Sample Hospital Listing:

ANYTOWN, Universal County

☒ **ANYTOWN HOSPITAL & CLINICS (777777)**, (Formerly Anytown Area
Community Hospital and Clinic), 100 South Main Street, Zip 12345–6789;
tel. 123/456–7890 **A**9 10] ①
F10 12 23 24 29 30 31 37 39 49 51 55 57 64 65 66 68 70 71 72 77
78 83 87 88 91 96 97 106 107 110 111 113 124 **P**1 2 3 **S** Universal ⑦
County Health System ② ③
Primary Contact: Ann M. Generic, Chief Executive Officer
COO: Ann M. Generic
CFO: Michael M. Generic ④
CMO: Peterl Van Generic, President Medical Staff
CHR: Jerry Generic, Human Resources Director
CNO: Danielle Generic, R.N., Chief Nursing Officer
Web address: www.website.org
Control: Other not–for–profit (including NFP Corporation) **Service:** General ⑤
Medical and Surgical

Staffed Beds: 25 **Admissions:** 892 **Census:** 9 **Outpatient Visits:** 44014
Births: 51 **Total Expense ($000):** 19210 **Payroll Expense ($000):** 5864
Personnel: 182

ANYTOWN, Universal County

☒ **ANYTOWN HOSPITAL & CLINICS (777777)**, (Formerly Anytown Area
Community Hospital and Clinic), 100 South Main Street, Zip 12345–6789;
tel. 123/456–7890 **A**9 10

① = Approval Codes
② = Physician Codes
③ = Health Care System Name
④ = Titles of Chief Administrators
⑤ = Control and Service Classifications
⑥ = Utilization Data
⑦ = Facility Codes

⑥

Hospital, Medicare Provider Number, Address, Telephone, Approval, Facility, and Physician Codes, Health Care System

★ American Hospital Association (AHA) membership ○ Healthcare Facilities Accreditation Program ⇑ Center for Improvement in Healthcare Quality Accreditation
☐ The Joint Commission accreditation ◇ DNV Healthcare Inc. accreditation △ Commission on Accreditation of Rehabilitation Facilities (CARF) accreditation

---

① Approval Codes

Reported by the approving bodies specified, as of the dates noted.

1 Accreditation under the hospital program of The
Joint Commission (February 2016).
2 Cancer program approved by American College
of Surgeons (March 2016).
3 Participating site recognized for one or more
Accreditation Council for Graduate Medical
Education accredited programs (March 2016).
5 Medical school affiliation, reported to the
American Medical Association (March 2016).
7 Accreditation by Commission on Accreditation of
Rehabilitation Facilities (March 2016).
8 Member of Council of Teaching Hospitals of the
Association of American Medical Colleges
(March 2016).

10 Certified for participation in the Health Insurance
for the Aged (Medicare) Program by the Centers
for Medicare and Medical Services (May 2016).
11 Healthcare Facilities Accreditation Program
(March 2016).
12 Internship approved by American Osteopathic
Association (March 2016).
13 Residency approved by American Osteopathic
Association (March 2016).
18 Critical Access Hospitals (March 2016).
19 Rural Referral Center (March 2016).
20 Sole Community Provider (March 2016).
21 Accreditation by DNV Healthcare Inc. (March
2016).

22 Accreditation by Center for Improvement in
Healthcare Quality (March 2016).

Nonreporting indicates that the 2015 Annual Survey
questionnaire for the hospital was not received prior to
publication.

---

② Physician Codes

Actually available within, and reported by the institution; for definitions, see page A12.

(Alphabetical/Numerical Order)
1 Closed physician–hospital organization (PHO)
2 Equity model
3 Foundation

4 Group practice without walls
5 Independent practice association (IPA)
6 Integrated salary model

7 Management service organization (MSO)
8 Open physician–hospital organization (PHO)

---

③ Health Care System Name

The inclusion of the letter "S" (1) indicates that the hospital belongs to a health care system and (2) identifies the specific system to which the hospital belongs.

---

④ Titles of Chief Administrators

⑤ Control and Service Classification
For a list of control and service classifications, see page A13.

Control–The type of organization that is
responsible for establishing policy for overall
operation of the hospital.

Service–The type of service the
hospital provides to the majority of
admissions.

---

⑥ Utilization Data

*Definitions are based on the American Hospital Association's Hospital Administration Terminology. In completing the survey, hospitals were requested to
report data for a full year, in accord with their fiscal year, ending in 2015.*

Beds–Number of beds regularly maintained
(set up and staffed for use) for inpatients as of
the close of the reporting period. Excludes
newborn bassinets.

Admissions–Number of patients accepted for
inpatient service during a 12–month period;
does not include newborn.

Census–Average number of inpatients
receiving care each day during the 12–month
reporting period; does not include newborn.

Outpatient Visits–A visit by a patient who is
not lodged in the hospital while receiving
medical, dental, or other services. Each
appearance of an outpatient in each unit
constitutes one visit regardless of the number
of diagnostic and/or therapeutic treatments
a patient receives.

Births–Number of infants born in the hos[pital]
and accepted for service in a newborn inf[ant]
bassinet during a 12–month period; exclu[des]
stillbirths.

Expense: Expense for a 12–month period;
both total expense and payroll components are
shown. Payroll expenses include all salaries
and wages.

Personnel: Represents personnel situations as
[report]ed at the end of the reporting period;
[part]–time
[full-time]
[par]t–time

D1441603

Sample Hospital Listing:

✠ **ANYTOWN HOSPITAL & CLINICS (777777)**, (Formerly Anytown Area Community Hospital and Clinic), 100 South Main Street, Zip 12345–6789; tel. 123/456–7890 **A**9 10] ①

F10 12 23 24 29 30 31 37 39 49 51 55 57 64 65 66 68 70 71 72 77 78 83 87 88 91 96 97 106 107 110 111 113 124 **P**1 2 3 **S** Universal — ⑦
County Health System — ② ③
Primary Contact: Ann M. Generic, Chief Executive Officer
COO: Ann M. Generic
CFO: Michael M. Generic
CMO: Peterl Van Generic, President Medical Staff — ④
CHR: Jerry Generic, Human Resources Director
CNO: Danielle Generic, R.N., Chief Nursing Officer
Web address: www.website.org
Control: Other not–for–profit (including NFP Corporation) **Service:** General — ⑤
Medical and Surgical

Staffed Beds: 25 **Admissions:** 892 **Census:** 9 **Outpatient Visits:** 44014
Births: 51 **Total Expense ($000):** 19210 **Payroll Expense ($000):** 5864 — ⑥
Personnel: 182

ANYTOWN, Universal County

✠ **ANYTOWN HOSPITAL & CLINICS (777777)**, (Formerly Anytown Area Community Hospital and Clinic), 100 South Main Street, Zip 12345–6789; tel. 123/456–7890 **A**9 10

① = Approval Codes
② = Physician Codes
③ = Health Care System Name
④ = Titles of Chief Administrators
⑤ = Control and Service Classifications
⑥ = Utilization Data
⑦ = Facility Codes

Hospital, Medicare Provider Number, Address, Telephone, Approval, Facility, and Physician Codes, Health Care System

★ American Hospital Association (AHA) membership
☐ The Joint Commission accreditation
◯ Healthcare Facilities Accreditation Program
◇ DNV Healthcare Inc. accreditation
⇧ Center for Improvement in Healthcare Quality Accreditation
△ Commission on Accreditation of Rehabilitation Facilities (CARF) accreditation

---

⑦ Facility Codes

Provided directly by the hospital; for definitions, see page A6.

(Numerical Order)

1. Acute long-term care
2. Adult day care program
3. Airborne infection isolation room
4. Alcoholism-drug abuse or dependency inpatient services
5. Alcoholism-drug abuse or dependency outpatient services
6. Alzheimer center
7. Ambulance services
8. Ambulatory surgery center
9. Arthritis treatment center
10. Assisted living
11. Auxiliary
12. Bariatric/weight control services
13. Birthing room-LDR room-LDRP room
14. Blood donor center
15. Breast cancer screening/mammograms
16. Burn care services
17. Cardiac intensive care
18. Adult cardiology services
19. Pediatric cardiology services
20. Adult diagnostic catheterization
21. Pediatric diagnostic catheterization
22. Adult interventional cardiac catheterization
23. Pediatric interventional cardiac catheterization
24. Adult cardiac surgery
25. Pediatric cardiac surgery
26. Adult cardiac electrophysiology
27. Pediatric cardiac electrophysiology
28. Cardiac rehabilitation
29. Case management
30. Chaplaincy/pastoral care services
31. Chemotherapy
32. Children's wellness program
33. Chiropractic services
34. Community health education
35. Community outreach
36. Complementary and alternative medicine services
37. Computer assisted orthopedic surgery (CAOS)
38. Crisis prevention
39. Dental services
40. Emergency department
41. Pediatric emergency department
42. Satellite emergency department
43. Trauma center (certified)
44. Enabling services
45. Optical colonoscopy
46. Endoscopic ultrasound
47. Ablation of Barrett's esophagus
48. Esophageal impedance study

49. Endoscopic retrograde cholangiopancreatography (ERCP)
50. Enrollment assistance services
51. Extracorporeal shock wave lithotripter (ESWL)
52. Fertility clinic
53. Fitness center
54. Freestanding outpatient care center
55. Genetic testing/counseling
56. Geriatric services
57. Health fair
58. Health research
59. Health screenings
60. Hemodialysis
61. HIV–AIDS services
62. Home health services
63. Hospice program
64. Hospital–based outpatient care center services
65. Immunization program
66. Indigent care clinic
67. Intermediate nursing care
68. Linguistic/translation services
69. Meals on wheels
70. Medical surgical intensive care services
71. Mobile health services
72. Neonatal intensive care
73. Neonatal intermediate care
74. Neurological services
75. Nutrition programs
76. Obstetrics
77. Occupational health services
78. Oncology services
79. Orthopedic services
80. Other special care
81. Outpatient surgery
82. Pain management program
83. Inpatient palliative care unit
84. Palliative care program
85. Patient controlled analgesia (PCA)
86. Patient education center
87. Patient representative services
88. Pediatric intensive care services
89. Pediatric medical–surgical care
90. Physical rehabilitation inpatient services
91. Assistive technology center
92. Electrodiagnostic services
93. Physical rehabilitation outpatient services
94. Prosthetic and orthotic services
95. Robot-assisted walking therapy
96. Simulated rehabilitation environment
97. Primary care department
98. Psychiatric care
99. Psychiatric child–adolescent services
100. Psychiatric consultation–liaison services

101. Psychiatric education services
102. Psychiatric emergency services
103. Psychiatric geriatric services
104. Psychiatric outpatient services
105. Psychiatric partial hospitalization services
106. Psychiatric residential treatment
107. CT scanner
108. Diagnostic radioisotope facility
109. Electron beam computed tomography (EBCT)
110. Full–field digital mammography (FFDM)
111. Magnetic resonance imaging (MRI)
112. Intraoperative magnetic resonance imaging
113. Magnetoencephalography (MEG)
114. Multi–slice spiral computed tomography (MSCT) (<64 slice CT)
115. Multi–slice spiral computed tomography (64 + slice CT)
116. Positron emission tomography (PET)
117. Positron emission tomography/CT (PET/CT)
118. Single photon emission computerized tomography (SPECT)
119. Ultrasound
120. Image–guided radiation therapy (IGRT)
121. Intensity–modulated radiation therapy (IMRT)
122. Proton beam therapy
123. Shaped beam radiation therapy
124. Stereotactic radiosurgery
125. Retirement housing
126. Robotic surgery
127. Rural health clinic
128. Skilled nursing care
129. Sleep center
130. Social work services
131. Sports medicine
132. Support groups
133. Swing bed services
134. Teen outreach services
135. Tobacco treatment/cessation program
136. Bone marrow transplant services
137. Heart transplant
138. Kidney transplant
139. Liver transplant
140. Lung transplant
141. Tissue transplant
142. Other transplant
143. Transportation to health services
144. Urgent care center
145. Virtual colonoscopy
146. Volunteer services department
147. Women's health center/services
148. Wound management services

AHA Guide® to the Health Care Field

2017 Edition

AHA Guide® to the Health Care Field

AHA Members $263
Nonmembers $391
AHA Item Number 010017
Telephone ORDERS 1–800–AHA–2626

ISSN 0094–8969
ISBN–13: 978–0–87258–971–1

Contents

Indexes

Acknowledgements and Advisements

Acknowledgements

The AHA Guide® to the Health Care Field is published annually by Health Forum LLC, an affiliate of the American Hospital Association. Contributions are made by Information Systems and Technology, Member Relations, Office of the President, Office of the Secretary, Printing Services Group, AHA Resource Center and the following participants:

Grant Denten	Peter Kralovec
Matthew Diener	Mary Krzywicki
Dianna Doyle	Andrea Liebig
DeAnn Ellis	Denise Loggins
Joan Finn	Rob Merrell
Deanna Frazier	Bethany Parnell
Robyn Gray	Kathy Poole
Tan Harris	Jennifer Sikora
Stella Hines	Susan Sheffey
Clisby Jackson	Elaine Singh
Danny Jackson	Jill Syftestad
Kimberly Jackson	Marty Weitzel
Maura Kennedy	

Health Forum LLC acknowledges the cooperation given by many professional groups and government agencies in the health care field, particularly the following: American College of Surgeons; American Medical Association; Council of Teaching Hospitals of the Association of American Medical Colleges; The Joint Commission; DNV Healthcare Inc.; Center for Improvement in Healthcare Quality; Commission on Accreditation of Rehabilitation Facilities; American Osteopathic Association, Centers for Medicare & Medicaid Services; and various offices within the U.S. Department of Health and Human Services.

Advisements

The data published here should be used with the following advisements: The data is based on replies to an annual survey that seeks a variety of information, not all of which is published in this book. The information gathered by the survey includes specific services, but not all of each hospital's services. Therefore, the data does not reflect an exhaustive list of all services offered by all hospitals. For information on the availability of additional data and products, please contact Health Forum LLC at 800/821–2039, or visit our web site.

Health Forum LLC does not assume responsibility for the accuracy of information voluntarily reported by the individual institutions surveyed. **The purpose of this publication is to provide basic data reflecting the delivery of health care in the United States and associated areas, and is not to serve as an official and all inclusive list of services offered by individual hospitals. The information reflected is based on data collected as of September 8, 2016.**

An Introduction to *AHA Guide*®

Welcome, and thank you for purchasing the 2017 edition of *AHA Guide*®. This section is designed to aid you in using the book. While the primary focus of *AHA Guide* is on hospitals, it also contains information on other areas of the health care field, divided across its two major sections:

A. Hospitals
B. Health care systems, networks, and alliances

The information contained within this publication was compiled using AHA membership, and the AHA Annual Survey of Hospitals. *AHA Guide* is the leading hospital directory and represents hospitals with or without AHA membership.

Additional information contained in the front of AHA Guide includes:

- A section by section table of contents
- Recognition of the source of data in the *Acknowledgements and Advisements* section
- Information on AHA's history as well as a listing of our awards in *AHA Offices, Officers, Historical Data, and Awards*

Getting Started: The AHA Guide Code Chart

Open the front cover and *AHA Guide* begins with the *2017 AHA Guide Code Chart*. This two page section (front and back) explains how to find and understand the most important elements of each hospital's listing. The chart is specially perforated and is meant to be extracted and used alongside Section A as a resource. The information found on these pages is repeated in the first section, so don't worry about removing the chart.

The *Code Chart* is a very useful tool to have when reading. It allows new users to become familiar with the data, and it aids returning users in understanding the new design and layout of *AHA Guide*. At the top of the chart, there is a sample listing. If you have used this publication before, you will notice the new columnar listing of all hospital entries by city. The city and county names are highlighted in gray, and all hospitals within the city follow. After the hospital name, you will find the address, telephone number, approval, facility and service codes, and health care systems to which the hospital belongs. Following this are the chief administrators and classifications for the hospital. Utilization data for the hospital is found in the box at the bottom of each hospital's entry in *AHA Guide*.

The chart further demonstrates how to understand these important elements:

1. **Approval codes** refer to certifications held by a hospital; they represent information supplied by various national approving and reporting bodies. For example, code A–3 indicates accreditation under one of the programs of the Accreditation Council for Graduate Medical Education, evidence that the hospital has been approved for participation in residency training.

2. **Physician codes** represent the different types of arrangements the hospital participates in with its physicians. In this section, code P-1 signifies a closed physician-hospital organization.

3. **Health Care System names** reference specific health care system headquarters to which the hospital belongs. The presence of a system name indicates that the hospital is a member. If no names are listed, the hospital does not belong to a system.

4. **Titles of Chief Administrators** including the Chief Executive Officer and, when available, other C-Suite officers such as the Chief Financial Officer, Chief Information Officer, Chief Medical Officer, Chief Operating Officer, Chief Human Resources Officer, and Chief Nursing Officer.

5. **Classification** refers to two items in *AHA Guide*. **Control** classification indicates the

---

2017 AHA Guide Code Chart

Sample Hospital Listing:

ANYTOWN, Universal County

☒ **ANYTOWN HOSPITAL & CLINICS (777777)**, (Formerly Anytown Area Community Hospital and Clinic), 100 South Main Street, Zip 12345–6789; tel. 123/456–7890 **A9** 10 ①
F10 12 23 24 29 30 31 37 39 49 51 55 57 64 65 66 68 70 71 72 77 78 83 87 88 91 96 97 106 107 110 111 113 124 **P1** 2 3 **S** Universal ⑦
County Health System ②③
Primary Contact: Ann M. Generic, Chief Executive Officer
COO: Ann M. Generic
CFO: Michael M. Generic
CMO: Peter/ Van Generic, President Medical Staff ④
CHR: Jerry Generic, Human Resources Director
CNO: Danielle Generic, R.N., Chief Nursing Officer
Web address: www.website.org
Control: Other not-for-profit (including NFP Corporation) **Service:** General ⑤ Medical and Surgical

Staffed Beds: 25 **Admissions:** 892 **Census:** 9 **Outpatient Visits:** 44014 **Births:** 51 **Total Expense ($000):** 19210 **Payroll Expense ($000):** 5864 **Personnel:** 182 ⑥

ANYTOWN, Universal County

☒ **ANYTOWN HOSPITAL & CLINICS (777777)**, (Formerly Anytown Area Community Hospital and Clinic), 100 South Main Street, Zip 12345–6789; tel. 123/456–7890 A9 10

① = Approval Codes
② = Physician Codes
③ = Health Care System Name
④ = Titles of Chief Administrators
⑤ = Control and Service Classifications
⑥ = Utilization Data
⑦ = Facility Codes

Hospital, Medicare Provider Number, Address, Telephone, Approval, Facility, and Physician Codes, Health Care System

★ American Hospital Association (AHA) membership ○ Healthcare Facilities Accreditation Program ‼ Center for Improvement in Healthcare Quality Accreditation
□ The Joint Commission accreditation ◇ DNV Healthcare Inc. accreditation △ Commission on Accreditation of Rehabilitation Facilities (CARF) accreditation

① Approval Codes
Reported by the approving bodies specified, as of the dates noted.

1 Accreditation under the hospital program of The Joint Commission (February 2016).
2 Cancer program approved by American College of Surgeons (March 2016).
3 Participating site recognized for one or more Accreditation Council for Graduate Medical Education accredited programs (March 2016).
5 Medical school affiliation, reported to the American Medical Association (March 2016).
7 Accreditation by Commission on Accreditation of Rehabilitation Facilities (March 2016).
8 Member of Council of Teaching Hospitals of the Association of American Medical Colleges (March 2016).

10 Certified for participation in the Health Insurance for the Aged (Medicare) Program by the Centers for Medicare and Medical Services (May 2016).
11 Healthcare Facilities Accreditation Program (March 2016).
12 Internship approved by American Osteopathic Association (March 2016).
13 Residency approved by American Osteopathic Association (March 2016).
18 Critical Access Hospitals (March 2016).
19 Rural Referral Center (March 2016).
20 Sole Community Provider (March 2016).
21 Accreditation by DNV Healthcare Inc (March 2016).

22 Accreditation by Center for Improvement in Healthcare Quality (March 2016).
Nonreporting indicates that the 2015 Annual Survey questionnaire for the hospital was not received prior to publication.

② Physician Codes
Actually available within, and reported by the institution; for definitions, see page A12.

(Alphabetical/Numerical Order)
1 Closed physician–hospital organization (PHO)
2 Equity model
3 Foundation
4 Group practice without walls
5 Independent practice association (IPA)
6 Integrated salary model
7 Management service organization (MSO)
8 Open physician–hospital organization (PHO)

③ Health Care System Name
The inclusion of the letter "S" (1) indicates that the hospital belongs to a health care system and (2) identifies the specific system to which the hospital belongs.

④ Titles of Chief Administrators

⑤ Control and Service Classification
For a list of control and service classifications, see page A13.

Control–The type of organization that is responsible for establishing policy for overall operation of the hospital.

Service–The type of service the hospital provides to the majority of admissions.

⑥ Utilization Data
Definitions are based on the American Hospital Association's Hospital Administration Terminology. In completing the survey, hospitals were requested to report data for a full year, in accord with their fiscal year, ending in 2015.

Beds–Number of beds regularly maintained (set up and staffed for use) for inpatients at the close of the reporting period. Excludes newborn bassinets.

Admissions–Number of patients accepted for inpatient service during a 12–month period; does not include newborn.

Census–Average number of inpatients receiving care each day during the 12–month reporting period; does not include newborn.

Outpatient Visits–A visit by a patient who is not lodged in the hospital while receiving medical, dental, or other services. Each appearance of an outpatient in each unit constitutes one visit regardless of the number of diagnostic and/or therapeutic treatments that a patient receives.

Births–Number of infants born in the hospital and accepted for service in a newborn infant bassinet during a 12–month period; excludes stillbirths.

Expense: Expense for a 12–month period; both total expense and payroll components are shown. Payroll expenses include all salaries and wages.

Personnel: Represents personnel situations as they existed at the end of the reporting period; includes full-time equivalents of part–time personnel. Full–time equivalents were calculated on the basis that two part–time persons equal one full-time person.

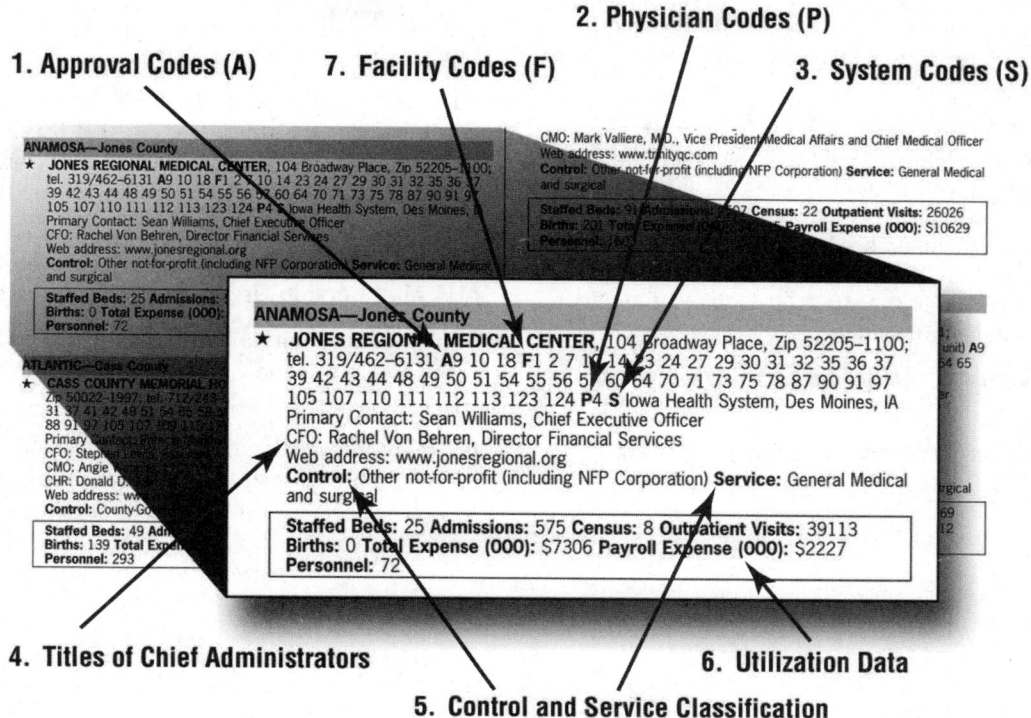

1. Approval Codes (A)
2. Physician Codes (P)
3. System Codes (S)
4. Titles of Chief Administrators
5. Control and Service Classification
6. Utilization Data
7. Facility Codes (F)

organization that operates the hospital, and **Service** classification refers to the type of service the hospital offers. Previously, this section utilized numerical codes corresponding with a literal value, but the new design of *AHA Guide* bypasses the codes and instead displays the literal classifications for control and service.

- **Control:** In this section, organizations are divided among nonfederal government hospitals, nongovernment not-for-profit hospitals, investor owned for-profit hospitals, and federal government hospitals.
- **Service:** This section displays the primary type of service that a hospital offers. The most common value is general hospital. Among the other services listed in this section are specialties such as psychiatric hospitals or children's hospitals.

6. **Utilization Data** contains the statistics related to the day-to-day and cumulative operation of the hospital. The information included in this section consists of:
  - **Beds:** Number of beds regularly maintained.
  - **Admissions:** Amount of patients accepted for inpatient services over a 12-month period.

- **Census:** Average number of patients receiving care each day.
- **Outpatient Visits:** Amount of visits by patients not lodged in the hospital while receiving care.
- **Births:** Number of infants born in the hospital and accepted for service in a newborn infant bassinet.
- **Expense:** Includes all expenses (including payroll) that the hospital had over the 12-month period.
- **Personnel:** Represents personnel situations as they existed at the end of the reporting period. In this area, full time equivalency is calculated on the basis that two part-time persons equal one full-time person.

7. **Facility codes** provide a description of the specific services offered by a hospital. Code F-14, for instance, indicates that the hospital contains a Blood Donor Center.

How To Use This Book

Section A begins with the *AHA Guide Hospital Listing Requirements*. This explains the requisite accreditations or characteristics a hospital must meet to be included in *AHA Guide*.

After this there is *An Explanation of the Hospital Listings*. These two pages review the information included in the Code Chart and are a vital resource in identifying the information, symbols, and codes for each hospital's listing.

Next up are the *Annual Survey* definitions, which go into even greater detail in explaining the facility and physician codes. Please note that these are arranged alphabetically and numerically to correspond with the code chart. Also included here are the definitions of the terms for Control and Service found in the Classification section. The listings of *Hospitals in the United States, by State* follow the definitions.

Finding Hospitals & Health Care Professionals in Section A

There are two ways to locate hospitals in the print version of *AHA Guide*. One is by the hospital's geographic classification. In Section A, hospitals are arranged alphabetically by state and then by city. The second method is through the *Hospital Index* that appears directly after the listings.

There is also an *Index of Health Care Professionals* which begins after the first index that lists key people from hospitals and health systems. Look for fold out tabs and tabs on the sides of pages that mark the indices.

AHA Membership Organizations

Section A ends with a description of the AHA Membership categories along with a listing of various AHA Membership organizations.

For more information on Systems, Networks, and Alliances, please read the introduction to Section B.

AHA Offices, Officers, and Historical Data

Chicago: 155 N. Wacker Drive, Chicago, IL 60606; tel. 312/422–3000

Washington: 800 10th Street, N.W., Two CityCenter, Suite 400, Washington, DC 20001; tel. 202/638–1100

Chairman of the Board of Trustees: Eugene A. Woods, Carolinas Healthcare System, PO Box 32861, Charlotte, NC
Chairman–Elect of the Board of Trustees: Nancy Howell Agee, Carilion Clinic, 1906 Belleview Avenue, Roanoke, VA 24014

Immediate Past Chairman of the Board of Trustees: James H. Skogsbergh, Advocate Health Care, 3075 Highland Parkway, Suite 600, Downers Grove, IL 60515
President & CEO: Richard J. Pollack , 800 10th Street, NW, Two CityCenter, Suite 400, Washington, DC 20001

Vice President and Secretary: Gail Lovinger Goldblatt, 155 N. Wacker Drive, Chicago, IL 60606
Senior Vice President, Association Services and Chief Financial Officer: Christina Fisher, 155 N. Wacker Drive, Chicago, IL 60606

Past Presidents/Chairs†

1899	★James S. Knowles	1939	★G. Harvey Agnew, M.D.	1979	W. Daniel Barker
1900	★James S. Knowles	1940	★Fred G. Carter, M.D.	1980	★Sister Irene Kraus
1901	★Charles S. Howell	1941	★B. W. Black, M.D.	1981	★Bernard J. Lachner
1902	★J. T. Duryea	1942	★Basil C. MacLean, M.D.	1982	★Stanley R. Nelson
1903	★John Fehrenbatch	1943	★James A. Hamilton	1983	Elbert E. Gilbertson
1904	★Daniel D. Test	1944	★Frank J. Walter	1984	Thomas R. Matherlee
1905	★George H. M. Rowe, M.D.	1945	★Donald C. Smelzer, M.D.	1985	★Jack A. Skarupa
1906	★George P. Ludlam	1946	★Peter D. Ward, M.D.	1986	Scott S. Parker
1907	★Renwick R. Ross, M.D.	1947	★John H. Hayes	1987	Donald C. Wegmiller
1908	★Sigismund S. Goldwater, M.D.	1948	★Graham L. Davis	1988	Eugene W. Arnett
1909	★John M. Peters, M.D.	1949	★Joseph G. Norby	1989	Edward J. Connors
1910	★H. B. Howard, M.D.	1950	★John N. Hatfield	1990	David A. Reed
1911	★W. L. Babcock, M.D.	1951	★Charles F. Wilinsky, M.D.	1991	C. Thomas Smith
1912	★Henry M. Hurd, M.D.	1952	★Anthony J. J. Rourke, M.D.	1992	D. Kirk Oglesby, Jr.
1913	★F. A. Washburn, M.D.	1953	★Edwin L. Crosby, M.D.	1993	Larry L. Mathis
1914	★Thomas Howell, M.D.	1954	★Ritz E. Heerman	1994	Carolyn C. Roberts
1915	★William O. Mann, M.D.	1955	★Frank R. Bradley	1995	Gail L. Warden
1916	★Winford H. Smith, M.D.	1956	★Ray E. Brown	1996	Gordon M. Sprenger
1917	★Robert J. Wilson, M.D.	1957	★Albert W. Snoke, M.D.	1997	Reginald M. Ballantyne III
1918	★A. B. Ancker, M.D.	1958	★Tol Terrell	1998	John G. King
1919	★A. R. Warner, M.D.	1959	★Ray Amberg	1999	Fred L. Brown
1920	★Joseph B. Howland, M.D.	1960	★Russell A. Nelson, M.D.	2000	★Carolyn Boone Lewis
1921	★Louis B. Baldwin, M.D.	1961	★Frank S. Groner	2001	Gary A. Mecklenburg
1922	★George O'Hanlon, M.D.	1962	★Jack Masur, M.D.	2002	Sr. Mary Roch Rocklage, RSM
1923	★Asa S. Bacon	1963	★T. Stewart Hamilton, M.D.	2003	Dennis R. Barry
1924	★Malcolm T. MacEachern, M.D.	1964	★Stanley A. Ferguson	2004	David L. Bernd
1925	★E. S. Gilmore	1965	★Clarence E. Wonnacott	2005	George F. Lynn
1926	★Arthur C. Bachmeyer, M.D.	1966	★Philip D. Bonnet, M.D.	January–April 2006 Richard J. Umbdenstock
1927	★R. G. Brodrick, M.D.	1967	★George E. Cartmill	April–December 2006 George F. Lynn
1928	★Joseph C. Doane, M.D.	1968	★David B. Wilson, M.D.	2007	Kevin E. Lofton
1929	★Louis H. Burlingham, M.D.	1969	★George William Graham, M.D.	2008	William D. Petasnick
1930	★Christopher G. Parnall, M.D.	1970	★Mark Berke	2009	Thomas M. Priselac
1931	★Lewis A. Sexton, M.D.	1971	★Jack A. L. Hahn	2010	Richard P. de Filippi
1932	★Paul H. Fesler	1972	★Stephen M. Morris	2011	John W. Bluford
1933	★George F. Stephens, M.D.	1973	★John W. Kauffman	2012	Teri G. Fontenot
1934	★Nathaniel W. Faxon, M.D.	1974	★Horace M. Cardwell	2013	Benjamin K. Chu, MD
1935	★Robert Jolly	1975	Wade Mountz	2014	James H. Hinton
1936	★Robin C. Buerki, M.D.	1976	H. Robert Cathcart	2015	Jonathan B. Perlin, MD, PhD
1937	★Claude W. Munger, M.D.	1977	★John M. Stagl	2016	James H. Skogsbergh
1938	★Robert E. Neff	1978	★Samuel J. Tibbitts		

Chief Executive Officers

1917–18	★William H. Walsh, M.D.	1954–72	★Edwin L. Crosby, M.D.	1991–2007	★Richard J. Davidson
1919–24	★Andrew Robert Warner, M.D.	1972	★Madison B. Brown, M.D. (acting)	2007–2015	Richard J. Umbdenstock
1925–27	★William H. Walsh, M.D.	1972–86	★J. Alexander McMahon	2015	Richard J. Pollack (current)
1928–42	★Bert W. Caldwell, M.D.	1986–91	Carol M. McCarthy, Ph.D., J.D.		
1943–54	★George Bugbee	1991	★Jack W. Owen (acting)		

Distinguished Service Award

The award recognizes significant lifetime contributions and service to health care institutions and associations.

1934	Matthew O. Foley	1965	Albert W. Snoke, M.D.	1992	David H. Hitt
1939	Malcolm T. MacEachern, M.D.	1966	Frank S. Groner	1993	Edward J. Connors
1940	Sigismund S. Goldwater, M.D.	1967	Rev. John J. Flanagan, S.J.		Jack W. Owen
1941	Frederic A. Washburn, M.D.	1968	Stanley W. Martin	1994	George Adams
1942	Winford H. Smith, M.D.	1969	T. Stewart Hamilton, M.D.	1995	Scott S. Parker
1943	Arthur C. Bachmeyer, M.D.	1970	Charles Patteson Cardwell, Jr.	1996	John A. Russell
1944	Rt. Rev. Msgr. Maurice F. Griffin, LL.D.	1971	Mark Berke	1997	D. Kirk Oglesby, Jr.
1945	Asa S. Bacon	1972	Stanley A. Ferguson	1998	Henry B. Betts, M.D.
1946	George F. Stephens, M.D.	1973	Jack A. L. Hahn	1999	Mitchell T. Rabkin, M.D.
1947	Robin C. Buerki, M.D.	1974	George William Graham, M.D.	2000	Gail L. Warden
1948	James A. Hamilton	1975	George E. Cartmill	2001	Gordon M. Sprenger
1949	Claude W. Munger, M.D.	1976	D. O. McClusky, Jr.	2002	Carolyn Boone Lewis
1950	Nathaniel W. Faxon, M.D.	1977	Boone Powell	2003	C. Thomas Smith
1951	Bert W. Caldwell, M.D.	1978	Richard J. Stull	2004	Michael C. Waters
1952	Fred G. Carter, M.D.	1979	Horace M. Cardwell	2005	John G. King
1953	Basil C. MacLean, M.D.	1980	Donald W. Cordes	2006	Gary A. Mecklenburg
1954	George Bugbee	1981	Sister Mary Brigh Cassidy		Sr. Mary Roch Rocklage, RSM
1955	Joseph G. Norby	1982	R. Zach Thomas, Jr.	2007	Richard J. Davidson
1956	Charles F. Wilinsky, M.D.	1983	H. Robert Cathcart	2008	Fred L. Brown
1957	John H. Hayes	1984	Matthew F. McNulty, Jr., Sc.D.	2009	George F. Lynn
1958	John N. Hatfield	1985	J. Alexander McMahon	2010	James J. Mongan, M.D.
1959	Edwin L. Crosby, M.D.	1986	Sister Irene Kraus	2011	Thomas C. Royer, M.D.
1960	Oliver G. Pratt	1987	W. Daniel Barker	2012	Karen Davis, Ph.D.
1961	E. M. Bluestone, M.D.	1988	Elbert E. Gilbertson	2013	Thomas C. Dolan, Ph.D., FACHE
1962	Mother Loretto Bernard, S.C., R.N.	1989	Donald G. Shropshire	2014	Thomas M. Priselac
1963	Ray E. Brown	1990	John W. Colloton	2015	Richard P. de Filippi
1964	Russell A. Nelson, M.D.	1991	Carol M. McCarthy, Ph.D., J.D.	2016	William Petasnick

★Deceased

†On June 3, 1972, the House of Delegates changed the title of the chief elected officer to chairman of the Board of Trustees, and the title of president was conferred on the chief executive officer of the Association.

Award of Honor

Awarded to individuals, organizations, or groups to recognize an exemplary contribution to the health and well being of the people through leadership on a major health policy or social initiative.

1966	Senator Lister Hill	1997	Paul B. Batalden, M.D.		Stanley F. Hupfeld
1967	Emory W. Morris, D.D.S.		Habitat for Humanity International	2008	Regina M. Benjamin, MD, MBA
1971	Special Committee on Provision of Health	1998	John E. Curley, Jr.		Alfred G. Stubblefield
	Services (staff also)		National Civic League	2009	The Center to Advance Palliative Care
1982	Walter J. McNemey	1999	Joseph Cardinal Bernardin, Literacy Volunteers		Paul B. Hofmann, Dr.PH
1989	Ruth M. Rothstein		of America	2010	Jack Bovender
1990	Joyce C. Clifford, R.N.	2000	Institute for Safe Medication Practices	2011	Cary Medical Center, Caribou, ME
1991	Haynes Rice	2001	Dennis R. Barry	2012	Ronald McDonald House Charities
1992	Donald W. Dunn	2002	Donald M. Berwick, M.D.		The Schwartz Center for Compassionate
	Ira M. Lane, Jr.	2003	Steven A. Schroeder, M.D.		Healthcare
1993	Elliott C. Roberts, Sr.		Dan S. Wilford	2013	George C. Halvorson
	William A. Spencer, M.D.	2004	Ron J. Anderson, M.D.		Reach Out and Read
1994	Robert A. Derzon		Johnson & Johnson	2014	Rhonda Anderson, RN
1995	Russell G. Mawby, Ph.D.	2005	Sr. Mary Jean Ryan		Ohio Hospital Association
	John K. Springer	2006	Jordan J. Cohen, M.D.	2015	Spencer C. Johnson
1996	Stephen J. Hegarty		James W. Varnum		Robert Wood Johnson Foundation
	Mothers Against Drunk Driving (MADD)	2007	Edward A. Eckenhoff	2016	Henry J. Kaiser Family Foundation

Justin Ford Kimball Innovators Award

Recognition to individuals or organizations that have made outstanding, innovative contributions to health care financing and/or delivery that improves access or coordination of care.

1958	E. A. van Steenwyk	1974	William H. Ford, Ph.D.	1995	E. George Middleton, Jr.
1959	George A. Newbury	1975	Earl H. Kammer		Glenn R. Mitchell
1960	C. Rufus Rorem, Ph.D.	1976	J. Ed McConnell	1997	Harvey Pettry
1961	James E. Stuart	1978	Edwin R. Werner		D. David Sniff
1962	Frank Van Dyk	1979	Robert M. Cunningham, Jr.	1998	Montana Health Research and Education
1963	William S. McNary	1981	Maurice J. Norby		Foundation
1964	Frank S. Groner	1982	Robert E. Rinehimer	1999	Kenneth W. Kizer, M.D.
1965	J. Douglas Colman	1983	John B. Morgan, Jr.	2002	David M. Lawrence, M.D.
1967	Walter J. McNemey	1984	Joseph F. Duplinsky	2003	Lowell C. Kruse
1968	John W. Paynter	1985	David W. Stewart	2006	Spencer Foreman, M.D.
1970	Edwin L. Crosby, M.D.	1988	Ernest W. Saward, M.D.	2009	On Lok
1971	H. Charles Abbott	1990	James A. Vohs	2012	Thomas S. Nesbitt, M.D.
1972	John R. Mannix	1993	John C. Lewin, M.D.	2015	Glenn D. Steele, Jr., MD
1973	Herman M. Somers	1994	Donald A. Brennan	2016	Dan Wolterman

Board of Trustees Award

Individuals or groups who have made substantial and noteworthy contributions to the work of the American Hospital Association.

1959	Joseph V. Friel		John E. Sullivan	2001	Spencer C. Johnson
	John H. Hayes	1982	John Bigelow		Michael M. Mitchel
1960	Duncan D. Sutphen, Jr.		Robert W. O'Leary	2002	Victor L. Campbell
1963	Eleanor C. Lambertsen, R.N., Ed.D.		Jack W. Owen		Joseph A. Parker
1964	John R. Mannix	1984	Howard J. Berman	2003	J. Richard Gaintner, M.D.
1965	Albert G. Hahn		O. Ray Hurst		Donald A. Wilson
	Maurice J. Norby		James R. Neely	2004	Richard L. Clarke
1966	Madison B. Brown, M.D.	1985	James E. Ferguson		Thelma Traut
	Kenneth Williamson		Cleveland Rodgers	2005	Merrill Gappmayer
1967	Alanson W. Wilcox	1986	Rex N. Olsen		Leo Greenawalt
1968	E. Dwight Barnett, M.D.	1987	Michael Lesparre	2006	Robert L. Harman
1969	Vane M. Hoge, M.D.	1988	Barbara A. Donaho, R.N.		Kenneth G. Stella
	Joseph H. McNinch, M.D.	1989	Walter H. MacDonald	2007	Deborah Freund, Ph.D.
1972	David F. Drake, Ph.D.		Donald R. Newkirk		Michael D. Stephens
	Paul W. Earle	1990	William T. Robinson	2008	James R. Castle
	Michael Lesparre	1992	Jack C. Bills	2009	Richard M. Knapp, Ph.D.
	Andrew Pattullo		Anne Hall Davis	2010	Fred Hessler
1973	Tilden Cummings	1993	Theodore C. Eickhoff, M.D.		John G. O'Brien
	Edmond J. Lanigan		Stephen W. Gamble	2011	Carolyn F. Scanlan
1974	James E. Hague		Yoshi Honkawa		Charlotte S. Yeh, MD
	Sister Marybelle	1994	Roger M. Busfield, Jr., Ph.D.	2012	Larry S. Gage
1975	Helen T. Yast	1995	Stephen E. Dorn		Larry McAndrews
1976	Boynton P. Livingston		William L. Yates	2013	Jeffrey D. Selberg
	James Ludlam	1996	Leigh E. Morris	2014	Russell D. Harrington, Jr.
	Helen McGuire		John Quigley		Daniel Sisto
1979	Newton J. Jacobson	1998	John D. Leech	2015	Todd C. Linden
	Edward W. Weimer	1999	Sister Carol Keehan		R. Timothy Rice
1980	Robert B. Hunter, M.D.		C. Edward McCauley	2016	Sandra Bennett Bruce
	Samuel J. Tibbitts		Stephen Rogness		Michael G. Rock, M.D.
1981	Vernon A. Knutson	2000	Dennis May		

Citation for Meritorious Service

1968	F. R. Knautz		Gordon McLachlan	1983	David M. Kinzer
	Sister Conrad Mary, R.N.	1977	Theodore Cooper, M.D.	1984	Donald L. Custis, M.D.
1971	Hospital Council of Southern California	1979	Norman D. Burkett	1985	John A. D. Cooper, M.D.
1972	College of Misericordia, Dallas, PA		John L. Quigley		Imperial Council of the Ancient Arabic Order of
1973	Madison B. Brown, M.D.		William M. Whelan		the Nobles of the Mystic Shrine for North
	Samuel J. Tibbitts	1980	Sister Grace Marie Hiltz		America
1975	Kenneth B. Babcock, M.D.		Leo J. Gehrig, M.D.	1986	Howard F. Cook
	Sister Mary Maurita Sengelaube	1981	Richard Davi	1987	David H. Hitt
1976	Chaiker Abbis		Pearl S. Fryar		Lucile Packard
	Susan Jenkins	1982	Jorge Brull Nater		

This citation is no longer awarded

AHA NOVA Awards

This award honors effective, collaborative programs focused on improving community health status.

1994

Health Partners of Philadelphi (PA): Albert Einstein Medical Center, Episcopal Hospital, Frankford Hospital, Medical College of Pennsylvania Hospital, St. Christopher's Hospital for Children, Temple University Hospital

Decker Family Development Center: Children's Hospital Medical Center of Akron (OH)
Denver (CO) School–Based Clinics: The Children's Hospital
Basic Health Plan: Dominican Network; Mount Carmel Hospital, Colville, WA; St. Joseph's

Hospital, Chewelah, WA; and Holy Family Hospital, Spokane, WA
HealthLink: Lakes Region General Hospital, Laconia, NH

1995

Bladen Community Care Network: Bladen County Hospital, Elizabethtown, NC
Building a Healthier Community: Community–Kimball Health Care System, Toms River, NJ

Injury Prevention Program: Harlem Hospital Center, New York City, NY
The Community Ministries & Outreach Program: Reaching Out to Our Vickery/Meadow

Neighborhood: Presbyterian Healthcare System, Dallas, TX
"CHOICES": Shriners Hospitals for Crippled Children, Tampa, FL

1996

Lincoln and Sunnyslope: John C. Lincoln Hospital and Health Center, Sunnyslope, AZ
Growing into Life Task Force: Aiken (SC) Regional Medical Centers

People Caring for People: Beatrice (NE) Community Hospital and Health Center
Injury Prevention Center of the Greater Dayton (OH) Area: The Children's Medical Center, Good

Samaritan Hospital and Health Center, Grandview Hospital, Kettering Memorial Hospital, Miami Valley Hospital, and St. Elizabeth Medical Center
Family Road: Hutzel Hospital, Detroit, MI

1997

Health Promotion Schools of Excellence Program: Alliant Health System and Kosair Children's Hospital, Louisville, KY
Health, Outreach, Prevention, and Education (HOPE): Health First Holmes Regional Medical Center, Melbourne, FL

Healthy Community Initiative: Roper Care Alliance, Charleston, SC
Obstetrical Care and Prenatal Counseling Program: St. Alexius Medical Center, Bismarck, ND
HIV/AIDS Neighborhood Service Program: Yale–New Haven Hospital, New Haven, CT

1998

Partners for a Healthier Community: Evergreen Community Health Care, Group Health Cooperative of Puget Sound, Overlake Hospital Medical Center, Providence Health System/Medalia HealthCare, Seattle, WA
Glenwood–Lyndale Community Clinic: Hennepin County Medical Center, Minneapolis, MN

Greater Dallas (TX) Injury Prevention Center: Parkland Health & Hospital System, Children's Medical Center of Dallas, Baylor Health Care System, Methodist Hospitals of Dallas, and Presbyterian Healthcare System
Network of Trust: Phoebe Putney Memorial Hospital, Albany, GA

The Lauderdale Court: A Community Partnership: St. Joseph Hospital and Health Centers, Memphis, TN

1999

Making a Case for Community Health: Middletown (OH) Regional Hospital
The Family Resource Center: Mount Carmel Medical Center, Pittsburgh, KS

The Health Neighborhood Project: St. Patrick Hospital, Missoula, MT
Kids for Health: Washington Regional Medical Center, Fayetteville, AR

Children's Village: Yakima Memorial Hospital, Yakima, WA

2000

Community Healthcare Network: Columbus (GA) Regional Healthcare System
Pasadena County Asthma Project: Huntington Memorial Hospital, Pasadena, CA

Ashe County Health Council "Health Carolinias Task Force": Ashe Memorial Hospital, Jefferson, NC
Caritas–Connection Project: St. Mary's Hospital, Passaic, NJ

Correctional Health Care Program: Baystate Health System, Springfield, MA

2001

J.C. Lewis Health Center: Memorial Health and St. Joseph's Candler Health System, Savannah, GA
Project C.A.R.E.: Mercy Medical Center, Canton, OH

TeenHealthFX.com: Atlantic Health System, Florham Park, NJ

Vista ElderCARE: Vista Health, Waukegan, IL

Western Village Enterprise School: INTEGRIS Health, Oklahoma City, OK

2002

Chester Community Connections: Crozer–Keystone Health System, Springfield, PA
The Hope Street Family Center: California Hospital Medical Center, Los Angeles, CA
Mobile Health Outreach Ministry: St. Vincent's Health System, Jacksonville, FL

Operation Access: Kaiser Foundation Hospitals, Oakland; Sutter Health, Sacramento; San Francisco General Hospital, San Francisco; St. Rose Hospital, Hayward; and Santa Rosa Memorial Hospital, Santa Rosa, CA

Wilmington Health Access for Teens: New Hanover Health Network, Wilmington, NC

2003

C.O.A.C.H. for Kids: Cedars–Sinai Medical Center, Los Angeles, CA
Community Action Network: Trinity Regional Medical Center, Fort Dodge, IA

Hearts N' Health: Glendale Adventist Medical Center, Glendale, CA
Saint Joseph Health Center: Saint Joseph Regional Medical Center, South Bend, IN

St. Mary Medical Center Bensalem Ministries: St. Mary Medical Center, Langhorne, PA

2004

Better Beginnings: Brockton Hospital, Brockton, MA
Buffalo County Community Health Partners: Good Samaritan Health Systems, Kearney, NE

Quad City Health Initiative: Genesis Health System, Davenport, IA and Trinity Regional Health System, Rock Island, IL
Quality of Life in the Truckee Meadows: Washoe Health System, Reno, NV

Solano Coalition for Better Health, Inc.: NorthBay Healthcare Group, Fairfield, CA; Sutter Solano Medical Center, Vallejo, CA; and Kaiser Permanente, Martinez, CA

2005

Children's Health Connection: McKay-Dee Hospital Center, Ogden, UT
Palmetto Health's Vision Health Initiative: Palmetto Health, Columbia, SC

Project Dulce, Whittier Institute for Diabetes: Scripps Health, San Diego, CA
Toledo/Lucas County CareNet: Mercy Health Partners, ProMedica Health System, and Medical

University of Ohio, all of Toledo, OH and St. Luke's Hospital, Maumee, OH
Volunteer Health Advisor (VHA) Program: Cambridge Health Alliance, Cambridge, MA

2006
Healthy Learners, Columbia, SC: Allendale County Hospital, Fairfax, SC; McLeod Medical Center–Dillon, Dillon, SC; Sisters of Charity Providence Hospitals, Columbia, SC; and Self Regional Healthcare, Greenwood, SC

Primary Care Access Network (PCAN): Health Central, Ocoee, FL; Florida Hospital, Winter Park, FL; and Orlando Regional Healthcare, Orlando, FL
ProHealth Care Community Health Outreach Initiative: ProHealth Care, Waukesha, WI

St. Joseph Mobile Health Services: Saint Joseph HealthCare Inc., Lexington, KY
Yonkers Childhood Health Initiative: St. John's Riverside, Yonkers, NY

2007
Medical-Legal Partnership for Children: Boston Medical Center, Boston, MA
NOW (Nutritional Options for Wellness) Program: Spectrum Health, Grand Rapids, MI

Richland Care: Palmetto Health, Columbia, SC
Trauma Nurses Talk Tough: Legacy Health System, Portland, OR

UMass Memorial Medical Center Healthy Youth Development Initiative: UMass Memorial Health Care, Worcester, MA
Youth Health Partnership-Patee Market Youth Dental Clinic: Heartland Health, St. Joseph, MO

2008
Partnership for Community Health: California Pacific Medical Center, San Francisco, CA
Every Child Succeeds: Cincinnati Children's Hospital Medical Center, Cincinnati, OH

Memorial Hermann Health Centers for Schools: Memorial Hermann, Houston, TX
Nutrition Center of Maine: Saint Mary's Health System, Lewiston, ME

***ENERGIZE!* Pediatric Diabetes Intervention Program:** WakeMed Health & Hospitals, Raleigh, NC

2009
Lighten Up 4 Life: Mission Health System, Asheville, NC
Project BRIEF: Jacobi Medical Center and North Central Bronx Hospital, Bronx, NY

Really Awesome Health (RAH) and Wholesome Routines: Duke Raleigh Hospital, Raleigh, NC
Student Success Jobs Program: Brigham and Women's Hospital, Boston, MA

Taos First Steps Program: Holy Cross Hospital, Taos, NM

2010
Community-Based Alternatives to the Emergency Room: Lee Memorial Health System, Fort Meyers, FL
Health-e-Access Telemedicine: University of Rochester Medical Center, Rochester, NY

Healthy Futures: Munson Healthcare System, Traverse City, MI
Healthy San Francisco: San Francisco General Hospital, University of California Medical Center, Chinese Hospital, California Pacific Medical Center,

Saint Francis Memorial Hospital, St. Mary's Medical Center, and Kaiser Permanente, San Francisco, CA
Pediatric Asthma Program: Sinai Health System, Chicago, IL

2011
Emergency Department Consistent Care Program: Providence St. Peter Hospital, Olympia, WA
Integrated Community Nursing Program at Parkview Health: Parkview Health, Fort Wayne, IN

Milwaukee Health Care Partnership: Aurora Health Care, Children's Hospital & Health System, Inc., Columbia St. Mary's, and Froedtert Health, all of Milwaukee, WI, and Wheaton Franciscan Healthcare, Glendale, WI

The Diabetes Collaborative: Northwestern Memorial Hospital, Chicago, IL
Rochester Youth Violence Partnership: University of Rochester Medical Center and Rochester General Health System, Rochester, NY

2012
The Beth Embraces Wellness: An Integrated Approach to Prevention in the Community: Newark Beth Israel Medical Center and Children's Hospital of New Jersey, Newark, NJ

CARE Network: St. Joseph Health Queen of the Valley Medical Center, Napa, CA
Fitness in the City: Boston Children's Hospital, Boston, MA

Puff City: Henry Ford Health System, Detroit, MI
Rural Health Initiative: Shawano Medical Center of ThedaCare, Shawano, WI

2013
Bangor Beacon Community: EMHS, Brewer, ME and St. Joseph Healthcare, Bangor, ME
Chippewa Health Improvement Partnership (CHIP): St. Joseph's Hospital, Chippewa Falls, WI

Core Health Program of Healthier Communities: Spectrum Health, Grand Rapids, MI
Free Preventive Screenings Program: Good Samaritan Hospital, Vincennes, IN

Hope Clinic and Pharmacy: Ephraim McDowell Health, Danville, KY

2014
FirstReach: FirstHealth of the Carolinas, Pinehurst, NC
Children's Hospital Center for Pediatric Medicine Asthma Action Team: Greenville Health System, Greenville, SC

Let's Go!: The Barbara Bush Children's Hospital at Maine Medical Center, Portland, ME
Hearts Beat Back: The Heart of New Ulm (HONU) Project: New Ulm Medical Center, part of Allina Health, New Ulm, MN

Finney County Community Health Coalition: St. Catherine Hospital, Garden City, KS

2015
Activate Whittier: PIH Health, Whittier, Calif. and Kaiser Permanente Downey Medical Center, Downey, CA
Bithlo Transformation Effort: Florida Hospital, Orlando, FL

Blood Pressure Advocate Program: University of Rochester Medical Center, Rochester, NY
Community Health: Healthy Eating: Presbyterian Healthcare Services, Albuquerque, NM

Mayor's Healthy City Initiative (Healthy BR): Baton Rouge General Medical Center, Ochsner Medical Center-Baton Rouge, Our Lady of the Lake Regional Medical Center and Woman's Hospital, Baton Rouge, LA

2016
Baylor Scott & White Health's Diabetes Health and Wellness Institute at the Juanita J. Craft Recreation Center: Baylor Scott & White Health, Dallas, TX
Building a Healthy Community Initiative, East Ocean View: Bon Secours Hampton Roads Health System, Norfolk, VA

Memorial Hermann Mobile Dental Program: Memorial Hermann Health System, Houston, TX
Spectrum Health Healthier Communities – Strong Beginnings: Spectrum Health, Grand Rapids, MI

Get Healthy, Live Well: Tanner Health System, Carrollton, GA

The Carolyn Boone Lewis Living the Vision Award
Organizations and individuals living AHA's vision of a society of healthy communities where all individuals reach their highest potential for health.

1998	Memorial Healthcare System, Hollywood, FL Baptist Health System, Montgomery, AL	2002	Health Improvement Collaborative of Greater Cincinnati, Cincinnati, OH	2011	Alaska Native Tribal Health Consortium, Anchorage, AK
1999	Robert A. DeVries, Battle Creek, MI Memorial Health System, South Bend, IN	2003	Franklin Memorial Hospital, Farmington, ME	2013	St. Joseph's Hospital Health Center, Syracuse, NY
2000	Rockingham Memorial Hospital, Harrisonburg, VA	2004	Jamaica Hospital Medical Center, Jamaica, NY		Cheshire Medical Center/Dartmouth–Hitchcock Keene, Keene, NH
2001	Salina Regional Health Center, Salina, KS	2005	Fairbanks Memorial Hospital, Fairbanks, AK Boston Medical Center, Boston, MA	2014	TPR Collaborative, MD
		2010	Lehigh Valley Health Network, Allentown, PA		

Circle of Life Award
This award celebrates innovation in palliative and end-of-life care.

2000

Improving Care through the End of Life, Franciscan Health System, Gig Harbor, WA	The Hospice of The Florida Suncoast, Largo, FL	Louisiana State Penitentiary Hospice Program, Angola, LA

2001

Department of Pain Medicine and Palliative Care, Beth Israel Medical Center, New York, NY	Palliative CareCenter & Hospice of the North Shore, Evanston , IL	St. Joseph's Manor, Trumbull, CT

2002

Children's Program of San Diego Hospice and Children's Hospital and Health Center of San Diego, San Diego, CA	Hospice of the Bluegrass, Lexington, KY Project Safe Conduct, Hospice of the Western Reserve and Ireland Cancer Center, Cleveland, OH	**Special Circle of Life Award** Population–based Palliative Care Research Network (PoPCRN), Denver, CO

2003

Hospice & Palliative CareCenter, Winston–Salem, NC	Providence Health System, Portland, OR	University of California Davis Health System, Sacramento, CA

2004

Hope Hospice and Palliative Care, Fort Myers, FL	St. Mary's Healthcare System for Children, Bayside, NY	University of Texas M.D. Anderson Cancer Center Palliative Care, Houston, TX

2005

High Point Regional Health System, High Point, NC	Palliative and End-of-life Care Program, Hoag Memorial Hospital Presbyterian, Newport Beach, CA	Thomas Palliative Care Unit, VCU Massey Cancer Center, Richmond, VA

2006

Continuum Hospice Care, New York, NY	Mercy Supportive Care, St. Joseph Mercy Oakland, Pontiac, MI	Transitions and Life Choices, Fairview Health Services, Minneapolis, MN

2007

UCSF Palliative Care Program, San Francisco, CA	Covenant Hospice, Pensacola, FL	Woodwell: A Program of Presbyterian SeniorCare and Family Hospice and Palliative Care, Oakmont, PA

2008

Children's Hospitals and Clinics of Minnesota, Pain and Palliative Care Program, Minneapolis, MN	Haven Hospice, Gainesville, FL	The Pediatric Advanced Care Team, The Children's Hospital of Philadelphia, Philadelphia, PA

2009

Four Seasons, Flat Rock, NC	Oregon Health and Science University Palliative Medicine & Comfort Care Program, Portland, OR	Wishard Health Services Palliative Care Program, Indianapolis, IN

2010

Department of Veteran Affairs, VA New York/New Jersey Healthcare Network, Brooklyn, NY	Kansas City Hospice & Palliative Care, Kansas City, MO	Snohomish Palliative Partnership, Everett, WA

2011

The Center for Hospice & Palliative Care, Cheektowaga, NY	Gilchrist Hospice Care, Hunt Valley, MD	St. John Providence Health System, Detroit, MI

2012

Haslinger Family Pediatric Palliative Care Center, Akron Children's Hospital, Akron, OH	Calvary Hospital, Bronx, NY	Sharp HealthCare, San Diego, CA

2013

The Denver Hospice and Optio Health Services, Denver, CO	Hertzberg Palliative Care Institute at the Mount Sinai Medical Center, New York, NY	UnityPoint Health, Iowa and Illinois

2014

OACIS/Palliative Medicine, Lehigh Valley Health Network, Allentown, PA	Supportive & Palliative Care, Baylor Health Care System, Dallas, TX	Yakima Valley Memorial Hospital, Yakima, WA

2015

Care Dimensions, Danvers, MA		

2016

Bon Secours Palliative Medicine, Richmond, VA	Cambia Palliative Care Center of Excellence at UW Medicine, Seattle, WA	Susquehanna Health Hospice and Palliative Care, Williamsport, PA

The American Hospital Association–McKesson Quest for Quality Prize
Honoring Leadership and Innovation in Patient Care Quality, Safety, and Commitment

2002

Missouri Baptist Medical Center, St. Louis, MO	**Finalist:** Fairview Hospital, Greater, Barrington, MA	**Finalist:** Minnesota Children's Hospital and Clinics, Minneapolis, MN

2003

Abington Memorial Hospital, Abington, PA	**Finalist:** Beaumont Hospitals, Royal Oak, MI	**Finalist:** University of Wisconsin Hospital and Clinics, Madison, WI

2004
Sentara Norfolk General Hospital, Norfolk, VA

Finalist: The Johns Hopkins Hospital, Baltimore, MD

Finalist: Mary Lanning Memorial Hospital, Hastings, NE

2005
North Mississippi Medical Center, Tupelo, MS

Finalist: El Camino Hospital, Mountain View, CA

Finalist: NewYork-Presbyterian Hospital, New York, NY

2006
Cincinnati Children's Hospital Medical Center, Cincinnati, OH

2007
Columbus Regional Hospital, Columbus, IN

Finalist: Cedars-Sinai Medical Center, Los Angeles, CA

Finalist: INTEGRIS Baptist Medical Center, Oklahoma City, OK

2008
Munson Medical Center, Traverse City, MI

Finalist: University of Michigan Hospitals & Health Centers, Ann Arbor, MI

2009
Bronson Methodist Hospital, Kalamazoo, MI

Finalist: Beth Israel Deaconess Medical Center, Boston, MA

2010
McLeod Regional Medical Center, Florence, SC

Finalist: Henry Ford Hospital, Detroit, MI

2011
Memorial Regional Hospital, Hollywood, FL

Finalist: AtlantiCare Regional Medical Center, Atlantic City, NJ

Finalist: Northwestern Memorial Hospital, Chicago, IL

2012
University Hospitals Case Medical Center, Cleveland, OH

Finalist: Lincoln Medical and Mental Health Center, Bronx, NY

Finalist: University of North Carolina Hospitals, Chapel Hill, NC and Life Choices, Fairview Health Services, Minneapolis, MN

2013
Beth Israel Deaconess Medical Center, Boston, MA

Finalist: Franklin Woods Community Hospital, Johnson City, TN

2014
VCU Medical Center, Richmond, VA

Finalist: Carolinas Medical Center-Northeast, Concord, NC

2015
Children's Hospital Colorado in Aurora, CO

Finalist: Duke University Hospital, Durham, NC

2016
Memorial Medical Center, Springfield, IL

Finalist: Memorial Hermann Greater Heights, Houston, TX

Foster G. McGaw Prize
Honors health delivery organizations that have demonstrated exceptional commitment to community service.

1986	Lutheran Medical Center, Brooklyn, NY	1995	Our Lady of Lourdes Medical Center, Camden, NJ	2006	Memorial Healthcare System, Hollywood, FL

1986 Lutheran Medical Center, Brooklyn, NY
1987 Copley Hospital, Morrisville, VT
Mount Sinai Hospital, Hartford, CT
1988 MetroHealth System, Cleveland, OH
1989 Greater Southeast Healthcare System, Washington, DC
1990 Mount Zion Medical Center of The University of California-San Francisco, San Francisco, CA
1991 Franklin Regional Hospital, Franklin, NH
1992 Mount Sinai Hospital Medical Center of Chicago, Chicago, IL
1993 The Cambridge Hospital, Cambridge, MA
1994 Parkland Memorial Hospital, Dallas, TX
2015 Massachusetts General Hospital, Boston

1995 Our Lady of Lourdes Medical Center, Camden, NJ
1996 St. Mary's Hospital, Rochester, NY
1997 Bladen County Hospital Rural Health Network, Elizabethtown, NC
1998 Allina Health System, Minneapolis, MN
1999 LAC+USC Healthcare Network, Los Angeles, CA
2000 Kaweah Delta Health Care District, Visalia, CA
2001 Memorial Hospital of South Bend, South Bend, IN
2002 John C. Lincoln Health Network, Phoenix, AZ
2003 Phoebe Putney Memorial Hospital, Albany, GA
2004 Henry Ford Health System, Detroit, MI
2005 Venice Family Clinic, Venice, CA

2006 Memorial Healthcare System, Hollywood, FL
2007 Harborview Medical Center, Seattle, WA
2008 St. Mary's Health System, Lewiston, ME
2009 Heartland Health, St. Joseph, MO
2010 Allegiance Health, Jackson, MI
2011 Mt. Ascutney Hospital and Health Center, Windsor, VT
2012 St. Joseph's/Candler Health System, Savannah, GA
2013 Crozer–Keystone Health System, Delaware County, PA
2014 Palmetto Health, Columbia, SC
2015 Massachusetts General Hospital, Boston

Dick Davidson Quality Milestone Award for Allied Association Leadership
The award recognizes state, regional or metropolitan hospital association leadership in improving health care quality.

2011 Michigan Health & Hospital Association
South Carolina Hospital Association
2012 Iowa Hospital Association
Washington State Hospital Association

2013 Florida Hospital Association
Tennessee Hospital Association
2014 Connecticut Hospital Association
Wisconsin Hospital Association

2015 Minnesota Hospital Association
2016 Maryland Hospital Association

AHA Equity of Care Award
The award is presented to hospitals or care systems that are noteworthy leaders and examples to the field in the area of equitable care.

2014 Massachusetts General Hospital, Boston, MA
2015 Henry Ford Health System, Detroit, MI
Robert Wood Johnson University Hospital, New Brunswick, NJ

2016 Cleveland Clinic, Cleveland, OH

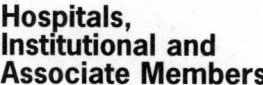

An institution may be listed by the American Hospital Association if it is accredited as a hospital by The Joint Commission, American Osteopathic Association, DNV Healthcare accredited, or Medicare certified as a provider of acute service under Title 18 of the Social Security Act. Membership in the American Hospital Association is not a prerequisite.

If none of the four conditions mentioned above are satisfied, an insititution licensed as a hospital by the appropriate state agency may be registered by AHA as a hospital by meeting the following alernative requirements:

Function: The primary function of the institution is to provide patient services, diagnostic and therapeutic, for particular or general medical conditions.

1. The institution shall maintain at least six inpatient beds, which shall be continuously available for the care of patients who are nonrelated and who stay on the average in excess of 24 hours per admission.
2. The institution shall be constructed, equipped, and maintained to ensure the health and safety of patients and to provide uncrowded, sanitary facilities for the treatment of patients.
3. There shall be an identifiable governing authority legally and morally responsible for the conduct of the hospital.
4. There shall be a chief executive to whom the governing authority delegates the continuous responsibility for the operation of the hospital in accordance with established policy.
5. There shall be an organized medical staff of fully licensed physicians* that may include other licensed individuals permitted by law and by the hospital to provide patient care services independently in the hospital. The medical staff shall be accountable to the governing authority for maintaining proper standards of medical care, and it shall be governed by bylaws adopted by said staff and approved by the governing authority.
6. Each patient shall be admitted on the authority of a member of the medical staff who has been granted the privilege to admit patients to inpatient services in accordance with state law and criteria for standards of medical care established by the individual medical staff. Each patient's general medical condition is the responsibility of a qualified physician member of the medical staff. When nonphysician members of the medical staff are granted privileges to admit patients, provision is made for prompt medical evaluation of these patients by a qualified physician. Any graduate of a foreign medical school who is permitted to assume responsibilities for patient care shall possess a valid license to practice medicine, or shall be certified by the Educational Commission for Foreign Medical Graduates, or shall have qualified for and have successfully completed an academic year of supervised clinical training under the direction of a medical school approved by the Liaison Committee on GAT Medical Education.
7. Registered nurse supervision and other nursing services are continuous.
8. A current and complete medical record shall be maintained by the institution for each patient and shall be available for reference.
9. Pharmacy service shall be maintained in the institution and shall be supervised by a registered pharmacist.
10. The institution shall provide patients with food service that meets their nutritional and therapeutic requirements; special diets shall also be available.

* Physician–Term used to describe an individual with an M.D. or D.O. degree who is fully licensed to practice medicine in all its phases.

‡ The completed records in general shall contain at least the following: the patient's identifying data and consent forms, medical history, record of physical examination, physicians' progress notes, operative notes, nurses' notes, routine x–ray and laboratory reports, doctors' orders, and final diagnosis.

Types of Hospitals

In addition to meeting these 10 general requirements, hospitals are listed as one of four types of hospitals: general, special, rehabilitation and chronic disease, or psychiatric. The following definitions of function by type of hospital and special requirements are:

General

The primary function of the institution is to provide patient services, diagnostic and therapeutic, for a variety of medical conditions. A general hospital also shall provide:
• diagnostic x–ray services with facilities and staff for a variety of procedures
• clinical laboratory service with facilities and staff for a variety of procedures and with anatomical pathology services regularly and conveniently available
• operating room service with facilities and staff.

Special

The primary function of the institution is to provide diagnostic and treatment services for patients who have specified medical conditions, both surgical and nonsurgical. A special hospital also shall provide:
• such diagnostic and treatment services as may be determined by the Executive Committee of the Board of Trustees of the American Hospital Association to be appropriate for the specified medical conditions for which medical services are provided shall be maintained in the institution with suitable facilities and staff. If such conditions do not normally require diagnostic x–ray service, laboratory service, or operating room service, and if any such services are therefore not maintained in the institution, there shall be written arrangements to make them available to patients requiring them.
• clinical laboratory services capable of providing tissue diagnosis when offering pregancy termination services.

Rehabilitation and Chronic Disease

The primary function of the institution is to provide diagnostic and treatment services to handicapped or disabled individuals requiring restorative and adjustive services. A rehabilitation and chronic disease hospital also shall provide:
• arrangements for diagnostic x–ray services, as required, on a regular and conveniently available basis
• arrangements for clinical laboratory service, as required on a regular and conveniently available basis
• arrangements for operating room service, as required, on a regular and conveniently available basis
• a physical therapy service with suitable facilities and staff in the institution
• an occupational therapy service with suitable facilities and staff in the institution

• arrangements for psychological and social work services on a regular and conveniently available basis
• arrangements for educational and vocational services on a regular and conveniently available basis
• written arrangements with a general hospital for the transfer of patients who require medical, obstetrical, or surgical services not available in the institution.

Psychiatric

The primary function of the institution is to provide diagnostic and treatment services for patients who have psychiatric–related illnesses. A psychiatric hospital also shall provide:
• arrangements for clinical laboratory service, as required, on a regular and conveniently available basis
• arrangements for diagnostic x–ray services, as required on a regular and conveniently available basis
• psychiatric, psychological, and social work service with facilities and staff in the institution
• arrangements for electroencephalograph services, as required, on a regular and conveniently available basis.
• written arrangements with a general hospital for the transfer of patients who require medical, obstetrical, or surgical services not available in the institution.

The American Hospital Association may, at the sole discretion of the Executive Committee of the Board of Trustees, grant, deny, or withdraw the listing of an institution.

---

* Physician–Term used to describe an individual with an M.D. or D.O. degree who is fully licensed to practice medicine in all its phases.

‡ The completed records in general shall contain at least the following: the patient's identifying data and consent forms, medical history, record of physical examination, physicians' progress notes, operative notes, nurses' notes, routine x–ray and laboratory reports, doctors' orders, and final diagnosis.

Explanation
of Hospital Listings

Sample Hospital Listing:

ANYTOWN, Universal County

☒ **ANYTOWN HOSPITAL & CLINICS (777777)**, (Formerly Anytown Area
Community Hospital and Clinic), 100 South Main Street, Zip 12345–6789;
tel. 123/456–7890 **A**9 10] ①
F10 12 23 24 29 30 31 37 39 49 51 55 57 64 65 66 68 70 71 72 77
78 83 87 88 91 96 97 106 107 110 111 113 124 **P**1 2 3 **S** Universal ⑦
County Health System ② ③
Primary Contact: Ann M. Generic, Chief Executive Officer
COO: Ann M. Generic
CFO: Michael M. Generic
CMO: Peterl Van Generic, President Medical Staff ④
CHR: Jerry Generic, Human Resources Director
CNO: Danielle Generic, R.N., Chief Nursing Officer
Web address: www.website.org
Control: Other not–for–profit (including NFP Corporation) **Service:** General ⑤
Medical and Surgical

Staffed Beds: 25 **Admissions:** 892 **Census:** 9 **Outpatient Visits:** 44014
Births: 51 **Total Expense ($000):** 19210 **Payroll Expense ($000):** 5864 ⑥
Personnel: 182

ANYTOWN, Universal County

☒ **ANYTOWN HOSPITAL & CLINICS (777777)**, (Formerly Anytown Area
Community Hospital and Clinic), 100 South Main Street, Zip 12345–6789;
tel. 123/456–7890 **A**9 10

① = Approval Codes
② = Physician Codes
③ = Health Care System Name
④ = Titles of Chief Administrators
⑤ = Control and Service Classifications
⑥ = Utilization Data
⑦ = Facility Codes

Hospital, Medicare Provider Number, Address, Telephone, Approval, Facility, and Physician Codes, Health Care System

★ American Hospital Association (AHA) membership ◯ Healthcare Facilities Accreditation Program ⇑ Center for Improvement in Healthcare Quality Accreditation
☐ The Joint Commission accreditation ◇ DNV Healthcare Inc. accreditation △ Commission on Accreditation of Rehabilitation Facilities (CARF) accreditation

---

① Approval Codes

Reported by the approving bodies specified, as of the dates noted.

1 Accreditation under the hospital program of The
Joint Commission (February 2016).
2 Cancer program approved by American College
of Surgeons (March 2016).
†3 Participating site recognized for one or more
Accreditation Council for Graduate Medical
Education accredited programs (March 2016).
†5 Medical school affiliation, reported to the
American Medical Association (March 2016).
7 Accreditation by Commission on Accreditation of
Rehabilitation Facilities (March 2016).
8 Member of Council of Teaching Hospitals of the
Association of American Medical Colleges
(March 2016).

10 Certified for participation in the Health Insurance
for the Aged (Medicare) Program by the Centers
for Medicare and Medical Services (May 2016).
11 Healthcare Facilities Accreditation Program
(March 2016).
12 Internship approved by American Osteopathic
Association (March 2016).
13 Residency approved by American Osteopathic
Association (March 2016).
18 Critical Access Hospitals (March 2016).
19 Rural Referral Center (March 2016).
20 Sole Community Provider (March 2016).
21 Accreditation by DNV Healthcare Inc. (March
2016).

22 Accreditation by Center for Improvement in
Healthcare Quality (March 2016).
Nonreporting indicates that the 2015 Annual Survey
questionnaire for the hospital was not received prior to
publication.

---

② Physician Codes

Actually available within, and reported by the institution; for definitions, see page A12.

(Alphabetical/Numerical Order)

1 Closed physician–hospital organization (PHO)
2 Equity model
3 Foundation
4 Group practice without walls
5 Independent practice association (IPA)
6 Integrated salary model
7 Management service organization (MSO)
8 Open physician–hospital organization (PHO)

---

③ Health Care System Name

The inclusion of the letter ''S'' (1) indicates that the hospital belongs to a health care system and (2) identifies the specific system to which the hospital belongs.

---

④ Titles of Chief Administrators

⑤ Control and Service Classification
For a list of control and service classifications, see page A13.

Control–The type of organization that is
responsible for establishing policy for overall
operation of the hospital.

Service–The type of service the
hospital provides to the majority of
admissions.

---

⑥ Utilization Data

Definitions are based on the American Hospital Association's Hospital Administration Terminology. In completing the survey, hospitals were requested to report data for a full year, in accord with their fiscal year, ending in 2015.

Beds–Number of beds regularly maintained
(set up and staffed for use) for inpatients as of
the close of the reporting period. Excludes
newborn bassinets.

Admissions–Number of patients accepted for
inpatient service during a 12–month period;
does not include newborn.

Census–Average number of inpatients
receiving care each day during the 12–month
reporting period; does not include newborn.

Outpatient Visits–A visit by a patient who is
not lodged in the hospital while receiving
medical, dental, or other services. Each
appearance of an outpatient in each unit
constitutes one visit regardless of the number
of diagnostic and/or therapeutic treatments that
a patient receives.

Births–Number of infants born in the hospital
and accepted for service in a newborn infant
bassinet during a 12–month period; excludes
stillbirths.

Expense: Expense for a 12–month period;
both total expense and payroll components are
shown. Payroll expenses include all salaries
and wages.

Personnel: Represents personnel situations as
they existed at the end of the reporting period;
includes full-time equivalents of part–time
personnel. Full–time equivalents were
calculated on the basis that two part–time
persons equal one full–time person.

Sample Hospital Listing:

ANYTOWN, Universal County

⊞ **ANYTOWN HOSPITAL & CLINICS (777777)**, (Formerly Anytown Area Community Hospital and Clinic), 100 South Main Street, Zip 12345–6789; tel. 123/456–7890 **A**9 10] ①
F10 12 23 24 29 30 31 37 39 49 51 55 57 64 65 66 68 70 71 72 77 78 83 87 88 91 96 97 106 107 110 111 113 124 **P**1 2 3 **S** Universal County Health System ② ③   ⑦
Primary Contact: Ann M. Generic, Chief Executive Officer
COO: Ann M. Generic
CFO: Michael M. Generic
CMO: Peterl Van Generic, President Medical Staff   ④
CHR: Jerry Generic, Human Resources Director
CNO: Danielle Generic, R.N., Chief Nursing Officer
Web address: www.website.org
Control: Other not–for–profit (including NFP Corporation) **Service:** General Medical and Surgical   ⑤

Staffed Beds: 25 **Admissions:** 892 **Census:** 9 **Outpatient Visits:** 44014
Births: 51 **Total Expense ($000):** 19210 **Payroll Expense ($000):** 5864
Personnel: 182

ANYTOWN, Universal County

⊞ **ANYTOWN HOSPITAL & CLINICS (777777)**, (Formerly Anytown Area Community Hospital and Clinic), 100 South Main Street, Zip 12345–6789; tel. 123/456–7890 **A**9 10

- ① = Approval Codes
- ② = Physician Codes
- ③ = Health Care System Name
- ④ = Titles of Chief Administrators
- ⑤ = Control and Service Classifications
- ⑥ = Utilization Data
- ⑦ = Facility Codes

Hospital, Medicare Provider Number, Address, Telephone, Approval, Facility, and Physician Codes, Health Care System

★ American Hospital Association (AHA) membership   ○ Healthcare Facilities Accreditation Program   ⇑ Center for Improvement in Healthcare Quality Accreditation
□ The Joint Commission accreditation   ◇ DNV Healthcare Inc. accreditation   △ Commission on Accreditation of Rehabilitation Facilities (CARF) accreditation

---

⑦ Facility Codes

Provided directly by the hospital; for definitions, see page A6.

(Numerical Order)

1. Acute long-term care
2. Adult day care program
3. Airborne infection isolation room
4. Alcoholism-drug abuse or dependency inpatient services
5. Alcoholism-drug abuse or dependency outpatient services
6. Alzheimer center
7. Ambulance services
8. Ambulatory surgery center
9. Arthritis treatment center
10. Assisted living
11. Auxiliary
12. Bariatric/weight control services
13. Birthing room-LDR room-LDRP room
14. Blood donor center
15. Breast cancer screening/mammograms
16. Burn care services
17. Cardiac intensive care
18. Adult cardiology services
19. Pediatric cardiology services
20. Adult diagnostic catheterization
21. Pediatric diagnostic catheterization
22. Adult interventional cardiac catheterization
23. Pediatric interventional cardiac catheterization
24. Adult cardiac surgery
25. Pediatric cardiac surgery
26. Adult cardiac electrophysiology
27. Pediatric cardiac electrophysiology
28. Cardiac rehabilitation
29. Case management
30. Chaplaincy/pastoral care services
31. Chemotherapy
32. Children's wellness program
33. Chiropractic services
34. Community health education
35. Community outreach
36. Complementary and alternative medicine services
37. Computer assisted orthopedic surgery (CAOS)
38. Crisis prevention
39. Dental services
40. Emergency department
41. Pediatric emergency department
42. Satellite emergency department
43. Trauma center (certified)
44. Enabling services
45. Optical colonoscopy
46. Endoscopic ultrasound
47. Ablation of Barrett's esophagus
48. Esophageal impedance study
49. Endoscopic retrograde cholangiopancreatography (ERCP)
50. Enrollment assistance services
51. Extracorporeal shock wave lithotripter (ESWL)
52. Fertility clinic
53. Fitness center
54. Freestanding outpatient care center
55. Genetic testing/counseling
56. Geriatric services
57. Health fair
58. Health research
59. Health screenings
60. Hemodialysis
61. HIV–AIDS services
62. Home health services
63. Hospice program
64. Hospital–based outpatient care center services
65. Immunization program
66. Indigent care clinic
67. Intermediate nursing care
68. Linguistic/translation services
69. Meals on wheels
70. Medical surgical intensive care services
71. Mobile health services
72. Neonatal intensive care
73. Neonatal intermediate care
74. Neurological services
75. Nutrition programs
76. Obstetrics
77. Occupational health services
78. Oncology services
79. Orthopedic services
80. Other special care
81. Outpatient surgery
82. Pain management program
83. Inpatient palliative care unit
84. Palliative care program
85. Patient controlled analgesia (PCA)
86. Patient education center
87. Patient representative services
88. Pediatric intensive care services
89. Pediatric medical–surgical care
90. Physical rehabilitation inpatient services
91. Assistive technology center
92. Electrodiagnostic services
93. Physical rehabilitation outpatient services
94. Prosthetic and orthotic services
95. Robot-assisted walking therapy
96. Simulated rehabilitation environment
97. Primary care department
98. Psychiatric care
99. Psychiatric child–adolescent services
100. Psychiatric consultation–liaison services
101. Psychiatric education services
102. Psychiatric emergency services
103. Psychiatric geriatric services
104. Psychiatric outpatient services
105. Psychiatric partial hospitalization services
106. Psychiatric residential treatment
107. CT scanner
108. Diagnostic radioisotope facility
109. Electron beam computed tomography (EBCT)
110. Full–field digital mammography (FFDM)
111. Magnetic resonance imaging (MRI)
112. Intraoperative magnetic resonance imaging
113. Magnetoencephalography (MEG)
114. Multi–slice spiral computed tomography (MSCT) (<64 slice CT)
115. Multi–slice spiral computed tomography (64 + slice CT)
116. Positron emission tomography (PET)
117. Positron emission tomography/CT (PET/CT)
118. Single photon emission computerized tomography (SPECT)
119. Ultrasound
120. Image–guided radiation therapy (IGRT)
121. Intensity–modulated radiation therapy (IMRT)
122. Proton beam therapy
123. Shaped beam radiation therapy
124. Stereotactic radiosurgery
125. Retirement housing
126. Robotic surgery
127. Rural health clinic
128. Skilled nursing care
129. Sleep center
130. Social work services
131. Sports medicine
132. Support groups
133. Swing bed services
134. Teen outreach services
135. Tobacco treatment/cessation program
136. Bone marrow transplant services
137. Heart transplant
138. Kidney transplant
139. Liver transplant
140. Lung transplant
141. Tissue transplant
142. Other transplant
143. Transportation to health services
144. Urgent care center
145. Virtual colonoscopy
146. Volunteer services department
147. Women's health center/services
148. Wound management services

Each year, an annual survey of hospitals is conducted by the American Hospital Association through its Health Forum affiliate.

The facilities and services found below are provided by the hospital. For data products reflecting the services provided by a hospital through its health care system, or network or through a formal arrangement with another provider contact Health Forum at 800/821–2039, or visit www.healthforum.com.

The AHA Guide to the Health Care Field does not include all data collected from the 2015 Annual Survey. Requests for purchasing other Annual Survey data should be directed to Health Forum LLC, an affiliate of the American Hospital Association, 155 N. Wacker Drive, Chicago, IL 60606, 800/821–2039.

Definitions of Facility Codes

1. **Acute long–term care.** Provides specialized acute hospital care to medically complex patients who are critically ill, have multisystem complications and/or failure, and require hospitalization averaging 25 days, in a facility offering specialized treatment programs and therapeutic intervention on a 24–hour/7 day a week basis.

2. **Adult day care program.** Program providing supervision, medical and psychological care, and social activities for older adults who live at home or in another family setting, but cannot be alone or prefer to be with others during the day. May include intake assessment, health monitoring, occupational therapy, personal care, noon meal, and transportation services.

3. **Airborne infection isolation room.** A single–occupancy room for patient care where environmental factors are controlled in an effort to minimize the transmission of those infectious agents, usually spread person to person by droplet nuclei associated with coughing and inhalation. Such rooms typically have specific ventilation requirements for controlled ventilation, air pressure and filtration.

4. **Alcoholism–drug abuse or dependency inpatient unit.** Provides diagnosis and therapeutic services to patients with alcoholism or other drug dependencies. Includes care for inpatient/residential treatment for patients whose course of treatment involves more intensive care than provided in an outpatient setting or where patient requires supervised withdrawal.

5. **Alcoholism–drug abuse or dependency outpatient unit.** Organized hospital services that provide medical care and/or rehabilitative treatment services to outpatients for whom the primary diagnosis is alcoholism or other chemical dependency.

6. **Alzheimer center.** Facility that offers care to persons with Alzheimer's disease and their families through an integrated program of clinical services, research, and education.

7. **Ambulance services.** Provision of ambulance services to the ill and injured who require medical attention on a scheduled or unscheduled basis.

8. **Ambulatory surgery center.** Facility that provides care to patients requiring surgery who are admitted and discharged on the same day. Ambulatory surgery centers are distinct from same day surgical units within the hospital outpatient departments for purposes of Medicare payments.

9. **Arthritis treatment center.** Specifically equipped and staffed center for the diagnosis and treatment of arthritis and other joint disorders.

10. **Assisted living.** A special combination of housing, supportive services, personalized assistance and health care designed to respond to the individual needs of those who need help in activities of daily living and instrumental activities of daily living. Supportive services are available, 24 hours a day, to meet scheduled and unscheduled needs, in a way that promotes maximum independence and dignity for each resident and encourages the involvement of a resident's family, neighbor and friends.

11. **Auxiliary.** A volunteer community organization formed to assist the hospital in carrying out its purpose and to serve as a link between the institution and the community.

12. **Bariatric/weight control services.** Bariatrics is the medical practice of weight reduction.

13. **Birthing room–LDR room–LDRP room.** A single room–type of maternity care with a more homelike setting for families than the traditional three–room unit (labor/delivery/recovery) with a separate postpartum area. A birthing room combines labor and delivery in one room. An LDR room accommodates three stages in the birthing process— labor, delivery, and recovery. An LDRP room accommodates all four stages of the birth process—labor, delivery, recovery and postpartum.

14. **Blood donor center.** A facility that performs, or is responsible for the collection, processing, testing or distribution of blood and components.

15. **Breast cancer screening/mammograms.** Mammography screening–the use of breast x–ray to detect unsuspected breast cancer in asymptomatic women. Diagnostic mammography–the x–ray imaging of breast tissue in symptomatic women who are considered to have a substantial likelihood of having breast cancer already.

16. **Burn care services.** Provides care to severely burned patients. Severely burned patients are those with any of the following: 1. Second–degree burns of more than 25% total body surface area for adults or 20% total body surface area for children; 2. Third–degree burns of more than 10% total body surface area; 3. Any severe burns of the hands, face, eyes, ears or feet or; 4. All inhalation injuries, electrical burns, complicated burn injuries involving fractures and other major traumas, and all other poor risk factors.

17. **Cardiac intensive care.** Provides patient care of a more specialized

nature than the usual medical and surgical care, on the basis of physicians' orders and approved nursing care plans. The unit is staffed with specially trained nursing personnel and contains monitoring and specialized support or treatment equipment for patients who, because of heart seizure, open–heart surgery, or other life–threatening conditions, require intensified, comprehensive observation and care. May include myocardial infarction, pulmonary care, and heart transplant units.

18. **Adult cardiology services.** An organized clinical service offering diagnostic and interventional procedures to manage the full range of adult heart conditions.

19. **Pediatric cardiology services.**

20. **Adult diagnostic catheterization.** (also called coronary angiography or coronary arteriography) is used to assist in diagnosing complex heart conditions. Cardiac angiography involves the insertion of a tiny catheter up into the artery in the groin then carefully threading the catheter up into the aorta where the coronary arteries originate. Once the catheter is in place, a dye is injected which allows the cardiologist to see the size, shape and distribution of the coronary arteries. These images are used to diagnose heart disease and to determine, among other things, whether or not surgery is indicated.

21. **Pediatric diagnostic catheterization.** (also called coronary angiography or coronary arteriography) is used to assist in diagnosing complex heart conditions. Cardiac angiography involves the insertion of a tiny catheter up into the artery in the groin then carefully threading the catheter up into the aorta where the coronary arteries originate. Once the catheter is in place, a dye is injected which allows the cardiologist to see the size, shape and distribution of the coronary arteries. These images are used to diagnose heart disease and to determine, among other things, whether or not surgery is indicated.

22. **Adult interventional cardiac catheterization.** Nonsurgical procedure that utilizes the same basic principles as diagnostic cathetereization and then uses advanced the techniques to improve the heart's function. It can be less invasive alternative to heart surgery.

23. **Pediatric diagnostic catheterization.** Nonsurgical procedure that utilizes the same basic principles as diagnostic cathetereization and then uses advanced the techniques to improve the heart's function. It can be less invasive alternative to heart surgery.

24. **Adult cardiac surgery.** Includes minimally invasive procedures that include surgery done with only a small incision or no incision at all, such as through a laparoscope or an endoscope and more invasive major surgical procedures that include open chest and open heart surgery.

25. **Pediatric cardiac surgery.** Includes minimally invasive procedures that include surgery done with only a small incision or no incision at all, such as through a laparoscope or an endoscope and more invasive major surgical procedures that include open chest and open heart surgery defibrillator implantation and follow-up.

26. **Adult cardiac electrophysiology.** Evaluation and management of patients with complex rhythm or conduction abnormalities, including diagnostic testing, treatment of arrhythmias by catheter ablation or drug therapy, and pacemaker/defibrillator implantation and follow-up.

27. **Pediatric cardiac electrophysiology.**

28. **Cardiac rehabilitation.** A medically supervised program to help heart patients recover quickly and improve their overall physical and mental functioning. The goal is to reduce risk of another cardiac event or to keep an already present heart condition from getting worse. Cardiac rehabilitation programs include: counseling to patients, an exercise program, helping patients modify risk factors such as smoking and high blood pressure, providing vocational guidance to enable the patient to return to work, supplying information on physical limitations and lending emotional support.

29. **Case management.** A system of assessment, treatment planning, referral and follow–up that ensures the provision of comprehensive and continuous services and the coordination of payment and reimbursement for care.

30. **Chaplaincy/pastoral care services.** A service ministering religious activities and providing pastoral counseling to patients, their families, and staff of a health care organization.

31. **Chemotherapy.** An organized program for the treatment of cancer by the use of drugs or chemicals.

32. **Children's wellness program.** A program that encourages improved health status and a healthful lifestyle of children through health education, exercise, nutrition and health promotion.

33. **Chiropractic services.** An organized clinical service including spinal manipulation or adjustment and related diagnostic and therapeutic services.

34. **Community health education.** Education that provides health information to individuals and populations as well as support for personal, family and community health decisions with the objective of improving health status.

35. **Community outreach.** A program that systematically interacts with the community to identify those in need of services, alerting persons and their families to the availability of services, locating needed services, and enabling persons to enter the service delivery system.

36. **Complementary and alternative medicine services.** Organized hospital services or formal arrangements to providers that provide care or treatment not based solely on traditional western allopathic medical teachings as instructed in most U.S. medical schools. Includes any of the following; acupuncture, chiropractic, homeopathy, osteopathy, diet and lifestyle changes, herbal medicine, massage therapy, etc.

37. **Computer assisted orthopedic surgery (CAOS).** Orthopedic surgery using computer technology, enabling three–dimensional graphic models to visualize a patient's anatomy.

38. **Crisis prevention** Services provided in order to promote physical and mental well being and the early identification of disease and ill health prior to the onset and recognition of symptoms so as to permit early treatment.

39. **Dental services.** An organized dental service, not necessarily involving special facilities, that provides dental or oral services to inpatients or outpatients.

40. **Emergency department.** Hospital facilities for the provision of

unscheduled outpatient services to patients whose conditions require immediate care. Must be staffed 24 hours a day.

41. **Pediatric emergency department.** Hospital facilities for the provision of unscheduled outpatient services to patients whose conditions require immediate care.

42. **Satellite emergency department.** A facility owned and operated by the hospital but physically separate from the hospital for the provision of unscheduled outpatient services to patients whose conditions require.

43. **Trauma center (certified).** A facility certified to provide emergency and specialized intensive care to critically ill and injured patients.

44. **Enabling services.** A program that is designed to help the patient access health care services by offering any of the following linguistic services, transportation services, and/or referrals to local social services agencies.

45. **Optical colonoscopy.** An examination of the interior of the colon using a long, flexible, lighted tube with a small built-in camera.

46. **Endoscopic ultrasound.** Specially designed endoscope that incorporates an ultrasound transducer used to obtain detailed images of organs in the chest and abdomen. The endoscope can be passed through the mouth or the anus. When combined with needle biopsy the procedure can assist in diagnosis and staging of cancer.

47. **Ablation of Barrett's esophagus.** Premalignant condition that can lead to adenocarcinoma of the esophagus. The non surgical ablation of the premalignant tissue in Barrett's esophagus by the application of thermal energy or light through an endoscope passed from the mouth into the esophagus.

48. **Esophageal impedance study.** A test in which a catheter is placed through the nose into the esophagus to measure whether gas or liquids are passing from the stomach into the esophagus and causing symptoms.

49. **Endoscopic retrograde cholangiopancreatography (ERCP).** A procedure in which a catheter is introduced through an endoscope into the bile ducts and pancreatic ducts. Injection of contrast materials permits detailed x–ray of these structures. The procedure is used diagnostically as

well as therapeutically to relieve obstruction or remove stones

50. **Enrollment assistance services.** A program that provides enrollment assistance for patients who are potentially eligible for public health insurance programs such as Medicaid, State Children's Health Insurance, or local/state indigent care programs. The specific services offered could include explanation of benefits, assist applicants in completing the application and locating all relevant documents, conduct eligibilty interviews, and/or forward applications and documentation to state/local social service or health agency.

51. **Extracorporeal shock wave lithotripter (ESWL).** A medical device used for treating stones in the kidney or urethra. The device disintegrates kidney stones noninvasively through the transmission of acoustic shock waves directed at the stones.

52. **Fertility clinic.** A specialized program set in an infertility center that provides counseling and education as well as advanced reproductive techniques such as: injectable therapy, reproductive surgeries, treatment for endometriosis, male factor infertility, tubal reversals, in vitro fertilization (IVF), donor eggs, and other such services to help patients achieve successful pregnancies.

53. **Fitness center.** Provides exercise, testing, or evaluation programs and fitness activities to the community and hospital employees.

54. **Freestanding outpatient care center.** A facility owned and operated by the hospital, but physically separate from the hospital, that provides various medical treatments on an outpatient basis only. In addition to treating minor illnesses or injuries, the center will stabilize seriously ill or injured patients before transporting them to a hospital. Laboratory and radiology services are usually available.

55. **Genetic testing/counseling** A service equipped with adequate laboratory facilities and directed by a qualified physician to advise parents and prospective parents on potential problems in cases of genetic defects. A genetic test is the analysis of human DNA, RNA, chromosomes, proteins, and certain metabolites in order to detect heritable disease–related genotypes, mutations,

phenotypes, or karyotypes for clinical purposes. Genetic tests can have diverse purposes, including the diagnosis of genetic diseases in newborns, children, and adults; the identification of future health risks; the prediction of drug responses; and the assessment of risks to future children.

56. **Geriatric services.** The branch of medicine dealing with the physiology of aging and the diagnosis and treatment of disease affecting the aged. Services could include: Adult day care program; Alzheimer's diagnostic–assessment services; Comprehensive geriatric assessment; Emergency response system; Geriatric acute care unit; and/or Geriatric clinics.

57. **Health fair.** Community health education events that focus on the prevention of disease and promotion of health through such activities as audiovisual exhibits and free diagnostic services.

58. **Health research.** Organized hospital research program in any of the following areas: basic research, clinical research, community health research, and/or research on innovative health care delivery.

59. **Health screenings.** A preliminary procedure, such as a test or examination to detect the most characteristic sign or signs of a disorder that may require further investigation.

60. **Hemodialysis.** Provision of equipment and personnel for the treatment of renal insufficiency on an inpatient or outpatient basis.

61. **HIV–AIDS services.** Services may include one or more of the following: HIV–AIDS unit (special unit or team designated and equipped specifically for diagnosis, treatment, continuing care planning, and counseling services for HIV–AIDS patients and their families.) General inpatient care for HIV–AIDS (inpatient diagnosis and treatment for human immunodeficiency virus and acquired immunodeficiency syndrome patients, but dedicated unit is not available.) Specialized outpatient program for HIV–AIDS (special outpatient program providing diagnostic, treatment, continuing care planning, and counseling for HIV–AIDS patients and their families.)

62. **Home health services.** Service providing nursing, therapy, and

health–related homemaker or social services in the patient's home.

63. **Hospice program.** A program providing palliative care, chiefly medical relief of pain and supportive services, addressing the emotional, social, financial, and legal needs of terminally ill patients and their families. Care can be provided in a variety of settings, both inpatient and at home.

64. **Hospital–based outpatient care center services.** Organized hospital health care services offered by appointment on an ambulatory basis. Services may include outpatient surgery, examination, diagnosis, and treatment of a variety of medical conditions on a nonemergency basis, and laboratory and other diagnostic testing as ordered by staff or outside physician referral.

65. **Immunization program.** Program that plans, coordinates and conducts immunization services in the community.

66. **Indigent care clinic.** Health care services for uninsured and underinsured persons where care is free of charge or charged on a sliding scale. This would include "free clinics" staffed by volunteer practitioners, but could also be staffed by employees with sponsoring health care organizations subsidizing the cost of service.

67. **Intermediate nursing care.** Provides health–related services (skilled nursing care and social services) to residents with a variety of physical conditions or functional disabilities. These residents do not require the care provided by a hospital or skilled nursing facility, but do need supervision and support services.

68. **Linguistic/translation services.** Services provided by the hospital designed to make health care more accessible to non–English speaking patients and their physicians.

69. **Meals on wheels.** A hospital sponsored program which delivers meals to people, usually the elderly, who are unable to prepare their own meals. Low cost, nutritional meals are delivered to individuals' homes on a regular basis.

70. **Medical surgical intensive care services.** Provides patient care of a more intensive nature than the usual medical and surgical care, on the basis of physicians' orders and approved nursing care plans. These units are staffed with specially trained nursing personnel and contain monitoring and specialized support equipment of patients who, because of shock, trauma, or other life–threatening conditions, require intensified, comprehensive observation and care. Includes mixed intensive care units.

71. **Mobile health services.** Vans and other vehicles used to deliver primary care services.

72. **Neonatal intensive care.** A unit that must be separate from the newborn nursery providing intensive care to all sick infants including those with the very lowest birth weights (less that 1500 grams). NICU has potential for providing mechanical ventilation, neonatal surgery, and special care for the sickest infants born in the hospital or transferred from another institution. A full–time neonatologist serves as director of the NICU.

73. **Neonatal intermediate care.** A unit that must be separate from the normal newborn nursery and that provides intermediate and/or recovery care and some specialized services, including immediate resuscitation, intravenous therapy, and capacity for prolonged oxygen therapy and monitoring.

74. **Neurological services.** Services provided by the hospital dealing with the operative and nonoperative management of disorders of the central, peripheral, and autonomic nervous system.

75. **Nutrition programs.** Those services within a health care facility which are designed to provide inexpensive, nutritionally sound meals to patients.

76. **Obstetrics.** Levels should be designated: (1) unit provides services for uncomplicated maternity and newborn cases; (2) unit provides services for uncomplicated cases, the majority of complicated problems, and special neonatal services; and (3) unit provides services for all serious illnesses and abnormalities and is supervised by a full–time maternal/fetal specialist.

77. **Occupational health services.** Includes services designed to protect the safety of employees from hazards in the work environment.

78. **Oncology services.** Inpatient and outpatient services for patients with cancer, including comprehensive care, support and guidance in addition to patient education and preventiion, chemotherapy, counseling, and other treatment methods.

79. **Orthopedic services.** Services provided for the prevention or correction of injuries or disorders of the skeletal system and associated muscles, joints, and ligaments.

80. **Other special care.** Provides care to patients requiring care more intensive than that provided in the acute area, yet not sufficiently intensive to require admission to an intensive care unit. Patients admitted to the area are usually transferred here from an intensive care unit once their condition has improved. These units are sometimes referred to as definitive observation, step–down, or progressive care units.

81. **Outpatient surgery.** Scheduled surgical services provided to patients who do not remain in the hospital overnight. The surgery may be performed in operating suites also used for inpatient surgery, specially designated surgical suites for outpatient surgery, or procedure rooms within an outpatient care facility.

82. **Pain management program.** A hospital wide formalized program that includes staff education for the management of chronic and acute pain based on guidelines and protocols like those developed by the agency for Health Care Policy Research, etc.

83. **Inpatient palliative care unit.** An inpatient palliative care ward is a physically discreet, inpatient nursing unit where the focus is palliative care. The patient care focus is on symptom relief for complex patients who may be continuing to undergo primary treatment. Care is delivered by palliative medicine specialists.

84. **Palliative care program.** An organized program providing specialized medical care, drugs or therapies for the management of acute or chronic pain and/or the control of symptoms adminstered by specially trained physicians and other clinicians; and supportive care services, such as counseling on advanced directives, spiritual care, and social services, to patients with advanced disease and their families.

85. **Patient controlled analgesia (PCA).** Patient Controlled Analgesia (PCA) is intravenously administered pain medicine under the patient's control. The patient has a button on the end of a cord than can be pushed at will, whenever more pain medicine is desired. This button will only deliver more pain medicine at pre–

determined intervals, as programmed by the doctor's order.

86. **Patient education center.** Written goals and objectives for the patient and/or family related to therapeutic regimens, medical procedures, and self care.

87. **Patient representative services.** Organized hospital services providing personnel through whom patients and staff can seek solutions to institutional problems affecting the delivery of high–quality care and services.

88. **Pediatric intensive care services.** Provides care to pediatric patients that is of a more intensive nature than that usually provided to pediatric patients. The unit is staffed with specially trained personnel and contains monitoring and specialized support equipment for treatment of patients who, because of shock, trauma, or other life–threatening conditions, require intensified, comprehensive observation and care.

89. **Pediatric medical–surgical care.** Provides acute care to pediatric patients on the basis of physicians' orders and approved nursing care plans.

90. **Physical rehabilitation inpatient services.** Provides care encompassing a comprehensive array of restoration services for the disabled and all support services necessary to help patients attain their maximum functional capacity.

91. **Assistive technology center.** A program providing access to specialized hardware and software with adaptations allowing individuals greater independence with mobility, dexterity, or increased communication options.

92. **Electrodiagnostic services.** Diagnostic testing services for nerve and muscle function including services such as nerve conduction studies and needle electromyography.

93. **Physical rehabilitation outpatient services.** Outpatient program providing medical, health–related, therapy, social, and/or vocational services to help disabled persons attain or retain their maximum functional capacity.

94. **Prosthetic and orthotic services.** Services providing comprehensive prosthetic and orthotic evaluation, fitting, and training.

95. **Robot-assisted walking therapy.** A form of physical therapy that uses a robotic device to assist patients who are relearning how to walk.

96. **Simulated rehabilitation environment.** Rehabilitation focused on retraining functional skills in a contextually appropriate environment (simulated home and community settings) or in a traditional setting (gymnasium) using motor learning principles.

97. **Primary care department.** A unit or clinic within the hospital that provides primary care services (e.g. general pediatric care, general internal medicine, family practice and gynecology) through hospital–salaried medical and or nursing staff, focusing on evaluating and diagnosing medical problems and providing medical treatment on an outpatient basis.

98. **Psychiatric care.** Provides acute or long–term care to emotionally disturbed patients, including patients admitted for diagnosis and those admitted for treatment of psychiatric problems, on the basis of physicians' orders and approved nursing care plans. Long–term care may include intensive supervision to the chronically mentally ill, mentally disordered, or other mentally incompetent persons.

99. **Psychiatric child–adolescent services.** Provides care to emotionally disturbed children and adolescents, including those admitted for diagnosis and those admitted for treatment.

100. **Psychiatric consultation–liaison services.** Provides organized psychiatric consultation/liaison services to nonpsychiatric hospital staff and/or department on psychological aspects of medical care that may be generic or specific to individual patients.

101. **Psychiatric education services.** Provides psychiatric educational services to community agencies and workers such as schools, police, courts, public health nurses, welfare agencies, clergy and so forth. The purpose is to expand the mental health knowledge and competence of personnel not working in the mental health field and to promote good mental health through improved understanding, attitudes, and behavioral patterns.

102. **Psychiatric emergency services.** Services or facilities available on a 24–hour basis to provide immediate unscheduled outpatient care, diagnosis, evaluation, crisis intervention, and assistance to persons suffering acute emotional or mental distress.

103. **Psychiatric geriatric services.** Provides care to emotionally disturbed elderly patients, including those admitted for diagnosis and those admitted for treatment.

104. **Psychiatric outpatient services.** Provides medical care, including diagnosis and treatment of psychiatric outpatients.

105. **Psychiatric partial hospitalization services.** Organized hospital services of intensive day/evening outpatient services of three hours or more duration, distinguished from other outpatient visits of one hour.

106. **Psychiatric residential treatment.**

107. **CT scanner.** Computed tomographic scanner for head and whole body scans.

108. **Diagnostic radioisotope facility.** The use of radioactive isotopes (Radiopharmaceutical) as tracers or indicators to detect an abnormal condition or disease.

109. **Electron beam computed tomography (EBCT).** A high tech computed tomography scan used to detect coronary artery disease by measuring coronary calcifications. This imaging procedure uses electron beams which are magnetically steered to produce a visual of the coronary artery and the images are produced faster than conventional CT scans.

110. **Full–field digital mammography (FFDM).** Combines the x–ray generators and tubes used in analog screen–film mammography (SFM) with a detector plate that converts the x–rays into a digital signal.

111. **Magnetic resonance imaging (MRI).** The use of a uniform magnetic field and radio frequencies to study tissue and structure of the body. This procedure enables the visualization of biochemical activity of the cell in vivo without the use of ionizing radiation, radioisotopic substances, or high–frequency sound.

112. **Intraoperative magnetic resonance imaging.** An integrated surgery system which provides an MRI system in an operating room. The system allows for immediate evaluation of the degree to tumor resection while the patient is undergoing a surgical resection. Intraoperative MRI exists when a MRI (low–field or high–field) is placed in the operating theater and is

used during surgical resection without moving the patient from the operating room to the diagnostic imaging suite.

113. **Magnetoencephalography (MEG).** A noninvasive neurophysiological measurement tool used to study magnetic fields generated by neuronal activity of the brain. MEG provides direct information about the dynamics of evoked and spontaneous neural activity and the location of their sources in the brain. The primary uses of MEG include assisting surgeons in localizing the source of epilepsy, sensory mapping and the study of brain function. When it is combined with structural imaging, it is known as magnetic source imaging (MSI).

114. **Multi–slice spiral computed tomography (MSCT) (<64 slice CT).** A specialized computed tomography procedure that provides three–dimensional processing and allows narrower and multiple slices with increased spatial resolution and faster scanning times as compared to a regular computed tomography scan.

115. **Multi–slice spiral computed tomography (64 + slice CT).** Involves the acquisition of volumetric tomographic x–ray absorption data expressed in Hounsfield units using multiple rows of detectors. 64+ systems reconstruct the equivalent of 64 or greater slices to cover the imaged volume.

116. **Positron emission tomography (PET).** A nuclear medicine imaging technology which uses radioactive (positron emitting) isotopes created in a cyclotron or generator and computers to produce composite pictures of the brain and heart at work. PET scanning produces sectional images depicting metabolic activity or blood flow rather than anatomy.

117. **Positron emission tomography/CT (PET/CT).** Provides metabolic functional information for the monitoring of chemotherapy, radiotherapy and surgical planning.

118. **Single photon emission computerized tomography (SPECT).** A nuclear medicine imaging technology that combines existing technology of gamma camera imaging with computed tomographic imaging technology to provide a more precise and clear image.

119. **Ultrasound.** The use of acoustic waves above the range of 20,000 cycles per second to visualize internal body structures.

120. **Image–guided radiation therapy (IGRT).** Automated system for image–guided radiation therapy that enables clinicians to obtain high–resolution x–ray images to pinpoint tumor sites, adjust patient positioning when necessary, and complete a treatment, all within the standard treatment time slot, allowing for more effective cancer treatments.

121. **Intensity–modulated radiation Therapy (IMRT).** A type of three–dimensional radiation therapy, which improves the targeting of treatment delivery in a way that is likely to decrease damage to normal tissues and allows varying intensities diagnosis of genetic diseases in newborns, children, and adults; the identification of future health risks; the prediction of drug responses; and the assessment of risks to future children.

122. **Proton beam therapy.** A form of radiation therapy which administers proton beams. While producing the same biologic effects as x–ray beams, the energy distribution of protons differs from conventional x–ray beams in that they can be more precisely focused in tissue volumes in a three–dimensional pattern resulting in less surrounding tissue damage than conventional radiation therapy permitting administration of higher doses.

123. **Shaped beam radiation therapy.** A precise, non–invasive treatment that involves targeting beams of radiation that mirror the exact size and shape of a tumor at a specific area of a tumor to shrink or destroy cancerous cells. This procedure delivers a therapeutic dose of radiation that conforms precisely to the shape of the tumor, thus minimizing the risk to nearby tissues.

124. **Stereotactic radiosurgery.** Stereotactic radiosurgery (SRS) is a radiotherapy modality that delivers a high dosage of radiation to a discrete treatment area in as few as one treatment session. Includes gamma knife, cyberknife, etc.

125. **Retirement housing.** A facility which provides social activities to senior citizens, usually retired persons, who do not require health care but some short–term skilled nursing care may be provided. A retirement center may furnish housing and may also have acute hospital and long–term care facilities, or it may

arrange for acute and long term care through affiliated institutions.

126. **Robotic surgery.** The use of mechanical guidance devices to remotely manipulate surgical instrumentation.

127. **Rural health clinic.** A clinic located in a rural, medically under-served area in the United States that has a separate reimbursement structure from the standard medical office under the Medicare and Medicaid programs.

128. **Skilled nursing care.** Provides non–acute medical and skilled nursing care services, therapy, and social services under the supervision of a licensed registered nurse on a 24–hour basis.

129. **Sleep center.** Specially equipped and staffed center for the diagnosis and treatment of sleep disorders.

130. **Social work services.** Services may include one or more of the following: Organized social work services (services that are properly directed and sufficiently staffed by qualified individuals who provide assistance and counseling to patients and their families in dealing with social, emotional, and environmental problems associated with illness or disability, often in the context of financial or discharge planning coordination.) Outpatient social work services (social work services provided in ambulatory care areas.) Emergency department social work services (social work services provided to emergency department patients by social workers dedicated to the emergency department or on call.)

131. **Sports medicine.** Provision of diagnostic screening and assessment and clinical and rehabilitation services for the prevention and treatment of sports–related injuries.

132. **Support groups.** A hospital sponsored program which allows a group of individuals with the same or similar problems who meet periodically to share experiences, problems, and solutions, in order to support each other.

133. **Swing bed services.** A hospital bed that can be used to provide either acute or long–term care depending on community or patients needs. To be eligible a hospital must have a Medicare provider agreement in place, have fewer than 100 beds, be located in a rural area, not have a 24 hour nursing service waiver in effect, have not been terminated from the

program in the prior two years, and meet various service conditions.

134. **Teen outreach services.** A program focusing on the teenager which encourages an improved health status and a healthful lifestyle including physical, emotional, mental, social, spiritual and economic health through education, exercise, nutrition and health promotion.

135. **Tobacco treatment/cessation program.** Organized hospital services with the purpose of ending tobacco–use habits of patients addicted to tobacco/nicotine.

136.–142. **Transplant services.** The branch of medicine that transfers an organ or tissue from one person to another or from one body part to another to replace a diseased structure or to restore function or to change appearance. Services could include: Bone marrow transplant program (**136. Bone marrow**); heart (**137. Heart transplant**), kidney (**138. Kidney transplant**), liver (**139. Liver transplant**) lung (**140. Lung transplant**), tissue (**141. Tissue**

transplant). Please include heart/lung or other multi– transplant surgeries in other (**142. Other Transplant**).

143. **Transportation to health services.** A long–term care support service designed to assist the mobility of the elderly. Some programs offer improved financial access by offering reduced rates and barrier–free buses or vans with ramps and lifts to assist the elderly or handicapped; others offer subsidies for public transport systems or operate mini–bus services exclusively for use by senior citizens.

144. **Urgent care center.** A facility that provides care and treatment for problems that are not life–threatening but require attention over the short term. These units function like emergency rooms but are separate from hospitals with which they may have backup affiliation arrangements.

145. **Virtual colonoscopy.** Noninvasive screening procedure used to visualize, analyze and detect cancerous or potentially cancerous polyps in the colon.

146. **Volunteer services department.** An organized hospital department responsible for coordinating the services of volunteers working within the institution.

147. **Women's center.** An area set aside for coordinated education and treatment services specifically for and promoted by women as provided by this special unit. Services may or may not include obstetrics but include a range of services other than OB.

148. **Wound management services.** Services for patients with chronic wounds and non–healing wounds often resulting from diabetes, poor circulation, improper seating and immunocompromising conditions. The goals are to progress chronic wounds through stages of healing, reduce and eliminate infections, increase physical function to minimize complications from current wounds and prevent future chronic wounds. Wound management services are provided on an inpatient or outpatient basis, depending on the intensity of service needed.

Definitions of Physician Codes

1. **Closed physician–hospital organization (PHO).** A PHO that restricts physician membership to those practitioners who meet criteria for cost effectiveness and/or high quality.

2. **Equity model.** Allows established practitioners to become shareholders in a professional corporation in exchange for tangible and intangible assets of their existing practices.

3. **Foundation.** A corporation, organized either as a hospital affiliate or subsidiary, which purchases both the tangible and intangible assets of one or more medical group practices. Physicians remain in a separate corporate entity but sign a professional services agreement with the foundation.

4. **Group practice without walls.** Hospital sponsors the formation of, or

provides capital to physicians to establish, a 'quasi' group to share administrative expenses while remaining independent practitioners.

5. **Independent practice association (IPA).** A legal entity that hold managed care contracts. The IPA then contracts with physicians, usually in solo practice, to provide care either on a fee–for–services or capitated basis. The purpose of an IPA is to assist solo physicians in obtaining managed care contracts.

6. **Integrated salary model.** Physicians are salaried by the hospital or another entity of a health system to provide medical services for primary care and specialty care.

7. **Management services organization (MSO).** A corporation, owned by the

hospital or a physician/hospital joint venture, that provides management services to one or more medical group practices. The MSO purchases the tangible assets of the practices and leases them back as part of a full–service management agreement, under which the MSO employs all non–physician staff and provides all supplies/administrative systems for a fee.

8. **Open physician–hospital organization (PHO).** A joint venture between the hospital and all members of the medical staff who wish to participate. The PHO can act as a unified agent in managed care contracting, own a managed care plan, own and operate ambulatory care centers or ancillary services projects, or provide administrative services to physician members.

Control and Service Classifications

Control

Government, nonfederal
State
County
City
City–county
Hospital district or authority

Nongovernment not-for-profit
Church operated
Other

Investor–owned (for–profit)
Individual
Partnership
Corporation

Government, federal
Air Force
Army
Navy
Public Health Service other than 47
Veterans Affairs

Federal other than 41–45, 47–48
Public Health Service Indian Service
Department of Justice

Osteopathic
Church operated
Other not–for–profit
Other
Individual for–profit
Partnership for–profit
Corporation for–profit

Service

General medical and surgical
Hospital unit of an institution
  (prison hospital, college infirmary, etc.)
Hospital unit within a facility for persons
  with intellectual disabilities
Surgical
Psychiatric
Tuberculosis and other respiratory
  diseases
Cancer
Heart

Obstetrics and gynecology
Eye, ear, nose, and throat
Rehabilitation
Orthopedic
Chronic disease
Other specialty
Children's general
Children's hospital unit of an institution
Children's psychiatric
Children's tuberculosis and other
  respiratory diseases
Children's eye, ear, nose, and throat

Children's rehabilitation
Children's orthopedic
Children's chronic disease
Children's other specialty
Intellectual disabilities
Long–Term Acute Care
Alcoholism and other chemical
  dependency
Children's Long–Term Acute Care
Children's Cancer
Children's Heart

ALABAMA

ALABASTER—Shelby County

☐ **NOLAND HOSPITAL SHELBY (012013)**, 1000 First Street North, 3rd Floor, Zip 35007–8703; tel. 205/620–8641 **A**1 10 **F**1 3 17 18 26 28 29 30 60 61 67 70 75 77 79 80 84 90 91 92 103 107 111 115 119 128 130 148 **S** Noland Health Services, Inc., Birmingham, AL
Primary Contact: Laura S. Wills, Administrator
Web address: www.nolandhospitals.com
Control: Other not–for–profit (including NFP Corporation) **Service:** Long–Term Acute Care hospital

Staffed Beds: 15 **Admissions:** 125 **Census:** 10 **Outpatient Visits:** 0 **Births:** 0 **Total Expense ($000):** 4311 **Payroll Expense ($000):** 1550 **Personnel:** 30

☒ **SHELBY BAPTIST MEDICAL CENTER (010016)**, 1000 First Street North, Zip 35007–8703; tel. 205/620–8100 **A**1 3 10 **F**3 8 11 12 13 15 17 18 20 22 24 26 28 29 30 31 34 35 40 43 45 47 48 49 50 57 59 64 70 72 74 75 76 77 79 81 82 84 85 87 93 98 103 107 108 110 111 114 115 118 119 124 126 127 129 130 131 135 146 147 148 **S** TENET Healthcare Corporation, Dallas, TX
Primary Contact: Robert A. Phillips, President
CFO: Jennifer Pittman, Chief Financial Officer
CMO: Mark Scofield, M.D., Chief Medical Officer
CIO: Mike Nighman, Facility Coordinator Information Systems
CHR: Cindy Nicholson, Director Human Resources
CNO: Ed Price, Chief Nurse Officer
Web address: www.brookwoodbaptisthealth.com
Control: Corporation, Investor–owned, for–profit **Service:** General Medical and Surgical

Staffed Beds: 231 **Admissions:** 12460 **Census:** 171 **Outpatient Visits:** 113520 **Births:** 1074 **Total Expense ($000):** 151778 **Payroll Expense ($000):** 58306 **Personnel:** 975

ALEXANDER CITY—Tallapoosa County

☒ **RUSSELL MEDICAL CENTER (010065)**, 3316 Highway 280, Zip 35010–3369, Mailing Address: P.O. Box 939, Zip 35011–0939; tel. 256/329–7100 **A**1 10 19 **F**3 11 13 15 18 20 22 28 29 30 31 34 35 40 43 45 50 51 53 57 58 59 60 64 67 68 74 75 76 77 78 79 80 81 82 85 87 89 93 107 108 110 111 115 116 119 121 123 126 129 131 132 143 146 148
Primary Contact: Lother E. Peace, III, President and Chief Executive Officer
CFO: J. Matthew Fisher, Chief Financial Officer
CMO: Michele Goldhagen, M.D., Chief of Staff
CIO: Tommy Spraggins, Director Information Services
CHR: Mary Shockley, Director Human Resources
Web address: www.russellmedcenter.com
Control: Other not–for–profit (including NFP Corporation) **Service:** General Medical and Surgical

Staffed Beds: 69 **Admissions:** 3127 **Census:** 28 **Outpatient Visits:** 94594 **Births:** 461 **Total Expense ($000):** 69793 **Payroll Expense ($000):** 23324 **Personnel:** 518

ANDALUSIA—Covington County

☒ **ANDALUSIA HEALTH (010036)**, 849 South Three Notch Street, Zip 36420–5325, Mailing Address: P.O. Box 760, Zip 36420–1214; tel. 334/222–8466 **A**1 10 **F**3 8 11 13 15 29 30 34 35 40 43 45 46 51 57 59 60 64 65 68 69 74 75 76 77 79 80 81 82 85 87 89 93 107 108 110 111 114 116 117 119 129 131 133 135 146 147 148 **S** LifePoint Health, Brentwood, TN
Primary Contact: John C. Yanes, Chief Executive Officer
COO: Melissa Davis, Chief Operating Officer
CFO: Shirley M. Smith, Chief Financial Officer
CIO: Matthew Perry, Director Information Systems
CHR: Brian Woods, Human Resources Director
CNO: Melissa Davis, Chief Clinical Officer
Web address: www.andalusiahealth.com
Control: Corporation, Investor–owned, for–profit **Service:** General Medical and Surgical

Staffed Beds: 88 **Admissions:** 3077 **Census:** 29 **Outpatient Visits:** 34874 **Births:** 456 **Total Expense ($000):** 30504 **Payroll Expense ($000):** 11438

ANNISTON—Calhoun County

☐ **NOLAND HOSPITAL ANNISTON (012011)**, 400 East 10th Street, 4th Floor, Zip 36207–4716; tel. 256/741–6141 **A**1 10 **F**1 3 29 148 **S** Noland Health Services, Inc., Birmingham, AL
Primary Contact: Trina Woods, Administrator
Web address: www.nolandhealth.com
Control: Other not–for–profit (including NFP Corporation) **Service:** Long–Term Acute Care hospital

Staffed Beds: 38 **Admissions:** 293 **Census:** 21 **Outpatient Visits:** 0 **Births:** 0 **Total Expense ($000):** 10055

☒ **NORTHEAST ALABAMA REGIONAL MEDICAL CENTER (010078)**, 400 East Tenth Street, Zip 36207–4716, Mailing Address: P.O. Box 2208, Zip 36202–2208; tel. 256/235–5121 **A**1 2 10 **F**3 8 11 12 13 15 17 18 20 22 24 28 29 30 31 34 35 40 43 44 45 46 47 48 49 50 51 53 54 56 57 59 60 61 64 68 70 74 76 77 78 79 81 82 83 84 85 86 87 89 98 102 103 104 107 108 110 111 114 115 116 117 118 119 120 121 123 124 126 127 129 130 132 135 144 146 147 148 **P**6
Primary Contact: Louis A. Bass, Chief Executive Officer
CMO: David Zinn, M.D., Vice President Medical Affairs
CIO: Pete Furlow, Director Information Technology Services
CHR: Michael S. Simms, Sr., Vice President Human Resources
CNO: Elaine Davis, Chief Nursing Officer and Vice President Patient Services
Web address: www.rmccares.org
Control: Hospital district or authority, Government, nonfederal **Service:** General Medical and Surgical

Staffed Beds: 276 **Admissions:** 12301 **Census:** 169 **Outpatient Visits:** 110047 **Births:** 1754 **Total Expense ($000):** 163928 **Payroll Expense ($000):** 63517 **Personnel:** 1295

☒ **STRINGFELLOW MEMORIAL HOSPITAL (010038)**, 301 East 18th Street, Zip 36207–3952; tel. 256/235–8900 **A**1 10 **F**12 15 18 19 20 22 24 26 29 30 31 34 35 40 43 45 47 48 49 50 51 56 57 59 60 64 65 68 69 70 71 74 75 77 78 79 81 82 85 86 87 93 97 107 108 111 114 119 129 130 131 132 135 141 146 148 **S** Community Health Systems, Inc., Franklin, TN
Primary Contact: Jay Hinesley, FACHE, Chief Executive Officer
CIO: Peggy Henderson, Director Health Information
CHR: Tamatha Johnson, Director Human Resources
Web address: www.stringfellowhealth.com
Control: Corporation, Investor–owned, for–profit **Service:** General Medical and Surgical

Staffed Beds: 75 **Admissions:** 3103 **Census:** 31 **Outpatient Visits:** 40430 **Births:** 0

ASHLAND—Clay County

CLAY COUNTY HOSPITAL (010073), 83825 Highway 9, Zip 36251–7981, Mailing Address: P.O. Box 1270, Zip 36251–1270; tel. 256/354–2131, (Total facility includes 83 beds in nursing home–type unit) **A**10 **F**3 10 11 15 29 30 34 35 40 45 49 50 53 57 59 62 63 64 68 70 75 77 79 81 85 87 91 93 96 100 107 108 114 119 128 129 130 135 145 146 148
Primary Contact: Joel W. Tate, FACHE, Chief Executive Officer
CFO: Kerry W. Tomlin, Associate Administrator
CMO: David Hensleigh, Director Medical Staff
CIO: Patrick Smith, Director Information Technology
CHR: Linda T. Smith, Director Human Resources
CNO: Charles Griffin, Director of Nursing
Web address: www.claycountyhospital.com
Control: Church–operated, Nongovernment, not–for profit **Service:** Surgical

Staffed Beds: 129 **Admissions:** 1312 **Census:** 88 **Outpatient Visits:** 13493 **Births:** 0 **Total Expense ($000):** 20034

Hospital, Medicare Provider Number, Address, Telephone, Approval, Facility, and Physician Codes, Health Care System

★ American Hospital Association (AHA) membership   ◯ Healthcare Facilities Accreditation Program   ⇧ Center for Improvement in Healthcare Quality Accreditation
☐ The Joint Commission accreditation   ◇ DNV Healthcare Inc. accreditation   △ Commission on Accreditation of Rehabilitation Facilities (CARF) accreditation

ATHENS—Limestone County

☐ **ATHENS–LIMESTONE HOSPITAL (010079)**, 700 West Market Street, Zip 35611–2457, Mailing Address: P.O. Box 999, Zip 35612–0999; tel. 256/233–9292 **A**1 5 10 **F**3 7 8 11 13 15 18 28 29 34 35 40 46 48 50 51 53 54 56 57 58 59 64 68 70 73 75 76 77 79 81 84 85 86 87 89 93 98 107 108 109 110 111 114 115 118 119 129 130 131 132 143 144 146 147 148 **S** Huntsville Hospital Health System, Huntsville, AL
Primary Contact: David Pryor, President
COO: Randy Comer, Chief Operating Officer
CFO: Randy Comer, Chief Financial Officer
CMO: Jon Bignault, M.D., Chief of Staff
CIO: Kim Hoback, Supervisor Information Systems
CHR: Rachel Frey, Director Human Resources
CNO: Jan Lenz, Chief Nursing Officer
Web address: www.athenslimestonehospital.com
Control: Hospital district or authority, Government, nonfederal **Service:** General Medical and Surgical

Staffed Beds: 101 **Admissions:** 3992 **Census:** 41 **Outpatient Visits:** 125568 **Births:** 503 **Total Expense ($000):** 72176 **Payroll Expense ($000):** 30849 **Personnel:** 722

ATMORE—Escambia County

ATMORE COMMUNITY HOSPITAL (010169), 401 Medical Park Drive, Zip 36502–3091; tel. 251/368–2500 **A**10 **F**3 11 15 29 30 34 40 56 57 62 64 70 81 85 87 91 93 97 107 115 119 127 128 133 144 146 148 **S** Infirmary Health System, Mobile, AL
Primary Contact: Douglas Tanner, Administrator
CFO: Keith Strickling, Chief Financial Officer
CHR: Linda Lowrey, Human Resources Officer
CNO: Ashley Chunn, Director of Nursing
Web address: www.ebaptisthealthcare.org/AtmoreCommunityHospital/
Control: County–Government, nonfederal **Service:** General Medical and Surgical

Staffed Beds: 33 **Admissions:** 1358 **Census:** 14 **Outpatient Visits:** 33287 **Births:** 0 **Total Expense ($000):** 14963

BAY MINETTE—Baldwin County

NORTH BALDWIN INFIRMARY (010129), 1815 Hand Avenue, Zip 36507–4110, Mailing Address: P.O. Box 1409, Zip 36507–1409; tel. 251/937–5521, (Nonreporting) **A**10 **S** Infirmary Health System, Mobile, AL
Primary Contact: Benjamin K. Hansert, Administrator
CFO: J. Patrick Murphy, Chief Financial Officer
Web address: www.mobileinfirmary.org
Control: Other not–for–profit (including NFP Corporation) **Service:** General Medical and Surgical

Staffed Beds: 50

BESSEMER—Jefferson County

☐ **MEDICAL WEST (010114)**, 995 Ninth Avenue S.W., Zip 35022–4527; tel. 205/481–7000 **A**1 3 10 **F**3 11 13 15 18 29 30 31 34 40 42 43 45 49 50 54 57 59 60 64 68 70 74 75 76 77 78 79 80 81 82 85 86 90 92 93 94 96 98 100 101 102 103 104 107 108 110 111 114 115 118 119 129 130 132 143 146 147 148 **P**6 **S** UAB Health System, Birmingham, AL
Primary Contact: Brian Keith Pennington, President and Chief Executive Officer
COO: Sean Tinney, FACHE, Chief Operating Officer
CFO: Brandon H. Slocum, Senior Vice President and Chief Financial Officer
CMO: Conrad De Los Santos, President Medical Staff
CIO: Bob Duckworth, Director Information Systems
CHR: Gannon Davis, Director Human Resources
CNO: Pamela Spencer Autrey, R.N., Chief Nursing Officer
Web address: www.medicalwesthospital.org
Control: Hospital district or authority, Government, nonfederal **Service:** General Medical and Surgical

Staffed Beds: 231 **Admissions:** 7122 **Census:** 111 **Outpatient Visits:** 223549 **Births:** 539 **Total Expense ($000):** 112621 **Payroll Expense ($000):** 46116 **Personnel:** 1066

BIRMINGHAM—Jefferson County

✠ **BIRMINGHAM VETERANS AFFAIRS MEDICAL CENTER**, 700 South 19th Street, Zip 35233–1927; tel. 205/933–8101, (Nonreporting) **A**1 2 3 5 8 **S** Department of Veterans Affairs, Washington, DC
Primary Contact: Thomas C. Smith, III, FACHE, Director
COO: Phyllis J. Smith, Associate Director
CFO: Mary S. Mitchell, Chief Resource Management Services
CMO: William F. Harper, M.D., Chief of Staff
CIO: Antonia Mohamed, Acting Chief Information Officer
CHR: Jacqueline Caron, Chief Human Resources
CNO: Cynthia Cleveland, Ph.D., Associate Director for Patient Care Services and Nurse Executive
Web address: www.birmingham.va.gov/
Control: Veterans Affairs, Government, federal **Service:** General Medical and Surgical

Staffed Beds: 151

✠ **BROOKWOOD BAPTIST MEDICAL CENTER (010139)**, 2010 Brookwood Medical Center Drive, Zip 35209–6875; tel. 205/877–1000 **A**1 2 3 5 10 **F**3 11 12 13 15 17 18 20 22 24 26 29 30 31 34 35 38 40 42 43 45 46 47 48 49 50 56 57 58 59 64 70 72 74 75 76 78 79 81 82 85 86 87 90 98 100 101 102 103 104 105 107 108 109 110 111 114 115 116 117 118 119 120 121 123 124 126 129 130 132 135 145 146 147 148 **S** TENET Healthcare Corporation, Dallas, TX
Primary Contact: Charles A. Stark, FACHE, President and Chief Executive Officer
COO: Kathy Healy–Collier, Chief Operating Officer
CFO: Brandon Willams, Chief Financial Officer
CMO: Mark Williams, Chief Physician Executive
CIO: Manuel Price, Director Information Systems
CHR: Ronnelle Stewart, SPHR, SHRM–SCP, Chief Human Resources Officer
CNO: Jacquelyn Martinek, R.N., Chief Nursing Officer
Web address: www.https://www.brookwoodbaptisthealth.com/
Control: Corporation, Investor–owned, for–profit **Service:** General Medical and Surgical

Staffed Beds: 607 **Admissions:** 25386 **Census:** 378 **Outpatient Visits:** 108289 **Births:** 4070 **Total Expense ($000):** 339737 **Payroll Expense ($000):** 107579 **Personnel:** 2035

✠ **CHILDREN'S OF ALABAMA (013300)**, 1600 Seventh Avenue South, Zip 35233–1785; tel. 205/638–9100 **A**1 3 5 10 **F**3 7 8 9 11 12 16 17 19 20 21 22 23 25 27 29 30 31 32 34 35 38 39 40 41 43 46 48 50 54 55 57 58 59 60 61 64 65 68 72 74 75 77 78 79 80 81 82 84 85 86 87 88 89 91 92 93 94 96 97 98 99 100 101 102 104 107 108 109 111 114 115 116 117 118 119 126 129 130 131 132 134 135 136 137 138 139 142 143 146 148 Primary Contact: Wm. Michael Warren, Jr., President and Chief Executive Officer
COO: Tom Shufflebarger, Chief Operating Officer
CFO: Dawn Walton, Chief Financial Officer
CMO: Crayton A. Fargason, M.D., Medical Director
CIO: Mike McDevitt, Chief Information Officer
CHR: Douglas B. Dean, Chief Human Resources Officer
CNO: Deb Wesley, MSN, Chief Nursing Officer
Web address: www.childrensal.org
Control: Other not–for–profit (including NFP Corporation) **Service:** Children's general

Staffed Beds: 345 **Admissions:** 15472 **Census:** 246 **Outpatient Visits:** 677037 **Total Expense ($000):** 680821 **Payroll Expense ($000):** 238195 **Personnel:** 4007

✠ **GRANDVIEW MEDICAL CENTER (010104)**, 3690 Grandview Parkway, Zip 35243–3326; tel. 205/971–1000 **A**1 2 3 5 10 13 **F**3 11 12 13 15 17 18 20 22 24 26 28 29 30 31 34 35 40 43 45 46 47 48 49 50 51 53 54 57 58 59 64 70 72 74 75 76 77 78 79 81 82 84 85 90 93 96 98 99 102 103 106 107 108 109 110 111 114 115 116 117 118 119 120 122 124 126 129 130 131 132 135 146 147 148 **S** Community Health Systems, Inc., Franklin, TN
Primary Contact: Keith Granger, President and Chief Executive Officer
COO: Drew Mason, Chief Operating Officer
CFO: Julie Soekoro, Chief Financial Officer
CMO: Rebecca Byrd, President Medical Staff
CIO: Tim Townes, Director Information Systems
CHR: Jeri Wink, Director Human Resources
CNO: James Epperson, Interim Chief Nursing Officer
Web address: www.grandviewhealth.com
Control: Corporation, Investor–owned, for–profit **Service:** General Medical and Surgical

Staffed Beds: 379 **Admissions:** 11523 **Census:** 184 **Outpatient Visits:** 225900 **Births:** 429 **Total Expense ($000):** 243693 **Payroll Expense ($000):** 83890 **Personnel:** 1687

✠ **HEALTHSOUTH LAKESHORE REHABILITATION HOSPITAL (013025)**, 3800 Ridgeway Drive, Zip 35209–5599; tel. 205/868–2000 **A**1 10 **F**3 29 75 77 86 87 90 91 93 95 96 130 132 148 **S** HEALTHSOUTH Corporation, Birmingham, AL
Primary Contact: Vickie Demers, Chief Executive Officer
CFO: Kimberly Thrasher, Controller
CMO: Michael Rosemore, M.D., Medical Director
CHR: Julie Smith, Director Human Resources
CNO: April Cobb, Chief Nursing Officer
Web address: www.healthsouthlakeshorerehab.com
Control: Corporation, Investor–owned, for–profit **Service:** Rehabilitation

Staffed Beds: 100 **Admissions:** 2708 **Census:** 91 **Outpatient Visits:** 10565 **Births:** 0 **Total Expense ($000):** 39463 **Payroll Expense ($000):** 16689 **Personnel:** 334

☐ **HILL CREST BEHAVIORAL HEALTH SERVICES (014000)**, 6869 Fifth Avenue South, Zip 35212–1866; tel. 205/833–9000 **A**1 10 **F**98 99 100 101 102 104 106 **S** Universal Health Services, Inc., King of Prussia, PA
Primary Contact: Steve McCabe, Chief Executive Officer
CFO: Mark Teske, Chief Financial Officer
Web address: www.hillcrestbhs.com
Control: Corporation, Investor–owned, for–profit **Service:** Psychiatric

Staffed Beds: 94 **Admissions:** 1264 **Census:** 67 **Outpatient Visits:** 0 **Births:** 0 **Total Expense ($000):** 20080

☐ **NOLAND HOSPITAL BIRMINGHAM (012009)**, 50 Medical Park East Drive, 8th Floor, Zip 35235; tel. 205/808–5100 **A**1 10 **F**1 29 130 148 **S** Noland Health Services, Inc., Birmingham, AL
Primary Contact: Laura S. Wills, Administrator
COO: Sharon Engle, Director Clinical Services
CMO: Mark Middlebrooks, M.D., Medical Director
CHR: Ashley Clark, Coordinator Human Resources
CNO: Rachel Chapman, Nurse Manager
Web address: www.nolandhealth.com
Control: Other not–for–profit (including NFP Corporation) **Service:** Long–Term Acute Care hospital

Staffed Beds: 45 **Admissions:** 340 **Census:** 26 **Outpatient Visits:** 0 **Births:** 0 **Total Expense ($000):** 11991

✉ **PRINCETON BAPTIST MEDICAL CENTER (010103)**, 701 Princeton Avenue S.W., Zip 35211–1303; tel. 205/783–3000 **A**1 2 3 5 10 **F**3 11 12 13 15 17 18 20 22 24 26 28 29 30 31 34 35 40 43 45 46 47 48 49 50 55 56 57 58 59 64 67 70 72 74 75 76 78 79 81 82 83 84 85 87 91 92 93 94 98 103 107 108 110 111 114 115 117 118 119 120 121 123 124 126 129 130 131 132 146 147 148 **S** TENET Healthcare Corporation, Dallas, TX
Primary Contact: Betsy Postlethwait, President
COO: Sarah Nunnelly, Chief Operating Officer
CFO: Beverly Haymon, Chief Financial Officer
CMO: Alan Craig, M.D., Physician Advisor
CNO: Paula Davenport, Chief Nursing Officer
Web address: www.bhsala.com
Control: Partnership, Investor–owned, for–profit **Service:** General Medical and Surgical

Staffed Beds: 309 **Admissions:** 14330 **Census:** 227 **Outpatient Visits:** 108606 **Births:** 347 **Total Expense ($000):** 221432 **Payroll Expense ($000):** 84405 **Personnel:** 1317

✉ **SELECT SPECIALTY HOSPITAL–BIRMINGHAM (012008)**, 2010 Brookwood Medical Center Drive, 3rd Floor, Zip 35209–6804; tel. 205/599–4600 **A**1 10 **F**1 60 77 82 84 103 105 111 115 116 117 118 119 148 **S** Select Medical Corporation, Mechanicsburg, PA
Primary Contact: Andrea White, Chief Executive Officer
CMO: Allan Goldstein, M.D., Medical Director and Chief of Staff
Web address: www.selectspecialtyhospitals.com/company/locations/birmingham.aspx
Control: Corporation, Investor–owned, for–profit **Service:** Long–Term Acute Care hospital

Staffed Beds: 38 **Admissions:** 306 **Census:** 28 **Outpatient Visits:** 0 **Births:** 0 **Total Expense ($000):** 14781

✉ **ST. VINCENT'S BIRMINGHAM (010056)**, 810 St. Vincent's Drive, Zip 35205–1695, Mailing Address: P.O. Box 12407, Zip 35202–2407; tel. 205/939–7000 **A**1 2 3 5 10 **F**3 11 12 13 15 17 18 20 22 24 26 28 29 30 31 34 35 37 40 43 45 50 53 57 58 59 60 62 65 66 68 70 72 74 75 77 78 79 81 82 84 85 86 87 91 93 94 107 101 114 114 115 119 120 121 123 126 129 130 131 132 135 146 147 **S** Ascension Health, Saint Louis, MO
Primary Contact: Evan Ray, FACHE, President
COO: Andy Davis, Chief Operating Officer
CFO: Wilma Newton, Executive Vice President and Chief Financial Officer
CMO: Gregory L. James, D.O., Chief Medical Officer
CIO: Timothy Stettheimer, Vice President and Chief Information Officer
CHR: Michelle Galipeau, Director Human Resources
Web address: www.stvhs.com
Control: Other not–for–profit (including NFP Corporation) **Service:** General Medical and Surgical

Staffed Beds: 409 **Admissions:** 19885 **Census:** 258 **Outpatient Visits:** 192518 **Births:** 3849 **Total Expense ($000):** 372197 **Payroll Expense ($000):** 99625 **Personnel:** 2026

✉ **ST. VINCENT'S EAST (010011)**, 50 Medical Park East Drive, Zip 35235–9987; tel. 205/838–3000 **A**1 2 3 5 10 **F**3 11 12 13 17 18 20 22 24 26 28 29 30 31 34 35 40 43 44 45 46 47 49 50 51 53 54 57 58 59 60 64 65 70 72 74 76 77 78 79 81 85 86 87 90 93 94 98 100 101 104 107 108 111 114 119 121 123 126 129 130 131 132 135 146 **S** Ascension Health, Saint Louis, MO
Primary Contact: Andrew Gnann, Vice President Operations
COO: Andrew Gnann, Vice President Operations
CFO: Jan DiCesare, Vice President Financial Operations
CMO: Frank Malensek, M.D., Chief Medical Officer
CIO: Beverly Golightly, Director Information Technology
CHR: Carol Maietta, Vice President Human Resources and Chief Learning Officer
CNO: Amy Shelton, Chief Nursing Officer
Web address: www.stvhs.com
Control: Other not–for–profit (including NFP Corporation) **Service:** General Medical and Surgical

Staffed Beds: 362 **Admissions:** 15972 **Census:** 249 **Outpatient Visits:** 128459 **Births:** 1017 **Total Expense ($000):** 219387 **Payroll Expense ($000):** 69812 **Personnel:** 1299

UAB HIGHLANDS See University of Alabama Hospital

✉ **UNIVERSITY OF ALABAMA HOSPITAL (010033)**, 619 19th Street South, Zip 35249–1900; tel. 205/934–4011, (Includes UAB HIGHLANDS, 1201 11th Avenue South, Zip 35205–5299; tel. 205/930–7000; Anthony Patterson, FACHE, Chief Operating Officer) **A**1 2 3 5 8 10 **F**1 3 4 5 8 9 11 12 13 15 16 17 18 20 22 24 26 28 29 30 31 33 34 35 37 38 39 40 43 44 45 46 47 48 49 50 52 53 54 55 56 57 58 59 60 61 62 64 65 66 67 68 70 71 72 73 74 75 76 77 78 79 80 81 82 83 84 85 86 87 88 89 90 91 92 93 94 95 96 97 98 99 100 101 102 103 104 107 108 110 111 113 114 115 116 117 118 119 120 121 123 124 126 128 129 130 131 132 135 136 137 138 139 140 141 142 143 144 145 146 147 148 **P**3 **S** UAB Health System, Birmingham, AL
Primary Contact: Anthony Patterson, FACHE, Senior Vice President Inpatient Services
CFO: Mary Beth Briscoe, Chief Financial Officer
CMO: Loring Rue, M.D., Senior Vice President, Quality Patient Safety and Clinical Effectiveness
CIO: Joan Hicks, Chief Information Officer
CHR: Alesia Jones, Chief Human Resources Officer
CNO: Terri Lyn Poe, Interim Chief Nursing Officer
Web address: www.uabmedicine.org
Control: State–Government, nonfederal **Service:** General Medical and Surgical

Staffed Beds: 1062 **Admissions:** 49641 **Census:** 951 **Outpatient Visits:** 702294 **Births:** 4123 **Total Expense ($000):** 1365148 **Payroll Expense ($000):** 507524 **Personnel:** 9036

VETERANS AFFAIRS MEDICAL CENTER See Birmingham Veterans Affairs Medical Center

BOAZ—Marshall County

☐ **MARSHALL MEDICAL CENTER SOUTH (010005)**, U.S. Highway 431 North, Zip 35957–0999, Mailing Address: P.O. Box 758, Zip 35957–0758; tel. 256/593–8310 **A**1 10 19 **F**3 7 8 11 12 13 15 18 20 22 26 28 29 31 32 34 35 37 40 43 45 46 50 51 53 54 57 59 64 68 70 74 75 76 78 79 81 84 85 86 87 89 92 93 100 107 108 110 111 114 115 117 119 121 123 129 130 131 132 135 141 145 146 147 148 **S** Marshall Health System, Guntersville, AL
Primary Contact: John D. Anderson, FACHE, Administrator
CFO: Kathy Nelson, Chief Financial Officer
Web address: www.mmcenters.com//index.php/facilities/marshall_south
Control: Hospital district or authority, Government, nonfederal **Service:** General Medical and Surgical

Staffed Beds: 114 **Admissions:** 4475 **Census:** 51 **Outpatient Visits:** 280570 **Births:** 623 **Total Expense ($000):** 90951 **Payroll Expense ($000):** 31977 **Personnel:** 590

BREWTON—Escambia County

☐ **D. W. MCMILLAN MEMORIAL HOSPITAL (010099)**, 1301 Belleville Avenue, Zip 36426–1306, Mailing Address: P.O. Box 908, Zip 36427–0908; tel. 251/867–8061 **A**1 10 **F**3 7 11 13 15 31 34 35 40 45 57 59 62 64 70 75 78 79 81 85 86 93 100 107 108 111 114 119 127 129 130 131 132 133 135 143 146 **P**6
Primary Contact: Christopher B. Griffin, Chief Executive Officer
CFO: Rick Owens, Chief Financial Officer
CIO: Ian Vickery, Director Information Technology
CHR: Autherine Davis, Director Human Resources
CNO: Bob Ellis, Director of Nursing
Web address: www.dwmmh.org
Control: Hospital district or authority, Government, nonfederal **Service:** General Medical and Surgical

Staffed Beds: 49 **Admissions:** 1728 **Census:** 17 **Outpatient Visits:** 48893 **Births:** 268 **Total Expense ($000):** 24692 **Payroll Expense ($000):** 9205 **Personnel:** 229

BUTLER—Choctaw County

CHOCTAW GENERAL HOSPITAL (011304), 401 Vanity Fair Avenue, Zip 36904–3032; tel. 205/459–9100 **A**10 18 **F**3 13 29 30 34 35 40 41 80 87 88 89 90 91 93 103 104 107 119 128 133 146 148 **S** Rush Health Systems, Meridian, MS
Primary Contact: J. W. Cowan, Administrator
Web address: www.choctawgeneral.com/cgh/
Control: Other not–for–profit (including NFP Corporation) **Service:** General Medical and Surgical

Staffed Beds: 25 **Admissions:** 242 **Census:** 6 **Outpatient Visits:** 13274 **Births:** 0

AL

CAMDEN—Wilcox County

J. PAUL JONES HOSPITAL (010102), 317 McWilliams Avenue,
Zip 36726–1610; tel. 334/682–4131 **A**10 20 **F**15 29 40 107 114 119 125
127 133
Primary Contact: Elizabeth M. Kennedy, Administrator
CMO: Willie White, M.D., Director Medical Staff
CIO: Jill Smith, Administrative Coordinator
CHR: Jill Smith, Administrative Coordinator
Control: City–County, Government, nonfederal **Service:** General Medical and
Surgical

Staffed Beds: 21 **Admissions:** 178 **Census:** 1 **Outpatient Visits:** 15399
Births: 0 **Total Expense ($000):** 3725 **Payroll Expense ($000):** 1584
Personnel: 50

CARROLLTON—Pickens County

PICKENS COUNTY MEDICAL CENTER (010109), 241 Robert K. Wilson Drive,
Zip 35447, Mailing Address: P.O. Box 478, Zip 35447–0478;
tel. 205/367–8111, (Nonreporting) **A**10 20
Primary Contact: Jim Marshall, Chief Executive Officer
CFO: Janice Winters, Controller
CMO: William R. Brooke, M.D., President Medical Staff
CHR: Dottie D. Wilson, Director Human Resources
Web address: www.dchsystem.com
Control: County–Government, nonfederal **Service:** General Medical and Surgical

Staffed Beds: 52

CENTRE—Cherokee County

✉ **CHEROKEE MEDICAL CENTER (010022)**, 400 Northwood Drive,
Zip 35960–1023; tel. 256/927–5531 **A**1 10 **F**3 5 8 11 15 29 30 34 35 40 43
45 48 50 51 57 59 62 63 64 70 74 75 77 81 85 87 92 93 107 108 110 114
119 127 130 131 132 133 146 **P**6 **S** Quorum Health, Brentwood, TN
Primary Contact: Terry Long, Chief Executive Officer
CFO: Zac Allen, CPA, Chief Financial Officer
CHR: Marlene Benefield, Director Human Resources
Web address: www.cherokeemedicalcenter.com
Control: Corporation, Investor–owned, for–profit **Service:** General Medical and
Surgical

Staffed Beds: 45 **Admissions:** 832 **Census:** 14 **Outpatient Visits:** 20834
Births: 0 **Total Expense ($000):** 16955 **Payroll Expense ($000):** 5004
Personnel: 145

CENTREVILLE—Bibb County

BIBB MEDICAL CENTER (010058), 208 Pierson Avenue, Zip 35042–2918;
tel. 205/926–4881, (Total facility includes 131 beds in nursing home–type unit)
A3 10 13 **F**3 11 15 29 35 40 50 57 59 64 81 93 107 114 119 125 127 128
130 133 143 144 146
Primary Contact: Joseph Marchant, Administrator
CFO: Heather Desmond, Chief Financial Officer
CMO: John Meigs, Jr., M.D., Chief of Staff
CHR: Karen Daniel, Director Human Resources
Web address: www.bibbmedicalcenter.com
Control: County–Government, nonfederal **Service:** General Medical and Surgical

Staffed Beds: 151 **Admissions:** 541 **Census:** 125 **Outpatient Visits:** 28115
Births: 0

CHATOM—Washington County

★ **WASHINGTON COUNTY HOSPITAL (011300)**, 14600 St. Stephens Avenue,
Zip 36518–9998, Mailing Address: P.O. Box 1299, Zip 36518–1299;
tel. 251/847–2223 **A**10 18 **F**29 34 40 57 59 64 107 114 119 128 133 148
Primary Contact: Teresa Grimes, Chief Executive Officer
CFO: Alyson Overstreet, Chief Financial Officer
CMO: Steve Donald, M.D., Chief of Staff
CIO: Brady Wright, Information Technology Network Administrator
CHR: Linda Randolph, Director Personnel Services
CNO: Michelle Alford, R.N., Director of Nursing
Web address: www.wchnh.org
Control: County–Government, nonfederal **Service:** General Medical and Surgical

Staffed Beds: 25 **Admissions:** 282 **Census:** 7 **Outpatient Visits:** 10832
Births: 0 **Total Expense ($000):** 6549 **Payroll Expense ($000):** 2757
Personnel: 98

CULLMAN—Cullman County

☐ **CULLMAN REGIONAL MEDICAL CENTER (010035)**, 1912 Alabama Highway
157, Zip 35055, Mailing Address: P.O. Box 1108, Zip 35056–1108;
tel. 256/737–2000 **A**1 10 **F**3 7 11 12 13 15 18 20 22 26 28 29 30 34 35 37
40 43 45 46 49 50 51 53 57 59 62 63 70 71 74 75 76 79 81 82 83 84 85
86 87 89 93 97 107 108 110 111 114 118 119 121 129 130 131 132 133
134 135 146 147 148
Primary Contact: James Clements, Chief Executive Officer
CFO: Nesha Donaldson, Chief Financial Officer
CMO: Bill Smith, M.D., Chief of Staff
CIO: Nancy Zavatchen, Director Information Technology
CHR: Toni Geddings, Director Human Resources
CNO: Cheryl Bailey, R.N., Chief Nursing Officer Vice President Patient Care
Services
Web address: www.crmchospital.com
Control: Other not–for–profit (including NFP Corporation) **Service:** General
Medical and Surgical

Staffed Beds: 115 **Admissions:** 7498 **Census:** 79 **Outpatient Visits:** 96883
Births: 639 **Total Expense ($000):** 100545 **Payroll Expense ($000):** 38429
Personnel: 905

DADEVILLE—Tallapoosa County

LAKE MARTIN COMMUNITY HOSPITAL (010052), 201 Mariarden Road,
Zip 36853–6251, Mailing Address: P.O. Box 629, Zip 36853–0629;
tel. 256/825–7821 **A**10 **F**11 29 40 45 50 59 62 63 64 65 68 81 82 107 111
119 127
Primary Contact: Michael D. Bruce, Chief Executive Officer
CHR: Karen Treadwell, Director Human Resources
Web address: www.lakemartincommunityhospital.com
Control: Partnership, Investor–owned, for–profit **Service:** General Medical and
Surgical

Staffed Beds: 25 **Admissions:** 705 **Census:** 7 **Outpatient Visits:** 15453
Births: 0 **Total Expense ($000):** 6256

DAPHNE—Baldwin County

✉ **EASTPOINTE HOSPITAL (014017)**, 7400 Roper Lane, Zip 36526–5274;
tel. 251/378–6500 **A**1 10 **F**98 130 143 **S** AltaPointe Health Systems, Mobile, AL
Primary Contact: Philip L. Cusa, Administrator
CFO: Kevin Markham, Chief Financial Officer
CMO: Sandra K. Parker, M.D., Chief Medical Officer
CIO: Steve Dolan, Chief Information Officer
CHR: Alicia Donoghue, Director Human Resources
Web address: www.altapointe.org/eastpointe.php
Control: Other not–for–profit (including NFP Corporation) **Service:** Psychiatric

Staffed Beds: 66 **Admissions:** 1367 **Census:** 47 **Outpatient Visits:** 0 **Births:**
0 **Total Expense ($000):** 11834 **Payroll Expense ($000):** 8071 **Personnel:**
176

DECATUR—Morgan County

☐ **DECATUR MORGAN HOSPITAL (010085)**, 1201 Seventh Street S.E.,
Zip 35601–3303, Mailing Address: P.O. Box 2239, Zip 35609–2239;
tel. 256/341–2000, (Includes DECATUR MORGAN HOSPITAL PARKWAY CAMPUS,
1874 Beltline Road S.W., Zip 35601–5509, Mailing Address: P.O. Box 2239,
Zip 35609–2239; tel. 256/350–2211; DECATUR MORGAN HOSPITAL–WEST,
2205 Beltline Road S.W., Zip 35601–3687, Mailing Address: P.O. Box 2240,
Zip 35609–2240; tel. 256/306–4000) **A**1 5 10 **F**3 6 11 13 15 18 20 28 29 30
31 34 35 38 40 41 43 45 49 50 51 53 55 56 57 59 60 61 65 68 70 73 74
75 76 77 78 79 81 85 86 87 89 91 92 93 97 98 99 100 101 102 103 104
105 107 108 110 111 113 114 119 120 121 123 126 129 130 131 132 134
135 145 146 147 148 **S** Huntsville Hospital Health System, Huntsville, AL
Primary Contact: Nathaniel Richardson, Jr., President
CFO: Kim Shrewsbury, Vice President and Chief Financial Officer
CMO: Allen J. Schmidt, M.D., President, Medical Staff
CIO: Mark Megehee, Vice President and Chief Information Officer
CNO: Anita Walden, Vice President and Chief Nursing Officer
Web address: www.decaturgeneral.org
Control: Hospital district or authority, Government, nonfederal **Service:** General
Medical and Surgical

Staffed Beds: 203 **Admissions:** 8563 **Census:** 108 **Outpatient Visits:**
134169 **Births:** 697 **Total Expense ($000):** 104283

PARKWAY MEDICAL CENTER See Decatur Morgan Hospital Parkway Campus

DEMOPOLIS—Marengo County

BRYAN W. WHITFIELD MEMORIAL HOSPITAL (010112), 105 U.S. Highway 80 East, Zip 36732–3616, Mailing Address: P.O. Box 890, Zip 36732–0890; tel. 334/289–4000 **A**3 10 20 **F**2 3 7 11 12 13 15 29 30 34 35 40 50 53 57 58 59 62 64 68 70 75 76 78 79 81 85 86 93 97 107 108 111 119 120 130 131 133 134 146 148
Primary Contact: Arthur D. Evans, Chief Executive Officer and Administrator
COO: Dereck Morrison, Assistant Administrator
CFO: Doug A. Brooker, Chief Financial Officer
CMO: John G. Kahler, M.D., Radiologist
CHR: Marsha Pugh, Director Human Resources
CNO: Marcia Pugh, M.D., Chief Nursing Officer
Web address: www.bwwmh.com
Control: Hospital district or authority, Government, nonfederal **Service:** General Medical and Surgical

Staffed Beds: 82 Admissions: 2666 Census: 36 Outpatient Visits: 37618 **Births: 122 Total Expense ($000):** 28584

DOTHAN—Houston County

FLOWERS HOSPITAL (010055), 4370 West Main Street, Zip 36305–4000, Mailing Address: P.O. Box 6907, Zip 36302–6907; tel. 334/793–5000 **A**1 2 10 **F**3 4 12 13 15 16 17 18 19 20 22 24 26 28 29 31 34 35 40 43 46 48 49 50 51 56 57 59 60 61 64 67 68 70 74 75 76 77 78 79 81 82 85 86 87 89 90 92 93 97 98 100 107 108 110 111 114 115 116 117 118 119 126 128 129 131 132 134 135 146 147 148 **P**6 **S** Community Health Systems, Inc., Franklin, TN
Primary Contact: Suzanne Woods, President and Chief Executive Officer
CFO: Talana Bell, Chief Financial Officer
CIO: Matthew Garrett, Director Information Systems
CHR: Jennifer Odom, Interim Director Human Resources
CNO: Dan L. Cumbie, Chief Nursing Officer
Web address: www.flowershospital.com
Control: Corporation, Investor–owned, for–profit **Service:** General Medical and Surgical

Staffed Beds: 141 Admissions: 10544 Census: 125 Outpatient Visits: 182162 **Births: 1247 Total Expense ($000):** 165809 **Payroll Expense ($000):** 51771 **Personnel:** 1184

HEALTHSOUTH REHABILITATION HOSPITAL (013030), 1736 East Main Street, Zip 36301–3040, Mailing Address: P.O. Box 6708, Zip 36302–6708; tel. 334/712–6333 **A**1 10 **F**28 29 34 35 56 57 59 64 74 75 77 79 90 91 93 95 96 130 132 **S** HEALTHSOUTH Corporation, Birmingham, AL
Primary Contact: Margaret A. Futch, Chief Executive Officer
CFO: Heath Watson, Controller
CHR: Lydia Christion, Director Human Resources
Web address: www.healthsouthdothan.com
Control: Corporation, Investor–owned, for–profit **Service:** Rehabilitation

Staffed Beds: 51 Admissions: 1377 Census: 49 Outpatient Visits: 850 **Births: 0 Total Expense ($000):** 18511

LAUREL OAKS BEHAVIORAL HEALTH CENTER (014013), 700 East Cottonwood Road, Zip 36301–3644; tel. 334/794–7373 **A**1 10 **F**29 98 99 106 130 **S** Universal Health Services, Inc., King of Prussia, PA
Primary Contact: Derek Johnson, Chief Executive Officer
CMO: Nelson Handol, M.D., Medical Director
CHR: Lorrie Evans, Director Human Resources
Web address: www.laureloaksbhc.com
Control: Corporation, Investor–owned, for–profit **Service:** Children's hospital psychiatric

Staffed Beds: 38 Admissions: 1106 Census: 37 Outpatient Visits: 0 Births: 0 Total Expense ($000): 11702

NOLAND HOSPITAL DOTHAN (012010), 1108 Ross Clark Circle, 4th Floor, Zip 36301–3022; tel. 334/699–4300 **A**1 10 **F**1 29 130 148 **S** Noland Health Services, Inc., Birmingham, AL
Primary Contact: Kaye Burk, Administrator
Web address: www.nolandhealth.com
Control: Other not–for–profit (including NFP Corporation) **Service:** Long–Term Acute Care hospital

Staffed Beds: 38 Admissions: 363 Census: 25 Outpatient Visits: 0 Births: 0 Total Expense ($000): 12334

SOUTHEAST ALABAMA MEDICAL CENTER (010001), 1108 Ross Clark Circle, Zip 36301–3024, Mailing Address: P.O. Box 6987, Zip 36302–6987; tel. 334/793–8111 **A**1 2 10 13 21 **F**3 8 12 13 15 18 20 22 24 26 28 29 30 31 32 34 35 37 40 43 44 45 49 50 51 53 54 56 57 59 60 62 63 64 68 70 71 74 75 76 77 78 79 81 82 84 85 86 87 89 92 93 94 98 100 101 102 103 104 105 107 108 110 111 114 115 116 117 118 119 120 121 123 124 126 127 129 130 132 135 146 147 148
Primary Contact: Richard O. Sutton, FACHE, Chief Executive Officer
COO: Charles C. Brannen, Senior Vice President and Chief Operating Officer
CFO: Derek Miller, Senior Vice President and Chief Financial Officer
CMO: Charles Harkness, D.O., Vice President Medical Affairs
CIO: Eric Allen Daffron, Division Director, Information Systems
CHR: Tony Welch, Vice President Human Resources
CNO: Diane Buntyn, MSN, Vice President Patient Care Services
Web address: www.samc.org
Control: Hospital district or authority, Government, nonfederal **Service:** General Medical and Surgical

Staffed Beds: 420 Admissions: 18675 Census: 244 Outpatient Visits: 133026 **Births: 1451 Total Expense ($000):** 316408 **Payroll Expense ($000):** 139212 **Personnel:** 2435

ENTERPRISE—Coffee County

MEDICAL CENTER ENTERPRISE (010049), 400 North Edwards Street, Zip 36330–2510; tel. 334/347–0584 **A**1 10 **F**3 13 15 29 34 40 45 57 59 70 79 81 85 93 107 110 111 114 118 119 130 131 **S** Community Health Systems, Inc., Franklin, TN
Primary Contact: Heath Phillips, Chief Executive Officer
CFO: Greg McGilvray, Chief Financial Officer
CMO: Rick Harrelson, M.D., President Medical Staff
CIO: Stephen Smothers, Director Information Systems
CHR: Toni Kaminski, Director Human Resources
CNO: Bobby Phillips, Chief Nursing Officer
Web address: www.mcehospital.com
Control: Corporation, Investor–owned, for–profit **Service:** General Medical and Surgical

Staffed Beds: 117 Admissions: 3437 Census: 23 Outpatient Visits: 36789 **Births: 971**

EUFAULA—Barbour County

MEDICAL CENTER BARBOUR (010069), 820 West Washington Street, Zip 36027–1899; tel. 334/688–7000 **A**10 20 **F**3 11 15 29 30 34 35 40 45 46 50 57 59 64 68 70 81 98 103 107 119 127 133 135 146
Primary Contact: Ralph H. Clark, Jr., FACHE, Chief Executive Officer
CFO: Debbie Norton, Chief Financial Officer
CHR: Cindy Griffin, Director Human Resources
CNO: Steven Skeen, R.N., Chief Clinical Officer
Web address: www.medctrbarbour.org
Control: Hospital district or authority, Government, nonfederal **Service:** General Medical and Surgical

Staffed Beds: 47 Admissions: 1428 Census: 23 Outpatient Visits: 38584 **Births: 0 Total Expense ($000):** 16822 **Payroll Expense ($000):** 7226 **Personnel:** 191

EUTAW—Greene County

GREENE COUNTY HEALTH SYSTEM (010051), 509 Wilson Avenue, Zip 35462–1099; tel. 205/372–3388, (Total facility includes 72 beds in nursing home–type unit) **A**10 **F**11 15 29 40 54 59 62 64 65 90 93 97 107 110 119 127 128 130 133 143 146 **P**6
Primary Contact: Elmore Patterson, Chief Executive Officer
Web address: www.gcheutaw.com
Control: County–Government, nonfederal **Service:** General Medical and Surgical

Staffed Beds: 20 Admissions: 286 Census: 52 Outpatient Visits: 8620 **Births: 0 Total Expense ($000):** 12193 **Payroll Expense ($000):** 6471 **Personnel:** 129

EVERGREEN—Conecuh County

EVERGREEN MEDICAL CENTER (010148), 101 Crestview Avenue, Zip 36401–3333, Mailing Address: P.O. Box 706, Zip 36401–0706; tel. 251/578–2480 **A**10 **F**3 29 30 34 40 49 50 53 57 59 62 81 87 93 97 98 107 111 114 119 127 130 135 **S** Gilliard Health Services, Montgomery, AL
Primary Contact: Tom McLendon, Administrator
CFO: Sharon Jones, Chief Financial Officer
CMO: William Farmer, M.D., Chief of Staff
CHR: Tracey Rhodes, Coordinator Human Resources
CNO: Angie Hendrix, Director of Nursing
Web address: www.evergreenmedical.org
Control: Partnership, Investor–owned, for–profit **Service:** General Medical and Surgical

Staffed Beds: 42 Admissions: 1549 Census: 13 Outpatient Visits: 17296 **Births: 0 Total Expense ($000):** 16628

Hospital, Medicare Provider Number, Address, Telephone, Approval, Facility, and Physician Codes, Health Care System

★ American Hospital Association (AHA) membership
□ The Joint Commission accreditation
○ Healthcare Facilities Accreditation Program
◇ DNV Healthcare Inc. accreditation
⇧ Center for Improvement in Healthcare Quality Accreditation
△ Commission on Accreditation of Rehabilitation Facilities (CARF) accreditation

FAIRHOPE—Baldwin County

☐ **THOMAS HOSPITAL (010100)**, 750 Morphy Avenue, Zip 36532–1812, Mailing Address: P.O. Box 929, Zip 36533–0929; tel. 251/928–2375 **A**1 10 19 **F**3 4 5 8 11 13 14 15 18 20 22 24 26 28 29 30 32 33 34 35 39 40 41 43 45 46 48 49 50 51 53 54 57 58 59 60 61 62 64 65 68 70 73 74 75 76 77 78 79 81 82 85 86 87 89 92 93 97 100 101 104 105 107 108 110 111 113 114 115 117 119 129 130 131 132 134 135 144 146 147 **S** Infirmary Health System, Mobile, AL
Primary Contact: Ormand P. Thompson, President
COO: Douglas Garner, Vice President
CMO: Michael McBrearty, M.D., Vice President Medical Affairs
CNO: Julie Rowell, R.N., Chief Nursing Officer
Web address: www.thomashospital.com
Control: Other not–for–profit (including NFP Corporation) **Service:** General Medical and Surgical

Staffed Beds: 136 **Admissions:** 8621 **Census:** 97 **Outpatient Visits:** 118066 **Births:** 1217 **Total Expense ($000):** 123960

FAYETTE—Fayette County

☐ **FAYETTE MEDICAL CENTER (010045)**, 1653 Temple Avenue North, Zip 35555–1314, Mailing Address: P.O. Drawer 710, Zip 35555–0710; tel. 205/932–5966, (Nonreporting) **A**1 10 **S** DCH Health System, Tuscaloosa, AL
Primary Contact: Donald J. Jones, FACHE, Administrator
CFO: Jeff Huff, Assistant Administrator Finance
CHR: Felicia Solomon–Owens, Director Human Resources
Web address: www.dchsystem.com
Control: Hospital district or authority, Government, nonfederal **Service:** General Medical and Surgical

Staffed Beds: 167

FLORENCE—Lauderdale County

☐ **ELIZA COFFEE MEMORIAL HOSPITAL (010006)**, 205 Marengo Street, Zip 35630–6033, Mailing Address: P.O. Box 818, Zip 35631–0818; tel. 256/768–9191 **A**1 10 17 18 22 24 26 28 29 31 40 43 45 49 50 51 55 57 59 60 64 68 70 74 75 76 77 78 79 80 81 84 85 87 89 90 92 93 103 107 108 114 115 116 117 118 119 129 130 145 146 148 **S** RCCH HealthCare Partners, Brentwood, TN
Primary Contact: Russell Pigg, Chief Executive Officer
COO: Mike Howard, Associate Administrator
CFO: Steve E. Hobbs, Chief Financial Officer
CMO: Oliver Matthews, M.D., Chief Medical Officer
CIO: Raul Velez, Director Information Systems
CHR: Cheryl Lee, Director Human Resources
CNO: Marye Elliott, Chief Nursing Officer
Web address: www.chgroup.org
Control: Hospital district or authority, Government, nonfederal **Service:** General Medical and Surgical

Staffed Beds: 278 **Admissions:** 15769 **Census:** 174 **Outpatient Visits:** 96433 **Births:** 1201

FOLEY—Baldwin County

⊠ **SOUTH BALDWIN REGIONAL MEDICAL CENTER (010083)**, 1613 North McKenzie Street, Zip 36535–2299; tel. 251/949–3400 **A**1 10 19 **F**3 12 13 15 18 20 28 29 30 31 34 35 38 40 43 45 49 50 51 54 57 59 60 62 64 65 68 70 75 76 77 79 81 82 85 86 87 93 107 108 110 111 114 116 117 118 119 130 131 132 133 134 135 144 146 147 148 **S** Community Health Systems, Inc., Franklin, TN
Primary Contact: Keith Newton, Chief Executive Officer
CFO: Brad Hardcastle, Chief Financial Officer
CMO: Lee Eslava, Chief Medical Officer
CHR: Pam Brunson, Director Human Resources
CNO: Margaret Roley, Chief Nursing Officer
Web address: www.southbaldwinrmc.com
Control: Corporation, Investor–owned, for–profit **Service:** General Medical and Surgical

Staffed Beds: 112 **Admissions:** 6410 **Census:** 68 **Outpatient Visits:** 134109 **Births:** 683

FORT PAYNE—Dekalb County

⊠ **DEKALB REGIONAL MEDICAL CENTER (010012)**, 200 Medical Center Drive, Zip 35968–3458, Mailing Address: P.O. Box 680778, Zip 35968–1608; tel. 256/845–3150 **A**1 10 20 **F**3 8 12 13 15 18 20 22 26 28 29 35 40 43 45 46 53 56 57 59 70 74 75 76 79 81 82 87 98 103 107 108 110 111 114 119 129 146 147 **S** Quorum Health, Brentwood, TN
Primary Contact: Patrick Trammell, Chief Executive Officer
CFO: Chris Benson, Chief Financial Officer
CMO: Anthony Sims, M.D., Chief of Staff
CIO: Joseph Helms, Director Information Systems
CHR: Diane McMichen, Director Human Resources
CNO: Marquita Bailey, Chief Nursing Officer
Web address: www.dekalbregional.com
Control: Corporation, Investor–owned, for–profit **Service:** General Medical and Surgical

Staffed Beds: 115 **Admissions:** 3493 **Census:** 44 **Outpatient Visits:** 62031 **Births:** 683 **Total Expense ($000):** 43765

GADSDEN—Etowah County

⊠ **GADSDEN REGIONAL MEDICAL CENTER (010040)**, 1007 Goodyear Avenue, Zip 35903–1195; tel. 256/494–4000 **A**1 2 10 **F**3 11 13 15 18 20 22 24 29 30 31 34 35 40 43 45 50 56 57 59 60 64 68 70 74 76 77 78 79 80 81 89 93 98 99 102 103 105 107 108 111 112 113 114 115 119 121 124 126 129 130 131 146 147 148 **S** Community Health Systems, Inc., Franklin, TN
Primary Contact: David Fuller, FACHE, Chief Executive Officer
CFO: Michael Cotton, Chief Financial Officer
CMO: William Haller, III, M.D., Chief of Staff
CIO: Glenn Phillips, Director Information Systems
CHR: Gale H. Sanders, Director
CNO: Donna Nicholson, Chief Nursing Officer
Web address: www.gadsdenregional.com
Control: Corporation, Investor–owned, for–profit **Service:** General Medical and Surgical

Staffed Beds: 274 **Admissions:** 14151 **Census:** 198 **Outpatient Visits:** 74883 **Births:** 1260 **Total Expense ($000):** 151332

⊠ **HEALTHSOUTH REHABILITATION OF GADSDEN (013032)**, 801 Goodyear Avenue, Zip 35903–1133; tel. 256/439–5000 **A**1 10 **F**28 30 90 91 94 95 96 148 **S** HEALTHSOUTH Corporation, Birmingham, AL
Primary Contact: Kayla Feazell, Chief Executive Officer
COO: Kayla Feazell, Chief Executive Officer
CFO: Lori Norman, Chief Financial Officer
CMO: Vladimir Slutsker, Medical Director
CIO: Lori Norman, Chief Financial Officer
CHR: Rhonda Young, Human Resource Director
CNO: Barry Eads, Chief Nursing Officer
Web address: www.healthsouthgadsden.com
Control: Corporation, Investor–owned, for–profit **Service:** Rehabilitation

Staffed Beds: 44 **Admissions:** 1084 **Census:** 39 **Outpatient Visits:** 1080 **Births:** 0 **Total Expense ($000):** 11830 **Payroll Expense ($000):** 6865 **Personnel:** 153

☐ **MOUNTAIN VIEW HOSPITAL (014006)**, 3001 Scenic Highway, Zip 35904–3047, Mailing Address: P.O. Box 8406, Zip 35902–8406; tel. 256/546–9265 **A**1 10 **F**2 54 98 99 104 105 130 132
Primary Contact: G. Michael Shehi, M.D., Chief Executive Officer
COO: Sara Romano, R.N., Vice President
CFO: Mary Jensen, Controller
CMO: G. Michael Shehi, M.D., Medical Director
CHR: Dave Jensen, Director Human Resources, Performance Improvement and Risk Management
Web address: www.mtnviewhospital.com
Control: Individual, Investor–owned, for–profit **Service:** Psychiatric

Staffed Beds: 68 **Admissions:** 1047 **Census:** 29 **Outpatient Visits:** 17784 **Births:** 0

⊠ **RIVERVIEW REGIONAL MEDICAL CENTER (010046)**, 600 South Third Street, Zip 35901–5399; tel. 256/543–5200 **A**1 10 **F**5 8 12 15 17 18 20 22 24 26 29 30 34 37 40 41 45 46 47 48 49 50 51 56 57 59 60 68 69 70 74 75 77 79 81 85 87 91 92 93 94 97 98 103 107 108 109 110 111 114 115 118 119 120 126 129 130 146 148 **S** Prime Healthcare Services, Ontario, CA
Primary Contact: Ruben Garza, Interim Chief Executive Officer
CIO: Jay Terrell, Manager Management Information Systems
CHR: Leslie Morton, Manager Human Resources
CNO: Tammy Harlow, Chief Nurse Executive
Web address: www.riverviewregional.com
Control: Corporation, Investor–owned, for–profit **Service:** General Medical and Surgical

Staffed Beds: 280 **Admissions:** 7162 **Census:** 106 **Outpatient Visits:** 69518 **Births:** 0

GENEVA—Geneva County

★ **WIREGRASS MEDICAL CENTER (010062)**, 1200 West Maple Avenue, Zip 36340–1694; tel. 334/684–3655, (Nonreporting) **A**10
Primary Contact: Samuel Johnson, Chief Executive Officer
CHR: Tim Tidwell, Human Resources Director
CNO: Ashley Tanner, Director of Nursing
Web address: www.alaweb.com/~tgarske
Control: Hospital district or authority, Government, nonfederal **Service:** General Medical and Surgical

Staffed Beds: 167

GEORGIANA—Butler County

GEORGIANA HOSPITAL (010047), 515 Miranda Street, Zip 36033–4519, Mailing Address: P.O. Box 548, Zip 36033–0548; tel. 334/376–2205 **A**10 **F**40 62 64 107 119 130
Primary Contact: Harry Cole, Jr., Administrator
Web address: www.georgianahospital.com/
Control: Partnership, Investor–owned, for–profit **Service:** General Medical and Surgical

Staffed Beds: 22 **Admissions:** 604 **Census:** 5 **Births:** 0

Many Facility Codes have changed. Please refer to the AHA Guide Code Chart.

© 2016 AHA Guide

GREENSBORO—Hale County

HALE COUNTY HOSPITAL (010095), 508 Green Street, Zip 36744–2316;
tel. 334/624–3024 **A**10 **F**29 40 62 81 107 119 133
Primary Contact: Shay Whaley, Administrator
Web address: www.halecountyhospital.com
Control: Hospital district or authority, Government, nonfederal **Service:** General Medical and Surgical

> **Staffed Beds:** 20 **Admissions:** 534 **Census:** 8 **Outpatient Visits:** 15079
> **Births:** 0 **Total Expense ($000):** 8848

GREENVILLE—Butler County

✠ **L. V. STABLER MEMORIAL HOSPITAL (010150)**, 29 L. V. Stabler Drive,
Zip 36037–3800; tel. 334/382–2671 **A**1 5 10 **F**3 15 17 29 35 40 56 57 62
64 81 93 98 103 107 111 119 133 146 147 **S** Quorum Health, Brentwood, TN
Primary Contact: Donald R. Rentfro, Chief Executive Officer
CMO: Norman F. McGowin, III, M.D., Chief of Staff
CIO: Doug Burkett, Manager Information Technology
CHR: Robert Foster, Director Human Resources
CNO: Kimberli Weaver, Chief Nursing Officer
Web address: www.lvstabler.com
Control: Corporation, Investor–owned, for–profit **Service:** General Medical and Surgical

> **Staffed Beds:** 15 **Admissions:** 1231 **Census:** 15 **Outpatient Visits:** 26022
> **Births:** 0 **Total Expense ($000):** 24317

GROVE HILL—Clarke County

★ **GROVE HILL MEMORIAL HOSPITAL (010091)**, 295 South Jackson Street,
Zip 36451–3231, Mailing Address: P.O. Box 935, Zip 36451–0935;
tel. 251/275–3191 **A**10 **F**3 11 13 15 28 29 30 32 34 35 40 43 56 57 59 64
66 75 76 81 86 87 89 97 98 101 103 104 107 114 119 127 129 132
135 146
Primary Contact: Emily Steadham, Administrator
CFO: Elaine Averett, Chief Financial Officer
CMO: Eniola Fagbongbe, M.D., Chief Medical Staff
CIO: Aaron Harrell, Director
CHR: Aubrey Sheffield, Administrative Assistant Human Resources and Public Relations
CNO: Karen Coleman, Director of Nursing
Web address: www.grovehillmemorial.org
Control: City–Government, nonfederal **Service:** General Medical and Surgical

> **Staffed Beds:** 33 **Admissions:** 1136 **Census:** 13 **Outpatient Visits:** 33313
> **Births:** 215 **Total Expense ($000):** 14257

GUNTERSVILLE—Marshall County

MARSHALL MEDICAL CENTER NORTH (010010), 8000 Alabama Highway 69,
Zip 35976; tel. 256/753–8000 **A**5 10 **F**3 11 12 13 15 26 28 29 32 34 35 37
38 40 43 45 49 50 51 53 54 57 59 64 68 70 74 75 76 79 81 82 85 86 87
92 93 99 100 102 103 104 107 108 110 111 114 115 119 130 131 132
135 141 146 147 **S** Marshall Health System, Guntersville, AL
Primary Contact: Cheryl M. Hays, FACHE, Administrator
COO: Cheryl M. Hays, FACHE, Administrator and Chief Operating Officer
CFO: Kathy Nelson, Chief Financial Officer
CIO: Kim Bunch, Director Information Technology
CHR: Jeff Stone, Director Human Resources
CNO: Kathy Woodruff, R.N., Chief Nursing Officer
Web address: www.mmcenters.com
Control: Hospital district or authority, Government, nonfederal **Service:** General Medical and Surgical

> **Staffed Beds:** 90 **Admissions:** 4114 **Census:** 52 **Outpatient Visits:** 165402
> **Births:** 375 **Total Expense ($000):** 55746 **Payroll Expense ($000):** 21315
> **Personnel:** 324

HALEYVILLE—Winston County

☐ **LAKELAND COMMUNITY HOSPITAL (010125)**, Highway 195 East,
Zip 35565–9536, Mailing Address: P.O. Box 780, Zip 35565–0780;
tel. 205/486–5213 **A**1 10 **F**3 15 29 30 34 40 43 62 70 77 81 93 98 103 107
110 115 119 130 131 133 146 **S** Curae Health, Clinton, TN
Primary Contact: Cynthia Nichols, R.N., MSN, Chief Executive Officer
CFO: Penny Westmoreland, Chief Financial Officer
Web address: www.lakelandcommunityhospital.com/
Control: Corporation, Investor–owned, for–profit **Service:** General Medical and Surgical

> **Staffed Beds:** 56 **Admissions:** 1526 **Census:** 19 **Outpatient Visits:** 17253
> **Births:** 0 **Total Expense ($000):** 13972

HAMILTON—Marion County

✠ **NORTH MISSISSIPPI MEDICAL CENTER–HAMILTON (010044)**, 1256 Military
Street South, Zip 35570–5003; tel. 205/921–6200 **A**1 10 **F**40 53 57 59 77 81
93 107 111 119 133 **S** North Mississippi Health Services, Inc., Tupelo, MS
Primary Contact: William Buck, Interim Chief Executive Officer
CMO: Jarred Sartain, M.D., President Medical Staff
CHR: Anne Lawler, Director Human Resources
CNO: Jennifer Cagle, Director of Nursing
Web address: www.nmhs.net
Control: Other not–for–profit (including NFP Corporation) **Service:** General Medical and Surgical

> **Staffed Beds:** 15 **Admissions:** 474 **Census:** 9 **Outpatient Visits:** 20668
> **Births:** 0 **Total Expense ($000):** 21090

HUNTSVILLE—Madison County

BEHAVIORAL HEALTHCARE CENTER AT HUNTSVILLE (014018), 5315
Millennium Drive N.W., Zip 35806–2458; tel. 256/964–6700 **A**10 **F**6 29 34 35
38 56 59 65 75 77 86 87 98 101 103 130 135 148 **S** Tennessee Health
Management, Parsons, TN
Primary Contact: Bradley Moss, Administrator
Web address: www.tnhealthmanagement.com/bhc/huntsville
Control: Corporation, Investor–owned, for–profit **Service:** Hospital unit within an institution for the mentally retarded

> **Staffed Beds:** 20 **Admissions:** 221 **Census:** 10 **Outpatient Visits:** 0 **Births:**
> 0 **Total Expense ($000):** 2963

✠ **CRESTWOOD MEDICAL CENTER (010131)**, One Hospital Drive,
Zip 35801–3403; tel. 256/429–4000 **A**1 5 10 **F**3 5 11 12 13 15 17 18 20 22
29 30 31 34 35 40 43 45 47 49 50 51 54 56 57 59 60 64 65 68 70 72 74
75 76 77 78 79 81 85 86 87 89 93 97 98 99 100 101 102 103 104 105 107
108 110 111 114 115 119 126 129 130 131 132 146 147 148 **S** Community
Health Systems, Inc., Franklin, TN
Primary Contact: Pamela Hudson, M.D., Chief Executive Officer
COO: Bobby Ginn, Chief Operating Officer
CFO: Sherry J. Jones, Chief Financial Officer
CHR: Elyria Sinclair, Director Human Resources
CNO: Martha Delaney Walls, R.N., Chief Nursing Officer
Web address: www.crestwoodmedcenter.com
Control: Corporation, Investor–owned, for–profit **Service:** General Medical and Surgical

> **Staffed Beds:** 147 **Admissions:** 11000 **Census:** 117 **Outpatient Visits:**
> 108534 **Births:** 720 **Total Expense ($000):** 14559

✠ **HEALTHSOUTH REHABILITATION HOSPITAL OF NORTH ALABAMA**
(013029), 107 Governors Drive S.W., Zip 35801–4326; tel. 256/535–2300,
(Nonreporting) **A**1 10 **S** HEALTHSOUTH Corporation, Birmingham, AL
Primary Contact: Douglas H. Beverly, Chief Executive Officer
Web address: www.healthsouthhuntsville.com
Control: Corporation, Investor–owned, for–profit **Service:** Rehabilitation

> **Staffed Beds:** 70

☐ **HUNTSVILLE HOSPITAL (010039)**, 101 Sivley Road S.W., Zip 35801–4470;
tel. 256/265–1000, (Includes HUNTSVILLE HOSPITAL FOR WOMEN AND
CHILDREN, 911 Big Cove Road S.E., Zip 35801–3784; tel. 256/265–1000;
MADISON HOSPITAL, 8375 Highway 72 West, Madison, Zip 35758–9573;
tel. 256/265–2012; Mary Lynne Wright, R.N., President) **A**1 2 3 5 10 **F**5 7 8 12
13 14 15 17 18 19 20 21 22 23 24 25 26 28 29 30 31 35 37 38 39 40 41
43 48 49 50 51 53 54 56 57 59 60 63 64 68 70 71 72 73 76 78 79 80 81
82 84 85 88 89 93 96 98 99 100 101 102 103 104 105 107 108 109 110
111 114 115 116 117 118 119 126 129 130 131 142 145 146 147 148
S Huntsville Hospital Health System, Huntsville, AL
Primary Contact: David S. Spillers, Chief Executive Officer
COO: Jeff Samz, Chief Operating Officer
CFO: Kelli Powers, Chief Financial Officer
CMO: Robert Chappell, M.D., Chief Medical Officer and Chief Quality Officer
CIO: Rick Corn, Chief Information Officer
CHR: Andrea P. Rosler, Vice President Human Resources
CNO: Karol Jones, Chief Nursing Officer
Web address: www.huntsvillehospital.org
Control: Hospital district or authority, Government, nonfederal **Service:** General Medical and Surgical

> **Staffed Beds:** 902 **Admissions:** 45230 **Census:** 601 **Outpatient Visits:**
> 781605 **Births:** 5218 **Total Expense ($000):** 777720 **Payroll Expense**
> **($000):** 307870 **Personnel:** 6655

Hospital, Medicare Provider Number, Address, Telephone, Approval, Facility, and Physician Codes, Health Care System

★ American Hospital Association (AHA) membership   ○ Healthcare Facilities Accreditation Program   ⇑ Center for Improvement in Healthcare Quality Accreditation
☐ The Joint Commission accreditation   ◇ DNV Healthcare Inc. accreditation   △ Commission on Accreditation of Rehabilitation Facilities (CARF) accreditation

JACKSON—Clarke County

JACKSON MEDICAL CENTER (010128), 220 Hospital Drive, Zip 36545–2459, Mailing Address: P.O. Box 428, Zip 36545–0428; tel. 251/246–9021 **A**10 **F**3 11 15 29 34 40 45 57 59 62 76 81 85 89 107 108 111 115 119 133 134 144 **S** Gilliard Health Services, Montgomery, AL
Primary Contact: Amy Gibson, Chief Executive Officer
COO: Jennifer M. Ryland, R.N., Chief Administrative Officer
CFO: Amy Gibson, Chief Executive Officer
CHR: Kathy Jones, Director Human Resources
Web address: www.jacksonmedicalcenter.org
Control: Partnership, Investor–owned, for–profit **Service:** General Medical and Surgical

Staffed Beds: 26 **Admissions:** 834 **Census:** 10 **Outpatient Visits:** 11859 **Births:** 0 **Total Expense ($000):** 9644

JACKSONVILLE—Calhoun County

☐ **RMC JACKSONVILLE (010146)**, 1701 Pelham Road South, Zip 36265–3399, Mailing Address: P.O. Box 999, Zip 36265–0999; tel. 256/435–4970 **A**1 10 **F**3 4 5 29 30 34 35 40 42 45 48 50 56 57 59 64 65 68 69 79 81 82 85 93 98 103 107 108 111 114 119 120 135 146
Primary Contact: Joe Weaver, Chief Executive Officer
COO: Carlos Farmer, R.N., Director Clinical Operations
CFO: Robbin Curlee, Controller
CMO: Rey Gavino, M.D., Chief of Staff
CIO: Richard Maust, Chief Information Officer
CHR: Doug Scott, Director Human Resources
CNO: Jean Ann McMurrey, R.N., Chief Nursing Officer
Web address: www.jmchealth.com
Control: Hospital district or authority, Government, nonfederal **Service:** General Medical and Surgical

Staffed Beds: 65 **Admissions:** 1036 **Census:** 18 **Outpatient Visits:** 18859 **Births:** 0 **Total Expense ($000):** 17453 **Payroll Expense ($000):** 7555 **Personnel:** 162

JASPER—Walker County

✠ **WALKER BAPTIST MEDICAL CENTER (010089)**, 3400 Highway 78 East, Zip 35501–8907, Mailing Address: P.O. Box 3547, Zip 35502–3547; tel. 205/387–4000 **A**1 10 20 **F**4 8 11 13 15 18 20 24 29 30 31 34 38 39 40 45 46 48 50 51 56 57 59 60 65 66 68 70 74 75 76 77 78 79 81 82 84 86 87 89 91 92 93 97 98 100 101 102 103 104 107 110 111 114 115 116 119 124 126 127 130 131 132 146 147 148 **S** TENET Healthcare Corporation, Dallas, TX
Primary Contact: John Langlois, Interim Administrator
CFO: Amanda Dyle, Chief Financial Officer
CIO: Kenny Horton, Director Information Systems
CHR: Pat Morrow, Director Human Resources
CNO: Robbie Hindman, Vice President Patient Care Services and Chief Nursing Officer
Web address: www.bhsala.com
Control: Corporation, Investor–owned, for–profit **Service:** General Medical and Surgical

Staffed Beds: 158 **Admissions:** 7582 **Census:** 105 **Outpatient Visits:** 78450 **Births:** 864 **Total Expense ($000):** 90173 **Payroll Expense ($000):** 31069 **Personnel:** 617

LUVERNE—Crenshaw County

☐ **BEACON CHILDREN'S HOSPITAL (014015)**, 150 Hospital Drive, Zip 36049; tel. 334/335–5040, (Nonreporting) **A**1 10
Primary Contact: Bradley Eisemann, Administrator
Web address: www.beaconchildrenshospital.com
Control: Other not–for–profit (including NFP Corporation) **Service:** Children's hospital psychiatric

Staffed Beds: 24

CRENSHAW COMMUNITY HOSPITAL (010008), 101 Hospital Circle, Zip 36049–7344; tel. 334/335–3374 **A**10 **F**3 4 11 13 15 29 38 40 53 60 64 76 79 81 98 100 101 102 103 107 119 143 144 148
Primary Contact: Lee Anne Montgomery, R.N., Administrator
COO: Victoria Lawrenson, Chief Operating Officer
CMO: Charles Tompkins, M.D., Chief of Staff
CHR: Patricia Jarry, Manager Human Resources
Control: Partnership, Investor–owned, for–profit **Service:** General Medical and Surgical

Staffed Beds: 65 **Admissions:** 1594 **Census:** 25 **Outpatient Visits:** 12462 **Births:** 0

MADISON—Madison County

BRADFORD HEALTH SERVICES AT HUNTSVILLE, 1600 Browns Ferry Road, Zip 35758–9601, Mailing Address: P.O. Box 1488, Zip 35758–0176; tel. 256/461–7272, (Nonreporting) **S** Bradford Health Services, Birmingham, AL
Primary Contact: Bob Hinds, Executive Director
Web address: www.bradfordhealth.com
Control: Corporation, Investor–owned, for–profit **Service:** Alcoholism and other chemical dependency

Staffed Beds: 84

MOBILE—Mobile County

BAYPOINTE BEHAVIORAL HEALTH (014014), 5800 Southland Drive, Zip 36693–3313; tel. 251/661–0153 **A**3 10 **F**38 98 99 100 101 102 130 132 **S** AltaPointe Health Systems, Mobile, AL
Primary Contact: Jack Lungu, Administrator
Web address: www.altapointe.org
Control: Other not–for–profit (including NFP Corporation) **Service:** Children's hospital psychiatric

Staffed Beds: 60 **Admissions:** 1452 **Census:** 33 **Outpatient Visits:** 0 **Births:** 0 **Total Expense ($000):** 7617 **Payroll Expense ($000):** 3906 **Personnel:** 393

☐ **INFIRMARY LONG TERM ACUTE CARE HOSPITAL (012006)**, 5 Mobile Infirmary Circle, Zip 36607–3513, Mailing Address: P.O. Box 2226, Zip 36652–2226; tel. 251/660–5239 **A**1 10 **F**1 29 30 56 59 75 82 84 86 91 103 119 132 148 **S** Infirmary Health System, Mobile, AL
Primary Contact: Susanne Marmande, Administrator
Web address: www.theinfirmary.com/
Control: Corporation, Investor–owned, for–profit **Service:** General Medical and Surgical

Staffed Beds: 38 **Admissions:** 262 **Census:** 18 **Outpatient Visits:** 0 **Births:** 0 **Total Expense ($000):** 8680

☐ △ **MOBILE INFIRMARY MEDICAL CENTER (010113)**, 5 Mobile Infirmary Drive North, Zip 36607–3513, Mailing Address: P.O. Box 2144, Zip 36652–2144; tel. 251/435–2400, (Includes ROTARY REHABILITATION HOSPITAL, 5 Mobile Infirmary Circle, Zip 36607, Mailing Address: P.O. Box 2144, Zip 36652; tel. 251/435–3400) **A**1 2 3 5 7 10 **F**1 3 8 11 12 13 15 17 18 20 22 24 26 28 29 30 34 35 40 41 43 45 46 47 48 49 50 51 52 53 54 56 57 59 60 64 68 70 74 75 76 77 78 79 80 81 82 85 86 87 89 90 91 92 93 96 98 102 103 107 108 110 111 114 115 118 119 120 121 124 126 129 130 131 132 145 146 147 148 **S** Infirmary Health System, Mobile, AL
Primary Contact: Jennifer Eslinger, President
CFO: Joe Denton, Executive Vice President and Chief Financial Officer
CMO: John Dixon, Chief Medical Officer
CIO: Eddy Stephens, Vice President Information Technology
CHR: Sheila Young, Vice President Human Resources
Web address: www.infirmaryhealth.org
Control: Other not–for–profit (including NFP Corporation) **Service:** General Medical and Surgical

Staffed Beds: 526 **Admissions:** 27378 **Census:** 435 **Outpatient Visits:** 209080 **Births:** 1098

✠ **PROVIDENCE HOSPITAL (010090)**, 6801 Airport Boulevard, Zip 36608–3785, Mailing Address: P.O. Box 850429, Zip 36685–0429; tel. 251/633–1000 **A**1 2 3 5 10 **F**3 11 13 15 17 18 20 22 24 26 28 29 30 31 34 35 40 44 45 50 51 53 54 55 57 58 59 60 61 64 65 68 70 73 74 75 76 77 78 79 80 81 82 83 84 85 86 87 89 92 93 96 102 107 108 110 111 114 115 117 119 120 121 124 126 129 130 131 132 135 142 146 148 **P**5 6 **S** Ascension Health, Saint Louis, MO
Primary Contact: Todd S. Kennedy, President and Chief Executive Officer
CFO: C. Susan Cornejo, Senior Vice President Finance and Chief Financial Officer
CMO: William M. Lightfoot, M.D., Vice President Medical Services
CIO: Kathy Ross, Chief Information Officer
CHR: Christopher Cockrell, Executive Director Human Resources
CNO: Peter Lindquist, Vice President and Chief Nursing Officer
Web address: www.providencehospital.org
Control: Church–operated, Nongovernment, not–for profit **Service:** General Medical and Surgical

Staffed Beds: 302 **Admissions:** 15572 **Census:** 213 **Outpatient Visits:** 94250 **Births:** 1791 **Total Expense ($000):** 221933

ROTARY REHABILITATION HOSPITAL See Mobile Infirmary Medical Center

☐ **SPRINGHILL MEMORIAL HOSPITAL (010144)**, 3719 Dauphin Street, Zip 36608–1798, Mailing Address: P.O. Box 8246, Zip 36689–0246; tel. 251/344–9630 **A**1 10 **F**11 13 15 17 18 20 22 24 26 28 29 30 31 34 40 46 47 49 50 51 57 60 70 74 75 76 77 78 79 81 82 85 86 87 88 89 90 93 107 110 111 115 118 119 126 127 129 130 132 146 147 148
Primary Contact: Jeffery M. St. Clair, President and Chief Executive Officer
COO: Rene Areaux, Vice President and Chief Operating Officer
CFO: Jan Grigsby, Vice President and Chief Financial Officer
CMO: Liston Jones, M.D., Medical Director
CIO: Mark Kilborn, Director Information Systems
CHR: Daniela Batchelor, Director Human Resources
CNO: Paul Read, R.N., Vice President and Chief Nursing Officer
Web address: www.springhillmedicalcenter.com
Control: Corporation, Investor–owned, for–profit **Service:** General Medical and Surgical

Staffed Beds: 207 **Admissions:** 10171 **Census:** 146 **Outpatient Visits:** 167535 **Births:** 760 **Total Expense ($000):** 148661 **Payroll Expense ($000):** 46616 **Personnel:** 1100

⊞ **UNIVERSITY OF SOUTH ALABAMA CHILDREN'S AND WOMEN'S HOSPITAL (013301)**, (Childrens and Womens), 1700 Center Street, Zip 36604–3301; tel. 251/415–1000 **A**1 3 5 10 **F**3 7 11 13 15 21 27 29 30 31 40 48 49 52 55 58 59 64 72 73 74 75 76 77 78 79 81 85 86 87 88 89 93 107 111 114 119 126 130 143 146 147 **S** University of South Alabama Hospitals, Mobile, AL
Primary Contact: Chris Jett, Administrator
CFO: Traci Jones, Chief Financial Officer
CIO: Mark Lauteren, Chief Information Officer
CHR: Janice Rehm, Manager Human Resources
CNO: Scotty Roberson, Assistant Administrator and Chief Nursing Officer
Web address: www.usahealthsystem.com/usacwh
Control: State–Government, nonfederal **Service:** Other specialty

> **Staffed Beds:** 182 **Admissions:** 8499 **Census:** 168 **Outpatient Visits:** 67666 **Births:** 2767 **Total Expense ($000):** 123582 **Payroll Expense ($000):** 55044 **Personnel:** 1225

⊞ **UNIVERSITY OF SOUTH ALABAMA MEDICAL CENTER (010087)**, 2451 Fillingim Street, Zip 36617–2293; tel. 251/471–7000 **A**1 2 3 5 8 10 **F**3 11 16 17 18 20 22 24 26 29 31 34 40 43 46 47 48 49 57 58 59 60 61 64 70 74 78 79 80 81 85 87 107 108 111 114 115 119 130 145 146 148 **S** University of South Alabama Hospitals, Mobile, AL
Primary Contact: A. Elizabeth Anderson, Administrator
CFO: Traci Jones, Chief Financial Officer
CIO: Mark Lauteren, Chief Information Officer
CHR: Anita Shirah, Director Human Resources
CNO: Lisa Mestas, Associate Administrator and System Chief Nursing Officer
Web address: www.usahealthsystem.com/usamc
Control: State–Government, nonfederal **Service:** General Medical and Surgical

> **Staffed Beds:** 142 **Admissions:** 6939 **Census:** 114 **Outpatient Visits:** 52813 **Births:** 1 **Total Expense ($000):** 217749 **Payroll Expense ($000):** 127628 **Personnel:** 1568

MONROEVILLE—Monroe County

☐ **MONROE COUNTY HOSPITAL (010120)**, 2016 South Alabama Avenue, Zip 36460–3044, Mailing Address: P.O. Box 886, Zip 36461–0886; tel. 251/575–3111 **A**1 10 20 **F**11 13 15 29 31 34 40 57 62 70 76 78 79 107 111 129 147
Primary Contact: Jeffrey M. Brannon, Chief Executive Officer
CFO: Wes Nall, Chief Financial Officer
CMO: David Stallworth, M.D., Chief of Staff
CIO: Jody Falkenberry, Director Information Systems
CHR: Tara Nowling, Director Human Resources
CNO: Barbara Harned, R.N., Chief Nursing Officer
Web address: www.mchcare.com
Control: Hospital district or authority, Government, nonfederal **Service:** General Medical and Surgical

> **Staffed Beds:** 44 **Admissions:** 1459 **Census:** 12 **Outpatient Visits:** 36643 **Births:** 209 **Total Expense ($000):** 23059

MONTGOMERY—Montgomery County

☐ **BAPTIST MEDICAL CENTER EAST (010149)**, 400 Taylor Road, Zip 36117–3512, Mailing Address: P.O. Box 241267, Zip 36124–1267; tel. 334/277–8330 **A**1 3 10 **F**3 11 12 13 15 29 30 34 35 40 44 45 47 49 50 56 57 63 64 68 70 72 73 75 76 77 79 81 82 85 86 89 90 93 94 107 108 111 114 115 119 126 129 130 132 135 146 147 **S** Baptist Health, Montgomery, AL
Primary Contact: Jeff G. Rains, Chief Executive Officer
CFO: Katrina Belt, Chief Financial Officer
CHR: Kay Bennett, Vice President Human Resources
CNO: Kathy Gaston, Chief Nursing Officer
Web address: www.baptistfirst.org
Control: Hospital district or authority, Government, nonfederal **Service:** General Medical and Surgical

> **Staffed Beds:** 164 **Admissions:** 9798 **Census:** 120 **Outpatient Visits:** 108582 **Births:** 3653 **Total Expense ($000):** 105979 **Payroll Expense ($000):** 41742 **Personnel:** 830

☐ **BAPTIST MEDICAL CENTER SOUTH (010023)**, 2105 East South Boulevard, Zip 36116–2409, Mailing Address: Box 11010, Zip 36111–0010; tel. 334/288–2100 **A**1 3 5 10 **F**3 5 11 12 13 15 17 18 20 22 24 26 28 29 30 31 34 35 40 44 45 47 49 50 56 57 58 59 60 61 63 64 68 70 72 74 75 76 78 79 81 82 84 85 86 87 89 90 93 94 98 100 101 102 103 104 105 107 108 110 111 114 115 116 117 118 119 126 129 130 131 132 135 146 147 148 **S** Baptist Health, Montgomery, AL
Primary Contact: J. Peter Selman, FACHE, Chief Executive Officer
CFO: Melissa Johnson, Chief Financial Officer
CMO: Donovan Kendrick, M.D., Chief Medical Officer
CIO: Steve Miller, Director Information Systems
CHR: Kay Bennett, System Director Human Resources
CNO: Karen McCaa, R.N., Vice President Patient Care Services and Chief Nursing Officer
Web address: www.baptistfirst.org
Control: Hospital district or authority, Government, nonfederal **Service:** General Medical and Surgical

> **Staffed Beds:** 387 **Admissions:** 17708 **Census:** 253 **Outpatient Visits:** 250427 **Births:** 788 **Total Expense ($000):** 376847 **Payroll Expense ($000):** 96760 **Personnel:** 1830

⊞ **CENTRAL ALABAMA VETERANS HEALTH CARE SYSTEM**, 215 Perry Hill Road, Zip 36109–3798; tel. 334/272–4670, (Includes MONTGOMERY DIVISION, 215 Perry Hill Road, tel. 334/272–4670; TUSKEGEE DIVISION, 2400 Hospital Road, Tuskegee, Zip 36083–5001; tel. 334/727–0550), (Nonreporting) **A**1 3 **S** Department of Veterans Affairs, Washington, DC
Primary Contact: Paul Bockelman, Director
CFO: Debra Nicholson, Manager Finance
CMO: Cliff Robinson, M.D., Chief of Staff
CIO: Rhoda Tyson, Chief Information Officer
CHR: Janice Hardy, Chief Human Resource Management Service
Web address: www.centralalabama.va.gov/
Control: Veterans Affairs, Government, federal **Service:** General Medical and Surgical

> **Staffed Beds:** 245

⊞ **HEALTHSOUTH REHABILITATION HOSPITAL OF MONTGOMERY (013028)**, 4465 Narrow Lane Road, Zip 36116–2900; tel. 334/284–7700 **A**1 10 **F**3 9 28 29 34 35 54 56 57 59 64 74 75 77 86 90 93 95 130 131 132 143 146 148 **P**5 **S** HEALTHSOUTH Corporation, Birmingham, AL
Primary Contact: Thomas Roddy, Chief Executive Officer
CFO: Heath Watson, Controller
CMO: Jeffrey Eng, M.D., Medical Director
CIO: Anidra Billingslea, Health Insurance Management
CHR: Kim McDaniel, Director Human Resources
CNO: Kim Headley, R.N., Chief Nursing Officer
Web address: www.healthsouthmontgomery.com
Control: Corporation, Investor–owned, for–profit **Service:** Rehabilitation

> **Staffed Beds:** 70 **Admissions:** 1768 **Census:** 62 **Outpatient Visits:** 4989 **Births:** 0 **Total Expense ($000):** 18485 **Payroll Expense ($000):** 10938 **Personnel:** 186

⊞ **JACKSON HOSPITAL AND CLINIC (010024)**, 1725 Pine Street, Zip 36106–1117; tel. 334/293–8000 **A**1 3 10 **F**13 15 17 18 20 22 24 26 29 30 31 34 40 45 46 49 57 59 64 68 70 74 76 77 78 79 81 82 84 85 86 87 89 107 108 111 115 116 117 118 119 126 130 131 135 144 146 147 **P**6
Primary Contact: Joe B. Riley, FACHE, President and Chief Executive Officer
COO: Michael James, Chief Operations Officer
CFO: Paul Peiffer, Chief Financial Officer and Vice President
CHR: Gilbert Darrington, Director Human Resources
CNO: Sharon A. Goodison, R.N., Chief Nursing Officer
Web address: www.jackson.org
Control: Other not–for–profit (including NFP Corporation) **Service:** General Medical and Surgical

> **Staffed Beds:** 230 **Admissions:** 13561 **Census:** 176 **Outpatient Visits:** 154678 **Births:** 1207 **Total Expense ($000):** 192613 **Payroll Expense ($000):** 72374 **Personnel:** 1402

LONG TERM CARE HOSPITAL See Noland Hospital Montgomery

MONTGOMERY DIVISION See Central Alabama Veterans Health Care System

☐ **NOLAND HOSPITAL MONTGOMERY (012007)**, 1725 Pine Street, 5 North, Zip 36106–1109; tel. 334/240–0532 **A**1 10 **F**1 29 130 148 **S** Noland Health Services, Inc., Birmingham, AL
Primary Contact: Dale Jones, Administrator
Web address: www.nolandhealth.com
Control: Other not–for–profit (including NFP Corporation) **Service:** Long–Term Acute Care hospital

> **Staffed Beds:** 65 **Admissions:** 283 **Census:** 20 **Outpatient Visits:** 0 **Births:** 0 **Total Expense ($000):** 10965

Hospital, Medicare Provider Number, Address, Telephone, Approval, Facility, and Physician Codes, Health Care System

★ American Hospital Association (AHA) membership ○ Healthcare Facilities Accreditation Program ⇑ Center for Improvement in Healthcare Quality Accreditation
☐ The Joint Commission accreditation ◇ DNV Healthcare Inc. accreditation △ Commission on Accreditation of Rehabilitation Facilities (CARF) accreditation

MOULTON—Lawrence County

☐ **LAWRENCE MEDICAL CENTER (010059)**, 202 Hospital Street, Zip 35650–1218, Mailing Address: P.O. Box 39, Zip 35650–0039; tel. 256/974–2200 **A**1 10 **F**3 15 28 29 30 34 35 40 45 46 47 50 54 56 57 59 62 64 65 66 68 70 75 81 85 86 87 93 97 107 108 111 114 118 119 127 130 132 135 146 147 **S** Huntsville Hospital Health System, Huntsville, AL
Primary Contact: Dean Griffin, Chief Executive Officer
CFO: Jim Crawford, Chief Financial Officer
CIO: Jeremy Duncan, Director Information Systems
CHR: Diane K. Secor, Director Human Resources
CNO: Sherry Jolley, Chief Clinical Officer
Web address: www.lawrencemedicalcenter.com
Control: County–Government, nonfederal **Service:** General Medical and Surgical

Staffed Beds: 53 **Admissions:** 683 **Census:** 8 **Outpatient Visits:** 29449 **Births:** 0

MUSCLE SHOALS—Colbert County

☐ **SHOALS HOSPITAL (010157)**, 201 Avalon Avenue, Zip 35661–2805, Mailing Address: P.O. Box 3359, Zip 35662–3359; tel. 256/386–1600 **A**1 10 **F**3 15 29 30 39 40 51 57 64 68 70 75 77 78 79 81 85 87 90 96 98 107 108 111 115 119 124 146 **S** RCCH HealthCare Partners, Brentwood, TN
Primary Contact: Kidada Hawkins, Chief Executive Officer
CFO: Steve E. Hobbs, Chief Financial Officer
CMO: Terry True, M.D., Chief of Staff
CIO: William Johnson, Director Information Systems
CHR: Nancy Bowling, Director Human Resources
CNO: Denida A. Cox, Chief Nursing Officer
Web address: www.shoalshospital.com
Control: Hospital district or authority, Government, nonfederal **Service:** General Medical and Surgical

Staffed Beds: 137 **Admissions:** 3280 **Census:** 61 **Outpatient Visits:** 32871 **Births:** 0 **Total Expense ($000):** 36225

ONEONTA—Blount County

✠ **ST. VINCENT'S BLOUNT (010050)**, 150 Gilbreath, Zip 35121–2827, Mailing Address: P.O. Box 1000, Zip 35121–0013; tel. 205/274–3000 **A**1 10 18 **F**3 11 15 18 29 30 35 40 43 45 57 59 64 65 70 75 77 78 79 81 82 85 86 87 91 93 107 108 110 119 133 135 **S** Ascension Health, Saint Louis, MO
Primary Contact: Lisa Nichols, R.N., Interim Administrator
CFO: Jennifer Kingry, Chief Financial Officer
CMO: David R. Wilson, M.D., Chief of Staff
CIO: John Laliberte, Chief Information Officer
CHR: Kristin L. Costanzo, Direct–In–Market Lead Human Relations Partner
CNO: Kira Schnittker, Director of Nursing
Web address: www.stvhs.com
Control: Other not–for–profit (including NFP Corporation) **Service:** General Medical and Surgical

Staffed Beds: 25 **Admissions:** 1128 **Census:** 15 **Outpatient Visits:** 37962 **Births:** 0 **Total Expense ($000):** 19523 **Payroll Expense ($000):** 6777 **Personnel:** 135

OPELIKA—Lee County

✠ **EAST ALABAMA MEDICAL CENTER (010029)**, 2000 Pepperell Parkway, Zip 36801–5452; tel. 334/749–3411, (Includes EAST ALABAMA MEDICAL CENTER–LANIER, 4800 48th Street, Valley, Zip 36854–3666; tel. 334/756–9180; Greg Nichols, Chief Executive Officer), (Total facility includes 26 beds in nursing home–type unit) **A**1 2 10 19 **F**7 10 11 13 15 17 18 20 22 24 26 28 29 30 31 32 34 40 43 45 50 51 53 54 56 57 59 60 61 64 65 66 67 68 70 74 75 76 77 78 79 81 82 83 84 85 86 87 89 92 93 97 98 99 100 101 102 104 107 108 110 111 114 115 116 117 118 119 120 121 124 125 126 128 129 130 131 132 143 144 146 147 148
Primary Contact: Terry W. Andrus, President
COO: Laura D. Grill, R.N., Executive Vice President and Administrator
CFO: Sam Price, Executive Vice President Finance/Chief Financial Officer
CIO: Sarah Gray, Vice President Information Services
CHR: Susan Johnston, Vice President Human Resources
CNO: Jane Fullum, Vice President Patient Care Services
Web address: www.eamc.org
Control: Hospital district or authority, Government, nonfederal **Service:** General Medical and Surgical

Staffed Beds: 296 **Admissions:** 13993 **Census:** 198 **Outpatient Visits:** 130280 **Births:** 1880

OPP—Covington County

★ **MIZELL MEMORIAL HOSPITAL (010007)**, 702 Main Street, Zip 36467–1626, Mailing Address: P.O. Box 1010, Zip 36467–1010; tel. 334/493–3541 **A**10 **F**11 17 29 30 35 40 53 79 81 98 103 107 110 111 114
Primary Contact: Jana Wyatt, Chief Executive Officer
CFO: Amy Bess, Chief Financial Officer
CIO: Elizabeth Cook, Chief Information Officer
CHR: Dianne Morrison, Director Human Resources
CNO: Steven Skeen, R.N., Chief Nursing Officer
Web address: www.mizellmh.com
Control: Other not–for–profit (including NFP Corporation) **Service:** General Medical and Surgical

Staffed Beds: 59 **Admissions:** 1689 **Census:** 25 **Outpatient Visits:** 11525 **Births:** 0 **Total Expense ($000):** 15588

OZARK—Dale County

DALE MEDICAL CENTER (010021), 126 Hospital Avenue, Zip 36360–2080; tel. 334/774–2601 **A**10 **F**8 11 13 15 17 29 40 51 53 54 57 59 62 63 70 75 76 77 81 85 86 89 93 98 103 107 108 111 118 119 144 147
Primary Contact: Vernon Johnson, Administrator
CFO: Brad Hull, Chief Financial Officer
CMO: Steve Brandt, M.D., Chief of Staff
CHR: Sheila Dunn, Assistant Administrator Human Resources
Web address: www.dalemedical.org
Control: Corporation, Investor–owned, for–profit **Service:** General Medical and Surgical

Staffed Beds: 75 **Admissions:** 1939 **Census:** 32 **Outpatient Visits:** 48989 **Births:** 0 **Total Expense ($000):** 30904

PELL CITY—St. Clair County

✠ **ST. VINCENT'S ST. CLAIR (010130)**, 7063 Veterans Parkway, Zip 35125–1499; tel. 205/814–2105 **A**1 10 **F**3 11 15 29 30 35 40 43 50 68 70 74 77 78 79 81 87 107 111 119 130 135 146 148 **S** Ascension Health, Saint Louis, MO
Primary Contact: Lisa Nichols, R.N., Administrator
CFO: Jason Lynn, Director Finance
Web address: www.stvhs.com
Control: Other not–for–profit (including NFP Corporation) **Service:** General Medical and Surgical

Staffed Beds: 40 **Admissions:** 1872 **Census:** 20 **Outpatient Visits:** 50435 **Births:** 0 **Total Expense ($000):** 27318 **Payroll Expense ($000):** 9419 **Personnel:** 194

PHENIX CITY—Russell County

☐ **JACK HUGHSTON MEMORIAL HOSPITAL (010168)**, 4401 Riverchase Drive, Zip 36867–7483; tel. 334/732–3000 **A**1 3 10 13 **F**3 29 40 42 70 79 81 89 107 111 115 119 131
Primary Contact: Mark A. Baker, Chief Executive Officer
COO: Rachel H. Crenshaw, Chief Operating Officer
CFO: Angela Hodzeda, Chief Financial Officer
CMO: Lamar Carden, M.D., Chief Medical Officer
CHR: Lana Thomas–Folds, System Director Human Resources
CNO: Sylvia Thomas, Chief Nursing Officer
Web address: www.hughston.com
Control: Corporation, Investor–owned, for–profit **Service:** General Medical and Surgical

Staffed Beds: 35 **Admissions:** 2585 **Census:** 21 **Outpatient Visits:** 22296 **Births:** 0 **Total Expense ($000):** 42581 **Payroll Expense ($000):** 12144 **Personnel:** 277

✠ **REGIONAL REHABILITATION HOSPITAL (013033)**, 3715 Highway 280/431 North, Zip 36867; tel. 334/732–2200 **A**1 10 **F**3 29 30 90 93 95 132 **S** HEALTHSOUTH Corporation, Birmingham, AL
Primary Contact: Michael Bartell, Chief Executive Officer
CFO: Bobby Edmondson, Controller
CMO: Nitin Desei, M.D., Medical Director
CIO: Jacki Cuevas, Director Health Information Services
CHR: Cindy Glynn, Director Human Resources
CNO: Wendy Lee, Chief Nursing Officer
Web address: www.regionalrehabhospital.com
Control: Partnership, Investor–owned, for–profit **Service:** Rehabilitation

Staffed Beds: 48 **Admissions:** 1237 **Census:** 45 **Outpatient Visits:** 3805 **Births:** 0 **Total Expense ($000):** 19215

Many Facility Codes have changed. Please refer to the AHA Guide Code Chart. © 2016 AHA Guide

PRATTVILLE—Autauga County

☐ **PRATTVILLE BAPTIST HOSPITAL (010108)**, 124 South Memorial Drive, Zip 36067–3619, Mailing Address: P.O. Box 681630, Zip 36068–1638; tel. 334/365–0651 **A**1 3 10 **F**3 11 12 15 18 29 30 34 35 40 44 45 50 56 57 59 60 63 64 68 70 74 75 81 82 84 85 86 87 93 107 111 114 119 129 132 146 **S** Baptist Health, Montgomery, AL
Primary Contact: Eric Morgan, Interim Chief Executive Officer
CFO: LaDonna McDaniel, Financial Manager
CIO: B. Blaine Brown, Vice President and General Counsel
CHR: Kymberli Skipper, Manager Human Resources
Web address: www.baptistfirst.org/facilities/prattville–baptist–hospital/default.aspx
Control: Hospital district or authority, Government, nonfederal **Service:** General Medical and Surgical

Staffed Beds: 50 **Admissions:** 2751 **Census:** 31 **Outpatient Visits:** 81837 **Births:** 0 **Total Expense ($000):** 38544 **Payroll Expense ($000):** 13393 **Personnel:** 282

RED BAY—Franklin County

★ **RED BAY HOSPITAL (011302)**, 211 Hospital Road, Zip 35582–3858, Mailing Address: P.O. Box 490, Zip 35582–0490; tel. 256/356–9532 **A**10 18 **F**11 15 29 34 35 40 43 50 53 54 56 57 59 64 65 68 75 77 81 82 86 90 91 92 93 94 97 107 114 119 127 130 131 132 133 135 146 147 148 **S** Huntsville Hospital Health System, Huntsville, AL
Primary Contact: Glen M. Jones, FACHE, Administrator
CFO: Penny Westmoreland, Chief Financial Officer
CMO: Kristy Crandell, M.D., Medical Staff President
CHR: Amy Leigh Bishop, Director Human Resources
CNO: Margaret Thorn, Interim Director of Nursing
Web address: www.redbayhospital.com
Control: Other not–for–profit (including NFP Corporation) **Service:** General Medical and Surgical

Staffed Beds: 22 **Admissions:** 364 **Census:** 10 **Outpatient Visits:** 12467 **Births:** 0 **Total Expense ($000):** 9020 **Payroll Expense ($000):** 4403 **Personnel:** 83

RUSSELLVILLE—Franklin County

☐ **RUSSELLVILLE HOSPITAL (010158)**, 15155 Highway 43, Zip 35653–1975, Mailing Address: P.O. Box 1089, Zip 35653–1089; tel. 256/332–1611 **A**1 10 **F**3 8 13 14 15 20 29 34 37 40 45 47 48 50 56 57 59 62 68 70 76 77 79 81 82 85 87 93 107 108 110 111 115 119 130 133 146 **S** Curae Health, Clinton, TN
Primary Contact: Christine R. Stewart, FACHE, Chief Executive Officer
CFO: Penny Westmoreland, Chief Financial Officer
CHR: Stephen Proctor, Director of Human Resources/Risk
CNO: Belinda Johnson, R.N., Chief Nursing Officer/Chief Clinical Officer
Web address: www.russellvillehospital.com
Control: Partnership, Investor–owned, for–profit **Service:** General Medical and Surgical

Staffed Beds: 92 **Admissions:** 1970 **Census:** 20 **Outpatient Visits:** 19509 **Births:** 0 **Total Expense ($000):** 20976

SCOTTSBORO—Jackson County

☐ **HIGHLANDS MEDICAL CENTER (010061)**, 380 Woods Cove Road, Zip 35768–2428, Mailing Address: P.O. Box 1050, Zip 35768–1050; tel. 256/259–4444 **A**1 5 10 20 **F**11 13 70 76 77 89 108 111 119 130 146
Primary Contact: Lonnie Albin, Interim Chief Executive Officer
CFO: Dan Newell, Chief Financial Officer
CIO: Doug Newby, Chief Information Officer
CHR: Susanna S. Sivley, Chief Personnel Officer
Web address: www.highlandsmedcenter.com
Control: Hospital district or authority, Government, nonfederal **Service:** General Medical and Surgical

Staffed Beds: 92 **Admissions:** 3504 **Census:** 34 **Outpatient Visits:** 49355 **Births:** 337 **Total Expense ($000):** 41261

SELMA—Dallas County

✉ **VAUGHAN REGIONAL MEDICAL CENTER (010118)**, 1015 Medical Center Parkway, Zip 36701–6352; tel. 334/418–4100 **A**1 3 5 10 **F**8 11 13 15 17 20 29 30 34 40 45 51 53 60 70 74 76 79 81 89 93 107 108 110 111 114 115 118 119 120 127 129 130 131 146 **S** LifePoint Health, Brentwood, TN
Primary Contact: J. David McCormack, Chief Executive Officer
CFO: Tyler Adkins, Chief Financial Officer
CMO: Walid Freij, M.D., Chief of Staff
CIO: Matthew McHugh, Director Information Services
CHR: Dionne Williams, Director Human Resources
CNO: Patricia Hannon, Chief Nursing Officer
Web address: www.vaughanregional.com
Control: Corporation, Investor–owned, for–profit **Service:** General Medical and Surgical

Staffed Beds: 149 **Admissions:** 5471 **Census:** 51 **Outpatient Visits:** 42707 **Births:** 626

SHEFFIELD—Colbert County

☐ **HELEN KELLER HOSPITAL (010019)**, 1300 South Montgomery Avenue, Zip 35660–6334, Mailing Address: P.O. Box 610, Zip 35660–0610; tel. 256/386–4196 **A**1 10 **F**3 7 8 11 13 15 18 20 21 28 29 30 31 34 35 40 45 47 49 50 51 53 57 59 60 64 65 68 70 74 75 76 77 78 79 80 81 82 83 84 85 86 87 89 91 92 93 94 107 108 110 111 114 115 117 118 119 126 129 130 131 132 135 145 146 147 148 **S** Huntsville Hospital Health System, Huntsville, AL
Primary Contact: Paul Storey, FACHE, President and Chief Executive Officer
CFO: Morris S. Strickland, Chief Financial Officer
CHR: Pam Bryant, Director Human Resources
Web address: www.helenkeller.com
Control: Hospital district or authority, Government, nonfederal **Service:** General Medical and Surgical

Staffed Beds: 145 **Admissions:** 6938 **Census:** 81 **Outpatient Visits:** 130042 **Births:** 861 **Total Expense ($000):** 93517

SYLACAUGA—Talladega County

☐ **COOSA VALLEY MEDICAL CENTER (010164)**, 315 West Hickory Street, Zip 35150–2996; tel. 256/401–4000 **A**1 10 **F**13 14 15 17 18 20 22 28 29 30 31 32 34 35 38 40 45 52 53 56 57 60 64 74 75 76 77 78 81 82 86 98 100 101 102 104 107 108 110 111 114 117 119 128 130 135 147 148
Primary Contact: Glenn C. Sisk, President
CFO: Janice Brown, Chief Financial Officer
CIO: Sandra Murchison, Director Medical Records
CHR: Christy Knowles, Chief Human Resources Officer
Web address: www.cvhealth.net
Control: Hospital district or authority, Government, nonfederal **Service:** General Medical and Surgical

Staffed Beds: 101 **Admissions:** 3401 **Census:** 37 **Outpatient Visits:** 64887 **Births:** 474 **Total Expense ($000):** 74382

TALLADEGA—Talladega County

✉ **CITIZENS BAPTIST MEDICAL CENTER (010101)**, 604 Stone Avenue, Zip 35160–2217, Mailing Address: P.O. Box 978, Zip 35161–0978; tel. 256/362–8111 **A**1 10 19 **F**3 4 11 13 15 29 30 34 35 40 49 50 53 57 59 60 62 63 64 65 67 70 74 75 76 79 81 82 86 87 93 98 103 107 108 110 111 112 114 118 119 129 131 132 135 146 **S** TENET Healthcare Corporation, Dallas, TX
Primary Contact: Zach Abercrombie, Administrator
CFO: Zach Abercrombie, Chief Financial Officer
CHR: Sandra Willis, Director of Human Resources
CNO: Ann McEntire, MSN, Chief Nursing Officer
Web address: www.brookwoodbaptisthealth.org
Control: Corporation, Investor–owned, for–profit **Service:** General Medical and Surgical

Staffed Beds: 72 **Admissions:** 2682 **Census:** 30 **Outpatient Visits:** 44273 **Births:** 245 **Total Expense ($000):** 33001 **Payroll Expense ($000):** 14817 **Personnel:** 283

TALLASSEE—Elmore County

★ **COMMUNITY HOSPITAL (010034)**, 805 Friendship Road, Zip 36078–1234; tel. 334/283–6541 **A**10 **F**18 21 28 29 35 40 62 63 64 70 81 82 86 87 98 100 101 102 103 104 107 119 146
Primary Contact: Jennie R. Rhinehart, Administrator and Chief Executive Officer
Web address: www.chal.org
Control: Other not–for–profit (including NFP Corporation) **Service:** General Medical and Surgical

Staffed Beds: 47 **Admissions:** 1300 **Census:** 20 **Outpatient Visits:** 27297 **Births:** 0 **Total Expense ($000):** 26498

Hospital, Medicare Provider Number, Address, Telephone, Approval, Facility, and Physician Codes, Health Care System

★ American Hospital Association (AHA) membership ☐ The Joint Commission accreditation ○ Healthcare Facilities Accreditation Program ◇ DNV Healthcare Inc. accreditation ⇑ Center for Improvement in Healthcare Quality Accreditation △ Commission on Accreditation of Rehabilitation Facilities (CARF) accreditation

TROY—Pike County

☐ **TROY REGIONAL MEDICAL CENTER (010126)**, 1330 Highway 231 South, Zip 36081–3058; tel. 334/670–5000 **A**1 10 **F**4 29 30 40 45 50 57 70 79 81 85 93 107 108 110 114 119 129 133 135 146
Primary Contact: Ronnie Dean, Chief Executive Officer
COO: Josh Hester, Chief Operating Officer
CFO: Janet Smith, Chief Financial Officer
CMO: Paul Dulaney, M.D., Chief of Staff
CIO: Michael Moore, Director Information Systems
CHR: Beth Nissen, Director Human Resources
CNO: Amy Minor, Chief Nursing Officer
Web address: www.troymedicalcenter.com
Control: Hospital district or authority, Government, nonfederal **Service:** General Medical and Surgical

Staffed Beds: 45 **Admissions:** 1835 **Census:** 20 **Births:** 0 **Total Expense ($000):** 27387

TUSCALOOSA—Tuscaloosa County

☐ **BRYCE HOSPITAL (014007)**, 200 University Boulevard, Zip 35401–1294; tel. 205/507–8299, (Nonreporting) **A**1 3 5 10
Primary Contact: Shelia Penn, Facility Director
CFO: Wendell Summerville, Chief Financial Officer
CMO: Cynthia Moore Sledge, M.D., Medical Director
CIO: Ronene Howell, Director Health Information Management
CHR: Jim Elliott, Director Human Resources
Web address: www.mh.alabama.gov/
Control: State–Government, nonfederal **Service:** Psychiatric

Staffed Beds: 820

☐ **DCH REGIONAL MEDICAL CENTER (010092)**, 809 University Boulevard East, Zip 35401–2029; tel. 205/759–7111, (Includes NORTHPORT MEDICAL CENTER, 2700 Hospital Drive, Northport, Zip 35476–3360; tel. 205/333–4500; Luke Standeffer, Administrator) **A**1 2 3 5 10 20 **F**3 11 12 13 15 17 18 20 22 24 26 28 29 30 31 35 38 40 43 45 48 49 50 51 57 59 60 61 62 64 66 68 70 72 74 75 76 77 78 79 81 82 86 87 88 89 90 93 94 96 98 100 101 102 103 104 105 106 107 108 110 111 114 115 116 117 118 119 121 126 129 130 131 132 146 147 148 **P**8 **S** DCH Health System, Tuscaloosa, AL
Primary Contact: William H. Cassels, Administrator
CFO: Nina Dusang, Vice President Finance and Chief Financial Officer
CMO: Kenneth Aldridge, M.D., Vice President Medical Affairs
CIO: Kim Ligon, Director Information Services
CHR: Peggy Sease, Vice President Human Resources
CNO: Lorraine Yehlen, R.N., Vice President Patient Care Services
Web address: www.dchsystem.com
Control: Hospital district or authority, Government, nonfederal **Service:** General Medical and Surgical

Staffed Beds: 684 **Admissions:** 33038 **Census:** 486 **Outpatient Visits:** 549373 **Births:** 3571 **Total Expense ($000):** 450944 **Payroll Expense ($000):** 195175 **Personnel:** 3909

☐ **MARY S HARPER GERIATRIC PSYCHIATRY CENTER (014012)**, 200 University Boulevard, Zip 35401–1250; tel. 205/759–0900, (Nonreporting) **A**1 10
Primary Contact: Beverly White, MS, Facility Director
CFO: Sarah Mitchell, Director Finance
CMO: Robin Barton Lariscy, M.D., Medical Director
CIO: Sarah Mitchell, Director Finance
CHR: Jim Elliott, Director Human Resources
Web address: www.mh.alabama.gov
Control: Corporation, Investor–owned, for–profit **Service:** Psychiatric

Staffed Beds: 96

☐ **NOLAND HOSPITAL TUSCALOOSA (012012)**, 809 University Boulevard E, 4th Floor, Zip 35401–2029; tel. 205/759–7241 **A**1 10 **F**1 29 130 148 **S** Noland Health Services, Inc., Birmingham, AL
Primary Contact: Jack Gibson, Administrator
Web address: www.nolandhealth.com
Control: Other not–for–profit (including NFP Corporation) **Service:** Long–Term Acute Care hospital

Staffed Beds: 32 **Admissions:** 322 **Census:** 23 **Outpatient Visits:** 0 **Births:** 0 **Total Expense ($000):** 11093

☐ **TAYLOR HARDIN SECURE MEDICAL FACILITY (014011)**, 1301 Jack Warner Parkway, Zip 35404–1060; tel. 205/556–7060, (Nonreporting) **A**1 10
Primary Contact: Barbara Jackson, Ed.D., Acting Facility Director
Web address: www.mh.alabama.gov/
Control: Corporation, Investor–owned, for–profit **Service:** Psychiatric

Staffed Beds: 114

☒ **TUSCALOOSA VETERANS AFFAIRS MEDICAL CENTER**, 3701 Loop Road East, Zip 35404–5015; tel. 205/554–2000, (Nonreporting) **A**1 5 **S** Department of Veterans Affairs, Washington, DC
Primary Contact: John F. Merkle, Medical Center Director
COO: Gary D. Trende, FACHE, Associate Director
CFO: Angelia Stevenson, Manager Finance
CMO: Carlos E. Berry, M.D., Acting Chief of Staff
Web address: www.tuscaloosa.va.gov
Control: Veterans Affairs, Government, federal **Service:** Psychiatric

Staffed Beds: 366

TUSKEGEE—Macon County

TUSKEGEE DIVISION See Central Alabama Veterans Health Care System, Montgomery

UNION SPRINGS—Bullock County

BULLOCK COUNTY HOSPITAL (010110), 102 West Conecuh Avenue, Zip 36089–1303; tel. 334/738–2140 **A**10 20 **F**3 15 29 30 32 35 40 50 57 62 64 77 93 98 101 102 103 107 119 130
Primary Contact: Jacques Jarry, Administrator
COO: Victoria Lawrenson, Chief Operating Officer
CMO: Maria Bernardo, M.D., Chief of Staff
Web address: www.unionspringsalabama.com/
Control: Corporation, Investor–owned, for–profit **Service:** General Medical and Surgical

Staffed Beds: 44 **Admissions:** 1388 **Census:** 27 **Outpatient Visits:** 8543 **Births:** 0

WARRIOR—Jefferson County

BRADFORD HEALTH SERVICES AT WARRIOR LODGE, 1189 Allbritt Road, Zip 35180, Mailing Address: P.O. Box 129, Zip 35180–0129; tel. 205/647–1945, (Nonreporting) **S** Bradford Health Services, Birmingham, AL
Primary Contact: Roy M. Ramsey, Executive Director
Web address: www.bradfordhealth.com
Control: Corporation, Investor–owned, for–profit **Service:** Alcoholism and other chemical dependency

Staffed Beds: 100

WEDOWEE—Randolph County

WEDOWEE HOSPITAL (010032), 209 North Main Street, Zip 36278–7428, Mailing Address: P.O. Box 307, Zip 36278–0307; tel. 256/357–2111 **A**10 **F**3 40 81 107 111 114 119 129 130 132 133
Primary Contact: Michael D. Alexander, MS, Administrator
Web address: www.wedoweehospital.org/
Control: Church–operated, Nongovernment, not–for profit **Service:** General Medical and Surgical

Staffed Beds: 26 **Admissions:** 420 **Census:** 4 **Outpatient Visits:** 15568 **Births:** 0 **Total Expense ($000):** 6323

WETUMPKA—Elmore County

ELMORE COMMUNITY HOSPITAL (010097), 500 Hospital Drive, Zip 36092–1625, Mailing Address: P.O. Box 130, Zip 36092–0003; tel. 334/567–4311 **A**10 **F**3 4 11 29 40 45 57 59 62 70 81 82 97 107 111 114 119 143 144
Primary Contact: Gordon Faulk, Administrator
CFO: Mike Bruce, Chief Financial Officer
CHR: Cindy Futral, Director Human Resources
Web address: www.elmorehospital.com/
Control: Partnership, Investor–owned, for–profit **Service:** General Medical and Surgical

Staffed Beds: 49 **Admissions:** 1233 **Census:** 11 **Outpatient Visits:** 34281 **Births:** 0 **Total Expense ($000):** 15802

WINFIELD—Marion County

☐ **NORTHWEST MEDICAL CENTER (010086)**, 1530 U.S. Highway 43, Zip 35594–5056; tel. 205/487–7000 **A**1 10 **F**3 8 15 18 29 34 35 40 50 53 56 57 59 64 68 70 79 81 85 90 98 103 107 108 110 111 114 119 127 130 132 133 135 **S** Curae Health, Clinton, TN
Primary Contact: Michael D. Windham, Chief Executive Officer
CFO: Glenda Reyes, Chief Financial Officer
CMO: David Corbett, M.D., Chief of Staff
Web address: www.northwestmedcenter.com
Control: Corporation, Investor–owned, for–profit **Service:** General Medical and Surgical

Staffed Beds: 76 **Admissions:** 1668 **Census:** 23 **Outpatient Visits:** 29248 **Births:** 0 **Total Expense ($000):** 21305

Many Facility Codes have changed. Please refer to the AHA Guide Code Chart.
© 2016 AHA Guide

HILL HOSPITAL OF SUMTER COUNTY (010138), 751 Derby Drive,
Zip 36925–2121; tel. 205/392–5263 **A**10 **F**33 40 57 58 62 107 119
Primary Contact: Loretta Wilson, Administrator
CFO: Joyce Wedgeworth, Financial Clerk
CMO: Gary Walton, M.D., Chief Medical Officer
CNO: Cynthia Brown, Director of Nursing
Control: Other not–for–profit (including NFP Corporation) **Service:** General
Medical and Surgical

Staffed Beds: 33 **Admissions:** 401 **Census:** 7 **Outpatient Visits:** 5968
Births: 0 **Total Expense ($000):** 4183

AK

ALASKA

ANCHORAGE—Anchorage Division

⊞ **ALASKA NATIVE MEDICAL CENTER (020026)**, 4315 Diplomacy Drive, Zip 99508–5926; tel. 907/563–2662 **A**1 3 5 10 **F**3 8 11 13 15 18 19 20 22 29 30 31 32 33 34 35 36 38 39 40 41 43 45 46 47 48 49 50 53 54 56 57 58 59 61 62 64 65 66 68 72 74 75 76 77 78 79 81 82 84 85 87 88 89 93 97 99 100 101 102 103 104 105 107 110 111 114 115 119 127 130 132 134 135 141 142 143 146 147 148
Primary Contact: Roald Helgesen, Chief Executive Officer
CMO: Paul Franke, M.D., Chief Medical Officer
CHR: Sonya Conant, Senior Director Human Resources
Web address: www.anmc.org
Control: Other not–for–profit (including NFP Corporation) **Service:** General Medical and Surgical

Staffed Beds: 146 **Admissions:** 7390 **Census:** 110 **Outpatient Visits:** 316203 **Births:** 1641

☐ **ALASKA PSYCHIATRIC INSTITUTE (024002)**, 3700 Piper Street, Zip 99508–4677; tel. 907/269–7100 **A**1 10 **F**98 99 100 103
Primary Contact: Gavin H. Carmichael, FACHE, Interim Chief Executive Officer
COO: Gavin H. Carmichael, FACHE, Chief Operating Officer
CFO: Gavin H. Carmichael, FACHE, Chief Operating Officer
CIO: Stephen Schneider, Manager Information Services
CHR: Katie E. Gratrix, Administrative Assistant III
CNO: Sharon Bergstedt, Director of Nursing
Web address: www.hss.state.ak.us/dbh/API/
Control: State–Government, nonfederal **Service:** Psychiatric

Staffed Beds: 80 **Admissions:** 1683 **Census:** 65 **Outpatient Visits:** 0 **Births:** 0 **Total Expense ($000):** 34579 **Payroll Expense ($000):** 17510 **Personnel:** 256

⊞ **ALASKA REGIONAL HOSPITAL (020017)**, 2801 Debarr Road, Zip 99508–2997, Mailing Address: P.O. Box 143889, Zip 99514–3889; tel. 907/264–1754, (Nonreporting) **A**1 2 10 **S** HCA, Nashville, TN
Primary Contact: Julie Taylor, FACHE, Chief Executive Officer
COO: Victor Rosenbaum, Chief Operating Officer
CFO: Lynn Kennington, Chief Financial Officer
CMO: David Cadogan, Chief Medical Officer
CIO: Gene Kaplanis, Director Information Technology
CHR: Tammy Kaminski, Director Human Resources
CNO: Linda Doughty, Chief Nursing Officer
Web address: www.alaskaregional.com
Control: Corporation, Investor–owned, for–profit **Service:** General Medical and Surgical

Staffed Beds: 132

⊞ **NORTH STAR BEHAVIORAL HEALTH SYSTEM (024001)**, 2530 DeBarr Circle, Zip 99508–2948; tel. 907/258–7575, (Includes NORTH STAR BEHAVIORAL HEALTH, 1650 South Bragaw, Zip 99508–3467; tel. 907/258–7575) **A**1 3 5 10 **F**98 99 106 130 **S** Universal Health Services, Inc., King of Prussia, PA
Primary Contact: Andrew Mayo, Ph.D., Chief Executive Officer and Managing Director
CFO: Alan Barnes, Chief Financial Officer
CMO: Ruth Dukoff, M.D., Medical Director
CIO: Brian O'Connell, Director Information Services
CHR: Sabrina Ben, Director Human Resources
CNO: Brandy Proctor, Director of Nursing
Web address: www.northstarbehavioral.com
Control: Corporation, Investor–owned, for–profit **Service:** Children's hospital psychiatric

Staffed Beds: 200 **Admissions:** 1050 **Census:** 144 **Outpatient Visits:** 0 **Births:** 0 **Total Expense ($000):** 28546 **Payroll Expense ($000):** 16196 **Personnel:** 269

⊞ **PROVIDENCE ALASKA MEDICAL CENTER (020001)**, 3200 Providence Drive, Zip 99508–4615, Mailing Address: P.O. Box 196604, Zip 99519–6604; tel. 907/562–2211, (Includes CHILDREN'S HOSPITAL AT PROVIDENCE, 3200 Providence Drive, Zip 99508; tel. 907/212–3130) **A**1 2 3 5 10 13 **F**3 8 11 12 13 17 18 19 20 21 22 24 25 26 28 29 30 31 34 35 38 39 40 41 43 45 46 47 49 50 53 55 56 57 58 59 60 62 63 65 67 68 70 72 74 75 76 77 78 79 81 82 83 84 85 86 87 88 89 90 92 93 94 97 98 99 100 101 102 104 105 106 107 108 111 115 118 119 120 121 123 124 126 130 131 132 146 148 **S** Providence St. Joseph Health, Renton, WA
Primary Contact: Richard Mandsager, M.D., Executive Officer
CFO: Anthony Dorsch, Chief Financial Officer
CMO: Roy Davis, M.D., Chief Medical Officer
CIO: Stephanie Morton, Chief Information Officer
CHR: Scott Jungwirth, Chief Human Resources Officer
Web address: www.providence.org/alaska/pamc/default.htm
Control: Church–operated, Nongovernment, not–for profit **Service:** General Medical and Surgical

Staffed Beds: 401 **Admissions:** 16428 **Census:** 285 **Outpatient Visits:** 389969 **Births:** 2936 **Total Expense ($000):** 423142 **Payroll Expense ($000):** 197145 **Personnel:** 2488

⊞ **ST. ELIAS SPECIALTY HOSPITAL (022001)**, 4800 Cordova Street, Zip 99503–7218; tel. 907/561–3333 **A**1 10 **F**1 107 114 119 129 **P**4
Primary Contact: Sharon H. Kurz, Ph.D., Chief Executive Officer
CFO: Andrew Fitch, Chief Financial Officer
Web address: www.st–eliashospital.com
Control: Partnership, Investor–owned, for–profit **Service:** Long–Term Acute Care hospital

Staffed Beds: 59 **Admissions:** 306 **Census:** 32 **Outpatient Visits:** 0 **Births:** 0 **Total Expense ($000):** 35275 **Payroll Expense ($000):** 13510 **Personnel:** 212

BARROW—North Slope Division

⊞ **SAMUEL SIMMONDS MEMORIAL HOSPITAL (021312)**, 7000 Uulu Street, Zip 99723, Mailing Address: P.O. Box 29, Zip 99723–0029; tel. 907/852–4611, (Nonreporting) **A**1 10 18
Primary Contact: Richard Hall, Chief Executive Officer
CMO: Devon Allen, M.D., Chief of Medical Staff
Web address: www.arcticslope.org
Control: Other not–for–profit (including NFP Corporation) **Service:** General Medical and Surgical

Staffed Beds: 14

BETHEL—Bethel Division

⊞ **YUKON–KUSKOKWIM DELTA REGIONAL HOSPITAL (020018)**, 700 Chief Eddie Hoffman Highway, Zip 99559–3000, Mailing Address: P.O. Box 528, Zip 99559–0528; tel. 907/543–6300 **A**1 3 5 10 **F**2 3 4 5 13 15 29 32 34 35 38 39 40 44 45 50 53 54 57 58 59 64 65 66 68 71 75 76 77 81 82 84 85 87 89 90 91 93 97 99 100 101 102 103 104 105 106 107 110 127 130 132 134 135 144 145 147 148 **P**6
Primary Contact: Dan Winkelman, President and Chief Executive Officer
CFO: Vanetta Van Cleave, Chief Financial Officer
CIO: William Pearch, Chief Information Officer
Web address: www.ykhc.org
Control: Other not–for–profit (including NFP Corporation) **Service:** General Medical and Surgical

Staffed Beds: 37 **Admissions:** 2000 **Census:** 18 **Outpatient Visits:** 240000 **Births:** 400 **Total Expense ($000):** 161108 **Payroll Expense ($000):** 71818 **Personnel:** 193

CORDOVA—Valdez–Cordova Division

★ **CORDOVA COMMUNITY MEDICAL CENTER (021307)**, 602 Chase Avenue, Zip 99574, Mailing Address: P.O. Box 160, Zip 99574–0160; tel. 907/424–8000, (Total facility includes 10 beds in nursing home–type unit) **A**10 18 **F**5 11 29 34 35 38 40 56 57 59 64 65 69 75 77 91 93 96 97 99 100 101 102 103 104 107 114 119 128 130 133 135 143 146
Primary Contact: Scot Mitchell, FACHE, Chief Executive Officer and Administrator
CFO: Lee W. Bennett, Interim Chief Financial Officer
CMO: Sam Blackadar, M.D., Medical Director
CHR: Kim Wilson, Human Resources Coordinator
CNO: Mary Rios, R.N., Interim Director of Nursing
Web address: www.cdvcmc.com
Control: City–Government, nonfederal **Service:** General Medical and Surgical

Staffed Beds: 23 **Admissions:** 77 **Census:** 11 **Outpatient Visits:** 970 **Births:** 1 **Total Expense ($000):** 9988 **Payroll Expense ($000):** 3271 **Personnel:** 57

Many Facility Codes have changed. Please refer to the AHA Guide Code Chart. © 2016 AHA Guide

DILLINGHAM—Dillingham Division

✣ **BRISTOL BAY AREA HEALTH CORPORATION (021309)**, 6000 Kanakanak Road, Zip 99576, Mailing Address: P.O. Box 130, Zip 99576–0130; tel. 907/842–5201 **A**1 10 18 **F**3 4 5 7 13 15 29 32 34 35 38 39 40 41 42 43 45 46 47 48 49 50 54 57 58 59 61 62 64 65 66 68 75 76 79 82 85 86 87 89 90 100 107 119 120 127 130 132 133 134 135 145 147 148
Primary Contact: Robert J. Clark, President and Chief Executive Officer
COO: Lucrecia Scotford, Executive Vice President and Chief Operations Officer
CFO: David Morgan, Vice President and Chief Financial Officer
CMO: Arnold Loera, M.D., Clinical Director
CIO: Bill Wilcox, Chief Information Technology Officer
CHR: John Davis, Chief Human Resources Officer
CNO: Starla Fox, Director of Nursing
Web address: www.bbahc.org
Control: PHS, Indian Service, Government, federal **Service:** General Medical and Surgical

Staffed Beds: 14 **Admissions:** 172 **Census:** 3 **Outpatient Visits:** 6595 **Births:** 49 **Total Expense ($000):** 63160 **Payroll Expense ($000):** 22549

ELMENDORF AFB—Anchorage Division

✣ **U. S. AIR FORCE REGIONAL HOSPITAL**, 5955 Zeamer Avenue, Zip 99506–3702; tel. 907/580–3006, (Nonreporting) **A**1 5 **S** Department of the Air Force, Washington, DC
Primary Contact: Major Mark Lamey, Commander
COO: Colonel Rebecca Seese, Chief Operating Officer
CFO: Major Felicia Burks, Chief Financial Officer
CMO: Colonel Marriner Oldham, M.D., Chief Medical Officer
CIO: Major Phillip Oliphant, Chief Information Officer
CHR: Mark Clark, Human Resources Liaison
Web address: www.elmendorf.af.mil/
Control: Air Force, Government, federal **Service:** General Medical and Surgical

Staffed Beds: 64

FAIRBANKS—Fairbanks North Star Division

✣ **FAIRBANKS MEMORIAL HOSPITAL (020012)**, 1650 Cowles Street, Zip 99701–5998; tel. 907/452–8181, (Total facility includes 90 beds in nursing home–type unit) **A**1 2 3 5 10 **F**3 13 15 18 20 22 28 29 30 34 35 40 45 48 50 51 57 59 60 62 63 64 67 68 70 74 75 76 77 78 79 81 82 84 85 86 87 89 93 96 98 100 101 102 103 107 108 110 111 114 115 119 120 121 125 126 128 129 130 132 146 148 **S** Banner Health, Phoenix, AZ
Primary Contact: Gregory Johnson, D.D.S., Chief Executive Officer
CFO: Steve Leslie, Chief Financial Officer
CIO: Carl J. Kegley, System Director Information Technology
CHR: Nicole Welch, Chief Human Resources Officer
CNO: Karen Justin-Tanner, R.N., Chief Nursing Officer
Web address: www.bannerhealth.com/locations/alaska/fairbanks+memorial+Hospital
Control: Other not–for–profit (including NFP Corporation) **Service:** General Medical and Surgical

Staffed Beds: 217 **Admissions:** 4821 **Census:** 127 **Outpatient Visits:** 320575 **Births:** 1046 **Total Expense ($000):** 234251 **Payroll Expense ($000):** 88214 **Personnel:** 1080

FORT WAINWRIGHT—Fairbanks North Star Division

✣ **BASSETT ARMY COMMUNITY HOSPITAL**, 1060 Gaffney Road, Box 7400, Zip 99703–5001, Mailing Address: 1060 Gaffney Road, Box 7440, Zip 99703–5001; tel. 907/361–4000, (Nonreporting) **A**1 **S** Department of the Army, Office of the Surgeon General, Falls Church, VA
Primary Contact: Timothy Bergeron, Deputy Commander, Administration
CMO: Colonel Leo Bennett, M.D., Deputy Commander Clinical Services
CHR: Terri Morefield, Deputy Chief Human Resources Division
Web address: www.alaska.amedd.army.mil
Control: Army, Government, federal **Service:** General Medical and Surgical

Staffed Beds: 24

HOMER—Kenai Peninsula Division

★ **SOUTH PENINSULA HOSPITAL (021313)**, 4300 Bartlett Street, Zip 99603–7000; tel. 907/235–8101, (Total facility includes 28 beds in nursing home–type unit) **A**10 18 **F**3 13 15 18 29 30 31 34 35 36 40 45 50 56 57 59 62 64 65 67 68 70 74 75 76 77 78 79 81 82 85 87 91 92 93 94 97 100 107 110 115 119 128 129 130 133 147 148 **P**6 8
Primary Contact: Robert F. Letson, FACHE, Chief Executive Officer
CMO: Sarah Spencer, M.D., Chief of Staff
CIO: Jim Bartilson, Manager Information Systems
CNO: Shara Sutherlin, R.N., Director Patient Care Services
Web address: www.sphosp.org
Control: Hospital district or authority, Government, nonfederal **Service:** General Medical and Surgical

Staffed Beds: 50 **Admissions:** 860 **Census:** 37 **Outpatient Visits:** 51060 **Births:** 137 **Total Expense ($000):** 59783 **Payroll Expense ($000):** 25696 **Personnel:** 334

JUNEAU—Juneau Division

✣ **BARTLETT REGIONAL HOSPITAL (020008)**, 3260 Hospital Drive, Zip 99801–7808; tel. 907/796–8900 **A**1 10 20 **F**3 4 5 13 15 28 29 31 34 40 43 45 50 51 57 59 64 70 75 77 81 85 86 91 93 98 99 100 102 104 105 107 108 110 111 114 115 119 120 129 130 132 135 148 **P**6
Primary Contact: Charles E. Bill, Chief Executive Officer
CFO: Alan Ulrich, Chief Financial Officer
CMO: Sharon Fisher, M.D., Chief of Staff
CIO: Martha Palicka, Director Information Systems
CHR: Dallas Hargrave, Human Resources Director
CNO: William Gardner, Chief Clinical Officer
Web address: www.bartletthospital.org
Control: City–Government, nonfederal **Service:** General Medical and Surgical

Staffed Beds: 73 **Admissions:** 2380 **Census:** 27 **Outpatient Visits:** 45237 **Births:** 362 **Total Expense ($000):** 99622 **Payroll Expense ($000):** 36961 **Personnel:** 353

KETCHIKAN—Ketchikan Gateway Division

★ ◇ **PEACEHEALTH KETCHIKAN MEDICAL CENTER (021311)**, 3100 Tongass Avenue, Zip 99901–5746; tel. 907/225–5171, (Total facility includes 25 beds in nursing home–type unit) **A**5 10 18 21 **F**11 13 15 18 19 29 30 31 40 43 45 46 50 62 63 65 70 74 75 77 78 79 81 82 84 87 93 94 97 102 104 107 108 109 110 111 115 119 128 129 130 131 132 146 147 148 **P**6 **S** PeaceHealth, Vancouver, WA
Primary Contact: Ken Tonjes, Interim Chief Administrative Officer
CFO: Ken Tonjes, Chief Financial Officer
CMO: Peter Rice, M.D., Medical Director
CIO: Tim Walker, Manager Information Services
CHR: Lanetta Lundberg, Vice President Culture and People
Web address: www.peacehealth.org
Control: Church–operated, Nongovernment, not–for profit **Service:** General Medical and Surgical

Staffed Beds: 50 **Admissions:** 1073 **Census:** 29 **Outpatient Visits:** 72451 **Births:** 205 **Total Expense ($000):** 65735 **Payroll Expense ($000):** 28495 **Personnel:** 335

KODIAK—Kodiak Island Division

✣ **PROVIDENCE KODIAK ISLAND MEDICAL CENTER (021306)**, 1915 East Rezanof Drive, Zip 99615–6602; tel. 907/486–3281, (Nonreporting) **A**1 10 18 **S** Providence St. Joseph Health, Renton, WA
Primary Contact: Barbara Bigelow, Administrator
COO: Brenda Zawacki, Chief Operating Manager
CFO: Timothy Hocum, Chief Financial Officer
CMO: Steve Smith, M.D., Chief of Staff
CIO: David Johnson, Manager Information Services
CNO: LeeAnn Horn, Chief Nurse Executive
Web address: www.providence.org
Control: Other not–for–profit (including NFP Corporation) **Service:** General Medical and Surgical

Staffed Beds: 25

AK

KOTZEBUE—Northwest Arctic Division

☐ **MANIILAQ HEALTH CENTER (021310)**, 436 5th Avenue, Zip 99752–0043, Mailing Address: P.O. Box 43, Zip 99752–0043; tel. 907/442–7344, (Nonreporting) **A**1 5 10 18
Primary Contact: Paul Hansen, Administrator
COO: Timothy Schuerch, President and Chief Executive Officer
CFO: Lucy Nelson, Director Finance, Vice President
CMO: Patricia Clancy, M.D., Director Medical Services
CIO: Eugene Smith, Chief Information Officer
CHR: Gerty Gallahom, Director Human Resources
CNO: Commander Donna K. Biagioni, R.N., Director of Nursing
Web address: www.maniilaq.org
Control: PHS, Indian Service, Government, federal **Service:** General Medical and Surgical

Staffed Beds: 17

NOME—Nome Division

⊠ **NORTON SOUND REGIONAL HOSPITAL (021308)**, Bering Straits, Zip 99762, Mailing Address: P.O. Box 966, Zip 99762–0966; tel. 907/443–3311, (Nonreporting) **A**1 10 18
Primary Contact: Angela Gorn, Vice President
COO: Roy Agloinga, Chief Administrative Officer
CMO: David Head, M.D., Chief Medical Staff
CIO: Dan Bailey, Director Information Systems
CHR: Tiffany Martinson, Director Human Resources
Web address: www.nortonsoundhealth.org
Control: Other not–for–profit (including NFP Corporation) **Service:** General Medical and Surgical

Staffed Beds: 36

PALMER—Matanuska–Susitna Division

⊠ **MAT–SU REGIONAL MEDICAL CENTER (020006)**, 2500 South Woodworth Loop, Zip 99645–8984, Mailing Address: P.O. Box 1687, Zip 99645–1687; tel. 907/861–6000 **A**1 3 10 20 **F**3 8 13 15 18 19 20 22 26 28 29 30 31 34 35 38 39 40 43 45 46 47 48 50 51 54 55 56 57 58 59 64 65 68 70 74 75 76 77 78 79 81 85 86 87 91 93 96 97 99 102 107 108 110 111 114 115 119 124 126 128 129 130 132 133 135 144 146 148 **P**6 **S** Community Health Systems, Inc., Franklin, TN
Primary Contact: John R. Lee, Chief Executive Officer
CMO: Christopher Sahlstrom, M.D., Chief of Staff
CIO: Bryan Meurer, Director Information Systems
CHR: Cathy Babuscio, Director Human Resources
CNO: Emily Stevens, Chief Nursing Officer
Web address: www.matsuregional.com
Control: Partnership, Investor–owned, for–profit **Service:** General Medical and Surgical

Staffed Beds: 74 **Admissions:** 4457 **Census:** 44 **Outpatient Visits:** 100535 **Births:** 749 **Personnel:** 457

PETERSBURG—Wrangell–Petersburg Division

★ **PETERSBURG MEDICAL CENTER (021304)**, 103 Fram Street, Zip 99833, Mailing Address: Box 589, Zip 99833–0589; tel. 907/772–4291, (Total facility includes 15 beds in nursing home–type unit) **A**10 18 **F**15 31 34 40 45 56 57 59 62 64 67 77 79 81 84 85 93 97 107 110 114 119 133 146 148 **P**6
Primary Contact: Elizabeth Woodyard, R.N., MSN, Chief Executive Officer
CFO: Doran Hammett, Chief Financial Officer
CHR: Cynthia Newman, Manager Human Resources
CNO: Jennifer Bryner, Director Nursing
Web address: www.pmcak.org
Control: City–County, Government, nonfederal **Service:** General Medical and Surgical

Staffed Beds: 27 **Admissions:** 106 **Census:** 19 **Outpatient Visits:** 10565 **Births:** 0

SEWARD—Kenai Peninsula Division

★ **PROVIDENCE SEWARD MEDICAL CENTER (021302)**, 417 First Avenue, Zip 99664, Mailing Address: P.O. Box 365, Zip 99664–0365; tel. 907/224–5205, (Nonreporting) **A**10 18 **S** Providence St. Joseph Health, Renton, WA
Primary Contact: Joseph Fong, Administrator
Web address: www.providence.org
Control: Other not–for–profit (including NFP Corporation) **Service:** General Medical and Surgical

Staffed Beds: 46

SITKA—Sitka Division

⊠ **SEARHC MT. EDGECUMBE HOSPITAL (020027)**, 222 Tongass Drive, Zip 99835–9416; tel. 907/966–2411 **A**1 5 10 **F**3 5 13 15 29 30 32 39 40 43 45 48 50 64 68 70 75 76 77 81 82 85 87 93 97 107 110 111 119 127 130 134 135 143 144 147
Primary Contact: Charles Clement, Chief Executive Officer
COO: Daniel P. Neumeister, Chief Operating Officer
CFO: Barbara Searls, Chief Financial Officer
CMO: David Vastola, Medical Director
CIO: Bob Cita, Chief Information Officer
CHR: Peggy Bernhardt–Kadlec, Chief Human Resources Officer
CNO: Patricia L. Giampa, Chief Nursing Officer
Web address: www.searhc.org
Control: Other not–for–profit (including NFP Corporation) **Service:** General Medical and Surgical

Staffed Beds: 25 **Admissions:** 398 **Census:** 8 **Outpatient Visits:** 95612 **Births:** 44 **Total Expense ($000):** 114635 **Payroll Expense ($000):** 55170 **Personnel:** 231

★ **SITKA COMMUNITY HOSPITAL (021303)**, 209 Moller Avenue, Zip 99835–7142; tel. 907/747–3241, (Total facility includes 15 beds in nursing home–type unit) **A**10 18 **F**3 11 13 15 28 29 31 32 33 34 35 40 43 44 45 50 53 56 59 62 64 65 76 77 81 82 85 87 89 90 93 94 96 97 102 107 110 114 119 128 130 131 133 135 148
Primary Contact: Rob Allen, Chief Executive Officer
CFO: Lee W. Bennett, Chief Financial Officer
CHR: Shannon Callahan, Director Human Resources
Web address: www.sitkahospital.org
Control: City–Government, nonfederal **Service:** Long–Term Acute Care hospital

Staffed Beds: 27 **Admissions:** 285 **Census:** 13 **Outpatient Visits:** 2362 **Births:** 36 **Total Expense ($000):** 30054 **Payroll Expense ($000):** 11273 **Personnel:** 142

SOLDOTNA—Kenai Peninsula Division

⊠ **CENTRAL PENINSULA HOSPITAL (020024)**, 250 Hospital Place, Zip 99669–6999; tel. 907/714–4404, (Total facility includes 58 beds in nursing home–type unit) **A**1 10 **F**3 4 5 11 13 15 28 29 30 31 34 35 36 38 40 45 46 47 48 49 57 59 65 68 70 74 75 76 77 78 79 81 82 84 85 86 87 93 97 99 100 102 103 104 105 106 107 108 110 111 115 119 128 129 130 131 132 133 134 135 145 146 147 148
Primary Contact: Richard Davis, Chief Executive Officer
COO: Matt Dammeyer, Ph.D., Chief Operating Officer
CFO: Shaun Keef, Chief Financial Officer
CMO: Gregg Motonaga, M.D., Chief of Staff
CIO: Bryan Downs, Director Information Systems
CHR: John Dodd, Vice President Human Resources
Web address: www.cpgh.org
Control: Other not–for–profit (including NFP Corporation) **Service:** General Medical and Surgical

Staffed Beds: 117 **Admissions:** 2664 **Census:** 79 **Outpatient Visits:** 96143 **Births:** 416 **Total Expense ($000):** 126509 **Payroll Expense ($000):** 56727 **Personnel:** 671

VALDEZ—Valdez–Cordova Division

★ **PROVIDENCE VALDEZ MEDICAL CENTER (021301)**, 911 Meals Avenue, Zip 99686–0550, Mailing Address: P.O. Box 550, Zip 99686–0550; tel. 907/835–2249, (Nonreporting) **A**10 18 **S** Providence St. Joseph Health, Renton, WA
Primary Contact: Jeremy O'Neil, Administrator
CMO: John Cullen, M.D., Chief of Staff and Medical Director Long Term Care
CHR: Maureen Radotich, Director Human Resources
Web address: www.providence.org/alaska
Control: City–Government, nonfederal **Service:** General Medical and Surgical

Staffed Beds: 21

WRANGELL—Wrangell Division

★ **WRANGELL MEDICAL CENTER (021305)**, First Avenue & Bennett Street, Zip 99929, Mailing Address: P.O. Box 1081, Zip 99929–1081; tel. 907/874–7000, (Total facility includes 14 beds in nursing home–type unit) **A**10 18 **F**1 40 45 57 67 80 89 90 93 107 128 130 133
Primary Contact: Robert A. Rang, R.N., Chief Executive Officer
CIO: Cathy Gross, Director Health Information Management Systems
CNO: Sherri Austin, MSN, Chief Nursing Officer
Web address: www.wrangellmedicalcenter.org/
Control: County–Government, nonfederal **Service:** General Medical and Surgical

Staffed Beds: 22 **Admissions:** 133 **Census:** 16 **Outpatient Visits:** 774 **Births:** 0

Many Facility Codes have changed. Please refer to the AHA Guide Code Chart. © 2016 AHA Guide

ARIZONA

APACHE JUNCTION—Pinal County

⊠ **BANNER GOLDFIELD MEDICAL CENTER (030134)**, 2050 West Southern Avenue, Zip 85120–7305; tel. 480/733–3300 **A**1 10 **F**3 29 30 34 36 38 40 41 44 45 47 50 61 68 70 74 75 77 79 81 85 86 87 100 102 107 114 119 130 132 135 145 146 148 **S** Banner Health, Phoenix, AZ
Primary Contact: Sharon Lind, MSN, FACHE, Chief Executive Officer
CFO: Tracy French, Chief Financial Officer
CMO: Jason Brown, M.D., Chief Medical Officer
CHR: Rebecca McLaughlin, Chief Human Resource Officer
CNO: Terri Paulus, Chief Nursing Officer
Web address: www.bannerhealth.com/Locations/Arizona/Banner+Goldfield+Medical+Center/_Welcome+to+Banner+Goldfield.htm
Control: Other not–for–profit (including NFP Corporation) **Service:** General Medical and Surgical

Staffed Beds: 30 **Admissions:** 764 **Census:** 7 **Total Expense ($000):** 20285 **Payroll Expense ($000):** 8265 **Personnel:** 115

BENSON—Cochise County

★ **BENSON HOSPITAL (031301)**, 450 South Ocotillo Street, Zip 85602–6403, Mailing Address: P.O. Box 2290, Zip 85602–2290; tel. 520/586–2261 **A**10 18 **F**3 11 29 30 34 40 43 50 57 59 64 75 77 87 93 107 111 114 119 132 133 146 148
Primary Contact: Richard Polheber, Chief Executive Officer
COO: Teresa Vincifora, Chief Operating Officer
CFO: Ken Goranson, Chief Financial Officer
CMO: Barbara Hartley, Chief Medical Officer
CIO: Rob Roberts, Director Information Technology
CHR: Ashley Dickey, Director Human Resources
Web address: www.bensonhospital.org
Control: Other not–for–profit (including NFP Corporation) **Service:** General Medical and Surgical

Staffed Beds: 22 **Admissions:** 335 **Census:** 6 **Outpatient Visits:** 15804 **Births:** 0 **Total Expense ($000):** 14105 **Payroll Expense ($000):** 6869 **Personnel:** 136

BISBEE—Cochise County

★ **COPPER QUEEN COMMUNITY HOSPITAL (031312)**, 101 Cole Avenue, Zip 85603–1399; tel. 520/432–5383 **A**10 18 **F**1 3 8 11 15 18 29 30 34 40 43 45 46 61 62 74 75 77 81 85 93 97 107 110 111 114 119 127 130 133 135 147
Primary Contact: James J. Dickson, Administrator and Chief Executive Officer
COO: Daniel Roe, M.D., Chief Operating Officer
CFO: James Ehasz, Chief Financial Officer
CMO: Daniel Roe, M.D., Chief Medical Officer
CIO: David Chmura, Chief Information Officer
CHR: Virginia Martinez, Director Human Resources
CNO: Sadie Maestas, Interim Chief Nursing Officer
Web address: www.cqch.org
Control: Other not–for–profit (including NFP Corporation) **Service:** General Medical and Surgical

Staffed Beds: 14 **Admissions:** 344 **Census:** 5 **Outpatient Visits:** 41201 **Births:** 6 **Total Expense ($000):** 22213 **Payroll Expense ($000):** 11863 **Personnel:** 231

BULLHEAD CITY—Mohave County

⊠ **WESTERN ARIZONA REGIONAL MEDICAL CENTER (030101)**, 2735 Silver Creek Road, Zip 86442–8303; tel. 928/763–2273, (Nonreporting) **A**1 10 19 **S** Community Health Systems, Inc., Franklin, TN
Primary Contact: Aaron Hazzard, Interim Chief Executive Officer
Web address: www.warmc.com
Control: Corporation, Investor–owned, for–profit **Service:** General Medical and Surgical

Staffed Beds: 139

CASA GRANDE—Pinal County

★ ◇ **BANNER CASA GRANDE MEDICAL CENTER (030016)**, 1800 East Florence Boulevard, Zip 85122–5399; tel. 520/381–6300 **A**10 21 **F**3 13 15 18 20 22 29 30 31 34 36 39 40 44 45 49 50 53 57 59 61 64 68 70 74 75 76 77 78 79 80 81 85 86 87 89 92 93 100 107 108 111 114 115 118 119 126 129 130 132 135 144 145 146 147 148 **S** Banner Health, Phoenix, AZ
Primary Contact: Rona Curphy, President and Chief Executive Officer
CFO: Robert Bender, Chief Financial Officer
CMO: Devin Minior, M.D., Chief Medical Officer
CHR: Carol D'Souza, Chief Human Resources Officer
CNO: Dan Lingle, Chief Nursing Officer
Web address: www.https://www.bannerhealth.com/Locations/Arizona/Banner+Casa+Grande+Medical+Center/_Banner+Casa+Grande+Medical+Center.htm
Control: Other not–for–profit (including NFP Corporation) **Service:** General Medical and Surgical

Staffed Beds: 135 **Admissions:** 5743 **Census:** 60 **Outpatient Visits:** 76009 **Births:** 727 **Total Expense ($000):** 119967 **Payroll Expense ($000):** 45205 **Personnel:** 670

CHANDLER—Maricopa County

☐ **ARIZONA ORTHOPEDIC SURGICAL HOSPITAL (030112)**, 2905 West Warner Road, Zip 85224–1674; tel. 480/603–9000 **A**1 10 **F**8 29 64 79 81 85 111 **S** United Surgical Partners International, Addison, TX
Primary Contact: Patricia Alice, Chief Executive Officer
Web address: www.azosh.com
Control: Corporation, Investor–owned, for–profit **Service:** Orthopedic

Staffed Beds: 24 **Admissions:** 891 **Census:** 5 **Births:** 0 **Personnel:** 79

⊠ **CHANDLER REGIONAL MEDICAL CENTER (030036)**, 1955 West Frye Road, Zip 85224–6282; tel. 480/728–3000 **A**1 3 10 **F**3 8 11 13 15 17 18 20 22 24 26 28 29 30 31 32 34 35 37 40 41 42 43 44 45 46 47 48 49 50 51 54 57 58 59 60 64 65 66 68 70 71 72 73 74 75 76 77 78 79 81 82 83 84 85 86 87 93 96 107 108 110 111 114 115 119 126 130 131 132 135 143 144 146 147 148 **P**6 **S** Dignity Health, San Francisco, CA
Primary Contact: Tim Bricker, President and Chief Executive Officer
COO: Jane E. Hanson, R.N., Chief Operating Officer
CFO: Mark Kem, Vice President Finance and Chief Financial Officer
CMO: Terry J. Happel, M.D., Vice President and Chief Medical Officer
CHR: Renea Brunke, Vice President Human Resources
CNO: Peg Smith, Vice President and Chief Nursing Officer
Web address: www.chandlerregional.com
Control: Other not–for–profit (including NFP Corporation) **Service:** General Medical and Surgical

Staffed Beds: 338 **Admissions:** 22448 **Census:** 251 **Outpatient Visits:** 184317 **Births:** 3839 **Total Expense ($000):** 415389 **Payroll Expense ($000):** 154234 **Personnel:** 2125

OASIS BEHAVIORAL HEALTH – CHANDLER, 2190 North Grace Boulevard, Zip 85225–3416; tel. 480/917–9301, (Nonreporting) **S** Acadia Healthcare Company, Inc., Franklin, TN
Primary Contact: James Gallagher, Chief Executive Officer
CFO: Dino Quarante, CPA, Chief Financial Officer
CHR: Barbara Mitchell, Director Human Resources
CNO: Charissa Davis, Chief Nursing Officer and Director of Nursing
Web address: www.obhhospital.com/about/location
Control: Corporation, Investor–owned, for–profit **Service:** Psychiatric

Staffed Beds: 47

CHINLE—Apache County

⊠ **CHINLE COMPREHENSIVE HEALTH CARE FACILITY (030084)**, Highway 191, Zip 86503, Mailing Address: P.O. Drawer PH, Zip 86503–8000; tel. 928/674–7001, (Nonreporting) **A**1 10 **S** U. S. Indian Health Service, Rockville, MD
Primary Contact: Ron Tso, Chief Executive Officer
CFO: Philene Tyler, Chief Finance Officer
CMO: Eric Ritchie, M.D., Clinical Director
CIO: Perry Francis, Supervisory Information Technology Specialist
CHR: Lorraine Begaye, Supervisory Human Resource Specialist
Web address: www.ihs.gov
Control: PHS, Indian Service, Government, federal **Service:** General Medical and Surgical

Staffed Beds: 60

Hospital, Medicare Provider Number, Address, Telephone, Approval, Facility, and Physician Codes, Health Care System

★ American Hospital Association (AHA) membership
☐ The Joint Commission accreditation
○ Healthcare Facilities Accreditation Program
◇ DNV Healthcare Inc. accreditation
⇑ Center for Improvement in Healthcare Quality Accreditation
△ Commission on Accreditation of Rehabilitation Facilities (CARF) accreditation

AZ

COTTONWOOD—Yavapai County

★ ◇ **VERDE VALLEY MEDICAL CENTER (030007)**, 269 South Candy Lane, Zip 86326–4170; tel. 928/639–6000 **A**10 13 20 21 **F**3 8 11 13 15 18 19 20 22 28 29 30 31 32 34 35 36 40 44 46 47 48 49 50 53 57 59 60 64 68 70 75 76 77 78 79 81 82 85 86 87 89 93 98 100 101 102 103 107 108 110 111 114 115 118 119 123 124 129 130 131 132 135 143 145 146 147 148 **S** Northern Arizona Healthcare, Flagstaff, AZ
Primary Contact: Barbara Firminger, Chief Administrative Officer
CFO: Jeffrey Treasure, Chief Financial Officer, Northern Arizona Healthcare
CMO: Amy Gottschalk, M.D., Chief Medical Officer, Verde Valley Medical Center; Vice President Quality, Northern Arizona Healthcare
CIO: Marilynn Black, Chief Information Officer, Northern Arizona Healthcare
CHR: Ronald Haase, Chief Human Resources Officer, Northern Arizona Healthcare
CNO: Lori A. Stevens, MSN, Interim Chief Nursing Officer
Web address: www.nahealth.com
Control: Other not–for–profit (including NFP Corporation) **Service:** General Medical and Surgical

Staffed Beds: 110 **Admissions:** 4491 **Census:** 54 **Outpatient Visits:** 109879 **Births:** 570 **Total Expense ($000):** 127367 **Payroll Expense ($000):** 49965 **Personnel:** 627

FLAGSTAFF—Coconino County

★ ◇ **FLAGSTAFF MEDICAL CENTER (030023)**, 1200 North Beaver Street, Zip 86001–3118; tel. 928/779–3366 **A**3 5 10 21 **F**3 5 7 8 11 13 15 17 18 20 22 24 26 28 29 30 31 32 34 35 37 40 43 44 45 49 50 54 57 58 59 60 61 64 65 66 68 70 72 75 76 77 78 79 81 82 84 85 86 87 88 89 93 94 98 99 100 101 102 103 104 105 107 108 111 114 115 116 117 118 119 120 121 123 124 126 130 131 132 145 146 147 148 **S** Northern Arizona Healthcare, Flagstaff, AZ
Primary Contact: Florence (Flo) Spyrow, Chief Administrative Officer
CFO: Jeffrey Treasure, Chief Financial Officer, Northern Arizona Healthcare
CMO: Richard Neff, M.D., Interim Chief Medical Officer
CIO: Marilynn Black, Chief Information Officer, Northern Arizona Healthcare
CHR: Ronald Haase, Chief Human Resources Officer, Northern Arizona Healthcare
CNO: Katy Wilkens, Chief Nursing Officer and Vice President, Northern Arizona Healthcare
Web address: www.nahealth.com
Control: Other not–for–profit (including NFP Corporation) **Service:** General Medical and Surgical

Staffed Beds: 267 **Admissions:** 14436 **Census:** 177 **Births:** 1234 **Total Expense ($000):** 355003 **Payroll Expense ($000):** 130130 **Personnel:** 1824

☐ **GUIDANCE CENTER (034023)**, 2187 North Vickey Street, Zip 86004–6121; tel. 928/527–1899, (Nonreporting) **A**1 10
Primary Contact: Jack Callaghan, M.D., Chief Executive Officer
Web address: www.tgcaz.org
Control: Other not–for–profit (including NFP Corporation) **Service:** Psychiatric

Staffed Beds: 10

FLORENCE—Pinal County

◇ **FLORENCE HOSPITAL AT ANTHEM (030132)**, 4545 North Hunt Highway, Zip 85132–6937; tel. 520/868–3333, (Nonreporting) **A**10 21
Primary Contact: Bryan J. Hargis, FACHE, Chief Executive Officer
CFO: Dennis E. Rutherford, CPA, Chief Financial Officer
CNO: Marla Meggers, Chief Nursing Officer and Chief Operating Officer
Web address: www.fhanthem.com
Control: Partnership, Investor–owned, for–profit **Service:** General Medical and Surgical

Staffed Beds: 36

FORT DEFIANCE—Apache County

★ **TSEHOOTSOOI MEDICAL CENTER (030071)**, Highway 12 & Bonito Drive, Zip 86504, Mailing Address: P.O. Box 649, Zip 86504–0649; tel. 928/729–8000, (Nonreporting) **A**10 **S** U. S. Indian Health Service, Rockville, MD
Primary Contact: Sandi Aretino, Chief Executive Officer
COO: Valonia Hardy, Chief Healthy Living Officer
CFO: Rachel Sorrell, Chief Financial Officer
CMO: Michael Tutt, M.D., Chief Medical Officer
CIO: Virgil Chavez, Director Information Technology
CHR: Vivian Santistevan, Chief Human Resources
CNO: Tori Davidson, R.N., Chief Nursing Officer
Web address: www.fdihb.org
Control: PHS, Indian Service, Government, federal **Service:** General Medical and Surgical

Staffed Beds: 52

FORT MOHAVE—Mohave County

☒ **VALLEY VIEW MEDICAL CENTER (030117)**, 5330 South Highway 95, Zip 86426–9225; tel. 928/788–2273, (Nonreporting) **A**1 10 **S** LifePoint Health, Brentwood, TN
Primary Contact: Feliciano Jiron, Chief Executive Officer
CFO: Emma Canlas, Chief Financial Officer
CIO: Monique Murphy–Mijares, Chief Information Officer
CHR: Bonnie Guerrero, Director Human Resources
CNO: Lesa Lock, Chief Nursing Officer
Web address: www.valleyviewmedicalcenter.net
Control: Corporation, Investor–owned, for–profit **Service:** General Medical and Surgical

Staffed Beds: 90

GANADO—Apache County

☒ **SAGE MEMORIAL HOSPITAL (031309)**, Highway 264, Zip 86505, Mailing Address: P.O. Box 457, Zip 86505–0457; tel. 928/755–4500 **A**1 10 18 **F**1 5 7 11 18 29 32 34 35 39 40 50 53 54 57 59 62 64 65 68 75 100 101 104 107 119 127 133 134 144
Primary Contact: Christi J. El–Meligi, R.N., Chief Executive Officer
COO: Netrisha Dalgai, Director of Operations
CFO: Michael Katigbak, Chief Financial Officer
CMO: Jeremy Wray, D.O., Medical Director
CIO: Michael Katigbak, Director Computer Services
CHR: Gary Pahe, Manager Human Resources
CNO: Ernasha McIntosh, Interim Director of Nursing
Web address: www.sagememorial.com
Control: Other not–for–profit (including NFP Corporation) **Service:** General Medical and Surgical

Staffed Beds: 25 **Admissions:** 305 **Census:** 7 **Births:** 0

GILBERT—Maricopa County

☒ **BANNER GATEWAY MEDICAL CENTER (030122)**, 1900 North Higley Road, Zip 85234–1604; tel. 480/543–2000 **A**1 3 10 **F**3 8 12 13 15 29 30 31 34 35 36 40 45 46 47 48 49 50 54 55 57 58 59 60 63 64 68 70 72 76 77 78 79 80 81 82 84 85 86 87 92 97 100 107 108 109 110 111 114 115 116 117 118 119 120 121 123 124 126 130 131 132 133 135 136 146 147 148 **S** Banner Health, Phoenix, AZ
Primary Contact: Lamont M. Yoder, R.N., MSN, FACHE, Chief Executive Officer
COO: James R. Powell, Associate Administrator
CFO: Thomas M. Matenaer, Chief Financial Officer
CMO: Nikunj Doshi, D.O., Chief Medical Officer
CHR: Michele Mustacchia, Chief Human Resources Officer
CNO: Debra Adornetto–Garcia, MSN, Chief Nursing Officer
Web address: www.bannerhealth.com/Locations/Arizona/Banner+Gateway+Medical+Center/
Control: Other not–for–profit (including NFP Corporation) **Service:** General Medical and Surgical

Staffed Beds: 177 **Admissions:** 12925 **Census:** 124 **Outpatient Visits:** 107983 **Births:** 3774 **Total Expense ($000):** 310858 **Payroll Expense ($000):** 84016 **Personnel:** 1454

GILBERT HOSPITAL (030120), 5656 South Power Road, Zip 85295–8487; tel. 480/984–2000 **A**10 **F**3 29 34 40 41 45 49 50 59 70 79 81 82 87 107 108 111 114 119
Primary Contact: Bryan J. Hargis, FACHE, Chief Executive Officer
CFO: Dennis E. Rutherford, CPA, Chief Financial Officer
CMO: Timothy Johns, M.D., Chief Medical Officer
CIO: Michelle Cianfrani, Director Information Technology
CNO: Marla Meggers, R.N., Chief Nursing Officer
Web address: www.gilberter.com
Control: Corporation, Investor–owned, for–profit **Service:** General Medical and Surgical

Staffed Beds: 19 **Admissions:** 740 **Census:** 7

☒ **MERCY GILBERT MEDICAL CENTER (030119)**, 3555 South Val Vista Road, Zip 85297–7323; tel. 480/728–8000 **A**1 10 **F**3 8 11 13 15 18 20 22 26 28 29 30 31 32 34 35 37 38 40 41 42 44 45 46 47 49 50 51 57 58 59 60 64 65 66 68 70 73 74 75 76 77 78 79 81 82 83 84 85 86 87 96 100 101 102 103 107 108 110 111 114 115 119 126 129 130 131 132 135 144 145 146 147 148 **P**6 **S** Dignity Health, San Francisco, CA
Primary Contact: Tim Bricker, President and Chief Executive Officer
COO: Jane E. Hanson, R.N., Chief Operating Officer
CFO: Chuck Sowers, Vice President Finance and Chief Financial Officer
CMO: Phil Fracica, M.D., Vice President and Chief Medical Officer
CIO: Larissa Spraker, Vice President Business Development and Chief Strategy Officer
CHR: Anita Harger, Director Human Resources
CNO: Julie Hoffman, Vice President Patient Care Services and Chief Nursing Officer
Web address: www.mercygilbert.org
Control: Other not–for–profit (including NFP Corporation) **Service:** General Medical and Surgical

Staffed Beds: 198 **Admissions:** 14162 **Census:** 135 **Outpatient Visits:** 87518 **Births:** 3578 **Total Expense ($000):** 233137 **Payroll Expense ($000):** 84090 **Personnel:** 1219

Many Facility Codes have changed. Please refer to the AHA Guide Code Chart. © 2016 AHA Guide

GLENDALE—Maricopa County

⊞ **ABRAZO ARROWHEAD CAMPUS (030094)**, 18701 North 67th Avenue, Zip 85308–7100; tel. 623/561–1000, (Includes ARIZONA HEART HOSPITAL, 1930 East Thomas Road, Phoenix, Zip 85016; tel. 602/532–1000), (Nonreporting) **A**1 3 10 **S** TENET Healthcare Corporation, Dallas, TX
Primary Contact: Frank L. Molinaro, Chief Executive Officer
CMO: Patrick Smith, M.D., Chief Medical Officer
CHR: Sharon M. Chadwick, Director Human Resources
Web address: www.arrowheadhospital.com
Control: Corporation, Investor–owned, for–profit **Service:** General Medical and Surgical

Staffed Beds: 234

☐ **AURORA BEHAVIORAL HEALTH SYSTEM WEST (034024)**, 6015 West Peoria Avenue, Zip 85302–1213; tel. 623/344–4400 **A**1 10 **F**5 11 29 30 34 35 38 44 50 54 57 68 75 86 87 98 99 101 102 104 130 132 134 135 146 **S** Signature Healthcare Services, Corona, CA
Primary Contact: Bruce Waldo, Chief Executive Officer
CFO: Rebekah Francis, JD, Chief Financial Officer
CHR: Vicki Thomsen, Director Human Resources
CNO: Lori Milus, R.N., Director of Nursing
Web address: www.aurorabehavioral.com
Control: Corporation, Investor–owned, for–profit **Service:** Psychiatric

Staffed Beds: 80 **Admissions:** 3921 **Census:** 79 **Outpatient Visits:** 2976 **Births:** 0 **Total Expense ($000):** 33122 **Payroll Expense ($000):** 16344 **Personnel:** 306

⊞ **BANNER THUNDERBIRD MEDICAL CENTER (030089)**, 5555 West Thunderbird Road, Zip 85306–4696; tel. 602/865–5555, (Includes BANNER BEHAVIORAL HEALTH CENTER–THUNDERBIRD CAMPUS, 5555 West Thunderbird Road, Zip 85306; tel. 602/588–5555) **A**1 10 **F**3 5 13 15 18 19 20 22 24 26 28 29 30 31 34 35 36 37 38 39 40 41 44 45 46 49 50 51 60 61 64 68 70 72 74 75 76 77 78 79 80 81 83 85 86 87 88 89 91 92 93 96 98 100 101 102 104 105 107 108 110 111 114 115 116 117 118 119 120 121 123 124 126 130 132 135 145 146 147 148 **S** Banner Health, Phoenix, AZ
Primary Contact: Debra J. Krmpotic, R.N., Chief Executive Officer
CFO: Richard Miller, Administrator Finance
CMO: Kathryn Perkins, M.D., Chief Medical Officer
CHR: Laura Witt, Administrator Human Resources
Web address: www.bannerhealth.com/Locations/Arizona/Banner+Thunderbird+Medical+Center/
Control: Other not–for–profit (including NFP Corporation) **Service:** General Medical and Surgical

Staffed Beds: 476 **Admissions:** 26950 **Census:** 349 **Outpatient Visits:** 137992 **Births:** 5327 **Total Expense ($000):** 441929 **Payroll Expense ($000):** 159218 **Personnel:** 2701

⊞ **HEALTHSOUTH VALLEY OF THE SUN REHABILITATION HOSPITAL (033032)**, 13460 North 67th Avenue, Zip 85304–1042; tel. 623/878–8800 **A**1 10 **F**29 62 64 75 90 93 132 **S** HEALTHSOUTH Corporation, Birmingham, AL
Primary Contact: Beth Bacher, Chief Executive Officer
CFO: Kathryn Haney, Controller
CMO: Michael Kravetz, M.D., Medical Director
CHR: Danette Garcia, Director Human Resources
CNO: Stephanie Palmer, Chief Nursing Officer
Web address: www.healthsouthvalleyofthesun.com
Control: Corporation, Investor–owned, for–profit **Service:** Rehabilitation

Staffed Beds: 75 **Admissions:** 1110 **Census:** 43 **Births:** 0 **Total Expense ($000):** 17723 **Payroll Expense ($000):** 9240 **Personnel:** 148

GLOBE—Gila County

COBRE VALLEY COMMUNITY HOSPITAL See Cobre Valley Regional Medical Center

★ **COBRE VALLEY REGIONAL MEDICAL CENTER (031314)**, 5880 South Hospital Drive, Zip 85501–9454; tel. 928/425–3261 **A**10 18 **F**3 11 12 13 15 18 29 30 34 35 40 43 45 46 49 51 57 59 64 70 74 75 76 78 79 81 82 87 92 93 97 107 108 110 111 115 117 118 119 127 129 130 133 135 146 147 148 **P**5 **S** HealthTech Management Services, Brentwood, TN
Primary Contact: Neal Jensen, Chief Executive Officer
CFO: Frank Napier, Interim Chief Financial Officer
CIO: Sharon Bennett, Manager Information Systems
CHR: Rita Murphy, Director Human Resources
Web address: www.cvrmc.org
Control: Other not–for–profit (including NFP Corporation) **Service:** General Medical and Surgical

Staffed Beds: 25 **Admissions:** 1635 **Census:** 15 **Outpatient Visits:** 55321 **Births:** 306 **Total Expense ($000):** 41634 **Payroll Expense ($000):** 17555 **Personnel:** 241

GOODYEAR—Maricopa County

⊞ **ABRAZO WEST CAMPUS (030110)**, 13677 West McDowell Road, Zip 85395–2635; tel. 623/882–1500, (Nonreporting) **A**1 10 **S** TENET Healthcare Corporation, Dallas, TX
Primary Contact: Stan V. Holm, FACHE, Chief Executive Officer
CFO: Richard Franco, Chief Financial Officer
CMO: Ron Kenneth, M.D., Chief Medical Officer
Web address: www.wvhospital.com
Control: Corporation, Investor–owned, for–profit **Service:** General Medical and Surgical

Staffed Beds: 106

⊞ **WESTERN REGIONAL MEDICAL CENTER (030127)**, 14200 West Celebrate Life way, Zip 85338–3005; tel. 623/207–3000 **A**1 2 10 **F**3 15 29 30 31 33 34 36 46 47 49 53 55 57 64 68 70 75 77 78 79 81 82 83 84 85 86 87 93 96 100 104 107 108 110 111 114 115 116 117 118 119 120 121 123 124 126 130 132 135 144 146 148 **P**6 **S** Cancer Treatment Centers of America, Schaumburg, IL
Primary Contact: Matthew McGuire, President and Chief Executive Officer
Web address: www.cancercenter.com/western–hospital.cfm
Control: Corporation, Investor–owned, for–profit **Service:** Cancer

Staffed Beds: 24 **Admissions:** 560 **Census:** 8 **Outpatient Visits:** 25307 **Births:** 0 **Personnel:** 558

GREEN VALLEY—Cochise County

GREEN VALLEY HOSPITAL (030137), 4455 South I–19 Frontage Road, Zip 85614; tel. 520/393–4700, (Nonreporting)
Primary Contact: David G. Covert, Chief Executive Officer
CFO: Sara Ghali, Chief Financial Officer
CNO: Mona R. Smith, Chief Nursing Officer
Web address: www.greenvalleyhospital.com
Control: Corporation, Investor–owned, for–profit **Service:** General Medical and Surgical

Staffed Beds: 98

KEAMS CANYON—Navajo County

⊞ **HOPI HEALTH CARE CENTER (031305)**, Highway 264 Mile Marker 388, Zip 86042, Mailing Address: P.O. Box 4000, Polacca, Zip 86042–4000; tel. 928/737–6000, (Nonreporting) **A**1 10 18 **S** U. S. Indian Health Service, Rockville, MD
Primary Contact: Daryl Melvin, Chief Executive Officer
COO: Leonard H. Lopez, Chief Operating Officer
CFO: Dorothy Sulu, Budget Analyst
CMO: Darren Vicenti, M.D., Clinical Director
CHR: Trudy Begay, Human Resources Specialist
CNO: Melissa Wyaco, Chief Nurse Executive
Web address: www.ihs.gov/index.asp
Control: PHS, Indian Service, Government, federal **Service:** General Medical and Surgical

Staffed Beds: 6

KINGMAN—Mohave County

★ ◇ **KINGMAN REGIONAL MEDICAL CENTER (030055)**, 3269 Stockton Hill Road, Zip 86409–3691; tel. 928/757–2101 **A**10 13 21 **F**3 11 13 15 17 18 22 24 28 29 30 31 34 35 40 42 43 49 51 53 57 59 60 62 63 64 70 74 75 77 78 79 81 82 84 85 86 87 90 93 97 107 108 110 111 114 115 116 117 118 119 121 123 127 129 130 132 135 143 144 146 147 148 **P**6
Primary Contact: Brian Turney, Chief Executive Officer
COO: Ryan Kennedy, Chief Operating Officer
CFO: Timothy D. Blanchard, Chief Financial Officer
CMO: Thomas Gaughan, M.D., Chief Medical Officer
CIO: Cheryl Martin, Chief Information Officer
CHR: Anita Harger, Chief Human Resource Officer
CNO: Kimberly Miyauchi, R.N., Chief Nursing Officer
Web address: www.azkrmc.com
Control: Hospital district or authority, Government, nonfederal **Service:** General Medical and Surgical

Staffed Beds: 180 **Admissions:** 8883 **Census:** 123 **Outpatient Visits:** 390703 **Births:** 648 **Total Expense ($000):** 242796 **Payroll Expense ($000):** 102956 **Personnel:** 1620

Hospital, Medicare Provider Number, Address, Telephone, Approval, Facility, and Physician Codes, Health Care System

★ American Hospital Association (AHA) membership   ○ Healthcare Facilities Accreditation Program   ⇑ Center for Improvement in Healthcare Quality Accreditation
☐ The Joint Commission accreditation   ◇ DNV Healthcare Inc. accreditation   △ Commission on Accreditation of Rehabilitation Facilities (CARF) accreditation

AZ

LAKE HAVASU CITY—Mohave County

⊞ **HAVASU REGIONAL MEDICAL CENTER (030069)**, 101 Civic Center Lane, Zip 86403–5683; tel. 928/855–8185, (Nonreporting) **A**1 10 **S** LifePoint Health, Brentwood, TN
Primary Contact: Michael N. Patterson, Chief Executive Officer
COO: Julie McCormack, Chief Operating Officer
CFO: Christina DiMambro, Chief Financial Officer
CMO: Michael Rosen, M.D., Chief Medical Officer
CIO: Linda Toy, Director Information Systems
CNO: Aphreikah DuHaney, Chief Nursing Officer
Web address: www.havasuregional.com
Control: Corporation, Investor–owned, for–profit **Service:** General Medical and Surgical

Staffed Beds: 162

LAKESIDE—Navajo County

CCC AT PINEVIEW HOSPITAL (034027), 1920 West Commerce Drive, Zip 85929; tel. 928/368–4110, (Nonreporting) **A**10
Primary Contact: Rosemary Anderson, Administrator
Web address: www.ccc–az.org
Control: Other not–for–profit (including NFP Corporation) **Service:** Psychiatric

Staffed Beds: 16

LAVEEN—Maricopa County

☐ **DIGNITY HEALTH ARIZONA GENERAL HOSPITAL (030136)**, 7171 South 51st Avenue, Zip 85339–2923; tel. 623/584–5100, (Nonreporting) **A**1
Primary Contact: Robert C. Honeycutt, Chief Executive Officer
CMO: David K. Butler, M.D., Chief Medical Officer
CNO: Kevin Lee Meek, R.N., Chief Nursing Officer
Web address: www.dignityhealth.org/arizonageneral/
Control: Other not–for–profit (including NFP Corporation) **Service:** Long–Term Acute Care hospital

Staffed Beds: 16

MESA—Maricopa County

☐ **ARIZONA SPINE AND JOINT HOSPITAL (030107)**, 4620 East Baseline Road, Zip 85206–4624; tel. 480/832–4770 **A**1 10 **F**29 34 77 79 81 82 85 111 146 **S** National Surgical Healthcare, Chicago, IL
Primary Contact: Todd Greene, Chief Executive Officer
CHR: Diane Hearne, Director Human Resources
CNO: Stacy Hayes, R.N., Chief Nursing Officer
Web address: www.azspineandjoint.com
Control: Corporation, Investor–owned, for–profit **Service:** Orthopedic

Staffed Beds: 23 Admissions: 964 Census: 5 Births: 0

⊞ **BANNER BAYWOOD MEDICAL CENTER (030088)**, 6644 East Baywood Avenue, Zip 85206–1797; tel. 480/321–2000 **A**1 10 **F**3 13 15 18 29 30 31 34 35 36 37 40 41 43 44 45 46 47 48 49 50 51 56 57 58 59 60 61 63 64 68 70 74 75 76 77 78 79 80 81 82 84 85 86 87 90 91 92 94 96 100 102 103 107 108 110 111 113 114 115 116 118 119 126 129 130 132 135 141 146 147 148 **S** Banner Health, Phoenix, AZ
Primary Contact: Julie Nunley, R.N., Chief Executive Officer
CFO: Derek Lythgoe, Chief Financial Officer
CMO: Michael P. O'Connor, M.D., Chief Medical Officer
CIO: Lori Matthews, Vice President Information Technology System
CHR: Lori Davis–Hill, Chief Human Resource Officer
CNO: Kelley Kieffer, Chief Nursing Officer
Web address: www.bannerhealth.com/locations/Arizona/banner+baywood+medical+center
Control: Other not–for–profit (including NFP Corporation) **Service:** General Medical and Surgical

Staffed Beds: 388 Admissions: 17859 Census: 232 Outpatient Visits: 105690 Births: 841 Total Expense ($000): 260658 Payroll Expense ($000): 95462 Personnel: 1654

BANNER CHILDREN'S HOSPITAL See Cardon Children's Medical Center

⊞ **BANNER DESERT MEDICAL CENTER (030065)**, 1400 South Dobson Road, Zip 85202–4707; tel. 480/412–3000, (Includes CARDON CHILDREN'S MEDICAL CENTER, 1400 South Dobson Road, tel. 480/412–3000; Justin Bradshaw, Chief Executive Officer; SAMARITAN BEHAVIORAL HEALTH CENTER–DESERT SAMARITAN MEDICAL CENTER, 2225 West Southern Avenue, Zip 85202; tel. 602/464–4000) **A**1 3 5 10 **F**3 11 13 18 19 20 21 22 23 24 25 26 27 28 29 30 31 32 34 35 36 37 38 40 41 45 46 47 48 49 50 51 57 58 59 60 61 64 68 70 71 72 74 75 76 77 78 79 80 81 82 84 85 87 89 92 93 96 97 102 107 108 111 114 115 118 119 120 123 124 126 129 130 132 134 146 147 148 **S** Banner Health, Phoenix, AZ
Primary Contact: Laura Robertson, R.N., Chief Executive Officer
CFO: Scott Leckey, Chief Financial Officer
CMO: Tanya Kne, M.D., Chief Medical Officer
CIO: Stacey Hinkle, Director Information Technology
CHR: Kevin McVeigh, Chief Human Resources Officer
Web address: www.bannerhealth.com/Locations/Arizona/Banner+Desert+Medical+Center
Control: Other not–for–profit (including NFP Corporation) **Service:** General Medical and Surgical

Staffed Beds: 595 Admissions: 31796 Census: 391 Outpatient Visits: 179992 Births: 4695 Total Expense ($000): 557353 Payroll Expense ($000): 196801 Personnel: 3285

⊞ **BANNER HEART HOSPITAL (030105)**, 6750 East Baywood Avenue, Zip 85206–1749; tel. 480/854–5000 **A**1 10 **F**3 17 18 20 22 24 26 28 29 30 34 35 36 44 45 46 50 56 57 58 59 60 61 64 68 74 75 77 81 82 84 85 86 87 92 94 100 103 113 119 126 130 132 135 141 146 147 148 **S** Banner Health, Phoenix, AZ
Primary Contact: Julie Nunley, R.N., Chief Executive Officer
CFO: Derek Lythgoe, Chief Financial Officer
CMO: Paul Hurst, M.D., Chief Medical Officer
CIO: Lori Matthews, Vice President, Information Technology System
CHR: Lori Davis–Hill, Chief Human Resource Officer
CNO: Kelley Kieffer, Chief Nursing Officer
Web address: www.bannerhealth.com/Locations/Arizona/Banner+Heart+Hospital/
Control: Other not–for–profit (including NFP Corporation) **Service:** Heart

Staffed Beds: 111 Admissions: 4793 Census: 57 Outpatient Visits: 8717 Births: 0 Total Expense ($000): 103886 Payroll Expense ($000): 27688 Personnel: 452

CARDON CHILDREN'S MEDICAL CENTER See Banner Desert Medical Center

⊞ **HEALTHSOUTH EAST VALLEY REHABILITATION HOSPITAL (033037)**, 5652 East Baseline Road, Zip 85206–4713; tel. 480/567–0350 **A**1 10 **F**28 29 64 74 75 77 79 82 90 91 93 94 95 96 130 132 148 **S** HEALTHSOUTH Corporation, Birmingham, AL
Primary Contact: Jerry Gray, Interim Chief Executive Officer
CMO: Martin Yee, M.D., Medical Director
CHR: Nancy Pickler, Director of Human Resources
CNO: Hope Dunn, Chief Nursing Officer
Web address: www.healthsoutheastvalley.com
Control: Corporation, Investor–owned, for–profit **Service:** Rehabilitation

Staffed Beds: 60 Admissions: 1498 Census: 56 Births: 0 Personnel: 230

★ ◇ **MOUNTAIN VISTA MEDICAL CENTER (030121)**, 1301 South Crismon Road, Zip 85209–3767; tel. 480/358–6100, (Nonreporting) **A**10 13 21 **S** IASIS Healthcare, Franklin, TN
Primary Contact: Eric Paul, Interim Chief Executive Officer
CNO: Bill Southwick, R.N., Chief Nursing Officer
Web address: www.mvmedicalcenter.com
Control: Corporation, Investor–owned, for–profit **Service:** General Medical and Surgical

Staffed Beds: 172

PROMISE HOSPITAL OF PHOENIX (032006), 433 East 6th Street, Zip 85203–7104; tel. 480/427–3000, (Nonreporting) **A**10 **S** Promise Healthcare, Boca Raton, FL
Primary Contact: Scott Floden, Chief Executive Officer
COO: Wendy Larson, Chief Clinical Officer
CFO: Theo Clark, Director Financial Services
CMO: Syed Shahryar, M.D., Medical Director
CHR: Christie Brea, Manager Human Resources
Web address: www.promise–phoenix.com
Control: Corporation, Investor–owned, for–profit **Service:** Long–Term Acute Care hospital

Staffed Beds: 40

SAMARITAN BEHAVIORAL HEALTH CENTER–DESERT SAMARITAN MEDICAL CENTER See Banner Desert Medical Center

Many Facility Codes have changed. Please refer to the AHA Guide Code Chart. © 2016 AHA Guide

NOGALES—Santa Cruz County

⊠ **CARONDELET HOLY CROSS HOSPITAL (031313)**, 1171 West Target Range Road, Zip 85621–2415; tel. 520/285–3000 **A**1 3 10 18 **F**3 11 13 29 30 31 32 34 35 40 50 51 56 57 59 64 65 68 70 75 76 77 79 81 85 86 87 89 93 107 111 115 119 130 132 133 134 135 146 **S** TENET Healthcare Corporation, Dallas, TX
Primary Contact: Debbie Knapheide, MSN, Site Administrator, Chief Nursing Officer and Chief Operating Officer
COO: Debbie Knapheide, MSN, Site Administrator, Chief Nursing Officer and Chief Operating Officer
CFO: Alan Strauss, Chief Financial Officer
CMO: Roy Farrell, M.D., Chief Medical Officer
CNO: Debbie Knapheide, MSN, Site Administrator, Chief Nursing Officer and Chief Operating Officer
Web address: www.carondelet.org
Control: Church–operated, Nongovernment, not–for profit **Service:** General Medical and Surgical

Staffed Beds: 25 **Admissions:** 912 **Census:** 6 **Outpatient Visits:** 37479 **Births:** 686 **Total Expense ($000):** 23010 **Payroll Expense ($000):** 10014 **Personnel:** 141

ORO VALLEY—Pima County

⊠ **ORO VALLEY HOSPITAL (030114)**, 1551 East Tangerine Road, Zip 85755–6213; tel. 520/901–3500 **A**1 10 **F**3 15 17 18 20 22 27 29 30 34 35 40 48 49 50 51 59 60 70 74 79 81 85 87 90 91 93 107 108 110 111 114 115 119 129 144 146 147 **S** Community Health Systems, Inc., Franklin, TN
Primary Contact: Jae Dale, Chief Executive Officer
CFO: Maurene Polashek, Chief Financial Officer
CNO: Julie Hunt, R.N., Chief Nursing Officer
Web address: www.orovalleyhospital.com
Control: Corporation, Investor–owned, for–profit **Service:** General Medical and Surgical

Staffed Beds: 144 **Admissions:** 5528 **Census:** 61 **Total Expense ($000):** 99709 **Payroll Expense ($000):** 40149 **Personnel:** 539

PAGE—Coconino County

⊠ **PAGE HOSPITAL (031304)**, 501 North Navajo Drive, Zip 86040, Mailing Address: P.O. Box 1447, Zip 86040–1447; tel. 928/645–2424 **A**1 10 18 **F**3 29 31 34 35 36 40 45 47 48 49 57 59 68 71 74 75 76 77 80 81 82 85 87 93 107 108 110 111 114 115 119 129 132 146 **S** Banner Health, Phoenix, AZ
Primary Contact: Brian Kellar, Chief Executive Officer
CFO: Darcy Robertson, Chief Financial Officer
CMO: Thomas Wood, M.D., Chief Medical Officer
CIO: Paul Caldwell, Facility Coordinator Information Technology Customer Relations
CHR: Ed Franklin, Chief Human Resources Officer
CNO: Susan Eubanks, Chief Nursing Officer
Web address: www.bannerhealth.com/Locations/Arizona/Page+Hospital
Control: Other not–for–profit (including NFP Corporation) **Service:** General Medical and Surgical

Staffed Beds: 25 **Admissions:** 459 **Census:** 3 **Outpatient Visits:** 18172 **Births:** 132 **Total Expense ($000):** 12979 **Payroll Expense ($000):** 6402 **Personnel:** 100

PARKER—La Paz County

LA PAZ REGIONAL HOSPITAL (031317), 1200 West Mohave Road, Zip 85344–6349; tel. 928/669–9201, (Nonreporting) **A**10 18
Primary Contact: Victoria Clark, Interim Chief Executive Officer
CFO: Carl J. Flanagan, Chief Financial Officer
CMO: Jack Dunn, M.D., Chief of Staff
CHR: Regina M. Martinez, Director Human Resources
CNO: Maria Martinez, Chief Nursing Officer
Web address: www.lapazhospital.org
Control: Other not–for–profit (including NFP Corporation) **Service:** General Medical and Surgical

Staffed Beds: 25

⊠ **U. S. PUBLIC HEALTH SERVICE INDIAN HOSPITAL (031307)**, 12033 Agency Road, Zip 85344–7718; tel. 928/669–2137, (Nonreporting) **A**1 10 18 **S** U. S. Indian Health Service, Rockville, MD
Primary Contact: Elizabeth Helsel, Chief Executive Officer
CFO: Robin Tahbo, Financial Management Officer
CMO: Laurence Norick, M.D., Clinical Director
CIO: JayLynn Saavedra, Chief Information Officer
Web address: www.ihs.gov
Control: Public Health Service, Government, federal **Service:** General Medical and Surgical

Staffed Beds: 20

PAYSON—Gila County

⊠ **BANNER PAYSON MEDICAL CENTER (030033)**, 807 South Ponderosa Street, Zip 85541–5599; tel. 928/474–3222, (Data for 153 days) **A**1 10 20 **F**3 11 13 15 18 26 29 30 31 34 35 38 40 44 45 50 57 59 68 70 75 76 77 79 80 81 85 87 93 100 107 110 111 119 127 130 132 135 145 146 **S** Banner Health, Phoenix, AZ
Primary Contact: Lance Porter, Chief Executive Officer
CFO: Peter Finelli, Chief Financial Officer
CMO: John Vandruff, M.D., Chief of Staff
CIO: Nick Vandermeer, Director Information Systems
CHR: Shawn M. Thomas, Director Human Resources
CNO: Hart Hintze, Chief Nursing Officer
Web address: www.paysonhospital.com
Control: Corporation, Investor–owned, for–profit **Service:** General Medical and Surgical

Staffed Beds: 44 **Admissions:** 678 **Census:** 12 **Outpatient Visits:** 13130 **Births:** 36 **Total Expense ($000):** 16351 **Payroll Expense ($000):** 5733

PEORIA—Maricopa County

KINDRED HOSPITAL ARIZONA–NORTHWEST PHOENIX See Kindred Hospital Arizona–Phoenix, Phoenix

PERIDOT—Gila County

⊠ **SAN CARLOS APACHE HEALTHCARE CORPORATION (030077)**, 103 Medicine Way Road, Zip 85542, Mailing Address: 10 Medicine Way Road, Zip 85542; tel. 928/475–2371, (Nonreporting) **A**1 10 **S** U. S. Indian Health Service, Rockville, MD
Primary Contact: Deven Parlikar, President and Chief Executive Officer
CFO: Vivie Hosteenez, Chief Financial Officer
CMO: Douglas Brinkerhoff, M.D., Clinical Director
CIO: Nimmy Mathews, Acting Director Quality Management
CHR: Shirley M. Boni, Administrative Officer
Web address: www.ihs.gov
Control: PHS, Indian Service, Government, federal **Service:** General Medical and Surgical

Staffed Beds: 8

PHOENIX—Maricopa County

⊠ **ABRAZO CENTRAL CAMPUS (030030)**, 2000 West Bethany Home Road, Zip 85015–2443; tel. 602/249–0212, (Nonreporting) **A**1 3 5 10 **S** TENET Healthcare Corporation, Dallas, TX
Primary Contact: Danny L. Jones, Jr., FACHE, Chief Executive Officer
COO: Jayleen Casano, Ph.D., Chief Operations and Nursing Officer
CFO: Paul Hymel, Chief Financial Officer
CHR: Dana George, Chief Human Resources Officer
Web address: www.abrazohealth.com
Control: Corporation, Investor–owned, for–profit **Service:** General Medical and Surgical

Staffed Beds: 215

⊠ **ABRAZO MARYVALE CAMPUS (030001)**, 5102 West Campbell Avenue, Zip 85031–1799; tel. 623/848–5000 **A**1 10 **F**3 13 18 20 22 26 29 34 35 40 45 49 59 68 70 73 74 75 76 81 85 86 107 108 111 119 130 146 147 **S** TENET Healthcare Corporation, Dallas, TX
Primary Contact: Crystal Hamilton, R.N., Chief Executive Officer
CFO: Julie Hastings–Smith, Chief Financial Officer
CHR: Erin Gonzalez, Director Chief Human Resources
CNO: Susan Kelley, R.N., Chief Nursing Officer
Web address: www.maryvalehospital.com
Control: Corporation, Investor–owned, for–profit **Service:** General Medical and Surgical

Staffed Beds: 100 **Admissions:** 3961 **Census:** 44 **Outpatient Visits:** 47006 **Births:** 252 **Total Expense ($000):** 47788 **Payroll Expense ($000):** 23080 **Personnel:** 379

⊠ **ABRAZO SCOTTSDALE CAMPUS (030083)**, 3929 East Bell Road, Zip 85032–2196; tel. 602/923–5000, (Nonreporting) **A**1 10 **S** TENET Healthcare Corporation, Dallas, TX
Primary Contact: David Tupponce, M.D., Chief Executive Officer
CFO: Jeffrey Zyla, Chief Financial Officer
CMO: David Tupponce, M.D., Chief Medical Officer
CHR: Kendrick Russell, Chief Human Resources Officer
CNO: Vicki Lynn Huber, R.N., Chief Nursing Officer
Web address: www.abrazoscottsdale.com
Control: Corporation, Investor–owned, for–profit **Service:** General Medical and Surgical

Staffed Beds: 142

AZ

☐ **ARIZONA STATE HOSPITAL (034021)**, 2500 East Van Buren Street, Zip 85008–6079; tel. 602/244–1331, (Nonreporting) **A**1 10
Primary Contact: Ann M. Froio, Interim Chief Executive Officer
COO: Donna Noriega, Chief Operating Officer
CFO: Donna Noriega, Chief Operating Officer
CMO: Steve Dingle, M.D., Chief Medical Officer
CIO: Bruce Randolph, Chief Information Technology
CHR: Jeanine Decker, Manager Human Resources
Web address: www.hs.state.az.us
Control: State–Government, nonfederal **Service:** Psychiatric

Staffed Beds: 299

⊠ △ **BANNER – UNIVERSITY MEDICAL CENTER PHOENIX (030002)**, 1111 East McDowell Road, Zip 85006–2666, Mailing Address: P.O. Box 2989, Zip 85062–2989; tel. 602/239–2000 **A**1 2 3 5 7 8 10 **F**3 6 7 8 9 11 12 13 15 17 18 20 22 24 26 28 29 30 31 34 35 36 37 39 40 43 44 45 46 47 48 49 50 51 53 54 55 56 57 58 59 60 64 66 68 70 72 74 75 76 77 78 79 80 81 82 83 84 85 86 87 90 91 92 93 94 96 97 98 100 101 102 103 104 107 108 110 111 113 114 115 116 117 118 119 120 121 123 124 126 129 130 131 132 135 138 139 141 142 145 146 147 148 **S** Banner Health, Phoenix, AZ
Primary Contact: Steve Narang, M.D., Chief Executive Officer
CFO: Kathy Kotin, Chief Financial Officer
CMO: Paul Stander, M.D., Chief Medical Officer
CIO: Michael S. Warden, Senior Vice President Information Technology
CHR: Michael Fleming, Chief People Officer
Web address: www.bannerhealth.com/Locations/Arizona/Banner+Good+Samaritan+Medical+Center
Control: Other not–for–profit (including NFP Corporation) **Service:** General Medical and Surgical

Staffed Beds: 685 Admissions: 33853 Census: 489 Outpatient Visits: 109688 Births: 5773 Total Expense ($000): 709439 Payroll Expense ($000): 261245 Personnel: 3674

⊠ **BANNER ESTRELLA MEDICAL CENTER (030115)**, 9201 West Thomas Road, Zip 85037–3332; tel. 623/327–4000 **A**1 3 10 **F**3 5 11 12 13 18 20 22 24 28 29 30 31 34 35 36 37 38 40 41 43 44 45 49 50 51 57 58 59 60 61 64 68 72 74 75 76 77 78 79 81 82 84 85 86 87 96 102 107 108 111 114 115 119 126 130 131 132 135 144 145 146 147 148 **S** Banner Health, Phoenix, AZ
Primary Contact: Courtney Ophaug, FACHE, Chief Executive Officer
COO: Gary Foster, R.N., Associate Administrator
CFO: Dean Shepardson, Chief Financial Officer
CHR: Wendy Labadie, Chief Human Resource Officer
CNO: Sheri Dahlstrom, R.N., Chief Nursing Officer
Web address: www.bannerhealth.com/Locations/Arizona/Banner+Estrella+Medical+Center/
Control: Other not–for–profit (including NFP Corporation) **Service:** General Medical and Surgical

Staffed Beds: 259 Admissions: 16321 Census: 167 Outpatient Visits: 108376 Births: 4472 Total Expense ($000): 241846 Payroll Expense ($000): 87320 Personnel: 1430

HAVEN SENIOR HORIZONS (034020), 1201 South 7th Avenue, Suite 200, Zip 85007–4076; tel. 623/236–2000 **A**10 **F**42 56 68 98 100 101 102 103 **P**5 **S** Haven Behavioral Healthcare, Nashville, TN
Primary Contact: Kathy Shaw, Chief Executive Officer
CHR: Erin McEldowney, Manager Human Resources
CNO: Char Ralstin, Director of Nursing
Web address: www.havenbehavioral.com
Control: Corporation, Investor–owned, for–profit **Service:** Psychiatric

Staffed Beds: 30 Admissions: 781 Census: 29 Outpatient Visits: 0 Births: 0 Personnel: 86

★ ○ ◇ **HONORHEALTH DEER VALLEY MEDICAL CENTER (030092)**, 19829 North 27th Avenue, Zip 85027–4002; tel. 623/879–6100 **A**10 11 21 **F**8 15 18 20 22 24 26 28 29 31 34 35 40 41 42 43 45 46 49 50 54 57 58 59 60 64 65 68 70 74 75 77 78 79 80 81 84 85 89 92 93 99 102 107 108 110 111 112 114 115 118 119 126 130 132 133 145 146 148 **S** HonorHealth, Scottsdale, AZ
Primary Contact: John L. Harrington, Jr., FACHE, Chief Executive Officer
CMO: Mary Ann Turley, D.O., Medical Director
CHR: Frank L. Cummins, Vice President Human Resources
Web address: www.jcl.com
Control: Other not–for–profit (including NFP Corporation) **Service:** General Medical and Surgical

Staffed Beds: 204 Admissions: 10401 Census: 147 Outpatient Visits: 96771 Births: 0 Total Expense ($000): 234909 Payroll Expense ($000): 79429

★ ◇ **HONORHEALTH JOHN C. LINCOLN MEDICAL CENTER (030014)**, 250 East Dunlap Avenue, Zip 85020–2825; tel. 602/943–2381 **A**10 13 21 **F**3 11 15 17 18 20 22 24 26 28 29 30 31 34 37 40 43 45 46 47 49 50 53 54 57 58 59 60 64 68 70 74 75 77 78 79 81 85 92 107 108 111 114 115 118 119 126 130 132 135 145 146 147 148 **S** HonorHealth, Scottsdale, AZ
Primary Contact: Margaret Elizabeth Griffin, Chief Executive Officer
CFO: Todd La Porte, Chief Financial Officer
CMO: Christopher Shearer, M.D., Chief Medical Officer
CNO: Jelden Arcilla, R.N., Vice President and Chief Nursing Officer
Web address: www.jcl.com
Control: Other not–for–profit (including NFP Corporation) **Service:** General Medical and Surgical

Staffed Beds: 262 Admissions: 13625 Census: 170 Births: 0 Personnel: 1393

⊠ **CURAHEALTH PHOENIX (032000)**, 40 East Indianola Avenue, Zip 85012–2059; tel. 602/280–7000, (Includes CURAHEALTH PHOENIX, 13216 North Plaza Del Rio Boulevard, Peoria, Zip 85381–4907; tel. 623/974–5463; Karen Shammas, Chief Executive Officer) **A**1 10 **F**3 29 30 40 47 60 70 75 85 119 148
Primary Contact: Karen Cawley, Chief Executive Officer
Control: Corporation, Investor–owned, for–profit **Service:** General Medical and Surgical

Staffed Beds: 58 Admissions: 291 Census: 25 Outpatient Visits: 0 Total Expense ($000): 17910 Payroll Expense ($000): 7292 Personnel: 110

LOS NINOS HOSPITAL (033301), 2303 East Thomas Road, Zip 85016–7827; tel. 602/954–7311, (Nonreporting) **A**10
Primary Contact: William Timmons, Chief Executive Officer
Web address: www.losninoshospital.com
Control: Other not–for–profit (including NFP Corporation) **Service:** Children's other specialty

Staffed Beds: 15

★ ◇ **MARICOPA INTEGRATED HEALTH SYSTEM (030022)**, 2601 East Roosevelt Street, Zip 85008–4956; tel. 602/344–5011, (Includes ARIZONA CHILDREN'S CENTER, 2601 East Roosevelt Street, Zip 85008–4973; tel. 602/344–5051) **A**3 5 8 10 21 **F**3 13 15 16 17 18 20 22 26 28 29 30 31 32 34 35 36 39 40 41 42 43 44 45 46 47 48 49 51 53 54 57 58 59 60 61 64 66 68 70 72 73 74 75 76 77 78 79 81 85 86 87 88 89 92 93 97 98 100 103 104 107 108 110 111 114 115 118 119 130 131 132 134 135 144 145 146 147 148 **P**1
Primary Contact: Stephen A. Purves, FACHE, President and Chief Executive Officer
COO: William F. Vanaskie, Executive Vice President and Chief Operating Officer
CFO: Michael Ayres, Senior Vice President and Chief Financial Officer
CMO: Robert Fromm, M.D., Chief Medical Officer
CIO: Kelly Summers, Chief Information Officer
CHR: Marshall Jones, Senior Vice President Human Resources
CNO: Sherry Stotler, R.N., Chief Nursing Officer
Web address: www.mihs.org
Control: Hospital district or authority, Government, nonfederal **Service:** General Medical and Surgical

Staffed Beds: 515 Admissions: 16511 Census: 367 Outpatient Visits: 510851 Births: 2848 Total Expense ($000): 512246 Payroll Expense ($000): 219489 Personnel: 3295

⊠ **MAYO CLINIC HOSPITAL (030103)**, 5777 East Mayo Boulevard, Zip 85054–4502; tel. 480/342–0960 **A**1 2 3 5 8 10 **F**3 6 8 9 11 12 15 17 18 20 22 24 26 28 29 30 31 34 35 36 39 40 45 46 47 48 49 50 51 54 55 56 57 58 59 60 61 64 65 68 70 74 75 77 78 79 80 81 82 84 85 86 87 90 92 93 96 97 100 103 104 107 108 110 111 112 114 115 116 117 118 119 120 121 123 124 126 129 130 131 132 135 136 137 138 139 141 142 145 146 147 148 **P**6 **S** Mayo Clinic, Rochester, MN
Primary Contact: Wyatt Decker, Chief Executive Officer
CFO: Jeffrey R. Froisland, Chief Financial Officer
CMO: Jeff T. Mueller, M.D., Chief Medical Officer, Medical Director
CIO: Paul Lenko, Unit Head, Information Technology
CHR: Nichelle A. Baker, Chair Human Resources
CNO: Teresa Connolly, R.N., Chief Nursing Officer
Web address: www.mayoclinic.org/arizona/
Control: Other not–for–profit (including NFP Corporation) **Service:** General Medical and Surgical

Staffed Beds: 268 Admissions: 13437 Census: 182 Outpatient Visits: 62617 Births: 0 Personnel: 2911

☐ **OASIS HOSPITAL (030131)**, 750 North 40th Street, Zip 85008–6486; tel. 602/797–7700 **A**1 3 10 **F**70 79 80 81 85 107 **P**7
Primary Contact: Tim Bogardus, Chief Executive Officer
Web address: www.oasishospital.com
Control: State–Government, nonfederal **Service:** Orthopedic

Staffed Beds: 64 Admissions: 3436 Census: 22 Outpatient Visits: 1226 Births: 0 Total Expense ($000): 63388 Payroll Expense ($000): 12359

AZ

✠ **PHOENIX CHILDREN'S HOSPITAL (033302)**, 1919 East Thomas Road, Zip 85016–7710; tel. 602/933–1000 **A**1 3 5 10 **F**3 8 11 15 17 19 21 23 25 27 29 30 31 32 34 35 37 38 39 40 41 42 43 44 46 48 49 50 54 55 57 58 59 60 61 64 65 66 68 71 72 73 74 75 77 78 79 81 82 84 85 86 87 88 89 91 92 93 94 96 97 98 99 100 101 102 104 105 107 108 111 113 114 115 116 117 118 119 129 130 131 132 134 135 136 137 138 139 144 146 148 **P**6
Primary Contact: Robert L. Meyer, President and Chief Executive Officer
COO: Betsy Kuzas, Executive Vice President and Chief Operating Officer
CFO: Craig L. McKnight, Senior Vice President and Chief Financial Officer
CMO: H. Stacy Nicholson, M.D., Physician in Chief
CIO: David Higginson, Executive Vice President and Chief Administrative Officer
CHR: Lisa Phelps, Senior Vice President, Human Resources
CNO: Julie Bowman, Senior Vice President, Patient Care and Chief Nursing Officer
Web address: www.phoenixchildrens.com
Control: Other not–for–profit (including NFP Corporation) **Service:** Children's general

Staffed Beds: 381 **Admissions:** 13332 **Census:** 211 **Outpatient Visits:** 269239 **Births:** 0 **Total Expense ($000):** 745720 **Payroll Expense ($000):** 302588 **Personnel:** 3568

✠ **PHOENIX VETERANS AFFAIRS HEALTH CARE SYSTEM**, 650 East Indian School Road, Zip 85012–1892; tel. 602/277–5551, (Nonreporting) **A**1 2 3 5 **S** Department of Veterans Affairs, Washington, DC
Primary Contact: Deborah Amdur, Director
CFO: Christine Hollingsworth, Chief Financial Officer
CMO: Raymond Chung, M.D., Chief of Staff
Web address: www.phoenix.va.gov/
Control: Veterans Affairs, Government, federal **Service:** General Medical and Surgical

Staffed Beds: 197

✠ **SELECT SPECIALTY HOSPITAL–PHOENIX (032001)**, 350 West Thomas Road, 3rd Floor Main, Zip 85013–4409; tel. 602/406–6802, (Nonreporting) **A**1 10 **S** Select Medical Corporation, Mechanicsburg, PA
Primary Contact: Sharon Anthony, Chief Executive Officer
Web address: www.phoenix.selectspecialtyhospitals.com/
Control: Corporation, Investor–owned, for–profit **Service:** Long–Term Acute Care hospital

Staffed Beds: 48

SELECT SPECIALTY HOSPITAL–PHOENIX DOWNTOWN See Select Specialty Hospital–Scottsdale, Scottsdale

✠ △ **ST. JOSEPH'S HOSPITAL AND MEDICAL CENTER (030024)**, 350 West Thomas Road, Zip 85013–4496, Mailing Address: P.O. Box 2071, Zip 85001–2071; tel. 602/406–3000, (Includes CHILDREN'S HEALTH CENTER, 350 West Thomas Road, Zip 85013–4409; ST. JOSEPH'S WESTGATE MEDICAL CENTER, 7300 North 99th Avenue, Glendale, Zip 85307–3003; tel. 602/406–0000) **A**1 2 3 5 7 8 10 **F**2 3 4 5 7 8 10 11 12 13 14 16 17 18 20 22 24 26 29 30 31 34 35 39 40 42 43 44 45 46 47 48 49 50 51 53 55 56 57 58 59 60 61 64 66 68 70 71 72 74 75 76 77 78 79 80 81 82 83 84 85 86 87 90 91 92 93 94 95 96 97 99 100 101 102 103 104 107 108 110 111 112 114 115 116 117 118 119 122 123 124 126 127 130 131 132 134 135 138 139 140 141 145 146 147 148 **P**5 6 **S** Dignity Health, San Francisco, CA
Primary Contact: Patty White, R.N., MS, President
CFO: Matthew Cox, Chief Financial Officer
CMO: Edward Donahue, M.D., Chief Medical Officer
CHR: Maureen Sterbach, Vice President Human Resources
CNO: Julie Ward, MSN, Chief Nursing Officer
Web address: www.stjosephs–phx.org
Control: Other not–for–profit (including NFP Corporation) **Service:** General Medical and Surgical

Staffed Beds: 595 **Admissions:** 29748 **Census:** 422 **Outpatient Visits:** 585699 **Births:** 4789 **Total Expense ($000):** 977716 **Payroll Expense ($000):** 390091 **Personnel:** 4544

☐ **ST. LUKE'S BEHAVIORAL HEALTH CENTER (034013)**, 1800 East Van Buren, Zip 85006–3742; tel. 602/251–8546, (Nonreporting) **A**1 10 **S** IASIS Healthcare, Franklin, TN
Primary Contact: Gregory L. Jahn, R.N., Chief Executive Officer
CFO: Ruby Majhail, Chief Financial Officer
CMO: Mario Tafur, M.D., Chief of Staff
CIO: Chris Ulrey, Director Management Information Systems
CHR: Amy M. Howell, Director Human Resources
Web address: www.iasishealthcare.com
Control: Corporation, Investor–owned, for–profit **Service:** Psychiatric

Staffed Beds: 85

★ ◇ **ST. LUKE'S MEDICAL CENTER (030037)**, 1800 East Van Buren Street, Zip 85006–3742; tel. 602/251–8100, (Includes TEMPE ST. LUKE'S HOSPITAL, 1500 South Mill Avenue, Tempe, Zip 85281–6699; tel. 480/784–5510; James Flinn, JD, FACHE, Chief Executive Officer) **A**3 10 21 **F**3 12 13 18 20 22 24 26 28 29 30 34 35 37 40 45 47 49 50 51 56 57 58 59 60 61 64 68 70 74 75 76 79 81 82 85 87 90 91 92 93 98 100 102 103 107 108 111 115 119 126 129 130 131 132 146 147 148 **P**4 **S** IASIS Healthcare, Franklin, TN
Primary Contact: James Flinn, JD, FACHE, Chief Executive Officer
CFO: Ken Walsh, Chief Financial Officer
CHR: Trinise Thompson, Director Human Resources
Web address: www.stlukesmedcenter.com
Control: Corporation, Investor–owned, for–profit **Service:** General Medical and Surgical

Staffed Beds: 284 **Admissions:** 8071 **Census:** 112 **Outpatient Visits:** 77416 **Births:** 372 **Total Expense ($000):** 150152 **Payroll Expense ($000):** 50296 **Personnel:** 852

☐ **THE CORE INSTITUTE SPECIALTY HOSPITAL (030108)**, 6501 North 19th Avenue, Zip 85015–1646; tel. 602/795–6020, (Nonreporting) **A**1 10
Primary Contact: Kurt Loveless, Chief Executive Officer
CFO: Barbara Chacon, Chief Financial Officer
CMO: Christopher A. Yeung, M.D., Chief of Staff
CHR: Sherrie A. Wagner, Manager Human Resources
CNO: Deborah Roberts, R.N., Chief Nursing Officer
Web address: www.thecoreinstitutehospital.com/
Control: Corporation, Investor–owned, for–profit **Service:** Surgical

Staffed Beds: 33

✠ **U. S. PUBLIC HEALTH SERVICE PHOENIX INDIAN MEDICAL CENTER (030078)**, 4212 North 16th Street, Zip 85016–5389; tel. 602/263–1200, (Nonreporting) **A**1 5 10 **S** U. S. Indian Health Service, Rockville, MD
Primary Contact: Captain Michael Weakhee, Chief Executive Officer
CFO: Geraldine Harney, Chief Financial Officer
CMO: Dave Civic, M.D., Associate Director Clinical Services
CIO: Vina Montour, Director Information Technology
CHR: Betty Weston, Chief Human Resources Officer
Web address: www.ihs.gov
Control: PHS, Indian Service, Government, federal **Service:** General Medical and Surgical

Staffed Beds: 127

☐ **VALLEY HOSPITAL PHOENIX (034026)**, 3550 East Pinchot Avenue, Zip 85018–7434; tel. 602/957–4000, (Nonreporting) **A**1 10 **S** Universal Health Services, Inc., King of Prussia, PA
Primary Contact: Michelle David, Chief Executive Officer
Web address: www.valleyhospital–phoenix.com
Control: Corporation, Investor–owned, for–profit **Service:** Psychiatric

Staffed Beds: 122

PRESCOTT—Yavapai County

✠ **NORTHERN ARIZONA VETERANS AFFAIRS HEALTH CARE SYSTEM**, 500 Highway 89 North, Zip 86313–5000; tel. 928/445–4860, (Nonreporting) **A**1 **S** Department of Veterans Affairs, Washington, DC
Primary Contact: Malcolm Keith Piatt, M.D., Interim Director
COO: James Belmont, Associate Director
CFO: Ame Callahan, Acting Manager Resource Management Service
CMO: A. Panneer Selvam, M.D., Chief of Staff
CIO: Scott McCrimmon, Manager Information Technology
CHR: Jane Lewerke, Manager Human Resources
Web address: www.prescott.va.gov/
Control: Veterans Affairs, Government, federal **Service:** General Medical and Surgical

Staffed Beds: 137

★ **YAVAPAI REGIONAL MEDICAL CENTER (030012)**, 1003 Willow Creek Road, Zip 86301–1668; tel. 928/445–2700 **A**10 **F**3 11 15 17 18 20 22 24 28 29 30 31 32 34 35 40 45 46 50 53 54 57 59 60 64 68 70 74 75 77 78 79 81 82 84 85 86 87 91 93 107 108 111 114 118 119 130 131 132 135 146 148 **P**6
Primary Contact: John Amos, President and Chief Executive Officer
COO: Larry P. Burns, Jr., Chief Operating Officer
CFO: Lee Livin, Chief Financial Officer
CMO: Joseph Goldberger, M.D., Chief Medical Officer
CHR: Mark Timm, Executive Director Human Resources
CNO: Diane Drexler, R.N., Chief Nursing Officer
Web address: www.yrmc.org
Control: Other not–for–profit (including NFP Corporation) **Service:** General Medical and Surgical

Staffed Beds: 134 **Admissions:** 6293 **Census:** 70 **Outpatient Visits:** 70656 **Births:** 0 **Total Expense ($000):** 182955 **Payroll Expense ($000):** 58468 **Personnel:** 893

Hospital, Medicare Provider Number, Address, Telephone, Approval, Facility, and Physician Codes, Health Care System		
★ American Hospital Association (AHA) membership	◯ Healthcare Facilities Accreditation Program	⇧ Center for Improvement in Healthcare Quality Accreditation
☐ The Joint Commission accreditation	◇ DNV Healthcare Inc. accreditation	△ Commission on Accreditation of Rehabilitation Facilities (CARF) accreditation

AZ

PRESCOTT VALLEY—Yavapai County

☐ **MOUNTAIN VALLEY REGIONAL REHABILITATION HOSPITAL (033036)**, 3700 North Windsong Drive, Zip 86314–1253; tel. 928/759–8800, (Nonreporting) **A**1 10 **S** Ernest Health, Inc., Albuquerque, NM
Primary Contact: Judy Baum, Chief Executive Officer
CFO: Mark A. Roth, Chief Financial Officer
CMO: Alan S. Berman, M.D., Medical Director
CHR: Troy Eagar, Director Human Resources
CNO: Leah Walters, R.N., Director of Nursing
Web address: www.mvrrh.ernesthealth.com
Control: Corporation, Investor–owned, for–profit **Service:** Rehabilitation

Staffed Beds: 16

WINDHAVEN PSYCHIATRIC HOSPITAL (034025), 3347 North Windsong Drive, Zip 86314–2283, Mailing Address: 3343 North Windsong Drive, Zip 86314–1213; tel. 928/445–5211 **A**10 **F**29 98 99 100
Primary Contact: Larry D. Green, Jr., Chief Executive Officer
COO: Pamela Pierce, Deputy Chief Executive Officer
CFO: Doug Oliver, Chief Financial Officer
CMO: Shane Russell-Jenkins, M.D., Medical Director
CIO: Laura Norman, Chief Development and Information Officer
CHR: Pamela Pierce, Deputy Chief Executive Officer
CNO: Esther Grear, Director Hospital Social Work and Assistant Hospital Administrator
Web address: www.wygc.org
Control: Other not–for–profit (including NFP Corporation) **Service:** Psychiatric

Staffed Beds: 16 **Admissions:** 769 **Census:** 13 **Outpatient Visits:** 0 **Births:** 0 **Total Expense ($000):** 4498 **Payroll Expense ($000):** 2615 **Personnel:** 29

★ **YAVAPAI REGIONAL MEDICAL CENTER – EAST (030118)**, 7700 East Florentine Road, Zip 86314–2245; tel. 928/445–2700 **A**10 **F**3 11 13 15 29 30 31 40 68 70 72 75 76 77 78 81 84 85 86 87 89 93 107 108 111 114 116 117 118 119 130 146 147 148
Primary Contact: John Amos, Chief Executive Officer
CFO: Lee Livin, Chief Financial Officer
CMO: Joseph Goldberger, M.D., Chief Medical Officer
CHR: Mark Timm, Executive Director Human Resources
CNO: Diane Drexler, R.N., Chief Nursing Officer
Web address: www.yrmc.org
Control: Other not–for–profit (including NFP Corporation) **Service:** General Medical and Surgical

Staffed Beds: 72 **Admissions:** 3804 **Census:** 32 **Outpatient Visits:** 78561 **Births:** 1022 **Total Expense ($000):** 52833 **Payroll Expense ($000):** 25868 **Personnel:** 415

SACATON—Pinal County

☐ **HUHUKAM MEMORIAL HOSPITAL (031308)**, 483 West Seed Farm Road, Zip 85147, Mailing Address: P.O. Box 38, Zip 85147–0001; tel. 602/528–1200 **A**1 3 10 18 **F**3 4 5 7 15 29 33 34 35 36 38 39 40 57 59 60 61 65 68 71 79 82 86 87 93 94 97 99 100 101 102 103 104 119 130 132 135 143 147 148
Primary Contact: Lorrie Henderson, Ph.D., Chief Executive Officer
COO: Pamela Thompson, Chief Operations Officer
CMO: Noel Habib, M.D., Chief Medical Officer
CHR: Michael Freeman, Director Human Resources
Web address: www.grhc.org
Control: PHS, Indian Service, Government, federal **Service:** General Medical and Surgical

Staffed Beds: 15 **Admissions:** 59 **Census:** 1 **Outpatient Visits:** 152043 **Births:** 0 **Total Expense ($000):** 135605 **Payroll Expense ($000):** 66768

SAFFORD—Graham County

★ **MT. GRAHAM REGIONAL MEDICAL CENTER (030068)**, 1600 South 20th Avenue, Zip 85546–4097; tel. 928/348–4000 **A**3 10 20 **F**3 11 13 15 18 29 30 31 34 35 40 43 45 46 47 48 49 50 57 59 63 64 66 70 75 76 77 78 79 81 84 85 97 107 108 110 111 114 119 127 129 130 132 133 135 145 146 147 **P**6
Primary Contact: Mark E. Marchetti, President and Chief Executive Officer
CFO: Keith Bryce, Vice President Finance and Chief Financial Officer
CIO: Anthon Ellsworth, Director Information Technology
CHR: Irvan "Wick" Lewis, Vice President Human Resources
CNO: Lori Burress, Vice President Patient Services and Chief Nursing Officer
Web address: www.mtgraham.org
Control: Hospital district or authority, Government, nonfederal **Service:** General Medical and Surgical

Staffed Beds: 49 **Admissions:** 1500 **Census:** 12 **Outpatient Visits:** 70968 **Births:** 614 **Total Expense ($000):** 57735 **Payroll Expense ($000):** 24783 **Personnel:** 463

SAN TAN VALLEY—Pinal County

⊞ **BANNER IRONWOOD MEDICAL CENTER (030130)**, 37000 North Gantzel Road, Zip 85140–7303; tel. 480/394–4000 **A**1 10 **F**3 13 29 30 34 36 38 40 41 44 45 47 50 61 68 74 75 76 77 79 80 81 85 86 87 100 102 107 111 114 119 130 132 135 141 145 146 147 148 **S** Banner Health, Phoenix, AZ
Primary Contact: Sharon Lind, MSN, FACHE, Chief Executive Officer
CFO: Tracy French, Chief Financial Officer
CMO: Darren West, M.D., Interim Chief Medical Officer
CHR: Janine Polito, Chief Human Resources Officer
CNO: Terri Paulus, Chief Nursing Officer
Web address: www.bannerhealth.com/Locations/Arizona/Banner+Ironwood/
Control: Other not–for–profit (including NFP Corporation) **Service:** General Medical and Surgical

Staffed Beds: 53 **Admissions:** 2527 **Census:** 21 **Outpatient Visits:** 35845 **Births:** 803 **Total Expense ($000):** 62475 **Payroll Expense ($000):** 19473 **Personnel:** 327

SCOTTSDALE—Maricopa County

⊞ **BANNER BEHAVIORAL HEALTH HOSPITAL – SCOTTSDALE (034004)**, 7575 East Earll Drive, Zip 85251–6915; tel. 480/941–7500 **A**1 3 10 **F**5 11 29 30 34 35 38 44 50 57 68 75 86 87 98 99 101 102 104 130 132 134 135 146 **S** Banner Health, Phoenix, AZ
Primary Contact: Brian Beutin, MS, Chief Executive Officer
CFO: Michael A. Cimino, Jr., Chief Financial Officer
CMO: Gagandeep Singh, M.D., Chief Medical Officer Behavioral Health
CHR: Zsaber Gere, Chief Human Resource Officer
CNO: Cherri Anderson, Chief Nursing Officer
Web address: www.bannerhealth.com/Locations/Arizona/Banner+Behavioral+Health
Control: Other not–for–profit (including NFP Corporation) **Service:** Psychiatric

Staffed Beds: 78 **Admissions:** 3921 **Census:** 79 **Births:** 0 **Total Expense ($000):** 28585 **Payroll Expense ($000):** 16344 **Personnel:** 352

FREEDOM PAIN HOSPITAL (030135), (Pain Specialty), 17500 North Perimeter Drive, Zip 85255–7808; tel. 480/586–2300 **A**10 **F**29 33 34 36 58 64 80 81 82 85 87
Primary Contact: Steven M. Siwek, M.D., President and Chief Executive Officer
COO: Michael Adams, Chief Operating Officer
CFO: Douglas B. Kell, Chief Financial Officer
CMO: Natalie Shand, M.D., Vice President Integrative Medicine and Chief Medical Officer
CIO: Milad Najjar, Information Technology
CHR: Samantha Mendez, Human Resources
CNO: Jani Manseau, Vice President Operations and Chief Nursing Officer
Web address: www.freedompainhospital.com
Control: Corporation, Investor–owned, for–profit **Service:** Other specialty

Staffed Beds: 12 **Admissions:** 24 **Census:** 1 **Births:** 0

⊞ **HEALTHSOUTH SCOTTSDALE REHABILITATION HOSPITAL (033025)**, 9630 East Shea Boulevard, Zip 85260–6267; tel. 480/551–5400, (Nonreporting) **A**1 10 **S** HEALTHSOUTH Corporation, Birmingham, AL
Primary Contact: Timothy T. Poore, Chief Executive Officer
CFO: Lisa Barrick, Controller
CMO: Keith W. Cunningham, M.D., Medical Director
CHR: Mary Beth Giczi, Director Human Resources
CNO: Diane M. Caruso, MSN, Chief Nursing Officer
Web address: www.healthsouthscottsdale.com
Control: Corporation, Investor–owned, for–profit **Service:** Rehabilitation

Staffed Beds: 60

★ ○ **HONORHEALTH REHABILITATION HOSPITAL (033038)**, 8850 East Pima Center Parkway, Zip 85258–4619; tel. 480/800–3900, (Nonreporting) **A**10 11 **S** Select Medical Corporation, Mechanicsburg, PA
Primary Contact: Scott R. Keen, Chief Executive Officer
Web address: www.scottsdale–rehab.com/
Control: Partnership, Investor–owned, for–profit **Service:** Rehabilitation

Staffed Beds: 50

★ ◇ **HONORHEALTH SCOTTSDALE OSBORN MEDICAL CENTER (030038)**, 7400 East Osborn Road, Zip 85251–6403; tel. 480/882–4000, (Nonreporting) **A**2 3 5 8 10 21 **S** HonorHealth, Scottsdale, AZ
Primary Contact: Kimberly Post, Senior Vice President and Chief Executive Officer
CFO: Todd La Porte, Senior Vice President and Chief Financial Officer
CMO: James Burke, M.D., Senior Vice President and Chief Medical Officer
CIO: James R. Cramer, Vice President and Chief Information Officer
Web address: www.shc.org
Control: Other not–for–profit (including NFP Corporation) **Service:** General Medical and Surgical

Staffed Beds: 347

★ ◇ **HONORHEALTH SCOTTSDALE SHEA MEDICAL CENTER (030087),**
9003 East Shea Boulevard, Zip 85260–6771; tel. 480/323–3000 **A**2 3 5 10 21
F7 8 12 13 15 17 18 20 26 28 29 31 34 35 40 41 45 56 57 58 59 62 64 70
72 73 75 76 78 79 81 82 88 89 91 97 107 111 114 115 119 126 130 131
132 133 135 146 147 148 **S** HonorHealth, Scottsdale, AZ
Primary Contact: Gary E. Baker, Senior Vice President and Chief Executive Officer
CFO: Todd La Porte, Senior Vice President and Chief Financial Officer
CMO: James Burke, M.D., Senior Vice President and Chief Medical Officer
CIO: James R. Cramer, Vice President and Chief Information Officer
Web address: www.shc.org
Control: Other not–for–profit (including NFP Corporation) **Service:** General
Medical and Surgical

Staffed Beds: 409 Admissions: 20162 Census: 217 Births: 4761

★ ◇ **HONORHEALTH SCOTTSDALE THOMPSON PEAK MEDICAL CENTER
(030123),** 7400 East Thompson Peak Parkway, Zip 85255–4109;
tel. 480/324–7000, (Nonreporting) **A**10 21 **S** HonorHealth, Scottsdale, AZ
Primary Contact: David Price, Chief Executive Officer
COO: Bruce Pearson, Senior Vice President and Chief Operating Officer
CFO: Alice H. Pope, Chief Financial Officer
CMO: Stephanie Jackson, M.D., Vice President and Chief Medical Officer
CIO: Charles Scully, Chief Information Officer
CHR: Wendy Crawford, Chief Human Resource Officer
CNO: Kimberly Post, Senior Vice President and Chief Clinical Officer
Web address: www.shc.org
Control: Other not–for–profit (including NFP Corporation) **Service:** General
Medical and Surgical

Staffed Beds: 64

⊞ **SELECT SPECIALTY HOSPITAL–SCOTTSDALE (032005),** 7400 East Osborn
Road, 3 West, Zip 85251–6432; tel. 480/882–4360, (Includes SELECT
SPECIALTY HOSPITAL–PHOENIX DOWNTOWN, 1012 East Wiletta Street, 4th Floor,
Phoenix, Zip 85006; tel. 602/239–6134; Sharon Anthony, Market Administrator),
(Nonreporting) **A**1 10 **S** Select Medical Corporation, Mechanicsburg, PA
Primary Contact: Meridell Sloterbeek, Chief Executive Officer
Web address: www.scottsdale.selectspecialtyhospitals.com/
Control: Corporation, Investor–owned, for–profit **Service:** Long–Term Acute Care
hospital

Staffed Beds: 62

SELLS—Pima County

⊞ **U. S. PUBLIC HEALTH SERVICE INDIAN HOSPITAL–SELLS (030074),**
Highway 86 & Topawa Road, Zip 85634, Mailing Address: P.O. Box 548,
Zip 85634–0548; tel. 520/383–7251, (Nonreporting) **A**1 10 **S** U. S. Indian Health
Service, Rockville, MD
Primary Contact: Angela Fallon, Acting Chief Executive Officer
COO: Diane Shanley, Deputy Service Unit Director
CFO: Vivian Draper, Chief Financial Officer
CMO: Peter Ziegler, M.D., Acting Chief Medical Officer
CIO: Karen Wade, Chief Information Officer
CNO: Donna Hobbs, Nurse Executive
Web address: www.ihs.gov
Control: PHS, Indian Service, Government, federal **Service:** General Medical and
Surgical

Staffed Beds: 12

SHOW LOW—Navajo County

★ **SUMMIT HEALTHCARE REGIONAL MEDICAL CENTER (030062),** 2200 East
Show Low Lake Road, Zip 85901–7800; tel. 928/537–4375 **A**10 20 **F**11 13 15
18 20 22 28 29 30 31 32 34 35 36 38 40 41 43 45 46 47 53 54 57 59 62
64 65 68 70 71 73 75 76 77 78 79 81 82 84 91 92 93 97 107 108 110 111
114 115 118 119 121 127 129 130 131 132 135 146 147 148
Primary Contact: Ronald L. McArthur, Chief Executive Officer
COO: Doug Gilchrist, Chief Operating Officer
CFO: Stanley Adams, Chief Financial Officer
CMO: Alan Neil DeWitt, Chief Medical Officer
CIO: Aaron Young, Chief Information Officer
CHR: Connie Kakavas, Chief Human Resources Officer
CNO: Cynthia Ebert–Loomis, R.N., Chief Nursing Officer
Web address: www.summithealthcare.net
Control: Other not–for–profit (including NFP Corporation) **Service:** General
Medical and Surgical

**Staffed Beds: 89 Admissions: 4306 Census: 35 Outpatient Visits: 60191
Births: 928 Total Expense ($000): 149680 Payroll Expense ($000): 63043**

SIERRA VISTA—Cochise County

☐ **CANYON VISTA MEDICAL CENTER (030043),** 5700 East Highway 90,
Zip 85635–9110; tel. 520/263–2000 **A**1 10 13 20 **F**3 13 15 18 20 22 28 29
30 31 34 35 40 43 45 51 57 59 60 61 63 64 68 70 73 74 75 77 79 81 84
85 93 94 96 98 102 103 107 108 110 111 115 119 130 131 145 146 147
148 **P**6 **S** RCCH HealthCare Partners, Brentwood, TN
Primary Contact: Randy Anderson, Chief Executive Officer
COO: Ashley L. Johnson, Chief Operations Officer
CIO: Jorge Moreno, Director Information Technology Operations
CHR: Traci Meyer, Director Human Resources
Web address: www.canyonvistamedicalcenter.com/
Control: Corporation, Investor–owned, for–profit **Service:** General Medical and
Surgical

**Staffed Beds: 100 Admissions: 5130 Census: 47 Outpatient Visits: 102113
Births: 1059 Total Expense ($000): 96626 Payroll Expense ($000): 32765
Personnel: 676**

SPRINGERVILLE—Apache County

WHITE MOUNTAIN REGIONAL MEDICAL CENTER (031315), 118 South
Mountain Avenue, Zip 85938–5104; tel. 928/333–4368, (Nonreporting) **A**10 18
Primary Contact: Gregory J. Was, CPA, Chief Executive Officer
CFO: James Hamblin, Chief Financial Officer
CMO: Scott Hamblin, M.D., President Medical Staff
Web address: www.wmrmc.com
Control: Other not–for–profit (including NFP Corporation) **Service:** General
Medical and Surgical

Staffed Beds: 20

SUN CITY—Maricopa County

⊞ **BANNER BOSWELL MEDICAL CENTER (030061),** 10401 West Thunderbird
Boulevard, Zip 85351–3004, Mailing Address: P.O. Box 1690, Zip 85372–1690;
tel. 623/832–4000, (Total facility includes 78 beds in nursing home–type unit) **A**1
2 3 10 **F**2 3 11 15 17 18 20 22 24 28 29 30 31 34 35 36 37 40 44 45
46 49 50 51 53 56 57 58 59 60 61 64 65 70 74 75 78 79 81 84 85 86 87
90 91 92 93 94 96 100 107 108 110 111 114 115 117 119 120 121 124
126 128 130 131 132 135 141 143 145 146 147 148 **S** Banner Health,
Phoenix, AZ
Primary Contact: David Cheney, Chief Executive Officer
CFO: Jeremy Williams, Chief Financial Officer
CMO: Kathryn Perkins, M.D., Chief Medical Officer
CHR: Brenda Dietrich, Chief Human Resources Officer
Web address: www.bannerhealth.com/Locations/Arizona/Banner+Boswell+
Medical+Center
Control: Other not–for–profit (including NFP Corporation) **Service:** General
Medical and Surgical

**Staffed Beds: 425 Admissions: 16814 Census: 249 Outpatient Visits:
83043 Births: 0 Total Expense ($000): 288267 Payroll Expense ($000):
99610 Personnel: 1698**

SUN CITY WEST—Maricopa County

⊞ **BANNER DEL E. WEBB MEDICAL CENTER (030093),** 14502 West Meeker
Boulevard, Zip 85375–5299; tel. 623/524–4000 **A**1 3 10 **F**3 5 9 13 15 18 20
22 28 29 30 31 34 35 36 37 39 40 41 44 45 46 47 48 49 50 51 56 57
58 59 60 61 64 65 68 70 74 75 76 77 78 79 80 81 82 84 85 86 87 90 91
92 93 94 96 98 100 102 103 104 105 107 108 110 111 114 115 118 119
126 130 131 132 135 145 146 147 148 **S** Banner Health, Phoenix, AZ
Primary Contact: Debbie Flores, Chief Executive Officer
CFO: Dan Stimpson, Chief Financial Officer
CMO: Scott Anderson, Chief Medical Officer
CNO: Nancy Adamson, Chief Nursing Officer
Web address: www.bannerhealth.com/Locations/Arizona/Banner+Del+Webb+
Medical+Center/
Control: Other not–for–profit (including NFP Corporation) **Service:** General
Medical and Surgical

**Staffed Beds: 365 Admissions: 15709 Census: 199 Outpatient Visits:
110569 Births: 1754 Total Expense ($000): 255128 Payroll Expense
($000): 89012 Personnel: 1527**

SURPRISE—Maricopa County

COBALT REHABILITATION HOSPITAL, 13060 West Bell Road,
Zip 85378–1200; tel. 623/499–9100, (Nonreporting)
Primary Contact: Sharon Noe, Chief Executive Officer
Web address: www.colbaltrehab.com
Control: Corporation, Investor–owned, for–profit **Service:** Rehabilitation

Staffed Beds: 40

Hospital, Medicare Provider Number, Address, Telephone, Approval, Facility, and Physician Codes, Health Care System

★ American Hospital Association (AHA) membership   ◯ Healthcare Facilities Accreditation Program   ⇑ Center for Improvement in Healthcare Quality Accreditation
☐ The Joint Commission accreditation   ◇ DNV Healthcare Inc. accreditation   △ Commission on Accreditation of Rehabilitation Facilities (CARF) accreditation

AZ

TEMPE—Maricopa County

☐ **AURORA BEHAVIORAL HEALTH SYSTEM EAST (034028)**, 6350 South Maple Street, Zip 85283–2857; tel. 480/345–5400, (Nonreporting) **A**1 10 **S** Signature Healthcare Services, Corona, CA
Primary Contact: Bruce Waldo, Chief Executive Officer
CFO: Rebekah Francis, JD, Chief Financial Officer
CMO: Jason Friday, M.D., Medical Director
CHR: Vicki Thomsen, Director Human Resources
Web address: www.auroraarizona.com
Control: Partnership, Investor–owned, for–profit **Service:** Psychiatric

Staffed Beds: 70

TUBA CITY—Coconino County

⊠ **TUBA CITY REGIONAL HEALTH CARE CORPORATION (030073)**, 167 Main Street, Zip 86045–0611, Mailing Address: P.O. Box 600, Zip 86045–0600; tel. 928/283–2501, (Nonreporting) **A**1 3 5 10
Primary Contact: Lynette Bonar, Chief Executive Officer
CFO: Christine Keyonnie, Chief Financial Officer
CMO: James Kyle, M.D., Chief Medical Officer
CIO: Shawn Davis, Chief Information Officer
CHR: Tanya Riggs, Chief Human Resources
CNO: Alvina Rosales, R.N., Chief Nursing Officer
Web address: www.tchealth.org
Control: Other not–for–profit (including NFP Corporation) **Service:** General Medical and Surgical

Staffed Beds: 73

TUCSON—Pima County

⊠ **BANNER – UNIVERSITY MEDICAL CENTER SOUTH (030111)**, 2800 East Ajo Way, Zip 85713–6289; tel. 520/874–2000 **A**1 3 5 10 **F**3 11 18 20 22 29 30 34 40 43 45 47 48 50 51 54 56 65 66 67 68 70 71 74 75 77 79 81 82 84 85 86 87 93 97 98 99 100 101 102 103 104 107 108 111 114 115 119 130 131 135 146 148 **S** Banner Health, Phoenix, AZ
Primary Contact: Thomas C. Dickson, Chief Executive Officer
COO: Sarah Frost, Administrator and Chief Operating Officer
CFO: Misty Hansen, Chief Financial Officer
CMO: John Kettelle, M.D., Chief Medical Officer
CIO: Ryan K. Smith, Senior Vice President Information Technology
CHR: John Marques, Vice President Chief Human Resources Officer
Web address: www.uahealth.com
Control: Other not–for–profit (including NFP Corporation) **Service:** General Medical and Surgical

Staffed Beds: 167 **Admissions:** 6154 **Census:** 90 **Births:** 0 **Total Expense ($000):** 129190 **Payroll Expense ($000):** 41350 **Personnel:** 894

⊠ **BANNER – UNIVERSITY MEDICAL CENTER TUCSON (030064)**, 1501 North Campbell Avenue, Zip 85724–5128; tel. 520/694–0111, (Includes DIAMOND CHILDREN'S HOSPITAL, 1501 North Campbell Avenue, Zip 85724–0001; tel. 520/694–0111), (Data for 306 days) **A**1 3 5 8 10 **F**3 11 12 13 15 16 18 19 20 21 22 23 24 25 26 27 28 29 30 31 34 35 40 41 43 45 46 47 49 50 51 53 54 55 56 57 58 59 60 61 64 65 67 68 70 71 72 74 75 76 77 78 79 80 81 82 84 85 86 87 88 89 92 93 97 100 104 107 108 110 111 114 115 116 117 118 119 120 121 123 124 126 129 130 131 132 136 137 138 139 140 141 145 146 147 148 **S** Banner Health, Phoenix, AZ
Primary Contact: Thomas C. Dickson, Chief Executive Officer
COO: Sarah Frost, Chief Operating Officer and Administrator, University of Arizona Medical Center – South Campus
CFO: Misty Hansen, Chief Financial Officer
CMO: Andreas Theodorou, Chief Medical Officer
CIO: Dan Critchley, Chief Information Officer
CHR: John Marques, Vice President Human Resources
Web address: www.uahealth.com
Control: Other not–for–profit (including NFP Corporation) **Service:** General Medical and Surgical

Staffed Beds: 451 **Admissions:** 17472 **Census:** 343 **Births:** 1263 **Total Expense ($000):** 576942 **Payroll Expense ($000):** 164839 **Personnel:** 3194

⊠ **CARONDELET ST. JOSEPH'S HOSPITAL (030011)**, 350 North Wilmot Road, Zip 85711–2678; tel. 520/873–3000 **A**1 5 10 **F**3 5 11 12 13 18 20 22 28 29 30 31 34 35 38 40 44 45 46 47 49 50 57 59 60 61 64 68 69 70 72 74 75 76 77 78 79 81 82 83 84 85 86 87 90 92 93 98 100 101 102 103 104 105 107 108 114 115 118 119 126 129 130 132 135 145 146 147 148 **S** TENET Healthcare Corporation, Dallas, TX
Primary Contact: Mark A. Benz, President and Chief Executive Officer
CFO: Alan Strauss, Chief Financial Officer
CMO: Donald Denmark, M.D., Chief Medical Officer
CIO: Sally Zambrello, Chief Information Officer
CHR: Igor Shegolev, Vice President Human Resources
CNO: Robin Conklin, R.N., Chief Nursing Officer
Web address: www.carondelet.org
Control: Church–operated, Nongovernment, not–for profit **Service:** General Medical and Surgical

Staffed Beds: 486 **Admissions:** 16549 **Census:** 219 **Outpatient Visits:** 120568 **Births:** 2555 **Total Expense ($000):** 256282 **Payroll Expense ($000):** 92359 **Personnel:** 1328

⊠ **CARONDELET ST. MARY'S HOSPITAL (030010)**, 1601 West St. Mary's Road, Zip 85745–2682; tel. 520/872–3000 **A**1 3 5 10 **F**3 11 15 17 18 20 22 24 26 28 29 30 31 34 38 40 44 45 46 47 49 50 51 56 57 58 59 60 61 63 64 68 70 74 77 78 79 81 82 84 85 87 90 92 93 96 98 100 101 102 103 107 108 110 111 114 115 118 119 129 130 131 132 146 148 **S** TENET Healthcare Corporation, Dallas, TX
Primary Contact: Amy Beiter, M.D., President and Chief Executive Officer
CMO: Donald Denmark, M.D., Chief Medical Officer
Web address: www.carondelet.org
Control: Church–operated, Nongovernment, not–for profit **Service:** General Medical and Surgical

Staffed Beds: 300 **Admissions:** 11863 **Census:** 173 **Outpatient Visits:** 185628 **Births:** 0 **Total Expense ($000):** 207234 **Payroll Expense ($000):** 79318 **Personnel:** 1177

☐ **CHG HOSPITAL TUCSON, LLC (032004)**, 7220 East Rosewood Drive, Zip 85710–1350; tel. 520/546–4595 **A**1 10 **F**1 3 29 30 75 77 82 84 85 **S** Cornerstone Healthcare Group, Dallas, TX
Primary Contact: Paul E. Qualls, Chief Executive Officer
CFO: Kurt Schultz, Group Chief Financial Officer
CMO: Haroon Haque, M.D., Medical Director
CIO: Adam Davis, Director Information Technology
CHR: Debra Ramage, Director Human Resources and Payroll
CNO: Michelle Laguna, Chief Nursing Officer
Web address: www.chghospitals.com
Control: Corporation, Investor–owned, for–profit **Service:** Long–Term Acute Care hospital

Staffed Beds: 34 **Admissions:** 310 **Census:** 22 **Births:** 0 **Total Expense ($000):** 11121 **Payroll Expense ($000):** 5248 **Personnel:** 86

⊠ **HEALTHSOUTH REHABILITATION HOSPITAL OF SOUTHERN ARIZONA (033029)**, 1921 West Hospital Drive, Zip 85704–7806; tel. 520/742–2800, (Nonreporting) **A**1 10 **S** HEALTHSOUTH Corporation, Birmingham, AL
Primary Contact: Donna Beifus, Chief Executive Officer
CFO: Kaleigh Hotchkiss, Controller
CMO: Susan Bulen, M.D., Medical Director
CHR: Neil Cullen, Director Human Resources
CNO: Virginia Ragonese–Green, Chief Nursing Officer
Web address: www.healthsouthsouthernarizona.com
Control: Corporation, Investor–owned, for–profit **Service:** Rehabilitation

Staffed Beds: 60

⊠ **HEALTHSOUTH REHABILITATION INSTITUTE OF TUCSON (033028)**, 2650 North Wyatt Drive, Zip 85712–6108; tel. 520/325–1300 **A**1 5 10 **F**29 34 35 62 90 93 96 130 132 **S** HEALTHSOUTH Corporation, Birmingham, AL
Primary Contact: Jeffrey Christensen, Chief Executive Officer
CFO: Mary Donovan, Controller
CMO: Jon Larson, M.D., Medical Director
CHR: Dawn Mosier, Director Human Resources
Web address: www.rehabinstituteoftucson.com
Control: Corporation, Investor–owned, for–profit **Service:** Rehabilitation

Staffed Beds: 80 **Admissions:** 1469 **Census:** 53 **Outpatient Visits:** 0 **Births:** 0 **Total Expense ($000):** 20226 **Payroll Expense ($000):** 11264 **Personnel:** 191

⊠ **CURAHEALTH TUCSON (032002)**, 355 North Wilmot Road, Zip 85711–2601; tel. 520/584–4500, (Nonreporting) **A**1 10
Primary Contact: Dianne Chartier, R.N., Resource Chief Executive Officer
CFO: Lynn Myers, Controller
CMO: Sunil Natrajan, M.D., Medical Director
CNO: Annette Lindeman, Chief Clinical Officer
Control: Corporation, Investor–owned, for–profit **Service:** Long–Term Acute Care hospital

Staffed Beds: 51

⊠ **NORTHWEST MEDICAL CENTER (030085)**, 6200 North La Cholla Boulevard, Zip 85741–3599; tel. 520/742–9000 **A**1 3 5 10 **F**3 8 12 13 15 17 18 19 20 22 24 26 28 29 30 31 34 35 37 40 49 53 57 59 68 70 72 74 75 76 78 79 81 85 91 93 102 107 108 110 111 113 114 118 119 126 130 135 144 146 147 148 **S** Community Health Systems, Inc., Franklin, TN
Primary Contact: Kevin Stockton, Chief Executive Officer
CFO: Ronald Patrick, Chief Financial Officer
CIO: David Bullock, Director Information Services
CNO: Kay Stubbs, Chief Nursing Officer
Web address: www.northwestmedicalcenter.com
Control: Corporation, Investor–owned, for–profit **Service:** General Medical and Surgical

Staffed Beds: 270 **Admissions:** 15987 **Census:** 164 **Births:** 2695 **Total Expense ($000):** 273859 **Payroll Expense ($000):** 104941 **Personnel:** 1532

Many Facility Codes have changed. Please refer to the AHA Guide Code Chart. © 2016 AHA Guide

AZ

PALO VERDE BEHAVIORAL HEALTH (034030), 2695 North Craycroft Road, Zip 85712–2244; tel. 520/322–2888, (Nonreporting) **A**5 10 **S** Universal Health Services, Inc., King of Prussia, PA
Primary Contact: P. P. Frayser, Chief Executive Officer
CFO: Richard N. England, Chief Financial Officer
CHR: Michelle Carrasco, Director Human Resources
Web address: www.paloverdebh.com/
Control: Other not–for–profit (including NFP Corporation) **Service:** Psychiatric

Staffed Beds: 48

☐ **SIERRA TUCSON**, 39580 South Lago Del Oro Parkway, Zip 85739–1091; tel. 520/624–4000 **A**1 **F**4 29 33 35 36 53 75 80 82 98 106 118 135 **S** CRC Health Group, Inc., Cupertino, CA
Primary Contact: Stephen P. Fahey, Executive Director
COO: Stephen P. Fahey, Executive Director
CFO: Amy Fritton, Controller
CMO: Jerome Lerner, M.D., Medical Director
CHR: Betty Dickens, Director Human Resources
CNO: Sue Menzie, R.N., Director Patient Care
Web address: www.sierratucson.com
Control: Corporation, Investor–owned, for–profit **Service:** Psychiatric

Staffed Beds: 139 Admissions: 1298 Census: 85 Births: 0

☐ **SONORA BEHAVIORAL HEALTH HOSPITAL (034022)**, 6050 North Corona Road, #3, Zip 85704–1096; tel. 520/469–8700 **A**1 3 10 **F**1 4 5 16 17 29 67 70 72 73 76 80 88 89 90 98 99 100 103 104 105 128 **S** Acadia Healthcare Company, Inc., Franklin, TN
Primary Contact: Edeli Kinsala, Chief Executive Officer
CMO: Steven Bupp, M.D., Medical Director
CHR: Ciria Soto, Director Human Resources
CNO: Angel Payne, Clinical Director, Director of Nursing
Control: Corporation, Investor–owned, for–profit **Service:** Psychiatric

Staffed Beds: 72 Admissions: 2958 Census: 62 Births: 0 Personnel: 139

✹ △ **SOUTHERN ARIZONA VETERANS AFFAIRS HEALTH CARE SYSTEM**, 3601 South 6th Avenue, Zip 85723–0002; tel. 520/792–1450, (Nonreporting) **A**1 3 5 7 8 **S** Department of Veterans Affairs, Washington, DC
Primary Contact: Jennifer S. Gutowski, FACHE, Acting Director
CFO: Larry Korn, Manager Finance
CMO: Jayendra H. Shah, M.D., Chief Medical Officer
CIO: John Walston, Chief Information Officer
CHR: Patrice Craig, Manager Human Resources
Web address: www.tucson.va.gov
Control: Veterans Affairs, Government, federal **Service:** General Medical and Surgical

Staffed Beds: 285

TMC FOR CHILDREN See TMC HealthCare

★ **TMC HEALTHCARE (030006)**, 5301 East Grant Road, Zip 85712–2874; tel. 520/324–1111, (Includes TMC FOR CHILDREN, 5301 East Grant Road, Zip 85712–2805; tel. 520/327–5461; Judy F. Rich, President and Chief Executive Officer) **A**3 5 10 **F**3 8 11 12 13 15 17 18 19 20 22 24 26 28 29 30 31 32 34 35 37 40 41 45 46 47 48 49 50 51 53 56 57 58 59 60 63 64 65 68 69 72 74 75 76 77 78 79 81 82 84 85 87 88 89 98 100 102 103 104 107 110 111 114 115 118 119 124 126 129 130 132 135 146 148 **P**6
Primary Contact: Judy F. Rich, President and Chief Executive Officer
COO: Karen Mlawsky, Senior Vice President and Chief Operations Officer
CFO: Stephen Bush, Chief Financial Officer
CMO: Rick Anderson, M.D., Senior Vice President and Chief Medical Officer
CIO: Frank Marini, Vice President and Chief Information Officer
CHR: Alex Horvath, Vice President and Chief Human Resources Officer
CNO: Marty Enriquez, MS, Vice President and Chief Nursing Officer
Web address: www.tmcaz.com
Control: Other not–for–profit (including NFP Corporation) **Service:** General Medical and Surgical

Staffed Beds: 586 Admissions: 31291 Census: 363 Outpatient Visits: 156895 Births: 5534 Total Expense ($000): 482096 Payroll Expense ($000): 185180 Personnel: 2998

WHITERIVER—Navajo County

☐ **U. S. PUBLIC HEALTH SERVICE INDIAN HOSPITAL–WHITERIVER (030113)**, 200 West Hospital Drive, Zip 85941–0860, Mailing Address: State Route 73, Box 860, Zip 85941–0860; tel. 928/338–4911 **A**1 10 **F**3 8 13 29 31 32 34 35 36 38 39 40 44 45 46 50 53 54 56 57 59 61 64 65 66 68 75 76 78 79 81 82 84 85 86 87 91 93 94 97 100 101 104 107 115 119 130 131 132 135 146 147 148 **S** U. S. Indian Health Service, Rockville, MD
Primary Contact: Michelle Martinez, Chief Executive Officer
COO: Brian Campbell, Director Professional Services
CFO: Desdemona Leslie, Finance Officer
CMO: John Umhau, M.D., Clinical Director
CIO: Russell Barker, Information Officer
CHR: Lena Fasthorse, Supervisor Human Resource
CNO: Jana Towne, Nurse Executive
Web address: www.ihs.gov
Control: PHS, Indian Service, Government, federal **Service:** General Medical and Surgical

Staffed Beds: 35 Admissions: 809 Census: 11 Births: 64 Personnel: 444

WICKENBURG—Maricopa County

★ **WICKENBURG COMMUNITY HOSPITAL (031300)**, 520 Rose Lane, Zip 85390–1447; tel. 928/684–5421 **A**10 18 **F**11 15 34 40 53 57 59 63 65 90 93 107 110 111 115 117 119 127 133 146 148
Primary Contact: James Tavary, Chief Executive Officer
CFO: Mike Ellis, Chief Financial Officer
CMO: Todd Kravetz, Chief of Staff
CIO: Michael McKay, Chief Information Officer
CHR: Kate Pina, Director Human Resources
CNO: Linda Brockwell, Chief Nursing Officer
Web address: www.wickhosp.com
Control: Other not–for–profit (including NFP Corporation) **Service:** General Medical and Surgical

Staffed Beds: 19 Admissions: 431 Census: 7 Births: 3 Total Expense ($000): 25322 Payroll Expense ($000): 11870 Personnel: 187

WILLCOX—Cochise County

★ **NORTHERN COCHISE COMMUNITY HOSPITAL (031302)**, 901 West Rex Allen Drive, Zip 85643–1009; tel. 520/384–3541, (Total facility includes 24 beds in nursing home–type unit) **A**10 18 **F**29 34 35 40 41 43 56 57 59 64 65 77 90 93 107 110 111 115 119 127 128 133 146
Primary Contact: Roland Knox, Chief Executive Officer
CFO: Kim Aguirre, Director Finance
CMO: Hisham Hamam, M.D., Chief of Staff
CIO: Dennis Drury, Director Information Technology
CNO: Pam Noland, Director of Nursing
Web address: www.ncch.com
Control: Hospital district or authority, Government, nonfederal **Service:** General Medical and Surgical

Staffed Beds: 48 Admissions: 415 Census: 22 Outpatient Visits: 17358 Births: 0 Total Expense ($000): 17549 Payroll Expense ($000): 7769 Personnel: 174

WINSLOW—Navajo County

LITTLE COLORADO MEDICAL CENTER (031311), 1501 Williamson Avenue, Zip 86047–2797; tel. 928/289–4691 **A**10 18 **F**29 34 40 50 65 79 81 107 127 130 133
Primary Contact: John J. Dempsey, Chief Executive Officer
CFO: Gina Reffner, Chief Financial Officer
CMO: Perry Mitchell, M.D., Chief of Staff
CIO: Jacob Garcia, Chief Information Officer
CHR: Nina L. Ferguson, Director Human Resources
Web address: www.lcmcwmh.com
Control: Other not–for–profit (including NFP Corporation) **Service:** General Medical and Surgical

Staffed Beds: 25 Admissions: 1142 Census: 11 Births: 221 Total Expense ($000): 28789 Payroll Expense ($000): 12411 Personnel: 226

Hospital, Medicare Provider Number, Address, Telephone, Approval, Facility, and Physician Codes, Health Care System

★ American Hospital Association (AHA) membership   ○ Healthcare Facilities Accreditation Program   ⇧ Center for Improvement in Healthcare Quality Accreditation
☐ The Joint Commission accreditation   ◇ DNV Healthcare Inc. accreditation   △ Commission on Accreditation of Rehabilitation Facilities (CARF) accreditation

YUMA—Yuma County

★ ○ **YUMA REGIONAL MEDICAL CENTER (030013)**, 2400 South Avenue A, Zip 85364–7170; tel. 928/344–2000 **A**2 3 5 10 11 **F**3 8 12 13 15 18 20 22 24 26 28 29 30 31 32 34 35 39 40 41 45 46 47 48 49 50 54 57 58 59 64 65 68 70 72 74 75 76 77 78 79 81 82 83 84 85 86 87 89 93 97 100 104 107 108 109 110 111 114 115 116 117 118 119 120 121 122 123 124 130 132 141 146 147 148
Primary Contact: Robert Trenschel, D.O., FACHE, M.P.H., President and Chief Executive Officer
CFO: David Willie, Chief Financial Officer
CMO: Bharat Magu, M.D., Chief Medical Officer
CIO: Fred Peet, Chief Information Officer
CHR: Marshall Jones, Vice President Human Resources
CNO: Deb Aders, MS, Interim Chief Nursing Officer
Web address: www.yumaregional.org
Control: Other not–for–profit (including NFP Corporation) **Service:** General Medical and Surgical

Staffed Beds: 406 **Admissions:** 17940 **Census:** 203 **Births:** 3313 **Total Expense ($000):** 349723 **Payroll Expense ($000):** 125388

⊠ **YUMA REHABILITATION HOSPITAL (033034)**, 901 West 24th Street, Zip 85364–6384; tel. 928/726–5000, (Nonreporting) **A**1 10 **S** HEALTHSOUTH Corporation, Birmingham, AL
Primary Contact: Ian Hodge, Chief Executive Officer
CMO: Rinely Aguiar–Olsen, M.D., Medical Director
CHR: Linda Woen, Director Human Resources
CNO: Kristin Parra, Chief Nursing Officer
Web address: www.yumarehabhospital.com
Control: Corporation, Investor–owned, for–profit **Service:** Rehabilitation

Staffed Beds: 41

Many Facility Codes have changed. Please refer to the AHA Guide Code Chart. © 2016 AHA Guide

ARKANSAS

ARKADELPHIA—Clark County

☒ **BAPTIST HEALTH MEDICAL CENTER–ARKADELPHIA (041321)**, 3050 Twin Rivers Drive, Zip 71923–4299; tel. 870/245–2622 **A**1 10 18 **F**3 11 13 15 29 30 34 35 40 41 45 46 50 57 58 59 64 65 67 69 71 75 76 79 81 82 87 89 90 93 96 97 107 110 111 114 119 127 128 129 130 131 133 146 **P**3 4 5 6 7 **S** Baptist Health, Little Rock, AR
Primary Contact: John Bowen, Assistant Vice President and Administrator
CFO: Robert C. Roberts, Vice President and Chief Financial Officer
CMO: Eddie Phillips, M.D., Chief Medical Officer
CIO: David House, Vice President and Chief Information Officer
CHR: Anthony Kendall, Vice President Human Resources
Web address: www.baptist-health.com/locations/accesspoint.aspx?accessPointID=187
Control: Other not–for–profit (including NFP Corporation) **Service:** General Medical and Surgical

Staffed Beds: 25 **Admissions:** 1332 **Census:** 14 **Outpatient Visits:** 28583
Births: 450 **Total Expense ($000):** 20588 **Payroll Expense ($000):** 8691
Personnel: 208

ASHDOWN—Little River County

★ **LITTLE RIVER MEMORIAL HOSPITAL (041320)**, 451 West Locke Street, Zip 71822–3325; tel. 870/898–5011 **A**10 18 **F**2 3 15 29 30 40 56 57 59 62 63 75 77 86 87 91 92 93 97 107 110 114 119 130 148
Primary Contact: James Dowell, Administrator and Chief Executive Officer
CFO: Jackie Rainey, Chief Financial Officer
CIO: Mitchell Jones, Director Information Technology
CHR: Vicki Keener, Administrative Assistant and Director Human Resources
CNO: Cynthia Metzger, Chief Nursing and Operations Officer
Control: County–Government, nonfederal **Service:** General Medical and Surgical

Staffed Beds: 25 **Admissions:** 217 **Census:** 2 **Outpatient Visits:** 8403
Births: 0 **Total Expense ($000):** 11445 **Payroll Expense ($000):** 6549
Personnel: 66

BARLING—Sebastian County

☐ **VALLEY BEHAVIORAL HEALTH SYSTEM (044006)**, 10301 Mayo Drive, Zip 72923–1660; tel. 479/494–5700, (Nonreporting) **A**1 10 **S** Acadia Healthcare Company, Inc., Franklin, TN
Primary Contact: Anthony Walters, Chief Executive Officer
CFO: Paul D. Ervin, Chief Financial Officer
CMO: Richard Livingston, M.D., Medical Director
CHR: Patricia J. Moore, Director Human Resource
CNO: Landon Horton, Director of Nursing
Web address: www.valleybehavioral.com
Control: Corporation, Investor–owned, for–profit **Service:** Psychiatric

Staffed Beds: 75

BATESVILLE—Independence County

★ **WHITE RIVER MEDICAL CENTER (040119)**, 1710 Harrison Street, Zip 72501–7303, Mailing Address: P.O. Box 2197, Zip 72503–2197; tel. 870/262–1200, (Total facility includes 11 beds in nursing home–type unit) **A**10 **F**3 8 11 12 13 15 17 20 22 28 29 30 31 34 35 38 40 42 43 44 45 48 50 51 56 57 59 60 64 68 70 74 75 76 77 78 79 81 82 84 85 86 87 90 92 93 98 100 101 103 104 107 108 110 111 114 115 119 121 126 127 128 129 130 131 132 135 144 146 147 148 **P**6 **S** White River Health System, Batesville, AR
Primary Contact: Gary Bebow, FACHE, Administrator and Chief Executive Officer
CFO: Phillip Hacker, Chief Financial Officer
CMO: Doug Bernard, M.D., Chief Medical Officer
CIO: Gary Paxson, Chief Information Officer
CHR: Gary McDonald, Chief Support Services Officer
CNO: Tammy Gavin, Chief Clinical Officer
Web address: www.whiteriverhealthsystem.com
Control: Other not–for–profit (including NFP Corporation) **Service:** General Medical and Surgical

Staffed Beds: 210 **Admissions:** 8283 **Census:** 105 **Outpatient Visits:** 268955 **Births:** 692 **Total Expense ($000):** 161717 **Payroll Expense ($000):** 63944 **Personnel:** 1114

BENTON—Saline County

☐ **RIVENDELL BEHAVIORAL HEALTH SERVICES OF ARKANSAS (044007)**, 100 Rivendell Drive, Zip 72019–9100; tel. 501/316–1255, (Nonreporting) **A**1 10 **S** Universal Health Services, Inc., King of Prussia, PA
Primary Contact: Jay Shehi, Chief Executive Officer
CFO: Mike Rainbolt, Chief Financial Officer
Web address: www.rivendellofarkansas.com
Control: Corporation, Investor–owned, for–profit **Service:** Children's hospital psychiatric

Staffed Beds: 77

★ **SALINE MEMORIAL HOSPITAL (040084)**, 1 Medical Park Drive, Zip 72015–3354; tel. 501/776–6000 **A**10 **F**3 7 11 12 13 15 17 18 20 22 29 30 34 35 39 40 41 43 50 57 59 62 63 64 70 74 75 76 77 79 81 84 85 87 89 90 91 93 96 98 107 108 110 111 114 115 118 119 129 130 131 132 135 144 146 148 **P**8
Primary Contact: Bob Trautman, Chief Executive Officer
COO: Carla Robertson, Chief Operating Officer and Chief Financial Officer
CFO: Carla Robertson, Chief Operating Officer and Chief Financial Officer
CIO: Andy Dick, Director Information Services
CHR: Carol Matthews, Director Human Resources
CNO: Debbie Burrow, R.N., Chief Nursing Officer
Web address: www.salinememorial.org
Control: Other not–for–profit (including NFP Corporation) **Service:** General Medical and Surgical

Staffed Beds: 124 **Admissions:** 6048 **Census:** 73 **Outpatient Visits:** 76157
Births: 598 **Total Expense ($000):** 87084 **Payroll Expense ($000):** 40212
Personnel: 612

BERRYVILLE—Carroll County

☒ **MERCY HOSPITAL BERRYVILLE (041329)**, 214 Carter Street, Zip 72616–4303; tel. 870/423–3355 **A**1 10 18 **F**3 11 15 28 29 30 31 34 35 40 43 45 46 48 50 57 59 61 64 75 78 81 85 93 107 108 114 119 129 130 131 132 133 146 148 **S** Mercy Health, Chesterfield, MO
Primary Contact: Douglas M. Stroemel, Administrator
CFO: Sherry Clouse Day, Vice President Finance
CHR: Taya James, Director
CNO: Michele Gann, Vice President Patient Services
Web address: www.mercy.net/berryvillear
Control: Church–operated, Nongovernment, not–for profit **Service:** General Medical and Surgical

Staffed Beds: 25 **Admissions:** 611 **Census:** 6 **Outpatient Visits:** 29722
Births: 0 **Total Expense ($000):** 16861 **Payroll Expense ($000):** 7859
Personnel: 131

BLYTHEVILLE—Mississippi County

☒ **GREAT RIVER MEDICAL CENTER (040069)**, 1520 North Division Street, Zip 72315–1448, Mailing Address: P.O. Box 108, Zip 72316–0108; tel. 870/838–7300 **A**1 10 **F**11 13 15 28 29 34 43 45 46 53 57 59 64 68 70 75 76 79 81 89 93 97 107 108 111 114 119 120 130 135 146 147 **P**7 **S** QHR, Brentwood, TN
Primary Contact: Chris Raymer, R.N., Chief Executive Officer
COO: Chris Raymer, R.N., Chief Executive Officer and Chief Operating Officer
CFO: Randy Nichols, Chief Financial Officer
CIO: Tammy Bratcher, Director System Information Technology
CHR: Cheri Blurton, Director Human Resources, HIPAA Privacy Officer
CNO: Felicia Pierce, R.N., Chief Nursing Officer
Web address: www.mchsys.org
Control: County–Government, nonfederal **Service:** General Medical and Surgical

Staffed Beds: 73 **Admissions:** 1964 **Census:** 14 **Outpatient Visits:** 29957
Births: 422 **Total Expense ($000):** 20121 **Payroll Expense ($000):** 8810
Personnel: 249

Hospital, Medicare Provider Number, Address, Telephone, Approval, Facility, and Physician Codes, Health Care System

★ American Hospital Association (AHA) membership
☐ The Joint Commission accreditation
○ Healthcare Facilities Accreditation Program
◇ DNV Healthcare Inc. accreditation
⇑ Center for Improvement in Healthcare Quality Accreditation
△ Commission on Accreditation of Rehabilitation Facilities (CARF) accreditation

BOONEVILLE—Logan County

★ **MERCY HOSPITAL BOONEVILLE (041318)**, 880 West Main Street, Zip 72927–3443, Mailing Address: P.O. Box 290, Zip 72927–0290; tel. 479/675–2800 **A**10 18 **F**3 11 40 43 57 59 62 64 65 68 81 85 107 119 133 148 **P**6 8 **S** Mercy Health, Chesterfield, MO
Primary Contact: Teresa Williams, R.N., Regional Administrator
CFO: J. Stuart Lisko, Regional Director Operations, Critical Access Hospital Operations
CMO: Michael Miranda, Chief of Staff
CHR: Doris Whitaker, Vice President and Manager
CNO: Candace Bollinger, Director of Nursing
Web address: www.mercy.net
Control: Church–operated, Nongovernment, not–for profit **Service:** General Medical and Surgical

Staffed Beds: 25 **Admissions:** 290 **Census:** 3 **Outpatient Visits:** 16197
Births: 0 **Total Expense ($000):** 11646 **Payroll Expense ($000):** 3865
Personnel: 79

CALICO ROCK— County

COMMUNITY MEDICAL CENTER OF IZARD COUNTY (041306), 61 Grasse Street, Zip 72519, Mailing Address: P.O. Box 438, Zip 72519–0438; tel. 870/297–3726 **A**10 18 **F**3 29 30 40 41 43 81 93 107 119 127 128 129 133 146
Primary Contact: Kim Skidmore, Chief Executive Officer
COO: Cathy Franks, RN, Chief Operating Officer
CMO: Bethany Knight, M.D., Chief of Staff
CIO: Quentin Wildhagen, Systems Administrator
CHR: Crystal R. Moody, Director Human Resources
CNO: Dana Hicks, Director of Nursing
Web address: www.cmcofic.org
Control: Other not–for–profit (including NFP Corporation) **Service:** General Medical and Surgical

Staffed Beds: 25 **Admissions:** 388 **Census:** 4 **Outpatient Visits:** 3595
Births: 0 **Total Expense ($000):** 6432 **Payroll Expense ($000):** 2804
Personnel: 76

CAMDEN—Ouachita County

★ **OUACHITA COUNTY MEDICAL CENTER (040050)**, 638 California Avenue S.W., Zip 71701–4699, Mailing Address: P.O. Box 797, Zip 71711–0797; tel. 870/836–1000 **A**10 20 **F**3 4 5 7 8 11 13 15 29 31 34 40 41 43 46 48 49 50 57 59 62 63 64 65 68 69 70 75 76 77 78 79 81 85 87 89 92 93 100 102 103 107 108 111 114 115 119 127 129 130 132 133 135 146 148
Primary Contact: Peggy L. Abbott, President and Chief Executive Officer
CFO: Robert Anders, Chief Financial Officer
CIO: Kenny Frachiseur, Chief Information Officer
CHR: Mary Bridges, Director Human Resources
CNO: Diane Isaacs, Director of Nursing
Web address: www.ouachitamedcenter.com
Control: Other not–for–profit (including NFP Corporation) **Service:** General Medical and Surgical

Staffed Beds: 65 **Admissions:** 1647 **Census:** 15 **Outpatient Visits:** 46670
Births: 224 **Total Expense ($000):** 32122 **Payroll Expense ($000):** 13776
Personnel: 395

OUACHITA MEDICAL CENTER See Ouachita County Medical Center

CLARKSVILLE—Johnson County

★ **JOHNSON REGIONAL MEDICAL CENTER (040002)**, 1100 East Poplar Street, Zip 72830–4419, Mailing Address: P.O. Box 738, Zip 72830–0738; tel. 479/754–5454 **A**10 **F**2 3 7 11 13 15 29 34 35 40 43 45 50 51 57 62 64 68 70 75 76 77 79 81 85 90 91 93 96 98 103 104 107 108 110 111 114 119 129 130 132 133 135 147 148 **P**3
Primary Contact: Edward Anderson, Interim Chief Executive Officer
CFO: Edward Anderson, Chief Financial Officer
CIO: Steve Sullivan, Chief Information Officer
CHR: Betty Collier, Chief Human Resources Officer
CNO: Nancy Hill, R.N., Chief Nursing Officer
Web address: www.jrmc.org
Control: Other not–for–profit (including NFP Corporation) **Service:** General Medical and Surgical

Staffed Beds: 90 **Admissions:** 2579 **Census:** 30 **Outpatient Visits:** 41876
Births: 334 **Total Expense ($000):** 35142 **Payroll Expense ($000):** 15078
Personnel: 327

CLINTON—Van Buren County

OZARK HEALTH MEDICAL CENTER (041313), Highway 65 South, Zip 72031–9045, Mailing Address: P.O. Box 206, Zip 72031–0206; tel. 501/745–7000, (Total facility includes 118 beds in nursing home–type unit) **A**10 18 **F**11 15 28 29 34 35 40 43 45 57 59 62 64 65 75 79 81 93 107 110 111 114 119 128 132 133 146
Primary Contact: David Deaton, Chief Executive Officer
CFO: Mike Deaton, Chief Financial Officer
CMO: Steve Schoettle, M.D., Chief Medical Staff
CHR: Sally Cassell, Manager Human Resources
CNO: Edna Prosser, Chief Nursing Officer
Web address: www.ozarkhealthinc.com
Control: Other not–for–profit (including NFP Corporation) **Service:** General Medical and Surgical

Staffed Beds: 143 **Admissions:** 1212 **Census:** 97 **Outpatient Visits:** 31754
Births: 0 **Total Expense ($000):** 19366 **Payroll Expense ($000):** 8666
Personnel: 216

CONWAY—Faulkner County

⊞ **CONWAY REGIONAL MEDICAL CENTER (040029)**, 2302 College Avenue, Zip 72034–6297; tel. 501/329–3831 **A**1 10 **F**3 8 11 13 15 17 18 20 22 24 28 29 30 31 35 40 43 45 49 50 51 53 56 57 59 60 62 64 70 74 75 77 78 79 81 84 85 87 93 103 107 108 110 111 115 117 119 120 127 130 131 132 146 147 148 **P**8
Primary Contact: Matthew Troup, Chief Executive Officer
COO: Alan Finley, Chief Operating Officer
CFO: Steven P. Rose, Chief Financial Officer
CMO: James France, M.D., Chief of Staff
CHR: Richard Tyler, Corporate Director Human Resources
CNO: Jacquelyn Wilkerson, R.N., Chief Nursing Officer
Web address: www.conwayregional.org
Control: Other not–for–profit (including NFP Corporation) **Service:** General Medical and Surgical

Staffed Beds: 154 **Admissions:** 8342 **Census:** 89 **Outpatient Visits:** 107135
Births: 1787 **Total Expense ($000):** 137270 **Payroll Expense ($000):** 50954 **Personnel:** 1030

CONWAY REGIONAL REHABILITATION HOSPITAL (043033), 2210 Robinson Avenue, Zip 72034–4943; tel. 501/932–3500 **A**10 **F**3 29 90 91 96 130 132 **P**8
Primary Contact: Alicia Kunert, MS, Executive Director
COO: Christy Scroggin, Chief Operating Officer
CMO: Roy Denton, M.D., Chief Medical Officer
CNO: Darrallyn Webb, R.N., Chief Nursing Officer
Web address: www.conwayregional.org
Control: Partnership, Investor–owned, for–profit **Service:** Rehabilitation

Staffed Beds: 26 **Admissions:** 446 **Census:** 16 **Outpatient Visits:** 0 **Births:** 0 **Total Expense ($000):** 3001 **Payroll Expense ($000):** 1675 **Personnel:** 48

CROSSETT—Ashley County

★ **ASHLEY COUNTY MEDICAL CENTER (041323)**, 1015 Unity Road, Zip 71635–9443, Mailing Address: P.O. Box 400, Zip 71635–0400; tel. 870/364–4111 **A**10 18 **F**3 11 13 15 18 29 30 31 34 35 40 45 50 53 56 57 59 62 64 68 70 75 76 77 78 79 81 85 93 98 100 103 104 105 107 108 110 111 115 119 127 129 130 132 133 148
Primary Contact: Phillip K. Gilmore, FACHE, Chief Executive Officer
CFO: Bill Couch, Chief Financial Officer
CMO: Brad Walsh, M.D., Chief of Staff
CIO: Dan Austin, Manager Data Processing
CHR: Shirley White, Director Human Resources
CNO: Emily Bendinelli, Director of Nurses
Web address: www.acmconline.org
Control: Other not–for–profit (including NFP Corporation) **Service:** General Medical and Surgical

Staffed Beds: 33 **Admissions:** 1131 **Census:** 16 **Outpatient Visits:** 92375
Births: 135 **Total Expense ($000):** 26138 **Payroll Expense ($000):** 12503
Personnel: 244

DANVILLE—Yell County

★ **CHAMBERS MEMORIAL HOSPITAL (040011)**, Highway 10 at Detroit, Zip 72833, Mailing Address: P.O. Box 639, Zip 72833–0639; tel. 479/495–2241 **A**10 20 **F**3 11 15 29 34 35 40 43 45 57 59 62 81 93 97 107 114 119 128 130 133
Primary Contact: Mike McCoy, Chief Executive Officer
CMO: Karl Sandberg, M.D., Chief Medical Officer
CIO: Ken Masters, Director Information Technology
CNO: Lynda Keeling, Director of Nursing
Web address: www.chambershospital.com
Control: Other not–for–profit (including NFP Corporation) **Service:** General Medical and Surgical

Staffed Beds: 41 **Admissions:** 1908 **Census:** 17 **Outpatient Visits:** 34098
Births: 0 **Total Expense ($000):** 19461 **Payroll Expense ($000):** 9097
Personnel: 209

Many Facility Codes have changed. Please refer to the AHA Guide Code Chart.

DARDANELLE—Yell County

RIVER VALLEY MEDICAL CENTER (041302), 200 North Third Street, Zip 72834–3802, Mailing Address: P.O. Box 578, Zip 72834–0578; tel. 479/229–4677 **A**10 18 **F**3 40 45 56 57 59 64 65 68 75 81 93 98 103 107 128 129 133 148 **S** Allegiance Health Management, Shreveport, LA
Primary Contact: Peter Savoy, III, Administrator
CMO: William P. Scott, M.D., Chief of Staff
CHR: Kathy Hastin, Administrative Assistant Human Resources
Control: Corporation, Investor–owned, for–profit **Service:** General Medical and Surgical

Staffed Beds: 35 **Admissions:** 784 **Census:** 4 **Births:** 0 **Total Expense ($000):** 11900 **Payroll Expense ($000):** 4928

DE QUEEN—Sevier County

DE QUEEN MEDICAL CENTER (041319), 1306 Collin Raye Drive, Zip 71832–2502; tel. 870/584–4111 **A**10 18 **F**3 11 15 29 40 41 57 59 75 77 90 93 107 114 119 129 133 146 148
Primary Contact: Jeremy Icenhower, Administrator and Chief Executive Officer
CFO: Vicky Kelly, Chief Financial Officer
CMO: Jason Lofton, M.D., Medical Director
CIO: David Harris, Director Information Systems
CHR: Ramona Driver, Director Human Resources
CNO: Kristy Richardson, Director of Nursing
Web address: www.dequeenhospital.com
Control: Corporation, Investor–owned, for–profit **Service:** General Medical and Surgical

Staffed Beds: 35 **Admissions:** 606 **Census:** 12 **Outpatient Visits:** 74618 **Births:** 0 **Personnel:** 161

DEWITT—Arkansas County

★ **DEWITT HOSPITAL (041314)**, 1641 South Whitehead Drive, Zip 72042–9481, Mailing Address: P.O. Box 32, Zip 72042–0032; tel. 870/946–3571, (Total facility includes 60 beds in nursing home–type unit) **A**10 18 **F**3 7 11 29 34 35 40 57 59 64 107 119 127 128 133 143 145 **P**6
Primary Contact: Philip S. Hanna, Chief Executive Officer
CFO: Brandon Cotten, Chief Financial Officer
CMO: Stan Burleson, M.D., Chief Medical Staff
CIO: Brian Brooks, Information Manager
CHR: Alisa Brown, Administrative Assistant
CNO: Jerrilyn Horton, R.N., Chief Nursing Officer
Web address: www.dhnh.org
Control: Other not–for–profit (including NFP Corporation) **Service:** General Medical and Surgical

Staffed Beds: 85 **Admissions:** 462 **Census:** 51 **Outpatient Visits:** 10481 **Births:** 0 **Total Expense ($000):** 11017 **Payroll Expense ($000):** 6350 **Personnel:** 150

DUMAS—Desha County

DELTA MEMORIAL HOSPITAL (041326), 811 South Highway 65, Zip 71639–3006, Mailing Address: P.O. Box 887, Zip 71639–0887; tel. 870/382–4303 **A**10 18 **F**3 11 13 15 29 34 35 40 45 50 55 57 59 62 64 68 75 76 77 78 81 86 87 93 97 107 114 119 120 127 128 130 133 134 135 148 **P**6
Primary Contact: Cris Bolin, Chief Executive Officer
CMO: Thomas Lewellen, D.O., Chief of Staff
CIO: Chris McTigrit, Manager Information Technology
CHR: Doris Fortenberry, Coordinator Human Resources
CNO: Dana Miles, Chief Nursing Officer and Chief Clinical Officer
Web address: www.deltamem.org
Control: Other not–for–profit (including NFP Corporation) **Service:** General Medical and Surgical

Staffed Beds: 25 **Admissions:** 820 **Census:** 9 **Outpatient Visits:** 31985 **Births:** 82 **Total Expense ($000):** 12648 **Payroll Expense ($000):** 5648 **Personnel:** 140

EL DORADO—Union County

⊞ **MEDICAL CENTER OF SOUTH ARKANSAS (040088)**, 700 West Grove Street, Zip 71730–4416; tel. 870/863–2000 **A**1 10 **F**3 11 13 15 17 18 20 22 24 28 29 31 34 40 43 45 46 50 56 57 59 64 70 73 75 76 77 78 79 80 81 82 85 87 89 90 93 107 108 110 111 114 115 119 130 131 146 147 148 **P**7 8 **S** Community Health Systems, Inc., Franklin, TN
Primary Contact: Robert Rupp, Chief Executive Officer
COO: Ross Korkmas, Chief Operating Officer
CFO: Dale Maddox, Chief Financial Officer
CMO: Misty Kneeland, Chief Medical Staff
CIO: Rob Robison, Director Information Technology
CHR: LaKeitha Davis, Director Human Resources
CNO: Kathy Degenstein Gartman, Chief Nursing Officer
Web address: www.themedcenter.net
Control: Corporation, Investor–owned, for–profit **Service:** General Medical and Surgical

Staffed Beds: 120 **Admissions:** 3871 **Census:** 40 **Outpatient Visits:** 52995 **Births:** 626 **Total Expense ($000):** 59579 **Payroll Expense ($000):** 22953 **Personnel:** 473

EUREKA SPRINGS—Carroll County

EUREKA SPRINGS HOSPITAL (041304), 24 Norris Street, Zip 72632–3541; tel. 479/253–7400 **A**10 18 **F**3 30 34 40 41 45 57 77 81 84 85 89 93 104 107 130 131 133 146 148 **S** Allegiance Health Management, Shreveport, LA
Primary Contact: Peter Savoy, III, Chief Executive Officer
CFO: Taylor Smith, Chief Financial Officer
CMO: John House, M.D., Chief of Staff
CIO: Drew Wood, Director Information Technology
CHR: Jodi Smith, Administrative Assistant Human Resources
CNO: Vicki Andert, Chief Nursing Officer
Web address: www.eurekaspringshospital.com
Control: Corporation, Investor–owned, for–profit **Service:** General Medical and Surgical

Staffed Beds: 15 **Admissions:** 313 **Census:** 6 **Outpatient Visits:** 5068 **Births:** 0 **Total Expense ($000):** 7368 **Payroll Expense ($000):** 2838 **Personnel:** 62

FAYETTEVILLE—Washington County

⊞ **HEALTHSOUTH REHABILITATION HOSPITAL (043032)**, 153 East Monte Painter Drive, Zip 72703–4002; tel. 479/444–2200 **A**1 10 **F**3 29 34 42 57 59 75 77 79 90 91 92 94 95 96 **P**8 **S** HEALTHSOUTH Corporation, Birmingham, AL
Primary Contact: Jack C. Mitchell, FACHE, Chief Executive Officer
CMO: Marty Hurlbut, M.D., Medical Director
CHR: Missy Cole, Director Human Resources
CNO: Miriam Irvin, CNO
Web address: www.healthsouthfayetteville.com
Control: Corporation, Investor–owned, for–profit **Service:** Rehabilitation

Staffed Beds: 66 **Admissions:** 1457 **Census:** 49 **Outpatient Visits:** 0 **Births:** 0 **Total Expense ($000):** 14714 **Payroll Expense ($000):** 8394 **Personnel:** 174

★ ○ **PHYSICIANS' SPECIALTY HOSPITAL (040152)**, 3873 North Parkview Drive, Zip 72703, Mailing Address: 3875 North Parkview Drive, Zip 72703; tel. 479/571–7070 **A**3 10 11 **F**3 12 29 40 45 79 81 82 85 107 111 114 119 131 **P**2 **S** Community Health Systems, Inc., Franklin, TN
Primary Contact: Rhonda McCabe, Chief Executive Officer
CFO: Rhonda McCabe, Chief Financial Officer
CIO: Walter Beadle, Chief Information Officer
CHR: Deborah Austin, Chief People Officer
CNO: Kelley Oliver, R.N., Chief Nursing Officer
Web address: www.pshfay.com
Control: Partnership, Investor–owned, for–profit **Service:** Surgical

Staffed Beds: 21 **Admissions:** 1134 **Census:** 5 **Births:** 0 **Total Expense ($000):** 32015 **Payroll Expense ($000):** 9270

⊞ **SPRINGWOODS BEHAVIORAL HEALTH HOSPITAL (044019)**, 1955 West Truckers Drive, Zip 72704–5637; tel. 479/973–6000 **A**1 10 **F**5 34 38 56 57 98 99 100 101 103 104 105 106 130 132 134 **P**6
Primary Contact: Mark Bethell, Chief Executive Officer
Web address: www.springwoodsbehavioral.com
Control: Corporation, Investor–owned, for–profit **Service:** Psychiatric

Staffed Beds: 80 **Admissions:** 2134 **Census:** 45 **Outpatient Visits:** 2032 **Births:** 0 **Total Expense ($000):** 13443 **Payroll Expense ($000):** 5499 **Personnel:** 181

Hospital, Medicare Provider Number, Address, Telephone, Approval, Facility, and Physician Codes, Health Care System

★ American Hospital Association (AHA) membership
□ The Joint Commission accreditation
○ Healthcare Facilities Accreditation Program
◇ DNV Healthcare Inc. accreditation
⇑ Center for Improvement in Healthcare Quality Accreditation
△ Commission on Accreditation of Rehabilitation Facilities (CARF) accreditation

AR

☐ **VANTAGE POINT OF NORTHWEST ARKANSAS (044004)**, 4253 North Crossover Road, Zip 72703–4596; tel. 479/521–5731 **A**1 10 **F**30 87 98 99 100 101 102 103 104 105 106 130 132 **P**6 **S** Acadia Healthcare Company, Inc., Franklin, TN
Primary Contact: Connie Borengasser, Chief Executive Officer
CFO: Ben Winbery, Chief Financial Officer
CMO: Norman Snyder, M.D., Medical Director
CIO: Margaret Brown, Director Medical Records
CHR: Kathy Vickers, Director Human Resources
CNO: Suzette Branscum, Director of Nursing
Web address: www.vantagepointnwa.com
Control: Corporation, Investor–owned, for–profit **Service:** Psychiatric

> **Staffed Beds:** 114 **Admissions:** 2378 **Census:** 96 **Outpatient Visits:** 142955 **Births:** 0 **Total Expense ($000):** 26420 **Payroll Expense ($000):** 15982 **Personnel:** 366

✖ **VETERANS HEALTH CARE SYSTEM OF THE OZARKS**, 1100 North College Avenue, Zip 72703–1944; tel. 479/443–4301, (Nonreporting) **A**1 2 3 **S** Department of Veterans Affairs, Washington, DC
Primary Contact: Bryan C. Matthews, Director
COO: Doris B. Cassidy, Associate Director
CMO: Bonnie Baker, M.D., Chief Medical Services
CIO: Michael Gracie, Chief Information Officer
CHR: Kathryn L. Barker, Chief Human Resources Management
Web address: www.fayettevillear.va.gov
Control: Veterans Affairs, Government, federal **Service:** General Medical and Surgical

> **Staffed Beds:** 72

✖ **WASHINGTON REGIONAL MEDICAL CENTER (040004)**, 3215 North Hills Boulevard, Zip 72703–4424; tel. 479/463–1000 **A**1 3 10 **F**3 11 12 13 14 15 17 18 20 22 24 26 28 29 30 31 34 35 39 40 43 45 46 47 48 49 50 51 53 54 56 57 58 59 60 61 62 63 64 68 70 71 72 73 74 75 76 77 78 79 80 81 82 83 84 85 86 87 89 93 100 102 107 108 111 115 118 119 126 129 130 131 132 135 144 146 147 148 **P**6 8
Primary Contact: William L. Bradley, President and Chief Executive Officer
CFO: Dan Eckels, Chief Financial Officer
CMO: David Ratcliff, M.D., Chief Medical Affairs
CIO: Becky Magee, Chief Information Officer
CHR: Steve Percival, Director Human Resources
CNO: Beverly Winney, Chief Nursing Officer
Web address: www.wregional.com
Control: Other not–for–profit (including NFP Corporation) **Service:** General Medical and Surgical

> **Staffed Beds:** 288 **Admissions:** 14179 **Census:** 163 **Outpatient Visits:** 163209 **Births:** 1240 **Total Expense ($000):** 213270 **Payroll Expense ($000):** 78385 **Personnel:** 2048

FORDYCE—Dallas County

★ **DALLAS COUNTY MEDICAL CENTER (041317)**, 201 Clifton Street, Zip 71742–3099; tel. 870/352–6300 **A**10 18 **F**3 11 29 30 34 35 40 43 45 57 59 64 81 86 93 107 119 127 133 146
Primary Contact: Tammy Rieves, Chief Executive Officer
CFO: Billie Launius, Director Business Finance
CMO: Michael Payne, M.D., Chief of Staff
CHR: Audrey Allen, Coordinator Benefits
CNO: Hollie Raney, Director of Nursing
Web address: www.dallascountymedicalcenter.com
Control: County–Government, nonfederal **Service:** General Medical and Surgical

> **Staffed Beds:** 25 **Admissions:** 286 **Census:** 2 **Outpatient Visits:** 45357 **Births:** 0 **Total Expense ($000):** 9417 **Payroll Expense ($000):** 3220 **Personnel:** 80

FORREST CITY—St. Francis County

✖ **FORREST CITY MEDICAL CENTER (040019)**, 1601 Newcastle Road, Zip 72335–2218; tel. 870/261–0000 **A**1 10 20 **F**3 13 15 29 34 40 41 43 57 68 70 79 81 85 87 89 98 107 111 114 119 133 135 141 145 146 **P**6 **S** Quorum Health, Brentwood, TN
Primary Contact: Kevin Decker, Chief Executive Officer
CFO: Todd Williams, Interim Chief Financial Officer
CMO: James Meredith, M.D., Chief of Staff
CIO: Scott Miller, Director Information Services
CHR: Sherry McLaughlin, Director Human Resources
CNO: Rhonda Nelson, Chief Nursing Officer
Web address: www.forrestcitymedicalcenter.com
Control: Corporation, Investor–owned, for–profit **Service:** General Medical and Surgical

> **Staffed Beds:** 70 **Admissions:** 2426 **Census:** 23 **Outpatient Visits:** 35160 **Births:** 943 **Total Expense ($000):** 30106 **Payroll Expense ($000):** 10271 **Personnel:** 216

FORT SMITH—Sebastian County

✖ **CHRISTUS DUBUIS HOSPITAL OF FORT SMITH (042008)**, 7301 Rogers Avenue, 4th Floor, Zip 72903–4100; tel. 479/314–4900 **A**1 10 **F**1 3 29 30 68 75 77 82 84 85 91 130 148 **S** CHRISTUS Health, Irving, TX
Primary Contact: Keith Rogers, Administrator
CFO: Paul Veillon, CPA, Chief Financial Officer
Web address: www.christusdubuis.org/fortsmith
Control: Church–operated, Nongovernment, not–for profit **Service:** Long–Term Acute Care hospital

> **Staffed Beds:** 25 **Admissions:** 220 **Census:** 17 **Outpatient Visits:** 0 **Births:** 0 **Total Expense ($000):** 7259 **Payroll Expense ($000):** 2830 **Personnel:** 53

✖ **HEALTHSOUTH REHABILITATION HOSPITAL OF FORT SMITH (043028)**, 1401 South J Street, Zip 72901–5155; tel. 479/785–3300 **A**1 10 **F**28 29 34 35 77 90 91 94 95 96 130 131 132 **S** HEALTHSOUTH Corporation, Birmingham, AL
Primary Contact: Dawn Watts, Chief Executive Officer
CFO: Brenda Forbes, Controller
CMO: Cygnet Schroeder, D.O., Medical Director
CIO: Donna England, Director Medical Records
CHR: S. Janette Daniels, Director Human Resources
CNO: Jacqueline Floyd, Chief Nursing Officer
Web address: www.healthsouthfortsmith.com
Control: Corporation, Investor–owned, for–profit **Service:** Rehabilitation

> **Staffed Beds:** 60 **Admissions:** 1392 **Census:** 45 **Outpatient Visits:** 4017 **Births:** 0 **Total Expense ($000):** 14457 **Payroll Expense ($000):** 8283 **Personnel:** 153

✖ **MERCY HOSPITAL FORT SMITH (040062)**, 7301 Rogers Avenue, Zip 72903–4189, Mailing Address: P.O. Box 17000, Zip 72917–7000; tel. 479/314–6000, (Includes MERCY ORTHOPEDIC HOSPITAL FORT SMITH, 3601 South 79th Street, Zip 72903–6255; tel. 479/709–8500; Ryan Gehrig, President) **A**1 2 10 13 **F**3 12 13 15 17 18 20 22 24 26 28 29 30 31 32 34 35 36 38 40 43 44 45 49 50 53 56 57 58 59 60 61 62 63 64 65 68 70 71 72 73 74 75 76 77 78 79 81 82 83 84 85 86 87 89 90 92 93 95 96 102 107 108 110 111 114 115 119 120 121 122 124 126 129 130 134 135 143 146 147 148 **P**8 **S** Mercy Health, Chesterfield, MO
Primary Contact: Ryan Gehrig, President
COO: Brent Hubbard, Chief Operating Officer
CFO: Greta Wilcher, Senior Vice President and Chief Financial Officer
CMO: David Hunton, M.D., Chief Medical Officer
CHR: Bryan Brown, Executive Director
CNO: Marianne Rataj, R.N., Chief Nursing Officer
Web address: www.mercy.net/fortsmithar
Control: Church–operated, Nongovernment, not–for profit **Service:** General Medical and Surgical

> **Staffed Beds:** 370 **Admissions:** 15353 **Census:** 194 **Outpatient Visits:** 190342 **Births:** 2298 **Total Expense ($000):** 254479 **Payroll Expense ($000):** 77045 **Personnel:** 1644

✖ **SELECT SPECIALTY HOSPITAL–FORT SMITH (042006)**, 1001 Towson Avenue, 6 Central, Zip 72901–4921; tel. 479/441–3960 **A**1 10 **F**1 3 29 34 45 46 57 74 75 78 79 94 148 **S** Select Medical Corporation, Mechanicsburg, PA
Primary Contact: Cindy McLain, Chief Executive Officer
Web address: www.selectspecialtyhospitals.com/company/locations/fortsmith.aspx
Control: Corporation, Investor–owned, for–profit **Service:** Long–Term Acute Care hospital

> **Staffed Beds:** 34 **Admissions:** 406 **Census:** 28 **Outpatient Visits:** 0 **Births:** 0 **Total Expense ($000):** 14289 **Payroll Expense ($000):** 5485 **Personnel:** 87

✖ **SPARKS REGIONAL MEDICAL CENTER (040055)**, 100 Towson Avenue, Zip 72901–2632, Mailing Address: P.O. Box 2406, Zip 72917–7006; tel. 479/441–4000 **A**1 3 10 **F**3 8 12 13 14 15 17 18 20 21 22 24 26 28 29 30 31 34 35 40 44 45 46 47 48 49 50 51 53 54 56 58 59 60 62 64 67 70 72 74 75 76 77 78 79 81 82 85 86 87 89 93 97 98 103 107 108 109 110 111 112 113 114 115 117 119 120 121 122 124 126 127 129 130 144 146 147 148 **P**8 **S** Community Health Systems, Inc., Franklin, TN
Primary Contact: Daniel E. McKay, Chief Executive Officer
COO: Jeremy Drinkwitz, Chief Operating Officer
CMO: Katherine Irish–Clardy, M.D., Chief Medical Officer
CIO: Tom Sallis, Director Information Systems
CHR: Robert Freeman, Director Human Resources
CNO: Cindy Slaydon, Chief Nursing Executive
Web address: www.sparks.org
Control: Corporation, Investor–owned, for–profit **Service:** General Medical and Surgical

> **Staffed Beds:** 303 **Admissions:** 16463 **Census:** 212 **Outpatient Visits:** 229054 **Births:** 1315 **Total Expense ($000):** 223078 **Payroll Expense ($000):** 64823

GRAVETTE—Benton County

OZARKS COMMUNITY HOSPITAL (041331), 1101 Jackson Street Sw,
Zip 72736–9121; tel. 479/787–5291 **A**10 18 **F**3 29 34 40 44 45 50 56 57 59
64 65 75 79 81 82 85 87 89 93 96 97 100 104 107 111 115 119 127 128
129 130 133 143 148 **P**6
Primary Contact: Paul Taylor, Administrator
Web address: www.ochonline.com/
Control: Corporation, Investor–owned, for–profit **Service:** General Medical and
Surgical

Staffed Beds: 25 **Admissions:** 662 **Census:** 20 **Outpatient Visits:** 43711
Births: 0 **Total Expense ($000):** 26995 **Payroll Expense ($000):** 11580
Personnel: 310

HARRISON—Boone County

★ **NORTH ARKANSAS REGIONAL MEDICAL CENTER (040017)**, 620 North Main
Street, Zip 72601–2911; tel. 870/414–4000 **A**10 **F**3 7 8 11 13 15 17 18 28
29 30 31 34 35 39 40 41 43 45 48 53 56 57 59 62 63 64 65 68 70 73 75
76 77 78 79 81 85 86 87 89 92 93 97 98 102 103 107 108 110 111 114
115 118 119 120 121 123 127 129 130 131 132 135 144 146 147 148 **P**8
Primary Contact: Vincent Leist, President and Chief Executive Officer
CFO: Deana Thomas, Vice President Finance and Chief Financial Officer
CIO: William J. Bogle, Director Information Systems
CNO: Sammie Cribbs, Vice President Clinical Services and Chief Nursing Officer
Web address: www.narmc.com
Control: Other not–for–profit (including NFP Corporation) **Service:** General
Medical and Surgical

Staffed Beds: 127 **Admissions:** 3696 **Census:** 29 **Outpatient Visits:** 157554
Births: 731 **Total Expense ($000):** 79484 **Payroll Expense ($000):** 33141
Personnel: 693

HEBER SPRINGS—Cleburne County

✠ **BAPTIST HEALTH MEDICAL CENTER–HEBER SPRINGS (041312)**, 1800
Bypass Road, Zip 72543–9135; tel. 501/887–3000 **A**1 10 18 **F**3 8 11 14 15
18 28 29 30 31 34 35 36 40 43 45 48 50 51 57 59 64 68 74 75 77 78 79
81 85 93 102 107 110 111 115 116 117 118 119 127 129 131 132 133 134
135 143 146 **S** Baptist Health, Little Rock, AR
Primary Contact: Edward L. Lacy, FACHE, Vice President and Administrator
Web address: www.baptist–health.com/maps–directions/bhmc–heber–springs
Control: Other not–for–profit (including NFP Corporation) **Service:** General
Medical and Surgical

Staffed Beds: 25 **Admissions:** 961 **Census:** 10 **Outpatient Visits:** 28728
Births: 0 **Total Expense ($000):** 19569 **Payroll Expense ($000):** 6712
Personnel: 138

HELENA—Phillips County

✠ **HELENA REGIONAL MEDICAL CENTER (040085)**, 1801 Martin Luther King
Drive, Zip 72342, Mailing Address: P.O. Box 788, Zip 72342–0788;
tel. 870/338–5800 **A**1 10 20 **F**3 11 13 15 28 29 34 40 43 50 59 62 70 74
76 79 81 82 86 87 89 91 93 97 107 108 111 113 114 119 130 132 133
135 145 146 147 148 **S** Quorum Health, Brentwood, TN
Primary Contact: Leah Osbahr, M.P.H., Chief Executive Officer
CFO: Amy Rice, Chief Financial Officer
CIO: Robert White, Director Information Technology
CHR: Juril Fonzie, Director Human Resources
CNO: Jodi Love, R.N., Chief Nursing Officer
Web address: www.helenarmc.com
Control: Corporation, Investor–owned, for–profit **Service:** General Medical and
Surgical

Staffed Beds: 105 **Admissions:** 1718 **Census:** 12 **Outpatient Visits:** 27174
Births: 218 **Total Expense ($000):** 27705 **Payroll Expense ($000):** 7589
Personnel: 143

HOPE—Hempstead County

◇ **WADLEY REGIONAL MEDICAL CENTER AT HOPE (040153)**, 2001 South
Main Street, Zip 71801–8194; tel. 870/722–3800 **A**10 21 **F**3 11 15 18 29 34
35 40 50 56 57 59 64 70 86 93 98 103 107 110 111 114 119 127 130
S IASIS Healthcare, Franklin, TN
Primary Contact: Thomas D. Gilbert, FACHE, Chief Executive Officer
CFO: Bonny Sorensen, Chief Financial Officer
CIO: Matt Kesterson, Director Information Services
CHR: Debby Butler, Director Human Resources
CNO: Shelly Strayhorn, R.N., Chief Nursing Officer
Web address: www.wadleyhealthathope.com
Control: Corporation, Investor–owned, for–profit **Service:** General Medical and
Surgical

Staffed Beds: 79 **Admissions:** 1022 **Census:** 15 **Outpatient Visits:** 26087
Births: 0 **Total Expense ($000):** 14190 **Payroll Expense ($000):** 5617
Personnel: 137

HOT SPRINGS—Garland County

✠ **CHI ST. VINCENT HOT SPRINGS (040026)**, 300 Werner Street,
Zip 71913–6406; tel. 501/622–1000 **A**1 2 10 19 **F**3 11 12 13 15 17 18 20
22 24 26 28 29 30 31 34 35 37 38 40 43 45 47 49 50 56 57 59 62 64 65
66 68 69 70 71 74 75 76 77 78 79 81 82 85 86 87 89 92 93 98 103 107
108 110 111 112 114 115 116 117 118 119 120 121 123 124 129 130 132
135 146 147 148 **P**6 **S** Catholic Health Initiatives, Englewood, CO
Primary Contact: Anthony Houston, FACHE, President
CFO: Tadd M. Richert, Chief Financial Officer
CMO: Thomas H. Cummins, M.D., Chief Medical Officer
CIO: Tracy Kirby, Assistant Vice President Business Relationship Management
CHR: Aaron Austin, Market Vice President Human Resources
CNO: Bryan Williams, R.N., Vice President Patient Care Services
Web address: www.chistvincent.com/Hospitals/st–vincent–hot–springs
Control: Church–operated, Nongovernment, not–for profit **Service:** General
Medical and Surgical

Staffed Beds: 262 **Admissions:** 12563 **Census:** 173 **Outpatient Visits:**
168887 **Births:** 975 **Total Expense ($000):** 262632 **Payroll Expense
($000):** 110093 **Personnel:** 1451

□ △ **NATIONAL PARK MEDICAL CENTER (040078)**, 1910 Malvern Avenue,
Zip 71901–7799; tel. 501/321–1000 **A**1 7 10 19 **F**3 11 12 13 15 17 18 20
22 24 28 29 30 31 34 35 40 45 46 47 49 56 57 59 64 70 73 74 75 76 78
79 81 85 87 89 90 92 93 98 103 107 110 111 119 124 130 131 132 146
148 **P**1 **S** RCCH HealthCare Partners, Brentwood, TN
Primary Contact: Jerry D. Mabry, FACHE, Chief Executive Officer
COO: Brian Bell, Associate Administrator and Chief Operating Officer
CFO: Robbie Pettey, Chief Financial Officer
CMO: Robert Breving, M.D., Chief of Staff
CIO: Brian Coffman, Director Information System
CHR: Tina Albright, Director Human Resources
CNO: Patsy Sue Crumpton, R.N., Chief Nursing Officer
Web address: www.nationalparkmedical.com
Control: Corporation, Investor–owned, for–profit **Service:** General Medical and
Surgical

Staffed Beds: 193 **Admissions:** 6009 **Census:** 88 **Outpatient Visits:** 51712
Births: 501 **Total Expense ($000):** 72887 **Payroll Expense ($000):** 26502
Personnel: 576

HOT SPRINGS NATIONAL PARK—Garland County

✠ **CHRISTUS DUBUIS HOSPITAL OF HOT SPRINGS (042004)**, 300 Werner
Street, 3rd Floor East, Zip 71913–6406; tel. 501/609–4300 **A**1 10 **F**1 3 29 30
45 68 77 79 85 87 118 130 135 148 **S** CHRISTUS Health, Irving, TX
Primary Contact: Keith Rogers, Administrator
CFO: Paul Veillon, CPA, Chief Financial Officer
CIO: David Cook, Manager Information Systems
Web address: www.christusdubuis.org/hotsprings
Control: Church–operated, Nongovernment, not–for profit **Service:** Long–Term
Acute Care hospital

Staffed Beds: 26 **Admissions:** 137 **Census:** 11 **Outpatient Visits:** 0 **Births:**
0 **Total Expense ($000):** 5326 **Payroll Expense ($000):** 2129 **Personnel:**
46

★ **LEVI HOSPITAL (040132)**, 300 Prospect Avenue, Zip 71901–4097;
tel. 501/624–1281 **A**10 **F**40 57 59 64 93 98 102 103 104 107 130 131 132
Primary Contact: Patrick G. McCabe, Jr., FACHE, President and Chief Executive
Officer
CFO: Stuart Lisko, Vice President, Chief Financial Officer and Compliance Officer
CMO: P. Ross Bandy, M.D., Chief Medical Officer and Chief of Staff
CIO: Stuart Lisko, Vice President, Chief Financial Officer and Compliance Officer
CHR: Susan Kramer, Director of Human Resources
CNO: Steven Boyd, R.N., Nurse Executive
Web address: www.levihospital.com
Control: Other not–for–profit (including NFP Corporation) **Service:** Psychiatric

Staffed Beds: 50 **Admissions:** 1445 **Census:** 18 **Outpatient Visits:** 18519
Births: 0 **Total Expense ($000):** 7576 **Payroll Expense ($000):** 4253
Personnel: 103

JACKSONVILLE—Pulaski County

NORTH METRO MEDICAL CENTER (040074), 1400 West Braden Street,
Zip 72076–3788; tel. 501/985–7000, (Nonreporting) **A**10 **S** Allegiance Health
Management, Shreveport, LA
Primary Contact: Joe Farrer, Interim Administrator
CFO: Lynn Muller, Chief Financial Officer
CMO: Ann Layton, M.D., Chief of Staff
CHR: Jane Rockwell, Director Support Services
Web address: www.northmetromed.com
Control: Other not–for–profit (including NFP Corporation) **Service:** General
Medical and Surgical

Staffed Beds: 76

Hospital, Medicare Provider Number, Address, Telephone, Approval, Facility, and Physician Codes, Health Care System

★ American Hospital Association (AHA) membership   ○ Healthcare Facilities Accreditation Program   ⇑ Center for Improvement in Healthcare Quality Accreditation
□ The Joint Commission accreditation   ◇ DNV Healthcare Inc. accreditation   △ Commission on Accreditation of Rehabilitation Facilities (CARF) accreditation

JONESBORO—Craighead County

⊠ **HEALTHSOUTH REHABILITATION HOSPITAL OF JONESBORO (043029)**, 1201 Fleming Avenue, Zip 72401–4311, Mailing Address: P.O. Box 1680, Zip 72403–1680; tel. 870/932–0440, (Nonreporting) **A**1 10 **S** HEALTHSOUTH Corporation, Birmingham, AL
Primary Contact: Donna Harris, Chief Executive Officer
CFO: Allan Jones, Controller
CMO: Virendar Verma, M.D., Medical Director
CHR: Tammy Barley, Director, Human Resources
CNO: Becky Kimble, R.N., Chief Nursing Officer
Web address: www.healthsouthjonesboro.com
Control: Corporation, Investor–owned, for–profit **Service:** Rehabilitation

Staffed Beds: 67

⊠ **NEA BAPTIST MEMORIAL HOSPITAL (040118)**, 4800 East Johnson Avenue, Zip 72401–8413; tel. 870/936–1000 **A**1 3 10 13 **F**3 11 12 13 15 17 18 20 22 24 26 28 29 30 31 34 39 40 43 45 46 48 49 57 58 59 60 74 75 77 78 79 81 82 84 85 86 87 90 93 96 107 108 110 111 115 118 119 120 121 123 124 126 130 132 135 146 148 **P**8 **S** Baptist Memorial Health Care Corporation, Memphis, TN
Primary Contact: Brad Parsons, FACHE, Administrator and Chief Executive Officer
CFO: Kyle Sanders, Chief Financial Officer
CMO: Stephen Woodruff, M.D., Chief Medical Officer
CIO: Terry Crider, Information Technology Site Manager
CHR: James Keller, Director Human Resources
CNO: Paula Grimes, R.N., Chief Nursing Officer
Web address: www.neabaptist.com
Control: Other not–for–profit (including NFP Corporation) **Service:** General Medical and Surgical

Staffed Beds: 216 Admissions: 10264 Census: 112 Outpatient Visits: 83828 Births: 921 Total Expense ($000): 160128 Payroll Expense ($000): 45888 Personnel: 901

⊠ **ST. BERNARDS MEDICAL CENTER (040020)**, 225 East Jackson Avenue, Zip 72401–3119; tel. 870/207–4100 **A**1 2 3 10 13 19 **F**3 5 11 12 13 15 17 18 19 20 22 24 26 27 28 29 30 31 32 34 35 38 39 40 43 45 46 49 50 51 53 54 56 57 59 60 62 63 64 68 70 71 72 74 75 76 77 78 79 81 82 83 84 85 86 87 89 92 93 98 100 101 102 103 104 105 107 108 109 110 111 114 115 116 117 118 119 120 121 123 126 129 130 131 132 135 141 145 146 147 148
Primary Contact: Chris B. Barber, FACHE, President and Chief Executive Officer
COO: Michael K. Givens, FACHE, Administrator
CFO: Harry Hutchison, Vice President Fiscal Services
CMO: Kasey Holder, M.D., Vice President Medical Affairs
CIO: Josh Melton, Chief Information Officer
CHR: Lori Smith, Vice President Human Resources
CNO: Susan Greenwood, R.N., Vice President and Chief Nursing Officer
Web address: www.stbernards.info
Control: Church–operated, Nongovernment, not–for profit **Service:** General Medical and Surgical

Staffed Beds: 386 Admissions: 17476 Census: 206 Outpatient Visits: 258263 Births: 1454 Total Expense ($000): 269351

LAKE VILLAGE—Chicot County

★ **CHICOT MEMORIAL MEDICAL CENTER (041328)**, 2729 Highway 65 and 82 South, Zip 71653; tel. 870/265–5351 **A**10 18 **F**3 7 11 13 15 29 34 35 40 43 49 50 53 57 59 62 64 71 75 76 77 80 81 82 85 87 93 107 111 114 119 128 129 130 132 133 146 147 148
Primary Contact: David Mantz, Chief Executive Officer
CFO: Vicki Allen, Chief Financial Officer
CMO: Michael Bradley Mayfield, M.D., Chief of Staff
CIO: David Andrews, Manager Information Systems
CNO: Eric Selby, R.N., Chief Nursing Officer
Web address: www.chicotmemorial.com
Control: Other not–for–profit (including NFP Corporation) **Service:** General Medical and Surgical

Staffed Beds: 25 Admissions: 1055 Census: 11 Outpatient Visits: 20503 Births: 87 Total Expense ($000): 17465 Payroll Expense ($000): 7089 Personnel: 176

SOUTHEAST REHABILITATION HOSPITAL (043034), 2729–A Highway 65 and 82 South, Zip 71653; tel. 870/265–4333, (Nonreporting) **A**10
Primary Contact: Stacy Noble, Administrator
CNO: Michael Vaughn, Director of Nursing
Web address: www.southeastrehab.com
Control: Partnership, Investor–owned, for–profit **Service:** Rehabilitation

Staffed Beds: 15

LITTLE ROCK—Pulaski County

ALLEGIANCE SPECIALTY HOSPITAL OF LITTLE ROCK See Cornerstone Hospital of Little Rock

⊠ **ARKANSAS CHILDREN'S HOSPITAL (043300)**, 1 Children's Way, Zip 72202–3500; tel. 501/364–1100 **A**1 3 5 8 10 **F**3 7 11 12 16 17 19 21 23 25 27 28 29 30 31 32 34 35 38 39 40 41 43 45 46 48 50 53 55 57 58 59 60 64 68 71 72 74 75 77 78 79 80 81 82 84 85 86 87 88 89 90 91 93 94 97 102 107 108 111 115 118 119 126 129 130 131 132 135 136 137 138 143 146 **P**8
Primary Contact: Marcella Doderer, FACHE, President and Chief Executive Officer
CFO: Gena Wingfield, Senior Vice President and Chief Financial Officer
CMO: Jay Deshpande, M.D., Senior Vice President and Chief Medical Officer
CIO: Jonathan Goldberg, Senior Vice President and Chief Information Officer
CHR: Andree Trosclair, Vice President Human Resources
CNO: Lee Anne Eddy, Senior Vice President and Chief Nursing Officer
COO: Chanda Cashen Chacon, Executive Vice President and Chief Operating Officer
Web address: www.archildrens.org
Control: Other not–for–profit (including NFP Corporation) **Service:** Children's general

Staffed Beds: 342 Admissions: 15529 Census: 224 Outpatient Visits: 365390 Births: 0 Total Expense ($000): 485183 Payroll Expense ($000): 205970 Personnel: 3436

⊠ **ARKANSAS HEART HOSPITAL (040134)**, 1701 South Shackleford Road, Zip 72211–4335; tel. 501/219–7000 **A**1 3 5 10 **F**3 11 17 18 20 22 24 26 29 30 34 35 40 57 58 59 64 70 74 75 81 85 86 102 107 111 114 119 127 129 130 132 148
Primary Contact: Bruce Murphy, M.D., President and Chief Executive Officer
CHR: Brent Davis, Human Resources Team Leader
Web address: www.arheart.com
Control: Partnership, Investor–owned, for–profit **Service:** Heart

Staffed Beds: 112 Admissions: 4762 Census: 50 Outpatient Visits: 10050 Births: 0 Total Expense ($000): 146058 Payroll Expense ($000): 39707 Personnel: 887

☐ **ARKANSAS STATE HOSPITAL (044011)**, 305 South Palm Street, Zip 72205–5432; tel. 501/686–9000 **A**1 3 5 10 **F**3 29 30 53 98 99 103 106 130 132 143 **P**6
Primary Contact: Steve Henson, Chief Executive Officer
CFO: Gary W. Hollis, Comptroller
CMO: Steven Domon, M.D., Medical Director
CIO: Tina Grissom, Chief Information Technology Officer
CHR: Donna Sadler, Director Human Resources
CNO: James Scoggins, Director of Nursing
Web address: www.state.ar.us/dhs/dmhs
Control: State–Government, nonfederal **Service:** Psychiatric

Staffed Beds: 222 Admissions: 589 Census: 203 Outpatient Visits: 0 Births: 0 Total Expense ($000): 50261 Payroll Expense ($000): 24352 Personnel: 598

★ **BAPTIST HEALTH EXTENDED CARE HOSPITAL (042012)**, 9601 Baptist Health Drive, Zip 72205–7202; tel. 501/202–1070 **A**10 **F**1 3 29 31 77 87 130 148 **S** Baptist Health, Little Rock, AR
Primary Contact: Mike Perkins, Vice President and Administrator
CFO: Robert C. Roberts, Vice President
CMO: Gail McCracken, M.D., Medical Director
CIO: David House, Vice President
CHR: Anthony Kendall, Vice President Human Resources
CNO: Diane Smith, Chief Nursing Officer
Web address: www.baptist–health.com/maps–directions/bh_extended_care/default.aspx
Control: Other not–for–profit (including NFP Corporation) **Service:** Long–Term Acute Care hospital

Staffed Beds: 55 Admissions: 339 Census: 30 Outpatient Visits: 0 Births: 0 Total Expense ($000): 15160 Payroll Expense ($000): 5892 Personnel: 97

⊠ **BAPTIST HEALTH MEDICAL CENTER–LITTLE ROCK (040114)**, 9601 Baptist Health Drive, Zip 72205–7299; tel. 501/202–2000 **A**1 3 5 10 **F**3 4 5 7 8 11 12 13 15 17 18 20 22 24 26 28 29 30 31 32 34 35 36 37 38 40 43 44 45 49 50 54 56 57 58 59 60 61 62 64 65 67 68 70 72 73 74 75 76 77 78 79 81 82 84 85 86 87 89 93 98 99 100 101 102 103 104 107 108 110 111 114 118 119 126 128 129 130 131 132 134 135 137 138 143 144 146 147 148 **S** Baptist Health, Little Rock, AR
Primary Contact: Greg Crain, FACHE, Vice President and Administrator
CFO: Robert C. Roberts, Senior Vice President Financial Services
CMO: Anthony Bennett, M.D., Chief Clinical Affairs
CIO: David House, Vice President and Chief Information Officer
CHR: Anthony Kendall, Vice President Human Resources
CNO: Jill Massiet, R.N., Vice President Patient Care
Web address: www.baptist–health.org/maps–directions/bhmc–lr
Control: Other not–for–profit (including NFP Corporation) **Service:** General Medical and Surgical

Staffed Beds: 694 Admissions: 29557 Census: 438 Outpatient Visits: 139055 Births: 2900 Total Expense ($000): 456439 Payroll Expense ($000): 142097 Personnel: 2741

AR

⊠ △ **BAPTIST HEALTH REHABILITATION INSTITUTE (043026)**, 9601
Interstate 630, Exit 7, Zip 72205–7202; tel. 501/202–7000 **A**1 3 5 7 10 **F**29
30 34 35 50 53 64 75 86 87 90 91 93 95 96 130 132 143 **S** Baptist Health,
Little Rock, AR
Primary Contact: Lee Gentry, FACHE, Vice President and Administrator
CFO: Robert C. Roberts, Senior Vice President
CIO: David House, Vice President and Chief Information Officer
CHR: Anthony Kendall, Vice President Human Resources
Web address: www.baptist–health.com/locations/accesspoint.
aspx?accessPointID=202
Control: Other not–for–profit (including NFP Corporation) **Service:** Rehabilitation

Staffed Beds: 120 **Admissions:** 1464 **Census:** 50 **Outpatient Visits:** 74788
Births: 0 **Total Expense ($000):** 29071 **Payroll Expense ($000):** 13401
Personnel: 220

⊠ **CENTRAL ARKANSAS VETERANS HEALTHCARE SYSTEM**, 4300 West
Seventh Street, Zip 72205–5446; tel. 501/257–1000, (Includes NORTH LITTLE
ROCK DIVISION, 2200 Fort Roots Drive, North Little Rock, Zip 72114–1706;
tel. 501/661–1202), (Total facility includes 152 beds in nursing home–type unit)
A1 2 3 5 8 **F**2 3 5 11 12 15 18 20 22 26 29 30 31 33 34 35 36 38 39 40 44
45 46 47 48 49 50 53 56 57 58 59 60 61 62 63 64 65 68 70 71 74 75 77
78 79 80 81 82 83 84 85 86 87 90 91 92 93 94 95 96 97 98 100 101 102
103 104 105 106 107 108 110 111 114 118 119 127 128 129 130 132 135
143 145 146 147 148 **P**1 **S** Department of Veterans Affairs, Washington, DC
Primary Contact: Cyril Ekeh, Interim Medical Center Director
CFO: Colonel Nate Todd, Chief Financial Officer
CMO: Margie Scott, M.D., Chief of Staff
CIO: Jim Hall, Acting Chief Information Officer
CHR: Richard Nelson, Chief of Human Resources Management Services
Web address: www.littlerock.va.gov/
Control: Veterans Affairs, Government, federal **Service:** General Medical and
Surgical

Staffed Beds: 637 **Admissions:** 8854 **Census:** 166 **Outpatient Visits:**
872952 **Births:** 0 **Total Expense ($000):** 590884 **Payroll Expense ($000):**
259968 **Personnel:** 3459

⊠ **CHI ST. VINCENT INFIRMARY MEDICAL CENTER (040007)**, Two St. Vincent
Circle, Zip 72205–5499; tel. 501/552–3000 **A**1 3 5 10 **F**3 11 13 17 18 20 22
24 26 27 28 29 30 31 34 35 37 40 43 44 45 46 48 49 50 51 53 54 56 57
58 59 60 61 64 68 70 72 74 75 76 77 78 79 80 81 82 83 84 85 86 87 91
92 93 96 97 98 100 101 102 107 108 109 110 111 112 114 115 116 117
118 119 124 126 129 130 132 135 143 146 147 148 **P**1 6 7 **S** Catholic
Health Initiatives, Englewood, CO
Primary Contact: Polly J. Davenport, FACHE, R.N., President
CFO: Tadd M. Richert, Chief Financial Officer
CMO: Thomas H. Cummins, M.D., Chief Medical Officer
CIO: Tracy Kirby, Assistant Vice President Business Relationship Management
CHR: Aaron Austin, Market Vice President Human Resources
CNO: Kathy E. Neely, R.N., Interim Vice President Patient Care Services
Web address: www.chistvincent.com/
Control: Church–operated, Nongovernment, not–for profit **Service:** General
Medical and Surgical

Staffed Beds: 447 **Admissions:** 20239 **Census:** 303 **Outpatient Visits:**
169302 **Births:** 1067 **Total Expense ($000):** 385573 **Payroll Expense
($000):** 134211 **Personnel:** 2297

CORNERSTONE HOSPITAL OF LITTLE ROCK (042010), 2 St. Vincent Circle,
6th Floor, Zip 72205; tel. 501/265–0600 **A**10 **F**1 18 29 85 91 93 119 148
S Cornerstone Healthcare Group, Dallas, TX
Primary Contact: James H. Rogers, FACHE, Chief Executive Officer
CNO: Joy Miller, Chief Nursing Officer
Web address: www.chghospitals.com/littlerock/
Control: Corporation, Investor–owned, for–profit **Service:** Long–Term Acute Care
hospital

Staffed Beds: 40 **Admissions:** 337 **Census:** 26 **Outpatient Visits:** 0 **Births:**
0 **Total Expense ($000):** 11771 **Payroll Expense ($000):** 5743 **Personnel:**
105

☐ **PINNACLE POINTE HOSPITAL (044013)**, 11501 Financial Center Parkway,
Zip 72211–3715; tel. 501/223–3322 **A**1 10 **F**29 34 35 50 54 55 75 87 98 99
101 102 105 106 130 134 135 143 **S** Universal Health Services, Inc., King of
Prussia, PA
Primary Contact: Shane Frazier, Chief Executive Officer
CFO: Gina Dailey, Chief Financial Officer
CMO: Ben Nimmo, M.D., Medical Director
CIO: James L. Howe, Director Human Resources
CHR: James L. Howe, Director Human Resources
CNO: Bobby Alexander, R.N., Chief Nursing Officer
Web address: www.pinnaclepointehospital.com
Control: Corporation, Investor–owned, for–profit **Service:** Children's hospital
psychiatric

Staffed Beds: 124 **Admissions:** 2792 **Census:** 114 **Outpatient Visits:** 84033
Births: 0 **Total Expense ($000):** 17332 **Payroll Expense ($000):** 10693
Personnel: 222

⊠ **UAMS MEDICAL CENTER (040016)**, 4301 West Markham Street,
Zip 72205–7101; tel. 501/686–7000 **A**1 3 5 8 10 **F**3 11 12 13 15 17 18 20
22 24 26 29 30 31 34 40 43 44 45 46 47 48 49 50 52 53 54 55 56 57 58
59 60 61 64 68 70 72 73 74 75 76 77 78 79 80 81 82 84 85 86 87 91 92
93 94 96 97 98 99 100 101 102 103 104 107 108 110 111 114 115 116
117 118 119 120 121 123 124 126 129 130 131 132 136 138 139 141 142
145 146 147 148 **P**6
Primary Contact: Roxane A. Townsend, M.D., Chief Executive Officer
COO: Melissa Fontaine, Chief Operating Officer
CFO: William Bowes, Chief Financial Officer
CMO: Nicholas P. Lang, M.D., Chief Medical Officer
CIO: David L. Miller, Chief Information Officer
CHR: Jeff Risinger, Director Human Resources
CNO: Mary Helen Forrest, R.N., Chief Nursing Officer
Web address: www.uams.edu/medcenter
Control: State–Government, nonfederal **Service:** General Medical and Surgical

Staffed Beds: 464 **Admissions:** 22897 **Census:** 407 **Outpatient Visits:**
501901 **Births:** 3361 **Total Expense ($000):** 646159 **Payroll Expense
($000):** 207621 **Personnel:** 4003

MAGNOLIA—Columbia County

★ **MAGNOLIA REGIONAL MEDICAL CENTER (040067)**, 101 Hospital Drive,
Zip 71753–2415; Mailing Address: P.O. Box 629, Zip 71754–0629;
tel. 870/235–3000 **A**3 10 20 **F**3 11 13 15 29 31 34 35 40 43 45 50 57 59
62 64 70 75 76 81 86 87 91 93 97 107 108 110 111 115 119 129 130 132
133 146 147 148
Primary Contact: Margaret M. West, MS, Chief Executive Officer
CFO: Roxane Stewart, Chief Financial Officer
CMO: James W. Chambliss, Chief of Staff
CHR: Shawnee Cooper, Director Human Resources
CNO: Joycelyn Watkins, R.N., Chief Nursing Officer
Web address: www.magnoliarmc.org
Control: City–Government, nonfederal **Service:** General Medical and Surgical

Staffed Beds: 49 **Admissions:** 1658 **Census:** 14 **Births:** 283 **Total Expense
($000):** 25065 **Payroll Expense ($000):** 11720 **Personnel:** 227

MALVERN—Hot Spring County

ARKANSAS DEPARTMENT OF CORRECTION HOSPITAL, 100 Walco Lane,
Zip 72104–6793; tel. 870/267–6999, (Nonreporting) **A**3 5
Primary Contact: Gregory McKinney, M.D., Medical Director
Control: State–Government, nonfederal **Service:** Hospital unit of an institution
(prison hospital, college infimary, etc.)

Staffed Beds: 27

★ **BAPTIST HEALTH MEDICAL CENTER–HOT SPRING COUNTY (040076)**,
1001 Schneider Drive, Zip 72104–4811; tel. 501/332–1000 **A**10 **F**3 11 15 17
28 29 34 35 40 43 45 57 59 64 70 75 81 98 102 107 110 111 115 119 130
132 146 **S** Baptist Health, Little Rock, AR
Primary Contact: Sheila Williams, Vice President and Administrator
CMO: Allen Gerber, M.D., Chief of Staff
CHR: Kelli Hopkins, Director Human Resources
CNO: Dee Schall, R.N., Chief Nursing Officer
Web address: www.https://www.baptist–health.org
Control: Other not–for–profit (including NFP Corporation) **Service:** General
Medical and Surgical

Staffed Beds: 72 **Admissions:** 2229 **Census:** 24 **Outpatient Visits:** 23923
Births: 0 **Total Expense ($000):** 19488 **Payroll Expense ($000):** 8938
Personnel: 199

Hospital, Medicare Provider Number, Address, Telephone, Approval, Facility, and Physician Codes, Health Care System

★ American Hospital Association (AHA) membership   ○ Healthcare Facilities Accreditation Program   ⇑ Center for Improvement in Healthcare Quality Accreditation
☐ The Joint Commission accreditation   ◇ DNV Healthcare Inc. accreditation   △ Commission on Accreditation of Rehabilitation Facilities (CARF) accreditation

MAUMELLE—Pulaski County

☐ **METHODIST BEHAVIORAL HOSPITAL OF ARKANSAS (044017)**, 1601 Murphy Drive, Zip 72113–6187; tel. 501/803–3388 **A**1 10 **F**30 32 38 50 54 64 75 86 87 98 99 102 104 106 130
Primary Contact: Andy Altom, Chief Executive Officer
Web address: www.umch.org
Control: Other not–for–profit (including NFP Corporation) **Service:** Children's hospital psychiatric

Staffed Beds: 60 **Admissions:** 1678 **Census:** 56 **Outpatient Visits:** 99350 **Births:** 0 **Total Expense ($000):** 17118 **Payroll Expense ($000):** 7623 **Personnel:** 121

MCGEHEE—Desha County

★ **MCGEHEE–DESHA COUNTY HOSPITAL (041308)**, 900 South Third, Zip 71654–2562, Mailing Address: P.O. Box 351, Zip 71654–0351; tel. 870/222–5600 **A**10 18 **F**3 11 29 40 57 59 62 64 68 107 114 119 132 133 135 146 148
Primary Contact: John E. Heard, Chief Executive Officer
CFO: Teresa Morgan, Chief Financial Officer
CMO: James Young, M.D., Chief of Staff
CIO: Shaun Perry, Chief Information Officer
CNO: Sarah Calvert, Chief Nursing Officer
Control: Other not–for–profit (including NFP Corporation) **Service:** General Medical and Surgical

Staffed Beds: 25 **Admissions:** 216 **Census:** 2 **Outpatient Visits:** 8276 **Births:** 0 **Total Expense ($000):** 10090 **Payroll Expense ($000):** 4913 **Personnel:** 121

MENA—Polk County

★ **MENA REGIONAL HEALTH SYSTEM (040015)**, 311 North Morrow Street, Zip 71953–2516; tel. 479/394–6100 **A**10 20 **F**3 11 13 15 29 30 32 34 35 40 43 45 50 56 57 59 64 68 70 75 76 77 79 81 86 87 90 91 93 96 98 99 100 101 103 104 107 108 111 115 119 129 130 131 133 144 146 147 **P**8
Primary Contact: Jay Quebedeaux, Chief Executive Officer
CFO: Mark Henke, Chief Financial Officer
CMO: Richard Lochala, Chief of Staff
CIO: Nicholas Dunn, Director Information Systems
CHR: JoAnna B. DesJardins, Director Human Resources
CNO: Teresa Wise, R.N., Chief Nursing Officer
Web address: www.menaregional.com
Control: City–Government, nonfederal **Service:** General Medical and Surgical

Staffed Beds: 60 **Admissions:** 1502 **Census:** 21 **Outpatient Visits:** 39966 **Births:** 306 **Total Expense ($000):** 27628 **Payroll Expense ($000):** 14560 **Personnel:** 262

MONTICELLO—Drew County

DREW MEMORIAL HOSPITAL (040051), 778 Scogin Drive, Zip 71655–5729; tel. 870/367–2411 **A**10 20 **F**3 11 13 15 29 31 34 35 40 43 45 50 57 59 62 64 68 70 75 77 78 81 82 86 87 91 93 94 96 100 103 107 110 111 115 119 128 129 130 132 133 147 148
Primary Contact: Scott G. Barrilleaux, FACHE, Chief Executive Officer
COO: Wade Smith, Chief Operating Officer
CFO: Melodie Colwell, Chief Financial Officer
CMO: Julia Nichoson, M.D., Chief Medical Officer
CIO: Rusty Bryant, Director Information Technology
CHR: Bobbie Ivey, Chief Human Resource Officer
CNO: Vonda Moore, Chief Nursing Officer
Web address: www.drewmemorial.org
Control: Other not–for–profit (including NFP Corporation) **Service:** General Medical and Surgical

Staffed Beds: 49 **Admissions:** 2490 **Census:** 20 **Outpatient Visits:** 55449 **Births:** 365 **Total Expense ($000):** 28082 **Payroll Expense ($000):** 11394 **Personnel:** 263

MORRILTON—Conway County

★ **CHI ST. VINCENT MORRILTON (041324)**, 4 Hospital Drive, Zip 72110–4510; tel. 501/977–2300 **A**10 18 **F**3 11 15 28 29 30 34 35 40 44 45 50 57 59 62 64 70 77 79 80 81 85 87 93 97 107 110 111 119 127 130 133 145 146 **P**1 6 **S** Catholic Health Initiatives, Englewood, CO
Primary Contact: Leslie Arnold, Chief Executive Officer and Administrator
CFO: Tadd M. Richert, Chief Financial Officer
CMO: Thomas H. Cummins, M.D., Chief Medical Officer
CIO: Tracy Kirby, Assistant Vice President Business Relatonship Management
CHR: Aaron Austin, Market Vice President Human Resources
CNO: Kathy E. Neely, R.N., Interim Vice President Patient Care Services
Web address: www.chistvincent.com/Hospitals/st–vincent–morrilton
Control: Church–operated, Nongovernment, not–for profit **Service:** General Medical and Surgical

Staffed Beds: 25 **Admissions:** 835 **Census:** 8 **Outpatient Visits:** 37327 **Births:** 0 **Total Expense ($000):** 16922 **Payroll Expense ($000):** 6634 **Personnel:** 118

ST. ANTHONY'S MEDICAL CENTER See CHI St. Vincent Morrilton

MOUNTAIN HOME—Baxter County

★ **BAXTER REGIONAL MEDICAL CENTER (040027)**, 624 Hospital Drive, Zip 72653–2955; tel. 870/508–1000 **A**10 **F**7 11 13 15 17 18 20 22 24 28 29 30 31 36 40 41 43 45 46 47 49 53 56 57 59 62 63 64 70 71 76 77 78 79 81 82 84 85 86 87 90 93 98 103 104 107 108 111 114 115 119 124 126 127 129 130 132 135 146 147 148 **P**6 8
Primary Contact: Ron Peterson, FACHE, President and Chief Executive Officer
COO: Rudy Darling, Chief Operating Officer
CFO: Ivan Holleman, Chief Financial Officer
CHR: Karen Adams, Vice President Human Resources
Web address: www.baxterregional.org
Control: Other not–for–profit (including NFP Corporation) **Service:** General Medical and Surgical

Staffed Beds: 209 **Admissions:** 8444 **Census:** 111 **Outpatient Visits:** 125750 **Births:** 699 **Total Expense ($000):** 169664 **Payroll Expense ($000):** 68535 **Personnel:** 1381

MOUNTAIN VIEW—Stone County

★ **STONE COUNTY MEDICAL CENTER (041310)**, 2106 East Main Street, Zip 72560–6439, Mailing Address: P.O. Box 510, Zip 72560–0510; tel. 870/269–4361 **A**10 18 **F**3 8 11 15 29 34 35 40 43 57 59 64 79 81 91 93 107 110 111 114 119 128 133 146 147 148 **S** White River Health System, Batesville, AR
Primary Contact: Stanley Townsend, Chief Executive Officer
CFO: Phillip Hacker, Chief Financial Officer
CIO: Gary Paxson, Associate Administrator Information Systems
CHR: Gary McDonald, Associate Administrator Human Resources
CNO: Diana Shelden, Chief Nursing Officer
Web address: www.whiteriverhealthsystem.com
Control: Other not–for–profit (including NFP Corporation) **Service:** General Medical and Surgical

Staffed Beds: 25 **Admissions:** 824 **Census:** 8 **Outpatient Visits:** 24025 **Births:** 0 **Total Expense ($000):** 13575 **Payroll Expense ($000):** 5123 **Personnel:** 108

NASHVILLE—Howard County

★ **HOWARD MEMORIAL HOSPITAL (041311)**, 130 Medical Circle, Zip 71852–8606; tel. 870/845–4400 **A**10 18 **F**3 11 15 28 29 30 34 35 40 43 45 50 53 57 64 65 70 77 81 85 87 93 102 103 107 108 110 115 119 133 146 **P**6
Primary Contact: Debra J. Wright, R.N., Chief Executive Officer
CFO: William J. Craig, CPA, Chief Financial Officer
CMO: John Hearnsberger, M.D., Chief of Staff
CHR: Gayla Lacefield, Director Human Resources
CNO: Alesha Danielle Collins, MSN, Chief Nursing Officer
Web address: www.howardmemorial.com
Control: Other not–for–profit (including NFP Corporation) **Service:** General Medical and Surgical

Staffed Beds: 20 **Admissions:** 527 **Census:** 6 **Outpatient Visits:** 29730 **Births:** 0 **Total Expense ($000):** 16328 **Payroll Expense ($000):** 7116 **Personnel:** 187

NORTH LITTLE ROCK—Pulaski County

☐ **ARKANSAS SURGICAL HOSPITAL (040147)**, 5201 North Shore Drive, Zip 72118–5312; tel. 501/748–8000 **A**1 10 **F**3 29 35 40 74 75 79 81 82 85 87 107 111 114 119 126 130 131 146 148
Primary Contact: Carrie Helm, Chief Executive Officer
CFO: Charles Powell, Chief Financial Officer
CMO: Kenneth A. Martin, M.D., Chief of Staff
CIO: Scott Davis, Manager Information Technology
CNO: Judy Jones, Chief Clinical Officer
Web address: www.ArkSurgicalHospital.com
Control: Corporation, Investor–owned, for–profit **Service:** General Medical and Surgical

Staffed Beds: 49 **Admissions:** 3286 **Census:** 18 **Outpatient Visits:** 16697 **Births:** 0 **Total Expense ($000):** 45669 **Payroll Expense ($000):** 12428 **Personnel:** 218

Many Facility Codes have changed. Please refer to the AHA Guide Code Chart. © 2016 AHA Guide

✷ △ **BAPTIST HEALTH MEDICAL CENTER – NORTH LITTLE ROCK (040036)**, 3333 Springhill Drive, Zip 72117–2922; tel. 501/202–3000 **A**1 3 7 10 **F**3 8 11 13 15 17 18 20 22 24 26 28 29 30 31 38 40 43 45 46 47 48 49 50 53 54 56 59 60 64 65 70 72 74 75 76 77 78 79 81 85 86 87 89 90 93 94 107 108 110 111 114 115 116 117 118 119 124 126 129 130 135 144 146 147 148 **S** Baptist Health, Little Rock, AR
Primary Contact: Steven B. Webb, FACHE, Vice President and Administrator
COO: Doug Weeks, Executive Vice President Operations
CFO: Robert C. Roberts, Senior Vice President Financial Services
CMO: Eddie Phillips, M.D., Chief Medical Affairs
CIO: David House, Vice President and Chief Information Officer
CHR: Cathy C. Dickinson, Vice President Human Resources
CNO: Kelley Hamby, Vice President Patient Care
Web address: www.baptist–health.com/locations/accesspoint. aspx?accessPointID=190
Control: Other not–for–profit (including NFP Corporation) **Service:** General Medical and Surgical

Staffed Beds: 225 **Admissions:** 11939 **Census:** 135 **Outpatient Visits:** 104027 **Births:** 1489 **Total Expense ($000):** 168148 **Payroll Expense ($000):** 57145 **Personnel:** 1041

NORTH LITTLE ROCK DIVISION See Central Arkansas Veterans Healthcare System, Little Rock

☐ **THE BRIDGEWAY (044005)**, 21 Bridgeway Road, Zip 72113–9516; tel. 501/771–1500 **A**1 10 **F**4 5 98 99 103 104 105 106 **P**5 6 **S** Universal Health Services, Inc., King of Prussia, PA
Primary Contact: Jason Miller, M.P.H., Chief Executive Officer
CFO: Fred Woods, Chief Financial Officer
CMO: Philip L. Mizell, M.D., Medical Director
CHR: Neely Robison, Director Human Resources
CNO: Sherrie James, R.N., Director of Nursing
Web address: www.thebridgeway.com
Control: Corporation, Investor–owned, for–profit **Service:** Psychiatric

Staffed Beds: 127 **Admissions:** 4312 **Census:** 87 **Outpatient Visits:** 27700 **Births:** 0 **Total Expense ($000):** 20911 **Payroll Expense ($000):** 8856 **Personnel:** 217

OSCEOLA—Mississippi County

✷ **SOUTH MISSISSIPPI COUNTY REGIONAL MEDICAL CENTER (041316)**, 611 West Lee Avenue, Zip 72370–3001, Mailing Address: P.O. Box 108, Blytheville, Zip 72316–0108; tel. 870/563–7000 **A**1 10 18 **F**29 40 57 59 68 75 81 93 107 114 130 133 146 **S** QHR, Brentwood, TN
Primary Contact: Chris Raymer, R.N., Chief Executive Officer
COO: Chris Raymer, R.N., Chief Operating Officer and Chief Nursing Officer
CFO: Randy Nichols, Chief Financial Officer
CMO: Pratapji Thakor, M.D., Chief of Staff
CIO: Tammy Bratcher, Director Information Technology
CHR: Cheri Blurton, Director Human Resources
CNO: Felicia Pierce, R.N., Chief Nursing Officer
Web address: www.mchsys.org
Control: County–Government, nonfederal **Service:** General Medical and Surgical

Staffed Beds: 25 **Admissions:** 635 **Census:** 7 **Outpatient Visits:** 12038 **Births:** 0 **Total Expense ($000):** 8959 **Payroll Expense ($000):** 3732 **Personnel:** 70

OZARK—Franklin County

★ **MERCY HOSPITAL OZARK (041303)**, 801 West River Street, Zip 72949–3023; tel. 479/667–4138 **A**10 18 **F**3 18 20 22 24 26 28 34 35 40 43 45 57 59 64 68 81 85 107 119 133 148 **P**6 8 **S** Mercy Health, Chesterfield, MO
Primary Contact: Teresa Williams, R.N., Administrator and Director of Nursing
COO: Brent Hubbard, Chief Operating Officer
CMO: John Lachowsky, M.D., Chief Medical Officer
CIO: Tiana Bolduc, Chief Information Officer
Web address: www.mercy.net/northwestarar/practice/mercy–hospital–ozark
Control: Church–operated, Nongovernment, not–for profit **Service:** General Medical and Surgical

Staffed Beds: 25 **Admissions:** 286 **Census:** 3 **Outpatient Visits:** 14150 **Births:** 0 **Total Expense ($000):** 10060 **Payroll Expense ($000):** 3592 **Personnel:** 52

PARAGOULD—Greene County

✷ △ **ARKANSAS METHODIST MEDICAL CENTER (040039)**, 900 West Kingshighway, Zip 72450–5942, Mailing Address: P.O. Box 339, Zip 72451–0339; tel. 870/239–7000 **A**1 7 10 13 19 **F**3 7 10 11 13 15 18 20 22 28 29 32 34 35 39 40 43 45 49 50 51 53 54 59 62 64 68 70 75 76 78 79 81 85 86 87 89 90 93 97 107 108 110 111 114 115 119 125 129 130 131 132 133 135 146 147 148 **P**6 8
Primary Contact: Barry L. Davis, FACHE, President and Chief Executive Officer
CFO: Brad Bloemer, Vice President Finance and Chief Financial Officer
CMO: John Hines, M.D., Chief of Staff
CIO: Dan Austin, Director Information Technology
CHR: Kevin Thielemier, Director Human Resources
CNO: Lana R. Williams, Chief Nursing Officer
Web address: www.arkansasmethodist.org
Control: Other not–for–profit (including NFP Corporation) **Service:** General Medical and Surgical

Staffed Beds: 125 **Admissions:** 4179 **Census:** 56 **Outpatient Visits:** 128545 **Births:** 506 **Total Expense ($000):** 59751 **Payroll Expense ($000):** 26078 **Personnel:** 629

PARIS—Logan County

★ **MERCY HOSPITAL PARIS (041300)**, 500 East Academy, Zip 72855–4040; tel. 479/963–6101 **A**10 18 **F**3 35 40 43 57 59 64 65 68 81 85 107 119 127 129 133 148 **P**6 8 **S** Mercy Health, Chesterfield, MO
Primary Contact: Sharon D. Sorey, R.N., Administrator
COO: Brent Hubbard, Chief Operating Officer
Web address: www.mercy.net/fortsmithar
Control: Church–operated, Nongovernment, not–for profit **Service:** General Medical and Surgical

Staffed Beds: 16 **Admissions:** 104 **Census:** 2 **Outpatient Visits:** 12879 **Births:** 0 **Total Expense ($000):** 8973 **Payroll Expense ($000):** 3602 **Personnel:** 50

PIGGOTT—Clay County

★ **PIGGOTT COMMUNITY HOSPITAL (041330)**, 1206 Gordon Duckworth Drive, Zip 72454–1911; tel. 870/598–3881 **A**10 18 **F**3 7 11 15 18 29 34 35 40 43 50 57 59 62 64 81 93 107 110 111 114 119 127 129 130 132 133 143 146 148
Primary Contact: James L. Magee, Executive Director
CFO: Linda Ort, Chief Financial Officer
Web address: www.piggottcommunityhospital.com
Control: City–Government, nonfederal **Service:** General Medical and Surgical

Staffed Beds: 25 **Admissions:** 637 **Census:** 6 **Outpatient Visits:** 14674 **Births:** 0 **Total Expense ($000):** 15498 **Payroll Expense ($000):** 6932 **Personnel:** 188

PINE BLUFF—Jefferson County

★ △ **JEFFERSON REGIONAL MEDICAL CENTER (040071)**, 1600 West 40th Avenue, Zip 71603–6301; tel. 870/541–7100 **A**3 7 10 20 **F**3 8 11 13 15 17 18 20 22 28 29 30 31 34 35 40 43 45 46 48 49 50 51 53 54 56 57 59 60 61 64 65 70 72 73 74 75 76 77 78 79 81 85 86 87 89 90 96 97 98 100 101 102 103 107 108 110 111 114 115 116 117 118 119 124 128 130 131 132 135 143 144 145 146 147 148 **P**6 7
Primary Contact: Brian N. Thomas, Interim Chief Executive Officer
COO: Brian N. Thomas, Senior Vice President and Chief Operating Officer
CFO: Bryan G. Jackson, Vice President and Chief Financial Officer
CMO: John Lytle, M.D., Chief of Staff
CIO: Patrick Neece, Chief Information Officer
CHR: M Daryl Scott, Assistant Vice President
CNO: Louise Hickman, R.N., Vice President of Patient Care Services
Web address: www.jrmc.org
Control: Other not–for–profit (including NFP Corporation) **Service:** General Medical and Surgical

Staffed Beds: 333 **Admissions:** 9574 **Census:** 154 **Outpatient Visits:** 202613 **Births:** 668 **Total Expense ($000):** 173049 **Payroll Expense ($000):** 71333 **Personnel:** 1208

POCAHONTAS—Randolph County

FIVE RIVERS MEDICAL CENTER (040047), 2801 Medical Center Drive, Zip 72455–9436; tel. 870/892–6000 **A**10 20 **F**3 11 18 29 40 43 45 50 57 59 62 68 70 79 81 85 93 98 103 107 111 115 119 129 130 133 146
Primary Contact: Luther J. Lewis, FACHE, Chief Executive Officer
CFO: Joey Radcliff, Chief Financial Officer
CHR: Anita Dickson, Director Human Resources
CNO: Paula Lewis, Interim Chief Nursing Officer
Web address: www.fiveriversmc.com
Control: Other not–for–profit (including NFP Corporation) **Service:** General Medical and Surgical

Staffed Beds: 48 **Admissions:** 802 **Census:** 14 **Births:** 0 **Personnel:** 163

Hospital, Medicare Provider Number, Address, Telephone, Approval, Facility, and Physician Codes, Health Care System

★ American Hospital Association (AHA) membership   ○ Healthcare Facilities Accreditation Program   ⇑ Center for Improvement in Healthcare Quality Accreditation
☐ The Joint Commission accreditation   ◇ DNV Healthcare Inc. accreditation   △ Commission on Accreditation of Rehabilitation Facilities (CARF) accreditation

AR

ROGERS—Benton County

✠ **MERCY HOSPITAL ROGERS (040010)**, 2710 Rife Medical Lane,
Zip 72758–1452; tel. 479/338–8000 **A**1 10 **F**3 8 11 12 13 15 17 18 20 22
24 26 28 29 30 34 40 42 43 45 46 49 54 57 59 62 64 68 70 71 72 74 75
76 77 79 81 82 84 85 86 89 93 103 107 108 110 111 115 118 119 129
130 135 146 148 **S** Mercy Health, Chesterfield, MO
Primary Contact: Eric Pianalto, President
COO: Brenda Chase, Chief Operating Officer
CFO: Benny Stover, Vice President Finance
CMO: Chris Johnson, M.D., Chief of Staff
CHR: Rick Barclay, Vice President Support Services
Web address: www.mercyhealthnwa.smhs.com
Control: Church–operated, Nongovernment, not–for profit **Service:** General
Medical and Surgical

> **Staffed Beds:** 189 **Admissions:** 10376 **Census:** 106 **Outpatient Visits:**
> 227801 **Births:** 1603 **Total Expense ($000):** 168246 **Payroll Expense**
> **($000):** 54980 **Personnel:** 1251

RUSSELLVILLE—Pope County

☐ **SAINT MARY'S REGIONAL MEDICAL CENTER (040041)**, 1808 West Main
Street, Zip 72801–2724; tel. 479/968–2841 **A**1 10 19 **F**3 11 13 15 18 20 22
29 34 35 40 43 45 50 51 53 54 56 57 59 64 68 70 74 75 76 78 79 80 81
85 86 87 89 90 93 98 102 107 108 109 110 111 114 115 118 119 120 121
127 129 130 131 132 146 147 148 **S** RCCH HealthCare Partners,
Brentwood, TN
Primary Contact: James Davidson, Chief Executive Officer
CFO: Wendell VanEs, Chief Financial Officer
CHR: Connie Gragg, Director Human Resources
CNO: Carol Gore, MSN, Chief Nursing Officer
Web address: www.saintmarysregional.com
Control: Corporation, Investor–owned, for–profit **Service:** General Medical and
Surgical

> **Staffed Beds:** 141 **Admissions:** 5584 **Census:** 66 **Outpatient Visits:** 83254
> **Births:** 1095 **Total Expense ($000):** 76003 **Payroll Expense ($000):** 24168
> **Personnel:** 489

SALEM—Fulton County

FULTON COUNTY HOSPITAL (041322), 679 North Main Street,
Zip 72576–9451, Mailing Address: P.O. Box 517, Zip 72576–0517;
tel. 870/895–2691 **A**10 18 **F**3 7 11 28 29 30 34 40 43 45 57 59 75 107 114
119 133 146 148
Primary Contact: Charles Willett, Administrator and Chief Executive Officer
Web address: www.fultoncountyhospital.org
Control: County–Government, nonfederal **Service:** General Medical and Surgical

> **Staffed Beds:** 25 **Admissions:** 830 **Census:** 11 **Outpatient Visits:** 9444
> **Births:** 0 **Total Expense ($000):** 10046 **Payroll Expense ($000):** 4252
> **Personnel:** 148

SEARCY—White County

ADVANCED CARE HOSPITAL OF WHITE COUNTY (042011), 1200 South
Main Street, Zip 72143–7321; tel. 501/278–3155 **A**10 **F**1 3 29 68 **P**5
Primary Contact: Terri L. Parsons, Administrator
CMO: Miguel Aguinaga, M.D., Medical Director
CNO: Mistie Vannatter, Chief Nursing Officer
Web address: www.advancedcarehospital.com
Control: Other not–for–profit (including NFP Corporation) **Service:** Long–Term
Acute Care hospital

> **Staffed Beds:** 27 **Admissions:** 188 **Census:** 14 **Outpatient Visits:** 0 **Births:**
> 0 **Total Expense ($000):** 6397 **Payroll Expense ($000):** 2855 **Personnel:**
> 60

★ **UNITY HEALTH WHITE COUNTY MEDICAL CENTER (040014)**, 3214 East
Race Avenue, Zip 72143–4810; tel. 501/268–6121, (Includes UNITY HEALTH
HARRIS MEDICAL CENTER, 1205 McLain Street, Newport, Zip 72112–3533;
tel. 870/523–8911; Darren Caldwell, Vice President and Administrator; UNITY
HEALTH SPECIALTY CARE, 1200 South Main Street, Zip 72143–7397;
tel. 501/278–3100) **A**10 13 20 **F**1 3 11 12 13 17 18 20 22 24 28 29 30 31
34 35 39 40 43 45 50 51 53 59 61 62 64 68 70 74 75 76 77 78 79 81 84
86 87 89 90 93 98 100 102 103 105 107 108 111 115 119 126 129 130
131 132 134 135 144 145 146 147 148 **P**2 6
Primary Contact: Raymond W. Montgomery, II, FACHE, President and Chief
Executive Officer
CFO: Stuart Hill, Vice President and Treasurer
CMO: John Henderson, M.D., Chief Medical Officer
CIO: Phil Miller, Chief Information Officer
CHR: Pamela G. Williams, Director Human Resources
CNO: Peggy Turner, Assistant Vice President and Director of Nursing
Web address: www.unity-health.org
Control: Other not–for–profit (including NFP Corporation) **Service:** General
Medical and Surgical

> **Staffed Beds:** 286 **Admissions:** 12284 **Census:** 159 **Outpatient Visits:**
> 98990 **Births:** 1179 **Total Expense ($000):** 207620 **Payroll Expense**
> **($000):** 96647 **Personnel:** 1811

SHERWOOD—Pulaski County

★ **CHI ST. VINCENT MEDICAL CENTER–NORTH (040137)**, 2215 Wildwood
Avenue, Zip 72120–5089; tel. 501/552–7100 **A**10 **F**3 11 15 18 20 22 26 29
30 35 40 43 44 45 50 64 68 70 74 79 81 85 87 107 110 111 115 118 119
129 130 146 **P**1 5 6 **S** Catholic Health Initiatives, Englewood, CO
Primary Contact: Polly J. Davenport, FACHE, R.N., Senior Vice President, Chief
Operating Officer, President CHI St. Vincent Infirmary Medical Center a
CFO: Tadd M. Richert, Senior Vice President and Chief Financial Officer
CMO: Thomas H. Cummins, M.D., Senior Vice President and Chief Medical Officer
Web address: www.stvincenthealth.com
Control: Church–operated, Nongovernment, not–for profit **Service:** General
Medical and Surgical

> **Staffed Beds:** 69 **Admissions:** 1305 **Census:** 11 **Outpatient Visits:** 34437
> **Births:** 0 **Total Expense ($000):** 23954 **Payroll Expense ($000):** 7703
> **Personnel:** 137

✠ **ST. VINCENT REHABILITATION HOSPITAL (043031)**, 2201 Wildwood Avenue,
Zip 72120–5074; tel. 501/834–1800 **A**1 10 **F**3 29 50 60 87 90 91 96 130
132 143 146 148 **S** HEALTHSOUTH Corporation, Birmingham, AL
Primary Contact: Lisa Watson, Chief Executive Officer
CFO: Stacy Shilling, Controller
CMO: Kevin J. Collins, M.D., Medical Director
CNO: Shannon Moreno–Cook, Chief Nursing Officer
Web address: www.stvincenthealth.com/svrehabhospital/index.html
Control: Corporation, Investor–owned, for–profit **Service:** Rehabilitation

> **Staffed Beds:** 71 **Admissions:** 1620 **Census:** 54 **Outpatient Visits:** 0 **Births:**
> 0 **Total Expense ($000):** 23080 **Payroll Expense ($000):** 11413
> **Personnel:** 207

SILOAM SPRINGS—Benton County

✠ **SILOAM SPRINGS REGIONAL HOSPITAL (040001)**, 603 North Progress
Avenue, Zip 72761–4352; tel. 479/215–3000 **A**1 10 **F**3 11 13 15 28 29 30 34
40 43 45 50 57 59 64 68 70 75 76 77 79 81 85 91 93 107 108 110 111
115 118 119 129 130 144 146 147 **P**6 **S** Community Health Systems, Inc.,
Franklin, TN
Primary Contact: Patrick Kerrwood, Chief Executive Officer
CFO: Todd Williams, Chief Financial Officer
CMO: Ashish Mathur, M.D., Chief of Staff
CHR: Carmen Burasco, Director Human Resources
CNO: Maria Wleklinski, Chief Nursing Officer
Web address: www.ssrh.net
Control: Corporation, Investor–owned, for–profit **Service:** General Medical and
Surgical

> **Staffed Beds:** 44 **Admissions:** 1799 **Census:** 12 **Outpatient Visits:** 39257
> **Births:** 582 **Total Expense ($000):** 28130 **Payroll Expense ($000):** 12085
> **Personnel:** 320

SPRINGDALE—Washington County

✠ **NORTHWEST MEDICAL CENTER – SPRINGDALE (040022)**, 609 West Maple
Avenue, Zip 72764–5394, Mailing Address: P.O. Box 47, Zip 72765–0047;
tel. 479/751–5711, (Includes NORTHWEST MEDICAL CENTER – BENTONVILLE,
3000 Medical Center Parkway, Bentonville, Zip 72712; tel. 479/553–1000;
Jeremy Barclay, Chief Executive Officer; WILLOW CREEK WOMEN'S HOSPITAL,
4301 Greathouse Springs Road, Johnson, Zip 72741–0544, Mailing Address:
P.O. Box 544, Zip 72741–0544; tel. 479/684–3000; Harrison Kiser, Assistant
Chief Executive Officer) **A**1 3 10 **F**3 8 11 12 13 15 17 18 20 22 24 26 28 29
30 37 40 43 45 46 47 48 49 50 51 56 60 61 70 72 74 76 77 79 81 82 85
86 87 90 91 92 93 96 98 102 107 108 110 111 114 115 118 119 124 126
129 130 131 135 146 147 148 **P**5 8 **S** Community Health Systems, Inc.,
Franklin, TN
Primary Contact: Sharif Omar, Chief Executive Officer
COO: Tom Sledge, Chief Operating Officer
CFO: Pamela Modisett, System Chief Financial Officer
CIO: Mark Bokon, Chief Information Officer
CNO: Karen Y. Labonte, Chief Nursing Officer
Web address: www.northwesthealth.com
Control: Corporation, Investor–owned, for–profit **Service:** General Medical and
Surgical

> **Staffed Beds:** 358 **Admissions:** 16341 **Census:** 167 **Outpatient Visits:**
> 163549 **Births:** 3669 **Total Expense ($000):** 211229 **Payroll Expense**
> **($000):** 73129 **Personnel:** 1563

✠ **REGENCY HOSPITAL OF NORTHWEST ARKANSAS – SPRINGDALE
(042009)**, 609 West Maple Avenue, 6th Floor, Zip 72764; tel. 479/757–2600
A1 10 **F**1 3 29 84 130 148 **S** Select Medical Corporation, Mechanicsburg, PA
Primary Contact: Jerry Alexander, Chief Executive Officer
COO: Ruth Jones, Chief Clinical Officer
CMO: Gary Templeton, M.D., Medical Director
CHR: Melissa Ross–Cole, Director Human Resources
Web address: www.regencyhospital.com
Control: Corporation, Investor–owned, for–profit **Service:** Long–Term Acute Care
hospital

> **Staffed Beds:** 25 **Admissions:** 291 **Census:** 20 **Outpatient Visits:** 0 **Births:**
> 0 **Total Expense ($000):** 11225 **Payroll Expense ($000):** 4671 **Personnel:**
> 84

Many Facility Codes have changed. Please refer to the AHA Guide Code Chart. © 2016 AHA Guide

AR

STUTTGART—Arkansas County

★ **BAPTIST HEALTH MEDICAL CENTER–STUTTGART (040072)**, 1703 North Buerkle Road, Zip 72160–1905, Mailing Address: P.O. Box 1905, Zip 72160–1905; tel. 870/673–3511 **A**10 **F**3 11 13 15 18 29 30 34 35 39 40 43 53 57 59 64 68 75 76 78 79 81 85 87 93 97 98 103 107 110 111 114 119 127 129 130 133 135 146 148 **S** Baptist Health, Little Rock, AR
Primary Contact: Kevin L. Storey, Vice President and Administrator
CMO: Seth M. Kleinbeck, M.D., Chief of Staff
CIO: Warren Horton, Information Technologist
CNO: Susan Williams, R.N., Chief Nursing Officer
Web address: www.https://www.baptist–health.com/location/baptist–health–medical–center–stuttgart–stuttgart
Control: Church–operated, Nongovernment, not–for profit **Service:** General Medical and Surgical

Staffed Beds: 49 **Admissions:** 1224 **Census:** 11 **Outpatient Visits:** 24196 **Births:** 228 **Total Expense ($000):** 26159 **Payroll Expense ($000):** 9008 **Personnel:** 207

TEXARKANA—Miller County

☐ **RIVERVIEW BEHAVIORAL HEALTH (044020)**, 701 Arkansas Boulevard, Zip 71854–2105; tel. 870/772–5028, (Nonreporting) **A**1 10 **S** Acadia Healthcare Company, Inc., Franklin, TN
Primary Contact: Michael A. Truman, Chief Executive Officer
CFO: Kimberly Hibschman, Chief Financial Officer
CIO: Jim Cruson, Chief Information Officer
CHR: Roberta Bachman, Director Human Resources
CNO: Carrie Gray, Director of Nursing
Web address: www.riverviewbehavioralhealth.com
Control: Corporation, Investor–owned, for–profit **Service:** Psychiatric

Staffed Beds: 62

VAN BUREN—Crawford County

✠ **SPARKS MEDICAL CENTER – VAN BUREN (040018)**, East Main and South 20th Streets, Zip 72956–5715, Mailing Address: P.O. Box 409, Zip 72957–0409; tel. 479/474–3401, (Nonreporting) **A**1 10 **S** Community Health Systems, Inc., Franklin, TN
Primary Contact: Daniel E. McKay, Chief Executive Officer
CHR: James Ford, Director Human Resources
CNO: Shelly L. Cordum, R.N., System Chief Nursing Officer
Web address: www.sparkshealth.com/locations/sparks–medical–center–van–buren
Control: Corporation, Investor–owned, for–profit **Service:** General Medical and Surgical

Staffed Beds: 103

WALDRON—Scott County

★ **MERCY HOSPITAL WALDRON (041305)**, 1341 West 6th Street, Zip 72958–7642; tel. 479/637–4135 **A**10 18 **F**3 35 40 43 45 57 59 64 65 68 81 85 107 119 127 129 133 148 **P**6 8 **S** Mercy Health, Chesterfield, MO
Primary Contact: Nick Hunt, Interim Director of Nursing
COO: Brent Hubbard, Chief Operating Officer
CFO: Greta Wilcher, Senior Vice President and Chief Financial Officer
CMO: Nathan Bennett, M.D., Chief Medical Officer
CNO: Nick Hunt, Interim Director of Nursing
Web address: www.stedwardmercy.com
Control: Church–operated, Nongovernment, not–for profit **Service:** General Medical and Surgical

Staffed Beds: 24 **Admissions:** 337 **Census:** 4 **Outpatient Visits:** 16387 **Births:** 0 **Total Expense ($000):** 10373 **Payroll Expense ($000):** 3918 **Personnel:** 53

WALNUT RIDGE—Lawrence County

✠ **LAWRENCE MEMORIAL HOSPITAL (041309)**, 1309 West Main, Zip 72476–1430, Mailing Address: P.O. Box 839, Zip 72476–0839; tel. 870/886–1200, (Includes LAWRENCE HALL NURSING HOME), (Total facility includes 179 beds in nursing home–type unit) **A**1 10 18 **F**3 11 15 28 29 32 34 35 40 45 46 47 57 59 84 85 97 107 111 114 119 127 128 129 130 133 135 146
Primary Contact: Gary R. Sparks, Interim President
COO: Junior Briner, Chief Operating Officer
CFO: Vanessa Wagner, Chief Financial Officer
CMO: Samantha L. Hatfield, M.D., Chief Medical Officer
CIO: Josh Wise, Director Information Technology
CHR: Brigett Rhodes, Director Human Resource
CNO: Rosalind C. Casillas, Chief Nursing Officer
Web address: www.lawrencehealth.net
Control: County–Government, nonfederal **Service:** General Medical and Surgical

Staffed Beds: 194 **Admissions:** 1207 **Census:** 158 **Outpatient Visits:** 27316 **Births:** 0 **Total Expense ($000):** 20808 **Payroll Expense ($000):** 10358 **Personnel:** 293

WARREN—Bradley County

★ **BRADLEY COUNTY MEDICAL CENTER (041327)**, 404 South Bradley Street, Zip 71671–3493; tel. 870/226–3731 **A**10 18 **F**3 11 13 15 29 30 34 35 40 43 45 49 50 56 57 59 62 68 76 81 87 89 93 98 103 104 107 108 111 115 118 119 129 130 131 132 133 146 147 **P**6
Primary Contact: Rex Jones, Chief Executive Officer
CFO: Brandon Gorman, Controller
CMO: Joe H. Wharton, M.D., Chief of Staff
CHR: Angela Lochridge, Director Human Resources
CNO: Tiffany Holland, Chief Nursing Officer
Web address: www.bradleycountymedicalcenter.com
Control: Other not–for–profit (including NFP Corporation) **Service:** General Medical and Surgical

Staffed Beds: 33 **Admissions:** 1423 **Census:** 16 **Outpatient Visits:** 63960 **Births:** 172 **Total Expense ($000):** 21084 **Payroll Expense ($000):** 9101 **Personnel:** 253

WYNNE—Cross County

✠ **CROSSRIDGE COMMUNITY HOSPITAL (041307)**, 310 South Falls Boulevard, Zip 72396–3013, Mailing Address: P.O. Box 590, Zip 72396–0590; tel. 870/238–3300 **A**1 10 18 **F**3 11 15 28 34 35 40 43 50 57 59 62 64 68 69 75 77 81 93 107 110 111 114 119 130 133 135 146
Primary Contact: Gary R. Sparks, Administrator
COO: Bryan Mattes, Associate Administrator
CFO: Janice Morris, Accountant
CIO: Gail Copeland, Director Management Information Systems
CHR: Bertha Ragle, Director Personnel
CNO: Amelia Davis, Director of Nursing
Control: Church–operated, Nongovernment, not–for profit **Service:** General Medical and Surgical

Staffed Beds: 15 **Admissions:** 799 **Census:** 10 **Outpatient Visits:** 19896 **Births:** 1 **Total Expense ($000):** 14467 **Payroll Expense ($000):** 6044 **Personnel:** 132

Hospital, Medicare Provider Number, Address, Telephone, Approval, Facility, and Physician Codes, Health Care System

★ American Hospital Association (AHA) membership
☐ The Joint Commission accreditation
○ Healthcare Facilities Accreditation Program
◇ DNV Healthcare Inc. accreditation
⇑ Center for Improvement in Healthcare Quality Accreditation
△ Commission on Accreditation of Rehabilitation Facilities (CARF) accreditation

CALIFORNIA

CA

ALAMEDA—Alameda County

★ **ALAMEDA HOSPITAL (050211)**, 2070 Clinton Avenue, Zip 94501–4397;
tel. 510/522–3700, (Total facility includes 181 beds in nursing home–type unit)
A10 **F**3 11 15 17 18 29 31 34 35 36 39 40 43 46 50 57 58 59 70 77 78 79
81 82 85 93 97 107 108 110 114 118 119 128 130 131 132 146 147 148
S Alameda Health System, San Leandro, CA
Primary Contact: Bonnie Panlasigui, Chief Administrative Officer
CFO: Robert C. Anderson, Interim Chief Financial Officer
CMO: Aika Sharma, M.D., President Medical Staff
CIO: Robert Lundy–Paine, Director Information Systems
CHR: Phyllis Weiss, Director Human Resources
Web address: www.alamedahospital.org
Control: Hospital district or authority, Government, nonfederal **Service:** General
Medical and Surgical

Staffed Beds: 126 **Admissions:** 2648 **Census:** 200 **Outpatient Visits:** 30617
Births: 0 **Total Expense ($000):** 85643 **Payroll Expense ($000):** 41678
Personnel: 492

ALHAMBRA—Los Angeles County

☐ **ALHAMBRA HOSPITAL MEDICAL CENTER (050281)**, 100 South Raymond
Avenue, Zip 91801–3199, Mailing Address: P.O. Box 510, Zip 91802–2510;
tel. 626/570–1606 **A**1 10 **F**29 31 34 40 49 57 59 60 68 70 77 78 79 81 85
87 90 107 108 130 146 **S** AHMC & Healthcare, Inc., Alhambra, CA
Primary Contact: Iris Lai, Chief Executive Officer
CFO: Linda Marsh, Vice President Financial Services and Chief Financial Officer
CMO: Stephen Chen, M.D., Chief Medicare
CIO: Johnson Legaspi, Director Information Systems
CHR: Elizabeth Sabandit, Director Human Resources
CNO: Eleanor Martinez, Chief Nursing Officer
Web address: www.alhambrahospital.com
Control: Partnership, Investor–owned, for–profit **Service:** General Medical and
Surgical

Staffed Beds: 144 **Admissions:** 5334 **Census:** 88 **Outpatient Visits:** 27411
Births: 0 **Total Expense ($000):** 146502 **Payroll Expense ($000):** 28878
Personnel: 576

ALTURAS—Modoc County

MODOC MEDICAL CENTER (051330), 228 West McDowell Avenue,
Zip 96101–3934; tel. 530/233–5131, (Total facility includes 71 beds in nursing
home–type unit) **A**10 18 **F**7 29 34 35 40 57 59 65 81 93 107 114 119 127
128 130 133 146 **P**5
Primary Contact: Kevin Kramer, Chief Executive Officer
CMO: Ed Richert, M.D., Chief of Staff
CHR: Diane Hagelthorn, Human Resources Generalist
Web address: www.modocmedicalcenter.org
Control: Hospital district or authority, Government, nonfederal **Service:** General
Medical and Surgical

Staffed Beds: 87 **Admissions:** 225 **Census:** 44 **Outpatient Visits:** 41224
Births: 1 **Total Expense ($000):** 14820 **Payroll Expense ($000):** 5522
Personnel: 151

ANAHEIM—Orange County

☐ **AHMC ANAHEIM REGIONAL MEDICAL CENTER (050226)**, 1111 West La
Palma Avenue, Zip 92801–2881; tel. 714/774–1450, (Nonreporting) **A**1 10
S AHMC & Healthcare, Inc., Alhambra, CA
Primary Contact: Patrick A. Petre, Chief Executive Officer
COO: Deborah G. Webber, Chief Operating Officer
CFO: Michael Chung, Chief Financial Officer
CMO: Amitabh Prakash, M.D., Chief Medical Officer
CIO: Jeff DesRoches, Manager Information Systems
CHR: Kathy Doi, Executive Director Human Resources
CNO: Phyllis Snyder, Chief Nursing Officer
Web address: www.anaheimregionalmc.com
Control: Other not–for–profit (including NFP Corporation) **Service:** General
Medical and Surgical

Staffed Beds: 223

☐ **ANAHEIM GLOBAL MEDICAL CENTER (050744)**, 1025 South Anaheim
Boulevard, Zip 92805–5806; tel. 714/533–6220, (Nonreporting) **A**1 10 **S** KPC
Healthcare, Inc., Santa Ana, CA
Primary Contact: Brian Cotter, Chief Executive Officer
CFO: John Collins, Chief Financial Officer
CMO: Beena Shah, M.D., Chief of Staff and Chief Medical Officer
CNO: Bonita Wells Veal, Chief Nursing Officer
Web address: www.westernmedanaheim.com
Control: Corporation, Investor–owned, for–profit **Service:** General Medical and
Surgical

Staffed Beds: 181

ANAHEIM MEDICAL CENTER See Kaiser Permanente Orange County Anaheim
Medical Center

✠ **KAISER PERMANENTE ORANGE COUNTY ANAHEIM MEDICAL CENTER
(050609)**, 3440 East La Palma Avenue, Zip 92806–2020; tel. 714/644–2000,
(Includes ORANGE COUNTY IRVINE MEDICAL CENTER, 6640 Alton Parkway, Irvine,
Zip 92618; tel. 949/932–5000; Mark E. Costa, Executive Director) **A**1 3 5 10 **F**3
13 14 15 17 18 19 20 29 30 31 35 37 40 44 45 46 47 48 49 50 59 61 62
63 64 65 68 70 72 74 75 76 78 79 80 81 82 84 85 87 89 92 93 100 107
108 111 114 115 119 130 135 143 146 148 **S** Kaiser Foundation Hospitals,
Oakland, CA
Primary Contact: Mark E. Costa, Executive Director
COO: Margie Harrier, MSN, Medical Center Chief Operations Officer
CFO: Marcus Hoffman, Area Chief Financial Officer
CMO: Nancy Gin, M.D., Area Associate Medical Director
CIO: James Brady, Area Information Officer
CHR: Jocelyn A. Herrera, Director Human Resources
CNO: Martha Dispoto, I, R.N., Chief Nurse Executive, Anaheim Medical Center
Web address: www.kp.org
Control: Other not–for–profit (including NFP Corporation) **Service:** General
Medical and Surgical

Staffed Beds: 436 **Admissions:** 26127 **Census:** 290 **Outpatient Visits:**
414779 **Births:** 6272 **Personnel:** 2511

✠ **WEST ANAHEIM MEDICAL CENTER (050426)**, 3033 West Orange Avenue,
Zip 92804–3183; tel. 714/827–3000 **A**1 10 13 **F**3 11 15 17 18 20 22 24 29
40 45 49 70 79 81 85 98 103 105 107 108 111 114 119 128 130 146
S Prime Healthcare Services, Ontario, CA
Primary Contact: Virgis Narbutas, Chief Executive Officer
CFO: Kora Guoyavatin, Chief Financial Officer
CMO: Hassan Alkhouli, M.D., Chief Medical Officer
CIO: Vic Mahan, Director Information Technology
CHR: Stephanie Sioson, Director Human Resources
CNO: Jason Black, Chie Nursing Officer
Web address: www.westanaheimmedctr.com
Control: Partnership, Investor–owned, for–profit **Service:** General Medical and
Surgical

Staffed Beds: 219 **Admissions:** 6045 **Census:** 105 **Outpatient Visits:** 50216
Births: 0

ANTIOCH—Contra Costa County

✠ **KAISER PERMANENTE ANTIOCH MEDICAL CENTER (050760)**, 4501 Sand
Creek Road, Zip 94531–8687; tel. 925/813–6500, (Nonreporting) **A**1 10
S Kaiser Foundation Hospitals, Oakland, CA
Primary Contact: Colleen McKeown, Senior Vice President and Area Manager
CFO: Kerry Easthope, Area Finance Officer
CMO: Dale Poppert, M.D., Chief of Staff
CIO: Mical Cayton, Area Information Officer
CHR: Davida Lindsay–Bell, Area Human Resources Leader
CNO: Janet Jule, Chief Nurse Executive
Web address: www.https://health.kaiserpermanente.org/wps/portal/facility/
100382
Control: Other not–for–profit (including NFP Corporation) **Service:** General
Medical and Surgical

Staffed Beds: 150

✠ **SUTTER DELTA MEDICAL CENTER (050523)**, 3901 Lone Tree Way,
Zip 94509–6253; tel. 925/779–7200 **A**1 10 **F**3 8 11 13 15 18 20 22 26 29
30 31 34 35 40 41 45 47 49 50 51 60 64 65 66 68 70 72 74 75 76 77 78
79 81 82 83 84 85 86 93 96 107 108 110 111 114 115 119 127 130 132
146 147 148 **P**3 **S** Sutter Health, Sacramento, CA
Primary Contact: Dori Stevens, Chief Executive Officer
CFO: Julie Peterson, Chief Financial Officer
CMO: Anupam Mapara, M.D., Chief of Staff
CIO: Kathy Frederickson, Information Systems Site Lead
CHR: Noemi Whitehead, Administrative Director Human Resources
CNO: James Christopher Reedy, Chief Nursing Officer
Web address: www.sutterdelta.org
Control: Other not–for–profit (including NFP Corporation) **Service:** General
Medical and Surgical

Staffed Beds: 132 **Admissions:** 8050 **Census:** 85 **Outpatient Visits:** 87686
Births: 995 **Total Expense ($000):** 186675 **Payroll Expense ($000):** 62777
Personnel: 991

Many Facility Codes have changed. Please refer to the AHA Guide Code Chart.

CA

APPLE VALLEY—San Bernardino County

✠ **ST. MARY MEDICAL CENTER (050300)**, 18300 Highway 18,
Zip 92307–2206, Mailing Address: P.O. Box 7025, Zip 92307–0725;
tel. 760/242–2311 **A**1 10 **F**8 11 13 15 18 20 22 24 26 28 29 30 34 35 40
45 46 50 57 59 60 64 65 68 70 71 72 75 76 77 78 79 81 82 83 84 85 86
87 89 93 107 108 111 115 119 126 127 130 132 135 143 146 148 **P**3 5
S Providence St. Joseph Health, Renton, WA
Primary Contact: Alan H. Garrett, President and Chief Executive Officer
COO: Kelly Linden, Senior Vice President, Chief Operating Officer
CFO: Tracey Fernandez, Chief Financial Officer
CMO: Dennis Haghighat, M.D., Vice President Medical Affairs
CIO: Doug Kleine, IT Director
CHR: Amanda Lens, Director, Human Resources
CNO: Marilyn Drone, R.N., Vice President, CNO
Web address: www.stmaryapplevalley.com/
Control: Church–operated, Nongovernment, not–for profit **Service:** General
Medical and Surgical

Staffed Beds: 210 **Admissions:** 15242 **Census:** 169 **Outpatient Visits:**
145354 **Births:** 2350 **Total Expense ($000):** 293652 **Payroll Expense
($000):** 94275 **Personnel:** 1432

ARCADIA—Los Angeles County

✠ **METHODIST HOSPITAL OF SOUTHERN CALIFORNIA (050238)**, 300 West
Huntington Drive, Zip 91007–3473, Mailing Address: P.O. Box 60016,
Zip 91066–6016; tel. 626/898–8000 **A**1 2 3 10 **F**3 12 13 14 15 17 18 20 22
24 26 28 29 30 31 34 35 37 38 40 45 46 48 49 50 51 55 56 57 58 59 60
64 65 68 70 72 73 74 75 76 77 78 79 81 82 84 85 86 87 90 92 94 96 107
108 111 114 115 119 130 132 135 146 147 148
Primary Contact: Dan F. Ausman, President and Chief Executive Officer
COO: Steven A. Sisto, Senior Vice President and Chief Operating Officer
CFO: William E. Grigg, Senior Vice President and Chief Financial Officer
CHR: Gwen Chambers, Executive Director Human Resources
CNO: Roberta McCaffrey, Vice President and Chief Nursing Officer
Web address: www.methodisthospital.org
Control: Other not–for–profit (including NFP Corporation) **Service:** General
Medical and Surgical

Staffed Beds: 260 **Admissions:** 16441 **Census:** 205 **Outpatient Visits:**
83274 **Births:** 1745 **Total Expense ($000):** 263250 **Payroll Expense
($000):** 123543 **Personnel:** 1444

ARCATA—Humboldt County

○ **MAD RIVER COMMUNITY HOSPITAL (050028)**, 3800 Janes Road,
Zip 95521–4788, Mailing Address: P.O. Box 1115, Zip 95518–1115;
tel. 707/822–3621, (Nonreporting) **A**10 11
Primary Contact: Douglas A. Shaw, Chief Executive Officer
COO: Steve Engle, Chief Operations Officer
CFO: Michael Young, Chief Financial Officer
CMO: Ronald Berman, M.D., Chief of Staff
CIO: Steve Engle, Chief Operations Officer
CHR: Peggy Shea, Human Resources Lead
CNO: Ken Terpening, Chief Nursing Officer
Web address: www.madriverhospital.com
Control: Corporation, Investor–owned, for–profit **Service:** General Medical and
Surgical

Staffed Beds: 68

ATASCADERO—San Luis Obispo County

□ **ATASCADERO STATE HOSPITAL**, 10333 El Camino Real, Zip 93422–5808,
Mailing Address: P.O. Box 7001, Zip 93423–7001; tel. 805/468–2000 **A**1 **F**3 29
30 31 34 38 39 53 57 59 75 82 86 87 98 102 103 130 132 144 146 **P**6
Primary Contact: Bob Hushing–Kline, Hospital Administrator
COO: David Landrum, Chief Police Services
CFO: Janie Pagnini, Administrator Accounting
CMO: David Fennell, M.D., Acting Medical Director
CIO: James Grover, Manager Data Processing
CHR: Elizabeth Andres, Director Human Resources
CNO: Liz Souza, Coordinator Nursing Services
Web address: www.dmh.ca.gov/statehospitals/atascadero
Control: State–Government, nonfederal **Service:** Psychiatric

Staffed Beds: 1184 **Admissions:** 1107 **Census:** 1174 **Outpatient Visits:** 0
Births: 0 **Total Expense ($000):** 223275 **Payroll Expense ($000):** 140214

AUBURN—Placer County

✠ **SUTTER AUBURN FAITH HOSPITAL (050498)**, 11815 Education Street,
Zip 95602–2410; tel. 530/888–4500 **A**1 2 10 **F**3 5 8 11 12 15 17 18 20 28
29 30 31 34 35 37 39 40 44 45 47 49 50 57 58 59 62 63 64 68 70 74 75
78 79 81 85 86 87 92 93 107 108 110 111 114 119 130 132 135 145 146
147 148 **P**3 **S** Sutter Health, Sacramento, CA
Primary Contact: Mitchell J. Hanna, Chief Executive Officer
CFO: Gary Hubschman, Administrative Director Finance
CMO: John Mesic, M.D., Chief Medical Officer
CIO: Tom Ream, Regional Chief Information Officer
CHR: Yvette Martinez, Director Human Resources
CNO: Gina Temple, Chief Nurse Executive
Web address: www.sutterhealth.org
Control: Other not–for–profit (including NFP Corporation) **Service:** General
Medical and Surgical

Staffed Beds: 72 **Admissions:** 3482 **Census:** 31 **Outpatient Visits:** 59023
Births: 0 **Total Expense ($000):** 127264 **Payroll Expense ($000):** 39382
Personnel: 411

AVALON—Los Angeles County

★ **CATALINA ISLAND MEDICAL CENTER (051307)**, 100 Falls Canyon Road,
Zip 90704, Mailing Address: P.O. Box 1563, Zip 90704–1563;
tel. 310/510–0700 **A**10 18 **F**3 11 28 34 36 40 50 57 64 65 75 93 96 107
113 119 127 128 130 133 146
Primary Contact: Jason Paret, Chief Executive Officer
CFO: John Lovrich, Chief Financial Officer
CMO: Laura Ulibarri, M.D., Chief of Staff
CIO: Jami Fuller, Manager Information Technology
CHR: Krista Steuter, Director Human Resources
CNO: Lorrie Mortensen, Chief Nursing Officer
Web address: www.catalinaislandmedicalcenter.org
Control: Other not–for–profit (including NFP Corporation) **Service:** General
Medical and Surgical

Staffed Beds: 12 **Admissions:** 15 **Census:** 5 **Outpatient Visits:** 6388 **Births:**
0 **Total Expense ($000):** 7891 **Payroll Expense ($000):** 3181 **Personnel:**
78

BAKERSFIELD—Kern County

□ **BAKERSFIELD HEART HOSPITAL (050724)**, 3001 Sillect Avenue,
Zip 93308–6337; tel. 661/316–6000 **A**1 10 **F**3 18 20 22 24 26 28 29 30 31
34 35 40 45 46 47 48 50 57 59 60 68 70 74 77 79 81 85 87 97 111 119
141 147 148
Primary Contact: Michelle Oxford, Chief Operating Officer, Acting Chief Executive
Officer
COO: Michelle Oxford, Chief Operating Officer, Acting Chief Executive Officer
CFO: Vickie Scharr, Chief Financial Officer
CMO: Brijesh Bhambi, M.D., Chief Medical Officer
CIO: Peter Mayer, Director Information Systems
CHR: Linda Hansen, Director Human Resources
Web address: www.bakersfieldhearthospital.com
Control: Partnership, Investor–owned, for–profit **Service:** General Medical and
Surgical

Staffed Beds: 47 **Admissions:** 3273 **Census:** 43 **Outpatient Visits:** 18114
Births: 0

✠ **BAKERSFIELD MEMORIAL HOSPITAL (050036)**, 420 34th Street,
Zip 93301–2237; tel. 661/327–1792 **A**1 3 5 10 13 **F**3 11 13 15 17 18 20 22
24 26 28 29 30 31 37 40 45 50 60 68 70 72 74 75 76 77 78 79 81 84 85
86 88 89 93 107 108 109 111 114 119 120 124 126 130 146 147 148
S Dignity Health, San Francisco, CA
Primary Contact: Jon Van Boening, President and Chief Executive Officer
COO: Bruce Peters, Vice President and Chief Operating Officer
CFO: Jesica Hanson, Vice President and Chief Financial Officer
CMO: Rodney Mark Root, D.O., Vice President Medical Affairs
CHR: Sheri Comaianni, Vice President Human Resources
Web address: www.bakersfieldmemorial.org
Control: Other not–for–profit (including NFP Corporation) **Service:** General
Medical and Surgical

Staffed Beds: 406 **Admissions:** 15210 **Census:** 169 **Outpatient Visits:**
148612 **Births:** 3208 **Total Expense ($000):** 384551 **Payroll Expense
($000):** 134819 **Personnel:** 1410

Hospital, Medicare Provider Number, Address, Telephone, Approval, Facility, and Physician Codes, Health Care System

★ American Hospital Association (AHA) membership ○ Healthcare Facilities Accreditation Program ⇑ Center for Improvement in Healthcare Quality Accreditation
□ The Joint Commission accreditation ◇ DNV Healthcare Inc. accreditation △ Commission on Accreditation of Rehabilitation Facilities (CARF) accreditation

---

CA

☐ **GOOD SAMARITAN HOSPITAL, (050257)**, 901 Olive Drive, Zip 93308–4144,
Mailing Address: P.O. Box 85002, Zip 93380–5002; tel. 661/215–7500,
(Nonreporting) **A**1 10
Primary Contact: Ganesh Acharya, Chief Executive Officer
COO: Anand Manohara, Chief Operating Officer
CFO: Rogelio Monzon, Chief Financial Officer
CMO: Gurmant Singh, Chief Medical Officer
CHR: Anand Manohara, Chief Operating Officer
CNO: Toby Davis, Chief Nursing Officer
Web address: www.goodsamhospital.com
Control: Partnership, Investor–owned, for–profit **Service:** General Medical and
Surgical

Staffed Beds: 120

☒ **HEALTHSOUTH BAKERSFIELD REHABILITATION HOSPITAL (053031)**, 5001
Commerce Drive, Zip 93309–0689; tel. 661/323–5500, (Nonreporting) **A**1 10
S HEALTHSOUTH Corporation, Birmingham, AL
Primary Contact: Martha Samora, R.N., FACHE, Chief Executive Officer
CFO: Robert Mosesian, Controller
CMO: Chris Yoon, M.D., Medical Director
CHR: Lori Brackett, Director Human Resources
CNO: Kathleen Szura, R.N., Chief Nursing Officer
Web address: www.healthsouthbakersfield.com
Control: Corporation, Investor–owned, for–profit **Service:** Rehabilitation

Staffed Beds: 66

☐ **KERN MEDICAL CENTER (050315)**, 1700 Mount Vernon Avenue,
Zip 93306–4018; tel. 661/326–2000, (Nonreporting) **A**1 2 3 5 10
Primary Contact: Russell V. Judd, Chief Executive Officer
COO: Jared Leavitt, Chief Operating Officer
CFO: Andrew Cantu, Chief Financial Officer
CMO: Glenn Goldis, Chief Medical Officer
CHR: Lisa K. Hockersmith, Vice P,resident Human Resources
CNO: Toni Smith, Chief Nursing Officer
Web address: www.kernmedical.com
Control: County–Government, nonfederal **Service:** General Medical and Surgical

Staffed Beds: 188

☒ **MERCY HOSPITALS OF BAKERSFIELD (050295)**, 2215 Truxtun Avenue,
Zip 93301–3698, Mailing Address: P.O. Box 119, Zip 93302–0119;
tel. 661/632–5000, (Includes MERCY SOUTHWEST HOSPITAL, 400 Old River
Road, Zip 93311; tel. 661/663–6000) **A**1 2 3 10 **F**11 12 13 15 29 30 31 32
34 35 37 38 40 44 45 46 47 48 49 50 51 55 59 60 62 64 65 68 70 72 74
75 76 78 79 81 84 85 87 107 108 110 111 119 130 132 146 148 **S** Dignity
Health, San Francisco, CA
Primary Contact: Bruce Peters, Chief Executive Officer
CFO: Rodney Winegarner, Chief Financial Officer
CIO: Jeff Vague, Regional Manager Information Systems
CHR: Jay King, Vice President Human Resources
Web address: www.mercybakersfield.org
Control: Other not–for–profit (including NFP Corporation) **Service:** General
Medical and Surgical

Staffed Beds: 187 **Admissions:** 12176 **Census:** 122 **Outpatient Visits:**
128886 **Births:** 2852 **Total Expense ($000):** 307063 **Payroll Expense**
($000): 119997 **Personnel:** 1267

☒ **SAN JOAQUIN COMMUNITY HOSPITAL (050455)**, 2615 Chester Avenue,
Zip 93301–2014, Mailing Address: P.O. Box 2615, Zip 93303–2615;
tel. 661/395–3000 **A**1 10 **F**3 8 11 12 13 15 16 18 20 22 24 26 28 29 30 31
34 35 36 40 45 46 47 48 49 50 51 54 55 56 57 59 64 65 68 70 71 72 74
75 76 77 78 79 81 82 84 85 86 87 91 107 108 110 111 114 115 116 117
118 119 120 121 123 124 126 130 132 135 146 147 148 **S** Adventist Health,
Roseville, CA
Primary Contact: Sharlet Briggs, Interim Chief Executive Officer
COO: Sharlet Briggs, Chief Operating Officer
CFO: Brent Soper, Chief Financial Officer
CHR: Marlene Kreidler, Executive Director Human Resources
Web address: www.sanjoaquinhospital.org
Control: Church–operated, Nongovernment, not–for profit **Service:** General
Medical and Surgical

Staffed Beds: 254 **Admissions:** 17936 **Census:** 192 **Outpatient Visits:**
182440 **Births:** 3576 **Total Expense ($000):** 354697 **Payroll Expense**
($000): 128968 **Personnel:** 1904

BALDWIN PARK—Los Angeles County

BALDWIN PARK MEDICAL CENTER See Kaiser Permanente Baldwin Park
Medical Center

☒ **KAISER PERMANENTE BALDWIN PARK MEDICAL CENTER (050723)**, 1011
Baldwin Park Boulevard, Zip 91706–5806; tel. 626/851–1011 **A**1 3 10 **F**3 8 13
15 18 29 30 31 34 35 40 41 49 56 57 58 59 60 61 62 63 64 65 68 70 72
74 75 76 77 78 79 81 82 84 85 86 87 93 94 107 111 119 130 146 147 148
S Kaiser Foundation Hospitals, Oakland, CA
Primary Contact: Margaret H. Pierce, Executive Director
COO: Payman Roshan, Chief Operating Officer
CFO: Rebecca Wheeler, Director Finance
CMO: John Bigley, M.D., Medical Director
CIO: Linda C. Salazar, Information Technology Leader
CNO: Michelle Nowicki, R.N., Chief Nurse Executive
Web address: www.kp.org
Control: Other not–for–profit (including NFP Corporation) **Service:** General
Medical and Surgical

Staffed Beds: 257 **Admissions:** 12392 **Census:** 117 **Outpatient Visits:**
359198 **Births:** 2876

☒ **KINDRED HOSPITAL–BALDWIN PARK (052045)**, 14148 Francisquito Avenue,
Zip 91706–6120; tel. 626/388–2700 **A**1 10 **F**1 3 29 45 60 68 77 84 87 97
107 111 119 130 148 **S** Kindred Healthcare, Louisville, KY
Primary Contact: Fiona Basa-Reyes, Chief Executive Officer
COO: Dina Garrow, Chief Nursing Officer and Chief Operating Officer
CFO: Christine Saltonstall, Chief Financial Officer
CMO: Anil Gupta, M.D., Chief of Staff
CHR: Antoinette Bibal, Director Human Resources
CNO: Dina Garrow, Chief Nursing Officer and Chief Operating Officer
Web address: www.khbaldwinpark.com
Control: Corporation, Investor–owned, for–profit **Service:** Long–Term Acute Care
hospital

Staffed Beds: 91 **Admissions:** 968 **Census:** 71 **Outpatient Visits:** 0 **Births:**
0 **Total Expense ($000):** 37258 **Payroll Expense ($000):** 17777
Personnel: 273

VISTA SPECIALTY HOSPITAL OF SAN GABRIEL VALLEY See Kindred
Hospital–Baldwin Park

BANNING—Riverside County

☒ **SAN GORGONIO MEMORIAL HOSPITAL (050054)**, 600 North Highland
Springs Avenue, Zip 92220–3046; tel. 951/845–1121 **A**1 10 22 **F**3 8 11 13 15
18 28 29 30 34 35 40 45 49 50 56 57 68 70 76 79 81 82 85 87 104 107
108 110 115 119 130 146 147 148
Primary Contact: Mark S. Turner, Chief Executive Officer
CFO: David Recupero, Chief Financial Officer
CMO: Richard Sheldon, M.D., Vice President Medical Affairs
CIO: Dan Howard, Director, Information Services
CHR: Annah Karam, Director Human Resources
CNO: Pat Brown, R.N., Chief Nursing Officer
Web address: www.sgmh.org
Control: Hospital district or authority, Government, nonfederal **Service:** General
Medical and Surgical

Staffed Beds: 79 **Admissions:** 3818 **Census:** 43 **Outpatient Visits:** 52719
Births: 493 **Total Expense ($000):** 74770 **Payroll Expense ($000):** 31363
Personnel: 564

BARSTOW—San Bernardino County

☒ **BARSTOW COMMUNITY HOSPITAL (050298)**, 820 East Mountain View Street,
Zip 92311–3004; tel. 760/256–1761, (Nonreporting) **A**1 10 20 **S** Quorum
Health, Brentwood, TN
Primary Contact: Steven Foster, Chief Executive Officer
CFO: Carrie Howell, Chief Financial Officer
CIO: Scott Bullock, Director Information Systems
CNO: Donna M. Smith, Chief Nursing Officer
Web address: www.barstowhospital.com
Control: Corporation, Investor–owned, for–profit **Service:** General Medical and
Surgical

Staffed Beds: 30

BERKELEY—Alameda County

☒ △ **ALTA BATES SUMMIT MEDICAL CENTER (050305)**, 2450 Ashby Avenue,
Zip 94705–2067; tel. 510/204–4444, (Includes ALTA BATES MEDICAL
CENTER–HERRICK CAMPUS, 2001 Dwight Way, Zip 94704; tel. 510/204–4444)
A1 3 5 7 10 **F**3 5 8 11 13 15 17 18 20 22 26 28 29 30 31 34 35 36 37 40
45 46 47 49 51 55 56 57 58 59 60 61 64 68 70 72 74 75 77 78 79 81 82
84 85 87 90 93 98 99 100 103 104 105 107 108 110 111 114 116 117 118
119 120 121 123 124 130 132 135 136 146 147 148 **P**3 **S** Sutter Health,
Sacramento, CA
Primary Contact: Charles Prosper, Chief Executive Officer
CFO: Robert Petrina, Chief Financial Officer
CMO: John Gentile, M.D., Vice President Medical Affairs
Web address: www.altabatessummit.org/
Control: Other not–for–profit (including NFP Corporation) **Service:** General
Medical and Surgical

Staffed Beds: 441 **Admissions:** 17568 **Census:** 230 **Outpatient Visits:**
158691 **Births:** 5361 **Total Expense ($000):** 646243 **Payroll Expense**
($000): 168771 **Personnel:** 1238

Many Facility Codes have changed. Please refer to the AHA Guide Code Chart. © 2016 AHA Guide

BIG BEAR LAKE—San Bernardino County

★ **BEAR VALLEY COMMUNITY HOSPITAL (051335)**, 41870 Garstin Drive, Zip 92315, Mailing Address: P.O. Box 1649, Zip 92315–1649; tel. 909/866–6501, (Total facility includes 21 beds in nursing home–type unit) **A**10 18 **F**3 15 29 34 35 40 50 57 59 81 85 93 97 104 107 110 114 119 127 128 133 146 **S** QHR, Brentwood, TN
Primary Contact: David M. Faulkner, Interim Chief Executive Officer
COO: Wade Sturgeon, Chief Operating Officer and Chief Financial Officer
CFO: Wade Sturgeon, Chief Operating Officer and Chief Financial Officer
CMO: Michael Norman, M.D., Chief Medical Staff
CHR: Kathy Norris, Director Human Resources
CNO: Mary Norman, R.N., Chief Nursing Officer
Web address: www.bvchd.com
Control: Hospital district or authority, Government, nonfederal **Service:** General Medical and Surgical

Staffed Beds: 30 Admissions: 168 Census: 17 Outpatient Visits: 19780 **Births: 0 Total Expense ($000):** 19877 **Payroll Expense ($000):** 8338 **Personnel:** 169

BISHOP—Inyo County

⊞ **NORTHERN INYO HOSPITAL (051324)**, 150 Pioneer Lane, Zip 93514–2599; tel. 760/873–5811, (Nonreporting) **A**1 10 18
Primary Contact: Kevin Flanigan, M.D., Chief Executive Officer
COO: Kelli Huntsinger, Chief Operating Officer
CMO: Thomas Boo, M.D., Chief of Staff
CIO: Adam Taylor, Manager Information Technology
CHR: Georgan L. Stottlemyre, Chief Human Relations Officer
CNO: Kathy Decker, Interim Chief Nursing Officer
Web address: www.nih.org
Control: Hospital district or authority, Government, nonfederal **Service:** General Medical and Surgical

Staffed Beds: 25

BLYTHE—Riverside County

◇ **PALO VERDE HOSPITAL (050423)**, 250 North First Street, Zip 92225–1702; tel. 760/922–4115 **A**10 20 21 **F**29 34 35 40 50 59 76 81 107 111 119 127
Primary Contact: Sandra J. Anaya, R.N., Chief Executive Officer
CFO: Christa Ronde, Assistant Chief Financial Officer
CMO: Hossain Sahlolbei, M.D., Chief of Staff
CIO: Jerome Learson, Manager Information Technology and Chief Security Officer
CHR: Myrna Davis, Manager Human Resources
CNO: Nena Foreman, Chief Nursing Officer
Web address: www.paloverdehospital.org
Control: Hospital district or authority, Government, nonfederal **Service:** General Medical and Surgical

Staffed Beds: 31 Admissions: 943 Census: 9 Outpatient Visits: 20206 **Births: 152 Total Expense ($000):** 22463 **Payroll Expense ($000):** 10593 **Personnel:** 126

BRAWLEY—Imperial County

★ ◇ **PIONEERS MEMORIAL HEALTHCARE DISTRICT (050342)**, 207 West Legion Road, Zip 92227–7780; tel. 760/351–3333 **A**3 10 21 **F**3 11 13 15 18 26 29 30 31 34 35 40 43 45 46 49 51 54 56 57 59 64 65 70 73 74 75 76 78 79 81 82 85 86 89 91 93 97 107 108 110 111 115 119 127 130 144 146 147 148
Primary Contact: Lawrence E. Lewis, Chief Executive Officer
COO: Stephen J. Campbell, Chief Operating Officer
CFO: Roger Armstrong, Interim Chief Financial Officer
CMO: Kestutis V. Kuraitis, M.D., Chief of Staff
CIO: Kathleen S. McKernan, Director Information Systems
CHR: Julie Cunningham, Associate Administrator and Chief Human Resources Officer
CNO: Robyn Atadero, R.N., Chief Nursing Officer
Web address: www.pmhd.org
Control: Hospital district or authority, Government, nonfederal **Service:** General Medical and Surgical

Staffed Beds: 107 Admissions: 5494 Census: 47 Outpatient Visits: 114362 **Births: 1917 Total Expense ($000):** 97437 **Payroll Expense ($000):** 41012 **Personnel:** 662

BREA—Orange County

⊞ **KINDRED HOSPITAL–BREA (052039)**, 875 North Brea Boulevard, Zip 92821–2699; tel. 714/529–6842 **A**1 10 **F**1 18 28 39 45 56 65 70 74 75 84 85 87 106 130 148 **S** Kindred Healthcare, Louisville, KY
Primary Contact: Diane Zeoli, Chief Executive Officer
COO: Denise Jenkins, Chief Clinical Officer
CFO: John Browne, Assistant Administrator Finance
CMO: Jyotika Wali, M.D., Chief of Staff
Web address: www.kindredhospitalbrea.com/
Control: Corporation, Investor–owned, for–profit **Service:** Long–Term Acute Care hospital

Staffed Beds: 48 Admissions: 757 Census: 39 Outpatient Visits: 0 Births: 0 Total Expense ($000): 26229 **Payroll Expense ($000):** 11422 **Personnel:** 214

BURBANK—Los Angeles County

⊞ △ **PROVIDENCE SAINT JOSEPH MEDICAL CENTER (050235)**, 501 South Buena Vista Street, Zip 91505–4866; tel. 818/843–5111 **A**1 2 3 7 10 **F**3 7 11 12 13 15 17 18 20 22 24 26 29 30 31 34 36 39 40 41 45 46 47 48 49 50 51 53 55 56 57 58 59 60 62 64 65 70 72 74 75 76 77 78 79 81 82 83 84 85 86 87 90 92 93 94 97 100 101 107 108 110 111 114 115 116 117 119 120 121 122 123 124 126 130 131 132 145 146 147 148 **P**2 3 5 **S** Providence St. Joseph Health, Renton, WA
Primary Contact: Julie Sprengel, Chief Executive Officer
CFO: Glenn Bales, Chief Financial Officer
CMO: Nick Testa, M.D., Chief Medical Officer
CIO: Anne Marie Brody, Director Information Systems Customer Service
CHR: LaDonna Najieb, Service Area Director Human Resources
CNO: Elizabeth Hart, R.N., Chief Nursing Officer
Web address: www.providence.org
Control: Church–operated, Nongovernment, not–for profit **Service:** General Medical and Surgical

Staffed Beds: 383 Admissions: 17340 Census: 213 Outpatient Visits: 264708 **Births: 2354 Total Expense ($000):** 288744 **Payroll Expense ($000):** 147723 **Personnel:** 1843

BURLINGAME—San Mateo County

⊞ **MILLS–PENINSULA HEALTH SERVICES (050007)**, 1501 Trousdale Drive, Zip 94010–3282; tel. 650/696–5400, (Includes MILLS HEALTH CENTER, 100 South San Mateo Drive, San Mateo, Zip 94401; tel. 650/696–4400; Janet Wagner, R.N., Chief Executive Officer; MILLS–PENINSULA MEDICAL CENTER, 1501 Trousdale Drive, Zip 94010–3205; tel. 650/696–5400; Janet Wagner, R.N., Chief Executive Officer) **A**1 2 10 **F**2 3 4 5 6 8 9 11 12 13 15 17 18 20 22 24 26 28 29 30 31 34 35 36 37 38 40 44 45 46 47 48 49 51 53 54 55 56 57 58 59 60 64 65 66 68 72 74 75 76 77 78 79 81 84 85 86 87 93 94 97 98 99 100 102 103 104 105 107 108 110 111 114 115 116 117 118 119 120 121 123 124 126 130 132 134 135 146 147 148 **P**3 **S** Sutter Health, Sacramento, CA
Primary Contact: Janet Wagner, R.N., Chief Executive Officer
COO: Dolores S. Gomez, R.N., Chief Operating Officer
CFO: Catherine Messman, Chief Financial Officer
CMO: Ranjit Hundal, M.D., Chief Medical Executive
CIO: Michael Reandeau, Chief Information Officer
CHR: Claudia Christensen, Director, Human Resources
CNO: Vicki White, R.N., Chief Nurse Executive
Web address: www.mills–peninsula.org
Control: Other not–for–profit (including NFP Corporation) **Service:** General Medical and Surgical

Staffed Beds: 258 Admissions: 13333 Census: 134 Outpatient Visits: 348841 **Births: 2247 Total Expense ($000):** 531463 **Payroll Expense ($000):** 145370 **Personnel:** 1485

CAMARILLO—Ventura County

★ **ST. JOHN'S PLEASANT VALLEY HOSPITAL (050616)**, 2309 Antonio Avenue, Zip 93010–1414; tel. 805/389–5800, (Nonreporting) **A**10 **S** Dignity Health, San Francisco, CA
Primary Contact: Darren W. Lee, President and Chief Executive Officer
COO: Richard Montmeny, Vice President Professional Services, On–Site Administrator
CFO: Donald P. Bernard, Chief Financial Officer
CMO: Sahin Yanik, M.D., Vice President Medical Associate
CIO: Jeff Perry, Director Information Technology
CHR: Ed Gonzales, Vice President Human Resources
CNO: Dana Littlepage, Interim Chief Nursing Officer
Web address: www.dignityhealth.org/pleasantvalley
Control: Other not–for–profit (including NFP Corporation) **Service:** General Medical and Surgical

Staffed Beds: 127

Hospital, Medicare Provider Number, Address, Telephone, Approval, Facility, and Physician Codes, Health Care System

★ American Hospital Association (AHA) membership   ○ Healthcare Facilities Accreditation Program   ⇑ Center for Improvement in Healthcare Quality Accreditation
□ The Joint Commission accreditation   ◇ DNV Healthcare Inc. accreditation   △ Commission on Accreditation of Rehabilitation Facilities (CARF) accreditation

CA

CAMP PENDLETON—San Diego County

✠ **NAVAL HOSPITAL CAMP PENDLETON**, Santa Margarita Road, Building H100,
Zip 92055–5191, Mailing Address: P.O. Box 555191, Zip 92055–5191;
tel. 760/725–1304, (Nonreporting) **A**1 3 5 **S** Bureau of Medicine and Surgery,
Department of the Navy, Falls Church, VA
Primary Contact: Captain Lisa Mulligan, Commanding Officer
CFO: Commander Gordon Blighton, Director Resource Management
CIO: Gabe Vallido, Chief Information Officer
CHR: Lieutenant Jet Ramos, Head Staff Administration
Web address: www.cpen.med.navy.mil/
Control: Navy, Government, federal **Service:** General Medical and Surgical

Staffed Beds: 72

CANOGA PARK—Los Angeles County, See Los Angeles

CARMICHAEL—Sacramento County

✠ **MERCY SAN JUAN MEDICAL CENTER (050516)**, 6501 Coyle Avenue,
Zip 95608–0306, Mailing Address: P.O. Box 479, Zip 95609–0479;
tel. 916/537–5000 **A**1 2 3 5 10 **F**3 8 11 12 13 15 17 18 20 22 24 26 28 29
30 31 34 35 37 40 43 45 46 47 48 49 50 51 57 58 62 63 64 70 72 74 75
76 77 78 79 81 82 83 84 85 87 89 92 93 100 107 108 111 115 118 119
126 129 130 132 135 146 148 **P**3 **S** Dignity Health, San Francisco, CA
Primary Contact: Brian K. Ivie, President
COO: Paul R. Luehrs, Chief Operating Officer
CFO: Robert Pascuzzi, Chief Financial Officer
CMO: Mark Owens, M.D., Vice President Medical Affairs
CHR: Donna Utley, Vice President Human Resources
Web address: www.mercysanjuan.org
Control: Church–operated, Nongovernment, not–for profit **Service:** General
Medical and Surgical

Staffed Beds: 359 **Admissions:** 23299 **Census:** 295 **Outpatient Visits:**
108247 **Births:** 2082 **Personnel:** 2057

CASTRO VALLEY—Alameda County

✠ **EDEN MEDICAL CENTER (050488)**, 20103 Lake Chabot Road,
Zip 94546–5305; tel. 510/537–1234 **A**1 2 3 10 **F**3 5 11 13 15 18 29 30 31
34 35 38 40 43 46 47 49 50 51 53 54 56 57 58 59 60 65 68 70 74 75 76
77 78 79 81 84 85 87 93 100 101 102 107 108 110 111 115 117 118 119
120 121 123 130 132 135 144 146 147 148 **P**3 **S** Sutter Health,
Sacramento, CA
Primary Contact: Theresa Glubka, R.N., Chief Executive Officer
Web address: www.edenmedcenter.org
Control: Other not–for–profit (including NFP Corporation) **Service:** General
Medical and Surgical

Staffed Beds: 130 **Admissions:** 7941 **Census:** 106 **Outpatient Visits:** 91146
Births: 1145 **Total Expense ($000):** 317914 **Payroll Expense ($000):**
100466 **Personnel:** 1009

CEDARVILLE—Modoc County

SURPRISE VALLEY HEALTH CARE DISTRICT (051308), 741 North Main
Street, Zip 96104, Mailing Address: P.O. Box 246, Zip 96104–0246;
tel. 530/279–6111, (Nonreporting) **A**10 18
Primary Contact: Richard Cornwell, Chief Executive Officer
CFO: Renae Sweet, Chief Financial Officer
CMO: Chuck Colas, M.D., Medical Director
CHR: William Bostic, Administrative Assistant Human Resources
Web address: www.svhospital.org/
Control: Hospital district or authority, Government, nonfederal **Service:** General
Medical and Surgical

Staffed Beds: 4

CERRITOS—Los Angeles County

☐ **COLLEGE HOSPITAL CERRITOS (054055)**, 10802 College Place,
Zip 90703–1579; tel. 562/924–9581, (Nonreporting) **A**1 10 **S** College Health
Enterprises, Santa Fe Springs, CA
Primary Contact: Stephen Witt, President and Chief Executive Officer
CFO: Roderick Bell, Chief Financial Officer
CHR: Holly Risha, Administrative Director Human Resources
Web address: www.collegehospitals.com
Control: Corporation, Investor–owned, for–profit **Service:** Psychiatric

Staffed Beds: 157

CHESTER—Plumas County

SENECA HEALTHCARE DISTRICT (051327), 130 Brentwood Drive,
Zip 96020–0737, Mailing Address: P.O. Box 737, Zip 96020–0737;
tel. 530/258–2151, (Nonreporting) **A**10 18
Primary Contact: Linda S. Wagner, MSN, R.N., FACHE, Chief Executive Officer
CFO: Carlene Slusher, Director Finance
CMO: Dana Ware, M.D., Chief of Staff
CIO: Elizabeth Steffen, Director Information Technology
CHR: Marie Stuersel, Director Human Resources
CNO: Teresa L. Whitfield, MS, Chief Nursing Officer
Web address: www.senecahospital.org
Control: Hospital district or authority, Government, nonfederal **Service:** General
Medical and Surgical

Staffed Beds: 26

CHICO—Butte County

✠ **ENLOE MEDICAL CENTER (050039)**, 1531 Esplanade, Zip 95926–3386;
tel. 530/332–7300, (Includes ENLOE MEDICAL CENTER–COHASSET, 560
Cohasset Road, Zip 95926; tel. 530/332–7300) **A**1 10 **F**3 7 8 11 12 13 17 18
19 20 22 24 26 28 29 30 31 34 35 36 38 39 40 43 44 45 46 49 50 51 54
57 59 61 62 63 64 65 68 69 70 73 74 75 76 77 78 79 81 84 85 87 89 90
91 92 93 94 96 98 99 100 101 102 103 107 108 109 111 114 115 116 117
118 119 120 121 123 124 130 132 143 144 146 147 148
Primary Contact: Michael C. Wiltermood, President and Chief Executive Officer
CMO: Forrest Olson, M.D., Chief Medical Officer
CHR: Carol Linscheid, Vice President Human Resources
Web address: www.enloe.org
Control: Other not–for–profit (including NFP Corporation) **Service:** General
Medical and Surgical

Staffed Beds: 265 **Admissions:** 15605 **Census:** 196 **Outpatient Visits:**
59729 **Births:** 1563 **Total Expense ($000):** 493970 **Payroll Expense
($000):** 165226 **Personnel:** 2273

CHINO—San Bernardino County

☐ **CANYON RIDGE HOSPITAL (054111)**, 5353 G Street, Zip 91710–5250;
tel. 909/590–3700, (Nonreporting) **A**1 3 10 **S** Universal Health Services, Inc.,
King of Prussia, PA
Primary Contact: Burt Harris, Acting Chief Executive Officer
CFO: Burt Harris, Chief Financial Officer
CMO: Mir Ali–Khan, M.D., Medical Director
CIO: Maria Patterson, Manager Health Information Management
CHR: Ericca Lopez, Director Human Resources
Web address: www.canyonridgehospital.com
Control: Corporation, Investor–owned, for–profit **Service:** Psychiatric

Staffed Beds: 106

★ ○ **CHINO VALLEY MEDICAL CENTER (050586)**, 5451 Walnut Avenue,
Zip 91710–2672; tel. 909/464–8600, (Nonreporting) **A**10 11 12 13 **S** Prime
Healthcare Services, Ontario, CA
Primary Contact: James M. Lally, D.O., President and Chief Medical Officer
CFO: Gregory Brentano, Chief Financial Officer
CIO: Vic Mahan, Chief Information Officer
Web address: www.cvmc.com
Control: Corporation, Investor–owned, for–profit **Service:** General Medical and
Surgical

Staffed Beds: 126

CHULA VISTA—San Diego County

SCRIPPS MERCY HOSPITAL CHULA VISTA See Scripps Mercy Hospital, San
Diego

✠ **SHARP CHULA VISTA MEDICAL CENTER (050222)**, 751 Medical Center
Court, Zip 91911–6699, Mailing Address: P.O. Box 1297, Zip 91912–1297;
tel. 619/502–5800, (Total facility includes 100 beds in nursing home–type unit)
A1 2 10 **F**8 11 12 13 15 17 18 20 22 24 26 28 29 30 31 34 35 40 46 47 49
51 53 54 57 59 60 63 64 65 70 72 75 76 77 78 79 81 82 84 85 86 87 93
94 107 114 115 119 120 121 123 124 126 128 130 132 143 146 147 148
P5 **S** Sharp HealthCare, San Diego, CA
Primary Contact: Pablo Velez, Chief Executive Officer
CMO: Lynn Welling, M.D., Chief Medical Officer
CHR: Zoe Gardner, Manager Human Resources
Web address: www.sharp.com
Control: Other not–for–profit (including NFP Corporation) **Service:** General
Medical and Surgical

Staffed Beds: 343 **Admissions:** 15486 **Census:** 270 **Outpatient Visits:**
165042 **Births:** 2866 **Total Expense ($000):** 360151 **Payroll Expense
($000):** 138932 **Personnel:** 1568

Many Facility Codes have changed. Please refer to the AHA Guide Code Chart. © 2016 AHA Guide

CA

CLEARLAKE—Lake County

⌦ **ST. HELENA HOSPITAL CLEAR LAKE (051317)**, 15630 18th Avenue, Zip 95422–9336, Mailing Address: P.O. Box 6710, Zip 95422; tel. 707/994–6486, (Nonreporting) **A**1 10 18 **S** Adventist Health, Roseville, CA
Primary Contact: David Santos, President and Chief Executive Officer
COO: David Santos, President Chief Executive Officer
CFO: Carlton Jacobson, Vice President of Finance
CMO: Marc Shapiro, M.D., Chief Medical Officer
CIO: Cambria Wheeler, Communications and Marketing
CHR: Audrey Barrall, Director Human Resources
CNO: Colleen Assavapisitkul, Chief Nursing Officer
Web address: www.adventisthealth.org
Control: Church–operated, Nongovernment, not–for profit **Service:** General Medical and Surgical

Staffed Beds: 25

CLOVIS—Fresno County

CLOVIS COMMUNITY MEDICAL CENTER (050492), 2755 Herndon Avenue, Zip 93611–6801; tel. 559/324–4000, (Nonreporting) **A**10 **S** Community Medical Centers, Fresno, CA
Primary Contact: Craig Castro, Chief Executive Officer
CFO: Tracy Kiritani, Vice President and Chief Financial Officer
CIO: George Vasquez, Chief Technology Officer
CHR: Ginny Burdick, Senior Vice President and Chief Human Resources Officer
Web address: www.communitymedical.org
Control: Other not–for–profit (including NFP Corporation) **Service:** General Medical and Surgical

Staffed Beds: 109

COALINGA—Fresno County

COALINGA REGIONAL MEDICAL CENTER (050397), 1191 Phelps Avenue, Zip 93210–9636; tel. 559/935–6400, (Total facility includes 99 beds in nursing home–type unit) **A**10 20 **F**15 32 35 40 41 50 57 59 65 66 68 89 93 102 107 110 115 119 127 128 130 143 148
Primary Contact: Sharon A. Spurgeon, Chief Executive Officer
CFO: Sandra Earls, Chief Financial Officer
CMO: Kenneth Smith, M.D., Emergency Medicine Medical Director
CIO: Chris Burrage, Manager Information Technology
CHR: Connie Pierce, Manager Human Resources
CNO: Rita Sypitkowski, Director of Patient Services
Web address: www.coalingamedicalcenter.com
Control: Hospital district or authority, Government, nonfederal **Service:** General Medical and Surgical

Staffed Beds: 123 **Admissions:** 220 **Census:** 80 **Outpatient Visits:** 27571 **Births:** 0 **Total Expense ($000):** 20701 **Payroll Expense ($000):** 9016 **Personnel:** 182

COLTON—San Bernardino County

★ ○ **ARROWHEAD REGIONAL MEDICAL CENTER (050245)**, 400 North Pepper Avenue, Zip 92324–1819; tel. 909/580–1000 **A**2 3 5 10 11 12 13 **F**3 8 13 15 16 18 20 22 28 29 30 31 32 34 35 36 39 40 43 45 47 49 50 51 52 54 55 56 57 60 64 66 68 70 71 72 74 75 76 77 78 79 81 82 84 85 86 87 89 91 92 93 97 98 100 101 102 108 110 111 114 115 116 118 119 120 121 130 132 135 146 147 148 **P**5
Primary Contact: William L. Gilbert, Hospital Director
CFO: Frank Arambula, Chief Financial Officer
CMO: Richard Pitts, D.O., Medical Director
CIO: Felix Ekpo, Manager, Information Systems
CHR: Kevin Saunders, Human Resources Officer III
CNO: Michelle Sayre, R.N., Chief Nursing Officer
Web address: www.arrowheadmedcenter.org
Control: County–Government, nonfederal **Service:** General Medical and Surgical

Staffed Beds: 436 **Admissions:** 21776 **Census:** 295 **Outpatient Visits:** 371270 **Births:** 2892 **Total Expense ($000):** 533878 **Payroll Expense ($000):** 177145 **Personnel:** 2920

CONCORD—Contra Costa County

⌦ **JOHN MUIR BEHAVIORAL HEALTH CENTER (054131)**, 2740 Grant Street, Zip 94520–2265; tel. 925/674–4100 **A**1 10 **F**5 34 50 56 57 59 87 92 98 99 100 101 103 104 105 130 132 134 135 143 **S** John Muir Health, Walnut Creek, CA
Primary Contact: Cindy Bolter, Chief Nursing and Operations Officer
COO: Arman Danielyan, M.D., Chief of Staff
CFO: Christian Pass, Senior Vice President and Chief Financial Officer
CMO: O. B. Towery, M.D., Chief of Staff
CIO: Jim Wesley, Senior Vice President and Chief Information Officer
CHR: Lisa Foust, Senior Vice President Human Resources
CNO: Cindy Bolter, Chief Nursing and Operations Officer
Web address: www.johnmuirhealth.com
Control: Other not–for–profit (including NFP Corporation) **Service:** Psychiatric

Staffed Beds: 73 **Admissions:** 3191 **Census:** 52 **Outpatient Visits:** 18965 **Births:** 0

⌦ **JOHN MUIR MEDICAL CENTER, CONCORD (050496)**, 2540 East Street, Zip 94520–1906; tel. 925/682–8200 **A**1 2 10 **F**3 12 15 17 18 20 22 24 26 28 29 30 31 34 37 39 40 44 45 47 48 49 50 55 56 57 58 59 61 64 68 70 74 75 77 78 79 80 81 82 83 84 85 86 87 93 100 102 107 108 110 115 118 119 120 121 123 126 130 132 141 145 146 148 **P**3 5 **S** John Muir Health, Walnut Creek, CA
Primary Contact: Michael S. Thomas, President and Chief Administrative Officer
COO: Michael S. Thomas, President and Chief Administrative Officer
CFO: Christian Pass, Interim Chief Financial Officer
CMO: John Merson, M.D., Chief of Staff
CIO: Jon Russell, Senior Vice President and Chief Information Officer
CHR: Lisa Foust, Senior Vice President Human Resources
CNO: Donna Brackley, R.N., Senior Vice President Patient Care Services
Web address: www.johnmuirhealth.com
Control: Other not–for–profit (including NFP Corporation) **Service:** General Medical and Surgical

Staffed Beds: 195 **Admissions:** 10546 **Census:** 132 **Outpatient Visits:** 175199 **Births:** 0 **Total Expense ($000):** 404152 **Payroll Expense ($000):** 154460 **Personnel:** 1120

CORONA—Riverside County

☐ **CORONA REGIONAL MEDICAL CENTER (050329)**, 800 South Main Street, Zip 92882–3400; tel. 951/737–4343, (Includes CORONA REGIONAL MEDICAL CENTER–REHABILITATION, 730 Magnolia Avenue, Zip 92879; tel. 951/736–7200) **A**1 10 **F**3 13 15 16 17 18 20 22 26 29 30 34 35 38 40 41 42 45 46 49 50 51 57 62 63 70 72 73 74 75 76 79 80 81 84 85 87 88 89 97 98 101 102 104 105 107 110 111 119 128 130 135 146 148 **S** Universal Health Services, Inc., King of Prussia, PA
Primary Contact: Mark H. Uffer, Chief Executive Officer
COO: Parrish Scarboro, Chief Operating Officer
CFO: Frederick J. Drewette, Chief Financial Officer
CMO: Nalin Nanayakkara, M.D., Chief of Staff
CIO: Irv Hoff, Director Information Systems
CHR: Berninia Bradley, Director, Human Resources
Web address: www.coronaregional.com
Control: Corporation, Investor–owned, for–profit **Service:** General Medical and Surgical

Staffed Beds: 238 **Admissions:** 8961 **Census:** 143 **Outpatient Visits:** 69308 **Births:** 930 **Total Expense ($000):** 151604 **Payroll Expense ($000):** 66073 **Personnel:** 780

CORONADO—San Diego County

⌦ **SHARP CORONADO HOSPITAL AND HEALTHCARE CENTER (050234)**, 250 Prospect Place, Zip 92118–1999; tel. 619/522–3600, (Total facility includes 122 beds in nursing home–type unit) **A**1 10 **F**3 11 15 29 30 34 35 36 37 40 45 46 49 53 57 59 64 65 68 70 74 75 77 79 81 82 85 86 87 93 107 111 114 119 126 128 130 135 146 148 **S** Sharp HealthCare, San Diego, CA
Primary Contact: Susan Stone, R.N., Ph.D., Senior Vice President and Chief Executive Officer
CFO: Victoria Day, Chief Financial Officer and Vice President of Ancillary Services
CHR: Rachel Davis, Director
CNO: Christopher Walker, Chief Nursing Officer
Web address: www.sharp.com
Control: Other not–for–profit (including NFP Corporation) **Service:** General Medical and Surgical

Staffed Beds: 181 **Admissions:** 2083 **Census:** 119 **Outpatient Visits:** 88663 **Births:** 0 **Total Expense ($000):** 86035 **Payroll Expense ($000):** 35094 **Personnel:** 401

Hospital, Medicare Provider Number, Address, Telephone, Approval, Facility, and Physician Codes, Health Care System

★ American Hospital Association (AHA) membership   ○ Healthcare Facilities Accreditation Program   ⇑ Center for Improvement in Healthcare Quality Accreditation
☐ The Joint Commission accreditation   ◇ DNV Healthcare Inc. accreditation   △ Commission on Accreditation of Rehabilitation Facilities (CARF) accreditation

CA

COSTA MESA—Orange County

☐ **COLLEGE HOSPITAL COSTA MESA (050543)**, 301 Victoria Street, Zip 92627–7131; tel. 949/642–2734, (Nonreporting) **A**1 10 **S** College Health Enterprises, Santa Fe Springs, CA
Primary Contact: Susan L. Taylor, JD, Chief Executive Officer
CFO: Dale Bracy, Chief Financial Officer
CMO: Michael Schwartz, M.D., Chief of Staff
CIO: Eladio Aldana, Manager Information Systems
CHR: Sharon DuBruyne, Director Human Resources
Web address: www.collegehospitals.com/cosHome
Control: Corporation, Investor–owned, for–profit **Service:** Psychiatric

Staffed Beds: 122

FAIRVIEW DEVELOPMENTAL CENTER (050548), 2501 Harbor Boulevard, Zip 92626; tel. 714/957–5000, (Nonreporting) **A**10
Primary Contact: Karen Larson, Chief Executive Officer
Web address: www.dds.ca.gov/fairview/index.cfm
Control: State–Government, nonfederal **Service:** Intellectual disabilities

Staffed Beds: 237

COVINA—Los Angeles County

☐ **AURORA CHARTER OAK HOSPITAL (054069)**, 1161 East Covina Boulevard, Zip 91724–1599; tel. 626/966–1632 **A**1 10 **F**4 5 29 35 87 98 101 102 104 105 130 135 **S** Signature Healthcare Services, Corona, CA
Primary Contact: Todd A. Smith, Chief Executive Officer
COO: Sheila Cordova, Director Clinical Services and Chief Operating Officer
CMO: Adib Bitar, M.D., Medical Director
CHR: Christine de la Paz, Director Human Resources
CNO: Sheila Cordova, Chief Operating Officer and Chief Nursing Officer
Web address: www.charteroakhospital.com
Control: Corporation, Investor–owned, for–profit **Service:** Psychiatric

Staffed Beds: 146 **Admissions:** 6358 **Census:** 127 **Outpatient Visits:** 16070 **Births:** 0

★ △ **CITRUS VALLEY MEDICAL CENTER–INTER COMMUNITY CAMPUS (050382)**, 210 West San Bernadino Road, Zip 91723–1515, Mailing Address: P.O. Box 6108, Zip 91722–5108; tel. 626/331–7331, (Includes CITRUS VALLEY MEDICAL CENTER–INTER–COMMUNITY CAMPUS, 210 West San Bernardino Road, Mailing Address: P.O. Box 6108, Zip 91722–5108; tel. 626/331–7331; CITRUS VALLEY MEDICAL CENTER–QUEEN OF THE VALLEY CAMPUS, 1115 South Sunset Avenue, West Covina, Zip 91790–3940, Mailing Address: P.O. Box 1980, Zip 91793–1980; tel. 626/962–4011) **A**7 10 **F**3 7 8 11 13 15 17 18 20 22 24 25 26 27 28 29 30 31 32 34 35 40 41 44 45 46 47 49 50 51 55 56 57 59 64 65 68 69 70 71 72 74 75 76 77 78 79 80 81 82 83 84 85 86 87 89 90 92 93 96 98 102 103 105 107 108 110 114 115 118 119 120 121 124 126 128 129 130 131 132 135 143 146 147 148 **P**5 **S** Citrus Valley Health Partners, Covina, CA
Primary Contact: Robert H. Curry, President and Chief Executive Officer
CFO: Roger Sharma, Chief Financial Officer
CIO: Pavel Bindra, M.D., Chief Medical Officer and Chief Information Officer
CHR: Paul Heredia, Chief Human Resources Officer
CNO: Diana Lugo–Zenner, R.N., Chief Nursing Officer
Web address: www.cvhp.org
Control: Other not–for–profit (including NFP Corporation) **Service:** General Medical and Surgical

Staffed Beds: 323 **Admissions:** 24506 **Census:** 284 **Outpatient Visits:** 168013 **Births:** 4172 **Total Expense ($000):** 381212 **Payroll Expense ($000):** 130541 **Personnel:** 1716

CRESCENT CITY—Del Norte County

☒ **SUTTER COAST HOSPITAL (050417)**, 800 East Washington Boulevard, Zip 95531–8359; tel. 707/464–8511 **A**1 10 20 **F**3 8 11 13 15 29 30 34 35 40 43 45 46 47 48 50 51 54 57 59 62 68 70 75 76 77 79 81 82 84 85 87 93 97 107 108 110 111 114 118 119 127 130 132 144 146 148 **P**3 **S** Sutter Health, Sacramento, CA
Primary Contact: Mitchell J. Hanna, Chief Executive Officer
CNO: Rose Corcoran, R.N., Chief Nursing Executive
Web address: www.sutterhealth.org
Control: Other not–for–profit (including NFP Corporation) **Service:** General Medical and Surgical

Staffed Beds: 49 **Admissions:** 1877 **Census:** 17 **Outpatient Visits:** 52321 **Births:** 288 **Total Expense ($000):** 65371 **Payroll Expense ($000):** 19848 **Personnel:** 320

CULVER CITY—Los Angeles County

☒ **SOUTHERN CALIFORNIA HOSPITAL AT CULVER CITY (050752)**, 3828 Delmas Terrace, Zip 90232–6806; tel. 310/836–7000, (Nonreporting) **S** Alta Healthcare System, Los Angeles, CA
Primary Contact: Gerald B. Clute, Chief Executive Officer
CFO: Vincent Rubin, Chief Financial Officer
CMO: Martha Sonnenberg, M.D., Chief of Staff
CIO: Carrie Bonar, Chief Information Officer
CHR: Betty J. Harris, Director Human Resources
Web address: www.sch–culvercity.com
Control: Corporation, Investor–owned, for–profit **Service:** General Medical and Surgical

Staffed Beds: 232

DALY CITY—San Mateo County

☒ **SETON MEDICAL CENTER (050289)**, 1900 Sullivan Avenue, Zip 94015–2229; tel. 650/992–4000, (Total facility includes 116 beds in nursing home–type unit) **A**1 2 3 10 **F**3 8 11 15 17 18 20 22 24 26 29 30 31 34 35 40 41 42 45 49 51 54 55 56 57 59 60 64 68 70 74 75 77 78 79 81 85 87 93 107 108 110 111 114 116 117 118 119 120 121 123 124 128 130 132 135 145 146 147 148 **S** Verity Health System, Los Angeles, CA
Primary Contact: John Ferrelli, Chief Executive Officer
COO: Stephanie Mearns, Vice President Patient Care Services and Chief Nurse Executive
CFO: Richard Wood, Chief Financial Officer
CMO: Timothy Ranney, M.D., Chief Medical Officer
CHR: Patricia White, Vice President Human Resources
Web address: www.setonmedicalcenter.org
Control: Other not–for–profit (including NFP Corporation) **Service:** General Medical and Surgical

Staffed Beds: 410 **Admissions:** 5472 **Census:** 228 **Outpatient Visits:** 131777 **Births:** 0 **Total Expense ($000):** 227656 **Payroll Expense ($000):** 112196 **Personnel:** 1148

DAVIS—Yolo County

☒ **SUTTER DAVIS HOSPITAL (050537)**, 2000 Sutter Place, Zip 95616–6201, Mailing Address: P.O. Box 1617, Zip 95617–1617; tel. 530/756–6440 **A**1 3 5 10 **F**3 5 8 11 13 15 18 28 29 30 31 40 45 57 65 70 75 76 78 79 81 83 85 86 87 92 107 108 111 119 124 130 131 141 142 146 147 **P**3 **S** Sutter Health, Sacramento, CA
Primary Contact: Jennifer Maher, Chief Executive Officer
CFO: Patti Pilgrim, Chief Financial Officer
CMO: Deven Merchant, M.D., Chief Medical Executive
CHR: Don Hartman, Director Human Resources
CNO: Myrna Chang, Chief Nursing Executive
Web address: www.sutterhealth.org
Control: Other not–for–profit (including NFP Corporation) **Service:** General Medical and Surgical

Staffed Beds: 48 **Admissions:** 3576 **Census:** 25 **Outpatient Visits:** 44347 **Births:** 1368 **Total Expense ($000):** 98770 **Payroll Expense ($000):** 30802 **Personnel:** 362

DELANO—Kern County

○ **DELANO REGIONAL MEDICAL CENTER (050608)**, 1401 Garces Highway, Zip 93215–3690, Mailing Address: P.O. Box 460, Zip 93216–0460; tel. 661/725–4800, (Nonreporting) **A**10 11
Primary Contact: Bahram Ghaffari, President
CFO: Bahram Ghaffari, President
CIO: Sandy Bakich, Director Information Management
CHR: Del Garbanzos, Director Human Resources
CNO: Amy Scroggs, Chief Nursing Officer
Web address: www.drmc.com
Control: Other not–for–profit (including NFP Corporation) **Service:** General Medical and Surgical

Staffed Beds: 100

DOWNEY—Los Angeles County

☒ **KAISER PERMANENTE DOWNEY MEDICAL CENTER (050139)**, 9333 Imperial Highway, Zip 90242–2812; tel. 562/657–9000 **A**1 3 10 **F**3 8 13 15 18 19 29 30 31 35 38 40 45 46 49 50 58 60 64 65 68 70 72 74 75 76 78 79 81 82 83 84 85 87 88 89 92 100 107 110 111 114 115 119 126 130 132 146 148 **S** Kaiser Foundation Hospitals, Oakland, CA
Primary Contact: James Branchick, R.N., MS, Executive Director
CNO: Patricia J. Clausen, R.N., Chief Nurse Executive
Web address: www.kaiserpermanente.org
Control: Other not–for–profit (including NFP Corporation) **Service:** General Medical and Surgical

Staffed Beds: 342 **Admissions:** 24534 **Census:** 274 **Outpatient Visits:** 199568 **Births:** 3907 **Personnel:** 3455

Many Facility Codes have changed. Please refer to the AHA Guide Code Chart. © 2016 AHA Guide

CA

★ ◇ **PIH HEALTH HOSPITAL – DOWNEY (050393)**, 11500 Brookshire Avenue, Zip 90241–4917; tel. 562/904–5000 **A**10 12 13 21 **F**3 8 11 13 15 17 18 20 22 24 29 30 40 41 42 45 49 50 56 60 69 70 72 74 75 76 77 79 81 85 91 93 107 108 110 111 115 118 119 130 146 148 **P**3 5 **S** PIH Health, Whittier, CA
Primary Contact: James R. West, President and Chief Executive Officer
COO: Ramona Pratt, Chief Operating Officer
CFO: Greg Williams, Chief Financial Officer
CIO: Jason Fischer, Chief Information Officer
CHR: Sherri Hollingsworth, Chief Human Resources Officer
CNO: Judy Pugach, Chief Nursing Officer
Web address: www.PIHHealth.org
Control: Other not–for–profit (including NFP Corporation) **Service:** General Medical and Surgical

Staffed Beds: 192 **Admissions:** 8290 **Census:** 82 **Outpatient Visits:** 93378 **Births:** 1088 **Total Expense ($000):** 163296 **Payroll Expense ($000):** 64960 **Personnel:** 950

□ △ **RANCHO LOS AMIGOS NATIONAL REHABILITATION CENTER (050717)**, 7601 East Imperial Highway, Zip 90242–3496; tel. 562/401–7111, (Nonreporting) **A**1 3 5 7 10 **S** Los Angeles County–Department of Health Services, Los Angeles, CA
Primary Contact: Jorge Orozco, Chief Executive Officer
COO: Benjamin Ovando, Chief Operations Officer
CFO: Robin Bayus, Chief Financial Officer
CMO: Mindy Aisen, M.D., Chief Medical Officer
CIO: Francis Tang, Chief Information Officer
CHR: Elizabeth Jacobi, Associate Director Human Resources
CNO: Aries Limbaga, R.N., Chief Nursing Officer
Web address: www.rancho.org
Control: County–Government, nonfederal **Service:** Rehabilitation

Staffed Beds: 207

DUARTE—Los Angeles County

✠ **CITY OF HOPE'S HELFORD CLINICAL RESEARCH HOSPITAL (050146)**, 1500 East Duarte Road, Zip 91010–3012; tel. 626/256–4673 **A**1 2 3 5 8 10 **F**3 8 11 14 15 18 26 29 30 31 34 35 36 38 44 45 46 47 49 50 55 56 57 58 59 61 63 64 68 70 74 75 77 78 79 80 81 82 84 85 86 87 88 89 92 93 96 99 100 101 102 103 104 107 108 110 111 115 117 118 119 120 121 123 124 126 130 132 134 135 136 141 142 144 145 146 147 148 **P**3
Primary Contact: Robert Stone, President and Chief Executive Officer
COO: Marty Sargeant, Chief Operating Officer
CFO: Gary F. Conner, Chief Financial Officer
CMO: Alexandra Levine, M.D., Chief Medical Officer
CIO: Paul Conocenti, Chief Information Officer
CHR: Stephanie Neuvirth, Chief Human Resource and Diversity Officer
Web address: www.cityofhope.org
Control: Other not–for–profit (including NFP Corporation) **Service:** Cancer

Staffed Beds: 215 **Admissions:** 6048 **Census:** 168 **Outpatient Visits:** 211275 **Births:** 0 **Total Expense ($000):** 806929 **Payroll Expense ($000):** 255690 **Personnel:** 3023

EL CENTRO—Imperial County

✠ **EL CENTRO REGIONAL MEDICAL CENTER (050045)**, 1415 Ross Avenue, Zip 92243–4398; tel. 760/339–7100, (Nonreporting) **A**1 10
Primary Contact: Adolphe Edward, Chief Executive Officer
COO: Tomas Virgen, R.N., Chief Operating Officer
CFO: Kathleen Farmer, Assistant Administrator Finance and Chief Financial Officer
CIO: John Gaede, Director Information Systems
CHR: Bill Moore, Chief Human Resources
Web address: www.ecrmc.org
Control: City–Government, nonfederal **Service:** General Medical and Surgical

Staffed Beds: 161

ELDRIDGE—Sonoma County

SONOMA DEVELOPMENTAL CENTER (050547), 15000 Arnold Drive, Zip 95431–8900, Mailing Address: P.O. Box 1493, Zip 95431–1493; tel. 707/938–6000, (Nonreporting) **A**10
Primary Contact: Aleana Carreon, Executive Director
COO: Karen Clark, Director Administrative Services
CMO: Carol Castillo, Medical Director
CHR: Brenda Dukes, Director Human Resources
Web address: www.dds.ca.gov/sonoma
Control: State–Government, nonfederal **Service:** Intellectual disabilities

Staffed Beds: 546

ENCINITAS—San Diego County

✠ △ **SCRIPPS MEMORIAL HOSPITAL–ENCINITAS (050503)**, 354 Santa Fe Drive, Zip 92024–5182, Mailing Address: P.O. Box 230817, Zip 92023–0817; tel. 760/633–6501 **A**1 2 7 10 **F**3 8 11 13 14 15 18 20 22 26 29 30 31 34 35 40 44 49 54 57 58 59 64 65 68 70 74 75 76 77 78 79 81 82 84 85 86 87 90 91 92 93 94 95 96 107 108 111 114 115 118 119 130 132 141 146 148 **P**3 5 **S** Scripps Health, San Diego, CA
Primary Contact: Carl J. Etter, Chief Executive and Senior Vice President
COO: Rebecca Cofinas, Vice President and Chief Operating Executive Operations
CFO: Sharon Creal, Vice President Financial Operations
CHR: Cara Williams, Director Human Resources
Web address: www.scripps.org
Control: Other not–for–profit (including NFP Corporation) **Service:** General Medical and Surgical

Staffed Beds: 194 **Admissions:** 10951 **Census:** 123 **Outpatient Visits:** 76445 **Births:** 2142 **Total Expense ($000):** 251382 **Payroll Expense ($000):** 91469 **Personnel:** 1230

ENCINO—Los Angeles County, See Los Angeles

ESCONDIDO—San Diego County

✠ △ **PALOMAR MEDICAL CENTER (050115)**, 2185 West Citracado Parkway, Zip 92029–4159; tel. 760/739–3000 **A**1 3 5 7 10 **F**3 11 12 13 15 17 18 20 22 24 26 28 29 30 31 40 42 43 45 46 47 50 51 62 64 68 70 74 75 76 77 78 79 81 82 84 85 87 90 93 96 98 100 102 103 104 105 107 108 111 112 114 115 119 120 121 123 124 126 129 130 131 146 147 148 **P**3 **S** Palomar Health, Escondido, CA
Primary Contact: Mariellena Sudak, R.N., MSN, Interim Vice President and Chief Nursing Officer
CMO: Duane Buringrud, M.D., Chief Medical and Quality Officer
CIO: Prudence August, Chief Information Officer
CHR: Brenda C. Turner, Chief Human Resources Officer
CNO: Mariellena Sudak, R.N., Chief Nursing Officer
Web address: www.palomarhealth.org
Control: Hospital district or authority, Government, nonfederal **Service:** General Medical and Surgical

Staffed Beds: 322 **Admissions:** 24531 **Census:** 273 **Outpatient Visits:** 206489 **Births:** 3262 **Total Expense ($000):** 497828 **Payroll Expense ($000):** 191934 **Personnel:** 1404

EUREKA—Humboldt County

HUMBOLDT COUNTY MENTAL HEALTH (054124), 720 Wood Street, Zip 95501–4413; tel. 707/268–2900 **A**10 **F**5 7 29 38 98 99 100 101 102 103 104 105 **P**4
Primary Contact: Jet L. DeKruse, Administrator
CMO: Harpreet Duggal, M.D., Medical Director, Department of Health and Human Services
CNO: Sherry Gallagher, Director Nursing, Department of Health and Human Services
Web address: www.https://co.humboldt.ca.us/hhs/mhb/
Control: County–Government, nonfederal **Service:** Psychiatric

Staffed Beds: 16 **Admissions:** 614 **Census:** 12 **Outpatient Visits:** 0 **Births:** 0 **Total Expense ($000):** 5768 **Personnel:** 45

★ ○ **ST. JOSEPH HOSPITAL (050006)**, 2700 Dolbeer Street, Zip 95501–4799; tel. 707/445–8121, (Includes GENERAL HOSPITAL, 2200 Harrison Avenue, Zip 95501–3299; tel. 707/445–5111) **A**2 10 11 19 **F**3 11 12 13 15 17 18 20 22 24 26 28 29 30 31 35 39 40 45 46 47 48 49 53 54 62 63 64 68 70 72 74 75 76 78 79 81 82 84 85 86 87 90 93 96 107 108 110 111 114 115 118 119 120 121 123 124 129 130 131 146 148 **P**5 **S** Providence St. Joseph Health, Renton, WA
Primary Contact: David O'Brien, M.D., President
CFO: Mich Riccioni, Chief Financial Officer
CMO: Mathew Miller, M.D., Vice President and Chief Medical Officer
CIO: Wendy Thorpe, Area Director Information Systems
CHR: Linda Cook, Vice President Human Resources
CNO: Carol Reeder, R.N., Chief Nursing Officer
Web address: www.stjosepheureka.org
Control: Church–operated, Nongovernment, not–for profit **Service:** General Medical and Surgical

Staffed Beds: 153 **Admissions:** 6196 **Census:** 87 **Outpatient Visits:** 177341 **Births:** 461 **Total Expense ($000):** 216918 **Payroll Expense ($000):** 57196 **Personnel:** 1054

Hospital, Medicare Provider Number, Address, Telephone, Approval, Facility, and Physician Codes, Health Care System

★ American Hospital Association (AHA) membership   ○ Healthcare Facilities Accreditation Program   ⇑ Center for Improvement in Healthcare Quality Accreditation
□ The Joint Commission accreditation   ◇ DNV Healthcare Inc. accreditation   △ Commission on Accreditation of Rehabilitation Facilities (CARF) accreditation

CA

FAIRFIELD—Solano County

⊞ **NORTHBAY MEDICAL CENTER (050367)**, 1200 B. Gale Wilson Boulevard, Zip 94533–3587; tel. 707/646–5000, (Includes NORTHBAY VACAVALLEY HOSPITAL, 1000 Nut Tree Road, Vacaville, Zip 95687–4100; tel. 707/624–7000; B. Konard Jones, President, Hospital Division) **A**1 2 5 10 **F**2 3 6 8 11 13 17 18 19 20 22 24 26 28 29 30 31 32 35 36 40 41 43 44 46 49 50 51 54 56 59 62 63 64 65 70 72 73 74 75 76 77 78 79 80 81 82 84 85 87 89 92 93 94 96 97 100 104 107 114 115 118 119 121 130 131 132 146 147 148 **P**3
Primary Contact: B. Konard Jones, President, Hospital Division
CFO: Arthur E. DeNio, Vice President and Chief Financial Officer
CIO: Christopher Timbers, Vice President and Chief Information Officer
CHR: Ken McCollum, Vice President, Human Resources
CNO: Traci A. Duncan, Vice President, Chief Nursing Officer
Web address: www.northbay.org
Control: Other not–for–profit (including NFP Corporation) **Service:** General Medical and Surgical

> **Staffed Beds:** 170 **Admissions:** 8090 **Census:** 100 **Outpatient Visits:** 315767 **Births:** 1347 **Total Expense ($000):** 461555 **Payroll Expense ($000):** 208387 **Personnel:** 1495

FALL RIVER MILLS—Shasta County

★ **MAYERS MEMORIAL HOSPITAL DISTRICT (051305)**, 43563 Highway 299 East, Zip 96028–0459, Mailing Address: P.O. Box 459, Zip 96028–0459; tel. 530/336–5511, (Total facility includes 87 beds in nursing home–type unit) **A**10 18 **F**3 6 7 11 13 18 28 34 40 41 45 50 53 56 57 59 63 64 65 75 76 79 81 85 86 89 93 107 114 119 128 130 132 133 135 146 148
Primary Contact: Louis James Ward, Interim Chief Executive Officer
COO: Louis James Ward, Chief Operating Officer
CFO: Travis Lakey, Chief Financial Officer
CMO: Thomas Watson, M.D., Chief of Staff
CIO: Chris Broadway, Manager Information Technology
CHR: Julie Thompson, Manager Personnel and Payroll
CNO: Sherry Wilson, R.N., Chief Nursing Officer
Web address: www.mayersmemorial.com
Control: Hospital district or authority, Government, nonfederal **Service:** General Medical and Surgical

> **Staffed Beds:** 97 **Admissions:** 505 **Census:** 79 **Outpatient Visits:** 21715 **Births:** 54 **Total Expense ($000):** 22673 **Payroll Expense ($000):** 10157

FOLSOM—Sacramento County

⊞ **MERCY HOSPITAL OF FOLSOM (050414)**, 1650 Creekside Drive, Zip 95630–3400; tel. 916/983–7400, (Nonreporting) **A**1 5 10 **S** Dignity Health, San Francisco, CA
Primary Contact: Edmundo Castaneda, President
COO: Randall Castillo, Vice President, Operations
CFO: Robin Rogness, Vice President and Chief Financial Officer
CHR: Anthony Robinson, Manager, Human Resources
CNO: Josh Freilich, Vice President and Chief Nurse Executive
Web address: www.mercyfolsom.org
Control: Other not–for–profit (including NFP Corporation) **Service:** General Medical and Surgical

> **Staffed Beds:** 106

⊞ **VIBRA HOSPITAL OF SACRAMENTO (052033)**, 330 Montrose Drive, Zip 95630–2720; tel. 916/351–9151 **A**1 10 **F**1 3 60 68 70 119 **P**4 **S** Vibra Healthcare, Mechanicsburg, PA
Primary Contact: Kimberly Horton, R.N., MSN, Chief Executive Officer
CFO: Todd Scott, Chief Financial Officer
CMO: S. Kwon Lee, M.D., Chief of Staff
CHR: Glenda Franco, Director, Human Resources
Web address: www.vhsacramento.com
Control: Individual, Investor–owned, for–profit **Service:** Children's Long–Term Acute Care

> **Staffed Beds:** 34 **Admissions:** 434 **Census:** 42 **Outpatient Visits:** 0 **Births:** 0 **Total Expense ($000):** 28496 **Payroll Expense ($000):** 12935 **Personnel:** 196

FONTANA—San Bernardino County

⊞ **KAISER PERMANENTE FONTANA MEDICAL CENTER (050140)**, 9961 Sierra Avenue, Zip 92335–6794; tel. 909/427–5000, (Includes KAISER PERMANENTE ONTARIO MEDICAL CENTER, 2295 South Vineyard Avenue, Ontario, Zip 91761–7925; tel. 909/724–5000; Greg Christian, Executive Director) **A**1 3 5 10 **F**3 8 11 13 15 17 18 20 22 24 28 29 30 31 35 40 41 44 45 46 48 49 50 51 57 58 59 60 62 63 64 65 68 70 72 73 74 75 76 77 78 79 81 82 84 85 86 87 88 89 100 102 107 108 110 111 114 115 117 118 119 126 130 135 141 145 146 148 **S** Kaiser Foundation Hospitals, Oakland, CA
Primary Contact: Greg Christian, Executive Director
CFO: Donald P. Bernard, Chief Financial Officer
CMO: David Quam, M.D., Area Medical Director
CIO: David Young, M.D., Area Information Officer
CHR: Kimberly Labiaga, Human Resources Leader
CNO: Toni Andersen, R.N., Chief Nurse Executive
Web address: www.kaiserpermanente.org
Control: Other not–for–profit (including NFP Corporation) **Service:** General Medical and Surgical

> **Staffed Beds:** 490 **Admissions:** 29514 **Census:** 330 **Outpatient Visits:** 170800 **Births:** 6088 **Personnel:** 4106

FORT BRAGG—Mendocino County

⊞ **MENDOCINO COAST DISTRICT HOSPITAL (051325)**, 700 River Drive, Zip 95437–5495; tel. 707/961–1234 **A**1 10 18 **F**7 11 15 29 30 31 34 36 40 57 59 62 63 64 75 76 77 78 79 81 82 87 96 97 107 111 115 119 127 132 133 146
Primary Contact: Bob S. Edwards, Jr., FACHE, Chief Executive Officer
CFO: Wayne Allen, Chief Financial Officer
CMO: John Kermen, D.O., Chief Medical Staff
CIO: Jeff Edwards, Manager Information Services
CHR: Ellen L. Hardin, Chief Human Resources Officer
CNO: Bonnie Kittner, R.N., Chief Nursing Officer
Web address: www.mcdh.org
Control: Hospital district or authority, Government, nonfederal **Service:** General Medical and Surgical

> **Staffed Beds:** 25 **Admissions:** 1168 **Census:** 13 **Outpatient Visits:** 54590 **Births:** 114

FORT IRWIN—San Bernardino County

⊞ **WEED ARMY COMMUNITY HOSPITAL**, Inner Loop Road and 4th Street, Building 166, Zip 92310–5065, Mailing Address: P.O. Box 105109, Zip 92310–5109; tel. 760/380–3108, (Nonreporting) **A**1 **S** Department of the Army, Office of the Surgeon General, Falls Church, VA
Primary Contact: Colonel Jason S. Wieman, Commander
CIO: Michael Haenelt, Chief Information Management
Web address: www.irwin.amedd.army.mil
Control: Army, Government, federal **Service:** General Medical and Surgical

> **Staffed Beds:** 27

FORTUNA—Humboldt County

★ **REDWOOD MEMORIAL HOSPITAL (051318)**, 3300 Renner Drive, Zip 95540–3198; tel. 707/725–3361 **A**2 10 18 **F**3 11 13 15 17 18 29 30 34 35 39 40 45 50 53 56 57 59 63 64 68 70 75 76 77 79 81 82 84 85 86 93 107 110 114 119 130 131 132 133 146 **S** Providence St. Joseph Health, Renton, WA
Primary Contact: David O'Brien, M.D., President
COO: Joseph J. Rogers, Vice President and Chief Operating Officer
CFO: Andrew Rybolt, Vice President and Chief Financial Officer
CHR: Bob Sampson, Vice President Human Resources
Web address: www.redwoodmemorial.org/
Control: Church–operated, Nongovernment, not–for profit **Service:** General Medical and Surgical

> **Staffed Beds:** 25 **Admissions:** 1456 **Census:** 15 **Outpatient Visits:** 49022 **Births:** 380 **Total Expense ($000):** 38898 **Payroll Expense ($000):** 13408 **Personnel:** 166

FOUNTAIN VALLEY—Orange County

⊞ **FOUNTAIN VALLEY REGIONAL HOSPITAL AND MEDICAL CENTER (050570)**, 17100 Euclid Street, Zip 92708–4043; tel. 714/966–7200, (Nonreporting) **A**1 2 5 10 **S** TENET Healthcare Corporation, Dallas, TX
Primary Contact: B. Joseph Badalian, Chief Executive Officer
COO: Edward Littlejohn, Chief Operating Officer
CFO: Ken Jordan, Chief Financial Officer
CMO: Daniel Hilton, M.D., Chief of Staff
CIO: Freddie Sanchez, Director Information Systems
CHR: Tim Howard, Chief Human Resources Officer
CNO: Barbara Vargas, Interim Chief Nursing Officer
Web address: www.fountainvalleyhospital.com
Control: Corporation, Investor–owned, for–profit **Service:** General Medical and Surgical

> **Staffed Beds:** 400

Many Facility Codes have changed. Please refer to the AHA Guide Code Chart. © 2016 AHA Guide

CA

✠ **ORANGE COAST MEMORIAL MEDICAL CENTER (050678)**, 9920 Talbert Avenue, Zip 92708–5115; tel. 714/378–7000 **A**1 2 10 **F**3 8 11 12 13 15 18 20 22 24 26 28 29 30 31 34 35 38 40 44 45 46 47 48 49 50 51 53 55 56 57 58 59 62 64 65 68 70 72 74 75 76 77 78 79 81 82 84 85 86 87 93 107 108 110 111 114 115 116 117 118 119 124 126 130 131 132 135 143 145 146 147 **S** MemorialCare, Fountain Valley, CA
Primary Contact: Marcia Manker, Chief Executive Officer
COO: Emily Randle, Vice President Operations
CFO: Steve McNamara, Chief Financial Officer
CIO: Scott Raymond, Director Information Systems
CHR: Michelle Gutierrez, Executive Director Human Resources
CNO: Dale Vital, Chief Nursing Officer
Web address: www.memorialcare.org
Control: Other not–for–profit (including NFP Corporation) **Service:** General Medical and Surgical

Staffed Beds: 218 Admissions: 12279 Census: 120 Outpatient Visits: 78549 Births: 1584 Total Expense ($000): 279690 Payroll Expense ($000): 75872 Personnel: 1102

FREMONT—Alameda County

✠ **FREMONT HOSPITAL (054110)**, 39001 Sundale Drive, Zip 94538–2005; tel. 510/796–1100 **A**1 10 **F**3 5 29 30 38 68 98 99 100 101 102 103 104 105 130 132 135 143 **S** Universal Health Services, Inc., King of Prussia, PA
Primary Contact: John C. Cooper, Chief Executive Officer
CMO: Vikas Duvvuri, M.D., Medical Director
CHR: Tom Piz, Director Human Resources
Web address: www.fremonthospital.com
Control: Corporation, Investor–owned, for–profit **Service:** Psychiatric

Staffed Beds: 148 Admissions: 5438 Census: 108 Outpatient Visits: 11020 Births: 0 Total Expense ($000): 29856 Payroll Expense ($000): 17352 Personnel: 212

✠ **FREMONT MEDICAL CENTER (050512)**, 39400 Paseo Padre Parkway, Zip 94538–2310; tel. 510/248–3000, (Nonreporting) **A**1 10 **S** Kaiser Foundation Hospitals, Oakland, CA
Primary Contact: Victoria O'Gorman, Administrator
Web address: www.kp.org
Control: Other not–for–profit (including NFP Corporation) **Service:** General Medical and Surgical

Staffed Beds: 106

✠ **WASHINGTON HOSPITAL HEALTHCARE SYSTEM (050195)**, 2000 Mowry Avenue, Zip 94538–1746; tel. 510/797–1111, (Nonreporting) **A**1 2 10
Primary Contact: Nancy D. Farber, Chief Executive Officer
COO: Edward J. Fayen, Associate Administrator Operations and Support
CFO: Chris Henry, Associate Administrator and Chief Financial Officer
CMO: Albert Brooks, M.D., Chief Medical Staff Services
CIO: Robert Thorwald, Chief Information Officer
CHR: Bryant Welch, Chief Human Resources
CNO: Stephanie Williams, R.N., Chief Nursing Officer
Web address: www.whhs.com
Control: Hospital district or authority, Government, nonfederal **Service:** General Medical and Surgical

Staffed Beds: 269

FRENCH CAMP—San Joaquin County

☐ **SAN JOAQUIN GENERAL HOSPITAL (050167)**, 500 West Hospital Road, Zip 95231–9693, Mailing Address: P.O. Box 1020, Stockton, Zip 95201–3120; tel. 209/468–6000, (Nonreporting) **A**1 3 5 10
Primary Contact: David K. Culberson, Chief Executive Officer
CFO: Ron Kreutner, Chief Financial Officer
CMO: Sheela Kapre, M.D., Chief Medical Officer
CIO: Don Johnston, Chief Information Officer
CHR: Lisa M. Lopez, Director Human Resources
CNO: Erlinda Bolor, R.N., Chief Nursing Officer
Web address: www.sjgeneral.org/
Control: County–Government, nonfederal **Service:** General Medical and Surgical

Staffed Beds: 110

FRESNO—Fresno County

COMMUNITY BEHAVIORAL HEALTH CENTER, 7171 North Cedar Avenue, Zip 93720–3311; tel. 559/449–8000, (Nonreporting) **S** Community Medical Centers, Fresno, CA
Primary Contact: Craig Wagoner, Chief Executive Officer
CFO: Stephen Walter, Senior Vice President and Chief Financial Officer
CMO: Tom Utecht, M.D., Senior Vice President and Chief Quality Officer
CIO: George Vasquez, Vice President Information Services
CHR: Ginny Burdick, Vice President Human Resources
CNO: Karen L. Buckley, R.N., Chief Nursing Officer
Web address: www.communitymedical.org
Control: Corporation, Investor–owned, for–profit **Service:** Psychiatric

Staffed Beds: 61

☐ **COMMUNITY REGIONAL MEDICAL CENTER (050060)**, 2823 Fresno Street, Zip 93721–1324, Mailing Address: P.O. Box 1232, Zip 93715–1232; tel. 559/459–6000, (Nonreporting) **A**1 2 3 5 8 10 **S** Community Medical Centers, Fresno, CA
Primary Contact: Craig Wagoner, Chief Executive Officer
COO: Patrick W. Rafferty, Executive Vice President and Chief Operating Officer
CFO: Stephen Walter, Senior Vice President and Chief Financial Officer
CMO: Tom Utecht, M.D., Chief Medical and Quality Officer
CIO: Craig Castro, Chief Information Officer
CHR: Ginny Burdick, Vice President Human Resources
Web address: www.communitymedical.org
Control: Other not–for–profit (including NFP Corporation) **Service:** General Medical and Surgical

Staffed Beds: 808

☐ **FRESNO HEART AND SURGICAL HOSPITAL (050732)**, 15 East Audubon Drive, Zip 93720–1542; tel. 559/433–8000, (Nonreporting) **A**1 3 10 **S** Community Medical Centers, Fresno, CA
Primary Contact: Wanda Holderman, R.N., Chief Executive Officer
CFO: Ben Armfield, Chief Financial Officer
CMO: Tom Utecht, M.D., Corporate Chief Quality Officer
CIO: George Vasquez, Corporate Chief Information Officer
CHR: Julie Adair, Interim Corporate Chief Human Resources Officer
CNO: Heather Rodriguez, Chief Nursing Officer
Web address: www.fresnoheartandsurgical.org
Control: Corporation, Investor–owned, for–profit **Service:** Heart

Staffed Beds: 60

FRESNO MEDICAL CENTER See Kaiser Permanente Fresno Medical Center

☐ **FRESNO SURGICAL HOSPITAL (050708)**, 6125 North Fresno Street, Zip 93710–5207; tel. 559/431–8000, (Nonreporting) **A**1 10
Primary Contact: Kristine Kassahn, Chief Executive Officer
CFO: Bruce Cecil, Chief Financial Officer
CMO: Bruce Witmer, M.D., Medical Director
CHR: Laura Patillo, Manager Human Resources
Web address: www.fresnosurgicalhospital.com
Control: Partnership, Investor–owned, for–profit **Service:** Surgical

Staffed Beds: 29

✠ **KAISER PERMANENTE FRESNO MEDICAL CENTER (050710)**, 7300 North Fresno Street, Zip 93720–2942; tel. 559/448–4500, (Nonreporting) **A**1 3 10 **S** Kaiser Foundation Hospitals, Oakland, CA
Primary Contact: Debbie Hemker, Senior Vice President and Area Manager
CFO: Richard Alves, Chief Financial Officer
CMO: Varouj Altebarmakian, M.D., Physician in Chief
CIO: David Bonnar, Chief Information Officer
CNO: Karen S. Strauman, R.N., Chief Nurse Executive
Web address: www.kaiserpermanente.org
Control: Other not–for–profit (including NFP Corporation) **Service:** General Medical and Surgical

Staffed Beds: 169

⊠ **SAINT AGNES MEDICAL CENTER (050093)**, 1303 East Herndon Avenue, Zip 93720–3397; tel. 559/450–3000 **A**1 2 3 10 **F**3 8 11 13 15 17 18 20 22 24 26 28 29 30 31 34 35 37 40 44 45 46 47 49 50 51 55 56 57 58 59 61 64 66 70 74 75 76 77 78 79 81 82 84 85 86 87 91 92 93 94 95 96 97 102 107 108 110 111 112 113 114 115 116 117 118 119 120 121 123 124 126 130 132 135 146 147 148 **P**1 5 **S** Trinity Health, Livonia, MI
Primary Contact: Nancy Hollingsworth, R.N., MSN, President and Chief Executive Officer
COO: Mark T. Bateman, Interim Chief Operating Officer
CFO: Phil Robinson, Chief Financial Officer
CMO: Stephen Soldo, M.D., Chief Medical Officer
CIO: Irfan Ali, Director Information Services
CHR: Stacy Vaillancourt, Vice President Marketing, Communications, Advocacy and Human Resources
Web address: www.samc.com
Control: Church–operated, Nongovernment, not–for profit **Service:** General Medical and Surgical

Staffed Beds: 436 **Admissions:** 20177 **Census:** 236 **Outpatient Visits:** 230360 **Births:** 3213 **Total Expense ($000):** 450726 **Payroll Expense ($000):** 152280 **Personnel:** 1831

⊠ △ **SAN JOAQUIN VALLEY REHABILITATION HOSPITAL (053032)**, 7173 North Sharon Avenue, Zip 93720–3329; tel. 559/436–3600, (Nonreporting) **A**1 7 10 **S** Vibra Healthcare, Mechanicsburg, PA
Primary Contact: Mary Jo Jacobson, Chief Executive Officer
CFO: Margaret Casarez, Chief Financial Officer
CMO: Michael Azevedo, M.D., Medical Director
CIO: Christi Rolff, Director Business Development
CHR: Jennifer Morrow, Director Human Resources
Web address: www.sanjoaquinrehab.com
Control: Corporation, Investor–owned, for–profit **Service:** Rehabilitation

Staffed Beds: 62

⊠ **VETERANS AFFAIRS CENTRAL CALIFORNIA HEALTH CARE SYSTEM**, 2615 East Clinton Avenue, Zip 93703–2223; tel. 559/225–6100, (Nonreporting) **A**1 3 5 **S** Department of Veterans Affairs, Washington, DC
Primary Contact: Wessel H. Meyer, M.D., Acting Director
CMO: Wessel H. Meyer, M.D., Chief of Staff
CHR: Sandra Stein, Chief Human Resources Management
Web address: www.fresno.va.gov/
Control: Veterans Affairs, Government, federal **Service:** General Medical and Surgical

Staffed Beds: 117

FULLERTON—Orange County

⊠ △ **ST. JUDE MEDICAL CENTER (050168)**, 101 East Valencia Mesa Drive, Zip 92835–3875; tel. 714/992–3000 **A**1 2 3 5 7 10 **F**2 3 5 7 8 10 18 20 22 24 26 28 29 30 31 32 34 39 40 43 44 45 46 47 48 49 50 51 53 54 55 56 57 58 59 60 61 62 63 64 65 66 68 70 71 72 74 75 76 77 78 79 81 82 83 84 85 86 87 90 91 92 93 95 96 97 100 107 108 109 110 111 112 114 115 116 117 118 121 123 124 126 129 130 131 132 134 135 143 146 147 148 **P**3 5 **S** Providence St. Joseph Health, Renton, WA
Primary Contact: Lee Penrose, President and Chief Executive Officer
COO: Brian Helleland, Executive Vice President and Chief Operating Officer
CFO: Ed Salvador, Chief Financial Officer
CIO: Ryan Olsen, Vice President of Operations
CHR: Mark Jablonski, Vice President Mission Integration
CNO: Linda Jenkins, R.N., Vice President Patient Care Services
Web address: www.stjudemedicalcenter.org
Control: Church–operated, Nongovernment, not–for profit **Service:** General Medical and Surgical

Staffed Beds: 351 **Admissions:** 13652 **Census:** 187 **Outpatient Visits:** 442348 **Births:** 2137 **Total Expense ($000):** 489578 **Payroll Expense ($000):** 140140 **Personnel:** 1963

GARBERVILLE—Humboldt County

★ **JEROLD PHELPS COMMUNITY HOSPITAL (051309)**, 733 Cedar Street, Zip 95542–3292; tel. 707/923–3921, (Total facility includes 8 beds in nursing home–type unit) **A**10 18 **F**34 35 40 50 65 77 82 91 93 97 110 119 127 128 133 **P**5
Primary Contact: Matthew Rees, Administrator
COO: Kent Scown, Director Operations and Information Services
CFO: Harry Jasper, Chief Financial Officer
CMO: Marcin Matuszkiewicz, M.D., Chief of Staff and Medical Director
CIO: Kent Scown, Director Operations and Information Services
CHR: Dee Way, Director Human Resources
CNO: Sarah Beach, Director of Nursing
Web address: www.shchd.org
Control: Hospital district or authority, Government, nonfederal **Service:** General Medical and Surgical

Staffed Beds: 17 **Admissions:** 58 **Census:** 8 **Outpatient Visits:** 16180 **Births:** 0

GARDEN GROVE—Orange County

⊠ **GARDEN GROVE HOSPITAL AND MEDICAL CENTER (050230)**, 12601 Garden Grove Boulevard, Zip 92843–1959; tel. 714/537–5160, (Nonreporting) **A**1 10 **S** Prime Healthcare Services, Ontario, CA
Primary Contact: Edward Mirzabegian, Chief Executive Officer
CFO: Kora Guoyavatin, Chief Financial Officer
CMO: Hassan Alkhouli, M.D., Chief Medical Officer
CIO: Vic Mahan, Director Information Systems
CHR: Stephanie Sioson, Director Human Resources
CNO: Wanda Ruben, R.N., Chief Nursing Officer
Web address: www.gardengrovehospital.com
Control: Corporation, Investor–owned, for–profit **Service:** General Medical and Surgical

Staffed Beds: 167

GARDENA—Los Angeles County

⊠ **KINDRED HOSPITAL SOUTH BAY (052050)**, 1246 West 155th Street, Zip 90247–4062; tel. 310/323–5330, (Nonreporting) **A**1 10 **S** Kindred Healthcare, Louisville, KY
Primary Contact: Isaac Lin, Chief Executive Officer
CHR: Michelle Parra, Director Human Resources
Web address: www.khsouthbay.com/
Control: Corporation, Investor–owned, for–profit **Service:** Long–Term Acute Care hospital

Staffed Beds: 84

⊠ **MEMORIAL HOSPITAL OF GARDENA (050468)**, 1145 West Redondo Beach Boulevard, Zip 90247–3528; tel. 310/532–4200 **A**1 10 **F**17 18 26 29 30 34 35 40 41 45 49 50 51 57 59 65 68 70 74 75 76 77 79 81 83 85 87 93 100 102 107 111 119 128 130 143 148 **S** Avanti Hospitals, El Segundo, CA
Primary Contact: Kathy Wojno, R.N., MSN, Interim Administrator
CFO: Daniel R. Heckathorne, Chief Financial Officer
CMO: Nosratian Farshao, M.D., Chief Medical Staff
CHR: Matthew Kempiak, Director Human Resources and Administrative Services
CNO: Glenda Luce, Chief Nursing Officer
Web address: www.mhglax.com/
Control: Partnership, Investor–owned, for–profit **Service:** General Medical and Surgical

Staffed Beds: 172 **Admissions:** 6365 **Census:** 129 **Outpatient Visits:** 45782 **Births:** 920 **Total Expense ($000):** 97197 **Payroll Expense ($000):** 47422 **Personnel:** 635

VISTA HOSPITAL OF SOUTH BAY See Kindred Hospital South Bay

GILROY—Santa Clara County

⊠ **SAINT LOUISE REGIONAL HOSPITAL (050688)**, 9400 No Name Uno, Zip 95020–3528; tel. 408/848–2000, (Nonreporting) **A**1 10 **S** Verity Health System, Los Angeles, CA
Primary Contact: Robert Minkin, Interim Chief Executive Officer
COO: Carol Furgurson, Chief Operating Officer
CFO: Nicole Thomson, Chief Financial Officer
CIO: Dick Hutsell, Vice President Information Technology Services
CHR: Lin Velasquez, Vice President Human Resources
CNO: Marilyn Gerrior, R.N., Chief Nursing Executive
Web address: www.verity.org
Control: Other not–for–profit (including NFP Corporation) **Service:** General Medical and Surgical

Staffed Beds: 93

GLENDALE—Los Angeles County

⊠ **GLENDALE MEMORIAL HOSPITAL AND HEALTH CENTER (050058)**, 1420 South Central Avenue, Zip 91204–2594; tel. 818/502–1900 **A**1 10 **F**12 13 15 17 18 20 22 24 26 28 29 30 31 34 35 37 40 41 45 46 47 48 49 50 51 53 56 57 58 59 64 68 70 72 74 75 78 79 81 82 84 85 90 91 92 93 98 99 102 107 108 110 111 114 115 119 120 128 130 131 132 146 147 148 **S** Dignity Health, San Francisco, CA
Primary Contact: Jack Ivie, President
CFO: Rebecca Cheng, Chief Financial Officer
CIO: Brian Gregor, Manager Information Technology Operations
CHR: Nga Nguyen, Manager Human Resources and Organizational Development
CNO: Claire H. Hanks, R.N., Vice President and Chief Nursing Officer
Web address: www.glendalememorial.com
Control: Other not–for–profit (including NFP Corporation) **Service:** General Medical and Surgical

Staffed Beds: 334 **Admissions:** 8906 **Census:** 114 **Outpatient Visits:** 101539 **Births:** 1997 **Total Expense ($000):** 262697 **Payroll Expense ($000):** 86073 **Personnel:** 1023

CA

★ ◇ **USC VERDUGO HILLS HOSPITAL (050124)**, 1812 Verdugo Boulevard, Zip 91208–1409; tel. 818/790–7100 **A**10 21 **F**3 11 12 13 14 15 17 28 29 30 31 34 35 38 40 41 44 45 49 50 51 53 56 57 58 59 60 63 65 68 70 74 75 76 77 79 81 83 84 85 86 87 91 93 98 101 102 103 104 105 107 108 110 111 115 119 124 126 128 130 132 135 145 146 147 148 **P**8 **S** Keck Medicine of USC, Los Angeles, CA
Primary Contact: Keith Hobbs, Chief Executive Officer
COO: Kenny Pawlek, Chief Operating Officer
CFO: Robert Allen, Chief Financial Officer
CMO: Stephanie Hall, M.D., Chief Medical Officer
CHR: Eva Herberger, Administrator Human Resources
CNO: Theresa Murphy, Chief Nursing Officer
Web address: www.uscvhh.org
Control: Other not–for–profit (including NFP Corporation) **Service:** General Medical and Surgical

Staffed Beds: 81 Admissions: 6020 **Census:** 81 **Outpatient Visits:** 64400 **Births:** 511 **Total Expense ($000):** 107046 **Payroll Expense ($000):** 42675 **Personnel:** 564

GLENDORA—Los Angeles County

✠ **FOOTHILL PRESBYTERIAN HOSPITAL (050597)**, 250 South Grand Avenue, Zip 91741–4218; tel. 626/963–8411 **A**1 10 **F**3 7 11 13 15 17 18 29 30 31 34 35 40 41 44 45 49 50 51 60 64 68 70 74 75 76 77 78 79 81 85 86 87 107 108 114 119 130 131 143 146 **S** Citrus Valley Health Partners, Covina, CA
Primary Contact: Robert H. Curry, President and Chief Executive Officer
COO: Elvia Foulke, Executive Vice President and Chief Operating Officer
CMO: John DiMare, M.D., Medical Director
CIO: David McCobb, Chief Information Officer
Web address: www.cvhp.org/Our_Facilities/Foothill_Presbyterian.aspx
Control: Other not–for–profit (including NFP Corporation) **Service:** Obstetrics and gynecology

Staffed Beds: 75 Admissions: 5892 **Census:** 58 **Outpatient Visits:** 57711 **Births:** 946 **Total Expense ($000):** 83695 **Payroll Expense ($000):** 33951 **Personnel:** 423

★ ○ **GLENDORA COMMUNITY HOSPITAL (050205)**, 150 West Route 66, Zip 91740–6207; tel. 626/852–5000, (Nonreporting) **A**10 11 **S** Prime Healthcare Services, Ontario, CA
Primary Contact: Edward Mirzabegian, Chief Executive Officer
CFO: Robert Bonner, Chief Financial Officer
CMO: Oliver Solomon, M.D., Chief Medical Officer
CIO: Jeffrey Cox, Chief Information Officer
CHR: Diana Cancel, Director Human Resources
CNO: Mary Ann Bennett, Chief Nursing Officer
Web address: www.evhmc.com
Control: Other not–for–profit (including NFP Corporation) **Service:** General Medical and Surgical

Staffed Beds: 128

GRANADA HILLS—Los Angeles County, See Los Angeles

GRASS VALLEY—Nevada County

✠ **SIERRA NEVADA MEMORIAL HOSPITAL (050150)**, 155 Glasson Way, Zip 95945–5723, Mailing Address: P.O. Box 1029, Zip 95945–1029; tel. 530/274–6000, (Nonreporting) **A**1 2 10 19 **S** Dignity Health, San Francisco, CA
Primary Contact: Katherine A. Medeiros, President and Chief Executive Officer
CFO: Carolyn Canady, Chief Financial Officer
CMO: Brian Evans, M.D., Chief of Medicine
CHR: Terri Labriola, Human Resources Officer
CNO: Jill McWilliams, Chief Nursing Officer
Web address: www.snmh.org
Control: Other not–for–profit (including NFP Corporation) **Service:** General Medical and Surgical

Staffed Beds: 121

GREENBRAE—Marin County

✠ **MARIN GENERAL HOSPITAL (050360)**, 250 Bon Air Road, Zip 94904–1784, Mailing Address: P.O. Box 8010, San Rafael, Zip 94912–8010; tel. 415/925–7000 **A**1 2 10 **F**3 8 13 15 18 20 22 24 26 28 29 30 31 34 35 36 37 40 43 45 47 49 57 58 59 60 68 70 72 74 75 76 77 78 79 81 84 85 86 87 89 93 98 100 104 105 107 108 110 111 114 115 116 117 118 119 120 121 123 124 126 130 132 141 146 148 **P**3 4 5
Primary Contact: Lee Domanico, Chief Executive Officer
CFO: David W. Cox, Chief Financial Officer
CMO: Joel Sklar, M.D., Chief Medical Officer
CIO: Mark Zielazinski, Chief Information and Technology Integration Officer
CHR: Linda Lang, Chief Human Resources Officer
Web address: www.maringeneral.org
Control: Other not–for–profit (including NFP Corporation) **Service:** General Medical and Surgical

Staffed Beds: 176 Admissions: 8698 **Census:** 113 **Outpatient Visits:** 194107 **Births:** 1322 **Total Expense ($000):** 349289 **Payroll Expense ($000):** 149312 **Personnel:** 1287

GRIDLEY—Butte County

★ ◇ **ORCHARD HOSPITAL (051311)**, 240 Spruce Street, Zip 95948–2216, Mailing Address: P.O. Box 97, Zip 95948–0097; tel. 530/846–5671, (Nonreporting) **A**10 18 21
Primary Contact: Steve Stark, Chief Executive Officer
COO: Tracy Atkins, Chief Operating and Nursing Officer
CFO: Kristina Sanke, Chief Financial Officer
CMO: Henry Starkes, M.D., Medical Director
CIO: John Helvey, Chief Information Officer
CNO: Tracy Atkins, Chief Operating and Nursing Officer
Web address: www.orchardhospital.com
Control: Other not–for–profit (including NFP Corporation) **Service:** General Medical and Surgical

Staffed Beds: 45

HANFORD—Kings County

✠ **ADVENTIST MEDICAL CENTER – HANFORD (050121)**, 115 Mall Drive, Zip 93230–3513; tel. 559/582–9000, (Includes ADVENTIST MEDICAL CENTER–SELMA, 1141 Rose Avenue, Selma, Zip 93662–3241; tel. 559/891–1000; Richard L. Rawson, President and Chief Executive Officer) **A**1 3 10 **F**3 8 13 14 15 20 22 29 30 34 35 40 56 57 59 68 70 76 79 81 93 106 107 111 119 130 146 147 148 **S** Adventist Health, Roseville, CA
Primary Contact: Wayne Ferch, President and Chief Executive Officer
CIO: Michael Aubry, Director Information Systems
Web address: www.adventisthealthcv.com/hospital_newhanfordhospital.aspx
Control: Church–operated, Nongovernment, not–for profit **Service:** General Medical and Surgical

Staffed Beds: 199 Admissions: 17347 **Census:** 110 **Outpatient Visits:** 392519 **Births:** 0 **Total Expense ($000):** 223152 **Payroll Expense ($000):** 87611 **Personnel:** 1594

✠ **CENTRAL VALLEY GENERAL HOSPITAL (050196)**, 1025 North Douty Street, Zip 93230–3722, Mailing Address: P.O. Box 480, Zip 93232–2113; tel. 559/583–2100, (Data for 334 days) **A**1 3 10 **F**8 13 18 19 29 34 39 50 54 57 59 64 65 76 87 97 107 109 110 111 114 119 129 130 135 144 146 147 **P**3 **S** Adventist Health, Roseville, CA
Primary Contact: Wayne Ferch, President and Chief Executive Officer
Web address: www.hanfordhealth.com
Control: Church–operated, Nongovernment, not–for profit **Service:** General Medical and Surgical

Staffed Beds: 49 Admissions: 2506 **Census:** 15 **Outpatient Visits:** 546114 **Births:** 2416 **Total Expense ($000):** 99158 **Payroll Expense ($000):** 32830 **Personnel:** 726

HARBOR CITY—Los Angeles County, See Los Angeles

HAWAIIAN GARDENS—Los Angeles County

◇ **GARDENS REGIONAL HOSPITAL AND MEDICAL CENTER (050575)**, 21530 South Pioneer Boulevard, Zip 90716–2608; tel. 562/860–0401, (Nonreporting) **A**10 21
Primary Contact: Gregory Padilla, Chief Executive Officer
CMO: Derek Dobalian, M.D., Chief of Staff
CIO: Anthony Carrasco, Director Information Systems
CHR: Gregg W. Yost, Chief Human Resources Officer
CNO: Juliet Miranda, Chief Nursing Officer
Web address: www.grhmc.org
Control: Other not–for–profit (including NFP Corporation) **Service:** General Medical and Surgical

Staffed Beds: 107

CA

Hospital, Medicare Provider Number, Address, Telephone, Approval, Facility, and Physician Codes, Health Care System

★ American Hospital Association (AHA) membership ○ Healthcare Facilities Accreditation Program ⇑ Center for Improvement in Healthcare Quality Accreditation
□ The Joint Commission accreditation ◇ DNV Healthcare Inc. accreditation △ Commission on Accreditation of Rehabilitation Facilities (CARF) accreditation

CA

HAYWARD—Alameda County

☐ **ST. ROSE HOSPITAL (050002)**, 27200 Calaroga Avenue, Zip 94545–4383; tel. 510/264–4000, (Nonreporting) **A**1 10
Primary Contact: Lex Reddy, President and Chief Executive Officer
CFO: Michael Taylor, Vice President Financial Services and Chief Financial Officer
CMO: Charles S. Feldstein, M.D., Vice President Medical Affairs
CHR: John Davini, Vice President
Web address: www.srhca.org
Control: Church–operated, Nongovernment, not–for profit **Service:** General Medical and Surgical

Staffed Beds: 150

HEALDSBURG—Sonoma County

☐ **HEALDSBURG DISTRICT HOSPITAL (051321)**, 1375 University Avenue, Zip 95448–3382; tel. 707/431–6500, (Nonreporting) **A**1 10 18
Primary Contact: Nancy Schmid, Chief Executive Officer
COO: Regina Novello, R.N., Chief Operating Officer
CFO: John S. Parigi, II, Interim Chief Financial Officer
CMO: Judy Widger, M.D., Chief of Staff
CIO: Steven Hansen, Director Information Technology
CHR: Kristina Holloway, Chief Human Resources Officer
CNO: Susan G. Spoelma, MSN, Chief Nursing Officer
Web address: www.nschd.org
Control: Hospital district or authority, Government, nonfederal **Service:** General Medical and Surgical

Staffed Beds: 24

HEMET—Riverside County

☐ **HEMET VALLEY MEDICAL CENTER (050390)**, 1117 East Devonshire Avenue, Zip 92543–3083; tel. 951/652–2811, (Nonreporting) **A**1 10 12 13 **S** Physicians for Healthy Hospitals, Hemet, CA
Primary Contact: Joel M. Bergenfeld, Chief Hospital Executive Officer
CFO: John R. Collins, Chief Financial Officer
CHR: Michele Bird, Chief Human Resources Officer
CNO: Kathryn McLaughlin, Chief Nursing Officer
Web address: www.physiciansforhealthyhospitals.com
Control: Hospital district or authority, Government, nonfederal **Service:** General Medical and Surgical

Staffed Beds: 159

HOLLISTER—San Benito County

⊞ **HAZEL HAWKINS MEMORIAL HOSPITAL (050296)**, 911 Sunset Drive, Zip 95023–5695; tel. 831/637–5711, (Includes WILLIAM AND INEZ MABIE SKILLED NURSING FACILITY, 911 Sunset Drive, Zip 95023; tel. 408/637–5711), (Total facility includes 119 beds in nursing home–type unit) **A**1 10 **F**3 8 11 13 15 29 30 34 35 39 40 45 49 50 51 57 59 62 64 65 66 68 70 74 75 76 77 79 81 82 84 85 86 87 91 93 97 107 110 111 112 115 119 127 128 129 130 131 132 146 147 148
Primary Contact: Ken Underwood, Chief Executive Officer
CFO: Mark Robinson, Associate Administrator and Chief Financial Officer
CIO: Julio Gil, Manager Information Services
CHR: Ysidro Gallardo, Associate Administrator Human Resources
Web address: www.hazelhawkins.com
Control: Hospital district or authority, Government, nonfederal **Service:** General Medical and Surgical

Staffed Beds: 181 Admissions: 2337 Census: 121 Outpatient Visits: 245704 Births: 430 Total Expense ($000): 98392 Payroll Expense ($000): 38361

HOLLYWOOD—Los Angeles County, See Los Angeles

HUNTINGTON BEACH—Orange County

⊞ **HUNTINGTON BEACH HOSPITAL (050526)**, 17772 Beach Boulevard, Zip 92647–6896; tel. 714/843–5000, (Nonreporting) **A**1 10 **S** Prime Healthcare Services, Ontario, CA
Primary Contact: Edward Mirzabegian, Chief Executive Officer
CFO: Alan H. Smith, Chief Financial Officer
CMO: Hassan Alkhouli, M.D., Medical Director
CIO: Adam Morquecho, Director Information Technology
CHR: Stephanie Sioson, Director Human Resources
CNO: Sofia Abrina, Administrator and Chief Nursing Officer
Web address: www.hbhospital.com
Control: Other not–for–profit (including NFP Corporation) **Service:** General Medical and Surgical

Staffed Beds: 131

HUNTINGTON PARK—Los Angeles County

COMMUNITY AND MISSION HOSPITALS OF HUNTINGTON PARK See Community Hospital of Huntington Park

○ **COMMUNITY HOSPITAL OF HUNTINGTON PARK (050091)**, 2623 East Slauson Avenue, Zip 90255–2926; tel. 323/583–1931, (Nonreporting) **A**10 11 **S** Avanti Hospitals, El Segundo, CA
Primary Contact: Araceli Lonergan, Chief Executive Officer
CFO: Cheryl Tong, Corporate Chief Financial Officer
CMO: Jose Rivas, M.D., Chief of Staff
CIO: Jason Cervantes, Corporate Chief Information Officer
CHR: Paul Celuch, Corporate Human Resources Director
CNO: Lisa Jacobson, Director of Nursing
Web address: www.chhplax.com
Control: Corporation, Investor–owned, for–profit **Service:** General Medical and Surgical

Staffed Beds: 81

INDIO—Riverside County

⊞ **JOHN F. KENNEDY MEMORIAL HOSPITAL (050534)**, 47111 Monroe Street, Zip 92201–6799; tel. 760/347–6191 **A**1 10 **F**3 8 18 20 29 30 34 35 37 40 46 47 48 49 50 54 56 57 59 68 70 74 76 78 79 81 85 87 89 97 107 108 111 118 119 126 130 146 148 **S** TENET Healthcare Corporation, Dallas, TX
Primary Contact: Gary Honts, Chief Executive Officer
COO: Philip Fitzgerald, Chief Operating Officer
CFO: Lorna Curtis, Chief Financial Officer
CMO: Charles Anderson, M.D., Market Chief Medical Officer
CHR: Raymond Konieczek, Chief Human Resources Officer
CNO: Pat Swaller, Interim Chief Nursing Officer
Web address: www.jfkmemorialhosp.com
Control: Corporation, Investor–owned, for–profit **Service:** General Medical and Surgical

Staffed Beds: 145 Admissions: 7195 Census: 61 Outpatient Visits: 49697 Births: 2180 Total Expense ($000): 116452 Payroll Expense ($000): 54451 Personnel: 570

INGLEWOOD—Los Angeles County

⊞ **CENTINELA HOSPITAL MEDICAL CENTER (050739)**, 555 East Hardy Street, Zip 90301–4011, Mailing Address: P.O. Box 720, Zip 90312–6720; tel. 310/673–4660, (Nonreporting) **A**1 10 **S** Prime Healthcare Services, Ontario, CA
Primary Contact: Linda Bradley, Chief Executive Officer
CFO: Paul Sennett, Chief Financial Officer
CMO: Paryus Patel, M.D., Chief Medical Officer
CIO: Martin Cordova, Director Information Services
CHR: George Akopyan, Director Human Resources
CNO: Mohammad Abdelnaser, Chief Nursing Officer
Web address: www.centinelamed.com
Control: Corporation, Investor–owned, for–profit **Service:** General Medical and Surgical

Staffed Beds: 369

IRVINE—Orange County

◇ **HOAG ORTHOPEDIC INSTITUTE (050769)**, 16250 Sand Canyon Avenue, Zip 92618–3714; tel. 949/517–3149, (Nonreporting) **A**3 21
Primary Contact: Deressa Reid, Interim Chief Executive Officer
Web address: www.hoag.org/Locations/Pages/HoagHospOrthoInstitute.aspx
Control: Other not–for–profit (including NFP Corporation) **Service:** Orthopedic

Staffed Beds: 20

ORANGE COUNTY IRVINE MEDICAL CENTER See Kaiser Permanente Orange County Anaheim Medical Center, Anaheim

JACKSON—Amador County

⊞ **SUTTER AMADOR HOSPITAL (050014)**, 200 Mission Boulevard, Zip 95642–2564; tel. 209/223–7500 **A**1 5 10 20 **F**29 34 35 40 46 47 49 54 59 64 65 70 75 77 78 79 81 84 85 87 93 102 107 108 110 111 115 119 129 130 132 146 148 **P**3 **S** Sutter Health, Sacramento, CA
Primary Contact: Anne Platt, Chief Executive Officer
CFO: Brett Moore, CPA, Assistant Administrator Finance
CMO: Ron Hood, M.D., Chief of Staff
CIO: Joy Bailey, Director Information Technology
CHR: Beverly Revels, Director Human Resources
CNO: Nikki Allen, Patient Care Executive
Web address: www.sutteramador.org
Control: Other not–for–profit (including NFP Corporation) **Service:** General Medical and Surgical

Staffed Beds: 52 Admissions: 2525 Census: 25 Outpatient Visits: 43550 Births: 413 Total Expense ($000): 73244 Payroll Expense ($000): 23328 Personnel: 290

Many Facility Codes have changed. Please refer to the AHA Guide Code Chart. © 2016 AHA Guide

KENTFIELD—Marin County

✠ **KENTFIELD REHABILITATION AND SPECIALTY HOSPITAL (052043)**, 1125 Sir Francis Drake Boulevard, Zip 94904–1455; tel. 415/456–9680 **A**1 10 **F**1 29 64 77 93 119 148 **S** Vibra Healthcare, Mechanicsburg, PA
Primary Contact: Ann Gors, Chief Executive Officer
CFO: Stephanie Lawrence, Chief Financial Officer
CMO: Curtis Roebken, M.D., Chief Medical Staff
CHR: Julene English, Director Human Resources
Web address: www.kentfieldrehab.com
Control: Corporation, Investor–owned, for–profit **Service:** Long–Term Acute Care hospital

Staffed Beds: 52 **Admissions:** 419 **Census:** 53 **Outpatient Visits:** 15840 **Births:** 0 **Total Expense ($000):** 40291 **Payroll Expense ($000):** 17467 **Personnel:** 195

KING CITY—Monterey County

☐ **MEE MEMORIAL HOSPITAL (050189)**, 300 Canal Street, Zip 93930–3431; tel. 831/385–6000, (Nonreporting) **A**1 10 20
Primary Contact: Susan M. Childers, CPA, Chief Executive Officer
CFO: Gary L. Wangsmo, Chief Financial Officer
CMO: Schindelheim Roy, M.D., Chief of Staff
CIO: Mike McNamara, Chief Information Officer
CHR: Karen Wong, Chief Human Resources Officer
Web address: www.meememorial.com
Control: Other not–for–profit (including NFP Corporation) **Service:** General Medical and Surgical

Staffed Beds: 119

LA JOLLA—San Diego County

✠ **SCRIPPS GREEN HOSPITAL (050424)**, 10666 North Torrey Pines Road, Zip 92037–1093; tel. 858/455–9100 **A**1 2 5 8 10 **F**3 8 11 12 14 15 17 18 20 22 24 26 28 29 30 31 34 35 36 37 44 45 46 47 49 50 51 54 57 58 59 61 64 68 70 74 75 77 78 79 80 81 82 84 85 86 87 93 107 108 110 111 114 115 118 119 120 121 123 124 126 130 131 132 136 138 139 141 142 146 148 **P**3 **S** Scripps Health, San Diego, CA
Primary Contact: Robin Brown, Chief Executive, Senior Vice President
CFO: Richard Rothberger, Corporate Executive Vice President and Chief Financial Officer
CMO: James LaBelle, M.D., Chief Medical Officer
CIO: Patric Thomas, Corporate Vice President Information Services
CHR: Victor Buzachero, Corporate Senior Vice President for Innovation, Human Resources and Performance Management
Web address: www.scrippshealth.org
Control: Other not–for–profit (including NFP Corporation) **Service:** General Medical and Surgical

Staffed Beds: 173 **Admissions:** 9234 **Census:** 103 **Outpatient Visits:** 86043 **Births:** 0 **Total Expense ($000):** 334096 **Payroll Expense ($000):** 99270 **Personnel:** 1336

✠ **SCRIPPS MEMORIAL HOSPITAL–LA JOLLA (050324)**, 9888 Genesee Avenue, Zip 92037–1200, Mailing Address: P.O. Box 28, Zip 92038–0028; tel. 858/626–4123 **A**1 2 3 5 10 **F**3 5 8 11 12 13 14 15 17 18 20 22 24 26 28 29 30 31 34 35 40 43 44 45 46 49 51 53 54 55 57 58 59 64 65 68 70 74 75 76 77 78 79 81 82 84 85 86 87 91 92 93 94 100 101 102 107 108 110 111 114 115 117 118 119 124 126 130 132 141 145 146 147 148 **P**3 5 **S** Scripps Health, San Diego, CA
Primary Contact: Gary G. Fybel, FACHE, Chief Executive, Senior Vice President
COO: Cindy Steckel, Ph.D., Vice President Chief Nurse and Operations Executive
CFO: Alan Mandal, Vice President Financial Operations
CMO: James LaBelle, M.D., Chief Medical Officer
CHR: Shelly Blazakis, Director Human Resources Services
CNO: Cindy Steckel, Ph.D., Vice President Chief Nurse and Operations Executive
Web address: www.scripps.org/locations/hospitals__scripps–memorial–hospital–la–jolla
Control: Other not–for–profit (including NFP Corporation) **Service:** General Medical and Surgical

Staffed Beds: 203 **Admissions:** 15899 **Census:** 189 **Outpatient Visits:** 97146 **Births:** 3813 **Total Expense ($000):** 470150 **Payroll Expense ($000):** 158850 **Personnel:** 2175

LA MESA—San Diego County

☐ **ALVARADO PARKWAY INSTITUTE BEHAVIORAL HEALTH SYSTEM (054075)**, 7050 Parkway Drive, Zip 91942–1535; tel. 619/465–4411 **A**1 10 **F**4 5 29 30 34 35 38 50 59 68 75 87 98 100 101 102 103 104 105 130 132 135
Primary Contact: Patrick C. Ziemer, Chief Executive Officer
CFO: Chad Engbrecht, Chief Financial Officer
CMO: R. Bradley Sanders, D.O., Executive Medical Director
CNO: Bonnie Asada, Chief Nursing Officer
Web address: www.apibhs.com
Control: Corporation, Investor–owned, for–profit **Service:** Psychiatric

Staffed Beds: 66 **Admissions:** 2567 **Census:** 60 **Outpatient Visits:** 119298 **Births:** 0 **Total Expense ($000):** 25328 **Payroll Expense ($000):** 12478 **Personnel:** 243

✠ △ **SHARP GROSSMONT HOSPITAL (050026)**, 5555 Grossmont Center Drive, Zip 91942–3019, Mailing Address: P.O. Box 158, Zip 91944–0158; tel. 619/740–6000, (Total facility includes 30 beds in nursing home–type unit) **A**1 2 3 7 10 **F**3 8 11 13 15 17 18 20 22 24 26 28 29 30 31 34 35 38 39 40 44 45 46 47 48 49 50 51 54 55 56 57 58 59 60 61 62 63 64 65 66 68 70 72 74 75 76 77 78 79 80 81 82 83 84 85 86 87 90 91 92 93 94 96 97 98 100 101 102 103 104 105 107 108 109 110 111 114 115 116 117 118 119 120 121 123 124 126 128 129 130 132 135 141 143 145 146 147 148 **S** Sharp HealthCare, San Diego, CA
Primary Contact: Scott Evans, FACHE, PharmD, Senior Vice President and Chief Executive Officer
COO: Maryann Cone, Chief Operating Officer
CFO: Kari Cornicelli, Chief Financial Officer
CMO: Michael Murphy, M.D., Chief Medical Officer
CIO: Kenneth Lawonn, Senior Vice President and Chief Information Officer
CHR: George Holtz, Director Human Resources
Web address: www.sharp.com
Control: Other not–for–profit (including NFP Corporation) **Service:** General Medical and Surgical

Staffed Beds: 528 **Admissions:** 27861 **Census:** 342 **Outpatient Visits:** 338569 **Births:** 3734 **Total Expense ($000):** 667861 **Payroll Expense ($000):** 253577 **Personnel:** 2766

LA MIRADA—Los Angeles County

✠ **KINDRED HOSPITAL–LA MIRADA (052038)**, 14900 East Imperial Highway, Zip 90638–2172; tel. 562/944–1900, (Includes KINDRED HOSPITAL SAN GABRIEL VALLEY, 845 North Lark Ellen Avenue, West Covina, Zip 91791–1069; tel. 626/339–5451; Julie Myers, Chief Executive Officer; KINDRED HOSPITAL SANTA ANA, 1901 North College Avenue, Santa Ana, Zip 92706–2334; tel. 714/564–7800), (Nonreporting) **A**1 10 **S** Kindred Healthcare, Louisville, KY
Primary Contact: David Kowalski, Chief Executive Officer
CFO: Rishab Punjabi, Chief Financial Officer
CMO: Prakash Chandra Patel, M.D., Chief of Staff
CHR: Susan Bergquist, Human Resources Generalist
CNO: Esperanza Sanchez, Chief Clinical Officer
Web address: www.kindredlamirada.com/
Control: Corporation, Investor–owned, for–profit **Service:** Long–Term Acute Care hospital

Staffed Beds: 216

LA PALMA—Orange County

✠ **LA PALMA INTERCOMMUNITY HOSPITAL (050580)**, 7901 Walker Street, Zip 90623–1764; tel. 714/670–7400 **A**1 10 **F**3 8 13 15 17 18 20 22 29 35 40 41 45 49 56 59 60 64 70 76 77 79 81 85 98 101 102 103 107 108 111 114 119 130 146 147 148 **S** Prime Healthcare Services, Ontario, CA
Primary Contact: Virgis Narbutas, Chief Executive Officer
CFO: Alan H. Smith, Chief Financial Officer
CMO: Sami Shoukair, M.D., Chief Medical Officer
CIO: Vic Mahan, Director Information Technology
CHR: Stephanie Sioson, Director Human Resources
CNO: Hilda Manzo–Luna, Chief Nursing Officer
Web address: www.lapalmaintercommunityhospital.com
Control: Other not–for–profit (including NFP Corporation) **Service:** General Medical and Surgical

Staffed Beds: 140 **Admissions:** 3376 **Census:** 54 **Outpatient Visits:** 26367 **Births:** 419 **Personnel:** 312

Hospital, Medicare Provider Number, Address, Telephone, Approval, Facility, and Physician Codes, Health Care System

★ American Hospital Association (AHA) membership ☐ The Joint Commission accreditation ○ Healthcare Facilities Accreditation Program ◇ DNV Healthcare Inc. accreditation ⇑ Center for Improvement in Healthcare Quality Accreditation △ Commission on Accreditation of Rehabilitation Facilities (CARF) accreditation

LAGUNA HILLS—Orange County

☒ **SADDLEBACK MEMORIAL MEDICAL CENTER (050603)**, 24451 Health Center Drive, Zip 92653–3689; tel. 949/837–4500 **A**1 2 10 **F**3 8 11 13 14 15 18 20 22 24 26 28 29 30 31 34 35 36 38 40 44 45 46 47 48 49 50 51 53 54 55 56 57 58 59 62 63 64 65 68 70 72 74 75 76 77 78 79 81 82 84 85 86 87 93 94 100 107 108 110 111 115 116 117 118 119 120 121 123 124 126 130 132 135 141 142 143 145 146 147 148 **P**7 **S** MemorialCare, Fountain Valley, CA
Primary Contact: Marcia Manker, Chief Executive Officer
COO: Cheryl Jacob, Chief Operating Officer
CFO: Adolfo Chanez, Vice President Finance and Chief Financial Officer
CMO: Ernest Hayward, M.D., Chief of Staff
CIO: J. Scott Joslyn, Senior Vice President and Chief Information Officer
CHR: Kayce H. Hudson, Executive Director Human Resources
CNO: Kathy Dawson, R.N., Chief Nursing Officer
Web address: www.memorialcare.org
Control: Other not–for–profit (including NFP Corporation) **Service:** General Medical and Surgical

Staffed Beds: 313 **Admissions:** 14250 **Census:** 143 **Outpatient Visits:** 228538 **Births:** 2825 **Total Expense ($000):** 340685 **Payroll Expense ($000):** 111613 **Personnel:** 1487

LAKE ARROWHEAD—San Bernardino County

☒ **SAN BERNARDINO MOUNTAINS COMMUNITY HOSPITAL DISTRICT (051312)**, 29101 Hospital Road, Zip 92352–9706, Mailing Address: P.O. Box 70, Zip 92352–0070; tel. 909/336–3651, (Nonreporting) **A**1 10 18
Primary Contact: Charles Harrison, Chief Executive Officer
COO: Terry Pena, Chief Operating Officer and Chief Nursing Officer
CFO: Yvonne Waggener, Chief Financial Officer
CMO: Walter M. Maier, Chief of Staff
CIO: Patrick Miller, Technology Coordinator
CHR: Julie Atwood, Director Human Resources
CNO: Terry Pena, Chief Operating Officer and Chief Nursing Officer
Web address: www.mchcares.com
Control: Hospital district or authority, Government, nonfederal **Service:** General Medical and Surgical

Staffed Beds: 37

LAKE ISABELLA—Kern County

KERN VALLEY HEALTHCARE DISTRICT (051314), 6412 Laurel Avenue, Zip 93240–9529, Mailing Address: P.O. Box 1628, Zip 93240–1628; tel. 760/379–2681, (Nonreporting) **A**10 18
Primary Contact: Timothy McGlew, Chief Executive Officer
CFO: Chester Beedle, Chief Financial Officer
CMO: Gary A. Finstad, M.D., Chief of Staff
CIO: Paul Quinn, Information Systems Manager
CHR: Debra Hoffman, Manager Human Resources
CNO: Mark Gordon, Chief Nursing Officer
Web address: www.kvhd.org
Control: Hospital district or authority, Government, nonfederal **Service:** General Medical and Surgical

Staffed Beds: 99

LAKEPORT—Lake County

☒ **SUTTER LAKESIDE HOSPITAL (051329)**, 5176 Hill Road East, Zip 95453–6300; tel. 707/262–5000 **A**1 10 18 **F**3 5 8 11 15 18 29 30 34 35 36 40 43 45 46 51 53 54 56 57 59 61 64 65 66 68 70 74 75 76 79 81 82 85 86 87 91 93 96 97 107 110 111 114 118 119 127 130 131 133 135 146 147 148 **P**3 **S** Sutter Health, Sacramento, CA
Primary Contact: Siri Nelson, Chief Administrative Officer
CFO: Linnea Humble, Director of Finance
CMO: Diane Pege, M.D., Vice President Medical Affairs
CIO: Jack Buell, Director Information Services
CHR: Brenda DeRamus, Manager Human Resources
CNO: Teresa Campbell, R.N., Chief Nursing Executive
Web address: www.sutterlakeside.org
Control: Other not–for–profit (including NFP Corporation) **Service:** General Medical and Surgical

Staffed Beds: 25 **Admissions:** 1697 **Census:** 17 **Outpatient Visits:** 71758 **Births:** 297 **Total Expense ($000):** 73548 **Payroll Expense ($000):** 22985 **Personnel:** 306

LAKEWOOD—Los Angeles County

☒ **LAKEWOOD REGIONAL MEDICAL CENTER (050581)**, 3700 East South Street, Zip 90712–1498, Mailing Address: P.O. Box 6070, Zip 90712; tel. 562/531–2550 **A**1 10 **F**3 11 15 17 18 20 22 24 26 29 30 34 35 38 40 45 49 50 51 57 59 64 68 70 74 75 77 81 85 87 93 107 108 109 111 115 118 119 120 126 130 132 143 146 148 **S** TENET Healthcare Corporation, Dallas, TX
Primary Contact: John A. Grah, FACHE, Chief Executive Officer
COO: Robert Shappley, Chief Operating Officer
CFO: Eric Delgado, Chief Financial Officer
CMO: Ronald L. Kaufman, M.D., Chief Medical Officer
CIO: Pat Pierce, Director Information Systems
CHR: Mary Okuhara, Chief Human Resource Officer
CNO: Terri Newton, Chief Nursing Officer
Web address: www.lakewoodregional.com
Control: Corporation, Investor–owned, for–profit **Service:** General Medical and Surgical

Staffed Beds: 153 **Admissions:** 8279 **Census:** 109 **Outpatient Visits:** 79586 **Births:** 0 **Total Expense ($000):** 152701 **Payroll Expense ($000):** 73321 **Personnel:** 826

LANCASTER—Los Angeles County

☒ **ANTELOPE VALLEY HOSPITAL (050056)**, 1600 West Avenue J, Zip 93534–2894; tel. 661/949–5000, (Nonreporting) **A**1 2 3 5 10
Primary Contact: John Rossfeld, Chief Executive Officer
COO: Ronald T. Bingham, Chief Operating Officer
CFO: Paul Brydon, Chief Financial Officer
CMO: Radha Krishnan, M.D., Chief Medical Officer
CIO: Dale Lepper, Chief Information Officer
CHR: George Leisher, Jr., Chief Human Resources Officer
CNO: Jack J. Burke, MS, Chief Operating Officer and Chief Nursing Officer
Web address: www.avhospital.org
Control: Hospital district or authority, Government, nonfederal **Service:** General Medical and Surgical

Staffed Beds: 368

LEMOORE—Kings County

★ **NAVAL HOSPITAL LEMOORE**, 937 Franklin Avenue, Zip 93246–0001; tel. 559/998–4481, (Nonreporting) **S** Bureau of Medicine and Surgery, Department of the Navy, Falls Church, VA
Primary Contact: Captain Mary A. Mahony, Commanding Officer
CFO: Thomas M. Brui, Director Resource Management
CMO: Scott Cota, M.D., Director Medical Services
CIO: Victor Dela Torre, Command Legal Officer
CHR: Billy Newman, Department Head
Web address: www.med.navy.mil/sites/nhlem/Pages/index.aspx
Control: Navy, Government, federal **Service:** General Medical and Surgical

Staffed Beds: 16

LIVERMORE—Alameda County

VALLEY MEMORIAL See Stanford Health Care – ValleyCare, Pleasanton

VETERANS AFFAIRS PALO ALTO HEALTH CARE SYSTEM, LIVERMORE DIVISION See VA Palo Alto Health Care System, Palo Alto

LODI—San Joaquin County

☒ **LODI MEMORIAL HOSPITAL (050336)**, 975 South Fairmont Avenue, Zip 95240–5118, Mailing Address: P.O. Box 3004, Zip 95241–1908; tel. 209/334–3411, (Includes LODI MEMORIAL HOSPITAL WEST, 800 South Lower Sacramento Road, Zip 95242; tel. 209/333–0211) **A**1 3 10 **F**2 3 11 12 18 20 28 29 30 31 32 34 35 40 45 46 47 49 50 53 55 56 57 59 60 62 64 65 66 68 70 74 75 76 77 79 81 82 84 85 86 87 90 91 92 93 96 97 107 108 111 114 115 119 120 121 126 127 130 131 132 135 144 146 148 **P**6 7 **S** Adventist Health, Roseville, CA
Primary Contact: Daniel Wolcott, President and Chief Executive Officer
CFO: Terry Deak, Chief Financial Officer
CHR: Mark T. Wallace, Director Human Resources
CNO: Debbie Moreno, Chief Nursing Officer
Web address: www.lodihealth.org
Control: Other not–for–profit (including NFP Corporation) **Service:** General Medical and Surgical

Staffed Beds: 214 **Admissions:** 7964 **Census:** 96 **Outpatient Visits:** 252965 **Births:** 1050 **Total Expense ($000):** 184836 **Payroll Expense ($000):** 78408 **Personnel:** 1113

Many Facility Codes have changed. Please refer to the AHA Guide Code Chart. © 2016 AHA Guide

CA

LOMA LINDA—San Bernardino County

LOMA LINDA UNIVERSITY CHILDREN'S HOSPITAL (050778), 11234 Anderson Street, Zip 92354–2804; tel. 909/558–8000 **A**5 **F**3 11 13 19 21 23 25 27 29 31 34 39 44 50 54 55 57 58 59 60 61 64 65 66 68 71 72 74 75 76 77 78 79 80 81 82 84 85 86 87 88 89 97 119 130 132 134 135 136 137 138 141 146 147 **P**3 **S** Loma Linda University Adventist Health Sciences Center, Loma Linda, CA
Primary Contact: Kerry Heinrich, JD, Chief Executive Officer
Web address: www.llu.edu/lluch
Control: Other not–for–profit (including NFP Corporation) **Service:** General Medical and Surgical

Staffed Beds: 337 Admissions: 10594 Census: 198 Outpatient Visits: 66986 Births: 2134 Total Expense ($000): 339389 Payroll Expense ($000): 145881 Personnel: 1234

LOMA LINDA UNIVERSITY HEART & SURGICAL HOSPITAL See Loma Linda University Medical Center

☒ △ **LOMA LINDA UNIVERSITY MEDICAL CENTER (050327)**, 11234 Anderson Street, Zip 92354–2804, Mailing Address: P.O. Box 2000, Zip 92354–0200; tel. 909/558–4000, (Includes LOMA LINDA UNIVERSITY EAST CAMPUS HOSPITAL, 25333 Barton Road, Zip 92354–3053; tel. 909/558–6000; LOMA LINDA UNIVERSITY HEART & SURGICAL HOSPITAL, 26780 Barton Road, Zip 92354; tel. 909/583–2900) **A**1 2 3 5 7 8 10 **F**2 3 8 11 12 15 17 18 20 22 24 26 28 29 30 31 34 35 37 40 41 43 44 45 46 47 48 49 50 54 57 58 59 60 64 65 68 70 74 75 77 78 79 81 82 84 85 86 87 90 91 92 93 94 96 107 108 110 111 114 115 117 118 119 120 121 122 123 124 126 129 130 132 137 138 139 141 142 143 144 146 147 148 **P**3 **S** Loma Linda University Adventist Health Sciences Center, Loma Linda, CA
Primary Contact: Kerry Heinrich, JD, Chief Executive Officer
COO: Trevor Wright, Chief Operating Officer
CFO: Steve Mohr, Senior Vice President Finance and Chief Financial Officer
CMO: H. Roger Hadley, M.D., Vice President, Medical Affairs
CIO: Mark Zirkelbach, Chief Information Officer
CNO: Judith Storfjell, Ph.D., Senior Vice President and Chief Nursing Officer
Web address: www.llumc.edu
Control: Other not–for–profit (including NFP Corporation) **Service:** General Medical and Surgical

Staffed Beds: 507 Admissions: 20411 Census: 356 Outpatient Visits: 637398 Births: 0 Total Expense ($000): 998525 Payroll Expense ($000): 336376 Personnel: 6121

☒ △ **VETERANS AFFAIRS LOMA LINDA HEALTHCARE SYSTEM**, 11201 Benton Street, Zip 92357–1000; tel. 909/825–7084, (Nonreporting) **A**1 2 3 5 7 8 **S** Department of Veterans Affairs, Washington, DC
Primary Contact: Barbara Fallen, FACHE, Director
COO: Shane Elliott, Associate Director Administration
CFO: Eric C. Sorenson, Chief Financial Officer
CMO: Dwight Evans, M.D., Chief of Staff
CIO: Doug Wirthgen, Facility Chief Information Officer
CHR: Eugene Wylie, Chief Human Resources Officer
CNO: Anne Gillespie, R.N., Associate Director Patient Care and Nursing Services
Web address: www.lomalinda.va.gov
Control: Veterans Affairs, Government, federal **Service:** General Medical and Surgical

Staffed Beds: 268

LOMPOC—Santa Barbara County

★ **LOMPOC VALLEY MEDICAL CENTER (050110)**, 1515 East Ocean Avenue, Zip 93436–7092, Mailing Address: P.O. Box 1058, Zip 93438–1058; tel. 805/737–3300, (Nonreporting) **A**10 22
Primary Contact: James J. Raggio, Chief Executive Officer
COO: Naishadh Buch, Chief Operating Officer
CFO: Robert M. Baden, Chief Financial Officer
CMO: Randall Michel, M.D., Chief of Staff
CIO: Jim White, Chief Information Officer
CHR: Edwin R. Braxton, Director Human Resources
CNO: Jayne Scalise, R.N., Chief Nursing Executive
Web address: www.lompocvmc.com
Control: Hospital district or authority, Government, nonfederal **Service:** General Medical and Surgical

Staffed Beds: 170

LONE PINE—Inyo County

SOUTHERN INYO HEALTHCARE DISTRICT (051302), 501 East Locust Street, Zip 93545–1009, Mailing Address: P.O. Box 1009, Zip 93545–1009; tel. 760/876–5501, (Nonreporting) **A**10 18
Primary Contact: Alan Germany, Chief Executive Officer and Chief Restructuring Officer
CFO: Marise Andrade, Controller
CIO: Phyllis Gregory, Registered Health Information Administrator
CHR: Nancy Erickson, Human Resource Director
CNO: Colleen Wilson, Chief Nursing Officer
Web address: www.sihd.org
Control: Hospital district or authority, Government, nonfederal **Service:** General Medical and Surgical

Staffed Beds: 37

LONG BEACH—Los Angeles County

◇ **COLLEGE MEDICAL CENTER (050776)**, 2776 Pacific Avenue, Zip 90806–2699, Mailing Address: P.O. Box 1268, Zip 90801–1268; tel. 562/595–1911, (Nonreporting) **A**10 12 13 21
Primary Contact: Joseph Avelino, Chief Executive Officer
COO: Jennifer Ensminger, Chief Operating Officer
CFO: Jim Canedo, Chief Financial Officer
CMO: Luke Watson, M.D., Chief of Staff
CIO: Rohan Corea, Director Healthcare Information Technology
CHR: Ann Mattia Schiller, Vice President Human Resources
Web address: www.collegemedicalcenter.com/
Control: Other not–for–profit (including NFP Corporation) **Service:** General Medical and Surgical

Staffed Beds: 157

☐ **COMMUNITY HOSPITAL LONG BEACH (050727)**, 1720 Termino Avenue, Zip 90804–2104; tel. 562/498–1000 **A**1 5 10 **F**3 4 5 8 11 12 14 18 26 28 29 30 31 34 35 38 40 45 46 49 50 53 54 56 57 59 64 65 68 70 71 75 77 79 81 82 85 86 87 93 98 100 101 102 103 104 105 107 108 111 115 119 130 132 135 146 148 **S** MemorialCare, Fountain Valley, CA
Primary Contact: John Bishop, Chief Executive Officer
CFO: Yair Katz, Chief Financial Officer
CMO: S. Gainer Pillsbury, M.D., Associate Chief Medical Officer
CIO: Richele Steele, Vice President, Marketing and Public Relations
CHR: Marcie Atchison, Vice President Human Resources
CNO: Sheryl Howland, R.N., Executive Director, Patient Care Services
Web address: www.memorialcare.org
Control: Other not–for–profit (including NFP Corporation) **Service:** General Medical and Surgical

Staffed Beds: 158 Admissions: 5502 Census: 64 Outpatient Visits: 30264 Births: 0 Total Expense ($000): 70383 Payroll Expense ($000): 28503 Personnel: 452

☒ △ **LONG BEACH MEMORIAL MEDICAL CENTER (050485)**, 2801 Atlantic Avenue, Zip 90806–1701, Mailing Address: P.O. Box 1428, Zip 90801–1428; tel. 562/933–2000 **A**1 2 3 5 7 8 10 **F**3 8 9 11 12 14 15 17 18 20 22 24 26 28 29 30 31 34 35 36 37 38 39 40 43 44 45 47 48 49 50 52 53 55 56 57 58 59 61 63 64 65 68 70 74 75 77 78 79 81 82 84 85 86 87 90 93 96 97 107 108 110 111 114 115 116 117 118 119 120 121 123 124 126 128 129 130 131 132 135 141 142 143 144 146 147 148 **S** MemorialCare, Fountain Valley, CA
Primary Contact: John Bishop, Chief Executive Officer
COO: Tamra Kaplan, Chief Operating Officer
CFO: Yair Katz, Chief Financial Officer
CMO: Susan Melvin, D.O., Chief Medical Officer
CIO: Danny Asaoka, Executive Director Information Systems
CHR: Marcie Atchison, Vice President, Human Resources
CNO: Judith A. Fix, R.N., Senior Vice President and Chief Nursing Officer
Web address: www.memorialcare.org/LongBeach
Control: Other not–for–profit (including NFP Corporation) **Service:** General Medical and Surgical

Staffed Beds: 458 Admissions: 20906 Census: 279 Outpatient Visits: 201087 Births: 0 Total Expense ($000): 590991 Payroll Expense ($000): 187305 Personnel: 3306

Hospital, Medicare Provider Number, Address, Telephone, Approval, Facility, and Physician Codes, Health Care System

★ American Hospital Association (AHA) membership
☐ The Joint Commission accreditation
○ Healthcare Facilities Accreditation Program
◇ DNV Healthcare Inc. accreditation
⇑ Center for Improvement in Healthcare Quality Accreditation
△ Commission on Accreditation of Rehabilitation Facilities (CARF) accreditation

☐ **MILLER CHILDREN'S & WOMEN'S HOSPITAL LONG BEACH (053309)**, 2801 Atlantic Avenue, Zip 90806–1701; tel. 562/933–5437 **A**1 2 3 5 10 **F**3 11 12 13 14 15 19 21 23 25 27 29 30 31 32 34 35 36 37 38 40 41 43 44 45 47 48 49 50 52 53 54 55 57 58 59 61 64 65 66 68 72 74 75 76 77 78 79 81 82 84 85 86 87 88 89 93 96 97 99 100 101 102 104 107 108 111 114 115 116 117 118 119 120 121 123 124 126 129 130 132 134 135 141 142 143 144 146 147 148 **S** MemorialCare, Fountain Valley, CA
Primary Contact: John Bishop, Chief Executive Officer
COO: Suzie Reinsvold, Chief Operating Officer
CFO: Yair Katz, Chief Financial Officer
CIO: Danny Asaoka, Executive Director Information Systems
CHR: Marcie Atchison, Vice President Human Resources
CNO: Joyce Volsch, Vice President, Nursing Services
Web address: www.memorialcare.org
Control: Other not–for–profit (including NFP Corporation) **Service:** Children's general

Staffed Beds: 371 **Admissions:** 15997 **Census:** 203 **Outpatient Visits:** 95920 **Births:** 6053 **Total Expense ($000):** 423794 **Payroll Expense ($000):** 134461 **Personnel:** 1273

✉ **ST. MARY MEDICAL CENTER (050191)**, 1050 Linden Avenue, Zip 90813–3321, Mailing Address: P.O. Box 887, Zip 90801–0887; tel. 562/491–9000 **A**1 2 3 5 10 **F**3 8 12 13 15 18 19 20 22 24 26 28 29 30 31 32 34 35 38 39 40 41 43 45 46 47 48 49 50 54 55 56 57 59 60 61 64 65 66 68 70 71 72 74 75 76 77 78 79 80 81 82 84 85 86 87 89 90 92 93 96 97 100 104 107 108 110 111 114 115 118 119 120 121 122 123 125 130 143 145 146 147 148 **P**5 **S** Dignity Health, San Francisco, CA
Primary Contact: Joel P. Yuhas, FACHE, President and Chief Executive Officer
COO: Paul M. Czajka, Vice President Chief Operating Officer
CFO: Leon Choiniere, Vice President, Chief Financial Officer
CIO: David Ung, Site Director
CHR: Denise Livingston, Director Human Resources
CNO: Jodi Hein, R.N., Vice President Chief Nurse Executive
Web address: www.stmarymedicalcenter.org
Control: Other not–for–profit (including NFP Corporation) **Service:** General Medical and Surgical

Staffed Beds: 302 **Admissions:** 10743 **Census:** 137 **Outpatient Visits:** 133571 **Births:** 2412 **Total Expense ($000):** 276828 **Payroll Expense ($000):** 102554 **Personnel:** 1111

✉ △ **VA LONG BEACH HEALTHCARE SYSTEM**, 5901 East 7th Street, Zip 90822–5201; tel. 562/826–8000, (Nonreporting) **A**1 2 3 5 7 8 **S** Department of Veterans Affairs, Washington, DC
Primary Contact: Tracye B. Davis, Acting Director
COO: Anthony DeFrancesco, Associate Director
CFO: Michael J. Rupert, Chief Financial Officer
CMO: Sandor Szabo, M.D., Chief of Staff
CIO: Rodney Sagmit, Chief Information Management
CHR: Mary E. McCartan, Manager Human Resources
Web address: www.longbeach.va.gov/
Control: Veterans Affairs, Government, federal **Service:** General Medical and Surgical

Staffed Beds: 356

LOS ALAMITOS—Orange County

✉ **LOS ALAMITOS MEDICAL CENTER (050551)**, 3751 Katella Avenue, Zip 90720–3164; tel. 562/598–1311 **A**1 10 13 **F**3 8 11 13 14 15 18 20 22 26 28 29 31 34 35 40 45 49 50 51 54 56 57 58 59 60 61 64 65 66 68 69 70 74 75 76 77 78 79 81 82 84 85 87 98 100 103 107 108 110 111 114 115 116 117 118 119 120 121 122 123 124 126 130 132 135 142 143 146 147 148 **S** TENET Healthcare Corporation, Dallas, TX
Primary Contact: Kent R. Clayton, Chief Executive Officer
COO: Clay Farell, Chief Operation Officer
CFO: Dave Vickers, Chief Financial Officer
CMO: Nirav Patel, M.D., Chief of Staff
CIO: Sally Andrada, Chief Information Officer
CHR: Lisa Oremus, Interim Chief Human Resource Officer
CNO: Judy Chabot, Chief Nursing Officer
Web address: www.losalamitosmedctr.com
Control: Corporation, Investor–owned, for–profit **Service:** General Medical and Surgical

Staffed Beds: 167 **Admissions:** 9448 **Census:** 123 **Outpatient Visits:** 84761 **Births:** 1239 **Total Expense ($000):** 173394 **Payroll Expense ($000):** 78175 **Personnel:** 684

LOS ANGELES—Los Angeles County

(Mailing Addresses - Canoga Park, Encino, Granada Hills, Harbor City, Hollywood, Mission Hills, North Hollywood, Northridge, Panorama City, San Pedro, Sepulveda, Sherman Oaks, Sun Valley, Sylmar, Tarzana, Van Nuys, West Hills, West Los Angeles, Woodland Hills)

✉ **BARLOW RESPIRATORY HOSPITAL (052031)**, 2000 Stadium Way, Zip 90026–2696; tel. 213/250–4200, (Nonreporting) **A**1 10
Primary Contact: Amit Mohan, President and Chief Executive Officer
CFO: Edward Engesser, Chief Financial Officer and Chief Information Officer
CMO: David Nelson, M.D., Medical Director
CIO: Edward Engesser, Chief Financial Officer and Chief Information Officer
CHR: Rashawn Woods, Vice President Human Resources
CNO: Gladys D'Souza, Chief Nursing Officer
Web address: www.barlow2000.org
Control: Other not–for–profit (including NFP Corporation) **Service:** Long–Term Acute Care hospital

Staffed Beds: 92

✉ **CALIFORNIA HOSPITAL MEDICAL CENTER (050149)**, 1401 South Grand Avenue, Zip 90015–3010; tel. 213/748–2411, (Total facility includes 31 beds in nursing home–type unit) **A**1 3 5 10 **F**3 11 15 17 18 20 22 24 26 29 30 31 34 35 40 43 45 49 50 51 57 59 64 70 72 75 76 78 79 81 82 84 87 89 102 107 108 110 111 114 118 119 120 121 128 130 132 135 143 146 147 **S** Dignity Health, San Francisco, CA
Primary Contact: Margaret R. Peterson, Ph.D., R.N., President
CFO: Rebecca Cheng, Chief Financial Officer
CMO: Joseph Nussbaum, M.D., Chief of Staff
CIO: David Ung, Director, Information Technology
CHR: Kristin Anderson, Director, Human Resources
CNO: Valarie Fleming, MSN, Chief Nursing Executive
Web address: www.chmcla.org
Control: Other not–for–profit (including NFP Corporation) **Service:** General Medical and Surgical

Staffed Beds: 318 **Admissions:** 17110 **Census:** 194 **Outpatient Visits:** 103940 **Births:** 3893 **Total Expense ($000):** 409027 **Payroll Expense ($000):** 141001

✉ △ **CEDARS–SINAI MEDICAL CENTER (050625)**, 8700 Beverly Boulevard, Zip 90048–1865, Mailing Address: Box 48750, Zip 90048–0750; tel. 310/423–5000 **A**1 2 3 5 7 8 10 **F**3 4 11 12 13 14 15 17 18 19 20 21 22 23 24 25 26 27 28 29 30 31 32 33 34 35 36 37 38 39 40 43 44 45 46 47 48 49 50 51 52 53 54 55 56 57 58 59 60 61 64 65 66 68 69 70 71 72 74 75 76 77 78 79 81 82 83 84 85 86 87 88 89 90 91 92 93 96 97 100 102 107 108 109 110 111 112 113 114 115 116 117 118 119 120 121 122 123 124 126 130 131 132 133 134 135 136 137 138 139 140 141 142 145 146 147 148 **P**3 5 6 **S** Cedars–Sinai, West Hollywood, CA
Primary Contact: Thomas M. Priselac, President and Chief Executive Officer
COO: Mark R. Gavens, Executive Vice President Health System Hospital Operations and Chief Operating Officer of Cedars–Sinai Medical Center
CFO: Edward M. Prunchunas, Executive Vice President and Chief Financial Officer
CMO: Michael L. Langberg, M.D., Senior Vice President Medical Affairs and Chief Medical Officer
CIO: Darren Dworkin, Senior Vice President Enterpirse Information Systems and Chief Information Officer
CHR: Jeanne Flores, Consultant to the President
CNO: Linda Burnes Bolton, R.N., Vice President and Chief Nursing Officer
CNO: Linda Burnes Bolton, R.N., Health System Chief Nurse Executive and Vice President and Chief Nursing Officer
Web address: www.cedars–sinai.edu
Control: Other not–for–profit (including NFP Corporation) **Service:** General Medical and Surgical

Staffed Beds: 885 **Admissions:** 47114 **Census:** 666 **Outpatient Visits:** 785639 **Births:** 6738 **Total Expense ($000):** 2711277 **Payroll Expense ($000):** 982339 **Personnel:** 11953

✉ **CHILDREN'S HOSPITAL LOS ANGELES (053302)**, 4650 West Sunset Boulevard, Zip 90027–6062, Mailing Address: 4650 West Sunset Boulevard, MS #1, Zip 90027–6062; tel. 323/660–2450 **A**1 3 5 10 **F**3 5 14 17 19 21 23 25 27 29 30 31 32 34 35 36 38 39 40 41 43 44 45 46 49 50 51 54 55 57 58 59 60 61 64 68 71 72 74 75 77 78 79 80 81 82 84 85 86 87 88 89 90 92 93 95 96 99 100 104 107 108 111 114 115 116 117 118 119 120 121 122 123 124 126 129 130 131 132 134 135 136 137 138 139 141 142 146 148
Primary Contact: Paul S. Viviano, President and Chief Executive Officer
CFO: Lannie Tonnu, Senior Vice President and Chief Financial Officer
CMO: Brent Polk, M.D., Chair Department of Pediatrics and Vice President Academic Affairs
CIO: TJ Malseed, Vice President and Chief Information Officer
CHR: Myra Gregorian, Vice President and Chief Human Resources Officer
CNO: Mary Dee Hacker, R.N., Vice President, Patient Care Services and Chief Nursing Officer
Web address: www.chla.org
Control: Other not–for–profit (including NFP Corporation) **Service:** Children's general

Staffed Beds: 357 **Admissions:** 15797 **Census:** 291 **Outpatient Visits:** 360117 **Births:** 0 **Total Expense ($000):** 1008587 **Payroll Expense ($000):** 347254 **Personnel:** 4969

☐ **EAST LOS ANGELES DOCTORS HOSPITAL (050641)**, 4060 Whittier Boulevard, Zip 90023–2526; tel. 323/268–5514, (Nonreporting) **A**1 10 **S** Avanti Hospitals, El Segundo, CA
Primary Contact: Araceli Lonergan, Chief Executive Officer
CFO: Steven Blake, Corporate Chief Financial Officer
CMO: Janine King, M.D., Chief of Staff
CIO: Jason Cervantes, Chief Information Officer
CHR: Paul Celuch, Chief Human Resource Officer
CNO: Kimberly Frazier, R.N., Chief Nursing Officer
Web address: www.avantihospitals.com
Control: Partnership, Investor–owned, for–profit **Service:** General Medical and Surgical

Staffed Beds: 127

☒ **ENCINO HOSPITAL MEDICAL CENTER (050158)**, 16237 Ventura Boulevard, Encino, Zip 91436–2272; tel. 818/995–5000, (Total facility includes 26 beds in nursing home–type unit) **A**1 10 **F**4 17 29 35 38 40 51 57 70 79 81 98 103 107 118 119 128 130 146 **S** Prime Healthcare Services, Ontario, CA
Primary Contact: Bockhi Park, Chief Executive Officer
CFO: Kanner Tillman, Chief Financial Officer
CMO: Muhammad Anwar, M.D., Chief Medical Officer
CIO: Edward Barrera, Director Communications
CHR: Barbara Back, Manager Human Resources
CNO: Vilma L. Dinham, R.N., Chief Nursing Officer
Web address: www.encinomed.com
Control: Other not–for–profit (including NFP Corporation) **Service:** General Medical and Surgical

Staffed Beds: 80 **Admissions:** 2669 **Census:** 58 **Outpatient Visits:** 12530 **Births:** 0 **Total Expense ($000):** 51921 **Payroll Expense ($000):** 21755 **Personnel:** 277

○ **GATEWAYS HOSPITAL AND MENTAL HEALTH CENTER (054028)**, 1891 Effie Street, Zip 90026–1793; tel. 323/644–2000 **A**10 11 **F**29 35 77 94 98 99 100 101 104 106 130 **P**6
Primary Contact: Mara Pelsman, Chief Executive Officer
COO: Phil Wong, PsyD, Chief Operating Officer
CMO: Imani Walker, M.D., Medical Director
CIO: Rozelle DeVera, Director of Information Systems
CHR: Vahan Demlakian, Director of Human Resources
Web address: www.gatewayshospital.org
Control: Other not–for–profit (including NFP Corporation) **Service:** Psychiatric

Staffed Beds: 55 **Admissions:** 990 **Census:** 32 **Outpatient Visits:** 103654 **Births:** 0 **Personnel:** 305

☒ ◇ **GLENDALE ADVENTIST MEDICAL CENTER (050239)**, 8700 Beverly Boulevard, NT–3138, Zip 90048, Mailing Address: 1509 Wilson Terrace, Glendale, Zip 91206–4098; tel. 818/409–8000 **A**1 2 3 5 10 21 **F**3 5 8 12 13 15 17 18 20 22 24 26 28 29 30 31 32 34 35 36 37 40 44 45 46 47 48 49 51 53 54 56 57 58 59 63 64 65 68 70 71 72 74 75 76 77 78 79 81 82 83 84 85 86 87 89 90 91 92 93 96 98 102 103 104 105 106 107 108 109 110 111 114 115 118 119 120 121 124 126 128 129 130 131 132 135 145 146 147 148 **P**3 **S** Adventist Health, Roseville, CA
Primary Contact: Kevin A. Roberts, FACHE, President and Chief Executive Officer
COO: Warren Tetz, Senior Vice President and Chief Operating Officer
CFO: Kelly Turner, Senior Vice President Finance and Chief Financial Officer
CMO: Arby Nahapetian, M.D., Vice President Medical Affairs and Quality
CIO: Sharon Correa, Vice President and Chief Information Officer
CNO: Judy Blair, Senior Vice President Clinical Services and Chief Nursing Officer
Web address: www.glendaleadventist.com
Control: Church–operated, Nongovernment, not–for profit **Service:** General Medical and Surgical

Staffed Beds: 462 **Admissions:** 19973 **Census:** 277 **Outpatient Visits:** 282218 **Births:** 2326 **Total Expense ($000):** 429378 **Payroll Expense ($000):** 154213 **Personnel:** 2459

☐ **GOOD SAMARITAN HOSPITAL (050471)**, 1225 Wilshire Boulevard, Zip 90017–2395; tel. 213/977–2121 **A**1 2 3 5 10 **F**3 7 8 11 13 14 15 17 18 20 22 24 26 28 29 30 31 34 35 37 40 43 45 46 47 48 49 50 51 53 57 58 59 60 64 65 68 70 72 74 75 76 77 78 79 81 85 86 87 93 107 108 110 111 114 115 117 118 119 120 121 123 124 126 129 130 132 143 145 146 148 **P**5
Primary Contact: Andrew B. Leeka, President and Chief Executive Officer
CFO: Alan Ino, Chief Financial Officer
CMO: Margaret Bates, Chief of Staff
CIO: Dean Campbell, Vice President Information Services and Chief Information Officer
CHR: Lexie Schuster, Vice President Human Resources
CNO: Margaret Pfeiffer, R.N., Vice President Patient Care Services
Web address: www.goodsam.org
Control: Other not–for–profit (including NFP Corporation) **Service:** General Medical and Surgical

Staffed Beds: 374 **Admissions:** 12595 **Census:** 160 **Outpatient Visits:** 74149 **Births:** 3444 **Total Expense ($000):** 338236 **Payroll Expense ($000):** 145430 **Personnel:** 1326

☒ **HOLLYWOOD PRESBYTERIAN MEDICAL CENTER (050063)**, 1300 North Vermont Avenue, Zip 90027–6306; tel. 213/413–3000 **A**1 3 5 10 **F**3 8 13 15 17 18 20 22 24 26 29 30 31 34 40 41 45 46 49 50 51 56 57 59 60 61 64 68 70 72 74 75 76 77 78 79 80 81 85 87 89 90 92 96 97 107 108 110 111 115 119 130 146 147 148 **P**3 5
Primary Contact: Gerald B. Clute, Chief Executive Officer
CFO: Janice Klostermeier, Vice President, Chief Financial Officer
CIO: Steve Giles, Chief Information Officer
CHR: George Leisher, Jr., Vice President Human Resources
CNO: Julieta M. Padilla, Chief Nursing Officer
Web address: www.hollywoodpresbyterian.com
Control: Partnership, Investor–owned, for–profit **Service:** General Medical and Surgical

Staffed Beds: 434 **Admissions:** 12390 **Census:** 153 **Outpatient Visits:** 52625 **Births:** 3716 **Total Expense ($000):** 246262 **Payroll Expense ($000):** 96032 **Personnel:** 1303

KAISER FOUNDATION MENTAL HEALTH CENTER See Kaiser Permanente Los Angeles Medical Center

☒ **KAISER PERMANENTE LOS ANGELES MEDICAL CENTER (050138)**, 4867 Sunset Boulevard, Zip 90027–5961; tel. 323/783–4011, (Includes KAISER FOUNDATION MENTAL HEALTH CENTER, 765 West College Street, Zip 90012; tel. 213/580–7200) **A**1 3 5 8 10 **F**3 5 8 13 15 17 18 19 20 21 22 23 24 26 28 29 30 31 35 36 38 40 41 44 45 46 47 49 50 51 54 55 56 57 58 59 60 61 62 63 64 65 66 68 70 72 73 74 75 76 77 78 79 80 81 82 83 84 85 86 87 88 89 92 93 94 97 98 99 100 101 102 103 104 105 106 107 108 109 110 111 113 114 115 118 119 120 121 122 123 124 126 129 130 131 132 135 144 146 147 148 **P**6 **S** Kaiser Foundation Hospitals, Oakland, CA
Primary Contact: William N. Grice, Executive Director
COO: Derek Berz, Chief Operating Officer
CFO: Brad Malsed, Area Chief Financial Officer
CMO: Michael Tome, M.D., Medical Director
CIO: David Strickland, Area Information Officer
CHR: Paul J. Martin, Director Human Resources
Web address: www.kaiserpermanente.org
Control: Other not–for–profit (including NFP Corporation) **Service:** General Medical and Surgical

Staffed Beds: 528 **Admissions:** 22614 **Census:** 347 **Outpatient Visits:** 83272 **Births:** 2016 **Personnel:** 5666

☒ **KAISER PERMANENTE PANORAMA CITY MEDICAL CENTER (050137)**, 13652 Cantara Street, Panorama City, Zip 91402–5497; tel. 818/375–2000, (Nonreporting) **A**1 3 5 10 **S** Kaiser Foundation Hospitals, Oakland, CA
Primary Contact: Payman Roshan, Senior Vice President and Area Manager
COO: Murtaza Sanwari, Chief Operating Officer
CFO: Karla Valle, Area Chief Financial Officer
CMO: James Lau, M.D., Area Medical Director
CIO: Earle Johnson, Area Information Officer
CHR: Carole L. Erken, Human Resources Leader
CNO: Celeste Farugia, R.N., Chief Nurse Executive
Web address: www.kaiserpermanente.org
Control: Other not–for–profit (including NFP Corporation) **Service:** General Medical and Surgical

Staffed Beds: 194

CA

Hospital, Medicare Provider Number, Address, Telephone, Approval, Facility, and Physician Codes, Health Care System

★ American Hospital Association (AHA) membership   ○ Healthcare Facilities Accreditation Program   ⇑ Center for Improvement in Healthcare Quality Accreditation
☐ The Joint Commission accreditation   ◇ DNV Healthcare Inc. accreditation   △ Commission on Accreditation of Rehabilitation Facilities (CARF) accreditation

KAISER PERMANENTE SOUTH BAY MEDICAL CENTER (050411), 25825 Vermont Avenue, Harbor City, Zip 90710–3599; tel. 310/325–5111 **A**1 3 10 **F**3 12 13 15 18 29 30 31 34 35 38 40 44 45 46 47 48 49 50 57 58 59 60 61 64 65 68 70 72 75 76 77 78 79 81 84 85 86 87 89 100 107 108 110 111 114 116 117 118 119 130 135 143 146 147 148 **P**6 **S** Kaiser Foundation Hospitals, Oakland, CA
Primary Contact: Lesley A. Wille, Executive Director
Web address: www.kaiserpermanente.org
Control: Other not–for–profit (including NFP Corporation) **Service:** General Medical and Surgical

Staffed Beds: 225 **Admissions:** 17937 **Census:** 121 **Outpatient Visits:** 84937 **Births:** 2457 **Personnel:** 3238

KAISER PERMANENTE WEST LOS ANGELES MEDICAL CENTER (050561), 6041 Cadillac Avenue, Zip 90034–1700; tel. 323/857–2201 **A**1 3 5 10 **F**3 9 12 13 15 29 30 31 32 34 35 37 40 45 46 47 48 49 50 55 56 57 59 60 61 64 65 68 70 72 73 74 77 78 79 80 81 82 83 84 85 86 87 97 100 101 103 104 105 107 108 110 111 114 115 116 117 119 126 130 131 132 135 144 146 147 148 **P**6 **S** Kaiser Foundation Hospitals, Oakland, CA
Primary Contact: Georgina R. Garcia, R.N., Executive Director
CFO: Alice H. Issai, Business Strategy and Finance Leader
CMO: Fred Alexander, M.D., Medical Director
CIO: Gregory M. Sincock, Information Technology Leader
Web address: www.kaiserpermanente.org
Control: Other not–for–profit (including NFP Corporation) **Service:** General Medical and Surgical

Staffed Beds: 133 **Admissions:** 15850 **Census:** 126 **Outpatient Visits:** 82855 **Births:** 1916 **Total Expense ($000):** 1254085 **Payroll Expense ($000):** 108738 **Personnel:** 2343

KAISER PERMANENTE WOODLAND HILLS MEDICAL CENTER (050677), 5601 DeSoto Avenue, Woodland Hills, Zip 91367–6798; tel. 818/719–2000 **A**1 3 5 10 **F**3 13 15 17 18 29 30 31 34 40 41 45 48 49 50 51 55 56 57 60 61 64 65 68 70 73 74 75 76 77 78 79 80 81 82 84 85 86 89 92 93 100 102 103 107 108 110 111 114 115 117 119 124 130 132 141 146 147 148 **P**6 **S** Kaiser Foundation Hospitals, Oakland, CA
Primary Contact: Dennis C. Benton, Senior Vice President and Area Manager
COO: Richard Trogman, FACHE, Chief Operating Officer
CFO: Marilou Cheung, Assistant Administrator Finance
CMO: Gregory Kelman, M.D., Area Medical Director
CIO: Earle Johnson, Area Information Officer
CHR: Cathy Cousineau, Director Human Resources
CNO: Nancy Tankel, R.N., Chief Nurse Executive
Web address: www.kaiserpermanente.org
Control: Other not–for–profit (including NFP Corporation) **Service:** General Medical and Surgical

Staffed Beds: 128 **Admissions:** 14049 **Census:** 117 **Outpatient Visits:** 42337 **Births:** 1662 **Personnel:** 1486

KECK HOSPITAL OF USC (050696), 1500 San Pablo Street, Zip 90033–5313; tel. 323/442–8500 **A**1 3 5 8 10 **F**3 6 8 9 11 12 15 17 18 20 22 24 26 28 29 30 31 34 35 36 37 38 39 44 45 46 47 48 49 50 51 52 53 54 55 56 57 58 59 60 61 64 65 68 70 71 74 75 77 78 79 81 82 84 85 86 87 90 92 93 94 96 97 100 101 104 107 108 110 111 112 114 115 116 117 118 119 123 124 126 129 130 131 132 135 137 138 139 140 141 142 143 145 146 147 148 **P**1 **S** Keck Medicine of USC, Los Angeles, CA
Primary Contact: Rodney B. Hanners, Chief Executive Officer
COO: Alice H. Issai, Chief Operating Officer
CFO: Robert Allen, Chief Financial Officer
CMO: Stephanie Hall, M.D., Chief Medical Officer
CHR: Matthew McElrath, Chief Human Resources Officer
CNO: Annette Sy, Chief Nursing Officer
Web address: www.keckhospitalofusc.org
Control: Other not–for–profit (including NFP Corporation) **Service:** General Medical and Surgical

Staffed Beds: 316 **Admissions:** 12147 **Census:** 243 **Outpatient Visits:** 290786 **Births:** 0 **Total Expense ($000):** 836374 **Payroll Expense ($000):** 294180 **Personnel:** 3069

KEDREN COMMUNITY MENTAL HEALTH CENTER (054083), 4211 South Avalon Boulevard, Zip 90011–5699; tel. 323/233–0425, (Nonreporting) **A**10
Primary Contact: John H. Griffith, Ph.D., President & Chief Executive Officer
COO: Madeline Valencerina, Chief Operating Officer
CFO: Rizwan A. Uraizee, Chief Financial Officer
CMO: Frank L. Williams, Executive Vice President/ Medical Director
CNO: Essie Adams, Director of Nursing
Web address: www.kedrenmentalhealth.com
Control: Other not–for–profit (including NFP Corporation) **Service:** Psychiatric

Staffed Beds: 72

KINDRED HOSPITAL–LOS ANGELES (052032), 5525 West Slauson Avenue, Zip 90056–1067; tel. 310/642–0325, (Nonreporting) **A**1 10 **S** Kindred Healthcare, Louisville, KY
Primary Contact: Phillip R. Wolfe, Chief Executive Officer
CFO: Charles Natcher, Chief Financial Officer
Web address: www.kindredhospitalla.com/
Control: Corporation, Investor–owned, for–profit **Service:** Long–Term Acute Care hospital

Staffed Beds: 81

LAC+USC MEDICAL CENTER (050373), 2051 Marengo Street, Zip 90033–1352; tel. 323/409–1000, (Includes GENERAL HOSPITAL, 1200 North State Street, Zip 90033; WOMEN'S AND CHILDREN'S HOSPITAL, 1240 North Mission Road, Zip 90033) **A**1 2 3 5 8 10 **F**3 12 13 15 16 17 18 19 20 21 22 23 24 25 26 28 29 30 31 32 34 35 39 40 41 43 44 45 46 47 48 49 50 51 52 53 54 55 56 57 58 59 60 61 63 64 65 66 68 70 71 72 73 74 75 76 77 78 79 80 81 83 84 85 86 87 88 89 91 92 93 94 97 98 99 100 101 102 103 104 107 108 110 111 114 115 116 117 118 119 120 121 129 130 131 132 133 134 141 144 146 147 148 **S** Los Angeles County–Department of Health Services, Los Angeles, CA
Primary Contact: Dan A. Castillo, FACHE, Chief Executive Officer
COO: Henry Ornelas, Chief Operating Officer
CFO: Mark Corbet, Interim Chief Financial Officer
CMO: Brad Spellberg, M.D., Chief Medical Officer
CIO: Oscar Autelli, Chief Information Officer
CHR: Elizabeth Jacobi, Human Resources Director
CNO: Isabel Milan, R.N., Chief Nursing Officer
Web address: www.lacusc.org
Control: County–Government, nonfederal **Service:** General Medical and Surgical

Staffed Beds: 664 **Admissions:** 27630 **Census:** 539 **Outpatient Visits:** 563866 **Births:** 1029 **Total Expense ($000):** 1405263 **Payroll Expense ($000):** 491831 **Personnel:** 7705

LAC–OLIVE VIEW–UCLA MEDICAL CENTER (050040), 14445 Olive View Drive, Sylmar, Zip 91342–1438; tel. 818/364–1555 **A**1 3 5 10 **F**3 13 15 18 19 20 22 26 29 30 31 40 41 45 46 48 49 50 51 58 59 60 61 62 63 64 65 66 68 70 72 74 76 78 79 81 83 84 85 87 89 93 94 97 98 100 102 103 104 105 107 108 110 111 114 115 116 117 118 119 130 143 144 146 147 148 **S** Los Angeles County–Department of Health Services, Los Angeles, CA
Primary Contact: Carolyn F. Rhee, Chief Executive Officer
COO: Niloo Shahi, Chief Operating Officer
CFO: Anthony Gray, Chief Financial Officer
CMO: Shannon Thyne, Chief Medical Officer
CIO: Susan Aintablian, Chief Information Officer
CHR: Thomas Beggane, Manager Human Resources
CNO: Dellone Pascascio, Chief Nursing Officer
Web address: www.ladhs.org
Control: County–Government, nonfederal **Service:** General Medical and Surgical

Staffed Beds: 275 **Admissions:** 11939 **Census:** 184 **Outpatient Visits:** 242663 **Births:** 602 **Total Expense ($000):** 468616 **Payroll Expense ($000):** 187581 **Personnel:** 2444

◇ **LOS ANGELES COMMUNITY HOSPITAL AT LOS ANGELES (050663)**, 4081 East Olympic Boulevard, Zip 90023–3330; tel. 323/267–0477, (Includes LOS ANGELES COMMUNITY HOSPITAL OF NORWALK, 13222 Bloomfield Avenue, Norwalk, Zip 90650; tel. 562/863–4763), (Nonreporting) **A**10 21 **S** Alta Healthcare System, Los Angeles, CA
Primary Contact: Omar Ramirez, Chief Executive Officer
CFO: Johnnette Chong, Chief Financial Officer
Control: Corporation, Investor–owned, for–profit **Service:** General Medical and Surgical

Staffed Beds: 180

LOS ANGELES COUNTY CENTRAL JAIL HOSPITAL, 441 Bauchet Street, Zip 90012–2906; tel. 213/473–6100, (Nonreporting)
Primary Contact: Tom Flaherty, Assistant Administrator
Control: County–Government, nonfederal **Service:** Hospital unit of an institution (prison hospital, college infimary, etc.)

Staffed Beds: 190

LOS ANGELES MEDICAL CENTER See Kaiser Permanente Los Angeles Medical Center

MARTIN LUTHER KING, JR. COMMUNITY HOSPITAL (050779), 1680 East 120th Street, Zip 90059–3026; tel. 424/338–8000, (Data for 41 days) **F**3 13 18 34 40 45 50 57 59 60 65 68 70 74 75 76 78 79 81 84 85 86 87 91 100 107 111 119 120 130 148
Primary Contact: Elaine Batchlor, M.D., M.P.H., Chief Executive Officer
COO: Myrna Allen, R.N., Chief Operating and Nursing Officer
CMO: John Fisher, M.D., Chief Medical Officer
CIO: Sajid Ahmed, Chief Information and Innovation Officer
CHR: Susan M. Burrows, Vice President Human Resources
CNO: Myrna Allen, R.N., Chief Operating and Nursing Officer
Web address: www.mlkcommunityhospital.org/
Control: Other not–for–profit (including NFP Corporation) **Service:** General Medical and Surgical

Staffed Beds: 46 **Admissions:** 30 **Census:** 4 **Outpatient Visits:** 0 **Births:** 0 **Total Expense ($000):** 53454 **Payroll Expense ($000):** 12398 **Personnel:** 1035

☐ **MIRACLE MILE MEDICAL CENTER (050751)**, 6000 San Vicente Boulevard, Zip 90036–4404; tel. 323/930–1040, (Nonreporting) **A**1 10
Primary Contact: Gil Tepper, M.D., Chief Executive Officer
COO: Liz Cheever, Administrator
CFO: Bert Roberts, Controller
CMO: Gil Tepper, M.D., Chief of Staff
CIO: Jonathan Lindell, Director Information Technology
CHR: Liz Cheever, Administrator
CNO: Melody Bradley, Chief Nursing Officer
Web address: www.miraclemilemedicalcenter.com
Control: Individual, Investor–owned, for–profit **Service:** General Medical and Surgical

Staffed Beds: 17

☐ **MISSION COMMUNITY HOSPITAL (050704)**, 14850 Roscoe Boulevard, Panorama City, Zip 91402–4677; tel. 818/787–2222, (Nonreporting) **A**1 5 10
Primary Contact: James Theiring, Chief Executive Officer
CMO: Glenn Marshak, M.D., Chief of Staff
CIO: Eric Rivers, Chief Information Officer
CHR: Carolyn Fish, Director Human Resources
CNO: Gwendolyn Dianne Wagner, R.N., Chief Nursing Officer
Web address: www.mchonline.org
Control: Other not–for–profit (including NFP Corporation) **Service:** General Medical and Surgical

Staffed Beds: 115

MOTION PICTURE AND TELEVISION FUND HOSPITAL AND RESIDENTIAL SERVICES (050552), 23388 Mulholland Drive, Woodland Hills, Zip 91364–2792; tel. 818/876–1888, (Nonreporting) **A**10
Primary Contact: Bob Beitcher, Chief Executive Officer
COO: David Asplund, Chief Operating Officer
CFO: Frank Guarrera, Executive Vice President and Chief Financial Officer
CHR: Nancy Rubin, Vice President Human Resources
Web address: www.mptvfund.org
Control: Other not–for–profit (including NFP Corporation) **Service:** General Medical and Surgical

Staffed Beds: 20

✠ △ **NORTHRIDGE HOSPITAL MEDICAL CENTER (050116)**, 18300 Roscoe Boulevard, Northridge, Zip 91328–4167; tel. 818/885–8500 **A**1 2 3 5 7 10 **F**1 2 3 5 8 11 12 13 14 15 17 18 20 22 24 26 28 29 30 31 34 35 38 40 41 43 48 49 56 57 58 59 60 61 64 68 70 72 73 74 75 76 77 78 79 81 82 84 85 86 87 88 89 90 93 97 98 99 100 101 102 103 104 105 107 108 110 111 114 117 118 119 121 124 126 129 130 132 134 146 147 148 **S** Dignity Health, San Francisco, CA
Primary Contact: Saliba Salo, President
CFO: Michael Taylor, Vice President Finance
CHR: Susan Paulsen, Director Human Resources
CNO: Mary Jane Jones, R.N., Vice President Nursing Operations
Web address: www.northridgehospital.org
Control: Other not–for–profit (including NFP Corporation) **Service:** General Medical and Surgical

Staffed Beds: 371 **Admissions:** 13952 **Census:** 176 **Outpatient Visits:** 61148 **Births:** 1134 **Total Expense ($000):** 395785 **Payroll Expense ($000):** 140369 **Personnel:** 1625

◇ **OLYMPIA MEDICAL CENTER (050742)**, 5900 West Olympic Boulevard, Zip 90036–4671; tel. 310/657–5900, (Nonreporting) **A**3 10 21
Primary Contact: John A. Calderone, Ph.D., Chief Executive Officer
CFO: Matthew Williams, R.N., Chief Financial Officer
CMO: Panch Jeyakumar, M.D., Chief of Staff
CIO: Jason Williams, Director Information Systems
CHR: Joseph Ambrosini, Director Human Resources
CNO: Sylvia A. Ventura, R.N., Chief Nursing Officer
Web address: www.olympiamc.com
Control: Partnership, Investor–owned, for–profit **Service:** General Medical and Surgical

Staffed Beds: 204

☐ **PACIFIC ALLIANCE MEDICAL CENTER (050018)**, 531 West College Street, Zip 90012–2385; tel. 213/624–8411, (Nonreporting) **A**1 10
Primary Contact: John R. Edwards, Administrator and Chief Executive Officer
CFO: Allan Shubin, Chief Financial Officer
CIO: John D. Brown, Director Information Systems
Web address: www.pamc.net
Control: Partnership, Investor–owned, for–profit **Service:** General Medical and Surgical

Staffed Beds: 138

☐ **PACIFICA HOSPITAL OF THE VALLEY (050378)**, 9449 San Fernando Road, Sun Valley, Zip 91352–1489; tel. 818/767–3310, (Nonreporting) **A**1 10
Primary Contact: Ayman Mousa, R.N., Ph.D., Chief Executive Officer
COO: Daniel Santos, Director Ancillary Services
CFO: Eileen Fisler, Chief Financial Officer
CMO: Joseph Eipe, M.D., Chief Medical Officer
CIO: Mubashir Hashmi, Chief Information Officer
CHR: Patti Alonzo, Manager Human Resources
CNO: Janet B. Latto, Chief Nursing Officer and Disaster Officer
Web address: www.pacificahospital.com
Control: Corporation, Investor–owned, for–profit **Service:** General Medical and Surgical

Staffed Beds: 231

PANORAMA CITY MEDICAL CENTER See Kaiser Permanente Panorama City Medical Center

☐ **PROMISE HOSPITAL OF EAST LOS ANGELES (052046)**, 443 South Soto Street, Zip 90033–4398; tel. 323/261–1181, (Includes PROMISE HOSPITAL OF EAST LOS ANGELES, SUBURBAN MEDICAL CENTER CAMPUS, 16453 South Colorado Avenue, Paramount, Zip 90723–5000; tel. 562/531–3110; Michael D. Kerr, Chief Executive Officer), (Nonreporting) **A**1 10 **S** Promise Healthcare, Boca Raton, FL
Primary Contact: Michael D. Kerr, Chief Executive Officer
Web address: www.promiseeastla.com
Control: Corporation, Investor–owned, for–profit **Service:** Long–Term Acute Care hospital

Staffed Beds: 36

✠ △ **PROVIDENCE HOLY CROSS MEDICAL CENTER (050278)**, 15031 Rinaldi Street, Mission Hills, Zip 91345–1207; tel. 818/365–8051, (Total facility includes 48 beds in nursing home–type unit) **A**1 2 7 10 **F**3 8 11 13 15 17 18 20 22 24 26 28 29 30 31 34 35 36 40 41 43 44 45 46 49 50 54 56 57 58 59 60 61 64 65 68 70 71 72 74 75 76 77 78 79 81 82 83 84 85 87 90 93 94 97 107 108 110 111 114 115 116 117 119 120 121 123 124 126 128 130 131 132 133 143 146 147 148 **S** Providence St. Joseph Health, Renton, WA
Primary Contact: Bernard Klein, M.D., Chief Executive
CFO: Paul Steinke, Chief Financial Officer
CMO: Bob Raggi, M.D., Chief Medical Officer
CHR: Pam Stahl, Regional Chief Human Resources Officer
CNO: Ann Dechairo–Marino, R.N., Chief Nursing Officer
Web address: www.https://california.providence.org/holy–cross/Pages/default.aspx
Control: Church–operated, Nongovernment, not–for profit **Service:** General Medical and Surgical

Staffed Beds: 377 **Admissions:** 18016 **Census:** 261 **Outpatient Visits:** 114394 **Births:** 3326 **Total Expense ($000):** 286071 **Payroll Expense ($000):** 148129 **Personnel:** 1938

✠ △ **PROVIDENCE LITTLE COMPANY OF MARY MEDICAL CENTER SAN PEDRO (050078)**, 1300 West Seventh Street, San Pedro, Zip 90732–3505; tel. 310/832–3311, (Total facility includes 125 beds in nursing home–type unit) **A**1 7 10 **F**2 3 4 5 11 13 14 15 18 29 30 32 34 35 40 44 45 49 50 51 57 59 60 65 66 68 70 71 72 74 75 76 77 78 79 81 82 84 85 86 87 90 92 93 94 96 98 100 101 102 103 104 107 108 110 111 119 120 123 128 130 131 132 133 135 145 146 **P**2 3 5 **S** Providence St. Joseph Health, Renton, WA
Primary Contact: Mary E. Kingston, FACHE, R.N., Chief Executive Officer
COO: Garry M. Olney, Chief Operating Officer
CFO: Elizabeth Zuanich, Chief Financial Officer
CMO: Richard Glimp, M.D., Chief Medical Officer
CIO: Kim Brant–Lucich, Director, Information Systems
CHR: Melissa Baker, Director, Human Resources
CNO: David Neal, MS, Chief Nursing Officer
Web address: www.https://california.providence.org/san–pedro
Control: Church–operated, Nongovernment, not–for profit **Service:** General Medical and Surgical

Staffed Beds: 317 **Admissions:** 7285 **Census:** 210 **Outpatient Visits:** 44986 **Births:** 549 **Total Expense ($000):** 112026 **Payroll Expense ($000):** 71022 **Personnel:** 912

CA

✠ **PROVIDENCE TARZANA MEDICAL CENTER (050761)**, 18321 Clark Street, Tarzana, Zip 91356–3521; tel. 818/881–0800 **A**1 10 **F**3 7 13 15 17 18 19 20 22 24 26 27 28 29 30 31 34 35 40 41 45 46 49 50 55 56 57 59 61 63 64 65 70 72 74 75 77 78 79 81 82 83 84 85 86 87 88 91 92 93 97 107 108 110 111 114 115 119 126 130 131 132 143 145 146 147 148 **P**2 3 5 **S** Providence St. Joseph Health, Renton, WA
Primary Contact: Dale Surowitz, Chief Executive
COO: Phyllis Bushart, R.N., Chief Operating Officer
CFO: Ted Wang, Chief Financial Officer
CIO: Alex Nury, Chief Information Officer
CHR: Wendy Regal, Director Human Resources
Web address: www.providence.org/tarzana.com
Control: Church–operated, Nongovernment, not–for profit **Service:** General Medical and Surgical

Staffed Beds: 249 **Admissions:** 13171 **Census:** 153 **Outpatient Visits:** 65484 **Births:** 2427 **Total Expense ($000):** 191920 **Payroll Expense ($000):** 102785 **Personnel:** 1174

✠ **RONALD REAGAN UCLA MEDICAL CENTER (050262)**, 757 Westwood Plaza, Zip 90095–8358; tel. 310/825–9111, (Includes MATTEL CHILDREN'S HOSPITAL, 757 Westwood Plaza, Zip 90095; tel. 310/825–9111) **A**1 3 5 8 10 **F**3 6 7 8 9 11 12 13 14 15 17 18 19 20 21 22 23 24 25 26 27 28 29 30 31 32 34 35 36 40 41 43 44 45 46 47 48 49 50 52 54 55 56 57 58 59 61 62 64 65 66 68 70 71 72 74 75 76 77 78 79 81 82 83 84 85 86 87 88 89 90 92 93 94 96 97 102 107 108 110 111 112 113 114 115 116 117 118 119 120 121 123 124 126 129 130 131 132 135 136 137 138 139 140 141 142 143 145 146 147 148 **P**6 **S** University of California Systemwide Administration, Oakland, CA
Primary Contact: Johnese Spisso, Chief Executive Officer
COO: J. Shannon O'Kelley, Chief Operating Officer
CFO: Paul Staton, Chief Financial Officer
CMO: Robert Cherry, M.D., Chief Medical and Quality Officer
CIO: Michael Pfeffer, M.D., Chief Information Officer
CHR: Susi Takeuchi, Chief Human Resources and Organization Development Officer
CNO: Karen A. Grimley, Chief Nursing Executive
Web address: www.uclahealth.org
Control: State–Government, nonfederal **Service:** General Medical and Surgical

Staffed Beds: 466 **Admissions:** 23953 **Census:** 456 **Outpatient Visits:** 564828 **Births:** 1898 **Total Expense ($000):** 1605370 **Payroll Expense ($000):** 637500 **Personnel:** 7549

✠ **SHERMAN OAKS HOSPITAL (050755)**, 4929 Van Nuys Boulevard, Sherman Oaks, Zip 91403–1777; tel. 818/981–7111, (Total facility includes 16 beds in nursing home–type unit) **A**1 5 10 **F**17 20 29 31 34 35 38 40 56 57 59 61 64 70 75 77 78 79 81 82 85 98 103 104 105 107 108 118 119 128 130 131 132 146 148 **S** Prime Healthcare Services, Ontario, CA
Primary Contact: Bockhi Park, Chief Executive Officer
CFO: Daniel Leon, Chief Financial Officer
CMO: Michael Malamed, M.D., Chief of Staff
Web address: www.shermanoakshospital.com
Control: Other not–for–profit (including NFP Corporation) **Service:** General Medical and Surgical

Staffed Beds: 90 **Admissions:** 6467 **Census:** 89 **Outpatient Visits:** 36780 **Births:** 0 **Total Expense ($000):** 87849 **Payroll Expense ($000):** 36302 **Personnel:** 619

✠ **SHRINERS HOSPITALS FOR CHILDREN–LOS ANGELES (053310)**, 3160 Geneva Street, Zip 90020–1199; tel. 213/388–3151 **A**1 3 5 10 **F**64 79 81 89 **P**1 **S** Shriners Hospitals for Children, Tampa, FL
Primary Contact: Lou Lazatin, Administrator
CFO: David Burkitt, Director Fiscal Services
CMO: Hugh Watts, M.D., Chief of Staff
CIO: Mark Garrett, Chief Information Officer
Web address: www.shrinershospitalsforchildren.org/Hospitals/Locations/Losangeles.aspx
Control: Other not–for–profit (including NFP Corporation) **Service:** Children's orthopedic

Staffed Beds: 30 **Admissions:** 33 **Census:** 1 **Outpatient Visits:** 6861 **Births:** 0 **Total Expense ($000):** 24578 **Payroll Expense ($000):** 9342 **Personnel:** 135

☐ **SILVER LAKE MEDICAL CENTER (050763)**, 1711 West Temple Street, Zip 90026–5421; tel. 213/989–6100, (Includes SILVER LAKE MEDICAL CENTER–INGLESIDE HOSPITAL, 7500 East Hellman Avenue, Rosemead, Zip 91770; tel. 626/288–1160), (Nonreporting) **A**1 10 **S** Success Healthcare, Boca Raton, FL
Primary Contact: Brent A. Cope, Chief Executive Officer
CFO: John Cowles, Chief Financial Officer
CMO: Louis Acosta, M.D., Chief of Staff
CIO: Scott Musack, Chief Information Officer
CHR: Sylvia Cloud, Director Human Resources
Web address: www.silverlakemc.com
Control: Corporation, Investor–owned, for–profit **Service:** General Medical and Surgical

Staffed Beds: 150

◇ **SOUTHERN CALIFORNIA HOSPITAL AT HOLLYWOOD (050135)**, 6245 De Longpre Avenue, Zip 90028–9001; tel. 323/462–2271, (Includes SOUTHERN CALIFORNIA HOSPITAL AT VAN NUYS, 14433 Emelita Street, Van Nuys, Zip 91401; tel. 818/787–1511), (Nonreporting) **A**10 21 **S** Alta Healthcare System, Los Angeles, CA
Primary Contact: Bruce P. Grimshaw, FACHE, Chief Executive Officer
Web address: www.hollywoodcommunityhospital.org/
Control: Corporation, Investor–owned, for–profit **Service:** General Medical and Surgical

Staffed Beds: 45

SOUTHERN CALIFORNIA HOSPITAL AT VAN NUYS See Southern California Hospital at Hollywood

✠ **ST. VINCENT MEDICAL CENTER (050502)**, 2131 West Third Street, Zip 90057–1901; Mailing Address: P.O. Box 57992, Zip 90057–0992; tel. 213/484–7111, (Nonreporting) **A**1 3 10 **S** Verity Health System, Los Angeles, CA
Primary Contact: Frank J. Cracolici, President and Chief Executive Officer
CFO: Michael Garko, Chief Financial Officer
CMO: Brian Itagaki, M.D., Chief of Staff
CIO: Dan Robbins, Information Technology and Account Executive
CHR: Gail Watts, Director
CNO: Judy McCurdy, R.N., Vice President and Chief Nursing Officer
Web address: www.stvincentmedicalcenter.com
Control: Other not–for–profit (including NFP Corporation) **Service:** General Medical and Surgical

Staffed Beds: 271

✠ **STEWART & LYNDA RESNICK NEUROPSYCHIATRIC HOSPITAL AT UCLA (054009)**, 150 UCLA Medical Plaza, Zip 90095–8353; tel. 310/825–9989 **A**1 3 5 10 **F**3 5 6 29 30 35 40 42 43 55 56 64 68 77 86 87 98 99 100 101 102 103 104 105 130 132 134 147 **P**1 **S** University of California Systemwide Administration, Oakland, CA
Primary Contact: Peter Whybrow, M.D., Chief Executive Officer
COO: Ruth Irwin, Associate Director Clinical Operations
CFO: Ronald Anthony Davis, Chief Financial Officer – UCLA Hospital System
CMO: Thomas Strouse, M.D., Medical Director and Professor of of Clinic Psych
CIO: Michael Pfeffer, M.D., Chief Medical Informatics Officer, UCLA Health
CHR: Monica Rodriquez, Director of Human Resources
CNO: Patricia Matos, Chief Nursing Officer
Web address: www.semel.ucla.edu/resnick
Control: State–Government, nonfederal **Service:** Psychiatric

Staffed Beds: 74 **Admissions:** 1852 **Census:** 68 **Outpatient Visits:** 16840 **Births:** 0 **Total Expense ($000):** 57475 **Payroll Expense ($000):** 34759 **Personnel:** 323

✠ **USC NORRIS COMPREHENSIVE CANCER CENTER (050660)**, 1441 Eastlake Avenue, Zip 90089–0112; tel. 323/865–3000 **A**1 2 3 5 8 10 **F**3 8 11 15 29 30 31 34 35 36 38 39 44 45 46 47 48 49 50 54 55 56 57 58 59 60 61 64 65 68 70 74 75 77 78 79 82 84 85 86 87 92 93 96 100 101 104 107 108 110 111 114 115 118 119 120 121 123 130 132 135 136 143 145 146 147 148 **P**1 **S** Keck Medicine of USC, Los Angeles, CA
Primary Contact: Rodney B. Hanners, Chief Executive Officer
COO: Tarek Salaway, Chief Operating Officer
CFO: Robert Allen, Chief Financial Officer
CMO: Stephanie Hall, M.D., Medical Director
CIO: Joshua Lee, Chief Information Officer
CHR: Matthew McElrath, Chief Human Resources Officer
CNO: Annette Sy, Chief Nursing Officer
Web address: www.uscnorriscancerhospital.org
Control: Other not–for–profit (including NFP Corporation) **Service:** Cancer

Staffed Beds: 60 **Admissions:** 1554 **Census:** 32 **Outpatient Visits:** 114709 **Births:** 0 **Total Expense ($000):** 159627 **Payroll Expense ($000):** 48376 **Personnel:** 368

USC UNIVERSITY HOSPITAL See Keck Hospital of USC

✠ △ **VA GREATER LOS ANGELES HEALTHCARE SYSTEM**, 11301 Wilshire Boulevard, Zip 90073–1003; tel. 310/478–3711, (Nonreporting) **A**1 5 7 8 **S** Department of Veterans Affairs, Washington, DC
Primary Contact: Ann R. Brown, M.D., Director
COO: Susan Shyshka, Associate Director
CFO: Joseph Schmitt, Chief Financial Officer
CIO: Eugene Archey, Chief Information Technology
CHR: Brenda Cabunoc, Chief Human Resources
CNO: James Doelling, Chief Nurse Executive
Web address: www.losangeles.va.gov/
Control: Veterans Affairs, Government, federal **Service:** General Medical and Surgical

Staffed Beds: 1087

Many Facility Codes have changed. Please refer to the AHA Guide Code Chart. © 2016 AHA Guide

★ ◇ **VALLEY PRESBYTERIAN HOSPITAL (050126)**, 15107 Vanowen Street, Van Nuys, Zip 91405–4597; tel. 818/782–6600 **A**5 10 21 **F**3 13 18 20 22 24 28 29 30 31 34 35 40 41 44 45 46 49 50 53 55 57 59 64 65 70 72 74 75 76 77 78 79 81 85 86 87 88 89 90 96 107 108 114 115 118 119 130 145 146 148 **P**5
Primary Contact: Gustavo A. Valdespino, President and Chief Executive Officer
COO: Gayathri S. Jith, M.P.H., Senior Vice President Strategy and Operations
CFO: Lori Cardle, Senior Vice President, Chief Financial Officer
CIO: Jeff Allport, Vice President, Chief Information Officer
CHR: Jonathan Wu, Vice President Human Resources
CNO: Lori Burnell, R.N., Senior Vice President and Chief Nursing Officer
Web address: www.valleypres.org
Control: Other not–for–profit (including NFP Corporation) **Service:** General Medical and Surgical

Staffed Beds: 350 **Admissions:** 14899 **Census:** 184 **Outpatient Visits:** 113056 **Births:** 3395 **Total Expense ($000):** 339873 **Payroll Expense ($000):** 112039 **Personnel:** 1345

⊞ **WEST HILLS HOSPITAL AND MEDICAL CENTER (050481)**, 7300 Medical Center Drive, West Hills, Zip 91307–1900; tel. 818/676–4000 **A**1 10 **F**3 12 13 14 15 16 18 20 22 24 26 28 29 31 34 35 37 40 41 45 46 50 54 57 64 66 68 70 72 74 75 76 77 78 79 81 85 86 87 91 92 93 94 107 108 110 111 114 118 119 130 131 132 146 147 148 **S** HCA, Nashville, TN
Primary Contact: Douglas Long, President and Chief Executive Officer
COO: Omar Chughtai, Vice President and Chief Operating Officer
CFO: David Cantrell, CPA, Vice President and Chief Financial Officer
CHR: Diana Steel, Vice President Human Resources
CNO: Stephanie Mearns, R.N., Vice President and Chief Nursing Officer
Web address: www.westhillshospital.com
Control: Corporation, Investor–owned, for–profit **Service:** General Medical and Surgical

Staffed Beds: 293 **Admissions:** 9264 **Census:** 122 **Outpatient Visits:** 92847 **Births:** 893

WEST LOS ANGELES MEDICAL CENTER See Kaiser Permanente West Los Angeles Medical Center

⊞ **WHITE MEMORIAL MEDICAL CENTER (050103)**, 1720 Cesar Chavez Avenue, Zip 90033–2414; tel. 323/268–5000, (Total facility includes 27 beds in nursing home–type unit) **A**1 2 3 5 8 10 **F**3 11 13 15 17 18 19 20 22 24 26 27 28 29 30 31 34 35 40 41 45 46 47 48 49 50 51 53 57 58 59 64 68 70 72 74 75 76 78 79 81 82 84 85 86 87 88 89 90 91 92 93 96 98 99 102 103 107 108 109 110 111 114 115 116 117 118 119 120 121 123 128 130 131 132 146 147 148 **S** Adventist Health, Roseville, CA
Primary Contact: John Raffoul, Chief Executive Officer
CIO: Ralf Weissenberger, Director Information Systems
CHR: Natasha Milatovich, Association Vice President Human Resources
CNO: Patricia Stone, R.N., Senior Vice President Operations and Chief Nursing Officer
Web address: www.whitememorial.com
Control: Church–operated, Nongovernment, not–for profit **Service:** General Medical and Surgical

Staffed Beds: 353 **Admissions:** 19595 **Census:** 238 **Outpatient Visits:** 69145 **Births:** 3699 **Total Expense ($000):** 390230 **Payroll Expense ($000):** 133683 **Personnel:** 1534

WOODLAND HILLS MEDICAL CENTER See Kaiser Permanente Woodland Hills Medical Center

LOS BANOS—Merced County

⊞ **MEMORIAL HOSPITAL LOS BANOS (050528)**, 520 West I Street, Zip 93635–3498; tel. 209/826–0591 **A**1 10 20 **F**3 11 13 15 18 29 30 34 35 40 45 46 49 50 57 59 64 66 68 70 75 76 81 85 87 107 110 111 115 119 127 130 132 135 146 **P**3 **S** Sutter Health, Sacramento, CA
Primary Contact: Doug Archer, Administrator
CFO: Timothy J. Noakes, Chief Financial Officer
CHR: Shawn Garcia, Manager Human Resources
CNO: Kristie Marion, Chief Nurse Executive
Web address: www.memoriallosbanos.org/
Control: Other not–for–profit (including NFP Corporation) **Service:** General Medical and Surgical

Staffed Beds: 35 **Admissions:** 1568 **Census:** 10 **Outpatient Visits:** 59957 **Births:** 661 **Total Expense ($000):** 48683 **Payroll Expense ($000):** 14909 **Personnel:** 224

LYNWOOD—Los Angeles County

⊞ **ST. FRANCIS MEDICAL CENTER (050104)**, 3630 East Imperial Highway, Zip 90262–2636; tel. 310/900–8900, (Nonreporting) **A**1 10 **S** Verity Health System, Los Angeles, CA
Primary Contact: Gerald T. Kozai, PharmD, President and Chief Executive Officer
CFO: Nancy Wilson, Senior Vice President and Chief Financial Officer
CIO: Judi Binderman, Chief Information Technology Officer and Chief Medical Informatics Officer
CHR: Laura Kato, Vice President Human Resources
CNO: Mary Lynne Knighten, R.N., Chief Nursing Officer and Vice President Patient Care Services
Web address: www.dochs.org
Control: Other not–for–profit (including NFP Corporation) **Service:** General Medical and Surgical

Staffed Beds: 323

MADERA—Madera County

◯ **MADERA COMMUNITY HOSPITAL (050568)**, 1250 East Almond Avenue, Zip 93637–5696, Mailing Address: P.O. Box 1328, Zip 93639–1328; tel. 559/675–5501 **A**10 11 19 **F**13 18 29 30 34 40 45 46 47 48 49 54 59 64 65 70 74 75 76 79 81 82 87 107 108 110 111 119 127 132 146 148 **P**5
Primary Contact: Evan J. Rayner, Chief Executive Officer
COO: Karen Paolmelli, Chief Operating Officer
CFO: Mark Foote, Chief Financial Officer
CIO: Jerry Kovalski, Director Information Systems
CHR: Christine M. Watts–Johnson, Assistant Vice President
CNO: Meri Combs, R.N., Vice President and Chief Nursing Officer
Web address: www.maderahospital.org
Control: Other not–for–profit (including NFP Corporation) **Service:** General Medical and Surgical

Staffed Beds: 106 **Admissions:** 3797 **Census:** 43 **Outpatient Visits:** 136930 **Births:** 1111 **Total Expense ($000):** 93812 **Payroll Expense ($000):** 30730 **Personnel:** 677

⊞ △ **VALLEY CHILDREN'S HEALTHCARE (053300)**, 9300 Valley Children's Place, Zip 93636–8761; tel. 559/353–3000 **A**1 3 5 7 8 10 **F**3 8 9 11 19 21 23 25 27 28 29 30 31 32 34 35 38 40 41 44 46 48 49 50 54 55 57 58 59 60 61 62 64 65 68 72 73 74 75 77 78 79 81 82 84 85 86 87 88 89 90 93 94 97 107 108 111 114 115 119 127 129 130 131 132 134 143 146 147 148
Primary Contact: Todd A. Suntrapak, President and Chief Executive Officer
CFO: Michele Waldron, Senior Vice President and Chief Financial Officer
CMO: David Christensen, M.D., Senior Vice President and Chief Medical Officer
CIO: Kevin Shimamoto, Vice President and Chief Informational Officer
CHR: Nat Ponticello, Vice President Human Resources
CNO: Beverly P. Hayden–Pugh, R.N., Senior Vice President and Chief Nursing Officer
Web address: www.valleychildrens.org
Control: Other not–for–profit (including NFP Corporation) **Service:** Children's general

Staffed Beds: 356 **Admissions:** 13704 **Census:** 208 **Outpatient Visits:** 282198 **Births:** 0 **Total Expense ($000):** 508287 **Payroll Expense ($000):** 182431 **Personnel:** 2202

MAMMOTH LAKES—Mono County

◇ **MAMMOTH HOSPITAL (051303)**, 85 Sierra Park Road, Zip 93546–2073, Mailing Address: P.O. Box 660, Zip 93546–0660; tel. 760/934–3311 **A**10 18 21 **F**3 13 15 29 31 34 35 39 40 45 46 50 53 57 59 64 65 68 70 74 75 77 78 79 81 82 85 93 94 97 107 110 111 114 119 127 131 132 146 147
Primary Contact: Gary Myers, Chief Executive Officer
CFO: Melanie Van Winkle, Chief Financial Officer
CMO: Yuri Parisky, M.D., Chief of Staff
CIO: Mark Lind, Chief Information Officer
CHR: Sarah Vigilante, Manager Human Resources
CNO: Kathleen Alo, Chief Nursing Officer
Web address: www.mammothhospital.com
Control: Hospital district or authority, Government, nonfederal **Service:** General Medical and Surgical

Staffed Beds: 17 **Admissions:** 583 **Census:** 3 **Outpatient Visits:** 88803 **Births:** 110 **Total Expense ($000):** 56665 **Payroll Expense ($000):** 17656 **Personnel:** 268

Hospital, Medicare Provider Number, Address, Telephone, Approval, Facility, and Physician Codes, Health Care System

★ American Hospital Association (AHA) membership ◯ Healthcare Facilities Accreditation Program ⇑ Center for Improvement in Healthcare Quality Accreditation
☐ The Joint Commission accreditation ◇ DNV Healthcare Inc. accreditation △ Commission on Accreditation of Rehabilitation Facilities (CARF) accreditation

CA

MANTECA—San Joaquin County

✠ **DOCTORS HOSPITAL OF MANTECA (050118)**, 1205 East North Street, Zip 95336–4900; tel. 209/823–3111 **A**1 10 **F**3 11 12 13 15 29 31 34 35 40 45 49 50 51 64 75 76 78 79 81 85 102 107 108 110 111 115 116 117 118 119 130 132 146 147 148 **S** TENET Healthcare Corporation, Dallas, TX
Primary Contact: Ikenna Mmeje, Chief Executive Officer
COO: Carmen Silva, R.N., Chief Operating Officer
CFO: Michael Szymanski, Chief Financial Officer
CHR: Traci Holzer, Chief Human Resources Officer
CNO: Kathy Daley, Chief Nursing Officer
Web address: www.doctorsmanteca.com
Control: Corporation, Investor–owned, for–profit **Service:** General Medical and Surgical

> **Staffed Beds:** 56 **Admissions:** 3916 **Census:** 38 **Outpatient Visits:** 70110 **Births:** 689 **Total Expense ($000):** 76679 **Payroll Expense ($000):** 38875 **Personnel:** 426

✠ **KAISER PERMANENTE MANTECA MEDICAL CENTER (050748)**, 1777 West Yosemite Avenue, Zip 95337–5187; tel. 209/825–3700, (Includes MODESTO MEDICAL CENTER, 4601 Dale Road, Modesto, Zip 95356–9718; tel. 209/735–5000; Corwin N. Harper, Administrator), (Nonreporting) **A**1 10 **S** Kaiser Foundation Hospitals, Oakland, CA
Primary Contact: Deborah G. Friberg, Senior Vice President and Area Manager
COO: Corwin N. Harper, Senior Vice President and Area Manager
CFO: Debra L. Brown, Area Financial Officer
CMO: Moses D. Elam, M.D., Physician–in–Chief
CIO: Tom J. Osteen, Director Area Technology
CHR: Pat McKeldin, Human Resource Business Partner
Web address: www.kaiserpermanente.org
Control: Other not–for–profit (including NFP Corporation) **Service:** General Medical and Surgical

> **Staffed Beds:** 239

MARINA DEL REY—Los Angeles County

✠ **MARINA DEL REY HOSPITAL (050740)**, 4650 Lincoln Boulevard, Zip 90292–6306; tel. 310/823–8911, (Nonreporting) **A**1 10 **S** Cedars–Sinai, West Hollywood, CA
Primary Contact: Paulette Heitmeyer, Administrator and Chief Operating Officer
COO: Phyllis Buchart, Chief Operating Officer
CFO: Stephen A. Hargett, Senior Vice President and Chief Financial Officer
Web address: www.marinahospital.com
Control: Corporation, Investor–owned, for–profit **Service:** General Medical and Surgical

> **Staffed Beds:** 90

MARIPOSA—Mariposa County

★ **JOHN C. FREMONT HEALTHCARE DISTRICT (051304)**, 5189 Hospital Road, Zip 95338–9524, Mailing Address: P.O. Box 216, Zip 95338–0216; tel. 209/966–3631, (Nonreporting) **A**10 18
Primary Contact: Alan MacPhee, Chief Executive Officer
CFO: Matthew Matthiessen, Chief Financial Officer
CMO: Kenneth P. Smith, Chief of Staff
CIO: Phil Blas, Chief Information Officer
CHR: Martha Robichaux, Chief Human Resources Officer
CNO: Theresa Loya, R.N., Chief Nursing Officer
Web address: www.jcf–hospital.com
Control: Hospital district or authority, Government, nonfederal **Service:** General Medical and Surgical

> **Staffed Beds:** 34

MARTINEZ—Contra Costa County

✠ **CONTRA COSTA REGIONAL MEDICAL CENTER (050276)**, 2500 Alhambra Avenue, Zip 94553–3156; tel. 925/370–5000 **A**1 2 3 10 **F**3 11 13 15 18 30 31 35 36 39 40 45 49 50 54 56 59 61 62 64 65 66 68 70 71 72 73 74 75 76 77 78 79 81 82 84 85 86 87 93 97 98 100 102 103 104 107 108 111 115 119 130 132 143 146 147 148 **P**6
Primary Contact: Anna M. Roth, R.N., MS, M.P.H., Chief Executive Officer
COO: Timothy Thompson–Cook, Chief Operating Officer
CFO: Patrick Godley, Chief Financial Officer
CMO: David Goldstein, M.D., Chief Medical Officer
CNO: Jaspreet Benepal, Chief Nursing Officer
Web address: www.cchealth.org/medical_center/
Control: County–Government, nonfederal **Service:** General Medical and Surgical

> **Staffed Beds:** 124 **Admissions:** 8675 **Census:** 124 **Outpatient Visits:** 466573 **Births:** 2278 **Total Expense ($000):** 506072 **Payroll Expense ($000):** 172638 **Personnel:** 1887

KAISER FOUNDATION HOSPITAL See Kaiser Permanente Walnut Creek Medical Center, Walnut Creek

MARYSVILLE—Yuba County

★ **RIDEOUT MEMORIAL HOSPITAL (050133)**, 726 Fourth Street, Zip 95901–5600; tel. 530/749–4300, (Includes FREMONT MEDICAL CENTER, 970 Plumas Street, Yuba City, Zip 95991–4087; tel. 530/751–4000) **A**2 10 20 **F**3 8 13 15 17 18 19 20 22 24 28 29 30 31 40 43 45 47 49 54 59 64 68 70 72 74 77 78 79 81 82 85 91 93 94 96 97 107 110 111 114 115 116 117 119 120 121 123 124 130 145 147 148 **P**3
Primary Contact: Gino Patrizio, Chief Executive Officer
COO: Melissa Burns, Chief Operating Officer
CIO: Tarun Ghosh, Chief Information Officer
CHR: Tresha Moreland, MS, Vice President Human Resources
Web address: www.frhg.org
Control: Other not–for–profit (including NFP Corporation) **Service:** General Medical and Surgical

> **Staffed Beds:** 212 **Admissions:** 10849 **Census:** 138 **Outpatient Visits:** 231088 **Births:** 1994 **Total Expense ($000):** 360946 **Payroll Expense ($000):** 108488 **Personnel:** 1607

MENLO PARK—San Mateo County

✠ **MENLO PARK SURGICAL HOSPITAL (050754)**, 570 Willow Road, Zip 94025–2617; tel. 650/324–8500 **A**1 10 **F**18 35 64 68 79 81 82 85 **P**3 **S** Sutter Health, Sacramento, CA
Primary Contact: Kathleen Palange, R.N., Chief Administrative Officer
CMO: Andrew Gutow, M.D., Medical Director
CNO: Marjorie Eckford, Chief Nursing Officer
Web address: www.pamf.org/mpsh
Control: Other not–for–profit (including NFP Corporation) **Service:** General Medical and Surgical

> **Staffed Beds:** 12 **Admissions:** 190 **Census:** 1 **Outpatient Visits:** 3287 **Births:** 0 **Total Expense ($000):** 13172 **Payroll Expense ($000):** 3997 **Personnel:** 40

MERCED—Merced County

✠ **MERCY MEDICAL CENTER MERCED (050444)**, 333 Mercy Avenue, Zip 95340–8319; tel. 209/564–5000, (Includes MERCY MEDICAL CENTER MERCED–DOMINICAN CAMPUS, 2740 M Street, Zip 95340–2880; tel. 209/384–6444; Charles Kassis, President) **A**1 3 5 10 19 **F**3 8 13 15 18 20 26 28 29 30 34 35 40 41 45 46 49 50 54 57 59 62 64 65 66 68 70 74 75 76 77 79 81 82 84 86 87 88 90 92 93 96 97 107 108 110 111 115 119 127 130 132 146 148 **P**3 **S** Dignity Health, San Francisco, CA
Primary Contact: Charles Kassis, President
CFO: Michael Strasser, Vice President and Chief Financial Officer
CMO: Robert Streeter, M.D., Vice President Medical Affairs
CIO: Daniel Andresen, Chief information Officer
CHR: Julie Rocha, Vice President Human Resources
CNO: Greg Rouleau, Vice President Nursing
Web address: www.mercymercedcares.org
Control: Other not–for–profit (including NFP Corporation) **Service:** General Medical and Surgical

> **Staffed Beds:** 186 **Admissions:** 10742 **Census:** 114 **Outpatient Visits:** 170632 **Births:** 2718 **Total Expense ($000):** 277772 **Payroll Expense ($000):** 95215 **Personnel:** 2813

MISSION HILLS—Los Angeles County, See Los Angeles

MISSION VIEJO—Orange County

☐ **CHOC CHILDREN'S AT MISSION HOSPITAL (053306)**, 27700 Medical Center Road, Zip 92691–6426; tel. 949/364–1400 **A**1 5 10 **F**3 11 36 72 74 79 81 85 88 89 129
Primary Contact: Kimberly C. Cripe, President and Chief Executive Officer
COO: Matthew S. Gerlach, Chief Operating Officer
CFO: Kerri Ruppert Schiller, Senior Vice President and Chief Financial Officer
CMO: Maria Minon, M.D., Vice President Medical Affairs and Chief Medical Officer
CIO: Mark Headland, Chief Information Officer
CHR: Mamoon Syed, Vice President Human Resources
Web address: www.choc.org
Control: Other not–for–profit (including NFP Corporation) **Service:** Children's general

> **Staffed Beds:** 54 **Admissions:** 2206 **Census:** 21 **Outpatient Visits:** 23731 **Births:** 0 **Total Expense ($000):** 51268 **Payroll Expense ($000):** 8368 **Personnel:** 88

Many Facility Codes have changed. Please refer to the AHA Guide Code Chart. © 2016 AHA Guide

✠ △ **MISSION HOSPITAL (050567)**, 27700 Medical Center Road, Zip 92691–6474; tel. 949/364–1400, (Includes MISSION HOSPITAL LAGUNA BEACH, 31872 Coast Highway, Laguna Beach, Zip 92651–6775; tel. 949/499–1311; Richard Afable, M.D., M.P.H., Interim President and Chief Executive Officer) **A**1 2 7 10 **F**3 4 5 8 11 13 14 15 17 18 20 22 24 26 28 29 30 31 34 35 36 40 43 44 45 46 47 48 49 50 53 54 57 58 59 64 65 66 68 70 74 75 76 77 78 79 80 81 82 84 85 86 87 90 92 93 96 98 100 101 104 105 107 108 110 111 112 114 115 116 117 118 119 120 121 123 126 129 130 131 132 134 135 141 143 145 146 147 148 **P**3 5 **S** Providence St. Joseph Health, Renton, WA
Primary Contact: Richard Afable, M.D., M.P.H., Interim President & Chief Executive Officer
COO: Tarek Salaway, Chief Operating Officer
CFO: Eileen Haubl, Senior Vice President and Chief Financial Officer
CMO: Linda Sieglen, M.D., Chief Medical Officer
CIO: Bill Russell, Senior Chief Information Officer
CHR: Terri Covert, Vice President Human Resources
Web address: www.mission4health.com
Control: Church–operated, Nongovernment, not–for profit **Service:** General Medical and Surgical

Staffed Beds: 235 **Admissions:** 19901 **Census:** 235 **Outpatient Visits:** 200003 **Births:** 2672 **Total Expense ($000):** 505088 **Payroll Expense ($000):** 139841 **Personnel:** 1989

MODESTO—Stanislaus County

★ ◇ **CENTRAL VALLEY SPECIALTY HOSPITAL (052055)**, 730 17th Street, Zip 95354–1209; tel. 209/248–7700, (Nonreporting) **A**21
Primary Contact: Gia Smith, Chief Executive Officer
Web address: www.centralvalleyspecialty.org/CVSH/
Control: Partnership, Investor–owned, for–profit **Service:** Long–Term Acute Care hospital

Staffed Beds: 100

✠ **DOCTORS MEDICAL CENTER OF MODESTO (050464)**, 1441 Florida Avenue, Zip 95350–4418, Mailing Address: P.O. Box 4138, Zip 95352–4138; tel. 209/578–1211 **A**1 2 3 10 **F**3 13 17 18 20 22 24 26 28 29 31 34 35 40 41 43 45 46 48 49 50 51 55 57 59 60 65 70 72 74 75 76 77 78 79 80 81 85 89 98 102 103 107 108 109 110 111 112 113 114 115 116 117 118 119 126 130 132 146 147 **S** TENET Healthcare Corporation, Dallas, TX
Primary Contact: Warren J. Kirk, Chief Executive Officer
CFO: Greg Berry, Chief Financial Officer
CMO: Edward Stanford, M.D., Chief Medical officer
CIO: Debbie Fuller, Director Health Information Systems and Chief Information Officer
CHR: Michele Bava, Director Human Resources
CNO: Cheryl Harless, Chief Nursing Officer
Web address: www.dmc–modesto.com
Control: Corporation, Investor–owned, for–profit **Service:** General Medical and Surgical

Staffed Beds: 455 **Admissions:** 24673 **Census:** 345 **Outpatient Visits:** 147530 **Births:** 3795 **Total Expense ($000):** 462636 **Payroll Expense ($000):** 206710 **Personnel:** 2309

✠ **MEMORIAL MEDICAL CENTER (050557)**, 1700 Coffee Road, Zip 95355–2869, Mailing Address: P.O. Box 942, Zip 95353–0942; tel. 209/526–4500, (Includes MEMORIAL MEDICAL CENTER, 1700 Coffee Road, Zip 95355, Mailing Address: Box 942, Zip 95353; tel. 209/526–4500) **A**1 2 10 **F**3 5 8 11 12 13 18 20 22 24 28 29 30 31 34 35 40 43 44 45 46 47 48 49 50 51 57 58 59 60 62 64 68 70 72 74 75 76 77 78 79 81 82 84 85 86 87 89 107 108 111 114 115 118 119 120 121 123 124 126 130 146 148 **P**3 **S** Sutter Health, Sacramento, CA
Primary Contact: Daryn J. Kumar, Chief Executive Officer
COO: Steve Mitchell, Chief Operating Officer
CFO: Eric Dalton, Chief Financial Officer
CIO: Patrick Anderson, Chief Information Officer
CHR: Paula Rafala, Director, Human Resources
CNO: Sandra Proctor, R.N., Chief Nurse Executive
Web address: www.memorialmedicalcenter.org
Control: Other not–for–profit (including NFP Corporation) **Service:** General Medical and Surgical

Staffed Beds: 196 **Admissions:** 16753 **Census:** 216 **Outpatient Visits:** 157919 **Births:** 1879 **Total Expense ($000):** 536153 **Payroll Expense ($000):** 163074 **Personnel:** 2023

MODESTO MEDICAL CENTER See Kaiser Permanente Manteca Medical Center, Manteca

★ **STANISLAUS SURGICAL HOSPITAL (050726)**, 1421 Oakdale Road, Zip 95355–3356; tel. 209/572–2700 **A**5 10 **F**3 15 45 46 47 51 74 79 81 82 93 107 111 116 117 119 147 148 **S** Sutter Health, Sacramento, CA
Primary Contact: Douglas V. Johnson, Chief Executive Officer
CFO: Richard Hart, Chief Financial Officer
CMO: Wesley Kinzie, M.D., Chief of Staff
CIO: Richard Hart, Chief Financial Officer
CHR: Tyson Hubbard, Director Human Resources
CNO: Susan Gonzalez, Director of Clinical Services
Web address: www.stanislaussurgical.com
Control: Corporation, Investor–owned, for–profit **Service:** Surgical

Staffed Beds: 23 **Admissions:** 550 **Census:** 4 **Outpatient Visits:** 7894 **Births:** 0 **Total Expense ($000):** 30015 **Payroll Expense ($000):** 11043 **Personnel:** 220

MONROVIA—Los Angeles County

○ **MONROVIA MEMORIAL HOSPITAL (052054)**, 323 South Heliotrope Avenue, Zip 91016–2914; tel. 626/408–9800, (Nonreporting) **A**10 11
Primary Contact: Ron Kupferstein, Chief Executive Officer
Web address: www.monroviamemorial.com
Control: Partnership, Investor–owned, for–profit **Service:** Long–Term Acute Care hospital

Staffed Beds: 49

MONTCLAIR—San Bernardino County

✠ **MONTCLAIR HOSPITAL MEDICAL CENTER (050758)**, 5000 San Bernardino Street, Zip 91763–2326; tel. 909/625–5411, (Nonreporting) **A**1 10 **S** Prime Healthcare Services, Ontario, CA
Primary Contact: Edward Mirzabegian, Chief Executive Officer
CFO: Robert Bonner, Chief Financial Officer
CMO: Joseph Hourany, Chief Medical Officer
CNO: Gail Aviado, Chief Nursing Officer
Web address: www.montclair–hospital.com
Control: Other not–for–profit (including NFP Corporation) **Service:** General Medical and Surgical

Staffed Beds: 102

MONTEBELLO—Los Angeles County

◇ **BEVERLY HOSPITAL (050350)**, 309 West Beverly Boulevard, Zip 90640–4308; tel. 323/726–1222, (Nonreporting) **A**10 21
Primary Contact: Alice Cheng, President and Chief Executive Officer
CFO: Larry Pugh, Vice President and Chief Financial Officer
CIO: Mark Turner, Director Information Systems
CHR: John Barnes, Administrative Director Human Resources
CNO: Kathy Wojno, R.N., Vice President Nursing Services and Chief Nursing Officer
Web address: www.beverly.org
Control: Other not–for–profit (including NFP Corporation) **Service:** General Medical and Surgical

Staffed Beds: 102

MONTEREY—Monterey County

✠ **COMMUNITY HOSPITAL OF THE MONTEREY PENINSULA (050145)**, 23625 Holman Highway, Zip 93940–5902, Mailing Address: Box 'HH', Zip 93942–6032; tel. 831/624–5311, (Total facility includes 28 beds in nursing home–type unit) **A**1 2 10 **F**3 5 11 12 13 15 17 18 20 22 24 26 28 29 30 31 32 34 35 37 40 44 45 46 47 48 49 50 51 53 54 57 58 59 60 61 62 63 64 68 70 73 74 75 76 77 78 79 81 82 83 84 85 86 87 89 90 91 92 93 94 96 98 99 100 101 102 103 104 105 107 110 111 114 115 116 117 118 119 120 121 123 124 128 129 130 132 134 135 145 146 148
Primary Contact: Steven J. Packer, M.D., President and Chief Executive Officer
CFO: Laura Zehm, Vice President and Chief Financial Officer
CMO: Anthony D. Chavis, M.D., Vice President Enterprise Medical Officer, Community Hospital Foundation
Web address: www.chomp.org
Control: Other not–for–profit (including NFP Corporation) **Service:** General Medical and Surgical

Staffed Beds: 248 **Admissions:** 11798 **Census:** 166 **Outpatient Visits:** 319199 **Births:** 1035 **Total Expense ($000):** 446037 **Payroll Expense ($000):** 159959 **Personnel:** 1707

Hospital, Medicare Provider Number, Address, Telephone, Approval, Facility, and Physician Codes, Health Care System

★ American Hospital Association (AHA) membership ○ Healthcare Facilities Accreditation Program ⇧ Center for Improvement in Healthcare Quality Accreditation
☐ The Joint Commission accreditation ◇ DNV Healthcare Inc. accreditation △ Commission on Accreditation of Rehabilitation Facilities (CARF) accreditation

CA

MONTEREY PARK—Los Angeles County

☐ **GARFIELD MEDICAL CENTER (050737)**, 525 North Garfield Avenue, Zip 91754–1205; tel. 626/573–2222 **A**1 10 **F**13 15 18 20 22 24 26 29 40 49 56 70 73 78 79 81 90 107 111 115 119 **P**5 **S** AHMC & Healthcare, Inc., Alhambra, CA
Primary Contact: Paul J. Hensler, Chief Executive Officer
COO: Herbert Villafuerte, Chief Operating Officer/Chief Nursing Officer
CFO: Steve Maekawa, Chief Financial Officer
CMO: Thomas Lam, Chief Medical Officer
CIO: Allan Carpenter, Chief Information Officer
CHR: Rebecca R. Ricartti, Interim Director Human Resources
CNO: Herbert Villafuerte, Chief Operating Officer and Chief Nursing Officer
Web address: www.garfieldmedicalcenter.com
Control: Corporation, Investor–owned, for–profit **Service:** General Medical and Surgical

Staffed Beds: 195 **Admissions:** 12933 **Census:** 165 **Outpatient Visits:** 33814 **Births:** 4160 **Total Expense ($000):** 262688 **Payroll Expense ($000):** 82092

☐ **MONTEREY PARK HOSPITAL (050736)**, 900 South Atlantic Boulevard, Zip 91754–4780; tel. 626/570–9000 **A**1 10 **F**3 15 29 34 35 40 49 50 57 59 60 70 75 76 81 86 87 89 107 113 114 119 130 142 143 146 **S** AHMC & Healthcare, Inc., Alhambra, CA
Primary Contact: Philip A. Cohen, Chief Executive Officer
COO: Ericka Smith, Chief Operating Officer
CFO: Daniel Song, Chief Financial Officer
CMO: Ruben Ramirez, M.D., Chief of Staff
CIO: Angelica Ching, Director Information Systems
CHR: Gretchen Lindeman, Director of Human Resources
CNO: Shirley Tang, R.N., Chief Nursing Officer
Web address: www.montereyparkhosp.com
Control: Partnership, Investor–owned, for–profit **Service:** General Medical and Surgical

Staffed Beds: 101 **Admissions:** 5738 **Census:** 53 **Outpatient Visits:** 24810 **Births:** 1612 **Total Expense ($000):** 100712 **Payroll Expense ($000):** 23816 **Personnel:** 322

MORENO VALLEY—Riverside County

☒ **KAISER PERMANENTE MORENO VALLEY MEDICAL CENTER (050765)**, 27300 Iris Avenue, Zip 92555–4800; tel. 951/243–0811 **A**1 10 **F**3 13 17 29 30 35 40 44 45 46 49 50 59 60 64 65 68 70 75 76 77 79 81 84 85 87 97 100 102 107 108 109 111 115 119 130 135 146 148 **S** Kaiser Foundation Hospitals, Oakland, CA
Primary Contact: Vita M. Willett, Senior Vice President
COO: Corey A. Seale, Chief Operating Officer
Control: Other not–for–profit (including NFP Corporation) **Service:** General Medical and Surgical

Staffed Beds: 71 **Admissions:** 7339 **Census:** 47 **Births:** 1279 **Personnel:** 244

☒ **RIVERSIDE UNIVERSITY HEALTH SYSTEM–MEDICAL CENTER (050292)**, 26520 Cactus Avenue, Zip 92555–3911; tel. 951/486–4000 **A**1 3 5 10 12 13 **F**3 11 13 15 18 19 29 30 31 32 34 35 39 40 43 45 46 49 50 51 56 57 58 59 64 66 68 70 71 72 74 75 76 77 78 79 81 82 84 85 87 88 89 91 93 97 98 99 100 102 107 108 110 111 114 115 118 119 126 130 132 135 146 147 148
Primary Contact: Zareh Sarrafian, Chief Executive Officer
COO: Jennifer Cruikshank, R.N., Chief Operating Officer
CFO: Christopher Hans, Chief Financial Officer
CMO: Arnold Tabuenca, M.D., Medical Director
CNO: Judi Nightingale, R.N., Chief Nursing Officer
Web address: www.rcrmc.org
Control: County–Government, nonfederal **Service:** General Medical and Surgical

Staffed Beds: 321 **Admissions:** 17978 **Census:** 283 **Outpatient Visits:** 255169 **Births:** 1639 **Total Expense ($000):** 462182 **Payroll Expense ($000):** 186220 **Personnel:** 2655

MOUNT SHASTA—Siskiyou County

☒ **MERCY MEDICAL CENTER MOUNT SHASTA (051319)**, 914 Pine Street, Zip 96067–2143; tel. 530/926–6111 **A**1 10 18 **F**3 11 13 15 29 30 35 40 43 50 53 56 57 59 62 63 64 68 70 75 76 77 79 81 82 84 89 93 107 108 110 111 114 118 119 121 127 130 131 132 133 143 146 148 **S** Dignity Health, San Francisco, CA
Primary Contact: Kenneth E. S. Platou, President
CFO: Kimberly Miranda, Chief Financial Officer
CMO: Gary Herfindahl, M.D., Chief of Staff
CHR: Michelle Michl, Director Human Resources
CNO: Sherie Ambrose, Vice President Patient Care Services
Web address: www.mercymtshasta.org
Control: Other not–for–profit (including NFP Corporation) **Service:** General Medical and Surgical

Staffed Beds: 33 **Admissions:** 1038 **Census:** 7 **Outpatient Visits:** 61849 **Births:** 151 **Total Expense ($000):** 52554 **Payroll Expense ($000):** 19306 **Personnel:** 214

MOUNTAIN VIEW—Santa Clara County

☒ **EL CAMINO HOSPITAL (050308)**, 2500 Grant Road, Zip 94040–4302, Mailing Address: P.O. Box 7025, Zip 94039–7025; tel. 650/940–7000, (Includes EL CAMINO HOSPITAL LOS GATOS, 815 Pollard Road, Los Gatos, Zip 95032–1438; tel. 408/378–6131) **A**1 2 3 10 **F**3 5 11 12 13 15 16 17 18 20 22 24 26 28 29 30 31 34 35 40 45 46 49 50 51 54 55 56 57 58 59 60 64 65 70 72 74 75 76 77 78 79 81 82 84 85 86 87 89 90 93 98 101 102 103 104 105 107 108 110 111 114 115 116 117 118 119 120 121 123 124 126 129 130 132 135 143 146 147
Primary Contact: Tomi S. Ryba, President and Chief Executive Officer
COO: Mike Zdeblick, Chief Operating Officer
CFO: Iftikhar Hussain, Chief Financial Officer
CMO: Eric Pifer, M.D., Chief Medical Officer
CIO: Greg Walton, Chief Information Officer
CHR: Kathryn M. Fisk, Chief Human Resources Officer
CNO: Cheryl Reinking, R.N., Chief Nursing Officer
Web address: www.elcaminohospital.org
Control: Hospital district or authority, Government, nonfederal **Service:** General Medical and Surgical

Staffed Beds: 420 **Admissions:** 19081 **Census:** 246 **Outpatient Visits:** 205453 **Births:** 5060 **Total Expense ($000):** 689631 **Payroll Expense ($000):** 314425 **Personnel:** 1916

MURRIETA—Riverside County

☐ **LOMA LINDA UNIVERSITY MEDICAL CENTER–MURRIETA (050770)**, 28062 Baxter Road, Zip 92563–1401; tel. 951/290–4000 **A**1 10 **F**3 8 11 13 15 18 20 22 24 26 28 29 30 31 34 35 37 40 41 44 45 46 47 48 49 50 54 57 58 59 60 64 65 68 70 74 75 76 77 78 79 81 82 85 86 87 90 91 92 93 96 107 108 110 111 114 115 117 118 119 120 121 123 124 126 129 130 143 146 147 148 **S** Loma Linda University Adventist Health Sciences Center, Loma Linda, CA
Primary Contact: Greg Henderson, Interim Administrator
COO: Richard M. Tibbits, Vice President and Chief Operating Officer
CFO: James Uli, Chief Financial Officer
CMO: Jeff Conner, M.D., Chief Medical Staff
Web address: www.llumcmurrieta.org
Control: Other not–for–profit (including NFP Corporation) **Service:** General Medical and Surgical

Staffed Beds: 106 **Admissions:** 8970 **Census:** 87 **Outpatient Visits:** 70744 **Births:** 1077 **Total Expense ($000):** 192448 **Payroll Expense ($000):** 53665 **Personnel:** 754

☒ **SOUTHWEST HEALTHCARE SYSTEM (050701)**, 25500 Medical Center Drive, Zip 92562–5965; tel. 951/696–6000, (Includes INLAND VALLEY MEDICAL CENTER, 36485 Inland Valley Drive, Wildomar, Zip 92595–9700; tel. 951/677–1111; Bradley D. Neet, FACHE, Chief Executive Officer; RANCHO SPRINGS MEDICAL CENTER, 25500 Medical Center Drive, tel. 951/696–6000) **A**1 10 **F**3 8 11 12 13 15 29 30 34 35 37 40 43 45 48 49 50 51 57 59 67 68 70 72 76 77 79 81 84 85 87 93 96 107 108 110 111 114 115 118 119 126 130 132 146 147 **S** Universal Health Services, Inc., King of Prussia, PA
Primary Contact: Bradley D. Neet, FACHE, Chief Executive Officer
COO: Jared Giles, Chief Operating Officer
CFO: Jon Zilkow, Chief Financial Officer
CMO: Reza Vaezazizi, M.D., Chief of Staff
CIO: Jeffrey Upcraft, Director Information Services
CHR: Della G. Stange, Director Human Resources
CNO: Kristen Johnson, Chief Nursing Officer
Web address: www.swhealthcaresystem.com/
Control: Corporation, Investor–owned, for–profit **Service:** General Medical and Surgical

Staffed Beds: 242 **Admissions:** 15448 **Census:** 159 **Outpatient Visits:** 102480 **Births:** 3424 **Total Expense ($000):** 226479 **Payroll Expense ($000):** 98480 **Personnel:** 1186

NAPA—Napa County

☐ **NAPA STATE HOSPITAL (054122)**, 2100 Napa–Vallejo Highway, Zip 94558–6293; tel. 707/253–5000 **A**1 3 5 10 **F**30 39 53 56 59 61 67 68 77 86 98 103 128 130 132 135 146 **P**6
Primary Contact: Dolly Matteucci, Executive Director
COO: Dolly Matteucci, Executive Director
Web address: www.dmh.ca.gov
Control: State–Government, nonfederal **Service:** Psychiatric

Staffed Beds: 1284 **Admissions:** 717 **Census:** 1175 **Outpatient Visits:** 0 **Births:** 0 **Total Expense ($000):** 288936 **Payroll Expense ($000):** 178773 **Personnel:** 2178

☒ **QUEEN OF THE VALLEY MEDICAL CENTER (050009)**, 1000 Trancas Street, Zip 94558–2906, Mailing Address: P.O. Box 2340, Zip 94558–0688; tel. 707/252–4411 **A**1 2 10 **F**3 7 13 15 17 18 20 22 24 26 29 30 31 32 34 35 37 39 40 41 43 44 45 46 47 48 49 50 51 54 57 59 63 64 68 70 72 74 75 76 77 78 79 81 82 83 84 85 86 87 90 91 92 93 96 97 107 108 110 111 114 115 116 117 118 119 120 121 123 126 130 132 135 146 **P**3 5 **S** Providence St. Joseph Health, Renton, WA
Primary Contact: Walt Mickens, FACHE, President and Chief Executive Officer
COO: Vincent Morgese, M.D., Executive Vice President, Chief Operating Officer and Chief Medical Officer
CFO: Mich Riccioni, Vice President and Chief Financial Officer, Northern California Region
CMO: Vincent Morgese, M.D., Executive Vice President, Chief Operating Officer and Chief Medical Officer
CHR: Robert A. Eisen, Vice President Human Resources, Northern California Region
Web address: www.thequeen.org
Control: Other not–for–profit (including NFP Corporation) **Service:** General Medical and Surgical

Staffed Beds: 120 **Admissions:** 6327 **Census:** 80 **Outpatient Visits:** 139618 **Births:** 785 **Total Expense ($000):** 259145 **Payroll Expense ($000):** 74197 **Personnel:** 1059

NATIONAL CITY—San Diego County

☒ △ **PARADISE VALLEY HOSPITAL (050024)**, 2400 East Fourth Street, Zip 91950–2099; tel. 619/470–4321, (Includes BAYVIEW BEHAVIORAL HEALTH CAMPUS, 330 Moss Street, Chula Vista, Zip 91911–2005; tel. 619/470–4321; Neerav Jadeja, Administrator) **A**1 3 7 10 **F**3 5 13 14 17 18 20 26 28 29 32 34 37 38 40 45 49 50 57 59 60 61 70 74 75 76 77 79 81 82 86 87 90 91 92 93 94 96 97 98 100 101 102 104 105 107 108 111 115 119 126 130 131 132 135 143 146 147 148 **S** Prime Healthcare Services, Ontario, CA
Primary Contact: Neerav Jadeja, Administrator
CFO: Becky Levy, Chief Financial Officer
CMO: Rosemarie Lim, M.D., Chief Medical Officer
CIO: Allan Tojino, Director, Information Systems
CHR: Lorraine Villegas, Manager Human Resources
CNO: Gemma Rama–Banaag, R.N., Chief Nursing Officer
Web address: www.paradisevalleyhospital.org
Control: Corporation, Investor–owned, for–profit **Service:** General Medical and Surgical

Staffed Beds: 256 **Admissions:** 7000 **Census:** 88 **Outpatient Visits:** 7000 **Births:** 1150

NEEDLES—San Bernardino County

★ **COLORADO RIVER MEDICAL CENTER (051323)**, 1401 Bailey Avenue, Zip 92363–3198; tel. 760/326–7100 **A**10 18 **F**3 4 29 30 34 40 45 50 53 57 59 65 68 75 81 100 104 107 111 119 128 130 144 145
Primary Contact: Steve Kelley Lopez, Chief Executive Officer
COO: Knaya Tabora, Chief Operating Officer and Chief Nursing Officer
CFO: Steve Kelley Lopez, Chief Financial Officer
CMO: Robert Strecker, M.D., Chief of Staff
CIO: Ron Chieffo, Chief Information Officer
CHR: Pam Barrett, Human Resources Director
CNO: Knaya Tabora, Chief Operating Officer and Chief Nursing Officer
Web address: www.crmccares.com
Control: Other not–for–profit (including NFP Corporation) **Service:** General Medical and Surgical

Staffed Beds: 25 **Admissions:** 525 **Census:** 4 **Outpatient Visits:** 9902 **Births:** 0 **Total Expense ($000):** 8997 **Payroll Expense ($000):** 3924 **Personnel:** 90

NEWPORT BEACH—Orange County

★ ◇ **HOAG MEMORIAL HOSPITAL PRESBYTERIAN (050224)**, One Hoag Drive, Zip 92663–4120, Mailing Address: P.O. Box 6100, Zip 92658–6100; tel. 949/764–4624, (Includes HOAG HOSPITAL IRVINE, 16200 Sand Canyon Avenue, Irvine, Zip 92618–3714; tel. 949/764–8240) **A**3 5 10 21 **F**3 4 5 6 8 11 13 14 15 17 18 20 22 24 26 28 29 30 31 34 35 36 37 40 44 45 46 47 48 49 50 51 53 54 55 57 58 59 64 68 70 71 72 74 75 76 77 78 79 81 82 84 85 86 87 92 93 94 96 97 100 102 103 107 108 110 111 113 114 115 116 117 118 119 120 121 123 124 126 129 130 131 132 135 141 143 144 145 146 147 148 **P**3
Primary Contact: Robert Braithwaite, President and Chief Executive Officer
COO: Michael R. Ricks, Chief Operating Officer
CFO: Andrew Guarni, Chief Financial Officer
CIO: Patrick Anderson, Chief Information Officer and Senior Vice President
CHR: Jan L. Blue, Vice President Human Resources
CNO: Richard A. Martin, MSN, Senior Vice President and Chief Nursing Officer
Web address: www.hoaghospital.org
Control: Other not–for–profit (including NFP Corporation) **Service:** General Medical and Surgical

Staffed Beds: 457 **Admissions:** 25491 **Census:** 286 **Outpatient Visits:** 394506 **Births:** 6208 **Total Expense ($000):** 830150 **Payroll Expense ($000):** 286748 **Personnel:** 4179

NEWPORT BAY HOSPITAL (054135), 1501 East 16th Street, Zip 92663–5924; tel. 949/650–9750, (Nonreporting) **A**10
Primary Contact: James E. Parkhurst, President and Chief Executive Officer
COO: Garry Hardwick, R.N., Chief Operating Officer
CFO: Rocky Gentner, Chief Financial Officer
CMO: Jason Kellogg, M.D., Chief of Staff
CIO: Nina Swenson, Director Business Services
CHR: Phyllis Parkhurst, Vice President Support Services
CNO: Diana Hakenson, Director of Patient Care Services
Web address: www.newportbayhospital.com
Control: Corporation, Investor–owned, for–profit **Service:** Psychiatric

Staffed Beds: 34

NORTH HOLLYWOOD—Los Angeles County, See Los Angeles

NORTHRIDGE—Los Angeles County, See Los Angeles

NORWALK—Los Angeles County

COAST PLAZA DOCTORS HOSPITAL See Coast Plaza Hospital

☐ **COAST PLAZA HOSPITAL (050771)**, 13100 Studebaker Road, Zip 90650–2500; tel. 562/868–3751, (Nonreporting) **A**1 10 **S** Avanti Hospitals, El Segundo, CA
Primary Contact: Richard Rowe, PharmD, Chief Executive Officer
CFO: Mihi Lee, Chief Financial Officer
CMO: Galal S. Gough, M.D., Chief of Staff
CIO: Linda K. Roman, Administrator
Web address: www.coastplaza.com
Control: Partnership, Investor–owned, for–profit **Service:** General Medical and Surgical

Staffed Beds: 123

LOS ANGELES COMMUNITY HOSPITAL OF NORWALK See Los Angeles Community Hospital at Los Angeles, Los Angeles

☐ **METROPOLITAN STATE HOSPITAL (054133)**, 11401 Bloomfield Avenue, Zip 90650–2015; tel. 562/863–7011, (Nonreporting) **A**1 10
Primary Contact: Michael Barsom, M.D., Executive Director
CFO: Maybelle Manlagnit, Senior Accounting Officer
CIO: Paul Mello, Manager Data Processing
CHR: Jorge Banuedos, Director Human Resources
Web address: www.dmh.ca.gov
Control: State–Government, nonfederal **Service:** Psychiatric

Staffed Beds: 657

NOVATO—Marin County

✠ **NOVATO COMMUNITY HOSPITAL (050131)**, 180 Rowland Way,
Zip 94945–5009, Mailing Address: P.O. Box 1108, Zip 94948–1108;
tel. 415/209–1300 **A**1 10 **F**3 15 18 26 29 30 31 34 40 45 49 50 51 54 56
59 60 64 68 70 75 77 79 81 84 85 87 93 107 108 111 115 119 130 131
132 143 144 146 148 **P**3 **S** Sutter Health, Sacramento, CA
Primary Contact: Brian Alexander, Chief Administrative Officer
CMO: Barbara Nylund, M.D., Chief of Staff
CIO: Kathryn Graham, Director Communications and Community Relations
CHR: Diana G. Johnson, Acting Chief Human Resources Officer
Web address: www.novatocommunity.sutterhealth.org
Control: Other not–for–profit (including NFP Corporation) **Service:** General
Medical and Surgical

> **Staffed Beds:** 40 **Admissions:** 1619 **Census:** 15 **Outpatient Visits:** 85416
> **Births:** 0 **Total Expense ($000):** 73269 **Payroll Expense ($000):** 22769
> **Personnel:** 235

OAKDALE—Stanislaus County

✠ **OAK VALLEY HOSPITAL DISTRICT (050067)**, 350 South Oak Avenue,
Zip 95361–3581; tel. 209/847–3011, (Nonreporting) **A**1 10
Primary Contact: John McCormick, President and Chief Executive Officer
CMO: Albert Gelders, M.D., Chief of Staff
CIO: Sherry Peral, Manager Information Systems
CHR: Brian Beck,PHR,MHROD, Vice President Human Resources
CNO: Joann L. Saporito, R.N., Vice President Nursing Services
Web address: www.oakvalleycares.org
Control: Hospital district or authority, Government, nonfederal **Service:** General
Medical and Surgical

> **Staffed Beds:** 150

OAKLAND—Alameda County

✠ △ **ALTA BATES SUMMIT MEDICAL CENTER – SUMMIT CAMPUS
(050043)**, 350 Hawthorne Avenue, Zip 94609–3100; tel. 510/655–4000 **A**1 2
5 7 19 **F**3 4 5 8 11 12 15 17 18 20 22 24 26 29 30 31 34 35 36 40 45 46
47 49 51 56 57 58 59 60 61 64 68 70 74 75 77 78 79 81 82 84 85 86 87
90 97 107 108 111 114 115 116 117 118 119 120 121 123 124 126 130
132 135 146 148 **P**3 **S** Sutter Health, Sacramento, CA
Primary Contact: Charles Prosper, Chief Executive Officer
CMO: John Gentile, M.D., Vice President Medical Affairs
CHR: Mark Beiting, Vice President Human Resources
Web address: www.altabatessummit.com
Control: Other not–for–profit (including NFP Corporation) **Service:** General
Medical and Surgical

> **Staffed Beds:** 333 **Admissions:** 13108 **Census:** 215 **Outpatient Visits:**
> 122126 **Births:** 0 **Total Expense ($000):** 443141 **Payroll Expense ($000):**
> 134479 **Personnel:** 1474

✠ **HIGHLAND HOSPITAL (050320)**, 1411 East 31st Street, Zip 94602–1018;
tel. 510/437–4800, (Includes FAIRMONT HOSPITAL, 15400 Foothill Boulevard,
San Leandro, Zip 94578–1009; tel. 510/895–4200; James E. T. Jackson,
M.P.H., Chief Administrative Officer; JOHN GEORGE PSYCHIATRIC HOSPITAL,
2060 Fairmont Drive, San Leandro, Zip 94578–1001; tel. 510/346–1300; Guy
C. Qvistgaard, Chief Executive Officer), (Total facility includes 109 beds in nursing
home–type unit) **A**1 3 5 10 **F**3 5 11 13 15 18 20 22 28 29 30 31 32 34 35 36
38 39 40 43 44 45 46 49 50 54 56 57 58 59 60 61 64 65 66 68 70 71 73
74 75 77 78 79 81 82 84 85 86 87 90 92 93 94 96 97 98 100 101 102 104
105 107 111 112 114 115 119 128 130 132 134 135 142 143 144 146 147
148 **S** Alameda Health System, San Leandro, CA
Primary Contact: Delvecchio Finley, Chief Executive Officer
CFO: Marion Schales, Chief Financial Officer
CMO: Sang–ick Chang, M.D., Chief Medical Officer
CHR: Jeanette L. Louden Corbett, Chief Human Resources Officer
Web address: www.alamedahealthsystem.org
Control: Hospital district or authority, Government, nonfederal **Service:** General
Medical and Surgical

> **Staffed Beds:** 387 **Admissions:** 14650 **Census:** 311 **Outpatient Visits:**
> 422172 **Births:** 1077 **Total Expense ($000):** 681901 **Payroll Expense
> ($000):** 312958 **Personnel:** 2856

✠ **KAISER PERMANENTE OAKLAND MEDICAL CENTER (050075)**, 3600
Broadway, Zip 94611–5693; tel. 510/752–1000, (Includes KAISER PERMANENTE
RICHMOND MEDICAL CENTER, 901 Nevin Avenue, Richmond, Zip 94801–2555;
tel. 510/307–1500), (Nonreporting) **A**1 3 5 8 10 **S** Kaiser Foundation Hospitals,
Oakland, CA
Primary Contact: Mark Fratzke, R.N., Senior Vice President and Area Manager
CFO: Dennis Morris, Area Finance Officer
CMO: John Loftus, M.D., Chief of Staff
CIO: Johnny Law, Area Information Officer
CHR: Rick Mead, Human Resources Leader
CNO: Charlene Boyer, Chief Nursing Officer
Web address: www.kaiserpermanente.org
Control: Other not–for–profit (including NFP Corporation) **Service:** General
Medical and Surgical

> **Staffed Beds:** 267

OAKLAND MEDICAL CENTER See Kaiser Permanente Oakland Medical Center

□ **TELECARE HERITAGE PSYCHIATRIC HEALTH CENTER (054146)**, 2633 East
27th Street, Zip 94601–1912; tel. 510/535–5115, (Nonreporting) **A**1 10
Primary Contact: Anne L. Bakar, President and Chief Executive Officer
Web address: www.tbhcare.com/
Control: Partnership, Investor–owned, for–profit **Service:** Psychiatric

> **Staffed Beds:** 26

✠ **USCF BENIOFF CHILDREN'S HOSPITAL OAKLAND (053301)**, 747 52nd
Street, Zip 94609–1859; tel. 510/428–3000, (Nonreporting) **A**1 3 5 10
Primary Contact: Bertram Lubin, M.D., President and Chief Executive Officer
CFO: Doug Myers, Senior Vice President and Chief Financial Officer
CIO: Don Livsey, Vice President and Chief Information Officer
Web address: www.childrenshospitaloakland.org
Control: Other not–for–profit (including NFP Corporation) **Service:** Children's
general

> **Staffed Beds:** 190

OCEANSIDE—San Diego County

✠ **TRI–CITY MEDICAL CENTER (050128)**, 4002 Vista Way, Zip 92056–4593;
tel. 760/724–8411 **A**1 2 3 5 8 11 **F**3 5 8 11 12 13 17 18 20 22 24 26 28
29 30 31 34 35 36 37 38 39 40 41 45 46 47 48 49 51 53 57 59 60 61 62
64 65 68 70 72 74 75 76 77 78 79 81 82 84 85 86 87 90 91 92 93 94 96
97 98 99 100 101 102 104 105 107 108 109 110 111 112 113 114 115
116 117 118 119 120 121 122 123 124 126 130 131 132 135 143 146
147 148
Primary Contact: Steve Dietlin, Chief Executive Officer
COO: Casey Fatch, Chief Operating Officer
CMO: Scott Worman, Chief of Staff
CIO: Kim Cook, Interim Clinical Applications Services Manager
CHR: Esther Beverly, Vice President Human Resources
CNO: Sharon A. Schultz, MSN, Chief Nurse Executive and Vice President
Web address: www.tricitymed.org
Control: Hospital district or authority, Government, nonfederal **Service:** General
Medical and Surgical

> **Staffed Beds:** 330 **Admissions:** 15226 **Census:** 191 **Outpatient Visits:**
> 187510 **Births:** 2586 **Total Expense ($000):** 335051 **Payroll Expense
> ($000):** 143757 **Personnel:** 1808

OJAI—Ventura County

◇ **OJAI VALLEY COMMUNITY HOSPITAL (051334)**, 1306 Maricopa Highway,
Zip 93023–3163; tel. 805/646–1401, (Nonreporting) **A**21 **S** Community
Memorial Health System, Ventura, CA
Primary Contact: Haady Lashkari, Chief Administrative Officer
CFO: David Glyer, Vice President Finance
CIO: Mark Turner, Manager Information Technology
CHR: Deborah Gallagher, Manager Human Resources
Web address: www.ojaihospital.org
Control: Other not–for–profit (including NFP Corporation) **Service:** General
Medical and Surgical

> **Staffed Beds:** 96

ONTARIO—San Bernardino County

✠ **KINDRED HOSPITAL–ONTARIO (052037)**, 550 North Monterey Avenue,
Zip 91764–3399; tel. 909/391–0333 **A**1 10 **F**26 29 35 46 49 60 63 65 68 70
71 79 84 86 87 91 97 107 111 119 130 148 **S** Kindred Healthcare,
Louisville, KY
Primary Contact: Vincent Trac, Chief Executive Officer
CFO: Omar Oregel, Controller
CMO: Marc Lynch, D.O., Chief of Staff
CHR: Laurel Scharber, Administrative Assistant and Coordinator Human Resources
CNO: Holly Ramos, R.N., Chief Clinical Officer
Web address: www.khontario.com/
Control: Corporation, Investor–owned, for–profit **Service:** Long–Term Acute Care
hospital

> **Staffed Beds:** 81 **Admissions:** 855 **Census:** 70 **Outpatient Visits:** 0 **Births:**
> 0 **Total Expense ($000):** 46655 **Payroll Expense ($000):** 18582

ORANGE—Orange County

□ **CHAPMAN GLOBAL MEDICAL CENTER (050745)**, 2601 East Chapman
Avenue, Zip 92869–3296; tel. 714/633–0011, (Nonreporting) **A**1 10 **S** KPC
Healthcare, Inc., Santa Ana, CA
Primary Contact: Ronald J. Galonsky, Jr., Chief Executive Officer
COO: Ada Yeh, Chief Operating Officer and Chief Nursing Officer
CFO: John Collins, Corporate Chief Financial Officer
CMO: Gary Bennett, M.D., Chief of Medical Staff
CIO: Sri Yarramsetti, Chief Information Officer
CHR: JoAnne Suehs, Manager Human Resources
CNO: Ada Yeh, Chief Operating Officer and Chief Nursing Officer
Web address: www.Chapman–GMC.com
Control: Corporation, Investor–owned, for–profit **Service:** General Medical and
Surgical

> **Staffed Beds:** 100

Many Facility Codes have changed. Please refer to the AHA Guide Code Chart. © 2016 AHA Guide

☐ **CHILDREN'S HOSPITAL OF ORANGE COUNTY (053304)**, 1201 West La Veta Avenue, Zip 92868–4203, Mailing Address: PO Box 5700, Zip 92863–5700; tel. 714/997–3000 **A**1 3 5 10 **F**3 14 17 19 21 23 25 27 29 30 31 32 34 35 40 41 43 50 55 57 58 59 61 64 65 66 68 71 72 74 75 77 78 79 81 85 86 87 88 89 91 92 93 97 99 100 101 104 107 111 113 114 115 116 117 118 119 120 121 123 126 129 130 131 132 134 136 146 **P**3 5
Primary Contact: Kimberly C. Cripe, President and Chief Executive Officer
COO: Matthew S. Gerlach, Chief Operating Officer
CFO: Kerri Ruppert Schiller, Senior Vice President and Chief Financial Officer
CMO: Maria Minon, M.D., Vice President Medical Affairs and Chief Medical Officer
CIO: Mark Headland, Chief Information Officer
CHR: Mamoon Syed, Vice President Human Resources
CNO: Melanie Patterson, DNP, R.N., Vice President Patient Care Services and Chief Nursing Officer
Web address: www.choc.org
Control: Other not–for–profit (including NFP Corporation) **Service:** Children's general

Staffed Beds: 279 **Admissions:** 11640 **Census:** 166 **Outpatient Visits:** 224418 **Births:** 0 **Total Expense ($000):** 573676 **Payroll Expense ($000):** 162029 **Personnel:** 2280

◇ **HEALTHBRIDGE CHILDREN'S HOSPITAL (053308)**, 393 South Tustin Street, Zip 92866–2501; tel. 714/289–2400 **A**10 21 **F**3 29 64 65 75 77 90 93 128 130 132 146 148 **S** Nexus Health Systems, Houston, TX
Primary Contact: Alex Villarruz, Chief Executive Officer
CIO: Roberta Consolver, Chief Information Officer
Web address: www.HealthBridgeOrange.com
Control: Partnership, Investor–owned, for–profit **Service:** Children's rehabilitation

Staffed Beds: 27 **Admissions:** 123 **Census:** 25 **Outpatient Visits:** 3077 **Births:** 0 **Total Expense ($000):** 12455 **Payroll Expense ($000):** 6254 **Personnel:** 95

✠ **ST. JOSEPH HOSPITAL (050069)**, 1100 West Stewart Drive, Zip 92868–3849, Mailing Address: P.O. Box 5600, Zip 92863–5600; tel. 714/633–9111 **A**1 2 3 5 10 **F**3 5 8 12 13 15 17 18 19 20 21 22 23 24 25 26 27 28 29 30 31 34 35 37 39 40 41 45 46 47 49 50 51 53 54 55 57 58 59 60 64 65 69 70 71 74 75 76 77 78 79 80 81 82 84 85 86 87 91 92 93 98 100 102 104 105 107 108 109 110 111 113 114 115 116 117 118 119 120 121 123 124 126 129 130 131 132 135 138 141 146 147 148 **P**3 5 **S** Providence St. Joseph Health, Renton, WA
Primary Contact: Steven C. Moreau, President and Chief Executive Officer
COO: Jeremy Zoch, Executive Vice President and Chief Operating Officer
CFO: Kristi Liberatore, Vice President and Chief Financial Officer
CMO: Paul Beck, Acting Chief Medical Officer
CIO: Jeremy Zoch, Executive Vice President and Chief Operating Officer
CHR: Mary P. Leahy, Vice President Human Resources
CNO: Katie Skelton, MSN, Vice President Nursing and Chief Nursing Officer
Web address: www.sjo.org
Control: Other not–for–profit (including NFP Corporation) **Service:** General Medical and Surgical

Staffed Beds: 379 **Admissions:** 19642 **Census:** 209 **Outpatient Visits:** 305991 **Births:** 4818 **Total Expense ($000):** 581804 **Payroll Expense ($000):** 164525 **Personnel:** 2369

✠ **UC IRVINE MEDICAL CENTER (050348)**, 101 The City Drive South, Zip 92868–3298; tel. 714/456–6011 **A**1 2 3 5 8 10 **F**3 6 8 9 11 12 13 14 15 16 17 18 19 20 22 24 26 28 29 30 31 32 34 35 36 37 39 40 41 43 44 45 46 47 48 49 50 51 53 54 55 56 57 58 59 60 61 64 66 70 71 72 74 75 76 77 78 79 80 81 82 84 85 86 87 88 89 90 91 92 93 96 97 98 99 100 101 102 104 105 107 108 110 111 112 115 116 117 118 119 120 121 123 124 126 130 131 132 134 135 138 141 142 144 145 146 147 148 **P**4 5 7 **S** University of California Systemwide Administration, Oakland, CA
Primary Contact: Howard Federoff, M.D., Vice Chancellor, Health Affairs & Chief Executive Officer, UC Irvine Health
COO: Larry Anstine, Interim Chief Operating Officer
CFO: Ajay Sial, Chief Financial Officer, UC Irvine Health
CMO: Doug Merill, M.D., Chief Medical Officer
CIO: Charles H. Podesta, Chief Information Officer
CHR: Ramona Agrela, Associate Chancellor & Chief Human Resources Executive
CNO: Sonia Lane, Interim Chief Nursing Officer
Web address: www.ucirvinehealth.org
Control: State–Government, nonfederal **Service:** General Medical and Surgical

Staffed Beds: 411 **Admissions:** 20226 **Census:** 317 **Outpatient Visits:** 656423 **Births:** 1596 **Total Expense ($000):** 880535 **Payroll Expense ($000):** 352214 **Personnel:** 4311

OROVILLE—Butte County

OROVILLE HOSPITAL (050030), 2767 Olive Highway, Zip 95966–6118; tel. 530/533–8500 **A**10 **F**3 5 11 13 15 18 19 26 27 28 29 30 31 32 33 34 35 36 38 39 40 41 44 45 46 47 48 49 50 51 52 54 56 57 59 60 61 62 63 64 65 66 68 70 74 75 76 77 78 79 81 82 83 84 85 86 87 91 93 94 96 97 107 108 110 111 114 115 116 117 118 119 120 121 123 124 126 127 129 130 131 132 134 135 144 145 146 147 148
Primary Contact: Robert J. Wentz, President and Chief Executive Officer
COO: Scott Chapple, Chief Operating Officer
CFO: Ashok Khanchandani, Chief Financial Officer
CMO: Mathew N. Fine, M.D., Chief Medical Officer
CIO: Denise LeFevre, Chief Information Officer
CHR: Scott Chapple, Chief Operating Officer
CNO: Carol Speer-Smith, R.N., Chief Nursing Officer
Web address: www.orovillehospital.com
Control: Other not–for–profit (including NFP Corporation) **Service:** General Medical and Surgical

Staffed Beds: 133 **Admissions:** 11875 **Census:** 114 **Outpatient Visits:** 378695 **Births:** 466 **Total Expense ($000):** 221855 **Payroll Expense ($000):** 85242 **Personnel:** 1244

OXNARD—Ventura County

✠ **ST. JOHN'S REGIONAL MEDICAL CENTER (050082)**, 1600 North Rose Avenue, Zip 93030–3723; tel. 805/988–2500, (Nonreporting) **A**1 2 10 **S** Dignity Health, San Francisco, CA
Primary Contact: Darren W. Lee, President and Chief Executive Officer
CFO: Donald P. Bernard, Chief Financial Officer
CMO: Sahin Yanik, M.D., Vice President Medical Administration
CIO: Jeff Perry, Director Information Technology
CHR: Ed Gonzales, Vice President Human Resources
Web address: www.stjohnshealth.org
Control: Other not–for–profit (including NFP Corporation) **Service:** General Medical and Surgical

Staffed Beds: 161

PALM SPRINGS—Riverside County

✠ **DESERT REGIONAL MEDICAL CENTER (050243)**, 1150 North Indian Canyon Drive, Zip 92262–4872; tel. 760/323–6511, (Total facility includes 30 beds in nursing home–type unit) **A**1 2 3 10 13 **F**3 12 13 15 17 18 20 22 24 26 28 29 30 31 34 35 40 43 45 46 47 48 49 50 51 52 53 54 55 56 57 58 59 60 61 62 64 65 68 70 72 74 75 76 77 78 79 81 82 85 86 87 89 90 92 93 94 100 102 107 108 109 110 111 114 115 116 117 118 119 124 126 128 130 131 132 144 146 147 148 **S** TENET Healthcare Corporation, Dallas, TX
Primary Contact: Carolyn P. Caldwell, Chief Executive Officer
CFO: Judi Stimson, Chief Financial Officer
CMO: Charles Anderson, M.D., Chief Medical Officer
CIO: Robert Klingseis, Director Information Systems
CHR: Frederick K. Owusu, Chief Human Resources Officer
CNO: Kristin Schmidt, R.N., Chief Nursing Officer
Web address: www.desertregional.com
Control: Individual, Investor–owned, for–profit **Service:** General Medical and Surgical

Staffed Beds: 382 **Admissions:** 18705 **Census:** 229 **Outpatient Visits:** 159534 **Births:** 3279 **Total Expense ($000):** 363705 **Payroll Expense ($000):** 173244 **Personnel:** 1925

PALMDALE—Los Angeles County

☐ **PALMDALE REGIONAL MEDICAL CENTER (050204)**, 38600 Medical Center Drive, Zip 93551–4483; tel. 661/382–5000, (Nonreporting) **A**1 10 **S** Universal Health Services, Inc., King of Prussia, PA
Primary Contact: Richard Allen, Chief Executive Officer
CFO: Kurt Broten, Chief Financial Officer
CIO: Roy Singleton, Director Computer Information Systems
CHR: Karen Hickling, Director Human Resources
CNO: Pat McClendon, MSN, Chief Nursing Officer
Web address: www.palmdaleregional.com
Control: Corporation, Investor–owned, for–profit **Service:** General Medical and Surgical

Staffed Beds: 157

Hospital, Medicare Provider Number, Address, Telephone, Approval, Facility, and Physician Codes, Health Care System

★ American Hospital Association (AHA) membership ○ Healthcare Facilities Accreditation Program ⇑ Center for Improvement in Healthcare Quality Accreditation
☐ The Joint Commission accreditation ◇ DNV Healthcare Inc. accreditation △ Commission on Accreditation of Rehabilitation Facilities (CARF) accreditation

PALO ALTO—Santa Clara County

✠ **LUCILE SALTER PACKARD CHILDREN'S HOSPITAL STANFORD (053305)**, 725 Welch Road, Zip 94304–1614; tel. 650/497–8000 **A**1 3 5 10 **F**3 7 8 11 12 13 17 19 25 27 28 29 30 31 32 34 35 36 38 44 45 46 47 48 49 50 52 54 55 57 58 59 60 61 64 65 66 68 71 72 73 74 75 76 77 78 79 80 81 82 84 85 86 87 88 89 91 92 93 96 97 99 100 101 104 107 111 115 119 124 126 129 130 131 132 134 136 137 138 139 140 141 142 144 145 146 148 **P**3
Primary Contact: Christopher G. Dawes, President and Chief Executive Officer
COO: Anne McCune, Chief Operating Officer
CMO: Kenneth Cox, M.D., Chief Medical Officer
CIO: James McCaughey, Chief Strategy Officer
CHR: Greg Souza, Vice President Human Resources
CNO: Susan Costello, Chief Nursing Officer
Web address: www.stanfordchildrens.org
Control: Other not–for–profit (including NFP Corporation) **Service:** Children's general

Staffed Beds: 257 Admissions: 13644 Census: 234 Outpatient Visits: 235637 **Births: 4472 Total Expense ($000):** 1003237 **Payroll Expense ($000):** 320944 **Personnel:** 3227

✠ **STANFORD HEALTH CARE (050441)**, 300 Pasteur Drive, Suite H3200, Zip 94304–2203; tel. 650/723–4000 **A**1 3 5 8 10 **F**3 5 6 7 8 9 11 12 14 15 17 18 20 21 22 23 24 26 27 28 29 30 31 33 34 35 36 37 38 39 40 41 43 44 45 46 47 48 49 50 51 52 54 55 56 57 58 59 60 61 63 64 65 66 68 70 74 75 77 78 79 80 81 82 84 85 86 87 91 92 93 94 95 96 97 98 100 101 102 103 104 107 108 110 111 114 115 117 118 119 120 121 123 124 126 129 130 131 132 135 136 137 138 139 140 141 142 143 145 146 147 148 **P**6 **S** Stanford Health Care, Palo Alto, CA
Primary Contact: Mariann Byerwalter, Interim President and Chief Executive Officer
COO: James Hereford, Chief Operating Officer
CFO: Daniel Morrissette, Chief Financial Officer
CMO: Norman Rizk, M.D., Chief Medical Officer
CIO: Pravene Nath, Chief Information Officer
CHR: Kety Duron, Vice President Human Resources
CNO: Nancy Lee, R.N., Vice President Patient Care Services and Chief Nursing Officer
Web address: www.stanfordhealthcare.org
Control: Other not–for–profit (including NFP Corporation) **Service:** General Medical and Surgical

Staffed Beds: 491 Admissions: 25299 Census: 412 Outpatient Visits: 1281737 **Births: 0 Total Expense ($000):** 3072561 **Payroll Expense ($000):** 870707 **Personnel:** 9279

✠ △ **VA PALO ALTO HEALTH CARE SYSTEM**, 3801 Miranda Avenue, Zip 94304–1207; tel. 650/493–5000, (Includes PALO ALTO DIVISION, 3801 Miranda Avenue, tel. 650/493–5000; VETERANS AFFAIRS PALO ALTO HEALTH CARE SYSTEM, LIVERMORE DIVISION, 4951 Arroyo Road, Livermore, Zip 94550; tel. 510/447–2560), (Nonreporting) **A**1 2 3 5 7 **S** Department of Veterans Affairs, Washington, DC
Primary Contact: Elizabeth Joyce Freeman, FACHE, Director
CFO: Mel Niese, Chief Fiscal Service
CMO: Lawrence Leung, M.D., Chief of Staff
CIO: Doug Wirthgen, Chief Information Officer
CHR: Lori Peery, Chief Human Resource Management Services
Web address: www.paloalto.va.gov/
Control: Veterans Affairs, Government, federal **Service:** General Medical and Surgical

Staffed Beds: 808

PANORAMA CITY—Los Angeles County, See Los Angeles

PARADISE—Butte County

✠ **FEATHER RIVER HOSPITAL (050225)**, 5974 Pentz Road, Zip 95969–5593; tel. 530/877–9361, (Nonreporting) **A**1 2 10 **S** Adventist Health, Roseville, CA
Primary Contact: Monty E. Knittel, Chief Executive Officer
CFO: Dan Gordon, Chief Financial Officer
CMO: Anthony Nasr, M.D., Chief Medical Staff
CIO: Dan Gordon, Chief Financial Officer
CHR: Denton Gruzensky, Director Human Resources
Web address: www.frhosp.org
Control: Church–operated, Nongovernment, not–for profit **Service:** General Medical and Surgical

Staffed Beds: 86

PASADENA—Los Angeles County

✠ **HUNTINGTON MEMORIAL HOSPITAL (050438)**, 100 West California Boulevard, Zip 91105–3097, Mailing Address: P.O. Box 7013, Zip 91109–7013; tel. 626/397–5000 **A**1 2 3 5 10 **F**1 3 4 5 8 11 12 13 14 15 16 17 18 20 22 24 26 28 29 30 31 34 35 37 40 41 43 44 45 46 47 48 49 50 51 53 56 58 59 60 61 63 64 65 66 67 68 70 72 73 74 75 76 77 78 79 80 81 82 84 86 87 88 89 90 92 93 97 98 100 101 102 103 104 105 106 107 108 111 114 115 118 119 120 121 123 126 128 129 130 132 146 147 148 **P**3 5 7
Primary Contact: Stephen A. Ralph, President and Chief Executive Officer
CFO: James S. Noble, Chief Financial Officer
CMO: Paula Verrette, M.D., Senior Vice President Quality and Physician Services and Chief Medical Officer
CIO: Debbie Tafoya, Vice President and Chief Information Officer
CHR: Debbie Ortega, Chief Human Resource Officer and Vice President Administrative Services
CNO: Gloria Sanchez–Rico, Chief Nursing Officer and Vice President
Web address: www.huntingtonhospital.com
Control: Other not–for–profit (including NFP Corporation) **Service:** General Medical and Surgical

Staffed Beds: 625 Admissions: 26792 Census: 327 Outpatient Visits: 135954 **Births: 3225 Total Expense ($000):** 593755 **Payroll Expense ($000):** 218671 **Personnel:** 3137

☐ **LAS ENCINAS HOSPITAL (054078)**, 2900 East Del Mar Boulevard, Zip 91107–4399; tel. 626/795–9901, (Nonreporting) **A**1 10 **S** Signature Healthcare Services, Corona, CA
Primary Contact: Joseph Murphy, Chief Executive Officer
CMO: Daniel Suzuki, M.D., Medical Director
CIO: Eric Kim, Chief Information Officer
CHR: Veronica Herrera, Director Human Resources
Web address: www.lasencinashospital.com
Control: Corporation, Investor–owned, for–profit **Service:** Psychiatric

Staffed Beds: 138

PATTON—San Bernardino County

☐ **PATTON STATE HOSPITAL**, 3102 East Highland Avenue, Zip 92369–7813; tel. 909/425–7000 **A**1 3 **F**3 29 30 39 53 57 58 59 61 65 74 75 77 86 87 98 100 101 103 130 132 135 143 146 **P**1
Primary Contact: Harry Oreol, Acting Chief Executive Officer
CFO: Kathleen Gamble, Fiscal Officer
CMO: George Christison, M.D., Medical Director
CIO: Cindy Barrett, Administrative Assistant
CHR: Nancy Varela, Director Human Resources
Web address: www.dmh.cahwnet.gov/statehospitals/patton
Control: State–Government, nonfederal **Service:** Psychiatric

Staffed Beds: 1527 Admissions: 1451 Census: 1527 Outpatient Visits: 0 **Births: 0 Total Expense ($000):** 315474 **Payroll Expense ($000):** 197383 **Personnel:** 2380

PERRIS—Riverside County

★ ○ **KINDRED HOSPITAL RIVERSIDE (052052)**, 2224 Medical Center Drive, Zip 92571–2638; tel. 951/436–3535, (Nonreporting) **A**10 11 **S** Kindred Healthcare, Louisville, KY
Primary Contact: Jonathan Jean–Marie, Administrator and Chief Executive Officer
COO: Guay Khim Fugate, Chief Operations Officer
CFO: John Browne, Senior Chief Financial Officer
CHR: Tom Wright, Director Human Resources
Web address: www.khriverside.com
Control: Corporation, Investor–owned, for–profit **Service:** Long–Term Acute Care hospital

Staffed Beds: 40

PETALUMA—Sonoma County

✠ **PETALUMA VALLEY HOSPITAL (050136)**, 400 North McDowell Boulevard, Zip 94954–2366; tel. 707/778–1111 **A**1 10 **F**3 11 13 15 29 30 31 35 40 44 45 46 49 50 51 57 60 63 64 68 70 74 75 76 77 78 79 81 84 85 87 91 92 93 100 107 108 110 111 115 119 130 146 148 **S** Providence St. Joseph Health, Renton, WA
Primary Contact: Todd Salnas, President
CFO: Mich Riccioni, Chief Financial Officer
CIO: Patrick Wylie, Director Information Systems
Web address: www.stjosephhealth.org/About–Us/Facilities/Petaluma–Valley–Hospital.aspx
Control: Other not–for–profit (including NFP Corporation) **Service:** General Medical and Surgical

Staffed Beds: 49 Admissions: 2605 Census: 25 Outpatient Visits: 62645 **Births: 418 Total Expense ($000):** 84029 **Payroll Expense ($000):** 28355 **Personnel:** 308

Many Facility Codes have changed. Please refer to the AHA Guide Code Chart. © 2016 AHA Guide

CA

PLACENTIA—Orange County

✠ **PLACENTIA–LINDA HOSPITAL (050589)**, 1301 North Rose Drive, Zip 92870–3899; tel. 714/993–2000 **A**1 10 **F**3 11 12 15 17 18 29 30 34 35 40 45 46 47 48 49 51 54 56 57 59 60 65 68 70 75 79 81 85 87 92 93 107 108 110 111 118 119 130 131 132 135 146 148 **S** TENET Healthcare Corporation, Dallas, TX
Primary Contact: Charles Orlando, Interim Chief Executive Officer
COO: Dwayne Richardson, Chief Operating Officer
CFO: Brittany Whitaker, Chief Financial Officer
CIO: Eleanor Laneaux, Director Information Systems
CHR: Diane McCluskey, Chief Human Resources Officer
CNO: Nancy Lee, Chief Nursing Officer
Web address: www.placentialinda.com
Control: Corporation, Investor–owned, for–profit **Service:** General Medical and Surgical

Staffed Beds: 114 **Admissions:** 3390 **Census:** 27 **Outpatient Visits:** 51648 **Births:** 0 **Total Expense ($000):** 55291 **Payroll Expense ($000):** 27194

PLACERVILLE—El Dorado County

✠ **MARSHALL MEDICAL CENTER (050254)**, 1100 Marshall Way, Zip 95667–5722; tel. 530/622–1441, (Total facility includes 14 beds in nursing home–type unit) **A**1 2 10 **F**3 8 11 13 15 18 20 22 28 29 31 34 43 46 49 50 51 56 57 59 62 65 66 70 74 75 76 77 78 79 81 84 85 86 87 89 93 107 108 110 111 115 116 117 119 126 127 128 129 130 135 143 146 147 148 **P**3
Primary Contact: James Whipple, Chief Executive Officer
COO: Shannon Truesdell, Chief Operating Officer
CFO: Laurie Eldridge, Chief Financial Officer
CMO: Rajiv Pathak, Chief of Staff
CIO: Mike Jones, Executive Director
CHR: Scott M. Comer, Vice President Human Resources
CNO: Kathy Blair Krejci, Chief Nursing Officer
Web address: www.marshallmedical.org
Control: Other not–for–profit (including NFP Corporation) **Service:** General Medical and Surgical

Staffed Beds: 113 **Admissions:** 5459 **Census:** 58 **Outpatient Visits:** 505502 **Births:** 528 **Total Expense ($000):** 206381 **Payroll Expense ($000):** 74991 **Personnel:** 1048

PLEASANTON—Alameda County

✠ **STANFORD HEALTH CARE – VALLEYCARE (050283)**, 5555 West Las Positas Boulevard, Zip 94588–4000; tel. 925/847–3000, (Includes VALLEY MEMORIAL, 1111 East Stanley Boulevard, Livermore, Zip 94550–4115; tel. 925/447–7000), (Total facility includes 22 beds in nursing home–type unit) **A**1 2 10 **F**3 8 10 11 12 13 15 17 18 20 22 24 26 28 29 30 31 34 35 39 40 41 45 47 50 53 56 57 59 60 69 70 72 74 75 76 77 78 79 81 84 85 89 93 98 103 107 111 116 119 126 128 129 130 131 132 144 146 147 **S** Stanford Health Care, Palo Alto, CA
Primary Contact: Scott Gregerson, President and Chief Executive Officer
COO: Cindy Noonan, Chief Operating Officer
CMO: Dat Nguyen, M.D., Chief of Staff
CIO: Bob Woods, Chief Information Officer
CHR: Chris Faber, Human Resources Analyst
Web address: www.valleycare.com
Control: Other not–for–profit (including NFP Corporation) **Service:** General Medical and Surgical

Staffed Beds: 207 **Admissions:** 7791 **Census:** 105 **Outpatient Visits:** 197192 **Births:** 1394 **Total Expense ($000):** 262538 **Payroll Expense ($000):** 102298 **Personnel:** 1092

POMONA—Los Angeles County

✠ △ **CASA COLINA HOSPITAL AND HEALTH SYSTEMS (053027)**, 255 East Bonita Avenue, Zip 91767–1923, Mailing Address: P.O. Box 6001, Zip 91769–6001; tel. 909/596–7733, (Nonreporting) **A**1 7 10 13
Primary Contact: Felice L. Loverso, Ph.D., President and Chief Executive Officer
CFO: David Morony, Chief Financial Officer
CMO: Christopher Chalian, M.D., Medical Director
CIO: Ross Lesins, Chief Information Officer
CHR: Karen Du Pont, Chief Human Resource Officer
CNO: Kathryn Johnson, Chief Nursing Officer
Web address: www.casacolina.org
Control: Other not–for–profit (including NFP Corporation) **Service:** Rehabilitation

Staffed Beds: 68

✠ **POMONA VALLEY HOSPITAL MEDICAL CENTER (050231)**, 1798 North Garey Avenue, Zip 91767–2918; tel. 909/865–9500 **A**1 2 3 5 10 **F**3 11 13 15 17 18 20 22 24 26 28 29 30 31 34 35 40 41 45 46 47 49 50 51 53 54 55 57 58 59 60 61 63 64 68 69 70 72 74 75 76 77 78 79 81 84 85 89 92 93 107 108 110 111 114 115 116 117 118 119 120 121 123 124 126 129 130 131 132 135 144 145 146 147 148 **P**5 7
Primary Contact: Richard E. Yochum, FACHE, President and Chief Executive Officer
CFO: Michael Nelson, Executive Vice President and Chief Financial Officer
CMO: Kenneth Nakamoto, M.D., Vice President Medical Affairs
CIO: Kent Hoyos, Chief Information Officer
CHR: Ray Inge, Vice President Human Resources
CNO: Darlene Scafiddi, R.N., Vice President Nursing and Patient Care Services
Web address: www.pvhmc.org
Control: Other not–for–profit (including NFP Corporation) **Service:** General Medical and Surgical

Staffed Beds: 399 **Admissions:** 21513 **Census:** 252 **Outpatient Visits:** 533624 **Births:** 7586 **Total Expense ($000):** 493591 **Payroll Expense ($000):** 224061

PORTERVILLE—Tulare County

PORTERVILLE DEVELOPMENTAL CENTER (050546), 26501 Avenue 140, Zip 93257–9109, Mailing Address: P.O. Box 2000, Zip 93258–2000; tel. 559/782–2222, (Nonreporting) **A**10
Primary Contact: Theresa Billeci, Executive Director
COO: Betty Davis, Director Administrative Services
CFO: Karen Warren, Fiscal Officer
CMO: Joseph Mendoza, M.D., Medical Director
CIO: Vincent Chandler, Director Information Services
CHR: Shawna Gregg, Director Human Resources
CNO: Tom Shelton, Coordinator of Nursing Services
Web address: www.pdc.dds.ca.gov/
Control: State–Government, nonfederal **Service:** Intellectual disabilities

Staffed Beds: 484

☐ **SIERRA VIEW MEDICAL CENTER (050261)**, 465 West Putnam Avenue, Zip 93257–3320; tel. 559/784–1110, (Total facility includes 35 beds in nursing home–type unit) **A**1 10 **F**3 13 15 29 30 31 34 35 40 42 45 47 49 54 57 59 60 65 68 70 72 75 76 78 79 81 85 87 89 93 107 108 110 111 114 115 119 120 121 123 130 132 135 146 147 148
Primary Contact: Donna J. Hefner, R.N., President and Chief Executive Officer
CFO: John Chivers, Senior Vice President Finance
CIO: Traci Follett, Director Clinical Infomatics
CHR: Sharon Brown, Vice President Human Resources
Web address: www.sierra–view.com
Control: Hospital district or authority, Government, nonfederal **Service:** General Medical and Surgical

Staffed Beds: 154 **Admissions:** 6252 **Census:** 100 **Outpatient Visits:** 159485 **Births:** 1542 **Total Expense ($000):** 130726 **Payroll Expense ($000):** 47257 **Personnel:** 753

PORTOLA—Plumas County

EASTERN PLUMAS HEALTH CARE (051300), 500 First Avenue, Zip 96122–9406; tel. 530/832–6500, (Total facility includes 58 beds in nursing home–type unit) **A**10 18 **F**3 7 39 40 45 50 57 59 65 66 68 79 81 82 87 90 91 97 104 107 114 119 120 127 128 135 145 146 148 **P**5
Primary Contact: Thomas P. Hayes, Chief Executive Officer
CFO: Jeri Nelson, Chief Financial Officer
CMO: Eric Bugna, M.D., Chief of Staff
CHR: Cathy Conant, Chief Human Resources and Personnel
Web address: www.ephc.org
Control: Hospital district or authority, Government, nonfederal **Service:** General Medical and Surgical

Staffed Beds: 75 **Admissions:** 243 **Census:** 51 **Outpatient Visits:** 32821 **Births:** 0 **Personnel:** 203

POWAY—San Diego County

✠ **POMERADO HOSPITAL (050636)**, 15615 Pomerado Road, Zip 92064–2460; tel. 858/613–4000, (Total facility includes 127 beds in nursing home–type unit) **A**1 10 **F**3 8 11 12 13 14 15 18 20 29 30 34 35 36 38 40 45 46 47 49 50 51 54 55 56 57 58 59 62 64 65 67 68 70 72 74 75 76 77 78 79 81 82 84 85 87 97 98 100 101 102 103 107 110 111 119 120 128 130 131 132 143 144 146 147 148 **P**3 **S** Palomar Health, Escondido, CA
Primary Contact: Cheryl Olson, Interim Vice President
CIO: Steven Tanaka, Chief Information Officer
CHR: Brenda C. Turner, Chief Human Resources Officer
Web address: www.pph.org
Control: Hospital district or authority, Government, nonfederal **Service:** General Medical and Surgical

Staffed Beds: 229 **Admissions:** 6465 **Census:** 184 **Outpatient Visits:** 115237 **Births:** 1299 **Total Expense ($000):** 147672 **Payroll Expense ($000):** 62038 **Personnel:** 531

QUINCY—Plumas County

☐ **PLUMAS DISTRICT HOSPITAL (051326)**, 1065 Bucks Lake Road, Zip 95971–9599; tel. 530/283–2121, (Nonreporting) **A**1 10 18
Primary Contact: Jeffrey Kepple, M.D., Chief Executive Officer
CMO: Vincent Frantz, M.D., Chief of Staff
CIO: Brenda Compton, Manager Information Technology
CHR: Denise Harding, Director Human Resources
Web address: www.pdh.org
Control: Hospital district or authority, Government, nonfederal **Service:** General Medical and Surgical

Staffed Beds: 25

RANCHO CUCAMONGA—San Bernardino County

✠ **KINDRED HOSPITAL RANCHO (052049)**, 10841 White Oak Avenue, Zip 91730–3811; tel. 909/581–6400, (Nonreporting) **A**1 10 **S** Kindred Healthcare, Louisville, KY
Primary Contact: Victor Carrasco, Chief Executive Officer
COO: Jody Knox, Chief Operating Officer
Web address: www.khrancho.com
Control: Corporation, Investor–owned, for–profit **Service:** Long–Term Acute Care hospital

Staffed Beds: 55

RANCHO MIRAGE—Riverside County

✠ △ **EISENHOWER MEDICAL CENTER (050573)**, 39000 Bob Hope Drive, Zip 92270–3221; tel. 760/340–3911 **A**1 2 3 7 10 **F**2 3 9 11 12 15 17 18 20 22 24 26 28 29 30 31 34 35 37 40 41 45 47 49 50 53 54 56 57 58 59 60 61 64 65 68 70 74 75 77 78 79 81 82 84 85 86 87 89 90 93 96 97 100 101 102 104 105 107 108 109 110 111 112 114 115 118 119 120 121 123 124 126 129 130 131 132 135 144 145 146 147 148 **P**3
Primary Contact: G. Aubrey Serfling, President and Chief Executive Officer
COO: Martin Massiello, Executive Vice President and Chief Operating Officer
CFO: Ken Wheat, Senior Vice President and Chief Financial Officer
CMO: Alan Williamson, M.D., Chief Medical Officer
CIO: David Perez, Vice President and Chief Information Officer
CHR: Liz Guignier, Vice President Human Resources
CNO: Ann R. Mostofi, MSN, Vice President Patient Care and Chief Nursing Officer
Web address: www.emc.org
Control: Other not–for–profit (including NFP Corporation) **Service:** General Medical and Surgical

Staffed Beds: 381 **Admissions:** 18801 **Census:** 208 **Outpatient Visits:** 795778 **Births:** 0 **Total Expense ($000):** 585273 **Payroll Expense ($000):** 205574 **Personnel:** 2994

RED BLUFF—Tehama County

✠ **ST. ELIZABETH COMMUNITY HOSPITAL (050042)**, 2550 Sister Mary Columba Drive, Zip 96080–4397; tel. 530/529–8000 **A**1 10 20 **F**3 7 8 11 13 15 29 30 34 35 40 43 45 51 54 62 63 64 68 70 75 76 81 82 84 85 89 93 107 108 110 111 114 119 130 131 132 133 145 146 148 **P**3 **S** Dignity Health, San Francisco, CA
Primary Contact: G. Todd Smith, President
CFO: Kim Miranda, Chief Financial Officer
CMO: James DeSoto, M.D., Vice President Medical Affairs
CIO: Henry Niessink, Senior Manager Information Technology Systems
CHR: Denise Little, Director Human Resources
Web address: www.mercy.org
Control: Church–operated, Nongovernment, not–for profit **Service:** General Medical and Surgical

Staffed Beds: 65 **Admissions:** 2886 **Census:** 22 **Outpatient Visits:** 66874 **Births:** 622 **Total Expense ($000):** 81131 **Payroll Expense ($000):** 33683 **Personnel:** 546

REDDING—Shasta County

✠ **MERCY MEDICAL CENTER REDDING (050280)**, 2175 Rosaline Avenue, Zip 96001–2549, Mailing Address: P.O. Box 496009, Zip 96049–6009; tel. 530/225–6000 **A**1 2 3 5 10 **F**2 3 7 11 13 15 17 18 20 22 24 28 29 30 31 34 35 37 40 43 45 46 47 48 49 50 54 57 59 61 62 63 64 66 68 70 72 75 76 77 78 79 81 82 84 85 89 91 97 107 108 111 114 115 118 119 126 130 132 135 143 144 145 146 147 148 **S** Dignity Health, San Francisco, CA
Primary Contact: Mark D. Korth, President
COO: Patrick Varga, Chief Operating Officer
CFO: Kimberly Miranda, Regional Vice President Finance and Chief Financial Officer
CMO: James DeSoto, M.D., Vice President Medical Affairs
CIO: Henry Niessink, Regional Director Information Technology Services
CHR: Stephan Hosler, Vice President Human Resources
CNO: Kimberly Shaw, Vice President Patient Care and Chief Nursing Executive
Web address: www.mercy.org
Control: Church–operated, Nongovernment, not–for profit **Service:** General Medical and Surgical

Staffed Beds: 267 **Admissions:** 12917 **Census:** 156 **Outpatient Visits:** 137846 **Births:** 1999 **Total Expense ($000):** 418015 **Payroll Expense ($000):** 147422 **Personnel:** 1506

NORTHERN CALIFORNIA REHABILITATION HOSPITAL See Vibra Hospital of Northern California

PATIENTS' HOSPITAL OF REDDING (050697), 2900 Eureka Way, Zip 96001–0220; tel. 530/225–8700, (Nonreporting) **A**10
Primary Contact: Shari Lejsek, Administrator
CFO: Kim Needles, Manager Business Office
CMO: James Tate, M.D., Chief of Staff
CIO: Kim Cameron, Manager Health Information Services
CHR: Brenda Meline, Manager Human Resources
CNO: Diane Rieke, Director Patient Care Services
Web address: www.patientshospital.com
Control: Individual, Investor–owned, for–profit **Service:** Surgical

Staffed Beds: 10

✠ **SHASTA REGIONAL MEDICAL CENTER (050764)**, 1100 Butte Street, Zip 96001–0853, Mailing Address: P.O. Box 496072, Zip 96049–6072; tel. 530/244–5400 **A**1 5 10 **F**3 11 17 18 20 22 24 26 28 29 30 34 37 40 43 45 46 49 50 51 56 59 70 74 77 79 81 85 98 103 107 108 111 114 115 119 135 146 147 148 **S** Prime Healthcare Services, Ontario, CA
Primary Contact: Cynthia Gordon, R.N., Chief Executive Officer
COO: Becky Levy, Chief Operating Officer
CFO: Becky Levy, Chief Financial Officer
CMO: Marcia McCampbell, M.D., Chief Medical Officer
CIO: Tony VanBoekel, Director Information Systems
CHR: Andrew Torge, Director Human Resources
CNO: Leslie Woodson, R.N., Chief Nursing Officer
Web address: www.shastaregional.com
Control: Corporation, Investor–owned, for–profit **Service:** General Medical and Surgical

Staffed Beds: 113 **Admissions:** 6841 **Census:** 87 **Outpatient Visits:** 75303 **Births:** 0 **Total Expense ($000):** 145406 **Payroll Expense ($000):** 44931 **Personnel:** 870

✠ **VIBRA HOSPITAL OF NORTHERN CALIFORNIA (052047)**, 2801 Eureka Way, Zip 96001–0222; tel. 530/246–9000, (Total facility includes 32 beds in nursing home–type unit) **A**1 10 **F**1 3 29 64 77 119 128 130 148 **S** Vibra Healthcare, Mechanicsburg, PA
Primary Contact: Chris Jones, Chief Executive Officer
COO: Lisa Stevens, Chief Clinical Officer and Chief Operating Officer
CFO: Rebecca Andrews, Chief Financial Officer
CMO: Nanda Kumar, M.D., Chief of Staff
CIO: Mark Cardenas, Director Plant Operations
CHR: Wendy Tempest, Director Human Resources
Web address: www.norcalrehab.com
Control: Corporation, Investor–owned, for–profit **Service:** Long–Term Acute Care hospital

Staffed Beds: 88 **Admissions:** 1053 **Census:** 77 **Outpatient Visits:** 3501 **Births:** 0 **Total Expense ($000):** 33647 **Payroll Expense ($000):** 14825 **Personnel:** 245

Many Facility Codes have changed. Please refer to the AHA Guide Code Chart. © 2016 AHA Guide

REDLANDS—San Bernardino County

☒ **LOMA LINDA UNIVERSITY BEHAVIORAL MEDICINE CENTER (054093)**, 1710 Barton Road, Zip 92373–5304; tel. 909/558–9200 **A**1 5 10 **F**4 5 29 30 34 38 50 57 87 98 99 100 101 102 103 104 105 130 132 134 135 **S** Loma Linda University Adventist Health Sciences Center, Loma Linda, CA
Primary Contact: Edward Field, Administrator
COO: Ruthita J. Fike, Chief Executive Officer
CFO: Steve Mohr, Senior Vice President Finance and Chief Financial Officer
CMO: William Murdoch, M.D., Medical Director
CIO: Mark Zirkelback, Chief Information Officer
CHR: Mark Hubbard, Vice President Risk Management
CNO: Norie Lee Reyes Bencito Aca–ac, R.N., Director of Nursing
Web address: www.llu.edu
Control: Other not–for–profit (including NFP Corporation) **Service:** Psychiatric

Staffed Beds: 89 **Admissions:** 4640 **Census:** 70 **Outpatient Visits:** 37473 **Births:** 0 **Total Expense ($000):** 34468 **Payroll Expense ($000):** 16328 **Personnel:** 301

☒ **REDLANDS COMMUNITY HOSPITAL (050272)**, 350 Terracina Boulevard, Zip 92373–0742, Mailing Address: P.O. Box 3391, Zip 92373–0742; tel. 909/335–5500, (Total facility includes 16 beds in nursing home–type unit) **A**1 3 10 **F**3 11 13 15 18 20 28 29 30 31 34 35 40 45 46 47 49 54 57 59 62 63 64 65 66 68 69 70 72 74 75 76 77 78 79 81 82 84 85 87 93 96 97 98 102 104 105 107 108 110 111 114 115 116 117 119 121 126 128 130 132 143 146 147 148 **P**5 7
Primary Contact: James R. Holmes, President and Chief Executive Officer
CFO: Michelle Mok, Chief Financial Officer
CHR: Lisa Guzman, Human Resource Vice President
CNO: Lauren Spilsbury, R.N., Vice President for Patient Care Services
Web address: www.redlandshospital.org
Control: Other not–for–profit (including NFP Corporation) **Service:** General Medical and Surgical

Staffed Beds: 189 **Admissions:** 11644 **Census:** 117 **Outpatient Visits:** 171042 **Births:** 2549 **Total Expense ($000):** 306012 **Payroll Expense ($000):** 92727 **Personnel:** 1325

REDWOOD CITY—San Mateo County

☒ **KAISER PERMANENTE REDWOOD CITY MEDICAL CENTER (050541)**, 1100 Veterans Boulevard, Zip 94063–2087; tel. 650/299–2000, (Nonreporting) **A**1 3 5 10 **S** Kaiser Foundation Hospitals, Oakland, CA
Primary Contact: Michelle Gaskill–Hames, R.N., Senior Vice President & Area Manager
COO: Sheila Gilson, R.N., Chief Operating Officer
CFO: Doug Reynolds, Area Finance Officer
CMO: William Firtch, M.D., Physician In Chief
CHR: Kimberly A. Seitz, Area Human Resources Leader
CNO: Jodi B. Galli, R.N., Chief Nursing Officer
Web address: www.kaiserpermanente.org
Control: Other not–for–profit (including NFP Corporation) **Service:** General Medical and Surgical

Staffed Beds: 213

☒ **SEQUOIA HOSPITAL (050197)**, 170 Alameda De Las Pulgas, Zip 94062–2799; tel. 650/369–5811 **A**1 10 **F**11 12 13 15 18 20 22 24 26 28 29 30 31 32 34 35 37 40 45 46 49 50 53 57 59 60 64 68 70 74 75 76 77 78 79 81 84 86 87 92 93 94 107 108 110 111 114 115 118 119 120 121 123 126 129 130 132 135 146 147 148 **P**3 5 **S** Dignity Health, San Francisco, CA
Primary Contact: Bill Graham, President
CFO: Kim Osborn, Chief Financial Officer
CMO: Anita Chandrasena, M.D., Vice President Medical Affairs
CIO: Ian Vallely, Information Technology Site Leader
CHR: Linde Cheema, Vice President Human Resources
CNO: Sherie Ambrose, Chief Nurse Executive
Web address: www.sequoiahospital.org
Control: Other not–for–profit (including NFP Corporation) **Service:** General Medical and Surgical

Staffed Beds: 131 **Admissions:** 5406 **Census:** 58 **Outpatient Visits:** 93697 **Births:** 1706 **Total Expense ($000):** 270820 **Payroll Expense ($000):** 87002 **Personnel:** 720

REEDLEY—Fresno County

☒ **ADVENTIST MEDICAL CENTER–REEDLEY (050192)**, 372 West Cypress Avenue, Zip 93654–2199; tel. 559/638–8155 **A**1 3 10 **F**13 15 29 30 40 45 50 64 76 77 81 87 107 110 111 114 119 127 133 135 **P**3 **S** Adventist Health, Roseville, CA
Primary Contact: Wayne Ferch, President and Chief Executive Officer
CFO: Teresa Jacques, Interim Chief Financial Officer
CMO: Todd Spencer, M.D., Chief Medical Staff
CIO: Valerie Alvarez, Executive Assistant
CHR: Ramona Alvarado, Interim Manager Human Resources
Web address: www.skdh.org
Control: Church–operated, Nongovernment, not–for profit **Service:** General Medical and Surgical

Staffed Beds: 49 **Admissions:** 2602 **Census:** 13 **Outpatient Visits:** 357928 **Births:** 1374 **Total Expense ($000):** 74969 **Payroll Expense ($000):** 29629 **Personnel:** 696

RESEDA—Los Angeles County

☐ **JOYCE EISENBERG–KEEFER MEDICAL CENTER (054147)**, 7150 Tampa Avenue, Zip 91335–3700; tel. 818/774–3000, (Total facility includes 239 beds in nursing home–type unit) **A**1 10 **F**3 30 39 50 53 56 62 63 65 68 74 75 77 82 84 98 101 103 125 128 130 143 146 148
Primary Contact: Molly Forrest, President and Chief Executive Officer
CNO: Haya Berci, Executive Director of Nursing
Web address: www.jha.org
Control: Other not–for–profit (including NFP Corporation) **Service:** Psychiatric

Staffed Beds: 249 **Admissions:** 522 **Census:** 243 **Outpatient Visits:** 0 **Births:** 0

RICHMOND—Contra Costa County

KAISER PERMANENTE RICHMOND MEDICAL CENTER See Kaiser Permanente Oakland Medical Center, Oakland

RIDGECREST—Kern County

★ ◇ **RIDGECREST REGIONAL HOSPITAL (051333)**, 1081 North China Lake Boulevard, Zip 93555–3130; tel. 760/446–3551, (Total facility includes 125 beds in nursing home–type unit) **A**10 18 21 **F**3 8 11 13 15 18 28 29 30 32 34 35 39 40 41 43 45 50 56 57 59 62 63 64 66 68 70 75 76 77 79 81 84 85 87 89 93 97 104 107 108 110 111 114 115 119 127 128 129 130 131 133 134 144 146 147 148
Primary Contact: James A. Suver, FACHE, Chief Executive Officer
CFO: Lois Johnson, Administrator Fiscal Services
CMO: Victoria Schauf, M.D., Chief of Staff
CIO: Randy Ferguson, Chief Information Officer
CHR: Dave Shary, Administrator Human Resources
Web address: www.rrh.org
Control: Other not–for–profit (including NFP Corporation) **Service:** General Medical and Surgical

Staffed Beds: 150 **Admissions:** 2140 **Census:** 107 **Outpatient Visits:** 203168 **Births:** 451 **Total Expense ($000):** 97708 **Payroll Expense ($000):** 35184 **Personnel:** 667

RIVERSIDE—Riverside County

☒ **KAISER PERMANENTE RIVERSIDE MEDICAL CENTER (050686)**, 10800 Magnolia Avenue, Zip 92505–3000; tel. 951/353–2000 **A**1 3 5 10 **F**3 13 15 17 28 29 30 31 34 35 40 44 45 46 48 49 50 51 59 60 62 63 64 65 68 70 72 74 75 76 77 78 79 81 82 84 85 86 87 89 92 93 97 100 102 107 108 109 110 111 114 115 117 118 119 130 144 146 147 148 **S** Kaiser Foundation Hospitals, Oakland, CA
Primary Contact: Vita M. Willett, Executive Director
COO: Robin D. Mackenroth, Chief Operating Officer
CFO: JiJi Abraham, Chief Financial Officer
CMO: Frank M. Flowers, M.D., Area Medical Director
CIO: Alfred T. Velasquez, Area Information Officer
CHR: Michelle Skipper, Director Human Resources
CNO: Rosemary M. Butler, R.N., Chief Nurse Executive
Web address: www.kaiserpermanente.org
Control: Other not–for–profit (including NFP Corporation) **Service:** General Medical and Surgical

Staffed Beds: 226 **Admissions:** 18228 **Census:** 159 **Births:** 3044 **Personnel:** 860

☐ **PACIFIC GROVE HOSPITAL (054130)**, 5900 Brockton Avenue, Zip 92506–1862; tel. 951/275–8400 **A**1 10 **F**3 4 5 34 35 53 64 68 86 98 101 102 103 104 105 130 132 **P**5 **S** Acadia Healthcare Company, Inc., Franklin, TN
Primary Contact: Nichol Sheffield, Chief Executive Officer
Web address: www.pacificgrovehospital.com
Control: Corporation, Investor–owned, for–profit **Service:** Psychiatric

Staffed Beds: 68 **Admissions:** 1319 **Census:** 22 **Outpatient Visits:** 4025 **Births:** 0 **Personnel:** 110

☐ **PARKVIEW COMMUNITY HOSPITAL MEDICAL CENTER (050102)**, 3865 Jackson Street, Zip 92503–3998; tel. 951/688–2211 **A**1 10 **F**3 8 11 12 13 15 18 29 34 35 40 45 46 49 50 56 57 59 60 62 65 68 70 72 74 75 76 77 79 81 84 85 86 87 89 100 107 110 111 114 115 119 130 132 135 143 145 146 147 148
Primary Contact: Steven Popkin, Chief Executive Officer
COO: Robert Brown, Chief Operating Officer
CFO: Patti Lepe, Chief Financial Officer
CMO: Dong Kim, M.D., Chief of Staff
CIO: John Ciccarelli, Director Information Technology
CNO: Thomas Santos, R.N., Chief Nursing Officer
Web address: www.pchmc.org
Control: Other not–for–profit (including NFP Corporation) **Service:** General Medical and Surgical

Staffed Beds: 193 **Admissions:** 10110 **Census:** 115 **Outpatient Visits:** 75801 **Births:** 2410 **Total Expense ($000):** 155164 **Payroll Expense ($000):** 61297 **Personnel:** 941

RIVERSIDE CENTER FOR BEHAVIORAL MEDICINE See Pacific Grove Hospital

☒ **RIVERSIDE COMMUNITY HOSPITAL (050022)**, 4445 Magnolia Avenue, Zip 92501–4199; tel. 951/788–3000, (Nonreporting) **A**1 2 5 10 **S** HCA, Nashville, TN
Primary Contact: Patrick D. Brilliant, President and Chief Executive Officer
COO: Daniel Bowers, Chief Operating Officer
CMO: David Tito, M.D., President Medical Staff
CIO: Cae Swanger, Chief Information Officer
CHR: Tammy Kaminski, Vice President Human Relations
Web address: www.riversidecommunityhospital.com
Control: Corporation, Investor–owned, for–profit **Service:** General Medical and Surgical

Staffed Beds: 373

RIVERSIDE MEDICAL CENTER See Kaiser Permanente Riverside Medical Center

ROSEMEAD—Los Angeles County

☐ **BHC ALHAMBRA HOSPITAL (054032)**, 4619 North Rosemead Boulevard, Zip 91770–1478, Mailing Address: P.O. Box 369, Zip 91770–0369; tel. 626/286–1191, (Nonreporting) **A**1 10 **S** Universal Health Services, Inc., King of Prussia, PA
Primary Contact: Peggy Minnick, R.N., Chief Executive Officer
CFO: Michelle Jackson, Chief Financial Officer
CMO: Wakelin McNeel, M.D., Medical Director
CIO: Debbie Irvin, Director Health Information Management
CHR: Venus Taylor, Director Human Resources
Web address: www.bhcalhambra.com
Control: Corporation, Investor–owned, for–profit **Service:** Psychiatric

Staffed Beds: 97

ROSEVILLE—Placer County

☒ **KAISER PERMANENTE ROSEVILLE MEDICAL CENTER (050772)**, 1600 Eureka Road, Zip 95661–3027; tel. 916/784–4000, (Nonreporting) **A**1 2 5 10 **S** Kaiser Foundation Hospitals, Oakland, CA
Primary Contact: Jeffrey A. Collins, M.D., Senior Vice President and Area Manager
Web address: www.kp.org
Control: Other not–for–profit (including NFP Corporation) **Service:** General Medical and Surgical

Staffed Beds: 340

☒ △ **SUTTER ROSEVILLE MEDICAL CENTER (050309)**, One Medical Plaza Drive, Zip 95661–3037; tel. 916/781–1000 **A**1 2 5 7 10 **F**3 5 8 12 13 15 18 20 22 28 29 30 31 34 35 40 43 45 46 50 55 56 58 59 60 63 64 65 68 70 72 74 75 76 78 79 81 82 84 85 89 90 93 94 96 107 108 109 111 114 116 119 126 130 131 132 141 146 147 148 **P**3 **S** Sutter Health, Sacramento, CA
Primary Contact: Patrick R. Brady, Chief Executive Officer
COO: Dionne Miller, Chief Operating Officer
CFO: Gary Hubschman, Administrative Director Finance
CMO: Stuart Bostrom, M.D., Director Medical Affairs
CIO: Nancy Turner, Director Communications
CHR: Lynda Dasaro, Director Human Resources
CNO: Barbara J. Nelson, Ph.D., Chief Nursing Executive
Web address: www.sutterroseville.org
Control: Other not–for–profit (including NFP Corporation) **Service:** General Medical and Surgical

Staffed Beds: 328 **Admissions:** 19575 **Census:** 230 **Outpatient Visits:** 126122 **Births:** 2779 **Total Expense ($000):** 487964 **Payroll Expense ($000):** 149157 **Personnel:** 1539

SACRAMENTO—Sacramento County

☐ **HERITAGE OAKS HOSPITAL (054104)**, 4250 Auburn Boulevard, Zip 95841–4164; tel. 916/489–3336 **A**1 3 5 10 **F**2 5 29 38 56 64 87 98 99 100 101 102 103 104 105 130 **P**8 **S** Universal Health Services, Inc., King of Prussia, PA
Primary Contact: Shawn Silva, Chief Executive Officer
CFO: Art Wong, Chief Financial Officer
CMO: Joseph Sison, M.D., Medical Director
CHR: Lisa Myers, Director Human Resources
Web address: www.heritageoakshospital.com
Control: Corporation, Investor–owned, for–profit **Service:** Psychiatric

Staffed Beds: 120 **Admissions:** 4044 **Census:** 108 **Outpatient Visits:** 20504 **Births:** 0 **Total Expense ($000):** 23949 **Payroll Expense ($000):** 13720 **Personnel:** 262

☒ **KAISER PERMANENTE SACRAMENTO MEDICAL CENTER (050425)**, 2025 Morse Avenue, Zip 95825–2100; tel. 916/973–5000, (Nonreporting) **A**1 2 3 5 10 **S** Kaiser Foundation Hospitals, Oakland, CA
Primary Contact: Sandy Sharon, Senior Vice President and Area Manager
CFO: Jim Eldridge, Area Financial Officer
CMO: Chris Palkowski, M.D., Physician in Chief
CIO: Philip Fasano, Chief Information Officer
CHR: Gay Westfall, Senior Vice President Human Resources
Web address: www.kp.org
Control: Other not–for–profit (including NFP Corporation) **Service:** General Medical and Surgical

Staffed Beds: 287

☒ **KAISER PERMANENTE SOUTH SACRAMENTO MEDICAL CENTER (050674)**, 6600 Bruceville Road, Zip 95823–4691; tel. 916/688–2430 **A**1 3 5 10 **F**3 8 12 13 15 20 22 29 30 31 34 35 40 43 44 45 49 50 58 59 61 62 63 64 65 68 70 73 74 75 76 77 78 79 81 82 84 85 86 87 93 96 97 100 104 107 108 109 110 111 114 115 126 129 130 131 135 144 146 147 148 **S** Kaiser Foundation Hospitals, Oakland, CA
Primary Contact: Patricia M. Rodriguez, Senior Vice President and Area Manager
CFO: Kevin L. Smith, Area Finance Officer
CIO: Michelle Odell, Director of Public Affairs
CHR: James Kevin Peterson, Human Resources Leader
CNO: Terri Owensby, R.N., Chief Nursing Executive
Web address: www.kp.org
Control: Other not–for–profit (including NFP Corporation) **Service:** General Medical and Surgical

Staffed Beds: 181 **Admissions:** 13736 **Census:** 133 **Outpatient Visits:** 130278 **Births:** 2400

☒ △ **MERCY GENERAL HOSPITAL (050017)**, 4001 J Street, Zip 95819–3600; tel. 916/453–4545 **A**1 2 3 5 7 10 **F**3 8 11 13 15 17 18 20 22 24 26 28 29 30 31 34 35 36 37 38 39 40 44 45 46 47 48 49 50 51 53 56 57 58 59 63 64 66 68 70 74 75 76 77 78 79 81 82 84 85 86 87 90 91 93 94 96 99 100 107 108 109 111 114 115 119 124 126 130 131 132 135 143 145 146 **P**3 5 **S** Dignity Health, San Francisco, CA
Primary Contact: Edmundo Castaneda, President
COO: Patricia Monczewski, Chief Operating Officer
CFO: Ronald Kroll, Chief Financial Officer
CMO: Robert Wiebe, M.D., Chief Medical Officer
CHR: Cyndi Kirch, Vice President Human Resources
Web address: www.mercygeneral.org
Control: Other not–for–profit (including NFP Corporation) **Service:** General Medical and Surgical

Staffed Beds: 254 **Admissions:** 16351 **Census:** 199 **Outpatient Visits:** 57047 **Births:** 1860 **Total Expense ($000):** 561769 **Payroll Expense ($000):** 191260 **Personnel:** 1590

☒ **METHODIST HOSPITAL OF SACRAMENTO (050590)**, 7500 Hospital Drive, Zip 95823–5477; tel. 916/423–3000, (Total facility includes 170 beds in nursing home–type unit) **A**1 3 5 10 **F**3 8 11 12 17 29 30 34 35 37 39 40 41 47 49 50 56 57 58 60 61 64 68 70 72 74 75 76 77 79 81 84 85 86 87 93 96 97 102 107 108 111 115 119 128 130 131 132 146 147 148 **P**5 **S** Dignity Health, San Francisco, CA
Primary Contact: Brian K. Ivie, President and Chief Executive Officer
COO: Anita J. Kennedy, Vice President Operations
CFO: Bonnie Jenkins, Chief Financial Officer
CMO: Amir Sweha, M.D., Vice President Medical Administration
CHR: Cyndi Kirch, Vice President Human Resources
CNO: Martina Evans–Harrison, R.N., Chief Nurse Executive
Web address: www.methodistsacramento.org
Control: Other not–for–profit (including NFP Corporation) **Service:** General Medical and Surgical

Staffed Beds: 281 **Admissions:** 11345 **Census:** 264 **Outpatient Visits:** 108694 **Births:** 1994 **Total Expense ($000):** 290015 **Payroll Expense ($000):** 118896 **Personnel:** 866

☐ **SHRINERS HOSPITALS FOR CHILDREN–NORTHERN CALIFORNIA (053311)**, 2425 Stockton Boulevard, Zip 95817–2215; tel. 916/453–2000, (Nonreporting) **A**1 3 5 10 **S** Shriners Hospitals for Children, Tampa, FL
Primary Contact: Margaret Bryan, Administrator
COO: Margaret Bryan, Administrator
CFO: William Dalby, Director Fiscal Services
CIO: John Bevel, Manager Information Systems
CHR: Deborah Rubens, Director Human Resources
Web address: www.shrinershospitalsforchildren.org/Hospitals/Locations/NorthernCalifornia.aspx
Control: Other not–for–profit (including NFP Corporation) **Service:** Children's general

Staffed Beds: 70

☐ **SIERRA VISTA HOSPITAL (054087)**, 8001 Bruceville Road, Zip 95823–2329; tel. 916/288–0300, (Nonreporting) **A**1 10 **S** Universal Health Services, Inc., King of Prussia, PA
Primary Contact: Mike Zauner, Chief Executive Officer
COO: Ixel Morell, Chief Operating Officer
CFO: Nicole Samuel, Chief Financial Officer
CMO: Alok Banga, M.D., Medical Director
CNO: Gwen Hubbard, Chief Nursing Officer
Web address: www.sierravistahospital.com
Control: Corporation, Investor–owned, for–profit **Service:** Psychiatric

Staffed Beds: 120

SOUTH SACRAMENTO MEDICAL CENTER See Kaiser Permanente South Sacramento Medical Center

☒ **SUTTER CENTER FOR PSYCHIATRY (054096)**, 7700 Folsom Boulevard, Zip 95826–2608; tel. 916/386–3000 **A**1 10 **F**29 30 34 35 44 68 98 99 100 101 104 105 130 132 133 134 143 **P**3 **S** Sutter Health, Sacramento, CA
Primary Contact: John W. Boyd, PsyD, Chief Executive Officer
CFO: Pamela Ansley, Director Finance
CMO: Cindy Thygeson, M.D., Director Medical Affairs
CHR: Kristin Daniels, Manager Human Resources
Web address: www.sutterpsychiatry.org
Control: Other not–for–profit (including NFP Corporation) **Service:** Psychiatric

Staffed Beds: 71 Admissions: 2937 Census: 55 Outpatient Visits: 4352 Births: 0 Total Expense ($000): 26564 Payroll Expense ($000): 12741 Personnel: 197

☒ **SUTTER MEDICAL CENTER, SACRAMENTO (050108)**, 2801 L Street, Zip 95816–5680; tel. 916/454–3333, (Includes SUTTER CHILDREN'S CENTER, 5151 F. Street, Zip 95819–3223; tel. 800/478–8837; SUTTER GENERAL HOSPITAL, 2801 L Street, Zip 95816; tel. 916/454–2222) **A**1 2 3 5 10 **F**3 5 11 12 15 17 18 19 20 21 22 23 24 25 26 27 28 29 30 31 34 35 36 37 39 40 41 45 46 48 49 55 56 58 59 61 63 64 68 70 72 74 75 76 77 78 79 81 84 85 86 87 88 89 93 102 107 108 111 114 115 118 119 124 126 129 130 132 134 136 137 146 147 148 **P**3 **S** Sutter Health, Sacramento, CA
Primary Contact: Michael J. Cohill, Interim Chief Executive Officer
COO: Faraaz Yousuf, Chief Operating Officer
CFO: Richard SooHoo, Chief Financial Officer
CMO: Muhammed Afzal, M.D., Chief of Staff
CIO: Jim Mills, Regional Director Information Technology
CHR: Colleen Peschel, Director Human Resources
CNO: Marchelle M. McGriff, Chief Nursing Executive
Web address: www.sutterhealth.org
Control: Other not–for–profit (including NFP Corporation) **Service:** General Medical and Surgical

Staffed Beds: 523 Admissions: 28793 Census: 353 Outpatient Visits: 205195 Births: 5975 Total Expense ($000): 988774 Payroll Expense ($000): 281646 Personnel: 3600

☒ **UNIVERSITY OF CALIFORNIA, DAVIS MEDICAL CENTER (050599)**, 2315 Stockton Boulevard, Zip 95817–2282; tel. 916/734–2011, (Includes UNIVERSITY OF CALIFORNIA DAVIS CHILDREN'S HOSPITAL, 2315 Stockton Boulevard, Zip 95817–2201; tel. 800/282–3284; Ann Madden Rice, Chief Executive Officer) **A**1 2 3 5 8 10 **F**3 6 8 9 11 12 13 15 16 18 19 20 21 22 23 24 25 26 27 28 29 30 31 32 34 35 36 37 38 39 40 41 43 44 45 46 47 48 49 50 51 53 54 55 56 57 58 59 60 61 62 63 64 65 66 68 70 71 72 73 74 75 76 77 78 79 81 82 84 85 86 87 88 89 90 91 92 93 94 96 97 99 100 102 103 104 107 108 110 111 114 115 116 117 118 119 120 121 123 124 126 129 130 131 132 134 135 136 138 141 142 143 144 145 146 147 148 **P**6 **S** University of California Systemwide Administration, Oakland, CA
Primary Contact: Ann Madden Rice, Chief Executive Officer
COO: Brad Simmons, Chief Operating Officer
CFO: Timothy Maurice, Chief Financial Officer
CMO: J. Douglas Kirk, M.D., Chief Medical Officer
CIO: John Cook, Interim Chief Information Officer
CHR: Stephen Chilcott, Associate Director Human Resources
CNO: Toby Marsh, MSN, Interim Chief Patient Care Services Officer
Web address: www.ucdmc.ucdavis.edu
Control: Other not–for–profit (including NFP Corporation) **Service:** General Medical and Surgical

Staffed Beds: 583 Admissions: 32526 Census: 479 Outpatient Visits: 1271741 Births: 1887 Total Expense ($000): 1675171 Payroll Expense ($000): 724819 Personnel: 7739

SAINT HELENA—Napa County

☒ **ST. HELENA HOSPITAL NAPA VALLEY (050013)**, 10 Woodland Road, Zip 94574–9554; tel. 707/963–3611 **A**1 10 **F**3 4 5 8 15 17 18 20 22 24 26 28 29 30 31 34 35 36 37 40 42 45 47 50 51 53 57 58 59 60 62 64 65 70 74 75 76 77 78 79 81 82 84 85 86 87 92 97 98 99 100 101 102 104 105 107 108 110 111 115 117 119 120 121 126 130 131 135 146 147 148 **P**3 **S** Adventist Health, Roseville, CA
Primary Contact: Steven Herber, M.D., President and Chief Executive Officer
COO: Hal Chilton, Senior Vice President and Chief Operating Officer
CMO: Steven Herber, M.D., President and Chief Executive Officer
CIO: Mark Heringer, Interim Director Information Systems
CHR: Sylvia Seals–Barnes, II, Director Human Resources
CNO: Nia Lendaris, Regional Vice President Patient Care
Web address: www.sthelenahospital.org
Control: Church–operated, Nongovernment, not–for profit **Service:** General Medical and Surgical

Staffed Beds: 116 Admissions: 4926 Census: 59 Outpatient Visits: 91618 Births: 251 Total Expense ($000): 206286 Payroll Expense ($000): 57825 Personnel: 770

SALINAS—Monterey County

☒ **NATIVIDAD MEDICAL CENTER (050248)**, 1441 Constitution Boulevard, Zip 93906–3100, Mailing Address: P.O. Box 81611, Zip 93912–1611; tel. 831/647–7611 **A**1 3 5 10 **F**3 11 12 13 15 18 19 29 30 34 35 37 39 40 43 44 45 46 47 48 49 50 51 57 59 61 64 65 68 70 72 74 75 76 78 79 81 82 84 85 86 87 89 90 91 92 93 96 97 98 100 102 107 108 110 111 114 115 118 119 124 130 132 135 143 146 147 148 **P**6
Primary Contact: Gary Gray, D.O., Chief Executive Officer
CMO: Craig Walls, M.D., Chief Medical Officer
CIO: Ari Entin, Chief Information Officer
CHR: Lawanda Janine Bouyea, Director Human Resources
Web address: www.natividad.com
Control: County–Government, nonfederal **Service:** General Medical and Surgical

Staffed Beds: 166 Admissions: 8139 Census: 99 Outpatient Visits: 160175 Births: 2652 Total Expense ($000): 214628 Payroll Expense ($000): 81059 Personnel: 839

☒ **SALINAS VALLEY MEMORIAL HEALTHCARE SYSTEM (050334)**, 450 East Romie Lane, Zip 93901–4098; tel. 831/757–4333 **A**1 2 10 **F**3 13 15 17 18 19 20 22 24 26 28 29 30 31 34 35 37 40 45 46 49 50 57 58 59 64 66 68 70 72 74 75 76 77 78 79 81 84 85 87 89 107 108 110 111 115 118 119 126 127 129 130 132 146 148
Primary Contact: Pete Delgado, President and Chief Executive Officer
COO: Henry Ornelas, Chief Operating Officer
CFO: Augustine Lopez, Chief Financial Officer
CMO: Allen Radner, M.D., Chief Medical Officer
CIO: Audrey Parks, Senior Administrative Director Information Technology
CHR: Michelle Childs, Senior Administrative Director Human Resources
CNO: Christie Gonder, Chief Nursing Officer
Web address: www.svmh.com
Control: Hospital district or authority, Government, nonfederal **Service:** General Medical and Surgical

Staffed Beds: 185 Admissions: 10139 Census: 121 Outpatient Visits: 101322 Births: 1821 Total Expense ($000): 320347 Payroll Expense ($000): 150222 Personnel: 1114

CA

Hospital, Medicare Provider Number, Address, Telephone, Approval, Facility, and Physician Codes, Health Care System

★ American Hospital Association (AHA) membership   ◯ Healthcare Facilities Accreditation Program   ⇈ Center for Improvement in Healthcare Quality Accreditation
☐ The Joint Commission accreditation   ◇ DNV Healthcare Inc. accreditation   △ Commission on Accreditation of Rehabilitation Facilities (CARF) accreditation

SAN ANDREAS—Calaveras County

☒ **MARK TWAIN MEDICAL CENTER (051332)**, 768 Mountain Ranch Road, Zip 95249–9998; tel. 209/754–3521 **A**1 10 18 **F**3 11 15 18 28 29 30 31 34 35 40 45 50 57 59 65 68 70 75 77 78 79 81 82 83 84 85 87 91 93 96 100 104 107 110 111 115 116 117 119 127 130 145 146 147 148 **P**6 **S** Dignity Health, San Francisco, CA
Primary Contact: Lawrence A. Philipp, Interim Chief Executive Officer
CFO: Jacob Lewis, Chief Financial Officer
CHR: Nancy Vargas, Director Human Resources
Web address: www.marktwainhospital.com
Control: Other not–for–profit (including NFP Corporation) **Service:** General Medical and Surgical

Staffed Beds: 25 **Admissions:** 1128 **Census:** 11 **Outpatient Visits:** 97559 **Births:** 0 **Total Expense ($000):** 66557 **Payroll Expense ($000):** 26440 **Personnel:** 253

SAN BERNARDINO—San Bernardino County

☒ △ **BALLARD REHABILITATION HOSPITAL (053037)**, 1760 West 16th Street, Zip 92411–1160; tel. 909/473–1200 **A**1 7 10 **F**29 34 35 50 64 79 90 93 96 130 132 135 148 **S** Vibra Healthcare, Mechanicsburg, PA
Primary Contact: Mary Miles Hunt, Chief Executive Officer
CFO: Jonathan Silver, Chief Financial Officer
CMO: Van Chen, M.D., Medical Director
CNO: Chris Bauman, Director of Nursing
Web address: www.ballardrehab.com
Control: Corporation, Investor–owned, for–profit **Service:** Rehabilitation

Staffed Beds: 55 **Admissions:** 1167 **Census:** 45 **Outpatient Visits:** 13378 **Births:** 0 **Total Expense ($000):** 21364 **Payroll Expense ($000):** 11125 **Personnel:** 196

☒ **COMMUNITY HOSPITAL OF SAN BERNARDINO (050089)**, 1805 Medical Center Drive, Zip 92411–1214; tel. 909/887–6333, (Total facility includes 122 beds in nursing home–type unit) **A**1 10 **F**2 3 8 11 13 15 20 28 29 30 31 32 34 35 40 45 46 47 48 49 50 51 57 59 60 65 68 70 72 74 75 76 77 79 81 82 83 84 86 87 89 94 98 100 101 104 105 107 108 111 119 128 130 132 135 146 147 148 **S** Dignity Health, San Francisco, CA
Primary Contact: June Collison, President
CFO: Dave Evans, Vice President Finance and Chief Financial Officer
CIO: James Borrenpohl, Market Site Director
CNO: Melissa Kolin, Chief Nursing Officer and Vice President Patient Care Services
Web address: www.dignityhealth.org/san–bernardino
Control: Other not–for–profit (including NFP Corporation) **Service:** General Medical and Surgical

Staffed Beds: 379 **Admissions:** 11956 **Census:** 250 **Outpatient Visits:** 78368 **Births:** 2151 **Total Expense ($000):** 250061 **Payroll Expense ($000):** 103158 **Personnel:** 1208

☒ **ST. BERNARDINE MEDICAL CENTER (050129)**, 2101 North Waterman Avenue, Zip 92404–4855; tel. 909/883–8711, (Nonreporting) **A**1 2 3 10 **S** Dignity Health, San Francisco, CA
Primary Contact: Darryl VandenBosch, President
CMO: Betty Daniels, M.D., Chief of Staff
CIO: James Croker, Director Information Systems
CHR: Dee Webb, Vice President Human Resources
Web address: www.stbernardinemedicalcenter.com
Control: Other not–for–profit (including NFP Corporation) **Service:** General Medical and Surgical

Staffed Beds: 342

SAN DIEGO—San Diego County

☒ **ALVARADO HOSPITAL MEDICAL CENTER (050757)**, 6655 Alvarado Road, Zip 92120–5208; tel. 619/287–3270, (Nonreporting) **A**1 2 3 10 **S** Prime Healthcare Services, Ontario, CA
Primary Contact: Robin Gomez, R.N., MSN, Administrator
CMO: Larry Emdur, D.O., Chief Medical Officer
CIO: Wayne Bartlett, Director Information Systems
CHR: Sara Turner, Director Human Resources
CNO: Peggy Jezsu, Chief Nursing Officer
Web address: www.alvaradohospital.com
Control: Corporation, Investor–owned, for–profit **Service:** General Medical and Surgical

Staffed Beds: 306

☐ **AURORA BEHAVIORAL HEALTHCARE SAN DIEGO (054095)**, 11878 Avenue of Industry, Zip 92128–3490; tel. 858/487–3200, (Nonreporting) **A**1 10 **S** Signature Healthcare Services, Corona, CA
Primary Contact: James S. Plummer, Chief Executive Officer
COO: Barbara Kennison, Director Clinical Services
CFO: Gene Fantano, Chief Financial Officer
CMO: Thomas Flanagan, M.D., Medical Director
CIO: Alain Azcona, Director Business Development
CHR: Susan Haas, Director Human Resources
Web address: www.sandiego.aurorabehavioral.com/
Control: Corporation, Investor–owned, for–profit **Service:** Psychiatric

Staffed Beds: 80

☒ **KAISER PERMANENTE SAN DIEGO MEDICAL CENTER (050515)**, 4647 Zion Avenue, Zip 92120–2507; tel. 619/528–5000 **A**1 3 5 10 **F**3 8 13 14 15 29 30 31 40 41 45 46 47 48 49 50 51 54 55 56 58 59 60 61 62 63 64 65 68 70 71 72 74 75 76 77 78 79 81 82 83 84 85 86 87 89 97 100 102 103 104 107 108 111 114 115 117 118 119 130 131 132 144 146 148 **S** Kaiser Foundation Hospitals, Oakland, CA
Primary Contact: Jane Finley, Senior Vice President & Area Manager
COO: Sam Totah, Chief Operating Officer
CFO: Lynette Seid, Area Chief Financial Officer
CMO: Paul E. Bernstein, M.D., Area Medical Director
CIO: Laura Sullivant, Area Chief Information Officer
CHR: Jocelyn A. Herrera, Human Resources Director
CNO: Anne Marie Watkins, Chief Nurse Executive
Web address: www.kaiserpermanente.org
Control: Other not–for–profit (including NFP Corporation) **Service:** General Medical and Surgical

Staffed Beds: 414 **Admissions:** 30031 **Census:** 414 **Outpatient Visits:** 133980 **Births:** 4427 **Personnel:** 2717

☒ **KINDRED HOSPITAL–SAN DIEGO (052036)**, 1940 El Cajon Boulevard, Zip 92104–1096; tel. 619/543–4500, (Nonreporting) **A**1 10 **S** Kindred Healthcare, Louisville, KY
Primary Contact: Natalie Germuska, R.N., MSN, Market Chief Executive Officer
CMO: Davies Wong, M.D., Medical Director
CHR: Jody Dewen Moore, District Director Human Resources
CNO: Maureen Bodine, Chief Clinical Officer
Web address: www.kindredsandiego.com
Control: Corporation, Investor–owned, for–profit **Service:** Long–Term Acute Care hospital

Staffed Beds: 70

☒ **NAVAL MEDICAL CENTER SAN DIEGO**, 34800 Bob Wilson Drive, Zip 92134–5000; tel. 619/532–6400, (Nonreporting) **A**1 2 3 5 **S** Bureau of Medicine and Surgery, Department of the Navy, Falls Church, VA
Primary Contact: Captain Joel A. Roos, Commanding Officer
CFO: Commander Thomas J. Piner, Director for Resources Management
CIO: Lieutenant Commander Ryan Jarmer, Chief Information Officer
Web address: www.med.navy.mil/sites/nmcsd/Pages/default.aspx
Control: Navy, Government, federal **Service:** General Medical and Surgical

Staffed Beds: 285

☐ **PROMISE HOSPITAL OF SAN DIEGO (052051)**, 5550 University Avenue, Zip 92105–2307; tel. 619/582–3800, (Nonreporting) **A**1 10 **S** Promise Healthcare, Boca Raton, FL
Primary Contact: William Mitchell, Chief Executive Officer
CFO: Kevin Ohler, Director of Finance
CMO: Larry Emdur, D.O., Chief of Staff
CIO: Jim Wilson, Vice President Information Technology
CHR: Kathleen Greene, Director Human Resources
CNO: Kevin Wood, Interim Chief Clinical Officer
Web address: www.promisesandiego.com
Control: Corporation, Investor–owned, for–profit **Service:** Long–Term Acute Care hospital

Staffed Beds: 100

☒ **RADY CHILDREN'S HOSPITAL – SAN DIEGO (053303)**, 3020 Childrens Way, Zip 92123–4223; tel. 858/576–1700, (Total facility includes 43 beds in nursing home–type unit) **A**1 3 5 10 **F**1 3 4 7 8 9 10 11 12 16 17 19 20 21 22 23 24 25 26 27 28 29 30 31 32 34 35 36 38 39 40 41 43 45 46 47 48 50 54 55 57 58 59 60 62 63 64 65 67 68 70 72 73 74 75 77 78 79 80 81 82 83 84 85 86 87 88 89 90 91 92 93 94 98 99 100 101 102 104 105 106 107 108 111 114 115 118 119 122 124 128 129 130 131 132 133 134 135 136 137 138 139 141 143 144 145 146 148 **P**3 5
Primary Contact: Donald Kearns, M.D., President and Chief Executive Officer
COO: Meg Norton, Executive Vice President and Chief Administrative Officer
CFO: Roger Roux, Chief Financial Officer
CMO: Irvin A. Kaufman, M.D., Chief Medical Officer
CIO: Albert Oriol, Vice President Information Management and Chief Information Officer
CHR: Mamoon Syed, Vice President Human Resources
CNO: Mary Fagan, MSN, Chief Nursing Officer
Web address: www.rchsd.org
Control: Other not–for–profit (including NFP Corporation) **Service:** Children's general

Staffed Beds: 427 **Admissions:** 19782 **Census:** 251 **Outpatient Visits:** 346663 **Births:** 0 **Total Expense ($000):** 913954 **Payroll Expense ($000):** 309717 **Personnel:** 4194

RADY CHILDREN'S HOSPITAL AND HEALTH CENTER See Rady Children's Hospital – San Diego

□ **SAN DIEGO COUNTY PSYCHIATRIC HOSPITAL (054114)**, 3853 Rosecrans Street, Zip 92110–3115, Mailing Address: P.O. Box 85524, Zip 92186–5524; tel. 619/692–8211, (Nonreporting) **A**1 10
Primary Contact: Izabela Karmach, R.N., Administrator
COO: Izabela Karmach, R.N., Administrator
CFO: Raul J. Loyo–Rodriguez, Administrative Analyst III
CMO: Michael Krelstein, M.D., Medical Director
CIO: Linda Cannon, Chief Medical Records Services
CHR: Francisco Puentes, Human Resource Officer
Web address: www.sdcounty.ca.gov
Control: County–Government, nonfederal **Service:** Psychiatric

Staffed Beds: 357

SAN DIEGO MEDICAL CENTER See Kaiser Permanente San Diego Medical Center

☒ **SCRIPPS MERCY HOSPITAL (050077)**, 4077 Fifth Avenue, Zip 92103–2105; tel. 619/294–8111, (Includes SCRIPPS MERCY HOSPITAL CHULA VISTA, 435 H Street, Chula Vista, Zip 91912–6617, Mailing Address: P.O. Box 1537, Zip 91910–1537; tel. 619/691–7000) **A**1 2 3 5 10 **F**3 8 11 12 13 14 15 17 18 20 22 24 26 28 29 30 31 32 34 35 39 40 43 44 45 46 49 50 51 54 56 57 58 59 61 64 65 66 68 70 73 74 75 76 77 78 79 81 82 84 85 86 87 92 93 97 98 100 101 102 103 104 105 107 108 110 111 114 115 119 126 129 130 132 134 135 141 146 147 148 **P**3 5 **S** Scripps Health, San Diego, CA
Primary Contact: Thomas A. Gammiere, Chief Executive, Senior Vice President
CFO: Edward Turk, Vice President Finance
CMO: Davis Cracroft, M.D., Senior Director Medical Affairs
CIO: Drexel DeFord, Chief Information Officer
Web address: www.scrippshealth.org
Control: Other not–for–profit (including NFP Corporation) **Service:** General Medical and Surgical

Staffed Beds: 392 Admissions: 32292 Census: 380 Outpatient Visits: 179463 Births: 3656 Total Expense ($000): 704440 Payroll Expense ($000): 250654 Personnel: 3274

☒ △ **SHARP MEMORIAL HOSPITAL (050100)**, 7901 Frost Street, Zip 92123–2701; tel. 858/939–3400 **A**1 2 3 7 10 **F**3 8 11 12 15 17 18 20 22 24 26 28 29 30 31 33 34 35 36 40 43 44 45 46 49 50 56 57 58 59 60 62 64 65 68 70 74 75 77 78 79 80 81 82 84 85 86 87 90 93 107 108 109 110 114 115 117 118 119 120 121 123 124 126 129 130 131 132 135 137 138 142 143 145 146 148 **P**5 **S** Sharp HealthCare, San Diego, CA
Primary Contact: Tim Smith, Senior Vice President and Chief Executive Officer
COO: Janie Kramer, Chief Operating Officer
CFO: Kari Cornicelli, Chief Financial Officer
CMO: Geoffrey Stiles, M.D., Chief Medical Officer
CIO: Kenneth Lawonn, Senior Vice President and Chief Information Officer
CHR: Connie Duquette, Director Human Resources
CNO: Pamela Wells, R.N., Chief Nursing Officer
Web address: www.sharp.com
Control: Other not–for–profit (including NFP Corporation) **Service:** General Medical and Surgical

Staffed Beds: 431 Admissions: 18893 Census: 271 Outpatient Visits: 436712 Births: 0 Total Expense ($000): 694043 Payroll Expense ($000): 250087 Personnel: 3417

☒ **SHARP MESA VISTA HOSPITAL (054145)**, 7850 Vista Hill Avenue, Zip 92123–2717; tel. 858/278–4110, (Includes SHARP MCDONALD CENTER, 7989 Linda Vista Road, Zip 92111–5106; tel. 858/637–6920; Trisha Khaleghi, Chief Executive Officer) **A**1 10 **F**4 5 11 29 30 34 35 37 40 49 56 57 58 59 64 68 87 98 99 100 101 102 103 104 105 130 132 135 143 146 **P**5 **S** Sharp HealthCare, San Diego, CA
Primary Contact: Trisha Khaleghi, Senior Vice President and Chief Executive Officer
CFO: Kari Cornicelli, Chief Financial Officer
CMO: Michael Plopper, M.D., Chief Medical Officer
CIO: Kenneth Lawonn, Senior Vice President Information Systems
CHR: Carlisle Lewis, III, Senior Vice President Legal and Human Resources
CNO: Cheryl Odell, R.N., Chief Nursing Officer
Web address: www.sharp.com
Control: Other not–for–profit (including NFP Corporation) **Service:** Psychiatric

Staffed Beds: 172 Admissions: 5297 Census: 124 Outpatient Visits: 90143 Births: 0 Total Expense ($000): 73528 Payroll Expense ($000): 41456 Personnel: 562

☒ **UC SAN DIEGO HEALTH (050025)**, 200 West Arbor Drive, Zip 92103–9000; tel. 619/543–6222, (Includes THORNTON HOSPITAL, 9300 Campus Point Drive, La Jolla, Zip 92037–1300; tel. 858/657–7000; UC SAN DIEGO SHILEY EYE INSTITUTE, 9415 Campus Point Drive, Room 2411 Dept Of, La Jolla, Zip 92093–0946, Mailing Address: 9415 Campus Point Drive, Zip 92093–0946; tel. 858/534–6290; Karen Anisko Ryan, Director Business Development and Communications) **A**1 2 3 5 8 10 **F**3 6 9 11 12 13 15 16 17 18 20 22 24 26 29 30 31 34 36 37 40 43 44 45 46 47 48 49 50 51 54 55 56 57 58 59 60 61 64 65 66 68 70 72 73 74 75 76 77 78 79 80 81 82 84 85 86 87 91 92 93 97 98 99 100 101 102 103 107 108 109 110 111 112 113 114 115 117 118 119 120 121 123 124 126 129 130 131 132 136 137 138 139 140 141 142 145 146 147 148 **P**1 **S** University of California Systemwide Administration, Oakland, CA
Primary Contact: Patty Maysent, Interim Chief Executive Officer
COO: Margarita Baggett, MSN, Interim Chief Operating Officer
CFO: Lori Donaldson, Chief Financial Officer
CMO: Angela Scioscia, M.D., Chief Medical Officer
CIO: Ed Babakanian, Chief Information Officer
CHR: William J. Murin, Chief Human Resources Officer
CNO: Margarita Baggett, MSN, Chief Nursing Officer
Web address: www.health.ucsd.edu
Control: State–Government, nonfederal **Service:** General Medical and Surgical

Staffed Beds: 542 Admissions: 28185 Census: 451 Outpatient Visits: 736092 Births: 2505 Total Expense ($000): 1301812 Payroll Expense ($000): 450894 Personnel: 5754

UNIVERSITY OF CALIFORNIA SAN DIEGO MEDICAL CENTER See UC San Diego Health

☒ △ **VA SAN DIEGO HEALTHCARE SYSTEM**, 3350 LaJolla Village Drive, Zip 92161–0002; tel. 858/552–8585, (Total facility includes 30 beds in nursing home–type unit) **A**1 3 5 7 8 **F**1 3 4 5 12 15 18 20 22 24 26 29 30 34 35 36 37 38 39 40 44 45 46 47 48 49 50 54 55 56 57 58 59 60 61 62 63 64 65 68 71 74 75 77 79 81 82 83 84 85 86 87 90 91 92 93 94 95 96 97 98 100 101 102 103 104 105 106 107 110 111 114 115 116 117 118 119 126 129 130 132 135 143 144 145 146 147 148 **S** Department of Veterans Affairs, Washington, DC
Primary Contact: Robert M. Smith, M.D., Director
COO: Cynthia Abair, Associate Director
CFO: Ronald Larson, Chief Financial Officer
CIO: Ruey Keller, Acting Chief Information Officer
CHR: Stephanie Wright, Director Human Resources Management
Web address: www.sandiego.va.gov
Control: Veterans Affairs, Government, federal **Service:** General Medical and Surgical

Staffed Beds: 248 Admissions: 7106 Census: 191 Outpatient Visits: 929345 Births: 0 Total Expense ($000): 668081 Payroll Expense ($000): 253593 Personnel: 3243

☒ **VIBRA HOSPITAL OF SAN DIEGO (052044)**, 555 Washington Street, Zip 92103–2294; tel. 619/260–8300 **A**1 10 **F**1 3 64 70 91 148 **P**5 **S** Vibra Healthcare, Mechanicsburg, PA
Primary Contact: Yameeka Jones, Chief Executive Officer
CFO: Mike Gonzales, Chief Financial Officer
CMO: John Fox, M.D., Medical Director
CHR: Tania Khalique, Director Human Resources
Web address: www.vhsandiego.com/
Control: Partnership, Investor–owned, for–profit **Service:** Long–Term Acute Care hospital

Staffed Beds: 110 Admissions: 867 Census: 68 Outpatient Visits: 1351 Births: 0 Total Expense ($000): 34944 Payroll Expense ($000): 16610 Personnel: 317

SAN DIMAS—Los Angeles County

☒ **SAN DIMAS COMMUNITY HOSPITAL (050588)**, 1350 West Covina Boulevard, Zip 91773–3219; tel. 909/599–6811 **A**1 10 **F**3 13 15 29 30 40 45 46 49 50 56 70 74 76 79 81 85 107 108 110 115 119 126 130 146 148 **S** Prime Healthcare Services, Ontario, CA
Primary Contact: Kurt Weinmeister, Chief Executive Officer
CFO: Robert Bonner, Chief Financial Officer
CMO: Rajnish Jandial, M.D., Chief Medical Officer
CIO: Jeffrey Cox, Director Information Technology
CHR: Elena Mayo, Manager, Human Resources
CNO: Holly Nagatoshi, R.N., Chief Nursing Officer
Web address: www.sandimashospital.com/
Control: Corporation, Investor–owned, for–profit **Service:** General Medical and Surgical

Staffed Beds: 101 Admissions: 3589 Census: 41 Outpatient Visits: 23352 Births: 522 Total Expense ($000): 60814 Payroll Expense ($000): 20444 Personnel: 377

CA

Hospital, Medicare Provider Number, Address, Telephone, Approval, Facility, and Physician Codes, Health Care System
★ American Hospital Association (AHA) membership ○ Healthcare Facilities Accreditation Program ⇑ Center for Improvement in Healthcare Quality Accreditation □ The Joint Commission accreditation ◇ DNV Healthcare Inc. accreditation △ Commission on Accreditation of Rehabilitation Facilities (CARF) accreditation

SAN FRANCISCO—San Francisco County

⊠ △ **CALIFORNIA PACIFIC MEDICAL CENTER (050047)**, 2333 Buchanan Street, Zip 94115–1925, Mailing Address: P.O. Box 7999, Zip 94120–7999; tel. 415/600–6000, (Total facility includes 38 beds in nursing home–type unit) **A**1 2 3 5 7 8 10 **F**2 3 5 6 7 8 12 13 15 18 19 20 22 24 26 28 29 30 31 32 34 35 36 37 38 39 40 41 45 46 47 48 49 50 51 52 55 56 57 58 59 60 61 63 65 68 70 72 74 75 76 77 78 79 81 82 83 84 85 86 87 88 89 90 91 92 93 96 97 98 99 100 101 102 104 107 108 110 111 114 115 116 117 118 119 120 121 123 124 126 128 130 132 133 135 137 138 139 141 142 143 144 145 146 147 148 **P**3 **S** Sutter Health, Sacramento, CA
Primary Contact: Warren S. Browner, M.D., M.P.H., Chief Executive Officer
COO: Hamila Kownacki, Chief Operating Officer
CFO: Henry Yu, Vice President Finance and Chief Financial Officer
CMO: Vernon Giang, M.D., Chief Medical Executive
CIO: Ann Barr, Chief Information Officer – Bay Area
CHR: Edward Battista, Vice President Human Resources
CNO: Diana M. Karner, R.N., Chief Nursing Officer
Web address: www.cpmc.org
Control: Other not–for–profit (including NFP Corporation) **Service:** General Medical and Surgical

Staffed Beds: 642 **Admissions:** 25306 **Census:** 391 **Outpatient Visits:** 496351 **Births:** 4608 **Total Expense ($000):** 1104914 **Payroll Expense ($000):** 353158 **Personnel:** 3852

★ **CALIFORNIA PACIFIC MEDICAL CENTER–DAVIES CAMPUS (050008)**, Castro and Duboce Streets, Zip 94114; tel. 415/600–6000, (Nonreporting) **A**3 5 **S** Sutter Health, Sacramento, CA
Primary Contact: Mary Lanier, Vice President, Post Acute Services and Site Administrator
Web address: www.cpmc.org
Control: Other not–for–profit (including NFP Corporation) **Service:** General Medical and Surgical

Staffed Beds: 205

⊠ **CHINESE HOSPITAL (050407)**, 845 Jackson Street, Zip 94133–4899; tel. 415/982–2400 **A**1 10 **F**3 11 15 18 29 30 31 34 35 40 45 47 49 50 57 59 60 64 65 70 75 77 78 79 81 86 87 97 107 110 115 118 119 130 132 135 145 146 147
Primary Contact: Brenda Yee, R.N., MSN, Chief Executive Officer
COO: Jian Q. Zhang, MSN, Chief Operating Officer
CFO: Scott Goodin, Interim Chief Financial Officer
CMO: William Chung, M.D., Chief of Staff
CIO: Keith Minard, Chief Information Officer
CHR: Lydia Mahr–Chan, Director of Human Resources
CNO: Peggy Cmiel, R.N., Chief Nursing Officer
Web address: www.chinesehospital–sf.org
Control: Other not–for–profit (including NFP Corporation) **Service:** General Medical and Surgical

Staffed Beds: 21 **Admissions:** 1687 **Census:** 21 **Outpatient Visits:** 80239 **Births:** 0 **Total Expense ($000):** 119290 **Payroll Expense ($000):** 33297 **Personnel:** 365

JEWISH HOME OF SAN FRANCISCO (054089), 302 Silver Avenue, Zip 94112–1510; tel. 415/334–2500, (Nonreporting) **A**10
Primary Contact: Daniel R. Ruth, President and Chief Executive Officer
COO: Kevin Ward, Chief Operating Officer
CFO: Victor E. Meinke, Chief Financial Officer
CNO: Edwin Cabigao, Chief Nursing Officer
Web address: www.jhsf.org
Control: Other not–for–profit (including NFP Corporation) **Service:** Psychiatric

Staffed Beds: 12

⊠ **KAISER PERMANENTE SAN FRANCISCO MEDICAL CENTER (050076)**, 2425 Geary Boulevard, Zip 94115–3358; tel. 415/833–2000, (Nonreporting) **A**1 3 5 10 **S** Kaiser Foundation Hospitals, Oakland, CA
Primary Contact: Ronald Groepper, Senior Vice President and Area Manager
COO: Helen Archer–Duste, Chief Operating Officer
CFO: Alex Khoo, Interim Area Finance Officer
CMO: Robert Mithun, M.D., Physician in Chief
CIO: Peti Arunamata, Interim Area Director Information Technology
CHR: Diane J. Easterwood, Human Resources Business Partner
Web address: www.kaiserpermanente.org
Control: Other not–for–profit (including NFP Corporation) **Service:** General Medical and Surgical

Staffed Beds: 215

★ **LAGUNA HONDA HOSPITAL AND REHABILITATION CENTER (050668)**, (General Acute Care Hospital with Distinct part SNF), 375 Laguna Honda Boulevard, Zip 94116–1499; tel. 415/759–2300, (Total facility includes 769 beds in nursing home–type unit) **A**10 **F**3 29 30 53 56 61 63 64 65 68 74 75 77 82 83 84 90 92 93 94 96 100 103 104 127 128 130 132 135 146 148
Primary Contact: Mivic Hirose, Executive Administrator
COO: Michael R. Llewellyn, Chief Operating Officer
CFO: Tess Navarro, Chief Financial Officer
CMO: Colleen Riley, M.D., Medical Director
CIO: Pat Skala, Chief Information Officer
CHR: Willie Ramirez, Manager Labor Relations
Web address: www.lagunahonda.org/
Control: City–County, Government, nonfederal **Service:** Other specialty

Staffed Beds: 780 **Admissions:** 1039 **Census:** 755 **Births:** 0 **Total Expense ($000):** 234169 **Payroll Expense ($000):** 124489

⊠ △ **SAINT FRANCIS MEMORIAL HOSPITAL (050152)**, 900 Hyde Street, Zip 94109–4899, Mailing Address: P.O. Box 7726, Zip 94120–7726; tel. 415/353–6000, (Nonreporting) **A**1 2 3 7 10 **S** Dignity Health, San Francisco, CA
Primary Contact: David G. Klein, M.D., President
CFO: Alan Fox, Chief Financial Officer
CHR: Richard Mead, Senior Director Human Resources
Web address: www.saintfrancismemorial.org
Control: Other not–for–profit (including NFP Corporation) **Service:** General Medical and Surgical

Staffed Beds: 239

SAN FRANCISCO MEDICAL CENTER See Kaiser Permanente San Francisco Medical Center

⊠ **SAN FRANCISCO VA MEDICAL CENTER**, 4150 Clement Street, Zip 94121–1545; tel. 415/221–4810, (Nonreporting) **A**1 2 3 5 **S** Department of Veterans Affairs, Washington, DC
Primary Contact: Bonnie S. Graham, Director
CFO: Brian Kelly, Acting Chief Fiscal Service
CMO: C. Diana Nicoll, M.D., Chief of Staff
CIO: Ryan Chun, Information Resources Management
CHR: Jerry Mills, Chief Human Resources Management Services
CNO: Shirley Pikula, MSN, Associate Director Patient Center Care
Web address: www.sanfrancisco.va.gov/
Control: Veterans Affairs, Government, federal **Service:** General Medical and Surgical

Staffed Beds: 244

⊠ **ST. LUKE'S HOSPITAL (050055)**, 3555 Cesar Chavez Street, Zip 94110–4403; tel. 415/600–6000, (Total facility includes 39 beds in nursing home–type unit) **A**1 3 5 10 **F**3 5 8 13 18 29 30 34 35 40 50 55 63 64 66 67 68 70 72 75 76 77 78 79 81 82 84 85 87 89 93 97 100 107 108 110 111 114 118 119 128 130 143 146 147 148 **P**3 **S** Sutter Health, Sacramento, CA
Primary Contact: Warren S. Browner, M.D., M.P.H., Chief Executive Officer
COO: Hamila Kownacki, Chief Operating Officer
CFO: Henry Yu, Vice President Finance and Chief Financial Officer
CMO: Vernon Giang, M.D., Chief Medical Executive
CIO: Ann Barr, Chief Information Officer – Bay Area
CHR: Edward Battista, Vice President Human Resources
CNO: Diana M. Karner, R.N., Chief Nursing Executive
Web address: www.stlukes–sf.org
Control: Other not–for–profit (including NFP Corporation) **Service:** General Medical and Surgical

Staffed Beds: 175 **Admissions:** 4233 **Census:** 101 **Outpatient Visits:** 77324 **Births:** 900 **Total Expense ($000):** 159321 **Payroll Expense ($000):** 52104 **Personnel:** 581

⊠ △ **ST. MARY'S MEDICAL CENTER (050457)**, 450 Stanyan Street, Zip 94117–1079; tel. 415/668–1000, (Nonreporting) **A**1 2 3 5 7 10 **S** Dignity Health, San Francisco, CA
Primary Contact: Michael C. Carter, Interim Chief Executive Officer
COO: Deborah Kolhede, Vice President and Chief Operating Officer
CFO: Eric Brettner, Vice President and Chief Financial Officer
CMO: Francis Charlton, Jr., M.D., Chief Medical Staff
CHR: Barbara Morrissett, Vice President Human Resources
CNO: Barbara Eusebio, R.N., Vice President, Chief Nurse Executive
Web address: www.stmarysmedicalcenter.com
Control: Other not–for–profit (including NFP Corporation) **Service:** General Medical and Surgical

Staffed Beds: 232

CA

CA

✠ **UCSF MEDICAL CENTER (050454)**, 500 Parnassus Avenue, Zip 94143–0296; Mailing Address: 500 Parnassus Avenue, Box 0296, Zip 94143–0296; tel. 415/476–1000, (Includes UCSF BENIOFF CHILDREN'S HOSPITAL, 500 Parnassus Avenue, Zip 94143–2203, Mailing Address: 505 Parnassus Avenue, Zip 94143–2203; tel. 888/689–8273; UCSF MEDICAL CENTER MISSION BAY, 1975 4th Street, Zip 94158–2351; tel. 415/353–3000) **A**1 2 3 5 8 10 **F**3 6 7 8 9 11 12 13 14 15 17 18 19 20 21 23 24 25 26 27 29 30 31 32 33 34 35 36 37 39 40 41 43 44 45 46 47 48 49 50 51 52 53 54 55 56 57 58 59 60 61 62 63 64 65 66 68 70 72 74 75 77 78 79 81 82 83 84 85 86 87 88 92 93 94 97 99 100 101 102 103 104 105 107 108 110 111 112 113 114 115 116 117 119 120 121 123 124 126 129 130 131 132 134 135 136 137 138 139 140 141 142 144 145 146 147 148 **S** University of California Systemwide Administration, Oakland, CA
Primary Contact: Mark R. Laret, Chief Executive Officer
COO: Ken M. Jones, Chief Operating Officer
CFO: Barrie Strickland, Chief Financial Officer
CMO: Josh Adler, M.D., Chief Medical Officer
CIO: Joe Bergfort, Chief Information Officer
CHR: David Odato, Chief Administrative and Chief Human Resources Officer
CNO: Sheila Antrum, R.N., President
Web address: www.ucsfhealth.org
Control: Other not–for–profit (including NFP Corporation) **Service:** General Medical and Surgical

Staffed Beds: 745 **Admissions:** 30504 **Census:** 517 **Outpatient Visits:** 1033169 **Births:** 2405 **Total Expense ($000):** 2616948 **Payroll Expense ($000):** 975792 **Personnel:** 7536

VETERANS AFFAIRS MEDICAL CENTER See San Francisco VA Medical Center

✠ **ZUCKERBERG SAN FRANCISCO GENERAL HOSPITAL AND TRAUMA CENTER (050228)**, 1001 Potrero Avenue, Zip 94110–3594; tel. 415/206–8000, (Nonreporting) **A**1 2 3 5 8 10
Primary Contact: Susan P. Ehrlich, M.D., Chief Executive Officer
COO: Iman Nazeeri–Simmons, Chief Operating Officer
CFO: Valerie Inouye, Chief Financial Officer
CMO: Todd May, M.D., Chief Medical Officer
CIO: Winona Windolovich, Associate Chief Information Officer
CHR: Karen Hill, Departmental Personnel Officer
CNO: Terry Dentoni, Chief Nursing Officer
Web address: www.zuckerbergsanfranciscogeneral.org/
Control: City–County, Government, nonfederal **Service:** General Medical and Surgical

Staffed Beds: 460

SAN JOSE—Santa Clara County

✠ **GOOD SAMARITAN HOSPITAL (050380)**, 2425 Samaritan Drive, Zip 95124–3997, Mailing Address: P.O. Box 240002, Zip 95154–2402; tel. 408/559–2011 **A**1 2 3 10 **F**3 5 8 11 12 13 15 17 18 19 20 21 22 23 24 25 26 27 28 29 30 31 34 35 37 38 40 44 45 46 47 48 49 50 54 57 58 59 60 63 64 68 70 72 74 75 76 77 78 79 81 82 83 84 85 86 87 88 89 90 93 96 98 101 102 104 105 107 108 110 111 114 115 117 118 119 120 121 123 124 126 130 132 135 146 147 148 **S** HCA, Nashville, TN
Primary Contact: Paul Beaupre, M.D., Chief Executive Officer
COO: Jordan Herget, Chief Operating Officer
CFO: Lana Arad, Chief Financial Officer
CMO: Bruce Wilbur, M.D., Chief Medical Officer
CIO: Darrell O'Dell, Director Information Services
CHR: Edward Battista, Vice President Human Resources
CNO: Darina Kavanagh, R.N., Chief Nursing Officer
Web address: www.goodsamsanjose.com
Control: Corporation, Investor–owned, for–profit **Service:** General Medical and Surgical

Staffed Beds: 349 **Admissions:** 16994 **Census:** 228 **Outpatient Visits:** 140908 **Births:** 3857 **Total Expense ($000):** 434042 **Payroll Expense ($000):** 193632 **Personnel:** 1149

✠ **KAISER PERMANENTE SAN JOSE MEDICAL CENTER (050604)**, 250 Hospital Parkway, Zip 95119–1199; tel. 408/972–7000 **A**1 5 10 **F**3 8 13 17 18 20 22 29 30 31 35 40 46 49 51 56 68 70 73 74 76 78 79 81 82 84 85 87 104 107 108 110 111 114 115 119 130 141 146 148 **S** Kaiser Foundation Hospitals, Oakland, CA
Primary Contact: Irene Chavez, Senior Vice President and Area Manager
COO: Irene Chavez, Senior Vice President and Area Manager
CFO: Stephen L. Kalsman, Area Finance Officer
CMO: Raj Bhandari, M.D., Physician–in–Chief
CIO: Greg Tuck, Area Information Officer
CHR: Susan Franzella, Human Resource Business Partner
CNO: Theresa R. Nero, R.N., Chief Nursing Officer
Web address: www.kaiserpermanente.org
Control: Other not–for–profit (including NFP Corporation) **Service:** General Medical and Surgical

Staffed Beds: 222 **Admissions:** 11010 **Census:** 114 **Outpatient Visits:** 240848 **Births:** 2259 **Personnel:** 1234

✠ **O'CONNOR HOSPITAL (050153)**, 2105 Forest Avenue, Zip 95128–1471; tel. 408/947–2500 **A**1 2 3 5 10 **F**1 3 8 11 13 15 18 19 20 22 24 26 28 29 30 31 34 35 37 40 44 46 48 49 50 53 54 57 59 60 64 66 68 70 72 74 75 76 77 78 79 81 84 85 86 87 89 93 97 100 107 108 110 111 114 116 117 118 119 121 123 128 130 131 132 135 146 147 148 **S** Verity Health System, Los Angeles, CA
Primary Contact: Robert Minkin, President and Chief Executive Officer
CIO: Richard Hutsell, Vice President and Chief Information Officer, Daughters of Charity Health System
CHR: Julie Hatcher, Vice President Human Resources
CNO: Dawn Marie Goeringer, Chief Clinical Care Officer
Web address: www.oconnorhospital.org
Control: Other not–for–profit (including NFP Corporation) **Service:** General Medical and Surgical

Staffed Beds: 202 **Admissions:** 10707 **Census:** 131 **Outpatient Visits:** 177284 **Births:** 2836 **Total Expense ($000):** 323250 **Payroll Expense ($000):** 135744

✠ **REGIONAL MEDICAL CENTER OF SAN JOSE (050125)**, 225 North Jackson Avenue, Zip 95116–1603; tel. 408/259–5000 **A**1 2 10 **F**3 13 15 18 20 22 24 26 28 29 30 31 34 40 45 46 51 57 58 60 64 70 72 74 75 76 77 78 79 81 85 87 89 90 93 107 110 111 114 115 119 124 126 130 131 132 135 146 147 **S** HCA, Nashville, TN
Primary Contact: Michael T. Johnson, FACHE, President and Chief Executive Officer
COO: Brian J. Knecht, Chief Operating Officer
CFO: Raju Iyer, Chief Financial Officer
CMO: William Scott, M.D., Vice President Medical Affairs
CIO: Shirley Joyal, Director Information Systems
CHR: Nancy Clark, Vice President Human Resources
Web address: www.regionalmedicalsanjose.com
Control: Corporation, Investor–owned, for–profit **Service:** General Medical and Surgical

Staffed Beds: 216 **Admissions:** 14173 **Census:** 200 **Outpatient Visits:** 116587 **Births:** 528 **Total Expense ($000):** 309331 **Payroll Expense ($000):** 157900 **Personnel:** 1250

SAN JOSE BEHAVORIAL HEALTH, 455 Silicon Valley Boulevard, Zip 95138–1858; tel. 888/210–2484, (Nonreporting) **S** Acadia Healthcare Company, Inc., Franklin, TN
Web address: www.sanjosebh.com
Control: Corporation, Investor–owned, for–profit **Service:** Psychiatric

Staffed Beds: 80

SAN JOSE MEDICAL CENTER See Kaiser Permanente San Jose Medical Center

☐ △ **SANTA CLARA VALLEY MEDICAL CENTER (050038)**, 751 South Bascom Avenue, Zip 95128–2699; tel. 408/885–5000 **A**1 3 5 7 10 **F**3 5 8 9 11 12 15 16 17 18 19 20 22 23 24 26 28 29 30 31 32 34 35 36 39 40 41 43 44 45 46 49 50 51 54 55 56 58 59 60 61 64 65 66 68 70 71 72 73 74 75 76 77 78 79 80 81 82 83 84 85 86 87 88 89 90 91 92 93 95 96 97 98 99 100 101 102 103 104 107 108 110 111 114 115 117 118 119 120 121 123 124 129 130 131 132 134 135 142 144 146 147 148 **P**6
Primary Contact: Paul E. Lorenz, Chief Executive Officer
COO: Benita McLarin, Chief Operating Officer
CMO: Jeffrey Arnold, M.D., Chief Medical Officer
CIO: Lee Herrmann, Chief Healthcare Technology Officer
CHR: David Manson, Manager Human Resources
CNO: Trudy Johnson, RN, R.N., Chief Nursing Officer
Web address: www.scvmed.org
Control: County–Government, nonfederal **Service:** General Medical and Surgical

Staffed Beds: 481 **Admissions:** 23055 **Census:** 352 **Outpatient Visits:** 827108 **Births:** 3442 **Total Expense ($000):** 1302896 **Payroll Expense ($000):** 503685 **Personnel:** 4762

SAN LEANDRO—Alameda County

FAIRMONT HOSPITAL See Highland Hospital, Oakland

✠ **KAISER PERMANENTE SAN LEANDRO MEDICAL CENTER (050777)**, 2500 Merced Street, Zip 94577–4201; tel. 510/454–1000, (Nonreporting) **A**1 10 **S** Kaiser Foundation Hospitals, Oakland, CA
Primary Contact: Thomas S. Hanenburg, Senior Vice President and Area Manager
Web address: www.kaiserpermanente.org
Control: Other not–for–profit (including NFP Corporation) **Service:** General Medical and Surgical

Staffed Beds: 264

Hospital, Medicare Provider Number, Address, Telephone, Approval, Facility, and Physician Codes, Health Care System

★ American Hospital Association (AHA) membership ○ Healthcare Facilities Accreditation Program ⇑ Center for Improvement in Healthcare Quality Accreditation
☐ The Joint Commission accreditation ◇ DNV Healthcare Inc. accreditation △ Commission on Accreditation of Rehabilitation Facilities (CARF) accreditation

☒ **KINDRED HOSPITAL–SAN FRANCISCO BAY AREA (052034)**, 2800 Benedict Drive, Zip 94577–6840; tel. 510/357–8300, (Nonreporting) **A**1 10 **S** Kindred Healthcare, Louisville, KY
Primary Contact: Jacob M. McCarty, Chief Executive Officer
CFO: Ziba Aflak, Chief Financial Officer
CHR: Erin Greene, Coordinator Human Resources
CNO: Emily Gard, Chief Clinical Officer
Web address: www.kindredhospitalsfba.com
Control: Corporation, Investor–owned, for–profit **Service:** Long–Term Acute Care hospital

Staffed Beds: 78

☐ **SAN LEANDRO HOSPITAL (050773)**, 13855 East 14th Street, Zip 94578–2600; tel. 510/357–6500 **A**1 10 **F**3 15 18 29 30 34 35 40 44 45 50 51 57 59 60 68 70 77 79 81 87 107 108 110 111 114 119 130 146 **S** Alameda Health System, San Leandro, CA
Primary Contact: James E. T. Jackson, M.P.H., Chief Administrative Officer
Web address: www.sanleandrohospital.org
Control: Hospital district or authority, Government, nonfederal **Service:** General Medical and Surgical

Staffed Beds: 45 Admissions: 2902 Census: 33 Outpatient Visits: 34916 Births: 0 Total Expense ($000): 73871 Payroll Expense ($000): 37995 Personnel: 336

☐ **WILLOW ROCK CENTER (054149)**, 2050 Fairmont Drive, Zip 94578–1001; tel. 510/895–5502, (Nonreporting) **A**1 10
Primary Contact: Anne L. Bakar, President and Chief Executive Officer
Web address: www.tbhcare.com
Control: County–Government, nonfederal **Service:** Psychiatric

Staffed Beds: 16

SAN LUIS OBISPO—San Luis Obispo County

CALIFORNIA MENS COLONY CORRECTIONAL TREATMENT CENTER, Highway 1, Zip 93409–8101, Mailing Address: P.O. Box 8101, Zip 93403–8101; tel. 805/547–7913, (Nonreporting)
Primary Contact: Martha Wallace, Administrator
CFO: William Cook, Associate Warden Business Service
CIO: Terry Knight, Public Information Officer and Administrative Assistant
Web address: www.yaca.ca.gov/visitors/fac_prison_cmc.html
Control: State–Government, nonfederal **Service:** Hospital unit of an institution (prison hospital, college infimary, etc.)

Staffed Beds: 39

☒ **FRENCH HOSPITAL MEDICAL CENTER (050232)**, 1911 Johnson Avenue, Zip 93401–4197; tel. 805/543–5353 **A**1 2 10 **F**8 11 15 18 20 22 24 28 29 30 34 35 40 46 50 53 54 57 59 64 68 70 75 76 77 78 79 81 84 85 86 87 89 97 100 107 108 110 111 114 115 117 119 124 130 132 134 146 147 148 **S** Dignity Health, San Francisco, CA
Primary Contact: Alan Iftiniuk, Chief Executive Officer
COO: Julia Fogelson, R.N., Chief Operating Officer and Chief Nursing Executive
CFO: Sue Andersen, Chief Financial Officer
CMO: Chris Voge, Chief of Staff
CIO: Cyndi Lang, Director Information Services
CHR: Barry Nateman, Manager Human Resources
CNO: Julia Fogelson, R.N., Chief Operating Officer and Chief Nursing Executive
Web address: www.frenchmedicalcenter.org
Control: Other not–for–profit (including NFP Corporation) **Service:** General Medical and Surgical

Staffed Beds: 72 Admissions: 4348 Census: 44 Births: 519

☒ **SIERRA VISTA REGIONAL MEDICAL CENTER (050506)**, 1010 Murray Avenue, Zip 93405–1806, Mailing Address: P.O. Box 1367, Zip 93405; tel. 805/546–7600 **A**1 2 10 19 **F**3 13 15 17 18 20 29 30 31 34 40 43 45 46 49 50 57 59 64 65 70 72 73 74 75 76 77 78 79 80 81 84 85 86 89 107 108 110 114 115 119 126 130 131 132 145 146 147 148 **S** TENET Healthcare Corporation, Dallas, TX
Primary Contact: Joseph DeSchryver, Chief Executive Officer
COO: Michael Bell, Chief Operating Officer
CFO: Rollie Pirkl, Chief Financial Officer
CIO: Robert Leonard, Director Information Services
CHR: Kristin Flynn, Chief Human Resources Officer
CNO: Nicki E. Edwards, Ph.D., Interim Chief Nursing Officer
Web address: www.sierravistaregional.com
Control: Corporation, Investor–owned, for–profit **Service:** General Medical and Surgical

Staffed Beds: 164 Admissions: 5554 Census: 62 Outpatient Visits: 42853 Births: 1333 Total Expense ($000): 122344 Payroll Expense ($000): 55024 Personnel: 582

SAN MATEO—San Mateo County

MILLS HEALTH CENTER See Mills–Peninsula Health Services, Burlingame

☐ **SAN MATEO MEDICAL CENTER (050113)**, 222 West 39th Avenue, Zip 94403–4398; tel. 650/573–2222, (Nonreporting) **A**1 3 5 10
Primary Contact: Chester Kunnappilly, M.D., Interim Chief Executive Officer
COO: John Thomas, Chief Operating Officer
CFO: David S. McGrew, Chief Financial Officer
CMO: Susan Fernyak, M.D., Interim Chief Medical Officer & Chief Quality Officer
CIO: Michael Aratow, M.D., Chief Information Officer
CHR: Angela Gonzales, Manager Human Resources
CNO: Joan G. Spicer, R.N., Chief Nursing Officer
Web address: www.sanmateomedicalcenter.org
Control: County–Government, nonfederal **Service:** General Medical and Surgical

Staffed Beds: 307

SAN PEDRO—Los Angeles County, See Los Angeles

SAN RAFAEL—Marin County

☒ **KAISER PERMANENTE SAN RAFAEL MEDICAL CENTER (050510)**, 99 Montecillo Road, Zip 94903–3397; tel. 415/444–2000, (Nonreporting) **A**1 10 **S** Kaiser Foundation Hospitals, Oakland, CA
Primary Contact: Judy Coffey, R.N., Senior Vice President and Area Manager
CFO: John Groesbeck, Area Finance Officer
CMO: Gary Mizono, M.D., Physician–in–Chief
CIO: Stanley Dobrawa, Area Technology Director
CHR: Michael G. Fanselau, Human Resource Leader
CNO: Dennis Kneeppel, R.N., Chief Nurse Executive and Chief Operating Officer
Web address: www.kaiserpermanente.org
Control: Other not–for–profit (including NFP Corporation) **Service:** General Medical and Surgical

Staffed Beds: 116

SAN RAMON—Contra Costa County

☒ **SAN RAMON REGIONAL MEDICAL CENTER (050689)**, 6001 Norris Canyon Road, Zip 94583–5400; tel. 925/275–9200 **A**1 10 **F**3 8 11 13 15 18 20 22 24 26 28 29 30 31 34 35 37 40 45 46 47 48 49 53 57 59 64 70 72 75 76 77 78 79 81 85 86 87 93 107 108 110 118 119 126 130 131 132 146 147 148 **P**3 5 **S** TENET Healthcare Corporation, Dallas, TX
Primary Contact: Gary Sloan, Chief Executive Officer
CFO: Beenu Chadha, Chief Financial Officer
CMO: Raymond Cheung, M.D., Chief of Staff
CIO: Anthony Abbate, Director of Information Services
CHR: Dennis Mills, Chief Human Resources Officer
CNO: Lani Dickinson, Interim Chief Nursing Officer
Web address: www.sanramonmedctr.com
Control: Partnership, Investor–owned, for–profit **Service:** General Medical and Surgical

Staffed Beds: 123 Admissions: 4710 Census: 49 Outpatient Visits: 73742 Births: 770 Total Expense ($000): 137869 Payroll Expense ($000): 64374 Personnel: 534

SANTA ANA—Orange County

☐ **ORANGE COUNTY GLOBAL MEDICAL CENTER, INC. (050746)**, 1001 North Tustin Avenue, Zip 92705–3577; tel. 714/953–3500, (Nonreporting) **A**1 3 5 10 **S** KPC Healthcare, Inc., Santa Ana, CA
Primary Contact: Suzanne Richards, Chief Executive Officer
COO: Ann Abe, Administrator and Chief Operating Officer
CFO: John Collins, Chief Financial Officer
CMO: Steven Bui, M.D., Chief of Staff
CIO: Sri Yarramsetti, Chief Information Officer
CHR: Terry Bohn, Director, Human Resources
CNO: Shela Kaneshiro, Chief Nursing Officer
Web address: www.orangecounty–gmc.com
Control: Corporation, Investor–owned, for–profit **Service:** General Medical and Surgical

Staffed Beds: 282

☐ **SOUTH COAST GLOBAL MEDICAL CENTER (050747)**, 2701 South Bristol Street, Zip 92704–6278; tel. 714/754–5454, (Nonreporting) **A**1 10 **S** KPC Healthcare, Inc., Santa Ana, CA
Primary Contact: Ronald J. Galonsky, Jr., Chief Executive Officer
CFO: John Collins, Chief Financial Officer
CHR: Cynthia Garren–Oster, Human Resource Manager
Web address: www.SouthCoast–GMC.com
Control: Corporation, Investor–owned, for–profit **Service:** General Medical and Surgical

Staffed Beds: 178

SANTA BARBARA—Santa Barbara County

COTTAGE REHABILITATION HOSPITAL See Santa Barbara Cottage Hospital

CA

Many Facility Codes have changed. Please refer to the AHA Guide Code Chart. © 2016 AHA Guide

CA

⊞ **GOLETA VALLEY COTTAGE HOSPITAL (050357)**, 351 South Patterson Avenue, Zip 93111–2496, Mailing Address: Box 6306, Zip 93160–6306; tel. 805/967–3411 **A**1 10 **F**8 11 12 15 29 40 65 68 70 79 81 107 110 114 119 124 130 148 **S** Cottage Health, Santa Barbara, CA
Primary Contact: Ronald C. Werft, President and Chief Executive Officer
COO: Steven A. Fellows, Executive Vice President and Chief Operating Officer
CFO: Joan Bricher, Senior Vice President Finance and Chief Financial Officer
CMO: Edmund Wroblewski, M.D., Vice President Medical Affairs and Chief Medical Officer
CIO: Alberto Kywi, Chief Information Officer
CHR: Patrice Ryan, Vice President Human Resources
Web address: www.sbch.org
Control: Other not–for–profit (including NFP Corporation) **Service:** General Medical and Surgical

Staffed Beds: 28 **Admissions:** 1597 **Census:** 21 **Outpatient Visits:** 43553 **Births:** 0 **Total Expense ($000):** 73917 **Payroll Expense ($000):** 27075 **Personnel:** 250

⊞ △ **SANTA BARBARA COTTAGE HOSPITAL (050396)**, 400 West Pueblo Street, Zip 93105–4390, Mailing Address: P.O. Box 689, Zip 93102–0689; tel. 805/682–7111, (Includes COTTAGE CHILDREN'S HOSPITAL, 400 West Pueblo Street, Zip 93105–4353; tel. 877/247–3260; COTTAGE REHABILITATION HOSPITAL, 2415 De la Vina Street, Zip 93105–3819; tel. 805/687–7444; Melinda Staveley, President and Chief Executive Officer) **A**1 2 3 5 7 10 **F**3 4 5 8 11 12 13 15 17 18 20 22 24 26 28 29 30 31 34 35 40 42 43 46 50 53 54 57 58 59 60 64 65 68 70 72 74 75 76 78 79 81 84 86 88 89 90 91 92 93 96 98 100 102 103 104 106 107 110 111 114 115 117 119 126 130 132 135 146 148 **S** Cottage Health, Santa Barbara, CA
Primary Contact: Ronald C. Werft, President and Chief Executive Officer
COO: Steven A. Fellows, Executive Vice President and Chief Operating Officer
CFO: Joan Bricher, Senior Vice President Finance and Chief Financial Officer
CMO: Edmund Wroblewski, M.D., Vice President Medical Affairs and Chief Medical Officer
CIO: Alberto Kywi, Chief Information Officer
CHR: Patrice Ryan, Vice President Human Resources
CNO: Herb J. Geary, Vice President Patient Care Services and Chief Nursing Officer
Web address: www.cottagehealthsystem.org
Control: Other not–for–profit (including NFP Corporation) **Service:** General Medical and Surgical

Staffed Beds: 351 **Admissions:** 17760 **Census:** 236 **Outpatient Visits:** 132771 **Births:** 2257 **Total Expense ($000):** 610087 **Payroll Expense ($000):** 214716 **Personnel:** 2150

SANTA BARBARA COUNTY PSYCHIATRIC HEALTH FACILITY (054125), 315 Camino Del Remedio, Zip 93110–1332; tel. 805/681–5244 **A**10 **F**29 38 50 66 68 75 82 86 87 98 101 102 130 132 135 **P**1 6
Primary Contact: Takashi Wada, Interim Director
CFO: Michael C. Evans, Chief Executive Officer and Deputy Director of Finance and Administration
CMO: Ole Behrendtsen, M.D., Medical Director
CIO: Dana Fahey, Manager Management Information Systems
CHR: Elena Molelus, Manager Human Resources
Web address: www.countyofsb.org
Control: County–Government, nonfederal **Service:** Psychiatric

Staffed Beds: 16 **Admissions:** 5000 **Census:** 16 **Births:** 0

SANTA CLARA—Santa Clara County

⊞ **KAISER PERMANENTE SANTA CLARA MEDICAL CENTER (050071)**, 700 Lawrence Expressway, Zip 95051–5173; tel. 408/851–1000 **A**1 2 3 5 10 **F**1 3 4 5 8 11 12 13 15 16 17 18 19 20 21 22 23 24 26 28 29 31 32 34 35 36 38 40 41 44 45 48 49 50 51 52 53 54 55 56 57 58 59 60 61 62 63 64 65 67 68 70 71 74 75 76 77 78 79 80 81 82 83 84 85 86 87 88 89 90 91 92 93 94 96 97 98 99 100 101 104 107 108 109 110 111 114 115 116 117 118 119 120 121 123 124 126 128 129 130 131 132 134 135 144 146 147 148 **S** Kaiser Foundation Hospitals, Oakland, CA
Primary Contact: Christopher L. Boyd, Senior Vice President and Area Manager
CFO: Tim O'Connor, Area Finance Officer
CMO: Susan Smarr, M.D., Physician–in–Chief
CIO: Scott May, Area Director Technology
CHR: Robert Hyde, Human Resources Business Partner
CNO: Lori Armstrong, R.N., Chief Nursing Officer
Web address: www.kaiserpermanente.org
Control: Other not–for–profit (including NFP Corporation) **Service:** General Medical and Surgical

Staffed Beds: 327 **Admissions:** 19341 **Census:** 225 **Outpatient Visits:** 83771 **Births:** 3472

SANTA CRUZ—Santa Cruz County

⊞ **DOMINICAN HOSPITAL (050242)**, 1555 Soquel Drive, Zip 95065–1794; tel. 831/462–7700, (Nonreporting) **A**1 2 10 **S** Dignity Health, San Francisco, CA
Primary Contact: Nanette Mickiewicz, M.D., President
COO: Chris Wernke, Chief Operating Officer
CFO: Rick Harron, Chief Financial Officer
CMO: Freddie Weinstein, M.D., Chief Medical Officer
CIO: Lee Vanderpool, Vice President
CHR: Vicki Miranda, Vice President Human Resources
Web address: www.dominicanhospital.org
Control: Other not–for–profit (including NFP Corporation) **Service:** General Medical and Surgical

Staffed Beds: 275

⊞ **SUTTER MATERNITY AND SURGERY CENTER OF SANTA CRUZ (050714)**, (Maternity and General Surgery), 2900 Chanticleer Avenue, Zip 95065–1816; tel. 831/477–2200 **A**1 10 **F**3 13 29 34 45 51 57 76 79 81 85 119 126 132 146 **P**3 **S** Sutter Health, Sacramento, CA
Primary Contact: Stephen Gray, Chief Administrative Officer
CFO: Bonnie Liang, Divisional Finance Officer
CMO: Joseph Fabry, D.O., Chief of Staff
CIO: Ann Barr, Chief Information Officer, Sutter Health Bay Area
CHR: Maynard Jenkins, Regional Vice President Human Resources
CNO: Sherri Stout–Torres, R.N., Chief Nursing Executive
Web address: www.suttersantacruz.org
Control: Other not–for–profit (including NFP Corporation) **Service:** Other specialty

Staffed Beds: 30 **Admissions:** 1431 **Census:** 11 **Outpatient Visits:** 12435 **Births:** 979 **Total Expense ($000):** 61351 **Payroll Expense ($000):** 19142 **Personnel:** 207

SANTA MARIA—Santa Barbara County

⊞ **MARIAN REGIONAL MEDICAL CENTER (050107)**, 1400 East Church Street, Zip 93454–5906; tel. 805/739–3000, (Includes ARROYO GRANDE COMMUNITY HOSPITAL, 345 South Halcyon Road, Arroyo Grande, Zip 93420–3896; tel. 805/489–4261; Kenneth Dalebout, Site Administrator), (Nonreporting) **A**1 2 3 10 13 **S** Dignity Health, San Francisco, CA
Primary Contact: Charles J. Cova, Senior Vice President, Operations
COO: Mark Allen, Chief Operating Officer
CFO: Sue Andersen, Vice President and Service Area and Chief Financial Officer
CMO: Chuck Merrill, M.D., Vice President Medical Affairs
CIO: Patricia Haase, Director Information Technology and Communications
CHR: Ed Gonzales, Vice President Human Resources
CNO: Candice Monge, R.N., Chief Nurse Executive Officer
Web address: www.marianmedicalcenter.org
Control: Other not–for–profit (including NFP Corporation) **Service:** General Medical and Surgical

Staffed Beds: 286

SANTA MONICA—Los Angeles County

⊞ **PROVIDENCE SAINT JOHN'S HEALTH CENTER (050290)**, 2121 Santa Monica Boulevard, Zip 90404–2091; tel. 310/829–5511 **A**1 2 10 **F**3 8 14 15 18 20 22 24 26 29 30 31 34 35 37 40 41 43 45 46 49 56 58 64 70 72 74 75 76 78 79 81 84 85 93 99 107 108 110 111 118 119 120 121 123 124 126 130 131 132 146 147 **P**2 3 5 **S** Providence St. Joseph Health, Renton, WA
Primary Contact: Marcel C. Loh, FACHE, Chief Executive Officer
COO: David A. Tam, M.D., Chief Operating Officer
CFO: James Uli, Chief Financial Officer
CMO: Donald Larsen, M.D., Chief Medical Officer
CIO: Martha Ponce, Director Information Technologies and Telecommunications
CHR: Laura Morton Rowe, Director Human Rescource
CNO: Dawna Hendel, R.N., Chief Nursing Officer and Vice President Patient Care Services
Web address: www.providence.org/saintjohns
Control: Church–operated, Nongovernment, not–for profit **Service:** General Medical and Surgical

Staffed Beds: 234 **Admissions:** 12687 **Census:** 146 **Outpatient Visits:** 151416 **Births:** 2146 **Total Expense ($000):** 261194 **Payroll Expense ($000):** 121158 **Personnel:** 1312

Hospital, Medicare Provider Number, Address, Telephone, Approval, Facility, and Physician Codes, Health Care System

★ American Hospital Association (AHA) membership ◯ Healthcare Facilities Accreditation Program ⇑ Center for Improvement in Healthcare Quality Accreditation
☐ The Joint Commission accreditation ◇ DNV Healthcare Inc. accreditation △ Commission on Accreditation of Rehabilitation Facilities (CARF) accreditation

✠ **UCLA MEDICAL CENTER–SANTA MONICA (050112)**, 1250 16th Street, Zip 90404–1249; tel. 310/319–4000 **A**1 3 5 10 **F**3 8 9 11 12 13 15 18 20 22 24 26 27 29 30 31 34 35 37 40 41 45 46 47 48 49 50 52 54 55 56 57 58 59 62 64 65 68 70 72 74 75 76 78 79 81 82 84 85 86 87 89 93 96 97 102 107 108 110 111 114 115 116 117 118 119 130 131 143 145 146 147 **P**6 **S** University of California Systemwide Administration, Oakland, CA
Primary Contact: Paul Watkins, Chief Administrative Officer
COO: Posie Carpenter, R.N., Chief Administrative Officer
CFO: Paul Staton, Chief Financial Officer
CMO: James Atkinson, M.D., Medical Director
CIO: Virginia McFerran, Chief Information Officer
CHR: Mark Speare, Senior Associate Director Patient Relations and Human Resources
Web address: www.healthcare.ucla.edu
Control: State–Government, nonfederal **Service:** General Medical and Surgical

Staffed Beds: 265 **Admissions:** 16442 **Census:** 213 **Outpatient Visits:** 184972 **Births:** 1400 **Total Expense ($000):** 425912 **Payroll Expense ($000):** 167640 **Personnel:** 1767

SANTA ROSA—Sonoma County

✠ **KAISER PERMANENTE SANTA ROSA MEDICAL CENTER (050690)**, 401 Bicentennial Way, Zip 95403–2192; tel. 707/571–4000, (Nonreporting) **A**1 3 10 **S** Kaiser Foundation Hospitals, Oakland, CA
Primary Contact: Judy Coffey, R.N., Senior Vice President and Area Manager
COO: Vicky Locey, R.N., Chief Operating and Chief Nursing Officer
CFO: John Groesbeck, Area Finance Officer
CMO: Kirk Pappas, M.D., Physician–in–Chief
CIO: Stanley Dobrawa, Area Technology Director
CHR: Michael G. Fanselau, Human Resource Leader
CNO: Vicky Locey, R.N., Chief Operating and Chief Nursing Officer
Web address: www.kaiserpermanente.org
Control: Other not–for–profit (including NFP Corporation) **Service:** General Medical and Surgical

Staffed Beds: 117

✠ **SANTA ROSA MEMORIAL HOSPITAL (050174)**, 1165 Montgomery Drive, Zip 95405–4897, Mailing Address: P.O. Box 522, Zip 95402–0522; tel. 707/546–3210 **A**1 2 10 **F**2 3 8 11 13 15 18 20 22 24 26 29 30 31 32 34 35 40 42 43 45 46 47 49 50 54 58 59 62 63 64 65 66 68 70 71 72 74 75 76 77 78 79 81 82 83 84 85 87 89 90 91 93 94 100 104 107 108 110 111 114 115 116 117 118 119 120 121 123 129 130 132 143 144 146 148 **S** Providence St. Joseph Health, Renton, WA
Primary Contact: Todd Salnas, President
CFO: Mich Riccioni, Chief Financial Officer
CMO: Richard Carvolth, M.D., Chief Medical Officer
CIO: Benjamin Richard, Regional Information Technology Director
CHR: John Omel, Regional Vice President, Human Resources
CNO: Vicki White, Chief Nursing Officer
Web address: www.stjosephhealth.org
Control: Other not–for–profit (including NFP Corporation) **Service:** General Medical and Surgical

Staffed Beds: 278 **Admissions:** 11403 **Census:** 179 **Outpatient Visits:** 259356 **Births:** 770 **Total Expense ($000):** 459902 **Payroll Expense ($000):** 121077 **Personnel:** 1345

✠ **SUTTER SANTA ROSA REGIONAL HOSPITAL (050291)**, 30 Mark West Springs Road, Zip 95403; tel. 707/576–4000, (Includes WARRACK CAMPUS, 2449 Summerfield Road, Zip 95405–7815; tel. 707/576–4200) **A**1 3 5 10 **F**3 11 12 13 18 20 22 24 26 29 30 31 34 35 36 40 45 49 50 51 56 59 60 61 64 65 68 70 72 75 76 77 78 79 81 84 85 87 107 108 111 119 126 130 146 148 **P**3 **S** Sutter Health, Sacramento, CA
Primary Contact: Mike Purvis, Chief Administrative Officer
CMO: William Carroll, M.D., Chief Medical Executive
Web address: www.sutterhealth.org
Control: Other not–for–profit (including NFP Corporation) **Service:** General Medical and Surgical

Staffed Beds: 84 **Admissions:** 6279 **Census:** 69 **Outpatient Visits:** 58595 **Births:** 1809 **Total Expense ($000):** 229843 **Payroll Expense ($000):** 67790 **Personnel:** 647

SEBASTOPOL—Sonoma County

◇ **SONOMA WEST MEDICAL CENTER**, 501 Petaluma Avenue, Zip 95472–4215, (Nonreporting) **A**10 21
Primary Contact: Luke Tharasri, Interim Chief Executive Officer
CFO: Robert Heinemeier, Interim Chief Financial Officer
Web address: www.sonomawesthealth.org/
Control: Hospital district or authority, Government, nonfederal **Service:** General Medical and Surgical

Staffed Beds: 25

SEPULVEDA—Los Angeles County, See Los Angeles

SHERMAN OAKS—Los Angeles County, See Los Angeles

SIMI VALLEY—Ventura County

✠ **SIMI VALLEY HOSPITAL (050236)**, 2975 North Sycamore Drive, Zip 93065–1277; tel. 805/955–6000 **A**1 2 10 **F**3 8 11 13 15 18 20 22 24 26 29 30 31 32 34 35 36 40 41 44 45 46 49 50 51 54 56 57 58 59 62 63 64 65 68 70 72 74 75 76 77 78 79 81 82 84 85 86 87 93 96 97 101 102 103 107 108 110 111 114 118 119 130 131 132 134 141 146 147 148 **P**2 3 4 **S** Adventist Health, Roseville, CA
Primary Contact: Jennifer Swenson, President and Chief Executive Officer
COO: Caroline Esparza, Sr. VP, COO & CNO
CFO: Brian Anderson, Chief Financial Officer
CMO: John Dingilian, M.D., Chief Medical Officer
CIO: Bridget Nakamura, Director Information Systems
CHR: Susan Crabtree, Director Human Resources
CNO: Caroline Esparza, Senior Vice President, Chief Operating Officer and Chief Nurse Officer
Web address: www.simivalleyhospital.com
Control: Church–operated, Nongovernment, not–for profit **Service:** General Medical and Surgical

Staffed Beds: 82 **Admissions:** 6298 **Census:** 76 **Outpatient Visits:** 82724 **Births:** 574 **Total Expense ($000):** 136993 **Payroll Expense ($000):** 57229 **Personnel:** 732

SOLVANG—Santa Barbara County

✠ **SANTA YNEZ VALLEY COTTAGE HOSPITAL (051331)**, 2050 Viborg Road, Zip 93463–2295; tel. 805/688–6431 **A**1 10 18 **F**15 28 40 57 68 81 85 107 111 114 119 143 146 **S** Cottage Health, Santa Barbara, CA
Primary Contact: Ronald C. Werft, President and Chief Executive Officer
COO: Steven A. Fellows, Executive Vice President and Chief Operating Officer
CFO: Brett Tande, Chief Financial Officer
CMO: Edmund Wroblewski, M.D., Vice President Medical Affairs and Chief Medical Officer
CHR: Patrice Ryan, Vice President Human Resources
CNO: Herb J. Geary, Chief Nursing Officer
Web address: www.cottagehealthsystem.org
Control: Other not–for–profit (including NFP Corporation) **Service:** General Medical and Surgical

Staffed Beds: 11 **Admissions:** 248 **Census:** 2 **Outpatient Visits:** 18816 **Births:** 0 **Total Expense ($000):** 15456 **Payroll Expense ($000):** 7377 **Personnel:** 65

SONOMA—Sonoma County

SONOMA VALLEY HOSPITAL (050090), 347 Andrieux Street, Zip 95476–6811, Mailing Address: P.O. Box 600, Zip 95476–0600; tel. 707/935–5000, (Nonreporting) **A**10 22
Primary Contact: Kelly Mather, Chief Executive Officer
CFO: Jeanette Tarver, Director of Finance
CMO: Robert Cohen, M.D., Chief Medical Officer
CIO: Fe Sendaydiego, Director Information Systems
CHR: Paula M. Davis, Chief Human Resources Officer
CNO: Leslie Lovejoy, R.N., Chief Nursing and Quality Officer
Web address: www.svh.com
Control: Hospital district or authority, Government, nonfederal **Service:** General Medical and Surgical

Staffed Beds: 65

SONORA—Tuolumne County

✠ **SONORA REGIONAL MEDICAL CENTER (050335)**, 1000 Greenley Road, Zip 95370–4819; tel. 209/536–5000, (Total facility includes 68 beds in nursing home–type unit) **A**1 10 **F**3 8 11 13 15 17 18 20 28 29 30 31 34 35 37 39 40 45 49 53 54 56 57 59 62 63 64 70 71 75 76 77 78 79 81 84 85 86 87 92 93 97 104 107 108 110 111 114 115 117 118 119 120 121 123 127 128 130 131 132 133 135 143 144 145 146 148 **P**6 **S** Adventist Health, Roseville, CA
Primary Contact: Andrew Jahn, President and Chief Executive Officer
CFO: Greg McCulloch, CPA, Vice President of Finance and Chief Financial Officer
CMO: Ed Clinite, D.O., Chief of Staff
CIO: Manty Drews, Chief Information Officer
CNO: Julie Kline, Senior Vice President Patient Services
Web address: www.sonoramedicalcenter.org/
Control: Church–operated, Nongovernment, not–for profit **Service:** General Medical and Surgical

Staffed Beds: 152 **Admissions:** 4866 **Census:** 123 **Outpatient Visits:** 352870 **Births:** 560 **Total Expense ($000):** 228582 **Payroll Expense ($000):** 81877 **Personnel:** 1269

Many Facility Codes have changed. Please refer to the AHA Guide Code Chart.

CA

SOUTH EL MONTE—Los Angeles County

☐ **GREATER EL MONTE COMMUNITY HOSPITAL (050738)**, 1701 Santa Anita Avenue, Zip 91733–3411; tel. 626/579–7777 **A**1 10 **F**3 13 14 17 18 29 34 35 40 41 45 49 50 57 59 64 68 70 75 76 77 78 79 81 82 85 87 89 92 93 107 108 119 128 130 146 **S** AHMC & Healthcare, Inc., Alhambra, CA
Primary Contact: Stanley Toy, Jr., M.D., Chief Executive Officer
COO: Jose Ortega, Chief Operating Officer
CFO: Michael Chung, Chief Financial Officer
CMO: Dilip Patel, M.D., Chief of Staff
CIO: Jay Geldhof, Director Information Systems
CHR: Jason Jaquez, Director Human Resources
CNO: Evelyn Calubaquib, Chief Nursing Officer
Web address: www.greaterelmonte.com
Control: Hospital district or authority, Government, nonfederal **Service:** General Medical and Surgical

Staffed Beds: 46 **Admissions:** 3522 **Census:** 45 **Outpatient Visits:** 19464 **Births:** 398 **Total Expense ($000):** 59131 **Payroll Expense ($000):** 18838 **Personnel:** 265

SOUTH LAKE TAHOE—El Dorado County

☒ **BARTON MEMORIAL HOSPITAL (050352)**, 2170 South Avenue, Zip 96150–7026, Mailing Address: P.O. Box 9578, Zip 96158–9578; tel. 530/541–3420, (Total facility includes 48 beds in nursing home–type unit) **A**1 5 10 20 **F**3 8 11 13 15 18 29 30 32 34 35 38 40 43 45 46 47 48 50 54 57 59 62 63 64 65 66 68 70 75 76 77 79 81 82 83 84 85 86 87 89 90 92 93 94 96 97 99 100 104 107 109 110 111 112 113 114 115 116 117 118 119 121 122 123 124 126 127 128 129 130 131 132 135 143 144 146 147 148
Primary Contact: Clint Purvance, M.D., President and Chief Executive Officer
CFO: Richard P. Derby, Vice President Finance
CMO: Rhonda Sneeringer, M.D., Chief Medical Officer
CIO: Jason Roberts, Director of Information Services
CNO: Susan Fairley, Chief Nursing Officer
Web address: www.bartonhealth.org
Control: Other not–for–profit (including NFP Corporation) **Service:** General Medical and Surgical

Staffed Beds: 111 **Admissions:** 2144 **Census:** 65 **Outpatient Visits:** 167191 **Births:** 324 **Total Expense ($000):** 113360 **Payroll Expense ($000):** 48583 **Personnel:** 791

SOUTH SAN FRANCISCO—San Mateo County

☒ **KAISER PERMANENTE SOUTH SAN FRANCISCO (050070)**, 1200 El Camino Real, Zip 94080–3208; tel. 650/742–2000, (Nonreporting) **A**1 3 10 **S** Kaiser Foundation Hospitals, Oakland, CA
Primary Contact: Ronald Groepper, Senior Vice President and Area Manager
CMO: Michelle Caughey, M.D., Physician In Chief
CIO: Angel Shew, Director Area Technology
CHR: Sharon Barncord, Human Resource Business Partner
Web address: www.kaiserpermanente.org
Control: Other not–for–profit (including NFP Corporation) **Service:** General Medical and Surgical

Staffed Beds: 120

STOCKTON—San Joaquin County

☐ **DAMERON HOSPITAL (050122)**, 525 West Acacia Street, Zip 95203–2484; tel. 209/944–5550, (Nonreporting) **A**1 10
Primary Contact: Lorraine P. Auerbach, FACHE, President and Chief Executive Officer
COO: Michael Glasberg, Senior Vice President, Chief Operating Officer
CFO: Elizabeth R. Propp, Vice President Finance and Chief Financial Officer
CMO: Bradley Reinke, M.D., Vice President Medical Affairs and Chief Medical Officer
CIO: David Kerrins, Vice President Information Services and Chief Information Officer
CHR: Tresha Moreland, MS, Regional Vice President Human Resources
CNO: Janine Hawkins, R.N., Vice President Patient Care Services and Chief Nursing Officer
Web address: www.dameronhospital.org
Control: Other not–for–profit (including NFP Corporation) **Service:** General Medical and Surgical

Staffed Beds: 202

☒ **ST. JOSEPH'S BEHAVIORAL HEALTH CENTER (054123)**, 2510 North California Street, Zip 95204–5568; tel. 209/461–2000 **A**1 10 **F**5 29 38 68 98 100 101 103 104 105 130 132 143 146 **S** Dignity Health, San Francisco, CA
Primary Contact: Paul Rains, R.N., MSN, President
CFO: Doreen Hartmann, Chief Financial Officer
CMO: David Robinson, D.O., Medical Director
CHR: Nancy Vargas, Chief Human Resources
CNO: Benny Lee Lucas, Jr., Chief Nursing Executive
Web address: www.stjosephscanhelp.org
Control: Church–operated, Nongovernment, not–for profit **Service:** Psychiatric

Staffed Beds: 35 **Admissions:** 2018 **Census:** 33 **Outpatient Visits:** 10675 **Births:** 0 **Total Expense ($000):** 17374 **Payroll Expense ($000):** 9439 **Personnel:** 111

☒ **ST. JOSEPH'S MEDICAL CENTER (050084)**, 1800 North California Street, Zip 95204–6019, Mailing Address: P.O. Box 213008, Zip 95213–9008; tel. 209/943–2000, (Nonreporting) **A**1 2 3 10 **S** Dignity Health, San Francisco, CA
Primary Contact: Donald J. Wiley, President and Chief Executive Officer
COO: Michael R. Ricks, Chief Operating Officer
CFO: Nikki Ochoa, Interim Chief Financial Officer
CIO: Randall Gamino, Director Perot Site
CHR: Nancy Vargas, Vice President Human Resources
Web address: www.stjosephsCARES.org
Control: Other not–for–profit (including NFP Corporation) **Service:** General Medical and Surgical

Staffed Beds: 273

SUN CITY—Riverside County

☐ **MENIFEE VALLEY MEDICAL CENTER (050684)**, 28400 McCall Boulevard, Zip 92585–9537; tel. 951/679–8888, (Nonreporting) **A**1 10 **S** Physicians for Healthy Hospitals, Hemet, CA
Primary Contact: Dan C. McLaughlin, Chief Executive Officer
CHR: Michele Bird, Chief Human Resources Officer
Web address: www.valleyhealthsystem.com
Control: Hospital district or authority, Government, nonfederal **Service:** General Medical and Surgical

Staffed Beds: 74

SUN VALLEY—Los Angeles County, See Los Angeles

SUSANVILLE—Lassen County

☒ **BANNER LASSEN MEDICAL CENTER (051320)**, 1800 Spring Ridge Drive, Zip 96130–6100; tel. 530/252–2000 **A**1 10 18 **F**3 13 15 29 30 31 34 38 39 40 45 59 76 79 81 85 87 93 107 110 111 114 119 129 130 146 148 **S** Banner Health, Phoenix, AZ
Primary Contact: Catherine S. Harshbarger, R.N., Chief Executive Officer
CFO: Jon R. McMillan, Chief Financial Officer
CMO: Hal Meadows, M.D., Chief Medical Officer
CIO: Randy Moore, Chief Information Officer
CHR: Ruth Smith, Chief Human Resource Officer
CNO: Sandy Goldstein, R.N., Chief Nursing Officer
Web address: www.bannerhealth.com/Locations/California/Banner+Lassen+Medical+Center
Control: Other not–for–profit (including NFP Corporation) **Service:** General Medical and Surgical

Staffed Beds: 25 **Admissions:** 1086 **Census:** 10 **Outpatient Visits:** 32475 **Births:** 237 **Total Expense ($000):** 33254 **Payroll Expense ($000):** 15614 **Personnel:** 185

SYLMAR—Los Angeles County, See Los Angeles

TARZANA—Los Angeles County, See Los Angeles

TEHACHAPI—Kern County

★ ◇ **TEHACHAPI VALLEY HEALTHCARE DISTRICT (051301)**, 115 West E Street, Zip 93561–1607, Mailing Address: P.O. Box 1900, Zip 93581–1900; tel. 661/823–3000, (Nonreporting) **A**10 18 21
Primary Contact: Eugene Suksi, Interim Chief Executive Officer
CFO: Chester Beedle, Interim Chief Financial Officer
CMO: Susan Cribbs, D.O., Chief of Staff
CIO: Dusty Colvard, Manager Information Technology
CHR: Susan Nelson–Jones, Director Human Resources
CNO: Juliana Kay Kirby, R.N., Chief Nursing Officer
Web address: www.tvhd.org
Control: Hospital district or authority, Government, nonfederal **Service:** General Medical and Surgical

Staffed Beds: 24

Hospital, Medicare Provider Number, Address, Telephone, Approval, Facility, and Physician Codes, Health Care System

★ American Hospital Association (AHA) membership
☐ The Joint Commission accreditation
○ Healthcare Facilities Accreditation Program
◇ DNV Healthcare Inc. accreditation
⇑ Center for Improvement in Healthcare Quality Accreditation
△ Commission on Accreditation of Rehabilitation Facilities (CARF) accreditation

CA

TEMECULA—Riverside County

⊠ **TEMECULA VALLEY HOSPITAL (050775)**, 31700 Temecula Parkway, Zip 92592–5896; tel. 951/331–2216, (Nonreporting) **A**1 10 **S** Universal Health Services, Inc., King of Prussia, PA
Primary Contact: Darlene Wetton, R.N., Chief Executive Officer
Web address: www.temeculavalleyhospital.com
Control: Corporation, Investor–owned, for–profit **Service:** General Medical and Surgical

Staffed Beds: 140

TEMPLETON—San Luis Obispo County

⊠ **TWIN CITIES COMMUNITY HOSPITAL (050633)**, 1100 Las Tablas Road, Zip 93465–9796; tel. 805/434–3500 **A**1 10 **F**3 8 13 18 29 30 31 34 37 39 40 45 46 47 48 49 50 55 56 57 59 60 64 67 68 70 74 75 77 78 79 81 84 85 87 107 108 111 115 119 130 146 148 **S** TENET Healthcare Corporation, Dallas, TX
Primary Contact: Mark P. Lisa, FACHE, Chief Executive Officer
COO: Mike Lane, Chief Operating Officer
CFO: Paul Posmoga, Chief Financial Officer
CHR: Keith Stanhill, Chief Human Resources Officer
CNO: Joan Fonda, Chief Nursing Officer
Web address: www.twincitieshospital.com
Control: Corporation, Investor–owned, for–profit **Service:** General Medical and Surgical

Staffed Beds: 89 **Admissions:** 4306 **Census:** 44 **Outpatient Visits:** 46524 **Births:** 646 **Total Expense ($000):** 82414 **Payroll Expense ($000):** 36516

THOUSAND OAKS—Ventura County

⊠ **LOS ROBLES HOSPITAL AND MEDICAL CENTER (050549)**, 215 West Janss Road, Zip 91360–1899; tel. 805/497–2727, (Includes THOUSAND OAKS SURGICAL HOSPITAL, 401 Rolling Oaks Drive, Zip 91361–1050; tel. 805/497–2727; Natalie Mussi, President and Chief Executive Officer), (Nonreporting) **A**1 2 10 **S** HCA, Nashville, TN
Primary Contact: Natalie Mussi, President and Chief Executive Officer
COO: Norair Jemjemian, Chief Operating Officer
CMO: Hannah Grossman, M.D., Chief Medical Officer
CIO: Alex Bryer, Director Information Management
CHR: John Bibby, Vice President Human Resources
CNO: Cynthia J. Johnson, R.N., Chief Nursing Officer
Web address: www.losrobleshospital.com
Control: Corporation, Investor–owned, for–profit **Service:** General Medical and Surgical

Staffed Beds: 334

TORRANCE—Los Angeles County

☐ **DEL AMO HOSPITAL (054053)**, 23700 Camino Del Sol, Zip 90505–5000; tel. 310/530–1151, (Nonreporting) **A**1 10 **S** Universal Health Services, Inc., King of Prussia, PA
Primary Contact: Steven Oppenheimer, Chief Executive Officer
Web address: www.delamohospital.com
Control: Corporation, Investor–owned, for–profit **Service:** Psychiatric

Staffed Beds: 70

☐ **HARBOR–UCLA MEDICAL CENTER (050376)**, 1000 West Carson Street, Zip 90502–2059; tel. 310/222–2345, (Nonreporting) **A**1 2 3 5 8 10 **S** Los Angeles County–Department of Health Services, Los Angeles, CA
Primary Contact: Kimberly McKenzie, R.N., MSN, Interim Chief Executive Officer
COO: Kimberly McKenzie, R.N., Chief Nursing Officer and Chief Operations Officer
CFO: Jody Nakasuji, Chief Financial Officer
CMO: Timothy Van Natta, M.D., Chief Medical Officer
CIO: Sandy Mungovan, Chief Information Officer
CHR: Karyl Smith, Director Human Resources
CNO: Kimberly McKenzie, R.N., Chief Nursing Officer and Chief Operations Officer
Web address: www.harbor–ucla.org
Control: County–Government, nonfederal **Service:** General Medical and Surgical

Staffed Beds: 350

⊠ **PROVIDENCE LITTLE COMPANY OF MARY MEDICAL CENTER – TORRANCE (050353)**, 4101 Torrance Boulevard, Zip 90503–4664; tel. 310/540–7676, (Total facility includes 77 beds in nursing home–type unit) **A**1 2 10 **F**3 8 11 13 14 15 18 19 20 22 24 26 28 29 30 31 34 35 37 40 41 43 44 45 46 49 51 57 59 60 62 64 68 70 72 73 74 75 76 77 78 79 81 82 84 85 86 87 88 89 91 92 93 100 107 108 110 111 114 115 116 117 118 119 120 121 123 126 128 130 131 132 133 143 145 146 147 148 **P**2 3 5 **S** Providence St. Joseph Health, Renton, WA
Primary Contact: Mary E. Kingston, FACHE, R.N., Chief Executive Officer, South Bay Community
COO: Garry M. Olney, Chief Operating Officer
CFO: Elizabeth Zuanich, Chief Financial Officer
CMO: Richard Glimp, M.D., Chief Medical Officer
CIO: Andrea Flores, Director, Information Systems
CHR: Melissa Baker, Director, Human Resources
CNO: Michael Jongsma, R.N., Chief Nursing Officer
Web address: www.providence.org
Control: Church–operated, Nongovernment, not–for profit **Service:** General Medical and Surgical

Staffed Beds: 376 **Admissions:** 22645 **Census:** 211 **Outpatient Visits:** 224039 **Births:** 2864 **Total Expense ($000):** 295776 **Payroll Expense ($000):** 162185 **Personnel:** 1820

⊠ **TORRANCE MEMORIAL MEDICAL CENTER (050351)**, 3330 Lomita Boulevard, Zip 90505–5073; tel. 310/325–9110 **A**1 2 10 **F**3 5 8 11 12 13 14 15 16 17 18 19 20 22 24 26 28 29 30 31 32 34 35 36 37 39 40 41 44 45 46 47 48 49 50 51 55 57 58 59 60 61 62 63 64 68 70 72 74 75 76 77 78 79 81 82 83 84 85 86 87 89 91 92 93 96 107 108 109 110 111 114 115 116 117 118 119 120 121 123 124 126 128 129 130 132 134 135 141 143 145 146 147 148 **P**2 3 5 7
Primary Contact: Craig Leach, President and Chief Executive Officer
CFO: Bill Larson, Vice President Finance and Chief Financial Officer
CMO: John McNamara, M.D., Senior Vice President, Chief Medical Officer
CIO: Bernadette Reid, Vice President, Information Technology and Chief Information Officer
CHR: Linda Dobie, R.N., Vice President, Legal Affairs
CNO: Margaret Berwald, R.N., Senior Vice President Patient Services
Web address: www.torrancememorial.org
Control: Other not–for–profit (including NFP Corporation) **Service:** General Medical and Surgical

Staffed Beds: 415 **Admissions:** 24875 **Census:** 299 **Outpatient Visits:** 381055 **Births:** 3129 **Total Expense ($000):** 571251 **Payroll Expense ($000):** 214027 **Personnel:** 2922

TRACY—San Joaquin County

⊠ **SUTTER TRACY COMMUNITY HOSPITAL (050313)**, 1420 North Tracy Boulevard, Zip 95376–3497; tel. 209/835–1500 **A**1 10 **F**3 11 13 15 18 29 30 31 34 35 39 40 45 46 49 50 54 57 59 60 64 68 70 74 75 76 77 78 79 81 82 85 86 87 93 107 108 110 111 115 119 124 130 132 135 146 148 **P**3 **S** Sutter Health, Sacramento, CA
Primary Contact: David M. Thompson, Chief Executive Officer
CFO: Eric Dalton, Chief Financial Officer
CIO: Catherine M. Larsen, Director Marketing
CHR: Melanie Wallace, Manager Human Resources
Web address: www.suttertracy.org
Control: Other not–for–profit (including NFP Corporation) **Service:** General Medical and Surgical

Staffed Beds: 81 **Admissions:** 3949 **Census:** 33 **Outpatient Visits:** 103970 **Births:** 718 **Total Expense ($000):** 106742 **Payroll Expense ($000):** 37080 **Personnel:** 472

TRAVIS AFB—Solano County

⊠ **DAVID GRANT USAF MEDICAL CENTER**, 101 Bodin Circle, Zip 94535–1809; tel. 707/423–7300, (Nonreporting) **A**1 3 5 **S** Department of the Air Force, Washington, DC
Primary Contact: Colonel Brian T. Hayes, Commander
CFO: Major Jonathan Richards, Chief Financial Officer
CMO: Colonel Chris Scharenbrock, M.D., Chief Medical Staff
Web address: www.travis.af.mil/units/dgmc/index.asp
Control: Air Force, Government, federal **Service:** General Medical and Surgical

Staffed Beds: 116

TRUCKEE—Nevada County

★ **TAHOE FOREST HOSPITAL DISTRICT (051328)**, 10121 Pine Avenue, Zip 96161–4856, Mailing Address: P.O. Box 759, Zip 96160–0759; tel. 530/587–6011, (Total facility includes 37 beds in nursing home–type unit) **A**2 3 5 10 18 **F**3 8 11 13 15 28 29 30 31 34 35 40 49 50 53 57 58 59 62 63 64 65 66 70 75 76 77 78 79 81 82 84 85 87 93 107 108 110 111 115 116 117 119 121 122 123 127 128 129 130 131 132 133 135 146 147 148 **P**3 7 **S** Tahoe Forest Health System, Truckee, CA
Primary Contact: Harry Weis, Chief Executive Officer
COO: Judy Newland, R.N., Chief Operating Officer
CFO: Crystal Betts, Chief Financial Officer
CMO: Jeff Dodd, M.D., Chief of Staff
CIO: Jake Dorst, Chief Information Officer
CHR: Jayne O'Flanagan, Chief Human Resources Officer
CNO: Judy Newland, R.N., Chief Nursing Officer
Web address: www.tfhd.com
Control: Hospital district or authority, Government, nonfederal **Service:** General Medical and Surgical

Staffed Beds: 62 **Admissions:** 1674 **Census:** 44 **Outpatient Visits:** 58852 **Births:** 388 **Total Expense ($000):** 111313 **Payroll Expense ($000):** 42056 **Personnel:** 571

TULARE—Tulare County

◇ **TULARE REGIONAL MEDICAL CENTER (050359)**, 869 North Cherry Street, Zip 93274–2287; tel. 559/688–0821 **A**10 21 **F**1 3 4 11 13 15 16 17 20 26 29 34 35 40 45 46 47 48 49 50 53 56 57 59 60 62 64 65 66 67 68 70 71 72 73 74 75 76 79 80 81 85 86 88 89 90 93 97 98 107 108 110 111 114 119 127 128 129 130 131 132 135 146 147 148
Primary Contact: Alan Germany, Interim Chief Executive Officer
COO: Alan Germany, Chief Operating Officer
CFO: Michael Bernstein, Chief Financial Officer
CMO: Pradeep Kamboj, M.D., Chief Medical Staff
CIO: Jim Peelgren, Chief Information Officer
CHR: John Barbadian, Vice President Human Resources
CNO: Patricia Mathewson, Chief Nursing Officer
Web address: www.tulareregional.org
Control: Hospital district or authority, Government, nonfederal **Service:** General Medical and Surgical

Staffed Beds: 103 **Admissions:** 3736 **Census:** 40 **Outpatient Visits:** 104572 **Births:** 987 **Total Expense ($000):** 71998 **Payroll Expense ($000):** 27560 **Personnel:** 376

TURLOCK—Stanislaus County

⊞ **EMANUEL MEDICAL CENTER (050179)**, 825 Delbon Avenue, Zip 95382–2016, Mailing Address: P.O. Box 819005, Zip 95382; tel. 209/667–4200 **A**1 2 10 **F**3 8 11 15 18 20 22 24 26 29 30 31 34 35 40 47 48 49 54 59 60 64 68 70 73 75 76 77 78 79 81 89 93 97 107 108 110 111 114 115 118 119 120 121 123 130 132 146 147 148 **S** TENET Healthcare Corporation, Dallas, TX
Primary Contact: Susan C. Micheletti, Chief Executive Officer
CFO: David Neapolitan, Chief Financial Officer
CIO: Beth Walker, Chief Information Officer
CHR: Terry Gray, Vice President Human Resources
CNO: Constance Fairchilds, R.N., Vice President Patient Care Services
Web address: www.emanuelmed.org
Control: Corporation, Investor–owned, for–profit **Service:** General Medical and Surgical

Staffed Beds: 209 **Admissions:** 9251 **Census:** 105 **Outpatient Visits:** 130475 **Births:** 1399 **Total Expense ($000):** 167106 **Payroll Expense ($000):** 75096 **Personnel:** 986

TUSTIN—Orange County

○ **FOOTHILL REGIONAL MEDICAL CENTER (052053)**, 14662 Newport Avenue, Zip 92780–6064; tel. 714/838–9600, (Nonreporting) **A**10 11
Primary Contact: Barbara Schneider, R.N., Chief Executive Officer
COO: Kara Bourne, R.N., Chief Nursing Officer and Chief Operating Officer
CIO: Darla Kennedy, Chief Information Officer
CHR: Aprille Major, Director Human Resources
Web address: www.newportspecialtyhospital.com/
Control: Corporation, Investor–owned, for–profit **Service:** Long–Term Acute Care hospital

Staffed Beds: 155

⊞ **HEALTHSOUTH TUSTIN REHABILITATION HOSPITAL (053034)**, 14851 Yorba Street, Zip 92780–2925; tel. 714/832–9200, (Nonreporting) **A**1 10 **S** HEALTHSOUTH Corporation, Birmingham, AL
Primary Contact: Diana C. Hanyak, Chief Executive Officer
CFO: Paula Redmond, Controller
CMO: Rodric Bell, M.D., Medical Director
CHR: JoAnn Roiz, Director Human Resources
Web address: www.tustinrehab.com
Control: Corporation, Investor–owned, for–profit **Service:** Rehabilitation

Staffed Beds: 48

TWENTYNINE PALMS—San Bernardino County

⊞ **ROBERT E. BUSH NAVAL HOSPITAL**, 1145 Sturgis Road, Zip 92278, Mailing Address: Box 788250, MCAGCC, Zip 92278–8250; tel. 760/830–2190, (Nonreporting) **A**1 3 **S** Bureau of Medicine and Surgery, Department of the Navy, Falls Church, VA
Primary Contact: Captain Jay C. Sourbeer, Commanding Officer
CHR: Virginia Ward, Human Resources Officer
CNO: Captain Sandra Mason, MSN, Director Nursing Services and Senior Nurse Executive
Web address: www.med.navy.mil/sites/nhtp/Pages/default.aspx
Control: Navy, Government, federal **Service:** General Medical and Surgical

Staffed Beds: 39

UKIAH—Mendocino County

⊞ **UKIAH VALLEY MEDICAL CENTER (050301)**, 275 Hospital Drive, Zip 95482–4531; tel. 707/462–3111 **A**1 5 10 **F**3 8 11 12 13 15 18 29 30 31 32 34 35 36 38 40 44 45 46 48 49 50 51 54 57 59 60 64 65 68 70 72 75 76 77 78 79 81 82 84 85 86 87 93 94 97 107 108 110 111 114 115 116 117 118 119 127 130 131 132 135 144 146 147 148 **P**3 **S** Adventist Health, Roseville, CA
Primary Contact: Gwen Matthews, R.N., MSN, Chief Executive Officer
CIO: David Eastman, Site Director
CHR: Rebecca Ryan, Interim Director Human Resources and Employee Health
Web address: www.adventisthealth.org
Control: Church–operated, Nongovernment, not–for profit **Service:** General Medical and Surgical

Staffed Beds: 50 **Admissions:** 3658 **Census:** 32 **Outpatient Visits:** 143811 **Births:** 852 **Total Expense ($000):** 143373 **Payroll Expense ($000):** 44999 **Personnel:** 645

UPLAND—San Bernardino County

⊞ **SAN ANTONIO REGIONAL HOSPITAL (050099)**, 999 San Bernardino Road, Zip 91786–4920, Mailing Address: Box 5001, Zip 91785–5001; tel. 909/985–2811 **A**1 2 10 **F**3 8 11 13 15 17 18 20 22 24 26 28 29 31 35 38 40 45 46 49 50 54 57 59 60 61 64 65 69 70 72 74 75 76 77 78 79 80 81 82 83 84 85 86 87 89 91 92 93 94 107 108 110 111 114 115 118 119 121 123 124 130 132 146 147 148
Primary Contact: Harris F. Koenig, President and Chief Executive Officer
CFO: Wah Chung Hsu, Senior Vice President Finance
CMO: Carlos Vigil, M.D., President Medical Staff
CIO: Kamel Pandya, Director Information Services
CHR: Laura Kato, Vice President of Human Resources
CNO: Gudrun Moll, R.N., Chief Nursing Officer
Web address: www.sarh.org
Control: Other not–for–profit (including NFP Corporation) **Service:** General Medical and Surgical

Staffed Beds: 279 **Admissions:** 15986 **Census:** 154 **Outpatient Visits:** 220226 **Births:** 2076 **Total Expense ($000):** 293811 **Payroll Expense ($000):** 122823 **Personnel:** 1650

VACAVILLE—Solano County

CALIFORNIA MEDICAL FACILITY, 1600 California Drive, Zip 95687; tel. 707/448–6841, (Nonreporting)
Primary Contact: Mary Lou Dunlap, Correctional Health Services Administrator
CMO: Raymond Andreasen, M.D., Chief Medical Officer–Inpatient
Web address: www.cya.ca.gov/visitors/fac_prison_cmf.html
Control: State–Government, nonfederal **Service:** Hospital unit of an institution (prison hospital, college infimary, etc.)

Staffed Beds: 215

⊞ **KAISER PERMANENTE VACAVILLE MEDICAL CENTER (050767)**, 1 Quality Drive, Zip 95688–9494; tel. 707/624–4000, (Nonreporting) **A**1 3 10 **S** Kaiser Foundation Hospitals, Oakland, CA
Primary Contact: Joseph M. Mark, Interim Chief Executive Officer
Web address: www.kp.org
Control: Other not–for–profit (including NFP Corporation) **Service:** General Medical and Surgical

Staffed Beds: 140

Hospital, Medicare Provider Number, Address, Telephone, Approval, Facility, and Physician Codes, Health Care System

★ American Hospital Association (AHA) membership
□ The Joint Commission accreditation
○ Healthcare Facilities Accreditation Program
◇ DNV Healthcare Inc. accreditation
⇑ Center for Improvement in Healthcare Quality Accreditation
△ Commission on Accreditation of Rehabilitation Facilities (CARF) accreditation

NORTHBAY VACAVALLEY HOSPITAL See NorthBay Medical Center, Fairfield

VALENCIA—Los Angeles County

⊠ **HENRY MAYO NEWHALL HOSPITAL (050624)**, 23845 McBean Parkway, Zip 91355–2083; tel. 661/200–2000 **A**1 2 10 **F**3 8 11 13 15 17 18 20 22 24 26 28 29 30 31 34 35 38 40 41 43 45 49 50 55 57 59 60 64 70 72 74 76 77 78 79 81 82 84 85 86 87 90 93 98 100 102 107 108 110 115 119 130 132 135 146 147 148
Primary Contact: Roger E. Seaver, President and Chief Executive Officer
COO: John V. Schleif, Senior Vice President and Chief Operating Officer
CFO: C. R. Hudson, Senior Vice President and Chief Financial Officer
CMO: Richard Frankenstein, M.D., Vice President and Chief Medical Officer
CIO: Cindy Peterson, Vice President and Chief Information Officer
CHR: Mark Puleo, Vice President and Chief Human Resources Officer
CNO: Larry R. Kidd, R.N., Vice President and Chief Nursing Officer
Web address: www.henrymayo.com
Control: Other not–for–profit (including NFP Corporation) **Service:** General Medical and Surgical

Staffed Beds: 238 **Admissions:** 12780 **Census:** 159 **Outpatient Visits:** 133332 **Births:** 1313 **Total Expense ($000):** 293412 **Payroll Expense ($000):** 91621 **Personnel:** 1563

VALLEJO—Solano County

⊠ △ **KAISER PERMANENTE VALLEJO MEDICAL CENTER (050073)**, 975 Sereno Drive, Zip 94589–2441; tel. 707/651–1000, (Nonreporting) **A**1 3 5 7 10 **S** Kaiser Foundation Hospitals, Oakland, CA
Primary Contact: Corwin N. Harper, Senior Vice President and Area Manager
COO: Karen Grisnak, R.N., Chief Operating Officer and Assistant Administrator Quality Services
CFO: Joseph D'Angina, Area Finance Officer
CMO: Steven Stricker, M.D., Physician in Chief
CIO: Gale Austin–Moore, Director Area Technology
CHR: Sherri Stegge, Director Human Resources
Web address: www.kaiserpermanente.org
Control: Other not–for–profit (including NFP Corporation) **Service:** General Medical and Surgical

Staffed Beds: 248

⊠ **ST. HELENA HOSPITAL CENTER FOR BEHAVIORAL HEALTH (054074)**, 525 Oregon Street, Zip 94590–3201; tel. 707/648–2200 **A**1 10 **F**29 30 42 50 64 65 68 98 99 104 105 130 146 **S** Adventist Health, Roseville, CA
Primary Contact: Steven Herber, M.D., President and Chief Executive Officer
CFO: Edward A. McDonald, Chief Financial Officer
Web address: www.sthelenahospitals.org/location/center–for–behavioral–health
Control: Other not–for–profit (including NFP Corporation) **Service:** Psychiatric

Staffed Beds: 61 **Admissions:** 2469 **Census:** 57 **Outpatient Visits:** 14968 **Births:** 0 **Total Expense ($000):** 23687 **Payroll Expense ($000):** 11510 **Personnel:** 119

⊠ **SUTTER SOLANO MEDICAL CENTER (050101)**, 300 Hospital Drive, Zip 94589–2574, Mailing Address: P.O. Box 3189, Zip 94590–0669; tel. 707/554–4444 **A**1 2 10 **F**3 8 11 13 15 18 26 29 30 31 34 35 40 45 49 50 51 55 57 58 59 64 68 70 74 75 76 77 78 79 81 84 85 86 87 100 107 108 110 111 114 118 119 120 121 123 124 130 132 146 **P**3 **S** Sutter Health, Sacramento, CA
Primary Contact: John W. Boyd, PsyD, Chief Executive Officer
CFO: Cynthia van Hoff, Chief Financial Officer
CHR: Jean Willhite, Director Human Resources
Web address: www.suttersolano.org
Control: Other not–for–profit (including NFP Corporation) **Service:** General Medical and Surgical

Staffed Beds: 102 **Admissions:** 3981 **Census:** 47 **Outpatient Visits:** 64211 **Births:** 581 **Total Expense ($000):** 149346 **Payroll Expense ($000):** 47931 **Personnel:** 453

VAN NUYS—Los Angeles County, See Los Angeles

VENTURA—Ventura County

★ ◇ **COMMUNITY MEMORIAL HOSPITAL (050394)**, 147 North Brent Street, Zip 93003–2809; tel. 805/652–5011, (Includes COMMUNITY MEMORIAL HOSPITAL, 147 North Brent Street, Zip 93003–2854; tel. 805/652–5011), (Total facility includes 66 beds in nursing home–type unit) **A**2 3 5 10 13 21 **F**3 8 11 12 13 15 17 18 19 20 22 24 26 28 29 30 31 32 34 35 40 45 46 47 48 49 53 54 57 59 64 65 66 68 70 71 72 74 75 77 78 79 81 82 83 84 85 86 91 93 97 104 107 108 110 111 114 115 118 119 126 127 128 130 131 132 141 144 145 146 147 148 **P**4 5 7 **S** Community Memorial Health System, Ventura, CA
Primary Contact: Gary Wilde, President and Chief Executive Officer
COO: Adam Thunell, Chief Operating Officer and Vice President Operations
CFO: David Glyer, Vice President Finance
CMO: Stanley Frochtzwajg, M.D., Chief Medical Officer
CIO: Ron Sandifer, Chief Information Officer
CHR: Diany Klein, Vice President Human Resources
Web address: www.cmhshealth.org
Control: Other not–for–profit (including NFP Corporation) **Service:** General Medical and Surgical

Staffed Beds: 345 **Admissions:** 12982 **Census:** 199 **Outpatient Visits:** 494613 **Births:** 2978 **Total Expense ($000):** 341959 **Payroll Expense ($000):** 122905 **Personnel:** 1461

⊠ **VENTURA COUNTY MEDICAL CENTER (050159)**, 3291 Loma Vista Road, Zip 93003–3099; tel. 805/652–6000, (Nonreporting) **A**1 3 10
Primary Contact: Kim S. Milstien, Chief Executive Officer
CMO: Bryan Wong, M.D., Medical Director
CIO: Terry Theobald, Chief Information Officer
CHR: Tim Rhyne, Personnel Officer
CNO: Susan Scott, Chief Nurse Executive
Web address: www.vchca.org
Control: County–Government, nonfederal **Service:** General Medical and Surgical

Staffed Beds: 160

☐ **VISTA DEL MAR HOSPITAL (054077)**, 801 Seneca Street, Zip 93001–1411; tel. 805/653–6434, (Nonreporting) **A**1 10 **S** Signature Healthcare Services, Corona, CA
Primary Contact: Mayla Krebsbach, Chief Executive Officer
CFO: Kurt Broten, Chief Financial Officer
CMO: Steve Ruths, M.D., Chief Medical Officer
Web address: www.vistadelmarhospital.com
Control: Corporation, Investor–owned, for–profit **Service:** Psychiatric

Staffed Beds: 87

VICTORVILLE—San Bernardino County

★ ○ **DESERT VALLEY HOSPITAL (050709)**, 16850 Bear Valley Road, Zip 92395–5795; tel. 760/241–8000, (Nonreporting) **A**10 11 **S** Prime Healthcare Services, Ontario, CA
Primary Contact: Fred Hunter, R.N., Chief Executive Officer
COO: Luis Leon, Chief Operating Officer
CFO: Martin Mansukhani, Chief Financial Officer
CIO: Sreekant Gotti, Director Information Systems
CNO: Patrick Reinhard, R.N., Chief Nursing Officer
Web address: www.dvmc.com
Control: Corporation, Investor–owned, for–profit **Service:** General Medical and Surgical

Staffed Beds: 75

☐ **VICTOR VALLEY GLOBAL MEDICAL CENTER (050517)**, 15248 Eleventh Street, Zip 92395–3704; tel. 760/245–8691, (Nonreporting) **A**1 10
Primary Contact: Suzanne Richards, R.N., M.P.H., FACHE, Chief Executive Officer
COO: Doreen Dann, R.N., Chief Operating Officer
CIO: Joe Archer, Chief Information Officer
CHR: Cesar Lugo, Director Human Resources
Web address: www.vvgmc.com
Control: Other not–for–profit (including NFP Corporation) **Service:** General Medical and Surgical

Staffed Beds: 115

Many Facility Codes have changed. Please refer to the AHA Guide Code Chart. © 2016 AHA Guide

VISALIA—Tulare County

☒ △ **KAWEAH DELTA MEDICAL CENTER (050057)**, 400 West Mineral King Boulevard, Zip 93291–6263; tel. 559/624–2000, (Includes SOUTH CAMPUS, 1633 South Court Street, Zip 93277; tel. 559/624–6090) **A**1 5 7 10 **F**3 13 15 17 18 20 22 24 26 28 29 30 31 34 35 40 41 43 45 49 50 51 53 54 56 57 59 60 62 63 64 65 68 70 73 74 75 76 77 78 79 81 82 84 85 86 87 89 90 93 97 98 99 100 101 102 103 104 107 108 110 111 114 116 117 118 119 123 124 126 127 128 129 130 131 132 134 135 144 146 147 148 **P**3 5 7
Primary Contact: Lindsay K. Mann, Chief Executive Officer
COO: Thomas J. Rayner, Senior Vice President and Chief Operating Officer
CFO: Gary Herbst, Senior Vice President and Chief Financial Officer
CMO: Edward Hirsch, M.D., Vice President Chief Medical and Quality Officer
CIO: Doug Leeper, Chief Information Officer
CHR: Dianne E. Cox, Vice President of Human Resources
CNO: Regina Sawyer, Vice President Chief Nursing Officer
Web address: www.kaweahdelta.org
Control: Hospital district or authority, Government, nonfederal **Service:** General Medical and Surgical

Staffed Beds: 437 **Admissions:** 23752 **Census:** 379 **Outpatient Visits:** 652422 **Births:** 4432 **Total Expense ($000):** 492064 **Payroll Expense ($000):** 209617 **Personnel:** 3768

WALNUT CREEK—Contra Costa County

☒ △ **JOHN MUIR MEDICAL CENTER, WALNUT CREEK (050180)**, 1601 Ygnacio Valley Road, Zip 94598–3194; tel. 925/939–3000 **A**1 2 7 10 **F**3 11 13 15 17 18 19 20 22 24 26 28 29 30 31 32 34 35 37 39 40 43 44 45 46 47 48 49 50 54 55 56 57 58 59 61 62 64 65 68 70 72 74 75 76 77 78 79 80 81 82 83 84 85 86 87 88 89 90 91 93 95 96 100 102 108 110 118 119 120 121 123 124 126 130 131 132 141 145 146 147 148 **P**3 5 **S** John Muir Health, Walnut Creek, CA
Primary Contact: Jane Willemsen, President and Chief Administrative Officer
COO: Raymond Nassief, Senior Vice President, Hospital Operations and Support Services
CFO: Christian Pass, Senior Vice President & Chief Financial Officer
CMO: Irving Pike, M.D., Senior Vice President and Chief Medical Officer
CIO: Jon Russell, Senior Vice President & Chief Information Officer
CHR: Lisa Foust, Senior Vice President, Human Resources
CNO: Michelle Anne Lopes, MSN, Senior Vice President, Patient Care Services & Chief Nursing Officer
Web address: www.https://www.johnmuirhealth.com/
Control: Other not–for–profit (including NFP Corporation) **Service:** General Medical and Surgical

Staffed Beds: 405 **Admissions:** 19152 **Census:** 264 **Outpatient Visits:** 317314 **Births:** 2887 **Total Expense ($000):** 746793 **Payroll Expense ($000):** 263968 **Personnel:** 2156

☒ **KAISER PERMANENTE WALNUT CREEK MEDICAL CENTER (050072)**, 1425 South Main Street, Zip 94596–5300; tel. 925/295–4000, (Includes KAISER FOUNDATION HOSPITAL, 200 Muir Road, Martinez, Zip 94553–4696; tel. 510/372–1000), (Nonreporting) **A**1 2 3 5 10 **S** Kaiser Foundation Hospitals, Oakland, CA
Primary Contact: Colleen McKeown, Senior Vice President and Area Manager
CFO: Yakesun Wing, Business Strategy and Finance Leader
CIO: Kevin Wheeler, Information Technology Leader
Web address: www.kaiserpermanente.org
Control: Other not–for–profit (including NFP Corporation) **Service:** General Medical and Surgical

Staffed Beds: 233

WATSONVILLE—Santa Cruz County

☒ **WATSONVILLE COMMUNITY HOSPITAL (050194)**, 75 Nielson Street, Zip 95076–2468; tel. 831/724–4741 **A**1 10 **F**3 11 13 15 18 20 29 34 35 40 45 49 50 51 57 60 64 68 70 72 74 76 77 79 81 87 89 93 97 107 111 115 119 130 144 146 148 **S** Quorum Health, Brentwood, TN
Primary Contact: Audra Earle, FACHE, Chief Executive Officer
CFO: Rachel Jones, Chief Financial Officer
CIO: Sergio Nell, Director Information Systems
CNO: Donna Salvi, Chief Nursing Officer
Web address: www.watsonvillehospital.com
Control: Corporation, Investor–owned, for–profit **Service:** General Medical and Surgical

Staffed Beds: 106 **Admissions:** 4332 **Census:** 44 **Outpatient Visits:** 76743 **Births:** 1157 **Total Expense ($000):** 105970 **Payroll Expense ($000):** 48686

WEAVERVILLE—Trinity County

TRINITY HOSPITAL (051315), 60 Easter Avenue, Zip 96093, Mailing Address: P.O. Box 1229, Zip 96093–1229; tel. 530/623–5541, (Nonreporting) **A**10 18
Primary Contact: Aaron Rogers, Chief Executive Officer
CFO: Kathy Walker, Chief Financial Officer
CMO: Donald Krouse, M.D., Chief of Staff
CIO: Jake Odom, Chief Information Officer
CHR: Heidi Corrigan, Manager Human Resources
CNO: Judy Nordlund, R.N., Chief Nursing Officer
Web address: www.mcmedical.org
Control: Hospital district or authority, Government, nonfederal **Service:** General Medical and Surgical

Staffed Beds: 47

WEST COVINA—Los Angeles County

☐ **WEST COVINA MEDICAL CENTER (050096)**, 725 South Orange Avenue, Zip 91790–2614; tel. 626/338–8481 **A**1 10 **F**29 79 81 104 105 108 128 130 148
Primary Contact: Gerald H. Wallman, Administrator
CFO: Kami Horvat, Chief Financial Officer
CMO: Erich Pollak, M.D., Chief of Staff
CHR: Lourdes Meza, Coordinator Human Resources
CNO: Guadalupe Ojeda, R.N., Chief Nursing Officer
Control: Corporation, Investor–owned, for–profit **Service:** General Medical and Surgical

Staffed Beds: 46 **Admissions:** 490 **Census:** 32 **Outpatient Visits:** 8006 **Births:** 0 **Total Expense ($000):** 14798 **Payroll Expense ($000):** 6455 **Personnel:** 287

WEST HILLS—Los Angeles County, See Los Angeles

WEST LOS ANGELES—Los Angeles County, See Los Angeles

WESTMINSTER—Orange County

☒ **KINDRED HOSPITAL–WESTMINSTER (052035)**, 200 Hospital Circle, Zip 92683–3910; tel. 714/893–4541 **A**1 10 **F**1 3 29 45 46 49 50 60 70 74 75 77 79 84 85 87 90 91 99 100 103 107 130 148 **S** Kindred Healthcare, Louisville, KY
Primary Contact: Scott Rifkin, Chief Executive Officer
CFO: Dale Wagner, Chief Financial Officer
Web address: www.khwestminster.com/
Control: Corporation, Investor–owned, for–profit **Service:** Long–Term Acute Care hospital

Staffed Beds: 99 **Admissions:** 1004 **Census:** 101 **Outpatient Visits:** 0 **Births:** 0

WHITTIER—Los Angeles County

☒ **PIH HEALTH HOSPITAL–WHITTIER (050169)**, 12401 Washington Boulevard, Zip 90602–1099; tel. 562/698–0811, (Total facility includes 35 beds in nursing home–type unit) **A**1 2 3 5 10 **F**3 11 12 13 14 15 18 20 22 24 26 28 29 30 31 34 35 36 37 40 44 45 46 49 50 51 54 55 56 57 58 59 60 61 62 63 64 65 66 68 69 70 72 74 75 76 77 78 79 81 84 85 86 87 89 90 92 93 96 107 108 110 111 114 115 116 117 118 119 120 121 123 124 128 130 131 132 135 143 145 146 147 148 **P**3 5 **S** PIH Health, Whittier, CA
Primary Contact: James R. West, President and Chief Executive Officer
COO: Reanna Thompson, R.N., Chief Operating Officer and Chief Nursing Officer
CFO: Greg Williams, Chief Financial Officer
CMO: Rosalio J. Lopez, M.D., Senior Vice President and Chief Medical Officer
CIO: Jason Fischer, Chief Information Officer
CHR: Sherri Hollingsworth, Chief Human Resources Officer
CNO: Reanna Thompson, R.N., Chief Operating Officer and Chief Nursing Officer
Web address: www.PIHHealth.org
Control: Other not–for–profit (including NFP Corporation) **Service:** General Medical and Surgical

Staffed Beds: 548 **Admissions:** 19491 **Census:** 236 **Outpatient Visits:** 278124 **Births:** 2744 **Total Expense ($000):** 534081 **Payroll Expense ($000):** 179966 **Personnel:** 3058

CA

Hospital, Medicare Provider Number, Address, Telephone, Approval, Facility, and Physician Codes, Health Care System

★ American Hospital Association (AHA) membership
☐ The Joint Commission accreditation
○ Healthcare Facilities Accreditation Program
◇ DNV Healthcare Inc. accreditation
⇧ Center for Improvement in Healthcare Quality Accreditation
△ Commission on Accreditation of Rehabilitation Facilities (CARF) accreditation

☐ **WHITTIER HOSPITAL MEDICAL CENTER (050735)**, 9080 Colima Road, Zip 90605–1600; tel. 562/945–3561, (Total facility includes 22 beds in nursing home–type unit) **A**1 10 **F**13 15 18 29 34 35 36 40 45 54 57 59 70 76 77 81 93 107 108 119 128 130 143 146 147 148 **S** AHMC & Healthcare, Inc., Alhambra, CA
Primary Contact: Richard Castro, Chief Executive Officer
COO: Mary Anne Monje, Chief Financial Officer and Chief Operating Officer
CFO: Mary Anne Monje, Chief Financial Officer and Chief Operating Officer
CIO: Jay Geldhof, Director Information Systems
CHR: Martha Salcedo, Interim Director Human Resources
CNO: Sarkis Vartanian, Chief Nursing Officer
Web address: www.whittierhospital.com
Control: Corporation, Investor–owned, for–profit **Service:** General Medical and Surgical

Staffed Beds: 100 **Admissions:** 9228 **Census:** 100 **Outpatient Visits:** 43892
Births: 3375

WILLITS—Mendocino County

☒ **FRANK R. HOWARD MEMORIAL HOSPITAL (051310)**, One Marcela Drive, Zip 95490–4298; tel. 707/459–6801 **A**1 10 18 **F**11 15 29 30 34 35 40 57 59 68 70 75 79 81 93 97 107 110 111 115 119 127 131 132 133 135 146 147 148 **S** Adventist Health, Roseville, CA
Primary Contact: Rick Bockmann, Chief Executive Officer
CFO: Chris Sauder, Chief Financial Officer
CMO: Kimberly Faucher, M.D., Chief Medical Officer
CIO: Cecilia Winiger, Community Outreach and Communication Manager
CHR: Darcy De Leon, Executive Director, Human Resources
CNO: Karen M. Scott, Vice President Patient Care
Web address: www.howardhospital.com
Control: Church–operated, Nongovernment, not–for profit **Service:** General Medical and Surgical

Staffed Beds: 25 **Admissions:** 1399 **Census:** 15 **Outpatient Visits:** 40315
Births: 0 **Total Expense ($000):** 54030 **Payroll Expense ($000):** 21434
Personnel: 281

WILLOWS—Glenn County

GLENN MEDICAL CENTER (051306), 1133 West Sycamore Street, Zip 95988–2745; tel. 530/934–1800, (Nonreporting) **A**10 18
Primary Contact: Barbara Rydgren, Administrator
CFO: John Lovrich, Chief Financial Officer
CHR: Deborah McMillan, Director Human Resources
Web address: www.glennmed.org
Control: Other not–for–profit (including NFP Corporation) **Service:** General Medical and Surgical

Staffed Beds: 15

WOODLAND—Yolo County

☒ **WOODLAND HEALTHCARE (050127)**, 1325 Cottonwood Street, Zip 95695–5199; tel. 530/662–3961 **A**1 5 10 **F**2 3 8 11 13 18 20 26 28 29 30 31 34 35 40 45 46 47 49 50 51 56 57 58 59 60 61 62 64 68 70 72 74 75 76 78 79 81 82 84 85 86 87 89 98 100 102 107 108 111 115 119 129 130 132 146 147 148 **P**3 **S** Dignity Health, San Francisco, CA
Primary Contact: H. Kevin Vaziri, President
Web address: www.woodlandhealthcare.org
Control: Other not–for–profit (including NFP Corporation) **Service:** General Medical and Surgical

Staffed Beds: 108 **Admissions:** 4329 **Census:** 57 **Outpatient Visits:** 62516
Births: 680 **Total Expense ($000):** 170647 **Payroll Expense ($000):** 59743
Personnel: 651

WOODLAND HILLS—Los Angeles County, See Los Angeles

YREKA—Siskiyou County

☐ **FAIRCHILD MEDICAL CENTER (051316)**, 444 Bruce Street, Zip 96097–3450; tel. 530/842–4121, (Nonreporting) **A**1 10 18
Primary Contact: Jonathon Andrus, Chief Executive Officer
CFO: Kelly Martin, Chief Financial Officer
CMO: David Della Lana, M.D., Chief of Staff
CIO: Joan Munson, Manager Information Systems
CHR: Joann Sarmento, Manager Human Resources
CNO: Kathy Shelvock, R.N., Assistant Administrator Patient Care Services
Web address: www.fairchildmed.org
Control: Other not–for–profit (including NFP Corporation) **Service:** General Medical and Surgical

Staffed Beds: 25

YUBA CITY—Sutter County

FREMONT MEDICAL CENTER See Rideout Memorial Hospital, Marysville

☐ **SUTTER SURGICAL HOSPITAL – NORTH VALLEY (050766)**, 455 Plumas Boulevard, Zip 95991–5074; tel. 530/749–5700 **A**1 10 **F**3 26 29 30 34 37 46 57 64 68 74 79 81 85 86 111 146 **P**3 **S** Sutter Health, Sacramento, CA
Primary Contact: Shawndra Simpson, Interim Chief Executive Officer
CHR: Michelle Guina, Manager Human Resources
CNO: David Cooke, Chief Nursing Officer
Web address: www.sshnv.org
Control: Corporation, Investor–owned, for–profit **Service:** Surgical

Staffed Beds: 14 **Admissions:** 526 **Census:** 4 **Outpatient Visits:** 2211
Births: 0 **Total Expense ($000):** 23184 **Payroll Expense ($000):** 1773
Personnel: 80

YUCCA VALLEY—San Bernardino County

☒ **HI–DESERT MEDICAL CENTER (050279)**, 6530 La Contenta, Suite 100, Zip 92284, Mailing Address: 6601 White Feather Road, Joshua Tree, Zip 92252–6607; tel. 760/366–3711, (Total facility includes 120 beds in nursing home–type unit) **A**1 10 **F**8 13 15 18 29 30 34 35 40 45 50 54 62 63 64 68 70 76 77 79 81 82 87 93 104 107 108 110 111 115 119 128 130 135 146 **S** TENET Healthcare Corporation, Dallas, TX
Primary Contact: Karen Faulis, Chief Executive Officer
CMO: Sumit Mahajan, M.D., Chief Medical Staff
CIO: Robin Schmelling, Chief Information Officer
CHR: Barbara Staresinic, Director Human Resources
Web address: www.hdmc.org
Control: Corporation, Investor–owned, for–profit **Service:** General Medical and Surgical

Staffed Beds: 179 **Admissions:** 3046 **Census:** 124 **Outpatient Visits:** 94660
Births: 477 **Total Expense ($000):** 73529 **Payroll Expense ($000):** 28282
Personnel: 473

Many Facility Codes have changed. Please refer to the AHA Guide Code Chart.

© 2016 AHA Guide

COLORADO

ALAMOSA—Alamosa County

★ **SAN LUIS VALLEY HEALTH (060008)**, 106 Blanca Avenue, Zip 81101–2393; tel. 719/589–2511 **A**10 20 **F**3 7 11 13 15 18 28 29 30 31 33 40 43 45 53 70 74 75 77 78 79 81 85 93 107 108 110 111 114 119 129 130 131 133 134 146 147 148 **P**6 **S** San Luis Valley Health, Alamosa, CO
Primary Contact: Konnie Martin, Chief Executive Officer
COO: Patti Thompson, Chief Operating Officer
CFO: Shane Mortensen, Chief Financial Officer
CMO: Gregory McAuliffe, M.D., Chief Medical Officer
CIO: Chuck Laufle, Director of Information Services
CHR: Mandy Lee Crockett, Director Human Resources
Web address: www.sanluisvalleyhealth.org
Control: Other not–for–profit (including NFP Corporation) **Service:** General Medical and Surgical

Staffed Beds: 44 **Admissions:** 2014 **Census:** 18 **Outpatient Visits:** 108201 **Births:** 504 **Total Expense ($000):** 72942 **Payroll Expense ($000):** 35085 **Personnel:** 581

ASPEN—Pitkin County

✠ **ASPEN VALLEY HOSPITAL DISTRICT (061324)**, 401 Castle Creek Road, Zip 81611–1159; tel. 970/925–1120 **A**1 10 18 **F**3 7 8 10 13 15 18 28 29 31 34 35 40 43 57 59 64 68 70 75 76 77 78 79 81 82 85 86 87 89 93 94 107 108 110 111 115 118 119 131 132 133 135 144 146 148
Primary Contact: Terry Collins, Interim Chief Executive Officer
CFO: Terry Collins, Chief Financial Officer
CMO: J. Christopher Beck, D.O., President Medical Staff
CIO: Ginny Dyche, Director Community Relations
CHR: Alicia Miller, Director Human Resources
CNO: Elaine Gerson, Chief Clinical Officer and General Counsel
Web address: www.avhaspen.org
Control: Hospital district or authority, Government, nonfederal **Service:** General Medical and Surgical

Staffed Beds: 25 **Admissions:** 890 **Census:** 7

AURORA—Adams County

✠ **CHILDREN'S HOSPITAL COLORADO (063301)**, 13123 East 16th Avenue, Zip 80045–7106; tel. 720/777–1234, (Includes CHILDREN'S HOSPITAL OF COLORADO AT MEMORIAL, 1400 East Boulder Street, Colorado Springs, Zip 80909–5533; tel. 719/365–5000) **A**1 3 5 10 **F**3 11 12 13 14 17 19 21 23 25 27 28 29 30 31 32 34 35 36 38 39 40 41 42 43 44 45 46 48 49 50 53 54 55 58 59 60 61 64 65 66 68 71 72 74 75 76 77 78 79 80 81 82 84 85 86 87 88 89 91 92 93 95 96 97 98 99 100 101 102 104 105 106 107 108 111 114 115 116 117 119 126 129 130 131 132 134 136 137 138 139 141 144 146 147 148
Primary Contact: Jena Hausmann, President and Chief Executive Officer
COO: David Biggerstaff, Chief Operating Officer
CFO: Jeff Harrington, Chief Financial Officer
CMO: Joan Bothner, M.D., Chief Medical Officer
CIO: Mary Anne Leach, Vice President and Chief Information Officer
CHR: Nita Mosby Henry, Senior Vice President Human Resources and Chief Inclusion Officer
CNO: Andrea Ferretti, Interim Chief Nursing Officer, Vice President and Associate Chief Nursing Officer Network of Care
Web address: www.thechildrenshospital.org
Control: Other not–for–profit (including NFP Corporation) **Service:** Children's general

Staffed Beds: 486 **Admissions:** 17547 **Census:** 291

✠ **KINDRED HOSPITAL–AURORA (062013)**, 700 Potomac Street 2nd Floor, Zip 80011–6844; tel. 720/857–8333, (Nonreporting) **A**1 10 **S** Kindred Healthcare, Louisville, KY
Primary Contact: Marc Lemon, Marketing Chief Executive Officer
CMO: Eric Yaeger, M.D., Chief Medical Officer
CHR: Becky Small, Chief Human Resources Officer
CNO: Paul Green, Chief Clinical Officer
Web address: www.khaurora.com/
Control: Corporation, Investor–owned, for–profit **Service:** Long–Term Acute Care hospital

Staffed Beds: 37

✠ **MEDICAL CENTER OF AURORA (060100)**, 1501 South Potomac Street, Zip 80012–5411; tel. 303/695–2600, (Includes MEDICAL CENTER OF AURORA, 700 Potomac Street, Zip 80011; tel. 303/360–3030; Daniel Miller, Chief Executive Officer; MEDICAL CENTER OF AURORA NORTH, 700 Potomac Street, Zip 80011–6792; tel. 303/363–7200; SOUTH CAMPUS, 1501 South Potomac, Zip 80012; tel. 303/695–2600) **A**1 2 10 **F**3 6 8 11 13 15 17 18 20 22 24 26 28 29 30 31 34 35 37 38 39 40 41 42 43 45 46 47 48 49 53 54 56 57 58 59 63 64 65 68 70 72 74 75 77 78 79 81 82 84 85 86 87 89 92 93 94 97 98 99 100 101 102 103 104 107 108 110 111 114 115 116 117 118 119 126 129 130 131 132 135 146 147 148 **P**6 8 **S** HCA, Nashville, TN
Primary Contact: Daniel Miller, Chief Executive Officer
COO: Mary Berrigan, Chief Operating Officer
CFO: Bryce DeHaven, Chief Financial Officer
CMO: Dianne McCallister, M.D., Chief Medical Officer
Web address: www.auroramed.com
Control: Corporation, Investor–owned, for–profit **Service:** General Medical and Surgical

Staffed Beds: 303 **Admissions:** 14801 **Census:** 204 **Outpatient Visits:** 139781 **Births:** 1310

✠ **SPALDING REHABILITATION HOSPITAL (063027)**, 900 Potomac Steet, Zip 80011–6716; tel. 303/367–1166, (Nonreporting) **A**1 10 **S** HCA, Nashville, TN
Primary Contact: Mark S. Deno, Chief Executive Officer
COO: Debbie Petersen, R.N., Chief Operating Officer and Chief Nursing Officer
CFO: Joyce Webber, Chief Financial Officer
CHR: Donna Greeley, Director Human Resources
CNO: Debbie Petersen, R.N., Chief Operating Officer and Chief Nursing Officer
Web address: www.spaldingrehab.com
Control: Partnership, Investor–owned, for–profit **Service:** Rehabilitation

Staffed Beds: 40

✠ **UNIVERSITY OF COLORADO HOSPITAL (060024)**, 12401 East 17th Avenue, MSF 417, Zip 80045–2545; tel. 720/848–0000 **A**1 2 3 5 8 10 **F**3 4 5 6 8 9 11 12 13 15 16 17 18 20 22 24 26 28 29 30 31 33 34 35 36 37 38 40 43 44 45 46 47 48 49 50 52 53 54 55 56 57 58 59 60 61 64 65 68 70 71 72 74 75 76 77 78 79 80 81 82 83 84 85 86 87 90 91 92 93 94 96 97 98 100 101 102 103 104 107 108 109 110 111 112 113 114 115 117 118 119 120 121 123 124 126 130 131 132 134 135 136 137 138 139 140 141 142 146 147 148 **S** University of Colorado Health, Fort Collins, CO
Primary Contact: William Cook, President and Chief Executive Officer
COO: Thomas Gronow, Chief Operating Officer
CFO: Barbara Carveth, Chief Financial Officer
CMO: Jean Kutner, M.D., Chief Medical Officer
CIO: Steve Hess, Vice President Information Services and Chief Information Officer
CNO: Carolyn Lucey Sanders, Senior Vice President Patient Services and Chief Nursing Officer
Web address: www.uchealth.org
Control: Hospital district or authority, Government, nonfederal **Service:** General Medical and Surgical

Staffed Beds: 648 **Admissions:** 28765 **Census:** 465 **Outpatient Visits:** 999256 **Births:** 3244 **Total Expense ($000):** 1146403 **Payroll Expense ($000):** 383899 **Personnel:** 5598

BOULDER—Boulder County

✠ △ **BOULDER COMMUNITY HEALTH (060027)**, 4747 Arapahoe Avenue, Zip 80303–1133, Mailing Address: P.O. Box 9019, Zip 80301–9019; tel. 303/415–7000, (Includes BOULDER COMMUNITY FOOTHILLS HOSPITAL, 4747 Arapahoe Avenue, Mailing Address: P.O. Box 9047, Zip 80301–9047; tel. 720/854–7000; Robert Vissers, M.D., President and Chief Executive Officer) **A**1 2 5 8 13 15 18 19 20 21 22 23 24 25 26 27 28 29 30 36 37 40 43 54 59 60 62 64 65 70 72 73 74 75 76 77 78 79 81 82 83 84 87 90 93 97 98 99 101 102 104 105 107 111 112 114 115 116 117 119 126 129 131 132 144 146 148 **P**4 5 6
Primary Contact: Robert Vissers, M.D., Chief Executive Officer
CFO: Bill Munson, Vice President and Chief Financial Officer
CMO: Paul Lewis, M.D., Chief Medical Officer, Vice President
CNO: Jacqueline M. Attlesey–Pries, MS, Chief Nursing Officer, Vice President
Web address: www.bch.org
Control: Other not–for–profit (including NFP Corporation) **Service:** General Medical and Surgical

Staffed Beds: 186 **Admissions:** 8470 **Census:** 100 **Outpatient Visits:** 403861 **Births:** 1055 **Total Expense ($000):** 330250 **Payroll Expense ($000):** 135076 **Personnel:** 1760

Hospital, Medicare Provider Number, Address, Telephone, Approval, Facility, and Physician Codes, Health Care System

★ American Hospital Association (AHA) membership ○ Healthcare Facilities Accreditation Program ⇑ Center for Improvement in Healthcare Quality Accreditation
□ The Joint Commission accreditation ◇ DNV Healthcare Inc. accreditation △ Commission on Accreditation of Rehabilitation Facilities (CARF) accreditation

BRIGHTON—Adams County

⊞ **PLATTE VALLEY MEDICAL CENTER (060004)**, 1600 Prairie Center Parkway, Zip 80601–4006; tel. 303/498–1600 **A**1 5 10 **F**3 7 13 15 18 20 22 26 28 29 30 31 34 35 40 43 45 49 57 68 70 72 74 75 76 77 78 79 81 85 87 90 92 93 107 108 110 111 115 119 130 132 135 146 147 148 **S** SCL Health, Broomfield, CO
Primary Contact: John R. Hicks, President and Chief Executive Officer
COO: Kurt Gensert, R.N., Vice President Operations
CFO: Harold Dupper, Chief Financial Officer
CMO: Kirk Quackenbush, M.D., Chief of Staff
CIO: Darrell Messersmith, Director Information Systems
CHR: Jackie J. Dunkin, Director Human Resources
Web address: www.pvmc.org
Control: Other not–for–profit (including NFP Corporation) **Service:** General Medical and Surgical

Staffed Beds: 70 **Admissions:** 2981 **Census:** 24 **Outpatient Visits:** 72003 **Births:** 963 **Total Expense ($000):** 96111 **Payroll Expense ($000):** 32134 **Personnel:** 535

BRUSH—Morgan County

★ **EAST MORGAN COUNTY HOSPITAL (061303)**, 2400 West Edison Street, Zip 80723–1640; tel. 970/842–6200 **A**10 18 **F**3 13 15 28 29 30 34 35 36 40 43 45 50 53 57 59 61 65 68 74 75 77 79 81 85 86 87 93 96 107 108 110 115 119 127 130 131 133 135 141 146 **S** Banner Health, Phoenix, AZ
Primary Contact: Linda Thorpe, Chief Executive Officer
CFO: Edith Pemberton, Chief Financial Officer
CHR: Cynthia Wentworth, Chief Human Resource Officer
CNO: Linda Lyn Roan, Chief Nursing Officer
Web address: www.emchbrush.com
Control: Other not–for–profit (including NFP Corporation) **Service:** General Medical and Surgical

Staffed Beds: 19 **Admissions:** 465 **Census:** 5 **Outpatient Visits:** 25150 **Births:** 8 **Total Expense ($000):** 24970 **Payroll Expense ($000):** 11866 **Personnel:** 156

BURLINGTON—Kit Carson County

★ **KIT CARSON COUNTY HEALTH SERVICE DISTRICT (061313)**, 286 16th Street, Zip 80807–1697; tel. 719/346–5311 **A**10 18 **F**3 13 15 29 31 34 35 40 43 45 47 48 57 75 76 78 79 81 84 93 107 110 111 127 128 130 133 **P**6
Primary Contact: Shauna Richarson, Interim Chief Operating Officer
CMO: Bong Pham, Chief Medical Officer
CIO: Paul Velasco, IT Manager
CHR: Robin Konecne, Manager Human Resources
CNO: Kandi Kuper, Chief Nursing Officer
Web address: www.kcchsd.org
Control: Hospital district or authority, Government, nonfederal **Service:** General Medical and Surgical

Staffed Beds: 19 **Admissions:** 263 **Census:** 1 **Outpatient Visits:** 14030 **Total Expense ($000):** 15858 **Payroll Expense ($000):** 5922

CANON CITY—Fremont County

⊞ **ST. THOMAS MORE HOSPITAL (060016)**, 1338 Phay Avenue, Zip 81212–2302; tel. 719/285–2000 **A**1 10 20 **F**3 8 11 13 15 29 30 34 35 40 43 51 53 57 59 64 66 69 70 75 77 79 81 82 85 86 87 93 97 107 108 110 111 119 127 129 131 132 133 135 146 147 148 **S** Catholic Health Initiatives, Englewood, CO
Primary Contact: Sheri Trahern, CPA, FACHE, Chief Executive Officer
COO: Dennis Bruens, Vice President Operations
CFO: Gwenyth Howard, Vice President Finance
CMO: Kern Low, M.D., Chief Medical Officer
CIO: Jillian Maes, Director Marketing and Public Relations
CHR: Janet Reedy, Manager Human Resources
CNO: James Woodard, Chief Nursing Officer
Web address: www.stmhospital.org
Control: Church–operated, Nongovernment, not–for profit **Service:** General Medical and Surgical

Staffed Beds: 25 **Admissions:** 1839 **Census:** 17 **Outpatient Visits:** 43162 **Births:** 239 **Total Expense ($000):** 43193 **Payroll Expense ($000):** 17080 **Personnel:** 367

CASTLE ROCK—Douglas County

⊞ **CASTLE ROCK ADVENTIST HOSPITAL (060125)**, 2350 Meadows Boulevard, Zip 80109–8405; tel. 720/455–5000 **A**1 10 **F**3 11 13 15 18 20 22 29 30 32 34 35 37 38 40 43 45 48 49 50 57 59 60 62 64 65 67 68 70 72 74 75 76 77 79 81 85 86 87 89 91 93 102 107 108 110 111 114 115 118 119 129 130 131 135 146 147 148 **P**6 **S** Adventist Health System Sunbelt Health Care Corporation, Altamonte Springs, FL
Primary Contact: Todd Folkenberg, Chief Executive Officer
CFO: Jeremy Pittman, Chief Financial Officer
Web address: www.castlerockhospital.org
Control: Church–operated, Nongovernment, not–for profit **Service:** General Medical and Surgical

Staffed Beds: 50 **Admissions:** 2542 **Census:** 21 **Outpatient Visits:** 28878 **Births:** 629 **Personnel:** 464

CHEYENNE WELLS—Cheyenne County

★ **KEEFE MEMORIAL HOSPITAL (060043)**, 602 North 6th Street West, Zip 80810, Mailing Address: P.O. Box 578, Zip 80810–0578; tel. 719/767–5661 **A**10 20 **F**3 15 29 34 35 36 40 43 45 57 59 64 68 89 93 97 107 108 110 114 119 127 128 133 147 **P**6
Primary Contact: Virginia Hallagin, Chief Executive Officer
CFO: Stella Worley, Director of Finance
CMO: Christine Connolly, M.D., Chief of Staff
CIO: Jeanne Moffat, Manager Information Technology
CHR: Carrie Rico, Chief Human Resource Officer
CNO: Jesse Smith, Director of Nursing
Web address: www.keefememorial.com
Control: County–Government, nonfederal **Service:** General Medical and Surgical

Staffed Beds: 11 **Admissions:** 53 **Census:** 1 **Outpatient Visits:** 3147 **Births:** 0 **Personnel:** 51

COLORADO SPRINGS—El Paso County

☐ **CEDAR SPRINGS HOSPITAL (064009)**, 2135 Southgate Road, Zip 80906–2693; tel. 719/633–4114, (Nonreporting) **A**1 10 **S** Universal Health Services, Inc., King of Prussia, PA
Primary Contact: Christopher Burke, Chief Executive Officer
CFO: Cynthia D. Deboer, Chief Financial Officer
CMO: Larry Shores, M.D., Executive Medical Director
CHR: Jessica McCoy, Director Human Resources
CNO: Jodi Mattson, Director of Nursing
Web address: www.cedarspringsbhs.com
Control: Corporation, Investor–owned, for–profit **Service:** Psychiatric

Staffed Beds: 110

⊞ **HEALTHSOUTH REHABILITATION HOSPITAL OF COLORADO SPRINGS (063030)**, 325 Parkside Drive, Zip 80910–3134; tel. 719/630–8000 **A**1 10 **F**29 93 95 132 148 **S** HEALTHSOUTH Corporation, Birmingham, AL
Primary Contact: Stephen Schaefer, Chief Executive Officer
CFO: Stephanie Davis, Controller
CHR: Diana Crepeau, Director Human Resources
Web address: www.healthsouthcoloradosprings.com
Control: Corporation, Investor–owned, for–profit **Service:** Rehabilitation

Staffed Beds: 60 **Admissions:** 1223 **Census:** 40 **Outpatient Visits:** 6274 **Births:** 0

⊞ **KINDRED HOSPITAL COLORADO SPRINGS (062016)**, 6001 East Woodmen Road, 6th Floor, Zip 80923–2601; tel. 719/571–6000, (Nonreporting) **A**1 10 **S** Kindred Healthcare, Louisville, KY
Primary Contact: Dawn Johantges, Resource Chief Executive Officer
CMO: Dave Call, M.D., Medical Director
CHR: Lisa Gayler, Director Human Resources
CNO: Jodie L. Green, Chief Nursing Officer
Web address: www.kindredcoloradosprings.com/
Control: Corporation, Investor–owned, for–profit **Service:** Long–Term Acute Care hospital

Staffed Beds: 30

⊞ △ **MEMORIAL HOSPITAL (060022)**, 1400 East Boulder Street, Zip 80909–5599; tel. 719/365–9888 **A**1 2 7 10 **F**3 8 11 13 15 17 18 19 20 21 22 23 24 26 27 28 29 30 31 34 35 36 40 41 43 44 45 46 48 49 54 55 57 58 59 64 68 70 72 74 76 77 78 79 81 82 84 85 86 87 88 89 90 92 93 96 97 107 108 109 110 111 114 115 116 117 118 119 120 121 123 124 126 129 130 132 135 141 144 146 148 **P**6 8 **S** University of Colorado Health, Fort Collins, CO
Primary Contact: George E. Hayes, FACHE, President and Chief Executive Officer
COO: Cherie Gorby, Chief Operations Officer
CFO: Dan Rieber, Chief Financial Officer
CMO: Jose Melendez, M.D., Chief Medical Officer
CHR: Jeffrey Johnson, Vice President
CNO: Kay J. Miller, MSN, Chief Nursing Officer
Web address: www.uchealth.org/southerncolorado
Control: Other not–for–profit (including NFP Corporation) **Service:** General Medical and Surgical

Staffed Beds: 548 **Admissions:** 21465 **Census:** 225 **Outpatient Visits:** 593739 **Births:** 4446 **Total Expense ($000):** 555784 **Payroll Expense ($000):** 232039 **Personnel:** 2420

☐ **PEAK VIEW BEHAVIORAL HEALTH (064026)**, 7353 Sisters Grove, Zip 80923–2615; tel. 719/444–8484 **A**1 10 13 **F**34 54 56 64 98 99 100 103 104 105 **S** Strategic Behavioral Health, LLC, Memphis, TN
Primary Contact: Lana Currance, R.N., MSN, Chief Executive Officer
Web address: www.strategicbh.com/peakview.html
Control: Corporation, Investor–owned, for–profit **Service:** Psychiatric

Staffed Beds: 92 **Admissions:** 3395 **Census:** 76 **Outpatient Visits:** 0 **Births:** 0 **Total Expense ($000):** 15118 **Payroll Expense ($000):** 8854 **Personnel:** 266

Many Facility Codes have changed. Please refer to the AHA Guide Code Chart. © 2016 AHA Guide

CO

CO

✠ △ **PENROSE–ST. FRANCIS HEALTH SERVICES (060031)**, 2222 North Nevada Avenue, Zip 80907–6799; tel. 719/776–5000, (Includes PENROSE HOSPITAL, 2222 North Nevada Avenue, Zip 80907; tel. 719/776–5000; Margaret D. Sabin, Chief Executive Officer; ST. FRANCIS MEDICAL CENTER, 6001 East Woodmen Road, Zip 80923–2601; tel. 719/776–5000; Margaret D. Sabin, Chief Executive Officer) **A**1 2 7 10 19 **F**3 5 11 12 13 14 15 17 18 20 22 24 26 28 29 30 31 34 35 36 37 38 39 40 41 42 43 44 45 46 47 48 49 50 52 53 54 55 56 57 58 59 61 62 64 65 68 70 71 72 74 75 76 77 78 81 82 84 85 86 87 89 90 91 93 96 97 99 100 101 102 103 107 108 110 114 115 118 119 120 121 123 124 126 127 129 130 131 132 135 144 146 147 148 **P**5 **S** Catholic Health Initiatives, Englewood, CO
Primary Contact: Margaret D. Sabin, President and Chief Executive Officer
COO: Lonnie Cramer, Chief Operating Officer
CFO: Danny Reeves, Chief Financial Officer
CMO: David Dull, M.D., Chief Medical Officer
CHR: James Humphrey, Vice President Talent Resources and Human Resources for South Side Operating Group
CNO: Cynthia Latney, Chief Nursing Officer
Web address: www.penrosestfrancis.org
Control: Church–operated, Nongovernment, not–for profit **Service:** General Medical and Surgical

Staffed Beds: 405 **Admissions:** 23009 **Census:** 261 **Outpatient Visits:** 191277 **Births:** 3130 **Total Expense ($000):** 460825 **Payroll Expense ($000):** 145522

CORTEZ—Montezuma County

★ ◇ **SOUTHWEST MEMORIAL HOSPITAL (061327)**, 1311 North Mildred Road, Zip 81321–2299; tel. 970/565–6666, (Nonreporting) **A**10 18 21
Primary Contact: W. Kent Rogers, Chief Executive Officer
CFO: Angela Kobel
CIO: Angela Kobel, Chief Information Officer
CHR: Travis Parker
CNO: Karen Pasquin
Web address: www.swhealth.org
Control: Other not–for–profit (including NFP Corporation) **Service:** General Medical and Surgical

Staffed Beds: 25

CRAIG—Moffat County

✠ ◇ **THE MEMORIAL HOSPITAL AT CRAIG (061314)**, 750 Hospital Loop, Zip 81625–8750; tel. 970/824–9411 **A**1 10 18 21 **F**3 7 11 13 15 18 29 31 32 34 35 40 43 45 49 50 51 57 59 68 70 75 76 77 78 79 81 85 86 87 91 93 97 102 107 108 110 111 112 114 119 129 130 131 132 133 135 146 147 148 **S** QHR, Brentwood, TN
Primary Contact: Andrew Daniels, Chief Executive Officer
CFO: Denise Arola, Chief Financial Officer
CMO: Scott Ellis, D.O., Chief Medical Officer
CIO: Bryan Curtis, Chief Information Officer
CNO: Annette Saylor, R.N., Chief Nursing Officer
Web address: www.thememorialhospital.com
Control: County–Government, nonfederal **Service:** General Medical and Surgical

Staffed Beds: 25 **Admissions:** 1022 **Census:** 8

DEL NORTE—Rio Grande County

★ **RIO GRANDE HOSPITAL (061301)**, 310 County Road 14, Zip 81132–8719; tel. 719/657–2510 **A**10 18 **F**34 40 43 57 65 81 93 107 111 115 119 127 129 133 **P**6
Primary Contact: Arlene Harms, Chief Executive Officer
CFO: Greg Porter, Chief Financial Officer
CMO: Heidi E. Helgeson, M.D., Chief Medical Officer
CIO: Denise Fietek, Information Technology
CHR: Paula Warner–Pacheco, Chief Human Resources
CNO: Candice Allen, Director of Nursing
Web address: www.rio–grande–hospital.org/
Control: Other not–for–profit (including NFP Corporation) **Service:** General Medical and Surgical

Staffed Beds: 17 **Admissions:** 481 **Census:** 6 **Outpatient Visits:** 44290 **Births:** 0 **Total Expense ($000):** 14401 **Payroll Expense ($000):** 7002 **Personnel:** 115

DELTA—Delta County

★ ◇ **DELTA COUNTY MEMORIAL HOSPITAL (060071)**, 1501 East 3rd Street, Zip 81416–2815, Mailing Address: P.O. Box 10100, Zip 81416–0008; tel. 970/874–7681 **A**10 21 **F**3 8 9 13 15 28 29 30 31 34 40 43 45 50 57 59 62 70 75 76 77 78 79 81 85 87 90 93 107 108 110 111 115 119 129 135 141 144 146 147 148 **P**5 8
Primary Contact: Jason Cleckler, Chief Executive Officer
CFO: Bev Carlson, Chief Financial Officer
CMO: John P. Knutson, M.D., Chief Medical Staff
CIO: Mitch Van Scoyk, Manager Information Systems
CHR: Larry Vincent, Director Human Resources
Web address: www.deltahospital.org
Control: Hospital district or authority, Government, nonfederal **Service:** General Medical and Surgical

Staffed Beds: 49 **Admissions:** 1766 **Census:** 14 **Outpatient Visits:** 89221 **Births:** 247 **Total Expense ($000):** 69353 **Payroll Expense ($000):** 27457 **Personnel:** 495

DENVER—Denver, Adams and Arapaho Coun Counties

✠ **COLORADO ACUTE LONG TERM HOSPITAL (062012)**, 1690 North Meade Street, Zip 80204–1552; tel. 303/264–6900, (Nonreporting) **A**1 10 **S** LifeCare Management Services, Plano, TX
Primary Contact: Craig Bailey, MS, Administrator
Web address: www.lifecare–hospitals.com/hospital/colorado
Control: Corporation, Investor–owned, for–profit **Service:** Long–Term Acute Care hospital

Staffed Beds: 63

☐ **COLORADO MENTAL HEALTH INSTITUTE AT FORT LOGAN (064003)**, 3520 West Oxford Avenue, Zip 80236–3197; tel. 303/866–7066, (Nonreporting) **A**1 3 5 10
Primary Contact: Nancy Kehiayan, Acting Director
CFO: Sabina Genesio, Finance Officer for Institutes
CMO: Bruce Leonard, M.D., Medical Director and Chief of Psychiatry
CNO: Nancy Kehiayan, Director of Nursing
Web address: www.cdhs.state.co.us/cmhifl
Control: State–Government, nonfederal **Service:** Psychiatric

Staffed Beds: 297

✠ **DENVER HEALTH (060011)**, 777 Bannock Street, Zip 80204–4507; tel. 303/436–6000 **A**1 3 5 8 10 **F**3 5 7 8 11 12 13 15 18 19 20 22 26 28 29 30 31 32 34 35 37 38 39 40 41 42 43 44 45 46 49 50 52 53 54 55 56 57 58 59 60 61 64 65 66 68 70 71 72 74 75 76 77 78 79 80 81 82 84 85 86 87 88 89 90 92 93 94 96 97 98 99 100 102 103 104 107 108 110 111 114 115 118 119 127 129 130 131 132 134 135 143 144 146 147 148 **P**6
Primary Contact: William Burman, M.D., Chief Executive Officer
COO: Tim Harlin, M.D., Chief Operations Officer
CFO: Peg Burnette, Chief Financial Officer
CMO: Connie Price, M.D., Chief Medical Officer
CIO: Jeff Pelot, Interim Chief Information Officer
CHR: Tim Hansen, Interim Chief Human Resource Officer
CNO: Kathy Boyle, R.N., Chief Nursing Officer
Web address: www.denverhealth.org
Control: Hospital district or authority, Government, nonfederal **Service:** General Medical and Surgical

Staffed Beds: 417 **Admissions:** 22080 **Census:** 304 **Outpatient Visits:** 971002 **Births:** 3442 **Total Expense ($000):** 936807 **Payroll Expense ($000):** 421675 **Personnel:** 5954

✠ **KINDRED HOSPITAL–DENVER (062009)**, 1920 High Street, Zip 80218–1213; tel. 303/320–5871, (Nonreporting) **A**1 10 **S** Kindred Healthcare, Louisville, KY
CFO: Tim Stecker, Chief Financial Officer
CMO: Eric Yaeger, M.D., Medical Director
Web address: www.kh–denver.com
Control: Corporation, Investor–owned, for–profit **Service:** Long–Term Acute Care hospital

Staffed Beds: 68

CO

✠ **NATIONAL JEWISH HEALTH (060107)**, (Respiratory Aller/Immun Card GI ID), 1400 Jackson Street, Zip 80206–2762; tel. 303/388–4461 **A**1 3 5 10 **F**1 3 9 11 12 18 20 28 29 30 31 32 34 35 36 44 45 46 47 48 50 53 54 55 57 58 59 61 62 64 65 66 68 70 74 75 77 78 84 86 87 89 90 93 96 97 98 99 100 101 104 107 108 111 114 115 116 117 118 119 127 129 130 132 134 135 143 145 146 147 **P**6
Primary Contact: Michael Salem, M.D., President and Chief Executive Officer
COO: Ron Berge, Executive Vice President and Chief Operating Officer
CFO: Christine Forkner, Executive Vice President and Chief Financial Officer
CMO: Gary Cott, M.D., Executive Vice President Medical and Clinical Services
CIO: Lots Pook, Chief Information Officer
CHR: Sarah Taylor, Chief Human Resources
CNO: Jeff Downing, R.N., Chief Nursing Officer
Web address: www.njhealth.org
Control: Other not–for–profit (including NFP Corporation) **Service:** Other specialty

> **Staffed Beds:** 76 **Admissions:** 61 **Census:** 1 **Outpatient Visits:** 98595 **Births:** 0 **Total Expense ($000):** 232949 **Payroll Expense ($000):** 113579 **Personnel:** 1504

✠ **PORTER ADVENTIST HOSPITAL (060064)**, 2525 South Downing Street, Zip 80210–5876; tel. 303/778–1955 **A**1 2 10 **F**3 4 5 6 8 11 15 17 18 20 22 24 26 28 29 30 31 34 35 36 37 38 39 40 43 44 45 46 47 48 49 50 53 54 55 56 57 58 59 60 63 64 65 68 70 74 75 77 78 79 81 82 83 84 85 86 87 90 91 92 93 94 96 97 98 100 101 102 103 104 105 106 107 108 109 110 111 112 114 115 116 117 118 119 120 121 122 123 124 125 126 129 130 131 132 135 138 139 141 142 146 147 148 **P**6 **S** Adventist Health System Sunbelt Health Care Corporation, Altamonte Springs, FL
Primary Contact: Morre Dean, Chief Executive Officer
COO: David Dookeeram, Chief Operating Officer
CFO: Andrew Gaasch, Chief Financial Officer
CHR: Oz Muller, Director Human Resources
CNO: Sharon H. Pappas, Ph.D., Chief Nursing Officer
Web address: www.porterhospital.org/poh/home/
Control: Church–operated, Nongovernment, not–for profit **Service:** General Medical and Surgical

> **Staffed Beds:** 250 **Admissions:** 9967 **Census:** 141 **Outpatient Visits:** 69247 **Births:** 0 **Total Expense ($000):** 262145 **Payroll Expense ($000):** 88107 **Personnel:** 1632

✠ **PRESBYTERIAN–ST. LUKE'S MEDICAL CENTER (060014)**, 1719 East 19th Avenue, Zip 80218–1281; tel. 303/839–6000, (Includes ROCKY MOUNTAIN HOSPITAL FOR CHILDREN, 1719 East 19th Avenue, Zip 80218–1235; tel. 720/754–1000; Maureen Tarrant, President and Chief Executive Officer) **A**1 2 3 5 10 **F**3 8 11 12 13 14 15 18 19 20 21 22 23 24 25 26 27 28 29 30 31 34 35 36 37 40 41 43 44 45 46 47 48 49 50 53 54 55 56 58 59 60 61 64 65 66 68 70 72 73 74 75 76 78 79 80 81 82 84 85 86 87 88 89 91 92 93 94 95 96 97 102 107 108 110 111 115 116 117 118 119 120 121 123 126 129 130 131 132 134 136 138 139 146 147 148 **P**2 4 6 **S** HCA, Nashville, TN
Primary Contact: Maureen Tarrant, Chief Executive Officer
CFO: Shari Collier, Chief Financial Officer
CMO: Steve Quach, M.D., Chief Medical Officer
CIO: Jason Brakenhoff, Director Information Services
CHR: Keri Moore, Vice President Human Resources and Support Services
Web address: www.pslmc.com
Control: Corporation, Investor–owned, for–profit **Service:** General Medical and Surgical

> **Staffed Beds:** 395 **Admissions:** 10675 **Census:** 212 **Outpatient Visits:** 68038 **Births:** 1525 **Personnel:** 1386

✠ **ROSE MEDICAL CENTER (060032)**, 4567 East Ninth Avenue, Zip 80220–3941; tel. 303/320–2121 **A**1 2 3 5 10 **F**3 8 9 11 12 13 15 18 20 22 24 26 28 29 30 31 34 35 40 43 44 45 46 49 50 52 53 54 55 58 59 60 61 64 68 70 72 74 75 76 77 78 79 81 82 84 85 86 87 91 92 93 94 97 100 101 102 107 108 110 111 112 114 115 116 117 118 119 120 121 122 123 126 129 130 131 132 135 146 147 148 **P**6 8 **S** HCA, Nashville, TN
Primary Contact: Kenneth H. Feiler, Chief Executive Officer
COO: Ryan Tobin, Chief Operating Officer
CFO: Jac Connelly, Chief Financial Officer
CMO: Andrew Ziller, M.D., Chief Medical Officer
CIO: Dave Trevathan, Director Information Systems
CHR: Clarence McDavid, Vice President Human Resources
CNO: Lynne Wagner, R.N., Chief Nursing Officer
Web address: www.rosebabies.com
Control: Corporation, Investor–owned, for–profit **Service:** General Medical and Surgical

> **Staffed Beds:** 262 **Admissions:** 11715 **Census:** 118 **Outpatient Visits:** 57294 **Births:** 3530

✠ **SAINT JOSEPH HOSPITAL (060028)**, 1375 East 19th Avenue, Zip 80218–1126; tel. 303/837–7111 **A**1 2 3 5 10 **F**3 8 11 12 13 15 18 20 22 24 26 28 29 30 31 34 35 37 40 43 45 46 49 50 55 58 60 63 64 66 68 70 71 72 74 75 76 77 78 79 81 82 84 85 87 93 107 108 110 111 115 116 117 119 120 121 123 124 126 130 145 146 **P**6 7 **S** SCL Health, Broomfield, CO
Primary Contact: Jameson Smith, Chief Executive Officer
COO: Barbara A. Jahn, Chief Operating Officer
CFO: Buzz Binder, Vice President Finance
CMO: Shawn Dufford, M.D., Vice President Medical Affairs and Chief Medical Officer
CHR: William R. Gould, Vice President Human Resources
CNO: Mary Shepler, R.N., Vice President and Chief Nursing Officer
Web address: www.saintjosephdenver.org/
Control: Other not–for–profit (including NFP Corporation) **Service:** General Medical and Surgical

> **Staffed Beds:** 400 **Admissions:** 18600 **Census:** 239 **Outpatient Visits:** 143795 **Births:** 4450 **Total Expense ($000):** 481942 **Payroll Expense ($000):** 150356 **Personnel:** 1953

★ **KINDRED HOSPITAL–DENVER SOUTH (062015)**, 2525 South Downing Street, 3 South, Zip 80210–5817; tel. 303/715–3737, (Nonreporting) **S** Select Medical Corporation, Mechanicsburg, PA
Primary Contact: George Welton, Chief Executive Officer
Control: Corporation, Investor–owned, for–profit **Service:** Long–Term Acute Care hospital

> **Staffed Beds:** 28

✠ **VETERANS AFFAIRS EASTERN COLORADO HEALTH CARE SYSTEM**, 1055 Clermont Street, Zip 80220–3877; tel. 303/399–8020, (Nonreporting) **A**1 3 5 **S** Department of Veterans Affairs, Washington, DC
Primary Contact: Sallie Houser–Hanfelder, FACHE, Director
CFO: Eliott R. Vanderstek, Chief Fiscal Service
CMO: Ellen Mangione, M.D., Chief of Staff
CIO: Don Huckaby, Chief Information Management Service
CHR: Lorene Connel, Chief Human Resources Management Service
Web address: www.denver.va.gov/
Control: Veterans Affairs, Government, federal **Service:** General Medical and Surgical

> **Staffed Beds:** 271

DURANGO—La Plata County

✠ **ANIMAS SURGICAL HOSPITAL (060117)**, 575 Rivergate Lane, Zip 81301–7487; tel. 970/247–3537, (Nonreporting) **A**10
Primary Contact: Brett Gosney, Chief Executive Officer
Web address: www.animassurgical.com/
Control: Corporation, Investor–owned, for–profit **Service:** Surgical

> **Staffed Beds:** 12

✠ **MERCY REGIONAL MEDICAL CENTER (060013)**, 1010 Three Springs Boulevard, Zip 81301–8296; tel. 970/247–4311 **A**1 2 10 20 **F**11 13 15 17 18 20 22 24 26 27 28 29 30 31 35 36 40 42 43 45 49 50 59 60 61 66 70 72 73 76 78 79 81 84 85 87 89 94 96 97 107 111 115 119 126 127 129 130 131 132 133 135 146 147 148 **P**6 **S** Catholic Health Initiatives, Englewood, CO
Primary Contact: Thomas Gessel, FACHE, President and Chief Executive Officer
COO: William McConnell, Ph.D., Vice President Operations and Strategic Outreach
CFO: Jane Strobel, Vice President and Chief Financial Officer
CMO: William Plauth, M.D., Vice President Operations and Chief Medical Officer
CIO: Neil Stock, Director Technology and Facilities
CHR: Cathy Roberts, Vice President Mission Integration and Human Resources
CNO: Nancy Hoyt, R.N., Vice President Operations/Clinical and Chief Nursing Officer
Web address: www.mercydurango.org
Control: Church–operated, Nongovernment, not–for profit **Service:** General Medical and Surgical

> **Staffed Beds:** 82 **Admissions:** 4281 **Census:** 39 **Outpatient Visits:** 129615 **Births:** 949 **Total Expense ($000):** 124565 **Payroll Expense ($000):** 40774 **Personnel:** 897

EADS—Kiowa County

★ **WEISBROD MEMORIAL COUNTY HOSPITAL (061300)**, 1208 Luther Street, Zip 81036, Mailing Address: P.O. Box 817, Zip 81036–0817; tel. 719/438–5401 **A**10 18 **F**2 7 29 30 34 40 57 59 64 75 82 87 93 96 97 127 133 135 143 148
Primary Contact: Tristen Sheridan, Chief Executive Officer and Administrator
CFO: Shannon Dixon, Manager Business Office
CMO: Jeff Waggoner, M.D., Chief of Staff
CHR: Shannon Dixon, Manager Business Office
CNO: Wendy McDowell, R.N., Director of Nursing
Web address: www.kchd.org
Control: Hospital district or authority, Government, nonfederal **Service:** General Medical and Surgical

> **Staffed Beds:** 25 **Admissions:** 91 **Census:** 1

ENGLEWOOD—Arapahoe County

⊠ **CRAIG HOSPITAL (062011)**, 3425 South Clarkson Street, Zip 80113–2899; tel. 303/789–8000 **A**1 3 5 10 **F**29 30 34 35 36 44 50 53 58 64 68 74 75 77 81 86 87 90 91 93 95 96 97 100 104 130 132 146 148
Primary Contact: Michael L. Fordyce, President and Chief Executive Officer
CFO: Julie Keegan, Vice President Finance
CMO: Thomas E. Balazy, M.D., Medical Director
CIO: Chris Watkins, Director of Information Technology
CHR: Stacy L. Abel, Director Human Resources
CNO: Diane Reinhard, R.N., Vice President of Patient Care Services
Web address: www.craighospital.org
Control: Other not–for–profit (including NFP Corporation) **Service:** Rehabilitation

Staffed Beds: 93 **Admissions:** 517 **Census:** 76 **Outpatient Visits:** 12974 **Births:** 0 **Total Expense ($000):** 84235 **Payroll Expense ($000):** 39913 **Personnel:** 587

⊠ **SWEDISH MEDICAL CENTER (060034)**, 501 East Hampden Avenue, Zip 80113–2702; tel. 303/788–5000 **A**1 2 3 10 13 **F**3 7 8 11 12 13 15 16 18 20 22 24 26 29 30 31 34 35 38 39 40 42 43 44 45 47 48 49 50 53 55 58 59 60 64 68 70 72 74 75 76 78 79 81 82 84 85 86 87 88 89 90 92 93 96 97 102 107 108 109 110 111 114 115 116 117 118 119 120 121 122 123 124 126 129 130 131 132 135 145 146 147 148 **P**6 8 **S** HCA, Nashville, TN
Primary Contact: Richard A. Hammett, Chief Executive Officer
CFO: Kathy Ashenfelter, Chief Financial Officer
CMO: Paul Hancock, M.D., Chief Medical Officer
CIO: Jeff Schnoor, Director Information Systems
CHR: Lisa Morris, Vice President Human Resources
CNO: Shari Chavez, Chief Nursing Officer
Web address: www.swedishhospital.com
Control: Partnership, Investor–owned, for–profit **Service:** General Medical and Surgical

Staffed Beds: 361 **Admissions:** 19783 **Census:** 264 **Outpatient Visits:** 136418 **Births:** 2019 **Personnel:** 1503

ESTES PARK—Larimer County

★ **ESTES PARK MEDICAL CENTER (061312)**, 555 Prospect Avenue, Zip 80517–6312, Mailing Address: P.O. Box 2740, Zip 80517–2740; tel. 970/586–2317, (Total facility includes 60 beds in nursing home–type unit) **A**10 18 **F**7 8 13 15 29 30 31 32 34 35 40 56 57 59 62 63 64 65 68 75 76 77 78 79 81 85 91 93 107 110 111 114 119 125 128 129 130 131 132 133 142 146 148
Primary Contact: Mark Gregson, Interim Chief Executive Officer
CFO: Mark Spafford, Interim Chief Financial Officer
CMO: Paul Fonken, M.D., Chief of Staff
CIO: Gary Hall, Vice President of Information Technology
CHR: Charles Frye, Director Human Resources
CNO: Cynthia Standlee, R.N., Chief Nursing Officer
Web address: www.epmedcenter.com
Control: Hospital district or authority, Government, nonfederal **Service:** General Medical and Surgical

Staffed Beds: 85 **Admissions:** 492 **Census:** 40 **Outpatient Visits:** 41812 **Births:** 92 **Total Expense ($000):** 40269 **Payroll Expense ($000):** 18587 **Personnel:** 263

FORT CARSON—El Paso County

⊠ **EVANS U. S. ARMY COMMUNITY HOSPITAL**, 1650 Cochrane Circle, Building 7500, Zip 80913–4613; tel. 719/526–7200, (Nonreporting) **A**1 3 **S** Department of the Army, Office of the Surgeon General, Falls Church, VA
Primary Contact: Patrick H. Garman, Commander
CFO: Major Bradley Robinson, Chief Financial Officer
CHR: Lieutenant Colonel Lory Gurr, Chief Human Resources Division
Web address: www.evans.amedd.army.mil
Control: Army, Government, federal **Service:** General Medical and Surgical

Staffed Beds: 57

FORT COLLINS—Larimer County

★ **BANNER FORT COLLINS MEDICAL CENTER**, 4700 Lady Moon Drive, Zip 80528–4426; tel. 970/229–4000, (Data for 270 days) **F**3 13 18 29 30 34 35 36 38 40 44 45 48 50 57 59 60 68 70 74 76 77 79 81 84 85 86 87 93 102 107 108 111 114 115 119 130 135 146 **S** Banner Health, Phoenix, AZ
Primary Contact: Margo Karsten, PhD, Interim Chief Executive Officer
COO: Marilyn Fain, R.N., Chief Operating Officer
CFO: Lori Sehrt, Associate Chief Financial Officer Northern Colorado
CMO: Bert Honea, M.D., Associate Chief Medical Officer Northern Colorado
CHR: Kelly Hurt, Chief Human Resources Officer Northern Colorado and Western Region
CNO: Roberta Bean, R.N., Associate Chief Nursing Officer
Web address: www.bannerhealth.com/Locations/Colorado/Banner+Fort+Collins+Medical+Center
Control: Other not–for–profit (including NFP Corporation) **Service:** General Medical and Surgical

Staffed Beds: 22 **Admissions:** 447 **Census:** 4 **Outpatient Visits:** 8501 **Births:** 104 **Total Expense ($000):** 34420 **Payroll Expense ($000):** 10313 **Personnel:** 160

⊠ **POUDRE VALLEY HOSPITAL (060010)**, 1024 South Lemay Avenue, Zip 80524–3998, Mailing Address: 2315 East Harmony Road, Zip 80528; tel. 970/495–7141, (Includes MOUNTAIN CREST HOSPITAL, 4601 Corbett Drive, Zip 80525; tel. 970/270–4800) **A**1 2 3 5 10 19 **F**3 5 7 11 12 13 14 15 18 20 22 28 29 30 31 32 34 35 38 39 40 42 43 44 45 46 47 48 49 50 53 54 55 57 58 59 60 61 64 65 66 68 69 70 72 73 74 75 76 77 78 79 80 81 82 83 84 85 86 87 89 92 93 98 99 100 101 102 103 104 105 106 107 108 110 111 114 115 118 119 120 121 123 124 126 129 130 131 132 134 135 143 146 147 148 **S** University of Colorado Health, Fort Collins, CO
Primary Contact: Kevin L. Unger, FACHE, Ph.D., President and Chief Executive Officer
COO: Marilyn Schock, Chief Operating Officer
CFO: Stephanie Doughty, Chief Financial Officer
CMO: William Neff, M.D., Chief Medical Officer
CIO: Fernando Pedroza, Vice President Information Technology
CNO: Donna D. Poduska, MS, Chief Nursing Officer
Web address: www.uchealth.org
Control: Other not–for–profit (including NFP Corporation) **Service:** General Medical and Surgical

Staffed Beds: 253 **Admissions:** 15348 **Census:** 152 **Outpatient Visits:** 289929 **Births:** 2317 **Total Expense ($000):** 381022 **Payroll Expense ($000):** 142299 **Personnel:** 1685

FORT MORGAN—Morgan County

⊠ **COLORADO PLAINS MEDICAL CENTER (060044)**, 1000 Lincoln Street, Zip 80701–3298; tel. 970/867–3391 **A**1 10 20 **F**3 11 13 15 28 29 31 34 35 40 43 44 45 46 47 48 50 51 53 56 57 59 62 64 65 70 75 76 77 79 80 81 86 87 89 93 94 97 98 100 101 103 104 105 107 108 110 111 114 119 129 130 131 133 146 147 148 **P**6 **S** LifePoint Health, Brentwood, TN
Primary Contact: Gene L. O'Hara, Interim Chief Executive Officer
CFO: Christina Patton, Chief Financial Officer
CHR: Janet Brinkman, Director Human Resources
CNO: Sonya Bass, MS, Chief Nursing Officer
Web address: www.coloradoplainsmedicalcenter.com
Control: Corporation, Investor–owned, for–profit **Service:** General Medical and Surgical

Staffed Beds: 50 **Admissions:** 1553 **Census:** 20 **Outpatient Visits:** 35324 **Births:** 410 **Total Expense ($000):** 33011 **Payroll Expense ($000):** 13500 **Personnel:** 225

FRISCO—Summit County

⊠ **ST. ANTHONY SUMMIT MEDICAL CENTER (060118)**, 340 Peak One Drive, Zip 80443, Mailing Address: P.O. Box 738, Zip 80443–0738; tel. 970/668–3300 **A**1 10 **F**3 34 40 42 43 45 57 59 68 70 75 76 77 79 81 82 84 85 97 107 110 111 119 129 130 132 144 146 147 **S** Catholic Health Initiatives, Englewood, CO
Primary Contact: Paul J. Chodkowski, Chief Executive Officer
CFO: David Thompson, Chief Financial Officer
CHR: Dana Laverdiere, Director Human Resources
Web address: www.summitmedicalcenter.org
Control: Church–operated, Nongovernment, not–for profit **Service:** General Medical and Surgical

Staffed Beds: 34 **Admissions:** 1251 **Census:** 9 **Outpatient Visits:** 20537 **Births:** 358 **Total Expense ($000):** 43158 **Payroll Expense ($000):** 15385 **Personnel:** 243

CO

CO

FRUITA—Mesa County

★ **COLORADO CANYONS HOSPITAL AND MEDICAL CENTER (061302)**, 300 West Ottley Avenue, Zip 81521–2118, Mailing Address: P.O. Box 130, Zip 81521–0130; tel. 970/858–9871, (Total facility includes 70 beds in nursing home–type unit) **A**10 18 **F**3 6 9 10 15 29 34 35 36 39 40 41 43 45 49 50 56 59 64 65 68 74 75 79 81 82 85 86 87 90 91 93 107 110 111 115 119 124 128 130 132 133 135 143 146 147 148 **P**6
Primary Contact: Mark J. Francis, President, Chief Executive Officer and Hospital Administrator
CFO: Mark J. Francis, President, Chief Executive Officer and Hospital Administrator
CMO: Christopher Wibblesman, M.D., Chief of Staff
CIO: Derrick Diddle, Chief Information Officer
CHR: Kelly Murphy, Director Human Resources
CNO: Lori Henderson, Chief Nursing Officer, Vice President Clinical
Web address: www.fhw.org
Control: Other not–for–profit (including NFP Corporation) **Service:** General Medical and Surgical

Staffed Beds: 86 **Admissions:** 641 **Census:** 75 **Outpatient Visits:** 31775 **Births:** 0 **Total Expense ($000):** 35614 **Payroll Expense ($000):** 13170 **Personnel:** 210

GLENWOOD SPRINGS—Garfield County

✠ **VALLEY VIEW HOSPITAL (060075)**, 1906 Blake Avenue, Zip 81601–4259; tel. 970/945–6535 **A**1 2 10 20 **F**3 4 11 13 14 15 18 20 22 26 28 29 30 31 32 34 35 36 40 43 45 49 50 51 54 57 58 59 68 69 70 73 74 75 76 77 78 79 81 82 85 86 87 92 93 94 97 99 100 104 107 108 110 111 114 115 116 117 118 119 120 121 123 124 126 129 130 131 132 135 145 146 147 148 **P**6
Primary Contact: Gary L. Brewer, Chief Executive Officer
COO: Dewane Pace, Chief Ancillary Operations
CFO: Larry L. Dupper, Chief Financial Officer
CIO: MariJo Rugh, Chief Information Officer
CHR: Daniel Biggs, Director Human Resources
CNO: Sandra Hurley, MS, Chief Nursing Officer
Web address: www.vvh.org
Control: Other not–for–profit (including NFP Corporation) **Service:** General Medical and Surgical

Staffed Beds: 49 **Admissions:** 2935 **Census:** 32 **Outpatient Visits:** 78680 **Births:** 693 **Total Expense ($000):** 193877 **Payroll Expense ($000):** 78347 **Personnel:** 859

GRAND JUNCTION—Mesa County

✠ ○ **COMMUNITY HOSPITAL (060054)**, 2351 G. Road, Zip 81505; tel. 970/242–0920 **A**1 10 11 **F**3 8 12 15 29 30 34 35 40 47 48 49 50 57 59 62 64 70 75 77 79 81 85 86 87 93 97 107 108 110 111 114 115 119 129 130 131 132 144 146 147 148 **S** QHR, Brentwood, TN
Primary Contact: Chris Thomas, FACHE, President and Chief Executive Officer
CMO: Donald Nicolay, M.D., Chief Medical Officer
CIO: Bart Butzine, Director Information Technology
CNO: Kristin Gundt, Chief Nursing Officer
Web address: www.yourcommunityhospital.com
Control: Other not–for–profit (including NFP Corporation) **Service:** General Medical and Surgical

Staffed Beds: 44 **Admissions:** 1849 **Census:** 17

✠ **GRAND JUNCTION VETERANS HEALTH CARE SYSTEM**, 2121 North Avenue, Zip 81501–6428; tel. 970/242–0731, (Nonreporting) **A**1 **S** Department of Veterans Affairs, Washington, DC
Primary Contact: Marc Magill, Medical Center Director
COO: Patricia A. Hitt, Associate Director
CFO: Laquita Gruver, Fiscal Officer
CMO: William R. Berryman, M.D., Chief of Staff
CIO: Craig Frerichs, Chief Information Technology Service
CHR: William Chester, Manager Human Resources
Web address: www.grandjunction.va.gov/
Control: Veterans Affairs, Government, federal **Service:** General Medical and Surgical

Staffed Beds: 23

✠ **ST. MARY'S MEDICAL CENTER (060023)**, 2635 North 7th Street, Zip 81501–8209, Mailing Address: P.O. Box 1628, Zip 81502–1628; tel. 970/298–2273 **A**1 2 3 10 **F**3 7 12 13 14 15 17 18 20 22 24 26 28 29 30 31 34 35 37 40 43 44 45 46 48 49 50 51 53 54 55 57 58 59 60 61 64 65 67 68 69 70 72 74 75 76 77 78 79 81 82 84 85 86 87 89 90 91 92 93 96 97 100 102 107 108 109 110 111 113 114 115 116 117 119 120 121 122 123 124 126 129 130 131 132 135 143 145 146 147 148 **P**6 **S** SCL Health, Broomfield, CO
Primary Contact: Brian Davidson, M.D., Interim President
COO: Reza Kaleel, Executive Vice President and Chief Operating Officer
CFO: Terri Chinn, Vice President Finance
CIO: John Bullard, Director Information Technology
CHR: Judy White House, Vice President Human Resources
CNO: Shelley Peterson, R.N., Vice President Patient Services and Chief Nursing Officer
Web address: www.stmarygj.com
Control: Church–operated, Nongovernment, not–for profit **Service:** General Medical and Surgical

Staffed Beds: 310 **Admissions:** 12731 **Census:** 178 **Outpatient Visits:** 191747 **Births:** 2101 **Total Expense ($000):** 359531 **Payroll Expense ($000):** 109074 **Personnel:** 1767

VETERANS AFFAIRS MEDICAL CENTER See Grand Junction Veterans Health Care System

WEST SPRINGS HOSPITAL (064023), 515 28 3/4 Road, Zip 81501–5016; tel. 970/263–4918 **A**10 **F**38 98 99 100 101 102 104
Primary Contact: Sharon Raggio, President and Chief Executive Officer
COO: Brandi Kroese, Director Operations
CFO: John Rattle, Chief Financial Officer
CMO: Jules Rosen, M.D., Chief Medical Officer
CIO: Shaun Charles, Director Information Technology
CHR: Karen Birmingham, Director Human Resources
CNO: Deborah Sharpe, RN, R.N., Director of Nursing
Web address: www.WestSpringsHospital.org
Control: Public Health Service, Government, federal **Service:** Psychiatric

Staffed Beds: 32 **Admissions:** 1100 **Census:** 24 **Outpatient Visits:** 0 **Births:** 0 **Total Expense ($000):** 8161 **Payroll Expense ($000):** 5043 **Personnel:** 137

GREELEY—Weld County

✠ **NORTH COLORADO MEDICAL CENTER (060001)**, 1801 16th Street, Zip 80631–5154; tel. 970/352–4121 **A**1 2 3 10 **F**3 7 11 13 14 15 17 18 20 22 24 26 28 29 30 31 34 35 36 38 40 42 43 44 46 49 50 51 53 54 55 57 58 59 60 61 64 65 68 70 72 74 75 76 77 78 79 80 81 82 84 85 86 87 89 93 96 100 102 107 108 110 111 114 115 116 117 118 119 120 121 123 126 129 130 131 132 133 135 141 143 146 148 **S** Banner Health, Phoenix, AZ
Primary Contact: Margo Karsten, PhD, Interim Chief Executive Officer
COO: Wendy Sparks, Chief Operating Officer
CFO: Mary McCabe, Chief Financial Officer
CHR: Jeannie Gallagher, Chief Human Resource Officer
CNO: Tiffany Erin Hettinger, Associate Chief Nursing Officer
Web address: www.ncmcgreeley.com
Control: Other not–for–profit (including NFP Corporation) **Service:** General Medical and Surgical

Staffed Beds: 223 **Admissions:** 11007 **Census:** 117 **Outpatient Visits:** 163727 **Births:** 1754 **Total Expense ($000):** 351331 **Payroll Expense ($000):** 99333 **Personnel:** 1892

GUNNISON—Gunnison County

✠ **GUNNISON VALLEY HOSPITAL (061320)**, 711 North Taylor Street, Zip 81230–2296; tel. 970/641–1456 **A**1 10 18 **F**3 7 11 13 15 29 30 31 32 34 35 40 43 44 45 56 57 59 64 68 76 77 78 85 87 93 97 107 110 111 114 119 129 132 133 135 146 147 148
Primary Contact: Robert J. Santilli, Chief Executive Officer
CFO: James P. Barbuat, Chief Financial Officer
CIO: Trevor Smith, Chief Management Information Services
CHR: Christina Lovelace, Director Human Resources
CNO: Lisa Loughran, Chief Nursing Officer
Web address: www.gvh–colorado.org
Control: County–Government, nonfederal **Service:** General Medical and Surgical

Staffed Beds: 24 **Admissions:** 554 **Census:** 4

Many Facility Codes have changed. Please refer to the AHA Guide Code Chart.

HAXTUN—Phillips County

★ **HAXTUN HOSPITAL DISTRICT (061304)**, 235 West Fletcher Street,
Zip 80731–2737; tel. 970/774–6123 **A**10 18 **F**7 40 54 59 64 65 75 77 87 93
97 107 114 119 129 133 146 **P**6
Primary Contact: Larry E. Schrage, FACHE, Chief Executive Officer
CFO: Rick Lee Nader, Chief Financial Officer
CMO: Colby Jolley, D.O., Acting Chief of Staff
CIO: Andrea Evers, Director Information Technology
CHR: Randy Brigham, Director Human Resources
CNO: Gail Phelps, R.N., Chief Nursing Officer
Web address: www.haxtunhealth.org
Control: Hospital district or authority, Government, nonfederal **Service:** General
Medical and Surgical

Staffed Beds: 25 **Admissions:** 60 **Census:** 19 **Outpatient Visits:** 29898
Births: 0 **Total Expense ($000):** 7804 **Payroll Expense ($000):** 4040
Personnel: 82

HOLYOKE—Phillips County

★ **MELISSA MEMORIAL HOSPITAL (061305)**, 1001 East Johnson Street,
Zip 80734–1854; tel. 970/854–2241, (Nonreporting) **A**10 18
Primary Contact: Trampas Hutches, Chief Executive Officer
CFO: Jason McCormick, Interim Chief Financial Officer
CMO: Dennis Jelden, M.D., Chief of Staff
CIO: David Bickford, Chief Information Officer
CHR: Sharon Greenman, Director Human Resources
CNO: Pat Notter, R.N., Chief Nursing Officer and Director Quality
Web address: www.melissamemorial.org
Control: Hospital district or authority, Government, nonfederal **Service:** General
Medical and Surgical

Staffed Beds: 15

HUGO—Lincoln County

★ **LINCOLN COMMUNITY HOSPITAL AND NURSING HOME (061306)**, 111 6th
Street, Zip 80821–0248, Mailing Address: P.O. Box 248, Zip 80821–0248;
tel. 719/743–2421, (Total facility includes 35 beds in nursing home–type unit)
A10 18 **F**7 28 40 43 45 62 63 64 81 82 89 93 97 99 100 101 102 103 104
107 110 111 114 119 128 130 133 143 **P**6
Primary Contact: Kevin M. Stansbury, Chief Executive Officer
CMO: Mark Olson, M.D., Chief of Staff
CIO: Michael Gaskins, Director Information Technology
CHR: Susan Petersen, Human Resources
CNO: Dan Walker, Chief Nursing Officer
Web address: www.lincolncommunityhospital.com
Control: County–Government, nonfederal **Service:** General Medical and Surgical

Staffed Beds: 50 **Admissions:** 241 **Census:** 27 **Outpatient Visits:** 30404
Births: 0 **Total Expense ($000):** 94661 **Personnel:** 190

JOHNSTOWN—Larimer County

☐ **NORTHERN COLORADO LONG TERM ACUTE HOSPITAL (062017)**, 4401
Union Street, Zip 80534; tel. 970/619–3663, (Nonreporting) **A**1 10 **S** Ernest
Health, Inc., Albuquerque, NM
Primary Contact: Lamar McBride, Chief Operating Officer
Web address: www.ncltah.ernesthealth.com/
Control: Partnership, Investor–owned, for–profit **Service:** Long–Term Acute Care
hospital

Staffed Beds: 20

⊞ **NORTHERN COLORADO REHABILITATION HOSPITAL (063033)**, 4401 Union
Street, Zip 80534–2800; tel. 970/619–3400 **A**1 10 **F**29 90 91 92 93 96 119
132 **S** Ernest Health, Inc., Albuquerque, NM
Primary Contact: Elizabeth Bullard, Chief Executive Officer
CFO: Bonnie Cushman, Chief Financial Officer
CMO: Revelyn Arrogante, M.D., Medical Director
CHR: Carolyn McCain, Director Human Resources
CNO: Christina Joder, Director Nursing Operations
Web address: www.ncrh.ernesthealth.com
Control: Corporation, Investor–owned, for–profit **Service:** Rehabilitation

Staffed Beds: 40 **Admissions:** 928 **Census:** 35 **Births:** 0

JULESBURG—Sedgwick County

SEDGWICK COUNTY HEALTH CENTER (061310), 900 Cedar Street,
Zip 80737–1199; tel. 970/474–3323, (Total facility includes 52 beds in nursing
home–type unit) **A**10 18 **F**3 10 13 15 31 32 34 40 45 53 56 57 59 65 66 67
76 81 89 107 110 111 114 119 127 128 131 133 145 148 **P**6
Primary Contact: David Garnas, Chief Executive Officer
COO: David Garnas, Chief Executive Officer
CFO: Karla Dunker, Director Finance
CMO: Donald Regier, M.D., Chief Medical Officer
CHR: Sonja Bell, Coordinator Human Resources
Control: County–Government, nonfederal **Service:** General Medical and Surgical

Staffed Beds: 67 **Admissions:** 150 **Census:** 49 **Outpatient Visits:** 14662
Births: 25 **Total Expense ($000):** 9565 **Payroll Expense ($000):** 4796
Personnel: 76

KREMMLING—Grand County

★ **MIDDLE PARK MEDICAL CENTER–KREMMLING (061318)**, 214 South Fourth
Street, Zip 80459, Mailing Address: P.O. Box 399, Zip 80459–0399;
tel. 970/724–3442 **A**10 18 **F**3 8 11 14 15 18 26 28 29 30 32 34 35 36 40
44 45 46 50 54 59 64 65 66 68 75 77 79 81 87 93 97 100 107 110 111
115 119 127 128 130 131 133 144 146 147 148 **P**6
Primary Contact: Robert Flake, Chief Executive Officer
CFO: Robert Flake, Chief Financial Officer
CMO: Thomas C. Coburn, M.D., Chief Medical Officer
CHR: Jason Bryan, Director Human Resources
CNO: Debra Plemmons, Chief Nursing Officer
Web address: www.mpmc.org
Control: Hospital district or authority, Government, nonfederal **Service:** General
Medical and Surgical

Staffed Beds: 10 **Admissions:** 122 **Census:** 1 **Births:** 1

LA JARA—Conejos County

★ **SAN LUIS VALLEY HEALTH CONEJOS COUNTY HOSPITAL (061308)**, 19021
U.S. Highway 285, Zip 81140–0639, Mailing Address: P.O. Box 639,
Zip 81140–0639; tel. 719/274–5121 **A**10 18 **F**3 29 40 43 54 56 59 64 70 76
87 89 93 97 107 114 119 127 128 133 **S** San Luis Valley Health, Alamosa, CO
Primary Contact: Ronnie Martin, Chief Executive Officer
CFO: Shane Mortensen, Chief Financial Officer
CMO: Gregory McAuliffe, M.D., Chief Medical Officer
CIO: Kathy Rogers, Vice President Marketing
CHR: Mandy Lee Crockett, Director Human Resources
CNO: Tandra Dunn, Director of Nursing
Web address: www.sanluisvalleyhealth.org/locations/conejos–county–hospital
Control: Other not–for–profit (including NFP Corporation) **Service:** General
Medical and Surgical

Staffed Beds: 17 **Admissions:** 147 **Census:** 2

LA JUNTA—Otero County

⊞ **ARKANSAS VALLEY REGIONAL MEDICAL CENTER (060036)**, 1100 Carson
Avenue, Zip 81050–2799; tel. 719/383–6000, (Total facility includes 81 beds in
nursing home–type unit) **A**1 10 20 **F**3 8 11 13 15 29 31 34 35 40 43 45 57 59
64 67 68 70 75 76 77 78 79 81 84 85 86 87 89 93 97 107 108 110 111
115 118 119 128 129 130 132 145 147 148 **P**6 **S** QHR, Brentwood, TN
Primary Contact: Lynn Crowell, Chief Executive Officer
CFO: Janette Bender, Chief Financial Officer
CMO: Michael Morley, M.D., Chief of Staff
CIO: Annette Cook, Application Support Specialist
CHR: Leigh Fitzpatrick, Director Human Resources
Web address: www.avrmc.org
Control: Other not–for–profit (including NFP Corporation) **Service:** General
Medical and Surgical

Staffed Beds: 145 **Admissions:** 1506 **Census:** 70 **Outpatient Visits:** 39485
Births: 201 **Total Expense ($000):** 40815 **Payroll Expense ($000):** 16804
Personnel: 400

CO

Hospital, Medicare Provider Number, Address, Telephone, Approval, Facility, and Physician Codes, Health Care System

★ American Hospital Association (AHA) membership   ◯ Healthcare Facilities Accreditation Program   ⇑ Center for Improvement in Healthcare Quality Accreditation
☐ The Joint Commission accreditation   ◇ DNV Healthcare Inc. accreditation   △ Commission on Accreditation of Rehabilitation Facilities (CARF) accreditation

Hospitals, U.S. / COLORADO

LAFAYETTE—Boulder County

✠ **GOOD SAMARITAN MEDICAL CENTER (060116)**, 200 Exempla Circle, Zip 80026–3370; tel. 303/689–4000 **A1** 2 10 **F3** 11 12 13 15 18 20 22 24 28 29 30 31 34 35 36 40 43 45 46 49 51 55 57 59 60 63 64 68 70 72 74 75 76 77 78 79 80 81 84 85 86 87 91 92 93 94 100 102 107 108 110 111 114 115 119 126 130 132 135 143 145 146 147 148 **P6 S** SCL Health, Broomfield, CO
Primary Contact: David Hamm, President and Chief Executive Officer
COO: Beth Forsyth, Chief Operating Officer
CFO: John Higgins, Vice President and Chief Financial Officer
CMO: Todd Mydler, M.D., Vice President and Chief Medical Officer
CHR: Amy Pacey, Vice President Human Resources
CNO: Susan Kerschen, MS, Vice President and Chief Nursing Officer
Web address: www.goodsamaritancolorado.org/
Control: Other not–for–profit (including NFP Corporation) **Service:** General Medical and Surgical

Staffed Beds: 183 **Admissions:** 12445 **Census:** 137 **Outpatient Visits:** 98338 **Births:** 2321 **Total Expense ($000):** 267284 **Payroll Expense ($000):** 81748 **Personnel:** 1079

LAKEWOOD—Jefferson County

✠ **ORTHOCOLORADO HOSPITAL (060124)**, 11650 West 2nd Place, Zip 80228–1527; tel. 720/321–5000, (Nonreporting) **A1** 10 **S** Catholic Health Initiatives, Englewood, CO
Primary Contact: Jude Torchia, Chief Executive Officer
Web address: www.orthocolorado.org
Control: Partnership, Investor–owned, for–profit **Service:** Orthopedic

Staffed Beds: 48

✠ **ST. ANTHONY HOSPITAL (060015)**, 11600 West Second Place, Zip 80228–1527; tel. 720/321–0000 **A1** 2 3 5 10 13 **F3** 7 11 12 17 18 20 22 24 26 28 29 30 31 34 35 36 40 42 43 45 46 47 48 49 50 53 56 57 59 64 65 68 70 74 75 76 77 78 79 81 82 84 85 87 90 91 92 93 96 97 102 107 108 111 114 115 116 117 118 119 120 121 123 124 126 129 130 132 133 134 135 146 147 148 **S** Catholic Health Initiatives, Englewood, CO
Primary Contact: Patrick Green, Interim Chief Executive Officer
COO: Patrick Green, Chief Operating Officer
CFO: David Thompson, Chief Financial Officer
CMO: Brian Erling, Group Chief Medical Officer
CIO: Dana Moore, Senior Vice President Information Services
CHR: Michelle Fornier–Johnson, Group Vice President Human Resources
CNO: Linda Goodwin, Group Chief Nursing Officer
Web address: www.stanthonyhosp.org
Control: Church–operated, Nongovernment, not–for profit **Service:** General Medical and Surgical

Staffed Beds: 224 **Admissions:** 11781 **Census:** 168 **Outpatient Visits:** 96813 **Births:** 0 **Total Expense ($000):** 313141 **Payroll Expense ($000):** 95724 **Personnel:** 1475

LAMAR—Prowers County

★ **PROWERS MEDICAL CENTER (061323)**, 401 Kendall Drive, Zip 81052–3993; tel. 719/336–4343 **A**10 18 **F3** 11 13 15 18 20 28 29 31 34 35 40 45 50 56 57 59 62 64 65 66 68 76 77 78 81 85 86 93 97 107 111 119 127 130 133 146 147 148 **P6 S** QHR, Brentwood, TN
Primary Contact: Craig Loveless, Chief Executive Officer
COO: Karen Bryant, Chief Support Services Officer
CFO: Audrey Kane, Interim Chief Financial Officer
CMO: Barry Portner, M.D., Chief of Staff
CIO: Jason Spano, Manager Information Technology
CHR: Karen Bryant, Chief Support Services Officer
Web address: www.prowersmedical.com
Control: Hospital district or authority, Government, nonfederal **Service:** General Medical and Surgical

Staffed Beds: 25 **Admissions:** 843 **Census:** 11 **Outpatient Visits:** 33680 **Births:** 158 **Total Expense ($000):** 24323 **Payroll Expense ($000):** 11147 **Personnel:** 200

LEADVILLE—Lake County

★ **ST. VINCENT GENERAL HOSPITAL DISTRICT (061319)**, 822 West 4th Street, Zip 80461–3897; tel. 719/486–0230 **A**10 18 **F**7 35 40 43 57 59 93 97 107 119 143 **P6**
Primary Contact: Sam Radke, Interim Chief Executive Officer and Interim Chief Financial Officer
CFO: Sam Radke, Interim Chief Executive Officer and Interim Chief Financial Officer
CMO: Gary Petry, M.D., Chief of Staff
CHR: Cheryl Snider, Director Human Resources
CNO: Von Kilpatrick, Chief Nursing Officer
Web address: www.svghd.org
Control: Hospital district or authority, Government, nonfederal **Service:** General Medical and Surgical

Staffed Beds: 2 **Admissions:** 5 **Census:** 1 **Outpatient Visits:** 2301 **Births:** 0

LITTLETON—Jefferson County

FEDERAL CORRECTIONAL INSTITUTE HOSPITAL, 9595 West Quincy Street, Zip 80123–1159; tel. 303/985–1566, (Nonreporting)
Primary Contact: Mike Hudson, Administrator
Control: Department of Justice, Government, federal **Service:** Hospital unit of an institution (prison hospital, college infirmary, etc.)

Staffed Beds: 6

✠ **HEALTHSOUTH REHABILITATION HOSPITAL OF LITTLETON (063034)**, 1001 West Mineral Avenue, Zip 80120–4507; tel. 303/334–1100, (Nonreporting) **A1** 10 **S** HEALTHSOUTH Corporation, Birmingham, AL
Primary Contact: David H. Shefte, Chief Executive Officer
CFO: Liz Freudenberg, Chief Financial Officer
CMO: Jill Castro, M.D., Medical Director
CHR: Sarah Thomas, Director of Human Resources
Web address: www.healthsouthdenver.com
Control: Corporation, Investor–owned, for–profit **Service:** Rehabilitation

Staffed Beds: 28

☐ **HIGHLANDS BEHAVIORAL HEALTH SYSTEM (064024)**, 8565 South Poplar Way, Zip 80130–3602; tel. 720/348–2800, (Nonreporting) **A1** 10 **S** Universal Health Services, Inc., King of Prussia, PA
Primary Contact: Lisa Strub, Interim Chief Executive Officer
Web address: www.highlandsbhs.com
Control: Corporation, Investor–owned, for–profit **Service:** Psychiatric

Staffed Beds: 86

✠ **LITTLETON ADVENTIST HOSPITAL (060113)**, 7700 South Broadway Street, Zip 80122–2628; tel. 303/730–8900 **A1** 2 5 10 **F3** 11 13 15 17 18 20 22 26 29 30 31 34 35 36 37 39 40 41 43 44 45 46 47 48 49 50 53 54 55 57 59 64 68 70 72 74 75 76 77 78 79 81 82 83 84 85 86 87 89 90 92 93 97 107 108 110 111 114 115 116 117 118 119 120 121 126 130 131 132 135 146 147 148 **P6 S** Adventist Health System Sunbelt Health Care Corporation, Altamonte Springs, FL
Primary Contact: Brett Spenst, Chief Executive Officer
COO: Geoff Lawton, Vice President Operations
CFO: Cheryl Curry, Chief Financial Officer
CMO: Lawrence Wood, M.D., Chief Medical Officer
CHR: Rita K. Arthur, Director Human Resources
CNO: Rhonda Ward, R.N., Chief Nursing Officer
Web address: www.centura.org
Control: Church–operated, Nongovernment, not–for profit **Service:** General Medical and Surgical

Staffed Beds: 201 **Admissions:** 9544 **Census:** 117 **Outpatient Visits:** 64620 **Births:** 1464 **Total Expense ($000):** 187717 **Payroll Expense ($000):** 68593 **Personnel:** 1275

LONE TREE—Douglas County

✠ **SKY RIDGE MEDICAL CENTER (060112)**, 10101 Ridge Gate Parkway, Zip 80124–5522; tel. 720/225–1000 **A1** 2 5 10 12 13 **F3** 8 12 13 15 17 18 19 20 22 28 29 30 31 34 35 36 37 40 41 43 45 46 47 48 49 54 58 59 64 70 72 73 74 75 76 77 78 79 81 82 84 85 86 87 89 93 97 107 108 111 114 115 119 120 121 123 126 129 130 131 132 135 146 147 148 **S** HCA, Nashville, TN
Primary Contact: Susan Hicks, Chief Executive Officer
CFO: Craig Sammons, Chief Financial Officer
CMO: David Markenson, M.D., Chief Medical Officer
CIO: Evan Tice, Director Information Technology and Systems
CHR: Jim Ritchey, Director Human Resources
CNO: Marian Savitsky, R.N., Chief Nursing Officer
Web address: www.skyridgemedcenter.com
Control: Corporation, Investor–owned, for–profit **Service:** General Medical and Surgical

Staffed Beds: 276 **Admissions:** 15007 **Census:** 142 **Outpatient Visits:** 95107 **Births:** 3315 **Personnel:** 1077

LONGMONT—Boulder County

✠ **LONGMONT UNITED HOSPITAL (060003)**, 1950 West Mountain View Avenue, Zip 80501–3162, Mailing Address: P.O. Box 1659, Zip 80502–1659; tel. 303/651–5111, (Total facility includes 15 beds in nursing home–type unit) **A1** 2 10 **F2** 3 11 13 15 18 20 22 28 29 30 31 34 35 36 37 40 43 44 45 47 48 49 50 53 54 56 57 59 61 64 68 70 73 74 75 76 77 78 79 81 82 84 85 86 87 89 92 93 107 108 110 111 114 115 118 119 121 123 126 128 129 130 131 132 135 146 148 **P6 S** Catholic Health Initiatives, Englewood, CO
Primary Contact: Mitchell C. Carson, President and Chief Executive Officer
CFO: Daniel Frank, Chief Financial Officer
CMO: Wyatt Hall, M.D., Chief Medical Officer
CHR: Warren Laughlin, Vice President Human Resources
CNO: Nancy Driscoll, Chief Nursing Officer
Web address: www.luhcares.org
Control: Other not–for–profit (including NFP Corporation) **Service:** General Medical and Surgical

Staffed Beds: 146 **Admissions:** 7081 **Census:** 83 **Outpatient Visits:** 188296 **Births:** 1049 **Total Expense ($000):** 185158 **Payroll Expense ($000):** 74182 **Personnel:** 1089

CO

A108 Hospitals *Many Facility Codes have changed. Please refer to the AHA Guide Code Chart.* © 2016 AHA Guide

LOUISVILLE—Boulder County

✠ **AVISTA ADVENTIST HOSPITAL (060103)**, 100 Health Park Drive, Zip 80027–9583; tel. 303/673–1000 **A**1 10 **F**3 8 11 13 15 17 18 20 22 28 29 30 34 40 43 44 45 47 48 49 50 56 59 60 62 63 64 68 70 72 74 75 76 77 79 81 82 84 85 86 87 89 93 107 108 111 114 115 119 129 130 131 132 135 146 147 **P**6 **S** Adventist Health System Sunbelt Health Care Corporation, Altamonte Springs, FL
Primary Contact: Dennis Barts, Chief Executive Officer
CFO: Brent Davis, Chief Financial Officer
CMO: David Ehrenberger, M.D., Chief Medical Officer
CHR: Becky Ortega, Manager Human Resources
CNO: Lavah Boyers Lowe, Chief Nursing Officer
Web address: www.avistahospital.org
Control: Church–operated, Nongovernment, not–for profit **Service:** General Medical and Surgical

Staffed Beds: 114 **Admissions:** 4151 **Census:** 36 **Outpatient Visits:** 47744 **Births:** 2013 **Total Expense ($000):** 87950 **Payroll Expense ($000):** 34007 **Personnel:** 586

☐ **CENTENNIAL PEAKS HOSPITAL (064007)**, 2255 South 88th Street, Zip 80027–9716; tel. 303/673–9990 **A**1 10 **F**4 5 38 87 98 99 100 101 102 104 105 135 **P**6 **S** Universal Health Services, Inc., King of Prussia, PA
Primary Contact: Elicia Bunch, Chief Executive Officer
COO: Lisa Strub, Chief Operating Officer
CFO: Tim Ryan, Chief Financial Officer
CMO: Konoy Mandal, M.D., Medical Director
CHR: Suzanne Martinez, Director Human Resources
CNO: Donia L. Andersen, Director of Nursing
Web address: www.centennialpeaks.com
Control: Individual, Investor–owned, for–profit **Service:** Psychiatric

Staffed Beds: 72 **Admissions:** 3139 **Census:** 61

LOVELAND—Larimer County

✠ **MCKEE MEDICAL CENTER (060030)**, 2000 Boise Avenue, Zip 80538–4281; tel. 970/669–4640 **A**1 2 10 **F**2 3 8 11 13 14 15 18 20 22 26 28 29 30 31 34 35 36 40 43 44 45 50 54 56 59 60 62 64 65 68 70 74 75 76 77 78 79 80 81 84 85 87 92 93 97 107 108 110 111 114 115 119 120 121 123 124 126 129 130 135 144 146 147 148 **S** Banner Health, Phoenix, AZ
Primary Contact: Margo Karsten, PhD, Interim Chief Executive Officer
COO: Julie Klein, Chief Operating Officer
CFO: Lori Sehrt, Chief Financial Officer
CMO: Bert Honea, M.D., Medical Director
CIO: Steve Rains, Director Information Services
CHR: Jeannie Gallagher, jeanie.gallagher@bannerhealth.com
CNO: Kelly Sturler, Chief Nursing Officer
Web address: www.mckeeloveland.com
Control: Other not–for–profit (including NFP Corporation) **Service:** General Medical and Surgical

Staffed Beds: 96 **Admissions:** 3949 **Census:** 33 **Outpatient Visits:** 87259 **Births:** 893 **Total Expense ($000):** 125904 **Payroll Expense ($000):** 36955 **Personnel:** 674

✠ **MEDICAL CENTER OF THE ROCKIES (060119)**, 2500 Rocky Mountain Avenue, Zip 80538–9004; tel. 970/624–2500 **A**1 3 5 10 **F**3 8 11 13 14 15 17 18 20 22 24 26 28 29 30 31 32 34 35 38 39 40 42 43 44 45 47 49 50 54 55 57 58 59 60 61 64 65 68 70 74 75 76 77 78 79 80 81 82 83 84 85 86 87 89 90 91 92 93 96 100 107 108 110 111 114 115 118 119 126 129 130 131 132 134 135 143 146 147 148 **S** University of Colorado Health, Fort Collins, CO
Primary Contact: Kevin L. Unger, FACHE, Ph.D., President and Chief Executive Officer
CFO: Stephanie Doughty, Chief Financial Officer
CMO: William Neff, M.D., Chief Medical Officer
CIO: Steve Hess, Vice President & Chief Information Officer
Web address: www.medctrrockies.org
Control: Other not–for–profit (including NFP Corporation) **Service:** General Medical and Surgical

Staffed Beds: 174 **Admissions:** 10589 **Census:** 120 **Outpatient Visits:** 92623 **Births:** 1343 **Total Expense ($000):** 325059 **Payroll Expense ($000):** 93576 **Personnel:** 993

MEEKER—Rio Blanco County

★ **PIONEERS MEDICAL CENTER (061325)**, 100 Pioneers Medical Center Drive, Zip 81641–3181; tel. 970/878–5047, (Includes WALBRIDGE MEMORIAL CONVALESCENT WING), (Total facility includes 30 beds in nursing home–type unit) **A**10 18 **F**1 3 8 15 28 29 34 35 40 43 45 50 53 56 57 59 62 64 65 68 69 75 76 77 79 81 82 84 85 87 91 93 97 107 110 111 115 119 127 128 129 130 131 132 133 135 143 146 147 148 **P**6 **S** QHR, Brentwood, TN
Primary Contact: Kenneth Harman, Chief Executive Officer
COO: Drew Varland, Chief Nursing Officer and Chief Operating Officer
CFO: James W. Worrell, Chief Financial Officer
CMO: Albert Krueger, M.D., Chief of Staff
CIO: Curtis Cooper, Manager Information Systems
CHR: Twyla Jensen, Director Human Resources
Web address: www.pioneershospital.org
Control: Hospital district or authority, Government, nonfederal **Service:** General Medical and Surgical

Staffed Beds: 40 **Admissions:** 231 **Census:** 21 **Outpatient Visits:** 10574 **Births:** 1 **Total Expense ($000):** 17663 **Payroll Expense ($000):** 6848 **Personnel:** 112

MONTROSE—Montrose County

✠ **MONTROSE MEMORIAL HOSPITAL (060006)**, 800 South Third Street, Zip 81401–4212; tel. 970/249–2211 **A**1 3 10 20 **F**13 14 15 18 20 22 24 28 29 30 31 34 40 43 45 47 48 50 51 57 59 65 68 70 74 75 76 78 79 81 82 85 86 87 90 92 93 94 102 107 108 109 110 111 112 115 118 119 126 129 130 132 143 148 **S** QHR, Brentwood, TN
Primary Contact: Steven Hannah, Chief Executive Officer
COO: Mary E. Snyder, Chief Operations Officer
CFO: Stephan A. Wilson, Chief Financial Officer
CMO: Richard Shannon, M.D., Chief of Staff
CIO: Carlos Lovera, Director Information Systems
CHR: Kathy McKie, Director Human Resources
Web address: www.montrosehospital.com
Control: Other not–for–profit (including NFP Corporation) **Service:** General Medical and Surgical

Staffed Beds: 66 **Admissions:** 2920 **Census:** 28 **Outpatient Visits:** 101192 **Births:** 411 **Total Expense ($000):** 89389 **Payroll Expense ($000):** 32285 **Personnel:** 528

PAGOSA SPRINGS—Archuleta County

PAGOSA SPRINGS MEDICAL CENTER (061328), 95 South Pagosa Boulevard, Zip 81147–8329; tel. 970/731–3700, (Nonreporting) **A**10 18
Primary Contact: Bradley Cochennet, Chief Executive Officer
Control: Other not–for–profit (including NFP Corporation) **Service:** General Medical and Surgical

Staffed Beds: 11

PARKER—Douglas County

✠ **PARKER ADVENTIST HOSPITAL (060114)**, 9395 Crown Crest Boulevard, Zip 80138–8573; tel. 303/269–4000 **A**1 2 10 **F**3 11 12 13 15 20 22 29 30 31 34 35 36 38 40 42 43 45 46 49 50 54 55 57 59 64 70 72 73 74 75 76 77 78 79 81 82 83 84 85 87 93 96 97 107 110 111 114 115 116 117 119 120 126 129 130 131 132 146 147 148 **P**6 **S** Adventist Health System Sunbelt Health Care Corporation, Altamonte Springs, FL
Primary Contact: Sam D. Huenergardt, Chief Executive Officer
CFO: Andrew Gaasch, Chief Financial Officer
Web address: www.parkerhospital.org
Control: Church–operated, Nongovernment, not–for profit **Service:** General Medical and Surgical

Staffed Beds: 145 **Admissions:** 7392 **Census:** 77 **Outpatient Visits:** 70025 **Births:** 1679 **Total Expense ($000):** 167048 **Payroll Expense ($000):** 55870 **Personnel:** 1095

PUEBLO—Pueblo County

☐ **COLORADO MENTAL HEALTH INSTITUTE AT PUEBLO (060115)**, 1600 West 24th Street, Zip 81003–1499; tel. 719/546–4000, (Nonreporting) **A**1 3 5 10
Primary Contact: Ron Hale, Superintendent
CFO: Jim Duff, Chief Financial Officer
CMO: Al Singleton, M.D., Chief Psychiatry and Chief Medical Staff
CIO: Eunice Wolther, Public Information Officer
CHR: Mary Young, Director Human Resources
Web address: www.cdhs.state.co.us/cmhip
Control: State–Government, nonfederal **Service:** Psychiatric

Staffed Beds: 514

Hospital, Medicare Provider Number, Address, Telephone, Approval, Facility, and Physician Codes, Health Care System

★ American Hospital Association (AHA) membership
☐ The Joint Commission accreditation
◯ Healthcare Facilities Accreditation Program
◇ DNV Healthcare Inc. accreditation
⇑ Center for Improvement in Healthcare Quality Accreditation
△ Commission on Accreditation of Rehabilitation Facilities (CARF) accreditation

CO

✠ △ **PARKVIEW MEDICAL CENTER (060020)**, 400 West 16th Street, Zip 81003–2781; tel. 719/584–4000, (Total facility includes 20 beds in nursing home–type unit) **A**1 7 10 13 **F**2 3 4 5 8 11 13 15 18 20 22 24 28 29 30 31 34 35 37 38 40 42 43 45 46 49 50 51 53 54 56 57 58 59 62 64 70 72 74 75 76 78 79 81 82 84 85 86 87 89 90 93 94 95 96 97 98 99 100 101 102 103 104 105 107 108 111 114 115 116 119 126 128 129 130 131 132 135 141 146 147 148 **P**6 8
Primary Contact: Michael T. Baxter, Chief Executive Officer
CFO: Leslie Barnes, Chief Financial Officer
CMO: Steve Nafziger, M.D., Vice President Medical Affairs
CIO: Steve Shirley, Chief Information Officer
CHR: Darrin Smith, Vice President Human Resources
CNO: Linda Flores, R.N., Vice President Nursing Services
Web address: www.parkviewmc.org
Control: Other not–for–profit (including NFP Corporation) **Service:** General Medical and Surgical

> **Staffed Beds:** 370 **Admissions:** 15637 **Census:** 242 **Outpatient Visits:** 219616 **Births:** 1627 **Total Expense ($000):** 282698 **Payroll Expense ($000):** 115128 **Personnel:** 2412

✠ **ST. MARY–CORWIN MEDICAL CENTER (060012)**, 1008 Minnequa Avenue, Zip 81004–3798; tel. 719/557–4000 **A**1 2 3 10 13 **F**3 13 15 18 20 22 26 28 29 30 31 34 35 40 43 45 47 48 49 50 51 53 55 57 58 59 64 68 70 72 73 75 76 78 79 81 82 84 85 86 87 89 90 107 108 110 111 114 115 117 119 120 121 123 124 126 129 130 131 132 135 146 147 148 **P**6 **S** Catholic Health Initiatives, Englewood, CO
Primary Contact: Brian Moore, President and Chief Executive Officer
COO: Michael Cafasso, Vice President Operations
CFO: Vanessa Kochevar, Chief Financial Officer
CMO: Robert Underwood, M.D., Chief Medical Officer
CHR: Timea Kennedy, Director Human Resources
CNO: Constance Schmidt, FACHE, Vice President Patient Care Services and Chief Nursing Officer
Web address: www.stmarycorwin.org
Control: Church–operated, Nongovernment, not–for profit **Service:** General Medical and Surgical

> **Staffed Beds:** 125 **Admissions:** 6081 **Census:** 71 **Outpatient Visits:** 95087 **Births:** 558 **Total Expense ($000):** 146434 **Payroll Expense ($000):** 52252 **Personnel:** 782

RANGELY—Rio Blanco County

★ **RANGELY DISTRICT HOSPITAL (061307)**, 225 Eagle Crest Drive, Zip 81648–2104; tel. 970/675–5011, (Nonreporting) **A**10 18
Primary Contact: Nick Goshe, Chief Executive Officer
COO: Bernard Rice, Chief Compliance Officer
CFO: Jim Dillon, Chief Financial Officer
CMO: Casey M. Aguirre, D.O., Chief of Staff
CHR: Cynthia S. Stults, Executive Assistant and Human Resources Director
CNO: Sharma Vaughn, Chief Nursing Officer
Web address: www.rangelyhospital.com
Control: Hospital district or authority, Government, nonfederal **Service:** General Medical and Surgical

> **Staffed Beds:** 25

RIFLE—Garfield County

★ **GRAND RIVER HOSPITAL DISTRICT (061317)**, 501 Airport Road, Zip 81650–8510, Mailing Address: P.O. Box 912, Zip 81650–0912; tel. 970/625–1510, (Total facility includes 57 beds in nursing home–type unit) **A**10 18 **F**3 11 12 15 29 34 35 39 40 41 45 50 55 57 59 64 68 69 75 77 79 81 85 87 93 96 97 107 108 110 111 112 115 118 119 127 128 129 130 131 132 133 144 145 146 148 **P**6
Primary Contact: James Coombs, Chief Executive Officer
COO: Bill Noel, Chief Operating Officer
CFO: Cris Bolin, Chief Financial Officer
CMO: Kevin Coleman, M.D., Chief Medical Officer
CIO: Diana Murray, Director Information Systems
CHR: Dawn Hodges, Director Human Resources
CNO: Stacy Pemberton, Chief Nursing Officer
Web address: www.grhd.org
Control: Hospital district or authority, Government, nonfederal **Service:** General Medical and Surgical

> **Staffed Beds:** 70 **Admissions:** 717 **Census:** 51 **Outpatient Visits:** 194354 **Births:** 0 **Total Expense ($000):** 66078 **Payroll Expense ($000):** 33837 **Personnel:** 440

SALIDA—Chaffee County

★ **HEART OF THE ROCKIES REGIONAL MEDICAL CENTER (061322)**, 1000 Rush Drive, Zip 81201–9627, Mailing Address: P.O. Box 429, Zip 81201–0429; tel. 719/530–2200 **A**10 18 **F**3 5 11 13 15 28 29 31 34 35 40 43 45 50 54 57 64 68 70 74 75 76 77 78 79 81 82 85 93 97 99 104 107 110 111 114 117 119 127 129 130 131 132 133 135 146 147 148
Primary Contact: Robert A. Morasko, Chief Executive Officer
CFO: Lesley Fagerberg, Vice President Fiscal Services
CMO: Daniel Wardrop, M.D., Medical Director
CIO: Andy Waldbart, Department Manager
CHR: Barbara Lutz, Vice President Human Resources
CNO: Linda Johnson, R.N., Vice President, Patient Services Risk Management and Chief Nursing Officer
Web address: www.hrrmc.com
Control: Hospital district or authority, Government, nonfederal **Service:** General Medical and Surgical

> **Staffed Beds:** 25 **Admissions:** 1084 **Census:** 10 **Outpatient Visits:** 68405 **Births:** 117 **Total Expense ($000):** 48805 **Payroll Expense ($000):** 21493 **Personnel:** 349

SPRINGFIELD—Baca County

★ **SOUTHEAST COLORADO HOSPITAL DISTRICT (061311)**, 373 East Tenth Avenue, Zip 81073–1699; tel. 719/523–4501, (Total facility includes 56 beds in nursing home–type unit) **A**10 18 **F**3 6 7 11 29 34 35 40 43 45 50 54 56 57 62 63 66 67 68 77 81 91 93 97 107 127 128 133 147 148 **P**6
Primary Contact: Michael E. Boyles, Chief Executive Officer and Administrator
CFO: Dorothy Burke, Chief Financial Officer
CMO: Jerry Flynn, M.D., Chief of Staff
CIO: Chris Westphal, Chief Information Technology Officer
CHR: Sherrilyn Turner, Director Human Resources
Web address: www.sechosp.org
Control: Hospital district or authority, Government, nonfederal **Service:** General Medical and Surgical

> **Staffed Beds:** 79 **Admissions:** 176 **Census:** 53 **Outpatient Visits:** 34151 **Births:** 0 **Total Expense ($000):** 13597 **Payroll Expense ($000):** 6715

STEAMBOAT SPRINGS—Routt County

✠ **YAMPA VALLEY MEDICAL CENTER (060049)**, 1024 Central Park Drive, Zip 80487–8813; tel. 970/879–1322 **A**1 2 10 20 **F**3 13 15 18 28 29 30 31 34 35 36 40 43 45 46 48 49 50 51 57 64 68 70 73 75 76 77 78 79 81 82 84 85 86 87 93 97 107 110 111 115 119 126 129 130 131 132 133 135 143 146 147
Primary Contact: Frank May, Chief Executive Officer
CFO: Bryan Roach, Chief Financial Officer
CMO: Lisa Kettering, Chief Medical Officer
CIO: Mark Clark, Chief Information Officer
CHR: Soniya Fidler, MS, Chief Human Resources and Compliance Officer
CNO: Marie Timlin, R.N., Chief Nursing Officer
Web address: www.yvmc.org
Control: Other not–for–profit (including NFP Corporation) **Service:** General Medical and Surgical

> **Staffed Beds:** 39 **Admissions:** 1475 **Census:** 12 **Outpatient Visits:** 67915 **Births:** 327 **Total Expense ($000):** 85630 **Payroll Expense ($000):** 27487 **Personnel:** 471

STERLING—Logan County

✠ **STERLING REGIONAL MEDCENTER (060076)**, 615 Fairhurst Street, Zip 80751–4523; tel. 970/522–0122 **A**1 10 20 **F**3 11 13 15 18 28 29 30 31 34 35 40 43 45 57 59 64 70 76 77 78 79 81 85 87 91 93 96 107 108 111 115 119 120 121 127 129 130 131 147 148 **S** Banner Health, Phoenix, AZ
Primary Contact: Jeffrey Shelton, Chief Executive Officer
CFO: Tiffany Weber, Chief Financial Officer
CMO: Jeff Bacon, D.O., Chief Medical Officer
CNO: Wade Alan Tyrrell, RN, Chief Nursing Officer
Web address: www.bannerhealth.com/Locations/Colorado/Sterling+Regional+MedCenter
Control: Other not–for–profit (including NFP Corporation) **Service:** General Medical and Surgical

> **Staffed Beds:** 25 **Admissions:** 1229 **Census:** 9 **Outpatient Visits:** 33200 **Births:** 274 **Total Expense ($000):** 41118 **Payroll Expense ($000):** 14667 **Personnel:** 214

CO

Many Facility Codes have changed. Please refer to the AHA Guide Code Chart. © 2016 AHA Guide

THORNTON—Adams County

✠ **NORTH SUBURBAN MEDICAL CENTER (060065)**, 9191 Grant Street,
Zip 80229–4341; tel. 303/451–7800 **A**1 10 **F**3 11 12 13 15 20 22 29 30 31
34 35 40 41 42 43 45 48 50 51 54 59 64 70 72 74 75 76 77 78 79 80 81
82 85 87 89 107 108 110 111 114 115 119 126 129 130 132 135 146 147
148 **S** HCA, Nashville, TN
Primary Contact: Jennifer Alderfer, Chief Executive Officer
COO: Tim O'Brien, Chief Operating Officer
CFO: Deborah Hart, Chief Financial Officer
CIO: Marty Hoesch, Director Information Systems
CHR: Dena Schmaedecke, Vice President Human Resources
CNO: Linnet Jung, Chief Nursing Officer
Web address: www.northsuburban.com
Control: Corporation, Investor–owned, for–profit **Service:** General Medical and
Surgical

Staffed Beds: 139 Admissions: 7083 Census: 75 Outpatient Visits: 97199
Births: 1183

✠ **VIBRA HOSPITAL OF DENVER (062014)**, 8451 Pearl Street, Zip 80229–4804;
tel. 303/288–3000, (Nonreporting) **A**1 10 **S** Vibra Healthcare, Mechanicsburg, PA
Primary Contact: Linda Tautz, Interim Chief Executive Officer
CMO: John Buckley, M.D., President Medical Staff
CHR: Lorna Fulton, Director Human Resources
Web address: www.vhdenver.com
Control: Corporation, Investor–owned, for–profit **Service:** Long–Term Acute Care
hospital

Staffed Beds: 71

TRINIDAD—Las Animas County

★ **MT. SAN RAFAEL HOSPITAL (061321)**, 410 Benedicta Avenue,
Zip 81082–2093; tel. 719/846–9213 **A**10 18 **F**3 11 15 28 34 35 40 45 46 50
65 75 81 82 85 89 93 94 96 97 107 111 114 119 127 129 133 146
147 148
Primary Contact: John Tucker, Chief Executive Officer
CFO: David W. Rollins, Chief Financial Officer
CIO: Michael Archuleta, Chief Information Technology Officer
CHR: Tammy Rogers, Director Human Resources
CNO: Mandy Shaiffer, Chief Nursing Officer
Web address: www.msrhc.org
Control: Other not–for–profit (including NFP Corporation) **Service:** General
Medical and Surgical

Staffed Beds: 18 Admissions: 515 Census: 5 Outpatient Visits: 37870
Births: 0 Total Expense ($000): 27570 Payroll Expense ($000): 12275
Personnel: 215

VAIL—Eagle County

✠ **VAIL VALLEY MEDICAL CENTER (060096)**, 181 West Meadow Drive,
Zip 81657–5242, Mailing Address: P.O. Box 40000, Zip 81658–7520;
tel. 970/476–2451, (Nonreporting) **A**1 3 10 20
Primary Contact: Doris Kirchner, Chief Executive Officer
CFO: Ted Sirotta, Chief Financial Officer
CMO: Barry Hammaker, M.D., Chief Medical Officer and Chief Clinical Officer
CIO: Brian Foster, Chief Information Officer
CHR: Rick Smith, Senior Vice President Human Resources and Chief
Administrative Officer
CNO: Sheila Sherman, Vice President Patient Care Services
Web address: www.vvmc.com
Control: Other not–for–profit (including NFP Corporation) **Service:** General
Medical and Surgical

Staffed Beds: 58

WALSENBURG—Huerfano County

★ **SPANISH PEAKS REGIONAL HEALTH CENTER (061316)**, 23500 U.S.
Highway 160, Zip 81089–9524; tel. 719/738–5100, (Nonreporting) **A**10 18
Primary Contact: Kay Whitley, President and Chief Executive Officer
CFO: Lionel J. Montoya, Chief Financial Officer
CMO: Michael A. Moll, M.D., Chief of Staff
CIO: Joe Camacho, Information Officer
CHR: Tony Marostica, Director Human Resources
CNO: Sherry Gomez, Chief Nursing Officer
Web address: www.sprhc.org
Control: Hospital district or authority, Government, nonfederal **Service:** General
Medical and Surgical

Staffed Beds: 20

WESTMINSTER—Adams County

✠ **ST. ANTHONY NORTH HEALTH CAMPUS (060104)**, 14300 Orchard Parkway,
Zip 80023–9206; tel. 720/627–0000 **A**1 2 3 10 **F**3 11 13 15 18 20 22 26 29
30 31 34 35 36 40 42 43 45 46 49 54 57 60 63 64 65 68 70 72 74 75 76
77 78 79 81 82 84 85 87 92 93 97 102 107 108 110 111 114 115 119 130
146 147 **S** Catholic Health Initiatives, Englewood, CO
Primary Contact: Carole Peet, R.N., MSN, President and Chief Executive Officer
CFO: Alison Mizer, Chief Financial Officer
CIO: Dana Moore, Senior Vice President Information Services
CHR: Robert Archibold, Director, Human Resources
CNO: Carol A. Butler, R.N., VP Patient Care Services & Operations
Web address: www.stanthonynorth.org
Control: Church–operated, Nongovernment, not–for profit **Service:** General
Medical and Surgical

Staffed Beds: 100 Admissions: 5329 Census: 53 Outpatient Visits: 55508
Births: 816 Total Expense ($000): 120251 Payroll Expense ($000): 41463
Personnel: 722

WHEAT RIDGE—Jefferson County

✠ **LUTHERAN MEDICAL CENTER (060009)**, 8300 West 38th Avenue,
Zip 80033–6005; tel. 303/425–4500, (Includes EXEMPLA WEST PINES, 3400
Lutheran Parkway, Zip 80033; tel. 303/467–4000), (Total facility includes 118
beds in nursing home–type unit) **A**1 2 3 10 **F**3 4 5 10 11 13 15 18 20 22 24
26 28 29 30 31 33 35 36 40 43 45 47 48 49 50 55 56 58 59 60 61 63 64
67 68 70 71 72 74 75 76 77 78 79 81 83 84 85 86 87 94 98 100 101 102
103 104 105 107 108 110 111 114 115 119 120 121 123 124 125 126 128
129 130 132 146 147 148 **P**6 **S** SCL Health, Broomfield, CO
Primary Contact: Grant Wicklund, President and Chief Executive Officer
COO: Peggy Cain Price, Vice President and Chief Operating Officer
CFO: Karen Scremin, Vice President Finance
CMO: Christina Johnson, M.D., Vice President and Chief Clinical and Quality Officer
CHR: Scott Day, Vice President Human Resources
CNO: Geraldine Towndrow, R.N., Senior Vice President Nursing
Web address: www.exempla.org
Control: Other not–for–profit (including NFP Corporation) **Service:** General
Medical and Surgical

Staffed Beds: 518 Admissions: 15436 Census: 310 Outpatient Visits:
243559 Births: 2549 Total Expense ($000): 325989 Payroll Expense
($000): 113479 Personnel: 1484

WOODLAND PARK—Teller County

◇ **PIKES PEAK REGIONAL HOSPITAL (061326)**, 16420 West Highway 24,
Zip 80863; tel. 719/687–9999 **A**10 18 21 **F**3 15 29 30 34 40 41 43 45 50 57
59 65 68 75 77 79 80 81 85 87 93 97 107 110 111 114 119 129 131
133 146 148 **S** IASIS Healthcare, Franklin, TN
Primary Contact: Kimberly Monjesky, Chief Executive Officer
CFO: Robin Ruff, Chief Financial Officer
CMO: Richard Malyszek, M.D., Chief of Staff
CHR: Arianne Randolph, Director Human Resources
CNO: Marsha Sensat, R.N., Chief Nursing Officer
Web address: www.pprmc.org
Control: Corporation, Investor–owned, for–profit **Service:** General Medical and
Surgical

Staffed Beds: 15 Admissions: 462 Census: 6

WRAY—Yuma County

★ **WRAY COMMUNITY DISTRICT HOSPITAL (061309)**, 1017 West 7th Street,
Zip 80758–1420; tel. 970/332–4811, (Nonreporting) **A**3 10 18
Primary Contact: Jennie Sullivan, Chief Executive Officer
CMO: Monte Uyemura, M.D., Chief of Staff
Web address: www.wraycommunitydistricthospital.com/
Control: Hospital district or authority, Government, nonfederal **Service:** General
Medical and Surgical

Staffed Beds: 15

CO

Hospital, Medicare Provider Number, Address, Telephone, Approval, Facility, and Physician Codes, Health Care System

★ American Hospital Association (AHA) membership   ○ Healthcare Facilities Accreditation Program   ⇑ Center for Improvement in Healthcare Quality Accreditation
□ The Joint Commission accreditation   ◇ DNV Healthcare Inc. accreditation   △ Commission on Accreditation of Rehabilitation Facilities (CARF) accreditation

YUMA—Yuma County

★ **YUMA DISTRICT HOSPITAL (061315)**, 1000 West 8th Avenue,
Zip 80759–2641; tel. 970/848–5405 **A**10 18 **F**3 11 13 15 28 29 30 31 34 35
36 40 43 44 50 53 57 59 62 64 65 68 74 75 77 78 79 81 82 87 93 97 99
101 102 103 104 107 111 115 119 127 130 133 148 **P**6
Primary Contact: Beth Saxton, R.N., Interim Chief Executive Officer and Vice
President Patient Care Services
CFO: Rick Korf, Chief Financial Officer
CMO: John Wolz, M.D., Chief Medical Staff
CIO: Jason Hawley, Manager Information Services
CHR: Gini Adams, Director Employee and Public Relations
CNO: Beth Saxton, R.N., Vice President Patient Care Services
Web address: www.yumahospital.org
Control: Hospital district or authority, Government, nonfederal **Service:** General
Medical and Surgical

Staffed Beds: 12 **Admissions:** 231 **Census:** 2 **Outpatient Visits:** 43968
Births: 1 **Total Expense ($000):** 21601 **Payroll Expense ($000):** 9261
Personnel: 119

CO

Many Facility Codes have changed. Please refer to the AHA Guide Code Chart.

CONNECTICUT

BETHLEHEM—Litchfield County

WELLSPRING FOUNDATION, 21 Arch Bridge Road, Zip 06751–1612, Mailing Address: P.O. Box 370, Zip 06751–0370; tel. 203/266–7235, (Nonreporting)
Primary Contact: Richard E. Beauvais, Ph.D., Chief Executive Officer
CFO: Richard E. Beauvais, Ph.D., Chief Executive Officer
Web address: www.wellspring.org
Control: Other not–for–profit (including NFP Corporation) **Service:** Psychiatric

Staffed Beds: 36

BRANFORD—New Haven County

☐ **THE CONNECTICUT HOSPICE (070038)**, 100 Double Beach Road, Zip 06405–4909; tel. 203/315–7500, (Nonreporting) **A**1 10
Primary Contact: Rosemary Johnson Hurzeler, President and Chief Executive Officer
Web address: www.hospice.com
Control: Other not–for–profit (including NFP Corporation) **Service:** Other specialty

Staffed Beds: 52

BRIDGEPORT—Fairfield County

⊠ **BRIDGEPORT HOSPITAL (070010)**, 267 Grant Street, Zip 06610–2805, Mailing Address: P.O. Box 5000, Zip 06610–0120; tel. 203/384–3000 **A**1 2 3 5 8 10 **F**3 5 6 8 11 12 13 14 15 16 18 19 20 22 24 26 28 29 30 31 32 34 35 36 38 39 40 41 43 44 45 46 47 48 49 50 51 52 54 55 56 57 58 59 61 64 65 66 68 70 74 75 76 77 78 79 80 81 82 84 85 86 87 90 93 96 97 98 99 100 101 102 103 104 105 107 108 110 111 114 115 116 117 118 119 120 121 123 124 126 129 130 131 132 134 144 145 146 147 148 **P**3 5 **S** Yale New Haven Health, New Haven, CT
Primary Contact: William M. Jennings, President and Chief Executive Officer
CFO: Patrick McCabe, Senior Vice President Finance and Chief Financial Officer
CMO: Michael Ivy, M.D., Senior Vice President for Medical Affairs and Chief Medical Officer
CIO: Daniel Barchi, Senior Vice President, Technical Services and Chief Information Officer
CHR: Melissa Turner, Senior Vice President Human Resources
CNO: MaryEllen Kosturko, R.N., Senior Vice President Patient Care Operations and Chief Nursing Officer
Web address: www.bridgeporthospital.org
Control: Other not–for–profit (including NFP Corporation) **Service:** General Medical and Surgical

Staffed Beds: 357 **Admissions:** 17511 **Census:** 275 **Outpatient Visits:** 299648 **Births:** 2519 **Total Expense ($000):** 443456 **Payroll Expense ($000):** 156620 **Personnel:** 2185

☐ **SOUTHWEST CONNECTICUT MENTAL HEALTH SYSTEM (074012)**, 1635 Central Avenue, Zip 06610–2717; tel. 203/551–7400 **A**1 10 **F**29 30 34 35 38 50 54 57 59 64 66 68 71 98 100 101 102 103 104 105 130 132 135 **S** Connecticut Department of Mental Health and Addiction Services, Hartford, CT
Primary Contact: Daniel Wartenberg, PsyD, M.P.H., Chief Executive Officer
COO: Cindy Perjon, Associate Director
CFO: Linda Woznikaitis, Chief Financial Officer
CMO: Sandra Gomez–Luna, Medical Director
CIO: Bernetta Witcher–Boateng, Ph.D., Director Quality Improvement Services and Compliance
CHR: Nancy Derman, Director Human Resources
Web address: www.ct.gov/dmhas/cwp/view.asp?a=2946&q=378936
Control: State–Government, nonfederal **Service:** Psychiatric

Staffed Beds: 62 **Admissions:** 65 **Census:** 60 **Births:** 0 **Personnel:** 124

⊠ **ST. VINCENT'S MEDICAL CENTER (070028)**, 2800 Main Street, Zip 06606–4292; tel. 203/576–6000, (Includes ST. VINCENT'S BEHAVIORAL HEALTH, 47 Long Lots Road, Westport, Zip 06880–3800; tel. 203/221–8813; Margaret Hardy, R.N., MS, Vice President) **A**1 2 3 5 10 **F**3 4 5 8 12 13 15 17 18 20 22 24 26 28 29 30 31 34 35 36 37 38 40 43 44 45 46 47 48 49 51 54 55 56 57 58 59 61 63 64 65 66 68 70 71 73 74 75 76 77 78 79 80 81 82 84 85 86 87 90 93 97 98 99 100 101 102 103 104 105 106 107 108 110 111 114 115 116 117 118 119 120 121 123 124 126 130 132 134 143 144 145 146 147 148 **P**1 **S** Ascension Health, Saint Louis, MO
Primary Contact: Vincent C. Caponi, President and Chief Executive Officer
COO: Vicki R. Briggs, Interim Chief Operating Officer
CFO: Stephen Franko, Senior Vice President and Chief Financial Officer
CMO: Dan Gottschall, Senior Vice President and Chief Clinical Officer
CIO: Rick McCarthy, Chief Information Officer
CNO: Dale G. Danowski, R.N., Senior Vice President, Chief Nursing Officer
Web address: www.stvincents.org
Control: Other not–for–profit (including NFP Corporation) **Service:** General Medical and Surgical

Staffed Beds: 403 **Admissions:** 17430 **Census:** 298 **Outpatient Visits:** 371007 **Births:** 1015 **Total Expense ($000):** 477048 **Payroll Expense ($000):** 207190 **Personnel:** 2096

BRISTOL—Hartford County

⊠ **BRISTOL HOSPITAL (070029)**, Brewster Road, Zip 06011, Mailing Address: P.O. Box 977, Zip 06011–0977; tel. 860/585–3000, (Nonreporting) **A**1 2 5 10
Primary Contact: Kurt A. Barwis, FACHE, President and Chief Executive Officer
COO: Marc D. Edelman, Vice President Operations
CFO: Peter Freytag, Senior Vice President Finance and Chief Financial Officer
CMO: Leonard Banco, M.D., Senior Vice President and Chief Medical Officer
CIO: David Rackliffe, Assistant Vice President Information Services
CHR: Jeanine Reckdenwald, Vice President Human Resources and Support Services
Web address: www.bristolhospital.org
Control: Other not–for–profit (including NFP Corporation) **Service:** General Medical and Surgical

Staffed Beds: 134

DANBURY—Fairfield County

⊠ **DANBURY HOSPITAL (070033)**, 24 Hospital Avenue, Zip 06810–6099; tel. 203/739–7000, (Includes NEW MILFORD HOSPITAL, 21 Elm Street, New Milford, Zip 06776–2993; tel. 860/355–2611; John M. Murphy, M.D., President and Chief Executive Officer, Western Connecticut Health Network) **A**1 2 3 5 8 10 **F**3 5 8 9 12 13 14 15 17 18 20 22 24 26 28 29 30 31 32 34 35 36 37 38 39 40 43 44 45 47 49 50 51 54 55 56 57 58 59 61 64 65 66 68 70 72 74 75 76 77 78 79 81 82 83 84 85 86 87 89 90 93 96 97 98 100 101 102 103 104 105 107 108 109 110 111 112 114 115 116 117 118 119 120 121 123 124 126 129 130 131 132 134 135 144 145 146 147 148 **P**8 **S** Western Connecticut Health Network, Danbury, CT
Primary Contact: John M. Murphy, M.D., President and Chief Executive Officer, Western Connecticut Health Network
COO: Sharon Adams, Chief Operating Officer
CFO: Steven Rosenberg, Chief Financial Officer
CMO: Matthew Miller, M.D., Chief Medical Officer – WCHN
CIO: Kathleen DeMatteo, Chief Information Officer
CHR: Cathy Frierson, Chief Human Resource Officer
CNO: Sharon Adams, Chief Nursing Officer
Web address: www.danburyhospital.org
Control: Other not–for–profit (including NFP Corporation) **Service:** General Medical and Surgical

Staffed Beds: 417 **Admissions:** 18727 **Census:** 270 **Outpatient Visits:** 444222 **Births:** 2065 **Total Expense ($000):** 624307 **Payroll Expense ($000):** 225712 **Personnel:** 2546

CT

Hospital, Medicare Provider Number, Address, Telephone, Approval, Facility, and Physician Codes, Health Care System

★ American Hospital Association (AHA) membership   ○ Healthcare Facilities Accreditation Program   ⇑ Center for Improvement in Healthcare Quality Accreditation
☐ The Joint Commission accreditation   ◇ DNV Healthcare Inc. accreditation   △ Commission on Accreditation of Rehabilitation Facilities (CARF) accreditation

CT

DERBY—New Haven County

✠ **GRIFFIN HOSPITAL (070031)**, 130 Division Street, Zip 06418–1326; tel. 203/735–7421 **A**1 2 3 5 10 **F**3 5 8 12 13 15 18 28 29 30 34 35 36 38 40 45 49 50 51 53 56 57 58 59 64 65 68 70 71 74 75 76 77 78 79 81 82 84 85 86 87 93 94 96 97 98 99 100 101 102 103 104 105 107 108 110 111 114 116 117 118 119 120 121 129 130 132 134 135 144 146 147 148 **P**8
Primary Contact: Patrick Charmel, President and Chief Executive Officer
CMO: Kenneth V. Schwartz, M.D., Medical Director
CIO: George Tomas, Director Information Services
CHR: Steve Mordecai, Director Human Resources
CNO: Barbara J. Stumpo, R.N., Vice President Patient Care Services
Web address: www.griffinhealth.org
Control: Other not–for–profit (including NFP Corporation) **Service:** General Medical and Surgical

Staffed Beds: 111 **Admissions:** 6419 **Census:** 81 **Outpatient Visits:** 184701 **Births:** 545 **Total Expense ($000):** 134870 **Payroll Expense ($000):** 57989 **Personnel:** 945

FARMINGTON—Hartford County

✠ **UNCONN JOHN DEMPSEY HOSPITAL (070036)**, 263 Farmington Avenue, Zip 06032–1941; tel. 860/679–2000, (Nonreporting) **A**1 2 3 5 8 10 12 13 19
Primary Contact: Anne Diamond, JD, Chief Executive Officer
COO: Kevin Larsen, Associate Vice President, Business and Ancillary Services
CFO: Jeffrey Geoghegan, Chief Financial Officer
CMO: Richard Simon, M.D., Chief of Staff
CIO: Jonathan Carroll, Chief Information Officer
CHR: Carolle Andrews, Vice President, Interim Human Resources Officer
CNO: Ann Marie Capo, R.N., Chief Nursing Officer
Web address: www.uchc.edu
Control: State–Government, nonfederal **Service:** General Medical and Surgical

Staffed Beds: 174

GREENWICH—Fairfield County

✠ **GREENWICH HOSPITAL (070018)**, 5 Perryridge Road, Zip 06830–4697; tel. 203/863–3000 **A**1 2 3 5 8 10 **F**3 5 8 11 12 13 14 15 18 20 22 26 28 29 30 31 32 34 35 36 37 38 39 40 44 45 46 47 48 49 50 51 52 53 54 55 56 57 58 59 61 63 64 65 66 68 70 72 74 75 76 77 78 79 80 81 82 84 85 86 87 89 93 96 97 99 100 101 102 103 104 107 108 110 111 114 115 116 117 118 119 120 121 123 124 126 129 130 131 132 134 135 146 147 148 **P**2 3 5 **S** Yale New Haven Health, New Haven, CT
Primary Contact: Norman G. Roth, Chief Executive Officer
COO: Norman G. Roth, Interim Chief Operating Officer
CFO: Eugene Colucci, Vice President Finance
CMO: A. Michael Marino, M.D., Senior Vice President Medical Administration
Web address: www.greenhosp.org
Control: Other not–for–profit (including NFP Corporation) **Service:** General Medical and Surgical

Staffed Beds: 184 **Admissions:** 10831 **Census:** 129 **Outpatient Visits:** 286716 **Births:** 2814 **Total Expense ($000):** 330759 **Payroll Expense ($000):** 117116 **Personnel:** 1458

HARTFORD—Hartford County

✠ **CONNECTICUT CHILDREN'S MEDICAL CENTER (073300)**, 282 Washington Street, Zip 06106–3322; tel. 860/545–9000 **A**1 3 5 10 **F**3 7 8 11 12 19 21 23 27 29 30 31 32 34 35 36 39 40 41 43 48 49 50 51 54 55 57 58 59 60 61 63 64 65 68 72 74 75 78 79 81 82 84 85 86 87 88 89 90 91 92 93 97 98 107 111 114 115 119 126 129 130 131 132 134 146
Primary Contact: James E. Shmerling, President
CFO: Gerald J. Boisvert, Vice President and Chief Financial Officer
CMO: Paul Dworkin, M.D., Physician–in–Chief
CIO: Kelly R. Styles, Vice President and Chief Information Officer
CHR: Elizabeth Rudden, Vice President Human Resources
Web address: www.ccmckids.org
Control: Other not–for–profit (including NFP Corporation) **Service:** Children's general

Staffed Beds: 166 **Admissions:** 6021 **Census:** 123 **Outpatient Visits:** 188829 **Births:** 0 **Total Expense ($000):** 288198 **Payroll Expense ($000):** 115451 **Personnel:** 2135

✠ **HARTFORD HOSPITAL (070025)**, 80 Seymour Street, Zip 06102–8000, Mailing Address: P.O. Box 5037, Zip 06102–5037; tel. 860/545–5000, (Includes INSTITUTE OF LIVING, 400 Washington Street, Zip 06106–3392; tel. 860/545–7000), (Total facility includes 104 beds in nursing home–type unit) **A**1 2 3 5 10 **F**2 3 5 6 7 8 9 10 11 12 13 15 17 18 20 22 24 26 28 29 30 31 34 35 36 37 38 39 40 43 44 45 46 47 48 49 50 51 52 53 54 55 56 57 58 59 60 61 63 64 65 66 68 70 71 74 75 76 77 78 79 80 81 82 83 84 85 86 87 91 92 93 94 96 97 98 99 100 101 102 103 104 105 106 107 108 110 111 112 114 115 116 117 118 119 120 121 123 124 125 126 128 129 130 131 132 134 135 137 138 139 141 143 145 146 147 148 **P**6 **S** Hartford HealthCare, Hartford, CT
Primary Contact: Stuart Markowitz, M.D., President
CMO: Stuart Markowitz, M.D., Chief Medical Officer
CIO: Stephan O'Neill, Vice President Information Services
CHR: Richard McAloon, Vice President Human Resources
Web address: www.harthosp.org
Control: Other not–for–profit (including NFP Corporation) **Service:** General Medical and Surgical

Staffed Beds: 870 **Admissions:** 39903 **Census:** 708 **Outpatient Visits:** 234200 **Births:** 3754 **Total Expense ($000):** 1043106 **Payroll Expense ($000):** 431298 **Personnel:** 6047

✠ **MOUNT SINAI REHABILITATION HOSPITAL (073025)**, 490 Blue Hills Avenue, Zip 06112–1513; tel. 860/714–3500 **A**1 10 **F**29 30 34 54 58 59 64 68 74 75 82 90 91 92 93 94 95 96 130 131 132 **P**8 **S** Trinity Health, Livonia, MI
Primary Contact: Robert J. Krug, M.D., Chief Executive Officer
CFO: David Bittner, Chief Financial Officer
Web address: www.stfranciscare.org
Control: Other not–for–profit (including NFP Corporation) **Service:** Rehabilitation

Staffed Beds: 30 **Admissions:** 706 **Census:** 23 **Outpatient Visits:** 42652 **Births:** 0 **Total Expense ($000):** 32875 **Payroll Expense ($000):** 13049 **Personnel:** 207

✠ **SAINT FRANCIS HOSPITAL AND MEDICAL CENTER (070002)**, 114 Woodland Street, Zip 06105–1208; tel. 860/714–4000 **A**1 2 3 5 8 10 **F**3 8 11 12 13 15 17 18 20 22 24 26 28 29 30 31 34 35 36 38 39 40 43 45 46 47 48 49 50 53 54 55 56 57 58 59 61 64 65 66 68 70 72 74 75 76 77 78 79 81 82 84 85 87 91 92 93 94 95 96 97 98 99 100 101 102 103 104 107 108 110 111 115 117 118 119 120 121 123 124 126 129 130 131 132 134 135 144 145 146 147 148 **P**8 **S** Trinity Health, Livonia, MI
Primary Contact: John F. Rodis, M.D., President
CFO: Jennifer S. Schneider, Vice President of Finance
CMO: Surendra Khera, M.D., Vice President Medical Affairs, Chief Medical Officer, Chief Quality Officer
CIO: Linda L. Shanley, Vice President, Chief Information Officer
CHR: Leonard F. Pansa, Senior Vice President, Chief Human Resources Officer
CNO: Denise Peterson, R.N., Vice President, Professional Nursing Practice & Quality, Chief Nursing Officer
Web address: www.saintfranciscare.com
Control: Church–operated, Nongovernment, not–for profit **Service:** General Medical and Surgical

Staffed Beds: 581 **Admissions:** 29097 **Census:** 401 **Outpatient Visits:** 249480 **Births:** 2793 **Total Expense ($000):** 681612 **Payroll Expense ($000):** 257621 **Personnel:** 4772

MANCHESTER—Hartford County

✠ **MANCHESTER MEMORIAL HOSPITAL (070027)**, 71 Haynes Street, Zip 06040–4188; tel. 860/646–1222, (Nonreporting) **A**1 2 5 10 12 13 **S** Eastern Connecticut Health Network, Manchester, CT
Primary Contact: Peter J. Karl, President and Chief Executive Officer
CFO: Michael D. Veillette, Senior Vice President and Chief Financial Officer
CMO: Joel R. Reich, M.D., Senior Vice President Medical Affairs
CIO: Richard Daigle, Chief Information Officer
CHR: Natalie Cook, Administrative Director of Human Resources
CNO: Mary Powers, MSN, Senior Vice President and Chief Nursing Officer
Web address: www.echn.org
Control: Other not–for–profit (including NFP Corporation) **Service:** General Medical and Surgical

Staffed Beds: 156

MANSFIELD CENTER—Tolland County

✠ **NATCHAUG HOSPITAL (074008)**, 189 Storrs Road, Zip 06250–1683; tel. 860/456–1311 **A**1 10 **F**5 98 99 100 103 104 105 106 **S** Hartford HealthCare, Hartford, CT
Primary Contact: Patricia Rehmer, President
COO: David Klein, Ph.D., Vice President Operations, Behavioral Health Network
CFO: Paul V. Maloney, Vice President Finance, Behavioral Health Network
CMO: Deborah Weidner, Medical Director
CIO: Mark Olson, Interim Chief Information Officer, Behavioral Health Network
CHR: Janet Keown, Vice President Human Resources, Behavioral Health Network
CNO: Justin Sleeper, Vice President Clinical Operations, Behavioral Health Network
Web address: www.natchaug.org
Control: Other not–for–profit (including NFP Corporation) **Service:** Psychiatric

Staffed Beds: 57 **Admissions:** 2031 **Census:** 51 **Outpatient Visits:** 60866 **Births:** 0 **Total Expense ($000):** 49783 **Payroll Expense ($000):** 28495 **Personnel:** 309

Many Facility Codes have changed. Please refer to the AHA Guide Code Chart. © 2016 AHA Guide

MERIDEN—New Haven County

✠ **MIDSTATE MEDICAL CENTER (070017)**, 435 Lewis Avenue, Zip 06451–2101; tel. 203/694–8200 **A**1 2 10 **F**3 11 12 13 15 18 28 29 30 31 34 35 36 38 39 40 44 45 46 47 48 49 50 51 53 54 56 57 59 61 63 64 68 70 74 75 76 78 79 81 82 84 85 86 87 97 102 107 108 110 111 114 115 117 118 119 120 121 123 124 126 129 130 131 132 144 145 146 147 148 **P**5 **S** Hartford HealthCare, Hartford, CT
Primary Contact: Lucille A. Janatka, President and Chief Executive Officer
CMO: Kenneth R. Kurz, M.D., Chief of Staff
CIO: Jennifer Comerford, Manager Information Services
CHR: Ken Cesca, Vice President Human Resources
Web address: www.midstatemedical.org
Control: Other not–for–profit (including NFP Corporation) **Service:** General Medical and Surgical

Staffed Beds: 88 **Admissions:** 8264 **Census:** 96 **Outpatient Visits:** 156995 **Births:** 914 **Total Expense ($000):** 210264 **Payroll Expense ($000):** 66714 **Personnel:** 826

MIDDLETOWN—Middlesex County

☐ **ALBERT J. SOLNIT PSYCHIATRIC CENTER – SOUTH CAMPUS**, 915 River Road, Zip 06457–3921, Mailing Address: P.O. Box 2792, Zip 06457–9292; tel. 860/704–4000, (Nonreporting) **A**1 3 5
Primary Contact: Michelle Sarofin, Superintendent
CFO: Connie Tessarzik, Business Manager
CMO: Lesley Siegel, M.D., Medical Director
CIO: Andrew J A Kass, M.D., Assistant Superintendent
Web address: www.ct.gov/
Control: State–Government, nonfederal **Service:** Children's hospital psychiatric

Staffed Beds: 75

☐ **CONNECTICUT VALLEY HOSPITAL (074003)**, Eastern Drive, Zip 06457–3947; tel. 860/262–5000, (Includes WHITING FORENSIC DIVISION OF CONNECTICUT VALLEY HOSPITAL, O'Brien Drive, Zip 06457, Mailing Address: Box 70, Zip 06457–3942; tel. 860/262–5000) **A**1 3 5 10 **F**3 4 29 30 34 36 39 50 53 56 57 58 59 60 61 65 68 74 75 77 82 84 86 87 90 91 94 97 98 99 100 101 102 103 106 119 130 132 135 144 146 148 **S** Connecticut Department of Mental Health and Addiction Services, Hartford, CT
Primary Contact: Helene M. Vartelas, MSN, Chief Executive Officer
COO: John D'Eramo, Chief Operating Officer
CFO: Cindy Butterfield, Director, Fiscal and Administrative Services
CMO: Thomas Pisano, M.D., Chief Professional Services
CIO: Kathryn Connelly, Manager Information Technology
CHR: Cheryl Thompson, Facility Director Human Resources
CNO: Jerilynn Lamb–Pagone, Nurse Executive
Web address: www.ct.gov/dmhas/cwp/view.asp?a=3519&q=416778
Control: State–Government, nonfederal **Service:** Psychiatric

Staffed Beds: 596 **Admissions:** 3587 **Census:** 562 **Outpatient Visits:** 0 **Births:** 0 **Total Expense ($000):** 154245 **Payroll Expense ($000):** 139226 **Personnel:** 1522

✠ **MIDDLESEX HOSPITAL (070020)**, 28 Crescent Street, Zip 06457–3650; tel. 860/358–6000 **A**1 2 3 5 10 **F**3 5 8 12 13 15 18 20 22 24 28 29 30 31 32 34 35 36 38 40 42 45 46 47 49 50 51 54 55 57 58 59 60 62 63 64 65 68 70 74 75 76 77 78 79 81 83 84 85 86 87 89 92 93 94 97 98 99 100 101 102 103 104 105 107 108 110 111 114 115 116 117 118 119 120 121 123 124 126 129 130 131 132 133 144 145 146 147 148 **P**6
Primary Contact: Vincent G. Capece, Jr., President and Chief Executive Officer
CFO: Susan Martin, Vice President Finance
CMO: Arthur V. McDowell, III, M.D., Vice President Clinical Affairs
CIO: Evan Jackson, Vice President Information Technology
CHR: Gregory Nokes, Vice President Human Resources
CNO: Jacquelyn Calamari, MSN, Vice President and Chief Nursing Officer
Web address: www.middlesexhospital.org
Control: Other not–for–profit (including NFP Corporation) **Service:** General Medical and Surgical

Staffed Beds: 237 **Admissions:** 12470 **Census:** 151 **Outpatient Visits:** 582453 **Births:** 1115 **Total Expense ($000):** 360551 **Payroll Expense ($000):** 168078 **Personnel:** 1801

WHITING FORENSIC DIVISION OF CONNECTICUT VALLEY HOSPITAL See Connecticut Valley Hospital

MILFORD—New Haven County

✠ **MILFORD HOSPITAL (070019)**, 300 Seaside Avenue, Zip 06460–4603; tel. 203/876–4000 **A**1 10 **F**3 8 11 13 15 29 32 34 35 37 38 40 45 46 49 50 54 59 63 64 68 70 74 75 76 78 79 81 82 85 87 89 102 107 108 111 114 118 119 126 130 132 135 144 146
Primary Contact: Joseph Pelaccia, President and Chief Executive Officer
COO: Lloyd Friedman, M.D., Vice President Medical Affairs and Chief Operating Officer
CFO: Joseph Pelaccia, President and Chief Executive Officer
CMO: Lloyd Friedman, M.D., Vice President Medical Affairs and Chief Operating Officer
CIO: Marilyn Christensen, Director Information Technology
CHR: Jeffrey Komornik, Director Human Resources
CNO: Beverly Lyon, R.N., Vice President Nursing
Web address: www.milfordhospital.org
Control: Other not–for–profit (including NFP Corporation) **Service:** General Medical and Surgical

Staffed Beds: 41 **Admissions:** 3237 **Census:** 33 **Outpatient Visits:** 49678 **Births:** 53 **Total Expense ($000):** 68666 **Payroll Expense ($000):** 32255 **Personnel:** 496

NEW BRITAIN—Hartford County

✠ △ **HOSPITAL FOR SPECIAL CARE (072004)**, 2150 Corbin Avenue, Zip 06053–2298; tel. 860/223–2761 **A**1 3 5 7 10 **F**1 3 11 29 30 35 39 53 56 64 77 80 89 90 91 92 93 96 119 130 131 132 135 146 148
Primary Contact: Lynn Ricci, President and Chief Operating Officer
CFO: Laurie A. Whelan, Senior Vice President Finance and Chief Financial Officer
CMO: Paul Scalise, M.D., Chief Pulmonary Medicine and Internal Medicine
CIO: Stan Jankowski, Vice President and Chief Information Officer
CHR: Judi Trczinski, Vice President and Chief Human Resources Officer
Web address: www.hfsc.org
Control: Other not–for–profit (including NFP Corporation) **Service:** Long–Term Acute Care hospital

Staffed Beds: 228 **Admissions:** 607 **Census:** 195 **Outpatient Visits:** 33267 **Births:** 0 **Total Expense ($000):** 95881 **Payroll Expense ($000):** 52873 **Personnel:** 775

✠ **THE HOSPITAL OF CENTRAL CONNECTICUT (070035)**, 100 Grand Street, Zip 06052–2017, Mailing Address: P.O. Box 100, Zip 06052–2017; tel. 860/224–5011, (Includes BRADLEY MEMORIAL, 81 Meriden Avenue, Southington, Zip 06489–3297; tel. 860/276–5000; NEW BRITAIN GENERAL, 100 Grand Street, Mailing Address: P.O. Box 100, Zip 06050–0100; tel. 860/224–5011) **A**1 2 3 5 10 **F**3 11 12 13 15 18 20 22 28 29 30 31 34 35 38 40 44 45 49 50 51 53 54 57 58 59 60 61 64 65 66 68 70 72 74 75 76 77 78 79 81 84 85 86 87 89 93 97 98 99 100 101 102 103 104 105 107 108 110 111 114 115 117 118 119 120 121 123 124 126 129 130 131 132 135 144 146 147 148 **P**6 **S** Hartford HealthCare, Hartford, CT
Primary Contact: Lucille A. Janatka, President and Chief Executive Officer, Hartford HealthCare Central Region
CFO: Brian Rogoz, Vice President Finance and Treasurer
CIO: Frank Pinto, Chief Information Officer
CHR: Elizabeth A. Lynch, Vice President Human Resources
Web address: www.thocc.org
Control: Other not–for–profit (including NFP Corporation) **Service:** General Medical and Surgical

Staffed Beds: 179 **Admissions:** 13634 **Census:** 179 **Outpatient Visits:** 369621 **Births:** 1571 **Total Expense ($000):** 356169 **Payroll Expense ($000):** 143110 **Personnel:** 1679

NEW CANAAN—Fairfield County

☐ **SILVER HILL HOSPITAL (074014)**, 208 Valley Road, Zip 06840–3899; tel. 203/966–3561, (Nonreporting) **A**1 10
Primary Contact: Sigurd H. Ackerman, M.D., President and Chief Executive Officer
COO: Elizabeth Moore, Chief Operating Officer
CFO: Ruurd Leegstra, Chief Financial Officer
CMO: Sigurd H. Ackerman, M.D., President and Chief Executive Officer
CIO: Maria Klinga, Director Management Information Systems
CHR: Rich Juliana, Director Human Resources
Web address: www.silverhillhospital.org
Control: Other not–for–profit (including NFP Corporation) **Service:** Psychiatric

Staffed Beds: 60

Hospital, Medicare Provider Number, Address, Telephone, Approval, Facility, and Physician Codes, Health Care System

★ American Hospital Association (AHA) membership
☐ The Joint Commission accreditation
○ Healthcare Facilities Accreditation Program
◇ DNV Healthcare Inc. accreditation
⇑ Center for Improvement in Healthcare Quality Accreditation
△ Commission on Accreditation of Rehabilitation Facilities (CARF) accreditation

NEW HAVEN—New Haven County

☐ **CONNECTICUT MENTAL HEALTH CENTER (074011)**, 34 Park Street, Zip 06519–1109, Mailing Address: P.O. Box 1842, Zip 06508–1842; tel. 203/974–7144, (Nonreporting) **A**1 3 5 10 **S** Connecticut Department of Mental Health and Addiction Services, Hartford, CT
Primary Contact: Michael Sernyak, M.D., Director
COO: Robert Cole, Chief Operating Officer
CFO: Robert Cole, Chief Operating Officer
CMO: Jeanne Steines, D.O., Medical Director
CIO: Paul Moore, Chief Information Officer
CHR: Carolyn Wallace, Director Human Resources
Web address: www.ct.gov/dmhas/cwp/view.asp?a=2906&q=334596
Control: State–Government, nonfederal **Service:** Psychiatric

Staffed Beds: 32

HOSPITAL OF SAINT RAPHAEL See Yale–New Haven Hospital–Saint Raphael Campus

☒ **YALE–NEW HAVEN HOSPITAL (070022)**, 20 York Street, Zip 06510–3202; tel. 203/688–4242, (Includes YALE–NEW HAVEN CHILDREN'S HOSPITAL, 1 Park Street, Zip 06504–8901; tel. 203/688–4242; Cynthia Sparer, Senior Vice President and Executive Director Women's & Children; YALE–NEW HAVEN HOSPITAL–SAINT RAPHAEL CAMPUS, 1450 Chapel Street, Zip 06511–4405; tel. 203/789–3000; Richard D'Aquila, President; YALE–NEW HAVEN PSYCHIATRIC HOSPITAL, 184 Liberty Street, Zip 06519–1625; tel. 203/688–9704; Mark Sevilla, Executive Director) **A**1 2 3 5 8 10 **F**3 5 6 8 9 11 12 13 14 15 17 18 19 20 21 22 23 24 25 26 27 28 29 30 31 34 35 36 37 38 39 40 41 42 43 44 45 46 47 48 49 50 51 52 53 54 55 56 57 58 59 61 64 65 66 68 72 74 75 76 77 78 79 80 81 82 84 85 86 87 88 89 90 91 92 93 94 96 97 98 99 100 101 102 103 104 105 107 108 109 110 111 112 114 115 116 117 118 119 120 121 123 124 126 129 130 131 132 134 135 136 137 138 139 141 142 143 144 145 146 147 148 **P**2 3 5 6 **S** Yale New Haven Health, New Haven, CT
Primary Contact: Marna P. Borgstrom, Chief Executive Officer
COO: Richard D'Aquila, President and Chief Operating Officer
CFO: Vincent Tammaro, Chief Financial Officer
CMO: Thomas Balcezak, M.D., Senior Vice President Medical Affairs and Chief Medical Officer
CIO: Lisa Stump, Interim Chief Information Officer
CHR: Kevin A. Myatt, Senior Vice President Human Resources
CNO: Patricia Sue Fitzsimons, R.N., Senior Vice President Patient Services
Web address: www.ynhh.org
Control: Other not–for–profit (including NFP Corporation) **Service:** General Medical and Surgical

Staffed Beds: 1391 Admissions: 73625 Census: 1091 Outpatient Visits: 1282539 Births: 5567 Total Expense ($000): 2429303 Payroll Expense ($000): 823371 Personnel: 11006

NEW LONDON—New London County

☒ △ **LAWRENCE + MEMORIAL HOSPITAL (070007)**, 365 Montauk Avenue, Zip 06320–4769; tel. 860/442–0711 **A**1 2 3 7 10 **F**3 8 11 13 15 17 18 20 22 26 28 29 30 31 34 35 38 39 40 41 42 45 46 47 48 49 50 51 54 57 58 59 61 68 70 72 74 75 76 77 78 79 81 82 84 85 86 87 89 90 91 92 93 96 98 99 100 101 102 103 107 108 110 111 114 115 116 117 118 119 120 121 123 124 126 129 130 131 132 146 148 **S** L+M Healthcare, New London, CT
Primary Contact: Bruce D. Cummings, President and Chief Executive Officer
COO: Daniel Rissi, M.D., Vice President, Chief Medical and Clinical Operations Officer
CFO: Seth Van Essendelft, Vice President and Chief Financial Officer
CMO: Daniel Rissi, M.D., Chief Medical and Clinical Operations
CIO: Kimberly Kalajainen, Vice President Operations and Chief Information Officer
CHR: Donna Epps, Vice President and Chief Human Resources Officer
CNO: Lauren Williams, MS, Vice President of Professional Services and Chief Nursing Officer
Web address: www.lmhospital.org
Control: Other not–for–profit (including NFP Corporation) **Service:** General Medical and Surgical

Staffed Beds: 235 Admissions: 12678 Census: 162 Personnel: 2036

NORWALK—Fairfield County

☒ **NORWALK HOSPITAL (070034)**, 34 Maple Street, Zip 06850–3894; tel. 203/852–2000 **A**1 2 3 5 8 10 **F**3 5 7 8 11 12 13 15 17 18 20 22 26 28 29 30 31 34 35 36 39 40 43 44 45 46 47 48 49 50 51 53 54 55 57 58 59 64 66 68 70 72 74 75 76 77 78 79 80 81 82 84 85 87 89 93 96 98 100 101 103 104 105 107 108 110 111 114 115 117 118 119 120 121 123 124 126 129 130 131 132 135 145 146 148 **P**8 **S** Western Connecticut Health Network, Danbury, CT
Primary Contact: Michael Daglio, President
CFO: Michael Kruzick, Acting Chief Financial Officer
CMO: Michael Marks, M.D., Chief of Staff
CHR: Anthony Aceto, Vice President Human Resources
Web address: www.norwalkhospital.org
Control: Other not–for–profit (including NFP Corporation) **Service:** General Medical and Surgical

Staffed Beds: 311 Admissions: 11437 Census: 150 Outpatient Visits: 267945 Births: 1370 Total Expense ($000): 357442 Payroll Expense ($000): 135722 Personnel: 1494

NORWICH—New London County

☒ **THE WILLIAM W. BACKUS HOSPITAL (070024)**, 326 Washington Street, Zip 06360–2740; tel. 860/889–8331 **A**1 2 3 5 10 **F**3 9 11 12 13 15 18 20 26 28 29 30 31 34 35 36 40 42 43 45 46 49 50 51 54 57 58 59 61 63 64 65 70 71 74 75 76 78 79 81 82 84 85 86 87 89 92 93 97 98 100 101 102 103 104 105 107 108 110 111 114 116 117 118 119 120 121 126 130 132 134 135 144 145 146 147 148 **S** Hartford HealthCare, Hartford, CT
Primary Contact: Bimal Patel, President, Hartford HealthCare East Region
COO: Carolyn Trantalis, R.N., Regional Vice President, Clinical Services and Operations
CFO: Daniel E. Lohr, Regional Vice President Finance
CMO: Robert Sidman, M.D., Regional Vice President, Medical Affairs
CIO: Angie Mathieu, System Director Information Technology and Regional Chief Information Officer
CHR: Karen James, Regional Director, Human Resources
CNO: Carolyn Trantalis, R.N., Regional Vice President, Clinical Services and Operations
Web address: www.backushospital.org
Control: Other not–for–profit (including NFP Corporation) **Service:** General Medical and Surgical

Staffed Beds: 184 Admissions: 9878 Census: 125 Outpatient Visits: 502664 Births: 903 Total Expense ($000): 251580 Payroll Expense ($000): 108506 Personnel: 1250

PUTNAM—Windham County

☒ **DAY KIMBALL HOSPITAL (070003)**, 320 Pomfret Street, Zip 06260–1836; tel. 860/928–6541 **A**1 2 5 10 **F**3 8 13 15 17 18 28 29 30 31 34 35 36 38 40 45 50 54 58 59 62 63 64 65 68 70 75 76 77 78 79 81 84 85 87 89 93 98 99 100 102 103 104 107 108 109 110 115 118 119 129 130 132 135 145 146 147 148 **P**3
Primary Contact: Robert E. Smanik, FACHE, President and Chief Executive Officer
CFO: James M. Burke, Chief Financial Officer
CMO: John Graham, M.D., Vice President Medical Affairs
CIO: Odile Romanick, Chief information Officer
CHR: Marlene Woods, Director Human Resources
CNO: John O'Keefe, Chief Nursing Officer
Web address: www.daykimball.org
Control: Other not–for–profit (including NFP Corporation) **Service:** General Medical and Surgical

Staffed Beds: 65 Admissions: 3891 Census: 42 Outpatient Visits: 684025 Births: 552 Total Expense ($000): 106930 Payroll Expense ($000): 46571 Personnel: 768

ROCKY HILL—Hartford County

CONNECTICUT VETERANS HOME AND HOSPITAL (072006), 287 West Street, Zip 06067–3501; tel. 860/616–3606, (Nonreporting) **A**10
Primary Contact: Seam Connolly, Commissioner
CFO: Michael Clark, Fiscal Administrative Manager
CMO: Vamseedhar Alla, M.D., Director Medical Staff
CIO: Sheri DeVaux, Information Technology Manager
CHR: Noreen Sinclair, Human Resources Administrator
CNO: Jeff Lord, Director of Nursing
Web address: www.ct.gov/ctva
Control: State–Government, nonfederal **Service:** Long–Term Acute Care hospital

Staffed Beds: 125

SHARON—Litchfield County

☐ **SHARON HOSPITAL (070004)**, 50 Hospital Hill Road, Zip 06069–2096, Mailing Address: P.O. Box 789, Zip 06069–0789; tel. 860/364–4000, (Nonreporting) **A**1 10 20 **S** RCCH HealthCare Partners, Brentwood, TN
Primary Contact: Peter Cordeau, Chief Executive Officer
CMO: Michael Parker, M.D., Chief of Staff
CHR: Kathleen Berlinghoff, Director Human Resources
Web address: www.sharonhospital.com
Control: Corporation, Investor–owned, for–profit **Service:** General Medical and Surgical

Staffed Beds: 78

SOMERS—Tolland County

CONNECTICUT DEPARTMENT OF CORRECTION'S HOSPITAL, 100 Bilton Road, Zip 06071–1059, Mailing Address: P.O. Box 100, Zip 06071–0100; tel. 860/749–8391, (Nonreporting)
Primary Contact: Edward A. Blanchette, M.D., Director
Control: State–Government, nonfederal **Service:** Hospital unit of an institution (prison hospital, college infimary, etc.)

Staffed Beds: 29

SOUTHINGTON—Hartford County

BRADLEY MEMORIAL See The Hospital of Central Connecticut, New Britain

Many Facility Codes have changed. Please refer to the AHA Guide Code Chart. © 2016 AHA Guide

STAFFORD SPRINGS—Tolland County

☒ **JOHNSON MEMORIAL MEDICAL CENTER (070008)**, 201 Chestnut Hill Road, Zip 06076–4005; tel. 860/684–4251, (Nonreporting) **A**1 2 10 **S** Trinity Health, Livonia, MI
Primary Contact: Stuart E. Rosenberg, President and Chief Executive Officer
CFO: John Grish, Chief Financial Officer
CMO: Ian Tucker, M.D., Vice President Medical Affairs
CHR: Donna M. Megliola, Assistant Vice President
CNO: Patricia Jagoe, Assistant Vice President Patient Care
Web address: www.jmmc.com
Control: Other not–for–profit (including NFP Corporation) **Service:** General Medical and Surgical

Staffed Beds: 72

STAMFORD—Fairfield County

☒ **STAMFORD HOSPITAL (070006)**, One Hospital Plaza, Zip 06902, Mailing Address: P.O. Box 9317, Zip 06904–9317; tel. 203/276–1000 **A**1 2 3 5 8 10 **F**3 8 12 13 15 18 19 20 22 24 26 28 29 30 31 32 34 35 36 37 38 40 41 43 44 45 46 47 48 49 50 52 53 54 55 56 57 58 59 60 61 64 65 66 68 70 71 72 74 75 76 77 78 79 81 82 84 85 86 87 89 90 91 92 93 95 96 97 98 100 101 102 103 104 107 108 110 111 114 115 116 117 118 119 120 121 123 124 126 129 130 131 132 135 144 145 146 147 148 **P**6
Primary Contact: Brian G. Grissler, President and Chief Executive Officer
COO: Kathleen A. Silard, R.N., Executive Vice President Operations and Chief Operating Officer
CFO: Kevin Gage, Chief Financial Officer
CMO: Sharon Kiely, M.D., Senior Vice President Medical Affairs and Chief Medical Officer
CIO: Steven Sakovits, Vice President Information Systems and Chief Information Officer
CHR: Elaine Guglielmo, Vice President Human Resources and Organizational Development
CNO: Ellen M. Komar, R.N., Vice President Patient Care Services and Chief Nursing Officer
Web address: www.stamhealth.org
Control: Other not–for–profit (including NFP Corporation) **Service:** General Medical and Surgical

Staffed Beds: 305 Admissions: 12716 Census: 184 Outpatient Visits: 455347 Births: 2131 Total Expense ($000): 447673 Payroll Expense ($000): 187562 Personnel: 2149

TORRINGTON—Litchfield County

☐ **THE CHARLOTTE HUNGERFORD HOSPITAL (070011)**, 540 Litchfield Street, Zip 06790–6679, Mailing Address: P.O. Box 988, Zip 06790–0988; tel. 860/496–6666 **A**1 2 10 **F**3 5 8 11 13 15 18 28 29 30 31 34 35 38 40 41 42 44 45 47 48 49 50 51 54 59 60 64 70 71 76 77 78 79 81 82 85 87 89 93 97 98 99 100 102 104 105 106 107 110 111 115 117 119 120 121 123 129 130 131 132 144 146 148 **P**6
Primary Contact: Daniel J. McIntyre, President and Chief Executive Officer
CFO: Susan Schapp, Vice President Finance and Treasurer
CMO: Mark Prete, M.D., Vice President Medical Affairs
CHR: R. James Elliott, Vice President Human Resources
Web address: www.charlottehungerford.org
Control: Other not–for–profit (including NFP Corporation) **Service:** General Medical and Surgical

Staffed Beds: 72 Admissions: 5580 Census: 68 Outpatient Visits: 284573 Births: 450 Total Expense ($000): 121979 Payroll Expense ($000): 55931 Personnel: 530

VERNON—Tolland County

☒ **ROCKVILLE GENERAL HOSPITAL (070012)**, 31 Union Street, Zip 06066–3160; tel. 860/872–0501, (Nonreporting) **A**1 5 10 **S** Eastern Connecticut Health Network, Manchester, CT
Primary Contact: Peter J. Karl, President and Chief Executive Officer
CFO: Michael D. Veillette, Senior Vice President and Chief Financial Officer
CMO: Joel R. Reich, M.D., Senior Vice President Medical Affairs
CIO: Richard Daigle, Chief Information Officer
CHR: Natalie Cook, Administrative Director, Human Resources
CNO: Mary Powers, MSN, Senior Vice President and Chief Nursing Officer
Web address: www.echn.org
Control: Other not–for–profit (including NFP Corporation) **Service:** General Medical and Surgical

Staffed Beds: 47

WALLINGFORD—New Haven County

☐ △ **GAYLORD HOSPITAL (072003)**, Gaylord Farm Road, Zip 06492–7048, Mailing Address: P.O. Box 400, Zip 06492–7048; tel. 203/284–2800 **A**1 5 7 10 **F**1 29 30 31 34 35 53 54 59 60 64 74 75 82 84 85 86 87 91 93 94 95 96 104 107 114 119 130 131 132 146 148 **P**5
Primary Contact: George M. Kyriacou, President and Chief Executive Officer
CFO: Art Tedesco, Interim Chief Financial Officer
CMO: Stephen Holland, M.D., Vice President Chief Medical Officer and Medical Director
CIO: Gerry Maroney, Chief Information Officer and Security Officer
CHR: Wally G. Harper SPHR, Vice President Human Resources
CNO: Virginia Staubach, R.N., Chief Nursing Officer and Senior Director of Nursing Services
Web address: www.gaylord.org
Control: Other not–for–profit (including NFP Corporation) **Service:** Long–Term Acute Care hospital

Staffed Beds: 123 Admissions: 1471 Census: 111 Outpatient Visits: 59343 Births: 0 Total Expense ($000): 72422 Payroll Expense ($000): 40085 Personnel: 457

★ **MASONICARE HEALTH CENTER (070039)**, 22 Masonic Avenue, Zip 06492–3048, Mailing Address: P.O. Box 70, Zip 06492–7001; tel. 203/679–5900, (Nonreporting) **A**3 5 10
Primary Contact: Stephen B. McPherson, President and Chief Executive Officer
COO: Jon–Paul Venoit, Chief Operating Officer
CFO: Raymond Scott Thelen, Vice President and Chief Financial Officer
CMO: Ronald Schwartz, M.D., Medical Director
CIO: Michael Nichols, Chief Information Officer
CHR: Edward Dooling, Vice President, Human Resources
CNO: Patti Russell, Vice President Nursing
Web address: www.masonicare.org
Control: Other not–for–profit (including NFP Corporation) **Service:** Other specialty

Staffed Beds: 65

WATERBURY—New Haven County

☒ **SAINT MARY'S HOSPITAL (070016)**, 56 Franklin Street, Zip 06706–1281; tel. 203/709–6000 **A**1 2 3 5 10 **F**3 5 8 11 13 15 17 18 20 22 24 26 28 29 30 31 32 34 35 36 37 39 40 41 43 45 46 47 49 50 51 53 54 55 57 59 64 70 72 73 74 75 76 77 78 79 80 81 85 87 92 93 96 98 100 102 104 107 108 110 111 114 115 118 119 126 129 130 132 135 144 145 146 147 148 **P**6 **S** Trinity Health, Livonia, MI
Primary Contact: Chad W. Wable, President and Chief Executive Officer
COO: Charles Flinn, Vice President, Chief Operating Officer
CFO: Ralph W. Becker, Vice President, Chief Financial Officer
CMO: Steven E. Schneider, M.D., Chief Medical Officer
CIO: Michael Novak, Vice President, Operations and Chief Information Officer
CHR: M. Clark Kearney, Vice President Human Resources
CNO: Elizabeth Bozzuto, R.N., Chief Nursing Officer and Vice President
Web address: www.stmh.org
Control: Church–operated, Nongovernment, not–for profit **Service:** General Medical and Surgical

Staffed Beds: 156 Admissions: 10932 Census: 133 Outpatient Visits: 255801 Births: 1042 Total Expense ($000): 241388 Payroll Expense ($000): 88793 Personnel: 1309

☒ **WATERBURY HOSPITAL (070005)**, 64 Robbins Street, Zip 06708–2600; tel. 203/573–6000 **A**1 2 3 5 10 **F**3 5 9 12 13 15 17 18 20 22 24 28 29 30 31 34 35 38 40 41 43 44 45 47 49 50 51 53 55 56 57 58 59 61 64 68 70 72 73 74 75 76 78 79 81 82 84 85 87 90 97 98 99 100 101 102 103 104 105 107 108 110 111 115 119 126 129 130 131 132 145 146 147 148
Primary Contact: Darlene Stromstad, FACHE, President and Chief Executive Officer
CFO: Colleen M. Scott, Vice President Finance
CMO: David Puzzuto, M.D., Vice President Medical Affairs and Chief Medical Officer
CIO: Michael J. Cemeno, Chief Information Officer
CHR: Diane Woolley, Vice President Human Resources
CNO: Sandra Ladarola, Chief Nursing Officer
Web address: www.waterburyhospital.org
Control: Other not–for–profit (including NFP Corporation) **Service:** General Medical and Surgical

Staffed Beds: 183 Admissions: 10507 Census: 146 Outpatient Visits: 162244 Births: 1106 Total Expense ($000): 210953 Payroll Expense ($000): 80844 Personnel: 1044

CT

Hospital, Medicare Provider Number, Address, Telephone, Approval, Facility, and Physician Codes, Health Care System

★ American Hospital Association (AHA) membership ○ Healthcare Facilities Accreditation Program ⇑ Center for Improvement in Healthcare Quality Accreditation
☐ The Joint Commission accreditation ◇ DNV Healthcare Inc. accreditation △ Commission on Accreditation of Rehabilitation Facilities (CARF) accreditation

WEST HARTFORD—Hartford County

★ **THE HOSPITAL AT HEBREW HEALTH CARE (070040)**, 1 Abrahms Boulevard, Zip 06117–1525; tel. 860/523–3800, (Nonreporting) **A**10
Primary Contact: Bonnie B. Gauthier, President and Chief Executive Officer
COO: Marcia H. Hickey, Senior Vice President Operations
CFO: David Houle, Executive Vice President and Chief Financial Officer
CMO: Ava Pannullo, M.D., Vice President Medical Services and Physician in Chief
CHR: Sam Vogt, Manager Human Resources
Web address: www.hebrewhealthcare.org
Control: Other not–for–profit (including NFP Corporation) **Service:** Other specialty

Staffed Beds: 322

WEST HAVEN—New Haven County

☒ **VETERANS AFFAIRS CONNECTICUT HEALTHCARE SYSTEM**, 950 Campbell Avenue, Zip 06516–2770; tel. 203/932–5711, (Includes WEST HAVEN DIVISION, 950 Campbell Avenue, Zip 06516–2700; tel. 203/932–5711), (Nonreporting) **A**1 2 3 5 8 **S** Department of Veterans Affairs, Washington, DC
Primary Contact: Gerald F. Culliton, Medical Center Director
CFO: Joseph LaMadeleine, Chief Financial Officer
CMO: Michael Ebert, M.D., Chief of Staff
CIO: Joseph Erdos, M.D., Chief Information Officer
CHR: Mark Bain, Chief Human Resources
Web address: www.connecticut.va.gov
Control: Veterans Affairs, Government, federal **Service:** General Medical and Surgical

Staffed Beds: 197

WESTPORT—Fairfield County

ST. VINCENT'S BEHAVIORAL HEALTH See St. Vincent's Medical Center, Bridgeport

WILLIMANTIC—Windham County

WINDHAM COMMUNITY MEMORIAL HOSPITAL See Windham Hospital

☒ **WINDHAM HOSPITAL (070021)**, 112 Mansfield Avenue, Zip 06226–2040; tel. 860/456–9116 **A**1 2 5 10 **F**3 8 11 12 13 14 15 18 28 29 30 31 32 34 35 36 40 45 48 50 51 54 56 57 59 60 61 64 65 66 68 75 76 77 78 79 81 82 83 84 85 86 87 90 93 94 100 102 107 108 110 111 115 116 117 118 119 129 130 131 132 134 135 144 146 147 148 **S** Hartford HealthCare, Hartford, CT
Primary Contact: Bimal Patel, President, Hartford Healthcare East Region
COO: Carolyn Trantalis, R.N., Chief Operating Officer, East Region
CFO: Daniel E. Lohr, Regional Vice President Finance
CMO: Nadia Nashid, M.D., Chief of Staff
CHR: Theresa L. Buss, Regional Vice President Human Resources
Web address: www.windhamhospital.org
Control: Other not–for–profit (including NFP Corporation) **Service:** General Medical and Surgical

Staffed Beds: 56 **Admissions:** 2737 **Census:** 32 **Outpatient Visits:** 95420 **Births:** 212 **Total Expense ($000):** 86657 **Payroll Expense ($000):** 35928 **Personnel:** 430

CT

DELAWARE

DOVER—Kent County

✠ **BAYHEALTH MEDICAL CENTER (080004)**, 640 South State Street, Zip 19901–3530; tel. 302/674–4700, (Includes BAYHEALTH MEDICAL CENTER AT KENT GENERAL, 640 South State Street, Zip 19901–3597; BAYHEALTH MEDICAL CENTER, MILFORD MEMORIAL HOSPITAL, 21 West Clarke Avenue, Milford, Zip 19963–1840, Mailing Address: P.O. Box 199, Zip 19963–0199; tel. 302/430–5738; Michael Ashton, Administrator) **A**1 2 3 5 10 **F**3 8 11 12 13 15 17 18 20 22 24 26 28 29 30 31 32 34 35 38 40 41 42 43 44 45 47 48 49 50 51 53 54 55 57 58 59 60 61 62 64 67 68 70 72 73 74 75 76 77 78 79 81 82 84 85 86 87 88 89 90 93 94 98 99 100 101 102 103 104 107 108 110 111 114 115 117 118 119 120 121 123 124 126 129 130 131 132 134 135 144 146 147 148
Primary Contact: Terry Murphy, President and Chief Executive Officer
COO: Deborah Watson, Senior Vice President and Chief Operating Officer
CFO: Mike Tretina, Senior Vice President and Chief Financial Officer
CMO: Gary M. Siegelman, M.D., Senior Vice President and Chief Medical Officer
CIO: Richard Mohnk, Vice President Corporate Services
CHR: Shana Ross, Vice President Human Resources
CNO: Bonnie I. Perratto, MSN, Senior Vice President, Chief Nurse Executive
Web address: www.bayhealth.org
Control: Other not–for–profit (including NFP Corporation) **Service:** General Medical and Surgical

> **Staffed Beds: 360 Admissions: 18755 Census: 288 Outpatient Visits: 603671 Births: 2317 Total Expense ($000): 528425 Payroll Expense ($000): 239203 Personnel: 3138**

☐ **DOVER BEHAVIORAL HEALTH SYSTEM (084004)**, 725 Horsepond Road, Zip 19901–7232; tel. 302/741–0140, (Nonreporting) **A**1 10 **S** Universal Health Services, Inc., King of Prussia, PA
Primary Contact: Jean–Charles Constant, Administrator
Web address: www.doverbehavioral.com
Control: Corporation, Investor–owned, for–profit **Service:** Psychiatric

> **Staffed Beds: 72**

LEWES—Sussex County

✠ **BEEBE HEALTHCARE (080007)**, 424 Savannah Road, Zip 19958–1462; tel. 302/645–3300 **A**1 2 3 10 19 **F**2 3 8 11 12 13 15 17 18 20 22 24 26 28 29 30 31 32 34 35 36 38 40 43 45 46 49 50 51 53 54 55 56 57 58 59 60 61 62 64 65 68 70 74 75 76 77 78 79 80 81 84 85 87 89 93 97 100 107 108 110 111 114 115 116 117 118 119 120 121 123 124 130 131 132 134 143 146 147 148 **P**4
Primary Contact: Jeffrey M. Fried, FACHE, President and Chief Executive Officer
CFO: Paul Pernice, Vice President Finance
CMO: Jeffrey Hawtof, M.D., Vice President Medical Operations and Informatics
CIO: Michael Maksymow, Vice President Information Systems
CHR: Catherine Halen, Vice President Human Resources
CNO: Steve Rhone, R.N., Vice President Patient Care Services
Web address: www.beebemed.org
Control: Other not–for–profit (including NFP Corporation) **Service:** General Medical and Surgical

> **Staffed Beds: 155 Admissions: 10003 Census: 122 Outpatient Visits: 505255 Births: 870 Total Expense ($000): 297622 Payroll Expense ($000): 109830 Personnel: 1950**

MILFORD—Sussex County

BAYHEALTH MEDICAL CENTER, MILFORD MEMORIAL HOSPITAL See Bayhealth Medical Center, Dover

NEW CASTLE—New Castle County

☐ **DELAWARE PSYCHIATRIC CENTER (084001)**, 1901 North Dupont Highway, Zip 19720–1199; tel. 302/255–2700 **A**1 3 5 10 **F**30 34 39 59 65 68 75 86 87 98 100 101 103 106 130 132 135 143 **P**1
Primary Contact: Melissa A. Smith, Deputy Director
CIO: James Nau, Manager Computer and Applications Support
Web address: www.dhss.delaware.gov
Control: State–Government, nonfederal **Service:** Psychiatric

> **Staffed Beds: 189 Admissions: 417 Census: 111 Outpatient Visits: 0 Births: 0 Total Expense ($000): 39777 Payroll Expense ($000): 17533 Personnel: 340**

☐ **MEADOW WOOD BEHAVIORAL HEALTH SYSTEM (084003)**, 575 South Dupont Highway, Zip 19720–4606; tel. 302/328–3330, (Nonreporting) **A**1 10 **S** Acadia Healthcare Company, Inc., Franklin, TN
Primary Contact: Bill A. Mason, Chief Executive Officer
CFO: Maria Valdenegro, Chief Financial Officer
Web address: www.meadowwoodhospital.com
Control: Corporation, Investor–owned, for–profit **Service:** Psychiatric

> **Staffed Beds: 53**

NEWARK—New Castle County

✠ **CHRISTIANA CARE HEALTH SYSTEM (080001)**, 4755 Ogletown–Stanton Road, Zip 19718–0002, Mailing Address: P.O. Box 6001, Zip 19718; tel. 302/733–1000 **A**1 2 3 5 8 10 12 13 **F**2 3 5 6 7 8 11 12 13 15 17 18 20 22 24 26 28 29 30 31 32 34 35 36 37 38 39 40 41 42 43 44 45 46 47 48 49 50 53 54 55 56 57 58 59 60 61 62 64 65 66 68 70 72 74 75 76 77 78 79 80 81 82 84 85 86 87 89 90 92 93 94 96 97 98 100 101 102 103 104 107 108 110 111 114 115 116 117 118 119 120 121 123 124 126 129 130 131 132 134 135 136 138 143 144 145 146 147 148 **P**6 **S** Christiana Care Health System, Wilmington, DE
Primary Contact: Janice E. Nevin, M.D., M.P.H., Chief Executive Officer
CFO: Thomas L. Corrigan, Senior Vice President Finance, Managed Care and Chief Financial Officer
CMO: Kenneth L. Silverstein, Chief Clinical Officer
CIO: Randall Gaboriault, Chief Information Officer
CHR: Audrey C. Van Luven, Senior Vice President and Chief Human Resources Officer
CNO: Ric Cuming, Chief Nurse Executive
Web address: www.christianacare.org
Control: Other not–for–profit (including NFP Corporation) **Service:** General Medical and Surgical

> **Staffed Beds: 1049 Admissions: 53072 Census: 767 Outpatient Visits: 587975 Births: 6469 Total Expense ($000): 1536251 Payroll Expense ($000): 739074 Personnel: 9685**

☐ **ROCKFORD CENTER (084002)**, 100 Rockford Drive, Zip 19713–2121; tel. 302/996–5480 **A**1 10 **F**98 99 102 103 104 105 **P**6 8 **S** Universal Health Services, Inc., King of Prussia, PA
Primary Contact: John F. McKenna, Chief Executive Officer and Managing Director
CFO: Kumar Purohit, Chief Financial Officer
CMO: Saurabh Gupta, Chief Medical Officer
CHR: Jessi Stewart, Director Human Resources
CNO: Michelle Singletary–Twyman, Chief Nursing Officer
Web address: www.rockfordcenter.com
Control: Corporation, Investor–owned, for–profit **Service:** Psychiatric

> **Staffed Beds: 128 Admissions: 4389 Census: 126 Outpatient Visits: 14201 Births: 0 Total Expense ($000): 27663 Payroll Expense ($000): 16061**

SEAFORD—Sussex County

✠ **NANTICOKE MEMORIAL HOSPITAL (080006)**, 801 Middleford Road, Zip 19973–3636; tel. 302/629–6611 **A**1 2 10 19 **F**3 13 15 18 20 22 28 29 30 31 32 34 35 37 40 43 45 50 51 54 57 59 60 64 65 68 70 74 75 76 77 78 79 81 84 85 86 87 89 93 107 108 111 114 115 117 119 120 121 123 129 130 132 135 144 146 147 148
Primary Contact: Steven A. Rose, R.N., President and Chief Executive Officer
COO: Penny Short, R.N., Chief Operating Officer
CFO: Denise Jester, Chief Financial Officer
CMO: Robert Ferber, M.D., Chief Clinical Innovation Officer
CIO: Charles Palmer, Director Information Technology
CHR: Barbara A. Hendricks, Vice President, Human Resources
CNO: Lori L. Lee, Assistant Vice President Nursing
Web address: www.nanticoke.org
Control: Other not–for–profit (including NFP Corporation) **Service:** General Medical and Surgical

> **Staffed Beds: 99 Admissions: 5232 Census: 52 Outpatient Visits: 136599 Births: 844 Total Expense ($000): 117046 Payroll Expense ($000): 40942 Personnel: 737**

DE

Hospital, Medicare Provider Number, Address, Telephone, Approval, Facility, and Physician Codes, Health Care System

★ American Hospital Association (AHA) membership
☐ The Joint Commission accreditation
◯ Healthcare Facilities Accreditation Program
◇ DNV Healthcare Inc. accreditation
⇑ Center for Improvement in Healthcare Quality Accreditation
△ Commission on Accreditation of Rehabilitation Facilities (CARF) accreditation

WILMINGTON—New Castle County

⊞ △ **ALFRED I. DUPONT HOSPITAL FOR CHILDREN (083300)**, 1600 Rockland Road, Zip 19803–3616, Mailing Address: Box 269, Zip 19899–0269; tel. 302/651–4000 **A**1 2 3 5 7 10 **F**3 8 11 12 17 18 19 20 21 22 23 24 25 26 27 29 30 31 32 34 35 36 37 39 40 41 43 44 45 48 50 53 54 55 56 57 58 59 60 61 64 65 68 72 73 74 75 77 78 79 80 81 82 84 85 86 87 88 89 90 91 92 93 94 96 97 99 100 101 102 104 107 111 115 118 119 126 127 129 130 131 132 136 137 138 139 143 146 148 **S** Nemours, Jacksonville, FL
Primary Contact: Roy Proujansky, M.D., Chief Executive Officer
COO: Paul D. Kempinski, Chief Operating Officer
CFO: William N. Britton, Associate Administrator Finance
CMO: Brent R. King, Chief Medical Officer and Chief Physician
Web address: www.nemours.org
Control: Other not–for–profit (including NFP Corporation) **Service:** Children's general

Staffed Beds: 194 **Admissions:** 9169 **Census:** 129 **Outpatient Visits:** 197059 **Births:** 0 **Total Expense ($000):** 402498 **Payroll Expense ($000):** 133090 **Personnel:** 2225

⊞ **SELECT SPECIALTY HOSPITAL–WILMINGTON (082000)**, 701 North Clayton Street, 5th Floor, Zip 19805–3948; tel. 302/421–4545 **A**1 10 **F**1 18 29 74 79 130 148 **S** Select Medical Corporation, Mechanicsburg, PA
Primary Contact: Donna Gares, R.N., FACHE, MSN, Chief Executive Officer
CFO: David Huffman, Vice President and Controller
CMO: Hummayun Ismail, M.D., Medical Director
CHR: Barbara A. Foster, Regional Human Resources Director
Web address: www.wilmington.selectspecialtyhospitals.com
Control: Corporation, Investor–owned, for–profit **Service:** Long–Term Acute Care hospital

Staffed Beds: 35 **Admissions:** 378 **Census:** 32 **Outpatient Visits:** 0 **Births:** 0 **Total Expense ($000):** 16920 **Payroll Expense ($000):** 7775 **Personnel:** 126

⊞ **ST. FRANCIS HOSPITAL (080003)**, Seventh and Clayton Streets, Zip 19805–0500, Mailing Address: P.O. Box 2500, Zip 19805–0500; tel. 302/421–4100, (Nonreporting) **A**1 2 3 5 10 **S** Trinity Health, Livonia, MI
Primary Contact: Brian E. Dietz, FACHE, Interim President and Chief Executive officer
CIO: Paul W. Rowe, Director Information Technology
CHR: Charlene J. Wilson, Vice President Human Resources
Web address: www.stfrancishealthcare.org
Control: Other not–for–profit (including NFP Corporation) **Service:** General Medical and Surgical

Staffed Beds: 214

⊞ **WILMINGTON VETERANS AFFAIRS MEDICAL CENTER**, 1601 Kirkwood Highway, Zip 19805–4989; tel. 302/994–2511, (Nonreporting) **A**1 3 5 8 **S** Department of Veterans Affairs, Washington, DC
Primary Contact: Robin C. Aube–Warren, Director
CFO: Mary Ann Kozel, Chief Fiscal
CMO: Enrique Guttin, M.D., Chief of Staff
CIO: Scott Vlars, Chief Information Technology Services
CHR: Louis McCloskey, Chief Human Resources
Web address: www.va.gov/wilmington
Control: Veterans Affairs, Government, federal **Service:** General Medical and Surgical

Staffed Beds: 120

DE

DISTRICT OF COLUMBIA

WASHINGTON—District Of Columbia County

☐ **BRIDGEPOINT HOSPITAL CAPITOL HILL (092002)**, 700 Constitution Avenue N.E., Zip 20002–6058; tel. 202/546–5700, (Nonreporting) **A**1 10 **S** BridgePoint Healthcare, Portsmouth, NH
Primary Contact: James Linhares, Chief Executive Officer
COO: Delores Clair Oliver, Chief Clinical Officer and Chief Operating Officer
CFO: Michael Grubb, Chief Financial Officer
CMO: Gerald Moawad, Chief Medical Officer
CHR: Karen Brown, Senior Director of Human Resources
CNO: Delores Clair Oliver, Chief Clinical Officer and Chief Operating Officer
Web address: www.bridgepointhealthcare.com/
Control: Corporation, Investor–owned, for–profit **Service:** Long–Term Acute Care hospital

Staffed Beds: 177

☐ **BRIDGEPOINT HOSPITAL NATIONAL HARBOR (092003)**, 4601 Martin Luther King Jr. Avenue, S.W., Zip 20032–1131; tel. 202/574–5700, (Nonreporting) **A**1 10 **S** BridgePoint Healthcare, Portsmouth, NH
Primary Contact: Kevin Chavez, Chief Executive Officer
CFO: Michael Grubb, Chief Financial Officer
CMO: Khosrow Davachi, Chief Medical Officer
CHR: Antoninette Saldivar, Vice President, Human Resources
CNO: Diane White, Chief Clinical Officer and Chief Nursing Officer
Web address: www.bridgepointhealthcare.com/
Control: Corporation, Investor–owned, for–profit **Service:** Long–Term Acute Care hospital

Staffed Beds: 82

⊞ **CHILDREN'S NATIONAL HEALTH SYSTEM (093300)**, 111 Michigan Avenue N.W., Zip 20010–2916; tel. 202/476–5000 **A**1 3 5 8 10 **F**1 3 4 5 7 8 11 12 14 16 17 18 19 21 23 25 27 29 30 31 32 34 35 36 38 39 40 41 42 43 44 45 46 48 49 50 51 54 55 57 58 59 60 61 64 65 66 67 68 70 71 72 73 74 75 77 78 79 80 81 82 83 84 85 86 87 88 89 90 91 92 93 94 96 97 98 99 100 102 104 107 111 112 115 116 117 118 119 126 128 129 130 131 132 134 136 137 138 141 142 146 148 **P**6
Primary Contact: Kurt Newman, M.D., President and Chief Executive Officer
COO: Kathleen Gorman, MSN, Executive Vice President Patient Care Services and Chief Operating Officer
CFO: Douglas Myers, Executive Vice President and Chief Financial Officer
CMO: Mark L. Batshaw, M.D., Physician–in–Chief, Executive Vice President and Chief Academic Officer
CIO: Brian Jacobs, M.D., Vice President Chief Information Officer and Chief Medical Information Officer
CHR: Darryl Varnado, Executive Vice President and Chief People Officer
CNO: Linda Talley, MS, Vice President and Chief Nursing Officer
Web address: www.childrensnational.org
Control: Other not–for–profit (including NFP Corporation) **Service:** Children's general

Staffed Beds: 313 **Admissions:** 15609 **Census:** 253 **Outpatient Visits:** 518796 **Births:** 0 **Total Expense ($000):** 726826 **Payroll Expense ($000):** 325264 **Personnel:** 5279

⊞ △ **GEORGE WASHINGTON UNIVERSITY HOSPITAL (090001)**, 900 23rd Street N.W., Zip 20037–2342; tel. 202/715–4000 **A**1 2 3 5 7 8 10 **F**3 8 12 13 15 17 18 20 22 24 26 29 31 34 35 40 43 45 46 47 48 49 50 51 54 55 56 57 58 59 64 70 72 74 75 76 77 78 79 81 82 84 85 86 87 90 91 92 93 94 96 98 107 108 110 111 114 115 116 117 118 119 120 121 123 126 129 130 131 132 135 136 138 141 146 **P**6 **S** Universal Health Services, Inc., King of Prussia, PA
Primary Contact: Kimberly Russo, Chief Executive Officer
COO: Kimberly Russo, Chief Operating Officer
CFO: Richard Davis, Chief Financial Officer
CMO: Gary Little, M.D., Medical Director
CIO: Louis Duhe, Senior Director Information Technology
CHR: Erin Fagan, Manager Human Resources
Web address: www.gwhospital.com
Control: Partnership, Investor–owned, for–profit **Service:** General Medical and Surgical

Staffed Beds: 385 **Admissions:** 19141 **Census:** 279 **Outpatient Visits:** 133961 **Births:** 3127 **Total Expense ($000):** 296364 **Payroll Expense ($000):** 153864 **Personnel:** 1802

GEORGETOWN UNIVERSITY HOSPITAL See MedStar Georgetown University Hospital

⊞ **HOWARD UNIVERSITY HOSPITAL (090003)**, 2041 Georgia Avenue N.W., Zip 20060–0002; tel. 202/865–6100 **A**1 2 3 5 8 10 **F**3 8 12 13 15 17 18 24 26 28 29 30 31 32 34 35 36 38 39 40 41 43 44 45 46 50 54 55 56 57 58 59 60 61 64 65 66 68 70 71 72 74 75 77 78 79 81 82 85 86 87 93 97 98 99 100 101 102 103 104 107 108 110 111 114 115 118 119 123 124 129 130 132 146 147 148 **P**4
Primary Contact: James D. Edwards, Chief Executive Officer
COO: Patrick J. Canavan, PsyD, Chief Operating Officer
CFO: James Corwin, Interim Chief Financial Officer
CMO: Shelly McDonald–Pinkett, Chief Medical Officer
CIO: Becky Quammen, Chief Information Officer
CHR: Jeronica Goodwin, Senior Director Human Resources
CNO: Gloria Gammage, Chief Nursing Officer
Web address: www.huhealthcare.com
Control: Other not–for–profit (including NFP Corporation) **Service:** General Medical and Surgical

Staffed Beds: 268 **Admissions:** 8893 **Census:** 107 **Outpatient Visits:** 150745 **Births:** 968 **Total Expense ($000):** 306126 **Payroll Expense ($000):** 112393 **Personnel:** 1800

⊞ **MEDSTAR GEORGETOWN UNIVERSITY HOSPITAL (090004)**, 3800 Reservoir Road N.W., Zip 20007–2197; tel. 202/444–2000 **A**1 2 3 5 8 10 **F**3 4 6 9 11 13 15 17 18 20 26 28 29 30 31 32 34 35 37 40 41 44 45 46 47 48 49 50 51 54 55 57 58 59 60 61 64 65 66 67 68 70 71 72 73 74 75 76 77 78 79 80 81 82 84 85 86 87 88 89 90 92 93 94 97 98 99 100 102 103 104 105 107 108 109 110 111 114 115 116 117 118 119 120 121 123 124 126 128 129 130 131 132 134 136 138 139 141 142 145 146 147 148 **P**6 **S** MedStar Health, Columbia, MD
Primary Contact: Michael Sachtleben, President
CFO: Paul Warda, Chief Financial Officer
CMO: Lisa Boyle, M.D., Vice President Medical Affairs and Medical Director
CIO: John Rasmussen, Vice President for Information Technology
CHR: Mary Jo Schweickhardt, Vice President Human Resources
CNO: Eileen Brennan Ferrell, MS, Vice President and Chief Nursing Officer
Web address: www.georgetownuniversityhospital.org
Control: Other not–for–profit (including NFP Corporation) **Service:** General Medical and Surgical

Staffed Beds: 415 **Admissions:** 16046 **Census:** 324 **Outpatient Visits:** 881135 **Births:** 1088 **Total Expense ($000):** 907855 **Payroll Expense ($000):** 413642 **Personnel:** 4615

⊞ △ **MEDSTAR NATIONAL REHABILITATION HOSPITAL (093025)**, 102 Irving Street N.W., Zip 20010–2949; tel. 202/877–1000 **A**1 3 5 7 10 **F**9 11 28 29 30 35 36 44 53 54 56 58 59 60 64 68 74 75 77 78 79 82 86 87 90 91 92 93 94 95 96 119 129 130 132 146 148 **P**6 **S** MedStar Health, Columbia, MD
Primary Contact: John D. Rockwood, President
CFO: Michael Boemmel, Vice President and Chief Financial Officer
CMO: Michael R. Yochelson, M.D., Vice President and Medical Director
CHR: Pamela Ashby, Vice President Human Resources
CNO: Rosemary C. Welch, R.N., Vice President and Chief Nursing Officer
Web address: www.medstarnrh.org
Control: Other not–for–profit (including NFP Corporation) **Service:** Rehabilitation

Staffed Beds: 137 **Admissions:** 2077 **Census:** 99 **Outpatient Visits:** 344543 **Births:** 0 **Total Expense ($000):** 117297 **Payroll Expense ($000):** 66899 **Personnel:** 1287

DC

Hospital, Medicare Provider Number, Address, Telephone, Approval, Facility, and Physician Codes, Health Care System

★ American Hospital Association (AHA) membership   ○ Healthcare Facilities Accreditation Program   ⇧ Center for Improvement in Healthcare Quality Accreditation
☐ The Joint Commission accreditation   ◇ DNV Healthcare Inc. accreditation   △ Commission on Accreditation of Rehabilitation Facilities (CARF) accreditation

✠ **MEDSTAR WASHINGTON HOSPITAL CENTER (090011)**, 110 Irving Street N.W., Zip 20010-3017; tel. 202/877-7000 **A**1 2 3 5 8 10 **F**3 4 5 12 13 15 16 17 18 20 22 24 26 28 29 30 31 34 35 36 37 38 39 40 43 44 45 46 47 48 49 50 51 54 55 56 57 58 59 60 61 62 63 64 65 66 68 70 72 73 74 75 76 77 78 79 80 81 82 84 85 86 87 92 97 98 100 101 102 103 104 105 107 108 109 110 111 112 114 115 116 117 118 119 120 121 124 126 130 131 132 134 135 137 138 142 144 146 147 148 **P**1 6 **S** MedStar Health, Columbia, MD
Primary Contact: John Sullivan, President
COO: Robert Ross, Chief Operating Officer
CFO: William Gayne, Chief Financial Officer
CMO: Gregory J. Argyros, M.D., Senior Vice President, Medical Affairs & Chief Medical Officer
CIO: Joe Brothman, Assistant Vice President, Information Systems
CHR: James P. Hill, Senior Vice President Administrative Services
CNO: Susan E. Eckert, R.N., Senior Vice President and Chief Nursing Officer
Web address: www.whcenter.org
Control: Other not-for-profit (including NFP Corporation) **Service:** General Medical and Surgical

Staffed Beds: 765 **Admissions:** 34795 **Census:** 607 **Outpatient Visits:** 389535 **Births:** 3361 **Total Expense ($000):** 1140282 **Payroll Expense ($000):** 512317 **Personnel:** 5750

NATIONAL REHABILITATION HOSPITAL See MedStar National Rehabilitation Hospital

✠ **PROVIDENCE HOSPITAL (090006)**, 1150 Varnum Street N.E., Zip 20017-2104; tel. 202/269-7000, (Total facility includes 252 beds in nursing home-type unit) **A**1 2 3 5 10 **F**4 5 12 13 15 17 20 22 26 29 30 31 32 34 35 40 44 45 46 47 48 49 50 53 54 56 57 59 61 64 65 68 70 72 74 75 76 78 79 81 84 85 86 87 93 94 97 98 100 104 107 110 111 114 115 116 119 124 128 129 130 131 132 135 143 144 146 147 **S** Ascension Health, Saint Louis, MO
Primary Contact: Darcy Burthay, MSN, R.N., President and Chief Executive Officer
CFO: Rick Talento, Senior Vice President and Chief Financial Officer
CMO: Raymond L. Cox, M.D., Chief Medical Officer
CIO: Alan Wyman, Chief Information Officer
CHR: Matt Lasecki, Interim Vice President Human Resources
CNO: Thedosia Munford, Senior Vice President and Chief Nursing Officer
Web address: www.provhosp.org
Control: Other not-for-profit (including NFP Corporation) **Service:** General Medical and Surgical

Staffed Beds: 448 **Admissions:** 11648 **Census:** 377 **Outpatient Visits:** 109244 **Births:** 2116 **Total Expense ($000):** 179521 **Payroll Expense ($000):** 73309 **Personnel:** 1363

☐ **PSYCHIATRIC INSTITUTE OF WASHINGTON (094004)**, 4228 Wisconsin Avenue N.W., Zip 20016-2138; tel. 202/885-5600 **A**1 5 10 **F**5 54 98 99 101 104 105 106 **P**5
Primary Contact: Charles J. Baumgardner, President and Chief Executive Officer
COO: Carol Desjeunes, Vice President and Chief Operating Officer
CFO: Aarti Subramanian, Vice President and Chief Financial Officer
CMO: Howard Hoffman, M.D., Medical Director
CIO: Ray Santina, Director Information Systems
CHR: Dawn Hatterer-Hoag, Director Human Resources
Web address: www.psychinstitute.com
Control: Corporation, Investor-owned, for-profit **Service:** Psychiatric

Staffed Beds: 114 **Admissions:** 4247 **Census:** 90 **Outpatient Visits:** 1787 **Births:** 0 **Total Expense ($000):** 35084 **Payroll Expense ($000):** 13777 **Personnel:** 238

★ **SAINT ELIZABETHS HOSPITAL (094001)**, 1100 Alabama Avenue S.E., Zip 20032-4540; tel. 202/299-5000 **A**3 5 10 **F**30 39 56 59 65 74 75 86 91 98 99 103 130 135 146 148
Primary Contact: Mark J. Chastang, M.P.H., Chief Executive Officer
CFO: James V. Jackson, Budget Director
CMO: Hannah Ong, Director, Medical Affairs
CIO: Brady Birdsong, Chief Information Officer
CHR: Frankie Wheeler, Director, Human Resources
CNO: Clotilde Vidoni-Clark, R.N., Chief Nurse Executive
Web address: www.dbh.dc.gov/
Control: State-Government, nonfederal **Service:** Psychiatric

Staffed Beds: 292 **Admissions:** 434 **Census:** 272 **Outpatient Visits:** 0 **Births:** 0 **Personnel:** 797

✠ **SIBLEY MEMORIAL HOSPITAL (090005)**, 5255 Loughboro Road N.W., Zip 20016-2633; tel. 202/537-4000, (Nonreporting) **A**1 3 5 10 **S** Johns Hopkins Health System, Baltimore, MD
Primary Contact: Richard O. Davis, Ph.D., President
COO: Sanjay K. Saha, Chief Operating Officer
CFO: Marty Basso, Chief Financial Officer
CMO: M. Therese McDonnell, M.D., Interim Vice President Patient Safety, Quality and Medical Affairs
CIO: Christopher T. Timbers, Chief Information Officer
CHR: Queenie C. Plater, Vice President Human Resources for JHM Community Division
CNO: Lynn Meuer, Interim Chief Nursing Officer
Web address: www.sibley.org
Control: Other not-for-profit (including NFP Corporation) **Service:** General Medical and Surgical

Staffed Beds: 246

✠ △ **THE HSC PEDIATRIC CENTER**, 1731 Bunker Hill Road N.E., Zip 20017-3096; tel. 202/832-4400 **A**1 7 **F**3 12 29 31 32 34 35 39 50 54 58 64 65 68 71 75 80 83 84 86 90 91 93 94 96 130 132 143 146 148 **P**6
Primary Contact: Debbie C. Holson, R.N., MSN, Chief Operating Officer
COO: Debbie C. Holson, R.N., Chief Operating Officer
CFO: Ray Vicks, Senior Vice President, Finance and Chief Financial Officer
CMO: Andrew Metinko, M.D., Chief Medical Officer
CIO: Khalil Bouharoun, Chief Information Officer
CHR: Lynne Hostetter, Vice President Human Resources
Web address: www.hscpediatriccenter.org/
Control: Other not-for-profit (including NFP Corporation) **Service:** Children's chronic disease

Staffed Beds: 118 **Admissions:** 229 **Census:** 27 **Outpatient Visits:** 12138 **Births:** 0 **Total Expense ($000):** 34843 **Payroll Expense ($000):** 15733 **Personnel:** 243

✠ **UNITED MEDICAL CENTER (090008)**, 1310 Southern Avenue S.E., Zip 20032-4623; tel. 202/574-6000, (Total facility includes 120 beds in nursing home-type unit) **A**1 10 **F**3 13 15 18 20 29 30 34 35 40 45 50 57 59 60 61 64 65 68 70 71 74 75 76 77 78 79 81 85 91 93 96 97 98 100 102 107 108 110 111 115 119 128 130 146 147 **P**6
Primary Contact: Luis Hernandez, Chief Executive Officer
COO: Charletta Washington, Chief Operations Officer
CFO: Lilian Chukwuma, Chief Financial Officer
CMO: Julian R. Craig, Chief Medical Officer
CIO: Thomas Hallisey, Chief Information Officer
CHR: Eric Johnson, Manager
CNO: Maribel Torres, Executive Vice President Patient Care Services and Chief Nursing Officer
Web address: www.united-medicalcenter.com
Control: Other not-for-profit (including NFP Corporation) **Service:** General Medical and Surgical

Staffed Beds: 354 **Admissions:** 6553 **Census:** 214 **Outpatient Visits:** 91443 **Births:** 365 **Total Expense ($000):** 122264 **Payroll Expense ($000):** 51441 **Personnel:** 1086

VETERANS AFFAIRS MEDICAL CENTER See Washington DC Veterans Affairs Medical Center

✠ △ **WASHINGTON DC VETERANS AFFAIRS MEDICAL CENTER**, 50 Irving Street N.W., Zip 20422-0002; tel. 202/745-8000, (Nonreporting) **A**1 2 3 5 7 **S** Department of Veterans Affairs, Washington, DC
Primary Contact: Brian A. Hawkins, Director
CFO: Frank Filosa, Fiscal Manager
CIO: Amanda Graves, Chief Information Systems
Web address: www.washingtondc.va.gov/
Control: Veterans Affairs, Government, federal **Service:** General Medical and Surgical

Staffed Beds: 291

WASHINGTON HOSPITAL CENTER See MedStar Washington Hospital Center

Many Facility Codes have changed. Please refer to the AHA Guide Code Chart. © 2016 AHA Guide

DC

FLORIDA

ALTAMONTE SPRINGS—Seminole County

FLORIDA HOSPITAL–ALTAMONTE See Florida Hospital, Orlando

☐ **HEALTHSOUTH REHABILITATION HOSPITAL OF ALTAMONTE SPRINGS**, 831 South State Road 434, Zip 32714–3502; tel. 407/587–8600 **A**1 **F**29 75 86 90 91 95 96 148 **S** HEALTHSOUTH Corporation, Birmingham, AL
Primary Contact: Jill Jordan, Chief Executive Officer
Web address: www.healthsouthaltamontesprings.com
Control: State–Government, nonfederal **Service:** Rehabilitation

Staffed Beds: 50 **Admissions:** 865 **Census:** 33 **Outpatient Visits:** 0 **Births:** 0 **Total Expense ($000):** 13326 **Payroll Expense ($000):** 7278 **Personnel:** 132

APALACHICOLA—Franklin County

GEORGE E. WEEMS MEMORIAL HOSPITAL (101305), 135 Avenue G., Zip 32320–1613, Mailing Address: P.O. Box 580, Zip 32329–0580; tel. 850/653–8853, (Nonreporting) **A**10 18
Primary Contact: Mike Cooper, Chief Executive Officer
CFO: James Robinson, Chief Financial Officer
CIO: Dennis Peterson, Chief Information Officer
CHR: Ginny Grimer, Director Human Resources
Web address: www.weemsmemorial.com
Control: Partnership, Investor–owned, for–profit **Service:** General Medical and Surgical

Staffed Beds: 25

APOPKA—Orange County

FLORIDA HOSPITAL–APOPKA See Florida Hospital, Orlando

ARCADIA—Desoto County

☐ **DESOTO MEMORIAL HOSPITAL (100175)**, 900 North Robert Avenue, Zip 34266–8712, Mailing Address: P.O. Box 2180, Zip 34265–2180; tel. 863/494–3535, (Nonreporting) **A**1 10 20
Primary Contact: Vincent A. Sica, President and Chief Executive Officer
CFO: Dan Hogan, Chief Financial Officer
CMO: Steven Mishkind, M.D., Chief of Staff
CIO: Kristen Spahr, Director of Marketing
CHR: Lois Hilton, Director Human Resources
CNO: Joseph La Cava, Chief Nursing Officer and Director Of Anesthesia
Web address: www.dmh.org
Control: Other not–for–profit (including NFP Corporation) **Service:** General Medical and Surgical

Staffed Beds: 49

ATLANTIS—Palm Beach County

☒ **JFK MEDICAL CENTER (100080)**, 5301 South Congress Avenue, Zip 33462–1197; tel. 561/965–7300, (Nonreporting) **A**1 2 3 5 10 **S** HCA, Nashville, TN
Primary Contact: Gina Melby, Chief Executive Officer
CFO: Jim Leamon, Chief Financial Officer
CIO: Jane Stewart, Director Information Services
CHR: Trudy Bromley, Vice President Human Resources
Web address: www.jfkmc.com
Control: Corporation, Investor–owned, for–profit **Service:** General Medical and Surgical

Staffed Beds: 424

AVENTURA—Miami–Dade County

☒ **AVENTURA HOSPITAL AND MEDICAL CENTER (100131)**, 20900 Biscayne Boulevard, Zip 33180–1407; tel. 305/682–7000, (Nonreporting) **A**1 2 3 10 **S** HCA, Nashville, TN
Primary Contact: Dianne Goldenberg, Chief Executive Officer
COO: Luanne Ansaldo, Chief Operating Officer
CFO: Alisa Bert, Chief Financial Officer
CMO: Martin Grossman, Chief of Staff
CHR: Rosemarie Amberson, Vice President Human Resources
CNO: Jesse Gabuat, Interim Chief Nursing Officer
Web address: www.aventurahospital.com
Control: Corporation, Investor–owned, for–profit **Service:** General Medical and Surgical

Staffed Beds: 359

BARTOW—Polk County

☒ **BARTOW REGIONAL MEDICAL CENTER (100121)**, 2200 Osprey Boulevard, Zip 33830–3308, Mailing Address: P.O. Box 1050, Zip 33831–1050; tel. 863/533–8111 **A**1 10 **F**3 8 11 15 18 20 26 29 30 31 34 35 40 45 46 49 50 51 57 58 59 60 64 68 70 74 75 77 78 79 81 82 84 85 86 87 92 93 94 99 100 101 104 107 108 110 111 114 118 119 123 124 126 129 130 131 132 135 144 146 147 148 **P**6 **S** Community Health Systems, Inc., Franklin, TN
Primary Contact: Philip Minden, Chief Executive Officer
CFO: Michael Boscia, Chief Financial Officer
CMO: Stuart Patterson, M.D., Chief of Staff
CIO: Vilakon Champavannarath, Director Information Systems
CHR: Marie Horton, Director Associate Relations
Web address: www.bartowregional.com
Control: Other not–for–profit (including NFP Corporation) **Service:** General Medical and Surgical

Staffed Beds: 72 **Admissions:** 2998 **Census:** 37 **Outpatient Visits:** 43189 **Births:** 0 **Total Expense ($000):** 43639 **Payroll Expense ($000):** 18400 **Personnel:** 314

BAY PINES—Pinellas County

☒ △ **BAY PINES VETERANS AFFAIRS HEALTHCARE SYSTEM**, 10000 Bay Pines Boulevard, Zip 33744–8200, Mailing Address: P.O. Box 5005, Zip 33744–5005; tel. 727/398–6661, (Total facility includes 112 beds in nursing home–type unit) **A**1 2 3 5 7 **F**3 4 5 8 12 15 18 20 22 26 28 29 30 31 36 38 39 40 45 46 47 49 51 53 54 56 57 58 59 60 61 62 63 64 65 68 70 74 75 77 78 79 81 82 83 84 85 86 87 90 91 93 94 97 98 100 101 102 103 104 105 106 107 108 110 111 114 115 116 117 118 119 120 121 123 128 129 130 131 132 135 143 144 146 147 148 **P**6 **S** Department of Veterans Affairs, Washington, DC
Primary Contact: Suzanne M. Klinker, Director
COO: Kris Brown, Associate Director
CFO: Jeanine Ergle, Chief Financial Officer
CMO: George F. Van Buskirk, M.D., Chief of Staff
CIO: John Williams, Chief Information Officer
CHR: Paula Buchele, Chief Human Resources
Web address: www.baypines.va.gov/
Control: Veterans Affairs, Government, federal **Service:** General Medical and Surgical

Staffed Beds: 396 **Admissions:** 10783 **Census:** 313 **Outpatient Visits:** 1417305 **Births:** 0 **Total Expense ($000):** 735028 **Payroll Expense ($000):** 281170 **Personnel:** 4112

BELLE GLADE—Palm Beach County

GLADES GENERAL HOSPITAL See Lakeside Medical Center

☒ **LAKESIDE MEDICAL CENTER (100130)**, 39200 Hooker Highway, Zip 33430–5368; tel. 561/996–6571 **A**1 10 13 **F**3 11 13 15 29 34 35 40 50 56 57 68 70 76 80 81 85 87 89 91 92 93 107 108 109 110 111 114 119 130 135 146
Primary Contact: Richard Roche, Administrator
COO: Darcy Davis, Chief Financial Officer
CFO: Darcy Davis, Chief Financial Officer
CMO: Ron Wiewora, M.D., Chief Medical Officer
Web address: www.lakesidemedical.org
Control: Hospital district or authority, Government, nonfederal **Service:** General Medical and Surgical

Staffed Beds: 70 **Admissions:** 2242 **Census:** 23 **Births:** 443 **Total Expense ($000):** 43822 **Payroll Expense ($000):** 16957

BLOUNTSTOWN—Calhoun County

CALHOUN–LIBERTY HOSPITAL (101304), 20370 N.E. Burns Avenue, Zip 32424–1045, Mailing Address: P.O. Box 419, Zip 32424–0419; tel. 850/674–5411 **A**10 18 **F**3 7 15 29 34 40 45 50 54 57 59 107 110 114 119 127 128 133
Primary Contact: James Heitzenrater, Interim Chief Executive Officer
CFO: Nathan Ebersole, Controller
CIO: Michael Flowers, Director Information Management
CHR: Lynn Pitts, Director Human Resources
CNO: Debra Summers, Chief Nursing Officer
Web address: www.calhounlibertyhospital.com
Control: Other not–for–profit (including NFP Corporation) **Service:** General Medical and Surgical

Staffed Beds: 25 **Admissions:** 457 **Census:** 5 **Births:** 0 **Total Expense ($000):** 10568 **Payroll Expense ($000):** 5603

FL

Hospital, Medicare Provider Number, Address, Telephone, Approval, Facility, and Physician Codes, Health Care System

★ American Hospital Association (AHA) membership   ◯ Healthcare Facilities Accreditation Program   ⇑ Center for Improvement in Healthcare Quality Accreditation
☐ The Joint Commission accreditation   ◇ DNV Healthcare Inc. accreditation   △ Commission on Accreditation of Rehabilitation Facilities (CARF) accreditation

BOCA RATON—Palm Beach County

BOCA RATON COMMUNITY HOSPITAL See Boca Raton Regional Hospital

☐ **BOCA RATON REGIONAL HOSPITAL (100168)**, 800 Meadows Road, Zip 33486–2368; tel. 561/955–7100 **A**1 2 3 5 10 **F**3 6 8 11 12 13 15 17 18 20 22 24 26 28 29 30 31 34 35 36 37 40 44 45 46 47 48 49 50 51 53 54 55 56 57 58 59 60 61 62 64 68 70 71 72 74 75 76 77 78 79 81 82 84 85 86 87 91 92 93 94 96 97 100 102 103 107 108 109 110 111 112 114 115 116 117 118 119 120 121 123 124 126 130 131 132 135 144 145 146 147 148 **P**6
Primary Contact: Jerry J. Fedele, President and Chief Executive Officer
COO: Karen Poole, Chief Operating Officer
CFO: Dawn Jauersack, Vice President and Chief Financial Officer
CMO: Charles Posternack, M.D., Vice President
CIO: Robin Hildwein, Chief Information Officer
CHR: Mindy Raymond, Vice President Human Resources
CNO: Melissa Durbin, R.N., Chief Nursing Officer
Web address: www.brrh.com
Control: Other not–for–profit (including NFP Corporation) **Service:** General Medical and Surgical

Staffed Beds: 374 Admissions: 18481 Census: 239 Outpatient Visits: 348351 Births: 2295 Total Expense ($000): 408403 Payroll Expense ($000): 164483 Personnel: 2297

✠ **WEST BOCA MEDICAL CENTER (100268)**, 21644 State Road 7, Zip 33428–1899; tel. 561/488–8000 **A**1 5 10 **F**8 13 15 18 19 29 31 35 39 40 41 42 49 54 57 64 70 72 74 76 79 80 81 85 86 88 89 93 107 108 109 110 111 114 115 117 118 119 126 129 130 131 146 147 148 **P**4 5 **S** TENET Healthcare Corporation, Dallas, TX
Primary Contact: Mitchell S. Feldman, Chief Executive Officer
COO: Ryan Lee, Chief Operating Officer
CFO: Brook Thomas, Chief Financial Officer
CMO: Jack L. Harari, M.D., Chief Medical Officer
CIO: Lauren Spagna, Marketing Director
CHR: Stephanie Sherman, Chief Human Resources Officer
CNO: Ruth Schwarzkopf, R.N., Chief Nursing Officer
Web address: www.westbocamedctr.com
Control: Corporation, Investor–owned, for–profit **Service:** General Medical and Surgical

Staffed Beds: 195 Admissions: 10761 Census: 113 Outpatient Visits: 74177 Births: 2074 Total Expense ($000): 126233 Payroll Expense ($000): 48840 Personnel: 638

BONIFAY—Holmes County

☐ **DOCTORS MEMORIAL HOSPITAL (101307)**, 2600 Hospital Drive, Zip 32425–4264, Mailing Address: P.O. Box 188, Zip 32425–0188; tel. 850/547–8000 **A**1 10 18 **F**3 11 15 29 30 40 45 50 57 59 64 70 77 81 90 93 107 110 114 119 131 133 146 148
Primary Contact: Joann Baker, Administrator
CFO: Celia F. Ward, Controller and Chief Financial Officer
CMO: Leisa Bailey, M.D., Chief of Staff
CIO: Rohan Anderson, Chief Information Officer
CHR: Christy Booth, Chief Human Resources Officer
CNO: Karla Rockwell, Director of Nursing
Web address: www.doctorsmemorial.org
Control: Hospital district or authority, Government, nonfederal **Service:** General Medical and Surgical

Staffed Beds: 20 Admissions: 557 Census: 6 Births: 0 Total Expense ($000): 12310 Payroll Expense ($000): 4810

BOYNTON BEACH—Palm Beach County

☐ **BETHESDA HOSPITAL EAST (100002)**, 2815 South Seacrest Boulevard, Zip 33435–7995; tel. 561/737–7733, (Includes BETHESDA HOSPITAL WEST, 9655 West Boynton Beach Boulevard, Zip 33472–4421; tel. 561/336–7000; Roger L. Kirk, President and Chief Executive Officer) **A**1 3 5 10 **F**3 8 11 12 13 17 18 20 22 24 26 28 29 31 32 37 40 41 45 46 49 50 51 56 58 60 61 64 68 70 72 74 75 77 78 79 81 86 87 88 90 91 92 93 94 96 107 108 109 110 111 112 113 114 115 116 117 118 119 124 126 129 131 143 145 146 147 148 **P**6
Primary Contact: Roger L. Kirk, President and Chief Executive Officer
COO: Ela C. Lena, Administrator and Vice President Operations
CFO: Joanne Aquilina, Vice President Finance and Chief Financial Officer
CMO: Albert Biehl, M.D., Vice President Medical Affairs
CIO: Leslie Albright, Vice President Information Systems
CHR: Regina Bellucy, Vice President Human Resources
CNO: Ela C. Lena, Interim System Chief Nursing Officer
Web address: www.bethesdaweb.com
Control: Other not–for–profit (including NFP Corporation) **Service:** General Medical and Surgical

Staffed Beds: 481 Admissions: 20597 Census: 284 Outpatient Visits: 243113 Births: 2930 Total Expense ($000): 302799 Payroll Expense ($000): 106764 Personnel: 2216

BRADENTON—Manatee County

✠ △ **BLAKE MEDICAL CENTER (100213)**, 2020 59th Street West, Zip 34209–4669; tel. 941/792–6611 **A**1 2 7 10 **F**3 11 15 16 17 18 20 22 24 26 28 29 30 31 34 35 40 43 45 48 49 50 53 57 58 59 64 68 70 74 75 77 78 79 80 81 85 87 90 91 92 93 94 96 100 107 108 110 111 114 115 118 119 126 129 130 131 132 144 146 147 148 **S** HCA, Nashville, TN
Primary Contact: Daniel J. Friedrich, III, Chief Executive Officer
CMO: Kirk Cianciolo, D.O., Chief Medical Officer
CIO: Shannon Piatkowski, Director Information Technology
CHR: Veronica Lequeux, Vice President Human Resources
Web address: www.blakemedicalcenter.com
Control: Corporation, Investor–owned, for–profit **Service:** General Medical and Surgical

Staffed Beds: 372 Admissions: 16315 Census: 214 Births: 0 Personnel: 1055

☐ **CENTERSTONE HOSPITAL (104040)**, (Substance Abuse, Mental Health and Addictions), 2020 26th Avenue East, Zip 34208–7753, Mailing Address: P.O. Box 9478, Zip 34206–9478; tel. 941/782–4600 **A**10 13 **F**4 5 38 50 61 98 99 101 102 103 104 132 134 135
Primary Contact: Mary Ruiz, Chief Executive Officer
CFO: Sean Gingras, CPA, Chief Financial Officer
CMO: Ranjay Halder, M.D., Chief Medical Director
CIO: Heidi L. Blair, Vice President Administration
CHR: Colleen O'Connor, Director Human Resources
Web address: www.manateeglens.org
Control: Other not–for–profit (including NFP Corporation) **Service:** Other specialty

Staffed Beds: 30 Admissions: 1610 Census: 29 Outpatient Visits: 0 Births: 0 Total Expense ($000): 5168 Payroll Expense ($000): 3250

☐ **LAKEWOOD RANCH MEDICAL CENTER (100299)**, 8330 Lakewood Ranch Boulevard, Zip 34202–5174; tel. 941/782–2100, (Nonreporting) **A**1 10 **S** Universal Health Services, Inc., King of Prussia, PA
Primary Contact: Linda S. Widra, FACHE, Ph.D., R.N., Interim Chief Executive Officer
COO: Linda S. Widra, FACHE, Chief Operating Officer
CFO: Gerald Christine, Chief Financial Officer
CHR: Trish Morales, Director Human Resources
Web address: www.lakewoodranchmedicalcenter.com
Control: Corporation, Investor–owned, for–profit **Service:** General Medical and Surgical

Staffed Beds: 120

☐ **MANATEE MEMORIAL HOSPITAL (100035)**, 206 Second Street East, Zip 34208–1000; tel. 941/746–5111, (Nonreporting) **A**1 2 5 10 12 13 **S** Universal Health Services, Inc., King of Prussia, PA
Primary Contact: Kevin DiLallo, Chief Executive Officer
CFO: Mark A. Tierney, Chief Financial Officer
CMO: Linda Christmann, M.D., Chief of Staff
CIO: Troy Beaubien, Director Information Services
CHR: Sheree Threewits, Director Human Resources
CNO: Darlette Tice, Chief Nursing Officer
Web address: www.manateememorial.com
Control: Partnership, Investor–owned, for–profit **Service:** General Medical and Surgical

Staffed Beds: 319

☐ **SUNCOAST BEHAVIORAL HEALTH CENTER**, 4480 51st Street West, Zip 34210–2855; tel. 941/251–5000 **A**1 **F**4 5 29 34 35 38 50 56 64 69 75 98 99 100 101 102 103 105 **S** Universal Health Services, Inc., King of Prussia, PA
Primary Contact: Brandy Hamilton, Chief Executive Officer
CFO: Linda Weymouth, Chief Financial Officer
CMO: Randolph Hemsath, M.D., Medical Director
CNO: Janey Sweeney, Chief Nursing Officer
Web address: www.suncoastbhc.com
Control: Corporation, Investor–owned, for–profit **Service:** Children's hospital psychiatric

Staffed Beds: 80 Admissions: 1601 Census: 23 Births: 0 Total Expense ($000): 7011 Payroll Expense ($000): 3402

BRANDON—Hillsborough County

✠ **BRANDON REGIONAL HOSPITAL (100243)**, 119 Oakfield Drive, Zip 33511–5779; tel. 813/681–5551, (Nonreporting) **A**1 5 10 **S** HCA, Nashville, TN
Primary Contact: Bland Eng, Chief Executive Officer
CFO: Michael T. Terrell, Chief Financial Officer
CMO: Joseph C. Corcoran, Chief Medical Officer
CIO: Aaron Fountain, Chief Information Officer
CHR: Doug Goodman, Vice President Human Resources
CNO: Chris Taramasco, R.N., Chief Nursing Officer
Web address: www.brandonhospital.com
Control: Corporation, Investor–owned, for–profit **Service:** General Medical and Surgical

Staffed Beds: 359

Many Facility Codes have changed. Please refer to the AHA Guide Code Chart. © 2016 AHA Guide

BROOKSVILLE—Hernando County

☒ **BAYFRONT HEALTH BROOKSVILLE (100071)**, 17240 Cortez Boulevard, Zip 34601–8921, Mailing Address: P.O. Box 37, Zip 34605–0037; tel. 352/796–5111, (Includes BAYFRONT HEALTH SPRING HILL, 10461 Quality Drive, Spring Hill, Zip 34609–9634; tel. 352/688–8200; Patrick Maloney, Market Chief Executive Officer), (Nonreporting) **A**1 10 **S** Community Health Systems, Inc., Franklin, TN
Primary Contact: Kenneth R. Wicker, Chief Executive Officer
COO: Scott Hartsell, Chief Operating Officer
CFO: Matthew Seagroves, Chief Financial Officer
CMO: Mohammad A. Joud, M.D., Chief of Staff
CIO: Lee Burch, Director Management Information Systems
CHR: Claudia L. Jack, Director Associate Relations
Web address: www.brooksvilleregionalhospital.org
Control: Corporation, Investor–owned, for–profit **Service:** General Medical and Surgical

Staffed Beds: 120

☒ **HEALTHSOUTH REHABILITATION HOSPITAL OF SPRING HILL (103042)**, 12440 Cortez Boulevard, Zip 34613–2628; tel. 352/592–4250 **A**1 10 **F**29 90 93 **S** HEALTHSOUTH Corporation, Birmingham, AL
Primary Contact: Lori Bedard, Chief Executive Officer
CFO: Kimberly Lunt, Controller
CMO: Mira Zelin, D.O., Medical Director
CIO: Myra Merillo, Supervisor Health Information Management
CHR: Mary Salamanca, Director Human Resources
Web address: www.healthsouthspringhill.com
Control: Corporation, Investor–owned, for–profit **Service:** Rehabilitation

Staffed Beds: 80 **Admissions:** 1649 **Census:** 66 **Outpatient Visits:** 5286 **Births:** 0 **Total Expense ($000):** 21476 **Payroll Expense ($000):** 11852 **Personnel:** 220

☒ **OAK HILL HOSPITAL (100264)**, 11375 Cortez Boulevard, Zip 34613–5409; tel. 352/596–6632 **A**1 2 3 10 **F**3 11 15 18 20 22 24 26 29 30 31 34 35 40 41 45 46 48 49 50 51 56 57 59 64 70 74 75 77 78 79 81 85 87 89 93 107 108 110 111 114 115 118 119 126 130 131 132 146 147 148 **P**6 **S** HCA, Nashville, TN
Primary Contact: Mickey Smith, Chief Executive Officer
COO: Sonia I. Wellman, Chief Operating Officer
CFO: Matt Romero, Chief Financial Officer
CMO: Ed Nast, M.D., Chief Medical Officer
CHR: Charles Snider, Vice President Human Resources
CNO: Leanne Salazar, Chief Nursing Officer
Web address: www.oakhillhospital.com
Control: Corporation, Investor–owned, for–profit **Service:** General Medical and Surgical

Staffed Beds: 262 **Admissions:** 14978 **Census:** 187 **Births:** 0 **Total Expense ($000):** 163269 **Payroll Expense ($000):** 57078

☐ **SPRINGBROOK HOSPITAL (104057)**, 7007 Grove Road, Zip 34609–8610; tel. 352/596–4306 **A**1 10 **F**4 5 98 103 104 105
Primary Contact: Stephen Reider, R.N., Administrator
Web address: www.springbrookhospital.org/
Control: Corporation, Investor–owned, for–profit **Service:** Psychiatric

Staffed Beds: 66 **Admissions:** 2401 **Census:** 66 **Outpatient Visits:** 0 **Births:** 0 **Total Expense ($000):** 17336 **Payroll Expense ($000):** 5774

CAPE CORAL—Lee County

★ ◇ **CAPE CORAL HOSPITAL (100244)**, 636 Del Prado Boulevard, Zip 33990–2695; tel. 239/424–2000 **A**10 21 **F**3 11 13 14 18 20 28 29 30 34 35 40 45 46 48 50 51 53 56 57 59 60 65 66 68 70 74 75 76 77 79 81 82 84 85 86 87 93 94 97 107 108 111 114 119 129 130 132 135 146 147 148 **S** Lee Memorial Health System, Fort Myers, FL
Primary Contact: James R. Nathan, President and Chief Executive Officer
COO: Lawrence Antonucci, M.D., Chief Operating Officer
CFO: Ben Spence, Chief Financial Officer
CMO: Mark Greenberg, M.D., Chief Medical Officer
CIO: Mike Smith, Chief Information Officer
CHR: Jon C. Cecil, Chief Human Resource Officer
Web address: www.leememorial.org
Control: Hospital district or authority, Government, nonfederal **Service:** General Medical and Surgical

Staffed Beds: 291 **Admissions:** 16837 **Census:** 194 **Outpatient Visits:** 237185 **Births:** 1316

CELEBRATION—Osceola County

FLORIDA HOSPITAL CELEBRATION HEALTH See Florida Hospital, Orlando

CHATTAHOOCHEE—Gadsden County

FLORIDA STATE HOSPITAL (104000), U.S. Highway 90 East, Zip 32324–1000, Mailing Address: P.O. Box 1000, Zip 32324–1000; tel. 850/663–7536, (Nonreporting) **A**10
Primary Contact: Marguerite J. Morgan, Administrator
CFO: Denise Smith, Director Financial Services
Web address: www.dcf.state.fl.us/institutions/fsh
Control: State–Government, nonfederal **Service:** Psychiatric

Staffed Beds: 987

CHIPLEY—Washington County

☐ **NORTHWEST FLORIDA COMMUNITY HOSPITAL (101308)**, 1360 Brickyard Road, Zip 32428–6303, Mailing Address: P.O. Box 889, Zip 32428–0889; tel. 850/638–1610, (Total facility includes 34 beds in nursing home–type unit) **A**1 10 18 **F**11 15 29 30 34 35 40 45 57 59 62 68 81 82 85 93 104 107 111 115 119 127 128 130 131 133 146 148 **S** Alliant Management Services, Louisville, KY
Primary Contact: Mark E. Bush, Chief Executive Officer
COO: Janet Kinney, Chief Operating Officer
CFO: Marcey Black, Chief Financial Officer
CHR: Shelia Schiefelbein, Coordinator Human Resources
CNO: Joan Beard, Chief Nursing Officer
Web address: www.nfch.org
Control: Corporation, Investor–owned, for–profit **Service:** General Medical and Surgical

Staffed Beds: 59 **Admissions:** 697 **Census:** 38 **Outpatient Visits:** 27919 **Births:** 0 **Total Expense ($000):** 22016 **Payroll Expense ($000):** 8602

CLEARWATER—Pinellas County

☒ **MORTON PLANT HOSPITAL (100127)**, 300 Pinellas Street, Zip 33756–3804, Mailing Address: P.O. Box 210, Zip 33757–0210; tel. 727/462–7000, (Total facility includes 126 beds in nursing home–type unit) **A**1 2 3 5 10 **F**3 6 11 13 15 17 18 20 22 24 26 28 29 30 31 34 35 37 38 40 42 45 46 47 48 49 50 51 53 54 55 56 57 58 59 60 61 62 64 65 66 68 70 72 74 75 76 77 78 79 80 81 82 84 85 86 87 92 93 98 100 101 102 107 108 109 110 111 114 115 116 117 118 119 120 121 123 124 126 128 129 130 131 132 143 145 146 147 148 **P**6 7 **S** Morton Plant Mease Health Care, Clearwater, FL
Primary Contact: N. Kristopher Hoce, President
CFO: Carl Tremonti, Chief Financial Officer
CMO: Jeff Jensen, D.O., Vice President, Medical Affairs
CIO: Timothy Thompson, Senior Vice President and Chief Information Officer
CHR: Angel Brown, Director Human Resources
CNO: Tom Doria, Vice President Patient Services – West
Web address: www.mortonplant.com
Control: Other not–for–profit (including NFP Corporation) **Service:** General Medical and Surgical

Staffed Beds: 620 **Admissions:** 25016 **Census:** 307 **Outpatient Visits:** 351375 **Births:** 2257 **Total Expense ($000):** 435656 **Payroll Expense ($000):** 133040 **Personnel:** 2931

☐ **WINDMOOR HEALTHCARE OF CLEARWATER (104017)**, 11300 U.S. 19 North, Zip 33764; tel. 727/541–2646, (Nonreporting) **A**1 10 **S** Universal Health Services, Inc., King of Prussia, PA
Primary Contact: Wendy Merson, Chief Executive Officer
Web address: www.windmoor.com
Control: Corporation, Investor–owned, for–profit **Service:** Psychiatric

Staffed Beds: 120

CLERMONT—Lake County

☐ **SOUTH LAKE HOSPITAL (100051)**, 1900 Don Wickham Drive, Zip 34711–1979; tel. 352/394–4071, (Total facility includes 30 beds in nursing home–type unit) **A**1 10 **F**3 8 11 13 15 18 20 22 26 28 29 30 31 32 34 35 37 40 45 46 47 48 49 50 51 53 54 57 59 60 62 64 66 68 70 74 75 76 77 78 79 81 82 85 86 87 89 92 93 107 108 110 111 114 115 116 117 119 120 121 124 126 127 128 130 131 132 135 146 147 148 **P**6 **S** Orlando Health, Orlando, FL
Primary Contact: John Moore, President
COO: Paul Johns, Chief Operating Officer
CFO: Lance Sewell, Chief Financial Officer
CHR: Joy L. Sylvester, Director, Human Resources and Education
CNO: Bonnie Onofre, Chief Nursing Officer
Web address: www.southlakehospital.com
Control: Hospital district or authority, Government, nonfederal **Service:** General Medical and Surgical

Staffed Beds: 170 **Admissions:** 8941 **Census:** 106 **Outpatient Visits:** 116276 **Births:** 593 **Total Expense ($000):** 154336 **Payroll Expense ($000):** 60800 **Personnel:** 1186

FL

Hospital, Medicare Provider Number, Address, Telephone, Approval, Facility, and Physician Codes, Health Care System

★ American Hospital Association (AHA) membership   ◯ Healthcare Facilities Accreditation Program   ⇑ Center for Improvement in Healthcare Quality Accreditation
☐ The Joint Commission accreditation   ◇ DNV Healthcare Inc. accreditation   △ Commission on Accreditation of Rehabilitation Facilities (CARF) accreditation

---

CLEWISTON—Hendry County

HENDRY REGIONAL MEDICAL CENTER (101309), 524 West Sagamore Avenue, Zip 33440–3514; tel. 863/902–3000 A1 10 18 F3 11 15 18 29 34 35 40 45 50 57 59 64 65 68 70 75 77 81 82 85 91 93 97 107 110 111 114 119 127 130 133 135 146 P6 S QHR, Brentwood, TN
Primary Contact: R. D. Williams, Chief Executive Officer
CFO: John Beltz, Chief Financial Officer
CMO: Karim Kaki, M.D., Chief Medical Director
CIO: Leon Hoover, Director Information Systems
CHR: Lisa Miller, Director Human Resources
CNO: Sandra E. Viall, MSN, Chief Nursing Officer
Web address: www.hendryregional.org
Control: Hospital district or authority, Government, nonfederal **Service:** General Medical and Surgical

Staffed Beds: 25 **Admissions:** 807 **Census:** 7 **Outpatient Visits:** 34029 **Births:** 2 **Total Expense ($000):** 27598 **Payroll Expense ($000):** 12094 **Personnel:** 225

COCOA BEACH—Brevard County

HEALTH FIRST CAPE CANAVERAL HOSPITAL (100177), 701 West Cocoa Beach Causeway, Zip 32931–5595, Mailing Address: P.O. Box 320069, Zip 32932–0069; tel. 321/799–7111 A1 10 F3 11 13 15 18 20 22 26 29 30 31 34 35 40 43 44 45 46 47 48 49 51 54 56 57 59 60 62 64 65 68 70 74 75 76 78 79 81 85 86 87 91 92 93 103 107 108 110 111 114 115 119 124 129 130 132 143 146 147 P6 7 S Health First, Inc., Rockledge, FL
Primary Contact: William Calhoun, President, Community Hospitals
CFO: Joseph G. Felkner, Senior Vice President Finance and Chief Financial Officer
CMO: Jeffrey Stalnaker, M.D., Vice President, Medical Affairs
CIO: Lori Delone, Senior Vice President Support Services and Chief Information Officer
CHR: Paula Just, Vice President Human Resources
CNO: Connie Bradley, R.N., Chief Nursing Officer
Web address: www.health–first.org
Control: Other not–for–profit (including NFP Corporation) **Service:** General Medical and Surgical

Staffed Beds: 145 **Admissions:** 7113 **Census:** 74 **Outpatient Visits:** 111766 **Births:** 690 **Total Expense ($000):** 88454 **Payroll Expense ($000):** 38090 **Personnel:** 439

CORAL GABLES—Miami–Dade County

BAPTIST HEALTH SOUTH FLORIDA, DOCTORS HOSPITAL (100296), 5000 University Drive, Zip 33146–2094; tel. 786/308–3000 A1 3 5 10 F3 11 18 29 30 31 34 35 37 40 45 47 49 53 57 58 59 60 63 64 68 70 74 75 77 78 79 81 82 84 85 86 87 93 94 100 102 107 108 111 114 115 119 124 126 130 131 132 135 143 146 148 S Baptist Health South Florida, Coral Gables, FL
Primary Contact: Nelson Lazo, Chief Executive Officer
CFO: Maria J. Yanez, Chief Financial Officer
Web address: www.baptisthealth.net
Control: Other not–for–profit (including NFP Corporation) **Service:** General Medical and Surgical

Staffed Beds: 146 **Admissions:** 6384 **Census:** 83 **Outpatient Visits:** 61071 **Births:** 0 **Total Expense ($000):** 193044 **Payroll Expense ($000):** 56996 **Personnel:** 878

CORAL GABLES HOSPITAL (100183), 3100 Douglas Road, Zip 33134–6914; tel. 305/445–8461, (Nonreporting) A1 10 S TENET Healthcare Corporation, Dallas, TX
Primary Contact: Patrick Downes, Chief Executive Officer
COO: Cristina Jimenez, Chief Operating Officer
CFO: Henry Capote, Interim Chief Financial Officer
CMO: Pedro Friarte, Director of Physician Services
CIO: Mercy Hermosa, Director of Information System
CHR: Ana Paguaga, Director of Human Resources
Web address: www.coralgableshospital.com
Control: Corporation, Investor–owned, for–profit **Service:** General Medical and Surgical

Staffed Beds: 256

CORAL SPRINGS—Broward County

BROWARD HEALTH CORAL SPRINGS (100276), 3000 Coral Hills Drive, Zip 33065–4108; tel. 954/344–3000 A1 10 F3 11 12 13 15 20 29 31 34 35 40 41 48 51 55 57 58 59 61 63 64 66 68 70 72 74 75 76 77 78 79 80 81 82 84 85 86 87 88 89 93 96 107 108 111 114 115 118 119 126 129 130 131 132 143 146 147 148 P6 S Broward Health, Fort Lauderdale, FL
Primary Contact: Drew Grossman, Chief Executive Officer
COO: Kimberley Graham, R.N., Chief Nursing Officer and Chief Operating Officer
CFO: Arthur Wallace, Chief Financial Officer
CMO: Azeem Sachedina, M.D., Chief of Staff
CHR: Eileen O'Brien, Director Human Resources
CNO: Kimberley Graham, R.N., Chief Nursing Officer and Chief Operating Officer
Web address: www.browardhealth.org
Control: Hospital district or authority, Government, nonfederal **Service:** General Medical and Surgical

Staffed Beds: 182 **Admissions:** 12378 **Census:** 133 **Outpatient Visits:** 141369 **Births:** 2296 **Total Expense ($000):** 148309 **Payroll Expense ($000):** 61238 **Personnel:** 982

CRESTVIEW—Okaloosa County

NORTH OKALOOSA MEDICAL CENTER (100122), 151 Redstone Avenue S.E., Zip 32539–6026; tel. 850/689–8100 A1 10 F3 8 11 13 15 18 20 22 28 29 30 34 35 40 47 49 50 54 59 64 70 75 76 79 81 85 86 87 89 107 108 109 110 111 114 115 116 117 118 119 126 127 129 130 131 146 147 148 S Community Health Systems, Inc., Franklin, TN
Primary Contact: Ronnie Daves, Chief Executive Officer
COO: Heath Evans, Assistant Chief Executive Officer
CFO: Jim Andrews, Chief Financial Officer
CMO: Michael Foley, M.D., Chief Medical Officer
CIO: Jenny Zeitler, Network Administrator
CHR: Melody M. Miller–Collette, Director Human Resources
CNO: Nina Perez, R.N., Chief Nursing Officer
Web address: www.northokaloosa.com
Control: Corporation, Investor–owned, for–profit **Service:** General Medical and Surgical

Staffed Beds: 110 **Admissions:** 4829 **Census:** 49 **Births:** 495 **Total Expense ($000):** 72883 **Payroll Expense ($000):** 26292

CRYSTAL RIVER—Citrus County

SEVEN RIVERS REGIONAL MEDICAL CENTER (100249), 6201 North Suncoast Boulevard, Zip 34428–6712; tel. 352/795–6560, (Nonreporting) A1 10 19 S Community Health Systems, Inc., Franklin, TN
Primary Contact: Austin Brown, Interim Chief Executive Officer
COO: Austin Brown, Chief Operating Officer
CFO: Vickie Magurean, Chief Financial Officer
CHR: Joann Mramor, Director Human Resources
CNO: Cynthia Heitzman, R.N., Chief Nursing Officer
Web address: www.srrmc.com
Control: Corporation, Investor–owned, for–profit **Service:** General Medical and Surgical

Staffed Beds: 128

CUTLER BAY—Miami–Dade County

HEALTHSOUTH REHABILITATION HOSPITAL See HEALTHSOUTH Rehabilitation Hospital of Miami

★ HEALTHSOUTH REHABILITATION HOSPITAL OF MIAMI (103038), 20601 Old Cutler Road, Zip 33189–2400; tel. 305/251–3800 A10 F3 29 77 86 90 91 96 130 132 135 148 S HEALTHSOUTH Corporation, Birmingham, AL
Primary Contact: Enrique A. Vicens–Rivera, Jr., JD, Chief Executive Officer
CFO: Reyna Hernandez, Chief Financial Officer
CIO: Miguel Cruz, Medical Staff Credentialing Coordinator
CHR: Susan Riley, Director Human Resources
CNO: Ellen Romanowski, Chief Nursing Officer
Web address: www.healthsouthmiami.com
Control: Corporation, Investor–owned, for–profit **Service:** Rehabilitation

Staffed Beds: 60 **Admissions:** 1479 **Census:** 46 **Outpatient Visits:** 0 **Births:** 0 **Total Expense ($000):** 18404 **Payroll Expense ($000):** 8460

DADE CITY—Pasco County

BAYFRONT HEALTH DADE CITY (100211), 13100 Fort King Road, Zip 33525–5294; tel. 352/521–1100, (Nonreporting) A1 10 S Community Health Systems, Inc., Franklin, TN
Primary Contact: Shauna McKinnon, Chief Executive Officer
CFO: Linda Stockton, Chief Financial Officer
CMO: Petros Tsambiras, M.D., Chief of Staff
CIO: Cheryl Kaufman, Director Health Information Management
CHR: Tabatha Wallace, Director Human Resources
Web address: www.pascoregionalmc.com
Control: Corporation, Investor–owned, for–profit **Service:** General Medical and Surgical

Staffed Beds: 120

DAVENPORT—Polk County

HEART OF FLORIDA REGIONAL MEDICAL CENTER (100137), 40100 Highway 27, Zip 33837–5906; tel. 863/422–4971 A1 10 19 F3 11 12 13 15 17 18 20 22 29 30 34 40 49 50 51 57 59 60 64 70 74 75 76 77 79 81 85 87 89 107 110 111 114 115 119 126 130 135 144 146 147 148 S Community Health Systems, Inc., Franklin, TN
Primary Contact: Ann Barnhart, Chief Executive Officer
CFO: Tonja Mosley, Chief Financial Officer
CMO: Claudio Manubens, M.D., Chief of Staff
CIO: Louis Jones, Director Management Information Systems
CHR: Joan Allard, Director Human Resources
CNO: Dottie Mileto, Chief Nursing Officer
Web address: www.heartofflorida.com
Control: Corporation, Investor–owned, for–profit **Service:** General Medical and Surgical

Staffed Beds: 193 **Admissions:** 8956 **Census:** 89 **Births:** 883 **Total Expense ($000):** 109671 **Payroll Expense ($000):** 36966

FL

Many Facility Codes have changed. Please refer to the AHA Guide Code Chart. © 2016 AHA Guide

DAYTONA BEACH—Volusia County

✠ **FLORIDA HOSPITAL MEMORIAL MEDICAL CENTER (100068)**, 301 Memorial Medical Parkway, Zip 32117–5167; tel. 386/676–6000, (Includes FLORIDA HOSPITAL–OCEANSIDE, 264 South Atlantic Avenue, Ormond Beach, Zip 32176–8192; tel. 386/672–4161) **A**1 2 10 **F**2 3 11 12 13 15 17 18 20 22 24 26 28 29 30 31 32 34 35 38 40 42 45 46 47 49 50 54 57 58 59 60 65 68 70 71 74 75 76 77 78 79 81 82 85 86 87 90 91 92 93 96 97 100 107 108 109 110 111 112 114 115 116 117 119 120 121 123 124 128 130 131 132 135 146 147 148 **P**6 **S** Adventist Health System Sunbelt Health Care Corporation, Altamonte Springs, FL
Primary Contact: Ed Noseworthy, Chief Executive Officer
COO: Darlinda Copeland, Chief Operating Officer
CFO: Debora Thomas, Chief Financial Officer
CMO: Kris David Gray, Chief Medical Officer
CHR: Opal R. Howard, Executive Director Human Resources
CNO: Michele Goeb–Burkett, R.N., Chief Nursing Officer
Web address: www.floridahospitalmemorial.org
Control: Church–operated, Nongovernment, not–for profit **Service:** General Medical and Surgical

Staffed Beds: 250 **Admissions:** 14838 **Census:** 208 **Outpatient Visits:** 254435 **Births:** 1530 **Total Expense ($000):** 276484 **Payroll Expense ($000):** 108748 **Personnel:** 1746

☐ **HALIFAX HEALTH MEDICAL CENTER OF DAYTONA BEACH (100017)**, 303 North Clyde Morris Boulevard, Zip 32114–2700; tel. 386/425–4000, (Includes HALIFAX BEHAVIORAL SERVICES, 841 Jimmy Ann Drive, Zip 32117–4599; tel. 386/425–3900; HALIFAX HEALTH MEDICAL CENTER OF PORT ORANGE, 1041 Dunlawton Avenue, Port Orange, Zip 32127; tel. 386/425–4700; Ann Martorano, Chief Operating Officer) **A**1 2 3 5 10 **F**3 11 12 13 17 18 20 22 24 26 28 29 30 31 34 40 43 45 46 47 49 50 53 55 57 59 60 65 66 70 72 76 77 78 79 81 85 86 87 88 89 90 91 93 94 96 97 98 99 100 101 102 103 105 107 108 111 114 115 118 119 120 121 123 124 126 130 131 132 135 138 146 147 148
Primary Contact: Jeff Feasel, Chief Executive Officer
COO: Ann Martorano, Chief Operating Officer
CFO: Eric Peburn, Chief Financial Officer
CMO: Donald Stoner, M.D., Chief Medical Officer
CIO: Tom Stafford, Chief Information Officer
CHR: Kimberly Fulcher, Chief Human Resources Officer
CNO: Catherine Luchsinger, R.N., Chief Nursing Officer
Web address: www.halifax.org
Control: Hospital district or authority, Government, nonfederal **Service:** General Medical and Surgical

Staffed Beds: 678 **Admissions:** 22492 **Census:** 350 **Outpatient Visits:** 256925 **Births:** 1925 **Total Expense ($000):** 436667 **Payroll Expense ($000):** 188819 **Personnel:** 2477

SELECT SPECIALTY HOSPITAL DAYTONA BEACH, 301 Memorial Medical Parkway, 11th Floor, Zip 32117–5167; tel. 386/231–3436, (Nonreporting) **S** Select Medical Corporation, Mechanicsburg, PA
Primary Contact: Adrianne Lutes, Chief Executive Officer
Web address: www.daytonabeach.selectspecialtyhospitals.com
Control: Corporation, Investor–owned, for–profit **Service:** Long–Term Acute Care hospital

Staffed Beds: 34

DEERFIELD BEACH—Broward County

★ △ **BROWARD HEALTH NORTH (100086)**, 201 East Sample Road, Zip 33064–3502; tel. 954/941–8300 **A**2 7 10 **F**3 6 11 15 17 18 20 28 29 30 31 34 35 37 40 43 45 46 49 51 55 57 58 59 60 61 64 66 68 70 74 75 77 78 79 80 81 82 83 84 85 86 87 90 92 93 94 96 100 107 108 110 111 114 115 117 118 119 120 121 123 124 129 130 131 132 143 145 146 148
S Broward Health, Fort Lauderdale, FL
Primary Contact: Robert Bugg, Acting Chief Executive Officer
COO: Kevin Fusco, Corporate Chief Operating Officer
CFO: Robert Bugg, Chief Financial Officer
CMO: Darren Hoffberger, D.O., Chief of Staff
CIO: Doris Crain, Vice President and Chief Information Officer
CHR: Grace King, Regional Director Human Resources
CNO: Bettiann S. Ruditz, MS, Chief Nursing Officer
Web address: www.browardhealth.org
Control: Hospital district or authority, Government, nonfederal **Service:** General Medical and Surgical

Staffed Beds: 334 **Admissions:** 13974 **Census:** 215 **Outpatient Visits:** 106604 **Births:** 0 **Total Expense ($000):** 227775 **Payroll Expense ($000):** 82875 **Personnel:** 1226

DEFUNIAK SPRINGS—Walton County

HEALTHMARK REGIONAL MEDICAL CENTER (100081), 4413 U.S. Highway 331 South, Zip 32435–6307; tel. 850/951–4500 **A**10 **F**11 34 40 41 45 46 48 56 57 59 62 63 75 81 87 93 107 111 115 119 127 133 143 146 148 **P**6
Primary Contact: James H. Thompson, Ph.D., FACHE, Owner and Chief Executive Officer
COO: Gerald C. Beard, Chief Operating Officer
CFO: Jim Brewer, M.P.H., Chief Financial Officer
CMO: Edward Tenewitz, M.D., Chief of Staff
CIO: Ray Downs, Senior Staff Accountant
CHR: Debra Tiller, Director Personnel and Administrative Secretary
Web address: www.healthmarkregional.com
Control: Individual, Investor–owned, for–profit **Service:** General Medical and Surgical

Staffed Beds: 50 **Admissions:** 725 **Census:** 9 **Outpatient Visits:** 22174 **Births:** 1 **Total Expense ($000):** 11442 **Payroll Expense ($000):** 5088 **Personnel:** 110

DELAND—Volusia County

★ **FLORIDA HOSPITAL DELAND (100045)**, 701 West Plymouth Avenue, Zip 32720–3236; tel. 386/943–4522 **A**2 10 **F**3 4 13 15 18 20 22 26 28 29 30 31 34 35 37 38 40 45 46 47 48 49 50 54 55 56 57 58 59 60 64 70 74 75 76 77 78 79 80 81 84 85 86 87 93 97 98 100 102 107 108 109 110 111 112 114 115 116 117 119 120 121 124 126 129 130 131 132 135 146 147 **P**6 **S** Adventist Health System Sunbelt Health Care Corporation, Altamonte Springs, FL
Primary Contact: Lorenzo Brown, Chief Executive Officer
COO: Hector M. De Jesus, Chief Operating Officer
CFO: Nigel Hinds, Chief Financial Officer
CMO: Samuel Edwards, M.D., Chief of Staff
CIO: Kevin Piper, Director Information Systems
CNO: Patricia Ann Stark, R.N., CNO
Web address: www.fhdeland.org
Control: Other not–for–profit (including NFP Corporation) **Service:** General Medical and Surgical

Staffed Beds: 156 **Admissions:** 8724 **Census:** 97 **Births:** 588 **Total Expense ($000):** 123580 **Payroll Expense ($000):** 54277

DELRAY BEACH—Palm Beach County

✠ **DELRAY MEDICAL CENTER (100258)**, 5352 Linton Boulevard, Zip 33484–6580; tel. 561/498–4440, (Includes FAIR OAKS PAVILION, 5440 Linton Boulevard, Zip 33484–6578; tel. 561/495–1000; PINECREST REHABILITATION HOSPITAL, 5360 Linton Boulevard, Zip 33484–6538; tel. 561/495–0400) **A**1 3 5 10 **F**3 4 11 12 15 17 18 20 22 24 26 28 29 31 34 35 37 38 40 41 42 43 45 46 49 50 51 56 57 58 59 60 64 65 70 74 75 77 78 79 80 81 82 83 84 85 87 90 91 93 94 96 97 98 100 101 102 103 104 107 108 111 115 118 119 126 129 130 132 133 135 143 144 146 147 148 **S** TENET Healthcare Corporation, Dallas, TX
Primary Contact: Mark Bryan, Chief Executive Officer
CMO: Anthony Dardano, M.D., Chief Medical Officer
CIO: Robens Rosena, Director Information Systems
CHR: Shannon Wills, Director Human Resources
Web address: www.delraymedicalctr.com
Control: Corporation, Investor–owned, for–profit **Service:** General Medical and Surgical

Staffed Beds: 439 **Admissions:** 19950 **Census:** 299 **Outpatient Visits:** 73874 **Births:** 0 **Personnel:** 1455

DUNEDIN—Pinellas County

☐ **BAYCARE ALLIANT HOSPITAL (102021)**, 601 Main Street, Zip 34698–5848; tel. 727/736–9991 **A**1 10 **F**1 3 28 29 34 36 57 130 148
Primary Contact: Jacqueline Arocho, Administrator
CFO: John Proni, CPA, Manager Finance and Operations
CMO: Leonard Dunn, M.D., Chief Medical Officer
CHR: Darlene Shelton, Coordinator Team Resources
Web address: www.baycare.org
Control: Other not–for–profit (including NFP Corporation) **Service:** Long–Term Acute Care hospital

Staffed Beds: 36 **Admissions:** 361 **Census:** 28 **Outpatient Visits:** 0 **Births:** 0 **Total Expense ($000):** 17250 **Payroll Expense ($000):** 6299 **Personnel:** 105

FL

Hospital, Medicare Provider Number, Address, Telephone, Approval, Facility, and Physician Codes, Health Care System

★ American Hospital Association (AHA) membership
☐ The Joint Commission accreditation
◯ Healthcare Facilities Accreditation Program
◇ DNV Healthcare Inc. accreditation
⇑ Center for Improvement in Healthcare Quality Accreditation
△ Commission on Accreditation of Rehabilitation Facilities (CARF) accreditation

✠ **MEASE DUNEDIN HOSPITAL (100043)**, 601 Main Street, Zip 34698–5891, Mailing Address: P.O. Box 760, Zip 34697–0760; tel. 727/733–1111 **A**1 10 **F**3 12 15 17 18 26 29 30 31 34 37 40 44 49 60 62 68 70 75 78 79 81 84 85 86 87 98 99 100 102 103 105 107 108 110 111 114 118 119 130 132 145 146 **P**6 **S** Trinity Health, Livonia, MI
Primary Contact: Lou Galdieri, R.N., President
CFO: Carl Tremonti, Chief Financial Officer
CMO: Donald Pocock, M.D., Chief Medical Officer
CHR: Sharon Collotta, Director Human Resources
Web address: www.mpmhealth.com
Control: Other not–for–profit (including NFP Corporation) **Service:** General Medical and Surgical

Staffed Beds: 120 **Admissions:** 6796 **Census:** 85 **Outpatient Visits:** 33239 **Births:** 0 **Total Expense ($000):** 78291 **Payroll Expense ($000):** 32741 **Personnel:** 610

EGLIN AFB—Okaloosa County

✠ **U. S. AIR FORCE REGIONAL HOSPITAL**, 307 Boatner Road, Suite 114, Zip 32542–1282; tel. 850/883–8221, (Nonreporting) **A**1 3 5 **S** Department of the Air Force, Washington, DC
Primary Contact: Colonel Eveline F. Yao, Commander
Web address: www.eglin.af.mil
Control: Air Force, Government, federal **Service:** General Medical and Surgical

Staffed Beds: 57

ENGLEWOOD—Sarasota County

✠ **ENGLEWOOD COMMUNITY HOSPITAL (100267)**, 700 Medical Boulevard, Zip 34223–3978; tel. 941/475–6571, (Nonreporting) **A**1 10 **S** HCA, Nashville, TN
Primary Contact: Valerie L. Powell–Stafford, Chief Executive Officer
COO: Alex Chang, Chief Operating Officer
CMO: Eric Pressman, D.O., Chair Department of Medicine
CNO: Kathleen Pace, MSN, Chief Nursing Officer
Web address: www.englewoodcommunityhospital.com
Control: Corporation, Investor–owned, for–profit **Service:** General Medical and Surgical

Staffed Beds: 100

FERNANDINA BEACH—Nassau County

✠ **BAPTIST MEDICAL CENTER NASSAU (100140)**, 1250 South 18th Street, Zip 32034–3098; tel. 904/321–3500 **A**1 10 **F**3 11 13 15 18 26 29 30 34 35 40 45 49 64 70 74 76 79 81 82 85 91 92 93 102 107 108 110 111 114 115 119 124 129 132 146 148
Primary Contact: Stephen Lee, FACHE, President
COO: Patricia K. Hausauer, Director Finance
CFO: Patricia K. Hausauer, Director Finance
CHR: Jodi Atkins, Human Resources Specialist
Web address: www.baptistjax.com/locations/baptist–medical–center–nassau
Control: Other not–for–profit (including NFP Corporation) **Service:** General Medical and Surgical

Staffed Beds: 52 **Admissions:** 3730 **Census:** 36 **Births:** 634 **Total Expense ($000):** 55028 **Payroll Expense ($000):** 20609

FORT LAUDERDALE—Broward County

☐ **ATLANTIC SHORES HOSPITAL (104065)**, 4545 North Federal Highway, Zip 33308–5274; tel. 954/771–2711, (Nonreporting) **A**1 10 **S** Universal Health Services, Inc., King of Prussia, PA
Primary Contact: Manuel R. Llano, Chief Executive Officer
CFO: Michel Duchaussee, Chief Financial Officer
CMO: Sherrie Bieniek, M.D., Medical Director
CHR: Carlos A. Gato, Director of Human Resources
Web address: www.atlanticshoreshospital.com
Control: Corporation, Investor–owned, for–profit **Service:** Psychiatric

Staffed Beds: 72

✠ **BROWARD HEALTH IMPERIAL POINT (100200)**, 6401 North Federal Highway, Zip 33308–1495; tel. 954/776–8500 **A**1 10 **F**3 11 12 15 20 29 34 35 40 45 51 53 55 57 58 59 61 63 64 68 70 74 75 77 78 79 80 81 82 84 85 86 87 93 98 100 102 104 105 107 108 111 114 115 118 119 126 129 130 131 132 143 146 147 148 **S** Broward Health, Fort Lauderdale, FL
Primary Contact: Alice Taylor, R.N., MSN, Chief Executive Officer
CFO: Susan Newton, Chief Financial Officer
CIO: Doris Peek, Chief Information Officer
CHR: Carl McDonald, Regional Director Human Resources
Web address: www.browardhealth.org
Control: Hospital district or authority, Government, nonfederal **Service:** General Medical and Surgical

Staffed Beds: 180 **Admissions:** 8468 **Census:** 104 **Outpatient Visits:** 85574 **Births:** 0 **Total Expense ($000):** 111086 **Payroll Expense ($000):** 42948 **Personnel:** 695

✠ **BROWARD HEALTH MEDICAL CENTER (100039)**, 1600 South Andrews Avenue, Zip 33316–2510; tel. 954/355–4400, (Includes CHRIS EVERT CHILDRENS HOSPITAL, 1600 South Andrews Avenue, tel. 954/355–4400; Calvin E. Glidewell, Jr., Chief Executive Officer) **A**1 2 3 5 10 12 13 **F**3 11 13 15 17 18 20 22 24 26 28 29 30 31 34 35 40 41 43 45 48 49 50 51 53 57 59 60 61 62 63 64 65 66 68 70 71 72 73 74 75 76 77 78 79 80 81 82 83 84 85 87 88 89 93 94 98 100 102 105 107 108 110 111 114 115 116 117 119 120 121 126 129 130 139 146 147 **S** Broward Health, Fort Lauderdale, FL
Primary Contact: Mark Sprada, R.N., Interim Chief Executive Officer
COO: Natassia Orr, Chief Operating Officer
CFO: Alexander Fernandez, Chief Financial Officer
CMO: Louis Yogel, M.D., Chief of Staff
CIO: Doris Crain, Vice President Information Services
CHR: Dionne Wong, Vice President and Chief Human Resources Officer
CNO: Robyn Farrington, Chief Nursing Officer
Web address: www.browardhealth.org
Control: Hospital district or authority, Government, nonfederal **Service:** General Medical and Surgical

Staffed Beds: 648 **Admissions:** 26233 **Census:** 423 **Outpatient Visits:** 248539 **Births:** 3702 **Total Expense ($000):** 469335 **Payroll Expense ($000):** 180209 **Personnel:** 2870

FLORIDA MEDICAL CENTER See Florida Medical Center – A Campus of North Shore

☐ **FORT LAUDERDALE HOSPITAL (104026)**, 1601 East Las Olas Boulevard, Zip 33301–2393; tel. 954/463–4321, (Nonreporting) **A**1 10 **S** Universal Health Services, Inc., King of Prussia, PA
Primary Contact: Manuel R. Llano, Chief Executive Officer
CFO: Varonica Oehl, Chief Financial Officer
CMO: Sherrie Bieniek, M.D., Medical Director
CHR: Carlos A. Gato, Director of Human Resources
CNO: Maria Spingos, Director of Nursing
Web address: www.fortlauderdalehospital.org
Control: Corporation, Investor–owned, for–profit **Service:** Psychiatric

Staffed Beds: 100

✠ **HOLY CROSS HOSPITAL (100073)**, 4725 North Federal Highway, Zip 33308–4668, Mailing Address: P.O. Box 23460, Zip 33307–3460; tel. 954/771–8000 **A**1 2 3 5 10 **F**3 8 11 12 13 15 17 18 20 22 24 26 28 29 30 31 32 34 35 36 37 39 40 44 45 46 47 48 49 50 51 53 54 55 56 57 58 59 61 62 64 65 66 67 68 70 71 72 74 75 76 77 78 79 81 82 84 85 86 87 90 91 92 93 95 96 97 100 107 108 110 111 114 115 116 117 118 119 120 121 123 124 126 129 130 131 132 134 143 144 145 146 147 **P**4 6 **S** Trinity Health, Livonia, MI
Primary Contact: Patrick Taylor, M.D., President and Chief Executive Officer
COO: Luisa Gutman, Senior Vice President and Chief Operating Officer
CFO: Linda Wilford, CPA, Senior Vice President and Chief Financial Officer
CMO: Kenneth Homer, M.D., Chief Medical Officer
CIO: Jeff Smith, Chief Information Officer
CNO: Taren Ruggiero, R.N., Vice President and Chief Nursing Officer
Web address: www.holy–cross.com
Control: Other not–for–profit (including NFP Corporation) **Service:** General Medical and Surgical

Staffed Beds: 367 **Admissions:** 16937 **Census:** 208 **Outpatient Visits:** 285308 **Births:** 1200 **Total Expense ($000):** 321738 **Payroll Expense ($000):** 110917 **Personnel:** 2564

IMPERIAL POINT MEDICAL CENTER See Broward Health Imperial Point

✠ **KINDRED HOSPITAL SOUTH FLORIDA–FORT LAUDERDALE (102010)**, 1516 East Las Olas Boulevard, Zip 33301–2399; tel. 954/764–8900, (Includes KINDRED HOSPITAL SOUTH FLORIDA–CORAL GABLES, 5190 S.W. Eighth Street, Coral Gables, Zip 33134–2495; tel. 305/445–1364; Charles Doten, Chief Executive Officer; KINDRED HOSPITAL SOUTH FLORIDA–HOLLYWOOD, 1859 Van Buren Street, Hollywood, Zip 33020–5127; tel. 954/920–9000; Craig A. Hoover, Administrator), (Nonreporting) **A**1 10 **S** Kindred Healthcare, Louisville, KY
Primary Contact: Michael S. Roffelsen, Chief Executive Officer
CFO: Dean Card, Chief Financial Officer
Web address: www.khfortlauderdale.com/
Control: Corporation, Investor–owned, for–profit **Service:** Long–Term Acute Care hospital

Staffed Beds: 123

FORT MYERS—Lee County

CHILDREN'S HOSPITAL OF SOUTHWEST FLORIDA See Lee Memorial Hospital

Many Facility Codes have changed. Please refer to the AHA Guide Code Chart.

© 2016 AHA Guide

FL

★ ◇ **GULF COAST MEDICAL CENTER (100220)**, 13681 Doctor's Way, Zip 33912–4300; tel. 239/343–1000 **A**10 21 **F**3 11 13 17 18 20 22 24 26 28 29 30 40 45 46 49 60 64 70 74 76 77 79 80 81 84 85 86 87 91 93 102 107 108 111 115 118 119 130 138 146 **S** Lee Memorial Health System, Fort Myers, FL
Primary Contact: James R. Nathan, President and Chief Executive Officer
COO: Lawrence Antonucci, M.D., Chief Operating Officer
CFO: Ben Spence, Chief Financial Officer
CMO: Mark Greenberg, M.D., Medical Director
CIO: Mike Smith, Chief Information Officer
CHR: Jon C. Cecil, Chief Human Resource Officer
CNO: Donna Giannuzzi, R.N., Chief Patient Care Officer
Web address: www.leememorial.org
Control: Hospital district or authority, Government, nonfederal **Service:** General Medical and Surgical

Staffed Beds: 349 **Admissions:** 23040 **Census:** 294 **Outpatient Visits:** 70488 **Births:** 1738

★ △ ◇ **LEE MEMORIAL HOSPITAL (100012)**, 2776 Cleveland Avenue, Zip 33901–5855, Mailing Address: P.O. Box 2218, Zip 33902–2218; tel. 239/343–2000, (Includes CHILDREN'S HOSPITAL OF SOUTHWEST FLORIDA, 9981 South HealthPark Drive, Zip 33908; tel. 239/433–7799; James R. Nathan, Chief Executive Officer; HEALTHPARK MEDICAL CENTER, 9981 South HealthPark Drive, Zip 33908; tel. 239/433–7799; James R. Nathan, Chief Executive Officer; THE REHABILITATION HOSPITAL, 2776 Cleveland Avenue, Zip 33901; tel. 239/343–3900; James R. Nathan, Chief Executive Officer), (Total facility includes 112 beds in nursing home–type unit) **A**2 3 7 10 21 **F**3 11 13 14 15 17 18 19 20 21 22 24 26 28 29 30 31 32 34 35 38 40 41 43 45 48 50 51 53 54 56 57 58 59 61 62 64 65 68 70 72 73 74 75 76 77 78 79 81 82 84 85 86 87 88 89 90 93 94 97 100 102 103 104 105 106 107 108 110 111 113 114 115 116 117 119 126 128 129 130 131 132 134 135 146 147 148 **S** Lee Memorial Health System, Fort Myers, FL
Primary Contact: James R. Nathan, President and Chief Executive Officer
COO: Lawrence Antonucci, M.D., Chief Operating Officer
CFO: Ben Spence, Chief Financial Officer
CMO: Chuck Krivenko, M.D., Chief Medical Officer, Clinical and Quality Services
CIO: Mike Smith, Chief Information Officer
CHR: Jon C. Cecil, Chief Human Resource Officer
CNO: Donna Giannuzzi, R.N., Chief Nursing Officer
Web address: www.leememorial.org
Control: Hospital district or authority, Government, nonfederal **Service:** General Medical and Surgical

Staffed Beds: 857 **Admissions:** 40489 **Census:** 520 **Outpatient Visits:** 167374 **Births:** 3769

☐ **PARK ROYAL HOSPITAL (104074)**, 9241 Park Royal Drive, Zip 33908–9204; tel. 239/985–2700, (Nonreporting) **A**1 10 **S** Acadia Healthcare Company, Inc., Franklin, TN
Primary Contact: Michael K. Evans, Chief Executive Officer
CFO: Amy Ciampa, Chief Financial Officer
CHR: Robert Raynor, Human Resources Director
Web address: www.ParkRoyalHospital.com
Control: Corporation, Investor–owned, for–profit **Service:** Psychiatric

Staffed Beds: 103

PROMISE HOSPITAL OF FORT MYERS, 3050 Champion Ring Road, Zip 33905–5599; tel. 239/313–2900, (Nonreporting) **S** Promise Healthcare, Boca Raton, FL
Primary Contact: Patrick G. Ryan, Chief Executive Officer
Web address: www.promisefortmyers.om
Control: Corporation, Investor–owned, for–profit **Service:** Long–Term Acute Care hospital

Staffed Beds: 60

✠ **LAWNWOOD REGIONAL MEDICAL CENTER & HEART INSTITUTE (100246)**, 1700 South 23rd Street, Zip 34950–4803; tel. 772/461–4000, (Includes LAWNWOOD PAVILION, 1860 North Lawnwood Circle, Zip 34950, Mailing Address: P.O. Box 1540, Zip 34954–1540; tel. 361/466–1500), (Nonreporting) **A**1 10 **S** HCA, Nashville, TN
Primary Contact: Greg Lowe, Chief Executive Officer
CFO: Robert Dunwoody, Chief Financial Officer
CIO: Eric Castle, Director Information Services
CHR: Pam Burchell, Director Human Resources
Web address: www.lawnwoodmed.com
Control: Corporation, Investor–owned, for–profit **Service:** General Medical and Surgical

Staffed Beds: 331

✠ **FORT WALTON BEACH MEDICAL CENTER (100223)**, 1000 Mar–Walt Drive, Zip 32547–6795; tel. 850/862–1111, (Nonreporting) **A**1 2 3 10 **S** HCA, Nashville, TN
Primary Contact: Mitchell P. Mongell, FACHE, Chief Executive Officer
CFO: Jeffrey Steve Moore, Chief Financial Officer
CMO: Colonel Tama Van Decar, M.D., Chief Medical Officer
CIO: Amy Caldeira, Director Information Technology and Systems
CHR: Julia Truman, Vice President Human Resources
CNO: Holly McGucken, R.N., Chief Nursing Officer
Web address: www.fwbmc.com
Control: Corporation, Investor–owned, for–profit **Service:** General Medical and Surgical

Staffed Beds: 257

✠ **NORTH FLORIDA REGIONAL MEDICAL CENTER (100204)**, 6500 Newberry Road, Zip 32605–4392, Mailing Address: P.O. Box 147006, Zip 32614–7006; tel. 352/333–4000 **A**1 2 3 10 **F**3 12 13 15 17 18 20 22 24 26 28 29 30 31 34 35 37 40 42 45 46 48 49 50 51 56 57 59 60 64 70 72 74 75 76 77 78 79 80 81 85 86 87 98 107 108 109 110 111 113 114 115 116 117 118 119 120 121 123 124 126 129 130 132 135 145 146 147 148 **S** HCA, Nashville, TN
Primary Contact: Brian Cook, FACHE, President and Chief Executive Officer
CFO: Jay St Pierre, Chief Financial Officer
CMO: Ann Weber, M.D., Chief Medical Officer
CIO: Eric Strand, Director Information Services
CHR: Jane Fuller, Vice President Human Resources
CNO: Natalie Ransom, Chief Nursing Officer
Web address: www.nfrmc.com
Control: Corporation, Investor–owned, for–profit **Service:** General Medical and Surgical

Staffed Beds: 349 **Admissions:** 25192 **Census:** 265 **Births:** 3132 **Total Expense ($000):** 319108 **Payroll Expense ($000):** 92272

✠ **NORTH FLORIDA/SOUTH GEORGIA VETERAN'S HEALTH SYSTEM**, 1601 S.W. Archer Road, Zip 32608–1135; tel. 352/376–1611, (Includes GAINESVILLE VETERANS AFFAIRS MEDICAL CENTER, 1601 S.W. Archer Road, Zip 32608–1197; tel. 352/376–1611; LAKE CITY VETERANS AFFAIRS MEDICAL CENTER, 619 South Marion Avenue, Lake City, Zip 32025–5898; tel. 386/755–3016), (Total facility includes 250 beds in nursing home–type unit) **A**1 3 5 **F**3 5 8 9 10 11 12 15 17 18 20 22 24 26 28 29 30 31 34 35 36 38 39 40 44 45 46 47 48 49 51 54 55 56 57 58 59 60 61 62 63 64 65 66 68 70 74 75 77 78 79 81 82 83 84 85 86 87 91 92 93 94 97 98 100 101 102 103 104 105 106 107 108 109 110 111 114 115 116 117 118 119 127 128 129 130 131 132 133 135 136 141 143 144 145 146 147 148 **P**6 **S** Department of Veterans Affairs, Washington, DC
Primary Contact: Thomas Wisnieski, FACHE, Director
COO: Thomas Sutton, Associate Director
CFO: Jim Taylor, Chief Business Office
CMO: Brad Bender, M.D., Chief of Staff
CIO: Deborah Michel–Ogborn, Chief Information Resource Management
CHR: Michelle Manderino, Chief Human Resources
Web address: www.northflorida.va.gov
Control: Veterans Affairs, Government, federal **Service:** General Medical and Surgical

Staffed Beds: 623 **Admissions:** 12067 **Census:** 40 **Outpatient Visits:** 1681054 **Births:** 0 **Total Expense ($000):** 1022311 **Payroll Expense ($000):** 417696 **Personnel:** 5460

✠ **SELECT SPECIALTY HOSPITAL–GAINESVILLE (102022)**, 2708 S.W. Archer Road, Zip 32608–1316; tel. 352/337–3240, (Nonreporting) **A**1 10 **S** Select Medical Corporation, Mechanicsburg, PA
Primary Contact: Kristopher Kitzke, Chief Executive Officer
Web address: www.selectspecialtyhospitals.com/company/locations/gainesville.aspx
Control: Corporation, Investor–owned, for–profit **Service:** Long–Term Acute Care hospital

Staffed Beds: 44

FL

Hospital, Medicare Provider Number, Address, Telephone, Approval, Facility, and Physician Codes, Health Care System		
★ American Hospital Association (AHA) membership	◯ Healthcare Facilities Accreditation Program	⇑ Center for Improvement in Healthcare Quality Accreditation
☐ The Joint Commission accreditation	◇ DNV Healthcare Inc. accreditation	△ Commission on Accreditation of Rehabilitation Facilities (CARF) accreditation

✠ △ **UF HEALTH SHANDS HOSPITAL (100113)**, 1600 S.W. Archer Road, Zip 32610–3003, Mailing Address: PO Box 100326, Zip 32610–0326; tel. 352/265–0111, (Includes UF HEALTH SHANDS CANCER HOSPITAL, 1515 S.W. Archer Road, Zip 32608–1134, Mailing Address: PO Box 100014, Zip 32610–0014; tel. 352/265–0111; Edward Jimenez, Chief Executive Officer; UF HEALTH SHANDS CHILDREN'S HOSPITAL, 1600 S.W. Archer Road, Mailing Address: PO Box 100326, Zip 32610–0326; tel. 352/265–0111; Edward Jimenez, Chief Executive Officer; UF HEALTH SHANDS PSYCHIATRIC HOSPITAL, 4101 N.W. 89th Boulevard, Zip 32606; tel. 352/265–5481; Marina T. Cecchini, Administrator; UF HEALTH SHANDS REHAB HOSPITAL, 4101 N.W. 89th Boulevard, Zip 32606–3813; tel. 352/265–5499; Marina T. Cecchini, Administrator) **A**1 2 3 5 7 8 10 **F**2 3 4 5 6 7 9 11 12 13 15 16 17 18 19 20 21 22 23 24 25 26 27 29 30 31 32 34 35 36 37 38 39 40 41 42 43 44 45 46 47 48 49 50 51 52 53 54 55 56 57 58 59 60 61 62 64 65 66 68 69 70 72 73 74 75 76 77 78 79 80 81 82 83 84 85 86 87 88 89 90 91 93 94 96 97 98 99 100 101 102 103 104 105 107 108 109 110 111 114 115 116 117 118 119 120 121 123 124 126 129 130 131 132 134 135 136 137 138 139 140 141 142 143 144 145 146 147 148 **P**6 **S** UF Health Shands, Gainesville, FL
Primary Contact: Edward Jimenez, Chief Executive Officer
CFO: James J. Kelly, Jr., Senior Vice President and Chief Financial Officer
CMO: Timothy C. Flynn, M.D., Chief of Staff
CIO: Kari Cassel, Senior Vice President and Chief Information Officer
CHR: Janet L. Christie, Senior Vice President Human Resources
CNO: Irene Alexaitis, R.N., Vice President of Nursing and Patient Services and Chief Nursing Officer
Web address: www.https://ufhealth.org/
Control: Other not–for–profit (including NFP Corporation) **Service:** General Medical and Surgical

Staffed Beds: 972 **Admissions:** 46235 **Census:** 808 **Outpatient Visits:** 948378 **Births:** 2792 **Total Expense ($000):** 1172049 **Payroll Expense ($000):** 427745 **Personnel:** 7904

UF HEALTH SHANDS REHAB HOSPITAL See UF Health Shands Hospital

GRACEVILLE—Jackson County

CAMPBELLTON GRACEVILLE HOSPITAL (101302), 5429 College Drive, Zip 32440–1897; tel. 850/263–4431 **A**10 18 **F**3 28 29 30 34 35 40 54 59 63 64 65 67 77 83 84 94 97 107 119 127 128 130 133 135 148
Primary Contact: George Perez, Chief Executive Officer
CFO: Dena Cooper, Chief Financial Officer
CMO: Steve Davis, M.D., Chief Medical Officer
CHR: Judy Austin, Director Human Resources
Web address: www.c–ghospital.com
Control: Hospital district or authority, Government, nonfederal **Service:** General Medical and Surgical

Staffed Beds: 25 **Admissions:** 144 **Census:** 4 **Births:** 0

GREEN COVE SPRINGS—Clay County

✠ **KINDRED HOSPITAL NORTH FLORIDA (102015)**, 801 Oak Street, Zip 32043–4317; tel. 904/284–9230 **A**1 10 **F**1 3 29 62 85 91 107 119 148 **P**5 **S** Kindred Healthcare, Louisville, KY
Primary Contact: Susan Drago, R.N., Chief Executive Officer
CFO: Beth Kalnajs, Controller
CMO: Uriel Nazario, M.D., Chief of Medical Staff
CIO: Rick Chapman, Chief Information Officer
CNO: Annette Sanchez, Chief Clinical Officer
Web address: www.khnorthflorida.com
Control: Corporation, Investor–owned, for–profit **Service:** Long–Term Acute Care hospital

Staffed Beds: 80 **Admissions:** 667 **Census:** 56 **Outpatient Visits:** 0 **Births:** 0 **Total Expense ($000):** 30378 **Payroll Expense ($000):** 11112 **Personnel:** 224

GULF BREEZE—Santa Rosa County

✠ **GULF BREEZE HOSPITAL (100266)**, 1110 Gulf Breeze Parkway, Zip 32561–4884; tel. 850/934–2000 **A**1 3 10 **F**3 8 11 15 20 26 29 30 31 40 44 45 46 50 54 57 59 64 68 70 74 75 78 79 81 82 84 85 86 91 93 106 107 110 111 114 119 120 121 123 129 130 131 132 143 146 147 148 **S** Baptist Health Care Corporation, Pensacola, FL
Primary Contact: Scott Raynes, President
CFO: Kerry Vermillion, Senior Vice President Finance and Chief Financial Officer
Web address: www.ebaptisthealthcare.org/GulfBreezeHospital/
Control: Other not–for–profit (including NFP Corporation) **Service:** General Medical and Surgical

Staffed Beds: 65 **Admissions:** 4159 **Census:** 44 **Outpatient Visits:** 116464 **Births:** 0 **Total Expense ($000):** 92858 **Payroll Expense ($000):** 24812 **Personnel:** 426

HIALEAH—Miami–Dade County

✠ **HIALEAH HOSPITAL (100053)**, 651 East 25th Street, Zip 33013–3878; tel. 305/693–6100 **A**1 10 **F**3 12 13 15 18 24 29 31 34 40 41 49 56 57 59 60 61 63 68 70 72 74 76 77 79 81 82 85 93 98 102 107 111 115 126 129 130 132 147 148 **S** TENET Healthcare Corporation, Dallas, TX
Primary Contact: Ben A. Rodriguez, Chief Executive Officer
CFO: Gary Nymoen, Chief Financial Officer
CMO: Orlando Garcia, M.D., Chief Medical Officer
CHR: Yamila Herrera, Director Human Resources
CNO: Lourdes Camps, R.N., Chief Nursing Officer
Web address: www.hialeahhosp.com
Control: Corporation, Investor–owned, for–profit **Service:** General Medical and Surgical

Staffed Beds: 191 **Admissions:** 12900 **Census:** 142 **Outpatient Visits:** 40996 **Births:** 1338 **Total Expense ($000):** 123069 **Payroll Expense ($000):** 47072 **Personnel:** 652

☐ **PALM SPRINGS GENERAL HOSPITAL (100050)**, 1475 West 49th Street, Zip 33012–3275, Mailing Address: P.O. Box 2804, Zip 33012–2804; tel. 305/558–2500, (Nonreporting) **A**1 10 12
Primary Contact: Nicholas T. Smith, Chief Executive Officer
CFO: Tony Milian, Chief Financial Officer
CHR: Lourdes Anton, Director Human Resources
Web address: www.psghosp.com
Control: Corporation, Investor–owned, for–profit **Service:** General Medical and Surgical

Staffed Beds: 190

✠ **PALMETTO GENERAL HOSPITAL (100187)**, 2001 West 68th Street, Zip 33016–1898; tel. 305/823–5000, (Nonreporting) **A**1 5 10 12 13 **S** TENET Healthcare Corporation, Dallas, TX
Primary Contact: Ana J. Mederos, Chief Executive Officer
COO: Georgina Diaz, Chief Operating Officer
CFO: Oscar Vicente, Chief Financial Officer
CMO: Eloy Roman, M.D., Chief of Staff
CHR: Ana Gonzalez–Fajardo, Human Resources Director
Web address: www.palmettogeneral.com
Control: Corporation, Investor–owned, for–profit **Service:** General Medical and Surgical

Staffed Beds: 360

SOUTHERN WINDS HOSPITAL See Westchester General Hospital, Miami

HOLLYWOOD—Broward County

☐ **LARKIN BEHAVIORAL HEALTH SERVICES (104015)**, 1201 North 37th Avenue, Zip 33021–5498; tel. 954/962–1355, (Nonreporting) **A**1
Primary Contact: Iris Berges, Chief Executive Officer
COO: Christopher Gabel, Chief Operating Officer
CFO: Rocky Davidson, Chief Financial Officer
CHR: Len Alpert, Director Human Resources
Web address: www.hollywoodpavilion.com
Control: Corporation, Investor–owned, for–profit **Service:** Psychiatric

Staffed Beds: 46

✠ △ **MEMORIAL REGIONAL HOSPITAL (100038)**, 3501 Johnson Street, Zip 33021–5421; tel. 954/987–2000, (Includes JOE DIMAGGIO CHILDREN'S HOSPITAL, 1005 Joe DiMaggio Drive, Zip 33021–5426; tel. 954/987–2000; Chantal Leconte, FACHE, Chief Executive Officer; MEMORIAL REGIONAL HOSPITAL SOUTH, 3600 Washington Street, Zip 33021–8216; tel. 954/966–4500; Douglas Zaren, FACHE, Administrator and CEO) **A**1 2 3 5 7 10 **F**3 5 11 12 13 15 17 18 19 20 21 22 23 24 25 26 27 28 29 30 31 32 34 37 38 39 40 41 43 45 46 47 49 50 51 53 55 56 57 58 59 60 61 64 65 66 67 68 70 71 72 73 74 75 76 77 78 79 81 82 84 85 87 88 89 90 91 93 95 96 97 98 99 100 101 102 103 104 107 108 110 111 114 115 119 120 121 123 126 129 130 131 132 134 135 137 145 146 147 148 **P**1 6 **S** Memorial Healthcare System, Hollywood, FL
Primary Contact: Zeff Ross, FACHE, Executive Vice President and Chief Executive Officer
CFO: Walter Bussell, Chief Financial Officer
CMO: Donald Kim, M.D., Chief Medical Officer
CIO: Forest Blanton, Administrator Process Engineering
CHR: Margie Vargas, Chief Human Resources Officer
CNO: Maggie Hansen, R.N., Chief Nursing Officer
Web address: www.mhs.net
Control: Hospital district or authority, Government, nonfederal **Service:** General Medical and Surgical

Staffed Beds: 1037 **Admissions:** 35667 **Census:** 579 **Outpatient Visits:** 419468 **Births:** 4956 **Total Expense ($000):** 837901 **Payroll Expense ($000):** 328013 **Personnel:** 4759

☐ **SOUTH FLORIDA STATE HOSPITAL (104001)**, 800 East Cypress Drive, Zip 33025–4543; tel. 954/392–3000, (Nonreporting) **A**1 10
Primary Contact: Lee Packer, Administrator
Web address: www.geocarellc.com/Locations/SouthFloridaStateHospital
Control: State–Government, nonfederal **Service:** Psychiatric

Staffed Beds: 355

FL

Many Facility Codes have changed. Please refer to the AHA Guide Code Chart.

© 2016 AHA Guide

HOMESTEAD—Miami-Dade County

☒ **BAPTIST HEALTH SOUTH FLORIDA, HOMESTEAD HOSPITAL (100125)**, 975 Baptist Way, Zip 33033-7600; tel. 786/243-8000 **A**1 10 **F**3 11 13 15 18 29 30 31 34 35 40 41 45 47 49 50 51 53 57 58 59 60 61 63 64 68 70 74 75 76 78 79 81 82 84 85 86 87 89 93 102 107 108 110 111 114 115 119 129 130 131 132 134 135 145 146 147 148 **S** Baptist Health South Florida, Coral Gables, FL
Primary Contact: William M. Duquette, Chief Executive Officer
COO: Kenneth R. Spell, Vice President Operations
CFO: David Abercrombie, Controller
CMO: George R. Tershakovec, M.D., President Medical Staff
CIO: Mimi Taylor, Corporate Vice President Information Technology
CHR: Adriene McCoy, MS, Corporate Vice President
CNO: Nancy Gail Gordon, R.N., Chief Nursing Officer and Vice President of Nursing
Web address: www.baptisthealth.net
Control: Other not-for-profit (including NFP Corporation) **Service:** General Medical and Surgical

Staffed Beds: 142 **Admissions:** 10393 **Census:** 93 **Outpatient Visits:** 119380 **Births:** 1568 **Total Expense ($000):** 214718 **Payroll Expense ($000):** 74553 **Personnel:** 1110

HUDSON—Pasco County

☒ **REGIONAL MEDICAL CENTER BAYONET POINT (100256)**, 14000 Fivay Road, Zip 34667-7199; tel. 727/869-5400 **A**1 2 10 13 **F**3 17 18 20 22 24 26 28 29 30 31 34 35 40 41 43 45 46 48 49 50 51 56 57 58 59 60 64 70 74 75 77 78 79 81 84 85 86 87 91 94 100 107 108 109 111 114 115 118 119 129 130 132 135 141 143 146 148 **S** HCA, Nashville, TN
Primary Contact: Shayne George, Chief Executive Officer
COO: Shalin Shah, Chief Operating Officer
CFO: Thomas Lawhorne, Chief Financial Officer
CMO: Joseph Pino, M.D., Chief Medical Officer
CIO: Mike Wilms, Director of Information Systems
CHR: Geoffrey A. Washburn, Vice President
CNO: Tanya Simpson, Chief Nursing Officer
Web address: www.rmchealth.com
Control: Corporation, Investor-owned, for-profit **Service:** General Medical and Surgical

Staffed Beds: 290 **Admissions:** 14612 **Census:** 188 **Births:** 0 **Total Expense ($000):** 183719 **Payroll Expense ($000):** 57162

INVERNESS—Citrus County

☒ **CITRUS MEMORIAL HEALTH SYSTEM (100023)**, 502 West Highland Boulevard, Zip 34452-4754; tel. 352/726-1551 **A**1 10 19 **F**17 18 20 22 24 28 29 30 31 34 35 40 45 46 49 57 59 64 65 70 75 76 78 79 81 82 84 85 86 87 93 94 102 105 107 108 111 114 115 119 124 132 135 146 147 148 **S** HCA, Nashville, TN
Primary Contact: Ralph A. Aleman, President and Chief Executive Officer
CFO: Mark Williams, Chief Financial Officer
CMO: C. Toumbis, M.D., Chief of Staff
CIO: Nick Brooks, Director of Information Systems
CHR: Lee Glotzback, Director Human Resources
CNO: Linda M. McCarthy, R.N., VP/ Chief Nursing Officer
Web address: www.citrusmh.com
Control: Corporation, Investor-owned, for-profit **Service:** General Medical and Surgical

Staffed Beds: 204 **Admissions:** 11056 **Census:** 123 **Outpatient Visits:** 151866 **Births:** 494

JACKSONVILLE—Duval County

☒ **BAPTIST MEDICAL CENTER JACKSONVILLE (100088)**, 800 Prudential Drive, Zip 32207-8202; tel. 904/202-2000, (Includes BAPTIST MEDICAL CENTER SOUTH, 14550 St. Augustine Road, Zip 32258-2160; tel. 904/821-6000; Ronald G. Robinson, Administrator; WOLFSON CHILDREN'S HOSPITAL, 800 Prudential Drive, Zip 32207; tel. 904/202-8000; Michael D. Aubin, President) **A**1 2 3 5 10 **F**3 5 6 8 11 12 13 15 17 18 19 20 21 22 23 24 25 26 27 28 29 30 31 32 34 35 36 37 38 39 40 41 42 45 46 47 48 49 50 51 53 55 56 57 58 59 60 61 62 64 68 70 72 73 74 75 76 78 79 80 81 82 83 85 86 87 88 89 92 93 94 98 99 100 101 102 103 104 105 107 108 109 110 111 112 113 114 115 116 117 118 119 120 121 123 124 126 129 130 132 134 135 136 145 146 147 148 **P**6 **S** Baptist Health, Jacksonville, FL
Primary Contact: Michael A. Mayo, FACHE, President
COO: John F. Wilbanks, FACHE, Chief Operating Officer
CFO: Scott Wooten, Senior Vice President and Chief Financial Officer
CMO: Keith L. Stein, M.D., Senior Vice President Medical Affairs and Chief Medical Officer
CIO: Roland Garcia, Senior Vice President and Chief Information Officer
CHR: M. Beth Mehaffey, SHRM-SCP, Senior Vice President Human Resources
Web address: www.e-baptisthealth.com
Control: Other not-for-profit (including NFP Corporation) **Service:** General Medical and Surgical

Staffed Beds: 903 **Admissions:** 51416 **Census:** 691 **Outpatient Visits:** 480331 **Births:** 4516 **Total Expense ($000):** 912885 **Payroll Expense ($000):** 272582 **Personnel:** 5681

☒ △ **BROOKS REHABILITATION HOSPITAL (103039)**, 3599 University Boulevard South, Zip 32216-4252; tel. 904/345-7600 **A**1 3 7 10 **F**10 29 30 54 62 64 90 91 93 95 96 130 132 146
Primary Contact: Douglas M. Baer, Chief Executive Officer
COO: Michael Spigel, Executive Vice President & Chief Operating Officer
CMO: Trevor Paris, M.D., Medical Director
CIO: Karen Green, Chief Information Officer
CHR: Karen Gallagher, Vice President Human Resources and Learning
CNO: Joanne Hoertz, Vice President of Nursing
Web address: www.brookshealth.org
Control: Other not-for-profit (including NFP Corporation) **Service:** Rehabilitation

Staffed Beds: 140 **Admissions:** 3091 **Census:** 131 **Outpatient Visits:** 279472 **Births:** 0 **Total Expense ($000):** 84023 **Payroll Expense ($000):** 32910 **Personnel:** 434

★ **MAYO CLINIC JACKSONVILLE (100151)**, 4500 San Pablo Road South, Zip 32224-1865; tel. 904/953-2000 **A**2 3 5 8 10 **F**3 6 8 9 11 12 14 15 17 18 20 22 24 26 28 29 30 31 34 35 36 37 39 40 45 46 47 48 49 50 51 54 55 56 57 58 59 60 61 64 65 68 70 74 75 77 78 79 80 81 82 84 85 86 87 92 93 96 97 100 103 104 105 107 108 110 111 112 114 115 116 117 118 119 120 121 123 124 126 129 130 131 132 135 136 137 138 139 140 141 142 145 146 148 **P**6 **S** Mayo Clinic, Rochester, MN
Primary Contact: Gianrico Farrugia, M.D., Vice President and Chief Executive Officer
CFO: Kevin Lockett, Interim Chief Financial Officer
CMO: Nancy Dawson, M.D., Medical Director
CIO: John Crooks, Chair Information Services
CHR: Daniel Tomlinson, Chair Human Resources
CNO: Ryannon Frederick, Chief Nursing Officer
Web address: www.mayoclinic.org/jacksonville/
Control: Other not-for-profit (including NFP Corporation) **Service:** General Medical and Surgical

Staffed Beds: 249 **Admissions:** 12625 **Census:** 165 **Outpatient Visits:** 44931 **Births:** 0 **Personnel:** 2626

☒ **MEMORIAL HOSPITAL JACKSONVILLE (100179)**, 3625 University Boulevard South, Zip 32216-4207, Mailing Address: P.O. Box 16325, Zip 32245-6325; tel. 904/702-6111 **A**1 2 3 10 **F**3 4 11 12 13 15 17 18 20 22 24 26 28 29 30 32 34 35 38 40 41 42 45 51 52 53 54 55 56 57 58 59 64 65 70 72 74 75 76 77 78 79 81 82 84 87 88 89 97 98 100 101 102 103 104 105 107 111 126 130 143 146 147 148 **S** HCA, Nashville, TN
Primary Contact: James F. O'Loughlin, President and Chief Executive Officer
COO: Bobby McCullough, Chief Operating Officer
CFO: Andy Miller, Chief Financial Officer
CMO: Aaron West, M.D., Chief Medical Officer
CIO: Lance Penton, Director, Information Services
CHR: Stuart Thompson, Vice President Human Resources
CNO: Suzanne Woods, Senior Vice President of Nursing
Web address: www.memorialhospitaljax.com
Control: Corporation, Investor-owned, for-profit **Service:** General Medical and Surgical

Staffed Beds: 418 **Admissions:** 22192 **Census:** 279 **Births:** 1410 **Total Expense ($000):** 304836 **Payroll Expense ($000):** 94587

FL

Hospital, Medicare Provider Number, Address, Telephone, Approval, Facility, and Physician Codes, Health Care System

★ American Hospital Association (AHA) membership
☐ The Joint Commission accreditation
○ Healthcare Facilities Accreditation Program
◇ DNV Healthcare Inc. accreditation
⇑ Center for Improvement in Healthcare Quality Accreditation
△ Commission on Accreditation of Rehabilitation Facilities (CARF) accreditation

✠ **NAVAL HOSPITAL JACKSONVILLE**, 2080 Child Street, Zip 32214–5000; tel. 904/542–7300, (Nonreporting) **A**1 3 5 **S** Bureau of Medicine and Surgery, Department of the Navy, Falls Church, VA
Primary Contact: Commander Darryl Green, Director Administration
CFO: Lieutenant Commander Michael Gregonis, Comptroller
CMO: Captain Christopher Quarles, M.D., Director Medical Services
CIO: Mike Haytaian, Head Director Information Resources Management
CHR: Captain Ruby Tennyson, Director Administration
Web address: www.med.navy.mil/SITES/NAVALHOSPITALJAX/Pages/default.aspx
Control: Navy, Government, federal **Service:** General Medical and Surgical

Staffed Beds: 64

☐ **RIVER POINT BEHAVIORAL HEALTH (104016)**, 6300 Beach Boulevard, Zip 32216–2782; tel. 904/724–9202, (Nonreporting) **A**1 10 **S** Universal Health Services, Inc., King of Prussia, PA
Primary Contact: Kevin McGee, Chief Executive Officer
CFO: Jenni Stackhouse, Chief Financial Officer
CIO: Bill Willis, Director Information Technology
CHR: Cathy Calhoun, Director Human Resources
Web address: www.riverpointbehavioral.com
Control: Corporation, Investor–owned, for–profit **Service:** Psychiatric

Staffed Beds: 92

✠ **SPECIALTY HOSPITAL JACKSONVILLE (102012)**, 4901 Richard Street, Zip 32207–7328; tel. 904/737–3120 **A**1 10 **F**1 18 29 60 75 85 119 130 148 **S** HCA, Nashville, TN
Primary Contact: Barbara McCarthy, Chief Executive Officer
CFO: Joshua Szostek, Chief Financial Officer
CMO: Wendell H. Williams, Jr., M.D., Medical Director
CIO: Patrick Adesso, Director Information Technology and Systems
CHR: Lisa Ayala, R.N., Director Human Resources
Web address: www.specialtyhospitaljax.com
Control: Corporation, Investor–owned, for–profit **Service:** Long–Term Acute Care hospital

Staffed Beds: 62 Admissions: 559 Census: 39 Outpatient Visits: 0 Births: 0 Total Expense ($000): 28451 Payroll Expense ($000): 11095

✠ **ST. VINCENT'S MEDICAL CENTER RIVERSIDE (100040)**, 1 Shircliff Way, Zip 32204–4748, Mailing Address: P.O. Box 2982, Zip 32203–2982; tel. 904/308–7300 **A**1 2 3 10 13 **F**3 12 13 15 17 18 20 22 24 26 28 29 30 31 34 40 44 45 46 47 48 49 53 55 57 58 61 64 65 70 72 74 76 78 79 81 85 86 87 91 93 107 108 110 111 114 118 119 120 121 123 124 126 130 131 132 146 147 **S** Ascension Health, Saint Louis, MO
Primary Contact: Michael Schatzlein, M.D., President and Chief Executive Officer
COO: Thomas J. VanOsdol, Chief Operating Officer
CFO: Pamela Hess, Chief Financial Officer
CMO: Kenneth Rothfield, M.D., System Vice President and Chief Medical Officer
CIO: Ann Carey, Vice President and Chief Information Officer
CHR: Michelle Adamolekun, Chief Human Resource Officer
CNO: Lorraine Keith, Chief Nursing Officer
Web address: www.jaxhealth.com
Control: Church–operated, Nongovernment, not–for profit **Service:** General Medical and Surgical

Staffed Beds: 482 Admissions: 25195 Census: 332 Outpatient Visits: 128759 Births: 1676 Total Expense ($000): 419988 Payroll Expense ($000): 131834 Personnel: 2272

✠ **ST. VINCENT'S MEDICAL CENTER SOUTHSIDE (100307)**, 4201 Belfort Road, Zip 32216–1431; tel. 904/296–3700 **A**1 5 10 **F**3 12 13 15 18 20 22 26 29 30 31 34 40 44 47 49 57 60 61 64 65 70 72 74 76 78 79 81 85 86 87 93 96 107 108 110 111 114 115 119 126 128 130 131 132 146 147 **S** Ascension Health, Saint Louis, MO
Primary Contact: Michael Schatzlein, M.D., President and Chief Executive Officer
COO: Thomas J. VanOsdol, Chief Operating Officer
CFO: Pamela Hess, Chief Financial Officer
CMO: Kenneth Rothfield, M.D., Chief Medical Officer
CIO: Ann Carey, Chief Information Officer
CHR: Kaye W. Lunsford, System Director Human Resources
CNO: Lorraine Keith, Chief Nursing Officer
Web address: www.jaxhealth.com
Control: Church–operated, Nongovernment, not–for profit **Service:** General Medical and Surgical

Staffed Beds: 288 Admissions: 12006 Census: 135 Outpatient Visits: 46351 Births: 1520 Total Expense ($000): 170423 Payroll Expense ($000): 45868 Personnel: 779

✠ **UF HEALTH JACKSONVILLE (100001)**, 655 West Eighth Street, Zip 32209–6595; tel. 904/244–0411, (Total facility includes 56 beds in nursing home–type unit) **A**1 2 3 5 8 10 **F**3 5 8 11 12 13 15 17 18 19 20 22 24 25 26 28 29 30 31 32 33 34 35 36 37 38 39 40 41 42 43 44 45 46 47 49 50 51 52 53 54 56 57 58 59 60 61 62 64 65 66 68 70 71 72 73 74 75 76 77 78 79 80 81 82 84 85 86 87 88 89 92 93 94 96 97 98 99 100 101 102 103 104 105 107 108 109 110 111 114 115 116 117 118 119 120 121 123 124 126 128 129 130 131 132 134 135 141 145 146 147 148 **S** UF Health Shands, Gainesville, FL
Primary Contact: Russell Armistead, Chief Executive Officer
COO: Greg Miller, Senior Vice President Operations
CFO: William Ryan, Vice President and Chief Financial Officer
CMO: David Vukich, M.D., Senior Vice President, Chief Medical Officer and Chief Quality Officer
CIO: Kari Cassel, Senior Vice President and Chief Information Officer
CHR: Lesli Ward, Vice President Human Resources
CNO: Patrice I. Jones, R.N., Vice President and Chief Nursing Officer
Web address: www.ufhealthjax.org/
Control: Other not–for–profit (including NFP Corporation) **Service:** General Medical and Surgical

Staffed Beds: 620 Admissions: 25850 Census: 451 Outpatient Visits: 454001 Births: 2950 Total Expense ($000): 542185 Payroll Expense ($000): 215503 Personnel: 3905

☐ **WEKIVA SPRINGS (104069)**, 3947 Salisbury Road, Zip 32216–6115; tel. 904/296–3533, (Nonreporting) **A**1 10 **S** Universal Health Services, Inc., King of Prussia, PA
Primary Contact: Sheila Carr, Chief Executive Officer
Web address: www.wekivacenter.com
Control: Other not–for–profit (including NFP Corporation) **Service:** Psychiatric

Staffed Beds: 60

JACKSONVILLE BEACH—Duval County

✠ **BAPTIST MEDICAL CENTER BEACHES (100117)**, 1350 13th Avenue South, Zip 32250–3205; tel. 904/627–2900 **A**1 10 **F**3 8 11 13 15 18 20 28 29 30 31 36 40 43 45 49 50 53 54 57 59 61 64 74 75 76 77 78 79 80 81 82 85 86 93 107 108 110 111 114 115 118 119 126 129 130 146 147 148 **S** Baptist Health, Jacksonville, FL
Primary Contact: Joseph M. Mitrick, FACHE, President
COO: John F. Wilbanks, FACHE, Chief Operating Officer
CFO: Scott Wooten, Senior Vice President and Chief Financial Officer
CMO: Keith L. Stein, M.D., Chief Medical Officer
CIO: Roland Garcia, Senior Vice President and Chief Information Officer
CHR: Dana Voiselle, Director Human Resources and Community Relations
Web address: www.community.e-baptisthealth.com/bmc/beaches/index.html
Control: Other not–for–profit (including NFP Corporation) **Service:** General Medical and Surgical

Staffed Beds: 136 Admissions: 7900 Census: 76 Outpatient Visits: 80967 Births: 1188 Total Expense ($000): 109365 Payroll Expense ($000): 35896 Personnel: 669

JAY—Santa Rosa County

★ **JAY HOSPITAL (100048)**, 14114 South Alabama Street, Zip 32565–1219; tel. 850/675–8000 **A**10 **F**3 11 15 18 29 30 34 35 40 45 48 50 57 59 64 75 77 81 82 85 91 93 107 110 114 119 127 130 133 135 146 **S** Baptist Health Care Corporation, Pensacola, FL
Primary Contact: Michael T. Hutchins, Administrator
CFO: Keith Strickling, Chief Accountant
CMO: Scott Moore, Chief of Staff
CHR: Heather Suggs, Manager Human Resources
CNO: Patsy Jackson, Director of Nursing
Web address: www.bhcpns.org/jayhospital/
Control: Other not–for–profit (including NFP Corporation) **Service:** General Medical and Surgical

Staffed Beds: 49 Admissions: 550 Census: 7 Outpatient Visits: 23422 Births: 0 Total Expense ($000): 11731 Payroll Expense ($000): 5361 Personnel: 94

JUPITER—Palm Beach County

✠ **JUPITER MEDICAL CENTER (100253)**, 1210 South Old Dixie Highway, Zip 33458–7299; tel. 561/263–2234 **A**1 2 10 **F**3 8 11 12 13 15 18 20 22 28 29 30 31 34 35 36 37 40 45 47 48 49 50 53 54 55 57 58 59 64 66 70 71 74 75 76 77 78 79 80 81 82 84 85 86 87 93 107 108 109 110 111 114 115 116 117 118 119 120 121 123 126 129 130 132 135 143 144 145 146 147 148 **P**6 8
Primary Contact: John D. Couris, President and Chief Executive Officer
COO: Steven Seeley, Vice President, Chief Operating Officer, Chief Nursing Officer
CFO: Dale E. Hocking, Chief Financial Officer
CIO: Tom Crawford, Chief Information Officer
CHR: Peter Gloggner, Chief Human Resources Officer
CNO: Steven Seeley, Vice President, Chief Operating Officer, Chief Nursing Officer
Web address: www.jupitermed.com
Control: Other not–for–profit (including NFP Corporation) **Service:** General Medical and Surgical

Staffed Beds: 207 Admissions: 10331 Census: 122 Outpatient Visits: 140766 Births: 1285 Total Expense ($000): 187765 Payroll Expense ($000): 66516 Personnel: 1313

FL

Many Facility Codes have changed. Please refer to the AHA Guide Code Chart. © 2016 AHA Guide

KEY WEST—Monroe County

✖ **LOWER KEYS MEDICAL CENTER (100150)**, 5900 College Road,
Zip 33040–4396, Mailing Address: P.O. Box 9107, Zip 33041–9107;
tel. 305/294–5531, (Includes DE POO HOSPITAL, 1200 Kennedy Drive,
Zip 33041; tel. 305/294–4692), (Nonreporting) **A**1 10 **S** Community Health
Systems, Inc., Franklin, TN
Primary Contact: Stephen G. Pennington, Interim Chief Executive Officer
COO: Meylan Love–Watler, Chief Operating Officer
CFO: Dale Guffey, Chief Financial Officer
CMO: Jerome Covington, M.D., Chief Medical Officer
CIO: Les Jackson, Manager Information Systems
CHR: Donald Canalejo, Director Human Resources
Web address: www.lkmc.com
Control: Corporation, Investor–owned, for–profit **Service:** General Medical and
Surgical

Staffed Beds: 90

KISSIMMEE—Osceola County

FLORIDA HOSPITAL KISSIMMEE See Florida Hospital, Orlando

✖ **OSCEOLA REGIONAL MEDICAL CENTER (100110)**, 700 West Oak Street,
Zip 34741–4996; tel. 407/846–2266, (Nonreporting) **A**1 2 3 5 10 13 **S** HCA,
Nashville, TN
Primary Contact: Robert M. Krieger, Chief Executive Officer
COO: W. Bryan Lee, Chief Operating Officer
CFO: Carrie Biggar, Chief Financial Officer
CMO: Stephens Stoops, M.D., Chief Medical Officer
CHR: Sylvia Lollis, Director Human Resources
Web address: www.osceolaregional.com
Control: Corporation, Investor–owned, for–profit **Service:** General Medical and
Surgical

Staffed Beds: 235

✖ **POINCIANA MEDICAL CENTER (100320)**, 325 Cypress Parkway, Zip 34758;
tel. 407/530–2000, (Nonreporting) **A**1 10 **S** HCA, Nashville, TN
Primary Contact: Joanna J. Conley, FACHE, Chief Executive Officer
Web address: www.poincianamedicalcenter.com
Control: Corporation, Investor–owned, for–profit **Service:** General Medical and
Surgical

Staffed Beds: 24

LAKE BUTLER—Union County

LAKE BUTLER HOSPITAL HAND SURGERY CENTER (101303), 850 East
Main Street, Zip 32054–1353, Mailing Address: P.O. Box 748, Zip 32054–0748;
tel. 386/496–2323 **A**10 18 **F**29 35 40 77 92 93 94 95 96 97 99 119 127
130 133
Primary Contact: Pamela B. Howard, R.N., Chief Executive Officer, Administrator
and Risk Manager
COO: Jennifer Thomas, Chief Operating Officer and Director of Public Relations
CFO: Paula Webb, Chief Financial Officer and Compliance Officer
CMO: Cynthia Larimer, M.D., Chief of Staff
CIO: Diane Cason, Chief Information Officer, Controller and Director Human
Resources
CNO: Mandy Dicks, Director of Nursing
Web address: www.lakebutlerhospital.com
Control: Corporation, Investor–owned, for–profit **Service:** General Medical and
Surgical

Staffed Beds: 25 **Admissions:** 30 **Census:** 1 **Births:** 0 **Total Expense**
($000): 8139 **Payroll Expense ($000):** 5730

RECEPTION AND MEDICAL CENTER, State Road 231 South, Zip 32054,
Mailing Address: P.O. Box 628, Zip 32054–0628;
tel. 386/496–6000, (Nonreporting)
Primary Contact: Maxine Streeter, Administrator
Web address: www.dc.state.fl.us
Control: State–Government, nonfederal **Service:** Hospital unit of an institution
(prison hospital, college infimary, etc.)

Staffed Beds: 120

LAKE CITY—Columbia County

✖ **LAKE CITY MEDICAL CENTER (100156)**, 340 N.W. Commerce Drive,
Zip 32055–4709; tel. 386/719–9000, (Nonreporting) **A**1 10 **S** HCA,
Nashville, TN
Primary Contact: Mark Miller, FACHE, Chief Executive Officer
COO: Jennifer B. Adams, Chief Operating Officer and Chief Financial Officer
CFO: Jennifer B. Adams, Chief Operating Officer and Chief Financial Officer
CMO: Miguel Tepedino, M.D., Chief Medicine
CIO: Taylor Dickerson, Chief Information Officer
CHR: Steve Gordon, Director Human Resources
Web address: www.lakecitymedical.com
Control: Corporation, Investor–owned, for–profit **Service:** General Medical and
Surgical

Staffed Beds: 67

✖ **SHANDS LAKE SHORE REGIONAL MEDICAL CENTER (100102)**, 368 N.E.
Franklin Street, Zip 32055–3047; tel. 386/292–8000, (Nonreporting) **A**1 3 10
S Community Health Systems, Inc., Franklin, TN
Primary Contact: Rhonda Kay Sherrod, R.N., MSN, Administrator
COO: Francis A. Pommett, Jr., Chief Operating Officer
CFO: Steve Davis, Chief Financial Officer
CMO: Mohammad Faisal, President Medical Staff
CHR: Angie Altman, Director Human Resources
CNO: Gary Goelz, R.N., Chief Nursing Officer
Web address: www.shandslakeshore.com
Control: Partnership, Investor–owned, for–profit **Service:** General Medical and
Surgical

Staffed Beds: 90

VETERANS AFFAIRS MEDICAL CENTER See Lake City Veterans Affairs Medical
Center

LAKE WALES—Polk County

✖ **LAKE WALES MEDICAL CENTER (100099)**, 410 South 11th Street,
Zip 33853–4256; tel. 863/676–1433 **A**1 10 **F**3 11 15 18 20 29 30 34 35 40
45 46 49 50 56 57 59 64 70 74 75 79 81 82 85 86 87 89 91 92 93 94 96
98 103 107 108 110 111 114 115 119 124 129 131 132 146 147 148
S Community Health Systems, Inc., Franklin, TN
Primary Contact: Rebecca Brewer, FACHE, Chief Executive Officer
CFO: Danny Warren, Chief Financial Officer
CMO: Sunil Nihalani, M.D., Chief Medical Staff
CIO: Erwin Jaropillo, Director Information Systems
CHR: Renee Latterner, Director Human Resources
CNO: Lee Clack, R.N., Chief Nursing Officer
Web address: www.lakewalesmedicalcenter.com
Control: Corporation, Investor–owned, for–profit **Service:** General Medical and
Surgical

Staffed Beds: 131 **Admissions:** 4699 **Census:** 60 **Births:** 0 **Total Expense**
($000): 55684 **Payroll Expense ($000):** 21956

LAKE WORTH—Palm Beach County

✖ **SELECT SPECIALTY HOSPITAL–PALM BEACH (102023)**, 3060 Melaleuca
Lane, Zip 33461–5174; tel. 561/357–7200, (Nonreporting) **A**1 10 **S** Select
Medical Corporation, Mechanicsburg, PA
Primary Contact: Larry Melby, Chief Executive Officer
Web address: www.selectspecialtyhospitals.com/company/locations/palmbeach.
aspx
Control: Corporation, Investor–owned, for–profit **Service:** Long–Term Acute Care
hospital

Staffed Beds: 60

FL

Hospital, Medicare Provider Number, Address, Telephone, Approval, Facility, and Physician Codes, Health Care System

★ American Hospital Association (AHA) membership   ○ Healthcare Facilities Accreditation Program   ⇑ Center for Improvement in Healthcare Quality Accreditation
□ The Joint Commission accreditation   ◇ DNV Healthcare Inc. accreditation   △ Commission on Accreditation of Rehabilitation Facilities (CARF) accreditation

LAKELAND—Polk County

✠ **LAKELAND REGIONAL HEALTH (100157)**, 1324 Lakeland Hills Boulevard, Zip 33805–4543, Mailing Address: P.O. Box 95448, Zip 33804–5448; tel. 863/687–1100 **A**1 2 3 5 10 **F**3 11 13 18 20 22 24 26 28 29 30 31 34 37 38 40 41 43 44 45 46 47 49 51 55 56 57 58 59 60 61 64 65 66 67 70 71 72 74 75 76 77 78 79 80 81 82 83 84 85 86 87 88 89 90 93 95 96 98 99 100 101 102 103 104 107 108 109 110 111 114 115 118 119 120 121 123 124 126 130 131 132 135 143 144 146 147 148
Primary Contact: Timothy Regan, President and Chief Medical Officer
COO: Sarah Bhagat, Chief Operating Officer and Vice President of Organizational Effectiveness
CFO: Evan Jones, Executive Vice President and Chief Financial Officer
CMO: Mack Reavis, M.D., President and Chief Medical Officer
CIO: Elizabeth Kerns, Senior Vice President and Chief Information Officer
CHR: Scott Dimmick, Senior Vice President and Chief Human Resources Officer
CNO: Janet Fansler, R.N., Executive Vice President and Chief Nurse Executive
Web address: www.mylrh.org
Control: Other not–for–profit (including NFP Corporation) **Service:** General Medical and Surgical

Staffed Beds: 794 **Admissions:** 43222 **Census:** 561 **Outpatient Visits:** 265831 **Births:** 3092 **Total Expense ($000):** 606967 **Payroll Expense ($000):** 240338 **Personnel:** 4416

LAND O'LAKES—Pasco County

✠ **FLORIDA HOSPITAL AT CONNERTON LONG TERM ACUTE CARE (102026)**, 9441 Health Center Drive, Zip 34637–5837; tel. 813/903–3701 **A**1 10 **F**3 29 30 34 70 107 119 146 148 **S** Adventist Health System Sunbelt Health Care Corporation, Altamonte Springs, FL
Primary Contact: Brian Adams, President and Chief Executive Officer
COO: Debora Martoccio, R.N., Chief Operating Officer
CMO: Sharad Patel, M.D., Medical Director
CNO: Rafael Padilla, R.N., Chief Nursing Officer
Web address: www.elevatinghealthcare.org
Control: Church–operated, Nongovernment, not–for profit **Service:** Long–Term Acute Care hospital

Staffed Beds: 50 **Admissions:** 670 **Census:** 49 **Outpatient Visits:** 0 **Births:** 0 **Total Expense ($000):** 24447 **Payroll Expense ($000):** 10924 **Personnel:** 180

LARGO—Pinellas County

✠ **HEALTHSOUTH REHABILITATION HOSPITAL (103037)**, 901 North Clearwater–Largo Road, Zip 33770–4126; tel. 727/586–2999 **A**1 10 **F**29 90 95 96 130 132 **S** HEALTHSOUTH Corporation, Birmingham, AL
Primary Contact: Tripp Smith, Chief Executive Officer
CFO: Judith Johnson, Controller
CMO: Richard A. Liles, M.D., Medical Director
CHR: Jackie Chalk, Director Human Resources
CNO: Pattie Brenner, R.N., Chief Nursing Officer
Web address: www.healthsouthlargo.com
Control: Corporation, Investor–owned, for–profit **Service:** Rehabilitation

Staffed Beds: 70 **Admissions:** 1589 **Census:** 55 **Outpatient Visits:** 0 **Births:** 0 **Total Expense ($000):** 19928 **Payroll Expense ($000):** 10374

✠ △ **LARGO MEDICAL CENTER (100248)**, 201 14th Street S.W., Zip 33770–3133; tel. 727/588–5200, (Includes LARGO MEDICAL CENTER – INDIAN ROCKS, 2025 Indian Rocks Road, Zip 33774–1096, Mailing Address: P.O. Box 2025, Zip 33779–2025; tel. 727/581–9474), (Nonreporting) **A**1 2 5 7 10 12 13 **S** HCA, Nashville, TN
Primary Contact: Anthony M. Degina, President and Chief Executive Officer
CFO: Robert E. Billings, Chief Financial Officer
CMO: David Weiland, M.D., Chief Medical Officer
CIO: David Saly, Director, Information Services
CNO: Brenda Simpson, R.N., Chief Nursing Officer
Web address: www.largomedical.com
Control: Corporation, Investor–owned, for–profit **Service:** General Medical and Surgical

Staffed Beds: 243

LAUDERDALE LAKES—Broward County

☐ △ **ST. ANTHONY'S REHABILITATION HOSPITAL (103027)**, 3485 N.W. 30th Street, Zip 33311–1890; tel. 954/739–6233 **A**1 7 10 **F**28 29 30 34 35 60 64 68 74 75 79 86 90 91 93 94 96 130 131 132 148 **S** Catholic Health Services, Lauderdale Lakes, FL
Primary Contact: Joseph M. Catania, Chief Executive Officer
COO: James Ball, Chief Operating Officer, Executive
CFO: David D'Amico
CMO: Mark Reiner, Chief Medical Office, Executive
CIO: Dario Achury, Director of Information Management
CHR: Barbara Griffith, Vice President Human Resources
Web address: www.catholichealthservices.org
Control: Church–operated, Nongovernment, not–for profit **Service:** Rehabilitation

Staffed Beds: 26 **Admissions:** 523 **Census:** 19 **Outpatient Visits:** 1029 **Births:** 0 **Total Expense ($000):** 7994 **Payroll Expense ($000):** 3719 **Personnel:** 87

LEESBURG—Lake County

✠ △ **LEESBURG REGIONAL MEDICAL CENTER (100084)**, 600 East Dixie Avenue, Zip 34748–5999; tel. 352/323–5762 **A**1 2 7 10 **F**3 8 11 13 15 17 18 20 22 24 26 28 29 30 31 34 35 40 45 47 48 49 53 54 57 59 64 68 70 74 75 76 77 78 79 81 82 84 85 87 89 90 93 96 107 108 110 111 114 115 119 130 132 135 144 146 147 **P**6 7 **S** Central Florida Health, Leesburg, FL
Primary Contact: Donald G. Henderson, FACHE, President and Chief Executive Officer
COO: Saad Ehtisham, R.N., Vice President and Chief Operating Officer
CFO: Diane P. Harden, Chief Financial Officer
CIO: David Steele, Vice President Information Technology
CHR: Amie Richason, Vice President Human Resources
CNO: Joshua Fleming, Vice President Chief Clinical Officer
Web address: www.cfhalliance.org
Control: Other not–for–profit (including NFP Corporation) **Service:** General Medical and Surgical

Staffed Beds: 330 **Admissions:** 15771 **Census:** 216 **Outpatient Visits:** 85022 **Births:** 1451 **Total Expense ($000):** 212120 **Payroll Expense ($000):** 80725 **Personnel:** 1327

LIFESTREAM BEHAVIORAL CENTER (104018), 2020 Tally Road, Zip 34748–3426, Mailing Address: P.O. Box 491000, Zip 34749–1000; tel. 352/315–7500, (Nonreporting) **A**10
Primary Contact: Jonathan M. Cherry, President and Chief Executive Officer
COO: David Braughton, Chief Operating Officer
CFO: Carol Dozier, Chief Financial Officer
CMO: T. J. Valente, M.D., Medical Director
CIO: Chad Heim, Management Information System Director
CHR: Ben Hargrove, Human Resources Director
Web address: www.lsbc.net
Control: Other not–for–profit (including NFP Corporation) **Service:** Psychiatric

Staffed Beds: 46

LEHIGH ACRES—Lee County

✠ **LEHIGH REGIONAL MEDICAL CENTER (100107)**, 1500 Lee Boulevard, Zip 33936–4835; tel. 239/369–2101, (Nonreporting) **A**1 10 **S** Prime Healthcare Services, Ontario, CA
Primary Contact: Thomas Marshall, Interim Chief Executive Officer
CFO: Osman Gruhonjic, Chief Financial Officer
CMO: Joe Lemmons, D.O., Chief of Staff
CIO: Jeff Hampton, Director Information Systems
CHR: Mary Gray, Director Human Resources
CNO: Julie G. Banker, R.N., Chief Nursing Officer
Web address: www.lehighregional.com
Control: Corporation, Investor–owned, for–profit **Service:** General Medical and Surgical

Staffed Beds: 88

LIVE OAK—Suwannee County

✠ **SHANDS LIVE OAK REGIONAL MEDICAL CENTER (101301)**, 1100 S.W. 11th Street, Zip 32064–3608; tel. 386/362–0800 **A**1 10 18 **F**15 18 29 34 35 40 41 45 50 54 56 57 59 64 68 75 81 91 92 93 97 102 107 108 110 111 119 127 135 146 147 **S** Community Health Systems, Inc., Franklin, TN
Primary Contact: Bayode Omosaiye, FACHE, Chief Executive Officer
CFO: Jennifer Grafton, Chief Financial Officer
CMO: Andrew C. Bass, M.D., Medical Director
CIO: Justin Marlowe, Information Technology Director
CHR: Dana Abbott, Market Human Resources Director
CNO: Donna Ragan, R.N., Chief Nursing Officer
Web address: www.shandsliveoak.com/
Control: Corporation, Investor–owned, for–profit **Service:** General Medical and Surgical

Staffed Beds: 25 **Admissions:** 1146 **Census:** 11 **Births:** 0 **Total Expense ($000):** 16678 **Payroll Expense ($000):** 7251

LOXAHATCHEE—Palm Beach County

✠ **PALMS WEST HOSPITAL (100269)**, 13001 Southern Boulevard, Zip 33470–9203; tel. 561/798–3300 **A**1 10 **F**3 8 13 15 18 19 20 22 29 30 31 34 35 39 40 41 45 46 49 50 51 56 57 58 60 61 64 68 70 74 75 76 77 78 79 80 81 82 84 85 86 87 88 89 90 93 107 108 110 111 114 115 119 124 126 130 131 141 146 147 148 **S** HCA, Nashville, TN
Primary Contact: Eric Goldman, Chief Executive Officer
COO: Lorna Kernivan, Chief Operating Officer
CFO: Steven Burroughs, Chief Financial Officer
CIO: Martha Stinson, Director of Information Technology
CHR: Marcy Mills–Mathews, Director Human Resources
CNO: Silvia Stradi, Chief Nursing Officer
Web address: www.palmswesthospital.com
Control: Corporation, Investor–owned, for–profit **Service:** General Medical and Surgical

Staffed Beds: 204 **Admissions:** 14054 **Census:** 158 **Births:** 1625 **Total Expense ($000):** 153467 **Payroll Expense ($000):** 48644

Many Facility Codes have changed. Please refer to the AHA Guide Code Chart. © 2016 AHA Guide

MACCLENNY—Baker County

ED FRASER MEMORIAL HOSPITAL AND BAKER COMMUNITY HEALTH CENTER (100134), 159 North Third Street, Zip 32063–2103, Mailing Address: P.O. Box 484, Zip 32063–0484; tel. 904/259–3151, (Nonreporting) **A**10 20
Primary Contact: Dennis R. Markos, Chief Executive Officer
CFO: W. Steve Dudley, CPA, Chief Financial Officer
CMO: Mark Hardin, M.D., Medical Director
CIO: Ernie Waller, Director Information Technology
CHR: Stacey Conner, Director Personnel
CNO: Valerie Markos, Chief Nursing Officer
Web address: www.bcmedsvcs.com
Control: Other not–for–profit (including NFP Corporation) **Service:** General Medical and Surgical

Staffed Beds: 68

MADISON—Madison County

MADISON COUNTY MEMORIAL HOSPITAL (101311), 224 N.W. Crane Avenue, Zip 32340–2561; tel. 850/973–2271, (Nonreporting) **A**10 18
Primary Contact: Tammy Stevens, Chief Executive Officer
CFO: Patrick Halfhill, Chief Financial Officer
CMO: Brett Perkins, M.D., Chief Medical Staff
CIO: Patrick Stiff, Coordinator Information Technology
CHR: Cindi Burnett, Chief Human Resources Officer
Web address: www.mcmh.us/
Control: Other not–for–profit (including NFP Corporation) **Service:** General Medical and Surgical

Staffed Beds: 25

MARATHON—Monroe County

⊞ **FISHERMEN'S HOSPITAL (101312)**, 3301 Overseas Highway, Zip 33050–2329; tel. 305/743–5533 **A**1 10 18 **F**3 11 15 17 18 29 34 35 40 45 46 50 51 57 59 64 68 70 75 79 81 82 85 91 93 107 108 110 111 114 119 124 130 133 141 146 **P**8 **S** QHR, Brentwood, TN
Primary Contact: Hal W. Leftwich, FACHE, Chief Executive Officer
COO: Lynn Mauck, R.N., Chief Operating Officer and Chief Nursing Officer
CFO: H. D. Cannington, Interim Chief Financial Officer
CMO: Harlan Pettit, M.D., Chief of Medical Staff
CIO: Patrick Stitt, Director of Information Systems
CHR: Chris Fletcher, Director of Human Resources
CNO: Lynn Mauck, R.N., Chief Operating Officer and Chief Nursing Officer
Web address: www.fishermenshospital.org
Control: Other not–for–profit (including NFP Corporation) **Service:** General Medical and Surgical

Staffed Beds: 25 **Admissions:** 608 **Census:** 5 **Outpatient Visits:** 12297 **Births:** 0 **Total Expense ($000):** 25399 **Payroll Expense ($000):** 10539 **Personnel:** 136

MARGATE—Broward County

⊞ **NORTHWEST MEDICAL CENTER (100189)**, 2801 North State Road 7, Zip 33063–5727; tel. 954/974–0400 **A**1 3 10 **F**3 8 11 12 13 15 17 18 22 24 26 29 31 34 35 40 41 44 45 46 47 49 50 53 56 57 59 60 61 63 64 65 68 70 73 74 75 76 77 78 79 80 81 82 83 85 86 87 89 93 107 108 110 111 114 115 117 118 119 126 129 130 131 132 135 146 147 148 **S** HCA, Nashville, TN
Primary Contact: Erica Gulrich, Chief Executive Officer
CFO: Ananda Rampat, Chief Financial Officer
CMO: Jose Martinez, M.D., Chief Medical Officer
CIO: David Irizarri, Director Information Technology
CHR: Lynda Bryan, Vice President Human Resources
CNO: Sandra Emeott, R.N., Chief Nursing Officer
Web address: www.northwestmed.com
Control: Corporation, Investor–owned, for–profit **Service:** General Medical and Surgical

Staffed Beds: 228 **Admissions:** 15596 **Census:** 154 **Births:** 1874 **Total Expense ($000):** 172041 **Payroll Expense ($000):** 52725

MARIANNA—Jackson County

⊞ **JACKSON HOSPITAL (100142)**, 4250 Hospital Drive, Zip 32446–1917, Mailing Address: P.O. Box 1608, Zip 32447–5608; tel. 850/526–2200 **A**1 10 20 **F**3 11 13 15 18 29 30 31 34 35 40 45 49 50 53 57 59 70 75 76 78 81 85 86 87 97 107 108 110 111 114 119 120 127 130 132 133 135 146 147 **S** QHR, Brentwood, TN
Primary Contact: Larry Meese, Chief Executive Officer
CFO: Kevin Rovito, Chief Financial Officer
CMO: Steven Walter Spence, M.D., Chief Medical Officer
CIO: Jamie Hussey, Chief Information Officer
CHR: Brooke G. Donaldson, Assistant Administrator Human Resources
CNO: Robbin K. Pumphrey, Chief Nursing Officer
Web address: www.jacksonhosp.com
Control: Hospital district or authority, Government, nonfederal **Service:** General Medical and Surgical

Staffed Beds: 68 **Admissions:** 2985 **Census:** 37 **Outpatient Visits:** 37734 **Births:** 457 **Total Expense ($000):** 46060 **Payroll Expense ($000):** 20595 **Personnel:** 468

MELBOURNE—Brevard County

☐ **CIRCLES OF CARE (104024)**, 400 East Sheridan Road, Zip 32901–3184; tel. 321/722–5200, (Nonreporting) **A**1 5 10
Primary Contact: James B. Whitaker, President
CFO: David L. Feldman, Executive Vice President and Treasurer
CMO: Jose Alvarez, M.D., Chief Medical Staff
CHR: Linda Brannon, Vice President Human Resources
Web address: www.circlesofcare.org
Control: Other not–for–profit (including NFP Corporation) **Service:** Psychiatric

Staffed Beds: 134

DEVEREUX HOSPITAL AND CHILDREN'S CENTER OF FLORIDA, 8000 Devereux Drive, Zip 32940–7907; tel. 321/242–9100, (Nonreporting) **S** Devereux, Villanova, PA
Primary Contact: Steven Murphy, Executive Director
COO: Eva Horner, Assistant Executive Director Operations
CFO: Kelly Messer, Director of Finance
CMO: Manal Durgin, Network Medical Director
CIO: Diana Deitrick, Director Information Services
CHR: Tim Dillion, Vice President of Human Resources
Web address: www.devereux.org
Control: Other not–for–profit (including NFP Corporation) **Service:** Children's hospital psychiatric

Staffed Beds: 100

⊞ **HEALTH FIRST HOLMES REGIONAL MEDICAL CENTER (100019)**, 1350 South Hickory Street, Zip 32901–3224; tel. 321/434–7000 **A**1 5 10 **F**3 7 11 13 15 17 18 20 22 24 26 29 30 31 34 35 40 43 45 46 47 48 49 56 57 59 60 65 68 70 72 73 74 75 76 77 78 79 81 82 83 84 85 87 89 91 92 93 100 107 108 110 111 114 115 116 117 118 119 124 126 129 130 132 146 147 148 **P**6 7 **S** Health First, Inc., Rockledge, FL
Primary Contact: Sean Gregory, Chief Executive Officer
CFO: Joseph G. Felkner, Executive Vice President, Finance and Chief Financial Officer
CMO: Mark Rosenbloom, Vice President of Medical Affairs
CIO: Dustin Leek, Vice President of Enterprise Technical Services
CHR: Paula Just, Chief Human Resources Officer
CNO: Barbara Seymour, Vice President of Nursing
Web address: www.health–first.org
Control: Other not–for–profit (including NFP Corporation) **Service:** General Medical and Surgical

Staffed Beds: 514 **Admissions:** 28135 **Census:** 364 **Outpatient Visits:** 215372 **Births:** 3030 **Total Expense ($000):** 389482 **Payroll Expense ($000):** 152879 **Personnel:** 1792

☐ **HEALTH FIRST VIERA HOSPITAL (100315)**, 8745 North Wickham Road, Zip 32940–5997; tel. 321/434–9164 **A**1 5 10 **F**3 11 12 15 18 29 30 31 34 35 40 41 44 45 46 47 48 49 50 57 59 60 64 68 70 74 77 78 79 81 85 86 87 93 97 107 108 110 111 115 117 118 119 126 129 130 132 146 148 **P**6 7 **S** Health First, Inc., Rockledge, FL
Primary Contact: William Calhoun, President, Community Hospitals
COO: Deborah Angerami, Chief Operating Officer
CFO: Joseph G. Felkner, Executive Vice President and Chief Financial Officer
CMO: Scott Gettings, M.D., Senior Vice President and Chief Medical Officer
CIO: Lori Delone, Senior Vice President and Chief Information Officer
CHR: Paula Just, Chief Human Resources Officer
CNO: Connie Bradley, R.N., Senior Vice President and Chief Nursing Officer
Web address: www.vierahospital.org
Control: Other not–for–profit (including NFP Corporation) **Service:** General Medical and Surgical

Staffed Beds: 84 **Admissions:** 4146 **Census:** 40 **Outpatient Visits:** 72199 **Births:** 0 **Total Expense ($000):** 81093 **Payroll Expense ($000):** 25879 **Personnel:** 300

FL

✠ **HEALTHSOUTH SEA PINES REHABILITATION HOSPITAL (103034)**, 101 East Florida Avenue, Zip 32901–8301; tel. 321/984–4600, (Nonreporting) **A**1 10 **S** HEALTHSOUTH Corporation, Birmingham, AL
Primary Contact: Denise B. McGrath, Chief Executive Officer
CFO: Dana Edwards, Chief Financial Officer
CMO: Juan Lebron, M.D., Medical Director
CHR: James L. Henry, Director Human Resources
CNO: Lisa Truman, Chief Nursing Officer
Web address: www.healthsouthseapines.com
Control: Corporation, Investor–owned, for–profit **Service:** Rehabilitation

> **Staffed Beds:** 90

✠ **KINDRED HOSPITAL MELBOURNE (102027)**, 765 West Nasa Boulevard, Zip 32901–1815; tel. 321/733–5725 **A**1 10 **F**1 3 29 70 107 114 148 **S** Kindred Healthcare, Louisville, KY
Primary Contact: Pamela R. Reed, Chief Executive Officer
Web address: www.khmelbourne.com
Control: Corporation, Investor–owned, for–profit **Service:** Long–Term Acute Care hospital

> **Staffed Beds:** 60 **Admissions:** 363 **Census:** 30 **Outpatient Visits:** 0 **Births:** 0 **Total Expense ($000):** 18261 **Payroll Expense ($000):** 6737

✠ **WUESTHOFF MEDICAL CENTER – MELBOURNE (100291)**, 250 North Wickham Road, Zip 32935–8625; tel. 321/752–1200 **A**1 10 **F**3 12 15 18 20 22 29 30 34 39 40 45 70 79 81 85 93 107 108 111 115 119 126 130 146 148 **S** Community Health Systems, Inc., Franklin, TN
Primary Contact: Ron Gicca, Chief Executive Officer
CFO: Steve Bender, Chief Financial Officer
Web address: www.wuesthoff.com/locations/wuesthoff–medical–center–melbourne
Control: Corporation, Investor–owned, for–profit **Service:** General Medical and Surgical

> **Staffed Beds:** 119 **Admissions:** 3571 **Census:** 44 **Births:** 0 **Total Expense ($000):** 63883 **Payroll Expense ($000):** 20519

MIAMI—Miami–Dade County

✠ △ **BAPTIST HEALTH SOUTH FLORIDA, BAPTIST HOSPITAL OF MIAMI (100008)**, 8900 North Kendall Drive, Zip 33176–2197; tel. 786/596–1960, (Includes BAPTIST CHILDREN'S HOSPITAL, 8900 North Kendall Drive, Zip 33176–2118; tel. 786/596–1960) **A**1 2 3 5 7 10 **F**3 8 11 13 15 17 18 19 20 22 24 26 28 29 30 34 40 41 45 46 47 49 50 51 53 54 55 56 57 58 59 60 61 62 63 64 66 68 70 72 73 74 75 76 77 78 79 81 82 84 85 86 87 88 89 90 91 92 93 96 100 102 107 108 109 110 111 114 115 116 117 118 119 120 121 123 124 126 129 130 132 135 144 145 146 147 148 **S** Baptist Health South Florida, Coral Gables, FL
Primary Contact: Albert Boulenger, Chief Executive Officer
COO: Randall Lee, Vice President and Chief Operating Officer
CFO: Ralph E. Lawson, Executive Vice President and Chief Financial Officer
CMO: Mark J. Hauser, M.D., Chief Medical Officer
CIO: Mimi Taylor, Corporate Vice President Information Technology
Web address: www.baptisthealth.net
Control: Other not–for–profit (including NFP Corporation) **Service:** General Medical and Surgical

> **Staffed Beds:** 720 **Admissions:** 34279 **Census:** 514 **Outpatient Visits:** 379503 **Births:** 4377 **Total Expense ($000):** 795511 **Payroll Expense ($000):** 276509 **Personnel:** 4110

✠ **BAPTIST HEALTH SOUTH FLORIDA, SOUTH MIAMI HOSPITAL (100154)**, 6200 S.W. 73rd Street, Zip 33143–4679; tel. 786/662–4000 **A**1 2 3 10 **F**3 5 11 12 13 15 17 18 20 22 24 26 28 29 30 31 34 35 36 40 46 49 50 51 52 53 54 57 58 59 60 61 64 68 70 72 74 75 76 77 78 79 81 82 84 85 86 87 93 107 108 110 111 114 115 116 117 118 119 120 121 123 124 126 129 130 132 135 144 146 147 148 **S** Baptist Health South Florida, Coral Gables, FL
Primary Contact: Lincoln S. Mendez, Chief Executive Officer
COO: Jeanette Stone, Vice President Operations
CFO: Erik Long, Controller
CMO: Jeremy Tabak, M.D., President Medical Staff
CIO: Mimi Taylor, Vice President Information Technology
CHR: Diana Montenegro, Director Human Resources
CNO: Kathy Sparger, R.N., Chief Nursing Officer
Web address: www.baptisthealth.net
Control: Other not–for–profit (including NFP Corporation) **Service:** General Medical and Surgical

> **Staffed Beds:** 335 **Admissions:** 16123 **Census:** 218 **Outpatient Visits:** 274973 **Births:** 4182 **Total Expense ($000):** 461058 **Payroll Expense ($000):** 154707 **Personnel:** 2005

✠ **BAPTIST HEALTH SOUTH FLORIDA, WEST KENDALL BAPTIST HOSPITAL (100314)**, 9555 S.W. 162nd Avenue, Zip 33196–6408; tel. 786/467–2000 **A**1 3 8 10 **F**3 11 13 18 19 29 30 31 34 35 40 41 45 49 50 51 53 57 58 59 60 63 64 68 70 74 75 76 78 79 81 82 84 85 86 87 93 100 102 107 108 109 111 114 115 119 126 130 131 132 135 146 147 148 **S** Baptist Health South Florida, Coral Gables, FL
Primary Contact: Javier Hernandez–Lichtl, Chief Executive Officer
CFO: Odalys Remigio, Assistant Vice President, Finance
CMO: Juan–Carlos Verdeja, M.D., President of Medical Staff
CHR: Hilde Zamora de Aguero, Human Resources Site Director
CNO: Denise H. Harris, R.N., Chief Nursing Officer
Web address: www.baptisthealth.net/en/facilities/West–Kendall–Baptist–Hospital/Pages/default.aspx
Control: Other not–for–profit (including NFP Corporation) **Service:** General Medical and Surgical

> **Staffed Beds:** 133 **Admissions:** 7598 **Census:** 83 **Outpatient Visits:** 81892 **Births:** 856 **Total Expense ($000):** 189854 **Payroll Expense ($000):** 64630 **Personnel:** 1050

✠ **BASCOM PALMER EYE INSTITUTE–ANNE BATES LEACH EYE HOSPITAL (100240)**, 900 N.W. 17th Street, Zip 33136–1199, Mailing Address: Box 016880, Zip 33101–6880; tel. 305/326–6000 **A**1 3 5 10 **F**31 40 44 50 57 58 59 64 66 68 71 78 79 81 85 87 90 93 94 111 129 130 141 146 **P**6 **S** University of Miami Health System, Miami, FL
Primary Contact: Michael B. Gittelman, Administrator
COO: Charles Pappas, M.D., Chief Operating Officer
CFO: Harry Rohrer, Chief Financial Officer
CMO: Eduardo Alfonso, M.D., Chairman Ophthalmology
CHR: Paul Hudgins, Associate Vice President Human Resources
Web address: www.bascompalmer.org
Control: Other not–for–profit (including NFP Corporation) **Service:** Eye, ear, nose, and throat

> **Staffed Beds:** 56 **Admissions:** 64 **Census:** 1 **Outpatient Visits:** 238956 **Births:** 0 **Total Expense ($000):** 107507 **Payroll Expense ($000):** 30884 **Personnel:** 663

JACKSON BEHAVIORAL HEALTH HOSPITAL See Jackson Health System

☐ △ **JACKSON HEALTH SYSTEM (100022)**, 1611 N.W. 12th Avenue, Zip 33136–1005; tel. 305/585–1111, (Includes HOLTZ CHILDREN'S HOSPITAL, 1611 N.W. 12th Avenue, tel. 305/585–5437; Don S. Steigman, Chief Executive Officer; JACKSON BEHAVIORAL HEALTH HOSPITAL, 1695 N.W. Ninth Avenue, Zip 33136–1409; tel. 305/324–4357; Nicolette B. Tessler, Chief Executive Officer of Behavioral Health Hospital; JACKSON MEMORIAL HOSPITAL, 1611 N.W. 12th Avenue, Zip 33136; tel. 305/585–1111; David Zambrana, Chief Executive Officer; JACKSON NORTH MEDICAL CENTER, 160 N.W. 170th Street, North Miami Beach, Zip 33169–5576; tel. 305/651–1100; Andre Boyd, Sr., Senior Vice President and Chief Executive Officer; JACKSON SOUTH COMMUNITY HOSPITAL, 9333 S.W. 152nd Street, Zip 33157–1780; tel. 305/251–2500; Georgina Diaz, Chief Executive Officer), (Total facility includes 342 beds in nursing home–type unit) **A**1 3 5 7 8 10 **F**1 3 4 5 8 11 12 13 18 19 20 21 22 23 24 25 26 27 28 29 30 31 34 35 38 39 40 41 43 44 45 49 50 54 55 56 57 58 59 60 61 63 64 65 66 67 68 70 71 72 74 75 76 77 78 79 80 81 82 83 84 85 86 87 88 89 90 93 94 96 97 98 99 100 101 102 103 104 106 107 108 109 110 111 114 115 116 117 118 119 120 121 123 124 126 128 129 130 131 132 135 136 137 138 139 140 141 142 146 147 148 **P**6
Primary Contact: Carlos A. Migoya, President and Chief Executive Officer
COO: Don S. Steigman, Chief Operating Officer
CFO: Mark T. Knight, Executive Vice President and Chief Financial Officer
CMO: Peter G. Paige, Chief Medical Officer
CIO: Michael A. Garcia, Vice President and Chief Information Officer
CHR: Julie Staub, Chief Human Resources Officer
Web address: www.jacksonhealth.org
Control: County–Government, nonfederal **Service:** General Medical and Surgical

> **Staffed Beds:** 1972 **Admissions:** 59742 **Census:** 1446 **Outpatient Visits:** 565029 **Births:** 6237 **Total Expense ($000):** 1606410 **Payroll Expense ($000):** 752898 **Personnel:** 10072

JACKSON SOUTH COMMUNITY HOSPITAL See Jackson Health System

✠ **KENDALL REGIONAL MEDICAL CENTER (100209)**, 11750 Bird Road, Zip 33175–3530; tel. 305/223–3000, (Nonreporting) **A**1 3 10 **S** HCA, Nashville, TN
Primary Contact: Scott A. Cihak, Chief Executive Officer
COO: Randy Gross, Chief Operating Officer
CFO: Scott Herndon, Chief Financial Officer
CMO: Bradley Shumaker, Chief Medical Officer
CIO: Matt Hernandez, Director of Information Technology and System
CHR: Knicole S. White, Director Human Resources
CNO: Wendy Stuart, Chief Nursing Officer
Web address: www.kendallmed.com
Control: Partnership, Investor–owned, for–profit **Service:** General Medical and Surgical

> **Staffed Beds:** 300

FL

Many Facility Codes have changed. Please refer to the AHA Guide Code Chart. © 2016 AHA Guide

☐ **MIAMI JEWISH HOME AND HOSPITAL FOR AGED (100277)**, 5200 N.E. Second Avenue, Zip 33137–2706; tel. 305/751–8626, (Nonreporting) **A**1 3 5 10
Primary Contact: Jeffrey P. Freimark, Chief Executive Officer
CFO: Lisa Jo Desmarteau, Chief Financial Officer
CMO: Brian Kiedrowski, M.D., Chief Medical Director
CHR: Larry McDonald, Director Human Resources
Web address: www.mjhha.org
Control: Other not–for–profit (including NFP Corporation) **Service:** General Medical and Surgical

Staffed Beds: 32

⊠ △ **MIAMI VETERANS AFFAIRS HEALTHCARE SYSTEM**, 1201 N.W. 16th Street, Zip 33125–1624; tel. 305/575–7000, (Nonreporting) **A**1 3 5 7 **S** Department of Veterans Affairs, Washington, DC
Primary Contact: Paul M. Russo, FACHE, Director
COO: Lance Davis, Associate Director
CFO: Albert Tucker, Chief Financial Officer
CMO: Vincent DeGennaro, M.D., Chief of Staff
CIO: Anthony Brooks, Chief Information Officer
CHR: Loyman Marin, Chief Human Resources
CNO: Marcia C. Lysaght, R.N., Associate Director Patient Care Services
Web address: www.miami.va.gov/
Control: Veterans Affairs, Government, federal **Service:** General Medical and Surgical

Staffed Beds: 401

⊠ **NICKLAUS CHILDREN'S HOSPITAL (103301)**, 3100 S.W. 62nd Avenue, Zip 33155–3009; tel. 305/666–6511 **A**1 2 3 5 8 10 12 13 **F**1 3 4 7 8 9 16 17 18 19 20 21 22 23 24 25 26 27 29 30 31 32 34 35 36 38 39 40 41 42 43 44 45 46 48 50 53 54 55 57 58 59 60 61 64 65 66 67 68 70 71 72 73 74 75 77 78 79 80 81 82 85 86 87 88 89 90 93 97 98 99 100 101 102 104 105 107 108 111 114 115 116 117 118 119 128 129 130 131 132 134 136 143 144 146 **P**6 7
Primary Contact: M. Narendra Kini, M.D., President and Chief Executive Officer
COO: Martha McGill, Executive Vice President and Chief Operating Officer
CFO: Timothy L. Birkenstock, Chief Financial Officer
CMO: Deise Granado–Villar, M.D., Chief Medical Officer and Senior Vice President Medical Affairs
CIO: Edward Martinez, Chief Information Officer
CHR: Michael S. Kushner, Senior Vice President and Chief Talent Officer
CNO: Jacqueline Gonzalez, Senior Vice President and Chief Nursing Officer
Web address: www.mch.com
Control: Other not–for–profit (including NFP Corporation) **Service:** Children's general

Staffed Beds: 272 **Admissions:** 10869 **Census:** 175 **Outpatient Visits:** 467074 **Births:** 0 **Total Expense ($000):** 593733 **Payroll Expense ($000):** 259568 **Personnel:** 3389

⊠ **NORTH SHORE MEDICAL CENTER (100029)**, 1100 N.W. 95th Street, Zip 33150–2098; tel. 305/835–6000, (Includes FLORIDA MEDICAL CENTER – A CAMPUS OF NORTH SHORE, 5000 West Oakland Park Boulevard, Fort Lauderdale, Zip 33313–1585; tel. 954/735–6000; Trey Abshier, Chief Executive Officer), (Nonreporting) **A**1 10 **S** TENET Healthcare Corporation, Dallas, TX
Primary Contact: Manuel Linares, Chief Executive Officer
COO: Shana Crittenden, Chief Operating Officer
CFO: Howard Brown, Chief Financial Officer
CMO: Marcia Bierman, M.D., Chief of Staff
CIO: Luis Estrada, Director Multifacility Information Systems
CHR: Carmen Gomez, Director Human Resources
CNO: Patrick Beaver, Chief Nursing Officer
Web address: www.northshoremedical.com
Control: Corporation, Investor–owned, for–profit **Service:** General Medical and Surgical

Staffed Beds: 357

PROMISE HOSPITAL OF MIAMI, 14001 N.W. 82nd Avenue, Zip 33158; tel. 786/609–9200, (Nonreporting) **S** Promise Healthcare, Boca Raton, FL
Primary Contact: Theodore L. Welding, Chief Executive Officer
Web address: www.promise–miami.com
Control: Corporation, Investor–owned, for–profit **Service:** Long–Term Acute Care hospital

Staffed Beds: 60

⊠ **SELECT SPECIALTY HOSPITAL–MIAMI (102001)**, 955 N.W. 3rd Street, Zip 33128–1274; tel. 305/416–5700, (Nonreporting) **A**1 10 **S** Select Medical Corporation, Mechanicsburg, PA
Primary Contact: Dionisio Bencomo, Chief Executive Officer
Web address: www.selectspecialtyhospitals.com/company/locations/miami.aspx
Control: Corporation, Investor–owned, for–profit **Service:** Long–Term Acute Care hospital

Staffed Beds: 47

⊠ **SISTER EMMANUEL HOSPITAL (102016)**, 3663 South Miami Avenue, Zip 33133–4253; tel. 305/285–2939 **A**1 10 **F**1 3 29 30 31 60 75 77 78 79 82 92 93 148
Primary Contact: Miguel Vasquez, Chief Executive Officer
CFO: Miguel Vasquez, Chief Financial Officer
CMO: Hugo Gonzalez, M.D., Chief Medical Officer
CIO: Macarena Restrepo, Manager Business Office
CHR: Kathy Mainieri, Human Resource Specialist
Web address: www.sisteremmanuelhospital.org/
Control: Corporation, Investor–owned, for–profit **Service:** Long–Term Acute Care hospital

Staffed Beds: 29 **Admissions:** 292 **Census:** 25 **Outpatient Visits:** 0 **Births:** 0 **Total Expense ($000):** 11463 **Payroll Expense ($000):** 4973 **Personnel:** 72

⊠ **UNIVERSITY OF MIAMI HOSPITAL (100009)**, 1400 N.W. 12th Avenue, Zip 33136–1003; tel. 305/325–5511 **A**1 2 3 5 10 **F**3 12 15 17 18 20 22 24 26 29 30 31 34 35 38 39 40 43 44 45 46 47 48 49 50 51 54 57 58 59 63 64 68 70 71 74 75 77 78 79 80 81 82 84 85 86 87 90 91 92 93 96 97 98 100 101 102 103 104 105 107 108 110 111 114 115 118 119 126 130 131 135 141 146 148 **S** University of Miami Health System, Miami, FL
Primary Contact: Michael B. Gittelman, Interim Chief Executive Officer
CFO: Harry Rohrer, Chief Financial Officer
CMO: Francisco Kerdel, M.D., President Medical Staff
CIO: Craig Scott, Interim Director Management Information Systems
CHR: Errol Douglas, Director Human Resources
Web address: www.umiamihospital.com
Control: Other not–for–profit (including NFP Corporation) **Service:** General Medical and Surgical

Staffed Beds: 464 **Admissions:** 22151 **Census:** 346 **Outpatient Visits:** 158661 **Births:** 0 **Total Expense ($000):** 393033 **Payroll Expense ($000):** 123504 **Personnel:** 2108

⊠ **UNIVERSITY OF MIAMI HOSPITAL AND CLINICS (100079)**, 1475 N.W. 12th Avenue, Zip 33136–1002; tel. 305/243–4000 **A**1 2 3 5 10 **F**3 11 12 15 18 19 29 30 31 32 34 35 36 38 44 45 46 47 48 49 50 52 54 55 57 58 59 61 63 64 65 68 70 74 75 77 78 79 80 81 82 84 85 86 87 91 92 93 97 99 100 101 103 104 107 108 110 111 114 115 117 118 119 120 121 123 124 126 130 132 135 136 141 145 146 147 148 **P**6 **S** University of Miami Health System, Miami, FL
Primary Contact: Richard R. Ballard, Chief Executive Officer and Administrator
COO: Joseph B. Natoli, Senior Vice President Business and Finance and Chief Financial Officer
CFO: Harry Rohrer, Chief Financial Officer
CMO: W. Jarrad Goodwin, M.D., Chief Medical Officer
CHR: Paul Hudgins, Associate Vice President Human Resources
Web address: www.uhealthsystem.com
Control: Other not–for–profit (including NFP Corporation) **Service:** Cancer

Staffed Beds: 40 **Admissions:** 1305 **Census:** 27 **Outpatient Visits:** 361127 **Births:** 0 **Total Expense ($000):** 394668 **Payroll Expense ($000):** 73926 **Personnel:** 1076

VETERANS AFFAIRS MEDICAL CENTER See Miami Veterans Affairs Healthcare System

⊠ △ **WEST GABLES REHABILITATION HOSPITAL (103036)**, 2525 S.W. 75th Avenue, Zip 33155–2800; tel. 305/262–6800 **A**1 7 10 **F**7 29 90 91 93 148 **S** Select Medical Corporation, Mechanicsburg, PA
Primary Contact: Walter Concepcion, Chief Executive Officer
CFO: Sara Reohr, Regional Controller
CMO: Jose L. Vargas, M.D., Medical Director
CHR: Barbara Etchason, HR Manager
CNO: Constance Hughes, Director of Nursing
Web address: www.westgablesrehabhospital.com/
Control: Corporation, Investor–owned, for–profit **Service:** Rehabilitation

Staffed Beds: 60 **Admissions:** 1700 **Census:** 54 **Outpatient Visits:** 10779 **Births:** 0 **Total Expense ($000):** 13255 **Payroll Expense ($000):** 11257

○ **WESTCHESTER GENERAL HOSPITAL (100284)**, 2500 S.W. 75th Avenue, Zip 33155–2805; tel. 305/264–5252, (Includes SOUTHERN WINDS HOSPITAL, 4225 West 20th Street, Hialeah, Zip 33012–5835; tel. 305/558–9700) **A**10 11 12 13 **F**3 15 18 29 31 40 45 49 56 65 70 74 75 77 78 79 81 85 87 98 99 100 102 103 107 108 110 114 115 119 130
Primary Contact: Gilda Baldwin, Chief Executive Officer
CFO: Joel Snook, Chief Financial Officer
CMO: Rogelio Zaldivar, M.D., Medical Director
CHR: Jennifer Ricardo, Director of Human Resources
Web address: www.westchesterhospital.com
Control: Corporation, Investor–owned, for–profit **Service:** General Medical and Surgical

Staffed Beds: 197 **Admissions:** 9671 **Census:** 139 **Outpatient Visits:** 34100 **Births:** 0 **Total Expense ($000):** 69263 **Payroll Expense ($000):** 33850 **Personnel:** 655

FL

Hospital, Medicare Provider Number, Address, Telephone, Approval, Facility, and Physician Codes, Health Care System

★ American Hospital Association (AHA) membership ◯ Healthcare Facilities Accreditation Program ⇑ Center for Improvement in Healthcare Quality Accreditation
☐ The Joint Commission accreditation ◇ DNV Healthcare Inc. accreditation △ Commission on Accreditation of Rehabilitation Facilities (CARF) accreditation

MIAMI BEACH—Dade County

MIAMI HEART CAMPUS AT MOUNT SINAI MEDICAL CENTER See Mount Sinai Medical Center

☐ △ **MOUNT SINAI MEDICAL CENTER (100034)**, 4300 Alton Road, Zip 33140-2948; tel. 305/674-2121, (Includes MIAMI HEART CAMPUS AT MOUNT SINAI MEDICAL CENTER, 4701 North Meridian Avenue, Zip 33140-2910; tel. 305/672-1111) **A**1 2 3 5 7 8 10 13 **F**1 3 4 6 8 12 13 14 15 16 17 18 19 20 22 24 26 28 29 30 31 34 35 36 37 38 39 40 41 42 44 45 46 47 48 49 50 51 53 54 55 56 57 58 59 60 61 62 63 64 65 66 67 68 70 71 72 73 74 75 76 77 78 79 80 81 82 83 84 85 86 87 88 89 90 91 92 93 96 97 98 100 101 102 103 104 107 108 110 111 112 114 115 118 119 120 121 123 124 126 128 129 130 131 132 135 143 145 146 147 148 **P**6
Primary Contact: Steven D. Sonenreich, President and Chief Executive Officer
COO: Angel Pallin, Senior Vice President of Operations
CFO: Alex A. Mendez, Executive Vice President of Operations and Chief Financial Officer
CMO: Robert Goldszer, M.D., Senior Vice President and Chief Medical Officer
CIO: Tom Gillette, Senior Vice President and Chief Information Officer
CHR: Georgia McLean, Director Human Resources
CNO: Karen W. Moyer, R.N., Senior Vice President and Chief Nursing Officer
Web address: www.msmc.com
Control: Other not-for-profit (including NFP Corporation) **Service:** General Medical and Surgical

Staffed Beds: 608 Admissions: 22682 Census: 363 Outpatient Visits: 194940 Births: 2711 Total Expense ($000): 426324 Payroll Expense ($000): 178602 Personnel: 3677

MIDDLEBURG—Clay County

✠ **ST. VINCENT'S MEDICAL CENTER CLAY COUNTY (100321)**, 1670 St. Vincent's Way, Zip 32068-8427, Mailing Address: 1670 St. Vincents Way, Zip 32068-8447; tel. 904/602-1000 **A**1 10 **F**3 15 18 20 29 30 34 40 44 49 57 61 64 65 70 74 79 81 84 85 86 87 93 107 108 110 111 114 115 118 119 124 130 131 132 146 147 **S** Ascension Health, Saint Louis, MO
Primary Contact: James Machado, President
Web address: www.jaxhealth.com/
Control: Church-operated, Nongovernment, not-for profit **Service:** General Medical and Surgical

Staffed Beds: 64 Admissions: 5303 Census: 53 Outpatient Visits: 41634 Births: 0 Total Expense ($000): 68117 Payroll Expense ($000): 22578 Personnel: 403

MILTON—Santa Rosa County

✠ **SANTA ROSA MEDICAL CENTER (100124)**, 6002 Berryhill Road, Zip 32570-5062; tel. 850/626-7762 **A**1 10 **F**3 11 13 15 18 20 29 30 34 35 40 45 49 54 57 59 64 65 74 75 76 77 79 81 85 87 97 107 108 111 115 119 126 129 130 132 135 144 146 147 148 **S** Community Health Systems, Inc., Franklin, TN
Primary Contact: Doug Sills, Chief Executive Officer
CFO: Jared Whipkey, Chief Financial Officer
CIO: Rick Payne, Director Information Systems
CHR: Christopher Foreman, Director Human Resources
CNO: Trish Davis, Chief Nursing Officer
Web address: www.santarosamedicalcenter.org
Control: Corporation, Investor-owned, for-profit **Service:** General Medical and Surgical

Staffed Beds: 68 Admissions: 3235 Census: 32 Births: 370 Total Expense ($000): 45135 Payroll Expense ($000): 16432

WEST FLORIDA COMMUNITY CARE CENTER (104027), 5500 Stewart Street, Zip 32570-4304; tel. 850/983-5500 **A**10 **F**29 30 98 103 106 130 143 **P**6
Primary Contact: Joshua Willis, Chief Executive Officer
Web address: www.elakeviewcenter.org/MentalHealth/Adult/Inpatient-WFCCC.aspx
Control: State-Government, nonfederal **Service:** Psychiatric

Staffed Beds: 100 Admissions: 119 Census: 78 Outpatient Visits: 0 Births: 0 Total Expense ($000): 7979 Payroll Expense ($000): 3583

MIRAMAR—Broward County

✠ **MEMORIAL HOSPITAL MIRAMAR (100285)**, 1901 S.W. 172nd Avenue, Zip 33029-5592; tel. 954/538-5000 **A**1 10 **F**3 13 15 29 30 40 41 45 49 50 57 59 61 64 68 70 72 74 75 76 78 79 81 82 84 85 86 87 91 93 107 108 110 111 114 115 118 119 126 130 131 132 135 145 146 147 **S** Memorial Healthcare System, Hollywood, FL
Primary Contact: Leah A. Carpenter, Administrator and Chief Executive Officer
CFO: Judy Sada, Chief Financial Officer
CMO: Stanley Marks, M.D., Chief Medical Officer
CIO: Forest Blanton, Senior VP and Chief Information Officer
CHR: Ray Kendrick, Chief Human Resources Officer
CNO: Denise Reynolds, Chief Nursing Officer
Web address: www.mhs.net
Control: Hospital district or authority, Government, nonfederal **Service:** General Medical and Surgical

Staffed Beds: 178 Admissions: 8595 Census: 86 Outpatient Visits: 128532 Births: 3204 Total Expense ($000): 131087 Payroll Expense ($000): 62686 Personnel: 800

MIRAMAR BEACH—Walton County

✠ **SACRED HEART HOSPITAL ON THE EMERALD COAST (100292)**, 7800 Highway 98 West, Zip 32550; tel. 850/278-3000, (Nonreporting) **A**1 10 **S** Ascension Health, Saint Louis, MO
Primary Contact: Roger L. Hall, President
CMO: Gary M. Pablo, M.D., Chief Medical Officer
Web address: www.sacredheartemerald.org
Control: Other not-for-profit (including NFP Corporation) **Service:** General Medical and Surgical

Staffed Beds: 58

NAPLES—Collier County

LANDMARK HOSPITAL OF SOUTHWEST FLORIDA, 1285 Creekside Boulevard East, Zip 34108; tel. 239/529-1800, (Nonreporting) **A**22 **S** Landmark Hospitals, Cape Girardeau, MO
Primary Contact: Jimmy Dascani, Chief Executive Officer
Web address: www.landmarkhospitals.com/naples.aspx
Control: Partnership, Investor-owned, for-profit **Service:** Long-Term Acute Care hospital

Staffed Beds: 50

✠ △ **NCH DOWNTOWN NAPLES HOSPITAL (100018)**, 350 Seventh Street North, Zip 34102-5754, Mailing Address: P.O. Box 413029, Zip 34101-3029; tel. 239/624-4000, (Includes NCH NORTH NAPLES HOSPITAL, 11190 Health Park Boulevard, Zip 34110-5729, Mailing Address: 11190 Health Park Boulevard, Zip 34110-5729; tel. 239/552-7000) **A**1 2 7 10 **F**3 11 13 14 17 18 20 22 24 26 28 29 30 31 34 37 40 41 45 47 49 50 53 57 59 64 68 70 72 74 75 76 77 78 79 81 84 85 86 87 88 89 90 91 92 93 95 96 98 100 102 103 107 108 111 114 115 119 126 130 135 146 147 148
Primary Contact: Allen S. Weiss, M.D., President and Chief Executive Officer
COO: Phillip C. Dutcher, Chief Operating Officer
CFO: Mike Stephens, Chief Financial Officer
CMO: Doug Ardion, M.D., Chief Medical Officer
CHR: John McGirl, Chief Human Resources Officer
CNO: Michele Thoman, R.N., Chief Nursing Officer
Web address: www.nchmd.org
Control: Other not-for-profit (including NFP Corporation) **Service:** General Medical and Surgical

Staffed Beds: 713 Admissions: 30487 Census: 383 Outpatient Visits: 294676 Births: 3422 Total Expense ($000): 395933 Payroll Expense ($000): 153323 Personnel: 2835

✠ **PHYSICIANS REGIONAL – PINE RIDGE (100286)**, 6101 Pine Ridge Road, Zip 34119-3900; tel. 239/348-4000, (Includes PHYSICIANS REGIONAL, 8300 Collier Boulevard, Zip 34114; tel. 239/354-6000; C. Scott Campbell, Market Chief Executive Officer), (Nonreporting) **A**1 10 **S** Community Health Systems, Inc., Franklin, TN
Primary Contact: Scott Lowe, Interim Market Chief Executive Officer
COO: Susan Takacs, Market Chief Operating Officer
CFO: Ken Warriner, Market Chief Financial Officer
CHR: Jill Gaffoli, Director Human Resources
Web address: www.physiciansregional.com
Control: Corporation, Investor-owned, for-profit **Service:** General Medical and Surgical

Staffed Beds: 201

☐ **THE WILLOUGH AT NAPLES (104063)**, 9001 Tamiami Trail East, Zip 34113-3304; tel. 239/775-4500, (Nonreporting) **A**1 10
Primary Contact: James E. O'Shea, Administrator
CFO: Steve Baldwin, Vice President Finance
Web address: www.thewilloughatnaples.com/
Control: Corporation, Investor-owned, for-profit **Service:** Psychiatric

Staffed Beds: 80

NEW PORT RICHEY—Pasco County

✠ △ **MORTON PLANT NORTH BAY HOSPITAL (100063)**, 6600 Madison Street, Zip 34652-1900; tel. 727/842-8468 **A**1 7 10 **F**3 11 18 20 22 29 30 31 34 35 40 44 45 47 49 50 57 58 59 64 68 70 74 75 78 79 81 84 85 86 87 90 91 93 96 98 99 100 102 107 108 111 114 115 118 119 129 130 132 135 143 146 147 **S** Morton Plant Mease Health Care, Clearwater, FL
Primary Contact: Michael Yungmann, President
CFO: Carl Tremonti, Chief Financial Officer
CMO: Jeff Jensen, D.O., Vice President, Medical Affairs
CIO: Timothy Thompson, Senior Vice President and Chief Information Officer
CHR: Kyle J. Barr, Senior Vice President, Chief Team Resources Officer
CNO: Tom Doria, Vice President and Patient Services – West
Web address: www.mpmhealth.com
Control: Other not-for-profit (including NFP Corporation) **Service:** General Medical and Surgical

Staffed Beds: 226 Admissions: 12105 Census: 156 Outpatient Visits: 36452 Births: 0 Total Expense ($000): 117823 Payroll Expense ($000): 47771 Personnel: 875

Many Facility Codes have changed. Please refer to the AHA Guide Code Chart. © 2016 AHA Guide

NEW SMYRNA BEACH—Volusia County

✠ **FLORIDA HOSPITAL NEW SMYRNA (100014)**, 401 Palmetto Street, Zip 32168–7399; tel. 386/424–5000 **A**1 10 **F**3 11 15 18 20 22 28 29 30 33 34 40 45 46 49 50 57 59 60 66 68 70 74 78 79 81 84 93 107 108 110 111 114 115 119 120 121 135 148 **P**5 **S** Adventist Health System Sunbelt Health Care Corporation, Altamonte Springs, FL
Primary Contact: Kenneth R. Mattison, Chief Executive Officer
COO: Steven W. Harrell, FACHE, Chief Operating Officer
CFO: Al W. Allred, Chief Financial Officer
CMO: Eric Lo, M.D., Chief Medical Staff
CIO: Calvin Patrick, II, Director Information Services
CHR: Nancy K. Evolga, Executive Director Human Resources
CNO: Linda G. Breum, R.N., Chief Nursing Officer
Web address: www.https://www.floridahospital.com/new-smyrna
Control: Hospital district or authority, Government, nonfederal **Service:** General Medical and Surgical

Staffed Beds: 112 **Admissions:** 4285 **Census:** 50 **Births:** 0 **Total Expense ($000):** 93930 **Payroll Expense ($000):** 31700

NICEVILLE—Okaloosa County

✠ **TWIN CITIES HOSPITAL (100054)**, 2190 Highway 85 North, Zip 32578–1045; tel. 850/678–4131 **A**1 10 **F**3 29 34 35 45 50 59 70 75 79 81 82 85 93 107 108 110 111 115 119 124 147 **S** HCA, Nashville, TN
Primary Contact: David Whalen, Chief Executive Officer
CFO: Mark Day, Chief Financial Officer
CHR: Cyndi Ronca, Director Human Resources
Web address: www.tchealthcare.com
Control: Corporation, Investor–owned, for–profit **Service:** General Medical and Surgical

Staffed Beds: 57 **Admissions:** 1979 **Census:** 18 **Births:** 0 **Total Expense ($000):** 38033 **Payroll Expense ($000):** 10753

NORTH MIAMI—Miami–Dade County

☐ △ **ST. CATHERINE'S REHABILITATION HOSPITAL (103026)**, 1050 N.E. 125th Street, Zip 33161–5881; tel. 305/357–1735, (Nonreporting) **A**1 7 10 **S** Catholic Health Services, Lauderdale Lakes, FL
Primary Contact: Jaime Gonzalez, Administrator
COO: Jim Ball, Chief Operating Officer
CFO: Mary Jo Frick, Director Finance
CMO: Miriam Feliz, M.D., Medical Director
Web address: www.catholichealthservices.org
Control: Other not–for–profit (including NFP Corporation) **Service:** Rehabilitation

Staffed Beds: 60

NORTH MIAMI BEACH—Miami–Dade County

JACKSON NORTH MEDICAL CENTER See Jackson Health System, Miami

OCALA—Marion County

✠ **HEALTHSOUTH REHABILITATION HOSPITAL OF OCALA (103043)**, 2275 S.W. 22nd Lane, Zip 34471–7710; tel. 352/282–4000, (Nonreporting) **A**1 10 **S** HEALTHSOUTH Corporation, Birmingham, AL
Primary Contact: Ellen Witterstaeter, FACHE, Chief Executive Officer
CFO: Sammy King, Controller
CMO: Amy Clunn, M.D., Medical Director
CHR: Tracy Sapp, Director Human Resources
CNO: Wendy Milam, Chief Nursing Officer
Web address: www.healthsouthocala.com
Control: Corporation, Investor–owned, for–profit **Service:** Rehabilitation

Staffed Beds: 40

✠ **KINDRED HOSPITAL OCALA (102019)**, 1500 S.W. 1st Avenue, Zip 34471–6504; tel. 352/369–0513, (Nonreporting) **A**1 10 **S** Kindred Healthcare, Louisville, KY
Primary Contact: Merlene Bhoorasingh, Administrator
CFO: Dean Cocchi, Chief Financial Officer
Web address: www.kindredocala.com/
Control: Corporation, Investor–owned, for–profit **Service:** Long–Term Acute Care hospital

Staffed Beds: 31

✠ **MUNROE REGIONAL MEDICAL CENTER (100062)**, 1500 S.W. 1st Avenue, Zip 34471–6504, Mailing Address: P.O. Box 6000, Zip 34478–6000; tel. 352/351–7200 **A**1 3 5 10 **F**12 13 17 18 20 22 24 26 28 29 30 34 35 38 40 41 42 45 49 50 51 53 57 59 60 64 65 67 68 70 74 75 76 77 79 81 84 85 86 87 89 91 92 93 96 100 107 108 109 110 111 112 113 114 115 119 120 124 126 130 132 136 141 146 147 148 **S** Community Health Systems, Inc., Franklin, TN
Primary Contact: Bob Moore, FACHE, Chief Executive Officer
COO: Philoron A. Wright, II, FACHE, Chief Operating Officer
CFO: Eric LaChance, Chief Financial Officer
CMO: Lon McPherson, M.D., Senior Vice President Medical Affairs and Chief Quality Officer
CIO: Carl Candullo, Chief Information Officer
CNO: Pamela W. Michell, R.N., Vice President, Chief Nursing Officer
Web address: www.munroeregional.com
Control: Corporation, Investor–owned, for–profit **Service:** General Medical and Surgical

Staffed Beds: 420 **Admissions:** 20848 **Census:** 263 **Outpatient Visits:** 174900 **Births:** 2463 **Total Expense ($000):** 248780 **Payroll Expense ($000):** 107740 **Personnel:** 1933

✠ **OCALA REGIONAL MEDICAL CENTER (100212)**, 1431 S.W. First Avenue, Zip 34471–6500, Mailing Address: P.O. Box 2200, Zip 34478–2200; tel. 352/401–1000, (Includes WEST MARION COMMUNITY HOSPITAL, 4600 S.W. 46th Court, Zip 34474; tel. 352/291–3000), (Nonreporting) **A**1 2 3 10 13 **S** HCA, Nashville, TN
Primary Contact: Randy McVay, Chief Executive Officer
CMO: Art Osberg, M.D., Chief Medical Officer
CIO: Brandon Holbert, Director, Information Services
CHR: Wayne Nielsen, Director Human Resources
Web address: www.ocalaregional.com
Control: Corporation, Investor–owned, for–profit **Service:** General Medical and Surgical

Staffed Beds: 270

THE CENTERS (104068), 5664 S.W. 60th Avenue, Zip 34474–5677; tel. 352/291–5500, (Nonreporting) **A**10
Primary Contact: Timothy Cowart, Chief Executive Officer
Web address: www.thecenters.us
Control: Other not–for–profit (including NFP Corporation) **Service:** Psychiatric

Staffed Beds: 61

THE VINES (104071), 3130 S.W. 27th Avenue, Zip 34471–4306; tel. 352/671–3130, (Nonreporting) **A**10 **S** Universal Health Services, Inc., King of Prussia, PA
Primary Contact: Stephen Quintyne, Chief Executive Officer
Web address: www.thevineshospital.com
Control: Corporation, Investor–owned, for–profit **Service:** Psychiatric

Staffed Beds: 64

OCOEE—Orange County

✠ **HEALTH CENTRAL HOSPITAL (100030)**, 10000 West Colonial Drive, Zip 34761–3499; tel. 407/296–1000, (Total facility includes 228 beds in nursing home–type unit) **A**1 10 **F**3 8 11 12 15 17 18 20 22 26 28 29 30 34 37 40 42 45 49 50 51 57 59 60 73 74 76 79 80 81 82 85 86 87 93 97 107 108 110 111 115 118 119 128 130 132 144 146 148 **P**6 **S** Orlando Health, Orlando, FL
Primary Contact: Mark A. Marsh, President
COO: Rick Smith, Chief Operating Officer
CFO: Michael E. Mueller, Chief Financial Officer
CMO: James Barton Rodier, M.D., Chief Quality Officer
CIO: John T. Sills, Chief Information Officer
CHR: Nancy Dinon, Vice President Human Resources
CNO: Christina Marie McGuirk, Chief Nursing Officer
Web address: www.healthcentral.org
Control: Other not–for–profit (including NFP Corporation) **Service:** General Medical and Surgical

Staffed Beds: 400 **Admissions:** 12053 **Census:** 343 **Outpatient Visits:** 99487 **Births:** 724 **Total Expense ($000):** 185168 **Payroll Expense ($000):** 80941 **Personnel:** 1185

FL

Hospital, Medicare Provider Number, Address, Telephone, Approval, Facility, and Physician Codes, Health Care System

★ American Hospital Association (AHA) membership
☐ The Joint Commission accreditation
◯ Healthcare Facilities Accreditation Program
◇ DNV Healthcare Inc. accreditation
⇑ Center for Improvement in Healthcare Quality Accreditation
△ Commission on Accreditation of Rehabilitation Facilities (CARF) accreditation

OKEECHOBEE—Okeechobee County

⊞ **RAULERSON HOSPITAL (100252)**, 1796 Highway 441 North,
Zip 34972–1918, Mailing Address: P.O. Box 1307, Zip 34973–1307;
tel. 863/763–2151, (Nonreporting) **A**1 10 20 **S** HCA, Nashville, TN
Primary Contact: Brian Melear, R.N., Chief Executive Officer
CFO: Heather Garvey, Chief Financial Officer
CMO: Mohammad Riaz, M.D., Chief of Staff
CIO: Doug Schneider, Director Information Systems
CHR: Janis Stevens, Director Human Resources
Web address: www.raulersonhospital.com
Control: Corporation, Investor–owned, for–profit **Service:** General Medical and Surgical

Staffed Beds: 100

ORANGE CITY—Volusia County

⊞ **FLORIDA HOSPITAL FISH MEMORIAL (100072)**, 1055 Saxon Boulevard,
Zip 32763–8468; tel. 386/917–5000 **A**1 10 **F**1 3 4 11 15 16 17 20 28 29 30
31 34 35 37 40 45 48 49 59 64 67 70 72 73 74 75 76 77 78 79 80 81 82
85 87 88 89 90 91 92 93 98 100 104 107 108 110 111 114 115 116 117
118 119 120 121 128 129 130 132 135 144 146 147 148 **P**8 **S** Adventist
Health System Sunbelt Health Care Corporation, Altamonte Springs, FL
Primary Contact: Robert Deininger, Chief Executive Officer
COO: Danielle Johnson, Chief Operating Officer
CFO: Eric Osterly, Chief Financial Officer
CMO: Leighton Smith, M.D., Chief Medical Officer
CHR: Jannina Garcia, Director of Human Resources
CNO: Jennifer Shull, R.N., Chief Nursing Officer
Web address: www.fhfishmemorial.org
Control: Church–operated, Nongovernment, not–for profit **Service:** General Medical and Surgical

Staffed Beds: 175 **Admissions:** 9182 **Census:** 116 **Outpatient Visits:** 62801 **Births:** 0 **Total Expense ($000):** 131886 **Payroll Expense ($000):** 53054

ORANGE PARK—Clay County

⊞ **ORANGE PARK MEDICAL CENTER (100226)**, 2001 Kingsley Avenue,
Zip 32073–5156; tel. 904/639–8500 **A**1 2 3 10 **F**3 8 11 15 16 17 18 20 22 24
26 28 29 30 31 34 35 40 45 46 48 49 50 60 67 68 70 72 74 76 77 79 81
84 85 87 93 94 97 98 100 101 102 103 104 107 108 110 111 114 115 118
119 126 131 132 135 146 147 148 **S** HCA, Nashville, TN
Primary Contact: Chad Patrick, President and Chief Executive Officer
COO: J. Christopher Mosley, Chief Operating Officer
CFO: Fred Ashworth, Chief Financial Officer
CMO: Lawrence Coots, M.D., Chief Medical Officer
CHR: Chris Marlin, Director Human Resources
CNO: Kathy Hester, Chief Nursing Officer
Web address: www.opmedical.com
Control: Corporation, Investor–owned, for–profit **Service:** General Medical and Surgical

Staffed Beds: 297 **Admissions:** 18243 **Census:** 206 **Births:** 2297 **Total Expense ($000):** 215266 **Payroll Expense ($000):** 68550

ORLANDO—Orange County

ARNOLD PALMER CHILDREN'S HOSPITAL See Orlando Regional Medical Center

ASPIRE HEALTH PARTNERS (104067), 1800 Mercy Drive, Zip 32808–5646;
tel. 407/875–3700, (Nonreporting) **A**10
Primary Contact: Jerry Kassab, President and Chief Executive Officer
Web address: www.lakesidecares.org
Control: Other not–for–profit (including NFP Corporation) **Service:** Psychiatric

Staffed Beds: 56

☐ **CENTRAL FLORIDA BEHAVIORAL HOSPITAL (104072)**, 6601 Central Florida
Parkway, Zip 32821–8064; tel. 407/370–0111, (Nonreporting) **A**1 5 10
S Universal Health Services, Inc., King of Prussia, PA
Primary Contact: Vickie Lewis, Chief Executive Officer
CFO: Marsha Burick, Chief Financial Officer
Web address: www.centralfloridabehavioral.com
Control: Other not–for–profit (including NFP Corporation) **Service:** Psychiatric

Staffed Beds: 126

★ △ ◇ **FLORIDA HOSPITAL (100007)**, 601 East Rollins Street,
Zip 32803–1248; tel. 407/303–6611, (Includes FLORIDA HOSPITAL
CELEBRATION HEALTH, 400 Celebration Place, Celebration, Zip 34747;
tel. 407/303–4000; Monica Reed, M.D., Administrator; FLORIDA HOSPITAL EAST
ORLANDO, 7727 Lake Underhill Drive, Zip 32822; tel. 407/277–8110; FLORIDA
HOSPITAL FOR CHILDREN–WALT DISNEY PAVILION, 601 East Rollins Street,
tel. 407/303–9732; Lars D. Houmann, President; FLORIDA HOSPITAL
KISSIMMEE, 2450 North Orange Blossom Trai, Kissimmee, Zip 34741;
tel. 407/846–4343; William Haupt, Administrator; FLORIDA
HOSPITAL–ALTAMONTE, 601 East Altamonte Drive, Altamonte Springs,
Zip 32701; tel. 407/830–4321; Rob Fulbright, Administrator; FLORIDA
HOSPITAL–APOPKA, 201 North Park Avenue, Apopka, Zip 32703;
tel. 407/889–2566; Verbelee Neilsen Swanson, Administrator; WINTER PARK
MEMORIAL HOSPITAL, 200 North Lakemont Avenue, Winter Park,
Zip 32792–3273; tel. 407/646–7000; Ken Bradley, Administrator) **A**2 3 5 7 8
10 21 **F**3 6 7 9 11 12 13 15 17 18 19 20 21 22 23 24 25 26 27 28 29 30
31 32 34 35 36 37 38 39 40 41 44 45 46 47 48 49 50 51 53 54 56 57 58
59 60 61 62 64 65 66 68 70 71 72 73 74 75 76 77 78 79 80 81 82 84 85
86 87 88 89 90 91 93 96 97 98 100 101 102 103 104 107 108 110 111
112 113 114 115 116 117 118 119 120 121 123 124 126 129 130 131 132
134 135 136 137 138 139 140 141 142 145 146 147 148 **P**1 5 6 **S** Adventist
Health System Sunbelt Health Care Corporation, Altamonte Springs, FL
Primary Contact: Lars D. Houmann, President
COO: Brian Paradis, Chief Operating Officer
CFO: Eddie Soler, Chief Financial Officer
CMO: David Moorhead, M.D., Chief Medical Officer
CHR: Sheryl Dodds, Chief Clinical Officer
Web address: www.flhosp.com
Control: Other not–for–profit (including NFP Corporation) **Service:** General Medical and Surgical

Staffed Beds: 2654 **Admissions:** 145842 **Census:** 1887 **Outpatient Visits:** 1108797 **Births:** 10672 **Total Expense ($000):** 4066945 **Payroll Expense ($000):** 1074711 **Personnel:** 19404

⊞ **NEMOURS CHILDREN'S HOSPITAL (103304)**, 13535 Nemours Parkway,
Zip 32827–7402; tel. 407/567–4000 **A**1 5 10 **F**3 19 29 30 31 32 34 35 36
39 40 41 45 46 48 50 51 53 54 55 57 58 59 60 61 65 68 72 73 74 75 78
79 81 82 85 86 87 88 89 91 93 94 97 99 100 101 104 107 108 111 115
119 129 130 131 132 143 144 146 **S** Nemours, Jacksonville, FL
Primary Contact: Dana Bledsoe, MS, R.N., Chief Executive Officer
CMO: Lane Donnelly, M.D., Chief Medical Officer
Web address: www.nemours.org
Control: Other not–for–profit (including NFP Corporation) **Service:** Children's general

Staffed Beds: 64 **Admissions:** 2527 **Census:** 32 **Outpatient Visits:** 57751 **Births:** 0 **Total Expense ($000):** 155470 **Payroll Expense ($000):** 44385 **Personnel:** 663

⊞ △ **ORLANDO REGIONAL MEDICAL CENTER (100006)**, 1414 Kuhl Avenue,
Zip 32806–2093; tel. 407/841–5111, (Includes ARNOLD PALMER CHILDREN'S
HOSPITAL, 92 West Miller Street, Zip 32806; tel. 407/649–6960; Kathy
Swanson, President; WINNIE PALMER HOSPITAL FOR WOMEN AND BABIES, 83
West Miller Street, Zip 32806; tel. 321/843–2201; Kathy Swanson, President) **A**1
2 3 5 7 10 **F**3 4 5 7 8 11 12 13 15 16 17 18 19 20 21 22 23 24 25 26 27
28 29 30 31 34 35 36 37 38 40 41 43 44 45 46 47 48 49 50 51 53 54 55
57 58 59 60 61 62 64 68 70 71 72 73 74 75 77 78 79 80 81 82 84 85 86
87 88 90 91 92 93 94 96 97 98 99 100 101 102 103 104 107 108 110 111
114 115 116 117 118 119 122 123 124 126 129 130 131 132 134 135
146 147 148 **P**6 **S** Orlando Health, Orlando, FL
Primary Contact: Mark A. Jones, President
COO: Carlos Carrasco, Chief Operating Officer
CFO: Bernadette Spong, Chief Financial Officer
CMO: Aurelio Duran, Chief of Staff
CIO: Rick Schooler, Vice President and Chief Information Officer
CHR: Greg Thompson, Corporate Director, Human Resources
CNO: Jayne Willis, Vice President Nursing and Chief Nursing Officer
Web address: www.orlandohealth.com/facilities/orlando–regional–medical–center
Control: Other not–for–profit (including NFP Corporation) **Service:** General Medical and Surgical

Staffed Beds: 1307 **Admissions:** 76208 **Census:** 1047 **Outpatient Visits:** 846442 **Births:** 14477 **Total Expense ($000):** 1565533 **Payroll Expense ($000):** 625669 **Personnel:** 11797

⊞ **SELECT SPECIALTY HOSPITAL–ORLANDO (102003)**, 2250 Bedford Road,
Zip 32803–1443; tel. 407/303–7869, (Includes SELECT SPECIALTY
HOSPITAL–ORLANDO SOUTH, 5579 South Orange Avenue, Zip 32809–3493;
tel. 407/241–4800), (Nonreporting) **A**1 10 **S** Select Medical Corporation,
Mechanicsburg, PA
Primary Contact: Nellie Castroman, Chief Executive Officer
Web address: www.selectspecialtyhospitals.com/company/locations/orlando.aspx
Control: Corporation, Investor–owned, for–profit **Service:** Long–Term Acute Care hospital

Staffed Beds: 75

WINNIE PALMER HOSPITAL FOR WOMEN AND BABIES See Orlando Regional Medical Center

Many Facility Codes have changed. Please refer to the AHA Guide Code Chart.

FL

OXFORD—Sumter County

PROMISE HOSPITAL OF FLORIDA AT THE VILLAGES (102028), 5050 County Road, Zip 34484; tel. 352/689–6400 **A**10 **F**1 29 75 77 82 84 90 98 107 119 **P**5 **S** Promise Healthcare, Boca Raton, FL
Primary Contact: Hoyt Ross, Chief Executive Officer
CNO: Janice M. McCoy, MS, Chief Clinical Officer
Web address: www.promise–villages.com
Control: Corporation, Investor–owned, for–profit **Service:** Long–Term Acute Care hospital

Staffed Beds: 40 **Admissions:** 468 **Census:** 36 **Outpatient Visits:** 0 **Births:** 0 **Personnel:** 128

PALATKA—Putnam County

✠ **PUTNAM COMMUNITY MEDICAL CENTER (100232)**, 611 Zeagler Drive, Zip 32177–3810, Mailing Address: P.O. Box 778, Zip 32178–0778; tel. 386/328–5711 **A**1 10 **F**3 11 13 15 18 20 22 29 30 34 35 40 45 49 50 51 54 57 59 60 64 68 70 74 75 76 77 79 81 85 87 93 107 108 110 111 114 115 119 129 130 133 135 146 147 148 **S** HCA, Nashville, TN
Primary Contact: J. Christopher Mosley, Chief Executive Officer
CFO: Stewart Whitmore, Chief Financial Officer
CIO: Yvette A. Jones, Health Information Management Director
CHR: John Schneider, Human Resources Director
CNO: Kari Bolin, Chief Nursing Officer
Web address: www.pcmcfl.com
Control: Corporation, Investor–owned, for–profit **Service:** General Medical and Surgical

Staffed Beds: 99 **Admissions:** 4777 **Census:** 52 **Outpatient Visits:** 81176 **Births:** 254 **Total Expense ($000):** 58291 **Payroll Expense ($000):** 23314 **Personnel:** 361

PALM BAY—Brevard County

☐ **HEALTH FIRST PALM BAY HOSPITAL (100316)**, 1425 Malabar Road N.E., Zip 32907–2506; tel. 321/434–8000 **A**1 5 10 **F**3 11 15 18 20 29 30 34 40 43 45 49 51 53 57 59 60 65 68 70 74 75 79 81 84 85 87 91 92 93 107 108 110 111 114 115 118 119 130 132 143 145 146 **P**6 7 **S** Health First, Inc., Rockledge, FL
Primary Contact: William Calhoun, President, Community Hospitals
COO: Judy Gizinski, Chief Operating Officer
CFO: Joseph G. Felkner, Executive Vice President and Chief Financial Officer
CMO: Scott Gettings, M.D., Senior Vice President and Chief Medical Officer
CIO: Alex Popowycz, Senior Vice President / Chief Information Officer
CHR: Paula Just, Chief Human Resources Officer
CNO: Connie Bradley, R.N., Senior Vice President and Chief Nursing Officer
Web address: www.health–first.org/hospitals_services/pbch/index.cfm
Control: Other not–for–profit (including NFP Corporation) **Service:** General Medical and Surgical

Staffed Beds: 119 **Admissions:** 5935 **Census:** 69 **Outpatient Visits:** 96267 **Births:** 0 **Total Expense ($000):** 78595 **Payroll Expense ($000):** 35363 **Personnel:** 376

PALM BEACH GARDENS—Palm Beach County

✠ **PALM BEACH GARDENS MEDICAL CENTER (100176)**, 3360 Burns Road, Zip 33410–4323; tel. 561/622–1411, (Nonreporting) **A**1 10 **S** TENET Healthcare Corporation, Dallas, TX
Primary Contact: Jeffrey M. Welch, Chief Executive Officer
CFO: Judi Stimson, Chief Financial Officer
CIO: James Vega, Director Information Systems
CHR: Kevin Caracciolo, Chief Human Resources Officer
Web address: www.pbgmc.com
Control: Corporation, Investor–owned, for–profit **Service:** General Medical and Surgical

Staffed Beds: 199

PALM COAST—Flagler County

✠ **FLORIDA HOSPITAL–FLAGLER (100118)**, 60 Memorial Medical Parkway, Zip 32164–5980; tel. 386/586–2000 **A**1 2 10 **F**11 15 18 20 22 28 29 30 31 34 35 40 45 46 47 49 50 51 54 57 59 60 62 63 64 68 70 74 75 77 78 79 81 85 86 87 93 97 107 108 110 111 114 115 117 119 120 121 123 124 126 130 132 135 146 147 **P**6 **S** Adventist Health System Sunbelt Health Care Corporation, Altamonte Springs, FL
Primary Contact: Ronald Jimenez, M.D., Chief Executive Officer
COO: JoAnne King, Chief Operating Officer
CFO: Cory Domayer, Chief Financial Officer
CMO: Ron Thomas, M.D., Chief Medical Officer
CHR: Joshua I. Champion, Director
CNO: Robert Davis, Chief Nursing Officer
Web address: www.floridahospitalflagler.com/
Control: Church–operated, Nongovernment, not–for profit **Service:** General Medical and Surgical

Staffed Beds: 99 **Admissions:** 7861 **Census:** 95 **Outpatient Visits:** 363168 **Births:** 0 **Total Expense ($000):** 150009 **Payroll Expense ($000):** 63311 **Personnel:** 922

PANAMA CITY—Bay County

✠ **BAY MEDICAL CENTER SACRED HEART HEALTH SYSTEM (100026)**, 615 North Bonita Avenue, Zip 32401–3600, Mailing Address: P.O. Box 59515, Zip 32412–0515; tel. 850/769–1511, (Nonreporting) **A**1 2 10 **S** LHP Hospital Group, Plano, TX
Primary Contact: Stephen Grubbs, Chief Executive Officer
COO: Randy Currin, Chief Operating Officer
CHR: Donna Baird, Vice President Corporate Services
CNO: Jan Thornton, Chief Nursing Officer
Web address: www.baymedical.org
Control: Hospital district or authority, Government, nonfederal **Service:** General Medical and Surgical

Staffed Beds: 273

☐ **EMERALD COAST BEHAVIORAL HOSPITAL (104073)**, 1940 Harrison Avenue, Zip 32405–4542; tel. 850/763–0017, (Nonreporting) **A**1 10 **S** Universal Health Services, Inc., King of Prussia, PA
Primary Contact: Tim Bedford, Chief Executive Officer
CFO: Michael J. Zenone, Chief Financial Officer
CMO: Roy Deal, Chief Medical Officer
CNO: Michael B. Barbour, Chief Nursing Officer
Web address: www.emeraldcoastbehavioral.com
Control: Corporation, Investor–owned, for–profit **Service:** Psychiatric

Staffed Beds: 80

✠ **GULF COAST MEDICAL CENTER (100242)**, 449 West 23rd Street, Zip 32405–4593, Mailing Address: P.O. Box 15309, Zip 32406–5309; tel. 850/769–8341 **A**1 2 10 **F**3 8 12 13 15 20 22 26 29 30 31 34 35 37 39 40 41 46 47 48 49 51 54 56 57 59 60 64 68 70 72 74 75 76 77 78 79 80 81 85 86 87 89 93 107 108 109 111 114 116 117 118 119 126 130 131 132 135 144 146 147 148 **S** HCA, Nashville, TN
Primary Contact: Carlton Ulmer, Chief Executive Officer
COO: Holly Jackson, Chief Operating Officer
CFO: Laurie Haynes, Chief Financial Officer
CHR: Tracy McGlon, Director Human Resources
CNO: Mary Reval, R.N., Chief Nursing Officer
Web address: www.egulfcoastmedical.com
Control: Corporation, Investor–owned, for–profit **Service:** General Medical and Surgical

Staffed Beds: 176 **Admissions:** 12295 **Census:** 127 **Births:** 2461 **Total Expense ($000):** 156861 **Payroll Expense ($000):** 46202

✠ **HEALTHSOUTH EMERALD COAST REHABILITATION HOSPITAL (103040)**, 1847 Florida Avenue, Zip 32405–4640; tel. 850/914–8600 **A**1 10 **F**3 28 29 34 57 59 68 75 77 85 86 87 90 91 95 96 130 131 132 148 **S** HEALTHSOUTH Corporation, Birmingham, AL
Primary Contact: Tony N. Bennett, Chief Executive Officer
CFO: Bradley Tilghman, Controller
CMO: Michael Hennigan, M.D., Medical Director
CHR: Traci Powell, Director Human Resources
CNO: Sharon Hamilton, Chief Nursing Officer
Web address: www.healthsouthpanamacity.com
Control: Corporation, Investor–owned, for–profit **Service:** Rehabilitation

Staffed Beds: 75 **Admissions:** 1595 **Census:** 56 **Outpatient Visits:** 0 **Births:** 0 **Total Expense ($000):** 19586 **Payroll Expense ($000):** 10119 **Personnel:** 221

FL

Hospital, Medicare Provider Number, Address, Telephone, Approval, Facility, and Physician Codes, Health Care System

★ American Hospital Association (AHA) membership ☐ The Joint Commission accreditation ○ Healthcare Facilities Accreditation Program ◇ DNV Healthcare Inc. accreditation ⇑ Center for Improvement in Healthcare Quality Accreditation △ Commission on Accreditation of Rehabilitation Facilities (CARF) accreditation

✠ **SELECT SPECIALTY HOSPITAL–PANAMA CITY (102017)**, 615 North Bonita Avenue, 3rd Floor, Zip 32401–3623; tel. 850/767–3180 **A**1 10 **F**1 3 29 148 **S** Select Medical Corporation, Mechanicsburg, PA
Primary Contact: Randal S. Hamilton, Chief Executive Officer
CMO: Amir Manzoor, M.D., Medical Director
Web address: www.selectspecialtyhospitals.com/company/locations/panamacity.aspx
Control: Corporation, Investor–owned, for–profit **Service:** Long–Term Acute Care hospital

Staffed Beds: 30 **Admissions:** 425 **Census:** 30 **Outpatient Visits:** 0 **Births:** 0 **Total Expense ($000):** 12536 **Payroll Expense ($000):** 5665

PEMBROKE PINES—Broward County

✠ **MEMORIAL HOSPITAL PEMBROKE (100230)**, 7800 Sheridan Street, Zip 33024–2536; tel. 954/883–8482 **A**1 10 **F**3 12 17 29 30 34 40 42 44 45 46 47 48 49 50 51 59 64 65 66 70 74 75 79 81 82 85 86 87 107 108 111 114 115 119 126 130 132 144 146 148 **S** Memorial Healthcare System, Hollywood, FL
Primary Contact: Mark Doyle, Administrator and Chief Executive Officer
CFO: Joseph Stuczynski, Assistant Administrator Finance and Support
CMO: Stanley Marks, M.D., Chief Medical Officer
CIO: Forest Blanton, Chief Information Officer
CNO: Judy Frum, R.N., Chief Nursing Officer
Web address: www.memorialpembroke.com/
Control: Hospital district or authority, Government, nonfederal **Service:** General Medical and Surgical

Staffed Beds: 157 **Admissions:** 6341 **Census:** 75 **Outpatient Visits:** 63399 **Births:** 0 **Total Expense ($000):** 124481 **Payroll Expense ($000):** 52041 **Personnel:** 737

✠ **MEMORIAL HOSPITAL WEST (100281)**, 703 North Flamingo Road, Zip 33028–1014; tel. 954/436–5000 **A**1 2 10 **F**3 12 13 15 17 18 20 22 26 28 29 30 31 34 35 36 40 41 45 46 47 49 53 55 56 57 58 59 60 61 64 68 70 72 74 75 76 78 79 81 82 84 85 87 91 93 107 108 110 111 114 115 119 120 121 123 124 126 130 131 132 136 145 146 147 **S** Memorial Healthcare System, Hollywood, FL
Primary Contact: C. Kennon Hetlage, FACHE, Administrator and Chief Executive Officer
CFO: Walter Bussell, Chief Financial Officer
CMO: Eric Freling, M.D., Director Medical Staff Affairs
CIO: Forest Blanton, Chief Information Officer
CHR: Maria Naranjo, Director Human Resources
CNO: Grisel Fernandez–Bravo, R.N., Chief Nursing Officer
Web address: www.mhs.net
Control: Hospital district or authority, Government, nonfederal **Service:** General Medical and Surgical

Staffed Beds: 384 **Admissions:** 21522 **Census:** 274 **Outpatient Visits:** 269511 **Births:** 4139 **Total Expense ($000):** 379085 **Payroll Expense ($000):** 148128 **Personnel:** 1935

PENSACOLA—Escambia County

✠ **BAPTIST HOSPITAL (100093)**, 1000 West Moreno, Zip 32501–2316, Mailing Address: P.O. Box 17500, Zip 32522–7500; tel. 850/434–4011 **A**1 2 3 10 **F**3 8 11 12 13 15 17 18 20 22 24 26 28 29 30 31 34 35 37 40 43 45 46 47 48 49 50 51 53 54 55 56 59 60 61 63 64 67 70 71 74 75 76 77 78 79 80 81 82 84 85 86 87 91 92 93 97 98 99 100 101 102 103 104 107 108 110 111 114 115 116 117 118 119 120 121 123 124 126 129 130 131 132 135 144 146 147 148 **S** Baptist Health Care Corporation, Pensacola, FL
Primary Contact: Scott Raynes, President
CFO: Sharon Nobles, Interim Chief Financial Officer
CMO: Mike Oleksyk, M.D., Vice President and Chief Medical Officer
CIO: Steven Sarros, Vice President and Chief Information Officer
CHR: Darlene Stone, Vice President Human Resources
CNO: Cynde Gamache, R.N., Vice President and Chief Nursing Officer
Web address: www.ebaptisthealthcare.org
Control: Other not–for–profit (including NFP Corporation) **Service:** General Medical and Surgical

Staffed Beds: 337 **Admissions:** 18724 **Census:** 229 **Outpatient Visits:** 245854 **Births:** 997 **Total Expense ($000):** 266045 **Payroll Expense ($000):** 88681 **Personnel:** 1546

✠ **NAVAL HOSPITAL PENSACOLA**, 6000 West Highway 98, Zip 32512–0003; tel. 850/505–6601, (Nonreporting) **A**1 3 5 **S** Bureau of Medicine and Surgery, Department of the Navy, Falls Church, VA
Primary Contact: Commander Devin Morrison, Director Administration
COO: Commander Devin Morrison, Director for Administration
CMO: Commander Carolyn Rice, M.D., Director Medical Services
CIO: Lieutenant Commander William Berg, Chief Information Officer
CHR: Commander Devin Morrison, Director for Administration
CNO: Captain Amy Tarbay, Director Nursing Services
Web address: www.med.navy.mil/sites/pcola/Pages/default.aspx
Control: Navy, Government, federal **Service:** General Medical and Surgical

Staffed Beds: 28

✠ **SACRED HEART HOSPITAL PENSACOLA (100025)**, 5151 North Ninth Avenue, Zip 32504–8795, Mailing Address: P.O. Box 2700, Zip 32513–2700; tel. 850/416–7000 **A**1 2 3 5 10 13 **F**3 8 12 13 15 17 18 19 20 21 22 24 26 28 29 30 31 34 40 41 43 45 46 47 48 49 50 54 55 57 58 59 60 61 65 66 70 71 72 73 74 75 76 77 78 79 81 82 84 85 87 88 89 90 92 93 96 97 107 108 110 111 112 114 116 117 119 120 124 126 128 130 131 132 135 144 145 146 147 148 **S** Ascension Health, Saint Louis, MO
Primary Contact: Henry Stovall, President
COO: Amy Wilson, Chief Operating Officer and Chief Nursing Officer
CFO: C. Susan Cornejo, Chief Financial Officer
CMO: Peter Jennings, M.D., Interim Chief Medical Officer
CIO: Kathy Ross, Chief Information Officer
CHR: Michelle Adamolekun, Vice President Human Resource Market Lead Florida/Alabama Ministry Market
CNO: Amy Wilson, Chief Operating Officer and Chief Nursing Officer
Web address: www.sacred–heart.org
Control: Other not–for–profit (including NFP Corporation) **Service:** General Medical and Surgical

Staffed Beds: 440 **Admissions:** 23747 **Census:** 280 **Births:** 3995 **Total Expense ($000):** 389767 **Payroll Expense ($000):** 118085

✠ **SELECT SPECIALTY HOSPITAL–PENSACOLA (102024)**, 7000 Cobble Creek Drive, Zip 32504–8638; tel. 850/473–4800, (Nonreporting) **A**1 10 **S** Select Medical Corporation, Mechanicsburg, PA
Primary Contact: David Goodson, Chief Executive Officer
CMO: John Bray, M.D., Medical Director
Web address: www.selectspecialtyhospitals.com/company/locations/pensacola.aspx
Control: Corporation, Investor–owned, for–profit **Service:** Long–Term Acute Care hospital

Staffed Beds: 75

✠ △ **WEST FLORIDA HOSPITAL (100231)**, 8383 North Davis Highway, Zip 32514–6088; tel. 850/494–4000, (Includes THE PAVILION, 8383 North Davis Highway, Zip 32523, Mailing Address: P.O. Box 18900, Zip 32523; tel. 904/494–5000; WEST FLORIDA REHABILITATION INSTITUTE, 8383 North Davis Highway, Zip 32514, Mailing Address: P.O. Box 18900, Zip 32523; tel. 850/494–6000), (Nonreporting) **A**1 2 7 10 **S** HCA, Nashville, TN
Primary Contact: Brian Baumgardner, Chief Executive Officer
COO: Kenneth C. Donahey, Chief Operating Officer
CFO: Randy Butler, Chief Financial Officer
CMO: Terry Stallings, M.D., Chief Medical Officer
CIO: Jeff Amerson, Director Information System
CHR: Wanda Salley, Vice President Human Resources
CNO: Karen White–Trevino, Chief Nursing Officer
Web address: www.westfloridahospital.com
Control: Corporation, Investor–owned, for–profit **Service:** General Medical and Surgical

Staffed Beds: 339

WEST FLORIDA REHABILITATION INSTITUTE See West Florida Hospital

---

PERRY—Taylor County

★ **DOCTOR'S MEMORIAL HOSPITAL (100106)**, 333 North Byron Butler Parkway, Zip 32347–2300; tel. 850/584–0800 **A**10 20 **F**3 7 11 15 29 30 34 35 40 45 50 57 59 62 70 81 85 89 90 93 107 110 111 114 119 127 129 132 133 146
Primary Contact: Thomas J. Stone, FACHE, Chief Executive Officer
CMO: Ron Emerick, M.D., Chief of Staff
CHR: Sarah Brus, Director Human Resources
CNO: Mary Lescher, Chief Clinical Officer
Web address: www.doctorsmemorial.com
Control: Other not–for–profit (including NFP Corporation) **Service:** General Medical and Surgical

Staffed Beds: 24 **Admissions:** 941 **Census:** 8 **Births:** 3 **Total Expense ($000):** 27738 **Payroll Expense ($000):** 12628 **Personnel:** 208

PLANT CITY—Hillsborough County

✠ **SOUTH FLORIDA BAPTIST HOSPITAL (100132)**, 301 North Alexander Street, Zip 33563–4303; tel. 813/757–1200 **A**1 10 **F**3 11 12 13 15 18 20 22 28 29 30 31 34 35 37 40 41 44 45 47 48 49 51 57 59 64 70 74 75 76 77 78 79 81 84 85 87 89 93 107 108 110 111 114 115 118 119 124 126 130 131 132 135 146 **P**6 **S** Trinity Health, Livonia, MI
Primary Contact: Karen Kerr, R.N., President
COO: Beth Tancredo, Director Operations
CFO: Carl Tremonti, Chief Financial Officer
CMO: Mark Vaaler, M.D., Chief Medical Officer
CIO: Tim Thompson, Senior Vice President, Chief Information Officer
CHR: Pat Lipton, Director Team Resources
CNO: Teresa Colletti, Director Patient Services
Web address: www.https://baycare.org/sfbh
Control: Other not–for–profit (including NFP Corporation) **Service:** General Medical and Surgical

Staffed Beds: 115 **Admissions:** 6671 **Census:** 68 **Outpatient Visits:** 56394 **Births:** 534 **Total Expense ($000):** 97391 **Payroll Expense ($000):** 38013 **Personnel:** 546

Many Facility Codes have changed. Please refer to the AHA Guide Code Chart. © 2016 AHA Guide

FL

PLANTATION—Broward County

☒ **PLANTATION GENERAL HOSPITAL (100167)**, 401 N.W. 42nd Avenue, Zip 33317–2882; tel. 954/587–5010, (Includes MERCY HOSPITAL – A CAMPUS OF PLANTATION GENERAL HOSPITAL, 3663 South Miami Avenue, Miami, Zip 33133–4237; tel. 305/854–4400; Barbara Simmons, R.N., Chief Executive Officer), (Nonreporting) **A**1 2 3 10 **S** HCA, Nashville, TN
Primary Contact: Patrick Rohan, Interim Chief Executive Officer
COO: Patrick Rohan, Chief Operating Officer
CFO: Irfan Mirza, Chief Financial Officer
CIO: Mia McGlynn, Director Management Information Systems
CHR: Jennifer Allen, Vice President Human Resources
Web address: www.plantationgeneral.com
Control: Corporation, Investor–owned, for–profit **Service:** General Medical and Surgical

Staffed Beds: 264

☒ **WESTSIDE REGIONAL MEDICAL CENTER (100228)**, 8201 West Broward Boulevard, Zip 33324–2701; tel. 954/473–6600 **A**1 10 **F**3 8 11 15 17 18 20 22 24 26 29 30 31 34 35 40 44 45 48 49 50 57 59 60 68 70 74 75 77 78 79 80 81 82 85 86 87 93 107 108 110 111 114 115 117 119 126 129 130 131 132 145 146 148 **S** HCA, Nashville, TN
Primary Contact: Barbara Simmons, R.N., Chief Executive Officer
COO: Shana Sappington–Crittenden, Chief Operating Officer
CFO: Kevin Corcoran, Chief Financial Officer
CMO: Brian Weinstein, M.D., Chief of Staff
CIO: Andres Blanco, Director Management Information Systems
CHR: Maria Rivera, Director Human Resources
Web address: www.westsideregional.com
Control: Corporation, Investor–owned, for–profit **Service:** General Medical and Surgical

Staffed Beds: 215 **Admissions:** 14258 **Census:** 176 **Births:** 0 **Total Expense ($000):** 170147 **Payroll Expense ($000):** 50081

PORT CHARLOTTE—Charlotte County

☒ **BAYFRONT HEALTH PORT CHARLOTTE (100077)**, 2500 Harbor Boulevard, Zip 33952–5000; tel. 941/766–4122 **A**1 5 10 **F**8 13 15 17 18 20 22 24 26 29 30 31 34 40 45 48 49 50 64 68 70 72 74 75 76 77 79 81 85 89 93 107 111 114 119 126 135 146 147 **S** Community Health Systems, Inc., Franklin, TN
Primary Contact: Richard H. Satcher, Chief Executive Officer
COO: Brian Cruddas, Chief Operating Officer
CFO: Jeffrey Mullis, Interim Chief Financial Officer
CMO: Thomas Noone, M.D., Chief Medical Officer
CHR: Karen Gardiner, Human Resources Director
CNO: Debra Clark, Chief Nursing Officer
Web address: www.bayfrontcharlotte.com
Control: Corporation, Investor–owned, for–profit **Service:** General Medical and Surgical

Staffed Beds: 190 **Admissions:** 9918 **Census:** 134 **Births:** 1166

☒ △ **FAWCETT MEMORIAL HOSPITAL (100236)**, 21298 Olean Boulevard, Zip 33952–6765; tel. 941/629–1181 **A**1 2 7 10 **F**3 8 15 18 20 22 26 29 30 31 34 35 40 45 46 47 48 49 51 57 59 64 70 74 75 77 78 79 81 85 86 87 90 91 93 96 107 108 110 111 114 119 131 132 146 147 148 **S** HCA, Nashville, TN
Primary Contact: William Hawley, President and Chief Executive Officer
COO: Sally Seymour, Chief Operating Officer
CFO: Phillip Baker, Vice President and Chief Financial Officer
CMO: Mark Callman, M.D., Chief Medical Officer
CHR: Linda Bryan, Vice President Human Resources
CNO: Marcy Frisina, Chief Nursing Officer
Web address: www.fawcetthospital.com
Control: Corporation, Investor–owned, for–profit **Service:** General Medical and Surgical

Staffed Beds: 237 **Admissions:** 11824 **Census:** 174 **Births:** 0 **Total Expense ($000):** 150251 **Payroll Expense ($000):** 50202

PORT ST. JOE—Gulf County

☒ **SACRED HEART HOSPITAL ON THE GULF (100313)**, 3801 East Highway 98, Zip 32456–5318; tel. 850/229–5600 **A**1 10 **F**1 3 4 11 15 16 17 29 30 31 34 35 40 44 45 48 50 54 57 59 64 67 68 70 72 73 79 80 81 85 88 89 90 93 98 107 110 111 114 119 128 130 131 133 146 147 **P**7 **S** Ascension Health, Saint Louis, MO
Primary Contact: Roger L. Hall, President
CNO: Katherine L. Chastain, R.N., Chief Nursing Officer
Web address: www.sacred–heart.org/gulf/
Control: Other not–for–profit (including NFP Corporation) **Service:** General Medical and Surgical

Staffed Beds: 19 **Admissions:** 430 **Census:** 5 **Births:** 0 **Total Expense ($000):** 20040 **Payroll Expense ($000):** 6119

PORT ST. LUCIE—St. Lucie County

☐ **PORT ST. LUCIE HOSPITAL (104070)**, 2550 S.E. Walton Road, Zip 34952–7168; tel. 772/335–0400 **A**1 10 **F**4 98 102 103 105 106 130 **P**6
Primary Contact: Michael Hogan, Chief Executive Officer
Web address: www.portstluciehospitalinc.com
Control: Corporation, Investor–owned, for–profit **Service:** Psychiatric

Staffed Beds: 75 **Admissions:** 1653 **Census:** 70 **Outpatient Visits:** 0 **Births:** 0 **Personnel:** 176

☒ **ST. LUCIE MEDICAL CENTER (100260)**, 1800 S.E. Tiffany Avenue, Zip 34952–7521; tel. 772/335–4000, (Nonreporting) **A**1 2 10 13 **S** HCA, Nashville, TN
Primary Contact: Jay Finnegan, Chief Executive Officer
COO: Calvin Thomas, IV, Chief Operating Officer
CFO: Kevin Keeling, Chief Financial Officer
Web address: www.stluciemed.com
Control: Corporation, Investor–owned, for–profit **Service:** General Medical and Surgical

Staffed Beds: 194

PUNTA GORDA—Charlotte County

☒ **BAYFRONT HEALTH PUNTA GORDA (100047)**, 809 East Marion Avenue, Zip 33950–3819, Mailing Address: P.O. Box 51–1328, Zip 33951–1328; tel. 941/639–3131 **A**1 10 **F**3 17 18 29 30 31 34 35 36 38 39 40 44 45 50 53 54 56 57 59 60 64 68 70 74 75 77 78 79 81 85 86 87 93 94 98 100 101 102 103 107 108 110 111 115 118 119 126 130 131 132 135 146 148 **S** Community Health Systems, Inc., Franklin, TN
Primary Contact: Andrew Emery, Chief Executive Officer
Web address: www.bayfrontcharlotte.com
Control: Corporation, Investor–owned, for–profit **Service:** General Medical and Surgical

Staffed Beds: 190 **Admissions:** 4731 **Census:** 81 **Births:** 0 **Total Expense ($000):** 62842 **Payroll Expense ($000):** 23056

RIVIERA BEACH—Palm Beach County

☒ **KINDRED HOSPITAL THE PALM BEACHES (102025)**, 5555 West Blue Heron Boulevard, Zip 33418–7813; tel. 561/840–0754 **A**1 10 **F**1 3 18 29 30 45 48 70 74 75 77 79 82 84 85 91 97 100 107 114 145 148 **S** Kindred Healthcare, Louisville, KY
Primary Contact: Mark Twilla, Chief Executive Officer
CFO: Dean Card, Chief Financial Officer
CNO: Elayne Lopreato, Chief Clinical Officer
Web address: www.khthepalmbeaches.com/
Control: Corporation, Investor–owned, for–profit **Service:** Long–Term Acute Care hospital

Staffed Beds: 70 **Admissions:** 510 **Census:** 45 **Outpatient Visits:** 0 **Births:** 0 **Total Expense ($000):** 23343 **Payroll Expense ($000):** 9283

ROCKLEDGE—Brevard County

☒ **WUESTHOFF MEDICAL CENTER – ROCKLEDGE (100092)**, 110 Longwood Avenue, Zip 32955–2887, Mailing Address: P.O. Box 565002, Mail Stop 1, Zip 32956–5002; tel. 321/636–2211 **A**1 2 10 **F**3 15 17 18 19 20 22 24 26 28 29 30 31 35 40 46 49 50 51 59 60 64 68 70 72 74 75 76 78 79 80 81 82 84 85 89 93 98 102 107 111 114 115 117 119 126 130 131 132 135 146 147 148 **S** Community Health Systems, Inc., Franklin, TN
Primary Contact: Gary Malaer, Chief Executive Officer
CFO: Richard Haun, Chief Financial Officer
CMO: Vinay Mehindru, M.D., Medical Director
CIO: David Barnhart, Director Information Systems
CHR: Marchita H. Marino, Vice President Human Resources
Web address: www.wuesthoff.org
Control: Corporation, Investor–owned, for–profit **Service:** General Medical and Surgical

Staffed Beds: 298 **Admissions:** 11857 **Census:** 147 **Births:** 597 **Total Expense ($000):** 136635 **Payroll Expense ($000):** 50837

FL

Hospital, Medicare Provider Number, Address, Telephone, Approval, Facility, and Physician Codes, Health Care System

★ American Hospital Association (AHA) membership
☐ The Joint Commission accreditation
○ Healthcare Facilities Accreditation Program
◇ DNV Healthcare Inc. accreditation
⇑ Center for Improvement in Healthcare Quality Accreditation
△ Commission on Accreditation of Rehabilitation Facilities (CARF) accreditation

SAFETY HARBOR—Pinellas County

✠ **MEASE COUNTRYSIDE HOSPITAL (100265)**, 3231 McMullen–Booth Road, Zip 34695–6607, Mailing Address: P.O. Box 1098, Zip 34695–1098; tel. 727/725–6111 **A**1 2 10 **F**3 8 13 15 17 18 20 22 26 28 29 30 31 34 35 37 40 41 44 46 49 51 59 60 62 64 68 70 72 73 75 76 77 78 79 81 84 85 86 87 89 92 107 108 109 111 114 115 116 117 118 119 126 129 130 131 132 145 146 147 148 **P**6 **S** Trinity Health, Livonia, MI
Primary Contact: Lou Galdieri, R.N., President
CFO: Carl Tremonti, Chief Financial Officer
CMO: Donald Pocock, M.D., Chief Medical Officer
CHR: Sharon Collotta, Director Human Resources
Web address: www.mpmhealth.com
Control: Other not–for–profit (including NFP Corporation) **Service:** General Medical and Surgical

Staffed Beds: 311 **Admissions:** 17787 **Census:** 211 **Outpatient Visits:** 128284 **Births:** 2415 **Total Expense ($000):** 245466 **Payroll Expense ($000):** 89026 **Personnel:** 1639

SAINT AUGUSTINE—St. Johns County

☐ **FLAGLER HOSPITAL (100090)**, 400 Health Park Boulevard, Zip 32086–5784; tel. 904/819–5155 **A**1 2 5 10 20 **F**1 3 5 8 11 12 13 14 15 18 20 22 24 28 29 30 31 34 35 38 40 45 49 56 57 58 59 60 65 67 70 72 73 74 75 76 78 79 80 81 82 85 86 87 89 90 93 98 100 101 102 104 105 106 107 108 110 111 114 115 119 120 126 128 129 130 131 132 135 146 **P**8
Primary Contact: Joseph S. Gordy, President and Chief Executive Officer
COO: Jason P. Barrett, Chief Operating Officer
CFO: Lynda I. Kirker, Chief Financial Officer
CMO: Douglas Dew, M.D., President Medical Staff
CIO: Bill Rieger, Chief Information Officer
CHR: Jeff Hurley, Vice President Human Resources
Web address: www.flaglerhospital.org
Control: Other not–for–profit (including NFP Corporation) **Service:** General Medical and Surgical

Staffed Beds: 336 **Admissions:** 14338 **Census:** 177 **Outpatient Visits:** 160358 **Births:** 1423 **Total Expense ($000):** 231552 **Payroll Expense ($000):** 83133 **Personnel:** 1699

SAINT CLOUD—Osceola County

✠ **ST. CLOUD REGIONAL MEDICAL CENTER (100302)**, 2906 17th Street, Zip 34769–6099; tel. 407/892–2135 **A**1 10 **F**3 15 18 29 30 34 35 40 45 46 49 51 57 59 70 74 75 77 78 79 81 82 85 86 87 91 93 94 96 97 107 108 110 111 115 119 146 **S** Community Health Systems, Inc., Franklin, TN
Primary Contact: Brent Burish, Chief Executive Officer
COO: Andrea Thomas, Chief Operating Officer
CFO: Carl Caley, Chief Financial Officer
CIO: James Devlin, Director Information Systems
CHR: Jennifer Harmon, Director of Human Resources
CNO: Perry Horne, Chief Nursing Officer
Web address: www.stcloudregional.com
Control: Corporation, Investor–owned, for–profit **Service:** General Medical and Surgical

Staffed Beds: 84 **Admissions:** 3745 **Census:** 46 **Births:** 0 **Total Expense ($000):** 42876 **Payroll Expense ($000):** 17725

SAINT PETERSBURG—Pinellas County

✠ **BAYFRONT HEALTH ST. PETERSBURG (100032)**, 701 Sixth Street South, Zip 33701–4891; tel. 727/823–1234, (Nonreporting) **A**1 3 5 10 **S** Community Health Systems, Inc., Franklin, TN
Primary Contact: Kathryn Gillette, President and Chief Executive Officer
COO: Lavah Lowe, Executive Vice President and Chief Operating Officer
CFO: Eric Smith, Chief Financial Officer
CIO: Kevin Murphy, Director, Information Technology Services
CHR: Jim Reames, Director Human Resources
CNO: Karen Long, R.N., Vice President Nursing
Web address: www.bayfrontstpete.com
Control: Corporation, Investor–owned, for–profit **Service:** General Medical and Surgical

Staffed Beds: 395

✠ **JOHNS HOPKINS ALL CHILDREN'S HOSPITAL (103300)**, 501 6th Avenue South, Zip 33701–4634; tel. 727/898–7451 **A**1 3 5 8 10 **F**3 11 12 17 18 19 20 21 22 23 24 25 26 27 29 30 31 32 34 35 36 37 39 40 41 43 44 45 46 47 48 49 50 51 54 55 57 58 59 60 61 64 65 68 72 73 74 75 77 78 79 81 82 84 85 86 87 88 89 92 93 96 97 99 100 107 111 114 115 116 118 119 129 130 131 132 134 135 136 137 141 142 143 144 146 147 148 **S** Johns Hopkins Health System, Baltimore, MD
Primary Contact: Jonathan M. Ellen, M.D., President
CFO: Nancy Templin, Vice President Finance and Chief Financial Officer
CMO: Michael Epstein, M.D., Senior Vice President Medical Affairs
CIO: John McLendon, Vice President and Chief Information Officer
CHR: Jay Kuhns, Vice President Human Resources
Web address: www.allkids.org
Control: Other not–for–profit (including NFP Corporation) **Service:** Children's general

Staffed Beds: 259 **Admissions:** 7686 **Census:** 182 **Outpatient Visits:** 377687 **Births:** 0 **Total Expense ($000):** 419092 **Payroll Expense ($000):** 163823 **Personnel:** 2584

✠ **NORTHSIDE HOSPITAL (100238)**, 6000 49th Street North, Zip 33709–2145; tel. 727/521–4411 **A**1 10 12 13 **F**3 11 17 18 20 22 24 26 28 29 30 34 40 45 49 50 51 53 56 57 58 59 63 65 68 70 74 75 77 79 81 85 87 92 93 100 107 108 111 114 115 119 126 135 146 148 **S** HCA, Nashville, TN
Primary Contact: Dia Nichols, Chief Executive Officer
COO: Jayme Chancellor, Chief Operating Officer
CFO: Gary Searls, Chief Financial Officer
CMO: Ira Siegman, M.D., Chief Medical Officer
CIO: Kirk Hendrick, Director Information Systems
CHR: Maggie Miklos, Director Human Resources
CNO: Wendy Lincoln, Chief Nursing Officer
Web address: www.northsidehospital.com
Control: Corporation, Investor–owned, for–profit **Service:** General Medical and Surgical

Staffed Beds: 217 **Admissions:** 10287 **Census:** 140 **Outpatient Visits:** 52029 **Births:** 0 **Total Expense ($000):** 142081 **Payroll Expense ($000):** 54678 **Personnel:** 786

✠ **PALMS OF PASADENA HOSPITAL (100126)**, 1501 Pasadena Avenue South, Zip 33707–3798; tel. 727/381–1000 **A**1 10 **F**3 12 15 29 30 34 35 37 39 40 41 45 46 47 48 49 50 54 56 57 59 60 63 64 65 66 67 68 70 74 75 77 79 81 82 84 85 86 87 90 107 108 110 111 114 115 118 119 130 132 135 146 148 **S** HCA, Nashville, TN
Primary Contact: Sharon Hayes, Chief Executive Officer
CFO: James B. Gilbert, Chief Financial Officer
CMO: George Hutter, M.D., Chief of Staff
CIO: Danny Waters, Director, Information Services
CHR: Karen Casteel, Director Human Resources
CNO: Andrea Clyne, R.N., Chief Nursing Officer
Web address: www.palmspasadena.com
Control: Corporation, Investor–owned, for–profit **Service:** General Medical and Surgical

Staffed Beds: 187 **Admissions:** 5178 **Census:** 80 **Outpatient Visits:** 35830 **Births:** 0 **Total Expense ($000):** 82766 **Payroll Expense ($000):** 36911 **Personnel:** 487

✠ **ST. ANTHONY'S HOSPITAL (100067)**, 1200 Seventh Avenue North, Zip 33705–1388, Mailing Address: P.O. Box 12588, Zip 33733–2588; tel. 727/825–1100 **A**1 2 5 10 **F**3 11 12 15 17 18 20 22 26 28 29 30 31 34 35 40 44 45 46 49 51 57 59 60 64 68 70 74 75 77 78 79 81 84 85 87 93 98 100 102 103 107 108 110 111 114 115 117 118 119 121 123 124 126 129 130 131 132 135 146 148 **P**6 **S** Trinity Health, Livonia, MI
Primary Contact: M. Scott Smith, President
CFO: Carl Tremonti, Chief Financial Officer
CMO: James McClintic, M.D., Vice President Medical Affairs
CIO: Tim Thompson, Senior Vice President and Chief Informatics Officer
CHR: Kristen A. Betts, Director Team Resources
CNO: Thomas Doria, Vice President and Patient Services West
Web address: www.stanthonys.com/
Control: Other not–for–profit (including NFP Corporation) **Service:** General Medical and Surgical

Staffed Beds: 393 **Admissions:** 18626 **Census:** 261 **Outpatient Visits:** 107497 **Births:** 0 **Total Expense ($000):** 257560 **Payroll Expense ($000):** 101365 **Personnel:** 1885

✠ **ST. PETERSBURG GENERAL HOSPITAL (100180)**, 6500 38th Avenue North, Zip 33710–1629; tel. 727/384–1414, (Nonreporting) **A**1 2 10 12 13 **S** HCA, Nashville, TN
Primary Contact: Janice Balzano, President and Chief Executive Officer
COO: Stephanie McNulty, Chief Operating Officer
CFO: Shawn Gregory, Chief Financial Officer
CMO: George Hutter, M.D., Chief Medical Officer
CHR: Jennifer B. Robinson, Vice President Human Resources
CNO: JoAnne Cattell, Chief Nursing Officer
Web address: www.stpetegeneral.com
Control: Corporation, Investor–owned, for–profit **Service:** General Medical and Surgical

Staffed Beds: 219

Many Facility Codes have changed. Please refer to the AHA Guide Code Chart. © 2016 AHA Guide

SANFORD—Seminole County

☒ △ **CENTRAL FLORIDA REGIONAL HOSPITAL (100161)**, 1401 West
Seminole Boulevard, Zip 32771–6764; tel. 407/321–4500, (Nonreporting) **A**1 7
10 **S** HCA, Nashville, TN
Primary Contact: Wendy H. Brandon, Chief Executive Officer
COO: Glenn Carney, Chief Operating Officer
CFO: Richard Read, Chief Financial Officer
CIO: Jerry Ballard, Director Information Systems
CHR: Linda V. Smith, Vice President Human Resources
CNO: Maria Calloway, R.N., Chief Nursing Officer
Web address: www.centralfloridaregional.com
Control: Corporation, Investor–owned, for–profit **Service:** General Medical and
Surgical

Staffed Beds: 226

SARASOTA—Sarasota County

☒ **COMPLEX CARE HOSPITAL AT RIDGELAKE (102018)**, 6150 Edgelake Drive,
Zip 34240–8803; tel. 941/342–3000 **A**1 10 **F**1 3 60 85 107 114 130
S LifeCare Management Services, Plano, TX
Primary Contact: Danny Mallicoat, Chief Executive Officer
CFO: Leah Drabant, Director of Finance
CMO: Craig Harcup, M.D., Hospital Medical Director
CHR: Jennifer Sparks, Human Resources Generalist
CNO: Timothy Mitchell, R.N., Chief Nursing Officer
Web address: www.lifecare–hospitals.com/hospital.php?id=23
Control: Corporation, Investor–owned, for–profit **Service:** Long–Term Acute Care
hospital

Staffed Beds: 40 **Admissions:** 430 **Census:** 35 **Outpatient Visits:** 0 **Births:**
0 **Total Expense ($000):** 20711 **Payroll Expense ($000):** 8678

☒ **DOCTORS HOSPITAL OF SARASOTA (100166)**, 5731 Bee Ridge Road,
Zip 34233–5056; tel. 941/342–1100, (Nonreporting) **A**1 2 10 **S** HCA,
Nashville, TN
Primary Contact: Robert C. Meade, Chief Executive Officer
COO: Stephen W. Young, Chief Operating Officer
CFO: Charles Schwaner, III, Chief Financial Officer
CMO: Thomas Trinchetto, M.D., Chief Medical Officer
CHR: Theresa Levering, Director Human Resources
CNO: Kathy Mitchell, R.N., Chief Nursing Officer
Web address: www.doctorsofsarasota.com
Control: Corporation, Investor–owned, for–profit **Service:** General Medical and
Surgical

Staffed Beds: 168

☒ △ **HEALTHSOUTH REHABILITATION HOSPITAL OF SARASOTA (103031)**,
6400 Edgelake Drive, Zip 34240–8813; tel. 941/921–8600 **A**1 7 10 **F**29 90 95
96 143 **S** HEALTHSOUTH Corporation, Birmingham, AL
Primary Contact: Marcus Braz, Chief Executive Officer
CFO: Barbara Bierut, Chief Financial Officer
CMO: Alexander De Jesus, M.D., Medical Director
CHR: Brenda Benner, Director Human Resources
CNO: Jacqueline Juenger, R.N., Chief Nursing Officer
Web address: www.healthsouthsarasota.com
Control: Corporation, Investor–owned, for–profit **Service:** Rehabilitation

Staffed Beds: 96 **Admissions:** 2290 **Census:** 80 **Outpatient Visits:** 0 **Births:**
0 **Total Expense ($000):** 23027 **Payroll Expense ($000):** 13378
Personnel: 246

HEALTHSOUTH RIDGELAKE HOSPITAL See Complex Care Hospital at
Ridgelake

☐ △ ◇ **SARASOTA MEMORIAL HEALTH CARE SYSTEM (100087)**, 1700
South Tamiami Trail, Zip 34239–3555; tel. 941/917–9000 **A**1 2 3 5 7 10 21 **F**3
6 7 8 11 12 13 15 17 18 19 20 22 24 26 28 29 30 31 32 34 35 36 37 38
39 40 42 43 44 45 46 47 48 49 50 51 53 54 55 56 57 58 59 60 61 64 66
68 70 72 73 74 75 76 77 78 79 80 81 82 84 85 86 87 88 89 90 93 96 98 99
100 101 102 103 107 108 110 111 114 115 118 119 124 126 129 130 131
132 135 143 144 145 146 147 148 **P**5
Primary Contact: David Verinder, President and Chief Executive Officer
COO: David Verinder, President and Chief Executive Officer
CFO: Bill Woeltjen, Chief Financial Officer
CMO: Steve Taylor, M.D., Chief Medical Officer
CIO: Denis Baker, Chief Information Officer
CHR: Laurie Bennett, Director Human Resources
CNO: Jan Mauck, R.N., Chief Nursing Officer
Web address: www.smh.com
Control: Hospital district or authority, Government, nonfederal **Service:** General
Medical and Surgical

Staffed Beds: 701 **Admissions:** 28042 **Census:** 383 **Outpatient Visits:**
541630 **Births:** 3347 **Total Expense ($000):** 530657 **Payroll Expense
($000):** 204909 **Personnel:** 4071

SEBASTIAN—Indian River County

☒ **SEBASTIAN RIVER MEDICAL CENTER (100217)**, 13695 North U.S. Highway
1, Zip 32958–3230, Mailing Address: Box 780838, Zip 32978–0838;
tel. 772/589–3186, (Total facility includes 33 beds in nursing home–type unit) **A**1
10 **F**3 11 12 15 18 20 22 28 29 30 31 34 40 45 47 48 49 50 51 54 60 63
68 70 74 75 77 78 79 81 82 83 84 85 87 89 93 94 107 108 109 111 114
115 116 117 119 126 128 129 130 132 135 145 146 148 **P**8 **S** Community
Health Systems, Inc., Franklin, TN
Primary Contact: Kelly Enriquez, Chief Executive Officer
CFO: John McEachern, Controller
CMO: Ralph Geiger, M.D., Chief of Staff
CHR: Kam Storey, Director Human Resources
Web address: www.sebastianrivermedical.com
Control: Corporation, Investor–owned, for–profit **Service:** General Medical and
Surgical

Staffed Beds: 154 **Admissions:** 5553 **Census:** 62 **Outpatient Visits:** 32084
Births: 0 **Total Expense ($000):** 12191 **Personnel:** 477

SEBRING—Highlands County

☒ **FLORIDA HOSPITAL HEARTLAND MEDICAL CENTER (100109)**, 4200 Sun'n
Lake Boulevard, Zip 33872–1986, Mailing Address: P.O. Box 9400,
Zip 33871–9400; tel. 863/314–4466, (Includes FLORIDA HOSPITAL LAKE
PLACID, 1210 U.S. 27 North, Lake Placid, Zip 33852–7948; tel. 863/465–3777;
Eric Stevens, Chief Executive Officer) **A**1 10 19 **F**11 13 15 18 20 22 24 26 28
29 30 34 35 37 40 44 45 49 50 51 53 54 57 59 60 62 64 70 75 76 78 79
81 86 87 89 97 98 100 101 103 104 107 108 110 111 114 115 116 117
118 119 126 127 129 130 132 135 146 147 148 **P**6 **S** Adventist Health
System Sunbelt Health Care Corporation, Altamonte Springs, FL
Primary Contact: Bruce Bergherm, Chief Executive Officer
CFO: Rosalie Oliver, Chief Financial Officer
CMO: Jorge F. Gonzalez, M.D., Chief Medical Officer
CHR: Anthony Stahl, Vice President
CNO: Gloria N. Santos, R.N., Chief Nursing Officer
Web address: www.fhheartland.org/
Control: Church–operated, Nongovernment, not–for profit **Service:** General
Medical and Surgical

Staffed Beds: 189 **Admissions:** 10577 **Census:** 142 **Outpatient Visits:**
129394 **Births:** 776 **Total Expense ($000):** 182541 **Payroll Expense
($000):** 77072 **Personnel:** 1397

☒ **HIGHLANDS REGIONAL MEDICAL CENTER (100049)**, 3600 South Highlands
Avenue, Zip 33870–5495, Mailing Address: Drawer 2066, Zip 33871–2066;
tel. 863/385–6101 **A**1 10 19 **F**3 11 12 13 15 18 20 22 29 34 40 45 49 50
51 57 59 64 70 76 79 81 85 87 93 97 107 108 110 114 119 124 129 135
146 **S** Community Health Systems, Inc., Franklin, TN
Primary Contact: John D. Montois, Interim Chief Executive Officer
CFO: Paul Damron, Chief Financial Officer
CIO: Nate Johnson, Chief Information Officer
CHR: Brenda Dane, Director, Human Resources
CNO: Adam Kless, Chief Nursing Officer
Web address: www.highlandsregional.com
Control: Corporation, Investor–owned, for–profit **Service:** General Medical and
Surgical

Staffed Beds: 80 **Admissions:** 5125 **Census:** 38 **Births:** 136 **Total Expense
($000):** 54510 **Payroll Expense ($000):** 16327

SOUTH MIAMI—Miami–Dade County

☒ **LARKIN COMMUNITY HOSPITAL (100181)**, 7031 S.W. 62nd Avenue,
Zip 33143–4781; tel. 305/284–7500 **A**1 3 10 12 13 **F**3 5 7 8 10 15 29 34 35
37 38 40 44 45 49 54 56 57 58 59 60 62 64 65 68 70 71 74 75 77 78 79
81 82 84 85 87 91 92 93 96 97 98 100 101 102 103 104 105 107 108 110
111 114 117 118 119 124 126 129 130 131 132 135 143 145 146 148
Primary Contact: Sandra Sosa–Guerrero, Chief Executive Officer
COO: George J. Michel, Chief Operating Officer
CFO: Edgar Castillo, Chief Financial Officer
CMO: Mario Almeida–Suarez, M.D., Chief of Staff
CIO: Orlando Suarez, Director Information Technology
CHR: Carolina Pena, Assistant Director Administrator
CNO: Mercedes Perez, Vice President Nursing
Web address: www.larkinhospital.com
Control: Individual, Investor–owned, for–profit **Service:** General Medical and
Surgical

Staffed Beds: 146 **Admissions:** 5623 **Census:** 83 **Outpatient Visits:** 28500
Births: 0 **Total Expense ($000):** 105682 **Payroll Expense ($000):** 46880
Personnel: 766

STARKE—Bradford County

SHANDS STARKE See Shands Starke Regional Medical Center

FL

SHANDS STARKE REGIONAL MEDICAL CENTER (101310), 922 East Call Street, Zip 32091–3699; tel. 904/368–2300 **A**1 3 10 18 **F**3 11 15 29 30 34 35 40 44 45 50 57 59 64 68 74 75 77 81 85 93 97 107 111 114 119 127 129 131 132 135 **P**6 **S** Community Health Systems, Inc., Franklin, TN
CFO: Wendy Martin, Chief Financial Officer
Web address: www.shandsstarke.com
Control: Partnership, Investor–owned, for–profit **Service:** General Medical and Surgical

Staffed Beds: 49 **Admissions:** 1537 **Census:** 15 **Births:** 0

STUART—Martin County

HEALTHSOUTH REHABILITATION HOSPITAL AT MARTIN HEALTH (103044), 5850 S.E. Community Drive, Zip 34997–6420; tel. 772/324–3500, (Nonreporting) **A**1 10 **S** HEALTHSOUTH Corporation, Birmingham, AL
Primary Contact: Ivette Miranda, Chief Executive Officer
CFO: Dawn Salas, Controller
CMO: Stephen L. Chastain, M.D., Chief Medical Officer
CHR: Annette DiPiero, Human Resource Director
Web address: www.healthsouthmartin.com
Control: Corporation, Investor–owned, for–profit **Service:** Rehabilitation

Staffed Beds: 34

MARTIN HEALTH SYSTEM (100044), 200 S.E. Hospital Avenue, Zip 34994–2346, Mailing Address: P.O. Box 9010, Zip 34995–9010; tel. 772/287–5200, (Includes MARTIN MEMORIAL HOSPITAL SOUTH, 2100 S.E. Salerno Road, Zip 34997; tel. 772/223–2300; Mark E. Robitaille, FACHE, President and Chief Executive Officer; TRADITION MEDICAL CENTER, 10000 S.W. Innovation Way, Port St. Lucie, Zip 34987–2111; tel. 772/345–8100; Mark E. Robitaille, FACHE, President and Chief Executive Officer) **A**1 2 10 **F**3 8 11 12 13 15 17 18 20 22 24 26 28 29 30 31 35 36 37 40 42 45 46 47 49 50 51 53 55 60 64 68 70 72 74 75 76 77 78 79 81 82 85 86 87 91 93 94 95 107 108 110 111 115 116 117 118 119 120 121 123 124 126 129 130 132 143 144 146 **P**6
Primary Contact: Robert L. Lord, JD, President and Chief Executive Officer
CFO: Chuck Cleaver, Vice President and Chief Financial Officer
CMO: Fernando Petry, M.D., Vice President and Chief Medical Officer
CIO: Edmund Collins, Chief Information Officer
CHR: Angie L. Metcalf, Vice President and Chief Human Resource Officer
CNO: Mary Elizabeth Flippo, R.N., Vice President and Chief Nursing Officer
Web address: www.martinhealth.org
Control: Other not–for–profit (including NFP Corporation) **Service:** General Medical and Surgical

Staffed Beds: 335 **Admissions:** 23609 **Census:** 293 **Outpatient Visits:** 138243 **Births:** 2542 **Total Expense ($000):** 404086 **Payroll Expense ($000):** 173443 **Personnel:** 3178

SUN CITY CENTER—Hillsborough County

SOUTH BAY HOSPITAL (100259), 4016 Sun City Center Boulevard, Zip 33573–5298; tel. 813/634–3301 **A**1 10 **F**3 15 18 29 30 31 34 35 37 40 45 49 50 57 59 64 68 70 74 75 77 78 79 81 82 85 86 87 93 107 108 110 111 114 118 119 132 146 148 **S** HCA, Nashville, TN
Primary Contact: Sharon L. Roush, Chief Executive Officer
COO: Daniel Bender, Chief Operating Officer
CFO: Phillip Sensing, Chief Financial Officer
CIO: Eric Young, Director Information Technology and Systems
CHR: Stacie Novosel, Vice President, Human Resources
CNO: Sherry Collins, Chief Nursing Officer
Web address: www.southbayhospital.com/
Control: Corporation, Investor–owned, for–profit **Service:** General Medical and Surgical

Staffed Beds: 112 **Admissions:** 6808 **Census:** 82 **Births:** 0 **Total Expense ($000):** 71699 **Payroll Expense ($000):** 24781

SUNRISE—Broward County

HEALTHSOUTH SUNRISE REHABILITATION HOSPITAL (103028), 4399 North Nob Hill Road, Zip 33351–5899; tel. 954/749–0300 **A**1 3 10 **F**3 18 29 34 35 56 57 59 62 82 90 91 93 95 96 130 132 148 **S** HEALTHSOUTH Corporation, Birmingham, AL
Primary Contact: Stacy Modlin, Chief Executive Officer
COO: Jay de los Reyes, Chief Operating Officer
CFO: Ruth Goodstein, Controller
CMO: Scott Tannenbaum, M.D., Medical Director
CIO: Angela Manning, Director Health Information Services
CHR: Barbara Dunkiel, Director Human Resources
CNO: Omaira D. Riano, Chief Nursing Officer
Web address: www.healthsouthsunrise.com
Control: Corporation, Investor–owned, for–profit **Service:** Rehabilitation

Staffed Beds: 126 **Admissions:** 2499 **Census:** 94 **Outpatient Visits:** 27069 **Births:** 0 **Total Expense ($000):** 35413 **Payroll Expense ($000):** 19464 **Personnel:** 366

TALLAHASSEE—Leon County

CAPITAL REGIONAL MEDICAL CENTER (100254), 2626 Capital Medical Boulevard, Zip 32308–4499; tel. 850/325–5000, (Nonreporting) **A**1 2 10 **S** HCA, Nashville, TN
Primary Contact: Mark Robinson, FACHE, President and Chief Executive Officer
CMO: Steve West, M.D., Chief Medical Officer
CIO: Robert A. Steed, Director Information Systems
CHR: Louise Truitt, Vice President Human Resources
Web address: www.capitalregionalmedicalcenter.com
Control: Individual, Investor–owned, for–profit **Service:** General Medical and Surgical

Staffed Beds: 198

EASTSIDE PSYCHIATRIC HOSPITAL (104059), 2634 Capital Circle N.E., Zip 32308–4106; tel. 850/523–3333, (Nonreporting) **A**10
Primary Contact: Jay A. Reeve, Ph.D., President and Chief Executive Officer
COO: Sue Conger, Chief Operating Officer
CFO: Virginia Kelly, Chief Financial Officer
CMO: Ludmila de Faria, M.D., Chief Medical Officer
CIO: Thad Moorer, Chief Information Officer
CHR: Candy Landry, Chief Human Resource Officer
CNO: Judy Goreau, R.N., Director of Nursing
Web address: www.apalacheecenter.org
Control: Other not–for–profit (including NFP Corporation) **Service:** Psychiatric

Staffed Beds: 24

HEALTHSOUTH REHABILITATION HOSPITAL OF TALLAHASSEE (103033), 1675 Riggins Road, Zip 32308–5315; tel. 850/656–4800, (Nonreporting) **A**1 10 **S** HEALTHSOUTH Corporation, Birmingham, AL
Primary Contact: K. Dale Neely, FACHE, Chief Executive Officer
CFO: Jennifer Spooner, Controller
CMO: Robert Rowland, M.D., Medical Director
CIO: Michael Spangler, Health Information Management Services Supervisor
CHR: Carol Bugayong, Human Resources Director
CNO: Elizabeth Squires, R.N., Chief Nursing Officer
Web address: www.healthsouthtallahassee.com
Control: Corporation, Investor–owned, for–profit **Service:** Rehabilitation

Staffed Beds: 76

SELECT SPECIALTY HOSPITAL–TALLAHASSEE (102020), 1554 Surgeons Drive, Zip 32308–4631; tel. 850/219–6950, (Nonreporting) **A**1 10 **S** Select Medical Corporation, Mechanicsburg, PA
Primary Contact: Lora Davis, FACHE, Chief Executive Officer
Web address: www.tallahassee.selectspecialtyhospitals.com/
Control: Corporation, Investor–owned, for–profit **Service:** Long–Term Acute Care hospital

Staffed Beds: 29

TALLAHASSEE MEMORIAL HEALTHCARE (100135), 1300 Miccosukee Road, Zip 32308–5054; tel. 850/431–1155, (Total facility includes 42 beds in nursing home–type unit) **A**1 2 3 5 10 **F**2 3 5 6 8 11 12 15 17 18 19 20 22 24 26 28 29 30 31 34 35 37 40 42 43 45 46 47 49 50 51 53 54 55 56 57 58 59 60 61 62 64 65 68 70 72 73 74 75 76 77 78 79 80 81 82 84 85 86 87 88 89 91 93 96 97 98 99 100 102 103 104 107 108 110 113 114 115 117 118 119 120 121 123 124 126 127 128 129 130 131 132 135 143 144 146 147 148 **P**6
Primary Contact: G. Mark O'Bryant, President and Chief Executive Officer
COO: Jason H. Moore, Vice President and Chief Operating Officer
CFO: William A. Giudice, Vice President and Chief Financial Officer
CMO: Dean Watson, M.D., Chief Medical Officer
CIO: Don Lindsey, Vice President and Chief Information Officer
CHR: Steven W. Adriaanse, Vice President and Chief Human Resources Officer
Web address: www.tmh.org
Control: Other not–for–profit (including NFP Corporation) **Service:** General Medical and Surgical

Staffed Beds: 491 **Admissions:** 28365 **Census:** 382 **Outpatient Visits:** 755435 **Births:** 3820 **Total Expense ($000):** 556328 **Payroll Expense ($000):** 233751 **Personnel:** 3696

TAMARAC—Broward County

UNIVERSITY HOSPITAL AND MEDICAL CENTER (100224), 7201 North University Drive, Zip 33321–2996; tel. 954/721–2200, (Includes UNIVERSITY PAVILION, 7425 North University Drive, Zip 33328; tel. 305/722–9933), (Nonreporting) **A**1 10 **S** HCA, Nashville, TN
Primary Contact: Joseph D. Melchiode, Chief Executive Officer
CFO: Aurelio Gonzalez, Chief Financial Officer
CMO: Ran Abrahamy, M.D., Chief of Staff
CIO: Tom Scharff, Director Information Services
Web address: www.uhmchealth.com
Control: Corporation, Investor–owned, for–profit **Service:** General Medical and Surgical

Staffed Beds: 317

Many Facility Codes have changed. Please refer to the AHA Guide Code Chart. © 2016 AHA Guide

TAMPA—Hillsborough County

✠ **FLORIDA HOSPITAL CARROLLWOOD (100069)**, 7171 North Dale Mabry Highway, Zip 33614–2665; tel. 813/932–2222 **A**1 3 10 **F**3 8 11 15 18 20 22 26 29 30 34 35 40 44 45 48 49 50 54 56 57 58 59 60 64 65 68 70 74 75 77 78 79 80 81 82 85 86 87 92 93 107 110 111 114 119 126 129 130 131 132 143 145 146 148 **S** Adventist Health System Sunbelt Health Care Corporation, Altamonte Springs, FL
Primary Contact: Joe Johnson, FACHE, Chief Executive Officer
COO: Mary C. Whillock, R.N., Associate Nursing Officer and Chief Operating Officer
CFO: Chris Sauder, Chief Financial Officer
Web address: www.elevatinghealthcare.org/locations/carrollwood
Control: Church–operated, Nongovernment, not–for profit **Service:** General Medical and Surgical

Staffed Beds: 96 Admissions: 4990 Census: 53 Outpatient Visits: 73383 Births: 0 Total Expense ($000): 125000 Payroll Expense ($000): 36387 Personnel: 470

✠ △ **FLORIDA HOSPITAL TAMPA (100173)**, 3100 East Fletcher Avenue, Zip 33613–4688; tel. 813/971–6000 **A**1 2 3 5 7 10 **F**3 12 13 15 17 18 19 20 21 22 24 25 26 27 28 29 30 31 34 35 37 40 41 44 45 46 47 48 49 50 54 57 58 59 60 64 65 70 72 74 75 76 77 78 79 80 81 82 84 85 86 87 88 89 90 91 92 93 96 107 108 109 110 111 112 114 115 116 117 118 119 120 121 123 124 126 129 130 132 135 143 144 146 147 148 **P**6 7 **S** Adventist Health System Sunbelt Health Care Corporation, Altamonte Springs, FL
Primary Contact: Brian Adams, President and CEO
COO: Dick Tibbits, Vice President and Chief Operating Officer
CFO: Dima Didenko, Chief Financial Officer
CMO: Brad Bjornstad, M.D., Vice President and Chief Medical Officer
CHR: Dick Tibbits, Vice President and Chief Operating Officer
CNO: Joy B. Solomita, R.N., Vice President and Chief Nursing Officer
Web address: www.floridahospital.com/tampa
Control: Other not–for–profit (including NFP Corporation) **Service:** General Medical and Surgical

Staffed Beds: 482 Admissions: 22454 Census: 325 Outpatient Visits: 124641 Births: 1493 Total Expense ($000): 428429 Payroll Expense ($000): 145209 Personnel: 2289

✠ **H. LEE MOFFITT CANCER CENTER AND RESEARCH INSTITUTE (100271)**, 12902 Magnolia Drive, Zip 33612–9497; tel. 813/745–4673 **A**1 2 3 5 10 **F**3 8 11 15 26 29 30 31 34 35 36 37 38 44 45 46 47 48 49 50 54 55 56 57 58 59 63 64 68 70 71 74 75 77 78 79 81 82 84 85 86 87 91 92 93 96 97 100 101 103 104 107 108 110 111 114 115 116 117 118 119 120 121 123 124 126 130 132 135 136 141 144 146 147 148 **P**6
Primary Contact: Alan F. List, President and Chief Executive Officer
COO: John A. Kolosky, Executive Vice President and Chief Operating Officer
CFO: Yvette Tremonti, Chief Financial Officer
CMO: Bob Keenan, Chief Medical Officer
CIO: Jennifer Greenman, Vice President Chief Information Officer
CHR: Mariana Bugallo–Muros, Vice President Chief Human Resources Officer
CNO: Jane Fusilero, Vice President Chief Nursing Officer
Web address: www.moffitt.org
Control: Other not–for–profit (including NFP Corporation) **Service:** Cancer

Staffed Beds: 206 Admissions: 9319 Census: 159 Outpatient Visits: 346471 Births: 0 Total Expense ($000): 906942 Payroll Expense ($000): 374346 Personnel: 4743

✠ △ **JAMES A. HALEY VETERANS' HOSPITAL–TAMPA**, 13000 Bruce B. Downs Boulevard, Zip 33612–4745; tel. 813/972–2000, (Total facility includes 64 beds in nursing home–type unit) **A**1 3 5 7 8 **F**3 5 9 12 15 17 18 20 22 24 26 28 29 30 31 34 35 36 38 39 40 45 46 47 48 49 50 51 53 54 55 56 57 58 59 60 61 62 63 64 65 70 71 74 75 77 78 79 80 81 82 83 84 85 86 87 90 91 92 93 94 95 96 97 98 100 101 102 103 104 105 106 107 108 109 110 111 113 114 115 116 117 118 119 120 121 123 127 128 129 130 131 132 135 143 144 146 147 148 **P**1 **S** Department of Veterans Affairs, Washington, DC
Primary Contact: Joe Battle, Director
COO: David Van Meter, Deputy Director
CFO: Robert Konkel, Manager Finance
CMO: Edward Cutolo, Jr., M.D., Chief of Staff
CIO: Jose Seymour, Chief Information Resource Management
CHR: Andrew Sutton, Chief, Human Resources Management Service
CNO: Laureen Doloresco, R.N., Associate Director for Patient Care and Nursing Services
Web address: www.tampa.va.gov/
Control: Veterans Affairs, Government, federal **Service:** General Medical and Surgical

Staffed Beds: 499 Admissions: 17614 Census: 403 Births: 0

✠ **KINDRED HOSPITAL BAY AREA–TAMPA (102009)**, 4555 South Manhattan Avenue, Zip 33611–2397; tel. 813/839–6341, (Includes KINDRED HOSPITAL–BAY AREA ST. PETERSBURG, 3030 Sixth Street South, Saint Petersburg, Zip 33705–3720; tel. 727/894–8719; Debra Plummer, Chief Executive Officer) **A**1 10 **F**1 3 18 28 29 30 34 56 57 59 68 74 75 82 84 85 87 100 119 **S** Kindred Healthcare, Louisville, KY
Primary Contact: Suthanthira M. Ratnasamy, R.N., FACHE, Chief Executive Officer
CFO: Frank Billy, Chief Financial Officer
CHR: Deborah Basria, Human Resources Payroll Administrator
Web address: www.khtampa.com/
Control: Hospital district or authority, Government, nonfederal **Service:** Long–Term Acute Care hospital

Staffed Beds: 73 Admissions: 508 Census: 50 Births: 0 Total Expense ($000): 26448 Payroll Expense ($000): 10800

✠ **KINDRED HOSPITAL CENTRAL TAMPA (102013)**, 4801 North Howard Avenue, Zip 33603–1411; tel. 813/874–7575, (Nonreporting) **A**1 10 **S** Kindred Healthcare, Louisville, KY
Primary Contact: Ralph Selner, Chief Executive Officer
CFO: John Miner, Chief Financial Officer
Web address: www.kindredcentraltampa.com/
Control: Corporation, Investor–owned, for–profit **Service:** Long–Term Acute Care hospital

Staffed Beds: 96

✠ **MEMORIAL HOSPITAL OF TAMPA (100206)**, 2901 Swann Avenue, Zip 33609–4057; tel. 813/873–6400, (Nonreporting) **A**1 5 10 **S** HCA, Nashville, TN
Primary Contact: Ward Boston, III, Chief Executive Officer
CFO: Shelley V. Kolseth, Chief Financial Officer
CIO: John Riton, Director Information Services
Web address: www.memorialhospitaltampa.com
Control: Corporation, Investor–owned, for–profit **Service:** General Medical and Surgical

Staffed Beds: 139

☐ **SHRINERS HOSPITALS FOR CHILDREN–TAMPA (103303)**, 12502 USF Pine Drive, Zip 33612–9499; tel. 813/972–2250 **A**1 3 5 10 **F**3 34 35 50 57 64 68 74 77 79 81 85 89 91 93 94 107 131 146 **S** Shriners Hospitals for Children, Tampa, FL
CFO: Ruth Gregos, Director Finance
CMO: Maureen Maciel, M.D., Chief of Staff
CHR: Amy Schenker, Human Resources Director
Web address: www.shrinershospitalsforchildren.org/Hospitals/Locations/Tampa.aspx
Control: Other not–for–profit (including NFP Corporation) **Service:** Children's orthopedic

Staffed Beds: 60 Admissions: 274 Census: 2 Births: 0 Total Expense ($000): 21390 Payroll Expense ($000): 9871

✠ **ST. JOSEPH'S HOSPITAL (100075)**, 3001 West Martin Luther King Jr. Boulevard, Zip 33607–6387, Mailing Address: P.O. Box 4227, Zip 33677–4227; tel. 813/870–4000, (Includes ST. JOSEPH'S CHILDREN'S HOSPITAL, 3001 Dr. Martin Luther King Jr. Boulevard, Zip 33607; tel. 813/554–8500; ST. JOSEPH'S HOSPITAL – NORTH, 4211 Van Dyke Road, Lutz, Zip 33558–8005; tel. 813/443–7000; Paula McGinnis, Chief Executive Officer; ST. JOSEPH'S HOSPITAL BEHAVIORAL HEALTH CENTER, 4918 North Habana Avenue, Zip 33614–6815; tel. 813/870–4300; ST. JOSEPH'S HOSPITAL–SOUTH, 6901 Simmons Loop, Riverview, Zip 33578–9498; tel. 813/302–8000; Scott Smith, President; ST. JOSEPH'S WOMEN'S HOSPITAL, 3030 West Dr. Martin L. King Boulevard, Zip 33607–6204; tel. 813/872–2950; Kimberly Guy, Chief Operating Officer) **A**1 2 3 5 10 **F**3 7 11 12 13 15 17 18 19 20 21 22 23 24 25 26 27 28 29 30 31 33 34 35 36 37 39 40 41 43 44 45 46 48 49 51 53 55 57 58 59 60 61 64 65 66 68 70 71 72 73 74 75 76 77 78 79 81 82 84 85 86 87 88 89 93 94 98 99 100 101 102 107 108 110 111 114 115 118 119 120 121 123 126 127 129 130 131 132 135 145 146 147 148 **P**6 **S** Trinity Health, Livonia, MI
Primary Contact: Lorraine Lutton, President
CFO: Cathy Yoder, Chief Financial Officer
CMO: Mark Vaaler, M.D., Vice President Medical Staff Affairs
CIO: Lindsey Jarrell, Vice President Information Services
CHR: Pat Lipton, Director Team Resources
Web address: www.sjbhealth.org
Control: Other not–for–profit (including NFP Corporation) **Service:** General Medical and Surgical

Staffed Beds: 1006 Admissions: 54993 Census: 717 Outpatient Visits: 521312 Births: 8682 Total Expense ($000): 888899 Payroll Expense ($000): 328675 Personnel: 4447

FL

Hospital, Medicare Provider Number, Address, Telephone, Approval, Facility, and Physician Codes, Health Care System

★ American Hospital Association (AHA) membership   ○ Healthcare Facilities Accreditation Program   ⇑ Center for Improvement in Healthcare Quality Accreditation
☐ The Joint Commission accreditation   ◇ DNV Healthcare Inc. accreditation   △ Commission on Accreditation of Rehabilitation Facilities (CARF) accreditation

⊞ **TAMPA COMMUNITY HOSPITAL (100255)**, 6001 Webb Road,
Zip 33615–3291; tel. 813/888–7060 **A**1 5 10 **F**3 4 5 15 18 20 29 40 45 46
47 48 49 70 74 79 81 82 85 92 93 98 102 103 107 110 111 114 115 118
119 126 128 130 146 148 **P**4 5 **S** HCA, Nashville, TN
Primary Contact: Jacob Fisher, Chief Executive Officer
COO: Paulina Tam, Vice President of Operations
CIO: Albert Lacy, Associate Director of Information Technology
CHR: Stephanie Kunkel, Vice President of Human Resources
CNO: Susan Laber, R.N., Chief Nursing Officer
Web address: www.tampacommunityhospital.com/
Control: Corporation, Investor–owned, for–profit **Service:** General Medical and
Surgical

Staffed Beds: 201 **Admissions:** 4977 **Census:** 61 **Births:** 0 **Total Expense
($000):** 65080 **Payroll Expense ($000):** 22650

⊞ △ **TAMPA GENERAL HOSPITAL (100128)**, 1 Tampa General Circle,
Zip 33606–3571, Mailing Address: P.O. Box 1289, Zip 33601–1289;
tel. 813/844–7000, (Includes TAMPA GENERAL HOSPITAL CHILDREN'S MEDICAL
CENTER, 1 Tampa General Circle, tel. 813/844–7000) **A**1 3 5 7 8 10 **F**3 7 9 11
12 13 15 16 17 18 19 20 22 24 26 28 29 30 31 32 34 35 36 37 38 39 40
41 43 44 45 46 47 48 49 50 51 52 53 54 55 56 57 58 59 60 61 64 65 66
68 70 72 73 74 75 76 77 78 79 81 82 83 84 85 86 87 88 89 90 91 92 93
94 96 97 99 100 101 102 103 107 108 109 110 111 112 114 115 119 120
121 123 124 126 129 130 132 134 135 137 138 139 140 141 142 143 145
146 147 148 **P**6
Primary Contact: James R. Burkhart, FACHE, President and Chief Executive Officer
COO: Deana Nelson, FACHE, Executive Vice President and Chief Operating Officer
CFO: Steve Short, Executive Vice President Finance and Administration and Chief
Financial Officer
CMO: Sally Houston, M.D., Executive Vice President and Chief Medical Officer
CIO: Scott Arnold, Senior Vice President Information Systems
CHR: Chris Roederer, Senior Vice President Human Resources
CNO: Janet Davis, R.N., Senior Vice President and Chief Nursing Officer
Web address: www.tgh.org
Control: Other not–for–profit (including NFP Corporation) **Service:** General
Medical and Surgical

Staffed Beds: 1011 **Admissions:** 46964 **Census:** 775 **Outpatient Visits:**
381533 **Births:** 5872 **Total Expense ($000):** 1125579 **Payroll Expense
($000):** 423137 **Personnel:** 7692

TARPON SPRINGS—Pinellas County

⊞ **FLORIDA HOSPITAL NORTH PINELLAS (100055)**, 1395 South Pinellas
Avenue, Zip 34689–3790; tel. 727/942–5000 **A**1 5 10 **F**3 11 13 15 17 18 20
22 26 28 29 30 31 34 35 40 45 46 48 49 50 57 59 64 70 71 75 76 78 79
81 93 94 96 97 107 108 110 111 114 115 117 119 126 128 129 130 131
132 146 147 148 **S** Adventist Health System Sunbelt Health Care Corporation,
Altamonte Springs, FL
Primary Contact: Tricia Williams, President and Chief Executive Officer
CFO: Steven Miller, Chief Financial Officer
CMO: Brian Williams, M.D., Chief of Medical Staff
CIO: Brett Peterson, Director of Information Services
CHR: Vernon Elarbee, Director of Human Resources
CNO: Karen Owensby, R.N., Chief Clinical Officer
Web address: www.fhnorthpinellas.com/
Control: Church–operated, Nongovernment, not–for profit **Service:** General
Medical and Surgical

Staffed Beds: 168 **Admissions:** 3558 **Census:** 65 **Births:** 395 **Total
Expense ($000):** 91859 **Payroll Expense ($000):** 32115

TAVARES—Lake County

⊞ **FLORIDA HOSPITAL WATERMAN (100057)**, 1000 Waterman Way,
Zip 32778–5266; tel. 352/253–3333 **A**1 2 10 **F**3 11 13 15 17 18 20 22 24
26 28 29 30 31 32 34 35 36 37 40 45 49 50 53 54 55 56 57 59 62 64 66
70 74 75 76 77 78 79 81 85 86 87 89 91 93 107 108 110 111 114 115 116
117 118 119 120 121 123 124 126 130 132 143 144 146 147 148 **P**8
S Adventist Health System Sunbelt Health Care Corporation, Altamonte
Springs, FL
Primary Contact: David Ottati, Chief Executive Officer
COO: Anita Young, Chief Operating Officer
CFO: Frances H. Crunk, Vice President and Chief Financial Officer
CMO: Vinay Mehindru, M.D., Vice President/Chief Medical Officer
CHR: Madge Springer, Director Human Resources
CNO: Patricia R. Dolan, R.N., Vice President/ Chief Nursing Officer
Web address: www.fhwat.org
Control: Church–operated, Nongovernment, not–for profit **Service:** General
Medical and Surgical

Staffed Beds: 269 **Admissions:** 14859 **Census:** 188 **Outpatient Visits:**
117881 **Births:** 575 **Total Expense ($000):** 218083 **Payroll Expense
($000):** 80316 **Personnel:** 1523

TAVERNIER—Monroe County

⊞ **BAPTIST HEALTH SOUTH FLORIDA, MARINERS HOSPITAL (101313)**, 91500
Overseas Highway, Zip 33070–2547; tel. 305/434–3000 **A**1 10 18 **F**3 11 15
18 28 29 30 31 34 35 40 45 47 50 53 57 59 68 70 74 75 78 79 81 84 85
93 97 102 107 108 110 111 114 115 119 129 130 131 132 133 145 146
147 148 **P**8 **S** Baptist Health South Florida, Coral Gables, FL
Primary Contact: Rick Freeburg, Chief Executive Officer
CFO: Erik Long, Controller
CIO: Mimi Taylor, Vice President Information Technology
CHR: John Williamson, Human Resources Site Manager
Web address: www.baptisthealth.net/en/facilities/mariners–hospital/Pages/
default.aspx
Control: Other not–for–profit (including NFP Corporation) **Service:** General
Medical and Surgical

Staffed Beds: 25 **Admissions:** 663 **Census:** 7 **Outpatient Visits:** 37956
Births: 0 **Total Expense ($000):** 48132 **Payroll Expense ($000):** 14830
Personnel: 204

THE VILLAGES—Sumter County

⊞ **THE VILLAGES REGIONAL HOSPITAL (100290)**, 1451 El Camino Real,
Zip 32159–0041; tel. 352/751–8000 **A**1 2 10 **F**3 8 11 15 18 20 22 24 28 29
30 31 34 35 40 45 51 54 57 59 64 68 70 74 75 77 78 79 81 84 85 87 93
107 108 110 111 114 115 116 119 130 132 135 144 146 **P**6 **S** Central
Florida Health, Leesburg, FL
Primary Contact: Donald G. Henderson, FACHE, President and Chief Executive
Officer
COO: Saad Ehtisham, R.N., Vice President and Chief Operating Officer
CFO: Diane P. Harden, Senior Vice President and Chief Financial Officer
CHR: Amie Richason, Vice President Human Resources
CNO: Mary Jane Curry–Pelyak, R.N., Vice President and Chief Clinical Officer
Web address: www.cfhalliance.org
Control: Other not–for–profit (including NFP Corporation) **Service:** General
Medical and Surgical

Staffed Beds: 277 **Admissions:** 13959 **Census:** 163 **Outpatient Visits:**
69230 **Births:** 0 **Total Expense ($000):** 148974 **Payroll Expense ($000):**
55306 **Personnel:** 946

TITUSVILLE—Brevard County

☐ **PARRISH MEDICAL CENTER (100028)**, 951 North Washington Avenue,
Zip 32796–2163; tel. 321/268–6111 **A**1 2 10 **F**3 11 13 15 18 20 22 28 29
30 34 35 40 45 47 50 51 53 54 56 57 59 60 62 64 68 69 70 74 75 76 77
78 79 80 81 82 83 84 85 86 87 89 92 93 94 107 108 110 111 116 126 129
130 132 134 135 143 144 146 147 148
Primary Contact: George Mikitarian, Jr., FACHE, President and Chief Executive
Officer
CFO: Timothy K. Skeldon, Senior Vice President and Chief Financial Officer
CMO: Lisa Alexanda, M.D., Vice President Medical Affairs
CIO: William Moore, Chief Information Officer
CHR: Roberta Chaildin, Manager Human Resources
Web address: www.parrishmed.com
Control: Hospital district or authority, Government, nonfederal **Service:** General
Medical and Surgical

Staffed Beds: 163 **Admissions:** 6724 **Census:** 77 **Births:** 640 **Total
Expense ($000):** 175875 **Payroll Expense ($000):** 65496

TRINITY—Pasco County

COMMUNITY HOSPITAL See Medical Center of Trinity

⊞ **MEDICAL CENTER OF TRINITY (100191)**, 9330 State Road 54,
Zip 34655–1808; tel. 727/834–4900 **A**1 2 10 **F**8 11 13 15 18 20 22 26 29
30 31 34 35 38 40 45 46 47 48 49 57 59 60 67 68 70 74 75 76 77 78 79
80 81 82 84 85 86 87 93 94 98 102 103 107 108 110 111 119 126 130
132 135 144 147 148 **S** HCA, Nashville, TN
Primary Contact: Leigh Massengill, Chief Executive Officer
COO: Kenneth West, Chief Operating Officer
CFO: Michael Wyers, Chief Financial Officer
CMO: Linda Badillo, M.D., Chief of Medical Staff
CIO: Kurt Hornung, Director
CHR: Christena Miano, Human Resources Director
CNO: Nancy Maysilles, R.N., Chief Nursing Officer
Web address: www.medicalcentertrinity.com
Control: Corporation, Investor–owned, for–profit **Service:** General Medical and
Surgical

Staffed Beds: 276 **Admissions:** 13943 **Census:** 171 **Births:** 1119 **Total
Expense ($000):** 198461 **Payroll Expense ($000):** 64544

FL

Many Facility Codes have changed. Please refer to the AHA Guide Code Chart. © 2016 AHA Guide

VENICE—Sarasota County

✠ **VENICE REGIONAL BAYFRONT HEALTH (100070)**, 540 The Rialto, Zip 34285–2900; tel. 941/485–7711 **A**1 10 **F**3 8 11 12 15 17 18 20 22 24 26 28 29 30 31 34 35 37 40 42 45 46 47 49 50 51 54 56 57 59 64 70 74 77 78 79 81 82 87 93 96 107 108 110 111 114 118 119 126 129 130 144 146 148 **S** Community Health Systems, Inc., Franklin, TN
Primary Contact: John R. McLain, Chief Executive Officer
COO: Kristen Gentry, Chief Operating Officer
CFO: Osman Gruhonjic, Chief Financial Officer
CIO: Eloy Rivas, Director of Information Systems
CHR: John Ware, Director of Human Resources
CNO: Walter A. Pannone, Chief Nursing Officer
Web address: www.veniceregional.com
Control: Corporation, Investor–owned, for–profit **Service:** General Medical and Surgical

Staffed Beds: 221 **Admissions:** 9559 **Census:** 109 **Outpatient Visits:** 100453 **Births:** 0 **Total Expense ($000):** 142350 **Payroll Expense ($000):** 49146 **Personnel:** 831

VERO BEACH—Indian River County

✠ **HEALTHSOUTH TREASURE COAST REHABILITATION HOSPITAL (103032)**, 1600 37th Street, Zip 32960–4863; tel. 772/778–2100, (Nonreporting) **A**1 10 **S** HEALTHSOUTH Corporation, Birmingham, AL
Primary Contact: Michael Kissner, Chief Executive Officer
CFO: Kevin Hardy, Chief Financial Officer
CMO: Jimmy Wayne Lockhart, M.D., Medical Director
CHR: Linda Rinehart, Director Human Resources
Web address: www.healthsouthtreasurecoast.com
Control: Corporation, Investor–owned, for–profit **Service:** Rehabilitation

Staffed Beds: 80

✠ **INDIAN RIVER MEDICAL CENTER (100105)**, 1000 36th Street, Zip 32960–6592; tel. 772/567–4311, (Includes BEHAVIORAL HEALTH CENTER, 1190 37th Street, Zip 32960–6507; tel. 772/563–4666; Jeffrey L. Susi, President and Chief Executive Officer) **A**1 2 10 **F**3 11 12 13 15 17 18 20 22 24 26 28 29 30 31 34 35 37 40 44 45 46 47 48 49 50 51 57 58 59 60 61 64 70 74 75 76 77 78 79 80 81 82 83 84 85 86 87 89 92 93 96 97 98 99 100 101 102 103 104 107 108 110 111 114 115 116 117 118 119 120 121 124 126 129 130 131 132 135 144 146 147 148 **P**6
Primary Contact: Jeffrey L. Susi, President and Chief Executive Officer
COO: Steven Salyer, Senior Vice President and Chief Operating Officer
CFO: Greg Gardner, Senior Vice President and Chief Financial Officer
CMO: Charles Mackett, M.D., Senior Vice President and Chief Medical Officer
CIO: William Neil, Vice President and Chief Information Officer
CNO: Lynn Hubbard, R.N., Vice President and Chief Nursing Officer
Web address: www.irmc.cc
Control: Other not–for–profit (including NFP Corporation) **Service:** General Medical and Surgical

Staffed Beds: 220 **Admissions:** 14033 **Census:** 170 **Outpatient Visits:** 126555 **Births:** 1018 **Total Expense ($000):** 223504 **Payroll Expense ($000):** 104332 **Personnel:** 1591

WAUCHULA—Hardee County

✠ **FLORIDA HOSPITAL WAUCHULA (101300)**, 533 West Carlton Street, Zip 33873–3407; tel. 863/773–3101 **A**1 10 18 **F**3 29 30 40 107 110 111 119 127 129 130 133 **P**6 **S** Adventist Health System Sunbelt Health Care Corporation, Altamonte Springs, FL
Primary Contact: Denise Grimsley, R.N., Vice President and Administrator
CFO: Rosalie Oliver, Senior Vice President and Chief Financial Officer
CMO: Jorge F. Gonzalez, M.D., Vice President and Chief Nursing Officer
CIO: Jeff McDonald, Information Technology Manager
CHR: Michelle F. Myers, Director Human Resources
CNO: Gloria N. Santos, R.N., Vice President and Chief Nursing Officer
Web address: www.fh.floridahospital.com/heartland/home.aspx
Control: Church–operated, Nongovernment, not–for profit **Service:** General Medical and Surgical

Staffed Beds: 25 **Admissions:** 641 **Census:** 22 **Outpatient Visits:** 25403 **Births:** 0 **Total Expense ($000):** 22233 **Payroll Expense ($000):** 8121 **Personnel:** 104

WESLEY CHAPEL—Pasco County

★ ◇ **FLORIDA HOSPITAL WESLEY CHAPEL (100319)**, 2600 Bruce B. Downs Bouelvard, Zip 33544–9207; tel. 813/929–5000 **A**5 10 21 **F**3 11 13 15 18 20 22 26 29 30 34 35 40 45 46 47 49 51 53 57 59 64 70 74 75 76 77 79 81 85 87 93 107 108 109 110 111 115 117 119 120 126 130 132 145 146 **S** Adventist Health System Sunbelt Health Care Corporation, Altamonte Springs, FL
Primary Contact: Denyse Bales–Chubb, President and Chief Executive Officer
Web address: www.https://www.floridahospital.com/wesley–chapel
Control: Other not–for–profit (including NFP Corporation) **Service:** General Medical and Surgical

Staffed Beds: 83 **Admissions:** 5643 **Census:** 57 **Outpatient Visits:** 58477 **Births:** 433 **Total Expense ($000):** 122230 **Payroll Expense ($000):** 39152 **Personnel:** 651

□ **NORTH TAMPA BEHAVIORAL HEALTH (104075)**, 29910 State Road 56, Zip 33543–8800; tel. 813/922–3300, (Nonreporting) **A**1 10 **S** Acadia Healthcare Company, Inc., Franklin, TN
Primary Contact: Jameson Norton, Chief Executive Officer
Web address: www.northtampabehavioralhealth.com
Control: Corporation, Investor–owned, for–profit **Service:** Psychiatric

Staffed Beds: 75

WEST PALM BEACH—Palm Beach County

✠ **GOOD SAMARITAN MEDICAL CENTER (100287)**, 1309 North Flagler Drive, Zip 33401–3499; tel. 561/655–5511, (Nonreporting) **A**1 2 5 10 **S** TENET Healthcare Corporation, Dallas, TX
Primary Contact: Mark Nosacka, Chief Executive Officer
CFO: Cynthia McCauley, Chief Financial Officer
CIO: Candace Helms, Director Information Services
CHR: Amy Linsin, Chief Human Resources Officer
Web address: www.goodsamaritanmc.com
Control: Corporation, Investor–owned, for–profit **Service:** General Medical and Surgical

Staffed Beds: 174

□ **JEROME GOLDEN CENTER FOR BEHAVIORAL HEALTH, INC. (104008)**, 1041 45th Street, Zip 33407–2494; tel. 561/383–8000, (Nonreporting) **A**1 10
Primary Contact: Linda De Piano, Ph.D., Chief Executive Officer
CFO: America Cordoves, Controller
CMO: Suresh Rajpara, M.D., Chief Medical Officer
CIO: Iris Garcia, Director, Information Services
CHR: Nadine Wilson, Manager, Human Resources
CNO: Holly Horvath, Director of Nursing
Web address: www.goldenctr.org
Control: Other not–for–profit (including NFP Corporation) **Service:** Psychiatric

Staffed Beds: 44

✠ ○ **JFK MEDICAL CENTER NORTH CAMPUS (100234)**, 2201 45th Street, Zip 33407–2047; tel. 561/842–6141 **A**1 10 11 **F**3 29 34 35 40 45 49 57 59 60 70 79 81 82 93 98 99 101 102 103 104 105 107 110 111 119 146 148 **S** HCA, Nashville, TN
Primary Contact: Dana C. Oaks, Chief Executive Officer
COO: Patrick Chapman, Assistant Vice President Operations
CMO: Paul Seltzer, M.D., Chief of Staff
CIO: Kenneth Vasquez, Associate Director
CHR: Donna Boyle, Director
CNO: Geraldine DeStefano, R.N., Chief Nursing Officer
Web address: www.westpalmhospital.com
Control: Corporation, Investor–owned, for–profit **Service:** General Medical and Surgical

Staffed Beds: 245 **Admissions:** 9335 **Census:** 111 **Births:** 0 **Total Expense ($000):** 91239 **Payroll Expense ($000):** 31318

FL

Hospital, Medicare Provider Number, Address, Telephone, Approval, Facility, and Physician Codes, Health Care System

★ American Hospital Association (AHA) membership   ○ Healthcare Facilities Accreditation Program   ⇑ Center for Improvement in Healthcare Quality Accreditation
□ The Joint Commission accreditation   ◇ DNV Healthcare Inc. accreditation   △ Commission on Accreditation of Rehabilitation Facilities (CARF) accreditation

☒ △ **ST. MARY'S MEDICAL CENTER (100288)**, 901 45th Street,
Zip 33407–2495; tel. 561/844–6300, (Includes PALM BEACH CHILDREN'S
HOSPITAL, 901 45th Street, Zip 33407; tel. 561/844–6300) **A**1 7 10 **F**3 6 8 11
12 13 15 17 18 19 20 21 22 23 24 25 29 30 31 34 35 38 39 40 41 43 44
45 47 48 49 50 51 56 57 58 59 60 64 65 68 70 72 73 74 75 76 77 78 79
81 85 86 87 88 89 90 92 93 94 96 98 100 101 102 103 107 108 110 111
114 115 119 121 123 130 131 132 134 135 146 147 148 **S** TENET
Healthcare Corporation, Dallas, TX
Primary Contact: Gabrielle Finley–Hazle, Chief Executive Officer
COO: Joey Bulfin, R.N., Interim Chief Executive Officer
CFO: Tom Schlemmer, Chief Financial Officer
CMO: Jeffrey Davis, D.O., Chief Medical Officer
CIO: Rich Avato, Director
CHR: Thomas J. Piszczatoski, Chief Human Resource Officer
CNO: Donna Small, R.N., Chief Nursing Officer
Web address: www.stmarysmc.com
Control: Corporation, Investor–owned, for–profit **Service:** General Medical and
Surgical

Staffed Beds: 464 **Admissions:** 17919 **Census:** 256 **Births:** 3416 **Total Expense ($000):** 272675 **Payroll Expense ($000):** 102259

VETERANS AFFAIRS MEDICAL CENTER See West Palm Beach Veterans Affairs
Medical Center

☐ **WELLINGTON REGIONAL MEDICAL CENTER (100275)**, 10101 Forest Hill
Boulevard, Zip 33414–6199; tel. 561/798–8500, (Nonreporting) **A**1 10 12 13
S Universal Health Services, Inc., King of Prussia, PA
Primary Contact: Robbin Lee, Chief Executive Officer
COO: Pamela S. Tahan, Chief Operating Officer
CFO: Joseph Paul, Chief Financial Officer
CMO: Richard Hays, M.D., Chief of Staff
CIO: Pierre Bergeron, Director Information Services
CHR: Mary Jo Caracciolo, Director Human Resources
CNO: Asenath Cassel, Chief Nursing Officer
Web address: www.wellingtonregional.com
Control: Corporation, Investor–owned, for–profit **Service:** General Medical and
Surgical

Staffed Beds: 158

☒ **WEST PALM BEACH VETERANS AFFAIRS MEDICAL CENTER**, 7305 North
Military Trail, Zip 33410–6400; tel. 561/422–8262, (Nonreporting) **A**1 3 5
S Department of Veterans Affairs, Washington, DC
Primary Contact: Charleen R. Szabo, FACHE, Director
CFO: Lori Hancock, Chief Business Officer
CMO: Deepak Mandi, M.D., Chief of Staff
CIO: Karen Gabaldon, Chief Management Information Systems
CHR: David Green, Chief Human Resources
Web address: www.westpalmbeach.va.gov/
Control: Veterans Affairs, Government, federal **Service:** General Medical and
Surgical

Staffed Beds: 297

WESTON—Broward County

☒ **CLEVELAND CLINIC FLORIDA (100289)**, 2950 Cleveland Clinic Boulevard,
Zip 33331–3602; tel. 954/659–5000 **A**1 2 3 5 10 **F**3 8 9 11 12 15 17 18 20
22 24 26 28 29 30 31 34 35 36 37 39 40 41 44 45 46 47 48 49 50 51 54
55 56 57 58 59 60 61 63 64 65 68 70 74 75 77 78 79 80 81 82 84 85 86
87 91 92 93 96 97 100 107 108 109 110 111 114 115 116 117 119 120
126 129 130 131 132 135 137 138 139 141 145 146 147 148 **P**6
S Cleveland Clinic Health System, Cleveland, OH
Primary Contact: Wael Barsoum, President
CFO: Keith Nilsson, Chief Financial Officer
CMO: Raul Rosenthal, M.D., Interim Chief of Staff
CIO: John Santangelo, Director Information Technology
CHR: Jackie Puntel, Senior Director Human Resources
CNO: Kerry Major, R.N., Chief Nursing Officer
Web address: www.clevelandclinic.org/florida
Control: Other not–for–profit (including NFP Corporation) **Service:** General
Medical and Surgical

Staffed Beds: 155 **Admissions:** 10500 **Census:** 125 **Outpatient Visits:**
57152 **Births:** 0 **Total Expense ($000):** 213993 **Payroll Expense ($000):**
78961 **Personnel:** 2350

WILLISTON—Levy County

NATURE COAST REGIONAL HOSPITAL See Regional General Hospital

REGIONAL GENERAL HOSPITAL (100322), 125 S.W. Seventh Street,
Zip 32696–2403; tel. 352/528–2801, (Nonreporting) **A**10
Primary Contact: Devaiah Pagidipati, M.D., Chief Executive Officer
CFO: Barbara Miller, Manager Business Office
CMO: Jeremie Young, M.D., Chief of Staff
CHR: Karla Dass, Director Human Resources
Web address: www.regionalgeneral.com/
Control: Partnership, Investor–owned, for–profit **Service:** General Medical and
Surgical

Staffed Beds: 20

WINTER HAVEN—Polk County

☒ △ **WINTER HAVEN HOSPITAL (100052)**, 200 Avenue F. N.E.,
Zip 33881–4193; tel. 863/293–1121 **A**1 7 10 19 **F**3 8 11 13 14 15 17 18 20
22 24 26 28 29 30 31 34 40 47 49 57 58 59 60 64 68 70 72 73 74 75 76
77 78 79 81 82 84 85 86 87 89 90 93 94 98 100 101 102 104 107 108 110
111 114 115 119 120 121 123 126 130 132 135 144 146 147 148 **P**6 7
S Trinity Health, Livonia, MI
Primary Contact: Stephen A. Nierman, President
COO: Jacques Vasconcellos, Director, Operations
CFO: Tina Solomon, Executive Director Finance
CMO: Khurram Kamran, M.D., Vice President, Physician Services
CIO: Cal Cole, Director Information Systems
CHR: Rosemary Myers, Manager, Team Resources
CNO: Carol Koeppel–Olsen, Vice President, Patient Care Services
Web address: www.winterhavenhospital.org
Control: Other not–for–profit (including NFP Corporation) **Service:** General
Medical and Surgical

Staffed Beds: 350 **Admissions:** 16915 **Census:** 218 **Outpatient Visits:**
117866 **Births:** 1548 **Total Expense ($000):** 259157 **Payroll Expense
($000):** 116112 **Personnel:** 2113

WINTER PARK—Orange County

WINTER PARK MEMORIAL HOSPITAL See Florida Hospital, Orlando

ZEPHYRHILLS—Pasco County

☒ **FLORIDA HOSPITAL ZEPHYRHILLS (100046)**, 7050 Gall Boulevard,
Zip 33541–1399; tel. 813/788–0411 **A**1 5 10 **F**3 12 13 14 15 17 18 20 22
24 26 28 29 30 31 32 34 35 37 40 44 45 46 47 48 49 51 53 54 56 57 59
60 62 63 64 68 70 74 76 77 79 81 82 83 86 87 91 92 93 97 107 108 110
111 114 116 119 124 126 129 130 132 133 135 146 147 148 **S** Adventist
Health System Sunbelt Health Care Corporation, Altamonte Springs, FL
Primary Contact: Randy Surber, Chief Executive Officer
COO: Donald E. Welch, Chief Operating Officer
CFO: Bill Heinrich, Chief Financial Officer
CMO: Hugar McNamee, D.O., Chief Medical Officer
CIO: Kelley Sasser, Director Information Systems
CHR: Laura Asaftei, Administrative Director
CNO: Gwen Alonso, Chief Nursing Officer
Web address: www.fhzeph.org
Control: Church–operated, Nongovernment, not–for profit **Service:** General
Medical and Surgical

Staffed Beds: 139 **Admissions:** 8348 **Census:** 92 **Outpatient Visits:** 99199
Births: 578 **Total Expense ($000):** 134069 **Payroll Expense ($000):** 49928
Personnel: 854

FL

GEORGIA

ADEL—Cook County

✠ **COOK MEDICAL CENTER–A CAMPUS OF TIFT REGIONAL MEDICAL CENTER (110101)**, 706 North Parrish Avenue, Zip 31620–1511; tel. 229/896–8000, (Total facility includes 95 beds in nursing home–type unit) **A**1 10 **F**11 15 29 30 34 35 40 45 46 47 56 57 59 63 64 65 68 75 77 81 84 85 86 87 93 97 98 101 103 104 107 108 110 111 114 118 119 127 129 130 133 135 146 147 148 **P**6 **S** Tift Regional Health System, Tifton, GA
Primary Contact: Michael L. Purvis, Chief Executive Officer
COO: Kim Wills, Chief Operating Officer
CIO: Barry Medley, Director Information Systems
CHR: Shirley Padgett, Director Human Resources
Web address: www.cookmedicalcenter.com
Control: Hospital district or authority, Government, nonfederal **Service:** General Medical and Surgical

Staffed Beds: 155 **Admissions:** 666 **Census:** 96 **Outpatient Visits:** 16542 **Births:** 0 **Total Expense ($000):** 19016 **Payroll Expense ($000):** 8315 **Personnel:** 201

ALBANY—Dougherty County

★ ◇ **PHOEBE PUTNEY MEMORIAL HOSPITAL (110007)**, 417 West Third Avenue, Zip 31701–1943, Mailing Address: P.O. Box 3770, Zip 31706–3770; tel. 229/312–4100, (Includes PHOEBE NORTH, 2000 Palmyra Road, Zip 31701–1528, Mailing Address: P.O. Box 1908, Zip 31702–1908; tel. 229/434–2000) **A**2 3 5 10 21 **F**3 5 7 11 12 13 15 17 18 20 22 24 26 28 29 30 31 34 35 40 45 46 49 50 51 53 54 56 57 59 60 62 63 64 68 70 72 73 74 75 76 77 78 79 81 82 83 84 85 86 87 89 90 91 92 93 94 96 97 98 100 101 102 103 104 105 107 108 110 111 114 115 116 117 118 119 120 121 123 124 126 127 129 130 131 132 134 135 136 144 145 146 147 148 **P**1 7 **S** Phoebe Putney Health System, Albany, GA
Primary Contact: Joel Wernick, President and Chief Executive Officer
COO: Joe Austin, Executive Vice President and Chief Operating Officer
CFO: Kerry Loudermilk, Senior Vice President and Chief Financial Officer
CMO: Frank Middleton, M.D., Interim Chief Medical Officer
CIO: Jesse Diaz, Chief Information Officer
CHR: David J. Baranski, Vice President Human Resources
CNO: Laura Shearer, R.N., Senior Vice President and Chief Nursing Officer
Web address: www.phoebeputney.com
Control: Other not–for–profit (including NFP Corporation) **Service:** General Medical and Surgical

Staffed Beds: 526 **Admissions:** 19504 **Census:** 293 **Outpatient Visits:** 1126012 **Births:** 2346 **Total Expense ($000):** 503609 **Payroll Expense ($000):** 144151 **Personnel:** 2597

ALMA—Bacon County

✠ **BACON COUNTY HOSPITAL AND HEALTH SYSTEM (111327)**, 302 South Wayne Street, Zip 31510–2922, Mailing Address: P.O. Drawer 1987, Zip 31510–0987; tel. 912/632–8961, (Total facility includes 88 beds in nursing home–type unit) **A**1 10 18 **F**13 15 29 34 35 40 45 48 50 56 57 59 64 70 79 81 93 107 110 111 114 117 119 127 128 129 133 146
Primary Contact: Cindy R. Turner, Chief Executive Officer
COO: Cindy R. Turner, Chief Executive Officer
CFO: Kyle Kimmel, Chief Financial Officer
CMO: Lou Ellen Hutcheson, M.D., Chief of Staff
CIO: Neil O'Steen, Director Information Technology
CHR: Kerry Hancock, Director Human Resources
CNO: Deanna Hoff, R.N., Director of Nursing
Web address: www.baconcountyhospital.com
Control: Hospital district or authority, Government, nonfederal **Service:** General Medical and Surgical

Staffed Beds: 113 **Admissions:** 1078 **Census:** 11 **Outpatient Visits:** 16293 **Births:** 151 **Total Expense ($000):** 32425 **Payroll Expense ($000):** 11738 **Personnel:** 450

AMERICUS—Sumter County

★ ◇ **PHOEBE SUMTER MEDICAL CENTER (110044)**, 126 Highway 280 West, Zip 31719; tel. 229/924–6011 **A**10 21 **F**3 8 11 12 13 15 29 31 34 35 40 41 49 53 57 60 63 64 70 74 75 76 78 79 81 85 92 97 107 108 111 127 129 130 141 146 **S** Phoebe Putney Health System, Albany, GA
Primary Contact: Brandi Lunneborg, Chief Executive Officer
CHR: Cassandra Haynes, Supervisor Human Resources and Employment
CNO: Susan Bruns, Chief Nursing Officer
Web address: www.phoebesumter.org
Control: Other not–for–profit (including NFP Corporation) **Service:** General Medical and Surgical

Staffed Beds: 44 **Admissions:** 2923 **Census:** 28 **Outpatient Visits:** 76974 **Births:** 449 **Total Expense ($000):** 59957 **Payroll Expense ($000):** 16849

ATHENS—Clarke County

✠ **ATHENS REGIONAL MEDICAL CENTER (110074)**, 1199 Prince Avenue, Zip 30606–2797; tel. 706/475–7000 **A**1 2 3 10 **F**3 8 11 13 15 17 18 20 22 24 26 28 29 30 31 32 34 35 36 40 43 45 46 47 48 49 50 51 54 55 56 57 58 59 60 61 62 68 70 71 72 73 74 76 77 78 79 80 81 83 84 85 86 87 89 91 92 93 94 96 100 102 107 108 110 111 115 116 117 118 119 120 121 123 124 129 130 131 132 135 145 146 147 148
Primary Contact: Charles A. Peck, M.D., Interim President and Chief Executive Officer
CFO: Wendy J. Cook, Senior Vice President and Chief Financial Officer
CMO: James L. Moore, M.D., Senior Vice President and Chief Medical Officer
CIO: Mike Koehler, Interim Chief Information Officer
CHR: Robert D. Finch, Vice President Human Resources
CNO: Lori Giles, Interim Chief Nursing Officer
Web address: www.armc.org
Control: Other not–for–profit (including NFP Corporation) **Service:** General Medical and Surgical

Staffed Beds: 338 **Admissions:** 19665 **Census:** 236 **Outpatient Visits:** 316033 **Births:** 2548 **Total Expense ($000):** 382500 **Payroll Expense ($000):** 146916 **Personnel:** 2279

☐ **LANDMARK HOSPITAL OF ATHENS (112017)**, 775 Sunset Drive, Zip 30606–2211; tel. 706/425–1500 **A**1 10 22 **F**1 3 29 45 119 130 148 **S** Landmark Hospitals, Cape Girardeau, MO
Primary Contact: Vivian Goff, R.N., Chief Executive Officer
Web address: www.landmarkhospitals.com
Control: Individual, Investor–owned, for–profit **Service:** Long–Term Acute Care hospital

Staffed Beds: 42 **Admissions:** 474 **Census:** 34 **Outpatient Visits:** 0 **Births:** 0 **Personnel:** 113

✠ △ **ST. MARY'S HEALTH CARE SYSTEM (110006)**, 1230 Baxter Street, Zip 30606–3791; tel. 706/389–3000 **A**1 3 7 10 **F**3 11 12 13 15 18 19 20 22 26 28 29 30 31 34 35 37 40 41 45 46 48 49 50 53 54 57 58 59 62 63 64 68 70 72 74 75 76 77 79 80 81 83 84 85 87 89 90 93 94 97 107 108 110 111 114 115 118 119 126 129 130 131 132 135 141 145 146 147 148 **P**5 **S** Trinity Health, Livonia, MI
Primary Contact: Donald McKenna, President and Chief Executive Officer
CFO: Marty Hutson, Chief Financial Officer
CMO: Bruce Middendorf, M.D., Chief Medical Officer
CIO: Kerry Vaughn, Chief Information Officer
CHR: Jeff English, Vice President Human Resources
CNO: Nina Evans, R.N., Vice President and Chief Nursing Officer
Web address: www.stmarysathens.com
Control: Church–operated, Nongovernment, not–for profit **Service:** General Medical and Surgical

Staffed Beds: 183 **Admissions:** 9060 **Census:** 120 **Outpatient Visits:** 188058 **Births:** 1407 **Total Expense ($000):** 170998 **Payroll Expense ($000):** 62978 **Personnel:** 1279

GA

Hospital, Medicare Provider Number, Address, Telephone, Approval, Facility, and Physician Codes, Health Care System

★ American Hospital Association (AHA) membership
☐ The Joint Commission accreditation
◯ Healthcare Facilities Accreditation Program
◇ DNV Healthcare Inc. accreditation
⇑ Center for Improvement in Healthcare Quality Accreditation
△ Commission on Accreditation of Rehabilitation Facilities (CARF) accreditation

ATLANTA—Fulton and De Kalb County

☐ **ANCHOR HOSPITAL (114032)**, 5454 Yorktowne Drive, Zip 30349–5317;
tel. 770/991–6044 **A**1 10 **F**4 98 99 103 105 130 **S** Universal Health Services,
Inc., King of Prussia, PA
Primary Contact: Randall G. Hines, Ph.D., Chief Executive Officer
CFO: John Kim, Chief Financial Officer
CMO: Athena Sotus–Nawar, M.D., Medical Director
CIO: Michael Delpleache, Specialist Information Technology
CHR: Rhian Sharp, Director Human Resources
CNO: Kim Butts, System Nurse Executive
Web address: www.anchorhospital.com
Control: Corporation, Investor–owned, for–profit **Service:** Psychiatric

Staffed Beds: 122 Admissions: 4436 Census: 102 Births: 0

☐ △ **CHILDREN'S HEALTHCARE OF ATLANTA (113301)**, 1600 Tullie Circle,
N.E., Zip 30329–2303; tel. 404/785–7000, (Includes CHILDREN'S HEALTHCARE
OF ATLANTA AT EGLESTON, 1600 Tullie Circle, Zip 30329; tel. 404/325–6000;
CHILDREN'S HEALTHCARE OF ATLANTA AT HUGHES SPALDING, 35 Jesse Hill Jr.
Drive, S.E., Zip 30303–3032; tel. 404/785–9500; CHILDREN'S HEALTHCARE OF
ATLANTA AT SCOTTISH RITE, 1001 Johnson Ferry Road N.E., Zip 30342–1600;
tel. 404/256–5252), (Nonreporting) **A**1 3 5 7 8 10
Primary Contact: Donna W. Hyland, President and Chief Executive Officer
COO: Carolyn Kenny, Executive Vice President Clinical Care
CFO: Ruth Fowler, Senior Vice President and Chief Financial Officer
CMO: Daniel Salinas, M.D., Senior Vice President and Chief Medical Officer
CIO: Allana Cummings, Chief Information Officer
CHR: Linda Matzigkeit, Senior Vice President Human Resources
Web address: www.choa.org
Control: Other not–for–profit (including NFP Corporation) **Service:** Children's
general

Staffed Beds: 496

✠ **EMORY REHABILITATION HOSPITAL (113031)**, 1441 Clifton Road N.E.,
Zip 30322–1004; tel. 404/712–5512 **A**1 10 **F**11 29 30 34 35 36 50 56 58 64
68 74 75 77 79 82 85 86 87 90 93 94 95 96 100 130 131 132 135 146 148
P6 **S** Emory Healthcare, Atlanta, GA
Primary Contact: Michael Eric Garrard, FACHE, Chief Executive Officer
CMO: S. Byron Milton, M.D., Medical Director
CHR: Janine Diaz, Human Resources Manager
CNO: Deborah Almauhy, R.N., Chief Nursing Officer
Web address: www.emoryhealthcare.org/rehabilitation
Control: Corporation, Investor–owned, for–profit **Service:** Rehabilitation

**Staffed Beds: 46 Admissions: 842 Census: 33 Outpatient Visits: 17072
Births: 0 Total Expense ($000): 19224 Payroll Expense ($000): 10731
Personnel: 160**

✠ **EMORY SAINT JOSEPH'S HOSPITAL OF ATLANTA (110082)**, 5665
Peachtree Dunwoody Road N.E., Zip 30342–1701; tel. 678/843–7001 **A**1 2 3
10 **F**3 11 15 17 18 20 22 24 26 28 29 30 31 34 35 37 40 44 45 46 47 49
50 51 53 54 55 57 58 59 60 64 68 70 71 74 75 77 78 79 81 82 84 85 87
93 107 108 110 111 114 115 117 119 120 121 123 124 126 130 132 135
145 146 147 148 **P**6 **S** Emory Healthcare, Atlanta, GA
Primary Contact: Heather Dexter, Chief Executive Officer
CFO: Kevin Brenan, Chief Financial Officer
CMO: Paul Scheinberg, M.D., Chief of Staff
CIO: Dedra Cantrell, Chief Information Officer
CHR: Audra Farish, Vice President Human Resources
Web address: www.stjosephsatlanta.org
Control: Other not–for–profit (including NFP Corporation) **Service:** General
Medical and Surgical

**Staffed Beds: 262 Admissions: 14577 Census: 194 Outpatient Visits:
114120 Births: 0 Total Expense ($000): 306992 Payroll Expense ($000):
97138 Personnel: 1475**

✠ **EMORY UNIVERSITY HOSPITAL (110010)**, 1364 Clifton Road N.E.,
Zip 30322; tel. 404/712–2000, (Includes EMORY UNIVERSITY ORTHOPAEDIC
AND SPINE HOSPITAL, 1455 Montreal Road, Tucker, Zip 30084;
tel. 404/251–3600; June Conner, R.N., Chief Operating Officer; EMORY WESLEY
WOODS GERIATRIC HOSPITAL, 1821 Clifton Road N.E., Atlanta, Zip 30329–4021;
tel. 404/728–6200; Jennifer Schuck, Associate Administrator) **A**1 2 3 5 8 10 **F**3
11 15 17 18 20 22 24 26 28 29 30 31 34 35 36 38 39 40 44 45 46 47
48 49 50 55 56 57 58 59 60 61 63 64 68 70 74 75 77 78 79 80 81 82 84
85 86 87 93 98 100 101 102 103 104 105 107 108 110 111 114 115 116
117 118 119 120 121 123 124 126 129 130 131 132 135 136 137 138 139
140 141 142 145 146 147 148 **P**6 **S** Emory Healthcare, Atlanta, GA
Primary Contact: Bryce D. Gartland, M.D., Chief Executive Officer
CFO: Greg E. Anderson, Chief Financial Officer, Emory Health System
CMO: Ira Horowitz, M.D., Chief Medical Officer
CIO: Dedra Cantrell, Chief Information Officer
CHR: Mary Beth Allen, Vice President Human Resources
CNO: Nancye R. Feistritzer, Chief Nursing Officer
Web address: www.emoryhealthcare.org
Control: Other not–for–profit (including NFP Corporation) **Service:** General
Medical and Surgical

**Staffed Beds: 548 Admissions: 25686 Census: 442 Outpatient Visits:
163835 Births: 0 Total Expense ($000): 743314 Payroll Expense ($000):
227718 Personnel: 3667**

✠ **EMORY UNIVERSITY HOSPITAL MIDTOWN (110078)**, 550 Peachtree Street
N.E., Zip 30308–2247; tel. 404/686–4411 **A**1 2 3 5 8 10 **F**3 11 12 13 15 17
18 20 22 24 26 28 29 30 31 34 35 36 38 40 44 45 46 47 48 49 50 51 52
55 57 58 59 60 61 63 64 68 70 72 73 74 75 76 77 78 79 81 82 84 85 86
87 92 93 100 102 104 107 108 110 111 114 115 116 117 118 119 120
121 123 124 126 130 131 132 135 141 146 147 148 **P**6 **S** Emory
Healthcare, Atlanta, GA
Primary Contact: Daniel Owens, Chief Executive Officer
CMO: James P. Steinberg, M.D., Chief Medical Officer
CIO: Dedra Cantrell, Chief Information Officer
CHR: Dallis Howard–Crow, Chief Human Resources Officer
Web address: www.emoryhealthcare.org
Control: Other not–for–profit (including NFP Corporation) **Service:** General
Medical and Surgical

**Staffed Beds: 468 Admissions: 21588 Census: 356 Outpatient Visits:
207784 Births: 4240 Total Expense ($000): 625605 Payroll Expense
($000): 181711 Personnel: 2569**

✠ **GRADY MEMORIAL HOSPITAL (110079)**, 80 Jesse Hill Jr. Drive S.E.,
Zip 30303–3031, Mailing Address: P.O. Box 26189, Zip 31329–0386;
tel. 404/616–1000, (Total facility includes 261 beds in nursing home–type unit)
A1 2 3 5 8 10 **F**2 3 5 7 8 13 15 16 18 20 22 24 26 29 30 31 34 35 38 39
40 43 45 46 47 49 50 51 52 53 54 55 56 57 58 59 60 61 62 63 64 65 66
68 70 72 73 74 75 76 77 78 79 80 81 82 84 85 86 87 93 94 97 98 100
101 102 103 104 105 107 108 109 110 111 112 113 114 115 116 117 118
119 120 121 128 129 130 132 134 135 143 144 146 147 148
Primary Contact: John M. Haupert, FACHE, Chief Executive Officer
COO: Christopher R. Mosley, FACHE, Chief Operating Officer
CFO: Mark Meyer, Chief Financial Officer
CMO: Curtis Lewis, M.D., Chief of Staff
CIO: Ben McKeeby, Senior Vice President and Chief Information Officer
CHR: Larry A. Callahan, Senior Vice President Human Resources
CNO: Rhonda A. Scott, Ph.D., Chief Nursing Officer and Executive Vice President
Web address: www.gradyhealthsystem.org
Control: Other not–for–profit (including NFP Corporation) **Service:** General
Medical and Surgical

**Staffed Beds: 971 Admissions: 30336 Census: 780 Outpatient Visits:
655040 Births: 3086 Total Expense ($000): 897000 Payroll Expense
($000): 333502 Personnel: 4924**

✠ **SELECT SPECIALTY HOSPITAL MIDTOWN ATLANTA (112004)**, 705 Juniper
Street N.E., Zip 30308–1307; tel. 404/873–2871, (Nonreporting) **A**1 10
Primary Contact: Robert Russell, Chief Executive Officer
CFO: Michael Nelson, Chief Financial Officer
CMO: David N. DeRuyter, M.D., President Medical Staff
CHR: Armetria Gibson, Human Resources Generalist
Web address: www.kindredatlanta.com/
Control: Partnership, Investor–owned, for–profit **Service:** Long–Term Acute Care
hospital

Staffed Beds: 70

✠ **NORTHSIDE HOSPITAL (110161)**, 1000 Johnson Ferry Road N.E.,
Zip 30342–1611; tel. 404/851–8000 **A**1 2 3 10 **F**3 5 8 11 12 13 15 17 18 20
22 26 28 29 30 31 34 35 37 40 44 45 46 47 48 49 50 54 55 57 58 59 60
64 68 70 71 72 73 74 75 76 77 78 79 80 81 82 84 85 86 87 93 100 104
105 107 108 110 111 114 115 117 118 120 121 123 124 126 129 130
132 135 136 145 146 147 148 **S** Northside Healthcare System, Atlanta, GA
Primary Contact: Robert Quattrocchi, President and Chief Executive Officer
CFO: Debbie Mitcham, Chief Financial Officer
CIO: Tina Wakim, Vice President Information
Web address: www.northside.com
Control: Other not–for–profit (including NFP Corporation) **Service:** General
Medical and Surgical

**Staffed Beds: 601 Admissions: 34745 Census: 378 Outpatient Visits:
767592 Births: 16010 Total Expense ($000): 1603885 Payroll Expense
($000): 482804 Personnel: 8046**

☐ **PEACHFORD BEHAVIORAL HEALTH SYSTEM (114010)**, 2151 Peachford
Road, Zip 30338–6599; tel. 770/455–3200, (Nonreporting) **A**1 10 **S** Universal
Health Services, Inc., King of Prussia, PA
Primary Contact: Matthew Crouch, Chief Executive Officer and Managing Director
COO: Sharon Stackhouse, Assistant Administrator and Director Risk Management
CFO: April Hughes, Chief Financial Officer
CMO: Asaf Aleem, M.D., Medical Director
CHR: Clay Boyles, Director Human Resources
Web address: www.peachfordhospital.com
Control: Corporation, Investor–owned, for–profit **Service:** Psychiatric

Staffed Beds: 246

◇ **PIEDMONT HOSPITAL (110083)**, 1968 Peachtree Road N.W., Zip 30309–1281; tel. 404/605–5000 **A**2 3 5 10 21 **F**3 8 11 12 13 15 17 18 20 22 24 26 28 29 30 31 34 35 40 44 45 46 47 48 49 50 51 53 54 55 56 57 58 59 60 61 64 65 68 70 72 73 74 75 76 77 78 79 81 82 84 85 86 87 92 93 107 108 110 111 114 115 116 117 118 119 120 121 123 124 126 129 130 131 132 135 137 138 139 141 142 145 146 147 148 **P**1 6 **S** Piedmont Healthcare, Atlanta, GA
Primary Contact: Patrick M. Battey, M.D., Chief Executive Officer
COO: Ed Lovern, Chief Operating Officer
CFO: Sheryl Klink, Chief Financial Officer
CMO: Mark Cohen, M.D., Chief Medical Officer
CHR: Greg Prokopchak, Senior Director Human Resources
CNO: Kelly Hulsey, Chief Nursing Officer
Web address: www.piedmonthospital.org
Control: Other not–for–profit (including NFP Corporation) **Service:** General Medical and Surgical

Staffed Beds: 510 **Admissions:** 26818 **Census:** 384 **Outpatient Visits:** 343025 **Births:** 3443 **Personnel:** 3083

SAINT JOSEPH'S HOSPITAL OF ATLANTA See Emory Saint Joseph's Hospital of Atlanta

⊞ **SELECT SPECIALTY HOSPITAL – NORTHEAST ATLANTA (112005)**, 1821 Clifton Road N.E., 2nd Floor, Zip 30329–4021; tel. 404/728–6200, (Nonreporting) **A**1 10 **S** Select Medical Corporation, Mechanicsburg, PA
Primary Contact: Matthew Paul Pearson, Chief Executive Officer
CFO: Theodore Saunders, Assistant Controller
CMO: Jeffrey Mikell, M.D., Chief Medical Officer
CIO: Vicky Goziah, Software Administrator
CNO: Annette Branan, Chief Nursing Officer and Vice President Patient Care Services
Web address: www.selectspecialtyhospitals.com/
Control: Corporation, Investor–owned, for–profit **Service:** Long–Term Acute Care hospital

Staffed Beds: 18

⊞ **SELECT SPECIALTY HOSPITAL–ATLANTA (112009)**, 550 Peachtree Street N.E., Zip 30308–2247; tel. 404/815–0348, (Nonreporting) **A**1 10 **S** Select Medical Corporation, Mechanicsburg, PA
Primary Contact: Matthew Paul Pearson, Chief Executive Officer
Web address: www.selectspecialtyhospitals.com/company/locations/atlanta.aspx
Control: Corporation, Investor–owned, for–profit **Service:** Long–Term Acute Care hospital

Staffed Beds: 30

☐ **SHEPHERD CENTER (112003)**, 2020 Peachtree Road N.W., Zip 30309–1465; tel. 404/352–2020, (Nonreporting) **A**1 3 5 10
Primary Contact: Gary R. Ulicny, Ph.D., President and Chief Executive Officer
COO: Sarah Morrison, Vice President Clinical Services
CFO: Stephen B. Holleman, Chief Financial Officer
CMO: Donald P. Leslie, M.D., Medical Director
CIO: Brian Barnette, Chief Information Officer
CHR: Lorie Hutcheson, Vice President of Human Resources
CNO: Tamara King, R.N., Chief Nurse Executive
Web address: www.https://www.shepherd.org
Control: Other not–for–profit (including NFP Corporation) **Service:** Long–Term Acute Care hospital

Staffed Beds: 100

⊞ **WELLSTAR ATLANTA MEDICAL CENTER (110115)**, 303 Parkway Drive N.E., Zip 30312–1212; tel. 404/265–4000, (Includes ATLANTA MEDICAL CENTER – SOUTH CAMPUS, 1170 Cleveland Avenue, Zip 30344–3665; tel. 404/466–1170; Daniel Jackson, Chief Administrative Officer), (Nonreporting) **A**1 2 3 5 8 10 **S** WellStar Health System, Marietta, GA
Primary Contact: Kimberly Ryan, President
COO: Greg Brickner, Vice President and Director, Business Development
CFO: Sandra Albrecht, Interim Chief Financial Officer
CMO: Albert Barrocas, M.D., Chief Medical Officer
CIO: Maryland McCarty, Director Information Systems
CHR: Stacey J. Hancock, Vice President, Human Resources
CNO: Paula Yvonne Butts, Chief Nursing Officer
Web address: www.atlantamedcenter.com
Control: Corporation, Investor–owned, for–profit **Service:** General Medical and Surgical

Staffed Beds: 536

WESLEY WOODS GERIATRIC HOSPITAL OF EMORY UNIVERSITY See Emory Wesley Woods Geriatric Hospital

WESLEY WOODS LONG TERM CARE HOSPITAL See Select Specialty Hospital – Northeast Atlanta

AUGUSTA—Richmond County

⊞ **AUGUSTA UNIVERSITY MEDICAL CENTER (110034)**, 1120 15th Street, Zip 30912–0004; tel. 706/721–0211, (Includes CHILDREN'S HOSPITAL OF GEORGIA, 1446 Harper Street, Zip 30912–0012; tel. 706/721–5437; Peter Buckley, M.D., Interim Chief Executive Officer) **A**1 2 3 5 8 10 13 **F**3 4 12 13 14 15 17 18 19 20 21 22 23 24 25 26 27 28 29 30 31 32 33 34 35 40 41 43 45 46 47 48 49 50 52 54 55 56 57 58 59 60 61 64 65 66 68 70 71 72 73 74 75 76 77 78 79 81 82 85 86 87 88 89 90 91 92 93 97 98 100 101 102 103 104 106 107 108 109 110 111 112 113 114 115 116 117 118 119 120 121 122 123 124 126 127 129 130 131 132 134 135 136 138 141 142 145 146 147 148
Primary Contact: Lee Ann Liska, Chief Executive Officer
COO: Shawn Vincent, Interim Chief Operating Officer
CFO: Greg Damron, Vice President Finance and Chief Financial Officer
CMO: Kevin Dellsperger, M.D., Chief Medical Officer
CIO: Charles Enicks, Chief Information Officer
CHR: Susan Norton, Vice President Human Resources
CNO: Laura E. Brower, R.N., Chief Nursing Officer
Web address: www.grhealth.org
Control: State–Government, nonfederal **Service:** General Medical and Surgical

Staffed Beds: 430 **Admissions:** 18580 **Census:** 283 **Outpatient Visits:** 466505 **Births:** 976

⊞ △ **CHARLIE NORWOOD VETERANS AFFAIRS MEDICAL CENTER**, 1 Freedom Way, Zip 30904–6285; tel. 706/733–0188, (Nonreporting) **A**1 2 3 5 7 8 **S** Department of Veterans Affairs, Washington, DC
Primary Contact: Maria R. Andrews, MS, Director
COO: John D. Stenger, Acting Associate Director
CFO: Earline Corder, Chief Fiscal
CIO: Sandy Williford, Chief Health Information Management and Revenue Administration
CHR: Roger W. Buterbaugh, Chief Human Resources Officer
CNO: Michelle Cox–Henley, R.N., Associate Director for Patient and Nursing Services
Web address: www.augusta.va.gov/
Control: Veterans Affairs, Government, federal **Service:** General Medical and Surgical

Staffed Beds: 338

⊞ **DOCTORS HOSPITAL (110177)**, 3651 Wheeler Road, Zip 30909–6426; tel. 706/651–3232, (Nonreporting) **A**1 2 3 5 10 **S** HCA, Nashville, TN
Primary Contact: Douglas Welch, Chief Executive Officer
CIO: Dona Hornung, Director Information and Technology Services
Web address: www.doctors–hospital.net
Control: Corporation, Investor–owned, for–profit **Service:** General Medical and Surgical

Staffed Beds: 307

☐ **EAST CENTRAL REGIONAL HOSPITAL (114029)**, 3405 Mike Padgett Highway, Zip 30906–3897; tel. 706/790–2011, (Includes EAST CENTRAL REGIONAL HOSPITAL, 100 Myrtle Boulevard, Gracewood, Zip 30812–1299; tel. 706/790–2011), (Total facility includes 250 beds in nursing home–type unit) **A**1 3 5 10 **F**29 34 38 39 59 65 67 75 77 98 101 102 128 130 132 135 **P**6
Primary Contact: Paul Brock, Administrator
CFO: Candace Walker, Chief Financial Officer
Web address: www.dbhdd.ga.gov
Control: State–Government, nonfederal **Service:** Psychiatric

Staffed Beds: 411 **Admissions:** 809 **Census:** 350 **Outpatient Visits:** 0 **Births:** 0 **Total Expense ($000):** 51789 **Payroll Expense ($000):** 33780 **Personnel:** 1205

⊞ **HEALTHSOUTH WALTON REHABILITATION HOSPITAL (113030)**, 1355 Independence Drive, Zip 30901–1037; tel. 706/724–7746, (Nonreporting) **A**1 3 5 10 **S** HEALTHSOUTH Corporation, Birmingham, AL
Primary Contact: Eric Crossan, Chief Executive Officer
CMO: Pamela Salazar, M.D., Chief of Staff
CIO: Ann Keller, Supervisor Health Information Management
CHR: Volante Henderson, Director Human Resources
CNO: Lynn Beaulieu, R.N., Chief Nursing Officer
Web address: www.healthsouthwalton.com/
Control: Corporation, Investor–owned, for–profit **Service:** Rehabilitation

Staffed Beds: 58

MEDICAL COLLEGE OF GEORGIA HEALTH See Augusta University Medical Center

---

Hospital, Medicare Provider Number, Address, Telephone, Approval, Facility, and Physician Codes, Health Care System

★ American Hospital Association (AHA) membership
☐ The Joint Commission accreditation
○ Healthcare Facilities Accreditation Program
◇ DNV Healthcare Inc. accreditation
⇑ Center for Improvement in Healthcare Quality Accreditation
△ Commission on Accreditation of Rehabilitation Facilities (CARF) accreditation

GA

✠ **SELECT SPECIALTY HOSPITAL–AUGUSTA (112013)**, 1537 Walton Way,
Zip 30904–3764; tel. 706/731–1200, (Nonreporting) **A**1 10 **S** Select Medical
Corporation, Mechanicsburg, PA
Primary Contact: Curt L. Roberts, Chief Executive Officer
CHR: Terrie Richardson, Coordinator Human Resources
CNO: Kim Pippin, Chief Nursing Officer
Web address: www.augusta.selectspecialtyhospitals.com
Control: Corporation, Investor–owned, for–profit **Service:** Long–Term Acute Care
hospital

Staffed Beds: 80

✠ **TRINITY HOSPITAL OF AUGUSTA (110039)**, 2260 Wrightsboro Road,
Zip 30904–4726; tel. 706/481–7000, (Nonreporting) **A**1 3 10 **S** Quorum Health,
Brentwood, TN
Primary Contact: Jason A. Studley, FACHE, President and Chief Executive Officer
CFO: Rodney Sisk, Chief Financial Officer
CMO: C. Judson Pickett, Chief of Staff
CIO: Charlotte Choate, Director Information Systems
CHR: Diana Maxson, Director Human Resources
CNO: Debbie Spells–Wilson, R.N., Chief Nursing Officer
Web address: www.trinityofaugusta.com
Control: Corporation, Investor–owned, for–profit **Service:** General Medical and
Surgical

Staffed Beds: 105

✠ **UNIVERSITY HOSPITAL (110028)**, 1350 Walton Way, Zip 30901–2629;
tel. 706/722–9011 **A**1 2 3 5 10 **F**3 12 13 15 17 18 20 22 24 26 28 29 30 31
34 35 37 38 40 41 44 48 49 50 54 55 56 57 59 60 62 64 68 70 72 73 74
75 76 77 78 79 80 81 82 83 84 85 86 87 89 93 97 100 107 108 110 111
114 115 116 117 118 119 124 129 130 132 134 135 144 146 147 148 **P**8
S University Health Care System, Augusta, GA
Primary Contact: James R. Davis, Chief Executive Officer
COO: Marilyn A. Bowcutt, R.N., President and Chief Operating Officer
CFO: David Belkoski, Senior Vice President and Chief Financial Officer
CMO: William L. Farr, M.D., Chief Medical Officer
CIO: Shirley Gabriel, Vice President and Chief Information Officer
CHR: Laurie Ott, Vice President Human Resources and President University Health
Care Foundation
CNO: Lynda Watts, R.N., Vice President Patient Care Services
Web address: www.universityhealth.org
Control: Other not–for–profit (including NFP Corporation) **Service:** General
Medical and Surgical

Staffed Beds: 489 Admissions: 23486 Census: 308 Outpatient Visits:
471596 Births: 3210 Total Expense ($000): 419069 Payroll Expense
($000): 149841 Personnel: 2404

VETERANS AFFAIRS MEDICAL CENTER See Charlie Norwood Veterans Affairs
Medical Center

WALTON REHABILITATION HOSPITAL See HEALTHSOUTH Walton Rehabilitation
Hospital

AUSTELL—Cobb County

✠ △ **WELLSTAR COBB HOSPITAL (110143)**, 3950 Austell Road,
Zip 30106–1121; tel. 770/732–4000 **A**1 2 3 7 10 **F**3 4 11 13 15 16 17 18 20
22 26 28 29 30 31 37 38 40 41 44 45 48 49 50 51 53 54 55 58 59 60 61
64 65 66 68 70 72 73 74 75 76 77 79 80 81 82 84 85 86 87 90 93 94
96 97 98 99 100 101 102 103 104 105 106 107 108 110 111 114 115 118
119 120 121 123 124 126 130 132 135 141 146 147 148 **P**5 6 **S** WellStar
Health System, Marietta, GA
Primary Contact: Amy Frey Carrier, President
COO: Callie Andrews, Chief Operating Officer and Facility Compliance Officer
CFO: Darold Etheridge, Vice President and Chief Financial Officer
CMO: Thomas McNamara, D.O., Vice President Medical Affairs
CIO: Jonathan B. Morris, M.D., Senior Vice President and Chief Information Officer
CHR: Danyale Ziglor, Assistant Vice President Human Resources
CNO: Kay Kennedy, Chief Nurse Executive
Web address: www.wellstar.org
Control: Other not–for–profit (including NFP Corporation) **Service:** General
Medical and Surgical

Staffed Beds: 402 Admissions: 21205 Census: 263 Outpatient Visits:
212035 Births: 3592 Personnel: 1994

BAINBRIDGE—Decatur County

◇ **MEMORIAL HOSPITAL AND MANOR (110132)**, 1500 East Shotwell Street,
Zip 39819–4256; tel. 229/246–3500, (Nonreporting) **A**10 21
Primary Contact: William J. Walker, Jr., Chief Executive Officer
COO: Lee Harris, Assistant Administrator Support Services
CFO: Karen Faircloth, Chief Financial Officer
CMO: Shawn Surratt, M.D., Chief of Staff
CIO: Nelda Moore, Director Data Processing
CHR: Angel Sykes, Director Human Resources
CNO: Cynthia Vickers, R.N., Assistant Administrator for Nursing Services
Web address: www.mh–m.org
Control: Hospital district or authority, Government, nonfederal **Service:** General
Medical and Surgical

Staffed Beds: 80

BAXLEY—Appling County

◇ **APPLING HEALTHCARE SYSTEM (110071)**, 163 East Tollison Street,
Zip 31513–0120; tel. 912/367–9841, (Nonreporting) **A**10 20 21
Primary Contact: Raymond J. Leadbetter, Jr., Interim Chief Executive Officer
COO: Judy M. Long, R.N., Chief Nursing Officer and Chief Operating Officer
CFO: Raymond J. Leadbetter, Jr., Revenue Cycle Consultant
CMO: Garland Martin, M.D., Chief of Staff
CIO: Gary Gower, Chief Information Officer
CHR: Carla McLendon, Director Human Resources
CNO: Judy M. Long, R.N., Chief Nursing Officer and Chief Operating Officer
Web address: www.appling–hospital.org
Control: County–Government, nonfederal **Service:** General Medical and Surgical

Staffed Beds: 150

BLAIRSVILLE—Union County

★ ◇ **UNION GENERAL HOSPITAL (110051)**, 35 Hospital Road,
Zip 30512–3139; tel. 706/745–2111, (Total facility includes 150 beds in nursing
home–type unit) **A**10 20 21 **F**7 11 13 15 18 28 29 30 34 35 40 45 49 51 53
56 57 59 63 64 65 66 70 76 79 81 85 93 96 97 100 103 104 107 108 110
111 115 119 127 129 130 132 133 135 143 146 147 148 **S** Union General
Hospital, Inc., Blairsville, GA
Primary Contact: Lewis Kelley, Interim Chief Executive Officer
COO: Lewis Kelley, Chief Operating Officer
CFO: Stephanie L. Fletcher, CPA, Chief Financial Officer
CMO: Andre Schaeffer, M.D., Chief of Staff
CIO: Mike Johnston, Director Facilities Operations
CHR: Kathy Hood, Administrative Assistant Human Resources
CNO: Julia Barnett, Chief Nursing Officer
Web address: www.uniongeneralhospital.com
Control: Other not–for–profit (including NFP Corporation) **Service:** General
Medical and Surgical

Staffed Beds: 195 Admissions: 2464 Census: 161 Outpatient Visits: 43690
Births: 376 Total Expense ($000): 70217 Payroll Expense ($000): 30965
Personnel: 411

BLAKELY—Early County

★ ◇ **PIONEER COMMUNITY HOSPITAL OF EARLY (111314)**, 11740
Columbia Street, Zip 39823–2574; tel. 229/723–4241, (Total facility includes
110 beds in nursing home–type unit) **A**10 18 21 **F**3 7 15 29 30 34 39 40 41 45
57 59 62 63 64 68 77 91 98 101 103 104 107 119 127 128 129 130 132
133 135 143 **P**5 6 **S** Pioneer Health Services, Magee, MS
Primary Contact: Ginger Cushing, Chief Executive Officer
Web address: www.pchearly.com
Control: County–Government, nonfederal **Service:** General Medical and Surgical

Staffed Beds: 152 Admissions: 25 Census: 10 Outpatient Visits: 15000
Births: 0

BLUE RIDGE—Fannin County

✠ **FANNIN REGIONAL HOSPITAL (110189)**, 2855 Old Highway 5,
Zip 30513–6248; tel. 706/632–3711, (Nonreporting) **A**1 10 **S** Quorum Health,
Brentwood, TN
Primary Contact: David S. Sanders, Chief Executive Officer
CFO: Phillip Fouts, Chief Financial Officer
CIO: Timothy Snider, Manager Information Systems
CHR: Terrasina Ensley, Director Human Resources
CNO: Jason L. Jones, R.N., Chief Nursing Officer
Web address: www.fanninregionalhospital.com
Control: Corporation, Investor–owned, for–profit **Service:** General Medical and
Surgical

Staffed Beds: 50

BRASELTON—Hall County

✠ **NORTHEAST GEORGIA MEDICAL CENTER BRASELTON**, 1400 River Place,
Zip 30517–5600; tel. 770/219–9000, (Nonreporting)
Primary Contact: Carol H. Burrell, Chief Executive Officer
Web address: www.nghs.com/locations/braselton
Control: Other not–for–profit (including NFP Corporation) **Service:** General
Medical and Surgical

Staffed Beds: 100

GA

Many Facility Codes have changed. Please refer to the AHA Guide Code Chart. © 2016 AHA Guide

BREMEN—Haralson County

⊞ **TANNER HIGGINS GENERAL HOSPITAL (111320)**, 200 Allen Memorial Drive, Zip 30110–2012; tel. 770/824–2000 **A**1 10 18 **F**3 11 15 29 30 40 45 48 50 56 57 59 60 68 81 107 110 111 114 119 127 130 133 146 148 **P**1 6 **S** Tanner Health System, Carrollton, GA
Primary Contact: Bonnie Boles, M.D., Administrator
COO: James D. Griffith, Chief Operating Officer
CFO: Carol Crews, Chief Financial Officer
CMO: Bill Waters, M.D., Chief Medical Officer
CIO: Terri Lee, Chief Information Office
CHR: Shari W. Gainey, Human Resource Director
CNO: B. J. Brock, Nursing Director
Web address: www.tanner.org/Main/HigginsGeneralHospitalBremen.aspx
Control: Other not–for–profit (including NFP Corporation) **Service:** General Medical and Surgical

> **Staffed Beds:** 23 **Admissions:** 709 **Census:** 14 **Outpatient Visits:** 80108 **Births:** 0 **Total Expense ($000):** 25722 **Payroll Expense ($000):** 13689 **Personnel:** 226

BRUNSWICK—Glynn County

⊞ **SOUTHEAST GEORGIA HEALTH SYSTEM BRUNSWICK CAMPUS (110025)**, 2415 Parkwood Drive, Zip 31520–4722, Mailing Address: P.O. Box 1518, Zip 31521–1518; tel. 912/466–7000, (Total facility includes 278 beds in nursing home–type unit) **A**1 2 10 **F**3 6 8 11 12 13 15 17 18 20 22 26 28 29 30 31 34 35 37 40 44 45 46 47 48 49 50 51 54 57 59 64 66 68 70 71 74 75 76 77 78 79 81 84 85 86 87 89 91 93 94 96 100 107 108 110 111 114 115 117 119 120 121 124 126 129 131 132 135 144 146 147 148 **P**5 **S** Southeast Georgia Health System, Brunswick, GA
Primary Contact: Michael D. Scherneck, President and Chief Executive Officer
CFO: Michael D. Scherneck, Executive Vice President and Chief Financial Officer
CIO: Chuck Bumgardner, Director Information Systems
CHR: Patrick D. Ebri, Ph.D., Vice President, Human Resources
CNO: Christine Kipp, Interim Vice President, Patient Care Services
Web address: www.sghs.org
Control: Hospital district or authority, Government, nonfederal **Service:** General Medical and Surgical

> **Staffed Beds:** 532 **Admissions:** 11915 **Census:** 374 **Outpatient Visits:** 230864 **Births:** 1327 **Total Expense ($000):** 302154 **Payroll Expense ($000):** 134173 **Personnel:** 1296

BRYON—Peach County

★ ◇ **MEDICAL CENTER OF PEACH COUNTY, NAVICENT HEALTH (111310)**, 1960 Highway 247 Connector, Zip 31008; tel. 478/654–2000, (Nonreporting) **A**10 18 21 **S** Navicent Health, Macon, GA
Primary Contact: Darren Pearce, Administrator and Chief Executive Officer
CFO: Lisa Urbistondo, Chief Financial Officer
CMO: Crystal Brown, M.D., Medical Director
CNO: Brenda Goodman, Chief Nursing Officer
Web address: www.navicenthealth.org
Control: Hospital district or authority, Government, nonfederal **Service:** General Medical and Surgical

> **Staffed Beds:** 25

CAIRO—Grady County

⊞ **GRADY GENERAL HOSPITAL (110121)**, 1155 Fifth Street S.E., Zip 39828–3142, Mailing Address: P.O. Box 360, Zip 39828–0360; tel. 229/377–1150 **A**1 10 **F**3 11 13 15 18 28 29 34 35 40 45 50 57 59 68 70 76 79 81 85 86 87 91 92 93 107 110 111 115 119 130 133 146 **P**6 **S** Archbold Medical Center, Thomasville, GA
Primary Contact: Crystal Ramm, Administrator
COO: Jim Carter, Chief Operating Officer
CFO: Skip Hightower, Chief Financial Officer
CIO: Tracy Gray, Chief Information Officer
CHR: Michelle Pledger, Coordinator Human Resources
CNO: Tammy Harlow, Director of Nursing
Web address: www.archbold.org
Control: Hospital district or authority, Government, nonfederal **Service:** General Medical and Surgical

> **Staffed Beds:** 48 **Admissions:** 1300 **Census:** 18 **Outpatient Visits:** 51092 **Births:** 215 **Total Expense ($000):** 20988 **Payroll Expense ($000):** 8366 **Personnel:** 135

CALHOUN—Gordon County

⊞ ◯ **GORDON HOSPITAL (110023)**, 1035 Red Bud Road, Zip 30701–2082, Mailing Address: P.O. Box 12938, Zip 30703–7013; tel. 706/629–2895 **A**1 2 10 11 19 **F**3 7 11 13 15 18 20 29 30 31 34 35 37 40 46 57 59 62 64 70 75 76 77 78 79 81 82 85 86 87 93 107 108 111 115 119 120 121 123 129 130 135 144 146 147 148 **P**1 6 **S** Adventist Health System Sunbelt Health Care Corporation, Altamonte Springs, FL
Primary Contact: Pete M. Weber, President and Chief Executive Officer
COO: Brandon M. Nudd, Chief Operating Officer
CFO: Cory Reeves, Chief Financial Officer
CMO: Will Theus, M.D., Chief of Staff
CHR: Jeni Hasselbrack, Director Human Resources
CNO: Amy Jordan, Chief Nursing Officer/Vice President of Nursing
Web address: www.gordonhospital.com
Control: Church–operated, Nongovernment, not–for profit **Service:** General Medical and Surgical

> **Staffed Beds:** 82 **Admissions:** 4049 **Census:** 44 **Outpatient Visits:** 258992 **Births:** 567 **Total Expense ($000):** 118541 **Payroll Expense ($000):** 47176 **Personnel:** 928

CAMILLA—Mitchell County

⊞ **MITCHELL COUNTY HOSPITAL (111331)**, 90 East Stephens Street, Zip 31730–1836, Mailing Address: P.O. Box 639, Zip 31730–0639; tel. 229/336–5284, (Total facility includes 156 beds in nursing home–type unit) **A**1 10 18 **F**3 11 15 18 29 34 35 40 50 57 59 68 75 87 93 97 107 110 111 114 119 127 128 130 133 146 **P**6 **S** Archbold Medical Center, Thomasville, GA
Primary Contact: James Womack, Administrator
COO: LaDon Toole, Vice President Network Operations
CFO: Skip Hightower, Senior Vice President and Chief Financial Officer
CIO: Tracy Gray, Chief Information Officer
CHR: Vickie County–Teemer, Coordinator Human Resources
CNO: Carla Beasley, Director of Nursing
Web address: www.archbold.org
Control: Hospital district or authority, Government, nonfederal **Service:** General Medical and Surgical

> **Staffed Beds:** 181 **Admissions:** 399 **Census:** 164 **Outpatient Visits:** 13274 **Births:** 0 **Total Expense ($000):** 25432 **Payroll Expense ($000):** 10905 **Personnel:** 139

CANTON—Cherokee County

⊞ **NORTHSIDE HOSPITAL–CHEROKEE (110008)**, 201 Hospital Road, Zip 30114–2408, Mailing Address: P.O. Box 906, Zip 30169–0906; tel. 770/720–5100 **A**1 10 **F**3 8 11 12 13 15 18 20 22 26 28 29 30 31 34 35 40 44 45 49 50 54 57 59 60 64 68 70 73 74 75 76 78 79 81 82 85 86 87 93 107 108 110 111 114 119 120 121 123 126 129 130 131 132 144 145 146 147 148 **S** Northside Healthcare System, Atlanta, GA
Primary Contact: William M. Hayes, Chief Executive Officer
COO: Mike Patterson, Director of Operations
CFO: Brian Jennette, Chief Financial Officer
CMO: Alexander Kessler, M.D., Chief of Staff
CIO: Bill Dunford, Manager
CHR: Roslyn Roberts, Manager
Web address: www.northside.com
Control: Other not–for–profit (including NFP Corporation) **Service:** General Medical and Surgical

> **Staffed Beds:** 88 **Admissions:** 5918 **Census:** 70 **Outpatient Visits:** 110714 **Births:** 1195 **Total Expense ($000):** 188288 **Payroll Expense ($000):** 79814 **Personnel:** 1333

CARROLLTON—Carroll County

⊞ **TANNER MEDICAL CENTER–CARROLLTON (110011)**, 705 Dixie Street, Zip 30117–3818; tel. 770/836–9666 **A**1 2 10 **F**3 11 13 15 18 20 22 26 28 29 30 31 34 35 40 45 47 49 56 57 58 59 60 62 63 64 68 70 71 73 74 75 76 78 79 81 82 85 87 89 90 107 108 110 111 115 116 117 118 119 120 121 123 124 126 129 130 132 143 146 147 148 **P**1 6 **S** Tanner Health System, Carrollton, GA
Primary Contact: James D. Griffith, Chief Operating Officer
COO: James D. Griffith, Chief Operating Officer
CHR: Vivian C. Barr, Director Human Resources
Web address: www.tanner.org
Control: Other not–for–profit (including NFP Corporation) **Service:** General Medical and Surgical

> **Staffed Beds:** 162 **Admissions:** 8430 **Census:** 99 **Outpatient Visits:** 258059 **Births:** 1293 **Total Expense ($000):** 252872 **Payroll Expense ($000):** 98406 **Personnel:** 1639

GA

Hospital, Medicare Provider Number, Address, Telephone, Approval, Facility, and Physician Codes, Health Care System

★ American Hospital Association (AHA) membership   ◯ Healthcare Facilities Accreditation Program   ⇑ Center for Improvement in Healthcare Quality Accreditation
□ The Joint Commission accreditation   ◇ DNV Healthcare Inc. accreditation   △ Commission on Accreditation of Rehabilitation Facilities (CARF) accreditation

---

CARTERSVILLE—Bartow County

⌧ **CARTERSVILLE MEDICAL CENTER (110030)**, 960 Joe Frank Harris Parkway,
Zip 30120–2129; tel. 770/382–1530, (Nonreporting) **A**1 2 10 **S** HCA,
Nashville, TN
Primary Contact: Keith Sandlin, Chief Executive Officer
COO: Lori Rakes, Chief Operating Officer
Web address: www.cartersvillemedical.com
Control: Corporation, Investor–owned, for–profit **Service:** General Medical and
Surgical

Staffed Beds: 80

CEDARTOWN—Polk County

⌧ **POLK MEDICAL CENTER (111330)**, 2360 Rockmart Highway,
Zip 30125–6029; tel. 770/748–2500 **A**1 10 18 **F**3 15 28 29 30 34 35 40 50
56 57 59 64 68 75 77 81 93 103 107 108 110 114 119 129 130 132 133
135 143 146 147 148
Primary Contact: Matt Gorman, Administrator
CFO: Rick Sheerin, Chief Financial Officer
CHR: Jeanna Smith, Administrative Assistant and Human Resources Officer
Web address: www.polkhospital.org
Control: Hospital district or authority, Government, nonfederal **Service:** General
Medical and Surgical

Staffed Beds: 25 Admissions: 370 Census: 9 Outpatient Visits: 38164 Births: 0 Total Expense ($000): 18793 Payroll Expense ($000): 7456 Personnel: 140

CHATSWORTH—Murray County

⌧ **MURRAY MEDICAL CENTER (110050)**, 707 Old Dalton Ellijay Road,
Zip 30705–2060, Mailing Address: P.O. Box 1406, Zip 30705–1406;
tel. 706/695–4564, (Data for 245 days) **A**1 10 **F**3 7 15 29 40 81 107 111 119
146 **S** Adventist Health System Sunbelt Health Care Corporation, Altamonte
Springs, FL
Primary Contact: Karen Steely, Administrator
CMO: Blaine Minor, M.D., Chief of Staff
CIO: Jose C. Rios, Director Information Services
CHR: Brandy Rymer, Coordinator Human Resources
CNO: Susan Shook, Interim Chief Executive officer
Web address: www.murraymedical.org/
Control: Church–operated, Nongovernment, not–for profit **Service:** General
Medical and Surgical

Staffed Beds: 33 Admissions: 206 Census: 2 Outpatient Visits: 18048 Births: 0 Total Expense ($000): 12551 Payroll Expense ($000): 3309 Personnel: 147

CLAXTON—Evans County

⌧ **EVANS MEMORIAL HOSPITAL (110142)**, 200 North River Street,
Zip 30417–1659, Mailing Address: P.O. Box 518, Zip 30417–0518;
tel. 912/739–2611 **A**1 10 **F**3 15 29 34 40 45 53 57 59 68 75 81 93 97 107
108 110 111 115 119 127 130 133 135 146
Primary Contact: Nikki NeSmith, Interim Chief Operating Officer
CFO: John Wiggins, Chief Financial Officer
CMO: Kyle Parks, M.D., Chief of Staff
CIO: Steve Schmidt, Director Information Systems
CHR: Gina Waters, Director Human Resources
CNO: Nikki NeSmith, Chief Nursing Officer
Web address: www.evansmemorial.org/Pages/default.aspx
Control: Hospital district or authority, Government, nonfederal **Service:** General
Medical and Surgical

Staffed Beds: 10 Admissions: 570 Census: 5 Outpatient Visits: 31050 Births: 0 Total Expense ($000): 13502 Payroll Expense ($000): 5041 Personnel: 107

CLAYTON—Rabun County

MOUNTAIN LAKES MEDICAL CENTER (111336), 196 Ridgecrest Circle,
Zip 30525–4111; tel. 706/782–4233, (Nonreporting) **A**10 18
Primary Contact: Joseph Forese, Chief Executive Officer
CFO: Jimmy Norman, Chief Financial Officer
CHR: Charles Harbaugh, Director Human Resources
Web address: www.mountainlakesmedicalcenter.com
Control: Hospital district or authority, Government, nonfederal **Service:** General
Medical and Surgical

Staffed Beds: 25

COCHRAN—Bleckley County

◇ **BLECKLEY MEMORIAL HOSPITAL (111302)**, 145 East Peacock Street,
Zip 31014–7846, Mailing Address: P.O. Box 536, Zip 31014–0536;
tel. 478/934–6211 **A**10 18 21 **F**3 11 29 40 41 63 64 65 68 77 79 86 87 89
90 92 93 107 119 128 129 133
Primary Contact: Courtney Moore, CPA, Chief Executive Officer
Web address: www.bleckleymemorial.com
Control: Hospital district or authority, Government, nonfederal **Service:** General
Medical and Surgical

Staffed Beds: 25 Admissions: 472 Census: 10 Outpatient Visits: 17442 Births: 0 Total Expense ($000): 9403 Payroll Expense ($000): 3667

COLQUITT—Miller County

◇ **MILLER COUNTY HOSPITAL (111305)**, 209 North Cuthbert Street,
Zip 39837–3518, Mailing Address: P.O. Box 7, Zip 39837–0007;
tel. 229/758–3305, (Total facility includes 163 beds in nursing home–type unit)
A10 18 21 **F**8 29 30 34 35 39 40 44 45 50 56 57 59 64 65 66 68 75 77 81
85 87 97 103 104 107 108 114 119 127 128 129 130 133 135 143 146
147 148
Primary Contact: Robin Rau, Chief Executive Officer
CFO: Jill Brown, Chief Financial Officer
CMO: William Swofford, M.D., Chief of Staff
CIO: Keith Lovering, Information Technician
CHR: Karie Spence, Director Human Resources
CNO: Shawn Whittaker, Chief Nursing Officer
Web address: www.millercountyhospital.com
Control: Hospital district or authority, Government, nonfederal **Service:** General
Medical and Surgical

Staffed Beds: 188 Admissions: 924 Census: 163 Outpatient Visits: 42080 Births: 0 Total Expense ($000): 30658 Payroll Expense ($000): 14928 Personnel: 340

COLUMBUS—Muscogee County

BRADLEY CENTER OF ST. FRANCIS See St. Francis Hospital

☐ **COLUMBUS SPECIALTY HOSPITAL (112012)**, 616 19th Street,
Zip 31901–1528, Mailing Address: P.O. Box 910, Zip 31902–0910;
tel. 706/494–4075 **A**1 10 **F**1 3 29 30 34 56 59 61 65 68 74 85 143
Primary Contact: Robert Saulnier, Chief Executive Officer
CFO: William Eckstein, Chief Financial Officer
CHR: Myra Whitley, Vice President, Human Resources
CNO: Robert Saulnier, Chief Executive Officer
Web address: www.columbusspecialtyhospital.net
Control: Other not–for–profit (including NFP Corporation) **Service:** Long–Term
Acute Care hospital

Staffed Beds: 33 Admissions: 300 Census: 24 Outpatient Visits: 0 Births: 0 Total Expense ($000): 12282 Payroll Expense ($000): 5149 Personnel: 89

HUGHSTON HOSPITAL See Northside Medical Center

☐ **MIDTOWN MEDICAL CENTER (110064)**, 710 Center Street, Zip 31901–1527,
Mailing Address: P.O. Box 951, Zip 31902–0951; tel. 706/571–1000,
(Nonreporting) **A**1 2 3 5 10 12 13 **S** Columbus Regional Healthcare System,
Columbus, GA
Primary Contact: Ryan Chandler, President and Chief Executive Officer
Web address: www.columbusregional.com
Control: Other not–for–profit (including NFP Corporation) **Service:** General
Medical and Surgical

Staffed Beds: 497

MIDTOWN MEDICAL CENTER WEST, 616 19th Street, Zip 31901–1528,
Mailing Address: P.O. Box 2188, Zip 31902–2188; tel. 706/494–4262,
(Nonreporting) **S** Columbus Regional Healthcare System, Columbus, GA
Primary Contact: Ryan Chandler, Chief Executive Officer
CMO: Thomas L. Theus, M.D., Chief of Medicine
CIO: Ryan Sanders, Director Information Services
Web address: www.columbusregional.com
Control: Other not–for–profit (including NFP Corporation) **Service:** General
Medical and Surgical

Staffed Beds: 171

☐ **NORTHSIDE MEDICAL CENTER (110200)**, 100 Frist Court, Zip 31909–3578,
Mailing Address: P.O. Box 7188, Zip 31908–7188; tel. 706/494–2100,
(Nonreporting) **A**1 3 10 **S** Columbus Regional Healthcare System, Columbus, GA
Primary Contact: Ryan Chandler, Interim Chief Executive Officer
COO: Michelle Breitfelder, Chief Operating Officer
CFO: Roland Thacker, Chief Financial Officer
CMO: Lyle Norwood, M.D., Chief of Staff
CIO: Douglas Colburn, Chief Information Officer
CHR: Becky Augustyniak, Director Human Resources
Web address: www.columbusregional.com
Control: Hospital district or authority, Government, nonfederal **Service:**
Orthopedic

Staffed Beds: 100

Many Facility Codes have changed. Please refer to the AHA Guide Code Chart. © 2016 AHA Guide

GA

☒ **ST. FRANCIS HOSPITAL (110129)**, 2122 Manchester Expressway,
Zip 31904–6878, Mailing Address: P.O. Box 7000, Zip 31908–7000;
tel. 706/596–4000, (Includes BRADLEY CENTER OF ST. FRANCIS, 2000 16th
Avenue, Zip 31906–0308; tel. 706/320–3700) **A**1 3 10 **F**3 10 11 13 15 17 18
20 22 24 26 28 29 30 31 34 35 40 45 46 49 50 51 53 54 56 59 60 64 70
74 75 76 77 78 79 81 82 85 86 92 93 94 98 99 100 101 102 103 104 105
106 107 108 110 111 115 119 126 129 130 131 144 145 146 147 148 **P**6
S LifePoint Health, Brentwood, TN
Primary Contact: David Koontz, Chief Executive Officer
CFO: Greg Hembree, Senior Vice President and Chief Financial Officer
CMO: Bobbi Farber, M.D., Chief Medical Officer
CIO: Jonathon R. Jager, Chief Information Officer
CHR: E. Rick Lowe, FACHE, Operations Support Risk Management and
Compliance
CNO: Shirley Hoskins, Interim Chief Nursing Officer
Web address: www.mystfrancis.com
Control: Other not–for–profit (including NFP Corporation) **Service:** General
Medical and Surgical

> **Staffed Beds:** 304 **Admissions:** 15232 **Census:** 215 **Outpatient Visits:**
> 186497 **Births:** 1413 **Total Expense ($000):** 246015 **Payroll Expense**
> **($000):** 90527 **Personnel:** 2379

☐ **WEST CENTRAL GEORGIA REGIONAL HOSPITAL (114013)**, 3000 Schatulga
Road, Zip 31907–3117, Mailing Address: P.O. Box 12435, Zip 31917–2435;
tel. 706/568–5000 **A**1 10 **F**98 106 130 135
Primary Contact: John L. Robertson, Administrator
COO: Marcia Capshaw, Chief Operating Officer
CFO: John Frederick, Chief Financial Officer
CMO: David Morton, M.D., Clinical Director
CIO: Karen Fisher–Ford, Director of Health Information Management
CHR: Peri Johnson, Human Resources Director
CNO: Nicolise Claassens, Nurse Executive
Web address: www.dbhdd.georgia.gov/west–central–georgia–regional–hospital–
columbus
Control: State–Government, nonfederal **Service:** Psychiatric

> **Staffed Beds:** 186 **Admissions:** 261 **Census:** 178 **Outpatient Visits:** 0
> **Births:** 0 **Personnel:** 699

COMMERCE—Jackson County

☒ **NORTHRIDGE MEDICAL CENTER (110040)**, 70 Medical Center Drive,
Zip 30529–1078; tel. 706/335–1000, (Total facility includes 167 beds in nursing
home–type unit) **A**1 10 **F**3 15 17 18 29 30 34 40 45 53 56 57 59 70 79 81 82
85 89 90 93 98 100 103 107 108 110 111 114 119 128 130 133 **P**6
Primary Contact: Larry W. Ebert, Jr., Chief Executive Officer
CMO: Narasimhulu Neelagaru, M.D., Chief of Staff
Web address: www.northridgemc.com
Control: Other not–for–profit (including NFP Corporation) **Service:** General
Medical and Surgical

> **Staffed Beds:** 257 **Admissions:** 1343 **Census:** 170 **Outpatient Visits:** 22445
> **Births:** 0 **Total Expense ($000):** 29836 **Payroll Expense ($000):** 12531
> **Personnel:** 334

CONYERS—Rockdale County

☒ **ROCKDALE MEDICAL CENTER (110091)**, 1412 Milstead Avenue N.E.,
Zip 30012–3877; tel. 770/918–3000 **A**1 5 10 **F**3 11 13 15 18 20 22 28 29
30 34 35 36 40 45 46 47 49 57 59 64 70 72 73 74 75 76 79 81 82 85 86
87 92 93 107 108 110 111 114 115 118 119 126 130 131 132 135 146
147 148 **S** LifePoint Health, Brentwood, TN
Primary Contact: Alan E. George, Chief Executive Officer
COO: Blake Watts, Chief Operating Officer
CFO: Diane Roth, Chief Financial Officer
CMO: Lisa Gillespie, M.D., Chief Medical Officer
CIO: Gail Waldo, Director Information Technology
CHR: Marianne Freeman, Vice President Human Resources
CNO: Eleanor Post, R.N., Chief Nursing Officer
Web address: www.rockdalemedicalcenter.org
Control: Corporation, Investor–owned, for–profit **Service:** General Medical and
Surgical

> **Staffed Beds:** 138 **Admissions:** 8899 **Census:** 101 **Outpatient Visits:**
> 121300 **Births:** 1831 **Total Expense ($000):** 128222 **Payroll Expense**
> **($000):** 48663 **Personnel:** 729

CORDELE—Crisp County

☒ **CRISP REGIONAL HOSPITAL (110104)**, 902 North Seventh Street,
Zip 31015–3234; tel. 229/276–3100, (Total facility includes 243 beds in nursing
home–type unit) **A**1 3 10 20 **F**3 10 11 13 15 28 29 30 31 34 35 40 43 44 45
48 50 51 54 56 57 58 59 60 61 62 63 64 65 68 70 75 76 77 78 79 81 84
85 86 87 89 90 93 96 97 107 108 110 111 115 125 127 128 129 132 133
135 144 146 147 148 **P**2 8
Primary Contact: Steven Gautney, Chief Executive Officer
COO: Mary Jim Montgomery, R.N., Chief Operating Officer
CFO: Jessica Y. Carter, Chief Financial Officer
CMO: David Kavtaradze, M.D., Chief of Staff
CHR: George M. Laurin, Interim Director Human Resources
CNO: Marsha L. Mulderig, R.N., Chief Nursing Officer
Web address: www.crispregional.org
Control: County–Government, nonfederal **Service:** General Medical and Surgical

> **Staffed Beds:** 316 **Admissions:** 2954 **Census:** 172 **Outpatient Visits:** 99790
> **Births:** 350 **Personnel:** 727

COVINGTON—Newton County

☐ **PIEDMONT NEWTON HOSPITAL (110018)**, 5126 Hospital Drive,
Zip 30014–2567; tel. 770/786–7053, (Nonreporting) **A**1 10 **S** Piedmont
Healthcare, Atlanta, GA
Primary Contact: James F. Weadick, Administrator and Chief Executive Officer
CFO: Troy Brooks, Assistant Administrator Fiscal Services
CMO: B. Carter Rogers, Chief of Staff
CIO: Brad Collier, Director
CHR: Greg H. Richardson, Assistant Administrator Human Resources
CNO: Patricia A. Waller, R.N., Assistant Administrator Patient Care Services
Web address: www.newtonmedical.com
Control: Other not–for–profit (including NFP Corporation) **Service:** General
Medical and Surgical

> **Staffed Beds:** 101

CUMMING—Forsyth County

☒ **NORTHSIDE HOSPITAL–FORSYTH (110005)**, 1200 Northside Forsyth Drive,
Zip 30041–7659; tel. 770/844–3200 **A**1 10 **F**3 8 11 12 13 15 18 20 22 26
28 29 30 31 34 35 37 40 44 45 48 49 50 54 57 59 60 64 68 70 71 72 73
74 75 76 78 79 81 82 85 86 87 93 107 108 110 111 114 115 117 119 120
121 123 124 126 129 130 132 135 144 145 146 147 148 **S** Northside
Healthcare System, Atlanta, GA
Primary Contact: Lynn Jackson, Administrator
CFO: Eric Caldwell, Director Finance
Web address: www.northside.com
Control: Other not–for–profit (including NFP Corporation) **Service:** General
Medical and Surgical

> **Staffed Beds:** 252 **Admissions:** 12976 **Census:** 171 **Outpatient Visits:**
> 205307 **Births:** 3069 **Total Expense ($000):** 364467 **Payroll Expense**
> **($000):** 129090 **Personnel:** 2297

CUTHBERT—Randolph County

★ ◇ **SOUTHWEST GEORGIA REGIONAL MEDICAL CENTER (111300)**, 361
Randolph Street, Zip 39840–6127; tel. 229/732–2181, (Nonreporting) **A**10 18
21 **S** Phoebe Putney Health System, Albany, GA
Primary Contact: Kim Gilman, Chief Executive Officer and Chief Nursing Officer
CFO: Candace Guarnieri, Chief Financial Officer
CNO: Kim Gilman, Chief Executive Officer and Chief Nursing Officer
Web address: www.phoebeputney.com/
Control: Hospital district or authority, Government, nonfederal **Service:** General
Medical and Surgical

> **Staffed Beds:** 105

DAHLONEGA—Lumpkin County

☐ **CHESTATEE REGIONAL HOSPITAL (110187)**, 227 Mountain Drive,
Zip 30533–1606; tel. 706/864–6136 **A**1 10 **F**2 3 15 29 34 49 50 54 56 57
59 64 65 79 81 85 86 87 98 103 105 107 108 110 111 114 119 127 129
130 133 143 147 **P**8 **S** Sunlink Health Systems, Atlanta, GA
Primary Contact: Jeanne Van Galder, Chief Executive Officer
CFO: Molly Lindquist, Interim Chief Financial Officer
CMO: Richard Wherry, M.D., Chief of Staff
CHR: Barbara Patrick, Director Human Resources
CNO: Barbara Arnau, R.N., Chief Nursing Officer
Web address: www.chestateeregionalhospital.com
Control: Corporation, Investor–owned, for–profit **Service:** General Medical and
Surgical

> **Staffed Beds:** 49 **Admissions:** 1008 **Census:** 14 **Outpatient Visits:** 17863
> **Births:** 0 **Total Expense ($000):** 15340 **Payroll Expense ($000):** 6570
> **Personnel:** 141

GA

Hospital, Medicare Provider Number, Address, Telephone, Approval, Facility, and Physician Codes, Health Care System

★ American Hospital Association (AHA) membership   ○ Healthcare Facilities Accreditation Program   ⇑ Center for Improvement in Healthcare Quality Accreditation
☐ The Joint Commission accreditation   ◇ DNV Healthcare Inc. accreditation   △ Commission on Accreditation of Rehabilitation Facilities (CARF) accreditation

DALTON—Whitfield County

⌧ **HAMILTON MEDICAL CENTER (110001)**, 1200 Memorial Drive,
Zip 30720–2529, Mailing Address: P.O. Box 1168, Zip 30722–1168;
tel. 706/272–6000 **A**1 2 10 19 **F**3 4 5 8 12 13 15 18 20 22 26 28 29 30 31
34 35 40 43 44 45 46 47 48 49 50 51 53 54 57 59 60 62 63 64 68 70 72
73 74 75 76 77 78 79 81 82 84 85 86 87 89 93 96 97 98 100 101 102 103
104 105 107 108 110 111 114 115 116 117 118 119 120 121 123 124 126
129 130 131 132 135 144 146 147 148
Primary Contact: Jeffrey D. Myers, President and Chief Executive Officer
COO: Sandra D. McKenzie, Executive Vice President and Chief Operating Officer
CFO: Gary L. Howard, Senior Vice President and Chief Financial Officer
CMO: Stephen G. Rohn, M.D., Vice President and Chief Medical Officer
CIO: John M. Forrester, Director Information Services
CHR: Jason Hopkins, Director, Human Resources
CNO: Cathy Ferguson, R.N., Vice President and Chief Nursing Officer
Web address: www.hamiltonhealth.com
Control: Other not–for–profit (including NFP Corporation) **Service:** General
Medical and Surgical

Staffed Beds: 227 **Admissions:** 9804 **Census:** 117 **Outpatient Visits:**
240561 **Births:** 1868 **Personnel:** 1173

DECATUR—Dekalb County

⌧ **ATLANTA VETERANS AFFAIRS MEDICAL CENTER**, 1670 Clairmont Road,
Zip 30033–4004; tel. 404/321–6111, (Nonreporting) **A**1 2 3 5 8 **S** Department
of Veterans Affairs, Washington, DC
Primary Contact: Annette Walker, Director
CFO: Pamela Watkins, Chief Financial Officer
CMO: David Bower, M.D., Chief of Staff
CIO: William Brock, Chief Information Officer
CHR: Zeta Ferguson, Chief Human Resources
CNO: Sandy Leake, MSN, Associate Director, Nursing and Patient Care Services
Web address: www.atlanta.va.gov/
Control: Veterans Affairs, Government, federal **Service:** General Medical and
Surgical

Staffed Beds: 239

☐ **DEKALB MEDICAL AT DOWNTOWN DECATUR (112006)**, 450 North Candler
Street, Zip 30030–2671; tel. 404/501–6700 **A**1 5 10 **F**1 3 11 29 30 75 87 90
146 148 **S** DeKalb Regional Health System, Decatur, GA
Primary Contact: John Shelton, President and Chief Executive Officer
COO: John Shelton, Executive Vice President and Chief Operating Officer
CMO: David Snyder, M.D., Chief of Staff
CHR: Tom Crawford, Vice President Human Resources
Web address: www.dekalbmedicalcenter.org
Control: Other not–for–profit (including NFP Corporation) **Service:** Long–Term
Acute Care hospital

Staffed Beds: 44 **Admissions:** 303 **Census:** 25 **Outpatient Visits:** 0 **Births:**
0 **Total Expense ($000):** 18577 **Payroll Expense ($000):** 8081 **Personnel:**
180

⌧ **DEKALB MEDICAL AT NORTH DECATUR (110076)**, 2701 North Decatur
Road, Zip 30033–5995; tel. 404/501–1000 **A**1 2 3 10 **F**3 11 12 13 15 18 20
22 26 28 29 30 31 34 35 36 40 45 46 48 49 50 53 55 56 57 58 59 60 64
70 71 72 73 74 75 76 77 78 79 81 82 85 87 90 93 96 97 98 100 101 102
105 107 108 111 114 115 117 119 120 121 124 126 129 130 131 132 134
135 146 147 148 **S** DeKalb Regional Health System, Decatur, GA
Primary Contact: John Shelton, President and Chief Executive Officer
COO: Dane Henry, Executive Vice President and Chief Operating Officer
CFO: John Katsianis, Senior Vice President and Chief Financial Officer
CIO: Beth Patino, Chief Information Officer
CHR: LeRoy Walker, Vice President Human Resources
CNO: Susan Breslin, R.N., Vice President Patient Care Services and Chief Nursing
Officer
Web address: www.dekalbmedical.org
Control: Other not–for–profit (including NFP Corporation) **Service:** General
Medical and Surgical

Staffed Beds: 417 **Admissions:** 19233 **Census:** 229 **Outpatient Visits:**
180322 **Births:** 4601 **Total Expense ($000):** 309185 **Payroll Expense**
($000): 109448 **Personnel:** 2158

☐ **GEORGIA REGIONAL HOSPITAL AT ATLANTA (114019)**, 3073 Panthersville
Road, Zip 30034–3828; tel. 404/243–2100, (Nonreporting) **A**1 3 5 10
Primary Contact: Susan Trueblood, Chief Executive Officer
COO: Sonny Slate, Chief Operating Officer
CFO: Reginald Jones, Business Manager
CMO: Emile Risby, M.D., Clinical Director
CIO: Elfie Early, Manager Data Services
CHR: Lorraine Farr, Manager Human Resources
Web address: www.atlantareg.dhr.state.ga.us
Control: State–Government, nonfederal **Service:** Psychiatric

Staffed Beds: 354

VETERANS AFFAIRS MEDICAL CENTER See Atlanta Veterans Affairs Medical
Center

DEMOREST—Habersham County

★ ◇ **HABERSHAM MEDICAL CENTER (110041)**, 541 Historic Highway 441,
Zip 30535–3118, Mailing Address: P.O. Box 37, Zip 30535–0037;
tel. 706/754–2161, (Total facility includes 84 beds in nursing home–type unit)
A10 21 **F**7 8 13 15 28 29 30 34 35 40 45 46 50 53 57 59 64 68 75 77 79
81 82 87 91 93 97 102 107 111 114 119 129 130 133 143 146
Primary Contact: Jerry R. Wise, Chief Executive Officer
COO: Michael Gay, Chief Operating Officer
CFO: Barbara Duncan, Chief Financial Officer
CMO: Josh Garrett, Chief of Staff
CHR: Ryan Snow, Director Human Resources
Web address: www.habershammedical.com/
Control: Hospital district or authority, Government, nonfederal **Service:** General
Medical and Surgical

Staffed Beds: 137 **Admissions:** 2145 **Census:** 26 **Outpatient Visits:** 50957
Births: 402 **Total Expense ($000):** 45000 **Payroll Expense ($000):** 23928

DONALSONVILLE—Seminole County

◇ **DONALSONVILLE HOSPITAL (110194)**, 102 Hospital Circle, Zip 39845–1199;
tel. 229/524–5217, (Nonreporting) **A**10 21
Primary Contact: Charles H. Orrick, Administrator
CFO: James Moody, Chief Financial Officer
CMO: C. O. Walker, M.D., Chief of Staff
CHR: Jo Adams, Director Human Resources
Control: Other not–for–profit (including NFP Corporation) **Service:** General
Medical and Surgical

Staffed Beds: 140

DOUGLAS—Coffee County

⌧ **COFFEE REGIONAL MEDICAL CENTER (110089)**, 1101 Ocilla Road,
Zip 31533–2207, Mailing Address: P.O. Box 1287, Zip 31534–1287;
tel. 912/384–1900 **A**1 10 20 **F**3 7 8 10 11 13 15 18 20 26 28 29 30 34 35
40 45 47 50 51 53 54 56 57 59 60 61 64 65 68 70 74 75 76 79 81 82 85
86 87 89 92 93 97 107 108 110 111 114 115 119 124 127 130 131 132
135 143 146 147 148
Primary Contact: Vicki Lewis, R.N., MS, FACHE, President and Chief Executive
Officer
CFO: Donald C. Lewis, Jr., Vice President and Chief Financial Officer
CHR: Laura Bloom, Director Human Resources
Web address: www.coffeeregional.org
Control: Other not–for–profit (including NFP Corporation) **Service:** General
Medical and Surgical

Staffed Beds: 88 **Admissions:** 4615 **Census:** 52 **Births:** 615 **Total Expense**
($000): 81822 **Payroll Expense ($000):** 30198

DOUGLASVILLE—Douglas County

★ **WELLSTAR DOUGLAS HOSPITAL (110184)**, 8954 Hospital Drive,
Zip 30134–2282; tel. 770/949–1500 **A**2 10 **F**3 11 13 15 18 20 22 28 29 30
31 37 38 40 44 45 48 49 50 51 54 58 59 60 61 64 68 70 74 75 76 77 78
79 81 82 85 86 87 93 94 102 107 108 110 111 114 115 117 118 119 129
130 132 135 146 147 148 **P**5 6 **S** WellStar Health System, Marietta, GA
Primary Contact: Craig A. Owens, President
CFO: Bradley Greene, Chief Financial Officer
CMO: Noel Holtz, M.D., Chief Medical Officer
CHR: Danyale Ziglor, Assistant Director Human Resources
Web address: www.wellstar.org
Control: Other not–for–profit (including NFP Corporation) **Service:** General
Medical and Surgical

Staffed Beds: 108 **Admissions:** 6914 **Census:** 73 **Outpatient Visits:** 128337
Births: 449 **Personnel:** 764

YOUTH VILLAGES INNER HARBOUR CAMPUS, 4685 Dorsett Shoals Road,
Zip 30135–4999; tel. 770/942–2391 **F**99 106
Primary Contact: Patrick Lawler, Chief Executive Officer
CFO: J. Steve Lewis, Director Finance
CIO: Laura Sellers, Director Information Systems
CHR: Sherry Kollmeyer, Vice President Human Resources
Web address: www.innerharbour.org
Control: Other not–for–profit (including NFP Corporation) **Service:** Children's
hospital psychiatric

Staffed Beds: 190 **Admissions:** 150 **Census:** 48 **Outpatient Visits:** 0 **Births:**
0

Many Facility Codes have changed. Please refer to the AHA Guide Code Chart. © 2016 AHA Guide

DUBLIN—Laurens County

☒ **CARL VINSON VETERANS AFFAIRS MEDICAL CENTER**, 1826 Veterans Boulevard, Zip 31021–3620; tel. 478/272–1210, (Nonreporting) **A**1
S Department of Veterans Affairs, Washington, DC
Primary Contact: Maryalice Morro, MSN, R.N., Director
COO: Gerald M. DeWorth, Associate Director
CFO: Angela Stevenson, Chief Financial Officer
CMO: Christopher Blasy, M.D., Chief of Staff
CIO: Mark Cowart, Chief Information Officer
CHR: Kurt Oster, Human Resources Officer
CNO: Connie Hampton, Nurse Executive
Web address: www.dublin.va.gov/
Control: Veterans Affairs, Government, federal **Service:** General Medical and Surgical

Staffed Beds: 178

☒ **FAIRVIEW PARK HOSPITAL (110125)**, 200 Industrial Boulevard, Zip 31021–2997, Mailing Address: P.O. Box 1408, Zip 31040–1408; tel. 478/275–2000, (Nonreporting) **A**1 10 19 **S** HCA, Nashville, TN
Primary Contact: Donald R. Avery, FACHE, President and Chief Executive Officer
COO: Matthew Steven Hasbrouck, Chief Operating Officer
CFO: Ted Short, Chief Financial Officer
CMO: Jeri Miller, M.D., President Medical Staff
CIO: Marsha Morris, Manager Information Services
CHR: Jeff Bruton, Director Human Resources
CNO: Donna Trickey, R.N., Chief Nursing Officer
Web address: www.fairviewparkhospital.com
Control: Corporation, Investor–owned, for–profit **Service:** General Medical and Surgical

Staffed Beds: 168

DULUTH—De Kalb County

GWINNETT MEDICAL CENTER–DULUTH See Gwinnett Hospital System, Lawrenceville

EAST POINT—Fulton County

☒ **REGENCY HOSPITAL OF SOUTH ATLANTA (112014)**, 1170 Cleveland Avenue, 4th Floor, Zip 30344–3615; tel. 404/466–6250, (Nonreporting) **A**1 3 10 **S** Select Medical Corporation, Mechanicsburg, PA
Primary Contact: Kathy A. Felps, R.N., Chief Executive Officer
Web address: www.regencyhospital.com
Control: Corporation, Investor–owned, for–profit **Service:** Long–Term Acute Care hospital

Staffed Beds: 40

EASTMAN—Dodge County

◇ **DODGE COUNTY HOSPITAL (110092)**, 901 Griffin Avenue, Zip 31023–6720, Mailing Address: PO BOX 4309, Zip 31023–4309; tel. 478/374–4000 **A**10 21 **F**3 11 13 15 29 30 31 40 45 53 57 59 64 69 70 75 76 79 81 85 86 98 101 103 107 108 110 111 114 119 146 147
Primary Contact: Kevin Bierschenk, Chief Executive Officer
CFO: Jan Hamrick, Chief Financial Officer
CIO: Victor Woodard, Manager Information Technology
CHR: Wendy Selph, Director Human Resources
CNO: Sandra M. Campbell, R.N., Chief Nursing Officer
Web address: www.dodgecountyhospital.com
Control: Hospital district or authority, Government, nonfederal **Service:** General Medical and Surgical

Staffed Beds: 35 **Admissions:** 1622 **Census:** 18 **Outpatient Visits:** 34548 **Births:** 115 **Total Expense ($000):** 19859 **Payroll Expense ($000):** 9019 **Personnel:** 241

EATONTON—Putnam County

☐ **PUTNAM GENERAL HOSPITAL (111313)**, 101 Lake Oconee Parkway, Zip 31024–6054; tel. 706/485–2711 **A**1 10 18 **F**3 11 15 18 28 29 34 40 45 49 57 59 64 68 77 81 91 93 107 111 114 119 129 133 146
Primary Contact: Alan Horton, Administrator
CFO: Judy Ware, Chief Financial Officer
CMO: Omar Akhras, M.D., Chief of Staff
CIO: Marcel Lundy, Chief Information Officer
CHR: Jeanine Martinez, Director Human Resources
CNO: Pam Douglas, Chief Nursing Officer
Web address: www.putnamgeneral.com
Control: Hospital district or authority, Government, nonfederal **Service:** General Medical and Surgical

Staffed Beds: 25 **Admissions:** 600 **Census:** 6 **Outpatient Visits:** 23845 **Births:** 0 **Total Expense ($000):** 12896 **Payroll Expense ($000):** 5130 **Personnel:** 105

ELBERTON—Elbert County

☒ **ELBERT MEMORIAL HOSPITAL (110026)**, 4 Medical Drive, Zip 30635–1897; tel. 706/283–3151, (Nonreporting) **A**1 10 20
Primary Contact: Brandon Clary, Chief Executive Officer
CIO: Greg Fields, Director Information Technology
CHR: Georgian Walton, Director Human Resources
CNO: Sonya Elrod, Interim Chief Nursing Officer
Web address: www.emhcare.net
Control: Hospital district or authority, Government, nonfederal **Service:** General Medical and Surgical

Staffed Beds: 42

FAYETTEVILLE—Fayette County

◇ **PIEDMONT FAYETTE HOSPITAL (110215)**, 1255 Highway 54 West, Zip 30214–4526; tel. 770/719–7000, (Nonreporting) **A**2 3 10 21 **S** Piedmont Healthcare, Atlanta, GA
Primary Contact: Michael Burnett, Chief Executive Officer
COO: Nathan Nipper, Chief Operating Officer
CFO: Scott Anthony Wolfe, Chief Financial Officer
CMO: Frederick Willms, M.D., Chief Medical Officer
CIO: Geoffrey Brown, Chief Information Officer
CHR: Holly Sawyer, Director and Human Resources Business Partner
CNO: Merry Heath, Chief Nursing Officer
Web address: www.piedmont.org
Control: Other not–for–profit (including NFP Corporation) **Service:** General Medical and Surgical

Staffed Beds: 172

FITZGERALD—Ben Hill County

◇ **DORMINY MEDICAL CENTER (110073)**, 200 Perry House Road, Zip 31750–8857, Mailing Address: P.O. Box 1447, Zip 31750–1447; tel. 229/424–7100 **A**10 21 **F**3 8 11 12 13 15 29 30 31 35 39 40 50 57 59 60 63 64 65 70 75 76 78 79 81 82 84 85 87 90 93 107 110 111 119 129 130 132 133 146 148
Primary Contact: Mel Pyne, Chief Executive Officer
CFO: Paige Wynn, Chief Financial Officer
CMO: Thomas Mann, M.D., Chief Medical Officer
CIO: Chris Ward, Director Management Information Systems
CHR: Denise Steverson, Director Human Resources
CNO: Staci Mims, Chief Nursing Officer
Web address: www.dorminymedical.org
Control: Hospital district or authority, Government, nonfederal **Service:** General Medical and Surgical

Staffed Beds: 58 **Admissions:** 1299 **Census:** 11 **Outpatient Visits:** 14772 **Births:** 113

FORSYTH—Monroe County

☐ **MONROE COUNTY HOSPITAL (111318)**, 88 Martin Luther King Jr. Drive, Zip 31029–1682, Mailing Address: P.O. Box 1068, Zip 31029–1068; tel. 478/994–2521 **A**1 10 18 **F**3 11 15 29 35 40 57 59 68 75 77 81 107 110 111 114 119 132 133 146 148 **P**1 2 3
Primary Contact: Darren Pearce, Chief Executive Officer
CFO: William H. Storck, Chief Financial Officer
CMO: Jeremy Goodwin, M.D., President, Medical Staff
CIO: Donna Hogg, Supervisor Medical Records
CHR: Deborah Flowers, Director Human Resources
CNO: Donna Nash, Director of Nursing
Web address: www.monroehospital.org
Control: Hospital district or authority, Government, nonfederal **Service:** General Medical and Surgical

Staffed Beds: 25 **Admissions:** 499 **Census:** 7 **Outpatient Visits:** 14939 **Births:** 0 **Total Expense ($000):** 10322 **Payroll Expense ($000):** 4237 **Personnel:** 146

FORT BENNING—Muscogee County

☒ **MARTIN ARMY COMMUNITY HOSPITAL**, 7950 Martin Loop, Zip 31905–5648, Mailing Address: 7950 Martin Loop, B9200, Room 010, Zip 31905–5648; tel. 706/544–2516, (Nonreporting) **A**1 3 5 **S** Department of the Army, Office of the Surgeon General, Falls Church, VA
Primary Contact: Colonel Marie Dominguez, Commander
CHR: Major Bernita Hightower, Chief Human Resources
Web address: www.martin.amedd.army.mil
Control: Army, Government, federal **Service:** General Medical and Surgical

Staffed Beds: 57

GA

Hospital, Medicare Provider Number, Address, Telephone, Approval, Facility, and Physician Codes, Health Care System

★ American Hospital Association (AHA) membership
☐ The Joint Commission accreditation
○ Healthcare Facilities Accreditation Program
◇ DNV Healthcare Inc. accreditation
⇑ Center for Improvement in Healthcare Quality Accreditation
△ Commission on Accreditation of Rehabilitation Facilities (CARF) accreditation

FORT GORDON—Richmond County

✠ **DWIGHT DAVID EISENHOWER ARMY MEDICAL CENTER**, 300 West Hospital Road, Zip 30905–5741; tel. 706/787–5811, (Nonreporting) **A**1 2 3 5 **S** Department of the Army, Office of the Surgeon General, Falls Church, VA
Primary Contact: Colonel John P. Lamoureux, Commander
CMO: Colonel James M. Baunchalk, Deputy Chief Clinical Services
CIO: Major Joseph A. Ponce, Chief Information Management
CHR: Elizabeth Shelt, Civilian Personnel Officer
Web address: www.ddeamc.amedd.army.mil
Control: Army, Government, federal **Service:** General Medical and Surgical

Staffed Beds: 107

FORT OGLETHORPE—Catoosa County

☐ **CORNERSTONE MEDICAL CENTER (110004)**, 100 Gross Crescent Circle, Zip 30742–3669; tel. 706/858–2000, (Nonreporting) **A**1 10
Primary Contact: Jessica Long, Chief Executive Officer
COO: Kevin Hopkins, Vice President of Operations
CFO: Farrell Hayes, Chief Financial Officer
CMO: John Erdman, M.D., Chief of Staff
CIO: Ruth Wright–Whitaker, Director Information Services
CHR: Cathy Hulsey, Manager of Human Resources
CNO: Sandra Siniard, Vice President of Patient Care Services
Web address: www.hutcheson.org
Control: Hospital district or authority, Government, nonfederal **Service:** General Medical and Surgical

Staffed Beds: 179

GAINESVILLE—Hall County

★ △ ◇ **NORTHEAST GEORGIA MEDICAL CENTER (110029)**, 743 Spring Street N.E., Zip 30501–3899; tel. 770/219–3553, (Total facility includes 53 beds in nursing home–type unit) **A**2 7 10 19 21 **F**3 4 5 7 11 12 13 15 17 18 20 22 24 26 28 29 30 31 34 35 38 39 40 43 44 45 46 47 48 49 50 51 54 56 57 58 59 60 61 63 64 65 66 68 70 72 73 74 75 76 77 78 79 81 82 84 85 86 87 89 90 93 98 99 100 101 102 103 104 105 106 107 108 110 111 114 115 116 117 119 120 121 123 124 126 128 129 130 131 132 143 144 146 147 148 **P**6
Primary Contact: Carol H. Burrell, Chief Executive Officer
CFO: Tony Herdener, Vice President Systems and Finance
CMO: Sam Johnson, M.D., Chief Medical Officer
CIO: Chris Paravate, Chief Information Officer
CHR: Deborah Weber, Chief Human Resource Officer
CNO: Brenda Simpson, Chief Nursing Officer
Web address: www.nghs.com
Control: Other not–for–profit (including NFP Corporation) **Service:** General Medical and Surgical

Staffed Beds: 609 **Admissions:** 31516 **Census:** 633 **Outpatient Visits:** 453944 **Births:** 4000 **Total Expense ($000):** 728574 **Payroll Expense ($000):** 276206 **Personnel:** 6510

GRACEWOOD—Richmond County

EAST CENTRAL REGIONAL HOSPITAL See East Central Regional Hospital, Augusta

GREENSBORO—Greene County

✠ **ST. MARY'S GOOD SAMARITAN HOSPITAL (111329)**, 5401 Lake Oconee Parkway, Zip 30642–4232; tel. 706/453–7331 **A**1 10 18 **F**3 11 15 26 29 30 34 35 40 45 51 57 59 64 65 68 74 75 77 79 81 85 87 93 107 108 115 119 129 130 133 146 147 148 **S** Trinity Health, Livonia, MI
Primary Contact: D. Montez Carter, President
CMO: Dave Ringer, M.D., Chief of Staff
CNO: Celia Covington, MSN, Director of Nursing
Web address: www.stmarysgoodsam.org
Control: Church–operated, Nongovernment, not–for profit **Service:** General Medical and Surgical

Staffed Beds: 25 **Admissions:** 925 **Census:** 14 **Outpatient Visits:** 33018 **Births:** 0 **Total Expense ($000):** 19360 **Payroll Expense ($000):** 7761 **Personnel:** 174

GRIFFIN—Spalding County

✠ **SPALDING REGIONAL HOSPITAL (110031)**, 601 South Eighth Street, Zip 30224–4294, Mailing Address: P.O. Drawer V, Zip 30224–1168; tel. 770/228–2721, (Nonreporting) **A**1 2 10 **S** WellStar Health System, Marietta, GA
Primary Contact: Tamara Ison, Senior Vice President and President
COO: Tamara Ison, Chief Operating Officer
CFO: Cameron Pophan, Chief Financial Officer
CMO: Philip Osehobo, M.D., Chief Medical Officer
CIO: Steve Brown, Director Information Systems
CHR: Amanda Remington, Director Human Resources
CNO: Wadra McCullough, Chief Nursing Officer
Web address: www.spaldingregional.com
Control: Corporation, Investor–owned, for–profit **Service:** General Medical and Surgical

Staffed Beds: 160

HAWKINSVILLE—Pulaski County

◇ **TAYLOR REGIONAL HOSPITAL (110135)**, Macon Highway, Zip 31036, Mailing Address: P.O. Box 1297, Zip 31036–7297; tel. 478/783–0200, (Nonreporting) **A**3 10 21
Primary Contact: E.R. McDannald, Interim Chief Executive Officer
CFO: Lisa Halliday, Director Accounting Services
CMO: Al Baggett, M.D., Interim Chief of Staff
CIO: Dawn Warnock, Director Medical Records
Web address: www.taylorregional.org
Control: Other not–for–profit (including NFP Corporation) **Service:** General Medical and Surgical

Staffed Beds: 57

HAZLEHURST—Jeff Davis County

☐ **JEFF DAVIS HOSPITAL (111333)**, 1215 South Tallahassee Street, Zip 31539–2921, Mailing Address: P.O. Box 1690, Zip 31539–1690; tel. 912/375–7781, (Nonreporting) **A**1 10 18
Primary Contact: Tammy Mims, Chief Executive Officer
CFO: Cathy Cason, Chief Financial Officer
CMO: Kirk Munsayac
CIO: Lane Layton, Information Technology Director
CHR: Brenda McEachin, Human Resources Director
CNO: Cindy Dale, Chief Nursing Officer
Web address: www.jeffdavishospital.org
Control: Hospital district or authority, Government, nonfederal **Service:** General Medical and Surgical

Staffed Beds: 25

HIAWASSEE—Towns County

CHATUGE REGIONAL HOSPITAL AND NURSING HOME (111324), 110 Main Street, Zip 30546–3408, Mailing Address: P.O. Box 509, Zip 30546–0509; tel. 706/896–2222, (Total facility includes 112 beds in nursing home–type unit) **A**10 18 **F**3 11 15 29 30 34 40 57 59 65 70 75 77 81 89 90 93 107 108 110 111 114 119 128 130 132 133 135 143 145 146 **P**4 **S** Union General Hospital, Inc., Blairsville, GA
Primary Contact: John Mark Gordon, Administrator
CFO: Tim Henry, Accountant
CMO: Robert F. Stahlkuppe, M.D., Chief of Staff
CIO: Walt Stafford, Director Information Technology
CHR: Rita Bradshaw, Director Human Resources
Web address: www.chatugeregionalhospital.org
Control: Hospital district or authority, Government, nonfederal **Service:** General Medical and Surgical

Staffed Beds: 137 **Admissions:** 637 **Census:** 116 **Outpatient Visits:** 24654 **Births:** 0 **Total Expense ($000):** 17275 **Payroll Expense ($000):** 8420 **Personnel:** 264

HINESVILLE—Liberty County

☐ **LIBERTY REGIONAL MEDICAL CENTER (111335)**, 462 Elma G. Miles Parkway, Zip 31313–4000, Mailing Address: P.O. Box 919, Zip 31310–0919; tel. 912/369–9400, (Nonreporting) **A**1 10 18
Primary Contact: Michael Hester, Chief Executive Officer
Web address: www.libertyregional.org
Control: Hospital district or authority, Government, nonfederal **Service:** General Medical and Surgical

Staffed Beds: 133

✠ **WINN ARMY COMMUNITY HOSPITAL**, 1061 Harmon Avenue, Zip 31314–5641, Mailing Address: 1061 Harmon Avenue, Suite 2311B, Zip 31314–5641; tel. 912/435–6965, (Nonreporting) **A**1 3 5 **S** Department of the Army, Office of the Surgeon General, Falls Church, VA
Primary Contact: Colonel Kirk W. Eggleston, Commanding Officer
CIO: Arthur N. Kirshner, Chief Information Management
CHR: Major Yvette McCrea, Chief Human Resources
CNO: Colonel Sharon Brown, Deputy Commander Nursing
Web address: www.winn.amedd.army.mil/
Control: Army, Government, federal **Service:** General Medical and Surgical

Staffed Beds: 37

GA

Many Facility Codes have changed. Please refer to the AHA Guide Code Chart. © 2016 AHA Guide

HIRAM—Paulding County

⊞ **WELLSTAR PAULDING HOSPITAL (110042)**, 2518 Jimmy Lee Smith Parkway, Zip 30141; tel. 470/644–7000, (Total facility includes 182 beds in nursing home–type unit) **A**1 2 10 **F**3 11 15 18 20 28 29 30 31 37 38 40 41 44 45 49 50 53 54 55 59 61 64 68 70 75 77 78 79 80 81 82 85 86 87 93 102 107 108 110 111 114 118 119 120 121 123 124 128 129 130 135 146 148 **P**5 6 **S** WellStar Health System, Marietta, GA
Primary Contact: Mark Haney, President
COO: Lindsay Rehn, Executive Director of Financial Operations
CFO: Lindsay Rehn, Executive Director of Financial Operations
CMO: Guillermo Pierluisi, Vice President of Medical Affairs
CHR: Jessica Bedsole, Director, Human Resources
CNO: Vicky Hogue, R.N., Vice President Patient Services and Chief Nursing Officer
Web address: www.wellstar.org
Control: Other not–for–profit (including NFP Corporation) **Service:** General Medical and Surgical

Staffed Beds: 238 **Admissions:** 4702 **Census:** 212 **Outpatient Visits:** 118110 **Births:** 0 **Personnel:** 682

HOMERVILLE—Clinch County

★ **CLINCH MEMORIAL HOSPITAL (111308)**, 1050 Valdosta Highway, Zip 31634–9701, Mailing Address: P.O. Box 516, Zip 31634–0516; tel. 912/487–5211 **A**10 18 **F**3 7 11 15 34 40 45 57 59 64 77 93 107 111 114 119 129 130 133 135 146
Primary Contact: Wallace D. Mincey, Interim Chief Executive Officer
COO: Wallace D. Mincey, Interim Chief Executive Officer
CFO: Sandra Hughes, Chief Financial Officer
CMO: Samuel Cobarrubias, M.D., Chief of Staff
CIO: Shelly Studebaker, Director Management Information Systems
CHR: Shelly Studebaker, Manager Human Resources
CNO: Kellie Register, Director of Nursing
Web address: www.clinchmemorialhospital.org
Control: County–Government, nonfederal **Service:** General Medical and Surgical

Staffed Beds: 25 **Admissions:** 246 **Census:** 3 **Outpatient Visits:** 14030 **Births:** 0 **Total Expense ($000):** 10544 **Payroll Expense ($000):** 3781 **Personnel:** 94

JACKSON—Butts County

★ **SYLVAN GROVE HOSPITAL (111319)**, 1050 McDonough Road, Zip 30233–1599; tel. 770/775–7861, (Nonreporting) **A**10 18 **S** WellStar Health System, Marietta, GA
Primary Contact: Tamara Ison, Senior Vice President and President
CFO: Tamara Ison, Chief Financial Officer
CIO: Steve Brown, Chief Information Officer
CHR: Amanda Remington, Director Human Resources
Web address: www.sylvangrovehospital.com
Control: Corporation, Investor–owned, for–profit **Service:** General Medical and Surgical

Staffed Beds: 24

JASPER—Pickens County

◇ **PIEDMONT MOUNTAINSIDE HOSPITAL (110225)**, 1266 Highway 515 South, Zip 30143–4872; tel. 706/692–2441 **A**10 21 **F**3 13 15 20 28 29 34 35 40 41 45 46 49 53 57 59 64 70 76 77 79 81 85 107 110 111 114 115 119 129 130 132 135 148 **S** Piedmont Healthcare, Atlanta, GA
Primary Contact: Denise Ray, President and Chief Executive Officer
CFO: Frank R. Powell, Chief Financial Officer
CIO: Geoffrey Brown, Chief Information Officer
CHR: Connie McLendon, Director Human Resources
CNO: Michelle Breitfelder, Chief Nursing Officer
Web address: www.piedmontmountainsidehospital.org
Control: Other not–for–profit (including NFP Corporation) **Service:** General Medical and Surgical

Staffed Beds: 52 **Admissions:** 2656 **Census:** 28 **Outpatient Visits:** 61474 **Births:** 329 **Total Expense ($000):** 49174 **Payroll Expense ($000):** 21379 **Personnel:** 382

JESUP—Wayne County

☐ **WAYNE MEMORIAL HOSPITAL (110124)**, 865 South First Street, Zip 31545–0210, Mailing Address: P.O. Box 410, Zip 31598–0410; tel. 912/427–6811, (Nonreporting) **A**1 10 20
Primary Contact: Joseph P. Ierardi, Chief Executive Officer
CFO: Greg Jones, Chief Financial Officer
CMO: Dan Collipp, M.D., Chief of Staff
CIO: Deborah Six, Coordinator Data Processing
CHR: John Mclwain, Director Human Resources
Web address: www.wmhweb.com
Control: County–Government, nonfederal **Service:** General Medical and Surgical

Staffed Beds: 84

JOHNS CREEK—Fulton County

⊞ **EMORY JOHNS CREEK HOSPITAL (110230)**, 6325 Hospital Parkway, Zip 30097–5775; tel. 678/474–7000 **A**1 2 3 10 **F**3 11 12 13 15 18 20 22 26 29 30 31 34 35 36 40 45 49 50 54 57 59 60 64 68 70 72 73 74 75 76 77 78 79 81 82 85 87 93 107 108 110 111 115 116 117 119 126 129 130 131 132 141 146 147 148 **P**6 **S** Emory Healthcare, Atlanta, GA
Primary Contact: Marilyn Margolis, MSN, Chief Executive Officer
COO: Laurie Hansen, Associate Administrator
CFO: JoAnn Manning, Chief Financial Officer
CMO: Adedapo Odetoyinbo, M.D., Chief Medical Office
CIO: Doug Allen, Information Technology and System Director
CHR: Alejandro Miguel Almanza, Vice President and Human Resources
CNO: Heather Redrick, Chief Nursing Officer
Web address: www.emoryjohnscreek.com
Control: Other not–for–profit (including NFP Corporation) **Service:** General Medical and Surgical

Staffed Beds: 113 **Admissions:** 6400 **Census:** 72 **Outpatient Visits:** 63817 **Births:** 1043 **Total Expense ($000):** 117991 **Payroll Expense ($000):** 39994 **Personnel:** 590

KENNESAW—Cobb County

DEVEREUX GEORGIA TREATMENT NETWORK, 1291 Stanley Road N.W., Zip 30152–4359; tel. 770/427–0147 **F**98 99 106 **S** Devereux, Villanova, PA
Primary Contact: Gwendolyn Skinner, Executive Director
COO: Mary H. Esposito, Assistant Executive Director
CFO: Kathy Goggin, Director Administrative Services
CMO: Yolanda Graham, M.D., Medical Director
CIO: Sam Maguta, Coordinator Information Systems
CHR: Rudie Delien, Director Human Resources
CNO: Debra Sharpton, Director of Nursing
Web address: www.devereuxga.org
Control: Other not–for–profit (including NFP Corporation) **Service:** Children's hospital psychiatric

Staffed Beds: 100 **Admissions:** 201 **Census:** 63 **Outpatient Visits:** 70 **Births:** 0 **Total Expense ($000):** 18692 **Payroll Expense ($000):** 9824 **Personnel:** 208

LAGRANGE—Troup County

⊞ **WEST GEORGIA HEALTH (110016)**, 1514 Vernon Road, Zip 30240–4131; tel. 706/882–1411, (Total facility includes 260 beds in nursing home–type unit) **A**1 2 10 19 **F**3 8 11 12 13 15 18 20 22 26 28 29 30 31 34 35 40 47 48 49 50 54 56 57 58 59 62 63 64 66 68 70 73 74 75 76 77 78 79 80 81 82 84 85 86 89 92 93 96 107 108 110 111 114 115 119 120 121 123 128 129 130 132 135 146 147 148 **P**6 **S** WellStar Health System, Marietta, GA
Primary Contact: Gerald N. Fulks, President
COO: Charis L. Acree, Vice President and Chief Operating Officer
CFO: Paul R. Perrotti, CPA, Chief Financial Officer
CIO: Alan Whitehouse, Chief Information Officer
CHR: Tommy Britt, Vice President of Human Resources
CNO: Tracy Gynther, R.N., Vice President and Chief Nursing Officer
Web address: www.wghealth.org/
Control: Other not–for–profit (including NFP Corporation) **Service:** General Medical and Surgical

Staffed Beds: 390 **Admissions:** 7699 **Census:** 314 **Outpatient Visits:** 142232 **Births:** 1111 **Total Expense ($000):** 186937 **Payroll Expense ($000):** 75546 **Personnel:** 1338

LAKELAND—Lanier County

⊞ **SOUTH GEORGIA MEDICAL CENTER LANIER CAMPUS (111326)**, 116 West Thigpen Avenue, Zip 31635–1011; tel. 229/482–3110, (Nonreporting) **A**1 10 18
Primary Contact: Janet Myers, Administrator
CFO: Libby Flemming, Controller and Chief Information Officer
CMO: Bruce Herrington, M.D., Chief Medical Officer
CIO: Libby Flemming, Controller and Chief Information Officer
CHR: Vicki Dinkins, Director Human Resources
Web address: www.sgmc.org
Control: Other not–for–profit (including NFP Corporation) **Service:** Other specialty

Staffed Beds: 87

GA

Hospital, Medicare Provider Number, Address, Telephone, Approval, Facility, and Physician Codes, Health Care System

★ American Hospital Association (AHA) membership   ○ Healthcare Facilities Accreditation Program   ⇑ Center for Improvement in Healthcare Quality Accreditation
☐ The Joint Commission accreditation   ◇ DNV Healthcare Inc. accreditation   △ Commission on Accreditation of Rehabilitation Facilities (CARF) accreditation

LAVONIA—Franklin County

★ ◇ **ST. MARY'S SACRED HEART HOSPITAL (110027)**, 367 Clear Creek Parkway, Zip 30553–4173; tel. 706/356–7800, (Nonreporting) **A**10 21 **S** Trinity Health, Livonia, MI
Primary Contact: Jeff English, Interim Chief Executive Officer
CIO: Tim Vickery, Chief Information Officer
CHR: Lauren Papka, Chief Administrative Officer
CNO: Evelyn Murphy, R.N., Chief Nursing Officer
Web address: www.stmaryssacredheart.org/
Control: Other not–for–profit (including NFP Corporation) **Service:** General Medical and Surgical

Staffed Beds: 35

LAWRENCEVILLE—Gwinnett County

✠ **GWINNETT HOSPITAL SYSTEM (110087)**, 1000 Medical Center Boulevard, Zip 30046–7694, Mailing Address: P.O. Box 348, Zip 30046–0348; tel. 678/312–1000, (Includes GWINNETT MEDICAL CENTER, 1000 Medical Center Boulevard, Zip 30245, Mailing Address: Box 348, Zip 30246; tel. 678/312–1000; Thomas Shepherd, Executive Vice President and Chief Operating Officer; GWINNETT MEDICAL CENTER–DULUTH, 3620 Howell Ferry Road, Duluth, Zip 30096; tel. 678/312–6800), (Total facility includes 89 beds in nursing home–type unit) **A**1 2 3 8 10 13 **F**3 8 11 12 13 15 17 18 20 22 24 26 28 29 30 31 34 35 36 37 38 40 41 43 44 45 46 47 48 49 50 53 54 55 56 58 59 64 67 68 70 71 72 73 74 75 76 77 78 79 81 82 84 85 86 87 90 93 96 97 107 108 110 111 114 115 116 117 118 119 126 128 129 130 131 132 134 135 146 147 148 **P**6 8
Primary Contact: Philip R. Wolfe, President and Chief Executive Officer
COO: Thomas Shepherd, Executive Vice President and Chief Operating Officer
CFO: Thomas Y. McBride, III, Executive Vice President and Chief Financial Officer
CMO: Alan Bier, M.D., Executive Vice President and Chief Medical Officer
CIO: Patricia A. Lavely, Senior Vice President and Chief Information Officer
CHR: Stephen Nadeau, Senior Vice President Human Resources
CNO: Carol Danielson, R.N., Senior Vice President and Chief Nursing Officer
Web address: www.gwinnettmedicalcenter.org
Control: Other not–for–profit (including NFP Corporation) **Service:** General Medical and Surgical

Staffed Beds: 569 Admissions: 29212 Census: 482 Outpatient Visits: 406919 Births: 5083 Total Expense ($000): 626908 Payroll Expense ($000): 246158 Personnel: 3329

☐ **SUMMITRIDGE HOSPITAL (114004)**, 250 Scenic Highway, Zip 30046–5675; tel. 678/442–5800 **A**1 10 **F**4 98 99 102 103 104 105
Primary Contact: Tim E. Merritt, Chief Executive Officer
Web address: www.summitridgehospital.net
Control: Corporation, Investor–owned, for–profit **Service:** Psychiatric

Staffed Beds: 86 Admissions: 3451 Census: 70 Outpatient Visits: 8788 Births: 0 Total Expense ($000): 16513 Payroll Expense ($000): 7477 Personnel: 150

LITHONIA—Dekalb County

☐ **DEKALB MEDICAL AT HILLANDALE (110226)**, 2801 DeKalb Medical Parkway, Zip 30058–4996; tel. 404/501–8700 **A**1 10 **F**3 11 15 29 30 31 33 34 35 40 45 47 48 49 56 57 59 60 70 74 75 77 78 79 81 85 87 93 102 107 108 111 114 119 120 130 146 **S** DeKalb Regional Health System, Decatur, GA
Primary Contact: John Shelton, President and Chief Executive Officer
COO: John Shelton, Chief Operating Officer
CMO: Duane Barclay, D.O., Chief Medical Officer
CIO: Mark Trocino, Chief Information Officer
CHR: Tom Crawford, Vice President Human Resources
Web address: www.dekalbmedical.org
Control: Other not–for–profit (including NFP Corporation) **Service:** General Medical and Surgical

Staffed Beds: 80 Admissions: 4524 Census: 47 Outpatient Visits: 101755 Births: 0 Total Expense ($000): 69446 Payroll Expense ($000): 25014 Personnel: 422

LOUISVILLE—Jefferson County

◇ **JEFFERSON HOSPITAL (110100)**, 1067 Peachtree Street, Zip 30434–1599; tel. 478/625–7000, (Nonreporting) **A**10 20 21
Primary Contact: Steve Widener, Chief Executive Officer
CMO: James Polhill, M.D., Chief Medical Officer
CHR: Catherine Hall, Manager Human Resources
CNO: Ben Doyle, R.N., Director of Nursing
Web address: www.jeffersonhosp.com
Control: City–County, Government, nonfederal **Service:** General Medical and Surgical

Staffed Beds: 37

MACON—Bibb County

✠ **COLISEUM MEDICAL CENTERS (110164)**, 350 Hospital Drive, Zip 31217–3871; tel. 478/765–7000, (Includes COLISEUM CENTER FOR BEHAVIORAL HEALTH, 340 Hospital Drive, Zip 31217–3838; tel. 478/741–1355; Lance Jones, Chief Executive Officer), (Nonreporting) **A**1 2 10 **S** HCA, Nashville, TN
Primary Contact: Lance Jones, Chief Executive Officer
COO: Todd Dixon, R.N., Chief Operating Officer
CFO: Heath King, Chief Financial Officer
CIO: Joan Morstad, Director Information Systems
CHR: Laura Booras, Vice President Human Resources
Web address: www.coliseumhealthsystem.com
Control: Corporation, Investor–owned, for–profit **Service:** General Medical and Surgical

Staffed Beds: 227

✠ **COLISEUM NORTHSIDE HOSPITAL (110201)**, 400 Charter Boulevard, Zip 31210–4853, Mailing Address: P.O. Box 4627, Zip 31208–4627; tel. 478/757–8200, (Nonreporting) **A**1 10 **S** HCA, Nashville, TN
Primary Contact: Stephen J. Daugherty, Chief Executive Officer
COO: Todd Dixon, R.N., Chief Operating Officer
CFO: Heath King, Chief Financial Officer
CHR: Louise Truitt, Human Resource Director
CNO: Patricia Derrico, FACHE, Chief Nursing Officer
Web address: www.coliseumhealthsystem.com
Control: Corporation, Investor–owned, for–profit **Service:** General Medical and Surgical

Staffed Beds: 103

★ ◇ **MEDICAL CENTER, NAVICENT HEALTH (110107)**, 777 Hemlock Street, Zip 31201–2155; tel. 478/633–1000, (Includes CHILDREN'S HOSPITAL, NAVICENT HEALTH, 888 Pine Street, tel. 478/633–1000) **A**2 3 5 8 10 21 **F**3 5 7 8 11 12 13 14 15 17 18 20 22 24 26 28 29 30 31 32 34 35 36 39 40 43 44 45 46 47 48 49 50 51 53 54 56 57 58 59 60 61 62 63 64 65 66 68 70 72 73 74 75 76 77 78 79 81 82 83 84 85 86 87 88 89 92 93 94 97 98 99 100 101 102 103 104 105 107 108 110 111 114 115 119 126 130 132 135 143 144 145 146 147 148 **P**1 **S** Navicent Health, Macon, GA
Primary Contact: Ninfa M. Saunders, Chief Executive Officer
COO: Susan Harris, R.N., Chief Operating Officer
CFO: Rhonda S. Perry, Chief Financial Officer
CMO: Christopher Hendry, M.D., Chief Medical Officer
CIO: Ed Brown, Chief Information Officer
CHR: Bernard J. Price, Chief Human Resources Officer
CNO: Tracey Blalock, MSN, Chief Nurse Executive
Web address: www.https://www.navicenthealth.org/
Control: Other not–for–profit (including NFP Corporation) **Service:** General Medical and Surgical

Staffed Beds: 659 Admissions: 30553 Census: 487 Outpatient Visits: 382985 Births: 2703 Total Expense ($000): 598291 Payroll Expense ($000): 220072 Personnel: 4008

✠ **REGENCY HOSPITAL OF CENTRAL GEORGIA (112016)**, 535 Coliseum Drive, Zip 31217–0104; tel. 478/803–7300, (Nonreporting) **A**1 10 **S** Select Medical Corporation, Mechanicsburg, PA
Primary Contact: Michael S. Boggs, Chief Executive Officer
Web address: www.regencyhospital.com
Control: Corporation, Investor–owned, for–profit **Service:** Long–Term Acute Care hospital

Staffed Beds: 60

★ ◇ **REHABILITATION HOSPITAL, NAVICENT HEALTH (113029)**, 3351 Northside Drive, Zip 31210–2587; tel. 478/201–6500 **A**3 10 21 **F**11 29 30 36 60 68 74 75 77 79 82 86 87 91 92 93 94 95 96 119 130 131 132 143 146 148 **P**1 **S** Navicent Health, Macon, GA
Primary Contact: Gina Tipton, Director of Operations
COO: Darren Pearce, Executive Director
CFO: Beverly Owens, Controller
CMO: Allison Scheetz, M.D., Medical Director
Web address: www.centralgarehab.com
Control: Other not–for–profit (including NFP Corporation) **Service:** Rehabilitation

Staffed Beds: 58 Admissions: 955 Census: 40 Outpatient Visits: 15281 Births: 0

MADISON—Morgan County

☐ **MORGAN MEMORIAL HOSPITAL (111304)**, 1077 South Main Street, Zip 30650–2073, Mailing Address: P.O. Box 860, Zip 30650–0860; tel. 706/342–1667, (Nonreporting) **A**1 10 18
Primary Contact: Ralph A. Castillo, CPA, Chief Executive Officer
CFO: Kyle Wilkinson, Chief Financial Officer
CMO: Dan Zant, M.D., Chief of Staff
CIO: Patrick Cook, Vice President Support Services
CHR: Sarah Phillips, Manager Human Resources
CNO: Beth O'Neill, Chief Nursing Officer
Web address: www.mmh.org
Control: Hospital district or authority, Government, nonfederal **Service:** General Medical and Surgical

Staffed Beds: 41

GA

Many Facility Codes have changed. Please refer to the AHA Guide Code Chart. © 2016 AHA Guide

MARIETTA—Cobb County

✉ △ **WELLSTAR KENNESTONE HOSPITAL (110035)**, 677 Church Street, Zip 30060–1148; tel. 770/793–5000 **A**1 2 3 5 7 10 **F**3 10 11 12 13 15 17 18 20 22 24 26 28 29 30 31 36 37 38 40 41 43 44 45 46 47 48 49 50 51 53 54 55 58 59 60 61 64 66 68 70 72 73 74 75 76 77 78 79 80 81 82 84 85 86 87 89 90 93 94 96 97 100 102 107 108 110 111 114 115 117 118 119 120 121 123 124 125 126 129 130 132 135 141 146 147 148 **P**5 6 **S** WellStar Health System, Marietta, GA
Primary Contact: Dan Woods, President
CFO: Douglas Arvin, Vice President Finance and Chief Financial Officer
CMO: Robert Lubitz, M.D., Vice President of Medical Affairs
CIO: Jonathan B. Morris, M.D., Senior Vice President and Chief Information Officer
CHR: Jimmy Duncan, Vice President Human Resources
CNO: Lynn Meurer, MSN, Interim Chief Nursing Officer
Web address: www.wellstar.org
Control: Other not–for–profit (including NFP Corporation) **Service:** General Medical and Surgical

Staffed Beds: 657 Admissions: 38895 Census: 491 Outpatient Visits: 429339 Births: 5463 Personnel: 3939

✉ **WELLSTAR WINDY HILL HOSPITAL (112007)**, 2540 Windy Hill Road, Zip 30067–8632; tel. 770/644–1000 **A**1 2 10 **F**1 3 5 11 15 28 29 30 44 45 50 51 60 61 64 68 75 77 79 81 82 85 86 87 93 100 101 107 108 110 111 114 118 119 129 130 131 135 141 146 147 148 **P**5 6 **S** WellStar Health System, Marietta, GA
Primary Contact: Kem Mullins, FACHE, President
CFO: Marsha Burke, Senior Vice President and Chief Financial Officer
CMO: Larry Haldeman, M.D., Executive Vice President and Chief Medical Officer
CIO: Leigh Cox, Chief Information Officer
Web address: www.wellstar.org
Control: Other not–for–profit (including NFP Corporation) **Service:** Long–Term Acute Care hospital

Staffed Beds: 55 Admissions: 346 Census: 32 Outpatient Visits: 55548 Births: 0 Personnel: 359

METTER—Candler County

☐ **CANDLER COUNTY HOSPITAL (111334)**, 400 Cedar Street, Zip 30439–3338, Mailing Address: P.O. Box 597, Zip 30439–0597; tel. 912/685–5741, (Nonreporting) **A**1 10 18
Primary Contact: Mel Pyne, Chief Executive Officer
COO: David Flanders, Chief Operating Officer
CNO: Christy Blackburn, R.N., Chief Nursing Officer
Web address: www.candlercountyhospital.com
Control: Hospital district or authority, Government, nonfederal **Service:** General Medical and Surgical

Staffed Beds: 25

MILLEDGEVILLE—Baldwin County

☐ **CENTRAL STATE HOSPITAL**, 620 Broad Street, Zip 31062–0001; tel. 478/445–4128, (Nonreporting) **A**1 3
Primary Contact: Susan Trueblood, Regional Hospital Administrator
COO: Terry McGee, Chief Operations Officer
CMO: Scott VanSant, M.D., Chief Medical Officer
CIO: Betsy Bradley, Coordinator Performance Improvement
CHR: Myra Holloway, Director Human Resources Management
Web address: www.centralstatehospital.org
Control: State–Government, nonfederal **Service:** Psychiatric

Staffed Beds: 297

✉ **OCONEE REGIONAL MEDICAL CENTER (110150)**, 821 North Cobb Street, Zip 31061–2351, Mailing Address: P.O. Box 690, Zip 31059–0690; tel. 478/454–3505, (Total facility includes 15 beds in nursing home–type unit) **A**1 10 19 **F**3 11 13 15 28 29 30 31 34 35 37 40 45 46 49 50 51 53 57 59 60 64 68 70 75 76 78 79 80 81 82 85 86 87 89 92 93 107 108 110 111 114 116 117 119 120 121 123 128 129 132 135 146 147 148 **S** Oconee Regional Health Systems, Milledgeville, GA
Primary Contact: Steven Johnson, Interim Chief Executive Officer
CFO: Brenda Qualls, Chief Financial Officer
CNO: Deborah Block, Vice President Nursing and Chief Nursing Officer
Web address: www.oconeeregional.com
Control: Other not–for–profit (including NFP Corporation) **Service:** General Medical and Surgical

Staffed Beds: 90 Admissions: 3293 Census: 45 Outpatient Visits: 118728 Births: 618 Total Expense ($000): 68120 Payroll Expense ($000): 23537 Personnel: 427

MONROE—Walton County

✉ **CLEARVIEW REGIONAL MEDICAL CENTER (110046)**, 2151 West Spring Street, Zip 30655–3115, Mailing Address: PO BOX 1346, Zip 30655–1346; tel. 770/267–8461, (Nonreporting) **A**1 10 **S** Quorum Health, Brentwood, TN
Primary Contact: Michael Johnson, Chief Executive Officer
CFO: Jeffrey Mullis, Interim Chief Financial Officer
CMO: Douglas Miller, M.D., Chief of Medical Staff
CIO: Cory Crayton, Director of Information Systems
CHR: Michele Monsrud, Director Human Resources
CNO: Sharon H. Queen, R.N., Chief Nursing Officer
Web address: www.clearviewregionalmedicalcenter.com/
Control: Corporation, Investor–owned, for–profit **Service:** General Medical and Surgical

Staffed Beds: 77

MONTEZUMA—Macon County

◇ **FLINT RIVER COMMUNITY HOSPITAL (110190)**, 509 Sumter Street, Zip 31063–1733, Mailing Address: P.O. Box 770, Zip 31063–2502; tel. 478/472–3100, (Nonreporting) **A**10 21
Primary Contact: Michael C. Patterson, Chief Executive Officer
CMO: Quincy Jordan, M.D., Chief of Staff
CHR: Vicki Stotts, Coordinator Human Resources
CNO: Lee Hughes, R.N., Chief Nursing Officer
Web address: www.flintriverhospital.com/
Control: Corporation, Investor–owned, for–profit **Service:** General Medical and Surgical

Staffed Beds: 49

MONTICELLO—Jasper County

JASPER MEMORIAL HOSPITAL (111303), 898 College Street, Zip 31064–1258; tel. 706/468–6411, (Total facility includes 55 beds in nursing home–type unit) **A**10 18 **F**11 18 29 34 40 57 59 65 77 93 97 107 111 119 128 133 146 148 **P**6 **S** Oconee Regional Health Systems, Milledgeville, GA
Primary Contact: Jan Gaston, Administrator
CFO: Stuart Abney, Controller
CHR: Laura Hammonds, Assistant Administrator
CNO: Robin Carey, Director of Nursing
Web address: www.jaspermemorialhospital.org
Control: Other not–for–profit (including NFP Corporation) **Service:** General Medical and Surgical

Staffed Beds: 67 Admissions: 139 Census: 53 Outpatient Visits: 12682 Births: 0 Total Expense ($000): 9307 Payroll Expense ($000): 4703 Personnel: 124

MOULTRIE—Colquitt County

✉ ○ **COLQUITT REGIONAL MEDICAL CENTER (110105)**, 3131 South Main Street, Zip 31768–6925, Mailing Address: P.O. Box 40, Zip 31776–0040; tel. 229/985–3420 **A**1 10 11 **F**3 7 11 12 13 15 17 20 29 30 33 34 35 39 40 45 47 48 49 56 57 59 60 61 62 63 65 68 70 74 75 76 77 78 79 81 82 85 86 87 89 91 93 97 107 108 110 111 115 119 126 127 129 130 131 132 135 143 144 146 147 148
Primary Contact: James L. Matney, President and Chief Executive Officer
COO: Greg K. Johnson, Chief Operating Officer
CFO: Shamb Purohit, Chief Financial Officer
CMO: Andy Wills, M.D., Medical Director
CIO: Bill Bishop, Chief Information Officer
CHR: Dawn Johns, Director Human Resources
CNO: Dena Zinker, MSN, Vice President Patient Services
Web address: www.colquittregional.com
Control: Hospital district or authority, Government, nonfederal **Service:** General Medical and Surgical

Staffed Beds: 99 Admissions: 4678 Census: 56 Outpatient Visits: 132058 Births: 526 Total Expense ($000): 88691 Payroll Expense ($000): 37363 Personnel: 846

GA

Hospital, Medicare Provider Number, Address, Telephone, Approval, Facility, and Physician Codes, Health Care System

★ American Hospital Association (AHA) membership
☐ The Joint Commission accreditation
○ Healthcare Facilities Accreditation Program
◇ DNV Healthcare Inc. accreditation
⇑ Center for Improvement in Healthcare Quality Accreditation
△ Commission on Accreditation of Rehabilitation Facilities (CARF) accreditation

TURNING POINT HOSPITAL (110209), 3015 Veterans Parkway South, Zip 31788–6705, Mailing Address: P.O. Box 1177, Zip 31776–1177; tel. 229/985–4815 **A**10 **F**4 5 30 75 87 98 130 135 143 **P**6 **S** Universal Health Services, Inc., King of Prussia, PA
Primary Contact: Judy H. Payne, Chief Executive Officer
COO: Stephen Smith, Associate Administrator
CFO: Edwin Bennett, Controller
CMO: Muhammed M. Alam, Medical Director
CHR: Jennifer Azar, Director Human Resources
CNO: Faith Connell, Director of Nursing
Web address: www.turningpointcare.com
Control: Corporation, Investor–owned, for–profit **Service:** Alcoholism and other chemical dependency

Staffed Beds: 59 **Admissions:** 3320 **Census:** 51 **Outpatient Visits:** 24824
Births: 0 **Total Expense ($000):** 22145 **Payroll Expense ($000):** 11922
Personnel: 226

NASHVILLE—Berrien County

✉ **SOUTH GEORGIA MEDICAL CENTER BERRIEN CAMPUS (110234)**, 1221 East McPherson Avenue, Zip 31639–2326, Mailing Address: P.O. Box 665, Zip 31639–0665; tel. 229/543–7100 **A**1 10 **F**3 15 29 34 35 38 40 45 50 56 57 59 68 77 78 86 87 93 98 103 107 108 110 111 115 119 130 135 146
Primary Contact: Janet Myers, Administrator
Web address: www.berrienhospital.com
Control: Hospital district or authority, Government, nonfederal **Service:** General Medical and Surgical

Staffed Beds: 39 **Admissions:** 406 **Census:** 13 **Outpatient Visits:** 14723
Births: 0 **Total Expense ($000):** 8966 **Payroll Expense ($000):** 3752

NEWNAN—Coweta County

◇ **PIEDMONT NEWNAN HOSPITAL (110229)**, 745 Poplar Road, Zip 30265–1618; tel. 770/400–1000 **A**2 10 21 **F**11 12 13 15 18 20 28 29 30 31 34 35 40 45 46 49 51 53 57 59 60 64 68 70 72 74 75 76 77 78 79 81 84 85 86 87 93 107 108 110 111 114 115 116 117 118 119 120 121 123 126 129 130 132 135 146 148 **S** Piedmont Healthcare, Atlanta, GA
Primary Contact: Michael Robertson, Chief Executive Officer
COO: Nathan Nipper, Vice President and Chief Operating Officer
CFO: John Miles, Chief Financial Officer
CMO: Jeffrey R. Folk, M.D., Vice President Medical Affairs and Chief Medical Officer
CIO: Henry Scott, Executive Director, Technical Services
CHR: Clay Boyles, Executive Director, Human Resources
CNO: Jason Smith, Chief Nursing Officer
Web address: www.piedmont.org/locations/piedmont–newnan/pnh–home
Control: Other not–for–profit (including NFP Corporation) **Service:** General Medical and Surgical

Staffed Beds: 136 **Admissions:** 8012 **Census:** 90 **Outpatient Visits:** 112506
Births: 1110 **Total Expense ($000):** 121801 **Payroll Expense ($000):** 48536 **Personnel:** 673

☐ **SOUTHEASTERN REGIONAL MEDICAL CENTER (110233)**, 600 Celebrate Life Parkway, Zip 30265–8000; tel. 770/400–6000 **A**1 10 **F**3 15 29 30 31 33 34 35 36 38 45 46 47 49 55 57 58 64 65 67 68 70 74 75 77 78 79 81 82 84 85 86 87 93 104 107 108 109 110 111 114 115 116 117 118 119 120 121 123 124 126 130 132 135 146 148 **P**6 **S** Cancer Treatment Centers of America, Schaumburg, IL
Primary Contact: Anne Meisner, MSN, President and Chief Executive Officer
COO: David Kent, Chief Operating Officer
CFO: Scott Walker, Chief Financial Officer
CNO: Gloria V. Barnes, MSN, Assistant Vice President Patient Care Services
Web address: www.cancercenter.com/southeastern–hospital.cfm
Control: Corporation, Investor–owned, for–profit **Service:** Cancer

Staffed Beds: 50 **Admissions:** 1447 **Census:** 27 **Outpatient Visits:** 22789
Births: 0 **Personnel:** 1059

NORCROSS—Gwinnett County

LAKEVIEW BEHAVIORAL HEALTH, 1 Technology Parkway South, Zip 30092–2928; tel. 888/834–4195, (Nonreporting) **S** Acadia Healthcare Company, Inc., Franklin, TN
Web address: www.lakeviewbehavioralhealth.com
Control: Corporation, Investor–owned, for–profit **Service:** Psychiatric

Staffed Beds: 70

OCILLA—Irwin County

✉ **IRWIN COUNTY HOSPITAL (110130)**, 710 North Irwin Avenue, Zip 31774–5011; tel. 229/468–3800, (Nonreporting) **A**1 10
Primary Contact: Paige Wynn, Administrator
CFO: Tami Gray, Chief Financial Officer
CMO: Ashfaq Saiyed, M.D., Medical Director
CHR: Becky Edwards, Manager Human Resources
Web address: www.irwincntyhospital.com
Control: County–Government, nonfederal **Service:** General Medical and Surgical

Staffed Beds: 64

PERRY—Houston County

✉ **PERRY HOSPITAL (110153)**, 1120 Morningside Drive, Zip 31069–2906; tel. 478/987–3600 **A**1 10 **F**3 11 15 18 29 30 34 35 39 40 45 48 50 56 57 58 59 61 68 70 75 79 81 82 85 86 87 89 93 100 107 110 111 114 115 119 129 130 131 132 133 134 135 146 147 148 **S** Houston Healthcare System, Warner Robins, GA
Primary Contact: David Campbell, Administrator
CFO: Sean Whilden, Chief Financial Officer
CMO: Charles Nutinsky, Chief Medical Officer
CIO: George Curtis, Director Information Systems
CHR: Michael O'Hara, Senior Executive Director
CNO: Melinda D. Hartley, R.N., Vice President Patient Care Services
Web address: www.hhc.org
Control: Other not–for–profit (including NFP Corporation) **Service:** General Medical and Surgical

Staffed Beds: 39 **Admissions:** 1645 **Census:** 21 **Outpatient Visits:** 39806
Births: 0 **Total Expense ($000):** 26388 **Payroll Expense ($000):** 9722
Personnel: 223

QUITMAN—Brooks County

✉ **BROOKS COUNTY HOSPITAL (111332)**, 903 North Court Street, Zip 31643–1315, Mailing Address: P.O. Box 5000, Zip 31643–5000; tel. 229/263–4171 **A**1 10 18 **F**11 15 18 29 34 35 40 50 57 59 64 68 75 86 87 97 107 110 111 114 119 127 130 133 135 146 **P**6 **S** Archbold Medical Center, Thomasville, GA
Primary Contact: Nancy Fincher Williams, Administrator
CFO: Skip Hightower, Chief Financial Officer
CMO: Michael Sopt, M.D., Chief of Staff
CHR: Janet Eldridge, Director Human Resources and Personnel
CNO: June Furney, R.N., Director of Nursing
Web address: www.archbold.org
Control: Hospital district or authority, Government, nonfederal **Service:** General Medical and Surgical

Staffed Beds: 25 **Admissions:** 438 **Census:** 14 **Outpatient Visits:** 12363
Births: 0 **Total Expense ($000):** 11176 **Payroll Expense ($000):** 4942
Personnel: 90

REIDSVILLE—Tattnall County

★ **OPTIM MEDICAL CENTER – TATTNALL (111323)**, 247 South Main Street, Zip 30453–4605; tel. 912/557–1000, (Nonreporting) **A**10 18 **S** National Surgical Healthcare, Chicago, IL
Primary Contact: Rob Snipes, Administrator
Web address: www.tattnallhospital.com
Control: Corporation, Investor–owned, for–profit **Service:** Orthopedic

Staffed Beds: 25

RIVERDALE—Clayton County

☐ **RIVERWOODS BEHAVIORAL HEALTH SYSTEM (114035)**, 233 Medical Center Drive, Zip 30274–2640; tel. 770/991–8500, (Nonreporting) **A**1 5 10 **S** Acadia Healthcare Company, Inc., Franklin, TN
Primary Contact: Kirk Kureska, Chief Executive Officer
COO: Jenifer Harcourt, Chief Operating Officer
CFO: Tricia Nelson, Chief Financial Officer
CIO: Hema Patel, Director Medical Records
CHR: Tareka Beasley, Director Human Resources
Web address: www.riverwoodsbehavioral.com
Control: Corporation, Investor–owned, for–profit **Service:** Psychiatric

Staffed Beds: 75

✉ **SOUTHERN CRESCENT HOSPITAL FOR SPECIALTY CARE (112015)**, 11 Upper Riverdale Road S.W., 6th Floor, Zip 30274–2615; tel. 770/897–7600 **A**1 10 **F**1 29 30 35 44 75 77 82 84 87 148 **S** CHRISTUS Health, Irving, TX
Primary Contact: Fiona Adams, Interim Director
Web address: www.christusdubuis.org/SouthernCrescentHospitalforSpecialtyCare
Control: Church–operated, Nongovernment, not–for profit **Service:** Long–Term Acute Care hospital

Staffed Beds: 30 **Admissions:** 250 **Census:** 21 **Outpatient Visits:** 0 **Births:** 0 **Total Expense ($000):** 10923 **Payroll Expense ($000):** 4319 **Personnel:** 79

✉ **SOUTHERN REGIONAL MEDICAL CENTER (110165)**, 11 Upper Riverdale Road S.W., Zip 30274–2615; tel. 770/991–8000, (Nonreporting) **A**1 2 3 5 10 **S** Prime Healthcare Services, Ontario, CA
Primary Contact: Charlotte W. Dupre, Interim Chief Executive Officer
COO: Therese O. Sucher, Senior Vice President Operations
CFO: Richard G. Stovall, Senior Vice President Fiscal Services and Chief Financial Officer
CMO: Willie Cochran, Jr., M.D., Chief of Staff
CIO: Karen Moore, Vice President Information Technology and Chief Information Officer
CHR: Norma Adams, Director Human Resources
Web address: www.southernregional.org
Control: Other not–for–profit (including NFP Corporation) **Service:** General Medical and Surgical

Staffed Beds: 331

Many Facility Codes have changed. Please refer to the AHA Guide Code Chart. © 2016 AHA Guide

GA

ROME—Floyd County

✠ **FLOYD MEDICAL CENTER (110054)**, 304 Turner McCall Boulevard,
Zip 30165–5621, Mailing Address: P.O. Box 233, Zip 30162–0233;
tel. 706/509–5000 **A**1 2 3 5 10 13 19 **F**3 4 5 6 7 8 9 11 12 13 15 17 18 20
22 26 28 29 30 31 32 34 35 36 37 38 39 40 43 44 45 46 48 49 50 51 53
54 56 57 58 59 61 63 64 65 66 68 70 71 72 74 75 76 77 78 79 81 82 84
85 86 87 88 89 90 93 96 97 98 100 101 102 103 104 107 108 110 111
114 115 118 119 129 130 131 132 134 135 143 144 146 147 148
Primary Contact: Kurt Stuenkel, FACHE, President and Chief Executive Officer
COO: Warren Alston Rigas, Executive Vice President and Chief Operating Officer
CFO: Rick Sheerin, Vice President Fiscal Services
CMO: Joseph Biuso, M.D., Vice President and Chief of Medical Affairs
CIO: Jeff Buda, Chief Information Officer
CHR: Beth Bradford, Director Human Resources
CNO: Sheila Bennett, R.N., Vice President & Chief Nursing Officer
Web address: www.floyd.org
Control: Other not–for–profit (including NFP Corporation) **Service:** General
Medical and Surgical

Staffed Beds: 327 **Admissions:** 14367 **Census:** 205 **Outpatient Visits:**
267406 **Births:** 2260 **Total Expense ($000):** 352713 **Payroll Expense
($000):** 154687 **Personnel:** 2531

✠ **KINDRED HOSPITAL ROME (112010)**, 304 Turner McCall Boulevard,
Zip 30165–5621; tel. 706/378–6800, (Nonreporting) **A**1 10 **S** Kindred
Healthcare, Louisville, KY
Primary Contact: Al Diaz, M.D., Chief Executive Officer
CFO: Julia Smith, Chief Financial Officer
CMO: Brij Singh, Medical Staff Director
CHR: Holly Murdock, Human Resources Coordinator
CNO: Jennifer Johnstone, Chief Clinical Officer
Web address: www.kindredrome.com
Control: Corporation, Investor–owned, for–profit **Service:** Long–Term Acute Care
hospital

Staffed Beds: 45

✠ **REDMOND REGIONAL MEDICAL CENTER (110168)**, 501 Redmond Road,
Zip 30165–1415, Mailing Address: P.O. Box 107001, Zip 30164–7001;
tel. 706/291–0291, (Nonreporting) **A**1 2 10 19 **S** HCA, Nashville, TN
Primary Contact: John Quinlivan, Chief Executive Officer
COO: David Bradley Stockton, Chief Operating Officer
CFO: Kenneth Metteauer, Chief Financial Officer
CMO: Julie Coffman Barnes, M.D., Chief Medical Officer
CIO: Brad Treglown, Director Information Systems
CHR: Patsy Adams, Vice President Human Resources
CNO: Lisa Wallace, R.N., Chief Nursing Officer
Web address: www.redmondregional.com
Control: Corporation, Investor–owned, for–profit **Service:** General Medical and
Surgical

Staffed Beds: 230

SPECIALTY HOSPITAL See Kindred Hospital Rome

ROSWELL—Fulton County

✠ **NORTH FULTON REGIONAL HOSPITAL (110198)**, 3000 Hospital Boulevard,
Zip 30076–3899; tel. 770/751–2500, (Nonreporting) **A**1 2 3 10 13 **S** WellStar
Health System, Marietta, GA
Primary Contact: Deborah C. Keel, Chief Executive Officer
COO: Lindsey Petrini, Chief Operating Officer
CFO: Felix Sotoizaguirre, Chief Financial Officer
CMO: Karim Godamunne, M.D., Chief Medical Officer
CHR: Susan Brown, Chief Human Resources Officer
CNO: Nancy Melcher, Chief Nursing Officer
Web address: www.nfultonhospital.com
Control: Corporation, Investor–owned, for–profit **Service:** General Medical and
Surgical

Staffed Beds: 196

SAINT MARYS—Camden County

✠ **SOUTHEAST GEORGIA HEALTH SYSTEM CAMDEN CAMPUS (110146)**,
2000 Dan Proctor Drive, Zip 31558–3810; tel. 912/576–6200 **A**1 10 20 **F**3 11
13 15 29 30 31 34 35 40 45 46 47 48 49 50 54 57 59 64 68 70 71 75 76
77 78 79 81 85 86 87 93 94 96 107 108 110 111 114 116 117 119 120
129 130 131 132 146 **P**5 **S** Southeast Georgia Health System, Brunswick, GA
Primary Contact: Howard W. Sepp, Jr., Vice President and Administrator
CFO: Michael D. Scherneck, President and Chief Executive Officer and Chief
Financial Officer
CMO: Steve Nickisch, Chief of Staff
CIO: Chuck Bumgardner, Director
CHR: Patrick D. Ebri, Ph.D., Vice President Human Resources
Web address: www.sghs.org
Control: City–County, Government, nonfederal **Service:** General Medical and
Surgical

Staffed Beds: 40 **Admissions:** 1884 **Census:** 18 **Outpatient Visits:** 81914
Births: 665 **Total Expense ($000):** 38574 **Payroll Expense ($000):** 14030
Personnel: 240

SAINT SIMONS ISLAND—Glynn County

☐ **SAINT SIMONS BY–THE–SEA HOSPITAL (114016)**, 2927 Demere Road,
Zip 31522–1620; tel. 912/638–1999 **A**1 10 **F**34 98 102 **S** Universal Health
Services, Inc., King of Prussia, PA
Primary Contact: Chuck Flavio, Chief Executive Officer
CMO: Kim Masters, M.D., Medical Director
CIO: Chisty Mosely, Director Information Management
Web address: www.ssbythesea.com
Control: Corporation, Investor–owned, for–profit **Service:** Psychiatric

Staffed Beds: 101 **Admissions:** 2679 **Census:** 66 **Births:** 0 **Total Expense
($000):** 10699 **Payroll Expense ($000):** 5769 **Personnel:** 116

SANDERSVILLE—Washington County

☐ **WASHINGTON COUNTY REGIONAL MEDICAL CENTER (110086)**, 610
Sparta Road, Zip 31082–1860, Mailing Address: P.O. Box 636, Zip 31082–0636;
tel. 478/240–2000, (Nonreporting) **A**1 10 20
Primary Contact: Robert M. Trimm, Chief Executive Officer
CFO: Cythia Parker, Fiscal Director
CMO: Robert Wright, M.D., Chief of Staff
CHR: Gayle Prince, Director Human Resources
CNO: Pamela Stewart, Director of Nursing
Web address: www.wcrmc.com
Control: Hospital district or authority, Government, nonfederal **Service:** General
Medical and Surgical

Staffed Beds: 116

SAVANNAH—Chatham County

✠ △ **CANDLER HOSPITAL (110024)**, 5353 Reynolds Street, Zip 31405–6015;
tel. 912/819–6000, (Total facility includes 11 beds in nursing home–type unit) **A**1
7 10 **F**2 3 11 13 15 18 20 29 30 31 32 34 35 36 37 38 39 40 44 45 46 47
48 49 50 53 54 57 58 59 60 61 64 65 68 70 71 73 74 75 76 77 78 80 81
82 84 85 86 87 89 90 91 93 94 96 107 108 110 111 115 117 118 119 120
121 123 124 126 128 129 130 131 135 146 147 148
Primary Contact: Paul P. Hinchey, President and Chief Executive Officer
CFO: Gregory J. Schaack, CPA, Vice President and Chief Financial Officer
CMO: James Scott, M.D., Vice President Medical Affairs
CIO: George Evans, Vice President and Chief Information Officer
CHR: Don Stubbs, Vice President Human Resources
CNO: Sherry Danello, MSN, Vice President and Chief Nursing Officer
Web address: www.sjchs.org
Control: Church–operated, Nongovernment, not–for profit **Service:** General
Medical and Surgical

Staffed Beds: 285 **Admissions:** 11774 **Census:** 186 **Outpatient Visits:**
238068 **Births:** 3046 **Total Expense ($000):** 253289 **Payroll Expense
($000):** 94974 **Personnel:** 1645

☐ **COASTAL HARBOR TREATMENT CENTER (114008)**, 1150 Cornell Avenue,
Zip 31406–2702; tel. 912/354–3911 **A**1 10 **F**5 98 99 103 105 106 **P**6
S Universal Health Services, Inc., King of Prussia, PA
Primary Contact: Sally Perry, Chief Executive Officer
COO: Ray Heckerman, Chief Executive Officer and Managing Director
CFO: Brad Lavoie, Chief Financial Officer
CMO: Reemon Bishara, M.D., Medical Director
CHR: Kellie Carlson, Director Human Resources
CNO: Jillisa Thornton, Director of Nursing
Web address: www.coastalharbor.com
Control: Corporation, Investor–owned, for–profit **Service:** Psychiatric

Staffed Beds: 191 **Admissions:** 3645 **Census:** 155 **Outpatient Visits:** 25587
Births: 0 **Total Expense ($000):** 31182 **Payroll Expense ($000):** 13663
Personnel: 302

GA

GEORGE AND MARIE BACKUS CHILDREN'S HOSPITAL See Memorial Children's Hospital

☐ **GEORGIA REGIONAL HOSPITAL AT SAVANNAH (114028)**, 1915 Eisenhower Drive, Zip 31406–5098; tel. 912/356–2011, (Nonreporting) **A**1 10
Primary Contact: Andy Mannich, Regional Administrator
COO: Thomas F. Kurtz, Jr., Chief Operating Officer
CFO: Janet Edenfield, Director Financial Services
CMO: Donald Manning, M.D., Clinical Director
CHR: Jamekia Powers, Assistant Director Human Resources
Web address: www.dbhdd.georgia.gov/georgia–regional–hospital–savannah
Control: State–Government, nonfederal **Service:** Psychiatric

Staffed Beds: 105

LANDMARK HOSPITAL OF SAVANNAH (110235), 800 East 68th Street, Zip 31405–4710; tel. 912/298–1000, (Nonreporting) **A**22 **S** Landmark Hospitals, Cape Girardeau, MO
Primary Contact: John Salandi, Chief Executive Officer
Web address: www.landmarkhospitals.com/savannah
Control: Partnership, Investor–owned, for–profit **Service:** Long–Term Acute Care hospital

Staffed Beds: 50

☒ △ **MEMORIAL HEALTH (110036)**, 4700 Waters Avenue, Zip 31404–6283, Mailing Address: P.O. Box 23089, Zip 31403–3089; tel. 912/350–8000, (Includes MEMORIAL CHILDREN'S HOSPITAL, 4700 Waters Avenue, Zip 31404–6220, Mailing Address: PO Box 23089, Zip 31403–3089; tel. 912/350–7337) **A**1 2 3 5 7 8 10 **F**3 8 11 12 13 14 15 17 18 19 20 22 24 26 28 29 30 31 32 34 35 36 37 39 40 41 43 44 45 46 49 50 53 54 55 56 57 59 60 61 64 65 66 68 70 71 72 73 74 75 76 77 78 79 80 81 82 83 84 85 86 87 88 89 92 93 96 97 98 100 101 102 103 104 107 110 111 115 117 118 119 120 121 122 123 124 126 129 130 131 132 135 143 144 146 147 148 **P**6
Primary Contact: Margaret Gill, President and Chief Executive Officer
COO: Mary Chatman, Ph.D., Senior Vice President, Chief Operating Officer and Chief Nursing Officer
CFO: Laura Dow, Chief Financial Officer
CMO: Ramon V. Meguiar, M.D., Chief Medical Officer
CIO: Kathryn McClellan, Chief Information Officer
CHR: Alisa R. Griner, Director, Human Resources
CNO: Mary Chatman, Ph.D., Senior Vice President, Chief Operating Officer and Chief Nursing Officer
Web address: www.memorialhealth.com
Control: Other not–for–profit (including NFP Corporation) **Service:** General Medical and Surgical

Staffed Beds: 508 Admissions: 26280 Census: 412 Outpatient Visits: 242338 Births: 2966 Total Expense ($000): 478049 Payroll Expense ($000): 169314 Personnel: 3324

REHABILITATION HOSPITAL OF SAVANNAH, 6510 Seawright DR, Zip 31406–2752; tel. 800/622–7269, (Nonreporting)
Primary Contact: Kathy Kleinsteuber, Chief Executive Officer
Web address: www.rehabilitationhospitalsavannah.com
Control: Corporation, Investor–owned, for–profit **Service:** Rehabilitation

Staffed Beds: 50

☒ **SELECT SPECIALTY HOSPITAL–SAVANNAH (112011)**, 5353 Reynolds Street, 4 South, Zip 31405–6015; tel. 912/819–7972, (Nonreporting) **A**1 10 **S** Select Medical Corporation, Mechanicsburg, PA
Primary Contact: Patrick McVey, Chief Executive Officer
Web address: www.selectspecialtyhospitals.com/company/locations/savannah. aspx
Control: Corporation, Investor–owned, for–profit **Service:** Long–Term Acute Care hospital

Staffed Beds: 40

ST. JOSEPH'S CANDLER HOSPITAL See Candler Hospital

☐ △ **ST. JOSEPH'S HOSPITAL (110043)**, 11705 Mercy Boulevard, Zip 31419–1791; tel. 912/819–4100, (Total facility includes 11 beds in nursing home–type unit) **A**1 2 7 10 **F**3 11 17 18 20 22 24 26 28 29 34 35 36 37 38 39 40 41 42 44 45 49 50 56 57 58 59 60 65 68 70 74 75 77 79 80 81 82 84 85 86 87 90 93 94 96 107 108 110 114 115 119 126 128 130 131 132 135 146 148
Primary Contact: Paul P. Hinchey, President and Chief Executive Officer
COO: Kyle McCann, Chief Operating Officer
CFO: Gregory J. Schaack, CPA, Vice President and Chief Financial Officer
CMO: James Scott, M.D., Vice President Medical Affairs
CIO: Nolan Henessee, Vice President and Chief Information Officer
CHR: Steve Pound, Vice President Human Resources
CNO: Sherry Danello, MSN, Vice President and Chief Nursing Officer
Web address: www.sjchs.org
Control: Church–operated, Nongovernment, not–for profit **Service:** General Medical and Surgical

Staffed Beds: 235 Admissions: 11185 Census: 174 Outpatient Visits: 84389 Births: 0 Total Expense ($000): 196416 Payroll Expense ($000): 70477 Personnel: 1155

SMYRNA—Cobb County

☒ **RIDGEVIEW INSTITUTE (114012)**, 3995 South Cobb Drive S.E., Zip 30080–6397; tel. 770/434–4567 **A**1 5 10 **F**4 5 29 35 38 75 87 98 99 100 101 103 104 105 130 132 147 **P**8
Primary Contact: Frank Sartor, President and Chief Executive Officer
CFO: Ruth Jenkins, Chief Financial Officer
CMO: Thomas Bradford Johns, M.D., Medical Director
CIO: Lynn Leger, Director Information Systems
CHR: Betty Sonderman, Manager Human Resources
Web address: www.ridgeviewinstitute.com
Control: Other not–for–profit (including NFP Corporation) **Service:** Psychiatric

Staffed Beds: 102 Admissions: 4987 Census: 80 Outpatient Visits: 40288 Births: 0 Total Expense ($000): 31627 Payroll Expense ($000): 18706 Personnel: 380

SNELLVILLE—Gwinnett County

☒ **EASTSIDE MEDICAL CENTER (110192)**, 1700 Medical Way, Zip 30078–2195; tel. 770/979–0200, (Nonreporting) **A**1 2 10 **S** HCA, Nashville, TN
Primary Contact: Trent Lind, Chief Executive Officer
COO: Callie Andrews, Chief Operating Officer
CMO: Michael O'Neill, M.D., Chief Medical Officer
CIO: Pattie Page, Director Marketing and Public Relations
Web address: www.eastsidemedical.com
Control: Corporation, Investor–owned, for–profit **Service:** General Medical and Surgical

Staffed Beds: 294

SPRINGFIELD—Effingham County

☒ **EFFINGHAM HOSPITAL (111306)**, 459 Highway 119 South, Zip 31329–3021, Mailing Address: P.O. Box 386, Zip 31329–0386; tel. 912/754–6451, (Total facility includes 105 beds in nursing home–type unit) **A**1 10 18 **F**3 6 11 15 18 26 27 29 32 34 35 40 43 45 49 50 54 56 57 59 61 64 74 77 79 81 85 86 97 107 110 111 114 119 127 128 130 133 134 135 146 147 148 **P**6
Primary Contact: Francine Baker–Witt, R.N., Interim Chief Executive Officer
CFO: Matthew Moore, Director of Financial Reporting
CMO: Claude Sanks, Chief Medical Staff
CIO: Mary Pizzino, Chief Information Officer
CHR: Marie Murphy, Director Human Resources
CNO: Betsy Smith, Chief Nursing Officer
Web address: www.effinghamhospital.org
Control: Hospital district or authority, Government, nonfederal **Service:** General Medical and Surgical

Staffed Beds: 130 Admissions: 450 Census: 109 Outpatient Visits: 44838 Births: 0 Total Expense ($000): 40350 Payroll Expense ($000): 17222 Personnel: 340

STATESBORO—Bulloch County

☒ **EAST GEORGIA REGIONAL MEDICAL CENTER (110075)**, 1499 Fair Road, Zip 30458–1683, Mailing Address: P.O. Box 1048, Zip 30459–1048; tel. 912/486–1000 **A**1 10 19 **F**3 11 13 15 18 20 22 26 29 35 37 40 45 46 47 48 49 50 51 54 57 59 60 64 67 68 70 74 75 77 78 79 81 82 85 87 93 107 108 110 111 112 114 115 116 117 118 119 126 129 132 145 146 147 148 **P**5 6 **S** Community Health Systems, Inc., Franklin, TN
Primary Contact: Paul Theriot, Chief Executive Officer
COO: Erin Smith, Chief Operating Officer
CFO: Elmer Polite, Chief Financial Officer
CMO: Andrew Cichelli, M.D., Chief of Staff
CIO: Conan Stuart, Director Information Services
CHR: Michael Black, Director Human Resources
CNO: Heidi Malez Coffee, Chief Nursing Officer
Web address: www.eastgeorgiaregional.com
Control: Corporation, Investor–owned, for–profit **Service:** General Medical and Surgical

Staffed Beds: 149 Admissions: 7654 Census: 81 Outpatient Visits: 114887 Births: 1566 Total Expense ($000): 111290 Payroll Expense ($000): 37420 Personnel: 605

WILLINGWAY HOSPITAL, 311 Jones Mill Road, Zip 30458–4765; tel. 912/764–6236, (Nonreporting) **A**3
Primary Contact: Barbara S. Reid, Chief Executive Officer
CMO: Robert W. Mooney, M.D., Medical Director
Web address: www.willingway.com
Control: Corporation, Investor–owned, for–profit **Service:** Alcoholism and other chemical dependency

Staffed Beds: 40

Many Facility Codes have changed. Please refer to the AHA Guide Code Chart. © 2016 AHA Guide

GA

STOCKBRIDGE—Henry County

◇ **PIEDMONT HENRY HOSPITAL (110191)**, 1133 Eagle's Landing Parkway, Zip 30281–5099; tel. 678/604–1000 **A**2 10 21 **F**3 8 11 13 15 18 20 22 26 29 30 31 34 35 37 40 45 46 49 53 54 57 59 61 64 70 72 73 74 75 76 77 78 79 81 82 84 85 86 87 93 100 107 108 110 111 114 115 118 119 120 121 122 124 130 132 135 144 146 147 148 **S** Piedmont Healthcare, Atlanta, GA
Primary Contact: Charles F. Scott, Chief Executive Officer
COO: Deborah Armstrong, Chief Operating Officer
CFO: Sherry Henderson, Chief Financial Officer
CMO: Lily Henson, M.D., Chief Medical Officer
CHR: Jana Warren, Human Resources Business Partner
CNO: Frances Marthone, Chief Nursing Officer
Web address: www.piedmonthenry.org
Control: Other not–for–profit (including NFP Corporation) **Service:** General Medical and Surgical

Staffed Beds: 214 **Admissions:** 13156 **Census:** 159 **Outpatient Visits:** 154945 **Births:** 2258 **Total Expense ($000):** 168110 **Payroll Expense ($000):** 66806 **Personnel:** 1077

SWAINSBORO—Emanuel County

◇ **EMANUEL MEDICAL CENTER (110109)**, 117 Kite Road, Zip 30401–3231, Mailing Address: P.O. Box 879, Zip 30401–0879; tel. 478/289–1100, (Nonreporting) **A**10 20 21
Primary Contact: Mel Pyne, Chief Executive Officer
CFO: Rhonda Durden, Chief Financial Officer
CMO: Cedric Porter, M.D., President Medical Staff
CIO: Damien Scott, Chief Information Officer
CHR: Ellen Boyd, Director Human Resources
Web address: www.emanuelmedical.org
Control: Hospital district or authority, Government, nonfederal **Service:** General Medical and Surgical

Staffed Beds: 91

SYLVANIA—Screven County

★ **OPTIM MEDICAL CENTER – SCREVEN (111312)**, 215 Mims Road, Zip 30467–2097; tel. 912/564–7426, (Nonreporting) **A**10 18 **S** National Surgical Healthcare, Chicago, IL
Primary Contact: Robert R. Sellers, Chief Executive Officer
CFO: Cindy Bierschenk, Director Financial Services
CIO: Christian Rekowski, Information Technology Director
CHR: Natalie Peterson, Human Resources Director
CNO: S. Lagina Evans, R.N., Assistant Chief Nursing Officer
Web address: www.optimhealth.com
Control: County–Government, nonfederal **Service:** General Medical and Surgical

Staffed Beds: 25

SYLVESTER—Worth County

★ ◇ **PHOEBE WORTH MEDICAL CENTER (111328)**, 807 South Isabella Street, Zip 31791–7554, Mailing Address: P.O. Box 545, Zip 31791–0545; tel. 229/776–6961 **A**10 18 21 **F**11 29 34 40 57 59 66 68 77 93 107 114 119 127 133 148 **P**6 **S** Phoebe Putney Health System, Albany, GA
Primary Contact: Kim Gilman, Chief Executive Officer
CFO: Candace Guarnieri, Chief Financial Officer
CMO: Natu M. Patel, M.D., Chief of Staff
CHR: Mandy Gordon, Human Resource Coordinator
CNO: Kim Gilman, Chief Nursing Officer
Web address: www.phoebeputney.com
Control: Other not–for–profit (including NFP Corporation) **Service:** General Medical and Surgical

Staffed Beds: 18 **Admissions:** 471 **Census:** 15 **Outpatient Visits:** 15141 **Total Expense ($000):** 15807 **Payroll Expense ($000):** 5745

THOMASTON—Upson County

★ ◇ **UPSON REGIONAL MEDICAL CENTER (110002)**, 801 West Gordon Street, Zip 30286–3426, Mailing Address: P.O. Box 1059, Zip 30286–0027; tel. 706/647–8111 **A**10 21 **F**3 11 13 15 28 29 30 31 34 35 36 40 45 46 49 50 57 59 61 64 70 76 78 79 80 81 82 85 86 87 89 107 108 111 114 115 118 119 124 130 131 132 135 148 **P**6 **S** HealthTech Management Services, Brentwood, TN
Primary Contact: Tripp Penn, Chief Executive Officer
CFO: John Williams, Chief Financial Officer
CIO: Douglas Thompson, Chief Information Officer
CHR: Rich Williams, Director Human Resources
CNO: Marilyn Ray, MSN, Chief Nursing Officer
Web address: www.urmc.org
Control: Other not–for–profit (including NFP Corporation) **Service:** General Medical and Surgical

Staffed Beds: 77 **Admissions:** 2930 **Census:** 34 **Outpatient Visits:** 77078 **Births:** 314 **Total Expense ($000):** 60201 **Payroll Expense ($000):** 23606 **Personnel:** 545

THOMASVILLE—Thomas County

⊠ **JOHN D. ARCHBOLD MEMORIAL HOSPITAL (110038)**, 915 Gordon Avenue, Zip 31792–6614, Mailing Address: P.O. Box 1018, Zip 31799–1018; tel. 229/228–2000, (Total facility includes 64 beds in nursing home–type unit) **A**1 2 10 19 **F**3 5 11 13 15 18 20 22 26 28 29 31 34 35 40 43 45 46 47 48 49 50 51 57 59 60 64 67 68 70 74 75 76 77 78 79 81 82 84 85 86 87 89 90 93 98 101 102 103 104 106 107 108 110 111 114 115 117 118 119 121 123 124 126 128 129 130 131 132 143 144 146 147 148 **P**6 **S** Archbold Medical Center, Thomasville, GA
Primary Contact: J. Perry Mustian, President and Chief Executive Officer
CFO: Skip Hightower, Senior Vice President and Chief Financial Officer
CIO: Tracy Gray, Senior Vice President Information Services
CHR: Zachariah P. Wheeler, Senior Vice President Human Resources
CNO: Amy Griffin, Vice President Patient Care Services
Web address: www.archbold.org
Control: Other not–for–profit (including NFP Corporation) **Service:** General Medical and Surgical

Staffed Beds: 302 **Admissions:** 10217 **Census:** 217 **Outpatient Visits:** 205537 **Births:** 787 **Total Expense ($000):** 225966 **Payroll Expense ($000):** 74939 **Personnel:** 1438

THOMSON—McDuffie County

⊠ **UNIVERSITY HOSPITAL MCDUFFIE (110111)**, 2460 Washington Road, N.E., Zip 30824; tel. 706/595–1411 **A**1 10 **F**3 11 15 29 30 34 40 45 50 57 59 64 68 79 81 87 107 110 114 119 129 130 132 133 146 148 **S** University Health Care System, Augusta, GA
Primary Contact: Bob Kepshire, R.N., MS, Administrator and Chief Nursing Officer
CFO: Dave Belkoski, Chief Financial Officer
CNO: Bob Kepshire, R.N., Administrator and Chief Nursing Officer
Web address: www.universityhealth.org/mcduffie
Control: Other not–for–profit (including NFP Corporation) **Service:** General Medical and Surgical

Staffed Beds: 12 **Admissions:** 631 **Census:** 6 **Outpatient Visits:** 32436 **Births:** 1 **Total Expense ($000):** 18692 **Payroll Expense ($000):** 7059 **Personnel:** 88

TIFTON—Tift County

⊠ **TIFT REGIONAL MEDICAL CENTER (110095)**, 901 East 18th Street, Zip 31794–3648, Mailing Address: Drawer 747, Zip 31793–0747; tel. 229/382–7120 **A**1 2 10 19 **F**3 8 9 11 12 13 15 18 20 22 26 28 29 31 33 34 35 40 45 47 49 50 54 57 59 60 63 64 68 70 74 75 76 77 78 79 81 82 84 85 86 87 89 92 93 97 100 104 107 108 110 111 114 115 118 119 120 121 123 126 129 130 131 132 135 143 144 146 147 148 **P**6 **S** Tift Regional Health System, Tifton, GA
Primary Contact: William T. Richardson, President and Chief Executive Officer
COO: Christopher Dorman, Senior Vice President/Chief Operating Officer
CFO: Dennis L. Crum, Senior Vice President and Chief Financial Officer
CMO: William Guest, M.D., Senior Vice President and Chief Medical Officer
CIO: Guy McAllister, Vice President and Chief Information Officer
CHR: Lori S. Folsom, Assistant Vice President Human Resources
CNO: Carol Smith, Vice President Patient Care and Chief Nursing Officer
Web address: www.tiftregional.com
Control: Hospital district or authority, Government, nonfederal **Service:** General Medical and Surgical

Staffed Beds: 181 **Admissions:** 9494 **Census:** 114 **Outpatient Visits:** 180881 **Births:** 1247 **Total Expense ($000):** 283213 **Payroll Expense ($000):** 122609 **Personnel:** 2074

GA

TOCCOA—Stephens County

✉ **STEPHENS COUNTY HOSPITAL (110032)**, 163 Hospital Drive, Zip 30577–6820; tel. 706/282–4200, (Total facility includes 92 beds in nursing home–type unit) **A**1 10 **F**3 7 11 13 15 28 30 34 35 40 51 57 59 60 64 68 70 75 76 77 79 81 85 86 89 93 107 110 111 115 119 125 129 130 146 148
Primary Contact: Lynne Anderson, Chief Executive Officer
CFO: Jeff Laird, Controller
CHR: Diane Hardeman, Director Personnel
CNO: Faye M. Taylor, R.N., Director of Nursing
Web address: www.stephenscountyhospital.com
Control: Hospital district or authority, Government, nonfederal **Service:** General Medical and Surgical

Staffed Beds: 188 **Admissions:** 2156 **Census:** 123 **Outpatient Visits:** 35982 **Births:** 392 **Total Expense ($000):** 47545 **Payroll Expense ($000):** 21408 **Personnel:** 490

VALDOSTA—Lowndes County

☐ **GREENLEAF CENTER (114036)**, 2209 Pineview Drive, Zip 31602–7316; tel. 229/247–4357 **A**1 10 **F**5 38 98 99 100 101 103 104 105 130 132 134 143 **P**5 6 **S** Acadia Healthcare Company, Inc., Franklin, TN
Primary Contact: Stephen Register, Chief Executive Officer
Web address: www.greenleafcounseling.net
Control: Corporation, Investor–owned, for–profit **Service:** Psychiatric

Staffed Beds: 73 **Admissions:** 2477 **Census:** 57 **Outpatient Visits:** 5909 **Births:** 0 **Total Expense ($000):** 11077 **Payroll Expense ($000):** 5784 **Personnel:** 126

✉ **SOUTH GEORGIA MEDICAL CENTER (110122)**, 2501 North Patterson Street, Zip 31602–1735, Mailing Address: P.O. Box 1727, Zip 31603–1727; tel. 229/333–1000, (Includes SMITH NORTHVIEW HOSPITAL, 4280 North Valdosta Road, Zip 31602, Mailing Address: P.O. Box 10010, Zip 31604; tel. 229/671–2000; Leonard Carter, Campus Administrator) **A**1 2 10 19 **F**3 7 8 11 13 15 17 18 20 22 24 26 28 29 30 31 32 34 35 39 40 45 46 47 49 50 51 54 57 58 59 60 64 68 70 72 73 74 75 76 77 78 79 81 82 84 85 86 87 89 90 96 107 108 110 111 113 114 115 117 118 119 120 121 123 124 126 129 130 131 132 135 143 144 146 147 **P**6
Primary Contact: Raymond A. Snead, FACHE, Interim Chief Executive Officer
COO: Andrew Flemer, Chief Operating Officer
CFO: Raymond A. Snead, FACHE, Interim Chief Financial Officer
CMO: Kimberly Megow, M.D., Chief Medical Officer
CIO: Bob Foster, Chief Information Officer
CHR: Johnny Percy Ball, III, Assistant Administrator Human Resources
Web address: www.sgmc.org
Control: Hospital district or authority, Government, nonfederal **Service:** General Medical and Surgical

Staffed Beds: 302 **Admissions:** 13793 **Census:** 177 **Outpatient Visits:** 202389 **Births:** 2074 **Total Expense ($000):** 322911 **Payroll Expense ($000):** 109563

VIDALIA—Toombs County

✉ **MEADOWS REGIONAL MEDICAL CENTER (110128)**, One Meadows Parkway, Zip 30474–8759, Mailing Address: P.O. Box 1048, Zip 30475–1048; tel. 912/535–5555 **A**1 10 20 **F**11 13 15 18 20 22 29 30 31 34 35 37 40 43 45 46 47 50 51 53 54 57 59 60 64 68 70 74 75 76 77 78 79 81 85 86 87 93 97 107 108 110 111 115 118 119 120 121 123 124 127 129 130 131 132 146 147 148
Primary Contact: Alan Kent, Chief Executive Officer
COO: Shirley Hoskins, Chief Operating Officer
CFO: John Cornell, Vice President Finance
CIO: Charles Bondurant, Chief Information Officer
Web address: www.meadowsregional.org
Control: Other not–for–profit (including NFP Corporation) **Service:** General Medical and Surgical

Staffed Beds: 57 **Admissions:** 4489 **Census:** 45 **Outpatient Visits:** 84701 **Births:** 823 **Total Expense ($000):** 106719 **Payroll Expense ($000):** 36161 **Personnel:** 670

VILLA RICA—Carroll County

✉ **TANNER MEDICAL CENTER–VILLA RICA (110015)**, 601 Dallas Highway, Zip 30180–1202; tel. 770/456–3000 **A**1 10 **F**3 5 11 13 15 18 20 22 29 30 31 34 38 40 45 49 50 51 59 60 64 68 74 76 78 79 81 85 91 98 99 100 101 102 103 104 105 107 108 110 111 115 118 119 129 135 148 **P**1 6 **S** Tanner Health System, Carrollton, GA
Primary Contact: Bonnie Boles, M.D., Administrator
CFO: Carol Crews, Senior Vice President and Chief Financial Officer
CMO: William Waters, IV, M.D., Executive Vice President
CIO: Terri Lee
CHR: Shari W. Gainey, Chief Human Resource Officer
CNO: Deborah Matthews, Senior Vice President
COO: Jerry Morris, Chief Operating Officer
Web address: www.tanner.org
Control: Other not–for–profit (including NFP Corporation) **Service:** General Medical and Surgical

Staffed Beds: 109 **Admissions:** 5192 **Census:** 69 **Outpatient Visits:** 102269 **Births:** 535 **Total Expense ($000):** 64176 **Payroll Expense ($000):** 29801 **Personnel:** 536

WARM SPRINGS—Meriwether County

☐ **ROOSEVELT WARM SPRINGS REHABILITATION AND SPECIALTY HOSPITALS – LTAC (112000)**, 6135 Roosevelt Highway, Zip 31830–2757, Mailing Address: P.O. Box 280, Zip 31830–2757; tel. 706/655–5291 **A**1 10 **F**1 29 30 34 35 57 67 74 75 77 84 86 87 90 91 100 101 119 148 **P**4
Primary Contact: David L. Mork, Jr., Chief Executive Officer
CFO: Susan Wilder, Director Financial Services
CMO: W. Burton McDaniel, Jr., M.D., Chief Medical Officer
CHR: Laura Stokes, Director Human Resources
CNO: Cathy Harbin, Chief Nursing Officer
Web address: www.augustahealth.org/roosevelt–warm–springs/rwsh
Control: Other not–for–profit (including NFP Corporation) **Service:** Long–Term Acute Care hospital

Staffed Beds: 20 **Admissions:** 170 **Census:** 13 **Outpatient Visits:** 0 **Births:** 0 **Personnel:** 82

✉ **ROOSEVELT WARM SPRINGS REHABILITATION AND SPECIALTY HOSPITALS – REHAB (113028)**, 6135 Roosevelt Highway, Zip 31830–2757, Mailing Address: P.O. Box 280, Zip 31830–0280; tel. 706/655–5515 **A**1 10 **F**28 29 30 35 60 74 75 77 85 86 87 90 100 119 130 148 **P**6
Primary Contact: David L. Mork, Jr., Chief Executive Officer
CFO: Susan Wilder, Director Financial Services
CMO: Burton McDaniel, M.D., Medical Director
CIO: Christen Carter, Director Public Relations
CHR: Laura Stokes, Director Human Resources
CNO: Cathy Harbin, Chief Nursing Officer
Web address: www.augustahealth.org/roosevelt–warm–springs/rwsh
Control: Other not–for–profit (including NFP Corporation) **Service:** Rehabilitation

Staffed Beds: 32 **Admissions:** 365 **Census:** 15 **Outpatient Visits:** 0 **Births:** 0 **Personnel:** 85

✉ **WARM SPRINGS MEDICAL CENTER (111316)**, 5995 Spring Street, Zip 31830–2149, Mailing Address: P.O. Box 8, Zip 31830–0008; tel. 706/655–3331, (Total facility includes 79 beds in nursing home–type unit) **A**1 10 18 **F**3 8 15 29 30 40 45 46 47 48 57 59 75 79 81 93 107 114 119 128 130 133 146
Primary Contact: Karen Daniel, Chief Executive Officer
CFO: Patrick Flynn, Chief Financial Officer
CMO: Alan Thompson, M.D., President Medical Staff
CIO: Milo Varnadoe, Director Information Systems
CHR: Theresa Passarelli, Human Resources Generalist
CNO: Lynda Ligon, Chief Nursing Officer
Web address: www.warmspringsmc.org
Control: Partnership, Investor–owned, for–profit **Service:** General Medical and Surgical

Staffed Beds: 104 **Admissions:** 305 **Census:** 69 **Outpatient Visits:** 10834 **Births:** 0 **Total Expense ($000):** 12311 **Payroll Expense ($000):** 5497 **Personnel:** 151

WARNER ROBINS—Houston County

✉ **HOUSTON MEDICAL CENTER (110069)**, 1601 Watson Boulevard, Zip 31093–3431, Mailing Address: P.O. Box 2886, Zip 31099–2886; tel. 478/922–4281 **A**1 10 13 **F**3 11 13 15 18 20 22 26 28 29 30 31 34 35 38 39 40 45 46 48 49 50 51 54 56 57 58 59 60 61 64 68 70 73 75 76 79 81 82 85 86 87 89 92 93 98 100 102 103 107 108 110 111 114 115 118 119 129 130 131 132 134 135 144 146 147 148 **P**6 **S** Houston Healthcare System, Warner Robins, GA
Primary Contact: Cary Martin, Chief Executive Officer
CFO: Sean Whilden, Chief Financial Officer
CIO: George Curtis, Chief Information Officer
CHR: Michael O'Hara, Senior Executive Director Human Resources
Web address: www.hhc.org
Control: Other not–for–profit (including NFP Corporation) **Service:** General Medical and Surgical

Staffed Beds: 237 **Admissions:** 13978 **Census:** 173 **Outpatient Visits:** 230150 **Births:** 2040 **Total Expense ($000):** 204663 **Payroll Expense ($000):** 82065 **Personnel:** 2005

WASHINGTON—Wilkes County

☐ **WILLS MEMORIAL HOSPITAL (111325)**, 120 Gordon Street, Zip 30673–1602, Mailing Address: P.O. Box 370, Zip 30673–0370; tel. 706/678–2151 **A**1 10 18 **F**15 18 20 29 30 40 54 59 71 75 77 79 81 93 107 111 119 129 130 133
Primary Contact: Tracie Haughey, Chief Executive Officer and Chief Financial Officer
CFO: Tracie Haughey, Chief Executive Officer and Chief Financial Officer
CMO: Robert J. Williams, M.D., Chief Medical Staff
CIO: David Harper, Chief Information Officer
CHR: Tom Urban, Director Human Resources
CNO: Angie Vickery, Director of Nursing
Web address: www.willsmemorialhospital.com
Control: Hospital district or authority, Government, nonfederal **Service:** General Medical and Surgical

Staffed Beds: 25 **Admissions:** 612 **Census:** 11 **Births:** 0

GA

Many Facility Codes have changed. Please refer to the AHA Guide Code Chart. © 2016 AHA Guide

WAYCROSS—Ware County

☒ **MAYO CLINIC HEALTH SYSTEM IN WAYCROSS (110003)**, 410 Darling
Avenue, Zip 31501–6357, Mailing Address: P.O. Box 139, Zip 31502–0139;
tel. 912/283–3030 **A**1 2 3 5 10 **F**3 13 15 17 18 20 22 28 29 30 34 35 40 45
49 51 57 59 60 70 73 74 75 76 77 78 79 80 81 85 87 89 90 92 93 98 107
108 111 114 115 116 117 118 119 129 130 132 135 146 **S** Mayo Clinic,
Rochester, MN
Primary Contact: Roger Forgey, Interim Chief Executive Officer
COO: Mary Hoffman, Chief Administrative Officer and Chief Financial Officer
CFO: Mary Hoffman, Chief Administrative Officer and Chief Financial Officer
CIO: Barry Rudd, Chief Information Officer
CHR: Brigitte Churchill, Director of Human Resources
CNO: Holli Sweat, Associate Administrator and Chief Nursing Officer
Web address: www.mayoclinichealthsystem.org
Control: Other not–for–profit (including NFP Corporation) **Service:** General
Medical and Surgical

Staffed Beds: 199 **Admissions:** 6586 **Census:** 80

WAYNESBORO—Burke County

☐ **BURKE MEDICAL CENTER (110113)**, 351 Liberty Street, Zip 30830–9686;
tel. 706/554–4435, (Nonreporting) **A**1 10
Primary Contact: Thomas K. Steiner, Interim Chief Executive Officer
CFO: Karen ONeal, Chief Financial Officer
CHR: Kim Anthony, Director Human Resources
CNO: Debra Burch, Chief Nursing Officer
Web address: www.burkemedical.net
Control: Hospital district or authority, Government, nonfederal **Service:** General
Medical and Surgical

Staffed Beds: 40

WINDER—Barrow County

☒ **BARROW REGIONAL MEDICAL CENTER (110045)**, 316 North Broad Street,
Zip 30680–2150, Mailing Address: P.O. Box 688, Zip 30680–0688;
tel. 770/867–3400 **A**1 10 **F**3 11 13 15 29 34 35 40 45 50 51 57 59 60 68
70 74 75 76 77 79 81 82 85 93 97 107 108 110 111 114 118 119 124 130
131 132 135 143 146 147 148 **S** Quorum Health, Brentwood, TN
Primary Contact: Chad Hatfield, Chief Executive Officer
CMO: Jon Horn, M.D., Chief of Staff
CIO: Cory Crayton, Director Information Systems
CHR: Carlotta Newman, Director Human Resources
CNO: Gene Street, Chief Nursing Officer
Web address: www.barrowregional.com
Control: Corporation, Investor–owned, for–profit **Service:** General Medical and
Surgical

Staffed Beds: 56 **Admissions:** 1525 **Census:** 14 **Outpatient Visits:** 32654
Births: 69 **Personnel:** 192

GA

HAWAII

AIEA—Honolulu County

✠ **PALI MOMI MEDICAL CENTER (120026)**, 98–1079 Moanalua Road,
Zip 96701–4713; tel. 808/486–6000 **A**1 2 5 10 **F**3 12 15 18 20 22 26 29 30
31 34 35 40 45 46 47 49 50 57 58 59 64 67 68 69 70 74 75 77 78 79 81
82 83 84 85 86 87 91 92 107 110 111 114 115 119 126 130 131 132 135
143 146 147 148 **S** Hawaii Pacific Health, Honolulu, HI
Primary Contact: Art Gladstone, R.N., President and Chief Executive Officer
CFO: David Okabe, Executive Vice President, Chief Financial Officer and Treasurer
CMO: James Kakuda, M.D., Chief of Staff
CIO: Steve Robertson, Senior Vice President
CHR: Gail Lerch, R.N., Vice President Human Resources
CNO: Brigitte McKale, MSN, Vice President and Chief Nurse Executive
Web address: www.palimomi.org
Control: Other not–for–profit (including NFP Corporation) **Service:** General
Medical and Surgical

Staffed Beds: 128 **Admissions:** 6255 **Census:** 103 **Outpatient Visits:**
200341 **Births:** 0 **Total Expense ($000):** 197613 **Payroll Expense ($000):**
72450 **Personnel:** 953

EWA BEACH—Honolulu County

✠ **KAHI MOHALA BEHAVIORAL HEALTH (124001)**, 91–2301 Old Fort Weaver
Road, Zip 96706–3602; tel. 808/671–8511 **A**1 3 10 **F**29 30 35 44 68 98 99
100 101 103 104 105 106 127 130 132 133 143 **P**3 **S** Sutter Health,
Sacramento, CA
Primary Contact: Leonard Licina, Chief Executive Officer
CFO: Quin Ogawa, Chief Financial Officer
CMO: Steven Chaplin, M.D., Medical Director
CHR: Christina Enoka, Director Human Resources and Risk Management
CNO: Charles St. Louis, Director of Patient Care Services
Web address: www.kahimohala.org
Control: Other not–for–profit (including NFP Corporation) **Service:** Psychiatric

Staffed Beds: 76 **Admissions:** 476 **Census:** 75 **Outpatient Visits:** 2526
Births: 0 **Total Expense ($000):** 21394 **Payroll Expense ($000):** 10543
Personnel: 181

HILO—Hawaii County

✠ **HILO MEDICAL CENTER (120005)**, 1190 Waianuenue Avenue,
Zip 96720–2089; tel. 808/932–3000, (Total facility includes 70 beds in nursing
home–type unit) **A**1 3 5 10 20 **F**1 3 8 15 17 18 29 30 31 34 40 43 45 49 50
57 59 64 67 68 70 74 75 76 77 78 79 81 82 85 86 87 89 93 97 98 100
101 102 103 107 108 111 115 119 121 123 128 130 135 146 148 **P**5 6
S Hawaii Health Systems Corporation, Honolulu, HI
Primary Contact: Dan Brinkman, R.N., Chief Executive Officer
COO: Dan Brinkman, R.N., Chief Operating Officer
CFO: Money Atwal, Chief Financial Officer
CMO: Ted Peskin, M.D., Acute Care Medical Director
CIO: Money Atwal, Chief Information Officer
CHR: Holly Ka'Akimaka, Director Human Resources
CNO: Arthur Sampaga, Assistant Director Nursing
Web address: www.https://www.hilomedicalcenter.org/
Control: State–Government, nonfederal **Service:** General Medical and Surgical

Staffed Beds: 199 **Admissions:** 7446 **Census:** 103 **Outpatient Visits:**
105960 **Births:** 2087 **Total Expense ($000):** 193618 **Payroll Expense
($000):** 74202 **Personnel:** 992

HONOKAA—Hawaii County

★ **HALE HO'OLA HAMAKUA (121307)**, 45–547 Plumeria Street,
Zip 96727–6902; tel. 808/932–4100, (Total facility includes 66 beds in nursing
home–type unit) **A**5 10 18 **F**3 30 40 41 42 56 67 68 77 80 91 93 103 128
130 143 146 148 **P**6 **S** Hawaii Health Systems Corporation, Honolulu, HI
Primary Contact: Kerry Pitcher, Administrator
CMO: Bruce Graves, M.D., Chief of Staff
CNO: Gayle Green, Director of Nursing
Web address: www.halehoolahamakua.org
Control: State–Government, nonfederal **Service:** General Medical and Surgical

Staffed Beds: 77 **Admissions:** 187 **Census:** 63 **Outpatient Visits:** 3638
Births: 0

HONOLULU—Honolulu County

✠ **KAISER PERMANENTE MEDICAL CENTER (120011)**, 3288 Moanalua Road,
Zip 96819–1469; tel. 808/432–0000, (Total facility includes 28 beds in nursing
home–type unit) **A**1 2 3 5 10 **F**3 12 13 15 17 18 19 20 21 22 24 26 29 30 31
32 34 35 36 38 40 41 45 46 47 48 49 50 51 54 55 56 57 58 59 60 61 62
64 65 68 70 72 74 75 76 77 78 79 81 82 83 84 85 86 87 88 89 92 93 94
97 99 100 101 104 107 108 110 111 115 119 128 129 130 131 134 135
146 148 **P**1 **S** Kaiser Foundation Hospitals, Oakland, CA
Primary Contact: Linda Puu, Hospital Administrator
CFO: Thomas Risse, Chief Financial Officer and Vice President Business Services
CMO: Keith Ogasawara, M.D., Associate Medical Director and Professional Chief
of Staff
CIO: Donna Scannell, Vice President Information Technology
CHR: Jean Melnikoff, Vice President Human Resources
CNO: Kecia Kelly, R.N., Chief Nurse Executive
Web address: www.kaiserpermanente.org
Control: Other not–for–profit (including NFP Corporation) **Service:** General
Medical and Surgical

Staffed Beds: 235 **Admissions:** 11084 **Census:** 175 **Outpatient Visits:**
64890 **Births:** 1517 **Personnel:** 1559

☐ **KAPIOLANI MEDICAL CENTER FOR WOMEN & CHILDREN (123300)**,
(Women & Children), 1319 Punahou Street, Zip 96826–1001; tel. 808/983–6000
A1 2 3 5 10 **F**8 13 15 19 25 29 31 32 34 35 36 38 40 41 43 50 52 53 54
55 57 58 59 64 65 68 70 72 74 76 78 79 81 82 84 85 87 88 89 91 92 93
94 99 100 102 107 108 110 111 114 115 119 126 130 131 132 134 135
136 146 147 148 **S** Hawaii Pacific Health, Honolulu, HI
Primary Contact: Martha Smith, Chief Executive Officer
CFO: David Okabe, Senior Vice President, Chief Financial Officer and Treasurer
CIO: Steve Robertson, Vice President
CHR: Gail Lerch, R.N., Vice President
Web address: www.kapiolani.org
Control: Other not–for–profit (including NFP Corporation) **Service:** Other specialty

Staffed Beds: 175 **Admissions:** 11497 **Census:** 173 **Outpatient Visits:**
192074 **Births:** 6192 **Total Expense ($000):** 284485 **Payroll Expense
($000):** 113943 **Personnel:** 1354

✠ **KUAKINI MEDICAL CENTER (120007)**, 347 North Kuakini Street,
Zip 96817–2381; tel. 808/536–2236 **A**1 2 3 5 10 **F**3 15 17 18 20 22 24 26
28 29 31 34 35 40 45 46 49 57 58 59 60 68 70 74 75 77 78 79 80 81 82
85 86 87 107 108 110 111 114 115 117 118 119 121 129 130 131 132
145 146 147 148 **P**1
Primary Contact: Gary K. Kajiwara, President and Chief Executive Officer
CFO: Quin Ogawa, Vice President Finance and Chief Financial Officer
CMO: Nobuyuki Miki, M.D., Vice President Medical Services and Chief Medical
Officer
CIO: Gary K. Kajiwara, President and Chief Executive Officer
CHR: Ann N. Choy, Manager Human Resources and Payroll
CNO: Virginia Walker, Vice President Nursing Services and Chief Nursing Officer
Web address: www.kuakini.org
Control: Other not–for–profit (including NFP Corporation) **Service:** General
Medical and Surgical

Staffed Beds: 70 **Admissions:** 4675 **Census:** 84 **Outpatient Visits:** 56251
Births: 0 **Total Expense ($000):** 137938 **Payroll Expense ($000):** 61877
Personnel: 960

★ **LEAHI HOSPITAL (122001)**, 3675 Kilauea Avenue, Zip 96816–2398;
tel. 808/733–8000, (Nonreporting) **A**10 **S** Hawaii Health Systems Corporation,
Honolulu, HI
Primary Contact: Reid Kondo, Interim Administrator
CFO: Edward Chu, Chief Financial Officer
CMO: Albert Yazawa, M.D., Regional Medical Director
CHR: Russel Higa, JD, Regional Director Human Resources
CNO: Amy Vasunaga, Chief Nurse Executive
Web address: www.hhsc.org
Control: State–Government, nonfederal **Service:** Long–Term Acute Care hospital

Staffed Beds: 164

Many Facility Codes have changed. Please refer to the AHA Guide Code Chart. © 2016 AHA Guide

HI

✠ THE QUEEN'S MEDICAL CENTER (120001), 1301 Punchbowl Street, Zip 96813–2499; tel. 808/691–5100, (Includes QUEEN'S MEDICAL CENTER – WEST OAHU, 91–2141 Fort Weaver Road, Ewa Beach, Zip 96706–1993; tel. 808/691–3000; Susan Murray, FACHE, Chief Operating Officer), (Total facility includes 28 beds in nursing home–type unit) **A**1 2 3 5 10 **F**3 5 11 12 13 15 17 18 20 22 24 26 28 29 31 34 35 37 38 39 40 43 44 45 46 47 48 49 50 51 55 56 57 58 59 60 61 62 63 64 66 68 70 73 74 75 76 77 78 79 81 82 84 85 86 87 93 96 97 98 99 100 101 102 103 104 105 107 108 110 111 115 117 118 119 120 121 124 126 128 129 130 131 132 135 138 139 143 146 147 148 **S** Queen's Health Systems, Honolulu, HI
Primary Contact: Arthur A. Ushijima, FACHE, President
COO: Jason Chang, Executive Vice President and Chief Operating Officer
CFO: Robert Nobriga, Executive Vice President and Chief Financial Officer
CMO: Whitney Limm, M.D., Executive Vice President and Chief Physician Executive
CIO: Brian Yoshii, Vice President Information Technology and Chief Information Officer
CHR: Nona Tamanaha, Vice President Human Resources
CNO: Madeline Harris, R.N., Vice President and Chief Nursing Officer
Web address: www.queensmedicalcenter.org
Control: Other not–for–profit (including NFP Corporation) **Service:** General Medical and Surgical

Staffed Beds: 516 **Admissions:** 29196 **Census:** 493 **Outpatient Visits:** 451023 **Births:** 1875 **Total Expense ($000):** 947912 **Payroll Expense ($000):** 366439 **Personnel:** 4272

✠ REHABILITATION HOSPITAL OF THE PACIFIC (123025), 226 North Kuakini Street, Zip 96817–2488; tel. 808/531–3511 **A**1 10 **F**3 11 28 29 34 36 44 54 58 64 68 74 75 77 79 90 91 93 94 95 96 130 131 132 135 143 146 147 148
Primary Contact: Timothy J. Roe, M.D., President and Chief Executive Officer
CFO: Wendy Manuel, Vice President and Chief Financial Officer
CMO: Jason Chang, M.D., Chief Medical Director
CIO: Scott Morimoto, Director Clinical Informatics
CHR: Faye Miyamoto, Assistant Vice President Human Resources
CNO: Brenda Hiromoto, Director of Nursing
Web address: www.rehabhospital.org
Control: Other not–for–profit (including NFP Corporation) **Service:** Rehabilitation

Staffed Beds: 70 **Admissions:** 1697 **Census:** 58 **Outpatient Visits:** 48325 **Births:** 0 **Total Expense ($000):** 42423 **Payroll Expense ($000):** 21491 **Personnel:** 309

☐ SHRINERS HOSPITALS FOR CHILDREN–HONOLULU (123301), 1310 Punahou Street, Zip 96826–1099; tel. 808/941–4466 **A**1 3 5 10 **F**3 29 35 39 53 58 64 74 75 77 79 81 89 93 94 119 130 132 146 **P**6 **S** Shriners Hospitals for Children, Tampa, FL
Primary Contact: John R. White, Administrator
CFO: Patricia Miyasawa, CPA, Director Fiscal Service
CMO: Craig Ono, M.D., Chief of Staff
CIO: Gregory A. Wolf, Director Information Systems
CHR: Derek Ito, Director Human Resources
CNO: Andrea Kubota, R.N., Director Patient Care Services and Nurse Executive
Web address: www.shrinershospitalsforchildren.org/Hospitals/Locations/Honolulu.aspx
Control: Other not–for–profit (including NFP Corporation) **Service:** Children's orthopedic

Staffed Beds: 16 **Admissions:** 157 **Census:** 3 **Outpatient Visits:** 9438 **Births:** 0

☐ STRAUB CLINIC & HOSPITAL (120022), 888 South King Street, Zip 96813–3097; tel. 808/522–4000 **A**1 2 3 5 10 **F**3 11 15 16 18 20 21 22 23 24 26 27 28 29 30 31 34 40 44 45 47 49 50 54 56 57 59 64 65 68 70 74 75 77 78 79 80 81 84 85 86 87 92 93 97 100 104 107 108 110 111 114 118 119 129 130 131 132 135 143 144 145 146 147 148 **P**6 **S** Hawaii Pacific Health, Honolulu, HI
Primary Contact: Art Gladstone, R.N., Chief Executive Officer
COO: Maureen Flannery, Vice President Clinic Operations
CFO: David Okabe, Executive Vice President, Chief Financial Officer and Treasurer
CMO: Randy Yates, M.D., Chief Medical Officer
CIO: Steve Robertson, Executive Vice President and Chief Information Officer
CHR: Gail Lerch, R.N., Executive Vice President Human Resources
CNO: Patricia Boeckmann, R.N., Chief Operating Officer and Chief Nursing Officer
Web address: www.straubhealth.org
Control: Other not–for–profit (including NFP Corporation) **Service:** General Medical and Surgical

Staffed Beds: 108 **Admissions:** 6846 **Census:** 121 **Outpatient Visits:** 867968 **Births:** 0 **Total Expense ($000):** 414482 **Payroll Expense ($000):** 187578 **Personnel:** 1802

✠ TRIPLER ARMY MEDICAL CENTER, 1 Jarret White Road, Zip 96859–5001; tel. 808/433–6661 **A**1 2 3 5 **F**3 7 8 12 13 14 15 18 19 20 21 22 23 24 25 26 27 29 30 31 32 33 34 35 36 38 39 40 41 43 44 45 46 47 48 49 50 51 52 53 54 55 56 57 58 59 60 64 65 67 68 70 72 74 75 76 77 78 79 81 82 85 86 87 88 89 91 92 93 94 96 97 98 99 100 101 102 103 104 105 106 107 108 110 111 115 116 117 118 119 120 121 123 124 126 127 129 130 131 132 133 134 135 143 144 145 146 147 148 **S** Department of the Army, Office of the Surgeon General, Falls Church, VA
Primary Contact: Andrew Barr, Commanding Officer
COO: Major Elias B. Lozano, Executive Officer
CFO: Lieutenant Colonel Christopher A. Wodarz, Chief, Resource Management Division
CMO: Captain Andrew L. Findlay, Deputy Commander Clinical Services
CIO: Lieutenant Colonel Donna E. Beed, Chief Information Management Division
CHR: Colonel James N. Davidson, Troop Commander
CNO: Colonel Jennifer L. Bedick, Deputy Commander Nursing
Web address: www.tamc.amedd.army.mil
Control: Army, Government, federal **Service:** General Medical and Surgical

Staffed Beds: 194 **Admissions:** 10648 **Census:** 112 **Outpatient Visits:** 1251697 **Births:** 2603 **Total Expense ($000):** 699146 **Payroll Expense ($000):** 366897

★ VETERANS AFFAIRS PACIFIC ISLANDS HEALTH CARE SYSTEM, 459 Patterson Road, Zip 96819; tel. 808/433–0600, (Nonreporting) **S** Department of Veterans Affairs, Washington, DC
Primary Contact: Tonia J. Bagby, PsyD, FACHE, Acting Director
Web address: www.hawaii.va.gov/
Control: Veterans Affairs, Government, federal **Service:** General Medical and Surgical

Staffed Beds: 0

KAHUKU—Honolulu County

KAHUKU MEDICAL CENTER (121304), 56–117 Pualalea Street, Zip 96731–2052; tel. 808/293–9221, (Total facility includes 6 beds in nursing home–type unit) **A**10 18 **F**3 29 34 35 40 41 59 64 69 75 82 86 87 91 93 97 107 108 114 119 128 130 132 133 146 148 **P**6
Primary Contact: Stephany Vaioleti, Chief Executive Officer
CFO: Francis Daquioag, Controller
CMO: P. Douglas Nielson, M.D., Chief of Staff
Web address: www.kahuku.hhsc.org/
Control: Other not–for–profit (including NFP Corporation) **Service:** General Medical and Surgical

Staffed Beds: 21 **Admissions:** 166 **Census:** 20 **Outpatient Visits:** 7310 **Births:** 0 **Total Expense ($000):** 13760 **Payroll Expense ($000):** 5359 **Personnel:** 75

KAILUA—Honolulu County

✠ CASTLE MEDICAL CENTER (120006), 640 Ulukahiki Street, Zip 96734–4454; tel. 808/263–5500 **A**1 3 10 **F**12 13 15 18 20 22 24 29 30 31 34 35 37 40 45 49 51 54 57 59 64 68 70 74 75 76 77 78 79 81 84 85 87 93 98 102 107 108 111 115 119 126 130 132 135 146 147 148 **P**8 **S** Adventist Health, Roseville, CA
Primary Contact: Kathryn A. Raethel, R.N., M.P.H., President and Chief Executive Officer
COO: Travis Clegg, Vice President, Operations
CFO: Jeff Nye, Chief Financial Officer
CMO: Alan Cheung, M.D., Vice President Medical Affairs
CHR: Todd Reese, Director Human Resources
CNO: Laura R. Westphal, Vice President Patient Care Services
Web address: www.castlemed.org
Control: Church–operated, Nongovernment, not–for profit **Service:** General Medical and Surgical

Staffed Beds: 160 **Admissions:** 7476 **Census:** 94 **Outpatient Visits:** 96905 **Births:** 1120 **Total Expense ($000):** 143870 **Payroll Expense ($000):** 60339 **Personnel:** 786

HI

KAMUELA—Hawaii County

⊞ **NORTH HAWAII COMMUNITY HOSPITAL (120028)**, 67–1125 Mamalahoa Highway, Zip 96743–8496; tel. 808/885–4444 **A**1 10 20 **F**1 3 4 8 13 15 16 17 18 26 29 30 31 34 35 36 40 43 45 46 49 50 53 57 58 59 62 64 67 68 70 72 73 75 76 77 78 79 80 81 84 85 86 88 89 90 93 97 98 107 108 110 111 115 119 128 130 131 146 147 148 **P**6 **S** Queen's Health Systems, Honolulu, HI
Primary Contact: Cynthia Kamikawa, R.N., MSN, President
CFO: Robert Nobriga, Chief Financial Officer
CMO: Gary Goldberg, M.D., Chief Medical Officer
CHR: Nona Tamanaha, Vice President, Human Resources
CNO: Miquel Noelani Simms, R.N., Chief Nursing Officer
Web address: www.nhch.com
Control: Other not–for–profit (including NFP Corporation) **Service:** General Medical and Surgical

Staffed Beds: 35 **Admissions:** 1754 **Census:** 16 **Outpatient Visits:** 18649 **Births:** 495 **Total Expense ($000):** 56231 **Payroll Expense ($000):** 22836 **Personnel:** 313

KANEOHE—Honolulu County

☐ **HAWAII STATE HOSPITAL**, 45–710 Keaahala Road, Zip 96744–3597; tel. 808/247–2191, (Nonreporting) **A**1 3 5
Primary Contact: William J. May, Administrator
COO: Anthony Fraiola, Associate Administrator Administrative and Support Services
CFO: Anthony Fraiola, Business Manager
CMO: William Sheehan, M.D., Medical Director
CIO: John Jansen, Management Information Specialist
CHR: Karen Hara, Personnel Management Specialist
CNO: Lani Tsuneishi, Chief Nursing Unit
Web address: www.hawaii.gov/health/
Control: State–Government, nonfederal **Service:** Psychiatric

Staffed Beds: 178

KAPAA—Kauai County

★ **SAMUEL MAHELONA MEMORIAL HOSPITAL (121306)**, (SNF/ICF LTC Facility), 4800 Kawaihau Road, Zip 96746–1971; tel. 808/822–4961, (Total facility includes 66 beds in nursing home–type unit) **A**10 18 **F**1 40 67 98 99 103 128 130 **S** Hawaii Health Systems Corporation, Honolulu, HI
Primary Contact: Peter Klune, Chief Executive Officer
CFO: Michael Perel, Regional Chief Financial Officer
CMO: Gerald Tomory, M.D., Regional Medical Director
CIO: Sandra McMaster, Regional Chief Information Officer
CHR: Lani Aranio, Regional Director Human Resources
Web address: www.smmh.hhsc.org
Control: State–Government, nonfederal **Service:** Other specialty

Staffed Beds: 80 **Admissions:** 200 **Census:** 58 **Outpatient Visits:** 6398 **Births:** 0

KAUNAKAKAI—Maui County

⊞ **MOLOKAI GENERAL HOSPITAL (121303)**, 280 Home Olu Place, Zip 96748–0408, Mailing Address: P.O. Box 408, Zip 96748–0408; tel. 808/553–5331 **A**1 10 18 **F**3 15 29 34 35 40 41 44 50 57 59 63 64 65 66 68 69 75 76 77 78 82 84 87 91 93 97 107 110 115 119 127 130 132 133 134 135 147 148 **P**6 **S** Queen's Health Systems, Honolulu, HI
Primary Contact: Janice Kalanihuia, President
CFO: Zessica L. Apiki, Accountant
CMO: William Thomas, Jr., M.D., Medical Director Clinical and Internal Affairs
CIO: Sampson Wescoatt, Manager Information Technology
CHR: Alicia Teves, Coordinator Human Resources
Web address: www.queens.org
Control: Other not–for–profit (including NFP Corporation) **Service:** General Medical and Surgical

Staffed Beds: 15 **Admissions:** 111 **Census:** 1 **Outpatient Visits:** 30158 **Births:** 38

KEALAKEKUA—Hawaii County

⊞ **KONA COMMUNITY HOSPITAL (120019)**, 79–1019 Haukapila Street, Zip 96750–7920; tel. 808/322–9311 **A**1 10 20 **F**3 11 12 13 15 29 30 31 34 35 40 43 44 47 50 68 70 74 79 81 84 98 107 108 109 111 115 119 120 121 123 128 130 133 **S** Hawaii Health Systems Corporation, Honolulu, HI
Primary Contact: Jay E. Kreuzer, FACHE, Chief Executive Officer
CFO: Dean Herzog, Chief Financial Officer
CMO: Richard McDowell, M.D., Medical Director
CHR: Kathryn Salomon, Director Human Resources
CNO: Patricia Kalua, Chief Nurse Executive
Web address: www.kch.hhsc.org
Control: State–Government, nonfederal **Service:** General Medical and Surgical

Staffed Beds: 94 **Admissions:** 3378 **Census:** 51 **Outpatient Visits:** 51500 **Births:** 523 **Total Expense ($000):** 88126 **Payroll Expense ($000):** 31500 **Personnel:** 479

KOHALA—Hawaii County

★ **KOHALA HOSPITAL (121302)**, 54–383 Hospital Road, Zip 96755, Mailing Address: P.O. Box 10, Kapaau, Zip 96755–0010; tel. 808/889–6211, (Nonreporting) **A**10 18 **S** Hawaii Health Systems Corporation, Honolulu, HI
Primary Contact: Eugene Amar, Jr., Administrator
CMO: Silvia Sonnenschein, M.D., Chief of Staff
Web address: www.koh.HHSC.org
Control: State–Government, nonfederal **Service:** General Medical and Surgical

Staffed Beds: 28

KULA—Maui County

★ **KULA HOSPITAL (121308)**, 100 Keokea Place, Zip 96790–7450; tel. 808/878–1221, (Nonreporting) **A**10 18 **S** Hawaii Health Systems Corporation, Honolulu, HI
Primary Contact: Paul Harper–O'Connor, Interim Regional Administrator
CFO: Nerissa Garrity, Chief Financial Officer
CMO: Nicole Apoliona, M.D., Medical Director
Web address: www.hhsc.org
Control: State–Government, nonfederal **Service:** General Medical and Surgical

Staffed Beds: 6

LANAI CITY—Maui County

★ **LANAI COMMUNITY HOSPITAL (121305)**, 628 Seventh Street, Zip 96763–0650, Mailing Address: P.O. Box 630650, Zip 96763–0650; tel. 808/565–8450, (Nonreporting) **A**10 18 **S** Hawaii Health Systems Corporation, Honolulu, HI
Primary Contact: Paul Harper–O'Connor, Interim Administrator
Web address: www.lch.HHSC.org
Control: Other not–for–profit (including NFP Corporation) **Service:** General Medical and Surgical

Staffed Beds: 24

LIHUE—Kauai County

☐ **WILCOX MEMORIAL HOSPITAL (120014)**, 3–3420 Kuhio Highway, Zip 96766–1099; tel. 808/245–1100 **A**1 2 10 20 **F**3 13 15 18 28 29 30 31 34 35 40 43 50 57 59 60 64 70 75 76 77 81 84 85 93 102 107 108 110 111 114 115 119 130 133 135 146 147 148 **S** Hawaii Pacific Health, Honolulu, HI
Primary Contact: Jen Chahanovich, President and Chief Executive Officer
CFO: David Okabe, Executive Vice President, Chief Financial Officer and Treasurer
CMO: Craig Netzer, M.D., President Medical Staff
CIO: Steve Robertson, Executive Vice President Revenue Cycle Management and Chief Information Officer
CNO: Mary Ann England, Chief Nurse Executive
Web address: www.wilcoxhealth.org
Control: Other not–for–profit (including NFP Corporation) **Service:** General Medical and Surgical

Staffed Beds: 65 **Admissions:** 3533 **Census:** 43 **Outpatient Visits:** 87483 **Births:** 526 **Total Expense ($000):** 101128 **Payroll Expense ($000):** 33349 **Personnel:** 441

PAHALA—Hawaii County

★ **KAU HOSPITAL (121301)**, 1 Kamani Street, Zip 96777, Mailing Address: P.O. Box 40, Zip 96777–0040; tel. 808/932–4200, (Nonreporting) **A**10 18 **S** Hawaii Health Systems Corporation, Honolulu, HI
Primary Contact: Merilyn Harris, Administrator
CFO: Money Atwal, Chief Financial Officer
CMO: Clifford Field, M.D., Medical Director
Web address: www.hhsc.org
Control: State–Government, nonfederal **Service:** General Medical and Surgical

Staffed Beds: 21

WAHIAWA—Honolulu County

⊞ **WAHIAWA GENERAL HOSPITAL (120004)**, 128 Lehua Street, Zip 96786–2036; tel. 808/621–8411, (Total facility includes 107 beds in nursing home–type unit) **A**1 3 5 10 **F**1 3 4 11 15 16 17 29 31 40 56 67 70 72 73 75 77 78 79 80 81 85 86 87 88 89 90 96 98 103 107 108 109 110 115 119 128 130 132 145 146 147 148 **P**8
Primary Contact: R. Don Olden, Chief Executive Officer
COO: R. Don Olden, Chief Executive Officer
CMO: Manuel Abundo, M.D., Chief of Staff
CIO: Jason Fujinaka, Manager Information System
CHR: Liflor Barrera, Manager Human Resources
CNO: Tammy Kohrer, Director of Nursing–Acute
Web address: www.wahiawageneral.org
Control: Other not–for–profit (including NFP Corporation) **Service:** General Medical and Surgical

Staffed Beds: 160 **Admissions:** 2311 **Census:** 122 **Outpatient Visits:** 29248 **Births:** 0 **Total Expense ($000):** 46382 **Payroll Expense ($000):** 20604 **Personnel:** 407

Many Facility Codes have changed. Please refer to the AHA Guide Code Chart. © 2016 AHA Guide

WAILUKU—Maui County

⊠ **MAUI MEMORIAL MEDICAL CENTER (120002)**, 221 Mahalani Street,
Zip 96793–2581; tel. 808/244–9056, (Nonreporting) **A**1 10 20 **S** Hawaii Health
Systems Corporation, Honolulu, HI
Primary Contact: Wesley Lo, Regional Chief Executive Officer
CIO: Dana Mendoza, Chief Information Officer
Web address: www.mmmc.HHSC.org
Control: State–Government, nonfederal **Service:** General Medical and Surgical

Staffed Beds: 213

WAIMEA—Kauai County

⊠ **KAUAI VETERANS MEMORIAL HOSPITAL (121300)**, 4643 Waimea Canyon
Road, Zip 96796, Mailing Address: P.O. Box 337, Zip 96796–0337;
tel. 808/338–9431, (Total facility includes 20 beds in nursing home–type unit) **A**1
10 18 **F**1 11 13 15 17 40 67 70 76 79 81 89 93 107 110 111 114 119 128
130 133 147 **S** Hawaii Health Systems Corporation, Honolulu, HI
Primary Contact: Peter Klune, Chief Executive Officer
CFO: Michael Perel, Regional Chief Financial Officer
CMO: Gerald Tomory, M.D., Regional Medical Director
CIO: Sandra McMaster, Regional Chief Information Officer
CHR: Solette Perry, Regional Director Human Resources
Web address: www.kvmh.HHSC.org
Control: State–Government, nonfederal **Service:** General Medical and Surgical

Staffed Beds: 45 **Admissions:** 1197 **Census:** 26 **Outpatient Visits:** 33990
Births: 289

IDAHO

AMERICAN FALLS—Power County

★ **POWER COUNTY HOSPITAL DISTRICT (131304)**, 510 Roosevelt Street, Zip 83211–1362, Mailing Address: P.O. Box 420, Zip 83211–0420; tel. 208/226–3200, (Nonreporting) **A**10 18
Primary Contact: Dallas Clinger, Administrator
COO: Rock Roy, Professional Services Director
CFO: Jeremy Claunch, Chief Financial Officer
CMO: Spencer Garrett Seibold, M.D., Chief of Medical Staff
CIO: Mindy Earl, Health Information Manager
CHR: Kendra Sweat, Director Human Resources
CNO: June Mortenson, R.N., Director of Nursing
Web address: www.pchd.net
Control: Hospital district or authority, Government, nonfederal **Service:** General Medical and Surgical

Staffed Beds: 36

ARCO—Butte County

LOST RIVERS MEDICAL CENTER (131324), 551 Highland Drive, Zip 83213–9771, Mailing Address: P.O. Box 145, Zip 83213–0145; tel. 208/527–8206, (Nonreporting) **A**10 18
Primary Contact: Brad Huerta, Chief Executive Officer and Administrator
CFO: Jon Smith, Chief Financial Officer
CMO: Jeffrey Haskell, M.D., Chief Medical Staff
CHR: Tina Akins, Director Human Resources
CNO: Geri Cammack, R.N., Director of Nursing
Web address: www.lostriversmedical.com
Control: Hospital district or authority, Government, nonfederal **Service:** General Medical and Surgical

Staffed Beds: 43

BLACKFOOT—Bingham County

⊞ **BINGHAM MEMORIAL HOSPITAL (131325)**, 98 Poplar Street, Zip 83221–1799; tel. 208/785–4100, (Total facility includes 70 beds in nursing home–type unit) **A**1 5 10 18 **F**3 12 13 15 18 20 22 26 29 34 35 36 37 40 44 45 46 47 50 51 52 55 56 57 58 59 64 66 68 70 76 77 79 81 82 85 86 87 92 93 97 107 108 109 110 111 115 119 127 128 129 130 131 132 133 134 135 144 146 147 148 **P**6
Primary Contact: D. Jeffery Daniels, Chief Executive Officer
COO: Jake Erickson, Chief Operating Officer
CFO: John Fullmer, Chief Financial Officer
CIO: Robert Weis, Director Information Systems
CHR: Tara Preston, Director Human Resources
CNO: Carolyn Hansen, Chief Nursing Officer
Web address: www.binghammemorial.org
Control: Other not–for–profit (including NFP Corporation) **Service:** General Medical and Surgical

Staffed Beds: 95 Admissions: 2163 Census: 55 Outpatient Visits: 137861 Births: 393 Total Expense ($000): 92712 Payroll Expense ($000): 39242 Personnel: 506

MOUNTAIN RIVER BIRTHING AND SURGERY CENTER (130067), 350 North Meridian Street, Zip 83221–1625; tel. 208/782–0300 **A**10 **F**8 68 81 87
Primary Contact: Louis D. Kraml, FACHE, Chief Executive Officer
COO: Dan Cochran, Chief Operating Officer
CIO: Robert Weis, Director Information Technology
CHR: Tara Preston, Director Human Resources
CNO: Nathan Buck, R.N., Nursing Manager
Web address: www.binghammemorial.org
Control: Partnership, Investor–owned, for–profit **Service:** Surgical

Staffed Beds: 8 Admissions: 71 Census: 1 Outpatient Visits: 7888 Births: 0 Total Expense ($000): 4693 Payroll Expense ($000): 853 Personnel: 16

☐ **STATE HOSPITAL SOUTH (134010)**, 700 East Alice Street, Zip 83221–4925, Mailing Address: P.O. Box 400, Zip 83221–0400; tel. 208/785–1200, (Total facility includes 29 beds in nursing home–type unit) **A**1 10 **F**3 50 53 98 99 119 128 130 135 143 146 **P**6
Primary Contact: Tracey Sessions, Administrator
COO: Greg Horton, Director Support Services
CFO: James Price, Assistant Administrator Finance and Operations
CMO: Kelly Palmer, D.O., Medical Director
CIO: Julie Sutton, Director Performance Improvement
CHR: Sheryl Donnelly, Human Resources Specialist
CNO: Randy Walker, Director Nursing Services
Web address: www.healthandwelfare.idaho.gov
Control: State–Government, nonfederal **Service:** Psychiatric

Staffed Beds: 135 Admissions: 696 Census: 84 Outpatient Visits: 0 Births: 0 Total Expense ($000): 23149 Payroll Expense ($000): 12875 Personnel: 303

BOISE—Ada County

BOISE BEHAVIORAL HEALTH HOSPITAL See Safe Haven Hospital of Treasure Valley

⊞ **BOISE VETERANS AFFAIRS MEDICAL CENTER**, 500 West Fort Street, Zip 83702–4598; tel. 208/422–1000, (Total facility includes 28 beds in nursing home–type unit) **A**1 3 5 **F**1 2 3 4 5 8 9 10 12 29 30 31 34 35 38 39 40 43 45 46 47 50 53 54 56 57 58 59 60 61 62 63 64 65 66 67 68 70 71 74 75 77 78 79 81 82 83 84 85 86 87 90 91 92 93 94 96 97 98 100 101 102 103 104 105 106 107 108 111 112 119 120 121 122 123 124 127 128 129 130 132 133 135 143 144 145 146 147 148 **S** Department of Veterans Affairs, Washington, DC
Primary Contact: David P. Wood, FACHE, Director
CFO: Ron Blanton, Chief Fiscal Services
CMO: Paul Lambert, M.D., Chief of Staff
CHR: Randy Turner, Chief Human Resource Management Services
Web address: www.boise.va.gov/
Control: Veterans Affairs, Government, federal **Service:** General Medical and Surgical

Staffed Beds: 100 Admissions: 2828 Census: 63 Outpatient Visits: 351245 Births: 0 Total Expense ($000): 226000 Payroll Expense ($000): 132000 Personnel: 1226

IDAHO ELKS REHABILITATION HOSPITAL See St. Luke's Rehabilitation Hospital

☐ **INTERMOUNTAIN HOSPITAL (134002)**, 303 North Allumbaugh Street, Zip 83704–9208; tel. 208/377–8400, (Nonreporting) **A**1 10 **S** Universal Health Services, Inc., King of Prussia, PA
Primary Contact: Jeffrey F. Morrell, Chief Executive Officer
CFO: JeDonne Hines, Chief Financial Officer
CMO: Charles Novak, M.D., Chief Medical Officer
CHR: Nancy Nelson, Director Human Resources
CNO: Jennifer Beaulieu, Director of Nursing
Web address: www.intermountainhospital.com
Control: Corporation, Investor–owned, for–profit **Service:** Psychiatric

Staffed Beds: 140

SAFE HAVEN HOSPITAL OF TREASURE VALLEY (134009), 8050 Northview Street, Zip 83704–7126; tel. 208/327–0504, (Nonreporting) **A**3 10 **S** Safe Haven Health Care, Pocatello, ID
Primary Contact: Scott Proctor, Chief Executive Officer
CMO: David Kent, M.D., Chief Medical Officer
CIO: Debra Alexander, Chief Information Officer
CHR: Kathy Cady, Coordinator Human Resources, Accounts Payable and Payroll
Web address: www.boisepsychhospital.com
Control: Corporation, Investor–owned, for–profit **Service:** Psychiatric

Staffed Beds: 22

⊞ △ **SAINT ALPHONSUS REGIONAL MEDICAL CENTER (130007)**, 1055 North Curtis Road, Zip 83706–1309, Mailing Address: 1055 North Curtis Road, Zip 83706–1309; tel. 208/367–2121 **A**1 2 3 5 7 10 **F**3 5 7 8 9 11 12 13 14 15 17 18 20 22 24 26 28 29 30 31 32 33 34 35 36 37 38 39 40 42 43 44 45 48 49 50 52 53 54 55 56 57 58 59 61 64 65 68 70 71 72 74 75 76 77 78 79 81 82 83 84 85 86 87 89 90 91 93 94 96 97 98 99 100 101 102 104 107 108 109 110 111 114 115 116 117 118 119 120 121 123 124 126 127 128 129 130 131 132 135 144 146 147 148 **P**6 8 **S** Trinity Health, Livonia, MI
Primary Contact: Rodney D. Reider, President
CFO: Kenneth Fry, Chief Financial Officer
CMO: Steve Brown, M.D., Chief Quality Officer
CIO: Dwight Pond, TIS Boise
CHR: Teresa Sargent, Vice President Human Resources
CNO: Sherry Parks, R.N., Chief Nursing Officer
Web address: www.saintalphonsus.org
Control: Church–operated, Nongovernment, not–for profit **Service:** General Medical and Surgical

Staffed Beds: 399 Admissions: 17113 Census: 224 Outpatient Visits: 1051796 Births: 1659 Total Expense ($000): 531032 Payroll Expense ($000): 216803 Personnel: 3364

⊞ **SOUTHWEST IDAHO ADVANCED CARE HOSPITAL (132003)**, 6651 West Franklin Road, Zip 83709–0914; tel. 208/685–2400 **A**1 3 10 **F**1 3 75 91 96 119 148 **S** Ernest Health, Inc., Albuquerque, NM
Primary Contact: Maureen Fakinos, Interim Chief Executive Officer
COO: Bridgette Hunter, Chief Operating Officer
CFO: Connie Johnson, Chief Financial Officer
Web address: www.siach.ernesthealth.com/
Control: Corporation, Investor–owned, for–profit **Service:** Long–Term Acute Care hospital

Staffed Beds: 22 Admissions: 335 Census: 24 Outpatient Visits: 0 Total Expense ($000): 13321 Payroll Expense ($000): 6564 Personnel: 142

Many Facility Codes have changed. Please refer to the AHA Guide Code Chart.
© 2016 AHA Guide

ID

⌧ **ST. LUKE'S REGIONAL MEDICAL CENTER (130006)**, 190 East Bannock Street, Zip 83712–6241; tel. 208/381–2222, (Includes ST. LUKE'S CHILDREN'S HOSPITAL, 190 East Bannock Street, tel. 208/381–2222; ST. LUKE'S MERIDIAN MEDICAL CENTER, 520 South Eagle Road, Meridian, Zip 83642, Mailing Address: 520 South Eagle RD, Zip 83642–6351; tel. 208/706–5000) **A**1 2 3 10 **F**7 8 11 12 13 15 17 18 19 20 21 22 23 24 25 26 27 28 29 30 31 32 34 35 36 37 40 41 42 46 47 48 49 53 54 56 57 58 59 60 61 62 63 64 68 69 70 71 72 74 75 76 77 78 79 81 82 84 86 87 88 89 90 93 107 108 110 111 114 115 116 117 118 119 120 121 124 126 127 129 130 131 132 134 135 136 144 146 147 **P**6 8 **S** St. Luke's Health System, Boise, ID
Primary Contact: Kathy D. Moore, Chief Executive Officer
CFO: Jeff Taylor, Vice President Finance
CMO: Jim Souza, Chief Medical Officer
CIO: Marc Chasin, M.D., Chief Information Officer
CHR: Phillip Johnson, Vice President, Chief Human Resources Officer
CNO: Cynthia Gearhard, Chief Nursing Officer
Web address: www.stlukesonline.org/boise
Control: Other not–for–profit (including NFP Corporation) **Service:** General Medical and Surgical

Staffed Beds: 604 Admissions: 29796 Census: 349 Outpatient Visits: 1675696 Births: 5462 Total Expense ($000): 1321745 Payroll Expense ($000): 530877 Personnel: 9503

★ △ **ST. LUKE'S REHABILITATION HOSPITAL (133025)**, 600 North Robbins Road, Zip 83702–4565, Mailing Address: P.O. Box 1100, Zip 83701–1100; tel. 208/489–4444, (Nonreporting) **A**5 7 10 **S** St. Luke's Health System, Boise, ID
Primary Contact: Nolan Hoffer, Senior Director
COO: Melissa Honsinger, Chief Operating Officer
CFO: Doug Lewis, Chief Financial Officer
CMO: Lee Kornfield, M.D., Medical Director
CIO: Scott Pyrah, Director Information Systems
CHR: Jim Atkins, Director Employee Services
Web address: www.idahoelksrehab.org
Control: Other not–for–profit (including NFP Corporation) **Service:** Rehabilitation

Staffed Beds: 31

☐ **TREASURE VALLEY HOSPITAL (130063)**, 8800 West Emerald Street, Zip 83704–8205; tel. 208/373–5000, (Nonreporting) **A**1 3 10
Primary Contact: Nick Genna, Administrator
CMO: Jeffrey Hessing, M.D., Medical Director
CHR: Kathleen Phelps, Director Human Resources
Web address: www.treasurevalleyhospital.com
Control: Corporation, Investor–owned, for–profit **Service:** General Medical and Surgical

Staffed Beds: 9

VETERANS AFFAIRS MEDICAL CENTER See Boise Veterans Affairs Medical Center

BONNERS FERRY—Boundary County

★ ◇ **BOUNDARY COMMUNITY HOSPITAL (131301)**, 6640 Kaniksu Street, Zip 83805–7532; tel. 208/267–3141, (Includes BOUNDARY COUNTY NURSING HOME), (Total facility includes 28 beds in nursing home–type unit) **A**10 18 21 **F**3 11 15 28 29 34 35 40 41 45 50 57 59 64 75 77 79 81 85 90 93 97 107 110 111 115 119 127 128 130 132 133 143
Primary Contact: Craig A. Johnson, Chief Executive Officer
CFO: Holly McDonald, Controller
CMO: Gregory T. Botkin, M.D., Chief of Staff
CHR: Ann Coughlin, Director Human Resources
CNO: Tari Yourzek, Chief Nursing Officer
Web address: www.boundarycommunityhospital.org
Control: County–Government, nonfederal **Service:** General Medical and Surgical

Staffed Beds: 48 Admissions: 108 Census: 24 Outpatient Visits: 22104 Births: 0 Total Expense ($000): 12962 Payroll Expense ($000): 7160 Personnel: 175

BURLEY—Cassia County

⌧ **CASSIA REGIONAL MEDICAL CENTER (131326)**, 1501 Hiland Avenue, Zip 83318–2688; tel. 208/678–4444 **A**1 10 18 **F**3 7 8 11 13 15 18 28 29 30 31 34 35 38 40 41 50 57 59 64 68 70 74 75 76 76 77 78 79 81 82 85 86 93 97 107 108 110 111 114 119 129 130 131 132 146 147 148 **P**6
S Intermountain Healthcare, Inc., Salt Lake City, UT
Primary Contact: Rod Barton, Administrator
CFO: Mark Christensen, Director, Finance
CMO: Bernard Boehmer, M.D., Medical Director
CIO: Carie Call, Computer Support
CHR: Keri Perrigot, Manager Human Resources
CNO: Michele Pond–Bell, R.N., Nurse Administrator
Web address: www.cassiaregional.org
Control: Other not–for–profit (including NFP Corporation) **Service:** General Medical and Surgical

Staffed Beds: 25 Admissions: 1362 Census: 9 Outpatient Visits: 113640 Births: 598 Total Expense ($000): 47986 Payroll Expense ($000): 20046 Personnel: 309

CALDWELL—Canyon County

⌧ **WEST VALLEY MEDICAL CENTER (130014)**, 1717 Arlington, Zip 83605–4802; tel. 208/459–4641, (Nonreporting) **A**1 3 5 10 **S** HCA, Nashville, TN
Primary Contact: Elizabeth Hunsicker, Chief Executive Officer
COO: Jennifer Opsut, Interim Chief Operating Officer
CFO: Kate Fowler, Chief Financial Officer
CMO: Richard Augustus, M.D., Chief Medical Officer
CIO: Jason Martinez, Director Information Technology
CHR: Senta Cornelius, Director Human Resources
CNO: Edith E. Irving, R.N., Chief Nursing Officer
Web address: www.westvalleymedctr.com
Control: Corporation, Investor–owned, for–profit **Service:** General Medical and Surgical

Staffed Beds: 118

CASCADE—Valley County

★ **CASCADE MEDICAL CENTER (131308)**, 402 Lake Cascade Parkway, Zip 83611–7702, Mailing Address: P.O. Box 1330, Zip 83611–1330; tel. 208/382–4242, (Nonreporting) **A**10 18
Primary Contact: Christopher R. Bjornberg, Chief Executive Officer
CFO: Penny Lancaster, Controller
CMO: Mikael Bedell, M.D., Medical Director
CNO: Teri Coombs, R.N., Director Nursing Services
Web address: www.cascademedicalcenter.net
Control: Hospital district or authority, Government, nonfederal **Service:** General Medical and Surgical

Staffed Beds: 10

COEUR D'ALENE—Kootenai County

★ ◇ **KOOTENAI HEALTH (130049)**, 2003 Kootenai Health Way, Zip 83814–2677; tel. 208/625–4000, (Includes KOOTENAI BEHAVIORAL HEALTH, 2301 North Ironwood Place, Zip 83814–2650; tel. 208/625–4800) **A**2 5 10 19 21 **F**2 3 4 5 11 13 14 15 17 18 20 22 24 26 28 29 30 31 32 34 35 37 40 41 43 44 45 46 47 48 49 50 51 53 54 56 57 58 59 60 63 64 65 68 70 71 72 74 75 76 78 79 81 82 83 84 85 86 87 89 91 93 95 96 97 98 99 100 101 102 103 104 107 108 110 111 114 115 116 117 119 121 124 126 127 129 130 131 132 135 143 145 146 148 **P**6
Primary Contact: Jon Ness, Chief Executive Officer
COO: Jeremy Evans, Vice President Operations
CFO: Kimberly Webb, Chief Financial Officer
CMO: Walter Fairfax, M.D., Chief Medical Officer
CHR: Daniel Klocko, Vice President Human Resources
CNO: Joan M. Simon, R.N., Chief Nursing Officer
Web address: www.kh.org
Control: Hospital district or authority, Government, nonfederal **Service:** General Medical and Surgical

Staffed Beds: 251 Admissions: 13322 Census: 174 Outpatient Visits: 295999 Births: 1766 Total Expense ($000): 397872 Payroll Expense ($000): 180565 Personnel: 2347

ID

Hospital, Medicare Provider Number, Address, Telephone, Approval, Facility, and Physician Codes, Health Care System

★ American Hospital Association (AHA) membership ◯ Healthcare Facilities Accreditation Program ⇑ Center for Improvement in Healthcare Quality Accreditation
☐ The Joint Commission accreditation ◇ DNV Healthcare Inc. accreditation △ Commission on Accreditation of Rehabilitation Facilities (CARF) accreditation

COTTONWOOD—Idaho County

★ **ST. MARY'S HOSPITAL (131321)**, Lewiston and North Streets, Zip 83522–9750, Mailing Address: P.O. Box 137, Zip 83522–0137; tel. 208/962–3251, (Nonreporting) **A**5 10 18 **S** Essentia Health, Duluth, MN
Primary Contact: Lenne Bonner, President
CFO: Jyl Ruland, Chief Financial Officer
CMO: Jack Secrest, M.D., Chief Medical Officer
CHR: Debbie Schumacher, Chief Human Resource Officer
Web address: www.smh–cvhc.org/getpage.php?name=index
Control: Other not–for–profit (including NFP Corporation) **Service:** General Medical and Surgical

Staffed Beds: 28

DRIGGS—Teton County

★ **TETON VALLEY HEALTH CARE (131313)**, 120 East Howard Street, Zip 83422–5112; tel. 208/354–2383 **A**10 18 **F**7 15 30 31 34 40 41 45 57 59 64 65 68 74 79 81 82 85 87 89 90 93 97 107 110 111 114 119 127 128 131 133 135 146 148
Primary Contact: Keith Gnagey, Chief Executive Officer
CFO: Wesley D. White, Chief Financial Officer
CMO: Nathan Levanger, M.D., Chief of Staff
CHR: Dory Harris, Director Human Resource
CNO: Angela Booker, Director of Nursing Services
Web address: www.tvhcare.org
Control: Other not–for–profit (including NFP Corporation) **Service:** General Medical and Surgical

Staffed Beds: 13 Admissions: 149 Census: 1 Outpatient Visits: 26948 **Births:** 1 **Total Expense ($000):** 16024 **Payroll Expense ($000):** 8524 **Personnel:** 103

EMMETT—Gem County

◇ **VALOR HEALTH (131318)**, 1202 East Locust Street, Zip 83617–2715; tel. 208/365–3561 **A**10 18 21 **F**11 13 29 31 34 35 40 45 48 50 57 59 75 76 78 81 83 85 89 97 107 111 115 119 127 129 133 135 144 146 148
Primary Contact: Wade C. Johnson, MS, FACHE, Chief Executive Officer
CHR: Susan Vahlberg, Director Employee and Community Relations
Web address: www.wkmh.org
Control: County–Government, nonfederal **Service:** General Medical and Surgical

Staffed Beds: 12 Admissions: 168 Census: 2 Outpatient Visits: 21205 **Births:** 58 **Total Expense ($000):** 14430 **Payroll Expense ($000):** 6176 **Personnel:** 116

GOODING—Gooding County

★ **NORTH CANYON MEDICAL CENTER (131302)**, 267 North Canyon Drive, Zip 83330–5500; tel. 208/934–4433 **A**10 18 **F**3 5 11 15 29 33 34 35 40 41 44 45 47 49 50 53 56 57 59 63 64 68 71 75 81 84 87 90 93 97 107 110 114 119 127 130 131 133 135 143 148 **S** St. Luke's Health System, Boise, ID
Primary Contact: Tim Powers, Chief Executive Officer
COO: J'Dee Adams, Chief Operating Officer
CFO: Sara DeMoe, Chief Financial Officer
CMO: Mark Spencer, D.O., Chief of Staff
CIO: Margie McLeod, Director Information Technology
CHR: Sara Otto, Chief Compliance Officer
Web address: www.ncm–c.org
Control: Hospital district or authority, Government, nonfederal **Service:** General Medical and Surgical

Staffed Beds: 18 Admissions: 548 Census: 5 Outpatient Visits: 28880 **Births:** 0 **Total Expense ($000):** 20158 **Payroll Expense ($000):** 7062 **Personnel:** 158

GRANGEVILLE—Idaho County

★ **SYRINGA HOSPITAL AND CLINICS (131315)**, 607 West Main Street, Zip 83530–1396; tel. 208/983–1700 **A**10 18 **F**7 13 29 30 40 50 59 63 76 81 89 93 107 119 127 130 133
Primary Contact: Joseph Cladouhos, Chief Executive Officer
CFO: Betty A. Watson, Chief Financial Officer
CMO: Daniel Griffis, M.D., Chief Medical Officer
CIO: Darla Whitley, Manager Health Information Technology
CHR: Katy Eimers, Human Resources Officer
CNO: Cindy Daly, R.N., Director of Nursing
Web address: www.syringahospital.org
Control: Hospital district or authority, Government, nonfederal **Service:** General Medical and Surgical

Staffed Beds: 14 Admissions: 463 Census: 4 Outpatient Visits: 25000 **Births:** 46 **Total Expense ($000):** 14738 **Payroll Expense ($000):** 6958 **Personnel:** 140

IDAHO FALLS—Bonneville County

⊠ **EASTERN IDAHO REGIONAL MEDICAL CENTER (130018)**, 3100 Channing Way, Zip 83404–7533, Mailing Address: P.O. Box 2077, Zip 83403–2077; tel. 208/529–6111, (Nonreporting) **A**1 10 19 **S** HCA, Nashville, TN
Primary Contact: Douglas Crabtree, Chief Executive Officer
COO: Sandee Moore, Chief Operating Officer
CFO: Jeffrey D. Baiocco, Chief Financial Officer
CMO: Todd Williams, M.D., President Medical Staff
CHR: Wendy Andersen, Director Human Resources
CNO: Kathleen Nelson, R.N., Chief Nursing Officer
Web address: www.eirmc.com
Control: Corporation, Investor–owned, for–profit **Service:** General Medical and Surgical

Staffed Beds: 309

MOUNTAIN VIEW HOSPITAL (130065), 2325 Coronado Street, Zip 83404–7407; tel. 208/557–2700, (Nonreporting) **A**5 10
Primary Contact: James Adamson, Chief Executive Officer
COO: Peter Fabrick, Vice President Clinical Operations
CHR: Eilene Horne, Manager Human Resources
Web address: www.mountainviewhospital.org
Control: Corporation, Investor–owned, for–profit **Service:** General Medical and Surgical

Staffed Beds: 42

JEROME—Jerome County

★ **ST. LUKE'S JEROME (131310)**, 709 North Lincoln Street, Zip 83338–1851, Mailing Address: 709 North Lincoln Avenue, Zip 83338–1851; tel. 208/814–9500 **A**10 18 **F**7 13 15 29 30 32 34 39 40 56 57 59 64 65 68 76 77 79 81 86 87 97 107 111 119 127 133 146 147 **P**6 **S** St. Luke's Health System, Boise, ID
Primary Contact: Chris Roth, Chief Executive Officer East Region – Interim
CMO: Elizabeth Sugden, M.D., Chief Medical Officer
CHR: Mark Stevens, Director Human Resources
CNO: Jill Howell, Chief Nursing Officer
Web address: www.stlukesonline.org/jerome/
Control: Other not–for–profit (including NFP Corporation) **Service:** General Medical and Surgical

Staffed Beds: 25 Admissions: 440 Census: 9 Outpatient Visits: 45894 **Births:** 158 **Total Expense ($000):** 16890 **Payroll Expense ($000):** 9427 **Personnel:** 226

KELLOGG—Shoshone County

◇ **SHOSHONE MEDICAL CENTER (131314)**, 25 Jacobs Gulch, Zip 83837–2023; tel. 208/784–1221, (Nonreporting) **A**10 18 21
Primary Contact: Jerry Brantz, Chief Executive Officer and Chief Financial Officer
CMO: David Lawhorn, M.D., Chief Medical Office
CIO: John Wohlman, Manager Information Systems
CHR: Dana Hemphill, Manager Human Resources
CNO: Beth Bates, Chief Nursing Officer
Web address: www.shoshonehealth.com
Control: Hospital district or authority, Government, nonfederal **Service:** General Medical and Surgical

Staffed Beds: 25

KETCHUM—Blaine County

⊠ **ST. LUKE'S WOOD RIVER MEDICAL CENTER (131323)**, 100 Hospital Drive, Zip 83340, Mailing Address: P.O. Box 100, Zip 83340–0100; tel. 208/727–8800 **A**1 5 10 18 **F**3 7 8 11 13 15 29 30 31 34 35 36 37 39 40 43 45 50 54 56 57 59 62 64 68 74 75 76 77 79 81 82 85 86 87 91 93 97 101 103 104 107 108 110 111 114 115 119 126 130 131 132 133 134 135 141 143 145 146 147 148 **P**6 **S** St. Luke's Health System, Boise, ID
Primary Contact: Chris Roth, Chief Executive Officer East Region–Interim
CNO: Suzanne Miller, R.N., Senior Director Patient Care Services and Nursing
Web address: www.slrmc.org
Control: Other not–for–profit (including NFP Corporation) **Service:** General Medical and Surgical

Staffed Beds: 25 Admissions: 1061 Census: 8 Outpatient Visits: 98049 **Births:** 220 **Total Expense ($000):** 61200 **Payroll Expense ($000):** 28722 **Personnel:** 385

Many Facility Codes have changed. Please refer to the AHA Guide Code Chart. © 2016 AHA Guide

ID

LEWISTON—Nez Perce County

✠ **ST. JOSEPH REGIONAL MEDICAL CENTER (130003)**, 415 Sixth Street,
Zip 83501–2431; tel. 208/743–2511 **A**1 2 10 **F**8 11 15 18 20 22 26 29 30
31 34 35 40 41 43 44 45 46 47 48 49 50 54 57 59 60 63 64 68 69 70 71
74 75 76 77 78 79 80 81 83 84 86 87 89 91 93 97 98 101 102 104 107
108 109 110 111 114 115 116 117 118 119 120 121 122 123 124 129 130
132 135 146 148 **S** Ascension Health, Saint Louis, MO
Primary Contact: Thomas E. Fitz, Jr., Interim President and Chief Executive Officer
CFO: Thomas Safley, Chief Financial Officer
CMO: Michael T. Rooney, M.D., Chief of Staff
CHR: Susan Dokken, Chief Human Resources
CNO: Joan Agee, Vice President Patient Care Services
Web address: www.sjrmc.org
Control: Church–operated, Nongovernment, not–for profit **Service:** General
Medical and Surgical

Staffed Beds: 123 **Admissions:** 4893 **Census:** 54 **Outpatient Visits:** 161061
Births: 767 **Total Expense ($000):** 145426 **Payroll Expense ($000):** 57832
Personnel: 797

MALAD CITY—Oneida County

NELL J. REDFIELD MEMORIAL HOSPITAL (131303), 150 North 200 West,
Zip 83252–1239, Mailing Address: Box 126, Zip 83252–0126;
tel. 208/766–2231, (Nonreporting) **A**10 18
Primary Contact: John Williams, Administrator and Chief Executive Officer
CFO: Cindy Howard, Director Financial Services
CHR: Kathy Hubbard, Manager Human Resources
Web address: www.oneidahospital.com
Control: County–Government, nonfederal **Service:** General Medical and Surgical

Staffed Beds: 11

MCCALL—Valley County

★ **ST. LUKE'S MCCALL (131312)**, 1000 State Street, Zip 83638–3704;
tel. 208/634–2221 **A**5 10 18 **F**3 8 9 11 15 30 32 34 35 36 38 40 45 46 50
57 59 64 66 68 79 81 85 86 87 93 97 107 115 119 130 132 133 134 135
146 **P**6 8 **S** St. Luke's Health System, Boise, ID
Primary Contact: Sean McCallister, Administrator
CFO: Matt Groenig, Vice President Finance
Web address: www.https://www.stlukesonline.org/communities–and–locations/
facilities/hospitals–and–medical–centers/st–lukes–mccall–medical–center
Control: Other not–for–profit (including NFP Corporation) **Service:** General
Medical and Surgical

Staffed Beds: 15 **Admissions:** 429 **Census:** 3 **Outpatient Visits:** 52339
Births: 74 **Total Expense ($000):** 27140 **Payroll Expense ($000):** 15335
Personnel: 264

MERIDIAN—Ada County

ST. LUKE'S MERIDIAN MEDICAL CENTER See St. Luke's Regional Medical
Center, Boise

✠ **VIBRA HOSPITAL OF BOISE (132002)**, 2131 South Bonito Way,
Zip 83642–1659; tel. 877/801–2244, (Nonreporting) **A**1 10 **S** Vibra Healthcare,
Mechanicsburg, PA
Primary Contact: Cynthia Newsom, Chief Executive Officer
Web address: www.vhboise.com
Control: Corporation, Investor–owned, for–profit **Service:** Long–Term Acute Care
hospital

Staffed Beds: 35

MONTPELIER—Bear Lake County

★ **BEAR LAKE MEMORIAL HOSPITAL (131316)**, 164 South Fifth Street,
Zip 83254–1597; tel. 208/847–1630, (Total facility includes 36 beds in nursing
home–type unit) **A**10 18 **F**1 2 3 10 11 12 13 18 29 32 34 35 40 45 50 53 56
57 59 60 62 64 65 68 70 76 79 81 82 85 86 87 89 90 93 97 102 105 107
114 119 120 127 128 129 130 131 133 135 146 148
Primary Contact: Rodney D. Jacobson, Administrator
Web address: www.blmhospital.com
Control: County–Government, nonfederal **Service:** General Medical and Surgical

Staffed Beds: 57 **Admissions:** 370 **Census:** 34 **Outpatient Visits:** 61148
Births: 71 **Total Expense ($000):** 21068 **Payroll Expense ($000):** 9848
Personnel: 181

MOSCOW—Latah County

✠ **GRITMAN MEDICAL CENTER (131327)**, 700 South Main Street,
Zip 83843–3056; tel. 208/882–4511 **A**1 10 18 **F**3 8 11 13 15 19 28 29 34
35 36 37 40 45 46 49 51 53 54 56 57 59 64 65 70 75 76 77 79 81 85 86
87 89 91 93 96 97 107 108 110 111 115 119 124 127 129 130 131 132
135 143 146 147 148 **S** QHR, Brentwood, TN
Primary Contact: Kara Besst, President and Chief Executive Officer
CIO: Kane Francetich, Chief Information Officer
CHR: Dennis Cockrell, Director Human Resources
CNO: Sheryl M. Washburn, MSN, Chief Nursing Officer
Web address: www.gritman.org
Control: Other not–for–profit (including NFP Corporation) **Service:** General
Medical and Surgical

Staffed Beds: 25 **Admissions:** 1310 **Census:** 10 **Outpatient Visits:** 64025
Births: 331 **Total Expense ($000):** 50203 **Payroll Expense ($000):** 22568
Personnel: 349

MOUNTAIN HOME—Elmore County

✠ **ST. LUKE'S ELMORE (131311)**, 895 North Sixth East Street, Zip 83647–2207,
Mailing Address: P.O. Box 1270, Zip 83647–1270; tel. 208/587–8401, (Total
facility includes 38 beds in nursing home–type unit) **A**1 10 18 **F**3 7 11 13 29 30
34 35 40 45 57 64 75 77 81 107 111 114 119 127 128 129 130 133 146
P6 **S** St. Luke's Health System, Boise, ID
Primary Contact: Michael Blauer, Administrator
COO: Cody Mangum, Director Operations
CFO: Tricia Senger, Chief Financial Officer
CNO: Lisa Sanford, Chief Nursing Officer
Web address: www.stlukesonline.org/elmore/
Control: Other not–for–profit (including NFP Corporation) **Service:** General
Medical and Surgical

Staffed Beds: 63 **Admissions:** 687 **Census:** 23 **Outpatient Visits:** 52132
Births: 102 **Total Expense ($000):** 23595 **Payroll Expense ($000):** 11898
Personnel: 218

NAMPA—Canyon County

MERCY MEDICAL CENTER See Saint Alphonsus Medical Center – Nampa

✠ **SAINT ALPHONSUS MEDICAL CENTER – NAMPA (130013)**, 1512 12th
Avenue Road, Zip 83686–6008; tel. 208/463–5000 **A**1 10 **F**3 11 12 13 14 15
18 20 22 28 29 30 31 32 34 35 37 40 41 42 43 44 45 50 54 57 59 64 65
67 68 69 70 71 72 75 76 77 78 79 80 81 82 85 86 87 89 92 107 108 110
111 114 115 118 119 126 129 130 132 133 134 135 141 143 145 146 147
148 **S** Trinity Health, Livonia, MI
Primary Contact: Karl Keeler, Chief Executive Officer
COO: Phil Harrop, Executive Director Operations
CFO: Lannie Checketts, Interim Assistant Chief Financial Officer
CMO: Dustan Hughes, M.D., Vice President Medical Affairs
CIO: Daniel Wright, Director Information Technology
CHR: Stefanie Thiel, Senior Human Resources Business Partner
CNO: Clint L. Child, R.N., Chief Nursing Officer
Web address: www.mercynampa.org
Control: Church–operated, Nongovernment, not–for profit **Service:** General
Medical and Surgical

Staffed Beds: 131 **Admissions:** 5702 **Census:** 47 **Outpatient Visits:** 116183
Births: 1183 **Total Expense ($000):** 96476 **Payroll Expense ($000):** 33420
Personnel: 634

OROFINO—Clearwater County

★ **CLEARWATER VALLEY HOSPITAL AND CLINICS (131320)**, 301 Cedar,
Zip 83544–9029; tel. 208/476–4555, (Nonreporting) **A**10 18 **S** Essentia Health,
Duluth, MN
Primary Contact: Lenne Bonner, President
CFO: Jyl Ruland, Chief Financial Officer
CMO: Kelly McGrath, Chief Medical Officer
CHR: Debbie Schumacher, Chief Human Resource Officer
Web address: www.smh–cvhc.org
Control: Other not–for–profit (including NFP Corporation) **Service:** General
Medical and Surgical

Staffed Beds: 23

STATE HOSPITAL NORTH, 300 Hospital Drive, Zip 83544–9034;
tel. 208/476–4511, (Nonreporting)
Primary Contact: Todd Hurt, Administrator
CMO: Karla Eisele, M.D., Clinical Director
CIO: James Sarbacher, Chief Information Officer
CHR: Heather Vandenbark, Human Resources Specialist
Web address: www.healthandwelfare.idaho.gov
Control: State–Government, nonfederal **Service:** Psychiatric

Staffed Beds: 60

ID

Hospital, Medicare Provider Number, Address, Telephone, Approval, Facility, and Physician Codes, Health Care System

★ American Hospital Association (AHA) membership ○ Healthcare Facilities Accreditation Program ⇑ Center for Improvement in Healthcare Quality Accreditation
□ The Joint Commission accreditation ◇ DNV Healthcare Inc. accreditation △ Commission on Accreditation of Rehabilitation Facilities (CARF) accreditation

POCATELLO—Bannock County

✠ **PORTNEUF MEDICAL CENTER (130028)**, 777 Hospital Way,
Zip 83201–5175; tel. 208/239–1000 **A**1 2 3 5 10 20 **F**3 7 11 12 13 14 15 17
18 19 20 22 24 26 28 29 31 34 35 37 39 40 43 44 45 46 47 48 49 50 56
57 58 59 60 61 64 65 68 70 71 72 74 75 76 77 78 79 80 81 82 85 86 87
88 89 90 92 93 96 97 98 100 101 102 103 104 107 108 109 110 111 114
115 118 119 120 121 123 124 126 129 130 131 132 143 146 147 **P**2
S LHP Hospital Group, Plano, TX
Primary Contact: Daniel Ordyna, Chief Executive Officer
COO: Don Wadle, Vice President Clinical and Support Services
CFO: John Abreu, Vice President and Chief Financial Officer
CHR: Don Wadle, Interim Director Human Resources
CNO: Natalie R. Smith, R.N., Vice President Patient Care Services and Chief
Nursing Officer
Web address: www.portmed.org
Control: Corporation, Investor–owned, for–profit **Service:** General Medical and
Surgical

Staffed Beds: 175 **Admissions:** 8322 **Census:** 93 **Outpatient Visits:** 310561
Births: 1454 **Total Expense ($000):** 209279 **Payroll Expense ($000):**
72891 **Personnel:** 1020

SAFE HAVEN HOSPITAL OF POCATELLO (134011), 1200 Hospital Way,
Zip 83201–2708; tel. 208/232–2570, (Total facility includes 84 beds in nursing
home–type unit) (Data for 130 days) **A**10 **F**56 98 103 128 130 143 **P**6 **S** Safe
Haven Health Care, Pocatello, ID
Primary Contact: Karen Neilson, Administrator
Web address: www.safehavenhealthcare.org/safehaven_hospital/index.html
Control: Corporation, Investor–owned, for–profit **Service:** Psychiatric

Staffed Beds: 87 **Admissions:** 241 **Census:** 216 **Outpatient Visits:** 0 **Births:**
0 **Total Expense ($000):** 10603 **Payroll Expense ($000):** 4916 **Personnel:**
232

POST FALLS—Kootenai County

☐ **NORTHERN IDAHO ADVANCED CARE HOSPITAL (132001)**, 600 North Cecil
Road, Zip 83854–6200; tel. 208/262–2800, (Nonreporting) **A**1 10 **S** Ernest
Health, Inc., Albuquerque, NM
Primary Contact: Maria Godley, R.N., Chief Executive Officer
Web address: www.niach.ernesthealth.com
Control: Corporation, Investor–owned, for–profit **Service:** Long–Term Acute Care
hospital

Staffed Beds: 40

☐ **NORTHWEST SPECIALTY HOSPITAL (130066)**, 1593 East Polston Avenue,
Zip 83854–5326; tel. 208/262–2300 **A**1 10 **F**3 29 34 35 54 59 64 65 75 77
79 81 82 87 107 111 119 129 144 **P**8 **S** National Surgical Healthcare,
Chicago, IL
Primary Contact: Rick Rasmussen, Chief Executive Officer
CIO: Craig McIntosh, Chief Information Officer
CHR: Gina Schneider, Director Human Resources
CNO: Christi Nance, R.N., Chief Nursing Officer
Web address: www.northwestspecialtyhospital.com
Control: Corporation, Investor–owned, for–profit **Service:** Surgical

Staffed Beds: 34 **Admissions:** 34 **Census:** 6 **Outpatient Visits:** 4287 **Births:**
0

PRESTON—Franklin County

FRANKLIN COUNTY MEDICAL CENTER (131322), 44 North First East Street,
Zip 83263–1399; tel. 208/852–0137, (Nonreporting) **A**10 18
Primary Contact: Alan Bird, Chief Executive Officer
CFO: Paul Smart, CPA, Chief Financial Officer
CHR: Courtney Dursteler, Chief Human Resources Officer
CNO: Patrica Bowles, R.N., Chief Nursing Officer
Web address: www.fcmc.org
Control: County–Government, nonfederal **Service:** General Medical and Surgical

Staffed Beds: 65

REXBURG—Madison County

★ ◇ **MADISON MEMORIAL HOSPITAL (130025)**, 450 East Main Street,
Zip 83440–2048, Mailing Address: P.O. Box 310, Zip 83440–0310;
tel. 208/359–6900 **A**10 21 **F**3 11 13 28 29 31 34 35 39 40 41 45 54 57 59
60 65 66 68 70 72 75 76 77 78 79 81 82 85 86 87 89 91 93 96 107 108
111 115 118 119 130 131 146 147 148 **P**8
Primary Contact: Rachel Ann Gonzales, Chief Executive Officer
COO: Audrey Fletcher, Chief Operating Officer
CFO: Troy Christensen, Chief Financial Officer
CMO: Clay Prince, M.D., Chief Medical Officer
CNO: Robert L. Kendrick, Chief Nursing Officer
Web address: www.madisonmemorial.org
Control: County–Government, nonfederal **Service:** General Medical and Surgical

Staffed Beds: 69 **Admissions:** 4099 **Census:** 19 **Outpatient Visits:** 29191
Births: 1547 **Total Expense ($000):** 54108 **Payroll Expense ($000):** 20610
Personnel: 323

RUPERT—Minidoka County

★ **MINIDOKA MEMORIAL HOSPITAL (131319)**, 1224 Eighth Street,
Zip 83350–1599; tel. 208/436–0481, (Total facility includes 43 beds in nursing
home–type unit) **A**10 18 **F**3 7 8 11 15 29 30 34 35 37 40 45 50 56 57 59 62
63 64 65 68 70 75 77 79 84 86 87 97 107 108 111 114 119 127
128 130 131 132 133 134 143 146 147 148 **P**1 3 5
Primary Contact: Tom Murphy, Chief Executive Officer
CFO: Jason Gibbons, Chief Financial Officer
CMO: Brian Muir, Chief of Staff
CIO: Nick Martin, Chief Information Officer
CHR: Tammy Hanks, Director Human Resources
CNO: Erinn Neilson, Chief Nursing Officer
Web address: www.minidokamemorial.com
Control: County–Government, nonfederal **Service:** General Medical and Surgical

Staffed Beds: 72 **Admissions:** 496 **Census:** 45 **Outpatient Visits:** 17987
Births: 0 **Total Expense ($000):** 18694 **Payroll Expense ($000):** 10380
Personnel: 201

MINIDOKA MEMORIAL HOSPITAL AND EXTENDED CARE FACILITY See
Minidoka Memorial Hospital

SAINT MARIES—Benewah County

BENEWAH COMMUNITY HOSPITAL (131317), 229 South Seventh Street,
Zip 83861–1803; tel. 208/245–5551 **A**10 18 **F**13 15 29 30 31 34 35 40 45
56 57 59 64 75 76 78 79 81 82 84 85 93 97 107 110 111 112 114 119 127
129 131 133 135 146 **P**6
Primary Contact: Anthony Koroush, Chief Executive Officer
CFO: Lori Stoltz, Chief Financial Officer
CMO: William Wheeler, M.D., Chief of Staff
CHR: Marlana Martin, Director Human Resources
CNO: Rhonda Smith, Chief Nursing Officer
Web address: www.bchmed.org
Control: County–Government, nonfederal **Service:** General Medical and Surgical

Staffed Beds: 19 **Admissions:** 335 **Census:** 3 **Outpatient Visits:** 17042
Births: 46 **Total Expense ($000):** 9072 **Payroll Expense ($000):** 7447
Personnel: 150

SALMON—Lemhi County

★ **STEELE MEMORIAL MEDICAL CENTER (131305)**, 203 South Daisy Street,
Zip 83467–4709; tel. 208/756–5600 **A**10 18 **F**3 11 13 15 18 28 29 31 34 35
40 45 55 57 59 64 65 66 68 75 76 77 78 79 81 82 85 86 87 90 93 97 104
107 110 111 115 119 127 131 132 133 135 146 148 **P**6 **S** QHR,
Brentwood, TN
Primary Contact: Jeanine Gentry, Chief Executive Officer
COO: Abner King, Chief Operating Officer
CFO: Jim Peterson, Chief Financial Officer
CMO: Richard Natelson, M.D., Chief of Staff
CHR: Libby Brittain, Director Human Resources
CNO: Stephanie Orr, Chief Nursing Officer
Web address: www.steelemh.org
Control: County–Government, nonfederal **Service:** General Medical and Surgical

Staffed Beds: 18 **Admissions:** 370 **Census:** 3 **Outpatient Visits:** 32060
Births: 42 **Total Expense ($000):** 21224 **Payroll Expense ($000):** 7731
Personnel: 136

SANDPOINT—Bonner County

★ ◇ **BONNER GENERAL HOSPITAL (131328)**, 520 North Third Avenue,
Zip 83864–1507; tel. 208/263–1441 **A**10 18 21 **F**3 11 13 15 17 22 26 28 29
30 34 35 40 45 46 47 48 54 57 59 62 63 64 68 75 76 77 79 81 85 86 87
93 102 107 108 110 111 114 118 119 130 131 132 142 144 146
Primary Contact: Sheryl Rickard, Chief Executive Officer
CFO: John Hennessy, Chief Financial Officer
CIO: Jeremy Welser, Director Information Systems
CHR: Brad Waterbury, Director Human Resources
CNO: Misty Robertson, R.N., Chief Nursing Officer
Web address: www.bonnergeneral.org
Control: Other not–for–profit (including NFP Corporation) **Service:** General
Medical and Surgical

Staffed Beds: 25 **Admissions:** 1358 **Census:** 11 **Outpatient Visits:** 67251
Births: 309 **Total Expense ($000):** 46652 **Payroll Expense ($000):** 20458
Personnel: 326

SODA SPRINGS—Caribou County

★ **CARIBOU MEMORIAL HOSPITAL AND LIVING CENTER (131309)**, 300 South
Third West, Zip 83276–1598; tel. 208/547–3341, (Total facility includes 30 beds
in nursing home–type unit) **A**10 18 **F**70 76 81 128 **P**6
Primary Contact: Jon Smith, Chief Executive Officer
CMO: John K. Franson, M.D., Chief Medical Staff
CIO: Johnathan Inskeep, Chief Information Officer
CHR: Michael D. Peck, Assistant Administrator
CNO: Brenda Bergholm, MSN, Chief Nursing Officer
Web address: www.cmhlc.org/
Control: County–Government, nonfederal **Service:** General Medical and Surgical

Staffed Beds: 55 **Admissions:** 309 **Census:** 25

ID

Many Facility Codes have changed. Please refer to the AHA Guide Code Chart.   © 2016 AHA Guide

TWIN FALLS—Twin Falls County

✉ △ **ST. LUKE'S MAGIC VALLEY MEDICAL CENTER (130002)**, 801 Pole Line
Road West, Zip 83301–5810, Mailing Address: P.O. Box 409, Zip 83303–0409;
tel. 208/814–1000 **A**1 2 3 7 10 **F**3 4 5 7 8 11 13 15 18 20 22 29 30 31 35
40 57 62 63 68 70 72 76 77 78 79 81 85 87 89 90 93 96 98 104 106 107
110 111 114 119 130 146 **P**6 7 8 **S** St. Luke's Health System, Boise, ID
Primary Contact: Chris Roth, Chief Executive Officer East Region – Interim
CFO: Joshua Custer, Director Finance
CIO: Melissa Capps, Site Leader Information Technology
CHR: Mark Stevens, Senior Director Human Resources
CNO: Amy Bearden, R.N., Vice President Patient Care Services and Chief Nursing
Officer
Web address: www.stlukesonline.org
Control: Other not–for–profit (including NFP Corporation) **Service:** General
Medical and Surgical

> **Staffed Beds:** 224 **Admissions:** 10410 **Census:** 114 **Outpatient Visits:**
> 665624 **Births:** 1813 **Total Expense ($000):** 318254 **Payroll Expense
> ($000):** 109196 **Personnel:** 2419

WEISER—Washington County

★ ◇ **WEISER MEMORIAL HOSPITAL (131307)**, 645 East Fifth Street,
Zip 83672–2202; tel. 208/549–0370, (Nonreporting) **A**10 18 21 **S** St. Luke's
Health System, Boise, ID
Primary Contact: Steven D. Hale, Chief Executive Officer
CFO: Kara Kunz, Administrative Director Finance
CMO: Evan W. Lee, M.D., Chief Medical Staff
CHR: Terri Kautz, Manager Human Resources
CNO: Reuben J. DeKastle, Chief Nursing Officer
Web address: www.weisermemorialhospital.org
Control: Hospital district or authority, Government, nonfederal **Service:** General
Medical and Surgical

> **Staffed Beds:** 25

ID

ILLINOIS

ALEDO—Mercer County

★ **GENESIS MEDICAL CENTER–ALEDO (141304)**, 409 N.W. Ninth Avenue, Zip 61231–1296; tel. 309/582–9100 **A**10 18 **F**3 5 11 15 28 29 34 40 45 50 56 57 59 64 75 81 82 87 94 97 104 107 108 115 119 127 130 131 133 144 146 **P**6 **S** Genesis Health System, Davenport, IA
Primary Contact: Ted Rogalski, Administrator
CFO: Mark G. Rogers, Chief Financial Officer
CMO: Julio Santiago, M.D., Chief of Staff
CIO: Robert Frieden, Vice President Information Systems
CHR: Megan Clark, Coordinator Human Resources
CNO: Heidi Hess, Chief Nursing Officer
Web address: www.genesishealth.com
Control: Other not–for–profit (including NFP Corporation) **Service:** General Medical and Surgical

> **Staffed Beds:** 22 **Admissions:** 260 **Census:** 5 **Outpatient Visits:** 16787 **Births:** 0 **Total Expense ($000):** 13733 **Payroll Expense ($000):** 5190 **Personnel:** 87

ALTON—Madison County

⊞ **ALTON MEMORIAL HOSPITAL (140002)**, One Memorial Drive, Zip 62002–6722; tel. 618/463–7311, (Total facility includes 62 beds in nursing home–type unit) **A**1 10 **F**3 6 7 11 13 15 18 20 22 29 30 31 34 35 36 38 40 45 46 49 50 56 57 59 64 69 70 74 75 76 77 78 79 81 82 85 86 87 89 92 93 96 98 107 108 110 111 114 115 116 117 118 119 120 121 123 128 129 130 131 132 146 148 **S** BJC HealthCare, Saint Louis, MO
Primary Contact: David A. Braasch, President
COO: Brad Goacher, Vice President Administration
CFO: Susan Koesterer, Regional Director Finance
CMO: Sebastian Rueckert, M.D., Vice President and Chief Medical Officer
CIO: David Weiss, Vice President Information System
CHR: Bryan Hartwick, Vice President Human Resources
CNO: Debra Turpin, R.N., Vice President Patient Care Services and Chief Nursing Officer
Web address: www.altonmemorialhospital.org
Control: Other not–for–profit (including NFP Corporation) **Service:** General Medical and Surgical

> **Staffed Beds:** 230 **Admissions:** 7618 **Census:** 82 **Outpatient Visits:** 139756 **Births:** 750 **Total Expense ($000):** 131970 **Payroll Expense ($000):** 48104 **Personnel:** 736

☐ **ALTON MENTAL HEALTH CENTER (144016)**, 4500 College Avenue, Zip 62002–5099; tel. 618/474–3800, (Nonreporting) **A**1 10 **S** Division of Mental Health, Department of Human Services, Springfield, IL
Primary Contact: Brian E. Thomas, Administrator
CFO: Susan Shobe, Director Administration and Support Services
CMO: Claudia Kachigion, M.D., Medical Director
Control: State–Government, nonfederal **Service:** Psychiatric

> **Staffed Beds:** 165

⊞ △ **OSF SAINT ANTHONY'S HEALTH CENTER (140052)**, 1 Saint Anthony's Way, Zip 62002–4579, Mailing Address: PO Box 340, Zip 62002–0340; tel. 618/465–2571, (Includes OSF SAINT CLARE'S HOSPITAL, 915 East Fifth Street, Zip 62002–6434; tel. 618/463–5151), (Total facility includes 30 beds in nursing home–type unit) **A**1 2 7 10 **F**2 3 5 10 11 15 18 20 22 29 30 31 34 35 37 38 39 40 41 44 45 46 47 48 49 50 51 53 56 57 58 59 60 61 64 65 68 69 70 74 75 76 77 78 79 81 82 84 85 86 87 89 90 91 92 93 95 96 99 100 101 102 103 104 107 108 110 111 114 115 116 117 118 119 120 121 123 125 128 129 130 131 132 134 135 146 147 148 **P**6 **S** OSF Healthcare System, Peoria, IL
Primary Contact: Ajay Pathak, President
COO: Sister M. Anselma, Chief Operating Officer
CFO: Matthew Hanley, Chief Financial Officer
CMO: James Piephoff, Chief Medical Officer
CIO: Georgia Henke, Operational Account Manager
CHR: Robyn Grissom, Director Employee Relations
CNO: Denise Boettger, Vice President Nursing and Chief Nursing Officer
Web address: www.osfsaintanthonys.org
Control: Church–operated, Nongovernment, not–for profit **Service:** General Medical and Surgical

> **Staffed Beds:** 203 **Admissions:** 3137 **Census:** 49 **Outpatient Visits:** 106263 **Births:** 307 **Total Expense ($000):** 76225 **Payroll Expense ($000):** 26955 **Personnel:** 538

ANNA—Union County

☐ **CHOATE MENTAL HEALTH CENTER (144038)**, 1000 North Main Street, Zip 62906–1699; tel. 618/833–5161 **A**1 10 **F**34 39 59 65 75 86 98 101 102 103 130 143 **S** Division of Mental Health, Department of Human Services, Springfield, IL
Primary Contact: Elaine Ray, Administrator
COO: Elaine Ray, Administrator
CMO: John Larcas, M.D., Acting Medical Director
CIO: Cindy Flamm, Manager Quality
CHR: Tammy Tellor, Acting Director Human Resources
Control: State–Government, nonfederal **Service:** Psychiatric

> **Staffed Beds:** 79 **Admissions:** 782 **Census:** 67 **Outpatient Visits:** 0 **Births:** 0 **Total Expense ($000):** 42354 **Payroll Expense ($000):** 34498 **Personnel:** 134

⊞ **UNION COUNTY HOSPITAL (141342)**, 517 North Main Street, Zip 62906–1696; tel. 618/833–4511, (Total facility includes 22 beds in nursing home–type unit) **A**1 10 18 **F**3 11 15 28 29 30 32 34 35 40 45 49 50 57 59 64 68 75 77 81 85 87 93 97 107 110 111 114 119 127 130 133 146 148 **P**6 **S** Quorum Health, Brentwood, TN
Primary Contact: James R. Farris, FACHE, Chief Executive Officer
CFO: Terry Paligo, Chief Financial Officer
CMO: Christine Lucas, Chief of Staff
CIO: John Hegger, Director Information Systems
CHR: Tammy Davis, Director Human Resources
CNO: Tammy H. Wheaton, Interim Chief Nursing Officer
Web address: www.unioncountyhospital.com
Control: Corporation, Investor–owned, for–profit **Service:** General Medical and Surgical

> **Staffed Beds:** 47 **Admissions:** 645 **Census:** 24 **Outpatient Visits:** 37571 **Births:** 0 **Total Expense ($000):** 21172 **Payroll Expense ($000):** 8232 **Personnel:** 152

ARLINGTON HEIGHTS—Cook County

⊞ **NORTHWEST COMMUNITY HOSPITAL (140252)**, 800 West Central Road, Zip 60005–2392; tel. 847/618–1000 **A**1 2 5 10 **F**3 5 8 13 15 18 20 22 24 26 28 29 30 31 32 33 34 35 37 38 39 40 41 43 44 45 46 47 49 50 53 54 55 56 57 59 61 62 63 64 65 68 70 71 72 73 74 75 76 77 78 79 81 82 84 85 86 87 89 92 93 94 96 98 99 100 101 102 103 104 105 106 107 108 110 111 114 115 116 117 118 119 120 121 123 124 126 129 130 131 132 135 144 145 146 147 148 **P**8
Primary Contact: Stephen Scogna, President and Chief Executive Officer
COO: Michael Hartke, Executive Vice President, Chief Operating Officer
CFO: Marsha Liu, Executive Vice President and Chief Financial Officer
CMO: Eric Benink, M.D., Chief Medical Officer
CIO: Glen Malan, Vice President Information Technology and Chief Information Officer
CHR: Ann M. Patrick, Vice President Human Resources
CNO: Kimberly Nagy, R.N., Executive Vice President, Patient Services and Chief Nursing Officer
Web address: www.nch.org
Control: Other not–for–profit (including NFP Corporation) **Service:** General Medical and Surgical

> **Staffed Beds:** 386 **Admissions:** 19856 **Census:** 223 **Outpatient Visits:** 347811 **Births:** 2816 **Total Expense ($000):** 420746 **Payroll Expense ($000):** 180750 **Personnel:** 3054

AURORA—Du Page and Kane Counties

⊞ **PRESENCE MERCY MEDICAL CENTER (140174)**, 1325 North Highland Avenue, Zip 60506–1449; tel. 630/859–2222 **A**1 2 10 **F**3 5 12 13 15 18 20 22 24 26 28 29 30 31 34 35 36 38 40 43 45 46 49 56 57 59 61 65 68 70 75 76 77 78 79 81 82 85 86 87 89 93 97 98 99 100 101 102 103 104 105 107 111 115 119 125 126 130 132 135 144 146 147 **P**5 **S** Presence Health, Chicago, IL
Primary Contact: Michael L. Brown, Regional President and Chief Executive Officer
COO: Roxann E. Barber, Regional Ambulatory Care and Ancillary Services Officer
CFO: Kevin Larkin, Regional Chief Financial Officer
CMO: Anil Gopinath, FACHE, Regional Chief Medical Officer
CIO: Anita Halvorsen, FACHE, Reginoal Strategy & Growth Officer
CHR: Michael O'Rourke, Regional Human Resource Officer
CNO: Grace McBride, Regional Chief Nursing Officer
Web address: www.presencehealth.org/mercy/
Control: Church–operated, Nongovernment, not–for profit **Service:** General Medical and Surgical

> **Staffed Beds:** 242 **Admissions:** 8721 **Census:** 108 **Outpatient Visits:** 225083 **Births:** 228 **Total Expense ($000):** 181667 **Payroll Expense ($000):** 49910 **Personnel:** 932

PROVENA MERCY MEDICAL CENTER See Presence Mercy Medical Center

◉ △ **RUSH–COPLEY MEDICAL CENTER (140029)**, 2000 Ogden Avenue, Zip 60504–7222; tel. 630/978–6200 **A**1 2 3 5 7 10 **F**3 7 9 13 15 17 18 19 20 22 24 26 28 29 30 31 32 34 35 36 37 38 39 40 42 43 44 45 46 47 49 50 51 52 53 54 55 56 57 58 59 60 61 62 64 65 66 68 70 72 73 74 75 76 77 78 79 81 82 84 85 86 87 89 90 92 93 94 96 97 107 108 110 111 114 115 117 118 119 120 121 123 124 130 131 132 134 135 143 144 145 146 147 148 **P**6 **S** Rush University Medical Center, Chicago, IL
Primary Contact: Barry C. Finn, President and Chief Executive Officer
COO: John A. Diederich, Senior Vice President Operations and Chief Operating Officer
CFO: Brenda VanWyhe, Senior Vice President Finance and Chief Financial Officer
CMO: Steve B. Lowenthal, M.D., Senior Vice President Medical Affairs and Chief Medical Officer
CIO: Dennis DeMasie, Vice President Information Systems and Chief Information Officer
CNO: Mary Shilkaitis, Vice President Patient Care and Chief Nursing Officer
Web address: www.rushcopley.com
Control: Other not–for–profit (including NFP Corporation) **Service:** General Medical and Surgical

Staffed Beds: 210 Admissions: 13097 Census: 152 Outpatient Visits: 223851 **Births: 3440 Total Expense ($000): 271256 Payroll Expense ($000): 112706 Personnel: 1727**

BARRINGTON—Lake County

★ ◇ **ADVOCATE GOOD SHEPHERD HOSPITAL (140291)**, 450 West Highway 22, Zip 60010–1919; tel. 847/381–0123 **A**2 10 21 **F**3 11 12 13 15 17 18 19 20 22 24 26 28 29 30 31 34 35 36 37 40 43 45 46 47 48 49 54 57 59 63 64 65 68 70 74 75 76 77 78 79 81 82 84 87 89 91 92 93 94 97 100 107 110 111 114 115 116 117 118 119 120 121 123 126 129 130 132 135 146 **P**8 **S** Advocate Health Care, Downers Grove, IL
Primary Contact: Karen A. Lambert, President
COO: Michael Ploszek, Vice President Physician Strategy and Clinical Operations
CFO: George Teufel, Vice President Finance
CMO: Barry Rosen, M.D., Vice President Medical Management
CIO: Chuck Malik, Director Information Systems
CHR: Jason Spigner, Vice President Human Resources
CNO: Marianne D. Araujo, R.N., Vice President Nursing and Chief Nurse Executive
Web address: www.advocatehealth.com/gshp/
Control: Church–operated, Nongovernment, not–for profit **Service:** General Medical and Surgical

Staffed Beds: 176 Admissions: 9652 Census: 107 Outpatient Visits: 260145 **Births: 1323 Total Expense ($000): 231192 Payroll Expense ($000): 72968 Personnel: 1122**

BELLEVILLE—St. Clair County

◉ △ **HSHS ST. ELIZABETH'S HOSPITAL (140187)**, 211 South Third Street, Zip 62220–1998; tel. 618/234–2120 **A**1 3 5 7 10 **F**3 4 5 11 13 15 18 20 22 24 26 28 29 30 35 39 40 45 46 49 50 53 54 56 57 59 60 64 65 68 70 74 75 76 77 78 79 81 82 85 86 87 90 93 97 98 100 101 102 103 104 105 107 108 111 115 116 117 118 119 121 124 129 130 131 132 135 144 146 147 148 **P**6 **S** Hospital Sisters Health System, Springfield, IL
Primary Contact: Peggy A. Sebastian, MSN, R.N., President and Chief Executive Officer
CFO: David Nosacka, Chief Financial Officer
CMO: Shelly Harkins, M.D., Chief Medical Officer
CIO: Leslee Martin, Manager Information Technology
CHR: Jason T. Snow, Director People Services
CNO: Shelley Harris, MSN, Chief Nursing Officer
Web address: www.steliz.org
Control: Church–operated, Nongovernment, not–for profit **Service:** General Medical and Surgical

Staffed Beds: 260 Admissions: 10479 Census: 115 Outpatient Visits: 187213 **Births: 1049 Total Expense ($000): 173792 Payroll Expense ($000): 58315 Personnel: 1141**

★ ○ **MEMORIAL HOSPITAL (140185)**, 4500 Memorial Drive, Zip 62226–5399; tel. 618/233–7750, (Total facility includes 82 beds in nursing home–type unit) **A**3 10 11 **F**3 11 13 15 18 20 22 24 26 28 29 30 31 34 35 40 45 46 47 48 49 53 54 57 59 60 62 64 70 71 74 76 77 79 81 82 84 85 86 87 89 92 93 94 96 107 108 110 111 112 114 115 118 119 126 128 129 130 131 132 135 145 146 147 148 **P**6 8 **S** BJC HealthCare, Saint Louis, MO
Primary Contact: Mark J. Turner, President and Chief Executive Officer
COO: Michael T. McManus, Chief Operating Officer
CFO: Amy Thomas, Vice President Finance
CMO: William Casperson, M.D., Vice President Medical Affairs
CIO: Jennifer Meinkoth, Chief Information Officer
CHR: John C. Ziegler, FACHE, Vice President Human Resources
CNO: Nancy R. Weston, R.N., Vice President Nursing Services
Web address: www.memhosp.com
Control: Other not–for–profit (including NFP Corporation) **Service:** General Medical and Surgical

Staffed Beds: 398 Admissions: 16447 Census: 252 Outpatient Visits: 352808 **Births: 1396 Total Expense ($000): 247872 Payroll Expense ($000): 100021 Personnel: 2394**

BENTON—Franklin County

★ **FRANKLIN HOSPITAL DISTRICT (141321)**, 201 Bailey Lane, Zip 62812–1969; tel. 618/439–3161 **A**10 18 **F**11 15 29 30 34 35 40 45 56 57 59 66 75 77 81 93 97 107 114 119 127 132 133 **P**6
Primary Contact: Hervey E. Davis, Chief Executive Officer
COO: Derek Johnson, Sr., Chief Operating Officer
CFO: James Johnson, Chief Financial officer
CMO: Tim Morthland, Chief of Staff
CIO: David Williams, Director Information Technology
CHR: Nancy Seibert, Director Human Resources
CNO: Terri Hermann, R.N., Chief Nursing Officer
Web address: www.franklinhospital.net
Control: Hospital district or authority, Government, nonfederal **Service:** General Medical and Surgical

Staffed Beds: 16 Admissions: 642 Census: 5 Outpatient Visits: 24545 Births: 0 Total Expense ($000): 18747 Payroll Expense ($000): 8768 Personnel: 190

BERWYN—Cook County

◉ **MACNEAL HOSPITAL (140054)**, 3249 South Oak Park Avenue, Zip 60402–0715; tel. 708/783–9100 **A**1 2 3 5 8 10 13 **F**3 5 11 12 13 15 18 19 20 22 24 26 28 29 30 31 34 35 37 38 40 41 43 44 45 46 47 49 50 54 57 58 59 62 63 64 65 68 70 73 74 75 76 77 79 81 82 85 86 87 89 90 91 93 96 97 98 100 101 102 103 104 105 107 108 110 111 113 114 115 116 117 118 119 126 130 131 132 141 143 144 146 147 148 **P**5 **S** TENET Healthcare Corporation, Dallas, TX
Primary Contact: J. Scott Steiner, Chief Executive Officer
COO: Sharon Oxendale, Chief Operating Officer
CFO: Mary Elizabeth Cleary, Chief Financial Officer
CMO: Charles Bareis, M.D., Medical Director
CIO: Tom Haslett, Interim Chief Information Officer
CHR: Richard Dodsworth, Chief Human Resource Officer
CNO: Kathleen Benjamin, R.N., Chief Nursing Officer
Web address: www.macneal.com
Control: Corporation, Investor–owned, for–profit **Service:** General Medical and Surgical

Staffed Beds: 357 Admissions: 14781 Census: 188 Outpatient Visits: 219064 **Births: 1749 Total Expense ($000): 207284 Payroll Expense ($000): 91379 Personnel: 1698**

BLOOMINGTON—Mclean County

◉ **OSF ST. JOSEPH MEDICAL CENTER (140162)**, 2200 East Washington Street, Zip 61701–4323; tel. 309/662–3311, (Total facility includes 12 beds in nursing home–type unit) **A**1 2 10 **F**3 11 12 13 15 18 20 22 24 28 29 30 31 34 35 37 40 43 45 49 50 51 53 54 57 59 60 61 64 65 68 70 74 75 76 77 78 79 81 82 84 85 86 87 89 92 93 96 97 107 108 110 111 114 115 118 119 127 128 129 130 131 132 135 144 146 147 148 **P**6 **S** OSF Healthcare System, Peoria, IL
Primary Contact: Chad Boore, President
CFO: John R. Zell, Chief Financial Officer
CMO: Paul E. Pedersen, M.D., Vice President and Chief Medical Officer
CHR: Sue A. Herriott, Executive Director Support Services
CNO: Deborah S. Smith, R.N., Vice President, Chief Nursing Officer
Web address: www.osfstjoseph.org
Control: Church–operated, Nongovernment, not–for profit **Service:** General Medical and Surgical

Staffed Beds: 149 Admissions: 6563 Census: 71 Outpatient Visits: 355252 Births: 807 Total Expense ($000): 156872 Payroll Expense ($000): 54960 Personnel: 846

BLUE ISLAND—Cook County

✠ **METROSOUTH MEDICAL CENTER (140118)**, 12935 South Gregory Street, Zip 60406–2470; tel. 708/597–2000, (Nonreporting) **A**1 10 **S** Quorum Health, Brentwood, TN
Primary Contact: John D. Baird, Chief Executive Officer
CFO: Mei Deng, Chief Financial Officer
CHR: Alanna Barker, Director Human Resources
CNO: Kathleen Hartman, Chief Nursing Officer
Web address: www.metrosouthmedicalcenter.com
Control: Corporation, Investor–owned, for–profit **Service:** General Medical and Surgical

Staffed Beds: 180

BOLINGBROOK—Will County

✠ **AMITA HEALTH ADVENTIST MEDICAL CENTER BOLINGBROOK (140304)**, 500 Remington Boulevard, Zip 60440–4906; tel. 630/312–5000 **A**1 10 **F**3 7 12 13 15 18 20 22 28 29 30 31 34 35 37 40 43 44 45 46 49 50 52 54 56 57 58 59 62 63 64 68 70 73 74 75 76 78 79 81 82 84 85 86 87 92 93 98 100 101 102 103 107 108 110 111 114 115 119 124 129 130 131 132 135 141 143 145 146 147 148 **P**5 8 **S** Adventist Health System Sunbelt Health Care Corporation, Altamonte Springs, FL
Primary Contact: Rick Mace, Chief Executive Officer
COO: Richard Roehr, Chief Operating Officer
CFO: Rebecca Mathis, Chief Financial Officer
CMO: Richard Carroll, M.D., Chief Medical officer
CIO: John McLendon, Senior Vice President and Chief Information Officer
CHR: Katie Baio, Human Resource Director
CNO: Jolene Albaugh, R.N., Chief Nursing Officer
Web address: www.keepingyouwell.com/abh/
Control: Church–operated, Nongovernment, not–for profit **Service:** General Medical and Surgical

Staffed Beds: 144 **Admissions:** 5704 **Census:** 54 **Outpatient Visits:** 102414 **Births:** 950 **Total Expense ($000):** 118711 **Payroll Expense ($000):** 32491 **Personnel:** 576

BREESE—Clinton County

✠ **HSHS ST. JOSEPH'S HOSPITAL (140145)**, 9515 Holy Cross Lane, Zip 62230–3618, Mailing Address: PO Box 99, Zip 62230–0099; tel. 618/526–4511 **A**1 10 **F**3 8 11 13 15 28 29 30 31 34 35 38 40 43 45 50 53 54 57 59 68 70 76 78 79 81 85 87 107 110 111 115 118 119 127 129 130 131 132 135 144 146 147 **P**6 **S** Hospital Sisters Health System, Springfield, IL
Primary Contact: Paulette Evans, R.N., MSN, President and Chief Executive Officer
CFO: John Jeffries, Director Finance
CHR: Robert J. Otrembiak, Director of Learning, Southern IL Division
CNO: Helen Essenpreis, MSN, Chief Nursing Officer
Web address: www.stjoebreese.com
Control: Church–operated, Nongovernment, not–for profit **Service:** General Medical and Surgical

Staffed Beds: 65 **Admissions:** 1401 **Census:** 10 **Outpatient Visits:** 97206 **Births:** 573 **Total Expense ($000):** 47583 **Payroll Expense ($000):** 18318 **Personnel:** 345

CANTON—Fulton County

✠ **GRAHAM HOSPITAL ASSOCIATION (140001)**, 210 West Walnut Street, Zip 61520–2497; tel. 309/647–5240, (Total facility includes 38 beds in nursing home–type unit) **A**1 10 20 **F**3 11 13 15 26 28 29 30 40 45 50 53 54 57 59 62 63 64 65 67 70 75 76 79 81 82 85 87 89 91 97 107 108 110 111 114 115 119 124 127 128 129 130 131 132 135 143 144 145 146 **P**3
Primary Contact: Robert G. Senneff, FACHE, President and Chief Executive Officer
CFO: Eric Franz, Vice President, Finance and Chief Financial Officer
CIO: Jim Schreiner, Chief Information Officer
CHR: Canise A. McComb, Director Human Resources
CNO: Teresa L. McConkey, MSN, Vice President of Nursing and Chief Nursing Officer
Web address: www.grahamhealthsystem.org
Control: Other not–for–profit (including NFP Corporation) **Service:** General Medical and Surgical

Staffed Beds: 87 **Admissions:** 2521 **Census:** 49 **Outpatient Visits:** 201514 **Births:** 260 **Total Expense ($000):** 74051 **Payroll Expense ($000):** 28421 **Personnel:** 594

CARBONDALE—Jackson County

✠ **MEMORIAL HOSPITAL OF CARBONDALE (140164)**, 405 West Jackson Street, Zip 62901–1467, Mailing Address: P.O. Box 10000, Zip 62902–9000; tel. 618/549–0721 **A**1 2 3 5 10 13 19 **F**3 11 13 18 20 22 24 26 28 29 30 31 34 35 40 45 46 48 49 54 56 57 59 64 68 70 72 74 75 76 77 78 79 81 82 83 84 85 86 87 89 107 108 111 114 115 119 120 121 126 130 131 132 135 145 146 147 **P**1 **S** Southern Illinois Hospital Services, Carbondale, IL
Primary Contact: Bart Millstead, Administrator
CFO: Michael Kasser, Vice President Chief Financial Officer and Treasurer
CMO: Marci Moore–Connelly, M.D., Vice President Chief Medical Officer
CIO: David Holland, Vice President Chief Innovation Officer
CHR: Pamela S. Henderson, Vice President Human Resources
CNO: Julie Firman, R.N., Vice President and Chief Nursing Officer
Web address: www.sih.net
Control: Other not–for–profit (including NFP Corporation) **Service:** General Medical and Surgical

Staffed Beds: 159 **Admissions:** 10759 **Census:** 97 **Outpatient Visits:** 120460 **Births:** 2111 **Total Expense ($000):** 261986 **Payroll Expense ($000):** 63411 **Personnel:** 1214

CARLINVILLE—Macoupin County

★ **CARLINVILLE AREA HOSPITAL (141347)**, 20733 North Broad Street, Zip 62626–1499; tel. 217/854–3141 **A**10 18 **F**11 15 28 29 34 35 40 45 64 77 79 81 91 93 107 110 115 127 129 133 148 **P**6 **S** HealthTech Management Services, Brentwood, TN
Primary Contact: Kenneth G. Reid, President and Chief Executive Officer
CFO: Mike Brown, Chief Financial Officer
CMO: Therese Polo, Medical Staff President
CIO: Jerod Cottingham, Director Information Systems
CHR: Tracy Koster, Director Human Resources
CNO: Sara McPeak, Chief Nursing Officer
Web address: www.cahcare.com
Control: Other not–for–profit (including NFP Corporation) **Service:** General Medical and Surgical

Staffed Beds: 25 **Admissions:** 457 **Census:** 6 **Outpatient Visits:** 20846 **Births:** 0 **Total Expense ($000):** 21183 **Payroll Expense ($000):** 7247 **Personnel:** 156

CARROLLTON—Greene County

THOMAS H. BOYD MEMORIAL HOSPITAL (141300), 800 School Street, Zip 62016–1498; tel. 217/942–6946, (Includes REISCH MEMORIAL NURSING HOME), (Nonreporting) **A**10 18
Primary Contact: Deborah Campbell, Administrator
CHR: Lisa Eldridge, Human Resources Officer
Control: Other not–for–profit (including NFP Corporation) **Service:** General Medical and Surgical

Staffed Beds: 25

CARTHAGE—Hancock County

☐ **MEMORIAL HOSPITAL (141305)**, 1454 North County Road 2050, Zip 62321–3551, Mailing Address: P.O. Box 160, Zip 62321–0160; tel. 217/357–8500, (Nonreporting) **A**1 10 18
Primary Contact: Ada Bair, Chief Executive Officer
COO: Florine Dixon, Chief Operating Officer
CFO: Teresa Smith, Chief Financial Officer
CIO: Syndi Horn, Director Information Systems
CHR: Dan Smith, Director Human Resources
Web address: www.mhtlc.org
Control: Other not–for–profit (including NFP Corporation) **Service:** General Medical and Surgical

Staffed Beds: 18

CENTRALIA—Marion County

✠ **SSM HEALTH ST. MARY'S HOSPITAL CENTRALIA (140034)**, 400 North Pleasant Avenue, Zip 62801–3056; tel. 618/436–8000 **A**1 2 10 **F**3 5 11 12 13 15 18 20 26 28 29 30 31 32 34 35 37 38 40 44 45 46 50 54 57 59 61 64 68 70 73 74 75 76 77 78 79 80 81 82 84 85 86 87 89 90 91 92 93 94 98 99 100 101 102 103 104 105 107 108 110 111 114 118 119 120 121 129 130 131 132 135 144 146 147 148 **P**6 8 **S** SSM Health, Saint Louis, MO
Primary Contact: John R. Sigsbury, President
COO: Mark A. Clark, Vice President Operations
CFO: Deland Evischi, Chief Financial Officer
CMO: Rajendra Shroff, M.D., Administrative Medical Director
CIO: Steve Murphy, Director Information Systems
CHR: Brenda Alexander, System Vice President, Human Resources
CNO: Sherry Dunlay, Chief Nursing Officer
Web address: www.ssmhealthillinois.com
Control: Church–operated, Nongovernment, not–for profit **Service:** General Medical and Surgical

Staffed Beds: 113 **Admissions:** 5059 **Census:** 52 **Outpatient Visits:** 203155 **Births:** 336 **Total Expense ($000):** 91399 **Payroll Expense ($000):** 30659 **Personnel:** 752

IL

CENTREVILLE—St. Clair County

☐ **TOUCHETTE REGIONAL HOSPITAL (140077)**, 5900 Bond Avenue, Zip 62207–2326; tel. 618/332–3060 **A**1 10 **F**3 11 13 15 18 29 39 40 45 47 50 54 55 62 64 68 70 73 75 76 79 81 85 87 92 98 99 101 102 103 104 105 107 108 110 114 119 125 130 135 143 146 148 **P**6
Primary Contact: Larry W. McCulley, President and Chief Executive Officer
COO: Tom Mikkelson, M.D., Interim Chief Operating Officer
CFO: John Majchrzak, Chief Financial Officer
CMO: Tom Mikkelson, M.D., Vice President Medical Affairs
Web address: www.touchette.org
Control: Other not–for–profit (including NFP Corporation) **Service:** General Medical and Surgical

Staffed Beds: 111 **Admissions:** 2424 **Census:** 25 **Outpatient Visits:** 59257 **Births:** 247 **Total Expense ($000):** 56311 **Payroll Expense ($000):** 26248 **Personnel:** 468

CHAMPAIGN—Champaign County

☐ **THE PAVILION (144029)**, 809 West Church Street, Zip 61820–3399; tel. 217/373–1700, (Nonreporting) **A**1 10 **S** Universal Health Services, Inc., King of Prussia, PA
Primary Contact: Joseph Sheehy, Chief Executive Officer and Managing Director
CFO: Edith Frasca, Controller and Chief Financial Officer
Web address: www.pavilionhospital.com
Control: Corporation, Investor–owned, for–profit **Service:** Psychiatric

Staffed Beds: 46

CHESTER—Randolph County

☐ **CHESTER MENTAL HEALTH CENTER**, Chester Road, Zip 62233–0031, Mailing Address: Box 31, Zip 62233–0031; tel. 618/826–4571, (Nonreporting) **A**1 **S** Division of Mental Health, Department of Human Services, Springfield, IL
Primary Contact: Leah Hammel, Acting Administrator
CFO: Sarah Imhoff, Business Administrator
CMO: Maitra Rupa, M.D., Acting Medical Director
CIO: Anthony Young, Information Services Specialist
CHR: Kim Holsapple, Human Resource Specialist
CNO: Jennifer Klingeman, Director of Nursing
Control: State–Government, nonfederal **Service:** Psychiatric

Staffed Beds: 245

☐ **MEMORIAL HOSPITAL (141338)**, 1900 State Street, Zip 62233–1116, Mailing Address: P.O. Box 609, Zip 62233–0609; tel. 618/826–4581, (Nonreporting) **A**1 10 18
Primary Contact: Brett Bollmann, Administrator
CFO: Gail Miesner, Chief Financial Officer
CMO: Alan Liefer, M.D., President Medical Staff
CIO: Becky Bunselmeyer, Director Information Services
CHR: May Rose, Director Human Resources
Web address: www.mhchester.com
Control: Hospital district or authority, Government, nonfederal **Service:** General Medical and Surgical

Staffed Beds: 25

CHICAGO—Cook County

ADVOCATE BETHANY HOSPITAL See RML Specialty Hospital

★ ◇ **ADVOCATE ILLINOIS MASONIC MEDICAL CENTER (140182)**, 836 West Wellington Avenue, Zip 60657–5147; tel. 773/975–1600 **A**2 3 5 8 10 13 21 **F**3 5 13 15 17 18 19 20 22 24 26 28 29 30 31 32 33 34 35 36 38 40 43 44 45 46 47 48 49 50 53 54 55 56 57 58 59 60 61 64 66 68 70 71 72 73 74 75 76 77 78 79 81 82 84 85 86 87 89 90 92 93 96 97 98 99 100 101 102 103 104 107 110 111 115 117 118 119 124 126 129 130 131 132 134 135 141 143 146 147 148 **P**6 8 **S** Advocate Health Care, Downers Grove, IL
Primary Contact: Susan Nordstrom Lopez, President
CFO: Jack Gilbert, Vice President Finance and Support Services
CMO: Robert Zadylak, M.D., Vice President Medical Management
CIO: Margaret Capannari, Director Information Systems
CHR: Katie Bata, Vice President Human Resources
CNO: Donna King, R.N., Vice President Clinical Operations and Chief Nursing Executive
Web address: www.advocatehealth.com/masonic
Control: Other not–for–profit (including NFP Corporation) **Service:** General Medical and Surgical

Staffed Beds: 333 **Admissions:** 14609 **Census:** 188 **Outpatient Visits:** 180381 **Births:** 2400 **Total Expense ($000):** 348464 **Payroll Expense ($000):** 137453 **Personnel:** 2097

★ ◇ **ADVOCATE TRINITY HOSPITAL (140048)**, 2320 East 93rd Street, Zip 60617; tel. 773/967–2000 **A**10 21 **F**1 3 4 13 15 16 17 18 20 22 24 26 28 29 30 31 34 35 40 45 49 50 55 56 57 58 59 60 61 64 65 67 68 70 72 73 74 75 76 77 78 79 80 81 82 87 88 89 90 92 93 98 107 110 111 114 115 119 126 128 130 132 135 146 148 **P**8 **S** Advocate Health Care, Downers Grove, IL
Primary Contact: Terika Richardson, M.P.H., President
CFO: Maureen Morrison, Vice President Financial Services
CMO: James Keller, Chief Medical Officer
CIO: Bonita Brown–Roberts, Director Information Systems
CHR: Kristin Landini, Senior Vice President Human Resources
CNO: Jacquelyn Whitten, R.N., Chief Nurse Executive and Vice President Nursing
Web address: www.advocatehealth.com/trinity
Control: Other not–for–profit (including NFP Corporation) **Service:** General Medical and Surgical

Staffed Beds: 186 **Admissions:** 9282 **Census:** 102 **Outpatient Visits:** 77786 **Births:** 1095 **Total Expense ($000):** 155885 **Payroll Expense ($000):** 54252 **Personnel:** 731

⊠ **ANN & ROBERT H. LURIE CHILDREN'S HOSPITAL OF CHICAGO (143300)**, 225 East Chicago Avenue, Zip 60611–2991; tel. 312/227–4000 **A**1 3 5 8 10 **F**3 8 9 11 12 17 18 19 21 23 24 25 27 29 30 31 32 34 35 36 37 38 39 40 41 43 44 45 46 48 49 50 51 52 54 55 57 58 59 60 61 63 64 65 68 72 74 75 78 79 81 82 84 85 86 87 88 89 91 92 93 94 96 97 98 99 100 101 102 104 105 107 108 111 115 116 117 118 119 124 126 129 130 131 132 134 136 137 138 139 141 142 144 146 148
Primary Contact: Patrick M. Magoon, President and Chief Executive Officer
COO: Gordon B. Bass, Chief Operating Officer
CFO: Paula Noble, Chief Financial Officer and Treasurer
CMO: Michael Kelleher, Chief Medical Officer
CIO: Lisa Dykstra, Senior Vice President and Chief Information Officer
CHR: Barbara Bowman, Chief Human Resource Officer
Web address: www.luriechildrens.org
Control: Other not–for–profit (including NFP Corporation) **Service:** Children's general

Staffed Beds: 288 **Admissions:** 12139 **Census:** 197 **Outpatient Visits:** 549043 **Births:** 0 **Total Expense ($000):** 683356 **Payroll Expense ($000):** 278323 **Personnel:** 4953

BERNARD MITCHELL HOSPITAL See University of Chicago Medical Center

☐ **CHICAGO LAKESHORE HOSPITAL (144005)**, 4840 North Marine Drive, Zip 60640–4296; tel. 773/878–9700, (Nonreporting) **A**1 3 5 10 **S** Signature Healthcare Services, Corona, CA
Primary Contact: Patrick Moallemian, Chief Executive Officer
CFO: Carol Peart, Chief Financial Officer
CMO: Peter Nierman, M.D., Chief Medical Officer
CHR: Michelle Culpepper, Director Human Resources
Web address: www.chicagolakeshorehospital.com
Control: Corporation, Investor–owned, for–profit **Service:** Psychiatric

Staffed Beds: 115

CHICAGO LYING–IN (CLI) See University of Chicago Medical Center

☐ **CHICAGO–READ MENTAL HEALTH CENTER (144010)**, 4200 North Oak Park Avenue, Zip 60634–1457; tel. 773/794–4000, (Nonreporting) **A**1 10 **S** Division of Mental Health, Department of Human Services, Springfield, IL
Primary Contact: Thomas Simpatico, M.D., Facility Director and Network System Manager
Control: State–Government, nonfederal **Service:** Psychiatric

Staffed Beds: 200

CHILDREN'S MEMORIAL HOSPITAL See Ann & Robert H. Lurie Children's Hospital of Chicago

COMER CHILDREN'S HOSPITAL See University of Chicago Medical Center

☐ **COMMUNITY FIRST MEDICAL CENTER (140251)**, 5645 West Addison Street, Zip 60634–4403; tel. 773/282–7000, (Nonreporting) **A**1 3 10
Primary Contact: Dennis FitzMaurice, Interim Chief Executive Officer
COO: Dennis FitzMaurice, Vice President, Professional Services
CFO: Richard Franco, Chief Financial Officer
CMO: David Bordo, M.D., Vice President and Chief Medical Officer
CIO: George Chessum, Senior Vice President and Chief Information Officer
CHR: Ivy McKinley, Regional Human Resources Officer
Web address: www.cfmedicalcenter.com
Control: Other not–for–profit (including NFP Corporation) **Service:** General Medical and Surgical

Staffed Beds: 279

Hospital, Medicare Provider Number, Address, Telephone, Approval, Facility, and Physician Codes, Health Care System

★ American Hospital Association (AHA) membership
☐ The Joint Commission accreditation
○ Healthcare Facilities Accreditation Program
◇ DNV Healthcare Inc. accreditation
⇑ Center for Improvement in Healthcare Quality Accreditation
△ Commission on Accreditation of Rehabilitation Facilities (CARF) accreditation

---

IL

☐ **GARFIELD PARK HOSPITAL (144039)**, 520 North Ridgeway Avenue, Zip 60624–1232; tel. 773/265–3700 **A**1 10 **F**29 35 59 68 75 86 87 98 99 101 105 130 **P**6 **S** Universal Health Services, Inc., King of Prussia, PA
Primary Contact: Len Kirby, Chief Executive Officer
CMO: Tina Mahera, M.D., Chief Medical Officer
CHR: Janice Clark, Manager Human Resources
Web address: www.garfieldparkhospital.com
Control: Corporation, Investor–owned, for–profit **Service:** Children's hospital psychiatric

Staffed Beds: 43 **Admissions:** 868 **Census:** 24 **Outpatient Visits:** 3723 **Births:** 0 **Total Expense ($000):** 9473 **Payroll Expense ($000):** 4130 **Personnel:** 76

☐ **HARTGROVE HOSPITAL (144026)**, 5730 West Roosevelt Road, Zip 60644–1580; tel. 773/413–1700, (Nonreporting) **A**1 10 **S** Universal Health Services, Inc., King of Prussia, PA
Primary Contact: Steven Airhart, Chief Executive Officer
CFO: Srbo Nikolic, Chief Financial Officer
CMO: Johnny Williamson, M.D., Chief Medical Officer
CHR: Anthony Rivera, Director Human Resources
CNO: Jody Bhambra, Chief Nursing Officer
Web address: www.hartgrovehospital.com
Control: Corporation, Investor–owned, for–profit **Service:** Psychiatric

Staffed Beds: 128

★ ○ **HOLY CROSS HOSPITAL (140133)**, 2701 West 68th Street, Zip 60629–1882; tel. 773/884–9000, (Nonreporting) **A**10 11 **S** Sinai Health System, Chicago, IL
Primary Contact: Lori Pacura, MSN, R.N., President
COO: Donnica Austin, Vice President, Operations
CFO: Charles Weis, Executive Vice President and Chief Financial Officer
CMO: James Richardson, Chief Medical Officer
CIO: Ben Patel, Chief Information Officer
CHR: Ann Hatches, Director, Human Resources
CNO: Deborah Davisson, MSN, Chief Nursing Officer and Vice President, Patient Care Services
Web address: www.holycrosshospital.org
Control: Corporation, Investor–owned, for–profit **Service:** General Medical and Surgical

Staffed Beds: 213

☐ **JACKSON PARK HOSPITAL AND MEDICAL CENTER (140177)**, 7531 Stony Island Avenue, Zip 60649–3993; tel. 773/947–7500, (Nonreporting) **A**1 3 10
Primary Contact: William Dorsey, M.D., Board Chairman and Chief Executive Officer
COO: Randall Smith, Executive Vice President
CFO: Nelson Vasquez, Vice President Finance
CMO: Bangalore Murthy, M.D., Director Medical Staff
CIO: Thomas Pankow, Chief Information Officer
CHR: Tracey Jones, Director Human Resources
Web address: www.jacksonparkhospital.org
Control: Other not–for–profit (including NFP Corporation) **Service:** General Medical and Surgical

Staffed Beds: 118

⊠ △ **JESSE BROWN VETERANS AFFAIRS MEDICAL CENTER**, 820 South Damen, Zip 60612–3776; tel. 312/569–8387 **A**1 3 5 7 8 **F**2 3 5 8 10 11 12 14 15 17 18 20 22 24 26 28 29 30 31 34 35 38 39 40 44 45 46 47 50 53 54 57 58 59 60 61 62 63 64 65 68 70 71 74 75 77 78 79 80 81 82 84 85 86 87 93 94 97 98 100 101 102 104 105 106 107 111 119 126 127 129 130 132 133 135 143 144 146 147 148 **S** Department of Veterans Affairs, Washington, DC
Primary Contact: Annette Walker, Acting Medical Center Director
COO: Michelle Blakely, Associate Director
CFO: Kalpana Mehta, Chief Fiscal Services
CMO: Wendy W. Brown, M.D., Chief of Staff
CIO: Howard Loewenstein, Chief Information Resource Management Services
CHR: Wayne Davis, Manager Human Resources
Web address: www.chicago.va.gov/
Control: Veterans Affairs, Government, federal **Service:** General Medical and Surgical

Staffed Beds: 240 **Admissions:** 8320 **Census:** 171 **Outpatient Visits:** 922572 **Births:** 0 **Total Expense ($000):** 419898 **Payroll Expense ($000):** 202565 **Personnel:** 2670

⊠ **JOHN H. STROGER JR. HOSPITAL OF COOK COUNTY (140124)**, 1969 West Ogden Avenue, Zip 60612–3714; tel. 312/864–6000 **A**1 2 3 5 8 10 13 **F**3 5 11 13 15 16 17 18 19 20 22 24 29 30 31 35 36 38 39 40 41 42 43 44 45 46 47 48 49 51 52 54 55 56 58 59 60 61 64 65 68 70 72 74 75 76 77 78 79 81 82 84 85 86 87 88 89 91 92 93 94 97 99 100 101 102 103 104 107 108 110 111 114 115 118 119 121 123 129 130 132 134 135 146 147 148 **P**6 **S** Cook County Health and Hospitals System, Chicago, IL
Primary Contact: John Jay Shannon, M.D., Chief Executive Officer
CFO: John R. Morales, Chief Financial Officer
CMO: Claudia Fegan, M.D., Chief Medical Officer
CIO: Bala Hota, Interim Chief Information Officer
CHR: Paris I. Partee, Associate Administrator and Director Human Resources
CNO: Antoinette Williams, Chief Nursing Officer
Web address: www.cookcountyhealth.net
Control: County–Government, nonfederal **Service:** General Medical and Surgical

Staffed Beds: 464 **Admissions:** 21517 **Census:** 271 **Outpatient Visits:** 950655 **Births:** 893 **Total Expense ($000):** 1119347 **Payroll Expense ($000):** 441490 **Personnel:** 5565

JOHNSTON R. BOWMAN HEALTH CENTER See Rush University Medical Center

KINDRED CHICAGO LAKESHORE See Kindred Chicago–Central Hospital

⊠ **KINDRED CHICAGO–CENTRAL HOSPITAL (142009)**, 4058 West Melrose Street, Zip 60641–4797; tel. 773/736–7000, (Includes KINDRED CHICAGO LAKESHORE, 6130 North Sheridan Road, Zip 60660; tel. 773/381–1222; Diane Otteman, Chief Executive Officer; KINDRED HOSPITAL CHICAGO NORTH, 2544 West Montrose Avenue, Zip 60618–1589; tel. 773/267–2622; Larry Foster, R.N., MSN, Chief Executive Officer), (Nonreporting) **A**1 10 **S** Kindred Healthcare, Louisville, KY
Primary Contact: Jonathan Cohee, Chief Executive Officer
COO: Joanne Garcia, Chief Operating Officer
CFO: Mary Treacy Shiff, Chief Financial Officer
Web address: www.khchicagocentral.com
Control: Corporation, Investor–owned, for–profit **Service:** Long–Term Acute Care hospital

Staffed Beds: 54

KINDRED HOSPITAL CHICAGO NORTH See Kindred Chicago–Central Hospital

⊠ **LA RABIDA CHILDREN'S HOSPITAL (143301)**, 6501 South Promontory Drive, Zip 60649–1003; tel. 773/363–6700 **A**1 3 5 10 **F**3 19 28 29 32 34 35 38 40 41 50 57 59 64 65 74 75 77 79 82 84 85 86 87 89 91 93 94 96 97 99 100 101 104 130 132 134 143 144 146 148 **P**6
Primary Contact: Brenda J. Wolf, President and Chief Executive Officer
CFO: Mark Renfree, Chief Financial Officer
CMO: David Soglin, Chief Medical Officer
CIO: Sheelah Cabrera, Chief Information Officer
CHR: Frances Lefkow, Director Human Resources
CNO: Aden Henry, R.N., Vice President, Patient Care
Web address: www.larabida.org
Control: Other not–for–profit (including NFP Corporation) **Service:** Children's chronic disease

Staffed Beds: 49 **Admissions:** 446 **Census:** 18 **Outpatient Visits:** 30011 **Births:** 0 **Total Expense ($000):** 48777 **Payroll Expense ($000):** 22943 **Personnel:** 412

☐ **LORETTO HOSPITAL (140083)**, 645 South Central Avenue, Zip 60644–5059; tel. 773/626–4300 **A**1 10 **F**2 3 4 5 15 18 29 30 31 34 35 38 40 44 45 50 54 57 59 60 61 64 65 68 70 74 75 78 79 81 85 86 87 89 92 93 98 102 103 104 105 106 107 108 115 119 130 132 143 146 147 148
Primary Contact: Sonia Mehta, M.D., Chief Executive Officer and Chief Medical Officer
CFO: John Valles, Senior Vice President and Chief Financial Officer
CMO: Sonia Mehta, M.D., Chief Executive Officer and Chief Medical Officer
CIO: Suresh Krishnan, Vice President and Chief Information Officer
CHR: Amy Coleman, Director Human Resources
CNO: James M. Renneker, MSN, Vice President and Chief Nursing Officer
Web address: www.lorettohospital.org
Control: Other not–for–profit (including NFP Corporation) **Service:** General Medical and Surgical

Staffed Beds: 113 **Admissions:** 4440 **Census:** 67 **Outpatient Visits:** 24302 **Births:** 0 **Total Expense ($000):** 55709 **Payroll Expense ($000):** 28423

⊠ **LOUIS A. WEISS MEMORIAL HOSPITAL (140082)**, 4646 North Marine Drive, Zip 60640–5759; tel. 773/878–8700 **A**1 2 3 5 10 **F**3 8 9 15 18 20 22 24 26 28 29 30 31 34 35 36 37 40 44 45 49 56 57 58 59 61 64 65 66 68 70 74 75 77 78 79 81 82 85 86 87 90 91 92 93 96 97 98 100 101 102 103 107 108 109 110 111 114 119 121 126 129 130 131 132 135 141 143 146 147 148 **P**5 6 8 **S** TENET Healthcare Corporation, Dallas, TX
Primary Contact: Anthony Tedeschi, M.D., M.P.H., Chief Executive Officer and Chief Medical Officer
CFO: Jeffrey L. Meigs, Chief Financial Officer
CMO: Anthony Tedeschi, M.D., Chief Executive Officer and Chief Medical Officer
CIO: Thomas Crawford, Chicago Market Chief Information Officer
CHR: Keoni Nader, Director Human Resources
Web address: www.weisshospital.com
Control: Corporation, Investor–owned, for–profit **Service:** General Medical and Surgical

Staffed Beds: 153 **Admissions:** 5992 **Census:** 90 **Outpatient Visits:** 72303 **Births:** 0 **Total Expense ($000):** 105967 **Payroll Expense ($000):** 46924 **Personnel:** 719

IL

★ ○ **MERCY HOSPITAL AND MEDICAL CENTER (140158)**, 2525 South Michigan Avenue, Zip 60616–2333; tel. 312/567–2000 **A**2 3 5 10 11 **F**3 5 12 13 15 17 18 20 22 24 26 28 29 30 31 32 33 34 35 36 40 44 45 46 49 50 51 52 53 54 55 56 57 58 59 61 64 65 66 70 74 77 78 79 81 82 84 85 86 87 90 91 92 93 96 97 98 99 100 101 102 103 104 105 107 108 110 111 114 115 117 118 119 121 123 124 126 129 130 131 132 133 134 135 143 144 145 146 147 148 **P**1 5 **S** Trinity Health, Livonia, MI
Primary Contact: Carol L. Schneider, President and Chief Executive Officer
COO: Richard Cerceo, Executive Vice President and Chief Operating Officer
CFO: Eric Krueger, Chief Financial Officer
CMO: Michael McDonnell, M.D., Chief Medical Officer
CIO: John Romeo, Chief Information Officer
CHR: Nancy L. Hill–Davis, Vice President Human Resources and Risk Management
CNO: Carla Campbell, R.N., Chief Nurse Officer
Web address: www.mercy–chicago.org
Control: Other not–for–profit (including NFP Corporation) **Service:** General Medical and Surgical

Staffed Beds: 189 **Admissions:** 14670 **Census:** 168 **Outpatient Visits:** 387142 **Births:** 2434 **Total Expense ($000):** 262705 **Payroll Expense ($000):** 100129 **Personnel:** 1467

○ **METHODIST HOSPITAL OF CHICAGO (140197)**, 5025 North Paulina Street, Zip 60640–2772; tel. 773/271–9040, (Nonreporting) **A**10 11
Primary Contact: Joseph Chandy, Administrator
CFO: Jim Gregory, Controller
Web address: www.bethanymethodist.org
Control: Other not–for–profit (including NFP Corporation) **Service:** General Medical and Surgical

Staffed Beds: 189

✠ **MOUNT SINAI HOSPITAL (140018)**, California Avenue at 15th Street, Zip 60608–1729; tel. 773/542–2000, (Includes SINAI CHILDREN'S HOSPITAL, California Avenue at 15th Street, Zip 60608; tel. 773/542–2000; Karen Teitelbaum, President and Chief Executive Officer), (Nonreporting) **A**1 2 3 5 8 10 **S** Sinai Health System, Chicago, IL
Primary Contact: Loren Chandler, President
CFO: Charles Weis, Chief Financial Officer
CMO: Mark Multach, M.D., Chief Medical Officer
CIO: Ben Patel, Chief Information Officer
CHR: Ann Hatches, Interim Director Human Resources
CNO: Michele A. Mazurek, Interim Vice President Patient Care Services and Chief Nursing Officer
Web address: www.sinai.org
Control: Other not–for–profit (including NFP Corporation) **Service:** General Medical and Surgical

Staffed Beds: 290

✠ **NORTHWESTERN MEMORIAL HOSPITAL (140281)**, 251 East Huron Street, Zip 60611–2908; tel. 312/926–2000, (Includes PRENTICE WOMEN'S HOSPITAL, 250 East Superior Street, Zip 60611; tel. 312/926–2000; STONE INSTITUTE OF PSYCHIATRY, 320 East Huron Street, Zip 60611; tel. 312/926–2000) **A**1 2 3 5 8 10 **F**3 4 5 6 8 9 11 12 13 15 17 18 20 22 24 26 28 29 30 31 32 33 34 35 36 37 38 39 40 43 44 45 46 47 48 49 50 51 52 54 55 56 57 58 59 60 61 63 64 65 66 68 70 72 73 74 75 76 77 78 79 80 81 82 83 84 85 86 87 92 93 96 97 98 99 100 101 102 103 104 107 108 110 111 114 115 116 117 118 119 120 121 123 124 126 129 130 131 132 135 136 137 138 139 140 141 142 144 146 147 148 **P**5 **S** Northwestern Memorial Healthcare, Chicago, IL
Primary Contact: Dean M. Harrison, Chief Executive Officer
CFO: Francis D. Fraher, Vice President and Chief Financial Officer, Northwestern Memorial Hospital
CMO: Gary Noskin, Senior Vice President and Chief Medical Officer, Northwestern Memorial Hospital
CIO: Carl Christensen, Senior Vice President and Chief Information Officer, Northwestern Memorial HealthCare
CHR: Dean Manheimer, Senior Vice President Human Resources, Northwestern Memorial Healthcare
CNO: Kristin Ramsey, R.N., Senior Vice President and Chief Nursing Executive, Northwestern Memorial Hospital
Web address: www.nm.org
Control: Other not–for–profit (including NFP Corporation) **Service:** General Medical and Surgical

Staffed Beds: 871 **Admissions:** 45998 **Census:** 648 **Outpatient Visits:** 1733680 **Births:** 11947 **Total Expense ($000):** 2006110 **Payroll Expense ($000):** 664045 **Personnel:** 8591

✠ **NORWEGIAN AMERICAN HOSPITAL (140206)**, 1044 North Francisco Avenue, Zip 60622–2743; tel. 773/292–8200 **A**1 3 5 10 **F**5 13 15 18 19 20 22 29 31 32 34 35 36 38 39 40 44 45 46 47 48 49 50 56 57 59 60 63 64 65 68 70 71 74 75 76 77 78 79 81 82 84 86 87 89 91 92 93 94 96 97 98 100 101 102 103 105 107 110 111 114 118 119 130 143 146 147 148 **P**8
Primary Contact: Jose R. Sanchez, President and Chief Executive Officer
COO: Justin Bynum, Chief Operating Officer
CFO: Gary M. Krugel, Chief Financial Officer
CMO: James Kolka, D.O., Chief Medical Officer
CIO: Stephen DePooter, Chief Information Officer
CHR: Neil Teatsorth, Vice President Human Resources
CNO: Deborah Jones, Interim Chief Nursing Officer
Web address: www.nahospital.org
Control: Other not–for–profit (including NFP Corporation) **Service:** General Medical and Surgical

Staffed Beds: 195 **Admissions:** 8357 **Census:** 111 **Outpatient Visits:** 83868 **Births:** 1025 **Total Expense ($000):** 111667 **Payroll Expense ($000):** 52002 **Personnel:** 768

OUR LADY OF THE RESURRECTION MEDICAL CENTER See Community First Medical Center

PRENTICE WOMEN'S HOSPITAL See Northwestern Memorial Hospital

✠ △ **PRESENCE RESURRECTION MEDICAL CENTER (140117)**, 7435 West Talcott Avenue, Zip 60631–3746; tel. 773/774–8000 **A**1 2 3 5 7 10 13 **F**3 11 13 15 17 18 19 20 22 24 26 27 28 29 30 31 34 35 37 38 39 40 41 45 46 47 49 50 53 57 58 59 60 62 64 66 68 70 73 74 75 76 78 79 81 82 83 84 85 87 89 90 92 93 96 100 107 108 110 111 114 115 117 118 119 120 121 123 124 126 130 131 132 133 146 147 148 **S** Presence Health, Chicago, IL
Primary Contact: Robert Dahl, President and Chief Executive Officer
CFO: Colleen Koppenhaver, Interim Chief Financial Officer
CMO: David Bordo, M.D., Chief Medical Officer
CHR: Ivy McKinley, Regional Lead Human Resources
CNO: Pam Bell, Vice President Patient Care Services and Chief Nursing Officer
Web address: www.presencehealth.org
Control: City–Government, nonfederal **Service:** General Medical and Surgical

Staffed Beds: 325 **Admissions:** 12710 **Census:** 190 **Outpatient Visits:** 189114 **Births:** 1074 **Total Expense ($000):** 257109 **Payroll Expense ($000):** 90379 **Personnel:** 1422

✠ **PRESENCE SAINT JOSEPH HOSPITAL (140224)**, 2900 North Lake Shore Drive, Zip 60657–6274; tel. 773/665–3000 **A**1 2 3 5 10 **F**3 5 11 12 13 15 18 19 20 22 24 25 26 28 29 30 31 32 33 34 35 36 38 39 40 41 45 46 47 48 49 50 53 54 55 56 57 58 59 60 61 63 64 65 66 68 70 72 74 75 76 77 78 79 81 82 84 85 86 87 89 90 92 93 96 97 98 100 101 103 104 107 108 110 111 114 115 117 118 119 120 121 122 123 124 126 128 129 130 131 132 135 143 145 146 147 148 **P**8 **S** Presence Health, Chicago, IL
Primary Contact: Roberta Luskin–Hawk, M.D., President and Chief Executive Officer
CFO: Stanley Kazmierczak, Controller
CMO: M. Todd Grendon, M.D., President Medical Staff
CIO: George Chessum, Senior Vice President Information Systems and Chief Information Officer
CHR: Denise Brown, Vice President Human Resources
Web address: www.reshealth.org
Control: Church–operated, Nongovernment, not–for profit **Service:** General Medical and Surgical

Staffed Beds: 327 **Admissions:** 11385 **Census:** 157 **Outpatient Visits:** 116968 **Births:** 1388 **Total Expense ($000):** 230928 **Payroll Expense ($000):** 78691 **Personnel:** 1228

IL

Hospital, Medicare Provider Number, Address, Telephone, Approval, Facility, and Physician Codes, Health Care System

★ American Hospital Association (AHA) membership ○ Healthcare Facilities Accreditation Program ⇑ Center for Improvement in Healthcare Quality Accreditation
□ The Joint Commission accreditation ◇ DNV Healthcare Inc. accreditation △ Commission on Accreditation of Rehabilitation Facilities (CARF) accreditation

✠ **PRESENCE SAINTS MARY & ELIZABETH MEDICAL CENTER (140180)**, 2233 West Division Street, Zip 60622–3086; tel. 312/770–2000, (Includes PRESENCE SAINTS MARY & ELIZABETH MEDICAL CENTER, CLAREMONT AVENUE, 1431 North Claremont Avenue, Zip 60622–1791; tel. 773/278–2000; Martin H. Judd, Regional President and Chief Executive Officer), (Total facility includes 25 beds in nursing home–type unit) **A**1 2 3 5 10 **F**3 4 13 15 18 19 20 22 24 26 28 29 30 31 32 34 35 36 38 40 45 49 50 52 57 58 59 60 64 65 66 68 70 74 75 76 77 78 79 81 82 84 85 86 87 89 90 91 92 93 94 96 97 98 99 100 101 102 103 107 108 110 111 114 115 119 121 123 126 128 129 130 132 135 143 146 147 148 **P**8 **S** Presence Health, Chicago, IL
Primary Contact: Martin H. Judd, Regional President and Chief Executive Officer
CFO: Bob Cech, Regional Finance Officer
CMO: Laura Concannon, M.D., Regional Chief Medical Officer
CIO: David Lundal, System Vice President, Information Systems and Chief Information Officer
CHR: Melanie Saenz, Regional Human Resources Officer
CNO: Suzanne Lambert, R.N., Regional Chief Nursing Officer and Support Services
Web address: www.presencehealth.org/presence–saints–mary–and–elizabeth–medical–center–chicago
Control: Church–operated, Nongovernment, not–for profit **Service:** General Medical and Surgical

Staffed Beds: 492 **Admissions:** 18947 **Census:** 285 **Outpatient Visits:** 196335 **Births:** 1406 **Total Expense ($000):** 252596 **Payroll Expense ($000):** 85402 **Personnel:** 1488

✠ **PROVIDENT HOSPITAL OF COOK COUNTY (140300)**, 500 East 51st Street, Zip 60615–2494; tel. 312/572–2000 **A**1 3 5 10 **F**3 8 15 18 29 30 34 35 40 45 50 53 57 59 61 64 66 68 78 81 85 87 92 94 104 107 119 130 132 135 143 146 147 **S** Cook County Health and Hospitals System, Chicago, IL
Primary Contact: John Jay Shannon, M.D., Chief Executive Officer
CFO: Barbara Patterson, Chief Financial Officer
CMO: Aaron Hamb, M.D., Chief Medical Officer
CIO: Donna Hart, Chief Information Officer
Web address: www.ccbhs.org/pages/ProvidentHospitalofCookCounty.htm
Control: County–Government, nonfederal **Service:** General Medical and Surgical

Staffed Beds: 25 **Admissions:** 745 **Census:** 8 **Outpatient Visits:** 30518 **Births:** 0 **Total Expense ($000):** 61954 **Payroll Expense ($000):** 33546 **Personnel:** 365

✠ **REHABILITATION INSTITUTE OF CHICAGO (143026)**, 345 East Superior Street, Zip 60611–2654; tel. 312/238–1000, (Nonreporting) **A**1 3 5 8 10
Primary Contact: Joanne C. Smith, M.D., President and Chief Executive Officer
COO: Peggy Kirk, Senior Vice President Clinical Operations
CFO: Ed Case, Executive Vice President and Chief Financial Officer
CMO: James Sliwa, M.D., Chief Medical Officer
CIO: Tim McKula, Vice President Information Systems and Chief Information Officer
CHR: Lois Huggins, Chief Human Resources Officer and Senior Vice President Human Resources
Web address: www.ric.org
Control: Other not–for–profit (including NFP Corporation) **Service:** Rehabilitation

Staffed Beds: 182

RESURRECTION MEDICAL CENTER See Presence Resurrection Medical Center

★ **RML SPECIALTY HOSPITAL (142012)**, 3435 West Van Buren Street, Zip 60624–3312; tel. 773/826–6300 **F**1 3 18 29 30 31 45 53 58 74 85 107 114 119 130 146 148 **P**6
Primary Contact: James R. Prister, President and Chief Executive Officer
COO: Ken Pawola, Chief Operating Officer
CFO: Tom Pater, Vice President Finance and Chief Financial Officer
CMO: Patrick Fahey, M.D., Chief Medical Director
CIO: Vincent S. Vitali, Chief Information Officer
CHR: John Landstrom, Vice President Human Resources and Operations
CNO: Marti Edwards, MSN, Chief Nursing Officer
Web address: www.rmlspecialtyhospital.org
Control: Other not–for–profit (including NFP Corporation) **Service:** Long–Term Acute Care hospital

Staffed Beds: 69 **Admissions:** 592 **Census:** 53 **Outpatient Visits:** 16 **Births:** 0 **Total Expense ($000):** 32164 **Payroll Expense ($000):** 16302 **Personnel:** 284

○ **ROSELAND COMMUNITY HOSPITAL (140068)**, 45 West 111th Street, Zip 60628–4294; tel. 773/995–3000 **A**10 11 **F**5 7 8 11 15 18 29 30 32 33 34 35 40 45 46 48 49 51 54 57 59 64 65 68 70 71 75 76 81 82 85 86 87 97 98 99 101 102 107 108 109 110 114 115 118 119 120 130 135 143 147 148
Primary Contact: Timothy Egan, President and Chief Executive Officer
CMO: Rogelio Cave, M.D., Medical Director
CIO: William Spence, Director
CNO: Winifred Lewis, R.N., Chief Nursing Officer
Web address: www.roselandhospital.org
Control: Other not–for–profit (including NFP Corporation) **Service:** General Medical and Surgical

Staffed Beds: 134 **Admissions:** 3721 **Census:** 49 **Outpatient Visits:** 38274 **Births:** 267 **Total Expense ($000):** 47237 **Payroll Expense ($000):** 24495 **Personnel:** 400

✠ △ **RUSH UNIVERSITY MEDICAL CENTER (140119)**, 1653 West Congress Parkway, Zip 60612–3833; tel. 312/942–5000, (Includes JOHNSTON R. BOWMAN HEALTH CENTER, 700 South Paulina, Zip 60612; tel. 312/942–7000; RUSH CHILDREN'S HOSPITAL, 1653 Wes Congress Parkway, tel. 888/352–7874) **A**1 2 3 5 7 8 10 **F**2 3 6 8 9 11 12 13 14 15 17 18 19 20 21 22 23 24 25 26 27 28 29 30 31 32 34 35 36 37 38 39 40 41 43 44 45 46 47 48 49 50 51 52 53 54 55 56 57 58 59 60 61 62 63 64 65 66 68 70 72 73 74 75 76 77 78 79 81 82 83 84 85 86 87 88 89 90 91 92 93 94 95 96 97 98 99 100 101 102 103 104 105 107 110 111 114 115 117 118 119 120 121 123 124 125 126 129 130 131 132 134 135 136 137 138 139 141 142 145 146 147 148 **P**8 **S** Rush University Medical Center, Chicago, IL
Primary Contact: Larry J. Goodman, M.D., Chief Executive Officer
COO: Michael J. Dandorph, President and Chief Operating Officer
CFO: John P. Mordach, Senior Vice President and Chief Financial Officer
CMO: David A. Ansell, M.D., Senior Vice President Clinical Affairs and Chief Medical Officer
CIO: Lac Tran, Senior Vice President Information Services
CHR: Mary Ellen Schopp, Senior Vice President Human Resources
CNO: Cynthia Barginere, MSN, Vice President Clinical Nursing and Chief Nursing Officer
Web address: www.rush.edu
Control: Other not–for–profit (including NFP Corporation) **Service:** General Medical and Surgical

Staffed Beds: 679 **Admissions:** 31810 **Census:** 483 **Outpatient Visits:** 569895 **Births:** 2251 **Total Expense ($000):** 1017036 **Payroll Expense ($000):** 315761 **Personnel:** 8755

✠ **SAINT ANTHONY HOSPITAL (140095)**, 2875 West 19th Street, Zip 60623–3596; tel. 773/484–1000 **A**1 3 10 **F**3 13 15 18 19 29 30 31 32 34 35 40 41 44 49 50 51 53 54 57 59 60 64 65 68 70 74 75 76 77 78 79 81 82 85 86 87 89 93 96 97 98 100 101 102 104 105 107 108 110 111 115 118 119 130 131 132 143 144 146 147 148 **P**8
Primary Contact: Guy A. Medaglia, President and Chief Executive Officer
CFO: Justin Bynum, Chief Financial Officer
CIO: Mark Jennings, Chief Information Officer
CHR: Malinda Yvonne Carter, Vice President Human Resources
Web address: www.sahchicago.org
Control: Church–operated, Nongovernment, not–for profit **Service:** General Medical and Surgical

Staffed Beds: 151 **Admissions:** 5747 **Census:** 73 **Outpatient Visits:** 160620 **Births:** 1546 **Total Expense ($000):** 109161 **Payroll Expense ($000):** 54990 **Personnel:** 831

SAINT JOSEPH HOSPITAL See Presence Saint Joseph Hospital

SAINTS MARY & ELIZABETH MEDICAL CENTER See Presence Saints Mary & Elizabeth Medical Center

✠ **SCHWAB REHABILITATION HOSPITAL (143025)**, 1401 South California Avenue, Zip 60608–1858; tel. 773/522–2010, (Nonreporting) **A**1 3 5 10 **S** Sinai Health System, Chicago, IL
Primary Contact: Karen Teitelbaum, Chief Executive Officer
CFO: Charles Weis, Chief Financial Officer
CMO: Michelle Gittler, M.D., Medical Director
CNO: Mary A. Gollinger, MS, Director of Nursing
Web address: www.schwabrehab.org
Control: Other not–for–profit (including NFP Corporation) **Service:** Rehabilitation

Staffed Beds: 102

☐ **SHRINERS HOSPITALS FOR CHILDREN–CHICAGO (143302)**, 2211 North Oak Park Avenue, Zip 60707–3392; tel. 773/622–5400, (Nonreporting) **A**1 3 5 10 **S** Shriners Hospitals for Children, Tampa, FL
Primary Contact: Mark L. Niederpruem, FACHE, Administrator
CFO: Philip Magid, Director Fiscal Services
CMO: Jeffrey D. Ackman, M.D., Chief of Staff
CHR: James E. Pawlowicz, Director Human Resources
CNO: Terry Wheat, R.N., Director of Patient Care Services
Web address: www.shrinershospitalsforchildren.org/Hospitals/Locations/Chicago.aspx
Control: Other not–for–profit (including NFP Corporation) **Service:** Children's orthopedic

Staffed Beds: 36

○ **SOUTH SHORE HOSPITAL (140181)**, 8012 South Crandon Avenue, Zip 60617–1124; tel. 773/768–0810, (Nonreporting) **A**10 11
Primary Contact: Timothy Caveney, President
CFO: Scott Spencer, Chief Financial Officer
CMO: James Bob Achebe, M.D., President Medical Staff
CIO: Jim Ritchie, Director Management Information Systems
CHR: Roger Rak, Director Human Resources
CNO: Laura Gonzalez, Interim Chief Nurse Executive
Web address: www.southshorehospital.com
Control: Other not–for–profit (including NFP Corporation) **Service:** General Medical and Surgical

Staffed Beds: 137

Many Facility Codes have changed. Please refer to the AHA Guide Code Chart.
© 2016 AHA Guide

IL

☐ **ST. BERNARD HOSPITAL AND HEALTH CARE CENTER (140103)**, 326 West 64th Street, Zip 60621–3146; tel. 773/962–3900, (Nonreporting) **A**1 10
Primary Contact: Charles Holland, President and Chief Executive Officer
COO: Roland Abellera, Vice President and Chief Operating Officer
CFO: James P. Porter, Chief Financial Officer
CNO: Evelyn Jones, R.N., Vice President Nursing Services
Web address: www.stbernardhospital.com
Control: Other not–for–profit (including NFP Corporation) **Service:** General Medical and Surgical

Staffed Beds: 100

○ **SWEDISH COVENANT HOSPITAL (140114)**, 5145 North California Avenue, Zip 60625–3661; tel. 773/878–8200 **A**2 3 5 10 11 13 **F**3 8 13 15 18 19 20 22 24 26 28 29 30 31 32 33 34 35 36 38 40 45 46 47 49 50 53 56 57 58 59 60 62 64 68 70 74 75 76 78 79 81 82 83 84 85 86 87 89 90 92 93 96 97 98 100 101 102 103 104 107 110 111 114 115 116 117 118 119 121 123 124 126 128 129 130 131 132 134 135 143 146 147 148 **P**1 5 7
Primary Contact: Anthony Guaccio, President and Chief Executive Officer
CFO: Thomas J. Garvey, Senior Vice President Operations and Chief Financial Officer
CMO: Derek J. Kelly, M.D., Vice President Transformation and Chief Medical Information Officer
CIO: Karen Sheehan, Vice President and Chief Information Officer
CNO: Mary Shehan, R.N., Senior Vice President and Chief Nursing Officer
Web address: www.schosp.org
Control: Church–operated, Nongovernment, not–for profit **Service:** General Medical and Surgical

Staffed Beds: 267 **Admissions:** 13570 **Census:** 182 **Outpatient Visits:** 273549 **Births:** 2116 **Total Expense ($000):** 257474 **Payroll Expense ($000):** 98381 **Personnel:** 1870

○ **THOREK MEMORIAL HOSPITAL (140115)**, 850 West Irving Park Road, Zip 60613–3077; tel. 773/525–6780, (Nonreporting) **A**3 10 11
Primary Contact: Edward Budd, President and Chief Executive Officer
COO: Peter N. Kamberos, Chief Operating Officer
CMO: Ilona Carlos, M.D., President Medical Staff
CIO: Tony Vavarutsos, Director Information Systems
CHR: Brett Wakefield, Director Human Resources
CNO: Mary McCahill, Chief Nursing Officer
Web address: www.thorek.org
Control: Other not–for–profit (including NFP Corporation) **Service:** General Medical and Surgical

Staffed Beds: 134

⊠ **UNIVERSITY OF CHICAGO MEDICAL CENTER (140088)**, 5841 South Maryland Avenue, Zip 60637–1447; tel. 773/702–1000, (Includes BERNARD MITCHELL HOSPITAL, 5815 South Maryland Avenue, Zip 60637, Mailing Address: 5841 S. Maryland Ave., Zip 60637; tel. 773/702–1000; Sharon L. O'Keefe, President, University of Chicago Medical Center; CHICAGO LYING–IN (CLI), 5815 South Maryland Avenue, Zip 60637, Mailing Address: 5841 South Maryland Avenue, Zip 60637; tel. 773/702–1000; Sharon L. O'Keefe, President, University of Chicago Medical Center; COMER CHILDREN'S HOSPITAL, 5721 South Maryland Avenue, Zip 60637, Mailing Address: 5841 South Maryland Avenue, Zip 60637; tel. 773/702–1000; Sharon L. O'Keefe, President, University of Chicago Medical Center) **A**1 2 3 5 8 10 **F**3 5 6 9 10 11 12 13 22 23 24 25 26 27 28 29 30 31 32 34 35 36 37 38 40 41 43 44 45 46 47 48 49 50 51 52 53 54 55 56 57 58 59 60 61 63 64 65 68 70 71 72 73 74 75 76 77 78 79 80 81 82 83 84 85 86 87 88 89 92 93 97 100 101 102 104 107 108 109 110 111 112 114 115 116 117 118 119 120 121 123 124 126 129 130 131 132 134 135 136 137 138 139 140 141 142 143 144 145 146 147 148 **P**1 **S** University of Chicago Medicine, Chicago, IL
Primary Contact: Sharon L. O'Keefe, President
COO: Jason Keeler, Executive Vice President and Chief Operating Officer
CFO: James Watson, Chief Financial Officer
CMO: Stephen Weber, M.D., Chief Medical Officer
CIO: Eric Yablonka, Vice President and Chief Information Officer
CHR: Bob Hanley, Chief Human Resources Officer
CNO: Debra Albert, MSN, Senior Vice President Patient Care and Chief Nursing Officer
Web address: www.uchospitals.edu
Control: Other not–for–profit (including NFP Corporation) **Service:** General Medical and Surgical

Staffed Beds: 624 **Admissions:** 28726 **Census:** 499 **Outpatient Visits:** 730088 **Births:** 1754 **Total Expense ($000):** 1459149 **Payroll Expense ($000):** 538502 **Personnel:** 8319

⊠ △ **UNIVERSITY OF ILLINOIS HOSPITAL & HEALTH SCIENCES SYSTEM (140150)**, 1740 West Taylor Street, Zip 60612–7232; tel. 312/996–7000 **A**1 2 3 5 7 8 10 **F**3 12 13 15 17 18 19 20 21 22 23 24 25 26 27 28 29 30 31 32 34 35 37 38 39 40 41 45 46 47 48 49 50 52 54 55 56 57 58 59 60 61 64 65 66 68 70 72 73 74 75 76 77 78 79 81 82 84 85 86 87 88 89 90 91 92 93 96 97 98 99 100 101 102 103 104 107 108 110 111 114 115 116 117 118 119 120 121 123 124 126 129 130 131 132 134 135 136 138 139 141 142 144 145 146 147 148 **P**4
Primary Contact: Avijit Ghosh, M.D., Chief Executive Officer
COO: David Loffing, Chief Operating Officer
CFO: Jeffrey Rooney, Chief Financial Officer
CMO: Bernard Pygon, M.D., Chief Medical Officer
CIO: Audrius Polikaitis, Chief Information Officer
CHR: Mary Jo Smith, Chief Human Resources Officer
CNO: Jodi S. Joyce, R.N., Associate Vice Chancellor, Quality & Patient Safety
Web address: www.hospital.uillinois.edu/
Control: State–Government, nonfederal **Service:** General Medical and Surgical

Staffed Beds: 398 **Admissions:** 20061 **Census:** 318 **Outpatient Visits:** 471598 **Births:** 2489 **Total Expense ($000):** 830568 **Payroll Expense ($000):** 286105 **Personnel:** 3644

CHICAGO HEIGHTS—Cook County

ST. JAMES HOSPITAL AND HEALTH CENTERS – CHICAGO HEIGHTS CAMPUS See Franciscan St. James Hospital and Health Centers, Olympia Fields

CLINTON—De Witt County

DR. JOHN WARNER HOSPITAL (141303), 422 West White Street, Zip 61727–2272; tel. 217/935–9571, (Nonreporting) **A**10 18
Primary Contact: Paul Skowron, Chief Executive Officer
CFO: Donna Wisner, Chief Financial Officer
CMO: Brit Williams, M.D., President Medical Staff
CIO: Larry Schleicher, Manager Information Services
CHR: Sarah Gerke, Manager Human Resources
CNO: Heidi Cook, Chief Nursing Officer
Web address: www.djwhospital.org
Control: City–Government, nonfederal **Service:** General Medical and Surgical

Staffed Beds: 25

DANVILLE—Vermilion County

⊠ **PRESENCE UNITED SAMARITANS MEDICAL CENTER (140093)**, 812 North Logan, Zip 61832–3788; tel. 217/443–5000 **A**1 2 5 10 19 **F**3 8 13 15 18 20 29 30 31 34 35 40 57 59 64 68 70 74 75 76 78 79 81 82 85 87 89 102 107 108 110 111 114 115 118 119 120 121 124 126 129 130 132 134 146 147 148 **S** Presence Health, Chicago, IL
Primary Contact: Jared Rogers, M.D., President and Chief Executive Officer
COO: Jennifer Cord, R.N., Vice President Operations
CFO: Deb Schimerowski, Chief Financial Officer
CMO: Vincent Kucich, FACHE, Chief Medical Officer
CIO: Paula Keele, Manager Information Systems
CHR: Michael Zimmerman, Human Resource Officer
CNO: Molly Nicholson, MS, Vice President of Patient Care/Chief Nurse Executive
Web address: www.presencehealth.org/usmc
Control: Church–operated, Nongovernment, not–for profit **Service:** General Medical and Surgical

Staffed Beds: 117 **Admissions:** 5482 **Census:** 53 **Outpatient Visits:** 197316 **Births:** 636 **Total Expense ($000):** 96690 **Payroll Expense ($000):** 31589 **Personnel:** 601

⊠ **VETERANS AFFAIRS ILLIANA HEALTH CARE SYSTEM**, 1900 East Main Street, Zip 61832–5198; tel. 217/554–3000, (Nonreporting) **A**1 3 5
S Department of Veterans Affairs, Washington, DC
Primary Contact: Diana Carranza, Interim Director
COO: Diana Carranza, Associate Director
CFO: Becky Tissier, Chief Fiscal Service
CMO: Khiem Tran, M.D., Acting Chief of Staff
CIO: Frank D. Jackson, III, Facility Chief Information Officer
CHR: Connie Ohl, Acting Chief Human Resources
Web address: www.danville.va.gov/
Control: Veterans Affairs, Government, federal **Service:** General Medical and Surgical

Staffed Beds: 221

Hospital, Medicare Provider Number, Address, Telephone, Approval, Facility, and Physician Codes, Health Care System

★ American Hospital Association (AHA) membership   ○ Healthcare Facilities Accreditation Program   ⇑ Center for Improvement in Healthcare Quality Accreditation
☐ The Joint Commission accreditation   ◇ DNV Healthcare Inc. accreditation   △ Commission on Accreditation of Rehabilitation Facilities (CARF) accreditation

IL

DECATUR—Macon County

✠ △ **DECATUR MEMORIAL HOSPITAL (140135)**, 2300 North Edward Street, Zip 62526–4192; tel. 217/876–8121 **A**1 2 3 5 7 10 19 **F**3 11 12 13 14 15 17 18 20 22 24 26 28 29 30 31 34 40 45 46 47 48 49 51 53 54 56 57 58 59 60 61 62 63 64 65 69 70 73 74 75 76 77 78 79 81 82 86 87 89 91 92 93 94 96 103 107 108 110 111 112 114 115 116 117 118 119 120 121 123 126 129 130 131 132 133 143 144 145 146 147 148 **P**8
Primary Contact: Timothy D. Stone, Jr., President and Chief Executive Officer
COO: John Ridley, Executive Vice President & Chief Operating Officer
CFO: Deborah L. Bragg, Senior Vice President, Finance
CMO: David Baumberger, M.D., Chief Medical Officer
CHR: Kevin Horath, Vice President Human Resources
CNO: Linda L. Fahey, R.N., Chief Nurse Executive
Web address: www.dmhcares.com
Control: Other not–for–profit (including NFP Corporation) **Service:** General Medical and Surgical

Staffed Beds: 202 **Admissions:** 9539 **Census:** 103 **Outpatient Visits:** 267171 **Births:** 803 **Total Expense ($000):** 270774 **Payroll Expense ($000):** 116113 **Personnel:** 1925

✠ △ **HSHS ST. MARY'S HOSPITAL (140166)**, 1800 East Lake Shore Drive, Zip 62521–3883; tel. 217/464–2966, (Total facility includes 14 beds in nursing home–type unit) **A**1 3 7 10 **F**2 3 5 11 13 15 18 20 22 28 29 30 31 34 35 40 44 45 50 54 56 57 59 64 66 70 74 75 76 77 78 79 81 82 85 86 87 89 90 92 93 96 98 99 100 101 102 103 104 105 107 108 110 111 114 115 117 119 120 121 123 124 126 128 129 130 131 132 141 142 146 148 **P**7 **S** Hospital Sisters Health System, Springfield, IL
Primary Contact: Daniel L. Perryman, President and Chief Executive Officer
CMO: Phil Barnell, Chief Medical Officer
CHR: Denise Smith, Director Human Resources
CNO: Michelle Oliver, Chief Nursing Officer
Web address: www.stmarysdecatur.com
Control: Church–operated, Nongovernment, not–for profit **Service:** General Medical and Surgical

Staffed Beds: 244 **Admissions:** 8147 **Census:** 110 **Outpatient Visits:** 177288 **Births:** 716 **Total Expense ($000):** 135599 **Payroll Expense ($000):** 41420 **Personnel:** 779

DEKALB—DeKalb County

✠ **NORTHWESTERN MEDICINE KISHWAUKEE HOSPITAL (140286)**, 1 Kish Hospital Drive, Zip 60115–9602, Mailing Address: P.O. Box 707, Zip 60115–0707; tel. 815/756–1521 **A**1 2 10 **F**3 8 11 13 15 18 20 22 26 28 29 30 31 32 34 35 36 37 38 40 43 45 46 48 49 57 58 59 60 64 68 70 71 73 74 75 76 77 78 79 81 82 85 86 87 89 93 96 102 104 107 108 110 111 114 115 117 118 119 127 129 130 131 132 133 135 143 145 146 147 148 **P**8 **S** Northwestern Memorial Healthcare, Chicago, IL
Primary Contact: Kevin Poorten, President
COO: Brad Copple, President
CFO: Loren Foelske, Vice President Finance
CMO: Michael Kulisz, D.O., Chief Medical Officer
CHR: Michele McClelland, Vice President Human Resources
CNO: Pamela Duffy, Vice President Operations and Chief Nursing Officer
Web address: www.kishhospital.org
Control: Other not–for–profit (including NFP Corporation) **Service:** General Medical and Surgical

Staffed Beds: 98 **Admissions:** 4922 **Census:** 50 **Outpatient Visits:** 210383 **Births:** 853 **Total Expense ($000):** 166533 **Payroll Expense ($000):** 50544 **Personnel:** 896

DES PLAINES—Cook County

HOLY FAMILY MEDICAL CENTER See Presence Holy Family Medical Center

✠ **PRESENCE HOLY FAMILY MEDICAL CENTER (142011)**, 100 North River Road, Zip 60016–1255; tel. 847/297–1800 **A**1 10 **F**1 3 5 15 18 29 30 34 42 45 46 50 53 54 56 57 59 60 62 63 64 65 66 68 81 82 84 85 87 93 107 109 110 111 118 129 130 135 143 146 147 148 **S** Presence Health, Chicago, IL
Primary Contact: Yolande Wilson–Stubbs, Regional Chief Operating Officer
CFO: Donna Pareti, Business Unit Chief Financial Officer
CMO: David Bordo, M.D., Chief Medical Officer
CIO: David Lundal, Senior Vice President Information Systems and Chief Information Officer
CHR: Ivy McKinley, Director Human Resources
Web address: www.presencehealth.org
Control: Church–operated, Nongovernment, not–for profit **Service:** Long–Term Acute Care hospital

Staffed Beds: 128 **Admissions:** 1461 **Census:** 94 **Outpatient Visits:** 29272 **Births:** 0 **Total Expense ($000):** 77171 **Payroll Expense ($000):** 32878 **Personnel:** 491

DIXON—Lee County

★ **KATHERINE SHAW BETHEA HOSPITAL (140012)**, 403 East First Street, Zip 61021–3187; tel. 815/288–5531 **A**3 5 10 **F**3 11 13 15 18 20 22 28 29 30 34 35 38 39 40 44 45 46 47 50 54 56 57 59 61 62 64 65 69 70 74 75 76 79 81 85 86 87 89 91 92 93 94 96 97 98 100 101 102 103 104 107 108 110 111 115 118 119 127 129 130 131 132 135 145 146 147 148 **P**6
Primary Contact: David L. Schreiner, FACHE, President and Chief Executive Officer
COO: Julie D. Mann, Vice President and Chief Administrative Officer
CFO: Anthony Evers, Chief Financial Officer
CMO: A. Timothy Appenheimer, M.D., Vice President and Chief Medical Officer
CHR: Christy Pierce, Director of Human Resources
CNO: Linda Clemen, R.N., Vice President and Chief Nursing Officer
Web address: www.ksbhospital.com
Control: Other not–for–profit (including NFP Corporation) **Service:** General Medical and Surgical

Staffed Beds: 80 **Admissions:** 2760 **Census:** 31 **Outpatient Visits:** 192974 **Births:** 351 **Total Expense ($000):** 131004 **Payroll Expense ($000):** 63781 **Personnel:** 753

DOWNERS GROVE—Dupage County

★ ◇ **ADVOCATE GOOD SAMARITAN HOSPITAL (140288)**, 3815 Highland Avenue, Zip 60515–1590; tel. 630/275–5900 **A**2 3 5 10 21 **F**3 4 5 11 12 13 15 17 18 20 22 24 26 28 29 30 31 32 34 35 36 37 38 40 41 43 44 45 46 47 49 50 53 54 55 56 57 59 60 63 64 68 70 72 73 74 75 76 78 79 81 82 84 85 86 87 89 93 98 100 101 102 103 104 105 107 108 109 110 111 114 115 118 119 120 121 123 124 126 129 130 131 132 135 144 145 146 147 148 **P**8 **S** Advocate Health Care, Downers Grove, IL
Primary Contact: David Fox, President
COO: Sandi Churchill, Vice President Business Development and Operations, Professional Services
CFO: Mary Treacy–Shiff, Vice President Finance
CMO: Charles Derus, M.D., Vice President Medical Management
CHR: Elizabeth Calby, Vice President Human Resources
CNO: Susan K. Okuno–Jones, Vice President Patient Care Services and Chief Nursing Executive
Web address: www.advocatehealth.com/gsam
Control: Church–operated, Nongovernment, not–for profit **Service:** General Medical and Surgical

Staffed Beds: 326 **Admissions:** 15209 **Census:** 183 **Outpatient Visits:** 161963 **Births:** 1859 **Total Expense ($000):** 329058 **Payroll Expense ($000):** 115376 **Personnel:** 1831

DU QUOIN—Perry County

✠ **MARSHALL BROWNING HOSPITAL (141331)**, 900 North Washington Street, Zip 62832–1233, Mailing Address: P.O. Box 192, Zip 62832–0192; tel. 618/542–2146 **A**1 10 18 **F**3 11 15 28 29 34 35 40 57 59 81 85 93 107 108 110 114 119 125 127 129 131 133
Primary Contact: Dan Eaves, Chief Executive Officer
CFO: Brice Harsy, Chief Financial Officer
CIO: Brian Schandl, Chief Information Officer
CHR: Sarah J. Dickey, Director Human Resources
CNO: Laurie Kellerman, MSN, Chief Clinical Officer
Web address: www.marshallbrowninghospital.com
Control: Other not–for–profit (including NFP Corporation) **Service:** General Medical and Surgical

Staffed Beds: 25 **Admissions:** 473 **Census:** 7 **Outpatient Visits:** 28874 **Births:** 0 **Total Expense ($000):** 17372 **Payroll Expense ($000):** 7119 **Personnel:** 155

EFFINGHAM—Effingham County

✠ **HSHS ST. ANTHONY'S MEMORIAL HOSPITAL (140032)**, 503 North Maple Street, Zip 62401–2099; tel. 217/342–2121 **A**1 2 3 5 10 19 **F**3 11 13 15 18 20 28 29 30 31 32 34 35 37 40 45 50 57 59 62 63 64 68 70 75 76 79 81 82 84 85 87 89 93 107 108 110 111 114 115 117 118 119 129 130 131 132 144 146 147 **S** Hospital Sisters Health System, Springfield, IL
Primary Contact: Theresa Rutherford, R.N., MS, FACHE, President and Chief Executive Officer
CFO: Dave Storm, Director Business Support
CNO: Kelly Sage, Chief Nursing Officer
Web address: www.stanthonyshospital.org
Control: Church–operated, Nongovernment, not–for profit **Service:** General Medical and Surgical

Staffed Beds: 133 **Admissions:** 5518 **Census:** 52 **Outpatient Visits:** 286275 **Births:** 690 **Total Expense ($000):** 108594 **Payroll Expense ($000):** 34959 **Personnel:** 639

IL

Many Facility Codes have changed. Please refer to the AHA Guide Code Chart. © 2016 AHA Guide

ELDORADO—Saline County

★ **FERRELL HOSPITAL (141324)**, 1201 Pine Street, Zip 62930–1634;
tel. 618/273–3361 **A**10 18 **F**3 11 15 28 29 30 34 35 40 45 57 59 65 68 81
85 86 91 93 101 103 104 107 110 114 118 119 127 130 133
Primary Contact: Alisa Coleman, Chief Executive Officer
CFO: Joseph Hohenberger, Chief Financial Officer
CIO: Brent Volkert, Director Information Technology
CHR: Caleigh Bruce, Vice President Human Resources
CNO: Rachael Prather, Chief Nursing Officer
Web address: www.ferrellhosp.org
Control: Other not–for–profit (including NFP Corporation) **Service:** General
Medical and Surgical

Staffed Beds: 25 **Admissions:** 716 **Census:** 7 **Outpatient Visits:** 37777
Births: 5 **Total Expense ($000):** 15144 **Payroll Expense ($000):** 6813
Personnel: 172

ELGIN—Kane County

★ ◇ **ADVOCATE SHERMAN HOSPITAL (140030)**, 1425 North Randall Road,
Zip 60123–2300; tel. 847/742–9800 **A**2 10 21 **F**3 11 13 15 18 20 22 24 26
28 29 30 31 34 35 38 40 43 45 46 47 48 49 50 54 57 59 64 65 68 70 71
73 74 75 76 77 78 79 81 82 85 87 89 92 93 100 102 107 108 110 111 114
115 118 119 120 121 126 129 130 132 135 144 146 147 148 **P**8
S Advocate Health Care, Downers Grove, IL
Primary Contact: Linda Deering, MSN, R.N., President
CMO: Bruce Hyman, M.D., Vice President Clinical Performance
CHR: Melissa O'Neill, Vice President Human Resources
CNO: Cheri Goll, MSN, Chief Nursing Executive
Web address: www.advocatehealth.com/sherman
Control: Other not–for–profit (including NFP Corporation) **Service:** General
Medical and Surgical

Staffed Beds: 255 **Admissions:** 14685 **Census:** 162 **Outpatient Visits:**
302753 **Births:** 2738 **Total Expense ($000):** 275579 **Payroll Expense**
($000): 94493 **Personnel:** 1353

☐ **ELGIN MENTAL HEALTH CENTER (144037)**, 750 South State Street,
Zip 60123–7692; tel. 847/742–1040, (Nonreporting) **A**1 5 10 **S** Division of
Mental Health, Department of Human Services, Springfield, IL
Primary Contact: Meredith Kiss, Administrator
CFO: Tajudeen Ibrahim, Interim Business Administrator
CMO: Malini Patel, M.D., Medical Director
CIO: Kelly Callahan, Public Information Officer
CHR: Darek Williams, Director Human Resources
Web address: www.dhs.state.il.us
Control: State–Government, nonfederal **Service:** Psychiatric

Staffed Beds: 500

✠ △ **PRESENCE SAINT JOSEPH HOSPITAL (140217)**, 77 North Airlite Street,
Zip 60123–4912; tel. 847/695–3200 **A**1 2 7 10 **F**5 11 12 15 17 18 20 22 24
26 28 29 30 31 34 35 36 37 38 40 43 44 49 50 53 54 56 57 58 59 60 61
62 63 64 65 68 69 70 74 75 77 78 79 81 82 84 85 86 87 90 93 94 96 97
98 99 100 101 102 103 104 105 107 108 111 114 115 117 119 120 121
123 124 126 130 132 134 135 143 145 146 147 148 **P**5 **S** Presence Health,
Chicago, IL
Primary Contact: Michael L. Brown, Regional President and Chief Executive Officer
CFO: Kevin Larkin, Regional Chief Financial Officer
CIO: Trevor O'Malley, Site Manager
CHR: Michael O'Rourke, Regional Human Resources Lead
Web address: www.provena.org
Control: Other not–for–profit (including NFP Corporation) **Service:** General
Medical and Surgical

Staffed Beds: 184 **Admissions:** 7035 **Census:** 111 **Outpatient Visits:**
158419 **Births:** 0 **Total Expense ($000):** 143595 **Payroll Expense ($000):**
41122 **Personnel:** 759

PROVENA SAINT JOSEPH HOSPITAL See Presence Saint Joseph Hospital

SHERMAN HOSPITAL See Advocate Sherman Hospital

ELK GROVE VILLAGE—Cook County

✠ **AMITA HEALTH ELK GROVE VILLAGE (140258)**, 800 Biesterfield Road,
Zip 60007–3397; tel. 847/437–5500, (Includes AMITA HEALTH REHABILITATION
HOSPITAL, 935 Beisner Road, Zip 60007; tel. 847/640–5600; John Dunkin,
Executive Director) **A**1 2 3 5 10 **F**3 12 13 15 17 18 20 22 24 26 28 29 30 31
34 35 36 37 40 41 43 44 45 46 47 48 49 50 54 55 57 59 62 63 64 70 73
74 75 76 78 79 81 82 84 85 86 87 89 90 91 92 93 95 96 103 107 108 110
111 114 115 116 117 119 120 121 124 126 129 130 132 135 143 145 146
147 148 **P**5 6 **S** Ascension Health, Saint Louis, MO
Primary Contact: John P. Werrbach, President and Chief Executive Officer
COO: Laurence Dry, Chief Operating Officer, Acute Care Hospitals Northern
Region
CFO: Henry Zeisel, Chief Financial Officer, Northern Region
CIO: Sherrie Russell, Senior Vice President & Chief Information Officer
CHR: Donald Russell, Senior Vice President and Chief Human Resources Officer
CNO: Chris Budzinsky, Vice President, Nursing and Chief Nursing Officer
Web address: www.AMITAHealth.org
Control: Church–operated, Nongovernment, not–for profit **Service:** General
Medical and Surgical

Staffed Beds: 375 **Admissions:** 18107 **Census:** 276 **Outpatient Visits:**
418409 **Births:** 2026 **Total Expense ($000):** 416027 **Payroll Expense**
($000): 138814 **Personnel:** 2077

ELMHURST—Dupage County

✠ **ELMHURST MEMORIAL HOSPITAL (140200)**, 155 East Brush Hill Road,
Zip 60126–5658; tel. 331/221–1000 **A**1 2 5 10 **F**3 5 7 12 13 15 18 19 20 22
24 26 28 29 30 31 32 34 35 37 38 39 40 41 43 44 45 46 47 48 49 50 54
55 57 58 59 61 63 64 65 68 70 73 74 75 76 77 78 79 81 82 84 85 86 87
89 91 92 93 96 97 99 100 101 102 103 104 107 108 109 110 111 114 115
117 119 120 121 123 124 126 129 130 131 132 135 144 146 147 148 **P**3
6 8 **S** Edward–Elmhurst Healthcare, Naperville, IL
Primary Contact: Mary Lou Mastro, FACHE, MS, R.N., President and Chief
Executive Officer
COO: Pamela L. Dunley, MS, Vice President Chief Nursing Officer and Chief
Operating Officer
CFO: Jeff Friant, Vice President Finance
CMO: Daniel Sullivan, D.O., Chief Medical Officer, Vice President Medical
Administration
CIO: Bobbie Byrne, M.D., Vice President Information Systems and Chief
Information Officer
CHR: Susan Mitchell, Senior Vice President Human Resources
CNO: Pamela L. Dunley, MS, Vice President Chief Nursing Officer and Chief
Operating Officer
Web address: www.emhc.org
Control: Other not–for–profit (including NFP Corporation) **Service:** General
Medical and Surgical

Staffed Beds: 259 **Admissions:** 15442 **Census:** 176 **Outpatient Visits:**
432388 **Births:** 2025 **Total Expense ($000):** 404595 **Payroll Expense**
($000): 142527 **Personnel:** 2197

EUREKA—Woodford County

★ ◇ **ADVOCATE EUREKA HOSPITAL (141309)**, 101 South Major Street,
Zip 61530–1246; tel. 309/467–2371 **A**10 18 21 **F**3 15 28 29 30 31 34 35 39
40 44 45 50 57 59 64 65 66 67 68 74 75 77 78 79 81 82 85 86 87 89 90
93 107 108 110 111 114 119 128 129 130 132 133 146 **P**8 **S** Advocate
Health Care, Downers Grove, IL
Primary Contact: Colleen Kannaday, FACHE, President
CFO: Aron Klein, Vice President of Finance
CMO: Steven K. Jones, M.D., Medical Director
CIO: David Harper, Director, Site Information Systems
CHR: Antonio Coletta, Vice President Human Resources
CNO: Nancy Allen, R.N., Director, Patient Services and Chief Nursing Executive
Web address: www.advocatehealth.com/eureka/
Control: Church–operated, Nongovernment, not–for profit **Service:** General
Medical and Surgical

Staffed Beds: 18 **Admissions:** 263 **Census:** 3 **Outpatient Visits:** 32653
Births: 0 **Total Expense ($000):** 14830 **Payroll Expense ($000):** 5733
Personnel: 131

EUREKA COMMUNITY HOSPITAL See Advocate Eureka Hospital

Hospital, Medicare Provider Number, Address, Telephone, Approval, Facility, and Physician Codes, Health Care System

★ American Hospital Association (AHA) membership
☐ The Joint Commission accreditation
◯ Healthcare Facilities Accreditation Program
◇ DNV Healthcare Inc. accreditation
⇑ Center for Improvement in Healthcare Quality Accreditation
△ Commission on Accreditation of Rehabilitation Facilities (CARF) accreditation

EVANSTON—Cook County

NORTHSHORE UNIVERSITY HEALTH SYSTEM (140010), 2650 Ridge Avenue, Zip 60201–1613; tel. 847/570–2000, (Includes NORTHSHORE EVANSTON HOSPITAL, 2650 Ridge Avenue, Zip 60201–1797; tel. 847/570–2000; Douglas M. Silverstein, President; NORTHSHORE GLENBROOK HOSPITAL, 2100 Pfingsten Road, Glenview, Zip 60025; tel. 847/657–5800; NORTHSHORE HIGHLAND PARK HOSPITAL, 718 Glenview Avenue, Highland Park, Zip 60035–2497; tel. 847/432–8000; NORTHSHORE SKOKIE HOSPITAL, 9600 Gross Point Road, Skokie, Zip 60076–1257; tel. 847/677–9600; Kristen Murtos, FACHE, President) **A**1 2 3 5 8 10 **F**5 8 9 11 12 13 14 15 18 19 20 22 24 26 28 29 30 31 32 34 35 36 37 38 39 40 43 44 45 46 47 48 49 50 54 55 56 57 58 59 60 61 62 63 64 66 68 74 75 77 78 79 81 82 83 84 85 86 87 92 93 96 97 99 100 101 102 103 104 105 107 108 110 111 114 115 116 117 118 119 120 121 123 124 126 129 130 131 132 134 135 136 145 146 147 148 **P**5
Primary Contact: Douglas M. Silverstein, President
COO: J. P. Gallagher, Chief Operating Officer
CFO: Gary Weiss, Chief Financial Officer
CIO: Steven Smith, Chief Information Officer
CHR: Bill Luehrs, Chief Human Resources Officer
CNO: Nancy Semerdjian, R.N., Chief Nursing Officer
Web address: www.northshore.org
Control: Other not–for–profit (including NFP Corporation) **Service:** General Medical and Surgical

Staffed Beds: 683 **Admissions:** 37409 **Census:** 465 **Outpatient Visits:** 2045976 **Births:** 4878 **Total Expense ($000):** 1319040 **Payroll Expense ($000):** 446673 **Personnel:** 5969

PRESENCE SAINT FRANCIS HOSPITAL (140080), 355 Ridge Avenue, Zip 60202–3399; tel. 847/316–4000 **A**1 2 3 5 10 **F**3 11 12 13 15 18 20 22 24 26 28 29 30 31 34 35 38 40 41 43 44 45 47 48 49 56 57 58 59 60 61 64 68 70 72 74 75 76 77 78 79 81 82 84 85 86 87 92 93 97 100 107 108 110 111 114 115 118 119 120 121 123 125 126 129 130 131 132 146 147 148 **P**8 **S** Presence Health, Chicago, IL
Primary Contact: Roberta Luskin–Hawk, M.D., Chief Executive Officer
CMO: David DiLoreto, M.D., Executive Vice President and Chief Medical Officer
CIO: George Chessum, Vice President Information Systems
CHR: Paul Skiem, Senior Vice President Human Resources
Web address: www.reshealth.org
Control: Church–operated, Nongovernment, not–for profit **Service:** General Medical and Surgical

Staffed Beds: 199 **Admissions:** 8239 **Census:** 88 **Outpatient Visits:** 114294 **Births:** 673 **Total Expense ($000):** 179685 **Payroll Expense ($000):** 53656 **Personnel:** 852

SAINT FRANCIS HOSPITAL See Presence Saint Francis Hospital

EVERGREEN PARK—Cook County

LITTLE COMPANY OF MARY HOSPITAL AND HEALTH CARE CENTERS (140179), 2800 West 95th Street, Zip 60805–2795; tel. 708/422–6200 **A**1 2 10 **F**3 5 11 12 13 15 17 18 20 22 26 29 30 31 34 35 36 38 40 41 45 46 47 49 50 54 56 57 59 60 62 63 64 65 71 73 74 75 76 77 78 79 81 82 83 84 85 86 87 89 92 93 94 98 100 101 102 103 104 105 107 108 110 111 114 115 119 120 121 124 126 129 130 131 132 133 135 144 146 147 148 **P**6 7 8 **S** American Province of Little Company of Mary Sisters, Evergreen Park, IL
Primary Contact: Dennis A. Reilly, President and Chief Executive Officer
COO: Mary Freyer, Chief Operating Officer
CFO: Randy Ruther, Vice President Finance and Chief Financial Officer
CMO: Kent A W Armbruster, M.D., Vice President Medical Affairs
CIO: Darryl Mazzuca, Director Management Information Systems
CHR: Colleen Rohan, Director Human Resources
CNO: Lisa DiMarco, R.N., Vice President Patient Care Service and Chief Nursing Officer
Web address: www.lcmh.org
Control: Other not–for–profit (including NFP Corporation) **Service:** General Medical and Surgical

Staffed Beds: 252 **Admissions:** 12163 **Census:** 148 **Outpatient Visits:** 218417 **Births:** 1167 **Total Expense ($000):** 198719 **Payroll Expense ($000):** 87627 **Personnel:** 1766

FAIRFIELD—Wayne County

FAIRFIELD MEMORIAL HOSPITAL (141311), 303 N.W. 11th Street, Zip 62837–1203; tel. 618/842–2611, (Total facility includes 30 beds in nursing home–type unit) **A**1 10 18 **F**3 11 15 18 28 31 34 35 38 40 41 45 46 50 56 57 59 62 64 70 75 77 81 82 85 86 87 93 97 99 103 104 107 108 110 115 119 127 128 130 132 135 146 148 **P**6 **S** Alliant Management Services, Louisville, KY
Primary Contact: Katherine Bunting, Chief Executive Officer
COO: Dana Shantel Taylor, Director Organizational Development
CFO: Melody Morgan, Chief Financial Officer
CMO: Wesley Thompson, M.D., President Medical Staff
CIO: Brad August, Director Information Systems
CHR: Robert Musoiu, Director Human Resources
CNO: Ann Ignas, R.N., Chief Nurse Executive
Web address: www.fairfieldmemorial.org
Control: Other not–for–profit (including NFP Corporation) **Service:** General Medical and Surgical

Staffed Beds: 55 **Admissions:** 975 **Census:** 27 **Outpatient Visits:** 61978 **Births:** 0 **Total Expense ($000):** 27545 **Payroll Expense ($000):** 11144 **Personnel:** 252

FLORA—Clay County

CLAY COUNTY HOSPITAL (141351), 911 Stacy Burk Drive, Zip 62839–3241, Mailing Address: P.O. Box 280, Zip 62839–0280; tel. 618/662–2131, (Nonreporting) **A**1 10 18 **S** SSM Health, Saint Louis, MO
Primary Contact: Amanda J. Basso, President
COO: Jamie Veach, Chief Operating Officer
CFO: Mike Hobbs, Chief Financial Officer
CMO: Colleen Murphy, M.D., Chief of Staff
CIO: Phil Bute, Manager Information Technology
CHR: Chelsea Musgrave, Director of Human Resources
Web address: www.claycountyhospital.org
Control: County–Government, nonfederal **Service:** General Medical and Surgical

Staffed Beds: 18

FOREST PARK—Cook County

RIVEREDGE HOSPITAL (144009), 8311 West Roosevelt Road, Zip 60130–2500; tel. 708/771–7000, (Nonreporting) **A**1 10 **S** Universal Health Services, Inc., King of Prussia, PA
Primary Contact: Carey Carlock, Chief Executive Officer
CFO: Michael E. Nelson, Chief Financial Officer
CMO: Lucyna M. Puszkarska, M.D., Medical Director
CIO: Kyle Heinze, Coordinator Information Technology
CHR: Joseph Baw, Director Human Resources
Web address: www.riveredgehospital.com
Control: Corporation, Investor–owned, for–profit **Service:** Psychiatric

Staffed Beds: 224

FREEPORT—Stephenson County

FHN MEMORIAL HOSPITAL (140160), 1045 West Stephenson Street, Zip 61032–4899; tel. 815/599–6000 **A**10 **F**3 11 13 14 15 18 20 22 28 29 30 31 32 34 38 40 46 47 48 49 50 51 53 57 59 61 63 64 65 68 69 74 75 76 77 78 79 81 82 84 85 86 87 93 97 99 100 101 102 103 104 107 108 109 110 111 114 119 129 130 131 132 135 146 **P**6 8
Primary Contact: Michael R. Perry, M.D., President and Chief Executive Officer
COO: Mark Gridley, FACHE, Executive Vice President and Chief Operating Officer
CFO: Michael Clark, Executive Vice President and Chief Financial Officer
CMO: Robert D. Geller, M.D., Vice President Medical Affairs
CIO: Mike Willams, Chief Information Officer
CHR: Leonard M. Carter, Vice President Human Resources
CNO: Kathryn J. Martinez, Chief Nursing Officer
Web address: www.fhn.org
Control: Other not–for–profit (including NFP Corporation) **Service:** General Medical and Surgical

Staffed Beds: 100 **Admissions:** 4016 **Census:** 39 **Outpatient Visits:** 107218 **Births:** 400 **Total Expense ($000):** 100873 **Payroll Expense ($000):** 31561 **Personnel:** 520

GALENA—Jo Daviess County

MIDWEST MEDICAL CENTER (141302), One Medical Center Drive, Zip 61036–1697; tel. 815/777–1340, (Nonreporting) **A**10 18
Primary Contact: Tracy Bauer, Chief Executive Officer
COO: Steve Busch, Chief Operating Officer
CMO: Grant Westenfelder, M.D., Chief Medical Officer
CHR: Melissa Conley, Director Human Resources
Web address: www.midwestmedicalcenter.org
Control: Corporation, Investor–owned, for–profit **Service:** General Medical and Surgical

Staffed Beds: 25

IL

Many Facility Codes have changed. Please refer to the AHA Guide Code Chart. © 2016 AHA Guide

GALESBURG—Knox County

⊞ **GALESBURG COTTAGE HOSPITAL (140040)**, 695 North Kellogg Street, Zip 61401–2885; tel. 309/343–8131, (Nonreporting) **A**1 10 19 **S** Quorum Health, Brentwood, TN
Primary Contact: Barry S. Schneider, Chief Executive Officer
COO: Hans Driessnack, Chief Operating Officer
CFO: Millie Smith, Interim Chief Financial Officer
CMO: Parthasarathy Srinivasan, M.D., President Medical Staff
CIO: Richard Tran, Director Information Technology
CHR: Anita Sells, Director Human Resources
CNO: Pam Davis, Chief Nursing Officer
Web address: www.cottagehospital.com
Control: Other not–for–profit (including NFP Corporation) **Service:** General Medical and Surgical

> **Staffed Beds:** 119

⊞ **OSF ST. MARY MEDICAL CENTER (140064)**, 3333 North Seminary Street, Zip 61401–1299; tel. 309/344–3161 **A**1 10 **F**3 11 13 15 18 28 29 30 31 34 40 41 43 45 49 50 51 53 56 57 59 61 63 64 68 70 74 75 76 77 78 79 81 82 84 85 86 87 89 93 96 107 108 110 111 115 117 119 129 130 132 135 145 146 147 **P**6 **S** OSF Healthcare System, Peoria, IL
Primary Contact: Roxanna Crosser, President
COO: Don Shadensack, Vice President Clinical Services
CFO: Curt Lipe, Vice President, Chief Financial Officer
CMO: Mark Meeker, D.O., Medical Staff President
CIO: Becky Lynch, Manager Business Entity Management and Information Systems
CHR: Jenny Jacobs, Director Human Resources
CNO: Alice Snyder, Vice President, Chief Nursing Officer
Web address: www.osfstmary.org
Control: Church–operated, Nongovernment, not–for profit **Service:** General Medical and Surgical

> **Staffed Beds:** 81 **Admissions:** 3064 **Census:** 30 **Outpatient Visits:** 169266 **Births:** 315 **Total Expense ($000):** 75380 **Payroll Expense ($000):** 28661 **Personnel:** 440

GENESEO—Henry County

★ ◇ **HAMMOND–HENRY HOSPITAL (141319)**, 600 North College Avenue, Zip 61254–1099; tel. 309/944–4625, (Total facility includes 38 beds in nursing home–type unit) **A**10 18 21 **F**3 8 11 13 15 17 18 19 28 29 34 35 40 44 45 49 50 57 59 62 70 75 76 79 81 82 87 88 89 93 107 111 114 119 128 129 130 131 132 133 144 146 **P**2 **S** HealthTech Management Services, Brentwood, TN
Primary Contact: Jeff Lingerfelt, Chief Executive Officer
CFO: Jodie Criswell, Vice President Fiscal Services
CIO: Heather Henry, Manager Information Systems
CHR: Hazel Butter, Manager Human Resources
CNO: Laura Domino, R.N., Vice President Patient Care Services
Web address: www.hammondhenry.com
Control: Hospital district or authority, Government, nonfederal **Service:** General Medical and Surgical

> **Staffed Beds:** 61 **Admissions:** 1514 **Census:** 46 **Outpatient Visits:** 100521 **Births:** 254 **Total Expense ($000):** 37491 **Payroll Expense ($000):** 13376 **Personnel:** 259

GENEVA—Kane County

⊞ **NORTHWESTERN MEDICINE DELNOR HOSPITAL (140211)**, 300 Randall Road, Zip 60134–4200; tel. 630/208–3000 **A**1 2 10 **F**3 12 13 15 18 19 20 22 26 28 29 30 31 32 33 34 35 36 39 40 43 44 45 46 47 48 49 50 53 55 57 59 60 64 65 68 70 74 75 76 77 78 79 81 82 85 86 87 89 93 94 96 97 99 100 101 102 104 107 108 110 111 114 115 116 117 118 119 120 121 123 126 129 130 131 132 135 146 147 148 **S** Northwestern Memorial Healthcare, Chicago, IL
Primary Contact: Maureen A. Bryant, FACHE, President
CFO: John Orsini, Executive Vice President and Chief Financial Officer
CMO: Mark Daniels, M.D., Vice President Physician Enterprise
CIO: Daniel F. Kinsella, Executive Vice President Information Technology
CHR: Michael Wukitsch, Vice President Human Resources
Web address: www.cadencehealth.org
Control: Other not–for–profit (including NFP Corporation) **Service:** General Medical and Surgical

> **Staffed Beds:** 159 **Admissions:** 7963 **Census:** 83 **Outpatient Visits:** 301528 **Births:** 1405 **Total Expense ($000):** 287089 **Payroll Expense ($000):** 104874 **Personnel:** 1618

GIBSON CITY—Ford County

⊞ **GIBSON AREA HOSPITAL AND HEALTH SERVICES (141317)**, 1120 North Melvin Street, Zip 60936–1477, Mailing Address: P.O. Box 429, Zip 60936–0429; tel. 217/784–4251, (Includes GIBSON COMMUNITY HOSPITAL NURSING HOME), (Total facility includes 42 beds in nursing home–type unit) **A**1 5 10 18 **F**3 7 11 13 15 18 20 29 31 34 35 40 43 44 45 49 50 51 53 55 56 57 59 63 64 65 67 68 69 70 75 76 77 79 81 82 85 87 93 99 100 101 103 104 107 108 110 111 115 119 127 128 129 131 132 133 143 146 147 148 **P**6 7 8 **S** Alliant Management Services, Louisville, KY
Primary Contact: Robert C. Schmitt, II, Chief Executive Officer
COO: Robin Rose, R.N., Chief Operating Officer
CMO: Mark Spangler, M.D., Chief Medical Officer
CIO: Julie Bowen, Executive Director of Information Technology
CHR: Ty Royal, Executive Director of Support Services and Human Resources
CNO: Cynthia Philipchuck, R.N., Executive Director of Nursing
Web address: www.gibsonhospital.org
Control: Other not–for–profit (including NFP Corporation) **Service:** General Medical and Surgical

> **Staffed Beds:** 67 **Admissions:** 1034 **Census:** 43 **Outpatient Visits:** 124531 **Births:** 196 **Total Expense ($000):** 79771 **Payroll Expense ($000):** 36626 **Personnel:** 597

GLENDALE HEIGHTS—DuPage County

⊞ **AMITA HEALTH GLENOAKS (140292)**, 701 Winthrop Avenue, Zip 60139–1403; tel. 630/545–8000 **A**1 10 **F**3 11 13 15 18 20 22 26 29 30 31 34 35 38 40 41 43 44 45 49 50 57 58 59 64 68 70 73 74 75 76 78 79 81 82 85 86 87 89 92 96 97 98 100 101 102 103 107 108 110 111 114 115 118 119 130 131 132 146 147 148 **P**7 8 **S** Adventist Health System Sunbelt Health Care Corporation, Altamonte Springs, FL
Primary Contact: Bruce Christian, President and Chief Executive Officer
COO: Laurence Dry, Chief Operating Officer, Acute Care Hospitals Northern Region
CFO: Henry Zeisel, Chief Financial Officer, Northern Region
CMO: Richard Carroll, M.D., Vice PResident and Chief Medical Officer
CIO: Sherrie Russell, Senior Vice President and Chief Information Officer
CHR: Donald Russell, Senior Vice President and Chief Human Resources Officer
CNO: Chris Budzinsky, Vice President, Nursing and Chief Nursing Officer
Web address: www.AMITAHealth.org
Control: Church–operated, Nongovernment, not–for profit **Service:** General Medical and Surgical

> **Staffed Beds:** 140 **Admissions:** 5630 **Census:** 78 **Outpatient Visits:** 35770 **Births:** 421 **Total Expense ($000):** 87679 **Payroll Expense ($000):** 33472 **Personnel:** 565

GLENVIEW—Cook County

NORTHSHORE GLENBROOK HOSPITAL See NorthShore University Health System, Evanston

GRANITE CITY—Madison County

⊞ **GATEWAY REGIONAL MEDICAL CENTER (140125)**, 2100 Madison Avenue, Zip 62040–4799; tel. 618/798–3000 **A**1 10 **F**3 8 11 13 15 17 18 20 22 24 26 28 29 31 34 35 40 45 49 50 51 54 59 64 70 74 75 76 77 78 79 81 85 87 90 91 92 93 94 97 98 99 100 101 102 103 107 108 110 111 114 115 119 126 128 129 130 132 135 144 146 147 148 **P**6 **S** Quorum Health, Brentwood, TN
Primary Contact: M. Edward Cunningham, Chief Executive Officer
COO: Matthew H. Blevins, Chief Operating Officer
CFO: Ronald Leazer, Chief Financial Officer
CMO: Mike Adams, M.D., Chief Medical Officer
CIO: Dennis Kampwerth, Director Management Information Systems
CHR: Reva S. Weems, Director Human Resources
CNO: Sam R. White, Chief Nursing Officer
Web address: www.gatewayregional.net
Control: Corporation, Investor–owned, for–profit **Service:** General Medical and Surgical

> **Staffed Beds:** 268 **Admissions:** 7404 **Census:** 106 **Outpatient Visits:** 98707 **Births:** 275 **Total Expense ($000):** 103795 **Payroll Expense ($000):** 33665 **Personnel:** 611

IL

GREENVILLE—Bond County

★ ○ **HSHS HOLY FAMILY HOSPITAL IN GREENVILLE (140137)**, 200 Healthcare Drive, Zip 62246–1154; tel. 618/664–1230, (Includes FAIR OAKS) **A**10 11 **F**3 11 13 15 18 28 29 31 34 40 41 45 49 50 56 57 59 76 78 79 81 85 89 93 94 97 98 103 104 107 110 111 115 119 125 127 129 130 133 **P**6 **S** Hospital Sisters Health System, Springfield, IL
Primary Contact: Brian Nall, President and Chief Executive Officer
CHR: Vicki Kloeckner, Director Human Resources
CNO: Tammy Lett, R.N., Chief Nursing Officer
Web address: www.greenvilleregionalhospital.com
Control: Other not-for-profit (including NFP Corporation) **Service:** General Medical and Surgical

Staffed Beds: 42 Admissions: 1304 Census: 14 Outpatient Visits: 37630 Births: 222 Total Expense ($000): 32679 Payroll Expense ($000): 14213 Personnel: 289

HARRISBURG—Saline County

✠ **HARRISBURG MEDICAL CENTER (140210)**, 100 Drive Warren Tuttle Drive, Zip 62946–2718, Mailing Address: P.O. Box 428, Zip 62946–0428; tel. 618/253–7671 **A**1 10 20 **F**3 8 11 15 28 29 30 31 34 40 45 50 56 57 59 61 62 64 75 77 78 81 85 87 89 91 93 97 98 100 101 102 103 104 105 107 108 110 115 118 119 127 129 130 131 133 146
Primary Contact: Rodney Smith, President and Chief Executive Officer
COO: Danny Lampley, Chief Operating Officer
CFO: June Hayes, Chief Financial Officer
CIO: Rick Pyle, Director Information Systems
CHR: Dorene L. Ewell, Director Human Resources and Education
CNO: Cindy Ford, R.N., Chief Nursing Officer
Web address: www.harrisburgmc.com
Control: Other not-for-profit (including NFP Corporation) **Service:** General Medical and Surgical

Staffed Beds: 76 Admissions: 3182 Census: 40 Outpatient Visits: 84216 Births: 0 Total Expense ($000): 52990 Payroll Expense ($000): 24569 Personnel: 453

HARVARD—Mchenry County

✠ **MERCY HARVARD HOSPITAL (141335)**, 901 Grant Street, Zip 60033–1898, Mailing Address: P.O. Box 850, Zip 60033–0850; tel. 815/943–5431, (Total facility includes 32 beds in nursing home–type unit) **A**1 10 18 **F**3 11 15 28 29 30 35 40 45 46 57 59 64 69 70 75 77 79 81 82 85 87 93 96 107 108 110 119 128 129 130 132 143 145 146 **P**6 **S** Mercy Health System, Janesville, WI
Primary Contact: Javon R. Bea, Chief Executive Officer
COO: Jennifer Hallatt, Chief Operating Officer
CFO: Shannon Dunphy–Alexander, Director
CMO: Douglas Bryan, President, Medical Staff
CHR: Heather Niles, Director Human Resources Operations
CNO: Caryn Lynn Oleston, MSN, Chief Nursing Officer
Web address: www.mercyhealthsystem.org
Control: Other not-for-profit (including NFP Corporation) **Service:** General Medical and Surgical

Staffed Beds: 45 Admissions: 563 Census: 29 Outpatient Visits: 57688 Births: 0 Total Expense ($000): 22355 Payroll Expense ($000): 8305 Personnel: 105

HARVEY—Cook County

★ △ ◇ **INGALLS MEMORIAL HOSPITAL (140191)**, One Ingalls Drive, Zip 60426–3591; tel. 708/333–2300 **A**2 3 5 7 10 21 **F**3 5 8 11 13 15 18 20 22 24 26 28 29 30 31 34 35 36 37 40 42 43 45 46 47 49 50 51 54 56 57 58 59 60 62 63 64 68 70 74 75 76 77 78 79 81 82 84 85 86 87 89 90 92 93 94 97 98 99 101 102 103 104 105 107 108 110 111 113 114 115 116 117 118 119 120 121 123 124 129 130 131 132 135 143 144 146 147 148 **P**8 **S** University of Chicago Medicine, Chicago, IL
Primary Contact: Kurt E. Johnson, President and Chief Executive Officer
COO: Michael L. Hicks, Senior Vice President and Chief Operating Officer
CFO: Andrew Stefo, Senior Vice President Finance and Chief Financial Officer
CHR: Aletha Ross, Vice President Human Resources
CNO: Kathleen A. Mikos, R.N., Vice President and Chief Nursing Officer
Web address: www.ingallshealthsystem.org
Control: Other not-for-profit (including NFP Corporation) **Service:** General Medical and Surgical

Staffed Beds: 478 Admissions: 13983 Census: 179 Outpatient Visits: 369878 Births: 977 Total Expense ($000): 278231 Payroll Expense ($000): 96339 Personnel: 1484

HAVANA—Mason County

✠ **MASON DISTRICT HOSPITAL (141313)**, 615 North Promenade Street, Zip 62644–1243, Mailing Address: P.O. Box 530, Zip 62644–0530; tel. 309/543–4431 **A**1 10 18 **F**3 7 8 11 15 18 28 29 30 34 35 40 45 49 50 53 54 56 57 59 62 64 65 68 75 77 79 81 93 97 102 103 107 108 110 114 118 119 127 129 130 131 132 133 143 146 **P**6
Primary Contact: Robert J. Stolba, Chief Executive Officer
COO: Douglas D. Kosier, Chief Operating Officer
CMO: Tad A. Yetter, M.D., President Medical Staff
CIO: Aaron Coots, Information Technology Director
CHR: Anne Davis, Director Human Resources
CNO: Rhonda Hine, R.N., Interim Chief Nursing Executive
Web address: www.masondistricthospital.org
Control: Hospital district or authority, Government, nonfederal **Service:** General Medical and Surgical

Staffed Beds: 20 Admissions: 223 Census: 2 Outpatient Visits: 23752 Births: 0 Total Expense ($000): 21944 Payroll Expense ($000): 10786 Personnel: 236

HAZEL CREST—Cook County

★ ◇ **ADVOCATE SOUTH SUBURBAN HOSPITAL (140250)**, 17800 South Kedzie Avenue, Zip 60429–0989; tel. 708/799–8000, (Total facility includes 35 beds in nursing home–type unit) **A**2 10 21 **F**3 11 13 15 18 20 22 24 26 28 29 30 31 34 35 36 40 45 46 47 49 50 51 53 55 57 59 60 63 64 68 70 75 76 78 79 81 82 85 87 89 92 93 100 107 108 110 111 114 115 118 119 126 128 129 130 132 145 146 147 148 **P**8 **S** Advocate Health Care, Downers Grove, IL
Primary Contact: Richard Heim, President
COO: Karen Clark, MS, Vice President Operations
CFO: Brian Kelly, Vice President Finance
CMO: Richard Multack, D.O., Vice President Medical Management
CIO: Beth Turek, Site Manager Information Systems
CHR: Kristin Landini, Vice President Human Resources
CNO: Sharon A. Otten, Vice President Nursing
Web address: www.advocatehealth.com/ssub/
Control: Church–operated, Nongovernment, not–for profit **Service:** General Medical and Surgical

Staffed Beds: 248 Admissions: 11340 Census: 143 Outpatient Visits: 143663 Births: 1366 Total Expense ($000): 210197 Payroll Expense ($000): 72490 Personnel: 898

HERRIN—Williamson County

☐ **HERRIN HOSPITAL (140011)**, 201 South 14th Street, Zip 62948–3631; tel. 618/942–2171 **A**1 5 10 **F**3 11 12 18 28 29 30 34 35 40 45 47 49 50 51 54 56 57 59 60 61 64 68 70 74 75 78 79 81 82 84 85 86 87 90 92 93 100 107 108 111 114 115 119 130 131 132 135 143 146 148 **P**1 **S** Southern Illinois Hospital Services, Carbondale, IL
Primary Contact: Terence Farrell, Vice President and Administrator
CFO: Michael Kasser, Chief Financial Officer
CMO: Michelle Jenkins, M.D., President Medical Staff
CIO: David Holland, Chief Information Officer
CHR: Teresa A. Lovellette, Manager Human Resources
Web address: www.sih.net
Control: Other not–for–profit (including NFP Corporation) **Service:** General Medical and Surgical

Staffed Beds: 114 Admissions: 6583 Census: 76 Outpatient Visits: 155005 Births: 0 Total Expense ($000): 139640 Payroll Expense ($000): 41948 Personnel: 876

HIGHLAND—Madison County

✠ **HSHS ST. JOSEPH'S HOSPITAL (141336)**, 12866 Troxler Avenue, Zip 62249–1698; tel. 618/651–2600, (Nonreporting) **A**1 10 18 **S** Hospital Sisters Health System, Springfield, IL
Primary Contact: John A Ludwig, RN, BSN, MHA, Interim President and Chief Executive Officer
CFO: David Nosacka, Southern Illinois Division Chief Financial Officer
CHR: Christie Silvey, Director People Services
CNO: Teresa Cornelius, R.N., Interim Chief Nursing Officer
Web address: www.stjosephshighland.com
Control: Other not–for–profit (including NFP Corporation) **Service:** General Medical and Surgical

Staffed Beds: 25

HIGHLAND PARK—Lake County

NORTHSHORE HIGHLAND PARK HOSPITAL See NorthShore University Health System, Evanston

HILLSBORO—Montgomery County

✠ **HILLSBORO AREA HOSPITAL (141332)**, 1200 East Tremont Street, Zip 62049–1900; tel. 217/532–6111 **A**1 10 18 **F**2 3 10 15 28 29 30 34 35 40 56 57 59 64 65 75 77 79 81 85 86 87 89 92 93 94 97 107 110 111 115 125 129 130 131 133 135 146 148 **S** HealthTech Management Services, Brentwood, TN
Primary Contact: Rex H. Brown, President and Chief Executive Officer
CFO: Terri L. Carroll, Vice President Financial Services
CHR: Sharon Clark, Director Human Resources
Web address: www.hillsborohealth.org
Control: Other not–for–profit (including NFP Corporation) **Service:** General Medical and Surgical

Staffed Beds: 25 **Admissions:** 461 **Census:** 7 **Outpatient Visits:** 20951 **Births:** 1 **Total Expense ($000):** 19250 **Payroll Expense ($000):** 6776 **Personnel:** 175

HINES—Cook County

✠ △ **EDWARD HINES, JR. VETERANS AFFAIRS HOSPITAL**, 5000 South Fifth Avenue, Zip 60141–3030, Mailing Address: P.O. Box 5000, Zip 60141–5000; tel. 708/202–8387 **A**1 2 3 5 7 8 9 12 14 15 17 18 20 22 24 26 28 29 30 31 34 35 36 38 39 40 44 45 46 47 48 49 50 53 56 57 58 59 60 61 63 64 65 66 68 70 71 74 75 77 78 79 80 81 82 83 84 86 87 90 91 92 93 94 96 97 98 100 101 102 103 104 105 106 107 108 109 110 111 112 113 115 116 117 119 120 121 122 123 124 126 127 129 130 131 132 135 143 144 146 147 148 **S** Department of Veterans Affairs, Washington, DC
Primary Contact: Drew Dewitt, FACHE, Acting Associate Director
CFO: Yolanda Martinez, Chief Fiscal Services
CMO: Jack Bulmash, M.D., Chief of Staff
CIO: Robert Tanjuakio, Chief Information Resources Management
CNO: Marianne Locke, R.N., Associate Director Patient Care Services
Web address: www.hines.va.gov/
Control: Veterans Affairs, Government, federal **Service:** General Medical and Surgical

Staffed Beds: 485 **Admissions:** 10900 **Census:** 512 **Outpatient Visits:** 1165200 **Births:** 0 **Total Expense ($000):** 550000 **Payroll Expense ($000):** 250000 **Personnel:** 3251

☐ **JOHN J. MADDEN MENTAL HEALTH CENTER (144028)**, 1200 South First Avenue, Zip 60141–0800; tel. 708/338–7202, (Nonreporting) **A**1 3 5 10 **S** Division of Mental Health, Department of Human Services, Springfield, IL
Primary Contact: Edith Newman, Interim Administrator
CFO: Janice Evans, Chief Financial Officer
Control: State–Government, nonfederal **Service:** Psychiatric

Staffed Beds: 150

VETERANS AFFAIRS EDWARD HINES, JR. HOSPITAL See Edward Hines, Jr. Veterans Affairs Hospital

HINSDALE—DuPage County

✠ **AMITA HEALTH ADVENTIST MEDICAL CENTER – HINSDALE (140122)**, 120 North Oak Street, Zip 60521–3890; tel. 630/856–6001 **A**1 2 3 5 10 13 **F**3 5 13 15 18 20 22 24 26 28 29 30 31 34 35 37 38 39 40 41 43 44 47 49 50 52 54 55 56 57 58 59 62 63 64 66 68 70 72 73 74 75 76 78 79 81 82 84 85 86 87 88 89 92 93 97 98 99 100 101 102 103 104 105 107 110 111 114 115 117 119 120 121 124 126 129 130 131 132 135 141 143 146 147 **P**5 8 **S** Adventist Health System Sunbelt Health Care Corporation, Altamonte Springs, FL
Primary Contact: Michael Goebel, FACHE, Vice President and Chief Executive Officer
CFO: Rebecca Mathis, Vice President and Chief Financial Officer
CMO: Bonny Chen, M.D., Vice President and Chief Medical Officer
CNO: Mary S. Murphy, MSN, Vice President and Chief Nursing Officer
Web address: www.AMITAhealth.org
Control: Church–operated, Nongovernment, not–for profit **Service:** General Medical and Surgical

Staffed Beds: 275 **Admissions:** 12032 **Census:** 136 **Outpatient Visits:** 304106 **Births:** 2410 **Total Expense ($000):** 268006 **Payroll Expense ($000):** 83978 **Personnel:** 1706

✠ **RML SPECIALTY HOSPITAL (142010)**, 5601 South County Line Road, Zip 60521–4875; tel. 630/286–4000 **A**1 3 5 10 **F**1 3 18 29 30 31 45 53 58 74 85 107 114 119 130 146 148 **P**6
Primary Contact: James R. Prister, President and Chief Executive Officer
COO: Ken Pawola, Chief Operating Officer
CFO: Tom Pater, Chief Financial Officer
CMO: Patrick Fahey, M.D., Chief Medical Officer
CIO: Vincent S. Vitali, Chief Information Officer
CHR: John Landstrom, Director Human Resources
CNO: Marti Edwards, MSN, Chief Nursing Officer
Web address: www.rmlspecialtyhospital.org
Control: Other not–for–profit (including NFP Corporation) **Service:** Long–Term Acute Care hospital

Staffed Beds: 95 **Admissions:** 1011 **Census:** 84 **Outpatient Visits:** 0 **Births:** 0 **Total Expense ($000):** 52211 **Payroll Expense ($000):** 27742 **Personnel:** 403

HOFFMAN ESTATES—Cook County

✠ **ALEXIAN BROTHERS BEHAVIORAL HEALTH HOSPITAL (144031)**, 1650 Moon Lake Boulevard, Zip 60169–1010; tel. 847/882–1600 **A**1 5 10 **F**4 5 29 30 34 35 38 50 56 57 68 75 98 99 100 101 102 103 104 105 130 132 134 146 **S** Ascension Health, Saint Louis, MO
Primary Contact: Clayton Ciha, President and Chief Executive Officer
COO: Christopher Novak, Chief Operating Officer
CFO: David Jones, Chief Financial Officer
CMO: Gregory Teas, M.D., Chief Medical Officer
CIO: Sherrie Russell, Vice President and Chief Information Officer
CNO: Christine Quinlan, MS, Chief Nursing Officer
Web address: www.abbhh.org
Control: Other not–for–profit (including NFP Corporation) **Service:** Psychiatric

Staffed Beds: 141 **Admissions:** 5901 **Census:** 128 **Outpatient Visits:** 168471 **Births:** 0 **Total Expense ($000):** 68054 **Payroll Expense ($000):** 36939

✠ **AMITA HEALTH HOFFMAN ESTATES (140290)**, 1555 Barrington Road, Zip 60169–1019; tel. 847/843–2000, (Includes AMITA HEALTH WOMEN & CHILDREN'S HOSPITAL, 1555 Barrington Road, tel. 847/843–2000; Kevin Rath, Vice President and Executive Director) **A**1 2 3 5 10 **F**3 8 12 13 15 18 20 22 26 29 30 31 32 34 35 37 39 40 41 43 44 45 46 47 48 49 50 54 55 57 59 63 64 70 72 73 74 75 76 77 78 79 81 82 84 85 86 87 88 89 93 107 108 110 111 114 115 119 120 121 124 126 130 132 145 146 147 148 **P**5 6 **S** Ascension Health, Saint Louis, MO
Primary Contact: Leonard Wilk, President and Chief Executive Officer
COO: Laurence Dry, Chief Operating Officer, Acute Care Hospitals Northern Region
CFO: Henry Zeisel, Chief Financial Officer, Northern Region
CIO: Sherrie Russell, Senior Vice President and Chief Information Officer
CHR: Donald Russell, Senior Vice President and Chief Human Resources Officer
CNO: Chris Budzinsky, Vice President Nursing and Chief Nursing Officer Alexian Brothers Acute Care Ministries
Web address: www.AMITAHealth.org
Control: Church–operated, Nongovernment, not–for profit **Service:** General Medical and Surgical

Staffed Beds: 286 **Admissions:** 17314 **Census:** 209 **Outpatient Visits:** 239878 **Births:** 3680 **Total Expense ($000):** 285251 **Payroll Expense ($000):** 100912 **Personnel:** 1339

HOOPESTON—Vermilion County

★ ◇ **CARLE HOOPESTON REGIONAL HEALTH CENTER (141316)**, 701 East Orange Street, Zip 60942–1801; tel. 217/283–5531, (Nonreporting) **A**10 18 21 **S** Carle Foundation, Urbana, IL
Primary Contact: Harry Brockus, Chief Executive Officer
CHR: Melodee Bowers, Director Human Resources
Web address: www.carle.org
Control: Other not–for–profit (including NFP Corporation) **Service:** General Medical and Surgical

Staffed Beds: 99

HOPEDALE—Tazewell County

HOPEDALE MEDICAL COMPLEX (141330), 107 Tremont Street, Zip 61747–7525; tel. 309/449–3321, (Nonreporting) **A**10 18
Primary Contact: Alfred N. Rossi, M.D., Chief Executive Officer
COO: Mark F. Rossi, Chief Operating Officer and General Counsel
CHR: Andrea Halley, Director Human Resources
CNO: Timothy Sondag, Senior Nursing Officer
Web address: www.hopedalemc.com
Control: Other not–for–profit (including NFP Corporation) **Service:** General Medical and Surgical

Staffed Beds: 25

IL

Hospital, Medicare Provider Number, Address, Telephone, Approval, Facility, and Physician Codes, Health Care System

★ American Hospital Association (AHA) membership
☐ The Joint Commission accreditation
◯ Healthcare Facilities Accreditation Program
◇ DNV Healthcare Inc. accreditation
⇑ Center for Improvement in Healthcare Quality Accreditation
△ Commission on Accreditation of Rehabilitation Facilities (CARF) accreditation

JACKSONVILLE—Morgan County

PASSAVANT AREA HOSPITAL (140058), 1600 West Walnut Street, Zip 62650–1136; tel. 217/245–9541, (Total facility includes 15 beds in nursing home–type unit) **A**1 10 **F**3 13 14 15 26 28 29 30 31 34 35 40 41 45 50 51 57 58 59 64 68 70 75 76 78 79 81 82 85 86 87 89 93 97 104 107 108 110 111 115 118 119 124 128 129 130 131 141 146 147 148 **S** Memorial Health System, Springfield, IL
Primary Contact: Douglas L. Rahn, President and Chief Executive Officer
CFO: David Bolen, Vice President and Chief Financial Officer
CMO: Charles Sheaff, M.D., President Medical Staff
CIO: Janie Cook, Director Information Systems
CHR: Jim Bormann, Director Human Resources
CNO: Karen Daum, R.N., Vice President and Chief Nursing Officer
Web address: www.passavanthospital.com
Control: Church–operated, Nongovernment, not–for profit **Service:** General Medical and Surgical

Staffed Beds: 108 **Admissions:** 3341 **Census:** 37 **Outpatient Visits:** 89541 **Births:** 428 **Total Expense ($000):** 77563 **Payroll Expense ($000):** 33742 **Personnel:** 708

JERSEYVILLE—Jersey County

JERSEY COMMUNITY HOSPITAL (140059), 400 Maple Summit Road, Zip 62052–2028, Mailing Address: P.O. Box 426, Zip 62052–0426; tel. 618/498–6402 **A**1 10 **F**3 7 11 15 18 28 29 31 32 34 35 36 38 40 41 46 51 53 57 59 64 70 79 81 85 87 94 97 107 111 114 115 117 118 119 127 129 130 131 132 133 146 147 **P**6
Primary Contact: Jonathan O. Wade, Chief Executive Officer
CFO: Beth King, Chief Financial Officer
CMO: Michael McNear, M.D., Chief Medical Officer
CIO: Shane Winters, Chief Information Officer
CHR: Sharon K. Sanford, Director Human Resources
CNO: Julie Smith, R.N., Director of Nursing
Web address: www.jch.org
Control: Hospital district or authority, Government, nonfederal **Service:** General Medical and Surgical

Staffed Beds: 46 **Admissions:** 942 **Census:** 9 **Outpatient Visits:** 87690 **Births:** 0 **Total Expense ($000):** 30975 **Payroll Expense ($000):** 13462 **Personnel:** 321

JOLIET—Will County

△ PRESENCE SAINT JOSEPH MEDICAL CENTER (140007), 333 North Madison Street, Zip 60435–8200; tel. 815/725–7133 **A**1 2 7 10 **F**3 5 8 11 12 13 15 17 18 20 22 24 26 28 29 30 31 32 33 34 35 36 37 38 39 40 41 43 44 45 46 49 50 53 54 56 57 58 59 60 61 64 65 68 70 71 72 74 75 76 77 78 79 80 81 82 84 85 86 87 88 89 90 92 93 96 97 98 99 100 101 102 103 105 107 108 110 111 114 115 118 119 120 121 123 124 126 129 130 131 132 134 135 143 144 145 146 147 148 **P**8 **S** Presence Health, Chicago, IL
Primary Contact: Lowell W. Johnson, LFACHE, Chief Executive Officer
CFO: Deb Schimerowski, Regional Finance Officer
CMO: Gary Lipinski, M.D., Regional Chief Medical Officer
CIO: Russell Soliman, System Manager Client Services and Management Information Services
CHR: Andre' Harrison, Regional Human Resource Officer
CNO: Jacqueline Medland, MS, Regional Chief Nursing Officer
Web address: www.presencehealth.org/stjoes
Control: Church–operated, Nongovernment, not–for profit **Service:** General Medical and Surgical

Staffed Beds: 443 **Admissions:** 22195 **Census:** 277 **Outpatient Visits:** 532575 **Births:** 1149 **Total Expense ($000):** 396447 **Payroll Expense ($000):** 130140 **Personnel:** 1937

PROVENA SAINT JOSEPH MEDICAL CENTER See Presence Saint Joseph Medical Center

KANKAKEE—Kankakee County

PRESENCE ST. MARY'S HOSPITAL (140155), 500 West Court Street, Zip 60901–3661; tel. 815/937–2400 **A**1 2 10 **F**3 5 11 12 13 15 18 20 22 26 28 29 30 31 32 34 35 36 38 39 40 43 45 48 49 50 53 54 56 57 58 59 60 61 64 65 68 70 74 75 76 77 78 79 81 82 83 84 85 86 87 89 92 93 97 98 99 100 101 102 103 104 105 106 107 108 110 111 114 115 116 119 129 130 131 132 135 143 146 147 148 **S** Presence Health, Chicago, IL
Primary Contact: Kathleen Rhine, President and Chief Executive Officer
CFO: Deb Schimerowski, Regional Chief Financial Officer
CMO: Gary Lipinski, M.D., Regional Chief Medical Officer
CIO: Russell Soliman, Director Information Services
CHR: Andre' Harrison, Regional Chief Human Resources Officer
CNO: Jacqueline Medland, MS, Regional Chief Nursing Officer
Web address: www.presencehealth.org/presence-st-marys-hospital-kankakee
Control: Church–operated, Nongovernment, not–for profit **Service:** General Medical and Surgical

Staffed Beds: 156 **Admissions:** 5455 **Census:** 62 **Outpatient Visits:** 212772 **Births:** 417 **Total Expense ($000):** 121646 **Payroll Expense ($000):** 36720 **Personnel:** 722

PROVENA ST. MARY'S HOSPITAL See Presence St. Mary's Hospital

★ △ ◇ **RIVERSIDE MEDICAL CENTER (140186)**, 350 North Wall Street, Zip 60901–2901; tel. 815/933–1671 **A**2 5 7 10 13 21 **F**3 4 5 6 7 8 9 12 13 15 17 18 19 20 22 24 26 28 29 30 31 32 33 34 35 36 38 39 40 41 43 44 45 46 47 48 49 50 51 54 55 56 57 58 59 61 62 64 65 66 68 70 71 74 75 76 77 78 79 81 82 84 85 86 87 89 90 92 93 96 97 98 99 100 101 102 103 104 105 106 107 108 110 111 114 115 118 119 120 121 123 124 126 127 129 131 132 134 135 141 143 144 145 146 147 148 **P**6
Primary Contact: Phillip M. Kambic, President and Chief Executive Officer
CFO: Bill Douglas, Senior Vice President and Chief Financial Officer
CMO: Keith A. Moss, Vice President & Chief Medical Informatics Officers
CIO: Kyle Hansen, Corporate Director Information Systems
CHR: Becky Kay Hinrichs, Vice President Human Resources
CNO: Michael Mutterer, Senior Vice President and Chief Nursing Officer
Web address: www.riversidehealthcare.org
Control: Other not–for–profit (including NFP Corporation) **Service:** General Medical and Surgical

Staffed Beds: 318 **Admissions:** 10199 **Census:** 144 **Outpatient Visits:** 503393 **Births:** 1077 **Total Expense ($000):** 282076 **Payroll Expense ($000):** 121021 **Personnel:** 2110

KEWANEE—Henry County

★ **OSF SAINT LUKE MEDICAL CENTER (141325)**, 1051 West South Street, Zip 61443–8354, Mailing Address: P.O. Box 747, Zip 61443–0747; tel. 309/852–7500 **A**10 18 **F**3 11 15 29 30 32 34 35 36 38 40 45 50 57 59 64 65 66 70 75 77 78 81 82 85 86 87 92 93 96 97 108 110 115 119 127 129 130 131 132 133 135 146 147 148 **P**6 **S** OSF Healthcare System, Peoria, IL
Primary Contact: Lynn Fulton, President
CFO: John Bowser, Vice President, Chief Financial Officer
CHR: Renee A. Salisbury, Director Human Resources
CNO: Jacqueline D. Kernan, Vice President, Chief Nursing Officer
Web address: www.osfsaintluke.org
Control: Other not–for–profit (including NFP Corporation) **Service:** General Medical and Surgical

Staffed Beds: 25 **Admissions:** 538 **Census:** 4 **Outpatient Visits:** 40002 **Births:** 0 **Total Expense ($000):** 28451 **Payroll Expense ($000):** 11079 **Personnel:** 179

LA GRANGE—Cook County

ADVENTIST LA GRANGE MEMORIAL HOSPITAL (140065), 5101 South Willow Spring Road, Zip 60525–2600; tel. 708/245–9000 **A**1 2 3 5 10 13 **F**3 13 15 18 20 22 24 28 29 30 31 34 35 37 40 41 43 44 49 50 52 54 56 57 58 59 62 63 64 66 68 70 73 74 75 76 78 79 81 82 84 85 86 87 90 91 93 96 97 100 102 107 108 110 111 114 115 119 124 126 129 130 131 132 135 141 143 146 147 148 **P**5 8 **S** Adventist Health System Sunbelt Health Care Corporation, Altamonte Springs, FL
Primary Contact: Michael Goebel, FACHE, Vice President and Chief Executive Officer
CFO: Rebecca Mathis, Chief Financial Officer
CIO: Thomas Schoenig, Chief Information Officer
CHR: Garry Giertuga, Site Manager Human Resources
CNO: Mary S. Murphy, MSN, Regional Chief Nursing Officer
Web address: www.keepingyouwell.com
Control: Church–operated, Nongovernment, not–for profit **Service:** General Medical and Surgical

Staffed Beds: 200 **Admissions:** 8059 **Census:** 98 **Outpatient Visits:** 112557 **Births:** 453 **Total Expense ($000):** 160963 **Payroll Expense ($000):** 51539 **Personnel:** 864

LAKE FOREST—Lake County

LAKE FOREST HOSPITAL See Northwestern Lake Forest Hospital

NORTHWESTERN LAKE FOREST HOSPITAL (140130), 660 North Westmoreland Road, Zip 60045–1696; tel. 847/234–5600, (Total facility includes 66 beds in nursing home–type unit) **A**1 2 3 5 10 **F**2 3 8 9 11 13 15 18 20 22 26 28 29 30 31 32 34 35 36 38 40 42 43 44 45 46 48 49 50 52 54 55 56 57 58 59 62 64 65 70 73 74 75 76 77 78 79 81 82 83 84 85 86 87 89 92 93 96 97 107 108 110 111 114 115 116 117 119 120 121 123 126 128 130 131 132 135 144 146 147 148 **P**5 **S** Northwestern Memorial Healthcare, Chicago, IL
Primary Contact: Thomas J. McAfee, President, North Market
CFO: Matthew J. Flynn, Senior Vice President and Chief Financial Officer
CMO: Michael G. Ankin, M.D., Vice President Medical Affairs & Chief Medical Officer
CNO: Denise Mageski, MSN, Chief Nurse Executive
Web address: www.lfh.org
Control: Other not–for–profit (including NFP Corporation) **Service:** General Medical and Surgical

Staffed Beds: 183 **Admissions:** 7200 **Census:** 84 **Outpatient Visits:** 438171 **Births:** 1440 **Total Expense ($000):** 333771 **Payroll Expense ($000):** 123811 **Personnel:** 1506

LAWRENCEVILLE—Lawrence County

LAWRENCE COUNTY MEMORIAL HOSPITAL (141344), 2200 West State Street, Zip 62439–1852; tel. 618/943–1000 **A**10 18 **F**3 11 15 28 29 30 40 75 77 81 93 107 114 127 130 133 **S** QHR, Brentwood, TN
Primary Contact: Doug Florkowski, Chief Executive Officer
CFO: Larry Spore, Chief Financial Officer
CIO: Gary Theriac, Director Information Technology
CHR: Kim Alldredge, Director Human Resources
CNO: Rita Garvey, Chief Nursing Officer
Web address: www.lcmhosp.org
Control: Other not–for–profit (including NFP Corporation) **Service:** General Medical and Surgical

Staffed Beds: 25 **Admissions:** 769 **Census:** 8 **Outpatient Visits:** 45601 **Births:** 0 **Total Expense ($000):** 14557 **Payroll Expense ($000):** 5882 **Personnel:** 142

LIBERTYVILLE—Lake County

★ ◇ **ADVOCATE CONDELL MEDICAL CENTER (140202)**, 801 South Milwaukee Avenue, Zip 60048–3199; tel. 847/362–2900 **A**2 10 21 **F**1 2 3 4 11 12 13 15 16 17 18 19 20 22 24 26 28 29 30 31 32 34 35 36 37 39 40 41 43 44 45 46 47 48 49 50 51 53 54 55 56 57 59 60 64 65 67 68 70 72 73 74 75 76 77 79 80 81 82 85 86 87 88 89 90 92 93 94 96 98 107 108 110 111 114 115 117 118 119 120 121 123 124 126 128 129 130 132 135 144 145 146 147 148 **P**8 **S** Advocate Health Care, Downers Grove, IL
Primary Contact: Dominica Tallarico, President
CFO: David A. Cartwright, Vice President Finance and Support Services
CMO: Debra Susie–Lattner, M.D., Vice President, Medical Management
CIO: Harold Kromer, Director, Site Information Systems
CHR: Jason Spigner, Vice President Human Resources
CNO: Mary Hillard, R.N., Vice President Patient Care Services and Clinical Operations, Chief Nursing Executive
Web address: www.advocatehealth.com/condell/
Control: Other not–for–profit (including NFP Corporation) **Service:** General Medical and Surgical

Staffed Beds: 277 **Admissions:** 16698 **Census:** 186 **Outpatient Visits:** 220644 **Births:** 2271 **Total Expense ($000):** 292827 **Payroll Expense ($000):** 98201 **Personnel:** 1499

LINCOLN—Logan County

✖ **ABRAHAM LINCOLN MEMORIAL HOSPITAL (141322)**, 200 Stahlhut Drive, Zip 62656–5066; tel. 217/732–2161 **A**1 10 18 **F**13 15 28 29 30 34 35 40 57 59 64 75 76 77 79 81 82 87 93 107 108 110 111 119 129 130 131 132 133 144 146 **P**5 **S** Memorial Health System, Springfield, IL
Primary Contact: Dolan Dalpoas, President and Chief Executive Officer
CFO: Andrew Costic, Regional Chief Financial Officer
CMO: Amir J. Wahab, M.D., Medical Staff President
CIO: Keenan Leesman, Director Information Systems
CHR: Michelle Long, Human Resources Business Partner
CNO: Jeanne Dennis, R.N., Chief Nursing Officer
Web address: www.almh.org
Control: Other not–for–profit (including NFP Corporation) **Service:** General Medical and Surgical

Staffed Beds: 25 **Admissions:** 1003 **Census:** 10 **Outpatient Visits:** 49405 **Births:** 215 **Total Expense ($000):** 39880 **Payroll Expense ($000):** 14255 **Personnel:** 304

LITCHFIELD—Montgomery County

✖ **HSHS ST. FRANCIS HOSPITAL (141350)**, 1215 Franciscan Drive, Zip 62056–1799, Mailing Address: P.O. Box 1215, Zip 62056–0999; tel. 217/324–2191 **A**1 10 18 **F**8 11 13 15 18 28 29 30 34 35 40 44 45 46 50 56 57 59 64 68 70 74 75 76 77 79 81 82 85 86 87 92 93 107 111 114 118 119 121 131 132 133 134 135 146 147 **S** Hospital Sisters Health System, Springfield, IL
Primary Contact: Patricia Fischer, FACHE, R.N., President and Chief Executive Officer
CFO: Marisa Murray, CPA, Director Finance
CNO: John Peipert, R.N., Chief Nursing Officer
Web address: www.stfrancis–litchfield.org
Control: Church–operated, Nongovernment, not–for profit **Service:** General Medical and Surgical

Staffed Beds: 25 **Admissions:** 1373 **Census:** 13 **Outpatient Visits:** 52709 **Births:** 250 **Total Expense ($000):** 32442 **Payroll Expense ($000):** 10615 **Personnel:** 224

MACOMB—Mcdonough County

✖ **MCDONOUGH DISTRICT HOSPITAL (140089)**, 525 East Grant Street, Zip 61455–3318; tel. 309/833–4101 **A**1 10 20 **F**2 3 5 7 11 13 15 28 29 31 34 35 38 40 45 47 48 50 51 54 56 57 59 62 63 64 68 70 75 76 77 78 79 81 82 84 85 86 91 93 94 96 97 98 99 100 101 102 103 104 107 108 110 115 119 124 127 129 130 131 132 133 135 146 148 **P**8
Primary Contact: Kenneth Boyd, Jr., President and Chief Executive Officer
CFO: Linda Dace, Vice President Finance
CMO: Edwin Card, President Medical Staff
CIO: Harlan T. Baker, Department Leader Information Systems
CHR: Sue Dexter, Administrative Department Leader Human Resources
CNO: Wanda Foster, R.N., Vice President Nursing
Web address: www.mdh.org
Control: Hospital district or authority, Government, nonfederal **Service:** General Medical and Surgical

Staffed Beds: 60 **Admissions:** 1615 **Census:** 15 **Outpatient Visits:** 206561 **Births:** 292 **Total Expense ($000):** 70178 **Payroll Expense ($000):** 34892 **Personnel:** 526

MARION—Williamson County

✖ **HEARTLAND REGIONAL MEDICAL CENTER (140184)**, 3333 West DeYoung, Zip 62959–5884; tel. 618/998–7000, (Nonreporting) **A**1 10 **S** Quorum Health, Brentwood, TN
Primary Contact: James Flynn, Chief Executive Officer
COO: Kolbe Sheridan, Chief Operating Officer
CFO: Jeff Thomas, Chief Financial Officer
CHR: Sam Hood, Director Human Resources
Web address: www.heartlandregional.com
Control: Corporation, Investor–owned, for–profit **Service:** General Medical and Surgical

Staffed Beds: 92

✖ **MARION VETERANS AFFAIRS MEDICAL CENTER**, 2401 West Main Street, Zip 62959–1188; tel. 618/997–5311 **A**1 3 5 **F**3 4 5 8 11 12 18 20 22 29 30 31 34 35 36 38 39 40 44 45 50 53 54 56 57 58 62 63 64 65 68 70 75 77 78 79 81 82 83 84 86 87 91 92 93 94 96 97 100 101 102 103 104 106 107 108 111 112 114 115 116 117 119 127 128 130 132 135 143 146 147 148 **S** Department of Veterans Affairs, Washington, DC
Primary Contact: Frank Kehus, Interim Director
COO: Frank Kehus, Associate Director for Operations
CFO: Connie McDonald, Chief Financial Officer
CMO: Michael Ladwig, M.D., Chief of Staff
CIO: Adam Powell, Program Manager
CHR: Tim Hartwell, Chief Human Resources
CNO: Rose Burke, Associate Director Patient Care Services
Web address: www.marion.va.gov
Control: Veterans Affairs, Government, federal **Service:** General Medical and Surgical

Staffed Beds: 99 **Admissions:** 1757 **Census:** 52 **Outpatient Visits:** 428033 **Births:** 0 **Personnel:** 1500

MARYVILLE—Madison County

✖ △ **ANDERSON HOSPITAL (140289)**, 6800 State Route 162, Zip 62062–8500; tel. 618/288–5711 **A**1 7 10 **F**3 11 13 15 18 20 22 28 29 30 34 35 40 49 50 57 59 62 70 74 75 76 78 79 81 85 90 93 107 110 111 115 118 119 126 129 130 132 144 146 147 148
Primary Contact: Keith Allen Page, President and Chief Executive Officer
CFO: Michael Marshall, Vice President Finance and Chief Financial Officer
CMO: Charles A. Lane, Chief Medical Officer
CIO: Michael Ward, Director Information Services
CHR: Robin Steinmann, Administrative Director Human Resources
CNO: Lisa Klaustermeier, R.N., Chief Nursing Officer
Web address: www.andersonhospital.org
Control: Other not–for–profit (including NFP Corporation) **Service:** General Medical and Surgical

Staffed Beds: 154 **Admissions:** 7485 **Census:** 80 **Outpatient Visits:** 173864 **Births:** 1732 **Total Expense ($000):** 120396 **Payroll Expense ($000):** 49364 **Personnel:** 913

IL

Hospital, Medicare Provider Number, Address, Telephone, Approval, Facility, and Physician Codes, Health Care System

★ American Hospital Association (AHA) membership
□ The Joint Commission accreditation
○ Healthcare Facilities Accreditation Program
◇ DNV Healthcare Inc. accreditation
⇑ Center for Improvement in Healthcare Quality Accreditation
△ Commission on Accreditation of Rehabilitation Facilities (CARF) accreditation

MATTOON—Coles County

☒ **SARAH BUSH LINCOLN HEALTH CENTER (140189)**, 1000 Health Center Drive, Zip 61938–9253; tel. 217/258–2525 **A**1 10 20 **F**3 11 12 13 15 18 20 22 28 29 30 31 32 34 35 36 38 39 40 44 47 48 49 50 53 54 56 57 59 61 62 63 64 65 66 68 69 70 71 74 75 76 77 78 79 81 82 84 85 86 87 89 93 97 98 99 100 101 102 103 104 105 107 110 111 115 117 119 120 121 123 127 129 130 131 132 134 135 144 145 146 147 148 **P**6
Primary Contact: Timothy A. Ols, FACHE, President and Chief Executive Officer
COO: Dennis Pluard, Vice President Finance and Operations
CFO: Dennis Pluard, Vice President Finance and Operations
CMO: James Hildebrandt, D.O., Vice President Medical Affairs
CIO: Maggie Ratliff, Vice President Information Systems
CHR: Eric Benson, Vice President Human Resources & Wellness
CNO: Lisa J. Woodward, R.N., Vice President, Patient Care Continuum and Chief Nursing Officer
Web address: www.sarahbush.org
Control: Other not–for–profit (including NFP Corporation) **Service:** General Medical and Surgical

Staffed Beds: 118 **Admissions:** 7378 **Census:** 72 **Outpatient Visits:** 500628 **Births:** 857 **Total Expense ($000):** 248021 **Payroll Expense ($000):** 122774 **Personnel:** 1958

MAYWOOD—Cook County

☒ △ **LOYOLA UNIVERSITY MEDICAL CENTER (140276)**, 2160 South First Avenue, Zip 60153–3328; tel. 708/216–9000, (Includes RONALD MCDONALD CHILDREN'S HOSPITAL, 2160 South 1St. Avenue, tel. 888/584–7888) **A**1 2 3 5 7 8 10 **F**3 6 7 8 9 11 12 13 14 15 16 17 18 19 20 21 22 23 24 25 26 27 28 29 30 31 32 33 34 35 36 39 40 41 43 44 45 46 47 48 49 50 51 54 55 56 57 58 59 60 61 64 65 66 68 70 71 72 73 74 75 76 77 78 79 80 81 82 84 85 86 87 88 89 90 91 92 93 94 96 97 99 100 101 102 103 104 107 108 110 111 114 115 116 117 118 119 120 121 123 124 126 129 130 131 132 134 135 136 137 138 139 140 141 142 143 144 145 146 147 148 **P**6 **S** Trinity Health, Livonia, MI
Primary Contact: Larry M. Goldberg, President and Chief Executive Officer
CFO: Jay Sial, Chief Financial Officer
CMO: Robert Cherry, M.D., Chief Medical Officer
CIO: Arthur J. Krumrey, Chief Information Officer
CHR: Vicky Piper, Vice President Human Resources
Web address: www.loyolamedicine.org/Medical_Services/index.cfm
Control: Other not–for–profit (including NFP Corporation) **Service:** General Medical and Surgical

Staffed Beds: 519 **Admissions:** 23059 **Census:** 387 **Outpatient Visits:** 1525807 **Births:** 1135 **Personnel:** 6699

MCHENRY—Mchenry County

☒ **CENTEGRA HOSPITAL – MCHENRY (140116)**, 4201 Medical Center Drive, Zip 60050–8409; tel. 815/344–5000, (Includes CENTEGRA HOSPITAL–HUNTLEY, 10400 Haligus Road, Huntley, Zip 60142; tel. 224/654–0000; Michael S. Eesley, Chief Executive Officer) **A**1 2 5 10 **F**3 4 11 12 13 15 18 20 22 24 26 28 29 30 31 34 35 37 38 39 40 43 44 45 49 50 51 54 55 57 58 59 62 64 68 69 70 74 75 76 78 79 81 82 85 86 87 90 92 93 96 100 101 102 107 108 110 111 114 115 117 118 119 120 121 123 124 126 129 130 131 132 143 144 146 147 148 **P**4 5 **S** Centegra Health System, Crystal Lake, IL
Primary Contact: Michael S. Eesley, Chief Executive Officer
COO: Jason Sciarro, President and Chief Operating Officer
CFO: David Tomlinson, Executive Vice President Chief Financial Officer and Chief Information Officer
CMO: Irfan Hafiz, Vice President Medical Affairs
CIO: David Tomlinson, Executive Vice President Chief Financial Officer and Chief Information Officer
CHR: Bernadette S. Szczepanski, Senior Vice President, Human Resources
Web address: www.centegra.org
Control: Other not–for–profit (including NFP Corporation) **Service:** General Medical and Surgical

Staffed Beds: 179 **Admissions:** 9928 **Census:** 116 **Outpatient Visits:** 155040 **Births:** 1459 **Total Expense ($000):** 235104 **Payroll Expense ($000):** 91069 **Personnel:** 1161

MCLEANSBORO—Hamilton County

HAMILTON MEMORIAL HOSPITAL DISTRICT (141326), 611 South Marshall Avenue, Zip 62859–1213, Mailing Address: P.O. Box 429, Mc Leansboro, Zip 62859–0429; tel. 618/643–2361 **A**10 18 **F**3 11 15 28 29 40 43 57 81 93 107 108 114 119 127 129 130 133 148
Primary Contact: Gregory F. Sims, Chief Executive Officer
CFO: Kent Mitchell, Chief Financial Officer
CIO: David Cutsinger, Chief Information Officer
CHR: Sheila Thompson, Director Human Resources
CNO: Patty Blazier, Chief Nursing Officer
Web address: www.hmhospital.org
Control: Hospital district or authority, Government, nonfederal **Service:** General Medical and Surgical

Staffed Beds: 25 **Admissions:** 620 **Census:** 5 **Outpatient Visits:** 34817 **Births:** 0 **Total Expense ($000):** 14214 **Payroll Expense ($000):** 5927 **Personnel:** 121

MELROSE PARK—Cook County

☒ **GOTTLIEB MEMORIAL HOSPITAL (140008)**, 701 West North Avenue, Zip 60160–1612; tel. 708/681–3200 **A**1 3 5 10 **F**2 3 11 12 13 15 18 20 22 24 26 28 29 30 31 34 35 36 39 40 43 44 45 47 49 50 53 54 56 57 59 60 64 65 68 70 74 75 76 77 78 79 81 85 86 87 89 92 93 96 97 98 103 107 108 110 111 114 116 117 118 119 126 128 129 130 131 132 143 144 145 146 147 148 **P**8 **S** Trinity Health, Livonia, MI
Primary Contact: Lori Price, President
CFO: Ellyn Chin, Vice President Finance
CMO: Gerald Luger, M.D., President Medical Staff
CIO: Maurita Adler, Director Information Services
CHR: Brett Wakefield, Vice President Human Resources
Web address: www.gottliebhospital.org
Control: Other not–for–profit (including NFP Corporation) **Service:** General Medical and Surgical

Staffed Beds: 205 **Admissions:** 7646 **Census:** 114 **Outpatient Visits:** 141037 **Births:** 852 **Personnel:** 877

☒ **WESTLAKE HOSPITAL (140240)**, 1225 Lake Street, Zip 60160–4000; tel. 708/681–3000, (Nonreporting) **A**1 3 5 10 **S** TENET Healthcare Corporation, Dallas, TX
Primary Contact: Patrick J. Maloney, Chief Executive Officer
COO: Michael Ditoro, Chief Operating Officer
CFO: Jennifer Lamont, Chief Financial Officer
CMO: Robert Chase, M.D., Chief Medical Officer
CHR: Nancy Gunnell, Chief Human Resource Officer
CNO: Ruth Matthei, R.N., Chief Nursing Officer
Web address: www.westlakehosp.com
Control: Corporation, Investor–owned, for–profit **Service:** General Medical and Surgical

Staffed Beds: 181

MENDOTA—Lasalle County

★ **OSF SAINT PAUL MEDICAL CENTER (141310)**, 1401 East 12th Street, Zip 61342–9216; tel. 815/539–7461 **A**10 18 **F**3 11 15 28 29 31 34 40 49 57 59 62 65 69 70 77 78 79 81 85 93 107 110 111 115 127 129 130 133 135 146 **P**6 **S** OSF Healthcare System, Peoria, IL
Primary Contact: Jennifer Junis, MSN, R.N., President
CFO: Dawn Trompeter, Vice President Finance I–80 Region and Chief Financial Officer
CMO: Leonardo Lopez, President Medical Staff
CHR: Kimberly Kennedy, Manager Human Resources
CNO: Heather Bomstad, MSN, Vice President Patient Care Services and Chief Nursing Officer
Web address: www.https://www.osfhealthcare.org/saint–paul
Control: Other not–for–profit (including NFP Corporation) **Service:** General Medical and Surgical

Staffed Beds: 25 **Admissions:** 626 **Census:** 7 **Outpatient Visits:** 44019 **Births:** 0 **Total Expense ($000):** 31130 **Payroll Expense ($000):** 13709 **Personnel:** 221

METROPOLIS—Massac County

★ **MASSAC MEMORIAL HOSPITAL (141323)**, 28 Chick Street, Zip 62960–2467, Mailing Address: P.O. Box 850, Zip 62960–0850; tel. 618/524–2176 **A**10 18 **F**11 15 18 28 29 30 31 32 34 40 45 46 47 48 49 50 59 64 66 68 75 81 82 93 94 97 104 107 108 110 111 115 119 127 128 129 133 143 148
Primary Contact: Tony Pfitzer, Chief Executive Officer
COO: Rick Goins, Chief Operating Officer
CFO: Randy Rushing, Chief Financial Officer
CHR: Johnna Douglas, Human Resources Manager
Web address: www.massachealth.org
Control: Hospital district or authority, Government, nonfederal **Service:** General Medical and Surgical

Staffed Beds: 25 **Admissions:** 768 **Census:** 9 **Births:** 0 **Total Expense ($000):** 21595 **Personnel:** 250

MOLINE—Rock Island County

UNITYPOINT HEALTH – TRINITY MOLINE See UnityPoint Health – Trinity Rock Island, Rock Island

MONMOUTH—Warren County

★ **OSF HOLY FAMILY MEDICAL CENTER (141318)**, 1000 West Harlem Avenue, Zip 61462–1007; tel. 309/734–3141 **A**10 18 **F**11 15 28 29 30 34 40 45 46 50 57 59 64 65 68 75 77 81 85 87 93 97 107 110 115 118 119 127 129 130 132 133 135 143 145 146 **P**6 **S** OSF Healthcare System, Peoria, IL
Primary Contact: Patricia A. Luker, President
CFO: Theresa Springer, Chief Financial Officer
CMO: Frank Lasala, M.D., President Medical Staff
CIO: Lew McCann, Director Management Information Systems
CHR: Jenny Jacobs, Director Human Resources
CNO: Shelley Wiborg, MS, Director of Nursing
Web address: www.osfholyfamily.org
Control: Church–operated, Nongovernment, not–for profit **Service:** General Medical and Surgical

Staffed Beds: 23 **Admissions:** 417 **Census:** 5 **Outpatient Visits:** 70186 **Births:** 0 **Total Expense ($000):** 27316 **Payroll Expense ($000):** 11294 **Personnel:** 155

MONTICELLO—Piatt County

⊠ **KIRBY MEDICAL CENTER (141301)**, 1000 Medical Center Drive, Zip 61856–2116; tel. 217/762–2115, (Nonreporting) **A**1 5 10 18
Primary Contact: Steven D. Tenhouse, FACHE, Chief Executive Officer
COO: Mark Fred, R.N., Chief Operating Officer
CFO: Alexander Nazarian, CPA, Chief Financial Officer
CMO: Narain Mandhan, M.D., Chief Medical Officer
CIO: Kyle Willams, Director Information Technology
CHR: Andrew Buffenbarger, Chief Compliance Officer
CNO: Jennifer Moss, MS, Chief Clinical Officer
Web address: www.kirbyhealth.org
Control: Other not–for–profit (including NFP Corporation) **Service:** General Medical and Surgical

Staffed Beds: 16

MORRIS—Grundy County

★ ○ **MORRIS HOSPITAL & HEALTHCARE CENTERS (140101)**, 150 West High Street, Zip 60450–1497; tel. 815/942–2932 **A**2 10 11 **F**3 11 13 15 18 19 20 22 26 28 29 34 35 40 43 47 49 50 54 57 59 64 66 69 70 74 75 76 77 78 79 81 82 85 86 87 89 93 97 102 107 108 110 111 114 115 118 119 120 121 123 130 132 135 143 144 146 **P**6
Primary Contact: Mark B. Steadham, President and Chief Executive Officer
COO: Patrick O'Connor, Chief Operating Officer
CFO: Dean M. Marketti, Vice President Finance
CIO: Dean M. Marketti, Chief Information Officer
CHR: Erin Murphy–Frobish, Vice President Human Resources
CNO: Kimberly A. Landers, MS, Vice President Patient Care Services
Web address: www.morrishospital.org
Control: Other not–for–profit (including NFP Corporation) **Service:** General Medical and Surgical

Staffed Beds: 89 **Admissions:** 4046 **Census:** 39 **Outpatient Visits:** 315181 **Births:** 557 **Total Expense ($000):** 136055 **Payroll Expense ($000):** 61414 **Personnel:** 800

MORRISON—Whiteside County

★ **MORRISON COMMUNITY HOSPITAL (141329)**, 303 North Jackson Street, Zip 61270–3042; tel. 815/772–4003, (Total facility includes 38 beds in nursing home–type unit) **A**10 18 **F**3 7 11 15 40 45 59 63 64 65 66 81 93 94 97 99 107 110 114 119 127 130 133 146 148 **P**6
Primary Contact: Pam Pfister, Chief Executive Officer
COO: Pam Pfister, Chief Executive Officer
CFO: Cami Megli, Controller
CMO: Duncan Dinkha, M.D., Chief of Staff
CIO: Pam Pfister, Chief Executive Officer
CHR: Amber L. Temple, Director Human Resources
Web address: www.morrisonhospital.com
Control: Hospital district or authority, Government, nonfederal **Service:** General Medical and Surgical

Staffed Beds: 63 **Admissions:** 288 **Census:** 21 **Outpatient Visits:** 17534 **Births:** 0 **Total Expense ($000):** 12772 **Payroll Expense ($000):** 6513

MOUNT CARMEL—Wabash County

⊠ **WABASH GENERAL HOSPITAL (141327)**, 1418 College Drive, Zip 62863–2638; tel. 618/262–8621, (Nonreporting) **A**1 10 18 **S** Alliant Management Services, Louisville, KY
Primary Contact: Jay Purvis, President and Chief Executive Officer
COO: Karissa Turner, Vice President Operations
CFO: Steve McGill, Vice President Finance and Chief Financial Officer
CMO: Justin Miller, M.D., Chief of Staff
CIO: Bobby Gage, Director Information Technology
CHR: Bridget Shepard, Vice President Human Resources
CNO: Tamara Gould, R.N., Vice President Clinical Services and Chief Nursing Officer
Web address: www.wabashgeneral.com
Control: County–Government, nonfederal **Service:** General Medical and Surgical

Staffed Beds: 25

MOUNT VERNON—Jefferson County

⊠ **CROSSROADS COMMUNITY HOSPITAL (140294)**, 8 Doctors Park Road, Zip 62864–6224; tel. 618/244–5500 **A**1 10 **F**3 8 11 15 18 29 34 35 40 45 50 53 56 57 59 60 64 68 70 74 75 77 79 81 85 93 94 96 107 110 111 115 119 126 127 129 135 145 146 147 148 **S** Quorum Health, Brentwood, TN
Primary Contact: Finny Mathew, Chief Executive Officer
CFO: Shawn Hartley, Chief Financial Officer
CIO: Bryan Delaney, Director Information Technology
CHR: Jessica Connaway, Director Human Resources
CNO: Stephanie Maines, Chief Nursing Officer
Web address: www.crossroadshospital.com
Control: Corporation, Investor–owned, for–profit **Service:** General Medical and Surgical

Staffed Beds: 47 **Admissions:** 1080 **Census:** 9 **Outpatient Visits:** 42816 **Births:** 0 **Total Expense ($000):** 43353 **Payroll Expense ($000):** 15317 **Personnel:** 246

⊠ **GOOD SAMARITAN REGIONAL HEALTH CENTER (140046)**, 1 Good Samaritan Way, Zip 62864–2402; tel. 618/242–4600 **A**1 2 10 19 **F**3 4 11 13 15 18 20 22 24 26 28 29 30 31 34 35 38 40 44 45 46 50 51 54 56 57 59 61 64 68 70 73 74 75 76 77 78 79 80 81 82 84 85 86 87 89 90 93 94 107 108 110 111 114 115 119 126 130 131 132 135 144 145 146 147 148 **P**6 8 **S** SSM Health, Saint Louis, MO
Primary Contact: Michael D. Warren, President
COO: Mark A. Clark, Vice President Operations
CFO: Deland Evischi, Regional Chief Financial Officer, Southern Illinois
CMO: Daniel Hoffman, M.D., Administrative Medical Director
CIO: Steve Murphy, FM–East Region IS
CHR: Thomas W. Blythe, System Vice President Human Resources
CNO: Chris Adams, Vice President Patient Care Services
Web address: www.smgsi.com
Control: Church–operated, Nongovernment, not–for profit **Service:** General Medical and Surgical

Staffed Beds: 134 **Admissions:** 8009 **Census:** 89 **Outpatient Visits:** 195104 **Births:** 1091 **Total Expense ($000):** 160635 **Payroll Expense ($000):** 49578 **Personnel:** 1141

MURPHYSBORO—Jackson County

★ **ST. JOSEPH MEMORIAL HOSPITAL (141334)**, 2 South Hospital Drive, Zip 62966–3333; tel. 618/684–3156 **A**10 18 **F**3 11 18 28 29 30 31 34 35 40 45 56 57 59 64 74 75 77 78 79 81 82 85 86 87 93 107 114 119 129 130 132 133 135 146 148 **P**1 **S** Southern Illinois Hospital Services, Carbondale, IL
Primary Contact: Susan Odle, Administrator
CMO: Emily Hanson, M.D., President, Medical Staff
CIO: David Holland, Vice President Information Services
CHR: Kelly Stevens, Manager Human Resources
CNO: Julie Firman, R.N., Chief Nursing Officer
Web address: www.sih.net
Control: Other not–for–profit (including NFP Corporation) **Service:** General Medical and Surgical

Staffed Beds: 25 **Admissions:** 683 **Census:** 12 **Outpatient Visits:** 76429 **Births:** 0 **Total Expense ($000):** 52713 **Payroll Expense ($000):** 12829 **Personnel:** 235

IL

Hospital, Medicare Provider Number, Address, Telephone, Approval, Facility, and Physician Codes, Health Care System

★ American Hospital Association (AHA) membership
□ The Joint Commission accreditation
○ Healthcare Facilities Accreditation Program
◇ DNV Healthcare Inc. accreditation
⇑ Center for Improvement in Healthcare Quality Accreditation
△ Commission on Accreditation of Rehabilitation Facilities (CARF) accreditation

NAPERVILLE—Dupage County

✠ **EDWARD HOSPITAL (140231)**, 801 South Washington Street, Zip 60540–7499; tel. 630/527–3000 **A**1 2 10 **F**3 7 12 13 15 17 18 19 20 22 24 26 28 29 30 31 32 34 35 37 38 39 40 41 42 43 44 45 46 47 48 49 50 53 54 55 57 58 59 61 63 64 65 68 70 72 73 74 75 76 77 78 79 81 82 84 85 86 87 88 89 91 92 93 96 97 99 100 101 102 107 108 110 111 114 115 117 118 119 120 121 123 124 126 129 130 131 132 135 144 146 147 148 **P**6 8 **S** Edward–Elmhurst Healthcare, Naperville, IL
Primary Contact: Bill Kottmann, President and Chief Executive Officer
COO: Marianne Spencer, R.N., Vice President Operations and Chief Operating Officer
CFO: Vincent Pryor, System Executive Vice President and Chief Financial Officer
CMO: Brent Smith, M.D., Chief Medical Officer and Vice President Clinical Integration
CIO: Bobbie Byrne, M.D., Executive Vice President and Chief Information Officer
CHR: Susan Mitchell, System Executive Vice President Human Resources
CNO: Patti Ludwig–Beymer, Ph.D., Vice President Chief Nursing Officer
Web address: www.eehealth.org
Control: Other not–for–profit (including NFP Corporation) **Service:** General Medical and Surgical

Staffed Beds: 350 **Admissions:** 22352 **Census:** 244 **Outpatient Visits:** 579650 **Births:** 3174 **Total Expense ($000):** 552865 **Payroll Expense ($000):** 205641 **Personnel:** 2296

✠ **LINDEN OAKS HOSPITAL (144035)**, 852 South West Street, Zip 60540–6400; tel. 630/305–5500 **A**1 3 5 10 **F**4 5 29 34 35 38 56 57 59 64 68 75 87 98 99 100 101 103 104 105 106 130 132 134 **P**6 8 **S** Edward–Elmhurst Healthcare, Naperville, IL
Primary Contact: Gina Sharp, FACHE, President
COO: Trish Jones–Fairbanks, R.N., Chief Operating Officer
CFO: Kristen Refness, Chief Financial Officer
CMO: Barry Rabin, M.D., Medical Director
CIO: Hugh Siddiqui, Senior Applications Analyst
CNO: Trish Jones–Fairbanks, R.N., Chief Nursing Officer
Web address: www.https://www.eehealth.org/services/behavioral–health
Control: Other not–for–profit (including NFP Corporation) **Service:** Psychiatric

Staffed Beds: 108 **Admissions:** 4569 **Census:** 87 **Outpatient Visits:** 57282 **Births:** 0 **Total Expense ($000):** 42455 **Payroll Expense ($000):** 23520 **Personnel:** 427

NASHVILLE—Washington County

✠ **WASHINGTON COUNTY HOSPITAL (141308)**, 705 South Grand Avenue, Zip 62263–1534; tel. 618/327–8236, (Total facility includes 28 beds in nursing home–type unit) **A**1 10 18 **F**8 11 15 28 29 31 34 40 49 50 57 59 64 65 78 81 85 93 104 107 114 119 127 129 133 145 146 148 **P**6
Primary Contact: Nancy M. Newby, R.N., Ph.D., FACHE, President and Chief Executive Officer
CFO: Elaine Matzenbacher, Chief Financial Officer
CMO: Alfonso Urdaneta, M.D., President Medical Staff
CIO: Kim Larkin, Chief Information Officer
CHR: David Davenport, Director Human Resources
Web address: www.washingtoncountyhospital.org
Control: Hospital district or authority, Government, nonfederal **Service:** General Medical and Surgical

Staffed Beds: 50 **Admissions:** 248 **Census:** 33 **Outpatient Visits:** 33530 **Births:** 0 **Total Expense ($000):** 14394 **Payroll Expense ($000):** 6728 **Personnel:** 156

NEW LENOX—Will County

✠ △ **SILVER CROSS HOSPITAL (140213)**, 1900 Silver Cross Boulevard, Zip 60451–9509; tel. 815/300–1100 **A**1 2 7 10 **F**3 5 7 11 12 13 15 18 19 20 22 26 27 28 29 30 31 32 34 35 38 40 42 43 44 46 47 48 49 50 54 57 59 60 62 64 68 70 71 74 75 76 77 78 79 81 82 83 84 85 89 90 91 92 93 96 98 100 101 102 103 104 105 107 108 110 111 114 115 118 119 120 121 126 129 130 131 132 134 135 146 147 148 **P**5 8
Primary Contact: Paul Pawlak, President and Chief Executive Officer
COO: Mary Bakken, Executive Vice President and Chief Operating Officer
CFO: John Krepps, Senior Vice President Finance
CMO: Christopher Udovich, M.D., Chief of Staff
CIO: Kevin Lane, Vice President Information Systems
CHR: Mark Jepson, Vice President
CNO: Peggy Gricus, R.N., Vice President, Patient Care Services and Chief Nursing Officer
Web address: www.silvercross.org
Control: Other not–for–profit (including NFP Corporation) **Service:** General Medical and Surgical

Staffed Beds: 296 **Admissions:** 20286 **Census:** 212 **Outpatient Visits:** 228804 **Births:** 2759 **Total Expense ($000):** 255259 **Payroll Expense ($000):** 109686 **Personnel:** 1536

NORMAL—McLean County

★ ◇ **ADVOCATE BROMENN MEDICAL CENTER (140127)**, 1304 Franklin Avenue, Zip 61761–3558, Mailing Address: P.O. Box 2850, Bloomington, Zip 61702–2850; tel. 309/454–1400, (Includes ADVOCATE BROMENN REGIONAL MEDICAL CENTER, Virginia and Franklin Streets, Zip 61761, Mailing Address: P.O. Box 2850, Bloomington, Zip 61702–2850; tel. 309/454–1400) **A**2 5 10 13 21 **F**2 3 4 11 12 13 15 17 18 20 22 24 26 28 29 30 31 32 34 35 37 38 39 40 43 44 45 49 50 51 54 57 59 64 65 66 68 70 74 75 76 77 78 79 81 82 84 85 86 87 89 90 93 96 97 98 100 101 102 103 107 108 110 111 114 115 118 119 126 130 131 132 135 141 146 147 148 **P**8 **S** Advocate Health Care, Downers Grove, IL
Primary Contact: Colleen Kannaday, FACHE, President
CFO: Aron Klein, Vice President Finance
CMO: James Nevin, M.D., Vice President Medical Management
CHR: Antonio Coletta, Vice President Human Resources
CNO: Laurie Round, MS, Chief Nurse Executive
Web address: www.advocatehealth.com
Control: Church–operated, Nongovernment, not–for profit **Service:** General Medical and Surgical

Staffed Beds: 198 **Admissions:** 8958 **Census:** 95 **Outpatient Visits:** 130631 **Births:** 1675 **Total Expense ($000):** 168386 **Payroll Expense ($000):** 55541 **Personnel:** 1068

ADVOCATE BROMENN REGIONAL MEDICAL CENTER See Advocate BroMenn Medical Center

NORTH CHICAGO—Lake County

✠ **CAPTAIN JAMES A. LOVELL FEDERAL HEALTH CARE CENTER**, 3001 Green Bay Road, Zip 60064–3049; tel. 847/688–1900, (Total facility includes 109 beds in nursing home–type unit) **A**1 3 5 8 **F**3 4 5 8 14 15 18 20 26 29 30 31 32 34 35 36 38 39 40 44 46 48 49 50 53 54 56 57 58 59 61 62 63 64 65 67 68 70 74 75 77 78 79 81 83 84 86 87 90 91 92 94 96 97 98 99 100 101 102 103 104 105 106 107 108 110 111 115 118 119 128 129 130 131 132 135 143 146 147 148 **P**6 **S** Department of Veterans Affairs, Washington, DC
Primary Contact: Stephen R. Holt, M.D., Director
CFO: Barbara Meadows, Chief Financial Manager
CMO: Tariq Hassan, M.D., Associate Director of Patient Care
CIO: Jonathan Friedman, Public Affairs Officer
CHR: Amy Sanders, Chief Human Resources
CNO: Sarah Fouse, Associate Director of Patient Services
Web address: www.lovell.fhcc.va.gov
Control: Veterans Affairs, Government, federal **Service:** General Medical and Surgical

Staffed Beds: 302 **Admissions:** 4645 **Census:** 45 **Outpatient Visits:** 657438 **Births:** 0 **Personnel:** 1748

NORTHLAKE—Cook County

✠ **KINDRED HOSPITAL CHICAGO–NORTHLAKE (142008)**, 365 East North Avenue, Zip 60164–2628; tel. 708/345–8100, (Nonreporting) **A**1 10 **S** Kindred Healthcare, Louisville, KY
Primary Contact: Beverly Foster, Chief Executive Officer
COO: Sandra Buckhoy, Chief Clinical Officer
CFO: Jay Schweikart, Chief Financial Officer
CMO: Maher Najjar, M.D., Medical Director
Web address: www.kindrednorthlake.com/
Control: Corporation, Investor–owned, for–profit **Service:** Long–Term Acute Care hospital

Staffed Beds: 94

OAK LAWN—Cook County

★ △ ◇ **ADVOCATE CHRIST MEDICAL CENTER (140208)**, 4440 West 95th Street, Zip 60453–2699; tel. 708/684–8000, (Includes ADVOCATE HOPE CHILDREN'S HOSPITAL, 4440 West 95th Street, Zip 60453–2600; tel. 708/684–8000) **A**2 3 5 7 8 10 13 21 **F**3 5 11 13 15 17 18 19 20 21 22 23 24 25 26 27 28 29 30 43 34 35 37 38 39 40 44 45 47 48 49 50 51 52 54 55 56 57 58 59 60 61 62 63 64 65 66 68 69 70 71 72 74 75 77 78 79 81 82 84 85 86 87 88 90 92 93 96 97 98 99 100 101 102 103 104 105 107 108 109 110 111 114 115 116 117 118 119 120 121 123 124 126 129 130 131 132 134 135 137 138 140 143 145 146 147 148 **P**8 **S** Advocate Health Care, Downers Grove, IL
Primary Contact: Kenneth W. Lukhard, President
COO: Michael Wilkins, Chief Operating Officer
CFO: Robert Pekofske, Vice President Finance
CMO: Robert Stein, M.D., Vice President Medical Management
CIO: Brian Banbury, Director Site Information Systems
Web address: www.advocatehealth.com/christ
Control: Other not–for–profit (including NFP Corporation) **Service:** General Medical and Surgical

Staffed Beds: 659 **Admissions:** 40517 **Census:** 576 **Outpatient Visits:** 343336 **Births:** 3859 **Total Expense ($000):** 964515 **Payroll Expense ($000):** 328223 **Personnel:** 4457

Many Facility Codes have changed. Please refer to the AHA Guide Code Chart. © 2016 AHA Guide

IL

OAK PARK—Cook County

✠ **RUSH OAK PARK HOSPITAL (140063)**, 520 South Maple Avenue,
Zip 60304–1097; tel. 708/383–9300, (Total facility includes 17 beds in nursing home–type unit) **A**1 3 5 10 **F**3 11 15 18 20 22 29 30 34 35 40 45 47 49 50 56 57 58 59 64 70 74 75 77 79 81 82 84 85 87 90 91 92 93 94 96 100 107 108 110 111 114 115 119 128 130 141 145 146 148 **P**8 **S** Rush University Medical Center, Chicago, IL
Primary Contact: Bruce M. Elegant, FACHE, President and Chief Executive Officer
COO: Robert S. Spadoni, Vice President of Hospital Operations
CFO: Elvy Yap, Director of Finance
CMO: Michael R. Silver, M.D., Vice President Medical Affairs
CIO: Michael R. Silver, M.D., Chief Information Officer
CHR: Arlene Cruz, Director
CNO: Karen Mayer, R.N., Senior Vice President Patient Care Services
Web address: www.roph.org
Control: Other not–for–profit (including NFP Corporation) **Service:** General Medical and Surgical

Staffed Beds: 95 **Admissions:** 4677 **Census:** 65 **Outpatient Visits:** 112366 **Births:** 0 **Total Expense ($000):** 108805 **Payroll Expense ($000):** 50423 **Personnel:** 817	

✠ **WEST SUBURBAN MEDICAL CENTER (140049)**, 3 Erie Court,
Zip 60302–2599; tel. 708/383–6200, (Nonreporting) **A**1 2 3 5 10 13 **S** TENET Healthcare Corporation, Dallas, TX
Primary Contact: Patrick J. Maloney, Chief Executive Officer
COO: Joseph Ottolino, Chief Operating Officer
CFO: Jennifer Lamont, Chief Financial Officer
CMO: Robert Chase, M.D., Physician Advisor
CHR: Nancy Gunnell, Chief Human Resource Officer
CNO: Roslyn J. Lennon, R.N., Chief Nursing Officer
Web address: www.westsuburbanmc.com/Home.aspx
Control: Corporation, Investor–owned, for–profit **Service:** General Medical and Surgical

Staffed Beds: 172

OLNEY—Richland County

★ ○ **RICHLAND MEMORIAL HOSPITAL (140147)**, 800 East Locust Street,
Zip 62450–2553; tel. 618/395–2131, (Total facility includes 34 beds in nursing home–type unit) **A**10 11 **F**3 7 11 13 15 28 29 31 34 35 40 45 57 59 61 62 63 64 68 69 70 75 76 78 79 81 85 87 89 93 97 98 100 102 103 107 108 110 111 115 119 127 128 129 130 131 132 133 135 143 146 147 **P**6
Primary Contact: David B. Allen, Chief Executive Officer
CFO: Mike Stoverink, Chief Financial Officer
CMO: Robert Nash, M.D., Chief of Staff
CIO: Tim Gillespie, Manager Information Systems
CHR: Jill Van Hyning, Director Human Resources
CNO: Gina Thomas, Chief Nursing Officer & Director of Patient Care Services
Web address: www.richlandmemorial.com
Control: Other not–for–profit (including NFP Corporation) **Service:** General Medical and Surgical

Staffed Beds: 90 **Admissions:** 2287 **Census:** 30 **Outpatient Visits:** 59392 **Births:** 309 **Total Expense ($000):** 48440 **Payroll Expense ($000):** 22290 **Personnel:** 457

OLYMPIA FIELDS—Cook County

★ ○ **FRANCISCAN ST. JAMES HOSPITAL AND HEALTH CENTERS (140172)**, 20201 South Crawford Avenue, Zip 60461–1010; tel. 708/747–4000, (Includes ST. JAMES HOSPITAL AND HEALTH CENTERS – CHICAGO HEIGHTS CAMPUS, 1423 Chicago Road, Chicago Heights, Zip 60411–3483; tel. 708/756–1000; ST. JAMES HOSPITALS AND HEALTH CENTERS – OLYMPIA FIELDS CAMPUS, 20201 Crawford Avenue, tel. 708/747–4000) **A**2 10 11 12 13 **F**12 13 15 18 20 22 24 26 28 29 30 31 35 40 45 46 49 50 53 57 60 62 63 64 66 68 70 75 76 77 78 81 82 84 90 91 93 97 107 111 114 115 116 117 119 120 121 124 126 129 130 132 135 143 144 146 148 **S** Franciscan Alliance, Mishawaka, IN
Primary Contact: Arnold Kimmel, Chief Executive Officer
CIO: Stephen Maes, Director Information Systems
Web address: www.franciscanalliance.org/hospitals/olympiafields/pages/default.aspx
Control: Church–operated, Nongovernment, not–for profit **Service:** General Medical and Surgical

Staffed Beds: 398 **Admissions:** 13696 **Census:** 151 **Outpatient Visits:** 242887 **Births:** 756 **Total Expense ($000):** 283397 **Payroll Expense ($000):** 96698 **Personnel:** 1221

ST. JAMES HOSPITAL AND HEALTH CENTERS See Franciscan St. James Hospital and Health Centers

OTTAWA—Lasalle County

✠ **OSF SAINT ELIZABETH MEDICAL CENTER (140110)**, 1100 East Norris Drive,
Zip 61350–1687; tel. 815/433–3100 **A**1 10 19 **F**3 11 13 15 18 28 29 30 34 35 40 45 48 49 53 56 57 59 68 70 75 76 77 79 81 82 84 85 86 87 93 94 98 99 100 101 102 103 104 105 107 108 110 111 115 118 119 129 130 131 132 135 143 144 146 148 **S** OSF Healthcare System, Peoria, IL
Primary Contact: Kenneth Beutke, President
CFO: Dawn Trompeter, Chief Financial Officer
CMO: Brian S. Rosborough, M.D., Chief Medical Officer
CHR: Robert L. Gibson, Director Employee Relations
CNO: Maeanne Stevens, R.N., Chief Nursing Officer
Web address: www.osfsaintelizabeth.org
Control: Church–operated, Nongovernment, not–for profit **Service:** General Medical and Surgical

Staffed Beds: 87 **Admissions:** 3697 **Census:** 35 **Outpatient Visits:** 97051 **Births:** 456 **Total Expense ($000):** 73050 **Payroll Expense ($000):** 29412 **Personnel:** 518

PALOS HEIGHTS—Cook County

☐ **PALOS COMMUNITY HOSPITAL (140062)**, 12251 South 80th Avenue,
Zip 60463–0930; tel. 708/923–4000, (Nonreporting) **A**1 2 10
Primary Contact: Terrence Moisan, M.D., Chief Executive Officer
CFO: Hugh Rose, Vice President Fiscal Management
CIO: Peggy Carroll, Chief Information Officer
CHR: Mary Denisienko, Vice President Human Resources
Web address: www.paloscommunityhospital.org
Control: Other not–for–profit (including NFP Corporation) **Service:** General Medical and Surgical

Staffed Beds: 362

PANA—Christian County

★ **PANA COMMUNITY HOSPITAL (141341)**, 101 East Ninth Street,
Zip 62557–1785; tel. 217/562–2131 **A**10 18 **F**3 11 15 28 29 30 31 34 35 40 50 53 56 57 59 61 62 63 69 75 77 78 81 87 90 93 107 114 124 127 130 131 132 133 143 147 148 **P**6
Primary Contact: Trina Casner, President and Chief Executive Officer
CFO: James Moon, Chief Financial Officer
CMO: Alan Frigy, M.D., President Medical Staff
CIO: Dianne Bailey, Chief Information Officer
CHR: Luann Funk, Administrative Assistant and Manager Human Resources
CNO: Vickie Coen, Chief Clinical Officer and Nurse Executive
Web address: www.panahospital.com
Control: Other not–for–profit (including NFP Corporation) **Service:** General Medical and Surgical

Staffed Beds: 22 **Admissions:** 279 **Census:** 2 **Outpatient Visits:** 48611 **Births:** 0 **Total Expense ($000):** 18928 **Payroll Expense ($000):** 8506 **Personnel:** 155

PARIS—Edgar County

✠ **PARIS COMMUNITY HOSPITAL (141320)**, 721 East Court Street,
Zip 61944–2460; tel. 217/465–4141 **A**1 10 18 **F**3 15 28 29 30 31 34 35 40 45 50 57 59 64 65 67 69 74 75 77 78 79 81 82 85 86 87 89 90 93 107 108 110 111 115 119 127 128 129 130 131 132 133 144 146 148 **P**6 **S** Alliant Management Services, Louisville, KY
Primary Contact: Oliver Smith, President and Chief Executive Officer
CFO: Martin D. Adams, CPA, Vice President Finance and Chief Financial Officer
CIO: Ed Weeks, Manager Information Services
CHR: Cathy Thompson, Manager Human Resources
CNO: Susan Livvix, R.N., Vice President Nursing Services
Web address: www.pariscommunityhospital.com
Control: Other not–for–profit (including NFP Corporation) **Service:** General Medical and Surgical

Staffed Beds: 25 **Admissions:** 645 **Census:** 6 **Outpatient Visits:** 117326 **Births:** 0 **Total Expense ($000):** 41717 **Payroll Expense ($000):** 19491 **Personnel:** 271

IL

Hospital, Medicare Provider Number, Address, Telephone, Approval, Facility, and Physician Codes, Health Care System
★ American Hospital Association (AHA) membership ○ Healthcare Facilities Accreditation Program ⇑ Center for Improvement in Healthcare Quality Accreditation ☐ The Joint Commission accreditation ◇ DNV Healthcare Inc. accreditation △ Commission on Accreditation of Rehabilitation Facilities (CARF) accreditation

PARK RIDGE—Cook County

★ △ ◇ **ADVOCATE LUTHERAN GENERAL HOSPITAL (140223)**, 1775 Dempster Street, Zip 60068–1174; tel. 847/723–2210 **A**2 3 5 7 8 10 13 21 **F**2 3 5 6 8 9 11 12 13 15 17 18 19 20 21 22 23 24 25 26 27 28 29 30 31 32 34 35 37 38 39 40 41 43 44 45 46 47 48 49 50 53 55 56 57 58 59 60 61 63 64 65 66 68 69 70 72 74 75 76 78 79 80 81 82 84 85 86 87 88 89 90 92 93 94 97 98 99 100 101 102 103 104 105 106 107 108 110 111 112 114 115 116 117 118 119 120 121 123 124 126 129 130 131 132 134 135 136 143 146 147 148 **P**6 8 **S** Advocate Health Care, Downers Grove, IL
Primary Contact: Richard B. Floyd, President
COO: Barbara Weber, Chief Operating Officer
CFO: Beth Hickey, Vice President Finance
CMO: Leo Kelly, M.D., Vice President Medical Management
CIO: Mark Beitzel, Director Information Systems
CHR: Katie Bata, Vice President Human Resources
CNO: Jane Denten, MSN, Vice President Nursing and Chief Nurse Executive
Web address: www.advocatehealth.com/luth/
Control: Other not–for–profit (including NFP Corporation) **Service:** General Medical and Surgical

Staffed Beds: 625 **Admissions:** 29103 **Census:** 419 **Outpatient Visits:** 321299 **Births:** 4216 **Total Expense ($000):** 655042 **Payroll Expense ($000):** 239234 **Personnel:** 3330

PEKIN—Tazewell County

✉ **PEKIN HOSPITAL (140120)**, 600 South 13th Street, Zip 61554–4936; tel. 309/347–1151, (Nonreporting) **A**1 5 10 **S** QHR, Brentwood, TN
Primary Contact: Bob J. Haley, Chief Executive Officer
CFO: Steve Hall, Chief Financial Officer
CMO: Kathryn Kramer, M.D., President Medical Staff
CHR: Anne Dierker, Vice President Hospital Services
Web address: www.pekinhospital.org
Control: Other not–for–profit (including NFP Corporation) **Service:** General Medical and Surgical

Staffed Beds: 107

PEORIA—Peoria County

GREATER PEORIA SPECIALTY HOSPITAL See Kindred Hospital Peoria

✉ **KINDRED HOSPITAL PEORIA (142013)**, 500 West Romeo B. Garrett Avenue, Zip 61605–2301; tel. 309/680–1500, (Nonreporting) **A**1 10 **S** Kindred Healthcare, Louisville, KY
Primary Contact: Ted Paarlberg, Chief Executive Officer
CMO: Michael Peil, M.D., Chief Medical Director
Web address: www.khpeoria.com/
Control: Corporation, Investor–owned, for–profit **Service:** Long–Term Acute Care hospital

Staffed Beds: 50

METHODIST MEDICAL CENTER OF ILLINOIS See UnityPoint Health – Peoria

✉ △ **OSF SAINT FRANCIS MEDICAL CENTER (140067)**, 530 N.E. Glen Oak Avenue, Zip 61637–0001; tel. 309/655–2000, (Includes CHILDREN'S HOSPITAL OF ILLINOIS, 530 N.E. Glen Oak Avenue, tel. 309/655–7171; Kelly Nierstedt, President) **A**1 2 3 5 7 8 10 **F**3 8 9 11 12 13 15 17 18 19 20 21 22 23 24 25 26 27 28 29 30 31 32 34 35 37 38 39 40 41 42 43 44 45 46 47 48 50 51 52 54 56 57 58 59 60 64 65 66 67 69 70 71 72 73 74 75 76 77 78 79 80 81 82 83 84 85 86 87 88 89 90 91 92 93 94 96 97 99 100 102 104 105 107 108 110 111 112 114 115 116 117 118 119 120 121 123 124 126 127 129 130 132 134 138 145 146 147 148 **P**6 **S** OSF Healthcare System, Peoria, IL
Primary Contact: Michael A. Cruz, M.D., President
COO: Robert G. Anderson, Jr., Executive Vice President and Chief Operating Officer
CFO: Ken Harbaugh, Vice President and Chief Financial Officer
CMO: Robert T. Sparrow, M.D., Vice President, Chief Medical Officer
CHR: Jacki L. Fugitt, Director Employee Relations
CNO: Jennifer Hopwood, Vice President, Chief Nursing Officer
Web address: www.osfsaintfrancis.org
Control: Church–operated, Nongovernment, not–for profit **Service:** General Medical and Surgical

Staffed Beds: 609 **Admissions:** 31413 **Census:** 470 **Outpatient Visits:** 1086356 **Births:** 2733 **Total Expense ($000):** 942804 **Payroll Expense ($000):** 348319 **Personnel:** 5083

✉ **UNITYPOINT HEALTH – PEORIA (140209)**, 221 N.E. Glen Oak Avenue, Zip 61636–4310; tel. 309/672–5522 **A**1 2 3 5 10 13 **F**3 8 9 11 12 13 15 17 18 20 22 24 26 29 30 31 32 34 35 36 38 40 43 44 45 46 47 48 49 50 53 54 56 57 58 59 60 62 63 64 68 70 74 75 76 77 78 79 81 82 84 85 86 87 89 90 92 93 96 98 99 100 101 102 103 104 105 107 108 110 111 114 115 116 117 118 119 120 121 126 127 129 130 131 132 134 135 136 143 144 145 146 147 148 **P**8 **S** UnityPoint Health, West Des Moines, IA
Primary Contact: Deborah R. Simon, R.N., President and Chief Executive Officer
COO: Keith Knepp, M.D., Executive Vice President and Chief Operating Officer
CFO: Robert Quin, Vice President Finance and Chief Financial Officer
CMO: Gary Knepp, D.O., Chief Medical Officer and Chief Quality Officer
CHR: Joy Ledbetter, Vice President, Chief Human Resources Officer
CNO: Jeanine R. Spain, R.N., Vice President Hospital Operations and Chief Nursing Officer
Web address: www.unitypoint.org/peoria
Control: Other not–for–profit (including NFP Corporation) **Service:** General Medical and Surgical

Staffed Beds: 277 **Admissions:** 14252 **Census:** 190 **Outpatient Visits:** 566329 **Births:** 1991 **Total Expense ($000):** 375877 **Payroll Expense ($000):** 151596 **Personnel:** 2229

☐ **UNITYPOINT HEALTH – PROCTOR (140013)**, 5409 North Knoxville Avenue, Zip 61614–5069; tel. 309/691–1000, (Total facility includes 20 beds in nursing home–type unit) **A**1 3 5 10 **F**3 4 5 11 15 18 20 22 24 28 29 30 34 40 45 49 51 53 57 59 60 64 70 74 75 79 81 85 86 87 93 98 103 104 105 107 108 110 111 115 118 119 128 129 130 132 135 145 146 148 **S** UnityPoint Health, West Des Moines, IA
Primary Contact: Deborah R. Simon, R.N., President and Chief Executive Officer
CFO: Roger Armstrong, Vice President Finance and Chief Financial Officer
CHR: Linda K. Buck, Vice President Human Resources
Web address: www.proctor.org
Control: Other not–for–profit (including NFP Corporation) **Service:** General Medical and Surgical

Staffed Beds: 138 **Admissions:** 4528 **Census:** 72 **Outpatient Visits:** 53809 **Births:** 0 **Total Expense ($000):** 87898 **Payroll Expense ($000):** 28160 **Personnel:** 547

PERU—Lasalle County

★ **ILLINOIS VALLEY COMMUNITY HOSPITAL (140234)**, 925 West Street, Zip 61354–2757; tel. 815/223–3300 **A**10 **F**2 3 11 13 15 28 29 30 31 34 35 38 40 45 46 47 48 49 50 51 54 57 59 63 64 65 66 68 69 70 74 75 77 79 81 82 85 87 93 96 97 104 107 110 111 114 118 119 127 129 130 131 132 133 135 143 144 146 147 148 **P**8
Primary Contact: Tommy Hobbs, Chief Executive Officer
COO: Bobby Smith, Vice President Physician Services and Quality
CFO: Stephen Davis, Chief Financial Officer
CMO: Mark Fernandez, M.D., Chief of Staff and President Medical Staff
CIO: Nancy McDonnell, Manager Information Systems
CHR: Mary Beth Herron, Director of Human Resources
CNO: Wilma Hart–Flynn, MSN, Vice President Patient Care Services and Chief Nursing Officer
Web address: www.ivch.org
Control: Other not–for–profit (including NFP Corporation) **Service:** General Medical and Surgical

Staffed Beds: 49 **Admissions:** 2555 **Census:** 20 **Outpatient Visits:** 178140 **Births:** 464 **Total Expense ($000):** 79127 **Payroll Expense ($000):** 28761 **Personnel:** 524

PINCKNEYVILLE—Perry County

★ **PINCKNEYVILLE COMMUNITY HOSPITAL (141307)**, 5383 State Route 154, Zip 62274–1099, Mailing Address: PO Box 437, Zip 62274–1099; tel. 618/357–2187 **A**10 18 **F**3 15 28 29 31 34 40 43 45 50 53 56 57 65 78 81 85 93 107 108 110 119 127 130 133 148 **P**6
Primary Contact: Randall W. Dauby, CPA, Chief Executive Officer
CFO: Kara Jo Carson, Chief Financial Officer
CIO: Jeff Roberts, Director Information Technology
CHR: Christie Gajewski, Director Human Resources
CNO: Eva Hopp, Chief Nurse Executive
Web address: www.pvillehosp.org/
Control: Hospital district or authority, Government, nonfederal **Service:** General Medical and Surgical

Staffed Beds: 25 **Admissions:** 498 **Census:** 7 **Outpatient Visits:** 42015 **Births:** 0 **Total Expense ($000):** 20490 **Payroll Expense ($000):** 9124 **Personnel:** 171

IL

PITTSFIELD—Pike County

✠ **ILLINI COMMUNITY HOSPITAL (141315)**, 640 West Washington Street, Zip 62363–1350; tel. 217/285–2113 **A**1 10 18 **F**3 15 18 19 28 29 30 31 34 40 46 50 53 59 64 65 68 70 75 78 81 82 85 87 89 93 97 107 110 115 119 127 129 130 131 133 146
Primary Contact: Kathy Hull, President and Chief Executive Officer
CFO: Tim Moore, Vice President Finance
CMO: Bashar Alzein, M.D., President Medical Staff
CHR: Becky Myers, Human Resources Specialist
CNO: Holly A. Jones, Administrative Director Nursing Services
Web address: www.illinihospital.org
Control: Other not–for–profit (including NFP Corporation) **Service:** General Medical and Surgical

Staffed Beds: 21 **Admissions:** 345 **Census:** 3 **Outpatient Visits:** 7629
Births: 0 **Total Expense ($000):** 21703 **Payroll Expense ($000):** 7787
Personnel: 188

PONTIAC—Livingston County

✠ **OSF SAINT JAMES – JOHN W. ALBRECHT MEDICAL CENTER (140161)**, 2500 West Reynolds, Zip 61764–9774; tel. 815/842–2828 **A**1 10 20 **F**3 8 11 13 15 18 28 29 30 32 34 35 40 45 50 56 57 59 64 68 70 75 76 77 79 81 82 84 85 86 87 89 90 91 93 96 97 107 110 111 115 117 118 119 127 128 129 130 131 132 133 135 144 146 147 **P**7 **S** OSF Healthcare System, Peoria, IL
Primary Contact: Bradley V. Solberg, FACHE, President
CFO: Paula Corrigan, Vice President and Chief Financial Officer
CMO: John M. Rinker, Chief Medical Officer
CNO: Elizabeth Davidson, R.N., Vice President, Patient Care Services
Web address: www.osfsaintjames.org
Control: Church–operated, Nongovernment, not–for profit **Service:** General Medical and Surgical

Staffed Beds: 42 **Admissions:** 1301 **Census:** 12 **Outpatient Visits:** 186735
Births: 181 **Total Expense ($000):** 67724 **Payroll Expense ($000):** 24760
Personnel: 279

PRINCETON—Bureau County

PERRY MEMORIAL HOSPITAL (141337), 530 Park Avenue East, Zip 61356–2598; tel. 815/875–2811 **A**10 18 **F**3 15 28 29 30 32 34 35 40 45 48 51 56 57 59 64 65 66 70 75 77 79 81 82 85 87 89 93 97 107 110 111 114 115 116 117 119 127 128 129 130 131 132 133 144 145 146
Primary Contact: Annette Schnabel, FACHE, President and Chief Executive Officer
COO: Chris J. Williams, FACHE, Vice President Operations
CFO: Mike DeFoe, Chief Financial Officer
CMO: T. Doran, M.D., Chief of Staff
CIO: Karen Behrens, Director Technology Services
CHR: James Lewandowski, Vice President Human Resources
Web address: www.perry–memorial.org
Control: City–Government, nonfederal **Service:** General Medical and Surgical

Staffed Beds: 24 **Admissions:** 841 **Census:** 7 **Outpatient Visits:** 70690
Births: 0 **Total Expense ($000):** 35316 **Payroll Expense ($000):** 14930
Personnel: 280

QUINCY—Adams County

✠ △ **BLESSING HOSPITAL (140015)**, Broadway at 11th Street, Zip 62305–7005, Mailing Address: P.O. Box 7005, Zip 62305–7005; tel. 217/223–1200, (Includes BLESSING HOSPITAL, Broadway & 14th Street, Zip 62301, Mailing Address: P.O. Box 7005, Zip 62305–7005; tel. 217/223–1200), (Total facility includes 20 beds in nursing home–type unit) **A**1 2 3 5 7 10 13 **F**3 5 8 11 12 13 15 17 18 20 22 24 26 28 29 30 31 32 34 35 40 43 44 48 49 50 53 56 57 58 59 60 61 62 63 64 66 68 70 73 74 75 76 77 78 79 81 82 84 85 86 87 89 90 94 96 98 99 100 101 102 103 104 107 108 110 111 114 115 118 119 120 121 123 124 126 127 128 129 130 131 132 135 144 146 147 148 **P**8
Primary Contact: Maureen A. Kahn, R.N., President and Chief Executive Officer
COO: Tim Moore, Chief Accounting Officer and Vice President Ancillary Services and Finance
CFO: Patrick M. Gerveler, Vice President Finance and Chief Financial Officer
CMO: George Liesmann, M.D., Chief Medical Officer
CNO: Jill K. Mason, MS, Chief Nursing Officer
Web address: www.blessinghospital.org
Control: Other not–for–profit (including NFP Corporation) **Service:** General Medical and Surgical

Staffed Beds: 306 **Admissions:** 13736 **Census:** 169 **Outpatient Visits:** 354221 **Births:** 1129 **Total Expense ($000):** 316604 **Payroll Expense ($000):** 104473 **Personnel:** 2160

RED BUD—Randolph County

✠ **RED BUD REGIONAL HOSPITAL (141348)**, 325 Spring Street, Zip 62278–1105; tel. 618/282–3831, (Total facility includes 115 beds in nursing home–type unit) **A**1 10 18 **F**1 3 8 15 29 30 35 40 45 50 56 57 59 64 65 68 75 81 87 93 97 103 104 107 108 110 111 115 119 127 129 130 133 135 143 146 147 148 **S** Quorum Health, Brentwood, TN
Primary Contact: Shane Watson, Chief Executive Officer
CFO: Benjamin Wells, Chief Financial Officer
CMO: Stephanie Skelly, President Medical Staff
CIO: Nick Behnken, Supervisor Information Technology
CHR: Lori Brooks, Director Human Resources
CNO: Linda Harbison, Chief Nursing Officer
Web address: www.redbudregional.com
Control: Corporation, Investor–owned, for–profit **Service:** General Medical and Surgical

Staffed Beds: 140 **Admissions:** 885 **Census:** 103 **Outpatient Visits:** 33672
Births: 0 **Total Expense ($000):** 27282 **Payroll Expense ($000):** 10803
Personnel: 177

ROBINSON—Crawford County

★ **CRAWFORD MEMORIAL HOSPITAL (141343)**, 1000 North Allen Street, Zip 62454–1167; tel. 618/544–3131, (Total facility includes 38 beds in nursing home–type unit) **A**10 18 **F**3 11 12 13 15 28 30 31 40 46 53 59 62 64 76 77 78 79 80 81 82 85 93 107 108 111 119 127 128 129 130 132 133 146 147 **S** QHR, Brentwood, TN
Primary Contact: Donald E. Annis, Chief Executive Officer
CFO: Richard Carlson, Chief Financial Officer
CMO: Gary Tennison, M.D., Chief of Staff
CIO: Tim Richard, IT Coordinator
CHR: Kristi Zane, Chief Human Resources Officer
CNO: Tammy Fralicker, MS, Chief Nursing Officer
Web address: www.crawfordmh.net
Control: Hospital district or authority, Government, nonfederal **Service:** General Medical and Surgical

Staffed Beds: 63 **Admissions:** 932 **Census:** 30 **Outpatient Visits:** 54435
Births: 200 **Total Expense ($000):** 46665 **Payroll Expense ($000):** 21255
Personnel: 366

ROCHELLE—Ogle County

✠ **ROCHELLE COMMUNITY HOSPITAL (141312)**, 900 North Second Street, Zip 61068–1764; tel. 815/562–2181 **A**1 10 18 **F**3 15 29 30 31 34 35 40 41 45 50 53 57 59 64 68 70 74 75 77 78 81 82 85 86 87 93 97 107 110 115 130 132 133 135 144 146 **P**6
Primary Contact: Mark Batty, Chief Executive Officer
CFO: Lori Gutierrez, Chief Financial Officer
CMO: Jason Popp, Chief of Medical Staff
CIO: Scott Stewart, Manager Information Services
CHR: Laura Cirone, Manager Human Resources
Web address: www.rcha.net
Control: Other not–for–profit (including NFP Corporation) **Service:** General Medical and Surgical

Staffed Beds: 16 **Admissions:** 618 **Census:** 5 **Outpatient Visits:** 46905
Births: 1 **Total Expense ($000):** 28543 **Payroll Expense ($000):** 10281
Personnel: 242

ROCK ISLAND—Rock Island County

✠ △ **UNITYPOINT HEALTH – TRINITY ROCK ISLAND (140280)**, 2701 17th Street, Zip 61201–5393; tel. 309/779–5000, (Includes UNITYPOINT HEALTH – TRINITY MOLINE, 500 John Deere Road, Moline, Zip 61265; tel. 309/779–5000), (Total facility includes 29 beds in nursing home–type unit) **A**1 2 7 10 **F**3 5 11 12 13 15 18 20 22 24 26 28 29 30 31 34 35 37 38 40 43 44 45 46 47 48 49 50 57 58 59 64 70 74 76 78 79 81 82 85 86 87 89 90 93 96 98 99 102 103 104 105 107 108 110 114 115 118 119 120 121 123 126 128 129 130 132 146 147 148 **P**8 **S** UnityPoint Health, West Des Moines, IA
Primary Contact: Richard A. Seidler, FACHE, President and Chief Executive Officer
CFO: Katie A. Marchik, Interim Chief Financial Officer
CMO: Paul McLoone, M.D., Chief Medical Officer
CHR: Cara Fuller, Vice President Human Resources
CNO: Ginger L. Renkiewicz, Chief Clinical Officer, Chief Nursing Executive, and Chief Quality Officer
Web address: www.trinityqc.com
Control: Other not–for–profit (including NFP Corporation) **Service:** General Medical and Surgical

Staffed Beds: 345 **Admissions:** 14678 **Census:** 192 **Outpatient Visits:** 288704 **Births:** 1495 **Total Expense ($000):** 315973 **Payroll Expense ($000):** 101993 **Personnel:** 1941

IL

Hospital, Medicare Provider Number, Address, Telephone, Approval, Facility, and Physician Codes, Health Care System

★ American Hospital Association (AHA) membership
☐ The Joint Commission accreditation
◯ Healthcare Facilities Accreditation Program
◇ DNV Healthcare Inc. accreditation
⇑ Center for Improvement in Healthcare Quality Accreditation
△ Commission on Accreditation of Rehabilitation Facilities (CARF) accreditation

ROCKFORD—Winnebago County

✠ **MERCYHEALTH ROCKTON AVENUE HOSPITAL (140239)**, 2400 North Rockton Avenue, Zip 61103–3655; tel. 815/971–5000 **A**1 2 3 5 10 **F**3 11 12 13 18 19 20 22 24 26 27 28 29 30 31 32 34 35 39 40 41 43 44 45 46 47 48 49 50 51 54 55 57 59 63 64 65 68 70 71 72 74 75 76 77 78 79 80 81 82 83 84 85 86 87 88 89 91 93 97 98 100 101 102 103 107 108 111 114 115 118 119 121 122 123 126 129 130 131 132 135 145 146 147 148 **P**6 **S** Mercy Health System, Janesville, WI
Primary Contact: Javon Bea, President and Chief Executive Officer
COO: Sue Ripsch, Senior Vice President & Chief Operating Officer
CFO: John Cook, Senior Vice President & Chief Financial Officer
CMO: John T. Dorsey, M.D., Vice President Physician Services and Chief Medical Officer
CIO: Ruth Yarbrough, Vice President
CHR: Heidi Elsbree, Vice President People and Culture
CNO: Susan Schreier, R.N., Vice President of Patient and Nursing Services and Chief Nursing Officer
Web address: www.rhsnet.org
Control: Other not–for–profit (including NFP Corporation) **Service:** General Medical and Surgical

Staffed Beds: 282 **Admissions:** 13364 **Census:** 180 **Outpatient Visits:** 289813 **Births:** 1482 **Total Expense ($000):** 316633 **Payroll Expense ($000):** 110590 **Personnel:** 2079

✠ **OSF SAINT ANTHONY MEDICAL CENTER (140233)**, 5666 East State Street, Zip 61108–2425; tel. 815/226–2000 **A**1 2 3 5 10 **F**3 11 12 13 15 16 17 18 20 22 24 26 28 29 30 31 32 34 35 36 37 38 39 40 41 43 44 45 46 49 50 51 53 55 56 57 58 59 64 66 70 73 74 75 76 77 78 79 81 82 84 85 86 87 89 92 93 107 108 110 111 114 115 116 117 118 119 120 121 123 124 129 130 131 132 135 145 146 147 148 **P**6 **S** OSF Healthcare System, Peoria, IL
Primary Contact: Paula A. Carynski, MS, R.N., President
COO: James Girardy, M.D., Vice President, Chief Surgical Officer
CFO: David Stenerson, Vice President and Chief Financial Officer
CMO: Harneet Bath, M.D., Vice President, Chief Medicine Officer
CIO: Kathy Peterson, Director Information Services
CHR: Karen C. Brown, Vice President Chief Operating Officer
Web address: www.osfhealth.com
Control: Church–operated, Nongovernment, not–for profit **Service:** General Medical and Surgical

Staffed Beds: 235 **Admissions:** 11196 **Census:** 136 **Outpatient Visits:** 411744 **Births:** 477 **Total Expense ($000):** 363109 **Payroll Expense ($000):** 124963 **Personnel:** 1690

✠ **SWEDISHAMERICAN – A DIVISION OF UW HEALTH (140228)**, 1401 East State Street, Zip 61104–2315; tel. 815/968–4400 **A**1 2 3 5 10 **F**3 13 15 17 18 20 22 24 26 28 29 30 31 34 35 36 37 38 39 40 43 44 45 46 49 50 51 56 57 58 59 60 61 64 65 68 70 73 74 75 76 77 78 79 81 82 84 85 86 87 89 92 93 98 99 100 101 102 103 104 105 107 108 110 111 114 115 118 119 126 129 130 132 135 146 147 148 **P**6
Primary Contact: William R. Gorski, M.D., President and Chief Executive Officer
COO: Don Daniels, Executive Vice President and Chief Operating Officer
CFO: Patti DeWane, Vice President Finance and Treasurer
CMO: Michael Born, M.D., Chief Medical Officer and Chief Quality Officer
CIO: Sheryl Johnson, Chief Information Officer
CHR: Gerard Guinane, Vice President Human Resources
CNO: Ann M. Gantzer, Ph.D., Vice President Patient Services and Chief Nursing Officer
Web address: www.swedishamerican.org
Control: Other not–for–profit (including NFP Corporation) **Service:** General Medical and Surgical

Staffed Beds: 269 **Admissions:** 15189 **Census:** 177 **Outpatient Visits:** 262787 **Births:** 2554 **Total Expense ($000):** 315025 **Payroll Expense ($000):** 120910 **Personnel:** 1936

✠ **VAN MATRE HEALTHSOUTH REHABILITATION HOSPITAL (143028)**, 950 South Mulford Road, Zip 61108–4274; tel. 815/381–8500 **A**1 10 **F**28 29 34 57 64 68 74 75 82 86 90 91 93 95 96 130 131 132 148 **P**5 **S** HEALTHSOUTH Corporation, Birmingham, AL
Primary Contact: Ken Bowman, Chief Executive Officer
CFO: Tim Anderson, Controller
CMO: Ricardo Knight, Interim Medical Director
CIO: Angela Bergman, Director Health Information Management
CHR: Dorothy Richardson, Director Human Resources
CNO: Nancy Miller, R.N., Chief Nursing Officer
Web address: www.healthsouth.com
Control: Partnership, Investor–owned, for–profit **Service:** Rehabilitation

Staffed Beds: 61 **Admissions:** 1508 **Census:** 52 **Outpatient Visits:** 8353 **Births:** 0 **Total Expense ($000):** 18789 **Payroll Expense ($000):** 10010 **Personnel:** 165

ROSICLARE—Hardin County

★ **HARDIN COUNTY GENERAL HOSPITAL (141328)**, 6 Ferrell Road, Zip 62982, Mailing Address: P.O. Box 2467, Zip 62982–2467; tel. 618/285–6634, (Nonreporting) **A**10 18
Primary Contact: Roby D. Williams, Administrator
CFO: Janie Parker, Chief Financial Officer
CMO: Marcos N. Sunga, M.D., Chief of Staff
CIO: Brian Casteel, Information Technology Technician
CHR: Joyce Shelby, Manager Human Resources
CNO: Courtney Spivey, Chief Nursing Officer
Web address: www.ilhcgh.org
Control: Other not–for–profit (including NFP Corporation) **Service:** General Medical and Surgical

Staffed Beds: 25

RUSHVILLE—Schuyler County

★ **SARAH D. CULBERTSON MEMORIAL HOSPITAL (141333)**, 238 South Congress Street, Zip 62681–1472; tel. 217/322–4321 **A**10 18 **F**11 15 28 29 31 34 40 56 57 59 65 69 75 77 81 85 93 96 97 103 104 107 110 114 119 125 127 129 130 132 133 135 146 148 **P**6
Primary Contact: Lynn E. Stambaugh, R.N., Chief Executive Officer
CFO: Alan Palo, Chief Financial Officer
CMO: Marguerite Taillefer, M.D., Acting President Medical Staff
CIO: Dan Wise, Manager Information Technology
CNO: Lisa M. Downs, R.N., Chief Nursing Officer
Web address: www.cmhospital.com
Control: Hospital district or authority, Government, nonfederal **Service:** General Medical and Surgical

Staffed Beds: 22 **Admissions:** 225 **Census:** 4 **Outpatient Visits:** 46210 **Births:** 0 **Total Expense ($000):** 20396 **Payroll Expense ($000):** 7855 **Personnel:** 167

SALEM—Marion County

★ **SALEM TOWNSHIP HOSPITAL (141345)**, 1201 Ricker Drive, Zip 62881–4263; tel. 618/548–3194, (Nonreporting) **A**10 18
Primary Contact: John E. Kessler, President and Chief Executive Officer
CFO: Teresa Stroud, Chief Financial Officer
CMO: Seth Hahs, Chief of Staff
CIO: Steve Turner, Director Information Technology
CHR: Diane Boswell, Director Human Resources and Marketing
Web address: www.sthcares.org
Control: City–County, Government, nonfederal **Service:** General Medical and Surgical

Staffed Beds: 22

SANDWICH—Dekalb County

✠ **NORTHWESTERN MEDICINE VALLEY WEST HOSPITAL (141340)**, 1302 North Main Street, Zip 60548–2587; tel. 815/786–8484 **A**1 10 18 **F**3 11 13 15 18 28 29 30 31 32 34 35 36 38 40 45 46 49 51 57 58 59 64 68 70 71 75 76 77 78 79 81 82 85 87 89 93 102 104 107 110 115 119 127 129 130 131 132 135 146 147 **S** Northwestern Memorial Healthcare, Chicago, IL
Primary Contact: Kevin Poorten, President
COO: Brad Copple, Vice President Operations
CFO: Loren Foelske, Vice President Finance
CMO: Michael Kulisz, D.O., Chief Medical Officer
CIO: Heath Bell, Vice President, Chief Information Officer
CHR: Michele McClelland, Vice President Human Resources
CNO: Pamela Duffy, Vice President Operations and Chief Nursing Officer
Web address: www.kishhealth.org
Control: Other not–for–profit (including NFP Corporation) **Service:** General Medical and Surgical

Staffed Beds: 25 **Admissions:** 979 **Census:** 7 **Outpatient Visits:** 34447 **Births:** 194 **Total Expense ($000):** 39657 **Payroll Expense ($000):** 11745 **Personnel:** 172

SHELBYVILLE—Shelby County

★ ◇ **SHELBY MEMORIAL HOSPITAL (140019)**, 200 South Cedar Street, Zip 62565–1838; tel. 217/774–3961 **A**10 20 21 **F**3 15 28 29 34 35 40 45 57 59 62 64 77 81 93 97 107 108 110 118 119 127 129 131 132 133 146 **P**5
Primary Contact: Marilyn Sears, President and Chief Executive Officer
CFO: Marilyn Sears, Chief Financial Officer
CMO: David Oligschlaeger, Medical Staff President
CIO: Ian Kuhlman, Manager Information Technology
CHR: Amy Koehler, Director Human Resources
CNO: Michelle Oliver, Chief Nursing Executive
Web address: www.mysmh.org
Control: Other not–for–profit (including NFP Corporation) **Service:** General Medical and Surgical

Staffed Beds: 30 **Admissions:** 505 **Census:** 4 **Outpatient Visits:** 31902 **Births:** 0 **Total Expense ($000):** 16779 **Payroll Expense ($000):** 6925 **Personnel:** 163

Many Facility Codes have changed. Please refer to the AHA Guide Code Chart. © 2016 AHA Guide

SHILOH—St. Clair County

MEMORIAL HOSPITAL EAST, 1404 Cross Street, Zip 62269–2988;
tel. 618/607–1000, (Nonreporting)
Primary Contact: Mark J. Turner, President and Chief Executive Officer
Web address: www.memhospeast.com
Control: Corporation, Investor–owned, for–profit **Service:** General Medical and Surgical

Staffed Beds: 94

SILVIS—Rock Island County

⊠ **GENESIS MEDICAL CENTER, ILLINI CAMPUS (140275)**, 801 Illini Drive,
Zip 61282–1893; tel. 309/281–4000 **A**1 10 **F**3 7 11 13 15 18 20 26 28 29
30 31 34 35 38 40 43 44 46 50 53 54 57 59 63 64 68 70 74 75 76 77 78
79 81 82 84 85 86 87 89 97 107 108 110 111 114 119 129 130 131 132
135 146 147 **P**6 **S** Genesis Health System, Davenport, IA
Primary Contact: Theresa Summers–Main, R.N., Interim President
CFO: Mark G. Rogers, Interim Vice President Finance and Chief Financial Officer
CMO: Peter Metcalf, M.D., President Medical Staff
CIO: Robert Frieden, Vice President Information Systems
CHR: Heidi Kahly–McMahon, Vice President Human Resources
Web address: www.genesishealth.com
Control: Other not–for–profit (including NFP Corporation) **Service:** General Medical and Surgical

Staffed Beds: 135 **Admissions:** 4379 **Census:** 33 **Outpatient Visits:** 107669 **Births:** 453 **Total Expense ($000):** 75841 **Payroll Expense ($000):** 23282 **Personnel:** 386

SPARTA—Randolph County

SPARTA COMMUNITY HOSPITAL (141349), 818 East Broadway Street,
Zip 62286–1820, Mailing Address: P.O. Box 297, Zip 62286–0297;
tel. 618/443–2177 **A**10 18 **F**3 11 15 28 34 35 38 40 41 45 53 57 59 62 64
65 75 77 81 82 89 93 97 99 104 107 108 110 111 115 119 127 130 132
133 143 146 147 **P**5
Primary Contact: Joann Emge, Chief Executive Officer
CFO: Paul Mueller, Chief Financial Officer
CMO: Mark Pruess, M.D., Chief Medical Staff
CIO: Susan Gutjahr, Reimbursement Specialist
CHR: Darla Shawgo, Director Human Resources
CNO: Lori Clinton, Chief Nursing Officer
Web address: www.spartahospital.com
Control: Hospital district or authority, Government, nonfederal **Service:** General Medical and Surgical

Staffed Beds: 25 **Admissions:** 543 **Census:** 3 **Outpatient Visits:** 37801 **Births:** 0 **Total Expense ($000):** 28500 **Payroll Expense ($000):** 12325 **Personnel:** 261

SPRING VALLEY—Bureau County

ST. MARGARET'S HOSPITAL (140143), 600 East First Street,
Zip 61362–1512; tel. 815/664–5311 **A**10 **F**3 11 13 15 28 29 30 31 32 34 35
38 40 44 45 46 47 49 53 57 58 59 63 70 74 75 76 77 79 81 82 84 85 87
90 93 96 107 108 110 111 115 118 119 129 130 131 132 133 135 143
144 146 147 148 **P**6 8 **S** Sisters of Mary of the Presentation Health System,
Fargo, ND
Primary Contact: Tim Muntz, President and Chief Executive Officer
CFO: Kim D. Santman, Vice President Finance
CIO: John Sabotta, Director Information Systems
CHR: Lisa R. Blackburn, Director Human Resources
CNO: Mary Vega, R.N., Vice President Nursing
Web address: www.aboutsmh.org
Control: Church–operated, Nongovernment, not–for profit **Service:** General Medical and Surgical

Staffed Beds: 54 **Admissions:** 1990 **Census:** 19 **Outpatient Visits:** 258016 **Births:** 343 **Total Expense ($000):** 74545 **Payroll Expense ($000):** 30737 **Personnel:** 509

SPRINGFIELD—Sangamon County

☐ **ANDREW MCFARLAND MENTAL HEALTH CENTER (144021)**, 901 East
Southwind Road, Zip 62703–5125; tel. 217/786–6994, (Nonreporting) **A**1 3 5
10 **S** Division of Mental Health, Department of Human Services, Springfield, IL
Primary Contact: Karen Schweighart, R.N., MS, Administrator
CFO: Jeff Frey, Business Administrator
CMO: Kasturi Kripakaran, M.D., Medical Director
CIO: Josh Kates, Information Technology Analyst
CNO: Frances Collins, Director of Nursing
Control: State–Government, nonfederal **Service:** Psychiatric

Staffed Beds: 118

KINDRED HOSPITAL SPRINGFIELD See Vibra Hospital of Springfield

☐ **LINCOLN PRAIRIE BEHAVIORAL HEALTH CENTER**, 5230 South Sixth Street,
Zip 62703–5128; tel. 217/585–1180 **A**1 3 5 **F**29 35 98 99 100 101 104 105
S Universal Health Services, Inc., King of Prussia, PA
Primary Contact: Mark Littrell, Chief Executive Officer
CFO: Chris Statz, Chief Financial Officer
CMO: Pamela Campbell, M.D., Medical Director
CNO: Renae Hale, Chief Nursing Officer
Web address: www.lincolnprairiebhc.com/
Control: Corporation, Investor–owned, for–profit **Service:** Children's hospital psychiatric

Staffed Beds: 97 **Admissions:** 1958 **Census:** 68 **Outpatient Visits:** 9188 **Total Expense ($000):** 18734 **Payroll Expense ($000):** 7390 **Personnel:** 118

⊠ △ **MEMORIAL MEDICAL CENTER (140148)**, 701 North First Street,
Zip 62781–0001; tel. 217/788–3000 **A**1 2 3 5 7 8 10 **F**3 8 11 12 13 14 15
16 17 18 20 22 24 26 28 29 30 31 32 34 35 36 37 40 43 44 45 46 47 48
49 50 51 54 57 58 59 60 61 63 64 68 69 70 74 75 76 77 78 79 81 82 84
85 86 87 89 90 92 93 96 97 98 100 101 102 103 104 105 107 108 110
111 114 115 116 117 118 119 120 121 124 126 129 130 131 132 134 135
138 141 142 145 146 147 148 **S** Memorial Health System, Springfield, IL
Primary Contact: Edgar J. Curtis, FACHE, President and Chief Executive Officer
COO: Charles D. Callahan, Ph.D., Executive Vice President and Chief Operating Officer
CFO: Robert W. Kay, Senior Vice President and Chief Financial Officer
CMO: Rajesh G. Govindaiah, M.D., Chief Medical Officer
CIO: David B. Graham, M.D., Senior Vice President and Chief Information Officer
CHR: Robert F. Scott, Vice President and Chief Human Resources Officer
CNO: Marsha A. Prater, Ph.D., Senior Vice President and Chief Nursing Officer
Web address: www.memorialmedical.com
Control: Other not–for–profit (including NFP Corporation) **Service:** General Medical and Surgical

Staffed Beds: 470 **Admissions:** 24469 **Census:** 325 **Outpatient Visits:** 421083 **Births:** 1570 **Total Expense ($000):** 613274 **Payroll Expense ($000):** 195553 **Personnel:** 3722

⊠ **ST. JOHN'S HOSPITAL (140053)**, 800 East Carpenter Street,
Zip 62769–0002; tel. 217/544–6464, (Includes ST. JOHN'S CHILDREN'S
HOSPITAL, 800 East Carpenter Street, Zip 62769; tel. 217/544–6464), (Total
facility includes 37 beds in nursing home–type unit) **A**1 2 3 5 10 **F**3 8 11 12 13
15 17 18 19 20 22 24 26 28 29 30 31 33 36 37 39 40 41 43 44 45 46
46 47 48 49 50 51 53 54 56 57 58 59 60 61 62 63 64 68 70 72 74 75 76
77 78 79 81 82 83 84 85 86 87 88 89 92 93 94 96 98 100 101 102 103
104 105 107 108 110 111 114 115 116 117 118 119 120 121 122 123 124
126 128 129 130 131 132 135 145 146 147 148 **S** Hospital Sisters Health
System, Springfield, IL
Primary Contact: Charles Lucore, M.D., President and Chief Executive Officer
COO: David R. Olejniczak, Chief Operating Officer
CFO: Patty Allen, St. John's Vice President Finance
CIO: Ryan Leach, Chief Information Officer
CHR: Becky Puclik, Division Chief People Officer
CNO: Sherri Greenwood, Chief Nursing Officer
Web address: www.st–johns.org
Control: Other not–for–profit (including NFP Corporation) **Service:** General Medical and Surgical

Staffed Beds: 432 **Admissions:** 19325 **Census:** 281 **Outpatient Visits:** 252690 **Births:** 1906 **Total Expense ($000):** 478021 **Payroll Expense ($000):** 138941 **Personnel:** 2515

⊠ **VIBRA HOSPITAL OF SPRINGFIELD (142014)**, 701 North Walnut Street,
Zip 62702–4931; tel. 217/528–1217 **A**1 10 **F**1 3 29 148 **P**6 **S** Vibra
Healthcare, Mechanicsburg, PA
Primary Contact: Larry Deal, R.N., Chief Executive Officer
CHR: Cyndi Dodge, Director Human Resources
CNO: Cathy Harding, Chief Clinical Officer
Web address: www.vhspringfield.com
Control: Corporation, Investor–owned, for–profit **Service:** Long–Term Acute Care hospital

Staffed Beds: 32 **Admissions:** 338 **Census:** 25 **Outpatient Visits:** 0 **Births:** 0 **Total Expense ($000):** 13728 **Payroll Expense ($000):** 6594 **Personnel:** 84

IL

Hospital, Medicare Provider Number, Address, Telephone, Approval, Facility, and Physician Codes, Health Care System

★ American Hospital Association (AHA) membership   ○ Healthcare Facilities Accreditation Program   ⇑ Center for Improvement in Healthcare Quality Accreditation
☐ The Joint Commission accreditation   ◇ DNV Healthcare Inc. accreditation   △ Commission on Accreditation of Rehabilitation Facilities (CARF) accreditation

---

STAUNTON—Macoupin County

COMMUNITY MEMORIAL HOSPITAL (141306), 400 Caldwell Street, Zip 62088–1499; tel. 618/635–2200 **A**10 18 **F**3 11 15 28 29 31 40 45 64 78 81 107 115 130 132 133 146 **P**5
Primary Contact: Susie Campbell, Chief Executive Officer
CFO: Brian Engelke, Chief Financial Officer
CMO: Joshua Poos, M.D., President Medical Staff
CIO: Cheryl Horner, Supervisor Data Processing
CHR: Marilyn Herbeck, Coordinator Human Resources
CNO: Roberta Brown, Chief Nursing Officer
Web address: www.stauntonhospital.org
Control: Other not-for-profit (including NFP Corporation) **Service:** General Medical and Surgical

Staffed Beds: 25 **Admissions:** 236 **Census:** 3 **Outpatient Visits:** 23308
Births: 0 **Total Expense ($000):** 14110 **Payroll Expense ($000):** 5558
Personnel: 126

STERLING—Whiteside County

✠ **CGH MEDICAL CENTER (140043)**, 100 East LeFevre Road, Zip 61081–1279; tel. 815/625–0400 **A**1 10 **F**3 7 8 11 13 15 18 20 22 28 29 30 31 34 35 40 45 47 49 50 51 57 59 62 64 68 70 74 76 78 79 81 82 85 86 87 93 97 105 107 108 110 111 112 115 116 117 118 119 124 129 130 132 133 135 144 145 146 148 **P**6
Primary Contact: Paul Steinke, D.O., President and Chief Executive Officer
COO: Cynthia L. Zander, Vice President and Chief Operating Officer
CFO: Ben Schaab, VP Fiscal Services/ Chief Financial Officer
CMO: Keith Martin, M.D., Vice President and Medical Director
CIO: Randy Davis, Vice President and Chief Information Officer
CHR: Shane Brown, Vice President and Chief Human Resources Officer
CNO: Kristie A. Geil, VP, Chief Nursing Officer
Web address: www.cghmc.com
Control: City–Government, nonfederal **Service:** General Medical and Surgical

Staffed Beds: 99 **Admissions:** 5074 **Census:** 40 **Outpatient Visits:** 374695
Births: 555 **Total Expense ($000):** 193740 **Payroll Expense ($000):** 86789
Personnel: 906

STREAMWOOD—Cook County

☐ **STREAMWOOD BEHAVIORAL HEALTH CENTER (144034)**, 1400 East Irving Park Road, Zip 60107–3203; tel. 630/837–9000, (Nonreporting) **A**1 10 **S** Universal Health Services, Inc., King of Prussia, PA
Primary Contact: Ron Weglarz, Chief Executive Officer and Managing Director
CFO: Patricia Ellison, Chief Financial Officer
CMO: Joseph McNally, M.D., Medical Director
CHR: Joseph Rinke, Director Human Resources
CNO: Olieth Lightbourne, Chief Nursing Officer
Web address: www.streamwoodhospital.com
Control: Corporation, Investor–owned, for–profit **Service:** Children's hospital psychiatric

Staffed Beds: 177

SYCAMORE—Dekalb County

✠ **KINDRED HOSPITAL–SYCAMORE (142006)**, 225 Edward Street, Zip 60178–2137; tel. 815/895–2144, (Nonreporting) **A**1 10 **S** Kindred Healthcare, Louisville, KY
Primary Contact: Jim Cohick, Chief Executive Officer
CFO: Jay Schweikart, Chief Financial Officer
CMO: Thomas Liske, M.D., Chief Medical Officer
CHR: Eileen Strachan, Coordinator Human Resources
Web address: www.kindredhospitalsyc.com/
Control: Corporation, Investor–owned, for–profit **Service:** Long–Term Acute Care hospital

Staffed Beds: 69

TAYLORVILLE—Christian County

✠ **TAYLORVILLE MEMORIAL HOSPITAL (141339)**, 201 East Pleasant Street, Zip 62568–1597; tel. 217/824–3331 **A**1 3 5 10 18 **F**8 15 28 29 30 34 35 40 45 46 50 57 59 64 75 77 79 81 87 89 93 103 107 108 110 111 115 119 129 130 131 132 133 144 146 **P**5 **S** Memorial Health System, Springfield, IL
Primary Contact: Kimberly L. Bourne, Chief Executive Officer
CFO: Andrew Costic, Regional Chief Financial Officer
CHR: Michelle Long, Regional Human Resource Manager
CNO: Tracy Seaton, Director of Nursing
Web address: www.taylorvillememorial.org
Control: Other not–for–profit (including NFP Corporation) **Service:** General Medical and Surgical

Staffed Beds: 25 **Admissions:** 1062 **Census:** 10 **Outpatient Visits:** 39150
Births: 0 **Total Expense ($000):** 37466 **Payroll Expense ($000):** 14541
Personnel: 229

URBANA—Champaign County

★ △ ◇ **CARLE FOUNDATION HOSPITAL (140091)**, 611 West Park Street, Zip 61801–2595; tel. 217/383–3311 **A**2 3 5 7 10 13 21 **F**3 5 7 8 11 12 13 15 17 18 20 22 24 26 28 29 30 31 32 34 35 40 43 44 45 46 47 48 49 50 51 53 56 57 58 59 60 61 62 63 64 65 68 70 72 74 75 76 78 79 80 81 84 85 86 87 89 90 91 93 94 96 107 108 110 111 114 115 116 117 119 126 129 130 131 132 135 145 146 148 **S** Carle Foundation, Urbana, IL
Primary Contact: James C. Leonard, M.D., President and Chief Executive Officer
COO: John Snyder, Executive Vice President and System Chief Operating Officer
CFO: Dennis Hesch, Executive Vice President Finance, System Chief Financial Officer
CMO: Matthew Gibb, M.D., Executive Vice President and System Chief Medical Officer
CIO: Rick Rinehart, Vice President, Chief Information Officer
CHR: L. J. Fallon, JD, Executive Vice President, Chief Legal and Human Resources Officer
CNO: Pamela Bigler, MSN, Senior Vice President, Chief Nursing Officer
Web address: www.carle.org
Control: Other not–for–profit (including NFP Corporation) **Service:** General Medical and Surgical

Staffed Beds: 376 **Admissions:** 22807 **Census:** 319 **Outpatient Visits:** 1157834 **Births:** 2679 **Total Expense ($000):** 561672 **Payroll Expense ($000):** 154023 **Personnel:** 2847

✠ △ **PRESENCE COVENANT MEDICAL CENTER (140113)**, 1400 West Park Street, Zip 61801–2396; tel. 217/337–2000 **A**1 3 5 7 10 **F**3 7 13 15 18 20 22 24 26 28 29 30 31 34 35 40 49 57 59 68 70 72 74 75 76 78 79 81 82 85 87 89 90 97 98 100 101 102 103 107 108 110 111 114 115 119 126 130 132 146 147 148 **S** Presence Health, Chicago, IL
Primary Contact: Jared Rogers, M.D., President and Chief Executive Officer
COO: Jennifer Cord, R.N., Chief Ambulatory, Ancillary, and Mission Officer
CFO: Deb Schimerowski, Vice President Finance and Chief Financial Officer
CMO: Vincent Kucich, FACHE, Chief Medical Officer
CIO: Paula Keele, Manager Information Systems
CHR: Michael Zimmerman, Human Resource Officer
CNO: Molly Nicholson, MS, Chief Nurse Executive
Web address: www.presencehealth.org/covenant
Control: Church–operated, Nongovernment, not–for profit **Service:** General Medical and Surgical

Staffed Beds: 181 **Admissions:** 7462 **Census:** 81 **Outpatient Visits:** 223301
Births: 714 **Total Expense ($000):** 139842 **Payroll Expense ($000):** 38970
Personnel: 725

VANDALIA—Fayette County

✠ **FAYETTE COUNTY HOSPITAL (141346)**, 650 West Taylor Street, Zip 62471–1296; tel. 618/283–1231, (Total facility includes 85 beds in nursing home–type unit) **A**1 10 18 **F**3 7 11 15 28 29 30 34 40 45 49 57 59 77 80 81 86 93 107 110 111 112 114 116 117 119 127 128 129 130 132 133 145 146 **P**5 **S** Alliant Management Services, Louisville, KY
Primary Contact: Gregory D. Starnes, Chief Executive Officer
CFO: Pete Fromme, Chief Financial Officer
CMO: Glenn Skow, M.D., Chief of Staff
CIO: Lisa Tessman, Manager Information Technology
CHR: Susan Crawford, Manager Human Resources
CNO: Marci Barth, Chief Nursing Officer
Web address: www.fayettecountyhospital.org
Control: Corporation, Investor–owned, for–profit **Service:** General Medical and Surgical

Staffed Beds: 110 **Admissions:** 760 **Census:** 56 **Outpatient Visits:** 49026
Births: 0 **Total Expense ($000):** 24508 **Payroll Expense ($000):** 8044
Personnel: 260

WATSEKA—Iroquois County

☐ **IROQUOIS MEMORIAL HOSPITAL AND RESIDENT HOME (140167)**, 200 Fairman Avenue, Zip 60970–1644; tel. 815/432–5841, (Total facility includes 35 beds in nursing home–type unit) **A**1 3 10 20 **F**3 7 11 13 15 17 18 26 28 29 30 31 34 35 40 44 45 46 49 50 57 59 62 63 64 65 68 69 70 75 76 77 78 79 81 85 92 93 94 96 97 102 107 108 109 110 111 115 119 127 128 129 130 132 133 135 143 144 145 146 147 148 **P**6
Primary Contact: Charles Bohlmann, Chief Executive Officer
COO: Christopher Curry, Chief Operating Officer
CMO: Philip Zumwalt, M.D., Chief of Staff
CIO: Tim Smith, Director Information Systems
CHR: Jamie Neumann, Director Human Resources
CNO: Leslie Cottrell, R.N., Nurse Lead
Web address: www.iroquoismemorial.com
Control: Other not–for–profit (including NFP Corporation) **Service:** General Medical and Surgical

Staffed Beds: 84 **Admissions:** 845 **Census:** 39 **Outpatient Visits:** 27973
Births: 89 **Total Expense ($000):** 38485 **Payroll Expense ($000):** 18217
Personnel: 303

Many Facility Codes have changed. Please refer to the AHA Guide Code Chart. © 2016 AHA Guide

IL

WAUKEGAN—Lake County

☒ **VISTA MEDICAL CENTER EAST (140084)**, 1324 North Sheridan Road, Zip 60085–2161; tel. 847/360–3000 **A**1 2 3 5 10 **F**3 12 13 15 18 20 22 24 26 28 29 30 31 34 35 38 39 40 41 42 43 44 45 46 47 48 49 50 57 59 68 70 73 74 76 78 79 81 82 84 85 87 89 93 100 102 107 108 110 111 114 115 119 126 129 130 132 146 147 148 **S** Quorum Health, Brentwood, TN
Primary Contact: Barbara J. Martin, R.N., President and Chief Executive Officer
COO: Kim Needham, Assistant Chief Executive Officer
CFO: Kerry Hill, Chief Financial Officer
CMO: Daniel Liesen, M.D., Chief Medical Officer
CHR: Michael R. Isaacs, Vice President Human Resources
CNO: Trisha E. Musich, R.N., Chief Nursing Officer
Web address: www.vistahealth.com
Control: Corporation, Investor–owned, for–profit **Service:** General Medical and Surgical

Staffed Beds: 190 Admissions: 10978 Census: 117 Outpatient Visits: 140639 **Births: 1275 Total Expense ($000): 166374 Payroll Expense ($000): 52603 Personnel: 838**

☒ △ **VISTA MEDICAL CENTER WEST (140033)**, 2615 Washington Street, Zip 60085–4988; tel. 847/249–3900 **A**1 7 10 **F**29 30 34 35 38 40 42 43 50 56 57 59 64 68 77 87 90 96 98 99 101 102 103 104 105 107 119 130 132 135 **S** Quorum Health, Brentwood, TN
Primary Contact: Barbara J. Martin, R.N., President and Chief Executive Officer
COO: Kim Needham, Assistant Chief Executive Officer
CFO: Kerry Hill, Chief Financial Officer
CMO: Daniel Liesen, M.D., Chief Medical Officer
CHR: Michael R. Isaacs, Vice President Human Resources
CNO: Trisha E. Musich, R.N., Chief Nursing Officer
Web address: www.vistahealth.com
Control: Corporation, Investor–owned, for–profit **Service:** Psychiatric

Staffed Beds: 67 Admissions: 1710 Census: 34 Outpatient Visits: 11952 Births: 0 Total Expense ($000): 15123 Payroll Expense ($000): 7150 Personnel: 111

WHEATON—Du Page County

☒ △ **MARIANJOY REHABILITATION HOSPITAL (143027)**, 26 West 171 Roosevelt Road, Zip 60187–0795, Mailing Address: P.O. Box 795, Zip 60187–0795; tel. 630/909–8000, (Total facility includes 27 beds in nursing home–type unit) **A**1 3 7 10 **F**11 29 30 34 35 36 50 56 58 64 68 75 77 79 82 86 87 90 91 93 95 96 128 132 143 146 148 **P**6 **S** Wheaton Franciscan Healthcare, Wheaton, IL
Primary Contact: Kathleen C. Yosko, President
COO: John Brady, Vice President Physician Services and Organizational Planning
CFO: Michael Hedderman, Senior Vice President Finance and Chief Financial Officer
CMO: Jeffrey Oken, Vice President of Medical Affairs
CIO: Robert Sinickas, Director Information Services
CHR: Teresa Chapman, Vice President Human Resources
CNO: Kathleen C. Yosko, President
Web address: www.marianjoy.org
Control: Church–operated, Nongovernment, not–for profit **Service:** Rehabilitation

Staffed Beds: 127 Admissions: 3045 Census: 114 Outpatient Visits: 45993 Births: 0 Total Expense ($000): 71055 Payroll Expense ($000): 39447 Personnel: 775

WINFIELD—DuPage County

☒ **NORTHWESTERN MEDICINE CENTRAL DUPAGE HOSPITAL (140242)**, 25 North Winfield Road, Zip 60190; tel. 630/933–1600, (Includes BEHAVIORAL HEALTH CENTER, 27 West 350 High Lake Road, tel. 630/653–4000) **A**1 2 3 5 10 **F**3 4 5 8 11 12 13 15 17 18 19 20 22 24 26 28 29 30 31 34 35 36 37 39 40 41 42 43 44 45 46 47 48 49 50 54 55 57 58 59 64 65 68 70 72 73 74 75 76 77 78 79 81 82 84 85 86 87 88 89 91 92 93 94 96 97 98 99 100 101 102 103 104 105 106 107 108 110 111 112 114 115 116 117 118 119 120 121 122 123 124 126 129 130 131 132 135 141 142 144 145 146 147 148 **S** Northwestern Memorial Healthcare, Chicago, IL
Primary Contact: Brian J. Lemon, President
CFO: John Orsini, Executive Vice President and Chief Financial Officer
CMO: Kevin Most, D.O., Vice President Medical Affairs
CIO: Daniel F. Kinsella, Vice President and Chief Information Officer
CHR: Michael Wukitsch, Vice President Human Resources
Web address: www.cdh.org
Control: Other not–for–profit (including NFP Corporation) **Service:** General Medical and Surgical

Staffed Beds: 379 Admissions: 21285 Census: 236 Outpatient Visits: 1466094 **Births: 3161 Total Expense ($000): 841209 Payroll Expense ($000): 319883 Personnel: 4422**

WOODSTOCK—Mchenry County

★ **CENTEGRA HOSPITAL – WOODSTOCK (140176)**, 3701 Doty Road, Zip 60098–7509, Mailing Address: P.O. Box 1990, Zip 60098–1990; tel. 815/338–2500 **A**2 10 **F**3 4 5 11 12 15 18 28 29 30 31 34 35 37 38 39 40 43 44 45 47 49 50 51 54 57 58 59 64 68 69 70 74 75 78 79 81 82 85 86 87 92 93 98 100 101 102 103 104 105 107 108 110 111 114 118 119 128 129 130 131 132 143 146 147 148 **P**4 5 **S** Centegra Health System, Crystal Lake, IL
Primary Contact: Michael S. Eesley, Chief Executive Officer
COO: Jason Sciarro, President and Chief Operating Officer
CFO: David Tomlinson, Executive Vice President Chief Financial Officer and Chief Information Officer
CMO: Irfan Hafiz, Vice President Medical Affairs
CIO: David Tomlinson, Senior Vice President, Chief Information Officer
CHR: Bernadette S. Szczepanski, Senior Vice President Human Resources
Web address: www.centegra.org
Control: Other not–for–profit (including NFP Corporation) **Service:** General Medical and Surgical

Staffed Beds: 96 Admissions: 5238 Census: 63 Outpatient Visits: 82735 Births: 192 Total Expense ($000): 121792 Payroll Expense ($000): 48620 Personnel: 589

ZION—Lake County

☒ **MIDWESTERN REGIONAL MEDICAL CENTER (140100)**, 2520 Elisha Avenue, Zip 60099–2587; tel. 847/872–4561 **A**1 2 3 10 **F**3 7 8 15 18 26 28 29 30 31 33 34 35 36 37 38 40 44 45 46 48 49 50 54 55 57 58 59 60 61 64 65 68 70 74 75 77 78 79 81 82 85 86 87 92 93 94 95 97 100 101 102 104 107 108 110 111 115 117 118 119 120 121 123 124 126 129 130 132 133 135 136 143 144 146 147 148 **P**6 **S** Cancer Treatment Centers of America, Schaumburg, IL
Primary Contact: Scott Jones, President and Chief Executive Officer
COO: Pete Govorchin, Senior Vice President Operations
CFO: Cecilia Taylor, Chief Financial Officer
CMO: Bradford Tan, M.D., Chief Medical Officer
CHR: Amy VanStrien, Director Talent Operations
CNO: Jacklynn Lesniak, R.N., Vice President Patient Care Services and Chief Nursing Officer
Web address: www.cancercenter.com
Control: Corporation, Investor–owned, for–profit **Service:** Cancer

Staffed Beds: 72 Admissions: 2099 Census: 32 Outpatient Visits: 35785 Births: 0 Personnel: 1260

IL

Hospital, Medicare Provider Number, Address, Telephone, Approval, Facility, and Physician Codes, Health Care System

★ American Hospital Association (AHA) membership   ○ Healthcare Facilities Accreditation Program   ⇑ Center for Improvement in Healthcare Quality Accreditation
□ The Joint Commission accreditation   ◇ DNV Healthcare Inc. accreditation   △ Commission on Accreditation of Rehabilitation Facilities (CARF) accreditation

INDIANA

ANDERSON—Madison County

⊞ **COMMUNITY HOSPITAL OF ANDERSON & MADISON COUNTY (150113)**, 1515 North Madison Avenue, Zip 46011–3453; tel. 765/298–4242 **A**1 2 10 **F**3 6 10 11 13 15 18 20 22 28 29 30 31 32 34 35 40 44 46 49 50 51 54 55 56 57 58 59 60 61 64 68 70 74 75 76 77 78 79 81 82 85 86 87 89 93 107 108 109 110 111 114 115 119 120 121 122 123 126 129 130 132 135 143 144 146 147 148 **P**6 **S** Community Health Network, Indianapolis, IN
Primary Contact: Beth S. Tharp, R.N., President and Chief Executive Officer
CFO: John B. Harris, Vice President Finance and Chief Financial Officer
CHR: Michael Harpe, Vice President Human Resources
CNO: Carol Whitesel, MSN, Vice President Patient Care Services and Chief Nursing Officer
Web address: www.communityanderson.com
Control: Other not–for–profit (including NFP Corporation) **Service:** General Medical and Surgical

Staffed Beds: 140 **Admissions:** 6210 **Census:** 61 **Outpatient Visits:** 197572 **Births:** 929 **Total Expense ($000):** 137670 **Payroll Expense ($000):** 56416 **Personnel:** 1049

⊞ **ST. VINCENT ANDERSON REGIONAL HOSPITAL (150088)**, 2015 Jackson Street, Zip 46016–4339; tel. 765/649–2511 **A**1 2 10 **F**3 4 5 8 11 13 14 15 18 20 22 28 29 30 31 32 34 35 36 38 39 40 43 44 45 46 49 50 51 54 55 56 57 58 59 60 61 64 65 66 68 70 74 75 76 77 78 79 81 82 84 85 86 87 89 90 92 93 94 96 98 99 100 101 102 103 104 105 106 107 108 110 111 114 115 116 117 118 119 120 121 123 124 129 130 132 134 135 145 146 147 148 **P**6 **S** Ascension Health, Saint Louis, MO
Primary Contact: Mike Schroyer, FACHE, MSN, R.N., President
COO: Nick Theohares, Executive Director, Operations
CFO: Laura L. Adams, Vice President, Finance
CIO: Robert Pope, Information Technology Director and Ministry Liaison
CHR: Ross Brodhead, Executive Director, Human Resources
CNO: Nancy Pitcock, Vice President Nursing and Chief Nursing Officer
Web address: www.stvincent.org/andersonregional
Control: Church–operated, Nongovernment, not–for profit **Service:** General Medical and Surgical

Staffed Beds: 141 **Admissions:** 6584 **Census:** 93 **Outpatient Visits:** 231250 **Births:** 462 **Total Expense ($000):** 180298 **Payroll Expense ($000):** 59662 **Personnel:** 813

ANGOLA—Steuben County

★ **CAMERON MEMORIAL COMMUNITY HOSPITAL (151315)**, 416 East Maumee Street, Zip 46703–2015; tel. 260/665–2141, (Nonreporting) **A**10 18
Primary Contact: Connie McCahill, R.N., President and Chief Executive Officer
CFO: Douglas Bomba, Chief Financial Officer
CMO: Jon Alley, D.O., President Medical Staff
CIO: Kris Keen, Chief Information Officer
CHR: Nancy Covell, Director Human Resources
CNO: Sharon Springer, Chief Nursing Officer
Web address: www.cameronmch.com
Control: Other not–for–profit (including NFP Corporation) **Service:** General Medical and Surgical

Staffed Beds: 25

AUBURN—Dekalb County

★ **DEKALB HEALTH (150045)**, 1316 East Seventh Street, Zip 46706–2515, Mailing Address: P.O. Box 542, Zip 46706–0542; tel. 260/925–4600 **A**10 **F**3 7 11 13 15 28 29 32 34 35 36 40 45 53 56 57 59 62 63 64 70 73 75 76 77 79 81 82 84 85 86 87 89 93 97 107 108 110 111 114 115 119 129 130 132 135 146 147 148 **P**4 6 8
Primary Contact: Craig Polkow, Chief Executive Officer
CMO: Emilio Vazquez, M.D., Chief Medical Officer
CIO: Ed Hobbs, Director Information Services
CNO: Donna S. Wisemore, R.N., Vice President and Chief Nursing Officer
Web address: www.dekalbhealth.com
Control: Other not–for–profit (including NFP Corporation) **Service:** General Medical and Surgical

Staffed Beds: 56 **Admissions:** 2327 **Census:** 18 **Outpatient Visits:** 76969 **Births:** 457 **Total Expense ($000):** 61006 **Payroll Expense ($000):** 26869 **Personnel:** 521

NORTHEASTERN CENTER (154050), 1850 Wesley Road, Zip 46706–3653; tel. 260/927–0726 **A**10 **F**98 103 133
Primary Contact: Jerry Hollister, Chief Executive Officer
Web address: www.necmh.org
Control: Other not–for–profit (including NFP Corporation) **Service:** Psychiatric

Staffed Beds: 16 **Admissions:** 744 **Census:** 10 **Outpatient Visits:** 0 **Births:** 0 **Total Expense ($000):** 3054 **Payroll Expense ($000):** 1375

AVON—Hendricks County

CLARIAN WEST MEDICAL CENTER See Indiana University Health West Hospital

⊞ **INDIANA UNIVERSITY HEALTH WEST HOSPITAL (150158)**, 1111 North Ronald Reagan Parkway, Zip 46123–7085; tel. 317/217–3000 **A**1 2 3 5 10 **F**3 13 15 18 22 26 28 29 30 34 35 40 45 47 48 49 50 51 57 59 64 70 73 74 75 76 77 78 79 81 82 85 86 87 89 93 100 107 110 111 113 114 115 119 120 121 129 130 132 135 146 147 148 **S** Indiana University Health, Indianapolis, IN
Primary Contact: Doug Puckett, President
CMO: Andrew Nigh, M.D., Chief of Staff
CHR: Lana Funkhouser, Vice President Human Resources
CNO: Lisa Sparks, R.N., Chief Nursing Officer and Vice President Patient Care Services
Web address: www.iuhealth.org
Control: Other not–for–profit (including NFP Corporation) **Service:** General Medical and Surgical

Staffed Beds: 127 **Admissions:** 6798 **Census:** 84 **Outpatient Visits:** 236676 **Births:** 1180 **Total Expense ($000):** 128763 **Payroll Expense ($000):** 42558 **Personnel:** 619

BATESVILLE—Ripley County

⊞ **MARGARET MARY HEALTH (151329)**, 321 Mitchell Avenue, Zip 47006–8909, Mailing Address: P.O. Box 226, Zip 47006–0226; tel. 812/934–6624 **A**1 2 10 18 **F**3 13 15 28 30 31 34 35 36 49 44 46 50 54 56 59 62 63 64 65 70 75 76 77 78 79 81 85 86 87 93 107 108 111 114 118 119 121 123 129 130 131 132 135 144 146 148 **P**1
Primary Contact: Timothy L. Putnam, FACHE, President and Chief Executive Officer
CFO: Brian Daeger, Vice President Financial Services
CMO: Charles McGovern, Chief of Staff
CIO: Trisha Prickel, Director Information Systems
CHR: Kimberly Inscho, Vice President Community Relations and Human Resources
CNO: Elizabeth Leising, Chief Nursing Officer and Vice President, Outpatient Services
Web address: www.mmhealth.org
Control: Other not–for–profit (including NFP Corporation) **Service:** General Medical and Surgical

Staffed Beds: 25 **Admissions:** 1668 **Census:** 13 **Outpatient Visits:** 163981 **Births:** 447 **Total Expense ($000):** 81999 **Payroll Expense ($000):** 33486 **Personnel:** 497

BEDFORD—Lawrence County

BEDFORD REGIONAL MEDICAL CENTER See Indiana University Health Bedford Hospital

DUNN MEMORIAL HOSPITAL See St. Vincent Dunn Hospital

⊞ **INDIANA UNIVERSITY HEALTH BEDFORD HOSPITAL (151328)**, 2900 West 16th Street, Zip 47421–3583; tel. 812/275–1200 **A**1 2 10 18 **F**3 7 11 15 18 28 29 30 31 34 35 36 37 38 39 40 41 44 45 46 49 50 53 57 59 64 65 68 71 74 75 77 78 79 81 85 86 87 89 91 92 93 94 97 102 107 108 110 111 115 118 119 129 130 131 132 133 134 135 144 146 **P**6 **S** Indiana University Health, Indianapolis, IN
Primary Contact: Bradford W. Dykes, President and Chief Executive Officer
CFO: Mike Craig, Vice President, Chief Financial Officer
CMO: Joanne F. Smart, M.D., Director Medical Affairs
CHR: Bruce Wade, Director Human Resources
CNO: Brenda Davis, R.N., Vice President Patient Services
Web address: www.iuhealth.org
Control: Other not–for–profit (including NFP Corporation) **Service:** General Medical and Surgical

Staffed Beds: 25 **Admissions:** 1087 **Census:** 12 **Outpatient Visits:** 78249 **Births:** 0 **Total Expense ($000):** 41594 **Payroll Expense ($000):** 14718 **Personnel:** 196

⊞ **ST. VINCENT DUNN HOSPITAL (151335)**, 1600 23rd Street, Zip 47421–4704; tel. 812/275–3331, (Nonreporting) **A**1 10 18 **S** Ascension Health, Saint Louis, MO
Primary Contact: Matt Balla, Chief Executive Officer
CFO: Crystal Plano, Controller
CMO: Deborah W. Craton, M.D., Chief Medical Officer
CIO: Chad Damon, Contractor
CHR: Darci Medlock, Manager Human Resources
CNO: Michelle Dotts–McCool, Chief Nursing Officer
Web address: www.stvincent.org/St-Vincent-Dunn/Default.aspx
Control: Other not–for–profit (including NFP Corporation) **Service:** General Medical and Surgical

Staffed Beds: 25

Many Facility Codes have changed. Please refer to the AHA Guide Code Chart. © 2016 AHA Guide

IN

BLOOMFIELD— County

✠ **MONROE HOSPITAL (150164)**, 5811 East Slick Rock lane, Zip 47424, Mailing Address: 4011 South Monroe Medical Park Boulevard, Bloomington, Zip 47403–8000; tel. 812/825–1111 **A**1 10 **F**3 15 18 20 29 37 40 45 50 59 64 65 68 70 79 80 81 85 97 107 108 109 111 114 115 119 126 127 135 136 137 138 139 140 141 142 144 148 **S** Prime Healthcare Services, Ontario, CA
Primary Contact: Phillip W. Lowe, Chief Executive Officer
CFO: Janice Wampler, Controller and Chief Information Technology Officer
CMO: Armandeep Singh, Chief Medical Officer
CIO: Janice Wampler, Controller and Chief Information Technology Officer
CHR: Pamela S. Hoffman, Director of Human Resources
CNO: Brenda Cook, Chief Nursing Officer
Web address: www.monroehospital.com
Control: Corporation, Investor–owned, for–profit **Service:** General Medical and Surgical

Staffed Beds: 32 **Admissions:** 4071 **Census:** 28 **Outpatient Visits:** 13831 **Births:** 0 **Total Expense ($000):** 28116 **Payroll Expense ($000):** 9873 **Personnel:** 276

BLOOMINGTON—Monroe County

BLOOMINGTON HOSPITAL See Indiana University Health Bloomington Hospital

☐ **BLOOMINGTON MEADOWS HOSPITAL (154041)**, 3600 North Prow Road, Zip 47404–1616; tel. 812/331–8000 **A**1 10 **F**4 98 99 101 102 103 104 105 106 **S** Universal Health Services, Inc., King of Prussia, PA
Primary Contact: Jean Scallon, Chief Executive Officer
CFO: Becky T. Nyberg, Chief Financial Officer
CMO: David Gilliam, M.D., Medical Director
CHR: Amanda Shettlesworth, Director Human Resources
CNO: Penny Caswell, Director of Nursing
Web address: www.bloomingtonmeadows.com
Control: Corporation, Investor–owned, for–profit **Service:** Psychiatric

Staffed Beds: 67 **Admissions:** 1540 **Census:** 54 **Outpatient Visits:** 5938 **Births:** 0 **Total Expense ($000):** 10332 **Payroll Expense ($000):** 6635 **Personnel:** 144

✠ △ **INDIANA UNIVERSITY HEALTH BLOOMINGTON HOSPITAL (150051)**, 601 West Second Street, Zip 47403–2317, Mailing Address: P.O. Box 1149, Zip 47402–1149; tel. 812/336–6821 **A**1 2 7 10 19 **F**3 7 8 11 12 13 15 18 19 20 22 24 26 28 29 30 31 32 34 35 38 40 45 46 47 48 49 50 53 54 55 57 59 61 62 63 64 65 69 70 74 75 76 77 78 79 81 82 84 85 86 87 89 90 92 93 94 97 98 100 101 102 103 104 107 108 111 114 115 119 120 121 124 126 129 130 131 132 135 143 144 146 147 148 **P**6 **S** Indiana University Health, Indianapolis, IN
Primary Contact: Mark E. Moore, President and Chief Executive Officer
COO: Matthew D. Bailey, FACHE, Chief Operating Officer
CFO: Mike Craig, Chief Financial Officer
CMO: Ken Marshall, M.D., Chief Medical Officer
CIO: Mark W. McMath, Chief Information Officer
CHR: Steven D. Deckard, Vice President Human Resources
Web address: www.iuhealth.org
Control: Other not–for–profit (including NFP Corporation) **Service:** General Medical and Surgical

Staffed Beds: 273 **Admissions:** 13024 **Census:** 151 **Outpatient Visits:** 150618 **Births:** 2154 **Total Expense ($000):** 305002 **Payroll Expense ($000):** 106094 **Personnel:** 1658

BLUFFTON—Wells County

✠ **BLUFFTON REGIONAL MEDICAL CENTER (150075)**, 303 South Main Street, Zip 46714–2503; tel. 260/824–3210, (Total facility includes 13 beds in nursing home–type unit) **A**1 10 **F**3 13 15 18 28 29 30 34 35 40 41 45 49 50 57 59 64 70 74 75 79 81 85 86 87 91 93 94 96 97 107 108 110 111 114 119 128 129 130 132 135 146 147 148 **S** Community Health Systems, Inc., Franklin, TN
Primary Contact: Aaron Garofola, Chief Executive Officer
COO: Julie Thompson, Chief Operating Officer and Chief Nursing Officer
CFO: Larry W. DeBolt, Chief Financial Officer
CMO: Harish Ardeshna, Chief Medical Officer
CNO: Julie Thompson, Chief Operating Officer and Chief Nursing Officer
Web address: www.blufftonregional.com
Control: Corporation, Investor–owned, for–profit **Service:** General Medical and Surgical

Staffed Beds: 79 **Admissions:** 1609 **Census:** 24 **Outpatient Visits:** 45594 **Births:** 211 **Total Expense ($000):** 33103 **Payroll Expense ($000):** 11794 **Personnel:** 226

BOONVILLE—Warrick County

✠ **ST. MARY'S WARRICK HOSPITAL (151325)**, 1116 Millis Avenue, Zip 47601–2204; tel. 812/897–4800 **A**1 10 18 **F**3 6 11 15 28 29 30 40 45 50 53 56 57 59 64 67 68 79 81 85 87 89 93 98 103 107 111 114 118 119 128 130 132 133 135 146 **S** Ascension Health, Saint Louis, MO
Primary Contact: Kathy J. Hall, Administrator
CFO: Crystal Heaton, Director of Finance
CNO: Karen Waters, Chief Nursing Officer
Web address: www.stmarys.org/warrick
Control: Other not–for–profit (including NFP Corporation) **Service:** General Medical and Surgical

Staffed Beds: 35 **Admissions:** 721 **Census:** 19 **Outpatient Visits:** 20644 **Births:** 0 **Total Expense ($000):** 14690 **Payroll Expense ($000):** 5007 **Personnel:** 113

BRAZIL—Clay County

✠ **ST. VINCENT CLAY HOSPITAL (151309)**, 1206 East National Avenue, Zip 47834–2797, Mailing Address: P.O. Box 489, Zip 47834–0489; tel. 812/442–2500 **A**1 10 18 **F**3 12 15 18 29 30 34 35 40 45 50 57 59 65 68 75 77 79 81 82 85 86 87 107 108 110 111 115 119 128 130 132 133 135 146 148 **S** Ascension Health, Saint Louis, MO
Primary Contact: Jerry Laue, Administrator
CFO: Wayne Knight, Director Finance
CMO: Craig Johnson, D.O., Medical Director
CHR: Danielle Abrams, Manager Human Resources, Marketing and Executive Assistant
CNO: Sandra Haggart, Chief Nursing Officer
Web address: www.stvincent.org
Control: Church–operated, Nongovernment, not–for profit **Service:** General Medical and Surgical

Staffed Beds: 25 **Admissions:** 575 **Census:** 8 **Outpatient Visits:** 35662 **Births:** 0 **Total Expense ($000):** 16739 **Payroll Expense ($000):** 5408 **Personnel:** 76

BREMEN—Marshall County

★ **COMMUNITY HOSPITAL OF BREMEN (151300)**, 1020 High Road, Zip 46506–1093, Mailing Address: P.O. Box 8, Zip 46506–0008; tel. 574/546–2211 **A**10 18 **F**3 11 13 15 29 34 35 40 45 50 57 59 64 69 75 76 77 79 81 82 85 93 107 110 111 114 119 129 130 132 133 135 146 **P**6 Primary Contact: David Bailey, FACHE, Chief Executive Officer
CFO: Amy Lashbrook, Chief Financial Officer
CMO: Jason Marker, M.D., Chief Medical Officer
CIO: Linda Barrett, Vice President of Information Services
CHR: Patricia Board, Vice President Human Resources
CNO: Sue Bettcher, R.N., Vice President of Nursing Services
Web address: www.bremenhospital.com
Control: Other not–for–profit (including NFP Corporation) **Service:** General Medical and Surgical

Staffed Beds: 24 **Admissions:** 342 **Census:** 3 **Outpatient Visits:** 47254 **Births:** 93 **Total Expense ($000):** 17330 **Payroll Expense ($000):** 6431 **Personnel:** 139

☐ **DOCTORS NEUROMEDICAL HOSPITAL (150180)**, 411 South Whitlock Street, Zip 46506–1626, Mailing Address: P.O. Box 36, Zip 46506–0036; tel. 574/546–3830, (Nonreporting) **A**1 10 **S** NeuroPsychiatric Hospitals, Mishawaka, IN
Primary Contact: Alan Fisher, Chief Executive Officer
COO: John M. Day, Chief Operating Officer
CFO: Bernie Hebert, Jr., Chief Financial Officer
CMO: Steven Posar, M.D., Chief of Medicine
CHR: Emyle Kruyer–Collins, Director Human Resources
Web address: www.physicianshospitalsystem.net
Control: Partnership, Investor–owned, for–profit **Service:** Rehabilitation

Staffed Beds: 20

DOCTORS NEUROPSYCHIATRIC HOSPITAL AND RESEARCH INSTITUTE (154058), 417 South Whitlock Street, Zip 46506–1626; tel. 574/546–0330, (Nonreporting) **A**10 **S** NeuroPsychiatric Hospitals, Mishawaka, IN
Primary Contact: Christy Gilbert, Interim Chief Executive Officer
Control: **Service:** Psychiatric

Staffed Beds: 20

CARMEL—Hamilton County

CLARIAN NORTH MEDICAL CENTER See Indiana University Health North Hospital

IN

○ **FRANCISCAN ST. FRANCIS HEALTH–CARMEL (150182)**, 12188B North Meridian Street, Zip 46032–4840; tel. 317/705–4500, (Nonreporting) **A**10 11 **S** Franciscan Alliance, Mishawaka, IN
Primary Contact: Stephen J. Wheatley, Director of Operations
CFO: Keith A. Lauter, Chief Financial Officer
CMO: Christopher Doehring, M.D., Vice President of Medical Affairs
CIO: Rebecca Merkel, Privacy Officer
CHR: Corey Baute, Vice President of Human Resource
CNO: Susan McRoberts, R.N., Chief Nursing Officer
Web address: www.franciscanalliance.org/hospitals/carmel/Pages/default.aspx
Control: Other not–for–profit (including NFP Corporation) **Service:** General Medical and Surgical

Staffed Beds: 6

☒ **INDIANA UNIVERSITY HEALTH NORTH HOSPITAL (150161)**, 11700 North Meridian Avenue, Zip 46032–4656; tel. 317/688–2000 **A**1 3 5 10 **F**3 13 15 18 19 20 22 25 29 30 31 34 35 36 37 40 45 47 49 55 57 59 60 64 68 70 72 74 75 76 78 79 81 85 87 88 89 91 92 93 107 108 110 111 115 119 124 126 130 132 135 146 147 148 **S** Indiana University Health, Indianapolis, IN
Primary Contact: Jonathan R. Goble, FACHE, President and Chief Executive Officer
COO: Randall C. Yust, Chief Operating Officer and Chief Financial Officer
CFO: Randall C. Yust, Chief Operating Officer and Chief Financial Officer
CMO: Paul Calkins, M.D., Chief Medical Officer
CIO: Steve Bodenham, Senior Manager Clinical Engineering
CHR: Steven Kile, Vice President Human Resources
CNO: Ruth Ann A. Kain, MSN, Interim Chief Nursing Officer and Vice President Patient Care Services
Web address: www.iuhealth.org/north
Control: Other not–for–profit (including NFP Corporation) **Service:** General Medical and Surgical

Staffed Beds: 161 Admissions: 6679 Census: 81 Outpatient Visits: 236558 Births: 2347 Total Expense ($000): 177226 Payroll Expense ($000): 53293 Personnel: 713

☒ **ST. VINCENT CARMEL HOSPITAL (150157)**, 13500 North Meridian Street, Zip 46032–1456; tel. 317/582–7000 **A**1 10 **F**3 12 13 15 29 30 34 35 36 37 40 44 45 49 50 54 57 58 59 61 64 68 69 70 72 75 76 78 79 80 81 85 87 92 96 107 108 110 111 119 126 130 132 135 146 147 148 **S** Ascension Health, Saint Louis, MO
Primary Contact: Michael D. Chittenden, President
COO: Daniel LaReau, Executive Director Operations and Information
CFO: Robert A. Bates, Executive Director Finance and Chief Financial Officer
CMO: Steven L. Priddy, M.D., Vice President Physician Affairs and Chief Medical Officer
CIO: Daniel LaReau, Executive Director Operations and Information
CHR: Charles Jeffras, Executive Director Human Resources
CNO: Gwynn Perlich, Vice President of Patient Services and Chief Nursing Officer
Web address: www.stvincent.org
Control: Church–operated, Nongovernment, not–for profit **Service:** General Medical and Surgical

Staffed Beds: 107 Admissions: 4665 Census: 44 Outpatient Visits: 112655 Births: 1445 Total Expense ($000): 117562 Payroll Expense ($000): 41959

CLARKSVILLE—Clark County

○ **KENTUCKIANA MEDICAL CENTER (150176)**, 4601 Medical Plaza Way, Zip 47129–9204; tel. 812/284–6100, (Nonreporting) **A**10 11
Primary Contact: Paul Newsom, Chief Operating Officer
Web address: www.kentuckianamedcen.com/
Control: Corporation, Investor–owned, for–profit **Service:** General Medical and Surgical

Staffed Beds: 40

CLINTON—Vermillion County

UNION HOSPITAL CLINTON (151326), 801 South Main Street, Zip 47842–2261; tel. 765/832–1234 **A**10 18 **F**3 11 15 18 29 30 34 35 40 45 50 57 59 64 65 68 70 75 81 85 86 87 91 93 97 107 108 110 115 119 130 132 133 146 **P**6
Primary Contact: Terri L. Hill, Vice President and Administrator
CFO: Wayne Hutson, Chief Financial Officer
CIO: Jack Hill, Vice President and Chief Operating Officer
CNO: Rhonda E. Smith, R.N., Chief Nursing Officer
Web address: www.myunionhospital.org/unionhospital/union–hospital–clinton
Control: Other not–for–profit (including NFP Corporation) **Service:** General Medical and Surgical

Staffed Beds: 21 Admissions: 961 Census: 7 Outpatient Visits: 44806 Births: 0 Total Expense ($000): 20131 Payroll Expense ($000): 8170 Personnel: 141

COLUMBIA CITY—Whitley County

☒ **PARKVIEW WHITLEY HOSPITAL (150101)**, 1260 East State Road 205, Zip 46725–9492; tel. 260/248–9000 **A**1 10 **F**3 5 7 8 13 15 28 29 34 35 38 40 45 50 54 57 59 64 69 70 75 76 79 81 82 85 89 91 93 96 102 107 108 110 111 114 119 129 132 135 143 146 148 **S** Parkview Health, Fort Wayne, IN
Primary Contact: Scott F. Gabriel, President
COO: Scott F. Gabriel, President
CFO: Lisa Peppler, Financial Manager
CMO: Jeffrey Brookes, M.D., Medical Director
CHR: Dianne P. Potter, Manager Human Resources
CNO: Bridget Dolohanty–Johnson, MSN, Vice President Patient Care Services
Web address: www.parkview.com
Control: Other not–for–profit (including NFP Corporation) **Service:** General Medical and Surgical

Staffed Beds: 30 Admissions: 1568 Census: 11 Outpatient Visits: 45793 Births: 461 Total Expense ($000): 44361 Payroll Expense ($000): 13056 Personnel: 222

COLUMBUS—Bartholomew County

★ ○ **COLUMBUS REGIONAL HOSPITAL (150112)**, 2400 East 17th Street, Zip 47201–5360; tel. 812/379–4441 **A**2 10 11 19 **F**3 7 11 12 13 15 18 20 22 24 26 28 29 30 31 34 35 38 39 40 45 47 49 50 51 53 58 59 68 70 73 74 75 76 77 78 79 81 85 86 87 89 90 93 98 100 101 102 103 107 108 110 111 114 115 117 118 119 120 121 123 126 129 130 131 132 135 146 147 148 **P**6 8
Primary Contact: Jim Bickel, Chief Executive Officer
CFO: Marlene Weatherwax, Vice President and Chief Financial Officer
CMO: Thomas Sonderman, M.D., Vice President and Chief Medical Officer
CIO: Steve Baker, Vice President and Chief Technology and Information Officer
CHR: John R. Loya, Vice President Human Resources and Organizational Development
CNO: Holly Cheek, Vice President and Chief Nursing Officer
Web address: www.crh.org
Control: County–Government, nonfederal **Service:** General Medical and Surgical

Staffed Beds: 198 Admissions: 9020 Census: 95 Outpatient Visits: 239176 Births: 1217 Total Expense ($000): 219235 Payroll Expense ($000): 70323 Personnel: 1479

CONNERSVILLE—Fayette County

○ **FAYETTE REGIONAL HEALTH SYSTEM (150064)**, 1941 Virginia Avenue, Zip 47331–2833; tel. 765/825–5131, (Nonreporting) **A**10 11
Primary Contact: Randall White, Chief Executive Officer
CFO: Debra Michalek, Chief Financial Officer
CMO: Mike Rowe, M.D., Chief of Staff
CIO: Andy Merida, Director Management Information Systems
CHR: Rhonda McPherson, Vice President Human Resources
CNO: Beth A. Wampler, R.N., Chief Nursing Officer
Web address: www.fayetteregional.org
Control: Other not–for–profit (including NFP Corporation) **Service:** General Medical and Surgical

Staffed Beds: 73

CORYDON—Harrison County

★ **HARRISON COUNTY HOSPITAL (151331)**, 1141 Hospital Drive North W., Zip 47112–1774; tel. 812/738–4251, (Nonreporting) **A**10 18
Primary Contact: Steven L. Taylor, Chief Executive Officer
CFO: Jeff Davis, Chief Financial Officer
CIO: Chuck Wiley, Manager Information Systems
CHR: Loren Haverstock, Manager Human Resources
CNO: Ruth Donahue, R.N., Chief Nursing Officer
Web address: www.hchin.org
Control: County–Government, nonfederal **Service:** General Medical and Surgical

Staffed Beds: 25

CRAWFORDSVILLE—Montgomery County

○ **FRANCISCAN ST. ELIZABETH HEALTH – CRAWFORDSVILLE (150022)**, 1710 Lafayette Road, Zip 47933–1099; tel. 765/362–2800 **A**10 11 **F**3 8 15 28 29 30 31 34 39 40 45 49 50 51 56 64 70 74 78 79 81 82 85 90 93 98 103 107 108 110 111 115 118 119 120 121 123 129 130 132 146 148 **S** Franciscan Alliance, Mishawaka, IN
Primary Contact: Terrance E. Wilson, President and CEO
COO: Terrence Klein, Vice President and Chief Operating Officer
CFO: Keith A. Lauter, Vice President Finance
Web address: www.stclaremedical.org
Control: Church–operated, Nongovernment, not–for profit **Service:** General Medical and Surgical

Staffed Beds: 42 Admissions: 1271 Census: 15 Births: 0 Total Expense ($000): 41159 Payroll Expense ($000): 9748 Personnel: 176

ST. CLARE MEDICAL CENTER See Franciscan St. Elizabeth Health – Crawfordsville

Many Facility Codes have changed. Please refer to the AHA Guide Code Chart. © 2016 AHA Guide

CROWN POINT—Lake County

○ **FRANCISCAN ST. ANTHONY HEALTH – CROWN POINT (150126)**, 1201 South Main Street, Zip 46307–8483; tel. 219/738–2100, (Nonreporting) **A**2 10 11 **S** Franciscan Alliance, Mishawaka, IN
Primary Contact: Barbara M. Anderson, President and Chief Executive Officer
CFO: Marc Golan, Chief Financial Officer
CMO: Daniel McCormick, M.D., Vice President Medical Staff Affairs
CIO: Tim Loosemore, Director
CNO: Carol E. Schuster, R.N., Chief Nursing Officer and Vice President Patient Care Services
Web address: www.franciscanalliance.org
Control: Other not–for–profit (including NFP Corporation) **Service:** General Medical and Surgical

Staffed Beds: 254

○ **PINNACLE HOSPITAL (150166)**, 9301 Connecticut Drive, Zip 46307–7486; tel. 219/756–2100, (Nonreporting) **A**10 11
Primary Contact: Haroon Naz, Chief Executive Officer
Web address: www.pinnaclehealthcare.net
Control: Partnership, Investor–owned, for–profit **Service:** General Medical and Surgical

Staffed Beds: 18

ST. ANTHONY MEDICAL CENTER See Franciscan St. Anthony Health – Crown Point

✉ **VIBRA HOSPITAL OF NORTHWESTERN INDIANA (152028)**, 9509 Georgia Street, Zip 46307–6518; tel. 219/472–2200 **A**1 10 **F**1 3 29 75 77 85 86 87 130 148 **S** Vibra Healthcare, Mechanicsburg, PA
Primary Contact: Rodney Midkiff, Chief Executive Officer
CFO: Douglas Morris, Chief Financial Officer
CMO: Raja Devanathan, M.D., Chief Medical Officer
CNO: Robert Beard, Chief Clinical Officer
Web address: www.vhnwindiana.com/
Control: Corporation, Investor–owned, for–profit **Service:** Long–Term Acute Care hospital

Staffed Beds: 40 Admissions: 513 Census: 34 Outpatient Visits: 0 Births: 0 Total Expense ($000): 17143 Payroll Expense ($000): 7167 Personnel: 110

DANVILLE—Hendricks County

★ ○ **HENDRICKS REGIONAL HEALTH (150005)**, 1000 East Main Street, Zip 46122–1948, Mailing Address: P.O. Box 409, Zip 46122–0409; tel. 317/745–4451 **A**2 5 10 11 **F**3 8 11 13 15 20 28 29 30 31 32 34 35 40 54 55 56 57 59 60 61 64 66 69 70 71 73 74 75 76 77 78 79 81 85 86 87 89 93 96 97 107 108 109 110 111 115 117 118 119 120 121 123 129 130 131 132 135 144 146 147 148
Primary Contact: Kevin Speer, Chief Executive Officer
CFO: John Komenda, Chief Financial Officer
CMO: John Sparzo, M.D., Vice President Medical Affairs
CIO: Lowell Nicodemus, Director Information Systems
CHR: Gary Lenard, Director Human Resources
Web address: www.hendrickshospital.org
Control: County–Government, nonfederal **Service:** General Medical and Surgical

Staffed Beds: 127 Admissions: 5358 Census: 51 Outpatient Visits: 340962 Births: 1294 Total Expense ($000): 233485 Payroll Expense ($000): 93570 Personnel: 1287

DECATUR—Adams County

★ **ADAMS MEMORIAL HOSPITAL (151330)**, 1100 Mercer Avenue, Zip 46733–2303, Mailing Address: P.O. Box 151, Zip 46733–0151; tel. 260/724–2145, (Total facility includes 195 beds in nursing home–type unit) **A**10 18 **F**3 5 7 10 13 15 29 34 35 38 40 45 47 50 53 57 59 64 65 66 67 68 70 74 75 76 77 79 81 82 85 86 87 92 93 96 97 98 100 101 102 103 104 107 108 110 111 115 119 125 128 129 130 131 132 133 135 143 144 145 146 147 148 **P**6
Primary Contact: JoEllen Eidam, FACHE, Chief Executive Officer
CFO: Dane Wheeler, Chief Financial Officer
CMO: Scott Smith, M.D., Chief Medical Officer
CIO: Nick Nelson, Director Support Services
CHR: Alison Kukelhan, Manager Human Resources
CNO: Theresa Bradtmiller, Chief Nursing Officer
Web address: www.adamshospital.com
Control: County–Government, nonfederal **Service:** General Medical and Surgical

Staffed Beds: 233 Admissions: 1907 Census: 192 Outpatient Visits: 113859 Births: 215 Total Expense ($000): 69249 Payroll Expense ($000): 31627 Personnel: 561

DYER—Lake County

FRANCISCAN ST. MARGARET HEALTH – DYER See Franciscan St. Margaret Health – Hammond, Hammond

SAINT MARGARET MERCY HEALTHCARE CENTERS–SOUTH CAMPUS See Franciscan St. Margaret Health – Dyer

EAST CHICAGO—Lake County

✉ **REGENCY HOSPITAL OF NORTHWEST INDIANA (152024)**, 4321 Fir Street, 4th Floor, Zip 46312–3049; tel. 219/392–7799, (Includes REGENCY HOSPITAL OF PORTER COUNTY, 3630 Willow Creek Road, Portage, Zip 46368; tel. 219/364–3800), (Nonreporting) **A**1 10 **S** Select Medical Corporation, Mechanicsburg, PA
Primary Contact: Cheryl G. Gentry, Chief Executive Officer
Web address: www.regencyhospital.com/company/locations/indiana–northwest–indiana.aspx
Control: Corporation, Investor–owned, for–profit **Service:** Long–Term Acute Care hospital

Staffed Beds: 61

☐ △ **ST. CATHERINE HOSPITAL (150008)**, 4321 Fir Street, Zip 46312–3097; tel. 219/392–1700 **A**1 7 10 **F**1 3 5 11 13 15 17 18 20 22 24 26 28 29 30 31 34 35 40 46 49 54 57 58 59 60 61 62 64 68 74 75 76 77 78 79 80 81 82 85 86 87 89 92 98 99 100 101 102 103 104 107 108 110 111 112 115 119 129 130 132 135 144 146 147 148 **P**8 **S** Community Healthcare System, Hammond, IN
Primary Contact: JoAnn Birdzell, Chief Executive Officer and Administrator
COO: Craig Bolda, Chief Operating Officer
CMO: John Griep, M.D., Chief Medical Director
CIO: Gary Weiner, Chief Information Officer
CNO: Paula C. Swenson, R.N., Vice President and Chief Nursing Officer
Web address: www.stcatherinehospital.org
Control: Other not–for–profit (including NFP Corporation) **Service:** General Medical and Surgical

Staffed Beds: 205 Admissions: 7558 Census: 107 Outpatient Visits: 146479 Births: 595 Total Expense ($000): 168063 Payroll Expense ($000): 53237 Personnel: 838

ELKHART—Elkhart County

★ ○ △ **ELKHART GENERAL HOSPITAL (150018)**, 600 East Boulevard, Zip 46514–2499, Mailing Address: P.O. Box 1329, Zip 46515–1329; tel. 574/294–2621 **A**2 7 10 11 **F**3 12 13 15 17 18 20 22 24 26 28 29 30 31 34 35 40 45 46 48 49 50 57 59 60 64 68 69 70 72 74 75 76 77 78 79 81 82 84 85 86 87 89 90 91 92 93 98 99 100 102 104 107 108 110 111 114 115 118 119 120 121 123 129 130 132 134 135 146 147 148 **P**8 **S** Beacon Health System, South Bend, IN
Primary Contact: Carl W. Risk, II, President
CFO: Jeff Costello, Chief Financial Officer
CMO: William Buckley, M.D., Chief of Staff
CIO: Steve Huffman, Chief Information Officer
CHR: Steven M. Eller, Vice President Human Resources
CNO: Karra Heggen, R.N., Vice President Nursing
Web address: www.egh.org
Control: Other not–for–profit (including NFP Corporation) **Service:** General Medical and Surgical

Staffed Beds: 265 Admissions: 11566 Census: 127 Outpatient Visits: 302905 Births: 1571 Total Expense ($000): 246679 Payroll Expense ($000): 79854 Personnel: 1475

ELWOOD—Madison County

✉ **ST. VINCENT MERCY HOSPITAL (151308)**, 1331 South A Street, Zip 46036–1942; tel. 765/552–4600 **A**1 2 10 18 **F**3 11 15 28 29 30 31 34 35 40 44 45 50 53 57 59 64 68 74 75 78 79 81 82 85 86 87 89 93 107 108 110 111 114 119 129 130 132 133 135 146 148 **S** Ascension Health, Saint Louis, MO
Primary Contact: Francis G. Albarano, Administrator
CFO: John Arthur, Chief Financial Officer
CMO: Gary Brazel, M.D., Chief Medical Officer
CHR: Ross Brodhead, Manager Human Resources
CNO: Ann C. Yates, R.N., Director Patient Care and Clinical Services
Web address: www.stvincent.org
Control: Church–operated, Nongovernment, not–for profit **Service:** General Medical and Surgical

Staffed Beds: 15 Admissions: 508 Census: 5 Outpatient Visits: 32481 Births: 0 Total Expense ($000): 21897 Payroll Expense ($000): 7614 Personnel: 141

IN

Hospital, Medicare Provider Number, Address, Telephone, Approval, Facility, and Physician Codes, Health Care System

★ American Hospital Association (AHA) membership
☐ The Joint Commission accreditation
○ Healthcare Facilities Accreditation Program
◇ DNV Healthcare Inc. accreditation
⇪ Center for Improvement in Healthcare Quality Accreditation
△ Commission on Accreditation of Rehabilitation Facilities (CARF) accreditation

---

EVANSVILLE—Vanderburgh County

★ ○ **DEACONESS HOSPITAL (150082)**, 600 Mary Street, Zip 47710–1658; tel. 812/450–5000, (Includes DEACONESS CROSS POINTE CENTER, 7200 East Indiana Street, Zip 47715; tel. 812/476–7200; Cheryl Rietman, Chief Administrative Officer) **A**2 3 10 11 **F**3 5 9 11 12 15 17 18 19 20 22 24 26 29 30 31 32 34 35 36 38 39 40 43 44 45 46 47 48 49 50 51 53 54 56 57 58 59 60 61 64 65 66 68 70 71 74 75 77 78 79 81 82 84 85 86 87 88 89 92 93 94 96 97 98 99 100 101 102 104 105 107 108 110 111 114 115 116 117 118 119 120 121 123 124 126 129 130 132 134 135 143 144 145 146 148 **P**6 8 **S** Deaconess Health System, Evansville, IN
Primary Contact: Shawn W. McCoy, Chief Administrative Officer
CFO: Cheryl A. Wathen, Interim Chief Financial Officer
CMO: James Porter, M.D., Vice President Medical Affairs
CHR: Larry Pile, Director Human Resources
Web address: www.deaconess.com
Control: Other not–for–profit (including NFP Corporation) **Service:** General Medical and Surgical

Staffed Beds: 506 **Admissions:** 27656 **Census:** 368 **Outpatient Visits:** 640294 **Births:** 0 **Total Expense ($000):** 596842 **Payroll Expense ($000):** 222922 **Personnel:** 3441

EVANSVILLE PSYCHIATRIC CHILDREN CENTER (15J200), 3300 East Morgan Avenue, Zip 47715–2232; tel. 812/477–6436 **A**10 **F**98 99
Primary Contact: Lottie Cook, Superintendent
COO: Melinda Kendle, Manager Business Office
CMO: Shannon Jones, M.D., Medical Director and Attending Psychiatrist
CIO: David Wirtz, Supervisor Information Technology
CHR: Jennifer Sontz, Director Human Resources
CNO: Elizabeth Angermeier, Director of Nursing
Web address: www.ih.gov
Control: State–Government, nonfederal **Service:** Children's hospital psychiatric

Staffed Beds: 28 **Admissions:** 25 **Census:** 12 **Outpatient Visits:** 0 **Births:** 0 **Total Expense ($000):** 3874 **Payroll Expense ($000):** 2003 **Personnel:** 57

□ **EVANSVILLE STATE HOSPITAL (154056)**, 3400 Lincoln Avenue, Zip 47714–0146; tel. 812/469–6800 **A**1 10 **F**30 98 130 132 135 146
Primary Contact: Cathe Fulcher, Superintendent
CFO: Melinda Kendle, Director Fiscal Management
CMO: Melba Briones, M.D., Medical Director
CIO: David Wirtz, Senior LAN Administrator
CHR: Jennifer Sontz, Director Human Resources
Control: State–Government, nonfederal **Service:** Psychiatric

Staffed Beds: 168 **Admissions:** 66 **Census:** 151 **Outpatient Visits:** 0 **Births:** 0 **Total Expense ($000):** 32233 **Payroll Expense ($000):** 12685 **Personnel:** 315

⊞ **HEALTHSOUTH DEACONESS REHABILITATION HOSPITAL (153025)**, 4100 Covert Avenue, Zip 47714–5567, Mailing Address: P.O. Box 5349, Zip 47716–5349; tel. 812/476–9983 **A**1 10 **F**28 29 57 64 68 75 87 90 91 93 94 95 96 130 132 143 148 **S** HEALTHSOUTH Corporation, Birmingham, AL
Primary Contact: Blake Bunner, Chief Executive Officer
CFO: Rhonda Ramsey, Controller
CMO: Ashok Dhingra, M.D., Executive Medical Director
CHR: Darlene Moog, Director Human Resources
CNO: Trish Draeger, Chief Nursing Officer
Web address: www.healthsouthdeaconess.com
Control: Corporation, Investor–owned, for–profit **Service:** Rehabilitation

Staffed Beds: 103 **Admissions:** 1843 **Census:** 68 **Outpatient Visits:** 6562 **Births:** 0 **Total Expense ($000):** 22969 **Payroll Expense ($000):** 11738 **Personnel:** 275

⊞ **SELECT SPECIALTY HOSPITAL–EVANSVILLE (152014)**, 400 S.E. 4th Street, Zip 47713–1206; tel. 812/421–2500, (Nonreporting) **A**1 10 **S** Select Medical Corporation, Mechanicsburg, PA
Primary Contact: Glen Winekauf, Chief Executive Officer
Web address: www.selectspecialtyhospitals.com/company/locations/evansville.aspx
Control: Corporation, Investor–owned, for–profit **Service:** Long–Term Acute Care hospital

Staffed Beds: 60

⊞ △ **ST. MARY'S MEDICAL CENTER OF EVANSVILLE (150100)**, 3700 Washington Avenue, Zip 47714–0541; tel. 812/485–4000 **A**1 2 7 10 **F**3 7 8 11 12 13 15 17 18 20 22 24 26 28 29 30 31 32 34 35 36 39 40 42 43 45 46 47 48 49 50 51 53 54 55 56 57 58 59 60 61 64 65 68 70 71 72 73 74 75 76 77 78 79 80 81 82 83 84 85 86 87 88 89 90 92 93 96 98 100 101 102 107 108 110 111 114 115 116 117 118 119 126 129 130 131 132 134 135 143 144 146 147 148 **P**6 **S** Ascension Health, Saint Louis, MO
Primary Contact: Keith Jewell, President
CFO: John Zabrowski, Chief Financial Officer
CMO: Vernon Maas, M.D., Vice President, Medical Affairs
CIO: Jose Diaz, Director Information Systems
CHR: Marty Mattingly, Chief Human Resources Officer
CNO: Darcy Ellison, R.N., Senior Vice President, Chief Nursing Officer and Inpatient Flow
Web address: www.stmarys.org
Control: Church–operated, Nongovernment, not–for profit **Service:** General Medical and Surgical

Staffed Beds: 436 **Admissions:** 17379 **Census:** 229 **Outpatient Visits:** 382931 **Births:** 1507 **Total Expense ($000):** 455144 **Payroll Expense ($000):** 133326 **Personnel:** 2431

FISHERS—Hamilton County

⊞ **ST. VINCENT FISHERS HOSPITAL (150181)**, 13861 Olio Road, Zip 46037–3487; tel. 317/415–9000 **A**1 10 **F**3 13 15 29 30 34 35 39 40 45 46 49 50 53 57 59 60 64 75 76 77 79 81 82 87 91 93 97 107 110 111 114 119 129 130 131 132 146 147 148 **S** Ascension Health, Saint Louis, MO
Primary Contact: Gary Fammartino, Administrator
CMO: Craig Wilson, Chief Medical Officer
Web address: www.stvincent.org
Control: Church–operated, Nongovernment, not–for profit **Service:** General Medical and Surgical

Staffed Beds: 46 **Admissions:** 1025 **Census:** 7 **Outpatient Visits:** 60517 **Births:** 311 **Total Expense ($000):** 43058 **Payroll Expense ($000):** 15807 **Personnel:** 165

FORT WAYNE—Allen County

⊞ **DUPONT HOSPITAL (150150)**, 2520 East Dupont Road, Zip 46825–1675; tel. 260/416–3000 **A**1 10 **F**3 8 13 15 18 29 30 34 35 39 40 45 50 56 57 58 59 60 64 65 68 70 72 73 74 75 76 77 78 79 81 82 83 84 85 86 87 89 107 110 111 114 115 118 119 126 129 130 131 132 135 141 146 147 148 **S** Community Health Systems, Inc., Franklin, TN
Primary Contact: Chad Towner, Chief Executive Officer
COO: Corey Lovelace, Chief Operating Officer
CFO: Brian Schneider, Chief Financial Officer
CIO: Janis Gray, Interim Chief Information Officer
Web address: www.thedupontdifference.com
Control: Partnership, Investor–owned, for–profit **Service:** General Medical and Surgical

Staffed Beds: 131 **Admissions:** 5022 **Census:** 52 **Outpatient Visits:** 99560 **Births:** 2429 **Total Expense ($000):** 89635 **Payroll Expense ($000):** 30899 **Personnel:** 507

⊞ **LUTHERAN HOSPITAL OF INDIANA (150017)**, 7950 West Jefferson Boulevard, Zip 46804–4140; tel. 260/435–7001, (Nonreporting) **A**1 2 3 5 10 **S** Community Health Systems, Inc., Franklin, TN
Primary Contact: Brian Bauer, Chief Executive Officer
CFO: Cully Chapman, Chief Financial Officer
CMO: Geoffrey Randolph, M.D., Chief Medical Officer
CIO: Keith A. Neuman, Chief Information Officer
CHR: Maria Kurtz, Director Human Resources
CNO: Angela Logan, Chief Nursing Officer
Web address: www.lutheranhospital.com
Control: Corporation, Investor–owned, for–profit **Service:** General Medical and Surgical

Staffed Beds: 379

⊞ **ORTHOPAEDIC HOSPITAL OF LUTHERAN HEALTH NETWORK (150168)**, 7952 West Jefferson Boulevard, Zip 46804–4140; tel. 260/435–2999 **A**1 10 **F**29 34 35 37 64 77 79 80 81 82 90 93 94 96 111 131 **P**8 **S** Community Health Systems, Inc., Franklin, TN
Primary Contact: Lorie Ailor, Chief Executive Officer
CFO: Amy Hochstetler, Chief Financial Officer
CMO: Kevin Rahn, President Medical Staff
CIO: Keith A. Neuman, Chief Information Officer
CHR: Maria Kurtz, Director Human Resources
CNO: Marci Hamilton, Chief Nursing Officer
Web address: www.theorthohospital.com
Control: Corporation, Investor–owned, for–profit **Service:** Orthopedic

Staffed Beds: 44 **Admissions:** 2594 **Census:** 16 **Outpatient Visits:** 50329 **Births:** 0 **Total Expense ($000):** 50313 **Payroll Expense ($000):** 12355 **Personnel:** 217

Many Facility Codes have changed. Please refer to the AHA Guide Code Chart. © 2016 AHA Guide

IN

⊞ **PARKVIEW ORTHO HOSPITAL (150167)**, 11130 Parkview Circle Drive, Zip 46845–1735; tel. 260/672–5000 **A**1 10 **F**3 8 29 30 34 42 45 50 58 65 68 79 81 82 84 85 86 87 90 91 93 94 96 107 111 119 131 135 141 **S** Parkview Health, Fort Wayne, IN
Primary Contact: Julie Fleck, Chief Operating Officer
Web address: www.parkview.com
Control: Corporation, Investor–owned, for–profit **Service:** Orthopedic

Staffed Beds: 37 **Admissions:** 2446 **Census:** 15 **Outpatient Visits:** 7573 **Births:** 0 **Total Expense ($000):** 60151 **Payroll Expense ($000):** 11662 **Personnel:** 306

⊞ **PARKVIEW REGIONAL MEDICAL CENTER (150021)**, 11109 Parkview Plaza Drive, Zip 46845–1701; tel. 260/266–1000, (Includes PARKVIEW HOSPITAL RANDALLIA, 2200 Randallia Drive, Zip 46805–4699; tel. 260/373–4000; Marlon Wardlow, Chief Operating Officer), (Total facility includes 31 beds in nursing home–type unit) **A**1 2 10 **F**3 5 7 11 13 14 15 17 18 20 22 24 26 28 29 30 31 32 34 35 39 40 41 43 44 45 46 47 48 49 50 51 53 54 55 56 57 58 59 60 61 62 63 64 65 67 68 69 70 72 74 75 76 78 79 81 82 84 85 86 87 88 89 90 91 92 93 96 98 99 100 101 102 103 104 105 107 108 109 111 114 115 118 119 120 121 123 124 126 128 129 130 131 132 135 141 146 147 148 **S** Parkview Health, Fort Wayne, IN
Primary Contact: Ben Miles, President
CNO: Judy Boerger, MSN, Chief Nursing Executive
Web address: www.parkview.com
Control: Other not–for–profit (including NFP Corporation) **Service:** General Medical and Surgical

Staffed Beds: 686 **Admissions:** 35113 **Census:** 495 **Outpatient Visits:** 448660 **Births:** 3075 **Total Expense ($000):** 725307 **Payroll Expense ($000):** 209584 **Personnel:** 3662

⊞ △ **REHABILITATION HOSPITAL OF FORT WAYNE (153030)**, 7970 West Jefferson Boulevard, Zip 46804–4140; tel. 260/435–6100 **A**1 7 10 **F**29 30 60 68 69 90 94 96 130 132 143 146 148 **S** Community Health Systems, Inc., Franklin, TN
Primary Contact: Shelley Boxell, R.N., Chief Nursing Officer and Interim Chief Operating Officer
COO: Shelley Boxell, R.N., Interim Chief Operating Officer
CFO: Edward Romero, Chief Financial Officer
CMO: Preeti Dembla, Chief Medical Officer and Medical Director
CIO: Janis Gray, Chief Information Officer
CHR: Deborah Giardina, Director Human Resources and Medical Staff Services
CNO: Shelley Boxell, R.N., Chief Nursing Officer
Web address: www.rehabhospital.com
Control: Corporation, Investor–owned, for–profit **Service:** Rehabilitation

Staffed Beds: 36 **Admissions:** 511 **Census:** 16 **Outpatient Visits:** 51 **Births:** 0 **Total Expense ($000):** 9130 **Payroll Expense ($000):** 4917 **Personnel:** 82

⊞ **SELECT SPECIALTY HOSPITAL–FORT WAYNE (152016)**, 700 Broadway, 7th Floor, Zip 46802–1402; tel. 260/425–3810, (Nonreporting) **A**1 10 **S** Select Medical Corporation, Mechanicsburg, PA
Primary Contact: Bill Underwood, Chief Executive Officer
CMO: Yogesh Amin, M.D., Medical Director
CNO: Marielle Lael, R.N., Chief Nursing Officer
Web address: www.fortwayne.selectspecialtyhospitals.com
Control: Corporation, Investor–owned, for–profit **Service:** Long–Term Acute Care hospital

Staffed Beds: 32

⊞ **ST. JOSEPH HOSPITAL (150047)**, 700 Broadway, Zip 46802–1493; tel. 260/425–3000, (Total facility includes 20 beds in nursing home–type unit) **A**1 3 5 10 13 **F**3 4 5 13 15 16 17 18 20 22 24 34 35 38 40 45 46 50 51 53 54 55 56 57 58 59 64 65 68 69 70 72 74 77 79 80 81 85 87 92 93 96 98 100 101 102 103 104 105 107 108 110 111 114 115 118 119 128 130 132 142 146 147 148 **P**6 **S** Community Health Systems, Inc., Franklin, TN
Primary Contact: Kenneth Jones, Chief Executive Officer
COO: Jeff Vice, Chief Operating Officer
CFO: Pamela Hess, Chief Financial Officer
CHR: Steve Heggen, Administrative Director Human Resources
Web address: www.stjoehospital.com
Control: Corporation, Investor–owned, for–profit **Service:** General Medical and Surgical

Staffed Beds: 182 **Admissions:** 5639 **Census:** 93 **Outpatient Visits:** 104813 **Births:** 401

⊞ **VETERANS AFFAIRS NORTHERN INDIANA HEALTH CARE SYSTEM**, 2121 Lake Avenue, Zip 46805–5100; tel. 260/426–5431, (Includes VETERANS AFFAIRS NORTHERN INDIANA HEALTH CARE SYSTEM–MARION CAMPUS, 1700 East 38th Street, Marion, Zip 46953–4589; tel. 765/674–3321), (Total facility includes 105 beds in nursing home–type unit) **A**1 **F**1 2 3 4 5 8 10 12 18 28 29 30 31 34 35 36 38 39 40 45 46 50 53 54 56 57 59 61 62 63 64 65 67 70 71 74 75 77 78 79 81 82 83 84 85 86 87 91 94 97 98 100 101 102 103 104 105 106 107 111 119 127 128 130 132 135 137 143 144 146 147 148 **S** Department of Veterans Affairs, Washington, DC
Primary Contact: Jay Miller, Acting Director
COO: Helen Rhodes, R.N., Associate Director Operations
CFO: Jay H. Vandermark, Chief Financial Officer
CMO: Ajay Dhawan, M.D., Chief of Staff
CIO: David Troyer, Chief Information Officer
CHR: Brian Flynn, Chief Human Resources Officer
Web address: www.northernindiana.va.gov/
Control: Veterans Affairs, Government, federal **Service:** General Medical and Surgical

Staffed Beds: 217 **Admissions:** 2441 **Census:** 191 **Births:** 0

⊞ **VIBRA HOSPITAL OF FORT WAYNE (152027)**, 2200 Randallia Drive, Zip 46805–4638; tel. 260/399–2900 **A**1 3 10 **F**1 3 85 148 **S** Vibra Healthcare, Mechanicsburg, PA
Primary Contact: Ryan Cassedy, Chief Executive Officer
Web address: www.vhfortwayne.com
Control: Corporation, Investor–owned, for–profit **Service:** Long–Term Acute Care hospital

Staffed Beds: 24 **Admissions:** 259 **Census:** 19 **Outpatient Visits:** 0 **Births:** 0 **Total Expense ($000):** 11472 **Payroll Expense ($000):** 4350 **Personnel:** 61

FRANKFORT—Clinton County

⊞ **ST. VINCENT FRANKFORT HOSPITAL (151316)**, 1300 South Jackson Street, Zip 46041–3313; tel. 765/656–3000 **A**1 10 18 **F**3 11 13 15 28 29 30 34 35 40 45 50 57 59 64 65 68 75 76 77 79 81 82 85 86 89 90 93 97 107 111 114 119 130 132 133 135 144 146 **S** Ascension Health, Saint Louis, MO
Primary Contact: Kristi Bledsoe, R.N., Administrator
CFO: Wayne Knight, Chief Financial Officer
CMO: Stephen Tharp, M.D., Medical Director
CHR: Krista Wright, Director Human Resources
Web address: www.stvincent.org
Control: Church–operated, Nongovernment, not–for profit **Service:** General Medical and Surgical

Staffed Beds: 25 **Admissions:** 886 **Census:** 9 **Outpatient Visits:** 30506 **Births:** 223 **Total Expense ($000):** 21201 **Payroll Expense ($000):** 8015 **Personnel:** 69

FRANKLIN—Johnson County

★ ○ **JOHNSON MEMORIAL HOSPITAL (150001)**, 1125 West Jefferson Street, Zip 46131–2140, Mailing Address: P.O. Box 549, Zip 46131–0549; tel. 317/736–3300 **A**5 10 11 **F**12 13 15 18 20 22 28 29 30 31 34 35 36 40 44 45 49 50 54 57 59 62 64 68 70 74 75 76 77 78 79 81 82 85 87 90 93 97 107 108 110 111 113 114 118 119 129 130 131 132 134 135 144 146 147 148 **P**8
Primary Contact: Larry Heydon, President and Chief Executive Officer
COO: Steve Wohlford, Chief Operating Officer
CFO: Tim Balasia, Chief Financial Officer
CMO: David Dunkle, Vice President Medical Affairs
CIO: Scott Krodel, Vice President Information Systems
CHR: Judy Ware, Director Human Resources
CNO: Anita M. Keller, R.N., Chief Nursing Officer
Web address: www.johnsonmemorial.org
Control: County–Government, nonfederal **Service:** General Medical and Surgical

Staffed Beds: 101 **Admissions:** 1887 **Census:** 19 **Outpatient Visits:** 130144 **Births:** 347 **Total Expense ($000):** 68469 **Payroll Expense ($000):** 33574 **Personnel:** 649

IN

Hospital, Medicare Provider Number, Address, Telephone, Approval, Facility, and Physician Codes, Health Care System

★ American Hospital Association (AHA) membership   ○ Healthcare Facilities Accreditation Program   ⇑ Center for Improvement in Healthcare Quality Accreditation
□ The Joint Commission accreditation   ◇ DNV Healthcare Inc. accreditation   △ Commission on Accreditation of Rehabilitation Facilities (CARF) accreditation

GARY—Lake County

★ ○ △ **METHODIST HOSPITALS (150002)**, 600 Grant Street, Zip 46402–6099; tel. 219/886–4000, (Includes SOUTHLAKE CAMPUS, 8701 Broadway, Merrillville, Zip 46410; tel. 219/738–5500) **A**2 3 5 7 10 11 **F**3 8 11 12 13 15 20 22 24 26 28 29 30 31 32 34 35 37 40 43 45 47 48 49 50 51 54 55 57 59 62 64 67 70 72 73 74 75 76 77 78 79 81 82 85 86 87 89 90 93 98 99 100 101 102 103 107 108 110 111 114 115 118 119 120 121 123 124 126 130 132 133 146 147 148 **P**6
Primary Contact: Raymond Grady, FACHE, President and Chief Executive Officer
CFO: Matthew Doyle, Chief Financial Officer
CIO: Timothy Diamond, Chief Information Officer
CHR: Alex Horvath, Vice President Human Resources
CNO: Shelly Major, Chief Nursing Officer
Web address: www.methodisthospitals.org
Control: Other not–for–profit (including NFP Corporation) **Service:** General Medical and Surgical

Staffed Beds: 504 **Admissions:** 17406 **Census:** 285 **Outpatient Visits:** 287900 **Births:** 1362 **Total Expense ($000):** 320901 **Payroll Expense ($000):** 141901 **Personnel:** 2041

GOSHEN—Elkhart County

GOSHEN GENERAL HOSPITAL See Indiana University Health Goshen Hospital

☒ **INDIANA UNIVERSITY HEALTH GOSHEN HOSPITAL (150026)**, 200 High Park Avenue, Zip 46526–4899, Mailing Address: P.O. Box 139, Zip 46527–0139; tel. 574/533–2141, (Nonreporting) **A**1 2 10 **S** Indiana University Health, Indianapolis, IN
Primary Contact: Randal Christophel, President and Chief Executive Officer
COO: Robert T. Myers, Chief Operating Officer
CMO: Randall Cammenga, M.D., Vice President Medical Affairs
CHR: Alan Weldy, Vice President Human Resources, Compliance and Legal Services
Web address: www.iuhealth.org
Control: Other not–for–profit (including NFP Corporation) **Service:** General Medical and Surgical

Staffed Beds: 122

OAKLAWN PSYCHIATRIC CENTER (154031), 330 Lakeview Drive, Zip 46528–9365, Mailing Address: P.O. Box 809, Zip 46527–0809; tel. 574/533–1234, (Nonreporting) **A**10
Primary Contact: Laurie N. Nafziger, President and Chief Executive Officer
CFO: Joseph Barkman, Vice President Financial Services
CMO: Daniel Kinsey, M.D., Medical Director
CIO: Jennifer Glick, Manager Clinical Informatics
CHR: Jill Seifer, Vice President Human Resources
CNO: Elaine G. Miller, Director of Nursing
Web address: www.oaklawn.org
Control: Other not–for–profit (including NFP Corporation) **Service:** Psychiatric

Staffed Beds: 16

GREENCASTLE—Putnam County

PUTNAM COUNTY HOSPITAL (151333), 1542 Bloomington Street, Zip 46135–2297; tel. 765/653–5121, (Nonreporting) **A**2 10 18
Primary Contact: Dennis Weatherford, Chief Executive Officer
CFO: Kevin Fowler, Director Finance
Web address: www.pchosp.org/
Control: County–Government, nonfederal **Service:** General Medical and Surgical

Staffed Beds: 25

GREENFIELD—Hancock County

★ ○ **HANCOCK REGIONAL HOSPITAL (150037)**, 801 North State Street, Zip 46140–1270, Mailing Address: P.O. Box 827, Zip 46140–0827; tel. 317/462–5544 **A**10 11 **F**3 11 12 13 15 17 18 20 22 28 29 30 31 32 34 35 38 40 44 45 47 48 49 50 53 54 56 57 59 63 64 69 70 74 75 76 78 79 81 82 84 85 86 87 89 90 92 93 96 98 103 107 108 110 111 114 115 118 119 120 121 123 124 127 129 130 132 134 135 146 147 148 **P**8
Primary Contact: Steven V. Long, FACHE, President and Chief Executive Officer
COO: Robert Lawrence Matt, Vice President and Chief Operating Officer
CFO: Rick Edwards, Vice President and Chief Financial Officer
CMO: Michael Fletcher, M.D., Vice President and Chief Medical Officer
CIO: Jon Miller, Director Accounting and Information Services
CHR: Laura L. Nichols, Director Human Resources
Web address: www.hancockregional.org
Control: County–Government, nonfederal **Service:** General Medical and Surgical

Staffed Beds: 71 **Admissions:** 3061 **Census:** 32 **Outpatient Visits:** 156074 **Births:** 338 **Total Expense ($000):** 107461 **Payroll Expense ($000):** 37356 **Personnel:** 677

GREENSBURG—Decatur County

★ ◇ **DECATUR COUNTY MEMORIAL HOSPITAL (151332)**, 720 North Lincoln Street, Zip 47240–1398; tel. 812/663–4331, (Total facility includes 370 beds in nursing home–type unit) **A**2 10 18 21 **F**3 7 11 13 15 18 28 29 31 34 40 45 50 54 57 59 62 64 65 68 69 74 75 77 78 79 80 81 82 85 86 87 92 93 94 96 97 107 108 110 111 115 116 118 119 128 129 130 131 132 133 135 144 145 146 147 148 **P**6
Primary Contact: Linda V. Simmons, President and Chief Executive Officer
COO: Eric Stokes, Vice President of Operations
CFO: Jerry Marks, Vice President Finance
CMO: Jennifer Fletcher, Chief of Staff
CHR: Amy Lynn Wickens, Executive Director Human Resources
CNO: Kathy Stephens, Vice President of Patient Care
Web address: www.dcmh.net
Control: County–Government, nonfederal **Service:** General Medical and Surgical

Staffed Beds: 395 **Admissions:** 1860 **Census:** 186 **Outpatient Visits:** 143113 **Births:** 215 **Total Expense ($000):** 68570 **Payroll Expense ($000):** 30969 **Personnel:** 388

GREENWOOD—Johnson County

☒ **KINDRED HOSPITAL INDIANAPOLIS SOUTH (152008)**, 607 Greenwood Springs Drive, Zip 46143–6377; tel. 317/888–8155, (Nonreporting) **A**1 10 **S** Kindred Healthcare, Louisville, KY
Primary Contact: Matthew Keppler, Market Chief Executive Officer
CFO: William Brenner, Chief Financial Officer
CMO: Steven Samuels, M.D., Medical Director
CNO: Jennifer Stallings, Chief Clinical Officer
Web address: www.khindysouth.com/
Control: Corporation, Investor–owned, for–profit **Service:** Long–Term Acute Care hospital

Staffed Beds: 60

☐ **VALLE VISTA HOSPITAL (154024)**, 898 East Main Street, Zip 46143–1400; tel. 317/887–1348, (Nonreporting) **A**1 10 **S** Universal Health Services, Inc., King of Prussia, PA
Primary Contact: Sherri R. Jewett, Chief Executive Officer
CFO: Tim Sides, Chief Financial Officer
CMO: Jennifer Comer, M.D., Medical Director
CIO: Karen Hayden, Director Health Information Services, Performance Improvement and Risk Management
CHR: Ismael Santos, Director Human Resources
Web address: www.vallevistahospital.com
Control: Corporation, Investor–owned, for–profit **Service:** Psychiatric

Staffed Beds: 102

HAMMOND—Lake County

○ △ **FRANCISCAN ST. MARGARET HEALTH – HAMMOND (150004)**, 5454 Hohman Avenue, Zip 46320–1999; tel. 219/932–2300, (Includes FRANCISCAN ST. MARGARET HEALTH – DYER, 24 Joliet Street, Dyer, Zip 46311–1799; tel. 219/865–2141; Matthew Teolis, Interim President and Chief Executive Officer, Vice President of Medical Affairs; SAINT MARGARET MERCY HEALTHCARE CENTERS–NORTH CAMPUS, 5454 Hohman Avenue, Zip 46320; tel. 219/932–2300) **A**2 7 10 11 **F**3 5 9 11 12 13 15 17 18 20 22 24 26 28 29 30 31 34 35 37 38 40 45 46 47 48 49 50 53 54 56 57 58 59 62 63 64 65 66 67 70 73 74 75 76 77 78 79 81 82 84 85 86 87 89 90 92 93 96 97 98 99 100 101 102 103 104 105 106 107 108 110 111 115 118 119 120 121 126 129 130 131 132 135 144 146 147 148 **S** Franciscan Alliance, Mishawaka, IN
Primary Contact: Matthew Teolis, Interim President and Chief Executive Officer, Vice President of Medical Affairs
CFO: Marc Golan, Chief Financial Officer
Web address: www.smmhc.com
Control: Church–operated, Nongovernment, not–for profit **Service:** General Medical and Surgical

Staffed Beds: 406 **Admissions:** 13354 **Census:** 217 **Births:** 497 **Total Expense ($000):** 323439 **Payroll Expense ($000):** 118959

☒ **KINDRED HOSPITAL NORTHWEST INDIANA (152012)**, 5454 Hohman Avenue, 5th Floor, Zip 46320–1931; tel. 219/937–9900, (Nonreporting) **A**1 10 **S** Kindred Healthcare, Louisville, KY
Primary Contact: Frank A. Solare, Chief Executive Officer
Web address: www.khnwindiana.com
Control: Corporation, Investor–owned, for–profit **Service:** Long–Term Acute Care hospital

Staffed Beds: 70

SAINT MARGARET MERCY HEALTHCARE CENTERS See Franciscan St. Margaret Health – Hammond

TRIUMPH HOSPITAL NORTHWEST INDIANA See Kindred Hospital Northwest Indiana

HARTFORD CITY—Blackford County

BLACKFORD COMMUNITY HOSPITAL See Indiana University Health Blackford Hospital

Many Facility Codes have changed. Please refer to the AHA Guide Code Chart. © 2016 AHA Guide

✠ **INDIANA UNIVERSITY HEALTH BLACKFORD HOSPITAL (151302)**, 410 Pilgrim Boulevard, Zip 47348–1897; tel. 765/348–0300 **A**1 10 18 **F**3 11 15 28 29 34 35 40 44 45 57 59 64 75 81 85 87 93 107 110 115 119 130 132 133 **S** Indiana University Health, Indianapolis, IN
Primary Contact: Steven J. West, Chief Executive Officer
CFO: Judy Coleman, Chief Financial Officer, Indiana University Health Ball Memorial Hospital
CIO: Steven J. West, Chief Executive Officer
CHR: Steven J. West, Chief Executive Officer
CNO: Rodney Stevens, R.N., East Central Region Director of Nursing Practice
Web address: www.iuhealth.org/blackford
Control: Other not–for–profit (including NFP Corporation) **Service:** General Medical and Surgical

> **Staffed Beds:** 15 **Admissions:** 478 **Census:** 6 **Outpatient Visits:** 30625 **Births:** 0 **Total Expense ($000):** 14451 **Payroll Expense ($000):** 5938 **Personnel:** 99

HOBART—Lake County

☐ △ **ST. MARY MEDICAL CENTER (150034)**, 1500 South Lake Park Avenue, Zip 46342–6699; tel. 219/942–0551 **A**1 2 7 10 **F**3 8 11 12 13 15 18 20 22 24 26 28 29 30 31 34 35 36 38 39 40 45 47 49 50 54 57 58 59 62 64 65 70 74 75 76 77 78 79 80 81 82 85 86 87 89 90 92 93 96 107 108 110 111 114 115 119 120 121 123 126 129 130 131 132 135 144 146 147 148 **P**8 **S** Community Healthcare System, Hammond, IN
Primary Contact: Janice L. Ryba, JD, Chief Executive Officer
CFO: Mary Sudicky, Chief Financial Officer
CIO: Gary Weiner, Vice President Information Technology and Chief Information Officer
CHR: Tony Ferracane, Vice President Human Resources
CNO: Tammie R. Jones, R.N., Chief Nursing Officer
Web address: www.comhs.org
Control: Other not–for–profit (including NFP Corporation) **Service:** General Medical and Surgical

> **Staffed Beds:** 200 **Admissions:** 11047 **Census:** 159 **Outpatient Visits:** 218220 **Births:** 619 **Total Expense ($000):** 216300 **Payroll Expense ($000):** 62387 **Personnel:** 980

HUNTINGTON—Huntington County

✠ **PARKVIEW HUNTINGTON HOSPITAL (150091)**, 2001 Stults Road, Zip 46750–1291; tel. 260/355–3000 **A**1 10 **F**3 7 8 13 15 28 29 30 31 32 34 35 36 38 39 40 44 45 46 50 53 56 57 59 64 68 69 70 75 76 77 78 79 81 85 86 87 93 96 97 107 108 111 119 129 130 131 132 134 135 146 148 **S** Parkview Health, Fort Wayne, IN
Primary Contact: Juli Johnson, MSN, R.N., President
CMO: Jeffrey Brooks, M.D., Chief Medical Officer
CIO: Ron Double, Chief Information Officer
CHR: Dena M. Jacquay, Chief Human Resource Officer
CNO: Doug R. Selig, Vice President of Patient Services
Web address: www.parkview.com
Control: Other not–for–profit (including NFP Corporation) **Service:** General Medical and Surgical

> **Staffed Beds:** 36 **Admissions:** 1707 **Census:** 13 **Outpatient Visits:** 42834 **Births:** 356 **Total Expense ($000):** 41311 **Payroll Expense ($000):** 13333 **Personnel:** 220

INDIANAPOLIS—Marion County

CLARIAN HEALTH PARTNERS See Indiana University Health University Hospital

✠ **COMMUNITY HOSPITAL EAST (150074)**, 1500 North Ritter Avenue, Zip 46219–3095; tel. 317/355–1411, (Includes COMMUNITY HEART AND VASCULAR HOSPITAL, 8075 North Shadeland Avenue, Zip 46250–2693; tel. 317/621–8000; Jason Fahrlander, FACHE, President; COMMUNITY WESTVIEW HOSPITAL, 3630 Guion Road, Zip 46222–1699; tel. 317/924–6661; David C. Williams, D.O., President and Chief Executive Officer) **A**1 2 3 5 10 **F**3 11 13 17 18 20 22 24 26 28 29 30 31 34 35 38 40 44 45 47 49 50 51 53 56 57 59 70 74 75 76 77 78 79 80 81 85 87 92 96 98 107 111 114 115 118 119 130 132 144 146 147 148 **S** Community Health Network, Indianapolis, IN
Primary Contact: Scott L. Teffeteller, President
Web address: www.ecommunity.com/east/
Control: Other not–for–profit (including NFP Corporation) **Service:** General Medical and Surgical

> **Staffed Beds:** 335 **Admissions:** 16460 **Census:** 192 **Outpatient Visits:** 406252 **Births:** 675 **Total Expense ($000):** 535713 **Payroll Expense ($000):** 172494 **Personnel:** 933

✠ **COMMUNITY HOSPITAL NORTH (150169)**, 7150 Clearvista Drive, Zip 46256–1695, Mailing Address: 7250 Clearvista Drive, Suite 200, Zip 46256–1695; tel. 317/355–2469 **A**1 3 10 **F**3 11 13 29 30 31 34 35 40 41 45 46 47 48 49 50 52 57 59 65 70 72 74 75 76 77 78 79 81 85 87 89 90 96 107 111 114 119 126 129 130 132 145 146 147 148 **P**8 **S** Community Health Network, Indianapolis, IN
Primary Contact: Kathleen R. Krusie, FACHE, President
CFO: Amy Campbell, Chief Financial Officer
CMO: Wesley Wong, M.D., Acting Vice President Medical and Academic Affairs
CIO: Ron Thieme, Ph.D., Chief Knowledge and Information Officer
CHR: Steve Pearcy, Director Human Resources
Web address: www.ecommunity.com/north
Control: Other not–for–profit (including NFP Corporation) **Service:** General Medical and Surgical

> **Staffed Beds:** 308 **Admissions:** 16515 **Census:** 208 **Outpatient Visits:** 226824 **Births:** 3905 **Total Expense ($000):** 297665 **Payroll Expense ($000):** 90054 **Personnel:** 1471

✠ **COMMUNITY HOSPITAL SOUTH (150128)**, 1402 East County Line Road South, Zip 46227–0963; tel. 317/887–7000 **A**1 3 10 **F**3 11 12 13 15 18 20 22 28 29 30 31 35 37 40 45 46 47 48 49 64 69 70 73 74 75 76 77 78 79 81 82 84 85 86 89 107 108 110 111 114 115 119 126 129 130 131 135 145 146 147 148 **P**8 **S** Community Health Network, Indianapolis, IN
Primary Contact: Anthony B. Lennen, President
CFO: Leslie Yoder, Executive Director, Finance
CMO: Randy Lee, M.D., Senior Vice President Medical Affairs
CHR: Edie Garriott, Director Human Resources
CNO: Anita Capps, R.N., Chief Nursing Executive
Web address: www.ecommunity.com
Control: Other not–for–profit (including NFP Corporation) **Service:** General Medical and Surgical

> **Staffed Beds:** 158 **Admissions:** 9374 **Census:** 95 **Outpatient Visits:** 130316 **Births:** 1720 **Total Expense ($000):** 163023 **Payroll Expense ($000):** 49372 **Personnel:** 714

☐ **ESKENAZI HEALTH (150024)**, 720 Eskenazi Avenue, Zip 46202–5166; tel. 317/880–0000 **A**1 3 5 8 10 **F**3 5 7 10 13 14 15 16 18 20 22 28 29 30 31 32 34 35 36 38 39 40 43 44 47 48 49 50 53 54 55 56 57 59 61 62 64 65 66 68 70 71 72 74 75 76 77 78 79 81 82 83 84 85 86 87 93 97 98 99 100 101 102 103 104 105 106 107 110 111 115 119 130 132 134 135 143 144 145 146 147 148
Primary Contact: Lisa E. Harris, M.D., Chief Executive Officer
COO: Parveen Chand, Chief Operating Officer
CFO: Kathi Johnson, Chief Financial Officer
CMO: Chris S. Weaver, M.D., Chief Medical Officer
CIO: David Shaw, Vice President Information Systems
CHR: Christia Hicks, Vice President Human Resources
CNO: Lee Ann Blue, MSN, Chief Nursing Officer and Executive Vice President Patient Care Services
Web address: www.eskenazihealth.edu
Control: County–Government, nonfederal **Service:** General Medical and Surgical

> **Staffed Beds:** 253 **Admissions:** 15438 **Census:** 203 **Outpatient Visits:** 839469 **Births:** 2233 **Total Expense ($000):** 613969 **Payroll Expense ($000):** 225245 **Personnel:** 3149

☐ **FAIRBANKS (150179)**, 8102 Clearvista Parkway, Zip 46256–4698; tel. 317/849–8222 **A**1 3 10 **F**4 5 29 30 35 36 75 87 100 105 130 132 135 146 **P**8
Primary Contact: Barb Elliott, Interim President and Chief Executive Officer
CFO: Barb Elliott, Chief Financial Officer
CMO: Dennis Rhyne, M.D., Acting Medical Director
CIO: Randy Walls, Manager Information Services
CHR: Sharon Baker, Director Support Services
CNO: Jennifer M. Horstman, R.N., Chief Nursing Officer and Chief Information Officer
Web address: www.fairbankscd.org
Control: Other not–for–profit (including NFP Corporation) **Service:** Alcoholism and other chemical dependency

IN

> **Staffed Beds:** 86 **Admissions:** 3897 **Census:** 54 **Outpatient Visits:** 24301 **Births:** 0 **Total Expense ($000):** 22364 **Payroll Expense ($000):** 11334 **Personnel:** 268

Hospital, Medicare Provider Number, Address, Telephone, Approval, Facility, and Physician Codes, Health Care System

★ American Hospital Association (AHA) membership
☐ The Joint Commission accreditation
○ Healthcare Facilities Accreditation Program
◇ DNV Healthcare Inc. accreditation
⇑ Center for Improvement in Healthcare Quality Accreditation
△ Commission on Accreditation of Rehabilitation Facilities (CARF) accreditation

---

○ △ **FRANCISCAN ST. FRANCIS HEALTH – INDIANAPOLIS (150162)**, 8111 South Emerson Avenue, Zip 46237–8601; tel. 317/528–5000, (Nonreporting) **A**2 3 5 7 10 11 **S** Franciscan Alliance, Mishawaka, IN
Primary Contact: James Callaghan, III, M.D., President and Chief Executive Officer
CFO: Keith A. Lauter, Regional Chief Financial Officer
CMO: Christopher Doehring, M.D., Vice President Medical Affairs
CIO: Barbara Coulter, Director Information Systems
CHR: Corey Baute, Vice President Human Resources
CNO: Susan McRoberts, R.N., Vice President and Chief Nursing Officer
Web address: www.stfrancishospitals.org
Control: Other not–for–profit (including NFP Corporation) **Service:** General Medical and Surgical

Staffed Beds: 455

○ **INDIANA ORTHOPAEDIC HOSPITAL (150160)**, 8400 Northwest Boulevard, Zip 46278–1381; tel. 317/956–1000, (Nonreporting) **A**3 10 11
Primary Contact: Jane Keller, R.N., Chief Executive Officer
COO: Stacie Vance, Chief Nursing Officer and Vice President Operations
CFO: Anthony Gioia, Chief Financial Officer
CMO: Joseph Randolph, M.D., Chairman Medical Executive Committee
CIO: Paul Frey, Director Information Technology Applications
CHR: Kristy Hensley, Director Human Resources
CNO: Stacie Vance, Chief Nursing Officer and Vice President Operations
Web address: www.orthoindy.com
Control: Corporation, Investor–owned, for–profit **Service:** Orthopedic

Staffed Beds: 37

INDIANA UNIVERSITY HEALTH METHODIST HOSPITAL See Indiana University Health University Hospital

✠ **INDIANA UNIVERSITY HEALTH UNIVERSITY HOSPITAL (150056)**, 550 University Boulevard, Mailing Address: P.O. Box 1367, Zip 46206–1367; tel. 317/944–5000, (Includes INDIANA UNIVERSITY HEALTH METHODIST HOSPITAL, 1701 North Senate Boulevard, Zip 46202, Mailing Address: 1701 North Senate Boulevard, Zip 46202; tel. 317/962–2000; Herbert Buchanan, President; INDIANA UNIVERSITY HEALTH SAXONY HOSPITAL, 13000 East 136th Street, Fishers, Zip 46037–9478; tel. 317/678–2000; Jonathan R. Goble, FACHE, Chief Executive Officer; INDIANA UNIVERSITY HOSPITAL, 550 North University Boulevard, Zip 46202–5262; tel. 317/274–5000; RILEY HOSPITAL FOR CHILDREN AT INDIANA UNIVERSITY HEALTH, 702 Barnhill Drive, Zip 46202–5225; tel. 317/274–5000) **A**1 2 3 5 8 10 **F**5 6 7 8 9 11 12 13 15 16 17 18 19 20 21 22 23 24 25 26 27 28 29 30 31 32 33 34 35 36 37 38 39 40 41 43 44 45 46 47 48 49 50 51 52 53 54 55 56 57 58 59 60 61 62 63 64 65 69 70 71 72 73 74 75 76 77 78 79 80 81 82 83 84 85 86 87 88 89 91 92 93 94 96 97 98 99 100 101 102 103 104 105 106 107 108 109 110 111 112 113 114 115 116 117 118 119 120 121 122 123 124 126 129 130 131 132 134 135 136 137 138 139 140 141 144 145 146 147 148 **S** Indiana University Health, Indianapolis, IN
Primary Contact: Herbert Buchanan, President
COO: Dennis M. Murphy, Chief Operating Officer
CIO: Richard F. Johnson, Senior Vice President and Chief Information Officer
Web address: www.iuhealth.org
Control: Other not–for–profit (including NFP Corporation) **Service:** General Medical and Surgical

Staffed Beds: 1253 Admissions: 48472 **Census:** 895 **Outpatient Visits:** 1217553 **Births:** 3300 **Total Expense ($000):** 2573978 **Payroll Expense ($000):** 880804 **Personnel:** 12731

INDIANA UNIVERSITY HOSPITAL See Indiana University Health University Hospital

✠ **KINDRED HOSPITAL–INDIANAPOLIS (152007)**, 1700 West 10th Street, Zip 46222–3802; tel. 317/636–4400, (Nonreporting) **A**1 10 **S** Kindred Healthcare, Louisville, KY
Primary Contact: Bryan Chatterton, Chief Executive Officer
COO: Angela Lynne Rotert, Chief Clinical Officer
CFO: William Brenner, Chief Financial Officer
CHR: Joe Housh, District Director Human Resources
Web address: www.kindredhospitalindy.com/
Control: Corporation, Investor–owned, for–profit **Service:** Long–Term Acute Care hospital

Staffed Beds: 59

□ **LARUE D. CARTER MEMORIAL HOSPITAL (154008)**, 2601 Cold Spring Road, Zip 46222–2273; tel. 317/941–4000, (Nonreporting) **A**1 3 5 10
Primary Contact: Eric Heeter, Superintendent
CFO: Michael Logar, Assistant Superintendent
CMO: Beth Pfau, M.D., Chief Medical Officer
CIO: Denton Gross, Director Information Services
CHR: Rebecca Dutton, Director Human Resources
CNO: Todd Rittman, Director of Nursing
Control: State–Government, nonfederal **Service:** Psychiatric

Staffed Beds: 148

METHODIST HOSPITAL See Indiana University Health Methodist Hospital

□ **OPTIONS BEHAVIORAL HEALTH SYSTEM (154057)**, 5602 Caito Drive, Zip 46226–1346; tel. 317/544–4340, (Nonreporting) **A**1 10 **S** Acadia Healthcare Company, Inc., Franklin, TN
Primary Contact: Matthew Love, Chief Executive Officer
Web address: www.optionsbehavioralhealthsystem.com/
Control: Corporation, Investor–owned, for–profit **Service:** Psychiatric

Staffed Beds: 42

□ △ **REHABILITATION HOSPITAL OF INDIANA (153028)**, 4141 Shore Drive, Zip 46254–2607; tel. 317/329–2000 **A**1 3 5 7 10 **F**28 29 30 33 54 58 64 75 79 86 87 90 91 92 93 96 130 131 132 146 148 **P**5 **S** Indiana University Health, Indianapolis, IN
Primary Contact: Daniel B. Woloszyn, Chief Executive Officer
COO: Monte Spence, Chief Operating Officer
CFO: Marjorie Basey, Chief Financial Officer
CMO: Flora Hammond, M.D., Chief Medical Affairs
CIO: Gary Skinner, Director Information Technology
CHR: Joni Brown, Director Human Resources
CNO: Debra Cordes, Chief Nursing Officer
Web address: www.rhin.com
Control: Other not–for–profit (including NFP Corporation) **Service:** Rehabilitation

Staffed Beds: 83 Admissions: 1353 **Census:** 56 **Outpatient Visits:** 20575 **Births:** 0 **Total Expense ($000):** 36739 **Payroll Expense ($000):** 18750 **Personnel:** 356

✠ △ **RICHARD L. ROUDEBUSH VETERANS AFFAIRS MEDICAL CENTER**, 1481 West Tenth Street, Zip 46202–2884; tel. 317/554–0000 **A**1 2 3 5 7 8 **F**3 5 18 20 22 24 26 28 29 30 31 33 34 35 38 39 40 44 45 46 47 49 50 53 54 56 57 58 59 60 61 62 63 64 65 67 70 71 74 75 77 78 79 80 81 82 83 84 85 86 87 90 91 92 93 94 96 97 98 100 101 102 103 104 105 106 107 108 111 115 117 118 119 120 121 123 124 126 127 130 132 135 143 144 146 147 148 **S** Department of Veterans Affairs, Washington, DC
Primary Contact: Brian Hancock, M.D., Director
COO: Ginny L. Creasman, Associate Director
CFO: Colin Lennon, Chief Financial Officer
CMO: Chowdry Bashir, M.D., Chief of Staff
CIO: Steve Stoner, Chief Information Officer
CHR: Chari Weddle, Chief Human Resource Management Service
CNO: Patricia Mathis, Associate Director Patient Care Service
Web address: www.indianapolis.va.gov
Control: Veterans Affairs, Government, federal **Service:** General Medical and Surgical

Staffed Beds: 209 Admissions: 7769 **Census:** 149 **Outpatient Visits:** 779258 **Births:** 0 **Total Expense ($000):** 538732 **Payroll Expense ($000):** 188760 **Personnel:** 2805

RILEY HOSPITAL FOR CHILDREN See Riley Hospital for Children at Indiana University Health

RILEY HOSPITAL FOR CHILDREN AT INDIANA UNIVERSITY HEALTH See Indiana University Health University Hospital

✠ **KINDRED HOSPITAL–INDIANAPOLIS NORTH (152013)**, 8060 Knue Road, Zip 46250–1976; tel. 317/783–8985, (Nonreporting) **A**1 10 **S** Select Medical Corporation, Mechanicsburg, PA
Primary Contact: Rick Ament, Chief Executive Officer
CHR: Kelly Becker, Administrative Coordinator Human Resources
Web address: www.indianapolis.selectspecialtyhospitals.com/
Control: Corporation, Investor–owned, for–profit **Service:** Long–Term Acute Care hospital

Staffed Beds: 45

ST. FRANCIS HOSPITAL AND HEALTH CENTERS – SOUTH CAMPUS See Franciscan St. Francis Health – Indianapolis

✠ **ST. VINCENT HEART CENTER (150153)**, 10580 North Meridian Street, Zip 46290–1028; tel. 317/583–5000 **A**1 10 **F**3 18 20 22 24 26 28 29 30 34 35 40 42 43 45 46 58 59 75 81 85 86 87 111 115 119 129 130 135 148 **P**2 **S** Ascension Health, Saint Louis, MO
Primary Contact: Blake A. Dye, President
CFO: Becky Jacobson, Vice President Finance
CMO: William Storer, M.D., Medical Director
CIO: Roger Strange, Chief Information Officer
Web address: www.bestheartcare.com/
Control: Partnership, Investor–owned, for–profit **Service:** Heart

Staffed Beds: 80 Admissions: 4531 **Census:** 53 **Outpatient Visits:** 10517 **Births:** 0 **Total Expense ($000):** 107433 **Payroll Expense ($000):** 29486 **Personnel:** 354

IN

✠ **ST. VINCENT INDIANAPOLIS HOSPITAL (150084)**, 2001 West 86th Street, Zip 46260–1991, Mailing Address: P.O. Box 40970, Zip 46240–0970; tel. 317/338–2345, (Includes PEYTON MANNING CHILDREN'S HOSPITAL, 1707 West 86th Street, Zip 46240, Mailing Address: P.O. Box 40407, Zip 46240; tel. 317/415–5500; Anne Coleman, Administrator; PEYTON MANNING CHILDREN'S HOSPITAL AT ST. VINCENT, 2001 West 86th Street, Zip 46260, Mailing Address: P.O. Box 40970, Zip 46240–0970; tel. 317/415–8111; Anne Coleman, Administrator; ST. VINCENT STRESS CENTER, 8401 Harcourt Road, Zip 46260, Mailing Address: P.O. Box 80160, Zip 46280; tel. 317/338–4600; Sheila Mishler, Chief Executive Officer; ST. VINCENT WOMEN'S HOSPITAL, 8111 Township Line Road, Zip 46260–8043; tel. 317/415–8111; Anne Coleman, Administrator) **A**1 2 3 5 8 10 **F**3 4 5 7 8 9 11 13 15 17 18 19 20 21 22 23 24 25 26 27 28 29 30 31 32 34 35 36 37 38 39 40 41 43 44 45 46 47 48 49 50 51 53 54 55 56 57 58 59 61 62 63 64 65 66 68 70 71 72 73 74 75 76 77 78 79 81 82 83 84 85 86 87 88 89 90 91 92 93 94 96 97 98 99 100 101 102 103 104 105 106 107 108 109 110 111 114 115 117 118 119 120 121 124 126 129 130 131 132 134 135 137 138 141 142 143 144 146 147 148 **P**6 **S** Ascension Health, Saint Louis, MO
Primary Contact: Joel Feldman, President
COO: Erica Wehrmeister, Chief Operating Officer
CFO: Terry Metzger, Vice President, Finance
CMO: Richard Freeman, Chief Medical Officer
CIO: Randy Cox, Chief Information Officer
CHR: Audra Pratt, Chief Human Resource Officer
CNO: Mary Myers, R.N., Chief Nursing Officer
Web address: www.stvincent.org
Control: Church–operated, Nongovernment, not–for profit **Service:** General Medical and Surgical

> **Staffed Beds:** 909 **Admissions:** 35140 **Census:** 557 **Outpatient Visits:** 843776 **Births:** 3394 **Total Expense ($000):** 1021957 **Payroll Expense ($000):** 351778 **Personnel:** 4279

✠ **ST. VINCENT SETON SPECIALTY HOSPITAL (152020)**, 8050 Township Line Road, Zip 46260–2478; tel. 317/415–8500 **A**1 10 **F**1 29 30 31 35 44 53 68 75 85 114 119 130 132 148 **P**8 **S** Ascension Health, Saint Louis, MO
Primary Contact: Joel Feldman, President and Chief Executive Officer
COO: Troy T. Reiff, Corporate Director Operations
CFO: David M. Girten, Corporate Director Financial Services
CMO: Ronald Reisman, M.D., Chief Medical Director
CHR: Terry A. Wignall, Director Human Resources
Web address: www.stvincent.org/
Control: Church–operated, Nongovernment, not–for profit **Service:** Long–Term Acute Care hospital

> **Staffed Beds:** 74 **Admissions:** 603 **Census:** 61 **Outpatient Visits:** 0 **Births:** 0 **Total Expense ($000):** 38092 **Payroll Expense ($000):** 18026 **Personnel:** 231

WESTVIEW HOSPITAL See Community Westview Hospital

JASPER—Dubois County

✠ **MEMORIAL HOSPITAL AND HEALTH CARE CENTER (150115)**, 800 West Ninth Street, Zip 47546–2516; tel. 812/996–2345, (Total facility includes 20 beds in nursing home–type unit) **A**1 2 10 19 **F**3 5 7 8 11 12 13 19 18 20 22 24 26 28 29 30 31 34 35 36 40 41 42 45 46 47 48 49 51 54 56 57 59 62 64 66 68 70 74 75 76 77 78 79 81 82 84 85 86 87 89 90 93 97 98 100 101 102 103 104 105 107 108 110 111 112 113 114 115 116 117 118 119 120 121 127 128 129 130 131 132 135 144 146 147 148 **P**6 **S** American Province of Little Company of Mary Sisters, Evergreen Park, IL
Primary Contact: E. Kyle Bennett, President and Chief Executive Officer
CFO: Randall Russell, Vice President and Chief Financial Officer
CMO: Stan Tretter, M.D., Chief Medical Officer
CIO: Gary Light, Vice President and Chief Information Officer
CHR: Richard Pea, Director Human Resources
CNO: Tonya Heim, R.N., Vice President Patient Services and Chief Nursing Officer
Web address: www.mhhcc.org
Control: Church–operated, Nongovernment, not–for profit **Service:** General Medical and Surgical

> **Staffed Beds:** 143 **Admissions:** 6065 **Census:** 70 **Outpatient Visits:** 227807 **Births:** 956 **Total Expense ($000):** 191160 **Payroll Expense ($000):** 85544 **Personnel:** 1303

JEFFERSONVILLE—Clark County

✠ **CLARK MEMORIAL HOSPITAL (150009)**, 1220 Missouri Avenue, Zip 47130–3743, Mailing Address: P.O. Box 69, Zip 47131–0600; tel. 812/282–6631, (Data for 153 days) **A**1 2 3 5 10 **F**3 5 8 11 12 15 17 18 20 22 26 28 29 30 31 34 35 38 40 45 46 49 50 54 56 57 59 64 65 70 74 75 76 77 78 79 81 82 85 86 87 91 92 97 98 100 101 102 103 104 105 107 108 110 111 114 115 119 124 130 132 135 144 145 146 147 148 **P**6 **S** LifePoint Health, Brentwood, TN
Primary Contact: Martin Padgett, President and Chief Executive Officer
CFO: Kirk Strack, Vice President and Chief Financial Officer
CMO: William Templeton, III, M.D., Medical Director
CIO: Larry Reverman, Director Information Systems
CHR: Scott Hicks, Vice President
CNO: Kathy Neuner, R.N., Chief Nursing Officer
Web address: www.clarkmemorial.org
Control: Partnership, Investor–owned, for–profit **Service:** General Medical and Surgical

> **Staffed Beds:** 185 **Admissions:** 4470 **Census:** 116 **Outpatient Visits:** 25017 **Births:** 567 **Total Expense ($000):** 76184 **Payroll Expense ($000):** 29978 **Personnel:** 1320

☐ **WELLSTONE REGIONAL HOSPITAL (154051)**, 2700 Vissing Park Road, Zip 47130–5989; tel. 812/284–8000 **A**1 10 **F**4 5 29 33 34 56 59 64 71 74 75 87 98 99 101 102 103 104 105 130 132 135 **P**5 **S** Universal Health Services, Inc., King of Prussia, PA
Primary Contact: Greg Stewart, Chief Executive Officer
CFO: Gracia Winsett, Chief Financial Officer
CMO: Asad Ismail, M.D., Medical Director
CIO: Billy Leftwitch, Director, Information Technology
CHR: Tiffany Smith, Director Human Resources
CNO: Anthony Aemmer, Director of Nursing
Web address: www.wellstonehospital.com
Control: Corporation, Investor–owned, for–profit **Service:** Psychiatric

> **Staffed Beds:** 100 **Admissions:** 3267 **Census:** 73 **Outpatient Visits:** 8024 **Births:** 0 **Total Expense ($000):** 15569 **Payroll Expense ($000):** 8554 **Personnel:** 180

KENDALLVILLE—Noble County

✠ **PARKVIEW NOBLE HOSPITAL (150146)**, 401 Sawyer Road, Zip 46755–2568; tel. 260/347–8700 **A**1 10 **F**3 7 13 15 28 29 34 35 40 45 46 47 50 54 57 59 64 70 74 75 76 79 81 82 85 87 93 94 97 107 108 110 111 114 118 119 129 130 132 135 143 145 146 **S** Parkview Health, Fort Wayne, IN
Primary Contact: Gary W. Adkins, President
COO: Gary W. Adkins, Chief Executive Officer
CFO: Kem Prince, Manager of Finance
CMO: Gerald Warrener, M.D., Chief Medical Officer
CIO: Ron Double, Chief Information Officer
CHR: Bruce Buttermore, Manager Human Resources
CNO: Catherine Byrd, Vice President Patient Services
Web address: www.parkview.com
Control: Other not–for–profit (including NFP Corporation) **Service:** General Medical and Surgical

> **Staffed Beds:** 31 **Admissions:** 1887 **Census:** 16 **Outpatient Visits:** 56474 **Births:** 287 **Total Expense ($000):** 43298 **Payroll Expense ($000):** 14031 **Personnel:** 231

KNOX—Starke County

✠ **STARKE HOSPITAL (150102)**, 102 East Culver Road, Zip 46534–2216, Mailing Address: P.O. Box 339, Zip 46534–0339; tel. 574/772–6231 **A**1 10 **F**3 15 18 29 30 32 34 35 38 40 45 46 49 50 53 57 59 65 68 74 75 77 79 81 85 87 93 94 107 108 110 111 114 115 116 117 119 130 132 135 146 147 148 **S** Community Health Systems, Inc., Franklin, TN
Primary Contact: Jeff Vice, Interim Chief Executive Officer
CFO: Rosemarie Heise, Vice President Finance
CMO: A. N. Damodaran, M.D., President Medical Staff
CIO: Ashley Norem, Chief Information Systems
CHR: Doug Jesch, Director Human Resources
Web address: www.iuhealth.org/starke/
Control: Other not–for–profit (including NFP Corporation) **Service:** General Medical and Surgical

> **Staffed Beds:** 15 **Admissions:** 466 **Census:** 4 **Outpatient Visits:** 26780 **Births:** 0 **Total Expense ($000):** 19751 **Payroll Expense ($000):** 6729 **Personnel:** 125

STARKE MEMORIAL HOSPITAL See Starke Hospital

IN

Hospital, Medicare Provider Number, Address, Telephone, Approval, Facility, and Physician Codes, Health Care System

★ American Hospital Association (AHA) membership
☐ The Joint Commission accreditation
○ Healthcare Facilities Accreditation Program
◇ DNV Healthcare Inc. accreditation
⇑ Center for Improvement in Healthcare Quality Accreditation
△ Commission on Accreditation of Rehabilitation Facilities (CARF) accreditation

KOKOMO—Howard County

✠ **COMMUNITY HOWARD REGIONAL HEALTH (150007)**, 3500 South Lafountain Street, Zip 46902–3803, Mailing Address: P.O. Box 9011, Zip 46904–9011; tel. 765/453–0702 **A**1 2 10 **F**3 5 7 11 13 15 17 18 20 22 24 26 28 29 30 31 32 34 35 38 40 45 47 48 49 54 55 57 58 59 61 64 65 67 70 71 72 74 75 76 77 78 79 80 81 84 85 86 87 89 92 93 94 96 97 98 99 100 101 102 103 104 105 106 107 108 109 110 111 119 120 121 129 131 132 134 135 141 145 146 147 148 **S** Community Health Network, Indianapolis, IN
Primary Contact: Joseph Hooper, President and Chief Executive Officer
COO: Theodore Brown, Chief Operating Officer
CFO: Theodore Brown, Vice President Financial Services
CIO: Kevin Purvis, Chief Information Officer
CHR: Michael L. Williams, FACHE, Vice President Human Resources
CNO: Melodi Greene, R.N., Chief Nursing Officer
Web address: www.howardregional.org
Control: Other not–for–profit (including NFP Corporation) **Service:** General Medical and Surgical

Staffed Beds: 137 Admissions: 4635 Census: 45 Outpatient Visits: 114668 Births: 472 Total Expense ($000): 109264 Payroll Expense ($000): 35595 Personnel: 593

✠ **COMMUNITY HOWARD SPECIALTY HOSPITAL (153039)**, 829 North Dixon Road, Zip 46901–7709; tel. 765/452–6700 **A**1 10 **F**28 29 30 34 57 77 90 93 129 131 132 **S** Community Health Network, Indianapolis, IN
Primary Contact: Clayton L. Clement, Interim Administrator
CFO: Julie Pena, Director Finance
CMO: Brad Vossberg, M.D., Chief Rehabilitation
CNO: Claudia Jean Lowry, R.N., Director of Nursing
Web address: www.communityhoward.org
Control: Partnership, Investor–owned, for–profit **Service:** Rehabilitation

Staffed Beds: 30 Admissions: 487 Census: 15 Outpatient Visits: 30133 Births: 0 Total Expense ($000): 11526 Payroll Expense ($000): 5897

HOWARD REGIONAL HEALTH SYSTEM See Community Howard Regional Health

HOWARD REGIONAL HEALTH SYSTEM WEST CAMPUS SPECIALTY HOSPITAL See Community Howard Specialty Hospital

✠ **ST. VINCENT KOKOMO (150010)**, 1907 West Sycamore Street, Zip 46901–4197; tel. 765/452–5611 **A**1 10 **F**3 4 5 7 8 13 15 18 20 28 29 30 31 34 35 36 40 44 45 49 50 51 53 55 57 59 64 66 68 69 70 73 74 75 76 77 78 79 81 82 85 86 87 89 90 93 96 98 99 100 101 102 103 104 105 107 108 110 111 115 119 120 121 123 129 130 131 132 135 143 145 146 147 148 **S** Ascension Health, Saint Louis, MO
Primary Contact: Margaret M. Johnson, President, St. Vincent Northwest Region
CFO: Dennis Ressler, Chief Financial Officer
CMO: David L. Williams, M.D., Chief Medical Officer
CIO: Jeffrey Scott, Chief Information Officer
CHR: Cindy Babb, Executive Director Human Resources and Organizational Effectiveness
CNO: Kathleen K. Peoples, R.N., Vice President of Nursing
Web address: www.stvincent.org/stjoseph
Control: Church–operated, Nongovernment, not–for profit **Service:** General Medical and Surgical

Staffed Beds: 138 Admissions: 4858 Census: 66 Outpatient Visits: 201459 Births: 773 Total Expense ($000): 117423 Payroll Expense ($000): 39479 Personnel: 653

LA PORTE—Laporte County

✠ **LA PORTE HOSPITAL (150006)**, 1007 Lincolnway, Zip 46350–3201, Mailing Address: P.O. Box 250, Zip 46352–0250; tel. 219/326–1234 **A**1 2 10 19 **F**1 3 4 8 11 13 15 16 17 18 19 20 22 24 26 28 29 30 31 32 34 35 36 39 40 45 46 47 48 49 50 51 53 54 56 57 59 60 63 64 70 71 72 73 74 75 76 77 78 79 81 85 86 87 88 91 92 93 94 96 97 98 107 108 110 111 115 118 119 126 128 129 130 131 132 135 144 145 146 147 148 **S** Community Health Systems, Inc., Franklin, TN
Primary Contact: Gigi Fergus, Interim Chief Executive Officer
Web address: www.iuhealth.org
Control: Other not–for–profit (including NFP Corporation) **Service:** General Medical and Surgical

Staffed Beds: 110 Admissions: 4210 Census: 48 Outpatient Visits: 93106 Births: 640 Total Expense ($000): 151273 Payroll Expense ($000): 56219 Personnel: 1310

LA PORTE REGIONAL HEALTH SYSTEM See La Porte Hospital

LAFAYETTE—Tippecanoe County

CLARIAN ARNETT HOSPITAL See Indiana University Health Arnett Hospital

○ **FRANCISCAN ST. ELIZABETH HEALTH – LAFAYETTE EAST (150109)**, 1701 South Creasy Lane, Zip 47905–4972; tel. 765/502–4000, (Includes FRANCISCAN ST. ELIZABETH HEALTH – LAFAYETTE CENTRAL, 1501 Hartford Street, Zip 47904–2134; tel. 765/423–6011; Terrance E. Wilson, President and CEO) **A**2 5 10 11 **F**3 5 10 17 26 28 29 30 31 34 35 39 40 45 49 50 51 60 62 63 64 68 70 72 74 76 79 81 82 84 85 87 89 90 93 98 107 108 110 111 112 113 114 115 116 119 120 121 123 126 129 130 132 135 146 147 148 **S** Franciscan Alliance, Mishawaka, IN
Primary Contact: Terrance E. Wilson, President and CEO
Web address: www.ste.org
Control: Church–operated, Nongovernment, not–for profit **Service:** General Medical and Surgical

Staffed Beds: 187 Admissions: 10834 Census: 123 Births: 2125 Total Expense ($000): 290049 Payroll Expense ($000): 84627 Personnel: 1509

★ ○ **INDIANA UNIVERSITY HEALTH ARNETT HOSPITAL (150173)**, 5165 McCarty Lane, Zip 47905–8764, Mailing Address: P.O. Box 5545, Zip 47903–5545; tel. 765/448–8000 **A**2 3 5 10 11 **F**3 11 12 13 15 17 18 20 22 24 26 28 29 30 31 34 35 40 43 45 46 49 50 51 54 57 59 60 61 64 65 68 69 70 72 74 75 76 77 78 79 80 81 82 85 87 89 93 97 100 104 107 108 110 111 114 115 116 117 118 120 121 126 129 130 131 132 144 146 147 148 **P**6 **S** Indiana University Health, Indianapolis, IN
Primary Contact: Donald Clayton, M.D., President
COO: Brian T. Shockney, FACHE, Chief Operating Officer
CFO: Cara Breidster, Chief Financial Officer
CMO: Jeffrey P. Brown, M.D., Chief Medical Officer
CIO: Rusty McGill, System Director Information Technology
CHR: Koreen H. Kyhnell, Vice President Human Resources
Web address: www.iuhealth.org
Control: Other not–for–profit (including NFP Corporation) **Service:** General Medical and Surgical

Staffed Beds: 191 Admissions: 9113 Census: 110 Outpatient Visits: 96916 Births: 1534 Total Expense ($000): 344635 Payroll Expense ($000): 152974 Personnel: 1635

✠ **LAFAYETTE REGIONAL REHABILITATION HOSPITAL (153042)**, 950 Park East Boulevard, Zip 47905–0792; tel. 765/447–4040, (Nonreporting) **A**1 10 **S** Ernest Health, Inc., Albuquerque, NM
Primary Contact: Michelle Russell, Chief Executive Officer
Web address: www.lrrh.ernesthealth.com
Control: Corporation, Investor–owned, for–profit **Service:** Rehabilitation

Staffed Beds: 40

ST. ELIZABETH CENTRAL See Franciscan St. Elizabeth Health – Lafayette Central

☐ **SYCAMORE SPRINGS HOSPITAL (154059)**, 833 Park East Boulevard, Zip 47905–0785; tel. 765/743–4400 **A**1 10 **F**4 5 98 102 103 104 105
Primary Contact: David Fletcher–Janzen, Chief Executive Officer
CFO: Michael Huth, Chief Financial Officer
CMO: Nizar El Khalili, M.D., Medical Director
CHR: Pam Sichts, Director Human Resources
CNO: Brooke Lavignette, Director of Nursing
Web address: www.sycamorespringshealth.com
Control: Corporation, Investor–owned, for–profit **Service:** Psychiatric

Staffed Beds: 48 Admissions: 1577 Census: 38 Outpatient Visits: 8643 Births: 0 Total Expense ($000): 10486 Payroll Expense ($000): 5472 Personnel: 116

LAGRANGE—Lagrange County

✠ **PARKVIEW LAGRANGE HOSPITAL (151323)**, 207 North Townline Road, Zip 46761–1325; tel. 260/463–9000 **A**1 10 18 **F**3 7 13 15 17 26 29 30 34 35 40 45 50 51 57 59 63 64 70 75 76 79 81 82 83 84 85 86 87 89 90 93 96 107 108 109 110 111 114 118 119 128 129 130 132 133 143 146 148 **S** Parkview Health, Fort Wayne, IN
Primary Contact: Jordi K. Disler, President
CFO: Vickie Stanski, Financial Manager
CMO: Jeffrey Brookes, M.D., Chief Medical Officer
CIO: Ron Double, Chief Information Technology Officer
CHR: Bruce Buttermore, Director Human Resources
CNO: Jared Beasley, R.N., Vice President Patient Care
Web address: www.parkview.com
Control: Other not–for–profit (including NFP Corporation) **Service:** General Medical and Surgical

Staffed Beds: 25 Admissions: 1037 Census: 10 Outpatient Visits: 23941 Births: 238 Total Expense ($000): 29447 Payroll Expense ($000): 9499 Personnel: 155

IN

Many Facility Codes have changed. Please refer to the AHA Guide Code Chart.   © 2016 AHA Guide

LAWRENCEBURG—Dearborn County

COMMUNITY MENTAL HEALTH CENTER (154011), 285 Bielby Road,
Zip 47025–1055; tel. 812/537–1302 **A**10 **F**98 100 101 102 103
Primary Contact: Tom Talbot, Chief Executive Officer
CFO: Georgii Zhirkin, Chief Financial Officer
CMO: Hasan Bakhtier, M.D., Medical Director
CIO: John McKinley, Director, Information Technology
CHR: Kelly Stewart, Director of Human Resources
Web address: www.cmhcinc.org
Control: Other not–for–profit (including NFP Corporation) **Service:** Psychiatric

Staffed Beds: 16 **Admissions:** 502 **Census:** 7 **Outpatient Visits:** 0 **Births:** 0
Total Expense ($000): 2251 **Payroll Expense ($000):** 1354 **Personnel:** 23

★ ○ **DEARBORN COUNTY HOSPITAL (150086)**, 600 Wilson Creek Road,
Zip 47025–2751; tel. 812/537–1010 **A**10 11 **F**3 4 11 13 15 20 28 30 34 35
37 40 43 44 45 46 47 49 50 57 59 62 63 64 70 75 76 77 79 81 84 85 86
87 92 93 107 108 110 111 114 116 117 118 119 129 130 131 132 146
148 **P**7
Primary Contact: Michael W. Schwebler, President and Chief Executive Officer
CFO: Philip A. Meyer, Vice President, Finance
CNO: Angela Scudder, MSN, Vice President Patient Care Services
Web address: www.dch.org
Control: County–Government, nonfederal **Service:** General Medical and Surgical

Staffed Beds: 88 **Admissions:** 4447 **Census:** 45 **Outpatient Visits:** 144623
Births: 404 **Total Expense ($000):** 75599 **Payroll Expense ($000):** 33289
Personnel: 610

LEBANON—Boone County

✠ **WITHAM HEALTH SERVICES (150104)**, 2605 North Lebanon Street,
Zip 46052–1476, Mailing Address: P.O. Box 1200, Zip 46052–3005;
tel. 765/485–8000 **A**1 10 **F**3 7 13 15 18 20 28 29 30 34 40 42 45 54 56 57
59 64 65 68 69 70 75 76 77 79 81 82 83 85 86 87 93 94 97 98 99 103
107 108 110 111 114 115 118 119 128 129 130 132 135 141 142 143 144
146 147 148 **P**1
Primary Contact: Raymond V. Ingham, Ph.D., President and Chief Executive Officer
COO: Diane Feder, R.N., Senior Vice President and Chief Operating Officer
CFO: George Pogas, CPA, Senior Vice President and Chief Financial Officer
CMO: Anthony Steele, M.D., Chief Medical Officer
CIO: George Pogas, CPA, Senior Vice President and Chief Financial Officer
CHR: Gary A. Deater, Vice President Administration, Human Resources and Risk
Management
CNO: Diane Feder, R.N., Senior Vice President and Chief Operating Officer
Web address: www.witham.org
Control: County–Government, nonfederal **Service:** General Medical and Surgical

Staffed Beds: 70 **Admissions:** 2616 **Census:** 31 **Outpatient Visits:** 136290
Births: 478 **Total Expense ($000):** 105933 **Payroll Expense ($000):** 42083
Personnel: 607

LINTON—Greene County

✠ **GREENE COUNTY GENERAL HOSPITAL (151317)**, 1185 North 1000 West,
Zip 47441–5282; tel. 812/847–2281 **A**1 10 18 **F**1 3 6 11 13 15 18 19 26 27
29 30 31 34 35 40 41 45 50 55 57 58 59 62 64 65 66 67 68 70 75 76 77
78 79 81 85 86 87 90 91 93 107 108 110 114 119 125 127 128 130 133
135 146 147 148 **P**6
Primary Contact: Brenda Reetz, FACHE, Chief Executive Officer
CFO: April Settles, Chief Financial Officer
CMO: Frederick R. Ridge, Chief of Staff
CIO: Steve Phillips, Information Officer
CHR: Jean Prather, Director of Human Resources
CNO: Lea Ann Camp, R.N., Chief Nursing Officer
Web address: www.greenecountyhospital.com
Control: County–Government, nonfederal **Service:** General Medical and Surgical

Staffed Beds: 25 **Admissions:** 847 **Census:** 8 **Outpatient Visits:** 581956
Births: 66 **Total Expense ($000):** 26233 **Payroll Expense ($000):** 11538
Personnel: 236

LOGANSPORT—Cass County

FOUR COUNTY COUNSELING CENTER (154035), 1015 Michigan Avenue,
Zip 46947–1526; tel. 574/722–5151, (Nonreporting) **A**10
Primary Contact: C.J. Davis, Chief Executive Officer/ Executive Director
COO: Carrie Cadwell, M.D., Chief Clinical Officer
CFO: Jason Cadwell, Chief Financial Officer
CMO: John Yarling, M.D., Medical Director
CIO: Becky Mulis, Director of Health Information Management Systems
CHR: Steve Curry, Regional Director Human Resources
CNO: Donna Henry, Vice President of Nursing Services
Web address: www.fourcounty.org
Control: Other not–for–profit (including NFP Corporation) **Service:** Psychiatric

Staffed Beds: 15

★ ○ **LOGANSPORT MEMORIAL HOSPITAL (150072)**, 1101 Michigan Avenue,
Zip 46947–1528, Mailing Address: P.O. Box 7013, Zip 46947–7013;
tel. 574/753–7541 **A**10 11 20 **F**3 11 13 15 28 29 32 34 35 36 40 44 45 48
49 50 51 57 59 64 65 68 69 70 75 76 77 78 79 81 85 86 87 93 97 107
108 110 111 114 119 124 129 130 132 133 135 146 147 **P**6
Primary Contact: Perry Gay, President and Chief Executive Officer
CFO: Sherri Gehlhausen, Assistant Chief Financial Officer
CIO: Beth Jump, Chief Information Officer
CHR: Lynda J. Shrock, Vice President Human Resources
CNO: Tara McVay, Chief Nursing Officer
Web address: www.logansportmemorial.org
Control: County–Government, nonfederal **Service:** General Medical and Surgical

Staffed Beds: 83 **Admissions:** 1799 **Census:** 15 **Outpatient Visits:** 106286
Births: 508 **Total Expense ($000):** 64458 **Payroll Expense ($000):** 29301
Personnel: 619

☐ **LOGANSPORT STATE HOSPITAL**, 1098 South State Road 25,
Zip 46947–6723; tel. 574/737–3633, (Nonreporting) **A**1
Primary Contact: Robert Clover, Superintendent and Chief Executive Officer
CFO: Misty Moss, Director Business Administration
CMO: Danny Meadows, M.D., Medical Director
CIO: Joe McIntosh, Director Management Information Systems
CHR: Dianne Renner, Director Human Resources
Web address: www.lshonline.org
Control: State–Government, nonfederal **Service:** Psychiatric

Staffed Beds: 170

MADISON—Jefferson County

★ ○ **KING'S DAUGHTERS' HEALTH (150069)**, 1373 East State Road 62,
Zip 47250–3357, Mailing Address: P.O. Box 447, Zip 47250–0447;
tel. 812/801–0800 **A**2 10 11 **F**3 7 8 13 15 18 20 22 28 29 30 31 32 34 35
40 43 44 50 56 57 59 62 63 64 65 68 70 74 75 76 77 78 79 81 82 84
85 86 87 91 93 94 97 107 108 110 111 115 119 120 121 123 129 130 131
132 134 135 144 145 146 147 148 **P**6
Primary Contact: Carol Dozier, President and Chief Executive Officer
CFO: Steve Meacham, Vice President Finance
CIO: Linda Darnell, Director Management Information Systems
CHR: Susan Poling, Director Human Resources
CNO: Lisa Morgan, R.N., Vice President Patient Services
Web address: www.kdhhs.org
Control: Other not–for–profit (including NFP Corporation) **Service:** General
Medical and Surgical

Staffed Beds: 77 **Admissions:** 3226 **Census:** 34 **Outpatient Visits:** 212890
Births: 491 **Total Expense ($000):** 119202 **Payroll Expense ($000):** 50600
Personnel: 835

☐ **MADISON STATE HOSPITAL (154019)**, 711 Green Road, Zip 47250–2199;
tel. 812/265–2611, (Nonreporting) **A**1 10
Primary Contact: Peggy Stephens, M.D., Superintendent and Medical Director
COO: Peggy Stephens, M.D., Superintendent and Medical Director
CFO: Carolyn Copeland, Business Administrator
CMO: Peggy Stephens, M.D., Superintendent and Medical Director
CIO: Ric Martin, Information Specialist
Web address: www.in.gov/fssa/msh
Control: State–Government, nonfederal **Service:** Psychiatric

Staffed Beds: 150

MARION—Grant County

☐ **GRANT–BLACKFORD MENTAL HEALTH CENTER (154021)**, 505 North
Wabash Avenue, Zip 46952–2608; tel. 765/662–3971, (Nonreporting) **A**1 10
Primary Contact: Paul Kuczora, Chief Executive Officer
Web address: www.cornerstone.org/
Control: Other not–for–profit (including NFP Corporation) **Service:** Psychiatric

Staffed Beds: 16

IN

★ ○ **MARION GENERAL HOSPITAL (150011)**, 441 North Wabash Avenue, Zip 46952–2690; tel. 765/660–6000 **A**2 10 11 **F**3 7 8 11 13 15 18 20 22 26 28 29 30 31 34 35 40 41 44 45 50 54 57 58 59 64 68 70 74 76 77 78 79 81 82 85 86 87 89 90 91 92 93 96 97 107 108 110 111 112 114 115 116 117 118 119 129 130 132 135 145 146 147 148 **P**6
Primary Contact: Stephanie Hilton–Siebert, MSN, President and Chief Executive Officer
CFO: Jeff Wakefield, CPA, Chief Financial Officer
CMO: Edward L. Keppler, M.D., Chief Medical Officer
CIO: Emmanuel Ndow, Chief Information Officer
CHR: Karen Jones, Administrative Director Human Resources
CNO: Cynthia Futrell, MSN, Chief Nursing Officer
Web address: www.mgh.net
Control: Other not–for–profit (including NFP Corporation) **Service:** General Medical and Surgical

Staffed Beds: 115 Admissions: 5288 Census: 59 Outpatient Visits: 228054 Births: 646 Total Expense ($000): 151540 Payroll Expense ($000): 49322 Personnel: 988

VETERANS AFFAIRS NORTHERN INDIANA HEALTH CARE SYSTEM–MARION CAMPUS See Veterans Affairs Northern Indiana Health Care System, Fort Wayne

MERRILLVILLE—Lake County

REGIONAL MENTAL HEALTH CENTER (154020), 8555 Taft Street, Zip 46410–6123; tel. 219/769–4005, (Nonreporting) **A**10
Primary Contact: Robert D. Krumwied, President and Chief Executive Officer
Web address: www.regionalmentalhealth.org/
Control: Corporation, Investor–owned, for–profit **Service:** Psychiatric

Staffed Beds: 16

SOUTHLAKE CAMPUS See Methodist Hospitals, Gary

MICHIGAN CITY—Laporte County

○ **FRANCISCAN ST. ANTHONY HEALTH – MICHIGAN CITY (150015)**, 301 West Homer Street, Zip 46360–4358; tel. 219/879–8511, (Nonreporting) **A**2 10 11 19 **S** Franciscan Alliance, Mishawaka, IN
Primary Contact: Dean Mazzoni, President and Chief Executive Officer
CFO: Marc Golan, Regional Chief Financial Officer
CIO: Tim Loosemore, Regional Director Information Systems
CHR: John Barrett, Regional Director Human Resources
CNO: Trish Weber, R.N., Vice President Operations and Chief Nursing Officer
Web address: www.franciscanalliance.org
Control: Other not–for–profit (including NFP Corporation) **Service:** General Medical and Surgical

Staffed Beds: 171

SAINT ANTHONY MEMORIAL See Franciscan St. Anthony Health – Michigan City

MISHAWAKA—St. Joseph County

⊠ **KINDRED HOSPITAL OF NORTHERN INDIANA (152018)**, 215 West Fourth Street, Suite 200, Zip 46544–1917; tel. 574/252–2000, (Nonreporting) **A**1 10 **S** Kindred Healthcare, Louisville, KY
Primary Contact: Lori Skora, Chief Executive Officer
CFO: Christy Henrich, Controller
CMO: Matthew F. Koscielski, M.D., Medical Director
CNO: Jennifer Pierce, Chief Clinical Officer
Web address: www.khnorthernindiana.com/
Control: Corporation, Investor–owned, for–profit **Service:** Long–Term Acute Care hospital

Staffed Beds: 32

□ **RIVERCREST SPECIALTY HOSPITAL (152026)**, 1625 East Jefferson Boulevard, Zip 46545–7103; tel. 574/255–1400 **A**1 10 **F**3 6 29 30 35 38 56 75 77 98 101 103 132 135 148 **S** NeuroPsychiatric Hospitals, Mishawaka, IN
Primary Contact: Christy Gilbert, Chief Executive Officer
Web address: www.physicianshospitalsystem.net/
Control: Corporation, Investor–owned, for–profit **Service:** Psychiatric

Staffed Beds: 30 Admissions: 459 Census: 25 Outpatient Visits: 0 Births: 0 Total Expense ($000): 5870 Payroll Expense ($000): 3249 Personnel: 66

⊠ **SAINT JOSEPH REGIONAL MEDICAL CENTER (150012)**, 5215 Holy Cross Parkway, Zip 46545–1469; tel. 574/335–5000 **A**1 2 3 5 10 **F**3 11 13 15 17 18 19 20 21 22 23 24 26 28 29 30 31 34 35 36 39 40 45 46 47 48 49 50 52 54 55 57 58 59 60 61 63 64 65 66 68 70 71 72 74 75 76 77 78 79 80 81 82 83 84 85 86 87 89 90 91 92 93 96 97 107 108 110 114 115 117 118 119 120 121 124 126 130 131 132 135 146 147 148 **S** Trinity Health, Livonia, MI
Primary Contact: Albert Gutierrez, FACHE, President and Chief Executive Officer
COO: Christopher J. Karam, Chief Operating Officer
CMO: Stephen Anderson, M.D., Chief Medical Officer
CIO: Gary L. Miller, Senior Director Information Systems
CHR: Kurt A. Meyer, Chief Human Resource Officer
CNO: Kenneth C. Hall, R.N., Chief Nursing Officer
Web address: www.sjmed.com
Control: Other not–for–profit (including NFP Corporation) **Service:** General Medical and Surgical

Staffed Beds: 294 Admissions: 14599 Census: 178 Outpatient Visits: 158520 Births: 1757 Total Expense ($000): 284093 Payroll Expense ($000): 79751 Personnel: 1348

TRIUMPH OUR LADY OF PEACE HOSPITAL See Kindred Hospital of Northern Indiana

○ **UNITY MEDICAL & SURGICAL HOSPITAL (150177)**, 4455 Edison Lakes Parkway, Zip 46545–1442; tel. 574/968–0867, (Nonreporting) **A**10 11
Primary Contact: John M. Day, Chief Executive Officer
COO: Donald Allen, Chief Operating Officer
CFO: Matthew M. Sherwood, Chief Financial Officer
CMO: Viraj Patel, M.D., Chief Medical Officer
CIO: Richard Leighton, Financial Application Analyst
CHR: Emyle Kruyer–Collins, Chief Human Resources Officer
CNO: Sylvia K. Coffing, R.N., Chief Nursing and Compliance Officer
Web address: www.umsh.net
Control: Partnership, Investor–owned, for–profit **Service:** Surgical

Staffed Beds: 15

MONTICELLO—White County

★ **INDIANA UNIVERSITY HEALTH WHITE MEMORIAL HOSPITAL (151312)**, 720 South Sixth Street, Zip 47960–8182; tel. 574/583–7111 **A**10 18 **F**3 11 15 29 30 31 34 35 40 45 50 57 59 64 75 77 78 80 81 85 91 93 107 108 110 111 114 119 129 133 135 146 147 **S** Indiana University Health, Indianapolis, IN
Primary Contact: Jeffrey C. Zeh, President
COO: Mary Minier, Vice President Operations
CMO: Adel Khdour, M.D., Chief Medical Officer
CIO: Michelle Baker, Director Information Systems
CHR: JoEllyn Brockmeyer, Director Human Resources
CNO: Robin C. Smith, Chief Nursing Officer
Web address: www.iuhealth.org/white–memorial
Control: Other not–for–profit (including NFP Corporation) **Service:** General Medical and Surgical

Staffed Beds: 25 Admissions: 638 Census: 7 Outpatient Visits: 36320 Births: 1 Total Expense ($000): 20878 Payroll Expense ($000): 7329 Personnel: 125

MOORESVILLE—Morgan County

○ **FRANCISCAN ST. FRANCIS HEALTH – MOORESVILLE (150057)**, 1201 Hadley Road, Zip 46158–1789; tel. 317/831–1160, (Nonreporting) **A**3 5 10 11 **S** Franciscan Alliance, Mishawaka, IN
Primary Contact: Peter J. Murphy, Senior Vice President and Chief Operating Officer
CIO: Barbara Coulter, Director Information Systems
CHR: John Ross, Vice President
Web address: www.franciscanalliance.org/hospitals/mooresville/Pages/default.aspx
Control: Other not–for–profit (including NFP Corporation) **Service:** General Medical and Surgical

Staffed Beds: 115

ST. FRANCIS HOSPITAL–MOORESVILLE See Franciscan St. Francis Health – Mooresville

MUNCIE—Delaware County

○ **AMG SPECIALTY HOSPITAL – MUNCIE (152025)**, 2401 West University Avenue, 8th Floor, Zip 47303–3428; tel. 765/751–5253, (Nonreporting) **A**10 11
Primary Contact: James Whitacre, Chief Executive Officer
CNO: Lisa G. Hayes, Chief Clinical Officer
Web address: www.amgmuncie.com/
Control: Corporation, Investor–owned, for–profit **Service:** Long–Term Acute Care hospital

Staffed Beds: 32

BALL MEMORIAL HOSPITAL See Indiana University Health Ball Memorial Hospital

IN

Many Facility Codes have changed. Please refer to the AHA Guide Code Chart. © 2016 AHA Guide

⊠ △ **INDIANA UNIVERSITY HEALTH BALL MEMORIAL HOSPITAL (150089)**, 2401 University Avenue, Zip 47303–3499; tel. 765/747–3111 **A**1 2 3 5 7 8 10 19 **F**3 7 11 12 13 15 17 18 20 22 24 26 28 29 30 31 32 34 35 39 40 43 45 49 50 51 53 54 56 57 58 59 60 64 65 66 69 70 72 74 75 76 77 78 79 80 81 82 83 84 85 86 87 89 90 91 92 93 94 97 99 100 102 107 110 111 114 115 116 117 118 119 120 121 123 124 126 129 130 132 146 147 148 **S** Indiana University Health, Indianapolis, IN
Primary Contact: Michael E. Haley, President
COO: Jeffrey C. Bird, M.D., Chief Operating Officer and Chief Medical Officer
CFO: Lori Luther, CPA, Chief Financial Officer
CMO: Jeffrey C. Bird, M.D., Chief Operating Officer and Chief Medical Officer
CHR: Ann M. McGuire, Regional Vice President Human Resources
CNO: Carla C. Cox, Chief Nursing Officer
Web address: www.iuhealth.org
Control: Other not–for–profit (including NFP Corporation) **Service:** General Medical and Surgical

Staffed Beds: 339 **Admissions:** 16303 **Census:** 234 **Outpatient Visits:** 289436 **Births:** 1448 **Total Expense ($000):** 306388 **Payroll Expense ($000):** 100172 **Personnel:** 1704

MERIDIAN HEALTH SERVICES (154053), 2401 West University Avenue, Zip 47303–3428; tel. 765/747–3281, (Nonreporting) **A**10
Primary Contact: Hank A. Milius, Chief Executive Officer
CMO: Sarfraz Khan, Medical Director
Web address: www.meridianhs.org
Control: Other not–for–profit (including NFP Corporation) **Service:** Psychiatric

Staffed Beds: 20

RENAISSANCE SPECIALTY HOSPITAL OF CENTRAL INDIANA See AMG Specialty Hospital – Muncie

MUNSTER—Lake County

☐ **COMMUNITY HOSPITAL (150125)**, 901 Macarthur Boulevard, Zip 46321–2959; tel. 219/836–1600 **A**1 2 10 **F**3 8 11 12 13 15 17 18 20 22 24 26 28 29 30 31 34 35 36 38 39 40 45 46 47 49 50 53 54 55 57 58 59 62 64 70 72 73 74 75 77 78 79 80 81 82 85 86 87 90 92 93 96 107 108 110 111 114 115 116 119 120 121 123 124 126 129 130 131 132 135 144 146 147 148 **S** Community Healthcare System, Hammond, IN
Primary Contact: Luis F. Molina, Chief Executive Officer and Administrator
CFO: Daniel R. O'Brien, Vice President and Chief Financial Officer
CMO: David Robinson, President Medical and Dental Staff
CIO: Gary Weiner, Vice President Information Technology, Chief Information Officer
CHR: Debbie Brandt, Director Human Resources
CNO: Ronda McKay, R.N., Vice President Patient Care Services, Chief Nursing Officer
Web address: www.comhs.org
Control: Other not–for–profit (including NFP Corporation) **Service:** General Medical and Surgical

Staffed Beds: 493 **Admissions:** 19310 **Census:** 299 **Outpatient Visits:** 385362 **Births:** 1906 **Total Expense ($000):** 435869 **Payroll Expense ($000):** 156504 **Personnel:** 2381

○ **FRANCISCAN HEALTHCARE – MUNSTER (150165)**, 701 Superior Avenue, Zip 46321–4037; tel. 219/924–1300, (Nonreporting) **A**10 11 **S** Franciscan Alliance, Mishawaka, IN
Primary Contact: Matthew Teolis, Interim President and Chief Executive Officer, Vice President of Medical Affairs
CFO: Harold E. Collins, JD, Chief Financial Officer
CMO: Vijay D. Gupta, M.D., President and Chief Executive Officer
CIO: Steven Krause, Manager Information Technology
Web address: www.franciscanphysicianshospital.org
Control: Partnership, Investor–owned, for–profit **Service:** General Medical and Surgical

Staffed Beds: 32

NEW ALBANY—Floyd County

★ ○ **BAPTIST HEALTH FLOYD (150044)**, 1850 State Street, Zip 47150–4997; tel. 812/949–5500, (Total facility includes 324 beds in nursing home–type unit) **A**2 3 5 10 11 **F**8 11 12 13 15 17 18 20 22 24 26 28 29 30 31 34 35 40 43 49 50 56 57 59 62 64 70 74 75 76 77 78 79 80 81 82 84 85 86 87 89 93 100 107 108 110 111 114 115 116 117 118 119 120 121 123 128 129 130 131 132 135 144 146 147 148
Primary Contact: Daniel J. Eichenberger, M.D., President and Chief Executive Officer
COO: Mark Truman, Vice President of Operations
CFO: Ted Miller, Chief Financial Officer
CIO: Brian Cox, Director Information Systems
CHR: Mike Ford, Vice President Human Resources
Web address: www.floydmemorial.com
Control: County–Government, nonfederal **Service:** General Medical and Surgical

Staffed Beds: 535 **Admissions:** 14043 **Census:** 439 **Outpatient Visits:** 611678 **Births:** 1180 **Total Expense ($000):** 324292 **Payroll Expense ($000):** 136894 **Personnel:** 1924

☐ **PHYSICIANS' MEDICAL CENTER (150172)**, 4023 Reas Lane, Zip 47150–2228; tel. 812/206–7660 **A**1 10 **F**3 12 45 51 79 81 82 85 86
Primary Contact: Dennis Medley, Chief Executive Officer and Administrator
COO: Rob Jones, Director of Nursing and Operations
CFO: Dennis Medley, Chief Executive Officer
CMO: Perry Cassady, M.D., Medical Director
CIO: Rob Jones, Director of Nursing and Operations
CHR: Mary Arntz, Manager Business Office and Executive Assistant
CNO: Rob Jones, Director of Nursing and Operations
Web address: www.pmcindiana.com
Control: Partnership, Investor–owned, for–profit **Service:** Surgical

Staffed Beds: 12 **Admissions:** 252 **Census:** 6 **Outpatient Visits:** 18338 **Births:** 0 **Total Expense ($000):** 6430 **Payroll Expense ($000):** 5522 **Personnel:** 128

⊠ △ **SOUTHERN INDIANA REHABILITATION HOSPITAL (153037)**, 3104 Blackiston Boulevard, Zip 47150–9579; tel. 812/941–8300 **A**1 7 10 **F**29 34 35 57 59 74 75 77 79 86 87 90 91 130 132 135 143 146 **P**5 **S** Catholic Health Initiatives, Englewood, CO
Primary Contact: Randy L. Napier, President
CFO: Robert Steltenpohl, Vice President
CMO: John C. Shaw, M.D., Medical Director
CHR: Lisa Burris, Director Human Resources
CNO: Suzann Byers, Director of Nursing
Web address: www.sirh.org
Control: Other not–for–profit (including NFP Corporation) **Service:** Rehabilitation

Staffed Beds: 60 **Admissions:** 1258 **Census:** 40 **Outpatient Visits:** 90567 **Births:** 0 **Total Expense ($000):** 17372 **Payroll Expense ($000):** 9351 **Personnel:** 207

NEW CASTLE—Henry County

★ ○ **HENRY COUNTY HOSPITAL (150030)**, 1000 North 16th Street, Zip 47362–4319, Mailing Address: P.O. Box 490, Zip 47362–0490; tel. 765/521–0890 **A**10 11 **F**3 8 11 13 15 28 29 30 32 34 35 36 37 40 44 45 46 48 53 54 57 59 62 63 64 68 70 75 76 79 81 82 85 87 89 92 93 94 96 97 107 108 110 111 115 118 119 127 129 130 131 132 135 141 144 145 146 **P**6
Primary Contact: Paul Janssen, President and Chief Executive Officer
COO: Brian K. Ring, Chief Operating Officer
CFO: Darin Brown, Vice President Finance
CMO: Wylie McGlothlin, M.D., Chief Medical Officer
CIO: Mike Spencer, Chief Information Officer
CHR: Deanna Malott, Director Human Resources
CNO: Leslie Cowan, R.N., Chief Nursing Officer
Web address: www.hcmhcares.org
Control: County–Government, nonfederal **Service:** General Medical and Surgical

Staffed Beds: 90 **Admissions:** 2173 **Census:** 21 **Outpatient Visits:** 124525 **Births:** 346 **Total Expense ($000):** 95764 **Payroll Expense ($000):** 43818

NEWBURGH—Warrick County

☐ **BRENTWOOD MEADOWS (154055)**, 4455 Roslin Road, Zip 47630; tel. 812/858–7200 **A**1 10 **F**4 5 98 102 104 105
Primary Contact: Jessica Black, Chief Executive Officer
Web address: www.brentwoodmeadows.com
Control: Corporation, Investor–owned, for–profit **Service:** Psychiatric

Staffed Beds: 48 **Admissions:** 1557 **Census:** 30 **Births:** 0

IN

Hospital, Medicare Provider Number, Address, Telephone, Approval, Facility, and Physician Codes, Health Care System

★ American Hospital Association (AHA) membership ○ Healthcare Facilities Accreditation Program ⇑ Center for Improvement in Healthcare Quality Accreditation
☐ The Joint Commission accreditation ◇ DNV Healthcare Inc. accreditation △ Commission on Accreditation of Rehabilitation Facilities (CARF) accreditation

★ ○ **THE HEART HOSPITAL AT DEACONESS GATEWAY (150175)**, 4007 Gateway Boulevard, Zip 47630–8947; tel. 812/842–4784 **A**10 11 **F**3 17 18 20 22 24 26 28 29 30 34 35 57 58 59 60 62 63 64 68 81 83 84 85 86 87 107 108 109 111 114 115 116 117 118 119 130 132 **S** Deaconess Health System, Evansville, IN
Primary Contact: Rebecca Malotte, Executive Director and Chief Nursing Officer
COO: Rebecca Malotte, Executive Director and Chief Nursing Officer
CFO: Tracy Hoefling, Chief Financial Officer
CMO: Lee Wagmeister, M.D., President Medical Staff
CIO: Lisa Hobgood, Chief Information Officer
CHR: Sarah Bryan, Manager Human Resources
CNO: Rebecca Malotte, Executive Director and Chief Nursing Officer
Web address: www.deaconess.com/
Control: Partnership, Investor–owned, for–profit **Service:** Heart

> **Staffed Beds:** 24 **Admissions:** 1702 **Census:** 18 **Outpatient Visits:** 11221 **Births:** 0 **Total Expense ($000):** 42680 **Payroll Expense ($000):** 7576 **Personnel:** 138

★ ○ **THE WOMEN'S HOSPITAL (150149)**, 4199 Gateway Boulevard, Zip 47630–8940; tel. 812/842–4200 **A**3 10 11 **F**3 13 15 29 30 34 35 36 40 50 53 55 57 59 63 64 65 72 75 76 77 81 84 85 86 87 93 110 119 126 130 132 134 135 147 **P**6 **S** Deaconess Health System, Evansville, IN
Primary Contact: Christina M. Ryan, R.N., Chief Executive Officer
CFO: Tina Cady, Controller
CIO: Jenny Skelton, System Integration Manager
CHR: Jerri Sue Traylor, Director Human Resources and Community and Employee Wellness
CNO: Christina M. Ryan, R.N., Chief Executive Officer and Chief Nursing Officer
Web address: www.deaconess.com
Control: Partnership, Investor–owned, for–profit **Service:** Obstetrics and gynecology

> **Staffed Beds:** 74 **Admissions:** 3655 **Census:** 46 **Outpatient Visits:** 38326 **Births:** 3046 **Total Expense ($000):** 72255 **Payroll Expense ($000):** 31288 **Personnel:** 446

NOBLESVILLE—Hamilton County

○ △ **RIVERVIEW HEALTH (150059)**, 395 Westfield Road, Zip 46060–1425, Mailing Address: P.O. Box 220, Zip 46061–0220; tel. 317/773–0760 **A**2 7 10 11 **F**3 8 11 12 13 15 17 18 20 22 24 26 28 29 30 31 34 35 37 38 39 40 45 46 49 50 53 54 56 57 59 60 62 63 64 65 66 70 73 74 75 76 77 78 79 81 82 85 86 87 89 90 91 93 94 97 100 102 107 108 110 111 114 115 116 117 118 119 120 121 123 128 129 130 131 132 135 144 146 147 148 **P**6
Primary Contact: Seth Warren, President and Chief Executive Officer
COO: Lawrence Christman, Chief Financial Officer and Chief Operating Officer
CFO: Brenda Baker, Chief Financial Officer
CMO: John Paris, M.D., Chief Medical Officer
CIO: Brant Bucciarelli, Chief Information Officer
CHR: Ann Kuzee, Executive Director Human Resources
CNO: Joyce Wood, Vice President Organizational Improvement and Chief Nursing Officer
Web address: www.riverview.org
Control: County–Government, nonfederal **Service:** General Medical and Surgical

> **Staffed Beds:** 156 **Admissions:** 4667 **Census:** 68 **Outpatient Visits:** 439679 **Births:** 641 **Total Expense ($000):** 170752 **Payroll Expense ($000):** 66483 **Personnel:** 1159

NORTH VERNON—Jennings County

⊠ **ST. VINCENT JENNINGS HOSPITAL (151303)**, 301 Henry Street, Zip 47265–1097; tel. 812/352–4200 **A**1 10 18 **F**3 15 18 29 30 32 34 35 40 44 45 50 56 57 59 64 65 66 77 79 81 85 97 107 111 115 119 128 132 133 135 144 146 148 **S** Ascension Health, Saint Louis, MO
CFO: Joseph Kubala, Chief Financial Officer
CMO: Jennifer Stanley, M.D., Chief Medical Officer
CHR: Kathryn Johnson, Manager Human Resources, Marketing and Public Relations
Web address: www.stvincent.org
Control: Other not–for–profit (including NFP Corporation) **Service:** General Medical and Surgical

> **Staffed Beds:** 25 **Admissions:** 311 **Census:** 3 **Outpatient Visits:** 31786 **Births:** 0 **Total Expense ($000):** 15173 **Payroll Expense ($000):** 4679 **Personnel:** 72

PAOLI—Orange County

BLOOMINGTON HOSPITAL OF ORANGE COUNTY See Indiana University Health Paoli Hospital

⊠ **INDIANA UNIVERSITY HEALTH PAOLI HOSPITAL (151306)**, 642 West Hospital Road, Zip 47454–9672, Mailing Address: P.O. Box 499, Zip 47454–0499; tel. 812/723–2811 **A**1 10 18 **F**3 13 15 29 30 35 40 45 50 57 59 64 77 81 84 85 89 93 107 110 111 114 119 129 132 133 135 146 148 **S** Indiana University Health, Indianapolis, IN
Primary Contact: Larry Bailey, Chief Executive Officer
COO: Sonya M. Zeller, R.N., Vice President, Chief Operating Officer and Chief Nursing Officer
CMO: Vincent John Waldron, M.D., President Medical Staff
CNO: Sonya M. Zeller, R.N., Vice President, Chief Operating Officer and Chief Nursing Officer
Web address: www.iuhealth.org/paoli
Control: Other not–for–profit (including NFP Corporation) **Service:** General Medical and Surgical

> **Staffed Beds:** 25 **Admissions:** 300 **Census:** 2 **Outpatient Visits:** 27355 **Births:** 134 **Total Expense ($000):** 19325 **Payroll Expense ($000):** 7485 **Personnel:** 102

PERU—Miami County

⊠ **DUKES MEMORIAL HOSPITAL (151318)**, 275 West 12th Street, Zip 46970–1638; tel. 765/472–8000 **A**1 10 18 **F**3 7 8 13 15 17 18 28 29 34 35 40 41 50 51 57 59 64 68 69 70 75 76 77 79 81 82 85 87 89 90 93 107 108 110 111 115 118 119 129 130 132 133 135 144 146 147 **P**6 **S** Community Health Systems, Inc., Franklin, TN
Primary Contact: Debra Close, Chief Executive Officer
CFO: Adam Cumbo, Chief Financial Officer
CMO: Neil Stalker, M.D., Chief of Staff
Web address: www.dukesmemorialhosp.com
Control: Corporation, Investor–owned, for–profit **Service:** General Medical and Surgical

> **Staffed Beds:** 25 **Admissions:** 1148 **Census:** 10 **Outpatient Visits:** 41099 **Births:** 189 **Total Expense ($000):** 39585 **Payroll Expense ($000):** 17134 **Personnel:** 262

PLYMOUTH—Marshall County

☐ **MICHIANA BEHAVIORAL HEALTH CENTER (154047)**, 1800 North Oak Drive, Zip 46563–3492; tel. 574/936–3784, (Nonreporting) **A**1 10 **S** Universal Health Services, Inc., King of Prussia, PA
Primary Contact: Michael Perry, Chief Executive Officer
CFO: Jeff Calvin, Chief Financial Officer
CMO: Robert Raster, M.D., Medical Director
CIO: Leslie McLaughlin, Director of Business Development
CHR: Becky Nowicki, Director Human Resources
CNO: Brandi Richard, Chief Nursing Officer
Web address: www.michianabhc.com
Control: Corporation, Investor–owned, for–profit **Service:** Psychiatric

> **Staffed Beds:** 75

⊠ **SAINT JOSEPH REGIONAL MEDICAL CENTER–PLYMOUTH CAMPUS (150076)**, 1915 Lake Avenue, Zip 46563–9366, Mailing Address: P.O. Box 670, Zip 46563–0670; tel. 574/948–4000 **A**1 10 **F**3 13 15 18 20 29 30 31 34 35 40 45 46 50 51 54 57 59 64 65 66 68 70 74 75 76 78 79 81 84 85 86 87 89 91 92 93 97 107 108 110 114 115 118 119 120 121 123 124 129 132 135 146 148 **S** Trinity Health, Livonia, MI
Primary Contact: Loretta Schmidt, President
COO: Tamara Awald, Chief Nursing Officer and Chief Operating Officer
CFO: Janice Dunn, Chief Financial Officer
CMO: Stephen Anderson, M.D., Chief Medical Officer
CIO: Gary L. Miller, Regional Director Information Systems
CHR: Kurt A. Meyer, Chief Human Resources Officer
CNO: Tamara Awald, Chief Nursing Officer and Chief Operating Officer
Web address: www.sjmed.com
Control: Other not–for–profit (including NFP Corporation) **Service:** General Medical and Surgical

> **Staffed Beds:** 48 **Admissions:** 1834 **Census:** 15 **Outpatient Visits:** 88238 **Births:** 251 **Total Expense ($000):** 43582 **Payroll Expense ($000):** 14944 **Personnel:** 231

PORTLAND—Jay County

⊠ **JAY COUNTY HOSPITAL (151320)**, 500 West Votaw Street, Zip 47371–1322; tel. 260/726–7131 **A**1 10 18 **F**3 8 11 15 28 29 30 32 34 35 40 45 50 57 59 68 70 75 76 77 81 85 86 87 103 107 108 110 111 114 119 129 130 132 133 135 146 148 **P**6 **S** Indiana University Health, Indianapolis, IN
Primary Contact: David W. Hyatt, Chief Executive Officer
CFO: Don Michael, Vice President, Chief Financial Officer
CIO: Jeff Horn, Vice President, Information and Support Services
CHR: Jerry Bozell, Vice President, Human Resources
CNO: Lisa Craiger, Vice President, Chief Nursing Officer
Web address: www.jaycountyhospital.com
Control: County–Government, nonfederal **Service:** General Medical and Surgical

> **Staffed Beds:** 35 **Admissions:** 912 **Census:** 12 **Outpatient Visits:** 98855 **Births:** 76 **Total Expense ($000):** 37083 **Payroll Expense ($000):** 15425 **Personnel:** 315

IN

PRINCETON—Gibson County

✠ **GIBSON GENERAL HOSPITAL (151319)**, 1808 Sherman Drive, Zip 47670–1043; tel. 812/385–3401, (Total facility includes 45 beds in nursing home–type unit) **A**1 10 18 **F**3 5 11 15 28 29 30 31 34 35 38 40 45 49 50 54 56 57 58 59 62 64 68 70 75 77 79 81 82 89 93 97 99 100 101 102 103 104 107 110 111 115 119 128 129 130 131 132 133 146 148 **P**6 **S** Alliant Management Services, Louisville, KY
Primary Contact: Emmett C. Schuster, President and Chief Executive Officer
CFO: James R. Childers, Vice President and Chief Financial Officer
CMO: Krishna Murthy, M.D., Chief of Medical Staff
CIO: James R. Childers, Vice President and Chief Financial Officer
CHR: D. Deann Hunt, Director Human Resources
CNO: Lori Phillips, Vice President and Chief Nursing Officer
Web address: www.gibsongeneral.com
Control: Other not–for–profit (including NFP Corporation) **Service:** General Medical and Surgical

Staffed Beds: 70 **Admissions:** 490 **Census:** 44 **Outpatient Visits:** 34577
Births: 0 **Total Expense ($000):** 23890 **Payroll Expense ($000):** 10688
Personnel: 279

RENSSELAER—Jasper County

FRANCISCAN HEALTH RENSSELEAR (151324), 1104 East Grace Street, Zip 47978–3296; tel. 219/866–5141, (Total facility includes 21 beds in nursing home–type unit) (Data for 122 days) **A**10 18 **F**3 11 15 28 29 30 31 34 35 39 40 43 49 50 51 53 54 59 62 63 64 65 67 68 69 70 74 75 77 78 79 81 82 85 86 87 93 96 107 108 110 111 114 115 118 119 127 128 129 130 131 132 133 135 146 148 **S** Franciscan Alliance, Mishawaka, IN
Primary Contact: Timothy M. Schreeg, President and Chief Executive Officer
CFO: Jeffrey D. Webb, CPA, Chief Financial Officer
CIO: Kirby Reed, Director Information Systems
CHR: Deana Brown, Director Administrative Services
CNO: Stacie Klingler, R.N., Vice President of Patient Services
Web address: www.jchh.com
Control: Church–operated, Nongovernment, not–for profit **Service:** General Medical and Surgical

Staffed Beds: 46 **Admissions:** 281 **Census:** 23 **Outpatient Visits:** 30438
Births: 0 **Total Expense ($000):** 12376 **Payroll Expense ($000):** 5056
Personnel: 262

RICHMOND—Wayne County

★ ○ **REID HEALTH (150048)**, 1100 Reid Parkway, Zip 47374–1157; tel. 765/983–3000 **A**2 10 11 13 **F**3 11 13 15 18 20 22 24 26 28 29 30 31 32 34 35 37 40 43 44 45 47 49 50 51 54 55 56 57 58 59 61 63 64 68 69 70 74 75 76 77 78 79 81 82 84 85 86 87 89 90 91 92 93 95 96 97 98 100 101 102 103 104 107 108 110 111 114 115 116 117 118 119 120 121 123 126 127 129 130 131 132 135 144 146 147 148 **P**6 7 8
Primary Contact: Craig C. Kinyon, President
CFO: Christopher D. Knight, Vice President Finance and Chief Financial Officer
CMO: Thomas Huth, M.D., Vice President Medical Affairs
CIO: Tim Love, Director Information Services
CHR: Scott C. Rauch, Vice President Human Resources
CNO: Kay B. Cartwright, R.N., Vice President and Chief Nursing Officer
Web address: www.reidhealth.org
Control: Other not–for–profit (including NFP Corporation) **Service:** General Medical and Surgical

Staffed Beds: 217 **Admissions:** 12114 **Census:** 140 **Outpatient Visits:** 348906 **Births:** 696 **Total Expense ($000):** 401634 **Payroll Expense ($000):** 156084 **Personnel:** 2326

☐ **RICHMOND STATE HOSPITAL (154018)**, 498 N.W. 18th Street, Zip 47374–2851; tel. 765/966–0511, (Nonreporting) **A**1 10
Primary Contact: Terry Suttle, Superintendent
CFO: Dave Shelford, Assistant Superintendent
CMO: Donald Graber, M.D., Medical Director
CIO: Robert Boatman, Director Information Technology
CHR: Sarah Witt, Director Human Resources
Web address: www.richmondstatehospital.org
Control: State–Government, nonfederal **Service:** Psychiatric

Staffed Beds: 213

ROCHESTER—Fulton County

★ **WOODLAWN HOSPITAL (151313)**, 1400 East Ninth Street, Zip 46975–8937; tel. 574/223–3141 **A**10 18 **F**3 11 13 15 29 30 31 34 40 46 56 57 59 63 65 68 69 75 77 78 79 81 82 93 94 97 107 108 111 115 116 119 129 130 132 133 135 143 146 147 148 **P**6
Primary Contact: John L. Alley, Chief Executive Officer
CFO: Dave Cholger, Chief Financial Officer
CHR: Debra J. Lemasters, Director Human Resources
Web address: www.woodlawnhospital.com
Control: County–Government, nonfederal **Service:** General Medical and Surgical

Staffed Beds: 25 **Admissions:** 1112 **Census:** 11 **Outpatient Visits:** 54282
Births: 226 **Total Expense ($000):** 51040 **Payroll Expense ($000):** 24046
Personnel: 357

RUSHVILLE—Rush County

★ **RUSH MEMORIAL HOSPITAL (151304)**, 1300 North Main Street, Zip 46173–1198, Mailing Address: P.O. Box 608, Zip 46173–0608; tel. 765/932–4111 **A**10 18 **F**3 7 11 15 18 24 28 29 31 35 36 40 46 51 52 57 59 64 65 74 75 77 78 79 81 85 93 97 107 111 114 117 120 121 122 129 130 131 132 133 135 146 147 148 **P**6
Primary Contact: Bradley Smith, President and Chief Executive Officer
COO: Debbie Jones–Browning, Vice President Operations and Physician Services and Chief Operating Officer
CFO: Karen Meyer, Vice President Finance and Chief Financial Officer
CMO: Daniel Stahl, D.O., Chief of Staff
CIO: Jim Boyer, Vice President Information Technology and Chief Information Officer
CHR: Dennis Fogle, Vice President of Human Resources
CNO: Gretchen Smith, Vice President Nursing and Compliance and Risk
Web address: www.rushmemorial.com
Control: County–Government, nonfederal **Service:** General Medical and Surgical

Staffed Beds: 25 **Admissions:** 472 **Census:** 4 **Outpatient Visits:** 32880
Births: 0 **Total Expense ($000):** 27819 **Payroll Expense ($000):** 12126
Personnel: 244

SALEM—Washington County

✠ **ST. VINCENT SALEM HOSPITAL (151314)**, 911 North Shelby Street, Zip 47167–1694; tel. 812/883–5881 **A**1 10 18 **F**3 11 15 28 29 30 32 34 40 45 47 49 57 59 75 77 79 81 82 85 93 104 107 111 114 119 129 130 132 133 148 **P**6 **S** Ascension Health, Saint Louis, MO
Primary Contact: Dana M. Muntz, Chief Executive Officer
CFO: Joseph Kubala, Director Financial and Support Services
CMO: S. E. Kemker, M.D., President Medical Staff
CIO: Jeremy Long, Manager Information Systems
CHR: Val Potter, Director Human Resources
Web address: www.stvincent.org/St–Vincent–Salem/Default.aspx
Control: Other not–for–profit (including NFP Corporation) **Service:** General Medical and Surgical

Staffed Beds: 25 **Admissions:** 202 **Census:** 2 **Outpatient Visits:** 29325
Births: 0 **Total Expense ($000):** 16501 **Payroll Expense ($000):** 5945
Personnel: 100

SCOTTSBURG—Scott County

✠ **SCOTT MEMORIAL HOSPITAL (151334)**, 1415 North Gardner Street, Zip 47170, Mailing Address: Box 430, Zip 47170–0430; tel. 812/752–3456, (Nonreporting) **A**1 10 18 **S** LifePoint Health, Brentwood, TN
Primary Contact: Michael Everett, Chief Executive Officer
CFO: Angela Doan, Chief Financial Officer
CNO: Dawn Mays, Chief Nursing Officer
Web address: www.scottmemorial.com
Control: County–Government, nonfederal **Service:** General Medical and Surgical

Staffed Beds: 25

IN

SEYMOUR—Jackson County

✠ **SCHNECK MEDICAL CENTER (150065)**, 411 West Tipton Street, Zip 47274–2363, Mailing Address: P.O. Box 2349, Zip 47274–5000; tel. 812/522–2349 **A**1 2 10 **F**3 12 13 15 18 28 29 30 31 34 35 36 40 45 56 57 59 62 63 64 65 68 70 74 75 76 77 78 79 81 82 84 85 87 89 93 94 98 104 107 110 111 115 119 120 121 123 126 129 130 131 132 133 135 146 147 148 **P**8
Primary Contact: Warren Forgey, CPA, FACHE, President and Chief Executive Officer
CFO: Deborah Ridlen, CPA, Vice President Fiscal Services and Chief Financial Officer
CMO: Douglas Towriss, Vice President and Chief Medical Officer
CIO: Craig Rice, Director Information
CHR: Kathy Covert, MSN, Vice President Human Resources
CNO: Amy Pettit, R.N., Vice President Nursing Services and Chief Nursing Officer
Web address: www.schneckmed.org
Control: County–Government, nonfederal **Service:** General Medical and Surgical

Staffed Beds: 93 **Admissions:** 3255 **Census:** 34 **Outpatient Visits:** 205356 **Births:** 753 **Total Expense ($000):** 118055 **Payroll Expense ($000):** 51345 **Personnel:** 771

SHELBYVILLE—Shelby County

★ ○ **MAJOR HOSPITAL (150097)**, 150 West Washington Street, Zip 46176–1236; tel. 317/392–3211 **A**2 10 11 **F**3 12 13 15 28 29 30 31 34 35 40 47 50 57 59 62 63 64 68 70 73 74 75 76 77 78 79 80 81 82 84 85 89 93 97 107 108 110 111 114 118 119 120 121 123 129 130 131 132 135 144 146 147 148 **P**6
Primary Contact: John M. Horner, President and Chief Executive Officer
CFO: Ralph Mercuri, Vice President and Chief Financial Officer
CMO: Douglas S. Carter, M.D., Vice President and Chief Medical Officer
CIO: Dan Van Gundy, Director of Information Technology Systems and Hardwire
CHR: Nicki Sparling, Manager Human Resources
CNO: Valerie L. Miller, MSN, Director of Nursing
Web address: www.majorhospital.org
Control: City–County, Government, nonfederal **Service:** General Medical and Surgical

Staffed Beds: 72 **Admissions:** 2715 **Census:** 27 **Outpatient Visits:** 160660 **Births:** 357 **Total Expense ($000):** 86549 **Payroll Expense ($000):** 39004 **Personnel:** 929

SOUTH BEND—St. Joseph County

✠ △ **MEMORIAL HOSPITAL OF SOUTH BEND (150058)**, 615 North Michigan Street, Zip 46601–1033; tel. 574/647–1000, (Includes MEMORIAL CHILDREN'S HOSPITAL, 615 North Michigan Street, Zip 46601; tel. 574/647–1000) **A**1 2 3 7 10 **F**3 7 8 11 12 13 15 17 18 19 20 22 24 26 28 29 30 31 35 36 38 40 43 46 49 50 53 55 56 58 59 60 61 64 65 67 68 70 72 73 74 75 76 77 78 79 81 82 84 85 86 87 88 89 90 91 92 93 96 98 99 102 103 107 108 110 114 115 116 117 118 119 120 121 123 124 126 129 130 131 132 135 146 147 148 **P**4 5 6 8 **S** Beacon Health System, South Bend, IN
Primary Contact: Philip A. Newbold, Chief Executive Officer, Beacon Health System
COO: Kreg Gruber, Chief Operating Officer
CFO: Jeff Costello, Chief Financial Officer
CMO: Cheryl Wibbens, M.D., Vice President Medical Staff Affairs
CIO: Mark Warlick, Chief Information Officer
CHR: Steven M. Eller, Chief Human Resources Officer, Beacon Health System
Web address: www.qualityoflife.org
Control: Other not–for–profit (including NFP Corporation) **Service:** General Medical and Surgical

Staffed Beds: 445 **Admissions:** 20180 **Census:** 296 **Outpatient Visits:** 200214 **Births:** 2541 **Total Expense ($000):** 407028 **Payroll Expense ($000):** 140824 **Personnel:** 2595

SULLIVAN—Sullivan County

★ **SULLIVAN COUNTY COMMUNITY HOSPITAL (151327)**, 2200 North Section Street, Zip 47882–7523, Mailing Address: P.O. Box 10, Zip 47882–0010; tel. 812/268–4311 **A**10 18 **F**3 8 13 15 28 29 32 34 35 40 44 45 47 48 53 56 57 59 61 62 69 70 75 76 77 78 79 81 86 87 93 97 107 110 111 114 127 129 130 131 133 146 147 148 **P**7 **S** QHR, Brentwood, TN
Primary Contact: Michelle Sly–Franklin, Chief Executive Officer
CFO: Scott Andritsch, Chief Financial Officer
CMO: Divyesh Purohit, M.D., Chief of Staff
CIO: Hap Beckes, Director Information Systems
CHR: Denise Hart, Director Human Resources
CNO: Lori Resler, R.N., Chief Nurse
Web address: www.schosp.com
Control: County–Government, nonfederal **Service:** General Medical and Surgical

Staffed Beds: 25 **Admissions:** 755 **Census:** 6 **Outpatient Visits:** 72040 **Births:** 122 **Total Expense ($000):** 23451 **Payroll Expense ($000):** 10599 **Personnel:** 196

TELL CITY—Perry County

★ **PERRY COUNTY MEMORIAL HOSPITAL (151322)**, 8885 State Road 237, Zip 47586–2750; tel. 812/547–7011 **A**10 18 **F**3 7 8 11 13 15 18 28 29 30 31 34 35 40 45 50 56 57 59 62 64 65 70 75 76 78 79 81 86 87 89 107 110 111 114 119 127 129 130 133 135 146 148 **P**5 **S** Alliant Management Services, Louisville, KY
Primary Contact: Brian J. Herwig, Chief Executive Officer
COO: Becky Elder, Vice President Clinical Services
CMO: Juan Cornejo, M.D., Chief of Staff
CIO: Mark Miller, Director Information Systems
CHR: Sheila Gaynor, Director Human Resources
CNO: Michele Howard, Director of Nursing
Web address: www.pchospital.org
Control: County–Government, nonfederal **Service:** General Medical and Surgical

Staffed Beds: 25 **Admissions:** 785 **Census:** 7 **Outpatient Visits:** 78813 **Births:** 83 **Total Expense ($000):** 33961 **Payroll Expense ($000):** 9852 **Personnel:** 268

TERRE HAUTE—Vigo County

HAMILTON CENTER (154009), 620 Eighth Avenue, Zip 47804–2744; tel. 812/231–8323, (Nonreporting) **A**10
Primary Contact: Melvin Burks, Chief Executive Officer
COO: Robb Johnson, Director Operations
CFO: Renee Utley, Chief Financial Officer
CMO: Ahsan Mahmood, M.D., Chief Medical Officer
CIO: Hans Eilbracht, Chief Information Officer
CHR: Margie Anshutz, Chief Development Officer
CNO: Rose Christy, Executive Director of Medical Services
Web address: www.hamiltoncenter.org
Control: State–Government, nonfederal **Service:** Psychiatric

Staffed Beds: 16

☐ **HARSHA BEHAVIORAL CENTER (154054)**, 1420 East Crossing Boulevard, Zip 47802–5316; tel. 866/644–8880 **A**1 10 **F**6 98 99 102 103
Primary Contact: Roopam Harshawat, Chief Executive Officer
COO: Holly Near, Chief Administrative Officer
CFO: Holly Near, Chief Administrative Officer
CMO: Paras Harshawat, M.D., Medical Director
CHR: Karen Hunt, Executive Director
CNO: Cindy Dowers, Chief Nursing Officer
Web address: www.harshacenter.com
Control: Corporation, Investor–owned, for–profit **Service:** Psychiatric

Staffed Beds: 44 **Admissions:** 1620 **Census:** 35 **Outpatient Visits:** 0 **Births:** 0 **Personnel:** 127

✠ **TERRE HAUTE REGIONAL HOSPITAL (150046)**, 3901 South Seventh Street, Zip 47802–5709; tel. 812/232–0021, (Nonreporting) **A**1 2 10 **S** HCA, Nashville, TN
Primary Contact: Mary Ann Conroy, Chief Executive Officer
COO: Tim Prestridge, Chief Operating Officer
CIO: Mike Kuckewich, Director Information Systems
CNO: Angela Ellis, R.N., Chief Nursing Officer
Web address: www.regionalhospital.com
Control: Corporation, Investor–owned, for–profit **Service:** General Medical and Surgical

Staffed Beds: 208

★ ○ **UNION HOSPITAL (150023)**, 1606 North Seventh Street, Zip 47804–2780; tel. 812/238–7000 **A**2 3 10 11 19 **F**3 8 13 15 18 20 22 24 26 28 29 30 31 34 35 36 40 45 46 48 49 50 51 53 54 57 59 60 64 68 70 72 73 74 75 76 77 78 79 81 85 86 87 89 90 91 92 93 94 95 96 97 100 107 108 110 111 112 114 115 116 117 118 119 120 121 123 126 127 130 131 132 135 144 146 147 148 **P**6
Primary Contact: Steve M. Holman, Chief Executive Officer
CFO: Wayne Hutson, Executive Vice President and Chief Financial Officer
CMO: John Bolinger, M.D., Vice President Medical Affairs
CIO: Kym Pfrank, Senior Vice President and Chief Operating Officer
CHR: Sally Zuel, Vice President Human Resources
CNO: Rhonda E. Smith, R.N., Vice President Patient Care Services and Chief Nursing Officer
Web address: www.uhhg.org
Control: Other not–for–profit (including NFP Corporation) **Service:** General Medical and Surgical

Staffed Beds: 238 **Admissions:** 14587 **Census:** 176 **Outpatient Visits:** 394353 **Births:** 1965 **Total Expense ($000):** 364956 **Payroll Expense ($000):** 116688 **Personnel:** 1707

Many Facility Codes have changed. Please refer to the AHA Guide Code Chart. © 2016 AHA Guide

IN

TIPTON—Tipton County

⊞ **INDIANA UNIVERSITY HEALTH TIPTON HOSPITAL (151311)**, 1000 South Main Street, Zip 46072–9799; tel. 765/675–8500 **A**1 10 18 **F**3 8 11 15 18 28 29 30 31 34 35 39 40 45 46 47 48 53 57 59 70 74 75 77 78 79 81 82 85 86 87 93 107 108 110 111 115 119 129 131 132 133 135 146 147 148 **S** Indiana University Health, Indianapolis, IN
Primary Contact: Michael Harlowe, President and Chief Executive Officer
CFO: Randall C. Yust, Chief Financial Officer NCR
CMO: Gaurau Arora, M.D., Chief Medical Officer
CHR: Shelly E. Huff, Manager Human Resources
CNO: Jo Ellen Scott, R.N., Senior Vice President of Patient Care Services and Chief Nursing Officer
Web address: www.iuhealth.org
Control: Other not–for–profit (including NFP Corporation) **Service:** General Medical and Surgical

Staffed Beds: 25 **Admissions:** 898 **Census:** 10 **Outpatient Visits:** 51538 **Births:** 0 **Total Expense ($000):** 32957 **Payroll Expense ($000):** 10227 **Personnel:** 162

TIPTON HOSPITAL See Indiana University Health Tipton Hospital

VALPARAISO—Porter County

⊞ **PORTER REGIONAL HOSPITAL (150035)**, 85 East U.S. Highway 6, Zip 46383–8947; tel. 219/983–8300, (Nonreporting) **A**1 5 10 **S** Community Health Systems, Inc., Franklin, TN
Primary Contact: Stephen Lunn, Chief Executive Officer
COO: Ashley Dickinson, Chief Operating Officer
CFO: Douglas Browning, Chief Financial Officer
CMO: Ramireddy K. Tummuru, M.D., Chief Medical Officer
CIO: Robert Richardson, Information Technology Administrator
CHR: Angie Hampton, Director Human Resources
Web address: www.porterhealth.com
Control: Corporation, Investor–owned, for–profit **Service:** General Medical and Surgical

Staffed Beds: 276

PORTER–STARKE SERVICES (154052), 601 Wall Street, Zip 46383–2512; tel. 219/531–3500 **A**10 **F**5 29 66 68 98 99 101 103 104 130 135 **P**6
Primary Contact: Rocco Schiralli, President/Chief Executive Officer
CFO: Mary Idstein, Chief Financial Officer
CMO: Anand Popli, Medical Director
Web address: www.porterstarke.org
Control: Other not–for–profit (including NFP Corporation) **Service:** Psychiatric

Staffed Beds: 16 **Admissions:** 671 **Census:** 8 **Outpatient Visits:** 124546 **Births:** 0 **Total Expense ($000):** 16287 **Payroll Expense ($000):** 9419 **Personnel:** 217

VINCENNES—Knox County

⊞ △ **GOOD SAMARITAN HOSPITAL (150042)**, 520 South Seventh Street, Zip 47591–1038; tel. 812/882–5220 **A**1 2 7 10 19 **F**1 3 4 5 8 11 13 15 16 17 18 19 20 22 28 29 30 31 32 34 35 38 40 44 45 46 47 48 49 53 54 56 57 58 59 63 64 65 66 67 68 70 72 73 74 75 76 77 78 79 80 81 84 85 87 88 89 90 92 93 96 97 98 100 101 102 103 104 106 107 108 110 111 115 118 119 120 121 123 127 128 129 130 131 132 134 135 144 145 146 147 148 **P**6
Primary Contact: Robert D. McLin, President and Chief Executive Officer
COO: Adam Thacker, Chief Operating Officer
CFO: Thomas M. Cook, Chief Financial Officer
CMO: Charles C. Hedde, M.D., Chief Medical Officer
CIO: Daniel Scott, Director of Information Systems
CHR: Dean Wagoner, Director Human Resources
CNO: Karen S. Haak, R.N., Chief Nursing Officer
Web address: www.gshvin.org/goodsamaritan
Control: County–Government, nonfederal **Service:** General Medical and Surgical

Staffed Beds: 191 **Admissions:** 7312 **Census:** 97 **Outpatient Visits:** 507091 **Births:** 476 **Total Expense ($000):** 320464 **Payroll Expense ($000):** 126440 **Personnel:** 1629

WABASH—Wabash County

⊞ **PARKVIEW WABASH COUNTY HOSPITAL (151310)**, 710 North East Street, Zip 46992–1924, Mailing Address: P.O. Box 548, Zip 46992–0548; tel. 260/563–3131 **A**1 10 18 **F**3 15 28 29 30 31 34 35 40 44 45 46 47 50 56 57 59 62 63 68 69 70 75 77 78 79 81 85 93 107 108 110 111 119 129 130 131 132 133 135 146 148 **S** Parkview Health, Fort Wayne, IN
Primary Contact: Marilyn J. Custer–Mitchell, President
CMO: Jeff Miller, M.D., Chief of Staff
CIO: David Brinson, Director Information Technology
CHR: Kimberly R. Shininger, Manger, Human Resources
CNO: Cathy Allyson Wolfe, Chief Nursing Officer
Web address: www.wchospital.com
Control: Other not–for–profit (including NFP Corporation) **Service:** General Medical and Surgical

Staffed Beds: 25 **Admissions:** 608 **Census:** 5 **Outpatient Visits:** 12090 **Births:** 0 **Total Expense ($000):** 35472 **Payroll Expense ($000):** 9534 **Personnel:** 166

WARSAW—Kosciusko County

⊞ **KOSCIUSKO COMMUNITY HOSPITAL (150133)**, 2101 East Dubois Drive, Zip 46580–3288; tel. 574/267–3200 **A**1 10 19 **F**3 8 12 13 15 28 29 30 31 32 34 35 40 43 44 49 50 51 53 57 58 59 64 65 68 70 74 75 76 77 78 79 81 82 85 86 89 90 93 107 108 110 111 114 115 116 117 118 119 120 121 129 130 131 132 144 146 147 148 **P**6 **S** Community Health Systems, Inc., Franklin, TN
Primary Contact: Kirk M. Ray, Chief Executive Officer
CFO: Douglas J. BeMent, Chief Financial Officer
CMO: Patrick Silveus, M.D., Medical Director
CIO: Tammy Lukens, Director Information
CHR: Joe Jarboe, Director Human Resources
CNO: Kim Finch, Chief Nursing Officer
Web address: www.kch.com
Control: Corporation, Investor–owned, for–profit **Service:** General Medical and Surgical

Staffed Beds: 72 **Admissions:** 3613 **Census:** 30 **Outpatient Visits:** 109444 **Births:** 520 **Total Expense ($000):** 64352 **Payroll Expense ($000):** 22775 **Personnel:** 550

★ **OTIS R. BOWEN CENTER FOR HUMAN SERVICES (154014)**, 2621 East Jefferson Street, Zip 46580–3880; tel. 574/267–7169, (Nonreporting) **A**10
Primary Contact: Kurt Carlson, Chief Executive Officer
Web address: www.bowencenter.org
Control: Other not–for–profit (including NFP Corporation) **Service:** Psychiatric

Staffed Beds: 16

WASHINGTON—Daviess County

⊞ △ **DAVIESS COMMUNITY HOSPITAL (150061)**, 1314 East Walnut Street, Zip 47501–2860, Mailing Address: P.O. Box 760, Zip 47501–0760; tel. 812/254–2760, (Nonreporting) **A**1 7 10 **S** QHR, Brentwood, TN
Primary Contact: David Bixler, Chief Executive Officer
CMO: Michael Baker, D.O., Chief of Staff
CIO: Richard Meinhart, Manager Information Systems
CHR: Marilyn Richard, Director Human Resources
Web address: www.dchosp.org
Control: County–Government, nonfederal **Service:** General Medical and Surgical

Staffed Beds: 80

WEST LAFAYETTE—Tippecanoe County

★ **RIVER BEND HOSPITAL (154005)**, 2900 North River Road, Zip 47906–3744; tel. 765/464–0400, (Nonreporting) **A**10
Primary Contact: Stephanie Long, President and Chief Executive Officer
COO: Tom Gillian, Chief Operating Officer
CFO: Jeff Nagy, Chief Financial Officer
CMO: Richard Rahdert, M.D., Medical Director
CIO: Craig Anderson, Director Management Information Systems
CHR: Jan Shaw, Director Personnel
CNO: Megan Gibson, Nurse Manager
Web address: www.nchsi.com/riverbendhospital.cfm
Control: Other not–for–profit (including NFP Corporation) **Service:** Psychiatric

Staffed Beds: 16

WABASH VALLEY HOSPITAL See River Bend Hospital

Hospital, Medicare Provider Number, Address, Telephone, Approval, Facility, and Physician Codes, Health Care System

★ American Hospital Association (AHA) membership
☐ The Joint Commission accreditation
◯ Healthcare Facilities Accreditation Program
◇ DNV Healthcare Inc. accreditation
⇑ Center for Improvement in Healthcare Quality Accreditation
△ Commission on Accreditation of Rehabilitation Facilities (CARF) accreditation

WILLIAMSPORT—Warren County

✠ **ST. VINCENT WILLIAMSPORT HOSPITAL (151307)**, 412 North Monroe Street, Zip 47993–1049; tel. 765/762–4000 **A**1 10 18 **F**3 7 15 29 30 34 35 40 45 50 51 57 59 64 75 77 79 81 85 86 87 93 97 107 111 114 119 127 131 132 133 135 143 146 **P**6 **S** Ascension Health, Saint Louis, MO
Primary Contact: Jane Craigin, Chief Executive Officer
CFO: Janet Merritt, Chief Financial Officer
Web address: www.stvincent.org
Control: Other not–for–profit (including NFP Corporation) **Service:** General Medical and Surgical

Staffed Beds: 16 **Admissions:** 732 **Census:** 7 **Outpatient Visits:** 68125 **Births:** 0 **Total Expense ($000):** 18900 **Payroll Expense ($000):** 8699 **Personnel:** 133

WINAMAC—Pulaski County

★ **PULASKI MEMORIAL HOSPITAL (151305)**, 616 East 13th Street, Zip 46996–1117, Mailing Address: P.O. Box 279, Zip 46996–0279; tel. 574/946–2100 **A**10 18 **F**3 11 13 15 18 28 29 30 31 34 35 40 43 45 50 53 56 57 59 62 63 64 65 68 73 75 76 77 78 79 80 81 82 85 86 87 89 90 91 93 96 97 103 107 110 114 119 127 128 130 131 132 133 135 146 148 **P**6
Primary Contact: Thomas Barry, Chief Executive Officer
CFO: Gregg Malott, Chief Financial Officer
CMO: Rex Allman, M.D., President Medical Staff
CIO: Jeff Boer, Director Information Technology
CHR: Mark Fenn, Director Human Resources
CNO: Linda Webb, R.N., Chief Nursing Executive
Web address: www.pmhnet.com
Control: County–Government, nonfederal **Service:** General Medical and Surgical

Staffed Beds: 25 **Admissions:** 672 **Census:** 7 **Outpatient Visits:** 28910 **Births:** 93 **Total Expense ($000):** 29605 **Payroll Expense ($000):** 13691 **Personnel:** 249

WINCHESTER—Randolph County

✠ **ST. VINCENT RANDOLPH HOSPITAL (151301)**, 473 Greenville Avenue, Zip 47394–9436; tel. 765/584–0004 **A**1 10 18 **F**3 11 13 15 28 29 30 31 34 35 40 44 45 50 57 59 64 65 68 75 76 77 79 81 85 86 87 89 93 107 110 111 114 119 129 130 131 132 133 135 146 147 148 **S** Ascension Health, Saint Louis, MO
Primary Contact: Francis G. Albarano, Administrator
CFO: John Arthur, Chief Financial Officer
CMO: Gary Brazel, M.D., Chief Medical Officer
CHR: Richard Ross Brodhead, Director Human Resources
CNO: Carla Fouse, Chief Nursing Officer
Web address: www.stvincent.org
Control: Other not–for–profit (including NFP Corporation) **Service:** General Medical and Surgical

Staffed Beds: 16 **Admissions:** 657 **Census:** 5 **Outpatient Visits:** 42529 **Births:** 247 **Total Expense ($000):** 21417 **Payroll Expense ($000):** 7585 **Personnel:** 164

IN

Many Facility Codes have changed. Please refer to the AHA Guide Code Chart. © 2016 AHA Guide

IOWA

ALBIA—Monroe County

★ **MONROE COUNTY HOSPITAL AND CLINICS (161342)**, 6580 165th Street,
Zip 52531–8793; tel. 641/932–2134 **A**10 18 **F**7 11 15 28 29 31 34 40 43 50
57 59 77 78 81 93 107 110 114 119 127 130 132 133 **P**6
Primary Contact: Veronica Fuhs, Chief Executive Officer
Web address: www.mchalbia.com
Control: County–Government, nonfederal **Service:** General Medical and Surgical

Staffed Beds: 25 **Admissions:** 349 **Census:** 5 **Outpatient Visits:** 48046
Births: 0 **Total Expense ($000):** 17368 **Payroll Expense ($000):** 6821
Personnel: 135

ALGONA—Kossuth County

★ **KOSSUTH REGIONAL HEALTH CENTER (161353)**, 1515 South Phillips Street,
Zip 50511–3649; tel. 515/295–2451 **A**10 18 **F**11 13 15 17 28 29 30 31 32
34 35 36 40 41 43 50 56 57 59 62 63 64 65 67 68 70 75 77 78 81 82 84
86 87 92 93 97 107 114 119 127 128 129 130 131 132 133 135 146 147
148 **P**8 **S** Trinity Health, Livonia, MI
Primary Contact: Scott A. Curtis, Administrator and Chief Executive Officer
CFO: Jason Feucht, Chief Financial Officer
CMO: Michael Lampe, M.D., Chief of Staff
CIO: Nancy Erickson, Administrator Information Systems
CHR: Paula Seely, Manager Human Resources
CNO: Darlene M. Elbert, R.N., Assistant Administrator and Chief Nursing Officer
Web address: www.krhc.com
Control: County–Government, nonfederal **Service:** General Medical and Surgical

Staffed Beds: 23 **Admissions:** 793 **Census:** 10 **Outpatient Visits:** 27589
Births: 137 **Total Expense ($000):** 31392 **Payroll Expense ($000):** 10713
Personnel: 202

AMES—Story County

⊠ △ ◇ **MARY GREELEY MEDICAL CENTER (160030)**, 1111 Duff Avenue,
Zip 50010–5745; tel. 515/239–2011 **A**1 2 7 10 19 21 **F**3 7 8 11 12 13 15 17
18 20 22 26 28 29 30 31 34 35 36 37 38 40 43 45 46 49 50 53 55 57 58
59 61 62 63 64 65 68 69 70 72 74 75 76 77 78 79 81 82 84 85 86 89 90
92 93 96 98 99 100 101 102 103 104 107 108 110 111 114 115 118 119
120 121 123 124 126 129 130 131 132 135 146 148
Primary Contact: Brian Dieter, President and Chief Executive Officer
CFO: Gary Botine, Vice President, Chief Financial Officer
CIO: Scott Carlson, Director
CHR: Betsy V. Schoeller, Director Human Resources and Education
Web address: www.mgmc.org
Control: City–Government, nonfederal **Service:** General Medical and Surgical

Staffed Beds: 171 **Admissions:** 8298 **Census:** 100 **Outpatient Visits:**
169940 **Births:** 1113 **Total Expense ($000):** 168892 **Payroll Expense
($000):** 61154 **Personnel:** 1046

ANAMOSA—Jones County

★ **UNITYPOINT HEALTH – JONES REGIONAL MEDICAL CENTER (161306)**,
1795 Highway 64 East, Zip 52205–2112; tel. 319/462–6131 **A**10 18 **F**3 7 11
12 15 28 29 30 31 34 35 38 40 43 45 50 56 57 59 64 68 71 75 77 81 82
84 85 87 93 96 97 99 100 101 102 103 104 107 110 114 118 119 126
130 132 133 135 145 146 148 **P**6 **S** UnityPoint Health, West Des Moines, IA
Primary Contact: Eric Briesemeister, Chief Executive Officer
CFO: Rachel Von Behren, Director Financial Services
CMO: Victor Salas, M.D., President Medical Staff
CHR: Donna Condry, Director Human Resources
Web address: www.jonesregional.org
Control: Other not–for–profit (including NFP Corporation) **Service:** General
Medical and Surgical

Staffed Beds: 22 **Admissions:** 617 **Census:** 7 **Outpatient Visits:** 82330
Births: 0 **Total Expense ($000):** 20112 **Payroll Expense ($000):** 7088
Personnel: 149

ATLANTIC—Cass County

★ **CASS COUNTY MEMORIAL HOSPITAL (161376)**, 1501 East Tenth Street,
Zip 50022–1997; tel. 712/243–3250 **A**10 18 **F**11 13 15 28 29 31 34 35 40
50 57 59 64 65 69 70 75 76 77 78 79 81 82 85 93 97 98 99 101 102 103
104 107 108 111 114 117 119 124 127 129 130 132 133 135 146 147 148
P6 8
Primary Contact: Patricia A. Markham, Interim Chief Executive Officer
COO: Alison Bruckner, Chief Operating Officer
CFO: Abbey Stangl, Chief Financial Officer
CMO: Todd Bean, Chief Medical Officer
CIO: Jeff Osegard, Chief Information Officer
CHR: Denise Coder, Chief Human Resource Officer
Web address: www.casshealth.org
Control: County–Government, nonfederal **Service:** General Medical and Surgical

Staffed Beds: 29 **Admissions:** 1009 **Census:** 12 **Outpatient Visits:** 101862
Births: 129 **Total Expense ($000):** 40916 **Payroll Expense ($000):** 14394
Personnel: 308

AUDUBON—Audubon County

AUDUBON COUNTY MEMORIAL HOSPITAL (161330), 515 Pacific Street,
Zip 50025–1056; tel. 712/563–2611 **A**10 18 **F**3 11 15 28 31 40 43 45 53 59
64 67 78 79 81 85 90 93 110 119 127 128 133 135
Primary Contact: Thomas G. Smith, Administrator and Chief Executive Officer
CFO: Melinda Alt, Chief Financial Officer
CMO: James Cunnigham, D.O., Chief of Staff
CIO: Mike Card, Chief Information Officer
CNO: Holly Kjergaard, Chief Nursing Officer
Web address: www.acmhhosp.org
Control: County–Government, nonfederal **Service:** General Medical and Surgical

Staffed Beds: 25 **Admissions:** 181 **Census:** 3 **Outpatient Visits:** 15774
Births: 1 **Total Expense ($000):** 11895 **Payroll Expense ($000):** 5103
Personnel: 107

BELMOND—Wright County

★ ◇ **IOWA SPECIALTY HOSPITAL–BELMOND (161301)**, 403 1st Street S.E.,
Zip 50421–1201; tel. 641/444–3223 **A**10 18 21 **F**3 7 11 12 15 28 29 32 34
35 40 43 45 46 50 56 57 59 62 63 64 65 67 68 75 77 79 81 82 85 87 89
92 93 96 97 100 101 102 104 107 110 119 127 128 129 130 131 132 133
135 146 148 **P**6 **S** Iowa Specialty Hospitals, Clarion, IA
Primary Contact: Amy McDaniel, Administrator and Chief Executive Officer
CFO: Greg Polzin, Chief Financial Officer
CMO: Charles B. Brindle, M.D., Chief Medical Staff
CHR: Holly Martin, Director Human Resource
CNO: Lisa Weatherwax, R.N., Chief Nursing Officer
Web address: www.iowaspecialtyhospital.com
Control: City–Government, nonfederal **Service:** General Medical and Surgical

Staffed Beds: 22 **Admissions:** 464 **Census:** 5 **Outpatient Visits:** 27350
Births: 0 **Total Expense ($000):** 22093 **Payroll Expense ($000):** 4591
Personnel: 126

BETTENDORF—Scott County

⊠ **UNITYPOINT HEALTH – TRINITY BETTENDORF (160104)**, 4500 Utica Ridge
Road, Zip 52722–1626; tel. 563/742–5000 **A**1 10 13 **F**3 11 13 15 18 20 22
24 26 29 30 34 35 37 40 44 45 46 48 50 57 59 64 70 73 74 75 76 79 81
82 85 86 87 93 96 97 102 104 107 108 110 114 119 130 132 135 146 147
148 **P**8 **S** UnityPoint Health, West Des Moines, IA
Primary Contact: Richard A. Seidler, FACHE, President and Chief Executive Officer
COO: Jay Willsher, Chief Operating Officer
CFO: Greg Pagliuzza, Chief Financial Officer
CMO: Paul McLoone, M.D., Chief Medical Officer
CHR: Cara Fuller, Vice President Human Resources
CNO: Jean B. Doerge, MS, Chief Nursing Executive
Web address: www.trinityqc.com
Control: Other not–for–profit (including NFP Corporation) **Service:** General
Medical and Surgical

Staffed Beds: 76 **Admissions:** 4140 **Census:** 34 **Outpatient Visits:** 53071
Births: 919 **Total Expense ($000):** 77353 **Payroll Expense ($000):** 22345
Personnel: 363

IA

BLOOMFIELD—Davis County

★ **DAVIS COUNTY HOSPITAL (161327)**, 509 North Madison Street,
Zip 52537–1271; tel. 641/664–2145 **A**10 18 **F**3 7 11 13 15 29 34 35 40 44
45 50 57 59 63 64 65 68 69 75 79 81 84 85 86 87 97 107 110 111 114
119 130 132 133 146 **P**6
Primary Contact: Kirby Johnson, Chief Executive Officer
CFO: Kendra Warning, Chief Financial Officer
CMO: Robert Floyd, D.O., Chief Medical Staff
CIO: Lynn Sims, Director Information Technology
CHR: Pam Young, Director Human Resources
CNO: Susan Kay Pankey, Chief Nursing Officer
Web address: www.daviscountyhospital.org
Control: County–Government, nonfederal **Service:** General Medical and Surgical

Staffed Beds: 25 **Admissions:** 308 **Census:** 4 **Outpatient Visits:** 24882
Births: 6 **Total Expense ($000):** 20785 **Payroll Expense ($000):** 7153
Personnel: 150

BOONE—Boone County

★ **BOONE COUNTY HOSPITAL (161372)**, 1015 Union Street, Zip 50036–4821;
tel. 515/432–3140, (Total facility includes 7 beds in nursing home–type unit) **A**10
18 **F**2 3 7 11 13 15 28 29 30 31 34 35 40 43 45 50 56 57 59 62 64 65 69
70 75 76 77 78 79 81 82 85 86 87 89 91 93 97 107 110 111 114 119 128
131 132 133 134 145 146 147 148 **P**6 **S** QHR, Brentwood, TN
Primary Contact: Joseph S. Smith, Chief Executive Officer
CFO: Joseph Devin, Chief Financial Officer
CMO: Tammara Chance, D.O., Chief of Staff
CIO: Matthew Sabus, Director Information Systems
CHR: Kim Schwartz, Assistant Administrator of Human Resources and Physician
Services
Web address: www.boonehospital.com
Control: County–Government, nonfederal **Service:** General Medical and Surgical

Staffed Beds: 32 **Admissions:** 1296 **Census:** 15 **Outpatient Visits:** 81494
Births: 104 **Total Expense ($000):** 40265 **Payroll Expense ($000):** 16471
Personnel: 312

BRITT—Hancock County

★ **HANCOCK COUNTY HEALTH SYSTEM (161307)**, 532 First Street N.W.,
Zip 50423–1227; tel. 641/843–5000 **A**10 18 **F**3 15 28 29 31 34 35 36 40 43
45 46 50 53 56 57 59 62 64 65 75 77 81 82 85 93 97 100 103 104 107
110 114 119 129 130 131 132 133 135 146 148 **P**1 **S** Trinity Health,
Livonia, MI
Primary Contact: Jeffry Stampohar, Chief Executive Officer
CFO: Julie Damm, Chief Financial Officer
CMO: Catherine Butler, M.D., Chief Medical Staff
CIO: Julie Damm, Chief Financial Officer
CHR: Denise Jakoubeck, Director Human Resources
CNO: Laura Zwiefel, Chief Nursing Officer and Assistant Administration
Web address: www.trusthchs.com/hancock–county–health–system
Control: County–Government, nonfederal **Service:** General Medical and Surgical

Staffed Beds: 25 **Admissions:** 586 **Census:** 9 **Outpatient Visits:** 21628
Births: 0 **Total Expense ($000):** 20072 **Payroll Expense ($000):** 6947
Personnel: 172

CARROLL—Carroll County

★ **ST. ANTHONY REGIONAL HOSPITAL (160005)**, 311 South Clark Street,
Zip 51401–3038, Mailing Address: P.O. Box 628, Zip 51401–0628;
tel. 712/792–3581, (Total facility includes 79 beds in nursing home–type unit)
A10 20 **F**6 11 13 15 28 29 30 31 34 35 37 38 39 40 43 44 45 46 50 51 56
57 59 60 61 62 63 64 65 67 68 69 70 74 75 76 77 78 79 81 82 84 85 86
87 89 93 97 98 99 100 101 102 103 104 107 108 110 111 115 118 119
125 126 127 129 130 131 132 133 134 135 145 146 147 148 **P**6
Primary Contact: Edward H. Smith, President and Chief Executive Officer
CFO: John Munson, Vice President and Chief Financial Officer
CMO: Kyle Ulveling, M.D., Chief of Staff
CIO: Randy Eischeid, Director Information Systems
CHR: Anna Fitzpatrick, Director Human Resources
CNO: Karen Timm, R.N., Vice President Patient Services
Web address: www.stanthonyhospital.org
Control: Church–operated, Nongovernment, not–for profit **Service:** General
Medical and Surgical

Staffed Beds: 155 **Admissions:** 2228 **Census:** 105 **Outpatient Visits:**
115783 **Births:** 369 **Total Expense ($000):** 67501 **Payroll Expense ($000):**
27823 **Personnel:** 540

CEDAR FALLS—Black Hawk County

⊠ **SARTORI MEMORIAL HOSPITAL (160040)**, 515 College Street,
Zip 50613–2500; tel. 319/268–3000 **A**1 10 **F**3 7 8 11 12 15 29 30 35 40 43
44 46 53 57 59 64 68 70 75 77 79 81 91 93 97 98 103 107 110 111 119
130 131 132 146 **P**1 6 **S** Wheaton Franciscan Healthcare, Wheaton, IL
Primary Contact: MaryJo Kavalier, Administrator
CFO: Michele Panicucci, Senior Vice President and Chief Financial Officer
CMO: James Lehman, M.D., Vice President Medical Affairs
CNO: Kelly Richards, MSN, Senior Vice President and Chief Nursing Officer
Web address: www.wheatoniowa.org
Control: Church–operated, Nongovernment, not–for profit **Service:** General
Medical and Surgical

Staffed Beds: 50 **Admissions:** 1459 **Census:** 20 **Outpatient Visits:** 41630
Births: 0 **Total Expense ($000):** 32671 **Payroll Expense ($000):** 10841
Personnel: 191

CEDAR RAPIDS—Linn County

☐ **CONTINUING CARE HOSPITAL AT ST. LUKE'S (162002)**, 1026 A Avenue
N.E., 6th Floor, Zip 52402–5036; tel. 319/369–8142 **A**1 10 **F**1 3 29 30 75 84
85 87 148 **S** CHRISTUS Health, Irving, TX
Primary Contact: Elly Steffen, Administrator
CNO: Mary Beth Keuter, Director Patient Care
Web address: www.unitypoint.org/cedarrapids/services–continuing–care–hospital.
aspx
Control: Other not–for–profit (including NFP Corporation) **Service:** Long–Term
Acute Care hospital

Staffed Beds: 16 **Admissions:** 159 **Census:** 11 **Outpatient Visits:** 0 **Births:**
0 **Total Expense ($000):** 7015 **Payroll Expense ($000):** 2159 **Personnel:**
51

⊠ **MERCY MEDICAL CENTER–CEDAR RAPIDS (160079)**, 701 Tenth Street S.E.,
Zip 52403–1292; tel. 319/398–6011, (Total facility includes 76 beds in nursing
home–type unit) **A**1 2 3 5 10 **F**3 5 11 12 13 15 18 20 22 26 28 29 30 31 32
34 35 36 38 40 43 44 45 48 49 50 54 55 56 57 59 60 61 62 63 64 65 67
68 70 71 72 74 75 76 77 78 79 81 82 84 85 86 87 88 89 90 91 92 93 94
98 99 100 101 102 103 104 107 108 109 110 114 115 116 117 118 119
120 121 123 124 126 128 130 131 132 135 143 145 146 147 148 **P**2 8
Primary Contact: Timothy L. Charles, President and Chief Executive Officer
CFO: Nathan VanGenderen, Executive Vice President and Chief Financial Officer
CMO: Mark Valliere, M.D., Senior Vice President Medical Affairs and Chief Medical
Officer
CIO: Jeff Cash, Senior Vice President and Chief Information Officer
CHR: Doug Jontz, Senior Vice President Human Resources
CNO: Mary Brobst, R.N., Senior Vice President Patient Care Services and Chief
Nursing Officer
Web address: www.mercycare.org
Control: Church–operated, Nongovernment, not–for profit **Service:** General
Medical and Surgical

Staffed Beds: 302 **Admissions:** 10570 **Census:** 188 **Outpatient Visits:**
302547 **Births:** 786 **Total Expense ($000):** 285814 **Payroll Expense
($000):** 105518 **Personnel:** 1876

ST. LUKE'S HOSPITAL See UnityPoint Health – St. Luke's Hospital

⊠ △ **UNITYPOINT HEALTH – ST. LUKE'S HOSPITAL (160045)**, 1026 A
Avenue N.E., Zip 52402–3026, Mailing Address: P.O. Box 3026,
Zip 52406–3026; tel. 319/369–7211 **A**1 2 3 5 7 10 **F**3 5 8 11 12 13 15 17
18 19 20 22 24 26 28 29 30 31 32 34 35 36 37 39 40 43 45 46 49 50 54
55 56 57 58 59 60 61 62 63 64 65 66 70 72 74 75 76 77 78 79 81 82 84
85 86 87 88 89 90 91 92 93 95 96 98 99 100 101 103 104 105 107 110
115 117 118 119 120 121 123 124 126 130 131 132 134 135 145 146 147
148 **P**6 **S** UnityPoint Health, West Des Moines, IA
Primary Contact: Theodore E. Townsend, FACHE, President and Chief Executive
Officer
COO: Michelle Niermann, Senior Vice President and Chief Operating Officer
CFO: Milton E. Aunan, II, CPA, Senior Vice President and Chief Financial Officer
CMO: Dustin Arnold, D.O., Chief Medical Officer
CHR: Susan L. Slattery, Director Human Resources
CNO: Mary Ann Osborn, R.N., Senior Vice President and Chief Care Coordinator
Officer
Web address: www.unitypoint.org
Control: Other not–for–profit (including NFP Corporation) **Service:** General
Medical and Surgical

Staffed Beds: 347 **Admissions:** 16649 **Census:** 212 **Outpatient Visits:**
551861 **Births:** 2573 **Total Expense ($000):** 326272 **Payroll Expense
($000):** 119502 **Personnel:** 2306

IA

Many Facility Codes have changed. Please refer to the AHA Guide Code Chart. © 2016 AHA Guide

CENTERVILLE—Appanoose County

★ **MERCY MEDICAL CENTER–CENTERVILLE (161377)**, 1 St. Joseph's Drive, Zip 52544–8055; tel. 641/437–4111, (Total facility includes 20 beds in nursing home–type unit) **A**10 18 **F**1 3 4 8 11 13 15 16 17 28 29 30 31 34 40 45 46 50 54 57 59 64 67 70 72 73 75 76 77 78 80 81 85 86 87 88 89 90 93 97 98 107 110 111 113 115 117 119 127 128 129 130 132 133 135 **P**6 **S** Catholic Health Initiatives, Englewood, CO
Primary Contact: Clinton J. Christianson, FACHE, President
CHR: Tonya Clawson, Manager Human Resources
CNO: Sherri L. Doggett, Vice President Patient Services
Web address: www.mercycenterville.org
Control: Church–operated, Nongovernment, not–for profit **Service:** General Medical and Surgical

Staffed Beds: 45 **Admissions:** 808 **Census:** 26 **Outpatient Visits:** 85360 **Births:** 64 **Total Expense ($000):** 25033 **Payroll Expense ($000):** 10007 **Personnel:** 175

CHARITON—Lucas County

★ **LUCAS COUNTY HEALTH CENTER (161341)**, 1200 North Seventh Street, Zip 50049–1258; tel. 641/774–3000 **A**10 18 **F**3 5 7 11 13 15 28 29 30 31 34 38 40 43 44 45 47 50 57 64 66 68 70 75 76 77 81 85 86 87 89 90 93 97 104 107 115 119 127 128 130 132 133 143 145 146 148
Primary Contact: Brian Sims, Chief Executive Officer
CMO: David Marcowitz, M.D., Chief of Staff
CIO: Terri Black, Network Manager
CHR: Lana Kuball, Director Administrative Services
CNO: JoBeth Lawless, Chief Nursing Officer, Nursing Services and Director Emergency Management Services
Web address: www.lchcia.com
Control: County–Government, nonfederal **Service:** General Medical and Surgical

Staffed Beds: 25 **Admissions:** 352 **Census:** 3 **Outpatient Visits:** 20324 **Births:** 70 **Total Expense ($000):** 18922 **Payroll Expense ($000):** 9363 **Personnel:** 192

CHARLES CITY—Floyd County

FLOYD COUNTY MEDICAL CENTER (161347), 800 Eleventh Street, Zip 50616–3499; tel. 641/228–6830 **A**10 18 **F**11 13 15 28 29 31 34 35 40 45 48 57 59 64 69 75 79 81 85 86 91 93 97 107 115 119 127 130 132 133 146 148 **S** Mayo Clinic, Rochester, MN
Primary Contact: Bill D. Faust, Administrator
CFO: Ron Timpe, Chief Financial Officer
CHR: Don Nosbisch, Director Human Resources
CNO: Viva Boerschel, Director of Nursing
Web address: www.fcmc.us.com/
Control: County–Government, nonfederal **Service:** General Medical and Surgical

Staffed Beds: 25 **Admissions:** 714 **Census:** 10 **Outpatient Visits:** 55343 **Births:** 79 **Total Expense ($000):** 22597 **Payroll Expense ($000):** 8650 **Personnel:** 174

CHEROKEE—Cherokee County

★ **CHEROKEE REGIONAL MEDICAL CENTER (161362)**, 300 Sioux Valley Drive, Zip 51012–1205; tel. 712/225–5101 **A**10 18 **F**7 11 13 15 17 28 29 34 35 40 43 45 53 56 57 59 62 63 64 65 67 68 69 75 76 77 78 81 84 86 87 89 93 96 97 107 111 114 119 125 127 128 129 130 131 132 133 135 146 147 148 **P**6
Primary Contact: Matthew Johnson, Chief Executive Officer and President
CFO: Joan Bierman, Vice President Finance
CIO: Kevin Naslund, Manager Information Technology
CHR: Theresa Conley, Manager Human Resources
CNO: Christy Syndergaard, Vice President Nursing
Web address: www.cherokeermc.org
Control: Other not–for–profit (including NFP Corporation) **Service:** General Medical and Surgical

Staffed Beds: 25 **Admissions:** 936 **Census:** 9 **Outpatient Visits:** 45107 **Births:** 147 **Total Expense ($000):** 21416 **Payroll Expense ($000):** 8926 **Personnel:** 173

☐ **MENTAL HEALTH INSTITUTE (164002)**, 1251 West Cedar Loop, Zip 51012–1599; tel. 712/225–2594 **A**1 10 **F**98 99 100 101 102 104 130 **P**6
Primary Contact: Chris Tosteberg, Superintendent
CFO: Tony Morris, Business Manager
CHR: Mary Ann Hanson, Director Personnel
Web address: www.dhs.state.ia.us
Control: State–Government, nonfederal **Service:** Psychiatric

Staffed Beds: 36 **Admissions:** 528 **Census:** 31 **Outpatient Visits:** 36 **Births:** 0 **Total Expense ($000):** 16792 **Payroll Expense ($000):** 9479 **Personnel:** 181

CLARINDA—Page County

★ **CLARINDA REGIONAL HEALTH CENTER (161352)**, 220 Essie Davison Drive, Zip 51632–2915, Mailing Address: P.O. Box 217, Zip 51632–0217; tel. 712/542–2176 **A**10 18 **F**3 7 11 15 28 29 31 34 36 40 43 50 57 59 64 65 69 75 79 81 85 86 87 93 97 107 110 111 114 118 119 127 128 129 130 133 135 143 146 148 **P**3 6
Primary Contact: Christopher R. Stipe, FACHE, Chief Executive Officer
COO: Elaine Otte, Chief Operating Officer
CMO: Autumn Morales, Chief Medical Staff Officer
CIO: Richard Morgan–Fine, IT Director
CHR: Melissa Walter, Director Human Resources
CNO: Sherrie L. Laubenthal, R.N., Chief Nursing Officer
Web address: www.clarindahealth.com
Control: City–Government, nonfederal **Service:** General Medical and Surgical

Staffed Beds: 25 **Admissions:** 614 **Census:** 6 **Outpatient Visits:** 66358 **Births:** 0 **Total Expense ($000):** 29104 **Payroll Expense ($000):** 11507 **Personnel:** 242

CLARION—Wright County

★ ◇ **IOWA SPECIALTY HOSPITAL–CLARION (161302)**, 1316 South Main Street, Zip 50525–2019; tel. 515/532–2811 **A**10 18 21 **F**11 13 15 28 29 31 32 34 35 40 43 45 46 50 56 57 59 63 64 65 68 69 75 76 77 79 81 82 85 86 87 92 93 97 107 110 111 114 119 125 127 129 131 132 133 134 135 146 148 **P**6 **S** Iowa Specialty Hospitals, Clarion, IA
Primary Contact: Steven J. Simonin, Chief Executive Officer
COO: Kirk Rier, Chief Operating Officer
CFO: Greg Polzin, Chief Financial Officer
CMO: Dennis Colby, M.D., Chief of Staff
CHR: Holly Martin, Human Resources Leader
CNO: Abby Young, Chief Nursing Officer
Web address: www.iowaspecialtyhospital.com
Control: City–Government, nonfederal **Service:** General Medical and Surgical

Staffed Beds: 25 **Admissions:** 1224 **Census:** 10 **Outpatient Visits:** 110964 **Births:** 287 **Total Expense ($000):** 50580 **Payroll Expense ($000):** 18939 **Personnel:** 324

CLINTON—Clinton County

⊞ **MERCY MEDICAL CENTER–CLINTON (160080)**, 1410 North Fourth Street, Zip 52732–2940; tel. 563/244–5555, (Includes MERCY SERVICES FOR AGING, 600 14th Avenue North, Zip 52732; tel. 563/244–3888), (Total facility includes 183 beds in nursing home–type unit) **A**1 10 **F**3 11 13 15 18 20 22 28 29 30 31 34 35 36 38 40 44 45 47 49 50 53 56 57 59 61 62 63 64 68 70 74 75 77 78 79 80 81 82 84 85 87 89 93 98 99 100 101 102 103 107 108 110 115 118 119 121 123 128 129 130 132 146 148 **S** Trinity Health, Livonia, MI
Primary Contact: Sean J. Williams, President and Chief Executive Officer
CFO: Paul Mangin, Vice President Finance
CHR: Shane Buer, Vice President, Human Resources
CNO: Amy Berentes, R.N., Vice President Patient Care Services
Web address: www.mercyclinton.com
Control: Church–operated, Nongovernment, not–for profit **Service:** General Medical and Surgical

Staffed Beds: 290 **Admissions:** 5385 **Census:** 194 **Outpatient Visits:** 75221 **Births:** 424 **Total Expense ($000):** 94256 **Payroll Expense ($000):** 38679 **Personnel:** 830

CORALVILLE—Johnson County

IOWA MEDICAL AND CLASSIFICATION CENTER, 2700 Coral Ridge Avenue, Zip 52241–4708, Mailing Address: 2700 Coral Rigde Avenue, Zip 52241; tel. 319/626–2391 **F**29 38 39 59 75 98 101 102 103 105 130 132 143
Primary Contact: James McKinney, Warden
Web address: www.oakdaleprison.com/
Control: State–Government, nonfederal **Service:** Psychiatric

Staffed Beds: 20 **Admissions:** 42 **Census:** 11 **Outpatient Visits:** 0 **Births:** 0 **Total Expense ($000):** 1588 **Personnel:** 26

Hospital, Medicare Provider Number, Address, Telephone, Approval, Facility, and Physician Codes, Health Care System

★ American Hospital Association (AHA) membership
☐ The Joint Commission accreditation
○ Healthcare Facilities Accreditation Program
◇ DNV Healthcare Inc. accreditation
⇑ Center for Improvement in Healthcare Quality Accreditation
△ Commission on Accreditation of Rehabilitation Facilities (CARF) accreditation

IA

CORNING—Adams County

★ **CHI HEALTH MERCY CORNING (161304)**, 603 Rosary Drive,
Zip 50841–1683; tel. 641/322–3121 **A**10 18 **F**3 11 15 17 28 30 31 34 40 43
46 50 53 56 57 59 64 67 70 74 75 77 78 79 81 85 89 90 97 107 110 115
119 127 128 129 130 132 133 135 146 147 148 **P**6 **S** Catholic Health
Initiatives, Englewood, CO
Primary Contact: Debra Goldsmith, Chief Executive Officer
CMO: Maen Haddadin, M.D., President Medical Staff
CIO: Kenneth Lawonn, Senior Vice President and Chief Information Officer
CHR: Sandra Lammers, Coordinator Human Resources and Finance
Web address: www.alegent.com
Control: Church–operated, Nongovernment, not–for profit **Service:** General
Medical and Surgical

Staffed Beds: 22 **Admissions:** 192 **Census:** 2 **Outpatient Visits:** 64255
Births: 0 **Total Expense ($000):** 17759 **Payroll Expense ($000):** 6595
Personnel: 105

CORYDON—Wayne County

★ **WAYNE COUNTY HOSPITAL (161358)**, 417 South East Street,
Zip 50060–1860, Mailing Address: P.O. Box 305, Zip 50060–0305;
tel. 641/872–2260 **A**10 18 **F**7 13 15 28 29 31 34 35 40 43 51 56 57 59 60
64 69 70 75 76 77 78 79 81 85 87 89 91 92 93 97 107 110 114 119 127
130 131 133 148 **P**6
Primary Contact: Daren Relph, Chief Executive Officer
COO: Michael Thomas, Associate Administrator
CFO: Diane Hook, Chief Financial Officer
CMO: Joel Baker, D.O., Chief Medical Officer
CIO: Laurie Ehrich, Chief Communications Officer
CHR: Dave Carlyle, Director Human Resources
CNO: Sheila Mattly, Chief Nursing Officer
Web address: www.waynecountyhospital.org
Control: County–Government, nonfederal **Service:** General Medical and Surgical

Staffed Beds: 25 **Admissions:** 660 **Census:** 7 **Outpatient Visits:** 27626
Births: 144 **Total Expense ($000):** 22659 **Payroll Expense ($000):** 11390
Personnel: 203

COUNCIL BLUFFS—Pottawattamie County

⊞ **CHI HEALTH MERCY COUNCIL BLUFFS (160028)**, 800 Mercy Drive,
Zip 51503–3128, Mailing Address: P.O. Box 1C, Zip 51502–3001;
tel. 712/328–5000 **A**1 2 5 10 **F**3 11 12 13 15 18 20 22 26 28 29 30 31 34
35 40 41 43 45 47 48 49 50 57 59 68 70 73 74 76 77 78 79 81 82 84 85
87 89 91 93 98 99 100 101 102 104 105 106 107 108 110 111 114 115
119 129 130 132 146 147 **P**8 **S** Catholic Health Initiatives, Englewood, CO
Primary Contact: Marie E. Knedler, R.N., FACHE, President
CFO: Jeanette Wojtalewicz, Chief Financial Officer
CMO: Joseph Hoagbin, M.D., Chief Quality Officer
CIO: Thomas Haley, Information Technology Services Site Director
CHR: Nancy Wallace, Senior Vice President Human Resources
CNO: Brenda Bergman–Evans, Interim Chief Nursing Officer
Web address: www.chihealth.com/chi–health–mercy–council–bluffs
Control: Church–operated, Nongovernment, not–for profit **Service:** General
Medical and Surgical

Staffed Beds: 166 **Admissions:** 7447 **Census:** 73 **Outpatient Visits:** 82002
Births: 543 **Total Expense ($000):** 75669 **Payroll Expense ($000):** 32824
Personnel: 568

JENNIE EDMUNDSON HOSPITAL See Methodist Jennie Edmundson Hospital

⊞ **METHODIST JENNIE EDMUNDSON HOSPITAL (160047)**, 933 East Pierce
Street, Zip 51503–4652, Mailing Address: P.O. Box 2C, Zip 51502–3002;
tel. 712/396–6000 **A**1 2 5 10 **F**3 11 13 15 18 20 22 26 28 30 31 34 35
39 40 43 44 45 47 49 50 57 58 59 61 64 68 70 74 75 76 78 79 81 82 85
86 87 89 92 93 98 100 101 102 103 107 108 110 111 115 118 119 121
123 129 130 131 132 135 143 145 146 147 148 **S** Nebraska Methodist Health
System, Inc., Omaha, NE
Primary Contact: Steven P. Baumert, President and Chief Executive Officer
CFO: Jeffrey Francis, Vice President Finance and Chief Financial Officer
CMO: Scott Bomgaars, M.D., Vice President Medical Affairs
CIO: Steven Zuber, Vice President
CHR: Holly Huerter, Vice President Human Resources
CNO: Peggy Helget, R.N., Vice President Patient Services and Chief Nursing
Officer
Web address: www.bestcare.org
Control: Other not–for–profit (including NFP Corporation) **Service:** General
Medical and Surgical

Staffed Beds: 114 **Admissions:** 5423 **Census:** 59 **Outpatient Visits:** 63548
Births: 385 **Total Expense ($000):** 94312 **Payroll Expense ($000):** 36223
Personnel: 511

CRESCO—Howard County

★ **REGIONAL HEALTH SERVICES OF HOWARD COUNTY (161328)**, 235 Eighth
Avenue West, Zip 52136–1098; tel. 563/547–2101 **A**10 18 **F**7 8 11 13 15 18
28 29 34 35 36 40 43 44 50 57 59 62 63 64 65 68 75 76 81 82 85 86 87
96 100 102 103 104 107 110 114 115 127 128 130 132 133 146 148 **P**8
S Trinity Health, Livonia, MI
Primary Contact: Robin M. Schluter, Chief Executive Officer
CFO: Greg Burkel, Chief Financial Officer
CMO: Paul Jensen, M.D., Chief of Staff
CIO: Greg Burkel, Chief Financial Officer
CHR: Jennalee Pedretti, Vice President Operations
CNO: Carol Kerian–Masters, RN, BSN, Chief Nursing Officer
Web address: www.rhshc.com
Control: County–Government, nonfederal **Service:** General Medical and Surgical

Staffed Beds: 18 **Admissions:** 249 **Census:** 4 **Outpatient Visits:** 21589
Births: 62 **Total Expense ($000):** 18227 **Payroll Expense ($000):** 7413
Personnel: 150

CRESTON—Union County

★ **GREATER REGIONAL MEDICAL CENTER (161365)**, 1700 West Townline
Street Suite 3, Zip 50801–1099; tel. 641/782–7091 **A**10 18 **F**3 7 11 13 15 28
29 31 34 35 40 43 45 50 56 57 59 64 65 66 70 75 76 77 78 79 81 82 84
85 86 93 96 97 107 108 109 110 111 115 119 120 121 122 123 124 125
127 129 130 131 132 133 135 146 148 **P**6 **S** UnityPoint Health, West Des
Moines, IA
Primary Contact: Monte Neitzel, Chief Executive Officer
CFO: Matt McCutchan, Chief Financial Officer
CMO: Steve Reeves, M.D., Chief Medical Staff
CIO: Karla Alford, Chief Information Officer
CHR: Amy Rieck, Human Resources Officer
CNO: Amanda Mohr, Chief Nursing Officer
Web address: www.greaterregional.org
Control: County–Government, nonfederal **Service:** General Medical and Surgical

Staffed Beds: 25 **Admissions:** 792 **Census:** 7 **Outpatient Visits:** 75317
Births: 158 **Total Expense ($000):** 41912 **Payroll Expense ($000):** 18080
Personnel: 310

DAVENPORT—Scott County

⊞ △ **GENESIS MEDICAL CENTER–DAVENPORT (160033)**, 1227 East
Rusholme Street, Zip 52803–2498; tel. 563/421–1000, (Includes GENESIS
MEDICAL CENTER–EAST CAMPUS, 1227 East Rusholme Street, Zip 52803;
tel. 563/421–1000; GENESIS MEDICAL CENTER–WEST CAMPUS, 1401 West
Central Park, Zip 52804–1769; tel. 563/421–1000) **A**1 2 3 5 7 10 **F**3 7 11 12
13 15 17 18 20 22 24 26 28 29 30 31 34 35 37 38 40 43 44 46 49 50 53
54 57 58 59 63 64 68 70 72 74 75 76 77 78 79 81 82 84 85 86 87 89 90
91 92 93 94 96 97 98 100 102 107 111 114 115 116 118 119 120 121 123
124 126 129 130 131 132 135 146 147 148 **P**6 **S** Genesis Health System,
Davenport, IA
Primary Contact: Jordan Voigt, Administrator
CFO: Mark G. Rogers, Interim Vice President Finance and Chief Financial Officer
CMO: Frank Claudy, M.D., Vice President Medical Staff Affairs
CIO: Robert Frieden, Vice President Information Systems
CHR: Heidi Kahly–McMahon, Interim Vice President Human Resources
Web address: www.genesishealth.com
Control: Other not–for–profit (including NFP Corporation) **Service:** General
Medical and Surgical

Staffed Beds: 352 **Admissions:** 19005 **Census:** 188 **Outpatient Visits:**
206838 **Births:** 2040 **Total Expense ($000):** 306317 **Payroll Expense
($000):** 86674 **Personnel:** 1348

⊞ **SELECT SPECIALTY HOSPITAL–QUAD CITIES (162001)**, 1111 West Kimberly
Road, Zip 52806–5711; tel. 563/468–2000 **A**1 10 **F**1 3 29 45 75 85 119 130
148 **S** Select Medical Corporation, Mechanicsburg, PA
Primary Contact: Connie K. Siffring, Chief Executive Officer
Web address: www.selectmedicalcorp.com
Control: Corporation, Investor–owned, for–profit **Service:** Long–Term Acute Care
hospital

Staffed Beds: 50 **Admissions:** 345 **Census:** 25 **Outpatient Visits:** 0 **Births:**
0 **Total Expense ($000):** 14393 **Payroll Expense ($000):** 6089 **Personnel:**
118

IA

Many Facility Codes have changed. Please refer to the AHA Guide Code Chart. © 2016 AHA Guide

DE WITT—Clinton County

⊠ **GENESIS MEDICAL CENTER, DEWITT (161313)**, 1118 11th Street,
Zip 52742–1296; tel. 563/659–4200, (Total facility includes 75 beds in nursing
home–type unit) **A**1 10 18 **F**7 11 15 29 30 31 34 35 38 40 43 44 50 53 57 59
64 74 75 77 78 79 81 85 86 87 97 102 107 110 111 114 119 129 130 131
132 133 135 **P**6 **S** Genesis Health System, Davenport, IA
Primary Contact: Curt Coleman, FACHE, Chief Executive Officer
CMO: Steven Fowler, M.D., President Medical Staff
CHR: Kristin Nicholson, Coordinator Human Resources
CNO: Wanda Haack, MSN, Chief Nursing Officer
Web address: www.genesishealth.com
Control: Other not–for–profit (including NFP Corporation) **Service:** General
Medical and Surgical

Staffed Beds: 86 Admissions: 321 Census: 74 Outpatient Visits: 19486
Births: 0 Total Expense ($000): 18599 **Payroll Expense ($000):** 7156
Personnel: 134

DECORAH—Winneshiek County

⊠ **WINNESHIEK MEDICAL CENTER (161371)**, 901 Montgomery Street,
Zip 52101–2325; tel. 563/382–2911 **A**1 10 18 **F**3 7 8 11 13 15 28 29 31 34
35 38 40 43 45 50 56 57 59 61 62 63 64 65 68 69 75 76 77 78 79 81 82
86 87 93 94 97 102 104 107 110 111 114 119 128 129 130 131 132 133
135 144 146 147 148 **S** Mayo Clinic, Rochester, MN
Primary Contact: Lisa Radtke, Chief Administrative Officer
COO: David Rooney, Administrator Operations
CFO: Lynn Luloff, Chief Financial Officer
CMO: Robert Flinchbaugh, D.O., Chief Medical Officer
CHR: Laurie Bulman, Director Human Resources
CNO: Susan Heitman, Chief Nursing Officer
Web address: www.winmedical.org
Control: County–Government, nonfederal **Service:** General Medical and Surgical

Staffed Beds: 25 Admissions: 1067 Census: 10 Outpatient Visits: 67285
Births: 238 Total Expense ($000): 50542 **Payroll Expense ($000):** 18503
Personnel: 371

DENISON—Crawford County

★ **CRAWFORD COUNTY MEMORIAL HOSPITAL (161369)**, 100 Medical
Parkway, Zip 51442–2299; tel. 712/265–2500 **A**10 18 **F**3 7 8 11 13 15 17 28
29 31 34 35 40 45 50 54 56 57 59 64 65 67 68 70 75 76 77 78 79 81 82
85 87 89 93 97 99 101 107 110 111 115 119 127 128 133 135 143 148 **P**6
Primary Contact: Bill Bruce, FACHE, Chief Executive Officer
CFO: Rachel Melby, Vice President, Chief Financial Officer
CIO: Angie Anderson, Director Information Technology
CHR: Brad Bonner, Executive Director, Human Resources and General Counsel
CNO: Erin Muck, Vice President, Clinical Nursing
Web address: www.ccmhia.com
Control: County–Government, nonfederal **Service:** General Medical and Surgical

Staffed Beds: 25 Admissions: 595 Census: 6 Outpatient Visits: 41015
Births: 124 Total Expense ($000): 31881 **Payroll Expense ($000):** 13794
Personnel: 221

DES MOINES—Polk County

⊠ **BROADLAWNS MEDICAL CENTER (160101)**, 1801 Hickman Road,
Zip 50314–1597; tel. 515/282–2200 **A**1 3 5 10 **F**3 5 11 13 15 18 29 30 31
32 34 35 38 39 40 43 44 45 48 50 52 53 56 57 58 59 64 65 66 68 70 74
75 76 77 78 79 81 82 85 86 87 92 93 94 97 98 99 100 101 102 103 104
105 106 107 111 114 119 129 130 131 132 135 144 146 147 148 **P**6
Primary Contact: Jody J. Jenner, President and Chief Executive Officer
CFO: Karlis Vilums, Chief Financial Officer
CMO: Vincent Mandracchia, DPM, Chief Medical Officer
CHR: Julie Kilgore, Vice President, Human Resources
CNO: Susan N. Kirstein, R.N., Chief Nursing Officer
Web address: www.broadlawns.org
Control: County–Government, nonfederal **Service:** General Medical and Surgical

Staffed Beds: 95 Admissions: 3103 Census: 52 Outpatient Visits: 217696
Births: 330 Total Expense ($000): 127397 **Payroll Expense ($000):** 61354
Personnel: 838

DES MOINES DIVISION See Veterans Affairs Central Iowa Health Care System

IOWA LUTHERAN HOSPITAL See UnityPoint Health–Iowa Lutheran Hospital

⊠ △ **MERCY MEDICAL CENTER–DES MOINES (160083)**, 1111 6th Avenue,
Zip 50314–2611; tel. 515/247–3121, (Includes MERCY MEDICAL CENTER–WEST
LAKES, 1755 59th Place, West Des Moines, Zip 50266–7737;
tel. 515/358–8000; Robert P. Ritz, President) **A**1 2 3 7 10 13 **F**3 4 5 6 7 8 9
11 13 15 16 17 18 19 20 21 22 23 24 25 26 27 28 29 30 31 32 34 35 36
38 39 40 41 43 44 46 48 49 50 53 54 56 57 58 59 60 61 62 63 64 65
66 68 70 71 72 73 74 75 76 77 78 79 81 82 84 85 86 87 88 89 90 91 92
93 94 96 97 98 99 100 101 102 103 104 105 106 107 108 109 110 111
114 115 116 117 118 119 120 121 123 124 126 129 130 131 132 134 135
138 141 142 143 144 145 146 147 148 **P**6 **S** Catholic Health Initiatives,
Englewood, CO
Primary Contact: Robert P. Ritz, President
COO: Michael Wegner, Senior Vice President and Chief Operating Officer
CFO: Randy Rubin, Senior Vice President and Chief Financial Officer
CMO: Tommy Ibrahim, M.D., Chief Physician Officer
CIO: James Strother, Site Director Information Technology Systems
CHR: Kevin Elsberry, Senior Vice President Human Resources
CNO: Mary J. Brown, MSN, Vice President and Chief Nursing Officer
Web address: www.mercydesmoines.org
Control: Church–operated, Nongovernment, not–for profit **Service:** General
Medical and Surgical

Staffed Beds: 539 Admissions: 29102 Census: 410 Outpatient Visits:
235561 **Births: 4631 Total Expense ($000):** 608571 **Payroll Expense**
($000): 220001 **Personnel:** 3303

⊠ **SELECT SPECIALTY HOSPITAL–DES MOINES (160157)**, 1111 6th Avenue,
4th Floor Main, Zip 50314–2610; tel. 515/247–4400 **A**1 10 **F**1 29 75 148
S Select Medical Corporation, Mechanicsburg, PA
Primary Contact: Glen Griesheim, Chief Executive Officer
Web address: www.selectspecialtyhospitals.com
Control: Corporation, Investor–owned, for–profit **Service:** Long–Term Acute Care
hospital

Staffed Beds: 30 Admissions: 217 Census: 18 Outpatient Visits: 0 Births:
0 **Total Expense ($000):** 10383 **Payroll Expense ($000):** 4772 **Personnel:**
81

★ △ ◇ **UNITYPOINT HEALTH – IOWA METHODIST MEDICAL CENTER**
(160082), 1200 Pleasant Street, Zip 50309–1406; tel. 515/241–6212,
(Includes POWELL CONVALESCENT CENTER, 1200 Pleasant, Zip 50309; UNITY
POINT HEALTH – JOHN STODDARD CANCER CENTER, 1221 Pleasant Street,
Zip 50309–1423; tel. 515/241–6212; UNITYPOINT HEALTH – BLANK
CHILDREN'S HOSPITAL, 1200 Pleasant Street, tel. 515/241–5437; David A.
Stark, FACHE, President; UNITYPOINT HEALTH – METHODIST WEST HOSPITAL,
1660 60th Street, West Des Moines, Zip 50266–7700; tel. 515/343–1000;
YOUNKER MEMORIAL REHABILITATION CENTER, 1200 Pleasant Road, Zip 50308)
A2 5 7 8 10 21 **F**3 7 8 11 12 13 17 18 20 22 24 26 28 29 30 31 32 34 35
39 40 41 43 44 45 46 47 49 50 53 54 55 56 57 58 59 60 61 64 65 68 70
71 72 74 75 76 77 78 79 81 82 84 85 86 87 88 89 90 91 92 93 94 96 97
100 107 108 111 114 115 116 117 118 119 120 121 123 124 126 129 130
131 132 134 135 138 146 147 148 **P**6 **S** UnityPoint Health, West Des
Moines, IA
Primary Contact: Eric T. Crowell, President and Chief Executive Officer
COO: David A. Stark, FACHE, Executive Vice President and Chief Operating Officer
CFO: Joe Corfits, Senior Vice President, Chief Financial Officer
CMO: Mark Purtle, M.D., Vice President Medical Affairs
CHR: Joyce McDanel, Vice President Human Resources and Education
CNO: Debra Moyer, R.N., Chief Nursing Executive and Vice President Nursing
Services
Web address: www.unitypoint.org
Control: Other not–for–profit (including NFP Corporation) **Service:** General
Medical and Surgical

Staffed Beds: 512 Admissions: 25308 Census: 347 Outpatient Visits:
275801 **Births: 4512 Total Expense ($000):** 544955 **Payroll Expense**
($000): 233924 **Personnel:** 3915

★ ◇ **UNITYPOINT HEALTH–IOWA LUTHERAN HOSPITAL (160024)**, 700 East
University Avenue, Zip 50316–2392; tel. 515/263–5612, (Total facility includes
16 beds in nursing home–type unit) **A**3 5 10 21 **F**3 4 5 8 11 13 15 17 18 20
22 26 28 29 30 34 35 38 39 40 43 44 45 49 50 51 53 56 57 59 60 61
64 65 68 70 71 74 75 76 79 81 82 84 85 86 87 91 93 97 98 99 100 101
102 103 104 105 107 108 110 111 114 115 118 119 128 130 132 134 135
146 147 148 **P**6 **S** UnityPoint Health, West Des Moines, IA
Primary Contact: Eric T. Crowell, President and Chief Executive Officer
COO: Eric L. Lothe, FACHE, Senior Vice President and Chief Operating Officer
CFO: Joe Corfits, Chief Financial Officer
CMO: Mark Purtle, M.D., Vice President Medical Affairs
CHR: Joyce McDanel, Vice President Human Resources and Education
CNO: Debra Moyer, R.N., Chief Nurse Executive
Web address: www.unitypoint.org
Control: Other not–for–profit (including NFP Corporation) **Service:** General
Medical and Surgical

Staffed Beds: 205 Admissions: 7975 Census: 120 Outpatient Visits: 59639
Births: 466 Total Expense ($000): 125237 **Payroll Expense ($000):** 53417
Personnel: 860

IA

Hospital, Medicare Provider Number, Address, Telephone, Approval, Facility, and Physician Codes, Health Care System

★ American Hospital Association (AHA) membership   ○ Healthcare Facilities Accreditation Program   ⇑ Center for Improvement in Healthcare Quality Accreditation
□ The Joint Commission accreditation   ◇ DNV Healthcare Inc. accreditation   △ Commission on Accreditation of Rehabilitation Facilities (CARF) accreditation

© 2016 AHA Guide   *Many Facility Codes have changed. Please refer to the AHA Guide Code Chart.*   Hospitals **A229**

⊠ △ **VETERANS AFFAIRS CENTRAL IOWA HEALTH CARE SYSTEM**, 3600 30th Street, Zip 50310–5753; tel. 515/699–5999, (Includes DES MOINES DIVISION, 3600 30th Street, Zip 50310–5774; tel. 515/699–5999; KNOXVILLE DIVISION, 1515 West Pleasant, Knoxville, Zip 50138–3399; tel. 515/842–3101), (Total facility includes 90 beds in nursing home–type unit) **A**1 3 5 7 **F**2 3 5 8 11 12 15 18 20 22 28 29 30 31 33 34 35 36 38 39 40 44 45 46 50 53 54 56 57 59 61 62 63 64 65 66 70 71 74 75 77 78 79 80 81 82 83 84 85 86 87 93 94 96 97 98 100 101 102 103 104 105 106 107 108 110 111 112 114 115 116 117 118 119 120 127 128 129 130 132 135 146 147 148 **S** Department of Veterans Affairs, Washington, DC
Primary Contact: Gail L. Graham, Director
CMO: Fredrick Bahls, M.D., Chief of Staff
CIO: James Danuser, Chief Information Officer
CHR: Sabrina Owen, Human Resources Officer
Web address: www.centraliowa.va.gov/
Control: Veterans Affairs, Government, federal **Service:** General Medical and Surgical

Staffed Beds: 258 Admissions: 3081 Census: 149 Outpatient Visits: 374417 Births: 0 Total Expense ($000): 301096 Payroll Expense ($000): 138262 Personnel: 1459

DUBUQUE—Dubuque County

FINLEY HOSPITAL See UnityPoint Health – Finley Hospital

⊠ △ **MERCY MEDICAL CENTER–DUBUQUE (160069)**, 250 Mercy Drive, Zip 52001–7360; tel. 563/589–8000, (Total facility includes 40 beds in nursing home–type unit) **A**1 7 10 **F**3 4 5 8 11 13 15 18 20 22 24 26 28 29 30 31 32 34 35 36 38 39 40 43 44 49 50 51 53 56 57 58 59 61 62 64 65 67 70 72 74 75 76 77 78 79 80 81 85 86 87 89 90 91 93 97 98 99 100 101 102 103 104 107 108 111 114 116 128 129 130 131 132 134 135 144 146 147 148 **P**8 **S** Trinity Health, Livonia, MI
Primary Contact: Kay Takes, R.N., President
CFO: Robert Shafer, Vice President Finance
CIO: Joe Billmeyer, Director, Information Services
CHR: Kathryn Roberts, Director Human Resources
CNO: Robert Wethal, R.N., Vice President and Chief Nursing Officer
Web address: www.mercydubuque.com
Control: Church–operated, Nongovernment, not–for profit **Service:** General Medical and Surgical

Staffed Beds: 235 Admissions: 9121 Census: 147 Outpatient Visits: 46038 Births: 845 Total Expense ($000): 153086 Payroll Expense ($000): 48664 Personnel: 1046

⊠ △ **UNITYPOINT HEALTH – FINLEY HOSPITAL (160117)**, 350 North Grandview Avenue, Zip 52001–6392; tel. 563/582–1881 **A**1 7 10 **F**3 11 12 13 15 18 20 22 26 28 29 30 31 34 35 39 40 43 44 45 46 48 49 50 53 56 57 59 60 61 62 64 65 70 72 74 75 76 77 78 79 81 82 84 85 86 87 90 91 93 96 97 98 99 103 107 108 110 111 115 117 118 119 120 121 123 124 126 129 130 131 132 135 144 146 147 148 **P**1 5 **S** UnityPoint Health, West Des Moines, IA
Primary Contact: David R. Brandon, President and Chief Executive Officer
COO: Tim Ahlers, Chief Operating Officer
CFO: Dan Carpenter, Chief Financial Officer
CMO: Bryan Pechous, M.D., Vice President Medical Affairs
CIO: Tim Loeffelholz, Account Executive Information Technology
CHR: Karla Waldbillig, Director Human Resources
CNO: Mary Peters, Chief Nursing Officer
Web address: www.unitypoint.org
Control: Other not–for–profit (including NFP Corporation) **Service:** General Medical and Surgical

Staffed Beds: 109 Admissions: 4660 Census: 60 Outpatient Visits: 96289 Births: 752 Total Expense ($000): 108172 Payroll Expense ($000): 48135 Personnel: 737

DYERSVILLE—Dubuque County

★ **MERCY MEDICAL CENTER–DYERSVILLE (161378)**, 1111 Third Street S.W., Zip 52040–1725; tel. 563/875–7101 **A**10 18 **F**11 15 34 35 36 39 40 44 50 56 57 59 64 65 75 79 81 85 86 93 119 130 131 132 133 134 135 146 147 **P**8 **S** Trinity Health, Livonia, MI
Primary Contact: Kay Takes, R.N., President
CFO: Robert Shafer, Vice President Finance
Web address: www.mercydubuque.com/mercy–dyersville
Control: Church–operated, Nongovernment, not–for profit **Service:** General Medical and Surgical

Staffed Beds: 20 Admissions: 131 Census: 3 Outpatient Visits: 3845 Births: 0 Total Expense ($000): 5068 Payroll Expense ($000): 2348 Personnel: 53

ELKADER—Clayton County

★ **CENTRAL COMMUNITY HOSPITAL (161319)**, 901 Davidson Street N.W., Zip 52043–9015; tel. 563/245–7000 **A**10 18 **F**7 11 15 28 34 35 40 43 50 56 57 59 64 67 68 75 81 85 87 91 93 107 110 128 130 132 133 134 146 **S** Trinity Health, Livonia, MI
Primary Contact: Frances J. Zichal, Chief Executive Officer
CFO: Patricia Borel, Chief Financial Officer
CIO: Jonathan Holliday, Manager Information Technology
CHR: Angie Gerndt, Human Resources Manager
CNO: Natalie Shea, Chief Nursing Officer
Web address: www.centralcommunityhospital.com
Control: Other not–for–profit (including NFP Corporation) **Service:** General Medical and Surgical

Staffed Beds: 25 Admissions: 196 Census: 2 Outpatient Visits: 5875 Births: 0 Total Expense ($000): 6017 Payroll Expense ($000): 2139 Personnel: 62

EMMETSBURG—Palo Alto County

★ **PALO ALTO COUNTY HEALTH SYSTEM (161357)**, 3201 First Street, Zip 50536–2516; tel. 712/852–5500, (Total facility includes 22 beds in nursing home–type unit) **A**10 18 **F**3 7 11 13 15 28 29 30 34 35 40 43 45 46 50 57 59 61 62 63 64 65 67 69 71 75 76 77 81 82 85 87 93 107 110 115 119 125 127 130 132 133 135 143 146 **S** Trinity Health, Livonia, MI
Primary Contact: Desiree Einsweiler, Chief Executive Officer
CFO: Renay Hauswirth, Chief Financial Officer
CMO: Paul Matthews, M.D., President of Medical Staff
CIO: Randy Beaver, Chief Information Officer
CHR: Amy Knoup, Director Human Resources
CNO: JoAnn Higgins, Chief Nursing Officer and Assistant Administrator
Web address: www.pachs.com
Control: County–Government, nonfederal **Service:** General Medical and Surgical

Staffed Beds: 47 Admissions: 445 Census: 26 Outpatient Visits: 22694 Births: 121 Total Expense ($000): 23628 Payroll Expense ($000): 9101 Personnel: 192

ESTHERVILLE—Emmet County

★ **AVERA HOLY FAMILY HOSPITAL (161351)**, 826 North Eighth Street, Zip 51334–1598; tel. 712/362–2631 **A**10 18 **F**3 11 13 15 28 29 30 31 34 35 40 45 50 57 59 63 64 68 69 70 75 76 77 78 79 81 85 87 93 97 107 110 111 114 119 130 131 132 133 146 **P**4 **S** Avera Health, Sioux Falls, SD
Primary Contact: Dale Hustedt, Administrator
CFO: Shannon Adams, Chief Financial Officer
CMO: Keith Probst, M.D., Chief of Staff
CHR: Janette Jensen, Manager Human Resources
CNO: Cathi Rae Scharnberg, R.N., Vice President Patient Services
Web address: www.avera–holyfamily.org
Control: Church–operated, Nongovernment, not–for profit **Service:** General Medical and Surgical

Staffed Beds: 25 Admissions: 811 Census: 7 Outpatient Visits: 68941 Births: 92 Total Expense ($000): 22821 Payroll Expense ($000): 9602 Personnel: 170

FAIRFIELD—Jefferson County

★ **JEFFERSON COUNTY HEALTH CENTER (161364)**, 2000 South Main, Zip 52556–9572, Mailing Address: P.O. Box 588, Zip 52556–0010; tel. 641/472–4111 **A**10 18 **F**11 15 28 30 31 34 35 36 40 43 45 50 57 59 67 68 70 75 77 78 79 81 85 89 93 96 102 107 110 114 115 119 127 128 129 132 133 135 143 144 146 148 **P**5
Primary Contact: Bryan Hunger, Chief Executive Officer
CFO: Larry Peach, Chief Financial Officer
CHR: Nanette Everly, Manager Human Resources and Administrative Assistant
Web address: www.jeffersoncountyhealthcenter.org
Control: County–Government, nonfederal **Service:** General Medical and Surgical

Staffed Beds: 25 Admissions: 963 Census: 15 Outpatient Visits: 67731 Births: 0 Total Expense ($000): 36223 Payroll Expense ($000): 12176 Personnel: 255

FORT DODGE—Webster County

★ ◇ **UNITYPOINT HEALTH – TRINITY REGIONAL MEDICAL CENTER (160016)**, 802 Kenyon Road, Zip 50501–5795; tel. 515/573–3101 **A**2 10 21 **F**3 7 8 11 13 15 18 20 22 24 26 28 29 31 32 34 35 36 40 43 44 45 46 47 49 50 53 59 64 68 70 74 75 76 77 78 79 81 82 84 86 87 89 92 93 102 107 108 110 111 115 118 119 120 121 123 129 130 131 132 135 145 146 148 **P**6 **S** UnityPoint Health, West Des Moines, IA
Primary Contact: Mike Dewerff, President and Chief Executive Officer
COO: Troy Martens, Chief Operating Officer
CFO: Brent Feickert, Chief Financial Officer
CHR: Ted W. Vaughn, Director Human Resources
CNO: Debra Shriver, R.N., Chief Nurse Executive
Web address: www.trmc.org
Control: Other not–for–profit (including NFP Corporation) **Service:** General Medical and Surgical

Staffed Beds: 107 Admissions: 3666 Census: 36 Outpatient Visits: 99039 Births: 500 Total Expense ($000): 100136 Payroll Expense ($000): 46341 Personnel: 653

Many Facility Codes have changed. Please refer to the AHA Guide Code Chart. © 2016 AHA Guide

IA

FORT MADISON—Lee County

⊠ **FORT MADISON COMMUNITY HOSPITAL (160122)**, 5445 Avenue O,
Zip 52627–9611, Mailing Address: P.O. Box 174, Zip 52627–0174;
tel. 319/372–6530 **A**1 10 **F**3 11 13 15 28 29 31 34 40 43 45 50 51 53 57
59 62 64 67 68 70 74 75 76 77 78 79 81 85 86 87 90 91 93 94 96 97 99
100 101 102 103 104 107 108 111 115 117 118 119 128 129 130 131
132 133 143 144 146 147 148 **P**6 **S** QHR, Brentwood, TN
Primary Contact: Lynn W. Beasley, FACHE, Interim Chief Executive Officer
CFO: Bradley J. Kokjohn, Chief Financial Officer
CMO: David Wenger–Keller, M.D., Chief of Staff
CIO: Shane Tapper, Director Management Information Systems
CHR: Vicki Kokjohn, Director Employee Relations
CNO: Shelby Dickens, Director, Patient Care Services
Web address: www.fmchosp.com
Control: Other not–for–profit (including NFP Corporation) **Service:** General
Medical and Surgical

**Staffed Beds: 50 Admissions: 1674 Census: 18 Outpatient Visits: 104088
Births: 419 Total Expense ($000): 56106 Payroll Expense ($000): 26201
Personnel: 459**

GREENFIELD—Adair County

★ **ADAIR COUNTY MEMORIAL HOSPITAL (161310)**, 609 S.E. Kent Street,
Zip 50849–9454; tel. 641/743–2123 **A**10 18 **F**3 7 8 11 15 18 28 31 34 35
40 43 45 50 57 59 62 64 65 69 75 81 97 107 108 110 114 119 127 128
133 135 **P**6
Primary Contact: Marcia Hendricks, R.N., FACHE, Chief Executive Officer
CMO: Cassie Rasmussen, M.D., Chief Medical Officer
CIO: Thom Richards, Chief Information Technology
CHR: Angie Frankl, Director Human Resources
CNO: Cindy K. Peeler, R.N., Chief Nursing Officer
Web address: www.adaircountyhealthsystem.org
Control: County–Government, nonfederal **Service:** General Medical and Surgical

**Staffed Beds: 17 Admissions: 141 Census: 2 Outpatient Visits: 11357
Births: 0 Total Expense ($000): 12518 Payroll Expense ($000): 4483
Personnel: 100**

GRINNELL—Poweshiek County

★ **GRINNELL REGIONAL MEDICAL CENTER (160147)**, 210 Fourth Avenue,
Zip 50112–1898; tel. 641/236–7511 **A**10 **F**3 11 12 13 15 28 29 30 31 32 34
35 36 37 38 40 43 44 45 46 47 50 53 54 56 57 59 61 62 63 64 65 66 70
75 76 77 78 79 81 84 85 86 87 89 93 97 99 100 101 102 103 104 107 108
110 111 115 118 119 126 127 130 131 132 133 134 135 144 146 147 148
P6 7
Primary Contact: Todd C. Linden, President and Chief Executive Officer
CFO: Kyle M. Wilcox, Vice President Finance
CIO: David L. Ness, Vice President Operations
CHR: Debra S. Nowachek, Director Human Resources
CNO: Doris Rindels, Vice President Operations
Web address: www.grmc.us
Control: Other not–for–profit (including NFP Corporation) **Service:** General
Medical and Surgical

**Staffed Beds: 49 Admissions: 1351 Census: 12 Outpatient Visits: 47398
Births: 147 Total Expense ($000): 46305 Payroll Expense ($000): 20423
Personnel: 343**

GRUNDY CENTER—Grundy County

★ **GRUNDY COUNTY MEMORIAL HOSPITAL (161303)**, 201 East J Avenue,
Zip 50638–2096; tel. 319/824–5421, (Total facility includes 55 beds in nursing
home–type unit) **A**10 18 **F**15 28 29 34 35 40 43 57 59 63 67 68 75 78 79 81
82 86 87 93 107 110 111 114 119 128 129 130 131 132 133 135 146 148
S UnityPoint Health, West Des Moines, IA
Primary Contact: Jennifer Havens, Chief Executive Officer and Director of Nursing
Operations
COO: Ryan Bingman, Director Operations
CFO: Lisa Zinkula, Chief Financial Officer
CMO: Douglas Cooper, M.D., Chief Medical Officer
CIO: Scott Lufkin, Director Information Technology
CHR: Aaron Wedo, Manager, Human Resources
Web address: www.grundycountyhospital.com
Control: County–Government, nonfederal **Service:** General Medical and Surgical

**Staffed Beds: 80 Admissions: 312 Census: 58 Outpatient Visits: 36631
Total Expense ($000): 19064 Payroll Expense ($000): 7948 Personnel:
143**

GUTHRIE CENTER—Guthrie County

★ **GUTHRIE COUNTY HOSPITAL (161314)**, 710 North 12th Street,
Zip 50115–1544; tel. 641/332–2201 **A**10 18 **F**11 15 18 28 29 31 34 35 40
43 45 53 56 57 59 64 69 75 79 81 85 93 107 110 119 128 130 132 133
143 148 **S** UnityPoint Health, West Des Moines, IA
Primary Contact: Patrick Peters, Chief Executive Officer
CFO: Melinda Alt, Chief Financial Officer
CMO: Steven Bascom, M.D., Chief Medical Officer
CIO: Jeff Cobb, Information Technologist
CHR: Kimberly Myers, Director Human Resources
Web address: www.guthriecountyhospital.org
Control: County–Government, nonfederal **Service:** General Medical and Surgical

**Staffed Beds: 17 Admissions: 327 Census: 3 Outpatient Visits: 45571
Births: 0 Total Expense ($000): 14687 Payroll Expense ($000): 6214
Personnel: 102**

GUTTENBERG—Clayton County

⊠ **GUTTENBERG MUNICIPAL HOSPITAL (161312)**, 200 Main Street,
Zip 52052–9108, Mailing Address: P.O. Box 550, Zip 52052–0550;
tel. 563/252–1121 **A**1 10 18 **F**3 7 8 11 13 15 28 34 35 40 43 45 50 57 59
64 68 76 81 85 93 97 102 107 110 111 115 119 127 128 130 132 133 **P**5
6 **S** UnityPoint Health, West Des Moines, IA
Primary Contact: Kimberley A. Gau, FACHE, Chief Executive Officer
CMO: Andrew Smith, M.D., Chief of Staff
CIO: Scott R. Pauls, Director Information Technology– HealthNet Connect
CHR: Linda Aulwes, Human Resources Coordinator
CNO: Kimberley A. Gau, FACHE, Interim Chief Nursing Officer
Web address: www.guttenberghospital.org
Control: City–Government, nonfederal **Service:** General Medical and Surgical

**Staffed Beds: 20 Admissions: 315 Census: 2 Outpatient Visits: 24708
Births: 33 Total Expense ($000): 14685 Payroll Expense ($000): 6121
Personnel: 126**

HAMBURG—Fremont County

GEORGE C GRAPE COMMUNITY HOSPITAL (161324), 2959 U.S. Highway
275, Zip 51640–5067; tel. 712/382–1515, (Total facility includes 6 beds in
nursing home–type unit) **A**10 18 **F**11 15 18 28 31 34 35 40 43 45 50 53 57
59 62 64 65 68 75 77 78 79 81 82 85 91 93 107 114 119 128 129 130 131
133 135 148
Primary Contact: Michael O'Neal, Administrator and Chief Executive Officer
CFO: Hilary Christiansen, Chief Financial Officer
CMO: Kelli Woltemath, D.O., Chief Medical Staff
CIO: Craig Wells, Chief Information Officer
CHR: Jackie Wertz, Director Human Resources
CNO: Gloria Mattice, R.N., Director Patient Care
Web address: www.grapehospital.com
Control: Other not–for–profit (including NFP Corporation) **Service:** General
Medical and Surgical

**Staffed Beds: 25 Admissions: 306 Census: 6 Outpatient Visits: 18092
Births: 0 Total Expense ($000): 10082 Payroll Expense ($000): 4080
Personnel: 88**

HAMPTON—Franklin County

★ **FRANKLIN GENERAL HOSPITAL (161308)**, 1720 Central Avenue East, Suite
A., Zip 50441–1867; tel. 641/456–5000, (Total facility includes 52 beds in
nursing home–type unit) **A**10 18 **F**7 10 11 15 28 30 34 40 43 57 59 63 64 65
67 68 75 77 79 81 82 85 86 89 90 93 107 111 114 119 127 128 129 130
131 132 133 135 146 148 **S** Trinity Health, Livonia, MI
Primary Contact: Kim Price, Chief Executive Officer
CFO: Bonnie Lettow, Chief Financial Officer
CHR: Victoria Kruse, Manager Human Resources
CNO: Ronda Reimer, R.N., Chief Nursing Officer and Assistant Administrator
Web address: www.franklingeneral.com
Control: County–Government, nonfederal **Service:** General Medical and Surgical

**Staffed Beds: 77 Admissions: 363 Census: 52 Outpatient Visits: 17035
Births: 0 Total Expense ($000): 17952 Payroll Expense ($000): 5486
Personnel: 134**

IA

Hospital, Medicare Provider Number, Address, Telephone, Approval, Facility, and Physician Codes, Health Care System

★ American Hospital Association (AHA) membership   ◯ Healthcare Facilities Accreditation Program   ⇑ Center for Improvement in Healthcare Quality Accreditation
☐ The Joint Commission accreditation   ◇ DNV Healthcare Inc. accreditation   △ Commission on Accreditation of Rehabilitation Facilities (CARF) accreditation

HARLAN—Shelby County

★ **MYRTUE MEDICAL CENTER (161374)**, 1213 Garfield Avenue, Zip 51537–2057; tel. 712/755–5161 **A**10 18 **F**3 11 13 15 28 29 31 32 34 35 38 40 43 45 46 50 53 56 57 59 62 63 64 65 68 75 76 77 78 81 85 87 92 93 97 99 101 102 103 104 107 110 114 119 127 129 130 131 132 133 135 146 148 **P**6 8
Primary Contact: Barry Jacobsen, CPA, Chief Executive Officer
CFO: Kristy Hansen, CPA, Chief Financial Officer
CMO: David Erlbacher, M.D., Chief of Staff
CIO: David Sirek, Chief Information Officer
CHR: Donna Christensen–Mores, JD, Director Human Resources
CNO: Karen Buman, Chief Nursing Executive
Web address: www.myrtuemedical.org
Control: County–Government, nonfederal **Service:** General Medical and Surgical

Staffed Beds: 25 **Admissions:** 1107 **Census:** 14 **Outpatient Visits:** 101431 **Births:** 95 **Total Expense ($000):** 35781 **Payroll Expense ($000):** 14581 **Personnel:** 288

HAWARDEN—Sioux County

★ **HAWARDEN REGIONAL HEALTHCARE (161311)**, 1111 11th Street, Zip 51023–1999; tel. 712/551–3100 **A**10 18 **F**1 4 11 15 16 17 28 29 31 34 35 40 43 53 59 64 67 69 70 72 73 75 77 80 81 88 89 90 92 93 98 107 108 114 127 128 132 133 135 148 **P**3 7 **S** Trinity Health, Livonia, MI
Primary Contact: Jayson Pullman, Chief Executive Officer
CFO: Jessica Hughes, Director Finance
CMO: Dale Nystrom, M.D., Chief Medical Officer, Physician
CHR: Maggie Hofer, Human Resources Representative
Web address: www.hawardenregionalhealthcare.com/
Control: City–Government, nonfederal **Service:** General Medical and Surgical

Staffed Beds: 18 **Admissions:** 85 **Census:** 1 **Outpatient Visits:** 18087 **Births:** 0 **Total Expense ($000):** 7814 **Payroll Expense ($000):** 3132 **Personnel:** 68

HUMBOLDT—Humboldt County

★ **HUMBOLDT COUNTY MEMORIAL HOSPITAL (161334)**, 1000 North 15th Street, Zip 50548–1008; tel. 515/332–4200, (Total facility includes 28 beds in nursing home–type unit) **A**10 18 **F**7 8 10 11 12 14 15 28 29 31 34 35 40 41 43 45 47 50 51 59 62 63 65 69 75 77 78 79 81 82 84 85 87 93 102 104 107 110 111 114 119 125 127 128 129 130 133 134 135 **S** UnityPoint Health, West Des Moines, IA
Primary Contact: Michelle Sleiter, Chief Executive Officer
CFO: Betty Etherington, Chief Financial Officer
CHR: Mary Moritz, Administrator Human Resources
Web address: www.humboldthospital.org
Control: County–Government, nonfederal **Service:** General Medical and Surgical

Staffed Beds: 49 **Admissions:** 424 **Census:** 31 **Outpatient Visits:** 76148 **Births:** 0 **Total Expense ($000):** 15401 **Payroll Expense ($000):** 6400 **Personnel:** 141

IDA GROVE—Ida County

★ **HORN MEMORIAL HOSPITAL (161354)**, 701 East Second Street, Zip 51445–1699; tel. 712/364–3311 **A**10 18 **F**11 15 28 29 34 40 45 50 57 59 62 63 64 65 66 68 75 77 78 79 81 82 85 89 93 97 107 108 110 111 115 119 127 129 130 131 132 133 135 146 147 148 **P**6
Primary Contact: Christopher Nichols, Chief Executive Officer
CFO: Marcia Fehring, Chief Financial Officer
CIO: Robbie Todd, Director Information Technology
CHR: Lorraine Davis, Vice President Human Resources
CNO: Jo Hayes, Chief Nursing Officer
Web address: www.hornmemorialhospital.org
Control: Other not–for–profit (including NFP Corporation) **Service:** General Medical and Surgical

Staffed Beds: 25 **Admissions:** 514 **Census:** 8 **Outpatient Visits:** 22937 **Births:** 0 **Total Expense ($000):** 17802 **Payroll Expense ($000):** 8063 **Personnel:** 158

INDEPENDENCE—Buchanan County

★ **BUCHANAN COUNTY HEALTH CENTER (161335)**, 1600 First Street East, Zip 50644–3155; tel. 319/332–0999, (Total facility includes 39 beds in nursing home–type unit) **A**10 18 **F**3 11 15 28 29 32 34 35 40 43 45 50 53 56 57 59 64 65 67 75 77 79 81 82 86 87 91 93 107 110 111 114 119 125 129 130 131 132 133 135 146 148
Primary Contact: Steve Robert Slessor, Chief Executive Officer
CFO: Ben Stevens, Chief Financial Officer
CNO: Rachel Goldenstein, R.N., Chief Nursing Officer
Web address: www.bchealth.info
Control: County–Government, nonfederal **Service:** General Medical and Surgical

Staffed Beds: 58 **Admissions:** 361 **Census:** 42 **Outpatient Visits:** 46723 **Births:** 0 **Total Expense ($000):** 21873 **Payroll Expense ($000):** 9336 **Personnel:** 184

□ **MENTAL HEALTH INSTITUTE (164003)**, 2277 Iowa Avenue, Zip 50644–9106; tel. 319/334–2583 **A**1 10 **F**65 98 99 101 102 106 130 143 146 **P**6
Primary Contact: Bhasker J. Dave, M.D., Superintendent
CFO: Kevin Jimmerson, Business Manager
CMO: Bhasker J. Dave, M.D., Superintendent
Web address: www.dhs.state.ia.us
Control: State–Government, nonfederal **Service:** Psychiatric

Staffed Beds: 75 **Admissions:** 203 **Census:** 51 **Outpatient Visits:** 14 **Births:** 0 **Total Expense ($000):** 22502 **Payroll Expense ($000):** 12904 **Personnel:** 227

IOWA CITY—Johnson County

⊠ **IOWA CITY VETERANS AFFAIRS HEALTH CARE SYSTEM**, 601 Highway 6 West, Zip 52246–2208; tel. 319/338–0581 **A**1 3 5 8 **F**3 5 8 11 12 17 18 20 22 24 29 30 31 33 34 35 36 38 39 40 43 44 45 46 47 50 51 53 54 56 57 58 59 60 61 62 64 65 70 71 74 75 78 79 81 82 83 84 85 86 87 91 92 93 94 97 98 100 101 102 103 104 106 107 108 111 114 115 116 117 118 119 129 130 135 138 142 143 146 147 148 **P**6 **S** Department of Veterans Affairs, Washington, DC
Primary Contact: Judith Johnson–Mekota, Director
COO: Kevin Kosek, Associate Director Operations
CFO: Jennifer Ruppert, Chief Financial Officer
CMO: Richard A. Charlat, Chief of Staff
CIO: Dwight Schuessler, Chief Information Officer
CHR: Dan Helle, Human Resources Officer
CNO: Dawn Oxley, R.N., Associate Director Patient Care Services and Nurse Executive
Web address: www.iowacity.va.gov/
Control: Veterans Affairs, Government, federal **Service:** General Medical and Surgical

Staffed Beds: 73 **Admissions:** 3496 **Census:** 52 **Outpatient Visits:** 504060 **Births:** 0 **Total Expense ($000):** 322557 **Payroll Expense ($000):** 130140 **Personnel:** 1880

⊠ **MERCY IOWA CITY (160029)**, 500 East Market Street, Zip 52245–2689; tel. 319/339–0300, (Total facility includes 16 beds in nursing home–type unit) **A**1 2 10 **F**3 5 8 11 12 13 15 18 20 22 24 26 28 29 30 31 34 35 38 40 41 43 44 45 47 48 50 54 56 57 58 59 62 63 64 65 70 72 73 74 75 76 77 78 79 81 82 85 86 87 89 97 98 100 101 102 103 104 107 108 110 111 114 115 119 126 128 130 132 135 144 145 146 148 **P**8
Primary Contact: Michael G. Heinrich, Interim President and Chief Executive Officer
CFO: Michael G. Heinrich, Executive Vice President and Chief Financial Officer
CMO: Martin Izakovic, M.D., Vice President Medical Staff Affairs and Chief Medical Officer
CIO: David Fishbaugher, Chief Medical Information
CHR: Dena M. Brockhouse, Director Human Resources
CNO: Cindy L. Penney, R.N., Vice President Nursing
Web address: www.mercyiowacity.org
Control: Church–operated, Nongovernment, not–for profit **Service:** General Medical and Surgical

Staffed Beds: 234 **Admissions:** 7881 **Census:** 83 **Outpatient Visits:** 328916 **Births:** 1258 **Total Expense ($000):** 146953 **Payroll Expense ($000):** 60949 **Personnel:** 947

UNIVERSITY HOSPITAL SCHOOL See Center for Disabilities and Development

⊠ **UNIVERSITY OF IOWA HOSPITALS AND CLINICS (160058)**, 200 Hawkins Drive, Zip 52242–1009; tel. 319/356–1616, (Includes CENTER FOR DISABILITIES AND DEVELOPMENT, 200 Hawkins Drive, Zip 52242; tel. 319/356–1347; CHEMICAL DEPENDENCY CENTER, 200 Hawkins Drive, Zip 52242–1007; tel. 319/384–8765; STATE PSYCHIATRIC HOSPITAL, 200 Hawkins Drive, Zip 52242; tel. 319/356–4658; UNIVERSITY OF IOWA CHILDREN'S HOSPITAL, 200 Hawkins Drive, tel. 888/573–5437) **A**1 2 3 5 8 10 **F**3 5 6 7 8 9 11 12 13 14 15 16 17 18 19 20 21 22 23 24 25 26 27 28 29 30 31 32 33 34 35 37 38 39 40 41 43 44 45 46 47 48 49 50 51 52 53 54 55 56 57 58 59 60 61 62 63 64 65 66 68 70 72 73 74 75 76 77 78 79 80 81 82 83 84 85 86 87 88 89 90 91 92 93 94 96 97 98 99 100 101 102 103 104 105 107 108 109 110 111 114 115 116 117 118 119 120 121 123 124 126 127 129 130 131 132 135 136 137 138 139 140 141 142 143 144 145 146 147 148 **P**1 7
Primary Contact: Kenneth P. Kates, Chief Executive Officer
COO: Scott Turner, Co–Chief Operating Officer
CFO: Kenneth Fisher, Associate Vice President Finance and Chief Financial Officer
CMO: Theresa Brennan, M.D., Chief Medical Officer
CIO: Lee Carmen, Associate Vice President Health Care Information Systems
CHR: Jana Wessels, Associate Vice President Human Resources
Web address: www.uihealthcare.org
Control: State–Government, nonfederal **Service:** General Medical and Surgical

Staffed Beds: 695 **Admissions:** 31748 **Census:** 565 **Outpatient Visits:** 1271144 **Births:** 2143 **Total Expense ($000):** 1237672 **Payroll Expense ($000):** 432181 **Personnel:** 7733

IA

Many Facility Codes have changed. Please refer to the AHA Guide Code Chart. © 2016 AHA Guide

IOWA FALLS—Hardin County

★ **HANSEN FAMILY HOSPITAL (161380)**, 920 South Oak, Zip 50126–9506; tel. 641/648–4631 **A**10 18 **F**3 11 13 15 28 34 40 43 45 50 53 57 59 64 65 75 76 77 81 82 85 86 87 89 93 97 100 104 107 110 115 119 133 135 147 **P**6 **S** Trinity Health, Livonia, MI
Primary Contact: Cherelle Montanye–Ireland, Chief Executive Officer
CFO: Mike White, Chief Financial Officer
CMO: George Pfaltzgraff, Chief Medical Officer
CHR: Cheri Geitz, Director Human Resources
CNO: Katie Rieks, Chief Nursing Officer
Web address: www.hansenfamilyhospital.com
Control: City–Government, nonfederal **Service:** General Medical and Surgical

Staffed Beds: 21 **Admissions:** 631 **Census:** 8 **Outpatient Visits:** 38343 **Births:** 92 **Total Expense ($000):** 24414 **Payroll Expense ($000):** 10355 **Personnel:** 234

JEFFERSON—Greene County

★ **GREENE COUNTY MEDICAL CENTER (161325)**, 1000 West Lincolnway, Zip 50129–1645; tel. 515/386–2114, (Total facility includes 65 beds in nursing home–type unit) **A**10 18 **F**3 11 13 15 28 29 31 34 35 36 40 46 56 57 59 63 64 65 67 68 75 76 77 79 81 82 85 93 107 110 114 119 125 128 130 131 132 133 147 **S** UnityPoint Health, West Des Moines, IA
Primary Contact: Carl P. Behne, Administrator and Chief Executive Officer
CFO: Mark A. VanderLinden, Chief Financial Officer
CMO: Jon Van Der Veer, D.O., Vice President Medical Affairs
CIO: Roger Overby, Executive Director Information Systems
CHR: Cathy Krieger, Human Resources Director
CNO: Katie Heldt, Chief Nursing Officer
Web address: www.gcmchealth.com
Control: County–Government, nonfederal **Service:** General Medical and Surgical

Staffed Beds: 90 **Admissions:** 357 **Census:** 51 **Outpatient Visits:** 33616 **Births:** 48 **Total Expense ($000):** 23102 **Payroll Expense ($000):** 9603 **Personnel:** 211

KEOKUK—Lee County

⊞ **KEOKUK AREA HOSPITAL (160008)**, 1600 Morgan Street, Zip 52632–3456; tel. 319/524–7150 **A**1 10 **F**3 11 15 28 29 34 35 40 43 45 46 57 59 62 64 68 70 79 81 85 86 87 93 96 107 108 111 114 115 118 119 129 130 131 132 133 146 148 **P**6
Primary Contact: Joseph K. Whiting, FACHE, Interim Chief Executive Officer
CMO: Neville Crenshaw, D.O., Chief of Staff
CIO: Linda Atterberg, Chief Information Officer
CHR: Lora Taylor, Director Human Resources and Compliance Officer
CNO: Vickie White, Director of Nursing
Web address: www.keokukhealthsystems.org
Control: Other not–for–profit (including NFP Corporation) **Service:** General Medical and Surgical

Staffed Beds: 42 **Admissions:** 983 **Census:** 8 **Outpatient Visits:** 32913 **Births:** 0 **Total Expense ($000):** 20383 **Payroll Expense ($000):** 8763 **Personnel:** 239

KEOSAUQUA—Van Buren County

★ **VAN BUREN COUNTY HOSPITAL (161337)**, 304 Franklin Street, Zip 52565–1164; tel. 319/293–3171 **A**10 18 **F**3 7 10 11 13 15 28 29 32 34 35 40 43 45 46 50 56 57 59 64 65 70 75 76 77 81 85 86 87 89 93 97 102 107 110 111 114 119 125 127 128 130 132 133 135 146 147 148 **P**6
Primary Contact: Ray Brownsworth, Chief Executive Officer
CFO: Kara McEntee, Chief Financial Officer
CIO: Chris McEntee, Network Specialist
CNO: Rhonda Fellows, R.N., Chief Nursing Officer
Web address: www.vbch.org
Control: County–Government, nonfederal **Service:** General Medical and Surgical

Staffed Beds: 25 **Admissions:** 397 **Census:** 4 **Outpatient Visits:** 16519 **Births:** 54 **Total Expense ($000):** 14606 **Payroll Expense ($000):** 7228 **Personnel:** 162

KNOXVILLE—Marion County

KNOXVILLE DIVISION See Veterans Affairs Central Iowa Health Care System, Des Moines

★ **KNOXVILLE HOSPITAL & CLINICS (161355)**, 1002 South Lincoln Street, Zip 50138–3155; tel. 641/842–2151 **A**10 18 **F**3 8 11 15 28 29 34 40 43 45 47 48 49 50 54 57 59 64 65 75 77 79 81 85 86 93 97 102 107 108 110 111 114 118 119 129 130 131 132 133 135 146 147 148 **P**6 **S** Catholic Health Initiatives, Englewood, CO
Primary Contact: Kevin Kincaid, Chief Executive Officer
CFO: Maggie Hamilton–Beyer, Chief Financial Officer
CMO: Brent Hoehns, M.D., Chief of Medical Staff
CIO: Thom Richards, Director Information Technology
CNO: MaryJane Applegate, Chief Clinical Officer
Web address: www.knoxvillehospital.org
Control: Other not–for–profit (including NFP Corporation) **Service:** General Medical and Surgical

Staffed Beds: 25 **Admissions:** 1014 **Census:** 10 **Outpatient Visits:** 66064 **Births:** 0 **Total Expense ($000):** 27753 **Payroll Expense ($000):** 11442 **Personnel:** 267

LAKE CITY—Calhoun County

★ **STEWART MEMORIAL COMMUNITY HOSPITAL (161350)**, 1301 West Main, Zip 51449–1585; tel. 712/464–3171 **A**10 18 **F**11 12 13 15 28 29 30 31 34 40 43 45 59 62 63 64 65 67 70 75 76 77 78 81 82 86 93 94 107 110 114 119 127 130 133 135 147 **P**5 6 **S** UnityPoint Health, West Des Moines, IA
Primary Contact: Cynthia L. Carstens, R.N., President and Chief Executive Officer
CFO: Jim Henkenius, Chief Financial Officer
CHR: Bill Albright, Director Human Resources
Web address: www.stewartmemorial.org
Control: Other not–for–profit (including NFP Corporation) **Service:** General Medical and Surgical

Staffed Beds: 25 **Admissions:** 573 **Census:** 6 **Outpatient Visits:** 40696 **Births:** 103 **Total Expense ($000):** 31264 **Payroll Expense ($000):** 13316 **Personnel:** 242

LE MARS—Plymouth County

★ **FLOYD VALLEY HEALTHCARE (161368)**, 714 Lincoln Street N.E., Zip 51031–3314; tel. 712/546–7871 **A**10 18 **F**3 10 11 13 15 28 29 31 32 34 35 40 43 45 50 53 57 59 62 64 65 67 68 76 78 79 80 81 85 86 87 89 107 110 111 114 119 128 130 132 133 135 146 148 **S** Avera Health, Sioux Falls, SD
Primary Contact: Michael T. Donlin, FACHE, Administrator
CFO: Daryl Friedenbach, Director Fiscal Services
CMO: Mark Stelzer, M.D., President Medical Staff
CIO: Jason Uhl, Chief Information Officer
CHR: Mary Helen Gibson, Director Human Resources
CNO: Loretta Myers, MS, Director, Patient Care
Web address: www.floydvalley.org
Control: City–Government, nonfederal **Service:** General Medical and Surgical

Staffed Beds: 25 **Admissions:** 771 **Census:** 7 **Outpatient Visits:** 52721 **Births:** 105 **Total Expense ($000):** 33416 **Payroll Expense ($000):** 11767 **Personnel:** 258

LEON—Decatur County

★ **DECATUR COUNTY HOSPITAL (161340)**, 1405 N.W. Church Street, Zip 50144–1299; tel. 641/446–4871 **A**10 18 **F**3 7 11 15 28 29 31 34 40 41 45 50 57 59 64 68 71 75 78 79 81 82 85 93 107 111 114 119 130 133 146 148
Primary Contact: Suzanne Cooner, R.N., MSN, Chief Executive Officer
CFO: Tara Spidle, Chief Financial Officer
CMO: Ed Wehling, Chief Medical Staff
CHR: Jo Beth Smith, Vice President Human Resources
Web address: www.decaturcountyhospital.org
Control: County–Government, nonfederal **Service:** General Medical and Surgical

Staffed Beds: 11 **Admissions:** 282 **Census:** 3 **Outpatient Visits:** 12418 **Births:** 0 **Total Expense ($000):** 12308 **Payroll Expense ($000):** 3785 **Personnel:** 96

IA

Hospital, Medicare Provider Number, Address, Telephone, Approval, Facility, and Physician Codes, Health Care System

★ American Hospital Association (AHA) membership
☐ The Joint Commission accreditation
○ Healthcare Facilities Accreditation Program
◇ DNV Healthcare Inc. accreditation
⇑ Center for Improvement in Healthcare Quality Accreditation
△ Commission on Accreditation of Rehabilitation Facilities (CARF) accreditation

MANCHESTER—Delaware County

★ **REGIONAL MEDICAL CENTER (161343)**, 709 West Main Street,
Zip 52057–1526, Mailing Address: P.O. Box 359, Zip 52057–0359;
tel. 563/927–3232 **A**10 18 **F**3 7 11 13 15 17 28 29 34 35 36 40 43 44 50
53 57 59 61 62 63 64 65 66 68 70 75 76 77 79 81 82 85 86 89 93 94 97
99 104 107 110 111 114 119 126 127 128 129 130 131 132 146 148 **P**6
Primary Contact: Lon D. Butikofer, R.N., Ph.D., Chief Executive Officer
CFO: Danette Kramer, Chief Financial Officer
CIO: Amy Mensen, Chief Administrative Officer
CHR: Amy Mensen, Chief Administrative Officer
CNO: Heather Ries, MSN, Chief Nursing Officer
Web address: www.regmedctr.org
Control: County–Government, nonfederal **Service:** General Medical and Surgical

Staffed Beds: 25 **Admissions:** 963 **Census:** 9 **Outpatient Visits:** 172052
Births: 204 **Total Expense ($000):** 44861 **Payroll Expense ($000):** 22212
Personnel: 365

MANNING—Carroll County

★ **MANNING REGIONAL HEALTHCARE CENTER (161332)**, 1550 6th Street,
Zip 51455–1093; tel. 712/655–2072, (Total facility includes 56 beds in nursing
home–type unit) **A**10 18 **F**3 4 5 11 13 15 31 34 35 38 40 43 45 50 56 57 59
64 68 75 76 81 85 89 92 93 97 107 110 114 119 128 130 132 133 148 **P**6 **S**
Primary Contact: John O'Brien, Chief Executive Officer
CFO: Amy McLaughlin, CPA, Chief Financial Officer
CMO: Douglas McLaws, D.O., Chief Medical Officer
CIO: Kim C. Jahn, Chief Plant Operations and Chief Information Officer
CHR: Shelli Lorenzen, Chief Human Resources Officer
CNO: Linn Block, R.N., Chief Nursing Officer
Web address: www.mrhcia.com
Control: Other not–for–profit (including NFP Corporation) **Service:** General
Medical and Surgical

Staffed Beds: 73 **Admissions:** 207 **Census:** 45 **Outpatient Visits:** 8417
Births: 19 **Total Expense ($000):** 15622 **Payroll Expense ($000):** 6327
Personnel: 179

MAQUOKETA—Jackson County

✉ **JACKSON COUNTY REGIONAL HEALTH CENTER (161329)**, 700 West Grove
Street, Zip 52060–2163; tel. 563/652–2474 **A**1 10 18 **F**3 7 11 15 28 34 40
43 45 53 64 75 81 85 87 93 107 110 114 119 128 129 133 146 148
S Genesis Health System, Davenport, IA
Primary Contact: Curt Coleman, FACHE, Administrator
CFO: Donna Roeder, Chief Financial Officer
CHR: Shannon Langenberg, Director Human Resources
Web address: www.jcrhc.org
Control: County–Government, nonfederal **Service:** General Medical and Surgical

Staffed Beds: 25 **Admissions:** 159 **Census:** 3 **Outpatient Visits:** 18341
Births: 0 **Total Expense ($000):** 13494 **Payroll Expense ($000):** 4616
Personnel: 114

MARENGO—Iowa County

★ **MARENGO MEMORIAL HOSPITAL (161317)**, 300 West May Street,
Zip 52301–1261; tel. 319/642–5543 **A**10 18 **F**3 15 28 29 31 34 35 38 40 43
45 50 59 64 69 75 81 85 87 96 97 107 110 115 127 130 131 133 135 143
146 **P**6 **S** UnityPoint Health, West Des Moines, IA
Primary Contact: Barry Goettsch, FACHE, Chief Executive Officer
COO: Mikaela Gehring, Chief Operating Officer
CFO: Matthew Murphy, Chief Financial Officer
CHR: Lesa Waddell, Director Human Resources
CNO: Teresa Sauerbrei, Chief Nursing Officer
Web address: www.marengohospital.org
Control: City–Government, nonfederal **Service:** General Medical and Surgical

Staffed Beds: 25 **Admissions:** 338 **Census:** 9 **Outpatient Visits:** 15197
Births: 1 **Total Expense ($000):** 17073 **Payroll Expense ($000):** 7911
Personnel: 137

MARSHALLTOWN—Marshall County

★ **CENTRAL IOWA HEALTHCARE (160001)**, 3 South Fourth Avenue,
Zip 50158–2998; tel. 641/754–5151 **A**10 **F**3 7 11 12 13 15 18 20 22 28 30
34 35 39 40 43 45 50 54 56 57 59 62 64 68 69 70 75 76 78 79 81 82 85
87 89 93 97 107 108 110 111 114 115 119 129 130 131 132 133 135 144
146 147 148
Primary Contact: John Hughes, FACHE, President and Chief Executive Officer
CFO: Hilary Dolbee, Chief Financial Officer
CMO: Milt Van Gundy, M.D., President Medical Staff
CHR: Jill Petermeier, Senior Executive Human Resources
Web address: www.marshmed.com/
Control: Other not–for–profit (including NFP Corporation) **Service:** General
Medical and Surgical

Staffed Beds: 49 **Admissions:** 2717 **Census:** 23 **Outpatient Visits:** 196102
Births: 480 **Total Expense ($000):** 80019 **Payroll Expense ($000):** 27733
Personnel: 389

MASON CITY—Cerro Gordo County

✉ **MERCY MEDICAL CENTER–NORTH IOWA (160064)**, 1000 Fourth Street
S.W., Zip 50401–2800; tel. 641/428–7000 **A**1 2 3 5 10 13 **F**3 11 12 13 15 18
20 22 24 26 28 29 30 31 34 35 37 39 40 42 43 44 45 46 47 48 49 50 54
55 56 57 58 59 60 61 62 63 64 65 68 70 71 72 74 75 76 77 78 79 81 82
84 85 86 87 89 90 91 93 96 97 98 99 100 101 102 103 104 107 108 110
111 113 115 117 118 119 120 121 123 124 125 126 128 129 130 131 132
135 144 145 146 147 148 **P**1 6 **S** Trinity Health, Livonia, MI
Primary Contact: Daniel Varnum, President and Chief Executive Officer
COO: Diane Fischels, Senior Vice President and Chief Operating Officer
CFO: Danette Zook, Chief Financial Officer
CMO: Paul Manternach, M.D., Senior Vice President Physician Integration
CIO: Terry Chartier, Director, Information Systems
CHR: Jackie Luecht, Chief Human Resources Officer
CNO: Kim Chamberlin, Vice President Patient Services and Chief Nursing Officer
Web address: www.mercynorthiowa.com
Control: Church–operated, Nongovernment, not–for profit **Service:** General
Medical and Surgical

Staffed Beds: 205 **Admissions:** 11450 **Census:** 132 **Outpatient Visits:**
453543 **Births:** 913 **Total Expense ($000):** 338633 **Payroll Expense
($000):** 136857 **Personnel:** 1963

MISSOURI VALLEY—Harrison County

★ **CHI HEALTH MISSOURI VALLEY (161309)**, 631 North Eighth Street,
Zip 51555–1102; tel. 712/642–2784 **A**10 18 **F**3 28 34 40 44 45 47 50 54 57
59 62 63 64 65 66 68 75 81 82 83 84 86 87 93 94 97 99 100 101 107 110
114 119 127 129 133 135 144 146 **P**8 **S** Catholic Health Initiatives,
Englewood, CO
Primary Contact: Robert A. Valentine, President
CMO: Daniel Richter, M.D., Chief of Staff
CIO: Ravae Smallwood, IS Coordinator
CHR: Heidi Winters, Business Partner Human Resources
CNO: Darcy Behrendt, R.N., Vice President, Patient Care Services
Web address: www.chihealth.com/chi–health–missouri–valley
Control: Other not–for–profit (including NFP Corporation) **Service:** General
Medical and Surgical

Staffed Beds: 16 **Admissions:** 630 **Census:** 4 **Outpatient Visits:** 33236
Births: 0 **Total Expense ($000):** 23006 **Payroll Expense ($000):** 9699
Personnel: 118

MOUNT AYR—Ringgold County

RINGGOLD COUNTY HOSPITAL (161373), 504 North Cleveland Street,
Zip 50854–2201; tel. 641/464–3226 **A**10 18 **F**7 15 28 29 31 34 35 38 40 43
50 56 57 59 64 65 81 93 97 107 111 115 119 127 133 148 **P**6
Primary Contact: Gordon W. Winkler, Administrator and Chief Executive Officer
CFO: Teresa Roberts, Chief Financial Officer
CIO: Beth Kosman, Director Health Information Management
CHR: Mitzi Hymbaugh, Chief Personnel
Web address: www.rchmtayr.org
Control: Hospital district or authority, Government, nonfederal **Service:** General
Medical and Surgical

Staffed Beds: 16 **Admissions:** 303 **Census:** 3 **Outpatient Visits:** 25391
Births: 0 **Total Expense ($000):** 17900 **Payroll Expense ($000):** 5992
Personnel: 125

MOUNT PLEASANT—Henry County

★ **HENRY COUNTY HEALTH CENTER (161356)**, 407 South White Street,
Zip 52641–2263; tel. 319/385–3141, (Total facility includes 49 beds in nursing
home–type unit) **A**10 18 **F**3 7 11 13 15 28 29 31 32 34 35 40 41 43 44 45 50
53 57 59 64 65 67 70 75 76 77 78 79 81 82 85 86 87 89 93 97 102 107
108 110 115 118 119 128 129 130 131 132 133 135 143 146 147 **P**6
Primary Contact: Robb Gardner, Chief Executive Officer
CFO: David Muhs, Chief Financial Officer
CMO: Joel Ryon, M.D., Chief of Staff
CHR: Lynn Humphreys, Director Human Resources
CNO: Jodi Geerts, Chief Nursing Officer
Web address: www.hchc.org
Control: County–Government, nonfederal **Service:** General Medical and Surgical

Staffed Beds: 74 **Admissions:** 597 **Census:** 47 **Outpatient Visits:** 50492
Births: 111 **Total Expense ($000):** 32822 **Payroll Expense ($000):** 11728
Personnel: 223

Many Facility Codes have changed. Please refer to the AHA Guide Code Chart. © 2016 AHA Guide

MUSCATINE—Muscatine County

☒ **UNITYPOINT HEALTH – TRINITY MUSCATINE (160013)**, 1518 Mulberry Avenue, Zip 52761–3499; tel. 563/264–9100 **A**1 10 20 **F**3 5 11 13 15 18 28 31 34 38 39 40 43 45 50 56 57 59 61 64 65 68 69 70 75 76 77 79 81 85 87 89 97 102 107 108 110 111 114 119 124 129 130 131 132 134 135 147 148 **S** UnityPoint Health, West Des Moines, IA
Primary Contact: James M. Hayes, Chief Executive Officer
CFO: Katie A. Marchik, Vice President, Consolidated Services, UnityPoint Health and Interim Chief Financial Officer, Trinity Regional Health Sy
CMO: Manasi Nadkarni, M.D., Vice President Medical Affairs
CIO: Sean Liddell, Manager Regional Service Information Technology
CHR: Karla Blaser, Director Human Resources
CNO: Pam Askew, R.N., Vice President Patient Care Services
Web address: www.unitypoint.org/quadcities/trinity–muscatine.aspx
Control: Other not–for–profit (including NFP Corporation) **Service:** General Medical and Surgical

Staffed Beds: 45 **Admissions:** 1337 **Census:** 10 **Outpatient Visits:** 85809 **Births:** 347 **Total Expense ($000):** 52119 **Payroll Expense ($000):** 20773 **Personnel:** 298

NEVADA—Story County

★ **STORY COUNTY MEDICAL CENTER (161333)**, 640 South 19th Street, Zip 50201–2902; tel. 515/382–2111, (Total facility includes 60 beds in nursing home–type unit) **A**10 18 **F**3 7 11 28 29 32 34 35 36 40 43 50 53 57 59 64 65 68 75 81 85 87 97 107 114 119 127 130 133 146 148 **P**6 **S** UnityPoint Health, West Des Moines, IA
Primary Contact: Nate Thompson, Chief Executive Officer
CFO: Jane Ramthun, Chief Financial Officer
CMO: Arthur Check, M.D., Chief Medical Officer
CHR: Jessica Lingo, Human Resource Generalist
CNO: Beth Rehbein, Chief Nursing and Quality Officer
Web address: www.storymedical.org
Control: County–Government, nonfederal **Service:** General Medical and Surgical

Staffed Beds: 77 **Admissions:** 448 **Census:** 65 **Outpatient Visits:** 26073 **Births:** 0 **Total Expense ($000):** 23739 **Payroll Expense ($000):** 10840 **Personnel:** 225

NEW HAMPTON—Chickasaw County

★ **MERCY MEDICAL CENTER–NEW HAMPTON (161331)**, 308 North Maple Avenue, Zip 50659–1142; tel. 641/394–4121 **A**10 18 **F**3 11 13 15 28 29 34 35 40 43 45 48 56 57 59 64 65 68 74 76 77 79 81 85 93 97 107 110 119 129 131 133 146 148 **P**1 **S** Trinity Health, Livonia, MI
Primary Contact: Aaron Flugum, Chief Executive Officer
CFO: Jennifer Rapenske, Manager Financial Services
CMO: Jack Kline, M.D., Chief of Staff
CIO: Terry Chartier, Director, Information Systems
CHR: Jackie Luecht, Director, Human Resources
CNO: Jody Wright, Interim Chief Nursing Officer
Web address: www.mercynewhampton.com
Control: Church–operated, Nongovernment, not–for profit **Service:** General Medical and Surgical

Staffed Beds: 18 **Admissions:** 377 **Census:** 4 **Outpatient Visits:** 21249 **Births:** 42 **Total Expense ($000):** 16577 **Payroll Expense ($000):** 6092 **Personnel:** 83

NEWTON—Jasper County

★ ○ **SKIFF MEDICAL CENTER (160032)**, 204 North Fourth Avenue East, Zip 50208–3100, Mailing Address: P.O. Box 1006, Zip 50208–1006; tel. 641/792–1273 **A**10 11 **F**3 11 13 15 17 28 29 30 31 34 35 40 43 44 45 50 57 59 62 63 64 65 70 75 76 77 78 79 81 82 85 89 90 93 96 102 107 108 110 111 115 119 128 130 131 132 133 135 145 146 148 **P**6 **S** Catholic Health Initiatives, Englewood, CO
Primary Contact: Brett Allen Altman, FACHE, President and Chief Executive Officer
COO: Sonja Ranck, MSN, Chief Operating Officer and Chief Nursing Officer
CIO: Amber Wentz, Director of Clinical Information Systems & Clinical Informatics
CHR: Teresa Wermager, Human Resources Business Partner
CNO: Sonja Ranck, MSN, Chief Operating Officer and Chief Nursing Officer
Web address: www.skiffmed.com
Control: City–Government, nonfederal **Service:** General Medical and Surgical

Staffed Beds: 48 **Admissions:** 1448 **Census:** 16 **Outpatient Visits:** 79049 **Births:** 157 **Total Expense ($000):** 35675 **Payroll Expense ($000):** 15733 **Personnel:** 263

OELWEIN—Fayette County

★ **MERCY HOSPITAL OF FRANCISCAN SISTERS (161338)**, 201 Eighth Avenue S.E., Zip 50662–2447; tel. 319/283–6000, (Total facility includes 39 beds in nursing home–type unit) **A**10 18 **F**7 11 15 29 30 34 35 40 57 59 69 75 79 81 93 97 107 110 111 119 127 128 130 132 133 146 147 **P**1 **S** Wheaton Franciscan Healthcare, Wheaton, IL
Primary Contact: Terri Derflinger, Administrator
CFO: Michele Panicucci, Senior Vice President and Chief Financial Officer
CMO: James Lehman, M.D., Vice President Medical Affairs
CNO: Kelly Richards, MSN, Senior Vice President and Chief Nursing Officer
Web address: www.wheatoniowa.org
Control: Church–operated, Nongovernment, not–for profit **Service:** General Medical and Surgical

Staffed Beds: 64 **Admissions:** 349 **Census:** 38 **Outpatient Visits:** 25539 **Births:** 0 **Total Expense ($000):** 12920 **Payroll Expense ($000):** 5401 **Personnel:** 120

ONAWA—Monona County

★ **BURGESS HEALTH CENTER (161359)**, 1600 Diamond Street, Zip 51040–1548; tel. 712/423–2311 **A**10 18 **F**3 7 11 13 15 28 29 31 32 34 35 40 45 47 53 56 57 59 62 63 64 65 67 68 70 75 76 77 78 79 81 82 85 93 97 99 100 101 103 104 107 111 114 119 127 128 130 132 133 135 146 148 **P**6
Primary Contact: Francis G. Tramp, President
CFO: Shawn Gosch, Chief Financial Officer
CMO: John Garred, Sr., M.D., Chief Medical Officer
CIO: Grady Warner, Director of Information Technology
CHR: Erin Brekke, Director Human Resources
CNO: Patty Sandmann, Senior Director of Nursing
Web address: www.burgesshc.org
Control: Other not–for–profit (including NFP Corporation) **Service:** General Medical and Surgical

Staffed Beds: 25 **Admissions:** 833 **Census:** 9 **Outpatient Visits:** 69172 **Births:** 39 **Total Expense ($000):** 27059 **Payroll Expense ($000):** 11825 **Personnel:** 271

ORANGE CITY—Sioux County

★ **ORANGE CITY AREA HEALTH SYSTEM (161360)**, 1000 Lincoln Circle S.E., Zip 51041–1862; tel. 712/737–4984, (Total facility includes 83 beds in nursing home–type unit) **A**10 18 **F**7 10 11 13 15 18 28 29 31 34 35 40 45 50 53 56 57 59 60 62 63 64 67 68 69 70 75 76 77 78 79 81 82 85 86 87 89 93 97 99 100 101 102 103 104 107 110 111 114 117 119 120 125 127 130 131 132 133 146 147 148 **P**6 **S** Sanford Health, Sioux Falls, SD
Primary Contact: Martin W. Guthmiller, Chief Executive Officer
COO: Daniel P. McCarty, Chief Operating Officer
CFO: Dina Baas, Director Financial Services
CMO: Alan Laird, M.D., Chief Medical Officer
CHR: Jason Jauron, Director Human Resources
Web address: www.ochealthsystem.org
Control: City–Government, nonfederal **Service:** General Medical and Surgical

Staffed Beds: 108 **Admissions:** 942 **Census:** 93 **Outpatient Visits:** 75636 **Births:** 238 **Total Expense ($000):** 42605 **Payroll Expense ($000):** 17865 **Personnel:** 405

OSAGE—Mitchell County

★ **MITCHELL COUNTY REGIONAL HEALTH CENTER (161323)**, 616 North Eighth Street, Zip 50461–1498; tel. 641/732–6000 **A**10 18 **F**7 8 11 15 18 28 29 34 35 40 45 50 57 59 63 64 65 70 75 81 85 87 93 107 110 114 119 127 128 130 132 133 144 146 **P**8 **S** Trinity Health, Livonia, MI
Primary Contact: Shelly Russell, Chief Executive Officer
CFO: Gregory Burkel, Chief Financial Officer
CMO: Jeff Nasstrom, D.O., Chief of Staff
CHR: Jodie Anderson, Director Human Resources
CNO: Shelly Russell, Chief Nursing Officer
Web address: www.mitchellcohospital–clinics.com
Control: County–Government, nonfederal **Service:** General Medical and Surgical

Staffed Beds: 25 **Admissions:** 356 **Census:** 5 **Outpatient Visits:** 59922 **Births:** 0 **Total Expense ($000):** 19793 **Payroll Expense ($000):** 7045 **Personnel:** 149

IA

Hospital, Medicare Provider Number, Address, Telephone, Approval, Facility, and Physician Codes, Health Care System

★ American Hospital Association (AHA) membership   ○ Healthcare Facilities Accreditation Program   ⇑ Center for Improvement in Healthcare Quality Accreditation
□ The Joint Commission accreditation   ◇ DNV Healthcare Inc. accreditation   △ Commission on Accreditation of Rehabilitation Facilities (CARF) accreditation

OSCEOLA—Clarke County

★ **CLARKE COUNTY HOSPITAL (161348)**, 800 South Fillmore Street, Zip 50213–1619; tel. 641/342–2184 **A**10 18 **F**7 11 15 18 28 29 31 34 35 40 45 50 57 59 64 67 68 75 77 78 79 81 89 90 93 94 96 107 111 115 116 117 118 119 128 129 130 131 132 133 135 148 **S** UnityPoint Health, West Des Moines, IA
Primary Contact: Brian G. Evans, FACHE, Chief Executive Officer
CFO: Michael Thilges, Chief Financial Officer
CMO: George Fotiadis, M.D., Chief of Staff
CIO: Dennis Blazek, Chief Information Officer
CHR: Kate Emanuel, Director Human Resources
Web address: www.clarkehosp.org
Control: County–Government, nonfederal **Service:** General Medical and Surgical

Staffed Beds: 25 **Admissions:** 309 **Census:** 10 **Outpatient Visits:** 17534 **Births:** 0 **Total Expense ($000):** 19336 **Payroll Expense ($000):** 6591 **Personnel:** 138

OSKALOOSA—Mahaska County

☒ **MAHASKA HEALTH PARTNERSHIP (161379)**, 1229 C Avenue East, Zip 52577–4298; tel. 641/672–3100 **A**1 10 18 **F**3 5 7 8 11 13 15 28 29 30 31 32 34 35 36 38 40 43 45 46 47 50 54 56 57 59 61 62 63 64 65 66 68 69 70 75 76 77 78 79 81 84 85 87 93 94 97 98 99 100 101 102 103 104 107 110 111 114 119 126 129 130 132 133 135 146 148 **P**6
Primary Contact: Jay Christensen, FACHE, Administrator
COO: Erin Baldwin, M.P.H., Chief Operating Officer
CMO: Matt Whitis, Chief Medical Officer
CHR: Jacky Bresnahan, Director Human Resources
Web address: www.mahaskahealth.com
Control: County–Government, nonfederal **Service:** General Medical and Surgical

Staffed Beds: 33 **Admissions:** 1723 **Census:** 21 **Outpatient Visits:** 208826 **Births:** 221 **Total Expense ($000):** 54318 **Payroll Expense ($000):** 28258 **Personnel:** 390

OTTUMWA—Wapello County

☐ △ **OTTUMWA REGIONAL HEALTH CENTER (160089)**, 1001 Pennsylvania Avenue, Zip 52501–2186; tel. 641/684–2300 **A**1 7 10 **F**3 7 8 11 13 15 18 20 22 28 29 30 31 34 35 40 41 43 45 46 47 48 50 51 53 54 56 57 59 60 62 64 73 74 75 76 77 79 80 81 82 85 87 89 90 93 98 102 103 107 108 110 111 114 115 118 119 120 121 123 126 129 130 131 132 135 144 146 147 148 **P**6 **S** RCCH HealthCare Partners, Brentwood, TN
Primary Contact: Philip J. Noel, III, Chief Executive Officer
COO: Jason Hotchkiss, CPA, Chief Financial Officer / Chief Operating Officer
CFO: Jason Hotchkiss, CPA, Chief Financial Officer
CMO: Sandro Younadam, M.D., Chief Medical Officer
CIO: Scott Garrett, Director of IS
CHR: Lidia Bryant, Director Human Resources
CNO: Lori Bailey, R.N., Vice President and Chief Nursing Officer
Web address: www.ottumwaregionalhealth.com
Control: Corporation, Investor–owned, for–profit **Service:** General Medical and Surgical

Staffed Beds: 101 **Admissions:** 3165 **Census:** 41 **Outpatient Visits:** 87702 **Births:** 475 **Total Expense ($000):** 71398 **Payroll Expense ($000):** 22429 **Personnel:** 453

PELLA—Marion County

☒ **PELLA REGIONAL HEALTH CENTER (161367)**, 404 Jefferson Street, Zip 50219–1257; tel. 641/628–3150, (Total facility includes 15 beds in nursing home–type unit) **A**1 10 18 **F**3 11 13 15 18 28 29 30 31 32 34 35 40 43 45 50 51 53 57 59 60 62 63 64 65 66 70 74 75 76 77 78 79 81 82 84 85 86 87 91 93 94 97 102 107 108 110 111 115 119 126 127 128 129 130 131 132 133 144 146 147 148 **P**6
Primary Contact: Robert D. Kroese, FACHE, Chief Executive Officer
COO: Robert D. Kroese, FACHE, Chief Executive Officer
CFO: Bruce Heifner, Chief Financial Officer
CIO: Tait Smock, Manager Information Systems
CHR: Teri Lickteig, Director Human Resources
CNO: Yvonne M. O'Brien-Evans, MS, Chief of Nursing
Web address: www.pellahealth.org
Control: Other not–for–profit (including NFP Corporation) **Service:** General Medical and Surgical

Staffed Beds: 40 **Admissions:** 1494 **Census:** 18 **Outpatient Visits:** 142813 **Births:** 475 **Total Expense ($000):** 51351 **Payroll Expense ($000):** 19830 **Personnel:** 577

PERRY—Dallas County

★ **DALLAS COUNTY HOSPITAL (161322)**, 610 10th Street, Zip 50220–2221; tel. 515/465–3547 **A**10 18 **F**15 18 28 29 31 34 35 39 40 41 43 45 47 50 57 59 68 75 77 78 79 81 82 85 89 93 107 110 114 119 128 130 132 133 135 146 148
Primary Contact: Angela Mortoza, Chief Executive Officer
CFO: Randy Loomis, Chief Financial Officer
CMO: Steven Sohn, M.D., President Medical Staff
CHR: Sherry Smith, Manager Human Resources
CNO: Tonya Summerson, Chief Clinical Officer
Web address: www.dallascohospital.org
Control: County–Government, nonfederal **Service:** General Medical and Surgical

Staffed Beds: 15 **Admissions:** 267 **Census:** 3 **Outpatient Visits:** 23921 **Births:** 0 **Total Expense ($000):** 13203 **Payroll Expense ($000):** 4319 **Personnel:** 89

POCAHONTAS—Pocahontas County

★ **POCAHONTAS COMMUNITY HOSPITAL (161305)**, 606 N.W. Seventh Street, Zip 50574–1099; tel. 712/335–3501 **A**10 18 **F**7 11 15 17 28 29 31 35 40 43 45 59 62 63 64 67 70 75 77 78 79 81 84 89 90 93 107 110 115 119 128 130 132 133 135 146 148 **P**6 **S** UnityPoint Health, West Des Moines, IA
Primary Contact: James D. Roetman, President and Chief Executive Officer
CFO: Lynn Raveling, Chief Financial Officer
CNO: Susie Aden, Director of IP Services
Web address: www.pocahontashospital.org
Control: City–Government, nonfederal **Service:** General Medical and Surgical

Staffed Beds: 20 **Admissions:** 229 **Census:** 3 **Outpatient Visits:** 23672 **Births:** 0 **Total Expense ($000):** 10173 **Payroll Expense ($000):** 3519 **Personnel:** 91

PRIMGHAR—O'brien County

★ **BAUM HARMON MERCY HOSPITAL (161300)**, 255 North Welch Avenue, Zip 51245–7765, Mailing Address: P.O. Box 528, Zip 51245–0528; tel. 712/957–2300 **A**10 18 **F**11 15 28 29 30 31 34 35 40 45 53 57 59 64 67 75 77 81 89 110 119 127 128 133 135 **P**6 **S** Trinity Health, Livonia, MI
Primary Contact: Angie Shilling, Chief Executive Officer
CFO: Sue E. McCauley, Director Finance
CMO: Shailesh Desai, M.D., Chief of Staff
Web address: www.baumharmon.org
Control: Church–operated, Nongovernment, not–for profit **Service:** General Medical and Surgical

Staffed Beds: 11 **Admissions:** 112 **Census:** 1 **Outpatient Visits:** 20433 **Births:** 0 **Total Expense ($000):** 7443 **Payroll Expense ($000):** 3873 **Personnel:** 65

RED OAK—Montgomery County

★ **MONTGOMERY COUNTY MEMORIAL HOSPITAL (161363)**, 2301 Eastern Avenue, Zip 51566–1300, Mailing Address: P.O. Box 498, Zip 51566–0498; tel. 712/623–7000 **A**10 18 **F**3 11 13 15 28 29 31 34 35 40 44 45 50 53 57 59 62 63 64 68 69 70 71 75 76 77 78 79 81 82 85 86 87 93 107 110 111 114 118 119 128 129 130 133 135 146 147 148
Primary Contact: David E. Abercrombie, Chief Executive Officer
CFO: Rick J. Leinen, Chief Financial Officer
CMO: Warren Hayes, Chief of Staff
CIO: Ron Kloewer, Chief Information Officer
CHR: Shayla Jennings, Human Resources Director
CNO: Diane McGrew, Chief Nurse Executive
Web address: www.mcmh.org
Control: County–Government, nonfederal **Service:** General Medical and Surgical

Staffed Beds: 25 **Admissions:** 1052 **Census:** 14 **Outpatient Visits:** 47519 **Births:** 72 **Total Expense ($000):** 31090 **Payroll Expense ($000):** 14448 **Personnel:** 282

ROCK RAPIDS—Lyon County

SANFORD MERRILL MEDICAL CENTER See Sanford Rock Rapids Medical Center

★ **SANFORD ROCK RAPIDS MEDICAL CENTER (161321)**, 801 South Greene Street, Zip 51246–1998; tel. 712/472–2591 **A**10 18 **F**11 28 31 34 40 41 45 53 57 59 65 68 75 77 81 87 89 97 107 119 127 130 131 133 146 **P**6 **S** Sanford Health, Sioux Falls, SD
Primary Contact: Tammy Loosbrock, Senior Director
CFO: Stanley Knobloch, Director Fiscal Services
CMO: Beta Hamon, Chief Medical Officer
CHR: Holly Anderson, Supervisor Human Resources
CNO: Jack Johnson, R.N., Director of Nursing
Web address: www.sanfordrockrapids.org
Control: Other not–for–profit (including NFP Corporation) **Service:** General Medical and Surgical

Staffed Beds: 14 **Admissions:** 370 **Census:** 4 **Outpatient Visits:** 19712 **Births:** 0 **Total Expense ($000):** 8395 **Payroll Expense ($000):** 3732 **Personnel:** 77

Many Facility Codes have changed. Please refer to the AHA Guide Code Chart. © 2016 AHA Guide

IA

ROCK VALLEY—Sioux County

★ **HEGG MEMORIAL HEALTH CENTER AVERA (161336)**, 1202 21st Avenue, Zip 51247–1497; tel. 712/476–8000, (Total facility includes 60 beds in nursing home–type unit) **A**10 18 **F**3 4 11 12 13 15 17 28 29 31 34 35 36 40 41 43 45 50 53 57 59 62 64 65 67 68 70 73 75 76 77 78 79 81 82 84 85 89 93 97 107 110 115 119 128 130 131 132 133 135 144 147 148 **S** Avera Health, Sioux Falls, SD
Primary Contact: Glenn Zevenbergen, Chief Executive Officer
CFO: Kari Timmer, Chief Financial Officer
CMO: Kevin Post, D.O., Chief Medical Officer
CHR: Tammy Faber, Director Human Resources
CNO: Linda VerSteeg, Director of Nursing
Web address: www.hegghc.org
Control: Other not–for–profit (including NFP Corporation) **Service:** General Medical and Surgical

Staffed Beds: 85 **Admissions:** 300 **Census:** 63 **Outpatient Visits:** 36466 **Births:** 88 **Total Expense ($000):** 17489 **Payroll Expense ($000):** 8910 **Personnel:** 208	

SAC CITY—Sac County

★ **LORING HOSPITAL (161370)**, 211 Highland Avenue, Zip 50583–2424; tel. 712/662–7105 **A**10 18 **F**3 11 15 28 29 30 31 34 35 40 43 45 57 59 64 68 75 78 79 81 84 86 87 93 107 110 115 119 125 130 132 133 146 **S** UnityPoint Health, West Des Moines, IA
Primary Contact: Brian Martin, Chief Executive Officer
CFO: Angie Fischer, Chief Financial Officer
CMO: Les Marczewski, M.D., Chief Medical Officer
CIO: Leah Snyder, Director Health Information Services
CHR: Becky Pontious, Human Resources/Accounting
Web address: www.loringhospital.org
Control: Other not–for–profit (including NFP Corporation) **Service:** General Medical and Surgical

Staffed Beds: 25 **Admissions:** 385 **Census:** 5 **Outpatient Visits:** 16951 **Births:** 0 **Total Expense ($000):** 12217 **Payroll Expense ($000):** 3938 **Personnel:** 95	

SHELDON—O'brien County

★ **SANFORD SHELDON MEDICAL CENTER (161381)**, 118 North Seventh Avenue, Zip 51201–1235, Mailing Address: P.O. Box 250, Zip 51201–0250; tel. 712/324–5041, (Total facility includes 70 beds in nursing home–type unit) **A**10 18 **F**3 11 13 15 28 29 31 32 34 35 38 40 43 45 50 53 57 59 62 63 64 65 67 68 74 75 76 77 78 79 81 82 84 86 87 91 93 96 97 99 100 101 102 103 104 107 108 110 111 114 119 127 129 130 131 132 133 135 146 148 **P**6 **S** Sanford Health, Sioux Falls, SD
Primary Contact: Richard E. Nordahl, Chief Executive Officer
CFO: Richard E. Nordahl, Chief Financial Officer
CMO: Scott Lichty, M.D., Physician
CIO: Jason Brown, Director Information Systems
CHR: Dianne Wolthuizen, Director Human Resources
CNO: Joni DeKok, Chief Nursing Officer
Web address: www.sanfordsheldon.org
Control: Other not–for–profit (including NFP Corporation) **Service:** General Medical and Surgical

Staffed Beds: 95 **Admissions:** 991 **Census:** 70 **Outpatient Visits:** 102613 **Births:** 149 **Total Expense ($000):** 27967 **Payroll Expense ($000):** 12457 **Personnel:** 253	

SHENANDOAH—Page County

★ **SHENANDOAH MEDICAL CENTER (161366)**, 300 Pershing Avenue, Zip 51601–2355; tel. 712/246–1230, (Total facility includes 50 beds in nursing home–type unit) **A**10 18 **F**3 13 15 18 28 29 31 34 36 38 40 41 43 45 50 53 56 57 59 62 63 64 65 67 68 69 70 74 75 76 77 78 79 81 83 84 85 87 91 93 104 107 108 110 111 115 117 118 119 127 129 130 131 132 133 135 144 146 147 148 **P**6
Primary Contact: Karen S. Cole, MS, FACHE, Chief Executive Officer
CFO: Matt Sells, CPA, Chief Financial Officer
CMO: Scott King, M.D., Chief Medical Officer
CIO: Chuck Dougherty, Chief Information Officer
CHR: Keli Royal, Chief Human Resources Officer
CNO: Alicia Sells, Interim Chief Nursing Officer
Web address: www.smchospital.com/
Control: Other not–for–profit (including NFP Corporation) **Service:** General Medical and Surgical

Staffed Beds: 75 **Admissions:** 620 **Census:** 47 **Outpatient Visits:** 118492 **Births:** 125 **Total Expense ($000):** 37115 **Payroll Expense ($000):** 19193 **Personnel:** 293	

SIBLEY— County

★ **OSCEOLA COMMUNITY HOSPITAL (161345)**, 600 Ninth Avenue North, Zip 51249–1012, Mailing Address: P.O. Box 258, Zip 51249–0258; tel. 712/754–2574 **A**10 18 **F**3 8 9 10 11 12 13 15 17 18 26 28 29 31 32 34 35 36 40 43 45 46 49 53 56 57 59 61 62 64 65 67 68 70 75 76 77 78 79 81 82 84 85 86 87 89 93 107 108 110 114 119 125 128 129 130 131 132 133 135 143 144 145 146 147 148 **P**5 **S** Avera Health, Sioux Falls, SD
Primary Contact: Janet H. Dykstra, Chief Executive Officer
CFO: Jerri Palsrok, Manager Business Office
CMO: Gregory J. Kosters, D.O., Chief Medical Officer
CIO: Sherry McElroy, Director Health Information Management
Web address: www.osceolacommunityhospital.org
Control: Other not–for–profit (including NFP Corporation) **Service:** General Medical and Surgical

Staffed Beds: 25 **Admissions:** 287 **Census:** 4 **Outpatient Visits:** 21677 **Births:** 23 **Total Expense ($000):** 11742 **Payroll Expense ($000):** 3663 **Personnel:** 89	

SIGOURNEY—Keokuk County

KEOKUK COUNTY HEALTH CENTER (161315), 23019 Highway 149, Zip 52591–8341; tel. 641/622–2720 **A**10 18 **F**1 2 3 7 11 12 28 29 30 34 35 38 40 43 45 46 50 56 57 59 63 64 65 67 75 77 82 84 86 87 90 91 93 97 107 128 130 131 132 133 134 135 144 146 147 148 **P**5 6
Primary Contact: Matthew Ives, Administrator and Chief Financial Officer
CFO: Matthew Ives, Interim Chief Executive Officer and Chief Financial Officer
Web address: www.kchc.net
Control: County–Government, nonfederal **Service:** General Medical and Surgical

Staffed Beds: 14 **Admissions:** 167 **Census:** 7 **Outpatient Visits:** 21119 **Births:** 0 **Total Expense ($000):** 9531 **Payroll Expense ($000):** 4698 **Personnel:** 94	

SIOUX CENTER—Sioux County

★ **SIOUX CENTER HEALTH (161346)**, 1101 9th Street S.E., Zip 51250; tel. 712/722–8107, (Total facility includes 69 beds in nursing home–type unit) **A**10 18 **F**3 8 10 13 15 17 18 28 29 33 35 40 41 43 45 50 56 57 59 62 63 64 67 68 74 75 76 77 78 79 81 82 84 85 86 87 89 93 96 97 107 110 111 114 119 125 128 130 131 132 133 144 146 147 148 **P**6 **S** Avera Health, Sioux Falls, SD
Primary Contact: Kayleen R. Lee, Chief Executive Officer
CFO: Jackson Schuiteman, Chief Financial Officer
CHR: Theresa Tucker, Human Resources Officer
Web address: www.siouxcenterhealth.org
Control: Other not–for–profit (including NFP Corporation) **Service:** General Medical and Surgical

Staffed Beds: 88 **Admissions:** 577 **Census:** 67 **Outpatient Visits:** 47630 **Births:** 153 **Total Expense ($000):** 35689 **Payroll Expense ($000):** 14765 **Personnel:** 349	

SIOUX CITY—Woodbury County

⊞ **MERCY MEDICAL CENTER–SIOUX CITY (160153)**, 801 Fifth Street, Zip 51101–1326, Mailing Address: P.O. Box 3168, Zip 51102–3168; tel. 712/279–2010 **A**1 2 3 5 10 **F**3 5 11 13 15 17 18 20 22 24 26 28 29 30 31 32 34 35 36 37 38 40 43 44 45 49 50 52 55 56 57 59 64 65 68 70 71 74 75 76 77 78 79 81 82 84 85 87 89 90 91 93 96 97 98 100 102 107 108 110 111 114 115 118 119 124 126 127 129 130 132 135 144 146 147 148 **P**6 8 **S** Trinity Health, Livonia, MI
Primary Contact: James G. Fitzpatrick, FACHE, Chief Executive Officer
CFO: Hugh DePaulis, Interim Vice President and Chief Financial Officer
CMO: Jerome Pierson, Chief Medical Officer
CIO: Steve Larson, M.D., Director Information Systems
CHR: Julie Anfinson, Director Human Resources
CNO: Tracy Larson, MS, Vice President Patient Care Services and Chief Nursing Officer
Web address: www.mercysiouxcity.com
Control: Church–operated, Nongovernment, not–for profit **Service:** General Medical and Surgical

Staffed Beds: 192 **Admissions:** 9382 **Census:** 125 **Outpatient Visits:** 211848 **Births:** 228 **Total Expense ($000):** 184871 **Payroll Expense ($000):** 75681 **Personnel:** 1200	

IA

Hospital, Medicare Provider Number, Address, Telephone, Approval, Facility, and Physician Codes, Health Care System
★ American Hospital Association (AHA) membership   ○ Healthcare Facilities Accreditation Program   ⇑ Center for Improvement in Healthcare Quality Accreditation
□ The Joint Commission accreditation   ◇ DNV Healthcare Inc. accreditation   △ Commission on Accreditation of Rehabilitation Facilities (CARF) accreditation

★ ◇ **UNITYPOINT HEALTH – ST. LUKE'S (160146)**, 2720 Stone Park Boulevard, Zip 51104–3734; tel. 712/279–3500 **A**3 5 10 21 **F**3 11 13 15 17 18 20 22 26 28 29 30 31 34 35 39 40 43 45 49 50 51 54 56 57 58 59 60 64 68 70 72 73 74 75 76 77 78 79 81 82 84 85 86 88 89 90 91 92 93 96 97 98 102 104 107 108 111 114 118 119 126 129 130 131 132 135 142 143 144 145 146 147 **P**6 **S** UnityPoint Health, West Des Moines, IA
Primary Contact: Lynn Wold, President and Chief Executive Officer
COO: Lynn Wold, Chief Operation Officer
CFO: James Gobell, Chief Financial Officer
CIO: James Gobell, Chief Financial Officer
CHR: Tammy Hartnett, Employee Relations Manager
CNO: Priscilla Stokes, MS, Vice President Patient Care and Hospital Operations
Web address: www.stlukes.org
Control: Other not–for–profit (including NFP Corporation) **Service:** General Medical and Surgical

Staffed Beds: 155 Admissions: 9176 Census: 103 Outpatient Visits: 90636 **Births:** 2064 **Total Expense ($000):** 157189 **Payroll Expense ($000):** 60240 **Personnel:** 1105

SPENCER—Clay County

★ **SPENCER HOSPITAL (160112)**, 1200 First Avenue East, Suite 1, Zip 51301–4342; tel. 712/264–6111 **A**10 **F**3 7 8 11 13 15 28 29 30 31 34 35 39 40 43 45 50 53 56 57 59 60 62 63 64 65 69 70 75 76 77 78 79 81 82 85 86 87 93 96 97 98 107 108 109 111 115 118 119 120 121 123 126 127 129 130 131 132 133 135 146 147 148
Primary Contact: William J. Bumgarner, President
CFO: Stacy E. Mol, CPA, Director Finance
CMO: Sonia Sather, M.D., President Medical Staff
CIO: Brenda Marie Tiefenthaler, R.N., Vice President Patient Care and Informatics
CHR: Stephen Deutsch, Vice President Operations and Support
CNO: Brenda Marie Tiefenthaler, R.N., Vice President Patient Care and Informatics
Web address: www.spencerhospital.org
Control: City–Government, nonfederal **Service:** General Medical and Surgical

Staffed Beds: 71 Admissions: 2524 Census: 29 Outpatient Visits: 121697 **Births:** 271 **Total Expense ($000):** 64003 **Payroll Expense ($000):** 22068 **Personnel:** 373

SPIRIT LAKE—Dickinson County

★ **LAKES REGIONAL HEALTHCARE (160124)**, 2301 Highway 71 South, Zip 51360–0159, Mailing Address: P.O. Box AB, Zip 51360–0159; tel. 712/336–1230 **A**10 **F**3 7 11 13 15 28 29 30 31 34 35 40 41 43 45 50 57 59 62 63 64 65 69 70 75 76 77 78 79 81 85 89 93 97 107 111 114 119 128 129 130 132 133 143 146 148 **P**6 **S** Avera Health, Sioux Falls, SD
Primary Contact: Jason Harrington, FACHE, President and Chief Executive Officer
CFO: Steve Alger, Senior Vice President and Chief Financial Officer
CMO: Brett J. Olson, M.D., Medical Chief of Staff
CIO: Derek Larson, Information Technology Network
CHR: Sonja Hamm, Vice President Human and Foundation Resources
CNO: Connie Lange, R.N., Vice President Quality, Inpatient and Community Services
Web address: www.lakeshealth.org
Control: County–Government, nonfederal **Service:** General Medical and Surgical

Staffed Beds: 30 Admissions: 819 Census: 8 Outpatient Visits: 89557 **Births:** 139 **Total Expense ($000):** 35966 **Payroll Expense ($000):** 11235 **Personnel:** 213

STORM LAKE—Buena Vista County

⊞ **BUENA VISTA REGIONAL MEDICAL CENTER (161375)**, 1525 West Fifth Street, Zip 50588–3027, Mailing Address: P.O. Box 309, Zip 50588–0309; tel. 712/732–4030 **A**1 10 18 **F**3 7 8 11 13 15 18 28 29 30 31 34 40 43 45 53 55 56 57 59 63 64 68 70 74 75 76 77 78 79 81 82 84 85 86 87 93 96 98 103 107 108 110 111 115 117 118 119 128 129 130 131 132 133 135 146 147 148 **S** UnityPoint Health, West Des Moines, IA
Primary Contact: Steven Colerick, Chief Executive Officer
CFO: Krista Ketcham, Chief Financial Officer
CMO: David Crippin, Chief Medical Officer
CIO: Brian Granville, Director Information Technology
CHR: Carrie Turnquist, Director Human Resources
CNO: Dawn M. Bach, MS, Chief Clinical Officer
Web address: www.bvrmc.org
Control: County–Government, nonfederal **Service:** General Medical and Surgical

Staffed Beds: 35 Admissions: 1263 Census: 15 Outpatient Visits: 69839 **Births:** 331 **Total Expense ($000):** 44609 **Payroll Expense ($000):** 17322 **Personnel:** 329

SUMNER—Bremer County

★ **COMMUNITY MEMORIAL HOSPITAL (161320)**, 909 West First Street, Zip 50674–1203, Mailing Address: P.O. Box 148, Zip 50674–0148; tel. 563/578–3275 **A**10 18 **F**3 11 15 28 29 34 40 45 57 59 64 81 85 86 97 107 114 127 128 129 131 133 135 148 **P**5 6 **S** UnityPoint Health, West Des Moines, IA
Primary Contact: Dustin Wright, Chief Executive Officer
CFO: Dawn Everding, Chief Financial Officer
CMO: Jeff Roske, D.O., Chief Medical Staff
CHR: Robin Elliott, Personnel Officer
CNO: Lynne Niemann, Director Nurses and Patient Care
Web address: www.cmhsumner.org
Control: Other not–for–profit (including NFP Corporation) **Service:** General Medical and Surgical

Staffed Beds: 16 Admissions: 216 Census: 3 Outpatient Visits: 25584 **Births:** 0 **Total Expense ($000):** 12769 **Payroll Expense ($000):** 4568 **Personnel:** 84

VINTON—Benton County

★ **VIRGINIA GAY HOSPITAL (161349)**, 502 North 9th Avenue, Zip 52349–2299; tel. 319/472–6200, (Total facility includes 40 beds in nursing home–type unit) **A**10 18 **F**3 15 28 29 34 40 43 45 53 59 62 64 75 77 81 85 86 87 96 97 107 111 114 119 125 127 129 130 131 132 133 143 146 **P**6
Primary Contact: Michael J. Riege, Administrator
CFO: Barry Dietsch, Chief Financial Officer
CMO: Brian Meeker, D.O., President Medical Staff
CIO: Sherri Isbell, Chief Information Officer
CHR: Kim Frank, Chief Human Resources Officer
CNO: Tina M. Eden, Director of Nursing
Web address: www.myvgh.org
Control: Other not–for–profit (including NFP Corporation) **Service:** General Medical and Surgical

Staffed Beds: 65 Admissions: 404 Census: 36 Outpatient Visits: 94248 **Births:** 0 **Total Expense ($000):** 23698 **Payroll Expense ($000):** 11679 **Personnel:** 231

WASHINGTON—Washington County

★ **WASHINGTON COUNTY HOSPITAL AND CLINICS (161344)**, 400 East Polk Street, Zip 52353–1237, Mailing Address: P.O. Box 909, Zip 52353–0909; tel. 319/653–5481, (Total facility includes 43 beds in nursing home–type unit) **A**10 18 13 15 18 28 29 34 40 43 45 50 57 59 64 67 68 75 76 77 81 82 85 86 93 96 97 107 110 111 114 119 127 130 132 133 146 147 148 **P**6
Primary Contact: Dennis Hunger, Chief Executive Officer
CFO: Steve Sanders, Chief Financial Officer
CMO: Matt Prihoda, M.D., Chief of Staff
CIO: Makyla Maize, Director Information Services
CHR: Tracy Ousey, Director Human Resources
CNO: Andrea Leyden, RN, Chief Nursing Officer
Web address: www.wchc.org
Control: County–Government, nonfederal **Service:** General Medical and Surgical

Staffed Beds: 68 Admissions: 1109 Census: 47 Outpatient Visits: 45966 **Births:** 148 **Total Expense ($000):** 29769 **Payroll Expense ($000):** 14189 **Personnel:** 280

WATERLOO—Black Hawk County

ALLEN MEMORIAL HOSPITAL See UnityPoint Health – Allen Hospital

⊞ △ **COVENANT MEDICAL CENTER (160067)**, 3421 West Ninth Street, Zip 50702–5401; tel. 319/272–8000, (Includes KIMBALL–RIDGE CENTER, 2101 Kimball Avenue, Zip 50702; tel. 319/272–8000; Jack Dusenbery, President and Chief Executive Officer) **A**1 2 3 5 7 10 **F**3 4 5 7 11 13 15 18 19 20 22 26 28 29 30 31 33 34 35 40 44 46 49 50 51 53 57 58 59 60 61 62 64 68 70 71 72 74 75 76 77 78 79 81 82 89 90 93 97 98 99 100 104 105 107 108 110 111 114 115 116 118 119 120 126 127 129 130 131 132 143 144 146 147 148 **P**1 6 **S** Wheaton Franciscan Healthcare, Wheaton, IL
Primary Contact: Jack Dusenbery, President and Chief Executive Officer
CFO: Michele Panicucci, Senior Vice President and Chief Financial Officer
CMO: James Lehman, M.D., Vice President Medical Affairs
CIO: Marge Ray, Director Information Systems
CHR: Suzanne M. Burt, Director Human Resources
CNO: Kelly Richards, MSN, Senior Vice President and Chief Nursing Officer
Web address: www.wheatoniowa.org
Control: Church–operated, Nongovernment, not–for profit **Service:** General Medical and Surgical

Staffed Beds: 229 Admissions: 8372 Census: 94 Outpatient Visits: 606859 **Births:** 1410 **Total Expense ($000):** 271005 **Payroll Expense ($000):** 123425 **Personnel:** 1937

☒ △ **UNITYPOINT HEALTH – ALLEN HOSPITAL (160110)**, 1825 Logan Avenue, Zip 50703–1916; tel. 319/235–3941 **A**1 3 5 7 10 **F**3 8 11 13 15 18 20 22 24 26 28 29 30 31 34 35 37 40 43 45 46 48 49 50 51 54 56 57 59 63 64 66 68 70 72 74 75 77 78 79 81 82 84 85 86 87 88 90 91 92 93 96 97 98 99 100 101 102 103 104 107 108 110 111 114 115 118 119 126 127 129 130 132 135 146 147 148 **P**6 **S** UnityPoint Health, West Des Moines, IA
Primary Contact: Pamela K. Delagardelle, President and Chief Executive Officer
COO: Jennifer Friedly, Chief Operating Officer and Vice President
CFO: Dan Carpenter, Chief Financial Officer
CMO: Timothy Horrigan, M.D., Chief Quality Officer
CIO: Daniel Norman, Regional Service Manager
CHR: Steven Sesterhenn, Vice President
CNO: Mary Hagen, R.N., VP and Chief Nursing Officer
Web address: www.allenhospital.org
Control: Other not–for–profit (including NFP Corporation) **Service:** General Medical and Surgical

Staffed Beds: 201 **Admissions:** 9730 **Census:** 99 **Outpatient Visits:** 279904 **Births:** 1056 **Total Expense ($000):** 207669 **Payroll Expense ($000):** 83117 **Personnel:** 1337

WAUKON—Allamakee County

★ **VETERANS MEMORIAL HOSPITAL (161318)**, 40 First Street S.E., Zip 52172–2099; tel. 563/568–3411 **A**10 18 **F**7 11 13 15 28 34 35 40 45 46 57 59 62 64 65 75 76 77 79 81 93 107 110 111 119 131 132 133 134 144 146
Primary Contact: Michael D. Myers, R.N., Chief Executive Officer
CFO: Scott Knode, Chief Financial Officer
CHR: Erin Berns, Director Human Resources
Web address: www.vmhospital.com
Control: City–Government, nonfederal **Service:** General Medical and Surgical

Staffed Beds: 25 **Admissions:** 670 **Census:** 7 **Outpatient Visits:** 43053 **Births:** 140 **Total Expense ($000):** 15935 **Payroll Expense ($000):** 6922 **Personnel:** 147

WAVERLY—Bremer County

☒ **WAVERLY HEALTH CENTER (161339)**, 312 Ninth Street S.W., Zip 50677–2999; tel. 319/352–4120 **A**1 10 18 **F**3 7 8 11 13 15 28 29 34 35 36 40 43 45 50 57 59 63 64 75 76 77 81 85 86 97 104 107 110 111 114 119 127 130 132 133 134 135 144 146 147 **P**6
Primary Contact: James Atty, Chief Executive Officer
CFO: Lisa Bennett, Chief Financial Officer
CMO: John Zehr, M.D., Chief Medical Officer
CIO: Jerry Tiedt, Director Information Systems
CHR: Angie Tye, Director Human Resources
CNO: Joanne Nathem, MSN, Chief Clinical and Nursing Officer
Web address: www.waverlyhealthcenter.org
Control: City–Government, nonfederal **Service:** General Medical and Surgical

Staffed Beds: 25 **Admissions:** 880 **Census:** 8 **Outpatient Visits:** 116169 **Births:** 264 **Total Expense ($000):** 50227 **Payroll Expense ($000):** 23902 **Personnel:** 328

WEBSTER CITY—Hamilton County

HAMILTON HOSPITAL See Van Diest Medical Center

★ **VAN DIEST MEDICAL CENTER (161361)**, 2350 Hospital Drive, Zip 50595–6600, Mailing Address: P.O. Box 430, Zip 50595–0430; tel. 515/832–9400 **A**10 18 **F**3 7 11 13 15 28 29 34 35 37 38 40 45 50 57 59 65 75 76 80 81 85 87 89 96 97 101 107 110 111 115 119 128 130 132 133 146 147 148 **P**5 6
Primary Contact: Lori Rathbun, Chief Executive Officer
CFO: Alice Heinrichs, CPA, Chief Financial Officer
CMO: Nicole Ehn, M.D., Chief of Staff
CIO: Erick Schrier, Supervisor Information Technology
CHR: Jodie Harker, Director Human Resources
CNO: Janet Naset–Payne, MS, Chief Nursing Officer
Web address: www.vandiestmc.org
Control: County–Government, nonfederal **Service:** General Medical and Surgical

Staffed Beds: 25 **Admissions:** 1129 **Census:** 13 **Outpatient Visits:** 20901 **Births:** 121 **Total Expense ($000):** 23256 **Payroll Expense ($000):** 8905 **Personnel:** 192

WEST BURLINGTON—Des Moines County

☒ △ **GREAT RIVER MEDICAL CENTER (160057)**, 1221 South Gear Avenue, Zip 52655–1681; tel. 319/768–1000, (Total facility includes 165 beds in nursing home–type unit) **A**1 7 10 19 **F**3 4 5 7 11 13 15 18 20 22 28 29 30 31 32 34 35 36 38 40 43 48 50 53 57 59 60 62 63 64 67 68 69 70 73 75 76 77 78 79 81 82 84 85 86 87 89 90 91 92 93 96 98 99 100 101 102 103 104 105 107 108 110 111 114 115 116 117 118 119 120 121 123 128 129 130 131 132 143 146 147 148 **P**6
Primary Contact: Mark D. Richardson, President and Chief Executive Officer
CFO: Todd J. Sladky, Chief Financial Officer
CMO: John Phillips, Chief of Staff
CIO: Gary Davis, Director Information Systems
CHR: James M. Kammerer, Vice President Support Services
CNO: Teresa Colgan, VP of Nursing
Web address: www.greatrivermedical.org
Control: Other not–for–profit (including NFP Corporation) **Service:** General Medical and Surgical

Staffed Beds: 378 **Admissions:** 6446 **Census:** 219 **Outpatient Visits:** 275000 **Births:** 533 **Total Expense ($000):** 164166 **Payroll Expense ($000):** 64838 **Personnel:** 1309

WEST DES MOINES—Polk County

★ **MERCY MEDICAL CENTER – WEST LAKES**, 1755 59th Place, Zip 50266–7737; tel. 515/358–8000 **A**3 **F**3 7 11 12 13 15 18 20 22 26 29 30 39 40 41 43 44 50 56 59 61 62 64 65 68 70 75 76 77 78 79 81 85 86 87 93 96 107 108 111 114 118 119 126 130 132 135 143 146 **P**6 **S** Catholic Health Initiatives, Englewood, CO
Primary Contact: Robert P. Ritz, President
COO: Kathy L. Goetz, Administrator
CFO: Randy Rubin, Senior Vice President and Chief Financial Officer
CMO: Tommy Ibrahim, M.D., Chief Physician Officer
CIO: James Strother, Site Director Information Technology Systems
CHR: Kevin Elsberry, Senior Vice President Human Resources
CNO: Deborah Willyard, R.N., Senior Director Clinical Services
Web address: www.mercywestlakes.org/
Control: Church–operated, Nongovernment, not–for profit **Service:** General Medical and Surgical

Staffed Beds: 74 **Admissions:** 4076 **Census:** 36 **Outpatient Visits:** 24249 **Births:** 331 **Total Expense ($000):** 46213 **Payroll Expense ($000):** 13837 **Personnel:** 274

WEST UNION—Fayette County

★ **PALMER LUTHERAN HEALTH CENTER (161316)**, 112 Jefferson Street, Zip 52175–1022; tel. 563/422–3811 **A**10 18 **F**3 8 11 13 15 28 29 30 31 34 40 43 56 57 59 62 63 64 65 68 70 76 77 78 79 81 82 85 86 93 96 107 111 114 119 128 129 130 131 132 133 135 144 146 148
Primary Contact: Tanya Tysland, Chief Executive Officer
CFO: Joni Gisleson, Director Finance
CMO: Chaudri Rasool, D.O., Chief of Staff
CIO: Kurt Chicken, Director Support Services
CHR: Cheryl Meyer, Director Human Resources
CNO: Kathy Begalske, Chief Nursing Officer
Web address: www.palmerlutheran.org
Control: Other not–for–profit (including NFP Corporation) **Service:** General Medical and Surgical

Staffed Beds: 25 **Admissions:** 334 **Census:** 5 **Outpatient Visits:** 52940 **Births:** 84 **Total Expense ($000):** 21908 **Payroll Expense ($000):** 7994 **Personnel:** 153

WINTERSET—Madison County

★ **MADISON COUNTY HEALTH CARE SYSTEM (161326)**, 300 West Hutchings Street, Zip 50273–2109; tel. 515/462–2373 **A**10 18 **F**3 15 18 28 31 35 37 40 43 45 57 59 78 79 81 89 93 97 107 110 114 119 127 128 129 130 131 133 135 146 **P**6 **S** Catholic Health Initiatives, Englewood, CO
Primary Contact: Marcia Hendricks, R.N., FACHE, Chief Executive Officer
CFO: Rebekah Mitchell, Chief Financial Officer
CMO: Sherri Broadbent, D.O., Chief of Staff
CIO: Dan VandenBosch, Chief Information Officer
CHR: Jennifer Hannon, Director Human Resources
CNO: Kim Hulbert, R.N., Chief Clinical Officer
Web address: www.madisonhealth.com
Control: County–Government, nonfederal **Service:** General Medical and Surgical

Staffed Beds: 25 **Admissions:** 425 **Census:** 5 **Outpatient Visits:** 59716 **Births:** 0 **Total Expense ($000):** 18893 **Payroll Expense ($000):** 7375 **Personnel:** 143

IA

Hospital, Medicare Provider Number, Address, Telephone, Approval, Facility, and Physician Codes, Health Care System

★ American Hospital Association (AHA) membership   ○ Healthcare Facilities Accreditation Program   ⇑ Center for Improvement in Healthcare Quality Accreditation
□ The Joint Commission accreditation   ◇ DNV Healthcare Inc. accreditation   △ Commission on Accreditation of Rehabilitation Facilities (CARF) accreditation

KANSAS

ABILENE—Dickinson County

★ **MEMORIAL HEALTH SYSTEM (171381)**, 511 N.E. Tenth Street,
Zip 67410–2153; tel. 785/263–2100, (Total facility includes 81 beds in nursing
home–type unit) **A**10 18 **F**2 3 11 13 15 18 28 29 31 34 36 40 45 53 57 59 62
63 64 68 69 75 76 77 78 79 81 82 85 87 89 93 98 103 107 108 110 111
115 119 127 128 129 130 131 132 133 134 135 143 146 148 **P**6
Primary Contact: Mark A. Miller, FACHE, Chief Executive Officer
CFO: Elgin Glanzer, Chief Financial Officer
CMO: W. L. Short, M.D., Chief Medical Officer
CIO: Blaine Cappel, Director Information Systems
CNO: Brenda L. Moffitt, Chief Nursing Officer
Web address: www.mhsks.org
Control: Hospital district or authority, Government, nonfederal **Service:** General
Medical and Surgical

Staffed Beds: 116 **Admissions:** 724 **Census:** 78 **Outpatient Visits:** 25834
Births: 109 **Total Expense ($000):** 32011 **Payroll Expense ($000):** 14563
Personnel: 340

ANDOVER—Butler County

KANSAS MEDICAL CENTER (170197), 1124 West 21st Street,
Zip 67002–5500; tel. 316/300–4000 **A**10 **F**3 17 18 20 22 24 29 30 40 49 51
60 64 68 70 75 77 79 81 82 85 87 93 102 107 108 111 115 119 126 130
131 146 148
Primary Contact: Badr Idbeis, M.D., Chief Executive Officer
COO: Daryl W. Thornton, Chief Operating Officer
CFO: Steven N. Hadley, Chief Financial Officer
CMO: G. Whitney Reader, M.D., Chief Medical Officer
CIO: Mike Buffington, Manager Information Technology
CHR: Norm Nevins, Manager Human Resources
CNO: Janet Kaiser, R.N., Chief Nursing Officer
Web address: www.ksmedcenter.com/
Control: Corporation, Investor–owned, for–profit **Service:** General Medical and
Surgical

Staffed Beds: 58 **Admissions:** 2502 **Census:** 26 **Outpatient Visits:** 10534
Births: 0 **Personnel:** 219

ANTHONY—Harper County

★ **ANTHONY MEDICAL CENTER (171346)**, 1101 East Spring Street,
Zip 67003–2122; tel. 620/842–5111 **A**10 18 **F**40 48 53 57 64 67 81 93 97
107 119 127 128 133 **P**6
Primary Contact: Lori Allen, Chief Financial Officer and Interim Chief Executive
Officer
CFO: Lori Allen, Chief Financial Officer
CMO: Sidney Stranathan, D.O., Chief of Staff
CIO: Jim Harbert, Chief Technology Officer
CHR: Kim Barwick, Vice President Human Resources
Control: Hospital district or authority, Government, nonfederal **Service:** General
Medical and Surgical

Staffed Beds: 25 **Admissions:** 236 **Census:** 8 **Outpatient Visits:** 20761
Births: 0 **Total Expense ($000):** 8775 **Payroll Expense ($000):** 4608
Personnel: 88

ARKANSAS CITY—Cowley County

★ **SOUTH CENTRAL KANSAS MEDICAL CENTER (170150)**, 6401 Patterson
Parkway, Zip 67005–5701, Mailing Address: P.O. Box 1107, Zip 67005–1107;
tel. 620/442–2500 **A**10 **F**3 11 12 13 15 29 30 34 35 39 40 45 50 52 59 64
68 70 75 76 77 79 81 82 85 87 93 107 108 110 111 115 119 129 132
133 148
Primary Contact: Virgil Watson, Chief Executive Officer
CFO: Holly Beaty, Chief Financial Officer
CMO: Kamran Shahzada, M.D., Chief Medical Staff
CHR: Clayton Pappan, Director Human Resources and Marketing
CNO: Patricia Davis, Chief Nursing Officer
Web address: www.sckrmc.org
Control: City–Government, nonfederal **Service:** General Medical and Surgical

Staffed Beds: 37 **Admissions:** 942 **Census:** 9 **Outpatient Visits:** 25684
Births: 149 **Total Expense ($000):** 18495 **Payroll Expense ($000):** 6812
Personnel: 197

ASHLAND—Clark County

★ **ASHLAND HEALTH CENTER (171304)**, 709 Oak Street, Zip 67831–0188,
Mailing Address: P.O. Box 188, Zip 67831–0188; tel. 620/635–2241 **A**10 18 **F**2
30 34 40 53 59 62 64 67 68 85 87 93 107 127 128 133 143 **P**6 **S** Great
Plains Health Alliance, Inc., Wichita, KS
Primary Contact: Michael Mages, Chief Executive Officer
CFO: Debbie Filson, Chief Financial Officer
CMO: Daniel Shuman, D.O., Chief Medical Officer
CIO: Alan Romans, Director Information Technology
CHR: Debbie Filson, Chief Financial Officer
CNO: Patty Young, R.N., Chief Nursing Officer
Web address: www.ashlandhc.org
Control: Hospital district or authority, Government, nonfederal **Service:** General
Medical and Surgical

Staffed Beds: 45 **Admissions:** 118 **Census:** 19 **Outpatient Visits:** 7280
Births: 0 **Total Expense ($000):** 5778 **Payroll Expense ($000):** 3085
Personnel: 71

ATCHISON—Atchison County

★ **ATCHISON HOSPITAL (171382)**, 800 Raven Hill Drive, Zip 66002–9204;
tel. 913/367–2131 **A**10 18 **F**3 11 13 15 28 29 30 31 34 35 40 45 49 50 57
59 62 63 64 65 68 70 75 76 77 79 81 82 85 87 89 92 93 97 107 108 110
111 114 118 119 127 129 130 131 132 133 135 146 147 148 **P**6
Primary Contact: John L. Jacobson, Chief Executive Officer
COO: Sandra Leggett, Chief Operating Officer
CFO: Gary R. Foll, Chief Financial Officer
CMO: McGarrett Groth, Chief of Staff
CIO: Terry Davis, Manager Information Systems
CHR: Jill Wenger, Director Human Resources
Web address: www.atchisonhospital.org
Control: Other not–for–profit (including NFP Corporation) **Service:** General
Medical and Surgical

Staffed Beds: 25 **Admissions:** 955 **Census:** 9 **Outpatient Visits:** 76982
Births: 142 **Total Expense ($000):** 36595 **Payroll Expense ($000):** 16972
Personnel: 267

ATWOOD—Rawlins County

★ **RAWLINS COUNTY HEALTH CENTER (171307)**, 707 Grant Street,
Zip 67730–1526, Mailing Address: P.O. Box 47, Zip 67730–0047;
tel. 785/626–3211 **A**10 18 **F**3 28 29 30 34 40 41 45 59 64 65 66 75 81 83
85 87 89 93 97 107 114 125 127 128 130 131 132 133 135 147 148 **P**6
S Great Plains Health Alliance, Inc., Wichita, KS
Primary Contact: Sharon K. Cox, FACHE, Chief Executive Officer
COO: Ryan Marvin, Support Services Director
CFO: Heather Prideaux, Chief Financial Officer
CMO: Brewster Kellogg, D.O., Chief Medical Officer
CIO: Destiny Schroeder, Information Systems Director
CHR: Tara Bowles, Employee Relations Director
CNO: Amber Withington, R.N., Chief Nursing Officer
Web address: www.rchc.us
Control: County–Government, nonfederal **Service:** General Medical and Surgical

Staffed Beds: 24 **Admissions:** 203 **Census:** 3 **Outpatient Visits:** 17582
Births: 0 **Total Expense ($000):** 7544 **Payroll Expense ($000):** 2742
Personnel: 55

BELLEVILLE—Republic County

★ **REPUBLIC COUNTY HOSPITAL (171361)**, 2420 G Street, Zip 66935–2400;
tel. 785/527–2254 **A**10 18 **F**3 13 15 28 29 30 31 35 39 40 45 56 57 64 67
68 75 76 77 78 79 81 85 86 87 89 93 107 108 114 119 128 130 131 133
S Great Plains Health Alliance, Inc., Wichita, KS
Primary Contact: Blaine K. Miller, Administrator
CFO: Barry Bottger, Chief Financial Officer
Web address: www.rphospital.org
Control: Other not–for–profit (including NFP Corporation) **Service:** General
Medical and Surgical

Staffed Beds: 63 **Admissions:** 857 **Census:** 43 **Outpatient Visits:** 14217
Births: 74 **Total Expense ($000):** 13819 **Payroll Expense ($000):** 6649
Personnel: 155

Many Facility Codes have changed. Please refer to the AHA Guide Code Chart. © 2016 AHA Guide

KS

BELOIT—Mitchell County

★ **MITCHELL COUNTY HOSPITAL HEALTH SYSTEMS (171375)**, 400 West Eighth, Zip 67420–1605, Mailing Address: P.O. Box 399, Zip 67420–0399; tel. 785/738–2266, (Total facility includes 40 beds in nursing home–type unit) **A**10 18 **F**3 11 13 15 28 29 31 34 40 43 45 48 50 56 59 62 63 64 68 69 74 76 77 81 82 84 86 87 93 98 103 106 107 111 114 119 128 129 130 132 133 148
Primary Contact: Jeremy Armstrong, FACHE, Chief Executive Officer
CFO: Eldon Koepke, Chief Financial Officer
CIO: Nate Richards, Director Information Technology
CHR: Phyllis Oetting, Director Human Resources
CNO: Jan Kemmerer, Director of Nursing
Web address: www.mchks.com
Control: County–Government, nonfederal **Service:** General Medical and Surgical

Staffed Beds: 75 **Admissions:** 1456 **Census:** 63 **Outpatient Visits:** 15547 **Births:** 111 **Total Expense ($000):** 25716 **Payroll Expense ($000):** 11641 **Personnel:** 274

BURLINGTON—Coffey County

★ **COFFEY COUNTY HOSPITAL (170094)**, 801 North 4th Street, Zip 66839–2602; tel. 620/364–2121, (Total facility includes 42 beds in nursing home–type unit) **A**10 20 **F**3 7 10 11 13 15 17 29 30 31 34 40 45 50 57 59 62 64 65 67 68 70 75 76 77 78 79 81 82 85 87 93 107 110 111 114 119 125 127 128 130 132 133 146 **P**6
Primary Contact: Leonard Hernandez, Chief Executive Officer
CFO: Jim Van Hoet, Chief Financial Officer
CMO: John Shell, M.D., Chief Medical Officer
CIO: Adam Haag, Manager Information Technology
CHR: Theresa Thoele, Director Human Resources
CNO: Melissa Hall, Chief Nursing Officer
Web address: www.coffeyhealth.org
Control: County–Government, nonfederal **Service:** General Medical and Surgical

Staffed Beds: 78 **Admissions:** 650 **Census:** 34 **Outpatient Visits:** 18976 **Births:** 97 **Total Expense ($000):** 25707 **Payroll Expense ($000):** 13889 **Personnel:** 261

CALDWELL—Sumner County

★ **SUMNER COUNTY HOSPITAL DISTRICT ONE (171329)**, 601 South Osage Street, Zip 67022–1654; tel. 620/845–6492 **A**10 18 **F**11 40 45 57 59 67 75 81 93 107 119 128 133 **P**5
Primary Contact: Thomas Henton, Chief Executive Officer
CFO: Jennifer Marcrum, Chief Financial Officer
CMO: Jim Blunk, D.O., Chief Medical Officer
CIO: Trey Watson, Network Administrator
Web address: www.schd1.com
Control: Hospital district or authority, Government, nonfederal **Service:** General Medical and Surgical

Staffed Beds: 16 **Admissions:** 103 **Census:** 1 **Outpatient Visits:** 3958 **Births:** 0 **Total Expense ($000):** 4473 **Payroll Expense ($000):** 1716 **Personnel:** 40

CHANUTE—Neosho County

★ ◇ **NEOSHO MEMORIAL REGIONAL MEDICAL CENTER (171380)**, 629 South Plummer, Zip 66720–1928, Mailing Address: P.O. Box 426, Zip 66720–0426; tel. 620/431–4000 **A**10 18 21 **F**3 7 11 13 15 28 29 30 34 40 43 47 48 50 52 53 57 62 63 64 76 77 79 81 82 85 89 93 107 108 110 111 114 119 126 127 128 129 130 133 143 146 147 **P**8 **S** QHR, Brentwood, TN
Primary Contact: Dennis Franks, FACHE, Chief Executive Officer
COO: Wendy Brazil, Chief Operating Officer
CFO: Nancy Woodyard, Chief Financial Officer
CMO: Charles Van Houden, M.D., Chief Medical Officer
CIO: Gretchen Keller, Director Health Information
CHR: R. C. Rowan, Director Human Resources
CNO: Jennifer Newton, R.N., Chief Nursing Officer
Web address: www.nmrmc.com
Control: County–Government, nonfederal **Service:** General Medical and Surgical

Staffed Beds: 25 **Admissions:** 1752 **Census:** 20 **Outpatient Visits:** 41211 **Births:** 328 **Total Expense ($000):** 45501 **Payroll Expense ($000):** 19061 **Personnel:** 322

CLAY CENTER—Clay County

★ **CLAY COUNTY MEDICAL CENTER (171371)**, 617 Liberty Street, Zip 67432–1564, Mailing Address: P.O. Box 512, Zip 67432–0512; tel. 785/632–2144 **A**10 18 **F**13 15 18 19 28 29 30 31 40 45 50 53 55 59 63 64 68 70 74 75 76 77 78 79 81 82 84 85 86 87 93 96 107 108 111 114 119 130 132 133 148
Primary Contact: Austin M. Gillard, Chief Executive Officer
CFO: James Garbarino, Chief Financial Officer
CIO: Chris Wolf, Director Information Technology
CHR: Cindy Rush, Director Human Resources
CNO: Sara Beikman, Director of Nursing
Web address: www.ccmcks.org
Control: County–Government, nonfederal **Service:** General Medical and Surgical

Staffed Beds: 25 **Admissions:** 705 **Census:** 10 **Outpatient Visits:** 45286 **Births:** 56 **Total Expense ($000):** 16923 **Payroll Expense ($000):** 7297 **Personnel:** 165

COFFEYVILLE—Montgomery County

✠ **COFFEYVILLE REGIONAL MEDICAL CENTER (170145)**, 1400 West Fourth, Zip 67337–3306; tel. 620/251–1200, (Total facility includes 20 beds in nursing home–type unit) **A**1 2 10 **F**3 7 11 13 15 28 29 30 31 34 40 45 46 47 50 57 59 62 64 70 74 75 76 77 78 79 81 82 85 93 97 107 108 110 111 112 114 115 117 119 120 121 123 128 130 131 132 135 145 146 147 **P**8
Primary Contact: Mark Woodring, Chief Executive Officer
CFO: Dean Ohmart, Chief Financial Officer
CIO: Kris Penco, Director Information Systems
CHR: Becky McCune, Director Human Resources, Community Relations and Education
CNO: Lori Rexwinkle, Chief Nursing Officer
Web address: www.crmcinc.com
Control: Other not–for–profit (including NFP Corporation) **Service:** General Medical and Surgical

Staffed Beds: 69 **Admissions:** 1985 **Census:** 25 **Outpatient Visits:** 49021 **Births:** 297 **Total Expense ($000):** 44668 **Payroll Expense ($000):** 15617 **Personnel:** 301

COLBY—Thomas County

★ **CITIZENS MEDICAL CENTER (171362)**, 100 East College Drive, Zip 67701–3799; tel. 785/462–7511, (Total facility includes 62 beds in nursing home–type unit) **A**10 18 **F**3 11 13 15 28 30 31 34 35 40 50 64 67 68 74 76 77 78 79 81 85 86 87 93 97 107 108 110 111 114 119 127 130 133 146 148 **P**6
Primary Contact: Greg Unruh, Chief Executive Officer
CFO: Darcy Howard, Chief Financial Officer
CMO: Kelly Gabel, Chief of Staff
CIO: Jacee Dobbs, Chief Information Officer
CHR: Margaret Kummer, Chief Human Resource Officer
CNO: Jenny Niblock, Chief Clinical Officer
Web address: www.cmciks.com
Control: Other not–for–profit (including NFP Corporation) **Service:** General Medical and Surgical

Staffed Beds: 87 **Admissions:** 587 **Census:** 53 **Outpatient Visits:** 11570 **Births:** 155 **Total Expense ($000):** 29764 **Payroll Expense ($000):** 14871 **Personnel:** 266

COLDWATER—Comanche County

★ **COMANCHE COUNTY HOSPITAL (171312)**, 202 South Frisco Street, Zip 67029–9101, Mailing Address: HC 65, Box 8A, Zip 67029–9500; tel. 620/582–2144 **A**10 18 **F**3 11 30 31 40 43 53 59 61 68 75 78 93 102 107 128 133 **P**6 **S** Great Plains Health Alliance, Inc., Wichita, KS
Primary Contact: Nancy Zimmerman, R.N., Administrator
CFO: Lisa Brooks, Chief Financial Officer
CMO: Daniel Schowengerdt, M.D., Chief of Staff
CIO: LaNell Wagnon, Director Medical Records
CHR: Lisa Brooks, Chief Financial Officer
CNO: Sandra Dobrinski, Director of Nursing
Web address: www.gpha.com
Control: County–Government, nonfederal **Service:** General Medical and Surgical

Staffed Beds: 12 **Admissions:** 118 **Census:** 2 **Outpatient Visits:** 12311 **Births:** 0 **Total Expense ($000):** 5404 **Payroll Expense ($000):** 2602 **Personnel:** 55

COLUMBUS—Cherokee County

★ **MERCY HOSPITAL COLUMBUS (171308)**, 220 North Pennsylvania Avenue, Zip 66725–1110; tel. 620/429–2545 **A**10 18 **F**11 15 40 45 59 77 93 119 133 **S** Mercy Health, Chesterfield, MO
Primary Contact: Angie Saporito, Administrator
Web address: www.mercy.net/newsroom–mercy–maude–norton–hospital–quick–facts
Control: Church–operated, Nongovernment, not–for profit **Service:** General Medical and Surgical

Staffed Beds: 18 **Admissions:** 88 **Census:** 1 **Outpatient Visits:** 10682
Births: 0 **Total Expense ($000):** 4737 **Payroll Expense ($000):** 2442
Personnel: 46

CONCORDIA—Cloud County

★ **CLOUD COUNTY HEALTH CENTER (171349)**, 1100 Highland Drive, Zip 66901–3923; tel. 785/243–1234 **A**10 18 **F**3 11 15 28 31 34 35 40 41 45 56 57 59 64 65 70 74 75 77 79 81 82 85 86 87 89 93 96 97 102 107 108 114 118 119 127 130 133 135 146 148 **P**6 **S** Salina Regional Health Center, Salina, KS
Primary Contact: Cherri Waites, Chief Executive Officer
CFO: Pamela Blochlinger, Acting Vice President Finance
CMO: Justin Poore, D.O., Chief Medical Staff
CIO: Jenny Bergstrom, Project Manager Information Technology
CHR: Dawn Thoman, Vice President Human Resources
CNO: Michelle Metro, Vice President Nursing
Web address: www.cchc.com
Control: Other not–for–profit (including NFP Corporation) **Service:** General Medical and Surgical

Staffed Beds: 25 **Admissions:** 444 **Census:** 6 **Outpatient Visits:** 35653
Births: 12 **Total Expense ($000):** 15726 **Payroll Expense ($000):** 6883
Personnel: 160

COUNCIL GROVE—Morris County

★ **MORRIS COUNTY HOSPITAL (171379)**, 600 North Washington Street, Zip 66846–1422; tel. 620/767–6811 **A**10 18 **F**7 11 13 15 18 28 31 35 40 45 59 64 65 70 76 77 81 87 93 94 96 107 110 111 130 132 133 146 148 **P**5
Primary Contact: James H. Reagan, Jr., Ph.D., Chief Executive Officer
CFO: Ron Christenson, Chief Financial Officer
CMO: Lora Siegle, M.D., Chief Medical Officer
CIO: Bill Lauer, Chief Information Officer
CHR: Don Zimmerman, Director Human Resources
CNO: Stephanne Wolf, Chief Nursing Officer
Web address: www.mrcohosp.com
Control: County–Government, nonfederal **Service:** General Medical and Surgical

Staffed Beds: 25 **Admissions:** 293 **Census:** 4 **Outpatient Visits:** 13566
Births: 28 **Total Expense ($000):** 9225 **Payroll Expense ($000):** 3213
Personnel: 84

DIGHTON—Lane County

★ **LANE COUNTY HOSPITAL (171303)**, 235 West Vine, Zip 67839–0969, Mailing Address: P.O. Box 969, Zip 67839–0969; tel. 620/397–5321, (Total facility includes 14 beds in nursing home–type unit) **A**10 18 **F**30 40 56 67 77 93 97 127 128 131 133 **P**6 **S** Great Plains Health Alliance, Inc., Wichita, KS
Primary Contact: Donna McGowan, Administrator
CFO: Marcia Gabel, Chief Financial Officer
CMO: Paul Chinburg, M.D., Medical Director
CHR: Dina Casey, Human Resources Officer
CNO: Jennifer Whipple, Director Nursing
Control: County–Government, nonfederal **Service:** General Medical and Surgical

Staffed Beds: 31 **Admissions:** 68 **Census:** 22 **Outpatient Visits:** 11074
Births: 0 **Total Expense ($000):** 5269 **Payroll Expense ($000):** 2229
Personnel: 50

DODGE CITY—Ford County

⊞ **WESTERN PLAINS MEDICAL COMPLEX (170175)**, 3001 Avenue A, Zip 67801–6508, Mailing Address: P.O. Box 1478, Zip 67801–1478; tel. 620/225–8400 **A**1 3 5 10 20 **F**3 8 11 13 15 17 18 20 22 28 29 30 34 35 40 50 57 60 64 70 72 73 74 75 76 77 79 81 85 88 89 93 107 108 110 111 115 119 129 130 133 146 **P**5 **S** LifePoint Health, Brentwood, TN
Primary Contact: Michael R. Burroughs, FACHE, Chief Executive Officer
CFO: Michael Gordian, Chief Financial Officer
CMO: Merrill Conant, M.D., Chief of Staff
CIO: Shawna Culver, Director Information Systems
CHR: Corry Israel, Director Human Resources
CNO: Edna Dunn, Chief Nursing Officer
Web address: www.westernplainsmc.com
Control: Corporation, Investor–owned, for–profit **Service:** General Medical and Surgical

Staffed Beds: 71 **Admissions:** 2193 **Census:** 18 **Outpatient Visits:** 38677
Births: 685 **Personnel:** 208

EL DORADO—Butler County

⊞ **SUSAN B. ALLEN MEMORIAL HOSPITAL (170017)**, 720 West Central Avenue, Zip 67042–2112; tel. 316/321–3300 **A**1 10 **F**3 11 13 15 28 30 40 45 59 60 62 68 69 70 76 79 81 85 92 93 96 97 107 108 110 111 115 119 121 123 130 133 144 146 148
Primary Contact: James B. Kirkbride, President and Chief Executive Officer
COO: David Shaw, Vice President and Chief Operating Officer
CFO: Robert E. Fisher, Interim Chief Financial Officer
CIO: Mark Rooker, Director Information Systems
CHR: D. Gay Kimble, Director Human Resources
CNO: Cecilia B. Goebel, R.N., Vice President and Chief Nursing Officer
Web address: www.sbamh.com
Control: Other not–for–profit (including NFP Corporation) **Service:** General Medical and Surgical

Staffed Beds: 52 **Admissions:** 1358 **Census:** 11 **Outpatient Visits:** 89517
Births: 288 **Total Expense ($000):** 48869 **Payroll Expense ($000):** 20362
Personnel: 360

ELKHART—Morton County

★ **MORTON COUNTY HEALTH SYSTEM (170166)**, 445 Hilltop Street, Zip 67950–0937, Mailing Address: P.O. Box 937, Zip 67950–0937; tel. 620/697–2141 **A**10 20 **F**3 10 28 29 34 40 45 54 56 57 59 64 70 81 83 86 87 93 94 96 97 107 114 119 130 131 132 133 135 143 146 148 **P**6
Primary Contact: Richard Q. Bergling, Chief Executive Officer
CHR: Sonja May, Director Human Resources
Web address: www.mchswecare.com
Control: County–Government, nonfederal **Service:** General Medical and Surgical

Staffed Beds: 28 **Admissions:** 409 **Census:** 53 **Outpatient Visits:** 6098
Births: 0 **Total Expense ($000):** 12690 **Payroll Expense ($000):** 5910
Personnel: 102

ELLINWOOD—Barton County

★ **ELLINWOOD DISTRICT HOSPITAL (171301)**, 605 North Main Street, Zip 67526–1440; tel. 620/564–2548 **A**10 18 **F**11 40 64 65 93 107 127 128 133 **P**6 **S** Great Plains Health Alliance, Inc., Wichita, KS
Primary Contact: Kile Magner, Administrator
CFO: Summer Zink, Chief Financial Officer
CMO: Charlie Joslin, M.D., Chief of Staff
CIO: Becky L. Burns, Manager Health Information Management
CHR: Chris Robl, Human Resources
CNO: Jill Ritchie, Director of Nursing
Web address: www.ellinwooddistricthospital.org
Control: Other not–for–profit (including NFP Corporation) **Service:** General Medical and Surgical

Staffed Beds: 25 **Admissions:** 229 **Census:** 7 **Outpatient Visits:** 13292
Births: 0 **Total Expense ($000):** 6171 **Payroll Expense ($000):** 3026
Personnel: 81

ELLSWORTH—Ellsworth County

★ **ELLSWORTH COUNTY MEDICAL CENTER (171327)**, 1604 Aylward Street, Zip 67439–0087, Mailing Address: P.O. Box 87, Zip 67439–0087; tel. 785/472–3111 **A**10 18 **F**3 11 28 29 34 35 40 45 47 53 57 59 64 67 77 85 86 87 93 97 107 115 119 127 128 130 133 146 **P**6
Primary Contact: Roger A. Masse, FACHE, Chief Executive Officer
CFO: Preston Sauers, Chief Financial Officer
CIO: Lynette Dick, Director of Support Services
CHR: Christa N. Bohnen, Director Human Resources
CNO: Amanda Thrasher, Director Nursing
Web address: www.ewmed.com
Control: County–Government, nonfederal **Service:** General Medical and Surgical

Staffed Beds: 20 **Admissions:** 664 **Census:** 4 **Outpatient Visits:** 16764
Births: 0 **Total Expense ($000):** 15636 **Payroll Expense ($000):** 7580
Personnel: 152

EMPORIA—Lyon County

★ **NEWMAN REGIONAL HEALTH (171384)**, 1201 West 12th Avenue, Zip 66801–2597; tel. 620/343–6800 **A**10 18 **F**3 11 13 15 17 18 20 22 26 28 29 31 39 40 41 45 51 53 59 61 63 64 65 68 70 76 77 78 79 81 82 84 85 86 87 89 90 93 96 102 107 108 111 114 118 119 129 130 131 132 133 135 144 146 147 148 **P**6
Primary Contact: Robert N. Wright, Chief Executive Officer
CFO: Holly French, Chief Financial Officer
CMO: James Geitz, M.D., Chief of Staff
CHR: Kathy Orear, Director Human Resources
CNO: Julia Pyle, R.N., Chief Nursing Officer
Web address: www.newmanrh.org
Control: County–Government, nonfederal **Service:** General Medical and Surgical

Staffed Beds: 32 **Admissions:** 2175 **Census:** 21 **Outpatient Visits:** 80107
Births: 395 **Total Expense ($000):** 60454 **Payroll Expense ($000):** 25432
Personnel: 462

KS

Many Facility Codes have changed. Please refer to the AHA Guide Code Chart.
© 2016 AHA Guide

EUREKA—Greenwood County

GREENWOOD COUNTY HOSPITAL (171339), 100 West 16th Street, Zip 67045–1064; tel. 620/583–7451 **A**10 18 **F**3 40 43 53 57 62 81 93 96 107 119 127 128 133 135 146 **P**6
Primary Contact: Nancy J. McKenzie, Chief Executive Officer
CFO: Marian Drake, Chief Financial Officer
CIO: Jason Clark, Director Quality Improvement, Risk Management and Information System
CHR: Janel M. Palmer, Director Human Resources
CNO: Tracy Harrod, Director of Nursing
Web address: www.gwch.org
Control: County–Government, nonfederal **Service:** General Medical and Surgical

Staffed Beds: 25 **Admissions:** 499 **Census:** 6 **Outpatient Visits:** 22903 **Births:** 0 **Total Expense ($000):** 10473 **Payroll Expense ($000):** 6130 **Personnel:** 119

FORT SCOTT—Bourbon County

✠ **MERCY HOSPITAL FORT SCOTT (170058)**, 401 Woodland Hills Boulevard, Zip 66701–8797; tel. 620/223–2200 **A**1 10 **F**3 7 11 13 15 28 29 30 34 35 40 53 57 59 62 63 65 70 72 75 76 77 79 81 82 84 85 93 97 107 108 110 111 114 118 119 127 129 130 131 132 133 143 144 145 146 148 **P**6 **S** Mercy Health, Chesterfield, MO
Primary Contact: Reta K. Baker, President
CFO: Shelly Hunter, Chief Financial Officer
CMO: Robert R. Nichols, M.D., Vice President Medical Affairs
CIO: Lori Sturgill, Vice President Business Partnership
CHR: Timothy Murphy, Vice President Human Resources
CNO: Patrick Callanan, Vice President Patient Care Services
Web address: www.mercykansas.com
Control: Church–operated, Nongovernment, not–for profit **Service:** General Medical and Surgical

Staffed Beds: 49 **Admissions:** 1575 **Census:** 14 **Outpatient Visits:** 81503 **Births:** 265 **Total Expense ($000):** 31849 **Payroll Expense ($000):** 13543 **Personnel:** 241

FREDONIA—Wilson County

★ **FREDONIA REGIONAL HOSPITAL (171374)**, 1527 Madison Street, Zip 66736–1751, Mailing Address: P.O. Box 579, Zip 66736–0579; tel. 620/378–2121 **A**10 18 **F**3 7 11 15 30 40 81 82 85 93 98 103 107 110 114 119 128 133 **S** Great Plains Health Alliance, Inc., Wichita, KS
Primary Contact: John Hart, Chief Executive Officer
CFO: Tracy Row, Manager Business Office
CMO: Jennifer McKenney, M.D., Chief Medical Officer
CIO: Tyler Row, Director Information Technology
CHR: Debbie Marr, Administrative Assistant and Director Human Resources
CNO: Ryan Duft, R.N., Chief Nursing Officer
Web address: www.fredoniaregionalhospital.org
Control: City–Government, nonfederal **Service:** General Medical and Surgical

Staffed Beds: 34 **Admissions:** 583 **Census:** 11 **Outpatient Visits:** 20842 **Births:** 0 **Total Expense ($000):** 13518 **Payroll Expense ($000):** 4644 **Personnel:** 116

GALENA—Cherokee County

◇ **PREMIER SURGICAL INSTITUTE (170203)**, 1619 West 7th Street, Zip 66739; tel. 620/783–1732, (Nonreporting) **A**10 21
Primary Contact: Travis W. Roderick, Chief Executive Officer
Web address: www.premiersurgicalinstitute.com/
Control: City–Government, nonfederal **Service:** General Medical and Surgical

Staffed Beds: 25

GARDEN CITY—Finney County

✠ **ST. CATHERINE HOSPITAL (170023)**, 401 East Spruce Street, Zip 67846–5679; tel. 620/272–2561 **A**1 10 20 **F**3 8 13 15 18 20 22 29 30 31 34 35 40 45 49 51 57 59 60 63 64 65 68 69 70 73 75 76 77 78 79 81 82 83 84 85 86 87 89 90 91 92 93 94 96 97 98 99 100 101 102 103 107 108 109 110 111 112 113 114 115 116 117 118 119 120 121 122 123 124 127 129 130 131 132 135 146 147 148 **P**5 6 **S** Catholic Health Initiatives, Englewood, CO
Primary Contact: Scott J. Taylor, President and Chief Executive Officer
CFO: Amanda Vaughan, Chief Financial Officer
CMO: Matthew C. Byrnes, M.D., Chief Medical Officer
CIO: Lance Kellenbarger, Site Director Information Systems
CHR: Kathy E. Morrison, Executive Director Human Resources
CNO: Margaret Elizabeth Prewitt, Vice President Patient Services and Chief Nursing Officer
Web address: www.StCatherineHosp.org
Control: Church–operated, Nongovernment, not–for profit **Service:** General Medical and Surgical

Staffed Beds: 110 **Admissions:** 3704 **Census:** 39 **Outpatient Visits:** 182182 **Births:** 619 **Total Expense ($000):** 97087 **Payroll Expense ($000):** 36536 **Personnel:** 587

GARDNER—Johnson County

★ △ **MEADOWBROOK REHABILITATION HOSPITAL (170180)**, 427 West Main Street, Zip 66030–1183; tel. 913/856–8747, (Total facility includes 42 beds in nursing home–type unit) **A**7 10 **F**29 34 87 90 91 92 128 130 132 135 143 148
Primary Contact: Jon W. Scott, Chief Executive Officer
CFO: Kelly Taul, Business Manager
CMO: David Edalati, M.D., Medical Director
CHR: Carrie Moore, Director Human Resources
CNO: Lisa Perez, R.N., Director Nursing
Web address: www.meadowbrookrehab.com
Control: Partnership, Investor–owned, for–profit **Service:** Rehabilitation

Staffed Beds: 96 **Admissions:** 524 **Census:** 69 **Outpatient Visits:** 0 **Births:** 0 **Total Expense ($000):** 13487 **Payroll Expense ($000):** 6085 **Personnel:** 156

GARNETT—Anderson County

★ **ANDERSON COUNTY HOSPITAL (171316)**, 421 South Maple, Zip 66032–1334, Mailing Address: P.O. Box 309, Zip 66032–0309; tel. 785/448–3131, (Total facility includes 36 beds in nursing home–type unit) **A**10 18 **F**7 8 11 15 29 30 34 35 40 41 43 45 56 57 59 64 65 67 75 79 81 87 91 93 97 107 108 110 114 127 130 133 **P**6 **S** Saint Luke's Health System, Kansas City, MO
Primary Contact: Rick McKain, Chief Executive Officer
CFO: Vicki L. Mills, Chief Financial Officer
CMO: Mackenzie Peterson, M.D., Chief of Staff
CHR: Karen Gillespie, Director Human Resources
CNO: Margo L. Williams, R.N., Chief Nursing Officer
Web address: www.saint–lukes.org
Control: Other not–for–profit (including NFP Corporation) **Service:** General Medical and Surgical

Staffed Beds: 48 **Admissions:** 242 **Census:** 38 **Outpatient Visits:** 45346 **Births:** 0 **Total Expense ($000):** 22011 **Payroll Expense ($000):** 8408 **Personnel:** 194

GIRARD—Crawford County

★ **GIRARD MEDICAL CENTER (171376)**, 302 North Hospital Drive, Zip 66743–2000; tel. 620/724–8291 **A**10 18 **F**3 6 8 11 12 15 29 34 35 40 43 45 47 50 51 53 56 57 59 62 64 65 70 75 77 79 81 87 93 97 98 100 101 102 103 104 105 107 114 119 127 128 130 131 132 133 146 148 **P**6
Primary Contact: Michael E. Payne, Administrator
CFO: Holly Koch, Chief Financial Officer
CIO: Jeff Barnes, Director Information Technology
CHR: Gregory Sullivan, Manager Human Resources
CNO: Joyce Geier, Director Nursing
Web address: www.girardmedicalcenter.com
Control: Hospital district or authority, Government, nonfederal **Service:** General Medical and Surgical

Staffed Beds: 35 **Admissions:** 655 **Census:** 14 **Outpatient Visits:** 19975 **Births:** 0 **Total Expense ($000):** 19354 **Payroll Expense ($000):** 9237 **Personnel:** 182

KS

Hospital, Medicare Provider Number, Address, Telephone, Approval, Facility, and Physician Codes, Health Care System

★ American Hospital Association (AHA) membership
☐ The Joint Commission accreditation
◯ Healthcare Facilities Accreditation Program
◇ DNV Healthcare Inc. accreditation
⇑ Center for Improvement in Healthcare Quality Accreditation
△ Commission on Accreditation of Rehabilitation Facilities (CARF) accreditation

GOODLAND—Sherman County

★ **GOODLAND REGIONAL MEDICAL CENTER (171370)**, 220 West Second Street, Zip 67735–1602; tel. 785/890–3625 **A**10 18 **F**11 13 15 28 29 31 34 40 57 59 60 64 65 69 75 76 77 78 79 81 82 87 93 96 97 107 110 114 119 127 130 132 133 135 148 **P**6
Primary Contact: William Widener, Chief Executive Officer
CFO: Donald Lee Wade, Chief Financial Officer
CIO: Christopher Biel, Chief Information Officer
CHR: Linda Taylor, Chief Human Resources Officer
Web address: www.goodlandregional.com
Control: County–Government, nonfederal **Service:** General Medical and Surgical

Staffed Beds: 25 **Admissions:** 497 **Census:** 5 **Outpatient Visits:** 37346
Births: 76 **Total Expense ($000):** 17472 **Payroll Expense ($000):** 7148
Personnel: 151

GREAT BEND—Barton County

GREAT BEND REGIONAL HOSPITAL (170191), 514 Cleveland Street, Zip 67530–3562; tel. 620/792–8833 **A**10 20 22 **F**3 7 8 13 15 29 30 34 40 43 45 50 57 59 64 65 68 70 75 76 79 81 82 89 107 110 111 114 119 127 130 135 146 147
Primary Contact: Kerry Noble, Chief Executive Officer
COO: Adina Gregory, Chief Operating Officer
CFO: Timothy Latimer, Chief Financial Officer
CMO: Randall Hildebrand, M.D., Chief Medical Officer
CHR: Brenda Kaiser, Director Human Resources
CNO: Adina Gregory, Chief Nursing Officer
Web address: www.gbregional.com
Control: Partnership, Investor–owned, for–profit **Service:** General Medical and Surgical

Staffed Beds: 33 **Admissions:** 1593 **Census:** 13 **Outpatient Visits:** 48943
Births: 353 **Total Expense ($000):** 39412 **Payroll Expense ($000):** 14698
Personnel: 283

GREENSBURG—Kiowa County

★ **KIOWA COUNTY MEMORIAL HOSPITAL (171332)**, 721 West Kansas Avenue, Zip 67054–1633; tel. 620/723–3341 **A**10 18 **F**3 7 11 34 40 50 53 59 64 68 107 114 127 128 133 **P**6 **S** Great Plains Health Alliance, Inc., Wichita, KS
Primary Contact: Mary Sweet, Administrator
CFO: Ron Tucker, Business Office Manager
CMO: Nizar Kibar, M.D., Chief Medical Staff
CIO: Jeremy Steven Hoover, Chief Information Officer
CHR: Cathy McFall, Human Resources Manager
CNO: Vanessa Kirk, Director of Nursing
Web address: www.kcmh.net
Control: Other not–for–profit (including NFP Corporation) **Service:** General Medical and Surgical

Staffed Beds: 15 **Admissions:** 114 **Census:** 4 **Outpatient Visits:** 11172
Births: 0 **Total Expense ($000):** 8052 **Payroll Expense ($000):** 3099
Personnel: 73

HANOVER—Washington County

★ **HANOVER HOSPITAL (171365)**, 205 South Hanover, Zip 66945–8924, Mailing Address: P.O. Box 38, Zip 66945–0038; tel. 785/337–2214 **A**10 18 **F**2 7 40 53 67 69 81 133 **P**4
Primary Contact: Brittany Oemke, Administrator
CFO: Sheryl Adam, Chief Financial Officer
Control: Hospital district or authority, Government, nonfederal **Service:** General Medical and Surgical

Staffed Beds: 25 **Admissions:** 135 **Census:** 4 **Outpatient Visits:** 1838
Births: 1 **Total Expense ($000):** 3740 **Payroll Expense ($000):** 2022
Personnel: 51

HARPER—Harper County

★ **HARPER HOSPITAL DISTRICT FIVE (171366)**, 700 West 13th Street, Zip 67058–1401; tel. 620/896–7324 **A**10 18 **F**3 10 29 34 35 40 43 45 46 50 53 54 59 64 65 67 68 75 77 79 81 84 87 90 93 97 107 111 114 119 125 127 128 130 131 133 135 146 147 148 **P**6
Primary Contact: Sandra Owen, Interim Chief Executive Officer
CFO: Sandra Owen, Director Fiscal and Accounting
CMO: Ralph Imlay, M.D., Chief of Staff
CIO: Cindi Beadman, Director Medical Records
CHR: Troy Hickman, Director Human Resources
CNO: Karen Aldis, Director of Nursing
Web address: www.hhd5.com
Control: Hospital district or authority, Government, nonfederal **Service:** General Medical and Surgical

Staffed Beds: 25 **Admissions:** 261 **Census:** 11 **Outpatient Visits:** 32869
Births: 0 **Total Expense ($000):** 9145 **Payroll Expense ($000):** 4258
Personnel: 107

HAYS—Ellis County

★ ◇ **HAYS MEDICAL CENTER (170013)**, 2220 Canterbury Drive, Zip 67601–2370, Mailing Address: P.O. Box 8100, Zip 67601–8100; tel. 785/623–5000 **A**3 5 10 21 **F**3 11 12 13 15 17 18 20 22 24 26 28 29 30 31 32 34 35 36 37 38 40 41 43 45 46 53 55 56 57 59 60 63 64 65 66 68 69 70 71 72 73 75 76 77 78 79 80 81 82 84 85 86 87 89 92 93 97 107 108 110 111 115 118 119 120 121 123 126 127 128 129 130 131 132 135 144 146 147 148 **P**6
Primary Contact: John H. Jeter, M.D., President and Chief Executive Officer
COO: Bryce A. Young, Chief Operating Officer
CFO: George Harms, Chief Financial Officer
CIO: Scott Rohleder, Chief Information Officer
CHR: Bryce A. Young, Chief Operating Officer
CNO: Terry Siek, MSN, Chief Nursing Officer
Web address: www.haysmed.com
Control: Other not–for–profit (including NFP Corporation) **Service:** General Medical and Surgical

Staffed Beds: 127 **Admissions:** 5275 **Census:** 62 **Outpatient Visits:** 303145
Births: 760 **Total Expense ($000):** 184853 **Payroll Expense ($000):** 81212
Personnel: 1197

HERINGTON—Dickinson County

HERINGTON MUNICIPAL HOSPITAL (171340), 100 East Helen Street, Zip 67449–1606; tel. 785/258–2207 **A**10 18 **F**3 11 15 28 29 40 45 50 54 57 59 64 68 75 77 81 93 97 107 114 115 119 127 133 144
Primary Contact: Alan Meisinger, Chief Financial Officer
CFO: Alan Meisinger, Chief Financial Officer
CMO: John Mosier, D.O., Chief of Staff
CHR: Nicole Will, Human Resources Officer
CNO: Roni Baker, Director of Nursing
Web address: www.heringtonhospital.org
Control: City–Government, nonfederal **Service:** General Medical and Surgical

Staffed Beds: 25 **Admissions:** 336 **Census:** 4 **Outpatient Visits:** 11576
Births: 0 **Total Expense ($000):** 8831 **Payroll Expense ($000):** 3097
Personnel: 62

HIAWATHA—Brown County

★ **HIAWATHA COMMUNITY HOSPITAL (171341)**, 300 Utah Street, Zip 66434–2314; tel. 785/742–2131 **A**10 18 **F**8 11 13 15 17 40 45 62 67 69 70 76 81 85 107 111 114 119 128 130 133 146 **P**6
Primary Contact: Jenny Knudson, Chief Financial Officer
CFO: Jenny Knudson, Controller
CMO: Steffen Shamburg, M.D., Chief of Staff
CIO: Cheryl Wenger, Manager Health Information and Quality Assurance
CHR: Alison Keri, Director Human Resources
CNO: Lisa Thompson, MSN, Director of Nursing
Web address: www.hch-ks.org
Control: Other not–for–profit (including NFP Corporation) **Service:** General Medical and Surgical

Staffed Beds: 25 **Admissions:** 705 **Census:** 6 **Outpatient Visits:** 27523
Births: 92 **Total Expense ($000):** 26066 **Payroll Expense ($000):** 11613
Personnel: 215

HILL CITY—Graham County

★ **GRAHAM COUNTY HOSPITAL (171325)**, 304 West Prout Street, Zip 67642–1435; tel. 785/421–2121 **A**10 18 **F**3 11 34 40 50 53 59 64 65 67 68 69 81 82 84 93 107 127 128 133 148
Primary Contact: Melissa Atkins, CPA, Chief Executive Officer
CHR: Donella Belleau, Director Human Resources
Web address: www.grahamcountyhospital.org
Control: County–Government, nonfederal **Service:** General Medical and Surgical

Staffed Beds: 20 **Admissions:** 313 **Census:** 4 **Outpatient Visits:** 942 **Births:** 0 **Total Expense ($000):** 7235 **Payroll Expense ($000):** 3593 **Personnel:** 78

HILLSBORO—Marion County

HILLSBORO COMMUNITY HOSPITAL (171357), 701 South Main Street, Zip 67063–1553; tel. 620/947–3114 **A**10 18 **F**3 11 29 30 34 35 40 45 47 50 57 59 64 65 75 77 79 81 82 85 86 87 93 97 107 114 127 130 131 133 146 **P**5 6 **S** Rural Community Hospitals of America, Kansas City, MO
Primary Contact: Marion Regier, Chief Executive Officer
COO: Johna Magnuson, Director Nursing
CIO: Marsha Setzkorn–Meyer, Director Public Relations and Marketing
CHR: Wendy McCarty, Director Human Resources
Web address: www.hchks.com
Control: Corporation, Investor–owned, for–profit **Service:** General Medical and Surgical

Staffed Beds: 10 **Admissions:** 136 **Census:** 1 **Outpatient Visits:** 6645
Births: 0 **Total Expense ($000):** 5217 **Payroll Expense ($000):** 2669
Personnel: 40

HOISINGTON—Barton County

★ **CLARA BARTON HOSPITAL (171333)**, 250 West Ninth Street,
Zip 67544–1706; tel. 620/653–2114 **A**10 18 **F**11 15 28 40 51 56 57 59 64
77 79 81 85 92 93 97 107 114 119 127 128 133 148 **P**6
Primary Contact: James Blackwell, President and Chief Executive Officer
CMO: Nathan Knackstedt, D.O., Chief of Staff
CHR: John Moshier, Director Human Resources
CNO: Jane Schepmann, Vice President and Chief Nursing Officer
Web address: www.clarabartonhospital.org
Control: Other not–for–profit (including NFP Corporation) **Service:** General
Medical and Surgical

Staffed Beds: 23 **Admissions:** 620 **Census:** 10 **Outpatient Visits:** 51387
Births: 0 **Total Expense ($000):** 20031 **Payroll Expense ($000):** 9617
Personnel: 186

HOLTON—Jackson County

★ **HOLTON COMMUNITY HOSPITAL (171319)**, 1110 Columbine Drive,
Zip 66436–8824; tel. 785/364–2116 **A**10 18 **F**3 7 11 13 15 18 28 29 34 40
43 45 50 59 62 63 64 65 74 75 76 77 79 81 82 87 93 97 107 114 119 127
128 130 131 132 133 135 146 147 148
Primary Contact: Carrie L. Saia, Chief Executive Officer
CFO: Bart Kenton, Chief Financial Officer
CMO: Joel Hutchsin, M.D., Chief Medical Staff
CIO: Holli Peters, Director Health Information Management
CHR: Gretchen Snavely, Director Human Resources
CNO: Mandy Bontrager, Director Nursing
Web address: www.holtonhospital.com
Control: Other not–for–profit (including NFP Corporation) **Service:** General
Medical and Surgical

Staffed Beds: 12 **Admissions:** 280 **Census:** 4 **Outpatient Visits:** 60351
Births: 42 **Total Expense ($000):** 13289 **Payroll Expense ($000):** 6606
Personnel: 139

HORTON—Brown County

HORTON COMMUNITY HOSPITAL (171320), 240 West 18th Street,
Zip 66439–1245; tel. 785/486–2642 **A**10 18 **F**7 15 28 29 40 45 46 64 81
107 114 119 127 128 133 **P**6 **S** Rural Community Hospitals of America, Kansas
City, MO
Primary Contact: James D. Noble, Chief Executive Officer
CFO: Sue Kidd, Chief Financial Officer
CMO: William Buck, Chief of Staff
CHR: Barbara McClain, Human Resources
CNO: Ty Compton, Chief Nursing Officer
Web address: www.horton–hospital.com
Control: Corporation, Investor–owned, for–profit **Service:** General Medical and
Surgical

Staffed Beds: 25 **Admissions:** 265 **Census:** 4 **Outpatient Visits:** 4816
Births: 0 **Total Expense ($000):** 6346 **Payroll Expense ($000):** 3265
Personnel: 58

HOXIE—Sheridan County

SHERIDAN COUNTY HEALTH COMPLEX (171347), 826 18th Street,
Zip 67740–0167, Mailing Address: P.O. Box 167, Zip 67740–0167;
tel. 785/675–3281, (Total facility includes 35 beds in nursing home–type unit)
A10 18 **F**3 10 11 29 30 34 35 40 45 50 53 56 57 59 66 67 68 69 75 81 85
86 87 93 107 115 127 130 133 135
Primary Contact: Niceta Farber, Chief Executive Officer
CFO: Michael O'Dell, Chief Financial Officer
CMO: Victor Nemechek, M.D., Chief of Staff and Chief Medical Officer
CHR: Shelby Moss, Human Resource Officer
CNO: Hannah Schoendaler, Chief Nursing Officer
Web address: www.sheridancountyhospital.com
Control: County–Government, nonfederal **Service:** General Medical and Surgical

Staffed Beds: 53 **Admissions:** 145 **Census:** 32 **Outpatient Visits:** 5922
Births: 0 **Total Expense ($000):** 8525 **Payroll Expense ($000):** 4234
Personnel: 110

HUGOTON—Stevens County

★ **STEVENS COUNTY HOSPITAL (171335)**, 1006 South Jackson Street,
Zip 67951–2858, Mailing Address: P.O. Box 10, Zip 67951–0010;
tel. 620/544–8511, (Total facility includes 83 beds in nursing home–type unit)
A10 18 **F**3 11 15 28 29 30 40 50 57 59 67 68 81 93 107 111 119 127 128
130 133 135 146
Primary Contact: Linda Stalcup, Chief Executive Officer
CMO: Samer Al–hashmi, M.D., Chief Medical Staff
Web address: www.stevenscountyhospital.com/
Control: County–Government, nonfederal **Service:** General Medical and Surgical

Staffed Beds: 100 **Admissions:** 212 **Census:** 69 **Outpatient Visits:** 22429
Births: 0 **Total Expense ($000):** 12186 **Payroll Expense ($000):** 4966
Personnel: 164

HUTCHINSON—Reno County

� △ **HUTCHINSON REGIONAL MEDICAL CENTER (170020)**, 1701 East 23rd
Avenue, Zip 67502–1191; tel. 620/665–2000, (Total facility includes 60 beds in
nursing home–type unit) **A**1 3 7 10 **F**3 7 11 13 18 20 22 24 26 28 29 30 31
34 35 40 43 47 48 49 50 51 53 57 60 64 68 70 74 76 77 78 79 81 82 83
85 87 88 89 90 93 98 102 103 106 107 108 111 114 115 119 120 121 123
125 126 128 129 130 143 146 148 **P**6
Primary Contact: Ken Johnson, President and Chief Executive Officer
CFO: Cassie Dolen, Vice President Finance and Chief Financial Officer
CMO: Thomas Smith, M.D., Vice President Medical Affairs
CIO: Calvin Wright, Chief Information Officer
CHR: Kevin Chiles, Vice President Human Resources
CNO: Julie R. Ward, MSN, Vice President Patient Care Services
Web address: www.hutchregional.com
Control: Other not–for–profit (including NFP Corporation) **Service:** General
Medical and Surgical

Staffed Beds: 258 **Admissions:** 6125 **Census:** 139 **Outpatient Visits:**
106280 **Births:** 554 **Total Expense ($000):** 113245 **Payroll Expense**
($000): 39290 **Personnel:** 938

SUMMIT SURGICAL (170198), 1818 East 23rd Avenue, Zip 67502–1106;
tel. 620/663–4800 **A**10 **F**3 29 45 50 64 79 81 82 85 **P**2
Primary Contact: Ann Hentzen Page, M.D., Chief Executive Officer
COO: Nancy Corwin, Chief Operating Officer
CMO: Ann Hentzen Page, M.D., Medical Director
CNO: Nancy Corwin, Chief Nursing Officer
Web address: www.summitks.com/index_surgical.htm
Control: Corporation, Investor–owned, for–profit **Service:** Surgical

Staffed Beds: 10 **Admissions:** 285 **Census:** 2 **Outpatient Visits:** 5581
Births: 0 **Total Expense ($000):** 8089 **Payroll Expense ($000):** 2394
Personnel: 31

IOLA—Allen County

✠ **ALLEN COUNTY REGIONAL HOSPITAL (171373)**, 3066 N. Kentucky Street,
Zip 66749, Mailing Address: P.O. Box 540, Zip 66749–0540; tel. 620/365–1000
A1 10 18 **F**3 13 15 29 30 31 34 35 40 56 57 59 62 63 64 65 68 75 76 77
78 81 82 84 85 86 87 89 93 103 104 107 110 114 119 127 129 130 132
133 146 147 148
Primary Contact: Marion A. Thompson, FACHE, Chief Executive Officer
CFO: Larry Peterson, Chief Financial Officer
CMO: Brian Wolfe, Chief of Staff
CHR: Paula Sell, Director Human Resources
CNO: Patty McGuffin, R.N., Chief Nursing Officer
Web address: www.allencountyhospital.com
Control: County–Government, nonfederal **Service:** General Medical and Surgical

Staffed Beds: 25 **Admissions:** 893 **Census:** 11 **Outpatient Visits:** 17286
Births: 76 **Total Expense ($000):** 22351 **Payroll Expense ($000):** 6478
Personnel: 158

JETMORE—Hodgeman County

★ **HODGEMAN COUNTY HEALTH CENTER (171369)**, 809 Bramley Street,
Zip 67854–9320, Mailing Address: P.O. Box 310, Zip 67854–0310;
tel. 620/357–8361, (Total facility includes 25 beds in nursing home–type unit)
A10 18 **F**3 40 53 67 81 107 114 125 127 130 133 143 **P**4
Primary Contact: Teresa L. Deuel, Chief Executive Officer
Web address: www.hchconline.org
Control: County–Government, nonfederal **Service:** General Medical and Surgical

Staffed Beds: 38 **Admissions:** 300 **Census:** 26 **Outpatient Visits:** 35862
Births: 0 **Total Expense ($000):** 7659 **Payroll Expense ($000):** 3389
Personnel: 81

Hospital, Medicare Provider Number, Address, Telephone, Approval, Facility, and Physician Codes, Health Care System

★ American Hospital Association (AHA) membership   ○ Healthcare Facilities Accreditation Program   ⇑ Center for Improvement in Healthcare Quality Accreditation
□ The Joint Commission accreditation   ◇ DNV Healthcare Inc. accreditation   △ Commission on Accreditation of Rehabilitation Facilities (CARF) accreditation

KS

JOHNSON—Stanton County

STANTON COUNTY HOSPITAL (171343), 404 North Chestnut Street,
Zip 67855–5001, Mailing Address: P.O. Box 779, Zip 67855–0779;
tel. 620/492–6250, (Total facility includes 25 beds in nursing home–type unit)
A10 18 **F**3 11 13 34 35 40 41 45 50 54 56 57 59 64 68 75 76 81 82 86 87
89 93 97 107 114 127 130 131 133 143 **P**6
Primary Contact: Jay Tusten, Chief Executive Officer
CFO: Robert Nahmensen, Chief Financial Officer and Chief Operations Officer
CMO: Bill Troup, M.D., Chief of Staff
CIO: Marco Medina, Chief Information Officer
CHR: Camille Davidson, Director Human Resources
CNO: Marianne Mills, R.N., Chairperson
Web address: www.stantoncountyhospital.com
Control: County–Government, nonfederal **Service:** General Medical and Surgical

Staffed Beds: 40 **Admissions:** 146 **Census:** 26 **Outpatient Visits:** 13802
Births: 22 **Total Expense ($000):** 9196 **Payroll Expense ($000):** 4477
Personnel: 97

JUNCTION CITY—Geary County

GEARY COMMUNITY HOSPITAL (170074), 1102 St. Mary's Road,
Zip 66441–4196, Mailing Address: P.O. Box 490, Zip 66441–0490;
tel. 785/238–4131 **A**1 10 **F**7 8 11 12 13 15 18 19 28 29 30 32 34 35 40 45
48 50 55 56 57 59 61 62 63 64 65 68 70 75 77 79 81 85 86 87 97 103
107 108 109 110 111 113 114 115 118 119 127 129 130 131 132 133 135
144 145 146 147 148 **P**6
Primary Contact: Joseph Stratton, FACHE, Chief Executive Officer
CFO: William Kloppe, Chief Financail Officer
CMO: Jimmy Jenkins, M.D., Chief Medical Officer
CIO: Kyle Ibarra, Director Information Systems
CHR: Loren Streit, Director Human Resources
CNO: Dawn M. Engel, Chief Nursing Officer
Web address: www.gchks.org
Control: County–Government, nonfederal **Service:** General Medical and Surgical

Staffed Beds: 49 **Admissions:** 1272 **Census:** 13 **Outpatient Visits:** 32555
Births: 388 **Total Expense ($000):** 44557 **Payroll Expense ($000):** 20556
Personnel: 332

IRWIN ARMY COMMUNITY HOSPITAL, 600 Caisson Hill Road,
Zip 66442–7037; tel. 785/239–7000, (Nonreporting) **A**1 2 3 5 **S** Department of
the Army, Office of the Surgeon General, Falls Church, VA
Primary Contact: Colonel Risa Ware, Commander
CMO: Lieutenant Colonel Mark S. Ochoa, M.D., Deputy Commander, Clinical
Services
CIO: David Dougherty, Chief Information Management Officer
CHR: Hope Brunton, Chief Manpower Branch
Web address: www.iach.amedd.army.mil
Control: Army, Government, federal **Service:** General Medical and Surgical

Staffed Beds: 44

KANSAS CITY—Wyandotte County

KVC PRAIRIE RIDGE PSYCHIATRIC HOSPITAL, 4300 Brenner Drive,
Zip 66104–1163; tel. 913/334–0294 **A**1 3 5 **F**32 38 50 98 99 106
Primary Contact: Jason R. Hooper, President and Chief Executive Officer
COO: Ryan Speier, Vice President Administration
CMO: Vishal Adma, M.D., Medical Director
Web address: www.kvc.org
Control: Other not–for–profit (including NFP Corporation) **Service:** Children's
hospital psychiatric

Staffed Beds: 100 **Admissions:** 2987 **Census:** 49 **Outpatient Visits:** 0
Births: 0 **Total Expense ($000):** 18866 **Payroll Expense ($000):** 8422
Personnel: 140

PROVIDENCE MEDICAL CENTER (170146), 8929 Parallel Parkway,
Zip 66112–1689; tel. 913/596–4000 **A**1 10 **F**3 13 15 17 18 20 22 24 28 29
30 31 34 35 40 41 44 45 49 50 53 56 57 59 64 70 74 75 76 77 78 79 81
82 84 85 87 89 93 97 102 103 107 108 110 111 114 119 120 121 123 124
126 129 130 131 132 135 143 146 147 148 **P**6 **S** Prime Healthcare Services,
Ontario, CA
Primary Contact: Randall G. Nyp, FACHE, Chief Executive Officer
CFO: David Dulny, Chief Financial Officer
CMO: Sabato Sisillo, M.D., Chief Medical Officer
CIO: Charles Soeken, Director Information Technology
CHR: Brenda Farwell, Director Human Resources
CNO: Karen Orr, Chief Nursing Officer
Web address: www.providencekc.com
Control: Individual, Investor–owned, for–profit **Service:** General Medical and
Surgical

Staffed Beds: 170 **Admissions:** 9358 **Census:** 103 **Outpatient Visits:**
206594 **Births:** 626 **Total Expense ($000):** 164699 **Payroll Expense**
($000): 62259 **Personnel:** 885

RAINBOW MENTAL HEALTH FACILITY (174010), 2205 West 36th Avenue,
Zip 66103–2107; tel. 913/755–7000, (Nonreporting) **A**5 10
Primary Contact: Jerry A. Rea, Ph.D., Interim Superintendent
CFO: Donna Dean, Chief Financial Officer
CMO: Maria Gustilo, M.D., Medical Director
CHR: Marilyn Williamson, Chief Human Resources Officer
Web address: www.srskansas.org/osh/osh-rmhf_main.html
Control: State–Government, nonfederal **Service:** Psychiatric

Staffed Beds: 36

SELECT SPECIALTY HOSPITAL–KANSAS CITY (172005), 1731 North 90th
Street, Zip 66112–1515; tel. 913/732–5900 **A**1 10 **F**1 3 18 29 82 85 91 107
130 148 **P**6 **S** Select Medical Corporation, Mechanicsburg, PA
Primary Contact: Larry Niemann, Chief Executive Officer
Web address: www.selectspecialtyhospitals.com
Control: Corporation, Investor–owned, for–profit **Service:** Long–Term Acute Care
hospital

Staffed Beds: 40 **Admissions:** 385 **Census:** 33 **Outpatient Visits:** 0 **Births:**
0 **Total Expense ($000):** 18689 **Payroll Expense ($000):** 7661 **Personnel:**
126

THE UNIVERSITY OF KANSAS HOSPITAL (170040), 3901 Rainbow Boulevard,
Zip 66160–7200; tel. 913/588–5000, (Includes THE UNIVERSITY OF KANSAS
HOSPITAL – INDIAN CREEK CAMPUS, 10720 Nall Avenue, Overland Park,
Zip 66211–1206; tel. 913/754–5000) **A**1 2 3 5 8 10 **F**3 8 11 12 13 15 16 17
18 20 22 23 24 25 26 27 28 29 30 31 34 35 36 37 38 39 40 41 43 44 45
46 47 48 49 50 54 55 56 57 58 59 60 61 63 64 65 68 70 72 74 75 76 77
78 79 80 81 82 83 84 85 86 87 88 89 90 92 93 96 97 98 99 100 101 102
103 104 107 108 110 111 114 115 116 117 118 119 120 121 123 124 126
129 130 131 132 135 136 138 139 141 142 144 145 146 147 148 **P**6
Primary Contact: Bob Page, Chief Executive Officer
COO: Tammy Peterman, R.N., Executive Vice President, Chief Operating Officer
and Chief Nursing Officer
CFO: Bill Marting, Senior Vice President and Chief Financial Officer
CMO: Lou Wetzel, M.D., Chief of Staff
CIO: Chris Hansen, Senior Vice President Ambulatory Services and Chief
Information Officer
CHR: Alisa Ford, Vice President Human Resources
CNO: Tammy Peterman, R.N., Executive Vice President, Chief Operating Officer
and Chief Nursing Officer
Web address: www.kumed.com
Control: Hospital district or authority, Government, nonfederal **Service:** General
Medical and Surgical

Staffed Beds: 773 **Admissions:** 32147 **Census:** 512 **Outpatient Visits:**
737453 **Births:** 1770 **Total Expense ($000):** 1350381 **Payroll Expense**
($000): 433609 **Personnel:** 6168

KINGMAN—Kingman County

KINGMAN COMMUNITY HOSPITAL (171378), 750 Avenue D. West,
Zip 67068–0376; tel. 620/532–3147 **A**10 18 **F**3 11 15 17 18 28 29 31 34 35
40 54 56 57 59 62 64 67 69 70 75 77 78 81 86 87 89 90 93 97 107 114
119 128 130 132 133 145 146 148 **P**6
Primary Contact: James E. Wahlmeier, Administrator and Chief Executive Officer
CFO: Kent Hudson, Chief Financial Officer
CIO: Jay Gehring, Director Information Systems
CHR: Nancy Stucky, Director Human Resources and Public Relations
CNO: Nita McFarland, Director of Nursing
Web address: www.kchks.com
Control: Other not–for–profit (including NFP Corporation) **Service:** General
Medical and Surgical

Staffed Beds: 25 **Admissions:** 568 **Census:** 8 **Outpatient Visits:** 23360
Births: 0 **Total Expense ($000):** 10317 **Payroll Expense ($000):** 5300
Personnel: 119

KINSLEY—Edwards County

EDWARDS COUNTY HOSPITAL AND HEALTHCARE CENTER (171317), 620
West Eighth Street, Zip 67547–2329, Mailing Address: P.O. Box 99,
Zip 67547–0099; tel. 620/659–3621 **A**10 18 **F**3 7 11 15 18 19 28 29 30 34
35 40 53 56 57 59 64 65 68 75 77 79 93 97 98 103 107 114 119 127 130
133 146 148
Primary Contact: Jimmie W. Hansel, Ph.D., Chief Executive Officer
CHR: Tammy K. Lampe, Director Human Resources
Web address: www.edwardscohospital.com
Control: County–Government, nonfederal **Service:** General Medical and Surgical

Staffed Beds: 22 **Admissions:** 374 **Census:** 12 **Outpatient Visits:** 8390
Births: 0 **Total Expense ($000):** 8257 **Payroll Expense ($000):** 3201
Personnel: 65

KS

Many Facility Codes have changed. Please refer to the AHA Guide Code Chart.

KIOWA—Barber County

★ **KIOWA DISTRICT HOSPITAL AND MANOR (171331)**, 810 Drumm Street,
Zip 67070–1626, Mailing Address: P.O. Box 184, Zip 67070–0184;
tel. 620/825–4131, (Total facility includes 29 beds in nursing home–type unit)
A10 18 **F**1 2 3 4 12 16 17 34 40 41 45 56 57 59 64 65 67 70 72 73 80 81
84 85 88 89 90 91 92 93 97 98 107 114 119 127 128 133 148 **P**6
Primary Contact: Margaret Grisner, Chief Executive Officer
CFO: Robin Lewis, Chief Financial Officer
CMO: Paul Wilhelm, M.D., Chief of Staff
CHR: Tara Girty, Director Human Resources
Control: Hospital district or authority, Government, nonfederal **Service:** General
Medical and Surgical

Staffed Beds: 39 Admissions: 180 Census: 20 Outpatient Visits: 6488
Births: 0 Total Expense ($000): 7074 **Payroll Expense ($000):** 3523
Personnel: 65

LA CROSSE—Rush County

★ **RUSH COUNTY MEMORIAL HOSPITAL (171342)**, 801 Locust Street,
Zip 67548–9673, Mailing Address: P.O. Box 520, Zip 67548–0520;
tel. 785/222–2545, **A**10 18 **F**3 40 45 50 53 59 64 77 81 93 97 107 111 114 119 127 133 **P**6
Primary Contact: Brenda Legleiter, R.N., Chief Executive Officer
CFO: Jane Oborny, Chief Financial Officer
CMO: Harley Calvin, D.O., Chief Medical Officer
CHR: Charlene Goodman, Director Human Resources
Web address: www.rushcountymemorialhospital.com
Control: County–Government, nonfederal **Service:** General Medical and Surgical

Staffed Beds: 36 Admissions: 162 Census: 22 Outpatient Visits: 6924
Births: 0 Total Expense ($000): 5888 **Payroll Expense ($000):** 2487
Personnel: 76

LAKIN—Kearny County

★ **KEARNY COUNTY HOSPITAL (171313)**, 500 Thorpe Street, Zip 67860–9625;
tel. 620/355–7111, (Total facility includes 75 beds in nursing home–type unit)
A10 18 **F**2 3 6 10 13 15 28 29 34 35 40 45 50 56 58 59 62 64 67 68 69 75
79 81 85 86 93 97 107 119 125 127 128 131 132 133 143 **P**6
Primary Contact: Benjamin Anderson, Chief Executive Officer and Administrator
COO: Shari Campbell, Chief Operating Officer
CFO: Kelly Ann Speckman, Chief Financial Officer
CMO: Arlo Reimer, M.D., Chief of Staff
CIO: Lisa Kay–Garcia, Chief Information Officer
CHR: Laci Williams, Director Human Resources
CNO: Susan D. Stingley, Chief Nursing Officer
Web address: www.kearnycountyhospital.com
Control: County–Government, nonfederal **Service:** General Medical and Surgical

Staffed Beds: 100 Admissions: 517 Census: 69 Outpatient Visits: 36263
Births: 197 Total Expense ($000): 20465 **Payroll Expense ($000):** 10623
Personnel: 235

LARNED—Pawnee County

☐ **LARNED STATE HOSPITAL (174006)**, 1301 Kansas Highway 264, Zip 67550;
tel. 620/285–2131 **A**1 10 **F**3 30 50 53 57 68 75 77 86 87 97 98 100 101
102 103 106 130 132 135 143 146
Primary Contact: Thomas Kinlen, Superintendent
COO: Steve Spain, Chief Operating Officer
CMO: Sayed Jehan, M.D., Interim Medical Director
CIO: Sid Smith, Director Information Resources
CHR: Kerri Barnard, Director Human Resources
CNO: Holly Hertel, Director Nursing
Web address: www.larnedstatehospital.org
Control: State–Government, nonfederal **Service:** Psychiatric

Staffed Beds: 612 Admissions: 685 Census: 321 Outpatient Visits: 0
Births: 0 Total Expense ($000): 59310 **Payroll Expense ($000):** 31428
Personnel: 685

★ **PAWNEE VALLEY COMMUNITY HOSPITAL (171345)**, 923 Carroll Avenue,
Zip 67550–2429; tel. 620/285–3161 **A**10 18 **F**3 11 28 29 30 34 40 43 45 46
57 68 77 81 82 84 85 86 87 91 93 94 102 104 107 111 115 119 127 129
130 131 132 133 135 147 148
Primary Contact: Eric Lybarger, Administrator
COO: Bryce A. Young, Chief Operating Officer
CFO: George Harms, Chief Financial Officer
CMO: David Sanger, M.D., Chief Medical Officer
CHR: Bruce Whittington, Vice President Human Resources
CNO: Paul Henry Carrington, Chief Nursing Officer
Web address: www.pawneevalleyhospital.com
Control: County–Government, nonfederal **Service:** General Medical and Surgical

Staffed Beds: 25 Admissions: 290 Census: 6 Outpatient Visits: 13440
Births: 0 Total Expense ($000): 12358 **Payroll Expense ($000):** 6449
Personnel: 116

LAWRENCE—Douglas County

✚ **LAWRENCE MEMORIAL HOSPITAL (170137)**, 325 Maine Street,
Zip 66044–1360; tel. 785/505–5000, (Total facility includes 14 beds in nursing
home–type unit) **A**1 3 5 10 20 **F**3 11 13 15 18 19 20 22 26 28 29 30 31 34
35 38 39 40 43 44 45 49 50 51 54 55 56 57 59 61 64 65 69 70 73 74 75
76 77 78 79 81 82 84 85 86 87 89 90 93 94 96 97 100 102 107 110 111
114 115 118 119 120 124 126 128 129 130 131 132 135 146 147 148
P6 8
Primary Contact: Russell W. Johnson, President and Chief Executive Officer
COO: Karen J. Shumate, R.N., Chief Operating Officer
CFO: Joe Pedley, CPA, Vice President and Chief Financial Officer
CIO: Michael Williams, Chief Information Officer
CHR: Carolyn Bowmer
CNO: Sarah Bradshaw, Vice President Nursing
Web address: www.lmh.org
Control: City–Government, nonfederal **Service:** General Medical and Surgical

Staffed Beds: 145 Admissions: 6691 Census: 61 Outpatient Visits: 168757
Births: 1210 Total Expense ($000): 191434 **Payroll Expense ($000):**
80169 **Personnel:** 1266

LEAVENWORTH—Leavenworth County

✚ **SAINT JOHN HOSPITAL (170009)**, 3500 South Fourth Street,
Zip 66048–5043; tel. 913/680–6000 **A**1 10 **F**3 8 15 18 29 30 34 40 44 45
46 50 54 56 57 59 64 68 70 74 75 77 83 98 100 103 107 115
119 130 133 146 147 148 **P**6 **S** Prime Healthcare Services, Ontario, CA
Primary Contact: Randall G. Nyp, FACHE, President and Chief Executive Officer
CFO: David Dulny, Chief Financial Officer
CMO: Sabato Sisillo, M.D., Chief Medical Officer
CIO: Charles Soeken, Director Information Technology
CHR: Brenda Farwell, Director Human Resources
CNO: Jodi Fincher, Vice President Patient Care Services
Web address: www.providence–health.org/sjh
Control: Individual, Investor–owned, for–profit **Service:** General Medical and
Surgical

Staffed Beds: 40 Admissions: 1428 Census: 21 Outpatient Visits: 58204
Births: 0 Total Expense ($000): 30582 **Payroll Expense ($000):** 12058
Personnel: 182

✚ **SAINT LUKE'S CUSHING HOSPITAL (170133)**, 711 Marshall Street,
Zip 66048–3235; tel. 913/684–1100 **A**1 10 **F**3 11 13 15 28 29 31 34 35 40
44 45 50 57 59 64 65 70 74 75 76 77 79 81 82 84 85 86 87 93 94 100
102 107 108 110 111 114 119 129 130 132 135 146 148 **S** Saint Luke's
Health System, Kansas City, MO
Primary Contact: Adele Ducharme, R.N., MSN, Chief Executive Officer
CFO: Julie Murphy, Chief Financial Officer
CMO: Nicholas Brockert, President
CHR: Donna Kunz, Director Human Resources
CNO: Karin Sundblom, MSN, Chief Nursing Officer
Web address: www.saintlukeshealthsystem.org/locations/saint–lukes–cushing–
hospital
Control: Other not–for–profit (including NFP Corporation) **Service:** General
Medical and Surgical

Staffed Beds: 25 Admissions: 861 Census: 7 Outpatient Visits: 33133
Births: 217 Total Expense ($000): 31830 **Payroll Expense ($000):** 10733
Personnel: 191

**VETERANS AFFAIRS EASTERN KANSAS HEALTH CARE SYSTEM–DWIGHT D.
EISENHOWER VETERANS AFFAIRS MEDICAL CENTER** See Veterans Affairs
Eastern Kansas Health Care System, Topeka

LEAWOOD—Johnson County

☐ **DOCTOR'S HOSPITAL (170194)**, 4901 College Boulevard, Zip 66211–1602;
tel. 913/529–1801 **A**1 10 **F**39 79 81 82 111 **P**5
Primary Contact: Phil Harness, Chief Executive Officer
Web address: www.dshospital.net
Control: Partnership, Investor–owned, for–profit **Service:** General Medical and
Surgical

Staffed Beds: 9 Admissions: 183 Census: 1 Outpatient Visits: 10814
Births: 0 Total Expense ($000): 17988 **Payroll Expense ($000):** 2616
Personnel: 44

KANSAS CITY ORTHOPAEDIC INSTITUTE (170188), 3651 College Boulevard,
Zip 66211–1910; tel. 913/338–4100 **A**3 5 10 **F**29 77 79 81 82 93 111
Primary Contact: Charles E. Rhoades, M.D., Chief Executive Officer
CIO: Jim Leveling, Director Information Technology
CHR: Laura Sinclair, Director Human Resources
Web address: www.kcoi.com
Control: Partnership, Investor–owned, for–profit **Service:** Orthopedic

Staffed Beds: 9 Admissions: 780 Census: 5 Outpatient Visits: 30986
Births: 0 Personnel: 102

Hospital, Medicare Provider Number, Address, Telephone, Approval, Facility, and Physician Codes, Health Care System

★ American Hospital Association (AHA) membership   ○ Healthcare Facilities Accreditation Program   ⇑ Center for Improvement in Healthcare Quality Accreditation
☐ The Joint Commission accreditation   ◇ DNV Healthcare Inc. accreditation   △ Commission on Accreditation of Rehabilitation Facilities (CARF) accreditation

KS

LENEXA—Johnson County

☐ **MINIMALLY INVASIVE SURGERY HOSPITAL (170199)**, 11217 Lakeview Avenue, Zip 66219–1399; tel. 913/322–7401 **A**1 10 **F**3 18 26 31 45 64 68 70 78 81 82 85 86 107 111 115 119 129 **P**6
Primary Contact: Parajeet Sabharrwal, Chief Executive Officer
Web address: www.mishhospital.com
Control: State–Government, nonfederal **Service:** Surgical

Staffed Beds: 9 **Admissions:** 101 **Census:** 1 **Outpatient Visits:** 3153 **Births:** 0 **Personnel:** 24

LEOTI—Wichita County

★ **WICHITA COUNTY HEALTH CENTER (171306)**, 211 East Earl Street, Zip 67861–9620; tel. 620/375–2233, (Total facility includes 15 beds in nursing home–type unit) **A**10 18 **F**2 3 11 29 34 35 40 41 45 50 56 57 59 64 69 75 77 86 87 93 97 102 107 119 127 130 133 135 146 148 **P**6
Primary Contact: Teresa Clark, Chief Executive Officer and Administrator
CFO: Janice Campas, Chief Financial Officer
CMO: Jeffrey Alpert, M.D., Medical Director
CHR: Patti Whalen, Manager Human Resources
Web address: www.wichitacountyhealthcenter.com
Control: County–Government, nonfederal **Service:** General Medical and Surgical

Staffed Beds: 40 **Admissions:** 140 **Census:** 27 **Outpatient Visits:** 5993 **Births:** 0 **Total Expense ($000):** 7685 **Payroll Expense ($000):** 3406 **Personnel:** 78

LIBERAL—Seward County

☐ **SOUTHWEST MEDICAL CENTER (170068)**, 315 West 15th Street, Zip 67901–2455, Mailing Address: Box 1340, Zip 67905–1340; tel. 620/624–1651, (Total facility includes 18 beds in nursing home–type unit) **A**1 10 **F**1 3 4 11 13 15 16 17 28 29 31 34 40 45 48 49 57 59 67 68 70 72 73 75 76 77 79 80 81 85 87 88 89 90 93 96 98 103 104 107 108 110 111 114 118 119 128 129 130 131 145 148
Primary Contact: William Ermann, President and Chief Executive Officer
COO: Robert Whitaker, Vice President of Operations
CFO: Amber Williams, Vice President and Chief Financial Officer
CHR: Lisa L. Mathes, Human Resources Director
CNO: Jo L. Harrison, Vice President of Patient Care Services
Web address: www.swmedcenter.com
Control: County–Government, nonfederal **Service:** General Medical and Surgical

Staffed Beds: 101 **Admissions:** 2009 **Census:** 17 **Outpatient Visits:** 47456 **Births:** 769 **Total Expense ($000):** 44425 **Payroll Expense ($000):** 19074 **Personnel:** 379

LINCOLN—Lincoln County

LINCOLN COUNTY HOSPITAL (171360), 624 North Second Street, Zip 67455–1738, Mailing Address: P.O. Box 406, Zip 67455–0406; tel. 785/524–4403 **A**10 18 **F**3 11 15 34 40 57 69 107 110 111 112 114 119 127 129 133 **P**6
Primary Contact: Steven L. Granzow, Chief Executive Officer
CFO: Tawnya Seitz, Chief Financial Officer
CNO: Christa Haesemeyer, Chief Nursing Officer
Web address: www.lincolncountyhospital.net
Control: County–Government, nonfederal **Service:** General Medical and Surgical

Staffed Beds: 14 **Admissions:** 129 **Census:** 1 **Outpatient Visits:** 5574 **Births:** 0 **Total Expense ($000):** 7757 **Payroll Expense ($000):** 2966 **Personnel:** 71

LINDSBORG—Mcpherson County

★ **LINDSBORG COMMUNITY HOSPITAL (171358)**, 605 West Lincoln Street, Zip 67456–2328; tel. 785/227–3308 **A**10 18 **F**3 28 29 40 53 57 59 62 64 65 67 81 93 97 107 115 119 128 130 133 144 **P**6 **S** Salina Regional Health Center, Salina, KS
Primary Contact: Larry VanDerWege, Administrator
CFO: Laraine Gengler, Chief Financial Officer
CIO: Jeremy Snapp, Director Information Systems
CHR: Brad Malm, Director Human Resources and Education
CNO: Beth Hedberg, R.N., Director Nursing
Web address: www.lindsborghospital.org
Control: Other not–for–profit (including NFP Corporation) **Service:** General Medical and Surgical

Staffed Beds: 21 **Admissions:** 351 **Census:** 6 **Outpatient Visits:** 22514 **Births:** 0 **Total Expense ($000):** 8696 **Payroll Expense ($000):** 4612 **Personnel:** 93

LYONS—Rice County

★ **HOSPITAL DISTRICT NO 1 OF RICE COUNTY (171330)**, 619 South Clark Street, Zip 67554–3003, Mailing Address: P.O. Box 828, Zip 67554–0828; tel. 620/257–5173 **A**10 18 **F**1 3 4 10 13 16 17 29 30 34 35 40 43 45 57 67 70 72 73 75 76 77 80 81 88 89 90 93 98 107 125 127 128 130 132 133 143
Primary Contact: George M. Stover, Chief Executive Officer
CFO: Terry Pound, Chief Financial Officer
CMO: Kristina Darnauer, M.D., Chief of Staff
CNO: Judy Hogdson, R.N., Chief Nursing Officer
Web address: www.ricecountyhospital.com
Control: Hospital district or authority, Government, nonfederal **Service:** General Medical and Surgical

Staffed Beds: 25 **Admissions:** 307 **Census:** 15 **Outpatient Visits:** 11895 **Births:** 83 **Total Expense ($000):** 14090 **Payroll Expense ($000):** 6794 **Personnel:** 127

MANHATTAN—Riley County

MANHATTAN SURGICAL (170190), 1829 College Avenue, Zip 66502–3381; tel. 785/776–5100 **A**10 **F**29 45 48 51 68 79 81 82 130
Primary Contact: Scott Chapman, Administrator
Web address: www.manhattansurgical.com
Control: Partnership, Investor–owned, for–profit **Service:** Surgical

Staffed Beds: 13 **Admissions:** 478 **Census:** 2 **Outpatient Visits:** 9952 **Births:** 0 **Personnel:** 79

★ ○ **VIA CHRISTI HOSPITAL MANHATTAN, INC. (170142)**, 1823 College Avenue, Zip 66502–3346; tel. 785/776–3322 **A**10 11 19 **F**7 11 12 13 15 18 20 22 28 29 30 31 34 35 37 40 41 44 45 49 50 51 60 67 70 73 77 79 81 82 83 84 85 86 87 90 93 95 96 102 104 107 108 109 110 111 115 119 126 129 130 132 133 145 146 147 148 **S** Ascension Health, Saint Louis, MO
Primary Contact: Robert C. Copple, FACHE, Senior Administrator
CFO: James Fraser, Administrator Finance
CIO: Andy Gagnon, Manager Information Technology
CHR: Renee Reed, Director Human Resources
CNO: Jennifer Goehring, R.N., Assistant Chief Nursing Officer
Web address: www.https://www.viachristi.org/manhattan
Control: Other not–for–profit (including NFP Corporation) **Service:** General Medical and Surgical

Staffed Beds: 96 **Admissions:** 4652 **Census:** 43 **Outpatient Visits:** 93435 **Births:** 1112 **Total Expense ($000):** 83353 **Payroll Expense ($000):** 31940 **Personnel:** 450

MANKATO—Jewell County

JEWELL COUNTY HOSPITAL (171309), 100 Crestvue Avenue, Zip 66956–2407, Mailing Address: P.O. Box 327, Zip 66956–0327; tel. 785/378–3137 **A**10 18 **F**2 3 29 40 50 64 75 77 87 93 107 127 128 130 133 148 **P**6
Primary Contact: Doyle L. McKimmy, FACHE, Chief Executive Officer
COO: Eric Borden, Chief Operating Officer and Chief Financial Officer
CFO: Eric Borden, Chief Operating Officer and Chief Financial Officer
Web address: www.jewellcountyhospital.com
Control: County–Government, nonfederal **Service:** General Medical and Surgical

Staffed Beds: 25 **Admissions:** 57 **Census:** 20 **Outpatient Visits:** 18624 **Births:** 0 **Total Expense ($000):** 4471 **Payroll Expense ($000):** 2172 **Personnel:** 61

MARION—Marion County

ST. LUKE HOSPITAL AND LIVING CENTER (171356), 535 South Freeborn, Zip 66861–1256; tel. 620/382–2177, (Total facility includes 32 beds in nursing home–type unit) **A**10 18 **F**3 11 15 28 29 34 40 43 45 56 57 59 62 64 67 68 75 77 81 85 97 102 107 108 110 114 119 127 128 133 135 143 146 147 148 **P**6
Primary Contact: Jeremy Ensey, Chief Executive Officer
CFO: Bev Reid, Chief Financial Officer
CMO: Don Hodson, M.D., Chief Medical Officer
CIO: Jeff Methvin, Manager Information Technology
CHR: Sharon Zogelman, Director Human Resources
Web address: www.slhmarion.org
Control: Hospital district or authority, Government, nonfederal **Service:** General Medical and Surgical

Staffed Beds: 37 **Admissions:** 160 **Census:** 32 **Outpatient Visits:** 31291 **Births:** 0 **Total Expense ($000):** 9897 **Payroll Expense ($000):** 4616 **Personnel:** 119

KS

Many Facility Codes have changed. Please refer to the AHA Guide Code Chart. © 2016 AHA Guide

MARYSVILLE—Marshall County

★ **COMMUNITY MEMORIAL HEALTHCARE (171363)**, 708 North 18th Street, Zip 66508–1338; tel. 785/562–2311 **A**10 18 **F**3 13 15 28 29 30 31 34 35 40 43 45 47 50 57 59 62 64 68 69 75 76 77 78 79 81 85 87 93 94 97 107 108 114 119 127 128 129 130 131 132 133 135 146 147 148 **P**6
Primary Contact: Curtis R. Hawkinson, Chief Executive Officer
CFO: Therese Landoll, Interim Chief Financial Officer
CMO: John Haefele, M.D., Chief Medical Officer
CIO: Colleen Behrens, Director Information Technology
CHR: Jessie Schneider, Director Human Resources
CNO: Diane Luebcke, R.N., Director Nursing
Web address: www.cmhcare.org
Control: Other not–for–profit (including NFP Corporation) **Service:** General Medical and Surgical

Staffed Beds: 25 **Admissions:** 782 **Census:** 11 **Outpatient Visits:** 24787 **Births:** 88 **Total Expense ($000):** 21009 **Payroll Expense ($000):** 9372 **Personnel:** 198

MCPHERSON—McPherson County

★ **MCPHERSON HOSPITAL (170105)**, 1000 Hospital Drive, Zip 67460–2326; tel. 620/241–2250 **A**10 **F**3 7 11 13 15 28 34 35 40 45 50 53 57 59 64 65 70 75 76 77 79 81 82 85 97 107 108 110 114 119 130 133 144 146 **P**6
Primary Contact: Robert Monical, President and Chief Executive Officer
COO: Terri Gehring, Vice President Operations
CFO: George Halama, Vice President Finance
CHR: Cathy Dunham, Vice President Human Resources
CNO: Beth Worden, Director Nursing Services
Web address: www.mcphersonhospital.org
Control: Other not–for–profit (including NFP Corporation) **Service:** General Medical and Surgical

Staffed Beds: 33 **Admissions:** 1031 **Census:** 10 **Outpatient Visits:** 53303 **Births:** 124 **Total Expense ($000):** 26825 **Payroll Expense ($000):** 12214 **Personnel:** 278

MEMORIAL HOSPITAL See McPherson Hospital

MEADE—Meade County

★ **MEADE DISTRICT HOSPITAL (171321)**, 510 East Carthage Street, Zip 67864–6401, Mailing Address: P.O. Box 820, Zip 67864–0820; tel. 620/873–2141, (Total facility includes 45 beds in nursing home–type unit) **A**10 18 **F**3 15 28 29 34 35 40 45 53 56 57 59 62 64 79 81 82 85 87 93 107 108 114 119 127 128 130 131 133 143 148 **P**6
Primary Contact: Steve Stewart, Administrator
CIO: Matt Bobo, Chief Information Officer
Web address: www.meadehospital.com
Control: Hospital district or authority, Government, nonfederal **Service:** General Medical and Surgical

Staffed Beds: 65 **Admissions:** 277 **Census:** 44 **Outpatient Visits:** 16264 **Births:** 0 **Total Expense ($000):** 14192 **Payroll Expense ($000):** 7172 **Personnel:** 189

MEDICINE LODGE—Barber County

★ **MEDICINE LODGE MEMORIAL HOSPITAL (171334)**, 710 North Walnut Street, Zip 67104–1019; tel. 620/886–3771 **A**10 18 **F**3 7 11 40 44 45 56 64 81 93 107 119 127 128 133 148 **P**6 **S** Great Plains Health Alliance, Inc., Wichita, KS
Primary Contact: Kevin A. White, Administrator
CFO: Thomas G. Lee, Chief Financial Officer
CHR: Johnnie Davis, Director Human Resources
CNO: Kathryn I. Burns, R.N., Director of Nursing
Web address: www.mlmh.net/
Control: Hospital district or authority, Government, nonfederal **Service:** General Medical and Surgical

Staffed Beds: 25 **Admissions:** 254 **Census:** 12 **Outpatient Visits:** 22784 **Births:** 0 **Total Expense ($000):** 10359 **Payroll Expense ($000):** 4447 **Personnel:** 88

MINNEAPOLIS—Ottawa County

★ **OTTAWA COUNTY HEALTH CENTER (171328)**, 215 East Eighth, Zip 67467–1902, Mailing Address: P.O. Box 290, Zip 67467–0290; tel. 785/392–2122, (Total facility includes 17 beds in nursing home–type unit) **A**10 18 **F**10 28 35 40 53 56 62 64 67 85 86 93 128 130 133 143 **S** Great Plains Health Alliance, Inc., Wichita, KS
Primary Contact: Jody Parks, Administrator
CFO: Cheryl Lanoue, Chief Financial Officer
CIO: Linda Wright, Director Information
CNO: Marlene Gawith, Director of Nursing
Web address: www.ottawacountyhealthcenter.com
Control: Other not–for–profit (including NFP Corporation) **Service:** General Medical and Surgical

Staffed Beds: 42 **Admissions:** 205 **Census:** 23 **Outpatient Visits:** 6135 **Births:** 0 **Total Expense ($000):** 5590 **Payroll Expense ($000):** 2688 **Personnel:** 74

MINNEOLA—Ford County

★ **MINNEOLA DISTRICT HOSPITAL (171368)**, 212 Main Street, Zip 67865–8511, Mailing Address: P.O. Box 127, Zip 67865–0127; tel. 620/885–4264, (Total facility includes 36 beds in nursing home–type unit) **A**10 18 **F**13 29 40 45 46 56 57 64 65 67 81 83 93 102 107 127 128 130 133 148 **P**6 **S** Great Plains Health Alliance, Inc., Wichita, KS
Primary Contact: Deborah Bruner, Chief Executive Officer and Administrator
CFO: Marion Zirger, Chief Financial Officer
CMO: Tony Luna, M.D., Chief of Staff
CHR: Vena Harris, Director Human Resources
CNO: Amanda Stout, Chief Nursing Officer
Web address: www.minneolahealthcare.com
Control: Hospital district or authority, Government, nonfederal **Service:** General Medical and Surgical

Staffed Beds: 54 **Admissions:** 346 **Census:** 37 **Outpatient Visits:** 25739 **Births:** 0 **Total Expense ($000):** 10754 **Payroll Expense ($000):** 5609 **Personnel:** 117

MOUNDRIDGE—Mcpherson County

★ **MERCY HOSPITAL (170075)**, 218 East Pack Street, Zip 67107–8815, Mailing Address: P.O. Box 180, Zip 67107–0180; tel. 620/345–6391 **A**10 **F**4 13 16 17 29 30 40 45 67 70 72 73 76 80 81 88 89 90 93 98 128 130 133
Primary Contact: Doyle K. Johnson, Administrator
CFO: Royce Holdeman, Chief Financial Officer
Web address: www.mercyh.org/
Control: Church–operated, Nongovernment, not–for profit **Service:** General Medical and Surgical

Staffed Beds: 18 **Admissions:** 222 **Census:** 4 **Outpatient Visits:** 8429 **Births:** 38 **Total Expense ($000):** 3289 **Payroll Expense ($000):** 1597 **Personnel:** 35

NEODESHA—Wilson County

★ **WILSON MEDICAL CENTER (171344)**, 2600 Ottawa Road, Zip 66757–1897, Mailing Address: P.O. Box 360, Zip 66757–0360; tel. 620/325–2611 **A**10 18 **F**3 11 15 29 34 35 40 45 53 57 59 64 81 82 85 86 89 93 107 108 110 114 119 127 128 130 132 133 148 **S** QHR, Brentwood, TN
Primary Contact: Dennis R. Shelby, Chief Executive Officer
CFO: John Gutschenritter, Chief Financial Officer
CIO: Kevin Myers, Director Information Technology
CHR: Laura Dean, Director Human Resources
CNO: Temple Monroe, Director Nursing Operations
Web address: www.wilsonmedical.org
Control: County–Government, nonfederal **Service:** General Medical and Surgical

Staffed Beds: 15 **Admissions:** 272 **Census:** 7 **Outpatient Visits:** 19156 **Births:** 0 **Total Expense ($000):** 13389 **Payroll Expense ($000):** 5391 **Personnel:** 130

NESS CITY—Ness County

★ **NESS COUNTY HOSPITAL DISTRICT NO 2 (171336)**, 312 Custer Street, Zip 67560–1654; tel. 785/798–2291, (Total facility includes 43 beds in nursing home–type unit) **A**10 18 **F**3 7 15 40 45 59 62 67 93 111 114 119 125 127 133
Primary Contact: Curt Thomas, Administrator
CFO: Debra Frank, Chief Financial Officer
CMO: Mikhail Imseis, M.D., Chief of Staff
CIO: Vicki Howe, Health Information Management
CHR: Shelly McDonald, Chief Human Resources Officer
CNO: Cindy Maier, R.N., Director of Nursing
Web address: www.nchospital.org
Control: Hospital district or authority, Government, nonfederal **Service:** General Medical and Surgical

Staffed Beds: 63 **Admissions:** 149 **Census:** 43 **Outpatient Visits:** 10123 **Births:** 0 **Total Expense ($000):** 8846 **Payroll Expense ($000):** 3906 **Personnel:** 102

NEWTON—Harvey County

★ ○ **NEWTON MEDICAL CENTER (170103)**, 600 Medical Center Drive, Zip 67114–8780, Mailing Address: P.O. Box 308, Zip 67114–0308; tel. 316/283–2700 **A**10 11 **F**3 11 13 15 20 22 28 29 30 31 34 40 45 49 51 59 64 68 70 73 74 75 76 79 81 85 86 90 103 107 108 110 111 115 119 126 130 131 132 133 146 147 148 **P**6
Primary Contact: Vallerie L. Gleason, Chief Executive Officer
COO: Todd Tangeman, Chief Operating Officer
CFO: Todd Kasitz, Vice President Finance
CIO: Mike Cottle, Chief Information Officer
CHR: Angela L. Anderson, Director Human Resources
CNO: Cindy Knoeppel, Chief Nursing Officer
Web address: www.newtonmedicalcenter.com
Control: Other not–for–profit (including NFP Corporation) **Service:** General Medical and Surgical

Staffed Beds: 103 **Admissions:** 2833 **Census:** 40 **Outpatient Visits:** 56022 **Births:** 527 **Total Expense ($000):** 68416 **Payroll Expense ($000):** 33360 **Personnel:** 641

☐ **PRAIRIE VIEW (174016)**, 1901 East First Street, Zip 67114–5010, Mailing Address: P.O. Box 467, Zip 67114–0467; tel. 316/284–6400, (Nonreporting) **A**1 10
Primary Contact: Jessie Kaye, Chief Executive Officer
CFO: Lisa Ramsey, Chief Financial Officer
CMO: Gary Fast, M.D., Medical Director
CIO: Chad Roth, Director Information Services
CHR: Joy Robb, Vice President Human Resources
CNO: Patrick Flaming, R.N., Director Inpatient Operations
Web address: www.prairieview.org
Control: Other not–for–profit (including NFP Corporation) **Service:** Psychiatric

Staffed Beds: 38

NORTON—Norton County

★ **NORTON COUNTY HOSPITAL (171348)**, 102 East Holme, Zip 67654–1406, Mailing Address: P.O. Box 250, Zip 67654–0250; tel. 785/877–3351 **A**10 18 **F**3 13 15 28 29 30 31 34 35 40 45 50 59 64 65 67 69 76 77 78 79 81 86 87 93 97 107 110 119 127 128 129 130 131 133 146 148 **P**6
Primary Contact: Ryan Stover, Chief Executive Officer
CHR: Shannan Hempler, Director Human Resources
Web address: www.ntcohosp.com
Control: County–Government, nonfederal **Service:** General Medical and Surgical

Staffed Beds: 25 **Admissions:** 376 **Census:** 6 **Outpatient Visits:** 61331 **Births:** 49 **Total Expense ($000):** 12372 **Payroll Expense ($000):** 6211 **Personnel:** 126

OAKLEY—Logan County

LOGAN COUNTY HOSPITAL (171326), 211 Cherry Street, Zip 67748–1201; tel. 785/672–3211, (Total facility includes 42 beds in nursing home–type unit) **A**10 18 **F**3 26 27 28 40 45 50 53 64 67 69 81 93 107 127 130 133 143 148 **P**6
Primary Contact: Meldon L. Snow, Chief Executive Officer
COO: Aimee Zimmerman, R.N., Chief Operations Officer
CFO: Bonnie Hagel, Chief Financial Officer
CMO: Celeste Rains, D.O., Chief of Staff
CIO: Russ Kahle, Chief Information Officer
CHR: Steve Allison, Director Human Resources
CNO: Marcia Kruse, R.N., Director Nursing
Web address: www.logancountyhospital.org
Control: County–Government, nonfederal **Service:** General Medical and Surgical

Staffed Beds: 59 **Admissions:** 280 **Census:** 37 **Outpatient Visits:** 9166 **Births:** 0 **Total Expense ($000):** 10431 **Payroll Expense ($000):** 5068 **Personnel:** 152

OBERLIN—Decatur County

DECATUR HEALTH SYSTEMS (171352), 810 West Columbia Street, Zip 67749–2450, Mailing Address: P.O. Box 268, Zip 67749–0268; tel. 785/475–2208, (Nonreporting) **A**10 18
Primary Contact: Johnathan Owens, Chief Executive Officer
CFO: Amanda Fortin, Manager Finance
CMO: Elizabeth Sliter, M.D., Chairman Medical Staff
CIO: Natasha Weishapl, Manager Business Office and Human Resources
CHR: Natasha Weishapl, Manager Business Office and Human Resources
Web address: www.decaturhealthsystems.org
Control: Other not–for–profit (including NFP Corporation) **Service:** General Medical and Surgical

Staffed Beds: 61

OLATHE—Johnson County

☐ **OLATHE MEDICAL CENTER (170049)**, 20333 West 151st Street, Zip 66061–5350; tel. 913/791–4200 **A**1 2 5 10 **F**3 8 11 12 13 15 18 20 22 24 26 28 29 30 31 34 35 39 40 41 45 46 47 48 49 56 57 58 59 61 62 63 64 65 68 70 74 75 76 77 78 79 81 82 84 85 86 87 89 92 93 107 108 110 111 115 116 117 118 119 120 121 129 130 131 132 135 144 145 146 147 148
Primary Contact: Frank H. Devocelle, President and Chief Executive Officer
COO: John Staton, Senior Vice President Operations
CFO: Tierney Lynn Grasser, Senior Vice President and Chief Financial Officer
CMO: James L. Wetzel, M.D., Senior Vice President, Chief Medical Officer
CIO: Randy Rahman, Vice President and Chief Information Officer
CHR: David Klimek, Vice President Human Resources
CNO: Amy J. Meglemre, R.N., Senior Vice President and Chief Nursing Officer
Web address: www.olathehealth.org
Control: Other not–for–profit (including NFP Corporation) **Service:** General Medical and Surgical

Staffed Beds: 235 **Admissions:** 10784 **Census:** 115 **Outpatient Visits:** 296933 **Births:** 1124 **Personnel:** 1322

ONAGA—Pottawatomie County

★ **COMMUNITY HEALTHCARE SYSTEM (171354)**, 120 West Eighth Street, Zip 66521–9574; tel. 785/889–4272, (Total facility includes 78 beds in nursing home–type unit) **A**10 18 **F**2 3 5 6 10 11 12 13 15 29 31 32 34 35 36 40 43 45 50 53 56 57 59 62 64 65 67 74 75 77 78 81 82 84 85 86 87 93 97 99 100 101 102 103 104 105 106 107 110 111 114 119 125 127 128 130 131 132 133 134 135 143 144 145 146 147 148 **P**6
Primary Contact: Todd Willert, Chief Executive Officer
COO: Marcia S. Walsh, M.P.H., Chief Operating Officer
CFO: Monica Holthaus, Chief Financial Officer
CMO: Marcus Weiser, D.O., Chief of Staff
CIO: Rod Evans, Chief Information Officer
CHR: Terry D. Bernatis, Director Human Resources
CNO: Rosalind Lewis, R.N., Chief Nursing Officer
Web address: www.chcsks.org
Control: Other not–for–profit (including NFP Corporation) **Service:** General Medical and Surgical

Staffed Beds: 150 **Admissions:** 955 **Census:** 71 **Outpatient Visits:** 105030 **Births:** 84 **Total Expense ($000):** 30851 **Payroll Expense ($000):** 18038 **Personnel:** 287

OSAWATOMIE—Miami County

☐ **OSAWATOMIE STATE HOSPITAL (174004)**, 500 State Hospital Drive, Zip 66064–1813, Mailing Address: P.O. Box 500, Zip 66064–0500; tel. 913/755–7000 **A**1 10 **F**30 50 75 86 87 98 101 103 130 132 135 146 **P**6
Primary Contact: Jerry A. Rea, Ph.D., Superintendent
CMO: Maria Gustilo, M.D., Medical Director
CHR: Dezerae Curran, Director Human Resources
Web address: www.srskansas.org/osh/osh–rmhf_info.html
Control: State–Government, nonfederal **Service:** Psychiatric

Staffed Beds: 206 **Admissions:** 2342 **Census:** 195 **Outpatient Visits:** 0 **Births:** 0 **Total Expense ($000):** 32964 **Payroll Expense ($000):** 16260 **Personnel:** 334

OSBORNE—Osborne County

★ **OSBORNE COUNTY MEMORIAL HOSPITAL (171364)**, 424 West New Hampshire Street, Zip 67473–2314, Mailing Address: P.O. Box 70, Zip 67473–0070; tel. 785/346–2121 **A**10 18 **F**3 11 13 40 45 64 69 76 81 107 119 127 128 133 **P**6 **S** Great Plains Health Alliance, Inc., Wichita, KS
Primary Contact: Marianna Harris, Administrator
CFO: Linda Murphy, Chief Financial Officer
CMO: Erin Baxa, M.D., Chief Medical Officer
CNO: Monica Mullender, Director of Nursing
Web address: www.ocmh.org
Control: County–Government, nonfederal **Service:** General Medical and Surgical

Staffed Beds: 25 **Admissions:** 242 **Census:** 7 **Outpatient Visits:** 10176 **Births:** 14 **Total Expense ($000):** 6023 **Payroll Expense ($000):** 2830 **Personnel:** 58

KS

Many Facility Codes have changed. Please refer to the AHA Guide Code Chart.

© 2016 AHA Guide

OSWEGO—Labette County

OSWEGO COMMUNITY HOSPITAL (171302), 800 Barker Drive,
Zip 67356–9014; tel. 620/795–2921 **A**10 18 **F**3 9 12 32 34 35 40 57 59 64
65 75 77 90 93 107 127 130 132 133 135 147 148 **P**6 **S** Rural Community
Hospitals of America, Kansas City, MO
Primary Contact: Daniel Hiben, Chief Executive Officer
CFO: Christina Schlatter, Chief Financial Officer
CMO: Gordon Kern, M.D., Medical Director
CHR: Christina Schlatter, Chief Financial Officer
Web address: www.oswegocommunityhospital.com
Control: Corporation, Investor–owned, for–profit **Service:** General Medical and
Surgical

Staffed Beds: 12 **Admissions:** 126 **Census:** 4 **Outpatient Visits:** 14441
Births: 0 **Total Expense ($000):** 4873 **Payroll Expense ($000):** 2550
Personnel: 47

OTTAWA—Franklin County

RANSOM MEMORIAL HOSPITAL (170014), 1301 South Main Street,
Zip 66067–3598; tel. 785/229–8200 **A**1 10 **F**3 11 13 15 28 29 30 32 34 35
40 41 43 44 45 46 47 49 50 53 56 57 59 64 65 68 70 74 76 77 78 79 81
82 85 86 87 91 93 102 107 108 109 110 111 115 116 119 127 129 130
131 132 144 145 146 148 **P**6
Primary Contact: Matthew M. Heyn, Chief Executive Officer
Web address: www.ransom.org
Control: County–Government, nonfederal **Service:** General Medical and Surgical

Staffed Beds: 44 **Admissions:** 1230 **Census:** 10 **Outpatient Visits:** 119575
Births: 160 **Total Expense ($000):** 37567 **Payroll Expense ($000):** 18390
Personnel: 334

OVERLAND PARK—Johnson County

○ **BLUE VALLEY HOSPITAL (170201)**, 12850 Metcalf Avenue, Zip 66213–2622;
tel. 913/220–2866 **A**11 **F**12 33 38 39 45 46 47 48 49 50 59 79 81 82 92
111 112 119 132
Primary Contact: Douglas C. Palzer, Chief Executive Officer
COO: Craig Storck, Chief Operating Officer
CMO: Lee Nigro, M.D., Chief Medical Officer
Web address: www.bluevalleysurgical.com/
Control: Corporation, Investor–owned, for–profit **Service:** General Medical and
Surgical

Staffed Beds: 7 **Admissions:** 99 **Census:** 1 **Outpatient Visits:** 3213 **Total
Expense ($000):** 15188 **Payroll Expense ($000):** 6025 **Personnel:** 66

□ **CHILDREN'S MERCY SOUTH (173300)**, 5808 West 110th Street,
Zip 66211–2504; tel. 913/696–8000 **A**1 10 **F**3 9 29 30 32 35 36 40 41 44
48 50 59 62 64 68 75 77 79 81 82 85 87 89 93 94 100 101 104 107 111
115 119 129 130 131 132 134 144 146 148 **P**6
Primary Contact: Randall L. O'Donnell, Ph.D., President and Chief Executive Officer
CFO: Sandra A J Lawrence, Executive Vice President and Chief Financial Officer
CMO: Charles Roberts, M.D., Medical Director
CIO: Jean Ann Breedlove, Chief Information Officer
CHR: Dan Wright, Vice President Human Resources
Web address: www.childrens–mercy.org
Control: Other not–for–profit (including NFP Corporation) **Service:** Children's
general

Staffed Beds: 50 **Admissions:** 2293 **Census:** 16 **Outpatient Visits:** 129005
Births: 0 **Total Expense ($000):** 105109 **Payroll Expense ($000):** 58225
Personnel: 679

HEARTLAND SPINE & SPECIALTY HOSPITAL See The University of Kansas
Hospital – Indian Creek Campus

MENORAH MEDICAL CENTER (170182), 5721 West 119th Street,
Zip 66209–3722; tel. 913/498–6000 **A**1 2 3 10 **F**3 12 13 15 18 20 22 24 26
28 29 30 31 34 35 38 40 45 46 47 49 55 57 58 59 60 64 65 68 70 72 74
75 76 77 78 79 81 82 85 86 87 90 93 97 102 107 108 110 111 114 115
117 119 121 124 126 129 130 131 132 135 144 145 146 147 148 **S** HCA,
Nashville, TN
Primary Contact: Charles Laird, Chief Executive Officer
COO: Lenetra S. King, Chief Operating Officer
CFO: Deborah Gafford, Chief Financial Officer
CMO: James Cheray, M.D., Chief Medical Officer
CIO: Christina McGinnis, Director Information Technology
CHR: Amy Hunt, Director Human Resources
CNO: Kelly Reno, R.N., Chief Nursing Officer
Web address: www.menorahmedicalcenter.com
Control: Corporation, Investor–owned, for–profit **Service:** General Medical and
Surgical

Staffed Beds: 158 **Admissions:** 7254 **Census:** 86 **Outpatient Visits:** 64781
Births: 581 **Total Expense ($000):** 163480 **Payroll Expense ($000):** 48128
Personnel: 694

OVERLAND PARK REGIONAL MEDICAL CENTER (170176), 10500 Quivira
Road, Zip 66215–2306, Mailing Address: P.O. Box 15959, Zip 66215–5959;
tel. 913/541–5000 **A**1 5 10 **F**3 8 13 15 18 20 22 24 26 28 29 30 31 34 35
37 40 42 43 45 49 50 56 57 59 60 61 64 65 67 70 72 73 74 75 76 77 78
79 81 82 83 84 85 86 87 91 92 93 107 108 110 111 114 115 119 126 129
130 131 135 144 145 146 147 148 **S** HCA, Nashville, TN
Primary Contact: Kevin J. Hicks, President and CEO
COO: Jim Beatty, Chief Operating Officer
CFO: Steven R. Cleary, Chief Financial Officer
CMO: George D. Stamos, M.D., Chief Medical Officer
CHR: Connie Miller, Vice President Human Resources
CNO: Teresa L. Collins, Chief Nursing Officer
Web address: www.oprmc.com
Control: Corporation, Investor–owned, for–profit **Service:** General Medical and
Surgical

Staffed Beds: 277 **Admissions:** 11108 **Census:** 148 **Outpatient Visits:**
81403 **Births:** 3331 **Total Expense ($000):** 165087 **Payroll Expense
($000):** 63370 **Personnel:** 877

□ **PROMISE HOSPITAL OF OVERLAND PARK (172004)**, 6509 West 103rd
Street, Zip 66212–1728; tel. 913/649–3701, (Total facility includes 52 beds in
nursing home–type unit) **A**1 10 **F**1 18 28 29 50 56 58 68 75 85 90 128 130
135 143 148 **P**8 **S** Promise Healthcare, Boca Raton, FL
Primary Contact: Karen Leverich, Chief Executive Officer
CFO: William Scott, Chief Financial Officer
CHR: Darren Enochs, Director Human Resources
Web address: www.promise–overlandpark.com
Control: Corporation, Investor–owned, for–profit **Service:** Long–Term Acute Care
hospital

Staffed Beds: 104 **Admissions:** 325 **Census:** 71 **Outpatient Visits:** 0 **Births:**
0 **Total Expense ($000):** 16322 **Payroll Expense ($000):** 7016 **Personnel:**
147

SAINT LUKE'S SOUTH HOSPITAL (170185), 12300 Metcalf Avenue,
Zip 66213–1324; tel. 913/317–7000 **A**1 10 **F**3 12 13 15 18 20 22 26 28 29
30 31 34 35 38 39 40 44 45 47 49 54 56 57 58 59 60 64 70 72 74 75 76
77 78 79 80 81 82 84 85 86 87 90 92 93 94 96 102 107 108 110 111 114
115 117 118 119 129 130 131 132 141 146 147 148 **S** Saint Luke's Health
System, Kansas City, MO
Primary Contact: Bobby Olm–Shipman, Chief Executive Officer
CFO: Shelby Frigon, Chief Financial Officer
CMO: Lisa Heath, M.D., President Medical Staff
CIO: Deborah Gash, Chief Information Officer
CHR: Donna Kunz, Manager Human Resources
CNO: Julia Woods, R.N., Vice President and Chief Nursing Officer
Web address: www.saintlukeshealthsystem.org/south
Control: Church–operated, Nongovernment, not–for profit **Service:** General
Medical and Surgical

Staffed Beds: 110 **Admissions:** 4937 **Census:** 54 **Outpatient Visits:** 85385
Births: 600 **Total Expense ($000):** 113973 **Payroll Expense ($000):** 30850
Personnel: 494

PAOLA—Miami County

□ **MIAMI COUNTY MEDICAL CENTER (170109)**, 2100 Baptiste Drive,
Zip 66071–1314, Mailing Address: P.O. Box 365, Zip 66071–0365;
tel. 913/294–2327 **A**1 5 10 **F**3 11 15 34 40 43 57 59 61 64 68 75 77 78 79
81 85 87 89 90 93 107 108 110 114 119 127 130 131 135 146 148
Primary Contact: Paul W. Luce, R.N., MSN, Vice President Operations
CFO: Cheryl Sharp, Chief Financial Office
CMO: Christopher Eckland, M.D., Chief Medical Officer
CIO: Randy Rahman, Chief Information Officer
CHR: David Klimek, Chief Human Resources Officer
CNO: Aubree Slayman, Director Patient Services
Web address: www.olathehealth.org
Control: Other not–for–profit (including NFP Corporation) **Service:** General
Medical and Surgical

Staffed Beds: 18 **Admissions:** 487 **Census:** 3 **Outpatient Visits:** 30694
Births: 0 **Personnel:** 118

KS

PARSONS—Labette County

★ ○ **LABETTE HEALTH (170120)**, 1902 South U.S. Highway 59,
Zip 67357–7404; tel. 620/421–4880 **A**10 11 **F**3 11 13 15 29 30 34 40 43 50
53 59 62 70 74 75 76 77 79 81 86 90 93 97 107 108 110 111 114 119 126
127 129 130 143 144 146 147 148 **P**6
Primary Contact: Brian A. Williams, Chief Executive Officer
CFO: Thomas Macaronas, Chief Financial Officer
CHR: Christina Sykes, Director Human Resources
Web address: www.labettehealth.com
Control: County–Government, nonfederal **Service:** General Medical and Surgical

Staffed Beds: 56 **Admissions:** 2306 **Census:** 23 **Outpatient Visits:** 74150
Births: 232 **Total Expense ($000):** 60968 **Payroll Expense ($000):** 25071
Personnel: 448

PARSONS STATE HOSPITAL AND TRAINING CENTER, 2601 Gabriel Avenue,
Zip 67357–2341, Mailing Address: P.O. Box 738, Zip 67357–0738;
tel. 620/421–6550 **F**35 39 67 130 146
Primary Contact: Jerry A. Rea, Ph.D., Superintendent
CFO: John Spare, Accountant
CMO: Rema Menon, M.D., Clinical Director
CIO: Ron Malmstrom, Information Research Specialist
CHR: Tim B. Posch, Business Manager and Director Personnel
Web address: www.pshtc.org
Control: State–Government, nonfederal **Service:** Intellectual disabilities

Staffed Beds: 188 **Admissions:** 9 **Census:** 170 **Outpatient Visits:** 0 **Births:**
0 **Total Expense ($000):** 27352 **Payroll Expense ($000):** 15698
Personnel: 439

PHILLIPSBURG—Phillips County

★ **PHILLIPS COUNTY HOSPITAL (171353)**, 1150 State Street, Zip 67661–1743,
Mailing Address: P.O. Box 607, Zip 67661–0607; tel. 785/543–5226 **A**10 18 **F**3
11 15 28 30 31 40 45 50 59 64 68 75 77 78 81 86 87 91 93 107 114 119
127 128 130 132 133 145 146 148 **P**6 **S** Great Plains Health Alliance, Inc.,
Wichita, KS
Primary Contact: David Engel, Chief Executive Officer
CFO: Christi Driggs, Chief Financial Officer
CMO: Ben Stephenson, M.D., Chief of Staff
CIO: Steven Seems, Director of Information Technology
CHR: Peggy Fabin, Director Human Resources
CNO: Vickie Gibbs, Director Nursing
Web address: www.phillipshospital.org
Control: Other not–for–profit (including NFP Corporation) **Service:** General
Medical and Surgical

Staffed Beds: 25 **Admissions:** 302 **Census:** 6 **Outpatient Visits:** 24964
Births: 2 **Total Expense ($000):** 12292 **Payroll Expense ($000):** 4716
Personnel: 102

PITTSBURG—Crawford County

⊠ **VIA CHRISTI HOSPITAL PITTSBURG (170006)**, 1 Mt. Carmel Way,
Zip 66762–7587; tel. 620/231–6100 **A**1 2 10 **F**3 5 8 11 12 13 15 18 20 22
26 28 29 30 31 34 35 40 42 43 45 46 47 48 50 51 53 54 56 57 58 59 62
64 68 69 70 74 75 76 77 78 79 81 82 84 85 86 89 90 93 99 100 101 103
104 107 108 109 110 111 112 114 115 116 117 118 119 120 121 122 123
126 129 130 131 132 133 135 143 144 145 146 147 148 **P**8 **S** Ascension
Health, Saint Louis, MO
Primary Contact: Randall R. Cason, FACHE, Senior Administrator
CFO: Mike Joy, Administrator, Finance
CIO: Missy McDown, Director Information Systems
CHR: Laurie Johnson, Director – Human Resources
CNO: Amy Katherine Renn, Interim Administrator, Patient Care and Nursing
Web address: www.viachristi.org/pittsburg
Control: Church–operated, Nongovernment, not–for profit **Service:** General
Medical and Surgical

Staffed Beds: 110 **Admissions:** 3442 **Census:** 42 **Outpatient Visits:** 107416
Births: 579 **Total Expense ($000):** 86502 **Payroll Expense ($000):** 34697
Personnel: 584

PLAINVILLE—Rooks County

★ **ROOKS COUNTY HEALTH CENTER (171311)**, 1210 North Washington Street,
Zip 67663–1632, Mailing Address: P.O. Box 389, Zip 67663–0389;
tel. 785/434–4553 **A**10 18 **F**3 13 15 28 29 31 34 35 40 43 45 47 50 57 59
64 67 76 77 79 81 82 87 89 93 96 107 110 114 119 125 128 130 131 133
135 143 144 146 147 148
Primary Contact: Michael Sinclair, Chief Executive Officer
COO: William D. Stahl, Chief Operating Officer
CFO: Julie Price, Chief Financial Officer
CMO: Lynn Fisher, M.D., Chief of Staff
CIO: Kathy Ramsay, R.N., Director Communications and Development
CHR: Cindi Knipp, Director Human Resources
Web address: www.rookscountyhealthcenter.com
Control: Hospital district or authority, Government, nonfederal **Service:** General
Medical and Surgical

Staffed Beds: 20 **Admissions:** 437 **Census:** 7 **Outpatient Visits:** 25716
Births: 38 **Total Expense ($000):** 14671 **Payroll Expense ($000):** 5801
Personnel: 128

PRATT—Pratt County

★ **PRATT REGIONAL MEDICAL CENTER (170027)**, 200 Commodore Street,
Zip 67124–2903; tel. 620/672–7451, (Total facility includes 45 beds in nursing
home–type unit) **A**10 20 **F**3 11 13 15 30 31 34 40 45 49 56 57 59 61 62 64
68 70 75 76 77 79 81 82 85 86 87 89 90 93 107 108 114 118 119 124 127
128 130 131 133 145 146 147 148 **P**6
Primary Contact: Susan M. Page, President and Chief Executive Officer
CFO: Vincent Scot Wilczek, Controller
CIO: Vikki Mader, Director Health Information Services
CHR: Ken Brown, Vice President and Chief Human Resource Officer
CNO: Jack L. Kennedy, R.N., Vice President and Chief Nursing Officer
Web address: www.prmc.org
Control: Other not–for–profit (including NFP Corporation) **Service:** General
Medical and Surgical

Staffed Beds: 80 **Admissions:** 1597 **Census:** 58 **Outpatient Visits:** 107401
Births: 294 **Total Expense ($000):** 47672 **Payroll Expense ($000):** 23352
Personnel: 408

QUINTER—Gove County

GOVE COUNTY MEDICAL CENTER (171367), 520 West Fifth Street,
Zip 67752–0129, Mailing Address: P.O. Box 129, Zip 67752–0129;
tel. 785/754–3341, (Total facility includes 43 beds in nursing home–type unit)
A10 18 **F**3 11 13 28 29 34 40 45 57 62 67 75 81 86 93 107 114 119 125
129 133 135 143 148
Primary Contact: Coleen Tummons, Chief Executive Officer
CFO: Alan Waites, Chief Financial Officer
CIO: Brad Mullins, Director Information Technology
CHR: Valerie Schneider, Director Human Resources
CNO: Renee Wagoner, R.N., Director of Nursing
Web address: www.govecountymedicalcenter.org
Control: County–Government, nonfederal **Service:** General Medical and Surgical

Staffed Beds: 64 **Admissions:** 692 **Census:** 41 **Outpatient Visits:** 10907
Births: 65 **Total Expense ($000):** 12955 **Payroll Expense ($000):** 5762
Personnel: 156

RANSOM—Ness County

★ **GRISELL MEMORIAL HOSPITAL DISTRICT ONE (171300)**, 210 South
Vermont Avenue, Zip 67572–9525; tel. 785/731–2231, (Total facility includes 34
beds in nursing home–type unit) **A**10 18 **F**3 40 56 67 69 85 93 97 127 128
133 **P**6 **S** Great Plains Health Alliance, Inc., Wichita, KS
Primary Contact: David Caudill, Administrator
CFO: Jolene Schuster, Chief Financial Officer
CMO: Allen McLain, M.D., Chief of Staff
CNO: Joni Pfaff, Chief Nursing Officer
Web address: www.grisellmemorialhospital.org
Control: Hospital district or authority, Government, nonfederal **Service:** General
Medical and Surgical

Staffed Beds: 46 **Admissions:** 49 **Census:** 28 **Outpatient Visits:** 6870
Births: 0 **Total Expense ($000):** 5383 **Payroll Expense ($000):** 2563
Personnel: 66

RUSSELL—Russell County

★ **RUSSELL REGIONAL HOSPITAL (171350)**, 200 South Main Street,
Zip 67665–2920; tel. 785/483–3131, (Total facility includes 22 beds in nursing
home–type unit) **A**10 18 **F**9 11 15 29 34 40 45 50 53 57 59 64 65 66 67 69
75 85 87 93 97 107 108 109 110 115 119 127 130 131 133 135 145 146
147 148 **P**6
Primary Contact: Harold Courtois, Chief Executive Officer
COO: Sharon Collins, Director Human Resources and Chief Operating Officer
CFO: Kevin Kreutzer, Chief Financial Officer
CMO: Tyrel Somers, M.D., Chief Medical Officer
CIO: David Schraeder, Director Information Systems
CHR: Sharon Collins, Director Human Resources and Chief Operating Officer
CNO: Deb Strobel, R.N., Chief Nursing Officer
Web address: www.russellhospital.org
Control: Other not–for–profit (including NFP Corporation) **Service:** General
Medical and Surgical

Staffed Beds: 47 **Admissions:** 450 **Census:** 28 **Outpatient Visits:** 37026
Births: 0 **Total Expense ($000):** 16251 **Payroll Expense ($000):** 7751
Personnel: 154

KS

Many Facility Codes have changed. Please refer to the AHA Guide Code Chart. © 2016 AHA Guide

SABETHA—Nemaha County

★ **SABETHA COMMUNITY HOSPITAL (171338)**, 14th and Oregon Streets, Zip 66534–0229, Mailing Address: P.O. Box 229, Zip 66534–0229; tel. 785/284–2121 **A**10 18 **F**3 11 13 15 28 34 35 40 43 45 50 56 57 59 62 63 64 68 75 76 77 78 79 81 82 84 85 86 93 107 110 114 119 128 130 132 133 146 148 **P**6 **S** Great Plains Health Alliance, Inc., Wichita, KS
Primary Contact: Lora Key, Chief Executive Officer
CFO: Lori Lackey, Chief Financial Officer
CMO: James Longabaugh, M.D., Chief Medical Staff
CIO: Garrett Colglazier, Director Health Information Management
CHR: Julie K. Holthaus, Director Human Resources
CNO: Rhonda Spellmeier, R.N., Director of Nursing
Web address: www.sabethahospital.com
Control: Other not–for–profit (including NFP Corporation) **Service:** General Medical and Surgical

Staffed Beds: 25 **Admissions:** 359 **Census:** 6 **Outpatient Visits:** 41872
Births: 60 **Total Expense ($000):** 12074 **Payroll Expense ($000):** 5724
Personnel: 110

SAINT FRANCIS—Cheyenne County

★ **CHEYENNE COUNTY HOSPITAL (171310)**, 210 West First Street, Zip 67756–3540, Mailing Address: P.O. Box 547, Zip 67756–0547; tel. 785/332–2104 **A**10 18 **F**3 8 11 13 28 29 31 40 57 59 64 65 66 68 76 77 78 81 85 89 93 97 107 119 127 128 133 148 **P**6 **S** Great Plains Health Alliance, Inc., Wichita, KS
Primary Contact: Scott Jenkins, Administrator
CFO: Heidi Tice, Chief Financial Officer
CMO: Mary Beth Miller, M.D., Chief of Staff
CIO: Carol Sloper, Manager Information Technology
CHR: Sara Wilson, Director Human Resources
CNO: Judith Ann Hodgson, Chief Nursing Officer
Web address: www.cheyennecountyhospital.com
Control: Other not–for–profit (including NFP Corporation) **Service:** General Medical and Surgical

Staffed Beds: 16 **Admissions:** 246 **Census:** 3 **Outpatient Visits:** 20449
Births: 23 **Total Expense ($000):** 9611 **Payroll Expense ($000):** 4508
Personnel: 90

SALINA—Saline County

★ ○ **SALINA REGIONAL HEALTH CENTER (170012)**, 400 South Santa Fe Avenue, Zip 67401–4198, Mailing Address: P.O. Box 5080, Zip 67402–5080; tel. 785/452–7000, (Includes SALINA REGIONAL HEALTH CENTER– PENN CAMPUS, 139 North Penn Street, Zip 67401, Mailing Address: P.O. Box 5080, Zip 67402–5080; tel. 913/452–7000; SALINA REGIONAL HEALTH CENTER–SANTA FE CAMPUS, 400 South Santa Fe Avenue, Zip 67401, Mailing Address: Box 5080, Zip 67402–5080; tel. 913/452–7000) **A**3 5 10 11 20 **F**3 13 15 18 19 20 22 24 28 29 30 31 35 40 43 45 46 47 48 49 51 53 54 55 57 59 63 64 65 68 70 71 72 73 74 76 77 78 79 81 85 86 87 89 90 98 99 100 101 102 103 104 105 107 108 110 111 114 115 116 117 118 119 120 121 122 123 124 126 129 130 143 144 145 146 147 148 **P**6 **S** Salina Regional Health Center, Salina, KS
Primary Contact: Micheal Terry, President and Chief Executive Officer
COO: Joel Phelps, Chief Operating Officer
CFO: Joe Tallon, Vice President Finance
CIO: Larry Barnes, Vice President Information Technology
CHR: David Moody, Vice President Human Resources
Web address: www.srhc.com
Control: Other not–for–profit (including NFP Corporation) **Service:** General Medical and Surgical

Staffed Beds: 205 **Admissions:** 9007 **Census:** 114 **Outpatient Visits:** 203093 **Births:** 1181 **Total Expense ($000):** 206658 **Payroll Expense ($000):** 92665 **Personnel:** 1551

SALINA SURGICAL HOSPITAL (170187), 401 South Santa Fe Avenue, Zip 67401–4143, Mailing Address: 401 South Sante Fe Avenue, Zip 67401–4143; tel. 785/827–0610 **A**5 10 **F**29 45 48 49 51 59 74 79 81 85 89 131
Primary Contact: LuAnn Puvogel, R.N., Chief Executive Officer
CFO: Elizabeth Bishop, Business Office Manager
CMO: Michael Johnson, M.D., Medical Director
CIO: Earl Akers, Supervisor Information Technology
CHR: Elizabeth Bishop, Business Office Manager
CNO: Jolene Glavin, R.N., Director Nursing
Web address: www.salinasurgical.com/
Control: Partnership, Investor–owned, for–profit **Service:** Surgical

Staffed Beds: 16 **Admissions:** 683 **Census:** 5 **Outpatient Visits:** 7384
Births: 0 **Total Expense ($000):** 17936 **Payroll Expense ($000):** 5457
Personnel: 100

SATANTA—Haskell County

★ **SATANTA DISTRICT HOSPITAL AND LONG TERM CARE (171324)**, 401 South Cheyenne Street, Zip 67870–0159, Mailing Address: P.O. Box 159, Zip 67870–0159; tel. 620/649–2761, (Total facility includes 44 beds in nursing home–type unit) **A**10 18 **F**3 11 40 43 45 57 64 67 68 75 81 82 87 93 104 107 119 127 128 130 133 **P**4 **S** Great Plains Health Alliance, Inc., Wichita, KS
Primary Contact: Jeremy Clingenpeel, Administrator
CFO: Libby Anderson, Chief Financial Officer
CMO: Virgilio Taduran, M.D., Chief Medical Officer
CIO: Ben Leppke, Chief Information Officer
CHR: Samantha Hett, Manager Human Resources
CNO: Tina Pendergraft, Chief Nursing Officer
Web address: www.satantahospital.org
Control: Hospital district or authority, Government, nonfederal **Service:** General Medical and Surgical

Staffed Beds: 57 **Admissions:** 170 **Census:** 42 **Outpatient Visits:** 24591
Births: 0 **Total Expense ($000):** 13203 **Payroll Expense ($000):** 5701
Personnel: 134

SCOTT CITY—Scott County

★ **SCOTT COUNTY HOSPITAL (171372)**, 201 East Albert Avenue, Zip 67871–1203; tel. 620/872–5811 **A**10 18 **F**3 7 13 15 28 29 30 31 35 40 45 46 50 57 59 64 68 69 75 76 77 81 82 85 93 107 110 111 119 127 128 129 130 133 135 145 148 **P**6
Primary Contact: Mark Burnett, President and Chief Executive Officer
COO: Karma Huck, Chief Operating Officer
CFO: Joe S. Meyer, Chief Financial Officer
CMO: Elizabeth Hineman, M.D., Chief Medical Staff
CHR: Pamela R. Wheeler, Director Human Resources
Web address: www.scotthospital.net
Control: Other not–for–profit (including NFP Corporation) **Service:** General Medical and Surgical

Staffed Beds: 22 **Admissions:** 745 **Census:** 11 **Outpatient Visits:** 23837
Births: 63 **Total Expense ($000):** 20338 **Payroll Expense ($000):** 10017
Personnel: 196

SEDAN—Chautauqua County

SEDAN CITY HOSPITAL (171318), 300 North Street, Zip 67361–1051, Mailing Address: P.O. Box C, Zip 67361–0427; tel. 620/725–3115 **A**10 18 **F**29 34 40 57 64 93 107 119 128 130 133 148
Primary Contact: Michelle Williams, Administrator
CFO: Jennifer Seever, Regional Chief Financial Officer
CMO: James McDermott, M.D., Chief of Staff
Control: City–Government, nonfederal **Service:** General Medical and Surgical

Staffed Beds: 18 **Admissions:** 205 **Census:** 2 **Outpatient Visits:** 9563
Births: 0 **Total Expense ($000):** 4516 **Payroll Expense ($000):** 1976
Personnel: 39

SENECA—Nemaha County

★ **NEMAHA VALLEY COMMUNITY HOSPITAL (171315)**, 1600 Community Drive, Zip 66538–9739; tel. 785/336–6181 **A**10 18 **F**11 12 13 15 28 31 40 56 57 59 64 75 76 77 78 79 81 84 85 89 93 107 114 119 127 129 130 131 132 133 **P**6
Primary Contact: Kiley Floyd, Chief Executive Officer
CFO: Connie Ingwerson, Chief Financial Officer
CMO: Angela Stueve, M.D., Chief Medical Officer
CHR: Lynn E. Hartter, Jr., Director Human Resources
CNO: Lynda Cross, R.N., Director of Nurses
Web address: www.nemvch.org
Control: Other not–for–profit (including NFP Corporation) **Service:** General Medical and Surgical

Staffed Beds: 24 **Admissions:** 240 **Census:** 3 **Outpatient Visits:** 18467
Births: 46 **Total Expense ($000):** 11879 **Payroll Expense ($000):** 5892
Personnel: 121

SHAWNEE MISSION—Johnson County

⊞ **MID–AMERICA REHABILITATION HOSPITAL (173026)**, 5701 West 110th Street, Zip 66211–2503; tel. 913/491–2400 **A**1 10 **F**29 35 56 64 86 87 90 91 93 95 96 130 132 135 143 148 **S** HEALTHSOUTH Corporation, Birmingham, AL
Primary Contact: Troy DeDecker, FACHE, Chief Executive Officer
CFO: Richard Lane, Chief Financial Officer
CMO: Cielo Dehning, M.D., Medical Director
CHR: Elizabeth Gibson, Director Human Resources
CNO: Amy McKay, Chief Nursing Officer
Web address: www.midamericarehabhospital.com
Control: Corporation, Investor–owned, for–profit **Service:** Rehabilitation

Staffed Beds: 98 **Admissions:** 1951 **Census:** 67 **Outpatient Visits:** 8828
Births: 0 **Total Expense ($000):** 26444 **Payroll Expense ($000):** 13436
Personnel: 201

Hospital, Medicare Provider Number, Address, Telephone, Approval, Facility, and Physician Codes, Health Care System

★ American Hospital Association (AHA) membership
□ The Joint Commission accreditation
○ Healthcare Facilities Accreditation Program
◇ DNV Healthcare Inc. accreditation
⇑ Center for Improvement in Healthcare Quality Accreditation
△ Commission on Accreditation of Rehabilitation Facilities (CARF) accreditation

✠ **SHAWNEE MISSION MEDICAL CENTER (170104)**, 9100 West 74th Street, Zip 66204–4004, Mailing Address: Box 2923, Zip 66201–1323; tel. 913/676–2000 **A**1 2 3 5 10 **F**3 4 5 8 11 12 13 15 17 18 20 22 24 26 28 29 30 31 32 34 35 36 40 42 45 46 47 48 49 52 53 54 55 56 57 58 59 60 61 62 64 65 70 72 74 75 76 77 78 79 80 81 82 83 84 85 86 87 89 93 96 97 98 100 101 102 103 104 105 107 108 110 111 114 115 117 118 119 120 121 123 124 126 129 130 131 132 135 144 145 146 147 148 **P**6 **S** Adventist Health System Sunbelt Health Care Corporation, Altamonte Springs, FL
Primary Contact: Ken J. Bacon, President and Chief Executive Officer
CFO: Karsten Randolph, Executive Vice President and Chief Financial Officer
CMO: Sherri Martin, M.D., President Medical Staff
CIO: Mike Allen, Director Information Services
CHR: Brad Hoffman, Administrative Director Human Resources
CNO: Sheri Hawkins, Chief Nursing Officer
Web address: www.shawneemission.org
Control: Church–operated, Nongovernment, not–for profit **Service:** General Medical and Surgical

Staffed Beds: 391 Admissions: 22232 Census: 240 Outpatient Visits: 536462 Births: 5022 Total Expense ($000): 388786 Payroll Expense ($000): 157133 Personnel: 2610

SMITH CENTER—Smith County

★ **SMITH COUNTY MEMORIAL HOSPITAL (171377)**, 614 South Main Street, Zip 66967–3001; tel. 785/282–6845, (Total facility includes 28 beds in nursing home–type unit) **A**10 18 **F**13 15 28 29 30 31 34 40 43 45 53 64 65 67 68 69 75 76 81 85 89 91 93 107 110 114 119 127 128 133 **P**6 **S** Great Plains Health Alliance, Inc., Wichita, KS
Primary Contact: Allen Van Driel, FACHE, Administrator
CFO: Julie Williams, Chief Financial Officer
CIO: Tammy Gaston, Chief Information Officer
CHR: Jody Maxwell, Manager Business Office
CNO: Sarah Ragsdale, R.N., Chief Nursing Officer
Web address: www.gpha.com
Control: Other not–for–profit (including NFP Corporation) **Service:** General Medical and Surgical

Staffed Beds: 53 Admissions: 444 Census: 28 Outpatient Visits: 28768 Births: 26 Total Expense ($000): 11977 Payroll Expense ($000): 5197 Personnel: 125

STAFFORD—Stafford County

★ **STAFFORD COUNTY HOSPITAL (171323)**, 502 South Buckeye Street, Zip 67578–2035, Mailing Address: P.O. Box 190, Zip 67578–0190; tel. 620/234–5221 **A**10 18 **F**3 15 29 35 40 57 59 62 64 67 77 93 107 128 130 133 **P**5
Primary Contact: Todd Taylor, Chief Executive Officer
CFO: MeKinzie Hudson, Chief Financial Officer
Web address: www.staffordcountyhospital.org
Control: Hospital district or authority, Government, nonfederal **Service:** General Medical and Surgical

Staffed Beds: 25 Admissions: 99 Census: 5 Outpatient Visits: 31451 Births: 0 Total Expense ($000): 3862 Payroll Expense ($000): 1678 Personnel: 39

SYRACUSE—Hamilton County

★ **HAMILTON COUNTY HOSPITAL (171322)**, 700 North Huser Street, Zip 67878–0948, Mailing Address: P.O. Box 948, Zip 67878–0948; tel. 620/384–7461, (Total facility includes 44 beds in nursing home–type unit) **A**10 18 **F**3 18 35 40 41 56 57 59 64 68 81 84 85 86 91 93 97 107 111 114 125 127 130 133 **P**6
Primary Contact: Robert Whitaker, Chief Executive Officer
CMO: Richard Carter, M.D., Chief Medical Director
CIO: Merlin Kuder, Chief Information Officer
CHR: Angela Talbot, Chief Manager Human Resource
CNO: Stacey Perry, Chief Nursing Officer
Web address: www.myhch.org
Control: County–Government, nonfederal **Service:** General Medical and Surgical

Staffed Beds: 69 Admissions: 99 Census: 24 Outpatient Visits: 7453 Births: 0 Total Expense ($000): 7071 Payroll Expense ($000): 3206 Personnel: 82

TOPEKA—Shawnee County

KANSAS NEUROLOGICAL INSTITUTE, 3107 West 21st Street, Zip 66604–3298; tel. 785/296–5301 **F**29 30 35 39 67 91 97 130 143 146 **P**6
Primary Contact: Brent Widick, Superintendent
CFO: Sara Hoyer, Director Administrative Services
CMO: Mary Gingrich, Director Health Care Services
CIO: Cheryl Fuller, Director Information Resources
CHR: Shawna Mercer, Director Human Resources
Web address: www.kdads.ks.gov/state–hospitals–and–institutions/kansas–neurological–institute
Control: State–Government, nonfederal **Service:** Intellectual disabilities

Staffed Beds: 142 Admissions: 4 Census: 142 Outpatient Visits: 0 Births: 0 Total Expense ($000): 26602 Payroll Expense ($000): 14588 Personnel: 419

✠ **KANSAS REHABILITATION HOSPITAL (173025)**, 1504 S.W. Eighth Avenue, Zip 66606–1632; tel. 785/235–6600 **A**1 10 **F**29 75 86 90 91 95 96 130 132 148 **S** HEALTHSOUTH Corporation, Birmingham, AL
Primary Contact: William J. Overbey, Chief Executive Officer
CMO: Joseph Sankoorikal, M.D., Chief Medical Staff
CHR: Dina Cox, Director Human Resources
CNO: Carol Swanger, Chief Nursing Officer
Web address: www.kansasrehabhospital.com
Control: Corporation, Investor–owned, for–profit **Service:** Rehabilitation

Staffed Beds: 57 Admissions: 1255 Census: 40 Outpatient Visits: 5871 Births: 0 Total Expense ($000): 16551 Payroll Expense ($000): 8579 Personnel: 156

✠ **ST. FRANCIS HEALTH (170016)**, 1700 S.W. 7th Street, Zip 66606–1690; tel. 785/295–8000 **A**1 2 10 **F**3 12 13 15 18 20 22 24 26 28 29 30 31 34 35 36 37 38 40 45 47 48 49 50 51 53 54 56 57 58 59 60 61 62 64 65 70 71 73 74 75 76 77 78 79 80 81 82 85 86 87 89 90 92 93 95 96 107 108 110 111 114 115 116 117 118 119 120 121 123 126 130 131 132 135 144 146 147 148 **P**6 **S** SCL Health, Broomfield, CO
Primary Contact: David P. Setchel, President
CFO: Debra Cartwright, Chief Financial Officer
CMO: Thomas Hamilton, D.O., Chief Medical Officer
CIO: Kevin Mapes, Director Kansas Division System and Technology Service Center
CHR: Steve Saffa, Director Human Resources
Web address: www.stfrancistopeka.org
Control: Church–operated, Nongovernment, not–for profit **Service:** General Medical and Surgical

Staffed Beds: 259 Admissions: 9066 Census: 110 Outpatient Visits: 248568 Births: 1014 Total Expense ($000): 203394 Payroll Expense ($000): 61446 Personnel: 1266

✠ **STORMONT VAIL HEALTH (170086)**, 1500 S.W. Tenth Avenue, Zip 66604–1353; tel. 785/354–6000 **A**1 2 5 10 **F**3 11 12 13 15 17 18 19 20 22 24 26 28 29 30 31 34 35 37 40 43 44 45 47 49 50 51 55 56 57 58 59 60 61 64 65 68 70 71 72 74 75 76 77 78 79 81 82 84 85 86 87 88 89 91 93 97 98 99 101 102 103 104 105 107 108 110 111 112 114 115 117 119 120 121 123 129 130 131 132 135 143 144 145 146 147 148 **P**6
Primary Contact: Randall Peterson, President and Chief Executive Officer
COO: Janet Stanek, Senior Vice President and Chief Operating Officer
CFO: Kevin Han, Vice President and Chief Financial Officer
CMO: Rob Kenagy, M.D., Senior Vice President and Chief Medical Officer
CIO: Judy Corzine, Administrative Director and Chief Information Officer
CHR: Bernard H. Becker, Vice President and Chief Human Resources Officer
CNO: Carol Perry, R.N., Vice President and Chief Nursing Officer
Web address: www.stormontvail.org
Control: Other not–for–profit (including NFP Corporation) **Service:** General Medical and Surgical

Staffed Beds: 394 Admissions: 20574 Census: 260 Outpatient Visits: 132549 Births: 1797 Total Expense ($000): 550904 Payroll Expense ($000): 290444 Personnel: 3889

✠ **VETERANS AFFAIRS EASTERN KANSAS HEALTH CARE SYSTEM**, 2200 South West Gage Boulevard, Zip 66622–0002; tel. 785/350–3111, (Includes VETERANS AFFAIRS EASTERN KANSAS HEALTH CARE SYSTEM–COLMERY–O'NEIL VETERANS AFFAIRS MEDICAL CENTER, 2200 South West Gage Boulevard, tel. 785/350–3111; VETERANS AFFAIRS EASTERN KANSAS HEALTH CARE SYSTEM–DWIGHT D. EISENHOWER VETERANS AFFAIRS MEDICAL CENTER, 4101 South 4th Street Trafficway, Leavenworth, Zip 66048–5055; tel. 913/682–2000), (Nonreporting) **A**1 3 5 **S** Department of Veterans Affairs, Washington, DC
Primary Contact: Anthony Rudy Klopfer, FACHE, Director
COO: John Moon, Associate Director
CMO: Rajeev Trehan, M.D., Chief of Staff
CIO: Joni Davin, Director Information and Business Management Service Line
Web address: www.topeka.va.gov/
Control: Veterans Affairs, Government, federal **Service:** General Medical and Surgical

Staffed Beds: 213

VETERANS AFFAIRS EASTERN KANSAS HEALTH CARE SYSTEM–COLMERY–O'NEIL VETERANS AFFAIRS MEDICAL CENTER See Veterans Affairs Eastern Kansas Health Care System

Many Facility Codes have changed. Please refer to the AHA Guide Code Chart.
© 2016 AHA Guide

KS

TRIBUNE—Greeley County

★ **GREELEY COUNTY HEALTH SERVICES (171359)**, 506 Third Street,
Zip 67879–9684, Mailing Address: P.O. Box 338, Zip 67879–0338;
tel. 620/376–4221, (Total facility includes 32 beds in nursing home–type unit)
A10 18 **F**3 17 28 34 40 45 59 64 65 66 69 81 89 107 127 133 147 **S** QHR,
Brentwood, TN
Primary Contact: Jamie W. Guin, Jr., Interim Administrator and Chief Executive Officer
CMO: Wendel Ellis, D.O., Chief Medical Staff
CIO: Shanon Schneider, Chief Information Officer
CHR: Katelyn Reynolds, Manager Human Resources
CNO: Janie Schmidt, Director of Nursing
Web address: www.mygchs.com
Control: Other not–for–profit (including NFP Corporation) **Service:** General Medical and Surgical

Staffed Beds: 50 **Admissions:** 274 **Census:** 35 **Outpatient Visits:** 17894
Births: 0 **Total Expense ($000):** 10104 **Payroll Expense ($000):** 4908
Personnel: 117

ULYSSES—Grant County

★ **BOB WILSON MEMORIAL GRANT COUNTY HOSPITAL (170110)**, 415 North Main Street, Zip 67880–2133; tel. 620/356–1266 **A**10 20 **F**3 11 13 15 29 30 34 35 40 45 50 57 59 64 68 75 76 79 81 82 85 86 87 91 93 96 97 107 119 127 130 133 146 148 **P**6 **S** Catholic Health Initiatives, Englewood, CO
Primary Contact: Deanna Mustin, R.N., Administrator
CFO: Robert Jacobi, Chief Financial Officer
CIO: Chris Moffet, Director Information Services
CHR: Tammy Oxford, Director Human Resources
Web address: www.bwmgch.com
Control: County–Government, nonfederal **Service:** General Medical and Surgical

Staffed Beds: 26 **Admissions:** 364 **Census:** 5 **Outpatient Visits:** 11255
Births: 39 **Total Expense ($000):** 11025 **Payroll Expense ($000):** 5320
Personnel: 106

WAKEENEY—Trego County

★ **TREGO COUNTY–LEMKE MEMORIAL HOSPITAL (171355)**, 320 North 13th Street, Zip 67672–2099; tel. 785/743–2182, (Total facility includes 37 beds in nursing home–type unit) **A**10 18 **F**3 8 10 11 15 28 29 34 40 45 53 57 59 62 64 67 69 71 81 86 89 93 107 110 114 127 128 130 133 143 146 148 **P**6 **S** Great Plains Health Alliance, Inc., Wichita, KS
Primary Contact: David Augustine, Chief Executive Officer
CFO: ReChelle Horinek, Chief Financial Officer
CMO: Gordon Lang, M.D., Chief of Staff
CHR: Jeff Bieker, Director Human Resource
CNO: Sandy Purinton, Chief Nursing Officer
Web address: www.tclmh.org
Control: County–Government, nonfederal **Service:** General Medical and Surgical

Staffed Beds: 62 **Admissions:** 686 **Census:** 51 **Outpatient Visits:** 36179
Births: 0 **Total Expense ($000):** 18268 **Payroll Expense ($000):** 7838
Personnel: 180

WAMEGO—Pottawatomie County

★ **WAMEGO HEALTH CENTER (171337)**, 711 Genn Drive, Zip 66547–1179;
tel. 785/456–2295 **A**10 18 **F**3 11 15 28 29 32 34 35 40 45 56 59 64 65 75 77 81 93 97 107 114 119 127 130 131 132 133 143 146 147 148 **P**6
Primary Contact: Steve Land, Senior Administrator
COO: Brian Smith, Director of Operations
CFO: Keith Zachariasen, Chief Financial Officer
CMO: Roland Darey, M.D., Medical Director
CIO: Wes Janzen, Chief Information Officer
CHR: Renee Reed, Director Human Resources
CNO: Tresha Flanary, R.N., Chief Clinical Services Officer
Web address: www.https://www.wamegohealthcenter.com
Control: Other not–for–profit (including NFP Corporation) **Service:** General Medical and Surgical

Staffed Beds: 18 **Admissions:** 213 **Census:** 4 **Outpatient Visits:** 37429
Births: 0 **Total Expense ($000):** 11987 **Payroll Expense ($000):** 7171
Personnel: 72

WASHINGTON—Washington County

WASHINGTON COUNTY HOSPITAL (171351), 304 East Third Street,
Zip 66968–2033; tel. 785/325–2211 **A**10 18 **F**1 3 11 13 15 28 29 31 34 35 40 41 44 45 64 67 68 76 81 83 85 89 90 91 93 97 107 110 114 133 148 **P**6
Primary Contact: Roxanne Schottel, Chief Executive Officer
CFO: Linda Rettig, Director Financial Services
CNO: Kelly Otott, R.N., Chief Nursing Officer
Web address: www.washingtoncountyhospital.net
Control: County–Government, nonfederal **Service:** General Medical and Surgical

Staffed Beds: 16 **Admissions:** 156 **Census:** 6 **Outpatient Visits:** 4980
Births: 15 **Total Expense ($000):** 4895 **Payroll Expense ($000):** 1629
Personnel: 42

WELLINGTON—Sumner County

★ **SUMNER REGIONAL MEDICAL CENTER (170039)**, 1323 North A Street,
Zip 67152–4350; tel. 620/326–7451, (Total facility includes 9 beds in nursing home–type unit) **A**10 **F**10 11 13 15 31 35 40 45 56 59 64 76 77 78 79 81 82 85 98 103 107 108 110 111 119 128 129 130
Primary Contact: Barry Harding, Interim Chief Executive Officer and Chief Financial Officer
CFO: Barry Harding, Interim Chief Executive Officer and Chief Financial Officer
CHR: Allen Keller, Director Human Resources
CNO: Darlene Cooney, Director Nursing
Web address: www.srmcks.org
Control: City–Government, nonfederal **Service:** General Medical and Surgical

Staffed Beds: 61 **Admissions:** 559 **Census:** 6 **Outpatient Visits:** 16310
Births: 172 **Total Expense ($000):** 23590 **Payroll Expense ($000):** 5810
Personnel: 130

WICHITA—Sedgwick County

☐ **AMG SPECIALTY HOSPITAL–WICHITA (172003)**, 8080 East Pawnee Street,
Zip 67207–5475; tel. 316/682–0004 **A**1 10 **F**1 29 30 77 130 148 **P**5 **S** AMG Integrated Healthcare Management, Lafayette, LA
Primary Contact: Robert A. Loepp, Jr., FACHE, Chief Executive Officer
CFO: Myra Dick, Manager Business Office
CIO: Michelle Bradley, Director Health Information Management
CHR: Adrienne Burkholder, Director Human Resources
Web address: www.amgwichita.com/
Control: Corporation, Investor–owned, for–profit **Service:** Long–Term Acute Care hospital

Staffed Beds: 26 **Admissions:** 271 **Census:** 19 **Outpatient Visits:** 0 **Births:** 0 **Total Expense ($000):** 8091 **Payroll Expense ($000):** 3450 **Personnel:** 98

KANSAS HEART HOSPITAL (170186), 3601 North Webb Road,
Zip 67226–8129; tel. 316/630–5000 **A**10 **F**3 17 18 20 22 24 26 29 30 64 81 85 86 107 115 119
Primary Contact: Thomas L. Ashcom, M.D., Ph.D., Chief Executive Officer
COO: Joyce Heismeyer, Chief Operating Officer
CFO: Steve Smith, Chief Financial Officer
CHR: Teresa E. Wolfe, Manager Human Resources
CNO: Susan Bradford, Director Nursing
Web address: www.kansasheart.com
Control: Corporation, Investor–owned, for–profit **Service:** Heart

Staffed Beds: 54 **Admissions:** 1824 **Census:** 22 **Outpatient Visits:** 9392
Births: 0 **Personnel:** 197

KANSAS SPINE AND SPECIALTY HOSPITAL (170196), 3333 North Webb Road, Zip 67226–8123; tel. 316/462–5000 **A**10 **F**3 29 79 81 82 85 87 107 111 114
Primary Contact: Thomas M. Schmitt, Chief Executive Officer
CFO: Kevin P. Vaughn, Chief Financial Officer
CIO: Michael Knocke, Chief Information Officer
CHR: Jean–Marie Jimeson, Manager Human Resources
CNO: John Coslett, R.N., Chief Nursing Officer
Web address: www.ksspine.com
Control: Corporation, Investor–owned, for–profit **Service:** General Medical and Surgical

Staffed Beds: 36 **Admissions:** 2039 **Census:** 12 **Outpatient Visits:** 6766
Births: 0 **Personnel:** 102

Hospital, Medicare Provider Number, Address, Telephone, Approval, Facility, and Physician Codes, Health Care System

★ American Hospital Association (AHA) membership
☐ The Joint Commission accreditation
◯ Healthcare Facilities Accreditation Program
◇ DNV Healthcare Inc. accreditation
⇑ Center for Improvement in Healthcare Quality Accreditation
△ Commission on Accreditation of Rehabilitation Facilities (CARF) accreditation

KS

KANSAS SURGERY AND RECOVERY CENTER (170183), 2770 North Webb Road, Zip 67226–8112; tel. 316/634–0090 **A**10 **F**45 51 64 68 81 85 87 93 107 111 114 119
Primary Contact: Ely Bartal, M.D., Chief Executive Officer
CFO: Ashley Simon, Chief Financial Officer
CMO: Ely Bartal, M.D., Chief Executive Officer and Medical Director
CIO: Jonathan Wells, Supervisor Information Technology
CNO: Becky Bailey, R.N., Director Nursing
Web address: www.ksrc.org
Control: Partnership, Investor–owned, for–profit **Service:** Surgical

Staffed Beds: 32 **Admissions:** 1777 **Census:** 11 **Outpatient Visits:** 6284
Births: 0 **Total Expense ($000):** 25573 **Payroll Expense ($000):** 6484
Personnel: 126

☒ **ROBERT J. DOLE VETERANS AFFAIRS MEDICAL CENTER**, 5500 East Kellogg, Zip 67218–1607; tel. 316/685–2221, (Nonreporting) **A**1 3 5
S Department of Veterans Affairs, Washington, DC
Primary Contact: Francisco Vazquez, Director
CFO: Ronald Dreher, Finance Officer
CMO: Kent Murray, M.D., Chief of Staff
CIO: Sharon Williamson, Chief Information Technology
CHR: Nancy Gerstner, Manager Human Resources
Web address: www.wichita.va.gov
Control: Veterans Affairs, Government, federal **Service:** General Medical and Surgical

Staffed Beds: 41

☒ **SELECT SPECIALTY HOSPITAL–WICHITA (172007)**, 929 North St. Francis Street, Zip 67214–3821; tel. 316/261–8303 **A**1 10 **F**1 3 12 18 29 50 56 61 75 82 84 85 86 87 130 148 **S** Select Medical Corporation, Mechanicsburg, PA
Primary Contact: Peggy Cliffe, Chief Executive Officer
CHR: Renee Schaffer, Coordinator Human Resources
CNO: Lindsey Cahoj, Chief Nursing Officer
Web address: www.selectspecialtyhospitals.com/company/locations/wichita.aspx
Control: Corporation, Investor–owned, for–profit **Service:** Long–Term Acute Care hospital

Staffed Beds: 48 **Admissions:** 567 **Census:** 42 **Outpatient Visits:** 0 **Births:** 0 **Total Expense ($000):** 21070 **Payroll Expense ($000):** 8351 **Personnel:** 140

☒ **VIA CHRISTI HOSPITAL ON ST. FRANCIS (170122)**, 929 North St. Francis Street, Zip 67214–3882; tel. 316/268–5000, (Includes GOOD SHEPHERD CAMPUS, 8901 East Orme, Zip 67207; tel. 316/858–0333; ST. FRANCIS CAMPUS, 929 North St. Francis Street, tel. 316/268–5000; Sherry Hausmann, Senior Administrator; ST. JOSEPH CAMPUS, 3600 East Harry Street, Zip 67218–3713; tel. 316/685–1111; Claudio J. Ferraro, President) **A**1 2 3 5 10 13 **F**3 5 7 11 12 13 15 16 17 18 19 20 21 22 23 24 26 27 28 29 30 31 32 34 35 38 40 43 44 45 46 48 49 50 51 54 56 57 58 59 60 61 62 64 68 70 72 74 75 76 77 78 79 80 81 82 84 85 86 87 88 89 92 93 97 98 99 100 101 102 103 104 105 107 108 110 111 114 115 116 117 118 119 120 121 123 124 126 130 131 132 135 136 141 142 143 146 147 148 **P**6
S Ascension Health, Saint Louis, MO
Primary Contact: Sherry Hausmann, Senior Administrator
CFO: Jeff Seirer, Interim Chief Financial Officer
CMO: Darrell Youngman, D.O., Chief Medical Officer
CIO: Donna Roach, Chief Information Officer
CHR: Judy Espinoza, Chief Human Resources Officer
Web address: www.via–christi.org
Control: Church–operated, Nongovernment, not–for profit **Service:** General Medical and Surgical

Staffed Beds: 717 **Admissions:** 32368 **Census:** 408 **Outpatient Visits:** 316950 **Births:** 2482 **Total Expense ($000):** 521020 **Payroll Expense ($000):** 200641 **Personnel:** 3448

☒ **VIA CHRISTI HOSPITAL ON ST. TERESA (170200)**, 14800 West St. Teresa, Zip 67235–9602; tel. 316/796–7000 **A**1 10 **F**3 8 18 20 22 29 30 34 35 40 45 50 64 68 70 75 78 79 81 85 87 107 108 111 114 118 119 130 146 147 148 **S** Ascension Health, Saint Louis, MO
Primary Contact: Claudio J. Ferraro, Senior Administrator
Web address: www.via–christi.org/st–teresa
Control: Church–operated, Nongovernment, not–for–profit **Service:** General Medical and Surgical

Staffed Beds: 40 **Admissions:** 1788 **Census:** 23 **Outpatient Visits:** 21001
Births: 0 **Total Expense ($000):** 36122 **Payroll Expense ($000):** 11382
Personnel: 167

VIA CHRISTI REGIONAL MEDICAL CENTER See Via Christi Hospital on St. Francis

☒ **VIA CHRISTI REHABILITATION HOSPITAL (173028)**, 1151 North Rock Road, Zip 67206–1262; tel. 316/634–3400 **A**1 10 **F**11 29 30 34 35 44 50 54 57 59 64 77 86 87 90 92 93 94 95 96 119 129 130 131 132 143 146 148
S Ascension Health, Saint Louis, MO
Primary Contact: Cindy LaFleur, Senior Administrator
CMO: Kevin Rieg, M.D., President Medical Staff
CNO: Cindy Hagerty, Assistant Chief Nurse Officer and Administrator of Operations
Web address: www.via–christi.org
Control: Church–operated, Nongovernment, not–for profit **Service:** Rehabilitation

Staffed Beds: 58 **Admissions:** 797 **Census:** 26 **Outpatient Visits:** 102379
Births: 0 **Total Expense ($000):** 23404 **Payroll Expense ($000):** 11111
Personnel: 220

☒ **WESLEY MEDICAL CENTER (170123)**, 550 North Hillside, Zip 67214–4976; tel. 316/962–2000, (Includes WESLEY CHILDREN'S HOSPITAL, 550 North Hillside Street, Zip 67214–4910; tel. 316/962–2000; WESLEY WOODLAWN HOSPITAL & ER, 2610 North Woodlawn, Zip 67220; tel. 316/858–2610) **A**1 3 5 10 **F**3 7 11 12 13 15 17 18 19 20 22 24 26 28 29 30 31 34 35 37 39 40 41 42 43 44 45 46 47 48 49 50 51 54 55 56 57 58 59 60 64 65 68 70 72 73 74 76 78 79 81 82 85 86 87 88 89 92 93 94 97 100 102 107 108 110 111 114 115 119 120 121 123 124 126 129 130 131 132 134 135 146 147 148 **P**6
S HCA, Nashville, TN
Primary Contact: Bill Voloch, President and Chief Executive Officer
CFO: Bradley Schultz, Chief Financial Officer
CMO: Francie H. Ekengren, M.D., Chief Medical Officer
CIO: Jeffrey Schauf, Director Information Systems
CHR: Jennifer Krier, Vice President Human Resources
CNO: Joyce M. Soule, R.N., Chief Nursing Officer
Web address: www.wesleymc.com
Control: Corporation, Investor–owned, for–profit **Service:** General Medical and Surgical

Staffed Beds: 562 **Admissions:** 27198 **Census:** 355 **Outpatient Visits:** 252418 **Births:** 6153 **Personnel:** 2442

☒ **WESLEY REHABILITATION HOSPITAL (173027)**, 8338 West 13th Street North, Zip 67212–2984; tel. 316/729–9999 **A**1 10 **F**29 34 35 62 64 68 90 91 93 95 96 132 148 **S** HEALTHSOUTH Corporation, Birmingham, AL
Primary Contact: James F. Grocholski, FACHE, Chief Executive Officer
CFO: Bob Peck, Chief Financial Officer
CIO: Debbie Patterson, Director Health Information Management
CHR: Betty Shuman, Director Human Resources
CNO: Jessika M. Workman, Chief Nursing Officer
Web address: www.wesleyrehabhospital.com
Control: Corporation, Investor–owned, for–profit **Service:** Rehabilitation

Staffed Beds: 65 **Admissions:** 1044 **Census:** 38 **Outpatient Visits:** 23143
Births: 0 **Total Expense ($000):** 18575 **Payroll Expense ($000):** 9076
Personnel: 152

WICHITA SPECIALTY HOSPITAL See AMG Specialty Hospital–Wichita

WINCHESTER—Jefferson County

★ **F. W. HUSTON MEDICAL CENTER (171314)**, 408 Delaware Street, Zip 66097–4003; tel. 913/774–4340, (Total facility includes 38 beds in nursing home–type unit) **A**10 18 **F**1 2 3 4 10 16 17 40 56 57 64 67 69 70 72 73 75 76 77 80 88 89 90 93 97 98 103 104 107 114 128 130 133 143 **P**6 8
Primary Contact: LaMont Cook, Administrator
CFO: Jason Johnson, Controller
CMO: William Greiner, M.D., Chief of Staff
CIO: Jason Johnson, Controller
CHR: Melody Keirns, Manager Human Resources
CNO: Heather R. Aranda, R.N., Chief Nursing Officer
Web address: www.jcmhospital.org
Control: Other not–for–profit (including NFP Corporation) **Service:** General Medical and Surgical

Staffed Beds: 74 **Admissions:** 76 **Census:** 33 **Outpatient Visits:** 5874
Births: 0 **Total Expense ($000):** 5240 **Payroll Expense ($000):** 3449
Personnel: 71

JEFFERSON COUNTY MEMORIAL HOSPITAL See F. W. Huston Medical Center

WINFIELD—Cowley County

★ **WILLIAM NEWTON HOSPITAL (171383)**, 1300 East Fifth Street, Zip 67156–2407; tel. 620/221–2300 **A**3 5 10 18 **F**3 8 9 10 11 12 13 15 28 29 34 35 39 40 43 45 56 57 59 62 64 68 69 70 76 77 79 81 85 87 89 93 96 97 107 108 110 111 114 118 119 127 129 130 133 146 147 148
Primary Contact: J. Ben Quinton, Administrator
COO: Shona Salzman, Chief Operating Officer
CFO: Debbie Hockenbury, Assistant Administrator and Chief Financial Officer
CMO: Bryan Dennett, M.D., Chief of Staff
CIO: Randy Mayo, Director Information Technology
CHR: Cathy McClurg, Director Human Resources
CNO: Tina Wheeler, R.N., Director Nursing
Web address: www.wnmh.org
Control: City–Government, nonfederal **Service:** General Medical and Surgical

Staffed Beds: 25 **Admissions:** 1029 **Census:** 9 **Outpatient Visits:** 76380
Births: 237 **Total Expense ($000):** 31711 **Payroll Expense ($000):** 13992
Personnel: 273

Many Facility Codes have changed. Please refer to the AHA Guide Code Chart.
© 2016 AHA Guide

KS

KENTUCKY

ALBANY—Clinton County

THE MEDICAL CENTER ALBANY (180106), 723 Burkesville Road, Zip 42602–1654; tel. 606/387–8000 **A**10 **F**3 10 11 15 29 30 40 41 45 50 64 81 82 93 107 114 119 133 146 **S** Commonwealth Health Corporation, Bowling Green, KY
Primary Contact: Laura Belcher, Interim Administrator
CFO: Ronald G. Sowell, Executive Vice President, Chief Financial Officer
CIO: Mark Brookman, Chief Information Officer
CHR: Lynn Williams, Vice President, Human Resources
Web address: www.chc.net/services/hospitals/the_medical_center_at_albany.aspx
Control: County–Government, nonfederal **Service:** General Medical and Surgical

Staffed Beds: 42 **Admissions:** 773 **Census:** 9 **Outpatient Visits:** 6241 **Personnel:** 129

ASHLAND—Boyd County

☐ **KING'S DAUGHTERS MEDICAL CENTER (180009)**, 2201 Lexington Avenue, Zip 41101–2874, Mailing Address: P.O. Box 151, Zip 41105–0151; tel. 606/408–4000, (Total facility includes 147 beds in nursing home–type unit) **A**1 2 10 **F**3 7 8 11 12 13 15 17 18 20 22 24 26 28 29 30 31 32 34 35 40 41 44 45 47 48 49 50 51 54 55 57 58 59 61 62 64 70 72 74 75 76 77 78 79 80 81 82 84 85 86 87 89 92 93 96 98 100 101 102 107 108 110 111 114 115 117 118 119 126 127 128 129 130 131 132 135 144 146 147 148 **P**6 8
Primary Contact: Kristie Whitlatch, President
COO: Bob Lucas, Vice President Operations
CFO: Paul L. McDowell, Vice President Finance and Chief Financial Officer
CMO: Phil Fioret, M.D., Vice President Medical Affairs
CIO: David Oliver, Director Information Systems
CHR: Larry Higgins, Vice President Human Resources
Web address: www.kdmc.com
Control: Other not–for–profit (including NFP Corporation) **Service:** General Medical and Surgical

Staffed Beds: 612 **Admissions:** 15611 **Census:** 488 **Outpatient Visits:** 859911 **Births:** 1150 **Total Expense ($000):** 464609 **Payroll Expense ($000):** 193676 **Personnel:** 3047

✠ **OUR LADY OF BELLEFONTE HOSPITAL (180036)**, St. Christopher Drive, Zip 41101, Mailing Address: P.O. Box 789, Zip 41105–0789; tel. 606/833–3333 **A**1 2 10 12 13 **F**3 4 5 8 11 12 15 18 19 20 28 29 30 31 34 35 37 39 40 44 45 49 50 53 54 55 56 57 58 59 62 64 65 66 69 70 71 74 75 77 78 79 81 82 84 85 86 87 89 93 96 97 98 100 101 102 103 104 105 106 107 108 110 111 114 115 118 119 126 129 130 131 132 135 143 144 145 146 147 148 **P**6 8 **S** Bon Secours Health System, Inc., Marriottsville, MD
Primary Contact: Kevin Halter, Chief Executive Officer
CFO: Joe Buchheit, Chief Financial Officer
CMO: Dan Goulson, M.D., Chief Medical Officer
CIO: Mike Gomez, Site Manager Medical Information Systems
CHR: Judy Daniels, Vice President Human Resources
Web address: www.olbh.com
Control: Church–operated, Nongovernment, not–for profit **Service:** General Medical and Surgical

Staffed Beds: 147 **Admissions:** 6595 **Census:** 78 **Outpatient Visits:** 246032 **Births:** 0 **Total Expense ($000):** 146128 **Payroll Expense ($000):** 45860 **Personnel:** 1386

BARBOURVILLE—Knox County

☐ **BARBOURVILLE ARH HOSPITAL (181328)**, 80 Hospital Drive, Zip 40906–7363, Mailing Address: P.O. Box 10, Zip 40906–0010; tel. 606/546–4175 **A**1 10 18 **F**28 29 40 45 49 50 57 70 77 81 107 119 130 133 **S** Pacer Health Corporation, Miami Lakes, FL
Primary Contact: Charles D. Lovell, Jr., FACHE, Chief Executive Officer
CFO: Amanda Ellis, Chief Financial Officer
CMO: Kamran Hasni, M.D., Chief of Medical Staff
CIO: Evan Davis, Director Technology and Environmental Services
CHR: Janet Wilder, Director Human Resources
CNO: Brenda Graham, Chief Nursing Officer
Web address: www.knoxcohospital.com
Control: Other not–for–profit (including NFP Corporation) **Service:** General Medical and Surgical

Staffed Beds: 25 **Admissions:** 2119 **Census:** 14 **Births:** 0 **Personnel:** 170

BARDSTOWN—Nelson County

✠ **FLAGET MEMORIAL HOSPITAL (180025)**, 4305 New Shepherdsville Road, Zip 40004–9019; tel. 502/350–5000, (Total facility includes 12 beds in nursing home–type unit) **A**1 2 10 **F**3 11 12 13 15 18 29 30 31 34 35 37 40 45 49 55 59 60 62 63 64 70 76 78 79 81 82 84 85 87 91 93 96 107 111 116 117 119 120 128 129 130 132 144 146 147 148 **P**6 **S** Catholic Health Initiatives, Englewood, CO
Primary Contact: Beverly Sue Downs, R.N., MSN, FACHE, President
COO: Norma Goss, R.N., Chief Operating Officer and Chief Nursing Officer
CFO: Mendy Evans, Vice President of Finance
CMO: Mickey Anderson, M.D., Vice President Medical Affairs
CNO: Norma Goss, R.N., Chief Operating Officer and Chief Nursing Officer
Web address: www.flaget.com
Control: Other not–for–profit (including NFP Corporation) **Service:** General Medical and Surgical

Staffed Beds: 42 **Admissions:** 2478 **Census:** 28 **Outpatient Visits:** 72775 **Births:** 264 **Total Expense ($000):** 64491 **Payroll Expense ($000):** 15330 **Personnel:** 305

BENTON—Marshall County

✠ **MARSHALL COUNTY HOSPITAL (181327)**, 615 Old Symsonia Road, Zip 42025–5042; tel. 270/527–4800 **A**1 10 18 **F**3 7 11 15 18 19 28 29 30 34 35 40 57 59 62 77 79 81 85 89 90 93 107 108 119 132 133 135 **P**6
Primary Contact: David G. Fuqua, Chief Executive Officer
CFO: Janice Kelley, Chief Financial Officer
CMO: Edwin Perez, M.D., Chief of Medical Staff
CIO: Dave Cope, Director Information Systems
CHR: Jeannie Lee, Director Human Resources
Web address: www.marshallcountyhospital.org
Control: Hospital district or authority, Government, nonfederal **Service:** General Medical and Surgical

Staffed Beds: 25 **Admissions:** 845 **Census:** 8 **Outpatient Visits:** 133657 **Births:** 0 **Total Expense ($000):** 22938 **Payroll Expense ($000):** 8141 **Personnel:** 219

BEREA—Madison County

✠ **SAINT JOSEPH BEREA (181329)**, 305 Estill Street, Zip 40403–1909; tel. 859/986–3151 **A**1 5 10 18 **F**3 29 40 45 70 77 79 81 82 91 97 107 111 114 119 133 **P**4 **S** Catholic Health Initiatives, Englewood, CO
Primary Contact: Eric Gilliam, Chief Executive Officer
CFO: Christy Spitser, Vice President Finance
CMO: Joshua Huffman, M.D., Chief Medical Staff
CHR: Sandra Turqueza, Human Resources Business Partner
CNO: Leslie Adams, Chief Nursing Executive
Web address: www.kentuckyonehealth.org/berea
Control: Church–operated, Nongovernment, not–for profit **Service:** General Medical and Surgical

Staffed Beds: 25 **Admissions:** 1223 **Census:** 13 **Outpatient Visits:** 53911 **Births:** 0 **Total Expense ($000):** 28704 **Payroll Expense ($000):** 9264 **Personnel:** 164

BOWLING GREEN—Warren County

☐ **COMMONWEALTH REGIONAL SPECIALTY HOSPITAL (182005)**, 250 Park Drive, 6th Floor, Zip 42101–1760, Mailing Address: P.O. Box 90010, Zip 42102–9010; tel. 270/796–6200 **A**1 10 **F**1 3 29 30 34 35 50 57 68 84 85 87 130 135 143 146 148 **P**6 **S** Commonwealth Health Corporation, Bowling Green, KY
Primary Contact: Christa Atkins, Administrator
CFO: Ronald G. Sowell, Executive Vice President
CMO: Doug Thomson, M.D., Chief Medical Officer
CIO: Jean Cherry, Executive Vice President
CHR: Lynn Williams, Vice President
Web address: www.commonwealthregionalspecialtyhospital.org
Control: Other not–for–profit (including NFP Corporation) **Service:** Long–Term Acute Care hospital

Staffed Beds: 28 **Admissions:** 217 **Census:** 18 **Outpatient Visits:** 0 **Births:** 0 **Personnel:** 58

Hospital, Medicare Provider Number, Address, Telephone, Approval, Facility, and Physician Codes, Health Care System

★ American Hospital Association (AHA) membership
☐ The Joint Commission accreditation
○ Healthcare Facilities Accreditation Program
◇ DNV Healthcare Inc. accreditation
⇑ Center for Improvement in Healthcare Quality Accreditation
△ Commission on Accreditation of Rehabilitation Facilities (CARF) accreditation

☐ **MEDICAL CENTER AT BOWLING GREEN (180013)**, 250 Park Street,
Zip 42101–1795, Mailing Address: P.O. Box 90010, Zip 42102–9010;
tel. 270/745–1000 **A**1 2 10 13 19 **F**1 3 7 12 13 15 17 18 20 22 24 26 28 29
30 31 34 35 37 39 40 45 46 48 49 50 51 56 57 59 60 62 64 68 70 72 74
75 76 78 79 81 82 85 86 87 89 91 92 93 98 100 102 103 104 107 108 110
111 115 116 117 118 119 120 121 122 123 124 126 129 130 132 135 145
146 147 148 **P**6 **S** Commonwealth Health Corporation, Bowling Green, KY
Primary Contact: Connie Smith, Chief Executive Officer
CFO: Ronald G. Sowell, Executive Vice President
CIO: Mark Brookman, Chief Information Officer
CHR: Lynn Williams, Vice President Human Resources
CNO: Betsy Kullman, R.N., Executive Vice President and Chief Nursing Officer
Web address: www.themedicalcenter.org
Control: Other not–for–profit (including NFP Corporation) **Service:** General
Medical and Surgical

Staffed Beds: 337 **Admissions:** 15858 **Census:** 231 **Outpatient Visits:**
135217 **Births:** 2370 **Personnel:** 1723

☐ **RIVENDELL BEHAVIORAL HEALTH (184017)**, 1035 Porter Pike,
Zip 42103–9581; tel. 270/843–1199, (Nonreporting) **A**1 10 **S** Universal Health
Services, Inc., King of Prussia, PA
Primary Contact: Matt Ours, Chief Executive Officer and Managing Director
CFO: Tim Gore, Chief Financial Officer
Web address: www.rivendellbehavioral.com
Control: Corporation, Investor–owned, for–profit **Service:** Psychiatric

Staffed Beds: 125

✠ △ **SOUTHERN KENTUCKY REHABILITATION HOSPITAL (183029)**, 1300
Campbell Lane, Zip 42104–4162; tel. 270/782–6900, (Nonreporting) **A**1 7 10
S Vibra Healthcare, Mechanicsburg, PA
Primary Contact: Stuart Locke, Chief Executive Officer
COO: Dana Lewis, Director Clinical Services
CMO: Jim Farrage, M.D., Medical Director
CHR: Suzanne Cornett, Director Human Resources
Web address: www.skyrehab.com
Control: Corporation, Investor–owned, for–profit **Service:** Rehabilitation

Staffed Beds: 60

✠ **TRISTAR GREENVIEW REGIONAL HOSPITAL (180124)**, 1801 Ashley Circle,
Zip 42104–3362; tel. 270/793–1000 **A**1 2 10 19 **F**3 8 11 15 18 20 22 29 30
31 34 35 37 40 45 46 48 49 50 51 57 64 65 68 70 74 75 78 79 81 82 85
86 87 107 108 110 111 114 118 119 126 128 130 132 133 135 145 146
S HCA, Nashville, TN
Primary Contact: Michael Sherrod, Chief Executive Officer
COO: Andrew Bedi, Chief Operating Officer
CMO: Wayne Bush, M.D., Chief of Staff
CIO: Cyndi Talley, Director Information Systems
CHR: Judy Fulkerson, Director Human Resources
CNO: Anne Leonard, R.N., Chief Nursing Officer
Web address: www.greenviewhospital.com
Control: Corporation, Investor–owned, for–profit **Service:** General Medical and
Surgical

Staffed Beds: 167 **Admissions:** 4964 **Census:** 59 **Outpatient Visits:** 62258
Births: 0 **Total Expense ($000):** 94852 **Payroll Expense ($000):** 31478
Personnel: 434

BURKESVILLE—Cumberland County

CUMBERLAND COUNTY HOSPITAL (181317), 299 Glasgow Road,
Zip 42717–9696, Mailing Address: P.O. Box 280, Zip 42717–0280;
tel. 270/864–2511, (Nonreporting) **A**10 18
Primary Contact: Richard Neikirk, Chief Executive Officer
CFO: Rick Capps, Chief Financial Officer
CMO: Christian Konsavage, M.D., Chief of Staff
CHR: Martha Young, Director Human Resources
Web address: www.cchospital.org
Control: Other not–for–profit (including NFP Corporation) **Service:** General
Medical and Surgical

Staffed Beds: 25

CADIZ—Trigg County

TRIGG COUNTY HOSPITAL (181304), 254 Main Street, Zip 42211–9153,
Mailing Address: P.O. Box 312, Zip 42211–0312; tel. 270/522–3215,
(Nonreporting) **A**10 18
Primary Contact: John Sumner, Chief Executive Officer
CFO: Liz Snodgrass, Chief Financial Officer
CMO: Stuart Harris, M.D., Chief of Staff
CHR: Janet James, Director Human Resources
Web address: www.trigghospital.org
Control: County–Government, nonfederal **Service:** General Medical and Surgical

Staffed Beds: 25

CAMPBELLSVILLE—Taylor County

✠ **TAYLOR REGIONAL HOSPITAL (180087)**, 1700 Old Lebanon Road,
Zip 42718–9600; tel. 270/465–3561 **A**1 2 10 **F**3 8 11 13 15 18 20 29 30 31
34 35 39 40 43 45 46 48 49 50 51 54 56 57 59 64 68 70 74 75 76 77 78
79 81 85 86 93 97 107 108 110 111 115 118 119 127 129 130 131 132
134 135 141 143 146 147 148 **S** Catholic Health Initiatives, Englewood, CO
Primary Contact: Jane Wheatley, Chief Executive Officer
CFO: Paul Phillips, Chief Financial Officer
CIO: Christopher Michael Gibbs, Director Information Management Systems
CHR: Andrea Settle, Director Human Resources
CNO: Dana M. Garrett, R.N., Nursing Services Administrator
Web address: www.trhosp.org
Control: Hospital district or authority, Government, nonfederal **Service:** General
Medical and Surgical

Staffed Beds: 90 **Admissions:** 2573 **Census:** 29 **Outpatient Visits:** 96399
Births: 335 **Total Expense ($000):** 67089 **Payroll Expense ($000):** 29698
Personnel: 576

CARROLLTON—Carroll County

★ **CARROLL COUNTY MEMORIAL HOSPITAL (181310)**, 309 11th Street,
Zip 41008–1400; tel. 502/732–4321 **A**10 18 **F**3 11 15 18 28 29 34 40 45 50
56 57 59 74 75 77 78 79 81 82 85 86 93 94 97 107 108 111 114 119 127
128 129 130 133 144 **P**6 **S** Alliant Management Services, Louisville, KY
Primary Contact: Harry Hays, Chief Executive Officer
CMO: Kathy Short, D.O., Family Practice
CHR: Kimberly Adams, Manager Human Resources
CNO: Lisa Penick, R.N., Chief Nursing Officer
Web address: www.ccmhosp.com
Control: Hospital district or authority, Government, nonfederal **Service:** General
Medical and Surgical

Staffed Beds: 25 **Admissions:** 587 **Census:** 5 **Outpatient Visits:** 16273
Births: 0

COLUMBIA—Adair County

✠ **T.J. HEALTH COLUMBIA (180149)**, 901 Westlake Drive, Zip 42728–1123,
Mailing Address: P.O. Box 1269, Zip 42728–6269; tel. 270/384–4753,
(Nonreporting) **A**1 10
Primary Contact: Bud Wethington, Chief Executive Officer
CFO: David R. Hayes, Chief Financial Officer
CMO: Charles Giles, M.D., President Medical Staff
CHR: Tonya Grant, Director Human Resources
CNO: Gidgett Warren, Director of Nursing
Web address: www.healthiercolumbia.org/
Control: Hospital district or authority, Government, nonfederal **Service:** General
Medical and Surgical

Staffed Beds: 32

CORBIN—Whitley County

★ ◇ **BAPTIST HEALTH CORBIN (180080)**, 1 Trillium Way, Zip 40701–8420;
tel. 606/528–1212 **A**10 19 21 **F**1 3 4 5 12 13 15 18 20 22 26 28 29 30 31
32 34 35 38 40 45 47 48 49 51 53 54 57 59 64 67 68 70 73 76 78 79 81
84 85 86 87 89 90 93 96 98 99 100 101 102 103 104 105 107 108 110
111 114 115 118 119 126 130 132 133 135 145 146 147 148 **S** Baptist
Health, Louisville, KY
Primary Contact: Larry Gray, President
CFO: Pamela K. Jones, Executive Director of Finance
CMO: David Worthy, M.D., Vice President and Chief Medical Officer
CIO: Rodney Richardson, Director of Information Technology
CHR: Tim Perry, Executive Director of Human Resources
CNO: Sherrie Mays, MSN, Vice President and Chief Nursing Officer
Web address: www.baptisthealth.com/corbin
Control: Other not–for–profit (including NFP Corporation) **Service:** General
Medical and Surgical

Staffed Beds: 273 **Admissions:** 9261 **Census:** 119 **Outpatient Visits:**
142221 **Births:** 933 **Total Expense ($000):** 138634 **Payroll Expense
($000):** 49468 **Personnel:** 995

◇ **CONTINUECARE HOSPITAL AT BAPTIST HEALTH CORBIN (182006)**, 1
Trillium Way, Lower Level, Zip 40701–8727; tel. 606/523–5150 **A**10 21 **F**1 3
29 30 39 60 130 148 **S** Community Hospital Corporation, Plano, TX
Primary Contact: R. Alan Coppock, FACHE, President and CEO
COO: Wilson Weber, Chief Operating Officer
CFO: Lisa Young, CPA, Chief Financial Officer
CMO: Steve Morton, M.D., Chief Medical Officer
CIO: Brian Doerr, Chief Information Officer
CHR: Amie Marcum, Human Resources Coordinator
CNO: Della Rains, Chief Nursing Officer
Web address: www.continuecare.org
Control: Other not–for–profit (including NFP Corporation) **Service:** Long–Term
Acute Care hospital

Staffed Beds: 32 **Admissions:** 385 **Census:** 29 **Outpatient Visits:** 0 **Births:**
0 **Total Expense ($000):** 12960 **Payroll Expense ($000):** 5363 **Personnel:**
99

COVINGTON—Kenton County

NORTHKEY COMMUNITY CARE (184006), 502 Farrell Drive,
Zip 41011–3799, Mailing Address: P.O. Box 2680, Zip 41012–2680;
tel. 859/578–3200, (Nonreporting) **A**10
Primary Contact: Owen Nichols, PsyD, President and Chief Executive Officer
CFO: John Metzger, Controller
Web address: www.northkey.org
Control: Other not–for–profit (including NFP Corporation) **Service:** Children's
hospital psychiatric

Staffed Beds: 34

ST. ELIZABETH MEDICAL CENTER–NORTH See St. Elizabeth Covington

CYNTHIANA—Harrison County

✠ **HARRISON MEMORIAL HOSPITAL (180079)**, 1210 KY Highway 36E,
Zip 41031–7498; tel. 859/234–2300 **A**1 10 **F**3 11 13 15 18 20 28 29 30 31
34 35 36 39 40 44 45 47 49 50 53 57 59 61 64 68 69 70 74 75 76 77 78
79 81 82 85 86 87 89 93 97 107 108 111 115 118 119 129 130 131 132
133 135 146 147 148 **P**6
Primary Contact: Sheila Currans, Chief Executive Officer
CFO: David Mellett, Chief Financial Officer
CIO: Martha Sullivan, Chief Information Officer
CHR: Rebecca Jenkins, Director Human Resources Management
CNO: Wendy Reeder, R.N., Chief Nursing Officer
Web address: www.harrisonmemhosp.com
Control: Other not–for–profit (including NFP Corporation) **Service:** General
Medical and Surgical

Staffed Beds: 50 **Admissions:** 1447 **Census:** 14 **Outpatient Visits:** 66207
Births: 235 **Total Expense ($000):** 40378 **Payroll Expense ($000):** 16616
Personnel: 392

DANVILLE—Boyle County

☐ **EPHRAIM MCDOWELL REGIONAL MEDICAL CENTER (180048)**, 217 South
Third Street, Zip 40422–1823; tel. 859/239–1000, (Total facility includes 24
beds in nursing home–type unit) **A**1 5 10 19 **F**1 3 4 8 10 11 13 15 16 17 18
20 22 28 29 30 31 32 34 35 40 43 45 46 49 51 53 56 57 59 60 64 65 66
67 70 72 73 74 75 76 77 78 79 80 81 82 84 85 87 88 89 90 93 96 97 98
100 101 102 103 107 108 110 111 114 117 118 119 124 125 127 128 129
130 132 144 146 147 148 **P**5 **S** Ephraim McDowell Health, Danville, KY
Primary Contact: Sally M. Davenport, R.N., MS, Chief Executive Officer
COO: Sally M. Davenport, R.N., Chief Nursing Officer and Chief Operating Officer
CFO: William R. Snapp, III, Vice President Finance and Chief Financial Officer
CMO: Eric Guerrant, M.D., President Medical Staff
CIO: Angela Allen–Johnson, Director Information Services
CHR: Carl Metz, Vice President Human Resources
CNO: Sally M. Davenport, R.N., Chief Nursing Officer and Chief Operating Officer
Web address: www.emrmc.org
Control: Other not–for–profit (including NFP Corporation) **Service:** General
Medical and Surgical

Staffed Beds: 159 **Admissions:** 7370 **Census:** 101 **Outpatient Visits:**
131213 **Births:** 658 **Total Expense ($000):** 141564 **Payroll Expense**
($000): 48197 **Personnel:** 990

EDGEWOOD—Kenton County

✠ **HEALTHSOUTH NORTHERN KENTUCKY REHABILITATION HOSPITAL
(183027)**, 201 Medical Village Drive, Zip 41017–3407; tel. 859/341–2044 **A**1
10 **F**28 29 64 79 82 90 91 93 94 95 96 148 **S** HEALTHSOUTH Corporation,
Birmingham, AL
Primary Contact: Richard R. Evens, Chief Executive Officer
CFO: Lisa McGue, Controller
CMO: Neal Moser, M.D., Medical Director
CHR: Bridgette Keith, Director Human Resources
CNO: Terri Ballard, Chief Nursing Officer
Web address: www.healthsouthkentucky.com
Control: Corporation, Investor–owned, for–profit **Service:** Rehabilitation

Staffed Beds: 40 **Admissions:** 1266 **Census:** 38 **Outpatient Visits:** 3548
Births: 0 **Personnel:** 134

☐ **ST. ELIZABETH EDGEWOOD (180035)**, 1 Medical Village Drive,
Zip 41017–3403; tel. 859/301–2000, (Includes ST. ELIZABETH COVINGTON,
1500 James Simpson Jr. Way, Covington, Zip 41014–1585; tel. 859/655–8800)
A1 2 3 5 10 **F**3 5 8 13 14 15 17 18 20 22 24 26 28 29 30 31 34 35 36 37
38 39 40 44 45 46 47 48 49 50 55 57 58 59 60 61 63 64 65 70 71 72 73
74 75 76 77 78 79 80 81 82 83 84 85 86 87 92 93 97 98 100 101 102 103
104 105 107 108 109 110 111 114 115 116 117 118 119 120 121 123 124
126 129 130 131 132 135 141 145 146 147 148 **S** St. Elizabeth Healthcare,
Edgewood, KY
Primary Contact: Garren Colvin, Chief Executive Officer
CMO: Karl Schmitt, M.D., Chief of Staff
CIO: Alex Rodriguez, Vice President and Chief Information Officer
CHR: Martin Oscadal, Vice President Human Resources
Web address: www.stelizabeth.com
Control: Church–operated, Nongovernment, not–for profit **Service:** General
Medical and Surgical

Staffed Beds: 508 **Admissions:** 27520 **Census:** 340 **Outpatient Visits:**
1049080 **Births:** 4330 **Total Expense ($000):** 629524 **Payroll Expense**
($000): 232178 **Personnel:** 3357

ST. ELIZABETH HEALTHCARE–EDGEWOOD See St. Elizabeth Edgewood

ELIZABETHTOWN—Hardin County

✠ **HARDIN MEMORIAL HOSPITAL (180012)**, 913 North Dixie Avenue,
Zip 42701–2503; tel. 270/737–1212, (Total facility includes 15 beds in nursing
home–type unit) **A**1 2 5 10 19 **F**3 8 11 12 13 15 17 18 20 22 24 28 29 30 31
32 34 35 37 39 40 44 45 48 49 50 51 52 54 57 58 59 64 68 70 71 72 74
75 76 77 78 79 80 81 82 84 85 86 87 89 93 94 96 98 102 107 108 110
111 114 115 117 118 119 120 121 124 126 128 129 130 131 132 134 135
144 146 147 148 **S** Baptist Health, Louisville, KY
Primary Contact: Dennis B. Johnson, President and Chief Executive Officer
COO: Tom Carrico, Vice President of Operations
CFO: Lennis Thompson, II, Vice President and Chief Financial Officer
CMO: John Godfrey, M.D., Vice President and Chief Executive Officer
CIO: Trey Hyberger, Director Information Technology
CHR: Myra Covault, Associate Vice President of Human Resources
CNO: Sharon Wright, R.N., Vice President and Chief Nursing Officer
Web address: www.hmh.net
Control: County–Government, nonfederal **Service:** General Medical and Surgical

Staffed Beds: 268 **Admissions:** 12941 **Census:** 152 **Outpatient Visits:**
388776 **Births:** 1629 **Total Expense ($000):** 240601 **Payroll Expense**
($000): 106314 **Personnel:** 1865

✠ **HEALTHSOUTH LAKEVIEW REHABILITATION HOSPITAL (183028)**, 134
Heartland Drive, Zip 42701–2778; tel. 270/769–3100, (Nonreporting) **A**1 10
S HEALTHSOUTH Corporation, Birmingham, AL
Primary Contact: Lori Jarboe, Chief Executive Officer
CFO: Scott Hart, Controller
CMO: Toni Abang, M.D., Medical Director
CHR: Janet Morris, Director Human Resources
Web address: www.healthsouthlakeview.com
Control: Corporation, Investor–owned, for–profit **Service:** Rehabilitation

Staffed Beds: 40

FLEMINGSBURG—Fleming County

✠ **FLEMING COUNTY HOSPITAL (180053)**, 55 Foundation Drive,
Zip 41041–9815, Mailing Address: P.O. Box 388, Zip 41041–0388;
tel. 606/849–5000 **A**1 10 **F**11 15 28 29 31 34 35 40 45 50 57 59 78 79 81
87 93 107 108 110 111 114 118 119 129 130 133 135 146 **P**6 **S** LifePoint
Health, Brentwood, TN
Primary Contact: Brian Springate, Chief Executive Officer
CFO: Theresa Fite, R.N., Chief Financial Officer
CMO: Samuel Gehring, M.D., Chief of Staff
CIO: Don Daugherty, Director Information Systems
CHR: Marsha Mitchell, Director Human Resources
CNO: Lynda Skaggs, Chief Nursing Officer
Web address: www.flemingcountyhospital.org
Control: Other not–for–profit (including NFP Corporation) **Service:** General
Medical and Surgical

Staffed Beds: 52 **Admissions:** 1214 **Census:** 12 **Outpatient Visits:** 28717
Births: 0 **Total Expense ($000):** 22214 **Payroll Expense ($000):** 8125
Personnel: 173

Hospital, Medicare Provider Number, Address, Telephone, Approval, Facility, and Physician Codes, Health Care System

★ American Hospital Association (AHA) membership ◯ Healthcare Facilities Accreditation Program ⇑ Center for Improvement in Healthcare Quality Accreditation
☐ The Joint Commission accreditation ◇ DNV Healthcare Inc. accreditation △ Commission on Accreditation of Rehabilitation Facilities (CARF) accreditation

FLORENCE—Boone County

☐ **GATEWAY REHABILITATION HOSPITAL (183030)**, 5940 Merchant Street, Zip 41042–1158; tel. 859/426–2400, (Nonreporting) **A**1 10 **S** Vibra Healthcare, Mechanicsburg, PA
Primary Contact: Frank Schneider, FACHE, Chief Executive Officer
CFO: Margaret Cesarez, Chief Financial Officer
CNO: Jenna Wellbrock, Chief Nursing Officer
Web address: www.gatewayflorence.com/
Control: Corporation, Investor–owned, for–profit **Service:** Rehabilitation

Staffed Beds: 40

☐ **ST. ELIZABETH FLORENCE (180045)**, 4900 Houston Road, Zip 41042–4824; tel. 859/212–5200, (Total facility includes 16 beds in nursing home–type unit) **A**1 10 **F**3 11 12 15 20 28 29 30 34 35 39 40 42 44 45 47 48 49 50 55 56 57 59 60 61 64 65 70 71 74 75 77 78 79 80 81 82 84 85 86 87 92 93 97 98 100 101 102 107 108 110 111 114 115 118 119 126 128 129 130 132 135 141 145 146 147 148 **S** St. Elizabeth Healthcare, Edgewood, KY
Primary Contact: Garren Colvin, Chief Executive Officer
COO: Chris Carle, Senior Vice President and Chief Operating Officer
CMO: George Hall, M.D., Vice President Medical Affairs
CIO: Alex Rodriguez, Vice President and Chief Information Officer
CHR: Martin Oscadal, Senior Vice President Human Resources
Web address: www.stelizabeth.com
Control: Church–operated, Nongovernment, not–for profit **Service:** General Medical and Surgical

Staffed Beds: 169 **Admissions:** 10466 **Census:** 118 **Outpatient Visits:** 171378 **Births:** 0 **Total Expense ($000):** 132420 **Payroll Expense ($000):** 51631 **Personnel:** 706

ST. ELIZABETH HEALTHCARE FLORENCE See St. Elizabeth Florence

FORT CAMPBELL—Christian County

✠ **COLONEL FLORENCE A. BLANCHFIELD ARMY COMMUNITY HOSPITAL**, 650 Joel Drive, Zip 42223–5318; tel. 270/798–8040, (Nonreporting) **A**1 3 5 **S** Department of the Army, Office of the Surgeon General, Falls Church, VA
Primary Contact: Colonel Telita Crosland, Commander
CMO: Lieutenant Colonel Michael Place, M.D., Deputy Commander Clinical Services
CHR: Major Travis Burchett, Troop Commander Human Resources
Web address: www.campbell.amedd.army.mil/
Control: Army, Government, federal **Service:** General Medical and Surgical

Staffed Beds: 66

FORT KNOX—Hardin County

✠ **IRELAND ARMY COMMUNITY HOSPITAL**, 289 Ireland Avenue, Zip 40121–5111; tel. 502/624–9333 **A**1 5 **F**3 7 11 12 13 15 18 29 30 32 33 34 35 39 40 44 45 50 53 57 59 64 65 68 74 75 76 77 79 81 87 89 91 93 97 99 100 101 104 105 107 108 110 111 115 118 119 130 131 132 135 146 **P**6 **S** Department of the Army, Office of the Surgeon General, Falls Church, VA
Primary Contact: Colonel Robert S. Cornes, Commander
Web address: www.iach.knox.amedd.army.mil/
Control: Army, Government, federal **Service:** General Medical and Surgical

Staffed Beds: 17 **Admissions:** 857 **Census:** 5 **Outpatient Visits:** 433921 **Births:** 248 **Total Expense ($000):** 124931 **Payroll Expense ($000):** 55973 **Personnel:** 860

FORT THOMAS—Campbell County

CARDINAL HILL SPECIALTY HOSPITAL See Select Specialty Hospital–Northern Kentucky

✠ **SELECT SPECIALTY HOSPITAL–NORTHERN KENTUCKY (182004)**, 85 North Grand Avenue, Zip 41075–1793; tel. 859/572–3880, (Nonreporting) **A**1 10 **S** Select Medical Corporation, Mechanicsburg, PA
Primary Contact: Teresa R. Detano, M.P.H., Chief Executive Officer
Web address: www.selectspecialtyhospitals.com
Control: Corporation, Investor–owned, for–profit **Service:** Long–Term Acute Care hospital

Staffed Beds: 33

☐ **ST. ELIZABETH FORT THOMAS (180001)**, 85 North Grand Avenue, Zip 41075–1796; tel. 859/572–3100, (Total facility includes 26 beds in nursing home–type unit) **A**1 2 10 **F**3 4 5 11 15 17 18 20 28 29 30 31 34 35 39 40 44 45 47 48 49 50 51 55 56 57 59 60 61 63 64 65 70 71 74 75 77 78 79 80 81 82 85 86 87 91 92 93 94 97 100 102 107 108 110 111 114 115 118 119 120 121 123 126 128 129 130 135 141 146 147 **S** St. Elizabeth Healthcare, Edgewood, KY
Primary Contact: Garren Colvin, Chief Executive Officer
COO: Thomas Saalfeld, Senior Vice President and Chief Operating Officer
CMO: George Hall, M.D., Vice President Medical Affairs
CIO: Alex Rodriguez, Vice President and Chief Information Officer
CHR: Martin Oscadal, Senior Vice President Human Resources
Web address: www.stelizabeth.com
Control: Church–operated, Nongovernment, not–for profit **Service:** General Medical and Surgical

Staffed Beds: 171 **Admissions:** 7781 **Census:** 102 **Outpatient Visits:** 131108 **Births:** 0 **Total Expense ($000):** 116824 **Payroll Expense ($000):** 47518 **Personnel:** 653

ST. ELIZABETH HEALTHCARE FORT THOMAS See St. Elizabeth Fort Thomas

FRANKFORT—Franklin County

✠ **FRANKFORT REGIONAL MEDICAL CENTER (180127)**, 299 King's Daughters Drive, Zip 40601–4186; tel. 502/875–5240 **A**1 2 3 10 19 **F**3 13 15 18 20 22 28 29 30 31 34 40 43 45 49 50 51 57 60 64 68 70 72 74 75 76 77 78 79 81 82 84 85 87 89 93 98 102 103 105 107 111 119 124 129 130 133 135 145 146 147 148 **S** HCA, Nashville, TN
Primary Contact: Chip Peal, Chief Executive Officer
CMO: Willis P. McKee, Jr., M.D., Chief Medical Officer
CIO: Craig Willard, Director Information Technology and Systems
CHR: Bev Young, Director Human Resources
Web address: www.frankfortregional.com
Control: Corporation, Investor–owned, for–profit **Service:** Long–Term Acute Care hospital

Staffed Beds: 128 **Admissions:** 5448 **Census:** 64 **Outpatient Visits:** 97223 **Births:** 820 **Total Expense ($000):** 82891 **Payroll Expense ($000):** 31739 **Personnel:** 432

FRANKLIN—Simpson County

✠ **MEDICAL CENTER AT FRANKLIN (181318)**, 1100 Brookhaven Road, Zip 42134–4800; tel. 270/598–4800 **A**1 10 18 **F**3 15 28 29 30 34 35 40 46 57 59 64 68 75 77 81 82 86 87 93 107 108 110 111 114 119 127 130 133 135 146 148 **P**6 **S** Commonwealth Health Corporation, Bowling Green, KY
Primary Contact: Annette Runyon, Vice President and Administrator
CFO: Ronald G. Sowell, Executive Vice President
CIO: Mark Brookman, Vice President and Chief Information Officer
Web address: www.themedicalcenterfranklin.org
Control: Other not–for–profit (including NFP Corporation) **Service:** General Medical and Surgical

Staffed Beds: 25 **Admissions:** 1088 **Census:** 21 **Outpatient Visits:** 24355 **Births:** 0 **Personnel:** 124

GEORGETOWN—Scott County

✠ **GEORGETOWN COMMUNITY HOSPITAL (180101)**, 1140 Lexington Road, Zip 40324–9362; tel. 502/868–1100 **A**1 5 10 **F**3 11 12 13 15 18 28 29 30 31 34 35 40 45 46 47 48 49 50 57 59 60 64 65 66 70 74 75 76 78 79 81 82 85 87 91 92 93 100 107 108 109 110 111 114 115 116 119 124 126 129 130 131 132 133 144 146 147 **S** LifePoint Health, Brentwood, TN
Primary Contact: William Haugh, Administrator
CFO: Patrick C. Bolander, Chief Financial Officer
CMO: Brian Allen, M.D., President Medical Staff
CHR: Marrianne Slonina, Director Human Resources
Web address: www.georgetowncommunityhospital.com
Control: Corporation, Investor–owned, for–profit **Service:** General Medical and Surgical

Staffed Beds: 58 **Admissions:** 2025 **Census:** 17 **Outpatient Visits:** 72098 **Births:** 241 **Total Expense ($000):** 47904 **Payroll Expense ($000):** 15742 **Personnel:** 365

Many Facility Codes have changed. Please refer to the AHA Guide Code Chart.

© 2016 AHA Guide

GLASGOW—Barren County

☐ **T. J. SAMSON COMMUNITY HOSPITAL (180017)**, 1301 North Race Street, Zip 42141–3483; tel. 270/651–4444, (Total facility includes 16 beds in nursing home–type unit) **A**1 3 5 10 19 **F**3 8 11 13 15 17 18 20 22 28 29 30 31 32 34 35 37 40 45 47 48 49 50 51 54 56 57 59 62 63 64 65 68 71 72 75 76 77 78 79 81 82 83 84 85 86 87 89 93 97 107 108 110 111 114 117 118 119 127 128 129 130 131 132 135 144 146 147 148 **P**6
Primary Contact: Bud Wethington, Chief Executive Officer
COO: Margie Gentry, Controller
CFO: Steve Fischer, Chief Financial Officer
CMO: Michael Shadowen, M.D., Chief of Staff
CIO: Scott Werkstell, Director Information System
CHR: LaDonna Rogers, Director Human Resources
CNO: Margaret Billingsley, R.N., Chief Nursing Officer
Web address: www.tjsamson.org
Control: Other not–for–profit (including NFP Corporation) **Service:** General Medical and Surgical

Staffed Beds: 141 **Admissions:** 5874 **Census:** 61 **Outpatient Visits:** 101770 **Births:** 1145 **Total Expense ($000):** 155760 **Payroll Expense ($000):** 60440 **Personnel:** 1194

GREENSBURG—Green County

JANE TODD CRAWFORD HOSPITAL (181325), 202–206 Milby Street, Zip 42743–1100, Mailing Address: P.O. Box 220, Zip 42743–0220; tel. 270/932–4211, (Nonreporting) **A**10 18
Primary Contact: Rex A. Tungate, Chief Executive Officer
CFO: Richard Hendershot, Chief Financial Officer
CMO: Shane DeSimone, M.D., Chief of Staff
Control: County–Government, nonfederal **Service:** General Medical and Surgical

Staffed Beds: 45

GREENVILLE—Muhlenberg County

☐ **OWENSBORO HEALTH MUHLENBERG COMMUNITY HOSPITAL (180004)**, 440 Hopkinsville Street, Zip 42345–1172, Mailing Address: P.O. Box 387, Zip 42345–0378; tel. 270/338–8000, (Nonreporting) **A**1 10 **S** Owensboro Health, Owensboro, KY
Primary Contact: Ed Heath, FACHE, Chief Executive Officer
CMO: Vincent P. Genovese, M.D., President Medical Staff
CIO: Alan Trail, Director Information Systems
CHR: Lisa R. Hope, Director Human Resources
CNO: Kathy Mitchell, Chief Nursing Officer
Web address: www.mchky.org
Control: Other not–for–profit (including NFP Corporation) **Service:** General Medical and Surgical

Staffed Beds: 105

HARDINSBURG—Breckinridge County

☒ **BRECKINRIDGE MEMORIAL HOSPITAL (181319)**, 1011 Old Highway 60, Zip 40143–2597; tel. 270/756–7000, (Nonreporting) **A**1 5 10 18 **S** Alliant Management Services, Louisville, KY
Primary Contact: Angela Portman, Chief Executive Officer
CFO: Timothy D. Crockett, Chief Financial Officer
CMO: Brian O'Donoghue, M.D., Chief Medical Officer
CHR: James Turpin, Human Resources
CNO: Tiffany Kennedy, Chief Nursing Officer
Web address: www.breckinridgehealth.org/
Control: Other not–for–profit (including NFP Corporation) **Service:** General Medical and Surgical

Staffed Beds: 43

HARLAN—Harlan County

☐ **HARLAN ARH HOSPITAL (180050)**, 81 Ball Park Road, Zip 40831–1792; tel. 606/573–8100 **A**1 10 19 **F**3 11 13 15 28 29 30 32 34 35 40 43 50 54 57 59 62 64 70 75 76 77 78 79 81 82 85 86 87 89 93 97 98 102 103 107 108 111 115 118 119 127 129 130 132 146 147 148 **P**6 **S** Appalachian Regional Healthcare, Inc., Lexington, KY
Primary Contact: Donald R. Fields, Community Chief Executive Officer
CFO: Brad Burkhart, Assistant Administrator
CHR: Sabra Howard, Manager Human Resources
Web address: www.arh.org
Control: Other not–for–profit (including NFP Corporation) **Service:** General Medical and Surgical

Staffed Beds: 145 **Admissions:** 4599 **Census:** 51 **Outpatient Visits:** 77576 **Births:** 146 **Total Expense ($000):** 52894 **Payroll Expense ($000):** 16390 **Personnel:** 542

HARRODSBURG—Mercer County

☒ **JAMES B. HAGGIN MEMORIAL HOSPITAL (181302)**, 464 Linden Avenue, Zip 40330–1862; tel. 859/734–5441, (Nonreporting) **A**1 5 10 18 **S** Alliant Management Services, Louisville, KY
Primary Contact: Victoria L. Reed, R.N., FACHE, Chief Executive Officer
CFO: Tony Patterson, Chief Financial Officer
Web address: www.hagginhosp.org
Control: Other not–for–profit (including NFP Corporation) **Service:** General Medical and Surgical

Staffed Beds: 25

HARTFORD—Ohio County

☒ **OHIO COUNTY HOSPITAL (181323)**, 1211 Main Street, Zip 42347–1619; tel. 270/298–7411, (Nonreporting) **A**1 10 18 **S** QHR, Brentwood, TN
Primary Contact: Blaine Pieper, Chief Executive Officer
CFO: John Tichenor, Chief Financial Officer
CMO: Joshua Skibba, Chief Medical Officer
CHR: Sue Wydick, Director Human Resources
CNO: Athena Minor, Chief Nursing Officer
Web address: www.ohiocountyhospital.com
Control: Other not–for–profit (including NFP Corporation) **Service:** General Medical and Surgical

Staffed Beds: 25

HAZARD—Perry County

☐ **HAZARD ARH REGIONAL MEDICAL CENTER (180029)**, 100 Medical Center Drive, Zip 41701–9421; tel. 606/439–6600 **A**1 2 3 5 10 19 **F**3 11 12 13 15 17 18 20 22 24 26 28 29 30 31 32 34 35 40 43 46 47 48 49 50 54 55 57 59 61 62 64 70 71 73 74 75 76 77 78 79 81 82 85 86 87 89 90 93 97 98 101 102 103 107 108 110 111 115 118 119 120 121 124 127 129 130 132 146 147 148 **P**6 **S** Appalachian Regional Healthcare, Inc., Lexington, KY
Primary Contact: Dan Stone, Senior Community Chief Executive Officer
CMO: J. D. Miller, M.D., Chief Medical Officer
CIO: Jeff Brady, Director Information Systems
CHR: Sheila Cornett, Manager Human Resources
Web address: www.arh.org
Control: Other not–for–profit (including NFP Corporation) **Service:** General Medical and Surgical

Staffed Beds: 358 **Admissions:** 12442 **Census:** 209 **Outpatient Visits:** 126205 **Births:** 396 **Total Expense ($000):** 133547 **Payroll Expense ($000):** 37636 **Personnel:** 1285

HENDERSON—Henderson County

☐ **METHODIST HOSPITAL (180056)**, 1305 North Elm Street, Zip 42420–2775, Mailing Address: P.O. Box 48, Zip 42419–0048; tel. 270/827–7700 **A**1 10 13 **F**3 11 12 13 15 18 20 29 30 31 34 35 36 40 45 46 47 48 49 50 51 53 54 57 58 59 64 66 68 70 72 74 75 76 77 78 79 81 82 85 86 87 89 92 93 107 108 110 111 114 115 118 119 126 127 129 130 131 132 135 146 147 148 **P**8
Primary Contact: Gary R. Colberg, FACHE, President and Chief Executive Officer
COO: David B. Park, Vice President, General Counsel
CFO: David Massengale, Vice President and Chief Financial Officer
CMO: James Fellows, M.D., Chief of Staff
CIO: Jamie Reid, Information Systems Director
CHR: Ty Kahle, Assistant Vice President Human Resources
CNO: Lois Morgan, R.N., Vice President and Chief Nursing Officer
Web address: www.methodisthospital.net
Control: Church–operated, Nongovernment, not–for profit **Service:** General Medical and Surgical

Staffed Beds: 136 **Admissions:** 4355 **Census:** 51 **Outpatient Visits:** 323171 **Births:** 696 **Total Expense ($000):** 101799 **Payroll Expense ($000):** 36685 **Personnel:** 1054

HOPKINSVILLE—Christian County

☐ **CUMBERLAND HALL HOSPITAL (184014)**, 270 Walton Way, Zip 42240–6808; tel. 270/886–1919, (Nonreporting) **A**1 10 **S** Universal Health Services, Inc., King of Prussia, PA
Primary Contact: Jason Staats, Chief Executive Officer
CFO: Mark Wallace, Chief Financial Officer
CMO: Deepak Patel, M.D., Medical Director
CIO: Patricia Gray, Director Health Information Management
CHR: Kelly Hagy, Director Human Resources
CNO: Denise Lyons, Chief Nursing Officer
Web address: www.cumberlandhallhospital.com
Control: Corporation, Investor–owned, for–profit **Service:** Psychiatric

Staffed Beds: 97

☒ **JENNIE STUART MEDICAL CENTER (180051)**, 320 West 18th Street, Zip 42240–1965, Mailing Address: P.O. Box 2400, Zip 42241–2400; tel. 270/887–0100, (Nonreporting) **A**1 3 10 **S** QHR, Brentwood, TN
Primary Contact: Eric A. Lee, President and Chief Executive Officer
CMO: Casey Covington, M.D., President Elect, Medical Staff
CIO: Jerry Houston, Director Information Systems
CHR: Austin Moss, Vice President Human Resources
Web address: www.jsmc.org
Control: Other not–for–profit (including NFP Corporation) **Service:** General Medical and Surgical

Staffed Beds: 139

☐ **WESTERN STATE HOSPITAL (184002)**, Russellville Road, Zip 42240–3017, Mailing Address: P.O. Box 2200, Zip 42241–2200; tel. 270/889–6025 **A**1 10 **F**98 102 103 130 **P**5
Primary Contact: Roger Westfall, Director
CFO: Jessica Cates, Fiscal Manager
CMO: Nayyar Iqbal, M.D., Director Medical Staff
CIO: Valerie Majors, Director Information Services
CHR: James L. Hayes, Director Human Resources
CNO: Jill Thomas, Director of Nursing
Web address: www.westernstatehospital.ky.gov
Control: State–Government, nonfederal **Service:** Psychiatric

Staffed Beds: 205 **Admissions:** 1954 **Census:** 136 **Outpatient Visits:** 0 **Births:** 0 **Total Expense ($000):** 18028 **Payroll Expense ($000):** 10151 **Personnel:** 587

HORSE CAVE—Hart County

★ **THE MEDICAL CENTER AT CAVERNA (181314)**, 1501 South Dixie Street, Zip 42749–1477; tel. 270/786–2191 **A**10 18 **F**3 15 29 34 40 45 57 59 64 71 77 81 87 89 91 103 104 107 110 111 114 119 127 128 133 **S** Commonwealth Health Corporation, Bowling Green, KY
Primary Contact: Alan B. Alexander, FACHE, Vice President and Administrator
CFO: Ronald G. Sowell, Executive Vice President and Chief Financial Officer
CIO: Mark Brookman, Vice President, Chief Information Officer
CHR: Lynn Williams, Vice President, Human Resources
Web address: www.TheMedicalCenterCaverna.org
Control: Other not–for–profit (including NFP Corporation) **Service:** General Medical and Surgical

Staffed Beds: 25 **Admissions:** 375 **Census:** 4 **Outpatient Visits:** 22053 **Births:** 0 **Total Expense ($000):** 10627 **Payroll Expense ($000):** 4196 **Personnel:** 132

HYDEN—Leslie County

MARY BRECKINRIDGE ARH HOSPITAL (181316), 130 Kate Ireland Drive, Zip 41749–9071, Mailing Address: P.O. Box 447–A, Zip 41749–0717; tel. 606/672–2901 **A**10 18 **F**2 3 11 15 29 30 32 34 35 40 50 57 59 62 65 68 75 77 81 86 87 93 107 110 115 119 130 132 133 135 146 **P**6 **S** Appalachian Regional Healthcare, Inc., Lexington, KY
Primary Contact: Mallie S. Noble, Administrator
COO: Nathan W. Lee, Chief Executive Officer
CFO: Robert Besten, Chief Financial Officer
CMO: Roy Varghese, M.D., Chief of Staff
CIO: Frank Baker, Chief Information Officer
CHR: Beulah Couch, Director Human Resources
Web address: www.frontiernursing.org
Control: Other not–for–profit (including NFP Corporation) **Service:** General Medical and Surgical

Staffed Beds: 25 **Admissions:** 422 **Census:** 7 **Outpatient Visits:** 20598 **Births:** 0 **Total Expense ($000):** 9700 **Payroll Expense ($000):** 3655 **Personnel:** 119

IRVINE—Estill County

★ **MARCUM AND WALLACE MEMORIAL HOSPITAL (181301)**, 60 Mercy Court, Zip 40336–1331; tel. 606/723–2115 **A**10 18 **F**3 15 29 30 34 35 40 43 45 50 56 57 59 64 75 77 81 83 93 107 115 119 127 129 130 131 133 147 **S** Mercy Health, Cincinnati, OH
Primary Contact: Susan Starling, President and Chief Executive Officer
CFO: Lori Witt, Site Finance Director
CMO: Maher Kassis, M.D., Chief Medical Staff
CHR: Dana Stepp, Human Resources Officer
CNO: Trena Stocker, Chief Nursing Executive
Web address: www.marcumandwallace.org
Control: Church–operated, Nongovernment, not–for profit **Service:** General Medical and Surgical

Staffed Beds: 25 **Admissions:** 1121 **Census:** 16 **Outpatient Visits:** 68898 **Births:** 0 **Total Expense ($000):** 18391 **Payroll Expense ($000):** 7798 **Personnel:** 158

JACKSON—Breathitt County

☒ **KENTUCKY RIVER MEDICAL CENTER (180139)**, 540 Jett Drive, Zip 41339–9622; tel. 606/666–6000, (Nonreporting) **A**1 10 20 **S** Quorum Health, Brentwood, TN
Primary Contact: John Ballard, Ph.D., Chief Executive Officer
CFO: Michael Ackley, Chief Financial Officer
CMO: Eunice Johnson, M.D., Chief Medical Staff
CIO: Diana Tyra, Director Health Information
CHR: Naomi Mitchell, Director Human Resources
Web address: www.kentuckyrivermc.com
Control: Corporation, Investor–owned, for–profit **Service:** General Medical and Surgical

Staffed Beds: 54

LA GRANGE—Oldham County

☒ **BAPTIST HEALTH LA GRANGE (180138)**, 1025 New Moody Lane, Zip 40031–9154; tel. 502/222–5388, (Total facility includes 24 beds in nursing home–type unit) **A**1 3 5 10 **F**3 7 11 13 15 18 28 29 30 31 34 35 36 40 43 45 46 49 50 54 56 57 59 64 68 70 74 75 76 77 78 79 81 82 85 86 87 93 97 107 108 110 111 114 119 128 129 130 131 132 133 135 146 147 148 **P**6 **S** Baptist Health, Louisville, KY
Primary Contact: Christopher Roty, President
CFO: Jim Morris, Vice President Finance
CMO: Matt McDanald, M.D., Chief Medical Officer
CIO: David Bensema, Chief Information Officer
CHR: Kayla Batts, Manager Human Resources
CNO: Nathan Wilson, R.N., Vice President and Chief Nursing Officer
Web address: www.baptisthealthlagrange.com
Control: Other not–for–profit (including NFP Corporation) **Service:** General Medical and Surgical

Staffed Beds: 65 **Admissions:** 2380 **Census:** 36 **Outpatient Visits:** 110193 **Births:** 535 **Total Expense ($000):** 72709 **Payroll Expense ($000):** 24337 **Personnel:** 436

LEBANON—Marion County

☒ **SPRING VIEW HOSPITAL (180024)**, 320 Loretto Road, Zip 40033–1300; tel. 270/692–3161 **A**1 10 **F**3 11 13 15 28 29 34 35 40 45 48 49 50 51 57 59 64 70 75 76 79 81 85 86 87 90 92 93 107 108 110 111 114 118 119 127 130 133 135 146 147 148 **P**6 **S** LifePoint Health, Brentwood, TN
Primary Contact: Timothy R. Trottier, Chief Executive Officer
CFO: Denise Thomas, Chief Financial Officer
CIO: Douglas Bland, Manager Information Services
CHR: Ann Dabney, Manager Human Resources
CNO: Linda Hunter, Chief Nursing Officer
Web address: www.springviewhospital.com
Control: Corporation, Investor–owned, for–profit **Service:** General Medical and Surgical

Staffed Beds: 60 **Admissions:** 1369 **Census:** 12 **Outpatient Visits:** 43592 **Births:** 311 **Total Expense ($000):** 27490 **Payroll Expense ($000):** 9843 **Personnel:** 200

LEITCHFIELD—Grayson County

☐ **TWIN LAKES REGIONAL MEDICAL CENTER (180070)**, 910 Wallace Avenue, Zip 42754–2414; tel. 270/259–9400, (Nonreporting) **A**1 10 **S** Alliant Management Services, Louisville, KY
Primary Contact: Wayne Meriwether, Chief Executive Officer
COO: Deneace Clemons, Chief Operating Officer
CFO: Scott Arndell, Chief Financial Officer
CIO: Robbie Lindsey, Chief Information Officer
CHR: Kim Rayls, Director Human Resources
CNO: David Logdson, Chief Nursing Officer
Web address: www.tlrmc.com
Control: Other not–for–profit (including NFP Corporation) **Service:** General Medical and Surgical

Staffed Beds: 75

LEXINGTON—Fayette County

☒ **BAPTIST HEALTH LEXINGTON (180103)**, 1740 Nicholasville Road, Zip 40503–1499; tel. 859/260–6100 **A**1 2 3 10 **F**3 11 12 13 15 18 20 22 24 26 28 29 30 31 34 35 36 40 44 48 49 53 54 55 56 57 58 59 60 64 68 70 72 74 75 76 77 78 79 81 84 85 86 87 89 92 93 97 107 108 110 111 114 115 117 118 119 120 121 124 126 129 130 131 132 135 144 146 147 148 **S** Baptist Health, Louisville, KY
Primary Contact: William G. Sisson, President
COO: Karen S. Hill, R.N., Chief Operating Officer and Chief Nursing Officer
CFO: John Franke, Chief Financial Officer
CMO: James Borders, M.D., Chief Medical Officer
CIO: Lisa Fluty, Director Information Services
CHR: Lynette Walker, R.N., Vice President Human Resources
Web address: www.baptisthealthlexington.com
Control: Other not–for–profit (including NFP Corporation) **Service:** General Medical and Surgical

Staffed Beds: 344 **Admissions:** 17983 **Census:** 229 **Outpatient Visits:** 318637 **Births:** 3477 **Total Expense ($000):** 396739 **Payroll Expense ($000):** 118221 **Personnel:** 2232

Many Facility Codes have changed. Please refer to the AHA Guide Code Chart.

★ △ **CARDINAL HILL REHABILITATION HOSPITAL (183026)**, 2050 Versailles Road, Zip 40504–1405; tel. 859/254–5701, (Total facility includes 74 beds in nursing home–type unit) **A**3 5 7 10 **F**3 28 29 58 62 64 68 79 87 90 91 93 94 95 96 128 130 143 146 **S** HEALTHSOUTH Corporation, Birmingham, AL
Primary Contact: Gary Payne, Chief Executive Officer
CFO: Marty Lautner, Vice President Finance and Chief Financial Officer
CMO: William Lester, M.D., Vice President Medical Affairs
CIO: LouAnn Hyder, Director Information Integrity Management
CHR: Barry K. Lindeman, Director Human Resources
CNO: Maureen Couture, Chief Nursing Officer and Vice President Nursing
Web address: www.cardinalhillhealthsouth.com
Control: Other not–for–profit (including NFP Corporation) **Service:** Rehabilitation

Staffed Beds: 232 Admissions: 2500 Census: 98 Outpatient Visits: 39463 **Births:** 0 **Total Expense ($000):** 61020 **Payroll Expense ($000):** 29901 **Personnel:** 689

★ **CONTINUING CARE HOSPITAL (182002)**, 150 North Eagle Creek Drive, 5th Floor, Zip 40509–1805; tel. 859/967–5744 **A**10 **F**1 3 29 30 **S** Catholic Health Initiatives, Englewood, CO
Primary Contact: Tonja Williams, R.N., President
CMO: Michael Miedler, M.D., Chief Medical Officer
CNO: Regina Masters, R.N., Director of Nursing
Control: Church–operated, Nongovernment, not–for profit **Service:** Long–Term Acute Care hospital

Staffed Beds: 43 Admissions: 445 Census: 38 Outpatient Visits: 0 **Births:** 0 **Total Expense ($000):** 18069 **Payroll Expense ($000):** 5759 **Personnel:** 104

☐ **EASTERN STATE HOSPITAL (184004)**, 1350 Bull Lea Road, Zip 40511; tel. 859/246–7000 **A**1 3 5 10 **F**29 30 35 56 75 77 87 96 97 98 101 103 130 132 135 143 146 **P**6
Primary Contact: Carrie Rudzik, Chief Administrative Officer
COO: Susan M. Griffith, Chief Operations Officer
CFO: Tambara Nalle, Chief Financial Officer
CMO: Scott A. Haas, M.D., Chief Medical Officer
CIO: Bud Stone, Director Information Systems
CHR: Jerry Kersey, Director Employee Relations
CNO: Kristan Mowder, Director Administration and Patient Care Services
Web address: www.ukhealthcare.uky.edu/ESH/
Control: State–Government, nonfederal **Service:** Psychiatric

Staffed Beds: 140 Admissions: 2286 Census: 118 Outpatient Visits: 0 **Births:** 0 **Total Expense ($000):** 42297 **Payroll Expense ($000):** 20289 **Personnel:** 341

FEDERAL MEDICAL CENTER, 3301 Leestown Road, Zip 40511–8799; tel. 859/255–6812, (Nonreporting)
Primary Contact: Francisco Quintana, Warden
CFO: Mike Kinsel, Controller
CMO: Michael Growse, M.D., Clinical Director
Control: Department of Justice, Government, federal **Service:** Hospital unit of an institution (prison hospital, college infirmary, etc.)

Staffed Beds: 22

☒ **LEXINGTON VETERANS AFFAIRS MEDICAL CENTER**, 1101 Veterans Drive, Zip 40502–2235; tel. 859/281–4901, (Nonreporting) **A**1 3 5 **S** Department of Veterans Affairs, Washington, DC
Primary Contact: Emma Metcalf, MSN, R.N., Director
CFO: Patricia Swisshelm, Acting Chief Fiscal Service
CMO: Patricia Breeden, M.D., Chief of Staff
CIO: Jeffrey Sutton, Chief Information Officer
CHR: Laura Faulkner, Chief Human Resource Management Service
CNO: Mary Kelly McCullough, Associate Director Patient Care Services
Web address: www.lexington.va.gov/
Control: Veterans Affairs, Government, federal **Service:** General Medical and Surgical

Staffed Beds: 199

☐ **RIDGE BEHAVIORAL HEALTH SYSTEM (184009)**, 3050 Rio Dosa Drive, Zip 40509–1540; tel. 859/269–2325, (Nonreporting) **A**1 3 5 10 **S** Universal Health Services, Inc., King of Prussia, PA
Primary Contact: Nina W. Eisner, Chief Executive Officer and Managing Director
CFO: Richard McDowell, Chief Financial Officer
CMO: Michael Rieser, M.D., Medical Director
CNO: Georgia Swank, Chief Nursing Officer
Web address: www.ridgebhs.com
Control: Corporation, Investor–owned, for–profit **Service:** Psychiatric

Staffed Beds: 110

☒ **SAINT JOSEPH EAST (180143)**, 150 North Eagle Creek Drive, Zip 40509–1805; tel. 859/967–5000, (Includes WOMEN'S HOSPITAL SAINT JOSEPH EAST, 170 North Eagle Creek Drive, Zip 40509–9087) **A**1 2 5 10 **F**3 8 12 13 15 18 20 22 24 26 28 29 30 31 40 47 49 50 60 68 70 72 74 75 76 77 78 79 81 82 85 86 93 107 108 111 114 118 119 120 121 122 123 126 129 142 146 147 148 **S** Catholic Health Initiatives, Englewood, CO
Primary Contact: Eric Gilliam, President
COO: Christine Mays, R.N., Chief Operating Officer and Chief Nurse Executive
CFO: Melinda S. Evans, Vice President Finance
CIO: Janie Fergus, Director and Chief Information Officer
Web address: www.sjhlex.org
Control: Church–operated, Nongovernment, not–for profit **Service:** General Medical and Surgical

Staffed Beds: 150 Admissions: 9071 Census: 99 Outpatient Visits: 116186 **Births:** 2779 **Total Expense ($000):** 155112 **Payroll Expense ($000):** 43217 **Personnel:** 761

☒ **SAINT JOSEPH HOSPITAL (180010)**, One St. Joseph Drive, Zip 40504–3754; tel. 859/278–3436 **A**1 2 3 10 **F**3 8 11 12 15 17 18 19 20 22 24 25 26 27 28 29 30 31 34 35 37 40 41 42 45 47 49 50 51 54 55 56 57 58 59 64 65 66 68 70 74 77 78 79 81 82 83 84 85 86 87 91 92 93 94 97 107 110 111 114 115 116 117 118 119 120 121 123 126 127 129 130 132 135 144 146 147 148 **S** Catholic Health Initiatives, Englewood, CO
Primary Contact: Bruce J. Tassin, President
COO: Christine Mays, R.N., Chief Operating Officer and Chief Nurse Executive
CFO: Melinda S. Evans, Vice President Finance
CIO: Janie Fergus, Director and Chief Information Officer
Web address: www.sjhlex.org
Control: Church–operated, Nongovernment, not–for profit **Service:** General Medical and Surgical

Staffed Beds: 307 Admissions: 13417 Census: 199 Outpatient Visits: 112440 **Births:** 0 **Total Expense ($000):** 287633 **Payroll Expense ($000):** 76269 **Personnel:** 1276

☒ **SELECT SPECIALTY HOSPITAL–LEXINGTON (182003)**, 310 South Limestone Street, 3rd Floor, Zip 40508–3008; tel. 859/226–7096, (Nonreporting) **A**1 10 **S** Select Medical Corporation, Mechanicsburg, PA
Primary Contact: Kim Pennington, Chief Executive Officer
CMO: Fadi Bacha, M.D., Chief Medical Officer
CHR: Tina Kirkland–Rose, Coordinator Human Resources
CNO: Katie Meredith, Chief Nursing Officer
Web address: www.lexington.selectspecialtyhospitals.com/
Control: Corporation, Investor–owned, for–profit **Service:** Long–Term Acute Care hospital

Staffed Beds: 41

☐ **SHRINERS HOSPITALS FOR CHILDREN–LEXINGTON (183300)**, 1900 Richmond Road, Zip 40502–1298; tel. 859/266–2101, (Nonreporting) **A**1 3 5 10 **S** Shriners Hospitals for Children, Tampa, FL
Primary Contact: Tony Lewgood, Administrator
CFO: Robert Montgomery, Chief Financial Officer
CMO: Chester Tylkowski, M.D., Chief of Staff
CIO: David Brian, Director Information Services
Web address: www.shrinershospitalsforchildren.org/Hospitals/Locations/Lexington.aspx
Control: Other not–for–profit (including NFP Corporation) **Service:** Children's orthopedic

Staffed Beds: 50

☒ **UNIVERSITY OF KENTUCKY ALBERT B. CHANDLER HOSPITAL (180067)**, 800 Rose Street, Zip 40536–0293; tel. 859/323–5000, (Includes KENTUCKY CHILDREN'S HOSPITAL, N–100 – 800 Rose Street, tel. 859/257–1000; UK HEALTHCARE GOOD SAMARITAN HOSPITAL, 310 South Limestone Street, Zip 40508–3008; tel. 859/226–7000; Michael Karpf, M.D., Executive Vice President of Health Affairs) **A**1 2 3 5 8 10 12 **F**3 5 6 7 9 11 12 13 15 16 17 18 19 20 21 22 23 24 26 27 28 29 30 31 32 34 35 36 37 38 39 40 41 43 44 45 46 47 48 49 50 52 54 55 56 57 59 60 61 64 65 66 68 70 72 73 74 75 76 77 78 79 81 82 84 85 86 87 88 89 92 93 94 95 96 97 98 100 102 104 107 108 110 111 113 114 115 118 119 120 121 123 124 126 130 131 132 134 135 136 137 138 139 140 141 142 145 146 147 148 **P**6
Primary Contact: Michael Karpf, M.D., Executive Vice President of Health Affairs
CHR: Kimberly P. Wilson, Director Human Resources
Web address: www.ukhealthcare.uky.edu
Control: State–Government, nonfederal **Service:** General Medical and Surgical

Staffed Beds: 854 Admissions: 37073 Census: 689 Outpatient Visits: 1335684 **Births:** 1749 **Total Expense ($000):** 1111255 **Payroll Expense ($000):** 343593 **Personnel:** 6885

UNIVERSITY OF KENTUCKY HOSPITAL See University of Kentucky Albert B. Chandler Hospital

---

Hospital, Medicare Provider Number, Address, Telephone, Approval, Facility, and Physician Codes, Health Care System

★ American Hospital Association (AHA) membership
☐ The Joint Commission accreditation
○ Healthcare Facilities Accreditation Program
◇ DNV Healthcare Inc. accreditation
⇑ Center for Improvement in Healthcare Quality Accreditation
△ Commission on Accreditation of Rehabilitation Facilities (CARF) accreditation

LIBERTY—Casey County

☐ **CASEY COUNTY HOSPITAL (181309)**, 187 Wolford Avenue, Zip 42539–3278; tel. 606/787–6275, (Nonreporting) **A**1 10 18
Primary Contact: Rex A. Tungate, Chief Executive Officer
CFO: Richard Hendershot, Chief Financial Officer
Control: County–Government, nonfederal **Service:** General Medical and Surgical

> **Staffed Beds:** 24

LONDON—Laurel County

✠ **SAINT JOSEPH LONDON (180011)**, 1001 Saint Joseph Lane, Zip 40741–8345; tel. 606/330–6000 **A**1 10 19 **F**3 13 15 20 22 26 28 29 30 31 34 35 40 42 45 47 49 50 51 57 59 60 61 64 70 74 75 76 78 79 80 81 82 85 87 89 92 93 97 107 108 110 111 114 115 119 127 129 130 131 135 146 147 **S** Catholic Health Initiatives, Englewood, CO
Primary Contact: Terrence G. Deis, CPA, FACHE, President
CFO: Christy Spitser, Vice President Finance and Business Development
CMO: Shelley Stanko, M.D., Chief Medical Officer
CHR: Sandra Turqueza, Senior Human Resources Business Partner
CNO: Lewis Stephen O'Neal, R.N., Chief Nursing Officer
Web address: www.saintjosephhealthsystem.org
Control: Church–operated, Nongovernment, not–for profit **Service:** General Medical and Surgical

> **Staffed Beds:** 116 **Admissions:** 6870 **Census:** 58 **Outpatient Visits:** 120822 **Births:** 1153 **Total Expense ($000):** 131001 **Payroll Expense ($000):** 35863 **Personnel:** 588

LOUISA—Lawrence County

✠ **THREE RIVERS MEDICAL CENTER (180128)**, 2485 Highway 644, Zip 41230–9242, Mailing Address: P.O. Box 769, Zip 41230–0769; tel. 606/638–9451 **A**1 10 20 **F**13 15 18 29 40 50 51 70 75 76 79 81 85 93 98 104 107 111 115 119 129 130 133 146 147 **S** Quorum Health, Brentwood, TN
Primary Contact: Greg Kiser, Chief Executive Officer
CFO: Michael Ackley, Chief Financial Officer
CHR: Pat Hart, Director Human Resources
CNO: Cathy Heston, Chief Nursing Officer
Web address: www.threeriversmedicalcenter.com
Control: Corporation, Investor–owned, for–profit **Service:** General Medical and Surgical

> **Staffed Beds:** 90 **Admissions:** 2562 **Census:** 25 **Outpatient Visits:** 29346 **Births:** 94

LOUISVILLE—Jefferson County

✠ △ **BAPTIST HEALTH LOUISVILLE (180130)**, 4000 Kresge Way, Zip 40207–4676; tel. 502/897–8100 **A**1 2 3 5 7 10 **F**3 5 8 11 12 13 15 17 18 20 22 24 26 28 29 30 31 34 35 37 38 40 44 45 46 47 48 49 50 51 54 56 57 58 59 60 61 62 64 70 72 74 75 76 78 79 81 82 83 84 85 86 87 89 90 91 93 98 100 101 102 103 104 105 107 108 110 111 114 115 116 117 118 119 120 121 123 124 126 129 130 132 135 146 147 148 **S** Baptist Health, Louisville, KY
Primary Contact: David L. Gray, FACHE, President
COO: Clint Kaho, Vice President
CFO: Jim Morris, Vice President Finance
CMO: Kenneth Anderson, M.D., Vice President and Chief Medical Officer
CIO: Shari Price, Director Information Services
CHR: Kim Scaglione, Vice President Human Resources
CNO: Karen Newman, Ed.D., Vice President and Chief Nursing Officer
Web address: www.baptisthealthlouisville.com
Control: Other not–for–profit (including NFP Corporation) **Service:** General Medical and Surgical

> **Staffed Beds:** 500 **Admissions:** 26572 **Census:** 366 **Outpatient Visits:** 331941 **Births:** 2965 **Total Expense ($000):** 454643 **Payroll Expense ($000):** 163516 **Personnel:** 2648

☐ **CENTRAL STATE HOSPITAL (184015)**, 10510 LaGrange Road, Zip 40223–1228; tel. 502/253–7000, (Nonreporting) **A**1 3 5 10
Primary Contact: Vital Shah, M.D., Chief Executive Officer ad Chief Medical Officer
CFO: Robert Underhill, Director of Business Services
CMO: Vital Shah, M.D., Chief Executive Officer and Chief Medical Officer
CIO: Randy Spicer, Information Technology Supervisor
CHR: Sonya Wheatley, Human Resources Manager
CNO: Michelle Napier, Director of Nursing
Control: State–Government, nonfederal **Service:** Psychiatric

> **Staffed Beds:** 112

★ △ **FRAZIER REHAB INSTITUTE**, 220 Abraham Flexner Way, Zip 40202–1887; tel. 502/582–7400 **A**3 5 7 **F**28 29 30 34 35 42 44 50 54 56 57 58 59 60 64 68 74 75 77 78 79 82 84 85 86 87 90 91 93 95 96 100 130 131 132 146 148 **P**6 **S** Catholic Health Initiatives, Englewood, CO
Primary Contact: Randy L. Napier, President
CFO: Robert Steltenpohl, Vice President and Chief Financial Officer
CMO: Darryl Kaelin, M.D., Medical Director
CHR: Lisa Burris, Manager Human Resources
Web address: www.frazierrehab.org
Control: Other not–for–profit (including NFP Corporation) **Service:** Rehabilitation

> **Staffed Beds:** 87 **Admissions:** 1584 **Census:** 65 **Outpatient Visits:** 85390 **Births:** 0 **Total Expense ($000):** 55269 **Payroll Expense ($000):** 22223 **Personnel:** 451

✠ **JEWISH HOSPITAL (180040)**, 200 Abraham Flexner Way, Zip 40202–1886; tel. 502/587–4011 **A**1 2 3 5 10 **F**1 3 8 11 14 15 18 20 22 24 26 28 29 30 31 34 35 36 37 40 42 43 44 45 46 47 48 49 50 53 54 56 57 58 59 60 61 64 67 68 70 74 75 78 79 81 82 84 85 87 92 97 100 107 108 110 111 112 114 115 116 117 118 119 121 123 124 126 130 131 132 135 136 137 138 139 140 141 142 145 146 **P**6 **S** Catholic Health Initiatives, Englewood, CO
Primary Contact: Joseph Gilene, President
CFO: Ronald Farr, Chief Financial Officer
CMO: James P. Ketterhagen, M.D., Senior Vice President and Chief Medical Officer
CIO: Thomas Wittman, Chief Information Officer
CHR: Julie McGregor, Vice President and Chief People Officer
CNO: Cheryl Fugatte, MSN, Vice President and Chief Nursing Officer
Web address: www.jewishhospital.org
Control: Other not–for–profit (including NFP Corporation) **Service:** General Medical and Surgical

> **Staffed Beds:** 342 **Admissions:** 16448 **Census:** 237 **Outpatient Visits:** 108504 **Births:** 0 **Total Expense ($000):** 364056 **Payroll Expense ($000):** 98293 **Personnel:** 1772

KINDRED HOSPITAL LOUISVILLE AT JEWISH HOSPITAL See Kindred Hospital–Louisville

✠ **KINDRED HOSPITAL–LOUISVILLE (182001)**, 1313 Saint Anthony Place, Zip 40204–1740; tel. 502/587–7001, (Includes KINDRED HOSPITAL LOUISVILLE AT JEWISH HOSPITAL, 200 Abraham Flexner Way, 2nd Floor, Zip 40202; tel. 502/587–3999; Jack Nicholson, Chief Executive Officer), (Nonreporting) **A**1 3 5 10 **S** Kindred Healthcare, Louisville, KY
Primary Contact: Wayne D. Blanchard, Chief Executive Officer
Web address: www.kindredlouisville.com/
Control: Corporation, Investor–owned, for–profit **Service:** Long–Term Acute Care hospital

> **Staffed Beds:** 164

★ **KOSAIR CHILDREN'S HOSPITAL**, 231 East Chestnut Street, Zip 40202–1821; tel. 502/629–6000 **A**2 3 5 **F**3 8 11 19 21 23 25 27 29 30 31 32 34 35 38 39 40 41 42 43 44 45 50 51 54 57 58 59 64 65 68 72 73 74 75 78 79 81 82 84 85 86 87 88 89 92 93 96 98 99 100 101 102 107 108 111 114 115 119 130 131 132 134 136 137 138 146 **S** Norton Healthcare, Louisville, KY
Primary Contact: Thomas D. Kmetz, Division President
Web address: www.kosairchildrens.com/
Control: Other not–for–profit (including NFP Corporation) **Service:** Children's general

> **Staffed Beds:** 267 **Admissions:** 10054 **Census:** 208 **Outpatient Visits:** 139368 **Births:** 0 **Total Expense ($000):** 327820 **Payroll Expense ($000):** 99983 **Personnel:** 1601

★ **NORTON AUDUBON HOSPITAL**, One Audubon Plaza Drive, Zip 40217–1300, Mailing Address: P.O. Box 17550, Zip 40217–0550; tel. 502/636–7111 **A**2 3 5 **F**3 5 11 15 17 18 20 22 24 26 28 29 30 31 34 35 37 40 45 46 47 48 49 50 56 57 59 64 68 70 74 75 78 79 81 82 85 86 87 107 108 110 111 114 115 118 119 129 130 131 132 146 147 **S** Norton Healthcare, Louisville, KY
Primary Contact: Jon Cooper, Chief Administrative Officer
CFO: Jonathan Presser, Vice President Finance and Operations
Web address: www.nortonhealthcare.com/NortonAudubonHospital
Control: Other not–for–profit (including NFP Corporation) **Service:** General Medical and Surgical

> **Staffed Beds:** 302 **Admissions:** 14429 **Census:** 215 **Outpatient Visits:** 149516 **Births:** 0 **Total Expense ($000):** 231986 **Payroll Expense ($000):** 79600 **Personnel:** 1397

★ **NORTON BROWNSBORO HOSPITAL**, 4960 Norton Healthcare Boulevard,
Zip 40241–2831; tel. 502/446–8000 **A**2 **F**3 15 18 20 22 29 30 31 34 35 36
37 40 44 45 46 47 48 49 56 57 58 59 64 68 70 74 75 78 79 81 82 85 86
87 92 107 108 110 111 114 115 119 129 130 131 132 146 148 **S** Norton
Healthcare, Louisville, KY
Primary Contact: Andrew Strausbaugh, Chief Administrative Officer
CFO: Michael Logan, Chief Financial Officer
CMO: Gregory Juhl, M.D., Medical Director
CNO: Regina J. Hymer, DNP, RN, CENP, MSN, Vice President Patient Care
Services and Chief Nursing Officer
Web address: www.nortonhealthcare.com/nortonbrownsborohospital
Control: Other not–for–profit (including NFP Corporation) **Service:** General
Medical and Surgical

> **Staffed Beds:** 124 **Admissions:** 8682 **Census:** 89 **Outpatient Visits:** 97399
> **Births:** 0 **Total Expense ($000):** 151614 **Payroll Expense ($000):** 48704
> **Personnel:** 854

NORTON HEALTHCARE PAVILION See Norton Hospital

⊠ **NORTON HOSPITAL (180088)**, 200 East Chestnut Street, Zip 40202–1800,
Mailing Address: P.O. Box 35070, Zip 40232–5070; tel. 502/629–8000,
(Includes NORTON HEALTHCARE PAVILION, 315 East Broadway,
Zip 40202–1703; tel. 502/629–2000) **A**1 2 3 5 10 **F**3 11 12 13 15 17 18 20
22 24 26 28 29 30 31 34 35 36 38 39 40 44 45 46 49 50 51 53 55 56 57
59 64 68 70 74 75 76 78 79 81 82 84 85 86 87 92 93 96 98 100 101 102
107 108 110 111 114 115 116 117 118 119 126 130 132 146 147 148
S Norton Healthcare, Louisville, KY
Primary Contact: Matthew Ayers, Chief Administrative Officer
CFO: Carl Amorose, Vice President Finance
Web address: www.nortonhealthcare.com/nortonhospital
Control: Other not–for–profit (including NFP Corporation) **Service:** General
Medical and Surgical

> **Staffed Beds:** 382 **Admissions:** 18561 **Census:** 272 **Outpatient Visits:**
> 104648 **Births:** 3201 **Total Expense ($000):** 334705 **Payroll Expense**
> **($000):** 107655 **Personnel:** 1728

★ **NORTON WOMEN'S AND KOSAIR CHILDREN'S HOSPITAL**, 4001 Dutchmans
Lane, Zip 40207–4799; tel. 502/893–1000 **A**2 3 5 **F**3 11 12 13 15 18 20 29
30 31 34 35 36 40 41 44 45 47 49 50 56 57 59 64 68 70 72 73 74 75 76
78 79 81 82 85 86 87 89 107 108 110 111 114 115 118 119 120 121 123
124 126 130 132 133 134 135 146 147 **S** Norton Healthcare, Louisville, KY
Primary Contact: Charlotte Ipsan, Chief Administrative Officer
CFO: Mark Kircher, Associate Vice President Finance
CMO: Steven Hester, M.D., Vice President Medical Affairs
CIO: Joseph DeVenuto, Vice President and Chief Information Officer
Web address: www.nortonhealthcare.com/nortonsuburbanhospital
Control: Other not–for–profit (including NFP Corporation) **Service:** General
Medical and Surgical

> **Staffed Beds:** 359 **Admissions:** 16003 **Census:** 197 **Outpatient Visits:**
> 124000 **Births:** 5442 **Total Expense ($000):** 226000 **Payroll Expense**
> **($000):** 78395 **Personnel:** 1385

★ **OUR LADY OF PEACE**, 2020 Newburg Road, Zip 40205–1879;
tel. 502/479–4500 **A**3 5 **F**5 29 30 34 35 43 53 59 68 98 99 100 101 104
105 106 130 132 143 146 **S** Catholic Health Initiatives, Englewood, CO
Primary Contact: Jennifer Nolan, President
COO: Martha S. Mather, Chief Operating Officer and Vice President
CFO: Beckie Kistler, Director of Finance
CHR: Jan Ostbloom, Human Resources Consultant
CNO: Brad Lincks, R.N., Chief Nursing Officer and Vice President
Web address: www.hopehasaplace.org
Control: Other not–for–profit (including NFP Corporation) **Service:** Psychiatric

> **Staffed Beds:** 211 **Admissions:** 8262 **Census:** 158 **Outpatient Visits:** 29312
> **Births:** 0 **Total Expense ($000):** 52659 **Payroll Expense ($000):** 24749
> **Personnel:** 549

⊠ **ROBLEY REX VETERANS AFFAIRS MEDICAL CENTER**, 800 Zorn Avenue,
Zip 40206–1499; tel. 502/287–4000, (Nonreporting) **A**1 3 5 **S** Department of
Veterans Affairs, Washington, DC
Primary Contact: Martin J. Traxler, Chief Executive Officer
CFO: Barbara Roberts, Chief Financial Officer
CMO: Marylee Rothschild, M.D., Chief of Staff
CIO: Augustine Bittner, Chief Information Officer
CHR: Angela Dutton, Chief Human Resources Management Service
Web address: www.louisville.va.gov
Control: Veterans Affairs, Government, federal **Service:** General Medical and
Surgical

> **Staffed Beds:** 116

★ **STS. MARY & ELIZABETH HOSPITAL**, 1850 Bluegrass Avenue,
Zip 40215–1199; tel. 502/361–6000 **A**3 5 **F**3 8 11 12 15 18 20 22 29 30 31
34 35 40 42 44 45 47 49 50 53 59 60 64 68 69 70 74 75 78 79 81 82 84
85 86 87 107 108 110 111 114 115 118 119 130 132 135 **P**6 **S** Catholic
Health Initiatives, Englewood, CO
Primary Contact: Jennifer Nolan, President
COO: Kenneth Johnson, Vice President
CFO: Elaine Hayes, Controller
CMO: Val Slayton, M.D., Vice President Medical Affairs
CHR: Julie McGregor, Director Human Resources
Web address: www.jhsmh.org
Control: Other not–for–profit (including NFP Corporation) **Service:** General
Medical and Surgical

> **Staffed Beds:** 174 **Admissions:** 8678 **Census:** 101 **Outpatient Visits:**
> 105810 **Births:** 0 **Total Expense ($000):** 123995 **Payroll Expense ($000):**
> 40717 **Personnel:** 682

TEN BROECK DUPONT See The Brook at Dupont

☐ **THE BROOK AT DUPONT (184007)**, 1405 Browns Lane, Zip 40207–4608;
tel. 502/896–0495, (Nonreporting) **A**1 10 **S** Universal Health Services, Inc., King
of Prussia, PA
Primary Contact: Paul Andrews, Chief Executive Officer
Web address: www.thebrookhospitals.com/
Control: Corporation, Investor–owned, for–profit **Service:** Psychiatric

> **Staffed Beds:** 88

☐ **THE BROOK HOSPITAL – KMI (184008)**, 8521 Old LaGrange Road,
Zip 40242–3800; tel. 502/426–6380 **A**1 3 5 10 **F**4 5 38 64 98 99 100 101
102 103 104 105 106 **S** Universal Health Services, Inc., King of Prussia, PA
Primary Contact: Paul Andrews, Chief Executive Officer
COO: Kim Peabody, Chief Operating Officer
CFO: Dennis Collins, Chief Financial Officer
CMO: Timothy Burke, M.D., Medical Director
CIO: Joel Roy, Manager Information Systems
CHR: Christina Taylor, Director Human Resources
Web address: www.thebrookhospitals.com
Control: Corporation, Investor–owned, for–profit **Service:** Psychiatric

> **Staffed Beds:** 110 **Admissions:** 2519 **Census:** 75 **Outpatient Visits:** 19867
> **Births:** 0 **Total Expense ($000):** 17988 **Payroll Expense ($000):** 7467
> **Personnel:** 187

⊠ **UNIVERSITY OF LOUISVILLE HOSPITAL (180141)**, 530 South Jackson Street,
Zip 40202–3611; tel. 502/562–3000 **A**1 2 3 5 8 10 **F**3 13 15 16 17 18 20 22
24 26 28 29 30 31 34 35 40 43 45 46 47 49 50 51 54 55 57 58 59 60 61
64 65 66 68 70 71 72 73 74 75 76 77 78 79 80 81 82 84 86 91 92 93 94
97 98 100 101 102 103 104 105 106 107 108 109 110 111 112 113 114
115 116 117 118 119 120 121 122 123 124 126 130 132 135 136 146 147
148 **S** Catholic Health Initiatives, Englewood, CO
Primary Contact: Charles W. Neumann, President
CMO: Mark P. Pfeifer, M.D., Senior Vice President and Chief Medical Officer
CIO: Troy May, Chief Information Officer
CNO: Mary Jane Adams, R.N., Senior Vice President and Chief Nursing Officer
Web address: www.ulh.org
Control: Other not–for–profit (including NFP Corporation) **Service:** General
Medical and Surgical

> **Staffed Beds:** 301 **Admissions:** 14402 **Census:** 222 **Outpatient Visits:**
> 186246 **Births:** 1376 **Total Expense ($000):** 467727 **Payroll Expense**
> **($000):** 118177 **Personnel:** 1814

VETERANS AFFAIRS MEDICAL CENTER–LOUISVILLE See Robley Rex Veterans
Affairs Medical Center

MADISONVILLE—Hopkins County

⊠ **BAPTIST HEALTH MADISONVILLE (180093)**, 900 Hospital Drive,
Zip 42431–1694; tel. 270/825–5100, (Total facility includes 20 beds in nursing
home–type unit) **A**1 2 3 5 10 22 **F**3 8 11 13 14 18 20 22 24 26 28 29 30 31
34 35 40 44 49 51 53 55 57 58 59 62 63 68 70 73 76 78 79 81 85 87 88
89 90 93 96 98 100 102 103 107 108 111 114 115 117 118 119 120 121
123 128 129 130 131 132 134 146 148 **P**8 **S** Baptist Health, Louisville, KY
Primary Contact: Robert L. Ramey, President
COO: Kevin Moser, Vice President of Operations
CFO: Kim Ashby, Vice President of Finance
CMO: Travis Sewalls, Chief Medical Officer
CIO: Karla Durham, Director of Information Systems
CHR: Lorie A. Oglesby, Director of Human Resources
CNO: Tiffany Cabibbo, Vice President of Nursing
Web address: www.baptisthealthmadisonville.com
Control: Other not–for–profit (including NFP Corporation) **Service:** General
Medical and Surgical

> **Staffed Beds:** 192 **Admissions:** 8089 **Census:** 118 **Outpatient Visits:**
> 138827 **Births:** 881 **Total Expense ($000):** 170535 **Payroll Expense**
> **($000):** 65026 **Personnel:** 1373

Hospital, Medicare Provider Number, Address, Telephone, Approval, Facility, and Physician Codes, Health Care System

★ American Hospital Association (AHA) membership   ○ Healthcare Facilities Accreditation Program   ⇑ Center for Improvement in Healthcare Quality Accreditation
☐ The Joint Commission accreditation   ◇ DNV Healthcare Inc. accreditation   △ Commission on Accreditation of Rehabilitation Facilities (CARF) accreditation

CONTINUECARE HOSPITAL AT MADISONVILLE, 900 Hospital Drive, 4th Floor, Zip 42431–1644; tel. 270/825–5450, (Nonreporting) **S** Community Hospital Corporation, Plano, TX
Primary Contact: Kathy DeVore, Administrator
Web address: www.continuecare.org/madisonville//
Control: Other not–for–profit (including NFP Corporation) **Service:** Long–Term Acute Care hospital

Staffed Beds: 36

MANCHESTER—Clay County

☒ ○ **MANCHESTER MEMORIAL HOSPITAL (180043)**, 210 Marie Langdon Drive, Zip 40962–6388; tel. 606/598–5104 **A**1 10 11 **F**3 13 15 18 29 30 34 35 40 45 50 57 59 62 65 68 70 71 75 76 77 79 81 85 86 87 93 97 107 108 110 111 115 119 127 130 135 143 146 147 **S** Adventist Health System Sunbelt Health Care Corporation, Altamonte Springs, FL
Primary Contact: Erika Skula, President and Chief Executive Officer
COO: Chris Self, Chief Operating Officer
CFO: Paul Merklin, Vice President Finance and Chief Financial Officer
CMO: Jeff Newswanger, M.D., Chief Medical Officer
CHR: Joe Skula, Director Human Resources
CNO: Michael Stimson, Chief Nursing Officer
Web address: www.manchestermemorial.org
Control: Church–operated, Nongovernment, not–for profit **Service:** General Medical and Surgical

Staffed Beds: 63 Admissions: 2141 Census: 19 Outpatient Visits: 52451 Births: 219 Total Expense ($000): 55625 Payroll Expense ($000): 23789 Personnel: 341

MARION—Crittenden County

☐ **CRITTENDEN COUNTY HOSPITAL (180095)**, 520 West Gum Street, Zip 42064–1516, Mailing Address: P.O. Box 386, Zip 42064–0386; tel. 270/965–5281, (Nonreporting) **A**1 10 20
Primary Contact: Greg R. McNeil, Chief Executive Officer
COO: Robin Curnel, MSN, Chief Operating Officer and Chief Nursing Officer
CFO: Karen Paris, Controller
CMO: Steven Burkhart, M.D., Chief Medical Officer
CIO: Reese Baker, Director Information Systems
CHR: Jan Gregory, Chief of Human Resources
CNO: Robin Curnel, MSN, Chief Operating Officer and Chief Nursing Officer
Web address: www.crittenden–health.org
Control: Other not–for–profit (including NFP Corporation) **Service:** General Medical and Surgical

Staffed Beds: 48

MARTIN—Floyd County

☒ **SAINT JOSEPH – MARTIN (181305)**, 11203 Main Street, Zip 41649; tel. 606/285–6400 **A**1 10 18 **F**3 15 18 28 35 40 56 81 104 111 114 119 130 **S** Catholic Health Initiatives, Englewood, CO
Primary Contact: Kathy Stumbo, President
CFO: Robert Brock, Vice President Finance
CMO: John Triplett, D.O., President Medical Staff
CIO: Chris Dye, Director Information Systems
Web address: www.saintjosephmartin.org
Control: Church–operated, Nongovernment, not–for profit **Service:** General Medical and Surgical

Staffed Beds: 25 Admissions: 703 Census: 9 Outpatient Visits: 31639 Births: 0 Total Expense ($000): 19927 Payroll Expense ($000): 7016 Personnel: 105

MAYFIELD—Graves County

☒ **JACKSON PURCHASE MEDICAL CENTER (180116)**, 1099 Medical Center Circle, Zip 42066–1159; tel. 270/251–4100 **A**1 10 19 **F**3 8 11 12 13 15 18 20 22 28 29 34 37 40 43 45 46 47 48 49 51 57 59 60 64 68 70 74 75 76 77 79 80 81 85 87 89 91 93 97 98 103 107 110 111 114 115 117 119 124 127 129 131 132 133 135 144 146 147 148 **S** LifePoint Health, Brentwood, TN
Primary Contact: David Anderson, Chief Executive Officer
CFO: Vicki Parks, Chief Financial Officer
CMO: Rudy Triana, M.D., Chief of Staff
CIO: Randy McDaniel, Information Systems Director
CHR: Tressa B. Hargrove, Director Human Resources
CNO: Julia Grove, Chief Nursing Officer
Web address: www.jacksonpurchase.com
Control: Corporation, Investor–owned, for–profit **Service:** General Medical and Surgical

Staffed Beds: 227 Admissions: 3944 Census: 46 Outpatient Visits: 69664 Births: 356 Total Expense ($000): 60266 Payroll Expense ($000): 26771 Personnel: 517

MAYSVILLE—Mason County

☒ **MEADOWVIEW REGIONAL MEDICAL CENTER (180019)**, 989 Medical Park Drive, Zip 41056–8750; tel. 606/759–5311, (Nonreporting) **A**1 10 **S** LifePoint Health, Brentwood, TN
Primary Contact: Robert Parker, Chief Executive Officer
CFO: Clayton Kolodziejczyk, Chief Financial Officer
CMO: Eric Lohman, M.D., Chief of Staff
CHR: Diana Kennedy, Director Human Resources
Web address: www.meadowviewregional.com
Control: Corporation, Investor–owned, for–profit **Service:** General Medical and Surgical

Staffed Beds: 101

MCDOWELL—Floyd County

☐ **MCDOWELL ARH HOSPITAL (181331)**, Route 122, Zip 41647, Mailing Address: P.O. Box 247, Zip 41647–0247; tel. 606/377–3400 **A**1 10 18 **F**3 11 15 29 30 34 35 40 43 50 57 59 62 64 65 70 75 77 81 82 86 87 89 90 93 97 98 107 111 115 119 127 130 131 133 146 **P**6 **S** Appalachian Regional Healthcare, Inc., Lexington, KY
Primary Contact: Russell Barker, Community Chief Executive Officer
COO: Russell Barker, Community Chief Executive Officer
CFO: Joseph Grossman, Chief Financial Officer
CMO: Mary A. Hall, Chief Medical Staff
CIO: Jeff Brady, Director Information Systems
CHR: Stephanie Owens, Manager Human Resources
Web address: www.arh.org
Control: Other not–for–profit (including NFP Corporation) **Service:** General Medical and Surgical

Staffed Beds: 25 Admissions: 587 Census: 7 Outpatient Visits: 31692 Births: 0 Total Expense ($000): 12918 Payroll Expense ($000): 5375 Personnel: 122

MIDDLESBORO—Bell County

☐ **MIDDLESBORO ARH HOSPITAL (180020)**, 3600 West Cumberland Avenue, Zip 40965–2614, Mailing Address: P.O. Box 340, Zip 40965–0340; tel. 606/242–1100 **A**1 10 **F**3 11 13 15 17 28 29 30 34 35 39 40 50 57 59 62 64 70 75 76 77 79 81 85 86 87 89 93 97 107 108 111 115 118 119 127 130 133 146 147 148 **P**6 **S** Appalachian Regional Healthcare, Inc., Lexington, KY
Primary Contact: Michael Slusher, Community Chief Executive Officer
CFO: Jeremy Hall, Assistant Administrator and Chief Financial Officer
CMO: Maria Hortillosa, M.D., Chief of Staff
CIO: Lisa Dooley, Health Information Director
CHR: Marina Cawood, Administrative Assistant
CNO: Stacy England, Community Chief Nursing Officer
Web address: www.arh.org/middlesboro
Control: Other not–for–profit (including NFP Corporation) **Service:** General Medical and Surgical

Staffed Beds: 96 Admissions: 1846 Census: 23 Outpatient Visits: 77682 Births: 256 Total Expense ($000): 34188 Payroll Expense ($000): 10565 Personnel: 263

MONTICELLO—Wayne County

WAYNE COUNTY HOSPITAL (181321), 166 Hospital Street, Zip 42633–2416; tel. 606/348–9343 **A**10 18 **F**3 15 29 30 40 47 75 81 107 108 114 119 127 133 135 146 **P**6
Primary Contact: Joseph Murrell, Chief Executive Officer
CFO: Anne Sawyer, Chief Financial Officer
CMO: David Mayer, Chief of Staff
CIO: Angela Burton, Privacy Officer
CHR: Mollie Dick, Coordinator Human Resources
CNO: Lora Elam, R.N., Chief Nursing Officer
Web address: www.waynehospital.org
Control: Other not–for–profit (including NFP Corporation) **Service:** General Medical and Surgical

Staffed Beds: 25 Admissions: 604 Census: 10 Outpatient Visits: 34289 Births: 0 Personnel: 153

MOREHEAD—Rowan County

☒ **ST. CLAIRE REGIONAL MEDICAL CENTER (180018)**, 222 Medical Circle, Zip 40351–1179; tel. 606/783–6500, (Total facility includes 10 beds in nursing home–type unit) **A**1 2 3 5 10 13 **F**3 5 11 13 15 18 20 22 28 29 30 31 34 35 38 39 40 45 48 49 50 51 54 56 57 58 59 60 61 62 63 64 65 68 70 74 75 76 77 78 79 81 82 84 85 86 87 89 90 93 97 98 99 100 101 102 103 104 107 108 110 111 115 118 119 128 130 133 135 146 147 148 **P**6
Primary Contact: Mark J. Neff, FACHE, President and Chief Executive Officer
CFO: Chris McClurg, Vice President Finance and Chief Financial Officer
CMO: William L. Melahn, M.D., Vice President Medical Affairs and Chief Medical Officer
CIO: Randy McCleese, Vice President Information Services and Chief Information Officer
CHR: Travis A. Bailey, Vice President Administration
CNO: Lerae Wilson, Vice President Patient Services and Chief Nursing Officer
Web address: www.st–claire.org
Control: Church–operated, Nongovernment, not–for profit **Service:** General Medical and Surgical

Staffed Beds: 133 **Admissions:** 4871 **Census:** 54 **Outpatient Visits:** 227878 **Births:** 418 **Total Expense ($000):** 128187 **Payroll Expense ($000):** 64214 **Personnel:** 1234

MORGANFIELD—Union County

☒ **METHODIST HOSPITAL UNION COUNTY (181306)**, 4604 Highway 60 West, Zip 42437–9570; tel. 270/389–5000 **A**1 10 18 **F**3 7 11 15 29 30 34 40 45 57 68 75 77 81 85 87 90 93 107 114 119 128 130 133 135 146
Primary Contact: Patrick Donahue, Vice President and Administrator
CFO: David Massingale, Chief Financial Officer
CMO: Maulik Desai, M.D., Chief of Staff
CHR: Ty Kahle, Assistant Vice President Human Resources
CNO: Peggy F. Creighton, R.N., Director of Nursing Services
Web address: www.methodisthospitaluc.net
Control: Church–operated, Nongovernment, not–for profit **Service:** General Medical and Surgical

Staffed Beds: 25 **Admissions:** 653 **Census:** 13 **Outpatient Visits:** 23021 **Births:** 0 **Total Expense ($000):** 13963 **Payroll Expense ($000):** 5640 **Personnel:** 142

MOUNT STERLING—Montgomery County

☒ **SAINT JOSEPH MOUNT STERLING (180064)**, 225 Falcon Drive, Zip 40353–1158, Mailing Address: P.O. Box 7, Zip 40353–0007; tel. 859/497–5000 **A**1 3 5 10 **F**3 13 15 17 28 29 34 35 40 45 46 57 59 64 68 70 74 75 76 77 78 79 81 86 87 93 97 107 114 119 129 130 132 133 135 146 147 148 **S** Catholic Health Initiatives, Englewood, CO
Primary Contact: Benny Nolen, President
CFO: Amanda Kinman, Director of Finance
CMO: Jeff McGinnis, M.D., President Medical Staff
CIO: Jeff Ryder, Director Information Systems
CHR: Annette Saadat, Human Resources Business Partner
CNO: Cinda Fluke, R.N., Chief Nursing Officer
Web address: www.sjhlex.org
Control: Church–operated, Nongovernment, not–for profit **Service:** General Medical and Surgical

Staffed Beds: 42 **Admissions:** 1741 **Census:** 21 **Outpatient Visits:** 64130 **Births:** 234 **Total Expense ($000):** 45266 **Payroll Expense ($000):** 11462 **Personnel:** 231

MOUNT VERNON—Rockcastle County

☒ **ROCKCASTLE REGIONAL HOSPITAL AND RESPIRATORY CARE CENTER (180115)**, 145 Newcomb Avenue, Zip 40456–2728, Mailing Address: P.O. Box 1310, Zip 40456–1310; tel. 606/256–2195, (Nonreporting) **A**1 10
Primary Contact: Stephen A. Estes, Chief Executive Officer
CFO: Charles Black, Jr., Chief Financial Officer
CMO: Jon A. Arvin, M.D., Chief Medical Officer
CIO: Maleigha Amyx, Chief Information Officer
CHR: Carmen Poynter, Director Human Resources
CNO: Cynthia Burton, R.N., Chief Nursing Officer
Web address: www.rockcastleregional.org
Control: Other not–for–profit (including NFP Corporation) **Service:** General Medical and Surgical

Staffed Beds: 105

MURRAY—Calloway County

☒ **MURRAY–CALLOWAY COUNTY HOSPITAL (180027)**, 803 Poplar Street, Zip 42071–2432; tel. 270/762–1100, (Total facility includes 150 beds in nursing home–type unit) **A**1 2 10 19 **F**2 3 7 11 12 13 14 15 18 20 28 29 30 31 34 35 40 45 47 49 50 51 53 57 59 62 63 66 68 70 74 75 76 77 78 79 81 82 84 85 87 90 92 93 94 104 107 108 111 114 115 119 121 127 128 129 130 131 132 135 146 147 148 **P**5
Primary Contact: Colonel Jerome Penner, Chief Executive Officer
CFO: Dirk Morgan, Vice President
CIO: Brian Benedict, Director of Information Technology
CHR: John R. Wilson, Vice President, Human Resources
CNO: Jeffrey L. Eye, R.N., Vice President Patient Care Services
Web address: www.murrayhospital.org
Control: City–County, Government, nonfederal **Service:** General Medical and Surgical

Staffed Beds: 247 **Admissions:** 4597 **Census:** 196 **Outpatient Visits:** 82455 **Births:** 609 **Total Expense ($000):** 115008 **Payroll Expense ($000):** 44520 **Personnel:** 973

OWENSBORO—Daviess County

☒ △ **OWENSBORO HEALTH REGIONAL HOSPITAL (180038)**, 1201 Pleasant Valley Road, Zip 42303; tel. 270/417–2000, (Includes HEALTHPARK, 1006 Ford Avenue, Zip 42301, Mailing Address: P.O. Box 2839, Zip 42302; tel. 270/688–5433), (Total facility includes 30 beds in nursing home–type unit) **A**1 2 5 7 10 **F**3 5 11 12 13 15 17 18 20 22 24 26 28 29 30 31 32 34 35 40 43 44 45 46 49 53 54 56 57 58 59 61 62 64 65 66 70 72 74 75 76 77 78 79 81 82 85 86 87 89 90 91 92 93 97 98 100 101 102 103 104 105 107 108 110 111 114 115 116 117 118 119 120 121 123 124 126 127 128 129 130 131 132 135 144 145 146 147 148 **P**6 8 **S** Owensboro Health, Owensboro, KY
Primary Contact: Greg Strahan, Interim Chief Executive Officer
COO: Greg Strahan, Chief Operating Officer
CFO: John Hackbarth, CPA, Senior Vice President Finance and Chief Financial Officer
CMO: Wathen Medley, M.D., Chief Medical Officer
CIO: Michael Elley, Chief Information Officer
CHR: Mia Suter, Chief Administration Officer
CNO: Vicki Stogsdill, R.N., Chief Nursing Officer
Web address: www.owensborohealth.org
Control: Other not–for–profit (including NFP Corporation) **Service:** General Medical and Surgical

Staffed Beds: 356 **Admissions:** 16914 **Census:** 223 **Outpatient Visits:** 781568 **Births:** 1961 **Total Expense ($000):** 425988 **Payroll Expense ($000):** 137906 **Personnel:** 3115

RIVERVALLEY BEHAVIORAL HEALTH HOSPITAL (184013), 1000 Industrial Drive, Zip 42301–8715; tel. 270/689–6500 **A**10 **F**4 29 38 40 41 59 98 99 100 101 102 104 105 130 **P**6
Primary Contact: Gayle DiCesare, President and Chief Executive Officer
COO: Michelle Parks, Administrator
CFO: J. Michael Mountain, Chief Financial Officer
CMO: David Harmon, D.O., Vice President Medical Services
CIO: Travis Taggart, Director Information Technology
CHR: Cathryn H. Gaddis, Director Human Resources
Web address: www.rvbh.com
Control: Other not–for–profit (including NFP Corporation) **Service:** Children's hospital psychiatric

Staffed Beds: 80 **Admissions:** 656 **Census:** 17 **Outpatient Visits:** 0 **Births:** 0 **Total Expense ($000):** 4478 **Payroll Expense ($000):** 2064 **Personnel:** 51

PADUCAH—Mccracken County

☒ **BAPTIST HEALTH PADUCAH (180104)**, 2501 Kentucky Avenue, Zip 42003–3200; tel. 270/575–2100 **A**1 2 10 19 22 **F**3 11 12 13 15 17 18 20 22 24 26 28 29 30 31 32 34 35 40 45 46 48 50 51 57 58 59 60 64 68 70 71 73 74 75 76 77 78 79 81 82 84 85 86 87 91 92 93 96 107 108 109 110 111 112 113 114 115 116 117 118 119 120 121 124 126 128 129 130 131 132 133 134 135 144 146 147 148 **S** Baptist Health, Louisville, KY
Primary Contact: William A. Brown, FACHE, President and CEO
COO: Bonnie W. Schrock, FACHE, Chief Operating Officer
CFO: Scott Leckey, Vice President Finance
CMO: Bradley W. Housman, M.D., Chief Medical Officer
CIO: Jay Orazine, Director Information Services
CHR: Kal Keitel, SPHR, Executive Director Human Resources
CNO: Sharon Freyer, R.N., Chief Nursing Officer
Web address: www.baptisthealthpaducah.com
Control: Other not–for–profit (including NFP Corporation) **Service:** General Medical and Surgical

Staffed Beds: 320 **Admissions:** 12381 **Census:** 163 **Outpatient Visits:** 189216 **Births:** 1425 **Total Expense ($000):** 244524 **Payroll Expense ($000):** 71582 **Personnel:** 1253

Hospital, Medicare Provider Number, Address, Telephone, Approval, Facility, and Physician Codes, Health Care System

★ American Hospital Association (AHA) membership
□ The Joint Commission accreditation
○ Healthcare Facilities Accreditation Program
◇ DNV Healthcare Inc. accreditation
⇑ Center for Improvement in Healthcare Quality Accreditation
△ Commission on Accreditation of Rehabilitation Facilities (CARF) accreditation

CONTINUECARE HOSPITAL AT BAPTIST HEALTH PADUCAH (180153), 2501 Kentucky Avenue, 5th Floor, Zip 42003–3813; tel. 270/575–2598, (Nonreporting) **S** Community Hospital Corporation, Plano, TX
Primary Contact: Arthur Rivas, Interim Chief Executive Officer
Web address: www.continuecare.org/paducah//
Control: Other not–for–profit (including NFP Corporation) **Service:** Long–Term Acute Care hospital

Staffed Beds: 37

⊠ △ **LOURDES HOSPITAL (180102)**, 1530 Lone Oak Road, Zip 42003–7900, Mailing Address: P.O. Box 7100, Zip 42002–7100; tel. 270/444–2444 **A**1 7 10 19 **F**3 7 8 11 13 15 17 18 20 22 24 26 28 29 30 31 34 35 40 45 46 54 57 59 60 62 63 64 68 70 73 74 75 76 77 78 79 81 82 83 84 85 87 90 93 96 97 98 100 101 102 103 104 105 107 108 110 111 114 115 116 118 119 129 130 131 132 135 141 143 144 146 147 148 **P**6 **S** Mercy Health, Cincinnati, OH
Primary Contact: Steven Grinnell, Chief Executive Officer
CHR: Kim Lindsey, Chief Human Resources Officer
Web address: www.lourdes–pad.org
Control: Church–operated, Nongovernment, not–for profit **Service:** General Medical and Surgical

Staffed Beds: 280 **Admissions:** 10414 **Census:** 133 **Outpatient Visits:** 454063 **Births:** 391 **Total Expense ($000):** 220122 **Payroll Expense ($000):** 82155

PAINTSVILLE—Johnson County

⊠ **PAUL B. HALL REGIONAL MEDICAL CENTER (180078)**, 625 James S. Trimble Boulevard, Zip 41240–0000; tel. 606/789–3511, (Nonreporting) **A**1 10 **S** Quorum Health, Brentwood, TN
Primary Contact: Deborah Trimble, R.N., Chief Executive Officer
CFO: Pattie Major, Chief Financial Officer
CMO: F. K. Belhasen, M.D., Medical Director
CHR: Carla J. Stapleton, Director Human Resources
Web address: www.pbhrmc.com
Control: Corporation, Investor–owned, for–profit **Service:** General Medical and Surgical

Staffed Beds: 72

PARIS—Bourbon County

⊠ **BOURBON COMMUNITY HOSPITAL (180046)**, 9 Linville Drive, Zip 40361–2196; tel. 859/987–3600 **A**1 10 **F**3 15 28 29 34 35 38 39 40 45 49 50 51 56 57 59 64 68 70 74 75 79 81 86 87 93 98 99 100 101 102 103 107 108 110 111 114 119 129 130 133 146 148 **P**7 **S** LifePoint Health, Brentwood, TN
Primary Contact: Joseph G. Koch, Chief Executive Officer
CFO: Michael Snedegar, Chief Financial Officer
CMO: C. Ray Young, M.D., Chief Medical Officer
CIO: Phil Osborne, Director Information Technology
CHR: Roger K. Davis, Director Human Resources
Web address: www.bourbonhospital.com
Control: Corporation, Investor–owned, for–profit **Service:** General Medical and Surgical

Staffed Beds: 58 **Admissions:** 2603 **Census:** 32 **Outpatient Visits:** 35447 **Births:** 0 **Personnel:** 167

PIKEVILLE—Pike County

☐ **PIKEVILLE MEDICAL CENTER (180044)**, 911 Bypass Road, Zip 41501–1689; tel. 606/218–3500 **A**1 2 10 13 **F**3 11 12 13 15 18 20 22 24 26 28 29 30 31 32 34 35 39 40 43 45 49 50 51 57 59 60 61 62 64 66 68 69 70 72 74 75 76 77 78 79 81 82 84 85 86 87 89 90 93 95 96 97 107 108 110 111 115 116 117 118 119 121 123 124 126 127 129 130 131 132 135 146 147 148 **P**6
Primary Contact: Walter E. May, President and Chief Executive Officer
COO: Juanita Deskins, Chief Operating Officer
CFO: Michelle Hagy, Chief Financial Officer
CMO: Aaron Crum, M.D., Chief Medical Officer
CIO: Tony Damron, Vice President Information Services
CNO: Debra Parsons, Chief Nursing Officer
Web address: www.pikevillehospital.org
Control: Other not–for–profit (including NFP Corporation) **Service:** General Medical and Surgical

Staffed Beds: 243 **Admissions:** 13240 **Census:** 194 **Outpatient Visits:** 483317 **Births:** 1024 **Total Expense ($000):** 392064 **Payroll Expense ($000):** 159955 **Personnel:** 2518

PINEVILLE—Bell County

○ **PINEVILLE COMMUNITY HOSPITAL ASSOCIATION (180021)**, 850 Riverview Avenue, Zip 40977–1452; tel. 606/337–3051, (Nonreporting) **A**10 11
Primary Contact: Gordon Larson, Administrator
CFO: Colan Kelly, Chief Financial Officer
CMO: Michael Peterson, M.D., Chief of Staff
CIO: David Hall, Chief Information Officer
CHR: Josh Collett, Director Human Resources
CNO: Dinah Jarvis, Director of Nursing
Web address: www.pinevillehospital.com
Control: Other not–for–profit (including NFP Corporation) **Service:** General Medical and Surgical

Staffed Beds: 150

PRESTONSBURG—Floyd County

★ ◇ **HIGHLANDS REGIONAL MEDICAL CENTER (180005)**, 5000 Kentucky Route 321, Zip 41653–1273, Mailing Address: P.O. Box 668, Zip 41653–0668; tel. 606/886–8511, (Nonreporting) **A**2 5 10 19 21
Primary Contact: Harold C. Warman, Jr., FACHE, President and Chief Executive Officer
COO: Chris Hoffman, Chief Operating Officer
CFO: Jack Blackwell, Chief Financial Officer
CIO: Michael Roberts, Chief Information Officer
CHR: Susan Renee' Ellis, R.N., Vice President of Human Resources
CNO: Terresa O. Booher, Vice President of Patient Care Services
Web address: www.hrmc.org
Control: Other not–for–profit (including NFP Corporation) **Service:** General Medical and Surgical

Staffed Beds: 145

PRINCETON—Caldwell County

⊠ **CALDWELL MEDICAL CENTER (181322)**, 100 Medical Center Drive, Zip 42445–2430, Mailing Address: P.O. Box 410, Zip 42445–0410; tel. 270/365–0300 **A**1 10 18 **F**11 15 28 29 34 35 40 57 59 62 68 77 81 85 107 108 111 118 119 129 133 135 146 **S** QHR, Brentwood, TN
Primary Contact: Kelley J. Rushing, Chief Executive Officer
CFO: Shane Whittington, Chief Financial Officer
CHR: Rhonda Burns, Director Human Resources
CNO: Douglas James, Chief Nursing Officer
Web address: www.caldwellhosp.org
Control: Other not–for–profit (including NFP Corporation) **Service:** General Medical and Surgical

Staffed Beds: 25 **Admissions:** 440 **Census:** 4 **Outpatient Visits:** 27970 **Total Expense ($000):** 14613 **Payroll Expense ($000):** 4260 **Personnel:** 49

RADCLIFF—Hardin County

☐ **LINCOLN TRAIL BEHAVIORAL HEALTH SYSTEM (184012)**, 3909 South Wilson Road, Zip 40160–8944, Mailing Address: P.O. Box 369, Zip 40159–0369; tel. 270/351–9444 **A**1 10 **F**4 5 29 30 56 87 98 99 100 101 102 103 104 105 130 135 **S** Universal Health Services, Inc., King of Prussia, PA
Primary Contact: Charles L. Webb, Jr., Chief Executive Officer
CFO: Debbie Ditto, CPA, Controller
CMO: Muhammad W. Sajid, M.D., Medical Director
CHR: Charlotte C. Davis, Director Human Resources
Web address: www.lincolnbehavioral.com
Control: Corporation, Investor–owned, for–profit **Service:** Psychiatric

Staffed Beds: 140 **Admissions:** 2198 **Census:** 94 **Births:** 0 **Personnel:** 155

RICHMOND—Madison County

★ ○ **BAPTIST HEALTH RICHMOND (180049)**, 801 Eastern Bypass, Zip 40475–2405, Mailing Address: P.O. Box 1600, Zip 40476–2603; tel. 859/623–3131 **A**10 11 19 **F**3 11 13 15 18 20 28 29 30 34 35 40 49 50 51 57 59 68 70 74 75 76 79 81 84 85 87 91 92 93 107 108 110 111 114 115 118 119 124 129 130 132 146 147 **S** Baptist Health, Louisville, KY
Primary Contact: Todd Jones, President
CMO: Richard Shelton, M.D., Chief Medical Officer
CIO: Kelly Bonzo, Director
CHR: Joy M. Benedict, Director Human Resources
CNO: Mendy Blair, Chief Nursing Officer
Web address: www.baptisthealthrichmond.com
Control: Other not–for–profit (including NFP Corporation) **Service:** General Medical and Surgical

Staffed Beds: 69 **Admissions:** 3084 **Census:** 34 **Outpatient Visits:** 84163 **Births:** 688 **Total Expense ($000):** 68028 **Payroll Expense ($000):** 23280 **Personnel:** 465

Many Facility Codes have changed. Please refer to the AHA Guide Code Chart.
© 2016 AHA Guide

RUSSELL SPRINGS—Russell County

★ **RUSSELL COUNTY HOSPITAL (181330)**, 153 Dowell Road, Zip 42642–4579, Mailing Address: P.O. Box 1610, Zip 42642–1610; tel. 270/866–4141 **A**10 18 **F**3 11 15 28 29 30 34 40 50 57 59 70 81 85 91 93 107 111 118 119 127 129 130 133 135 146 148
Primary Contact: Bill Kindred, Chief Executive Officer
CFO: Janie Landis, Chief Financial Officer
CMO: Jerry Lawson, M.D., Chief of Medical Staff
CIO: Monte Monsanto, Chief Information Systems
CHR: Jennifer Goode, Director Human Resources
CNO: Judy Chenoweth, Chief Nursing Officer
Web address: www.russellcohospital.org
Control: Hospital district or authority, Government, nonfederal **Service:** General Medical and Surgical

Staffed Beds: 25 **Admissions:** 653 **Census:** 7 **Outpatient Visits:** 45893 **Births:** 0 **Total Expense ($000):** 20925 **Payroll Expense ($000):** 10190 **Personnel:** 271

RUSSELLVILLE—Logan County

✠ **LOGAN MEMORIAL HOSPITAL (180066)**, 1625 South Nashville Road, Zip 42276–8834, Mailing Address: P.O. Box 10, Zip 42276–0010; tel. 270/726–4011 **A**1 10 **F**3 15 28 29 30 34 40 45 50 51 57 59 64 70 75 79 81 87 93 107 110 111 114 119 127 129 130 132 133 135 146 **S** LifePoint Health, Brentwood, TN
Primary Contact: James Bills, Chief Executive Officer
CFO: Tracy Martin, Chief Financial Officer
CIO: Randy Compton, Information Technology and System Director
CHR: Susan Renodin Deaton, Human Resources Director
CNO: Deborah Brown, Chief Nursing Officer
Web address: www.loganmemorial.com
Control: Corporation, Investor–owned, for–profit **Service:** General Medical and Surgical

Staffed Beds: 53 **Admissions:** 776 **Census:** 10 **Outpatient Visits:** 12883 **Births:** 0 **Total Expense ($000):** 21545 **Payroll Expense ($000):** 7696 **Personnel:** 198

SALEM—Livingston County

LIVINGSTON HOSPITAL AND HEALTHCARE SERVICES (181320), 131 Hospital Drive, Zip 42078–8043; tel. 270/988–2299 **A**10 18 **F**3 8 11 15 29 30 34 35 40 41 43 45 47 48 56 57 59 64 65 68 75 81 85 86 87 89 90 93 103 107 110 115 119 127 128 130 133 144 146 **S** Alliant Management Services, Louisville, KY
Primary Contact: Kent Giles, Interim Chief Executive Officer
CMO: William Guyette, M.D., President Medical Staff
CIO: Shannan Landreth, Information Systems
CHR: Carla Wiggins, Director Human Resources
CNO: Joanna Stone, Chief Nursing Officer
Web address: www.lhhs.org
Control: Other not–for–profit (including NFP Corporation) **Service:** General Medical and Surgical

Staffed Beds: 25 **Admissions:** 847 **Census:** 10 **Outpatient Visits:** 18941 **Births:** 0 **Total Expense ($000):** 14365 **Payroll Expense ($000):** 5826 **Personnel:** 150

SCOTTSVILLE—Allen County

MEDICAL CENTER AT SCOTTSVILLE (181324), 456 Burnley Road, Zip 42164–6355; tel. 270/622–2800, (Total facility includes 110 beds in nursing home–type unit) **A**10 18 **F**3 15 28 29 30 34 35 40 56 57 59 64 68 71 74 75 79 81 82 85 86 87 93 97 102 103 104 107 110 111 114 119 127 128 130 132 133 135 143 146 148 **P**6 **S** Commonwealth Health Corporation, Bowling Green, KY
Primary Contact: Eric Hagan, R.N., Executive Vice President and Administrator
CFO: Ronald G. Sowell, Chief Financial Officer
CIO: Mark Brookman, Chief Information Officer
CHR: Lynn Williams, Vice President Human Resources
Web address: www.themedicalcenterscottsville.org/
Control: Other not–for–profit (including NFP Corporation) **Service:** General Medical and Surgical

Staffed Beds: 135 **Admissions:** 666 **Census:** 124 **Outpatient Visits:** 23745 **Births:** 0 **Personnel:** 191

SHELBYVILLE—Shelby County

✠ **JEWISH HOSPITAL–SHELBYVILLE (180016)**, 727 Hospital Drive, Zip 40065–1699; tel. 502/647–4000 **A**1 10 **F**3 11 15 18 28 29 34 35 39 40 44 45 46 50 57 59 64 68 75 79 80 81 82 84 85 87 91 93 107 108 110 111 114 119 129 132 135 146 147 148 **P**6 **S** Catholic Health Initiatives, Englewood, CO
Primary Contact: Tonya Brady, Director of Operations
CFO: Erika McGimsey, Controller
CMO: Tony Perez, M.D., President Medical Staff
CHR: Cindy Stewart Rattray, Director Human Resources
Web address: www.jhsmh.org
Control: Other not–for–profit (including NFP Corporation) **Service:** General Medical and Surgical

Staffed Beds: 30 **Admissions:** 1129 **Census:** 10 **Outpatient Visits:** 39629 **Births:** 0 **Total Expense ($000):** 30993 **Payroll Expense ($000):** 9226 **Personnel:** 146

SOMERSET—Pulaski County

✠ **LAKE CUMBERLAND REGIONAL HOSPITAL (180132)**, 305 Langdon Street, Zip 42503–2750, Mailing Address: P.O. Box 620, Zip 42502–0620; tel. 606/679–7441, (Total facility includes 12 beds in nursing home–type unit) **A**1 2 10 13 **F**3 8 11 12 13 15 17 18 20 22 24 29 30 31 34 39 40 41 45 46 49 50 51 54 56 57 58 59 64 65 68 70 73 74 75 76 77 78 79 81 82 85 86 87 89 90 91 93 96 97 98 100 102 103 107 108 109 110 111 114 115 119 120 127 128 129 130 131 132 135 144 146 147 148 **S** LifePoint Health, Brentwood, TN
Primary Contact: Timothy A. Bess, Chief Executive Officer
COO: Rebecca Segal, Chief Operating Officer
CFO: Steve Sloan, Chief Financial Officer
CMO: Michael Citak, M.D., Chief Medical Officer
CIO: Thomas Gilbert, Director Information Technology Services
CHR: James Hughes, Director Human Resources
CNO: Sheryl Glasscock, Chief Nursing Officer
Web address: www.lakecumberlandhospital.com
Control: Corporation, Investor–owned, for–profit **Service:** General Medical and Surgical

Staffed Beds: 295 **Admissions:** 11043 **Census:** 148 **Outpatient Visits:** 120070 **Births:** 1260 **Total Expense ($000):** 141807 **Payroll Expense ($000):** 53379 **Personnel:** 1250

SOUTH WILLIAMSON—Pike County

☐ **TUG VALLEY ARH REGIONAL MEDICAL CENTER (180069)**, 260 Hospital Drive, Zip 41503–4072; tel. 606/237–1710, (Total facility includes 35 beds in nursing home–type unit) **A**1 10 **F**3 11 15 29 30 34 35 40 43 50 54 57 59 60 62 64 67 70 74 75 76 77 79 81 82 85 86 87 89 90 93 97 107 108 110 111 115 118 119 127 128 129 130 132 146 147 **P**6 **S** Appalachian Regional Healthcare, Inc., Lexington, KY
Primary Contact: Timothy A. Hatfield, Community Chief Executive Officer
CMO: J. D. Miller, M.D., Vice President Medical Affairs
CIO: Jeff Brady, Chief Information Officer
Web address: www.arh.org/locations/tug_valley/about_us.aspx
Control: Other not–for–profit (including NFP Corporation) **Service:** General Medical and Surgical

Staffed Beds: 141 **Admissions:** 2530 **Census:** 47 **Outpatient Visits:** 59751 **Births:** 110 **Total Expense ($000):** 38280 **Payroll Expense ($000):** 12129 **Personnel:** 330

STANFORD—Lincoln County

☐ **EPHRAIM MCDOWELL FORT LOGAN HOSPITAL (181315)**, 110 Metker Trail, Zip 40484–1020; tel. 606/365–4600 **A**1 10 18 **F**3 11 13 15 29 30 34 35 40 43 57 59 64 76 81 87 89 107 110 111 119 130 133 135 146 **S** Ephraim McDowell Health, Danville, KY
Primary Contact: Sally M. Davenport, R.N., MS, Interim Chief Executive Officer
CFO: William R. Snapp, III, Vice President and Chief Financial Officer
CMO: James Turpin, Chief of Staff
CIO: Gary Neat, Director Information Systems
CHR: Carl Metz, Vice President
CNO: Ina Louise Glass, Administrator
Web address: www.fortloganhospital.org
Control: Other not–for–profit (including NFP Corporation) **Service:** General Medical and Surgical

Staffed Beds: 25 **Admissions:** 674 **Census:** 7 **Outpatient Visits:** 32660 **Births:** 353 **Total Expense ($000):** 13967 **Payroll Expense ($000):** 6318 **Personnel:** 139

Hospital, Medicare Provider Number, Address, Telephone, Approval, Facility, and Physician Codes, Health Care System

★ American Hospital Association (AHA) membership
☐ The Joint Commission accreditation
◯ Healthcare Facilities Accreditation Program
◇ DNV Healthcare Inc. accreditation
⇑ Center for Improvement in Healthcare Quality Accreditation
△ Commission on Accreditation of Rehabilitation Facilities (CARF) accreditation

TOMPKINSVILLE—Monroe County

☒ **MONROE COUNTY MEDICAL CENTER (180105)**, 529 Capp Harlan Road, Zip 42167–1840; tel. 270/487–9231, (Nonreporting) **A**1 10 **S** QHR, Brentwood, TN
Primary Contact: Vicky McFall, Chief Executive Officer
CFO: Rickie F. Brown, Chief Financial Officer
CIO: Paul McKiddy, Director Information Technology
CHR: Sue Page, Director Human Resources
Web address: www.mcmccares.com
Control: Other not–for–profit (including NFP Corporation) **Service:** General Medical and Surgical

Staffed Beds: 49

VERSAILLES—Woodford County

★ **BLUEGRASS COMMUNITY HOSPITAL (181308)**, 360 Amsden Avenue, Zip 40383–1286; tel. 859/873–3111, (Nonreporting) **A**10 18 **S** LifePoint Health, Brentwood, TN
Primary Contact: Tommy Haggard, Chief Executive Officer
CFO: Shellie Shouse, Chief Financial Officer
CMO: Michele Welling, M.D., Chief of Staff
CHR: Marcia Carter, Director Human Resources
CNO: Kathy Russell, R.N., Chief Nursing Officer
Web address: www.bluegrasscommunityhospital.com
Control: Other not–for–profit (including NFP Corporation) **Service:** General Medical and Surgical

Staffed Beds: 16

WEST LIBERTY—Morgan County

☐ **MORGAN COUNTY ARH HOSPITAL (181307)**, 476 Liberty Road, Zip 41472–2049, Mailing Address: P.O. Box 579, Zip 41472–0579; tel. 606/743–3186 **A**1 10 18 **F**11 15 29 30 34 35 40 54 57 59 62 64 75 82 86 87 93 97 107 114 119 129 130 132 133 146 **P**6 **S** Appalachian Regional Healthcare, Inc., Lexington, KY
Primary Contact: Stephen M. Gavalchik, FACHE, Community Chief Executive Officer
COO: Paul V. Miles, Chief Operating Officer
CMO: J. D. Miller, M.D., Vice President Medical Affairs
CIO: Jeff Brady, Director Information Systems
CHR: Lisa Redding, Manager Human Resources
Web address: www.arh.org
Control: Other not–for–profit (including NFP Corporation) **Service:** General Medical and Surgical

Staffed Beds: 25 Admissions: 301 Census: 3 Outpatient Visits: 25132 Births: 0 Total Expense ($000): 13073 Payroll Expense ($000): 4562 Personnel: 109

WHITESBURG—Letcher County

☐ **WHITESBURG ARH HOSPITAL (180002)**, 240 Hospital Road, Zip 41858–7627; tel. 606/633–3500 **A**1 10 **F**3 11 12 13 15 18 20 28 29 30 31 32 34 35 40 43 50 54 57 59 62 64 70 75 76 77 81 82 85 86 87 89 93 97 107 108 110 111 114 118 119 127 129 130 133 146 147 **P**6 **S** Appalachian Regional Healthcare, Inc., Lexington, KY
Primary Contact: Dena C. Sparkman, FACHE, Community Chief Executive Officer
COO: Paul V. Miles, Vice President Administration
CFO: Joseph Grossman, Vice President Fiscal Affairs
CMO: Ricky M. Collins, M.D., Chief of Staff
CIO: Brent Styer, Director Information Technology
CHR: Daniel Fitzpatrick, Director Human Resources
Web address: www.arh.org/whitesburg
Control: Other not–for–profit (including NFP Corporation) **Service:** General Medical and Surgical

Staffed Beds: 87 Admissions: 3297 Census: 37 Outpatient Visits: 67150 Births: 442 Total Expense ($000): 38372 Payroll Expense ($000): 12171 Personnel: 330

WILLIAMSTOWN—Grant County

ST. ELIZABETH GRANT (181311), 238 Barnes Road, Zip 41097–9482; tel. 859/824–8240 **A**10 18 **F**3 11 15 18 26 29 30 31 34 35 38 40 44 46 50 57 59 63 64 65 74 75 78 79 84 93 97 107 108 110 111 114 119 129 130 131 132 135 141 146 148 **S** St. Elizabeth Healthcare, Edgewood, KY
Primary Contact: Garren Colvin, Chief Executive Officer
Web address: www.stelizabeth.com
Control: Church–operated, Nongovernment, not–for profit **Service:** General Medical and Surgical

Staffed Beds: 16 Admissions: 271 Census: 2 Outpatient Visits: 55439 Births: 0 Total Expense ($000): 16612 Payroll Expense ($000): 7055 Personnel: 95

ST. ELIZABETH MEDICAL CENTER–GRANT COUNTY See St. Elizabeth Grant

WINCHESTER—Clark County

☒ **CLARK REGIONAL MEDICAL CENTER (180092)**, 175 Hospital Drive, Zip 40391–9591; tel. 859/745–3500 **A**1 5 10 **F**13 15 18 19 29 30 31 34 35 38 40 41 45 46 49 50 51 56 57 59 60 61 64 65 68 70 71 74 75 76 77 78 79 81 82 87 92 93 97 107 108 110 111 115 116 117 119 124 127 128 129 130 133 135 144 146 147 **S** LifePoint Health, Brentwood, TN
Primary Contact: Cherie Sibley, R.N., Chief Executive Officer
CFO: Amber Goodpaster, Chief Financial Officer
CMO: Ben McQuaide, M.D., Chief of Staff
CHR: Deidre Bradley, Vice President Human Resources
CNO: Barbara Kinder, R.N., Chief Clinical Officer
Web address: www.clarkregional.org
Control: Corporation, Investor–owned, for–profit **Service:** General Medical and Surgical

Staffed Beds: 79 Admissions: 2720 Census: 45 Outpatient Visits: 54211 Births: 681 Total Expense ($000): 54245 Payroll Expense ($000): 18801 Personnel: 497

Many Facility Codes have changed. Please refer to the AHA Guide Code Chart. © 2016 AHA Guide

LOUISIANA

ABBEVILLE—Vermilion Parish

✈ **ABBEVILLE GENERAL HOSPITAL (190034)**, 118 North Hospital Drive, Zip 70510–4077, Mailing Address: P.O. Box 580, Zip 70511–0580; tel. 337/893–5466 **A**1 10 **F**3 11 13 15 29 30 31 34 40 45 50 54 59 60 64 66 68 70 75 76 79 81 82 85 86 87 89 97 98 103 105 107 108 114 119 127 128 130 133 146 **P**6
Primary Contact: Ray A. Landry, Chief Executive Officer
COO: Charles W. Guidry, Chief Operating Officer
CFO: Troy Hair, Chief Financial Officer
CMO: Weston Miller, M.D., Chief Medical Officer
CIO: Kelly Hair, Director Information Technology
CNO: Heidi Broussard, Chief Nursing Officer
Web address: www.abbgen.net
Control: Hospital district or authority, Government, nonfederal **Service:** General Medical and Surgical

Staffed Beds: 60 **Admissions:** 1876 **Census:** 29 **Outpatient Visits:** 99351 **Births:** 257 **Total Expense ($000):** 41462 **Payroll Expense ($000):** 19503 **Personnel:** 386

ALEXANDRIA—Rapides Parish

◇ **CENTRAL LOUISIANA SURGICAL HOSPITAL (190298)**, 651 North Bolton Avenue, Zip 71301–7449, Mailing Address: P.O. Box 8646, Zip 71306–1646; tel. 318/443–3511 **A**10 21 **F**12 68 74 81 85 86 90 107 111 130
Primary Contact: Louise Barker, R.N., Chief Executive Officer
CFO: Michael Fuselier, FACHE, Chief Financial Officer
CMO: Renick Webb, M.D., Chief Medical Director
CHR: Debbie Norman, Director Human Resources
CNO: Carol Wells, R.N., Chief Nursing Officer
Web address: www.clshospital.com
Control: Partnership, Investor–owned, for–profit **Service:** Surgical

Staffed Beds: 24 **Admissions:** 1285 **Census:** 8 **Outpatient Visits:** 34040 **Births:** 0 **Total Expense ($000):** 47284 **Payroll Expense ($000):** 12044 **Personnel:** 229

✈ **CHRISTUS DUBUIS HOSPITAL OF ALEXANDRIA (192012)**, 3330 Masonic Drive, 4th Floor, Zip 71301–3841; tel. 318/448–4938 **A**1 10 **F**1 3 29 77 84 85 148 **S** CHRISTUS Health, Irving, TX
Primary Contact: Kimberly Bennett, R.N., Interim Chief Executive Officer and Director of Nursing
CNO: Kimberly Bennett, R.N., Director Patient Care
Web address: www.christusdubuis.org/CHRISTUSDubuisHospitalofAlexandriaLA
Control: Church–operated, Nongovernment, not–for profit **Service:** Long–Term Acute Care hospital

Staffed Beds: 25 **Admissions:** 244 **Census:** 16 **Outpatient Visits:** 0 **Births:** 0 **Total Expense ($000):** 7662 **Payroll Expense ($000):** 3313 **Personnel:** 49

✈ **CHRISTUS ST. FRANCES CABRINI HOSPITAL (190019)**, 3330 Masonic Drive, Zip 71301–3899; tel. 318/487–1122 **A**1 2 10 **F**3 11 12 13 15 18 20 22 24 26 28 29 30 31 34 35 40 45 46 49 57 58 59 64 66 70 72 74 75 78 79 81 82 84 85 86 87 90 91 93 98 102 107 108 111 114 115 116 117 118 119 120 121 124 126 129 130 131 132 135 144 146 147 148 **P**6 **S** CHRISTUS Health, Irving, TX
Primary Contact: Nancy R. Hellyer, R.N., FACHE, Chief Executive Officer
COO: Lisa R. Lauve, R.N., Regional Chief Nursing Executive and Chief Operating Officer
CFO: Suzette Fatula, Vice President Finance
CHR: Wendy White, Regional Vice President Human Resources
Web address: www.cabrini.org/
Control: Church–operated, Nongovernment, not–for profit **Service:** General Medical and Surgical

Staffed Beds: 281 **Admissions:** 11929 **Census:** 182 **Outpatient Visits:** 185835 **Births:** 990 **Total Expense ($000):** 225382 **Payroll Expense ($000):** 70514 **Personnel:** 1338

□ **COMPASS BEHAVIORAL CENTER OF ALEXANDRIA (194106)**, 6410 Masonic Drve, Zip 71301–2319; tel. 318/442–3163 **A**1 10 **F**29 34 35 38 64 98 100 101 102 103 104 105 130 133 135 **P**5 **S** Compass Health, Crowley, LA
Primary Contact: Phillip Maxwell, Administrator
CNO: Cheryl Lachney, Director of Nursing
Web address: www.compasshealthcare.com/site191.php
Control: State–Government, nonfederal **Service:** Psychiatric

Staffed Beds: 16 **Admissions:** 351 **Census:** 10 **Outpatient Visits:** 0 **Births:** 0 **Total Expense ($000):** 2918 **Payroll Expense ($000):** 1390

✈ **HEALTHSOUTH REHABILITATION HOSPITAL OF ALEXANDRIA (193031)**, 104 North Third Street, Zip 71301–8581; tel. 318/449–1370, (Nonreporting) **A**1 10 **S** HEALTHSOUTH Corporation, Birmingham, AL
Primary Contact: James W. McClung, Chief Executive Officer
CFO: Linda Wright, Chief Financial Officer
CMO: Vasudeva Dhulipala, M.D., Medical Director
CHR: Suzie Wagner, Director Human Resources
CNO: Karin Jones, Chief Nursing Officer
Web address: www.healthsouthalexandria.com
Control: Partnership, Investor–owned, for–profit **Service:** Rehabilitation

Staffed Beds: 47

LONGLEAF HOSPITAL (194022), 110 John Eskew Drive, Zip 71303; tel. 318/445–5111, (Nonreporting) **A**10 **S** Acadia Healthcare Company, Inc., Franklin, TN
Primary Contact: Monica Tatum, Chief Executive Officer and Administrator
Web address: www.longleafhospital.com/
Control: Corporation, Investor–owned, for–profit **Service:** Psychiatric

Staffed Beds: 70

□ **OCEANS BEHAVIORAL HOSPITAL OF ALEXANDRIA (194096)**, 2621 North Bolton Avenue, Zip 71303–4506; tel. 318/448–8473, (Nonreporting) **A**1 10 **S** Oceans Healthcare, Lake Charles, LA
Primary Contact: Nicholas D. Guillory, MSN, Interim Administrator
Web address: www.obha.info/
Control: Corporation, Investor–owned, for–profit **Service:** Psychiatric

Staffed Beds: 24

✈ **RAPIDES REGIONAL MEDICAL CENTER (190026)**, 211 Fourth Street, Zip 71301–8421; tel. 318/769–3000 **A**1 2 3 5 10 **F**3 11 13 15 17 18 19 20 22 24 26 28 29 30 31 32 34 35 36 38 40 41 43 44 45 46 47 48 49 50 51 52 54 55 57 59 60 61 64 65 66 68 70 72 74 75 76 77 78 79 81 82 84 85 86 87 88 89 97 107 108 110 111 114 115 118 119 120 121 123 124 129 130 131 132 135 144 146 147 148 **P**1 **S** HCA, Nashville, TN
Primary Contact: Jason E. Cobb, FACHE, Chief Executive Officer
COO: Becky Barnes, Chief Operating Officer
CFO: Randy Rogers, FACHE, Chief Financial Officer
CMO: David Rhodes, M.D., Senior Vice President Medical Affairs and Chief Medical Officer
CHR: Stephen W. Scull, Vice President Ethics and Compliance officer
CNO: Diane Fulton, MSN, Chief Nursing Officer
Web address: www.rapidesregional.com
Control: Partnership, Investor–owned, for–profit **Service:** General Medical and Surgical

Staffed Beds: 357 **Admissions:** 16104 **Census:** 238 **Outpatient Visits:** 222963 **Births:** 1975 **Total Expense ($000):** 224670 **Payroll Expense ($000):** 80803 **Personnel:** 1393

□ **RIVERSIDE HOSPITAL OF LOUISIANA (192043)**, 211 Fourth Street, 5th Floor, Zip 71301–8421; tel. 318/767–2900, (Nonreporting) **A**1 10
Primary Contact: Chris G. Voinche, Chief Executive Officer
Web address: www.riversidehospital.net
Control: Corporation, Investor–owned, for–profit **Service:** Long–Term Acute Care hospital

Staffed Beds: 27

AMITE—Tangipahoa Parish

★ **HOOD MEMORIAL HOSPITAL (191309)**, 301 West Walnut Street, Zip 70422–2098; tel. 985/748–9485 **A**10 18 **F**3 29 35 40 57 59 64 65 75 86 97 107 108 114 119 127 133 144 146 **P**6
Primary Contact: Edward Dugar, RN, Chief Executive Officer
CFO: Mike Estay, Chief Financial Officer
CMO: Richard Bridges, M.D., Chief of Staff
CIO: Schley Harvin, Information Technology Technician
CHR: Alicia Chatelain, Director Human Resource
CNO: Fran St. Pierre, Chief Nursing Officer
Web address: www.hoodmemorial.com
Control: Hospital district or authority, Government, nonfederal **Service:** General Medical and Surgical

Staffed Beds: 25 **Admissions:** 514 **Census:** 13 **Outpatient Visits:** 25501 **Births:** 0 **Total Expense ($000):** 13461 **Payroll Expense ($000):** 5815

Hospital, Medicare Provider Number, Address, Telephone, Approval, Facility, and Physician Codes, Health Care System

★ American Hospital Association (AHA) membership ○ Healthcare Facilities Accreditation Program ⇑ Center for Improvement in Healthcare Quality Accreditation
□ The Joint Commission accreditation ◇ DNV Healthcare Inc. accreditation △ Commission on Accreditation of Rehabilitation Facilities (CARF) accreditation

LA

ARCADIA—Bienville Parish

BIENVILLE MEDICAL CENTER (191320), 1175 Pine Street, Suite 200, Zip 71001–3122; tel. 318/263–4700, (Nonreporting) **A**10 18 **S** Allegiance Health Management, Shreveport, LA
Primary Contact: Kirk Lemoine, Chief Executive Officer
Web address: www.bienvillemedicalcenter.net/
Control: Other not–for–profit (including NFP Corporation) **Service:** General Medical and Surgical

Staffed Beds: 21

BASTROP—Morehouse Parish

☐ **LIBERTY HEALTHCARE SYSTEMS (194083)**, 4673 Eugene Ware Boulevard, Zip 71220–1425; tel. 318/281–2448 **A**1 10 **F**98 99 130 **P**6
Primary Contact: Raphael Rhymes, Administrator
COO: Christine Murphy, MS, Chief Operating Officer
CFO: Paul Coburn, Chief Financial Officer
CMO: Tommy Dansby, Chief Medical Officer
CHR: Lindsay Cobb, Director Human Resources
CNO: Carla Sams, R.N., Director of Nursing
Web address: www.libertybh.com/
Control: Partnership, Investor–owned, for–profit **Service:** Children's hospital psychiatric

Staffed Beds: 60 **Admissions:** 997 **Census:** 23 **Outpatient Visits:** 15584 **Births:** 0 **Total Expense ($000):** 6075 **Payroll Expense ($000):** 3534 **Personnel:** 63

★ **MOREHOUSE GENERAL HOSPITAL (190116)**, 323 West Walnut Avenue, Zip 71220–4521, Mailing Address: P.O. Box 1060, Zip 71221–1060; tel. 318/283–3600 **A**3 10 **F**11 13 15 29 34 39 40 45 50 64 65 70 76 77 79 81 85 86 89 93 97 102 107 108 110 111 114 118 119 127 133 145 146 147 148 **P**5 6 **S** Community Hospital Corporation, Plano, TX
Primary Contact: Gary G. Kendrick, Interim Chief Executive Officer
CFO: James Allbritton, Chief Financial Officer
CMO: John Coats, M.D., Chief Medical Staff
CIO: B. J. Vail, Director Information Systems
CHR: Debbie Spann, Director Human Resources
CNO: Melinda Jones, R.N., Chief Nursing Officer
Web address: www.mghospital.com
Control: Hospital district or authority, Government, nonfederal **Service:** General Medical and Surgical

Staffed Beds: 49 **Admissions:** 1901 **Census:** 16 **Outpatient Visits:** 41367 **Births:** 405 **Total Expense ($000):** 28261 **Payroll Expense ($000):** 13236 **Personnel:** 235

STERLINGTON REHABILITATION HOSPITAL (193069), 370 West Hickory Avenue, Zip 71220–4442, Mailing Address: P.O. Box 627, Zip 71221–0627; tel. 318/665–9950 **A**10 **F**28 34 35 50 54 56 57 59 64 65 66 68 75 86 87 90 91 93 94 95 96 97 100 101 103 104 127 130 132 135 143 147 148 **P**6
Primary Contact: Catherine M. Waldrop, Administrator
Web address: www.www.sterlingtonrehab.com
Control: Corporation, Investor–owned, for–profit **Service:** Rehabilitation

Staffed Beds: 10 **Admissions:** 284 **Census:** 10 **Outpatient Visits:** 1200 **Births:** 0 **Total Expense ($000):** 8252 **Payroll Expense ($000):** 4150 **Personnel:** 82

BATON ROUGE—East Baton Rouge Parish

☐ **BATON ROUGE BEHAVIORAL HOSPITAL (194107)**, 4040 North Boulevard, Zip 70806–3829; tel. 225/300–8470, (Nonreporting) **A**1 10
Primary Contact: Rick Bennett, Administrator
COO: James O'Shea, Chief Operating Officer
CFO: Warren Knight, Chief Financial Officer
CMO: Richard Capiola, M.D., Chief Medical Officer
CNO: Francine Mineau, Chief Nursing Officer
Web address: www.batonrougebehavioral.com
Control: Corporation, Investor–owned, for–profit **Service:** Psychiatric

Staffed Beds: 15

☐ **BATON ROUGE GENERAL MEDICAL CENTER (190065)**, 8585 Picardy Avenue, Zip 70809–3679; tel. 225/763–4000, (Includes BATON ROUGE GENERAL MEDICAL CENTER–BLUEBONNET, 8585 Picardy Avenue, Mailing Address: P.O. Box 84330, Zip 70884–4330; tel. 225/763–4000; Edgardo J. Tenreiro, Interim Chief Executive Officer and Chief Operating Officer) **A**1 2 3 5 8 10 **F**3 8 11 12 13 15 16 17 18 19 20 22 24 26 28 29 30 31 34 35 38 40 44 45 46 47 49 50 53 56 57 58 59 60 61 64 65 68 70 72 74 75 76 77 78 79 81 82 84 86 87 88 89 90 91 93 96 97 98 101 102 103 104 105 107 108 110 111 114 115 117 118 119 120 121 123 124 126 128 129 130 131 132 135 143 144 146 147 148 **P**4 6
Primary Contact: Edgardo J. Tenreiro, Interim Chief Executive Officer and Chief Operating Officer
COO: Edgardo J. Tenreiro, Executive Vice President and Chief Operating Officer
CFO: Kendall Johnson, Chief Financial Officer
CIO: Bennett Cheramie, Vice President Information Technology
CHR: Paul Douglas, Vice President Human Resources
CNO: Anna Leah Cazes, Chief Nursing Officer
Web address: www.brgeneral.org
Control: Other not–for–profit (including NFP Corporation) **Service:** General Medical and Surgical

Staffed Beds: 566 **Admissions:** 16115 **Census:** 248 **Outpatient Visits:** 195658 **Births:** 605 **Total Expense ($000):** 367659 **Payroll Expense ($000):** 125376 **Personnel:** 2521

☐ **BATON ROUGE REHABILITATION HOSPITAL (193028)**, 8595 United Plaza Boulevard, Zip 70809–2251; tel. 225/927–0567, (Nonreporting) **A**1 10
Primary Contact: Trisha Guidry, Administrator
CFO: Nicholas Hluchy, Business Analyst, Support Services Manager
CMO: Sundararama R. Vatsavai, M.D., Medical Director
CIO: John Derrick Landreneau, Director of Marketing
CHR: Michelle Smith, Coordinator Human Resources
CNO: John Derrick Landreneau, Director of Nursing
Web address: www.brrehab.com
Control: Corporation, Investor–owned, for–profit **Service:** Rehabilitation

Staffed Beds: 80

BETHESDA REHABILITATION HOSPITAL (193092), 7414 Sumrall Drive, Zip 70812–1240, Mailing Address: 8225 Summa Avenue, Suite B., Zip 70809–3422; tel. 225/767–2034, (Nonreporting) **A**10
Primary Contact: Lionel Murphy, Chief Executive Officer and Administrator
Web address: www.bethesdarh.com/
Control: Corporation, Investor–owned, for–profit **Service:** Rehabilitation

Staffed Beds: 18

HEALTHSOUTH REHABILITATION HOSPITAL OF BATON ROUGE See Baton Rouge Rehabilitation Hospital

OCEANS BEHAVIORAL HOSPITAL OF BATON ROUGE (194086), 11135 Florida Boulevard, Zip 70815–2013; tel. 225/356–7030, (Nonreporting) **A**10 **S** Oceans Healthcare, Lake Charles, LA
Primary Contact: Valerie Dalton, R.N., Administrator
Web address: www.obhbr.info/
Control: Corporation, Investor–owned, for–profit **Service:** Psychiatric

Staffed Beds: 20

✠ **OCHSNER MEDICAL CENTER–BATON ROUGE (190202)**, 17000 Medical Center Drive, Zip 70816–3224; tel. 225/752–2470 **A**1 10 **F**3 11 12 13 15 18 20 22 24 26 29 30 31 34 35 40 42 45 46 47 48 49 51 57 58 59 60 64 68 70 72 74 75 76 77 78 79 81 82 85 86 87 93 97 104 107 108 110 111 114 116 117 119 126 129 130 132 135 144 146 147 148 **P**6 **S** Ochsner Health System, New Orleans, LA
Primary Contact: Eric McMillen, Chief Executive Officer
CFO: Stephanie Bushart, Chief Financial Officer
CMO: F. Ralph Dauterive, M.D., Vice President Medical Affairs
CHR: Jan Rivers, Director Human Resources
Web address: www.ochsner.org/page.cfm?id=103
Control: Other not–for–profit (including NFP Corporation) **Service:** General Medical and Surgical

Staffed Beds: 152 **Admissions:** 7353 **Census:** 73 **Outpatient Visits:** 87897 **Births:** 1404 **Total Expense ($000):** 134975 **Payroll Expense ($000):** 46591 **Personnel:** 638

Many Facility Codes have changed. Please refer to the AHA Guide Code Chart. © 2016 AHA Guide

✠ **OUR LADY OF THE LAKE REGIONAL MEDICAL CENTER (190064)**, 5000 Hennessy Boulevard, Zip 70808–4375; tel. 225/765–6565, (Includes OUR LADY OF THE LAKE CHILDREN'S HOSPITAL, 5000 Hennessy Boulevard, tel. 225/765–8886), (Total facility includes 390 beds in nursing home–type unit) **A**1 2 3 5 8 10 **F**3 4 5 8 10 11 12 14 15 17 18 19 20 21 22 24 26 28 29 30 31 34 35 37 38 39 40 41 42 43 46 47 49 50 51 53 54 55 56 57 58 59 60 61 64 66 68 70 71 74 75 77 78 79 81 84 85 86 87 88 89 90 93 94 96 97 98 99 100 101 102 103 104 105 107 108 110 111 114 115 116 117 118 119 125 126 127 129 130 131 132 135 141 142 143 146 148 **P**6 **S** Franciscan Missionaries of Our Lady Health System, Inc., Baton Rouge, LA
Primary Contact: K. Scott Wester, FACHE, President and Chief Executive Officer
COO: Terrie Sterling, R.N., Chief Operating Officer
CFO: Jeff Limbocker, Chief Financial Officer
CMO: Richard Vath, M.D., Vice President Medical Affairs
CIO: Vindell Washington, M.D., Vice President Performance Excellence and Technology
CHR: Cora Ford, Vice President Human Resources
CNO: Nicole Telhiard, Chief Nursing Officer
Web address: www.ololrmc.com
Control: Church–operated, Nongovernment, not–for profit **Service:** General Medical and Surgical

Staffed Beds: 1111 **Admissions:** 34858 **Census:** 781 **Outpatient Visits:** 1490616 **Births:** 0 **Total Expense ($000):** 1022563 **Payroll Expense ($000):** 372684 **Personnel:** 6037

☐ **PROMISE HOSPITAL BATON ROUGE – MAIN CAMPUS (192045)**, 5130 Mancuso Lane, Zip 70809–3583; tel. 225/490–9600, (Nonreporting) **A**1 **S** Promise Healthcare, Boca Raton, FL
Primary Contact: Kiley P. Cedotal, FACHE, Chief Executive Officer
COO: Michael R. Sanders, MS, Chief Operating Officer
CFO: Trina Arceneaux, Assistant Chief Financial Officer
CMO: Subhaker Gummadi, M.D., Chief Medical Staff
CIO: Charmaine T. Mosby, Area Director Health Information Management
CHR: Marilyn Hamilton, Director Human Resources
CNO: Larrie Arceneaux, Chief Clinical Officer
Web address: www.promise–batonrouge.com
Control: Corporation, Investor–owned, for–profit **Service:** Long–Term Acute Care hospital

Staffed Beds: 50

PROMISE HOSPITAL OF BATON ROUGE – MID–CITY CAMPUS (192004), 3600 Florida Boulevard, 4th Floor, Zip 70806–3842; tel. 225/387–7770, (Nonreporting) **A**10 **S** Promise Healthcare, Boca Raton, FL
Primary Contact: Kiley P. Cedotal, FACHE, Chief Executive Officer
CMO: Subhaker Gummadi, M.D., President Medical Staff
Web address: www.promise–batonrougemidcity.com
Control: Corporation, Investor–owned, for–profit **Service:** Long–Term Acute Care hospital

Staffed Beds: 57

PROMISE HOSPITAL OF BATON ROUGE – OCHSNER CAMPUS (192049), 17000 Medical Center Drive, 3rd Floor, Zip 70816–3246; tel. 225/236–5440, (Nonreporting) **A**10 **S** Promise Healthcare, Boca Raton, FL
Primary Contact: Kiley P. Cedotal, FACHE, Chief Executive Officer
CMO: Venkat Banda, M.D., President Medical Staff
CHR: Wendy Cobbs, Director of Human Resources
Web address: www.promise–batonrougeochsner.com
Control: Corporation, Investor–owned, for–profit **Service:** Long–Term Acute Care hospital

Staffed Beds: 22

SAGE REHABILITATION HOSPITAL (193078), 8000 Summa Avenue, Zip 70809–3423, Mailing Address: P.O. Box 82681, Zip 70884–2681; tel. 225/819–0703, (Total facility includes 15 beds in nursing home–type unit) **A**10 **F**29 54 74 75 77 90 91 93 128 130
Primary Contact: Linda Coulon, R.N., Administrator
CMO: Christopher Belleau, M.D., Medical Director
CHR: Kathy Ringe, Director Human Resources
CNO: Beth Sibley, Director of Nursing
Web address: www.sage–rehab.org
Control: Individual, Investor–owned, for–profit **Service:** Rehabilitation

Staffed Beds: 42 **Admissions:** 624 **Census:** 28 **Outpatient Visits:** 0 **Births:** 0 **Personnel:** 157

☐ **SEASIDE HEALTH SYSTEM (194103)**, 4363 Convention Street, Zip 70806–3906; Mailing Address: TX, tel. 225/238–3043, (Nonreporting) **A**1 10
Primary Contact: Eric Gintoli, Administrator
Web address: www.seasidehc.com/seaside–health–system–locations/
Control: Partnership, Investor–owned, for–profit **Service:** Psychiatric

Staffed Beds: 24

SPINE HOSPITAL OF LOUISIANA (FORMALLY THE NEUROMEDICAL CENTER SURGICAL HOSPITAL) (190266), 10105 Park Rowe Avenue, Suite 250, Zip 70810–1684; tel. 225/763–9900, (Nonreporting) **A**10
Primary Contact: Robert D. Blair, Chief Executive Officer
CFO: Allison Doherty, Chief Financial Officer
CMO: Greg Fautheree, M.D., Medical Director
CIO: Jeremy Deprato, Director Information Technology
CHR: Kimberly Jones, Coordinator Human Resources
CNO: Monica Nijoka, Chief Nursing Office
Web address: www.theneuromedicalcenter.com
Control: Corporation, Investor–owned, for–profit **Service:** Surgical

Staffed Beds: 23

☐ **SURGICAL SPECIALTY CENTER OF BATON ROUGE (190251)**, 8080 Bluebonnet Boulevard, Zip 70810–7827; tel. 225/408–8080, (Nonreporting) **A**1 10
Primary Contact: Ann Heine, Chief Executive Officer
Web address: www.sscbr.com
Control: Corporation, Investor–owned, for–profit **Service:** Surgical

Staffed Beds: 14

THE NEUROMEDICAL CENTER REHABILITATION HOSPITAL (193090), 10101 Park Rowe Avenue, Suite 500, Zip 70810–1685; tel. 225/906–2999, (Nonreporting) **A**10 **S** AMG Integrated Healthcare Management, Lafayette, LA
Primary Contact: Elizabeth Wilson, Administrator
Web address: www.theneuromedicalcenter.com
Control: Corporation, Investor–owned, for–profit **Service:** Rehabilitation

Staffed Beds: 23

✠ **WOMAN'S HOSPITAL (190128)**, 100 Woman's Way, Zip 70817–5100, Mailing Address: P.O. Box 95009, Zip 70895–9009; tel. 225/927–1300 **A**1 2 3 5 10 **F**3 11 12 13 15 29 31 32 34 35 36 38 40 45 50 53 54 57 58 59 61 64 65 66 68 70 71 72 74 75 76 77 78 79 81 84 85 86 87 93 102 107 110 111 115 119 126 129 130 131 132 134 135 146 147 148 **P**6
Primary Contact: Teri G. Fontenot, FACHE, President and Chief Executive Officer
COO: Stephanie Anderson, Executive Vice President and Chief Operating Officer
CFO: Greg Smith, CPA, Chief Financial Officer
CMO: Susan Puyau, M.D., Medical Director
CIO: Paul Kirk, Vice President
CHR: Donna L. Bodin, Vice President
CNO: Patricia Johnson, R.N., Senior Vice President
Web address: www.womans.org
Control: Other not–for–profit (including NFP Corporation) **Service:** Obstetrics and gynecology

Staffed Beds: 216 **Admissions:** 11848 **Census:** 140 **Outpatient Visits:** 118749 **Births:** 8720 **Total Expense ($000):** 251464 **Payroll Expense ($000):** 119573 **Personnel:** 1658

BERNICE—Union Parish

REEVES MEMORIAL MEDICAL CENTER (191326), 409 First Street, Zip 71222–4001, Mailing Address: P.O. Box 697, Zip 71222–0697; tel. 318/285–9066, (Nonreporting) **A**10 18
Primary Contact: David Caston, Chief Executive Officer
COO: Beth Jones, Chief Operating Officer
CFO: Charolette Thompson, Chief Financial Officer
CMO: R. Brian Harris, M.D., Chief of Staff
CIO: Scott Dickson, Director Information Technology
CHR: Robin Adams, Director Human Resources
CNO: Beth Jones, Director of Nursing
Web address: www.reevesmemorial.com/
Control: Hospital district or authority, Government, nonfederal **Service:** General Medical and Surgical

Staffed Beds: 11

TRI–WARD GENERAL HOSPITAL See Reeves Memorial Medical Center

LA

BOGALUSA—Washington Parish

✠ **OUR LADY OF THE ANGELS HOSPITAL (190312)**, 433 Plaza Street, Zip 70427–3793; tel. 985/730–6700, (Includes BOGALUSA COMMUNITY MEDICAL CENTER, 433 Plaza Street, tel. 985/730–6700) **A**1 3 5 10 **F**3 13 15 18 28 29 30 32 34 35 40 45 47 48 49 50 51 57 59 60 61 64 65 66 68 70 74 75 76 77 79 81 85 89 97 98 99 102 104 107 108 110 111 119 130 135 146 147 148 **S** Franciscan Missionaries of Our Lady Health System, Inc., Baton Rouge, LA
Primary Contact: Rene Ragas, Chief Operating Officer
COO: Rene Ragas, Chief Operating Officer
CFO: Brooke Cummings, Chief Financial Officer
CMO: Hamid Hussain, M.D., Medical Director
CIO: Mike Gilly, Chief Information Officer
CHR: Christi Brown, Director Human Resources
CNO: Mark Kellar, R.N., Interim Chief Nursing Officer
Web address: www.oloah.org
Control: Church–operated, Nongovernment, not–for profit **Service:** General Medical and Surgical

Staffed Beds: 57 Admissions: 2174 Census: 23 Outpatient Visits: 100366 Births: 226

BOSSIER CITY—Bossier Parish

☐ **CORNERSTONE HOSPITAL OF BOSSIER CITY (192006)**, 4900 Medical Drive, Zip 71112–4521; tel. 318/747–9500, (Nonreporting) **A**1 10 **S** Cornerstone Healthcare Group, Dallas, TX
Primary Contact: Sheri Burnette, R.N., Chief Executive Officer and Administrator
CFO: Billy Wilcox, Group Controller
CMO: James Jackson, M.D., Chief of Staff
CNO: Tamara Grimm, R.N., Chief Clinical Officer and Chief Nursing Officer
Web address: www.chghospitals.com/
Control: Corporation, Investor–owned, for–profit **Service:** Long–Term Acute Care hospital

Staffed Beds: 54

◇ **PATHWAY REHABILITATION HOSPITAL (193094)**, 4900 Medical Drive, Zip 71112–4521; tel. 318/841–5555, (Nonreporting) **A**10 21
Primary Contact: James Manning, Administrator
Web address: www.pathrehab.com
Control: Corporation, Investor–owned, for–profit **Service:** Rehabilitation

Staffed Beds: 24

RED RIVER BEHAVIORAL CENTER (194079), 2800 Melrose Avenue, Zip 71111–5870; tel. 318/549–2033 **A**10 **F**29 38 56 98 100 101 103 130 135 143
Primary Contact: Susan Kottenbrook, Chief Executive Officer
Web address: www.redriverbehavioral.com/
Control: Partnership, Investor–owned, for–profit **Service:** Psychiatric

Staffed Beds: 20 Admissions: 328 Census: 16 Outpatient Visits: 0 Births: 0 Total Expense ($000): 3589 Payroll Expense ($000): 1530 Personnel: 51

WILLIS–KNIGHTON BOSSIER HEALTH CENTER See WK Bossier Health Center

✠ △ **WK BOSSIER HEALTH CENTER (190236)**, 2400 Hospital Drive, Zip 71111–2385; tel. 318/212–7000 **A**1 2 7 10 **F**3 8 11 12 13 15 18 20 22 28 29 30 34 35 38 40 44 45 46 47 48 49 50 53 54 56 57 59 60 61 64 65 68 70 74 75 76 77 78 79 80 81 82 84 85 86 87 89 93 96 97 100 101 102 103 107 108 109 110 111 114 115 118 119 126 127 129 130 131 132 135 144 146 147 148 **P**7 **S** Willis–Knighton Health System, Shreveport, LA
Primary Contact: Clifford M. Broussard, FACHE, Administrator
COO: Charles D. Daigle, Chief Operating Officer
CFO: Ramona D. Fryer, Chief Financial Officer
CMO: Charles Powers, M.D., Administrative Medical Director
CIO: Charles Laster, Director Information Management
CHR: Debbie McCall, Director Human Resources
CNO: Sharon Hudnell, R.N., Chief Nursing Officer
Web address: www.wkhs.com/wkb/
Control: Other not–for–profit (including NFP Corporation) **Service:** General Medical and Surgical

Staffed Beds: 166 Admissions: 13027 Census: 102 Outpatient Visits: 128918 Births: 969 Personnel: 961

BREAUX BRIDGE—St. Martin Parish

★ **GENESIS BEHAVIORAL HOSPITAL (194089)**, 606 Latiolais Drive, Zip 70517–4231; Mailing Address: PO BOX 159, Zip 70517–0159; tel. 337/442–6084 **A**10 **F**98 100 101 102 103 104 105 **P**1
Primary Contact: William Alredge, Administrator
COO: Gretchen Kaltenbach, R.N., Chief Operating Officer
CFO: William Alredge, Chief Financial Officer
Web address: www.genesisbh.com/
Control: Corporation, Investor–owned, for–profit **Service:** Psychiatric

Staffed Beds: 18 Admissions: 554 Census: 15 Outpatient Visits: 17000 Births: 0 Personnel: 71

★ **ST. MARTIN HOSPITAL (191302)**, 210 Champagne Boulevard, Zip 70517–3700, Mailing Address: P.O. Box 357, Zip 70517–0357; tel. 337/332–2178 **A**10 18 **F**15 18 29 34 35 40 64 75 77 90 93 107 110 111 114 119 128 130 133 146 **S** Lafayette General Health, Lafayette, LA
Primary Contact: Karen Wyble, R.N., Chief Executive Officer
CFO: Shadelle Huval, Director Finance
CHR: Rena B. Mouisset, Director Human Resources and Contract Compliance
Web address: www.stmartinhospital.org
Control: Other not–for–profit (including NFP Corporation) **Service:** General Medical and Surgical

Staffed Beds: 25 Admissions: 357 Census: 13 Outpatient Visits: 131140 Births: 0 Total Expense ($000): 15075 Payroll Expense ($000): 6835 Personnel: 126

BROUSSARD—Lafayette Parish

☐ **OCEANS BEHAVIORAL HOSPITAL OF BROUSSARD (194073)**, 418 Albertson Parkway, Zip 70518–4971; tel. 337/237–6444, (Nonreporting) **A**1 10 **S** Oceans Healthcare, Lake Charles, LA
Primary Contact: Amy Dysart–Credeur, Administrator
Web address: www.obhb.info/
Control: Corporation, Investor–owned, for–profit **Service:** Psychiatric

Staffed Beds: 38

BUNKIE—Avoyelles Parish

BEACON BEHAVIORAL HOSPITAL (194112), 323 Evergreen Street, Zip 71322–1307; tel. 318/346–3143, (Nonreporting) **S** Beacon Health System, South Bend, IN
Primary Contact: Gene Amons, R.N., Administrator
Web address: www.beaconbh.com
Control: Other not–for–profit (including NFP Corporation) **Service:** Psychiatric

Staffed Beds: 17

BUNKIE GENERAL HOSPITAL (191311), 427 Evergreen Highway, Zip 71322, Mailing Address: P.O. Box 380, Zip 71322–0380; tel. 318/346–6681, (Nonreporting) **A**10 18
Primary Contact: Linda F. Deville, Chief Executive Officer
CFO: Frances Deglandon, Chief Financial Officer
CMO: Mohit Srivastava, M.D., Chief of Staff
CIO: Johnny Bergeron, Chief Information Officer
CHR: Tina Louise Juneau, Director Human Resources
CNO: Corey Jeansonne, Chief Nursing Officer
Web address: www.bunkiegeneral.com
Control: Hospital district or authority, Government, nonfederal **Service:** General Medical and Surgical

Staffed Beds: 18

CAMERON—Cameron Parish

SOUTH CAMERON MEMORIAL HOSPITAL (190307), 5360 West Creole Highway, Zip 70631–5127; tel. 337/542–4111, (Nonreporting) **A**10
Primary Contact: Leslie Trahan, Chief Executive Officer
Control: Hospital district or authority, Government, nonfederal **Service:** General Medical and Surgical

Staffed Beds: 49

CHALMETTE—Saint Bernard Parish

✠ **ST. BERNARD PARISH HOSPITAL (190308)**, 8000 West Judge Perez Drive, Zip 70043–1668; tel. 504/826–9500 **A**1 10 **F**3 8 15 17 18 20 22 24 29 34 40 45 46 49 53 57 59 67 70 72 73 76 77 79 80 81 88 90 91 107 108 110 111 114 119 129 148
Primary Contact: Charles Lindell, Chief Executive Officer
CFO: Joseph Kemka, Chief Financial Officer
CMO: Paul Verrette, M.D., Chief Medical Officer
CIO: Zane Looney, Chief Information Officer
CHR: Melody M. O'Connell, Director Human Resources
CNO: Janice Kishner, Chief Nursing Officer
Web address: www.sbph.net
Control: Hospital district or authority, Government, nonfederal **Service:** General Medical and Surgical

Staffed Beds: 40 Admissions: 2102 Census: 25 Outpatient Visits: 35000 Births: 0

CHURCH POINT—Acadia Parish

ACADIA–ST. LANDRY HOSPITAL (191319), 810 South Broadway Street, Zip 70525–4497; tel. 337/684–5435, (Nonreporting) **A**10 18
Primary Contact: Cindy Walters, Chief Executive Officer
CFO: Lucille LeJeune, Assistant Administrator and Chief Financial Officer
CMO: Ty Hargroder, M.D., Chief of Staff
Web address: www.aslh.org
Control: Other not–for–profit (including NFP Corporation) **Service:** General Medical and Surgical

Staffed Beds: 25

Many Facility Codes have changed. Please refer to the AHA Guide Code Chart. © 2016 AHA Guide

CLINTON—East Feliciana Parish

AMG SPECIALTY HOSPITAL–FELICIANA (192041), 9725 Grace Lane,
Zip 70722–4925; tel. 225/683–1600, (Nonreporting) **A**10 **S** AMG Integrated
Healthcare Management, Lafayette, LA
Primary Contact: Michael Sanders, Chief Executive Officer
Web address: www.amgfeliciana.com/
Control: Corporation, Investor–owned, for–profit **Service:** Long–Term Acute Care
hospital

Staffed Beds: 16

COLUMBIA—Caldwell Parish

CALDWELL MEMORIAL HOSPITAL (190190), 411 Main Street,
Zip 71418–6704, Mailing Address: P.O. Box 899, Zip 71418–0899;
tel. 318/649–6111 **A**10 **F**90
Primary Contact: Heather Clark, Chief Executive Officer
COO: Lisa Patrick, Chief Operating Officer
CFO: William H. Clark, Chief Financial Officer
Control: Other, Government, federal **Service:** General Medical and Surgical

Staffed Beds: 47 **Admissions:** 1030 **Census:** 12 **Outpatient Visits:** 0 **Births:**
0

CITIZENS MEDICAL CENTER (190184), 7939 U.S. Highway 165,
Zip 71418–1079, Mailing Address: P.O. Box 1079, Zip 71418–1079;
tel. 318/649–6106, (Nonreporting) **A**10
Primary Contact: Steve Barbo, R.N., Administrator
Web address: www.citizensmedcenter.com/
Control: Hospital district or authority, Government, nonfederal **Service:** General
Medical and Surgical

Staffed Beds: 40

COUSHATTA—Red River Parish

CHRISTUS COUSHATTA HEALTH CARE CENTER (191312), 1635 Marvel
Street, Zip 71019–9022, Mailing Address: P.O. Box 589, Zip 71019–0589;
tel. 318/932–2000 **A**1 10 18 **F**3 15 29 30 34 35 39 40 41 50 54 56 57 59
64 65 66 67 68 75 77 78 81 82 91 93 97 103 107 110 115 116 117 119
120 127 128 130 133 135 147 148 **S** CHRISTUS Health, Irving, TX
Primary Contact: Brandon Hillman, Interim Administrator, Director of Hospital
Services
CFO: Scott Merryman, Chief Financial Officer
CMO: Jonathan Weisul, M.D., Vice President Medical Affairs and Chief Medical
Officer
CIO: Bruce Honea, Director Information Services
CHR: Donnette Craig, Director Human Resources
Web address: www.christuscoushatta.org
Control: Church–operated, Nongovernment, not–for profit **Service:** General
Medical and Surgical

Staffed Beds: 25 **Admissions:** 778 **Census:** 10 **Births:** 0

SPECIALTY REHABILITATION HOSPITAL OF COUSHATTA (193080), 1110
Ringgold Avenue Suite B., Zip 71019–9073; tel. 318/932–1770,
(Nonreporting) **A**10
Primary Contact: Craig Ball, Chief Executive Officer
COO: Charlie Ball, Chief Operating Officer
CFO: Connie Ball, Chief Financial Officer
CMO: Jalal Joudeh, M.D., Chief Medical Officer
CHR: Denise Logan, Director Human Resources
Web address: www.specialtyhealthcare.com
Control: Individual, Investor–owned, for–profit **Service:** Rehabilitation

Staffed Beds: 12

COVINGTON—St. Tammany Parish

AMG SPECIALTY HOSPITAL – COVINGTON (192051), 195 Highland Park
Entrance, Zip 70433–7164; tel. 985/867–3977, (Nonreporting) **A**1 10 **S** AMG
Integrated Healthcare Management, Lafayette, LA
Primary Contact: Tim Deaton, Chief Executive Officer
CMO: Merrill Laurent, M.D., Medical Director
CHR: MaryAnn O'Brien, Coordinator Human Resource
CNO: Michelle Moreau, Chief Clinical Officer
Web address: www.amgcovington.com/
Control: Corporation, Investor–owned, for–profit **Service:** Long–Term Acute Care
hospital

Staffed Beds: 38

FAIRWAY MEDICAL SURGICAL HOSPITAL (190267), 67252 Industry Lane,
Zip 70433–8704; tel. 985/809–9888, (Nonreporting) **A**10 21
Primary Contact: Benjamin Patterson, Chief Executive Officer
CFO: Denise Businelle, Chief Financial Officer
CMO: William Preau, M.D., Medical Director
CIO: Skip Federico, Director Information Systems
CHR: Pam Collins, Director Human Resources
Web address: www.fairwaymedical.com
Control: Corporation, Investor–owned, for–profit **Service:** General Medical and
Surgical

Staffed Beds: 21

GREENBRIER BEHAVIOR HEALTH HOSPITAL (194069), 201 Greenbrier
Boulevard, Zip 70433–7236; tel. 985/893–2970 **A**10 **F**54 56 64 98 100 101
102 103 104 105 **S** Acadia Healthcare Company, Inc., Franklin, TN
Primary Contact: Wes Crawford, Chief Executive Officer
CFO: Terri Logsdon, Chief Financial Officer
CMO: Jason Coe, M.D., Medical Director
Web address: www.greenbrierhospital.com/
Control: Corporation, Investor–owned, for–profit **Service:** Psychiatric

Staffed Beds: 60 **Admissions:** 2000 **Census:** 41 **Births:** 0

LAKEVIEW REGIONAL MEDICAL CENTER (190177), 95 Judge Tanner
Boulevard, Zip 70433–7507; tel. 985/867–3800, (Nonreporting) **A**1 3 10 **S** HCA,
Nashville, TN
Primary Contact: Bret G. Kolman, CPA, FACHE, Chief Executive Officer
COO: Hirat Patel, M.D., Chief Operating Officer
CFO: Carolyn Ridge, Chief Financial Officer
CMO: George Barnes, M.D., Medical Director
CIO: Jinilinn Cass, Director Medical Records
CHR: Lyle Theriot, Director Human Resources
Web address: www.lakeviewregional.com
Control: Corporation, Investor–owned, for–profit **Service:** General Medical and
Surgical

Staffed Beds: 172

NORTHSHORE SPECIALTY HOSPITAL See PAM Specialty Hospital of Covington

PAM SPECIALTY HOSPITAL OF COVINGTON (192048), 20050 Crestwood
Boulevard, Zip 70433–5207; tel. 985/875–7525 **A**1 10 **F**1 29 75 130 143
S Post Acute Medical, LLC, Enola, PA
Primary Contact: J. Cullen Meyers, Chief Executive Officer
COO: John Bauer, Chief Operating Officer
CFO: Karick Stober, Chief Financial Officer
CMO: Adam Burick, M.D., Chief Medical Officer
CIO: Bryan Munchel, Senior Vice President and Chief Information Officer
CHR: Waynea Finley, Senior Vice President Human Resources
CNO: Marsha Medlin, Senior Vice President of Clinical and Operations
Web address: www.postacutemedical.com
Control: Individual, Investor–owned, for–profit **Service:** Long–Term Acute Care
hospital

Staffed Beds: 58 **Admissions:** 404 **Census:** 28 **Outpatient Visits:** 0 **Births:**
0 **Total Expense ($000):** 15682 **Payroll Expense ($000):** 6615 **Personnel:**
100

ST. TAMMANY PARISH HOSPITAL (190045), 1202 South Tyler Street,
Zip 70433–2330; tel. 985/898–4000 **A**1 2 10 **F**3 8 11 12 13 15 17 18 20 22
24 26 28 29 30 31 34 35 37 40 43 44 45 46 48 49 50 54 57 59 62 63 64
65 69 70 72 74 75 76 77 78 79 81 82 84 85 86 87 89 90 92 93 96 97 107
108 109 110 111 114 115 119 124 126 129 130 132 135 146 147 148 **P**6
Primary Contact: Patti M. Ellish, FACHE, President and Chief Executive Officer
COO: Sharon A. Toups, Senior Vice President and Chief Operating Officer
CFO: Sandra P. Dipietro, Chief Financial Officer
CMO: Robert Capitelli, M.D., Senior Vice President and Chief Medical Officer
CIO: Craig Doyle, Director and Chief Information Officer
CHR: Carolyn Adema, Vice President, Human Resources
CNO: Kerry K. Milton, R.N., Chief Nursing Officer
Web address: www.stph.org
Control: Hospital district or authority, Government, nonfederal **Service:** General
Medical and Surgical

Staffed Beds: 218 **Admissions:** 10415 **Census:** 126 **Outpatient Visits:**
315324 **Births:** 1811 **Total Expense ($000):** 264405 **Payroll Expense
($000):** 106965 **Personnel:** 1803

LA

CROWLEY—Acadia Parish

★ **ACADIA GENERAL HOSPITAL (190044)**, 1305 Crowley Rayne Highway, Zip 70526–8202; tel. 337/783–3222, (Nonreporting) **A**10 **S** Lafayette General Health, Lafayette, LA
Primary Contact: Donald D. Trexler, Chief Executive Officer
CFO: Charmaine R. Vidrine, CPA, Chief Financial Officer
CNO: Caroline Marceaux, R.N., Chief Nursing Officer
Web address: www.acadiageneral.com
Control: Other not–for–profit (including NFP Corporation) **Service:** General Medical and Surgical

Staffed Beds: 178

★ **COMPASS BEHAVIORAL CENTER OF CROWLEY (194085)**, 1526 North Avenue I., Zip 70526–2434; tel. 337/788–3380, (Nonreporting) **A**10 **S** Compass Health, Crowley, LA
Primary Contact: Allison Kidder–Tuck, Administrator
Web address: www.compasshealthcare.com
Control: Corporation, Investor–owned, for–profit **Service:** Psychiatric

Staffed Beds: 34

CUT OFF—Lafourche Parish

★ ◇ **LADY OF THE SEA GENERAL HOSPITAL (191325)**, 200 West 134th Place, Zip 70345–4143; tel. 985/632–6401 **A**10 18 21 **F**3 15 29 34 35 40 45 57 59 60 62 64 65 70 81 85 87 107 108 110 111 114 119 127 130 132 133 135 146 148 **P**6
Primary Contact: Karen S. Collins, R.N., Chief Executive Officer
COO: Lloyd Guidry, Chief Operating Officer
CFO: Jacquelyn Richoux, Chief Financial Officer
CMO: William Crenshaw, M.D., Chief of Staff
CIO: Bennie Smith, Chief Information Officer
CHR: Bennie Smith, Director Human Resources and Risk Management
CNO: Holly Griffin, R.N., Chief Nursing Officer
Web address: www.losgh.org
Control: Hospital district or authority, Government, nonfederal **Service:** General Medical and Surgical

Staffed Beds: 25 Admissions: 725 Census: 8 Outpatient Visits: 38119
Births: 0 Total Expense ($000): 30780 Payroll Expense ($000): 12433
Personnel: 282

DE RIDDER—Beauregard Parish

✠ **BEAUREGARD MEMORIAL HOSPITAL (190050)**, 600 South Pine Street, Zip 70634–4942, Mailing Address: P.O. Box 730, Zip 70634–0730; tel. 337/462–7100 **A**1 10 **F**3 11 13 15 18 20 26 28 29 30 31 34 35 39 40 45 46 50 53 57 64 70 75 76 78 79 81 85 89 91 93 96 107 108 110 111 114 119 129 130 131 133 148 **P**6
Primary Contact: Darrell L. Kingham, CPA, Interim Chief Executive Officer and Chief Financial Officer
CFO: Darrell L. Kingham, CPA, Vice President Finance
CMO: David Jones, M.D., Chief Medical Officer
CIO: Meg Jackson, Director Information Technology
CHR: Kelli C. Broocks, Director Human Resources, Public Relations and Physician Recruitment
CNO: Anita Thibodeaux, Chief Nursing Officer
Web address: www.beauregard.org
Control: Hospital district or authority, Government, nonfederal **Service:** General Medical and Surgical

Staffed Beds: 60 Admissions: 2585 Census: 27 Outpatient Visits: 79550
Births: 456 Total Expense ($000): 39452 Payroll Expense ($000): 18258
Personnel: 375

DELHI—Richland Parish

RICHLAND PARISH HOSPITAL (191323), 407 Cincinnati Street, Zip 71232–3007; tel. 318/878–5171 **A**10 18 **F**3 15 18 28 29 34 35 39 40 50 54 56 57 59 64 65 66 71 75 77 81 91 97 103 104 107 111 114 119 127 129 130 132 133 134 135 143 146 148
Primary Contact: Michael W. Carroll, Administrator
CIO: Barbra Hutchison, Director Medical Records
CHR: Patsy Stout, Director Personnel
Web address: www.delhihospital.com
Control: Hospital district or authority, Government, nonfederal **Service:** General Medical and Surgical

Staffed Beds: 25 Admissions: 632 Census: 8 Outpatient Visits: 44508
Births: 0 Total Expense ($000): 19121 Payroll Expense ($000): 9124
Personnel: 214

DENHAM SPRINGS—Livingston Parish

AMG SPECIALTY HOSPITAL–DENHAM SPRINGS (192008), 8375 Florida Boulevard, Zip 70726–7806; tel. 225/665–2664, (Nonreporting) **A**10 **S** AMG Integrated Healthcare Management, Lafayette, LA
Primary Contact: Karen Crayton, Administrator
CFO: Jessica McGee, Chief Financial Officer
CMO: Durwin Walker, M.D., Chief Medical Officer
CHR: Kim Hernandez, Chief Human Resources Officer
CNO: Sharon Faulkner, Chief Nursing Officer
Web address: www.amgdenham.com/
Control: Corporation, Investor–owned, for–profit **Service:** Long–Term Acute Care hospital

Staffed Beds: 117

DEQUINCY—Calcasieu Parish

☐ **DEQUINCY MEMORIAL HOSPITAL (191307)**, 110 West Fourth Street, Zip 70633–3508, Mailing Address: P.O. Box 1166, Zip 70633–1166; tel. 337/786–1200, (Nonreporting) **A**1 10 18
Primary Contact: Patrick C. Robinson, M.D., Interim Chief Executive Officer
CFO: Vicky Kelley, Chief Financial Officer
CMO: Jalal Joudeh, M.D., Chief of Staff
Web address: www.dequincyhospital.com
Control: City–Government, nonfederal **Service:** General Medical and Surgical

Staffed Beds: 19

DERIDDER—Beauregard Parish

☐ **OCEANS BEHAVIORAL HOSPITAL OF DE RIDDER (194081)**, 1420 Blankenship Drive, Zip 70634–4604; tel. 337/460–9472, (Nonreporting) **A**1 10 **S** Oceans Healthcare, Lake Charles, LA
Primary Contact: Lynette Dhillon, Administrator
Web address: www.obhd.info/
Control: Corporation, Investor–owned, for–profit **Service:** Psychiatric

Staffed Beds: 20

DONALDSONVILLE—Ascension Parish

✠ **PREVOST MEMORIAL HOSPITAL (191308)**, 301 Memorial Drive, Zip 70346–4376; tel. 225/473–7931 **A**1 10 18 **F**3 11 15 29 40 57 59 107 110 119 130 133 146
Primary Contact: Vincent A. Cataldo, Administrator
CFO: Nobie Landry, Chief Financial Officer
CMO: Glenn Schexnayder, M.D., Chief of Staff
CHR: Linda Cataldo, Human Resources Secretary
Web address: www.prevosthospital.net
Control: Hospital district or authority, Government, nonfederal **Service:** General Medical and Surgical

Staffed Beds: 25 Admissions: 45 Census: 1 Outpatient Visits: 21679
Births: 0 Total Expense ($000): 6623 Payroll Expense ($000): 2536
Personnel: 59

FARMERVILLE—Union Parish

UNION GENERAL HOSPITAL (191301), 901 James Avenue, Zip 71241–2234, Mailing Address: P.O. Box 398, Zip 71241–0398; tel. 318/368–9751 **A**10 18 **F**15 29 32 35 40 45 56 81 93 104 107 110 114 119 127 128 133 143 **P**6
Primary Contact: Evalyn Ormond, Chief Executive Officer
COO: Dianne Davidson, Chief Operating Officer
CFO: William Adcock, Chief Financial Officer
CHR: Sheri Cooper, Director Human Resources
CNO: Darra Jung, Director of Nursing
Web address: www.uniongen.com
Control: Other not–for–profit (including NFP Corporation) **Service:** General Medical and Surgical

Staffed Beds: 15 Admissions: 331 Census: 3 Outpatient Visits: 32531
Births: 0 Total Expense ($000): 12905 Payroll Expense ($000): 4803
Personnel: 104

FERRIDAY—Concordia Parish

RIVERLAND MEDICAL CENTER (191318), 1700 EE Wallace Boulevard, Zip 71334–0111, Mailing Address: P.O. Box 111, Zip 71334–0111; tel. 318/757–6551 **A**10 18 **F**3 15 29 30 34 35 40 45 57 59 70 75 77 81 85 87 104 107 110 119 133 146 **P**6
Primary Contact: William H. Rucker, Administrator
CFO: Spencer Holder, Chief Financial Officer
CMO: Carrie Bonomo, M.D., Chief of Staff
CIO: Nekisha Smith, Director Health Information Systems
CHR: Debra Stephens, Director Personnel
CNO: Shelia James, Director of Nursing
Web address: www.riverlandmedical.com/
Control: Hospital district or authority, Government, nonfederal **Service:** General Medical and Surgical

Staffed Beds: 25 Admissions: 958 Census: 8 Outpatient Visits: 99693
Births: 0 Total Expense ($000): 16399 Payroll Expense ($000): 7247
Personnel: 161

Many Facility Codes have changed. Please refer to the AHA Guide Code Chart. © 2016 AHA Guide

FORT POLK—Vernon Parish

⌘ **BAYNE–JONES ARMY COMMUNITY HOSPITAL**, 1585 3rd Street,
Zip 71459–5102; tel. 337/531–3928, (Nonreporting) **A1 S** Department of the
Army, Office of the Surgeon General, Falls Church, VA
Primary Contact: Colonel Carlene Blanding, Commander
COO: Larry R. Patterson, Deputy Commander Administration
CFO: Captain Dustin Mullins, Chief Resource Management
CMO: Colonel Thomas Starkey, M.D., Deputy Commander FDR Clinical Services
CIO: Major William Callahan, Chief Information Management Division
CHR: Captain Dustin Mullins, Chief Human Resources
CNO: Colonel Bridget Little, Deputy Commander Nursing
Web address: www.polk.amedd.army.mil
Control: Army, Government, federal **Service:** General Medical and Surgical

Staffed Beds: 22

FRANKLIN—St. Mary Parish

⌘ **FRANKLIN FOUNDATION HOSPITAL (191310)**, 1097 Northwest Boulevard,
Zip 70538–3407, Mailing Address: P.O. Box 577, Zip 70538–0577;
tel. 337/828–0760 **A1** 10 18 **F**3 11 13 15 18 26 28 29 34 40 45 50 57 59
68 70 74 75 76 77 79 81 85 93 107 110 111 114 119 130 133 135 146
147 148 **P**6 **S** QHR, Brentwood, TN
Primary Contact: Craig R. Cudworth, Chief Executive Officer
CFO: Ron Bailey, Chief Financial Officer
CMO: Jesus Chua, M.D., Chief of Staff
CIO: John Spradlin, Information Systems Director
CHR: Elmo Vinas, Director Human Resources
CNO: Jennifer Wise, Chief Nursing Officer
Web address: www.franklinfoundation.org
Control: Hospital district or authority, Government, nonfederal **Service:** General
Medical and Surgical

Staffed Beds: 22 **Admissions:** 726 **Census:** 9 **Outpatient Visits:** 27060
Births: 113 **Total Expense ($000):** 23431 **Payroll Expense ($000):** 10955
Personnel: 171

FRANKLINTON—Washington Parish

☐ **RIVERSIDE MEDICAL CENTER (191313)**, 1900 Main Street, Zip 70438–3688;
tel. 985/839–4431, (Nonreporting) **A1** 10 18
Primary Contact: Peter Sullivan, Chief Executive Officer
CFO: Michael J. Magee, Chief Financial Officer
CMO: Chris Foret, M.D., Chief of Staff
CHR: John Seal, Director Human Resources
Web address: www.rmchospital.com
Control: Hospital district or authority, Government, nonfederal **Service:** General
Medical and Surgical

Staffed Beds: 25

GONZALES—Ascension Parish

SOUTH BATON ROUGE REHABILITATION HOSPITAL See United Medical
Rehabilitation Hospital – Gonzales

⌘ **ST. ELIZABETH HOSPITAL (190242)**, 1125 West Highway 30,
Zip 70737–5004; tel. 225/647–5000 **A1** 10 **F**3 8 11 12 15 18 29 30 34 35
40 43 45 46 47 48 49 51 57 59 64 66 70 74 75 77 79 81 82 84 85 87 92
107 108 110 111 114 115 119 129 130 131 132 146 147 **P**6 **S** Franciscan
Missionaries of Our Lady Health System, Inc., Baton Rouge, LA
Primary Contact: Robert L. Burgess, President and Chief Executive Officer
COO: Sue Knight, CPA, Chief Operating Officer
CFO: Scott Richard, Vice President Finance and Chief Financial Officer
CMO: Chris Trevino, M.D., Chief Medical Officer
CIO: Shannon Simpson, Director Information Services
CHR: Melissa Miller, Director Human Resources
CNO: Yvonne Pellerin, Chief Nursing Officer
Web address: www.steh.com
Control: Church–operated, Nongovernment, not–for profit **Service:** General
Medical and Surgical

Staffed Beds: 44 **Admissions:** 2324 **Census:** 29 **Outpatient Visits:** 287044
Births: 0 **Total Expense ($000):** 111021 **Payroll Expense ($000):** 42194
Personnel: 807

☐ **ST. JAMES BEHAVIORAL HEALTH HOSPITAL (194088)**, 3136 South Saint
Landry Road, Zip 70737–5801; tel. 225/647–7524, (Nonreporting) **A1** 10
Primary Contact: Rick Bennett, Administrator
COO: Wendell Smith, Chief Operating Officer
CFO: Rama Kongara, Chief Financial Officer
CMO: Lance Bullock, M.D., Medical Director
CHR: Dessa Frederick, Manager Human Resources
Web address: www.sjbhh.net
Control: Corporation, Investor–owned, for–profit **Service:** Psychiatric

Staffed Beds: 10

GREENSBURG—St. Helena Parish

ST. HELENA PARISH HOSPITAL (191300), 16874 Highway 43,
Zip 70441–4834; tel. 225/222–6111, (Nonreporting) **A10** 18
Primary Contact: Naveed Awan, FACHE, Chief Executive Officer
CFO: Theresa Brinkhaus, Chief Financial Officer
CMO: Anjanette Varnado, M.D., Chief Medical Officer
CHR: Lorraine L. Ballard, Director Human Resources
Web address: www.sthelenaparishhospital.com
Control: Other not–for–profit (including NFP Corporation) **Service:** General
Medical and Surgical

Staffed Beds: 97

GRETNA—Jefferson Parish

UNITED MEDICAL REHABILITATION HOSPITAL (193074), 3201 Wall
Boulevard, Suite B., Zip 70056–7755; tel. 504/433–5551 **A10 F**29 90 91
S United Medical Rehabilitation Hospitals, Gretna, LA
Primary Contact: John E.H. Mills, President and Chief Executive Officer
Web address: www.umrhospital.com/
Control: Individual, Investor–owned, for–profit **Service:** Rehabilitation

Staffed Beds: 21 **Admissions:** 254 **Census:** 11 **Outpatient Visits:** 0 **Births:**
0 **Total Expense ($000):** 4508 **Payroll Expense ($000):** 2357

HAMMOND—Tangipahoa Parish

◇ **CYPRESS POINTE SURGICAL HOSPITAL (190303)**, 42570 South Airport
Road, Zip 70403–0946; tel. 985/510–6200, (Nonreporting) **A10** 21
Primary Contact: Glenda Dobson, Chief Executive Officer
COO: Scot Treitler, Chief Financial Officer and Chief Operating Officer
CFO: Scot Treitler, Chief Financial Officer and Chief Operating Officer
CNO: Denise Fortenberry, Chief Nursing Officer and Chief Compliance Officer
Web address: www.cpsh.org
Control: Corporation, Investor–owned, for–profit **Service:** Surgical

Staffed Beds: 24

⌘ △ **NORTH OAKS MEDICAL CENTER (190015)**, 15790 Paul Vega, MD, Drive,
Zip 70403–1436, Mailing Address: P.O. Box 2668, Zip 70404–2668;
tel. 985/345–2700 **A1** 7 10 19 **F**3 12 13 15 18 20 22 24 26 28 29 30 31 32
34 40 45 49 50 54 56 57 58 59 63 64 68 70 72 73 74 75 76 77 78 79 81
82 84 85 86 87 89 93 94 96 102 107 108 110 111 114 115 118 119 126
129 130 131 132 135 143 144 146 147 148 **P**6 **S** North Oaks Health System,
Hammond, LA
Primary Contact: Michele K. Sutton, FACHE, Administrator and Chief Executive
Officer
CFO: Shirley Hsing, Senior Vice President and Chief Financial Officer
CMO: Robert Peltier, M.D., Senior Vice President and Chief Medical Officer
CIO: Jacob Goodson, Director Information Technology
CHR: Jeff Jarreau, Senior Vice President Human Resources
CNO: Shelly Welch, Senior Vice President Patient Services and Chief Nursing
Officer
Web address: www.northoaks.org
Control: Hospital district or authority, Government, nonfederal **Service:** General
Medical and Surgical

Staffed Beds: 248 **Admissions:** 10381 **Census:** 156 **Outpatient Visits:**
447243 **Births:** 1297 **Total Expense ($000):** 279707 **Payroll Expense
($000):** 149183 **Personnel:** 2374

☐ **NORTH OAKS REHABILITATION HOSPITAL (193044)**, 1900 South Morrison
Boulevard, Zip 70403–5742; tel. 985/542–7777 **A1** 10 **F**29 56 75 86 87 90
130 132 143 **P**6 **S** North Oaks Health System, Hammond, LA
Primary Contact: Sybil K. Paulson, Administrator
COO: Michele K. Sutton, FACHE, Senior Vice President, Chief Operating Officer,
North Oaks Health System
CFO: Shirley Hsing, Senior Vice President, Chief Financial Officer, North Oaks
Health System
CMO: Robert Peltier, M.D., Senior Vice President, Chief Medical Officer, North
Oaks Health System
CIO: Herbert Robinson, M.D., Vice President, Chief Medical Information Officer,
North Oaks Health System
CHR: Jeff Jarreau, Senior Vice President, Human Resources, North Oaks Health
System
CNO: Shelly Welch, Senior Vice President, Patient Services, Chief Nursing Officer,
North Oaks Health System
Web address: www.northoaks.org
Control: Hospital district or authority, Government, nonfederal **Service:**
Rehabilitation

Staffed Beds: 27 **Admissions:** 494 **Census:** 16 **Outpatient Visits:** 0 **Births:**
0 **Total Expense ($000):** 11940 **Payroll Expense ($000):** 2305 **Personnel:**
40

Hospital, Medicare Provider Number, Address, Telephone, Approval, Facility, and Physician Codes, Health Care System

★ American Hospital Association (AHA) membership
☐ The Joint Commission accreditation
○ Healthcare Facilities Accreditation Program
◇ DNV Healthcare Inc. accreditation
⇑ Center for Improvement in Healthcare Quality Accreditation
△ Commission on Accreditation of Rehabilitation Facilities (CARF) accreditation

LA

✠ **PAM SPECIALTY HOSPITAL OF HAMMOND (192036)**, 42074 Veterans
Avenue, Zip 70403–1408; tel. 985/902–8148 **A**1 10 **F**1 3 29 75 77 146 148
P1 **S** Post Acute Medical, LLC, Enola, PA
Primary Contact: Nicholas Paul Mendez, Chief Executive Officer
Web address: www.postacutemedical.com
Control: Partnership, Investor–owned, for–profit **Service:** Long–Term Acute Care
hospital

Staffed Beds: 40 **Admissions:** 360 **Census:** 26 **Outpatient Visits:** 0 **Births:**
0 **Total Expense ($000):** 13151 **Payroll Expense ($000):** 5176 **Personnel:**
90

UNITED MEDICAL REHABILITATION HOSPITAL (193079), 15717 Belle Drive,
Zip 70403–1439; tel. 985/340–5998, (Includes UNITED MEDICAL
REHABILITATION HOSPITAL – GONZALES, 333 East Worthy Road, Gonzales,
Zip 70737–4234; tel. 225/450–2231; Bruce Walker, MSN, R.N., Chief Executive
Officer), (Nonreporting) **A**10 **S** United Medical Rehabilitation Hospitals, Gretna, LA
Primary Contact: Cyrillia Bonds, Administrator
CFO: Warren Swenson, Chief Financial Officer
CMO: Luis Franco, M.D., Medical Director
CHR: Mark Gros, Director Human Resources
Web address: www.umrhospital.com
Control: Corporation, Investor–owned, for–profit **Service:** Rehabilitation

Staffed Beds: 20

HOMER—Claiborne Parish

★ ◇ **CLAIBORNE MEMORIAL MEDICAL CENTER (190114)**, 620 East College
Street, Zip 71040–3202; tel. 318/927–2024 **A**10 21 **F**3 15 29 35 38 40 45 50
54 56 57 62 64 65 70 75 81 85 86 87 98 101 103 104 107 108 114 119
130 132 133 143 146 **S** QHR, Brentwood, TN
Primary Contact: Antonia M. Goodin, Interim Chief Executive Officer
CFO: Antonia M. Goodin, Chief Financial Officer
CMO: Mark Haynes, M.D., Chief of Staff
CIO: Angie Costakis, Chief Information Officer
CHR: William Colvin, Human Resources Officer
CNO: Kristie M. Copeland, Interim Chief Nursing Officer
Web address: www.claibornemedical.com/
Control: Hospital district or authority, Government, nonfederal **Service:** General
Medical and Surgical

Staffed Beds: 57 **Admissions:** 1276 **Census:** 21 **Outpatient Visits:** 18532
Births: 0 **Total Expense ($000):** 34138 **Payroll Expense ($000):** 6550

HOUMA—Terrebonne Parish

AMG SPECIALTY HOSPITAL–HOUMA (192037), 629 Dunn Street,
Zip 70360–4707; tel. 985/274–0001 **A**10 **F**1 29 130 **S** AMG Integrated
Healthcare Management, Lafayette, LA
Primary Contact: Keith Carruth, Chief Executive Officer
Web address: www.amghouma.com/
Control: Corporation, Investor–owned, for–profit **Service:** Long–Term Acute Care
hospital

Staffed Beds: 40 **Admissions:** 456 **Census:** 33 **Outpatient Visits:** 0 **Births:**
0 **Total Expense ($000):** 14042 **Payroll Expense ($000):** 5851 **Personnel:**
105

☐ **COMPASS BEHAVIORAL CENTER OF HOUMA (194109)**, 4701 West Park
Avenue, Zip 70364–4426; tel. 985/876–1715 **A**1 10 **F**98 101 102 103 104
105 **S** Compass Health, Crowley, LA
Primary Contact: Cheryl Turner, Administrator
Web address: www.compasshealthcare.com/site83.php
Control: Individual, Investor–owned, for–profit **Service:** Psychiatric

Staffed Beds: 20 **Admissions:** 484 **Census:** 15 **Outpatient Visits:** 0 **Births:**
0

✠ **LEONARD J. CHABERT MEDICAL CENTER (190183)**, 1978 Industrial
Boulevard, Zip 70363–7094; tel. 985/873–2200 **A**1 3 5 10 **F**3 15 18 20 29 31
32 34 35 38 40 44 45 46 47 48 49 50 51 55 58 59 61 64 65 66 68 70 74
75 77 78 79 81 82 84 85 86 87 89 91 92 93 94 97 98 100 101 102 107
108 110 111 114 115 119 130 132 146 147 148 **S** Ochsner Health System,
New Orleans, LA
Primary Contact: Timothy J. Allen, FACHE, Chief Executive Officer
COO: Kendrick Duet, Chief Operating Officer
CNO: Jana Semere, Chief Nursing Officer
Web address: www.ochsner.org/locations/leonard_j_chabert_medical_center/
Control: State–Government, nonfederal **Service:** General Medical and Surgical

Staffed Beds: 72 **Admissions:** 3654 **Census:** 47 **Outpatient Visits:** 166950
Births: 0 **Total Expense ($000):** 93854 **Payroll Expense ($000):** 31805
Personnel: 577

PHYSICIANS ALLIANCE HOSPITAL OF HOUMA See AMG Specialty
Hospital–Houma

PHYSICIANS MEDICAL CENTER (190241), 218 Corporate Drive,
Zip 70360–2768; tel. 985/853–1390, (Nonreporting) **A**10
Primary Contact: Connie Martin, Chief Executive Officer and Administrator
Web address: www.physicianshouma.com/
Control: Partnership, Investor–owned, for–profit **Service:** Surgical

Staffed Beds: 10

✠ △ **TERREBONNE GENERAL MEDICAL CENTER (190008)**, 8166 Main
Street, Zip 70360–3498; tel. 985/873–4141, (Total facility includes 8 beds in
nursing home–type unit) **A**1 2 7 10 **F**8 11 13 14 15 17 18 20 22 24 26 29 30
31 34 35 40 44 49 50 57 58 59 64 65 68 70 72 74 75 76 77 78 79 81 84
85 86 87 89 90 91 92 93 107 108 109 110 111 114 117 118 119 121 123
124 128 130 131 132 134 135 146 147 148 **P**3 5 6
Primary Contact: Phyllis L. Peoples, President and Chief Executive Officer
COO: Diane Yeates, Chief Operating Officer
CFO: Dean Verret, Vice President Financial Services
CMO: Robert Gamble, M.D., Chief of Staff
CIO: Jeff Sardella, Director Information Technology
CHR: Mickie Rousseau, Director Human Resources
CNO: Teresita McNabb, R.N., Vice President Nursing Services
Web address: www.tgmc.com
Control: Hospital district or authority, Government, nonfederal **Service:** General
Medical and Surgical

Staffed Beds: 230 **Admissions:** 9583 **Census:** 136 **Outpatient Visits:**
126656 **Births:** 1931 **Total Expense ($000):** 195713 **Payroll Expense
($000):** 67453 **Personnel:** 1397

INDEPENDENCE—Tangipahoa Parish

☐ **LALLIE KEMP MEDICAL CENTER (191321)**, 52579 Highway 51 South,
Zip 70443–2231; tel. 985/878–9421, (Nonreporting) **A**1 3 5 10 18
Primary Contact: Sherre Pack–Hookfin, Administrator
COO: Lisa G. Bruhl, Chief Operating Officer
CFO: Chad Thompson, Chief Financial Officer
CMO: Kathy Willis, M.D., Medical Director
CIO: Charles Tate, Director Information Technology
CHR: Diane Farnham, Acting Director Human Resources
Web address: www.lsuhospitals.org/Hospitals/LK/LK.aspx
Control: State–Government, nonfederal **Service:** General Medical and Surgical

Staffed Beds: 25

JACKSON—East Feliciana Parish

☐ **EASTERN LOUISIANA MENTAL HEALTH SYSTEM (194008)**, 4502 Highway
951, Zip 70748–5842, Mailing Address: P.O. Box 498, Zip 70748–0498;
tel. 225/634–0100 **A**1 3 10 **F**29 30 35 39 50 59 74 75 87 98 100 101 103
104 106 130 135 143 146 **P**6 **S** Louisiana State Hospitals, Baton Rouge, LA
Primary Contact: Hampton P. S. Lea, Acting Chief Executive Officer
CFO: Laura Lott, Administrative Director
CMO: John W. Thompson, M.D., Chief of Staff
CIO: Deborah Brandon, Director Total Quality Management
CHR: Vikki Riggle, Director Human Resources
CNO: Mary Fontenelle, Executive Nurse Director
Web address: www.wwwprd.doa.louisiana.gov/laservices/publicpages/
ServiceDetail.cfm?service_id=2445
Control: State–Government, nonfederal **Service:** Psychiatric

Staffed Beds: 473 **Admissions:** 1070 **Census:** 481 **Outpatient Visits:** 0
Births: 0 **Total Expense ($000):** 103970 **Payroll Expense ($000):** 49413
Personnel: 999

VILLA FELICIANA MEDICAL COMPLEX (190199), 5002 Highway 10,
Zip 70748–3627, Mailing Address: P.O. Box 438, Zip 70748–0438;
tel. 225/634–4017, (Total facility includes 297 beds in nursing home–type unit)
A10 **F**1 29 65 67 85 86 91 94 106 128 130 132 135 143 148 **P**8
Primary Contact: Mark Anders, Administrator
CFO: Kim Jelks, Fiscal Officer
CMO: John F. Piker, M.D., Medical Director
CIO: Michael James, Information Technology Technical Support Specialist 1
CHR: Sandra Delatte, Director Human Resources
CNO: Linda Williams, Director of Nursing
Web address: www.dhh.state.la.us/
Control: State–Government, nonfederal **Service:** Long–Term Acute Care hospital

Staffed Beds: 307 **Admissions:** 18 **Census:** 11 **Outpatient Visits:** 0 **Births:**
0 **Total Expense ($000):** 18396 **Payroll Expense ($000):** 8893 **Personnel:**
193

JENA—La Salle Parish

★ **LASALLE GENERAL HOSPITAL (190145)**, 187 Ninth Street, Zip 71342–3901,
Mailing Address: P.O. Box 2780, Zip 71342–2780; tel. 318/992–9200 **A**10 **F**7
11 15 18 29 33 40 53 57 59 62 64 71 81 89 93 107 108 110 111 115 119
127 130 133 **P**6
Primary Contact: Lana B. Francis, Chief Executive Officer
CHR: Allyson Fannin, Human Resources Officer
CNO: Carolyn Francis, R.N., Director of Nursing
Web address: www.lasallegeneralhospital.com
Control: Hospital district or authority, Government, nonfederal **Service:** General
Medical and Surgical

Staffed Beds: 20 **Admissions:** 502 **Census:** 5 **Outpatient Visits:** 36446
Births: 0 **Total Expense ($000):** 16907 **Payroll Expense ($000):** 8422
Personnel: 195

JENNINGS—Jefferson Davis Parish

☐ **JENNINGS AMERICAN LEGION HOSPITAL (190053)**, 1634 Elton Road, Zip 70546–3614; tel. 337/616–7000 **A**1 10 **F**3 15 18 20 28 29 40 45 64 70 76 79 81 89 107 108 111 115 119 127 133 146 147
Primary Contact: Dana D. Williams, Chief Executive Officer
COO: Keith J. Simpson, Chief Operating Officer
CFO: Chris Kohlenberg, Chief Financial Officer
CIO: Gary Courrege, Chief Information Officer
CHR: Ruth Carnes, Manager Human Resources
CNO: Theresa L. Woods, MSN, Chief Nursing Officer
Web address: www.jalh.com
Control: Other not–for–profit (including NFP Corporation) **Service:** General Medical and Surgical

Staffed Beds: 49 **Admissions:** 2749 **Census:** 29 **Outpatient Visits:** 34656 **Births:** 295 **Total Expense ($000):** 37998 **Payroll Expense ($000):** 15393 **Personnel:** 379

JENNINGS SENIOR CARE HOSPITAL (194082), 1 Hospital Drive, Suite 201, Zip 70546–3641; tel. 337/824–1558 **A**10 **F**98 103 104 105 130
Primary Contact: Kirk Perron, Administrator and Chief Administrative Officer
Web address: www.compasshealthcare.com/site74.php
Control: Individual, Investor–owned, for–profit **Service:** Psychiatric

Staffed Beds: 16 **Admissions:** 291 **Census:** 11 **Outpatient Visits:** 15814 **Births:** 0 **Total Expense ($000):** 4724 **Payroll Expense ($000):** 1912 **Personnel:** 26

REHABILITATION HOSPITAL OF JENNINGS (193067), 1 Hospital Drive, Suite 101, Zip 70546–3641; tel. 337/821–5353 **A**10 **F**29 30 34 35 56 57 62 65 68 75 77 87 90 91 130 148
Primary Contact: Michael Holland, M.D., Chief Executive Officer
Web address: www.jenningsrehab.com
Control: Partnership, Investor–owned, for–profit **Service:** Rehabilitation

Staffed Beds: 16 **Admissions:** 214 **Census:** 8 **Outpatient Visits:** 0 **Births:** 0 **Total Expense ($000):** 4779 **Payroll Expense ($000):** 1388 **Personnel:** 44

☐ **WESTEND HOSPITAL (194075)**, 1530 Highway 90 West, Zip 70546–4022; tel. 337/616–8122, (Nonreporting) **A**1 10 **S** Acadia Healthcare Company, Inc., Franklin, TN
Primary Contact: Luis Betances, Administrator
CMO: Phillip Lafleur, M.D., Medical Director
CHR: Susanna Rodriguez, Director Human Resources
Web address: www.westendbh.com
Control: Corporation, Investor–owned, for–profit **Service:** Psychiatric

Staffed Beds: 20

JONESBORO—Jackson Parish

★ **JACKSON PARISH HOSPITAL (191317)**, 165 Beech Springs Road, Zip 71251–2059; tel. 318/259–4435, (Nonreporting) **A**10 18
Primary Contact: Bobby Jordan, Chief Executive Officer
COO: Eric Cripps, Chief Financial Officer and Chief Operating Officer
CFO: Eric Cripps, Chief Financial Officer and Chief Operating Officer
CMO: W. James (Jamie) Slusher, M.D., Chief of Staff
CIO: Monie Phillips, III, Director Clinical Informatics
CHR: Phillip Thomas, Jr., Director Human Resources
CNO: Christy Wyatt, R.N., Interim Chief Nursing Officer
Web address: www.jacksonparishhospital.com
Control: Hospital district or authority, Government, nonfederal **Service:** General Medical and Surgical

Staffed Beds: 25

KAPLAN—Vermilion Parish

ABROM KAPLAN MEMORIAL HOSPITAL (191322), 1310 West Seventh Street, Zip 70548–2910; tel. 337/643–8300, (Nonreporting) **A**10 18 **S** Lafayette General Health, Lafayette, LA
Primary Contact: Bryce Quebodeaux, Chief Executive Officer
CFO: Michael G. Johnson, CPA, Chief Financial Officer
CMO: Scott Bergeaux, M.D., Chief Medical Staff
CIO: Michael Cardiff, Systems Supervisor
CHR: Linda Guidry, Human Resources Generalist
CNO: Darnell Kohlenberg, R.N., Director of Nursing
Web address: www.lafayettegeneral.com
Control: Hospital district or authority, Government, nonfederal **Service:** General Medical and Surgical

Staffed Beds: 35

KENNER—Jefferson Parish

LOUISIANA EXTENDED CARE HOSPITAL OF KENNER See Ochsner Extended Care Hospital of Kenner

☐ **OCEANS BEHAVIORAL HOSPITAL OF GREATER NEW ORLEANS (194098)**, 716 Village Road, Zip 70065–2751; tel. 504/464–8895 **A**1 10 **F**34 35 38 56 57 98 100 101 102 103 104 105 135 143 **S** Oceans Healthcare, Lake Charles, LA
Primary Contact: Deborah Spier, Administrator
Web address: www.obhgno.info/
Control: Corporation, Investor–owned, for–profit **Service:** Psychiatric

Staffed Beds: 30 **Admissions:** 715 **Census:** 28 **Outpatient Visits:** 0 **Births:** 0

☐ **OCHSNER EXTENDED CARE HOSPITAL OF KENNER (192015)**, 180 West Esplanade Avenue, 5th Floor, Zip 70065–2467; tel. 504/464–8658, (Nonreporting) **A**1 3 10 **S** LHC Group, Lafayette, LA
Primary Contact: Frederick Nelson, Administrator
Web address: www.lhcgroup.com/
Control: Corporation, Investor–owned, for–profit **Service:** Long–Term Acute Care hospital

Staffed Beds: 32

⊞ **OCHSNER MEDICAL CENTER – KENNER (190274)**, 180 West Esplanade Avenue, Zip 70065–6001; tel. 504/468–8600 **A**1 3 5 10 **F**3 4 13 15 17 18 20 22 24 29 30 31 34 35 37 38 40 42 45 46 47 49 50 51 53 54 56 57 58 59 60 61 64 65 66 68 70 72 74 75 76 77 78 79 81 82 84 85 86 87 90 91 93 97 98 102 107 110 111 114 116 117 119 120 129 130 131 132 135 146 147 148 **S** Ochsner Health System, New Orleans, LA
Primary Contact: Stephen Robinson, Chief Executive Officer
COO: Eddy Ramirez, Assistant Vice President Business Development
CFO: Mark Eckert, Vice President Finance
CMO: James Tebbe, M.D., Vice President Medical Affairs
CIO: Dere Krummel, Director Information Systems
Web address: www.ochsner.org/locations/ochsner_health_center_kenner_w_esplanade_ave/
Control: Other not–for–profit (including NFP Corporation) **Service:** General Medical and Surgical

Staffed Beds: 110 **Admissions:** 5945 **Census:** 65 **Outpatient Visits:** 147748 **Births:** 953 **Total Expense ($000):** 126404 **Payroll Expense ($000):** 46032 **Personnel:** 843

☐ **ST. THERESA SPECIALTY HOSPITAL (192030)**, 3601 Loyola Drive, Zip 70065–1797; tel. 504/904–7600, (Nonreporting) **A**1 10
Primary Contact: Ethan Thompson, Chief Executive Officer
CFO: Ethan Thompson, Chief Executive Officer
CMO: Ricardo Febry, M.D., Medical Director
CHR: Nicole Wilson, Manager Human Resources
CNO: Collette Jackson, R.N., Director of Clinical Services
Web address: www.stmck.com
Control: Corporation, Investor–owned, for–profit **Service:** Long–Term Acute Care hospital

Staffed Beds: 73

KENTWOOD—Tangipahoa Parish

OCEANS BEHAVIORAL HOSPITAL OF KENTWOOD (194091), 921 Avenue G., Zip 70444–2636; tel. 985/229–0717 **A**10 **F**98 100 101 102 103 **S** Oceans Healthcare, Lake Charles, LA
Primary Contact: Sarah Chisholm, Administrator
Web address: www.obhk.info/
Control: Corporation, Investor–owned, for–profit **Service:** Psychiatric

Staffed Beds: 16 **Admissions:** 379 **Census:** 14 **Outpatient Visits:** 0 **Births:** 0

SOUTHEAST REGIONAL MEDICAL CENTER (192040), 719 Avenue G., Zip 70444–2601; tel. 985/229–9193, (Nonreporting) **A**10
Primary Contact: Lionel Murphy, Chief Executive Officer
Control: Corporation, Investor–owned, for–profit **Service:** Long–Term Acute Care hospital

Staffed Beds: 14

Hospital, Medicare Provider Number, Address, Telephone, Approval, Facility, and Physician Codes, Health Care System

★ American Hospital Association (AHA) membership
☐ The Joint Commission accreditation
○ Healthcare Facilities Accreditation Program
◇ DNV Healthcare Inc. accreditation
⇑ Center for Improvement in Healthcare Quality Accreditation
△ Commission on Accreditation of Rehabilitation Facilities (CARF) accreditation

---

LA

KINDER—Allen Parish

★ **ALLEN PARISH HOSPITAL (190133)**, 108 Sixth Avenue, Zip 70648–3187, Mailing Address: P.O. Box 1670, Zip 70648–1670; tel. 337/738–2527 **A**10 **F**29 32 34 38 40 50 56 57 59 62 64 65 87 93 98 101 102 107 119 127 130 133 148
Primary Contact: Jackie Reviel, R.N., Chief Executive Officer
COO: Terry Willet, Chief Financial Officer
CFO: Ken Cox, Chief Financial Officer
CMO: Ejiro Ughouwa, M.D., Chief of Staff
CIO: Bill Marcantel, Chief Information Systems
CHR: Amand Lambert, Director Human Resources
Web address: www.allenparishhospital.com
Control: Hospital district or authority, Government, nonfederal **Service:** General Medical and Surgical

Staffed Beds: 49 **Admissions:** 916 **Census:** 17 **Outpatient Visits:** 11380 **Births:** 0 **Total Expense ($000):** 6428 **Personnel:** 170

LACOMBE—St. Tammany Parish

BEACON BEHAVIORAL HEALTHCARE (194080), 64026 Highway 434, Suite 300, Zip 70445–5417; tel. 985/882–0226, (Data for 275 days) **A**10 **F**98 103 104 130
Primary Contact: Jessika Scallion, Administrator
Web address: www.magnoliabh.com/
Control: Corporation, Investor–owned, for–profit **Service:** Psychiatric

Staffed Beds: 22 **Admissions:** 375 **Census:** 14 **Outpatient Visits:** 3469 **Births:** 0 **Personnel:** 55

☐ **LOUISIANA HEART HOSPITAL (190250)**, 64030 Louisiana Highway 434, Zip 70445–3456; tel. 985/690–7500 **A**1 3 10 **F**3 17 18 20 22 24 26 28 29 34 35 40 45 46 54 55 57 58 59 60 64 65 68 70 74 75 77 79 81 82 85 87 93 97 107 111 115 119 130 132 135 146 147 148 **P**6 7
Primary Contact: Scott Boudreaux, Chief Executive Officer
COO: Glenn L. Craig, Chief Operating Officer
CFO: Suzette Duhe, Chief Financial Officer
CMO: Anthony Morales, M.D., Medical Director
CIO: Jack Fayard, Director Information Technology
CHR: Wendy F. Alexander, Director Human Resources
CNO: Regina Crow, R.N., Interim Chief Nursing Officer
Web address: www.louisianaheart.com
Control: Corporation, Investor–owned, for–profit **Service:** General Medical and Surgical

Staffed Beds: 68 **Admissions:** 3427 **Census:** 36 **Outpatient Visits:** 34326 **Births:** 0 **Total Expense ($000):** 88356 **Payroll Expense ($000):** 26751 **Personnel:** 395

LAFAYETTE—Lafayette Parish

ACADIA OPTIMA HOSPITAL (194078), 1131 Rue De Belier, Zip 70506–6532; tel. 337/991–0571, (Nonreporting) **A**3 10 **S** Acadia Healthcare Company, Inc., Franklin, TN
Primary Contact: Glynis R. DeRoche, Administrator
Web address: www.optimaspecialtyhospital.com/
Control: Corporation, Investor–owned, for–profit **Service:** General Medical and Surgical

Staffed Beds: 24

ACADIA VERMILION HOSPITAL (194044), 2520 North University Avenue, Zip 70507–5306; tel. 337/234–5614, (Nonreporting) **A**10 **S** Acadia Healthcare Company, Inc., Franklin, TN
Primary Contact: Stephanie Bonin, Chief Executive Officer
CFO: Margot Mokdessi, Interim Chief Financial Officer
CMO: Bob Winston, M.D., Medical Director
CHR: Claire Rowland, Director Human Resources
CNO: Amy LaHood, R.N., Director of Nursing
Web address: www.acadiavermilion.com
Control: Corporation, Investor–owned, for–profit **Service:** Psychiatric

Staffed Beds: 54

AMG SPECIALTY HOSPITAL–LAFAYETTE (192029), 310 Youngsville Highway, Zip 70508–4524; tel. 337/839–9880, (Nonreporting) **A**10 **S** AMG Integrated Healthcare Management, Lafayette, LA
Primary Contact: Ben Miller, Chief Executive Officer
CFO: Jessica McGee, Chief Financial Officer
CMO: Maximo LaMarche, M.D., Chief Medical Officer
CHR: Heather Lamarche, Manager Human Resources
CNO: Mary Bollich, Director of Nurses
Web address: www.amglafayette.com
Control: Corporation, Investor–owned, for–profit **Service:** Long–Term Acute Care hospital

Staffed Beds: 58

⊞ **HEART HOSPITAL OF LAFAYETTE (190263)**, 1105 Kaliste Saloom Road, Zip 70508–5705; tel. 337/521–1000 **A**1 10 **F**3 17 18 20 22 24 26 28 29 30 34 35 40 46 50 57 59 64 68 74 75 81 85 87 107 108 115 135 **P**5 7 8
Primary Contact: Michelle B. Crain, R.N., MSN, Administrator and Chief Operating Officer
CFO: Rachel Hebert, Chief Financial Officer
CHR: Thomas Duhon, Director Human Resources
Web address: www.hearthospitaloflafayette.com
Control: Partnership, Investor–owned, for–profit **Service:** Heart

Staffed Beds: 32 **Admissions:** 1461 **Census:** 15 **Outpatient Visits:** 19242 **Births:** 0 **Total Expense ($000):** 35322 **Payroll Expense ($000):** 10619 **Personnel:** 214

KINDRED HOSPITAL LAFAYETTE See PAM Specialty Hospital of Lafayette

⊞ **LAFAYETTE GENERAL MEDICAL CENTER (190002)**, 1214 Coolidge Avenue, Zip 70503–2696, Mailing Address: P.O. Box 52009 OCS, Zip 70505–2009; tel. 337/289–7991, (Includes LAFAYETTE BEHAVIORAL HEALTH, 302 Dulles Drive, Zip 70506–3008; tel. 337/262–4190; Kandy Collins, MSN, Director; LAFAYETTE GENERAL SOUTHWEST, 2810 Ambassador Caffery Parkway, Zip 70506–5906; tel. 337/981–2949; David L. Callecod, President and Chief Executive Officer) **A**1 2 3 5 10 **F**3 8 11 12 13 15 18 20 22 24 26 28 29 30 31 34 35 37 40 41 45 46 47 48 49 50 52 53 54 55 57 58 59 64 65 70 72 74 75 76 77 78 79 81 82 85 87 89 90 92 93 96 98 99 100 107 108 110 111 115 117 118 119 120 121 123 124 126 129 130 132 135 146 147 148 **P**8 **S** Lafayette General Health, Lafayette, LA
Primary Contact: Patrick W. Gandy, CPA, Executive Vice President and Chief Executive Officer
COO: Court LeMaistre, FACHE, Chief Operating Officer
CFO: Lana Adams, Chief Financial Officer
CMO: Angela Mayeux–Hebert, Vice President Medical Affairs
CIO: Michael Dozier, Vice President, Chief Information Officer
CHR: Sheena Bouquet, Vice President
CNO: Rebecca Benoit, R.N., Chief Nursing Officer
Web address: www.lafayettegeneral.com
Control: Other not–for–profit (including NFP Corporation) **Service:** General Medical and Surgical

Staffed Beds: 324 **Admissions:** 18853 **Census:** 249 **Outpatient Visits:** 219580 **Births:** 2875 **Total Expense ($000):** 331630 **Payroll Expense ($000):** 105534 **Personnel:** 1534

LAFAYETTE GENERAL SURGICAL HOSPITAL (190268), 1000 West Pinhook Road, Zip 70503–2460; tel. 337/289–8088, (Nonreporting) **A**10 **S** Lafayette General Health, Lafayette, LA
Primary Contact: Carrie E. Templeton, FACHE, Chief Executive Officer
CFO: Sandi Hernandez, Controller
CHR: Sheena Bouquet, Vice President
CNO: Kim H. Dooley, Director of Nursing
Web address: www.lgsh.us
Control: Partnership, Investor–owned, for–profit **Service:** General Medical and Surgical

Staffed Beds: 10

LAFAYETTE PHYSICAL REHABILITATION HOSPITAL (193093), 307 Polly Lane, Zip 70508–4960; tel. 337/314–1111 **A**10 **F**29 75 77 79 90 91 143 148 **S** AMG Integrated Healthcare Management, Lafayette, LA
Primary Contact: Carol Washington, R.N., MSN, Chief Executive Officer
Web address: www.lafayettephysicalrehab.com/
Control: Partnership, Investor–owned, for–profit **Service:** Rehabilitation

Staffed Beds: 32 **Admissions:** 713 **Census:** 29 **Outpatient Visits:** 0 **Births:** 0 **Total Expense ($000):** 10584 **Payroll Expense ($000):** 5128 **Personnel:** 53

☐ **LAFAYETTE SURGICAL SPECIALTY HOSPITAL (190259)**, 1101 Kaliste Saloom Road, Zip 70508–5705; tel. 337/769–4100, (Nonreporting) **A**1 10 **S** National Surgical Healthcare, Chicago, IL
Primary Contact: Buffy Domingue, Chief Executive Officer
CFO: Stephanie Guidry, Chief Financial Officer
CNO: Selina Guidry, Chief Nursing Officer
Web address: www.lafayettesurgical.com
Control: Corporation, Investor–owned, for–profit **Service:** Surgical

Staffed Beds: 20

LONG TERM ACUTE CARE OF ACADIANA See AMG Specialty Hospital–Lafayette

LOUISIANA EXTENDED CARE HOSPITAL OF LAFAYETTE (192032), 1214 Coolidge Boulevard, Floors 9 & 10, Zip 70503–2621; tel. 337/289–8180, (Includes EUNICE EXTENDED CARE HOSPITAL, 3879 Highway 190, Eunice, Zip 70535; tel. 337/546–0024; Kevin Frank, Administrator; IBERIA EXTENDED CARE HOSPITAL, 2315 East Main Street, 3rd Floor, New Iberia, Zip 70560–4031; tel. 337/289–8190; Kevin Frank, Administrator), (Nonreporting) **A**10 **S** LHC Group, Lafayette, LA
Primary Contact: Kevin Frank, Administrator
Web address: www.lhcgroup.com
Control: Other not–for–profit (including NFP Corporation) **Service:** Long–Term Acute Care hospital

Staffed Beds: 42

OPTIMA SPECIALTY HOSPITAL See Acadia Optima Hospital

Many Facility Codes have changed. Please refer to the AHA Guide Code Chart.

☒ **OUR LADY OF LOURDES REGIONAL MEDICAL CENTER (190102)**, 4801 Ambassador Caffery Parkway, Zip 70508–6917; tel. 337/470–2000 **A**1 2 10 **F**3 9 11 12 15 16 18 20 22 24 26 28 29 30 31 32 34 35 38 39 40 42 43 46 48 49 50 51 53 54 56 57 58 59 60 61 64 65 66 68 70 71 74 75 77 78 79 81 82 84 85 86 87 90 93 94 96 107 108 110 111 114 115 117 118 119 126 127 129 130 132 134 135 143 144 146 147 148 **P**6 **S** Franciscan Missionaries of Our Lady Health System, Inc., Baton Rouge, LA
Primary Contact: William F. Barrow, II, President and Chief Executive Officer
COO: Donna F. Landry, Chief Operating Officer
CFO: Ronald E. Hogan, Chief Financial Officer
CMO: Anthony P. Blalock, M.D., Chief Medical Officer
CIO: Ryan J. Latiolais, Director Information Systems
CHR: Jennifer Lynch Trahan, Assistant Vice President Human Resources
CNO: Terry J. Broussard, Interim Chief Nursing Officer
Web address: www.lourdesrmc.com
Control: Church–operated, Nongovernment, not–for profit **Service:** General Medical and Surgical

Staffed Beds: 186 **Admissions:** 9776 **Census:** 136 **Outpatient Visits:** 132736 **Births:** 0 **Total Expense ($000):** 200686 **Payroll Expense ($000):** 58934 **Personnel:** 1343

☒ **PAM SPECIALTY HOSPITAL OF LAFAYETTE (192033)**, 204 Energy Parkway, Zip 70508–3816; tel. 337/232–1905 **A**1 10 **F**1 3 28 29 30 34 35 50 56 57 59 60 67 74 75 77 85 91 135 143 148 **P**5 **S** Post Acute Medical, LLC, Enola, PA
Primary Contact: Jason Branson, Chief Executive Officer
CMO: Vitalis C. Okechukwu, M.D., President Medical Staff
CNO: Patricia Tweedel, Chief Nursing Officer
Web address: www.postacutemedical.com
Control: Partnership, Investor–owned, for–profit **Service:** Long–Term Acute Care hospital

Staffed Beds: 50 **Admissions:** 339 **Census:** 23 **Outpatient Visits:** 0 **Births:** 0 **Total Expense ($000):** 14012 **Personnel:** 88

◇ **PARK PLACE SURGICAL HOSPITAL (190255)**, 4811 Ambassador Caffery Parkway, Zip 70508–6917; tel. 337/237–8119, (Nonreporting) **A**10 21
Primary Contact: Brandon Moore, FACHE, Administrator and Chief Executive Officer
Web address: www.parkplacesurgery.com/
Control: Partnership, Investor–owned, for–profit **Service:** Surgical

Staffed Beds: 10

☐ **UNIVERSITY HOSPITAL AND CLINICS (190006)**, 2390 West Congress Street, Zip 70506–4298; tel. 337/261–6000 **A**1 2 3 5 10 **F**3 4 15 18 20 29 30 31 34 35 39 40 43 45 46 47 48 49 50 54 56 57 58 59 60 61 63 64 65 66 68 70 74 75 77 78 79 81 82 84 85 86 87 107 110 111 114 115 119 129 130 135 144 147 148 **S** Lafayette General Health, Lafayette, LA
Primary Contact: Katherine D. Hebert, Chief Executive Officer
CMO: James B. Falterman, Jr., M.D., Medical Director
CNO: Laurence Marie Vincent, Chief Nursing Officer
Web address: www.lafayettegeneral.com
Control: Other not–for–profit (including NFP Corporation) **Service:** General Medical and Surgical

Staffed Beds: 100 **Admissions:** 3247 **Census:** 38 **Outpatient Visits:** 337244 **Births:** 0 **Total Expense ($000):** 126101 **Payroll Expense ($000):** 36926

☒ **WOMEN'S AND CHILDREN'S HOSPITAL (190205)**, 4600 Ambassador Caffery Parkway, Zip 70508–6923, Mailing Address: P.O. Box 88030, Zip 70598–8030; tel. 337/521–9100 **A**1 5 10 **F**3 8 13 15 19 29 30 31 35 39 40 41 50 52 55 57 59 65 68 70 72 74 75 76 77 78 79 81 85 86 87 88 89 91 93 107 111 114 115 117 119 126 129 130 132 146 147 **S** HCA, Nashville, TN
Primary Contact: Kathy Bobbs, FACHE, President and Chief Executive Officer
COO: Leona Boullion, Chief Operating Officer
CFO: James Miller, Chief Financial Officer
CMO: Donald Mickal, M.D., Chief Medical Officer
CIO: John Trahan, Director Information Systems
CHR: Candice Chopin, Vice President Human Resources
CNO: John Marker, Chief Nursing Officer
Web address: www.womens–childrens.com
Control: Corporation, Investor–owned, for–profit **Service:** Obstetrics and gynecology

Staffed Beds: 161 **Admissions:** 6192 **Census:** 98 **Outpatient Visits:** 55885 **Births:** 3200 **Total Expense ($000):** 80326 **Payroll Expense ($000):** 32281 **Personnel:** 501

LAKE CHARLES—Calcasieu Parish

CALCASIEU OAKS GERIATRIC PSYCHIATRIC HOSPITAL, 2837 Ernest Street, Zip 70601–8785; tel. 337/439–8111, (Nonreporting) **A**10 **S** Pacer Health Corporation, Miami Lakes, FL
Primary Contact: Charles Getwood, Assistant Chief Executive Officer
Control: Corporation, Investor–owned, for–profit **Service:** Psychiatric

Staffed Beds: 24

☒ △ **CHRISTUS ST. PATRICK HOSPITAL OF LAKE CHARLES (190027)**, 524 Dr. Michael Debakey Drive, Zip 70601–5799, Mailing Address: P.O. Box 3401, Zip 70601; tel. 337/436–2511 **A**1 2 7 10 **F**3 11 15 17 18 20 22 24 26 28 29 30 31 32 34 35 37 38 40 44 45 46 47 48 49 50 56 57 59 61 64 65 70 74 75 78 79 81 84 85 86 87 89 90 93 96 97 98 100 101 102 103 104 105 107 108 110 118 119 120 121 122 123 124 126 130 131 132 134 135 146 147 148 **P**8 **S** CHRISTUS Health, Irving, TX
Primary Contact: Donald H. Lloyd, II, Chief Executive Officer
COO: Marsha L. White, Chief Nursing Executive
CFO: Scott Merryman, Chief Financial Officer
CMO: Rick Tyler, M.D., Vice President Medical Affairs
CHR: Wendy White, Assistant Administrator Human Resources
Web address: www.stpatrickhospital.org
Control: Church–operated, Nongovernment, not–for profit **Service:** General Medical and Surgical

Staffed Beds: 160 **Admissions:** 6712 **Census:** 108 **Outpatient Visits:** 72796 **Births:** 0 **Total Expense ($000):** 137320 **Payroll Expense ($000):** 37143 **Personnel:** 696

☒ **LAKE AREA MEDICAL CENTER (190201)**, 4200 Nelson Road, Zip 70605–4118; tel. 337/474–6370, (Nonreporting) **A**1 10 **S** Community Health Systems, Inc., Franklin, TN
Primary Contact: Bryan S. Bateman, Chief Executive Officer
CFO: Dawn Johnson–Hatcher, Chief Financial Officer
CIO: Aaron Cook, Director Information Services
CHR: Lisa Friday, Director Human Resources
CNO: Robbin Odom, R.N., Chief Nursing Officer
Web address: www.Lakeareamc.com
Control: Corporation, Investor–owned, for–profit **Service:** Other specialty

Staffed Beds: 88

☒ **LAKE CHARLES MEMORIAL HOSPITAL (190060)**, 1701 Oak Park Boulevard, Zip 70601–8911; tel. 337/494–3000, (Includes LAKE CHARLES MEMORIAL HOSPITAL FOR WOMEN, 1900 West Gauthier Road, Zip 70605–7170; tel. 337/480–7000; Marilyn McSwain, MSN, R.N., Administrator) **A**1 2 3 5 10 **F**3 8 11 15 17 18 20 22 24 25 26 28 29 30 31 34 37 40 45 49 50 53 54 56 57 58 60 62 64 66 70 71 72 73 74 75 76 77 78 79 81 82 85 86 87 89 90 93 98 99 102 103 107 108 110 111 114 115 119 120 121 123 124 127 129 130 131 132 144 146 147 148 **P**1 6 7
Primary Contact: Larry M. Graham, FACHE, President and Chief Executive Officer
COO: Timothy O. Coffey, Senior Vice President Operations
CFO: Charles P. Whitson, CPA, Senior Vice President Finance
CMO: Kevin Mocklin, M.D., Director Medical Staff
CIO: Belinda Sommers, Chief Information Officer
CHR: Ginger Consigney, Vice President Human Resources
Web address: www.lcmh.com
Control: Other not–for–profit (including NFP Corporation) **Service:** General Medical and Surgical

Staffed Beds: 308 **Admissions:** 12052 **Census:** 174 **Outpatient Visits:** 321346 **Births:** 1833 **Total Expense ($000):** 260542 **Payroll Expense ($000):** 84835 **Personnel:** 2328

MEMORIAL SPECIALTY HOSPITAL (192019), 524 Doctor Michael Debakey Drive, 3rd Floor, Zip 70601–5725; tel. 337/480–8990, (Nonreporting) **A**10
Primary Contact: Robert R. LaFleur, R.N., Administrator
CNO: Julie LeBlanc, Director of Nursing
Web address: www.lcmh.com/
Control: Other not–for–profit (including NFP Corporation) **Service:** Long–Term Acute Care hospital

Staffed Beds: 29

OCEANS BEHAVIORAL HOSPITAL OF LAKE CHARLES (194090), 302 West Mcneese Street, Zip 70605–5604; tel. 337/474–7581 **A**10 **F**29 35 57 98 100 101 102 103 104 130 132 143 **S** Oceans Healthcare, Lake Charles, LA
Primary Contact: William L. Willis, Administrator
Web address: www.obhlc.info/
Control: Corporation, Investor–owned, for–profit **Service:** Psychiatric

Staffed Beds: 40 **Admissions:** 362 **Census:** 15 **Outpatient Visits:** 0 **Births:** 0 **Personnel:** 78

Hospital, Medicare Provider Number, Address, Telephone, Approval, Facility, and Physician Codes, Health Care System

★ American Hospital Association (AHA) membership
☐ The Joint Commission accreditation
○ Healthcare Facilities Accreditation Program
◇ DNV Healthcare Inc. accreditation
⇑ Center for Improvement in Healthcare Quality Accreditation
△ Commission on Accreditation of Rehabilitation Facilities (CARF) accreditation

LA

LAKE PROVIDENCE—East Carroll Parish

EAST CARROLL PARISH HOSPITAL (190208), 336 North Hood Street,
Zip 71254–2140; tel. 318/559–4023, (Nonreporting) **A**10
Primary Contact: LaDonna Englerth, Administrator
Control: Hospital district or authority, Government, nonfederal **Service:** General Medical and Surgical

Staffed Beds: 11

LEESVILLE—Vernon Parish

☒ **BYRD REGIONAL HOSPITAL (190164)**, 1020 West Fertitta Boulevard,
Zip 71446–4645; tel. 337/239–9041, (Nonreporting) **A**1 10 **S** Community Health Systems, Inc., Franklin, TN
Primary Contact: Roger C. LeDoux, Chief Executive Officer
CFO: Jared Graves, Chief Financial Officer
CMO: Charles Caldwell, M.D., Chief of Staff
CHR: Karolyne Christian, Director Human Resources
CNO: Beth Westerchil, Chief Nursing Officer
Web address: www.byrdregional.com
Control: Corporation, Investor–owned, for–profit **Service:** General Medical and Surgical

Staffed Beds: 60

DOCTOR'S HOSPITAL OF DEER CREEK (190297), 815 South 10th Street,
Zip 71446–4611, Mailing Address: P.O. Box 1391, Zip 71496–1391;
tel. 337/392–5088, (Nonreporting) **A**10
Primary Contact: Jeffrey Morrow, Chief Executive Officer
CMO: Gregory D. Lord, M.D., Medical Director
CIO: Kim Smith, Director Business Office
CHR: Annette Hillman, Director Human Resources
CNO: Brenda Willis, Director of Nursing
Web address: www.dhdc.md
Control: Corporation, Investor–owned, for–profit **Service:** General Medical and Surgical

Staffed Beds: 10

☐ **LEESVILLE REHABILITATION HOSPITAL (193086)**, 900 South 6th Street,
Zip 71446–4723; tel. 337/392–8118, (Nonreporting) **A**1 10
Primary Contact: Jack M. Causey, Chief Executive Officer
CMO: Gregory D. Lord, M.D., Chief Medical Officer
CHR: Jackie Rubar, Administrative Assistant and Director Human Resources
Web address: www.leesvillerehab.com
Control: Corporation, Investor–owned, for–profit **Service:** Rehabilitation

Staffed Beds: 16

☐ **TRI PARISH REHABILITATION HOSPITAL (193050)**, 8088 Hawks Road,
Zip 71446–6649; tel. 337/462–8880, (Nonreporting) **A**1 10
Primary Contact: Lloyd Monger, Administrator
Web address: www.triparishrehab.com
Control: Corporation, Investor–owned, for–profit **Service:** Rehabilitation

Staffed Beds: 20

LULING—St. Charles Parish

☒ **ST. CHARLES PARISH HOSPITAL (190079)**, 1057 Paul Maillard Road,
Zip 70070–4349, Mailing Address: P.O. Box 87, Zip 70070–0087;
tel. 985/785–6242, (Nonreporting) **A**1 10 **S** Ochsner Health System, New Orleans, LA
Primary Contact: Ritchie Dupre, Chief Executive Officer
CFO: Peter Torsch, Chief Financial Officer
CMO: Vadakkipalayam N. Devarajan, Chief Medical Staff
CIO: Angela Boudreaux, Director Information Technology
CHR: Karen Ann Judlin, Director Human Resources
CNO: Jean Hill, Chief Nursing Officer and Chief Clinical Officer
Web address: www.ochsner.org/locations/st_charles_parish_hospital/
Control: Hospital district or authority, Government, nonfederal **Service:** General Medical and Surgical

Staffed Beds: 56

LUTCHER—St. James Parish

BEACON BEHAVIORAL HOSPITAL (194102), 2471 Louisiana Avenue,
Zip 70071–5413; tel. 225/258–6103, (Nonreporting)
Primary Contact: Sean Wendell, Chief Executive Officer
Web address: www.beaconbh.com
Control: Other not–for–profit (including NFP Corporation) **Service:** Psychiatric

Staffed Beds: 19

☒ **ST. JAMES PARISH HOSPITAL (191305)**, 1645 Lutcher Avenue,
Zip 70071–5150; tel. 225/869–5512 **A**1 10 18 **F**3 15 29 30 34 35 40 45 50 57 59 64 75 77 80 81 107 110 111 114 119 128 129 132 133 135 144
Primary Contact: Mary Ellen Pratt, FACHE, Chief Executive Officer
CFO: Tracy L. George, Chief Financial Officer
CIO: Jeremy Martin, Chief Support Services Officer
CHR: Lisa Faucheux, Director Human Resources
CNO: Rhonda Zeringue, R.N., Chief Nursing Officer
Web address: www.sjph.org
Control: Hospital district or authority, Government, nonfederal **Service:** General Medical and Surgical

Staffed Beds: 25 Admissions: 708 Census: 10 Outpatient Visits: 32498 Births: 1 Total Expense ($000): 25311 Payroll Expense ($000): 9682 Personnel: 194

MAMOU—Evangeline Parish

☒ **SAVOY MEDICAL CENTER (190025)**, 801 Poinciana Avenue,
Zip 70554–2298; tel. 337/468–5261, (Nonreporting) **A**1 10 **S** CHRISTUS Health, Irving, TX
Primary Contact: Sherman Fookes, Chief Executive Officer
COO: Gerald Fuselier, Chief Operating Officer
CMO: Greg Savoy, M.D., Chief Medical Officer
CIO: Daniel Lahaye, Manager
CHR: Annette Thibodeaux, Director Human Resources
Web address: www.savoymedical.com/
Control: City–Government, nonfederal **Service:** General Medical and Surgical

Staffed Beds: 180

MANDEVILLE—St. Tammany Parish

☐ **NORTHLAKE BEHAVIORAL HEALTH SYSTEM (194007)**, 23515 Highway 190,
Zip 70448–7334; tel. 985/626–6300, (Nonreporting) **A**1 3 5 10
Primary Contact: Richard Kramer, Chief Executive Officer
CFO: Melissa S. Clayton, CPA, Chief Financial Officer
CMO: Hyon Su Kim, M.D., Medical Director
CIO: Archie Carriere, Information Technology Technician
CHR: Nicole Messa–Gill, Manager Human Resources
CNO: Jo Nell King, Director of Nursing
Web address: www.northlakebehavioralhealth.com
Control: State–Government, nonfederal **Service:** Psychiatric

Staffed Beds: 153

MANSFIELD—De Soto Parish

DE SOTO REGIONAL HEALTH SYSTEM (190118), 207 Jefferson Street,
Zip 71052–2603, Mailing Address: P.O. Box 1636, Zip 71052–1636;
tel. 318/872–4610, (Nonreporting) **A**10 20 **S** Willis–Knighton Health System, Shreveport, LA
Primary Contact: Todd Eppler, FACHE, Chief Executive Officer
CFO: Sandra Anderson, Chief Financial Officer
CMO: Denis Kamberov, M.D., Chief of Staff
CNO: Vernadine Mitchell, R.N., Chief Nursing Officer
Web address: www.desotoregional.com
Control: Other not–for–profit (including NFP Corporation) **Service:** General Medical and Surgical

Staffed Beds: 10

MANY—Sabine Parish

SABINE MEDICAL CENTER (190218), 240 Highland Drive, Zip 71449–3718;
tel. 318/256–5691 **A**10 20 **F**3 29 40 50 64 107 119 127 133 **S** Allegiance Health Management, Shreveport, LA
Primary Contact: Chris Beddoe, Chief Executive Officer
COO: Doug Plummer, Chief Operating Officer
CFO: Frances F. Hopkins, Chief Financial Officer
CNO: Karen Ford, Chief Nursing Officer
Web address: www.sabinemedicalcenter.net
Control: Corporation, Investor–owned, for–profit **Service:** General Medical and Surgical

Staffed Beds: 24 Admissions: 540 Census: 5 Outpatient Visits: 43367 Births: 0 Total Expense ($000): 15209 Payroll Expense ($000): 6417 Personnel: 130

MARKSVILLE—Avoyelles Parish

☐ **AVOYELLES HOSPITAL (190099)**, 4231 Highway 1192, Zip 71351–4711,
Mailing Address: P.O. Box 249, Zip 71351–0249; tel. 318/253–8611 **A**1 10 **F**3 15 29 30 34 40 56 57 64 65 70 75 81 85 86 107 110 114 119 133 135 146
Primary Contact: David M. Mitchel, Chief Executive Officer
CFO: Douglas Lahasky, Chief Financial Officer
CMO: Robert Scott York, M.D., Chief of Staff
CHR: Allison Ferguson, Director Human Resources
CNO: Cindy K. Juneau, Chief Nursing Officer, Manger Quality and Risk
Web address: www.avoyelleshospital.com
Control: Corporation, Investor–owned, for–profit **Service:** General Medical and Surgical

Staffed Beds: 35 Admissions: 1026 Census: 11 Outpatient Visits: 36920 Births: 0 Total Expense ($000): 12769 Payroll Expense ($000): 6224 Personnel: 167

Many Facility Codes have changed. Please refer to the AHA Guide Code Chart. © 2016 AHA Guide

MARRERO—Jefferson Parish

LOUISIANA CONTINUING CARE HOSPITAL (192007), 1111 Medical Center Boulevard, Suite S–550, Zip 70072–3151; tel. 504/349–2470, (Nonreporting) **A**10
Primary Contact: Phyllis Hauro, Chief Executive Officer
Control: Corporation, Investor–owned, for–profit **Service:** Long–Term Acute Care hospital

Staffed Beds: 56

☒ △ **WEST JEFFERSON MEDICAL CENTER (190039)**, 1101 Medical Center Boulevard, Zip 70072–3191; tel. 504/347–5511 **A**1 2 3 5 7 10 **F**3 6 7 11 12 13 15 17 18 20 22 24 26 28 29 30 31 34 35 37 38 39 40 41 43 45 46 47 49 50 51 53 56 57 59 61 64 65 68 70 72 74 75 76 78 79 81 82 84 85 86 87 89 91 93 96 97 98 100 101 102 104 105 107 108 110 111 114 115 117 118 119 120 121 124 126 127 129 130 132 135 144 146 147 148 **P**6 7
Primary Contact: Nancy R. Cassagne, FACHE, Chief Executive Officer
COO: Angela Greener, Chief Administrative Officer
CMO: Mark Workman, M.D., Chief Medical Officer
CIO: Nicholas Thimis, Chief Information Officer
CHR: Frank Martinez, Vice President Human Resources
Web address: www.wjmc.org
Control: Other not–for–profit (including NFP Corporation) **Service:** General Medical and Surgical

Staffed Beds: 243 Admissions: 11306 Census: 160 Outpatient Visits: 191533 Births: 1230 Total Expense ($000): 246261 Payroll Expense ($000): 81810 Personnel: 1526

METAIRIE—Jefferson Parish

☒ △ **EAST JEFFERSON GENERAL HOSPITAL (190146)**, 4200 Houma Boulevard, Zip 70006–2996; tel. 504/503–4000, (Includes DOCTORS HOSPITAL OF JEFFERSON, 4320 Houma Boulevard, Zip 70006–2973; tel. 504/849–4000) **A**1 2 3 5 7 10 **F**3 7 8 11 13 14 15 17 18 20 22 24 26 28 29 30 31 34 35 36 37 40 44 45 46 47 48 49 50 51 53 54 55 56 57 58 59 60 64 65 68 70 72 73 74 75 76 77 78 79 81 82 84 85 86 87 89 90 91 92 93 96 97 98 102 103 107 108 110 111 114 115 117 118 119 120 121 123 124 126 128 129 130 131 132 135 141 142 145 146 147 148 **P**6
Primary Contact: Mark J. Peters, M.D., President and Chief Executive Officer
COO: Judy Brown, Executive Vice President and Chief Operating Officer
CFO: Bruce Naremore, Senior Vice President and Chief Financial Officer
CMO: Raymond P. DeCorte, M.D., Chief Medical Officer
CHR: Frank Martinez, Senior Vice President Human Resources
CNO: Ruby Brewer, RN, Senior Vice President, Chief Nursing and Quality Officer
Web address: www.ejgh.org
Control: Hospital district or authority, Government, nonfederal **Service:** General Medical and Surgical

Staffed Beds: 424 Admissions: 15528 Census: 246 Outpatient Visits: 222217 Births: 1948 Total Expense ($000): 343554 Payroll Expense ($000): 111993 Personnel: 2290

◇ **OMEGA HOSPITAL (190302)**, 2525 Severn Avenue, Zip 70002–5932; tel. 504/832–4200, (Nonreporting) **A**10 21
Primary Contact: Debbie Schenck, Administrator
Web address: www.omega–institute.com
Control: Individual, Investor–owned, for–profit **Service:** Surgical

Staffed Beds: 10

MINDEN—Webster Parish

☒ **MINDEN MEDICAL CENTER (190144)**, 1 Medical Plaza, Zip 71055–3330, Mailing Address: P.O. Box 5003, Zip 71058–5003; tel. 318/377–2321 **A**1 10 19 **F**11 13 15 18 20 22 29 30 34 40 45 46 56 57 59 62 64 70 75 76 77 79 81 82 87 89 90 93 98 103 107 111 115 119 129 130 132 146 147 148 **S** LifePoint Health, Brentwood, TN
Primary Contact: Stephen R. Selzer, Interim Chief Executive Officer
CFO: Jim Williams, Chief Financial Officer
CMO: G. Max Stell, M.D., Medical Director
CIO: Mace Morgan, Director Information Systems
CHR: Mary Winget, Director Human Resources
CNO: Donna Carter, MSN, Chief Nursing Officer
Web address: www.mindenmedicalcenter.com
Control: Corporation, Investor–owned, for–profit **Service:** General Medical and Surgical

Staffed Beds: 161 Admissions: 3650 Census: 39 Outpatient Visits: 44202 Births: 771 Total Expense ($000): 52998 Payroll Expense ($000): 19537 Personnel: 456

MONROE—Ouachita Parish

BASTROP REHABILITATION HOSPITAL (193058), 4310 South Grand Street, Zip 71202–6322; tel. 318/654–8300, (Nonreporting) **A**10
Primary Contact: Stephen J. Florentine, Administrator
COO: Tena Paulk, R.N., Program Director and Director Nursing
CMO: James M. Smith, M.D., Medical Director
CIO: Debbie Chunn, Director Medical Records
CHR: Renee Walker, Director Human Resources
Control: Corporation, Investor–owned, for–profit **Service:** Rehabilitation

Staffed Beds: 10

E. A. CONWAY MEDICAL CENTER See University Health Conway

◇ **MONROE SURGICAL HOSPITAL (190245)**, 2408 Broadmoor Boulevard, Zip 71201–2963; tel. 318/410–0002, (Nonreporting) **A**3 10 21
Primary Contact: Robyn Hemphill, Interim Chief Executive Officer and Chief Nursing Officer
Web address: www.monroesurgical.com
Control: Corporation, Investor–owned, for–profit **Service:** Surgical

Staffed Beds: 10

★ ◇ **P & S SURGICAL HOSPITAL (190246)**, 312 Grammont Street Suite 101, Zip 71201–7403; tel. 318/388–4040, (Nonreporting) **A**10 21
Primary Contact: Linda S. Holyfield, R.N., MSN, President and Chief Executive Officer
COO: Terri Hicks, Chief Operating Officer and Chief Financial Officer
CFO: Terri Hicks, Chief Operating Officer and Chief Financial Officer
CMO: Bart Liles, M.D., Chief of Staff
CIO: Christy Childers, Director Information Technology
CHR: Cheniere Craig, Director Human Resources
CNO: Debbie W. Austin, MSN, Vice President Patient Care Services
Web address: www.pssurgery.com
Control: Partnership, Investor–owned, for–profit **Service:** Surgical

Staffed Beds: 22

SPECIALTY HOSPITAL (192016), 309 Jackson Street, 7th Floor, Zip 71201–7407, Mailing Address: P.O. Box 1532, Zip 71210–1532; tel. 318/966–7045, (Nonreporting) **A**10 **S** LHC Group, Lafayette, LA
Primary Contact: Cleta Munholland, Administrator
Web address: www.lhcgroup.com
Control: Other not–for–profit (including NFP Corporation) **Service:** Long–Term Acute Care hospital

Staffed Beds: 32

☒ **ST. FRANCIS MEDICAL CENTER (190125)**, 309 Jackson Street, Zip 71201–7407, Mailing Address: P.O. Box 1901, Zip 71210–1901; tel. 318/966–4000, (Includes ST. FRANCIS NORTH HOSPITAL, 3421 Medical Park Drive, Zip 71203–2399; tel. 318/388–1946) **A**1 10 **F**12 13 15 17 18 20 22 24 26 28 29 30 34 35 38 40 42 45 47 49 50 51 54 57 59 63 64 65 66 68 69 70 72 74 75 76 77 81 83 84 85 87 88 89 90 93 96 97 98 107 108 109 110 111 114 115 116 117 118 119 124 126 128 129 130 132 134 135 146 147 148 **P**6 8 **S** Franciscan Missionaries of Our Lady Health System, Inc., Baton Rouge, LA
Primary Contact: Kristin Wolkart, R.N., President and Chief Executive Officer
CFO: Ronald E. Hogan, Regional Chief Financial Officer
CNO: Kayla Johnson, R.N., Vice President Patient Care Services and Chief Nursing Officer
Web address: www.stfran.com
Control: Church–operated, Nongovernment, not–for profit **Service:** General Medical and Surgical

Staffed Beds: 331 Admissions: 13858 Census: 212 Outpatient Visits: 264021 Births: 1772 Total Expense ($000): 254880 Payroll Expense ($000): 103204 Personnel: 1722

ST. FRANCIS SPECIALTY HOSPITAL See Specialty Hospital

☐ **UNIVERSITY HEALTH CONWAY (190011)**, 4864 Jackson Street,
Zip 71202–6497, Mailing Address: P.O. Box 1881, Zip 71210–8005;
tel. 318/330–7000 **A**1 3 5 10 **F**3 8 11 13 15 18 20 22 24 26 28 29 30 31 32
34 35 36 38 40 41 45 46 50 54 56 57 59 61 64 65 66 68 70 71 72 73 75
76 77 78 79 81 85 86 87 89 91 93 97 98 100 101 102 103 107 108 110
111 112 114 115 119 124 130 135 143 144 146 147 **S** University Health
System, Shreveport, LA
Primary Contact: Larry Donner, Administrator
CFO: Dorothy Whittington, Chief Financial Officer
CMO: Richard Cavell, M.D., Medical Director
CIO: Todd Walters, Director of UHC Information Technology Services
CHR: Rob Hartmann, Assistant Director Human Resources Management
CNO: Traci S. Jordan, MS, Chief Nursing Officer
Web address: www.uhsystem.com
Control: Other not–for–profit (including NFP Corporation) **Service:** General
Medical and Surgical

Staffed Beds: 108 **Admissions:** 6200 **Census:** 76 **Outpatient Visits:** 140000 **Births:** 984 **Total Expense ($000):** 90000 **Payroll Expense ($000):** 36000 **Personnel:** 593

MORGAN CITY—St. Mary Parish

✖ **TECHE REGIONAL MEDICAL CENTER (190014)**, 1125 Marguerite Street,
Zip 70380–1855, Mailing Address: P.O. Box 2308, Zip 70381–2308;
tel. 985/384–2200 **A**1 10 20 **F**3 13 15 18 29 30 34 40 45 50 57 59 70 76
79 81 82 84 85 89 90 93 98 100 101 102 104 105 107 108 110 111 114
117 118 119 129 130 146 147 **S** LifePoint Health, Brentwood, TN
Primary Contact: James P. Frazier, III, Chief Executive Officer
COO: Don Knight, Assistant Administrator and Risk Manager
CFO: Lynn Kliebert, Chief Financial Officer
CMO: Eric Melancon, Chief of Staff
CIO: Cheryl Lipari, Manager Information Systems
CHR: Timothy Hebert, Director Human Resources
Web address: www.techeregional.com
Control: Corporation, Investor–owned, for–profit **Service:** General Medical and
Surgical

Staffed Beds: 165 **Admissions:** 2884 **Census:** 38 **Outpatient Visits:** 55198 **Births:** 436 **Total Expense ($000):** 45447 **Payroll Expense ($000):** 14659 **Personnel:** 251

NAPOLEONVILLE—Assumption Parish

★ **ASSUMPTION COMMUNITY HOSPITAL (191303)**, 135 Highway 402,
Zip 70390–2217; tel. 985/369–3600 **A**10 18 **F**32 34 35 40 57 58 59 64 65
127 135 **S** Franciscan Missionaries of Our Lady Health System, Inc., Baton
Rouge, LA
Primary Contact: Wayne M. Arboneaux, Chief Executive Officer
CHR: Letonia Pierre, Coordinator Human Resources
CNO: Donna Mullings, Director of Nursing
Control: Other not–for–profit (including NFP Corporation) **Service:** General
Medical and Surgical

Staffed Beds: 6 **Admissions:** 69 **Census:** 1 **Outpatient Visits:** 21058 **Births:** 0 **Total Expense ($000):** 6529 **Payroll Expense ($000):** 2209 **Personnel:** 49

NATCHITOCHES—Natchitoches Parish

LOUISIANA EXTENDED CARE HOSPITAL OF NATCHITOCHES (192035), 501
Keyser Avenue, Zip 71457–6018; tel. 318/354–2044 **A**10 **F**1 3 28 29 34 38 44
50 57 59 68 74 75 85 86 87 91 97 130 148 **S** LHC Group, Lafayette, LA
Primary Contact: John Rivoire, R.N., MSN, Administrator
Web address: www.lhcgroup.com
Control: Partnership, Investor–owned, for–profit **Service:** Long–Term Acute Care
hospital

Staffed Beds: 21 **Admissions:** 257 **Census:** 17 **Outpatient Visits:** 0 **Births:** 0 **Personnel:** 44

✖ **NATCHITOCHES REGIONAL MEDICAL CENTER (190007)**, 501 Keyser
Avenue, Zip 71457–6036, Mailing Address: P.O. Box 2009, Zip 71457–2009;
tel. 318/214–4200 **A**1 10 20 **F**3 5 7 8 10 11 13 15 18 28 29 30 31 32 34 35
36 37 38 39 40 41 42 43 45 46 47 50 51 53 54 55 56 57 58 59 60 61 65
66 69 70 71 74 75 76 77 78 79 81 82 85 86 87 93 94 97 98 100 101 102
103 104 105 106 107 108 109 110 111 112 114 119 120 121 124 125 126
127 129 130 131 132 133 135 143 144 145 146 147 148 **P**5 7 8
S CHRISTUS Health, Irving, TX
Primary Contact: D. Kirk Soileau, FACHE, Chief Executive Officer
CFO: Brad McCormick, Chief Financial Officer
CMO: Phyllis Mason, M.D., Chief Medical Officer
CIO: Raymond Bruels, Manager Information Technology
CHR: Ernie Scott, Director Human Resources
CNO: Dawna DeBlieux, Vice President Patient Care Services and Chief Nurse
Executive
Web address: www.nrmchospital.org
Control: Hospital district or authority, Government, nonfederal **Service:** General
Medical and Surgical

Staffed Beds: 91 **Admissions:** 3800 **Census:** 43 **Outpatient Visits:** 95000 **Births:** 675

NEW IBERIA—Iberia Parish

☐ **IBERIA MEDICAL CENTER (190054)**, 2315 East Main Street,
Zip 70560–4031, Mailing Address: P.O. Box 13338, Zip 70562–3338;
tel. 337/364–0441 **A**1 10 **F**3 11 13 15 18 20 22 28 29 30 31 34 39 40 45
46 47 48 49 50 57 68 70 72 74 75 77 78 79 81 85 93 97 107 108 110 115
119 127 130 135 146 **P**6 **S** HealthTech Management Services, Brentwood, TN
Primary Contact: Parker A. Templeton, FACHE, Chief Executive Officer
COO: Shane P. Myers, Chief Operating Officer
CFO: Dionne Viator, CPA, Chief Financial Officer
CMO: Shawn Baquet, Chief of Staff
CIO: Vance Robinson, Chief Information Officer
CHR: Lori Spann, Director Human Resources
CNO: Josie Fletcher, Interim Chief Nursing Officer
Web address: www.iberiamedicalcenter.com
Control: Hospital district or authority, Government, nonfederal **Service:** General
Medical and Surgical

Staffed Beds: 84 **Admissions:** 3732 **Census:** 35 **Outpatient Visits:** 97949 **Births:** 591 **Total Expense ($000):** 62736 **Payroll Expense ($000):** 25524 **Personnel:** 573

☐ **IBERIA REHABILITATION HOSPITAL (190304)**, 532 Jefferson Terrace,
Zip 70560–4948; tel. 337/364–6923, (Nonreporting) **A**1 10
Primary Contact: Athan Olivier III, RN, MSN, Administrator and Chief Executive
Officer
Web address: www.iberiarehab.net/
Control: Partnership, Investor–owned, for–profit **Service:** Rehabilitation

Staffed Beds: 24

NEW ORLEANS—Orleans Parish

☐ **BEACON BEHAVIORAL HOSPITAL – NEW ORLEANS (194084)**, 14500 Hayne
Boulevard, Suite 200, Zip 70128–1751; tel. 504/210–0460, (Nonreporting)
A1 10
Primary Contact: Jessika Scallion, Administrator
Control: Corporation, Investor–owned, for–profit **Service:** Psychiatric

Staffed Beds: 24

☐ △ **CHILDREN'S HOSPITAL (193300)**, 200 Henry Clay Avenue,
Zip 70118–5720; tel. 504/899–9511 **A**1 2 3 5 7 10 **F**17 19 25 29 30 31 32
41 54 58 60 64 65 68 72 74 79 81 82 87 88 89 90 93 97 98 99 104 106
107 108 111 115 118 119 126 130 131 134 136 146 148 **S** LCMC Health,
New Orleans, LA
Primary Contact: Mary R. Perrin, President and Chief Executive Officer
COO: Justin Olsen, Chief Operating Officer
CFO: Courtney Garrett, CPA, Senior Vice President, Chief Financial Officer
CMO: John Heaton, M.D., Senior Vice President and Medical Director
CIO: Tanya Townsend, Senior Vice President, Chief Information Officer (part of
LCMC)
CHR: Wendy L. Willis, Vice President Human Resources
CNO: Diane Michel, Senior Vice President, Chief Nursing Officer
Web address: www.chnola.org
Control: Other not–for–profit (including NFP Corporation) **Service:** Children's
general

Staffed Beds: 210 **Admissions:** 7148 **Census:** 143 **Births:** 0

☐ **COMMUNITY CARE HOSPITAL (194056)**, 1421 General Taylor Street,
Zip 70115–3717; tel. 504/899–2500, (Nonreporting) **A**1 10
Primary Contact: Paul B. Kavanaugh, President and Chief Executive Officer
Web address: www.communitycarehospital.com
Control: State–Government, nonfederal **Service:** Psychiatric

Staffed Beds: 36

✖ **CURAHEALTH NEW ORLEANS (192009)**, 3601 Coliseum Street,
Zip 70115–3606; tel. 504/899–1555 **A**1 3 10 **F**1 3 28 29 30 46 70 75 77 86
87 91 96 98 103 130 135 148
Primary Contact: Theresa Barrios, Interim Administrator
CFO: Laurie Champagne, Controller
Control: Corporation, Investor–owned, for–profit **Service:** Long–Term Acute Care
hospital

Staffed Beds: 80 **Admissions:** 496 **Census:** 41 **Outpatient Visits:** 0 **Births:** 0

MEDICAL CENTER OF LOUISIANA AT NEW ORLEANS See University Medical
Center

☐ **NEW ORLEANS EAST HOSPITAL (190313)**, 5620 Read Boulevard, Zip 70127–3106, Mailing Address: 5620 Read Boulevard, Zip 70127–3106; tel. 504/592–6600 **A**1 **F**3 11 15 18 20 22 28 29 30 34 35 38 40 44 45 50 57 59 60 63 64 68 70 74 75 77 79 81 85 86 87 91 93 97 107 108 110 111 115 118 119 129 130 146 **P**8 **S** LCMC Health, New Orleans, LA
Primary Contact: Takeisha C. Davis, M.D., M.P.H., President and Chief Executive Officer
COO: Dante Green, Assistant Vice President Operations
CFO: Anthony Saul, Chief Financial Officer
CHR: Brion Stanford, Director Human Resources
CNO: Martha Smith, R.N., Chief Nursing Officer
Web address: www.noehospital.org
Control: Hospital district or authority, Government, nonfederal **Service:** General Medical and Surgical

Staffed Beds: 34 **Admissions:** 643 **Census:** 7 **Outpatient Visits:** 28092 **Births:** 0 **Total Expense ($000):** 39462 **Payroll Expense ($000):** 10708 **Personnel:** 198

✦ △ **OCHSNER MEDICAL CENTER (190036)**, 1514 Jefferson Highway, Zip 70121–2429; tel. 504/842–3000, (Includes OCHSNER BAPTIST MEDICAL CENTER, 2700 Napoleon Avenue, Zip 70115–6914; tel. 504/899–9311; Dawn Anuszkiewicz, Chief Executive Officer; OCHSNER MEDICAL CENTER – WEST BANK, 2500 Belle Chasse Highway, Gretna, Zip 70056–7127; tel. 504/392–3131; Anthony DiGerolamo, R.N., MSN, Chief Executive Officer; OCHSNER MEDICAL CENTER FOR CHILDREN, 1514 Jefferson Highway, tel. 504/842–3000), (Total facility includes 38 beds in nursing home–type unit) **A**1 2 3 5 7 8 10 **F**3 4 5 6 7 8 9 11 12 13 14 15 17 18 19 20 21 22 23 24 25 26 27 28 29 30 31 32 34 35 36 37 38 40 41 43 44 45 46 47 48 49 50 51 54 55 56 57 58 59 60 61 63 64 65 68 70 71 72 73 74 75 76 77 78 79 80 81 82 84 85 86 87 88 89 90 91 92 93 94 96 97 98 99 100 101 102 103 104 105 107 108 110 111 114 115 116 117 118 119 120 121 123 124 126 128 129 130 131 132 134 135 136 137 138 139 140 141 142 145 146 147 148 **P**6 **S** Ochsner Health System, New Orleans, LA
Primary Contact: Robert K. Wolterman, Chief Executive Officer
CFO: Scott J. Posecai, Executive Vice President and Chief Financial Officer
CMO: Patrick J. Quinlan, M.D., Chief Executive Officer
CIO: Lynn Witherspoon, Vice President and Chief Information Officer
CHR: Joan Mollohan, Vice President Human Resources
Web address: www.ochsner.org
Control: Other not–for–profit (including NFP Corporation) **Service:** General Medical and Surgical

Staffed Beds: 813 **Admissions:** 40052 **Census:** 606 **Outpatient Visits:** 393746 **Births:** 3764 **Total Expense ($000):** 1166368 **Payroll Expense ($000):** 401881 **Personnel:** 7832

PSYCHIATRIC PAVILION NEW ORLEANS See Beacon Behavioral Hospital – New Orleans

☐ **RIVER OAKS HOSPITAL (194031)**, 1525 River Oaks Road West, Zip 70123–2162; tel. 504/734–1740, (Includes RIVER OAKS CHILD AND ADOLESCENT HOSPITAL, 1525 River Oaks Road West, tel. 504/734–1740), (Nonreporting) **A**1 3 10 **S** Universal Health Services, Inc., King of Prussia, PA
Primary Contact: Evelyn Nolting, Chief Executive Officer and Managing Director
CFO: Brandon Frazier, Chief Financial Officer
CMO: Lincoln Paine, M.D., Medical Director
CIO: Vincent Chatelain, Director Business Development
CHR: Wanda Hoffmann, Director Human Resources
CNO: Michelle Wells, Director of Nursing
Web address: www.riveroakshospital.com
Control: Corporation, Investor–owned, for–profit **Service:** Psychiatric

Staffed Beds: 126

SEASIDE BEHAVIORAL CENTER (194100), 4201 Woodland Drive, Zip 70131–7339; tel. 504/393–4223, (Nonreporting) **A**3 10
Primary Contact: Mary L. Matamoros, R.N., Chief Executive Officer
CHR: Sherry May Campbell, Director of Human Resources, Medical Records
CNO: Justin Bernier, R.N., Director of Nursing
Web address: www.seasidehc.com
Control: Partnership, Investor–owned, for–profit **Service:** Psychiatric

Staffed Beds: 24

☐ **ST. CATHERINE MEMORIAL HOSPITAL (192023)**, 14500 Hayne Boulevard, Zip 70128–1751; tel. 504/210–3000, (Nonreporting) **A**1 10
Primary Contact: Lexis Landry Nunez, Chief Executive Officer
Web address: www.stcatherine–hospital.com
Control: Corporation, Investor–owned, for–profit **Service:** Long–Term Acute Care hospital

Staffed Beds: 21

◇ **ST. CHARLES SURGICAL HOSPITAL (190300)**, 1717 Saint Charles Avenue, Zip 70130–5223; tel. 504/529–6600, (Nonreporting) **A**10 21
Primary Contact: Cheri Saltaformaggio, Chief Executive Officer
Web address: www.scsh.com
Control: Corporation, Investor–owned, for–profit **Service:** Surgical

Staffed Beds: 39

✦ △ **TOURO INFIRMARY (190046)**, 1401 Foucher Street, Zip 70115–3593; tel. 504/897–7011, (Includes TOURO REHABILITATION CENTER, 1401 Foucher Street, Zip 70115–3515; tel. 504/897–8560; Susan E. Andrews, Chief Executive Officer) **A**1 2 3 5 7 10 **F**3 8 10 11 13 15 18 20 24 28 29 30 31 34 35 36 37 39 40 44 45 46 50 53 54 55 57 59 60 61 62 63 64 68 70 72 74 75 76 77 78 79 81 83 84 85 86 87 90 92 93 96 97 107 108 109 110 111 114 115 116 117 118 119 120 121 123 124 125 126 130 131 132 135 143 146 147 148 **P**8 **S** LCMC Health, New Orleans, LA
Primary Contact: Susan E. Andrews, Chief Executive Officer
COO: David Elgarico, Chief Operating Officer
CFO: Mark Wack, Senior Vice President and Chief Financial Officer
CMO: Jeffrey Coco, M.D., Chief Medical Officer
CIO: Leann Hughes–Mickel, Chief Information Officer
CHR: Cindy Mousa, Director Human Resources
CNO: Danita S. Sullivan, R.N., Chief Nursing Officer
Web address: www.touro.com
Control: Other not–for–profit (including NFP Corporation) **Service:** General Medical and Surgical

Staffed Beds: 280 **Admissions:** 11084 **Census:** 190 **Outpatient Visits:** 311899 **Births:** 3516 **Total Expense ($000):** 255481 **Payroll Expense ($000):** 93893 **Personnel:** 1547

✦ **TULANE MEDICAL CENTER (190176)**, 1415 Tulane Avenue, Zip 70112–2600; tel. 504/988–5263, (Includes TULANE–LAKESIDE HOSPITAL, 4700 South I. 10 Service Road West, Metairie, Zip 70001–1269; tel. 504/780–4223) **A**1 2 3 5 8 10 **F**3 12 13 15 17 18 20 21 22 23 24 25 26 27 28 29 30 31 32 34 35 40 41 45 46 47 48 49 50 51 52 53 55 58 60 61 64 65 70 72 74 75 76 77 78 79 80 81 85 87 88 89 90 91 92 93 97 99 100 101 102 104 107 108 109 110 111 114 115 118 119 120 121 122 123 124 126 129 130 131 132 136 138 139 141 142 146 147 **P**4 5 **S** HCA, Nashville, TN
Primary Contact: William Lunn, M.D., Chief Executive Officer
COO: Jyric Sims, FACHE, Chief Operating Officer
CFO: Todd LaCaze, Chief Financial Officer
CMO: John Pigott, M.D., Chief Medical Officer
CIO: Sue Rachuig, Director Information Services
CHR: Leah Grau, Director Human Resources
CNO: Jana S. Stonestreet, R.N., Chief Nursing Officer
Web address: www.tuhc.com
Control: Corporation, Investor–owned, for–profit **Service:** General Medical and Surgical

Staffed Beds: 294 **Admissions:** 13822 **Census:** 195 **Outpatient Visits:** 363520 **Births:** 2334 **Total Expense ($000):** 366389 **Payroll Expense ($000):** 111099 **Personnel:** 1529

☐ **UNIVERSITY MEDICAL CENTER (190005)**, 2000 Canal Street, Zip 70112–3018; tel. 504/903–3000 **A**1 2 5 8 10 **F**3 11 15 18 20 22 24 26 29 30 31 34 35 39 40 43 45 46 49 50 51 58 61 64 65 66 70 74 78 79 81 85 86 87 93 94 97 98 102 107 108 110 111 114 115 116 117 118 119 123 126 130 135 141 146 147 148 **S** LCMC Health, New Orleans, LA
Primary Contact: William J. Masterton, President and Chief Executive Officer
Web address: www.umcno.org
Control: Other not–for–profit (including NFP Corporation) **Service:** General Medical and Surgical

Staffed Beds: 255 **Admissions:** 10822 **Census:** 178 **Outpatient Visits:** 294937 **Births:** 0 **Total Expense ($000):** 502131 **Payroll Expense ($000):** 117627 **Personnel:** 1838

NEW ROADS—Pointe Coupee Parish

★ **POINTE COUPEE GENERAL HOSPITAL (191316)**, 2202 False River Drive, Zip 70760–2614; tel. 225/638–6331 **A**10 18 **F**40 45 64 75 81 89 93 107 111 119 128 129 130 133
Primary Contact: Chad E. Olinde, CPA, Administrator and Chief Executive Officer
CFO: John Cazayoux, Chief Financial Officer
CMO: Paul Rachal, M.D., Chief Medical Officer
CIO: Anthony Sauro, Chief Information Officer
CHR: Lisa Patterson, Director Human Resources
CNO: Valerie Sparks Jarreau, R.N., Chief Nursing Officer
Web address: www.pcgh.org
Control: Hospital district or authority, Government, nonfederal **Service:** General Medical and Surgical

Staffed Beds: 25 **Admissions:** 433 **Census:** 6 **Outpatient Visits:** 46414 **Births:** 0 **Total Expense ($000):** 15507 **Payroll Expense ($000):** 6972 **Personnel:** 182

Hospital, Medicare Provider Number, Address, Telephone, Approval, Facility, and Physician Codes, Health Care System

★ American Hospital Association (AHA) membership
☐ The Joint Commission accreditation
○ Healthcare Facilities Accreditation Program
◇ DNV Healthcare Inc. accreditation
⇑ Center for Improvement in Healthcare Quality Accreditation
△ Commission on Accreditation of Rehabilitation Facilities (CARF) accreditation

LA

OAK GROVE—West Carroll Parish

WEST CARROLL MEMORIAL HOSPITAL (190081), 706 Ross Street,
Zip 71263–9798; tel. 318/428–3237, (Nonreporting) **A**10
Primary Contact: R. Randall Morris, Administrator
Control: Other not–for–profit (including NFP Corporation) **Service:** General
Medical and Surgical

Staffed Beds: 21

OAKDALE—Allen Parish

☐ **OAKDALE COMMUNITY HOSPITAL (190106)**, 130 North Hospital Drive,
Zip 71463–3035, Mailing Address: P.O. Box 629, Zip 71463–0629;
tel. 318/335–3700, (Nonreporting) **A**1 10
Primary Contact: Billy Tingle, Interim Chief Executive Officer
CMO: Tommy Davis, M.D., Chief of Staff
CIO: Melissa Welch, Director Health Information Management
CHR: Becky Johnson, Director Human Resources
Web address: www.oakdalecommunityhospital.com/
Control: Partnership, Investor–owned, for–profit **Service:** General Medical and
Surgical

Staffed Beds: 27

OLLA—Caldwell Parish

HARDTNER MEDICAL CENTER (191315), 1102 North Pine Road,
Zip 71465–4804; tel. 318/495–3131, (Nonreporting) **A**10 18
Primary Contact: Paul G. Mathews, CPA, Administrator
CIO: Sarah Thompson, Director Health Information Management
CNO: Cherry B. Salter, Director of Nursing
Web address: www.hardtnermedical.com
Control: Hospital district or authority, Government, nonfederal **Service:** General
Medical and Surgical

Staffed Beds: 35

OPELOUSAS—St. Landry Parish

☐ **OCEANS BEHAVIORAL HOSPITAL OF OPELOUSAS (194095)**, 1310 Heather
Drive, Zip 70570–7714; tel. 337/948–8820, (Nonreporting) **A**1 10 **S** Oceans
Healthcare, Lake Charles, LA
Primary Contact: Theresa Fontenot, Executive Director
Web address: www.obho.info/
Control: Corporation, Investor–owned, for–profit **Service:** Psychiatric

Staffed Beds: 20

✠ **OPELOUSAS GENERAL HEALTH SYSTEM (190017)**, 539 East Prudhomme
Street, Zip 70570–6499, Mailing Address: P.O. Box 1389, Zip 70571–1389;
tel. 337/948–3011, (Includes OPELOUSAS GENERAL HEALTH SYSTEM–SOUTH
CAMPUS, 3983 I–49 South Service Road, Zip 70570–8975; tel. 337/948–2100;
Kenneth Cochran, R.N., FACHE, President and Chief Executive Officer) **A**1 2 10
19 **F**3 13 15 28 31 34 37 40 44 45 48 49 50 53 57 60 65 68 70 73 77 78
79 80 81 85 87 90 91 93 96 97 98 102 103 104 105 107 108 110 111 112
114 115 116 117 119 121 126 129 130 131 132 146 147 148 **P**6
Primary Contact: Kenneth Cochran, R.N., FACHE, President and Chief Executive
Officer
COO: Bob Hardy, Chief Operating Officer
CFO: James B. Juneau, Chief Financial Officer
CMO: Hunt Deblanc, M.D., Chief of Staff
CIO: Jared Lormand, Vice President Information Technology
CHR: Suzanne F. Kidder, Human Resources Officer
CNO: Kimberly Probus, Chief Nursing Officer
Web address: www.opelousasgeneral.com
Control: Hospital district or authority, Government, nonfederal **Service:** General
Medical and Surgical

Staffed Beds: 201 Admissions: 7285 Census: 96 Outpatient Visits: 143419
Births: 1082 Total Expense ($000): 126682 Payroll Expense ($000):
46049 Personnel: 872

ST. LANDRY EXTENDED CARE HOSPITAL (192034), 3983 I–49 South
Service Road, 2nd Floor, Zip 70570; tel. 337/948–2251, (Nonreporting) **A**10
S LHC Group, Lafayette, LA
Primary Contact: Biff David, R.N., Administrator
Web address: www.lhcgroup.com
Control: Corporation, Investor–owned, for–profit **Service:** Long–Term Acute Care
hospital

Staffed Beds: 41

PINEVILLE—Rapides Parish

☒ **ALEXANDRIA VETERANS AFFAIRS HEALTH CARE SYSTEM**, 2495 Shreveport
Highway, 71 N., Zip 71360–4044, Mailing Address: P.O. Box 69004, Alexandria,
Zip 71306–9004; tel. 318/473–0010, (Nonreporting) **A**1 2 3 5 **S** Department of
Veterans Affairs, Washington, DC
Primary Contact: Peter Dancy, Director
CFO: Bianca A. Obey, Chief Financial Officer
CMO: Robert Bernard, M.D., Chief of Staff
CIO: Robin McBryde, Chief Information Officer
CHR: Alex Love, Acting Manager Human Resources
CNO: Amy Lesniewski, Associate Director Patient Care Services
Web address: www.alexandria.va.gov/
Control: Veterans Affairs, Government, federal **Service:** General Medical and
Surgical

Staffed Beds: 143

☐ **CENTRAL LOUISIANA STATE HOSPITAL (194025)**, 242 West Shamrock
Avenue, Zip 71360–6439, Mailing Address: P.O. Box 5031, Zip 71361–5031;
tel. 318/484–6200 **A**1 10 **F**98 **S** Louisiana State Hospitals, Baton Rouge, LA
Primary Contact: Ronald G. Williams, Administrator
COO: Paul Benoit, Associate Administrator
CFO: Tina Darbonne, Chief Financial Officer
CMO: L. Lee Tynes, Jr., M.D., Medical Director
CIO: William Haynes, Director Information Technology
CHR: Tom Crout, MS, Director Human Resources
Web address: www.dhh.louisiana.gov/index.cfm/directory/detail/217
Control: State–Government, nonfederal **Service:** Psychiatric

Staffed Beds: 120 Admissions: 55 Census: 118 Outpatient Visits: 0 Births:
0

VETERANS AFFAIRS MEDICAL CENTER – ALEXANDRIA See Alexandria
Veterans Affairs Health Care System

PLAQUEMINE—Iberville Parish

MMO REHABILITATION AND WELLNESS CENTER (193070), 59213
Riverwest Drive, Zip 70764–6552; tel. 225/687–8100, (Nonreporting) **A**10
Primary Contact: Shannon Hawkins Ragusa, Acting Administrator
Web address: www.mmoinc.com
Control: Other not–for–profit (including NFP Corporation) **Service:** Rehabilitation

Staffed Beds: 8

RACELAND—Lafourche Parish

☒ **OCHSNER ST. ANNE GENERAL HOSPITAL (191324)**, 4608 Highway 1,
Zip 70394–2623; tel. 985/537–6841 **A**1 10 18 **F**3 4 5 13 15 17 18 29 30 34
35 40 45 57 59 63 65 70 72 74 75 76 79 81 85 86 87 88 89 98 99 100
101 102 103 104 107 108 114 118 119 127 130 133 135 146 147
S Ochsner Health System, New Orleans, LA
Primary Contact: Timothy J. Allen, FACHE, Chief Executive Officer
COO: Fernis LeBlanc, Chief Operating Officer
CNO: Jana Semere, Chief Nursing Officer
Web address: www.ochsner.org/locations/ochsner-st-anne
Control: Other not–for–profit (including NFP Corporation) **Service:** General
Medical and Surgical

Staffed Beds: 38 Admissions: 1698 Census: 18 Outpatient Visits: 57888
Births: 322 Total Expense ($000): 31122 Payroll Expense ($000): 14310
Personnel: 228

RAYNE—Acadia Parish

☐ **PHOENIX BEHAVIORAL HOSPITAL (194097)**, 2021 Crowley Rayne Highway,
Zip 70578–4027; tel. 337/788–0091 **A**1 10 **F**29 34 59 64 98 100 101 103
104 105 135 143 **P**6
Primary Contact: Joseph Tidwell, Administrator
Control: Individual, Investor–owned, for–profit **Service:** Psychiatric

Staffed Beds: 16 Admissions: 416 Census: 11 Outpatient Visits: 0 Births:
0

RAYVILLE—Richland Parish

RICHARDSON MEDICAL CENTER (190151), 254 Highway 3048 Christian
Drive, Zip 71269–0388, Mailing Address: P.O. Box 388, Zip 71269–0388;
tel. 318/728–4181 **A**10 **F**3 15 17 18 22 29 32 34 35 38 40 41 44 45 48 50
53 56 57 59 64 65 66 68 70 81 86 87 89 107 110 111 119 127 129 130
133 136 **P**5
Primary Contact: James W. Barrett, Jr., Chief Executive Officer
CFO: Mallory Gulley Wells, CPA, Chief Financial Officer
CMO: David Thompson, M.D., Chief of Staff
CHR: Rita Brown, Director Human Resources
Web address: www.richardsonmed.org
Control: State–Government, nonfederal **Service:** General Medical and Surgical

Staffed Beds: 32 Admissions: 814 Census: 9 Outpatient Visits: 15444
Births: 0

Many Facility Codes have changed. Please refer to the AHA Guide Code Chart.

RUSTON—Lincoln Parish

ALLEGIANCE HEALTH CENTER OF RUSTON (194087), 1401 Ezell Street, Zip 71270–7218; tel. 318/255–8085, (Nonreporting) **A**10 **S** Allegiance Health Management, Shreveport, LA
Primary Contact: Donna K. Thompson, Chief Executive Officer
Web address: www.ahmgt.com
Control: Corporation, Investor–owned, for–profit **Service:** Psychiatric

Staffed Beds: 14

LIBERTY HEALTHCARE SYSTEMS See Serenity Springs Specialty Hospital

☒ **LIFECARE SPECIALTY HOSPITAL OF NORTH LOUISIANA (192022)**, 1401 Ezell Street, Zip 71270–7218; tel. 318/251–3126, (Nonreporting) **A**1 10 **S** LifeCare Management Services, Plano, TX
Primary Contact: Brent Martin, Administrator
Web address: www.lifecare–hospitals.com/hospital.php?id=19
Control: Corporation, Investor–owned, for–profit **Service:** Long–Term Acute Care hospital

Staffed Beds: 55

☒ **NORTHERN LOUISIANA MEDICAL CENTER (190086)**, 401 East Vaughn Avenue, Zip 71270–5950; tel. 318/254–2100, (Includes GREEN CLINIC SURGICAL HOSPITAL, 1118 Farmerville Street, Zip 71270–5914; tel. 318/232–7700; Chad Conner, Administrator), (Nonreporting) **A**1 10 19 **S** Community Health Systems, Inc., Franklin, TN
Primary Contact: Roy Finch, Chief Executive Officer
CFO: Frank Malek, Chief Financial Officer
CMO: Derek McClusky, M.D., Chief of Staff
CIO: Heather Nolan, Director Information Services
CHR: Tonya Duggan, Director Human Resources
CNO: Ronnie Ursin, R.N., Chief Nursing Officer
Web address: www.northernlouisianamedicalcenter.com
Control: Other not–for–profit (including NFP Corporation) **Service:** General Medical and Surgical

Staffed Beds: 104

SERENITY SPRINGS SPECIALTY HOSPITAL (194074), 1495 Frazier Road, Zip 71270–1632; tel. 318/202–3860, (Nonreporting) **A**10
Primary Contact: Adrian Williams, Chief Executive Officer
Web address: www.serenityhospital.com
Control: Corporation, Investor–owned, for–profit **Service:** Psychiatric

Staffed Beds: 18

SAINT FRANCISVILLE—West Feliciana Parish

☒ **WEST FELICIANA PARISH HOSPITAL (191306)**, 5266 Commerce Street, Zip 70775, Mailing Address: P.O. Box 368, Zip 70775–0368; tel. 225/635–3811, (Nonreporting) **A**1 10 18
Primary Contact: Lee Chastant, Chief Executive Officer
CFO: Linda Harvey, Chief Financial Officer
CHR: Neta F. Leake, Administrative Assistant Human Resources
CNO: Angela Noble, Director of Nursing
Web address: www.wfph.org
Control: Hospital district or authority, Government, nonfederal **Service:** General Medical and Surgical

Staffed Beds: 22

SHREVEPORT—Caddo Parish

☐ **BRENTWOOD HOSPITAL (194020)**, 1006 Highland Avenue, Zip 71101–4103; tel. 318/678–7500 **A**1 10 **F**4 5 35 50 54 56 75 87 98 99 100 101 102 103 104 105 **P**6 **S** Universal Health Services, Inc., King of Prussia, PA
Primary Contact: William Weaver, Chief Executive Officer
COO: Charles Lee, Director Clinical Operations
CFO: Kae Bell, Chief Financial Officer
CMO: Colonel Daniel Feeney, M.D., Medical Director
CHR: Talicia Johnson, Director Human Resources
CNO: Carey Ouzts, Director of Nursing
Web address: www.brentwoodbehavioral.com
Control: Corporation, Investor–owned, for–profit **Service:** Psychiatric

Staffed Beds: 176 **Admissions:** 5895 **Census:** 152 **Outpatient Visits:** 12053 **Births:** 0 **Total Expense ($000):** 25185 **Payroll Expense ($000):** 13043 **Personnel:** 341

☒ **CHRISTUS HEALTH SHREVEPORT–BOSSIER (190041)**, 1453 East Bert Koun Industrial Loop, Zip 71105–6800; tel. 318/681–5000, (Includes CHRISTUS HIGHLAND MEDICAL CENTER, 1453 East Bert Kouns Industrial Loop, Zip 71105–6050; tel. 318/681–5000; Isaac Palmer, Chief Executive Officer) **A**1 2 3 5 10 **F**3 11 12 13 15 17 18 20 22 24 26 28 29 30 31 32 34 35 40 45 46 47 48 49 50 53 54 55 56 57 58 59 61 64 70 72 73 74 75 76 77 78 79 81 82 84 85 86 87 89 90 93 96 97 102 107 108 110 111 114 115 119 120 121 123 124 126 130 131 132 134 135 146 147 148 **S** CHRISTUS Health, Irving, TX
Primary Contact: Isaac Palmer, Chief Executive Officer
COO: Billy Porter, Vice President Clinical Operations
CFO: Scott Merryman, Chief Financial Officer
CMO: Marisa Johnson, M.D., Vice President Medical Affairs
CIO: Mary Merryman, Regional Director Information Management
CHR: Wendy White, Vice President Human Resources
CNO: Charlotte Knoll, R.N., Chief Nursing Executive
Web address: www.christushealthsb.org
Control: Church–operated, Nongovernment, not–for profit **Service:** General Medical and Surgical

Staffed Beds: 154 **Admissions:** 6559 **Census:** 97 **Outpatient Visits:** 124714 **Births:** 610 **Total Expense ($000):** 165139 **Payroll Expense ($000):** 48868 **Personnel:** 774

☒ **LIFECARE HOSPITALS OF SHREVEPORT (192011)**, 9320 Linwood Avenue, Zip 71106–7003; tel. 318/688–8504, (Includes LIFECARE HOSPITALS OF SHREVEPORT–WILLIS KNIGHTON, 8001 Youree Drive, Zip 71115–2302; Keith Cox, Chief Executive Officer and Administrator; LIFECARE HOSPITALS OF SOUTH SHREVEPORT–WILLIS KNIGHTON NORTH, 2550 Kings Highway, Zip 71103–3922; Keith Cox, Chief Executive Officer and Administrator), (Nonreporting) **A**1 10 **S** LifeCare Management Services, Plano, TX
Primary Contact: Brent Martin, Administrator
Web address: www.lifecare–hospitals.com
Control: Corporation, Investor–owned, for–profit **Service:** Long–Term Acute Care hospital

Staffed Beds: 119

☒ **OVERTON BROOKS VETERANS AFFAIRS MEDICAL CENTER**, 510 East Stoner Avenue, Zip 71101–4295; tel. 318/221–8411, (Nonreporting) **A**1 2 3 5 **S** Department of Veterans Affairs, Washington, DC
Primary Contact: Toby T. Mathew, Medical Center Director
CFO: Kim Lane, Chief Fiscal Service
CIO: Janey Taylor, Chief Information and Technology
CHR: Michael L. Palmier, Chief Human Resources Management
Web address: www.shreveport.va.gov/
Control: Veterans Affairs, Government, federal **Service:** General Medical and Surgical

Staffed Beds: 100

PHYSICIANS BEHAVIORAL HOSPITAL (194094), 2025 Desoto Street, Zip 71103–4717; tel. 318/550–0520 **A**10 **F**4 5 98 104 105
Primary Contact: Allison Cooper, Administrator
Control: Individual, Investor–owned, for–profit **Service:** Psychiatric

Staffed Beds: 24 **Admissions:** 368 **Census:** 10 **Outpatient Visits:** 0 **Births:** 0

☐ **PROMISE HOSPITAL OF LOUISIANA – SHREVEPORT CAMPUS (192010)**, 1800 Irving Place, Zip 71101–4608; tel. 318/425–4096, (Includes PROMISE HOSPITAL OF LOUISIANA – BOSSIER CITY CAMPUS, 2525 Viking Drive, Bossier City, Zip 71111–2103; tel. 318/841–2525), (Nonreporting) **A**1 10 **S** Promise Healthcare, Boca Raton, FL
Primary Contact: Rick Stockton, Chief Executive Officer
Web address: www.promise–shreveport.com
Control: Corporation, Investor–owned, for–profit **Service:** Long–Term Acute Care hospital

Staffed Beds: 146

PROMISE SPECIALTY HOSPITAL OF SHREVEPORT See Promise Hospital of Louisiana – Shreveport Campus

---

Hospital, Medicare Provider Number, Address, Telephone, Approval, Facility, and Physician Codes, Health Care System

★ American Hospital Association (AHA) membership
☐ The Joint Commission accreditation
○ Healthcare Facilities Accreditation Program
◇ DNV Healthcare Inc. accreditation
⇧ Center for Improvement in Healthcare Quality Accreditation
△ Commission on Accreditation of Rehabilitation Facilities (CARF) accreditation

LA

☐ **SHRINERS HOSPITALS FOR CHILDREN–SHREVEPORT (193301)**, 3100 Samford Avenue, Zip 71103–4289; tel. 318/222–5704 **A**1 3 5 10 **F**34 50 59 64 68 79 81 85 89 93 94 119 130 131 146 **S** Shriners Hospitals for Children, Tampa, FL
Primary Contact: Garry Kim Green, FACHE, Administrator
CFO: Randy Tabor, Director Fiscal Services
CMO: John A. Fox, M.D., Chief of Staff
CIO: Michael Lyons, Regional Information Systems Director
CHR: Rena Arbuthnot, Director Human Resources
CNO: Gail Rains, R.N., Director Patient Care Services
Web address: www.shrinershospitalsforchildren.org/Hospitals/Locations/Shreveport.aspx
Control: Other not–for–profit (including NFP Corporation) **Service:** Children's orthopedic

Staffed Beds: 45 **Admissions:** 264 **Census:** 2 **Outpatient Visits:** 16483 **Births:** 0 **Personnel:** 175

SPECIALISTS HOSPITAL – SHREVEPORT (190278), 1500 Line Avenue, Zip 71101–4639; tel. 318/213–3800, (Nonreporting) **A**10
Primary Contact: Kandi Moore, Administrator
CFO: Daniel Montgomery, Chief Financial Officer
CNO: Mary Virginia Loftus, Chief Nursing Officer
Web address: www.specialistshospitalshreveport.com/
Control: Corporation, Investor–owned, for–profit **Service:** Orthopedic

Staffed Beds: 15

UNIVERSITY HEALTH SHREVEPORT (190098), 1501 Kings Highway, Zip 71103–4228, Mailing Address: P.O. Box 33932, Zip 71130–3932; tel. 318/675–5000, (Includes CHILDREN'S HOSPITAL OF SHREVEPORT, 1501 Kings Highway, Mailing Address: PO Box 33932, Zip 71130–3932; tel. 318/675–5000), (Nonreporting) **A**2 3 5 10 **S** University Health System, Shreveport, LA
Primary Contact: Roderick L. Williams, M.P.H., President
COO: Betty Johnson, Associate Administrator
CFO: Harold White, Vice Chancellor
CMO: Kevin Sittig, M.D., Senior Associate Dean and Chief Medical Officer
CIO: Marcus Hobgood, Director Information Services
CHR: David Fuqua, Director Human Resources Management
Web address: www.lsuhscshreveport.edu
Control: State–Government, nonfederal **Service:** General Medical and Surgical

Staffed Beds: 459

☒ △ **WILLIS–KNIGHTON MEDICAL CENTER (190111)**, 2600 Greenwood Road, Zip 71103–3908, Mailing Address: P.O. Box 32600, Zip 71130–2600; tel. 318/212–4600, (Includes WILLIS–KNIGHTON PIERREMONT HEALTH CENTER, 8001 Youree Drive, Zip 71115; tel. 318/212–3000; WILLIS–KNIGHTON SOUTH – THE CENTER FOR WOMEN'S HEALTH, 2510 Bert Kouns Industrial Loop, Zip 71118; tel. 318/212–5000; Keri Elrod, Administrator), (Total facility includes 24 beds in nursing home–type unit) **A**1 2 3 5 7 10 **F**3 4 5 7 8 12 13 15 18 20 22 24 26 28 29 30 31 34 35 40 44 45 46 50 52 53 54 55 56 57 59 60 62 63 64 65 66 68 70 72 74 75 76 77 78 79 81 82 84 85 86 87 88 89 90 91 93 97 98 99 100 101 102 103 104 106 107 108 109 111 114 115 116 117 119 120 121 122 126 127 128 129 130 131 132 134 135 138 139 142 143 144 145 147 148 **P**7 **S** Willis–Knighton Health System, Shreveport, LA
Primary Contact: James K. Elrod, FACHE, Chief Executive Officer
COO: Charles D. Daigle, Senior Vice President and Chief Operating Officer
CMO: Dan Moller, M.D., Chief Medical Officer
CHR: Jaf Fielder, Vice President and Administrator
CNO: Debbie D. Olds, R.N., Director of Nursing
Web address: www.wkhs.com
Control: Other not–for–profit (including NFP Corporation) **Service:** General Medical and Surgical

Staffed Beds: 720 **Admissions:** 42937 **Census:** 504 **Outpatient Visits:** 387529 **Births:** 2751 **Personnel:** 4720

SLIDELL—St. Tammany Parish

NORTHSHORE REGIONAL MEDICAL CENTER See Ochsner Medical Center – North Shore

☒ **OCHSNER MEDICAL CENTER – NORTH SHORE (190204)**, 100 Medical Center Drive, Zip 70461–5520; tel. 985/649–7070 **A**1 10 **F**3 12 13 15 17 18 20 22 24 26 29 30 31 34 35 38 40 41 43 44 45 46 49 50 51 57 59 60 61 64 68 70 72 74 75 77 78 79 81 84 85 86 87 88 89 90 91 93 95 96 97 102 107 108 110 111 114 116 117 118 119 129 130 132 135 146 147 148 **S** Ochsner Health System, New Orleans, LA
Primary Contact: John William Davis, Chief Executive Officer
CFO: Forrest Whichard, Chief Financial Officer
CMO: James Newcomb, M.D., Vice President Medical
CHR: Terri Joseph–Taylor, Chief Human Resource Manager
CNO: Cheryl Woods, Chief Nursing Officer
Web address: www.https://www.ochsner.org/locations/ochsner–medical–center–north–shore/
Control: Other not–for–profit (including NFP Corporation) **Service:** General Medical and Surgical

Staffed Beds: 110 **Admissions:** 4705 **Census:** 61 **Outpatient Visits:** 78066 **Births:** 82 **Total Expense ($000):** 84070 **Payroll Expense ($000):** 34256 **Personnel:** 663

☒ **SLIDELL MEMORIAL HOSPITAL (190040)**, 1001 Gause Boulevard, Zip 70458–2987; tel. 985/280–2200 **A**1 2 3 5 10 **F**3 11 13 15 18 20 22 24 26 28 29 30 31 32 34 35 40 45 47 49 54 56 57 59 62 64 65 70 72 75 76 78 79 81 82 85 86 87 89 90 91 93 96 97 102 107 108 110 111 114 115 116 117 118 119 120 121 124 129 130 132 135 **P**6
Primary Contact: John William Davis, Chief Executive Officer
COO: Bruce Clement, Chief Operating Officer
CFO: Sandy Badinger, Chief Financial Officer
CMO: James Griffee, M.D., Chief Medical Officer
CHR: Jeanne M. Stachovsky, Director Human Resources
CNO: Lynn Strain, R.N., Chief Nursing Officer
Web address: www.slidellmemorial.org
Control: Hospital district or authority, Government, nonfederal **Service:** General Medical and Surgical

Staffed Beds: 170 **Admissions:** 7118 **Census:** 79 **Outpatient Visits:** 127763 **Births:** 1269 **Total Expense ($000):** 146318 **Payroll Expense ($000):** 61074

☐ **SOUTHERN SURGICAL HOSPITAL (190270)**, 1700 Lindberg Drive, Zip 70458–8062; tel. 985/641–0600 **A**1 10 **F**3 8 12 29 45 57 59 60 70 79 81 82 107 111 114 119 130 131 132 **P**5
Primary Contact: Michael J. Piscotta, Chief Executive Officer
CFO: Michael J. Maurin, Chief Financial Officer
CMO: J. Gosey, M.D., Medical Director
CIO: Buddy Graves, Chief Information Officer
CHR: Lorrie Alfred, Director Human Resources
Web address: www.sshla.com/
Control: Partnership, Investor–owned, for–profit **Service:** Surgical

Staffed Beds: 37 **Admissions:** 1182 **Census:** 14 **Outpatient Visits:** 5312 **Births:** 0

STERLING SURGICAL HOSPITAL (190256), 989 Robert Boulevard, Zip 70458–2009; tel. 985/690–8200, (Nonreporting) **A**10
Primary Contact: Christopher W. Daniel, Administrator
Web address: www.sterlingsurgical.net/
Control: Corporation, Investor–owned, for–profit **Service:** Surgical

Staffed Beds: 10

SPRINGHILL—Webster Parish

☐ **SPRINGHILL MEDICAL CENTER (190088)**, 2001 Doctors Drive, Zip 71075–4526, Mailing Address: P.O. Box 920, Zip 71075–0920; tel. 318/539–1000 **A**1 10 20 **F**3 15 18 26 29 30 32 34 35 40 45 47 48 49 50 51 54 57 59 64 65 66 68 70 75 79 81 85 86 87 93 98 103 107 108 110 111 114 119 127 129 130 131 133 135 146 148 **P**6 **S** Willis–Knighton Health System, Shreveport, LA
Primary Contact: Vince Sedminik, Chief Executive Officer
CFO: David Sanders, Chief Financial Officer
CMO: Jerry W. Sessions, M.D., Chief Medical Staff
CIO: Brian Griffin, Director Information Services
CHR: Ashley Ortego, Director Human Resources and Marketing
CNO: Dana Jones, R.N., Chief Nursing Officer
Web address: www.smccare.com
Control: Other not–for–profit (including NFP Corporation) **Service:** General Medical and Surgical

Staffed Beds: 58 **Admissions:** 1107 **Census:** 15 **Outpatient Visits:** 38663 **Births:** 0 **Total Expense ($000):** 20063 **Payroll Expense ($000):** 10152 **Personnel:** 175

SULPHUR—Calcasieu Parish

☐ **CORNERSTONE HOSPITAL OF SOUTHWEST LOUISIANA (192013)**, 703 Cypress Street, Zip 70663–5053; tel. 337/310–6000, (Nonreporting) **A**1 10 **S** Cornerstone Healthcare Group, Dallas, TX
Primary Contact: David Smith, President
CFO: Amy Bryant, Chief Financial Officer
Web address: www.chghospitals.com/sulphur/
Control: Partnership, Investor–owned, for–profit **Service:** Long–Term Acute Care hospital

Staffed Beds: 30

☐ **WEST CALCASIEU CAMERON HOSPITAL (190013)**, 701 Cypress Street, Zip 70663–5000, Mailing Address: P.O. Box 2509, Zip 70664–2509; tel. 337/527–7034, (Nonreporting) **A**1 10
Primary Contact: Janie Fruge, R.N., MSN, FACHE, Chief Executive Officer
CFO: Jobie James, Chief Financial Officer
CIO: Trey Rion, Chief Information Officer
CHR: Christi Kingsley, Vice President Human Resources
CNO: Brenda Quesnel, R.N., Vice President of Patient Care and Chief Nursing Officer
Web address: www.wcch.com
Control: Hospital district or authority, Government, nonfederal **Service:** General Medical and Surgical

Staffed Beds: 79

Many Facility Codes have changed. Please refer to the AHA Guide Code Chart. © 2016 AHA Guide

LA

TALLULAH—Madison Parish

MADISON PARISH HOSPITAL (191314), 900 Johnson Street,
Zip 71282–4537; tel. 318/574–2374, (Nonreporting) **A**10 18
Primary Contact: Ted Topolewski, Chief Executive Officer
CFO: W. Robert Laurents, CPA, Chief Financial Officer
CIO: Charles Whitaker, Director Information Technology
CHR: Chasity Whitaker, Administrative Assistant
Web address: www.madisonparishhospital.com
Control: Other not–for–profit (including NFP Corporation) **Service:** General
Medical and Surgical

Staffed Beds: 25

THIBODAUX—Lafourche Parish

⊠ △ **THIBODAUX REGIONAL MEDICAL CENTER (190004)**, 602 North Acadia
Road, Zip 70301–4847, Mailing Address: P.O. Box 1118, Zip 70302–1118;
tel. 985/447–5500 **A**1 2 7 10 **F**3 8 11 12 13 15 18 19 20 22 24 28 29 30 31
32 34 39 40 46 49 57 59 62 64 70 73 74 75 76 77 78 79 81 82 85 86 87
89 90 92 93 96 97 98 103 104 105 107 108 110 111 115 116 117 119 120
121 123 124 126 127 129 130 131 132 135 146 147 148
Primary Contact: Greg K. Stock, Chief Executive Officer
COO: Scott Flowers, Vice President Professional Services
CFO: Steve C. Gaubert, Chief Financial Officer
CMO: Allen Vander, M.D., Chief Medical Staff
CIO: Bernie Clement, Chief Information Officer
CHR: Eric Degravelle, Director Human Resources
Web address: www.thibodaux.com
Control: Hospital district or authority, Government, nonfederal **Service:** General
Medical and Surgical

Staffed Beds: 154 **Admissions:** 8170 **Census:** 93 **Outpatient Visits:** 164550
Births: 1160 **Total Expense ($000):** 158225 **Payroll Expense ($000):**
64992 **Personnel:** 1002

VIDALIA—Concordia Parish

☐ **PROMISE HOSPITAL OF MISS LOU (192028)**, 209 Front Street,
Zip 71373–2837; tel. 318/336–6500, (Nonreporting) **A**1 10 **S** Promise
Healthcare, Boca Raton, FL
Primary Contact: Michael Harrell, R.N., Chief Executive Officer
COO: Howard B. Koslow, President and Chief Executive Officer
CFO: James Hopwood, Chief Financial Officer
CMO: Randy Tillman, M.D., Chief Medical Staff
CIO: Robert Greene, Director Information Technology
CHR: Roxan Houghton, Director Human Resources
CNO: Regetta Woods, Chief Nursing Officer and Chief Clinical Officer
Web address: www.promise–misslou.com
Control: Corporation, Investor–owned, for–profit **Service:** Long–Term Acute Care
hospital

Staffed Beds: 40

VILLE PLATTE—Evangeline Parish

⊠ **MERCY REGIONAL MEDICAL CENTER (190167)**, 800 East Main Street,
Zip 70586–4618; tel. 337/363–5684, (Includes ACADIAN MEDICAL CENTER,
3501 Highway 190, Eunice, Zip 70535–5129; tel. 337/580–7500; Scott M.
Smith, Chief Executive Officer), (Nonreporting) **A**1 10 **S** LifePoint Health,
Brentwood, TN
Primary Contact: Scott M. Smith, Chief Executive Officer
COO: John Whiteside, Chief Operating Officer
CFO: Micheal Fontenot, Chief Financial Officer
CMO: Zebediah Stearns, M.D., Chief of Staff
CIO: Courtney Bieber, Director Information Systems
CHR: Cody Ardoin, Director Human Resources
CNO: Sandy Morein, Chief Nursing Officer
Web address: www.mercyregionalmedicalcenter.com
Control: Corporation, Investor–owned, for–profit **Service:** General Medical and
Surgical

Staffed Beds: 109

VIVIAN—Caddo Parish

NORTH CADDO MEDICAL CENTER (191304), 1000 South Spruce Street,
Zip 71082–3232, Mailing Address: P.O. Box 792, Zip 71082–0792;
tel. 318/375–3235, (Nonreporting) **A**3 5 10 18
Primary Contact: David C. Jones, Administrator
CFO: Carol Reisz, Chief Financial Officer
CMO: John H. Haynes, Jr., M.D., Chief of Medical Staff
CIO: Allyson Allums, Director Medical Records
CHR: Lanell Audirsch, Administrative Assistant
Web address: www.northcaddomedicalcenter.com
Control: Hospital district or authority, Government, nonfederal **Service:** General
Medical and Surgical

Staffed Beds: 27

WEST MONROE—Ouachita Parish

☐ **CORNERSTONE HOSPITAL–WEST MONROE (192031)**, 6198 Cypress Street,
Zip 71291–9010; tel. 318/396–5600, (Nonreporting) **A**1 10 **S** Cornerstone
Healthcare Group, Dallas, TX
Primary Contact: Chris Simpson, Chief Executive Officer
COO: Jay Quintana, Vice President Operations
CFO: Kurt Schultz, Chief Financial Officer
CMO: Khaled Shafici, M.D., President Medical Staff
CIO: Adam Davis, Chief Information Officer
CHR: Dan Perkins, Corporate Director Human Resources
Web address: www.chghospitals.com/chwm.html
Control: Corporation, Investor–owned, for–profit **Service:** Long–Term Acute Care
hospital

Staffed Beds: 40

◇ **GLENWOOD REGIONAL MEDICAL CENTER (190160)**, 503 McMillan Road,
Zip 71291–5327; tel. 318/329–4200, (Includes GLENWOOD SURGERY CENTER,
1275 Glenwood Drive, Zip 71291–5539, Mailing Address: 503 McMillan Road,
Zip 71291–5327; tel. 318/322–1339; Matthew S. Roberts, Chief Executive
Officer), (Nonreporting) **A**10 21 **S** IASIS Healthcare, Franklin, TN
Primary Contact: Matthew S. Roberts, Chief Executive Officer
COO: Jeremy Tinnerello, R.N., Chief Operations Officer
CFO: John DeSantis, Chief Financial Officer
CMO: Steve McMahan, M.D., Chief Medical Officer
CIO: Ronnie Maxwell, Director Information Systems
CHR: Jan Walker, Director Human Resources
CNO: Debbie Vaughn, R.N., Chief Nursing Officer
Web address: www.grmc.com
Control: Corporation, Investor–owned, for–profit **Service:** General Medical and
Surgical

Staffed Beds: 278

LOUISIANA EXTENDED CARE HOSPITAL WEST MONROE (192055), 503
McMillan Road, 3rd Floor, Zip 71291–5327; tel. 318/329–4378, (Nonreporting)
A10 **S** LHC Group, Lafayette, LA
Primary Contact: Cleta Munholland, Administrator
Control: Corporation, Investor–owned, for–profit **Service:** Long–Term Acute Care
hospital

Staffed Beds: 18

WINNFIELD—Winn Parish

☐ **SPECIALTY HOSPITAL OF WINNFIELD (192052)**, 915 First Street,
Zip 71483–2945; tel. 318/648–0212, (Nonreporting) **A**1 10
Primary Contact: Chuck Jurek, Interim Administrator and Chief Operating Officer
CFO: Chuck Jurek, Business Office Manager
CIO: Shamada Venzant, Manager Health Information
Control: Corporation, Investor–owned, for–profit **Service:** Long–Term Acute Care
hospital

Staffed Beds: 20

WINN PARISH MEDICAL CENTER (190090), 301 West Boundary Street,
Zip 71483–3427, Mailing Address: P.O. Box 152, Zip 71483–0152;
tel. 318/648–3000, (Nonreporting) **A**10
Primary Contact: Bryan Bogle, Chief Executive Officer
CFO: Douglas Lahasky, Chief Financial Officer
CMO: Ricky Hendrix, M.D., Chief of Staff
CHR: Ashley S. Files, Director Human Resources and Public Relations and
Marketing
CNO: Toby Wise, Chief Nursing Officer
Web address: www.winnparishmedical.com
Control: Partnership, Investor–owned, for–profit **Service:** General Medical and
Surgical

Staffed Beds: 60

WINNSBORO—Franklin Parish

★ **FRANKLIN MEDICAL CENTER (190140)**, 2106 Loop Road, Zip 71295–3344,
Mailing Address: P.O. Box 1300, Zip 71295–1300; tel. 318/435–9411,
(Nonreporting) **A**3 10
Primary Contact: Blake Kramer, Chief Executive Officer
CFO: William E. Page, CPA, Chief Financial Officer
CMO: Jay Busby, M.D., President Medical Staff
CIO: Judy Ogden, Director Information Technology
Web address: www.fmc–cares.com
Control: Hospital district or authority, Government, nonfederal **Service:** General
Medical and Surgical

Staffed Beds: 43

Hospital, Medicare Provider Number, Address, Telephone, Approval, Facility, and Physician Codes, Health Care System

★ American Hospital Association (AHA) membership   ○ Healthcare Facilities Accreditation Program   ⇑ Center for Improvement in Healthcare Quality Accreditation
☐ The Joint Commission accreditation   ◇ DNV Healthcare Inc. accreditation   △ Commission on Accreditation of Rehabilitation Facilities (CARF) accreditation

LA

☒ **LANE REGIONAL MEDICAL CENTER (190020)**, 6300 Main Street, Zip 70791–4037; tel. 225/658–4000, (Total facility includes 38 beds in nursing home–type unit) **A**1 10 **F**3 11 12 13 15 18 20 22 26 29 34 35 36 39 40 45 46 48 50 54 56 57 59 62 64 67 70 73 75 76 77 79 80 81 85 87 90 93 107 108 110 111 114 115 119 130 146 148 **P**6
Primary Contact: Randall M. Olson, Chief Executive Officer
COO: David Beck, Chief Operating Officer
CFO: Mark Anderson, Chief Financial Officer
CMO: Thomas Kang, M.D., Chief, Medical Staff
CIO: Paul Murphy, Chief Information Officer
CNO: Staci Sullivan, R.N., Chief Nursing Officer
Web address: www.lanermc.org
Control: Hospital district or authority, Government, nonfederal **Service:** General Medical and Surgical

Staffed Beds: 179 **Admissions:** 4488 **Census:** 95 **Outpatient Visits:** 97141 **Births:** 551 **Total Expense ($000):** 80722 **Payroll Expense ($000):** 33347 **Personnel:** 680

Many Facility Codes have changed. Please refer to the AHA Guide Code Chart. © 2016 AHA Guide

MAINE

AUGUSTA—Kennebec County

� **MAINE VETERANS AFFAIRS MEDICAL CENTER**, 1 VA Center,
Zip 04330–6719; tel. 207/623–8411 **A**1 3 **F**3 5 8 18 20 28 29 30 31 33 34
35 36 38 39 40 44 45 53 54 56 57 58 59 60 61 62 63 64 65 66 68 70 71
74 75 77 78 79 81 82 83 84 85 87 93 94 97 98 100 102 103 104 105 107
108 111 114 115 118 119 127 129 130 132 135 143 146 147 148 **P**6
S Department of Veterans Affairs, Washington, DC
Primary Contact: Ryan S. Lilly, Director
CFO: Daniel Howard, Chief Financial Officer
CMO: Timothy J. Richardson, M.D., Chief of Staff
CIO: Richard McNaughton, Chief Information Management Service
CHR: Christine Miller, Chief Human Resources Management Services
Web address: www.maine.va.gov/
Control: Veterans Affairs, Government, federal **Service:** General Medical and
Surgical

Staffed Beds: 167 **Admissions:** 2969 **Census:** 58 **Outpatient Visits:** 440136
Births: 0 **Total Expense ($000):** 300146 **Payroll Expense ($000):** 134123
Personnel: 1555

✦ **MAINEGENERAL MEDICAL CENTER (200039)**, 35 Medical Center Parkway,
Zip 04330; tel. 207/626–1000, (Includes MAINEGENERAL MEDICAL
CENTER–AUGUSTA CAMPUS, 35 Medical Center Parkway, Zip 04330–9988;
tel. 207/626–1000; Chuck Hays, President and Chief Executive Officer),
(Nonreporting) **A**1 2 10 19
Primary Contact: Chuck Hays, President and Chief Executive Officer
COO: Paul Stein, Chief Operating Officer
CFO: Terry Brann, Chief Financial Officer
CMO: Steve Diaz, M.D., Chief Medical Officer
CIO: Daniel Burgess, Chief Information Officer
CHR: Rebecca Lamey, Vice President Human Resources
CNO: Jennifer Riggs, R.N., Chief Nurse Officer
Web address: www.mainegeneral.org
Control: Other not–for–profit (including NFP Corporation) **Service:** General
Medical and Surgical

Staffed Beds: 258

MAINEGENERAL MEDICAL CENTER–AUGUSTA CAMPUS See MaineGeneral
Medical Center

☐ **RIVERVIEW PSYCHIATRIC CENTER (204007)**, 250 Arsenal Street,
Zip 04330–5742; tel. 207/624–3900, (Nonreporting) **A**1 10
Primary Contact: Rodney Bouffard, Superintendent
COO: David Lovejoy, Chief Operations Officer
CFO: Samantha Kavanaugh, Chief Financial Officer
CMO: Brendan Kirby, M.D., Medical Director
CHR: Aimee Rice, Human Resources Manager
CNO: Roland Pushard, Director of Nursing
Web address: www.state.me.us/dhhs/riverview
Control: State–Government, nonfederal **Service:** Psychiatric

Staffed Beds: 92

VETERANS AFFAIRS MEDICAL CENTER See Maine Veterans Affairs Medical
Center

BANGOR—Penobscot County

☐ **DOROTHEA DIX PSYCHIATRIC CENTER (204004)**, 656 State Street,
Zip 04401–5609, Mailing Address: P.O. Box 926, Zip 04402–0926;
tel. 207/941–4000, (Nonreporting) **A**1 10
Primary Contact: Sharon Sprague, Superintendent
CMO: Michelle Gardner, M.D., Clinical Director
CHR: Tamra Hanson, Human Resource Manager
CNO: Janet Babcock, Director of Nursing
Web address: www.maine.gov/dhhs/ddpc/index.shtml
Control: State–Government, nonfederal **Service:** Psychiatric

Staffed Beds: 51

✦ **EASTERN MAINE MEDICAL CENTER (200033)**, 489 State Street,
Zip 04401–6674, Mailing Address: P.O. Box 404, Zip 04402–0404;
tel. 207/973–7000, (Includes ROSS SKILLED NURSING FACILITY) **A**1 2 3 5 10
13 **F**3 11 12 13 15 17 18 19 20 22 24 26 27 28 29 30 31 32 34 36 37 39
40 43 44 45 46 47 48 49 50 51 53 54 55 57 58 59 61 64 70 72 74 75 76
77 78 79 81 82 84 85 86 87 88 89 90 92 93 94 96 97 102 107 108 110
111 114 115 117 118 119 120 121 123 124 126 129 130 131 132 144 145
146 147 148 **P**6 **S** Eastern Maine Healthcare Systems, Brewer, ME
Primary Contact: Deborah Carey Johnson, R.N., President and Chief Executive
Officer
CMO: James Raczek, M.D., Sr. Vice President of Operations and Chief Medical
Officer
CIO: Catherine Bruno, FACHE, Chief Information Officer
CHR: Greg Howat, Vice President Human Resources
Web address: www.emh.org
Control: Other not–for–profit (including NFP Corporation) **Service:** General
Medical and Surgical

Staffed Beds: 361 **Admissions:** 19086 **Census:** 284 **Outpatient Visits:**
480827 **Births:** 1691 **Total Expense ($000):** 680823 **Payroll Expense
($000):** 279898 **Personnel:** 3626

✦ **ST. JOSEPH HOSPITAL (200001)**, 360 Broadway, Zip 04401–3979, Mailing
Address: P.O. Box 403, Zip 04402–0403; tel. 207/262–1000 **A**1 10 **F**8 15 18
29 30 31 35 40 48 49 51 55 56 57 62 63 64 70 75 78 81 84 85 86
87 107 108 110 114 118 119 129 130 132 135 146 147 148 **S** Covenant
Health, Tewksbury, MA
Primary Contact: Mary Prybylo, President and Chief Executive Officer
CFO: Michael A. Hendrix, Jr., Chief Financial Officer
CMO: William Wood, M.D., Vice President Medical Affairs
CHR: Paige A. Hagerstrom, System Director of Talent Management
CNO: Dianne Swandal, R.N., Vice President Patient Care
Web address: www.sjhhealth.com
Control: Church–operated, Nongovernment, not–for profit **Service:** General
Medical and Surgical

Staffed Beds: 84 **Admissions:** 4206 **Census:** 56 **Outpatient Visits:** 140255
Births: 0 **Total Expense ($000):** 121657 **Payroll Expense ($000):** 49867
Personnel: 914

✦ **THE ACADIA HOSPITAL (204006)**, 268 Stillwater Avenue, Zip 04401–3945,
Mailing Address: P.O. Box 422, Zip 04402–0422; tel. 207/973–6100 **A**1 10 **F**5
29 30 50 57 66 68 75 77 82 87 98 99 100 101 103 104 105 130 132 **P**6
S Eastern Maine Healthcare Systems, Brewer, ME
Primary Contact: Daniel B. Coffey, President and Chief Executive Officer
CFO: Marie Suitter, Chief Financial Officer
CMO: Anthony Ng, M.D., Vice President and Chief Medical Officer
CIO: Jeanne Paradis, Director Information Services
CHR: Paul Bolin, Vice President Human Resources
CNO: Wayne Steller, Vice President Chief Nursing Officer
Web address: www.acadiahospital.org
Control: Other not–for–profit (including NFP Corporation) **Service:** Psychiatric

Staffed Beds: 68 **Admissions:** 1469 **Census:** 55 **Outpatient Visits:** 98560
Births: 0 **Total Expense ($000):** 49070 **Payroll Expense ($000):** 26107
Personnel: 484

BAR HARBOR—Hancock County

★ **MOUNT DESERT ISLAND HOSPITAL (201304)**, 10 Wayman Lane,
Zip 04609–1625, Mailing Address: P.O. Box 8, Zip 04609–0008;
tel. 207/288–5081 **A**5 10 18 **F**3 5 6 10 11 13 15 28 29 31 34 35 36 39 40
50 54 56 57 59 64 65 70 74 75 76 77 78 79 81 82 84 85 87 91 92 93 97
99 100 101 104 107 108 111 114 119 125 127 130 131 132 133 135 145
146 147 **P**6 7
Primary Contact: Arthur J. Blank, President and Chief Executive Officer
CFO: Christina Harding, Vice President Finance
CMO: Stuart Davidson, President Medical Staff
CIO: Bruce Donlin, Director Information Services
CHR: Joanne Harris, Director Human Resources
CNO: Karen Mueller, R.N., Chief Nursing Officer
Web address: www.mdihospital.org
Control: Other not–for–profit (including NFP Corporation) **Service:** General
Medical and Surgical

Staffed Beds: 25 **Admissions:** 970 **Census:** 8 **Outpatient Visits:** 177003
Births: 100 **Total Expense ($000):** 49742 **Payroll Expense ($000):** 23206
Personnel: 373

Hospital, Medicare Provider Number, Address, Telephone, Approval, Facility, and Physician Codes, Health Care System

★ American Hospital Association (AHA) membership ○ Healthcare Facilities Accreditation Program ⇑ Center for Improvement in Healthcare Quality Accreditation
☐ The Joint Commission accreditation ◇ DNV Healthcare Inc. accreditation △ Commission on Accreditation of Rehabilitation Facilities (CARF) accreditation

ME

BELFAST—Waldo County

WALDO COUNTY GENERAL HOSPITAL (201312), 118 Northport Avenue, Zip 04915–6072, Mailing Address: P.O. Box 287, Zip 04915–0287; tel. 207/338–2500 **A**10 18 **F**3 11 13 15 18 19 28 29 30 31 34 35 39 40 45 46 51 57 59 62 63 64 65 70 74 75 76 78 79 81 83 85 93 97 107 108 110 111 114 117 118 119 127 129 130 132 133 135 145 146 147 148 **P**8
S MaineHealth, Portland, ME
Primary Contact: Mark A. Biscone, Chief Executive Officer
COO: Dan Bennett, Director Operations
CFO: Linda Drinkwater, Chief Financial Officer
CMO: Kent Clark, M.D., Chief Medical Affairs and Quality
CIO: David Felton, Manager Information Systems
CHR: Karen Littlefield, Director Human Resources
CNO: Paula Delahanty, Regional Chief Nursing Officer
Web address: www.wcgh.org
Control: Other not–for–profit (including NFP Corporation) **Service:** General Medical and Surgical

Staffed Beds: 25 **Admissions:** 1437 **Census:** 15 **Outpatient Visits:** 142271 **Births:** 148 **Total Expense ($000):** 77648 **Payroll Expense ($000):** 38102 **Personnel:** 521

BIDDEFORD—York County

☒ **SOUTHERN MAINE HEALTH CARE – BIDDEFORD MEDICAL CENTER (200019)**, One Medical Center Drive, Zip 04005–9496, Mailing Address: P.O. Box 626, Zip 04005–0626; tel. 207/283–7000, (Includes SOUTHERN MAINE HEALTH CARE – BIDDEFORD MEDICAL CENTER, One Medical Center Drive, Mailing Address: P.O. Box 626, Zip 04005–0626; tel. 207/283–7000; Edward J. McGeachey, President and Chief Executive Officer), (Nonreporting) **A**1 2 10
Primary Contact: Edward J. McGeachey, President and Chief Executive Officer
COO: Patricia Aprile, Chief Operating Officer
CFO: Norman Belair, Senior Vice President and Chief Financial Officer
CMO: Michael Albaum, M.D., Senior Vice President and Chief Medical Officer
CIO: Ralph Johnson, Chief Information Officer
CHR: Yvonne McAllister, Senior Director Human Resources
CNO: Joanna Salamone, Senior Vice President Clinical Services and Chief Nursing Officer
Web address: www.smhc.org
Control: Other not–for–profit (including NFP Corporation) **Service:** General Medical and Surgical

Staffed Beds: 246

BLUE HILL—Hancock County

★ **BLUE HILL MEMORIAL HOSPITAL (201300)**, 57 Water Street, Zip 04614–5231; tel. 207/374–3400 **A**10 18 **F**8 15 18 28 29 31 32 34 35 40 41 43 44 45 50 51 57 59 64 65 66 75 78 79 80 81 82 85 86 87 91 93 96 97 107 110 119 130 132 133 135 146 147 148 **S** Eastern Maine Healthcare Systems, Brewer, ME
Primary Contact: John Ronan, President and Chief Executive Officer
CFO: Wendy Jones, Interim Chief Financial Officer
CHR: David Wheaton, Director Human Resources
CNO: Kathy Lirakis, R.N., Chief Nursing Officer
Web address: www.bhmh.org
Control: Other not–for–profit (including NFP Corporation) **Service:** General Medical and Surgical

Staffed Beds: 23 **Admissions:** 751 **Census:** 11 **Outpatient Visits:** 174763 **Births:** 0 **Total Expense ($000):** 37030 **Payroll Expense ($000):** 16334 **Personnel:** 277

BRIDGTON—Cumberland County

★ **BRIDGTON HOSPITAL (201310)**, 10 Hospital Drive, Zip 04009–1148; tel. 207/647–6000 **A**3 10 18 **F**3 7 8 11 13 15 18 20 29 30 31 34 35 40 43 44 45 50 57 59 64 65 67 68 75 76 77 78 79 80 81 85 87 90 91 93 94 96 97 107 108 110 114 119 127 130 131 132 133 135 143 144 146 148 **P**5 8
S Central Maine Healthcare, Lewiston, ME
Primary Contact: R. David Frum, President
COO: John A. Ludwig, R.N., Vice President Operations
CFO: Philip Morissette, Chief Financial Officer
CMO: Alan Verrill, M.D., President Medical Staff
CHR: Kirk Miklavic, Director Human Resources
Web address: www.bridgtonhospital.org
Control: Other not–for–profit (including NFP Corporation) **Service:** General Medical and Surgical

Staffed Beds: 25 **Admissions:** 1034 **Census:** 13 **Outpatient Visits:** 96083 **Births:** 132 **Total Expense ($000):** 46354 **Payroll Expense ($000):** 18975 **Personnel:** 285

BRUNSWICK—Cumberland County

☒ **MID COAST HOSPITAL (200021)**, 123 Medical Center Drive, Zip 04011–2652; tel. 207/373–6000 **A**1 2 5 10 **F**3 5 11 12 13 15 18 20 28 29 30 31 32 34 35 36 40 41 44 45 46 47 48 51 53 54 57 58 59 61 64 66 68 70 74 75 76 77 78 79 81 82 84 85 86 87 89 92 93 97 98 103 105 107 108 110 111 115 118 119 129 130 131 132 134 135 144 146 147 148 **P**6
Primary Contact: Lois N. Skillings, R.N., MSN, President and Chief Executive Officer
COO: Philip A. Ortolani, Vice President Operations
CFO: Robert N. McCue, Vice President Finance
CMO: Scott Mills, M.D., Vice President Medical Staff Administration and Chief Medical Officer
CIO: Gale Stoy, Manager Information Systems
CHR: Coleen M. Farrell, Vice President Human Resources
CNO: Deborah MacLeod, MS, Vice President Nursing and Patient Care Services
Web address: www.midcoasthealth.com
Control: Other not–for–profit (including NFP Corporation) **Service:** General Medical and Surgical

Staffed Beds: 93 **Admissions:** 4653 **Census:** 56 **Outpatient Visits:** 204069 **Births:** 564 **Total Expense ($000):** 149627 **Payroll Expense ($000):** 70217 **Personnel:** 1052

CALAIS—Washington County

★ **CALAIS REGIONAL HOSPITAL (201305)**, 24 Hospital Lane, Zip 04619–1398; tel. 207/454–7521 **A**10 18 **F**3 8 11 13 15 28 29 31 32 34 35 36 40 41 42 45 46 50 57 59 62 63 64 65 68 76 77 79 80 81 85 87 90 93 97 107 108 110 111 114 119 127 128 129 130 132 133 146 147 148 **S** QHR, Brentwood, TN
Primary Contact: Rodney Boula, Chief Executive Officer
CFO: Nancy Glidden, Chief Financial Officer
CMO: David Feiner, M.D., Chief Staff
CIO: Dee Dee Travis, Director Community Relations
CHR: Kristi K. Saunders, Director and Compliance Officer
CNO: Erika Marshall, Interim Chief Nursing Officer
Web address: www.calaishospital.com
Control: Other not–for–profit (including NFP Corporation) **Service:** General Medical and Surgical

Staffed Beds: 25 **Admissions:** 1159 **Census:** 14 **Outpatient Visits:** 40216 **Births:** 71 **Total Expense ($000):** 36235 **Payroll Expense ($000):** 20975 **Personnel:** 247

CARIBOU—Aroostook County

☒ **CARY MEDICAL CENTER (200031)**, 163 Van Buren Road, Suite 1, Zip 04736–3567; tel. 207/498–3111, (Total facility includes 9 beds in nursing home–type unit) **A**1 10 **F**3 8 11 13 15 28 29 31 32 34 35 36 38 40 43 44 51 53 54 56 57 59 61 64 67 68 70 75 76 77 78 79 81 82 84 85 86 87 89 90 93 97 107 108 111 115 118 119 121 130 131 132 135 144 146 147 148 **S** QHR, Brentwood, TN
Primary Contact: Kris A. Doody, R.N., Chief Executive Officer
COO: Shawn Anderson, Chief Operating Officer
CFO: Galen Dickinson, Chief Financial Officer
CMO: Regen Gallagher, M.D., Chief Medical Officer
CIO: Dave Silsbee, Chief Information Officer
CHR: Paula A. Parent, Chief Nursing Officer and Director of Human Resources
CNO: Paula A. Parent, Chief Nursing Officer
Web address: www.carymedicalcenter.org
Control: City–Government, nonfederal **Service:** General Medical and Surgical

Staffed Beds: 49 **Admissions:** 1902 **Census:** 31 **Outpatient Visits:** 74298 **Births:** 230 **Total Expense ($000):** 52808 **Payroll Expense ($000):** 21083 **Personnel:** 417

DAMARISCOTTA—Lincoln County

★ **LINCOLNHEALTH (201302)**, 35 Miles Street, Zip 04543–4047; tel. 207/563–1234, (Includes LINCOLNHEALTH MILES CAMPUS, 35 Miles Street, tel. 207/563–1234; James W. Donovan, President and Chief Executive Officer; LINCOLNHEALTH ST. ANDREWS CAMPUS, 6 St. Andrews Lane, Boothbay Harbor, Zip 04538–1732, Mailing Address: P.O. Box 417, Zip 04538–0417; tel. 207/633–2121), (Total facility includes 54 beds in nursing home–type unit) **A**10 18 **F**3 11 13 15 29 30 32 34 35 40 43 44 45 50 57 59 64 65 67 70 75 76 79 81 85 86 87 93 96 97 107 108 110 111 114 115 118 119 127 128 130 132 133 135 144 146 147 148 **P**6 **S** MaineHealth, Portland, ME
Primary Contact: James W. Donovan, President and Chief Executive Officer
COO: Cynthia Wade, RN, BSN, R.N., Executive Vice President and Chief Operating Officer
CFO: Wayne Printy, Chief Financial Officer and Senior Vice President Finance
CMO: Mark Fourre, Senior Vice President and Chief Medical Officer
CIO: David Felton, Regional Chief Information Officer
CHR: Thomas R. Girard, Vice President Human Resources
CNO: Christine Anderson, Chief Nursing Officer and Vice President of Patient Care Services
Web address: www.lchcare.org
Control: Other not–for–profit (including NFP Corporation) **Service:** General Medical and Surgical

Staffed Beds: 79 **Admissions:** 1845 **Census:** 61 **Outpatient Visits:** 103370 **Births:** 115 **Total Expense ($000):** 71637 **Payroll Expense ($000):** 21956 **Personnel:** 456

Many Facility Codes have changed. Please refer to the AHA Guide Code Chart.
© 2016 AHA Guide

DOVER–FOXCROFT—Piscataquis County

★ **MAYO REGIONAL HOSPITAL (201309)**, 897 West Main Street,
Zip 04426–1099; tel. 207/564–8401 **A**10 18 **F**3 5 7 8 11 13 15 28 29 30 31
34 35 38 40 45 50 57 59 64 65 70 71 75 76 77 78 79 81 85 86 87 93 96
97 99 104 107 110 111 114 119 127 128 129 130 132 133 135 146
147 148
Primary Contact: Marie E. Vienneau, FACHE, President and Chief Executive Officer
CFO: Nancy Glidden, Chief Financial Officer and Vice President Finance
CMO: Challa Reddy, M.D., President Medical Staff
CHR: James R. Godley, Vice President of Human Resources
CNO: Denise Scuderi, Vice President Patient Care Services
Web address: www.mayohospital.com
Control: Hospital district or authority, Government, nonfederal **Service:** General
Medical and Surgical

Staffed Beds: 25 **Admissions:** 1171 **Census:** 11 **Outpatient Visits:** 123729
Births: 90 **Total Expense ($000):** 48036 **Payroll Expense ($000):** 24724
Personnel: 420

ELLSWORTH—Hancock County

⊞ **MAINE COAST MEMORIAL HOSPITAL (200050)**, 50 Union Street,
Zip 04605–1599; tel. 207/664–5311, (Nonreporting) **A**1 10 **S** Eastern Maine
Healthcare Systems, Brewer, ME
Primary Contact: Charles D. Therrien, President and Chief Executive Officer
CFO: Chris Frauenhofer, Chief Financial Officer
CMO: Sheena Whittaker, M.D., Chief Medical Officer
CIO: Scott Burtchell, Director Information Systems
CHR: Noah Lundy, Director of Human Resources
CNO: Ardelle Bigos, R.N., Chief Nursing Officer and Vice President Patient Care
Services
Web address: www.mainehospital.org
Control: Other not–for–profit (including NFP Corporation) **Service:** General
Medical and Surgical

Staffed Beds: 48

FARMINGTON—Franklin County

⊞ **FRANKLIN MEMORIAL HOSPITAL (200037)**, 111 Franklin Health Commons,
Zip 04938–6144; tel. 207/778–6031 **A**1 5 10 20 **F**3 5 7 8 11 13 15 28 29 30
31 32 34 35 36 40 41 45 46 50 51 54 56 59 61 64 65 66 70 75 76 77 78
79 81 82 83 84 85 86 87 89 93 94 97 99 104 107 108 110 111 115 118
119 129 130 131 132 135 146 147 148
Primary Contact: Timothy A. Churchill, Interim Chief Executive Officer
COO: Gerald Cayer, Executive Vice President and Chief Operating Officer
CFO: Wayne Bennett, Chief Financial Officer
CMO: Michael Rowland, M.D., Vice President Medical Affairs
CIO: Ralph Johnson, Chief Information Officer
CHR: Joline Hart, Vice President Human Resources
Web address: www.fchn.org
Control: Other not–for–profit (including NFP Corporation) **Service:** General
Medical and Surgical

Staffed Beds: 48 **Admissions:** 2406 **Census:** 24

FORT FAIRFIELD—Aroostook County

COMMUNITY GENERAL HEALTH CENTER See The Aroostook Medical Center,
Presque Isle

FORT KENT—Aroostook County

⊞ **NORTHERN MAINE MEDICAL CENTER (200052)**, 194 East Main Street,
Zip 04743–1497; tel. 207/834–3155, (Total facility includes 45 beds in nursing
home–type unit) **A**1 10 20 **F**13 15 29 31 34 40 45 54 57 59 62 64 67 68 70
75 76 77 78 79 81 82 86 87 89 98 99 100 101 102 103 104 107 108 111
115 119 127 128 130 131 132 133 135 146 147 148 **P**6
Primary Contact: Peter Sirois, Chief Executive Officer
CFO: Cindy Daigle, Chief Financial Officer
CMO: Michael Sullivan, M.D., Chief Medical Officer
CIO: Adam Landry, Coordinator Computer Systems
CHR: Robin Damboise, Director Human Resources
CNO: Alain Bois, R.N., Director of Nursing
Web address: www.nmmc.org
Control: Other not–for–profit (including NFP Corporation) **Service:** General
Medical and Surgical

Staffed Beds: 81 **Admissions:** 1449 **Census:** 59 **Outpatient Visits:** 50347
Births: 54 **Total Expense ($000):** 46739 **Payroll Expense ($000):** 25124
Personnel: 416

GREENVILLE—Piscataquis County

★ **CHARLES A. DEAN MEMORIAL HOSPITAL (201301)**, 364 Pritham Avenue,
Zip 04441–1395, Mailing Address: P.O. Box 1129, Zip 04441–1129;
tel. 207/695–5200 **A**10 18 **F**1 2 3 7 8 15 18 28 29 30 32 34 35 36 38 40 44
45 46 50 52 53 55 56 57 59 63 64 65 66 67 68 75 77 78 79 81 82 83 84
85 86 87 90 93 97 101 102 103 104 107 110 119 124 127 128 130 131
132 133 135 143 144 145 146 147 148 **P**4 **S** Eastern Maine Healthcare
Systems, Brewer, ME
Primary Contact: Geno Murray, President and Chief Executive Officer
CFO: Edward Olivier, Chief Financial Officer
CMO: Darin Peck, M.D., Chief of Staff
Web address: www.cadean.org
Control: State–Government, nonfederal **Service:** General Medical and Surgical

Staffed Beds: 23 **Admissions:** 3994 **Census:** 13 **Outpatient Visits:** 1191
Births: 0 **Total Expense ($000):** 15159 **Payroll Expense ($000):** 7987

HOULTON—Aroostook County

★ **HOULTON REGIONAL HOSPITAL (201308)**, 20 Hartford Street,
Zip 04730–1891; tel. 207/532–9471 **A**1 3 4 11 13 15 16 17 28 29
30 34 40 43 45 46 50 59 65 67 70 72 73 75 76 79 80 81 83 84 85 86 87
88 89 90 93 97 98 107 108 110 111 114 118 119 127 128 130 132 133
135 146 148
Primary Contact: Thomas J. Moakler, Chief Executive Officer
CHR: Vicky Moody, Director Human Resources
Web address: www.houlton.net/hrh
Control: Other not–for–profit (including NFP Corporation) **Service:** General
Medical and Surgical

Staffed Beds: 25 **Admissions:** 1227 **Census:** 19 **Outpatient Visits:** 96180
Births: 132 **Total Expense ($000):** 45820 **Payroll Expense ($000):** 20359
Personnel: 345

LEWISTON—Androscoggin County

⊞ △ **CENTRAL MAINE MEDICAL CENTER (200024)**, 300 Main Street,
Zip 04240–7027; tel. 207/795–0111 **A**1 2 3 5 7 10 13 **F**3 11 12 13 15 18 19
20 22 24 26 28 29 30 31 32 34 35 36 40 41 43 44 45 46 47 48 49 50 51
52 53 54 55 56 57 58 59 61 64 65 66 67 68 70 71 73 74 75 76 77 78 79
81 82 84 85 86 87 89 90 91 92 93 97 100 101 102 104 107 108 110 114
115 118 119 120 121 123 124 129 130 131 132 135 143 144 146 147 148
P5 8 **S** Central Maine Healthcare, Lewiston, ME
Primary Contact: Tina Legere, President
CFO: Philip Morissette, Chief Financial Officer
CMO: David Lauver, M.D., Chief Division Hospital Based Care
CIO: Denis Tanguay, Chief Information Officer
CHR: Kirk Miklavic, Director, Human Resources
CNO: Sharron Chalke, R.N., VP, Nursing
Web address: www.cmmc.org
Control: Other not–for–profit (including NFP Corporation) **Service:** General
Medical and Surgical

Staffed Beds: 190 **Admissions:** 10593 **Census:** 128 **Outpatient Visits:**
708804 **Births:** 700 **Total Expense ($000):** 351060 **Payroll Expense
($000):** 149597 **Personnel:** 1871

⊞ **ST. MARY'S REGIONAL MEDICAL CENTER (200034)**, 318 Sabattus Street,
Zip 04240–5553, Mailing Address: P.O. Box 291, Zip 04243–0291;
tel. 207/777–8100, (Total facility includes 210 beds in nursing home–type unit)
A1 2 5 10 **F**3 4 5 7 12 13 15 17 18 20 22 28 29 30 31 34 35 36 37 38 39
40 44 45 49 50 54 56 57 59 64 65 66 68 70 74 75 77 78 79 80 81 82
84 85 86 87 89 93 97 98 99 100 101 102 103 104 105 107 108 110 111
114 115 116 117 118 119 127 128 129 130 131 132 134 135 143 144 146
147 148 **P**1 6 **S** Covenant Health, Tewksbury, MA
Primary Contact: Christopher A. Chekouras, President and Chief Executive Officer
COO: Susan Keiler, Chief Operating Officer
CFO: Carolyn Kasabian, Chief Financial Officer
CMO: Ira Shapiro, M.D., Chief Medical Officer
CIO: Rene Dumont, Vice President Strategic Growth
CHR: Nicole Morin–Scribner, Director Human Resources
CNO: Karen Clark, Vice President Patient Care Services
Web address: www.stmarysmaine.com
Control: Other not–for–profit (including NFP Corporation) **Service:** General
Medical and Surgical

Staffed Beds: 380 **Admissions:** 5825 **Census:** 112 **Outpatient Visits:**
302123 **Births:** 570 **Total Expense ($000):** 150911 **Payroll Expense
($000):** 72818 **Personnel:** 1331

Hospital, Medicare Provider Number, Address, Telephone, Approval, Facility, and Physician Codes, Health Care System

★ American Hospital Association (AHA) membership   ○ Healthcare Facilities Accreditation Program   ⇑ Center for Improvement in Healthcare Quality Accreditation
☐ The Joint Commission accreditation   ◇ DNV Healthcare Inc. accreditation   △ Commission on Accreditation of Rehabilitation Facilities (CARF) accreditation

ME

LINCOLN—Penobscot County

★ **PENOBSCOT VALLEY HOSPITAL (201303)**, 7 Transalpine Road,
Zip 04457–4222, Mailing Address: P.O. Box 368, Zip 04457–0368;
tel. 207/794–3321, (Nonreporting) **A**10 18 **S** QHR, Brentwood, TN
Primary Contact: Gary R. Poquette, FACHE, Chief Executive Officer
CFO: Ann Marie Rush, Chief Financial Officer
CHR: Sarah Loman, Director Human Resources
Web address: www.pvhme.org
Control: Other not–for–profit (including NFP Corporation) **Service:** General
Medical and Surgical

Staffed Beds: 25

MACHIAS—Washington County

★ **DOWN EAST COMMUNITY HOSPITAL (201311)**, 11 Hospital Drive,
Zip 04654–3325; tel. 207/255–3356, (Total facility includes 28 beds in nursing
home–type unit) **A**10 18 **F**3 11 15 28 29 34 35 40 43 57 59 64 65 75 76 77
79 81 82 83 84 85 89 93 97 107 108 110 111 114 119 127 128 129 130
133 146 147 148
Primary Contact: Dennis Welsh, Chief Executive Officer
COO: Steve Lail, Vice President Operations and Chief Operating Officer
CFO: Lynnette Parr, Chief Financial Officer
CMO: Aziz Massaad, M.D., Medical Staff President
CHR: Ernestine O. Reisman, Vice President Human Resources
CNO: Kevin McEwan, Vice President of Patient Care Service and Chief Nursing
Officer
Web address: www.dech.org
Control: Other not–for–profit (including NFP Corporation) **Service:** General
Medical and Surgical

Staffed Beds: 53 **Admissions:** 907 **Census:** 33 **Outpatient Visits:** 29710
Births: 138 **Total Expense ($000):** 38808 **Payroll Expense ($000):** 19074
Personnel: 264

MARS HILL—Aroostook County

AROOSTOOK HEALTH CENTER See The Aroostook Medical Center, Presque
Isle

MILLINOCKET—Penobscot County

★ **MILLINOCKET REGIONAL HOSPITAL (201307)**, 200 Somerset Street,
Zip 04462–1298; tel. 207/723–5161 **A**10 18 **F**3 8 11 15 28 29 31 34 35 40
41 45 50 53 56 57 59 64 65 68 75 77 78 79 80 81 85 87 93 97 107 108
110 111 118 119 127 128 130 131 132 133 135
Primary Contact: Robert Peterson, Chief Executive Officer
CFO: Catherine LeMay, Vice President Finance
CMO: Daniel Herbert, M.D., Medical Administrative Officer
CHR: Lisa Arsenault, Vice President Human Resources and Compliance
CNO: Jason Fugleberg, R.N., Vice President Patient Services and Chief Nursing
Officer
Web address: www.mrhme.org
Control: Other not–for–profit (including NFP Corporation) **Service:** General
Medical and Surgical

Staffed Beds: 25 **Admissions:** 730 **Census:** 9 **Outpatient Visits:** 26409
Births: 0 **Total Expense ($000):** 26152 **Payroll Expense ($000):** 13029
Personnel: 204

NORWAY—Oxford County

★ **STEPHENS MEMORIAL HOSPITAL (201315)**, 181 Main Street,
Zip 04268–5664; tel. 207/743–5933 **A**5 10 18 **F**3 7 13 15 28 29 30 31 34
35 40 43 45 57 59 61 64 65 68 75 76 78 79 80 81 85 87 89 93 96 97 102
107 108 110 111 115 119 127 130 132 133 146 148 **S** MaineHealth, Portland, ME
Primary Contact: Timothy A. Churchill, President
CMO: James Eshleman, D.O., President Medical Staff
CHR: Roberta Metivier, Vice President Human Resources and Administrator,
Western Main Nursing Home
Web address: www.wmhcc.com
Control: Other not–for–profit (including NFP Corporation) **Service:** General
Medical and Surgical

Staffed Beds: 25 **Admissions:** 1334 **Census:** 12 **Outpatient Visits:** 104937
Births: 143 **Total Expense ($000):** 56431 **Payroll Expense ($000):** 24149
Personnel: 378

PITTSFIELD—Somerset County

⊠ **SEBASTICOOK VALLEY HEALTH (201313)**, 447 North Main Street,
Zip 04967–3707; tel. 207/487–4000 **A**1 10 18 **F**3 7 11 15 18 28 29 30 32
34 35 40 45 46 50 51 57 59 64 65 70 75 77 78 79 81 87 93 96 97 104
107 108 111 119 127 129 130 132 133 135 143 146 147 148 **P**6 **S** Eastern
Maine Healthcare Systems, Brewer, ME
Primary Contact: Terri Vieira, President and Chief Executive Officer
COO: Michael Peterson, FACHE, Chief Operating Officer
CFO: Randal Clark, Vice President Finance
CMO: Robert Schlager, M.D., Chief Medical Officer
CIO: Michael Peterson, FACHE, Chief Operating Officer
CHR: Tammy Hatch, Manager
Web address: www.sebasticookvalleyhealth.org
Control: Other not–for–profit (including NFP Corporation) **Service:** General
Medical and Surgical

Staffed Beds: 25 **Admissions:** 813 **Census:** 12 **Outpatient Visits:** 59541
Births: 0 **Total Expense ($000):** 36361 **Payroll Expense ($000):** 16784
Personnel: 293

PORTLAND—Cumberland County

⊠ **MAINE MEDICAL CENTER (200009)**, 22 Bramhall Street, Zip 04102–3175;
tel. 207/662–0111, (Includes BARBARA BUSH CHILDREN'S HOSPITAL, 22
Bramhall Street, Zip 04102–3134; tel. 207/662–0111; Richard W. Petersen,
President and Chief Executive Officer; MAINE MEDICAL CENTER, BRIGHTON
CAMPUS, 335 Brighton Avenue, Zip 04102–9735, Mailing Address: P.O. Box
9735, Zip 04102–9735; tel. 207/879–8000; Richard W. Petersen, President and
Chief Executive Officer) **A**1 2 3 5 8 10 **F**3 5 6 8 11 12 13 15 17 18 19 20 21
22 23 24 25 26 27 28 29 30 31 32 34 35 36 38 40 41 42 43 44 45 46 47
48 49 51 54 55 56 57 58 59 60 61 64 65 66 68 70 72 73 74 75 76 78 79
80 81 82 84 85 86 87 88 89 91 92 97 98 99 100 101 102 103 104 105 107
108 110 111 115 116 117 118 119 120 121 123 124 126 129 130 131 132
134 135 138 141 144 146 147 148 **P**6 8 **S** MaineHealth, Portland, ME
Primary Contact: Richard W. Petersen, President and Chief Executive Officer
COO: Jeff Sanders, Senior Vice President, Chief Operating Officer
CFO: Lou Inzana, Senior Vice President and Chief Financial Officer
CMO: Joel Botler, M.D., Chief Medical Officer
CHR: Judith M. West, Senior Vice President Human Resources and Chief Human
Resources Officer
CNO: Marjorie Wiggins, Senior Vice President, Chief Nursing Officer
Web address: www.mmc.org
Control: Other not–for–profit (including NFP Corporation) **Service:** General
Medical and Surgical

Staffed Beds: 637 **Admissions:** 27915 **Census:** 400 **Outpatient Visits:**
554309 **Births:** 1831 **Total Expense ($000):** 1002984 **Payroll Expense
($000):** 413078 **Personnel:** 6127

⊠ **MERCY HOSPITAL OF PORTLAND (200008)**, 144 State Street,
Zip 04101–3795; tel. 207/879–3000 **A**1 2 3 10 **F**3 4 5 11 15 18 20 26 29
30 31 33 35 36 40 44 45 48 49 50 51 54 55 56 57 58 59 61 64 68 70 72
74 75 76 78 79 81 82 84 86 87 93 96 97 100 102 107 108 110 111 114
115 117 119 130 132 135 143 144 146 147 148 **P**6 **S** Eastern Maine
Healthcare Systems, Brewer, ME
Primary Contact: Jay Eckersley, Interim Chief Executive Officer
CFO: Michael Hachey, Senior Vice President and Chief Financial Officer
CMO: Scott Rusk, M.D., Vice President Medical Administration
CIO: Craig Dreher, Chief Information Officer
CHR: Elizabeth B. Christensen, Director Human Resources
CNO: Bette Neville, R.N., Vice President and Chief Nursing Officer
Web address: www.mercyhospital.org
Control: Other not–for–profit (including NFP Corporation) **Service:** General
Medical and Surgical

Staffed Beds: 121 **Admissions:** 6375 **Census:** 59 **Outpatient Visits:** 437585
Births: 834 **Total Expense ($000):** 239788 **Payroll Expense ($000):**
101594 **Personnel:** 1166

⊠ **NEW ENGLAND REHABILITATION HOSPITAL OF PORTLAND (203025)**, 335
Brighton Avenue, Zip 04102–2363; tel. 207/775–4000 **A**1 3 10 **F**29 34 35 75
79 82 90 93 95 96 131 132 135 146 **S** HEALTHSOUTH Corporation,
Birmingham, AL
Primary Contact: Jeanine Chesley, Chief Executive Officer
CFO: James Paladino, Controller
CMO: Thomas Morrione, Medical Director
CHR: Mary Cote, Director Human Resources
CNO: Elizabeth Glidden, Chief Nursing Officer
Web address: www.nerhp.org
Control: Partnership, Investor–owned, for–profit **Service:** Rehabilitation

Staffed Beds: 90 **Admissions:** 1828 **Census:** 71 **Outpatient Visits:** 11206
Births: 0 **Total Expense ($000):** 23804 **Payroll Expense ($000):** 14036
Personnel: 219

Many Facility Codes have changed. Please refer to the AHA Guide Code Chart. © 2016 AHA Guide

PRESQUE ISLE—Aroostook County

☒ **THE AROOSTOOK MEDICAL CENTER (200018)**, 140 Academy Street, Zip 04769–3171, Mailing Address: P.O. Box 151, Zip 04769–0151; tel. 207/768–4000, (Includes AROOSTOOK HEALTH CENTER, 15 Highland Avenue, Mars Hill, Zip 04758; tel. 207/768–4900; ARTHUR R. GOULD MEMORIAL HOSPITAL, 140 Academy Street, Zip 04769, Mailing Address: P.O. Box 151, Zip 04769; tel. 207/768–4000; COMMUNITY GENERAL HEALTH CENTER, 3 Green Street, Fort Fairfield, Zip 04742; tel. 207/768–4700), (Total facility includes 64 beds in nursing home–type unit) **A**1 10 **F**3 7 8 12 13 15 18 20 28 29 30 31 32 34 35 36 38 39 40 43 45 46 51 52 53 54 56 57 59 60 61 64 65 67 68 69 70 74 75 76 77 78 79 80 81 82 84 85 86 87 89 90 91 93 96 97 99 104 107 108 110 114 115 118 119 121 123 128 129 130 131 132 134 135 143 146 147 148 **P**6 **S** Eastern Maine Healthcare Systems, Brewer, ME
Primary Contact: Glenda E. Dwyer, Interim President
COO: Jay Reynolds, M.D., Chief Medical Officer and Chief Clinical Officer
CFO: C. Bruce Sandstrom, Vice President and Chief Financial Officer
CMO: Jay Reynolds, M.D., Chief Medical Officer and Chief Clinical Officer
CIO: Kyle Johnson, Chief Information Officer
CHR: Joseph Siddiqui, Vice President Human Resources
CNO: Roland Eugene Joy, Jr., Vice President and Chief Nursing Officer
Web address: www.tamc.org
Control: Other not–for–profit (including NFP Corporation) **Service:** General Medical and Surgical

Staffed Beds: 114 **Admissions:** 2062 **Census:** 84 **Outpatient Visits:** 193496 **Births:** 202 **Total Expense ($000):** 116049 **Payroll Expense ($000):** 59067 **Personnel:** 840

ROCKPORT—Knox County

☐ **PEN BAY MEDICAL CENTER (200063)**, 6 Glen Cove Drive, Zip 04856–4240; tel. 207/921–8000, (Total facility includes 84 beds in nursing home–type unit) **A**1 2 5 10 20 **F**3 4 5 6 13 15 17 18 28 29 30 31 32 34 35 40 43 45 51 58 59 61 64 65 67 70 74 75 76 77 78 79 81 82 83 85 86 87 89 93 97 98 100 107 108 110 111 114 119 128 129 130 131 132 134 135 144 146 147 148 **P**1 **S** MaineHealth, Portland, ME
Primary Contact: Mark A. Biscone, Chief Executive Officer
COO: Eric Waters, Vice President Operations
CFO: Maura Kelly, Vice President Fiscal Services
CMO: Dana L. Goldsmith, M.D., Vice President Medical Affairs
CIO: Brooks Betts, Director Information Systems and Chief Information Officer
CHR: Thomas R. Girard, Vice President Human Resources
CNO: Paula Delahanty, Regional Chief Nursing Officer
Web address: www.penbayhealthcare.org
Control: Other not–for–profit (including NFP Corporation) **Service:** General Medical and Surgical

Staffed Beds: 165 **Admissions:** 5774 **Census:** 167 **Outpatient Visits:** 179111 **Births:** 320 **Total Expense ($000):** 126771 **Payroll Expense ($000):** 62036 **Personnel:** 894

PENOBSCOT BAY MEDICAL CENTER See Pen Bay Medical Center

RUMFORD—Oxford County

★ **RUMFORD HOSPITAL (201306)**, 420 Franklin Street, Zip 04276–2145; tel. 207/369–1000 **A**10 18 **F**3 8 11 13 15 18 28 29 30 31 34 35 40 43 44 45 50 57 59 64 65 67 68 75 76 77 78 79 80 81 85 87 89 90 91 93 94 96 97 101 114 119 127 128 130 132 133 135 143 144 146 148 **P**5 8 **S** Central Maine Healthcare, Lewiston, ME
Primary Contact: R. David Frum, President
CNO: Becky Hall, R.N., Director Nursing
Web address: www.rumfordhospital.org
Control: Other not–for–profit (including NFP Corporation) **Service:** General Medical and Surgical

Staffed Beds: 21 **Admissions:** 1104 **Census:** 13 **Outpatient Visits:** 73324 **Births:** 88 **Total Expense ($000):** 37951 **Payroll Expense ($000):** 15481 **Personnel:** 243

SKOWHEGAN—Somerset County

★ **REDINGTON–FAIRVIEW GENERAL HOSPITAL (201314)**, 46 Fairview Avenue, Zip 04976, Mailing Address: P.O. Box 468, Zip 04976–0468; tel. 207/474–5121 **A**5 10 18 **F**3 7 11 13 15 18 28 29 30 31 34 35 40 45 47 50 53 56 57 59 65 68 70 74 75 76 77 78 79 81 82 84 85 91 92 93 97 107 108 110 114 115 118 119 130 131 132 133 134 135 146 147 **P**6
Primary Contact: Richard Willett, Chief Executive Officer
CFO: Elmer H. Doucette, Chief Financial Officer
CMO: Michael Lambke, M.D., Medical Director
CHR: Lisa G. Landry, Human Resources Director
CNO: Sherry L. Rogers, MS, Chief Nursing Officer
Web address: www.rfgh.net
Control: Other not–for–profit (including NFP Corporation) **Service:** General Medical and Surgical

Staffed Beds: 25 **Admissions:** 1505 **Census:** 13 **Outpatient Visits:** 82104 **Births:** 146 **Total Expense ($000):** 79175 **Payroll Expense ($000):** 39749 **Personnel:** 586

WATERVILLE—Kennebec County

★ ○ **INLAND HOSPITAL (200041)**, 200 Kennedy Memorial Drive, Zip 04901–4595; tel. 207/861–3000 **A**10 11 **F**3 13 15 18 28 29 30 34 35 40 45 46 50 51 56 57 59 64 68 70 74 75 76 77 79 81 82 85 92 93 97 107 108 109 110 111 115 127 129 130 132 146 147 148 **P**6 **S** Eastern Maine Healthcare Systems, Brewer, ME
Primary Contact: John Dalton, President and Chief Executive Officer
COO: Daniel Booth, Vice President Operations and Chief Human Resources Officer
CFO: Dean Bither, Chief Financial Officer
CMO: Michael Palumbo, D.O., Vice President Medical Affairs and Chief Education
CIO: Kevin Dieterich, Director Information Services
CHR: Daniel Booth, Vice President Operations
Web address: www.inlandhospital.org
Control: Other not–for–profit (including NFP Corporation) **Service:** General Medical and Surgical

Staffed Beds: 29 **Admissions:** 1250 **Census:** 13 **Outpatient Visits:** 14549 **Births:** 357 **Total Expense ($000):** 71201 **Payroll Expense ($000):** 30255 **Personnel:** 514

WESTBROOK—Cumberland County

☒ **SPRING HARBOR HOSPITAL (204005)**, 123 Andover Road, Zip 04092–3850; tel. 207/761–2200, (Nonreporting) **A**1 10 **S** MaineHealth, Portland, ME
Primary Contact: Mary Jane Krebs, FACHE, President
CFO: Michael Abbatiello, Chief Financial Officer
CMO: Girard Robinson, M.D., Senior Vice President Medical and Clinical Affairs
CIO: Susan Moulton, Director Health Information Management
CHR: Timothy McNulty, Director Human Resources
Web address: www.springharbor.org
Control: Other not–for–profit (including NFP Corporation) **Service:** Psychiatric

Staffed Beds: 88

YORK—York County

★ **YORK HOSPITAL (200020)**, 15 Hospital Drive, Zip 03909–1099; tel. 207/363–4321 **A**2 10 **F**3 5 8 13 15 17 18 20 22 26 28 29 30 31 32 33 34 35 36 37 40 42 43 45 48 49 50 51 53 54 55 56 57 59 62 64 65 69 70 71 74 75 76 77 78 79 81 85 87 89 91 92 93 96 97 100 103 104 107 108 110 111 112 114 119 126 129 130 132 135 143 144 146 148 **P**6
Primary Contact: Jud Knox, President
CFO: Robin LaBonte, Leader Financial Care
CMO: Lawrence Petrovich, M.D., Chief Medical Officer
CIO: Robin LaBonte, Leader Financial Care
CHR: Olivia Chayer, Director, Human Resources
CNO: Eleanor Milo, Chief Nursing Officer
Web address: www.yorkhospital.com
Control: Other not–for–profit (including NFP Corporation) **Service:** General Medical and Surgical

Staffed Beds: 68 **Admissions:** 3244 **Census:** 34 **Outpatient Visits:** 302446 **Births:** 727 **Personnel:** 1044

Hospital, Medicare Provider Number, Address, Telephone, Approval, Facility, and Physician Codes, Health Care System

★ American Hospital Association (AHA) membership
☐ The Joint Commission accreditation
○ Healthcare Facilities Accreditation Program
◇ DNV Healthcare Inc. accreditation
⇧ Center for Improvement in Healthcare Quality Accreditation
△ Commission on Accreditation of Rehabilitation Facilities (CARF) accreditation

MARYLAND

ANNAPOLIS—Anne Arundel County

☒ **ANNE ARUNDEL MEDICAL CENTER (210023)**, 2001 Medical Parkway, Zip 21401–3019; tel. 443/481–1000, (Total facility includes 40 beds in nursing home–type unit) **A**1 2 3 5 10 **F**3 4 5 6 9 11 12 13 14 15 18 20 22 26 28 29 30 31 32 34 35 36 37 38 39 40 41 44 45 46 49 50 51 53 54 55 56 57 58 59 60 61 63 64 65 66 68 70 71 72 74 75 76 77 78 79 81 82 83 84 85 86 87 89 91 92 93 94 96 97 99 100 101 102 103 105 107 108 110 111 114 115 116 117 118 119 120 121 123 124 126 129 130 131 132 134 135 144 145 146 147 148 **P**1 6 7
Primary Contact: Victoria Bayless, President and Chief Executive Officer
COO: Maulik Joshi, Executive Vice President, Integrated Care Delivery and Chief Operating Officer
CFO: Robert Reilly, Vice President and Chief Financial Officer
CMO: Mitchell B. Schwartz, M.D., Chief Medical Officer
CIO: Barbara Baldwin, Chief Information Officer
CHR: Julie McGovern, Vice President Human Resources
CNO: Barbara S. Jacobs, MSN, Vice President, Nursing and Chief Nursing Officer
Web address: www.aahs.org
Control: Other not–for–profit (including NFP Corporation) **Service:** General Medical and Surgical

Staffed Beds: 454 **Admissions:** 26667 **Census:** 293 **Outpatient Visits:** 491564 **Births:** 5559 **Total Expense ($000):** 504335 **Payroll Expense ($000):** 192665 **Personnel:** 3540

BALTIMORE—Baltimore City County

☒ **BON SECOURS BALTIMORE HEALTH SYSTEM (210013)**, 2000 West Baltimore Street, Zip 21223–1558; tel. 410/362–3000 **A**1 10 **F**3 11 15 18 20 26 29 30 31 40 44 49 58 59 60 64 66 70 78 79 81 84 85 87 98 99 100 101 102 103 104 105 107 108 110 111 115 119 130 143 146 148 **S** Bon Secours Health System, Inc., Marriottsville, MD
Primary Contact: Samuel Lee Ross, M.D., MS, Chief Executive Officer
CFO: Laura Ellison, Chief Financial Officer
CMO: Arsalan Sheikh, Chief of Medicine
CIO: Sanjay Purushotham, Executive Director Information Systems
CHR: Danielle Jorden–Ellis, Director
CNO: Shelly Buck, Chief Nursing Executive and Chief Operating Officer
Web address: www.bonsecoursbaltimore.com
Control: Church–operated, Nongovernment, not–for profit **Service:** General Medical and Surgical

Staffed Beds: 93 **Admissions:** 4336 **Census:** 52 **Births:** 0

FRANKLIN SQUARE HOSPITAL CENTER See MedStar Franklin Square Medical Center

GOOD SAMARITAN HOSPITAL OF MARYLAND See MedStar Good Samaritan Hospital

☒ **GREATER BALTIMORE MEDICAL CENTER (210044)**, 6701 North Charles Street, Zip 21204–6892; tel. 443/849–2000, (Total facility includes 25 beds in nursing home–type unit) **A**1 2 3 5 10 **F**3 8 11 12 13 18 20 22 26 29 30 31 34 35 40 41 44 45 46 47 48 49 50 51 55 56 57 58 59 60 61 63 64 66 68 70 72 73 74 75 76 77 78 79 81 82 83 84 85 86 87 89 92 93 96 97 102 107 108 114 115 119 120 121 123 124 126 128 129 130 132 135 136 142 145 146 147 148 **P**4
Primary Contact: John B. Chessare, M.D., M.P.H., FACHE, President and Chief Executive Officer
COO: Keith R. Poisson, Executive Vice President and Chief Operating Officer
CFO: Eric L. Melchior, Executive Vice President and Chief Financial Officer
CMO: John R. Saunders, M.D., Senior Vice President Medical Affairs and Chief Medical Officer
CHR: Deloris Simpson–Tuggle, Vice President Human Resources and Organizational Development and Chief Human Resources Officer
CNO: Jody Porter, R.N., Senior Vice President Patient Care Services and Chief Nursing Officer
Web address: www.gbmc.org
Control: Other not–for–profit (including NFP Corporation) **Service:** General Medical and Surgical

Staffed Beds: 249 **Admissions:** 15943 **Census:** 163 **Outpatient Visits:** 126311 **Births:** 3924 **Total Expense ($000):** 392457 **Payroll Expense ($000):** 190139 **Personnel:** 3110

HARBOR HOSPITAL See MedStar Harbor Hospital

☒ **JOHNS HOPKINS BAYVIEW MEDICAL CENTER (210029)**, 4940 Eastern Avenue, Zip 21224–2780; tel. 410/550–0100 **A**1 2 3 5 8 10 **F**1 2 3 4 5 6 8 9 11 12 13 15 16 17 18 20 22 26 28 29 30 34 35 36 38 40 41 43 44 45 46 47 48 49 50 51 54 55 56 57 58 59 60 61 64 65 66 68 70 71 72 74 75 76 77 78 79 80 81 82 84 85 86 87 89 90 91 92 93 94 97 98 99 100 101 102 103 104 105 107 110 111 115 117 118 119 120 121 126 129 130 131 132 134 135 141 143 146 147 148 **S** Johns Hopkins Health System, Baltimore, MD
Primary Contact: Richard G. Bennett, M.D., President
COO: Charlie Reuland, Sc.D., Executive Vice President and Chief Operating Officer
CFO: Carl H. Francioli, Vice President Finance
CIO: Sandy Reckert, Director Communications and Public Affairs
CHR: Craig R. Brodian, Vice President Human Resources
Web address: www.hopkinsbayview.org
Control: Other not–for–profit (including NFP Corporation) **Service:** General Medical and Surgical

Staffed Beds: 421 **Admissions:** 19221 **Census:** 321 **Outpatient Visits:** 442797 **Births:** 1326 **Total Expense ($000):** 511116 **Payroll Expense ($000):** 173856 **Personnel:** 3084

☒ △ **JOHNS HOPKINS HOSPITAL (210009)**, 733 North Broadway MRB 104, Zip 21205–1832; tel. 410/955–5000, (Includes JOHNS HOPKINS CHILDREN'S CENTER, 1800 Orleans Street, Zip 21287–0010; tel. 410/955–5000) **A**1 2 3 5 7 8 10 **F**3 5 6 7 8 9 11 13 14 15 16 17 18 19 20 21 22 23 24 25 26 27 28 29 30 31 32 34 35 36 38 39 40 41 43 44 45 46 47 48 49 50 51 52 54 55 56 57 58 59 60 61 63 64 65 66 68 70 72 74 75 76 77 78 79 80 81 82 83 84 85 86 87 88 89 90 92 93 94 96 97 98 99 100 101 102 103 104 105 107 108 110 111 112 114 115 116 117 118 119 120 121 123 124 126 129 130 131 132 134 135 136 137 138 139 140 141 142 143 145 146 147 148 **S** Johns Hopkins Health System, Baltimore, MD
Primary Contact: Redonda G. Miller, M.D., President
COO: Judy A. Reitz, Sc.D., Executive Vice President and Chief Operating Officer
CFO: Ronald J. Werthman, Senior Vice President Finance, Chief Financial Officer and Treasurer
CIO: Stephanie L. Reel, Senior Vice President Information Services
CHR: Bonnie Windsor, Senior Vice President Human Resources
CNO: Deborah Baker, Interim Vice President, Nursing and Patient Care Services
Web address: www.hopkinsmedicine.org
Control: Other not–for–profit (including NFP Corporation) **Service:** General Medical and Surgical

Staffed Beds: 977 **Admissions:** 48459 **Census:** 861 **Outpatient Visits:** 620902 **Births:** 2249 **Total Expense ($000):** 2047447 **Payroll Expense ($000):** 575064 **Personnel:** 9897

☐ △ **KENNEDY KRIEGER INSTITUTE (213301)**, 707 North Broadway, Zip 21205–1890; tel. 443/923–9200, (Nonreporting) **A**1 3 5 7 10
Primary Contact: Gary W. Goldstein, M.D., President and Chief Executive Officer
COO: James M. Anders, Jr., Administrator and Chief Operating Officer
CFO: Michael J. Neuman, Vice President Finance
CMO: Michael V. Johnston, M.D., Chief Medical Officer and Senior Vice President Medical Programs
CIO: Kenneth Davis, Assistant Vice President Information Systems
CHR: Michael Loughran, Vice President Human Resources
Web address: www.kennedykrieger.org
Control: Other not–for–profit (including NFP Corporation) **Service:** Children's other specialty

Staffed Beds: 70

☐ △ **LEVINDALE HEBREW GERIATRIC CENTER AND HOSPITAL (210064)**, 2434 West Belvedere Avenue, Zip 21215–5267; tel. 410/601–2400, (Nonreporting) **A**1 7 10 **S** LifeBridge Health, Baltimore, MD
Primary Contact: Idriz Limaj, Chief Operating Officer and Executive Director
CMO: Susan M. Levy, M.D., Vice President Medical Affairs
CIO: Tressa Springmann, Vice President and Chief Information Officer
CHR: Cheryl T. Boyer, Vice President Human Resources
CNO: Candy Hamner, Vice President and Chief Nursing Officer
Web address: www.sinai–balt.com
Control: Other not–for–profit (including NFP Corporation) **Service:** Long–Term Acute Care hospital

Staffed Beds: 490

✠ **MEDSTAR FRANKLIN SQUARE MEDICAL CENTER (210015)**, 9000 Franklin Square Drive, Zip 21237–3901; tel. 443/777–7000 **A**1 2 3 5 8 10 **F**3 5 11 12 13 14 15 18 20 22 26 28 29 30 31 32 34 35 36 37 38 39 40 41 44 45 46 47 48 49 50 51 55 56 57 58 59 60 61 64 65 66 68 70 71 72 74 75 76 77 78 79 81 82 85 86 87 89 92 93 94 97 98 99 100 101 102 103 104 107 108 109 110 111 115 118 119 126 129 130 131 132 134 135 145 146,147 148 **P**6 **S** MedStar Health, Columbia, MD
Primary Contact: Samuel E. Moskowitz, President
CFO: Robert P. Lally, Jr., Vice President Finance
CMO: Tony Sclama, M.D., Vice President Medical Affairs
CIO: Stephen Mannion, Assistant Vice President Information Systems Customer Service
CHR: Karen Robertson–Keck, Vice President Human Resources
CNO: Lawrence F. Strassner III, Ph.D., Senior Vice President Operations and Chief Nursing Officer
Web address: www.medstarfranklin.org
Control: Other not–for–profit (including NFP Corporation) **Service:** General Medical and Surgical

Staffed Beds: 404 **Admissions:** 21189 **Census:** 255 **Outpatient Visits:** 469285 **Births:** 2969 **Total Expense ($000):** 487703 **Payroll Expense ($000):** 216109 **Personnel:** 2937

✠ △ **MEDSTAR GOOD SAMARITAN HOSPITAL (210056)**, 5601 Loch Raven Boulevard, Zip 21239–2995; tel. 443/444–8000, (Total facility includes 30 beds in nursing home–type unit) **A**1 2 3 5 7 10 **F**3 6 9 11 14 15 17 18 20 26 28 29 30 31 34 35 36 37 38 40 43 44 45 49 50 51 53 55 56 57 58 59 60 61 64 65 66 68 70 74 75 77 78 79 80 81 82 84 85 86 87 90 91 93 96 97 99 100 101 102 103 104 107 108 110 111 114 117 118 119 124 128 129 130 132 135 146 148 **P**6 **S** MedStar Health, Columbia, MD
Primary Contact: Bradley Chambers, President and Chief Executive Officer
CFO: Deana Stout, Vice President Financial Services
Web address: www.goodsam–md.org
Control: Other not–for–profit (including NFP Corporation) **Service:** General Medical and Surgical

Staffed Beds: 305 **Admissions:** 11370 **Census:** 180 **Outpatient Visits:** 291952 **Births:** 0 **Total Expense ($000):** 308230 **Payroll Expense ($000):** 126027 **Personnel:** 1885

✠ **MEDSTAR HARBOR HOSPITAL (210034)**, 3001 South Hanover Street, Zip 21225–1290; tel. 410/350–3200 **A**1 2 3 5 10 **F**3 9 11 13 14 15 18 20 26 29 30 31 34 35 36 40 43 44 45 46 48 49 50 51 53 55 56 57 58 59 60 61 64 65 66 68 70 72 74 75 76 77 78 79 81 82 84 85 86 87 89 92 93 94 97 102 103 107 108 110 111 114 115 118 119 120 121 129 130 131 132 135 146 147 **P**6 **S** MedStar Health, Columbia, MD
Primary Contact: Dennis W. Pullin, FACHE, President
COO: Jill Donaldson, Vice President Operations
CFO: David R. Pitman, Vice President Finance
CMO: Allan Birenberg, Vice President Medical Affairs
CIO: Cynthia Tanebaum, Director Information Services
CHR: Karen Evelius, Director Human Resources
CNO: Lenora Addison, Vice President Patient Care and Nursing
Web address: www.harborhospital.org
Control: Other not–for–profit (including NFP Corporation) **Service:** General Medical and Surgical

Staffed Beds: 150 **Admissions:** 7143 **Census:** 79 **Outpatient Visits:** 175162 **Births:** 1407 **Total Expense ($000):** 196535 **Payroll Expense ($000):** 80300 **Personnel:** 1049

✠ △ **MEDSTAR UNION MEMORIAL HOSPITAL (210024)**, 201 East University Parkway, Zip 21218–2895; tel. 410/554–2000 **A**1 2 3 5 7 10 **F**3 5 8 9 11 14 15 17 18 20 22 24 26 28 29 30 31 34 35 37 38 39 40 41 43 44 45 46 47 48 49 50 51 52 53 54 55 56 57 58 59 60 61 63 64 65 66 68 70 74 75 77 78 79 80 81 82 84 85 86 87 91 92 93 94 96 97 98 100 101 102 103 104 105 107 108 110 111 114 115 118 119 120 121 123 129 130 131 132 135 142 146 **S** MedStar Health, Columbia, MD
Primary Contact: Bradley Chambers, President
COO: Neil MacDonald, Vice President Operations
CFO: Deana Stout, Vice President Finance
CMO: Stuart Bell, M.D., Vice President Medical Affairs
CIO: Janet Decker, Assistant Vice President
CHR: Ashley Handwerk, Director, Human Resources
CNO: Sharon A. Bottcher, R.N., Vice President Patient Care Services
Web address: www.medstarunionmemorial.org
Control: Other not–for–profit (including NFP Corporation) **Service:** General Medical and Surgical

Staffed Beds: 218 **Admissions:** 12059 **Census:** 162 **Outpatient Visits:** 143540 **Births:** 0 **Total Expense ($000):** 432797 **Payroll Expense ($000):** 162830 **Personnel:** 1951

✠ **MERCY MEDICAL CENTER (210008)**, 301 St. Paul Place, Zip 21202–2165; tel. 410/332–9000 **A**1 2 3 10 **F**3 4 8 11 13 14 15 18 20 29 30 31 34 35 36 37 39 40 41 44 45 46 47 48 49 50 51 55 57 58 59 64 65 66 68 70 72 74 75 76 77 78 79 81 82 85 86 87 89 92 93 94 100 102 107 108 110 111 114 115 116 117 118 119 120 121 123 124 126 128 129 130 131 132 135 141 142 143 144 145 146 147 148 **P**6
Primary Contact: Thomas R. Mullen, President and Chief Executive Officer
COO: Susan D. Finlayson, MSN, Senior Vice President of MMC Operations
CFO: Justin Deibel, Senior Vice President and Chief Financial Officer
CMO: Scott A. Spier, M.D., Senior Vice President Medical Affairs
CIO: Kathleen Perry, Senior Vice President and Chief Information Officer
CHR: Tammy Janus, Senior Vice President Human Resources
CNO: Kim Bushnell, MSN, Vice President, Patient Care Services
Web address: www.mdmercy.com
Control: Church–operated, Nongovernment, not–for profit **Service:** General Medical and Surgical

Staffed Beds: 262 **Admissions:** 14391 **Census:** 175 **Outpatient Visits:** 301591 **Births:** 2791 **Total Expense ($000):** 458517 **Payroll Expense ($000):** 161998 **Personnel:** 3469

✠ △ **MT. WASHINGTON PEDIATRIC HOSPITAL (213300)**, 1708 West Rogers Avenue, Zip 21209–4545; tel. 410/578–8600, (Nonreporting) **A**1 3 5 7 10 **S** University of Maryland Medical System, Baltimore, MD
Primary Contact: Sheldon J. Stein, President and Chief Executive Officer
CFO: Mary Miller, Vice President Finance and Business Development
CMO: Richard Katz, M.D., Vice President Medical Affairs
CIO: Tim Brady, Director Information Systems
CHR: Thomas J. Ellis, Vice President Human Resources
Web address: www.mwph.org
Control: Other not–for–profit (including NFP Corporation) **Service:** Children's other specialty

Staffed Beds: 61

✠ **SAINT AGNES HOSPITAL (210011)**, 900 Caton Avenue, Zip 21229–5201; tel. 410/368–6000 **A**1 2 3 5 10 **F**3 8 11 12 13 14 15 17 18 20 22 26 28 29 30 31 32 34 35 40 41 44 46 49 50 53 54 55 56 57 58 59 60 61 64 65 68 70 72 74 75 76 77 78 79 81 82 84 85 86 87 88 89 92 93 96 97 100 107 108 110 111 114 115 117 118 119 120 121 123 124 126 129 130 131 132 134 135 144 146 147 148 **P**6 **S** Ascension Health, Saint Louis, MO
Primary Contact: Keith Vander Kolk, President and Chief Executive Officer
CFO: Scott Furniss, Senior Vice President and Chief Financial Officer
CMO: Adrian Long, M.D., Executive Vice President and Chief Medical Officer
CIO: William Greskovich, Chief Information Officer
CHR: James Bobbitt, Vice President Human Resources
CNO: Yolanda Copeland, R.N., Senior Vice President and Chief Nursing Officer
Web address: www.stagnes.org
Control: Church–operated, Nongovernment, not–for profit **Service:** General Medical and Surgical

Staffed Beds: 363 **Admissions:** 16363 **Census:** 194 **Outpatient Visits:** 511212 **Births:** 1987 **Total Expense ($000):** 415189 **Payroll Expense ($000):** 207872 **Personnel:** 2520

☐ **SHEPPARD PRATT HEALTH SYSTEM (214000)**, 6501 North Charles Street, Zip 21204–6819, Mailing Address: P.O. Box 6815, Zip 21285–6815; tel. 410/938–3000 **A**1 3 5 10 **F**10 30 35 38 56 58 64 75 87 98 99 101 103 104 105 106 130 132 135 143 144 146
Primary Contact: Harsh Trivedi, M.D., President and Chief Executive Officer
COO: Bonnie B. Katz, Vice President, Business Development and Support Operations
CFO: Gerald Noll, Vice President and Chief Financial Officer
CMO: Robert Roca, M.D., Vice President Medical Affairs
CIO: Matthew Knudsen, Director, Information Systems
CHR: Cathy Doughty, Vice President Human Resources
CNO: Ernestine Y. Cosby, Vice President Clinical Services and Chief Nursing Officer
Web address: www.sheppardpratt.org
Control: Other not–for–profit (including NFP Corporation) **Service:** Psychiatric

Staffed Beds: 340 **Admissions:** 9200 **Census:** 283 **Outpatient Visits:** 79862 **Births:** 0 **Total Expense ($000):** 201220 **Payroll Expense ($000):** 105933 **Personnel:** 2288

Hospital, Medicare Provider Number, Address, Telephone, Approval, Facility, and Physician Codes, Health Care System

★ American Hospital Association (AHA) membership
☐ The Joint Commission accreditation
○ Healthcare Facilities Accreditation Program
◇ DNV Healthcare Inc. accreditation
⇑ Center for Improvement in Healthcare Quality Accreditation
△ Commission on Accreditation of Rehabilitation Facilities (CARF) accreditation

MD

✠ △ **SINAI HOSPITAL OF BALTIMORE (210012)**, 2401 West Belvedere Avenue, Zip 21215–5271; tel. 410/601–9000 **A**1 2 3 5 7 10 **F**3 5 6 8 9 11 12 13 15 17 18 19 20 22 24 26 28 29 30 31 32 34 35 36 38 39 40 41 43 44 45 46 47 48 49 50 51 55 56 57 58 59 60 61 63 64 65 66 68 70 72 73 74 75 76 77 78 79 80 81 82 83 84 85 86 87 88 89 90 92 93 94 95 96 97 98 99 100 101 102 103 104 105 107 108 110 111 113 114 115 116 117 118 119 120 121 123 124 126 129 130 131 132 134 135 143 146 147 **P**6
Primary Contact: Amy Perry, President
CFO: David Krajewski, Senior Vice President and Chief Financial Officer
CMO: Daniel C. Silverman, M.D., Vice President and Chief Medical Officer
CIO: Karen Barker, Vice President and Chief Information Officer
CHR: Cheryl T. Boyer, Vice President Human Resources
CNO: Diane Johnson, R.N., Vice President Patient Care Services and Chief Nursing Officer
Web address: www.lifebridgehealth.org
Control: Other not–for–profit (including NFP Corporation) **Service:** General Medical and Surgical

Staffed Beds: 473 **Admissions:** 22169 **Census:** 318 **Outpatient Visits:** 185961 **Births:** 2173 **Total Expense ($000):** 698383 **Payroll Expense ($000):** 299738 **Personnel:** 4060

☐ **SPRING GROVE HOSPITAL CENTER (214018)**, 55 Wade Avenue, Zip 21228–4663; tel. 410/402–6000, (Nonreporting) **A**1 3 5 10
Primary Contact: David S. Helsel, M.D., Chief Executive Officer
CFO: Edward Swartz, Chief Financial Officer
CMO: Kelly Phillips, M.D., Clinical Director and Chief Staff
Web address: www.springgrove.com
Control: State–Government, nonfederal **Service:** Psychiatric

Staffed Beds: 365

UNION MEMORIAL HOSPITAL See MedStar Union Memorial Hospital

✠ **UNIVERSITY OF MARYLAND MEDICAL CENTER (210002)**, 22 South Greene Street, Zip 21201–1595; tel. 410/328–8667, (Includes UNIVERSITY OF MARYLAND HOSPITAL FOR CHILDREN, 22 South Greene Street, Zip 21201–1544; tel. 800/492–5538) **A**1 2 3 5 8 10 **F**3 5 6 7 9 11 12 13 14 15 17 18 19 20 21 22 23 24 25 26 27 28 29 30 31 32 34 35 36 38 39 40 41 43 44 45 46 47 48 49 50 51 52 54 55 56 57 58 59 60 61 64 65 66 68 70 71 72 74 75 76 77 78 79 80 81 82 84 85 86 87 88 89 91 92 93 94 97 98 99 100 101 102 103 104 105 106 107 108 109 110 111 114 115 116 117 118 119 120 121 123 124 126 130 131 132 134 135 136 137 138 139 140 141 142 143 144 145 146 147 148 **S** University of Maryland Medical System, Baltimore, MD
Primary Contact: Mohan Suntha, M.D., President and Chief Executive Officer
CFO: Keith D. Persinger, Senior Vice President Finance and Chief Financial Officer
CMO: Jonathan Gottlieb, M.D., Senior Vice President and Chief Medical Officer
CIO: Jon P. Burns, Chief Information Officer
CHR: R. Keith Allen, Senior Vice President Human Resources
CNO: Lisa Rowen, R.N., Senior Vice President and Chief Nursing Officer
Web address: www.umm.edu
Control: Other not–for–profit (including NFP Corporation) **Service:** General Medical and Surgical

Staffed Beds: 630 **Admissions:** 29464 **Census:** 583 **Outpatient Visits:** 412412 **Births:** 1778 **Total Expense ($000):** 1361148 **Payroll Expense ($000):** 454241 **Personnel:** 7779

✠ **UNIVERSITY OF MARYLAND MEDICAL CENTER MIDTOWN CAMPUS (210038)**, 827 Linden Avenue, Zip 21201–4606; tel. 410/225–8000 **A**1 3 5 10 **F**1 5 11 15 18 20 29 30 31 34 35 40 44 45 49 50 56 57 59 60 61 64 65 66 68 70 74 75 77 78 79 81 82 84 85 87 91 93 94 96 97 98 100 101 102 103 104 106 107 108 111 114 115 118 119 129 143 148 **S** University of Maryland Medical System, Baltimore, MD
Primary Contact: John W. Ashworth, Interim President and Chief Executive Officer
COO: Donald Ray, Vice President Operations
CFO: Craig Fleischmann, Vice President Finance
CMO: W. Eugene Egerton, M.D., Chief Medical Officer
CIO: Jon P. Burns, Senior Vice President and Chief Information Officer
CHR: Paula Henderson, Vice President Human Resources
CNO: Lisa Rowen, R.N., Chief Nursing Officer
Web address: www.ummidtown.org/
Control: Other not–for–profit (including NFP Corporation) **Service:** General Medical and Surgical

Staffed Beds: 170 **Admissions:** 5604 **Census:** 116 **Outpatient Visits:** 151614 **Births:** 0 **Total Expense ($000):** 193293 **Payroll Expense ($000):** 78424 **Personnel:** 1239

✠ △ **UNIVERSITY OF MARYLAND REHABILITATION & ORTHOPAEDIC INSTITUTE (210058)**, 2200 Kernan Drive, Zip 21207–6697; tel. 410/448–2500 **A**1 3 5 7 10 **F**1 8 29 34 35 36 39 57 68 70 74 77 79 81 82 90 91 93 94 95 96 107 115 120 131 132 133 143 146 148 **S** University of Maryland Medical System, Baltimore, MD
Primary Contact: Cynthia Kelleher, M.P.H., President and Chief Executive Officer
CFO: W. Walter Augustin, III, CPA, Vice President Financial Services and Chief Financial Officer
CMO: John P. Straumanis, M.D., Vice President Medical Affairs and Chief Medical Officer
CIO: Linda Hines, Vice President Information Technology and Information Systems
CHR: Paula Henderson, Vice President Human Resources
CNO: Cheryl D. Lee, R.N., Vice President of Patient Care Services and Chief Nursing Officer
Web address: www.umrehabortho.org
Control: Other not–for–profit (including NFP Corporation) **Service:** Rehabilitation

Staffed Beds: 104 **Admissions:** 3242 **Census:** 103 **Outpatient Visits:** 57756 **Births:** 0 **Total Expense ($000):** 112948 **Payroll Expense ($000):** 43491 **Personnel:** 609

✠ **VETERANS AFFAIRS MARYLAND HEALTH CARE SYSTEM–BALTIMORE DIVISION**, 10 North Greene Street, Zip 21201–1524; tel. 410/605–7001, (Includes VETERANS AFFAIRS MARYLAND HEALTH CARE SYSTEM–PERRY POINT DIVISION, Circle Drive, Perry Point, Zip 21902; tel. 410/642–2411; Dennis H. Smith, Director), (Nonreporting) **A**1 2 3 5 8 **S** Department of Veterans Affairs, Washington, DC
Primary Contact: Adam M. Robinson, Director
CFO: Major Tom Scheffler, Chief Fiscal Officer
CMO: Dorothy Snow, M.D., Chief of Staff
CIO: Sharon Zielinski, Chief Information Resource Officer
CHR: Jeff Craig, Chief Human Resource Management
Web address: www.maryland.va.gov/
Control: Veterans Affairs, Government, federal **Service:** General Medical and Surgical

Staffed Beds: 727

BEL AIR—Harford County

✠ **UNIVERSITY OF MARYLAND UPPER CHESAPEAKE MEDICAL CENTER (210049)**, 500 Upper Chesapeake Drive, Zip 21014–4324; tel. 443/643–1000, (Nonreporting) **A**1 2 3 10 **S** University of Maryland Medical System, Baltimore, MD
Primary Contact: Lyle Ernest Sheldon, FACHE, President and Chief Executive Officer
CFO: Joseph E. Hoffman, III, Executive Vice President and Chief Financial Officer
CMO: Peggy Vaughan, M.D., Senior Vice President Medical Affairs
CIO: Rick Casteel, Vice President Management Information Systems and Chief Information Officer
CHR: Toni M. Shivery, Vice President Human Resources
Web address: www.uchs.org
Control: Other not–for–profit (including NFP Corporation) **Service:** General Medical and Surgical

Staffed Beds: 181

BERLIN—Worcester County

✠ **ATLANTIC GENERAL HOSPITAL (210061)**, 9733 Healthway Drive, Zip 21811–1155; tel. 410/641–1100 **A**1 10 **F**3 8 11 12 15 18 29 30 31 34 35 38 40 45 50 51 54 57 58 59 64 65 66 70 74 75 77 78 79 81 82 84 85 87 92 97 99 104 107 108 110 111 114 119 129 146 147 148 **P**7
Primary Contact: Michael A. Franklin, FACHE, President and Chief Executive Officer
COO: Kim Justice, Vice President Planning and Operations
CFO: Cheryl Nottingham, Chief Financial Officer
CMO: Stephen F. Waters, M.D., Medical Director
CIO: Andrew Fowler, Vice President Information Services
CHR: Jim Brannon, Vice President Human Resources
CNO: Colleen Wareing, Vice President Patient Care Services
Web address: www.atlanticgeneral.org
Control: Other not–for–profit (including NFP Corporation) **Service:** General Medical and Surgical

Staffed Beds: 45 **Admissions:** 3348 **Census:** 34 **Outpatient Visits:** 116881 **Births:** 0 **Total Expense ($000):** 108171 **Payroll Expense ($000):** 46650 **Personnel:** 739

BETHESDA—Montgomery County

☒ **NATIONAL INSTITUTES OF HEALTH CLINICAL CENTER**, (Biomedical Research), 9000 Rockville Pike, Building 10, Room 6–2551, Zip 20892–1504; tel. 301/496–4000, (Includes CHILDREN'S INN AT NIH, 7 West Drive, Zip 20814–1509; tel. 301/496–5672) **A**1 3 5 8 **F**3 4 5 14 20 22 26 30 31 36 39 45 53 55 58 59 60 61 64 65 68 70 74 75 77 78 79 81 82 84 85 86 87 89 91 92 93 94 95 96 98 99 100 101 104 105 107 108 111 112 114 115 116 117 118 119 120 121 124 126 129 130 132 135 136 141 142 145 146 148 **S** U. S. Indian Health Service, Rockville, MD
Primary Contact: John I. Gallin, M.D., Director
COO: Maureen E. Gormley, R.N., Chief Operating Officer
CFO: Maria Joyce, Chief Financial Officer
CMO: David K. Henderson, M.D., Deputy Director Clinical Care
CIO: Jon W. McKeeby, Chief Information Officer
CHR: Bonnie Tuma, Human Resources Team Lead
CNO: Clare Hastings, R.N., Chief Nurse Officer
Web address: www.clinicalcenter.nih.gov
Control: Public Health Service, Government, federal **Service:** Other specialty

Staffed Beds: 146 **Admissions:** 5448 **Census:** 131 **Outpatient Visits:** 100507 **Births:** 0 **Total Expense ($000):** 413121 **Payroll Expense ($000):** 175130 **Personnel:** 1804

NATIONAL NAVAL MEDICAL CENTER See Walter Reed National Military Medical Center

☒ **SUBURBAN HOSPITAL (210022)**, 8600 Old Georgetown Road, Zip 20814–1497; tel. 301/896–3100 **A**1 2 3 5 10 **F**3 5 8 11 15 17 18 20 22 24 26 28 29 30 31 34 35 36 37 38 39 40 41 43 44 45 46 49 50 51 56 57 58 59 60 64 70 71 74 75 77 78 79 81 82 84 85 87 89 92 93 98 99 100 101 102 103 104 105 107 108 110 111 115 118 119 120 121 123 126 130 132 135 146 148 **P**6 **S** Johns Hopkins Health System, Baltimore, MD
Primary Contact: Jacky Schultz, R.N., MSN, Interim President
COO: Joseph Linstrom, Vice President Operations
CFO: Marty Basso, Senior Vice President Finance
CMO: Robert Rothstein, M.D., Vice President Medical Affairs
CIO: Jason Cole, Senior Director, Management Information Systems
CNO: Jacky Schultz, R.N., Chief Nurse Officer
Web address: www.suburbanhospital.org
Control: Other not–for–profit (including NFP Corporation) **Service:** General Medical and Surgical

Staffed Beds: 236 **Admissions:** 13861 **Census:** 167 **Outpatient Visits:** 110793 **Births:** 0 **Total Expense ($000):** 263007 **Payroll Expense ($000):** 97106 **Personnel:** 1506

☒ **WALTER REED NATIONAL MILITARY MEDICAL CENTER**, 8901 Wisconsin Avenue, Zip 20889–5600; tel. 301/295–4611, (Nonreporting) **A**1 2 3 5 **S** Bureau of Medicine and Surgery, Department of the Navy, Falls Church, VA
Primary Contact: Brigadier General Jeffrey B. Clark, Director
CFO: Commander Joseph Pickel, Director Resource Management
CIO: Commander Cayetano Thornton, Chief Information Officer
CHR: Captain Jaime Carroll, Department Head
Web address: www.wrnmmc.capmed.mil/SitePages/home.aspx
Control: Navy, Government, federal **Service:** General Medical and Surgical

Staffed Beds: 240

CAMBRIDGE—Dorchester County

☐ **EASTERN SHORE HOSPITAL CENTER (214002)**, 5262 Woods Road, Zip 21613–3796, Mailing Address: P.O. Box 800, Zip 21613–0800; tel. 410/221–2300 **A**1 10 **F**10 11 29 59 75 98 100 101 106 135 146 **P**6
Primary Contact: Randy L. Bradford, Chief Executive Officer
COO: William Webb, Assistant Superintendent
CFO: William Webb, Assistant Superintendent
CMO: Evangeline Garcia, M.D., Clinical Director
CHR: Cassandra Stanley, Director Personnel
CNO: Lisa Hines, Director Nursing
Web address: www.dhmh.state.md.us/eshc
Control: State–Government, nonfederal **Service:** Psychiatric

Staffed Beds: 80 **Admissions:** 91 **Census:** 37 **Outpatient Visits:** 0 **Births:** 0

☒ **UNIVERSITY OF MARYLAND SHORE MEDICAL CENTER AT DORCHESTER**, 300 Byrn Street, Zip 21613–1908; tel. 410/228–5511 **A**1 **F**3 11 15 18 20 29 30 31 34 35 40 43 44 45 50 57 59 62 64 68 70 74 75 77 78 81 82 84 85 86 87 91 93 98 99 100 101 102 103 104 105 107 108 110 111 113 118 119 129 130 132 146 **P**3 5 **S** University of Maryland Medical System, Baltimore, MD
Primary Contact: Kenneth D. Kozel, FACHE, President and Chief Executive Officer
COO: Robert A. Frank, Senior Vice President Operations
CFO: Joanne A. Hahey, Senior Vice President and Chief Financial Officer
CMO: William Huffner, M.D., Vice President Medical Affairs
CIO: Elizabeth Fish, Chief Information Officer
CHR: Susan Coe, Regional Vice President Human Resources
Web address: www.shorehealth.org
Control: Other not–for–profit (including NFP Corporation) **Service:** General Medical and Surgical

Staffed Beds: 47 **Admissions:** 2606 **Census:** 34 **Outpatient Visits:** 50592 **Births:** 0 **Total Expense ($000):** 40176 **Payroll Expense ($000):** 18346 **Personnel:** 253

CHESTERTOWN—Kent County

CHESTER RIVER HOSPITAL CENTER See University of Maryland Shore Medical Center at Chestertown

☒ **UNIVERSITY OF MARYLAND SHORE MEDICAL CENTER AT CHESTERTOWN (210030)**, 100 Brown Street, Zip 21620–1499; tel. 410/778–3300, (Total facility includes 94 beds in nursing home–type unit) **A**1 10 **F**3 11 15 18 28 29 30 31 34 35 39 40 41 42 45 46 47 50 53 55 56 57 59 60 62 63 64 65 68 70 75 78 79 81 82 84 85 87 89 97 102 107 110 111 115 119 128 129 130 132 143 146 147 **S** University of Maryland Medical System, Baltimore, MD
Primary Contact: Kenneth D. Kozel, FACHE, President and Chief Executive Officer
COO: Robert A. Frank, Senior Vice President of Operations
CFO: Joanne A. Hahey, Vice President Finance and Chief Financial Officer
CMO: William Huffner, M.D., Chief Medical Officer
CIO: Elizabeth Fish, Senior Director Site Executive and Information Technology
CHR: Susan Coe, Vice President Human Resources
CNO: Ruth Ann Jones, Ed.D., Senior Vice President, Chief Nursing Officer
Web address: www.umms.org/hospitals/shore–health–system.htm
Control: Other not–for–profit (including NFP Corporation) **Service:** General Medical and Surgical

Staffed Beds: 124 **Admissions:** 1859 **Census:** 103 **Outpatient Visits:** 47797 **Births:** 0 **Total Expense ($000):** 49435 **Payroll Expense ($000):** 17495 **Personnel:** 358

CHEVERLY—Prince George's County

GLADYS SPELLMAN SPECIALTY HOSPITAL AND NURSING CENTER, 2900 Mercy Lane, Zip 20785–1157; tel. 301/618–2010, (Nonreporting)
Primary Contact: Stewart R. Seitz, Chief Executive Officer
CFO: Ketty Taboado, Chief Financial Officer
CMO: Paul A. Devore, M.D., Medical Director
CHR: Michael Jacobs, Vice President Human Resources
Web address: www.dimensionshealth.org
Control: Corporation, Investor–owned, for–profit **Service:** Chronic disease

Staffed Beds: 30

☐ **PRINCE GEORGE'S HOSPITAL CENTER (210003)**, 3001 Hospital Drive, Zip 20785–1189; tel. 301/618–2000 **A**1 3 5 10 **F**3 11 13 15 17 18 20 22 24 26 28 29 31 34 35 38 40 42 43 45 46 47 48 50 54 55 56 57 59 60 61 63 64 65 66 68 69 70 72 74 75 76 77 78 79 81 82 84 85 86 87 89 92 93 97 98 100 101 102 103 104 105 107 108 110 111 114 115 118 119 130 131 132 134 135 142 144 146 148 **P**6 **S** Dimensions Healthcare System, Cheverly, MD
Primary Contact: K. Singh Taneja, Chief Operating Officer
CMO: David Goldman, M.D., Vice President Medical Affairs and Education
CIO: Don Chenoweth, Chief Information Officer
CHR: Michael Jacobs, Vice President Human Resources
Web address: www.princegeorgeshospital.org
Control: Other not–for–profit (including NFP Corporation) **Service:** General Medical and Surgical

Staffed Beds: 156 **Admissions:** 11944 **Census:** 170 **Outpatient Visits:** 56378 **Births:** 2327 **Total Expense ($000):** 246500 **Payroll Expense ($000):** 110550 **Personnel:** 1204

Hospital, Medicare Provider Number, Address, Telephone, Approval, Facility, and Physician Codes, Health Care System

★ American Hospital Association (AHA) membership   ◯ Healthcare Facilities Accreditation Program   ⇑ Center for Improvement in Healthcare Quality Accreditation
☐ The Joint Commission accreditation   ◇ DNV Healthcare Inc. accreditation   △ Commission on Accreditation of Rehabilitation Facilities (CARF) accreditation

MD

CLINTON—Prince George's County

☒ **MEDSTAR SOUTHERN MARYLAND HOSPITAL CENTER (210062)**, 7503 Surratts Road, Zip 20735–3358; tel. 301/868–8000, (Total facility includes 20 beds in nursing home–type unit) **A**1 2 10 **F**3 11 12 13 15 17 18 20 22 26 28 29 30 31 32 34 35 36 37 39 40 43 44 45 46 47 48 49 50 57 59 64 65 68 70 73 74 75 76 77 78 79 80 81 82 85 86 87 89 91 92 93 96 98 100 101 102 103 105 107 108 114 115 118 119 126 128 129 130 135 145 146 147 148 **S** MedStar Health, Columbia, MD
Primary Contact: Christine R. Wray, President
CFO: Daniel Feeley, Interim Chief Financial Officer
CMO: Yvette Johnson–Threat, Vice President Medical Affairs
CIO: Lou Mavromatis, Vice President Information Technology
CHR: Paul Zeller, Vice President Human Resources
CNO: Patricia A. Scalfari, Vice President Nursing
Web address: www.medstarsouthernmaryland.org
Control: Other not–for–profit (including NFP Corporation) **Service:** General Medical and Surgical

Staffed Beds: 255 **Admissions:** 13183 **Census:** 169 **Outpatient Visits:** 116832 **Births:** 1422 **Total Expense ($000):** 233356 **Payroll Expense ($000):** 90564 **Personnel:** 1255

SOUTHERN MARYLAND HOSPITAL CENTER See MedStar Southern Maryland Hospital Center

COLUMBIA—Howard County

☒ **HOWARD COUNTY GENERAL HOSPITAL (210048)**, 5755 Cedar Lane, Zip 21044–2999; tel. 410/740–7890 **A**1 2 5 10 **F**3 8 11 13 15 18 20 22 26 28 29 30 31 32 34 35 36 39 40 41 44 45 46 47 49 50 51 55 56 57 58 59 60 61 64 65 68 70 72 74 75 76 77 78 79 81 82 84 85 86 87 89 91 92 93 96 98 100 101 102 103 107 108 110 111 115 119 129 130 131 132 134 135 146 147 148 **S** Johns Hopkins Health System, Baltimore, MD
Primary Contact: Steven C. Snelgrove, President
CFO: James Young, Senior Vice President Finance and Chief Financial Officer
CMO: Mohammed Shafeeq Ahmed, M.D., Vice President of Medical Affairs and Chief Medical Officer
CHR: Jon Oravec, Vice President, Human Resources
CNO: Karen Davis, Chief Nursing Officer and Vice President, Nursing
Web address: www.hcgh.org
Control: Other not–for–profit (including NFP Corporation) **Service:** General Medical and Surgical

Staffed Beds: 256 **Admissions:** 16527 **Census:** 187 **Outpatient Visits:** 144409 **Births:** 3596 **Total Expense ($000):** 235477 **Payroll Expense ($000):** 88669 **Personnel:** 1386

CRISFIELD—Somerset County

☐ **MCCREADY HEALTH (210045)**, 201 Hall Highway, Zip 21817–1299; tel. 410/968–1200, (Nonreporting) **A**1 10
Primary Contact: Joy A. Strand, Chief Executive Officer
CFO: Gary W. Broadwater, Chief Financial Officer
Web address: www.mccreadyfoundation.org
Control: Other not–for–profit (including NFP Corporation) **Service:** General Medical and Surgical

Staffed Beds: 89

CUMBERLAND—Allegany County

☐ **THOMAS B. FINAN CENTER (214012)**, 10102 Country Club Road S.E., Zip 21502–8339, Mailing Address: P.O. Box 1722, Zip 21501–1722; tel. 301/777–2405, (Nonreporting) **A**1 10
Primary Contact: Judith Hott, Chief Executive Officer
COO: John Cullen, Assistant Superintendent
CFO: Craig Alexander, Fiscal Specialist
CMO: David Millis, M.D., Clinical Director
CIO: John Cullen, Assistant Superintendent
CHR: Chris Loney, Director Personnel
CNO: Gayle Walter, Director of Nursing
Web address: www.dhmh.state.md.us
Control: State–Government, nonfederal **Service:** Psychiatric

Staffed Beds: 80

☒ △ **WESTERN MARYLAND REGIONAL MEDICAL CENTER (210027)**, 12500 Willowbrook Road S.E., Zip 21502–6393, Mailing Address: P.O. Box 539, Zip 21501–0539; tel. 240/964–7000, (Total facility includes 88 beds in nursing home–type unit) **A**1 2 7 10 **F**3 5 11 13 14 15 17 18 20 22 24 26 28 29 30 31 32 34 35 40 43 44 45 47 50 51 53 54 56 57 58 59 60 62 63 64 66 68 70 73 74 75 76 77 78 79 80 81 82 84 85 86 87 89 90 93 94 96 97 98 100 102 103 104 107 108 111 114 115 116 117 118 119 120 121 124 128 129 130 132 134 135 144 145 146 148 **P**6
Primary Contact: Barry P. Ronan, President and Chief Executive Officer
COO: Nancy D. Adams, R.N., Senior Vice President Chief Operating Officer and Chief Nurse Executive
CFO: Kimberly S. Repac, Senior Vice President and Chief Financial Officer
CMO: Gerald Goldstein, M.D., Senior Vice President and Chief Medical Officer
CIO: William Byers, Chief Technology Officer
CHR: Christopher Bumbaugh, Executive Director, Human Resources
CNO: Nancy D. Adams, R.N., Senior Vice President Chief Operating Officer and Chief Nurse Executive
Web address: www.wmhs.com
Control: Other not–for–profit (including NFP Corporation) **Service:** General Medical and Surgical

Staffed Beds: 313 **Admissions:** 11880 **Census:** 226 **Outpatient Visits:** 555195 **Births:** 941 **Total Expense ($000):** 290770 **Payroll Expense ($000):** 96401 **Personnel:** 1570

EAST NEW MARKET—Dorchester County

WARWICK MANOR BEHAVIORAL HEALTH, 3680 Warwick Road, Zip 21631–1420; tel. 410/943–8108, (Nonreporting)
Primary Contact: L. Wesley Fuhrman, President and Chief Executive Officer
Web address: www.warwickmanor.org/
Control: Corporation, Investor–owned, for–profit **Service:** Alcoholism and other chemical dependency

Staffed Beds: 42

EASTON—Talbot County

☒ △ **UNIVERSITY OF MARYLAND SHORE MEDICAL CENTER AT EASTON (210037)**, 219 South Washington Street, Zip 21601–2996; tel. 410/822–1000 **A**1 2 7 10 **F**3 8 11 13 15 18 20 22 28 29 30 31 34 35 36 37 39 40 42 43 44 45 49 51 54 57 58 59 60 62 63 64 65 70 74 76 78 79 81 82 83 84 85 86 89 90 91 93 100 102 107 108 111 114 116 117 118 119 120 121 123 124 126 129 130 132 144 147 148 **P**3 5 **S** University of Maryland Medical System, Baltimore, MD
Primary Contact: Kenneth D. Kozel, FACHE, President and Chief Executive Officer
COO: Robert A. Frank, Senior Vice President of Operations
CFO: Joanne A. Hahey, Senior Vice President and Chief Financial Officer
CMO: William Huffner, M.D., Chief Medical Officer
CIO: Elizabeth Fish, Chief Information Officer
CHR: Susan Coe, Regional Vice President Human Resources
CNO: Ruth Ann Jones, Ed.D., Senior Vice President, Chief Nursing Officer
Web address: www.shorehealth.org
Control: Other not–for–profit (including NFP Corporation) **Service:** General Medical and Surgical

Staffed Beds: 132 **Admissions:** 7911 **Census:** 90 **Outpatient Visits:** 387702 **Births:** 1048 **Total Expense ($000):** 169189 **Payroll Expense ($000):** 63787 **Personnel:** 1252

ELKTON—Cecil County

☒ **UNION HOSPITAL (210032)**, 106 Bow Street, Zip 21921–5596; tel. 410/398–4000 **A**1 2 3 5 10 **F**2 3 11 12 13 15 18 26 29 30 31 34 35 38 40 44 45 46 49 50 51 53 54 57 59 61 63 64 69 70 74 75 76 77 78 79 81 82 84 85 86 87 89 92 93 97 98 100 102 104 105 107 108 110 111 114 118 119 129 130 131 132 135 146 147 148 **P**6
Primary Contact: Richard C. Szumel, M.D., Chief Executive Officer
CFO: Laurie Beyer, Senior Vice President and Chief Financial Officer
CMO: Cydney Teal, M.D., Vice President Medical Affairs
CIO: Anne Lara, Chief Information Officer
CHR: Terrence Lovell, Vice President Human Resources
CNO: Katie Boston, Senior Vice President Patient Care Services
Web address: www.uhcc.com
Control: Other not–for–profit (including NFP Corporation) **Service:** General Medical and Surgical

Staffed Beds: 109 **Admissions:** 5453 **Census:** 61 **Outpatient Visits:** 143445 **Births:** 582 **Total Expense ($000):** 150962 **Payroll Expense ($000):** 67882 **Personnel:** 944

Many Facility Codes have changed. Please refer to the AHA Guide Code Chart. © 2016 AHA Guide

FREDERICK—Frederick County

⊠ **FREDERICK MEMORIAL HOSPITAL (210005)**, 400 West Seventh Street,
Zip 21701–4593; tel. 240/566–3300 **A**1 2 5 10 **F**3 8 11 12 13 15 18 20 22
26 28 29 30 31 34 35 38 40 41 45 46 49 50 54 55 56 59 62 63 64 65 66
68 70 72 75 76 78 79 81 82 83 84 85 86 87 89 93 98 100 102 103 105
107 110 111 114 115 116 117 119 120 121 123 124 126 129 130 132 135
144 146 147 148 **P**6 7
Primary Contact: Thomas A. Kleinhanzl, President and Chief Executive Officer
COO: John R. Verbus, Senior Vice President and Chief Operating Officer
CFO: Michelle K. Mahan, Senior Vice President and Chief Financial Officer
CMO: Manuel Casiano, M.D., Senior Vice President Medical Affairs
CIO: David Quirke, Vice President Information Services
CNO: Cheryl Cioffi, R.N., Senior Vice President Patient Care Services and Chief
Nursing Officer
Web address: www.fmh.org
Control: Other not–for–profit (including NFP Corporation) **Service:** General
Medical and Surgical

Staffed Beds: 308 **Admissions:** 16221 **Census:** 191 **Outpatient Visits:**
404571 **Births:** 2383 **Total Expense ($000):** 324532 **Payroll Expense
($000):** 104888 **Personnel:** 1662

GERMANTOWN—Montgomery County

★ **HOLY CROSS GERMANTOWN HOSPITAL**, 19801 Observation Drive,
Zip 20876–4070; tel. 301/754–7000, (Data for 273 days) **F**3 11 13 26 29 30
39 40 49 50 59 64 66 68 70 73 74 75 76 77 79 81 85 86 87 97 98 100
102 107 108 111 114 115 118 119 126 130 146 147 **S** Trinity Health,
Livonia, MI
Primary Contact: Doug Ryder, President
Web address: www.holycrosshealth.org/germantown
Control: Church–operated, Nongovernment, not–for profit **Service:** General
Medical and Surgical

Staffed Beds: 101 **Admissions:** 2540 **Census:** 40 **Outpatient Visits:** 22191
Births: 302 **Total Expense ($000):** 62123 **Payroll Expense ($000):** 23290
Personnel: 512

GLEN BURNIE—Anne Arundel County

⊠ **UNIVERSITY OF MARYLAND BALTIMORE WASHINGTON MEDICAL CENTER
(210043)**, 301 Hospital Drive, Zip 21061–5899; tel. 410/787–4000 **A**1 2 3 5
10 **F**3 11 13 14 18 19 20 22 26 28 29 30 31 34 35 37 40 41 42 43 44 45
46 48 49 50 54 55 56 57 58 59 60 64 65 68 70 74 75 76 77 78 79 81 82
84 85 86 87 89 93 98 100 101 102 103 104 105 107 111 114 115 118 119
120 121 122 123 124 126 129 130 131 132 135 146 147 148 **P**6
S University of Maryland Medical System, Baltimore, MD
Primary Contact: Karen E. Olscamp, President and Chief Executive Officer
COO: Kathleen McCollum, Senior Vice President, Clinical Integration and Chief
Operating Officer
CFO: Al Pietsch, CPA, Senior Vice President and Chief Financial Officer
CMO: Neel Vibhakar, M.D., Senior Vice President and Chief Medical Officer
CHR: Kathy Poehler, Vice President, Human Resources
CNO: Catherine Whitaker, MSN, Vice President and Chief Nursing Officer
Web address: www.mybwmc.org
Control: Other not–for–profit (including NFP Corporation) **Service:** General
Medical and Surgical

Staffed Beds: 310 **Admissions:** 18986 **Census:** 218 **Outpatient Visits:**
156234 **Births:** 860 **Total Expense ($000):** 330447 **Payroll Expense
($000):** 139989 **Personnel:** 2332

HAGERSTOWN—Washington County

☐ **BROOK LANE HEALTH SERVICES (214003)**, 13121 Brook Lane,
Zip 21742–1435, Mailing Address: P.O. Box 1945, Zip 21742–1945;
tel. 301/733–0330 **A**1 10 **F**5 26 27 30 56 68 98 99 100 101 103 104 105
130 143 146 **P**4 6
Primary Contact: R. Lynn Rushing, Chief Executive Officer
CFO: Floyd Klauka, Chief Financial Officer
CMO: David Gonzalez, M.D., Medical Director
CIO: Sharon Gladfelter, Health Information Officer
CHR: Nicole Twigg, Director Human Resources
CNO: Jason Allen, Director Patient Care Services
Web address: www.brooklane.org
Control: Other not–for–profit (including NFP Corporation) **Service:** Psychiatric

Staffed Beds: 57 **Admissions:** 1770 **Census:** 39 **Outpatient Visits:** 82887
Births: 0 **Total Expense ($000):** 24895 **Payroll Expense ($000):** 16082
Personnel: 361

⊠ △ **MERITUS MEDICAL CENTER (210001)**, 11116 Medical Campus Road,
Zip 21742–6710; tel. 301/790–8000 **A**1 2 7 10 13 **F**3 5 11 12 13 15 17 18
20 22 26 28 29 30 31 34 35 38 40 43 44 49 51 52 54 56 57 58 59 60 61
62 64 65 70 74 75 76 77 78 79 81 82 83 84 85 86 87 89 90 93 94 96 97
98 99 100 101 102 103 104 105 107 108 111 114 115 118 119 120 121
123 130 131 132 135 143 144 145 146 147 148 **P**6 8
Primary Contact: Joseph P. Ross, President and Chief Executive Officer
COO: Jesus Cepero, Ph.D., Chief Operating Officer and Chief Nursing Officer
CFO: Thomas T. Chan, Chief Financial Officer
CMO: Heather Lorenzo, M.D., Vice President and Chief Medical Officer
CHR: Christopher Bumbaugh, Executive Human Resources
CNO: Jesus Cepero, Ph.D., Chief Operating Officer and Chief Nursing Officer
Web address: www.meritushealth.com
Control: Other not–for–profit (including NFP Corporation) **Service:** General
Medical and Surgical

Staffed Beds: 278 **Admissions:** 17029 **Census:** 173 **Outpatient Visits:**
193694 **Births:** 1938 **Total Expense ($000):** 298835 **Payroll Expense
($000):** 91903 **Personnel:** 1709

WASHINGTON COUNTY HEALTH SYSTEM See Meritus Medical Center

☐ △ **WESTERN MARYLAND HOSPITAL CENTER (212002)**, 1500 Pennsylvania
Avenue, Zip 21742–3194; tel. 301/745–4200, (Nonreporting) **A**1 7 10
Primary Contact: Michael Reyka, Chief Executive Officer
COO: David Davis, Chief Operating Officer
CFO: Kelly Edmonds, Chief Financial Officer
CMO: Monica Stallworth, M.D., Chief of Staff
CIO: Ron Keplinger, Chief Information Officer
CHR: David Davis, Chief Operating Officer
Web address: www.wmhc.us
Control: State–Government, nonfederal **Service:** Long–Term Acute Care hospital

Staffed Beds: 120

HAVRE DE GRACE—Harford County

⊠ **UNIVERSITY OF MARYLAND HARFORD MEMORIAL HOSPITAL (210006)**,
501 South Union Avenue, Zip 21078–3493; tel. 443/843–5000 **A**1 2 10 **F**3 11
12 15 29 30 31 34 35 36 38 40 42 46 49 50 51 57 59 60 64 65 66 68 70
71 74 75 77 78 79 81 82 84 85 86 87 92 93 96 98 102 103 104 107 108
110 111 114 115 118 119 129 130 131 132 135 146 148 **S** University of
Maryland Medical System, Baltimore, MD
Primary Contact: Lyle Ernest Sheldon, FACHE, President and Chief Executive
Officer
CFO: Joseph E. Hoffman, III, Executive Vice President and Chief Financial Officer
CMO: Peggy Vaughan, M.D., Senior Vice President Medical Affairs
CIO: Rick Casteel, Vice President Management Information Systems and Chief
Information Officer
CHR: Toni M. Shivery, Vice President Human Resources
Web address: www.uchs.org
Control: Other not–for–profit (including NFP Corporation) **Service:** General
Medical and Surgical

Staffed Beds: 49 **Admissions:** 4174 **Census:** 58 **Births:** 0

JESSUP—Howard County

☐ **CLIFTON T. PERKINS HOSPITAL CENTER**, 8450 Dorsey Run Road,
Zip 20794–9486; tel. 410/724–3000, (Nonreporting) **A**1 3 5
Primary Contact: Thomas D. Lewis, Acting Chief Executive Officer
COO: Steve Mason, Assistant Superintendent and Chief Operating Officer
CFO: George Parnel, Chief Financial Officer
CMO: Muhammed Ajanah, M.D., Clinical Director
CIO: Chanda Hamilton, Chief Information Officer
CHR: Beverly Stacie, Director Human Resources
Web address: www.dhmh.state.md.us/perkins/
Control: State–Government, nonfederal **Service:** Psychiatric

Staffed Beds: 250

Hospital, Medicare Provider Number, Address, Telephone, Approval, Facility, and Physician Codes, Health Care System

★ American Hospital Association (AHA) membership   ○ Healthcare Facilities Accreditation Program   ⇑ Center for Improvement in Healthcare Quality Accreditation
☐ The Joint Commission accreditation   ◇ DNV Healthcare Inc. accreditation   △ Commission on Accreditation of Rehabilitation Facilities (CARF) accreditation

MD

LA PLATA—Charles County

☒ **UNIVERSITY OF MARYLAND CHARLES REGIONAL MEDICAL CENTER (210035)**, 5 Garrett Avenue, Zip 20646–5960, Mailing Address: P.O. Box 1070, Zip 20646–1070; tel. 301/609–4000 **A**1 2 10 **F**3 11 13 15 18 28 29 30 31 34 35 36 38 40 44 45 50 51 56 57 59 60 61 64 70 74 76 77 78 79 81 82 85 86 87 89 91 92 93 96 107 108 110 111 115 118 119 129 130 132 135 145 146 147 148 **S** University of Maryland Medical System, Baltimore, MD
Primary Contact: Noel A. Cervino, President and Chief Executive Officer
CFO: Erik Boas, Vice President Finance
CMO: Sanjeeb Mishra, M.D., Chief of Staff
CHR: Stacey M. Cook, MS, Vice President, Human Resources
Web address: www.charlesregional.org
Control: Other not–for–profit (including NFP Corporation) **Service:** General Medical and Surgical

Staffed Beds: 115 **Admissions:** 6744 **Census:** 74 **Outpatient Visits:** 82773 **Births:** 866 **Total Expense ($000):** 113418 **Payroll Expense ($000):** 44944 **Personnel:** 738

LANHAM—Prince George's County

☒ **DOCTORS COMMUNITY HOSPITAL (210051)**, 8118 Good Luck Road, Zip 20706–3574; tel. 301/552–8118 **A**1 10 **F**3 8 12 15 18 20 26 28 29 30 31 34 35 40 44 45 49 50 51 53 54 57 59 64 70 71 75 77 78 79 81 84 85 86 87 90 93 107 108 111 114 115 119 120 121 123 126 130 131 132 135 146 **P**6 7
Primary Contact: Philip B. Down, Chief Executive Officer
COO: Paul Grenaldo, Executive Vice President and Chief Operating Officer
CFO: Camille Bash, Chief Financial Officer
CMO: Sunil Madan, M.D., Chief Medical Officer and Chief Population Health Officer
CIO: Alan Johnson, Chief Information Officer
CHR: Paul Hagens, Vice President Human Resources
Web address: www.dchweb.org
Control: Other not–for–profit (including NFP Corporation) **Service:** General Medical and Surgical

Staffed Beds: 144 **Admissions:** 8643 **Census:** 119 **Outpatient Visits:** 64235 **Births:** 0 **Total Expense ($000):** 176538 **Payroll Expense ($000):** 77206 **Personnel:** 1211

LAUREL—Prince George's County

☐ △ **LAUREL REGIONAL HOSPITAL (210055)**, 7300 Van Dusen Road, Zip 20707–9463; tel. 301/725–4300 **A**1 7 10 **F**1 3 11 13 15 18 20 29 30 31 34 35 40 46 49 50 51 57 59 60 61 63 64 65 66 68 69 70 74 75 76 77 78 79 80 81 82 84 85 87 90 92 93 98 100 102 103 104 105 107 108 110 111 114 115 118 119 129 130 132 146 148 **P**6 **S** Dimensions Healthcare System, Cheverly, MD
Primary Contact: John Spearman, President and Chief Operating Officer
COO: John Spearman, Interim Chief Operating Officer
CFO: Lisa Goodlett, Senior Vice President and Chief Financial Officer
CMO: Trudy Hall, M.D., Vice President Medical Affairs
CIO: David Peterson, Chief Information Officer
CHR: John Peeples, Senior Vice President Human Resources
CNO: June Meyer, MSN, Vice President Chief Nursing Officer
Web address: www.laurelregionalhospital.org
Control: Other not–for–profit (including NFP Corporation) **Service:** General Medical and Surgical

Staffed Beds: 136 **Admissions:** 4717 **Census:** 50 **Outpatient Visits:** 37751 **Births:** 671 **Total Expense ($000):** 100432 **Payroll Expense ($000):** 41905 **Personnel:** 395

LEONARDTOWN—St. Mary's County

☒ **MEDSTAR ST. MARY'S HOSPITAL (210028)**, 25500 Point Lookout Road, Zip 20650–2015, Mailing Address: PO Box 527, Zip 20650–0527; tel. 301/475–6001 **A**1 2 10 **F**3 11 13 15 18 28 29 30 31 32 34 35 36 39 40 44 45 48 50 51 53 54 56 57 59 60 63 64 65 66 68 70 71 74 75 76 77 78 79 81 82 84 85 86 87 89 93 98 100 101 102 103 104 105 107 108 110 111 114 115 118 119 129 130 132 134 135 144 146 147 148 **S** MedStar Health, Columbia, MD
Primary Contact: Christine R. Wray, President
COO: Stephen T. Michaels, M.D., Chief Operating Officer and Chief Medical Officer
CFO: Richard Braam, Vice President Finance
CIO: Donald Sirk, Director Information Systems
CHR: Evelyn Campos–Diaz, Director Human Resources
Web address: www.medstarstmarys.org
Control: Other not–for–profit (including NFP Corporation) **Service:** General Medical and Surgical

Staffed Beds: 82 **Admissions:** 6954 **Census:** 66 **Outpatient Visits:** 171779 **Births:** 1288 **Total Expense ($000):** 140130 **Payroll Expense ($000):** 59570 **Personnel:** 999

OAKLAND—Garrett County

☒ **GARRETT REGIONAL MEDICAL CENTER (210017)**, 251 North Fourth Street, Zip 21550–1375; tel. 301/533–4000, (Total facility includes 10 beds in nursing home–type unit) **A**1 10 **F**3 11 13 28 29 30 31 32 34 35 38 40 45 50 53 56 57 59 64 65 68 70 75 76 78 79 81 85 87 89 102 107 108 114 118 119 128 130 135 141 146 148 **P**6
Primary Contact: Mark Boucot, FACHE, President and Chief Executive Officer
CFO: Tracy Lipscomb, CPA, Vice President Financial Services and Chief Financial Officer
CMO: Marjorie Fridkin, M.D., Chief Medical Officer
CIO: Stephen Peterson, Vice President, Operations and Chief Information Officer
CHR: Laura M. Waters, Vice President Human Resources
CNO: Kendra Thayer, MSN, Vice President, Clinical Services and Chief Nursing Officer
Web address: www.https://www.gcmh.com
Control: Other not–for–profit (including NFP Corporation) **Service:** General Medical and Surgical

Staffed Beds: 59 **Admissions:** 1894 **Census:** 18 **Outpatient Visits:** 72105 **Births:** 283 **Total Expense ($000):** 41597 **Payroll Expense ($000):** 17148 **Personnel:** 311

OLNEY—Montgomery County

☒ **MEDSTAR MONTGOMERY MEDICAL CENTER (210018)**, 18101 Prince Philip Drive, Zip 20832–1512; tel. 301/774–8882 **A**1 2 3 10 **F**3 5 11 12 13 18 20 26 28 29 30 31 34 35 37 38 40 41 45 46 48 49 50 51 53 55 56 57 59 64 65 68 70 74 75 76 77 78 79 80 81 82 84 85 86 87 89 92 93 98 99 100 102 103 104 105 107 108 111 114 115 118 119 120 121 126 129 130 131 132 134 135 146 147 **S** MedStar Health, Columbia, MD
Primary Contact: Thomas J. Senker, FACHE, Chief Executive Officer
CFO: David A. Havrilla, Chief Financial Officer
CMO: Frederick Finelli, M.D., Vice President Medical Affairs
CIO: Chistiane Brown, Assistant Vice President
CHR: Kevin Mell, Vice President Operations
CNO: Connie Stone, R.N., Chief Nursing Officer
Web address: www.medstarmontgomery.org
Control: Other not–for–profit (including NFP Corporation) **Service:** General Medical and Surgical

Staffed Beds: 151 **Admissions:** 8011 **Census:** 87 **Outpatient Visits:** 81233 **Births:** 719 **Total Expense ($000):** 148886 **Payroll Expense ($000):** 58376 **Personnel:** 750

OXEN HILL—Prince George's County

☒ **FORT WASHINGTON MEDICAL CENTER (210060)**, 174 Waterfront Street, Suite 225, Zip 20744; tel. 301/292–7000 **A**1 10 **F**3 8 15 18 29 30 34 35 40 44 45 50 57 59 68 70 74 77 79 81 85 87 107 108 110 119 133
Primary Contact: Reginald Jones, Interim President and Chief Executive Officer
CFO: Joseph B. Tucker, Senior Vice President and Chief Financial Officer
CMO: Elias Debbas, M.D., President Medical Staff
CIO: Fred Ashby, Director Information Technology
CHR: Alexander Morris, Corporate Director Human Resources
CNO: Marjorie Quint–Bouzid, Chief Nursing Officer and Vice President Patient Care Services
Web address: www.fortwashingtonmc.org
Control: Other not–for–profit (including NFP Corporation) **Service:** General Medical and Surgical

Staffed Beds: 37 **Admissions:** 2250 **Census:** 23 **Outpatient Visits:** 51012 **Births:** 0

PERRY POINT—Cecil County

VETERANS AFFAIRS MARYLAND HEALTH CARE SYSTEM–PERRY POINT DIVISION See Veterans Affairs Maryland Health Care System–Baltimore Division, Baltimore

PRINCE FREDERICK—Calvert County

☒ **CALVERT MEMORIAL HOSPITAL (210039)**, 100 Hospital Road, Zip 20678–4017; tel. 410/535–4000, (Total facility includes 18 beds in nursing home–type unit) **A**1 10 **F**3 11 13 14 20 26 28 29 30 31 32 34 35 36 38 39 40 41 45 46 47 48 49 50 51 54 55 56 57 59 64 65 66 68 70 71 74 75 76 77 78 79 81 82 84 85 86 87 89 93 98 99 100 101 102 104 105 107 108 111 112 114 115 119 124 127 129 130 132 134 135 144 146 147 148 **P**4
Primary Contact: Dean Teague, Chief Executive Officer
CFO: Robert Kertis, Vice President Finance
CMO: Barbara Estes, M.D., Chief of Staff
CIO: Ed Grogan, Vice President Information Services and Chief Information Officer
CHR: Anthony M. Bladen, Vice President Human Resources
CNO: Diane Couchman, Vice President Patient Care Services and Chief Nursing Executive
Web address: www.calverthospital.com
Control: Other not–for–profit (including NFP Corporation) **Service:** General Medical and Surgical

Staffed Beds: 132 **Admissions:** 5611 **Census:** 66 **Outpatient Visits:** 144908 **Births:** 731 **Total Expense ($000):** 124914 **Payroll Expense ($000):** 54120 **Personnel:** 1020

RANDALLSTOWN—Baltimore County

☐ **NORTHWEST HOSPITAL (210040)**, 5401 Old Court Road, Zip 21133–5185; tel. 410/521–2200, (Nonreporting) **A**1 2 3 10 **S** LifeBridge Health, Baltimore, MD
Primary Contact: Brian M. White, President
CFO: Nancy Kane, Assistant Vice President Finance LifeBridge Health
CMO: Ronald L. Ginsberg, M.D., Vice President Medical Affairs
CIO: Tressa Springmann, Vice President and Chief Information Officer
CHR: Valerie Brandenburg, Director Human Resources
CNO: Susan L. Jalbert, R.N., Vice President Patient Care Services and Chief Nursing Officer
Web address: www.lifebridgehealth.org
Control: Other not–for–profit (including NFP Corporation) **Service:** General Medical and Surgical

Staffed Beds: 253

ROCKVILLE—Montgomery County

☐ **ADVENTIST BEHAVIORAL HEALTH ROCKVILLE (214013)**, 14901 Broschart Road, Zip 20850–3318; tel. 301/251–4500, (Nonreporting) **A**1 10 **S** Adventist HealthCare, Gaithersburg, MD
Primary Contact: Kevin Young, FACHE, President
CFO: Randy Reimer, Chief Financial Officer
CMO: Peter H. Levine, M.D., Executive Medical Director Behavioral Health Services
CIO: Kathleen Dyer, Vice President and Chief Information Officer
CHR: Mary Cloutier, Director Human Resources
Web address: www.adventistbehavioralhealth.com
Control: Other not–for–profit (including NFP Corporation) **Service:** Psychiatric

Staffed Beds: 283

☐ **ADVENTIST HEALTHCARE SHADY GROVE MEDICAL CENTER (210057)**, 9901 Medical Center Drive, Zip 20850–3395; tel. 240/826–6000 **A**1 2 3 10 **F**3 12 13 15 18 20 22 26 28 29 30 31 36 39 40 41 42 45 47 48 50 51 53 55 57 60 61 64 66 68 70 72 74 75 76 77 78 79 81 82 83 84 85 87 89 102 107 108 110 111 114 115 116 117 119 120 121 126 129 130 135 146 148 **P**5 6 **S** Adventist HealthCare, Gaithersburg, MD
Primary Contact: John Sackett, President SGMC and Executive Vice President and Chief Operating Officer
COO: Eunmee Shim, R.N., Vice President Operations
CFO: Daniel Cochran, Vice President and Chief Financial Officer
CMO: Kevin Smothers, M.D., Vice President Chief Medical Officer
CIO: christopher Ghion, Vice President and Chief Information Officer
CNO: Joan M. Vincent, Vice President Patient Care Services and Chief Nurse Executive
Web address: www.adventisthealthcare.com
Control: Church–operated, Nongovernment, not–for profit **Service:** General Medical and Surgical

Staffed Beds: 321 **Admissions:** 16525 **Census:** 182 **Outpatient Visits:** 94957 **Births:** 4636 **Total Expense ($000):** 330016 **Payroll Expense ($000):** 121401 **Personnel:** 1692

☐ △ **ADVENTIST REHABILITATION HOSPITAL OF MARYLAND (213029)**, 9909 Medical Center Drive, Zip 20850–6361; tel. 240/864–6000, (Nonreporting) **A**1 7 10 **S** Adventist HealthCare, Gaithersburg, MD
Primary Contact: Brent Reitz, President
COO: Jason Makaroff, Chief Operating Officer and Associate Vice President
CMO: Terrence P. Sheehan, M.D., Medical Director
CHR: Carrie Hibbard, Human Resource Business Partner
CNO: Valerie Summerlin, R.N., Chief Nursing Officer
Web address: www.adventistrehab.com
Control: Other not–for–profit (including NFP Corporation) **Service:** Rehabilitation

Staffed Beds: 77

POTOMAC RIDGE BEHAVIORAL HEALTH See Adventist Behavioral Health Rockville

SALISBURY—Wicomico County

☒ **DEER'S HEAD HOSPITAL CENTER (212003)**, 351 Deer's Head Hospital Road, Zip 21801–3201, Mailing Address: PO Box 2018, Zip 21802–2018; tel. 410/543–4000, (Nonreporting) **A**1 10
Primary Contact: Mary Beth Waide, JD, MS, R.N., Chief Executive Officer
CFO: Kenneth Waller, Fiscal Administrator
CMO: Michael P. Buchness, M.D., Director Medical
CIO: Mac Beattie, Computer Network Specialist
CHR: Luanne G. Dashield, Personnel Administrator
CNO: Cheri Porcelli, MSN, Chief Nursing Officer
Web address: www.deershead.org
Control: State–Government, nonfederal **Service:** Long–Term Acute Care hospital

Staffed Beds: 69

☒ △ **HEALTHSOUTH CHESAPEAKE REHABILITATION HOSPITAL (213028)**, 220 Tilghman Road, Zip 21804–1921; tel. 410/546–4600, (Nonreporting) **A**1 7 10 **S** HEALTHSOUTH Corporation, Birmingham, AL
Primary Contact: Steven Walas, Chief Executive Officer
CFO: Karen Rounsley, Controller
CHR: Belinda Thompson, Coordinator Human Resources
CNO: Belle Goslee, Chief Nursing Officer
Web address: www.healthsouthchesapeake.com
Control: Corporation, Investor–owned, for–profit **Service:** Rehabilitation

Staffed Beds: 54

☒ **PENINSULA REGIONAL MEDICAL CENTER (210019)**, 100 East Carroll Street, Zip 21801–5422; tel. 410/546–6400 **A**1 2 10 **F**3 11 12 13 15 17 18 20 22 24 26 28 29 30 31 32 34 35 40 43 45 46 47 48 49 50 51 53 54 57 58 59 60 61 62 64 68 70 71 73 74 75 76 77 78 79 81 82 84 85 86 87 89 93 97 98 99 100 102 104 105 107 108 110 111 114 115 118 119 120 121 123 124 126 130 132 143 144 145 146 147 148 **P**5 8
Primary Contact: Margaret Naleppa, Ph.D., President and Chief Executive Officer
COO: Cindy Lunsford, Executive Vice President and Chief Operating Officer
CFO: Bruce Ritchie, Vice President of Finance and Chief Financial Officer
CMO: Charles B. Silvia, M.D., Chief Medical Officer and Vice President Medical Affairs
CIO: Raymond Adkins, Chief Information Officer
CHR: Scott Peterson, Vice President of People and Organizational Development
CNO: Karen C. Poisker, MSN, Vice President Patient Care Services and Chief Nursing Officer
Web address: www.peninsula.org
Control: Other not–for–profit (including NFP Corporation) **Service:** General Medical and Surgical

Staffed Beds: 285 **Admissions:** 17558 **Census:** 210 **Outpatient Visits:** 541630 **Births:** 1863 **Total Expense ($000):** 391325 **Payroll Expense ($000):** 155405 **Personnel:** 2512

SILVER SPRING—Montgomery County

☒ **HOLY CROSS HOSPITAL (210004)**, 1500 Forest Glen Road, Zip 20910–1487; tel. 301/754–7000 **A**1 2 3 5 8 10 **F**3 11 12 13 15 17 18 19 20 22 26 29 30 31 39 40 41 45 46 49 50 56 58 59 60 64 66 68 70 72 74 75 76 77 78 79 81 82 84 85 86 87 89 93 97 100 107 108 110 111 114 115 119 120 121 123 124 126 129 130 132 134 144 146 147 **S** Trinity Health, Livonia, MI
Primary Contact: Judith Rogers, R.N., Ph.D., President and Chief Executive Officer
CFO: Anne Gillis, Chief Financial Officer
CMO: Blair Eig, M.D., Senior Vice President Medical Affairs
CIO: Matthew Trimmer, Director Information Services
CHR: J. Manuel Ocasio, Vice President Human Resources
CNO: Celia Guarino, R.N., Vice President and Chief Nursing Officer
Web address: www.holycrosshealth.org
Control: Church–operated, Nongovernment, not–for profit **Service:** General Medical and Surgical

Staffed Beds: 425 **Admissions:** 27742 **Census:** 338 **Outpatient Visits:** 175424 **Births:** 8510 **Total Expense ($000):** 398445 **Payroll Expense ($000):** 177068 **Personnel:** 2511

SAINT LUKE INSTITUTE, 8901 New Hampshire Avenue, Zip 20903–3611; tel. 301/445–7970, (Nonreporting)
Primary Contact: David Songy, President and Chief Executive Officer
COO: Sister Danile Lynch, Chief Operating Officer
Web address: www.sli.org
Control: Other not–for–profit (including NFP Corporation) **Service:** Psychiatric

Staffed Beds: 24

SYKESVILLE—Carroll County

☐ **SPRINGFIELD HOSPITAL CENTER (214004)**, 6655 Sykesville Road, Zip 21784–7966; tel. 410/970–7000 **A**1 3 10 **F**11 30 35 39 44 50 53 56 57 68 75 77 86 87 98 101 103 130 132 135 146 **P**6
Primary Contact: Paula A. Langmead, Chief Executive Officer
COO: Daniel Triplett, Acting Chief Operating Officer
CFO: Keith Hardesty, Chief Financial Officer
CMO: Kim Bright, M.D., Clinical Director
CIO: Denise Maskell, Chief Information Officer
CNO: Gloria Merek, Director of Nursing
Web address: www.dhmh.state.md.us/springfield
Control: State–Government, nonfederal **Service:** Psychiatric

Staffed Beds: 232 **Admissions:** 276 **Census:** 232 **Outpatient Visits:** 0 **Births:** 0

Hospital, Medicare Provider Number, Address, Telephone, Approval, Facility, and Physician Codes, Health Care System

★ American Hospital Association (AHA) membership
☐ The Joint Commission accreditation
○ Healthcare Facilities Accreditation Program
◇ DNV Healthcare Inc. accreditation
⇑ Center for Improvement in Healthcare Quality Accreditation
△ Commission on Accreditation of Rehabilitation Facilities (CARF) accreditation

TAKOMA PARK—Montgomery County

☐ △ **WASHINGTON ADVENTIST HOSPITAL (210016)**, 7600 Carroll Avenue,
Zip 20912–6392; tel. 301/891–7600 **A**1 2 3 5 7 10 **F**3 13 15 17 18 20 22 24
26 28 29 30 31 34 35 40 45 49 51 55 59 60 64 68 70 74 76 77 78 79 81
84 85 91 92 93 98 100 102 103 105 107 108 110 111 114 115 118 119
120 121 126 130 131 132 135 146 147 148 **S** Adventist HealthCare,
Gaithersburg, MD
Primary Contact: Erik Wangsness, President
Web address: www.adventisthealthcare.com
Control: Church–operated, Nongovernment, not–for profit **Service:** General
Medical and Surgical

Staffed Beds: 230 **Admissions:** 10398 **Census:** 152 **Outpatient Visits:**
78400 **Births:** 1747 **Personnel:** 1087

TOWSON—Baltimore County

✠ **UNIVERSITY OF MARYLAND ST. JOSEPH MEDICAL CENTER (210063)**,
7601 Osler Drive, Zip 21204–7582; tel. 410/337–1000 **A**1 2 3 10 **F**3 11 13 15
17 18 20 22 24 26 28 29 30 31 34 35 36 37 40 41 44 45 46 47 48 49 50
54 55 56 57 58 59 60 61 64 65 66 68 70 71 72 74 75 76 77 78 79 81 82
84 85 86 87 89 91 92 93 97 98 99 100 101 102 103 104 105 107 108 110
114 115 118 119 120 121 122 123 124 126 129 130 131 132 134 135 144
146 147 148 **P**6 **S** University of Maryland Medical System, Baltimore, MD
Primary Contact: Thomas Smyth, President and Chief Executive Officer
COO: Craig Carmichael, Vice President, Operations
CMO: Gail Cunningham, Interim Chief Medical Officer
CIO: Thomas Gronert, Chief Information Officer
CNO: Pamela Jamieson, Vice President Patient Care Services and Chief Nursing
Officer
Web address: www.stjosephtowson.com/home.aspx
Control: Other not–for–profit (including NFP Corporation) **Service:** General
Medical and Surgical

Staffed Beds: 314 **Admissions:** 16435 **Census:** 180 **Outpatient Visits:**
108582 **Births:** 2345 **Total Expense ($000):** 402534 **Payroll Expense
($000):** 163914 **Personnel:** 1701

WESTMINSTER—Carroll County

✠ **CARROLL HOSPITAL (210033)**, 200 Memorial Avenue, Zip 21157–5799;
tel. 410/848–3000 **A**1 2 10 **F**3 5 11 13 15 18 19 20 22 26 28 29 30 31 32
34 35 36 37 38 39 40 44 45 46 49 50 51 54 55 56 57 58 59 62 63 64 68
70 74 75 76 77 78 79 81 82 83 84 85 86 87 89 93 94 96 98 99 100 101
102 103 104 105 107 108 109 111 114 115 118 119 120 121 126 129 130
131 132 134 135 145 146 147 148 **P**6 8 **S** LifeBridge Health, Baltimore, MD
Primary Contact: Leslie Simmons, R.N., FACHE, R.N., President and Chief
Executive Officer
CFO: Kevin Kelbly, Senior Vice President Finance and Corporate Fiscal Affairs
CMO: Mark Olszyk, M.D., Vice President Medical Affairs and Chief Medical Officer
CHR: Tracey Ellison, Vice President Human Resources
CNO: Stephanie Reid, R.N., Vice President of Quality and Chief Nursing Officer
Web address: www.carrollhospitalcenter.org
Control: Other not–for–profit (including NFP Corporation) **Service:** General
Medical and Surgical

Staffed Beds: 147 **Admissions:** 10767 **Census:** 101 **Outpatient Visits:**
169825 **Births:** 1079 **Personnel:** 2332

Many Facility Codes have changed. Please refer to the AHA Guide Code Chart.   © 2016 AHA Guide

MASSACHUSETTS

ATHOL—Worcester County

☐ **ATHOL MEMORIAL HOSPITAL (221303)**, 2033 Main Street, Zip 01331–3598; tel. 978/249–3511, (Nonreporting) **A**1 10 18
Primary Contact: Winfield S. Brown, FACHE, President and Chief Executive Officer
COO: Michael Grimmer, Chief Operating Officer
CFO: Robert Crosby, Chief Financial Officer
CMO: Mohsen Noreldin, M.D., President Medical Staff
CIO: Carol Roosa, Vice President Information Services and Chief Information Officer
CNO: Lucille Songer, Chief Nursing Officer
Web address: www.atholhospital.org
Control: Other not–for–profit (including NFP Corporation) **Service:** General Medical and Surgical

Staffed Beds: 12

ATTLEBORO—Bristol County

☐ **ARBOUR–FULLER HOSPITAL (224021)**, 200 May Street, Zip 02703–5520; tel. 508/761–8500, (Nonreporting) **A**1 10 **S** Universal Health Services, Inc., King of Prussia, PA
Primary Contact: Rachel Legend, MSH, LICSW, Interim Chief Executive Officer
CFO: James Rollins, Chief Financial Officer
CMO: Aminadav Zakai, M.D., Medical Director
CHR: Brian Jenkins, Director Human Resources
Web address: www.arbourhealth.com
Control: Corporation, Investor–owned, for–profit **Service:** Psychiatric

Staffed Beds: 46

★ ◇ **STURDY MEMORIAL HOSPITAL (220008)**, 211 Park Street, Zip 02703–3137, Mailing Address: PO Box 2963, Zip 02703–0963; tel. 508/222–5200 **A**2 5 10 21 **F**3 8 13 15 18 20 28 29 30 31 32 34 35 36 39 40 44 45 46 49 50 56 57 58 59 61 64 70 74 75 76 77 78 79 81 82 85 86 87 89 93 97 100 107 108 109 110 111 115 118 119 129 130 131 132 134 144 146 147 148 **P**5 6
Primary Contact: Bruce S. Auerbach, M.D., President and Chief Executive Officer
CFO: Joseph Casey, Chief Financial Officer
CMO: Brian Kelly, M.D., Vice President Medical Affairs and Medical Director
CHR: Cheryl Barrows, Vice President Human Resources
CNO: Marita Prater, MS, Vice President Patient Care Services
Web address: www.sturdymemorial.org
Control: Other not–for–profit (including NFP Corporation) **Service:** General Medical and Surgical

Staffed Beds: 128 **Admissions:** 6237 **Census:** 77 **Outpatient Visits:** 214105 **Births:** 661 **Total Expense ($000):** 153815 **Payroll Expense ($000):** 80343 **Personnel:** 849

AYER—Middlesex County

☐ **NASHOBA VALLEY MEDICAL CENTER (220098)**, 200 Groton Road, Zip 01432–3300; tel. 978/784–9000, (Nonreporting) **A**1 10 **S** Steward Health Care System, LLC, Boston, MA
Primary Contact: Salvatore Perla, President
CFO: Ben Moll, Assistant Chief Financial Officer
CMO: Michael Older, M.D., President Medical Staff
Web address: www.nashobamed.com
Control: Corporation, Investor–owned, for–profit **Service:** General Medical and Surgical

Staffed Beds: 48

BEDFORD—Middlesex County

✠ **BEDFORD VETERANS AFFAIRS MEDICAL CENTER, EDITH NOURSE ROGERS MEMORIAL VETERANS HOSPITAL**, 200 Springs Road, Zip 01730–1198; tel. 781/687–2000 **A**1 3 5 **F**4 5 6 11 18 29 30 34 35 38 39 44 50 53 54 56 57 58 59 61 62 63 64 66 67 74 75 77 82 84 86 87 90 91 93 94 96 97 98 100 101 103 104 105 106 128 130 132 135 143 144 146 147 148 **S** Department of Veterans Affairs, Washington, DC
Primary Contact: Karen Acerra–Williams, Acting Director
COO: Mark Fontaine–Westhart, Associate Director
CFO: Edward Koetting, Chief Financial Officer
CMO: Dan Berlowitz, M.D., Acting Chief of Staff
CHR: Robert Colpitts, Chief Human Resource Service
CNO: Mary Ann Petrillo, R.N., Acting Associate Director Nursing and Patient Clinical Services
Web address: www.bedford.va.gov
Control: Veterans Affairs, Government, federal **Service:** Psychiatric

Staffed Beds: 461 **Admissions:** 1842 **Census:** 341 **Outpatient Visits:** 222677 **Births:** 0 **Total Expense ($000):** 123367 **Payroll Expense ($000):** 91169 **Personnel:** 1479

BELMONT—Middlesex County

✠ **MCLEAN HOSPITAL (224007)**, 115 Mill Street, Zip 02478–1064; tel. 617/855–2000 **A**1 3 5 10 **F**4 5 29 50 53 56 58 64 68 77 86 98 99 100 101 103 104 105 106 111 119 130 132 134 146 **P**6 **S** Partners HealthCare System, Inc., Boston, MA
Primary Contact: Scott L. Rauch, M.D., President
COO: Michele L. Gougeon, Executive Vice President and Chief Operating Officer
CFO: David A. Lagasse, Senior Vice President Fiscal Affairs
CMO: Joseph Gold, M.D., Chief Medical Officer
CIO: Andrew Laband, Chief Information Officer
CHR: Lisa D. Pratt, Vice President, Human Resources
CNO: Linda Flaherty, R.N., Senior Vice President, Patient Care Services
Web address: www.mcleanhospital.org
Control: Other not–for–profit (including NFP Corporation) **Service:** Psychiatric

Staffed Beds: 182 **Admissions:** 5756 **Census:** 164 **Outpatient Visits:** 124638 **Births:** 0 **Total Expense ($000):** 193757 **Payroll Expense ($000):** 81472 **Personnel:** 1672

BEVERLY—Essex County

✠ **BEVERLY HOSPITAL (220033)**, 85 Herrick Street, Zip 01915–1777; tel. 978/922–3000, (Includes ADDISON GILBERT HOSPITAL, 298 Washington Street, Gloucester, Zip 01930–4887; tel. 978/283–4000), (Nonreporting) **A**1 2 3 5 10 **S** Lahey Health, Burlington, MA
Primary Contact: Philip M. Cormier, Chief Executive Officer
COO: Pauline Pike, Chief Operating Officer
CFO: Gary P. Marlow, Chief Financial Officer
CMO: Peter H. Short, M.D., Senior Vice President Medical Affairs
CIO: Robert Laramie, Chief Information Officer
CHR: Althea C. Lyons, Vice President Human Resources and Development
Web address: www.beverlyhospital.org
Control: Other not–for–profit (including NFP Corporation) **Service:** General Medical and Surgical

Staffed Beds: 404

BOSTON—Suffolk County

☐ **ARBOUR HOSPITAL (224013)**, 49 Robinwood Avenue, Zip 02130–2156; tel. 617/522–4400, (Nonreporting) **A**1 10 **S** Universal Health Services, Inc., King of Prussia, PA
Primary Contact: Laura Ames, Chief Executive Officer
Web address: www.arbourhealth.com
Control: Other not–for–profit (including NFP Corporation) **Service:** Psychiatric

Staffed Beds: 118

Hospital, Medicare Provider Number, Address, Telephone, Approval, Facility, and Physician Codes, Health Care System

★ American Hospital Association (AHA) membership
☐ The Joint Commission accreditation
◯ Healthcare Facilities Accreditation Program
◇ DNV Healthcare Inc. accreditation
⇑ Center for Improvement in Healthcare Quality Accreditation
△ Commission on Accreditation of Rehabilitation Facilities (CARF) accreditation

MA

☒ **BETH ISRAEL DEACONESS MEDICAL CENTER (220086)**, 330 Brookline Avenue, Zip 02215–5491; tel. 617/667–7000 **A**1 2 3 5 8 10 **F**3 6 9 11 12 13 14 15 17 18 20 22 24 26 28 29 30 31 34 35 36 37 38 40 43 44 45 46 47 48 49 50 51 52 53 54 55 56 57 58 59 60 61 63 64 65 66 68 70 71 72 73 74 75 76 77 78 79 81 82 84 85 86 87 92 93 97 98 100 101 102 103 104 107 108 109 110 111 112 113 114 115 116 117 118 119 120 121 123 124 126 129 130 131 132 135 136 138 139 141 142 143 144 145 146 147 148 **P**8
Primary Contact: Kevin Tabb, M.D., President and Chief Executive Officer
COO: Nancy A. Formella, R.N., Chief Operating Officer
CFO: Steven P. Fischer, Chief Financial Officer
CIO: John Halamka, M.D., Chief Information Officer
CHR: Judi Bieber, Senior Vice President Human Resources
CNO: Marsha L. Maurer, R.N., Chief Nursing Officer Patient Care Services
Web address: www.bidmc.harvard.edu
Control: Other not–for–profit (including NFP Corporation) **Service:** General Medical and Surgical

Staffed Beds: 672 **Admissions:** 33878 **Census:** 516 **Outpatient Visits:** 677150 **Births:** 5072 **Total Expense ($000):** 1476845 **Payroll Expense ($000):** 594217 **Personnel:** 7987

☐ **BOSTON CHILDREN'S HOSPITAL (223302)**, 300 Longwood Avenue, Zip 02115–5737; tel. 617/355–6000 **A**1 3 5 8 10 **F**3 5 8 11 12 14 18 19 20 21 22 23 24 25 26 27 28 29 34 35 36 37 38 39 40 41 43 44 45 46 48 49 50 51 54 55 57 58 59 60 61 62 63 64 65 67 68 72 74 75 77 78 79 80 81 82 83 84 85 86 87 88 89 92 93 94 97 98 99 100 101 102 104 107 108 109 111 112 113 114 115 116 117 118 119 120 121 123 124 126 129 130 131 132 134 135 136 137 138 139 140 141 142 143 144 146 147 148 **P**3 5
Primary Contact: Sandra L. Fenwick, M.P.H., President and Chief Executive Officer
COO: Kevin B. Churchwell, M.D., Chief Operating Officer and Executive Vice President Health Affairs
CFO: Douglas M. Vanderslice, Senior Vice President and Chief Financial Officer
CIO: Daniel Nigrin, M.D., Vice President Information Services and Chief Information Officer
CHR: Inez Stewart, Vice President
Web address: www.childrenshospital.org/
Control: Other not–for–profit (including NFP Corporation) **Service:** Children's general

Staffed Beds: 415 **Admissions:** 15817 **Census:** 312 **Outpatient Visits:** 666560 **Births:** 0 **Total Expense ($000):** 1383220 **Payroll Expense ($000):** 503153 **Personnel:** 8438

☒ **BOSTON MEDICAL CENTER (220031)**, 1 Boston Medical Center Place, Zip 02118–2908; tel. 617/638–8000 **A**1 2 3 5 8 10 **F**3 5 8 9 12 13 15 17 18 20 22 24 26 28 29 30 31 32 35 36 38 40 41 43 44 45 46 47 49 50 51 54 55 56 57 58 59 61 64 65 66 68 70 72 73 74 75 76 77 78 79 81 82 84 85 86 87 88 89 93 97 99 100 101 102 103 104 107 108 110 111 114 116 117 118 119 120 121 123 124 126 129 130 131 132 134 135 136 138 142 143 144 145 146 147 148 **P**7
Primary Contact: Kate Walsh, M.P.H., President and Chief Executive Officer
CFO: Ronald E. Bartlett, Chief Financial Officer
CMO: Ravin Davidoff, M.D., Chief Medical Officer
CHR: Stephanie Lovell, Vice President and General Counsel
Web address: www.bmc.org
Control: Other not–for–profit (including NFP Corporation) **Service:** General Medical and Surgical

Staffed Beds: 458 **Admissions:** 22547 **Census:** 323 **Outpatient Visits:** 1050976 **Births:** 2437 **Total Expense ($000):** 1125334 **Payroll Expense ($000):** 405586 **Personnel:** 5068

☒ **BRIGHAM AND WOMEN'S FAULKNER HOSPITAL (220119)**, 1153 Centre Street, Zip 02130–3446; tel. 617/983–7000 **A**1 3 5 8 10 **F**3 5 9 11 12 15 17 18 28 29 30 32 34 35 40 41 45 46 47 49 50 51 54 56 57 58 59 64 65 68 70 74 75 77 79 81 82 84 85 86 87 90 91 93 94 96 98 100 101 102 103 104 105 107 108 110 111 114 115 118 119 126 129 130 131 132 133 145 146 147 148 **P**6 **S** Partners HealthCare System, Inc., Boston, MA
Primary Contact: Michael Gustafson, M.D., President
CFO: Gerard Hadley, Vice President Finance for Brigham & Women's Faulkner Hospital and Vice President Finance and Controller
CMO: Margaret M. Duggan, M.D., Chief Medical Officer
CIO: Catherine Schroeder, Deputy Chief Information Officer
CHR: Laura Barnett, Executive Director, Human Resources
CNO: Judy M. Hayes, R.N., Vice President Nursing and Chief Nursing Officer
Web address: www.brighamandwomensfaulkner.org/index.asp
Control: Other not–for–profit (including NFP Corporation) **Service:** General Medical and Surgical

Staffed Beds: 83 **Admissions:** 8460 **Census:** 100 **Outpatient Visits:** 212588 **Births:** 0 **Total Expense ($000):** 216053 **Payroll Expense ($000):** 94374 **Personnel:** 949

☒ **BRIGHAM AND WOMEN'S HOSPITAL (220110)**, 75 Francis Street, Zip 02115–6110; tel. 617/732–5500 **A**1 2 3 5 8 10 **F**3 5 6 8 9 11 12 13 14 15 16 17 18 20 22 24 26 28 29 30 31 32 33 34 35 36 37 38 39 40 43 44 45 46 47 48 49 50 51 52 54 55 56 57 58 59 60 61 64 65 66 68 70 71 72 74 75 76 77 78 79 81 82 83 84 85 86 87 92 93 97 99 100 101 102 103 104 105 107 108 110 111 112 114 115 116 117 118 119 120 121 123 124 126 129 130 131 132 133 134 135 136 137 138 140 141 142 143 144 145 146 147 148 **P**6 **S** Partners HealthCare System, Inc., Boston, MA
Primary Contact: Elizabeth Nabel, M.D., President
COO: Ron Walls, M.D., Executive Vice President and COO
CFO: Christopher Dunleavy, Senior Vice President Finance and Chief Financial Officer
CMO: Stanley Ashley, M.D., Chief Medical Officer
CIO: Adam Landman, M.D., Chief Information Officer
CHR: Julie Celano, Vice President Human Resources
CNO: Jacqueline G. Somerville, R.N., Senior Vice President for Patient Care Services and Chief Nursing Officer
Web address: www.brighamandwomens.org
Control: Other not–for–profit (including NFP Corporation) **Service:** General Medical and Surgical

Staffed Beds: 741 **Admissions:** 39917 **Census:** 656 **Outpatient Visits:** 1259087 **Births:** 6617 **Total Expense ($000):** 2521962 **Payroll Expense ($000):** 752606 **Personnel:** 13245

☐ **CARNEY HOSPITAL (220017)**, 2100 Dorchester Avenue, Zip 02124–5615; tel. 617/296–4000, (Nonreporting) **A**1 2 3 5 10 **S** Steward Health Care System, LLC, Boston, MA
Primary Contact: Walter J. Ramos, President and Chief Executive Officer
COO: Christian Stroucken, Chief Operating Officer
CFO: David McGrail, Vice President Finance
CMO: Alexander White, Vice President Medical Affairs
CHR: Mary Orlandi, Manager Human Resources
Web address: www.carneyhospital.org
Control: Corporation, Investor–owned, for–profit **Service:** General Medical and Surgical

Staffed Beds: 120

☒ **DANA–FARBER CANCER INSTITUTE (220162)**, 450 Brookline Avenue, Zip 02215–5418; tel. 617/632–3000 **A**1 2 3 5 8 10 **F**3 11 15 29 30 31 32 34 35 36 44 50 54 55 57 58 59 64 65 66 68 71 75 77 78 82 83 84 85 86 87 99 100 101 104 107 108 110 111 114 115 117 118 119 120 121 123 124 130 132 134 135 136 146 147 148 **P**6
Primary Contact: Edward J. Benz, Jr., M.D., President and Chief Executive Officer
COO: Dorothy E. Puhy, Executive VP and Chief Operating Officer
CIO: Jeffrey R. Kessler, Vice President Information Services
CHR: Emily Barclay, Vice President Human Resources
Web address: www.dana–farber.org
Control: Other not–for–profit (including NFP Corporation) **Service:** Cancer

Staffed Beds: 30 **Admissions:** 1296 **Census:** 27 **Outpatient Visits:** 367336 **Births:** 0 **Total Expense ($000):** 1157940 **Payroll Expense ($000):** 342599 **Personnel:** 4328

DR. SOLOMON CARTER FULLER MENTAL HEALTH CENTER (224040), 85 East Newton Street, Zip 02118–2340; tel. 617/626–8700, (Nonreporting) **A**3 5 10
Primary Contact: Mary–Louise White, M.D., Chief Executive Officer
Control: Other not–for–profit (including NFP Corporation) **Service:** Psychiatric

Staffed Beds: 32

☒ **FRANCISCAN HOSPITAL FOR CHILDREN (223300)**, 30 Warren Street, Zip 02135–3680; tel. 617/254–3800 **A**1 3 10 **F**1 29 30 38 39 58 59 64 65 68 75 77 81 86 87 90 91 93 97 98 99 100 104 105 106 130 132 **P**8
Primary Contact: John D. Nash, FACHE, President and Chief Executive Officer
COO: Donna Polselli, Chief Operating Officer
CFO: Alex Denucci, Chief Financial Officer
CMO: Jane E. O'Brien, M.D., Medical Director
CIO: Sean McKeon, Director, Information Technology
CHR: Nancy Murphy, Vice President, Human Resources
CNO: Mary Lou Kelleher, R.N., Vice President, Nursing
Web address: www.franciscanhospital.org
Control: Other not–for–profit (including NFP Corporation) **Service:** Children's Long–Term Acute Care

Staffed Beds: 72 **Admissions:** 804 **Census:** 59 **Outpatient Visits:** 28547 **Births:** 0 **Total Expense ($000):** 58857 **Payroll Expense ($000):** 30646 **Personnel:** 418

Many Facility Codes have changed. Please refer to the AHA Guide Code Chart. © 2016 AHA Guide

MA

★ △ **HEBREW REHABILITATION CENTER (222007)**, 1200 Centre Street, Zip 02131–1097; tel. 617/363–8000, (Total facility includes 675 beds in nursing home–type unit) **A**7 10 **F**1 2 6 18 29 30 35 39 50 58 59 60 64 65 68 69 75 77 82 83 84 93 97 100 103 104 119 128 130 132 143 146 148 **P**6
Primary Contact: Mary K. Moscato, FACHE, President
COO: Brian Murphy, Senior Director Admissions and Referral Services
CFO: Lise Paul, Vice President Reimbursement and Network Planning
CMO: Helen Chen, M.D., Chief Medical Officer
CIO: Eric Rogers, Chief Information Officer
CHR: Deborah Lemmerman, Vice President, Human Resources
CNO: Tammy B. Retalic, R.N., Chief Nursing Officer
Web address: www.hebrewseniorlife.org
Control: Other not–for–profit (including NFP Corporation) **Service:** Long–Term Acute Care hospital

Staffed Beds: 725 **Admissions:** 1432 **Census:** 688 **Outpatient Visits:** 36630 **Births:** 0 **Total Expense ($000):** 128317 **Payroll Expense ($000):** 77295 **Personnel:** 1098

☐ **MASSACHUSETTS EYE AND EAR INFIRMARY (220075)**, 243 Charles Street, Zip 02114–3002; tel. 617/523–7900 **A**1 3 5 10 **F**3 7 8 11 29 30 31 34 35 36 40 41 44 50 54 55 56 57 58 59 64 65 66 68 74 75 77 78 81 82 85 86 87 89 107 111 114 119 130 132 141 143 144 146 148 **P**6
Primary Contact: John R. Fernandez, President and Chief Executive Officer
CFO: CarolAnn Williams, Chief Financial Officer
CIO: Leo Hill, Chief Information Officer
CHR: Martha Pyle Farrell, Vice President Human Resources and General Counsel
Web address: www.masseyeandear.org
Control: Other not–for–profit (including NFP Corporation) **Service:** Eye, ear, nose, and throat

Staffed Beds: 41 **Admissions:** 1263 **Census:** 13 **Outpatient Visits:** 394513 **Births:** 0 **Total Expense ($000):** 252784 **Payroll Expense ($000):** 71324 **Personnel:** 1901

⊠ **MASSACHUSETTS GENERAL HOSPITAL (220071)**, 55 Fruit Street, Zip 02114–2696; tel. 617/726–2000, (Includes MASSGENERAL HOSPITAL FOR CHILDREN, 55 Fruit Street, Zip 02114–2621; tel. 888/644–3248) **A**1 3 5 8 10 **F**3 5 6 8 9 11 12 13 14 15 16 17 18 19 20 21 22 23 24 25 26 27 28 29 30 31 32 33 34 35 36 37 38 39 40 41 43 44 45 46 47 48 49 50 51 52 53 54 55 56 57 58 59 60 61 62 63 64 65 66 68 70 72 73 74 75 76 77 78 79 81 82 84 85 86 87 88 89 91 92 93 94 96 97 98 99 100 101 102 103 104 107 108 110 111 112 113 114 115 116 117 118 119 120 121 122 123 124 126 129 130 131 132 134 135 136 137 138 139 140 141 142 143 144 145 146 147 148 **P**6 7 **S** Partners HealthCare System, Inc., Boston, MA
Primary Contact: Peter L. Slavin, M.D., President
CFO: Sally Mason Boemer, Senior Vice President Finance
CMO: Britain Nicholson, M.D., Chief Medical Officer
CIO: Keith Jennings, Chief Information Officer
CHR: Jeff Davis, Senior Vice President Human Resources
CNO: Jeanette R. Ives Erickson, MS, Senior Vice President Patient Care and Chief Nurse
Web address: www.massgeneral.org
Control: Other not–for–profit (including NFP Corporation) **Service:** General Medical and Surgical

Staffed Beds: 1016 **Admissions:** 50800 **Census:** 829 **Outpatient Visits:** 919934 **Births:** 3840 **Total Expense ($000):** 3251871 **Payroll Expense ($000):** 1001586 **Personnel:** 17398

⊠ **NEW ENGLAND BAPTIST HOSPITAL (220088)**, 125 Parker Hill Avenue, Zip 02120–2847; tel. 617/754–5800 **A**1 3 5 10 **F**3 8 9 14 18 20 26 29 30 34 35 36 37 44 45 46 50 51 53 54 57 58 59 64 65 66 68 70 74 75 77 79 81 82 85 86 87 91 92 93 96 97 100 107 108 111 115 119 126 130 131 132 135 141 143 146 148
Primary Contact: Trish Hannon, FACHE, R.N., President and Chief Executive Officer
CFO: Thomas Gheringhelli, Senior Vice President, Chief Financial Officer
CHR: Linda Thompson, Senior Vice President, Human Resources and Service Excellence
CNO: Mary Sullivan Smith, R.N., Senior Vice President, Chief Operating Officer and Chief Nursing Officer
Web address: www.nebh.org
Control: Other not–for–profit (including NFP Corporation) **Service:** Orthopedic

Staffed Beds: 118 **Admissions:** 8214 **Census:** 68 **Outpatient Visits:** 124527 **Births:** 0 **Total Expense ($000):** 238693 **Payroll Expense ($000):** 84299 **Personnel:** 911

☐ **SHRINERS HOSPITALS FOR CHILDREN–BOSTON (223304)**, (Pediatric Burns, Orthopaedics, Cleft Lip & Palate), 51 Blossom Street, Zip 02114–2601; tel. 617/722–3000 **A**1 3 5 10 **F**3 16 29 30 34 35 57 64 68 75 77 79 81 85 86 87 93 99 104 130 132 141 143 146 148 **S** Shriners Hospitals for Children, Tampa, FL
Primary Contact: John Patrick ONeill, Administrator
CFO: Maria Chung, CPA, Director Fiscal Services
CMO: Matthias B. Donelan, M.D., Chief of Staff
CIO: Mary Dolan, Regional Director Information Services and HIPAA Security Official
CHR: John Donlin, Regional Director Human Resources – Boston, Erie, and Springfield
Web address: www.shrinershospitalsforchildren.org/Hospitals/Locations/Boston
Control: Other not–for–profit (including NFP Corporation) **Service:** Children's other specialty

Staffed Beds: 14 **Admissions:** 179 **Census:** 6 **Outpatient Visits:** 5905 **Births:** 0 **Total Expense ($000):** 36224 **Payroll Expense ($000):** 14593 **Personnel:** 193

⊠ **TUFTS MEDICAL CENTER (220116)**, 800 Washington Street, Zip 02111–1552; tel. 617/636–5000 **A**1 2 3 5 8 10 **F**3 12 13 14 15 17 18 19 20 21 22 23 24 25 26 27 28 29 30 31 32 34 35 39 40 41 43 44 45 47 49 50 51 52 55 56 57 58 59 61 64 65 68 70 71 72 74 75 76 77 78 79 81 82 84 85 86 87 88 89 93 97 98 99 100 102 104 107 108 111 114 115 116 117 118 119 120 121 123 124 126 129 130 131 132 134 135 136 137 138 143 146 147 148 **P**5
Primary Contact: Michael Wagner, M.D., President and Chief Executive Officer
CFO: Kristine Hanscom, Chief Financial Officer
CMO: David Fairchild, M.D., Chief Medical Officer
CIO: William Shickolovich, Chief Information Officer
CNO: Therese M. Hudson–Jinks, R.N., Chief Nursing Officer
Web address: www.tuftsmedicalcenter.org
Control: Other not–for–profit (including NFP Corporation) **Service:** General Medical and Surgical

Staffed Beds: 258 **Admissions:** 16610 **Census:** 254 **Outpatient Visits:** 402086 **Births:** 1263 **Total Expense ($000):** 659874 **Payroll Expense ($000):** 261322 **Personnel:** 4291

★ △ **VETERANS AFFAIRS BOSTON HEALTHCARE SYSTEM**, 1400 VFW Parkway, Zip 02132–4927; tel. 617/323–7700, (Nonreporting) **A**3 5 7 8 **S** Department of Veterans Affairs, Washington, DC
Primary Contact: Vincent Ng, Director
CFO: Joe Costa, Chief Financial Officer
CMO: Brian Hoffman, M.D., Chief Medical Services
CIO: David M. Goodman, Ph.D., Chief Information Officer
CHR: William Warfield, Chief Human Resources Management
Web address: www.boston.va.gov/
Control: Veterans Affairs, Government, federal **Service:** General Medical and Surgical

Staffed Beds: 361

BRADFORD—Essex County

⊠ **WHITTIER REHABILITATION HOSPITAL (222047)**, 145 Ward Hill Avenue, Zip 01835–6928; tel. 978/372–8000, (Nonreporting) **A**1 10 **S** Whittier Health Network, Haverhill, MA
Primary Contact: Alfred J. Arcidi, M.D., Senior Vice President
Web address: www.whittierhealth.com
Control: Partnership, Investor–owned, for–profit **Service:** Long–Term Acute Care hospital

Staffed Beds: 60

BRAINTREE—Norfolk County

⊠ **HEALTHSOUTH BRAINTREE REHABILITATION HOSPITAL (223027)**, 250 Pond Street, Zip 02184–5351; tel. 781/348–2500 **A**1 3 5 10 **F**29 34 35 54 57 59 64 74 75 77 78 79 86 87 90 91 92 93 108 119 130 131 132 146 148 **P**5 **S** HEALTHSOUTH Corporation, Birmingham, AL
Primary Contact: Randy Doherty, CPA, Chief Executive Officer
CMO: Arthur Williams, M.D., Medical Director
CHR: Cathryn Wigman, Director Human Resources
CNO: Jinia Drinkwater, R.N., Director Patient Care Services
Web address: www.braintreerehabhospital.com
Control: Corporation, Investor–owned, for–profit **Service:** Rehabilitation

Staffed Beds: 187 **Admissions:** 2181 **Census:** 95 **Outpatient Visits:** 77897 **Births:** 0

Hospital, Medicare Provider Number, Address, Telephone, Approval, Facility, and Physician Codes, Health Care System

★ American Hospital Association (AHA) membership ○ Healthcare Facilities Accreditation Program ⇑ Center for Improvement in Healthcare Quality Accreditation
☐ The Joint Commission accreditation ◇ DNV Healthcare Inc. accreditation △ Commission on Accreditation of Rehabilitation Facilities (CARF) accreditation

MA

BRIDGEWATER—Plymouth County

BRIDGEWATER STATE HOSPITAL, 20 Administration Road, Zip 02324–3201; tel. 508/279–4521, (Nonreporting) **A**3 5
Primary Contact: Daniel Calais, Superintendent
CFO: Diane Wholley, Director Fiscal Services
Control: State–Government, nonfederal **Service:** Psychiatric

Staffed Beds: 350

BRIGHTON—Suffolk County

CARITAS ST. ELIZABETH'S MEDICAL CENTER See St. Elizabeth's Medical Center

☒ **KINDRED HOSPITAL–BOSTON (222045)**, 1515 Commonwealth Avenue, Zip 02135–3617; tel. 617/254–1100, (Nonreporting) **A**1 10 **S** Kindred Healthcare, Louisville, KY
Primary Contact: Susan Downey, R.N., MS, Chief Executive Officer
CFO: Lawrence J. Toye, Chief Financial Officer
CMO: Mark Rohrer, M.D., Chief Medical Officer
Web address: www.kindredbos.com/
Control: Corporation, Investor–owned, for–profit **Service:** Long–Term Acute Care hospital

Staffed Beds: 59

☐ **ST. ELIZABETH'S MEDICAL CENTER (220036)**, 736 Cambridge Street, Zip 02135–2997; tel. 617/789–3000, (Nonreporting) **A**1 2 3 5 8 10 **S** Steward Health Care System, LLC, Boston, MA
Primary Contact: Beth Hughes, Chief Executive Officer
CFO: Jeffrey P. Dion, Vice President Finance
CIO: Joseph Schmitt, Chief Information Officer
CHR: Claudia Henderson, Chief Human Resources
Web address: www.stewardhealth.org/St_Elizabeths
Control: Corporation, Investor–owned, for–profit **Service:** General Medical and Surgical

Staffed Beds: 338

BROCKTON—Plymouth County

CARITAS GOOD SAMARITAN MEDICAL CENTER See Good Samaritan Medical Center

☐ **GOOD SAMARITAN MEDICAL CENTER (220111)**, 235 North Pearl Street, Zip 02301–1794; tel. 508/427–3000, (Includes GOOD SAMARITAN MEDICAL CENTER – CUSHING CAMPUS, 235 North Pearl Street, Zip 02401–1794; tel. 508/427–3000), (Nonreporting) **A**1 2 3 5 10 **S** Steward Health Care System, LLC, Boston, MA
Primary Contact: John A. Jurczyk, FACHE, Interim President
COO: Donna Rubinate, R.N., Chief Operating Officer
CFO: Thomas Whalen, Vice President Finance
CMO: Scott Stewart, M.D., Vice President Medical Management
CIO: Lori Caswell, Director Information Technology
CHR: David J. Cronin, Regional Vice President Human Resources
Web address: www.stewardhealth.org/Good–Samaritan
Control: Corporation, Investor–owned, for–profit **Service:** General Medical and Surgical

Staffed Beds: 189

☒ **SIGNATURE HEALTHCARE BROCKTON HOSPITAL (220052)**, 680 Centre Street, Zip 02302–3395; tel. 508/941–7000, (Total facility includes 29 beds in nursing home–type unit) **A**1 2 3 10 **F**3 11 12 13 15 17 18 20 22 24 28 29 30 31 32 34 35 38 40 45 46 47 48 49 50 51 52 54 55 56 57 58 59 60 61 64 65 66 68 70 73 74 75 76 77 78 79 81 82 84 85 87 89 93 97 98 100 101 102 103 104 105 107 108 110 111 114 115 116 117 118 119 120 121 123 128 130 131 132 135 143 144 146 147 148 **P**6 8
Primary Contact: Kim Norton Hollon, FACHE, President and Chief Executive Officer
CFO: James Papadakos, Chief Financial Officer
CMO: Vera De Palo, M.D., Chief Medical Officer
CIO: Marc Delacroix, Chief Information Officer
CHR: David Fisher, Vice President Human Resources
CNO: Kim Walsh, Chief Nursing Officer
Web address: www.signature–healthcare.org
Control: Other not–for–profit (including NFP Corporation) **Service:** General Medical and Surgical

Staffed Beds: 245 Admissions: 11749 Census: 150 Outpatient Visits: 385512 Births: 1005 Total Expense ($000): 245667 Payroll Expense ($000): 109693 Personnel: 1374

★ **VETERANS AFFAIRS BOSTON HEALTHCARE SYSTEM BROCKTON DIVISION**, 940 Belmont Street, Zip 02301–5596; tel. 508/583–4500, (Includes VETERANS AFFAIRS MEDICAL CENTER WEST ROXBURY DIVISION, 1400 VFW Parkway, West Roxbury, Zip 02132, Mailing Address: 1400 VVF Parkway, West Roxbury, Boston, Zip 02132; tel. 617/323–7700; William H. Kelleher, Director), (Nonreporting) **A**3 5 8 **S** Department of Veterans Affairs, Washington, DC
Primary Contact: Vincent Ng, Interim Director
CFO: Joe Costa, Acting Chief Fiscal Officer
Web address: www.boston.va.gov/
Control: Veterans Affairs, Government, federal **Service:** General Medical and Surgical

Staffed Beds: 375

BROOKLINE—Norfolk County

☐ **ARBOUR H. R. I. HOSPITAL (224018)**, 227 Babcock Street, Zip 02446–6799; tel. 617/731–3200, (Nonreporting) **A**1 10 **S** Universal Health Services, Inc., King of Prussia, PA
Primary Contact: William Zella, Chief Executive Officer
CFO: James Rollins, Chief Financial Officer
CMO: Anthony Raynes, M.D., Psychiatrist in Chief
CHR: Kris Munson, Director Human Resources
Web address: www.arbourhealth.com
Control: Corporation, Investor–owned, for–profit **Service:** Psychiatric

Staffed Beds: 68

BOURNEWOOD HEALTH SYSTEMS (224022), 300 South Street, Zip 02467–3658; tel. 617/469–0300 **A**3 5 10 **F**4 5 98 99 104 105 130 132 **P**1
Primary Contact: Philip A. Mason, Chief Executive Officer
CFO: Michael Gale, Chief Financial Officer
CMO: Carmel Heinsohn, M.D., Medical Director
CHR: Paula Berardi, Manager Human Resources
Web address: www.bournewood.com
Control: Corporation, Investor–owned, for–profit **Service:** Psychiatric

Staffed Beds: 90 Admissions: 3808 Census: 86 Outpatient Visits: 10240 Births: 0 Total Expense ($000): 24665 Payroll Expense ($000): 14915 Personnel: 202

BURLINGTON—Middlesex County

☒ **LAHEY HOSPITAL & MEDICAL CENTER, BURLINGTON (220171)**, 41 Mall Road, Zip 01805–0001; tel. 781/744–5100, (Includes LAHEY MEDICAL CENTER, PEABODY, 1 Essex Center Drive, Peabody, Zip 01960–2901; tel. 978/538–4000) **A**1 2 3 5 8 10 **F**3 5 6 8 9 11 12 15 17 18 20 22 24 26 28 29 30 31 34 35 36 38 40 43 44 45 46 47 48 49 50 51 53 54 55 56 57 58 59 60 61 63 64 65 68 70 74 75 77 78 79 81 82 84 85 86 87 91 92 93 96 97 100 101 102 103 104 107 108 110 111 114 115 116 117 118 119 120 121 123 124 126 129 130 131 132 135 136 138 139 141 142 144 145 146 147 148 **P**6 **S** Lahey Health, Burlington, MA
Primary Contact: Joanne Conroy, M.D., Chief Executive Officer
COO: Richard R. Bias, Chief Operating Officer
CFO: Timothy P. O'Connor, Executive Vice President and Chief Financial Officer
CMO: Andrew Villanueva, M.D., Interim Chief Medical Officer
CIO: Bruce Metz, Ph.D., Senior Vice President and Chief Information Officer
CHR: Elizabeth P. Conrad, Senior Vice President and Chief Human Resource Officer
Web address: www.lahey.org
Control: Other not–for–profit (including NFP Corporation) **Service:** General Medical and Surgical

Staffed Beds: 345 Admissions: 22303 Census: 294 Outpatient Visits: 910155 Births: 0 Total Expense ($000): 806225 Payroll Expense ($000): 283457 Personnel: 5639

CAMBRIDGE—Middlesex County

☒ **CAMBRIDGE HEALTH ALLIANCE (220011)**, 1493 Cambridge Street, Zip 02139–1099; tel. 617/665–1000, (Includes CAMBRIDGE HOSPITAL, 1493 Cambridge Street, tel. 617/498–1000; SOMERVILLE HOSPITAL, 230 Highland Avenue, Somerville, Zip 02143; tel. 617/666–4400; WHIDDEN MEMORIAL HOSPITAL, 103 Garland Street, Everett, Zip 02149–5095; tel. 617/389–6270) **A**1 2 3 5 8 10 **F**4 5 11 12 13 15 29 30 31 32 34 35 36 38 39 40 42 44 45 46 47 48 49 50 56 57 58 59 61 64 65 66 68 70 75 76 77 78 79 81 82 86 87 93 97 98 99 100 101 102 103 104 107 108 110 111 114 115 119 129 130 131 132 134 135 143 146 147 148 **P**6
Primary Contact: Patrick R. Wardell, Chief Executive Officer
CFO: Jill I. Batty, Chief Financial Officer
CMO: Assaad Sayah, M.D., Chief Medical Officer
CIO: Judith S. Klickstein, Chief Information Officer
CHR: Joy U. Curtis, Senior Vice President Human Resources
CNO: Elizabeth Cadigan, R.N., Senior Vice President Patient Care Services and Chief Nursing Officer
Web address: www.challiance.org
Control: Hospital district or authority, Government, nonfederal **Service:** General Medical and Surgical

Staffed Beds: 212 Admissions: 10526 Census: 155 Outpatient Visits: 675750 Births: 1174 Total Expense ($000): 577117 Payroll Expense ($000): 312416 Personnel: 3296

Many Facility Codes have changed. Please refer to the AHA Guide Code Chart. © 2016 AHA Guide

MA

✠ **MOUNT AUBURN HOSPITAL (220002)**, 330 Mount Auburn Street, Zip 02138–5597; tel. 617/492–3500 **A**1 2 3 5 8 10 **F**3 5 11 12 13 14 15 17 18 20 22 24 26 28 29 30 31 34 35 36 37 40 45 49 50 51 52 55 56 57 58 59 60 61 62 64 65 68 70 73 74 75 76 77 78 79 81 82 86 87 93 97 98 100 101 102 103 104 107 108 110 111 114 115 117 118 119 120 121 123 124 126 129 130 131 132 135 144 145 146 147 **P**5 6 7
Primary Contact: Jeanette G. Clough, President and Chief Executive Officer
COO: Nicholas T. Dileso, R.N., Chief Operating Officer
CFO: William Sullivan, Chief Financial Officer
CIO: Bob Todd, Director Information Systems
CHR: Tom Fabiano, Director Human Resources
CNO: Deborah Baker, Vice President, Patient Care Services
Web address: www.mountauburnhospital.org
Control: Other not–for–profit (including NFP Corporation) **Service:** General Medical and Surgical

Staffed Beds: 199 Admissions: 11421 Census: 144 Outpatient Visits: 171055 Births: 2854 Total Expense ($000): 309106 Payroll Expense ($000): 145570 Personnel: 2493

SPAULDING HOSPITAL CAMBRIDGE See Spaulding Hospital for Continuing Medical Care Cambridge

✠ **SPAULDING HOSPITAL FOR CONTINUING MEDICAL CARE CAMBRIDGE (222000)**, 1575 Cambridge Street, Zip 02138–4308; tel. 617/876–4344 **A**1 10 **F**1 7 28 29 30 31 34 35 36 50 54 57 58 60 64 68 **S** Partners HealthCare System, Inc., Boston, MA
Primary Contact: Maureen Banks, FACHE, MS, R.N., President
CFO: Mary Shaughnessy, Vice President Finance
CMO: Jonathon Schwartz, M.D., Chief Medical Officer
CIO: John Campbell, Chief Information Officer
CHR: Jack Carroll, Director Human Resources
CNO: Adrienne Sarnecki, R.N., Chief Nurse Executive
Web address: www.spauldingnetwork.org
Control: Other not–for–profit (including NFP Corporation) **Service:** Long–Term Acute Care hospital

Staffed Beds: 128 Admissions: 1548 Census: 129 Outpatient Visits: 0 Births: 0

CANTON—Norfolk County

✠ **MASSACHUSETTS HOSPITAL SCHOOL (222025)**, 3 Randolph Street, Zip 02021–2351; tel. 781/828–2440, (Nonreporting) **A**1 10 **S** Massachusetts Department of Public Health, Boston, MA
Primary Contact: Brian V. Devin, Chief Executive Officer
CFO: Sharon Porter, Chief Financial Officer
CMO: Aruna Sachdev, M.D., Medical Director
CIO: Robert Lima, Director Information Systems
CHR: Trish Scully, Manager Employment Services
Web address: www.mhsf.us/
Control: State–Government, nonfederal **Service:** Children's Long–Term Acute Care

Staffed Beds: 93

CHARLESTOWN—Suffolk County

✠ △ **SPAULDING REHABILITATION HOSPITAL (223034)**, 300 First Avenue, Zip 02129–3109; tel. 617/952–5000 **A**1 3 5 7 10 **F**3 7 29 30 34 35 36 39 50 54 57 58 60 64 68 74 75 77 82 85 86 87 90 91 92 93 94 95 96 100 104 119 129 130 131 132 143 146 148 **S** Partners HealthCare System, Inc., Boston, MA
Primary Contact: David E. Storto, President
COO: Maureen Banks, FACHE, Chief Operating Officer
CFO: Mary Shaughnessy, Vice President Finance
CMO: Ross Zafonte, D.O., Vice President, Physical Medicine and Rehabilitation and Vice President Medical Affairs, Research and Education
CIO: John Campbell, Chief Information Officer
CHR: Russell Averna, Vice President Human Resources
Web address: www.spauldingrehab.org
Control: Other not–for–profit (including NFP Corporation) **Service:** Rehabilitation

Staffed Beds: 132 Admissions: 2370 Census: 126 Outpatient Visits: 268499 Births: 0 Total Expense ($000): 132158 Payroll Expense ($000): 59211 Personnel: 1011

CLINTON—Worcester County

★ ◇ **CLINTON HOSPITAL (220058)**, 201 Highland Street, Zip 01510–1096; tel. 978/368–3000 **A**3 5 10 21 **F**3 11 29 34 35 40 44 50 59 64 68 75 77 81 85 93 98 103 107 108 110 115 119 130 146 **P**6 **S** UMass Memorial Health Care, Inc., Worcester, MA
Primary Contact: Lisa Colombo, R.N., Chief Executive Officer
CFO: Steven McCue, Chief Financial Officer
CHR: Martha Chiarchiaro, Vice President Human Resources
CNO: Charlene Elie, Vice President Patient Care Services
Web address: www.clintonhospital.org
Control: Other not–for–profit (including NFP Corporation) **Service:** General Medical and Surgical

Staffed Beds: 41 Admissions: 1054 Census: 25 Outpatient Visits: 14661 Births: 0 Total Expense ($000): 27741 Payroll Expense ($000): 12125 Personnel: 172

CONCORD—Middlesex County

✠ **EMERSON HOSPITAL (220084)**, 133 Old Road to Nine Acre Corner, Zip 01742–9120; tel. 978/369–1400 **A**1 5 10 **F**3 5 7 8 11 12 13 14 15 17 18 28 29 30 31 32 34 35 36 37 38 40 45 48 49 50 51 54 57 59 60 62 64 65 68 70 72 73 74 75 76 77 78 79 81 82 85 86 87 89 93 98 100 101 102 103 104 105 107 110 111 114 115 119 128 129 130 131 132 135 145 146 148 **P**5 8
Primary Contact: Christine C. Schuster, R.N., President and Chief Executive Officer
CFO: Michael Hachey, Senior Vice President and Chief Financial Officer
CMO: C. Gregory Martin, M.D., Chief Medical Officer
CIO: Renee Fosberg, Chief Information Officer
CHR: Eric Stastny, Vice President Human Resources
CNO: Joyce Welsh, R.N., Vice President of Clinical Services and Chief Nursing Officer
Web address: www.emersonhospital.org
Control: Other not–for–profit (including NFP Corporation) **Service:** General Medical and Surgical

Staffed Beds: 170 Admissions: 7689 Census: 97 Outpatient Visits: 252748 Births: 1153 Total Expense ($000): 199971 Payroll Expense ($000): 90462 Personnel: 1156

DARTMOUTH—Bristol County

SOUTHCOAST BEHAVIORAL HEALTH (224041), 581 Faunce Corner Road, Zip 02747–1242; tel. 888/210–2475, (Nonreporting) **S** Acadia Healthcare Company, Inc., Franklin, TN
Primary Contact: Kevin R. Burchill, Chief Executive Officer
Web address: www.southcoastbehavioral.com
Control: Corporation, Investor–owned, for–profit **Service:** Psychiatric

Staffed Beds: 120

EAST SANDWICH—Barnstable County

✠ △ **SPAULDING REHABILITATION HOSPITAL CAPE COD (223032)**, 311 Service Road, Zip 02537–1370; tel. 508/833–4000 **A**1 7 10 **F**3 28 29 30 32 34 35 36 50 56 60 64 74 75 77 79 82 90 91 92 93 94 96 130 131 132 146 147 148 **P**4 6 **S** Partners HealthCare System, Inc., Boston, MA
Primary Contact: Maureen Banks, FACHE, MS, R.N., President
COO: Stephanie Nadolny, Vice President of Hospital Operations
CFO: Mary Shaughnessy, Vice President Finance
CMO: David Lowell, M.D., Chief Medical Officer
CIO: John Campbell, Chief Information Officer
CHR: Russell Averna, Vice President of Human Resources
CNO: Adrienne Sarnecki, R.N., Chief Nursing Officer
Web address: www.spauldingrehab.org
Control: State–Government, nonfederal **Service:** Rehabilitation

Staffed Beds: 60 Admissions: 1131 Census: 43 Outpatient Visits: 111381 Births: 0 Total Expense ($000): 38294 Payroll Expense ($000): 21237 Personnel: 344

EVERETT—Middlesex County

WHIDDEN MEMORIAL HOSPITAL See Cambridge Health Alliance, Cambridge

FALL RIVER—Bristol County

CHARLTON MEMORIAL HOSPITAL See Southcoast Hospitals Group

□ **DR. J. CORRIGAN MENTAL HEALTH CENTER (224028)**, 49 Hillside Street, Zip 02720–5266; tel. 508/235–7200, (Nonreporting) **A**1 10 **S** Massachusetts Department of Mental Health, Boston, MA
Primary Contact: Frank O'Reilly, Director
Control: State–Government, nonfederal **Service:** Psychiatric

Staffed Beds: 16

MA

☐ **SAINT ANNE'S HOSPITAL (220020)**, 795 Middle Street, Zip 02721–1798; tel. 508/674–5741, (Nonreporting) **A**1 2 10 **S** Steward Health Care System, LLC, Boston, MA
Primary Contact: Craig A. Jesiolowski, FACHE, President
CFO: Michael Bushell, Vice President Operations, Chief Financial Officer
CMO: John Conlon, M.D., Chief Medical Officer
CIO: Julie Berry, Chief Information Officer
CHR: Sandra Dellicker, Director of Human Resources
CNO: Carole Billington, R.N., Vice President Operations, Chief Nursing Officer
Web address: www.saintanneshospital.org
Control: Corporation, Investor–owned, for–profit **Service:** General Medical and Surgical

Staffed Beds: 160

✠ **SOUTHCOAST HOSPITALS GROUP (220074)**, 363 Highland Avenue, Zip 02720–3703; tel. 508/679–3131, (Includes CHARLTON MEMORIAL HOSPITAL, 363 Highland Avenue, tel. 508/679–3131; Keith A. Hovan, R.N., President and Chief Executive Officer; ST. LUKE'S HOSPITAL, 101 Page Street, New Bedford, Zip 02740; tel. 508/997–1515; Keith A. Hovan, R.N., President and Chief Executive Officer; TOBEY HOSPITAL, 43 High Street, Wareham, Zip 02571; tel. 508/295–0880; Keith A. Hovan, R.N., President and Chief Executive Officer) **A**1 2 10 **F**3 8 11 12 13 15 17 18 20 22 24 26 28 29 30 31 34 35 37 40 41 44 45 46 47 48 49 50 51 54 56 57 58 59 60 61 64 65 68 70 71 73 74 75 76 77 78 79 81 82 83 84 85 86 87 89 90 91 92 93 95 96 100 101 102 103 107 108 110 111 114 115 116 117 118 119 120 121 123 124 126 130 131 132 134 135 144 146 147 148 **P**5 6
Primary Contact: Keith A. Hovan, R.N., President and Chief Executive Officer
COO: Renee Clark, Senior Vice President and Chief Operating Officer
CFO: Robert Tarola, Executive Vice President and Chief Financial Officer
CMO: Robert Caldas, D.O., Chief Medical Officer
CIO: Joan McFaul, Senior Vice President and Chief Information Officer
CHR: David DeJesus, Senior Vice President Human Resources
CNO: Timothy D. Eixenberger, Chief Nursing Officer
Web address: www.southcoast.org
Control: Other not–for–profit (including NFP Corporation) **Service:** General Medical and Surgical

Staffed Beds: 666 Admissions: 37454 Census: 453 Outpatient Visits: 907028 Births: 3458 Total Expense ($000): 741761 Payroll Expense ($000): 319351 Personnel: 4130

FALMOUTH—Barnstable County

✠ **FALMOUTH HOSPITAL (220135)**, 100 Ter Heun Drive, Zip 02540–2599; tel. 508/548–5300 **A**1 2 10 **F**3 8 11 13 15 18 20 28 29 30 34 35 36 38 40 45 50 53 54 57 59 61 64 65 68 70 74 75 76 77 79 81 82 85 86 87 89 93 96 102 107 108 110 111 115 118 119 129 130 131 132 135 143 144 146 147 148 **P**6 8 **S** Cape Cod Healthcare, Inc., Hyannis, MA
Primary Contact: Michael K. Lauf, President and Chief Executive Officer
COO: Lori Jewett, R.N., Vice President of Nursing and Chief Operating Officer
CFO: Michael Connors, Senior Vice President and Chief Financial Officer
CMO: Alex Heard, Chief Medical Officer
CIO: Jeanne M. Fallon, Chief Information Officer
CHR: Emily Schorer, Vice President, Human Resources
CNO: Lori Jewett, R.N., Vice President of Nursing
Web address: www.capecodhealth.org
Control: Other not–for–profit (including NFP Corporation) **Service:** General Medical and Surgical

Staffed Beds: 95 Admissions: 5866 Census: 68 Outpatient Visits: 139222 Births: 425 Total Expense ($000): 143533 Payroll Expense ($000): 64159 Personnel: 530

FRAMINGHAM—Middlesex County

✠ **METROWEST MEDICAL CENTER (220175)**, 115 Lincoln Street, Zip 01702–6342; tel. 508/383–1000, (Includes FRAMINGHAM UNION HOSPITAL, 115 Lincoln Street, Zip 01702; tel. 508/383–1000; LEONARD MORSE HOSPITAL, 67 Union Street, Natick, Zip 01760; tel. 508/650–7000) **A**1 2 3 5 10 **F**3 5 12 13 14 15 18 20 22 26 28 29 30 31 32 34 35 36 40 41 44 45 49 50 54 56 57 59 61 62 63 64 65 68 70 73 74 75 76 77 78 79 81 84 85 87 89 93 97 98 99 100 102 103 104 105 107 108 110 114 115 118 119 120 121 129 130 131 132 134 135 143 146 147 148 **S** TENET Healthcare Corporation, Dallas, TX
Primary Contact: Barbara J. Doyle, R.N., MS, Chief Executive Officer
CHR: Rebecca Heffernan, Director Human Resources
CNO: Donna T. Gemme, R.N., Chief Nursing Officer Vice President Patient Care Services
Web address: www.mwmc.com
Control: Corporation, Investor–owned, for–profit **Service:** General Medical and Surgical

Staffed Beds: 155 Admissions: 11270 Census: 150 Outpatient Visits: 358014 Births: 895 Total Expense ($000): 246956 Payroll Expense ($000): 115595 Personnel: 1684

GARDNER—Worcester County

☐ **HEYWOOD HOSPITAL (220095)**, 242 Green Street, Zip 01440–1373; tel. 978/632–3420 **A**1 3 5 10 **F**3 11 15 18 28 29 30 31 34 35 38 40 44 45 50 53 56 57 58 59 64 65 68 70 75 76 77 78 79 81 82 84 85 86 87 89 92 96 98 99 100 101 102 103 104 105 107 108 110 111 114 115 116 117 118 119 129 130 132 134 135 146 **P**8
Primary Contact: Winfield S. Brown, FACHE, President and Chief Executive Officer
CFO: Robert Crosby, Senior Vice President and Chief Financial Officer
CHR: Thomas Cady, Vice President Human Resources
Web address: www.heywood.org
Control: Other not–for–profit (including NFP Corporation) **Service:** General Medical and Surgical

Staffed Beds: 93 Admissions: 4524 Census: 64 Outpatient Visits: 156809 Births: 441 Total Expense ($000): 101224 Payroll Expense ($000): 47393 Personnel: 541

GLOUCESTER—Essex County

ADDISON GILBERT HOSPITAL See Beverly Hospital, Beverly

GREAT BARRINGTON—Berkshire County

✠ **FAIRVIEW HOSPITAL (221302)**, 29 Lewis Avenue, Zip 01230–1713; tel. 413/528–0790 **A**1 10 18 **F**3 11 13 15 18 28 29 32 34 35 36 40 50 54 56 57 59 64 65 68 70 75 77 79 81 85 86 87 92 93 94 107 108 110 114 119 130 131 132 133 135 146 147 148 **P**6 **S** Berkshire Health Systems, Inc., Pittsfield, MA
Primary Contact: Eugene A. Dellea, President
COO: Doreen M. Sylvia–Hutchinson, Vice President Operations and Chief Nurse Executive
CFO: Anthony Rinaldi, Executive Vice President
CMO: Brian Burke, M.D., President Medical Staff
CHR: Laura Farkas, Director Human Resources
Web address: www.bhs1.org/body_fh.cfm?id=39
Control: Other not–for–profit (including NFP Corporation) **Service:** General Medical and Surgical

Staffed Beds: 24 Admissions: 820 Census: 9 Outpatient Visits: 77214 Births: 128 Total Expense ($000): 45810 Payroll Expense ($000): 22316 Personnel: 246

GREENFIELD—Franklin County

✠ **BAYSTATE FRANKLIN MEDICAL CENTER (220016)**, 164 High Street, Zip 01301–2613; tel. 413/773–0211 **A**1 3 10 **F**3 11 12 13 14 15 18 24 28 29 30 31 34 35 36 40 45 46 47 48 50 51 55 57 59 64 68 70 74 75 76 77 78 79 81 82 85 86 87 89 93 98 100 101 105 107 108 110 111 115 118 119 129 130 131 132 146 147 148 **S** Baystate Health, Inc., Springfield, MA
Primary Contact: Cindy Russo, MS, President and Chief Administrative Officer
CFO: Andrea Nathanson, Director Finance
CMO: Thomas Higgins, M.D., Chief Medical Officer
CHR: Kerry Damon, Director Human Resources
CNO: Leesa–Lee Keith, R.N., Chief Nursing Officer
Web address: www.baystatehealth.org
Control: Other not–for–profit (including NFP Corporation) **Service:** General Medical and Surgical

Staffed Beds: 89 Admissions: 4595 Census: 53 Outpatient Visits: 110810 Births: 491 Personnel: 442

HAVERHILL—Essex County

BALDPATE HOSPITAL (224033), 83 Baldpate Road, Zip 01833–2303; tel. 978/352–2131, (Nonreporting) **A**10
Primary Contact: Lucille M. Batal, Administrator
Web address: www.baldpateh.com
Control: Corporation, Investor–owned, for–profit **Service:** Psychiatric

Staffed Beds: 59

WHITTIER PAVILION (224039), 76 Summer Street, Zip 01830–5814; tel. 978/373–8222 **A**10 **F**77 98 103 104 **S** Whittier Health Network, Haverhill, MA
Primary Contact: Alfred L. Arcidi, M.D., Chief Executive Officer
Web address: www.whittierhealth.com
Control: Individual, Investor–owned, for–profit **Service:** Psychiatric

Staffed Beds: 65 Admissions: 1850 Census: 51 Outpatient Visits: 5338 Births: 0

HOLYOKE—Hampden County

◇ **HOLYOKE MEDICAL CENTER (220024)**, 575 Beech Street, Zip 01040–2223; tel. 413/534–2500, (Nonreporting) **A**2 5 10 21
Primary Contact: Spiros Hatiras, FACHE, President and Chief Executive Officer
CFO: Antonio Correia, Chief Financial Officer
CMO: Karen Ferroni, M.D., Medical Director
CIO: Carl Cameron, Director Information Systems
CHR: Mary Kelleher, Vice President Human Resources
Web address: www.holyokehealth.com
Control: Other not–for–profit (including NFP Corporation) **Service:** General Medical and Surgical

Staffed Beds: 198

HYANNIS—Barnstable County

✠ **CAPE COD HOSPITAL (220012)**, 27 Park Street, Zip 02601–5230;
tel. 508/771–1800 **A**1 2 5 10 20 **F**3 11 13 14 15 17 18 20 22 24 26 28 29
30 31 34 35 37 38 40 45 49 50 51 54 57 61 64 65 68 70 74 75 76 77 78
79 81 82 85 86 87 89 93 97 98 99 100 101 102 103 104 105 107 108 110
111 114 115 118 119 120 121 123 124 126 130 131 132 143 144 146 147
P6 8 **S** Cape Cod Healthcare, Inc., Hyannis, MA
Primary Contact: Michael K. Lauf, President and Chief Executive Officer
COO: Michael N. Bundy, Chief Operating Officer
CFO: Michael Connors, Senior Vice President and Chief Financial Officer
CMO: Donald Guadagnoli, M.D., Chief Medical Officer
CIO: Jeanne M. Fallon, Senior Vice President and Chief Information Officer
CHR: Emily Schorer, Senior Vice President Human Resources
CNO: Judith Quinn, Vice President Patient Care Services
Web address: www.capecodhealth.org
Control: Other not–for–profit (including NFP Corporation) **Service:** General
Medical and Surgical

Staffed Beds: 259 **Admissions:** 15966 **Census:** 191 **Outpatient Visits:**
581798 **Births:** 750 **Total Expense ($000):** 438185 **Payroll Expense
($000):** 168453 **Personnel:** 1468

JAMAICA PLAIN—Suffolk County

☐ **LEMUEL SHATTUCK HOSPITAL (222006)**, 170 Morton Street,
Zip 02130–3735; tel. 617/522–8110, (Nonreporting) **A**1 3 5 10
S Massachusetts Department of Public Health, Boston, MA
Primary Contact: Rosette Martinez, Acting Chief Executive Officer
CFO: Mike Donovan, Chief Financial Officer
CMO: Kenneth Freedman, M.D., Chief Medical Officer
CIO: Kathryn Noonan, Director Information Management
CHR: Jill Sampson, Director Human Resources
Web address: www.mass.gov/shattuckhospital
Control: State–Government, nonfederal **Service:** Long–Term Acute Care hospital

Staffed Beds: 260

LAWRENCE—Essex County

✠ **LAWRENCE GENERAL HOSPITAL (220010)**, 1 General Street,
Zip 01841–2961, Mailing Address: P.O. Box 189, Zip 01842–0389;
tel. 978/683–4000, (Nonreporting) **A**1 2 3 5 10
Primary Contact: Dianne J. Anderson, MS, R.N., President and Chief Executive
Officer
CFO: Deborah J. Wilson, Senior Vice President and Chief Financial Officer
CMO: Neil S. Meehan, D.O., Chief Medical Officer and Chief Medical Information
Officer
CIO: Jeffrey L. Brown, Director Information Systems
CHR: Cynthia Phelan, Vice President Human Resources
Web address: www.lawrencegeneral.org
Control: Other not–for–profit (including NFP Corporation) **Service:** General
Medical and Surgical

Staffed Beds: 189

LEEDS—Hampshire County

✠ **VETERANS AFFAIRS CENTRAL WESTERN MASSACHUSETTS HEALTHCARE
SYSTEM**, 421 North Main Street, Zip 01053–9764; tel. 413/582–3000,
(Nonreporting) **A**1 5 **S** Department of Veterans Affairs, Washington, DC
Primary Contact: John P. Collins, Medical Center Director
COO: Joyce Fredrick, Associate Director
CFO: Andrew McMahon, Chief Fiscal Officer
CMO: Neil Nusbaum, M.D., Chief of Staff
CIO: Michael Marley, Chief Information Officer
CHR: Pablo Feliciano, Manager Human Resources
Web address: www.centralwesternmass.va.gov/
Control: Veterans Affairs, Government, federal **Service:** Psychiatric

Staffed Beds: 167

LEOMINSTER—Worcester County

✠ **HEALTHALLIANCE HOSPITALS (220001)**, 60 Hospital Road, Zip 01453–2205;
tel. 978/466–2000 **A**1 2 3 5 10 **F**3 15 28 29 30 31 34 35 36 40 45 46 47 49
50 51 59 60 62 63 64 65 68 70 74 75 76 77 78 79 81 82 84 85 89 92 93 97
107 108 110 114 115 119 130 135 144 146 **P**6 **S** UMass Memorial Health
Care, Inc., Worcester, MA
Primary Contact: Deborah K. Weymouth, FACHE, President and Chief Executive
Officer
COO: Paul MacKinnon, R.N., Chief Operating Officer
CFO: John Bronhard, Chief Financial Officer
CMO: Daniel H. O'Leary, M.D., Chief Medical Officer
CNO: Mary Fortunato–Habib, Chief Nursing Officer
Web address: www.healthalliance.com
Control: Other not–for–profit (including NFP Corporation) **Service:** General
Medical and Surgical

Staffed Beds: 103 **Admissions:** 6604 **Census:** 73 **Outpatient Visits:** 271052
Births: 855 **Total Expense ($000):** 159429 **Payroll Expense ($000):** 65746
Personnel: 864

LOWELL—Middlesex County

✠ **LOWELL GENERAL HOSPITAL (220063)**, 295 Varnum Avenue,
Zip 01854–2134; tel. 978/937–6000, (Includes LOWELL GENERAL HOSPITAL,
SAINTS CAMPUS, 1 Hospital Drive, Zip 01852–1311, Mailing Address: 295
Varnum Avenue, Zip 01854–2134; tel. 978/458–1411; Normand E. Deschene,
FACHE, Chief Executive Officer) **A**1 2 3 5 10 **F**3 8 11 12 13 15 18 20 22 26 28
29 30 31 32 34 35 36 38 40 41 43 44 45 46 47 48 49 50 51 54 55 56 57
58 59 60 61 62 63 64 65 66 68 70 73 74 75 76 77 78 79 81 82 84 85 86
87 89 93 97 107 108 110 114 115 118 119 120 121 123 124 126 129 130
131 132 134 135 144 146 147 **P**5 6 8
Primary Contact: Normand E. Deschene, FACHE, Chief Executive Officer
COO: Amy J. Hoey, R.N., Executive Vice President and Chief Operating Officer
CFO: Susan Green, Senior Vice President Finance, Chief Financial Officer
CMO: David Pickul, M.D., Chief Medical Officer, Circle Health
CIO: Brian Sandager, Chief Information Officer
CHR: Sabrina M. Granville, Senior Vice President and Chief Human Resources
Officer
CNO: Cecelia Lynch, R.N., Vice President Patient Care Services and Chief Nursing
Officer
Web address: www.lowellgeneral.org
Control: Other not–for–profit (including NFP Corporation) **Service:** General
Medical and Surgical

Staffed Beds: 316 **Admissions:** 19761 **Census:** 227 **Outpatient Visits:**
535784 **Births:** 2348 **Total Expense ($000):** 416657 **Payroll Expense
($000):** 165092 **Personnel:** 2697

SAINTS MEDICAL CENTER See Lowell General Hospital, Saints Campus

LUDLOW—Hampden County

✠ **HEALTHSOUTH REHABILITATION HOSPITAL OF WESTERN
MASSACHUSETTS (223030)**, 222 State Street, Zip 01056–3437;
tel. 413/308–3300 **A**1 10 **F**74 90 91 93 **P**5 **S** HEALTHSOUTH Corporation,
Birmingham, AL
Primary Contact: John R. Hunt, Chief Executive Officer
CFO: John Flaherty, Chief Financial Officer
CMO: Adnan Dahdul, M.D., Medical Director
CHR: Mary Mazza, Director Human Resources
CNO: Deborah Santos, R.N., Chief Nursing Officer
Web address: www.healthsouthrehab.org
Control: Individual, Investor–owned, for–profit **Service:** Rehabilitation

Staffed Beds: 53 **Admissions:** 1111 **Census:** 49 **Outpatient Visits:** 10800
Births: 0

LYNN—Essex County

UNION CAMPUS See North Shore Medical Center, Salem

UNION HOSPITAL See Union Campus

MA

MA

MARLBOROUGH—Middlesex County

✠ **UMASS MEMORIAL–MARLBOROUGH HOSPITAL (220049)**, 157 Union ST, Zip 01752–1297; tel. 508/481–5000 **A**1 3 5 10 **F**3 11 15 18 24 28 29 30 34 35 40 49 50 51 53 57 68 77 78 79 81 82 85 93 98 100 101 105 107 114 119 132 146 147 **S** UMass Memorial Health Care, Inc., Worcester, MA
Primary Contact: Steven P. Roach, FACHE, President and Chief Executive Officer
COO: John Kelly, R.N., Chief Nursing Officer and Chief Operating Officer
CFO: Steven McCue, Chief Financial Officer
CMO: Habib Sioufi, M.D., Chief Medical Officer
CHR: Francis Meringolo, Vice President Human Resources
CNO: John Kelly, R.N., Chief Nursing Officer and Chief Operating Officer
Web address: www.marlboroughhospital.org
Control: Other not–for–profit (including NFP Corporation) **Service:** General Medical and Surgical

Staffed Beds: 67 **Admissions:** 3877 **Census:** 45 **Outpatient Visits:** 27986 **Births:** 0 **Total Expense ($000):** 76155 **Payroll Expense ($000):** 29997 **Personnel:** 401

MEDFORD—Middlesex County

LAWRENCE MEMORIAL HOSPITAL OF MEDFORD See Hallmark Health System, Melrose

MELROSE—Middlesex County

✠ **HALLMARK HEALTH SYSTEM (220070)**, 585 Lebanon Street, Zip 02176–3225; tel. 781/979–3000, (Includes LAWRENCE MEMORIAL HOSPITAL OF MEDFORD, 170 Governors Avenue, Medford, Zip 02155–1643; tel. 781/306–6000; MELROSE–WAKEFIELD HOSPITAL, 585 Lebanon Street, Zip 02176–3000; tel. 781/979–3000; Michael V. Sack, FACHE, Chief Executive Officer) **A**1 2 3 10 **F**2 3 11 12 13 15 18 20 22 26 28 29 30 31 34 35 38 40 41 45 46 47 49 50 51 54 55 56 57 58 59 60 61 62 63 64 65 68 70 72 74 75 76 77 78 79 81 82 84 85 86 87 93 97 98 100 101 102 103 104 107 108 110 111 114 115 116 117 118 119 120 121 123 124 129 130 131 132 135 144 146 147 148 **P**5 6
Primary Contact: Alan G. Macdonald, President and Chief Executive Officer
COO: William J. Doherty, M.D., Executive Vice President and Chief Operating Officer
CFO: James A. Nania, System Vice President and Chief Financial Officer
CMO: Steven Sbardella, M.D., Chief Medical Officer
CIO: Carol Ann Dresser, Vice President Information Services and Chief Information Officer
CHR: David P. Ryan, Vice President Human Resources
Web address: www.hallmarkhealth.org
Control: Other not–for–profit (including NFP Corporation) **Service:** General Medical and Surgical

Staffed Beds: 250 **Admissions:** 10781 **Census:** 152 **Outpatient Visits:** 544133 **Births:** 934 **Total Expense ($000):** 256791 **Payroll Expense ($000):** 127489 **Personnel:** 1511

METHUEN—Essex County

☐ **HOLY FAMILY HOSPITAL (220080)**, 70 East Street, Zip 01844–4597; tel. 978/687–0151, (Includes HOLY FAMILY HOPSITAL AT MERRIMACK VALLEY, 140 Lincoln Avenue, Haverhill, Zip 01830–6798; tel. 978/374–2000; Michael F. Collins, Chief Executive Officer), (Nonreporting) **A**1 2 10 **S** Steward Health Care System, LLC, Boston, MA
Primary Contact: Joseph Roach, Chief Executive Officer
COO: Martha M. McDrury, R.N., Chief Operating Officer and Chief Nursing Officer
CFO: Kevin Kilday, Vice President Finance
CHR: Patricia Gauron, Director Human Resources
CNO: Martha M. McDrury, R.N., Chief Operating Officer and Chief Nursing Officer
Web address: www.stewardhealth.org/Holy–Family–Hospital
Control: Corporation, Investor–owned, for–profit **Service:** General Medical and Surgical

Staffed Beds: 329

MILFORD—Worcester County

✠ **MILFORD REGIONAL MEDICAL CENTER (220090)**, 14 Prospect Street, Zip 01757–3003; tel. 508/473–1190, (Includes WHITINSVILLE MEDICAL CENTER, 18 Granite Street, Whitinsville, Zip 01588; tel. 508/234–6311) **A**1 2 3 5 10 **F**3 11 12 13 15 18 20 28 29 30 31 32 34 35 40 41 47 49 50 51 52 57 59 64 65 68 70 74 75 76 77 79 80 81 82 83 84 85 86 87 89 93 107 108 110 114 115 118 119 124 126 130 131 132 134 135 146 147 148 **P**6
Primary Contact: Edward Kelly, Chief Executive Officer and President
COO: Peggy Novick, Vice President, Clinical Support and Outpatient Services
CFO: Jeanne Lynskey, Vice President and Chief Financial Officer
CMO: Mary Czymbor, Chief Medical Officer
CIO: Nicole Heim, Chief Information Officer
CHR: Linda Greason, Vice President Human Resources
CNO: Nancy Tomaso, Vice President, Patient Care Services
Web address: www.milfordregional.org
Control: Other not–for–profit (including NFP Corporation) **Service:** General Medical and Surgical

Staffed Beds: 145 **Admissions:** 7708 **Census:** 75 **Outpatient Visits:** 381520 **Births:** 963 **Total Expense ($000):** 191831 **Payroll Expense ($000):** 91049 **Personnel:** 1661

MILTON—Norfolk County

☐ **BETH ISRAEL DEACONESS HOSPITAL–MILTON (220108)**, 199 Reedsdale Road, Zip 02186–3926; tel. 617/696–4600 **A**1 10 **F**12 15 17 18 26 28 29 30 34 35 37 40 41 50 51 56 57 59 64 68 70 74 75 77 79 81 82 85 87 93 107 108 110 111 115 119 126 129 130 131 132 146 147 148
Primary Contact: Peter J. Healy, Chief Executive Officer
CIO: Jean Fernandez, Chief Information Officer
CHR: Kathleen Harrington, Vice President Human Resources
Web address: www.miltonhospital.org
Control: Other not–for–profit (including NFP Corporation) **Service:** General Medical and Surgical

Staffed Beds: 88 **Admissions:** 6710 **Census:** 61 **Outpatient Visits:** 138829 **Births:** 0 **Total Expense ($000):** 90042 **Payroll Expense ($000):** 38388 **Personnel:** 604

NANTUCKET—Nantucket County

✠ **NANTUCKET COTTAGE HOSPITAL (220177)**, 57 Prospect Street, Zip 02554–2799; tel. 508/825–8100 **A**1 10 **F**13 15 28 29 31 35 40 45 50 57 59 60 64 68 70 75 76 77 78 79 81 84 85 86 87 89 93 100 102 107 110 111 115 119 130 132 133 147 148 **P**5 **S** Partners HealthCare System, Inc., Boston, MA
Primary Contact: Margot Hartmann, M.D., Ph.D., President and Chief Executive Officer
COO: Jim Kelly, Chief Operating Officer
CFO: David J. Burke, Director Finance and Chief Financial Officer
CMO: Jock Lawrason, M.D., Chief Medical Officer
CIO: Terry Hughes, Director Information Systems
CHR: Susan Partridge, Director Human Resources
CNO: Bonnie J. Kester, R.N., Vice President Patient Care Services and Chief Nursing Officer
Web address: www.nantuckethospital.org
Control: Other not–for–profit (including NFP Corporation) **Service:** General Medical and Surgical

Staffed Beds: 19 **Admissions:** 728 **Census:** 5 **Outpatient Visits:** 35707 **Births:** 137 **Total Expense ($000):** 41573 **Payroll Expense ($000):** 16644 **Personnel:** 192

NATICK—Middlesex County

LEONARD MORSE HOSPITAL See MetroWest Medical Center, Framingham

NEEDHAM—Norfolk County

☐ **BETH ISRAEL DEACONESS HOSPITAL–NEEDHAM CAMPUS (220083)**, 148 Chestnut Street, Zip 02492; tel. 781/453–3000 **A**1 2 3 **F**3 15 18 29 30 34 35 40 45 49 50 51 54 59 64 65 68 69 70 74 75 77 78 79 81 82 85 87 93 100 102 107 108 110 111 115 118 119 129 130 131 144 146 148
Primary Contact: John M. Fogarty, President and Chief Executive Officer
CFO: Brian Smith, Chief Financial Officer
CMO: Peter Ostrow, M.D., President Medical Staff
Web address: www.bidneedham.org/
Control: Other not–for–profit (including NFP Corporation) **Service:** General Medical and Surgical

Staffed Beds: 31 **Admissions:** 2206 **Census:** 20 **Outpatient Visits:** 174017 **Births:** 0 **Total Expense ($000):** 74512 **Payroll Expense ($000):** 29024 **Personnel:** 326

NEW BEDFORD—Bristol County

ST. LUKE'S HOSPITAL See Southcoast Hospitals Group, Fall River

✠ **VIBRA HOSPITAL OF SOUTHEASTERN MASSACHUSETTS (222043)**, 4499 Acushnet Avenue, Zip 02745–4707; tel. 508/995–6900 **A**1 10 **F**1 12 18 28 29 50 56 57 64 74 75 77 79 87 93 94 96 101 103 104 130 135 146 148 **P**6 **S** Vibra Healthcare, Mechanicsburg, PA
Primary Contact: Edward B. Leary, Chief Executive Officer
CFO: Cheryl Perry, Chief Financial Officer
CMO: Albert Loerinc, M.D., Medical Director
CHR: Ilene Mirabella, Director Human Resources
CNO: Emmanuel Berthil, Chief Clinical Officer
Web address: www.newbedfordrehab.com
Control: Corporation, Investor–owned, for–profit **Service:** Long–Term Acute Care hospital

Staffed Beds: 90 **Admissions:** 595 **Census:** 70 **Outpatient Visits:** 2925 **Births:** 0 **Total Expense ($000):** 24593 **Payroll Expense ($000):** 15466 **Personnel:** 154

Many Facility Codes have changed. Please refer to the AHA Guide Code Chart.
© 2016 AHA Guide

MA

NEWBURYPORT—Essex County

⊠ **ANNA JAQUES HOSPITAL (220029)**, 25 Highland Avenue, Zip 01950–3894; tel. 978/463–1000 **A**1 10 **F**3 13 14 15 18 20 26 28 29 31 34 40 43 45 46 50 64 65 70 75 76 77 78 79 80 81 82 85 89 92 93 98 102 105 107 108 110 111 115 116 117 118 119 129 130 135 146 148 **P**5 8
Primary Contact: Mark L. Goldstein, President and Chief Executive Officer
CFO: Kevin Kilday, Chief Financial Officer
CMO: Gail Fayre, M.D., Medical Director
CIO: Robert Buchanan, Chief Information Officer
CHR: Stephen Salvo, Vice President Human Resources
CNO: Richard Maki, R.N., Vice President Nursing and Chief Nursing Officer
Web address: www.ajh.org
Control: Other not–for–profit (including NFP Corporation) **Service:** General Medical and Surgical

Staffed Beds: 123 **Admissions:** 6571 **Census:** 79 **Outpatient Visits:** 255811 **Births:** 720 **Total Expense ($000):** 114145 **Payroll Expense ($000):** 54064 **Personnel:** 709

NEWTON LOWER FALLS—Middlesex County

⊠ **NEWTON–WELLESLEY HOSPITAL (220101)**, 2014 Washington Street, Zip 02462–1699; tel. 617/243–6000, (Includes MASSGENERAL FOR CHILDREN AT NEWTON–WELLESLEY HOSPITAL, 2000 Washington Street, Newton, Zip 02462–1650; tel. 617/243–6585) **A**1 2 3 5 10 **F**3 8 11 12 13 15 18 26 28 29 30 31 34 35 36 38 40 41 44 45 46 47 48 49 50 51 52 53 54 55 56 57 58 59 60 61 64 65 68 70 74 75 76 77 78 79 81 82 84 85 86 87 89 93 94 97 98 99 100 101 102 107 108 110 111 113 114 115 116 117 118 119 129 130 131 132 135 143 144 146 147 148 **P**1 6 **S** Partners HealthCare System, Inc., Boston, MA
Primary Contact: Ellen Moloney, Interim President
CFO: Jeffrey P. Dion, Vice President Finance and Chief Financial Officer
CMO: Timothy Foster, Acting Chief Medical Officer
CIO: Beth Downie, Chief Information Officer
CHR: Beth Taylor, Vice President, Human Resources
CNO: Karen A. Conley, R.N., Chief Nursing Officer and Senior Vice President Patient Care Services
Web address: www.nwh.org
Control: Other not–for–profit (including NFP Corporation) **Service:** General Medical and Surgical

Staffed Beds: 264 **Admissions:** 13838 **Census:** 174 **Outpatient Visits:** 572953 **Births:** 4568 **Total Expense ($000):** 416453 **Payroll Expense ($000):** 187212 **Personnel:** 2395

NORTHAMPTON—Hampshire County

⊠ **COOLEY DICKINSON HOSPITAL (220015)**, 30 Locust Street, Zip 01060–2093, Mailing Address: P.O. Box 5001, Zip 01061–5001; tel. 413/582–2000 **A**1 2 10 **F**2 3 11 13 14 15 18 20 26 28 29 30 31 34 35 36 38 39 40 49 50 51 54 55 56 57 59 60 61 64 68 70 74 75 76 78 79 81 82 85 86 87 89 93 96 98 100 102 107 108 110 111 114 115 119 120 121 123 126 130 131 132 134 135 144 146 147 148 **P**8 **S** Partners HealthCare System, Inc., Boston, MA
Primary Contact: Joanne Marqusee, President and Chief Executive Officer
CFO: Laurie Lamoureux, Director of Finance
CMO: Mark Novotny, M.D., Chief Medical Officer
CIO: Lee Martinez, Chief Information Officer
CHR: Lori A. Kerwood, Director Human Resources
Web address: www.cooley–dickinson.org
Control: Other not–for–profit (including NFP Corporation) **Service:** General Medical and Surgical

Staffed Beds: 86 **Admissions:** 6400 **Census:** 75 **Outpatient Visits:** 222317 **Births:** 582 **Total Expense ($000):** 152463 **Payroll Expense ($000):** 71596

NORWOOD—Norfolk County

☐ **NORWOOD HOSPITAL (220126)**, 800 Washington Street, Zip 02062–3487; tel. 781/769–4000, (Nonreporting) **A**1 2 10 **S** Steward Health Care System, LLC, Boston, MA
Primary Contact: Kimberly S. Bassett, R.N., Interim President
COO: William P. Fleming, Chief Operating Officer
CFO: Mark Johnson, Chief Financial Officer
CHR: Kimberly Brosnan, Director Human Resources
CNO: Mary Kinneman, R.N., Chief Nursing Officer, Vice President Patient Care Services
Web address: www.stewardhealth.org/Norwood–Hospital
Control: Corporation, Investor–owned, for–profit **Service:** General Medical and Surgical

Staffed Beds: 188

OAK BLUFFS—Dukes County

⊠ **MARTHA'S VINEYARD HOSPITAL (221300)**, One Hospital Road, Zip 02557, Mailing Address: P.O. Box 1477, Zip 02557–1477; tel. 508/693–0410 **A**1 10 18 **F**3 8 13 15 28 29 30 31 39 40 45 50 57 59 60 64 70 75 78 79 81 82 85 86 87 93 97 107 110 111 115 119 130 133 135 146 147 **P**6 **S** Partners HealthCare System, Inc., Boston, MA
Primary Contact: Joseph L. Woodin, Chief Executive Officer
CFO: Edward Olivier, Chief Financial Officer
CMO: Pieter Pil, M.D., Chief Medical Staff
CHR: Ken Chisholm, Director Human Resources
CNO: Carol A. Bardwell, R.N., Chief Nurse Executive
Web address: www.marthasvineyardhospital.org
Control: Other not–for–profit (including NFP Corporation) **Service:** General Medical and Surgical

Staffed Beds: 25 **Admissions:** 1182 **Census:** 16 **Outpatient Visits:** 128377 **Births:** 140 **Personnel:** 355

PALMER—Hampden County

⊠ **BAYSTATE WING HOSPITAL (220030)**, 40 Wright Street, Zip 01069–1138; tel. 413/283–7651 **A**1 5 10 **F**3 5 11 15 18 29 30 33 34 36 37 40 45 49 50 51 56 57 59 61 62 63 64 65 68 70 74 75 79 81 85 89 92 93 97 98 99 100 101 103 104 107 108 110 115 118 119 130 131 132 146 147 148 **P**6 **S** Baystate Health, Inc., Springfield, MA
Primary Contact: Michael Francis Moran, Interim President and Chief Administrative Officer
CFO: Keary T. Allicon, Vice President Finance and Chief Financial Officer
CMO: David L. Maguire, M.D., Vice President Medical Affairs
CIO: Kenneth Riley, Director Information Systems
CHR: Thomas Guilfoil, Director Human Resources
Web address: www.baystatewinghospital.org/
Control: Other not–for–profit (including NFP Corporation) **Service:** General Medical and Surgical

Staffed Beds: 74 **Admissions:** 2882 **Census:** 46 **Outpatient Visits:** 213297 **Births:** 0 **Total Expense ($000):** 79292 **Payroll Expense ($000):** 40124 **Personnel:** 604

PEABODY—Essex County

⊠ **CURAHEALTH BOSTON NORTH SHORE (222044)**, 15 King Street, Zip 01960–4379; tel. 978/531–2900, (Nonreporting)
Primary Contact: Amber Hester, Chief Executive Officer
COO: Beth Cullum, Chief Operating Officer
CMO: M. Akbarian, M.D., Medical Director
CHR: Jan Pray, Coordinator Payroll and Benefits
CNO: Michelle Mastin, Chief Clinical Officer
Control: Corporation, Investor–owned, for–profit **Service:** Long–Term Acute Care hospital

Staffed Beds: 50

PEMBROKE—Plymouth County

PEMBROKE HOSPITAL, 199 Oak Street, Zip 02359–1953; tel. 781/829–7000, (Nonreporting) **S** Universal Health Services, Inc., King of Prussia, PA
Primary Contact: Thomas P. Hickey, Chief Executive Officer and Managing Director
CFO: Diane Airosus, Chief Financial Officer
CMO: Gary Jacobson, M.D., Chief Medical Officer
Web address: www.arbourhealth.com/organizations/pembroke–hospital/
Control: Partnership, Investor–owned, for–profit **Service:** Psychiatric

Staffed Beds: 115

Hospital, Medicare Provider Number, Address, Telephone, Approval, Facility, and Physician Codes, Health Care System

★ American Hospital Association (AHA) membership
☐ The Joint Commission accreditation
○ Healthcare Facilities Accreditation Program
◇ DNV Healthcare Inc. accreditation
⇑ Center for Improvement in Healthcare Quality Accreditation
△ Commission on Accreditation of Rehabilitation Facilities (CARF) accreditation

MA

PITTSFIELD—Berkshire County

✠ **BERKSHIRE MEDICAL CENTER (220046)**, 725 North ST, Zip 01201–4124, Mailing Address: 725 North Street, Zip 01201–4124; tel. 413/447–2000, (Includes HILLCREST HOSPITAL, 165 Tor Court, Zip 01201–3099, Mailing Address: Box 1155, Zip 01202–1155; tel. 413/443–4761) **A**1 2 3 5 8 10 12 13 **F**3 4 8 12 13 14 15 17 18 20 26 28 29 30 31 32 34 35 37 38 39 40 42 43 44 45 46 48 49 50 51 53 54 55 56 57 58 59 60 61 62 63 64 65 68 70 71 74 75 77 78 79 81 82 83 85 86 87 89 90 92 93 94 98 99 100 101 102 103 104 105 107 108 110 111 112 114 115 116 117 118 119 120 121 122 123 124 126 129 130 131 132 134 135 145 146 147 148 **P**6 **S** Berkshire Health Systems, Inc., Pittsfield, MA
Primary Contact: David E. Phelps, President and Chief Executive Officer
COO: Diane Kelly, Chief Operating Officer
CFO: Darlene Rodowicz, Chief Financial Officer
CIO: William Young, Chief Information Officer
CHR: Arthur D. Milano, Vice President Human Resources
CNO: Brenda E. Cadorette, Chief Nursing Officer
Web address: www.berkshirehealthsystems.org
Control: Other not–for–profit (including NFP Corporation) **Service:** General Medical and Surgical

Staffed Beds: 274 **Admissions:** 14307 **Census:** 175 **Outpatient Visits:** 625968 **Births:** 828 **Total Expense ($000):** 406799 **Payroll Expense ($000):** 189769 **Personnel:** 2306

PLYMOUTH—Plymouth County

✠ **BETH ISRAEL DEACONESS HOSPITAL PLYMOUTH (220060)**, 275 Sandwich Street, Zip 02360–2196; tel. 508/746–2000 **A**1 2 5 10 **F**3 5 8 10 19 20 22 26 28 29 30 31 34 35 36 37 40 44 45 51 57 58 59 61 64 68 70 74 75 76 77 78 79 81 82 85 86 87 89 93 96 98 100 102 103 104 107 108 109 110 111 115 117 118 119 120 121 123 126 129 130 131 132 134 135 143 146 147 148 **P**6
Primary Contact: Peter J. Holden, President and Chief Executive Officer
COO: Kevin E. Coughlin, Senior Vice President System Development
CFO: Jason Radzevich, Vice President Finance
CMO: John Connolly, M.D., Vice President Medical Affairs
CIO: Ronald Rutherford, Chief Information Officer
CHR: Lisa Berry–Barbosa, Vice President Human Resources
CNO: Donna Doherty, R.N., Vice President of Nursing and Chief Nursing Officer
Web address: www.bidplymouth.org
Control: Other not–for–profit (including NFP Corporation) **Service:** General Medical and Surgical

Staffed Beds: 155 **Admissions:** 8339 **Census:** 108 **Outpatient Visits:** 263402 **Births:** 710 **Total Expense ($000):** 211078 **Payroll Expense ($000):** 86992 **Personnel:** 997

POCASSET—Barnstable County

☐ **CAPE COD & ISLAND COMMUNITY MENTAL HEALTH CENTER (224031)**, 830 County Road, Zip 02559–2110; tel. 508/564–9600, (Nonreporting) **A**1 10
Primary Contact: Steven Jochim, Administrator
Control: Other not–for–profit (including NFP Corporation) **Service:** Psychiatric

Staffed Beds: 24

ROCHDALE—Worcester County

VIBRA HOSPITAL OF WESTERN MASSACHUSETTS–CENTRAL CAMPUS See Vibra Hospital of Western Massachusetts, Springfield

SALEM—Essex County

NORTH SHORE CHILDREN'S HOSPITAL See MassGeneral for Children at North Shore Medical Center

✠ **NORTH SHORE MEDICAL CENTER (220035)**, 81 Highland Avenue, Zip 01970–2714; tel. 978/741–1200, (Includes MASSGENERAL FOR CHILDREN AT NORTH SHORE MEDICAL CENTER, 57 Highland Avenue, Zip 01970–6508; tel. 978/745–2100; SALEM CAMPUS, 81 Highland Avenue, Zip 01970; tel. 978/741–1200; Robert G. Norton, President; UNION CAMPUS, 500 Lynnfield Street, Lynn, Zip 01904–1487; tel. 781/581–9200; Robert G. Norton, President) **A**1 3 5 10 **F**5 12 13 15 17 18 20 22 24 26 28 29 30 31 32 34 35 36 38 40 41 43 45 46 49 50 51 55 57 59 61 63 64 68 70 73 74 75 76 77 78 79 81 82 84 85 86 87 89 93 98 99 100 101 102 103 104 105 107 108 111 114 116 118 119 121 123 129 130 131 132 135 143 146 147 148 **P**6 8
S Partners HealthCare System, Inc., Boston, MA
Primary Contact: Robert G. Norton, President
CFO: Sally Mason Boemer, Chief Financial Officer
CMO: Mitchell S. Rein, M.D., Chief Medical Officer
CIO: Fran X. Hinckley, Chief Information Officer
CHR: Arthur Bowes, Senior Vice President Human Resources
CNO: Cheryl Bhima Merrill, MSN, Senior Vice President Patient Care Services and Chief Nursing Officer
Web address: www.nsmc.partners.org
Control: Other not–for–profit (including NFP Corporation) **Service:** General Medical and Surgical

Staffed Beds: 406 **Admissions:** 17698 **Census:** 248 **Outpatient Visits:** 632133 **Births:** 1340 **Total Expense ($000):** 451888 **Payroll Expense ($000):** 201045 **Personnel:** 2369

SALEM HOSPITAL See Salem Campus

SOMERVILLE—Middlesex County

SOMERVILLE HOSPITAL See Cambridge Health Alliance, Cambridge

SOUTH WEYMOUTH—Norfolk County

✠ **SOUTH SHORE HOSPITAL (220100)**, 55 Fogg Road, Zip 02190–2432; tel. 781/624–8000 **A**1 2 3 5 10 **F**3 7 11 13 15 17 18 20 22 24 26 28 29 30 31 32 34 35 36 37 40 41 43 44 45 46 50 51 53 54 55 57 58 59 60 62 63 64 65 68 70 72 73 74 75 76 78 79 81 82 84 85 86 87 89 91 92 93 96 107 108 110 111 114 115 118 119 124 126 129 130 132 134 135 143 146 147 148 **P**1
Primary Contact: Gene E. Green, M.D., Chief Executive Officer
COO: Joseph Cahill, Executive Vice President and Chief Operating Officer
CFO: Michael Cullen, Senior Vice President and Chief Financial Officer
CMO: John Stevenson, M.D., Senior Vice President and Chief Medical Officer
CIO: Del Dixon, Chief Information Officer
CHR: Robert Wheeler, Vice President Human Resources
Web address: www.southshorehospital.org
Control: Other not–for–profit (including NFP Corporation) **Service:** General Medical and Surgical

Staffed Beds: 387 **Admissions:** 23888 **Census:** 274 **Outpatient Visits:** 588293 **Births:** 3394 **Total Expense ($000):** 513779 **Payroll Expense ($000):** 249872 **Personnel:** 3348

SOUTHBRIDGE—Worcester County

✠ **HARRINGTON MEMORIAL HOSPITAL (220019)**, 100 South Street, Zip 01550–4051; tel. 508/765–9771 **A**1 2 5 10 **F**3 5 8 11 13 15 17 18 19 28 29 30 31 32 34 35 38 39 40 42 45 48 49 50 51 54 57 59 61 64 65 68 70 71 74 75 76 77 78 79 81 82 85 86 87 89 92 93 94 96 98 99 100 101 102 103 104 105 107 108 110 111 114 115 117 118 119 129 130 131 132 134 135 145 146 147 148 **P**6 8
Primary Contact: Edward H. Moore, President and Chief Executive Officer
COO: Kristin Morales, Chief Operating Officer
CFO: Thomas Sullivan, Vice President Fiscal Services
CMO: Arthur Russo, M.D., Director Medical Affairs
CIO: Harry Lemieux, Chief Information Officer
CHR: Christopher Canniff, Executive Director, Human Resources
CNO: Thomas W. Hijeck, R.N., Vice President Nursing Services and Chief Nursing Officer
Web address: www.harringtonhospital.org
Control: Other not–for–profit (including NFP Corporation) **Service:** General Medical and Surgical

Staffed Beds: 114 **Admissions:** 3987 **Census:** 48 **Outpatient Visits:** 353785 **Births:** 257 **Total Expense ($000):** 116876 **Payroll Expense ($000):** 55824 **Personnel:** 701

SPRINGFIELD—Hampden County

✠ **BAYSTATE MEDICAL CENTER (220077)**, 759 Chestnut Street, Zip 01199–0001; tel. 413/794–0000, (Includes BAYSTATE CHILDREN'S HOSPITAL, 759 Chestnut Street, Zip 01199–1001; tel. 413/794–0000; Mark A. Keroack, M.D., M.P.H., President and Chief Executive Officer, Baystate Health) **A**1 3 5 8 10 **F**3 8 12 13 14 15 17 18 19 20 22 24 26 29 30 31 32 35 37 38 40 41 43 44 45 46 47 48 49 50 51 52 53 54 55 56 57 58 59 60 61 64 65 66 68 70 72 74 75 76 77 78 79 80 81 82 83 84 85 86 87 88 89 92 93 96 97 98 99 100 101 103 104 105 107 108 110 111 114 115 118 119 120 121 123 124 126 129 130 131 132 135 138 143 145 146 147 148 **P**5 8
S Baystate Health, Inc., Springfield, MA
Primary Contact: Mark A. Keroack, M.D., M.P.H., President and Chief Executive Officer
COO: Tejas Gandhi, Ph.D., Chief Operating Officer
CFO: Dennis Chalke, Senior Vice President, Chief Financial Officer and Treasurer
CMO: Andrew Artenstein, M.D., Chief Physician Executive, Chief Academic Officer and President, Baystate Medical Practices
CIO: Joel L. Vengco, MS, Vice President, Chief Information Officer
CHR: Paula C. Squires, Senior Vice President, Chief Human Resources Officer and Chief Human Resources Officer
CNO: Nancy Shendell–Falik, R.N., Senior Vice President, Chief Operating Officer and Chief Nursing Officer
Web address: www.baystatehealth.org/bmc
Control: Other not–for–profit (including NFP Corporation) **Service:** General Medical and Surgical

Staffed Beds: 710 **Admissions:** 37076 **Census:** 529 **Outpatient Visits:** 354069 **Births:** 3990 **Total Expense ($000):** 1029318 **Payroll Expense ($000):** 404889 **Personnel:** 7626

KINDRED HOSPITAL PARK VIEW See Vibra Hospital of Western Massachusetts

⊠ △ **MERCY MEDICAL CENTER (220066)**, 271 Carew Street, Zip 01104–2398, Mailing Address: P.O. Box 9012, Zip 01102–9012; tel. 413/748–9000 **A**1 2 7 10 **F**3 4 5 8 12 13 14 15 18 20 26 29 30 31 34 35 38 40 44 45 46 47 48 49 50 51 55 56 57 58 59 62 64 68 70 74 75 76 77 78 79 81 82 83 84 85 86 87 89 90 91 92 93 96 98 99 100 101 102 103 104 105 106 107 108 110 111 113 114 115 116 117 118 119 120 121 123 124 126 130 131 132 134 135 143 146 147 148 **P**6 **S** Trinity Health, Livonia, MI
Primary Contact: Scott A. Wolf, D.O., President and Chief Executive Officer
COO: Scott A. Wolf, D.O., Senior Vice President, Medical Affairs, Chief Medical Officer and Chief Operating Officer
CFO: Thomas W. Robert, Senior Vice President of Finance and Chief Financial Officer
CMO: Scott A. Wolf, D.O., Senior Vice President, Medical Affairs, Chief Medical Officer and Chief Operating Officer
CIO: Joan Methe, Chief Information Officer
CHR: Leonard F. Pansa, Senior Vice President Human Resources and Administrative Services
CNO: Sharon Adams, R.N., Senior Vice President Patient Care Services and Chief Quality Officer
Web address: www.mercycares.com
Control: Other not–for–profit (including NFP Corporation) **Service:** General Medical and Surgical

Staffed Beds: 336 **Admissions:** 14713 **Census:** 214 **Outpatient Visits:** 588588 **Births:** 1223 **Total Expense ($000):** 256043 **Payroll Expense ($000):** 98443 **Personnel:** 388

☐ **SHRINERS HOSPITALS FOR CHILDREN–SPRINGFIELD (223303)**, 516 Carew Street, Zip 01104–2396; tel. 413/787–2000 **A**1 3 5 10 **F**3 29 32 34 35 55 58 59 64 66 68 71 74 75 77 79 81 85 86 89 91 92 93 94 119 130 143 146 **P**1 **S** Shriners Hospitals for Children, Tampa, FL
Primary Contact: H. Lee Kirk, Jr., FACHE, Administrator
CFO: Richard Fulkerson, Director Fiscal Services
CMO: David M. Drvaric, M.D., Chief of Staff
CIO: Eric Kamens, Regional Director Information Systems
CHR: John Donlin, Director Human Resources
CNO: Diane Brunelle, MSN, Director Patient Care Services and Chief Nursing Officer
Web address: www.shrinershospitalsforchildren.org/Hospitals/Locations/Springfield.aspx
Control: Other not–for–profit (including NFP Corporation) **Service:** Children's orthopedic

Staffed Beds: 10 **Admissions:** 89 **Census:** 1 **Outpatient Visits:** 11765 **Births:** 0 **Total Expense ($000):** 17094 **Payroll Expense ($000):** 8111 **Personnel:** 144

⊠ **VIBRA HOSPITAL OF WESTERN MASSACHUSETTS (222046)**, 1400 State Street, Zip 01109–2550; tel. 413/726–6700, (Includes VIBRA HOSPITAL OF WESTERN MASSACHUSETTS–CENTRAL CAMPUS, 111 Huntoon Memorial Highway, Rochdale, Zip 01542; tel. 508/892–6000; Scott MacLean, Administrator), (Total facility includes 172 beds in nursing home–type unit) **A**1 10 **F**3 29 50 75 82 96 98 128 130 148 **S** Vibra Healthcare, Mechanicsburg, PA
Primary Contact: Edward B. Leary, Interim Chief Executive Officer
CFO: Anna Dyrkacz, Chief Financial Officer
CHR: Donna Ciarefella, Director Human Resources
Web address: www.vhwmass.com
Control: Corporation, Investor–owned, for–profit **Service:** Long–Term Acute Care hospital

Staffed Beds: 346 **Admissions:** 660 **Census:** 299 **Outpatient Visits:** 0 **Births:** 0 **Total Expense ($000):** 32912 **Payroll Expense ($000):** 15115 **Personnel:** 197

⊠ **AUSTEN RIGGS CENTER**, 25 Main Street, Zip 01262, Mailing Address: P.O. Box 962, Zip 01262–0962; tel. 413/298–5511 **A**1 3 5 **F**98 105 106 130
Primary Contact: Andrew Gerber, M.D., Ph.D., Medical Director and Chief Executive Officer
COO: Chauncey Collins, Chief Operating Officer and Chief Financial Officer
CFO: Chauncey Collins, Chief Operating Officer and Chief Financial Officer
CIO: Ave Schwartz, Chief Information Officer
CHR: Bertha Mary Connelley, Director Human Resources
CNO: Barbara Turner, Director of Nursing
Web address: www.austenriggs.org
Control: Other not–for–profit (including NFP Corporation) **Service:** Psychiatric

Staffed Beds: 74 **Admissions:** 78 **Census:** 61 **Outpatient Visits:** 0 **Births:** 0 **Total Expense ($000):** 17028 **Payroll Expense ($000):** 9459 **Personnel:** 148

⊠ **CURAHEALTH STOUGHTON (222002)**, 909 Sumner Street, 1st Floor, Zip 02072–3396; tel. 781/297–8200, (Nonreporting) **A**1 10 Primary Contact: Robert A. Gundersen, Market Chief Executive Officer
Control: Corporation, Investor–owned, for–profit **Service:** Long–Term Acute Care hospital

Staffed Beds: 111

☐ **NEW ENGLAND SINAI HOSPITAL AND REHABILITATION CENTER (222027)**, 150 York Street, Zip 02072–1881; tel. 781/344–0600, (Nonreporting) **A**1 3 5 10 **S** Steward Health Care System, LLC, Boston, MA
Primary Contact: Judith C. Waterston, R.N., MS, President and Chief Executive Officer
CFO: Victoria Lobban, Vice President Finance
CMO: Lawrence S. Hotes, M.D., Chief Medical Officer
CIO: Michael West, Manager Systems Account
CHR: Julie Burke, Director Human Resources
CNO: Mary Beth Urquhart, Vice President Patient Care Services and Director of Quality
Web address: www.newenglandsinai.org
Control: Other not–for–profit (including NFP Corporation) **Service:** Long–Term Acute Care hospital

Staffed Beds: 212

☐ **MORTON HOSPITAL AND MEDICAL CENTER (220073)**, 88 Washington Street, Zip 02780–2465; tel. 508/828–7000, (Nonreporting) **A**1 2 10 **S** Steward Health Care System, LLC, Boston, MA
Primary Contact: Deborah Bitsoli, CPA, President
COO: Donna Maher, R.N., Chief Operating Officer
CFO: Heidi Taylor, Chief Financial Officer
CMO: Charles Thayer, M.D., Chief Medical Officer
CNO: Lisa Coggins, Chief Nursing Officer
Web address: www.mortonhospital.org
Control: Other not–for–profit (including NFP Corporation) **Service:** General Medical and Surgical

Staffed Beds: 154

☐ **TAUNTON STATE HOSPITAL (224001)**, 60 Hodges Avenue Extension, Zip 02780–3034, Mailing Address: PO Box 4007, Zip 02780–0997; tel. 508/977–3000, (Nonreporting) **A**1 10 **S** Massachusetts Department of Mental Health, Boston, MA
Primary Contact: Joyce O. Connor, Chief Operating Officer
CHR: Trish Scully, Director Human Resources
Control: State–Government, nonfederal **Service:** Psychiatric

Staffed Beds: 45

☐ **TEWKSBURY HOSPITAL (222003)**, 365 East Street, Zip 01876–1998; tel. 978/851–7321, (Nonreporting) **A**1 3 10 **S** Massachusetts Department of Public Health, Boston, MA
Primary Contact: Debra Tosti, Chief Executive Officer
COO: Betsy L. Schwechheimer, Chief Operating Officer
CFO: Maureen DiPalma, Chief Financial Officer
CMO: James DeVita, M.D., Chief Medical Officer
CNO: Janice E. Bishop, R.N., Chief Nursing Officer
Web address: www.mass.gov
Control: State–Government, nonfederal **Service:** Long–Term Acute Care hospital

Staffed Beds: 381

☐ **WALDEN PSYCHIATRIC CARE (224038)**, 9 Hope Avenue, Zip 02453–2741; tel. 781/647–6700 **A**1 10 **F**98 99 101 104 105 106 **P**6
Primary Contact: Stuart Koman, Ph.D., President and Chief Executive Officer
COO: Paula Vass, Vice President Clinical Operations
CFO: Lawrence Behan, Vice President Administration and Finance, Chief Financial Officer
CMO: James Greenblatt, M.D., Chief Medical Officer, Vice President Medical Clinical Services
CIO: Lawrence Behan, Vice President Administration and Finance, Chief Financial Officer
CHR: Carol Pender, Assistant Vice President Human Resources
CNO: Stephen Reider, R.N., Director of Nursing, Assistant Vice President Patient Care Services
Web address: www.waldenbehavioralcare.com/
Control: Partnership, Investor–owned, for–profit **Service:** Psychiatric

Staffed Beds: 47 **Admissions:** 1531 **Census:** 45 **Outpatient Visits:** 24183 **Births:** 0

Hospital, Medicare Provider Number, Address, Telephone, Approval, Facility, and Physician Codes, Health Care System

★ American Hospital Association (AHA) membership
☐ The Joint Commission accreditation
○ Healthcare Facilities Accreditation Program
◇ DNV Healthcare Inc. accreditation
⇑ Center for Improvement in Healthcare Quality Accreditation
△ Commission on Accreditation of Rehabilitation Facilities (CARF) accreditation

MA

WAREHAM—Plymouth County

TOBEY HOSPITAL See Southcoast Hospitals Group, Fall River

WEST ROXBURY—Suffolk County

VETERANS AFFAIRS MEDICAL CENTER WEST ROXBURY DIVISION See Veterans Affairs Boston Healthcare System Brockton Division, Brockton

WESTBOROUGH—Worcester County

☐ **WHITTIER REHABILITATION HOSPITAL (222048)**, 150 Flanders Road, Zip 01581–1017; tel. 508/871–2000 **A**1 10 **F**1 18 29 34 35 54 56 60 62 64 65 68 74 75 79 85 86 93 94 95 96 119 130 131 135 146 148 **S** Whittier Health Network, Haverhill, MA
Primary Contact: Alfred J. Arcidi, M.D., Senior Vice President
Web address: www.whittierhealth.com
Control: Corporation, Investor–owned, for–profit **Service:** Long–Term Acute Care hospital

> **Staffed Beds:** 60 **Admissions:** 722 **Census:** 50 **Outpatient Visits:** 26909
> **Births:** 0

WESTFIELD—Hampden County

✠ **BAYSTATE NOBLE HOSPITAL (220065)**, 115 West Silver Street, Zip 01085–3628; tel. 413/568–2811 **A**1 2 5 10 **F**8 14 15 18 28 29 30 31 34 40 57 59 68 70 75 77 78 79 80 81 86 89 90 93 98 100 101 102 103 104 105 107 108 110 111 115 116 117 119 130 132 143 144 146 147 148 **P**8 **S** Baystate Health, Inc., Springfield, MA
Primary Contact: Ronald Bryant, President
CFO: John Shaver, Chief Financial Officer
CMO: Stanley Strzempko, M.D., Vice President Medical Affairs and Chief Medical Officer
CIO: Steven Cummings, Chief Operating Officer and Chief Information Officer
CHR: Joanne Ollson, Vice President Human Resources
Web address: www.baystatehealth.org/locations/noble–hospital
Control: Other not–for–profit (including NFP Corporation) **Service:** General Medical and Surgical

> **Staffed Beds:** 97 **Admissions:** 3046 **Census:** 47 **Outpatient Visits:** 92223
> **Births:** 0 **Total Expense ($000):** 58154 **Payroll Expense ($000):** 25603
> **Personnel:** 328

☐ **WESTERN MASSACHUSETTS HOSPITAL (222023)**, 91 East Mountain Road, Zip 01085–1801; tel. 413/562–4131 **A**1 10 **F**75 82 84 100 130 132 146 148 **P**5 **S** Massachusetts Department of Public Health, Boston, MA
Primary Contact: Valenda M. Liptak, Chief Executive Officer
CMO: Chabilal Neergheen, M.D., Medical Director
CHR: James E. Duggan, Director Human Resources
Web address: www.mass.gov/eohhs/gov/departments/dph/programs/western–massachusetts–hospital.html
Control: State–Government, nonfederal **Service:** Obstetrics and gynecology

> **Staffed Beds:** 80 **Admissions:** 69 **Census:** 86 **Outpatient Visits:** 0 **Births:** 0

WESTWOOD—Norfolk County

☐ **WESTWOOD LODGE HOSPITAL (224023)**, 45 Clapboardtree Street, Zip 02090–2903; tel. 781/762–7764, (Nonreporting) **A**1 5 10 **S** Universal Health Services, Inc., King of Prussia, PA
Primary Contact: Gregory Brownstein, Chief Executive Officer
CFO: Charles Denno, Chief Financial Officer
Web address: www.arbourhealth.com
Control: Corporation, Investor–owned, for–profit **Service:** Psychiatric

> **Staffed Beds:** 130

WHITINSVILLE—Worcester County

WHITINSVILLE MEDICAL CENTER See Milford Regional Medical Center, Milford

WINCHESTER—Middlesex County

✠ **WINCHESTER HOSPITAL (220105)**, 41 Highland Avenue, Zip 01890–1496; tel. 781/729–9000 **A**1 2 3 5 10 **F**3 8 12 16 26 28 29 30 31 32 34 35 36 38 40 41 44 45 46 49 50 51 54 55 56 57 59 62 64 68 70 73 74 75 76 77 78 79 81 82 85 86 87 89 92 93 107 108 110 114 115 118 119 120 121 126 129 130 131 132 135 144 145 146 147 148 **S** Lahey Health, Burlington, MA
Primary Contact: Dale M. Lodge, Chief Executive Officer
CFO: Matthew Woods, Vice President Finance
CMO: Richard Iseke, M.D., Vice President Medical Affairs
CHR: Stephanie M. Bettinelli, Vice President of Human Resources
CNO: Kathy Schuler, R.N., Vice President of Patient Care Services
Web address: www.winchesterhospital.org
Control: Other not–for–profit (including NFP Corporation) **Service:** General Medical and Surgical

> **Staffed Beds:** 197 **Admissions:** 10980 **Census:** 125 **Outpatient Visits:** 549527 **Births:** 1957 **Total Expense ($000):** 266275 **Payroll Expense ($000):** 117388 **Personnel:** 1737

WOBURN—Middlesex County

✠ **HEALTHSOUTH NEW ENGLAND REHABILITATION HOSPITAL (223026)**, Two Rehabilitation Way, Zip 01801–6098; tel. 781/935–5050, (Nonreporting) **A**1 3 10 **S** HEALTHSOUTH Corporation, Birmingham, AL
Primary Contact: Laura Ames, Chief Executive Officer
CFO: Lester Felege, Controller
CHR: Annamarie Cronin, Director Human Resources
Web address: www.newenglandrehab.com
Control: Corporation, Investor–owned, for–profit **Service:** Rehabilitation

> **Staffed Beds:** 210

WORCESTER—Worcester County

ADCARE HOSPITAL OF WORCESTER (220062), 107 Lincoln Street, Zip 01605–2499; tel. 508/799–9000, (Nonreporting) **A**3 5 10
Primary Contact: David W. Hillis, Chairman and Chief Executive Officer
COO: Jeffrey W. Hillis, Chief Operating Officer
CFO: Christine Judycki–Crepeault, Chief Financial Officer
CMO: Ronald F. Pike, M.D., Medical Director
CHR: Joan L. Bertrand, Vice President Human Resources
CNO: Judith Richards, Director of Nursing
Web address: www.adcare.com
Control: Other not–for–profit (including NFP Corporation) **Service:** Alcoholism and other chemical dependency

> **Staffed Beds:** 114

✠ **FAIRLAWN REHABILITATION HOSPITAL (223029)**, 189 May Street, Zip 01602–4339; tel. 508/791–6351 **A**1 3 5 10 **F**3 28 29 34 35 56 57 59 64 74 75 77 79 82 86 87 90 91 93 95 96 130 132 135 148 **P**8 **S** HEALTHSOUTH Corporation, Birmingham, AL
Primary Contact: R. David Richer, Chief Executive Officer
CFO: John Flaherty, Controller
CMO: Peter Bagley, M.D., Medical Director
CIO: Anna Francis, Chief Information Officer
CHR: Rosalie Lawless, Director Human Resources
Web address: www.fairlawnrehab.org
Control: Corporation, Investor–owned, for–profit **Service:** Rehabilitation

> **Staffed Beds:** 110 **Admissions:** 2477 **Census:** 88 **Outpatient Visits:** 10935
> **Births:** 0 **Total Expense ($000):** 34884 **Payroll Expense ($000):** 16676
> **Personnel:** 339

✠ **SAINT VINCENT HOSPITAL (220176)**, 123 Summer Street, Zip 01608–1216; tel. 508/363–5000 **A**1 2 3 5 10 **F**3 8 12 13 15 17 18 20 22 24 26 28 29 30 31 35 38 40 45 46 48 49 50 57 59 60 64 68 70 74 75 76 77 78 79 81 82 84 85 86 87 89 92 93 97 98 100 101 102 107 108 110 111 114 115 116 117 118 119 120 121 123 124 126 129 130 131 132 135 146 147 148 **P**5 **S** TENET Healthcare Corporation, Dallas, TX
Primary Contact: Steven MacLauchlan, Chief Executive Officer
CFO: Peter D'Elia, Chief Financial Officer
CMO: Douglas Waite, M.D., Chief Medical Officer
CHR: Jan Peters, Vice President Human Resources
CNO: JoAnn Piedrafite, R.N., Chief Nursing Officer
Web address: www.stvincenthospital.com
Control: Corporation, Investor–owned, for–profit **Service:** General Medical and Surgical

> **Staffed Beds:** 283 **Admissions:** 17236 **Census:** 198 **Outpatient Visits:** 254269 **Births:** 2087 **Total Expense ($000):** 357653 **Payroll Expense ($000):** 147061 **Personnel:** 1613

✠ **UMASS MEMORIAL MEDICAL CENTER (220163)**, 119 Belmont Street, Zip 01605–2982; tel. 508/334–1000, (Includes HAHNEMANN CAMPUS, 281 Lincoln Street, Zip 01605; tel. 508/334–1000; MEMORIAL CAMPUS, 119 Belmont Street, Zip 01605; tel. 508/334–1000; UMASS MEMORIAL CHILDREN'S MEDICAL CENTER, 55 Lake Avenue North, Zip 01655–0002; tel. 508/334–1000; UNIVERSITY CAMPUS, 55 Lake Avenue North, Zip 01655–0002; tel. 508/334–1000) **A**1 2 3 5 8 10 **F**3 5 7 8 9 12 13 14 15 16 17 18 19 20 22 24 26 29 30 31 32 34 38 40 41 43 45 46 47 48 49 50 51 52 55 56 58 59 60 61 64 65 68 70 71 72 73 74 75 78 79 81 82 84 85 87 88 92 93 97 98 99 100 101 102 103 104 105 107 108 110 114 115 118 119 120 121 123 124 126 127 130 131 132 134 135 136 138 139 142 144 145 146 147 148 **P**5 6 **S** UMass Memorial Health Care, Inc., Worcester, MA
Primary Contact: Patrick L. Muldoon, FACHE, President
COO: Andrew Sussman, M.D., Chief Operating Officer
CFO: Therese Day, Chief Financial Officer
CMO: Stephen E. Tosi, M.D., Chief Medical Officer
CIO: George Brenkle, Chief Information Officer
Web address: www.umassmemorial.org
Control: Other not–for–profit (including NFP Corporation) **Service:** General Medical and Surgical

> **Staffed Beds:** 654 **Admissions:** 38396 **Census:** 564 **Outpatient Visits:** 975529 **Births:** 3734 **Total Expense ($000):** 1463132 **Payroll Expense ($000):** 503432 **Personnel:** 7418

Many Facility Codes have changed. Please refer to the AHA Guide Code Chart.

© 2016 AHA Guide

☐ **WORCESTER RECOVERY CENTER AND HOSPITAL (224032)**, 305 Belmont Street, Zip 01604–1695; tel. 508/368–3300, (Nonreporting) **A**1 3 5 10
S Massachusetts Department of Mental Health, Boston, MA
Primary Contact: Anthony Riccitelli, Chief Operating Officer
COO: Anthony Riccitelli, Chief Operating Officer
CIO: Ron Medciros, Director Applied Information Technology
Control: State–Government, nonfederal **Service:** Psychiatric

Staffed Beds: 126

MA

MICHIGAN

MI

ADRIAN—Lenawee County

★ ○ **PROMEDICA BIXBY HOSPITAL (230005)**, 818 Riverside Avenue, Zip 49221–1446; tel. 517/265–0900 **A**2 10 11 **F**3 11 13 15 18 28 30 34 35 40 45 46 50 51 55 57 59 64 68 70 74 75 76 78 79 81 82 85 91 92 93 100 102 107 108 111 114 116 117 118 119 120 121 126 130 131 132 135 143 145 146 148 **P**6 8 **S** ProMedica Health System, Toledo, OH
Primary Contact: Julie Yaroch, D.O., President
CFO: Bernie Nawrocki, Administrative Director Finance
CIO: Stephanie Sonnenberg, Director Information Technology
CHR: Cathy J. Davis, Director Human Resources
CNO: Kathryn M. Greenlee, R.N., Vice President, Clinical Services/CNO
Web address: www.promedica.org
Control: Other not–for–profit (including NFP Corporation) **Service:** General Medical and Surgical

Staffed Beds: 66 **Admissions:** 3805 **Census:** 37 **Outpatient Visits:** 133267 **Births:** 703 **Total Expense ($000):** 75248 **Payroll Expense ($000):** 26030 **Personnel:** 434

ALLEGAN—Allegan County

★ ◇ **ALLEGAN GENERAL HOSPITAL (231328)**, 555 Linn Street, Zip 49010–1524; tel. 269/673–8424 **A**10 18 21 **F**3 12 15 28 29 31 34 35 40 45 47 48 50 57 59 62 70 75 77 78 79 81 82 85 86 87 96 99 100 101 104 107 108 110 114 119 127 129 130 131 132 135 146 147 **S** QHR, Brentwood, TN
Primary Contact: Gerald J. Barbini, President and Chief Executive Officer
CFO: Richard Harning, Vice President Finance and Chief Financial Officer
CMO: Nabil Nouna, M.D., Chief of Staff
CIO: David Federinko, Chief Information Officer
CHR: Denise A. Eberth, Chief Human Resources Officer
CNO: Kathy Chapman, Chief Clinical Officer and Vice President of Patient Services
Web address: www.aghosp.org
Control: Other not–for–profit (including NFP Corporation) **Service:** General Medical and Surgical

Staffed Beds: 25 **Admissions:** 867 **Census:** 8 **Outpatient Visits:** 81774 **Births:** 0 **Total Expense ($000):** 46149 **Payroll Expense ($000):** 17372 **Personnel:** 250

ALMA—Gratiot County

GRATIOT MEDICAL CENTER See MidMichigan Medical Center–Gratiot

⊞ △ **MIDMICHIGAN MEDICAL CENTER–GRATIOT (230030)**, 300 East Warwick Drive, Zip 48801–1014; tel. 989/463–1101 **A**1 5 7 10 19 **F**3 11 12 13 15 18 20 28 29 31 34 35 40 45 50 51 56 57 59 61 64 68 70 74 76 77 78 79 81 82 85 86 87 89 90 92 93 96 97 98 100 101 102 103 104 105 107 108 110 111 115 117 118 119 127 129 130 132 135 144 145 146 147 148 **S** MidMichigan Health, Midland, MI
Primary Contact: Mark A. Santamaria, President
CFO: Jeff Provenzano, Vice President and Chief Financial Officer
CNO: Robin Whitmore, Chief Nursing Officer
Web address: www.midmichigan.org/gratiot
Control: Other not–for–profit (including NFP Corporation) **Service:** General Medical and Surgical

Staffed Beds: 79 **Admissions:** 4146 **Census:** 54 **Outpatient Visits:** 140738 **Births:** 556 **Total Expense ($000):** 95707 **Payroll Expense ($000):** 28824 **Personnel:** 513

ALPENA—Alpena County

⊞ **MIDMICHIGAN MEDICAL CENTER – ALPENA (230036)**, 1501 West Chisholm Street, Zip 49707–1401; tel. 989/356–7390 **A**1 2 10 **F**3 11 13 15 20 26 28 29 31 34 35 40 44 45 46 47 48 49 50 59 62 64 65 70 71 73 74 75 76 77 78 79 81 82 85 86 87 90 92 93 96 97 98 99 100 101 102 103 104 106 107 108 110 111 114 115 118 119 129 130 131 132 135 146 147 148 **P**6 **S** MidMichigan Health, Midland, MI
Primary Contact: Karmon T. Bjella, Chief Executive Officer
COO: Charles H. Sherwin, Vice President of Business Development and Clinical Services
CFO: George J. Smart, Vice President Finance and Information Technology
CMO: Richard Bates, Vice President of Medical Affairs
CHR: Diane Shields, Chief Human Resources Officer
CNO: Charles H. Sherwin, Chief Nursing Officer
Web address: www.alpenaregionalmedicalcenter.org
Control: County–Government, nonfederal **Service:** General Medical and Surgical

Staffed Beds: 125 **Admissions:** 4851 **Census:** 59 **Outpatient Visits:** 214953 **Births:** 374 **Total Expense ($000):** 125469 **Payroll Expense ($000):** 50820 **Personnel:** 883

ANN ARBOR—Washtenaw County

⊞ **UNIVERSITY OF MICHIGAN HOSPITALS AND HEALTH CENTERS (230046)**, 1500 East Medical Center Drive, Zip 48109; tel. 734/936–4000, (Includes C. S. MOTT CHILDREN'S HOSPITAL, 1540 East Hospital Drive, Zip 48109–5475; tel. 734/936–4000; Paul A. King, Executive Director) **A**1 2 3 5 8 10 **F**3 5 6 8 9 11 12 13 15 16 17 18 19 20 21 22 23 24 25 26 27 28 29 30 31 32 34 35 36 37 38 39 40 41 43 44 45 46 47 48 49 50 51 52 53 54 55 56 57 58 59 60 61 62 64 65 66 68 69 70 72 74 75 76 77 78 79 80 81 82 84 85 86 87 88 89 90 91 92 93 94 95 97 98 99 100 101 102 103 104 107 108 110 111 112 114 115 116 117 118 119 120 121 123 124 126 127 129 130 131 132 134 135 136 137 138 139 140 141 142 145 146 147 148 **P**1
Primary Contact: David Spahlinger, M.D., President
COO: Tony Denton, JD, Senior Vice President and Chief Operating Officer
CFO: Paul Castillo, Chief Financial Officer
CMO: Jeffrey Desmond, M.D., Chief Medical Officer
CIO: Andrew Rosenberg, M.D., Chief Information Officer
CHR: Joseph Fournier, Chief Human Resources Officer
CNO: Marge Calarco, Chief Nursing Executive
Web address: www.med.umich.edu
Control: Other not–for–profit (including NFP Corporation) **Service:** General Medical and Surgical

Staffed Beds: 993 **Admissions:** 49557 **Census:** 804 **Outpatient Visits:** 2267117 **Births:** 4378 **Total Expense ($000):** 2661584 **Payroll Expense ($000):** 1013648 **Personnel:** 15351

⊞ **VETERANS AFFAIRS ANN ARBOR HEALTHCARE SYSTEM**, 2215 Fuller Road, Zip 48105–2399; tel. 734/769–7100 **A**1 2 3 5 8 **F**3 5 12 18 20 22 24 26 28 29 30 31 34 35 36 39 40 45 46 48 49 50 54 56 57 58 59 60 61 62 63 64 65 68 70 74 75 77 78 79 81 82 83 84 85 86 87 91 92 93 94 96 97 98 100 101 102 103 104 105 107 108 111 114 115 116 117 118 119 120 121 123 126 128 129 130 132 135 143 144 146 147 148 **P**6 **S** Department of Veterans Affairs, Washington, DC
Primary Contact: Robert P. McDivitt, FACHE, Director
COO: Himanshu Singh, M.D., Associate Director
CFO: Joel Wallinga, Chief Financial Officer
CMO: Eric Young, M.D., Chief of Staff
CIO: Rob Whitehurst, Chief, Office of Information and Technology
CHR: Stephanie Hunter, Chief Human Resources Officer
CNO: Stacey Breedveld, R.N., Associate Director for Patient Care
Web address: www.annarbor.va.gov
Control: Veterans Affairs, Government, federal **Service:** General Medical and Surgical

Staffed Beds: 109 **Admissions:** 5532 **Census:** 87 **Outpatient Visits:** 633039 **Births:** 0 **Total Expense ($000):** 452939 **Payroll Expense ($000):** 198730 **Personnel:** 2502

AUBURN HILLS—Oakland County

☐ **HAVENWYCK HOSPITAL (234023)**, 1525 University Drive, Zip 48326–2673; tel. 248/373–9200 **A**1 10 **F**98 99 102 103 105 106 130 **P**8 **S** Universal Health Services, Inc., King of Prussia, PA
Primary Contact: Diane Henneman, Chief Executive Officer
COO: Julie Szyska, Chief Operating Officer
CFO: Steve Sacharski, Chief Financial Officer
CMO: Hani Mekhael, M.D., Chief Staff
CHR: Amy Giannosa, Director Human Resources
CNO: Mitzi Sawicki, Director of Nursing
Web address: www.havenwyckhospital.com
Control: Corporation, Investor–owned, for–profit **Service:** Psychiatric

Staffed Beds: 235 **Admissions:** 6766 **Census:** 184 **Outpatient Visits:** 4446 **Births:** 0 **Total Expense ($000):** 42931 **Payroll Expense ($000):** 16530 **Personnel:** 377

BAD AXE—Huron County

HURON MEDICAL CENTER (230118), 1100 South Van Dyke Road, Zip 48413–9615; tel. 989/269–9521 **A**5 10 20 **F**3 11 13 14 15 18 20 28 29 31 32 34 35 40 45 53 56 57 59 64 70 74 75 76 77 78 79 81 82 85 90 93 97 107 108 114 119 126 127 130 132 134 135 144 146 148 **P**6
Primary Contact: Jeffery Longbrake, President and Chief Executive Officer
CFO: Bill Castle, Chief Financial Officer
CMO: Christopher Gong, M.D., Chief Staff
CHR: Nancy Bouck, Director Human Resources
CNO: Carrie Franzel, Chief Nursing Officer
Web address: www.huronmedicalcenter.org
Control: Other not–for–profit (including NFP Corporation) **Service:** General Medical and Surgical

Staffed Beds: 41 **Admissions:** 1574 **Census:** 13 **Outpatient Visits:** 53396 **Births:** 415 **Total Expense ($000):** 43363 **Payroll Expense ($000):** 16667 **Personnel:** 320

Many Facility Codes have changed. Please refer to the AHA Guide Code Chart. © 2016 AHA Guide

BATTLE CREEK—Calhoun County

⊠ **BATTLE CREEK VETERANS AFFAIRS MEDICAL CENTER**, 5500 Armstrong Road, Zip 49037–7314; tel. 269/966–5600, (Total facility includes 75 beds in nursing home–type unit) **A**1 5 **F**3 4 5 7 12 18 29 30 33 34 35 36 38 39 50 53 54 56 57 58 59 61 62 63 64 65 68 74 75 77 82 83 84 86 87 91 92 93 94 96 97 98 100 101 102 103 104 106 107 108 111 114 115 119 127 128 130 132 135 143 144 146 147 148 **S** Department of Veterans Affairs, Washington, DC
Primary Contact: Mary Beth Skupien, Director
COO: Edward G. Dornoff, Associate Director
CFO: James M. Rupert, Chief Fiscal Services
CMO: Wilfredo Rodriguez, M.D., Chief of Staff
CIO: Scott Hershberger, Acting Chief Information Management Services
CHR: Palma Simkins, Chief Human Resources Management Services
CNO: Kay Bower, Associate Director for Patient Care Services
Web address: www.battlecreek.va.gov/
Control: Veterans Affairs, Government, federal **Service:** Psychiatric

Staffed Beds: 242 **Admissions:** 2164 **Census:** 206 **Outpatient Visits:** 538014 **Births:** 0 **Personnel:** 1524

⊠ **BRONSON BATTLE CREEK (230075)**, 300 North Avenue, Zip 49017–3307; tel. 269/245–8000, (Includes FIELDSTONE CENTER, 165 North Washington Avenue, Zip 49037; tel. 269/245–8570; MAIN CAMPUS, 300 North Avenue, Zip 49017; tel. 616/966–8000) **A**1 2 10 **F**3 4 5 6 9 11 13 15 18 20 26 28 29 30 31 34 35 38 40 43 44 45 46 49 50 51 54 55 56 57 58 59 60 62 64 65 66 68 70 71 74 75 76 77 78 79 81 82 84 85 86 87 91 92 93 94 96 97 98 100 101 102 103 104 107 108 110 111 114 115 116 117 118 119 120 121 123 124 126 129 130 131 132 135 143 144 146 147 148 **P**6 **S** Bronson Healthcare Group, Kalamazoo, MI
Primary Contact: Frank J. Sardone, President and Chief Executive Officer
COO: James E. Mckernan, Chief Operating Officer
CFO: Mary Meitz, Senior Vice President and Chief Financial Officer
CMO: Daniel Stewart, M.D., Senior Vice President Medical Affairs
CHR: John Hayden, Senior Vice President and Human Resources Officer
CNO: Susan Watson, MSN, Vice President
Web address: www.bronsonhealth.com
Control: Other not–for–profit (including NFP Corporation) **Service:** General Medical and Surgical

Staffed Beds: 198 **Admissions:** 8383 **Census:** 108 **Outpatient Visits:** 487504 **Births:** 814 **Total Expense ($000):** 222967 **Payroll Expense ($000):** 74661 **Personnel:** 1477

⊠ **SELECT SPECIALTY HOSPITAL–BATTLE CREEK (232035)**, 300 North Avenue, Zip 49017–3307; tel. 269/245–4675, (Nonreporting) **A**1 10 **S** Select Medical Corporation, Mechanicsburg, PA
Primary Contact: Salvatore Iweimrin, R.N., Chief Executive Officer
Web address: www.battlecreek.selectspecialtyhospitals.com/
Control: Corporation, Investor–owned, for–profit **Service:** Long–Term Acute Care hospital

Staffed Beds: 25

VETERANS AFFAIRS MEDICAL CENTER See Battle Creek Veterans Affairs Medical Center

BAY CITY—Bay County

☐ △ **MCLAREN BAY REGION (230041)**, 1900 Columbus Avenue, Zip 48708–6831; tel. 989/894–3000, (Includes MCLAREN BAY REGION–WEST CAMPUS, 3250 East Midland Road, Zip 48706; tel. 989/667–6750) **A**1 2 5 7 10 12 13 **F**3 7 11 13 15 17 18 20 22 26 28 29 30 31 32 33 40 43 40 44 45 46 47 48 49 50 57 58 59 64 65 68 70 73 74 75 76 78 79 81 82 85 86 87 89 90 92 93 96 97 98 100 102 103 107 108 110 111 114 115 119 120 121 123 124 129 130 131 132 135 141 143 146 147 148 **P**6 **S** McLaren Health Care Corporation, Flint, MI
Primary Contact: Clarence Sevillian, President and Chief Executive Officer
CFO: Damon Sorensen, Chief Financial Officer
CMO: Jason White, M.D., Chief Medical Officer
CIO: Ronald Strachan, Chief Information Officer
CHR: Carolyn Potter, Vice President Human Resources
CNO: Ellen E. Talbott, R.N., Vice President Patient Care Services
Web address: www.bayregional.org
Control: Other not–for–profit (including NFP Corporation) **Service:** General Medical and Surgical

Staffed Beds: 338 **Admissions:** 15236 **Census:** 203 **Outpatient Visits:** 304146 **Births:** 841 **Total Expense ($000):** 273758 **Payroll Expense ($000):** 124000 **Personnel:** 2094

○ **MCLAREN BAY SPECIAL CARE (232020)**, 3250 East Midland Road, Suite 1, Zip 48706–2835; tel. 989/667–6802 **A**10 11 **F**1 3 29 31 79 87 96 148 **S** McLaren Health Care Corporation, Flint, MI
Primary Contact: Cheryl A. Burzynski, MSN, President
CFO: Damon Sorensen, Chief Financial Officer
CMO: Janet Sutton, M.D., Medical Director
CIO: Greg Jacobs, Manager
CHR: Carolyn Potter, Vice President Human Resources
Web address: www.bayspecialcare.org
Control: Other not–for–profit (including NFP Corporation) **Service:** Long–Term Acute Care hospital

Staffed Beds: 26 **Admissions:** 301 **Census:** 21 **Outpatient Visits:** 0 **Births:** 0 **Total Expense ($000):** 7850 **Payroll Expense ($000):** 3789 **Personnel:** 64

BIG RAPIDS—Mecosta County

⊠ **SPECTRUM HEALTH BIG RAPIDS HOSPITAL (230093)**, 605 Oak Street, Zip 49307–2099; tel. 231/796–8691 **A**1 5 10 20 **F**3 8 13 15 17 28 29 34 35 40 45 53 59 62 63 64 65 70 75 76 77 79 81 85 86 87 89 90 91 93 96 97 107 108 110 111 115 119 124 127 129 132 135 146 147 148 **P**1 **S** Spectrum Health, Grand Rapids, MI
Primary Contact: Mary Kay VanDriel, President
COO: Catherine Rybicki, Vice President Physician Services and Chief Operating Officer
CFO: Thomas Khoerl, Vice President Finance
CMO: Christopher Skinner, Chief of Staff
CIO: Patrick Whiteside, Manager Information Services
CHR: Ricky Green, Senior Human Resources Business Partner
CNO: Caroline A. Ring, Chief Nursing Officer
Web address: www.mcmcbr.com
Control: Other not–for–profit (including NFP Corporation) **Service:** General Medical and Surgical

Staffed Beds: 61 **Admissions:** 2196 **Census:** 19 **Outpatient Visits:** 343998 **Births:** 588 **Total Expense ($000):** 65702 **Payroll Expense ($000):** 28294 **Personnel:** 458

BRIGHTON—Livingston County

★ **BRIGHTON CENTER FOR RECOVERY (230279)**, 12851 Grand River Road, Zip 48116–8506; tel. 810/227–1211 **A**10 **F**4 5 35 68 75 104 132 143 146 **S** Ascension Health, Saint Louis, MO
Primary Contact: Raymond A. Waller, Director
COO: Raymond A. Waller, Director
CFO: Marie Allard, Finance Manager
CMO: Ismael David Yanga, M.D., Chief Medical Officer
CIO: Frank Sanzone, Manager Information Technology
CHR: Marney Daugherty, Worklife Services Consultant
CNO: Barbara Shoup, R.N., Chief Nursing Officer
Web address: www.brightonrecovery.org
Control: Church–operated, Nongovernment, not–for profit **Service:** Alcoholism and other chemical dependency

Staffed Beds: 99 **Admissions:** 4138 **Census:** 89 **Outpatient Visits:** 20201 **Births:** 0 **Total Expense ($000):** 15283 **Payroll Expense ($000):** 7410 **Personnel:** 143

CADILLAC—Wexford County

⊠ **MUNSON HEALTHCARE CADILLAC HOSPITAL (230081)**, 400 Hobart Street, Zip 49601–2389; tel. 231/876–7200 **A**1 10 20 **F**3 11 13 15 18 28 29 30 31 34 35 40 44 45 50 51 59 64 68 70 76 77 78 79 81 85 87 89 91 93 97 107 108 111 114 115 116 119 127 129 130 132 146 **P**6 8 **S** Munson Healthcare, Traverse City, MI
Primary Contact: Tonya Smith, President
COO: Michael Zdrodowski, Vice President of Operations and Ambulatory Services
CFO: Kristin Ellis, Controller
CMO: Joe Santangelo, M.D., Vice President of Medical Affairs
CIO: Randi Terry, Site Director Management Information Systems
CHR: Kelley Whittington–Geppert, Director Human Resources
CNO: Kathryn Bandfield–Keough, Vice President Patient Care Services
Web address: www.mercyhealthcadillac.com/welcome-cadillac
Control: Other not–for–profit (including NFP Corporation) **Service:** General Medical and Surgical

Staffed Beds: 65 **Admissions:** 3388 **Census:** 32 **Outpatient Visits:** 132428 **Births:** 369 **Total Expense ($000):** 72228 **Payroll Expense ($000):** 28658 **Personnel:** 466

MI

Hospital, Medicare Provider Number, Address, Telephone, Approval, Facility, and Physician Codes, Health Care System

★ American Hospital Association (AHA) membership
☐ The Joint Commission accreditation
○ Healthcare Facilities Accreditation Program
◇ DNV Healthcare Inc. accreditation
⇑ Center for Improvement in Healthcare Quality Accreditation
△ Commission on Accreditation of Rehabilitation Facilities (CARF) accreditation

MI

CARO—Tuscola County

☐ **CARO CENTER (234025)**, 2000 Chambers Road, Zip 48723–9296;
tel. 989/673–3191, (Nonreporting) **A**1 10
Primary Contact: Rose Laskowski, R.N., Director
COO: Rose Laskowski, R.N., Director
CFO: Mary Jo Drzewiecki–Burger, Administrative Manager
CMO: William Clark, M.D., Chief Clinical Affairs
CIO: Michele Wills, Registered Health Information Administrator
CHR: Barbara Frank, Human Resource Specialist
Control: State–Government, nonfederal **Service:** Psychiatric

Staffed Beds: 193

★ **CARO COMMUNITY HOSPITAL (231329)**, 401 North Hooper Street,
Zip 48723–1476, Mailing Address: P.O. Box 435, Zip 48723–0435;
tel. 989/673–3141 **A**5 10 18 **F**3 11 15 29 34 35 40 45 50 57 59 65 75 81
82 85 87 92 93 97 107 108 110 115 119 129 130 131 135 **P**6
Primary Contact: Marc Augsburger, R.N., President and Chief Executive Officer
CFO: Ron Srebinski, Chief Financial Officer
CMO: T. Gard Adams, M.D., Chief of Staff
CHR: Allyson Joyce, Vice President Human Resources
CNO: Kelly Whittaker, Vice President Nursing
Web address: www.cch–mi.org
Control: Other not–for–profit (including NFP Corporation) **Service:** General
Medical and Surgical

**Staffed Beds: 25 Admissions: 196 Census: 1 Outpatient Visits: 30297
Births: 0 Total Expense ($000): 13132 Payroll Expense ($000): 5397
Personnel: 118**

CARSON CITY—Montcalm County

★ ○ **SPARROW CARSON HOSPITAL (230208)**, 406 East Elm Street,
Zip 48811–9693, Mailing Address: P.O. Box 879, Zip 48811–0879;
tel. 989/584–3131, (Nonreporting) **A**3 5 10 11 19 **S** Sparrow Health System,
Lansing, MI
Primary Contact: Matthew J. Thompson, Chief Executive Officer
CFO: Richard Reid, Vice President Chief Finance Officer
CMO: Robert Seals, D.O., Medical Director
CIO: Richard Terry, Vice President & Chief Information Officer
CHR: Georgette Russell, Vice President of Talent & Organizational Effectiveness
Web address: www.carsoncityhospital.com
Control: Other not–for–profit (including NFP Corporation) **Service:** General
Medical and Surgical

Staffed Beds: 62

CASS CITY—Tuscola County

★ **HILLS & DALES GENERAL HOSPITAL (231316)**, 4675 Hill Street,
Zip 48726–1099; tel. 989/872–2121 **A**5 10 18 **F**3 11 15 29 30 31 32 34 35
40 45 46 53 56 57 59 61 64 68 74 75 77 79 81 85 86 87 93 97 107 108
109 110 115 118 119 127 129 130 131 132 133 135 144 146 147 148 **P**6
Primary Contact: Jean Anthony, R.N., President and Chief Executive Officer
CFO: Kenneth Baranski, Chief Financial Officer
CMO: Donald Robbins, Jr., M.D., Chief Staff
CNO: Jennifer TerBush, Vice President, Patient Services
Web address: www.hdghmi.org
Control: Other not–for–profit (including NFP Corporation) **Service:** General
Medical and Surgical

**Staffed Beds: 25 Admissions: 487 Census: 4 Outpatient Visits: 81363
Births: 0 Total Expense ($000): 27946 Payroll Expense ($000): 12883
Personnel: 241**

CHARLEVOIX—Charlevoix County

⊞ **MUNSON HEALTHCARE CHARLEVOIX HOSPITAL (231322)**, 14700 Lake
Shore Drive, Zip 49720–1999; tel. 231/547–4024, (Nonreporting) **A**1 5 10 18
S Munson Healthcare, Traverse City, MI
Primary Contact: Lyn Jenks, Chief Executive Officer
COO: Christine Wilhelm, Chief Operating Officer
CFO: Robert Zimmerman, Vice President Financial Services
CMO: Craig Boss, M.D., Chief Medical Officer
CIO: David Priest, Director Information Systems
CHR: Patty Fitzgerald, Staff Services
CNO: Bernadette Green Cole, R.N., Chief Nursing Officer
Web address: www.cah.org
Control: Other not–for–profit (including NFP Corporation) **Service:** General
Medical and Surgical

Staffed Beds: 25

CHARLOTTE—Eaton County

⊞ **HAYES GREEN BEACH MEMORIAL HOSPITAL (231327)**, 321 East Harris
Street, Zip 48813–1629; tel. 517/543–1050 **A**1 10 18 **F**3 7 11 15 18 26 28
29 34 35 36 40 45 46 50 53 57 59 62 64 65 68 69 75 77 79 81 82 85 87
89 92 93 97 107 108 110 111 114 118 119 129 130 131 132 135 143 144
146 148 **P**6 **S** QHR, Brentwood, TN
Primary Contact: Matthew Rush, FACHE, President and Chief Executive Officer
CFO: Kim Capps, Chief Financial Officer
CMO: Hugh Lindsey, M.D., Chief Medical Officer
CIO: Kevin Neugent, Chief Information Officer
CHR: Jennifer C. Bucienski, Vice President Human Resources
CNO: Maureen Hillary, Chief Nursing Officer
Web address: www.hgbhealth.com
Control: Other not–for–profit (including NFP Corporation) **Service:** General
Medical and Surgical

**Staffed Beds: 25 Admissions: 634 Census: 5 Outpatient Visits: 159901
Births: 0 Total Expense ($000): 47615 Payroll Expense ($000): 20718
Personnel: 376**

CHELSEA—Washtenaw County

⊞ **ST. JOSEPH MERCY CHELSEA (230259)**, 775 South Main Street,
Zip 48118–1383; tel. 734/593–6000 **A**1 3 5 10 **F**3 5 8 11 15 28 29 30 31 34
35 40 45 50 51 56 57 59 62 64 65 70 74 75 77 78 79 81 82 84 85 86 87
90 91 92 93 97 98 99 100 101 102 104 107 110 111 114 115 119 129 130
131 132 134 135 146 147 **P**6 **S** Trinity Health, Livonia, MI
Primary Contact: Nancy Kay Graebner, President and Chief Executive Officer
CFO: Barb Fielder, Vice President Finance
CMO: Randall T. Forsch, M.D., Chief Medical Officer
CHR: Jeremy Stephens, Vice President and Chief Human Resources Officer
CNO: Kathy M. Brubaker, R.N., Vice President and Chief Nursing Officer
Web address: www.cch.org
Control: Other not–for–profit (including NFP Corporation) **Service:** General
Medical and Surgical

**Staffed Beds: 96 Admissions: 5018 Census: 46 Outpatient Visits: 272468
Births: 0 Total Expense ($000): 123737 Payroll Expense ($000): 55353
Personnel: 732**

CLARE—Clare County

⊞ **MIDMICHIGAN MEDICAL CENTER–CLARE (230180)**, 703 North McEwan
Street, Zip 48617–1440; tel. 989/802–5000 **A**1 5 10 **F**3 11 15 18 20 28 29
30 34 35 40 45 50 53 57 58 59 61 64 75 77 79 80 81 85 87 91 93 97 107
108 110 111 115 118 119 127 129 130 132 135 144 146 **S** MidMichigan
Health, Midland, MI
Primary Contact: Raymond Stover, President and Chief Executive Officer
CFO: Jeff Provenzano, Vice President and Chief Financial Officer
CMO: David Bremer, D.O., Chief of Staff
CIO: Michael Larson, Vice President Chief Information Officer
CNO: Glenn King, R.N., Vice President, Chief Nursing Officer
Web address: www.midmichigan.org
Control: Other not–for–profit (including NFP Corporation) **Service:** General
Medical and Surgical

**Staffed Beds: 49 Admissions: 1179 Census: 8 Outpatient Visits: 107030
Births: 0 Total Expense ($000): 43128 Payroll Expense ($000): 14088
Personnel: 224**

CLINTON TOWNSHIP—Macomb County

⊞ **HENRY FORD MACOMB HOSPITALS (230047)**, 15855 19 Mile Road,
Zip 48038–6324; tel. 586/263–2300, (Includes HENRY FORD MACOMB
HOSPITAL – MOUNT CLEMENS CAMPUS, 215 North Avenue, Mount Clemens,
Zip 48043; tel. 586/466–9300; ST. JOSEPH'S MERCY HOSPITAL–WEST, 15855
19 Mile Road, Zip 48038; tel. 586/263–2707; ST. JOSEPH'S MERCY–NORTH,
80650 North Van Dyke, Romeo, Zip 48065; tel. 810/798–3551) **A**1 2 3 10 13
F3 7 11 12 13 15 18 20 22 24 26 29 30 31 32 34 35 36 38 40 41 43 44
45 46 47 49 50 51 54 56 57 58 59 60 61 62 63 64 65 66 68 69 70 73 74
75 76 77 78 79 81 82 84 85 86 87 89 90 92 93 96 97 98 99 100 101 102
103 104 107 108 110 111 114 115 116 117 118 119 120 121 123 124 126
129 130 131 132 134 135 144 146 147 148 **P**6 8 **S** Henry Ford Health
System, Detroit, MI
Primary Contact: Barbara W. Rossmann, R.N., President and Chief Executive
Officer
COO: Gary Beaulac, Chief Operating Officer
CFO: Terry Goodbalian, Vice President Finance and Chief Financial Officer
CMO: Charles Kelly, D.O., Vice President Medical Affairs and Chief Medical Officer
CHR: Joel Gibson, Vice President Human Resources
Web address: www.henryfordmacomb.com
Control: Other not–for–profit (including NFP Corporation) **Service:** General
Medical and Surgical

**Staffed Beds: 418 Admissions: 21278 Census: 308 Outpatient Visits:
600769 Births: 1672 Total Expense ($000): 428999 Payroll Expense
($000): 170411 Personnel: 2819**

Many Facility Codes have changed. Please refer to the AHA Guide Code Chart.

© 2016 AHA Guide

COLDWATER—Branch County

⊠ **COMMUNITY HEALTH CENTER OF BRANCH COUNTY (230022)**, 274 East Chicago Street, Zip 49036–2041; tel. 517/279–5400 **A**1 10 13 19 **F**3 8 11 12 13 15 28 29 30 31 34 37 40 43 45 57 59 61 62 63 64 65 70 74 75 76 78 79 81 84 85 87 89 91 92 93 96 97 98 100 101 102 103 107 108 110 111 115 118 119 127 129 130 132 134 146 148 **P**6 8
Primary Contact: Randy DeGroot, President and Chief Executive Officer
COO: Mary R. Rose, R.N., Chief Clinical Officer
CFO: Amy Crouch, Chief Financial Officer
CMO: Joudat Daoud, M.D., Chief of Staff
CIO: Joel Lederman, Director Information Systems
CHR: Amy Jensen, Director Human Resources
Web address: www.chcbc.com
Control: County–Government, nonfederal **Service:** General Medical and Surgical

Staffed Beds: 87 **Admissions:** 3345 **Census:** 33 **Outpatient Visits:** 143467 **Births:** 302 **Total Expense ($000):** 64543 **Payroll Expense ($000):** 27600 **Personnel:** 458

COMMERCE TOWNSHIP—Oakland County

⊠ **DMC HURON VALLEY–SINAI HOSPITAL (230277)**, 1 William Carls Drive, Zip 48382–2201; tel. 248/937–3300 **A**1 3 5 10 **F**3 11 12 13 15 18 20 22 26 28 29 30 31 34 35 37 39 40 44 45 46 47 48 49 50 51 53 57 58 59 61 64 65 70 73 74 75 76 77 78 79 81 82 84 85 86 87 89 93 96 107 108 110 111 114 115 117 118 119 121 123 124 126 129 130 131 132 135 141 146 147 148 **P**1 6 **S** TENET Healthcare Corporation, Dallas, TX
Primary Contact: Karen Fordham, President
COO: Samuel Pieh, Chief Operating Officer
CFO: William Lantzy, Chief Financial Officer
CMO: Binesh Patel, Chief Medical Officer
CHR: Nicole Williams, Director of Human Resources Operations
CNO: Lori Stallings–Sicard, R.N., Chief Nursing Officer
Web address: www.hvsh.org
Control: Corporation, Investor–owned, for–profit **Service:** General Medical and Surgical

Staffed Beds: 148 **Admissions:** 8483 **Census:** 87 **Outpatient Visits:** 93969 **Births:** 1115 **Total Expense ($000):** 158413 **Payroll Expense ($000):** 57417 **Personnel:** 894

DEARBORN—Wayne County

⊠ **BEAUMONT HOSPITAL–DEARBORN (230020)**, 18101 Oakwood Boulevard, Zip 48124–4089, Mailing Address: P.O. Box 2500, Zip 48123–2500; tel. 313/593–7000 **A**1 2 3 5 8 10 **F**3 11 12 13 15 17 18 20 22 24 26 28 29 30 31 32 34 35 37 38 39 40 41 43 44 47 49 50 52 55 56 57 58 59 60 61 64 65 68 70 72 74 75 76 77 78 79 81 82 84 85 86 87 89 92 93 96 97 100 102 107 108 110 111 114 115 118 119 120 121 123 124 126 130 131 132 135 146 147 148 **P**8 **S** Beaumont Health, Southfield, MI
Primary Contact: Kelly C. Smith, Senior Vice President and Division President
COO: Carolyn Wilson, Chief Operating Officer
CFO: Timothy Jodway, Chief Financial Administrator
CMO: Parvez Khan, Chief of Staff
CIO: Subra Sripada, Executive Vice President, Chief Transformation Officer and Chief Information Officer
CHR: Sherry Huffman, Administrator Human Resources
CNO: Mary Ellen Kochis, MSN, Administrator Nursing Operations
Web address: www.beaumont.org
Control: Other not–for–profit (including NFP Corporation) **Service:** General Medical and Surgical

Staffed Beds: 632 **Admissions:** 30282 **Census:** 433 **Outpatient Visits:** 191323 **Births:** 4235 **Total Expense ($000):** 610553 **Payroll Expense ($000):** 229182 **Personnel:** 3110

DECKERVILLE—Sanilac County

DECKERVILLE COMMUNITY HOSPITAL (231311), 3559 Pine Street, Zip 48427–7703, Mailing Address: P.O. Box 126, Zip 48427–0126; tel. 810/376–2835, (Nonreporting) **A**10 18
Primary Contact: David West, Administrator
COO: David West, Administrator
CFO: Valerie Bryant, Chief Financial Officer
CMO: Bassam Afaneh, M.D., Chief of Staff
Web address: www.deckervillehosp.org
Control: Other not–for–profit (including NFP Corporation) **Service:** General Medical and Surgical

Staffed Beds: 15

DETROIT—Wayne County

BCA STONECREST HOSPITAL See Stonecrest Center

⊠ △ **DMC – CHILDREN'S HOSPITAL OF MICHIGAN (233300)**, 3901 Beaubien Street, Zip 48201–2119; tel. 313/745–5437 **A**1 3 5 7 10 **F**3 11 16 17 18 19 20 21 22 23 24 25 26 27 29 30 31 32 34 35 38 39 40 41 43 44 45 48 49 50 51 54 55 57 58 59 60 61 64 65 66 68 72 74 75 77 78 79 80 81 82 84 85 86 87 88 89 90 91 92 93 95 96 97 99 100 107 108 111 114 115 116 117 119 120 121 123 124 129 130 131 132 134 136 137 138 139 141 142 144 146 148 **P**1 6 **S** TENET Healthcare Corporation, Dallas, TX
Primary Contact: Luanne T. Ewald, Interim Chief Executive Officer
CMO: Rudolph Valentini, M.D., Chief Medical Officer
CHR: Walter Tetteh, Director Human Resources
CNO: Claudine N. Hoppen, MSN, Interim Chief Nursing Officer
Web address: www.chmkids.org
Control: Corporation, Investor–owned, for–profit **Service:** Children's general

Staffed Beds: 225 **Admissions:** 11659 **Census:** 149 **Outpatient Visits:** 305361 **Births:** 0 **Total Expense ($000):** 347534 **Payroll Expense ($000):** 127875 **Personnel:** 2049

⊠ **DMC – DETROIT RECEIVING HOSPITAL (230273)**, 4201 Saint Antoine Street, Zip 48201–2153; tel. 313/745–3000 **A**1 3 5 10 **F**3 16 17 18 29 30 34 35 38 39 40 43 44 49 50 56 57 58 59 60 61 64 65 66 70 74 75 77 79 81 82 84 85 86 87 93 97 98 100 102 103 104 107 114 115 119 129 130 131 132 135 141 144 146 148 **P**1 6 **S** TENET Healthcare Corporation, Dallas, TX
Primary Contact: Reginald J. Eadie, M.D., Chief Executive Officer
CFO: Gloria Larkins, Vice President Finance
CMO: Safwan Badr, M.D., Executive Vice President and Chief Medical Officer
CIO: Michael LeRoy, Senior Vice President and Chief Information Officer
CHR: Paulette Griffin, Vice President Human Resources
Web address: www.dmc.org
Control: Corporation, Investor–owned, for–profit **Service:** General Medical and Surgical

Staffed Beds: 191 **Admissions:** 14100 **Census:** 191 **Outpatient Visits:** 142717 **Births:** 0 **Total Expense ($000):** 256627 **Payroll Expense ($000):** 93344 **Personnel:** 1536

⊠ △ **DMC – REHABILITATION INSTITUTE OF MICHIGAN (233027)**, 261 Mack Avenue, Zip 48201–2495; tel. 313/745–1203 **A**1 3 5 7 10 **F**3 28 29 30 34 35 44 53 54 58 59 64 68 75 82 86 87 90 91 92 93 94 95 96 119 130 131 132 134 146 148 **P**1 6 **S** TENET Healthcare Corporation, Dallas, TX
Primary Contact: William H. Restum, Ph.D., Chief Executive Officer
COO: Patty Jobbitt, Chief Operating Officer
CFO: Dan Babb, Chief Financial Officer
CMO: Ali Bitar, M.D., Vice President Medical Affairs
CHR: Paul Sturgis, Director Human Resources
CNO: Julia Libcke, R.N., VP Patient Care Services
Web address: www.rimrehab.org
Control: Corporation, Investor–owned, for–profit **Service:** Rehabilitation

Staffed Beds: 69 **Admissions:** 1376 **Census:** 55 **Outpatient Visits:** 250726 **Births:** 0 **Total Expense ($000):** 79921 **Payroll Expense ($000):** 46480 **Personnel:** 583

⊠ **DMC – SINAI–GRACE HOSPITAL (230024)**, 6071 West Outer Drive, Zip 48235–2679; tel. 313/966–3300 **A**1 3 5 10 12 13 **F**3 8 11 13 15 18 20 22 24 26 28 29 30 31 32 34 35 38 40 43 44 45 49 50 51 54 55 57 58 59 60 61 64 65 70 72 74 75 76 77 78 79 80 81 82 84 85 86 87 90 93 96 97 98 100 102 104 107 108 110 111 114 115 117 118 119 120 121 123 126 129 130 132 134 135 141 144 146 147 148 **P**1 6 **S** TENET Healthcare Corporation, Dallas, TX
Primary Contact: Paula R. Autry, FACHE, Chief Executive Officer
COO: London Quicci, Chief Operating Officer
CFO: Michael Prusatis, Vice President Finance
CMO: Matthew Griffin, M.D., Vice President Medical Affairs
CHR: Paulette Griffin, Director Human Resources
Web address: www.sinaigrace.org
Control: Corporation, Investor–owned, for–profit **Service:** General Medical and Surgical

Staffed Beds: 295 **Admissions:** 21388 **Census:** 264 **Outpatient Visits:** 213709 **Births:** 1471 **Total Expense ($000):** 333900 **Payroll Expense ($000):** 128808 **Personnel:** 2005

MI

Hospital, Medicare Provider Number, Address, Telephone, Approval, Facility, and Physician Codes, Health Care System

★ American Hospital Association (AHA) membership
□ The Joint Commission accreditation
○ Healthcare Facilities Accreditation Program
◇ DNV Healthcare Inc. accreditation
⇑ Center for Improvement in Healthcare Quality Accreditation
△ Commission on Accreditation of Rehabilitation Facilities (CARF) accreditation

MI

✠ **DMC HARPER UNIVERSITY HOSPITAL (230104)**, 3990 John R Street, Zip 48201–2018; tel. 313/745–8040 **A**1 3 5 10 **F**3 8 9 11 12 13 15 17 18 20 22 24 26 28 29 30 34 35 40 43 44 45 46 47 48 49 50 51 52 54 55 57 58 59 60 61 64 65 66 70 72 73 74 75 76 77 78 79 80 81 82 84 85 86 87 93 97 100 107 108 111 118 119 126 130 131 132 134 135 138 141 146 147 148 **P**1 6 **S** TENET Healthcare Corporation, Dallas, TX
Primary Contact: Reginald J. Eadie, M.D., Chief Executive Officer
COO: Valerie Gibson, Chief Operating Officer
CFO: Tina Wood, Chief Financial Officer
CMO: Patricia Wilkerson–Uddyback, M.D., Chief Medical Officer
CIO: Michael LeRoy, Senior Vice President and Chief Information Officer
CHR: Deloris Hunt, Corporate Vice President Human Resources
CNO: Christine Bowen, R.N., Chief Nursing Officer
Web address: www.harperhospital.org
Control: Corporation, Investor–owned, for–profit **Service:** General Medical and Surgical

Staffed Beds: 397 **Admissions:** 21299 **Census:** 258 **Outpatient Visits:** 217117 **Births:** 4407 **Total Expense ($000):** 470343 **Payroll Expense ($000):** 163070 **Personnel:** 2517

HARPER UNIVERSITY HOSPITAL See DMC Harper University Hospital

✠ **HENRY FORD HOSPITAL (230053)**, 2799 West Grand Boulevard, Zip 48202–2608; tel. 313/916–2600 **A**1 2 3 5 8 9 10 **F**3 4 5 6 8 9 11 12 13 15 17 18 19 20 22 24 26 28 29 30 31 32 33 34 35 36 38 40 41 42 43 44 45 46 47 48 49 50 51 52 53 54 55 56 57 58 59 60 61 62 63 64 65 66 68 70 71 72 73 74 75 76 77 78 79 80 81 82 83 84 85 86 87 91 92 93 96 97 99 100 101 102 103 104 105 107 108 110 111 112 113 114 115 116 117 118 119 120 121 123 124 126 129 130 131 132 134 135 136 137 138 139 140 141 142 144 145 146 147 148 **P**6 **S** Henry Ford Health System, Detroit, MI
Primary Contact: John Popovich, M.D., President and Chief Executive Officer
COO: Veronica Hall, R.N., Chief Operating Officer
CFO: Joseph Schmitt, III, Senior Vice President Finance and Chief Financial Officer
CMO: John Popovich, M.D., President and Chief Executive Officer
CIO: Mary Alice Annecharico, System Vice President and Chief Information Officer
CHR: Kathy Oswald, Senior Vice President and Chief Human Resources Officer
CNO: Gwen Gnam, R.N., Chief Nursing Officer
Web address: www.henryfordhealth.org
Control: Other not–for–profit (including NFP Corporation) **Service:** General Medical and Surgical

Staffed Beds: 681 **Admissions:** 37779 **Census:** 550 **Outpatient Visits:** 2928144 **Births:** 2519 **Total Expense ($000):** 1883296 **Payroll Expense ($000):** 866784 **Personnel:** 11678

✠ △ **JOHN D. DINGELL VETERANS AFFAIRS MEDICAL CENTER**, 4646 John R Street, Zip 48201–1932; tel. 313/576–1000, (Total facility includes 55 beds in nursing home–type unit) **A**1 2 3 5 7 **F**3 5 8 9 11 12 18 20 26 28 29 30 31 33 34 35 36 38 39 40 44 45 46 49 50 54 56 57 58 59 60 61 62 63 64 65 66 67 68 70 74 75 77 78 79 81 82 83 84 85 86 87 90 93 94 97 98 100 101 102 103 104 105 107 108 111 114 115 118 119 121 123 126 127 128 129 130 132 135 143 146 147 148 **P**6 **S** Department of Veterans Affairs, Washington, DC
Primary Contact: Pamela J. Reeves, M.D., Director
COO: Annette Walker, Associate Director
CFO: Sherry Riedel, Chief Financial Management Service
CMO: Scott Gruber, M.D., Chief of Staff
CIO: Jonathan Small, Chief Operations Information and Technology
CHR: Kathleen Osinski, Chief Human Resources Service
CNO: Belina Brown–Tezera, MSN, Associate Director Patient Care Services
Web address: www.detroit.va.gov/
Control: Veterans Affairs, Government, federal **Service:** General Medical and Surgical

Staffed Beds: 242 **Admissions:** 4297 **Census:** 204 **Outpatient Visits:** 526500 **Births:** 0 **Total Expense ($000):** 367563 **Payroll Expense ($000):** 158727 **Personnel:** 1785

☐ **KARMANOS CANCER CENTER (230297)**, 4100 John R Street, Zip 48201–2013; tel. 313/576–8670 **A**1 2 3 5 10 **F**3 8 14 15 29 30 31 34 35 36 39 44 45 46 47 48 49 50 51 54 55 57 58 59 60 63 64 65 70 74 75 78 79 81 82 83 84 85 86 87 100 107 108 110 111 113 114 115 116 117 118 119 120 121 123 124 126 130 132 135 136 144 146 147 148 **P**6
Primary Contact: Gerold Bepler, M.D., Ph.D., President and Chief Executive Officer
CFO: Brian Gamble, Chief Financial Officer
CMO: George Yoo, M.D., Chief Medical Officer
CIO: Scott McCarter, Chief Information Officer
CHR: David Jansen, Vice President Human Resources
Web address: www.karmanos.org
Control: Other not–for–profit (including NFP Corporation) **Service:** Cancer

Staffed Beds: 85 **Admissions:** 3481 **Census:** 66 **Outpatient Visits:** 83134 **Births:** 0 **Total Expense ($000):** 235216 **Payroll Expense ($000):** 56825 **Personnel:** 974

✠ **KINDRED HOSPITAL DETROIT (232027)**, 4777 East Outer Drive, Zip 48234–3241; tel. 313/369–5800, (Nonreporting) **A**1 10 **S** Kindred Healthcare, Louisville, KY
Primary Contact: Mary Hoskins, Chief Executive Officer
CFO: Clayton Kubacki, Controller
CMO: Kevin Potts, M.D., Medical Director
CHR: Karen McGrail, District Director Human Resource
Web address: www.kindreddetroit.com/
Control: Corporation, Investor–owned, for–profit **Service:** Long–Term Acute Care hospital

Staffed Beds: 77

✠ **SELECT SPECIALTY HOSPITAL–NORTHWEST DETROIT (232032)**, 6071 West Outer Drive, Zip 48235–2624; tel. 313/966–4747, (Nonreporting) **A**1 10 **S** Select Medical Corporation, Mechanicsburg, PA
Primary Contact: Marilouise Riska, Chief Executive Officer
Web address: www.selectspecialtyhospitals.com/company/locations/northwestdetroit.aspx
Control: Corporation, Investor–owned, for–profit **Service:** Long–Term Acute Care hospital

Staffed Beds: 36

✠ **ST. JOHN HOSPITAL AND MEDICAL CENTER (230165)**, 22101 Moross Road, Zip 48236–2148; tel. 313/343–4000 **A**1 2 3 5 8 10 **F**3 8 9 11 12 13 14 15 17 18 20 22 24 26 28 29 30 31 32 34 35 36 37 38 39 40 41 42 43 44 45 46 47 48 49 50 54 55 56 57 58 59 60 61 65 66 68 70 72 74 75 76 77 78 79 80 81 82 84 85 86 87 88 89 90 91 92 93 95 96 97 98 100 101 102 103 107 108 110 111 114 115 116 117 118 119 120 121 123 124 126 130 131 132 135 138 141 143 144 146 147 148 **P**3 6 8 **S** Ascension Health, Saint Louis, MO
Primary Contact: Robert E. Hoban, Chief Executive Officer
COO: Brant Russell, R.N., Chief Operating Officer
CFO: Tomasine Marx, Chief Financial Officer
CMO: Kevin Grady, M.D., Chief Medical Officer
CIO: Ralph Tenney, Chief Information Officer
CHR: Joanne E. Tuscany, Director Human Resources
Web address: www.stjohn.org
Control: Church–operated, Nongovernment, not–for profit **Service:** General Medical and Surgical

Staffed Beds: 635 **Admissions:** 29448 **Census:** 406 **Outpatient Visits:** 1036160 **Births:** 2981 **Total Expense ($000):** 731640 **Payroll Expense ($000):** 257948 **Personnel:** 3323

☐ **STONECREST CENTER (234038)**, 15000 Gratiot Avenue, Zip 48205–1973; tel. 313/245–0600 **A**1 10 **F**98 99 100 101 103 **S** Acadia Healthcare Company, Inc., Franklin, TN
Primary Contact: Steve Savage, Chief Executive Officer
Web address: www.stonecrestcenter.com
Control: Corporation, Investor–owned, for–profit **Service:** Psychiatric

Staffed Beds: 104 **Admissions:** 3409 **Census:** 93 **Outpatient Visits:** 0 **Births:** 0 **Total Expense ($000):** 20799 **Payroll Expense ($000):** 10017 **Personnel:** 196

TRIUMPH HOSPITAL DETROIT See Kindred Hospital Detroit

DOWAGIAC—Cass County

✠ **BORGESS–LEE MEMORIAL HOSPITAL (231315)**, 420 West High Street, Zip 49047–1943; tel. 269/782–8681 **A**1 10 18 **F**3 11 15 18 28 29 30 31 34 35 40 41 50 54 57 59 64 65 68 70 75 77 78 79 81 85 86 87 93 97 100 104 107 108 110 114 119 127 128 130 132 133 135 146 148 **P**6 **S** Ascension Health, Saint Louis, MO
Primary Contact: John E. Ryder, Chief Operating Officer
COO: John E. Ryder, Chief Operating Officer
CFO: Richard Felbinger, Chief Financial Officer
CMO: Robert Hill, M.D., Chief Medical Officer
CIO: James Keller, Chief Information Officer
CHR: Pete Krueger, Director Human Resources
CNO: Janice K. Troeger, R.N., Chief Nursing Officer
Web address: www.borgess.com
Control: Church–operated, Nongovernment, not–for profit **Service:** General Medical and Surgical

Staffed Beds: 25 **Admissions:** 405 **Census:** 4 **Outpatient Visits:** 89784 **Births:** 0 **Total Expense ($000):** 25269 **Payroll Expense ($000):** 12422 **Personnel:** 183

Many Facility Codes have changed. Please refer to the AHA Guide Code Chart.   © 2016 AHA Guide

EAST CHINA—St. Clair County

⊞ **ST. JOHN RIVER DISTRICT HOSPITAL (230241)**, 4100 River Road, Zip 48054–2909; tel. 810/329–7111 **A**1 3 10 **F**3 7 11 13 15 18 20 29 30 34 35 36 39 40 45 49 50 57 59 64 65 68 70 75 76 77 79 80 81 82 84 85 87 92 93 97 107 108 110 111 115 116 117 119 129 130 132 146 147 **S** Ascension Health, Saint Louis, MO
Primary Contact: Frank W. Poma, President
CMO: H. Lee Bacheldor, D.O., Chief Medical Officer
CHR: Dawn Beindit, Director Work Life Services
CNO: Joyce Kasperski, Director Nursing
Web address: www.stjohn.org
Control: Church–operated, Nongovernment, not–for profit **Service:** General Medical and Surgical

Staffed Beds: 68 **Admissions:** 1909 **Census:** 17 **Outpatient Visits:** 50773 **Births:** 297 **Total Expense ($000):** 37668 **Payroll Expense ($000):** 16925 **Personnel:** 272

EATON RAPIDS—Eaton County

★ ◇ **EATON RAPIDS MEDICAL CENTER (231324)**, 1500 South Main Street, Zip 48827–1952, Mailing Address: P.O. Box 130, Zip 48827–0130; tel. 517/663–2671 **A**10 18 21 **F**3 15 28 29 34 35 40 41 45 46 50 53 56 57 59 64 65 66 68 75 77 81 85 86 91 93 97 107 115 117 119 127 129 130 131 132 133 146 147 148 **P**6
Primary Contact: Timothy Johnson, President and Chief Executive Officer
CFO: Shari Glynn, Vice President Finance and Chief Financial Officer
CMO: Ashok K. Gupta, M.D., Chief of Staff
CIO: Mark Rodge, Director Information Systems
CHR: Laurie Field, Director Human Resources
Web address: www.eatonrapidsmedicalcenter.org
Control: Other not–for–profit (including NFP Corporation) **Service:** General Medical and Surgical

Staffed Beds: 20 **Admissions:** 384 **Census:** 3 **Outpatient Visits:** 62245 **Births:** 0 **Total Expense ($000):** 22420 **Payroll Expense ($000):** 10231 **Personnel:** 186

ESCANABA—Delta County

⊞ **OSF ST. FRANCIS HOSPITAL AND MEDICAL GROUP (231337)**, 3401 Ludington Street, Zip 49829–1377; tel. 906/786–3311 **A**1 10 18 **F**3 11 13 15 18 28 29 30 31 34 35 40 44 45 46 53 56 57 59 62 63 64 65 66 68 70 74 75 76 77 78 79 81 83 84 85 86 92 93 96 97 107 108 110 111 115 119 127 129 130 131 132 133 144 145 146 147 148 **P**6 **S** OSF Healthcare System, Peoria, IL
Primary Contact: David Lord, President
COO: Kelly Jefferson, Vice President, Operations
CFO: Fred Wagner, Chief Financial Officer
CMO: Mark Povich, D.O., Medical Director
CIO: Mark Irving, Manager Management Information Systems
CHR: Elizabeth Zorza, Assistant Administrator
CNO: Joy Hopkins, Vice President Patient Care Services
Web address: www.osfstfrancis.org
Control: Church–operated, Nongovernment, not–for profit **Service:** General Medical and Surgical

Staffed Beds: 25 **Admissions:** 1830 **Census:** 14 **Outpatient Visits:** 122126 **Births:** 295 **Total Expense ($000):** 79821 **Payroll Expense ($000):** 30135 **Personnel:** 397

FARMINGTON HILLS—Oakland County

★ ○ **BEAUMONT HOSPITAL – FARMINGTON HILLS (230151)**, 28050 Grand River Avenue, Zip 48336–5933; tel. 248/471–8000 **A**2 3 10 11 12 13 **F**3 8 11 13 15 18 20 22 26 28 29 30 32 33 34 35 36 38 39 40 41 43 44 45 46 47 48 49 50 51 54 56 57 58 59 60 61 63 64 65 68 70 74 75 76 77 78 79 81 82 83 84 85 87 89 90 92 93 94 96 97 98 100 101 102 103 107 108 110 111 114 115 118 119 120 121 123 124 126 129 130 131 132 134 135 144 146 147 148 **P**1 6 **S** Beaumont Health, Southfield, MI
Primary Contact: Constance O'Malley, President
COO: Carolyn Wilson, R.N., Chief Operating Officer
CFO: Barbara Hrit, Controller
CMO: Michael Rebock, Chief Medical Officer
CIO: Subra Sripada, Executive Vice President, Chief Transportation Officer and Chief Information Officer
CHR: Dalph Watson, Director of Human Resources
CNO: Marge Hasler, R.N., Vice President Patient Care Services and Chief Nursing Officer
Web address: www.beaumont.org
Control: Other not–for–profit (including NFP Corporation) **Service:** General Medical and Surgical

Staffed Beds: 330 **Admissions:** 14442 **Census:** 201 **Outpatient Visits:** 426117 **Births:** 736 **Total Expense ($000):** 291720 **Payroll Expense ($000):** 149207 **Personnel:** 2197

FERNDALE—Oakland County

⊞ **HENRY FORD KINGSWOOD HOSPITAL (234011)**, 10300 West Eight Mile Road, Zip 48220–2100; tel. 248/398–3200 **A**1 10 **F**4 29 30 32 34 35 44 50 56 57 59 68 75 77 80 82 86 87 98 99 101 103 130 134 135 **P**6 **S** Henry Ford Health System, Detroit, MI
Primary Contact: DoreeAnn V. Espiritu, M.D., Interim Chair, Behavioral Health Services
CMO: Robert Lagrou, D.O., Medical Director
CNO: Cheryl Taylor, R.N., Director of Nursing
Web address: www.henryford.com
Control: Other not–for–profit (including NFP Corporation) **Service:** Psychiatric

Staffed Beds: 136 **Admissions:** 3886 **Census:** 57 **Outpatient Visits:** 0 **Births:** 0 **Total Expense ($000):** 20949 **Payroll Expense ($000):** 13440 **Personnel:** 225

FLINT—Genesee County

⊞ **HURLEY MEDICAL CENTER (230132)**, One Hurley Plaza, Zip 48503–5993; tel. 810/262–6887, (Includes HURLEY CHILDREN'S HOSPITAL, 1 Hurley Plaza, Zip 48503–5902) **A**1 2 3 5 8 10 **F**3 5 11 12 13 15 16 17 18 19 20 22 26 28 29 30 31 32 33 35 39 40 41 43 46 49 50 52 54 55 56 57 58 59 61 64 66 70 72 74 75 76 77 78 79 80 81 82 84 85 86 87 88 89 90 93 96 97 98 100 101 102 103 104 107 108 110 111 114 115 118 119 120 121 123 124 126 129 130 131 132 135 141 143 144 146 147 148
Primary Contact: Melany Gavulic, President & Chief Executive Officer
COO: Melany Gavulic, Senior Vice President Operations & COO
CFO: Cass Wisniewski, Interim Chief Financial Officer
CMO: Michael Jaggi, D.O., Vice President and Chief Medical Officer
CIO: Gary Townsend, Chief Information Officer
CHR: Beth Brophy, Interim VP for Human Resources
CNO: Teresa Bourque, Sr. Administrator for Nursing/Chief Nurse
Web address: www.hurleymc.com
Control: City–Government, nonfederal **Service:** General Medical and Surgical

Staffed Beds: 418 **Admissions:** 18942 **Census:** 273 **Outpatient Visits:** 463901 **Births:** 2670 **Total Expense ($000):** 387042 **Payroll Expense ($000):** 165893 **Personnel:** 2382

☐ **MCLAREN FLINT (230141)**, 401 South Ballenger Highway, Zip 48532–3685; tel. 810/342–2000 **A**1 2 3 5 8 10 **F**3 5 8 11 12 13 15 17 18 20 22 24 26 28 29 30 31 32 34 35 36 38 39 40 43 44 45 46 49 50 52 53 54 55 56 57 58 59 61 64 68 70 74 75 76 77 78 79 81 82 84 85 86 87 89 90 91 93 96 97 98 99 100 101 102 103 104 105 107 108 111 114 115 118 119 120 121 123 124 126 129 130 131 132 135 141 144 146 147 148 **P**6 7 **S** McLaren Health Care Corporation, Flint, MI
Primary Contact: Donald C. Kooy, President and Chief Executive Officer
COO: Brent Wheeler, Vice President Ancillary and Support Services
CFO: Fred Korte, Chief Financial Officer
CMO: Jason White, M.D., Vice President of Medical Affairs
CIO: Ronald Strachan, Chief Information Officer
CHR: Rachelle Hulett, Vice President Human Resources
CNO: Diane Kallas, Vice President of Nursing Services
Web address: www.mclarenregional.org
Control: Other not–for–profit (including NFP Corporation) **Service:** General Medical and Surgical

Staffed Beds: 348 **Admissions:** 20718 **Census:** 271 **Outpatient Visits:** 391582 **Births:** 557 **Total Expense ($000):** 413627 **Payroll Expense ($000):** 182787 **Personnel:** 2253

⊞ **SELECT SPECIALTY HOSPITAL–FLINT (232012)**, 401 South Ballenger Highway, 5th Floor Central, Zip 48532–3638; tel. 810/342–4545, (Nonreporting) **A**1 10 **S** Select Medical Corporation, Mechanicsburg, PA
Primary Contact: Christina DeBlouw, Chief Executive Officer
CMO: Jitendra P. Katneni, M.D., Medical Director
CHR: Gayle Barthel, Coordinator Human Resources
CNO: Kathleen Gallardo, Chief Nursing Officer
Web address: www.selectspecialtyhospitals.com/company/locations/flint.aspx
Control: Corporation, Investor–owned, for–profit **Service:** Long–Term Acute Care hospital

Staffed Beds: 26

Hospital, Medicare Provider Number, Address, Telephone, Approval, Facility, and Physician Codes, Health Care System

★ American Hospital Association (AHA) membership   ○ Healthcare Facilities Accreditation Program   ⇑ Center for Improvement in Healthcare Quality Accreditation
☐ The Joint Commission accreditation   ◇ DNV Healthcare Inc. accreditation   △ Commission on Accreditation of Rehabilitation Facilities (CARF) accreditation

MI

FRANKFORT—Benzie County

★ **PAUL OLIVER MEMORIAL HOSPITAL (231300)**, 224 Park Avenue, Zip 49635–9658; tel. 231/352–2200, (Total facility includes 39 beds in nursing home–type unit) **A**10 18 **F**11 15 28 30 34 35 40 45 50 53 57 59 60 64 75 77 81 86 87 93 107 110 111 115 119 129 130 132 133 143 146 148 **S** Munson Healthcare, Traverse City, MI
Primary Contact: Peter Marinoff, President
CMO: George Ryckman, D.O., Chief of Staff
CHR: Julie Banktson, Manager Human Resources
Web address: www.munsonhealthcare.org
Control: Other not–for–profit (including NFP Corporation) **Service:** General Medical and Surgical

Staffed Beds: 47 **Admissions:** 112 **Census:** 36 **Outpatient Visits:** 52956 **Births:** 0 **Total Expense ($000):** 15818 **Payroll Expense ($000):** 5797 **Personnel:** 128

FREMONT—Newaygo County

⊞ **SPECTRUM HEALTH GERBER MEMORIAL (230106)**, 212 South Sullivan Avenue, Zip 49412–1548; tel. 231/924–3300 **A**1 3 10 18 **F**3 11 13 15 28 29 31 32 34 35 36 40 43 45 47 50 53 59 64 68 70 75 76 77 78 79 81 86 87 93 96 107 108 110 111 115 118 119 127 129 130 131 132 135 146 147 **S** Spectrum Health, Grand Rapids, MI
Primary Contact: Randall Stasik, President
COO: Janice Stone, Chief Operating Officer
CFO: Kevin Nichols, Controller
CMO: Nicholas Kuhl, M.D., Chief of Staff
CIO: Dave Mitchell, Manager Information Services
CHR: Christine Schurkamp, Senior Human Resources Business Partner
CNO: Meleah Mariani, Chief Nursing Officer
Web address: www.spectrumhealth.org
Control: Other not–for–profit (including NFP Corporation) **Service:** General Medical and Surgical

Staffed Beds: 25 **Admissions:** 2009 **Census:** 13 **Outpatient Visits:** 142780 **Births:** 505 **Total Expense ($000):** 73867 **Payroll Expense ($000):** 28040 **Personnel:** 520

GARDEN CITY—Wayne County

★ ○ **GARDEN CITY HOSPITAL (230244)**, 6245 Inkster Road, Zip 48135–4001; tel. 734/421–3300 **A**10 11 12 13 **F**3 4 11 13 15 17 18 20 22 26 28 29 31 34 35 36 40 43 44 45 46 47 49 50 59 62 64 65 68 70 71 74 75 76 77 78 79 80 81 82 85 87 89 90 91 92 93 96 107 109 110 111 112 115 119 129 130 131 132 135 143 146 147 148 **P**5 6 **S** Prime Healthcare Services, Ontario, CA
Primary Contact: Saju George, Chief Executive Officer
CFO: Gina Butcher, Chief Financial Officer
CMO: H. Rex Reuttinger, D.O., Chief Medical Officer, Administration
CIO: Randall Sanborn, Director Information Systems
CHR: Josie Ciccone, Director, Human Resources
Web address: www.gch.org
Control: Corporation, Investor–owned, for–profit **Service:** General Medical and Surgical

Staffed Beds: 176 **Admissions:** 9645 **Census:** 109 **Outpatient Visits:** 147357 **Births:** 760 **Total Expense ($000):** 138691 **Payroll Expense ($000):** 60321 **Personnel:** 973

GAYLORD—Otsego County

⊞ **OTSEGO MEMORIAL HOSPITAL (230133)**, 825 North Center Avenue, Zip 49735–1592; tel. 989/731–2100, (Includes MCREYNOLDS HALL), (Total facility includes 34 beds in nursing home–type unit) **A**1 5 10 20 **F**3 13 15 28 29 31 32 34 35 36 40 43 44 45 46 49 50 53 57 59 64 65 70 74 75 76 77 78 79 81 82 85 86 87 93 96 97 104 107 108 110 111 115 118 119 124 127 128 130 131 132 134 135 144 146 147 148 **P**6
Primary Contact: Thomas R. Lemon, Chief Executive Officer
COO: James Flickema, Vice President Market Development
CFO: Robert Courtois, Vice President Finance
CMO: Kevin Smith, D.O., Chief of Staff
CIO: Timothy Hella, Chief Information Officer
CHR: Terra Deming, Director Human Resources
CNO: Diane Fisher, R.N., VP, Patient Care Services
Web address: www.myomh.org
Control: Other not–for–profit (including NFP Corporation) **Service:** General Medical and Surgical

Staffed Beds: 80 **Admissions:** 2046 **Census:** 47 **Outpatient Visits:** 251515 **Births:** 377 **Total Expense ($000):** 85130 **Payroll Expense ($000):** 43003 **Personnel:** 700

GLADWIN—Gladwin County

⊞ **MIDMICHIGAN MEDICAL CENTER–GLADWIN (231325)**, 515 Quarter Street, Zip 48624–1959; tel. 989/426–9286 **A**1 5 10 18 **F**3 11 15 18 28 29 30 31 34 35 40 45 53 57 59 64 75 77 81 85 86 93 97 107 108 110 111 114 118 119 127 129 130 132 135 144 146 **S** MidMichigan Health, Midland, MI
Primary Contact: Raymond Stover, President and Chief Executive Officer
CFO: Jeff Provenzano, Vice President and Chief Financial Officer
CMO: Cheryl Loubert, M.D., Chief Medical Staff
CIO: Dan Waltz, Vice President and Chief Information Officer
CNO: Glenn King, R.N., Vice President and Chief Nursing Officer
Web address: www.midmichigan.org
Control: Other not–for–profit (including NFP Corporation) **Service:** General Medical and Surgical

Staffed Beds: 25 **Admissions:** 570 **Census:** 4 **Outpatient Visits:** 56027 **Births:** 0 **Total Expense ($000):** 25056 **Payroll Expense ($000):** 8068 **Personnel:** 117

GRAND BLANC—Genesee County

⊞ **GENESYS REGIONAL MEDICAL CENTER (230197)**, One Genesys Parkway, Zip 48439–8066; tel. 810/606–5000 **A**1 3 5 10 12 13 **F**3 11 13 18 20 22 24 26 28 29 30 31 32 35 40 43 44 45 47 48 49 50 51 56 57 58 60 61 64 68 70 73 74 75 76 78 79 81 82 84 85 86 87 89 90 91 92 96 97 102 107 108 111 114 115 117 118 119 126 129 130 132 135 144 145 146 147 148 **P**1 6 7 **S** Ascension Health, Saint Louis, MO
Primary Contact: Chris Palazzolo, President and Chief Executive Officer
COO: Joy Finkenbiner, Vice President, Operations
CFO: Nancy Haywood, Chief Financial Officer
CMO: Charles Husson, Regional Chief Medical Officer
CIO: Daniel Stross, Chief Information Officer
CNO: Julie A. Gorczyca, R.N., Chief Nursing Officer
Web address: www.genesys.org
Control: Church–operated, Nongovernment, not–for profit **Service:** General Medical and Surgical

Staffed Beds: 415 **Admissions:** 21174 **Census:** 280 **Outpatient Visits:** 552378 **Births:** 2004 **Total Expense ($000):** 399178 **Payroll Expense ($000):** 180060 **Personnel:** 2685

GRAND HAVEN—Ottawa County

★ ◇ **NORTH OTTAWA COMMUNITY HOSPITAL (230174)**, 1309 Sheldon Road, Zip 49417–2488; tel. 616/842–3600 **A**10 21 **F**3 7 11 12 13 15 29 30 34 35 40 43 45 50 51 57 59 61 62 63 64 65 68 69 70 74 75 76 79 81 83 84 86 87 97 107 108 115 119 126 128 129 130 131 132 135 143 144 145 146 147 148 **P**6
Primary Contact: Shelleye Yaklin, President and Chief Executive Officer
CFO: Donald J. Longpre, Vice President Finance and Chief Financial Officer
CMO: Haney Assaad, Vice President Medical Affairs
CIO: Joe Abbott, Director Information Systems
CHR: Carla Wallis, Director Human Resources
CNO: Cindy Van Kampen, Chief Nursing Officer
Web address: www.noch.org
Control: Other not–for–profit (including NFP Corporation) **Service:** General Medical and Surgical

Staffed Beds: 58 **Admissions:** 2043 **Census:** 15 **Outpatient Visits:** 120349 **Births:** 344 **Total Expense ($000):** 72232 **Payroll Expense ($000):** 27227 **Personnel:** 472

GRAND RAPIDS—Kent County

☐ **FOREST VIEW PSYCHIATRIC HOSPITAL (234030)**, 1055 Medical Park Drive S.E., Zip 49546–3607; tel. 616/942–9610 **A**1 10 **F**87 98 99 100 101 102 103 104 105 130 132 **S** Universal Health Services, Inc., King of Prussia, PA
Primary Contact: Andrew Hotaling, Chief Executive Officer
CFO: Andre Pierre, Chief Financial Officer
CMO: James VanHaren, M.D., Medical Director
CHR: Mike Henderson, Director Human Resources
CNO: Jo ell Harris, Director of Nursing
Web address: www.forestviewhospital.com
Control: Corporation, Investor–owned, for–profit **Service:** Psychiatric

Staffed Beds: 109 **Admissions:** 2928 **Census:** 77 **Outpatient Visits:** 11538 **Births:** 0 **Total Expense ($000):** 18249 **Payroll Expense ($000):** 8319 **Personnel:** 158

⊞ **GREAT LAKES SPECIALTY HOSPITAL–GRAND RAPIDS (232026)**, 200 S.E. Jefferson Avenue, 5th Floor, Zip 49503–4502; tel. 616/965–8650, (Nonreporting) **A**1 10 **S** Select Medical Corporation, Mechanicsburg, PA
Primary Contact: Jevne Conover, Chief Executive Officer
CMO: Mark J. Ivey, M.D., Medical Director
CNO: Tracie Peterson, R.N., Chief Nursing Officer
Web address: www.selectmedicalcorp.com
Control: Corporation, Investor–owned, for–profit **Service:** Long–Term Acute Care hospital

Staffed Beds: 20

LIFECARE HOSPITALS OF WESTERN MICHIGAN See Great Lakes Specialty Hospital–Grand Rapids

Many Facility Codes have changed. Please refer to the AHA Guide Code Chart.
© 2016 AHA Guide

✠ △ **MARY FREE BED REHABILITATION HOSPITAL (233026)**, 235 Wealthy Street S.E., Zip 49503–5247; tel. 616/840–8000 **A**1 3 5 7 10 **F**2 30 34 54 56 57 58 62 64 68 75 77 78 79 82 86 90 91 92 93 94 95 96 100 104 119 130 131 132 143 146 **P**6
Primary Contact: Kent Riddle, Chief Executive Officer
CFO: Randall DeNeff, Vice President Finance
CMO: Michael Jakubowski, M.D., Chief Medical Officer
CIO: Jeff Burns, Manager of Information Technology
CNO: Ingrid Cheslek, R.N., Chief Nursing Officer
Web address: www.maryfreebed.com
Control: Other not–for–profit (including NFP Corporation) **Service:** Rehabilitation

Staffed Beds: 80 **Admissions:** 1387 **Census:** 63 **Outpatient Visits:** 62488 **Births:** 0 **Total Expense ($000):** 70027 **Payroll Expense ($000):** 41022 **Personnel:** 895

✠ **MERCY HEALTH SAINT MARY'S (230059)**, 200 Jefferson Avenue S.E., Zip 49503–4598; tel. 616/685–5000, (Includes MERCY HEALTH ROCKFORD, 6050 Northland Drive N.E., Rockford, Zip 49341–9244; tel. 616/685–7950) **A**1 2 3 5 10 **F**3 13 15 18 20 22 26 28 29 30 34 35 36 37 39 40 42 43 44 45 46 48 49 50 54 55 56 57 58 59 61 64 65 66 68 70 72 74 75 76 77 78 79 80 81 82 83 84 85 86 87 97 98 100 102 105 107 108 110 111 114 115 116 117 118 119 120 121 123 124 126 129 130 132 135 138 144 146 148 **P**6 8 **S** Trinity Health, Livonia, MI
Primary Contact: Bill Manns, President
COO: Randall J. Wagner, Chief Operating Officer
CFO: Steve Eavenson, Vice President Finance
CMO: Rolland Mambourg, M.D., Vice President Medical Affairs
CIO: Jim Keller, Site Director Information Services
CHR: Thomas L. Karel, Vice President Organization and Talent Effectiveness
CNO: Elizabeth A. Murphy, R.N., Vice President for Patient Care Services
Web address: www.mercyhealthsaintmarys.org
Control: Church–operated, Nongovernment, not–for profit **Service:** General Medical and Surgical

Staffed Beds: 371 **Admissions:** 21520 **Census:** 279 **Outpatient Visits:** 1128344 **Births:** 2205 **Total Expense ($000):** 466612 **Payroll Expense ($000):** 162614 **Personnel:** 3242

✠ **PINE REST CHRISTIAN MENTAL HEALTH SERVICES (234006)**, 300 68th Street S.E., Zip 49548–6927, Mailing Address: P.O. Box 165, Zip 49501–0165; tel. 616/455–5000 **A**1 5 10 **F**4 5 6 29 30 32 34 35 38 55 56 58 59 66 68 75 77 82 86 87 98 99 100 101 102 103 104 105 106 130 132 134 135 146 **P**6
Primary Contact: Mark C. Eastburg, Ph.D., President and Chief Executive Officer
COO: Robert Nykamp, Vice President and Chief Operating Officer
CFO: Paul H. Karsten, Vice President Finance and Chief Financial Officer
CMO: Alan Armstrong, M.D., Chief Medical Officer
Web address: www.pinerest.org
Control: Other not–for–profit (including NFP Corporation) **Service:** Psychiatric

Staffed Beds: 451 **Admissions:** 6521 **Census:** 169 **Outpatient Visits:** 332312 **Births:** 0 **Total Expense ($000):** 127130 **Payroll Expense ($000):** 73610 **Personnel:** 1314

✠ **SPECTRUM HEALTH – BUTTERWORTH HOSPITAL (230038)**, 100 Michigan Street N.E., Zip 49503–2560; tel. 616/774–7444, (Includes HELEN DEVOS CHILDREN'S HOSPITAL, 100 Michigan Street N.E., tel. 616/391–9000; Robert Connors, M.D., President; SPECTRUM HEALTH, 100 Michigan Street N.E., Zip 49503–2551; tel. 616/391–1774; Christina Freese–Decker, FACHE, President, Spectrum Health Hospital Group; SPECTRUM HEALTH – BLODGETT CAMPUS, 1840 Wealthy Street S.E., Zip 49506–2921; tel. 616/774–7444; Julie Wolowitz, Vice President, Imaging, Lab) **A**1 2 3 5 10 **F**3 8 9 11 12 13 15 16 17 18 19 20 21 22 23 24 25 26 27 28 29 30 31 32 34 35 36 37 38 40 41 43 44 45 46 47 48 49 50 51 52 54 55 56 57 58 59 60 61 64 65 66 68 70 71 72 73 74 75 76 77 78 79 80 81 82 84 85 86 87 88 89 90 93 96 99 100 101 102 107 108 110 111 112 114 115 116 117 118 119 120 121 123 124 126 130 131 132 134 135 136 137 138 140 145 146 147 148 **P**6 8 **S** Spectrum Health, Grand Rapids, MI
Primary Contact: Christina Freese–Decker, FACHE, President, Spectrum Health Hospital Group
COO: Gwen L. Sandefur, Chief Operating Officer
CFO: Doug Welday, Senior Vice President Finance
CMO: David Krhovsky, M.D., Vice President, Medical Affairs
CIO: Jason Joseph, Vice President, Information Services
CHR: Ovell Barbee, Senior Vice President, Human Resources
CNO: Shawn Ulreich, R.N., Vice President Clinical Operations and Chief Nursing Executive
Web address: www.spectrumhealth.org
Control: Other not–for–profit (including NFP Corporation) **Service:** General Medical and Surgical

Staffed Beds: 1126 **Admissions:** 58777 **Census:** 764 **Outpatient Visits:** 1438608 **Births:** 7553 **Total Expense ($000):** 1674780 **Payroll Expense ($000):** 457703 **Personnel:** 6934

✠ △ **SPECTRUM HEALTH SPECIAL CARE HOSPITAL (232029)**, 750 Fuller Avenue N.E., Zip 49503–1995; tel. 616/486–3000 **A**1 7 10 **F**1 29 30 50 56 59 68 75 77 84 87 91 96 130 146 148 **S** Spectrum Health, Grand Rapids, MI
Primary Contact: Chad Tuttle, President
COO: Linda Joel, Vice President Operations
CFO: Larry Oberst, Vice President Finance
CMO: Peter Sholler, M.D., Medical Director
CIO: Mary Nader, Director Information Technology
CHR: Mark Pakkala, Director Human Resources
CNO: Jennifer Groeneweg, R.N., Director of Nursing
Web address: www.spectrum–health.org
Control: Other not–for–profit (including NFP Corporation) **Service:** Long–Term Acute Care hospital

Staffed Beds: 40 **Admissions:** 166 **Census:** 14 **Births:** 0

GRAYLING—Crawford County

✠ **MUNSON HEALTHCARE GRAYLING HOSPITAL (230058)**, 1100 East Michigan Avenue, Zip 49738–1312; tel. 989/348–5461, (Total facility includes 39 beds in nursing home–type unit) **A**1 5 10 20 **F**3 11 13 15 28 29 30 32 34 35 36 38 40 44 45 50 51 54 56 57 58 59 64 65 66 70 75 76 77 78 79 81 85 86 87 93 97 107 108 111 115 119 127 129 130 131 135 146 147 148 **P**6 8 **S** Munson Healthcare, Traverse City, MI
Primary Contact: Stephanie J. Riemer, President
COO: Kirsten Korth–White, Vice President Physician Network and Ambulatory Service
CFO: Lori Shively, Vice President of Finance
CMO: Vince Schultz, M.D., Chief Medical Officer
CHR: Kirsten Korth–White, Vice President Physician Network and Ambulatory Services
CNO: Carla Gardner, Director of Nursing
Web address: www.mercygrayling.munsonhealthcare.org/
Control: Other not–for–profit (including NFP Corporation) **Service:** General Medical and Surgical

Staffed Beds: 110 **Admissions:** 3148 **Census:** 56 **Outpatient Visits:** 149367 **Births:** 380 **Total Expense ($000):** 49665 **Payroll Expense ($000):** 20489 **Personnel:** 356

GREENVILLE—Montcalm County

✠ **SPECTRUM HEALTH UNITED HOSPITAL (230035)**, 615 South Bower Street, Zip 48838–2614; tel. 616/754–4691, (Includes SPECTRUM HEALTH KELSEY HOSPITAL, 418 Washington Avenue, Lakeview, Zip 48850; tel. 989/352–7211), (Total facility includes 70 beds in nursing home–type unit) **A**1 10 **F**3 8 11 13 15 18 28 29 30 31 32 34 35 40 41 43 44 45 46 50 54 57 59 64 65 66 70 71 75 76 77 78 79 81 85 86 87 89 93 96 97 107 108 110 111 115 119 124 127 128 129 130 132 133 134 135 143 146 147 148 **P**6 **S** Spectrum Health, Grand Rapids, MI
Primary Contact: Brian Brasser, President
COO: Priscilla Mahar, Chief Clinical Officer
CFO: Ryan K. Johnson, Vice President Finance
CMO: Kevin O'Connor, D.O., President Medical Staff
CIO: David Dutmers, Manager Technology Information System
CHR: Mary Fenske, Human Resource Business Partner
CNO: Andrea M. Leslie, MSN, Chief Nursing Officer
Web address: www.spectrumhealth.org/
Control: Other not–for–profit (including NFP Corporation) **Service:** General Medical and Surgical

Staffed Beds: 116 **Admissions:** 3160 **Census:** 90 **Outpatient Visits:** 184771 **Births:** 388 **Total Expense ($000):** 88086 **Payroll Expense ($000):** 34164 **Personnel:** 694

MI

GROSSE POINTE—Wayne County

☒ **BEAUMONT HOSPITAL – GROSSE POINTE (230089)**, 468 Cadieux Road, Zip 48230–1507; tel. 313/473–1000 **A**1 2 3 5 10 **F**3 6 11 12 13 15 18 20 22 26 28 29 30 31 32 34 35 36 39 40 43 44 45 46 47 48 49 50 51 53 54 55 56 57 58 59 60 61 62 63 64 65 66 68 69 70 71 74 75 76 77 78 79 80 81 82 84 85 86 87 89 91 92 93 94 96 97 100 107 108 110 111 114 115 116 117 118 119 126 129 130 131 132 134 135 145 146 147 148 **P**1 6 **S** Beaumont Health, Southfield, MI
Primary Contact: Richard P. Swaine, President
COO: Carolyn Wilson, R.N., Chief Operating Officer
CFO: Maria Miller, Controller
CMO: Donna Hoban, M.D., Senior Vice President and Chief Medical Officer
CIO: Subra Sripada, Executive Vice President, Chief Transportation Officer and Chief Information Officer
CHR: Pandora Walker, Director, Human Resources
CNO: Anne Stewart, Vice President and Chief Nursing Officer
Web address: www.beaumont.org
Control: Other not–for–profit (including NFP Corporation) **Service:** General Medical and Surgical

Staffed Beds: 250 **Admissions:** 11915 **Census:** 127 **Outpatient Visits:** 313817 **Births:** 839 **Total Expense ($000):** 169422 **Payroll Expense ($000):** 60888 **Personnel:** 1249	

☒ **SELECT SPECIALTY HOSPITAL–GROSSE POINTE (232038)**, 468 Cadieux Road, 3 North East, Zip 48230–1507; tel. 313/473–6131, (Nonreporting) **A**1 10 **S** Select Medical Corporation, Mechanicsburg, PA
Primary Contact: Zaahra Butt, Chief Executive Officer
Web address: www.grossepointe.selectspecialtyhospitals.com/
Control: Corporation, Investor–owned, for–profit **Service:** Long–Term Acute Care hospital

Staffed Beds: 30	

HANCOCK—Houghton County

☒ **UP HEALTH SYSTEM–PORTAGE (230108)**, 500 Campus Drive, Zip 49930–1569; tel. 906/483–1000, (Nonreporting) **A**1 5 10 20 **S** LifePoint Health, Brentwood, TN
Primary Contact: Jeff Lang, President
CFO: Steve Bishop, Chief Financial Officer
CMO: Mary Beth Hines, D.O., Chief Medical Officer
CHR: Robbyn Lucier, Director Human Resources
Web address: www.portagehealth.org
Control: Other not–for–profit (including NFP Corporation) **Service:** General Medical and Surgical

Staffed Beds: 96	

HARBOR BEACH—Huron County

HARBOR BEACH COMMUNITY HOSPITAL (231313), 210 South First Street, Zip 48441–1236; tel. 989/479–3201, (Nonreporting) **A**5 10 18
Primary Contact: Paul Clabuesch, President and Chief Executive Officer
CFO: Jill Wehner, Vice President Financial Services
CMO: Richard Lloyd, D.O., Chief of Staff
CIO: Tami Nickrand, Director Information Technology
CHR: Tina Osantoski, Director Human Resources
CNO: Deb Geiger, Executive Director of Acute Care
Web address: www.hbch.org
Control: Other not–for–profit (including NFP Corporation) **Service:** General Medical and Surgical

Staffed Beds: 54	

HASTINGS—Barry County

☒ **SPECTRUM HEALTH PENNOCK (230040)**, 1009 West Green Street, Zip 49058–1710; tel. 269/945–3451 **A**1 10 **F**3 11 13 15 29 30 32 34 35 36 39 40 44 45 50 53 54 56 57 62 63 64 65 68 70 74 75 76 77 79 81 82 84 85 86 87 89 91 92 93 96 97 107 108 110 111 115 119 125 126 127 130 131 132 135 144 146 147 148 **P**6 8 **S** Spectrum Health, Grand Rapids, MI
Primary Contact: Sheryl Lewis Blake, FACHE, President
COO: Carla Wilson–Neil, FACHE, Chief Operating Officer
CFO: Deidre Weller, CPA, Controller
CMO: Douglas Smendik, M.D., Chief Medical Officer
CIO: Teri VanTongeren, Director Information Services
CHR: Sherri Thrasher, Executive Human Resources Partner
CNO: Steve Marzolf, R.N., Chief Nursing Officer
Web address: www.spectrumhealth.org
Control: Other not–for–profit (including NFP Corporation) **Service:** General Medical and Surgical

Staffed Beds: 39 **Admissions:** 2450 **Census:** 24 **Outpatient Visits:** 436526 **Births:** 329 **Total Expense ($000):** 69905 **Payroll Expense ($000):** 33386 **Personnel:** 490	

HILLSDALE—Hillsdale County

★ ○ **HILLSDALE HOSPITAL (230037)**, 168 South Howell Street, Zip 49242–2081; tel. 517/437–4451, (Total facility includes 39 beds in nursing home–type unit) **A**10 11 12 13 19 **F**3 11 12 13 15 28 29 31 34 35 38 40 45 46 48 49 50 57 59 62 70 74 75 76 78 79 81 82 87 93 97 98 102 107 110 111 115 119 127 128 130 131 132 135 146 147 148 **P**6 8
Primary Contact: Duke Anderson, President and Chief Executive Officer
CFO: Valerie Fetters, Chief Financial Officer
CMO: Dan McCance, D.O., Chief of Staff
CIO: Sheila Puffenberger, Manager Information Technology
CHR: Stacy Mellon, Manager Human Resource
CNO: Julie Walters, Chief Nursing Officer
Web address: www.hillsdalehospital.com
Control: Other not–for–profit (including NFP Corporation) **Service:** General Medical and Surgical

Staffed Beds: 93 **Admissions:** 2988 **Census:** 57 **Outpatient Visits:** 105506 **Births:** 325 **Total Expense ($000):** 58619 **Payroll Expense ($000):** 21701 **Personnel:** 410	

HOLLAND—Ottawa County

★ ◇ **HOLLAND HOSPITAL (230072)**, 602 Michigan Avenue, Zip 49423–4999; tel. 616/392–5141, (Nonreporting) **A**10 21
Primary Contact: Dale Sowders, President and Chief Executive Officer
CFO: Terry L. Steele, Vice President Finance and Chief Financial Officer
CMO: William Vandervliet, M.D., Vice President Medical Affairs
CIO: Randy J. Paruch, Director, Information Systems
CHR: Michael Matthews, Vice President Human Resources
CNO: Patti J. VanDort, MSN, Vice President Nursing/Chief Nursing Officer
Web address: www.hollandhospital.org
Control: Other not–for–profit (including NFP Corporation) **Service:** General Medical and Surgical

Staffed Beds: 130	

HOWELL—Livingston County

☒ **ST. JOSEPH MERCY LIVINGSTON HOSPITAL (230069)**, 620 Byron Road, Zip 48843–1093; tel. 517/545–6000 **A**1 3 5 10 13 **F**3 5 8 11 15 18 28 29 30 31 34 35 40 41 42 45 50 51 54 56 57 59 62 63 64 65 66 68 70 74 75 77 78 79 81 82 84 85 86 87 93 97 100 104 107 108 110 111 115 117 118 119 120 121 123 124 130 131 132 134 135 141 145 146 147 148 **P**1 **S** Trinity Health, Livonia, MI
Primary Contact: David Brooks, President
COO: Robin Damschroder, Chief Operating Officer
CFO: Kathy O'Connor, Vice President Finance and Controller
CMO: Rosalie Tocco–Bradley, Ph.D., Chief Medical Officer
CIO: Frank Rademacher, Director, Information Systems
CHR: Tonia Schemer, Interim Chief Human Resources
CNO: Joyce Young, Ph.D., Vice President, Patient Services and Chief Nursing Officer
Web address: www.stjoeslivingston.org/livingston
Control: Church–operated, Nongovernment, not–for profit **Service:** General Medical and Surgical

Staffed Beds: 42 **Admissions:** 2917 **Census:** 25 **Outpatient Visits:** 272347 **Births:** 0 **Total Expense ($000):** 98247 **Payroll Expense ($000):** 34306 **Personnel:** 532	

IONIA—Ionia County

☒ **SPARROW IONIA HOSPITAL (231331)**, 3565 South State Road, Zip 48846–1870, Mailing Address: Box 1001, Zip 48846–6001; tel. 616/523–1400 **A**1 10 18 **F**3 12 15 29 31 34 35 40 45 50 54 57 59 64 65 68 70 75 77 78 79 81 85 93 107 108 110 115 119 127 129 130 131 146 148 **P**6 **S** Sparrow Health System, Lansing, MI
Primary Contact: William Roeser, President and Chief Executive Officer
COO: Kevin A. Price, Vice President and Chief Operating Officer
CFO: Mark Brisboe, VP and Chief Financial Officer
CMO: Amy Jentz, M.D., Chief of Staff
CIO: Bob Neal, Information Technology
CHR: Debbie Olsen, Human Resource Partner
Web address: www.sparrow.org/sparrowionia
Control: Other not–for–profit (including NFP Corporation) **Service:** General Medical and Surgical

Staffed Beds: 22 **Admissions:** 591 **Census:** 4 **Outpatient Visits:** 52652 **Births:** 3 **Total Expense ($000):** 37534 **Payroll Expense ($000):** 16428 **Personnel:** 271	

Many Facility Codes have changed. Please refer to the AHA Guide Code Chart. © 2016 AHA Guide

MI

IRON MOUNTAIN—Dickinson County

✠ **DICKINSON COUNTY HEALTHCARE SYSTEM (230055)**, 1721 South Stephenson Avenue, Zip 49801–3637; tel. 906/774–1313 **A**1 10 20 **F**3 11 13 15 18 28 29 30 31 34 35 40 45 46 50 53 59 62 64 65 70 75 76 77 78 79 80 81 85 87 89 91 92 93 96 107 108 110 111 114 115 119 120 121 123 127 129 130 131 132 133 135 144 145 146 148 **P**6
Primary Contact: John Schon, Administrator and Chief Executive Officer
COO: Peggy Freeman, Chief Physicians Services Officer
CFO: Eileen Sparpana, Chief Financial Officer
CMO: Don Kube, M.D., Chief of Staff
CIO: Dean Decremer, Information Systems Manager
CHR: Paula Swartout, Human Resources Manager
CNO: Susan Hadley, R.N., Chief Nursing Officer
Web address: www.dchs.org
Control: County–Government, nonfederal **Service:** General Medical and Surgical

Staffed Beds: 96 **Admissions:** 2810 **Census:** 27 **Outpatient Visits:** 271420 **Births:** 409 **Total Expense ($000):** 106700 **Payroll Expense ($000):** 44587 **Personnel:** 643

✠ **OSCAR G. JOHNSON VETERANS AFFAIRS MEDICAL CENTER**, 325 East H Street, Zip 49801–4792; tel. 906/774–3300, (Nonreporting) **A**1 **S** Department of Veterans Affairs, Washington, DC
Primary Contact: James W. Rice, Director
Web address: www.ironmountain.va.gov/
Control: Veterans Affairs, Government, federal **Service:** General Medical and Surgical

Staffed Beds: 17

VETERANS AFFAIRS MEDICAL CENTER See Oscar G. Johnson Veterans Affairs Medical Center

IRON RIVER—Iron County

✠ **ASPIRUS IRON RIVER HOSPITALS & CLINICS (231318)**, 1400 West Ice Lake Road, Zip 49935–9526; tel. 906/265–6121 **A**1 10 18 **F**11 15 28 29 31 32 34 35 40 43 50 54 56 57 59 60 63 64 70 75 77 78 79 81 86 87 89 93 97 107 111 115 119 128 130 131 132 133 135 144 145 146 147 148 **S** Aspirus, Inc., Wausau, WI
Primary Contact: Connie L. Koutouzos, R.N., MSN, Chief Executive Officer
CFO: Glenn E. Dobson, Vice President, Finance and Chief Financial Officer
CMO: Nasseem Rizkalla, M.D., Chief Medical Officer
CHR: Carol Bastianello, Director Human Resources
CNO: Nancy Lynn Ponozzo, MSN, Chief Nursing Officer
Web address: www.aspirus.org
Control: Other not–for–profit (including NFP Corporation) **Service:** General Medical and Surgical

Staffed Beds: 12 **Admissions:** 844 **Census:** 9 **Outpatient Visits:** 55020 **Births:** 0 **Total Expense ($000):** 38016 **Payroll Expense ($000):** 14692 **Personnel:** 228

IRONWOOD—Gogebic County

✠ **ASPIRUS GRAND VIEW (231333)**, N10561 Grand View Lane, Zip 49938–9622; tel. 906/932–2525 **A**1 10 18 **F**3 11 13 15 28 29 31 34 35 40 50 56 57 59 62 64 65 70 75 77 78 79 81 85 93 97 107 110 114 115 119 127 129 130 132 133 135 144 146 147 148 **P**6 **S** Aspirus, Inc., Wausau, WI
Primary Contact: Paula L. Chermside, Chief Executive Officer
COO: Paula L. Chermside, Chief Executive Officer
CFO: Shane Jacques, Regional Chief Financial Officer
CMO: Chris Pogliano, M.D., Chief Medical Staff
CIO: John Steenport, Information Systems Manager
CHR: Keri Van Epern, Manager Human Resources
CNO: Grace Tousignant, R.N., Chief Nursing Officer
Web address: www.aspirus.org
Control: Other not–for–profit (including NFP Corporation) **Service:** General Medical and Surgical

Staffed Beds: 25 **Admissions:** 1089 **Census:** 10 **Outpatient Visits:** 59706 **Births:** 127 **Total Expense ($000):** 52034 **Payroll Expense ($000):** 23012 **Personnel:** 232

ISHPEMING—Marquette County

★ **UP HEALTH SYSTEM–BELL (231321)**, 901 Lakeshore Drive, Zip 49849–1367; tel. 906/486–4431 **A**10 18 **F**3 11 13 15 29 30 34 40 50 51 53 57 59 65 68 70 75 77 79 81 82 85 87 92 93 96 97 107 108 110 119 129 133 135 144 146 147 **P**6 **S** LifePoint Health, Brentwood, TN
Primary Contact: Mitchell D. Leckelt, Chief Executive Officer
CFO: Teresa J. Perry, Chief Financial Officer
CMO: Douglas LaBelle, M.D., Chief Medical Officer
CIO: Mike Brady, Director Information Technology
CHR: Tami Ketchem, Human Resource Director
CNO: Sandra McGovern, Chief Nursing Officer
Web address: www.bellhospital.org
Control: Corporation, Investor–owned, for–profit **Service:** General Medical and Surgical

Staffed Beds: 25 **Admissions:** 945 **Census:** 8 **Outpatient Visits:** 58792 **Births:** 278 **Total Expense ($000):** 32535 **Payroll Expense ($000):** 13477 **Personnel:** 190

JACKSON—Jackson County

✠ **CARELINK OF JACKSON (232036)**, 110 North Elm Avenue, Zip 49202–3595; tel. 517/787–1440, (Nonreporting) **A**1 10
Primary Contact: J. Mark Fall, Chief Executive Officer
COO: Charlotte Hyatt, MSN, Chief Operating Officer and Chief Nursing Officer
CFO: Dale L. Friesen, Chief Financial Officer
CMO: Robert Albertson, M.D., Chief Medical Officer
CNO: Charlotte Hyatt, MSN, Chief Operating Officer and Chief Nursing Officer
Web address: www.carelinkofjackson.org
Control: Other not–for–profit (including NFP Corporation) **Service:** Long–Term Acute Care hospital

Staffed Beds: 44

DUANE L. WATERS HOSPITAL, 3857 Cooper Street, Zip 49201–7521; tel. 517/780–5600, (Nonreporting)
Primary Contact: Carol Griffes, Administrator
Control: State–Government, nonfederal **Service:** Hospital unit of an institution (prison hospital, college infimary, etc.)

Staffed Beds: 150

✠ **HENRY FORD ALLEGIANCE HEALTH (230092)**, 205 North East Avenue, Zip 49201–1753; tel. 517/788–4800, (Total facility includes 20 beds in nursing home–type unit) **A**1 2 3 5 10 12 13 **F**3 4 5 8 9 11 13 15 17 18 20 22 24 26 28 29 30 31 34 35 38 40 44 45 46 47 48 49 50 51 53 56 57 58 59 61 62 63 64 65 68 69 70 73 74 75 77 78 79 81 82 84 85 87 92 93 96 98 99 100 101 102 103 104 105 106 107 108 110 111 114 115 119 121 123 126 128 129 130 131 132 135 146 147 148 **P**6 **S** Henry Ford Health System, Detroit, MI
Primary Contact: Georgia R. Fojtasek, R.N., President and Chief Executive Officer
COO: Ondrea Bates, Senior Vice President, Operations and Continuum of Care
CMO: Ray King, M.D., Senior Vice President and Chief Medical Officer
CIO: Aaron Wootton, Vice President Health Information Systems
CHR: Patricia Seagram, Vice President Human Resources
CNO: Wendy Boersma, Vice President and Chief Nursing Officer
Web address: www.allegiancehealth.org
Control: Other not–for–profit (including NFP Corporation) **Service:** General Medical and Surgical

Staffed Beds: 302 **Admissions:** 17542 **Census:** 212 **Outpatient Visits:** 475698 **Births:** 1746 **Total Expense ($000):** 468366 **Payroll Expense ($000):** 210351 **Personnel:** 3403

KALAMAZOO—Kalamazoo County

✠ △ **BORGESS MEDICAL CENTER (230117)**, 1521 Gull Road, Zip 49048–1640; tel. 269/226–7000 **A**1 3 5 7 10 12 13 **F**3 7 8 9 11 12 13 15 17 18 20 22 24 26 28 29 30 31 32 33 34 35 36 37 38 39 40 43 44 45 46 49 50 53 54 56 57 58 59 60 61 64 68 70 74 75 76 77 78 79 81 82 84 85 86 87 90 91 92 93 94 96 97 98 99 100 101 102 103 104 105 107 108 110 114 115 118 119 126 129 130 131 132 135 144 146 147 148 **P**3 6 8 **S** Ascension Health, Saint Louis, MO
Primary Contact: Kathlene A. Young, MS, FACHE, Chief Executive Officer
COO: Mark Anthony, Executive Vice President and Chief Operating Officer
CFO: Richard Felbinger, Senior Vice President and Chief Financial Officer
CMO: Robert Hill, M.D., Vice President Medical Staff Affairs
CHR: Laura Lentenbrink, Vice President, Human Resources
CNO: Lori J. Brown, R.N., Vice President and Chief Nursing Executive
Web address: www.borgess.com
Control: Church–operated, Nongovernment, not–for profit **Service:** General Medical and Surgical

Staffed Beds: 347 **Admissions:** 19371 **Census:** 248 **Outpatient Visits:** 508842 **Births:** 1376 **Total Expense ($000):** 404014 **Payroll Expense ($000):** 184953 **Personnel:** 2535

MI

Hospital, Medicare Provider Number, Address, Telephone, Approval, Facility, and Physician Codes, Health Care System

★ American Hospital Association (AHA) membership
□ The Joint Commission accreditation
○ Healthcare Facilities Accreditation Program
◇ DNV Healthcare Inc. accreditation
⇑ Center for Improvement in Healthcare Quality Accreditation
△ Commission on Accreditation of Rehabilitation Facilities (CARF) accreditation

MI

⊞ **BRONSON METHODIST HOSPITAL (230017)**, 601 John Street,
Zip 49007–5346; tel. 269/341–6000, (Includes BRONSON VICKSBURG
HOSPITAL, 13326 North Boulevard, Vicksburg, Zip 49097–1099;
tel. 269/649–2321; Frank J. Sardone, President and Chief Executive Officer;
CHILDREN'S HOSPITAL AT BRONSON, 601 John Street, Zip 49007–5341;
tel. 269/341–7654) **A**1 3 5 10 12 13 **F**3 8 9 11 12 13 15 16 17 18 19 20 22
24 26 28 29 30 31 32 34 35 37 39 40 41 42 43 44 45 46 47 49 50 51 55
56 57 58 59 60 61 62 64 65 66 68 70 71 72 74 75 77 78 79 80 81 82 83
84 85 86 87 88 89 90 92 93 97 102 107 108 110 111 114 115 117 118
119 126 129 130 131 132 134 135 141 144 145 146 147 148 **P**6 **S** Bronson
Healthcare Group, Kalamazoo, MI
Primary Contact: Frank J. Sardone, President and Chief Executive Officer
COO: Kenneth L. Taft, Executive Vice President and Chief Operating Officer
CFO: Mary Meitz, Vice President Finance
CMO: Scott Larson, M.D., Vice President Medical Affairs and Chief Medical Officer
CHR: John Hayden, Vice President and Chief Human Resources Officer
CNO: Denise Neely, R.N., Vice President and Chief Nursing Officer
Web address: www.bronsonhealth.com
Control: Other not–for–profit (including NFP Corporation) **Service:** General
Medical and Surgical

Staffed Beds: 410 **Admissions:** 21362 **Census:** 278 **Outpatient Visits:**
655437 **Births:** 3611 **Total Expense ($000):** 605468 **Payroll Expense
($000):** 286312 **Personnel:** 3620

☐ **KALAMAZOO PSYCHIATRIC HOSPITAL (234026)**, 1312 Oakland Drive,
Zip 49008–1205; tel. 269/337–3000 **A**1 10 12 13 **F**3 39 50 53 56 65 75 77
86 87 97 98 101 103 130 132 135 143 146 148 **P**6
Primary Contact: Jill A. Krause, Director
CMO: V.R. Kanaparti, M.D., Director Medical Services
CIO: Brian Bayer, Information Technology Site Leader
CHR: Holly Hiday, Director Human Resources
CNO: Kathleen Millard, Acting Director Nursing
Control: State–Government, nonfederal **Service:** Psychiatric

Staffed Beds: 203 **Admissions:** 133 **Census:** 129 **Outpatient Visits:** 0
Births: 0 **Personnel:** 470

KALKASKA—Kalkaska County

★ **KALKASKA MEMORIAL HEALTH CENTER (231301)**, 419 South Coral Street,
Zip 49646–2503; tel. 231/258–7500, (Total facility includes 88 beds in nursing
home–type unit) **A**10 18 **F**2 10 15 28 34 35 40 44 45 50 53 56 57 59 60 64
65 66 79 81 84 87 93 97 107 110 111 115 128 129 130 132 134
143 144 146 147 148 **S** Munson Healthcare, Traverse City, MI
Primary Contact: Kevin L. Rogols, FACHE, Administrator
CHR: Kimberly Babcock, Administrative Director of Operations
CNO: Christine Bissonette, R.N., Service Line Director for Acute Services
Web address: www.munsonhealthcare.org
Control: Hospital district or authority, Government, nonfederal **Service:** General
Medical and Surgical

Staffed Beds: 96 **Admissions:** 165 **Census:** 81 **Outpatient Visits:** 83546
Births: 0 **Total Expense ($000):** 32630 **Payroll Expense ($000):** 14350
Personnel: 274

L'ANSE—L'Anse County

☐ **BARAGA COUNTY MEMORIAL HOSPITAL (231307)**, 18341 U.S. Highway 41,
Zip 49946–8024; tel. 906/524–3300 **A**1 10 18 **F**3 5 11 15 28 31 34 40 45
53 57 59 62 63 64 74 75 77 78 79 81 82 84 85 89 93 107 108 110 114
118 119 127 130 132 133 146 **P**6
Primary Contact: Margie Hale, R.N., MSN, Chief Executive Officer
CFO: Gail Jestila–Peltola, Chief Financial Officer
CMO: Sharon Gilliland, Chief of Staff
CIO: Taylor Makela, Director Information Technology
CHR: Janelle E. Beeler, Human Resource Manager
CNO: Bonny Cotter, Chief Nursing Officer
Web address: www.bcmh.org
Control: County–Government, nonfederal **Service:** General Medical and Surgical

Staffed Beds: 15 **Admissions:** 518 **Census:** 7 **Outpatient Visits:** 23782
Births: 0 **Total Expense ($000):** 22036 **Payroll Expense ($000):** 8458
Personnel: 121

LAKEVIEW—Montcalm County

SPECTRUM HEALTH KELSEY HOSPITAL See Spectrum Health United Hospital,
Greenville

LANSING—Ingham County

○ **MCLAREN GREATER LANSING (230167)**, 401 West Greenlawn Avenue,
Zip 48910–2819; tel. 517/975–6000, (Includes MCLAREN GREATER LANSING,
401 West Greenlawn Avenue, tel. 517/795–6000; MCLAREN ORTHOPEDIC
HOSPITAL, 2727 South Pennsylvania Avenue, Zip 48910–3490;
tel. 517/975–6000; Thomas Mee, R.N., President and Chief Executive Officer) **A**2
3 5 10 11 13 **F**3 8 11 13 15 18 20 22 24 26 28 29 30 31 34 35 37 39 40
44 45 46 47 49 50 51 56 57 58 59 60 61 63 64 65 66 70 74 75 77 78 79
80 81 82 84 85 86 87 92 93 97 98 100 101 102 103 104 107 108 110 111
114 115 118 119 120 121 124 126 130 131 132 135 144 146 147 148
P8 **S** McLaren Health Care Corporation, Flint, MI
Primary Contact: Thomas Mee, R.N., President and Chief Executive Officer
CFO: Dale Thompson, Chief Financial Officer
CMO: Linda Peterson, M.D., Vice President Medical Affairs
CHR: Amy Dorr, Vice President Human Resources
CNO: Camille Jensen, R.N., Chief Nursing Officer
Web address: www.mclaren.org
Control: Other not–for–profit (including NFP Corporation) **Service:** General
Medical and Surgical

Staffed Beds: 321 **Admissions:** 12500 **Census:** 148 **Outpatient Visits:**
500000 **Births:** 1100

⊞ △ **SPARROW HOSPITAL (230230)**, 1215 East Michigan Avenue,
Zip 48912–1811; tel. 517/364–1000, (Includes SPARROW CHILDREN'S CENTER,
1215 East Michigan Avenue, tel. 517/364–1000) **A**1 2 3 5 7 8 10 12 13 **F**3 4 5
11 12 13 15 17 18 20 22 24 26 28 29 30 31 34 35 36 38 40 41 43 44 45
46 49 50 51 54 56 57 58 59 60 63 64 65 66 67 68 70 72 74 75 76 77 78
79 81 82 84 85 86 87 88 89 90 91 92 93 94 96 97 98 99 100 101 102 103
104 105 107 108 109 110 114 115 116 117 118 119 120 121 123 124 126
128 129 130 131 132 135 144 146 147 148 **P**1 6 **S** Sparrow Health System,
Lansing, MI
Primary Contact: Dennis A. Swan, JD, FACHE, President and Chief Executive
Officer
COO: Joseph Ruth, Executive Vice President and Chief Operating Officer
CFO: Paula Reichle, Senior Vice President and Chief Operating Officer
CMO: Brian D. Schroeder, M.D., Senior Vice President and Chief Medical Officer
CIO: Thomas Bres, Senior Vice President and Chief Administrative Officer
CHR: Paul Sturgis, Vice President and Chief Human Resources Officer
CNO: Mary Lou Wesley, R.N., Senior Vice President and Chief Nursing Officer
Web address: www.sparrow.org
Control: Other not–for–profit (including NFP Corporation) **Service:** General
Medical and Surgical

Staffed Beds: 666 **Admissions:** 33874 **Census:** 449 **Outpatient Visits:**
387863 **Births:** 4271 **Total Expense ($000):** 847253 **Payroll Expense
($000):** 401132 **Personnel:** 5653

★ ○ **SPARROW SPECIALTY HOSPITAL (232037)**, 8 West Sparrow Hospital
Tower, Zip 48912; tel. 517/364–4840 **A**10 11 **F**1 3 29 30 60 68 85 100 101
119 130 148 **S** Sparrow Health System, Lansing, MI
Primary Contact: Lou Little, President and Chief Executive Officer
CFO: David Przybylski, Controller
CMO: Paul Entler, D.O., Medical Director
CHR: Paul Sturgis, Chief Human Resource Officer
CNO: Tina Gross, MSN, Chief Nursing Officer
Web address: www.sparrowspecialty.org
Control: Other not–for–profit (including NFP Corporation) **Service:** Long–Term
Acute Care hospital

Staffed Beds: 30 **Admissions:** 313 **Census:** 27 **Outpatient Visits:** 0 **Births:**
0 **Total Expense ($000):** 13561 **Payroll Expense ($000):** 6322 **Personnel:**
115

LAPEER—Lapeer County

○ **MCLAREN LAPEER REGION (230193)**, 1375 North Main Street,
Zip 48446–1350; tel. 810/667–5500, (Total facility includes 19 beds in nursing
home–type unit) **A**2 10 11 **F**3 11 13 15 18 20 28 29 30 31 34 35 38 40 43 45
49 50 51 54 56 59 61 64 68 70 74 75 76 77 78 79 81 82 85 87 92 93 97
98 102 107 108 110 111 114 115 119 128 129 130 143 144 146 148
S McLaren Health Care Corporation, Flint, MI
Primary Contact: Barton Buxton, Ed.D., President and Chief Executive Officer
CFO: Mary Beth Callahan, Chief Financial Officer
CMO: Gary Salem, M.D., Vice President Medical Affairs
CIO: Gayle Consiglio, Chief Information Officer
CHR: Amy Dorr, Vice President Human Resources
Web address: www.lapeerregional.org
Control: Other not–for–profit (including NFP Corporation) **Service:** General
Medical and Surgical

Staffed Beds: 159 **Admissions:** 7016 **Census:** 94 **Outpatient Visits:** 141972
Births: 283 **Total Expense ($000):** 107959 **Payroll Expense ($000):** 49402
Personnel: 600

Many Facility Codes have changed. Please refer to the AHA Guide Code Chart.   © 2016 AHA Guide

LAURIUM—Houghton County

ASPIRUS KEWEENAW HOSPITAL (231319), 205 Osceola Street,
Zip 49913–2134; tel. 906/337–6500 **A**1 10 18 **F**3 7 11 13 15 17 18 28 29
30 31 34 35 36 40 45 52 53 56 57 59 61 64 65 66 70 75 76 77 78 79 81
85 87 89 92 93 94 97 107 108 110 111 115 118 119 127 129 130 131 132
133 135 146 147 148 **P**6 **S** Aspirus, Inc., Wausau, WI
Primary Contact: Michael Hauswirth, Chief Operating Officer
COO: Michael Hauswirth, Chief Operating Officer
CFO: Shane Jacques, Regional Chief Financial Officer – U.P.
CMO: Michael Luoma, M.D., Chief of Staff
CIO: Dave Olsson, Director of Marketing
CHR: Chad Rowe, Human Resource Director
CNO: Grace Tousignant, R.N., Chief Nursing Officer
Web address: www.aspirus.org
Control: Other not–for–profit (including NFP Corporation) **Service:** General
Medical and Surgical

**Staffed Beds: 25 Admissions: 1074 Census: 9 Outpatient Visits: 39706
Births: 116 Total Expense ($000): 44757 Payroll Expense ($000): 20831
Personnel: 294**

LINCOLN PARK—Wayne County

VIBRA HOSPITAL OF SOUTHEASTERN MICHIGAN, LLC (232019), 26400
West Outer Drive, Zip 48146–2088; tel. 313/386–2000, (Nonreporting) **A**1 10
S Vibra Healthcare, Mechanicsburg, PA
Primary Contact: Denise Wayne, Chief Executive Officer
COO: Cindy Brassinger, Chief Operating Officer
CFO: Douglas Morris, Chief Financial Officer
CHR: Karen D. Gray, Director Human Resources
Web address: www.vhsemichigan.com/
Control: Corporation, Investor–owned, for–profit **Service:** Long–Term Acute Care
hospital

Staffed Beds: 220

LIVONIA—Wayne County

ST. MARY MERCY HOSPITAL (230002), 36475 Five Mile Road,
Zip 48154–1988; tel. 734/655–4800 **A**1 2 3 10 12 13 **F**3 4 5 12 13 15 18 20
22 26 28 29 30 31 34 35 36 38 40 45 46 47 49 50 51 53 56 57 58 59 63
64 68 70 74 75 76 78 79 81 84 85 87 90 93 97 98 100 101 102 103 104
107 108 110 111 114 115 116 117 118 119 120 121 126 128 129 130 131
132 135 143 145 146 147 148 **P**6 **S** Trinity Health, Livonia, MI
Primary Contact: David A. Spivey, President and Chief Executive Officer
COO: Shannon Striebich, Chief Operating Officer
CFO: Mike Samyn, Vice President, Finance and Chief Financial Officer
CIO: Janet Yim, Director Information Services
CHR: Kenneth Antczak, Vice President Human Resources
Web address: www.stmarymercy.org
Control: Church–operated, Nongovernment, not–for profit **Service:** General
Medical and Surgical

**Staffed Beds: 303 Admissions: 17840 Census: 207 Outpatient Visits:
219625 Births: 869 Total Expense ($000): 257224 Payroll Expense
($000): 107492 Personnel: 1443**

LUDINGTON—Mason County

★ ◇ **SPECTRUM HEALTH LUDINGTON HOSPITAL (230110)**, One Atkinson
Drive, Zip 49431–1906; tel. 231/843–2591 **A**10 20 21 **F**8 11 13 15 17 28 29
31 32 34 35 40 41 45 49 50 54 57 59 62 64 65 68 70 75 76 77 78 79 81
82 85 86 87 89 92 93 98 100 102 103 104 107 108 110 111 114 115 118
119 127 129 130 131 132 135 146 147 148 **S** Spectrum Health, Grand
Rapids, MI
Primary Contact: Randall Stasik, Interim President
CFO: Kerri Nelson, Chief Financial Officer
CMO: Steve Strbich, D.O., Chief of Staff
CIO: Jeremy Vronko, Manager, Information Services
CHR: Jill Vasquez, Manager Human Resources
CNO: Helen Johnson, R.N., Vice President Patient Services
Web address: www.mmcwm.com
Control: Other not–for–profit (including NFP Corporation) **Service:** General
Medical and Surgical

**Staffed Beds: 44 Admissions: 2523 Census: 27 Births: 337 Total Expense
($000): 66230 Payroll Expense ($000): 24169**

MANISTEE—Manistee County

WEST SHORE MEDICAL CENTER (231335), 1465 East Parkdale Avenue,
Zip 49660–9709; tel. 231/398–1100 **A**3 10 20 **F**3 7 11 13 15 28 29 31 34
35 39 40 45 48 50 51 53 54 57 59 64 74 75 76 77 79 80 81 85 86 92 93
96 107 108 110 111 115 118 119 127 129 132 135 141 146 147 148 **P**6
Primary Contact: James Barker, Chief Executive Officer
COO: Donn J. Lemmer, Chief Financial Officer and Chief Operating Officer
CFO: Donn J. Lemmer, Chief Financial Officer and Chief Operating Officer
CMO: Marion Fuller, Chief of Staff
CHR: Kim Weckesser, Director Human Resources
CNO: Thomas Kane, R.N., Vice President Patient Services and Chief Nursing
Officer
Web address: www.westshoremedcenter.org
Control: County–Government, nonfederal **Service:** General Medical and Surgical

**Staffed Beds: 45 Admissions: 1522 Census: 15 Outpatient Visits: 93586
Births: 193 Total Expense ($000): 61544 Payroll Expense ($000): 24466
Personnel: 302**

MANISTIQUE—Schoolcraft County

★ **SCHOOLCRAFT MEMORIAL HOSPITAL (231303)**, 7870W U.S. Highway 2,
Zip 49854–8992; tel. 906/341–3200 **A**10 18 **F**3 11 15 28 29 30 31 32 34 35
40 41 44 45 50 53 56 57 59 62 63 64 65 66 68 70 75 77 78 79 81 82 84
85 93 97 107 108 110 114 118 119 127 129 130 132 133 144 146 147
148 **P**6
Primary Contact: Robert Crumb, Chief Executive Officer
CFO: Duane C. Coulter, Interim Chief Financial Officer
CMO: John P. Galey, M.D., Chief Medical Officer
CIO: Kent La Croix, Supervisor Information Technology
CHR: Fawn Freeborn, Human Resources Generalist
CNO: Cindy Olli, R.N., Chief Nursing Officer
Web address: www.scmh.org
Control: County–Government, nonfederal **Service:** General Medical and Surgical

**Staffed Beds: 12 Admissions: 391 Census: 3 Outpatient Visits: 37501
Births: 0 Total Expense ($000): 26914 Payroll Expense ($000): 13499
Personnel: 194**

MARLETTE—Sanilac County

MARLETTE REGIONAL HOSPITAL (231330), 2770 Main Street,
Zip 48453–1141, Mailing Address: P.O. Box 307, Zip 48453–0307;
tel. 989/635–4000, (Nonreporting) **A**5 10 18
Primary Contact: Daniel Babcock, Chief Executive Officer
CFO: James L. Singles, Chief Financial Officer
CMO: Daniel Kulick, M.D., Chief of Staff
CIO: Paul Gugel, Manager Information Technology
CHR: Connie Kennedy, Director Human Resources
CNO: Hilda Hebberd, R.N., Senior Director Clinical Services
Web address: www.marletteregionalhospital.org
Control: Other not–for–profit (including NFP Corporation) **Service:** General
Medical and Surgical

Staffed Beds: 74

MARQUETTE—Marquette County

UP HEALTH SYSTEM–MARQUETTE (230054), 580 West College Avenue,
Zip 49855–2736; tel. 906/228–9440 **A**1 2 3 5 10 13 **F**3 4 5 7 8 11 12 13 14
15 17 18 20 22 24 26 28 29 30 31 32 34 35 37 38 40 43 45 46 48 49 50
51 53 55 56 57 58 59 60 62 63 64 65 68 70 72 74 75 76 77 78 79 81 82
85 86 87 89 90 93 94 98 99 100 101 102 103 104 107 108 110 111 114
115 116 117 119 120 121 122 123 124 127 129 130 131 132 135 145
147 148 **P**6 **S** Duke LifePoint Healthcare, Brentwood, TN
Primary Contact: Brian Sinotte, Chief Executive Officer
COO: Jeff Perry, Chief Operating Officer
CFO: Steve Embree, Chief Financial Officer
CMO: Tom Noren, M.D., Chief Medical Officer
CIO: Doug Stacy, Director Information Technology
CHR: Ruth Solinski, Senior Director Human Resources
Web address: www.mgh.org
Control: Corporation, Investor–owned, for–profit **Service:** General Medical and
Surgical

**Staffed Beds: 268 Admissions: 10302 Census: 138 Outpatient Visits:
204609 Births: 595 Total Expense ($000): 331382 Payroll Expense
($000): 125609 Personnel: 1875**

MI

MI

MARSHALL—Calhoun County

★ ◇ **OAKLAWN HOSPITAL (230217)**, 200 North Madison Street, Zip 49068–1199; tel. 269/781–4271, (Nonreporting) **A**10 21
Primary Contact: Ginger Williams, M.D., FACHE, President and Chief Executive Officer
COO: Sharon Thomas–Boyd, Chief Operating Officer
CFO: Gregg M. Beeg, FACHE, Chief Financial Officer
CIO: Mac McClurkan, Chief Information Officer
CNO: Theresa Dawson, MSN, Chief Nursing Officer
Web address: www.oaklawnhospital.org
Control: Other not–for–profit (including NFP Corporation) **Service:** General Medical and Surgical

Staffed Beds: 78

MIDLAND—Midland County

✠ **MIDMICHIGAN MEDICAL CENTER–MIDLAND (230222)**, 4000 Wellness Drive, Zip 48670–2000; tel. 989/839–3000 **A**1 2 3 5 10 **F**3 7 8 10 12 13 14 15 17 18 20 22 24 26 28 29 30 31 32 34 35 36 37 40 43 44 45 46 47 48 49 50 51 53 54 55 56 57 58 59 60 61 62 63 64 65 66 68 70 71 74 75 76 77 78 79 80 81 82 84 85 86 87 89 91 92 93 94 96 97 98 100 101 102 103 104 107 108 109 110 111 114 115 116 117 118 119 120 121 122 123 124 126 127 129 130 131 132 135 143 144 146 147 148 **P**3 **S** MidMichigan Health, Midland, MI
Primary Contact: Gregory H. Rogers, President
CFO: Scott D. Currie, Vice President and Chief Financial Officer
CMO: Margueritte Kuhn, M.D., Vice President Medical Affairs
CIO: C. Harlan Goodrich, Vice President and Chief Information Officer
CNO: Jan Penney, R.N., Vice President and Chief Nursing Officer
Web address: www.midmichigan.org
Control: Other not–for–profit (including NFP Corporation) **Service:** General Medical and Surgical

Staffed Beds: 308 **Admissions:** 12688 **Census:** 132 **Outpatient Visits:** 269768 **Births:** 1322 **Total Expense ($000):** 322460 **Payroll Expense ($000):** 99953 **Personnel:** 1968

MONROE—Monroe County

✠ **PROMEDICA MONROE REGIONAL HOSPITAL (230099)**, 718 North Macomb Street, Zip 48162–7815; tel. 734/240–8400, (Total facility includes 69 beds in nursing home–type unit) **A**1 2 10 13 **F**3 5 8 11 13 15 18 20 28 29 30 34 35 38 40 41 44 45 46 49 50 51 54 56 57 59 62 63 64 65 66 69 70 71 74 75 76 77 79 81 84 85 86 87 89 92 93 97 98 99 100 101 102 103 104 107 108 109 110 111 113 114 115 116 117 118 119 126 128 129 130 131 132 135 145 146 147 148 **P**6 **S** ProMedica Health System, Toledo, OH
Primary Contact: Daniel Schwanke, Interim President
CMO: Gary L. Moorman, D.O., Chief Medical Officer and Senior Vice President Medical Affairs
CNO: Pamela A. Urbanski, R.N., Chief Nursing Officer, Senior Vice President, Patient Care Services
Web address: www.promedica.org
Control: Other not–for–profit (including NFP Corporation) **Service:** General Medical and Surgical

Staffed Beds: 173 **Admissions:** 8792 **Census:** 94 **Outpatient Visits:** 163973 **Births:** 733 **Total Expense ($000):** 162771 **Payroll Expense ($000):** 69879 **Personnel:** 1304

MOUNT CLEMENS—Macomb County

◯ **MCLAREN MACOMB (230227)**, 1000 Harrington Boulevard, Zip 48043–2992; tel. 586/493–8000 **A**2 10 11 12 13 **F**3 8 11 12 13 15 18 19 20 22 24 26 28 29 30 31 34 35 36 37 40 43 45 46 47 48 49 50 51 54 55 56 59 64 65 66 68 70 71 74 75 76 77 78 79 81 82 85 87 89 92 93 96 100 102 107 108 110 111 114 115 118 119 120 121 123 124 126 129 130 131 132 135 145 146 147 148 **P**8 **S** McLaren Health Care Corporation, Flint, MI
Primary Contact: Thomas M. Brisse, President and Chief Executive Officer
COO: Sue Durst, R.N., Vice President Plant Operations
CFO: Brian Baluntanski, Chief Financial Officer
CMO: Michael K. Smith, D.O., Vice President Medical Affairs
Web address: www.mclaren.org/macomb/macomb.aspx
Control: Other not–for–profit (including NFP Corporation) **Service:** General Medical and Surgical

Staffed Beds: 288 **Admissions:** 14512 **Census:** 159 **Outpatient Visits:** 159733 **Births:** 1007 **Total Expense ($000):** 292290 **Payroll Expense ($000):** 121117 **Personnel:** 1803

✠ **SELECT SPECIALTY HOSPITAL–MACOMB COUNTY (232023)**, 215 North Avenue, Zip 48043–1700; tel. 586/307–9000, (Nonreporting) **A**1 10 **S** Select Medical Corporation, Mechanicsburg, PA
Primary Contact: Jon P. O'Malley, Chief Executive Officer
CFO: Sharon Ryan, Regional Controller
CMO: Arsenio V. Deleon, M.D., Chief Medical Officer
CHR: Katelyn Andre, Human Resource Coordinator
CNO: Lydia Alaszewski, Chief Nursing Officer
Web address: www.macomb.selectspecialtyhospitals.com/
Control: Corporation, Investor–owned, for–profit **Service:** Long–Term Acute Care hospital

Staffed Beds: 30

MOUNT PLEASANT—Isabella County

◯ **MCLAREN CENTRAL MICHIGAN (230080)**, 1221 South Drive, Zip 48858–3257; tel. 989/772–6700 **A**2 5 10 11 19 **F**3 12 13 15 18 20 22 26 28 29 30 31 34 35 40 44 45 48 49 50 51 54 57 59 62 64 65 68 70 74 75 76 77 78 79 81 82 85 86 87 89 96 97 107 108 110 111 114 117 118 119 120 121 123 124 129 130 131 132 144 145 146 147 148 **S** McLaren Health Care Corporation, Flint, MI
Primary Contact: William P. Lawrence, President and Chief Executive Officer
CFO: Gregg Beeg, Chief Financial Officer
CMO: Ashok Vashishta, M.D., Vice President Medical Affairs
CIO: Nicolette Zalud, Customer Site Manager
CHR: Carolyn Potter, Vice President Human Resources
CNO: Sheri Myers, Vice President Patient Care Services
Web address: www.cmch.org
Control: Other not–for–profit (including NFP Corporation) **Service:** General Medical and Surgical

Staffed Beds: 78 **Admissions:** 3380 **Census:** 27 **Outpatient Visits:** 129275 **Births:** 538 **Total Expense ($000):** 82461 **Payroll Expense ($000):** 34991 **Personnel:** 524

MUNISING—Alger County

MUNISING MEMORIAL HOSPITAL (231308), 1500 Sand Point Road, Zip 49862–1406; tel. 906/387–4110, (Nonreporting) **A**10 18
Primary Contact: Kevin P. Calhoun, Chief Executive Officer
CFO: Wendy Rautio, Chief Financial Officer
CMO: Christine Krueger, M.D., Chief of Staff
CHR: Melissa Hall, Human Resources
CNO: Andrea Wills, R.N., Chief Nursing Executive
Web address: www.munisingmemorial.org
Control: Other not–for–profit (including NFP Corporation) **Service:** General Medical and Surgical

Staffed Beds: 25

MUSKEGON—Muskegon County

✠ **MERCY HEALTH HACKLEY CAMPUS (230066)**, 1700 Clinton Street, Zip 49442–5502; Mailing Address: P.O. Box 3302, Zip 49443–3302; tel. 231/726–3511, (Includes MERCY HEALTH, GENERAL CAMPUS, 1700 Oak Avenue, Zip 49442; tel. 231/672–3311; Greg Loomis, Interim President and Chief Operating Officer; MERCY HEALTH, MERCY CAMPUS, 1500 East Sherman Boulevard, Zip 49444–1849; tel. 231/672–2000; Greg Loomis, President) **A**1 2 10 13 **F**3 7 11 12 13 15 26 29 30 35 40 45 49 50 51 53 54 57 59 61 64 68 70 74 76 77 79 81 82 84 85 87 89 90 91 93 96 97 98 100 101 102 103 104 105 106 107 108 109 111 114 115 116 117 118 119 127 144 146 147 148 **P**6 7 8 **S** Trinity Health, Livonia, MI
Primary Contact: Greg Loomis, President
CFO: Gary Allore, Chief Financial Officer
CMO: F. Remington Sprague, M.D., Chief Medical Officer
CIO: William Stefl, Director Information Systems
CNO: Kimberly Maguire, R.N., Chief Nursing Officer
Web address: www.mercyhealthmuskegon.com
Control: Other not–for–profit (including NFP Corporation) **Service:** General Medical and Surgical

Staffed Beds: 401 **Admissions:** 19635 **Census:** 199 **Outpatient Visits:** 992206 **Births:** 2007 **Total Expense ($000):** 470337 **Payroll Expense ($000):** 207364 **Personnel:** 3208

✠ **SELECT SPECIALTY HOSPITAL–MUSKEGON (232021)**, 1700 Clinton Street, 3 South, Zip 49442–5502; tel. 231/728–5811, (Nonreporting) **A**1 10 **S** Select Medical Corporation, Mechanicsburg, PA
Primary Contact: Sharon Purkis, Administrator
Web address: www.greatlakesspecialtyhospital.com
Control: Corporation, Investor–owned, for–profit **Service:** Long–Term Acute Care hospital

Staffed Beds: 31

SELECT SPECIALTY HOSPITAL–WESTERN MICHIGAN See Select Specialty Hospital–Muskegon

NEW BALTIMORE—Macomb County

HARBOR OAKS HOSPITAL (234021), 35031 23 Mile Road, Zip 48047–3649; tel. 586/725–5777, (Nonreporting) **A**10 **S** Acadia Healthcare Company, Inc., Franklin, TN
Primary Contact: Sari Abromovich, Chief Executive Officer
CFO: Michael Ferguson, Chief Financial Officer
CMO: James D. Adamo, M.D., Medical Director
CHR: Zena Ridley, Director Human Resources
CNO: Leeann Duncan, Director Patient Care Services
Web address: www.harboroaks.com
Control: Corporation, Investor–owned, for–profit **Service:** Psychiatric

Staffed Beds: 45

Many Facility Codes have changed. Please refer to the AHA Guide Code Chart. © 2016 AHA Guide

NEWBERRY—Luce County

★ ◇ **HELEN NEWBERRY JOY HOSPITAL (231304)**, 502 West Harrie Street, Zip 49868–1209; tel. 906/293–9200, (Includes HELEN NEWBERRY JOY HOSPITAL ANNEX), (Total facility includes 39 beds in nursing home–type unit) **A**10 18 21 **F**3 15 28 29 31 34 35 40 45 53 57 59 64 65 75 78 81 87 93 97 107 108 111 114 118 119 127 128 129 130 131 132 133 143 144 148 **P**6
Primary Contact: Scott Pillion, Chief Executive Officer
CFO: Hunter Nostrant, Chef Financial Officer
CMO: Michael Gregory Beaulieu, M.D., Chief Medical Officer
CIO: Howard Bliss, Director of Information Systems
CNO: Deborah Baker, Chief Nursing Officer
Web address: www.hnjh.org
Control: County–Government, nonfederal **Service:** General Medical and Surgical

Staffed Beds: 64 **Admissions:** 602 **Census:** 45 **Outpatient Visits:** 35695 **Births:** 0 **Total Expense ($000):** 34199 **Payroll Expense ($000):** 15006 **Personnel:** 279

NORTHVILLE—Wayne County

☐ **HAWTHORN CENTER**, 18471 Haggerty Road, Zip 48168–9575; tel. 248/735–6771, (Nonreporting) **A**1 3
Primary Contact: Roy Kelly, Facility Director
CIO: Robert W. Bailey, Chief Information Officer
Web address: www.https://www.michigan.gov
Control: State–Government, nonfederal **Service:** Children's hospital psychiatric

Staffed Beds: 69

NOVI—Oakland County

PROVIDENCE – PROVIDENCE PARK HOSPITAL, NOVI CAMPUS See Providence – Providence Park Hospital, Southfield Campus, Southfield

ONTONAGON—Ontonagon County

⊞ **ASPIRUS ONTONAGON HOSPITAL (231309)**, 601 South Seventh Street, Zip 49953–1459; tel. 906/884–8000, (Total facility includes 46 beds in nursing home–type unit) **A**1 10 18 **F**3 15 28 29 31 34 35 40 41 45 47 53 56 59 64 65 68 75 78 79 81 85 87 90 93 94 97 107 110 114 119 127 128 131 132 133 **P**6 **S** Aspirus, Inc., Wausau, WI
Primary Contact: Michael Hauswirth, Chief Operating Officer
COO: Michael Hauswirth, Chief Operating Officer
CMO: Richard Chaltry, M.D., Director Medical Staff
CHR: Gina Linna, Manager Human Resources
CNO: Deanna Wilson, VP Patient Care Services/Site Manager
Web address: www.aspirus.org
Control: Other not–for–profit (including NFP Corporation) **Service:** General Medical and Surgical

Staffed Beds: 64 **Admissions:** 150 **Census:** 44 **Outpatient Visits:** 17978 **Births:** 0 **Total Expense ($000):** 13337 **Payroll Expense ($000):** 4836 **Personnel:** 79

OWOSSO—Shiawassee County

⊞ **MEMORIAL HEALTHCARE (230121)**, 826 West King Street, Zip 48867–2120; tel. 989/723–5211, (Total facility includes 32 beds in nursing home–type unit) **A**1 2 5 10 **F**11 13 15 28 29 30 31 32 34 35 36 38 40 45 50 51 56 57 59 62 63 64 65 69 70 74 75 76 77 78 79 81 82 85 87 89 93 97 98 100 101 102 107 108 110 111 115 119 127 128 129 130 131 132 143 144 146 147 148 **P**6 7
Primary Contact: Brian Long, FACHE, President and Chief Executive Officer
COO: Tim Susterich, Chief Financial Officer and Chief Operating Officer
CFO: Tim Susterich, Chief Financial Officer and Chief Operating Officer
CMO: Wael Salman, M.D., Vice President Medical Affairs
CIO: Tom Kurtz, Vice President Information Services and Chief Information Officer
CHR: Ruthann Liagre, Vice President Human Resources
CNO: Jim Nemeth, Senior Vice President of Patient Care Services and Chief Nursing Officer
Web address: www.memorialhealthcare.org
Control: Other not–for–profit (including NFP Corporation) **Service:** General Medical and Surgical

Staffed Beds: 149 **Admissions:** 3692 **Census:** 77 **Outpatient Visits:** 406558 **Births:** 457 **Total Expense ($000):** 118638 **Payroll Expense ($000):** 54963 **Personnel:** 972

PAW PAW—Van Buren County

⊞ **BRONSON LAKEVIEW HOSPITAL (231332)**, 408 Hazen Street, Zip 49079–1019, Mailing Address: P.O. Box 209, Zip 49079–0209; tel. 269/657–3141 **A**1 10 18 **F**3 6 11 15 29 30 34 35 40 44 50 56 57 59 64 65 66 68 74 75 77 79 81 82 85 86 87 90 93 97 98 100 101 102 103 107 110 114 119 127 129 130 132 146 147 148 **P**6 **S** Bronson Healthcare Group, Kalamazoo, MI
Primary Contact: Kirk Richardson, R.N., Vice President, Chief Operating Officer, and Chief Nursing Officer
COO: Kirk Richardson, R.N., Vice President, Chief Operating Officer, and Chief Nursing Officer
CFO: Becky East, Senior Vice President, Chief Financial Officer
CMO: Matthew Dommer, M.D., Chief Medical Officer
CIO: Paul Peabody, Vice President Information Technology and Chief Information Officer
CHR: John Hayden, Senior Vice President and Chief Human Resources Officer
CNO: Kirk Richardson, R.N., Vice President, Chief Operating Officer, and Chief Nursing Officer
Web address: www.bronsonhealth.com/lakeview
Control: Other not–for–profit (including NFP Corporation) **Service:** General Medical and Surgical

Staffed Beds: 35 **Admissions:** 935 **Census:** 12 **Outpatient Visits:** 96888 **Births:** 0 **Total Expense ($000):** 46418 **Payroll Expense ($000):** 14783 **Personnel:** 317

PETOSKEY—Emmet County

☐ **MCLAREN NORTHERN MICHIGAN (230105)**, 416 Connable Avenue, Zip 49770–2297; tel. 231/487–4000 **A**1 2 5 10 **F**3 12 13 15 17 18 20 22 24 26 28 29 30 31 32 34 35 36 38 40 42 44 45 48 49 50 51 53 57 58 59 60 64 68 70 74 75 76 77 78 79 81 82 85 86 87 89 90 91 93 94 96 107 108 110 111 114 115 119 120 121 123 124 129 130 132 135 146 148 **S** McLaren Health Care Corporation, Flint, MI
Primary Contact: David M. Zechman, FACHE, President and Chief Executive Officer
CFO: David Bellamy, Chief Financial Officer
CMO: Kirk Lufkin, M.D., VPMA
CIO: David Bellamy, Chief Financial Officer
CHR: Gene Kaminski, Vice President Human Resources and Hospitality Services
CNO: Jennifer Woods, R.N., Chief Nursing Officer
Web address: www.northernhealth.org
Control: Other not–for–profit (including NFP Corporation) **Service:** General Medical and Surgical

Staffed Beds: 188 **Admissions:** 10171 **Census:** 108 **Outpatient Visits:** 220475 **Births:** 609 **Total Expense ($000):** 212888 **Payroll Expense ($000):** 79795 **Personnel:** 1290

PIGEON—Huron County

⊞ **SCHEURER HOSPITAL (231310)**, 170 North Caseville Road, Zip 48755–9781; tel. 989/453–3223, (Total facility includes 19 beds in nursing home–type unit) **A**1 5 10 18 **F**3 7 8 10 11 15 28 29 30 31 32 34 35 40 44 45 50 53 54 56 57 59 64 65 68 69 75 77 78 79 81 85 86 87 91 93 97 107 108 110 115 119 125 127 130 131 132 133 134 144 146 **P**6
Primary Contact: Terrance Lerash, Interim President and Chief Executive Officer
CFO: Terry Lutz, Chief Financial Officer
CMO: Ross Ramsey, M.D., Chief of Staff
CIO: Carleen Giddings, Information Technology System Leader
CHR: Gregory S. Foy, Human Resources System Leader
CNO: Kendra Kretzschmer, Patient Care System Leader
Web address: www.scheurer.org
Control: Other not–for–profit (including NFP Corporation) **Service:** General Medical and Surgical

Staffed Beds: 44 **Admissions:** 739 **Census:** 30 **Outpatient Visits:** 44999 **Births:** 0 **Total Expense ($000):** 39766 **Payroll Expense ($000):** 18354 **Personnel:** 354

PLAINWELL—Allegan County

⊞ **BORGESS–PIPP HOSPITAL (232034)**, 411 Naomi Street, Zip 49080–1222; tel. 269/685–6811, (Nonreporting) **A**1 10 **S** Ascension Health, Saint Louis, MO
Primary Contact: John E. Ryder, Administrator and Chief Operating Officer
Web address: www.borgess.com
Control: Other not–for–profit (including NFP Corporation) **Service:** Long–Term Acute Care hospital

Staffed Beds: 43

Hospital, Medicare Provider Number, Address, Telephone, Approval, Facility, and Physician Codes, Health Care System

★ American Hospital Association (AHA) membership   ◯ Healthcare Facilities Accreditation Program   ⇧ Center for Improvement in Healthcare Quality Accreditation
☐ The Joint Commission accreditation   ◇ DNV Healthcare Inc. accreditation   △ Commission on Accreditation of Rehabilitation Facilities (CARF) accreditation

MI

PONTIAC—Oakland County

☐ **DOCTORS' HOSPITAL OF MICHIGAN (230013)**, 461 West Huron Street, Zip 48341–1601; tel. 248/857–7200, (Nonreporting) **A**1 3 10
Primary Contact: Robert Barrow, Chief Executive Officer
COO: Dennis Franks, Vice President Operations
CFO: Dennis Franks, Interim Chief Financial Officer
CMO: Ray Breitenbach, M.D., Chief of Staff
CIO: Albert Sinisi, Director Information Systems
Web address: www.dhofm.com
Control: Other not-for-profit (including NFP Corporation) **Service:** General Medical and Surgical

Staffed Beds: 106

☐ ○ **MCLAREN OAKLAND (230207)**, 50 North Perry Street, Zip 48342–2253; tel. 248/338–5000, (Total facility includes 120 beds in nursing home–type unit) **A**1 2 10 11 12 13 **F**3 4 7 8 11 12 14 15 18 20 24 26 28 29 30 31 32 33 34 35 36 40 42 43 44 45 50 53 54 57 59 62 63 64 65 66 68 70 74 75 77 78 79 81 82 85 90 92 93 94 98 103 107 108 111 114 118 119 124 128 129 130 131 132 135 136 137 138 139 140 141 142 143 144 146 148 **P**4 8 **S** McLaren Health Care Corporation, Flint, MI
Primary Contact: Chad M. Grant, President and Chief Executive Officer
COO: Nicholle Mehr, Vice President Operations
CFO: Matthew LeGault, Chief Financial Officer
CMO: Steven Calkin, D.O., Vice President Medical Affairs
CIO: Darin Boka, Chief Information Officer
CHR: Dwan Cosby, Manager Human Resources
CNO: Calandra Anderson, Vice President Patient Care and Chief Nursing Officer
Web address: www.mclaren.org/oakland
Control: Other not-for-profit (including NFP Corporation) **Service:** General Medical and Surgical

Staffed Beds: 263 **Admissions:** 5545 **Census:** 195 **Outpatient Visits:** 173900 **Births:** 0 **Total Expense ($000):** 164376 **Payroll Expense ($000):** 68266 **Personnel:** 1214

PIONEER SPECIALTY HOSPITAL, 50 North Perry Street, 6th Floor, Zip 48342–2217; tel. 248/338–5430, (Nonreporting)
Primary Contact: Daniel Oddo, Chief Executive Officer
Web address: www.pioneerspecialtyhospital.com
Control: Individual, Investor-owned, for-profit **Service:** Long-Term Acute Care hospital

Staffed Beds: 30

☒ **SELECT SPECIALTY HOSPITAL–PONTIAC (232030)**, 44405 Woodward Avenue, 8th Floor, Zip 48341–5023; tel. 248/452–5252, (Nonreporting) **A**1 10 **S** Select Medical Corporation, Mechanicsburg, PA
Primary Contact: Peggy Kingston, Chief Executive Officer
CMO: Fadi Salloum, M.D., Medical Director
CNO: Cathy Boyd, Chief Nursing Officer
Web address: www.selectspecialtyhospitals.com/company/locations/pontiac.aspx
Control: Corporation, Investor-owned, for-profit **Service:** Long-Term Acute Care hospital

Staffed Beds: 30

☒ **ST. JOSEPH MERCY OAKLAND (230029)**, 44405 Woodward Avenue, Zip 48341–5023; tel. 248/858–3000 **A**1 2 3 5 10 13 **F**3 8 11 12 13 15 16 17 18 20 22 24 26 28 29 30 31 34 35 36 39 40 41 43 44 45 46 50 53 54 55 56 57 58 59 61 64 65 66 68 72 74 75 76 77 78 79 80 81 82 84 85 86 87 88 89 90 93 94 96 97 98 100 103 105 107 108 110 111 114 115 119 126 129 130 131 132 135 144 146 147 148 **S** Trinity Health, Livonia, MI
Primary Contact: Shannon Striebich, Chief Executive Officer
CFO: Michael Gusho, Chief Financial Officer
CMO: Michael Smith, M.D., Vice President Medical Affairs
CIO: Robert Jones, Director Management Information Systems
CHR: Ane McNeil, Vice President Human Resources
CNO: Douglas R. Dascenzo, MSN, Chief Nursing Officer
Web address: www.stjoesoakland.com
Control: Church-operated, Nongovernment, not-for profit **Service:** General Medical and Surgical

Staffed Beds: 413 **Admissions:** 20135 **Census:** 272 **Outpatient Visits:** 345356 **Births:** 1857 **Total Expense ($000):** 385073 **Payroll Expense ($000):** 146868 **Personnel:** 2449

PORT HURON—St. Clair County

☒ **LAKE HURON MEDICAL CENTER (230031)**, 2601 Electric Avenue, Zip 48060–6518; tel. 810/985–1500 **A**1 2 10 **F**3 11 12 15 18 20 28 29 30 31 34 35 37 40 45 49 50 54 56 57 58 59 61 64 66 70 74 75 77 78 79 81 82 85 86 87 90 91 93 96 97 107 108 110 114 118 119 120 121 123 126 130 131 132 135 146 147 148 **P**6 8 **S** Prime Healthcare Services, Ontario, CA
Primary Contact: Rebekah Smith, R.N., President and Chief Executive Officer
COO: Janet Herbert, Vice President Operations and Chief Nursing Officer
CFO: Chris Fulks, Vice President Finance
CMO: Robert Camara, M.D., Chief Medical Officer
CIO: Peggy Assessor, Director Information Services
CNO: Janet Herbert, Vice President Operations and Chief Nursing Officer
Web address: www.mymercy.us
Control: Church-operated, Nongovernment, not-for profit **Service:** General Medical and Surgical

Staffed Beds: 119 **Admissions:** 3851 **Census:** 44 **Outpatient Visits:** 122033 **Births:** 0 **Total Expense ($000):** 78635 **Payroll Expense ($000):** 31618 **Personnel:** 606

☒ ○ **MCLAREN PORT HURON (230216)**, 1221 Pine Grove Avenue, Zip 48060–3511; tel. 810/987–5000 **A**1 2 10 11 **F**1 3 4 5 11 12 13 15 16 17 18 20 22 24 26 29 30 31 32 34 35 36 39 40 44 45 46 48 49 50 51 54 56 57 58 59 61 64 65 66 67 68 70 71 72 73 74 75 76 77 78 79 80 81 82 84 85 86 87 88 89 90 92 93 94 96 97 98 99 100 101 102 103 104 107 108 110 111 114 115 116 117 118 119 126 128 129 130 131 132 134 135 144 145 146 147 148 **P**6 **S** McLaren Health Care Corporation, Flint, MI
Primary Contact: Jennifer Montgomery, R.N., FACHE, President and Chief Executive Officer
COO: John Liston, Chief Operating Officer
CFO: Bridget Sholtis, Chief Financial Officer
CMO: Michael W. Tawney, D.O., Vice President Medical Affairs
CIO: Abby Bishop, Chief Information Officer
CHR: Doris A. Seidl, Vice President Human Resources
CNO: Christine R. Sansom, Chief Nursing Officer
Web address: www.porthuronhospital.org
Control: Other not-for-profit (including NFP Corporation) **Service:** General Medical and Surgical

Staffed Beds: 186 **Admissions:** 10521 **Census:** 118 **Outpatient Visits:** 202275 **Births:** 1072 **Total Expense ($000):** 159608 **Payroll Expense ($000):** 69214 **Personnel:** 1094

REED CITY—Osceola County

☒ **SPECTRUM HEALTH REED CITY HOSPITAL (231323)**, 300 North Patterson Road, Zip 49677–8041, Mailing Address: P.O. Box 75, Zip 49677–0075; tel. 231/832–3271, (Total facility includes 50 beds in nursing home–type unit) **A**1 5 10 18 **F**3 8 15 29 31 34 35 40 45 53 54 57 59 64 65 70 75 77 78 79 81 84 85 86 87 93 96 97 107 108 110 111 115 119 120 121 123 124 127 128 129 130 131 133 146 147 **P**6 **S** Spectrum Health, Grand Rapids, MI
Primary Contact: Mary Kay VanDriel, President
COO: Cathy Rybicki, Chief Operating Officer
CFO: Thomas Knoerl, Vice President Finance
CMO: Thomas Campana, M.D., Chief of Staff
CIO: Brandi Johnson, Site Manager Technology Information Systems
CHR: Kris Miller, Senior Human Resources Business Partner
CNO: Scott Lombard, Director of Care Management and Community Out Reach
Web address: www.spectrumhealth.org/reedcity
Control: Other not-for-profit (including NFP Corporation) **Service:** General Medical and Surgical

Staffed Beds: 75 **Admissions:** 807 **Census:** 57 **Outpatient Visits:** 410824 **Births:** 0 **Total Expense ($000):** 53111 **Payroll Expense ($000):** 18426 **Personnel:** 365

ROCHESTER—Oakland County

☒ △ **CRITTENTON HOSPITAL MEDICAL CENTER (230254)**, 1101 West University Drive, Zip 48307–1831; tel. 248/652–5000, (Nonreporting) **A**1 3 5 7 10 **S** Ascension Health, Saint Louis, MO
Primary Contact: Margaret Dimond, Ph.D., President and Chief Executive Officer
CFO: Donna Kopinski, Chief Financial Officer
CMO: Sheryl Wissman, M.D., Chief Medical Officer
CIO: Ralph Tenney, Chief Information Officer
CHR: Ann Vano, Vice President, Human Resources
CNO: Ken Sanger, R.N., Chief Nursing Officer
Web address: www.crittenton.com
Control: Other not-for-profit (including NFP Corporation) **Service:** General Medical and Surgical

Staffed Beds: 254

ROMEO—Macomb County

ST. JOSEPH'S MERCY–NORTH See Henry Ford Macomb Hospitals, Clinton Township

Many Facility Codes have changed. Please refer to the AHA Guide Code Chart.

© 2016 AHA Guide

ROYAL OAK—Oakland County

✠ **BEAUMONT HOSPITAL – ROYAL OAK (230130)**, 3601 West Thirteen Mile Road, Zip 48073–6712; tel. 248/898–5000, (Includes BEAUMONT CHILDREN'S HOSPITAL, 3601 West 13 Mile Road, tel. 248/898–5000) **A**1 2 3 5 8 10 **F**3 6 8 11 12 13 15 17 18 19 20 22 24 26 28 29 30 31 32 34 35 36 37 38 39 40 41 43 44 45 46 47 48 49 50 51 54 55 56 57 58 59 60 61 62 63 64 65 66 68 70 71 72 73 74 75 76 77 78 79 80 81 82 83 84 85 86 87 88 89 90 91 92 93 94 95 96 97 98 99 100 101 102 103 104 105 107 108 109 110 111 114 115 116 117 118 119 120 121 123 124 126 129 130 131 132 134 135 138 139 141 142 143 144 145 146 147 148 **P**1 6 **S** Beaumont Health, Southfield, MI
Primary Contact: Rosanna Morris, Hospital President
COO: Carolyn Wilson, R.N., Chief Operating Officer
CFO: Steve Thompson, Vice President, Finance
CMO: Leslie Rocher, Senior Vice President and Chief Medical Officer
CIO: Subra Sripada, Executive Vice President, Chief Transportation Officer and Chief Information Officer
CHR: Michael L. Dixon, Director, Human Resources
CNO: Maureen Bowman, Vice President and Chief Nursing Officer
Web address: www.beaumont.org
Control: Other not–for–profit (including NFP Corporation) **Service:** General Medical and Surgical

Staffed Beds: 1070 **Admissions:** 60558 **Census:** 862 **Outpatient Visits:** 1490793 **Births:** 6046 **Total Expense ($000):** 1152163 **Payroll Expense ($000):** 403058 **Personnel:** 8624

SAGINAW—Saginaw County

✠ **ALEDA E. LUTZ VETERANS AFFAIRS MEDICAL CENTER**, 1500 Weiss Street, Zip 48602–5298; tel. 989/497–2500, (Total facility includes 81 beds in nursing home–type unit) **A**1 3 **F**3 5 8 11 12 15 18 29 30 31 34 35 36 38 39 44 45 50 53 54 56 57 58 59 61 63 64 68 74 75 77 78 81 82 83 84 85 86 87 93 94 97 100 101 102 103 104 107 108 119 127 128 130 131 132 133 135 136 137 138 139 140 141 142 143 144 146 147 148 **P**6 **S** Department of Veterans Affairs, Washington, DC
Primary Contact: Ginny L. Creasman, Director
COO: Stephanie Young, Associate Director
CFO: Jeff Drew, Fiscal Officer
CMO: Gregory Movsesian, M.D., Acting Chief of Staff
CIO: Angie Schmus, Chief Information Technology
CHR: Thomas Stredney, Chief Human Resources Management Service
CNO: Penny Holland, Associate Director for Patient Care Services
Web address: www.saginaw.va.gov/
Control: Veterans Affairs, Government, federal **Service:** General Medical and Surgical

Staffed Beds: 89 **Admissions:** 1030 **Census:** 40 **Outpatient Visits:** 414249 **Births:** 0 **Total Expense ($000):** 217194 **Payroll Expense ($000):** 78667 **Personnel:** 1123

★ ○ △ **COVENANT HEALTHCARE (230070)**, 1447 North Harrison Street, Zip 48602–4727; tel. 989/583–0000, (Includes COVENANT MEDICAL CENTER–COOPER, 700 Cooper Avenue, Zip 48602–5399; tel. 989/583–0000; Edward Bruff, President and Chief Executive Officer; COVENANT MEDICAL CENTER–HARRISON, 1447 North Harrison Street, Zip 48602–4785; tel. 989/583–0000; Edward Bruff, President and Chief Executive Officer), (Total facility includes 20 beds in nursing home–type unit) **A**2 3 5 7 10 11 **F**3 8 11 12 13 15 17 18 19 20 22 24 25 26 27 28 29 30 31 35 36 40 41 42 43 45 46 47 48 49 50 54 57 58 59 60 61 63 64 65 70 72 74 75 76 77 78 79 81 82 83 84 86 87 88 89 90 91 92 93 94 97 107 108 110 111 113 114 115 118 119 120 121 123 124 126 128 129 130 131 132 135 143 144 146 147 148 **P**7 8
Primary Contact: Edward Bruff, President and Chief Executive Officer
COO: Daniel M. George, Executive Vice President, Operations
CFO: Kevin Albosta, Vice President, Chief Financial Officer
CMO: John Kosanovich, M.D., Executive Vice President Physician Enterprise and Chief Executive Officer, Covenant Medical Group
CHR: Kevin Birchmeier, Director Human Resources
CNO: Beth Charlton, Vice President Patient Services and Chief Nursing Officer
Web address: www.covenanthealthcare.com
Control: Other not–for–profit (including NFP Corporation) **Service:** General Medical and Surgical

Staffed Beds: 532 **Admissions:** 26909 **Census:** 401 **Outpatient Visits:** 433755 **Births:** 3022 **Total Expense ($000):** 538395 **Payroll Expense ($000):** 233023 **Personnel:** 3867

☐ **HEALTHSOURCE SAGINAW, INC. (230275)**, 3340 Hospital Road, Zip 48603–9622; tel. 989/790–7700, (Total facility includes 213 beds in nursing home–type unit) **A**1 5 10 **F**4 5 64 66 90 91 93 98 99 100 101 102 104 128 130 143 146 **P**6
Primary Contact: Lisa Lapham, President and Chief Executive Officer
CFO: Glen Chipman, Chief Financial Officer
CMO: Daniel Duffy, D.O., Chief Medical Director
CIO: Greg Sieg, Director Information Technology
CHR: Krystal Hadaway, Director Human Resources
CNO: Susan Graham, R.N., Nurse Executive
Web address: www.healthsourcesaginaw.org
Control: Other not–for–profit (including NFP Corporation) **Service:** Psychiatric

Staffed Beds: 330 **Admissions:** 3849 **Census:** 275 **Outpatient Visits:** 0 **Births:** 0 **Total Expense ($000):** 46483 **Payroll Expense ($000):** 21166 **Personnel:** 497

✠ **SELECT SPECIALTY HOSPITAL–SAGINAW (232033)**, 1447 North Harrison Street, 8th Floor, Zip 48602–4785; tel. 989/583–4235, (Nonreporting) **A**1 10 **S** Select Medical Corporation, Mechanicsburg, PA
Primary Contact: Matthew Cannon, Chief Executive Officer
Web address: www.selectspecialtyhospitals.com/company/locations/saginaw.aspx
Control: Corporation, Investor–owned, for–profit **Service:** Long–Term Acute Care hospital

Staffed Beds: 32

✠ **ST. MARY'S OF MICHIGAN (230077)**, 800 South Washington Avenue, Zip 48601–2594; tel. 989/907–8000 **A**1 2 3 5 10 **F**2 3 11 12 15 17 18 20 22 24 26 28 29 30 31 34 35 40 42 43 44 45 49 50 54 57 58 59 64 66 68 70 74 77 78 79 80 81 82 84 85 86 87 92 93 96 97 100 102 107 108 110 111 114 115 118 119 120 121 123 124 126 129 130 132 146 **P**6 8 **S** Ascension Health, Saint Louis, MO
Primary Contact: Chris Palazzolo, Health System President and Chief Executive Officer Mid–Michigan
CFO: Nancy Haywood, Chief Financial Officer
CMO: Raghu Sarvepalli, M.D., Vice President of Medical Affairs
CIO: Daniel Stross, Chief Information Officer
CHR: Paula Coffee, Director Human Resources
CNO: Bernie Jore, Chief Nursing Officer
Web address: www.stmarysofmichigan.org
Control: Church–operated, Nongovernment, not–for profit **Service:** General Medical and Surgical

Staffed Beds: 236 **Admissions:** 9440 **Census:** 132 **Outpatient Visits:** 204768 **Births:** 0 **Total Expense ($000):** 251144 **Payroll Expense ($000):** 98076 **Personnel:** 1362

SAINT IGNACE—Mackinac County

★ **MACKINAC STRAITS HEALTH SYSTEM, INC. (231306)**, 1140 North State Street, Zip 49781–1048; tel. 906/643–8585, (Total facility includes 48 beds in nursing home–type unit) **A**10 18 **F**8 15 18 28 29 31 32 40 42 43 53 54 56 59 60 64 65 74 75 77 78 79 81 91 93 97 107 110 111 114 119 127 128 130 133 135 144 146 147 148
Primary Contact: Rodney M. Nelson, Chief Executive Officer
CFO: Jason Anderson, Chief Financial Officer
CMO: Matthew Bowes, M.D., Chief of Staff
CHR: Karen Cheeseman, Executive Vice President
CNO: Dawn Stageman–Tyrer, R.N., Chief Nursing Officer
Web address: www.mackinacstraitshealth.org
Control: Other not–for–profit (including NFP Corporation) **Service:** General Medical and Surgical

Staffed Beds: 63 **Admissions:** 287 **Census:** 49 **Outpatient Visits:** 36140 **Births:** 0 **Total Expense ($000):** 35962 **Payroll Expense ($000):** 12627 **Personnel:** 192

SAINT JOHNS—Clinton County

✠ **SPARROW CLINTON HOSPITAL (231326)**, 805 South Oakland Street, Zip 48879–2253; tel. 989/227–3400 **A**1 10 18 **F**3 8 11 15 18 19 31 32 34 35 40 45 50 53 57 59 64 68 70 75 77 78 79 81 85 93 107 108 110 111 114 119 129 130 131 133 135 145 146 148 **P**6 **S** Sparrow Health System, Lansing, MI
Primary Contact: Edward Bruun, President and Chief Executive Officer
COO: Kevin A. Price, Vice President and Chief Operating Officer
CFO: Mark Brisboe, VP and Chief Financial Officer
CMO: Christopher Beal, M.D., Chief of Staff
CNO: Beth Ann Daugherty, R.N., Vice President Care Services and Chief Nursing Executive
Web address: www.sparrowclinton.com
Control: Other not–for–profit (including NFP Corporation) **Service:** General Medical and Surgical

Staffed Beds: 25 **Admissions:** 725 **Census:** 6 **Outpatient Visits:** 59541 **Births:** 0 **Total Expense ($000):** 39088 **Payroll Expense ($000):** 14596 **Personnel:** 218

MI

MI

SAINT JOSEPH—Berrien County

☐ **LAKELAND MEDICAL CENTER, ST. JOSEPH (230021)**, 1234 Napier Avenue, Zip 49085–2158; tel. 269/983–8300, (Includes LAKELAND HOSPITAL, NILES, 31 North Saint Joseph Avenue, Niles, Zip 49120; tel. 269/683–5510; Debra Johnson, R.N., Chief Administrator), (Nonreporting) **A**1 2 10 13 **S** Lakeland Health, Saint Joseph, MI
Primary Contact: Loren Hamel, M.D., President and Chief Executive Officer
CFO: Timothy Calhoun, Vice President Finance and Chief Financial Officer
CMO: Stephen Hempel, M.D., President Medical Staff
CIO: Emily Gallay, Vice President and Chief Information Officer
Web address: www.lakelandhealth.org
Control: Other not–for–profit (including NFP Corporation) **Service:** General Medical and Surgical

Staffed Beds: 250

SALINE—Washtenaw County

☐ **CENTER FOR FORENSIC PSYCHIATRY (234041)**, 8303 Platt Road, Zip 48176–9773, Mailing Address: P.O. Box 2060, Ann Arbor, Zip 48106–2060; tel. 734/429–2531 **A**1 10 **F**30 39 50 98
Primary Contact: Diane Heisel, Acting Director
Web address: www.michigan.gov
Control: State–Government, nonfederal **Service:** Psychiatric

Staffed Beds: 210 Admissions: 227 Census: 210 Outpatient Visits: 0
Births: 0 Total Expense ($000): 72961 Payroll Expense ($000): 36767

SANDUSKY—Sanilac County

MCKENZIE HEALTH SYSTEM (231314), 120 North Delaware Street, Zip 48471–1087; tel. 810/648–3770, (Nonreporting) **A**10 18
Primary Contact: Steve Barnett, President and Chief Executive Officer
COO: Billi Jo Hennika, Vice President Operations
CFO: Amy Ruedisueli, Vice President of Finance
CMO: Michael Merkler, Chief of Staff
CHR: Carrie Krampits, Director Human Resources
CNO: Patricia Schafsnitz, Director of Nursing Services
Web address: www.mckenziehealth.org
Control: Other not–for–profit (including NFP Corporation) **Service:** General Medical and Surgical

Staffed Beds: 25

SAULT SAINTE MARIE—Chippewa County

★ ◇ **WAR MEMORIAL HOSPITAL (230239)**, 500 Osborn Boulevard, Zip 49783–1884; tel. 906/635–4460, (Total facility includes 51 beds in nursing home–type unit) **A**5 10 20 21 **F**3 11 12 13 15 18 28 29 30 31 34 35 36 38 40 43 44 50 51 53 54 56 57 59 60 61 64 65 66 68 70 74 75 76 77 78 79 81 82 85 87 92 93 96 97 98 100 101 103 104 107 108 110 111 115 119 127 128 129 130 131 132 133 135 143 144 146 147 148 **P**6
Primary Contact: David B. Jahn, President and Chief Executive Officer
COO: Marla Bunker, Vice President Nursing and Chief Operating Officer
CFO: Kevin Kalchik, Chief Financial Officer
CMO: Paula Rechner, M.D., Chief Medical Officer
CIO: Sandy DePlonty, Senior Director Clinical Services
CHR: Susan Sliger, Director Human Resources
CNO: Marla Bunker, Vice President Nursing and Chief Operating Officer
Web address: www.warmemorialhospital.org
Control: Other not–for–profit (including NFP Corporation) **Service:** General Medical and Surgical

Staffed Beds: 133 Admissions: 3231 Census: 89 Outpatient Visits: 157450
Births: 347 Total Expense ($000): 98979 Payroll Expense ($000): 44035
Personnel: 808

SHELBY—Oceana County

⊠ **MERCY HEALTH, LAKESHORE CAMPUS (231320)**, 72 South State Street, Zip 49455–1299; tel. 231/861–2156 **A**1 10 18 **F**3 11 15 29 30 34 35 40 45 47 50 57 59 68 81 83 84 85 87 89 97 107 110 111 114 119 127 129 131 132 146 **S** Trinity Health, Livonia, MI
Primary Contact: Jay Bryan, President and Chief Executive Officer
CFO: Mark Gross, Senior Business Director Finance
Web address: www.mercyhealthmuskegon.com
Control: Other not–for–profit (including NFP Corporation) **Service:** General Medical and Surgical

Staffed Beds: 24 Admissions: 311 Census: 3 Outpatient Visits: 38104
Births: 0 Total Expense ($000): 23452 Payroll Expense ($000): 11923
Personnel: 182

SHERIDAN—Montcalm County

★ **SHERIDAN COMMUNITY HOSPITAL (231312)**, 301 North Main Street, Zip 48884–9235, Mailing Address: P.O. Box 279, Zip 48884–0279; tel. 989/291–3261 **A**5 10 18 **F**3 15 18 34 40 45 50 54 57 59 64 65 66 77 79 81 85 93 97 107 115 119 127 129 132 133 146
Primary Contact: Randolph K. Flechsig, Administrator
COO: Steve Scott, Chief Operating Officer
CFO: Randolph K. Flechsig, Administrator
CMO: Maria Charlotte Alvarez, M.D., Chief of Staff
CIO: David Bussler, Chief Information Officer
CHR: Sharon Bowers, R.N., Manager of Community, Public and Employee Relations
CNO: Kim Christensen, Interim Chief Nursing Executive
Web address: www.sheridanhospital.com
Control: Other not–for–profit (including NFP Corporation) **Service:** General Medical and Surgical

Staffed Beds: 22 Admissions: 242 Census: 3 Outpatient Visits: 25654
Births: 0 Total Expense ($000): 15445 Payroll Expense ($000): 7831
Personnel: 178

SOUTH HAVEN—Van Buren County

SOUTH HAVEN COMMUNITY HOSPITAL See South Haven Health System

⊠ **SOUTH HAVEN HEALTH SYSTEM (230085)**, 955 South Bailey Avenue, Zip 49090–6743; tel. 269/637–5271 **A**1 10 **F**3 11 15 18 28 29 30 31 34 35 36 40 41 45 46 50 53 54 57 59 62 64 65 68 75 77 78 79 81 82 85 87 89 91 93 96 97 107 108 110 114 115 119 127 129 130 131 132 135 144 146 147 **P**4
Primary Contact: Joanne Schroeder, President and Chief Executive Officer
CFO: Mark Gross, Executive Vice President and Chief Financial Officer
CMO: Allan Caudill, M.D., Chief of Staff
CIO: Dennis Sorenson, Supervisor Information Technology
CHR: Kim Wise, Director Human Resources
CNO: Donna Cassidy, Chief Nursing Executive
Web address: www.sh–hs.org
Control: Hospital district or authority, Government, nonfederal **Service:** General Medical and Surgical

Staffed Beds: 49 Admissions: 645 Census: 5 Outpatient Visits: 123425
Births: 0 Total Expense ($000): 41091 Payroll Expense ($000): 18904
Personnel: 314

SOUTHFIELD—Oakland County

★ ○ **OAKLAND REGIONAL HOSPITAL (230301)**, 22401 Foster Winter Drive, Zip 48075–3724; tel. 248/423–5100, (Total facility includes 26 beds in nursing home–type unit) **A**10 11 **F**45 64 79 81 82 85 87 90 93 111 115 119 128 130
Primary Contact: Amelia Jones, Chief Operating Officer and Acting Chief Executive Officer
COO: Amelia Jones, Chief Operating Officer
CMO: John Jack Ryan, M.D., Chief Medical Officer
CIO: William Moncrief, ORH IT Client Executive
CHR: Gordon Meyer, Director Human Resources
CNO: Lola Evans, Director of Nursing
Web address: www.oaklandregionalhospital.com
Control: Corporation, Investor–owned, for–profit **Service:** General Medical and Surgical

Staffed Beds: 71 Admissions: 604 Census: 24 Outpatient Visits: 10958
Births: 0 Total Expense ($000): 25693 Payroll Expense ($000): 6865
Personnel: 136

⊠ **PROVIDENCE – PROVIDENCE PARK HOSPITAL, SOUTHFIELD CAMPUS (230019)**, 16001 West Nine Mile Road, Zip 48075–4818, Mailing Address: P.O. Box 2043, Zip 48037–2043; tel. 248/424–3000, (Includes PROVIDENCE – PROVIDENCE PARK HOSPITAL, NOVI CAMPUS, 47601 Grand River Avebue, Novi, Zip 48374–1233; tel. 248/465–4100; Peter Karadjoff, President) **A**1 2 3 5 10 **F**3 5 8 9 11 12 13 15 17 18 20 22 24 26 28 29 30 31 34 35 36 38 39 40 44 45 46 47 48 49 50 51 54 55 56 57 58 59 60 61 63 64 65 66 68 70 72 74 75 76 77 78 79 80 81 82 84 85 86 87 89 90 92 93 97 98 100 101 102 103 105 107 108 110 111 114 115 116 117 118 119 120 121 123 124 126 129 130 131 132 135 141 143 146 147 148 **S** Ascension Health, Saint Louis, MO
Primary Contact: Michael Wiemann, M.D., President
CFO: Douglas Winner, Chief Financial Officer
CHR: Sue Gronbach, Director Human Resources
Web address: www.providence–stjohnhealth.org
Control: Church–operated, Nongovernment, not–for profit **Service:** General Medical and Surgical

Staffed Beds: 635 Admissions: 34160 Census: 420 Outpatient Visits: 306528 Births: 4149 Total Expense ($000): 638660 Payroll Expense ($000): 241581 Personnel: 3417

⊠ **STRAITH HOSPITAL FOR SPECIAL SURGERY (230071)**, 23901 Lahser Road, Zip 48033–6035; tel. 248/357–3360, (Nonreporting) **A**1 10
Primary Contact: Jan Rys, Chief Executive Officer
CFO: Bradley Bescoe, Chief Financial Officer
CNO: Michelle Holder, Nurse Executive
Web address: www.straith.org/
Control: Other not–for–profit (including NFP Corporation) **Service:** Surgical

Staffed Beds: 24

Many Facility Codes have changed. Please refer to the AHA Guide Code Chart.

STANDISH—Arenac County

✠ **ST. MARY'S OF MICHIGAN STANDISH HOSPITAL (231305)**, 805 West Cedar Street, Zip 48658–9526; tel. 989/846–4521, (Nonreporting) **A**1 5 10 18 **S** Ascension Health, Saint Louis, MO
Primary Contact: Chris Palazzolo, President and Chief Executive Officer
CFO: Tony Doud, Controller
CMO: Jaya Sankaran, M.D., Chief of Staff
CIO: Tammy Copes, Director Information Systems
CHR: Renee Reetz, Director Human Resources
Web address: www.stmarysofmichigan.org/standish
Control: Other not–for–profit (including NFP Corporation) **Service:** General Medical and Surgical

Staffed Beds: 64

STURGIS—St. Joseph County

★ ◇ **STURGIS HOSPITAL (230096)**, 916 Myrtle Street, Zip 49091–2326; tel. 269/651–7824 **A**10 21 **F**3 11 13 15 28 29 30 31 34 35 40 45 49 50 57 59 62 63 64 65 68 70 75 76 77 79 81 85 87 89 93 97 102 107 108 110 115 118 119 127 129 130 132 144 145 146 147 148 **P**6 **S** QHR, Brentwood, TN
Primary Contact: Robert J. LaBarge, President and Chief Executive Officer
CFO: Robert J. Morin, Vice President Finance and Chief Financial Officer
CMO: Bharat Vakharia, M.D., President Medical Staff
CIO: Rita Denison, Director of Information Systems
CHR: Mary Kay Schultz, Director Human Resources
CNO: Charlotte J. Pavilanis, R.N., Vice President of Clinical Services and Chief Nursing Officer
Web address: www.sturgishospital.com
Control: Other not–for–profit (including NFP Corporation) **Service:** General Medical and Surgical

Staffed Beds: 49 **Admissions:** 1555 **Census:** 12 **Outpatient Visits:** 164771 **Births:** 396 **Total Expense ($000):** 46610 **Payroll Expense ($000):** 21138 **Personnel:** 277

TAWAS CITY—Iosco County

✠ **ST. JOSEPH HEALTH SYSTEM (230100)**, 200 Hemlock Street, Zip 48763–9237, Mailing Address: P.O. Box 659, Zip 48764–0659; tel. 989/362–3411, (Nonreporting) **A**1 10 20 **S** Ascension Health, Saint Louis, MO
Primary Contact: Ann M. Balfour, R.N., President
CFO: Tony Doud, Controller
CIO: Daniel Stross, Chief Information Officer
CHR: Nancy Bodenner, Director Human Resources
Web address: www.sjhsys.org
Control: Other not–for–profit (including NFP Corporation) **Service:** General Medical and Surgical

Staffed Beds: 20

TAYLOR—Wayne County

✠ **BEAUMONT HOSPITAL – TAYLOR (230270)**, 10000 Telegraph Road, Zip 48180–3330; tel. 313/295–5000 **A**1 3 5 10 **F**3 11 15 29 30 34 35 37 38 39 40 44 46 49 50 56 57 59 60 61 64 65 68 70 74 75 78 79 81 82 84 85 86 87 90 92 93 96 98 100 101 102 103 104 105 107 108 111 114 118 119 130 131 132 135 146 148 **P**8 **S** Beaumont Health, Southfield, MI
Primary Contact: Lee Ann Odom, Division President
COO: Carolyn Wilson, R.N., Chief Operating Officer
CFO: Mark Deming, Administrator, Finance and Support
CMO: Kassem Charara, Chief Medical Officer
CIO: Subra Sripada, Exec. Vice President, Chief Transformation Officer and Chief Information Officer
CHR: Karen Krolicki, Director, Human Resources
CNO: Kristine Marie Donahue, Administrator, Clinical Operations
Web address: www.beaumont.org
Control: Other not–for–profit (including NFP Corporation) **Service:** General Medical and Surgical

Staffed Beds: 189 **Admissions:** 7532 **Census:** 128 **Outpatient Visits:** 75671 **Births:** 0 **Total Expense ($000):** 145278 **Payroll Expense ($000):** 59840 **Personnel:** 945

TECUMSEH—Lenawee County

★ **PROMEDICA HERRICK HOSPITAL (231334)**, 500 East Pottawatamie Street, Zip 49286–2018; tel. 517/424–3000, (Total facility includes 25 beds in nursing home–type unit) **A**10 18 **F**3 11 15 29 30 40 43 45 46 53 64 68 74 75 77 79 81 85 91 92 93 98 100 101 102 104 107 108 110 114 119 128 129 130 132 135 145 146 147 **P**6 8 **S** ProMedica Health System, Toledo, OH
Primary Contact: Julie Yaroch, D.O., President
CFO: Bernie Nawrocki, Administrative Director Finance
CIO: Stephanie Sonnenberg, Director Information Technology
CHR: Cathy J. Davis, Director Human Resources
CNO: Kathryn M. Greenlee, R.N., Vice President, Clinical Services/CNO
Web address: www.promedica.org
Control: Other not–for–profit (including NFP Corporation) **Service:** General Medical and Surgical

Staffed Beds: 60 **Admissions:** 1267 **Census:** 34 **Outpatient Visits:** 40867 **Total Expense ($000):** 32774 **Payroll Expense ($000):** 10871 **Personnel:** 142

THREE RIVERS—St. Joseph County

★ ○ △ **THREE RIVERS HEALTH (230015)**, 701 South Health Parkway, Zip 49093–8352; tel. 269/278–1145, (Nonreporting) **A**7 10 11 **S** QHR, Brentwood, TN
Primary Contact: William B. Russell, Chief Executive Officer
COO: Laurie Herbert, Vice President Operations
CFO: Steve Andrews, Chief Financial Officer
CIO: Dave Parks, Chief Information Officer
Web address: www.threerivershealth.org
Control: Hospital district or authority, Government, nonfederal **Service:** General Medical and Surgical

Staffed Beds: 35

TRAVERSE CITY—Grand Traverse County

✠ **MUNSON MEDICAL CENTER (230097)**, 1105 Sixth Street, Zip 49684–2386; tel. 231/935–5000 **A**1 2 3 5 10 13 **F**3 4 5 6 11 12 13 15 17 18 20 22 24 26 28 29 30 31 32 34 35 36 38 39 40 43 44 45 47 48 49 50 53 54 55 56 57 58 59 60 61 62 63 64 65 68 70 71 72 74 75 76 77 78 79 81 82 84 85 86 87 89 90 92 93 94 96 97 98 100 101 102 103 104 105 107 108 110 115 116 117 118 119 120 121 123 124 126 129 130 131 132 134 135 141 142 143 144 145 146 147 148 **P**6 **S** Munson Healthcare, Traverse City, MI
Primary Contact: Alfred E. Pilong, Jr., FACHE, President, Munson Medical Center and Chief Operating Officer, Munson HEalthcare
COO: Derk F. Pronger, Chief Operating Officer
CFO: Mark A. Helper, Vice President, Chief Financial Officer
CMO: David S. McGreaham, M.D., Vice President Medical Affairs
CIO: Christopher J. Podges, Chief Information Officer and Vice President Outpatient and Retail Services
CHR: Suzanne K. Peters, Vice President Human Resources
CNO: Loraine Frank–Lightfoot, R.N., Vice President, Patient Care Services and Chief Nursing Officer
Web address: www.munsonhealthcare.org
Control: Other not–for–profit (including NFP Corporation) **Service:** General Medical and Surgical

Staffed Beds: 391 **Admissions:** 21468 **Census:** 279 **Outpatient Visits:** 554335 **Births:** 1897 **Total Expense ($000):** 509090 **Payroll Expense ($000):** 197430 **Personnel:** 2934

TRENTON—Wayne County

✠ **BEAUMONT HOSPITAL – TRENTON (230176)**, 5450 Fort Street, Zip 48183–4625; tel. 734/671–3800 **A**1 3 10 12 13 **F**3 8 11 13 15 18 20 22 26 28 29 30 34 35 38 39 40 43 44 45 46 47 49 50 56 57 59 60 61 64 65 68 70 74 75 76 78 79 80 81 82 85 86 87 92 93 96 100 102 107 108 110 111 115 118 119 130 131 132 135 146 147 148 **P**8 **S** Beaumont Health, Southfield, MI
Primary Contact: Chris Stesney–Ridenour, President
COO: Carolyn Wilson, R.N., Chief Operating Officer
CFO: Paul Lauzau, Controller
CMO: Jonathan Kaper, Chief Medical Officer
CIO: Subra Sripada, Executive Vice President, Chief Transformation Officer and Chief Information Officer
CHR: Juliet Hafford, Director Human Resources
CNO: Susan G. Schulz, Director Patient Care Services
Web address: www.beaumont.org
Control: Other not–for–profit (including NFP Corporation) **Service:** General Medical and Surgical

Staffed Beds: 193 **Admissions:** 9297 **Census:** 99 **Outpatient Visits:** 79271 **Births:** 586 **Total Expense ($000):** 154642 **Payroll Expense ($000):** 55305 **Personnel:** 779

Hospital, Medicare Provider Number, Address, Telephone, Approval, Facility, and Physician Codes, Health Care System

★ American Hospital Association (AHA) membership
□ The Joint Commission accreditation
○ Healthcare Facilities Accreditation Program
◇ DNV Healthcare Inc. accreditation
⇑ Center for Improvement in Healthcare Quality Accreditation
△ Commission on Accreditation of Rehabilitation Facilities (CARF) accreditation

TROY—Oakland County

⌖ **BEAUMONT HOSPITAL – TROY (230269)**, 44201 Dequindre Road,
Zip 48085–1117; tel. 248/964–5000 **A**1 2 3 5 10 13 **F**3 8 11 12 13 15 17 18
20 22 24 26 28 29 30 31 32 34 35 36 39 40 41 44 45 46 47 48 49 50 51
53 54 55 56 57 58 59 60 61 62 63 64 65 66 68 70 71 72 74 75 76 77 78
79 80 81 82 84 85 86 87 89 90 91 92 93 94 96 97 100 102 107 108 109
110 111 114 115 116 117 118 119 120 121 123 124 126 129 130 131 132
135 141 142 143 145 146 147 148 **P**1 6 **S** Beaumont Health, Southfield, MI
Primary Contact: Nancy Susick, MSN, President
COO: Carolyn Wilson, R.N., Chief Operating Officer
CFO: Mark Leonard, Vice President Finance
CMO: James Lynch, Senior Vice President and Chief Medical Officer
CIO: Subra Sripada, Executive Vice President, Chief Transportation Officer and
Chief Information Officer
CHR: Lisa Ouelette, Director Human Resources
CNO: Debra Guido–Allen, Vice President and Chief Nursing Officer
Web address: www.beaumont.org
Control: Other not–for–profit (including NFP Corporation) **Service:** General
Medical and Surgical

Staffed Beds: 458 **Admissions:** 35650 **Census:** 404 **Outpatient Visits:**
928207 **Births:** 3736 **Total Expense ($000):** 543577 **Payroll Expense
($000):** 253357 **Personnel:** 3615

VICKSBURG—Kalamazoo County

BRONSON VICKSBURG HOSPITAL See Bronson Methodist Hospital, Kalamazoo

WARREN—Macomb County

☐ **BEHAVIORAL CENTER OF MICHIGAN (234042)**, 4050 East 12 Mile Road,
Zip 48092–2534; tel. 586/261–2266, (Nonreporting) **A**1 10
Primary Contact: Ryan Gunabalan, Chief Executive Officer
COO: Efren Lusterio, Director of Nursing
CFO: Mark Corey, Chief Financial Officer
CMO: Eleanor Medina, M.D., Chief Medical Officer
CIO: Kashmira Khade, Coordinator Non–Clinical Services
CHR: Erin R. Youngblood, Chief Human Resources Officer
Web address: www.behavioralcenter.com
Control: Corporation, Investor–owned, for–profit **Service:** Psychiatric

Staffed Beds: 42

☐ **SOUTHEAST MICHIGAN SURGICAL HOSPITAL (230264)**, 21230 Dequindre,
Zip 48091–2287; tel. 586/427–1000, (Nonreporting) **A**1 10 **S** National Surgical
Healthcare, Chicago, IL
Primary Contact: Yvonne Kughn, Chief Executive Officer
CMO: Benjamin Paolucci, D.O., Chief of Staff
CHR: Dawn Meiers, Coordinator Medical Staff and Personnel Services
Web address: www.nshinc.com
Control: Corporation, Investor–owned, for–profit **Service:** Surgical

Staffed Beds: 13

⌖ **ST. JOHN MACOMB–OAKLAND HOSPITAL (230195)**, 11800 East 12 Mile
Road, Zip 48093–3472; tel. 586/573–5000, (Includes ST. JOHN
MACOMB–OAKLAND HOSPITAL, MADISON HEIGHTS CAMPUS, 27351 Dequindre,
Madison Heights, Zip 48071–3487; tel. 248/967–7000; Terry Hamilton,
President; ST. JOHN MACOMB–OAKLAND HOSPITAL, WARREN CAMPUS, 11800
East Twelve Mile Road, tel. 586/573–5000; Terry Hamilton, President) **A**1 2 3 10
12 13 **F**3 11 12 13 15 17 18 20 22 24 26 28 29 30 31 34 35 36 38 39 40
44 45 46 47 48 49 50 51 56 57 58 59 60 61 63 64 65 68 70 74 75 76 77
78 79 80 81 82 84 85 86 87 90 91 92 93 95 96 97 98 100 101 102 103
105 107 108 111 115 116 117 118 119 121 123 126 129 130 131 132 135
141 143 146 147 148 **S** Ascension Health, Saint Louis, MO
Primary Contact: Terry Hamilton, President
COO: William Mott, Chief Operating Officer
CFO: Tomasine Marx, Chief Financial Officer
CMO: Gary L. Berg, D.O., Chief Medical Officer
CIO: Ralph Tenney, Chief Information Officer
CHR: Joanne E. Tuscany, Director Worklife Services
Web address: www.stjohnprovidence.org/macomb–oakland/
Control: Church–operated, Nongovernment, not–for profit **Service:** General
Medical and Surgical

Staffed Beds: 535 **Admissions:** 26112 **Census:** 377 **Outpatient Visits:**
407731 **Births:** 927 **Total Expense ($000):** 375040 **Payroll Expense
($000):** 152967 **Personnel:** 2411

WATERVLIET—Berrien County

COMMUNITY HOSPITAL See Lakeland Hospital, Watervliet

☐ △ **LAKELAND HOSPITAL, WATERVLIET (230078)**, 400 Medical Park Drive,
Zip 49098–9225; tel. 269/463–3111 **A**1 7 10 **F**3 11 15 29 30 34 35 38 40
45 50 54 57 59 64 68 75 77 79 81 85 86 87 90 93 97 107 119 127 130
131 132 135 144 146 **S** Lakeland Health, Saint Joseph, MI
Primary Contact: Ray Cruse, Chief Executive Officer
CFO: Timothy Calhoun, Vice President Finance, Chief Financial Officer
CIO: Norma Tirado, Vice President, Human Resources and Health Information
Technology
CHR: Norma Tirado, Vice President, Human Resources and Health Information
Technology
CNO: Connie Harmon, Director of Nursing
Control: Other not–for–profit (including NFP Corporation) **Service:** General
Medical and Surgical

Staffed Beds: 38 **Admissions:** 731 **Census:** 10 **Outpatient Visits:** 90773
Births: 0 **Total Expense ($000):** 35458 **Payroll Expense ($000):** 15417
Personnel: 264

WAYNE—Wayne County

⌖ **BEAUMONT HOSPITAL – WAYNE (230142)**, 33155 Annapolis Street,
Zip 48184–2405; tel. 734/467–4000 **A**1 3 10 **F**3 11 13 15 18 20 22 26 28
29 30 31 34 35 38 40 43 44 47 49 50 57 59 60 61 64 65 68 70 74 75 76
78 79 81 82 84 85 86 87 92 93 96 100 102 107 108 111 114 115 118 119
130 131 132 135 146 147 148 **P**8 **S** Beaumont Health, Southfield, MI
Primary Contact: Eric W. Widner, Division President
COO: Carolyn Wilson, R.N., Chief Operating Officer
CFO: Jacqueline Nash, Controller
CMO: Ashok Jain, M.D., Senior Vice President and Chief Medical Officer
CIO: Subra Sripada, Executive Vice President, Chief Transformation Officer and
Chief Information Officer
CHR: Robert L. James, Director Human Resources
CNO: Diane L. Hartley, Director of Patient Care Services
Web address: www.beaumont.org
Control: Other not–for–profit (including NFP Corporation) **Service:** General
Medical and Surgical

Staffed Beds: 215 **Admissions:** 8258 **Census:** 80 **Outpatient Visits:** 99504
Births: 972 **Total Expense ($000):** 162866 **Payroll Expense ($000):** 69834
Personnel: 831

WEST BLOOMFIELD—Oakland County

★ ◇ **HENRY FORD WEST BLOOMFIELD HOSPITAL (230302)**, 6777 West
Maple Road, Zip 48322–3013; tel. 248/661–4100 **A**2 10 21 **F**3 6 11 12 13 15
18 20 22 26 28 29 30 31 32 34 35 36 38 40 41 44 45 46 49 50 51 53 55
56 57 58 59 60 61 62 63 64 65 66 68 70 73 74 75 76 77 78 79 80 81 82
84 85 86 87 89 91 92 93 97 100 101 102 103 107 108 110 111 114 115
116 117 118 119 120 121 123 124 126 130 131 132 135 146 147 148 **P**6
S Henry Ford Health System, Detroit, MI
Primary Contact: Lynn M. Torossian, President and Chief Executive Officer
COO: Karen Harris, R.N., Chief Nursing and Operations Officer
CFO: Terry Goodbalian, Regional Chief Financial Officer
CMO: Betty Chu, M.D., Chief Medical Officer and Vice President of Medical Affairs
CIO: Mary Alice Annecharico, System Vice President and Chief Information Officer
CNO: Karen Harris, R.N., Chief Nursing and Operations Officer
Web address: www.henryford.com
Control: Other not–for–profit (including NFP Corporation) **Service:** General
Medical and Surgical

Staffed Beds: 198 **Admissions:** 13017 **Census:** 147 **Outpatient Visits:**
293441 **Births:** 2086 **Total Expense ($000):** 261037 **Payroll Expense
($000):** 101660 **Personnel:** 1891

WEST BRANCH—Ogemaw County

★ ○ **WEST BRANCH REGIONAL MEDICAL CENTER (230095)**, 2463 South
M–30, Zip 48661–1199; tel. 989/345–3660 **A**5 10 11 20 **F**3 11 15 17 20 28
29 30 34 35 40 50 57 59 63 64 75 77 79 81 84 93 107 111 114 115 117
119 130 135 146 148 **P**6
Primary Contact: Robert McGrail, Chief Executive Officer
CFO: Kathy Kohr, Chief Financial Officer
CMO: Mark Weber, M.D., President Medical Staff
CHR: Kent Allen, Director Human Resources
CNO: Nicole Gillette, R.N., Chief Nursing Officer
Web address: www.wbrmc.com
Control: City–Government, nonfederal **Service:** General Medical and Surgical

Staffed Beds: 88 **Admissions:** 2471 **Census:** 26 **Outpatient Visits:** 63612
Births: 0 **Total Expense ($000):** 40936 **Payroll Expense ($000):** 13244
Personnel: 300

WESTLAND—Wayne County

☐ **WALTER P. REUTHER PSYCHIATRIC HOSPITAL (234035)**, 30901 Palmer
Road, Zip 48186–5389; tel. 734/367–8400, (Nonreporting) **A**1 10
Primary Contact: Richard T. Young, FACHE, Director
CMO: H. Bandla, M.D., Chief Clinical Affairs
CHR: Deborah Moore, Director Human Resources
CNO: E. McDade, R.N.
Web address: www.mhweb.org/wayne/reuther.htm
Control: State–Government, nonfederal **Service:** Psychiatric

Staffed Beds: 239

Many Facility Codes have changed. Please refer to the AHA Guide Code Chart. © 2016 AHA Guide

WYANDOTTE—Wayne County

★ △ ◇ **HENRY FORD WYANDOTTE HOSPITAL (230146)**, 2333 Biddle Avenue, Zip 48192–4668; tel. 734/246–6000 **A**3 7 10 12 13 21 **F**3 5 6 8 11 12 13 15 17 18 22 26 28 29 30 31 32 34 35 36 38 40 41 42 43 44 45 46 47 49 50 51 54 56 57 58 59 60 61 62 63 64 65 66 68 70 73 74 75 76 77 78 79 80 81 82 84 85 86 87 90 92 93 94 96 97 98 100 101 102 103 107 108 110 111 114 115 116 117 118 119 126 129 130 131 132 135 144 146 147 148 **P**1 6 **S** Henry Ford Health System, Detroit, MI
Primary Contact: Denise Brooks–Williams, President and Chief Executive Officer
CFO: Terry Goodbalian, Vice President, Finance and Chief Financial Officer
CMO: Dennis R. Lemanski, D.O., Senior Vice President Medical Affairs and Medical Education/CMO
CIO: Mary Alice Annecharico, System Vice President and Chief Information Officer
CNO: Josephine Sclafani Wahl, R.N., VP, Patient Care Services & CNO
Web address: www.henryfordhealth.org
Control: Other not–for–profit (including NFP Corporation) **Service:** General Medical and Surgical

Staffed Beds: 351 **Admissions:** 17109 **Census:** 239 **Outpatient Visits:** 394002 **Births:** 1648 **Total Expense ($000):** 282045 **Payroll Expense ($000):** 122004 **Personnel:** 1850

⊞ **SELECT SPECIALTY HOSPITAL–DOWNRIVER (232031)**, 2333 Biddle Avenue, 8th Floor, Zip 48192–4668; tel. 734/246–5500, (Nonreporting) **A**1 10 **S** Select Medical Corporation, Mechanicsburg, PA
Primary Contact: Angela Kudla, MSN, R.N., Chief Nursing Officer
CMO: Roderick Boyer, M.D., Medical Director
CHR: Barb Wierzbicki, Manager Human Resources
CNO: Angela Kudla, MSN, Chief Nursing Officer
Web address: www.downriver.selectspecialtyhospitals.com/
Control: Corporation, Investor–owned, for–profit **Service:** Long–Term Acute Care hospital

Staffed Beds: 35

WYOMING—Kent County

★ ◯ **METRO HEALTH HOSPITAL (230236)**, 5900 Byron Center Avenue S.W., Zip 49519–9606, Mailing Address: P.O. Box 916, Zip 49509–0916; tel. 616/252–7200 **A**3 5 10 11 12 13 **F**3 12 13 15 18 20 22 26 29 30 31 34 35 40 44 45 48 49 50 54 57 58 59 64 65 66 70 71 74 75 76 77 78 79 80 81 82 85 86 87 92 94 97 107 108 110 111 115 119 126 129 130 131 132 135 146 147 148 **P**8
Primary Contact: Michael D. Faas, President and Chief Executive Officer
CFO: Kris Kurtz, Controller
CIO: William Lewkowski, Executive Vice President Information Services and Chief Information Officer
Web address: www.metrohealth.net
Control: Other not–for–profit (including NFP Corporation) **Service:** General Medical and Surgical

Staffed Beds: 208 **Admissions:** 9832 **Census:** 125 **Outpatient Visits:** 498002 **Births:** 1671 **Total Expense ($000):** 318237 **Payroll Expense ($000):** 109210 **Personnel:** 2078

YPSILANTI—Washtenaw County

☐ **FOREST HEALTH MEDICAL CENTER (230144)**, 135 South Prospect Street, Zip 48198–7914; tel. 734/547–4700 **A**1 10 **F**12 30 46 64 74 75 79 81 82 85 111 119 130 132
Primary Contact: Trevor J. Dyksterhouse, President
COO: Andrea Walrath, Chief Operating Officer
CFO: David Althoen, Director Financial Planning and Analysis
CMO: Jason Adams, M.D., Medical Staff President
CIO: Andrea Walrath, Chief Operating Officer
CHR: Amy Mohr, Coordinator Human Resources
Web address: www.fhmc–mi.com
Control: Corporation, Investor–owned, for–profit **Service:** General Medical and Surgical

Staffed Beds: 24 **Admissions:** 951 **Census:** 5 **Outpatient Visits:** 10018 **Births:** 0 **Personnel:** 46

⊞ **SELECT SPECIALTY HOSPITAL–ANN ARBOR (232024)**, 5301 East Huron River Drive, 5th Floor, Zip 48197–1051; tel. 734/712–6751, (Nonreporting) **A**1 10 **S** Select Medical Corporation, Mechanicsburg, PA
Primary Contact: Bryan Cutliff, Chief Executive Officer
CMO: Hamid Halimi, M.D., Medical Director
CHR: Leah Warshaw, Coordinator Human Resources
CNO: Tim Varney, R.N., Chief Nursing Officer
Web address: www.annarbor.selectspecialtyhospitals.com/
Control: Corporation, Investor–owned, for–profit **Service:** Long–Term Acute Care hospital

Staffed Beds: 36

★ **ST. JOSEPH MERCY ANN ARBOR (230156)**, 5301 Mcauley Drive, Zip 48197–1051, Mailing Address: P.O. Box 995, Ann Arbor, Zip 48106–0995; tel. 734/712–3456 **A**2 3 5 8 10 **F**3 4 5 6 8 9 11 12 13 15 17 18 20 22 24 26 28 29 30 31 32 34 35 36 38 40 41 42 43 44 45 46 47 48 49 50 51 53 54 55 56 57 58 59 61 62 63 64 65 66 67 68 70 71 72 73 74 75 76 77 78 79 80 81 82 83 84 85 86 87 89 90 91 92 93 94 97 98 99 100 101 102 103 104 105 107 108 109 110 111 114 115 119 120 121 123 124 125 126 128 129 130 131 132 134 135 141 143 144 146 147 148 **P**1 **S** Trinity Health, Livonia, MI
Primary Contact: David Brooks, President
CFO: Kathy O'Connor, Vice President Finance
CMO: Rosalie Tocco–Bradley, Ph.D., Chief Medical Officer
CIO: Frank Rademacher, Senior Director Information Systems
CNO: Joyce Young, Ph.D., Vice President, Patient Services and Chief Nursing Officer
Web address: www.sjmercyhealth.org
Control: Church–operated, Nongovernment, not–for profit **Service:** General Medical and Surgical

Staffed Beds: 481 **Admissions:** 32084 **Census:** 390 **Outpatient Visits:** 1108599 **Births:** 3304 **Total Expense ($000):** 716269 **Payroll Expense ($000):** 266444 **Personnel:** 5654

ZEELAND—Ottawa County

⊞ **SPECTRUM HEALTH ZEELAND COMMUNITY HOSPITAL (230003)**, 8333 Felch Street, Zip 49464–2608; tel. 616/772–4644 **A**1 10 **F**3 12 13 15 18 29 32 34 35 39 40 42 43 45 46 47 50 57 59 64 65 68 69 70 74 75 76 78 79 81 85 86 87 89 91 92 93 97 107 108 110 111 115 119 129 130 132 134 135 144 146 147 **S** Spectrum Health, Grand Rapids, MI
Primary Contact: Ron Lewis, President
CFO: Ryan J. Powers, Vice President Finance
CMO: Ruel R. Lirio, M.D., Clinical Physician Advisor
CIO: Imran Syed, Manager Technology Information Services
CHR: Jennifer F. Becksvoort, Senior Human Resource Business Partner
CNO: Jane Czerew, Vice President Clinical Services and Quality
Web address: www.spectrumhealth.org/zeeland
Control: Other not–for–profit (including NFP Corporation) **Service:** General Medical and Surgical

Staffed Beds: 50 **Admissions:** 2596 **Census:** 20 **Outpatient Visits:** 91973 **Births:** 496 **Total Expense ($000):** 48419 **Payroll Expense ($000):** 16506 **Personnel:** 340

ZEELAND COMMUNITY HOSPITAL See Spectrum Health Zeeland Community Hospital

MI

Hospital, Medicare Provider Number, Address, Telephone, Approval, Facility, and Physician Codes, Health Care System

★ American Hospital Association (AHA) membership ◯ Healthcare Facilities Accreditation Program ⇑ Center for Improvement in Healthcare Quality Accreditation
☐ The Joint Commission accreditation ◇ DNV Healthcare Inc. accreditation △ Commission on Accreditation of Rehabilitation Facilities (CARF) accreditation

MINNESOTA

ADA—Norman County

BRIDGES MEDICAL CENTER See Essentia Health Ada

★ **ESSENTIA HEALTH ADA (241313)**, 201 9th Street West, Zip 56510–1279; tel. 218/784–5000, (Nonreporting) **A**10 18 **S** Essentia Health, Duluth, MN
Primary Contact: Erin Stoltman, Administrator
CMO: Jeff Peterson, M.D., Chief of Staff
CHR: Shayla Hennenberg, Director Human Resources
Web address: www.essentiahealth.org
Control: Other not–for–profit (including NFP Corporation) **Service:** General Medical and Surgical

Staffed Beds: 14

AITKIN—Aitkin County

✠ **RIVERWOOD HEALTHCARE CENTER (241305)**, 200 Bunker Hill Drive, Zip 56431–1865; tel. 218/927–2121 **A**1 2 10 18 **F**3 8 11 13 15 28 29 31 32 34 35 40 43 45 53 54 56 57 59 64 65 70 75 76 77 78 79 81 82 86 87 93 97 104 107 110 111 114 119 127 129 130 131 132 133 135 144 145 146 147 148 **P**6
Primary Contact: Chad D. Cooper, Chief Executive Officer
COO: Cindi Sorensen–Baker, Chief Operating Officer
CFO: Casey R. Johnson, Chief Financial Officer
CMO: Mark Heggem, M.D., Chief Medical Officer
CIO: Daryl Kallevig, Chief Information Officer
CHR: Cindi Hills, Director Human Resources
CNO: Kristine Layne, R.N., Chief Nursing Officer
Web address: www.riverwoodhealthcare.org
Control: Other not–for–profit (including NFP Corporation) **Service:** General Medical and Surgical

Staffed Beds: 25 **Admissions:** 1221 **Census:** 10 **Outpatient Visits:** 72531 **Births:** 72 **Total Expense ($000):** 54868 **Payroll Expense ($000):** 21277

ALBERT LEA—Freeborn County

☐ **MAYO CLINIC HEALTH SYSTEM IN ALBERT LEA (240043)**, 404 West Fountain Street, Zip 56007–2473; tel. 507/373–2384, (Nonreporting) **A**1 3 5 10 20 **S** Mayo Clinic, Rochester, MN
Primary Contact: Mark Ciota, M.D., Chief Executive Officer
CFO: Sheri Dankert, Chief Financial Officer
CMO: John Grzybowski, M.D., Medical Director
CHR: Monica Fleegel, Director Human Resources
CNO: Lori Routh, R.N., Nurse Administrator
Web address: www.almedcenter.org
Control: Other not–for–profit (including NFP Corporation) **Service:** General Medical and Surgical

Staffed Beds: 129

ALEXANDRIA—Sherburne County

☐ **COMMUNITY BEHAVIORAL HEALTH HOSPITAL – ALEXANDRIA (244012)**, 1610 8th Avenue East, Zip 56308–2472; tel. 320/335–6201, (Nonreporting) **A**1 10 **S** Minnesota Department of Human Services, Saint Paul, MN
Primary Contact: Jennifer Westrum, Administrator
CFO: Shirley Jacobson, Chief Financial Officer
Web address: www.health.state.mn.us
Control: State–Government, nonfederal **Service:** Psychiatric

Staffed Beds: 16

★ ◇ **DOUGLAS COUNTY HOSPITAL (240030)**, 111 17th Avenue East, Zip 56308–3798; tel. 320/762–1511 **A**2 10 11 **F**3 8 11 13 15 28 29 30 31 32 34 35 36 40 43 45 50 57 61 64 65 68 69 70 76 77 78 79 81 82 85 86 87 89 91 93 97 107 108 111 115 117 118 119 129 130 131 132 135 144 146 **P**6
Primary Contact: Carl P. Vaagenes, Chief Executive Officer
CFO: Nate Meyer, Director Finance
CHR: Shelly Gompf, Director Human Resources
Web address: www.dchospital.com
Control: County–Government, nonfederal **Service:** General Medical and Surgical

Staffed Beds: 99 **Admissions:** 3509 **Census:** 37 **Outpatient Visits:** 66691 **Births:** 676 **Personnel:** 610

ANNANDALE—Wright County

☐ **COMMUNITY BEHAVIORAL HEALTH HOSPITAL – ANNANDALE (244011)**, 400 Annandale Boulevard, Zip 55302–3141; tel. 651/259–3850, (Nonreporting) **A**1 10 **S** Minnesota Department of Human Services, Saint Paul, MN
Primary Contact: Pamela R. Bajari, R.N., Interim Administrator
CMO: Shabeer A. Ahmed, M.D., Clinical Director
CNO: Lennetta M. Reynolds, Administrative Supervisor
Web address: www.health.state.mn.us
Control: State–Government, nonfederal **Service:** Psychiatric

Staffed Beds: 16

ANOKA—Anoka County

☐ **ANOKA–METROPOLITAN REGIONAL TREATMENT CENTER (244002)**, 3301 Seventh Avenue, Zip 55303–4516; tel. 651/431–5000, (Nonreporting) **A**1 10 **S** Minnesota Department of Human Services, Saint Paul, MN
Primary Contact: Wade Brost, Interim Executive Director
Web address: www.health.state.mn.us
Control: State–Government, nonfederal **Service:** Psychiatric

Staffed Beds: 112

APPLETON—Swift County

★ **APPLETON AREA HEALTH SERVICES (241341)**, 30 South Behl Street, Zip 56208–1699; tel. 320/289–2422, (Nonreporting) **A**10 18
Primary Contact: Jeffrey A. Cook, Chief Executive Officer
CFO: Anne Kells, Interim Chief Financial Officer
Web address: www.appletonareahealth.com
Control: City–Government, nonfederal **Service:** General Medical and Surgical

Staffed Beds: 68

ARLINGTON—Sibley County

★ ◇ **RIDGEVIEW SIBLEY MEDICAL CENTER (241311)**, 601 West Chandler Street, Zip 55307–2127; tel. 507/964–2271, (Nonreporting) **A**10 18 21 **S** Ridgeview Medical Center, Waconia, MN
Primary Contact: Todd Sandberg, Chief Executive Officer and Administrator
CFO: Darla Anderson, Chief Financial Officer
CMO: Ehtaisham Mohammed, M.D., Chief Medical Officer
CIO: Chris Bulau, Manager Information Technology
CHR: Sara Christiansen, Interim Director Human Resources
CNO: Sandy Domeier, Director Patient Care Services
Web address: www.sibleymedical.org
Control: City–Government, nonfederal **Service:** General Medical and Surgical

Staffed Beds: 17

AURORA—St. Louis County

★ **ESSENTIA HEALTH NORTHERN PINES MEDICAL CENTER (241340)**, 5211 Highway 110, Zip 55705–1599; tel. 218/229–2211, (Total facility includes 50 beds in nursing home–type unit) **A**10 18 **F**28 29 34 38 40 50 56 59 65 75 77 79 81 82 87 91 93 97 99 100 101 102 103 104 107 128 130 133 **P**6 **S** Essentia Health, Duluth, MN
Primary Contact: Laura Ackman, Chief Operating Officer and Administrator
CFO: Kevin Boren, Chief Financial Officer
CMO: Michelle Oman, D.O., Chief Medical Officer
CHR: Kim Carlson, Director Human Resources
CNO: Cindy Loe, R.N., Director of Nursing
Web address: www.essentiahealth.org/NorthernPines/FindaClinic/Essentia–HealthNorthern–Pines–36.aspx
Control: Other not–for–profit (including NFP Corporation) **Service:** General Medical and Surgical

Staffed Beds: 58 **Admissions:** 187 **Census:** 48 **Outpatient Visits:** 20204 **Births:** 0 **Total Expense ($000):** 16210 **Payroll Expense ($000):** 7974 **Personnel:** 126

WHITE COMMUNITY HOSPITAL See Essentia Health Northern Pines Medical Center

Many Facility Codes have changed. Please refer to the AHA Guide Code Chart.

MN

AUSTIN—Mower County

MAYO CLINIC HEALTH SYSTEM–ALBERT LEA AND AUSTIN (240117), 1000 First Drive N.W., Zip 55912–2904; tel. 507/433–7351 **A**3 5 **F**3 5 11 13 15 18 28 29 30 31 34 35 40 43 45 50 52 56 57 59 61 62 63 64 65 70 74 75 76 77 78 79 81 82 84 86 87 93 96 97 98 99 100 101 102 103 104 105 106 107 110 111 115 118 119 129 130 131 132 135 143 144 146 147 148 **P**6 **S** Mayo Clinic, Rochester, MN
Primary Contact: Mark Ciota, M.D., Chief Executive Officer
CFO: Sheri Dankert, Vice President Finance
CMO: Cynthia Dube, M.D., Medical Director
CIO: Tammy Kritzer, Vice President Clinic Operations
CHR: Rodney Nording, Vice President Organizational Support
CNO: Lori Routh, R.N., Nurse Administrator
Web address: www.austinmedicalcenter.org
Control: Other not–for–profit (including NFP Corporation) **Service:** General Medical and Surgical

Staffed Beds: 69 **Admissions:** 4432 **Census:** 42 **Outpatient Visits:** 316349 **Births:** 762 **Personnel:** 1636

BAGLEY—Clearwater County

★ **SANFORD BAGLEY MEDICAL CENTER (241328)**, 203 Fourth Street N.W., Zip 56621–8307; tel. 218/694–6501 **A**10 18 **F**3 7 15 28 34 40 45 53 59 65 75 77 79 81 87 89 93 97 104 107 114 119 127 128 133 143 **P**6 **S** Sanford Health, Sioux Falls, SD
Primary Contact: Sammi Davidson, Administrative Director
CMO: Andre Spence, Chief Medical Staff
CNO: Stephanie McKnight, Hospital Nursing Manager
Web address: www.sanfordhealth.org
Control: Other not–for–profit (including NFP Corporation) **Service:** General Medical and Surgical

Staffed Beds: 25 **Admissions:** 138 **Census:** 2 **Outpatient Visits:** 18947 **Births:** 0 **Total Expense ($000):** 9537 **Payroll Expense ($000):** 3958 **Personnel:** 80

BAUDETTE—Lake Of The Woods County

★ **CHI LAKEWOOD HEALTH (241301)**, 600 Main Avenue South, Zip 56623–2855; tel. 218/634–2120, (Nonreporting) **A**10 18 **S** Catholic Health Initiatives, Englewood, CO
Primary Contact: Benjamin Koppelman, Interim President
CFO: Jay Ross, Vice President of Finance
CMO: Justin Quo, Chief of Staff
CIO: Dan Leadbetter, Information Technology Systems Site Lead
CHR: Lois Slick, Director Human Resources
CNO: Danielle Abel, Vice President of Patient Care Services
Web address: www.lakewoodhealthcenter.org
Control: Other not–for–profit (including NFP Corporation) **Service:** General Medical and Surgical

Staffed Beds: 55

BAXTER—Crow Wing County

☐ **COMMUNITY BEHAVIORAL HEALTH HOSPITAL – BAXTER (244015)**, 14241 Grand Oaks Drive, Zip 56425–8749; tel. 218/316–3101, (Nonreporting) **A**1 10 **S** Minnesota Department of Human Services, Saint Paul, MN
Primary Contact: Richard G. Slieter, Jr., Administrator
Control: State–Government, nonfederal **Service:** Psychiatric

Staffed Beds: 16

BEMIDJI—Beltrami County

☐ **COMMUNITY BEHAVIORAL HEALTH HOSPITAL – BEMIDJI (244014)**, 800 Bemidji Avenue North, Zip 56601–3054; tel. 218/308–2400, (Nonreporting) **A**1 10 **S** Minnesota Department of Human Services, Saint Paul, MN
Primary Contact: Larry A. Laudon, Administrator
Control: State–Government, nonfederal **Service:** Psychiatric

Staffed Beds: 16

NORTH COUNTRY REGIONAL HOSPITAL See Sanford Bemidji Medical Center

★ **SANFORD BEMIDJI MEDICAL CENTER (240100)**, 1300 Anne Street N.W., Zip 56601–5103; tel. 218/751–5430, (Total facility includes 78 beds in nursing home–type unit) **A**2 10 **F**3 7 8 10 11 13 14 15 18 20 22 28 29 30 31 34 35 40 43 44 45 46 49 50 51 53 54 55 56 57 58 59 60 62 63 64 65 68 70 74 75 76 77 78 79 81 82 85 86 87 90 93 96 97 103 104 107 108 110 111 114 115 117 119 120 121 123 124 125 126 127 128 129 130 131 132 133 135 141 142 144 145 146 148 **P**6 **S** Sanford Health, Sioux Falls, SD
Primary Contact: Bryan Nermoe, President
CFO: Craig Boyer, Vice President Finance
CMO: Daniel DeKrey, M.D., Chief of Staff
CIO: Dan Moffatt, Chief Information Officer
Web address: www.nchs.com
Control: Other not–for–profit (including NFP Corporation) **Service:** General Medical and Surgical

Staffed Beds: 196 **Admissions:** 5952 **Census:** 141 **Outpatient Visits:** 266218 **Births:** 912 **Total Expense ($000):** 137939 **Payroll Expense ($000):** 51065 **Personnel:** 1074

BENSON—Swift County

★ **SWIFT COUNTY–BENSON HOSPITAL (241365)**, 1815 Wisconsin Avenue, Zip 56215–1653; tel. 320/843–1311, (Nonreporting) **A**10 18
Primary Contact: Kurt Waldbillig, Chief Executive Officer
CFO: Jayne Thielke, Chief Financial Officer
CMO: Richard Horecka, Chief Medical Officer
CIO: Jayne Thielke, Chief Financial Officer
CHR: Naomi Sands, Administrative Assistant and Manager Human Resources
Web address: www.scbh.org
Control: Hospital district or authority, Government, nonfederal **Service:** General Medical and Surgical

Staffed Beds: 18

BIGFORK—Itasca County

★ **BIGFORK VALLEY HOSPITAL (241316)**, 258 Pine Tree Drive, Zip 56628, Mailing Address: P.O. Box 258, Zip 56628–0258; tel. 218/743–3177, (Total facility includes 47 beds in nursing home–type unit) **A**10 18 **F**2 3 8 10 11 15 28 29 31 33 34 35 40 45 53 56 57 59 62 64 77 79 80 81 82 85 89 92 93 97 110 119 125 128 130 132 133 143 146 148
Primary Contact: Aaron Saude, Chief Executive Officer
CFO: Christine Lokken, Director of Finance
CMO: Edwin Anderson, M.D., Chief of Staff and Chief Medical Officer
CIO: Amanda Niemala, Director of Information Services
CHR: Angela Kleffman, Director of Ancillary Services
CNO: Nancy Probst, R.N., Chief Nursing Officer
Web address: www.bigforkvalley.org
Control: Hospital district or authority, Government, nonfederal **Service:** General Medical and Surgical

Staffed Beds: 67 **Admissions:** 429 **Census:** 42 **Outpatient Visits:** 20508 **Total Expense ($000):** 23381 **Payroll Expense ($000):** 8106 **Personnel:** 173

BLUE EARTH—Faribault County

⊞ **UNITED HOSPITAL DISTRICT (241369)**, 515 South Moore Street, Zip 56013–2158, Mailing Address: P.O. Box 160, Zip 56013–0160; tel. 507/526–3273 **A**1 10 18 **F**3 5 7 8 11 13 15 17 28 29 30 34 35 40 45 46 47 48 50 53 56 57 59 62 63 64 65 68 69 70 75 76 77 79 81 82 85 86 89 91 93 96 97 107 110 111 114 115 119 129 130 132 133 134 135 144 146 148 **P**6
Primary Contact: Richard M. Ash, Chief Executive Officer
CFO: Patrick Justine, Chief Financial Officer
CMO: Bob Karp, M.D., Chief Medical Officer
CIO: Mary Hynes, Manager Information Services
CHR: Shanna Gudahl, Manager Human Resources
CNO: Candace Arends, R.N., Chief Nursing Officer
Web address: www.uhd.org
Control: Other not–for–profit (including NFP Corporation) **Service:** General Medical and Surgical

Staffed Beds: 25 **Admissions:** 520 **Census:** 6 **Outpatient Visits:** 54230 **Births:** 66 **Total Expense ($000):** 27896 **Payroll Expense ($000):** 11806 **Personnel:** 177

Hospital, Medicare Provider Number, Address, Telephone, Approval, Facility, and Physician Codes, Health Care System

★ American Hospital Association (AHA) membership
☐ The Joint Commission accreditation
○ Healthcare Facilities Accreditation Program
◇ DNV Healthcare Inc. accreditation
⇑ Center for Improvement in Healthcare Quality Accreditation
△ Commission on Accreditation of Rehabilitation Facilities (CARF) accreditation

BRAINERD—Crow Wing County

✠ **ESSENTIA HEALTH ST. JOSEPH'S MEDICAL CENTER (240075)**, 523 North Third Street, Zip 56401–3098; tel. 218/829–2861 **A**1 2 10 **F**3 4 5 11 13 15 17 18 20 22 26 28 29 30 31 32 34 35 40 43 45 49 50 51 54 57 59 64 65 70 74 75 76 77 78 81 82 86 87 89 91 93 96 97 98 100 102 107 111 118 119 126 130 131 132 135 144 148 **P**2 **S** Essentia Health, Duluth, MN
Primary Contact: Adam Rees, President
COO: Mike Larson, Chief Operating Officer
CFO: Dave Pilot, Chief Financial Officer
CMO: Peter Henry, M.D., Chief Medical Officer
CIO: Pam Marlatt, Business Systems Director
CHR: Sarah Carlson, Director Human Resources
CNO: Patricia DeLong, Chief Nursing Officer
Web address: www.essentiahealth.org
Control: Church–operated, Nongovernment, not–for profit **Service:** General Medical and Surgical

Staffed Beds: 136 **Admissions:** 4930 **Census:** 55 **Outpatient Visits:** 294324 **Births:** 455 **Total Expense ($000):** 180675 **Payroll Expense ($000):** 79373 **Personnel:** 990

ST. JOSEPH'S MEDICAL CENTER See Essentia Health St. Joseph's Medical Center

BRECKENRIDGE—Wilkin County

★ **CHI ST. FRANCIS HEALTH (241377)**, 2400 St. Francis Drive, Zip 56520–1025; tel. 218/643–3000, (Total facility includes 80 beds in nursing home–type unit) **A**5 10 18 **F**3 8 11 13 15 28 29 30 34 35 38 40 43 45 50 56 57 59 64 65 75 79 81 87 93 96 97 99 100 101 103 104 107 110 111 115 119 125 127 128 129 130 131 132 133 146 **P**6 **S** Catholic Health Initiatives, Englewood, CO
Primary Contact: David A. Nelson, President
CFO: Becky Thompson, Chief Financial Officer
CHR: Gail Grant, Director Human Resources
Web address: www.sfcare.org
Control: Church–operated, Nongovernment, not–for profit **Service:** General Medical and Surgical

Staffed Beds: 105 **Admissions:** 828 **Census:** 86 **Outpatient Visits:** 19234 **Births:** 141 **Total Expense ($000):** 30658 **Payroll Expense ($000):** 10645

BUFFALO—Wright County

✠ **BUFFALO HOSPITAL (240076)**, 303 Catlin Street, Zip 55313–1947; tel. 763/682–1212 **A**1 10 **F**3 11 13 15 18 28 29 30 31 32 34 35 36 40 43 44 45 50 53 57 59 64 75 76 77 78 79 80 81 85 86 87 89 93 107 110 111 114 118 119 129 130 131 132 135 146 148 **S** Allina Health, Minneapolis, MN
Primary Contact: Jennifer Myster, President
COO: Heather Johnson, Director of Finance, Operations and Business Development
CFO: Heather Johnson, Director of Finance, Operations and Business Development
CMO: Corey Martin, M.D., Director Medical Affairs
CIO: Jonathan Cloutier, Manager, Information Services
CHR: Leah Schmoyer, Human Resources Director
CNO: Gretchen A. Frederick, R.N., Director Patient Care Services
Web address: www.buffalohospital.org
Control: Other not–for–profit (including NFP Corporation) **Service:** General Medical and Surgical

Staffed Beds: 44 **Admissions:** 2335 **Census:** 16 **Outpatient Visits:** 77328 **Births:** 606 **Total Expense ($000):** 63782 **Payroll Expense ($000):** 26571 **Personnel:** 342

BURNSVILLE—Dakota County

✠ **FAIRVIEW RIDGES HOSPITAL (240207)**, 201 East Nicollet Boulevard, Zip 55337–5799; tel. 952/892–2000 **A**1 2 3 5 10 **F**3 13 15 18 19 20 22 28 29 30 31 34 35 40 41 43 44 45 46 49 50 52 55 57 59 64 65 68 70 72 74 75 76 77 78 79 81 82 84 85 87 89 93 100 107 108 110 111 114 115 116 117 118 119 126 130 132 146 148 **P**6 **S** Fairview Health Services, Minneapolis, MN
Primary Contact: Patrick Belland, President
COO: Brian A. Knapp, Vice President Operations
CFO: Alan Lem, Vice President Finance
CMO: John Stoltenberg, M.D., Vice President Medical Affairs
CHR: Michelle LeDell, Director Human Resource
CNO: Julie Sethney, R.N., Vice President Patient Care
Web address: www.fairview.org
Control: Other not–for–profit (including NFP Corporation) **Service:** General Medical and Surgical

Staffed Beds: 162 **Admissions:** 10623 **Census:** 111 **Outpatient Visits:** 112629 **Births:** 2426 **Total Expense ($000):** 183122 **Payroll Expense ($000):** 86817 **Personnel:** 953

CAMBRIDGE—Isanti County

✠ **CAMBRIDGE MEDICAL CENTER (240020)**, 701 South Dellwood Street, Zip 55008–1920; tel. 763/689–7700 **A**1 2 10 **F**3 4 5 11 13 14 15 18 28 29 30 31 32 34 35 38 40 43 45 50 55 56 57 59 61 64 65 69 70 74 75 76 77 78 79 81 82 85 86 87 89 93 97 98 99 100 101 102 103 104 107 108 111 114 119 125 129 130 131 132 134 135 144 145 146 147 148 **P**5 6 **S** Allina Health, Minneapolis, MN
Primary Contact: Gary Shaw, President
CFO: Nancy Treacy, Director Finance
CHR: Diane Rasmussen, Director Human Resources
CNO: Sherri Abrahamson–Baty, Director Patient Care Services
Web address: www.allina.com/ahs/cambridge.nsf
Control: Other not–for–profit (including NFP Corporation) **Service:** General Medical and Surgical

Staffed Beds: 75 **Admissions:** 3099 **Census:** 34 **Outpatient Visits:** 91565 **Births:** 450 **Total Expense ($000):** 73826 **Payroll Expense ($000):** 32620 **Personnel:** 639

CANBY—Yellow Medicine County

★ **SANFORD CANBY MEDICAL CENTER (241347)**, 112 St. Olaf Avenue South, Zip 56220–1433; tel. 507/223–7277, (Includes SENIOR HAVEN CONVALESCENT NURSING CENTER), (Total facility includes 68 beds in nursing home–type unit) **A**10 18 **F**3 7 10 11 13 15 28 29 31 34 35 39 40 45 46 53 56 59 60 62 64 65 70 71 75 79 81 85 89 92 93 107 110 119 127 128 130 132 133 135 144 **P**6 **S** Sanford Health, Sioux Falls, SD
Primary Contact: Lori Sisk, R.N., Chief Executive Officer
CFO: Allison Nelson, Chief Financial Officer
CMO: Maritza Lopez, M.D., Chief of Staff
CIO: Cheryl L. Ferguson, Associate Administrator
Web address: www.sanfordcanby.org
Control: Other not–for–profit (including NFP Corporation) **Service:** General Medical and Surgical

Staffed Beds: 93 **Admissions:** 362 **Census:** 59 **Outpatient Visits:** 29783 **Births:** 0 **Total Expense ($000):** 21032 **Payroll Expense ($000):** 9935 **Personnel:** 199

CANNON FALLS—Goodhue County

☐ **MAYO CLINIC HEALTH SYSTEM IN CANNON FALLS (241346)**, 32021 County Road 24 Boulevard, Zip 55009–1898; tel. 507/263–4221 **A**1 10 18 **F**3 11 15 18 28 29 34 35 40 45 57 59 64 67 69 74 75 77 79 81 87 93 97 104 107 111 115 119 130 133 **P**6 **S** Mayo Clinic, Rochester, MN
Primary Contact: Thomas J. Witt, M.D., President and Chief Executive Officer
COO: Glenn Christian, Administrator
CFO: Edward A. Tusa, Chief Financial Officer
CMO: Tarlochan Turna, M.D., Medical Director
CHR: Mary Garlets, Director Human Resources
Web address: www.mayoclinichealthsystem.org/locations/cannon–falls
Control: Other not–for–profit (including NFP Corporation) **Service:** General Medical and Surgical

Staffed Beds: 15 **Admissions:** 374 **Census:** 8 **Outpatient Visits:** 21589 **Births:** 0 **Personnel:** 141

CASS LAKE—Cass County

★ **U. S. PUBLIC HEALTH SERVICE INDIAN HOSPITAL (241358)**, 425 7th Street North West, Zip 56633; tel. 218/335–3200, (Nonreporting) **A**5 10 18 **S** U. S. Indian Health Service, Rockville, MD
Primary Contact: Robert Malone, Chief Executive Officer
CMO: Antonio Guimaraes, M.D., Clinical Director
CHR: Terrance Lascano, Administrative Officer
CNO: Roberta A. Williams, Director of Nursing
Web address: www.ihs.gov
Control: PHS, Indian Service, Government, federal **Service:** General Medical and Surgical

Staffed Beds: 9

CLOQUET—Carlton County

★ **COMMUNITY MEMORIAL HOSPITAL (241364)**, 512 Skyline Boulevard, Zip 55720–1199; tel. 218/879–4641, (Total facility includes 44 beds in nursing home–type unit) **A**10 18 **F**13 15 28 29 30 31 34 35 40 43 45 46 47 48 49 50 64 70 75 76 77 79 81 82 85 93 107 108 110 111 115 119 124 128 129 130 131 132 133 146 147 **P**6 7
Primary Contact: Rick Breuer, Chief Executive Officer and Administrator
CFO: Brad Anderson, Chief Financial Officer
CIO: Sam Jacobson, Director Management Information Systems
Web address: www.cloquethospital.com
Control: Other not–for–profit (including NFP Corporation) **Service:** General Medical and Surgical

Staffed Beds: 69 **Admissions:** 1051 **Census:** 52 **Outpatient Visits:** 44878 **Births:** 85 **Total Expense ($000):** 47701 **Payroll Expense ($000):** 22543 **Personnel:** 319

Many Facility Codes have changed. Please refer to the AHA Guide Code Chart. © 2016 AHA Guide

MN

MN

COOK—St. Louis County

★ **COOK HOSPITAL AND CONVALESCENT NURSING CARE UNIT (241312)**, 10 Fifth Street S.E., Zip 55723–9745; tel. 218/666–5945, (Total facility includes 28 beds in nursing home–type unit) **A**10 18 **F**2 3 11 15 28 29 35 40 43 50 53 56 57 64 77 81 93 96 107 110 111 119 128 130 133 148
Primary Contact: Teresa Debevec, Chief Executive Officer
CFO: Kaylee S. Hoard, Chief Financial Officer
Web address: www.cookhospital.org
Control: Hospital district or authority, Government, nonfederal **Service:** General Medical and Surgical

Staffed Beds: 42 **Admissions:** 219 **Census:** 30 **Outpatient Visits:** 16388 **Births:** 0 **Total Expense ($000):** 13217 **Payroll Expense ($000):** 5592 **Personnel:** 116

COON RAPIDS—Anoka County

✠ **MERCY HOSPITAL (240115)**, 4050 Coon Rapids Boulevard, Zip 55433–2586; tel. 763/236–6000 **A**1 2 3 5 10 **F**3 8 11 13 17 18 20 22 24 26 28 29 30 31 34 35 36 37 38 40 43 45 46 49 53 55 59 63 64 65 68 69 70 74 75 76 77 78 79 81 82 85 87 89 93 97 98 99 100 101 102 103 104 105 107 108 111 115 119 126 130 132 135 146 147 148 **P**4 5 6 **S** Allina Health, Minneapolis, MN
Primary Contact: Sara J. Criger, President
CFO: Gerald Pietz, Vice President Finance
CMO: Ryan Else, M.D., Vice President Medical Affairs
CIO: Susan Heichert, Chief Information Officer
CHR: Nancy Watson, Director Human Resources
CNO: MariBeth Olson, R.N., Vice President Patient Care Services
Web address: www.allinamercy.org
Control: Other not–for–profit (including NFP Corporation) **Service:** General Medical and Surgical

Staffed Beds: 258 **Admissions:** 19552 **Census:** 194 **Outpatient Visits:** 150572 **Births:** 2529 **Total Expense ($000):** 388045 **Payroll Expense ($000):** 139817 **Personnel:** 1506

CROOKSTON—Polk County

✠ **RIVERVIEW HEALTH (241320)**, 323 South Minnesota Street, Zip 56716–1601; tel. 218/281–9200, (Total facility includes 24 beds in nursing home–type unit) **A**1 5 10 18 **F**2 3 5 6 11 13 15 29 34 35 36 40 45 46 47 48 49 56 57 59 62 65 66 69 70 76 77 79 81 82 85 87 93 94 96 97 99 107 108 110 111 112 115 119 127 128 129 130 132 133 135 144 145 146 147
Primary Contact: Carrie Michalski, President and Chief Executive Officer
COO: Chris Bruggeman, Chief Operating Officer
CFO: Betty Arvidson, Chief Financial Officer
CMO: Colin Fennell, M.D., Chief Medical Officer
CIO: Nichole Beauchane, Director Information Technology
CHR: Jean Tate, Vice President Human Resources
CNO: April Grunhovd, Chief Nursing Officer
Web address: www.riverviewhealth.org
Control: Other not–for–profit (including NFP Corporation) **Service:** General Medical and Surgical

Staffed Beds: 49 **Admissions:** 888 **Census:** 28 **Outpatient Visits:** 39518 **Births:** 82 **Total Expense ($000):** 26070 **Payroll Expense ($000):** 22096 **Personnel:** 327

CROSBY—Crow Wing County

✠ **CUYUNA REGIONAL MEDICAL CENTER (241353)**, 320 East Main Street, Zip 56441–1690; tel. 218/546–7000, (Total facility includes 117 beds in nursing home–type unit) **A**1 2 3 5 10 18 **F**3 7 12 13 15 18 28 29 31 34 35 40 43 45 46 47 48 49 50 51 56 57 59 62 63 64 69 68 70 75 76 77 78 79 81 82 84 85 86 87 91 92 93 94 97 99 100 101 103 104 107 110 111 115 116 117 118 119 124 127 128 130 131 132 133 143 144 146 147 148 **P**6
Primary Contact: John H. Solheim, Chief Executive Officer
COO: Amy Hart, Chief Operating Officer
CFO: Kyle Bauer, Chief Financial Officer
CMO: Robert Westin, M.D., Chief Medical Officer
CHR: Caity Eggen, Chief Human Resource Officer
CNO: Renee Steffin, Chief Nursing Officer
Web address: www.cuyunamed.org
Control: Hospital district or authority, Government, nonfederal **Service:** General Medical and Surgical

Staffed Beds: 142 **Admissions:** 2181 **Census:** 116 **Outpatient Visits:** 132941 **Births:** 255 **Total Expense ($000):** 96715 **Payroll Expense ($000):** 36366 **Personnel:** 595

DAWSON—Lac Qui Parle County

JOHNSON MEMORIAL HEALTH SERVICES (241314), 1282 Walnut Street, Zip 56232–2333; tel. 320/769–4323, (Total facility includes 56 beds in nursing home–type unit) **A**10 18 **F**3 7 8 10 11 12 15 28 31 32 34 40 41 43 45 50 56 57 62 64 65 68 69 70 71 75 77 78 79 81 82 84 89 93 97 107 110 111 119 127 128 129 130 133 135 145 146 148 **P**6
Primary Contact: Stacey Lee, CPA, JD, Chief Executive Officer
COO: Lori Andreas, Chief Operating Officer
CFO: Crystal Bothun, Chief Financial Officer
CMO: Ayaz Virji, M.D., Chief of Staff
CIO: Derrick Ochsendorf, Manager Information Technology and Systems
CHR: Megan Lynch, Manager Human Resources
CNO: Lori Andreas, Director Patient Care Services
Web address: www.jmhsmn.org
Control: Hospital district or authority, Government, nonfederal **Service:** General Medical and Surgical

Staffed Beds: 78 **Admissions:** 139 **Census:** 53 **Outpatient Visits:** 9897 **Births:** 0 **Total Expense ($000):** 15137 **Payroll Expense ($000):** 7148 **Personnel:** 147

DEER RIVER—Itasca County

★ **ESSENTIA HEALTH–DEER RIVER (241360)**, 115 10th Avenue N.E., Zip 56636–8795; tel. 218/246–2900, (Total facility includes 32 beds in nursing home–type unit) **A**10 18 **F**2 3 7 11 12 13 15 28 29 31 34 35 40 45 46 50 56 57 59 62 64 65 70 71 74 75 76 77 79 81 82 85 91 92 93 96 97 107 108 110 115 118 119 125 128 130 131 133 135 143 146 147 148 **P**6 **S** Essentia Health, Duluth, MN
Primary Contact: Marsha Green, Chief Executive Officer
CMO: David Goodall, M.D., Chief Medical Staff
CHR: Brittany Mohler, Director Human Resources
Web address: www.essentiahealth.org
Control: Other not–for–profit (including NFP Corporation) **Service:** General Medical and Surgical

Staffed Beds: 52 **Admissions:** 551 **Census:** 30 **Outpatient Visits:** 23625 **Births:** 82 **Total Expense ($000):** 27711 **Payroll Expense ($000):** 13101 **Personnel:** 232

DETROIT LAKES—Becker County

✠ **ESSENTIA HEALTH ST. MARY'S – DETROIT LAKES (240101)**, 1027 Washington Avenue, Zip 56501–3409; tel. 218/847–5611, (Total facility includes 96 beds in nursing home–type unit) **A**1 5 10 20 **F**7 10 11 13 15 18 28 29 30 31 40 41 43 45 56 57 59 62 64 65 70 75 76 77 79 81 89 93 97 104 107 110 111 119 125 128 130 131 132 135 144 146 147 148 **S** Essentia Health, Duluth, MN
Primary Contact: Peter Jacobson, President
CMO: Rich Vetter, M.D., Associate Chief
CIO: Ken Gilles, Associate Chief Information Officer
CHR: Diane Sundrud, Human Resource Service Partner
CNO: Kay Larson, R.N., Chief Nursing Officer
Web address: www.essentiahealth.org
Control: Other not–for–profit (including NFP Corporation) **Service:** General Medical and Surgical

Staffed Beds: 131 **Admissions:** 2387 **Census:** 101 **Outpatient Visits:** 277221 **Births:** 511 **Total Expense ($000):** 96603 **Payroll Expense ($000):** 45249 **Personnel:** 504

ST. MARY'S INNOVIS HEALTH See Essentia Health St. Mary's – Detroit Lakes

DULUTH—St. Louis County

✠ △ **ESSENTIA HEALTH DULUTH (240019)**, 502 East Second Street, Zip 55805–1982; tel. 218/727–8762 **A**1 3 5 7 10 **F**3 5 11 12 15 16 29 30 31 32 34 35 49 50 51 52 54 55 56 57 59 61 64 65 70 74 75 77 78 79 81 82 84 85 86 87 90 91 92 93 94 96 97 98 99 100 101 103 104 105 107 108 110 111 114 115 116 117 118 119 120 121 123 124 130 131 132 134 135 141 144 146 147 148 **P**6 **S** Essentia Health, Duluth, MN
Primary Contact: James Garvey, Administrator
CFO: Kevin Boren, Chief Financial Officer
CMO: Hugh Renier, M.D., Vice President Medical Affairs
CIO: Dennis Dassenko, Chief Information Officer
CHR: Diane Davidson, Senior Vice President Human Resources
CNO: Sandee Carlson, Director of Nursing
Web address: www.smdcmedicalcenter.org
Control: Other not–for–profit (including NFP Corporation) **Service:** General Medical and Surgical

Staffed Beds: 154 **Admissions:** 3461 **Census:** 76 **Outpatient Visits:** 38497 **Births:** 21 **Total Expense ($000):** 385156 **Payroll Expense ($000):** 197753 **Personnel:** 2150

Hospital, Medicare Provider Number, Address, Telephone, Approval, Facility, and Physician Codes, Health Care System

★ American Hospital Association (AHA) membership   ○ Healthcare Facilities Accreditation Program   ⇑ Center for Improvement in Healthcare Quality Accreditation
□ The Joint Commission accreditation   ◇ DNV Healthcare Inc. accreditation   △ Commission on Accreditation of Rehabilitation Facilities (CARF) accreditation

✠ **ESSENTIA HEALTH ST. MARY'S MEDICAL CENTER (240002)**, 407 East Third Street, Zip 55805–1984; tel. 218/786–4000, (Includes ST. MARY'S CHILDREN'S HOSPITAL, 407 East Third Street, Zip 55805–1950; tel. 218/786–5437) **A**1 2 3 5 10 **F**3 11 12 13 17 18 20 22 24 26 28 29 30 34 35 37 38 40 41 43 45 46 47 48 49 50 57 59 63 65 67 70 72 74 76 78 79 81 83 84 85 86 87 88 89 91 102 107 108 111 115 119 126 129 130 132 135 141 146 **P**6 **S** Essentia Health, Duluth, MN
Primary Contact: James Garvey, Executive Vice President, Operations and Administrator
CMO: Hugh Renier, M.D., Vice President Medical Affairs
CIO: Tess Jettergren, Director Clinical Informatics
CHR: Glen Porter, Vice President Human Resources
Web address: www.essentiahealth.org/StMarysMedicalCenter/FindaClinic/Essentia–HealthSt–Marys–Medical–Center–46.aspx
Control: Other not–for–profit (including NFP Corporation) **Service:** General Medical and Surgical

Staffed Beds: 306 **Admissions:** 18395 **Census:** 240 **Outpatient Visits:** 121772 **Births:** 1343 **Total Expense ($000):** 351859 **Payroll Expense ($000):** 153665 **Personnel:** 2103

SMDC MEDICAL CENTER See Essentia Health Duluth

✠ △ **ST. LUKE'S HOSPITAL (240047)**, 915 East First Street, Zip 55805–2193; tel. 218/249–5555 **A**1 2 3 7 10 **F**3 5 8 11 12 13 15 17 18 20 22 24 26 28 29 30 31 34 35 39 40 43 46 47 48 49 51 53 54 57 58 59 60 61 62 63 64 65 70 74 75 76 77 78 79 81 82 83 84 85 86 87 89 90 92 93 97 98 100 102 104 107 108 110 114 115 117 118 119 120 121 123 124 126 129 130 131 132 144 145 146 148 **P**6
Primary Contact: John Strange, President and Chief Executive Officer
CFO: Eric Lohn, Vice President and Chief Financial Officer
CMO: Gary Peterson, M.D., Vice President Medical Affairs and Chief Medical Officer
CIO: Clark Averill, Director Information Technology
CHR: Marla Halvorson, Director Human Resources
CNO: Susan Hamel, Chief Nursing Officer
Web address: www.slhduluth.com
Control: Other not–for–profit (including NFP Corporation) **Service:** General Medical and Surgical

Staffed Beds: 267 **Admissions:** 10267 **Census:** 144 **Outpatient Visits:** 731611 **Births:** 735 **Total Expense ($000):** 386035 **Payroll Expense ($000):** 186955 **Personnel:** 2051

ST. MARY'S MEDICAL CENTER See Essentia Health St. Mary's Medical Center

EDINA—Hennepin County

✠ **FAIRVIEW SOUTHDALE HOSPITAL (240078)**, 6401 France Avenue South, Zip 55435–2199; tel. 952/924–5000 **A**1 2 3 5 10 **F**3 5 8 11 12 13 15 17 18 20 22 24 26 28 29 30 31 34 35 38 39 40 43 45 46 49 50 51 55 56 57 59 60 64 65 68 70 72 74 75 76 77 78 79 81 82 83 84 85 87 93 94 96 98 100 102 107 108 110 111 114 115 117 118 119 121 124 126 129 130 131 132 134 135 146 147 148 **P**6 **S** Fairview Health Services, Minneapolis, MN
Primary Contact: Bradley Beard, Regional President
CFO: Alan Lem, Vice President Finance
CHR: Michelle LeDell, Director Human Resources
Web address: www.fairview.org
Control: Other not–for–profit (including NFP Corporation) **Service:** General Medical and Surgical

Staffed Beds: 338 **Admissions:** 17157 **Census:** 200 **Outpatient Visits:** 127237 **Births:** 2827 **Total Expense ($000):** 396354 **Payroll Expense ($000):** 154353 **Personnel:** 1678

ELBOW LAKE—Grant County

ELEAH MEDICAL CENTER See Prairie Ridge Hospital and Health Services

★ **PRAIRIE RIDGE HOSPITAL AND HEALTH SERVICES (241379)**, 1411 Highway 79 E., Zip 56531–4611; tel. 218/685–7300 **A**10 18 **F**3 7 28 31 40 42 43 45 46 47 48 59 64 79 81 93 107 114 133 148 **P**5
Primary Contact: Jim Gingerich, Administrator
CFO: Loraine Martineau, Controller
CMO: Phillip Walter Holmes, M.D., Chief of Staff
CNO: Alycia Athey, Director of Nursing
Web address: www.prairiehealth.org
Control: Other not–for–profit (including NFP Corporation) **Service:** General Medical and Surgical

Staffed Beds: 10 **Admissions:** 134 **Census:** 2 **Outpatient Visits:** 23033 **Births:** 0 **Total Expense ($000):** 19392 **Payroll Expense ($000):** 4473 **Personnel:** 130

ELY—St. Louis County

★ **ELY–BLOOMENSON COMMUNITY HOSPITAL (241318)**, 328 West Conan Street, Zip 55731–1198; tel. 218/365–3271 **A**10 18 **F**3 13 15 28 31 40 45 53 62 64 76 81 107 110 119 128 130 133 148 **P**6
Primary Contact: John Fossum, Chief Executive Officer
CFO: Scott Kellerman, Chief Financial Officer
CHR: Rochelle Sjoberg, Director Human Resources
CNO: Becky Gaulke, Chief Nursing Officer
Web address: www.ebch.org
Control: Other not–for–profit (including NFP Corporation) **Service:** General Medical and Surgical

Staffed Beds: 20 **Admissions:** 319 **Census:** 3 **Outpatient Visits:** 3649 **Births:** 14 **Total Expense ($000):** 16155 **Payroll Expense ($000):** 5363 **Personnel:** 89

FAIRMONT—Martin County

☐ **MAYO CLINIC HEALTH SYSTEM IN FAIRMONT (240166)**, 800 Medical Center Drive, Zip 56031–4575; tel. 507/238–8100, (Includes LUTZ WING CONVALESCENT AND NURSING CARE UNIT), (Total facility includes 40 beds in nursing home–type unit) **A**1 10 20 **F**3 12 13 15 18 28 29 30 31 34 36 40 43 45 56 57 59 64 65 68 74 75 76 77 78 79 81 82 84 85 86 87 92 93 97 99 100 101 103 104 107 108 110 111 115 118 119 128 129 130 132 133 144 146 148 **P**6 **S** Mayo Clinic, Rochester, MN
Primary Contact: Robert Bartingale, Administrator
COO: Gayle B. Hansen, R.N., Chief Operating Officer
CFO: Brian Suter, Chief Financial Officer
CMO: Rufus Rodriguez, M.D., Medical Director
Web address: www.fairmontmedicalcenter.org
Control: Other not–for–profit (including NFP Corporation) **Service:** General Medical and Surgical

Staffed Beds: 63 **Admissions:** 2023 **Census:** 50 **Outpatient Visits:** 104771 **Births:** 229 **Personnel:** 345

FARIBAULT—Rice County

★ **DISTRICT ONE HOSPITAL (240071)**, 200 State Avenue, Zip 55021–6345; tel. 507/334–6451, (Nonreporting) **A**10 **S** Allina Health, Minneapolis, MN
Primary Contact: Stephen J. Pribyl, FACHE, President
COO: Rick Miller, Director, Operations and Finance
CFO: Rick Miller, Chief Financial Officer
CMO: Amy Elliott, M.D., Director Medical Affairs
Web address: www.allinahealth.org/District–One–Hospital/
Control: Hospital district or authority, Government, nonfederal **Service:** General Medical and Surgical

Staffed Beds: 42

FERGUS FALLS—Otter Tail County

☐ **COMMUNITY BEHAVIORAL HEALTH HOSPITAL – FERGUS FALLS (244013)**, 1801 West Alcott Avenue, Zip 56537–2661, Mailing Address: P.O. Box 478, Zip 56538–0478; tel. 218/332–5001, (Nonreporting) **A**1 10 **S** Minnesota Department of Human Services, Saint Paul, MN
Primary Contact: Brenda Schleske, Administrator
Control: State–Government, nonfederal **Service:** Psychiatric

Staffed Beds: 16

✠ △ **LAKE REGION HEALTHCARE (240052)**, 712 South Cascade Street, Zip 56537–2900, Mailing Address: P.O. Box 728, Zip 56538–0728; tel. 218/736–8000 **A**1 7 10 20 **F**3 10 11 13 15 17 18 26 28 29 30 31 32 34 35 36 40 43 44 45 50 51 53 54 56 57 58 59 61 64 65 70 74 75 76 77 78 79 81 82 84 85 86 87 89 90 92 93 94 96 97 98 100 101 102 103 104 107 108 110 111 115 118 119 120 121 123 130 131 132 135 144 146 147 148
Primary Contact: Larry A. Schulz, Chief Executive Officer
CFO: Brett Longtin, Chief Financial Officer
CMO: Greg Smith, Chief Medical Officer
CIO: Wade A. Jyrkas, Director Computer Information Systems
CHR: Kim Blank, Director Human Resources
CNO: Lucia E. Anderson, Senior Vice President Operations and Chief Nurse Executive
Web address: www.lrhc.org
Control: Other not–for–profit (including NFP Corporation) **Service:** General Medical and Surgical

Staffed Beds: 108 **Admissions:** 2573 **Census:** 28 **Outpatient Visits:** 57890 **Births:** 298 **Total Expense ($000):** 117866 **Payroll Expense ($000):** 38718 **Personnel:** 737

MN

FOSSTON—Polk County

★ **ESSENTIA HEALTH FOSSTON (241357)**, 900 Hilligoss Boulevard S.E., Zip 56542–1599; tel. 218/435–1133, (Total facility includes 50 beds in nursing home–type unit) **A**10 18 **F**3 7 10 11 13 15 28 29 31 34 35 40 43 44 50 56 57 59 62 63 65 68 69 70 75 76 77 78 79 81 82 84 85 87 93 97 99 104 107 110 114 127 128 129 130 131 132 133 135 146 148 **P**6 **S** Essentia Health, Duluth, MN
Primary Contact: Kevin Gish, Administrator and Vice President
CFO: Kim Bodensteiner, Chief Financial Officer
CHR: Diane Sundrud, Director Human Resources
Web address: www.essentiahealth.org
Control: Other not–for–profit (including NFP Corporation) **Service:** General Medical and Surgical

Staffed Beds: 75 **Admissions:** 577 **Census:** 46 **Outpatient Visits:** 55826 **Births:** 80 **Total Expense ($000):** 25789 **Payroll Expense ($000):** 12448 **Personnel:** 188

FIRST CARE MEDICAL SERVICES See Essentia Health Fosston

FRIDLEY—Anoka County

⊞ **UNITY HOSPITAL (240132)**, 550 Osborne Road N.E., Zip 55432–2799; tel. 763/236–5000 **A**1 2 5 10 **F**3 4 5 11 12 13 18 20 22 24 26 28 29 30 31 34 35 36 40 43 45 50 53 55 56 57 59 64 65 69 70 73 75 76 77 78 79 81 82 85 86 87 88 93 96 98 99 100 101 102 103 104 107 108 111 114 115 119 126 130 132 135 145 146 147 148 **S** Allina Health, Minneapolis, MN
Primary Contact: Helen J. Strike, R.N., President
COO: Daniel Steffen, Vice President Operations
CFO: Gerald Pietz, Vice President Finance
CMO: Paul Kettler, M.D., Vice President Medical Affairs
CIO: Susan Heichert, Chief Information Officer
CHR: Nancy Watson, Vice President Human Resources
Web address: www.allina.com
Control: Other not–for–profit (including NFP Corporation) **Service:** General Medical and Surgical

Staffed Beds: 167 **Admissions:** 11179 **Census:** 116 **Outpatient Visits:** 91020 **Births:** 635 **Total Expense ($000):** 185900 **Payroll Expense ($000):** 80522 **Personnel:** 783

GLENCOE—Mcleod County

★ **GLENCOE REGIONAL HEALTH SERVICES (241355)**, 1805 Hennepin Avenue North, Zip 55336–1416; tel. 320/864–3121, (Total facility includes 110 beds in nursing home–type unit) **A**10 18 **F**3 11 13 15 28 29 31 34 40 43 45 48 56 64 68 75 76 77 78 79 81 86 87 89 93 97 107 111 115 118 119 125 128 130 132 133 135 144 146 **P**6 **S** HealthPartners, Bloomington, MN
Primary Contact: Jon D. Braband, FACHE, President and Chief Executive Officer
CFO: John C. Doidge, Vice President Finance
CMO: John H. Bergseng, D.O., Vice President Medical Affairs
CIO: Ryan Lake, Director Medical Imaging and Information Technology
CHR: Jill Hatlestad, Vice President Human Resources and Marketing
CNO: Patricia Henderson, R.N., Vice President Nursing and Clinical Services
Web address: www.grhsonline.org
Control: Other not–for–profit (including NFP Corporation) **Service:** General Medical and Surgical

Staffed Beds: 135 **Admissions:** 940 **Census:** 107 **Outpatient Visits:** 21488 **Births:** 142 **Total Expense ($000):** 51773 **Payroll Expense ($000):** 24689 **Personnel:** 371

GLENWOOD—Pope County

★ **GLACIAL RIDGE HEALTH SYSTEM (241376)**, 10 Fourth Avenue S.E., Zip 56334–1898; tel. 320/634–4521 **A**10 18 **F**7 11 12 13 15 17 28 31 34 35 40 41 43 53 59 62 63 64 75 76 79 81 93 107 110 111 114 119 127 130 133 146 148 **P**6
Primary Contact: Kirk A. Stensrud, Chief Executive Officer
CFO: Kyle Chase, Chief Financial Officer
CMO: Gustave Mellgren, M.D., Chief of Staff
CIO: Jeff Ofstedal, Manager Information Technology
CHR: Gordon Paulson, Manager Human Resources
CNO: Lynn Flesner, Director of Nursing
Web address: www.glacialridge.org
Control: Hospital district or authority, Government, nonfederal **Service:** General Medical and Surgical

Staffed Beds: 19 **Admissions:** 623 **Census:** 6 **Outpatient Visits:** 15923 **Births:** 64 **Total Expense ($000):** 27860 **Payroll Expense ($000):** 14157 **Personnel:** 199

GOLDEN VALLEY—Hennepin County

⊞ **REGENCY HOSPITAL OF MINNEAPOLIS (242005)**, 1300 Hidden Lakes Parkway, Zip 55422–4286; tel. 763/588–2750, (Nonreporting) **A**1 10 **S** Select Medical Corporation, Mechanicsburg, PA
Primary Contact: Marshall E. Smith, Chief Executive Officer
CMO: Alaka Nagaraj, M.D., Medical Director
CNO: Caren Gaytko, Chief Nursing Officer
Web address: www.regencyhospital.com
Control: Corporation, Investor–owned, for–profit **Service:** Long–Term Acute Care hospital

Staffed Beds: 64

GRACEVILLE—Big Stone County

★ **ESSENTIA HEALTH–GRACEVILLE (241321)**, 115 West Second Street, Zip 56240–4845, Mailing Address: P.O. Box 157, Zip 56240–0157; tel. 320/748–7223, (Nonreporting) **A**10 18 **S** Essentia Health, Duluth, MN
Primary Contact: Julie Rosenberg, Administrator
CMO: Arthur Van Vranken, M.D., Chief Medical Officer
CIO: Brad Tostenson, Chief Information Officer
CHR: Jenny Lee, Human Resources Generalist
CNO: Jill Johnsrud, Director of Nursing
Web address: www.essentiahealth.org/HolyTrinityHospital/FindaClinic/Essentia–HealthHoly–Trinity–Hospital–96.aspx
Control: Other not–for–profit (including NFP Corporation) **Service:** General Medical and Surgical

Staffed Beds: 65

GRACEVILLE HEALTH CENTER See Essentia Health–Graceville

GRAND MARAIS—Cook County

★ **NORTH SHORE HEALTH (241317)**, 515 5th Avenue West, Zip 55604–3017; tel. 218/387–3040, (Total facility includes 37 beds in nursing home–type unit) **A**10 18 **F**3 7 11 15 28 31 40 45 50 56 59 62 64 75 84 85 89 93 107 110 111 114 119 128 130 133 148
Primary Contact: Kimber L. Wraalstad, FACHE, Administrator
CFO: Vera Schumann, Director of Finance and Controller
CMO: Milan Schmidt, Medical Director
CIO: Greg Johnson, IT Coordinator
CHR: Robert Willis, Director Human Resources
CNO: Bridget Sobieck, Director of Nursing
Web address: www.nshorehospital.com
Control: Hospital district or authority, Government, nonfederal **Service:** General Medical and Surgical

Staffed Beds: 53 **Admissions:** 229 **Census:** 30 **Outpatient Visits:** 12100 **Births:** 5 **Total Expense ($000):** 14400 **Payroll Expense ($000):** 5899 **Personnel:** 114

GRAND RAPIDS—Itasca County

⊞ **GRAND ITASCA CLINIC AND HOSPITAL (240064)**, 1601 Golf Course Road, Zip 55744–8648; tel. 218/326–5000, (Nonreporting) **A**1 10 20
Primary Contact: Michael Youso, Chief Executive Officer
CFO: Sarah S. Gustafson, Vice President of Finance
CHR: Julie Schmidt, Director Human Resources
CNO: Sue Skinner, Vice President of Patient Care Services
Web address: www.granditasca.org
Control: Other not–for–profit (including NFP Corporation) **Service:** General Medical and Surgical

Staffed Beds: 31

GRANITE FALLS—Yellow Medicine County

★ **GRANITE FALLS MUNICIPAL HOSPITAL AND MANOR (241343)**, 345 Tenth Avenue, Zip 56241–1499; tel. 320/564–3111, (Nonreporting) **A**10 18
Primary Contact: Thomas Kooiman, Chief Executive Officer
CFO: Val Hoffman, Chief Financial Officer
CIO: Kris Wilke, Manager Health Information
CHR: Sue Tollefson, Coordinator Payroll Personnel
CNO: Patty Massman, Director of Nursing
Web address: www.granitefallshealthcare.com
Control: City–Government, nonfederal **Service:** General Medical and Surgical

Staffed Beds: 82

MN

MN

HALLOCK—Kittson County

★ **KITTSON MEMORIAL HEALTHCARE CENTER (241336)**, 1010 South Birch Street, Zip 56728–4215, Mailing Address: P.O. Box 700, Zip 56728–0700; tel. 218/843–3612, (Total facility includes 60 beds in nursing home–type unit) **A**10 18 **F**7 10 11 15 28 32 34 35 40 45 50 53 54 59 62 63 65 68 93 107 117 127 128 130 133 143 148
Primary Contact: Cindy Urbaniak, Chief Executive Officer
CFO: Todd Christensen, Chief Financial Officer
CMO: Thomas Lohstreter, M.D., Chief of Staff
CIO: Holly Knutson, Manager Information Technology
CHR: Carlene Cole, Manager Human Resources
CNO: Tawnya Sorenson, Director of Nursing
Web address: www.kmhc.net
Control: Other not–for–profit (including NFP Corporation) **Service:** General Medical and Surgical

Staffed Beds: 75 **Admissions:** 162 **Census:** 67 **Outpatient Visits:** 1085
Births: 0

HASTINGS—Dakota County

✣ **REGINA HOSPITAL (240059)**, 1175 Nininger Road, Zip 55033–1098; tel. 651/480–4100 **A**1 10 **F**3 8 11 13 15 28 29 30 34 35 40 43 45 46 50 57 59 68 70 75 76 77 79 81 83 87 93 103 107 110 114 119 129 130 132 145 146 148 **S** Allina Health, Minneapolis, MN
Primary Contact: Thomas R. Thompson, Chief Executive Officer
CFO: Andy Rolling, Director of Finance
CMO: James Noreen, M.D., Chief Medical Officer
CHR: Robert P. Verchota, Vice President Support Services
Web address: www.reginamedical.org
Control: Other not–for–profit (including NFP Corporation) **Service:** General Medical and Surgical

Staffed Beds: 115 **Admissions:** 1484 **Census:** 20 **Outpatient Visits:** 49374
Births: 298 **Total Expense ($000):** 50346 **Payroll Expense ($000):** 17438
Personnel: 279

HENDRICKS—Lincoln County

★ **HENDRICKS COMMUNITY HOSPITAL ASSOCIATION (241339)**, 503 East Lincoln Street, Zip 56136–9598, Mailing Address: P.O. Box 106, Zip 56136–0106; tel. 507/275–3134, (Total facility includes 58 beds in nursing home–type unit) **A**10 18 **F**2 3 7 10 11 15 17 28 29 31 34 35 40 50 59 62 63 70 81 89 93 125 127 128 130 132 133 146 148
Primary Contact: Jeffrey Gollaher, Chief Executive Officer
CMO: Tabb McCluskey, M.D., Chief Medical Officer
CHR: Lynn R. Olson, Director Human Resources
Web address: www.hendrickshosp.org
Control: Other not–for–profit (including NFP Corporation) **Service:** General Medical and Surgical

Staffed Beds: 70 **Admissions:** 221 **Census:** 57 **Outpatient Visits:** 12007
Births: 0 **Total Expense ($000):** 12872 **Payroll Expense ($000):** 6874
Personnel: 116

HIBBING—St. Louis County

✣ **RANGE REGIONAL HEALTH SERVICES (240040)**, 750 East 34th Street, Zip 55746–4600; tel. 218/262–4881 **A**1 2 10 **F**3 6 11 13 15 28 29 30 31 33 34 35 40 43 50 57 62 63 64 65 68 70 75 76 77 78 79 81 82 84 85 87 89 93 97 98 102 104 107 108 110 111 115 116 117 119 120 129 130 131 132 135 143 144 146 147 148 **P**6 **S** Fairview Health Services, Minneapolis, MN
Primary Contact: Debra K. Boardman, FACHE, President and Chief Executive Officer
COO: Patrick Sharp, Chief Operating Officer
CFO: Tom Fink, Vice President Regional Finance Officer
CMO: Susan Rudberg, M.D., Chief Medical Officer
CIO: Jessica Valento, Director Information Systems
CHR: Mitch Vincent, Vice President Organizational Support
CNO: Connie Harle, Chief Nursing Officer
Web address: www.range.fairview.org
Control: Other not–for–profit (including NFP Corporation) **Service:** General Medical and Surgical

Staffed Beds: 57 **Admissions:** 2561 **Census:** 32 **Outpatient Visits:** 46536
Births: 375 **Total Expense ($000):** 107304 **Payroll Expense ($000):** 55144
Personnel: 754

HUTCHINSON—Mcleod County

✣ **HUTCHINSON HEALTH (240187)**, 1095 Highway 15 South, Zip 55350–3182; tel. 320/234–5000 **A**1 10 20 **F**3 5 11 13 15 28 29 31 34 35 36 38 40 43 45 56 57 59 64 65 69 70 75 76 77 78 79 81 82 85 86 87 93 96 97 98 99 100 101 103 104 107 110 111 115 119 127 129 130 131 132 144 146 147 148 **P**6 **S** Allina Health, Minneapolis, MN
Primary Contact: Steven Mulder, M.D., President and Chief Executive Officer
COO: Glen Kegley, Chief Operating Officer
CFO: Pamela Larson, Division Director Financial Services
CMO: Brian Pollman, Chief Medical Officer
CIO: Jim Lyons, Chief Clinic Officer
CHR: Rebecca Streich, Manager Human Resources and Education Manager
CNO: Mary Kay Henze, Chief Nursing Officer
Web address: www.hutchhealth.com
Control: Other not–for–profit (including NFP Corporation) **Service:** General Medical and Surgical

Staffed Beds: 57 **Admissions:** 2117 **Census:** 23 **Outpatient Visits:** 219777
Births: 218 **Total Expense ($000):** 85636 **Payroll Expense ($000):** 31134
Personnel: 467

INTERNATIONAL FALLS—Koochiching County

✣ **RAINY LAKE MEDICAL CENTER (241322)**, 1400 Highway 71, Zip 56649–2189; tel. 218/283–4481, (Nonreporting) **A**1 10 18
Primary Contact: Bonnie Erickson, Chief Executive Officer
CFO: Melissa Marcotte, Chief Financial Officer
CIO: Michael Blesi, Director Information Technology
CNO: Donita Ettestad, R.N., Chief Nursing Officer
Web address: www.rainylakemedical.com
Control: Other not–for–profit (including NFP Corporation) **Service:** General Medical and Surgical

Staffed Beds: 25

JACKSON—Jackson County

★ **SANFORD JACKSON MEDICAL CENTER (241315)**, 1430 North Highway, Zip 56143–1093; tel. 507/847–2420 **A**10 18 **F**1 3 15 18 28 29 31 34 35 40 41 43 45 46 50 56 57 59 64 65 67 68 75 77 78 79 81 82 85 86 87 89 90 93 97 107 108 110 111 114 118 119 127 128 129 131 132 133 148 **P**6 **S** Sanford Health, Sioux Falls, SD
Primary Contact: Mary J. Ruyter, Chief Executive Officer
CFO: Gail Eike, Chief Financial Officer
CMO: Sister Marie Paul Lockerd, M.D., Chief Medical Officer
CNO: Dawn Schnell, Chief Nursing Officer
Web address: www.sanfordjackson.org
Control: Other not–for–profit (including NFP Corporation) **Service:** General Medical and Surgical

Staffed Beds: 14 **Admissions:** 193 **Census:** 2 **Outpatient Visits:** 24222
Births: 0 **Total Expense ($000):** 8721 **Payroll Expense ($000):** 3712
Personnel: 58

LAKE CITY—Goodhue County

☐ **MAYO CLINIC HEALTH SYSTEM IN LAKE CITY (241338)**, 500 West Grant Street, Zip 55041–1143; tel. 651/345–3321, (Total facility includes 90 beds in nursing home–type unit) **A**1 10 18 **F**15 18 28 29 30 34 35 40 45 57 59 64 67 69 75 79 81 87 92 93 97 107 110 111 114 119 128 130 132 133 146 148 **P**6 **S** Mayo Clinic, Rochester, MN
Primary Contact: Thomas J. Witt, M.D., President and Chief Executive Officer
CFO: David Biren, Chief Financial Officer
CMO: Dennis Spano, M.D., Medical Director
CHR: Jacqueline Ryan, Director Human Resources
Web address: www.lakecitymedicalcenter.org
Control: Other not–for–profit (including NFP Corporation) **Service:** General Medical and Surgical

Staffed Beds: 101 **Admissions:** 483 **Census:** 92 **Outpatient Visits:** 52379
Births: 16 **Personnel:** 194

LE SUEUR—Le Sueur County

★ **MINNESOTA VALLEY HEALTH CENTER (241375)**, 621 South Fourth Street, Zip 56058–2298; tel. 507/665–3375, (Includes GARDENVIEW NURSING HOME), (Nonreporting) **A**10 18 **S** Essentia Health, Duluth, MN
Primary Contact: Pam Williams, Chief Executive Officer
CFO: Patricia Schlegel, Executive Director Finance
CMO: Carolyn Stelter, M.D., Chief of Staff
CHR: Bonnie Barnhardt, Executive Director Human Resources
CNO: Kim Putz, R.N., Director, Nursing Hospital
Web address: www.mvhc.org
Control: Other not–for–profit (including NFP Corporation) **Service:** General Medical and Surgical

Staffed Beds: 64

LITCHFIELD—Meeker County

★ **MEEKER MEMORIAL HOSPITAL (241366)**, 612 South Sibley Avenue,
Zip 55355–3398; tel. 320/693–4500 **A**10 18 **F**11 13 15 28 29 31 34 40 43
45 57 59 70 75 77 78 81 93 107 110 111 114 119 130 133 146 148
Primary Contact: Kyle R. Rasmussen, Chief Executive Officer
CFO: Stephen Plaisance, Chief Financial Officer
CMO: Tim Peterson, M.D., Chief of Staff
CIO: Troy Bruning, Director Information Technology
CHR: Cindi Twardy, Manager Human Resources
CNO: Joan Bitz, Chief Nursing Officer
Web address: www.meekermemorial.org
Control: County–Government, nonfederal **Service:** General Medical and Surgical

Staffed Beds: 38 **Admissions:** 937 **Census:** 15 **Outpatient Visits:** 31095
Births: 150 **Total Expense ($000):** 28985 **Payroll Expense ($000):** 10662
Personnel: 151

LITTLE FALLS—Morrison County

⊠ **CHI ST. GABRIEL'S HEALTH (241370)**, 815 Second Street S.E.,
Zip 56345–3596; tel. 320/632–5441, (Nonreporting) **A**1 10 18 **S** Catholic Health
Initiatives, Englewood, CO
Primary Contact: Lee Boyles, President
CFO: Steve Smith, Assistant Vice President Finance
CMO: Susan Okoniewski, M.D., Chief of Staff
Web address: www.stgabriels.com
Control: Other not–for–profit (including NFP Corporation) **Service:** General
Medical and Surgical

Staffed Beds: 25

LONG PRAIRIE—Todd County

★ **CENTRACARE HEALTH–LONG PRAIRIE (241326)**, 20 Ninth Street S.E.,
Zip 56347–1404; tel. 320/732–2141, (Nonreporting) **A**5 10 18 **S** CentraCare
Health, Saint Cloud, MN
Primary Contact: Daniel J. Swenson, FACHE, Administrator and Chief Executive
Officer
CFO: Larry Knutson, Director Finance
CMO: Rene Eldidy, M.D., Chief of Staff
Web address: www.centracare.com
Control: Other not–for–profit (including NFP Corporation) **Service:** General
Medical and Surgical

Staffed Beds: 20

LONG PRAIRIE MEMORIAL HOSPITAL AND HOME See CentraCare
Health–Long Prairie

LUVERNE—Rock County

★ **SANFORD LUVERNE MEDICAL CENTER (241371)**, 1600 North Kniss Avenue,
Zip 56156–1067; tel. 507/283–2321 **A**10 18 **F**3 4 5 7 8 11 13 15 18 19 28
29 31 32 34 35 40 43 45 56 57 59 63 64 65 67 68 74 75 76 77 78 79 81
82 83 84 85 86 87 90 93 96 97 107 111 114 118 119 128 129 131 132
133 135 146 147 148 **P**6 **S** Sanford Health, Sioux Falls, SD
Primary Contact: Tammy Loosbrock, Senior Director
COO: Nancy E. Drenth, R.N., Director Ancillary Services
CFO: Stanley Knobloch, Director Fiscal Services
CMO: Judy S. Chesley, M.D., Chief of Staff
CNO: Nyla H. Sandbulte, R.N., Director of Nursing
Web address: www.sanfordluverne.org
Control: Other not–for–profit (including NFP Corporation) **Service:** General
Medical and Surgical

Staffed Beds: 25 **Admissions:** 506 **Census:** 6 **Outpatient Visits:** 31348
Births: 83 **Total Expense ($000):** 22340 **Payroll Expense ($000):** 9378
Personnel: 141

MADELIA—Watonwan County

⊠ **MADELIA COMMUNITY HOSPITAL (241323)**, 121 Drew Avenue S.E.,
Zip 56062–1899; tel. 507/642–3255 **A**1 3 5 10 18 **F**3 11 13 15 34 35 40 57
59 62 64 68 69 75 76 77 81 84 85 86 93 102 107 110 114 128 130 132
133 144 145
Primary Contact: Candace Fenske, Chief Executive Officer
CFO: Donna M. Klinkner, Chief Financial Officer
CMO: Todd Gavin, Chief Medical Officer
CIO: Valerie Juhl, Director of Health
CHR: Donna M. Klinkner, Chief Financial Officer
CNO: Deidre Hruby, Director of Patient Care
Web address: www.mchospital.org
Control: Other not–for–profit (including NFP Corporation) **Service:** General
Medical and Surgical

Staffed Beds: 21 **Admissions:** 189 **Census:** 3 **Outpatient Visits:** 4683
Births: 0 **Total Expense ($000):** 10903 **Payroll Expense ($000):** 4075
Personnel: 73

MADISON—Lac Qui Parle County

★ **MADISON HEALTHCARE SERVICES (241372)**, 900 Second Avenue,
Zip 56256–1006; tel. 320/598–7556 **A**10 18 **F**10 11 15 28 29 30 34 40 43
57 59 62 64 65 77 78 79 81 82 84 93 97 107 110 111 119 127 130 132
133 145 147 **P**5
Primary Contact: Erik Bjerke, Chief Executive Officer
CFO: Carol Borgerson, Business Office Manager and Chief Financial Officer
CIO: Jerry Harberts, Information Technologist
CHR: Allen Anderson, Director Human Resources
Web address: www.mlhmn.org/
Control: Other not–for–profit (including NFP Corporation) **Service:** General
Medical and Surgical

Staffed Beds: 12 **Admissions:** 194 **Census:** 2 **Outpatient Visits:** 11900
Births: 7 **Total Expense ($000):** 10174 **Payroll Expense ($000):** 3650
Personnel: 57

MAHNOMEN—Mahnomen County

★ **MAHNOMEN HEALTH CENTER (241300)**, 414 West Jefferson Avenue,
Zip 56557–4912, Mailing Address: P.O. Box 396, Zip 56557–0396;
tel. 218/935–2511, (Total facility includes 38 beds in nursing home–type unit)
A10 18 **F**2 3 7 11 15 34 40 43 57 59 62 110 128 130 132 133 146
S Sanford Health, Sioux Falls, SD
Primary Contact: Dale K. Kruger, Chief Executive Officer
CFO: Mary Pazdernik, Chief Financial Officer
CMO: Anju Gurung, M.D., Chief Medical Officer
CHR: Kristi Stall, Chief Human Resources Officer
Web address: www.mahnomenhealthcenter.com
Control: City–County, Government, nonfederal **Service:** General Medical and
Surgical

Staffed Beds: 56 **Admissions:** 116 **Census:** 20 **Outpatient Visits:** 3657
Births: 0 **Total Expense ($000):** 8919 **Payroll Expense ($000):** 2447
Personnel: 77

MANKATO—Blue Earth County

⊠ **MAYO CLINIC HEALTH SYSTEM IN MANKATO (240093)**, 1025 Marsh Street,
Zip 56001–4752; tel. 507/625–4031 **A**1 3 5 10 13 **F**3 7 11 12 13 15 18 19
20 22 26 28 29 30 31 33 34 35 36 38 40 41 43 45 49 53 54 56 57 58 59
60 61 63 64 65 66 68 70 73 74 75 76 77 78 79 81 82 83 84 85 87 89 91
92 93 97 98 99 100 102 103 104 107 108 110 111 114 118 119 120 121
126 127 129 130 131 132 135 144 146 147 148 **P**6 **S** Mayo Clinic,
Rochester, MN
Primary Contact: Gregory Kutcher, M.D., President and Chief Executive Officer
CFO: James Tarasovitch, Chief Financial Officer
CMO: Susan Pearson, M.D., Chief Medical Officer
CIO: Sarah Daniels, Vice President, Information Technology
CHR: Beth Dittbenner, Regional Director, Human Resources
Web address: www.isj–mhs.org
Control: Other not–for–profit (including NFP Corporation) **Service:** General
Medical and Surgical

Staffed Beds: 166 **Admissions:** 9579 **Census:** 102 **Outpatient Visits:**
288208 **Births:** 1477 **Personnel:** 1612

MAPLE GROVE—Hennepin County

⊠ ◇ **MAPLE GROVE HOSPITAL (240214)**, 9875 Hospital Drive,
Zip 55369–4648; tel. 763/581–1000 **A**1 10 21 **F**3 13 15 18 29 30 40 43 45
53 60 68 70 72 76 77 79 81 84 85 89 100 102 107 108 111 115 118 119
126 130 146 148 **P**8 **S** North Memorial Health Care, Robbinsdale, MN
Primary Contact: Andrew S. Cochrane, Chief Executive Officer
CFO: Aaron Bloomquist, Chief Financial Officer
CMO: Pamela Doorenbos, Medical Director, Medical Affairs
CHR: Rebecca A. Thiesfeld Rauen, Director Human Resources
CNO: Faith Zwirchitz, Director Nursing and Professional Practice
Web address: www.maplegrovehospital.org
Control: Other not–for–profit (including NFP Corporation) **Service:** General
Medical and Surgical

Staffed Beds: 108 **Admissions:** 8903 **Census:** 66 **Outpatient Visits:** 196893
Births: 4557 **Total Expense ($000):** 144507 **Payroll Expense ($000):**
50185 **Personnel:** 630

MN

Hospital, Medicare Provider Number, Address, Telephone, Approval, Facility, and Physician Codes, Health Care System

★ American Hospital Association (AHA) membership   ○ Healthcare Facilities Accreditation Program   ⇑ Center for Improvement in Healthcare Quality Accreditation
□ The Joint Commission accreditation   ◇ DNV Healthcare Inc. accreditation   △ Commission on Accreditation of Rehabilitation Facilities (CARF) accreditation

MAPLEWOOD—Ramsey County

⊞ ST. JOHN'S HOSPITAL (240210), 1575 Beam Avenue, Zip 55109–1126; tel. 651/232–7000 **A**1 2 3 5 10 **F**3 13 15 17 28 29 30 31 34 35 36 37 38 40 43 44 49 50 54 55 57 59 61 63 64 68 70 72 74 75 76 77 78 79 81 85 86 87 89 93 96 97 100 102 104 107 108 110 111 114 115 116 117 118 119 121 123 126 130 131 132 146 147 148 **P**8 **S** HealthEast Care System, Saint Paul, MN
Primary Contact: Catherine Barr, Chief Operating Officer
COO: Brian Gager, Vice President Operations, Acute Care Hospitals
CFO: Douglas Davenport, Senior Vice President and Chief Financial Officer
CMO: Kevin C. Garrett, M.D., Chief Medical Officer
CIO: Joanne Sundquist, Chief Information Officer
CHR: Dawn Kessler, Senior Vice President Human Resources
CNO: Debra J. Hurd, R.N., Vice President Nursing Acute Care
Web address: www.stjohnshospital–mn.org
Control: Other not–for–profit (including NFP Corporation) **Service:** General Medical and Surgical

Staffed Beds: 192 **Admissions:** 12664 **Census:** 115 **Outpatient Visits:** 109910 **Births:** 2483 **Total Expense ($000):** 231508 **Payroll Expense ($000):** 87803 **Personnel:** 961

MARSHALL—Lyon County

★ AVERA MARSHALL REGIONAL MEDICAL CENTER (241359), 300 South Bruce Street, Zip 56258–3900; tel. 507/532–9661, (Total facility includes 76 beds in nursing home–type unit) **A**10 18 **F**1 2 11 12 13 15 28 29 30 31 40 43 45 46 50 54 59 62 63 64 70 75 77 78 79 81 82 84 90 93 97 98 102 104 107 110 111 115 119 120 129 130 132 133 144 146 148 **P**6 **S** Avera Health, Sioux Falls, SD
Primary Contact: Mary B. Maertens, FACHE, President and Chief Executive Officer
CFO: Sharon Williams, Vice President Finance and Information Technology
CMO: Edward Woiske, M.D., Chief Medical Officer
CIO: Sharon Williams, Vice President Finance and Information Technology
CHR: Sonya J. Kayser, Human Resources Officer
CNO: Dodie Derynck, Chief Nursing Officer
Web address: www.avera.org
Control: Other not–for–profit (including NFP Corporation) **Service:** General Medical and Surgical

Staffed Beds: 111 **Admissions:** 2103 **Census:** 95 **Outpatient Visits:** 107320 **Births:** 534

MELROSE—Stearns County

★ CENTRACARE HEALTH–MELROSE (241330), 525 Main Street West, Zip 56352–1043; tel. 320/256–4231, (Nonreporting) **A**10 18 **S** CentraCare Health, Saint Cloud, MN
Primary Contact: Gerry Gilbertson, FACHE, Administrator
COO: Gerry Gilbertson, FACHE, Administrator
CFO: Adam Paulson, Director Finance
CMO: Dante Beretta, M.D., Chief of Staff
CIO: Janet Kruzel, Business Office Manager
CHR: Joyce Chan, Chief Human Resources Officer
CNO: Keri Wimmer, R.N., Patient Care Director
Web address: www.centracare.com
Control: Other not–for–profit (including NFP Corporation) **Service:** General Medical and Surgical

Staffed Beds: 93

MINNEAPOLIS—Hennepin County

⊞ ◇ ABBOTT NORTHWESTERN HOSPITAL (240057), 800 East 28th Street, Zip 55407–3799; tel. 612/863–4000, (Includes SISTER KENNY REHABILITATION INSTITUTE, 810 East 27th Street, Zip 55407; tel. 612/874–4000), (Total facility includes 44 beds in nursing home–type unit) **A**1 2 3 5 10 21 **F**3 8 9 12 13 15 17 18 19 20 22 24 26 28 29 30 31 34 35 36 38 39 40 41 42 43 44 45 46 47 48 49 50 51 52 53 54 55 56 57 58 59 60 61 63 64 65 66 68 70 71 74 75 76 77 78 79 81 82 83 84 85 86 87 90 91 92 93 94 95 96 97 98 99 100 101 102 103 104 105 107 108 109 110 111 112 113 114 115 116 117 118 119 120 121 123 124 126 129 130 131 132 135 136 137 138 141 143 144 145 146 147 148 **P**6 **S** Allina Health, Minneapolis, MN
Primary Contact: Ben Bache–Wiig, M.D., President
CFO: Brian Weinreis, Vice President Operations and Finance
CMO: Penny Ann Wheeler, M.D., President and Chief Medical Officer
CIO: Susan Heichert, Senior Vice President and Chief Information Officer
CHR: Margaret Butler, Vice President Human Resources
CNO: Terry J. Graner, R.N., Vice President Patient Care
Web address: www.abbottnorthwestern.com
Control: Other not–for–profit (including NFP Corporation) **Service:** General Medical and Surgical

Staffed Beds: 675 **Admissions:** 36297 **Census:** 485 **Outpatient Visits:** 433505 **Births:** 5415 **Total Expense ($000):** 1056583 **Payroll Expense ($000):** 449193 **Personnel:** 3925

⊞ CHILDREN'S HOSPITALS AND CLINICS OF MINNESOTA (243302), 2525 Chicago Avenue South, Zip 55404–4518; tel. 612/813–6100, (Includes CHILDREN'S HOSPITALS AND CLINICS OF MINNESOTA, 345 North Smith Avenue, Saint Paul, Zip 55102–2346; tel. 651/220–6000; Robert Bonar, Jr., Chief Executive Officer) **A**1 3 5 10 **F**3 9 17 18 19 20 21 22 23 24 25 26 27 28 29 30 31 32 34 35 36 38 39 40 43 45 50 51 54 55 57 58 59 61 62 63 64 65 68 71 72 73 74 75 77 78 79 80 81 82 84 85 86 87 88 89 92 93 97 99 100 101 102 104 107 108 111 112 114 115 119 129 130 131 132 134 135 136 143 145 146 148
Primary Contact: Robert Bonar, Jr., Chief Executive Officer
COO: David S. Overman, President and Chief Operating Officer
CFO: Todd Ostendorf, Chief Financial Officer
CMO: Phillip M. Kibort, M.D., Vice President Medical Affairs and Chief Medical Officer
CIO: Jeffrey D. Young, Chief Information Officer
CHR: Samantha Hanson, Chief Human Resources Officer
CNO: Roxanne Fernandes, R.N., Chief Nursing Officer
Web address: www.childrensmn.org
Control: Other not–for–profit (including NFP Corporation) **Service:** Children's general

Staffed Beds: 428 **Admissions:** 14688 **Census:** 276 **Outpatient Visits:** 334570 **Births:** 0 **Total Expense ($000):** 721986 **Payroll Expense ($000):** 342602 **Personnel:** 3808

FAIRVIEW RIVERSIDE HOSPITAL See University of Minnesota Medical Center, Fairview

□ △ HENNEPIN COUNTY MEDICAL CENTER (240004), 701 Park Avenue South, Zip 55415–1829; tel. 612/873–3000, (Includes HCMC DEPARTMENT OF PEDIATRICS, 701 Park Avenue, Zip 55415–1623; tel. 612/873–2064) **A**1 2 3 5 7 8 10 **F**3 5 7 12 13 15 16 18 20 22 24 26 28 29 30 31 32 33 34 35 36 38 39 40 41 43 44 45 46 47 48 49 50 51 53 54 55 56 57 58 59 60 61 64 65 66 68 70 72 74 75 76 77 78 79 81 82 84 85 86 87 88 89 90 92 93 94 96 97 98 99 100 101 102 103 104 105 107 108 110 111 112 114 115 117 118 119 120 121 129 130 131 132 134 135 138 141 144 145 146 147 148 **P**6
Primary Contact: Jon Pryor, M.D., Chief Executive Officer
CFO: Larry Kryzaniak, Chief Financial Officer
CMO: William Heegaard, M.D., Chief Medical Officer
CIO: Nancy Garrett, Chief Analytics and Information Technology Officer
CHR: Walter Chesley, Senior Vice President Human Resources
CNO: Kathy R. Wilde, R.N., Chief Nursing Officer
Web address: www.hcmc.org
Control: County–Government, nonfederal **Service:** General Medical and Surgical

Staffed Beds: 460 **Admissions:** 22437 **Census:** 347 **Outpatient Visits:** 692077 **Births:** 2115 **Total Expense ($000):** 878263 **Payroll Expense ($000):** 484874 **Personnel:** 5720

⊞ △ MINNEAPOLIS VETERANS AFFAIRS HEALTH CARE SYSTEM, One Veterans Drive, Zip 55417–2399; tel. 612/725–2000 **A**1 2 3 5 7 8 **F**1 2 3 5 8 9 12 15 18 20 22 24 26 28 29 30 31 33 35 36 38 39 40 46 47 49 52 53 56 57 58 59 60 61 62 63 64 65 70 74 75 77 78 79 80 81 82 83 84 85 86 87 90 91 92 93 94 95 96 97 100 101 102 103 104 105 107 108 109 110 111 112 113 114 115 116 117 118 119 120 121 122 123 124 126 127 130 131 132 135 143 144 146 147 148 **S** Department of Veterans Affairs, Washington, DC
Primary Contact: Patrick J. Kelly, FACHE, Director
COO: Kurt Thielen, Associate Director
CFO: LeAnn Stomberg, Chief Financial Officer
CMO: Kent Crossley, M.D., Chief of Staff
CIO: Brian Bornick, Chief Information Officer
CHR: Tom Johnson, Chief Human Resource Officer
CNO: Helen Pearlman, Nurse Executive
Web address: www.minneapolis.va.gov
Control: Veterans Affairs, Government, federal **Service:** General Medical and Surgical

Staffed Beds: 305 **Admissions:** 8689 **Census:** 200 **Outpatient Visits:** 903280 **Births:** 0 **Personnel:** 3586

⊞ PHILLIPS EYE INSTITUTE (240196), 2215 Park Avenue, Zip 55404–3756; tel. 612/775–8800 **A**1 10 **F**81 **S** Allina Health, Minneapolis, MN
Primary Contact: Daniel S. Conrad, M.D., President
CFO: Chris Verdon, Director Finance
CMO: Emmett Carpel, M.D., Medical Director and Chief of Staff
CNO: Margaret Watry, Director of Patient Care Services and Nurse Executive
Web address: www.allinahealth.org/ahs/pei.nsf/
Control: Other not–for–profit (including NFP Corporation) **Service:** Eye, ear, nose, and throat

Staffed Beds: 8 **Admissions:** 17 **Census:** 1 **Outpatient Visits:** 15021 **Births:** 0 **Total Expense ($000):** 32187 **Payroll Expense ($000):** 10265 **Personnel:** 126

Many Facility Codes have changed. Please refer to the AHA Guide Code Chart. © 2016 AHA Guide

☐ **SHRINERS HOSPITALS FOR CHILDREN–TWIN CITIES (243303)**, 2025 East River Parkway, Zip 55414–3696; tel. 612/596–6100, (Nonreporting) **A**1 3 5 10 **S** Shriners Hospitals for Children, Tampa, FL
Primary Contact: Charles C. Lobeck, Administrator
CMO: Kenneth Guidera, M.D., Chief of Staff
CHR: Karen Frigen, Director Human Resources
Web address: www.shrinershospitalsforchildren.org/Hospitals/Locations/twincities.aspx
Control: Other not–for–profit (including NFP Corporation) **Service:** Children's orthopedic

Staffed Beds: 40

SISTER KENNY REHABILITATION INSTITUTE See Abbott Northwestern Hospital

ST. MARY'S HOSPITAL AND REHABILITATION CENTER See University of Minnesota Medical Center, Fairview

UNIVERSITY OF MINNESOTA HOSPITAL AND CLINIC See University of Minnesota Medical Center, Fairview

⊠ **UNIVERSITY OF MINNESOTA MEDICAL CENTER, FAIRVIEW (240080)**, 2450 Riverside Avenue, Zip 55454–1400; tel. 612/672–6000, (Includes FAIRVIEW RIVERSIDE HOSPITAL, 2312 South Sixth Street, Zip 55454; tel. 612/371–6300; ST. MARY'S HOSPITAL AND REHABILITATION CENTER, 2414 South Seventh Street, Zip 55454; tel. 612/338–2229; UNIVERSITY OF MINNESOTA HOSPITAL AND CLINIC, 420 S.E. Delaware Street, Zip 55455–0392; tel. 612/626–3000; UNIVERSITY OF MINNESOTA MASONIC CHILDREN'S HOSPITAL, 420 Delaware Street, S.E., Zip 55455–0341; tel. 888/543–7866), (Total facility includes 36 beds in nursing home–type unit) **A**1 3 5 8 10 **F**2 3 4 5 9 11 12 13 15 17 18 19 20 21 22 23 24 25 26 27 28 29 30 31 32 33 34 35 36 37 38 39 40 41 43 44 45 46 47 48 49 50 51 54 55 56 57 58 59 60 61 64 65 68 70 71 72 74 75 76 77 78 79 80 81 82 84 85 86 87 88 89 90 91 92 93 96 97 98 99 100 101 102 103 104 105 106 107 108 109 110 111 112 113 114 115 116 117 118 119 120 121 123 124 126 128 129 130 131 132 134 135 136 137 138 139 140 141 142 145 146 147 148 **P**5 **S** Fairview Health Services, Minneapolis, MN
Primary Contact: David Murphy, Interim Chief Executive Officer
CFO: John Doherty, Vice President Finance
CMO: Barbara Gold, M.D., Chief Medical Officer
CHR: Don Moschkau, Senior Director Human Resources
Web address: www.fairview.org
Control: Other not–for–profit (including NFP Corporation) **Service:** General Medical and Surgical

Staffed Beds: 863 **Admissions:** 32823 **Census:** 605 **Outpatient Visits:** 797040 **Births:** 2271 **Total Expense ($000):** 1384092 **Payroll Expense ($000):** 471559 **Personnel:** 7315

VETERANS AFFAIRS MEDICAL CENTER See Minneapolis Veterans Affairs Health Care System

MONTEVIDEO—Chippewa County

★ **CHIPPEWA COUNTY–MONTEVIDEO HOSPITAL (241325)**, 824 North 11th Street, Zip 56265–1683; tel. 320/269–8877, (Nonreporting) **A**10 18
Primary Contact: Mark E. Paulson, Chief Executive Officer
CFO: Darlene Boike, Chief Financial Officer
CIO: Jeff Plemel, Director Health Information
CHR: Vonnie Erickson, Human Resource Manager
CNO: Terry Anderson, R.N., Director of Nursing Services
Web address: www.montevideomedical.com
Control: City–County, Government, nonfederal **Service:** General Medical and Surgical

Staffed Beds: 25

MONTICELLO—Wright County

⊠ **CENTRACARE HEALTH–MONTICELLO (241362)**, 1013 Hart Boulevard, Zip 55362–8230; tel. 763/295–2945, (Total facility includes 89 beds in nursing home–type unit) **A**1 3 5 10 18 **F**3 7 11 13 15 30 31 34 35 40 45 50 57 59 66 68 69 70 76 78 79 81 85 89 90 96 97 107 110 111 114 117 119 120 121 123 128 129 130 132 133 146 148 **S** CentraCare Health, Saint Cloud, MN
Primary Contact: Mary Ellen Wells, FACHE, Administrator
CFO: Nancy Friesen, Chief Financial Officer
CMO: Mark Dietz, Chief Medical Officer
CIO: Ruth Kremer, Director Information Services
CHR: Kathy Voss, Director Human Resources
CNO: Euretta Sorenson, R.N., Chief Nursing Officer
Web address: www.newrivermedical.com
Control: Other not–for–profit (including NFP Corporation) **Service:** General Medical and Surgical

Staffed Beds: 126 **Admissions:** 935 **Census:** 93 **Outpatient Visits:** 14547 **Births:** 290 **Total Expense ($000):** 63189 **Payroll Expense ($000):** 28098 **Personnel:** 356

MOOSE LAKE—Carlton County

★ **MERCY HOSPITAL (241350)**, 4572 County Road 61, Zip 55767–9405; tel. 218/485–4481 **A**10 18 **F**3 7 8 11 13 15 28 29 31 34 35 40 41 43 45 46 53 57 59 62 64 68 70 75 76 77 79 81 85 86 87 93 107 111 114 119 130 131 132 133 135 143 144 146 148 **P**5
Primary Contact: Michael Delfs, Chief Executive Officer
CHR: Sonya Towle, Director Human Resources
CNO: Donita Korpela, R.N., Director of Patient Care Services
Web address: www.mercymooselake.org
Control: Hospital district or authority, Government, nonfederal **Service:** General Medical and Surgical

Staffed Beds: 25 **Admissions:** 744 **Census:** 7 **Outpatient Visits:** 27589 **Births:** 130 **Total Expense ($000):** 32403 **Payroll Expense ($000):** 13519 **Personnel:** 164

MORA—Kanabec County

⊠ **FIRSTLIGHT HEALTH SYSTEM (241367)**, 301 South Highway 65 South, Zip 55051–1899; tel. 320/679–1212 **A**1 10 18 **F**3 7 11 12 13 15 28 30 31 34 35 40 43 51 53 57 59 70 75 76 77 78 79 81 84 85 87 93 94 107 110 111 115 118 119 127 130 131 132 133 135 146 148
Primary Contact: Randy Ulseth, Chief Executive Officer
COO: Sandy Zutz–Wiczek, Chief Operating Officer
CFO: Gordy Forbort, Chief Financial Officer
CIO: Becky Gallik, Information Systems Manager
CHR: Kim Carlson, Senior Vice President Human Resources
CNO: Diane Bankers, Senior Vice President, Nursing Services
Web address: www.firstlighthealthsystem.org
Control: County–Government, nonfederal **Service:** General Medical and Surgical

Staffed Beds: 25 **Admissions:** 1178 **Census:** 7 **Outpatient Visits:** 32244 **Births:** 135 **Total Expense ($000):** 61643 **Payroll Expense ($000):** 20870 **Personnel:** 361

MORRIS—Stevens County

★ **STEVENS COMMUNITY MEDICAL CENTER (241363)**, 400 East First Street, Zip 56267–1408, Mailing Address: P.O. Box 660, Zip 56267–0660; tel. 320/589–1313 **A**10 18 **F**3 11 13 15 28 29 31 34 35 40 44 45 50 57 59 64 70 76 77 79 81 85 86 87 89 97 107 110 111 115 119 130 131 132 133 135 145 146 148 **P**6
Primary Contact: Jason Breuer, Chief Executive Officer
CFO: Kerrie Erickson, Vice President of Finance
CIO: Kerrie Erickson, Vice President of Finance
CHR: Karla Larson, Director Human Resources
Web address: www.scmcinc.org
Control: Other not–for–profit (including NFP Corporation) **Service:** General Medical and Surgical

Staffed Beds: 25 **Admissions:** 844 **Census:** 8 **Outpatient Visits:** 69762 **Births:** 85 **Total Expense ($000):** 34231 **Payroll Expense ($000):** 16716 **Personnel:** 236

NEW PRAGUE—Scott County

☐ **MAYO CLINIC HEALTH SYSTEM IN NEW PRAGUE (241361)**, 301 Second Street N.E., Zip 56071–1799; tel. 952/758–4431 **A**1 10 18 **F**11 13 15 28 29 30 31 34 35 36 40 43 45 46 53 57 59 64 68 74 75 76 77 78 79 81 82 85 87 93 97 107 108 110 111 114 116 117 119 125 128 129 130 131 132 133 146 147 **P**6 **S** Mayo Clinic, Rochester, MN
Primary Contact: Mary J. Klimp, FACHE, Administrator
Web address: www.mayoclinichealthsystem.org/locations/new-prague
Control: Other not–for–profit (including NFP Corporation) **Service:** General Medical and Surgical

Staffed Beds: 25 **Admissions:** 808 **Census:** 10 **Outpatient Visits:** 60106 **Births:** 139 **Personnel:** 193

NEW ULM—Brown County

⊠ **NEW ULM MEDICAL CENTER (241378)**, 1324 Fifth Street North, Zip 56073–1553; tel. 507/217–5000 **A**1 10 18 **F**3 4 5 11 13 15 28 29 31 32 34 35 36 40 43 45 55 56 57 59 64 65 68 70 75 76 77 78 79 81 82 85 87 93 94 97 98 99 100 101 102 103 104 107 108 111 114 119 129 130 131 132 135 144 146 148 **S** Allina Health, Minneapolis, MN
Primary Contact: Toby Freier, President
CFO: Steve Schneider, Manager Behavioral Services and Director Operations
CMO: Daniel Holmberg, M.D., Director of Medical Affairs
CHR: Anne Makepeace, Director Human Resources
CNO: Jennifer Brehmer, Director of Patient Care
Web address: www.newulmmedicalcenter.com
Control: Other not–for–profit (including NFP Corporation) **Service:** General Medical and Surgical

Staffed Beds: 45 **Admissions:** 2265 **Census:** 20 **Outpatient Visits:** 124163 **Births:** 528 **Total Expense ($000):** 78745 **Payroll Expense ($000):** 27140 **Personnel:** 402

MN

NORTHFIELD—Dakota County

★ **NORTHFIELD HOSPITAL (240014)**, 2000 North Avenue, Zip 55057–1498; tel. 507/646–1000, (Includes LONG TERM CARE CENTER), (Total facility includes 40 beds in nursing home–type unit) **A**10 **F**3 7 11 13 15 30 31 40 43 59 62 63 64 68 69 70 75 76 77 78 79 81 85 87 89 93 107 110 111 115 119 128 129 130 131 132 133 144 146 **P**6
Primary Contact: Steve Underdahl, Chief Executive Officer
COO: Jerry Ehn, Chief Operating Officer
CFO: Scott D. Edin, Vice President, Finance and Chief Financial Officer
CMO: Jeff Meland, M.D., Vice President, Chief Medical Officer
CHR: Vicki Stevens, Human Resources Executive
CNO: Tammy A. Hayes, R.N., Chief Nurse Executive and Long Term Care Administrator
Web address: www.northfieldhospital.org
Control: City–Government, nonfederal **Service:** General Medical and Surgical

Staffed Beds: 77 **Admissions:** 1840 **Census:** 51 **Outpatient Visits:** 133659 **Births:** 513 **Total Expense ($000):** 88410 **Payroll Expense ($000):** 40117 **Personnel:** 532

OLIVIA—Renville County

★ **RC HOSPITAL AND CLINICS (241306)**, 611 East Fairview Avenue, Zip 56277–4213; tel. 320/523–1261 **A**10 18 **F**3 8 15 17 28 29 34 35 40 41 43 45 46 57 59 63 64 65 68 70 75 76 77 79 81 82 85 86 89 93 94 96 97 107 111 114 119 127 129 130 131 132 133 146 148
Primary Contact: Nathan Blad, Chief Executive Officer
CFO: Nathan Blad, Chief Financial Officer
CIO: Cherry Weigel, Director Health Information Management
Web address: www.rchospital.com
Control: County–Government, nonfederal **Service:** General Medical and Surgical

Staffed Beds: 16 **Admissions:** 352 **Census:** 4 **Outpatient Visits:** 40185 **Births:** 41 **Total Expense ($000):** 21815 **Payroll Expense ($000):** 9938 **Personnel:** 138

ONAMIA—Mille Lacs County

★ **MILLE LACS HEALTH SYSTEM (241356)**, 200 North Elm Street, Zip 56359–7901; tel. 320/532–3154, (Total facility includes 57 beds in nursing home–type unit) **A**10 18 **F**7 11 15 28 29 31 33 34 40 43 45 50 59 62 63 64 75 77 81 85 93 98 103 107 110 114 115 127 129 130 132 133 135 144 **P**6
Primary Contact: Bill Nelson, Chief Executive Officer
COO: Kim Kucera, Chief Operating Officer
CFO: John Unzen, Chief Financial Officer
CMO: Thomas H. Bracken, M.D., Vice President Medical Affairs
Web address: www.mlhealth.org
Control: Other not–for–profit (including NFP Corporation) **Service:** General Medical and Surgical

Staffed Beds: 85 **Admissions:** 851 **Census:** 66 **Outpatient Visits:** 24165 **Births:** 2 **Total Expense ($000):** 37632 **Payroll Expense ($000):** 18584 **Personnel:** 325

ORTONVILLE—Big Stone County

★ **ORTONVILLE AREA HEALTH SERVICES (241342)**, 450 Eastvold Avenue, Zip 56278–1133; tel. 320/839–2502, (Total facility includes 53 beds in nursing home–type unit) **A**5 10 18 **F**2 3 6 7 8 10 11 13 15 18 19 20 21 28 29 30 31 32 34 35 40 44 45 46 47 50 56 59 60 62 63 64 65 68 69 74 75 76 77 78 79 81 85 86 89 93 94 96 100 101 107 110 111 112 114 115 116 117 118 119 125 127 128 129 130 131 132 133 135 143 147 148 **S** Sanford Health, Sioux Falls, SD
Primary Contact: David Rogers, Chief Executive Officer
CFO: Kevin Benson, Chief Financial Officer
CMO: Stacy Longnecker, Chief of Staff
CIO: Barbara Voecks, Chief Information Officer
CHR: Kim McCrea, Chief Human Resources Officer
CNO: Jennifer Wiik, Chief Nursing Officer
Web address: www.oahs.us
Control: City–Government, nonfederal **Service:** General Medical and Surgical

Staffed Beds: 115 **Admissions:** 493 **Census:** 55 **Outpatient Visits:** 23423 **Births:** 65 **Total Expense ($000):** 28443 **Payroll Expense ($000):** 11356 **Personnel:** 243

OWATONNA—Steele County

✠ **OWATONNA HOSPITAL (240069)**, 2250 N.W. 26th Street, Zip 55060–5503; tel. 507/451–3850 **A**1 10 **F**11 13 28 29 34 35 40 57 76 77 79 80 81 89 93 98 100 101 102 103 107 108 119 129 130 131 145 **S** Allina Health, Minneapolis, MN
Primary Contact: David L. Albrecht, President
COO: Mark T. Gillen, Director of Operations
CFO: Mark T. Gillen, Director Finance and Operations
CHR: Sarah Stumme, Director Human Resources
CNO: Anne Draeger, Chief Nursing Officer
Web address: www.owatonnahospital.com
Control: Other not–for–profit (including NFP Corporation) **Service:** General Medical and Surgical

Staffed Beds: 43 **Admissions:** 2467 **Census:** 25 **Outpatient Visits:** 38248 **Births:** 514 **Total Expense ($000):** 46474 **Payroll Expense ($000):** 17338 **Personnel:** 218

PARK RAPIDS—Hubbard County

✠ **CHI ST. JOSEPH'S HEALTH (241380)**, 600 Pleasant Avenue, Zip 56470–1431; tel. 218/732–3311 **A**1 5 10 18 **F**3 11 12 13 15 28 29 30 32 34 35 39 40 43 45 47 50 57 59 63 64 65 70 75 76 77 79 81 82 84 85 93 107 108 110 115 118 129 130 131 132 133 134 146 **S** Catholic Health Initiatives, Englewood, CO
Primary Contact: Benjamin Koppelman, President
CFO: Jay Ross, Chief Financial Officer
CMO: Darryl Beehler, D.O., Chief of Staff
CHR: John Tormanen, Director Mission and Human Resources
CNO: Deb Haagenson, R.N., Vice President of Patient Care
Web address: www.sjahs.org
Control: Church–operated, Nongovernment, not–for profit **Service:** General Medical and Surgical

Staffed Beds: 25 **Admissions:** 1344 **Census:** 13 **Outpatient Visits:** 46429 **Births:** 109 **Total Expense ($000):** 45379 **Payroll Expense ($000):** 16923 **Personnel:** 230

PAYNESVILLE—Stearns County

★ **CENTRACARE HEALTH–PAYNESVILLE (241349)**, 200 West 1st Street, Zip 56362–1496; tel. 320/243–3767, (Total facility includes 52 beds in nursing home–type unit) **A**10 18 **F**7 10 11 13 15 28 31 34 40 43 45 56 57 64 70 76 81 85 93 107 110 111 115 119 125 127 128 130 133 145 146 148 **S** CentraCare Health, Saint Cloud, MN
Primary Contact: Dennis C. Miley, Administrator
CFO: Gregg Redfield, Director Finance
CMO: Timothy Malling, M.D., Chief of Staff
CHR: Paulette Hagen, Human Resources and Administrative Services Director
CNO: Rachel A. Walz, Director Patient Care
Web address: www.centracare.com
Control: Other not–for–profit (including NFP Corporation) **Service:** General Medical and Surgical

Staffed Beds: 82 **Admissions:** 575 **Census:** 57 **Outpatient Visits:** 32186 **Births:** 99 **Total Expense ($000):** 36962 **Payroll Expense ($000):** 17276 **Personnel:** 194

PERHAM—Otter Tail County

✠ **PERHAM HEALTH (241373)**, 1000 Coney Street West, Zip 56573–1108; tel. 218/347–4500, (Total facility includes 96 beds in nursing home–type unit) **A**1 10 18 **F**2 3 7 10 11 13 15 28 29 30 33 34 35 36 40 43 45 56 57 59 62 64 69 75 76 77 79 81 85 86 89 92 93 97 104 107 110 111 115 119 125 128 129 130 131 132 133 144 146 147 148 **S** Sanford Health, Sioux Falls, SD
Primary Contact: Chuck Hofius, Chief Executive Officer
CFO: Brad D. Wurgler, Chief Financial Officer
CMO: Tim Studer, President Medical Staff
CIO: Jim Rieber, Director Information Systems
CNO: Bonnie Johnson, R.N., Vice President of Patient Services
Web address: www.perhamhealth.org
Control: Hospital district or authority, Government, nonfederal **Service:** General Medical and Surgical

Staffed Beds: 121 **Admissions:** 1009 **Census:** 99 **Outpatient Visits:** 306086 **Births:** 153 **Total Expense ($000):** 46042 **Payroll Expense ($000):** 19728 **Personnel:** 240

PIPESTONE—Pipestone County

★ **PIPESTONE COUNTY MEDICAL CENTER AVERA (241374)**, 916 4th Avenue S.W., Zip 56164–1890; tel. 507/825–5811 **A**10 18 **F**8 13 15 28 29 31 34 35 40 45 46 47 48 50 53 56 57 59 62 63 64 65 68 75 77 79 81 82 85 93 97 107 110 111 115 119 130 131 132 133 135 146 148 **P**6 **S** Avera Health, Sioux Falls, SD
Primary Contact: Bradley D. Burris, Chief Executive Officer
CFO: Dave Keeler, Chief Financial Officer
CHR: Judy Raschke, Director Human Resources
CNO: Jessica Smidt, R.N., Director of Nursing
Web address: www.pcmchealth.org
Control: County–Government, nonfederal **Service:** General Medical and Surgical

Staffed Beds: 25 **Admissions:** 442 **Census:** 4 **Outpatient Visits:** 32593 **Births:** 77 **Total Expense ($000):** 27049 **Payroll Expense ($000):** 8801 **Personnel:** 189

MN

Many Facility Codes have changed. Please refer to the AHA Guide Code Chart.
© 2016 AHA Guide

PRINCETON—Sherburne County

✠ **FAIRVIEW NORTHLAND MEDICAL CENTER (240141)**, 911 Northland Drive, Zip 55371–2173; tel. 763/389–1313 **A**1 5 10 **F**3 11 13 15 18 28 29 30 31 32 34 35 36 40 43 45 46 50 57 59 64 70 75 76 77 78 79 81 82 85 86 87 89 91 93 94 100 107 110 111 114 115 119 130 131 132 146 147 148 **P**6 **S** Fairview Health Services, Minneapolis, MN
Primary Contact: John W. Herman, President
CFO: Kim Ericson, Vice President Finance
CMO: Greg Schoen, M.D., Regional Medical Director
CHR: Erich Spencer, Chief Human Resource Officer
CNO: Karen Whiley, R.N., Vice President Patient Care Services
Web address: www.northland.fairview.org
Control: Other not–for–profit (including NFP Corporation) **Service:** General Medical and Surgical

Staffed Beds: 37 **Admissions:** 1652 **Census:** 13 **Outpatient Visits:** 48945 **Births:** 420 **Total Expense ($000):** 52062 **Payroll Expense ($000):** 25342 **Personnel:** 246

RED LAKE—Beltrami County

☐ **RED LAKE INDIAN HEALTH SERVICE HOSPITAL (240206)**, 24760 Hospital Drive, Zip 56671, Mailing Address: P.O. Box 497, Zip 56671–0497; tel. 218/679–3912, (Nonreporting) **A**1 10 **S** U. S. Indian Health Service, Rockville, MD
Primary Contact: Norine Smith, Chief Executive Officer
CMO: Paul Ditmanson, M.D., Clinical Director
CNO: Mary Ann Cook, R.N., Director of Nursing
Web address: www.rlnnredlakehospital.com/
Control: PHS, Indian Service, Government, federal **Service:** General Medical and Surgical

Staffed Beds: 19

RED WING—Goodhue County

✠ **MAYO CLINIC HEALTH SYSTEM IN RED WING (240018)**, 701 Hewitt Boulevard, Zip 55066–2848, Mailing Address: P.O. Box 95, Zip 55066–0095; tel. 651/267–5000 **A**1 10 **F**3 11 13 15 18 28 29 30 31 34 35 36 40 43 45 57 59 62 63 64 70 74 75 76 77 78 79 81 87 93 94 96 97 99 100 104 107 111 115 119 129 130 131 132 146 147 **P**6 **S** Mayo Clinic, Rochester, MN
Primary Contact: Thomas J. Witt, M.D., President and Chief Executive Officer
CMO: Jack Alexander, M.D., Chief Medical Officer
CHR: Kim Trittin, Manager Human Resources
Web address: www.mayoclinichealthsystem.org/locations/red–wing
Control: Other not–for–profit (including NFP Corporation) **Service:** General Medical and Surgical

Staffed Beds: 22 **Admissions:** 1876 **Census:** 15 **Outpatient Visits:** 111595 **Births:** 304 **Personnel:** 613

REDWOOD FALLS—Redwood County

★ **REDWOOD AREA HOSPITAL (241351)**, 100 Fallwood Road, Zip 56283–1828; tel. 507/637–4500 **A**10 18 **F**2 3 11 13 15 29 31 34 35 40 45 46 57 59 62 63 75 77 79 81 84 93 107 111 115 119 129 130 131 133 146 148
Primary Contact: Bryan Lydick, Chief Executive Officer
CFO: Thomas Richard, Director Budget and Revenue Cycle
CIO: Tom Balko, Manager Information Systems
CHR: Jody Rindfleisch, Manager Human Resources
CNO: Dawn Allen, R.N., Chief Clinical Officer
Web address: www.redwoodareahospital.org
Control: City–Government, nonfederal **Service:** General Medical and Surgical

Staffed Beds: 25 **Admissions:** 585 **Census:** 5 **Outpatient Visits:** 20444 **Births:** 88 **Total Expense ($000):** 23237 **Payroll Expense ($000):** 8576 **Personnel:** 130

ROBBINSDALE—Hennepin County

★ △ ◇ **NORTH MEMORIAL MEDICAL CENTER (240001)**, 3300 Oakdale Avenue North, Zip 55422–2926; tel. 763/520–5200 **A**2 3 5 7 10 21 **F**3 7 11 12 13 15 17 18 20 22 24 26 28 29 30 31 32 34 35 38 40 43 44 45 46 49 50 53 54 55 56 57 58 59 60 62 63 64 68 70 72 73 74 75 76 77 78 79 81 82 84 85 86 87 89 90 91 92 93 96 97 98 100 102 103 104 105 107 108 110 111 114 115 117 118 119 124 126 129 130 132 133 135 143 144 146 147 148 **P**8 **S** North Memorial Health Care, Robbinsdale, MN
Primary Contact: Jeff Wicklander, President
COO: Laura Latt, Vice President of Operations
CFO: Aaron Bloomquist, Chief Financial Officer
CIO: Patrick Taffe, Vice President Information Services
CHR: David Abrams, Vice President Human Resources
CNO: Kelly Lynn White, Vice President of Patient Care and Chief Nursing Officer
Web address: www.northmemorial.com
Control: Other not–for–profit (including NFP Corporation) **Service:** General Medical and Surgical

Staffed Beds: 355 **Admissions:** 18030 **Census:** 218 **Outpatient Visits:** 65557 **Births:** 985 **Total Expense ($000):** 713167 **Payroll Expense ($000):** 348660 **Personnel:** 2075

ROCHESTER—Olmsted County

☐ **COMMUNITY BEHAVIORAL HEALTH HOSPITAL – ROCHESTER (244017)**, 251 Wood Lake Drive S.E., Zip 55904–5530; tel. 507/206–2561 **A**1 10 **F**98 103 106 **P**5 **S** Minnesota Department of Human Services, Saint Paul, MN
Primary Contact: Stephanie Juhl, Administrator
CFO: Shirley Jacobson, Chief Financial Officer
CMO: Peter S. Millen, Chief Medical Officer MHSATS
CIO: Thomas Baden, Jr., Chief Information Officer
CHR: Connie Jones, Director Human Resources
CNO: Pamela R. Bajari, R.N., Nurse Executive MHSATS
Web address: www.health.state.mn.us
Control: State–Government, nonfederal **Service:** Psychiatric

Staffed Beds: 8 **Admissions:** 67 **Census:** 1 **Outpatient Visits:** 0 **Births:** 0

✠ △ **MAYO CLINIC HOSPITAL – ROCHESTER (240010)**, 1216 Second Street S.W., Zip 55902–1906; tel. 507/255–5123, (Includes MAYO CLINIC HOSPITAL – METHODIST CAMPUS, 201 West Center Street, Zip 55902–3084; tel. 507/266–7890; MAYO CLINIC HOSPITAL – SAINT MARYS CAMPUS, 1216 Second Street S.W., Zip 55902–1970; tel. 507/255–5123) **A**1 2 3 5 7 8 10 20 **F**3 5 6 8 9 11 12 13 14 15 17 18 19 20 21 22 23 24 25 26 27 28 29 30 31 34 35 36 37 38 39 40 41 43 44 45 46 47 48 49 50 51 52 53 54 55 56 57 58 59 60 61 64 65 66 68 70 72 73 74 75 76 77 78 79 80 81 82 84 85 86 87 88 89 90 91 92 93 94 95 96 97 98 99 100 101 102 103 104 105 106 107 108 110 111 112 114 115 116 117 118 119 122 124 126 130 132 134 135 136 137 138 139 140 141 142 143 144 145 146 147 148 **P**6 **S** Mayo Clinic, Rochester, MN
Primary Contact: F. Kenneth Ackerman, Chair, Hospital Operations
COO: Jeffrey W. Bolton, Chief Administrative Officer
CFO: Kedrick D. Adkins, Chief Financial Officer
CMO: Amy W. Williams, M.D., Chief Medical Officer
CIO: Christopher Ross, Chief Information Technology Officer
CHR: Cathryn Fraser, Chief Human Resources Officer
CNO: Pamela O. Johnson, MS, Chief Nursing Officer
Web address: www.mayoclinic.org
Control: Other not–for–profit (including NFP Corporation) **Service:** General Medical and Surgical

Staffed Beds: 1263 **Admissions:** 54713 **Census:** 863 **Outpatient Visits:** 280568 **Births:** 2449 **Personnel:** 30238

★ ◇ **OLMSTED MEDICAL CENTER (240006)**, 1650 Fourth Street S.E., Zip 55904–4717, Mailing Address: 210 Ninth Street S.E., Zip 55904–6756; tel. 507/288–3443 **A**10 21 **F**3 11 12 13 15 18 26 28 29 30 34 40 44 45 46 50 51 53 64 65 68 74 75 76 77 79 80 81 82 84 85 86 87 92 93 97 100 102 104 107 108 110 111 115 129 130 131 132 135 146 147 148 **P**6
Primary Contact: Tim W. Weir, Chief Executive Officer
CFO: Kevin A. Higgins, Chief Financial Officer
CIO: Susan M. Schuett, Chief Information Officer
CHR: Tom Hunsberger, Director Human Resources
CNO: Susan Klenner, Chief Nursing Officer and Vice President of Hospital Operations
Web address: www.olmmed.org
Control: Other not–for–profit (including NFP Corporation) **Service:** General Medical and Surgical

Staffed Beds: 42 **Admissions:** 1919 **Census:** 13 **Outpatient Visits:** 361445 **Births:** 927 **Total Expense ($000):** 172155 **Payroll Expense ($000):** 87479 **Personnel:** 920

MN

ROSEAU—Roseau County

⊠ **LIFECARE MEDICAL CENTER (241344)**, 715 Delmore Drive,
Zip 56751–1599; tel. 218/463–2500, (Total facility includes 90 beds in nursing
home–type unit) **A**1 5 10 18 **F**3 7 10 11 13 15 28 29 30 31 32 34 35 36 40
43 45 53 56 57 59 62 63 64 65 68 75 76 77 81 82 84 85 86 93 104 107
110 111 115 118 119 128 129 130 132 133 135 144 146 147 148 **P**6
Primary Contact: Keith Okeson, President and Chief Executive Officer
COO: Susan C. Lisell, Vice President of Clinical Services
CFO: Cathy Huss, Chief Financial Officer
CIO: Kevin Schumacher, Director of Information Systems
CHR: Kristy S. McFarlane, Director Human Resources
CNO: Roxanne Fabian, Director of Nursing–Acute Care
Web address: www.lifecaremedicalcenter.org
Control: Other not–for–profit (including NFP Corporation) **Service:** General
Medical and Surgical

Staffed Beds: 115 **Admissions:** 736 **Census:** 93 **Outpatient Visits:** 40636 **Births:** 163 **Total Expense ($000):** 38453 **Payroll Expense ($000):** 17052 **Personnel:** 278	

SAINT CLOUD—Stearns County

⊠ △ **ST. CLOUD HOSPITAL (240036)**, 1406 Sixth Avenue North,
Zip 56303–1901; tel. 320/251–2700 **A**1 2 3 5 7 10 20 **F**3 5 11 12 13 14 15
17 18 19 20 22 24 26 27 28 29 30 31 32 34 35 36 37 38 39 40 43 44 45
46 47 48 49 50 51 54 56 57 58 59 60 61 62 63 64 66 68 69 70 72 74 75
76 77 78 79 80 81 82 84 85 86 87 88 89 90 92 93 94 96 97 98 99 100
101 102 103 104 105 106 107 108 110 111 115 117 118 119 120 121 123
126 129 130 131 132 134 135 141 144 145 146 147 148 **P**6 **S** CentraCare
Health, Saint Cloud, MN
Primary Contact: Craig J. Broman, FACHE, President
COO: Linda A. Chmielewski, R.N., Vice President Operations
CFO: Greg Klugherz, Vice President Corporate Services and Chief Financial Officer
CMO: Mark Matthias, M.D., Vice President of Medical Affairs
CIO: Amy Porwoll, Vice President of Information Systems
CHR: Duane Rasmusson, Vice President Human Resources
CNO: Linda A. Chmielewski, R.N., Vice President Operations
Web address: www.centracare.com
Control: Other not–for–profit (including NFP Corporation) **Service:** General
Medical and Surgical

Staffed Beds: 487 **Admissions:** 26069 **Census:** 314 **Outpatient Visits:** 499093 **Births:** 2689 **Total Expense ($000):** 661574 **Payroll Expense ($000):** 282748 **Personnel:** 4662	

⊠ **ST. CLOUD VETERANS AFFAIRS HEALTH CARE SYSTEM**, 4801 Veterans
Drive, Zip 56303–2099; tel. 320/252–1670, (Total facility includes 225 beds in
nursing home–type unit) **A**1 **F**2 3 4 5 6 8 9 11 12 15 18 29 30 31 34 35 36 38
39 44 45 47 50 53 54 56 57 58 59 63 64 65 68 74 75 77 78 79 81 82 83
84 85 86 87 91 92 93 94 97 98 100 101 102 103 104 105 106 107 111
115 119 128 130 132 135 143 144 146 147 148 **S** Department of Veterans
Affairs, Washington, DC
Primary Contact: Cheryl Thieschafer, Acting Director
COO: Barry I. Bahl, Director
CFO: Joseph Schmitz, Chief Financial Officer
CMO: Susan Markstrom, M.D., Chief of Staff
CIO: Denise Hanson, Information Technology Specialist
CHR: Lisa Rosendahl, Director Human Resources
CNO: Meri Hauge, R.N., Associate Director of Patient Care Services and Nurse
Executive
Web address: www.stcloud.va.gov
Control: Veterans Affairs, Government, federal **Service:** General Medical and
Surgical

Staffed Beds: 388 **Admissions:** 2745 **Census:** 342 **Outpatient Visits:** 420969 **Births:** 0 **Total Expense ($000):** 262355 **Payroll Expense ($000):** 111451 **Personnel:** 1577	

VETERANS AFFAIRS MEDICAL CENTER See St. Cloud Veterans Affairs Health
Care System

SAINT JAMES—Watonwan County

☐ **MAYO CLINIC HEALTH SYSTEM IN SAINT JAMES (241333)**, 1101 Moulton
and Parsons Drive, Zip 56081–5550; tel. 507/375–3261 **A**1 10 18 **F**3 15 18 28
34 35 40 43 53 57 59 64 75 81 86 87 97 107 110 114 119 128 129 130
132 133 144 146 148 **P**6 **S** Mayo Clinic, Rochester, MN
Primary Contact: Ryan J. Smith, Administrator
COO: Richard Grace, Chief Administrative Officer
CFO: James Tarasovich, Chief Financial Officer
CMO: Jennifer Langbehn, Medical Director
CIO: Thomas Borowski, Chief Information Officer
CHR: Gayle B. Hansen, R.N., Chief Integration Officer
Web address: www.mayoclinichealthsystem.org/locations/st–james
Control: Other not–for–profit (including NFP Corporation) **Service:** General
Medical and Surgical

Staffed Beds: 13 **Admissions:** 260 **Census:** 4 **Outpatient Visits:** 31835 **Births:** 0 **Personnel:** 63	

SAINT LOUIS PARK—Hennepin County

☐ **PARK NICOLLET METHODIST HOSPITAL (240053)**, 6500 Excelsior
Boulevard, Zip 55426–4702; Mailing Address: Minneapolis, tel. 952/993–5000,
(Nonreporting) **A**1 2 3 5 10 **S** HealthPartners, Bloomington, MN
Primary Contact: Steven Connelly, M.D., President and Chief Medical Officer
COO: Michael Kaupa, Executive Vice President and Chief Operating Officer
CFO: Sheila McMillan, Chief Financial Officer
CMO: Steven Connelly, M.D., President and Chief Medical Officer
CIO: Julie Flaschenriem, Chief Information Officer
CHR: Paul Dominski, Vice President Human Resources
CNO: Roxanna L. Gapstur, Ph.D., Chief Nursing Officer
Web address: www.parknicollet.com
Control: Other not–for–profit (including NFP Corporation) **Service:** General
Medical and Surgical

Staffed Beds: 393	

SAINT PAUL—Ramsey County

⊠ **BETHESDA HOSPITAL (242004)**, 559 Capitol Boulevard, Zip 55103–2101;
tel. 651/232–2000 **A**1 3 5 10 **F**1 3 6 11 29 30 38 44 45 50 53 56 60 61 64
68 74 75 77 79 85 86 87 91 93 100 101 104 105 107 111 114 119
130 132 146 **P**8 **S** HealthEast Care System, Saint Paul, MN
Primary Contact: Catherine Barr, Chief Operating Officer
COO: Eric Nelson, Vice President, Ambulatory Services
CFO: Douglas Davenport, Chief Financial Officer
CMO: Kevin C. Garrett, M.D., Chief Medical Officer
CIO: Joanne Sunquist, Chief Information Officer
CNO: Linda Barnhart, Vice President and Chief Nursing Officer
Web address: www.healtheast.org
Control: Other not–for–profit (including NFP Corporation) **Service:** Long–Term
Acute Care hospital

Staffed Beds: 126 **Admissions:** 1221 **Census:** 98 **Outpatient Visits:** 5660 **Births:** 0 **Total Expense ($000):** 77548 **Payroll Expense ($000):** 36235 **Personnel:** 406	

⊠ △ **GILLETTE CHILDREN'S SPECIALTY HEALTHCARE (243300)**, 200
University Avenue East, Zip 55101–2507; tel. 651/291–2848 **A**1 3 5 7 10 **F**3
28 29 30 34 35 36 39 43 50 54 63 64 68 71 74 79 81 82 84 85 86 87 88
89 90 91 92 93 94 95 96 107 111 115 119 127 129 130 146 148 **P**6
Primary Contact: Barbara Walczyk–Joers, President and Chief Executive Officer
CFO: James Haddican, Chief Financial Officer, Vice President Finance
CMO: Steven Koop, M.D., Chief Medical Officer, Medical Director
CIO: Timothy Getsay, Chief Information Officer, Vice President of Performance &
Information Mgmt
CHR: Kit Brady, Vice President Human Resources
CNO: Karen Brill, R.N., Chief Nursing Officer, Vice President Care
Web address: www.gillettechildrens.org
Control: Other not–for–profit (including NFP Corporation) **Service:** Children's
general

Staffed Beds: 60 **Admissions:** 2477 **Census:** 34 **Outpatient Visits:** 155517 **Births:** 0 **Total Expense ($000):** 223155 **Payroll Expense ($000):** 101638 **Personnel:** 1083	

☐ △ **REGIONS HOSPITAL (240106)**, 640 Jackson Street, Zip 55101–2595;
tel. 651/254–3456 **A**1 2 3 5 7 8 10 **F**3 4 5 7 8 13 15 16 17 18 20 22 24 26
28 29 30 31 34 35 36 38 40 42 43 45 46 47 48 49 50 51 53 54 55 56 57
58 59 60 64 65 68 70 71 72 74 75 76 77 78 79 81 82 84 85 86 87 88 90
92 93 96 98 100 101 102 103 104 105 106 107 108 109 110 111 112 114
115 116 117 119 120 121 122 124 126 129 130 131 132 135 143 146 147
148 **S** HealthPartners, Bloomington, MN
Primary Contact: Megan Remark, Chief Executive Officer
CFO: Heidi Conrad, Vice President and Chief Financial Officer
CMO: Charles Fazio, Chief Health Officer and Medical Director Health Plan
CIO: Kim LaReau, Vice President and Chief Information Officer
CHR: Kim Egan, Executive Director Human Resources
CNO: Chris Boese, Vice President and Chief Nursing Officer
Web address: www.regionshospital.com
Control: Other not–for–profit (including NFP Corporation) **Service:** General
Medical and Surgical

Staffed Beds: 463 **Admissions:** 25350 **Census:** 341 **Outpatient Visits:** 140201 **Births:** 2552 **Total Expense ($000):** 678441 **Payroll Expense ($000):** 325310 **Personnel:** 3647	

Many Facility Codes have changed. Please refer to the AHA Guide Code Chart.
© 2016 AHA Guide

✠ **ST. JOSEPH'S HOSPITAL (240063)**, 45 West 10th Street, Zip 55102–1053; tel. 651/232–3000 **A**1 2 3 5 10 **F**3 4 5 11 12 13 15 17 18 20 22 24 26 28 29 30 31 34 35 36 37 38 40 43 44 49 50 57 59 61 63 64 68 70 74 75 76 77 78 79 81 82 85 86 87 92 96 97 98 100 101 102 103 104 105 107 108 111 114 115 119 120 121 124 130 132 146 148 **P**8 **S** HealthEast Care System, Saint Paul, MN
Primary Contact: Catherine Barr, Chief Operating Officer
COO: Brian Gager, Vice President, Acute Care Operations
CFO: Douglas Davenport, Senior Vice President and Chief Financial Officer
CMO: Kevin C. Garrett, M.D., Chief Medical Officer
CIO: Joanne Sunquist, Information System, Senior Vice President and Chief Information Officer
CHR: Dawn Kessler, Senior Vice President Human Resources
CNO: Debra J. Hurd, R.N., Vice President Nursing
Web address: www.healtheast.org
Control: Other not–for–profit (including NFP Corporation) **Service:** General Medical and Surgical

Staffed Beds: 234 **Admissions:** 11492 **Census:** 154 **Outpatient Visits:** 54651 **Births:** 877 **Total Expense ($000):** 257141 **Payroll Expense ($000):** 95041 **Personnel:** 1125

✠ △ ◇ **UNITED HOSPITAL (240038)**, 333 North Smith Avenue, Zip 55102–2389; tel. 651/241–8000 **A**1 2 3 5 7 10 21 **F**3 8 12 13 15 17 18 20 22 24 26 28 29 30 31 34 35 36 37 40 43 46 47 49 51 53 56 58 60 61 64 65 70 74 75 76 77 78 79 81 82 85 87 90 91 92 93 97 98 99 100 101 102 103 104 105 107 108 110 111 112 113 114 115 118 119 120 121 123 124 126 129 130 132 146 148 **P**6 **S** Allina Health, Minneapolis, MN
Primary Contact: Thomas O'Connor, President
CFO: John Bien, Vice President Finance
CMO: Alison Peterson, Vice President Medical Affairs
CIO: Susan Heichert, Senior Vice President
CHR: James McGlade, Director Human Resources
CNO: Mandy Richards, R.N., Vice President Patient Care
Web address: www.allina.com
Control: Other not–for–profit (including NFP Corporation) **Service:** General Medical and Surgical

Staffed Beds: 370 **Admissions:** 22251 **Census:** 258 **Outpatient Visits:** 174345 **Births:** 3267 **Total Expense ($000):** 465648 **Payroll Expense ($000):** 189428 **Personnel:** 2236

SAINT PETER—Nicollet County

☐ **COMMUNITY BEHAVIORAL HEALTH HOSPITAL – ST. PETER (244010)**, 2000 Klein Street, Zip 56082–5800; tel. 507/933–5001 **A**1 10 **F**98 101 103 130 **S** Minnesota Department of Human Services, Saint Paul, MN
Primary Contact: Christopher Schiffer, Administrator
CFO: Shirley Jacobson, Chief Financial Officer
Web address: www.health.state.mn.us
Control: State–Government, nonfederal **Service:** Psychiatric

Staffed Beds: 10 **Admissions:** 69 **Census:** 6 **Outpatient Visits:** 0 **Births:** 0

★ ◇ **RIVER'S EDGE HOSPITAL AND CLINIC (241334)**, 1900 North Sunrise Drive, Zip 56082–5376; tel. 507/931–2200 **A**10 18 21 **F**3 7 15 28 29 40 53 63 75 77 81 90 107 110 115 119 130 133 144
Primary Contact: George A. Rohrich, FACHE, Chief Executive Officer
CFO: Lori Zook, Chief Financial Officer
CIO: Kevin Schaefer, Manager Information Services
CHR: Jackie Kimmet, Chief Human Resource Officer
CNO: Paula Meskan, R.N., Chief Nursing Officer
Web address: www.rehc.org
Control: City–Government, nonfederal **Service:** General Medical and Surgical

Staffed Beds: 14 **Admissions:** 700 **Census:** 6 **Outpatient Visits:** 24928 **Births:** 0 **Total Expense ($000):** 10759 **Payroll Expense ($000):** 8293 **Personnel:** 129

SANDSTONE—Pine County

★ **ESSENTIA HEALTH SANDSTONE (241309)**, 109 Court Avenue South, Zip 55072–5120; tel. 320/245–2212, (Total facility includes 45 beds in nursing home–type unit) **A**10 18 **F**7 11 12 15 28 29 30 34 35 40 45 59 64 65 75 77 80 81 85 87 91 92 93 107 110 114 128 130 132 133 135 143 144 148 **P**5 6 **S** Essentia Health, Duluth, MN
Primary Contact: Michael D. Hedrix, Administrator and President
CMO: Sarah Aldredge, M.D., Chief Medical Officer
Web address: www.pinemedicalcenter.org
Control: Hospital district or authority, Government, nonfederal **Service:** General Medical and Surgical

Staffed Beds: 85 **Admissions:** 284 **Census:** 41 **Outpatient Visits:** 12739 **Births:** 0 **Total Expense ($000):** 17920 **Payroll Expense ($000):** 8277 **Personnel:** 134

SAUK CENTRE—Stearns County

★ **CENTRACARE HEALTH–SAUK CENTRE (241368)**, 425 North Elm Street, Zip 56378–1010; tel. 320/352–2221, (Nonreporting) **A**5 10 18 **S** CentraCare Health, Saint Cloud, MN
Primary Contact: Delano Christianson, Administrator
CFO: Delano Christianson, Administrator
Web address: www.centracare.com/hospitals/sauk_centre/index.html
Control: City–Government, nonfederal **Service:** General Medical and Surgical

Staffed Beds: 85

SHAKOPEE—Scott County

✠ **ST. FRANCIS REGIONAL MEDICAL CENTER (240104)**, 1455 St. Francis Avenue, Zip 55379–3380; tel. 952/428–3000 **A**1 2 5 10 **F**3 12 13 15 28 29 30 31 34 35 36 38 40 41 43 45 46 50 51 57 58 59 64 68 75 77 78 79 80 81 82 84 86 87 93 107 108 110 111 114 117 118 119 120 124 129 130 131 132 144 146 147 148 **S** Allina Health, Minneapolis, MN
Primary Contact: Mike McMahan, President
CFO: Cynthia Vincent, Vice President Finance and Operations
CMO: Monte Johnson, Vice President, Medical Affairs
CIO: Joe Delveaux, Manager Information Services
CHR: Ann Glaves, Vice President Human Resources
CNO: Debora Ryan, R.N., Vice President Patient Care
Web address: www.stfrancis–shakopee.com
Control: Other not–for–profit (including NFP Corporation) **Service:** General Medical and Surgical

Staffed Beds: 86 **Admissions:** 5735 **Census:** 42 **Outpatient Visits:** 119535 **Births:** 1328 **Total Expense ($000):** 124298 **Payroll Expense ($000):** 47084 **Personnel:** 519

SLAYTON—Murray County

★ **MURRAY COUNTY MEDICAL CENTER (241319)**, 2042 Juniper Avenue, Zip 56172–1017; tel. 507/836–6111, (Nonreporting) **A**10 18 **S** Sanford Health, Sioux Falls, SD
Primary Contact: Dennis Goebel, Chief Executive Officer
CFO: Renee Logan, Chief Financial Officer
CMO: Joyce Tarbet, M.D., Chief Medical Officer
CIO: Justin Keller, Chief Information Officer
CHR: Nancy Andert, Director Human Resources
CNO: Lorrie Mortensen, R.N., Chief Patient Services
Web address: www.murraycountymed.org
Control: County–Government, nonfederal **Service:** General Medical and Surgical

Staffed Beds: 18

SLEEPY EYE—Brown County

SLEEPY EYE MEDICAL CENTER (241327), 400 Fourth Avenue N.W., Zip 56085–1109, Mailing Address: P.O. Box 323, Zip 56085–0323; tel. 507/794–3571 **A**10 18 **F**8 13 15 18 28 29 34 40 41 43 45 57 59 64 65 76 81 89 91 93 97 107 110 114 127 130 133 144 148 **P**6
Primary Contact: Kevin Sellheim, Administrator
CHR: Connie Dahlberg, Director Business and Employee
CNO: Karee Schmiesing, Director of Nursing
Web address: www.semedicalcenter.org
Control: City–Government, nonfederal **Service:** General Medical and Surgical

Staffed Beds: 16 **Admissions:** 312 **Census:** 3 **Outpatient Visits:** 11697 **Births:** 42 **Total Expense ($000):** 11631 **Payroll Expense ($000):** 5337 **Personnel:** 92

SPRINGFIELD—Brown County

☐ **MAYO CLINIC HEALTH SYSTEM IN SPRINGFIELD (241352)**, 625 North Jackson Avenue, Zip 56087–1714, Mailing Address: P.O. Box 146, Zip 56087–0146; tel. 507/723–6201 **A**1 10 18 **F**3 15 28 29 32 34 35 40 45 57 59 64 65 75 81 85 89 93 97 107 110 114 128 133 135 146 148 **P**6 **S** Mayo Clinic, Rochester, MN
Primary Contact: Scott D. Thoreson, FACHE, Administrator
CFO: James Tarasovich, Chief Financial Officer
CMO: Jennifer White, Chief of Staff
Web address: www.mayoclinichealthsystem.org
Control: Other not–for–profit (including NFP Corporation) **Service:** General Medical and Surgical

Staffed Beds: 23 **Admissions:** 348 **Census:** 4 **Outpatient Visits:** 15383 **Births:** 0 **Personnel:** 60

MN

Hospital, Medicare Provider Number, Address, Telephone, Approval, Facility, and Physician Codes, Health Care System

★ American Hospital Association (AHA) membership
☐ The Joint Commission accreditation
◯ Healthcare Facilities Accreditation Program
◇ DNV Healthcare Inc. accreditation
⇑ Center for Improvement in Healthcare Quality Accreditation
△ Commission on Accreditation of Rehabilitation Facilities (CARF) accreditation

STAPLES—Todd County

LAKEWOOD HEALTH SYSTEM (241329), 49725 County 83, Zip 56479–5280; tel. 218/894–1515, (Total facility includes 100 beds in nursing home–type unit) **A**10 18 **F**3 6 7 8 10 11 12 13 15 28 29 30 31 34 35 36 39 40 43 50 52 53 56 57 59 62 63 64 65 68 75 76 77 78 79 81 82 84 85 86 87 93 97 98 99 100 101 102 103 104 105 107 110 114 119 125 127 128 129 130 131 132 133 135 143 146 147 148 **P**7
Primary Contact: Tim Rice, President and Chief Executive Officer
CMO: John Halfen, M.D., Medical Director
CHR: Janet Jacobson, Director Human Resources
CNO: Teresa Fisher, Chief Nursing Officer
Web address: www.lakewoodhealthsystem.com
Control: Other not–for–profit (including NFP Corporation) **Service:** General Medical and Surgical

Staffed Beds: 135 **Admissions:** 1731 **Census:** 120 **Outpatient Visits:** 212383 **Births:** 425 **Total Expense ($000):** 91582 **Payroll Expense ($000):** 37024 **Personnel:** 712

STILLWATER—Washington County

✠ **LAKEVIEW HOSPITAL (240066)**, 927 Churchill Street West, Zip 55082–6605; tel. 651/439–5330 **A**1 3 5 10 **F**3 7 8 13 15 18 26 28 29 30 31 34 35 40 43 45 50 62 63 64 68 70 75 76 77 78 79 81 84 85 87 91 92 96 107 108 110 111 115 118 119 129 130 132 135 141 146 147 148 **S** HealthPartners, Bloomington, MN
Primary Contact: Theodore Wegleitner, Chief Executive Officer
CFO: Douglas E. Johnson, Chief Financial Officer
CMO: Thomas Anderson, Vice President Medical Affairs
CIO: Emad Awwad, Director Care Delivery Sites Information Systems and Technology
CHR: Angy Duchesneau, Senior Director Human Resources
CNO: Robbi Hagelberg, Vice President Nursing Services and Chief Nursing Officer
Web address: www.lakeview.org
Control: Other not–for–profit (including NFP Corporation) **Service:** General Medical and Surgical

Staffed Beds: 54 **Admissions:** 3736 **Census:** 29 **Outpatient Visits:** 61852 **Births:** 533 **Total Expense ($000):** 92686 **Payroll Expense ($000):** 37564 **Personnel:** 494

THIEF RIVER FALLS—Pennington County

MERITCARE THIEF RIVER FALLS NORTHWEST MEDICAL CENTER See Sanford Medical Center Thief River Falls

★ **SANFORD MEDICAL CENTER THIEF RIVER FALLS (241381)**, 3001 Sanford Parkway, Zip 56701–2700; tel. 218/681–4240 **A**10 18 **F**3 5 11 13 15 28 29 31 33 34 35 38 39 40 43 45 54 60 64 65 68 70 74 75 76 78 79 81 82 85 87 93 94 98 99 100 101 102 104 106 107 110 111 115 119 129 130 131 132 133 135 144 146 147 148 **P**6 **S** Sanford Health, Sioux Falls, SD
Primary Contact: Brian J. Carlson, FACHE, Chief Executive Officer
COO: Rob Lovejoy, Chief Operating Officer
CFO: Todd Christensen, Executive Director Fiscal Services
CMO: Ashok Patel, M.D., Chief of Staff
CHR: Rob Lovejoy, Chief Operating Officer
CNO: Janell Hudson, Chief Clinical Officer
Web address: www.sanfordhealth.org
Control: Other not–for–profit (including NFP Corporation) **Service:** General Medical and Surgical

Staffed Beds: 35 **Admissions:** 1591 **Census:** 16 **Outpatient Visits:** 90999 **Births:** 297 **Total Expense ($000):** 69451 **Payroll Expense ($000):** 22674 **Personnel:** 418

SANFORD THIEF RIVER FALLS BEHAVIORAL HEALTH CENTER, 120 LaBree Avenue South, Zip 56701–2819, Mailing Address: 3001 Sanford Parkway, Zip 56701–2819; tel. 218/683–4349, (Nonreporting) **S** Sanford Health, Sioux Falls, SD
Primary Contact: Brian J. Carlson, FACHE, Chief Executive Officer
COO: Rob Lovejoy, Chief Operating Officer
CFO: Todd Christensen, Executive Director Finance
Web address: www.sanfordhealth.org/Locations/1766896362
Control: Other not–for–profit (including NFP Corporation) **Service:** Psychiatric

Staffed Beds: 16

TRACY—Lyon County

★ **SANFORD TRACY MEDICAL CENTER (241303)**, 251 Fifth Street East, Zip 56175–1536; tel. 507/629–3200 **A**10 18 **F**3 28 29 31 32 34 40 41 42 43 45 50 56 57 59 62 64 65 68 77 81 85 87 89 91 93 97 107 108 111 114 125 127 129 130 131 132 133 135 143 **S** Sanford Health, Sioux Falls, SD
Primary Contact: Stacy Barstad, Chief Executive Officer
CMO: Muhammad Ali, M.D., Chief Medical Officer
CIO: Janet Theisen, Chief Information Officer
CHR: Becky Foster, Manager Human Resources
CNO: Jeri Schons, R.N., Chief Nursing Officer
Web address: www.sanfordtracy.org
Control: Other not–for–profit (including NFP Corporation) **Service:** General Medical and Surgical

Staffed Beds: 25 **Admissions:** 181 **Census:** 2 **Outpatient Visits:** 18396 **Births:** 0 **Total Expense ($000):** 10345 **Payroll Expense ($000):** 4523 **Personnel:** 92

TWO HARBORS—Lake County

LAKE VIEW MEMORIAL HOSPITAL (241308), 325 11th Avenue, Zip 55616–1360; tel. 218/834–7300 **A**10 18 **F**15 28 35 40 43 50 53 59 63 64 75 77 81 82 84 93 97 115 119 130 133 144 148
Primary Contact: Greg Ruberg, Administrator
CFO: Eric Lohn, Chief Financial Officer
Web address: www.lvmhospital.com
Control: Other not–for–profit (including NFP Corporation) **Service:** General Medical and Surgical

Staffed Beds: 16 **Admissions:** 261 **Census:** 6 **Outpatient Visits:** 33140 **Births:** 0 **Total Expense ($000):** 13685 **Payroll Expense ($000):** 5614 **Personnel:** 83

TYLER—Lincoln County

TYLER HEALTHCARE CENTER AVERA (241348), 240 Willow Street, Zip 56178–1166; tel. 507/247–5521, (Nonreporting) **A**10 18 **S** Avera Health, Sioux Falls, SD
Primary Contact: Jonathan Moe, Chief Executive Officer
Web address: www.www1.avera.org/amck/regionalfacilities/tyler/index.aspx
Control: Other not–for–profit (including NFP Corporation) **Service:** General Medical and Surgical

Staffed Beds: 56

VIRGINIA—St. Louis County

✠ △ **ESSENTIA HEALTH–VIRGINIA (240084)**, 901 Ninth Street North, Zip 55792–2398; tel. 218/741–3340, (Total facility includes 90 beds in nursing home–type unit) **A**1 7 10 **F**3 11 13 15 17 18 28 29 30 31 34 35 40 41 43 45 47 48 56 59 63 64 65 70 75 76 77 79 80 81 84 85 87 89 90 96 97 107 108 110 111 115 119 124 128 129 130 132 135 146 147 148 **P**6 **S** Essentia Health, Duluth, MN
Primary Contact: Daniel Milbridge, Administrator and Chief Operating Officer
CFO: Steven Feltman, CPA, Chief Financial Officer
CMO: Michelle Oman, D.O., Chief Medical Officer
CNO: Michelle M. Fleming, Chief Nursing Officer
Web address: www.essentiahealth.org
Control: Other not–for–profit (including NFP Corporation) **Service:** General Medical and Surgical

Staffed Beds: 173 **Admissions:** 1805 **Census:** 94 **Outpatient Visits:** 51955 **Births:** 242 **Total Expense ($000):** 76026 **Payroll Expense ($000):** 36503 **Personnel:** 494

WABASHA—Wabasha County

★ **SAINT ELIZABETH'S MEDICAL CENTER (241335)**, 1200 Grant Boulevard West, Zip 55981–1042; tel. 651/565–4531, (Total facility includes 146 beds in nursing home–type unit) **A**10 18 **F**2 6 10 11 12 15 28 29 30 34 35 40 43 45 46 49 50 53 56 59 62 65 75 77 81 85 93 94 107 110 114 119 125 128 130 133 135 143 145 146 148 **S** Ascension Health, Saint Louis, MO
Primary Contact: Thomas Crowley, President and Chief Executive Officer
CFO: John Wolfe, Chief Financial Officer
CMO: Brian E. Kelly, M.D., President Medical Staff
CHR: Jim Root, Vice President Human Resources
CNO: Kathy Lueders, R.N., Director of Nursing–Acute Care
Web address: www.stelizabethswabasha.org
Control: Church–operated, Nongovernment, not–for profit **Service:** General Medical and Surgical

Staffed Beds: 164 **Admissions:** 482 **Census:** 139 **Outpatient Visits:** 24403 **Births:** 0 **Total Expense ($000):** 26279 **Payroll Expense ($000):** 12327 **Personnel:** 231

WACONIA—Carver County

★ ◇ **RIDGEVIEW MEDICAL CENTER (240056)**, 500 South Maple Street, Zip 55387–1791; tel. 952/442–2191, (Nonreporting) **A**2 10 21 **S** Ridgeview Medical Center, Waconia, MN
Primary Contact: Robert Stevens, President and Chief Executive Officer
CFO: Gordon Gablenz, Vice President Finance
CIO: Tamara Korbel, Director Management Information Systems
CHR: Sarah M. Hastings, Executive Director
Web address: www.ridgeviewmedical.org
Control: Other not–for–profit (including NFP Corporation) **Service:** General Medical and Surgical

Staffed Beds: 102

Many Facility Codes have changed. Please refer to the AHA Guide Code Chart. © 2016 AHA Guide

MN

WADENA—Wadena County

✠ **TRI–COUNTY HOSPITAL (241354)**, 415 Jefferson Street North,
Zip 56482–1297; tel. 218/631–3510 **A**1 10 18 **F**3 7 11 13 15 17 28 31 34
35 40 50 54 57 59 64 65 70 75 76 77 81 85 86 87 89 93 99 104 107 110
111 114 115 118 119 127 129 130 131 132 133 135 146 147 148 **P**6
Primary Contact: Joel Beiswenger, Chief Executive Officer
CFO: Kim Aagard, Chief Financial Officer
CMO: John Pate, M.D., Chief Medical Officer
CIO: Bill Blaha, Manager Information Technology
CHR: Bryan Pederson, Human Resources Manager
CNO: Kathy Kleen, Chief Nursing Officer
Web address: www.tchc.org
Control: Other not–for–profit (including NFP Corporation) **Service:** General
Medical and Surgical

> **Staffed Beds:** 25 **Admissions:** 1100 **Census:** 8 **Outpatient Visits:** 109681
> **Births:** 163 **Total Expense ($000):** 56386 **Payroll Expense ($000):** 22516
> **Personnel:** 353

WARREN—Marshall County

★ **NORTH VALLEY HEALTH CENTER (241337)**, 300 West Good Samaritan Drive,
Zip 56762; tel. 218/745–4211, (Nonreporting) **A**10 18
Primary Contact: Jon E. Linnell, Interim Chief Executive Officer
CFO: Mitchell Kotrba, Chief Financial Officer
CNO: Sara Marie Kazmierczak, R.N., Director of Nursing
Web address: www.northvalleyhealth.org
Control: Other not–for–profit (including NFP Corporation) **Service:** General
Medical and Surgical

> **Staffed Beds:** 20

WASECA—Waseca County

☐ **MAYO CLINIC HEALTH SYSTEM IN WASECA (241345)**, 501 North State
Street, Zip 56093–2811; tel. 507/835–1210 **A**1 3 5 10 18 **F**3 11 15 18 28 29
30 34 35 40 45 53 57 59 64 65 74 75 77 81 82 85 86 87 93 97 107 110
114 119 128 130 132 133 144 146 148 **P**6 **S** Mayo Clinic, Rochester, MN
Primary Contact: Thomas Borowski, Administrator
CMO: Christopher Schimming, M.D., Medical Director
Web address: www.mayoclinichealthsystem.org
Control: Other not–for–profit (including NFP Corporation) **Service:** General
Medical and Surgical

> **Staffed Beds:** 25 **Admissions:** 239 **Census:** 6 **Outpatient Visits:** 30431
> **Births:** 0 **Personnel:** 99

WESTBROOK—Cottonwood County

★ **SANFORD WESTBROOK MEDICAL CENTER (241302)**, 920 Bell Avenue,
Zip 56183–9669, Mailing Address: P.O. Box 188, Zip 56183–0188;
tel. 507/274–6121 **A**10 18 **F**3 29 31 34 35 40 42 43 56 57 59 62 64 65 68
71 75 77 81 85 86 87 89 91 93 97 99 100 101 102 103 104 107 108 114
125 127 130 131 132 133 135 143 **P**6 **S** Sanford Health, Sioux Falls, SD
Primary Contact: Stacy Barstad, Chief Executive Officer
COO: Gordon Kopperud, Director Operations
CIO: Janet Theisen, Chief Information Officer
CHR: Becky Foster, Manager Human Resources
Web address: www.sanfordwestbrook.org
Control: Other not–for–profit (including NFP Corporation) **Service:** General
Medical and Surgical

> **Staffed Beds:** 6 **Admissions:** 109 **Census:** 1 **Outpatient Visits:** 11267
> **Births:** 0 **Total Expense ($000):** 6537 **Payroll Expense ($000):** 2339
> **Personnel:** 35

WHEATON—Traverse County

★ **SANFORD WHEATON MEDICAL CENTER (241304)**, 401 12th Street North,
Zip 56296–1099; tel. 320/563–8226 **A**10 18 **F**3 7 11 15 18 28 29 30 34 40
43 45 57 59 64 65 81 86 97 107 110 114 119 127 128 132 133 **P**6
S Sanford Health, Sioux Falls, SD
Primary Contact: JoAnn M. Foltz, R.N., Chief Executive Officer
CFO: Shane Ayres, Chief Financial Officer
CHR: Brenda Petersen, Human Resources
CNO: Chelsie Falk, Chief Nursing Officer
Web address: www.sanfordhealth.org
Control: Other not–for–profit (including NFP Corporation) **Service:** General
Medical and Surgical

> **Staffed Beds:** 15 **Admissions:** 93 **Census:** 1 **Outpatient Visits:** 14025
> **Births:** 0 **Total Expense ($000):** 7491 **Payroll Expense ($000):** 2747
> **Personnel:** 56

WILLMAR—Kandiyohi County

☐ **CHILD AND ADOLESCENT BEHAVIORAL HEALTH SERVICES (244005)**,
1701 Technology Drive Northeast, Zip 56201–2275; tel. 320/231–5421,
(Nonreporting) **A**1 10
Primary Contact: Pamela Peters, Administrator
Web address: www.dhs.state.mn.us
Control: County–Government, nonfederal **Service:** Psychiatric

> **Staffed Beds:** 16

✠ **RICE MEMORIAL HOSPITAL (240088)**, 301 Becker Avenue S.W.,
Zip 56201–3395; tel. 320/235–4543, (Total facility includes 78 beds in nursing
home–type unit) **A**1 2 10 **F**3 7 11 12 13 28 29 30 34 35 39 40 43 45 47 48
49 57 59 60 63 64 65 68 70 73 75 76 78 79 81 82 85 86 87 89 90 93
98 100 101 102 103 104 105 107 108 111 115 118 119 121 128 130 132
143 146 147 148
Primary Contact: Michael Schramm, Chief Executive Officer
CFO: Bill Fenske, Chief Financial Officer
CMO: Kenneth Flowe, M.D., Chief Medical Officer
CIO: Teri Beyer, Chief Information Officer, Quality
CNO: Wendy Ulferts, R.N., Chief Nursing Officer
Web address: www.ricehospital.com
Control: City–Government, nonfederal **Service:** General Medical and Surgical

> **Staffed Beds:** 184 **Admissions:** 3782 **Census:** 89 **Outpatient Visits:** 72134
> **Births:** 821 **Total Expense ($000):** 103469 **Payroll Expense ($000):** 43827
> **Personnel:** 542

WINDOM—Cottonwood County

★ **WINDOM AREA HOSPITAL (241332)**, 2150 Hospital Drive, Zip 56101–0339,
Mailing Address: P.O. Box 339, Zip 56101–0339; tel. 507/831–2400 **A**10 18
F11 13 15 28 31 34 35 40 45 53 57 64 76 77 81 93 107 114 119 130 133
148 **S** Sanford Health, Sioux Falls, SD
Primary Contact: Shelby Medina, Chief Executive Officer
CFO: Kim Armstrong, Chief Financial Officer
CIO: Lori Ling, Information Technician
CHR: Emily Masters, Director Human Resources and Marketing
CNO: Kari Witte, Director Patient Care
Web address: www.windomareahospital.com
Control: City–Government, nonfederal **Service:** General Medical and Surgical

> **Staffed Beds:** 18 **Admissions:** 412 **Census:** 4 **Outpatient Visits:** 32262
> **Births:** 121 **Total Expense ($000):** 15545 **Payroll Expense ($000):** 6009
> **Personnel:** 99

WINONA—Winona County

★ **WINONA HEALTH (240044)**, 855 Mankato Avenue, Zip 55987–4868, Mailing
Address: P.O. Box 5600, Zip 55987–0600; tel. 507/454–3650 **A**2 10 20 **F**11
13 15 28 29 30 31 32 34 35 38 40 43 50 53 56 57 59 60 61 70 74 75 76
77 78 79 81 82 84 85 86 87 89 93 96 97 98 99 100 101 102 103 104 107
108 110 111 115 118 119 127 129 130 131 132 135 144 146 147 148
Primary Contact: Rachelle H. Schultz, President and Chief Executive Officer
CFO: Jan Brosnahan, Chief Financial Officer
CMO: Dan Parker, M.D., Chief of Staff
CIO: Polly Peterson, Information Technology Director
CHR: Ashley Anderson, Manager Human Resources
Web address: www.winonahealth.org
Control: Other not–for–profit (including NFP Corporation) **Service:** General
Medical and Surgical

> **Staffed Beds:** 53 **Admissions:** 2376 **Census:** 24 **Outpatient Visits:** 225253
> **Births:** 308 **Total Expense ($000):** 113574 **Payroll Expense ($000):** 49076
> **Personnel:** 786

WOODBURY—Washington County

✠ **WOODWINDS HEALTH CAMPUS (240213)**, 1925 Woodwinds Drive,
Zip 55125–4445; tel. 651/232–0228 **A**1 3 5 10 **F**3 13 15 28 29 30 31 34 35
36 37 38 40 43 44 49 50 57 59 61 63 64 68 70 74 75 76 77 78 79 81 85
86 87 93 96 97 100 102 104 106 107 108 110 111 115 118 119 120 121
124 130 132 146 **P**8 **S** HealthEast Care System, Saint Paul, MN
Primary Contact: Catherine Barr, Chief Operating Officer
COO: Brian Gager, Vice President of Operations, Acute Care Hospitals
CFO: Douglas Davenport, Senior Vice President and Chief Financial Officer
CMO: Kevin C. Garrett, M.D., Chief Medical Officer
CIO: Joanne Sunquist, Chief Information Officer
CHR: Dawn Kessler, System Director Human Resources Operations
CNO: Debra J. Hurd, R.N., Vice President of Nursing, Acute Care Hospitals
Web address: www.woodwinds.org
Control: Other not–for–profit (including NFP Corporation) **Service:** General
Medical and Surgical

> **Staffed Beds:** 86 **Admissions:** 7829 **Census:** 82 **Outpatient Visits:** 60164
> **Births:** 1725 **Total Expense ($000):** 123328 **Payroll Expense ($000):**
> 45760 **Personnel:** 492

MN

Hospital, Medicare Provider Number, Address, Telephone, Approval, Facility, and Physician Codes, Health Care System

★ American Hospital Association (AHA) membership
☐ The Joint Commission accreditation
○ Healthcare Facilities Accreditation Program
◇ DNV Healthcare Inc. accreditation
⇑ Center for Improvement in Healthcare Quality Accreditation
△ Commission on Accreditation of Rehabilitation Facilities (CARF) accreditation

WORTHINGTON—Nobles County

SANFORD REGIONAL HOSPITAL WORTHINGTON See Sanford Worthington Medical Center

★ **SANFORD WORTHINGTON MEDICAL CENTER (240022)**, 1018 Sixth Avenue, Zip 56187–2202, Mailing Address: P.O. Box 997, Zip 56187–0997; tel. 507/372–2941 **A**10 20 **F**3 11 13 15 18 19 26 27 28 31 34 35 40 43 45 50 57 59 60 62 64 68 69 70 75 76 78 79 81 85 86 93 97 107 110 111 114 116 119 120 121 126 129 130 131 132 133 135 144 146 147 148 **S** Sanford Health, Sioux Falls, SD
Primary Contact: Michael Hammer, Chief Executive Officer
CFO: Linda Wagner, Chief Financial Officer
CMO: Charles Dike, M.D., Chief of Staff
CIO: Brad Klassen, Information Technology Coordinator
CNO: Jennifer Weg, R.N., Chief Nursing Officer
Web address: www.sanfordhealth.org
Control: Other not–for–profit (including NFP Corporation) **Service:** General Medical and Surgical

Staffed Beds: 48 **Admissions:** 1348 **Census:** 10 **Outpatient Visits:** 66821 **Births:** 437 **Total Expense ($000):** 34777 **Payroll Expense ($000):** 13906 **Personnel:** 226

WYOMING—Chisago County

✠ **FAIRVIEW LAKES HEALTH SERVICES (240050)**, 5200 Fairview Boulevard, Zip 55092–8013; tel. 651/982–7000 **A**1 10 **F**3 11 13 15 18 28 29 30 32 34 35 40 43 45 51 57 59 62 63 64 65 68 70 75 76 79 81 82 85 87 93 96 107 110 111 115 119 130 131 132 134 144 146 147 148 **P**6 **S** Fairview Health Services, Minneapolis, MN
Primary Contact: John W. Herman, President
CFO: Kim Ericson, Vice President Finance
CMO: David Milbrandt, M.D., Vice President Medical Affairs
CNO: Margaret J. Swanson, Chief Nursing Officer
Web address: www.fairview.org/
Control: Other not–for–profit (including NFP Corporation) **Service:** General Medical and Surgical

Staffed Beds: 49 **Admissions:** 2864 **Census:** 23 **Outpatient Visits:** 91187 **Births:** 692 **Total Expense ($000):** 74250 **Payroll Expense ($000):** 41636 **Personnel:** 381

MN

Many Facility Codes have changed. Please refer to the AHA Guide Code Chart. © 2016 AHA Guide

MISSISSIPPI

ABERDEEN—Monroe County

★ ◇ **PIONEER COMMUNITY HOSPITAL OF ABERDEEN (251302)**, 400 South Chestnut Street, Zip 39730–3335, Mailing Address: P.O. Box 548, Zip 39730–0548; tel. 662/369–2455 **A**10 18 21 **F**3 8 10 11 29 35 40 41 45 53 56 70 75 77 81 85 86 87 89 90 93 96 97 98 100 101 102 103 104 105 106 107 112 115 119 125 127 128 130 131 133 135 143 146 **S** Pioneer Health Services, Magee, MS
Primary Contact: Christopher Chandler, Chief Executive Officer
CFO: Julie Gieger, Chief Financial Officer
CMO: Kevin Hayes, M.D., Chief of Staff
CHR: Lee Rob, Director Human Resources
Web address: www.pchaberdeen.com
Control: Corporation, Investor–owned, for–profit **Service:** General Medical and Surgical

Staffed Beds: 35 **Admissions:** 456 **Census:** 17 **Outpatient Visits:** 14268 **Births:** 0 **Personnel:** 217

ACKERMAN—Choctaw County

☐ **CHOCTAW REGIONAL MEDICAL CENTER (251334)**, 311 West Cherry Street, Zip 39735–8708; tel. 662/285–6235 **A**1 10 18 **F**3 29 34 40 43 50 57 58 65 77 87 89 90 93 107 114 119 127 130 133 **P**4 6 8
Primary Contact: Jamie Rodgers, Interim Chief Executive Officer
Control: Corporation, Investor–owned, for–profit **Service:** General Medical and Surgical

Staffed Beds: 15 **Admissions:** 112 **Census:** 1 **Outpatient Visits:** 27466 **Births:** 0 **Total Expense ($000):** 14831 **Payroll Expense ($000):** 7886 **Personnel:** 262

AMORY—Monroe County

✠ **MERIT HEALTH GILMORE MEMORIAL (250025)**, 1105 Earl Frye Boulevard, Zip 38821–5500, Mailing Address: P.O. Box 459, Zip 38821–0459; tel. 662/256–7111 **A**1 10 **F**3 13 15 17 18 29 32 34 35 40 41 43 45 49 50 53 55 57 59 64 65 68 70 72 73 75 76 77 81 85 86 87 88 89 90 107 108 110 111 114 115 119 126 130 135 146 147 **P**8 **S** Community Health Systems, Inc., Franklin, TN
Primary Contact: J. Allen Tyra, Chief Executive
COO: Carol Upton, Regional Area Practice Manager
CFO: Bert Pickard, Chief Financial Officer
CMO: William Rogers, Chief Medical Officer
CIO: Jeff Wideman, Director Information Systems
CHR: Angie L. Weaver, Director Human Resources
Web address: www.gilmorehealth.com
Control: Corporation, Investor–owned, for–profit **Service:** General Medical and Surgical

Staffed Beds: 95 **Admissions:** 2569 **Census:** 75 **Outpatient Visits:** 53511 **Births:** 586 **Personnel:** 245

BATESVILLE—Panola County

★ **MERIT HEALTH BATESVILLE (250128)**, 303 Medical Center Drive, Zip 38606–8608; tel. 662/563–5611 **A**10 **F**3 4 5 11 12 13 15 18 19 28 29 30 32 34 35 38 40 43 45 48 50 56 57 59 64 65 68 70 76 77 81 85 87 89 97 98 100 101 102 103 104 107 108 114 119 127 129 130 132 146 147 **S** Community Health Systems, Inc., Franklin, TN
Primary Contact: Travis Sisson, Chief Executive Officer
COO: Vince Brummett, Director Administrative Services
CMO: Michael R. Hovens, M.D., Chief Medical Officer
CIO: Will Morris, Director Information Technology
CHR: Arthur A. Wasek, Director Human Resources
Web address: www.trilakesmc.com
Control: Corporation, Investor–owned, for–profit **Service:** General Medical and Surgical

Staffed Beds: 112 **Admissions:** 2700 **Census:** 41 **Outpatient Visits:** 24464 **Births:** 226 **Total Expense ($000):** 31903 **Payroll Expense ($000):** 12155 **Personnel:** 269

BAY SAINT LOUIS—Hancock County

✠ **HANCOCK MEDICAL CENTER (250162)**, 149 Drinkwater Boulevard, Zip 39520–1658, Mailing Address: 149 Drinkwater Road, Zip 39520–1658; tel. 228/467–8600 **A**1 10 **F**3 13 15 17 18 28 29 30 34 35 39 40 43 45 51 54 57 59 64 65 70 75 76 77 79 81 82 85 86 87 89 90 93 97 107 108 110 111 114 115 118 119 127 130 131 135 144 146 147 **S** Ochsner Health System, New Orleans, LA
Primary Contact: Alan Hodges, Chief Executive Officer
CFO: Thomas Ramsey, Chief Financial Officer
CIO: Craig Hodges, Director Information Services
CHR: Cathy Benvenutti, Human Resource Director
CNO: Virginia Kenny, Chief Nursing Officer
Web address: www.hmc.org
Control: County–Government, nonfederal **Service:** General Medical and Surgical

Staffed Beds: 102 **Admissions:** 2114 **Census:** 17 **Outpatient Visits:** 45980 **Births:** 222 **Total Expense ($000):** 34571 **Payroll Expense ($000):** 16942 **Personnel:** 270

BAY SPRINGS—Jasper County

★ **JASPER GENERAL HOSPITAL (250018)**, 15 A South Sixth Street, Zip 39422–9738, Mailing Address: P.O. Box 527, Zip 39422–0527; tel. 601/764–2101, (Includes JASPER COUNTY NURSING HOME), (Total facility includes 110 beds in nursing home–type unit) **A**10 **F**10 55 59 62 64 108 119 128 130 133
Primary Contact: Michael Nester, Chief Executive Officer
CFO: Steve Green, Comptroller
CMO: A. K. Lay, Jr., M.D., Chief Medical Officer
CHR: Beth Gable, Administrative Assistant
CNO: Becky Ulmer, R.N., Director of Nursing
Web address: www.jaspergeneralhospital.com
Control: County–Government, nonfederal **Service:** General Medical and Surgical

Staffed Beds: 122 **Admissions:** 41 **Census:** 109 **Outpatient Visits:** 0 **Births:** 0 **Total Expense ($000):** 8354 **Payroll Expense ($000):** 5404 **Personnel:** 153

BILOXI—Harrison County

✠ **MERIT HEALTH BILOXI (250007)**, 150 Reynoir Street, Zip 39530–4199, Mailing Address: P.O. Box 128, Zip 39533–0128; tel. 228/432–1571 **A**1 10 **F**3 8 11 12 13 15 17 18 20 22 26 29 31 34 35 37 40 43 45 46 47 48 49 50 54 59 61 64 65 68 70 73 74 75 76 77 78 79 81 82 85 86 87 89 90 92 93 94 97 98 99 100 102 103 104 105 106 107 108 110 111 112 114 115 118 119 120 121 122 123 126 130 135 143 146 147 148 **P**8 **S** Community Health Systems, Inc., Franklin, TN
COO: Tonda V. Haigler, Chief Operating Officer
CMO: George Loukatos, M.D., President Medical Staff Affairs
CIO: George Bickel, Director, Information Systems
CHR: Brion Stanford, Director Human Resources
CNO: Mary Franklin, R.N., Chief Nursing Officer
Web address: www.merithealthbiloxi.com
Control: Corporation, Investor–owned, for–profit **Service:** General Medical and Surgical

Staffed Beds: 198 **Admissions:** 6940 **Census:** 86 **Outpatient Visits:** 104512 **Births:** 825 **Personnel:** 665

✠ **VETERANS AFFAIRS GULF COAST VETERANS HEALTH CARE SYSTEM**, 400 Veterans Avenue, Zip 39531–2410; tel. 228/523–5000, (Nonreporting) **A**1 3 5 **S** Department of Veterans Affairs, Washington, DC
Primary Contact: Anthony L. Dawson, FACHE, Director
COO: Alexander Murray, Interim Associate Director
CFO: John D. Williams, Jr., Chief Financial Officer
CMO: Kenneth B. Simon, M.D., Chief of Staff
CIO: David D. Wagner, Chief Information Management Service
CHR: Andrew Roberts, Interim Chief Human Resources Officer
CNO: Deatosha D. Haynes, Interim Associates Director for Patient
Web address: www.biloxi.va.gov/
Control: Veterans Affairs, Government, federal **Service:** General Medical and Surgical

Staffed Beds: 392

MS

BOONEVILLE—Prentiss County

✠ **BAPTIST MEMORIAL HOSPITAL–BOONEVILLE (250044)**, 100 Hospital Street, Zip 38829–3359; tel. 662/720–5000 **A**1 10 **F**3 12 15 17 18 28 29 30 35 40 43 57 59 68 70 75 81 85 87 89 90 93 98 103 107 108 111 118 119 130 132 133 146 **P**3 **S** Baptist Memorial Health Care Corporation, Memphis, TN
Primary Contact: James Grantham, Administrator and Chief Executive Officer
CFO: Donavan Leonard, Chief Financial Officer
CMO: Nathan Baldwin, M.D., President Medical Staff
CIO: Linda Chaffin, Director Medical Review
CHR: Shannon Bolen, Director Human Resources
Web address: www.bmhcc.org/booneville
Control: Other not–for–profit (including NFP Corporation) **Service:** General Medical and Surgical

Staffed Beds: 66 **Admissions:** 1212 **Census:** 19 **Outpatient Visits:** 27110 **Births:** 0 **Total Expense ($000):** 20503 **Payroll Expense ($000):** 7445 **Personnel:** 181

BRANDON—Rankin County

✠ **MERIT HEALTH RANKIN (250096)**, 350 Crossgates Boulevard, Zip 39042–2698; tel. 601/825–2811 **A**1 5 10 **F**3 6 15 17 29 30 34 40 43 45 50 57 59 64 70 78 79 81 85 87 90 93 97 98 103 106 107 108 109 110 111 112 114 119 129 130 146 **P**8 **S** Community Health Systems, Inc., Franklin, TN
Primary Contact: Barry Moss, Chief Executive Officer
CFO: Christy Wilson, Chief Financial Officer
CMO: Edward Rigdon, M.D., Chief Medical Officer
CIO: Heather Holmes, Director Health Information Systems
CHR: Joy M. Hutson, Director Human Resources
CNO: Jacqueline C. Sullins, R.N., Chief Nursing Officer
Web address: www.crossgatesriveroaks.com
Control: Corporation, Investor–owned, for–profit **Service:** General Medical and Surgical

Staffed Beds: 134 **Admissions:** 2287 **Census:** 37 **Outpatient Visits:** 63190 **Births:** 0 **Total Expense ($000):** 42115 **Payroll Expense ($000):** 14498 **Personnel:** 288

BROOKHAVEN—Lincoln County

★ ◇ **KING'S DAUGHTERS MEDICAL CENTER (250057)**, 427 Highway 51 North, Zip 39601–2350, Mailing Address: P.O. Box 948, Zip 39602–0948; tel. 601/833–6011, (Nonreporting) **A**10 20 21 **S** QHR, Brentwood, TN
Primary Contact: Alvin Hoover, FACHE, Chief Executive Officer
COO: Tom Hood, Chief Operating Officer
CFO: Randy B. Pirtle, Chief Financial Officer
CMO: Richard Rushing, Chief of Staff
CIO: Carl Smith, Director Information Systems
CHR: Celine H. Craig, Director Human Resources
CNO: Cheri Walker, R.N., Chief Nursing Officer
Web address: www.kdmc.org
Control: Other not–for–profit (including NFP Corporation) **Service:** General Medical and Surgical

Staffed Beds: 122

CALHOUN CITY—Calhoun County

★ **CALHOUN HEALTH SERVICES (251331)**, 140 Burke–Calhoun City Road, Zip 38916–9690; tel. 662/628–6611, (Total facility includes 120 beds in nursing home–type unit) **A**10 18 **F**7 40 43 64 68 70 81 87 89 93 98 103 107 114 119 128 130 133 **S** North Mississippi Health Services, Inc., Tupelo, MS
Primary Contact: James P. Franklin, Administrator
CFO: Kenneth Conley, Controller
CMO: Bruce Longest, M.D., President Medical Staff
Web address: www.nmhs.net/calhoun_city
Control: City–County, Government, nonfederal **Service:** General Medical and Surgical

Staffed Beds: 145 **Admissions:** 337 **Census:** 107 **Births:** 0 **Total Expense ($000):** 17656 **Payroll Expense ($000):** 7577 **Personnel:** 243

CANTON—Madison County

✠ **MERIT HEALTH MADISON (250038)**, 161 River Oaks Drive, Zip 39046–5375, Mailing Address: PO Box 1607, Zip 39046–5375; tel. 601/855–4000, (Nonreporting) **A**1 10 **S** Community Health Systems, Inc., Franklin, TN
Primary Contact: Britton Phelps, Chief Executive Officer
CFO: Shea Sutherland, Chief Financial Officer
CMO: Vibha Vig, Chief of Staff
CIO: Rick Hartzog, Chief Information Officer
CHR: Jackie Williams, Director Human Resources
CNO: Terri Meadows, Chief Nursing Executive
Web address: www.merithealthmadison.com
Control: Partnership, Investor–owned, for–profit **Service:** General Medical and Surgical

Staffed Beds: 44

CARTHAGE—Leake County

★ **BAPTIST MEDICAL CENTER LEAKE (251315)**, 1100 Highway 16 E., Zip 39051–3809, Mailing Address: P.O. Box 909, Zip 39051–0909; tel. 601/267–1100, (Total facility includes 44 beds in nursing home–type unit) **A**10 18 **F**3 15 29 32 34 40 41 43 46 57 59 65 66 81 87 107 108 110 114 119 127 130 133 135 **P**6 **S** Baptist Health Systems, Jackson, MS
Primary Contact: Daryl W. Weaver, Interim Chief Executive Officer
COO: C. Gerald Cotton, Interim Chief Operating Officer
CFO: David Jackson, Chief Financial Officer
CMO: Doug Perry, M.D., Chief of Staff
Web address: www.mbhs.com/locations/baptist–medical–center–leake/
Control: Other not–for–profit (including NFP Corporation) **Service:** General Medical and Surgical

Staffed Beds: 69 **Admissions:** 828 **Census:** 60 **Births:** 1 **Personnel:** 195

CENTREVILLE—Wilkinson County

✠ **FIELD MEMORIAL COMMUNITY HOSPITAL (251309)**, 270 West Main Street, Zip 39631, Mailing Address: P.O. Box 639, Zip 39631–0639; tel. 601/645–5221 **A**1 10 18 **F**15 18 29 30 34 39 40 43 45 57 59 61 64 75 77 79 81 89 90 93 107 114 118 127 130 133 135 **P**6
Primary Contact: Chad Netterville, Administrator
CFO: Bryan N. Stevens, Chief Financial Officer
CIO: Locke Wheeles, Information Technology Manager
CHR: Dana McNabb, Human Resources Manager
CNO: Robin Walker, Chief Nursing Officer
Web address: www.fmch.org
Control: County–Government, nonfederal **Service:** General Medical and Surgical

Staffed Beds: 25 **Admissions:** 541 **Census:** 5 **Outpatient Visits:** 14702 **Births:** 0 **Personnel:** 153

CHARLESTON—Tallahatchie County

◇ **TALLAHATCHIE GENERAL HOSPITAL (251304)**, 201 South Market, Zip 38921–2236, Mailing Address: P.O. Box 230, Zip 38921–0240; tel. 662/647–5535, (Total facility includes 98 beds in nursing home–type unit) **A**10 18 21 **F**29 34 40 42 53 57 64 70 86 87 93 107 114 127 128 130 133 135 143 **P**6
Primary Contact: Jim Blackwood, Chief Executive Officer
CFO: Sammie Bell, Jr., Chief Financial Officer
Control: County–Government, nonfederal **Service:** General Medical and Surgical

Staffed Beds: 116 **Admissions:** 223 **Census:** 94 **Outpatient Visits:** 3579 **Births:** 0 **Total Expense ($000):** 26185 **Payroll Expense ($000):** 10581 **Personnel:** 352

CLARKSDALE—Coahoma County

✠ **MERIT HEALTH NORTHWEST MISSISSIPPI (250042)**, 1970 Hospital Drive, Zip 38614–7202, Mailing Address: P.O. Box 1218, Zip 38614–1218; tel. 662/627–3211 **A**1 10 19 **F**3 13 15 17 18 20 22 28 29 30 31 34 35 40 43 46 49 50 53 57 59 64 65 70 73 74 76 79 80 81 85 87 89 92 93 107 108 110 111 114 115 118 119 126 130 131 132 **P**8 **S** Community Health Systems, Inc., Franklin, TN
Primary Contact: Joel Southern, R.N., MSN, Chief Executive Officer
CFO: Charles H. Hester, Jr., CPA, Chief Financial Officer
CMO: Maha Wasef, M.D., Chief of Staff
CIO: Patricia Keenum, Health Information Management Systems Officer
CNO: Steven W. Brackeen, R.N., Chief Nursing Officer
Web address: www.merithealthnorthwestms.com
Control: Corporation, Investor–owned, for–profit **Service:** General Medical and Surgical

Staffed Beds: 181 **Admissions:** 3712 **Census:** 42 **Outpatient Visits:** 53060 **Births:** 785 **Personnel:** 389

CLEVELAND—Bolivar County

✠ **BOLIVAR MEDICAL CENTER (250093)**, 901 East Sunflower Road, Zip 38732–2833, Mailing Address: P.O. Box 1380, Zip 38732–1380; tel. 662/846–0061, (Nonreporting) **A**1 10 20 **S** LifePoint Health, Brentwood, TN
Primary Contact: Robert L. Marshall, Jr., FACHE, Chief Executive Officer
CMO: Mark Blackwood, M.D., Chief of Staff
CIO: Cagri Sapmaz, Information Technology Director
CHR: Ben Bufkin, Human Resource Director
CNO: Joann McCollum, Chief Nursing Officer
Web address: www.bolivarmedical.com
Control: Corporation, Investor–owned, for–profit **Service:** General Medical and Surgical

Staffed Beds: 127

MS

COLLINS—Covington County

★ ◇ **COVINGTON COUNTY HOSPITAL (251325)**, Gerald McRaney Street, Zip 39428–3899, Mailing Address: P.O. Box 1149, Zip 39428–1149; tel. 601/765–6711, (Total facility includes 60 beds in nursing home–type unit) **A**10 18 21 **F**3 7 34 40 41 43 45 50 54 57 59 64 65 66 68 70 81 89 93 94 98 103 107 114 119 127 128 133 135 144 146 147
Primary Contact: Gregg Gibbes, Chief Executive Officer
CFO: Kirstie Evans, Chief Financial Officer
CMO: Word Johnston, Medical Director
CIO: Ransom Jones, Information Technology Director
CHR: Beverly K. Ponder, Executive Assistant and Human Resources Coordinator
CNO: Martha Lynn Scott, Chief Patient Care Officer
Web address: www.covingtoncountyhospital.com
Control: County–Government, nonfederal **Service:** General Medical and Surgical

Staffed Beds: 94 Admissions: 481 Census: 64 Outpatient Visits: 26239 **Births: 0 Total Expense ($000):** 30983 **Payroll Expense ($000):** 11084 **Personnel:** 246

COLUMBIA—Marion County

MARION GENERAL HOSPITAL (250085), 1560 Sumrall Road, Zip 39429–2654, Mailing Address: P.O. Box 630, Zip 39429–0630; tel. 601/736–6303 **A**10 **F**11 29 35 39 40 43 61 70 75 81 87 89 90 93 97 107 108 111 118 119 130 133 144 146
Primary Contact: Bryan K. Maxie, Administrator
CMO: Mark Stevens, M.D., Chief Medical Staff
CIO: Donny Bracey, Director Information Services
CNO: Patricia Reid, Director of Nursing
Control: County–Government, nonfederal **Service:** General Medical and Surgical

Staffed Beds: 49 Admissions: 1154 Census: 24 Outpatient Visits: 29765 **Births: 0 Total Expense ($000):** 16403 **Payroll Expense ($000):** 7452 **Personnel:** 143

COLUMBUS—Lowndes County

✈ **BAPTIST MEMORIAL HOSPITAL–GOLDEN TRIANGLE (250100)**, 2520 Fifth Street North, Zip 39705–2095, Mailing Address: P.O. Box 1307, Zip 39703–1307; tel. 662/244–1000 **A**1 10 19 **F**3 4 5 7 11 13 15 17 18 20 22 26 28 29 30 31 34 38 39 40 43 49 51 55 57 59 61 64 65 70 73 75 76 77 78 79 80 81 84 85 87 88 89 93 96 98 100 102 104 105 106 107 108 110 111 114 115 116 117 118 119 120 121 123 126 130 132 134 135 146 147 **P**6 **S** Baptist Memorial Health Care Corporation, Memphis, TN
Primary Contact: Paul Cade, Administrator and Chief Executive Officer
CFO: David Webb, Chief Financial Officer
CMO: John E. Reed, M.D., Medical Director
CIO: Sheila Bardwell, Director Information Systems
CHR: Bob McCallister, Director Human Resources
CNO: Mary Ellen Sumrall, Chief Nursing Officer
Web address: www.baptistonline.org/golden–triangle/
Control: Other not–for–profit (including NFP Corporation) **Service:** General Medical and Surgical

Staffed Beds: 236 Admissions: 8284 Census: 102 Outpatient Visits: 116234 **Births: 917 Total Expense ($000):** 143879 **Payroll Expense ($000): 43902 Personnel:** 918

CORINTH—Alcorn County

☐ **MAGNOLIA REGIONAL HEALTH CENTER (250009)**, 611 Alcorn Drive, Zip 38834–9321; tel. 662/293–1000 **A**1 10 13 19 **F**13 15 17 29 35 39 40 43 51 53 62 63 70 75 76 77 78 81 82 86 87 89 93 98 100 101 102 103 107 108 111 116 118 119 127 130 131 132 143 146 147 **P**7 8
Primary Contact: Ronny Humes, Chief Executive Officer
COO: Angela Nowlin, R.N., Senior VP, Operations
CFO: Brian Craven, Senior Vice President Finance
CMO: Felton Combest, M.D., Vice President Medical Affairs
CIO: David Parker, VP Information Technology
CHR: Regenia Brown, Vice President Human Resources
CNO: Pam B. Wallis, MSN, Vice President Nursing Services
Web address: www.mrhc.org
Control: City–County, Government, nonfederal **Service:** General Medical and Surgical

Staffed Beds: 200 Admissions: 8293 Census: 101 Outpatient Visits: 160083 **Births: 679 Total Expense ($000):** 184803 **Payroll Expense ($000): 65773 Personnel:** 1210

DE KALB—Kemper County

JOHN C. STENNIS MEMORIAL HOSPITAL (251335), 14365 Highway 16 West, Zip 39328–7974; tel. 769/486–1000 **A**10 18 **F**29 40 43 75 107 119 127 133 **P**6 **S** Rush Health Systems, Meridian, MS
Primary Contact: Justin Palmer, Administrator
Web address: www.johncstennismemorialhospital.com/jcsmh/
Control: Other not–for–profit (including NFP Corporation) **Service:** General Medical and Surgical

Staffed Beds: 25 Admissions: 327 Census: 8 Outpatient Visits: 56989 **Births: 0 Total Expense ($000):** 5339 **Payroll Expense ($000):** 2742 **Personnel:** 170

EUPORA—Webster County

✈ **NORTH MISSISSIPPI MEDICAL CENTER–EUPORA (250020)**, 70 Medical Plaza, Zip 39744–4018; tel. 662/258–6221, (Total facility includes 35 beds in nursing home–type unit) **A**1 10 **F**3 7 8 11 12 18 20 22 24 26 28 29 30 31 32 34 35 37 38 40 42 43 53 57 59 64 65 68 71 74 79 83 84 86 87 89 90 93 97 107 111 115 117 119 126 127 128 129 130 133 135 146 148 **S** North Mississippi Health Services, Inc., Tupelo, MS
Primary Contact: Wes Sigler, Administrator
CFO: Adonna Mitchell, Director Fiscal Services
CMO: Christy Vowell, D.O., Chief of Staff
CIO: Helen Reed, Director Health Information
CHR: Dorothy Castle, Director Human Resources
Web address: www.nmhs.net/eupora
Control: Other not–for–profit (including NFP Corporation) **Service:** General Medical and Surgical

Staffed Beds: 73 Admissions: 1098 Census: 46 Outpatient Visits: 18165 **Births: 0 Total Expense ($000):** 20550 **Payroll Expense ($000):** 10787 **Personnel:** 182

FAYETTE—Jefferson County

★ **JEFFERSON COUNTY HOSPITAL (250060)**, 870 South Main Street, Zip 39069–5695, Mailing Address: P.O. Box 577, Zip 39069–0577; tel. 601/786–3401 **A**10 **F**3 40 42 105 106 130
Primary Contact: Wanda C. Fleming, Chief Executive Officer
CMO: Khar Omolara, M.D., Chief Medical Staff
CHR: Patricia Selmon, Director Public Relations and Chief Human Resources
Control: County–Government, nonfederal **Service:** General Medical and Surgical

Staffed Beds: 30 Admissions: 215 Census: 5 Outpatient Visits: 25341 **Births: 1 Personnel:** 104

FLOWOOD—Rankin County

✈ **MERIT HEALTH RIVER OAKS (250138)**, 1030 River Oaks Drive, Zip 39232–9553, Mailing Address: P.O. Box 5100, Jackson, Zip 39296–5100; tel. 601/932–1030 **A**1 3 10 **F**3 11 12 13 15 18 20 29 30 31 35 39 40 43 45 49 51 60 61 63 70 72 73 74 75 76 77 78 79 81 82 85 87 89 93 107 108 110 111 115 119 126 130 144 146 147 **P**5 **S** Community Health Systems, Inc., Franklin, TN
Primary Contact: L. Dwayne Blaylock, Chief Executive Officer
COO: Heather Sistrunk, R.N., Chief Operating Officer
CFO: Brad Sinclair, Chief Financial Officer
CIO: Pat Jones, Director Information Systems
CHR: Warren Weed, Director Human Resources
CNO: Sherry P. Cook, R.N., Chief Nursing Executive
Web address: www.riveroakshosp.com
Control: Corporation, Investor–owned, for–profit **Service:** General Medical and Surgical

Staffed Beds: 158 Admissions: 4316 Census: 45 Births: 1487 Total Expense ($000): 93425 **Payroll Expense ($000):** 31308 **Personnel:** 552

✈ **MERIT HEALTH WOMAN'S HOSPITAL (250136)**, 1026 North Flowood Drive, Zip 39232–9532, Mailing Address: 1026 North Flowood Drive, Zip 39232; tel. 601/932–1000 **A**1 10 **F**8 13 15 30 34 35 39 59 64 72 73 76 81 85 105 108 119 130 147 **S** Community Health Systems, Inc., Franklin, TN
Primary Contact: Sherry J. Pitts, Chief Executive Officer
CFO: Nick Renda, Chief Financial Officer
CMO: Ed Barham, M.D., Chief of Staff
CHR: Warren Weed, Director Associate Relations
CNO: Linda Atwood, Chief Nursing Officer
Web address: www.merithealthwomanshospital.com
Control: Corporation, Investor–owned, for–profit **Service:** Obstetrics and gynecology

Staffed Beds: 60 Admissions: 1731 Census: 17 Births: 1281 Total Expense ($000): 28129 **Payroll Expense ($000):** 10391 **Personnel:** 184

MS

Hospital, Medicare Provider Number, Address, Telephone, Approval, Facility, and Physician Codes, Health Care System

★ American Hospital Association (AHA) membership   ◯ Healthcare Facilities Accreditation Program   ⇑ Center for Improvement in Healthcare Quality Accreditation
☐ The Joint Commission accreditation   ◇ DNV Healthcare Inc. accreditation   △ Commission on Accreditation of Rehabilitation Facilities (CARF) accreditation

FOREST—Scott County

★ ◇ **LACKEY MEMORIAL HOSPITAL (251300)**, 330 Broad Street,
Zip 39074–3508, Mailing Address: P.O. Box 428, Zip 39074–0428;
tel. 601/469–4151, (Total facility includes 20 beds in nursing home–type unit)
A10 18 21 **F**3 8 11 15 18 29 34 35 38 40 41 43 45 50 54 55 56 57 59 64
65 66 68 70 81 86 87 89 92 97 98 103 104 106 107 108 110 111 114 119
127 128 130 133 143 **P**6 **S** Pioneer Health Services, Magee, MS
Primary Contact: Mark Norman, Chief Executive Officer
CFO: Julie Gieger, Chief Financial Officer
CMO: John Paul Lee, M.D., Chief of Staff
CIO: Eddie Pope, Chief Information Officer
CHR: Donn Paul, Chief Human Resources
Web address: www.lackeymemorialhospital.com
Control: Other not–for–profit (including NFP Corporation) **Service:** General
Medical and Surgical

Staffed Beds: 45 **Admissions:** 1053 **Census:** 32 **Outpatient Visits:** 19022
Births: 0 **Personnel:** 199

GREENVILLE—Washington County

★ ◇ **ALLEGIANCE SPECIALTY HOSPITAL OF GREENVILLE (252013)**, 300
South Washington Avenue, 3rd Floor, Zip 38701–4719; tel. 662/332–7344 **A**10
21 **F**1 3 29 34 57 85 87 130 148 **S** Allegiance Health Management,
Shreveport, LA
Primary Contact: Vernail Herzog, Chief Executive Officer
CMO: Parvez Karim, M.D., Chief Medical Officer
CIO: Sharon Scott, Health Information Director
CHR: Sharon Taylor, Human Resources Director
CNO: John Read, Chief Nursing Officer
Web address: www.ahmgt.com
Control: Corporation, Investor–owned, for–profit **Service:** Long–Term Acute Care
hospital

Staffed Beds: 39 **Admissions:** 363 **Census:** 27 **Outpatient Visits:** 0 **Births:**
0 **Total Expense ($000):** 11395 **Payroll Expense ($000):** 4724 **Personnel:**
106

★ **DELTA REGIONAL MEDICAL CENTER (250082)**, 1400 East Union Street,
Zip 38704–5247; tel. 662/378–3783, (Includes THE KING'S DAUGHTERS
HOSPITAL, 300 Washington Avenue, Zip 38701–3614, Mailing Address: P.O. Box
1857, Zip 38702–1857; tel. 662/378–2020; Scott Christensen, Chief Executive
Officer) **A**10 19 **F**3 4 11 13 15 18 20 22 28 29 30 31 34 35 38 39 40 43 45
46 50 51 55 57 59 60 62 63 64 65 66 68 70 72 73 75 76 77 78 79 81 84
85 89 90 93 94 96 97 98 102 103 104 107 108 109 110 111 114 115 116
118 119 127 129 130 131 132 135 144 146 147 148
Primary Contact: Scott Christensen, Chief Executive Officer
CFO: C. Thomas Moore, Chief Financial Officer
CIO: Andy Altenburger, Chief Information Officer
CHR: Chrissy Nicholson, Vice President Human Resources
CNO: Amy Walker, Chief Nursing Officer
Web address: www.deltaregional.com
Control: County–Government, nonfederal **Service:** General Medical and Surgical

Staffed Beds: 171 **Admissions:** 6323 **Census:** 89 **Outpatient Visits:** 90360
Births: 754 **Total Expense ($000):** 109215 **Payroll Expense ($000):** 50294
Personnel: 765

GREENWOOD—Leflore County

AMG SPECIALTY HOSPITAL–GREENWOOD (252010), 1401 River Road Floor
2, Zip 38930–4030; tel. 662/459–2681 **A**10 **F**1 3 18 34 50 59 130 **S** AMG
Integrated Healthcare Management, Lafayette, LA
Primary Contact: Jennifer Wallace, Chief Executive Officer
CMO: Gutti Rao, M.D., Medical Director
CNO: Brenda Small, Chief Clinical Officer
Web address: www.amggreenwood.com/
Control: Partnership, Investor–owned, for–profit **Service:** Long–Term Acute Care
hospital

Staffed Beds: 40 **Admissions:** 363 **Census:** 26 **Outpatient Visits:** 0 **Births:**
0 **Personnel:** 80

□ △ **GREENWOOD LEFLORE HOSPITAL (250099)**, 1401 River Road,
Zip 38930–4030, Mailing Address: Drawer 1410, Zip 38935–1410;
tel. 662/459–7000 **A**1 7 10 19 **F**3 8 13 15 17 18 20 29 31 32 33 35 39 40
43 45 53 56 57 59 61 68 70 74 75 76 79 81 82 85 86 87 89 90 93 94 96
103 107 108 110 111 114 117 118 119 127 129 130 132 145 146 147 148
P6 8
Primary Contact: James H. Jackson, Jr., Executive Director
COO: Dodie McElmurray, Chief Operating Officer
CFO: Dawne Holmes, Chief Financial Officer
CMO: Gutti Rao, M.D., Chief of Staff
CIO: Mark S. Hutson, Chief Information Officer
CHR: Key Britt, Associate Director
CNO: Rebecca Edwards, Chief Nursing Officer
Web address: www.glh.org
Control: City–County, Government, nonfederal **Service:** General Medical and
Surgical

Staffed Beds: 208 **Admissions:** 6512 **Census:** 81 **Outpatient Visits:** 156103
Births: 571 **Total Expense ($000):** 119571 **Payroll Expense ($000):** 56834
Personnel: 948

GRENADA—Grenada County

★ ◇ **UNIVERSITY OF MISSISSIPPI MEDICAL CENTER GRENADA (250168)**,
960 Avent Drive, Zip 38901–5230; tel. 662/227–7000 **A**10 20 21 **F**3 7 8 11
13 15 17 29 30 32 34 35 39 40 43 53 56 57 59 60 62 64 65 70 73 76 77
79 80 81 82 85 87 89 90 93 94 96 97 98 103 107 108 110 111 115 118
119 127 130 143 146 147 **P**6 **S** University Hospitals and Health System,
Jackson, MS
Primary Contact: Donald Hutson, Chief Executive Officer
COO: Molly B. Brown, Chief Operating Officer
CFO: Scott Whittemore, Chief Financial Officer
CIO: John Farrish, Health Information Director
CHR: Claudette Hathcock, Administrative Director Human Resources
Web address: www.ummchealth.com/grenada
Control: State–Government, nonfederal **Service:** General Medical and Surgical

Staffed Beds: 93 **Admissions:** 2636 **Census:** 31 **Outpatient Visits:** 50167
Births: 415 **Total Expense ($000):** 45735 **Payroll Expense ($000):** 18985
Personnel: 423

GULFPORT—Harrison County

⊠ **GARDEN PARK MEDICAL CENTER (250123)**, 15200 Community Road,
Zip 39503–3085, Mailing Address: P.O. Box 1240, Zip 39502–1240;
tel. 228/575–7000 **A**1 10 **F**3 12 13 15 18 19 29 34 35 40 41 43 45 46 49
57 59 70 74 76 79 81 85 86 87 89 90 97 98 103 107 108 110 111 112 114
115 116 118 119 126 130 132 146 147 **S** HCA, Nashville, TN
Primary Contact: Brenda M. Waltz, FACHE, Chief Executive Officer
COO: Regina Ramazani, Chief Operating Officer
CFO: Regina Ramazani, Chief Financial Officer
CMO: T. Paul Mace, Chief Medical Officer
CIO: Chris Oubre, Information Technology Director
CHR: Michael Pocchiari, Director Human Resources
CNO: Cheryl Thompson, Chief Nursing Officer
Web address: www.gpmedical.com
Control: Corporation, Investor–owned, for–profit **Service:** General Medical and
Surgical

Staffed Beds: 130 **Admissions:** 3666 **Census:** 46 **Outpatient Visits:** 64779
Births: 470 **Total Expense ($000):** 69983 **Payroll Expense ($000):** 23061
Personnel: 320

⊠ △ **MEMORIAL HOSPITAL AT GULFPORT (250019)**, 4500 13th Street,
Zip 39501–2569, Mailing Address: P.O. Box 1810, Zip 39502–1810;
tel. 228/867–4000, (Includes MEMORIAL BEHAVIORAL HEALTH, 11150 Highway
49 North, Zip 39503–4110; tel. 228/831–1700; Michael A. Zieman,
Administrator) **A**1 2 3 7 10 **F**3 4 8 11 13 15 17 18 20 22 26 28 29 30 31 34
35 40 43 44 45 46 48 49 50 51 53 54 57 59 64 65 66 68 70 71 72 73 74
76 77 78 79 80 81 84 85 87 89 90 92 93 95 96 98 99 100 101 102 104
105 107 108 110 111 114 115 116 117 118 119 120 121 124 126 130 132
135 145 146 **P**8
Primary Contact: Gary G. Marchand, President and Chief Executive Officer
COO: Kent Nicaud, Chief Operating Officer
CFO: Jeffrey T. Steiner, Vice President Finance
CMO: Larry Couvillon, M.D., Chief Medical Officer
CIO: Gene Thomas, Vice President, Information Systems, Chief Information Officer
CHR: Cathy Wood, Vice President, Human Resources
CNO: Jennifer Dumal, R.N., Chief Operating Officer of Clinical and Chief Nursing
Officer
Web address: www.gulfportmemorial.com
Control: City–County, Government, nonfederal **Service:** General Medical and
Surgical

Staffed Beds: 445 **Admissions:** 15855 **Census:** 228 **Outpatient Visits:**
607801 **Births:** 1399 **Total Expense ($000):** 391713 **Payroll Expense
($000):** 167895 **Personnel:** 2966

⊠ **SELECT SPECIALTY HOSPITAL–GULFPORT (252005)**, 1520 Broad Avenue,
Suite 300, Zip 39501–3601; tel. 228/575–7500 **A**1 10 **F**1 29 70 82 87 90 130
S Select Medical Corporation, Mechanicsburg, PA
Primary Contact: John O'Keefe, Chief Executive Officer
Web address: www.selectspecialtyhospitals.com/company/locations/gulfcoast.
aspx
Control: Corporation, Investor–owned, for–profit **Service:** Long–Term Acute Care
hospital

Staffed Beds: 61 **Admissions:** 446 **Census:** 25 **Outpatient Visits:** 0 **Births:**
0 **Total Expense ($000):** 16532 **Payroll Expense ($000):** 7858 **Personnel:**
139

MS

HATTIESBURG—Forrest County

★ △ ◇ **FORREST GENERAL HOSPITAL (250078)**, 6051 U.S. Highway 49, Zip 39401–7200, Mailing Address: P.O. Box 16389, Zip 39404–6389; tel. 601/288–7000 **A**2 3 5 7 10 19 21 **F**3 4 5 8 12 13 15 17 18 20 22 26 28 29 30 31 34 35 37 39 40 43 45 46 47 48 49 53 57 58 59 60 62 63 64 68 70 72 73 75 76 77 78 79 81 85 86 87 89 90 91 92 93 95 96 98 99 100 102 103 104 106 107 108 111 114 115 118 119 120 121 123 124 126 128 130 131 132 135 146 147 **P**1
Primary Contact: Evan S. Dillard, M.P.H., FACHE, President and Chief Executive Officer
COO: Douglas A. Jones, Chief Operating Officer
CFO: Andy Woodard, Chief Financial Officer
CMO: Steven E. Farrell, M.D., Chief Medical Officer
CHR: Troy P. Daniels, Chief Human Resources Officer
CNO: Micah Rehm, Chief Nursing Officer
Web address: www.forrestgeneral.com
Control: County–Government, nonfederal **Service:** General Medical and Surgical

Staffed Beds: 512 **Admissions:** 27619 **Census:** 349 **Outpatient Visits:** 147320 **Births:** 2369 **Total Expense ($000):** 392368 **Payroll Expense ($000):** 147707 **Personnel:** 3061

⊞ **MERIT HEALTH WESLEY (250094)**, 5001 Hardy Street, Zip 39402–1308, Mailing Address: P.O. Box 16509, Zip 39404–6509; tel. 601/268–8000 **A**1 10 19 **F**13 15 17 29 35 39 40 43 53 60 61 70 72 73 75 76 77 81 87 89 90 93 97 107 108 111 118 119 130 132 146 **P**6 7 **S** Community Health Systems, Inc., Franklin, TN
Primary Contact: Michael Neuendorf, Chief Executive Officer
CFO: Randy Humphrey, Chief Financial Officer
CMO: William Reno, III, M.D., President Medical Staff
CHR: Terry Trigg, Director Human Resources
Web address: www.wesley.com
Control: Corporation, Investor–owned, for–profit **Service:** General Medical and Surgical

Staffed Beds: 211 **Admissions:** 6802 **Census:** 97 **Outpatient Visits:** 86379 **Births:** 1192 **Personnel:** 813

⊞ **REGENCY HOSPITAL OF HATTIESBURG (252009)**, 6051 U.S. Highway 49, 5th Floor, Zip 39401–6031; tel. 601/288–8510 **A**1 10 **F**1 40 70 **S** Select Medical Corporation, Mechanicsburg, PA
Primary Contact: William Heath, Chief Executive Officer
CMO: Ralph Kahler, M.D., Medical Director
CHR: Joseph Worley, Human Resources Coordinator
Web address: www.hattiesburg.regencyhospital.com/
Control: Corporation, Investor–owned, for–profit **Service:** Long–Term Acute Care hospital

Staffed Beds: 33 **Admissions:** 397 **Census:** 29 **Outpatient Visits:** 0 **Births:** 0 **Total Expense ($000):** 8217 **Payroll Expense ($000):** 5750 **Personnel:** 146

HAZLEHURST—Copiah County

★ **HARDY WILSON MEMORIAL HOSPITAL (251327)**, 233 Magnolia Street, Zip 39083–2228, Mailing Address: P.O. Box 889, Zip 39083–0889; tel. 601/894–4541 **A**10 18 **F**15 29 35 39 40 51 75 81 93 104 107 111 119 130 133
Primary Contact: Benjamin Lott, Chief Executive Officer
CFO: David Abel, Chief Financial Officer
Web address: www.hwmhospital.com
Control: County–Government, nonfederal **Service:** General Medical and Surgical

Staffed Beds: 25 **Admissions:** 743 **Census:** 13 **Outpatient Visits:** 0 **Births:** 0 **Total Expense ($000):** 12440 **Payroll Expense ($000):** 5090 **Personnel:** 157

HOLLY SPRINGS—Marshall County

ALLIANCE HEALTHCARE SYSTEM (250012), 1430 Highway 4 East, Zip 38635–2140, Mailing Address: P.O. Box 6000, Zip 38634–6000; tel. 662/252–1212 **A**10 20 **F**15 29 35 40 43 57 75 81 87 89 98 103 104 107 119 130 132 133 143
Primary Contact: Perry E. Williams, Sr., Administrator and Chief Executive Officer
COO: Cecelia Bost, Chief Operating Officer
CFO: William F. Magee, Chief Financial Officer
CMO: Subbu Rayudu, M.D., Chief of Staff
CIO: Saul Mbenga, Manager Information Technology
CHR: Judy Eggers, Manager Human Resources
Web address: www.alliancehealth.us
Control: Corporation, Investor–owned, for–profit **Service:** General Medical and Surgical

Staffed Beds: 40 **Admissions:** 710 **Census:** 12 **Outpatient Visits:** 7615 **Births:** 0 **Total Expense ($000):** 10468 **Payroll Expense ($000):** 4456 **Personnel:** 95

HOUSTON—Chickasaw County

TRACE REGIONAL HOSPITAL (250017), Highway 8 East, Zip 38851–9396, Mailing Address: P.O. Box 626, Zip 38851–0626; tel. 662/456–3700 **A**10 **F**3 11 15 30 34 35 45 57 59 61 64 66 75 82 90 91 93 98 101 102 103 107 111 119 127 130 133 135 146 148 **P**6 **S** Sunlink Health Systems, Atlanta, GA
Primary Contact: Gary L. Staten, Chief Executive Officer
CFO: Pamela W. Cook, Chief Financial Officer
CMO: Bill Brohawn, Chief of Staff
CHR: Sherry Craig, Director Human Resources
CNO: Marianne Johnson, Chief Nursing Officer
Web address: www.traceregional.com
Control: Corporation, Investor–owned, for–profit **Service:** General Medical and Surgical

Staffed Beds: 84 **Admissions:** 621 **Census:** 12 **Outpatient Visits:** 13629 **Births:** 0 **Total Expense ($000):** 12138 **Payroll Expense ($000):** 7125 **Personnel:** 188

INDIANOLA—Sunflower County

★ **SOUTH SUNFLOWER COUNTY HOSPITAL (250095)**, 121 East Baker Street, Zip 38751–2498; tel. 662/887–5235 **A**10 20 **F**13 15 40 43 76 80 81 107 110 111 119 127 130 **P**8
Primary Contact: Courtney Phillips, Chief Executive Officer
COO: Holly H. Sparks, Chief Clinical Officer
CFO: Katie Yates, Chief Financial Officer
CMO: John H. Jones, Chief of Staff
CIO: Benjamin Rosenthal, Information Systems Director
CHR: Meredith Taylor, Controller
Control: County–Government, nonfederal **Service:** General Medical and Surgical

Staffed Beds: 46 **Admissions:** 1087 **Census:** 10 **Births:** 112 **Total Expense ($000):** 16204 **Payroll Expense ($000):** 5451 **Personnel:** 116

IUKA—Tishomingo County

⊞ **NORTH MISSISSIPPI MEDICAL CENTER–IUKA (250002)**, 1777 Curtis Drive, Zip 38852–1001, Mailing Address: P.O. Box 860, Zip 38852–0860; tel. 662/423–6051 **A**1 10 **F**7 15 17 29 34 35 40 43 53 57 64 65 68 70 75 82 86 87 89 90 91 93 107 108 111 119 130 132 133 134 **S** North Mississippi Health Services, Inc., Tupelo, MS
Primary Contact: Fred A. Truesdale, Jr., Administrator
CFO: Betty Moore, Business Manager
CMO: Margaret Glynn, M.D., Chief Medical Officer
CIO: Fred A. Truesdale, Jr., Administrator
CHR: Jane Chamblee, Manager Human Resources
Web address: www.nmhs.net
Control: Other not–for–profit (including NFP Corporation) **Service:** General Medical and Surgical

Staffed Beds: 48 **Admissions:** 690 **Census:** 6 **Outpatient Visits:** 21853 **Births:** 1 **Total Expense ($000):** 15841 **Payroll Expense ($000):** 7472 **Personnel:** 143

JACKSON—Hinds County

☐ **BRENTWOOD BEHAVIORAL HEALTHCARE OF MISSISSIPPI (254007)**, 3531 East Lakeland Drive, Zip 39232–8839; tel. 601/936–2024 **A**1 10 **F**35 98 99 101 102 104 105 130 132 134 **S** Universal Health Services, Inc., King of Prussia, PA
Primary Contact: Michael J. Carney, Chief Executive Officer
Web address: www.brentwoodjackson.com
Control: Corporation, Investor–owned, for–profit **Service:** Psychiatric

Staffed Beds: 105 **Admissions:** 2994 **Census:** 75 **Outpatient Visits:** 2905 **Births:** 0 **Personnel:** 220

⊞ **G.V. (SONNY) MONTGOMERY VETERANS AFFAIRS MEDICAL CENTER**, 1500 East Woodrow Wilson Drive, Zip 39216–5199; tel. 601/362–4471, (Nonreporting) **A**1 2 3 5 **S** Department of Veterans Affairs, Washington, DC
Primary Contact: David M. Walker, M.D., Medical Center Director
COO: Jed Fillingim, Acting Chief Operating Officer and Associate Director
CFO: Joy Willis, Acting Chief Fiscal Service
CMO: Kent Kirchner, M.D., Chief of Staff
CIO: Robert Wolak, Chief Information Resource Management Service
CHR: Sam Evans, Chief Human Resources Management
Web address: www.jackson.va.gov/
Control: Veterans Affairs, Government, federal **Service:** General Medical and Surgical

Staffed Beds: 323

Hospital, Medicare Provider Number, Address, Telephone, Approval, Facility, and Physician Codes, Health Care System

★ American Hospital Association (AHA) membership   ◯ Healthcare Facilities Accreditation Program   ⇑ Center for Improvement in Healthcare Quality Accreditation
☐ The Joint Commission accreditation   ◇ DNV Healthcare Inc. accreditation   △ Commission on Accreditation of Rehabilitation Facilities (CARF) accreditation

MS

MERIT HEALTH CENTRAL (250072), 1850 Chadwick Drive, Zip 39204–3479; Mailing Address: P.O. Box 59001, Zip 39284–9001; tel. 601/376–1000 **A**1 2 3 10 **F**4 13 15 16 17 29 35 40 43 51 61 70 72 75 76 77 78 81 86 87 89 90 93 97 98 100 102 107 108 111 116 118 119 130 132 146 147 **S** Community Health Systems, Inc., Franklin, TN
Primary Contact: Jon–Paul Croom, President and Chief Executive Officer
COO: Sam Dean, Chief Operating Officer
CFO: Justin Stroud, Chief Financial Officer
CMO: Greg Oden, Chief Medical Officer
CIO: Tracy Holifield, Director Information Systems
CHR: Sean Jones, Director Human Resources
CNO: Laura Knight, Chief Nursing Officer
Web address: www.merithealthcentral.com/
Control: Corporation, Investor–owned, for–profit **Service:** General Medical and Surgical

Staffed Beds: 319 **Admissions:** 8337 **Census:** 111 **Outpatient Visits:** 102890 **Births:** 780 **Personnel:** 851

△ **METHODIST REHABILITATION CENTER (250152)**, 1350 Woodrow Wilson Drive, Zip 39216–5198; tel. 601/981–2611, (Total facility includes 60 beds in nursing home–type unit) **A**1 3 5 7 10 **F**35 81 82 86 87 90 93 119 130 131 132 146
Primary Contact: Mark A. Adams, President and Chief Executive Officer
COO: Joseph M. Morette, Executive Vice President
CFO: Gary Armstrong, Executive Vice President
CIO: Gary Armstrong, Executive Vice President
CHR: Steve Hope, Vice President Corporate Services
Web address: www.methodistrehab.org
Control: Other not–for–profit (including NFP Corporation) **Service:** Rehabilitation

Staffed Beds: 184 **Admissions:** 1281 **Census:** 112 **Outpatient Visits:** 52937 **Births:** 0 **Total Expense ($000):** 51220 **Payroll Expense ($000):** 24987 **Personnel:** 591

MISSISSIPPI BAPTIST MEDICAL CENTER (250102), 1225 North State Street, Zip 39202–2064; tel. 601/968–1000 **A**1 2 3 5 10 **F**3 4 5 8 11 12 13 15 17 18 19 20 22 24 26 27 28 29 30 31 34 35 36 39 40 43 44 45 46 47 48 49 50 51 52 53 54 55 57 59 60 64 65 68 70 71 72 74 75 76 78 79 80 81 82 85 86 89 91 92 93 94 98 100 103 107 108 109 110 111 113 114 115 116 117 118 119 126 130 132 144 145 146 147 **S** Baptist Health Systems, Jackson, MS
Primary Contact: Chris Anderson, President & Chief Executive Officer
COO: Bobbie K. Ware, R.N., Vice President Patient Care and Chief Nursing Officer
CFO: William Thompson, Chief Financial Officer
CMO: Michael Maples, M.D., Vice President and Chief Medical Officer
CIO: Steve M. Stanic, Vice President and Chief Information Officer
CHR: Lee Ann Foreman, Vice President Human Resources
CNO: Bobbie K. Ware, R.N., Vice President Patient Care and Chief Nursing Officer
Web address: www.mbhs.org
Control: Other not–for–profit (including NFP Corporation) **Service:** General Medical and Surgical

Staffed Beds: 483 **Admissions:** 19830 **Census:** 298 **Outpatient Visits:** 221371 **Births:** 1674 **Personnel:** 2891

SELECT SPECIALTY HOSPITAL – BELHAVEN (252003), 1225 North State Street, Zip 39202–2097, Mailing Address: P.O. Box 23695, Zip 39225–3695; tel. 601/968–1000 **A**1 10 **F**1 3 29 39 56 61 80 82 130 **P**7 **S** Select Medical Corporation, Mechanicsburg, PA
Primary Contact: Bobbie K. Ware, R.N., FACHE, Chief Executive Officer and Chief Nursing Officer
CFO: Russell W. York, Vice President and Chief Financial Officer
CMO: Holland M. Addison, M.D., Medical Director
CIO: Steve M. Stanic, Vice President and Chief Information Officer
CHR: Lee Ann Foreman, Vice President Human Resources
Web address: www.mbhs.org
Control: Other not–for–profit (including NFP Corporation) **Service:** Long–Term Acute Care hospital

Staffed Beds: 24 **Admissions:** 232 **Census:** 19 **Outpatient Visits:** 0 **Births:** 0

SELECT SPECIALTY HOSPITAL–JACKSON (252007), 5903 Ridgewood Road, Suite 100, Zip 39211–3700; tel. 601/899–3800 **A**1 10 **F**1 107 119 **P**7 **S** Select Medical Corporation, Mechanicsburg, PA
Primary Contact: Chandler Ewing, Chief Executive Officer
CFO: Melissa Smith, Controller
CIO: Jacqueline Barnes, Manager Health Information
CHR: Vicki Watson, Manager Human Resources
Web address: www.selectspecialtyhospitals.com/company/locations/jackson.aspx
Control: Corporation, Investor–owned, for–profit **Service:** Long–Term Acute Care hospital

Staffed Beds: 53 **Admissions:** 638 **Census:** 47 **Outpatient Visits:** 0 **Births:** 0 **Personnel:** 212

ST. DOMINIC–JACKSON MEMORIAL HOSPITAL (250048), 969 Lakeland Drive, Zip 39216–4606; tel. 601/200–2000, (Nonreporting) **A**1 2 3 5 10
Primary Contact: Lester K. Diamond, President
CFO: Matt Fisher, Vice President Finance
CMO: Lawrence Riddles, M.D., Executive Vice President Medical Affairs and Quality
CIO: Keith Van Camp, Vice President Information Services
CHR: Lorraine Washington, Vice President Human Resources
CNO: Theresa Horne, MS, Vice President Patient Care Services
Web address: www.stdom.com
Control: Other not–for–profit (including NFP Corporation) **Service:** General Medical and Surgical

Staffed Beds: 476

△ **UNIVERSITY OF MISSISSIPPI MEDICAL CENTER (250001)**, 2500 North State Street, Zip 39216–4505; tel. 601/984–1000, (Includes BLAIR E. BATSON HOSPITAL FOR CHILDREN, 2500 North State State Room W019, Zip 39216–4500; tel. 601/984–1000; CHILDREN'S HEALTHCARE OF MISSISSIPPI, 2500 North State Street, Zip 39216–4500) **A**1 2 3 5 7 8 10 13 **F**3 6 7 8 11 12 13 15 17 18 19 20 21 22 23 24 25 26 27 28 29 30 31 32 34 35 37 39 40 41 43 44 45 46 47 48 49 50 52 53 54 55 56 57 58 59 60 61 64 65 66 68 70 71 72 73 74 75 76 77 78 79 80 81 84 85 86 87 88 89 90 92 93 94 96 97 98 99 100 101 102 103 104 107 108 110 111 112 114 115 116 117 118 119 120 121 123 124 126 127 129 130 131 132 134 135 136 137 138 139 141 142 143 144 146 147 148 **P**6 **S** University Hospitals and Health System, Jackson, MS
Primary Contact: Kevin S. Cook, Chief Executive Officer
CFO: Dan Janicak, Chief Financial Officer
CMO: William H. Cleland, M.D., Chief Medical Officer
CHR: Michael Estes, Director Human Resources
Web address: www.umc.edu
Control: State–Government, nonfederal **Service:** General Medical and Surgical

Staffed Beds: 680 **Admissions:** 29831 **Census:** 543 **Outpatient Visits:** 232136 **Births:** 2219 **Total Expense ($000):** 731950 **Payroll Expense ($000):** 261664 **Personnel:** 4631

KEESLER AFB—Harrison County

U. S. AIR FORCE MEDICAL CENTER KEESLER, 301 Fisher Street, Room 1A132, Zip 39534–2519; tel. 228/376–2550, (Nonreporting) **A**1 2 3 5 **S** Department of the Air Force, Washington, DC
Primary Contact: Colonel Thomas Harrell, M.D., Commander
COO: Brigadier General James Dougherty, Commander
CFO: Major Brenda Yi, Director Medical Resource Management and Chief Financial Officer
CMO: Colonel James Gasque, M.D., Chief Hospital Services
CIO: Major Samuel Silverthorne, Chief Information Officer
CHR: Major Brenda Yi, Director Medical Resource Management and Chief Financial Officer
Web address: www.keesler.af.mil
Control: Air Force, Government, federal **Service:** General Medical and Surgical

Staffed Beds: 56

KOSCIUSKO—Attala County

★ ◇ **BAPTIST MEDICAL CENTER ATTALA (251336)**, 220 Highway 12 West, Zip 39090–3208, Mailing Address: P.O. Box 887, Zip 39090–0887; tel. 662/289–4311, (Data for 335 days) **A**10 18 21 **F**3 15 29 34 35 40 43 56 57 59 63 64 65 81 85 89 90 92 93 103 107 108 110 115 116 118 119 130 133 148 **S** Baptist Health Systems, Jackson, MS
Primary Contact: John Dawson, Chief Executive Officer
CHR: Stephanie Washington, Human Resources Director
CNO: Allison Schuler, R.N., Chief Nursing Officer
Web address: www.mbhs.org/locations/baptist–medical–center–attala/
Control: County–Government, nonfederal **Service:** General Medical and Surgical

Staffed Beds: 25 **Admissions:** 762 **Census:** 11 **Births:** 0 **Total Expense ($000):** 4387 **Payroll Expense ($000):** 1387 **Personnel:** 99

LAUREL—Jones County

★ ◇ **SOUTH CENTRAL REGIONAL MEDICAL CENTER (250058)**, 1220 Jefferson Street, Zip 39440–4374, Mailing Address: P.O. Box 607, Zip 39441–0607; tel. 601/426–4000, (Total facility includes 252 beds in nursing home–type unit) **A**10 21 **F**3 4 7 10 12 13 15 17 18 20 28 29 30 31 34 35 37 39 40 43 48 49 51 53 56 57 59 62 63 64 68 69 70 73 74 75 76 77 78 79 81 82 84 85 86 87 89 90 92 93 100 102 104 105 107 108 110 111 114 115 117 118 119 127 128 130 131 132 134 143 144 146 147 148 **P**6
Primary Contact: G. Douglas Higginbotham, President and Chief Executive Officer
CFO: Tom Canizaro, Vice President and Chief Financial Officer
CIO: Dell Blakeney, Vice President and Chief Information Officer
CHR: Janet Staples, Vice President Human Resources
CNO: Beth W. Endom, R.N., Vice President and Chief Nursing Officer
Web address: www.scrmc.com
Control: County–Government, nonfederal **Service:** General Medical and Surgical

Staffed Beds: 402 **Admissions:** 8319 **Census:** 333 **Outpatient Visits:** 90171 **Births:** 883 **Total Expense ($000):** 136597 **Payroll Expense ($000):** 73683 **Personnel:** 1570

Many Facility Codes have changed. Please refer to the AHA Guide Code Chart.   © 2016 AHA Guide

MS

LEAKESVILLE—Greene County

GREENE COUNTY HOSPITAL (251329), 1017 Jackson Avenue,
Zip 39451–9105; tel. 601/394–4139 **A**10 18 **F**40 43 70 107 128 133
Primary Contact: Deborah Berry, Director of Operations
CFO: Debbie Brannan, Chief Financial Officer
CMO: Larry Henderson, M.D., Medical Director
CHR: Carla Shows, Payroll Clerk
Web address: www.georgeregional.com
Control: County–Government, nonfederal **Service:** General Medical and Surgical

Staffed Beds: 7 **Admissions:** 37 **Census:** 1 **Births:** 0 **Total Expense ($000):** 3521 **Payroll Expense ($000):** 1907 **Personnel:** 47

LEXINGTON—Holmes County

✠ **UNIVERSITY OF MISSISSIPPI MEDICAL CENTER HOLMES COUNTY (251319)**, 239 Bowling Green Road, Zip 39095–5167; tel. 601/496–5200 **A**1 10 18 **F**3 11 15 29 34 40 43 45 50 56 57 59 64 86 87 89 93 104 107 108 114 118 119 127 130 133 146 **P**6 **S** University Hospitals and Health System, Jackson, MS
Primary Contact: Donald Hutson, Chief Executive Officer
COO: Paige Lawrence, Assistant Administrator
CFO: Scott Whittemore, Chief Financial Officer
CMO: Mark Smothers, M.D., Chief Medical Officer
CIO: Sammuel Townsend, LAN Administrator
CHR: Claudette Hathcock, Human Resources Director
Web address: www.ummchealth.com/holmes/
Control: State–Government, nonfederal **Service:** General Medical and Surgical

Staffed Beds: 25 **Admissions:** 399 **Census:** 3 **Outpatient Visits:** 15633 **Births:** 0 **Total Expense ($000):** 12138 **Payroll Expense ($000):** 6455 **Personnel:** 99

LOUISVILLE—Winston County

WINSTON MEDICAL CENTER (250027), 562 East Main Street,
Zip 39339–2742, Mailing Address: P.O. Box 967, Zip 39339–0967;
tel. 662/773–6211, (Total facility includes 74 beds in nursing home–type unit) **A**10 20 **F**15 29 34 35 40 43 57 59 65 89 93 103 107 110 114 119 127 128 130 133 146
Primary Contact: Paul S. Black, Interim Administrator
Web address: www.winstonmedical.org
Control: Other not–for–profit (including NFP Corporation) **Service:** General Medical and Surgical

Staffed Beds: 91 **Admissions:** 606 **Census:** 74 **Outpatient Visits:** 19793 **Births:** 0 **Personnel:** 193

LUCEDALE—Jackson County

GEORGE REGIONAL HOSPITAL (250036), 859 Winter Street,
Zip 39452–6603, Mailing Address: P.O. Box 607, Zip 39452–0607;
tel. 601/947–3161 **A**10 20 **F**3 11 13 15 18 29 30 34 40 43 45 47 48 49 53 54 57 59 65 68 70 76 81 86 87 93 107 108 111 119 127 129 130 133 135 146 148 **P**8
Primary Contact: Greg Havard, Chief Executive Officer
CFO: Debbie Brannan, Chief Financial Officer
CMO: Jay Pinkerton, Chief of Staff
CIO: Anthoney Fryfogle, Chief Information Officer
CHR: Carla Shows, Human Resource and Payroll Clerk
CNO: Joel Turner, Director of Nursing
Web address: www.georgeregional.com
Control: County–Government, nonfederal **Service:** General Medical and Surgical

Staffed Beds: 48 **Admissions:** 1247 **Census:** 12 **Outpatient Visits:** 44389 **Births:** 264 **Total Expense ($000):** 20223 **Payroll Expense ($000):** 12249 **Personnel:** 328

MACON—Noxubee County

NOXUBEE GENERAL HOSPITAL (251307), 606 North Jefferson Street,
Zip 39341–2242, Mailing Address: P.O. Box 480, Zip 39341–0480;
tel. 662/726–4231, (Total facility includes 60 beds in nursing home–type unit) **A**10 18 **F**40 89 107 127 128 130 133
Primary Contact: Danny H. McKay, Administrator
Web address: www.noxubeecountyms.com/quality–of–life–noxubee–mississipp/health–care–noxubee–mississippi/
Control: County–Government, nonfederal **Service:** General Medical and Surgical

Staffed Beds: 85 **Admissions:** 728 **Census:** 65 **Births:** 0 **Total Expense ($000):** 15015 **Payroll Expense ($000):** 7975 **Personnel:** 195

MAGEE—Simpson County

★ **MAGEE GENERAL HOSPITAL (250124)**, 300 Third Avenue S.E.,
Zip 39111–3698; tel. 601/849–5070 **A**10 **F**13 15 29 35 40 43 76 81 89 97 107 108 111 119 130 133 146
Primary Contact: Amy Tolliver, Administrator
CMO: Kelli Smith, M.D., Chief of Staff
CIO: Kirby Craft, Chief Information Officer
CHR: Steve Beckham, Director Human Resources
CNO: Cindy McIntyre, R.N., Administrative Director Clinical Services
Web address: www.mghosp.org
Control: Other not–for–profit (including NFP Corporation) **Service:** General Medical and Surgical

Staffed Beds: 64 **Admissions:** 1294 **Census:** 16 **Births:** 274 **Personnel:** 227

MAGNOLIA—Pike County

BEACHAM MEMORIAL HOSPITAL (250049), 205 North Cherry Street,
Zip 39652–2819, Mailing Address: P.O. Box 351, Zip 39652–0351;
tel. 601/783–2351 **A**10 **F**3 34 35 36 57 59 65 68 98 100 101 103 107 114 127 130 133 146 148
Primary Contact: Jason Reed, Chief Executive Officer
CMO: Lucius Lampton, M.D., Medical Director
CHR: Jackie McKenzie, Director Administrative Services
Web address: www.beachammemhos.com
Control: Other not–for–profit (including NFP Corporation) **Service:** General Medical and Surgical

Staffed Beds: 37 **Admissions:** 976 **Census:** 24 **Outpatient Visits:** 0 **Births:** 0 **Personnel:** 44

MARKS—Quitman County

QUITMAN COUNTY HOSPITAL (251314), 340 Getwell Drive, Zip 38646–9785;
tel. 662/326–8031 **A**10 18 **F**3 29 35 40 43 56 64 75 89 90 93 103 105 106 107 114 119 130 133 **P**8
Primary Contact: Jeff Geraci, Administrator
CFO: Jane Moore, Director, Fiscal Services
CMO: James E. Warrington, Sr., M.D., Chief of Staff
CHR: Sandra Biffle, Personnel Clerk
CNO: Dana Hall, Director of Nursing
Control: Corporation, Investor–owned, for–profit **Service:** General Medical and Surgical

Staffed Beds: 33 **Admissions:** 332 **Census:** 6 **Outpatient Visits:** 9881 **Births:** 0 **Total Expense ($000):** 6557 **Payroll Expense ($000):** 3584 **Personnel:** 117

MCCOMB—Pike County

★ ◇ **SOUTHWEST MISSISSIPPI REGIONAL MEDICAL CENTER (250097)**, 215 Marion Avenue, Zip 39648–2705, Mailing Address: P.O. Box 1307, Zip 39649–1307; tel. 601/249–5500 **A**10 19 21 **F**3 8 11 12 13 15 17 18 20 22 24 26 28 29 30 31 34 35 37 39 40 41 43 44 45 47 48 49 50 53 55 57 59 64 65 70 72 73 74 75 76 77 78 79 81 85 86 87 92 93 107 108 109 110 111 115 118 119 120 121 126 127 129 130 131 132 135 145 146 148 **P**6 **S** Southwest Health Systems, Mccomb, MS
Primary Contact: Norman M. Price, FACHE, Chief Executive Officer
COO: Richard Williams, Chief Operating Officer
CFO: Charla Rowley, Chief Financial Officer
CMO: Kevin Richardson, M.D., Chief of Staff
CIO: Ron Noreen, Director, Information Services
CHR: Don Haskins, Administrative Director Human Resources
CNO: Michelle Gough, MSN, RN–B, Chief Nursing Officer
Web address: www.smrmc.com
Control: Hospital district or authority, Government, nonfederal **Service:** General Medical and Surgical

Staffed Beds: 143 **Admissions:** 6323 **Census:** 63 **Outpatient Visits:** 80480 **Births:** 782 **Personnel:** 894

MEADVILLE—Franklin County

FRANKLIN COUNTY MEMORIAL HOSPITAL (251330), 40 Union Church Road,
Zip 39653–8336, Mailing Address: P.O. Box 636, Zip 39653–0636;
tel. 601/384–5801 **A**10 18 **F**29 35 39 40 43 56 86 93 103 104 107 119 127 130 133 143 148 **P**6
Primary Contact: Mike Boleware, Administrator
Web address: www.fcmh.net
Control: County–Government, nonfederal **Service:** General Medical and Surgical

Staffed Beds: 25 **Admissions:** 460 **Census:** 18 **Births:** 0 **Total Expense ($000):** 15188 **Payroll Expense ($000):** 9184 **Personnel:** 198

Hospital, Medicare Provider Number, Address, Telephone, Approval, Facility, and Physician Codes, Health Care System

★ American Hospital Association (AHA) membership ○ Healthcare Facilities Accreditation Program ⇑ Center for Improvement in Healthcare Quality Accreditation
□ The Joint Commission accreditation ◇ DNV Healthcare Inc. accreditation △ Commission on Accreditation of Rehabilitation Facilities (CARF) accreditation

MENDENHALL—Simpson County

SIMPSON GENERAL HOSPITAL (251317), 1842 Simpson Highway 149, Zip 39114–3438; tel. 601/847–2221 **A**10 18 **F3** 11 29 30 34 35 40 43 44 54 56 57 59 61 64 65 66 68 81 85 86 87 90 93 98 100 101 102 103 104 107 114 119 127 130 132 133 134 143 146 **P**5
Primary Contact: Randall Neely, Chief Executive Officer
COO: Al Gary, COO
CFO: Al Gary, COO
CMO: Chip Holbrook, M.D., Chief of Staff
CIO: David Welch, Director Information Technology
CHR: Randall Neely, CEO
CNO: Sharon Burnham, Director of Nursing
Web address: www.simpsongeneralhospital.com
Control: Other not–for–profit (including NFP Corporation) **Service:** General Medical and Surgical

Staffed Beds: 35 **Admissions:** 728 **Census:** 16 **Outpatient Visits:** 13954 **Births:** 0 **Total Expense ($000):** 12035 **Payroll Expense ($000):** 7773 **Personnel:** 163

MERIDIAN—Lauderdale County

☐ **ALLIANCE HEALTH CENTER (250151)**, 5000 Highway 39 North, Zip 39301–1021; tel. 601/483–6211 **A**1 10 **F4** 32 34 35 36 38 54 57 59 64 70 71 86 87 98 99 101 102 103 105 106 135 **P**6 **S** Universal Health Services, Inc., King of Prussia, PA
Primary Contact: Brennan Francois, Chief Executive Officer
CFO: Robert Jackson, Chief Financial Officer
CMO: Terry Jordan, M.D., Chief of Staff
CIO: Brenda Smith, Director Financial Services
CHR: Shrea Johnson, Director Human Resources
Web address: www.alliancehealthcenter.com
Control: Corporation, Investor–owned, for–profit **Service:** Psychiatric

Staffed Beds: 154 **Admissions:** 3480 **Census:** 81 **Outpatient Visits:** 0 **Births:** 0 **Total Expense ($000):** 21169 **Payroll Expense ($000):** 11123 **Personnel:** 298

⌧ **ANDERSON REGIONAL HEALTH SYSTEM (250104)**, 2124 14th Street, Zip 39301–4040; tel. 601/553–6000 **A**1 2 10 19 **F3** 13 15 17 18 20 22 24 28 30 31 34 35 39 40 43 45 48 49 50 53 57 59 65 68 70 72 73 74 75 76 77 78 79 80 81 84 85 86 87 88 89 90 93 94 98 107 108 110 111 114 115 116 117 118 119 120 121 123 126 127 129 130 131 132 135 146 **P**7 8
Primary Contact: John G. Anderson, FACHE, President and Chief Executive Officer
CFO: Steven Brown, Vice President Finance
CMO: Scot Bell, Chief Medical Officer
CHR: Joel Windham, Vice President Human Resources
CNO: Matt Edwards, Vice President Nursing Services and Chief Nursing Officer
Web address: www.andersonregional.org
Control: Other not–for–profit (including NFP Corporation) **Service:** General Medical and Surgical

Staffed Beds: 260 **Admissions:** 10078 **Census:** 137 **Outpatient Visits:** 115508 **Births:** 1338 **Total Expense ($000):** 149571 **Payroll Expense ($000):** 53738 **Personnel:** 1197

☐ △ **ANDERSON REGIONAL HEALTH SYSTEM SOUTH (250081)**, 1102 Constitution Avenue, Zip 39301–4001; tel. 601/553–6000 **A**1 7 10 **F3** 18 29 34 35 50 57 59 60 61 64 68 74 75 81 82 84 86 87 90 97 103 106 107 114 115 117 119 127 130 132 133 135 144 146 **P**7 8
Primary Contact: John G. Anderson, FACHE, President and Chief Executive Officer
CFO: Steven Brown, Vice President Finance
CIO: Steve Taylor, Chief Information Officer
CHR: Joel Windham, Vice President Human Resources
CNO: Betty Cryer, R.N., Administrator/Chief Nursing Officer
Web address: www.andersonregional.org
Control: Other not–for–profit (including NFP Corporation) **Service:** General Medical and Surgical

Staffed Beds: 69 **Admissions:** 1037 **Census:** 38 **Outpatient Visits:** 41751 **Births:** 0 **Total Expense ($000):** 23356 **Payroll Expense ($000):** 7548 **Personnel:** 172

☐ **EAST MISSISSIPPI STATE HOSPITAL**, 1818 College Drive, Zip 39307, Mailing Address: Box 4128, West Station, Zip 39304–4128; tel. 601/482–6186, (Total facility includes 210 beds in nursing home–type unit) **A**1 **F4** 29 39 56 82 86 87 98 99 101 103 128 130 143 146 **S** Mississippi State Department of Mental Health, Jackson, MS
Primary Contact: Charles Carlisle, Director
CFO: Geri Doggett, Director Business
CMO: Gloria Gomez, M.D., Medical Director
CIO: Scotty Taylor, Information Technology Director
CHR: Shearmaine Calaway, Director Human Resources
CNO: Diane Nobles, Nurse Executive
Web address: www.emsh.state.ms.us
Control: State–Government, nonfederal **Service:** Psychiatric

Staffed Beds: 411 **Admissions:** 931 **Census:** 344 **Outpatient Visits:** 0 **Births:** 0 **Personnel:** 945

⌧ **REGENCY HOSPITAL OF MERIDIAN (252006)**, 1102 Constitution Avenue, 2nd Floor, Zip 39301–4001; tel. 601/484–7900 **A**1 10 **F1** 40 70 **S** Select Medical Corporation, Mechanicsburg, PA
Primary Contact: Clifton Quinn, Chief Executive Officer
Web address: www.regencyhospital.com
Control: Corporation, Investor–owned, for–profit **Service:** Long–Term Acute Care hospital

Staffed Beds: 40 **Admissions:** 410 **Census:** 30 **Outpatient Visits:** 0 **Births:** 0 **Total Expense ($000):** 14324 **Payroll Expense ($000):** 6036 **Personnel:** 121

RILEY HOSPITAL See Anderson Regional Health System South

★ ◇ **RUSH FOUNDATION HOSPITAL (250069)**, 1314 19th Avenue, Zip 39301–4195; tel. 601/483–0011, (Nonreporting) **A**10 19 21 **S** Rush Health Systems, Meridian, MS
Primary Contact: Larkin Kennedy, Chief Executive Officer
COO: Jason Payne, Executive Vice President and Chief Operating Officer
CMO: W. Scot Bell, M.D., Chief Medical Officer
CIO: Angela Sherrill, Corporate Director Information System
CHR: Donnie Smith, Director Human Resources
CNO: Casey Bland, Director of Nursing
Web address: www.rushhealthsystems.org/rfh/
Control: Other not–for–profit (including NFP Corporation) **Service:** General Medical and Surgical

Staffed Beds: 182

SPECIALTY HOSPITAL OF MERIDIAN (252004), 1314 19th Avenue, Zip 39301–4116; tel. 601/703–4211 **A**10 **F1** 3 18 20 22 30 31 34 57 59 65 68 74 78 79 85 87 94 96 127 133 135 144 **S** Rush Health Systems, Meridian, MS
Primary Contact: Elizabeth C. Mitchell, Chief Executive Officer and Chief Operating Officer
COO: Elizabeth C. Mitchell, Chief Operating Officer
CFO: Christopher Rush, Chief Financial Officer
CMO: John Johnston, Chief Medical Officer
CIO: Angela Sherrill, Corporate Director Information System
CHR: Donnie Smith, Director of Human Resources
CNO: Kawanda Johnson, Director of Nursing
Web address: www.specialtyhospitalofmeridian.com/shm/
Control: Other not–for–profit (including NFP Corporation) **Service:** Long–Term Acute Care hospital

Staffed Beds: 49 **Admissions:** 608 **Census:** 47 **Outpatient Visits:** 0 **Births:** 0 **Personnel:** 167

MONTICELLO—Lawrence County

LAWRENCE COUNTY HOSPITAL (251305), Highway 84 East, Zip 39654–0788, Mailing Address: P.O. Box 788, Zip 39654–0788; tel. 601/587–4051 **A**10 18 **F3** 30 45 87 107 111 114 119 127 133 **P**5 **S** Southwest Health Systems, Mccomb, MS
Primary Contact: Semmes Ross, Jr., Administrator
CFO: Jennifer Moak, Business Office Manager
Web address: www.smrmc.com
Control: County–Government, nonfederal **Service:** General Medical and Surgical

Staffed Beds: 25 **Admissions:** 511 **Census:** 22 **Outpatient Visits:** 7697 **Births:** 0 **Total Expense ($000):** 11082 **Payroll Expense ($000):** 3839 **Personnel:** 108

MORTON—Scott County

SCOTT REGIONAL HOSPITAL (251323), 317 Highway 13 South, Zip 39117–3353, Mailing Address: P.O. Box 259, Zip 39117–0259; tel. 601/732–6301 **A**10 18 **F3** 30 35 40 43 55 57 70 77 81 89 93 107 111 112 114 119 127 130 133 **S** Rush Health Systems, Meridian, MS
Primary Contact: Michael R. Edwards, Administrator
CFO: Paul S. Black, Chief Financial Officer
CHR: Amy Sugg, Director Human Resources
Web address: www.scottregional.org/srh/
Control: Other not–for–profit (including NFP Corporation) **Service:** General Medical and Surgical

Staffed Beds: 25 **Admissions:** 373 **Census:** 4 **Outpatient Visits:** 12724 **Births:** 0 **Personnel:** 148

Many Facility Codes have changed. Please refer to the AHA Guide Code Chart.
© 2016 AHA Guide

MS

NATCHEZ—Adams County

☒ △ **MERIT HEALTH NATCHEZ (250084)**, 54 Seargent S Prentiss Drive, Zip 39120–4726; tel. 601/443–2100 **A**1 7 10 **F**13 15 17 29 35 40 43 60 70 73 75 76 77 78 81 82 86 87 88 89 90 93 103 107 108 111 116 118 119 130 131 132 134 146 147 **P**5 **S** Community Health Systems, Inc., Franklin, TN
Primary Contact: Eric Robinson, Chief Executive Officer
CFO: Charles Mack, Vice President Finance and Chief Financial Officer
CMO: Leslie England, Chief of Staff
CIO: Leslie Makoro, Director Information management Systems
CHR: Jean E. Juchnowicz, Director Human Resources
Web address: www.natchezregional.com
Control: Corporation, Investor–owned, for–profit **Service:** General Medical and Surgical

Staffed Beds: 104 **Admissions:** 1918 **Census:** 32 **Births:** 141 **Total Expense ($000):** 35482 **Payroll Expense ($000):** 11998 **Personnel:** 385

☒ **NATCHEZ COMMUNITY HOSPITAL (250122)**, 129 Jefferson Davis Boulevard, Zip 39120–5100, Mailing Address: P.O. Box 1203, Zip 39121–1203; tel. 601/445–6200, (Nonreporting) **A**1 10 **S** Community Health Systems, Inc., Franklin, TN
Primary Contact: Eric Robinson, Chief Executive Officer
Web address: www.natchezcommunityhospital.com/default.aspx
Control: Partnership, Investor–owned, for–profit **Service:** General Medical and Surgical

Staffed Beds: 101

NEW ALBANY—Union County

☒ **BAPTIST MEMORIAL HOSPITAL–UNION COUNTY (250006)**, 200 Highway 30 West, Zip 38652–3112; tel. 662/538–7631 **A**1 10 **F**2 3 7 11 13 15 17 29 30 34 35 39 40 41 51 57 59 70 75 76 77 79 81 85 86 87 89 90 93 107 108 110 111 118 119 130 132 133 146 147 **S** Baptist Memorial Health Care Corporation, Memphis, TN
Primary Contact: Walter Grace, Chief Executive Officer and Administrator
CFO: Kim High, Chief Financial Officer
CMO: Justin Lohmeier, M.D., Chief of Staff
CIO: Missy Coltharp, Director
CHR: Lori Goode, Director Human Resources
CNO: Randy White, Chief Nursing Officer
Web address: www.baptistonline.org/union–county/
Control: Other not–for–profit (including NFP Corporation) **Service:** General Medical and Surgical

Staffed Beds: 153 **Admissions:** 3173 **Census:** 28 **Outpatient Visits:** 55776 **Births:** 967 **Total Expense ($000):** 47547 **Payroll Expense ($000):** 16190 **Personnel:** 320

OCEAN SPRINGS—Jackson County

OCEAN SPRINGS HOSPITAL See Singing River Health System, Pascagoula

OLIVE BRANCH—Desoto County

☐ **METHODIST OLIVE BRANCH HOSPITAL (250167)**, 4250 Bethel Road, Zip 38654–8737; tel. 662/932–9000 **A**1 10 **F**4 13 15 16 17 29 35 40 43 60 62 63 70 76 77 78 80 81 82 86 87 88 89 90 93 102 107 108 111 118 119 130 132 138 144 146 147 **P**8 **S** Methodist Le Bonheur Healthcare, Memphis, TN
Primary Contact: David G. Baytos, Chief Executive Officer
CFO: Kris Sanders, Chief Financial Officer
CHR: Robin Mathis, Director of Human Resources
CNO: Annelise Jensen, Chief Nursing Officer
Web address: www.methodisthealth.org/olivebranch
Control: Church–operated, Nongovernment, not–for profit **Service:** General Medical and Surgical

Staffed Beds: 67 **Admissions:** 1803 **Census:** 17 **Births:** 333 **Personnel:** 289

☐ **PARKWOOD BEHAVIORAL HEALTH SYSTEM (254005)**, 8135 Goodman Road, Zip 38654–2103; tel. 662/895–4900, (Total facility includes 40 beds in nursing home–type unit) **A**1 10 **F**4 5 29 34 35 54 57 64 71 75 82 86 87 98 99 100 101 102 103 104 105 106 130 135 **P**5 **S** Universal Health Services, Inc., King of Prussia, PA
Primary Contact: Ethan Permenter, Chief Executive Officer
CFO: David Denegri, Chief Financial Officer
CMO: Paul King, M.D., Medical Director
CHR: Julie Dorman, Human Resources Director
CNO: Alicia Plunkett, Chief Nurse Executive
Web address: www.parkwoodbhs.com
Control: Corporation, Investor–owned, for–profit **Service:** Psychiatric

Staffed Beds: 148 **Admissions:** 2969 **Census:** 108 **Outpatient Visits:** 5904 **Births:** 0 **Personnel:** 127

OXFORD—Lafayette County

☒ △ **BAPTIST MEMORIAL HOSPITAL–NORTH MISSISSIPPI (250034)**, 2301 South Lamar Boulevard, Zip 38655–5373, Mailing Address: P.O. Box 946, Zip 38655–6002; tel. 662/232–8100 **A**1 2 7 10 19 **F**3 7 8 11 12 13 15 17 18 20 22 24 25 26 28 29 30 31 34 35 40 43 47 48 49 50 53 57 59 64 68 70 73 74 76 78 79 81 84 85 86 87 89 90 93 96 107 108 110 111 114 115 116 117 118 119 126 130 131 132 146 147 **P**7 **S** Baptist Memorial Health Care Corporation, Memphis, TN
Primary Contact: William C. Henning, Administrator and Chief Executive Officer
CFO: Dana Williams, Chief Financial Officer
CMO: Dennis P. Morgan, Chief of Staff
CIO: Linda Britt, Director Information Systems
CHR: Debbie Swan, Director Human Resources
CNO: Mark Ottens, Chief Nursing Officer
Web address: www.baptistonline.org/north–mississippi/
Control: Other not–for–profit (including NFP Corporation) **Service:** General Medical and Surgical

Staffed Beds: 217 **Admissions:** 7960 **Census:** 97 **Outpatient Visits:** 77904 **Births:** 964 **Total Expense ($000):** 186462 **Payroll Expense ($000):** 42541 **Personnel:** 687

PASCAGOULA—Jackson County

☐ △ **SINGING RIVER HEALTH SYSTEM (250040)**, 2809 Denny Avenue, Zip 39581–5301; tel. 228/809–5000, (Includes OCEAN SPRINGS HOSPITAL, 3109 Bienville Boulevard, Ocean Springs, Zip 39564–4361; tel. 228/818–1111; Heath Thompson, R.N., Administrator; SINGING RIVER HOSPITAL, 2809 Denny Avenue, tel. 228/809–5000; Laurin St. Pe', Administrator) **A**1 2 7 10 **F**3 11 13 15 17 18 19 20 21 22 24 26 28 29 30 31 38 39 40 41 43 44 45 47 48 49 53 54 61 64 70 72 73 74 76 78 80 81 82 83 84 85 86 87 88 89 90 92 94 95 96 98 99 100 101 102 103 104 106 107 108 110 111 114 115 118 119 120 121 123 124 126 127 129 130 135 144 145 146 148 **P**8
Primary Contact: Kevin Holland, Chief Executive Officer
COO: Lee Bond, Chief Operating Officer
CFO: Brian Argo, Chief Financial Officer
CMO: Randy Roth, Chief Medical Officer
CHR: Craig Summerlin, Chief Human Resources Officer
CNO: Susan Russell, Chief Nursing Officer
Web address: www.singingriverhealthsystem.com
Control: County–Government, nonfederal **Service:** General Medical and Surgical

Staffed Beds: 376 **Admissions:** 16710 **Census:** 212 **Outpatient Visits:** 374487 **Births:** 1483 **Total Expense ($000):** 357003 **Payroll Expense ($000):** 129626 **Personnel:** 1374

PHILADELPHIA—Neshoba County

◇ **CHOCTAW HEALTH CENTER (250127)**, 210 Hospital Circle, Zip 39350–6781; tel. 601/656–2211 **A**10 21 **F**29 40 43 77 80 93 107 119 133 **P**4 6 8
Primary Contact: Tina Scott, Acting Health Director
CFO: Myrna Hancock, Director Financial Services
CMO: Juantina Johnson, Chief of Staff
CIO: Raymond Willis, IT Manager
CHR: Anna Denson, Human Resources Specialist
CNO: Regina Isaac, Director of Nursing
Web address: www.choctaw.org
Control: County–Government, nonfederal **Service:** General Medical and Surgical

Staffed Beds: 25 **Admissions:** 112 **Census:** 1 **Outpatient Visits:** 27466 **Births:** 0 **Total Expense ($000):** 14831 **Payroll Expense ($000):** 7886 **Personnel:** 262

NESHOBA COUNTY GENERAL HOSPITAL (250043), 1001 Holland Avenue, Zip 39350–2161, Mailing Address: P.O. Box 648, Zip 39350–0648; tel. 601/663–1200, (Total facility includes 160 beds in nursing home–type unit) **A**10 20 **F**3 7 11 15 29 32 34 40 43 45 46 57 59 64 65 81 82 89 90 93 103 104 107 108 110 111 114 118 119 127 128 130 132 133 143 144 146
Primary Contact: Lee McCall, Chief Executive Officer
CFO: Scott McNair, Chief Financial Officer
CMO: Jessica Myers, Medical Director
CHR: Hedda Stewart, Director Human Resources
CNO: Scott Breazeale, Chief Nursing Officer
Web address: www.neshobageneral.com
Control: County–Government, nonfederal **Service:** General Medical and Surgical

Staffed Beds: 208 **Admissions:** 1920 **Census:** 176 **Births:** 0 **Total Expense ($000):** 42455 **Payroll Expense ($000):** 20887 **Personnel:** 508

MS

Hospital, Medicare Provider Number, Address, Telephone, Approval, Facility, and Physician Codes, Health Care System

★ American Hospital Association (AHA) membership
☐ The Joint Commission accreditation
○ Healthcare Facilities Accreditation Program
◇ DNV Healthcare Inc. accreditation
⇑ Center for Improvement in Healthcare Quality Accreditation
△ Commission on Accreditation of Rehabilitation Facilities (CARF) accreditation

PICAYUNE—Pearl River County

HIGHLAND COMMUNITY HOSPITAL (250117), 130 Highland Parkway,
Zip 39466–5574, Mailing Address: P.O. Box 909, Zip 39466–0909;
tel. 601/358–9400 **A**10 **F**3 13 15 18 29 34 40 43 45 56 57 59 64 65 70 75
76 81 86 87 89 93 106 107 108 110 111 119 130 131 146 147
Primary Contact: Mark Stockstill, R.N., Administrator
CMO: Robert Lopez, Chief Medical Officer
CHR: Cynthia Render–Leach, Director Human Resources
CNO: Kim Varnado, R.N., Chief Nursing Officer
Web address: www.highlandch.com
Control: County–Government, nonfederal **Service:** General Medical and Surgical

Staffed Beds: 60 **Admissions:** 1934 **Census:** 21 **Outpatient Visits:** 48736
Births: 324 **Total Expense ($000):** 39559 **Payroll Expense ($000):** 15454
Personnel: 298

PONTOTOC—Pontotoc County

✠ **NORTH MISSISSIPPI MEDICAL CENTER–PONTOTOC (251308)**, 176 South
Main Street, Zip 38863–3311, Mailing Address: P.O. Box 790, Zip 38863–0790;
tel. 662/488–7640, (Total facility includes 44 beds in nursing home–type unit) **A**1
10 18 **F**3 11 34 35 40 43 57 65 68 82 83 84 86 87 93 107 114 119 128
130 133 146 **S** North Mississippi Health Services, Inc., Tupelo, MS
Primary Contact: Leslia Carter, Administrator
CFO: M. Denise Heard, Director Business Services
CHR: P. Marie Barnes, Director, Human Resources
CNO: Cathy Waldrop, Director, Hospital Nursing Services
Web address: www.nmhs.net
Control: Other not–for–profit (including NFP Corporation) **Service:** General
Medical and Surgical

Staffed Beds: 69 **Admissions:** 483 **Census:** 58 **Births:** 0 **Personnel:** 161

POPLARVILLE—Pearl River County

PEARL RIVER COUNTY HOSPITAL (251333), 305 West Moody Street,
Zip 39470–7338, Mailing Address: P.O. Box 392, Zip 39470–0392;
tel. 601/795–4543 **A**10 18 **F**3 35 40 43 64 65 93 103 107 119 127 130 133
143 146
Primary Contact: Steve Vaughan, Chief Executive Officer
CNO: Lisa Brown, Director of Nursing
Control: County–Government, nonfederal **Service:** General Medical and Surgical

Staffed Beds: 24 **Admissions:** 31 **Census:** 1 **Outpatient Visits:** 12389
Births: 0 **Personnel:** 234

PORT GIBSON—Claiborne County

CLAIBORNE COUNTY MEDICAL CENTER (251320), 123 McComb Avenue,
Zip 39150–2915, Mailing Address: P.O. Box 1004, Zip 39150–1004;
tel. 601/437–5141, (Nonreporting) **A**10 18
Primary Contact: Linda Dunigan, Chief Executive Officer
CFO: Linda Caho–Mooney, Chief Financial Officer
CIO: Ada Ratliff, Chief Information Officer
Control: County–Government, nonfederal **Service:** General Medical and Surgical

Staffed Beds: 32

PRENTISS—Jefferson Davis County

JEFFERSON DAVIS COMMUNITY HOSPITAL (251326), 1102 Rose Street,
Zip 39474–5200, Mailing Address: P.O. Box 1288, Zip 39474–1288;
tel. 601/792–4276, (Total facility includes 60 beds in nursing home–type unit)
A10 18 **F**3 35 40 43 53 56 57 64 65 66 70 86 87 89 93 98 103 107 111
119 127 128 130 132 133
Primary Contact: Jimmy Graves, Interim Chief Executive Officer
CHR: Diane Daughdrill, Director Human Resources
Web address: www.jdchospital.com
Control: County–Government, nonfederal **Service:** General Medical and Surgical

Staffed Beds: 95 **Admissions:** 395 **Census:** 60 **Outpatient Visits:** 12457
Births: 0 **Total Expense ($000):** 15462 **Payroll Expense ($000):** 4743
Personnel: 129

PURVIS—Lamar County

☐ **SOUTH MISSISSIPPI STATE HOSPITAL (254008)**, 823 Highway 589,
Zip 39475–4194; tel. 601/794–0100 **A**1 10 **F**3 98 106 130 146 **S** Mississippi
State Department of Mental Health, Jackson, MS
Primary Contact: Clint Ashley, Director
CFO: Andy Tucker, Chief Financial Officer
CMO: Allen Harris, M.D., Clinical Director
CIO: Sabrina Young, Administrative Support Director
CHR: Kelly Reid, Human Resources Director
CNO: Pam Brinson, Nurse Executive
Web address: www.smsh.state.ms.us
Control: State–Government, nonfederal **Service:** Psychiatric

Staffed Beds: 50 **Admissions:** 648 **Census:** 44 **Outpatient Visits:** 0 **Births:**
0 **Personnel:** 99

QUITMAN—Clarke County

H. C. WATKINS MEMORIAL HOSPITAL (251316), 605 South Archusa Avenue,
Zip 39355–2331; tel. 601/776–6925 **A**10 18 **F**29 40 43 81 89 104 107 127
130 133 **P**6 **S** Rush Health Systems, Meridian, MS
Primary Contact: Michael Nester, Administrator
CFO: Paul S. Black, Controller
CMO: O. Wayne Byrd, M.D., Chief of Staff
CIO: Melinda Smith, Chief Information Systems
CHR: Leigh Moore, Administrative Assistant Human Resources
Web address: www.watkinsmemorialhospital.com/hcwmh/
Control: Other not–for–profit (including NFP Corporation) **Service:** General
Medical and Surgical

Staffed Beds: 25 **Admissions:** 508 **Census:** 15 **Births:** 0 **Total Expense**
($000): 9791 **Payroll Expense ($000):** 5104 **Personnel:** 190

RALEIGH—Smith County

PATIENTS CHOICE MEDICAL CENTER OF SMITH COUNTY (250163), 347
Magnolia Drive, Zip 39153–6011; tel. 601/782–9997 **A**10 **F**98 101 103 104
108 130 **P**6
Primary Contact: Tim Cockrell, Chief Executive Officer
Control: Corporation, Investor–owned, for–profit **Service:** General Medical and
Surgical

Staffed Beds: 20 **Admissions:** 136 **Census:** 5 **Births:** 0 **Personnel:** 26

RICHTON—Perry County

PERRY COUNTY GENERAL HOSPITAL (251306), 206 Bay Avenue,
Zip 39476–2941; tel. 601/788–6316 **A**10 18 **F**3 34 40 41 43 57 59 64 65
107 115 119 127 133 146
Primary Contact: David Paris, Chief Executive Officer
Web address: www.pcghospital.com/
Control: Partnership, Investor–owned, for–profit **Service:** General Medical and
Surgical

Staffed Beds: 22 **Admissions:** 208 **Census:** 4 **Outpatient Visits:** 10606
Births: 0 **Total Expense ($000):** 4865 **Payroll Expense ($000):** 3725
Personnel: 53

RIPLEY—Tippah County

★ **TIPPAH COUNTY HOSPITAL (250010)**, 1005 City Avenue North,
Zip 38663–1414, Mailing Address: P.O. Box 499, Zip 38663–0499;
tel. 662/837–9221, (Total facility includes 40 beds in nursing home–type unit)
A10 20 **F**29 40 43 53 81 89 90 93 107 119 128 130 131 133 **P**1
Primary Contact: Patrick Chapman, Ed.D., Chief Executive Officer
CFO: Stephanie McAlister, Controller
CMO: Troy Cappleman, M.D., Chief of Staff
CHR: Heather Taylor, Human Resources Manager
CNO: Carol Anne Hurt, Chief Nursing Officer
Web address: www.tippahcountyhospital.com/
Control: County–Government, nonfederal **Service:** General Medical and Surgical

Staffed Beds: 65 **Admissions:** 572 **Census:** 44 **Outpatient Visits:** 14555
Births: 0 **Total Expense ($000):** 9706 **Payroll Expense ($000):** 3582
Personnel: 170

ROLLING FORK—Sharkey County

SHARKEY–ISSAQUENA COMMUNITY HOSPITAL (250079), 108 South Fourth
Street, Zip 39159–5146, Mailing Address: P.O. Box 339, Zip 39159–0339;
tel. 662/873–4395 **A**10 **F**40 53 56 98 103 104 105 107 111 119 133
Primary Contact: Jerry Keever, Administrator
Control: County–Government, nonfederal **Service:** General Medical and Surgical

Staffed Beds: 29 **Admissions:** 606 **Census:** 12 **Births:** 0 **Total Expense**
($000): 8342 **Payroll Expense ($000):** 3359 **Personnel:** 71

RULEVILLE—Sunflower County

★ **NORTH SUNFLOWER MEDICAL CENTER (251318)**, 840 North Oak Avenue,
Zip 38771–3227, Mailing Address: P.O. Box 369, Zip 38771–0369;
tel. 662/756–2711, (Total facility includes 60 beds in nursing home–type unit)
A10 18 **F**15 29 35 40 43 53 56 63 75 77 81 82 87 90 93 97 100 103 104
107 119 128 130 132 133 134 143 147 **P**6
Primary Contact: Sam Miller, Chief Executive Officer
COO: Rodney Clark, Chief Operating Officer
CFO: Nickie Moore, Chief Financial Officer
CMO: Bennie B. Wright, M.D., Chief of Staff
CIO: Roger Goss, Director, Information Services
CHR: Robbie Taylor, Director Human Resources
CNO: Lisa Miller, R.N., Director of Nursing
Web address: www.northsunflower.com
Control: Navy, Government, federal **Service:** General Medical and Surgical

Staffed Beds: 95 **Admissions:** 898 **Census:** 70 **Outpatient Visits:** 50138
Births: 0 **Total Expense ($000):** 57102 **Payroll Expense ($000):** 20700
Personnel: 386

MS

Many Facility Codes have changed. Please refer to the AHA Guide Code Chart. © 2016 AHA Guide

SENATOBIA—Tate County

☐ **NORTH OAK REGIONAL MEDICAL CENTER (250126)**, 401 Getwell Drive, Zip 38668–2213, Mailing Address: P.O. Box 648, Zip 38668–0648; tel. 662/562–3100 **A**1 10 **F**3 29 34 35 40 43 45 56 57 64 81 86 98 103 107 114 119 130 132
Primary Contact: Sonja Graham, Chief Executive Officer
CHR: Vickie Barksdale, Manager Human Resources
Web address: www.normc.org
Control: Corporation, Investor–owned, for–profit **Service:** General Medical and Surgical

Staffed Beds: 41 **Admissions:** 909 **Census:** 13 **Outpatient Visits:** 11740 **Births:** 0 **Total Expense ($000):** 10435 **Payroll Expense ($000):** 5329 **Personnel:** 124

SOUTHAVEN—Desoto County

⊠ △ **BAPTIST MEMORIAL HOSPITAL–DESOTO (250141)**, 7601 Southcrest Parkway, Zip 38671–4742; tel. 662/772–4000 **A**1 3 7 10 **F**3 5 11 15 17 18 20 22 26 28 29 30 31 35 39 40 43 44 45 46 47 48 49 50 57 59 60 61 68 70 73 74 75 76 77 78 79 80 81 82 84 85 86 87 90 93 96 107 108 109 110 111 114 115 116 117 118 119 120 121 123 124 126 130 131 132 135 143 144 146 147 **P**1 **S** Baptist Memorial Health Care Corporation, Memphis, TN
Primary Contact: James Huffman, Chief Executive Officer and Administrator
CFO: Joe McWherter, Chief Financial Officer
CMO: Joann Wood, M.D., Chief Medical Officer
CHR: Walter Banks, Director Human Resources
Web address: www.baptistonline.org/desoto/
Control: Other not–for–profit (including NFP Corporation) **Service:** General Medical and Surgical

Staffed Beds: 233 **Admissions:** 15678 **Census:** 220 **Outpatient Visits:** 103245 **Births:** 1669 **Total Expense ($000):** 236618 **Payroll Expense ($000):** 76181 **Personnel:** 1211

STARKVILLE—Oktibbeha County

★ ◇ **OCH REGIONAL MEDICAL CENTER (250050)**, 400 Hospital Road, Zip 39759–2163, Mailing Address: P.O. Box 1506, Zip 39760–1506; tel. 662/323–4320 **A**10 21 **F**3 7 11 13 15 17 28 29 32 34 35 39 40 41 43 45 47 48 51 53 57 59 61 64 65 66 70 73 74 75 76 77 79 81 82 85 87 88 89 90 93 97 98 107 108 110 111 114 115 118 119 126 130 131 132 133 135 146 147 **P**6
Primary Contact: Richard G. Hilton, Administrator and Chief Executive Officer
COO: Mike Andrews, Associate Administrator and Chief Operating Officer
CFO: Susan Russell, Chief Financial Officer
CIO: Chamath Wijewardane, Director Information Technology
CHR: Mike Andrews, Associate Administrator and Chief Operating Officer
CNO: Martha Fulcher, MSN, Chief Nursing Officer
Web address: www.och.org
Control: County–Government, nonfederal **Service:** General Medical and Surgical

Staffed Beds: 96 **Admissions:** 2505 **Census:** 27 **Outpatient Visits:** 267523 **Births:** 898 **Total Expense ($000):** 72278 **Payroll Expense ($000):** 34564 **Personnel:** 614

TUPELO—Lee County

⊠ △ **NORTH MISSISSIPPI MEDICAL CENTER – TUPELO (250004)**, 830 South Gloster Street, Zip 38801–4934; tel. 662/377–3000, (Total facility includes 107 beds in nursing home–type unit) **A**1 2 3 5 7 10 **F**3 4 5 7 11 12 13 15 17 18 19 20 22 24 26 28 29 30 31 32 34 35 37 38 40 41 43 44 46 47 48 49 50 51 53 56 57 58 59 61 62 63 64 66 68 70 71 72 73 74 75 76 77 78 79 80 81 83 84 85 86 87 88 89 90 91 92 93 96 97 98 100 101 103 104 106 107 108 109 110 111 112 113 114 115 116 117 118 119 120 121 122 123 124 126 128 129 130 131 132 134 135 146 147 148 **P**6 7 **S** North Mississippi Health Services, Inc., Tupelo, MS
Primary Contact: David C. Wilson, Chief Executive Officer
CFO: Joseph A. Reppert, Executive Vice President and Chief Financial Officer
CHR: Rodger Brown, Vice President Human Resources
Web address: www.nmhs.net
Control: Other not–for–profit (including NFP Corporation) **Service:** General Medical and Surgical

Staffed Beds: 757 **Admissions:** 24941 **Census:** 508 **Outpatient Visits:** 259890 **Births:** 2145 **Total Expense ($000):** 603798 **Payroll Expense ($000):** 199363 **Personnel:** 4534

NORTH MISSISSIPPI STATE HOSPITAL (254009), 1937 Briar Ridge Road, Zip 38804–5963; tel. 662/690–4200 **A**1 10 **F**3 29 30 34 87 98 101 106 130 143 146 **S** Mississippi State Department of Mental Health, Jackson, MS
Primary Contact: Paul A. Callens, Ph.D., Director
CFO: Joe Rials, Director Fiscal Services
CMO: Ken Lippincott, M.D., Chief of Staff
CIO: James Wilhite, Director Systems Information
Web address: www.nmsh.state.ms.us
Control: State–Government, nonfederal **Service:** Psychiatric

Staffed Beds: 50 **Admissions:** 547 **Census:** 45 **Outpatient Visits:** 0 **Births:** 0 **Personnel:** 116

TYLERTOWN—Walthall County

★ **WALTHALL COUNTY GENERAL HOSPITAL (251324)**, 100 Hospital Drive, Zip 39667–2099; tel. 601/876–2122 **A**10 18 **F**40 43 81 89 93 107 111 119 127 130 133 146
Primary Contact: Bryan K. Maxie, Administrator
Web address: www.walthallhospitalms.org
Control: County–Government, nonfederal **Service:** General Medical and Surgical

Staffed Beds: 25 **Admissions:** 574 **Census:** 9 **Outpatient Visits:** 16919 **Births:** 0 **Total Expense ($000):** 9499 **Payroll Expense ($000):** 4770 **Personnel:** 94

UNION—Newton County

LAIRD HOSPITAL (251322), 25117 Highway 15, Zip 39365–9099; tel. 601/774–8214, (Nonreporting) **A**10 18 **S** Rush Health Systems, Meridian, MS
Primary Contact: Thomas G. Bartlett, III, Administrator
COO: Morris A. Reece, EVP/COO
CFO: Jennifer Flint, Chief Financial Officer
CMO: John Mutziger, M.D., Chief Medical Officer
CIO: Angela Sherrill, Chief Information Officer
CHR: Donnie Smith, Chief Human Resources Officer
CNO: Pam Rigdon, Director Nursing
Web address: www.lairdhospital.com/lh/
Control: Other not–for–profit (including NFP Corporation) **Service:** General Medical and Surgical

Staffed Beds: 25

VICKSBURG—Warren County

⊠ **MERIT HEALTH RIVER REGION (250031)**, 2100 Highway 61 North, Zip 39183–8211, Mailing Address: P.O. Box 590, Zip 39181–0590; tel. 601/883–5000, (Includes RIVER REGION WEST CAMPUS, 1111 North Frontage Road, Zip 39180–5102; tel. 601/883–5000) **A**1 10 **F**3 4 7 13 15 17 18 20 22 24 26 29 30 35 38 39 40 43 47 49 50 51 56 60 64 65 70 73 75 76 77 78 79 81 82 85 87 89 90 93 97 98 100 101 102 103 107 108 110 111 114 115 118 119 126 127 130 131 132 135 146 147 **S** Community Health Systems, Inc., Franklin, TN
Primary Contact: Gregory Pearson, Chief Executive Officer
CFO: John Milazzo, Chief Financial Officer
CMO: W. Briggs Hopson, M.D., Clinical Medical Director
CIO: J. B. White, Director Information Systems
CHR: Hal Harrington, Vice President Human Resources
Web address: www.riverregion.com
Control: Corporation, Investor–owned, for–profit **Service:** General Medical and Surgical

Staffed Beds: 361 **Admissions:** 7780 **Census:** 118 **Births:** 694 **Personnel:** 871

PROMISE HOSPITAL OF VICKSBURG (252008), 1111 North Frontage Road, 2nd Floor, Zip 39180–5102; tel. 601/619–3526 **A**10 **F**1 3 11 70 77 90 148 **S** Promise Healthcare, Boca Raton, FL
Primary Contact: Michael Harrell, R.N., Chief Executive Officer
COO: Dawn Posey, Chief Operating Officer
CFO: Christopher A. Stegall, Regional Chief Financial Officer and Chief Operating Officer
CMO: Daniel Edney, M.D., Chief of Staff
CIO: Barbara Whiting, Director Health Information Management
CHR: Debbie Carson, Director Human Resources
Web address: www.promise–vicksburg.com
Control: Corporation, Investor–owned, for–profit **Service:** Long–Term Acute Care hospital

Staffed Beds: 33 **Admissions:** 377 **Census:** 28 **Outpatient Visits:** 0 **Births:** 0 **Personnel:** 78

MS

Hospital, Medicare Provider Number, Address, Telephone, Approval, Facility, and Physician Codes, Health Care System

★ American Hospital Association (AHA) membership ○ Healthcare Facilities Accreditation Program ⇑ Center for Improvement in Healthcare Quality Accreditation
☐ The Joint Commission accreditation ◇ DNV Healthcare Inc. accreditation △ Commission on Accreditation of Rehabilitation Facilities (CARF) accreditation

WATER VALLEY—Yalobusha County

★ **YALOBUSHA GENERAL HOSPITAL (250061)**, 630 South Main,
Zip 38965–3468, Mailing Address: P.O. Box 728, Zip 38965–0728;
tel. 662/473–1411, (Total facility includes 122 beds in nursing home–type unit)
A10 **F**2 3 7 15 29 30 32 33 59 64 65 70 107 110 115 119 127 128 130 133
143 146 **P**6
Primary Contact: Terry Varner, Administrator
COO: Ashlee Langdon, Controller
CHR: Katie Rotenberry–Baggett, Administrative Assistant and Human Resources
Web address: www.yalobushageneral.com/
Control: County–Government, nonfederal **Service:** General Medical and Surgical

Staffed Beds: 148 **Admissions:** 546 **Census:** 123 **Outpatient Visits:** 0
Births: 0 **Total Expense ($000):** 20852 **Payroll Expense ($000):** 13402
Personnel: 196

WAYNESBORO—Wayne County

◇ **WAYNE GENERAL HOSPITAL (250077)**, 950 Matthew Drive, Zip 39367–2590,
Mailing Address: P.O. Box 1249, Zip 39367–1249; tel. 601/735–5151 **A**10 20
21 **F**13 15 29 35 39 40 43 53 61 62 63 70 75 76 81 86 89 93 107 108 111
119 127 130 132 133 146
Primary Contact: Kathy Waddell, Administrator
Web address: www.waynegeneralhospital.org
Control: County–Government, nonfederal **Service:** General Medical and Surgical

Staffed Beds: 80 **Admissions:** 2023 **Census:** 31 **Outpatient Visits:** 33688
Births: 226 **Total Expense ($000):** 28635 **Payroll Expense ($000):** 15558
Personnel: 361

WEST POINT—Clay County

⊠ **NORTH MISSISSIPPI MEDICAL CENTER–WEST POINT (250067)**, 835
Medical Center Drive, Zip 39773–9320; tel. 662/495–2300 **A**1 10 **F**3 7 8 11 13
15 17 28 29 30 31 32 34 35 40 42 43 45 48 53 57 59 64 65 70 73 75 76
78 79 80 81 85 86 87 89 90 97 107 108 109 110 114 119 120 130 132
133 135 143 145 146 147 **S** North Mississippi Health Services, Inc., Tupelo, MS
Primary Contact: Barry L. Keel, Administration
CFO: Kay Lawler, Business Office Manager
CMO: B. Keith Watson, M.D., Chief Medical Staff
CIO: Stacie Griggs, MIS Analyst
CHR: Brenda Johnson, Director Human Resources
CNO: Jane Windle, R.N., Director of Nurses
Web address: www.nmhs.net/westpoint
Control: Other not–for–profit (including NFP Corporation) **Service:** General
Medical and Surgical

Staffed Beds: 60 **Admissions:** 1564 **Census:** 15 **Outpatient Visits:** 44628
Births: 377 **Total Expense ($000):** 27893 **Payroll Expense ($000):** 13189
Personnel: 261

WHITFIELD—Rankin County

⊠ **MISSISSIPPI STATE HOSPITAL (254010)**, 3550 Highway 468 West,
Zip 39193–5529, Mailing Address: P.O. Box 157–A, Zip 39193–0157;
tel. 601/351–8000, (Includes WHITFIELD MEDICAL SURGICAL HOSPITAL, Oak
Circle, Zip 39193; tel. 601/351–8023) **A**1 3 10 **F**4 29 39 56 75 86 87 98 100
101 103 104 107 119 128 130 143 146 **P**1 **S** Mississippi State Department of
Mental Health, Jackson, MS
Primary Contact: James G. Chastain, FACHE, Director
COO: Kelly R. Breland, CPA, Director Support Services
CFO: Alicia Harris, Director Fiscal Services
CMO: Duncan Stone, D.D.S., Chief Medical Staff
CIO: Bart Uharriet, Director Information Services
CHR: Katie Storr, Director of Human Resources
CNO: Jackie Yates, R.N., Nurse Executive
Web address: www.msh.state.ms.us
Control: State–Government, nonfederal **Service:** Psychiatric

Staffed Beds: 395 **Admissions:** 1766 **Census:** 169 **Outpatient Visits:** 3311
Births: 0 **Personnel:** 1244

WIGGINS—Stone County

STONE COUNTY HOSPITAL (251303), 1434 East Central Avenue,
Zip 39577–9602; tel. 601/928–6600 **A**10 18 **F**3 7 29 34 35 40 43 46 57 59
64 70 77 79 81 89 90 97 107 111 112 114 115 119 127 130 133 135 143
146 **P**6
Primary Contact: Joan Strayham, R.N., Chief Executive Officer
Web address: www.schospital.net/
Control: Corporation, Investor–owned, for–profit **Service:** General Medical and
Surgical

Staffed Beds: 25 **Admissions:** 462 **Census:** 4 **Births:** 0 **Total Expense
($000):** 20321 **Payroll Expense ($000):** 7209 **Personnel:** 174

WINONA—Montgomery County

TYLER HOLMES MEMORIAL HOSPITAL (251312), 409 Tyler Holmes Drive,
Zip 38967–1599; tel. 662/283–4114 **A**10 18 **F**3 11 34 35 40 41 43 50 51 57
59 66 87 104 107 111 114 119 130 133 135 **P**8
Primary Contact: Rosamond M. Tyler, Administrator
CFO: Cori Bailey, Accountant
CHR: Becky Corley, Director Human Resources
Control: County–Government, nonfederal **Service:** General Medical and Surgical

Staffed Beds: 25 **Admissions:** 612 **Census:** 11 **Births:** 0 **Total Expense
($000):** 12750 **Payroll Expense ($000):** 6265 **Personnel:** 138

YAZOO CITY—Yazoo County

★ **BAPTIST MEDICAL CENTER YAZOO (251313)**, 823 Grand Avenue,
Zip 39194–3233; tel. 662/746–2261 **A**10 18 **F**8 11 15 29 30 40 53 54 56 81
93 97 107 110 111 114 119 133 **S** Baptist Health Systems, Jackson, MS
Primary Contact: Sean Johnson, Chief Executive Officer
COO: Marsha Jones, R.N., Director Nursing
CFO: James L. Miller, Chief Financial Officer
CMO: Marion Sigrest, M.D., Chief of Staff
CIO: Benton D. Estes, Materials Management
CHR: Stephanie Washington, Director Community Relations and Human Resources
CNO: Marsha Jones, R.N., Director of Nursing
Web address: www.kdhyazoo.com
Control: Other not–for–profit (including NFP Corporation) **Service:** General
Medical and Surgical

Staffed Beds: 25 **Admissions:** 743 **Census:** 7 **Outpatient Visits:** 14777
Births: 2 **Total Expense ($000):** 18751 **Payroll Expense ($000):** 7234
Personnel: 172

MS

MISSOURI

ALBANY—Gentry County

★ **NORTHWEST MEDICAL CENTER (261328)**, 705 North College Street, Zip 64402–1433; tel. 660/726–3941 **A**10 18 **F**3 11 15 18 28 29 34 35 40 44 45 50 56 57 59 62 64 65 68 74 75 77 79 81 85 86 87 90 93 97 104 107 108 110 111 114 118 119 127 128 130 131 133 135 148 **P**6
Primary Contact: Jon D. Doolittle, President and Chief Executive Officer
COO: Nate Blackford, Chief Operating Officer
CFO: Tina Gillespie, Vice President and Chief Financial Officer
CMO: Angelia Martin, M.D., Chief of Staff
CIO: James Crouch, Vice President Technical Services
CHR: Vickie Cline, Director Human Resources
CNO: Miranda Floyd, R.N., Chief Nursing Officer
Web address: www.northwestmedicalcenter.org
Control: Other not–for–profit (including NFP Corporation) **Service:** General Medical and Surgical

Staffed Beds: 25 **Admissions:** 350 **Census:** 6 **Outpatient Visits:** 47873
Births: 0 **Total Expense ($000):** 21092 **Payroll Expense ($000):** 7944
Personnel: 163

APPLETON CITY—St. Clair County

★ **ELLETT MEMORIAL HOSPITAL (261301)**, 610 North Ohio Avenue, Zip 64724–1609, Mailing Address: P.O. Box 6, Zip 64724–0006; tel. 660/476–2111 **A**10 18 **F**3 7 11 18 34 40 45 50 57 59 77 79 81 97 107 111 114 119 127 129 133 143 **P**6
Primary Contact: Tom Hollis, Chief Executive Officer
CMO: Richard R. Dailey, D.O., President Medical Staff
CIO: Gina Raybourn, Director Health Information
CHR: Cathy Grishow, Director Human Resources
CNO: Cathy Menninga, R.N., Chief Nursing Officer
Web address: www.ellettmemorial.com
Control: Hospital district or authority, Government, nonfederal **Service:** General Medical and Surgical

Staffed Beds: 12 **Admissions:** 259 **Census:** 4 **Outpatient Visits:** 11681
Births: 0 **Total Expense ($000):** 8770 **Payroll Expense ($000):** 3663
Personnel: 91

AURORA—Lawrence County

⊞ **MERCY HOSPITAL AURORA (261316)**, 500 Porter Street, Zip 65605–2365; tel. 417/678–2122 **A**1 10 18 **F**3 11 13 15 28 29 30 34 35 40 41 45 50 57 59 64 65 75 76 77 81 85 86 87 89 92 93 94 96 107 108 110 111 114 119 129 132 133 135 148 **P**6 **S** Mercy Health, Chesterfield, MO
Primary Contact: Douglas M. Stroemel, President
CFO: Sherry Clouse Day, CPA, Vice President Finance and Regional Chief Financial Officer
CMO: Christie Hurt, M.D., Chief of Staff and Medical Director
CHR: George Roden, Vice President Human Resources
CNO: Nicki Gamet, R.N., Vice President and Chief Nursing Officer
Web address: www.stjohns.com/aboutus/aurora.aspx
Control: Church–operated, Nongovernment, not–for profit **Service:** General Medical and Surgical

Staffed Beds: 25 **Admissions:** 648 **Census:** 6 **Outpatient Visits:** 31877
Births: 209 **Total Expense ($000):** 18483 **Payroll Expense ($000):** 8331
Personnel: 144

BELTON—Cass County

⊞ **BELTON REGIONAL MEDICAL CENTER (260214)**, 17065 South 71 Highway, Zip 64012–4631; tel. 816/348–1200 **A**1 2 10 **F**3 15 18 20 29 30 31 34 35 37 40 43 45 57 59 65 68 70 74 75 77 78 79 81 82 85 87 90 93 107 108 110 111 118 119 129 130 131 132 146 **P**5 **S** HCA, Nashville, TN
Primary Contact: Todd Krass, Chief Executive Officer
CFO: Ronnie Thompson, Chief Financial Officer
CMO: Douglas Bradley, M.D., Chief Medical Officer
CIO: Sarah Richardson, Director Information Systems
CHR: Jessica Sulzen, Director Human Resources
CNO: Karen Lee, MSN, Chief Nursing Officer
Web address: www.beltonregionalmedicalcenter.com
Control: Corporation, Investor–owned, for–profit **Service:** General Medical and Surgical

Staffed Beds: 46 **Admissions:** 2605 **Census:** 25 **Outpatient Visits:** 104170
Births: 0 **Total Expense ($000):** 53826 **Payroll Expense ($000):** 16821
Personnel: 207

RESEARCH BELTON HOSPITAL See Belton Regional Medical Center

BETHANY—Harrison County

★ **HARRISON COUNTY COMMUNITY HOSPITAL (261312)**, 2600 Miller Street, Zip 64424–2701, Mailing Address: P.O. Box 428, Zip 64424–0428; tel. 660/425–2211 **A**10 18 **F**3 11 15 28 29 34 40 41 44 45 50 57 59 62 64 75 77 79 81 82 87 89 90 92 93 96 98 103 104 107 108 110 111 115 119 127 128 130 131 133 143 **P**5
Primary Contact: Kelly Pottorff, Chief Executive Officer
COO: Tina Gillespie, Chief Operating Officer
CFO: Lee Ann Miles, Chief Financial Officer
CMO: Terry E. Hall, Chief of Staff
CIO: Will Holt, Director Information Technology
CHR: Cathie Chalfant, Director Human Resources
CNO: Crystal Hicks, R.N., Chief Nursing Officer
Web address: www.hcchospital.org
Control: Hospital district or authority, Government, nonfederal **Service:** General Medical and Surgical

Staffed Beds: 19 **Admissions:** 432 **Census:** 7 **Outpatient Visits:** 61265
Births: 0 **Total Expense ($000):** 22289 **Payroll Expense ($000):** 9895
Personnel: 230

BLUE SPRINGS—Jackson County

⊞ **ST. MARY'S MEDICAL CENTER (260193)**, 201 Northwest R. D. Mize Road, Zip 64014–2518; tel. 816/228–5900, (Data for 322 days) **A**1 10 13 **F**3 8 15 18 20 22 28 29 30 34 35 40 49 50 53 57 59 60 64 68 70 74 77 78 79 80 81 82 83 84 85 87 90 93 96 107 108 110 111 113 114 115 119 123 129 130 131 135 143 145 146 148 **S** Prime Healthcare Services, Ontario, CA
Primary Contact: Debra Ohnoutka, Chief Executive Officer
Web address: www.stmaryskc.com/
Control: Corporation, Investor–owned, for–profit **Service:** General Medical and Surgical

Staffed Beds: 88 **Admissions:** 4478 **Census:** 53 **Outpatient Visits:** 101927
Births: 0 **Total Expense ($000):** 65346 **Payroll Expense ($000):** 24252
Personnel: 420

BOLIVAR—Polk County

⊞ **CITIZENS MEMORIAL HOSPITAL (260195)**, 1500 North Oakland Avenue, Zip 65613–3011; tel. 417/326–6000 **A**1 10 20 **F**3 7 11 13 15 18 20 22 26 28 29 31 34 35 36 40 43 44 50 51 54 56 57 59 64 66 70 74 75 76 77 78 79 80 81 82 84 85 86 87 89 90 93 94 96 97 98 100 102 103 104 107 108 110 111 115 117 119 127 128 129 130 131 132 133 135 146 147 148 **P**6
Primary Contact: Donald J. Babb, Chief Executive Officer
COO: Jeff Miller, Chief Operating Officer
CFO: Gary D. Fullbright, Comptroller
CMO: Michael Misko, M.D., Chief Medical Officer
CIO: Denni McColm, Chief Information Officer
CHR: Jeremy MacLaughlin, Director Human Resources
CNO: Lesa Stock, R.N., Chief Clinical Officer
Web address: www.citizensmemorial.com
Control: Hospital district or authority, Government, nonfederal **Service:** General Medical and Surgical

Staffed Beds: 72 **Admissions:** 3090 **Census:** 26 **Outpatient Visits:** 315973
Births: 502 **Total Expense ($000):** 125595 **Payroll Expense ($000):** 58787
Personnel: 901

BONNE TERRE—St. Francois County

★ **PARKLAND HEALTH CENTER–BONNE TERRE (261315)**, 7245 Raider Road, Zip 63628–3767; tel. 573/358–1400 **A**10 18 **F**3 11 29 30 31 34 35 40 50 53 57 59 64 65 75 77 78 86 90 93 107 129 130 146 **S** BJC HealthCare, Saint Louis, MO
Primary Contact: Christinia Jepsen, R.N., Administrator
CFO: Cheri L. Goldsmith, Director Financial Services
CHR: Sheri Graham, Director Human Resources and Administrative Services
CNO: Jeanne Boyer, R.N., Director of Nurses
Web address: www.parklandhealthcenter.org
Control: Other not–for–profit (including NFP Corporation) **Service:** General Medical and Surgical

Staffed Beds: 3 **Admissions:** 3 **Census:** 1 **Outpatient Visits:** 23873 **Births:** 0 **Personnel:** 61

MO

BOONVILLE—Cooper County

★ **COOPER COUNTY MEMORIAL HOSPITAL (260004)**, 17651 B Highway, Zip 65233–2839, Mailing Address: P.O. Box 88, Zip 65233–0088; tel. 660/882–7461, (Total facility includes 14 beds in nursing–type unit) **A**10 20 **F**7 11 28 29 34 35 40 45 53 57 59 62 64 67 68 75 79 81 85 89 93 94 107 111 114 119 127 128 130 131 132 133 135 146 148 **S** Rural Community Hospitals of America, Kansas City, MO
Primary Contact: Danielle Gearhart, Chief Executive Officer
CFO: Patricia Nowlin, Director Accounting
CMO: Mona Brownfield, M.D., Chief Medical Staff
CIO: Bill Fletcher, Director Information Technology
CHR: Patricia Nowlin, Director Human Resources
CNO: Nancy Fredrich, R.N., Chief Clinical Officer
Web address: www.coopercmh.com
Control: County–Government, nonfederal **Service:** General Medical and Surgical

Staffed Beds: 32 **Admissions:** 381 **Census:** 16 **Outpatient Visits:** 33490 **Births:** 0 **Total Expense ($000):** 12905 **Payroll Expense ($000):** 6055 **Personnel:** 136

BRANSON—Taney County

★ △ ◇ **COX MEDICAL CENTER BRANSON (260094)**, 251 Skaggs Road, Zip 65616–2031, Mailing Address: P.O. Box 650, Zip 65615–0650; tel. 417/335–7000 **A**7 10 21 **F**3 8 13 15 17 18 20 22 26 28 29 31 32 34 35 40 41 44 45 46 47 50 53 56 57 59 60 61 62 63 64 65 66 68 70 74 75 76 77 78 79 80 81 82 84 85 86 87 89 90 93 97 98 100 103 106 107 108 110 111 114 117 118 119 120 121 123 127 129 130 131 132 135 143 144 146 147 148 **P**6 **S** CoxHealth, Springfield, MO
Primary Contact: William K. Mahoney, President and Chief Executive Officer
CFO: David Strong, Chief Financial Officer/Vice President Finance
CHR: Carol Murrow, Vice President Business Development
Web address: www.coxhealth.com
Control: Other not–for–profit (including NFP Corporation) **Service:** General Medical and Surgical

Staffed Beds: 113 **Admissions:** 6553 **Census:** 77 **Outpatient Visits:** 252220 **Births:** 597 **Total Expense ($000):** 155471 **Payroll Expense ($000):** 54256 **Personnel:** 1033

BRIDGETON—St. Louis County

✠ △ **SSM DEPAUL HEALTH CENTER (260104)**, 12303 De Paul Drive, Zip 63044–2512; tel. 314/344–6000, (Total facility includes 52 beds in nursing home–type unit) **A**1 2 5 7 10 **F**3 4 5 11 12 13 15 17 18 20 22 24 26 28 29 30 31 34 35 36 38 40 43 44 49 50 51 53 55 56 57 58 59 60 61 64 68 70 73 74 75 76 78 79 81 82 84 85 86 87 89 98 99 100 101 102 104 105 107 108 110 111 114 115 117 118 119 120 121 124 126 128 130 132 135 144 146 147 148 **P**6 8 **S** SSM Health, Saint Louis, MO
Primary Contact: Sean Hogan, President
COO: Tina Garrison, Vice President Operations
CFO: Hal Holder, Director Finance
CMO: John Moore, M.D., Vice President Medical Affairs
CIO: Scott Feldmann, Director Information Technology
CHR: Gloria Reed, Leader Human Resources
Web address: www.ssmdepaul.com
Control: Church–operated, Nongovernment, not–for profit **Service:** General Medical and Surgical

Staffed Beds: 477 **Admissions:** 23389 **Census:** 356 **Outpatient Visits:** 238450 **Births:** 1066 **Total Expense ($000):** 362614 **Payroll Expense ($000):** 116894 **Personnel:** 1980

BROOKFIELD—Linn County

GENERAL JOHN J. PERSHING MEMORIAL HOSPITAL (261307), 130 East Lockling Avenue, Zip 64628–2337, Mailing Address: P.O. Box 408, Zip 64628–0408; tel. 660/258–2222 **A**10 18 **F**11 15 28 29 34 36 40 57 59 64 75 77 81 87 89 93 97 107 111 114 119 127 129 130 133 146 **P**6
Primary Contact: Phil Hamilton, R.N., Chief Executive Officer
CFO: Gary R. Tandy, Chief Financial Officer
CMO: B. K. Knowles, D.O., Chief of Staff
CIO: Elaine Sutton, Chief Information Officer
CHR: Amy Sayre, Director Human Resources
Web address: www.pershinghealthsystem.com
Control: Other not–for–profit (including NFP Corporation) **Service:** General Medical and Surgical

Staffed Beds: 25 **Admissions:** 664 **Census:** 7 **Outpatient Visits:** 46849 **Births:** 0 **Total Expense ($000):** 16822 **Payroll Expense ($000):** 6589 **Personnel:** 154

BUTLER—Bates County

★ **BATES COUNTY MEMORIAL HOSPITAL (260034)**, 615 West Nursery Street, Zip 64730–1840, Mailing Address: P.O. Box 370, Zip 64730–0370; tel. 660/200–7000 **A**10 20 **F**3 7 11 15 28 29 30 31 34 40 45 50 59 64 68 70 77 78 79 81 87 90 93 107 108 109 110 111 115 118 119 127 129 130 132 133 **P**5 6
Primary Contact: Edward J. Hannon, Chief Executive Officer
CFO: Terri Floyd, Chief Financial Officer
CMO: John P. Bustle, Medical Chief of Staff
CIO: Marcia Cook, Director Information Technology
CHR: Melinda R. Jackson, Director Human Resources
CNO: Rebecca Tarver, Chief Nursing Officer
Web address: www.bcmhospital.com
Control: County–Government, nonfederal **Service:** General Medical and Surgical

Staffed Beds: 49 **Admissions:** 960 **Census:** 11 **Outpatient Visits:** 76305 **Births:** 0 **Total Expense ($000):** 35546 **Payroll Expense ($000):** 13377 **Personnel:** 263

CAMERON—Clinton County

CAMERON REGIONAL MEDICAL CENTER (260057), 1600 East Evergreen, Zip 64429–2400, Mailing Address: P.O. Box 557, Zip 64429–0557; tel. 816/632–2101 **A**3 5 10 **F**3 11 12 13 15 28 29 30 31 34 35 39 40 46 47 49 56 57 59 61 62 63 64 67 70 74 75 76 77 78 79 81 82 84 85 86 87 89 90 98 100 104 107 110 111 115 119 128 129 130 131 133 143 146 147 148 **P**6
Primary Contact: Joseph F. Abrutz, Jr., Administrator
CFO: Rosa Patti, Chief Financial Officer
CIO: Bill Walser, Coordinator Technology
CHR: Pat Bestgen, Manager Human Resources
Web address: www.cameronregional.org
Control: Other not–for–profit (including NFP Corporation) **Service:** General Medical and Surgical

Staffed Beds: 58 **Admissions:** 1994 **Census:** 33 **Outpatient Visits:** 308542 **Births:** 146 **Total Expense ($000):** 55913 **Payroll Expense ($000):** 23709 **Personnel:** 369

CAPE GIRARDEAU—Cape Girardeau County

□ **LANDMARK HOSPITAL OF CAPE GIRARDEAU (262015)**, 3255 Independence Street, Zip 63701–4914; tel. 573/335–1091, (Nonreporting) **A**1 10 22 **S** Landmark Hospitals, Cape Girardeau, MO
Primary Contact: Rodney Brown, Chief Executive Officer
COO: Michael L. Norman, Executive Vice President and Chief Operating Officer
CFO: Richard H. Hogan, CPA, Chief Financial Officer
CMO: William Fritsch, M.D., Medical Director
CIO: Renee Hesselrode, Director Health Information Management
CHR: Angela Kisner, Director Human Resources and Coordinator Medical Staff
Web address: www.landmarkhospitals.com
Control: Partnership, Investor–owned, for–profit **Service:** Long–Term Acute Care hospital

Staffed Beds: 30

✠ **SAINT FRANCIS HEALTHCARE SYSTEM (260183)**, 211 St. Francis Drive, Zip 63703–5049; tel. 573/331–3000 **A**1 2 10 19 **F**3 9 11 12 13 15 17 18 20 22 24 26 28 29 30 31 32 34 35 39 40 43 44 45 46 47 48 49 50 53 54 56 57 58 59 60 61 62 63 64 65 68 70 72 73 74 75 76 77 78 79 80 81 82 83 84 85 86 87 89 90 91 92 93 96 97 107 108 110 111 114 115 117 118 119 120 121 123 124 126 129 130 131 132 135 141 142 143 144 145 146 147 148 **P**6
Primary Contact: Steven C. Bjelich, President and Chief Executive Officer
COO: Maryann Reese, R.N., Chief Operating Officer
CFO: Tony Balsano, Vice President Finance
CMO: James Schell, M.D., Vice President Medical Affairs
CIO: Edward E. Duryee, Director Information Systems
CHR: Teri Kreitzer, Director Human Resources
CNO: Jeannie Fadler, R.N., Vice President Patient Care Services
Web address: www.sfmc.net
Control: Church–operated, Nongovernment, not–for profit **Service:** General Medical and Surgical

Staffed Beds: 284 **Admissions:** 11366 **Census:** 158 **Outpatient Visits:** 518044 **Births:** 924 **Total Expense ($000):** 421114 **Payroll Expense ($000):** 162599 **Personnel:** 2379

Many Facility Codes have changed. Please refer to the AHA Guide Code Chart. © 2016 AHA Guide

SOUTHEAST HOSPITAL (260110), 1701 Lacey Street, Zip 63701–5230; tel. 573/334–4822 **A**1 10 19 **F**3 11 13 15 17 18 20 22 24 26 28 29 30 31 32 34 35 40 44 45 48 49 50 51 53 54 57 58 59 60 61 62 63 64 65 70 72 73 74 75 76 77 78 79 80 81 82 84 85 86 87 88 89 90 92 93 96 97 98 100 102 107 108 110 111 115 117 119 120 121 123 124 126 127 129 130 131 132 135 146 147 **S** SoutheastHEALTH, Cape Girardeau, MO
Primary Contact: Kenneth Bateman, CPA, Chief Executive Officer
COO: Sylvia Moore, Vice President and Chief Operating Officer
CFO: Bruce Fairbanks, Vice President and Chief Financial Officer
CMO: Matt Shoemaker, D.O., Vice President and Chief Medical Officer
CIO: Mike Dozier, Chief Information Officer
CHR: Lincoln Scott, Vice President Human Resources
CNO: Judy Aslin, MSN, Vice President and Chief Nursing Officer
Web address: www.sehealth.org/
Control: Other not-for-profit (including NFP Corporation) **Service:** General Medical and Surgical

Staffed Beds: 199 Admissions: 9287 Census: 109 Outpatient Visits: 331240 **Births:** 1013 **Total Expense ($000):** 303525 **Payroll Expense ($000):** 116600 **Personnel:** 1833

CARROLLTON—Carroll County

★ **CARROLL COUNTY MEMORIAL HOSPITAL (261332)**, 1502 North Jefferson Street, Zip 64633–1948; tel. 660/542–1695 **A**10 18 **F**3 11 15 28 29 30 31 34 35 38 40 45 50 53 56 57 59 62 64 65 74 75 77 78 79 81 86 87 90 91 92 93 96 103 104 107 108 110 111 114 119 125 127 129 130 131 132 133 143 146 148 **P**6
Primary Contact: Jeff A. Tindle, Chief Executive Officer
COO: Tim Braun, Assistant Administrator
CFO: Amy Ireland, Chief Financial Officer
CMO: Richard Smith, Chief of Staff
CIO: Bill Bollinger, Chief Information Officer
CHR: Michael Schubach, Director Human Resources
CNO: Jeanne Rector, Chief Nursing Officer
Web address: www.carrollcountyhospital.org
Control: Other not-for-profit (including NFP Corporation) **Service:** General Medical and Surgical

Staffed Beds: 25 Admissions: 300 Census: 4 Outpatient Visits: 47506 **Births:** 0 **Total Expense ($000):** 17104 **Payroll Expense ($000):** 6931 **Personnel:** 167

CARTHAGE—Jasper County

★ **MERCY HOSPITAL CARTHAGE (260228)**, 3125 Drive Russell Smith Way, Zip 64836–7402; tel. 417/358–8121 **A**10 18 **F**3 7 11 13 15 28 29 30 31 34 35 40 45 50 53 57 59 62 64 67 68 69 70 75 79 81 89 90 98 104 107 110 111 115 119 127 129 130 131 132 133 135 146 147 **P**6 **S** Mercy Health, Chesterfield, MO
Primary Contact: Robert Watson, JD, Administrator
CFO: Douglas Culver, Chief Financial Officer
CIO: Cheryl Lease–Homeyer, Lead Information Technology Business Partner
CHR: Colette St. Peter, Senior Manager Human Resources
Web address: www.mercy.net
Control: Church-operated, Nongovernment, not-for profit **Service:** General Medical and Surgical

Staffed Beds: 13 Admissions: 1163 Census: 9 Outpatient Visits: 112570 **Births:** 167 **Total Expense ($000):** 42201 **Payroll Expense ($000):** 12836 **Personnel:** 225

CASSVILLE—Barry County

MERCY HOSPITAL CASSVILLE (261317), 94 Main Street, Zip 65625–1610; tel. 417/847–6000 **A**1 10 18 **F**3 11 15 28 29 30 34 40 41 45 50 53 57 59 64 65 75 77 81 85 86 87 89 92 93 94 96 103 107 110 111 114 119 132 133 135 148 **P**6 **S** Mercy Health, Chesterfield, MO
Primary Contact: Douglas M. Stroemel, President
CFO: Sherry Clouse Day, CPA, Chief Financial Officer
CMO: Jamie Zengotita, M.D., Chief Medical Staff
CHR: George Roden, Vice President Human Resources
CNO: Nicki Gamet, R.N., Chief Nursing Officer
Web address: www.mercy.net/northwestarar/practice/mercy–hospital–cassville
Control: Church-operated, Nongovernment, not-for profit **Service:** General Medical and Surgical

Staffed Beds: 18 Admissions: 295 Census: 3 Outpatient Visits: 31946 **Births:** 0 **Total Expense ($000):** 14868 **Payroll Expense ($000):** 6560 **Personnel:** 103

CHESTERFIELD—St. Louis County

□ △ **MERCY REHABILITATION HOSPITAL (263029)**, 14561 North Outer Forty Road, Zip 63017; tel. 314/881–4000 **A**1 7 10 **F**16 29 30 90 130 132 148 **S** Kindred Healthcare, Louisville, KY
Primary Contact: Donna M. Flannery, Chief Executive Officer
CMO: Siresha Samudrala, M.D., Medical Director
Web address: www.stjohnsmercyrehab.com
Control: Partnership, Investor-owned, for-profit **Service:** Rehabilitation

Staffed Beds: 90 Admissions: 1593 Census: 60 Outpatient Visits: 0 **Births:** 0 **Total Expense ($000):** 25707 **Payroll Expense ($000):** 11971 **Personnel:** 249

ST. LUKE'S HOSPITAL (260179), 232 South Woods Mill Road, Zip 63017–3417; tel. 314/434–1500, (Total facility includes 140 beds in nursing home–type unit) **A**1 2 3 10 **F**3 10 11 13 15 17 18 20 22 24 26 28 29 30 31 32 34 35 36 38 39 40 41 42 44 45 46 48 49 50 52 53 54 55 56 57 58 59 60 61 62 63 64 65 66 68 69 70 71 73 74 75 76 77 78 79 81 82 83 84 85 86 87 89 90 93 97 107 108 110 111 114 115 117 118 119 120 121 123 124 126 128 129 130 131 132 135 144 145 146 147 148 **P**6 8
Primary Contact: Christine M. Candio, R.N., FACHE, President and Chief Executive Officer
COO: Donald L. Miller, FACHE, Vice President, Operations
CFO: Scott H. Johnson, Vice President Finance and Chief Financial Officer
CIO: William Meyers, Chief Information Officer
CHR: Janette Taaffe, Vice President, Human Resource
CNO: Diane Ray, R.N., Vice President and Chief Nursing Officer Patient Services
Web address: www.stlukes–stl.com
Control: Church–operated, Nongovernment, not-for profit **Service:** General Medical and Surgical

Staffed Beds: 542 Admissions: 15543 Census: 293 Outpatient Visits: 967253 **Births:** 1871 **Total Expense ($000):** 485297 **Payroll Expense ($000):** 216980 **Personnel:** 3242

ST. LUKE'S REHABILITATION HOSPITAL (263030), 14709 Olive Boulevard, Zip 63017–2221; tel. 314/317–5700 **A**1 10 **F**3 12 18 28 29 34 75 79 90 96 100 130 132 148
Primary Contact: Christopher Baechle, Chief Executive Officer
Web address: www.khrehabstluke.com
Control: Partnership, Investor–owned, for-profit **Service:** Rehabilitation

Staffed Beds: 35 Admissions: 646 Census: 21 Outpatient Visits: 0 **Births:** 0 **Total Expense ($000):** 8511 **Payroll Expense ($000):** 4085 **Personnel:** 78

CHILLICOTHE—Livingston County

HEDRICK MEDICAL CENTER (261321), 2799 North Washington Street, Zip 64601–2902; tel. 660/646–1480 **A**1 10 18 **F**3 11 13 15 18 28 29 30 31 34 35 39 40 41 43 44 45 50 54 57 59 64 65 68 69 70 74 75 76 77 78 79 81 85 86 87 89 90 92 93 96 97 100 104 107 108 110 111 115 118 119 127 128 129 130 131 133 146 147 148 **P**6 **S** Saint Luke's Health System, Kansas City, MO
Primary Contact: Steven M. Schieber, FACHE, Chief Executive Officer
CHR: Lisa Hecker, Director Human Resources
CNO: Catherine Hamilton, Chief Nursing Officer
Web address: www.saintlukeskc.org
Control: Other not-for-profit (including NFP Corporation) **Service:** General Medical and Surgical

Staffed Beds: 25 Admissions: 1140 Census: 14 Outpatient Visits: 107626 **Births:** 203 **Total Expense ($000):** 41633 **Payroll Expense ($000):** 16138 **Personnel:** 275

CLINTON—Henry County

GOLDEN VALLEY MEMORIAL HEALTHCARE (260175), 1600 North Second Street, Zip 64735–1192; tel. 660/885–5511 **A**1 10 **F**3 7 11 13 15 17 18 28 29 30 31 34 35 40 45 47 48 49 53 57 59 61 62 64 68 70 74 75 76 77 78 79 81 85 86 87 89 90 92 93 96 107 108 111 115 118 119 127 128 129 130 131 132 133 143 146 147 148
Primary Contact: Randy S. Wertz, Chief Executive Officer
COO: Craig Thompson, Chief Operating Officer
CFO: Tammy R. Nadler, Chief Financial Officer
CIO: Mike Gaul, Director Information Technology
CHR: Greg Shannon, Director Human Resources
CNO: Mark David Mattes, R.N., Assistant Administrator/Patient Care Services
Web address: www.gvmh.org
Control: Hospital district or authority, Government, nonfederal **Service:** General Medical and Surgical

Staffed Beds: 55 Admissions: 2581 Census: 23 Outpatient Visits: 275043 **Births:** 0 **Total Expense ($000):** 77984 **Payroll Expense ($000):** 36888 **Personnel:** 668

MO

COLUMBIA—Boone County

⊞ **BOONE HOSPITAL CENTER (260068)**, 1600 East Broadway, Zip 65201–5844; tel. 573/815–8000 **A**1 2 3 5 10 **F**3 7 11 12 13 15 17 18 20 22 24 26 28 29 31 34 35 36 40 45 46 47 48 49 50 51 53 56 57 59 60 61 64 65 68 70 71 72 73 74 75 76 77 78 79 80 81 82 84 85 86 87 89 90 93 96 107 108 110 111 114 115 117 118 119 126 129 130 131 132 135 145 146 147 148 **S** BJC HealthCare, Saint Louis, MO
Primary Contact: James J. Sinek, FACHE, President
CFO: Randy Morrow, Vice President and Chief Operating Officer
CMO: Jerry Kennett, M.D., Chief Medical Officer
CHR: Michelle Zvanut, Vice President Human Resources
Web address: www.boone.org
Control: Other not–for–profit (including NFP Corporation) **Service:** General Medical and Surgical

Staffed Beds: 311 **Admissions:** 15260 **Census:** 180 **Outpatient Visits:** 167425 **Births:** 2051 **Total Expense ($000):** 309232 **Payroll Expense ($000):** 85400 **Personnel:** 1495

ELLIS FISCHEL CANCER CENTER See University of Missouri Hospitals and Clinics

⊞ **HARRY S. TRUMAN MEMORIAL VETERANS HOSPITAL**, 800 Hospital Drive, Zip 65201–5275; tel. 573/814–6000, (Total facility includes 41 beds in nursing home–type unit) **A**1 3 5 **F**3 4 5 17 18 20 22 24 28 29 30 31 34 35 36 38 39 40 44 49 54 56 58 59 61 62 63 64 67 70 74 75 78 79 81 82 84 85 86 87 90 92 93 94 97 98 100 101 102 103 104 106 107 108 111 115 117 118 119 127 128 129 130 132 135 146 147 **P**6 **S** Department of Veterans Affairs, Washington, DC
Primary Contact: David Isaacks, Director
COO: Robert G. Ritter, FACHE, Associate Director
CFO: Deborah Henderson, Acting Chief Financial Officer
CMO: Lana Zerrer, M.D., Chief of Staff
CIO: Donna Krause, Chief Information Officer
CHR: Jimmy Powell, Manager Human Resources
Web address: www.columbiamo.va.gov
Control: Veterans Affairs, Government, federal **Service:** General Medical and Surgical

Staffed Beds: 123 **Admissions:** 3864 **Census:** 83 **Outpatient Visits:** 524850 **Births:** 0 **Total Expense ($000):** 340612 **Payroll Expense ($000):** 107908 **Personnel:** 1440

⊞ **HOWARD A. RUSK REHABILITATION CENTER (263027)**, 315 Business Loop 70 West, Zip 65203–3248; tel. 573/817–2703 **A**1 3 5 10 **F**29 34 58 68 75 90 91 94 95 96 132 143 148 **S** HEALTHSOUTH Corporation, Birmingham, AL
Primary Contact: Larry Meeker, Chief Executive Officer
CFO: Jeff Reese, Chief Financial Officer
CMO: Gregory Worsowicz, M.D., Medical Director
CHR: Robin Prater, Director Human Resources
CNO: Lori Mann, R.N., Chief Nursing Officer
Web address: www.ruskrehab.com
Control: Partnership, Investor–owned, for–profit **Service:** Rehabilitation

Staffed Beds: 60 **Admissions:** 1135 **Census:** 46 **Outpatient Visits:** 0 **Births:** 0 **Total Expense ($000):** 19766 **Payroll Expense ($000):** 8631 **Personnel:** 156

LANDMARK HOSPITAL OF COLUMBIA (262020), 604 Old 63 North, Zip 65201–6308; tel. 573/499–6600, (Nonreporting) **A**3 5 10 22 **S** Landmark Hospitals, Cape Girardeau, MO
Primary Contact: Deborah Sabella, R.N., Chief Executive Officer
Web address: www.landmarkhospitals.com
Control: Partnership, Investor–owned, for–profit **Service:** Long–Term Acute Care hospital

Staffed Beds: 42

⊞ **UNIVERSITY OF MISSOURI HOSPITALS AND CLINICS (260141)**, One Hospital Drive, Zip 65212–0001; tel. 573/882–4141, (Includes ELLIS FISCHEL CANCER CENTER, 115 Business Loop 70 West, Zip 65203; tel. 573/882–5460; WOMEN'S AND CHILDREN'S HOSPITAL, 404 Keene Street, Zip 65201–6626; tel. 573/875–9000; Keri Simon, Executive Director) **A**1 2 3 5 8 10 **F**3 4 7 9 11 12 13 15 16 17 18 19 20 22 24 26 28 29 30 31 32 34 35 37 38 39 40 41 42 43 44 45 46 47 48 49 50 51 52 53 54 55 56 57 58 59 60 61 64 65 66 68 70 71 72 73 74 75 76 77 78 79 80 81 82 83 84 85 86 87 88 89 91 92 93 97 98 99 100 101 102 103 104 107 108 110 111 114 115 116 117 118 119 120 121 123 124 126 127 129 130 131 132 134 135 136 138 141 142 143 144 146 147 148 **P**1 6 **S** University of Missouri Health Care, Columbia, MO
Primary Contact: Mitchell L. Wasden, Ed.D., Chief Executive Officer and Chief Operating Officer
CFO: Kevin Necas, Chief Financial Officer
CMO: Stevan Whitt, M.D., Chief Medical Officer
CHR: Sue Kopfle, Chief Human Resources Officer
CNO: Deborah Pasch, Chief Nurse Executive
Web address: www.muhealth.org
Control: State–Government, nonfederal **Service:** General Medical and Surgical

Staffed Beds: 538 **Admissions:** 25703 **Census:** 348 **Outpatient Visits:** 872639 **Births:** 1838 **Total Expense ($000):** 746616 **Payroll Expense ($000):** 230459 **Personnel:** 4781

CRYSTAL CITY—Jefferson County

⊞ △ **MERCY HOSPITAL JEFFERSON (260023)**, Highway 61 South, Zip 63019, Mailing Address: P.O. Box 350, Zip 63019–0350; tel. 636/933–1000 **A**1 7 10 **F**3 4 5 8 11 12 13 15 18 20 22 24 26 28 29 30 31 34 35 40 44 45 47 49 50 51 53 54 57 59 60 62 63 64 68 70 74 75 76 77 78 79 81 82 84 85 86 87 89 90 92 93 94 96 97 98 100 101 102 103 104 107 110 111 114 115 116 117 118 119 129 130 131 132 135 143 144 146 147 148 **P**6 **S** Mercy Health, Chesterfield, MO
Primary Contact: Eric Ammons, President
CMO: Mark Briete, M.D., Vice President Medical Affairs
CIO: Jan Poneta, Director Information Services
CHR: Saundra G. Turner, Director Human Resources
Web address: www.mercy.net/crystalcitymo
Control: Other not–for–profit (including NFP Corporation) **Service:** General Medical and Surgical

Staffed Beds: 209 **Admissions:** 10040 **Census:** 125 **Outpatient Visits:** 188895 **Births:** 359 **Total Expense ($000):** 138545 **Payroll Expense ($000):** 53818 **Personnel:** 1032

DEXTER—Stoddard County

SOUTHEAST HEALTH CENTER OF STODDARD COUNTY (260160), 1200 North One Mile Road, Zip 63841–1000; tel. 573/624–5566 **A**10 **F**3 11 15 28 29 31 34 39 40 45 59 62 65 70 75 77 78 81 85 89 90 93 97 107 108 111 115 118 119 127 129 133 135 146 **P**6 **S** SoutheastHEALTH, Cape Girardeau, MO
Primary Contact: Sue Ann Williams, Chief Executive Officer
CHR: Judy Bowling, Director Human Resources
Web address: www.sehealth.org
Control: Other not–for–profit (including NFP Corporation) **Service:** General Medical and Surgical

Staffed Beds: 16 **Admissions:** 866 **Census:** 6 **Outpatient Visits:** 103666 **Births:** 0 **Total Expense ($000):** 21216 **Payroll Expense ($000):** 8632 **Personnel:** 165

DONIPHAN—Ripley County

★ **SOUTHEAST HEALTH CENTER OF RIPLEY COUNTY (260080)**, 109 Plum Street, Zip 63935–1299; tel. 573/996–2141 **A**10 **F**3 29 34 40 57 59 62 64 65 93 107 111 115 119 127 129 130 133 **P**6 **S** SoutheastHEALTH, Cape Girardeau, MO
Primary Contact: Cheryl Barton, R.N., Chief Executive Officer
CFO: Rickie Maples, Interim Chief Financial Officer
CMO: Ureej Mansoor, M.D., Chief of Staff
CIO: Riley March, Manager Information Technology
CHR: Peggy Teasdale, Director Human Resources
Web address: www.sehealth.org/southeast–health–center–of–ripley–county/SoutheastHEALTH.aspx?nd=41
Control: Other not–for–profit (including NFP Corporation) **Service:** General Medical and Surgical

Staffed Beds: 10 **Admissions:** 278 **Census:** 2 **Outpatient Visits:** 44205 **Births:** 0 **Total Expense ($000):** 9796 **Payroll Expense ($000):** 3986 **Personnel:** 87

EL DORADO SPRINGS—Cedar County

CEDAR COUNTY MEMORIAL HOSPITAL (261323), 1401 South Park Street, Zip 64744–2037; tel. 417/876–2511 **A**10 18 **F**11 15 18 28 29 30 34 35 40 45 53 56 57 59 62 64 65 68 74 77 81 85 87 89 90 93 102 103 107 110 111 114 119 127 129 130 133 146 147 148 **P**6
Primary Contact: Jana Witt, Chief Executive Officer
CFO: Carla Gilbert, Director Finance
CMO: Rick Casey, D.O., Chief Medical Staff
CIO: Lois Willmore, Supervisor Health Information Management
CHR: Diana Pyle, Director Human Resources and Executive Assistant to Chief Executive Officer
CNO: Drew Alexander, Chief Nursing Officer
Web address: www.cedarcountyhospital.org
Control: County–Government, nonfederal **Service:** General Medical and Surgical

Staffed Beds: 25 **Admissions:** 382 **Census:** 12 **Outpatient Visits:** 35247 **Births:** 0 **Total Expense ($000):** 12256 **Payroll Expense ($000):** 4439 **Personnel:** 115

EXCELSIOR SPRINGS—Clay County

★ **EXCELSIOR SPRINGS HOSPITAL (261322)**, 1700 Rainbow Boulevard, Zip 64024–1190; tel. 816/630–6081, (Total facility includes 80 beds in nursing home–type unit) **A**10 18 **F**3 10 11 15 18 29 30 31 32 34 35 39 40 45 49 56 57 59 62 63 64 67 68 70 75 77 78 79 81 82 84 85 86 87 89 90 93 102 107 108 110 111 114 116 117 118 119 125 128 129 130 133 143 146 147
Primary Contact: Sally S. Nance, Chief Executive Officer
CFO: Dennis Hartman, Chief Financial Officer
CMO: Manoch Kuangparichat, M.D., President Medical Staff
CIO: Alicia Harrison, Data Management Officer
CHR: Joni Schwan, Director Human Resources
Web address: www.esmc.org
Control: City–Government, nonfederal **Service:** General Medical and Surgical

Staffed Beds: 105 **Admissions:** 456 **Census:** 73 **Outpatient Visits:** 29764 **Births:** 0 **Total Expense ($000):** 26189 **Payroll Expense ($000):** 10495 **Personnel:** 249

MO

Many Facility Codes have changed. Please refer to the AHA Guide Code Chart. © 2016 AHA Guide

FAIRFAX—Atchison County

COMMUNITY HOSPITAL ASSOCIATION See Community Hospital–Fairfax

★ ◇ **COMMUNITY HOSPITAL–FAIRFAX (261303)**, 26136 U.S. Highway 59, Zip 64446–9105, Mailing Address: P.O. Box 107, Zip 64446–0107; tel. 660/686–2211 **A**10 18 21 **F**3 11 13 15 28 29 30 34 40 45 50 57 59 62 64 67 76 79 81 85 87 89 107 110 114 117 119 128 130 132 133
Primary Contact: Roger W. Steinkruger, Chief Executive Officer
CFO: Jon Davis, Chief Financial Officer
CIO: Chris Hedlund, Director Information Systems
CHR: Amber Durr, Human Resources Executive
CNO: Julie L. Jones, Chief Nursing Officer
Web address: www.fairfaxmed.com
Control: Other not–for–profit (including NFP Corporation) **Service:** General Medical and Surgical

Staffed Beds: 18 **Admissions:** 485 **Census:** 4 **Outpatient Visits:** 18157 **Births:** 43 **Total Expense ($000):** 13460 **Payroll Expense ($000):** 4347 **Personnel:** 96

FARMINGTON—St. Francois County

⊞ **PARKLAND HEALTH CENTER – LIBERTY STREET (260163)**, 1101 West Liberty Street, Zip 63640–1921; tel. 573/756–6451 **A**1 10 **F**3 4 11 13 15 18 28 29 30 34 35 40 45 46 49 50 53 57 59 64 65 68 69 70 75 76 77 79 81 85 86 87 89 93 98 103 107 108 111 115 118 119 130 135 143 146 147 148 **S** BJC HealthCare, Saint Louis, MO
Primary Contact: Thomas P. Karl, President
COO: Steven R. Marler, Assistant Administrator
CFO: Cheri L. Goldsmith, Director Financial Services
CMO: Jamesy Smith, D.O., Chief of Staff
CHR: Sheri Graham, Director Human Resources and Administrative Services
CNO: Lauren A. Beckmann, Chief Nursing Officer
Web address: www.parklandhealthcenter.org
Control: Other not–for–profit (including NFP Corporation) **Service:** General Medical and Surgical

Staffed Beds: 103 **Admissions:** 3372 **Census:** 28 **Outpatient Visits:** 90836 **Births:** 656 **Total Expense ($000):** 79526 **Payroll Expense ($000):** 29249 **Personnel:** 480

☐ **SOUTHEAST MISSOURI MENTAL HEALTH CENTER (264005)**, 1010 West Columbia Street, Zip 63640–2997; tel. 573/218–6792 **A**1 10 **F**4 11 30 39 53 65 75 77 86 87 97 98 101 103 106 130 132 135 143 146
Primary Contact: Julie Inman, Regional Executive Officer
CMO: Jay Englehart, M.D., Medical Director
CHR: Mark Remspecher, Director Human Resources
Web address: www.dmh.missouri.gov/southeast/
Control: State–Government, nonfederal **Service:** Psychiatric

Staffed Beds: 323 **Admissions:** 41 **Census:** 302 **Outpatient Visits:** 0 **Births:** 0 **Total Expense ($000):** 61396 **Payroll Expense ($000):** 32401 **Personnel:** 890

FENTON—St. Louis County

⊞ **SSM ST. CLARE HOSPITAL (260081)**, 1015 Bowles Avenue, Zip 63026–2394; tel. 636/496–2000 **A**1 2 10 **F**3 11 13 15 17 18 20 22 24 28 29 30 31 34 35 40 44 45 49 50 51 53 54 56 57 59 61 64 70 73 74 75 76 78 79 81 82 84 85 86 87 89 100 102 103 107 108 110 111 115 117 119 120 124 130 132 135 143 144 146 147 148 **P**6 8 **S** SSM Health, Saint Louis, MO
Primary Contact: Ellis Hawkins, President
COO: Lee Bernstein, Regional Executive Vice President and Chief Operating Officer
CFO: Hal Holder, Regional Chief Financial Officer–Hospital Operations
CMO: Timothy J. Pratt, M.D., Vice President Medical Affairs and Chief Medical Officer
CIO: Michael Paasch, Vice President, Regional Chief Information Officer
CHR: Renee Roach, System Vice President, Human Resources
CNO: Wayne Laramie, Vice President Nursing
Web address: www.ssmstclare.com
Control: Church–operated, Nongovernment, not–for profit **Service:** General Medical and Surgical

Staffed Beds: 184 **Admissions:** 10526 **Census:** 116 **Outpatient Visits:** 117247 **Births:** 1152 **Total Expense ($000):** 178898 **Payroll Expense ($000):** 55250 **Personnel:** 877

FORT LEONARD WOOD—Pulaski County

⊞ **GENERAL LEONARD WOOD ARMY COMMUNITY HOSPITAL**, 126 Missouri Avenue, Zip 65473–8952; tel. 573/596–0414, (Nonreporting) **A**1 3
S Department of the Army, Office of the Surgeon General, Falls Church, VA
Primary Contact: Colonel Christian Meko, Hospital Commander
CFO: Major Michael Hogan, Chief Resource Management
CMO: Lieutenant Colonel John Lowery, M.D., Deputy Commander Clinical Services
CHR: Major Sandra Roper, Chief Human Resources
Web address: www.glwach.amedd.army.mil/
Control: Army, Government, federal **Service:** General Medical and Surgical

Staffed Beds: 54

FREDERICKTOWN—Madison County

MADISON MEDICAL CENTER (261302), 611 West Main Street, Zip 63645–1111; tel. 573/783–3341, (Total facility includes 80 beds in nursing home–type unit) **A**10 18 **F**6 11 15 18 28 31 35 40 45 59 62 64 67 70 74 77 78 79 81 85 87 92 93 97 103 107 111 119 127 128 130 133 146
Primary Contact: Lisa Twidwell, Administrator
CMO: P. A. George, M.D., Chief of Staff
CHR: Jennifer Penuel, Director Human Resources
Web address: www.madisonmedicalcenter.net
Control: County–Government, nonfederal **Service:** General Medical and Surgical

Staffed Beds: 97 **Admissions:** 349 **Census:** 76 **Outpatient Visits:** 52013 **Births:** 0 **Total Expense ($000):** 19104 **Payroll Expense ($000):** 9364 **Personnel:** 246

FULTON—Callaway County

☐ **FULTON MEDICAL CENTER (260209)**, 10 South Hospital Drive, Zip 65251–2510; tel. 573/642–3376 **A**1 3 5 10 **F**3 11 15 29 34 35 40 45 50 54 59 67 68 75 79 81 85 89 90 93 97 98 103 107 108 111 114 119 127 128 130 133 **P**6
Primary Contact: Mike Powell, Chief Executive Officer
COO: Isabel Schmedemann, R.N., Chief Nursing Officer and Chief Operating Officer
CNO: Isabel Schmedemann, R.N., Chief Nursing Officer and Chief Operating Officer
Web address: www.fultonmed.com
Control: Corporation, Investor–owned, for–profit **Service:** General Medical and Surgical

Staffed Beds: 37 **Admissions:** 420 **Census:** 13 **Outpatient Visits:** 35053 **Births:** 0 **Total Expense ($000):** 17458 **Payroll Expense ($000):** 7451 **Personnel:** 140

☐ **FULTON STATE HOSPITAL (264004)**, 600 East Fifth Street, Zip 65251–1753; tel. 573/592–4100 **A**1 3 5 10 **F**3 4 11 29 30 39 44 50 53 56 57 58 59 65 75 77 82 86 87 98 100 101 102 103 130 132 135 143 146 **P**6
Primary Contact: Robert Reitz, Ph.D., Chief Executive Officer
COO: Anthony Menditto, Ph.D., Interim Chief Operating Officer
CFO: Forrest "Bud" H. Smith, Jr., Chief Financial Officer
CMO: Sanjiv Sethi, M.D., Medical Director
CIO: Thomas Gillespie, Chief Information Officer
CHR: Lori Hollinger, Manager Human Resources
CNO: Sherry Lee, Chief Nurse Executive
Web address: www.dmh.missouri.gov/fulton
Control: State–Government, nonfederal **Service:** Psychiatric

Staffed Beds: 376 **Admissions:** 163 **Census:** 353 **Outpatient Visits:** 0 **Births:** 0 **Total Expense ($000):** 93220 **Payroll Expense ($000):** 48023 **Personnel:** 1187

HANNIBAL—Marion County

⊞ **HANNIBAL REGIONAL HOSPITAL (260025)**, 6000 Hospital Drive, Zip 63401–6887, Mailing Address: P.O. Box 551, Zip 63401–0551; tel. 573/248–1300 **A**1 2 10 **F**3 13 15 20 22 26 28 29 31 34 40 45 47 49 51 57 59 64 68 70 74 75 76 78 79 81 82 85 86 87 89 90 92 107 108 110 111 114 115 117 118 119 120 121 123 124 129 130 132 135 **P**1
Primary Contact: C. Todd Ahrens, President and Chief Executive Officer
CFO: Roger J. Dix, Vice President Finance
CMO: Bryson McHardy, M.D., President Medical Staff
CIO: Jeff W. Evans, Vice President Information and Technology
CHR: Susan R. Wathen, Vice President Human Resources
Web address: www.hrhonline.org
Control: Other not–for–profit (including NFP Corporation) **Service:** General Medical and Surgical

Staffed Beds: 99 **Admissions:** 4223 **Census:** 44 **Outpatient Visits:** 137861 **Births:** 620 **Total Expense ($000):** 117490 **Payroll Expense ($000):** 50572 **Personnel:** 766

MO

HARRISONVILLE—Cass County

✠ **CASS REGIONAL MEDICAL CENTER (261324)**, 2800 East Rock Haven Road, Zip 64701–4411; tel. 816/380–3474 **A**1 10 18 **F**3 11 12 15 17 18 28 29 30 31 32 34 35 40 43 44 45 46 48 50 54 56 57 59 64 65 66 70 74 75 77 78 79 81 82 84 85 86 87 92 93 96 97 98 107 110 111 114 115 119 127 129 130 131 132 133 135 146 147 **P**6
Primary Contact: John Christopher Lang, Chief Executive Officer
CFO: Brent Probasco, Chief Financial Officer
CIO: Lester Vohs, Manager Information Systems
CHR: Carla Wallen, Manager Human Resources
CNO: Twila Buckner, R.N., Chief Nursing Officer
Web address: www.cassregional.org
Control: County–Government, nonfederal **Service:** General Medical and Surgical

Staffed Beds: 35 **Admissions:** 1343 **Census:** 17 **Outpatient Visits:** 107823
Births: 0 **Total Expense ($000):** 61487 **Payroll Expense ($000):** 22503
Personnel: 390

HAYTI—Pemiscot County

PEMISCOT MEMORIAL HEALTH SYSTEM (260070), 946 East Road, Zip 63851–1245, Mailing Address: P.O. Box 489, Zip 63851–0489; tel. 573/359–1372, (Nonreporting) **A**10
Primary Contact: Mark Davis, Chief Executive Officer
CFO: Kerry L. Noble, Chief Financial Officer
CHR: Jackie Powell, Director Human Resources
Web address: www.pemiscot.org/
Control: County–Government, nonfederal **Service:** General Medical and Surgical

Staffed Beds: 167

HERMANN—Gasconade County

HERMANN AREA DISTRICT HOSPITAL (261314), 509 West 18th Street, Zip 65041–1547, Mailing Address: P.O. Box 470, Zip 65041–0470; tel. 573/486–2191 **A**10 18 **F**3 11 15 18 28 29 34 35 40 41 44 45 53 56 57 59 62 64 67 69 71 75 77 78 81 85 86 87 89 90 93 96 97 104 107 111 114 119 128 143 146 **P**6
Primary Contact: Dan McKinney, Administrator
COO: Matt Siebert, Assistant Administrator Ancillary Services
CFO: Christine Lewis, Controller
CMO: Michael Rothermich, M.D., Chief of Staff
CIO: Jeffrey Wehmeyer, Director Information Technology
CHR: Brandon Hughes, Director Human Resources
CNO: Sue Daller, R.N., Assistant Administrator Nursing
Web address: www.hadh.org
Control: Hospital district or authority, Government, nonfederal **Service:** General Medical and Surgical

Staffed Beds: 24 **Admissions:** 548 **Census:** 11 **Outpatient Visits:** 60465
Births: 0 **Total Expense ($000):** 18250 **Payroll Expense ($000):** 8178
Personnel: 175

HOUSTON—Texas County

TEXAS COUNTY MEMORIAL HOSPITAL (260024), 1333 South Sam Houston Boulevard, Zip 65483–2046; tel. 417/967–3311 **A**10 20 **F**3 7 13 15 28 29 34 40 45 57 59 62 63 64 70 76 81 85 86 87 89 93 97 107 110 111 115 119 127 129 130 133 143 148 **P**6
Primary Contact: Wesley E. Murray, Chief Executive Officer
CFO: Linda Pamperien, Chief Financial Officer
CMO: Charles Mueller, M.D., Chief of Staff
CHR: Anita Kuhn, Controller
Web address: www.tcmh.org
Control: County–Government, nonfederal **Service:** General Medical and Surgical

Staffed Beds: 47 **Admissions:** 1496 **Census:** 16 **Outpatient Visits:** 102207
Births: 210 **Total Expense ($000):** 30443 **Payroll Expense ($000):** 14740
Personnel: 340

INDEPENDENCE—Jackson County

✠ **CENTERPOINT MEDICAL CENTER (260095)**, 19600 East 39th Street, Zip 64057–2301; tel. 816/698–7000 **A**1 2 10 **F**3 8 12 13 15 18 20 22 24 26 28 29 30 31 34 35 38 40 43 46 47 48 49 50 54 55 57 59 60 64 68 70 72 74 75 76 77 78 79 80 81 82 85 86 87 92 93 107 108 110 111 114 115 118 119 126 129 130 131 132 144 145 146 147 148 **S** HCA, Nashville, TN
Primary Contact: David R. Williams, Chief Executive Officer
COO: Phil Buttell, Chief Operating Officer
CFO: James H. Brown, Chief Financial Officer
CMO: Christopher Sullivan, M.D., Chief Medical Officer
CIO: Carl Sifers, Director Information Technology and System Services
CHR: Kyla Stoltz, Vice President Human Resources
CNO: Lynn Barrett, Chief Nursing Officer
Web address: www.centerpointmedical.com
Control: Corporation, Investor–owned, for–profit **Service:** General Medical and Surgical

Staffed Beds: 221 **Admissions:** 15934 **Census:** 178 **Outpatient Visits:** 152700 **Births:** 1425 **Total Expense ($000):** 226748 **Payroll Expense ($000):** 73514 **Personnel:** 946

JEFFERSON CITY—Cole County

✠ **CAPITAL REGION MEDICAL CENTER (260047)**, 1125 Madison Street, Zip 65101–5200, Mailing Address: P.O. Box 1128, Zip 65102–1128; tel. 573/632–5000 **A**1 3 5 10 12 13 **F**3 5 11 13 15 17 18 20 22 24 26 28 29 30 31 32 34 35 36 38 40 45 46 47 48 51 53 54 56 57 58 59 61 62 64 65 66 70 73 74 75 76 77 78 79 80 81 85 87 89 90 92 93 94 97 99 100 102 104 107 108 110 111 115 118 119 120 121 123 129 130 131 132 135 144 146 147 **P**2 6 **S** University of Missouri Health Care, Columbia, MO
Primary Contact: Gaspare Calvaruso, President
COO: Janet Weckenborg, Vice President Operations
CFO: Tom Luebbering, Vice President Finance
CMO: Mitchell Godbee, Chief of Staff
CIO: Jason Cecil, Vice President, Information
CHR: Sarah Morrow, Vice President Human Resources
CNO: Lynne Voskamp, R.N., Vice President of Nursing
Web address: www.crmc.org
Control: Other not–for–profit (including NFP Corporation) **Service:** General Medical and Surgical

Staffed Beds: 114 **Admissions:** 5007 **Census:** 54 **Outpatient Visits:** 446431
Births: 780 **Total Expense ($000):** 167126 **Payroll Expense ($000):** 74868
Personnel: 1266

✠ **SSM HEALTH ST. MARY'S HOSPITAL – JEFFERSON CITY (260011)**, 2505 Mission Drive, Zip 65109; tel. 573/681–3000 **A**1 10 19 **F**3 5 11 13 15 17 18 20 22 24 28 29 30 31 34 40 45 47 48 49 50 51 54 57 59 60 64 70 73 74 75 76 77 78 79 81 82 85 86 87 89 93 96 98 100 101 102 104 107 108 111 115 117 118 119 120 121 122 123 127 129 130 131 132 135 141 144 146 147 148 **P**6 **S** SSM Health, Saint Louis, MO
Primary Contact: R. Brent VanConia, President
CFO: James Stratton, Vice President Finance
CMO: Stephen Stewart, M.D., Vice President Medical Affairs
CHR: Susan Mankoski, Vice President Human Resources
CNO: Alice M. Chatley, R.N., Vice President Acute Care Services
Web address: www.lethealingbegin.com
Control: Church–operated, Nongovernment, not–for profit **Service:** General Medical and Surgical

Staffed Beds: 154 **Admissions:** 6887 **Census:** 75 **Outpatient Visits:** 208678
Births: 1013 **Total Expense ($000):** 162411 **Payroll Expense ($000):** 47689 **Personnel:** 889

JOPLIN—Newton County

★ ○ **FREEMAN HEALTH SYSTEM (260137)**, 1102 West 32nd Street, Zip 64804–3503; tel. 417/347–1111, (Includes FREEMAN HOSPITAL EAST, 932 East 34th Street, Zip 64804–3999, Mailing Address: 1102 West 32nd Street, Zip 64804–3999; tel. 417/347–1111; Paula F. Baker, President and Chief Executive Officer) **A**10 11 13 **F**3 8 11 12 13 15 17 18 20 22 24 26 28 29 30 31 34 35 40 42 43 44 45 46 47 48 49 50 54 56 57 59 60 61 62 64 65 68 70 72 73 74 75 76 77 78 79 81 82 84 85 86 87 89 90 93 96 97 98 100 102 103 107 108 110 111 115 117 119 120 121 124 129 130 131 132 144 145 146 147 148 **P**1 6 **S** Freeman Health System, Joplin, MO
Primary Contact: Paula F. Baker, President and Chief Executive Officer
CFO: Steve W. Graddy, Chief Financial Officer
CMO: Saba Habis, M.D., Chief Medical Officer
CIO: Skip Rollins, Chief Information Officer
CHR: Mary Frerer, Chief Human Resources Officer
CNO: Jeffrey Carrier, R.N., Chief Clinical Officer
Web address: www.freemanhealth.com
Control: Other not–for–profit (including NFP Corporation) **Service:** General Medical and Surgical

Staffed Beds: 396 **Admissions:** 17849 **Census:** 267 **Outpatient Visits:** 759625 **Births:** 2169 **Total Expense ($000):** 451303 **Payroll Expense ($000):** 207608 **Personnel:** 3138

LANDMARK HOSPITAL OF JOPLIN (262016), 2040 West 32nd Street, Zip 64804–3512; tel. 417/627–1300, (Nonreporting) **A**10 22 **S** Landmark Hospitals, Cape Girardeau, MO
Primary Contact: Kevin J. Clement, Chief Executive Officer
CMO: Jack Rhoads, M.D., Medical Director
CHR: Janice Nordstrom, Director Human Resources
CNO: Stephanie Slater-Nesuold, Director of Nursing
Web address: www.landmarkhospitals.com
Control: Partnership, Investor–owned, for–profit **Service:** Long–Term Acute Care hospital

Staffed Beds: 30

MO

Many Facility Codes have changed. Please refer to the AHA Guide Code Chart. © 2016 AHA Guide

⊞ **MERCY HOSPITAL JOPLIN (260001)**, 100 Mercy Way, Zip 64804–1626; tel. 417/781–2727, (Includes ST. JOHN'S REHABILITATION CENTER, 2727 McClelland Boulevard, Zip 64804; tel. 417/659–6716) **A**1 2 10 13 **F**3 4 5 7 11 12 13 15 17 18 20 22 24 26 28 29 30 31 34 35 37 38 39 40 43 44 45 46 47 48 49 50 51 54 57 58 59 60 61 62 63 64 65 66 68 70 72 73 74 75 76 77 78 79 81 82 84 85 86 87 89 90 93 94 97 98 99 100 101 102 103 104 105 106 107 108 110 111 114 115 117 118 119 120 121 123 124 126 127 129 130 131 132 134 135 144 146 147 148 **P**6 **S** Mercy Health, Chesterfield, MO
Primary Contact: Gary W. Pulsipher, President and Chief Executive Officer
COO: Michele Stewart, R.N., Chief Operating Officer
CFO: Shelly Hunter, Chief Financial Officer
CHR: Timothy Murphy, Vice President Human Resources
CNO: Dennis Manley, R.N., Chief Nursing Officer
Web address: www.mercy.net/joplinmo
Control: Church–operated, Nongovernment, not–for profit **Service:** General Medical and Surgical

Staffed Beds: 240 **Admissions:** 9179 **Census:** 116 **Outpatient Visits:** 159174 **Births:** 737 **Total Expense ($000):** 195575 **Payroll Expense ($000):** 56584 **Personnel:** 1285

KANSAS CITY—Jackson County

☐ **CENTER FOR BEHAVIORAL MEDICINE (264008)**, 1000 East 24th Street, Zip 64108–2776; tel. 816/512–7000, (Total facility includes 68 beds in nursing home–type unit) **A**1 3 5 10 **F**4 29 35 36 38 50 53 86 87 98 128
Primary Contact: Denise Norbury, Chief Executive Officer
COO: Jeanette Simmons, Chief Operating Officer
CFO: Randy Riley, Chief Financial Officer
CMO: Nashaat Boutros, M.D., Clinical Director
CIO: Robert Curren, Director Information Technology
CHR: Silva Ward, Director Human Resources
CNO: John Tucker, Chief Nursing Executive
Web address: www.dmhonline.dmh.state.mo.us
Control: State–Government, nonfederal **Service:** Psychiatric

Staffed Beds: 133 **Admissions:** 47 **Census:** 119 **Outpatient Visits:** 0 **Births:** 0 **Total Expense ($000):** 24138 **Payroll Expense ($000):** 13864 **Personnel:** 383

⊞ **CHILDREN'S MERCY HOSPITALS AND CLINICS (263302)**, 2401 Gillham Road, Zip 64108–4619; tel. 816/234–3000 **A**1 2 3 5 8 10 **F**3 7 8 9 11 12 16 19 20 21 22 23 24 25 26 27 29 30 31 32 34 35 36 39 40 41 43 44 48 50 54 55 57 58 59 60 61 62 64 65 68 72 73 74 75 77 78 79 81 82 84 85 86 87 88 89 90 91 92 93 94 96 97 100 101 104 107 108 111 115 117 118 119 130 131 132 134 136 137 138 139 141 142 144 146 148 **P**6
Primary Contact: Randall L. O'Donnell, Ph.D., President and Chief Executive Officer
COO: Jo W. Stueve, Executive Vice President and Co–Chief Operating Officer
CFO: Sandra A J Lawrence, Executive Vice President and Chief Financial Officer
CMO: Charles Roberts, M.D., Executive Vice President and Executive Medical Director
CIO: Jean Ann Breedlove, Chief Information Officer
CNO: Cheri Hunt, R.N., Vice President Patient Care Services and Chief Nursing Officer
Web address: www.childrensmercy.org
Control: Other not–for–profit (including NFP Corporation) **Service:** Children's general

Staffed Beds: 301 **Admissions:** 12245 **Census:** 222 **Outpatient Visits:** 392212 **Births:** 141 **Total Expense ($000):** 928486 **Payroll Expense ($000):** 463216 **Personnel:** 5658

⊞ **CRITTENTON CHILDREN'S CENTER (264018)**, 10918 Elm Avenue, Zip 64134–4108; tel. 816/765–6600 **A**1 10 **F**5 29 30 32 34 35 68 75 77 86 87 98 99 100 101 102 104 106 130 132 146 **P**6 **S** Saint Luke's Health System, Kansas City, MO
Primary Contact: Janine Hron, Chief Executive Officer
CFO: Willard Staron, Chief Financial Officer
CMO: Eileen Duggan, M.D., Medical Director
CIO: Deborah Gash, Vice President and Chief Information Officer
CHR: Terri Neal, Director Human Resources
CNO: Belva Giesing, Chief Nursing Officer
Web address: www.crittentonkc.org
Control: Other not–for–profit (including NFP Corporation) **Service:** Children's hospital psychiatric

Staffed Beds: 46 **Admissions:** 2574 **Census:** 39 **Outpatient Visits:** 15596 **Births:** 0 **Total Expense ($000):** 29761 **Payroll Expense ($000):** 15825 **Personnel:** 295

⊞ **KANSAS CITY VETERANS AFFAIRS MEDICAL CENTER**, 4801 East Linwood Boulevard, Zip 64128–2226; tel. 816/861–4700, (Nonreporting) **A**1 2 3 5 **S** Department of Veterans Affairs, Washington, DC
Primary Contact: Kathleen R. Fogarty, MS, Director
CFO: Bryan Bieri, Manager Finance
CMO: Ahmad Batrash, Chief of Staff
CIO: Eddie Johnson, Chief Information Technology Officer
CHR: Kathi Nippert, Acting Chief Human Resources Officer
Web address: www.kansascity.va.gov/
Control: Veterans Affairs, Government, federal **Service:** General Medical and Surgical

Staffed Beds: 157

⊞ **KINDRED HOSPITAL KANSAS CITY (262011)**, 8701 Troost Avenue, Zip 64131–2767; tel. 816/995–2000 **A**1 10 **F**1 18 29 56 70 82 85 87 100 107 130 148 **S** Kindred Healthcare, Louisville, KY
Primary Contact: Alexander Gill, Chief Executive Officer
CFO: Brett Stevenson, Controller
CNO: Cheryl Hunt, Chief Clinical Officer
Web address: www.kindredhospitalkc.com
Control: Corporation, Investor–owned, for–profit **Service:** Long–Term Acute Care hospital

Staffed Beds: 130 **Admissions:** 530 **Census:** 50 **Outpatient Visits:** 0 **Births:** 0 **Total Expense ($000):** 31921 **Payroll Expense ($000):** 10073 **Personnel:** 123

⊞ **KINDRED HOSPITAL NORTHLAND (262018)**, 500 Northwest 68th Street, Zip 64118–2455; tel. 816/420–6300 **A**1 10 **F**1 3 16 18 28 29 30 80 82 84 85 90 100 130 135 142 148 **S** Kindred Healthcare, Louisville, KY
Primary Contact: Jason Grundstrom, Chief Executive Officer
CFO: Brett Stevenson, Controller
CMO: Sean R. Muldoon, M.D., Senior Vice President and Chief Medical Officer–Kindred Healthcare, Hospital Division
CNO: Laura Inge, Chief Clinical Officer
Web address: www.khnorthland.com
Control: Corporation, Investor–owned, for–profit **Service:** Long–Term Acute Care hospital

Staffed Beds: 35 **Admissions:** 423 **Census:** 31 **Outpatient Visits:** 0 **Births:** 0 **Total Expense ($000):** 17679 **Payroll Expense ($000):** 6699 **Personnel:** 85

NORTHLAND LTAC HOSPITAL See Kindred Hospital Northland

⊞ **RESEARCH MEDICAL CENTER (260027)**, 2316 East Meyer Boulevard, Zip 64132–1136; tel. 816/276–4000, (Includes RESEARCH PSYCHIATRIC CENTER, 2323 East 63rd Street, Zip 64130–3462; tel. 816/444–8161; Lisa St. Aubyn, Chief Executive Officer) **A**1 2 3 5 10 **F**3 4 5 8 11 13 15 16 17 18 20 22 24 26 28 29 30 31 34 35 38 39 40 42 43 44 45 46 47 49 50 52 53 54 55 57 58 59 60 61 64 68 70 72 73 74 75 76 77 78 79 81 82 84 85 86 87 90 91 93 94 96 97 98 99 100 101 102 103 104 105 107 108 110 111 112 114 115 116 118 119 120 121 122 124 126 129 130 131 132 134 135 138 142 143 146 147 148 **S** HCA, Nashville, TN
Primary Contact: Jacqueline DeSouza, Chief Executive Officer
COO: Eric Becker, Chief Operating Officer
CFO: Susan Shreeve, Chief Financial Officer
CMO: James Bower, M.D., Chief Medical Officer
CIO: Shawn Kegley, Director Information Services
CHR: Charlotte O'Neal, Vice President Human Resources
Web address: www.researchmedicalcenter.com
Control: Corporation, Investor–owned, for–profit **Service:** General Medical and Surgical

Staffed Beds: 456 **Admissions:** 19419 **Census:** 304 **Outpatient Visits:** 167827 **Births:** 1100 **Total Expense ($000):** 401115 **Payroll Expense ($000):** 118321 **Personnel:** 1992

MO

Hospital, Medicare Provider Number, Address, Telephone, Approval, Facility, and Physician Codes, Health Care System

★ American Hospital Association (AHA) membership
☐ The Joint Commission accreditation
○ Healthcare Facilities Accreditation Program
◇ DNV Healthcare Inc. accreditation
⇧ Center for Improvement in Healthcare Quality Accreditation
△ Commission on Accreditation of Rehabilitation Facilities (CARF) accreditation

SAINT LUKE'S HOSPITAL OF KANSAS CITY (260138), 4401 Wornall Road, Zip 64111–3220; tel. 816/932–3800 **A**1 2 3 5 8 10 **F**3 4 6 8 9 11 12 13 15 17 18 20 22 24 25 26 28 29 30 31 32 34 35 36 37 38 39 40 43 44 45 46 47 48 49 50 55 56 57 58 59 60 61 64 65 66 68 70 71 72 73 74 75 76 77 78 79 80 81 82 84 85 86 87 89 90 91 92 93 94 95 96 97 100 101 102 103 104 107 108 110 111 114 115 116 117 118 119 120 121 123 124 126 129 130 131 132 134 135 137 138 139 141 145 146 147 148 **P**6 **S** Saint Luke's Health System, Kansas City, MO
Primary Contact: Jani L. Johnson, R.N., MSN, Chief Executive Officer
COO: Brad Simmons, Chief Operating Officer
CFO: Amy Nachtigal, Chief Financial Officer
CMO: Peter Holt, M.D., Director Medical Affairs
CIO: Deborah Gash, Chief Information Officer
CHR: Doris Rogers, Vice President Human Resources
CNO: Debra Wilson, Vice President and Chief Nursing Officer
Web address: www.saint–lukes.org
Control: Church–operated, Nongovernment, not–for profit **Service:** General Medical and Surgical

Staffed Beds: **442** Admissions: **18185** Census: **310** Outpatient Visits: **401790** Births: **2267** Total Expense ($000): **619909** Payroll Expense ($000): **157755** Personnel: **2646**

SAINT LUKE'S NORTH HOSPITAL – BARRY ROAD (260062), 5830 N.W. Barry Road, Zip 64154–2778; tel. 816/891–6000, (Includes SAINT LUKE'S NORTH HOSPITAL–SMITHVILLE CAMPUS, 601 South 169 Highway, Smithville, Zip 64089–9317; tel. 816/532–3700; Matthew Wenzel, Chief Executive Officer) **A**1 10 **F**3 11 13 15 18 20 22 26 28 29 30 31 34 35 36 38 40 44 45 49 50 53 56 57 58 59 60 64 65 69 70 73 74 75 76 77 78 79 80 81 82 84 85 86 87 89 90 92 93 96 98 99 100 101 102 103 107 108 110 111 114 115 116 117 118 119 129 130 131 132 135 141 143 146 147 148 **S** Saint Luke's Health System, Kansas City, MO
Primary Contact: Matthew Wenzel, President and Chief Executive Officer
CFO: Julie Murphy, Chief Financial Officer
CMO: Leonardo J. Lozada, M.D., Chief Physician Executive
CIO: LaDonna Seger, Director Information Services
CHR: Donna Kunz, Director Human Resources
CNO: Amy Brummer, R.N., Chief Nursing Officer
Web address: www.saint–lukes.org
Control: Church–operated, Nongovernment, not–for profit **Service:** General Medical and Surgical

Staffed Beds: **142** Admissions: **7483** Census: **83** Outpatient Visits: **88912** Births: **864** Total Expense ($000): **121889** Payroll Expense ($000): **38127** Personnel: **624**

SELECT SPECIALTY HOSPITAL–WESTERN MISSOURI (262014), 2316 East Meyer Boulevard, 3 West, Zip 64132–1136; tel. 816/276–3300 **A**1 10 **F**1 3 29 148 **S** Select Medical Corporation, Mechanicsburg, PA
Primary Contact: Jeffrey Alexander, Chief Executive Officer
Web address: www.selectspecialtyhospitals.com/company/locations/westernmissouri.aspx
Control: Corporation, Investor–owned, for–profit **Service:** Long–Term Acute Care hospital

Staffed Beds: **34** Admissions: **396** Census: **27** Outpatient Visits: **0** Births: **0** Total Expense ($000): **14702** Payroll Expense ($000): **6210** Personnel: **104**

SIGNATURE PSYCHIATRIC HOSPITAL (264030), 2900 Clay Edwards Drive, Zip 64116–3235; tel. 816/691–5101, (Nonreporting)
Primary Contact: Dennis Anderson, Administrator and Director of Nursing
CFO: Tariq F. Malik, CPA, Chief Financial Officer
CMO: Azfar Malik, M.D., Chief Medical Officer
CIO: Mike Solom, Director Information Technology
CHR: Sheila Shipley, Human Resources Educator
CNO: Dennis Anderson, Administrator and Director of Nursing
Web address: www.signaturepsychiatrichospitalkc.com
Control: Corporation, Investor–owned, for–profit **Service:** Psychiatric

Staffed Beds: **24**

ST. JOSEPH MEDICAL CENTER (260085), 1000 Carondelet Drive, Zip 64114–4673; tel. 816/942–4400, (Data for 322 days) **A**1 2 10 **F**3 11 12 13 15 17 18 20 22 24 26 28 29 34 35 40 45 47 49 50 51 57 58 59 60 64 68 70 72 74 75 76 77 78 79 80 81 82 84 85 87 90 93 96 107 108 110 111 114 115 116 118 119 129 130 132 146 147 148 **P**6 **S** Prime Healthcare Services, Ontario, CA
Primary Contact: Robert J. Erickson, Chief Executive Officer
CFO: Debra Cartwright, Chief Financial Officer
CMO: Tommy Ko, M.D., Chief Medical Officer
CIO: Cheryl Johnson, Regional Chief Information Officer
CHR: Donna Sumner, Director, Human Resources and Organizational Development
CNO: Greg Simpson, Chief Nursing Officer
Web address: www.stjosephkc.com/
Control: Individual, Investor–owned, for–profit **Service:** General Medical and Surgical

Staffed Beds: **185** Admissions: **7826** Census: **113** Outpatient Visits: **81595** Births: **536** Total Expense ($000): **142512** Payroll Expense ($000): **46945** Personnel: **1143**

TRUMAN MEDICAL CENTER–HOSPITAL HILL (260048), 2301 Holmes Street, Zip 64108–2640; tel. 816/404–1000 **A**1 2 3 5 8 10 13 **F**3 4 5 11 12 13 14 15 17 18 20 22 26 28 29 31 34 35 36 37 38 39 40 41 43 44 45 46 48 49 50 52 53 55 57 58 59 61 64 65 66 68 70 71 72 73 74 75 76 77 78 79 81 82 84 85 86 90 93 94 97 98 99 100 101 102 103 104 107 108 110 111 114 115 119 129 130 131 132 134 135 143 146 147 148 **P**5 6 **S** Truman Medical Centers, Kansas City, MO
Primary Contact: Charlie Shields, President and Chief Executive Officer
CFO: Allen Johnson, Chief Financial Officer
CMO: Mark Steele, M.D., Chief Medical Officer
CIO: Mitzi Cardenas, Chief Information Officer
CHR: Marcos DeLeon, Vice President Community Engagement
CNO: Lynette Wheeler, MSN, Chief Nursing Officer
Web address: www.trumed.org
Control: Other not–for–profit (including NFP Corporation) **Service:** General Medical and Surgical

Staffed Beds: **249** Admissions: **16413** Census: **203** Outpatient Visits: **615870** Births: **1866** Total Expense ($000): **363145** Payroll Expense ($000): **148783** Personnel: **2453**

TRUMAN MEDICAL CENTER–LAKEWOOD (260102), 7900 Lee's Summit Road, Zip 64139–1236; tel. 816/404–7000, (Total facility includes 188 beds in nursing home–type unit) **A**1 3 5 10 **F**3 4 5 6 11 13 15 18 29 30 32 34 35 36 38 39 40 44 45 50 53 56 57 58 59 64 65 66 67 68 70 71 72 74 75 76 77 78 79 81 85 86 87 89 90 92 93 94 97 98 99 100 101 102 103 104 107 112 115 119 126 128 129 130 131 132 134 135 143 146 147 **P**5 6 **S** Truman Medical Centers, Kansas City, MO
Primary Contact: Charlie Shields, President and Chief Executive Officer
COO: Amy Peters, R.N., Interim Chief Operating Officer
CFO: Allen Johnson, Chief Financial Officer
CMO: Mark Steele, M.D., Chief Medical Officer
CIO: Mitzi Cardenas, Chief Information Officer
CHR: Marcos DeLeon, Vice President Community Engagement
CNO: Lynette Wheeler, MSN, Chief Nursing Officer
Web address: www.trumed.org
Control: Other not–for–profit (including NFP Corporation) **Service:** General Medical and Surgical

Staffed Beds: **298** Admissions: **6246** Census: **227** Outpatient Visits: **448271** Births: **1626** Total Expense ($000): **140071** Payroll Expense ($000): **59209** Personnel: **841**

TWO RIVERS BEHAVIORAL HEALTH SYSTEM (264017), 5121 Raytown Road, Zip 64133–2141; tel. 816/382–6300 **A**1 10 **F**4 5 34 75 98 99 101 102 104 105 130 132 143 **P**6 **S** Universal Health Services, Inc., King of Prussia, PA
Primary Contact: Terry Trafton, Chief Executive Officer
CFO: Teresa Martin, Chief Financial Officer
CMO: Shahbaz Khan, M.D., Medical Director
CHR: Diane Peoples, Director Human Resources
CNO: Kristie Baker, Chief Nursing Officer
Web address: www.tworivershospital.com
Control: Corporation, Investor–owned, for–profit **Service:** Psychiatric

Staffed Beds: **105** Admissions: **2898** Census: **47** Outpatient Visits: **3524** Births: **0** Total Expense ($000): **16094** Payroll Expense ($000): **7760** Personnel: **181**

VETERANS AFFAIRS MEDICAL CENTER See Kansas City Veterans Affairs Medical Center

KENNETT—Dunklin County

TWIN RIVERS REGIONAL MEDICAL CENTER (260015), 1301 First Street, Zip 63857–2508, Mailing Address: P.O. Box 728, Zip 63857–0728; tel. 573/888–4522 **A**1 10 **F**3 11 13 15 18 29 30 31 35 40 50 56 57 59 60 64 68 70 75 76 78 79 81 85 89 90 98 99 100 101 102 103 104 107 108 110 111 114 115 117 119 127 129 130 135 147 148 **P**5 **S** Community Health Systems, Inc., Franklin, TN
Primary Contact: Gerald Faircloth, FACHE, Chief Executive Officer
CFO: Michelle Beachman, Chief Financial Officer
CHR: Mark Niemeier, Director Human Resources
CNO: Judy Haney, Chief Nursing Officer
Web address: www.twinriversregional.com
Control: Corporation, Investor–owned, for–profit **Service:** General Medical and Surgical

Staffed Beds: **100** Admissions: **2971** Census: **31** Outpatient Visits: **89352** Births: **413** Total Expense ($000): **45611** Payroll Expense ($000): **15506** Personnel: **282**

KIRKSVILLE—Adair County

★ ○ **NORTHEAST REGIONAL MEDICAL CENTER (260022)**, 315 South Osteopathy, Zip 63501–6401, Mailing Address: P.O. Box C8502, Zip 63501–8599; tel. 660/785–1000 **A**10 11 12 13 **F**3 12 13 15 18 20 24 28 29 30 34 35 39 40 43 45 46 49 50 51 53 57 59 60 62 64 68 70 74 75 76 77 79 81 82 85 86 87 89 90 93 107 108 110 111 114 115 119 127 129 130 131 132 133 135 146 147 148 **S** Community Health Systems, Inc., Franklin, TN
Primary Contact: Ranee C. Brayton, R.N., MSN, Chief Executive Officer
CFO: Carol Cross, CPA, Chief Financial Officer
CMO: Brent Speak, Chief of Staff
CIO: Chad Tatro, Supervisor Information Systems
CHR: Jim Bergman, Director Human Resources
CNO: Mary Knudsen, Chief Nursing Officer
Web address: www.nermc.com
Control: Corporation, Investor–owned, for–profit **Service:** General Medical and Surgical

Staffed Beds: 93 **Admissions:** 2612 **Census:** 29 **Outpatient Visits:** 76260 **Births:** 536 **Total Expense ($000):** 51433 **Payroll Expense ($000):** 18658 **Personnel:** 465

LAKE SAINT LOUIS—St. Charles County

▣ **SSM HEALTH ST. JOSEPH HOSPITAL – LAKE SAINT LOUIS (260200)**, 100 Medical Plaza, Zip 63367–1366; tel. 636/625–5200 **A**1 2 10 **F**3 11 13 15 17 18 20 22 28 29 30 31 34 35 36 38 40 41 43 44 49 50 51 53 54 55 56 57 59 60 61 64 68 70 73 74 75 76 78 79 81 82 84 85 86 87 89 102 107 108 110 111 114 117 118 119 129 130 132 135 145 146 147 148 **P**6 8 **S** SSM Health, Saint Louis, MO
Primary Contact: Lisle Wescott, President
COO: Lee Bernstein, Regional Executive Vice President of Hospital and Chief Operating Officer
CFO: Hal Holder, Regional Chief Financial Officer
CMO: Michael Handler, M.D., Vice President Medical Affairs and Chief Medical Officer
CIO: Sharon Gardner, Manager Information Systems
CHR: Renee Roach, System Vice President
CNO: Janet K. Pestle, R.N., Vice President Nursing and Chief Nursing Officer
Web address: www.ssmstjoseph.com
Control: Church–operated, Nongovernment, not–for profit **Service:** General Medical and Surgical

Staffed Beds: 119 **Admissions:** 9303 **Census:** 94 **Outpatient Visits:** 145427 **Births:** 1173 **Total Expense ($000):** 142978 **Payroll Expense ($000):** 51249 **Personnel:** 779

LAMAR—Barton County

BARTON COUNTY MEMORIAL HOSPITAL (261325), 29 N.W. First Lane, Zip 64759–8105; tel. 417/681–5100 **A**10 18 **F**3 11 15 18 28 30 34 35 36 40 44 45 50 57 59 64 65 68 74 75 77 79 81 84 85 86 87 89 90 92 93 97 107 108 110 111 114 119 127 128 129 130 132 133 135 143 146 148
Primary Contact: Wendy Duvall, Chief Executive Officer
CIO: Brad Butler, Network Administrator
CHR: Sheila Boice, Director Human Resources
CNO: Marlys Buckner, Chief Nursing Officer
Web address: www.bcmh.net
Control: County–Government, nonfederal **Service:** General Medical and Surgical

Staffed Beds: 25 **Admissions:** 927 **Census:** 11 **Outpatient Visits:** 45079 **Births:** 0 **Total Expense ($000):** 18458 **Payroll Expense ($000):** 7657 **Personnel:** 162

LEBANON—Laclede County

▣ **MERCY HOSPITAL LEBANON (260059)**, 100 Hospital Drive, Zip 65536–9210; tel. 417/533–6100 **A**1 10 20 **F**3 11 13 15 28 29 30 31 35 36 37 40 45 47 50 53 57 59 64 65 68 70 71 74 75 76 77 78 79 81 82 83 85 86 87 89 90 93 94 102 107 108 110 111 114 119 129 130 131 132 135 146 147 148 **P**6 **S** Mercy Health, Chesterfield, MO
Primary Contact: David R. Steinmann, Administrator
CFO: Douglas M. Hoban, Vice President and Chief Financial Officer
CNO: Judy O'Connor–Snyder, Chief Nursing Officer
Web address: www.mercy.net/practice/mercy–hospital–lebanon
Control: Church–operated, Nongovernment, not–for profit **Service:** General Medical and Surgical

Staffed Beds: 58 **Admissions:** 2418 **Census:** 18 **Outpatient Visits:** 141509 **Births:** 427 **Total Expense ($000):** 70860 **Payroll Expense ($000):** 26408 **Personnel:** 462

LEE'S SUMMIT—Jackson County

▣ **LEE'S SUMMIT MEDICAL CENTER (260190)**, 2100 S.E. Blue Parkway, Zip 64063–1007; tel. 816/282–5000 **A**1 10 **F**15 18 20 22 28 29 30 31 34 40 43 49 57 59 60 64 65 68 69 70 74 75 77 78 79 81 82 84 85 87 93 107 108 110 111 115 119 126 129 130 131 132 145 146 148 **S** HCA, Nashville, TN
Primary Contact: Matt Sogard, Chief Executive Officer
CFO: John Heurtin, Chief Financial Officer
CIO: Andrew Beechy, Manager Information Technology Systems
CHR: Linda Duncan, Director Human Resources
CNO: Paige Baker, MSN, Chief Nursing Officer
Web address: www.leessummitmedicalcenter.com
Control: Corporation, Investor–owned, for–profit **Service:** General Medical and Surgical

Staffed Beds: 64 **Admissions:** 3984 **Census:** 38 **Outpatient Visits:** 98057 **Births:** 0 **Total Expense ($000):** 77596 **Payroll Expense ($000):** 32502 **Personnel:** 309

▣ **SAINT LUKE'S EAST HOSPITAL (260216)**, 100 N.E. Saint Luke's Boulevard, Zip 64086–6000; tel. 816/347–5000 **A**1 10 **F**3 13 15 18 20 22 26 28 29 30 31 34 35 38 40 43 44 45 46 49 50 56 57 58 59 60 64 65 70 71 72 73 74 75 76 77 78 79 80 81 82 84 85 86 87 90 92 93 94 96 100 102 107 108 110 111 114 115 117 118 119 120 121 123 126 129 130 131 132 135 145 146 147 148 **S** Saint Luke's Health System, Kansas City, MO
Primary Contact: Ronald L. Baker, Chief Executive Officer
CFO: Joseph P. Stasi, Chief Financial Officer
CHR: John Clabaugh, Director Human Resources
CNO: Gloria Solis, R.N., Chief Nursing Officer
Web address: www.saintlukeskc.org
Control: Church–operated, Nongovernment, not–for profit **Service:** General Medical and Surgical

Staffed Beds: 161 **Admissions:** 10421 **Census:** 110 **Outpatient Visits:** 128247 **Births:** 1847 **Total Expense ($000):** 182289 **Payroll Expense ($000):** 51478 **Personnel:** 875

LEXINGTON—Lafayette County

▣ **LAFAYETTE REGIONAL HEALTH CENTER (261320)**, 1500 State Street, Zip 64067–1107; tel. 660/259–2203 **A**1 10 18 **F**11 15 29 31 40 64 68 70 75 78 79 81 85 93 107 110 111 114 116 119 127 129 130 133 147 148 **P**6 **S** HCA, Nashville, TN
Primary Contact: Darrel Box, Chief Executive Officer
COO: Daniel Astleford, Vice President Operations
CFO: Teri James, Chief Financial Officer
CIO: Keith Richcreek, Manager Technical Services
CHR: Stephen Davidson, Director Human Resources
CNO: Kim Leakey, R.N., Chief Nursing Officer
Web address: www.lafayetteregionalhealthcenter.com
Control: Corporation, Investor–owned, for–profit **Service:** General Medical and Surgical

Staffed Beds: 25 **Admissions:** 1106 **Census:** 10 **Outpatient Visits:** 67932 **Births:** 0 **Total Expense ($000):** 27922 **Payroll Expense ($000):** 9897 **Personnel:** 226

LIBERTY—Clay County

▣ **LIBERTY HOSPITAL (260177)**, 2525 Glenn Hendren Drive, Zip 64068–9600, Mailing Address: P.O. Box 1002, Zip 64069–1002; tel. 816/781–7200 **A**1 2 10 **F**3 9 11 13 15 18 20 22 24 28 29 30 34 35 37 40 43 44 47 53 54 59 62 63 64 68 69 70 73 74 75 76 77 79 80 81 82 84 85 86 87 89 90 92 93 96 97 102 107 108 110 111 114 115 118 119 126 129 130 131 132 135 144 146 147 148
Primary Contact: David Feess, President and Chief Executive Officer
CFO: Dan Williams, Vice President Finance and Support
CMO: Robert Haas, M.D., Chief Medical Officer
CIO: Paul Klehn, Chief Information Technology Officer
CHR: Nancy E. Cattell, Vice President Human Resources
CNO: Shirley Heintz, R.N., Vice President Patient Care
Web address: www.Libertyhospital.org
Control: Hospital district or authority, Government, nonfederal **Service:** General Medical and Surgical

Staffed Beds: 226 **Admissions:** 9268 **Census:** 97 **Outpatient Visits:** 270721 **Births:** 1087 **Total Expense ($000):** 188022 **Payroll Expense ($000):** 85700 **Personnel:** 961

MO

Hospital, Medicare Provider Number, Address, Telephone, Approval, Facility, and Physician Codes, Health Care System

★ American Hospital Association (AHA) membership
□ The Joint Commission accreditation
○ Healthcare Facilities Accreditation Program
◇ DNV Healthcare Inc. accreditation
⇧ Center for Improvement in Healthcare Quality Accreditation
△ Commission on Accreditation of Rehabilitation Facilities (CARF) accreditation

LOUISIANA—Pike County

✉ **PIKE COUNTY MEMORIAL HOSPITAL (261333)**, 2305 Georgia Street, Zip 63353–2559; tel. 573/754–5531 **A**1 10 18 **F**3 7 11 15 18 28 29 30 34 35 40 45 50 53 54 56 57 59 64 65 68 74 75 77 79 81 85 86 87 89 90 93 97 100 107 110 114 127 130 131 132 133 147 148
Primary Contact: Justin Selle, Chief Executive Officer
CFO: Ann Tran, Chief Financial Officer
CIO: Jeremy Gruen, Director Information Systems
CHR: Connie Bair, Human Resources Assistant
CNO: Judith Prater, Director of Nursing
Web address: www.pcmh–mo.org
Control: County–Government, nonfederal **Service:** General Medical and Surgical

Staffed Beds: 25 **Admissions:** 530 **Census:** 6 **Outpatient Visits:** 38887
Births: 0 **Total Expense ($000):** 17604 **Payroll Expense ($000):** 7118
Personnel: 162

MACON—Macon County

★ **SAMARITAN MEMORIAL HOSPITAL (261313)**, 1205 North Missouri Street, Zip 63552–2095; tel. 660/385–8700 **A**10 18 **F**3 7 8 11 15 28 29 31 34 35 40 45 46 53 56 57 59 63 64 65 68 71 74 75 77 78 79 81 82 84 85 86 87 89 90 93 94 107 111 115 119 127 128 129 130 133 143 146 148 **P**5
Primary Contact: Bernard A. Orman, Jr., Administrator
CFO: Susan Spencer, Chief Financial Officer
CHR: Suzanne Britt, Director Human Resources
Web address: www.samaritanhospital.net
Control: County–Government, nonfederal **Service:** General Medical and Surgical

Staffed Beds: 25 **Admissions:** 798 **Census:** 13 **Outpatient Visits:** 61936
Births: 0 **Total Expense ($000):** 27402 **Payroll Expense ($000):** 9276
Personnel: 204

MARSHALL—Saline County

★ **FITZGIBBON HOSPITAL (260142)**, 2305 South 65 Highway, Zip 65340–0250, Mailing Address: P.O. Box 250, Zip 65340–0250; tel. 660/886–7431 **A**5 10 20 **F**3 11 13 15 30 31 34 35 40 45 50 57 59 62 63 64 68 70 74 75 76 77 78 79 81 82 85 87 89 90 93 98 103 104 107 110 111 115 118 119 120 121 127 128 129 130 131 132 133 135 143 146 147 148
Primary Contact: Darin L. Haug, D.O., President and Chief Executive Officer
COO: Angela P. Littrell, CPA, Chief Financial Officer and Chief Operating Officer
CFO: Angela P. Littrell, CPA, Chief Financial Officer and Chief Operating Officer
CMO: Darin L. Haug, D.O., President & Chief Executive Officer
CIO: Tom Jones, Chief Information Officer
CHR: Jessica Henderson, Employee Relations Specialist
CNO: Angela Igo, MSN, Chief Nursing Officer
Web address: www.fitzgibbon.org
Control: Other not–for–profit (including NFP Corporation) **Service:** General Medical and Surgical

Staffed Beds: 52 **Admissions:** 2025 **Census:** 18 **Outpatient Visits:** 109347
Births: 236 **Total Expense ($000):** 49960 **Payroll Expense ($000):** 22820
Personnel: 488

MARYLAND HEIGHTS—St. Louis County

★ **RANKEN JORDAN PEDIATRIC BRIDGE HOSPITAL (263303)**, 11365 Dorsett Road, Zip 63043–3411; tel. 314/872–6400 **A**10 **F**1 3 12 29 30 32 34 35 38 44 50 68 82 86 87 89 90 91 92 93 94 96 98 99 104 130 132 146 148 **P**6
Primary Contact: Laureen K. Tanner, R.N., MSN, FACHE, President and Chief Executive Officer
COO: Brett Moorehouse, FACHE, Vice President and Chief Operating Officer
CFO: Jean Bardwell, Vice President and Chief Financial Officer
CMO: Nicholas Holekamp, M.D., Chief Medical Officer
CIO: Jean Bardwell, Vice President and Chief Financial Officer
CHR: Thomas M. Irvin, Administrator Human Resources
CNO: Laureen K. Tanner, R.N., President and Chief Executive Officer
Web address: www.rankenjordan.org
Control: Other not–for–profit (including NFP Corporation) **Service:** Children's rehabilitation

Staffed Beds: 34 **Admissions:** 301 **Census:** 27 **Outpatient Visits:** 8460
Births: 0 **Total Expense ($000):** 30637 **Payroll Expense ($000):** 15269
Personnel: 274

MARYVILLE—Nodaway County

✉ **SSM HEALTH ST. FRANCIS HOSPITAL – MARYVILLE (260050)**, 2016 South Main Street, Zip 64468–2655; tel. 660/562–2600 **A**1 10 20 **F**3 11 13 15 28 29 30 34 35 38 40 45 57 59 64 65 68 70 75 76 77 79 81 82 84 85 86 89 90 93 96 97 98 102 103 104 107 110 111 115 117 118 119 127 128 130 131 132 133 135 **P**6 **S** SSM Health, Saint Louis, MO
Primary Contact: Michael A. Baumgartner, President
COO: Frank Grispino, Vice President Operations
CFO: Jocelyn Skidmore, Director Finance
CMO: Shirley Harris, M.D., President Medical Staff
CIO: Dave Lewis, Director Information Services
CHR: Krista Barcus, Human Resources Leader
CNO: Debbie Hoffman, Vice President Patient Services
Web address: www.ssmhealthstfrancis.com
Control: Church–operated, Nongovernment, not–for profit **Service:** General Medical and Surgical

Staffed Beds: 56 **Admissions:** 1547 **Census:** 17 **Outpatient Visits:** 132749
Births: 300 **Total Expense ($000):** 60486 **Payroll Expense ($000):** 26041
Personnel: 415

MEMPHIS—Scotland County

★ **SCOTLAND COUNTY HOSPITAL (261310)**, 450 Sigler Avenue, Zip 63555–1726, Mailing Address: 450 East Sigler Avenue, Zip 63555–1726; tel. 660/465–8511, (Nonreporting) **A**10 18
Primary Contact: Randy Tobler, M.D., Chief Executive Officer
CFO: Sheryl Templeton, Chief Financial Officer
CMO: Randy Tobler, M.D., Chief Medical Officer
CIO: Ken McMinn, Director Information Technology
CHR: Missy Smith, Coordinator Human Resources
CNO: Carla Cook, Director of Nursing
Web address: www.scotlandcountyhospital.com
Control: Hospital district or authority, Government, nonfederal **Service:** General Medical and Surgical

Staffed Beds: 25

SCOTLAND COUNTY MEMORIAL HOSPITAL See Scotland County Hospital

MEXICO—Audrain County

✉ **SSM HEALTH ST. MARY'S HOSPITAL – AUDRAIN (260064)**, 620 East Monroe Street, Zip 65265–2919; tel. 573/582–5000 **A**1 2 10 **F**3 11 13 15 18 20 22 26 28 29 30 31 34 40 45 54 57 59 64 65 70 73 74 75 76 77 78 79 81 82 85 86 87 89 90 93 107 108 110 111 115 118 119 121 123 127 129 130 131 132 146 147 **P**6 **S** SSM Health, Saint Louis, MO
Primary Contact: Donna K. Jacobs, FACHE, President
CFO: James Stratton, Regional Vice President Finance
CMO: Diane Jacobi, Chief of Staff
CIO: Dawn Evans, Manager Information Technology
CHR: Christy Smiley, Leader Human Resources
CNO: Kari Wilson, R.N., Vice President Patient Care Services and Chief Nursing Officer
Web address: www.ssmhealthmidmo.com
Control: Church–operated, Nongovernment, not–for profit **Service:** General Medical and Surgical

Staffed Beds: 51 **Admissions:** 1769 **Census:** 15 **Outpatient Visits:** 131991
Births: 226 **Total Expense ($000):** 59992 **Payroll Expense ($000):** 21607
Personnel: 360

MILAN—Sullivan County

★ **SULLIVAN COUNTY MEMORIAL HOSPITAL (261306)**, 630 West Third Street, Zip 63556–1076; tel. 660/265–4212, (Total facility includes 14 beds in nursing home–type unit) **A**10 18 **F**28 29 32 33 34 40 57 59 64 65 67 68 77 79 87 93 97 99 103 104 107 111 114 119 127 128 130 133 147 148 **P**5 6
Primary Contact: Jerry Dover, Chief Executive Officer
COO: Amy J. Michael, Chief Operating Officer
CMO: Dale Essmyer, M.D., Chief of Staff
CIO: Vern Johnson, Director Information Technology
CHR: Billie Ryals, Director Human Resources
CNO: Carol Fordyce, Director Patient Care Services
Web address: www.scmhospital.org
Control: County–Government, nonfederal **Service:** General Medical and Surgical

Staffed Beds: 29 **Admissions:** 237 **Census:** 20 **Outpatient Visits:** 15361
Births: 0 **Total Expense ($000):** 7715 **Payroll Expense ($000):** 2994
Personnel: 72

MO

MOBERLY—Randolph County

✠ **MOBERLY REGIONAL MEDICAL CENTER (260074)**, 1515 Union Avenue,
Zip 65270–9449; tel. 660/263–8400 **A**1 10 20 **F**3 18 20 22 26 28 29 30 34
35 38 39 40 44 45 46 50 51 53 56 57 59 64 65 70 74 75 77 79 81 85 86
87 89 93 97 98 100 103 107 108 111 115 118 119 127 129 130 132 135
146 147 148 **P**5 **S** Community Health Systems, Inc., Franklin, TN
Primary Contact: John M. Dawes, FACHE, Chief Executive Officer
COO: Tracey Matheis, Chief Operating Officer
CFO: Tracey Matheis, Chief Financial Officer
CMO: Heather Gessling, M.D., Chief Medical Officer
CHR: Michael Turner, Director Human Resources
CNO: Jennifer Dunkin, Chief Nursing Officer
Web address: www.moberlyhospital.com
Control: Corporation, Investor–owned, for–profit **Service:** General Medical and
Surgical

Staffed Beds: 94 **Admissions:** 1279 **Census:** 16 **Outpatient Visits:** 58579
Births: 0 **Total Expense ($000):** 46027 **Payroll Expense ($000):** 13435
Personnel: 207

MONETT—Barry County

◇ **COX MONETT (261329)**, 801 North Lincoln Avenue, Zip 65708–1641;
tel. 417/235–3144 **A**10 18 21 **F**3 11 13 15 28 29 30 31 32 34 35 40 45 50
56 57 59 64 76 77 81 85 89 90 93 107 111 114 119 127 128 129 130 131
133 135 146 147 **P**6 **S** CoxHealth, Springfield, MO
Primary Contact: Darren Bass, President
CFO: Josh Powell, Facility Controller
CMO: Frank Romero, M.D., Vice President Medical Affairs and Chief Medical
Officer
CHR: Debra Isenmann, Human Resources Generalist
CNO: Bev Eli, Chief Nursing Officer
Web address: www.coxhealth.com
Control: Other not–for–profit (including NFP Corporation) **Service:** General
Medical and Surgical

Staffed Beds: 25 **Admissions:** 752 **Census:** 7 **Outpatient Visits:** 57844
Births: 249 **Total Expense ($000):** 27429 **Payroll Expense ($000):** 12936
Personnel: 232

MOUNTAIN VIEW—Howell County

✠ **MERCY ST. FRANCIS HOSPITAL (261335)**, 100 West Highway 60,
Zip 65548–7125; tel. 417/934–7000 **A**1 10 18 **F**3 11 15 28 29 30 34 40 45
50 57 59 64 65 75 77 81 85 89 90 93 107 110 111 114 119 129 131 132
133 148 **P**6 **S** Mercy Health, Chesterfield, MO
Primary Contact: David R. Steinmann, Administrator
CFO: Sherry Clouse Day, CPA, Chief Financial Officer
CMO: Barry Spoon, M.D., Chief of Staff
CHR: Tracy Smith, Director Human Resources
Web address: www.stjohns.com/aboutus/stfrancis.aspx
Control: Church–operated, Nongovernment, not–for profit **Service:** General
Medical and Surgical

Staffed Beds: 20 **Admissions:** 377 **Census:** 4 **Outpatient Visits:** 25321
Births: 0 **Total Expense ($000):** 15030 **Payroll Expense ($000):** 6766
Personnel: 102

NEOSHO—Newton County

★ **FREEMAN NEOSHO HOSPITAL (261331)**, 113 West Hickory Street,
Zip 64850–1705; tel. 417/455–4352 **A**10 18 **F**3 11 15 28 29 30 34 35 40 44
45 47 56 57 59 64 68 70 75 77 79 81 84 85 86 87 90 93 97 107 110 114
119 130 131 132 133 146 147 148 **P**1 6 **S** Freeman Health System, Joplin, MO
Primary Contact: Paula F. Baker, President and Chief Executive Officer
CFO: Steve W. Graddy, Chief Financial Officer
CMO: Rodney McFarland, M.D., Medical Director
CIO: Sue Annesser, Director Information Systems
CHR: Mary Frerer, Chief Human Resources Officer
Web address: www.freemanhealth.com
Control: Other not–for–profit (including NFP Corporation) **Service:** General
Medical and Surgical

Staffed Beds: 25 **Admissions:** 1009 **Census:** 11 **Outpatient Visits:** 64550
Births: 0 **Total Expense ($000):** 24053 **Payroll Expense ($000):** 11465
Personnel: 201

NEVADA—Vernon County

☐ **HEARTLAND BEHAVIORAL HEALTH SERVICES**, 1500 West Ashland Street,
Zip 64772–1710; tel. 417/667–2666 **A**1 **F**98 99 101 102 106 **P**6 **S** Universal
Health Services, Inc., King of Prussia, PA
Primary Contact: Alyson Wysong–Harder, Chief Executive Officer
CFO: Bryan Bishop, Chief Financial Officer
CMO: Ahmad Tarar, M.D., Medical Director
CHR: Carri Compton–Ogle, Administrative Officer
CNO: Nathan Taylor, Director of Nursing
Web address: www.heartlandbehavioral.com
Control: Corporation, Investor–owned, for–profit **Service:** Psychiatric

Staffed Beds: 69 **Admissions:** 1795 **Census:** 46 **Outpatient Visits:** 0 **Births:**
0 **Total Expense ($000):** 14046 **Payroll Expense ($000):** 7597 **Personnel:**
112

✠ **NEVADA REGIONAL MEDICAL CENTER (260061)**, 800 South Ash Street,
Zip 64772–3223; tel. 417/667–3355 **A**1 10 **F**3 11 13 15 26 27 28 29 30 31
32 34 35 39 40 41 45 50 54 57 59 62 63 64 65 66 70 74 75 76 77 78 79
81 82 83 84 85 86 87 89 90 91 93 94 96 98 101 102 103 104 107 110 111
114 119 127 129 130 131 132 133 135 143 144 146 147 148 **S** QHR,
Brentwood, TN
Primary Contact: Kevin Leeper, Chief Executive Officer
CFO: Mike Harbor, Chief Financial Officer
CMO: Russ Kemm, M.D., Chief Medical Officer
CIO: Marci Hardin, Manager Information Technology
CHR: Heather Brockmeyer, Human Resource Administrative Officer
CNO: Cory Vokoun, Chief Nursing Officer
Web address: www.nrmchealth.com
Control: City–Government, nonfederal **Service:** General Medical and Surgical

Staffed Beds: 71 **Admissions:** 2837 **Census:** 31 **Outpatient Visits:** 58053
Births: 328 **Total Expense ($000):** 38723 **Payroll Expense ($000):** 13863
Personnel: 312

NORTH KANSAS CITY—Clay County

✠ **NORTH KANSAS CITY HOSPITAL (260096)**, 2800 Clay Edwards Drive,
Zip 64116–3220; tel. 816/691–2000 **A**1 2 3 5 10 **F**3 11 12 13 15 17 18 20
22 24 26 28 29 30 31 34 35 37 40 43 44 45 46 47 48 49 50 51 53 54 57
58 59 60 62 63 64 70 72 74 75 76 77 78 79 80 81 82 83 84 85 86 87 89
90 93 96 100 107 108 109 110 111 114 115 116 117 118 119 120 121
123 124 126 129 130 132 135 146 147 148
Primary Contact: Peggy Schmitt, President and Chief Executive Officer
COO: Jody Abbott, Senior Vice President and Chief Operating Officer
CFO: Jim McNey, Senior Vice President Finance and Chief Financial Officer
CMO: Gary L. Carter, M.D., Vice President and Chief Medical Officer
CIO: Paul Foelsch, Vice President and Chief Information Technology Officer
CHR: Dawn Bryant, Vice President Human Resources
CNO: Sarah G. Oakley, Vice President Nursing
Web address: www.nkch.org
Control: City–Government, nonfederal **Service:** General Medical and Surgical

Staffed Beds: 413 **Admissions:** 20978 **Census:** 272 **Outpatient Visits:**
233549 **Births:** 1630 **Total Expense ($000):** 433943 **Payroll Expense
($000):** 157844 **Personnel:** 2496

O'FALLON—St. Charles County

✠ **PROGRESS WEST HOSPITAL (260219)**, Two Progress Point Parkway,
Zip 63368–2208; tel. 636/344–1000 **A**1 10 **F**3 13 15 18 20 22 29 30 34 40
41 45 49 51 57 59 60 70 76 79 81 85 87 89 107 108 110 111 115 118 119
130 135 146 148 **S** BJC HealthCare, Saint Louis, MO
Primary Contact: Lee F. Fetter, Interim President
CFO: Glen Schwaegel, Chief Financial Officer
CMO: Dane Glueck, M.D., Chief of Staff
CHR: Michael J. Miller, Director Human Resources
CNO: Jill Skyles, R.N., Vice President Patient Care Services and Chief Nurse
Executive
Web address: www.progresswest.org
Control: Other not–for–profit (including NFP Corporation) **Service:** General
Medical and Surgical

Staffed Beds: 44 **Admissions:** 3236 **Census:** 29 **Outpatient Visits:** 51284
Births: 665 **Total Expense ($000):** 68695 **Payroll Expense ($000):** 24574
Personnel: 330

MO

Hospital, Medicare Provider Number, Address, Telephone, Approval, Facility, and Physician Codes, Health Care System

★ American Hospital Association (AHA) membership ◯ Healthcare Facilities Accreditation Program ⇑ Center for Improvement in Healthcare Quality Accreditation
☐ The Joint Commission accreditation ◇ DNV Healthcare Inc. accreditation △ Commission on Accreditation of Rehabilitation Facilities (CARF) accreditation

---

OSAGE BEACH—Camden County

✠ **LAKE REGIONAL HEALTH SYSTEM (260186)**, 54 Hospital Drive, Zip 65065–3050; tel. 573/348–8000, (Total facility includes 16 beds in nursing home–type unit) **A**1 2 10 **F**3 11 12 13 15 17 18 20 22 24 28 29 30 31 32 34 35 38 39 40 43 44 45 48 49 50 51 53 57 59 60 62 64 65 68 70 73 74 75 76 77 78 79 81 82 84 85 86 87 89 93 96 107 108 111 114 115 118 119 120 121 122 123 124 127 128 129 130 131 132 135 144 145 146 148 **P**6
Primary Contact: Michael E. Henze, Chief Executive Officer
COO: Kevin G. McRoberts, FACHE, Senior Vice President of Operations
CFO: David Halsell, Senior Vice President and Chief Financial Officer
CMO: Robert Hyatt, M.D., Senior Vice President Medical Affairs
CIO: Scott Poest, Chief Information Officer
CHR: Tom Williams, Vice President Human Resources
CNO: Janice L. Dungan, Senior Vice President Clinical Services
Web address: www.lakeregional.com
Control: Other not–for–profit (including NFP Corporation) **Service:** General Medical and Surgical

Staffed Beds: 116 **Admissions:** 4880 **Census:** 57 **Outpatient Visits:** 303180 **Births:** 528 **Total Expense ($000):** 166249 **Payroll Expense ($000):** 65610 **Personnel:** 1061

☐ **OSAGE BEACH CENTER FOR COGNITIVE DISORDERS**, 840 Passover Road, Zip 65065; tel. 573/302–0319, (Nonreporting) **A**1
Primary Contact: Lorri Steffen, Chief Executive Officer and Administrator
Web address: www.osagebeachccd.com
Control: Corporation, Investor–owned, for–profit **Service:** Psychiatric

Staffed Beds: 14

PERRYVILLE—Perry County

✠ **PERRY COUNTY MEMORIAL HOSPITAL (261311)**, 434 North West Street, Zip 63775–1398; tel. 573/547–2536 **A**1 10 18 **F**3 7 8 11 13 15 28 29 30 31 34 35 40 44 48 51 53 54 56 57 59 62 64 66 68 75 76 77 78 79 81 85 87 89 90 92 93 97 99 100 101 102 103 104 107 111 115 117 119 129 130 131 132 133 135 143 144 145 147 148
Primary Contact: Patrick E. Carron, FACHE, President and Chief Executive Officer
CFO: Randall Wolf, Vice President Finance
CMO: Michael Steele, M.D., Chief of Staff
CIO: Ron Heuring, Director Information Systems
CHR: Christopher Wibbenmeyer, Director Human Resources
Web address: www.pchmo.org
Control: Other not–for–profit (including NFP Corporation) **Service:** General Medical and Surgical

Staffed Beds: 25 **Admissions:** 976 **Census:** 14 **Outpatient Visits:** 49602 **Births:** 142 **Total Expense ($000):** 32677 **Payroll Expense ($000):** 13214 **Personnel:** 311

PILOT KNOB—Iron County

IRON COUNTY MEDICAL CENTER (261336), 301 North Highway 21, Zip 63663–0548, Mailing Address: P.O. Box 548, Zip 63663–0548; tel. 573/546–1260 **A**10 18 **F**3 11 15 18 29 34 35 38 40 44 45 57 59 64 66 79 81 82 89 90 93 96 97 100 102 104 107 111 114 119 127 129 130 133 148 **P**6
Primary Contact: Terry Nichols, Chief Executive Officer
COO: Cyndi Basler, Chief Operating Officer
CFO: Justin Lattimore, Chief Financial Officer
CNO: Cindy Finley, Chief Nursing Officer
Web address: www.ironhospital.com
Control: Hospital district or authority, Government, nonfederal **Service:** General Medical and Surgical

Staffed Beds: 15 **Admissions:** 209 **Census:** 4 **Outpatient Visits:** 19613 **Births:** 0 **Personnel:** 123

POPLAR BLUFF—Butler County

✠ **BLACK RIVER MEDICAL CENTER (260227)**, 217 Physicians Park Drive, Zip 63901–3956; tel. 573/727–9080 **A**1 10 **F**3 15 29 34 39 40 45 57 59 64 65 81 86 107 108 110 111 115 118 119 135
Primary Contact: Christy Shawan, Chief Executive Officer
CFO: Phillip Crocker, Accounting Specialist
CMO: Christopher Pinderski, M.D., Medical Director of Emergency Room
CIO: TJ Mcmeans, Information Technology Technician
CHR: Denyce Keele, Administrative Assistant and Human Resources Coordinator
CNO: E. Kay Fox, Director of Nursing
Web address: www.blackrivermedical.com
Control: Other not–for–profit (including NFP Corporation) **Service:** General Medical and Surgical

Staffed Beds: 3 **Admissions:** 419 **Census:** 2 **Outpatient Visits:** 9609 **Births:** 0 **Total Expense ($000):** 15796 **Payroll Expense ($000):** 4802 **Personnel:** 119

✠ **JOHN J. PERSHING VETERANS AFFAIRS MEDICAL CENTER**, 1500 North Westwood Boulevard, Zip 63901–3318; tel. 573/686–4151, (Total facility includes 40 beds in nursing home–type unit) **A**1 **F**3 5 11 15 29 30 33 34 36 38 39 40 45 53 54 56 59 62 63 64 65 75 77 79 81 82 83 84 86 87 90 93 94 97 100 104 107 111 114 119 127 128 129 130 135 143 144 146 147
S Department of Veterans Affairs, Washington, DC
Primary Contact: Patricia Ten Haaf, R.N., MSN, Ph.D., Director
COO: Seth Barlage, Associate Medical Center Director
CFO: Kristy Siebert, Manager Finance
CMO: Vijayachandran Nair, M.D., Chief of Staff
CIO: Michael Gustin, Information Technology
CHR: Genise Denton, Manager Human Resources
CNO: Elizabeth A. Smith, Director of Nursing
Web address: www.poplarbluff.va.gov
Control: Veterans Affairs, Government, federal **Service:** General Medical and Surgical

Staffed Beds: 58 **Admissions:** 624 **Census:** 33 **Outpatient Visits:** 118954 **Births:** 0 **Total Expense ($000):** 131686 **Payroll Expense ($000):** 48217 **Personnel:** 341

✠ **POPLAR BLUFF REGIONAL MEDICAL CENTER (260119)**, 3100 Oak Grove Road, Zip 63901, Mailing Address: P.O. Box 88, Zip 63902–0088; tel. 573/776–2000, (Includes POPLAR BLUFF REGIONAL MEDICAL CENTER–SOUTH CAMPUS, 621 Pine Boulevard, tel. 573/785–7721) **A**1 2 10 **F**3 11 13 15 17 18 20 22 24 29 30 31 35 40 43 45 46 49 50 51 53 54 57 59 60 64 65 68 70 74 75 76 77 78 79 80 81 82 85 87 89 90 93 98 102 107 108 111 114 117 118 119 120 121 126 127 130 131 132 146 148
S Community Health Systems, Inc., Franklin, TN
Primary Contact: Larry Rodgers, Chief Executive Officer
CFO: Steve Dorris, Chief Financial Officer
CMO: Steve Pu, D.O., Chief Medical Officer
CIO: Gary Dollins, Director Management Information Systems
CHR: Denise Rushin, Director Human Resources
CNO: Melissa A. Samuelson, R.N., Chief Nurse Executive
Web address: www.poplarbluffregional.com
Control: Individual, Investor–owned, for–profit **Service:** General Medical and Surgical

Staffed Beds: 252 **Admissions:** 10496 **Census:** 120 **Outpatient Visits:** 95916 **Births:** 1409 **Total Expense ($000):** 147959 **Payroll Expense ($000):** 40239 **Personnel:** 1001

POTOSI—Washington County

★ **WASHINGTON COUNTY MEMORIAL HOSPITAL (261308)**, 300 Health Way, Zip 63664–1420; tel. 573/438–5451 **A**10 18 **F**3 11 15 28 29 33 34 35 40 45 57 59 64 65 74 75 77 79 81 87 90 93 97 98 104 106 107 108 110 111 114 119 127 129 130 133 144 145 146 147 148 **P**6
Primary Contact: Kenneth Marx, Chief Executive Officer
CFO: Yvonne Fourez, Chief Financial Officer
CMO: Jonathan Borchers, M.D., Chief Medical Officer
CIO: Jim Smith, Director Information Systems
CHR: Christy Aubuchon, Director Personnel
CNO: Beverly Williams, R.N., Chief Nursing Officer
Web address: www.wcmhosp.org
Control: County–Government, nonfederal **Service:** General Medical and Surgical

Staffed Beds: 25 **Admissions:** 817 **Census:** 9 **Outpatient Visits:** 96818 **Births:** 0 **Total Expense ($000):** 27817 **Payroll Expense ($000):** 11758 **Personnel:** 245

RICHMOND—Ray County

★ **RAY COUNTY MEMORIAL HOSPITAL (261327)**, 904 Wollard Boulevard, Zip 64085–2229; tel. 816/470–5432 **A**10 18 **F**3 11 15 29 31 40 45 56 57 62 64 68 74 75 78 79 81 82 85 87 93 103 107 108 110 111 115 117 119 130 133 146
Primary Contact: Earl N. Sheehy, Administrator
CFO: Donald Harr, Controller
CHR: Donna Strain, Director Human Resources
Web address: www.raycountyhospital.com
Control: County–Government, nonfederal **Service:** General Medical and Surgical

Staffed Beds: 25 **Admissions:** 853 **Census:** 10 **Outpatient Visits:** 18901 **Births:** 0 **Total Expense ($000):** 21249 **Payroll Expense ($000):** 9525 **Personnel:** 213

RICHMOND HEIGHTS—St. Louis County

✠ △ **SSM SELECT REHABILITATION HOSPITAL (263031)**, 1027 Bellevue Avenue, 3rd Floor, Zip 63117–1851, Mailing Address: 1027 Bellevue Avenue, Zip 63117–1851; tel. 314/768–5300, (Includes SSM SELECT REHABILITATION HOSPITAL, 12380 De Paul Drive, Bridgeton, Zip 63044–2511; tel. 314/447–9700; Timothy Wadman, Chief Executive Officer), (Nonreporting) **A**1 7 10 **S** Select Medical Corporation, Mechanicsburg, PA
Primary Contact: Timothy Wadman, Chief Executive Officer
Web address: www.ssm–select.com
Control: Partnership, Investor–owned, for–profit **Service:** Rehabilitation

Staffed Beds: 95

Many Facility Codes have changed. Please refer to the AHA Guide Code Chart.
© 2016 AHA Guide

MO

ROLLA—Phelps County

☒ △ **PHELPS COUNTY REGIONAL MEDICAL CENTER (260017)**, 1000 West Tenth Street, Zip 65401–2905; tel. 573/458–8899, (Total facility includes 20 beds in nursing home–type unit) **A**1 2 7 10 **F**3 7 8 11 13 15 18 20 22 28 29 30 31 34 35 39 40 45 47 49 50 51 54 56 57 58 59 60 62 63 68 70 73 74 75 76 77 78 79 81 82 84 85 86 87 89 90 93 96 98 100 101 102 103 104 107 108 110 111 114 115 117 118 119 120 121 127 128 129 130 131 132 135 143 146 147 148 **P**6
Primary Contact: Edward Clayton, Chief Executive Officer
CMO: Donald James, D.O., Chief Medical Officer
CIO: Jeff McKune, Chief Health Informatics Officer
CHR: Frank A. Lazzaro, III, Chief Human Resources Officer
CNO: Keri S. Brookshire–Heavin, Chief Nurse Executive
Web address: www.pcrmc.com
Control: County–Government, nonfederal **Service:** General Medical and Surgical

Staffed Beds: 161 Admissions: 6221 Census: 80 Outpatient Visits: 468234 Births: 851 Total Expense ($000): 210152 Payroll Expense ($000): 91324 Personnel: 1080

SAINT CHARLES—St. Charles County

☒ **CENTERPOINTE HOSPITAL (264012)**, 4801 Weldon Spring Parkway, Zip 63304–9101; tel. 636/441–7300 **A**1 10 **F**4 5 34 35 38 44 54 80 87 98 99 100 101 102 103 104 105 106 130 132 143
Primary Contact: Susan Mathis, MSN, R.N., Chief Executive Officer
CFO: Tom Croffut, Chief Financial Officer
CMO: Azfar Malik, M.D., Chief Medical Officer
CIO: Jennifer Bourn, Director, Health Information Services and Medical Staff Services
CHR: Kelli White, Director, Human Resources
Web address: www.centerpointehospital.com
Control: Corporation, Investor–owned, for–profit **Service:** Psychiatric

Staffed Beds: 150 Admissions: 5007 Census: 102 Outpatient Visits: 0 Births: 0 Total Expense ($000): 33985 Payroll Expense ($000): 17729 Personnel: 439

☒ **SELECT SPECIALTY HOSPITAL–ST. LOUIS (262013)**, 300 First Capitol Drive, Unit 1, Zip 63301–2844; tel. 636/947–5010 **A**1 10 **F**1 29 74 75 148 **S** Select Medical Corporation, Mechanicsburg, PA
Primary Contact: Donna Mansard, Chief Executive Officer
Web address: www.selectspecialtyhospitals.com/company/locations/stlouis.aspx
Control: Corporation, Investor–owned, for–profit **Service:** Long–Term Acute Care hospital

Staffed Beds: 33 Admissions: 357 Census: 28 Outpatient Visits: 0 Births: 0 Total Expense ($000): 15818 Payroll Expense ($000): 6588 Personnel: 92

☒ **SSM ST. JOSEPH HEALTH CENTER (260005)**, 300 First Capitol Drive, Zip 63301–2844; tel. 636/947–5000, (Includes SSM ST. JOSEPH HEALTH CENTER – WENTZVILLE, 500 Medical Drive, Wentzville, Zip 63385–3421; tel. 636/327–1000) **A**1 2 10 **F**3 4 11 13 15 17 18 20 22 24 26 28 29 30 31 34 35 38 40 41 42 43 44 45 46 49 50 53 54 55 56 57 58 59 60 64 68 70 73 74 75 76 78 79 81 82 84 85 86 87 90 96 97 98 99 100 101 102 103 104 105 107 108 110 111 114 118 119 120 121 129 130 132 135 144 146 147 148 **P**6 8 **S** SSM Health, Saint Louis, MO
Primary Contact: Michael E. Bowers, President
COO: Lee Bernstein, Regional Executive Vice President and Chief Operating Officer
CFO: Karen Rewerts, System Vice President Finance
CIO: Margaret Feilner, Director Information Services
CHR: Debbie G. Walkenhorst, System Vice President Talent Management
Web address: www.ssmstjoseph.com
Control: Church–operated, Nongovernment, not–for profit **Service:** General Medical and Surgical

Staffed Beds: 331 Admissions: 14137 Census: 198 Outpatient Visits: 172348 Births: 756 Total Expense ($000): 227255 Payroll Expense ($000): 80169 Personnel: 1282

SAINT JOSEPH—Buchanan County

★ **LONG–TERM ACUTE CARE HOSPITAL, MOSAIC LIFE CARE AT ST. JOSEPH (262019)**, 5325 Faraon Street, Zip 64506–3488; tel. 816/271–6000 **A**10 **F**1 3 29 85 130 148
Primary Contact: Dana Anderson, Administrator
CNO: Douglas Schmitz, Director of Nursing
Web address: www.https://www.mymosaiclifecare.org/General/Long–Term–Acute–Care–Hospital/
Control: Other not–for–profit (including NFP Corporation) **Service:** Long–Term Acute Care hospital

Staffed Beds: 41 Admissions: 231 Census: 21 Outpatient Visits: 0 Births: 0 Total Expense ($000): 11403 Payroll Expense ($000): 3327 Personnel: 51

☒ **MOSAIC LIFE CARE AT ST. JOSEPH (260006)**, 5325 Faraon Street, Zip 64506–3488; tel. 816/271–6000 **A**1 2 10 20 **F**3 8 9 11 12 13 15 17 18 20 22 24 26 28 29 30 31 32 33 34 35 36 40 43 45 46 48 49 50 53 54 57 58 59 62 63 64 65 66 70 74 75 76 77 78 79 80 81 82 84 85 86 87 89 90 92 93 94 96 97 98 100 102 103 104 107 108 110 111 114 115 118 119 120 121 123 129 130 131 134 135 143 144 146 147 148 **P**6
Primary Contact: Samuel Mark Laney, M.D., Chief Executive Officer
COO: Curt Kretzinger, Chief Operating Officer
CFO: Dwain Stilson, Chief Financial Officer
CIO: Brennan Lehman, Chief Information Officer
CHR: Michael Pulido, Chief Administrative Officer
Web address: www.https://www.mymosaiclifecare.org/Main/Location/st-joseph-mo/mosaic–life–care–at–st.–joseph/
Control: Other not–for–profit (including NFP Corporation) **Service:** General Medical and Surgical

Staffed Beds: 352 Admissions: 15666 Census: 186 Outpatient Visits: 1036648 Births: 1653 Total Expense ($000): 565371 Payroll Expense ($000): 250114 Personnel: 3217

☐ **NORTHWEST MISSOURI PSYCHIATRIC REHABILITATION CENTER (264007)**, 3505 Frederick Avenue, Zip 64506–2914; tel. 816/387–2300 **A**1 10 **F**4 29 30 34 58 59 65 68 75 77 86 87 97 98 101 102 103 130 132 135 143 146 **P**6
Primary Contact: Denise Norbury, Regional Executive Officer
COO: Mary Attebury, Chief Operating Officer
CFO: Randy Riley, Fiscal and Administrative Manager
CMO: James B. Reynolds, M.D., Medical Director
CIO: Robert Curren, Western Region Chief Information Technology Officer
CHR: Mary Blakey Gorman, Director Human Resources
CNO: Pam Nold, Chief Nurse Executive
Web address: www.dmh.mo.gov/nmprc/index.htm
Control: State–Government, nonfederal **Service:** Psychiatric

Staffed Beds: 108 Admissions: 59 Census: 107 Outpatient Visits: 0 Births: 0 Total Expense ($000): 22242 Payroll Expense ($000): 11283 Personnel: 309

SAINT LOUIS—St. Louis City County

☒ **BARNES–JEWISH HOSPITAL (260032)**, 1 Barnes–Jewish Hospital Plaza, Zip 63110–1003; tel. 314/747–3000, (Includes BARNES–JEWISH HOSPITAL PSYCHIATRIC SUPPORT CENTER, 5355 Delmar Boulevard, Zip 63112–3146; tel. 314/273–0040; John M. Eiler, President), (Total facility includes 120 beds in nursing home–type unit) **A**1 2 3 5 8 10 **F**3 4 6 8 9 11 12 13 14 15 16 17 18 20 22 24 26 28 29 30 31 34 35 36 37 38 39 40 43 44 45 46 47 48 49 50 51 52 53 54 55 58 59 60 61 63 64 65 66 68 70 71 73 74 75 76 77 78 79 80 81 82 84 85 86 87 89 90 91 92 93 94 95 96 97 98 100 101 102 103 104 105 107 108 109 110 111 112 114 115 116 117 118 119 120 121 122 123 124 126 128 129 130 131 132 134 135 136 137 138 139 140 141 142 143 144 145 146 147 148 **P**6 **S** BJC HealthCare, Saint Louis, MO
Primary Contact: Robert W. Cannon, President
CFO: Mark Krieger, Vice President and Chief Financial Officer
CMO: John Lynch, M.D., Vice President and Chief Medical Officer
CIO: Jerry Vuchak, Vice President Information Systems
CHR: John Beatty, Vice President Human Resources
CNO: Coreen Vlodarchyk, R.N., Vice President, Patient Care Services and Chief Nursing Officer
Web address: www.barnesjewish.org
Control: Other not–for–profit (including NFP Corporation) **Service:** General Medical and Surgical

Staffed Beds: 1390 Admissions: 55114 Census: 948 Outpatient Visits: 750936 Births: 3408 Total Expense ($000): 1849623 Payroll Expense ($000): 564657 Personnel: 10670

☒ **BARNES–JEWISH WEST COUNTY HOSPITAL (260162)**, 12634 Olive Boulevard, Zip 63141–6337; tel. 314/996–8000 **A**1 3 5 10 **F**3 12 15 18 29 34 35 40 45 46 47 49 50 51 57 59 60 64 65 70 74 75 77 78 79 81 82 85 90 93 107 110 111 114 115 119 120 121 126 129 130 131 142 145 146 148 **S** BJC HealthCare, Saint Louis, MO
Primary Contact: Trisha Lollo, President
CFO: Diane M. Glen, Assistant Administrator
CMO: Sam B. Bhayani, M.D., Chief Medical Officer
CIO: Jerry Vuchak, Vice President Information Systems
CNO: Yoany Finetti, R.N., Chief Nursing Officer
Web address: www.barnesjewishwestcounty.org
Control: Other not–for–profit (including NFP Corporation) **Service:** General Medical and Surgical

Staffed Beds: 77 Admissions: 2745 Census: 19 Outpatient Visits: 139624 Births: 0 Total Expense ($000): 104676 Payroll Expense ($000): 33051 Personnel: 416

MO

Hospital, Medicare Provider Number, Address, Telephone, Approval, Facility, and Physician Codes, Health Care System		
★ American Hospital Association (AHA) membership	◯ Healthcare Facilities Accreditation Program	⇑ Center for Improvement in Healthcare Quality Accreditation
☐ The Joint Commission accreditation	◇ DNV Healthcare Inc. accreditation	△ Commission on Accreditation of Rehabilitation Facilities (CARF) accreditation

✠ **CHRISTIAN HOSPITAL (260180)**, 11133 Dunn Road, Zip 63136–6119; tel. 314/653–5000 **A**1 2 10 **F**3 4 5 7 8 11 15 17 18 20 22 24 26 28 29 30 31 34 35 36 38 40 42 44 45 46 47 49 50 53 56 57 58 59 60 63 64 65 68 69 70 74 75 77 78 79 80 81 82 83 84 85 86 87 90 92 93 94 96 98 107 108 109 110 111 112 113 114 115 116 117 118 119 120 121 123 126 129 130 132 135 143 146 147 148 **P**6 **S** BJC HealthCare, Saint Louis, MO
Primary Contact: Rick Stevens, President
CMO: Sebastian Rueckert, M.D., Chief Medical Officer
CIO: Michael Kelly, Vice President
CHR: Bryan Hartwick, Vice President Human Resources
CNO: Jennifer Cordia, Vice President and Chief Nursing Executive
Web address: www.christianhospital.org
Control: Other not–for–profit (including NFP Corporation) **Service:** General Medical and Surgical

Staffed Beds: 220 **Admissions:** 13104 **Census:** 192 **Outpatient Visits:** 296758 **Births:** 0 **Total Expense ($000):** 292177 **Payroll Expense ($000):** 110657 **Personnel:** 1704

✠ **DES PERES HOSPITAL (260176)**, 2345 Dougherty Ferry Road, Zip 63122–3313; tel. 314/966–9100 **A**1 3 5 10 12 13 **F**3 12 15 17 18 20 22 24 26 29 30 31 34 35 36 37 40 44 48 49 50 56 57 58 59 60 64 68 69 70 75 77 79 81 82 85 86 87 93 107 108 110 111 115 119 126 130 132 143 146 148 **S** TENET Healthcare Corporation, Dallas, TX
Primary Contact: David E. Loving, Chief Executive Officer
COO: Alex Lovshin, Chief Operating Officer
CFO: Rhonda Rogers, Chief Financial Officer
CMO: Karen Webb, M.D., Chief Medical Officer
CIO: Kay Hannon, Director Information Systems
CHR: Kathaleen Clutts, Chief Human Resources Officer
CNO: Mary Ann Hampton, R.N., Chief Nursing Officer
Web address: www.despereshospital.com
Control: Corporation, Investor–owned, for–profit **Service:** General Medical and Surgical

Staffed Beds: 143 **Admissions:** 4691 **Census:** 46 **Outpatient Visits:** 33078 **Births:** 0 **Total Expense ($000):** 112200 **Payroll Expense ($000):** 33324 **Personnel:** 504

□ **HAWTHORN CHILDREN PSYCHIATRIC HOSPITAL (264028)**, 1901 Pennsylvania, Zip 63133–1325; tel. 314/512–7800, (Nonreporting) **A**1 3 10
Primary Contact: Laurent D. Javois, Regional Executive Officer
COO: Marcia F. Ford, Chief Operating Officer
CFO: James D. Martin, Chief Financial Officer
CMO: Joshua Calhoun, M.D., Medical Director
CHR: Michael McFarlane, Director Human Resource
CNO: Melody Chilese, Chief Nurse Executive
Web address: www.dmh.missouri.gov/hcph/
Control: State–Government, nonfederal **Service:** Hospital unit within an institution for the mentally retarded

Staffed Beds: 52

✠ **KINDRED HOSPITAL–ST. LOUIS (262010)**, 4930 Lindell Boulevard, Zip 63108–1510; tel. 314/361–8700, (Includes KINDRED HOSPITAL ST. LOUIS–ST. ANTHONY'S, 10018 Kennerly Road, 3rd Floor, Zip 63128; tel. 314/525–8100; Stephanie Bridges, Interim Chief Executive Officer), (Nonreporting) **A**1 10 **S** Kindred Healthcare, Louisville, KY
Primary Contact: Stephanie Bridges, Chief Executive Officer
COO: Dakota Redd, R.N., Chief Clinical Officer
CFO: Maureen Roach, Senior Chief Financial Officer
CMO: Michael Holtzman, M.D., Medical Director
CIO: Thomas C. Christman, Director Plant Operations
CHR: Cindy Sander, Coordinator Human Resources
Web address: www.kindredstlouis.com/
Control: Corporation, Investor–owned, for–profit **Service:** Long–Term Acute Care hospital

Staffed Beds: 98

✠ **KINDRED HOSPITAL–ST. LOUIS AT MERCY (260230)**, 615 South New Ballas Road, 7th Floor, Zip 63141–8221; tel. 314/567–4326 **A**1 10 **F**1 3 29 67 77 85 90 128 130 148 **S** Kindred Healthcare, Louisville, KY
Primary Contact: Robert S. Adcock, Chief Executive Officer
CFO: Paul Veillon, CPA, Chief Financial Officer
CMO: Rekha Lakshmanan, M.D., Medical Director
Web address: www.kindredstlouismercy.com
Control: Corporation, Investor–owned, for–profit **Service:** Long–Term Acute Care hospital

Staffed Beds: 53 **Admissions:** 332 **Census:** 28 **Outpatient Visits:** 0 **Births:** 0 **Total Expense ($000):** 15383 **Payroll Expense ($000):** 5366 **Personnel:** 117

MERCY CONTINUING CARE HOSPITAL See Kindred Hospital–St. Louis at Mercy

✠ **MERCY HOSPITAL ST. LOUIS (260020)**, 615 South New Ballas Road, Zip 63141–8277; tel. 314/569–6000, (Includes MERCY CHILDREN'S HOSPITAL ST. LOUIS, 615 South New Ballas Road, Zip 63141–8221; tel. 314/251–6000), (Total facility includes 120 beds in nursing home–type unit) **A**1 2 3 5 8 10 **F**1 3 4 5 8 11 12 13 14 15 16 17 18 19 20 22 24 25 26 27 28 29 30 31 32 33 34 35 36 38 39 40 41 43 45 46 47 48 49 50 51 52 53 54 55 56 57 58 59 60 61 64 66 67 68 69 70 71 72 73 74 75 76 77 78 79 80 81 82 84 85 86 87 88 89 90 92 93 94 96 97 98 99 100 101 102 103 104 105 106 107 108 110 111 114 115 116 117 118 119 120 121 123 124 126 128 129 130 131 132 134 135 143 144 146 147 148 **P**6 8 **S** Mercy Health, Chesterfield, MO
Primary Contact: Jeffrey A. Johnston, President
CFO: Cheryl Matejka, Chief Financial Officer
CMO: Paul Hintze, M.D., Vice President Medical Affairs
CIO: Eugene Roth, Vice President Information Services
CHR: Rocky Ruello, Vice President Human Resources
Web address: www.mercy.net/stlouismo
Control: Other not–for–profit (including NFP Corporation) **Service:** General Medical and Surgical

Staffed Beds: 962 **Admissions:** 42183 **Census:** 608 **Outpatient Visits:** 1024156 **Births:** 8598 **Total Expense ($000):** 839350 **Payroll Expense ($000):** 298336 **Personnel:** 4844

□ **METROPOLITAN ST. LOUIS PSYCHIATRIC CENTER (264025)**, 5351 Delmar, Zip 63112–3198; tel. 314/877–0501, (Nonreporting) **A**1 3 10
Primary Contact: Laurent D. Javois, Regional Executive Officer
COO: Michael Bruce Anderson, Ph.D., Chief Operating Officer
CFO: James D. Martin, Chief Financial Officer
CMO: Roy Wilson, M.D., Medical Director
CHR: Michael McFarlane, Director Human Resources
CNO: Sarah Jones, Chief Nurse Executive
Web address: www.dmh.missouri.gov/mpc
Control: State–Government, nonfederal **Service:** Psychiatric

Staffed Beds: 50

✠ **MISSOURI BAPTIST MEDICAL CENTER (260108)**, 3015 North Ballas Road, Zip 63131–2329; tel. 314/996–5000 **A**1 2 3 5 10 **F**3 11 13 14 15 17 18 20 22 24 26 28 29 30 31 32 34 35 36 40 41 45 46 48 49 50 51 54 56 57 58 59 60 63 64 65 68 70 72 74 75 76 77 78 79 81 82 83 84 85 86 87 89 90 92 93 94 96 97 102 107 108 110 111 114 115 116 117 118 119 120 121 123 124 126 130 132 135 145 146 147 148 **P**6 **S** BJC HealthCare, Saint Louis, MO
Primary Contact: John Antes, President
COO: Michael Kelly, Vice President Operations
CFO: Amy Desart, Vice President, Chief Financial Officer
CMO: Mitchell Botney, M.D., Vice President Medical Affairs and Chief Medical Officer
CIO: Tracie Johnson, Director Information Services
CHR: Cyndy Donato, Vice President, Human Resources
CNO: Tim Mislan, MS, Vice President and Chief Nurse Executive
Web address: www.missouribaptist.org
Control: Other not–for–profit (including NFP Corporation) **Service:** General Medical and Surgical

Staffed Beds: 448 **Admissions:** 20773 **Census:** 252 **Outpatient Visits:** 402089 **Births:** 3895 **Total Expense ($000):** 519303 **Payroll Expense ($000):** 169913 **Personnel:** 2441

□ **SHRINERS HOSPITALS FOR CHILDREN–ST. LOUIS (263304)**, 4400 Clayton Avenue, Zip 63110–1624; tel. 314/432–3600 **A**1 3 5 10 **F**3 29 58 64 74 75 79 81 85 86 87 89 93 94 130 131 146 148 **S** Shriners Hospitals for Children, Tampa, FL
Primary Contact: John Gloss, FACHE, Administrator
CFO: Sandra K. Lawson, Interim Director Fiscal Services
CMO: Perry L. Schoenecker, M.D., Chief of Staff
CIO: Jeanne Hall, Director Information Systems
CHR: Mark Venable, Interim Director Human Resources
Web address: www.shrinershospitalsforchildren.org/Hospitals/Locations/Stlouis.aspx
Control: Other not–for–profit (including NFP Corporation) **Service:** Children's orthopedic

Staffed Beds: 12 **Admissions:** 265 **Census:** 3 **Outpatient Visits:** 9191 **Births:** 0 **Total Expense ($000):** 24936 **Payroll Expense ($000):** 8786 **Personnel:** 146

MO

Many Facility Codes have changed. Please refer to the AHA Guide Code Chart.
© 2016 AHA Guide

★ **SSM CARDINAL GLENNON CHILDREN'S MEDICAL CENTER (269807)**, 1465 South Grand Boulevard, Zip 63104–1095; tel. 314/577–5600 **A**3 5 10 **F**3 11 19 21 23 25 27 29 30 31 32 34 35 38 39 40 41 43 44 45 46 47 48 49 50 54 55 57 59 60 61 64 66 68 72 73 74 75 77 78 79 80 81 82 84 85 86 87 88 89 90 93 94 97 99 100 101 102 104 107 108 111 115 118 119 124 127 129 130 131 132 134 136 137 138 139 141 142 146 148 **P**6 8 **S** SSM Health, Saint Louis, MO
Primary Contact: Steven Burghart, President
CFO: Karen Rewerts, System Vice President of Finance
CMO: John Peter, M.D., Vice President Medical Affairs
CIO: Michael Paasch, Regional Vice President and Chief Information Officer
CHR: Debbie G. Walkenhorst, Network Vice President
Web address: www.cardinalglennon.com
Control: Church–operated, Nongovernment, not–for profit **Service:** Children's general

Staffed Beds: 176 **Admissions:** 7591 **Census:** 134 **Outpatient Visits:** 243413 **Births:** 0 **Total Expense ($000):** 314683 **Payroll Expense ($000):** 94639 **Personnel:** 1565

⊞ **SSM HEALTH SAINT LOUIS UNIVERSITY HOSPITAL (260105)**, 3635 Vista at Grand Boulevard, Zip 63110–0250, Mailing Address: P.O. Box 15250, Zip 63110–0250; tel. 314/577–8000, (Includes SSM HEALTH SAINT LOUIS UNIVERSITY HOSPITAL–SOUTH, 1755 South Grand Boulevard, Zip 63104–1540; tel. 314/577–6027; Raymond Alvey, Chief Financial Officer) **A**1 2 3 5 8 10 **F**3 4 6 7 8 9 11 14 15 17 18 20 22 24 26 28 29 30 31 34 35 36 37 38 39 40 43 44 45 46 47 48 49 50 51 55 56 57 58 59 60 61 63 64 65 68 70 74 75 77 78 79 81 82 84 85 86 87 90 91 92 93 94 96 97 98 100 101 102 103 104 107 108 110 111 112 113 114 115 116 117 118 119 121 123 124 126 129 130 131 132 135 136 138 139 141 142 146 147 148 **P**6 8 **S** SSM Health, Saint Louis, MO
Primary Contact: Kathleen R. Becker, M.P.H., JD, President
COO: Robert William Hoefer, FACHE, Chief Operating Officer
CFO: Raymond Alvey, Chief Financial Officer
CMO: Nirav Patel, M.D., Interim Chief Medical Officer
CIO: Patrick Brennan, Director Information System Technology
CNO: Russell Schroeder, Chief Nursing Officer
Web address: www.sluhospital.com
Control: Church–operated, Nongovernment, not–for profit **Service:** General Medical and Surgical

Staffed Beds: 352 **Admissions:** 16972 **Census:** 260 **Outpatient Visits:** 150869 **Births:** 0 **Total Expense ($000):** 419278 **Payroll Expense ($000):** 96707 **Personnel:** 1488

★ **SSM ST. MARY'S HEALTH CENTER (260091)**, 6420 Clayton Road, Zip 63117–1811; tel. 314/768–8000 **A**2 5 **F**3 4 13 15 17 18 20 22 24 26 28 29 30 31 34 35 37 38 40 44 45 46 49 50 51 52 55 56 57 58 59 60 61 64 66 70 72 73 74 75 76 78 79 81 82 84 85 86 87 97 98 100 101 102 103 104 105 107 108 110 111 114 115 119 120 121 129 130 132 135 143 144 146 147 148 **P**6 8 **S** SSM Health, Saint Louis, MO
Primary Contact: Travis Capers, FACHE, President
CFO: Karen Rewerts, System Vice President of Finance
CMO: Stephen Kelly, M.D., Chief Medical Officer
CIO: Michael Paasch, Regional Chief Information Officer
Web address: www.stmarys–stlouis.com
Control: Church–operated, Nongovernment, not–for profit **Service:** General Medical and Surgical

Staffed Beds: 381 **Admissions:** 19592 **Census:** 267 **Outpatient Visits:** 220287 **Births:** 3507 **Total Expense ($000):** 334051 **Payroll Expense ($000):** 111044 **Personnel:** 1784

☐ **ST. ALEXIUS HOSPITAL – BROADWAY CAMPUS (260210)**, 3933 South Broadway, Zip 63118–4601; tel. 314/865–7000, (Includes SOUTHPOINTE HOSPITAL, 2639 Miami Street, Zip 63118–3929; tel. 314/772–1456; ST. ALEXIUS HOSPITAL – FOREST PARK CAMPUS, 6150 Oakland Avenue, Zip 63139–3215; tel. 314/768–3000; Michael J. Motte, Chief Executive Officer) **A**1 5 10 **F**3 12 15 20 29 30 35 38 39 40 56 57 59 60 68 70 74 77 78 79 81 86 87 98 101 102 103 104 107 108 111 118 119 130 143 146 148 **P**6 **S** Success Healthcare, Boca Raton, FL
Primary Contact: Michael J. Motte, Chief Executive Officer
CFO: Matthew Brandt, Chief Financial Officer
Web address: www.stalexiushospital.com
Control: Corporation, Investor–owned, for–profit **Service:** General Medical and Surgical

Staffed Beds: 189 **Admissions:** 3869 **Census:** 99 **Outpatient Visits:** 28620 **Births:** 0 **Total Expense ($000):** 58756 **Payroll Expense ($000):** 31304 **Personnel:** 674

⊞ △ **ST. ANTHONY'S MEDICAL CENTER (260077)**, 10010 Kennerly Road, Zip 63128–2106; tel. 314/525–1000 **A**1 2 3 5 7 10 **F**3 4 5 11 12 13 15 17 18 20 22 24 26 28 29 30 31 34 35 36 38 40 41 43 47 48 49 50 51 53 54 56 57 58 59 60 61 62 63 64 65 68 69 70 73 74 75 76 77 78 79 80 81 82 84 85 86 87 89 90 91 92 93 94 95 96 97 98 99 100 101 102 103 104 105 107 108 110 111 114 115 116 117 118 119 120 121 122 123 124 126 129 130 131 132 143 144 146 147 148 **P**6
Primary Contact: David Sindelar, Chief Executive Officer
CFO: Brent Singer, Chief Financial Officer
CIO: Jim Weldon, Chief Information Officer
CNO: Beverly Bokovitz, R.N., Chief Nursing Officer
Web address: www.stanthonysmedcenter.com
Control: Other not–for–profit (including NFP Corporation) **Service:** General Medical and Surgical

Staffed Beds: 540 **Admissions:** 27093 **Census:** 325 **Outpatient Visits:** 713007 **Births:** 1118 **Total Expense ($000):** 490740 **Payroll Expense ($000):** 213336 **Personnel:** 3239

ST. JOHN'S MERCY CHILDREN'S HOSPITAL See Mercy Children's Hospital St. Louis

ST. JOHN'S MERCY MEDICAL CENTER See Mercy Hospital St. Louis

⊞ △ **ST. LOUIS CHILDREN'S HOSPITAL (263301)**, One Children's Place, Zip 63110–1002; tel. 314/454–6000 **A**1 3 5 7 8 10 **F**5 7 8 11 16 17 19 20 21 22 23 25 26 27 29 30 31 32 34 35 38 39 40 41 42 43 44 45 46 47 48 49 50 54 55 58 59 60 61 62 63 64 65 68 71 72 74 75 77 78 79 81 82 83 84 85 86 87 88 89 90 92 93 96 99 100 101 102 104 107 108 109 111 112 114 115 119 129 130 131 132 134 135 136 137 138 139 140 141 142 143 145 146 148 **S** BJC HealthCare, Saint Louis, MO
Primary Contact: Joan Magruder, President
CFO: Michele McKee, Vice President and Chief Financial Officer
CMO: F. Sessions Cole, M.D., Chief Medical Officer
Web address: www.stlouischildrens.org
Control: Other not–for–profit (including NFP Corporation) **Service:** Children's general

Staffed Beds: 280 **Admissions:** 10448 **Census:** 197 **Outpatient Visits:** 300981 **Births:** 0 **Total Expense ($000):** 538530 **Payroll Expense ($000):** 185010 **Personnel:** 2981

☐ **ST. LOUIS PSYCHIATRIC REHABILITATION CENTER (264010)**, 5300 Arsenal Street, Zip 63139–1463; tel. 314/877–6501 **A**1 10 **F**11 30 39 65 68 75 86 87 98 100 101 106 130 143 146
Primary Contact: Laurent D. Javois, Chief Executive Officer
COO: Felix T. Vincenz, Chief Operating Officer
CFO: James D. Martin, Chief Financial Officer
CMO: Roy Wilson, M.D., Medical Director
CHR: Michael McFarlane, Chief Human Resource Officer
CNO: Deborah Mokry, Chief Nurse Executive
Web address: www.dmh.missouri.gov
Control: State–Government, nonfederal **Service:** Psychiatric

Staffed Beds: 180 **Admissions:** 27 **Census:** 180 **Outpatient Visits:** 0 **Births:** 0 **Total Expense ($000):** 35806 **Payroll Expense ($000):** 18144 **Personnel:** 511

⊞ △ **THE REHABILITATION INSTITUTE OF ST. LOUIS (263028)**, 4455 Duncan Avenue, Zip 63110–1111; tel. 314/658–3800 **A**1 7 10 **F**29 44 56 58 64 68 74 75 79 82 87 90 91 93 94 100 130 132 143 146 148 **S** HEALTHSOUTH Corporation, Birmingham, AL
Primary Contact: Tara Diebling, Chief Executive Officer
CFO: Tara Diebling, Chief Executive Officer
CMO: David Carr, M.D., Physician Medical Director
CHR: Heather Savage, Director Human Resources
CNO: Angelina Sherman, R.N., Chief Nursing Officer
Web address: www.rehabinstitutestl.com
Control: Partnership, Investor–owned, for–profit **Service:** Rehabilitation

Staffed Beds: 96 **Admissions:** 2001 **Census:** 78 **Outpatient Visits:** 40516 **Births:** 0 **Total Expense ($000):** 36271 **Payroll Expense ($000):** 18177 **Personnel:** 260

⊞ △ **VETERANS AFFAIRS ST. LOUIS HEALTH CARE SYSTEM**, 915 North Grand, Zip 63106–1621; tel. 314/652–4100, (Nonreporting) **A**1 3 5 7 **S** Department of Veterans Affairs, Washington, DC
Primary Contact: Keith D. Repko, Director
CFO: Karen Westerheide, Chief Financial Officer
CIO: Steve Warmbold, Director Information Management Service Line
CHR: Marie Lewis, Human Resources Liaison
CNO: Richard Holt, R.N., Associate Director Patient Care Services
Web address: www.stlouis.va.gov/
Control: Veterans Affairs, Government, federal **Service:** General Medical and Surgical

Staffed Beds: 356

MO

Hospital, Medicare Provider Number, Address, Telephone, Approval, Facility, and Physician Codes, Health Care System

★ American Hospital Association (AHA) membership ○ Healthcare Facilities Accreditation Program ⇑ Center for Improvement in Healthcare Quality Accreditation
☐ The Joint Commission accreditation ◇ DNV Healthcare Inc. accreditation △ Commission on Accreditation of Rehabilitation Facilities (CARF) accreditation

SAINT PETERS—St. Charles County

⊠ **BARNES–JEWISH ST. PETERS HOSPITAL (260191)**, 10 Hospital Drive, Zip 63376–1659; tel. 636/916–9000 **A**1 3 5 10 **F**3 8 11 15 18 20 22 28 29 30 31 34 35 40 45 46 49 51 57 59 64 70 75 77 78 79 81 85 86 90 93 107 108 110 111 114 115 118 119 120 121 123 129 130 132 135 146 147 148 **S** BJC HealthCare, Saint Louis, MO
Primary Contact: Lee F. Fetter, Interim President
CFO: Glen Schwaegel, Vice President and Chief Financial Officer
CMO: Feliipe Orellana, Chief Medical Officer
CIO: Cindy Gross, Director of Finance
CHR: Michael J. Miller, Director Human Resources
CNO: Jill Skyles, R.N., Vice President Patient Care Services and Chief Nurse Executive
Web address: www.bjsph.org/
Control: Other not–for–profit (including NFP Corporation) **Service:** General Medical and Surgical

Staffed Beds: 101 **Admissions:** 5019 **Census:** 60 **Outpatient Visits:** 90975 **Births:** 0 **Total Expense ($000):** 123287 **Payroll Expense ($000):** 38749 **Personnel:** 547

SALEM—Dent County

★ **SALEM MEMORIAL DISTRICT HOSPITAL (261318)**, Highway 72 North, Zip 65560–0774, Mailing Address: P.O. Box 774, Zip 65560–0774; tel. 573/729–6626, (Total facility includes 18 beds in nursing home–type unit) **A**10 18 **F**3 7 11 29 30 34 40 59 60 62 67 75 81 85 87 89 107 115 119 127 128 130 133 135 146
Primary Contact: Kasey Lucas, Administrator
CFO: Becky Cunningham, Controller
CMO: John Demorlis, M.D., Chief Medical Staff
CHR: Jodie Gorman, Director Human Resources
Web address: www.smdh.net
Control: Hospital district or authority, Government, nonfederal **Service:** General Medical and Surgical

Staffed Beds: 43 **Admissions:** 645 **Census:** 26 **Outpatient Visits:** 36723 **Births:** 0 **Total Expense ($000):** 19587 **Payroll Expense ($000):** 8189 **Personnel:** 178

SEDALIA—Pettis County

⊠ **BOTHWELL REGIONAL HEALTH CENTER (260009)**, 601 East 14th Street, Zip 65301–5972, Mailing Address: P.O. Box 1706, Zip 65302–1706; tel. 660/826–8833, (Total facility includes 10 beds in nursing home–type unit) **A**1 10 **F**3 9 11 13 14 15 18 20 22 28 29 30 31 34 35 39 40 51 54 56 57 59 60 64 65 68 70 73 74 75 76 77 78 79 80 81 82 84 85 86 87 89 92 93 107 108 110 111 114 115 116 117 118 119 120 121 123 124 127 128 129 130 131 132 135 146 147 148
Primary Contact: James A. Robertson, Jr., Chief Executive Officer
COO: Mark I. Hirshberg, Chief Operating Officer
CIO: Tom Fairfax, Director Information Systems
CHR: Deb Clemmer, Vice President Human Resources
CNO: Regina W. Crow, R.N., Chief Nursing Officer
Web address: www.brhc.org
Control: City–Government, nonfederal **Service:** General Medical and Surgical

Staffed Beds: 137 **Admissions:** 5416 **Census:** 62 **Outpatient Visits:** 114945 **Births:** 561 **Total Expense ($000):** 98004 **Payroll Expense ($000):** 38444 **Personnel:** 693

SIKESTON—Scott County

☐ **MISSOURI DELTA MEDICAL CENTER (260113)**, 1008 North Main Street, Zip 63801–5044; tel. 573/471–1600 **A**1 10 **F**3 13 15 18 28 29 30 31 34 35 37 40 50 51 53 54 56 57 59 60 62 64 68 70 74 75 76 77 78 79 81 82 84 85 86 87 89 90 93 97 98 103 107 108 109 110 111 115 116 117 118 119 126 127 129 130 131 132 144 146 147 148
Primary Contact: Jason Schrumpf, President
CFO: Greg Carda, Vice President Finance
Web address: www.missouridelta.com
Control: Other not–for–profit (including NFP Corporation) **Service:** General Medical and Surgical

Staffed Beds: 110 **Admissions:** 4136 **Census:** 58 **Outpatient Visits:** 237271 **Births:** 379 **Total Expense ($000):** 90255 **Payroll Expense ($000):** 42188 **Personnel:** 759

SPRINGFIELD—Greene County

★ ◇ **COX MEDICAL CENTERS (260040)**, 1423 North Jefferson Street, Zip 65802–1988; tel. 417/269–3000, (Includes COX MEDICAL CENTER NORTH, 1423 North Jefferson Avenue, Zip 65802; tel. 417/269–3000; COX MEDICAL CENTER SOUTH, 3801 South National Avenue, Zip 65807; tel. 417/269–6000) **A**2 3 5 10 21 **F**3 4 5 7 11 12 13 15 17 18 19 20 22 24 26 28 29 30 31 32 34 35 38 39 40 41 42 43 44 45 46 47 48 49 50 51 52 53 54 55 56 57 58 59 60 61 62 64 65 68 69 70 71 72 74 75 76 77 78 79 80 81 82 84 85 86 87 88 89 90 92 93 94 95 96 97 98 99 100 101 102 103 104 107 108 110 111 114 115 117 118 119 120 121 124 126 127 128 129 130 131 132 134 135 143 144 146 147 148 **P**3 6 **S** CoxHealth, Springfield, MO
Primary Contact: Steven D. Edwards, President and Chief Executive Officer
CFO: Jacob McWay, Senior Vice President and Chief Financial Officer
CMO: Frank Romero, M.D., Chief Medical Officer
CIO: Bruce Robison, Vice President and Chief Information Officer
CHR: John Hursh, Vice President Human Resources
CNO: Karen Kramer, R.N., Vice President and System Chief Nursing Officer
Web address: www.coxhealth.com
Control: Other not–for–profit (including NFP Corporation) **Service:** General Medical and Surgical

Staffed Beds: 621 **Admissions:** 33015 **Census:** 441 **Outpatient Visits:** 1373826 **Births:** 3206 **Total Expense ($000):** 980274 **Payroll Expense ($000):** 309469 **Personnel:** 6869

☐ **LAKELAND BEHAVIORAL HEALTH SYSTEM (264024)**, 440 South Market Street, Zip 65806–2026; tel. 417/865–5581 **A**1 10 **F**98 99 103 106 130 **S** Acadia Healthcare Company, Inc., Franklin, TN
Primary Contact: Nathan Duncan, Chief Executive Officer
COO: Randy Fox, Director Performance Improvement and Risk Management
CFO: Rick Crump, Chief Financial Officer
CMO: Richard Aiken, M.D., Medical Director
CIO: Brad Strothkamp, Chief Information Systems
CHR: Dave England, Director Human Resources
Web address: www.lakeland–hospital.com
Control: Corporation, Investor–owned, for–profit **Service:** Psychiatric

Staffed Beds: 132 **Admissions:** 2409 **Census:** 107 **Outpatient Visits:** 0 **Births:** 0 **Total Expense ($000):** 22147 **Payroll Expense ($000):** 12912 **Personnel:** 323

⊠ **MERCY HOSPITAL SPRINGFIELD (260065)**, 1235 East Cherokee Street, Zip 65804–2263; tel. 417/820–2000, (Includes MERCY CHILDREN'S HOSPITAL SPRINGFIELD, 1235 East Cherokee Street, Zip 65804–2203; tel. 417/820–2000; MERCY ORTHOPEDIC HOSPITAL SPRINGFIELD, 3050 East Riverbluff Boulevard, Ozark, Zip 65721; tel. 417/820–5611; Robert Steele, M.D., President), (Total facility includes 97 beds in nursing home–type unit) **A**1 2 3 5 10 **F**3 5 6 7 8 9 11 12 13 14 15 16 17 18 19 20 22 24 26 28 29 30 31 34 35 36 37 38 39 40 43 44 45 46 48 49 50 51 54 55 56 57 58 59 60 61 62 63 64 65 66 67 68 70 71 72 73 74 75 76 77 78 79 81 82 84 85 86 87 88 89 90 91 92 93 94 96 97 98 99 100 101 102 103 104 107 108 110 111 114 115 116 117 118 119 120 121 123 124 126 127 128 129 130 131 132 134 135 143 146 147 148 **P**6 8 **S** Mercy Health, Chesterfield, MO
Primary Contact: Alan Scarrow, M.D., President
COO: Jay Guffey, Senior Vice President and Chief Operating Officer
CFO: Scott Reynolds, Vice President Finance
CMO: Allan Allphin, M.D., Chief of Staff
CIO: Lori Sturgill, Vice President Business Partnership
CHR: Tanya Maricn, Interim Vice President Human Resources
CNO: Lisa Person, MSN, Vice President and Chief Nursing Officer
Web address: www.mercy.net/springfieldmo
Control: Church–operated, Nongovernment, not–for profit **Service:** General Medical and Surgical

Staffed Beds: 703 **Admissions:** 36223 **Census:** 458 **Outpatient Visits:** 626111 **Births:** 3170 **Total Expense ($000):** 887881 **Payroll Expense ($000):** 258170 **Personnel:** 7966

☐ **MERCY REHABILITION HOSPITAL SPRINGFIELD (263032)**, 5904 South Southwood Road, Zip 65804–5234; tel. 417/227–9000 **A**1 10 **F**29 30 90 130 132
Primary Contact: Bruce Eady, Chief Executive Officer
CFO: Melissa Campbell, Controller
CMO: Hollis Bell, M.D., Medical Director
CHR: Sarah Eiffert, Director Human Resources
CNO: Jennifer Friedline, R.N., Director of Nursing
Web address: www.mercy.net
Control: Partnership, Investor–owned, for–profit **Service:** Rehabilitation

Staffed Beds: 60 **Admissions:** 1101 **Census:** 38 **Outpatient Visits:** 0 **Births:** 0 **Total Expense ($000):** 14049 **Payroll Expense ($000):** 6547 **Personnel:** 175

○ **OZARKS COMMUNITY HOSPITAL (260207)**, 2828 North National, Zip 65803–4306; tel. 417/837–4000, (Nonreporting) **A**10 11
Primary Contact: Paul Taylor, Chief Executive Officer
CFO: Misty Hampshire, Chief Financial Officer
Web address: www.ochonline.com
Control: Corporation, Investor–owned, for–profit **Service:** General Medical and Surgical

Staffed Beds: 21

Many Facility Codes have changed. Please refer to the AHA Guide Code Chart.

MO

⊠ **SELECT SPECIALTY HOSPITAL–SPRINGFIELD (262017)**, 1630 East Primrose Street, Zip 65804–7929; tel. 417/885–4700 **A**1 10 **F**1 3 29 45 85 107 114 148 **S** Select Medical Corporation, Mechanicsburg, PA
Primary Contact: Mark S. Brodeur, FACHE, Chief Executive Officer
CHR: Tonya Eddington, Coordinator Human Resources
Web address: www.selectspecialtyhospitals.com/company/locations/springfield.aspx
Control: Corporation, Investor–owned, for–profit **Service:** Long–Term Acute Care hospital

Staffed Beds: 44 **Admissions:** 507 **Census:** 36 **Outpatient Visits:** 0 **Births:** 0 **Total Expense ($000):** 21067 **Payroll Expense ($000):** 8588 **Personnel:** 168

STE. GENEVIEVE—Ste. Genevieve County

★ **STE. GENEVIEVE COUNTY MEMORIAL HOSPITAL (261330)**, 800 Suite Genevieve Drive, Zip 63670–1434; tel. 573/883–2751 **A**10 18 **F**2 3 11 13 14 15 18 28 29 31 34 35 39 40 50 53 56 57 59 62 64 65 66 68 75 76 77 78 79 81 82 85 86 87 89 92 93 107 110 111 115 119 124 127 129 130 131 132 133 135 145 146 147 148 **P**6
Primary Contact: Thomas Keim, Chief Executive Officer
CFO: Susan Eckenfels, Chief Financial Officer
CMO: Joseph Sharlow, M.D., Chief of Staff
CHR: Sarah Jo Kelley, Director Human Resources
CNO: Rita Brumfield, R.N., Chief Nursing Officer
Web address: www.stegenevievehospital.org
Control: County–Government, nonfederal **Service:** General Medical and Surgical

Staffed Beds: 25 **Admissions:** 995 **Census:** 10 **Outpatient Visits:** 108819 **Births:** 153 **Total Expense ($000):** 40889 **Payroll Expense ($000):** 16935 **Personnel:** 329

SULLIVAN—Crawford County

★ **MISSOURI BAPTIST SULLIVAN HOSPITAL (261337)**, 751 Sappington Bridge Road, Zip 63080–2354; tel. 573/468–4186 **A**10 18 **F**3 4 7 11 13 15 28 29 30 31 34 35 40 53 56 57 59 63 64 65 70 75 76 77 78 79 81 82 83 84 85 86 87 89 90 93 97 98 102 103 104 107 111 115 119 127 129 130 131 132 133 146 **S** BJC HealthCare, Saint Louis, MO
Primary Contact: Tony Schwarm, President
CFO: Angela Wilks, Finance Director
CMO: Alison Baker, M.D., Chief of Staff
CHR: Kathleen Reed, Manager Human Resources
CNO: Carmen J. Bartolotta, Chief Nursing Officer
Web address: www.missouribaptistsullivan.org
Control: Other not–for–profit (including NFP Corporation) **Service:** General Medical and Surgical

Staffed Beds: 35 **Admissions:** 2258 **Census:** 25 **Outpatient Visits:** 100955 **Births:** 291 **Total Expense ($000):** 47725 **Payroll Expense ($000):** 18089 **Personnel:** 336

SWEET SPRINGS—Saline County

I–70 COMMUNITY HOSPITAL (261334), 105 Hospital Drive, Zip 65351–2229; tel. 660/335–4700, (Nonreporting) **A**10 18 **S** Rural Community Hospitals of America, Kansas City, MO
Primary Contact: Jeff Bloemker, Chief Executive Officer
CFO: Cathy Berube, Chief Financial Officer
CMO: Deborah Herrmann, M.D., Chief of Staff
CIO: Diane Swift, Director Medical Records
CHR: Tina Bredehoeft, Human Resources
CNO: Nancy Gardner, Chief Nursing Officer
Web address: www.i70medcenter.com
Control: Corporation, Investor–owned, for–profit **Service:** General Medical and Surgical

Staffed Beds: 15

TRENTON—Grundy County

★ **WRIGHT MEMORIAL HOSPITAL (261309)**, 191 Iowa Boulevard, Zip 64683–8343; tel. 660/358–5700 **A**10 18 **F**3 11 13 15 28 29 30 31 34 35 40 45 50 56 57 58 59 64 68 75 76 77 78 79 81 82 84 85 87 89 90 93 102 104 107 108 110 111 115 119 127 129 130 133 146 148 **P**6 **S** Saint Luke's Health System, Kansas City, MO
Primary Contact: Gary W. Jordan, FACHE, Chief Executive Officer
CFO: Leslie Reed, Chief Financial Officer
CMO: Gerald C. Zabielski, M.D., Chief Medical Staff
CHR: Jenny Donovan, Director Human Resources
Web address: www.saintlukeshealthsystem.org
Control: Other not–for–profit (including NFP Corporation) **Service:** General Medical and Surgical

Staffed Beds: 25 **Admissions:** 726 **Census:** 8 **Outpatient Visits:** 65445 **Births:** 226 **Total Expense ($000):** 28113 **Payroll Expense ($000):** 9988 **Personnel:** 166

TROY—Lincoln County

⊠ **MERCY HOSPITAL LINCOLN (261319)**, 1000 East Cherry Street, Zip 63379–1513; tel. 636/528–8551 **A**1 10 18 **F**3 11 15 17 18 28 29 30 34 35 40 44 45 50 51 57 59 62 64 65 68 69 70 75 77 79 80 81 85 86 87 89 90 93 104 107 110 111 113 114 119 127 129 130 131 132 133 135 144 146 148 **P**6 **S** Mercy Health, Chesterfield, MO
Primary Contact: Anthony Rothermich, Administrator
CFO: Mark Thorn, FACHE, Executive Director, Finance
CIO: Travis Boyd, Manager, Information Technology
CHR: Mary Kay Kunza, Manager Human Resources
CNO: Breanne Griffin, R.N., Executive Director, Nursing
Web address: www.mercy.net
Control: Other not–for–profit (including NFP Corporation) **Service:** General Medical and Surgical

Staffed Beds: 25 **Admissions:** 348 **Census:** 4 **Outpatient Visits:** 17173 **Births:** 0 **Total Expense ($000):** 11847 **Payroll Expense ($000):** 5316 **Personnel:** 276

UNIONVILLE—Putnam County

PUTNAM COUNTY MEMORIAL HOSPITAL (261305), 1926 Oak Street, Zip 63565–1180, Mailing Address: P.O. Box 389, Zip 63565–0389; tel. 660/947–2411 **A**10 18 **F**3 11 15 18 28 29 34 35 40 45 50 57 59 75 77 81 85 90 93 97 98 102 104 105 107 111 112 115 119 127 128 129 130 133 135 143 145 147 148 **P**5
Primary Contact: Richard Morrow, Executive Committee Chairman
COO: Jerry Cummings, Chief Operating Officer
CMO: Dawn Ann Fairley, M.D., Chief of Staff
CHR: Debbie Douglas, Director Human Resources
CNO: Gayle Pickens, Chief Nursing Officer
Web address: www.pcmhosp.com
Control: County–Government, nonfederal **Service:** General Medical and Surgical

Staffed Beds: 25 **Admissions:** 202 **Census:** 9 **Outpatient Visits:** 15501 **Births:** 0 **Total Expense ($000):** 14242 **Payroll Expense ($000):** 5555 **Personnel:** 108

WARRENSBURG—Johnson County

⊠ **WESTERN MISSOURI MEDICAL CENTER (260097)**, 403 Burkarth Road, Zip 64093–3101; tel. 660/747–2500 **A**1 10 20 **F**3 8 11 12 13 15 17 18 28 29 30 31 32 34 35 40 45 47 57 59 61 64 65 68 70 74 75 76 77 78 79 81 82 85 89 90 93 102 107 108 110 111 115 117 118 119 127 129 130 131 132 133 135 144 146 147 148 **P**6
Primary Contact: Darinda Reberry, MSN, R.N., President and Chief Executive Officer
CFO: Terri Bradley, CPA, Vice President Financial Services and Chief Financial Officer
CIO: Bill Ladd, Director Information Services
CHR: Dennis Long, Director Human Resources
CNO: Jennifer Koepke, R.N., Vice President of Patient Care Services and Chief Nursing Officer
Web address: www.wmmc.com
Control: County–Government, nonfederal **Service:** General Medical and Surgical

Staffed Beds: 72 **Admissions:** 2508 **Census:** 22 **Outpatient Visits:** 136256 **Births:** 718 **Total Expense ($000):** 80071 **Payroll Expense ($000):** 28548 **Personnel:** 513

WASHINGTON—Franklin County

⊠ **MERCY HOSPITAL WASHINGTON (260052)**, 901 East Fifth Street, Zip 63090–3127; tel. 636/239–8000 **A**1 10 **F**3 8 11 12 13 14 15 17 18 20 22 28 29 30 31 32 34 35 39 40 43 44 48 49 50 51 52 53 54 57 59 61 64 66 68 69 70 73 74 75 76 77 78 79 80 81 82 84 85 87 89 90 93 94 96 97 100 101 104 107 108 110 111 114 116 117 118 119 127 129 130 131 132 134 135 143 144 146 147 148 **P**6 8 **S** Mercy Health, Chesterfield, MO
Primary Contact: Eric J. Eoloff, President
COO: Joan Frost, R.N., Chief Operating Officer
CFO: Cheryl Matejka, Chief Financial Officer
CMO: Thomas Riechers, M.D., Chief Medical Staff
CIO: Michael McCreary, Chief of Services
CHR: Barbara Grayson, Vice President Human Resources
CNO: Stacy Blankenship, Chief Nursing Officer
Web address: www.mercy.net
Control: Other not–for–profit (including NFP Corporation) **Service:** General Medical and Surgical

Staffed Beds: 166 **Admissions:** 6001 **Census:** 53 **Outpatient Visits:** 311988 **Births:** 844 **Total Expense ($000):** 142834 **Payroll Expense ($000):** 54409 **Personnel:** 773

MO

Hospital, Medicare Provider Number, Address, Telephone, Approval, Facility, and Physician Codes, Health Care System

★ American Hospital Association (AHA) membership ○ Healthcare Facilities Accreditation Program ⇑ Center for Improvement in Healthcare Quality Accreditation
□ The Joint Commission accreditation ◇ DNV Healthcare Inc. accreditation △ Commission on Accreditation of Rehabilitation Facilities (CARF) accreditation

WENTZVILLE—St. Charles County

SSM ST. JOSEPH HEALTH CENTER – WENTZVILLE See SSM St. Joseph Health Center, Saint Charles

WEST PLAINS—Howell County

☒ **OZARKS MEDICAL CENTER (260078)**, 1100 Kentucky Avenue, Zip 65775–2029, Mailing Address: P.O. Box 1100, Zip 65775–1100; tel. 417/256–9111 **A**1 10 **F**2 3 5 11 13 15 17 18 20 22 24 28 29 30 31 34 38 40 44 45 49 50 57 59 61 62 63 64 68 70 74 75 76 77 78 79 81 82 84 85 86 87 89 90 91 93 94 98 99 100 101 102 103 104 107 108 110 111 115 118 119 120 121 127 129 130 131 132 135 144 145 146 147 148 **P**8
Primary Contact: Thomas Keller, President and Chief Executive Officer
CFO: Kim Thompson, Vice President and Chief Financial Officer
CMO: Walter R. Holloway, Chief Medical Officer
CIO: John Wilcox, Chief Information Officer
CHR: Connie Schott, Vice President, Human Resources
CNO: Kurtis Abbey, Chief Nursing Officer
Web address: www.ozarksmedicalcenter.com
Control: Other not–for–profit (including NFP Corporation) **Service:** General Medical and Surgical

Staffed Beds: 103 **Admissions:** 5683 **Census:** 57 **Outpatient Visits:** 538787 **Births:** 641 **Total Expense ($000):** 140466 **Payroll Expense ($000):** 63546 **Personnel:** 896

WINDSOR—Henry County

☐ **ROYAL OAKS HOSPITAL (264020)**, 307 North Main, Zip 65360–1449; tel. 660/647–2182 **A**1 3 5 10 **F**75 98 99 100 101 102
Primary Contact: Alan W. Greiman, Chief Executive Officer and President
CFO: Dave Turner, Chief Financial Officer
CMO: Syed Arshad Husain, M.D., Executive Vice President and Chief Medical Officer
CIO: Richard Colvert, Chief Information Officer
CHR: Diane Coletta, Director Human Resources
CNO: Erin Allee, R.N., Director of Nursing
Web address: www.royal–oaks–hospital.org
Control: Other not–for–profit (including NFP Corporation) **Service:** Psychiatric

Staffed Beds: 41 **Admissions:** 1320 **Census:** 27 **Outpatient Visits:** 0 **Births:** 0 **Total Expense ($000):** 13040 **Payroll Expense ($000):** 6601 **Personnel:** 160

MO

Many Facility Codes have changed. Please refer to the AHA Guide Code Chart.

MONTANA

ANACONDA—Deer Lodge County

★ **COMMUNITY HOSPITAL OF ANACONDA (271335)**, 401 West Pennsylvania Street, Zip 59711; tel. 406/563–8500, (Total facility includes 62 beds in nursing home–type unit) **A**10 18 **F**1 3 6 8 11 13 15 29 30 31 34 40 43 45 50 57 59 62 63 64 75 76 77 79 81 82 87 93 107 111 114 116 119 128 130 133 135 143 144 146 148 **P**6 **S** Providence St. Joseph Health, Renton, WA
Primary Contact: Steve McNeece, Chief Executive Officer
COO: Laura Austin, Chief Financial Officer and Chief Operating Officer
CFO: Laura Austin, Chief Financial Officer and Chief Operating Officer
CMO: Shawna Baker, M.D., Chief of Staff
CIO: Laura Austin, Chief Financial Officer and Chief Operating Officer
CHR: Meg Hickey–Boynton, Director Human Resources and Marketing
CNO: Jamie Johnson, R.N., Vice President Nursing
Web address: www.communityhospitalofanaconda.org
Control: Other not–for–profit (including NFP Corporation) **Service:** General Medical and Surgical

Staffed Beds: 87 **Admissions:** 1273 **Census:** 66 **Outpatient Visits:** 49424
Births: 197 **Total Expense ($000):** 41500 **Payroll Expense ($000):** 21371
Personnel: 320

BAKER—Fallon County

FALLON MEDICAL COMPLEX (271301), 202 South 4th Street West, Zip 59313–9156, Mailing Address: P.O. Box 820, Zip 59313–0820; tel. 406/778–3331, (Total facility includes 15 beds in nursing home–type unit) **A**10 18 **F**11 15 32 34 40 56 57 59 62 64 65 66 68 69 75 93 97 107 110 114 119 127 128 130 133 146 148 **P**6
Primary Contact: David Espeland, Chief Executive Officer
CFO: Selena Nelson, Chief Financial Officer
CMO: Darryl Espeland, D.O., Chief Medical Staff
CIO: Susan Stevens, Information Technology Specialist
CHR: Theresa Myers, Personnel Director
CNO: Susan Lunde, R.N., Director of Nursing
Web address: www.fallonmedical.org
Control: Other not–for–profit (including NFP Corporation) **Service:** General Medical and Surgical

Staffed Beds: 40 **Admissions:** 149 **Census:** 23 **Outpatient Visits:** 19307
Births: 0 **Total Expense ($000):** 9338 **Payroll Expense ($000):** 4407
Personnel: 87

BIG SANDY—Chouteau County

★ **BIG SANDY MEDICAL CENTER (271311)**, 166 Montana Avenue East, Zip 59520–8474, Mailing Address: P.O. Box 530, Zip 59520–0530; tel. 406/378–2188, (Total facility includes 22 beds in nursing home–type unit) **A**10 18 **F**40 64 93 127 128 133
Primary Contact: Leah Griffith, Chief Executive Officer
CFO: Nora Grubb, Chief Financial Officer
Web address: www.bsmc.org
Control: Other not–for–profit (including NFP Corporation) **Service:** General Medical and Surgical

Staffed Beds: 30 **Admissions:** 53 **Census:** 16 **Outpatient Visits:** 2668
Births: 0 **Total Expense ($000):** 3262 **Payroll Expense ($000):** 1740
Personnel: 33

BIG SKY—Gallatin County

BOZEMAN HEALTH BIG SKY MEDICAL CENTER, 334 Town Center Avenue, Zip 59716; tel. 406/995–6995, (Nonreporting)
Primary Contact: Tracy Reamy, Administrator
Web address: www.https://www.bigskymedicalcenter.com/
Control: Other not–for–profit (including NFP Corporation) **Service:** General Medical and Surgical

Staffed Beds: 4

BIG TIMBER—Sweet Grass County

★ **PIONEER MEDICAL CENTER (271313)**, 301 West Seventh Avenue, Zip 59011–7893, Mailing Address: P.O. Box 1228, Zip 59011–1228; tel. 406/932–4603, (Total facility includes 25 beds in nursing home–type unit) **A**10 18 **F**2 7 10 29 34 35 40 41 45 57 59 63 64 65 69 75 77 93 97 107 114 127 128 130 131 132 133
Primary Contact: Erik Wood, Chief Executive Officer
CFO: Kyle Gee, Chief Financial Officer
CMO: Benjamin P. Bullington, M.D., Chief of Staff
CHR: Miki Gregorich, Director Human Resources
CNO: Randi Pike, Director of Nursing
Web address: www.pmcmt.org/
Control: County–Government, nonfederal **Service:** General Medical and Surgical

Staffed Beds: 50 **Admissions:** 189 **Census:** 31 **Outpatient Visits:** 17235
Births: 0

BILLINGS—Yellowstone County

☐ **ADVANCED CARE HOSPITAL OF MONTANA (272001)**, 3528 Gabel Road, Zip 59102–7307; tel. 406/373–8000 **A**1 10 **F**1 3 **P**6 8 **S** Ernest Health, Inc., Albuquerque, NM
Primary Contact: Judi Powers, Chief Executive Officer
Web address: www.achm.ernesthealth.com
Control: Corporation, Investor–owned, for–profit **Service:** Long–Term Acute Care hospital

Staffed Beds: 40 **Admissions:** 373 **Census:** 29

⊞ **BILLINGS CLINIC (270004)**, 801 North 24th Street, Zip 59101–0905, Mailing Address: P.O. Box 37000, Zip 59107–7000; tel. 406/657–4000, (Total facility includes 125 beds in nursing home–type unit) **A**1 2 10 19 **F**3 7 8 9 10 11 12 13 15 17 18 19 20 22 24 26 27 28 29 30 31 32 34 35 36 38 40 43 44 45 46 48 49 50 51 52 54 55 56 57 58 59 60 61 62 63 64 65 66 68 70 71 72 74 75 76 77 78 79 81 82 84 85 86 87 91 92 93 97 98 99 100 101 102 103 104 105 107 108 110 111 114 115 116 117 118 119 120 121 124 126 128 129 130 131 132 134 135 143 144 146 147 148 **P**6
Primary Contact: Nicholas Wolter, M.D., Chief Executive Officer
CFO: Connie F. Prewitt, Chief Financial Officer
CMO: Randall K. Gibb, M.D., Chief Medical Officer
CIO: Chris E. Stevens, Chief Information Officer
CHR: Karla Stauffer, Executive Director People Resources
CNO: Lu Byrd, R.N., Vice President Hospital Operations and Chief Nursing Officer
Web address: www.billingsclinic.com
Control: Other not–for–profit (including NFP Corporation) **Service:** General Medical and Surgical

Staffed Beds: 393 **Admissions:** 15674 **Census:** 305 **Outpatient Visits:** 914896 **Births:** 1388 **Total Expense ($000):** 562742 **Payroll Expense ($000):** 275630 **Personnel:** 3528

⊞ △ **ST. VINCENT HEALTHCARE (270049)**, 1233 North 30th Street, Zip 59101–0165, Mailing Address: P.O. Box 35200, Zip 59107–5200; tel. 406/237–7000 **A**1 2 7 10 **F**3 7 11 12 13 15 18 19 20 22 24 28 29 30 31 32 34 35 36 37 38 39 40 43 44 46 47 49 50 51 56 57 58 59 60 61 64 68 70 71 72 74 75 76 77 78 79 81 82 84 85 86 87 88 89 90 92 93 97 99 100 101 103 104 107 108 111 114 115 116 117 118 119 120 121 123 124 126 129 130 131 132 134 135 143 144 145 146 147 148 **P**6 **S** SCL Health, Broomfield, CO
Primary Contact: Steve Loveless, President and Chief Executive Officer
CMO: Michael Schweitzer, M.D., Chief Medical Officer
CIO: Al Rooney, Director Information Systems
Web address: www.svh–mt.org
Control: Church–operated, Nongovernment, not–for profit **Service:** General Medical and Surgical

Staffed Beds: 221 **Admissions:** 11585 **Census:** 151 **Outpatient Visits:** 174377 **Births:** 1584 **Total Expense ($000):** 332004 **Payroll Expense ($000):** 105056 **Personnel:** 1740

MT

Hospital, Medicare Provider Number, Address, Telephone, Approval, Facility, and Physician Codes, Health Care System

★ American Hospital Association (AHA) membership   ○ Healthcare Facilities Accreditation Program   ⇑ Center for Improvement in Healthcare Quality Accreditation
☐ The Joint Commission accreditation   ◇ DNV Healthcare Inc. accreditation   △ Commission on Accreditation of Rehabilitation Facilities (CARF) accreditation

BOZEMAN—Gallatin County

✠ **BOZEMAN HEALTH DEACONESS HOSPITAL (270057)**, 915 Highland Boulevard, Zip 59715–6902; tel. 406/585–5000, (Nonreporting) **A**1 2 10 20 **S** Bozeman Health, Bozeman, MT
Primary Contact: John Hill, President and Chief Executive Officer
CFO: Gordon L. Davidson, Chief Financial Officer
CMO: David Chen, M.D., Chief Medical Officer
Web address: www.bozemandeaconess.org
Control: Corporation, Investor–owned, for–profit **Service:** General Medical and Surgical

Staffed Beds: 86

BUTTE—Silver Bow County

✠ **ST. JAMES HEALTHCARE (270017)**, 400 South Clark Street, Zip 59701–2328; tel. 406/723–2500 **A**1 10 **F**3 11 13 15 18 20 22 26 28 29 30 31 34 35 40 43 45 47 48 49 50 51 56 57 59 64 65 68 70 71 72 75 76 77 78 79 81 82 85 86 87 89 91 92 93 94 97 107 108 110 111 114 115 118 119 120 121 123 126 127 130 131 132 135 146 147 148 **S** SCL Health, Broomfield, CO
Primary Contact: Charles T. Wright, President and Chief Executive Officer
CFO: David Brain, Interim Vice President Finance
CMO: Dennis Salisbury, M.D., Vice President for Medical Affairs
CHR: Trisha Palmer, Director
CNO: Mary Winters, Interim Chief Nursing Officer
Web address: www.stjameshealthcare.org
Control: Other not–for–profit (including NFP Corporation) **Service:** General Medical and Surgical

Staffed Beds: 67 **Admissions:** 3231 **Census:** 34 **Outpatient Visits:** 62321 **Births:** 314 **Total Expense ($000):** 96404 **Payroll Expense ($000):** 32255 **Personnel:** 485

CHESTER—Liberty County

LIBERTY MEDICAL CENTER (271334), 315 West Madison Avenue, Zip 59522, Mailing Address: P.O. Box 705, Zip 59522–0705; tel. 406/759–5181 **A**10 18 **F**2 3 10 11 34 35 40 43 45 56 57 59 64 67 81 86 87 93 97 107 114 119 127 128 130 133 **P**6
Primary Contact: Derek Daly, Chief Executive Officer
CFO: Shari Dolan, Chief Financial Officer
CMO: Anna Earl, M.D., Chief of Staff
CHR: Bev Halter, Director Human Resources and Payroll
CNO: Shirley Morkrid, Chief Nursing Officer
Web address: www.lchnh.org
Control: Other not–for–profit (including NFP Corporation) **Service:** General Medical and Surgical

Staffed Beds: 25 **Admissions:** 41 **Census:** 1 **Outpatient Visits:** 9273 **Births:** 0 **Total Expense ($000):** 6378 **Payroll Expense ($000):** 3327 **Personnel:** 89

CHOTEAU—Teton County

★ **BENEFIS TETON MEDICAL CENTER (271307)**, 915 4th Street North West, Zip 59422–9123; tel. 406/466–5763, (Total facility includes 36 beds in nursing home–type unit) **A**10 18 **F**2 3 34 35 40 41 43 56 57 59 68 77 87 93 107 127 128 133 143 146 **S** Benefis Health System, Great Falls, MT
Primary Contact: Louie King, Chief Executive Officer
Web address: www.tetonmedicalcenter.net
Control: Hospital district or authority, Government, nonfederal **Service:** General Medical and Surgical

Staffed Beds: 46 **Admissions:** 195 **Census:** 24 **Outpatient Visits:** 7153 **Births:** 0 **Total Expense ($000):** 6437 **Payroll Expense ($000):** 3469 **Personnel:** 68

CIRCLE—McCone County

★ **MCCONE COUNTY HEALTH CENTER (271305)**, 605 Sullivan Avenue, Zip 59215, Mailing Address: P.O. Box 48, Zip 59215–0048; tel. 406/485–3381 **A**10 18 **F**2 3 11 34 40 41 58 65 69 86 87 93 133 135 143 146
Primary Contact: Nancy Rosaaen, Chief Executive Officer
CFO: Nancy Rosaaen, Chief Executive Officer
CHR: Jacque Gardner, Administrative Assistant, Clinic Manager, Co–Chief Financial Officer and Chief Human Resources
Web address: www.mcconehealth.org/
Control: County–Government, nonfederal **Service:** General Medical and Surgical

Staffed Beds: 25 **Admissions:** 66 **Census:** 23 **Outpatient Visits:** 3048 **Births:** 0 **Total Expense ($000):** 3460 **Payroll Expense ($000):** 1547 **Personnel:** 41

COLUMBUS—Stillwater County

★ **STILLWATER COMMUNITY HOSPITAL (271330)**, 44 West Fourth Avenue North, Zip 59019–0959, Mailing Address: P.O. Box 959, Zip 59019–0959; tel. 406/322–5316 **A**10 18 **F**3 15 28 29 32 34 35 40 43 45 50 57 59 62 64 65 68 75 83 91 107 110 114 127 133 144 **P**1
Primary Contact: Kelley Evans, Chief Administrative Officer
Web address: www.billingsclinic.com
Control: Other not–for–profit (including NFP Corporation) **Service:** General Medical and Surgical

Staffed Beds: 10 **Admissions:** 114 **Census:** 1 **Outpatient Visits:** 12221 **Births:** 0 **Total Expense ($000):** 8134 **Payroll Expense ($000):** 1878 **Personnel:** 42

CONRAD—Pondera County

PONDERA MEDICAL CENTER (271324), 805 Sunset Boulevard, Zip 59425–1717, Mailing Address: P.O. Box 668, Zip 59425–0668; tel. 406/271–3211, (Total facility includes 59 beds in nursing home–type unit) **A**10 18 **F**3 6 7 11 13 15 28 29 34 35 40 43 53 57 59 62 63 65 66 77 81 87 91 93 97 102 107 119 128 130 133 144 146 148 **P**6
Primary Contact: Bill O'Leary, Chief Executive Officer
CFO: Randy Nightengale, Chief Financial Officer
CMO: Jay Taylor, M.D., Chief of Staff
CIO: Sean Kavanagh, Director Information Technology
CHR: Patrick Johnson, Director Human Resources
Web address: www.ponderamedical.org
Control: Other not–for–profit (including NFP Corporation) **Service:** General Medical and Surgical

Staffed Beds: 79 **Admissions:** 137 **Census:** 53 **Outpatient Visits:** 6785 **Births:** 0 **Total Expense ($000):** 12593 **Payroll Expense ($000):** 6564 **Personnel:** 190

CROW AGENCY—Big Horn County

CROW/NORTHERN CHEYENNE HOSPITAL (271339), 10110 South 7650 East, Zip 59022–0009, Mailing Address: P.O. Box 9, Zip 59022–0009; tel. 406/638–2626, (Nonreporting) **A**10 18 **S** U. S. Indian Health Service, Rockville, MD
Primary Contact: Darren Crowe, Chief Executive Officer
CMO: Jim Upchurch, M.D., Chief Medical Officer
CIO: Melanie Falls Down, Site Manager
Web address: www.ihs.gov/facilitiesservices/areaoffices/billings/crow/index.asp
Control: Public Health Service, Government, federal **Service:** General Medical and Surgical

Staffed Beds: 24

CULBERTSON—Roosevelt County

★ **ROOSEVELT MEDICAL CENTER (271308)**, 818 Second Avenue East, Zip 59218, Mailing Address: P.O. Box 419, Zip 59218–0419; tel. 406/787–6401 **A**10 18 **F**2 3 7 15 34 35 40 43 50 56 57 59 65 69 77 93 97 119 127 128 130 133 143 146 **P**6
Primary Contact: Audrey Stromberg, Administrator
CFO: Jennifer Kessner, Financial Director
CMO: Don Helland, M.D., Chief Medical Officer
CIO: Brian Fordyce, Director Information Technology
CHR: Elizabeth Raaum, Manger Business Office
CNO: Jessica Schmitz, Director of Nursing
Web address: www.roosmem.org
Control: Other not–for–profit (including NFP Corporation) **Service:** General Medical and Surgical

Staffed Beds: 25 **Admissions:** 60 **Census:** 23 **Outpatient Visits:** 8881 **Births:** 1 **Total Expense ($000):** 5508 **Payroll Expense ($000):** 2973 **Personnel:** 58

CUT BANK—Glacier County

★ **NORTHERN ROCKIES MEDICAL CENTER (271337)**, 802 Second Street S.E., Zip 59427–3329; tel. 406/873–2251 **A**10 18 **F**57 59 65 76 81 93 107 119 127 128 133
Primary Contact: Cherie Taylor, Chief Executive Officer
CFO: Treasure Berkram, Chief Financial Officer
CMO: Adron Medley, M.D., Chief Medical Staff
CHR: Kandie Lemieux, Administrative Assistant and Director Human Resources
Web address: www.nrmcinc.org
Control: Other not–for–profit (including NFP Corporation) **Service:** General Medical and Surgical

Staffed Beds: 29 **Admissions:** 277 **Census:** 2 **Outpatient Visits:** 7324 **Births:** 60 **Total Expense ($000):** 5895 **Payroll Expense ($000):** 4189 **Personnel:** 87

MT

Many Facility Codes have changed. Please refer to the AHA Guide Code Chart.

DEER LODGE—Powell County

DEER LODGE MEDICAL CENTER (271314), 1100 Hollenbeck Lane,
Zip 59722–2317; tel. 406/846–2212, (Nonreporting) **A**10 18
Primary Contact: Tony Pfaff, Chief Executive Officer
CFO: Jaena Richards, Chief Financial Officer
CMO: Michelle Corbin, M.D., Chief of Staff
CIO: Chris Foster, Director Health Information Management
Web address: www.dlmed.org/
Control: Other not–for–profit (including NFP Corporation) **Service:** General
Medical and Surgical

Staffed Beds: 16

DILLON—Beaverhead County

★ **BARRETT HOSPITAL & HEALTHCARE (271318)**, 600 MT Highway 91,
Zip 59725–7379; tel. 406/683–3000 **A**5 10 18 **F**3 13 15 28 31 34 40 45 50
57 59 62 63 64 65 69 75 76 77 79 81 83 84 85 87 89 93 96 97 107 110
111 115 119 130 133 135 144 146 **P**6 **S** HealthTech Management Services,
Brentwood, TN
Primary Contact: Ken Westman, Chief Executive Officer
CFO: Dick Achter, Chief Financial Officer
CMO: Carol Kennedy, Chief Clinical Officer
CIO: Dick Achter, Chief Financial Officer
CHR: Geoff Roach, Director Human Resources
Web address: www.barretthospital.org
Control: Hospital district or authority, Government, nonfederal **Service:** General
Medical and Surgical

Staffed Beds: 18 **Admissions:** 478 **Census:** 4 **Outpatient Visits:** 32140
Births: 60 **Total Expense ($000):** 31511 **Payroll Expense ($000):** 14035
Personnel: 232

EKALAKA—Carter County

DAHL MEMORIAL HEALTHCARE ASSOCIATION (271302), 215 Sandy Street,
Zip 59324, Mailing Address: P.O. Box 46, Zip 59324–0046; tel. 406/775–8730,
(Total facility includes 23 beds in nursing home–type unit) **A**10 18 **F**2 7 40 41 57
59 65 69 127 128 130 131 133 135 143 146 148 **P**6
Primary Contact: Nadine Elmore, Chief Executive Officer
CFO: Nadine Elmore, Chief Executive Officer
CMO: Darryl Espeland, D.O., Medical Director
CIO: Davie Ann Barrere, Coordinator Information Technology
CHR: Melissa Matthews, Director Human Resources
CNO: Patricia Rogers, Director of Nursing
Web address: www.dahlmemorial.com
Control: Other not–for–profit (including NFP Corporation) **Service:** General
Medical and Surgical

Staffed Beds: 31 **Admissions:** 38 **Census:** 17 **Outpatient Visits:** 3612
Births: 0 **Total Expense ($000):** 2764 **Payroll Expense ($000):** 1305
Personnel: 31

ENNIS—Madison County

MADISON VALLEY MEDICAL CENTER (271329), 305 North Main Street,
Zip 59729–8001; tel. 406/682–4222, (Nonreporting) **A**10 18
Primary Contact: Allen Rohrback, Chief Executive Officer
CFO: John Bishop, Chief Executive Officer
CMO: Cindy Sharp, M.D., Chief Medical Officer
CIO: Bo Nix, Chief Information Officer
Web address: www.mvmedcenter.org
Control: Other not–for–profit (including NFP Corporation) **Service:** General
Medical and Surgical

Staffed Beds: 10

FORSYTH—Rosebud County

★ **ROSEBUD HEALTH CARE CENTER (271327)**, 383 North 17th Avenue,
Zip 59327–0268, Mailing Address: P.O. Box 268, Zip 59327–0268;
tel. 406/346–2161, (Nonreporting) **A**10 18
Primary Contact: Ryan Tooke, Chief Executive Officer
CMO: William Anderson, M.D., Medical Director
CHR: Karla Allies, Director Human Resources
Web address: www.rosebudhealthcare.com/
Control: Other not–for–profit (including NFP Corporation) **Service:** General
Medical and Surgical

Staffed Beds: 55

FORT BENTON—Chouteau County

MISSOURI RIVER MEDICAL CENTER (271304), 1501 St. Charles Street,
Zip 59442–0249, Mailing Address: P.O. Box 249, Zip 59442–0249;
tel. 406/622–3331, (Total facility includes 41 beds in nursing–type unit)
A10 18 **F**1 2 3 29 40 41 50 56 57 59 62 64 65 67 89 90 93 107 127 128
130 133 135 143 148 **P**6 **S** Benefis Health System, Great Falls, MT
Primary Contact: Louie King, President, Harry Bold Nursing Home Administrator
CMO: Jace Bird, M.D., Chief Medical Officer
CIO: Bryan Cartwright, Chief Information Technology Officer
CHR: Carolyn Johnsrud, Manager Human Resources
CNO: Janice Woodhouse, Director of Nursing
Web address: www.mrmcfb.org
Control: Hospital district or authority, Government, nonfederal **Service:**
Long–Term Acute Care hospital

Staffed Beds: 52 **Admissions:** 79 **Census:** 28 **Outpatient Visits:** 5387
Births: 0 **Total Expense ($000):** 5857 **Payroll Expense ($000):** 2978
Personnel: 63

FORT HARRISON—Lewis And Clark County

☒ **VETERANS AFFAIRS MONTANA HEALTH CARE SYSTEM**, 3687 Veterans
Drive, Zip 59636–9703, Mailing Address: P.O. Box 1500, Zip 59636–1500;
tel. 406/442–6410, (Total facility includes 30 beds in nursing home–type unit) **A**1
F3 4 5 28 29 30 31 33 35 36 38 39 40 44 45 50 51 53 54 55 56 59 63 64
65 66 70 71 74 75 77 78 79 81 82 83 84 85 87 91 92 93 94 97 100 101
102 103 104 105 106 107 108 111 115 116 117 118 119 127 129 130 132
135 143 144 146 147 148 **P**6 **S** Department of Veterans Affairs,
Washington, DC
Primary Contact: Dr. Kathy Berger, RN, Interim Director
CFO: Brian Gustafson, Chief Financial Officer
CMO: Kurt Werner, M.D., Chief of Staff
CIO: Paul Gauthier, Chief Information Resources Management
CHR: Aggie Hamilton, Chief Human Resources
Web address: www.montana.va.gov/
Control: Veterans Affairs, Government, federal **Service:** General Medical and
Surgical

Staffed Beds: 65 **Admissions:** 2171 **Census:** 37 **Outpatient Visits:** 480056
Births: 0 **Total Expense ($000):** 331485 **Payroll Expense ($000):** 87032
Personnel: 1177

GLASGOW—Valley County

☒ **FRANCES MAHON DEACONESS HOSPITAL (271316)**, 621 Third Street
South, Zip 59230–2699; tel. 406/228–3500 **A**1 10 18 **F**3 7 11 13 15 28 29
30 31 34 35 40 42 43 53 56 57 59 61 64 70 75 76 78 79 81 82 86 87 89
93 100 102 105 107 108 110 111 114 118 119 127 128 130 131 133 135
145 146 **P**6 7
Primary Contact: Randall G. Holom, Chief Executive Officer
COO: Ellen Guttenberg, Chief Operating Officer
CFO: Cami Kalinski, Director Financial Services
CMO: Gordon Bell, M.D., Chief of Staff
CIO: David L. Nixdorf, Director Support Services
CHR: Charam Orth, Director Human Resources
CNO: Brenda Koessl, R.N., Director of Nursing Services
Web address: www.fmdh.org
Control: Other not–for–profit (including NFP Corporation) **Service:** General
Medical and Surgical

Staffed Beds: 25 **Admissions:** 566 **Census:** 5 **Outpatient Visits:** 34356
Births: 130 **Total Expense ($000):** 21563 **Payroll Expense ($000):** 9834
Personnel: 161

GLENDIVE—Dawson County

★ **GLENDIVE MEDICAL CENTER (271332)**, 202 Prospect Drive,
Zip 59330–1999; tel. 406/345–3306, (Total facility includes 71 beds in nursing
home–type unit) **A**10 18 **F**3 10 11 13 15 28 29 30 31 35 38 40 41 43 50 56
57 59 61 62 63 64 67 69 70 75 76 77 78 79 81 82 87 89 93 94 98 102
104 107 108 111 115 119 127 128 130 131 132 133 143 144 146 147 148
P6 7 8
Primary Contact: Parker Powell, Chief Executive Officer
CFO: Barbara Markham, Chief Financial Officer
CMO: Joseph M. Leal, Jr., M.D., Chief of Staff
CIO: Barbara Markham, Chief Financial Officer
CHR: Joetta J. Pearcy, Director, Human Resources
Web address: www.gmc.org
Control: Other not–for–profit (including NFP Corporation) **Service:** General
Medical and Surgical

Staffed Beds: 96 **Admissions:** 691 **Census:** 55 **Outpatient Visits:** 30230
Births: 108 **Total Expense ($000):** 29836 **Payroll Expense ($000):** 12628
Personnel: 237

MT

Hospital, Medicare Provider Number, Address, Telephone, Approval, Facility, and Physician Codes, Health Care System

★ American Hospital Association (AHA) membership   ○ Healthcare Facilities Accreditation Program   ⇑ Center for Improvement in Healthcare Quality Accreditation
☐ The Joint Commission accreditation   ◇ DNV Healthcare Inc. accreditation   △ Commission on Accreditation of Rehabilitation Facilities (CARF) accreditation

---

GREAT FALLS—Cascade County

△ **BENEFIS HEALTH SYSTEM (270012)**, 1101 26th Street South,
Zip 59405–5104; tel. 406/455–5000, (Includes BENEFIS HEALTH CARE–EAST
CAMPUS, 1101 26th Street, Zip 59405; tel. 406/761–1200; BENEFIS HEALTH
CARE–WEST CAMPUS, 500 15th Avenue South, Zip 59405, Mailing Address: P.O.
Box 5013, Zip 59403–5013; tel. 406/727–3333), (Total facility includes 146
beds in nursing home–type unit) **A**2 7 10 20 **F**3 4 5 6 8 10 11 12 13 15 18 20
22 24 26 28 29 30 31 34 35 36 37 38 40 43 45 48 49 50 52 53 54 55 56
57 58 59 61 62 63 64 65 70 71 72 73 74 75 76 77 78 79 81 82 83 84 85
86 87 88 89 90 92 93 96 97 98 100 101 102 103 104 105 107 108 110
111 114 115 116 117 119 120 121 123 124 126 127 128 129 130 131 132
133 134 135 136 141 143 144 145 146 147 148 **P**6 8 **S** Benefis Health
System, Great Falls, MT
Primary Contact: John H. Goodnow, Chief Executive Officer
CFO: Forrest Ehlinger, System Chief Financial Officer
CMO: Gregory Tierney, M.D., President, BMG and BHS Chief Medical Officer
CIO: Mark Simon, System Chief Information Officer
CNO: Rayn Ginnaty, Vice President Nursing
Web address: www.benefis.org
Control: Other not–for–profit (including NFP Corporation) **Service:** General
Medical and Surgical

Staffed Beds: 507 Admissions: 12495 Census: 342 Outpatient Visits:
489511 Births: 1502 Total Expense ($000): 387347 Payroll Expense
($000): 167482 Personnel: 2478

GREAT FALLS CLINIC MEDICAL CENTER (270086), 1400 29th Street South,
Zip 59405–5353; tel. 406/216–8000, (Nonreporting) **A**10
Primary Contact: Vicki Newhiller, Chief Executive Officer
COO: Vicki Newmiller, Chief Operating Officer
CFO: Cheryl Cornwell, Chief Financial Officer
CMO: Nicholas Bonfilio, M.D., Chief of Staff
Web address: www.greatfallsclinicmedicalcenter.com
Control: Corporation, Investor–owned, for–profit **Service:** Surgical

Staffed Beds: 20

HAMILTON—Ravalli County

★ **MARCUS DALY MEMORIAL HOSPITAL (271340)**, 1200 Westwood Drive,
Zip 59840–2345; tel. 406/363–2211 **A**10 18 **F**3 7 8 11 13 15 17 28 29 30
34 35 40 45 50 57 59 62 63 64 65 70 74 75 76 77 79 81 83 84 89 93 97
102 105 107 110 111 115 119 127 128 129 130 131 132 133 144 145
146 148
Primary Contact: John M. Bartos, Chief Executive Officer
CFO: Donja Erdman, Chief Financial Officer
CMO: John Moreland, M.D., Chief Medical Officer
CIO: Brad Kowalski, Director Information Technology
CHR: Debbie M. Morris, Director Human Resources
CNO: Kathy Padilla, Director of Nursing
Web address: www.mdmh.org
Control: Other not–for–profit (including NFP Corporation) **Service:** General
Medical and Surgical

Staffed Beds: 31 Admissions: 1454 Census: 13 Outpatient Visits: 50229
Births: 141 Total Expense ($000): 52841 Payroll Expense ($000): 28002
Personnel: 442

HARDIN—Big Horn County

★ **BIG HORN COUNTY MEMORIAL HOSPITAL (271338)**, 17 North Miles Avenue,
Zip 59034–2323; tel. 406/665–2310, (Total facility includes 36 beds in nursing
home–type unit) **A**10 18 **F**10 11 15 40 43 50 57 59 64 65 68 75 76 77 81 85
86 87 93 107 110 111 114 119 125 128 130 132 133 143 146
Primary Contact: Kristi Gatrell, Chief Executive Officer
CFO: Roxie Cain, Chief Financial Officer
CHR: Paula Small–Plenty, Human Resources Officer
CNO: Kirsten Willoughby, Director of Nursing
Web address: www.bighornhospital.org
Control: Other not–for–profit (including NFP Corporation) **Service:** General
Medical and Surgical

Staffed Beds: 61 Admissions: 404 Census: 42 Outpatient Visits: 7750
Births: 42 Total Expense ($000): 13648 Payroll Expense ($000): 7392
Personnel: 154

HARLEM—Blaine County

**FORT BELKNAP U. S. PUBLIC HEALTH SERVICE INDIAN HOSPITAL
(271315)**, 669 Agency Main Street, Zip 59526–9455; tel. 406/353–3100,
(Nonreporting) **A**10 18 **S** U. S. Indian Health Service, Rockville, MD
Primary Contact: Alan Barlow, Chief Executive Officer
CMO: Ethel L. Moore, M.D., Director of Medical Affairs
CIO: Mikki Grant, Chief Information Officer
CHR: Charlotte Lamebull, Administrative Officer
CNO: Diana Hunter, Director of Nursing
Web address: www.ihs.gov
Control: PHS, Indian Service, Government, federal **Service:** General Medical and
Surgical

Staffed Beds: 6

HARLOWTON—Wheatland County

★ **WHEATLAND MEMORIAL HEALTHCARE (271321)**, 530 Third Street North
West, Zip 59036, Mailing Address: P.O. Box 287, Zip 59036–0287;
tel. 406/632–4351, (Nonreporting) **A**10 18
Primary Contact: Bradley Howell, Interim Chief Executive Officer
CFO: Doug Lewis, Chief Financial Officer
CMO: Kathy Jutila, M.D., Chief of Staff
CIO: Ray Hetherington, Network Administrator
CHR: Peggy Hiner, Director Human Resources
CNO: Lauri Ann Cooney, Director Nursing
Web address: www.wheatlandmemorial.org
Control: Other not–for–profit (including NFP Corporation) **Service:** General
Medical and Surgical

Staffed Beds: 25

HAVRE—Hill County

★ **NORTHERN MONTANA HOSPITAL (270032)**, 30 13th Street,
Zip 59501–5222, Mailing Address: P.O. Box 1231, Zip 59501–1231;
tel. 406/265–2211, (Total facility includes 115 beds in nursing–type unit)
A10 20 **F**10 11 13 15 28 29 34 35 36 38 40 43 45 50 53 56 57 59 60 63
64 68 70 75 76 77 79 81 82 84 85 89 93 97 99 101 102 103 104 105 107
108 110 111 115 118 119 127 128 129 130 132 133 135 146 148 **P**6
Primary Contact: David Henry, President and Chief Executive Officer
COO: Julia Mariani, Vice President Business Operations
CFO: Kim Lucke, Vice President Finance
CNO: Eric Koch, Chief Nursing Officer
Web address: www.nmhcare.org
Control: Other not–for–profit (including NFP Corporation) **Service:** General
Medical and Surgical

Staffed Beds: 142 Admissions: 1625 Census: 111 Outpatient Visits: 96535
Births: 398 Total Expense ($000): 57587 Payroll Expense ($000): 30491
Personnel: 512

HELENA—Lewis And Clark County

⊠ **SHODAIR CHILDREN'S HOSPITAL (274004)**, 2755 Colonial Drive,
Zip 59601–4926, Mailing Address: P.O. Box 5539, Zip 59604–5539;
tel. 406/444–7500 **A**1 10 **F**55 98 99 101 104 106 130 **P**6
Primary Contact: Craig E. Aasved, Chief Executive Officer
CFO: Ron Wiens, Chief Financial Officer
CMO: Heather Zaluski, M.D., President Medical Staff
CIO: Judy Jackson, Director Health Information Management and Privacy Officer
CNO: Christine Bates, Chief Nursing Officer
Web address: www.shodair.org
Control: Other not–for–profit (including NFP Corporation) **Service:** Children's
hospital psychiatric

Staffed Beds: 84 Admissions: 864 Census: 63 Outpatient Visits: 2958
Births: 0 Total Expense ($000): 22690 Payroll Expense ($000): 13462
Personnel: 338

⊠ **ST. PETER'S HOSPITAL (270003)**, 2475 Broadway, Zip 59601–4928;
tel. 406/442–2480 **A**1 2 10 20 **F**3 7 11 13 15 18 20 22 28 29 30 31 34 35
40 43 45 46 49 50 51 54 56 57 59 60 62 63 64 65 70 74 75 76 78 79 81
82 84 85 87 89 92 93 98 100 102 103 107 108 110 111 114 115 116 117
119 120 121 122 129 130 132 133 135 144 146 147 148 **P**6
Primary Contact: Fred Olson, Interim Chief Executive Officer
CFO: John Green, Vice President Finance
CIO: Tammy K. Buyok, Vice President Support Services
CHR: Thomas Gregg, Vice President Human Resources
Web address: www.stpetes.org
Control: Other not–for–profit (including NFP Corporation) **Service:** General
Medical and Surgical

Staffed Beds: 123 Admissions: 5596 Census: 77 Outpatient Visits: 206570
Births: 775 Total Expense ($000): 175488 Payroll Expense ($000): 71899
Personnel: 1050

JORDAN—Garfield County

GARFIELD COUNTY HEALTH CENTER (271310), 332 Leavitt Avenue,
Zip 59337, Mailing Address: P.O. Box 389, Zip 59337–0389;
tel. 406/557–2500, (Nonreporting) **A**10 18
Primary Contact: Chris Hopkins, Chief Executive Officer
CFO: Charlotte Herbold, Manager Business Officer
CMO: David M. Kidder, D.O., Chief Medical Officer
CIO: Charlotte Herbold, Manager Business Officer
CHR: Hanz Arnston, R.N., Chief Executive Officer
CNO: Sarah Nordlund, Director of Nursing
Control: County–Government, nonfederal **Service:** General Medical and Surgical

Staffed Beds: 24

KALISPELL—Flathead County

HEALTHCENTER NORTHWEST See The HealthCenter

MT

★ △ **KALISPELL REGIONAL HEALTHCARE (270051)**, 310 Sunnyview Lane, Zip 59901–3129; tel. 406/752–5111, (Includes PATHWAYS TREATMENT CENTER, 200 Heritage Way, Zip 59901; tel. 406/756–3950) **A**2 3 5 7 10 **F**3 4 5 8 13 15 18 20 22 24 26 28 29 30 31 35 36 40 43 45 46 49 50 56 57 58 59 62 63 64 68 70 72 74 75 76 77 78 79 81 84 85 86 87 89 98 99 100 101 102 103 104 105 107 108 114 115 118 119 120 121 123 126 129 130 131 132 143 144 145 146 147 148 **P**6
Primary Contact: Velinda Stevens, President
COO: Ted W. Hirsch, Senior Executive Director
CFO: Charles T. Pearce, Chief Financial and Information Officer
CHR: Deb Wilson, Director Human Resources
Web address: www.krmc.org
Control: Other not-for-profit (including NFP Corporation) **Service:** General Medical and Surgical

Staffed Beds: 160 **Admissions:** 7731 **Census:** 98 **Outpatient Visits:** 198396 **Births:** 640 **Total Expense ($000):** 269133 **Payroll Expense ($000):** 124813 **Personnel:** 3559

★ **THE HEALTHCENTER (270087)**, 320 Sunnyview Lane, Zip 59901–3129; tel. 406/751–7550 **A**10 **F**3 8 15 31 36 39 64 68 74 78 79 81 82 85 87 90 93 96 97 100 107 110 111 114 115 117 119 126 147 **P**6
Primary Contact: Tate J. Kreitinger, Chief Executive Officer
CFO: Charles T. Pearce, Chief Financial and Information Officer
CIO: Charles T. Pearce, Chief Financial and Information Officer
CHR: Susan Stevens, Director Human Resources
CNO: Victoria Johnson, R.N., Nursing Director of Surgical and Medical Services
Web address: www.krmc.org
Control: Corporation, Investor-owned, for-profit **Service:** General Medical and Surgical

Staffed Beds: 30 **Admissions:** 600 **Census:** 4 **Outpatient Visits:** 34736 **Births:** 0 **Total Expense ($000):** 36805 **Payroll Expense ($000):** 8003 **Personnel:** 198

LEWISTOWN—Fergus County

★ **CENTRAL MONTANA MEDICAL CENTER (271345)**, 408 Wendell Avenue, Zip 59457–2261; tel. 406/535–7711, (Nonreporting) **A**10 18
Primary Contact: Michael Dowdy, Chief Executive Officer
CFO: Alan Aldrich, Chief Financial Officer
CHR: Torie A. Lynch, Manager Human Resources
CNO: Delilah Duffy, Interim Chief Nurse Officer
Web address: www.cmmccares.com
Control: Other not-for-profit (including NFP Corporation) **Service:** General Medical and Surgical

Staffed Beds: 90

LIBBY—Lincoln County

★ **CABINET PEAKS MEDICAL CENTER (271320)**, 209 Health Park Drive, Zip 59923–2130; tel. 406/283–7000 **A**5 10 18 **F**3 11 13 15 17 28 29 30 31 34 35 40 45 50 56 57 59 64 68 70 75 76 77 79 81 84 85 86 87 89 91 93 97 102 107 110 111 114 119 128 129 130 131 132 133 135 144 146 147 148 **P**6
Primary Contact: Bruce Whitfield, CPA, Chief Executive Officer and Chief Financial Officer
CFO: Bruce Whitfield, CPA, Chief Executive Officer and Chief Financial Officer
CMO: Jay Maloney, M.D., Chief of Staff
Web address: www.sjlh.com
Control: Other not-for-profit (including NFP Corporation) **Service:** General Medical and Surgical

Staffed Beds: 25 **Admissions:** 778 **Census:** 7 **Outpatient Visits:** 34223 **Births:** 112 **Total Expense ($000):** 28782 **Payroll Expense ($000):** 12646 **Personnel:** 212

LIVINGSTON—Park County

★ **LIVINGSTON HEALTHCARE (271317)**, 320 Alpenglow Lane, Zip 59047–8506; tel. 406/222–3541 **A**5 10 18 **F**3 13 15 17 28 29 31 34 35 36 40 43 45 50 57 59 62 63 64 65 66 67 68 70 75 76 77 78 79 81 82 85 86 87 89 93 100 101 102 104 107 108 110 111 114 119 124 128 129 130 131 133 135 **P**3
Primary Contact: Bren Lowe, Chief Executive Officer
CFO: Ryan Speas, Director Finance
CMO: D. Scott Coleman, Medical Director
CIO: Jody Duran, Manager Information Systems
CHR: Vicki Axtell, Director Human Resources
CNO: Dave Noble, Director of Nursing
Web address: www.livingstonhealthcare.org
Control: Other not-for-profit (including NFP Corporation) **Service:** General Medical and Surgical

Staffed Beds: 25 **Admissions:** 1055 **Census:** 11 **Outpatient Visits:** 25485 **Births:** 91 **Total Expense ($000):** 32524 **Payroll Expense ($000):** 16080 **Personnel:** 288

MALTA—Phillips County

★ **PHILLIPS COUNTY HOSPITAL (271312)**, 311 South 8th Avenue East, Zip 59538–0640, Mailing Address: P.O. Box 640, Zip 59538–0640; tel. 406/654–1100 **A**10 18 **F**3 29 31 34 40 41 43 56 57 59 62 66 84 90 91 93 107 114 127 130 132 133 **P**4
Primary Contact: Ward C. VanWichen, Chief Executive Officer
CFO: Stephanie Denham, Chief Financial Officer and Human Resources Officer
CMO: Ed Medina, M.D., Medical Director
CHR: Stephanie Denham, Chief Financial Officer and Human Resources Officer
CNO: Lonna Crowder, Director of Nursing
Web address: www.pchospital.us/
Control: Other not-for-profit (including NFP Corporation) **Service:** General Medical and Surgical

Staffed Beds: 6 **Admissions:** 206 **Census:** 2 **Outpatient Visits:** 6743 **Births:** 0 **Total Expense ($000):** 5486 **Payroll Expense ($000):** 2777 **Personnel:** 64

MILES CITY—Custer County

✠ **HOLY ROSARY HEALTHCARE (271347)**, 2600 Wilson Street, Zip 59301–5094; tel. 406/233–2600, (Total facility includes 65 beds in nursing home–type unit) **A**1 10 18 **F**3 13 15 28 29 30 31 32 34 37 39 45 48 56 57 59 63 64 65 68 70 75 76 77 78 79 81 84 85 89 93 94 97 99 100 101 103 104 107 108 110 111 115 119 124 127 129 130 131 133 135 143 144 146 147 148 **P**6 **S** SCL Health, Broomfield, CO
Primary Contact: Paul Lewis, Chief Executive Officer
CFO: Travis Scheving, Chief Financial Officer
CMO: Michael Bush, M.D., Chief Medical Officer
CHR: Cathy Rodenbaugh, Director Human Resources
CNO: Lisa Sanford, VP Patient Care/CNO
Web address: www.holyrosaryhealthcare.org
Control: Church-operated, Nongovernment, not-for profit **Service:** General Medical and Surgical

Staffed Beds: 90 **Admissions:** 1334 **Census:** 107 **Outpatient Visits:** 29761 **Births:** 303 **Total Expense ($000):** 33526 **Payroll Expense ($000):** 12950 **Personnel:** 218

MISSOULA—Missoula County

✠ △ **COMMUNITY MEDICAL CENTER (270023)**, 2827 Fort Missoula Road, Zip 59804–7408; tel. 406/728–4100 **A**1 3 5 7 10 19 **F**3 11 13 15 17 18 20 22 26 28 29 30 31 34 35 37 40 43 46 47 48 49 51 54 57 59 64 65 68 70 72 74 75 78 79 81 82 83 84 85 87 88 90 91 92 93 94 96 97 107 108 110 111 114 115 116 117 118 119 120 121 123 124 126 130 132 134 135 141 143 144 145 146 147 148 **P**6 7
Primary Contact: Dean French, M.D., Chief Executive Officer
COO: Devin Huntley, Vice President Operations
CFO: David Richhart, Vice President Fiscal Services
CMO: David Lechner, M.D., Chief Medical Officer and Vice President Innovation
CNO: Jan Perry, R.N., Vice President Patient Care Services
Web address: www.communitymed.org
Control: Corporation, Investor-owned, for-profit **Service:** General Medical and Surgical

Staffed Beds: 135 **Admissions:** 4789 **Census:** 64 **Outpatient Visits:** 132037 **Births:** 1399 **Total Expense ($000):** 158301 **Payroll Expense ($000):** 59626 **Personnel:** 939

✠ △ **ST. PATRICK HOSPITAL (270014)**, 500 West Broadway, Zip 59802–4096, Mailing Address: P.O. Box 4587, Zip 59806–4587; tel. 406/543–7271 **A**1 2 3 5 7 10 19 **F**3 5 8 11 12 13 15 18 20 22 24 26 28 29 30 31 34 35 38 40 43 45 46 48 49 50 53 57 58 59 60 61 64 65 68 70 74 75 77 78 79 81 82 84 85 86 88 89 90 92 93 96 97 98 99 100 101 102 103 104 105 107 108 109 110 111 113 114 115 116 117 118 119 120 121 123 124 126 127 129 130 131 132 135 141 146 147 148 **P**4 **S** Providence St. Joseph Health, Renton, WA
Primary Contact: Jeff Fee, Chief Executive Officer
CFO: Kirk Bodlovic, Regional Chief Financial Officer
CHR: Karyn Trainor, Director Human Resources
CNO: Joyce Dombrouski, R.N., Regional Chief Nursing Officer
Web address: www.saintpatrick.org
Control: Church-operated, Nongovernment, not-for profit **Service:** General Medical and Surgical

Staffed Beds: 200 **Admissions:** 9558 **Census:** 124 **Outpatient Visits:** 286321 **Births:** 189 **Total Expense ($000):** 210600 **Payroll Expense ($000):** 66958 **Personnel:** 1483

MT

Hospital, Medicare Provider Number, Address, Telephone, Approval, Facility, and Physician Codes, Health Care System

★ American Hospital Association (AHA) membership ○ Healthcare Facilities Accreditation Program ⇑ Center for Improvement in Healthcare Quality Accreditation
□ The Joint Commission accreditation ◇ DNV Healthcare Inc. accreditation △ Commission on Accreditation of Rehabilitation Facilities (CARF) accreditation

MT

PHILIPSBURG—Granite County

GRANITE COUNTY MEDICAL CENTER (271303), 310 Sansome Street,
Zip 59858–0729, Mailing Address: P.O. Box 729, Zip 59858–0729;
tel. 406/859–3271, (Nonreporting) **A**10 18
Primary Contact: Maria Stoppler, Chief Executive Officer
CFO: Susan Ossello, Chief Financial Officer
CMO: John Moore, M.D., Medical Director
Web address: www.gcmedcenter.org/
Control: County–Government, nonfederal **Service:** General Medical and Surgical

Staffed Beds: 25

PLAINS—Sanders County

★ **CLARK FORK VALLEY HOSPITAL (271323)**, 10 Kruger Road, Zip 59859,
Mailing Address: P.O. Box 768, Zip 59859–0768; tel. 406/826–4800, (Total
facility includes 28 beds in nursing home–type unit) **A**10 18 **F**3 11 13 15 28 29
30 32 34 35 36 40 43 44 45 50 57 58 59 62 63 64 65 68 70 74 75 76 77
81 82 83 84 85 87 89 91 93 97 107 110 114 118 119 127 128 130 132
133 135 143 146 147 148 **P**3 6
Primary Contact: Gregory S. Hanson, M.D., Chief Executive Officer
CFO: Carla Neiman, Chief Financial Officer
CMO: Jeanne Williams, M.D., Chief of Staff
CIO: Carla Neiman, Chief Financial Officer
CHR: Barry Fowler, Director Human and System Resources
CNO: Lisa Eberhardt, Chief Nursing Officer
Web address: www.cfvh.org
Control: Other not–for–profit (including NFP Corporation) **Service:** General Medical and Surgical

Staffed Beds: 44 **Admissions:** 397 **Census:** 39 **Outpatient Visits:** 28293
Births: 57 **Total Expense ($000):** 17604 **Payroll Expense ($000):** 8072
Personnel: 126

PLENTYWOOD—Sheridan County

SHERIDAN MEMORIAL HOSPITAL (271322), 440 West Laurel Avenue,
Zip 59254–1596; tel. 406/765–3700, (Total facility includes 78 beds in nursing
home–type unit) **A**10 18 **F**3 7 11 13 15 17 29 30 35 40 50 56 59 62 63 64 70
75 77 80 81 87 93 97 107 110 114 119 127 128 130 132 133 145 146
147 148
Primary Contact: Gregory L. Maurer, Chief Executive Officer
CIO: Troy McClymont, Chief Information Technology Officer
Web address: www.sheridanmemorial.net/
Control: Other not–for–profit (including NFP Corporation) **Service:** General Medical and Surgical

Staffed Beds: 97 **Admissions:** 261 **Census:** 52 **Outpatient Visits:** 18225
Births: 0 **Total Expense ($000):** 12235 **Personnel:** 116

POLSON—Lake County

⊠ **PROVIDENCE ST. JOSEPH MEDICAL CENTER (271343)**, 6 Thirteenth Avenue
East, Zip 59860–5315, Mailing Address: P.O. Box 1010, Zip 59860–1010;
tel. 406/883–5377 **A**1 10 18 **F**3 10 13 15 28 29 30 34 35 40 43 46 50 57
59 64 68 75 76 77 79 81 82 85 87 89 93 97 100 102 107 110 111 114 119
125 127 129 130 131 133 146 147 148 **P**6 **S** Providence St. Joseph Health,
Renton, WA
Primary Contact: James R. Kiser, II, Chief Executive Officer
COO: Colleen Nielsen, Director Operations
CFO: Kirk Bodlovic, Vice President and Chief Financial Officer
CMO: Kelly Bagnell, M.D., Chief of Staff
Web address: www.saintjoes.org
Control: Church–operated, Nongovernment, not–for profit **Service:** General Medical and Surgical

Staffed Beds: 22 **Admissions:** 622 **Census:** 6 **Outpatient Visits:** 77090
Births: 137 **Total Expense ($000):** 23886 **Payroll Expense ($000):** 13775
Personnel: 171

POPLAR—Roosevelt County

★ **POPLAR COMMUNITY HOSPITAL (271300)**, 211 H Street, Zip 59255–9519,
Mailing Address: P.O. Box 38, Zip 59255–0038; tel. 406/768–3452 **A**10 18 **F**1
3 7 17 40 43 50 57 59 67 70 73 78 87 88 89 98 99 100 101 102 103 104
107 110 119 128 130 133 143 147 **P**3 6
Primary Contact: Margaret B. Norgaard, Chief Executive Officer
CHR: Annie Block, Director Human Resources
Web address: www.nemhs.net
Control: Other not–for–profit (including NFP Corporation) **Service:** General Medical and Surgical

Staffed Beds: 20 **Admissions:** 115 **Census:** 4 **Outpatient Visits:** 7865
Births: 3 **Total Expense ($000):** 9025 **Payroll Expense ($000):** 4426
Personnel: 87

RED LODGE—Carbon County

★ **BEARTOOTH BILLINGS CLINIC (271326)**, 2525 North Broadway Avenue,
Zip 59068–9222, Mailing Address: P.O. Box 590, Zip 59068–0590;
tel. 406/446–2345, (Data for 181 days) **A**10 18 **F**3 11 15 18 28 29 34 35 40
43 44 45 50 56 57 59 62 63 64 65 68 75 77 81 84 85 86 87 91 93 94 96
97 107 110 114 119 130 131 133 135 146 147 148 **P**6
Primary Contact: Kelley Evans, Chief Administrative Officer
CFO: Kyle Gee, Chief Financial Officer
CMO: William George, M.D., Chief of Staff
CHR: Katie Nordstrom, Director Human Resources
CNO: Bridgett Chartier, Director of Nursing
Web address: www.beartoothbillingsclinic.org
Control: Other not–for–profit (including NFP Corporation) **Service:** General Medical and Surgical

Staffed Beds: 10 **Admissions:** 141 **Census:** 4 **Outpatient Visits:** 31541
Births: 0 **Total Expense ($000):** 6216 **Payroll Expense ($000):** 2083
Personnel: 97

RONAN—Lake County

★ **ST. LUKE COMMUNITY HEALTHCARE (271325)**, 107 Sixth Avenue S.W.,
Zip 59864–2634; tel. 406/676–4441, (Total facility includes 75 beds in nursing
home–type unit) **A**10 18 **F**2 13 15 28 29 34 40 43 45 53 54 56 57 59 61 64
65 68 75 76 79 81 85 93 97 107 108 110 111 115 119 127 128 129 130
131 132 133 135 144 145 147 **P**6
Primary Contact: Steve J. Todd, Chief Executive Officer
CFO: Paul Soukup, Chief Financial Officer
CMO: Hikmat A. Maaliki, M.D., Chief of Staff
CHR: Theresa Jones, Manager Human Resources
CNO: Leah Emerson, Director of Nursing
Web address: www.stlukehealthcare.org
Control: Other not–for–profit (including NFP Corporation) **Service:** General Medical and Surgical

Staffed Beds: 100 **Admissions:** 996 **Census:** 61 **Outpatient Visits:** 74248
Births: 137 **Total Expense ($000):** 36033 **Payroll Expense ($000):** 17642
Personnel: 303

ROUNDUP—Musselshell County

★ **ROUNDUP MEMORIAL HEALTHCARE (271346)**, 1202 Third Street West,
Zip 59072–1816, Mailing Address: P.O. Box 40, Zip 59072–0040;
tel. 406/323–2301 **A**10 18 **F**11 29 30 34 35 40 45 50 57 59 65 66 85 87 97
102 107 119 127 130 132 133 146
Primary Contact: Bradley Howell, Chief Executive Officer
CFO: Kyle Gee, Regional Vice President Financial Operations
CMO: Mark Ward, M.D., Chief of Staff
CHR: Michelle Clement, Executive Assistant/Human Resources Director
CNO: Emily Shoup, Director Nursing Services
Web address: www.rmhmt.org
Control: Other not–for–profit (including NFP Corporation) **Service:** General Medical and Surgical

Staffed Beds: 25 **Admissions:** 117 **Census:** 1 **Outpatient Visits:** 10024

SAINT MARY—Glacier County

**U. S. PUBLIC HEALTH SERVICE BLACKFEET COMMUNITY HOSPITAL
(270074)**, 760 New Hospital Circle, Zip 59417–0760, Mailing Address: P.O. Box
760, Browning, Zip 59417–0760; tel. 406/338–6100, (Nonreporting) **A**5 10 **S** U.
S. Indian Health Service, Rockville, MD
Primary Contact: Dee Hutchison, Chief Executive Officer
CFO: Cleo Main, Finance Officer
CMO: Neil Sun Rhodes, M.D., Chief Medical Officer
CNO: Susan Head, Director Nursing Services
Web address: www.ihs.gov
Control: PHS, Indian Service, Government, federal **Service:** General Medical and Surgical

Staffed Beds: 25

SCOBEY—Daniels County

DANIELS MEMORIAL HEALTHCARE CENTER (271342), 105 Fifth Avenue
East, Zip 59263, Mailing Address: P.O. Box 400, Zip 59263–0400;
tel. 406/487–2296, (Total facility includes 30 beds in nursing home–type unit)
A10 18 **F**2 11 29 34 35 40 43 50 56 59 64 65 67 69 75 77 85 86 87 91 93
97 107 114 119 127 130 133 143 146 148 **P**6
Primary Contact: David Ryerse, Chief Executive Officer
CMO: Don Sawdey, M.D., Medical Director
CHR: Edith Huda, Director Human Resources
CNO: Kathy Ware, Director of Nursing
Web address: www.danielsmemorialhealthcare.org
Control: Hospital district or authority, Government, nonfederal **Service:** General Medical and Surgical

Staffed Beds: 54 **Admissions:** 65 **Census:** 24 **Outpatient Visits:** 7210
Births: 0 **Total Expense ($000):** 7232 **Payroll Expense ($000):** 3184
Personnel: 91

Many Facility Codes have changed. Please refer to the AHA Guide Code Chart.

SHELBY—Toole County

★ **MARIAS MEDICAL CENTER (271328)**, 640 Park Drive, Zip 59474–1663, Mailing Address: P.O. Box 915, Zip 59474–0915; tel. 406/434–3200, (Total facility includes 63 beds in nursing home–type unit) **A**10 18 **F**3 7 10 11 13 15 17 28 34 40 45 56 57 59 64 70 76 77 81 85 89 91 93 102 107 110 111 114 119 125 128 129 130 133
Primary Contact: Jessica Brusven, Chief Executive Officer
CFO: Melissa Ostberg, Chief Financial Officer
CMO: Melanie Hardy, D.O., Chief of Staff
CIO: Jayce Yarn, Director Information Technology
CHR: Cindy Lamb, Director Human Resources
CNO: Tamra Fender, Chief Nursing Officer
Web address: www.mmcmt.org
Control: County–Government, nonfederal **Service:** General Medical and Surgical

Staffed Beds: 84 **Admissions:** 246 **Census:** 36 **Outpatient Visits:** 10910 **Births:** 32 **Total Expense ($000):** 14655 **Payroll Expense ($000):** 5690 **Personnel:** 146

SHERIDAN—Madison County

★ **RUBY VALLEY HOSPITAL (271319)**, 220 East Crofoot Street, Zip 59749–7714, Mailing Address: P.O. Box 336, Zip 59749–0336; tel. 406/842–5453 **A**10 18 **F**2 11 28 29 34 35 38 40 43 56 57 59 64 65 66 75 82 86 90 91 93 97 107 114 119 127 128 130 133 135 147 148 **P**6
Primary Contact: John H. Semingson, Chief Executive Officer
CFO: Dennis Holschbach, Chief Financial Officer and Director Human Resources
CMO: Roman Hendrickson, M.D., Medical Director
CHR: Dennis Holschbach, Chief Financial Officer and Director Human Resources
CNO: Ted Woirhaye, R.N., Director of Nursing
Web address: www.rubyvalleyhospital.com/
Control: Hospital district or authority, Government, nonfederal **Service:** General Medical and Surgical

Staffed Beds: 8 **Admissions:** 155 **Census:** 2 **Outpatient Visits:** 3902 **Births:** 0 **Total Expense ($000):** 5424 **Payroll Expense ($000):** 3210 **Personnel:** 53

SIDNEY—Richland County

★ **SIDNEY HEALTH CENTER (271344)**, 216 14th Avenue S.W., Zip 59270–3586; tel. 406/488–2100, (Total facility includes 56 beds in nursing home–type unit) **A**10 18 **F**2 3 11 13 15 17 28 30 31 34 35 40 41 45 50 56 59 62 63 64 68 70 75 76 78 79 81 82 84 85 86 87 89 93 96 97 107 108 110 111 115 119 120 121 122 123 128 129 130 133 144 145 146 147 148 **P**6
Primary Contact: Richard Haraldson, Chief Executive Officer
CFO: Tina Montgomery, Chief Financial Officer
CMO: Rajohn Karanjai, M.D., Chief Medical Officer
CIO: Brian Fay, Director Information Systems
CHR: Lisa Aisenbrey, Administrator Human Resources and Support Services
Web address: www.sidneyhealth.org
Control: Other not–for–profit (including NFP Corporation) **Service:** General Medical and Surgical

Staffed Beds: 81 **Admissions:** 1594 **Census:** 58 **Outpatient Visits:** 50155 **Births:** 146 **Total Expense ($000):** 53236 **Payroll Expense ($000):** 19830 **Personnel:** 341

SUPERIOR—Mineral County

MINERAL COMMUNITY HOSPITAL (271331), 1208 6th Avenue East, Zip 59872–9618; tel. 406/822–4841 **A**10 18 **F**10 29 40 45 57 69 75 77 81 93 107 110 114 119 133 143
Primary Contact: Ronald M. Gleason, Chief Executive Officer
CFO: Cliff Case, Chief Financial Officer
CMO: Roger Pafford, M.D., Medical Director
CHR: Stacy Conrow–Ververis, Director Human Resources
CNO: Jenifer Mitchell, R.N., Director of Nursing Services
Web address: www.mineralcommunityhospital.com/
Control: Other not–for–profit (including NFP Corporation) **Service:** General Medical and Surgical

Staffed Beds: 25 **Admissions:** 145 **Census:** 16 **Outpatient Visits:** 5824 **Births:** 0 **Total Expense ($000):** 6358 **Payroll Expense ($000):** 3276 **Personnel:** 63

TERRY—Prairie County

PRAIRIE COMMUNITY HEALTH CENTER See Prairie Community Hospital

★ **PRAIRIE COMMUNITY HOSPITAL (271309)**, 312 South Adams Avenue, Zip 59349–0156, Mailing Address: P.O. Box 156, Zip 59349–0156; tel. 406/635–5511 **A**10 18 **F**1 2 32 34 40 41 57 59 64 65 67 69 75 87 90 93 127 128 133 135 146 147 148 **P**6
Primary Contact: Laurie Lea Durham, Chief Executive Officer
CFO: Laurie Chandler, Financial Officer
CIO: Laurie Chandler, Chairman
CNO: Susan Morgan, Director of Nursing Services
Web address: www.prairiecommunityhospital.org/
Control: Hospital district or authority, Government, nonfederal **Service:** General Medical and Surgical

Staffed Beds: 22 **Admissions:** 54 **Census:** 20 **Outpatient Visits:** 3683 **Births:** 1 **Total Expense ($000):** 2435 **Payroll Expense ($000):** 978 **Personnel:** 33

TOWNSEND—Broadwater County

BROADWATER HEALTH CENTER (271333), 110 North Oak Street, Zip 59644–2306; tel. 406/266–3186 **A**10 18 **F**3 7 9 15 29 32 34 40 41 43 50 53 54 55 57 59 64 66 67 71 75 77 79 87 91 93 97 107 111 128 130 131 133 135 143 144 146 147 148 **P**6
Primary Contact: Kyle Hopstad, Chief Executive Officer
CFO: Jennifer Clowes, Chief Financial Officer
CMO: Carol Bridges, M.D., Medical Director
CHR: April Campbell, Director Human Resources
CNO: Fran Wright, Director of Nursing
Web address: www.broadwaterhealthcenter.com
Control: Other not–for–profit (including NFP Corporation) **Service:** Long–Term Acute Care hospital

Staffed Beds: 44 **Admissions:** 90 **Census:** 2 **Births:** 0

WARM SPRINGS—Deer Lodge County

MONTANA STATE HOSPITAL (274086), 100 Garnet Way, Zip 59756–9705; tel. 406/693–7000 **A**10 **F**39 50 59 75 77 86 97 98 102 103 106 130 135 **P**6
Primary Contact: Jay Pottenger, Administrator
CFO: Tracey Thun, Director Business and Support Services
CMO: Thomas Gray, M.D., Medical Director
CIO: Melinda Bridgewater, Director, Information Services
CHR: Todd Thun, Director Human Resources
CNO: Dave Olson, Director of Nursing
Web address: www.msh.mt.gov
Control: State–Government, nonfederal **Service:** Psychiatric

Staffed Beds: 264 **Admissions:** 691 **Census:** 216 **Outpatient Visits:** 0 **Births:** 0 **Total Expense ($000):** 40451 **Payroll Expense ($000):** 20191 **Personnel:** 408

WHITE SULPHUR SPRINGS—Meagher County

MOUNTAINVIEW MEDICAL CENTER (271306), 16 West Main Street, Zip 59645–9036, Mailing Address: P.O. Box Q, Zip 59645–0817; tel. 406/547–3321 **A**10 18 **F**1 3 11 34 35 40 56 57 59 64 65 67 82 90 93 97 107 114 119 127 128 133
Primary Contact: Rob Brandt, Chief Executive Officer
Web address: www.mvmc.org
Control: Other not–for–profit (including NFP Corporation) **Service:** General Medical and Surgical

Staffed Beds: 21 **Admissions:** 116 **Census:** 1 **Outpatient Visits:** 3433 **Births:** 0

WHITEFISH—Flathead County

★ **NORTH VALLEY HOSPITAL (271336)**, 1600 Hospital Way, Zip 59937–7849; tel. 406/863–3500 **A**10 18 **F**3 11 13 15 28 29 30 31 34 35 37 40 43 45 50 51 54 56 59 64 68 70 75 76 79 81 85 86 87 97 99 100 102 103 104 107 110 111 114 119 126 127 129 130 131 132 133 135 144 146 148 **P**6
S QHR, Brentwood, TN
Primary Contact: Tate J. Kreitinger, Interim Chief Executive Officer
COO: Christina Bogers, Chief Clinical Officer
CFO: Arebi Garsa, Interim Chief Financial Officer
CMO: Jason Cohen, M.D., Chief Medical Officer
CIO: Michael Barnes, Chief Information Officer
CHR: Joseph Schmier, Interim Director Human Resources
Web address: www.nvhosp.org
Control: Other not–for–profit (including NFP Corporation) **Service:** General Medical and Surgical

Staffed Beds: 25 **Admissions:** 1621 **Census:** 13 **Outpatient Visits:** 67049 **Births:** 541 **Total Expense ($000):** 49171 **Payroll Expense ($000):** 18480 **Personnel:** 301

MT

Hospital, Medicare Provider Number, Address, Telephone, Approval, Facility, and Physician Codes, Health Care System

★ American Hospital Association (AHA) membership   ○ Healthcare Facilities Accreditation Program   ⇑ Center for Improvement in Healthcare Quality Accreditation
□ The Joint Commission accreditation   ◇ DNV Healthcare Inc. accreditation   △ Commission on Accreditation of Rehabilitation Facilities (CARF) accreditation

★ **TRINITY HOSPITAL (271341)**, 315 Knapp Street, Zip 59201–1826;
tel. 406/653–6500, (Total facility includes 60 beds in nursing home–type unit)
A10 **F**3 6 7 8 13 15 29 31 32 34 40 43 45 50 56 57 59 64 70 75 76 78 81
92 110 119 120 125 127 128 130 133 143 145 **P**5
Primary Contact: Margaret B. Norgaard, Chief Executive Officer
Web address: www.nemhs.net
Control: Other not–for–profit (including NFP Corporation) **Service:** General
Medical and Surgical

Staffed Beds: 82 **Admissions:** 434 **Census:** 58 **Outpatient Visits:** 13680
Births: 166 **Total Expense ($000):** 19246 **Payroll Expense ($000):** 10221
Personnel: 201

MT

Many Facility Codes have changed. Please refer to the AHA Guide Code Chart. © 2016 AHA Guide

NEBRASKA

AINSWORTH—Brown County

BROWN COUNTY HOSPITAL (281325), 945 East Zero Street,
Zip 69210–1547; tel. 402/387–2800, (Nonreporting) **A**10 18
Primary Contact: Shannon Sorensen, Chief Executive Officer
CFO: Lisa Wood, Chief Financial Officer
CMO: Melvin Campbell, M.D., Medical Staff Chairman
CIO: Mike Depko, Director Information Technology
CHR: Lisa Fischer, Director Human Resources
CNO: Matt Lentz, R.N., Director of Patient Services
Web address: www.browncountyhospital.org
Control: County–Government, nonfederal **Service:** General Medical and Surgical

Staffed Beds: 18

ALBION—Boone County

★ **BOONE COUNTY HEALTH CENTER (281334)**, 723 West Fairview Street,
Zip 68620–1725, Mailing Address: P.O. Box 151, Zip 68620–0151;
tel. 402/395–2191, (Nonreporting) **A**5 10 18
Primary Contact: Victor N. Lee, FACHE, President and Chief Executive Officer
CFO: Tanya Sharp, Vice President of Fiscal Services and Chief Financial Officer
CMO: Lynette Kramer, M.D., Chief Medical Officer
CIO: Larry Zoucha, Chief Information Officer
CHR: Jennifer Beierman, Director Human Resources
CNO: Cindy Lesiak, Vice President Patient Care Services and Director of Nursing
Web address: www.boonecohealth.org
Control: County–Government, nonfederal **Service:** General Medical and Surgical

Staffed Beds: 25

ALLIANCE—Box Butte County

⊞ **BOX BUTTE GENERAL HOSPITAL (281360)**, 2101 Box Butte Avenue,
Zip 69301–4445, Mailing Address: P.O. Box 810, Zip 69301–0810;
tel. 308/762–6660 **A**1 5 10 18 **F**3 5 11 13 15 28 29 32 34 35 36 38 40 43
47 48 50 53 57 59 60 64 68 69 75 77 78 79 81 82 85 86 87 92 93 97 100
101 104 107 108 111 114 116 118 119 127 129 130 131 132 133 134 135
146 148
Primary Contact: Lori Mazanec, Interim Chief Executive Officer
COO: Lori Mazanec, Chief Operating Officer
CFO: Tracy E. Jatczak, CPA, Chief Financial Officer
CHR: Lisa L. Hillyer, Human Resources Manager
CNO: Carolyn Jones, R.N., Chief Nursing Officer
Web address: www.bbgh.org
Control: County–Government, nonfederal **Service:** General Medical and Surgical

Staffed Beds: 25 **Admissions:** 889 **Census:** 10 **Outpatient Visits:** 34228
Births: 106 **Total Expense ($000):** 30121 **Payroll Expense ($000):** 12929
Personnel: 251

ALMA—Harlan County

★ **HARLAN COUNTY HEALTH SYSTEM (281300)**, 717 North Brown Street,
Zip 68920–2132, Mailing Address: P.O. Box 836, Zip 68920–0836;
tel. 308/928–2151 **A**10 18 **F**1 3 4 11 15 16 17 29 30 31 40 45 46 50 57 59
64 67 70 72 73 80 81 85 86 88 89 90 93 98 107 110 114 119 127 128 130
132 133 135 146 147 **P**6 **S** Great Plains Health Alliance, Inc., Wichita, KS
Primary Contact: Manuela Wolf, R.N., Chief Executive Officer
CFO: Sue Lans, Comptroller
CMO: Cameron Knackstedt, D.O., Chief Medical Staff
CIO: Michael Andrews, Coordinator Information Systems
CHR: Ana Schluntz, Coordinator Human Resources and Benefits
CNO: Katherine Fleischmann, Director of Nursing
Web address: www.harlancountyhealth.com
Control: County–Government, nonfederal **Service:** General Medical and Surgical

Staffed Beds: 19 **Admissions:** 105 **Census:** 3 **Outpatient Visits:** 19307
Births: 0 **Total Expense ($000):** 8375 **Payroll Expense ($000):** 3379
Personnel: 59

ATKINSON—Holt County

WEST HOLT MEMORIAL HOSPITAL (281343), 406 West Neely Street,
Zip 68713–4801; tel. 402/925–2811, (Nonreporting) **A**10 18 **S** Faith Regional
Health Services, Norfolk, NE
Primary Contact: Bradley D. Pfeifer, Chief Executive Officer
CFO: Karen Nollette, Chief Financial Officer
CMO: John Tubbs, M.D., Chief of Staff
CIO: Mark Johnson, Chief Information Officer
CHR: Margaret Linse, Administrative Secretary and Director Human Resources
CNO: Tana O'Neill, R.N., Chief Nursing Officer
Web address: www.westholtmed.org
Control: Other not–for–profit (including NFP Corporation) **Service:** General
Medical and Surgical

Staffed Beds: 17

AUBURN—Nemaha County

★ ◇ **NEMAHA COUNTY HOSPITAL (281324)**, 2022 13th Street,
Zip 68305–1799; tel. 402/274–4366 **A**10 18 21 **F**3 7 12 15 28 29 30 31 34
35 40 43 62 64 68 74 75 77 78 79 81 82 85 86 87 93 94 104 107 110 111
114 117 119 128 129 130 131 133 135 141 147 148
Primary Contact: Marty Fattig, Chief Executive Officer
COO: Kermit Moore, R.N., Chief Operating Officer and Chief Nursing Officer
CFO: Stacy Taylor, Chief Financial Officer
CHR: Susan Shupp, Chief Human Resources Officer
Web address: www.nchnet.org
Control: County–Government, nonfederal **Service:** General Medical and Surgical

Staffed Beds: 16 **Admissions:** 242 **Census:** 4 **Outpatient Visits:** 18620
Births: 0 **Total Expense ($000):** 11723 **Payroll Expense ($000):** 4791
Personnel: 88

AURORA—Hamilton County

★ **MEMORIAL COMMUNITY HEALTH (281320)**, 1423 Seventh Street,
Zip 68818–1197; tel. 402/694–3171, (Total facility includes 48 beds in nursing
home–type unit) **A**10 18 **F**10 11 13 15 28 29 31 34 35 40 41 43 45 50 51 57
59 64 65 67 75 76 77 78 79 81 82 85 86 87 93 94 97 107 108 110 114
119 130 131 132 133 146 **P**6
Primary Contact: Diane R. Keller, Chief Executive Officer
CFO: Phil Fendt, Chief Financial Officer
CMO: Jeff Muilenburg, Chief of Staff
CIO: Brad Tiede, Director Information Systems
CHR: Laura Teichmeier, Director Human Resources
CNO: Lindy Mosel, Director of Nursing
Web address: www.memorialcommunityhealth.org
Control: Other not–for–profit (including NFP Corporation) **Service:** General
Medical and Surgical

Staffed Beds: 64 **Admissions:** 259 **Census:** 44 **Outpatient Visits:** 22306
Births: 31 **Total Expense ($000):** 22223 **Payroll Expense ($000):** 10164
Personnel: 221

MEMORIAL HOSPITAL See Memorial Community Health

BASSETT—Rock County

ROCK COUNTY HOSPITAL (281333), 102 East South Street,
Zip 68714–5508; tel. 402/684–3366, (Total facility includes 30 beds in nursing
home–type unit) **A**10 18 **F**7 11 15 28 40 53 57 81 84 107 110 127 128 133
Primary Contact: Stacey A. Knox, Administrator
CMO: John Tubbs, M.D., Chief of Staff
CIO: Cal Alder, Director Information Technology
CHR: Jackie Carpenter, Office Manager
CNO: Katie Aase, Director of Nursing
Web address: www.rockcountyhospital.com
Control: County–Government, nonfederal **Service:** General Medical and Surgical

Staffed Beds: 54 **Admissions:** 183 **Census:** 30 **Outpatient Visits:** 6547
Births: 0 **Total Expense ($000):** 8101 **Payroll Expense ($000):** 2939
Personnel: 84

NE

Hospital, Medicare Provider Number, Address, Telephone, Approval, Facility, and Physician Codes, Health Care System

★ American Hospital Association (AHA) membership   ○ Healthcare Facilities Accreditation Program   ⇑ Center for Improvement in Healthcare Quality Accreditation
□ The Joint Commission accreditation   ◇ DNV Healthcare Inc. accreditation   △ Commission on Accreditation of Rehabilitation Facilities (CARF) accreditation

BEATRICE—Gage County

☒ **BEATRICE COMMUNITY HOSPITAL AND HEALTH CENTER (281364)**, 4800 Hospital Parkway, Zip 68310–6906, Mailing Address: P.O. Box 278, Zip 68310–0278; tel. 402/228–3344 **A**1 10 18 **F**3 13 15 28 29 31 34 35 40 45 57 62 63 64 65 68 69 70 75 76 78 79 81 82 84 85 87 93 107 110 111 114 119 127 129 130 131 132 133 135 146 147
Primary Contact: Thomas W. Sommers, FACHE, Chief Executive Officer
CFO: Alan W. Streeter, Chief Financial Officer
CMO: John T Findley, M.D., Chief Medical Officer
CHR: Kathryn G. Humble, Chief Human Resources Officer
CNO: Arlinda K. Ament, R.N., Interim Chief Nursing Officer
Web address: www.beatricecommunityhospital.com
Control: Other not-for-profit (including NFP Corporation) **Service:** General Medical and Surgical

Staffed Beds: 25 **Admissions:** 1062 **Census:** 11 **Outpatient Visits:** 196057
Births: 200 **Total Expense ($000):** 66134 **Payroll Expense ($000):** 30108
Personnel: 453

BELLEVUE—Sarpy County

MADONNA REHABILITATION SPECIALTY HOSPITAL (280136), 2500 Bellevue Medical Center Drive, Fourth Floor, Zip 68123–1591; tel. 402/401–3000, (Nonreporting)
Primary Contact: Paul Dongilli, Jr., Ph.D., FACHE, President and Chief Executive Officer
Web address: www.madonna.org
Control: Other not-for-profit (including NFP Corporation) **Service:** General Medical and Surgical

Staffed Beds: 32

☐ **NEBRASKA MEDICINE – BELLEVUE (280132)**, 2500 Bellevue Medical Center Drive, Zip 68123–1591; tel. 402/763–3000 **A**1 3 5 10 **F**3 13 15 18 20 22 28 29 30 31 34 35 40 41 44 45 47 48 49 50 51 53 55 57 58 59 63 64 65 68 70 74 76 77 78 79 81 82 84 85 86 87 97 107 108 110 111 114 119 130 131 132 135 141 143 145 146 147 148
Primary Contact: Matt E. Pospisil, Vice President, Clinical Operations
CFO: Stephanie Daubert, Chief Financial Officer
CMO: Jeffrey D. Akerson, M.D., Chief Medical Officer
CIO: Brian Lancaster, Executive Director Information Management
CNO: Ray D. Dial, Director of Nursing
Web address: www.bellevuemed.com
Control: Other not-for-profit (including NFP Corporation) **Service:** General Medical and Surgical

Staffed Beds: 32 **Admissions:** 3734 **Census:** 32 **Outpatient Visits:** 78331
Births: 829 **Total Expense ($000):** 65496 **Payroll Expense ($000):** 21554
Personnel: 334

BENKELMAN—Dundy County

★ **DUNDY COUNTY HOSPITAL (281340)**, 1313 North Cheyenne Street, Zip 69021–3074, Mailing Address: P.O. Box 626, Zip 69021–0626; tel. 308/423–2204, (Nonreporting) **A**10 18
Primary Contact: Rita A. Jones, Chief Executive Officer
COO: Wendy Elkins, Director Operations
CFO: Renee Fink, CPA, Chief Financial Officer
CMO: Jose Garcia, M.D., Chief Medical Staff
CIO: David Craw, Coordinator Information Technology
CHR: Sandy Noffsinger, Executive Assistant, Risk Manager and Director Marketing
CNO: Laken Vrbas, R.N., Director of Nursing
Web address: www.bwtelcom.net/dch
Control: County-Government, nonfederal **Service:** General Medical and Surgical

Staffed Beds: 14

BLAIR—Washington County

★ **MEMORIAL COMMUNITY HOSPITAL AND HEALTH SYSTEM (281359)**, 810 North 22nd Street, Zip 68008–1199, Mailing Address: P.O. Box 250, Zip 68008–0250; tel. 402/426–2182, (Nonreporting) **A**10 18
Primary Contact: Tim Plante, MSN, R.N., President and Chief Executive Officer
CMO: John F. Simonson, M.D., President Medical Staff
CHR: Kristine Nielsen, Manager Human Resources
CNO: Laura Stawniak, R.N., Chief Nursing Executive
Web address: www.mchhs.org
Control: Other not-for-profit (including NFP Corporation) **Service:** General Medical and Surgical

Staffed Beds: 25

BRIDGEPORT—Morrill County

MORRILL COUNTY COMMUNITY HOSPITAL (281318), 1313 S Street, Zip 69336–0579; tel. 308/262–1616 **A**10 18 **F**7 28 32 35 40 57 59 62 64 65 69 77 81 82 93 97 107 108 111 112 119 120 121 122 123 124 127 129 130 133 135 144 148
Primary Contact: Robin Stuart, Chief Executive Officer
CFO: Connie Christensen, Chief Financial Officer
CMO: John Post, M.D., Medical Director
CIO: Lori Shengle, Director Information Technology
CHR: Rhea Basa, Director Human Resources
CNO: Sylvia Marie Lichius, R.N., Chief Nursing Officer
Web address: www.morrillcountyhospital.org
Control: County-Government, nonfederal **Service:** General Medical and Surgical

Staffed Beds: 20 **Admissions:** 116 **Census:** 1 **Outpatient Visits:** 4489
Births: 0 **Total Expense ($000):** 5840 **Payroll Expense ($000):** 4793
Personnel: 120

BROKEN BOW—Custer County

JENNIE M. MELHAM MEMORIAL MEDICAL CENTER (281365), 145 Memorial Drive, Zip 68822–1378, Mailing Address: P.O. Box 250, Zip 68822–0250; tel. 308/872–4100, (Total facility includes 50 beds in nursing home–type unit) **A**10 18 **F**3 10 11 13 15 28 31 34 40 43 45 53 57 59 67 76 79 81 107 110 115 119 125 129 130 133
Primary Contact: Michael J. Steckler, President and Chief Executive Officer
CFO: Tim Schuckman, Chief Financial Officer
CIO: Tim Schuckman, Chief Financial Officer
CHR: Teri Sell, Payroll and Personnel Coordinator
CNO: Shelly Amsberry, Director of Nursing
Web address: www.brokenbow-ne.com/community/healthcare/melham.htm
Control: Other not-for-profit (including NFP Corporation) **Service:** General Medical and Surgical

Staffed Beds: 73 **Admissions:** 638 **Census:** 72 **Outpatient Visits:** 15711
Births: 95 **Total Expense ($000):** 16747 **Payroll Expense ($000):** 6896

CALLAWAY—Custer County

★ **CALLAWAY DISTRICT HOSPITAL (281335)**, 211 East Kimball, Zip 68825–2589, Mailing Address: P.O. Box 100, Zip 68825–0100; tel. 308/836–2228, (Nonreporting) **A**10 18
Primary Contact: Marvin Neth, Chief Executive Officer
CHR: Carol Koch, Manager Human Resources
Web address: www.callawayhospital.org
Control: Hospital district or authority, Government, nonfederal **Service:** General Medical and Surgical

Staffed Beds: 12

CAMBRIDGE—Furnas County

★ **TRI VALLEY HEALTH SYSTEM (281348)**, 1305 West Highway 6 and 34, Zip 69022–0488, Mailing Address: P.O. Box 488, Zip 69022–0488; tel. 308/697–3329, (Total facility includes 32 beds in nursing home–type unit) **A**10 18 **F**3 8 10 11 13 15 28 29 30 31 32 34 35 40 41 45 46 53 56 57 59 64 65 67 68 69 71 75 76 77 78 79 81 82 86 87 91 93 107 110 115 119 125 127 128 129 130 131 132 133 135 143 145 146 147 148 **P**6 **S** HealthTech Management Services, Brentwood, TN
Primary Contact: Deborah L. Herzberg, R.N., MS, FACHE, Chief Executive Officer
COO: Keith Luedders, Chief Operations Officer
CFO: Diana Rippe, Chief Financial Officer
CMO: Lennie Deaver, M.D., Chief of Staff
CIO: Ciprian Galarneau, Director Information Systems
CHR: Tammy Claussen, Chief Human Resource Officer
CNO: Melissa Bodkins, R.N., Chief Clinical Officer
Web address: www.trivalleyhealth.com
Control: Other not-for-profit (including NFP Corporation) **Service:** General Medical and Surgical

Staffed Beds: 52 **Admissions:** 380 **Census:** 29 **Outpatient Visits:** 16424
Births: 63 **Total Expense ($000):** 20685 **Payroll Expense ($000):** 7892
Personnel: 155

CENTRAL CITY—Merrick County

★ **LITZENBERG MEMORIAL COUNTY HOSPITAL (281328)**, 1715 26th Street, Zip 68826–9620; tel. 308/946–3015, (Nonreporting) **A**10 18
Primary Contact: Julie Murray, Chief Executive Officer
CHR: Shauna Graham, Director of Professional Services Human Resources, Marketing Foundation
Web address: www.lmchealth.com
Control: County-Government, nonfederal **Service:** General Medical and Surgical

Staffed Beds: 65

Many Facility Codes have changed. Please refer to the AHA Guide Code Chart.

NE

CHADRON—Dawes County

★ **CHADRON COMMUNITY HOSPITAL AND HEALTH SERVICES (281341)**, 825 Centennial Drive, Zip 69337–9400; tel. 308/432–5586 **A**3 10 18 **F**3 10 13 15 28 31 34 35 40 59 60 62 63 65 75 76 77 78 79 81 84 85 93 96 107 110 111 114 119 125 127 129 130 133 135
Primary Contact: Harold L. Krueger, Jr., Chief Executive Officer
COO: Anna Turman, Chief Operating Officer
CFO: Russ Bohnenkamp, Chief Financial Officer
CMO: Ed Pelton, Chief of Staff
CIO: Anna Turman, Chief Information Officer
CHR: Ellen Krueger, Director Human Resources
CNO: Cheryl Cassiday, R.N., Director of Nursing
Web address: www.chadronhospital.com
Control: Corporation, Investor–owned, for–profit **Service:** General Medical and Surgical

Staffed Beds: 25 **Admissions:** 527 **Census:** 4 **Outpatient Visits:** 22341 **Births:** 107 **Total Expense ($000):** 21265 **Payroll Expense ($000):** 8116 **Personnel:** 182

COLUMBUS—Platte County

⊠ **COLUMBUS COMMUNITY HOSPITAL (280111)**, 4600 38th Street, Zip 68601–1664, Mailing Address: P.O. Box 1800, Zip 68602–1800; tel. 402/564–7118, (Nonreporting) **A**1 10 20
Primary Contact: Michael T. Hansen, FACHE, President and Chief Executive Officer
COO: James P. Goulet, Vice President Operations
CFO: Chad Van Cleave, Chief Financial Officer
CMO: Mark Howerter, M.D., President Medical Staff
CIO: Cheryl Tira, Director Information Systems
CHR: Scott E. Messersmith, Director Human Resources
CNO: Linda K. Walline, R.N., Vice President Nursing
Web address: www.columbushosp.org
Control: Other not–for–profit (including NFP Corporation) **Service:** General Medical and Surgical

Staffed Beds: 51

COZAD—Dawson County

★ **COZAD COMMUNITY HOSPITAL (281327)**, 300 East 12th Street, Zip 69130–1505, Mailing Address: P.O. Box 108, Zip 69130–0108; tel. 308/784–2261 **A**5 10 18 **F**3 10 13 15 28 30 31 34 35 40 43 50 53 56 57 59 62 63 68 70 75 76 77 81 82 84 86 93 94 97 107 110 114 119 127 128 129 130 131 132 133 135 146 148 **P**6
Primary Contact: Lyle E. Davis, Administrator
Web address: www.cozadhealthcare.com
Control: Hospital district or authority, Government, nonfederal **Service:** General Medical and Surgical

Staffed Beds: 20 **Admissions:** 403 **Census:** 5 **Outpatient Visits:** 8744 **Births:** 51 **Total Expense ($000):** 13628 **Payroll Expense ($000):** 6249 **Personnel:** 132

CREIGHTON—Knox County

★ **AVERA CREIGHTON HOSPITAL (281331)**, 1503 Main Street, Zip 68729–3007, Mailing Address: P.O. Box 186, Zip 68729–0186; tel. 402/358–5700, (Nonreporting) **A**10 18 **S** Avera Health, Sioux Falls, SD
Primary Contact: Jennifer Neukirch, Chief Executive Officer
CHR: Jane E. Miller, Director Human Resources
CNO: Jean M. Henes, MSN, RN–B, R.N., Director of Nursing
Web address: www.avera.org/creighton/
Control: Other not–for–profit (including NFP Corporation) **Service:** General Medical and Surgical

Staffed Beds: 54

CRETE—Saline County

★ **CRETE AREA MEDICAL CENTER (281354)**, 2910 Betten Drive, Zip 68333–3084, Mailing Address: P.O. Box 220, Zip 68333–0220; tel. 402/826–2102, (Nonreporting) **A**10 18 **S** Bryan Health, Lincoln, NE
Primary Contact: Rebekah Mussman, Chief Executive Officer
CFO: Doug Kucera, Chief Financial Officer
CMO: Amy Vertin, M.D., Chief of Staff
CIO: Drew Kotil, Director Information Technology
CHR: Bobbie Wilson, Director Human Resources
CNO: Jeaniffr P. Snide, Chief Nursing Officer
Web address: www.creteareamedicalcenter.com
Control: Other not–for–profit (including NFP Corporation) **Service:** General Medical and Surgical

Staffed Beds: 24

DAVID CITY—Butler County

★ **BUTLER COUNTY HEALTH CARE CENTER (281332)**, 372 South Ninth Street, Zip 68632–2116; tel. 402/367–1200, (Nonreporting) **A**5 10 18
Primary Contact: Donald T. Naiberk, Administrator
CFO: Jodi Prochaska, Chief Financial Officer
CMO: Victor Thoendel, M.D., Chief Medical Officer
CIO: Cindy Neesen, Director of Information Technology
CHR: Andra Vandenberg, Director Human Resources
CNO: Sue M. Birkel, R.N., Director of Nursing
Web address: www.bchccnet.org
Control: County–Government, nonfederal **Service:** General Medical and Surgical

Staffed Beds: 20

ELKHORN—Douglas County

METHODIST WOMEN'S HOSPITAL See Nebraska Methodist Hospital, Omaha

FAIRBURY—Jefferson County

★ **JEFFERSON COMMUNITY HEALTH CENTER (281319)**, 2200 H Street, Zip 68352–1119, Mailing Address: P.O. Box 277, Zip 68352–0277; tel. 402/729–3351, (Total facility includes 40 beds in nursing home–type unit) **A**10 18 **F**2 3 13 15 28 29 30 31 34 35 40 45 50 53 57 59 62 64 75 76 77 78 79 81 85 86 87 93 107 110 114 119 128 130 131 132 133 135 146
Primary Contact: Chad Jurgens, Chief Executive Officer
CFO: Chance Klasek, CPA, Chief Financial Officer
CIO: Dennis Ahl, Director Information Technology
CHR: Sandra A. Bauer, Director Human Resources
Web address: www.jchc.us
Control: Other not–for–profit (including NFP Corporation) **Service:** General Medical and Surgical

Staffed Beds: 57 **Admissions:** 321 **Census:** 39 **Outpatient Visits:** 26373 **Births:** 26 **Total Expense ($000):** 17048 **Payroll Expense ($000):** 6979 **Personnel:** 168

FALLS CITY—Richardson County

★ **COMMUNITY MEDICAL CENTER, INC. (281352)**, 3307 Barada Street, Zip 68355–2470, Mailing Address: P.O. Box 399, Zip 68355–0399; tel. 402/245–2428 **A**10 18 **F**3 13 15 28 31 34 35 40 43 45 59 75 76 78 79 81 85 93 97 107 111 119 127 130 133 135 **P**6
Primary Contact: Ryan C. Larsen, FACHE, Chief Executive Officer
CFO: Scott Sawyer, Chief Financial Officer
CMO: David E. Borg, Chief of Medical Staff
CIO: Joe Buckminster, Manager Information Technology
CHR: Shannon Weinmann, Human Resources Manager
CNO: Ivy Campbell, Director of Nursing
Web address: www.cmcfc.org
Control: Other not–for–profit (including NFP Corporation) **Service:** General Medical and Surgical

Staffed Beds: 24 **Admissions:** 829 **Census:** 9 **Outpatient Visits:** 52794 **Births:** 44 **Total Expense ($000):** 22875 **Payroll Expense ($000):** 7623 **Personnel:** 168

FRANKLIN—Franklin County

★ **FRANKLIN COUNTY MEMORIAL HOSPITAL (281311)**, 1406 Q Street, Zip 68939–0315, Mailing Address: 1406 Q. Street, Zip 68939–0315; tel. 308/425–6221 **A**10 18 **F**28 29 33 34 35 40 41 46 50 54 57 59 64 65 75 89 93 107 119 127 129 130 133 148 **P**6
Primary Contact: Theresa Rizzo, Administrator
CFO: Amy Kahrs, Director of Finance
CMO: Linda Mazour, M.D., President
CIO: Cathy Webber, Director of Health Information Management
CNO: Kari Yelken, R.N., Director of Nursing
Web address: www.fcmh.com
Control: Other not–for–profit (including NFP Corporation) **Service:** General Medical and Surgical

Staffed Beds: 14 **Admissions:** 92 **Census:** 1 **Births:** 0

NE

FREMONT—Dodge County

☐ **FREMONT HEALTH (280077)**, 450 East 23rd Street, Zip 68025–2387;
tel. 402/721–1610, (Total facility includes 112 beds in nursing home–type unit)
A1 2 5 10 20 **F**3 8 11 13 15 17 18 20 22 26 28 29 30 31 34 35 37 40 45
56 57 59 62 63 64 68 70 72 74 75 76 77 78 79 81 85 86 87 89 93 99 100
103 104 107 108 110 111 114 119 120 121 123 124 126 128 129 130 131
132 135 143 146
Primary Contact: Patrick M. Booth, FACHE, Chief Executive Officer
CFO: Michael Sindelar, Vice President and Chief Financial Officer
CIO: Matt Sakalosky, Director Information Services and Chief Information Officer
CHR: Bethany Childers, Director Human Resources
CNO: Peggy S. Kennedy, R.N., Vice President and Chief Nurse Executive
Web address: www.fremonthealth.com
Control: County–Government, nonfederal **Service:** General Medical and Surgical

Staffed Beds: 202 **Admissions:** 3261 **Census:** 110 **Outpatient Visits:** 73565
Births: 343 **Total Expense ($000):** 99771 **Payroll Expense ($000):** 43840
Personnel: 681

FRIEND—Saline County

FRIEND COMMUNITY HEALTHCARE SYSTEM (281330), 905 Second Street,
Zip 68359–1133; tel. 402/947–2541, (Nonreporting) **A**10 18
Primary Contact: Chad Thompson, Chief Executive Officer
CFO: Mackenzie Svarc, Finance Director
CMO: Roger Meyer, M.D., Chief of Staff
CHR: Shyanne Scholl, Interim Human Resources Director
CNO: Dayna Pulver, Director of Nursing
Web address: www.friendmed.com/
Control: City–Government, nonfederal **Service:** General Medical and Surgical

Staffed Beds: 60

GENEVA—Fillmore County

FILLMORE COUNTY HOSPITAL (281301), 1900 F Street, Zip 68361–1325,
Mailing Address: P.O. Box 193, Zip 68361–0193; tel. 402/759–3167,
(Nonreporting) **A**10 18
Primary Contact: Paul Utemark, Chief Executive Officer
COO: Debbie Domann, Director of Operations
CFO: Jeanne Ackland, Director of Finance
CMO: Jason Bespalec, M.D., Chief of Staff
CIO: Tyler Gewecke, Information Technology Technician
CHR: Abby Tuberville, Human Resource Manager
Web address: www.fhsofgeneva.org
Control: County–Government, nonfederal **Service:** General Medical and Surgical

Staffed Beds: 25

GENOA—Nance County

GENOA MEDICAL FACILITIES (281312), 706 Ewing Avenue, Zip 68640–3035,
Mailing Address: P.O. Box 310, Zip 68640–0310; tel. 402/993–2283, (Total
facility includes 39 beds in nursing home–type unit) **A**10 18 **F**3 8 10 28 29 30
34 35 40 41 43 45 46 47 48 49 53 56 57 59 64 65 71 75 77 79 81 82 84
90 92 93 107 119 128 130 131 133 143 146 148 **P**3
Primary Contact: Cory Nelson, Administrator
CFO: Angie Sutton, Chief Financial Officer
CMO: Brian Buhlke, M.D., Medical Director
CHR: Brianna Molt, Human Resources Director
CNO: Amanda Roebuck, Director Patient Care Services
Web address: www.genoamedical.org/
Control: City–Government, nonfederal **Service:** General Medical and Surgical

Staffed Beds: 58 **Admissions:** 103 **Census:** 28 **Outpatient Visits:** 6258
Births: 0

GORDON—Sheridan County

★ **GORDON MEMORIAL HOSPITAL (281358)**, 300 East Eighth Street,
Zip 69343–1123; tel. 308/282–0401, (Nonreporting) **A**10 18
Primary Contact: William Giles, Chief Executive Officer
CFO: Heidi Cushing, Director Finance
CMO: Christopher P. Costa, M.D., Chief of Staff
CIO: Ray Waldron, Director Information Technology
CHR: Lisa Woodcock, Director Human Resources
CNO: Glenda Capler, Interim Director of Nursing
Web address: www.gordonmemorial.org
Control: Hospital district or authority, Government, nonfederal **Service:** General
Medical and Surgical

Staffed Beds: 25

GOTHENBURG—Dawson County

★ **GOTHENBURG MEMORIAL HOSPITAL (281313)**, 910 20th Street,
Zip 69138–1237, Mailing Address: P.O. Box 469, Zip 69138–0469;
tel. 308/537–3661 **A**10 18 **F**3 13 15 28 29 31 34 35 40 43 45 50 53 57 59
65 75 77 78 79 81 97 107 110 111 119 124 127 129 130 133 147 **P**2 6
Primary Contact: Mick Brant, FACHE, Chief Executive Officer
CFO: Michael Pracheil, Chief Financial Officer
CMO: Carol Shackleton, M.D., Medical Director
CIO: Tinna Therrien, Chief Information Officer and Director Clinical Infomatics
CHR: Jim Imler, Director Human Resources
CNO: Cassie Hilbers, R.N., Chief Nursing Officer
Web address: www.gothenburghealth.org
Control: Hospital district or authority, Government, nonfederal **Service:** General
Medical and Surgical

Staffed Beds: 12 **Admissions:** 298 **Census:** 4 **Outpatient Visits:** 12147
Births: 93 **Total Expense ($000):** 14773 **Payroll Expense ($000):** 5557
Personnel: 139

GRAND ISLAND—Hall County

✠ **CHI HEALTH SAINT FRANCIS (280023)**, 2620 West Faidley Avenue,
Zip 68803–4297, Mailing Address: P.O. Box 9804, Zip 68802–9804;
tel. 308/384–4600, (Includes ST. FRANCIS MEDICAL PLAZA, 2116 West Faidley
Avenue, Zip 68803, Mailing Address: P.O. Box 9804, Zip 68802;
tel. 308/384–4600) **A**1 2 3 5 10 19 **F**3 5 11 12 13 15 17 18 19 20 22 28 30
31 34 35 40 43 45 47 50 51 53 59 60 62 63 64 65 68 70 72 74 75 76 77
78 79 81 82 84 85 89 90 91 97 104 105 110 120 121 123 128 129 130
132 135 145 146 148 **P**8 **S** Catholic Health Initiatives, Englewood, CO
Primary Contact: Daniel P. McElligott, FACHE, President
CFO: Lisa Webb, Vice President Operational Finance
CMO: Shu–Ming Wang, MD, Vice President Medical Affairs
CHR: Nancy Wallace, Vice President Human Resources, CHI Health
CNO: Beth Bartlett, MSN, Vice President Nursing
Web address: www.saintfrancisgi.org
Control: Church–operated, Nongovernment, not–for profit **Service:** General
Medical and Surgical

Staffed Beds: 159 **Admissions:** 6066 **Census:** 72 **Outpatient Visits:** 77050
Births: 940 **Total Expense ($000):** 137403 **Payroll Expense ($000):** 36807
Personnel: 733

GRANT—Perkins County

★ **PERKINS COUNTY HEALTH SERVICES (281356)**, 900 Lincoln Avenue,
Zip 69140–3095; tel. 308/352–7200, (Includes GOLDEN OURS CONVALESCENT
HOME), (Total facility includes 50 beds in nursing home–type unit) **A**10 18 **F**3 10
13 15 17 18 30 31 34 35 40 41 43 45 57 59 62 65 75 76 77 81 93 97 107
110 111 114 119 127 133 135 143 **P**6
Primary Contact: James LeBrun, Chief Executive Officer
CFO: Derick Lorentz, Chief Financial Officer
CMO: Ruth Demmel, M.D., Chief Medical Officer
CIO: Jennifer Baumgartner, Chief Information Officer
CHR: Julie Bevard, Director Human Resources
CNO: Dana McArtor, R.N., Director of Nursing
Web address: www.pchsgrant.com
Control: Hospital district or authority, Government, nonfederal **Service:** General
Medical and Surgical

Staffed Beds: 70 **Admissions:** 411 **Census:** 5 **Outpatient Visits:** 13117
Births: 53 **Total Expense ($000):** 16337 **Payroll Expense ($000):** 7351

HASTINGS—Adams County

✠ **MARY LANNING HEALTHCARE (280032)**, 715 North St. Joseph Avenue,
Zip 68901–4497; tel. 402/463–4521, (Nonreporting) **A**1 2 10
Primary Contact: Eric A. Barber, President and Chief Executive Officer
COO: Mark Callahan, Chief Operating Officer
CFO: Shawn A. Nordby, Chief Financial Officer
CMO: Michael Skoch, M.D., Chief Medical Officer
CIO: Lisa Nonneman, Director Information Technology Services
CHR: Bruce E. Cutright, MS, Vice President Human Resources
CNO: Ronda S. Ehly, R.N., Chief Nursing Officer
Web address: www.marylanning.org
Control: Other not–for–profit (including NFP Corporation) **Service:** General
Medical and Surgical

Staffed Beds: 148

HEBRON—Thayer County

★ **THAYER COUNTY HEALTH SERVICES (281304)**, 120 Park Avenue,
Zip 68370–2019, Mailing Address: P.O. Box 49, Zip 68370–0049;
tel. 402/768–6041, (Nonreporting) **A**10 18
Primary Contact: Michael G. Burcham, Sr., FACHE, Chief Executive Officer
CFO: Doug Wismer, Chief Financial Officer
CMO: Bryan Hubl, M.D., Chief of Staff
CIO: Dan Engle, Chief Information Officer
CHR: Tamara Francik, Human Resources Generalist
CNO: Jamie Koch, R.N., Director of Nursing
Web address: www.thayercountyhealth.com
Control: County–Government, nonfederal **Service:** General Medical and Surgical

Staffed Beds: 19

Many Facility Codes have changed. Please refer to the AHA Guide Code Chart. © 2016 AHA Guide

HENDERSON—York County

HENDERSON HEALTH CARE SERVICES (281308), 1621 Front Street,
Zip 68371–8902; tel. 402/723–4512, (Nonreporting) **A**10 18
Primary Contact: Cheryl Brown, Administrator
CMO: James M. Ohrt, M.D., Director Medical Staff
CHR: Lynette Friesen, Manager Human Resources
CNO: Carrie Peterson, Director of Nursing
Web address: www.hendersonhealthcare.org/getpage.php?name=message
Control: Other not–for–profit (including NFP Corporation) **Service:** General
Medical and Surgical

Staffed Beds: 56

HOLDREGE—Phelps County

★ ◇ **PHELPS MEMORIAL HEALTH CENTER (281362)**, 1215 Tibbals Street,
Zip 68949–1255; tel. 308/995–2211, (Nonreporting) **A**10 18 21 **S** QHR,
Brentwood, TN
Primary Contact: Mark Harrel, Chief Executive Officer
CFO: Loren D. Schroder, Chief Financial Officer
CMO: Stuart Embury, M.D., Chief Medical Officer
CIO: Leora Smith, Information System and Health Information Management Team
Leader
CHR: Cindy Jackson, Director Human Resources
Web address: www.phelpsmemorial.com
Control: Other not–for–profit (including NFP Corporation) **Service:** General
Medical and Surgical

Staffed Beds: 25

IMPERIAL—Chase County

★ **CHASE COUNTY COMMUNITY HOSPITAL (281351)**, 600 West 12th Street,
Zip 69033–3130, Mailing Address: P.O. Box 819, Zip 69033–0819;
tel. 308/882–7111 **A**10 18 **F**11 13 15 28 29 30 31 34 35 40 41 42 43 45 57
59 64 75 76 81 91 93 107 110 114 127 133 **P**6
Primary Contact: Stephen Lewis, Chief Executive Officer
CFO: Abigail Cyboron, Chief Financial Officer
CMO: Jonathan Richman, M.D., Chief of Staff
CIO: Jen Harris, Director Health Information Management
CHR: Julie Sharp, Supervisor Human Resources
CNO: Kathy Geier, Director of Nursing
Web address: www.chasecountyhospital.com
Control: County–Government, nonfederal **Service:** General Medical and Surgical

Staffed Beds: 22 **Admissions:** 117 **Census:** 1 **Outpatient Visits:** 11032 **Births:** 13 **Total Expense ($000):** 10748 **Payroll Expense ($000):** 4411 **Personnel:** 73

KEARNEY—Buffalo County

⊠ **CHI HEALTH GOOD SAMARITAN (280009)**, 10 East 31st Street,
Zip 68847–2926, Mailing Address: P.O. Box 1990, Zip 68848–1990;
tel. 308/865–7100, (Includes RICHARD H. YOUNG BEHAVIORAL HEALTH CENTER,
1755 Prairie View Place, Zip 68848, Mailing Address: P.O. Box 1750,
Zip 68848–1705; tel. 308/865–2000; Michelle Hansen, Director), (Nonreporting)
A1 2 3 5 10 **S** Catholic Health Initiatives, Englewood, CO
Primary Contact: Michael H. Schnieders, FACHE, President
CFO: Lisa Webb, Vice President for Operational Finance
CMO: Dennis Edwards, M.D., Vice President Medical Affairs
CIO: Katie Gartner, Director Health Information Management
CNO: Carol R. Wahl, R.N., Vice President Patient Care Services
Web address: www.gshs.org
Control: Other not–for–profit (including NFP Corporation) **Service:** General
Medical and Surgical

Staffed Beds: 233

GOOD SAMARITAN HEALTH SYSTEMS See CHI Health Good Samaritan

★ ◯ **KEARNEY REGIONAL MEDICAL CENTER (280134)**, 804 22nd Avenue,
Zip 68845–2206; tel. 855/404–5762, (Nonreporting) **A**10 11
Primary Contact: Larry Speicher, Chief Executive Officer
CFO: Steve Regier, Chief Financial Officer
CIO: Travis Gregg, Director Support Services
CHR: Steve Beck, MS, Director Human Resources
CNO: Adrienne Carney, R.N., Director Nursing and Surgical Services
Web address: www.kearneyregional.com
Control: Partnership, Investor–owned, for–profit **Service:** General Medical and
Surgical

Staffed Beds: 44

KIMBALL—Kimball County

★ **KIMBALL HEALTH SERVICES (281305)**, 505 South Burg Street,
Zip 69145–1398; tel. 308/235–1952, (Nonreporting) **A**10 18
Primary Contact: Ken Hunter, R.N., Chief Executive Officer
CFO: Melissa Prante, Chief Financial Officer
CMO: James Plate, M.D., Chief of Staff
CIO: Charles Walker, Director Information Technology
CHR: Jim Imler, Director Human Resources
CNO: Richard Harriger, Director of Emergency Services
Web address: www.kimballhealth.org
Control: County–Government, nonfederal **Service:** General Medical and Surgical

Staffed Beds: 12

LEXINGTON—Dawson County

★ ◇ **LEXINGTON REGIONAL HEALTH CENTER (281361)**, 1201 North Erie
Street, Zip 68850–1560, Mailing Address: P.O. Box 980, Zip 68850–0980;
tel. 308/324–5651, (Nonreporting) **A**5 10 18 21
Primary Contact: Leslie Marsh, Chief Executive Officer
COO: Jim Hain, Chief Operating Officer
CFO: Wade Eschenbrenner, Chief Financial Officer
CMO: Francisca Acosta–Carlson, M.D., Chief of Staff
CIO: Robb Hanna, Executive Director Information Technology
CHR: Jill Denker, Executive Director Human Resources
CNO: Nicole Thorell, R.N., Chief Nursing Officer
Web address: www.lexingtonregional.org
Control: Hospital district or authority, Government, nonfederal **Service:** General
Medical and Surgical

Staffed Beds: 25

LINCOLN—Lancaster County

⊠ △ **BRYAN MEDICAL CENTER (280003)**, 1600 South 48th Street,
Zip 68506–1299; tel. 402/489–0200, (Includes BRYAN MEDICAL CENTER–EAST,
1600 South 48th Street, tel. 402/489–0200; BRYAN MEDICAL CENTER–WEST,
2300 South 16th Street, Zip 68502–3781; tel. 402/475–1011) **A**1 2 7 10 **F**3 4
5 12 13 15 17 18 19 20 22 24 26 28 29 30 31 34 35 37 38 39 40 43 45 46
47 48 49 50 54 56 57 58 59 61 64 68 70 71 72 74 75 76 77 78 79 81 82
85 86 87 89 90 92 93 96 98 99 101 102 103 104 105 107 108 110 111
114 115 116 117 118 119 120 123 126 129 130 131 132 135 145 146 147
148 **S** Bryan Health, Lincoln, NE
Primary Contact: John T. Woodrich, President and Chief Operating Officer
CFO: Russell Gronewold, Chief Financial Officer
CMO: John Trapp, Vice President Medical Affairs
CIO: George Carr, Chief Information Officer
CHR: Jan Garvin, Vice President Human Resources
CNO: Lisa M. Vail, R.N., Chief Nursing Officer and Vice President of Patient Care
Services
Web address: www.bryanhealth.com
Control: Other not–for–profit (including NFP Corporation) **Service:** General
Medical and Surgical

Staffed Beds: 540 **Admissions:** 26078 **Census:** 318 **Outpatient Visits:** 193842 **Births:** 3376 **Total Expense ($000):** 479908 **Payroll Expense ($000):** 169919 **Personnel:** 2885

★ **CHI HEALTH NEBRASKA HEART (280128)**, 7500 South 91st Street,
Zip 68526–9437; tel. 402/327–2700, (Nonreporting) **A**10 **S** Catholic Health
Initiatives, Englewood, CO
Primary Contact: Dan Schonlau, Interim President
CFO: Dan Schonlau, Chief Financial Officer and Vice President of Finance
CMO: Peter Dionisopoulos, Chief Medical Officer
CNO: Jackie Mendoza, Chief Nursing Officer
Web address: www.CHIhealthNebraskaHeart.com
Control: Other not–for–profit (including NFP Corporation) **Service:** Heart

Staffed Beds: 52

NE

Hospital, Medicare Provider Number, Address, Telephone, Approval, Facility, and Physician Codes, Health Care System

★ American Hospital Association (AHA) membership ◯ Healthcare Facilities Accreditation Program ⇑ Center for Improvement in Healthcare Quality Accreditation
□ The Joint Commission accreditation ◇ DNV Healthcare Inc. accreditation △ Commission on Accreditation of Rehabilitation Facilities (CARF) accreditation

✠ **CHI HEALTH ST ELIZABETH (280020)**, 555 South 70th Street, Zip 68510–2494; tel. 402/219–8000 **A**1 2 3 5 10 **F**3 8 11 12 13 15 16 29 30 31 34 35 37 39 40 44 45 46 47 48 49 50 51 53 55 58 59 60 61 64 65 68 70 72 74 75 76 78 79 80 81 84 85 86 87 89 92 107 108 110 111 114 115 116 117 118 119 120 121 123 124 126 129 130 131 132 144 145 146 147 148 **P**8 **S** Catholic Health Initiatives, Englewood, CO
Primary Contact: Kim S. Moore, FACHE, President
CFO: Dan Schonlau, Chief Financial Officer and Vice President of Finance
CMO: Michael Ferris, M.D., Chief Medical Officer
CIO: Richard Bohaty, Director Information Technology
CHR: Nancy Wallace, Senior Vice President, Chief Human Resources Officer
CNO: Elizabeth A. Raetz, R.N., Vice President Nursing and Chief Nursing Officer
Web address: www.saintelizabethonline.com
Control: Other not–for–profit (including NFP Corporation) **Service:** General Medical and Surgical

Staffed Beds: 260 **Admissions:** 8538 **Census:** 100 **Outpatient Visits:** 88880 **Births:** 1548 **Total Expense ($000):** 186372 **Payroll Expense ($000):** 55572 **Personnel:** 964

LINCOLN DIVISION See Veterans Affairs Nebraska–Western Iowa Health Care System – Lincoln

☐ **LINCOLN REGIONAL CENTER (284003)**, West Prospector Place and South Folsom, Zip 68522–2299, Mailing Address: P.O. Box 94949, Zip 68509–4949; tel. 402/479–5207, (Nonreporting) **A**1 10
Primary Contact: William R. Gibson, Chief Executive Officer
COO: Stacey Werth–Sweeney, Facility Operating Officer
CFO: Randy Willey, Business Manager
CMO: Vijay Dewan, M.D., Clinical Director
CHR: Scott Rasmussen, Director Human Resources
Web address: www.hhs.state.ne.us/beh/rc
Control: State–Government, nonfederal **Service:** Psychiatric

Staffed Beds: 244

LINCOLN SURGICAL HOSPITAL (280127), 1710 South 70th Street, Suite 200, Zip 68506–1677; tel. 402/484–9090, (Nonreporting) **A**10
Primary Contact: Robb Linafelter, Chief Executive Officer
Web address: www.lincolnsurgery.com
Control: Corporation, Investor–owned, for–profit **Service:** Surgical

Staffed Beds: 7

MADONNA REHABILITATION HOSPITAL (282000), 5401 South Street, Zip 68506–2150; tel. 402/413–3000, (Nonreporting)
Primary Contact: Paul Dongilli, Jr., Ph.D., FACHE, President and Chief Executive Officer
Web address: www.madonna.org/
Control: Other not–for–profit (including NFP Corporation) **Service:** Long–Term Acute Care hospital

Staffed Beds: 300

△ **MADONNA REHABILITATION HOSPITAL (283025)**, 5401 South Street, Zip 68506–2134; tel. 402/489–7102, (Nonreporting) **A**7 10
Primary Contact: Paul Dongilli, Jr., Ph.D., FACHE, President and Chief Executive Officer
CFO: Victor J. Witkowicz, Senior Vice President and Chief Financial Officer
CMO: Thomas Stadler, M.D., Vice President Medical Affairs and Chief Medical Officer
CIO: David Rolfe, Chief Information Officer
CHR: Lou Ann Manske, Director Human Resources
Web address: www.madonna.org
Control: Other not–for–profit (including NFP Corporation) **Service:** Rehabilitation

Staffed Beds: 308

NEBRASKA PENAL AND CORRECTIONAL HOSPITAL, 14th And Pioneer Streets, Zip 68501, Mailing Address: P.O. Box 94661, Zip 94661; tel. 402/471–3161, (Nonreporting)
Primary Contact: Randy T. Kohl, M.D., Deputy Director, Health Services
Web address: www.corrections.nebraska.gov
Control: State–Government, nonfederal **Service:** Hospital unit of an institution (prison hospital, college infimary, etc.)

Staffed Beds: 12

✠ **SELECT SPECIALTY HOSPITAL – LINCOLN (282002)**, 2300 South 16th Street, 7th Floor, Zip 68502–3704; tel. 402/483–8444, (Nonreporting) **A**1 10 **S** Select Medical Corporation, Mechanicsburg, PA
Primary Contact: Scott Butterfield, Chief Executive Officer
Control: Corporation, Investor–owned, for–profit **Service:** Long–Term Acute Care hospital

Staffed Beds: 24

★ **VETERANS AFFAIRS NEBRASKA–WESTERN IOWA HEALTH CARE SYSTEM – LINCOLN**, 600 South 70th Street, Zip 68510–2493; tel. 402/489–3802, (Includes LINCOLN DIVISION, 600 South 70th Street, tel. 402/489–3802), (Nonreporting) **S** Department of Veterans Affairs, Washington, DC
Primary Contact: Don Burman, Director
CIO: David Daiker, Chief Information Resource Management
CHR: Dave Peters, Chief Human Resources Officer
Web address: www.nebraska.va.gov/
Control: Veterans Affairs, Government, federal **Service:** General Medical and Surgical

Staffed Beds: 132

LYNCH—Boyd County

NIOBRARA VALLEY HOSPITAL (281303), 401 South Fifth Street, Zip 68746–0118, Mailing Address: P.O. Box 118, Zip 68746–0118; tel. 402/569–2451, (Nonreporting) **A**10 18 **S** Faith Regional Health Services, Norfolk, NE
Primary Contact: Kelly Kalkowski, Chief Executive Officer
CFO: Martha Nelson, Chief Financial Officer
CMO: James Keil, M.D., Chief Medical Officer
CHR: Trudy Nelson, Chief Human Resource Officer
CNO: Debra Dawn Hanzlik, R.N., Director of Nursing
Web address: www.nvhcares.org
Control: Other not–for–profit (including NFP Corporation) **Service:** General Medical and Surgical

Staffed Beds: 20

MCCOOK—Red Willow County

✠ **COMMUNITY HOSPITAL (281363)**, 1301 East H Street, Zip 69001–1328, Mailing Address: P.O. Box 1328, Zip 69001–1328; tel. 308/344–2650 **A**1 10 18 **F**3 11 13 15 28 29 31 34 35 40 41 45 48 50 51 57 62 63 64 75 77 78 79 81 85 107 110 111 114 119 120 121 127 129 130 131 132 133 135
Primary Contact: James P. Ulrich, Jr., President and Chief Executive Officer
CFO: Troy Bruntz, Vice President Finance and Chief Financial Officer
CMO: Jason Blomstedt, Chief of Staff
CIO: Lori Beeby, Director Information Systems
CHR: Leanne R. Miller, Director Human Resources
Web address: www.chmccook.org
Control: Other not–for–profit (including NFP Corporation) **Service:** General Medical and Surgical

Staffed Beds: 25 **Admissions:** 870 **Census:** 6 **Outpatient Visits:** 30256 **Births:** 143 **Total Expense ($000):** 42760 **Payroll Expense ($000):** 14880 **Personnel:** 253

MINDEN—Kearney County

★ **KEARNEY COUNTY HEALTH SERVICES (281306)**, 727 East First Street, Zip 68959–1705; tel. 308/832–3400, (Total facility includes 34 beds in nursing home–type unit) **A**10 18 **F**10 15 28 34 40 41 45 59 64 65 67 81 97 99 103 104 107 110 115 119 127 128 130 133 145 146 147 148 **P**6
Primary Contact: Luke Poore, Chief Executive Officer
CFO: Kayla Rhynalds, Interim Chief Financial Officer
CMO: Douglas Althouse, Chief Medical Staff
CHR: Rebecca L. Cooke, Director Human Resources
CNO: Mary Bunger, R.N., Director Nursing Services
Web address: www.kchs.org
Control: County–Government, nonfederal **Service:** General Medical and Surgical

Staffed Beds: 44 **Admissions:** 138 **Census:** 28 **Outpatient Visits:** 7887 **Births:** 0 **Total Expense ($000):** 10204 **Payroll Expense ($000):** 4491 **Personnel:** 123

NEBRASKA CITY—Otoe County

★ **CHI HEALTH ST. MARY'S (281342)**, 1301 Grundman Boulevard, Zip 68410; tel. 402/873–3321 **A**10 18 **F**3 13 15 18 28 31 34 35 40 43 45 57 59 64 66 67 68 69 75 76 78 79 81 82 85 87 89 97 107 110 111 114 115 118 119 127 128 129 130 132 133 135 146 147 148 **S** Catholic Health Initiatives, Englewood, CO
Primary Contact: Daniel J. Kelly, President
CFO: Tim H. Schnack, Vice President Operations Finance
CMO: Jonathan Stelling, M.D., Vice President Medical Affairs
CNO: Brenda Jean Sebek, R.N., Vice President Patient Care Services
Web address: www.chihealthstmarys.com
Control: Church–operated, Nongovernment, not–for–profit **Service:** General Medical and Surgical

Staffed Beds: 18 **Admissions:** 395 **Census:** 3 **Outpatient Visits:** 30734 **Births:** 126 **Total Expense ($000):** 25752 **Payroll Expense ($000):** 9126 **Personnel:** 140

NELIGH—Antelope County

★ **ANTELOPE MEMORIAL HOSPITAL (281326)**, 102 West Ninth Street,
Zip 68756–1114, Mailing Address: P.O. Box 229, Zip 68756–0229;
tel. 402/887–4151 **A**10 18 **F**7 8 13 15 28 35 36 40 41 53 56 57 59 62 63
64 68 75 76 77 79 81 89 93 107 110 119 127 128 130 131 133 147 **P**6
Primary Contact: Jack W. Green, Administrator
CFO: Martha Nelson, Chief Financial Officer
CMO: Troy Dawson, M.D., President Medical Staff
CIO: Kevin Trease, Chief Information Officer
CHR: Mary A. Schwager, Director Human Resources
CNO: Merry Sprout, R.N., Chief Nursing Officer
Web address: www.amhne.org/
Control: Other not–for–profit (including NFP Corporation) **Service:** General
Medical and Surgical

Staffed Beds: 25 **Admissions:** 352 **Census:** 6 **Outpatient Visits:** 18875
Births: 19 **Total Expense ($000):** 14489 **Payroll Expense ($000):** 6201
Personnel: 121

NORFOLK—Madison County

⊠ **FAITH REGIONAL HEALTH SERVICES (280125)**, 2700 West Norfolk Avenue,
Zip 68701–4438, Mailing Address: P.O. Box 869, Zip 68702–0869;
tel. 402/644–7201, (Includes EAST CAMPUS, 1500 Koenigstein Avenue,
Zip 68701; tel. 402/371–3402; WEST CAMPUS, 2700 Norfolk Avenue,
Zip 68701, Mailing Address: P.O. Box 869, Zip 68702–0869;
tel. 402/371–4880), (Total facility includes 62 beds in nursing home–type unit)
A1 2 3 5 10 20 **F**3 4 8 10 11 13 15 16 17 18 20 22 24 26 28 29 30 31 34
35 40 43 44 45 46 49 50 53 57 58 59 61 62 63 64 65 67 68 70 71 72 73
74 75 76 77 78 79 80 81 82 84 85 86 87 88 89 90 91 92 93 96 98 100
102 107 110 111 114 115 119 120 121 123 128 129 130 131 132 135 146
147 148 **P**6 **S** Faith Regional Health Services, Norfolk, NE
Primary Contact: Mark D. Klosterman, FACHE, President and Chief Executive
Officer
CFO: Johnathan Wilker, Vice President Finance and Chief Financial Officer
CMO: Dean O. French, M.D., Chief of Staff
CIO: Brian Sterud, Chief Information Officer
CHR: Janet Pinkelman, Director Human Resources
Web address: www.frhs.org
Control: Other not–for–profit (including NFP Corporation) **Service:** General
Medical and Surgical

Staffed Beds: 146 **Admissions:** 5009 **Census:** 132 **Outpatient Visits:** 87894
Births: 908 **Total Expense ($000):** 150743 **Payroll Expense ($000):** 48170
Personnel: 1026

NORTH PLATTE—Lincoln County

⊠ **GREAT PLAINS HEALTH (280065)**, 601 West Leota Street, Zip 69101–6598,
Mailing Address: P.O. Box 1167, Zip 69103–1167; tel. 308/568–8000 **A**1 2 3 5
10 **F**3 8 12 13 15 18 20 22 28 29 30 31 34 35 40 43 45 48 50 51 57 59 60
62 63 68 70 73 74 75 76 78 79 81 82 84 85 89 93 98 99 102 103 104 105
107 108 110 111 115 116 117 119 120 121 122 124 129 130 131 132 135
145 146 147 148 **P**8
Primary Contact: Melvin McNea, Chief Executive Officer
CFO: Krystal Claymore, Chief Financial Officer
CMO: Howard Shaw, M.D., Chief Medical Officer
CIO: Brandon Kelliher, Chief Information Officer
CHR: Jayne Johnson, Director Human Resources
Web address: www.gphealth.org
Control: Other not–for–profit (including NFP Corporation) **Service:** General
Medical and Surgical

Staffed Beds: 114 **Admissions:** 5745 **Census:** 60 **Outpatient Visits:** 277081
Births: 511 **Total Expense ($000):** 142748 **Payroll Expense ($000):** 53980
Personnel: 968

O'NEILL—Holt County

★ **AVERA ST. ANTHONY'S HOSPITAL (281329)**, 300 North Second Street,
Zip 68763–1514, Mailing Address: P.O. Box 270, Oneill, Zip 68763–0270;
tel. 402/336–2611 **A**5 10 18 **F**3 8 13 15 18 28 29 30 31 32 34 35 38 40 41
43 44 45 46 48 57 59 60 64 65 68 74 75 76 77 78 79 81 82 83 84 86 87
90 91 93 94 96 97 100 101 107 108 110 111 112 114 119 124 127
128 129 130 131 133 135 143 146 148 **P**1 6 **S** Avera Health, Sioux Falls, SD
Primary Contact: Todd Consbruck, President and Chief Executive Officer
CFO: Michael Garman, Chief Financial Officer
CIO: Michael Garman, Chief Financial Officer
CHR: Kathryn Benson, Human Resources Partner
Web address: www.avera.org/st-anthonys
Control: Church–operated, Nongovernment, not–for profit **Service:** General
Medical and Surgical

Staffed Beds: 25 **Admissions:** 895 **Census:** 9 **Outpatient Visits:** 46535
Births: 167 **Total Expense ($000):** 32425 **Payroll Expense ($000):** 13334
Personnel: 203

OAKLAND—Burt County

★ **OAKLAND MERCY HOSPITAL (281321)**, 601 East Second Street,
Zip 68045–1499; tel. 402/685–5601 **A**10 18 **F**11 15 18 20 22 24 26 28 29
30 31 34 35 40 43 44 50 57 59 75 81 93 97 107 108 110 114 119 127 128
132 133 148 **P**6 **S** Trinity Health, Livonia, MI
Primary Contact: John W. Werner, Chief Executive Officer
COO: John W. Werner, Chief Executive Officer
CFO: Terri Mentink, Chief Financial Officer
CMO: Tracie Martin, M.D., Chief Medical Officer
CNO: Jayma Brown, Director of Nursing
Web address: www.oaklandhospital.org
Control: Church–operated, Nongovernment, not–for profit **Service:** General
Medical and Surgical

Staffed Beds: 18 **Admissions:** 130 **Census:** 2 **Outpatient Visits:** 5615
Births: 0 **Personnel:** 50

OGALLALA—Keith County

★ **OGALLALA COMMUNITY HOSPITAL (281355)**, 2601 North Spruce Street,
Zip 69153–2465; tel. 308/284–4011 **A**10 18 **F**3 13 15 29 31 34 35 40 41 43
45 59 75 77 78 79 81 82 85 87 93 94 97 107 110 115 119 129 133 147
S Banner Health, Phoenix, AZ
Primary Contact: Drew H. Dostal, R.N., FACHE, Chief Executive Officer
CFO: Dena Klockman, Chief Financial Officer
CMO: Shane Banks, M.D., Chief of Staff
CHR: Patricia Shaner, Interim Chief Human Resources Officer
CNO: Aileen Chandler, Chief Nursing Officer
Web address: www.bannerhealth.com/Locations/Nebraska/Ogallala+Community+
Hospital
Control: Other not–for–profit (including NFP Corporation) **Service:** General
Medical and Surgical

Staffed Beds: 18 **Admissions:** 448 **Census:** 4 **Outpatient Visits:** 21212
Births: 53 **Total Expense ($000):** 14752 **Payroll Expense ($000):** 6106
Personnel: 107

OMAHA—Douglas County

☐ **BOYS TOWN NATIONAL RESEARCH HOSPITAL (283300)**, 555 North 30th
Street, Zip 68131–2198; tel. 402/498–6511 **A**1 3 5 10 **F**3 34 35 58 65 68 79
81 86 87 89 97 99 104 106 107 108 111 119 129 130 131 **P**6
Primary Contact: John K. Arch, FACHE, Director
CFO: Leigh Jean Koinzan, Director Finance
CMO: Edward Kolb, M.D., Medical Director
CIO: Ann Ducey, Chief Information Officer
CHR: Michael Gell, Director Human Resources
CNO: Patricia Allgeier, R.N., Chief Nursing Officer
Web address: www.boystownhospital.org
Control: Other not–for–profit (including NFP Corporation) **Service:** Children's
general

Staffed Beds: 131 **Admissions:** 167 **Census:** 1 **Outpatient Visits:** 211146
Births: 0 **Total Expense ($000):** 106729 **Payroll Expense ($000):** 46069
Personnel: 874

⊠ **CHI HEALTH BERGAN MERCY (280060)**, 7500 Mercy Road,
Zip 68124–2319; tel. 402/398–6060, (Includes CHI HEALTH CREIGHTON
UNIVERSITY MEDICAL CENTER, 601 North 30th Street, Zip 68131–2197;
tel. 402/449–4000; Kevin J. Nokels, FACHE, President; LASTING HOPE
RECOVERY CENTER, 415 South 25th Avenue, Zip 68131; tel. 402/717–5300;
Robin Conyers, Administrator) **A**1 2 3 5 8 10 **F**3 8 11 13 15 17 18 20 22 24
26 28 29 30 31 32 34 35 37 38 40 43 44 45 46 47 48 49 50 51 53 54 55
56 57 58 59 60 61 62 63 64 65 68 70 72 74 75 76 77 78 79 80 81 82 83
84 85 86 87 89 92 93 97 98 100 105 107 108 109 110 111 114 115 116
117 118 119 120 121 123 124 126 127 130 131 132 134 143 144 145 146
147 148 **P**8 **S** Catholic Health Initiatives, Englewood, CO
Primary Contact: Marie E. Knedler, R.N., FACHE, President
COO: Chris Evans, Vice President Operations
CFO: Tim H. Schnack, Vice President Financial Services
CMO: Kevin Reagan, M.D., Chief Medical Officer
CIO: Karun Kapur, Chief Information Officer
CHR: Nancy Wallace, Vice President Human Resources
Web address: www.alegent.com/bergan
Control: Church–operated, Nongovernment, not–for profit **Service:** General
Medical and Surgical

Staffed Beds: 336 **Admissions:** 11639 **Census:** 146 **Outpatient Visits:**
103550 **Births:** 3295 **Total Expense ($000):** 91597 **Payroll Expense
($000):** 70927 **Personnel:** 1270

NE

Hospital, Medicare Provider Number, Address, Telephone, Approval, Facility, and Physician Codes, Health Care System

★ American Hospital Association (AHA) membership   ◯ Healthcare Facilities Accreditation Program   ⇑ Center for Improvement in Healthcare Quality Accreditation
☐ The Joint Commission accreditation   ◇ DNV Healthcare Inc. accreditation   △ Commission on Accreditation of Rehabilitation Facilities (CARF) accreditation

✠ △ **CHI HEALTH IMMANUEL (280081)**, 6901 North 72nd Street, Zip 68122–1799; tel. 402/572–2121 **A**1 2 3 5 7 10 **F**3 4 5 6 11 12 13 15 17 18 20 22 26 28 29 30 31 32 34 35 36 37 38 40 43 44 45 49 50 51 53 55 56 57 58 59 62 63 64 68 70 72 73 74 75 76 77 78 79 80 81 82 83 84 85 86 87 88 89 90 91 92 93 96 97 98 99 100 101 102 103 104 105 106 107 108 109 110 111 114 115 117 118 119 120 121 123 124 126 128 129 130 131 132 134 136 142 146 147 148 **P**8 **S** Catholic Health Initiatives, Englewood, CO
Primary Contact: Ann Schumacher, R.N., MSN, FACHE, President
CFO: Tim H. Schnack, Chief Financial Officer
CMO: Joseph Hoagbin, M.D., Chief Medical Officer
CHR: Nancy Wallace, Vice President Human Resources
Web address: www.alegent.com/immanuel
Control: Church–operated, Nongovernment, not–for profit **Service:** General Medical and Surgical

Staffed Beds: 289 **Admissions:** 9591 **Census:** 141 **Outpatient Visits:** 108353 **Births:** 528 **Total Expense ($000):** 139172 **Payroll Expense ($000):** 55079 **Personnel:** 991

✠ **CHI HEALTH LAKESIDE (280130)**, 16901 Lakeside Hills Court, Zip 68130–2318; tel. 402/717–8000 **A**1 2 5 10 **F**3 8 12 13 15 17 18 20 22 26 28 29 30 31 32 34 35 36 38 44 45 46 49 53 54 55 56 59 60 63 64 68 70 72 73 74 75 76 77 78 79 81 82 83 84 85 86 93 94 97 99 100 102 103 104 107 108 110 111 114 115 118 119 120 121 122 123 124 126 129 130 131 132 134 143 146 147 148 **P**8 **S** Catholic Health Initiatives, Englewood, CO
Primary Contact: Cindy Alloway, President
COO: Joan E. Neuhaus, Division Senior Vice President Chief Operating Officer
CFO: Tyler DeJong, Director, Operational Finance
CMO: Patricia Murdock–Langan, M.D., Chief Medical Officer
CIO: Thomas Haley, Information Technology Systems Site Director
CHR: Nancy Wallace, Division Senior Vice President, Chief Human Resource Officer
CNO: Brenda Bergman–Evans, Chief Nursing Officer
Web address: www.CHIhealth.com
Control: Church–operated, Nongovernment, not–for profit **Service:** General Medical and Surgical

Staffed Beds: 135 **Admissions:** 6261 **Census:** 66 **Outpatient Visits:** 83590 **Births:** 854 **Total Expense ($000):** 248299 **Payroll Expense ($000):** 33450 **Personnel:** 595

✠ **CHILDREN'S HOSPITAL AND MEDICAL CENTER (283301)**, 8200 Dodge Street, Zip 68114–4113; tel. 402/955–5400 **A**1 3 5 10 **F**3 7 11 12 13 19 21 23 25 27 29 30 31 32 34 35 40 41 43 45 46 47 48 49 50 54 55 58 59 60 62 64 65 68 72 74 75 76 77 78 79 81 82 84 85 87 88 89 92 93 99 104 107 108 111 115 116 117 130 131 132 137 143 144 145 146 148 **P**6
Primary Contact: Richard G. Azizkhan, M.D., President and Chief Executive Officer
COO: Kathy L. English, R.N., Executive Vice President and Chief Operating Officer
CFO: Amy Hatcher, Chief Financial Officer
CMO: Carl H. Gumbiner, M.D., Senior Vice President Medical Affairs and Chief Medical Officer
CIO: Mark Stastny, Vice President and Chief Information Officer
CHR: Patricia Schulz, Vice President, Human Resources
CNO: Debra Arnow, R.N., VP Patient Care & Chief Nursing Officer
Web address: www.childrensomaha.org
Control: Other not–for–profit (including NFP Corporation) **Service:** Children's general

Staffed Beds: 126 **Admissions:** 4547 **Census:** 94 **Outpatient Visits:** 345171 **Births:** 5 **Total Expense ($000):** 327733 **Payroll Expense ($000):** 143292 **Personnel:** 1765

★ ○ **DOUGLAS COUNTY COMMUNITY MENTAL HEALTH CENTER (284009)**, 4102 Woolworth Avenue, Zip 68105–1899; tel. 402/444–7000 **A**3 5 10 11 **F**5 29 38 98 101 104 105
Primary Contact: Sherry L. Glasnapp, Director
CFO: DeDe Will, Director Finance
CMO: Sidney A. Kauzlarich, M.D., Medical Director
CIO: Dianne Wallace, County Information Manager
CHR: Karen Buche, Chief Human Resource Officer
CNO: Marti Christensen, Director of Psychiatric Nursing
Web address: www.co.douglas.ne.us
Control: County–Government, nonfederal **Service:** Psychiatric

Staffed Beds: 16 **Admissions:** 889 **Census:** 10 **Outpatient Visits:** 0 **Births:** 0

MIDWEST SURGICAL HOSPITAL (280131), 7915 Farnam Drive, Zip 68114–4504; tel. 402/399–1900, (Nonreporting) **A**3 10
Primary Contact: Charles Livingston, Chief Executive Officer
Web address: www.mwsurgicalhospital.com
Control: Corporation, Investor–owned, for–profit **Service:** Surgical

Staffed Beds: 19

✠ **NEBRASKA MEDICINE – NEBRASKA MEDICAL CENTER (280013)**, 987400 Nebraska Medical Center, Zip 68198–7400; tel. 402/552–2000 **A**1 2 3 5 8 10 **F**3 6 8 9 11 12 13 15 16 17 18 20 22 24 25 26 28 29 30 31 32 34 35 36 37 38 39 40 41 43 44 45 46 47 48 49 50 51 53 54 55 56 57 58 59 60 61 62 63 64 65 66 68 70 71 72 74 75 76 77 78 79 80 81 82 84 85 86 87 88 89 91 92 93 94 96 97 98 99 100 101 102 103 104 107 108 110 111 113 114 115 116 117 118 119 120 121 123 124 126 127 129 130 131 132 134 135 136 137 138 139 140 141 142 143 144 145 146 147 148 **P**5 6 8
Primary Contact: Daniel J. DeBehnke, M.D., Chief Executive Officer
COO: Dennis Bierle, Chief Operating Officer
CFO: Stephanie Daubert, Chief Financial Officer
CMO: Harris Frankel, M.D., Interim Chief Medical Officer
CIO: Michael A. Ash, Chief Transformation Officer
CHR: Frank Venuto, Chief Human Capital Officer
CNO: Suzanne Langan Nuss, M.D., Chief Nursing Officer
Web address: www.nebraskamed.com
Control: Other not–for–profit (including NFP Corporation) **Service:** General Medical and Surgical

Staffed Beds: 540 **Admissions:** 24521 **Census:** 376 **Outpatient Visits:** 459274 **Births:** 1786 **Total Expense ($000):** 847350 **Payroll Expense ($000):** 327168 **Personnel:** 5374

✠ △ **NEBRASKA METHODIST HOSPITAL (280040)**, 8303 Dodge Street, Zip 68114–4199; tel. 402/354–4000, (Includes METHODIST WOMEN'S HOSPITAL, 707 North 190th Plaza, Elkhorn, Zip 68022–3974; tel. 402/815–4000; Susan Korth, M.P.H., Ph.D., Vice President and Chief Operating Officer) **A**1 2 3 5 7 10 **F**3 8 11 12 13 15 17 18 20 22 24 26 28 29 30 31 34 35 40 45 46 47 48 49 50 51 52 53 54 55 56 57 58 59 62 63 64 65 66 68 70 72 74 75 76 77 78 79 81 82 83 84 85 86 87 90 91 92 93 96 100 101 104 107 108 110 111 114 115 117 118 119 120 121 123 124 126 129 130 132 135 136 141 143 146 147 148 **S** Nebraska Methodist Health System, Inc., Omaha, NE
Primary Contact: Stephen L. Goeser, FACHE, President and Chief Executive Officer
CFO: Linda K. Burt, Corporate Vice President Finance
CMO: William Shiffermiller, M.D., Vice President Medical Affairs
CHR: Holly Huerter, Vice President Human Resources
CNO: Teri Tipton, MSN, Chief Nursing Officer and Vice President Patient Care Services
Web address: www.bestcare.org
Control: Other not–for–profit (including NFP Corporation) **Service:** General Medical and Surgical

Staffed Beds: 377 **Admissions:** 19240 **Census:** 268 **Outpatient Visits:** 133583 **Births:** 5377 **Total Expense ($000):** 452224 **Payroll Expense ($000):** 169000 **Personnel:** 2705

☐ **NEBRASKA ORTHOPAEDIC HOSPITAL (280129)**, 2808 South 143rd Plaza, Zip 68144–5611; tel. 402/609–1600, (Nonreporting) **A**1 3 5 10
Primary Contact: Levi Scheppers, Chief Executive Officer
COO: Mark E. Longacre, FACHE, Chief Operating Officer
CFO: Anna McCaslin, Chief Financial Officer
CMO: Ian Crabb, M.D., Chief Medical Officer
CIO: Tim Pugsley, Chief Information Officer
CHR: Lori L. Thompson, Manager Human Resources
CNO: Nancy Laughlin, R.N., Chief Nursing Officer
Web address: www.neorthohospital.com
Control: Partnership, Investor–owned, for–profit **Service:** Orthopedic

Staffed Beds: 24

✠ **NEBRASKA SPINE HOSPITAL (280133)**, 6901 North 72nd Street, Suite 20300, Zip 68122–1755, Mailing Address: 6901 North 72nd Street, Zip 68122–1709; tel. 402/572–3000, (Nonreporting) **A**1 10
Primary Contact: Cory Kruger, Interim Chief Executive Officer
CNO: Teresa Hawlik, MSN, Chief Nurse Executive
Web address: www.nebraskaspinehospital.com
Control: Partnership, Investor–owned, for–profit **Service:** Orthopedic

Staffed Beds: 34

✠ **SELECT SPECIALTY HOSPITAL–OMAHA (282001)**, 1870 South 75th Street, Zip 68124–1700; tel. 402/361–5700, (Nonreporting) **A**1 10 **S** Select Medical Corporation, Mechanicsburg, PA
Primary Contact: Thomas N. Theroult, Chief Executive Officer
COO: Joel White, Chief Operating Officer
CMO: Guillermo Huerta, M.D., Chief Medical Officer
CHR: Laurna Hoss, Human Resource Coordinator
CNO: Brenda O'Gorman, R.N., Interim Chief Nursing Officer
Web address: www.selectspecialtyhospitals.com/company/locations/omahacentral.aspx
Control: Corporation, Investor–owned, for–profit **Service:** Long–Term Acute Care hospital

Staffed Beds: 52

NE

☒ **VETERANS AFFAIRS NEBRASKA–WESTERN IOWA HEALTH CARE SYSTEM**, 4101 Woolworth Avenue, Zip 68105–1873; tel. 402/346–8800, (Total facility includes 38 beds in nursing home–type unit) **A**1 2 3 5 8 **F**3 4 5 8 9 12 18 20 22 29 30 31 34 35 36 38 39 40 45 46 47 48 49 50 51 53 54 56 57 58 59 60 61 63 64 65 70 71 74 75 77 78 79 81 82 83 84 85 86 87 91 92 93 94 95 96 97 98 100 101 102 103 104 105 106 107 111 115 117 118 119 127 128 129 130 132 135 143 144 145 146 147 148 **S** Department of Veterans Affairs, Washington, DC
Primary Contact: Don Burman, Director
COO: Denise Harrison, Associate Director
CFO: Kirk Kay, Chief Financial Officer
CMO: Grace Stringfellow, M.D., Chief of Staff
CIO: Jennifer Rosenbalm, Manager Business Office
CHR: Cheryl M. DeWispelare, Chief Human Resources Officer
CNO: Eileen M. Kingston, R.N., Nurse Executive, Associate Director Patient Care
Web address: www.nebraska.va.gov/
Control: Veterans Affairs, Government, federal **Service:** General Medical and Surgical

Staffed Beds: 100 **Admissions:** 5903 **Census:** 100 **Outpatient Visits:** 934870 **Births:** 0 **Total Expense ($000):** 408721 **Payroll Expense ($000):** 156505 **Personnel:** 2051

ORD—Valley County

★ **VALLEY COUNTY HEALTH SYSTEM (281353)**, 2707 L. Street, Zip 68862–1275; tel. 308/728–4200 **A**10 18 **F**3 7 11 28 29 31 34 35 40 43 45 50 57 59 62 63 64 65 67 75 77 81 82 87 93 97 103 107 111 115 119 127 128 129 130 132 133 143 148 **P**8
Primary Contact: Nancy Glaubke, Chief Executive Officer
CFO: Ashley Woodward, Director Financial Services
CMO: Jennifer Bengston, M.D., Chief Medical Officer
CIO: Shane Molacek, Chief Information Officer
CHR: Danielle Proskocil, Director Human Resources
CNO: Vicki Bredthauer, R.N., Director of Nursing
Web address: www.valleycountyhealthsystem.org
Control: County–Government, nonfederal **Service:** General Medical and Surgical

Staffed Beds: 16 **Admissions:** 439 **Census:** 6 **Outpatient Visits:** 30614 **Births:** 2 **Total Expense ($000):** 23627 **Payroll Expense ($000):** 9466 **Personnel:** 156

OSCEOLA—Polk County

ANNIE JEFFREY MEMORIAL COUNTY HEALTH CENTER (281314), 531 Beebe Street, Zip 68651–5537, Mailing Address: P.O. Box 428, Zip 68651–0428; tel. 402/747–2031, (Nonreporting) **A**10 18
Primary Contact: Joseph W. Lohrman, Chief Executive Officer
CFO: Joseph W. Lohrman, Chief Executive Officer
CMO: David Jameson, M.D., Chief of Staff
CIO: Frank Vrba, Chief Information Officer
CHR: Sue Leif, R.N., Director Human Resources
Web address: www.ajhc.org
Control: County–Government, nonfederal **Service:** General Medical and Surgical

Staffed Beds: 12

OSHKOSH—Garden County

★ **REGIONAL WEST GARDEN COUNTY (281310)**, 1100 West Second Street, Zip 69154–6152; tel. 308/772–3283, (Nonreporting) **A**10 18
Primary Contact: Chad Thompson, Chief Executive Officer
CFO: Jennifer Moffat, Staff Accountant
CMO: Steve Boyer, M.D., Chief Medical Officer
CHR: Ricca Sanford, Director Human Resources
CNO: Trish Davison, R.N., Chief Nursing Officer
Web address: www.gchealth.org
Control: County–Government, nonfederal **Service:** General Medical and Surgical

Staffed Beds: 50

OSMOND—Pierce County

★ **OSMOND GENERAL HOSPITAL (281347)**, 402 North Maple Street, Zip 68765–5726, Mailing Address: P.O. Box 429, Zip 68765–0429; tel. 402/748–3393 **A**10 18 **F**3 28 34 40 57 59 64 69 81 107 133 143 **P**5 6
Primary Contact: Lon Knievel, Chief Executive Officer
CFO: Jodi Aschoff, Chief Financial Officer
CMO: David Mwebe, M.D., Chief of Staff
CNO: Kristen Colsden, Director of Nursing
Web address: www.osmondhospital.com
Control: Other not–for–profit (including NFP Corporation) **Service:** General Medical and Surgical

Staffed Beds: 21 **Admissions:** 105 **Census:** 1 **Outpatient Visits:** 4439 **Births:** 0 **Total Expense ($000):** 7187 **Payroll Expense ($000):** 3410 **Personnel:** 64

PAPILLION—Sarpy County

☒ **CHI HEALTH MIDLANDS (280105)**, 11111 South 84th Street, Zip 68046–4122; tel. 402/593–3000 **A**1 2 5 10 **F**3 11 15 17 18 20 22 26 28 29 30 34 35 36 38 40 42 43 44 45 46 49 50 51 53 56 57 59 60 61 62 63 64 65 68 70 77 79 81 84 85 86 87 93 97 107 110 111 114 115 117 118 119 129 130 131 132 135 143 146 147 **P**8 **S** Catholic Health Initiatives, Englewood, CO
Primary Contact: Cindy Alloway, President
COO: Joan E. Neuhaus, Division Senior Vice President, Chief Operating Officer
CFO: Tyler DeJong, Director of Operational Finance
CMO: Patricia Murdock–Langan, M.D., Chief Medical Officer
CIO: Thomas Haley, Information Technology Systems Site Director
CHR: Nancy Wallace, Division Senior Vice President, Chief Human Resource Officer
CNO: Brenda Bergman–Evans, Chief Nursing Officer
Web address: www.CHIhealth.com
Control: Church–operated, Nongovernment, not–for profit **Service:** General Medical and Surgical

Staffed Beds: 54 **Admissions:** 1596 **Census:** 17 **Outpatient Visits:** 35033 **Births:** 0 **Total Expense ($000):** 35484 **Payroll Expense ($000):** 13148 **Personnel:** 231

PAWNEE CITY—Pawnee County

★ **PAWNEE COUNTY MEMORIAL HOSPITAL AND RURAL HEALTH CLINIC (281302)**, 600 I Street, Zip 68420–3001, Mailing Address: P.O. Box 433, Zip 68420–0433; tel. 402/852–2231 **A**10 18 **F**3 7 15 28 29 30 40 43 45 59 107 119 127 128 130 133 147 **P**6
Primary Contact: Ruth M. Stephens, MSN, R.N., Administrator
CHR: Jennifer Bartels, Director Human Resources
CNO: Eulala Mitchell, Director of Nursing
Web address: www.pawneehospital.com
Control: County–Government, nonfederal **Service:** General Medical and Surgical

Staffed Beds: 11 **Admissions:** 34 **Census:** 1 **Outpatient Visits:** 903 **Births:** 0

PENDER—Thurston County

★ **PENDER COMMUNITY HOSPITAL (281349)**, 100 Hospital Drive, Zip 68047–0100, Mailing Address: P.O. Box 100, Zip 68047–0100; tel. 402/385–3083, (Nonreporting) **A**10 18 **S** Trinity Health, Livonia, MI
Primary Contact: Melissa Kelly, Administrator
COO: Melissa Kelly, Chief Operating Officer
CFO: Melissa Kelly, Chief Financial Officer
CMO: Matt Timm, M.D., Medical Director
CIO: Teresa Heise, Coordinator Management Information Systems
CHR: Nancy Suhr, Manager Human Resources
CNO: Katie Peterson, R.N., Chief Nursing Officer
Web address: www.pendercommunityhospital.com
Control: Hospital district or authority, Government, nonfederal **Service:** General Medical and Surgical

Staffed Beds: 67

PLAINVIEW—Pierce County

★ **CHI HEALTH PLAINVIEW (281346)**, 704 North Third Street, Zip 68769–2047, Mailing Address: P.O. Box 489, Zip 68769–0489; tel. 402/582–4245 **A**10 18 **F**2 12 28 29 30 34 35 40 50 57 59 62 65 67 68 75 81 87 92 94 100 104 107 114 127 128 129 130 132 133 135 143 148 **P**6 **S** Catholic Health Initiatives, Englewood, CO
Primary Contact: Gregory Beckmann, Chief Executive Officer
CFO: Tim H. Schnack, Chief Financial Officer
CMO: Steve Peterson, M.D., Chief of Staff
CHR: Diane Blair, Human Resources and Admissions
CNO: Debra K. Rutledge, R.N., Vice President Nursing Services
Web address: www.alegentcreighton.com/plainview–hospital
Control: Church–operated, Nongovernment, not–for profit **Service:** General Medical and Surgical

Staffed Beds: 15 **Admissions:** 164 **Census:** 2 **Outpatient Visits:** 4154 **Births:** 0 **Total Expense ($000):** 7558 **Payroll Expense ($000):** 2612 **Personnel:** 52

NE

Hospital, Medicare Provider Number, Address, Telephone, Approval, Facility, and Physician Codes, Health Care System

★ American Hospital Association (AHA) membership
□ The Joint Commission accreditation
○ Healthcare Facilities Accreditation Program
◇ DNV Healthcare Inc. accreditation
⇑ Center for Improvement in Healthcare Quality Accreditation
△ Commission on Accreditation of Rehabilitation Facilities (CARF) accreditation

RED CLOUD—Webster County

WEBSTER COUNTY COMMUNITY HOSPITAL (281316), Sixth Avenue and Franklin Street, Zip 68970–0465, Mailing Address: P.O. Box 465, Zip 68970–0465; tel. 402/746–5600 **A**10 18 **F**3 15 18 28 29 30 32 34 35 40 41 42 45 50 56 57 59 64 65 68 70 75 77 78 79 81 82 83 84 90 91 93 94 96 97 107 110 111 112 114 115 116 117 119 127 128 129 130 133 135 145 146 147 148
Primary Contact: Mirya Hallock, Administrator
CFO: Marcia Olson, Business Office Manager
CMO: Amy Springer, Medical Director
CHR: Marcia Olson, Business Office Manager
CNO: Candace Peters, R.N., Director of Nursing
Web address: www.websterhospital.org
Control: County–Government, nonfederal **Service:** General Medical and Surgical

Staffed Beds: 13 **Admissions:** 143 **Census:** 3 **Outpatient Visits:** 874 **Births:** 0 **Total Expense ($000):** 5048 **Payroll Expense ($000):** 2300 **Personnel:** 47

SAINT PAUL—Howard County

HOWARD COUNTY COMMUNITY HOSPITAL See Howard County Medical Center

★ **HOWARD COUNTY MEDICAL CENTER (281338)**, 1113 Sherman Street, Zip 68873–1546, Mailing Address: P.O. Box 406, Zip 68873–0406; tel. 308/754–4421, (Nonreporting) **A**10 18
Primary Contact: Arlan D. Johnson, Chief Executive Officer
COO: Jillyn Klein, Chief Operating Officer
CFO: Morgan Meyer, Chief Financial Officer
CMO: Angela Brennan, M.D., Chief of Staff
CIO: Cheryl Watson, Chief Information Officer
CHR: Leslie Belzer, Director Human Resources
CNO: Janelle Morgan, Interim Director of Nursing
Web address: www.hcmc.us.com
Control: County–Government, nonfederal **Service:** General Medical and Surgical

Staffed Beds: 25

SCHUYLER—Colfax County

★ **CHI HEALTH SCHUYLER (281323)**, 104 West 17th Street, Zip 68661–1304; tel. 402/352–2441, (Nonreporting) **A**10 18 **S** Catholic Health Initiatives, Englewood, CO
Primary Contact: Connie Peters, R.N., President
CFO: Tim H. Schnack, Chief Financial Officer
CIO: Kenneth Lawonn, Senior Vice President and Chief Information Officer
CHR: Nancy Wallace, Vice President Human Resources
Web address: www.alegent.org
Control: Other not–for–profit (including NFP Corporation) **Service:** General Medical and Surgical

Staffed Beds: 25

SCOTTSBLUFF—Scotts Bluff County

⊠ △ **REGIONAL WEST MEDICAL CENTER (280061)**, 4021 Avenue B, Zip 69361–4695; tel. 308/635–3711 **A**1 2 3 5 7 10 **F**3 7 8 11 12 13 14 15 17 28 29 30 31 34 40 43 45 47 50 59 60 62 63 64 65 68 69 70 72 74 76 77 78 81 83 85 89 90 92 93 98 107 108 110 111 114 115 119 120 121 128 129 130 146 147 148
Primary Contact: John Mentgen, FACHE, President and Chief Executive Officer
COO: Tadd Greenfield, Executive Vice President and Chief Operating Officer
CFO: Stan Moser, Interim Chief Financial Officer
CMO: Lisa Scheppers, Chief Medical Officer
CIO: Montie Hodge, Vice President Information Technology and Chief Information Officer
CHR: Brenda J. Forge, Vice President, Human Resources
CNO: Connie Rupp, MSN, Executive Vice President and Chief Nursing Officer
Web address: www.rwhs.org
Control: Other not–for–profit (including NFP Corporation) **Service:** General Medical and Surgical

Staffed Beds: 122 **Admissions:** 6922 **Census:** 84 **Outpatient Visits:** 393257 **Births:** 785 **Total Expense ($000):** 171961 **Payroll Expense ($000):** 58788 **Personnel:** 904

SEWARD—Seward County

★ **MEMORIAL HEALTH CARE SYSTEMS (281339)**, 300 North Columbia Avenue, Zip 68434–2228; tel. 402/643–2971, (Nonreporting) **A**10 18
Primary Contact: Roger J. Reamer, Chief Executive Officer
CFO: Greg Jerger, Chief Financial Officer
CMO: Joel Gabriel, M.D., Medical Director
CIO: Mark Criner, Director Information Technology
CHR: Corey Mann, Director Human Resources
Web address: www.mhcs.us
Control: Other not–for–profit (including NFP Corporation) **Service:** General Medical and Surgical

Staffed Beds: 36

SIDNEY—Cheyenne County

★ **SIDNEY REGIONAL MEDICAL CENTER (281357)**, 1000 Pole Creek Crossing, Zip 69162–1799; tel. 308/254–5825, (Nonreporting) **A**3 5 10 18
Primary Contact: Jason Petik, Chief Executive Officer
CMO: Mandy Shaw, M.D., Chief of Staff
CIO: Jennifer Brockhaus, Chief Information Officer
CHR: Catherine T. Arterburn, R.N., Vice President Human Resources
CNO: Julie A. Slagle, R.N., Vice President Patient Care Services
Web address: www.sidneyrmc.com
Control: Other not–for–profit (including NFP Corporation) **Service:** General Medical and Surgical

Staffed Beds: 88

SUPERIOR—Nuckolls County

★ **BRODSTONE MEMORIAL HOSPITAL (281315)**, 520 East Tenth Street, Zip 68978–1225, Mailing Address: P.O. Box 187, Zip 68978–0187; tel. 402/879–3281 **A**10 18 **F**3 8 11 13 15 17 28 29 30 31 34 35 40 41 57 59 62 65 66 67 70 74 75 76 77 79 81 82 85 86 87 89 93 97 107 110 111 114 119 127 128 129 130 131 132 133 135 146 148
Primary Contact: John E. Keelan, Administrator and Chief Executive Officer
COO: Dena C. Alvarez, R.N., COO & Chief Compliance Officer
CFO: Sandy Borden, Chief Financial Officer
CMO: Timothy Blecha, M.D., Medical Director
CIO: Tim Hiatt, Chief Information Officer
CHR: Jeremy Littrell, Director Human Resources
CNO: Kori Field, Director of Nursing
Web address: www.brodstonehospital.org
Control: Other not–for–profit (including NFP Corporation) **Service:** General Medical and Surgical

Staffed Beds: 25 **Admissions:** 441 **Census:** 3 **Outpatient Visits:** 18000 **Births:** 37 **Total Expense ($000):** 20977 **Payroll Expense ($000):** 8598 **Personnel:** 168

SYRACUSE—Otoe County

★ **COMMUNITY MEMORIAL HOSPITAL (281309)**, 1579 Midland Street, Zip 68446–9732, Mailing Address: P.O. Box N., Zip 68446–0518; tel. 402/269–2011 **A**10 18 **F**1 3 11 15 28 29 40 43 45 53 59 62 64 67 79 81 85 89 90 93 107 110 119 127 128 133
Primary Contact: Michael Harvey, FACHE, President and Chief Executive Officer
CFO: Karrie Beach, Vice President Finance
CMO: Zak Tempelmeyer, M.D., Chief Medical Staff
CIO: Matthew Steinblock, Director Information Systems
CHR: Nancy R. Brack, Vice President Human Resources
CNO: Pat Howell, Chief Nursing Officer
Web address: www.syracusecmh.org
Control: Hospital district or authority, Government, nonfederal **Service:** General Medical and Surgical

Staffed Beds: 10 **Admissions:** 136 **Census:** 2 **Outpatient Visits:** 13362 **Births:** 0 **Total Expense ($000):** 13184 **Payroll Expense ($000):** 5947 **Personnel:** 105

TECUMSEH—Johnson County

★ **JOHNSON COUNTY HOSPITAL (281350)**, 202 High Street, Zip 68450–2443, Mailing Address: P.O. Box 599, Zip 68450–0599; tel. 402/335–3361, (Nonreporting) **A**10 18
Primary Contact: Diane Newman, FACHE, Administrator
COO: Diane Newman, FACHE, Administrator
CFO: Jennifer Deal, Chief Financial Officer
CMO: Keith Shuey, M.D., Chief Medical Staff
CIO: Fred Pooch, Supervisor Information Technology
CHR: Susan Hessheimer, Director Human Resources
CNO: Matthew Snyder, R.N., Director of Nursing
Web address: www.jchosp.com
Control: County–Government, nonfederal **Service:** General Medical and Surgical

Staffed Beds: 25

VALENTINE—Cherry County

★ **CHERRY COUNTY HOSPITAL (281344)**, 510 North Green Street, Zip 69201–1932, Mailing Address: P.O. Box 410, Zip 69201–0410; tel. 402/376–2525, (Nonreporting) **A**10 18
Primary Contact: Brent A. Peterson, Administrator
CFO: Peggy Snell, Chief Finance Officer
Control: County–Government, nonfederal **Service:** General Medical and Surgical

Staffed Beds: 25

Many Facility Codes have changed. Please refer to the AHA Guide Code Chart. © 2016 AHA Guide

WAHOO—Saunders County

★ **SAUNDERS MEDICAL CENTER (281307)**, 1760 County Road J.,
Zip 68066–4152; tel. 402/443–4191, (Nonreporting) **A**10 18 **S** Bryan Health,
Lincoln, NE
Primary Contact: Tyler Toline, FACHE, Chief Executive Officer
COO: Julie A. Rezac, R.N., Chief Operating Officer
CFO: Chase Manstedt, Chief Financial Officer
CMO: Jared Pehrson, M.D., Chief of Staff
CIO: Carrie Stephens, Director Information Technology
CHR: Joanna Peters, Director Human Resources
CNO: Lalah Landers, R.N., Director of Nursing
Web address: www.saundersmedicalcenter.com
Control: County–Government, nonfederal **Service:** General Medical and Surgical

Staffed Beds: 87

WAYNE—Wayne County

★ **PROVIDENCE MEDICAL CENTER (281345)**, 1200 Providence Road,
Zip 68787–1299; tel. 402/375–3800 **A**10 18 **F**3 7 13 15 28 29 30 31 34 35
36 40 50 53 57 59 62 63 64 68 75 76 81 84 85 93 107 110 111 114 119
128 130 132 133 135
Primary Contact: Jim Frank, CPA, Chief Executive Officer
COO: Kristine A. Giese, Chief Operating Officer
CFO: Kim Hixson, Vice President of Financial Officer and Chief Financial Officer
CHR: Jacqueline Ann Backer, Vice President of Human Resources
CNO: Nicole Haglund, Vice President of Nursing Services
Web address: www.providencemedical.com
Control: Other not–for–profit (including NFP Corporation) **Service:** General
Medical and Surgical

Staffed Beds: 25 Admissions: 435 Census: 5 Outpatient Visits: 14054
Births: 52 Total Expense ($000): 18007 Payroll Expense ($000): 8184
Personnel: 156

WEST POINT—Cuming County

★ **ST. FRANCIS MEMORIAL HOSPITAL (281322)**, 430 North Monitor Street,
Zip 68788–1555; tel. 402/372–2404, (Total facility includes 63 beds in nursing
home–type unit) **A**10 18 **F**3 6 11 13 15 28 29 30 31 34 35 40 43 45 50 53 57
59 62 63 64 68 75 76 77 78 79 81 82 85 86 90 92 93 94 98 99 100 103
107 111 114 119 127 128 129 130 131 132 133 135 146 147 148 **P**6
S Franciscan Sisters of Christian Charity Sponsored Ministries, Inc.,
Manitowoc, WI
Primary Contact: Jerry Wordekemper, President and Chief Executive Officer
CFO: Dennis Dinslage, Vice President Finance and Chief Financial Officer
CMO: Renae Meyer, M.D., Chief Medical Officer
CIO: Jean Meiergerd, Chief Information Officer
CHR: Terri Ridder, Director Human Resources
CNO: Carol Kampschnieder, Vice President Clinical and Regulatory Services
Web address: www.fcswp.org
Control: Church–operated, Nongovernment, not–for profit **Service:** General
Medical and Surgical

Staffed Beds: 88 Admissions: 572 Census: 62 Outpatient Visits: 71624
Births: 61

WINNEBAGO—Thurston County

☐ ◇ **U. S. PUBLIC HEALTH SERVICE INDIAN HOSPITAL (280119)**, Highway
7577, Zip 68071; tel. 402/878–2231, (Nonreporting) **A**1 10 21 **S** U. S. Indian
Health Service, Rockville, MD
Primary Contact: Patricia Medina, Service Unit Director
CFO: Audrey Parker, Budget Analyst
Web address: www.ihs.gov
Control: PHS, Indian Service, Government, federal **Service:** General Medical and
Surgical

Staffed Beds: 30

YORK—York County

★ **YORK GENERAL HOSPITAL (281336)**, 2222 North Lincoln Avenue,
Zip 68467–1095; tel. 402/362–6671, (Total facility includes 129 beds in nursing
home–type unit) **A**10 18 **F**3 10 11 12 13 15 28 29 31 34 35 40 45 53 56 57
59 60 62 64 68 70 75 76 77 78 79 81 82 85 86 87 89 93 96 107 108 110
111 115 117 118 119 125 128 129 130 131 132 133 145 146 148
Primary Contact: Charles K. Schulz, Chief Executive Officer
CFO: Bob McQuistan, Vice President Finance
CMO: Ye Ye, Chief of Staff
CIO: Chris Kraft, Director Information Systems
CHR: Cathy Norquest, Director Human Resources
CNO: Jenny Obermier, VP, Director of Nursing
Web address: www.yorkgeneral.org
Control: Other not–for–profit (including NFP Corporation) **Service:** General
Medical and Surgical

Staffed Beds: 154 Admissions: 862 Census: 120 Outpatient Visits: 37869
Births: 85 Total Expense ($000): 38965 Payroll Expense ($000): 18302
Personnel: 398

NE

Hospital, Medicare Provider Number, Address, Telephone, Approval, Facility, and Physician Codes, Health Care System

★ American Hospital Association (AHA) membership   ◯ Healthcare Facilities Accreditation Program   ⇑ Center for Improvement in Healthcare Quality Accreditation
☐ The Joint Commission accreditation   ◇ DNV Healthcare Inc. accreditation   △ Commission on Accreditation of Rehabilitation Facilities (CARF) accreditation

NEVADA

BATTLE MOUNTAIN—Lander County

BATTLE MOUNTAIN GENERAL HOSPITAL (291303), 535 South Humboldt Street, Zip 89820–1988; tel. 775/635–2550, (Nonreporting) **A**10 18
Primary Contact: Kelley Price, R.N., Interim Chief Executive Officer
CFO: Cindy Fagg, Fiscal Officer
CMO: Mark S. Meyers, M.D., Chief of Staff
CIO: Terry Dunn, Director Information Technology
CHR: Lori Sherbondy, Director Human Resources
CNO: Kelley Price, R.N., Chief Nursing Officer
Web address: www.bmgh.org
Control: Hospital district or authority, Government, nonfederal **Service:** General Medical and Surgical

Staffed Beds: 7

BOULDER CITY—Clark County

BOULDER CITY HOSPITAL (291309), 901 Adams Boulevard, Zip 89005–2213; tel. 702/293–4111, (Nonreporting) **A**10 18
Primary Contact: Thomas Maher, Chief Executive Officer and Administrator
CFO: Douglas Lewis, Chief Financial Officer
CMO: Herve Bezard, M.D., Chief of Staff
CHR: Belinda McGraw, Director Human Resources
CNO: Andre Pastian, R.N., Chief Nursing Officer
Web address: www.bouldercityhospital.org
Control: Other not–for–profit (including NFP Corporation) **Service:** General Medical and Surgical

Staffed Beds: 63

CALIENTE—Lincoln County

GROVER C. DILS MEDICAL CENTER (291312), 700 North Spring Street, Zip 89008, Mailing Address: P.O. Box 1010, Zip 89008–1010; tel. 775/726–3171, (Nonreporting) **A**10 18
Primary Contact: Jason Bleak, Administrator and Chief Executive Officer
COO: Jason Bleak, Administrator and Chief Executive Officer
CFO: Sherlyn Fackrell, Finance Controller
CMO: R. William Katschke, Jr., M.D., Medical Director
CHR: Rozanne Mangum, Administrative Assistant and Director Human Resources
Web address: www.gcdmc.org
Control: Other not–for–profit (including NFP Corporation) **Service:** Other specialty

Staffed Beds: 20

CARSON CITY—Carson City County

CARSON TAHOE CONTINUING CARE HOSPITAL (292008), 775 Fleischmann Way, 2nd Floor, Zip 89703–2995; tel. 775/445–7795, (Nonreporting) **A**10
Primary Contact: Kelly Wilcher, Chief Executive Officer
CFO: Ann Beck, Vice President and Chief Financial Officer
CMO: Jose Aguirre, M.D., Medical Director
CHR: Angie Rodriguez, Human Resource Manager
CNO: Kristin Madsen, Chief Nursing Officer
Web address: www.carsontahoe.com
Control: Other not–for–profit (including NFP Corporation) **Service:** Long–Term Acute Care hospital

Staffed Beds: 29

✠ **CARSON TAHOE HEALTH (290019)**, 1600 Medical Parkway, Zip 89703–4625, Mailing Address: P.O. Box 2168, Zip 89702–2168; tel. 775/445–8672, (Includes SIERRA SURGERY HOSPITAL, 1400 Medical Parkway, Zip 89703–4624; tel. 775/883–1700; Ken Doran, Interim Chief Executive Officer) **A**1 2 5 10 22 **F**3 4 5 8 11 13 15 17 18 20 22 24 26 28 29 30 31 34 35 40 42 46 47 49 50 51 54 56 57 59 64 65 68 70 74 75 77 78 79 81 82 85 86 87 93 96 98 99 100 101 102 103 104 105 107 108 110 111 115 116 117 118 119 130 132 135 144 146 147 148 **P**8
Primary Contact: Edward L. Epperson, Chief Executive Officer
COO: Michelle L. Joy, Chief Operating Officer
CFO: Ann Beck, Vice President Finance
CMO: Jeffrey Sanders, M.D., Chief of Staff
CHR: Jim Lewandowski, Interim Director of Human Resources
CNO: Anna Anders, Vice President and Chief Nursing Officer
Web address: www.carsontahoe.com
Control: Other not–for–profit (including NFP Corporation) **Service:** General Medical and Surgical

Staffed Beds: 205 Admissions: 11881 Census: 140 Outpatient Visits: 261906 Births: 993 Total Expense ($000): 229390 Payroll Expense ($000): 76550 Personnel: 1394

ELKO—Elko County

✠ **NORTHEASTERN NEVADA REGIONAL HOSPITAL (290008)**, 2001 Errecart Boulevard, Zip 89801–8333; tel. 775/738–5151 **A**1 10 20 **F**3 8 11 13 15 20 22 28 29 30 31 34 40 41 45 46 49 50 51 57 59 60 68 70 75 76 79 81 82 85 89 93 102 107 108 111 114 115 119 129 **S** LifePoint Health, Brentwood, TN
Primary Contact: Richard L. Palagi, Chief Executive Officer
CFO: Grant Trollope, Chief Financial Officer
CIO: Jeff Morgan, Director Information Systems
CHR: Laura Elliott, Director Human Resources
Web address: www.nnrhospital.com
Control: Corporation, Investor–owned, for–profit **Service:** General Medical and Surgical

Staffed Beds: 50 Admissions: 2152 Census: 17 Outpatient Visits: 54025 Births: 518 Total Expense ($000): 46772 Payroll Expense ($000): 16075 Personnel: 260

ELY—White Pine County

✠ **WILLIAM BEE RIRIE HOSPITAL (291302)**, 1500 Avenue H, Zip 89301–2699; tel. 775/289–3001, (Nonreporting) **A**1 10 18
Primary Contact: Matthew Walker, Chief Executive Officer and Administrator
CMO: G. N. Christensen, M.D., Chief Medical Officer
CIO: Destin Brandis, Chief Information Officer
CHR: Vicki Pereace, Manager Human Resources
Web address: www.wbrhely.org/getpage.php?name=index
Control: Hospital district or authority, Government, nonfederal **Service:** General Medical and Surgical

Staffed Beds: 15

FALLON—Churchill County

✠ **BANNER CHURCHILL COMMUNITY HOSPITAL (290006)**, 801 East Williams Avenue, Zip 89406–3052; tel. 775/423–3151 **A**1 10 18 **F**3 7 11 13 15 29 30 31 34 35 40 41 45 47 50 57 59 65 68 70 75 76 79 80 81 85 86 87 93 97 107 108 110 111 115 119 129 130 146 **S** Banner Health, Phoenix, AZ
Primary Contact: Hoyt Skabelund, Chief Executive Officer
CFO: Steve Fraker, Chief Financial Officer
CMO: Tedd McDonald, M.D., Chief Medical Officer
CHR: Darlene Hanefeld, Chief Human Resources Officer
CNO: Robert H. Carnahan, II, R.N., Chief Nursing Officer
Web address: www.bannerhealth.com/churchill
Control: Other not–for–profit (including NFP Corporation) **Service:** General Medical and Surgical

Staffed Beds: 25 Admissions: 1577 Census: 13 Outpatient Visits: 51549 Births: 329 Total Expense ($000): 35746 Payroll Expense ($000): 15174 Personnel: 264

GARDNERVILLE—Douglas County

★ **CARSON VALLEY MEDICAL CENTER (291306)**, 1107 Highway 395, Zip 89410; tel. 775/782–1500 **A**3 10 18 **F**3 8 11 15 29 31 34 35 40 45 50 53 54 56 57 59 64 65 68 70 75 77 78 79 81 85 86 87 91 93 102 103 104 107 108 110 111 115 119 127 129 130 131 132 133 135 144 146 148 **P**6
Primary Contact: Preston Becker, Chief Executive Officer
COO: Linda Lilleboe, R.N., Director Operations
CMO: Evan Easley, M.D., Chief Medical Officer
CIO: Jason Roberts, Director Information System
CHR: Lisa Tremaine, Manager Human Resources
CNO: Kathy Cocking, R.N., Director of Clinical Services
Web address: www.cvmchospital.org
Control: Other not–for–profit (including NFP Corporation) **Service:** General Medical and Surgical

Staffed Beds: 23 Admissions: 953 Census: 7 Births: 0

HAWTHORNE—Mineral County

MOUNT GRANT GENERAL HOSPITAL (291300), First and A Street, Zip 89415, Mailing Address: P.O. Box 1510, Zip 89415–1510; tel. 775/945–2461, (Nonreporting) **A**10 18
Primary Contact: Richard Munger, Administrator
Web address: www.mtgrantgenhospital.org/
Control: Other not–for–profit (including NFP Corporation) **Service:** General Medical and Surgical

Staffed Beds: 11

NV

Many Facility Codes have changed. Please refer to the AHA Guide Code Chart. © 2016 AHA Guide

HENDERSON—Clark County

☒ **HEALTHSOUTH REHABILITATION HOSPITAL – HENDERSON (293032)**, 10301 Jeffreys Street, Zip 89052–3922; tel. 702/939–9400, (Nonreporting) **A**1 10 **S** HEALTHSOUTH Corporation, Birmingham, AL
Primary Contact: Samantha Billig, Chief Executive Officer
CFO: Robert Bollard, Chief Financial Officer
Web address: www.hendersonrehabhospital.com
Control: Corporation, Investor–owned, for–profit **Service:** Rehabilitation

Staffed Beds: 90

SEVEN HILLS HOSPITAL (294012), 3021 West Horizon Ridge Parkway, Zip 89052–3990; tel. 702/646–5000 **A**10 **F**4 5 29 34 38 56 64 98 99 101 103 104 105 130 132 135 143 148 **P**8 **S** Acadia Healthcare Company, Inc., Franklin, TN
Primary Contact: Robert L. Turner, Ph.D., Chief Executive Officer
CFO: Mars Patricio, Jr., Chief Financial Officer
CMO: Jonathan Wirjo, M.D., Medical Director
CIO: Jessica Raub, Director Health Information Management
CHR: Teresa Sulit, Director of Human Resources
CNO: Rustin Park, Director of Nursing
Web address: www.sevenhillsbi.com
Control: Corporation, Investor–owned, for–profit **Service:** Psychiatric

Staffed Beds: 94 Admissions: 4951 Census: 87 Outpatient Visits: 4610 Births: 0 Total Expense ($000): 16616 Payroll Expense ($000): 9154 Personnel: 182

☒ **ST. ROSE DOMINICAN HOSPITALS – ROSE DE LIMA CAMPUS (290012)**, 102 East Lake Mead Parkway, Zip 89015–5524; tel. 702/616–5000 **A**1 10 **F**3 8 12 15 18 20 29 30 31 32 34 35 38 40 43 44 45 49 50 57 59 61 62 63 64 65 68 70 74 75 77 78 79 81 82 84 85 86 87 90 93 95 96 102 107 110 111 115 119 130 131 132 135 143 146 147 148 **S** Dignity Health, San Francisco, CA
Primary Contact: Teressa Conley, President and Chief Executive Officer
COO: Teressa Conley, Vice President and Chief Operating Officer
CFO: Kevin Walters, Chief Financial Officer
CMO: Stephen K. Jones, M.D., Vice President Medical Staff Affairs
Web address: www.strosehospitals.org
Control: Church–operated, Nongovernment, not–for profit **Service:** General Medical and Surgical

Staffed Beds: 110 Admissions: 5306 Census: 83 Outpatient Visits: 44010 Births: 0 Total Expense ($000): 143739 Payroll Expense ($000): 63123 Personnel: 673

☒ **ST. ROSE DOMINICAN HOSPITALS – SIENA CAMPUS (290045)**, 3001 St. Rose Parkway, Zip 89052; tel. 702/616–5000 **A**1 3 5 10 **F**3 7 8 13 15 18 19 20 22 24 26 28 29 30 31 32 34 35 38 40 41 43 44 45 46 50 51 57 59 61 62 63 64 68 70 72 74 75 76 78 79 81 82 84 85 87 88 89 93 102 107 108 110 111 115 116 117 119 126 130 131 132 135 146 147 148 **S** Dignity Health, San Francisco, CA
Primary Contact: Brian G. Brannman, President and Chief Executive Officer
CFO: Brian Kleven, Chief Financial Officer
CMO: Robert Pretzlaff, M.D., Chief Medical Officer
CIO: Russ Patterson, Director Information Technology
CHR: Linda Gerstenberger, Vice President Human Resources
CNO: Cathleen Hamel, Chief Nurse Executive
Web address: www.strosehospitals.com
Control: Church–operated, Nongovernment, not–for profit **Service:** General Medical and Surgical

Staffed Beds: 230 Admissions: 15238 Census: 195 Outpatient Visits: 83062 Births: 3367 Total Expense ($000): 346125 Payroll Expense ($000): 141315 Personnel: 1722

INCLINE VILLAGE—Washoe County

★ **INCLINE VILLAGE COMMUNITY HOSPITAL (291301)**, 880 Alder Avenue, Zip 89451–8335; tel. 775/833–4100, (Nonreporting) **A**3 5 10 18 **S** Tahoe Forest Health System, Truckee, CA
Primary Contact: Judy Newland, R.N., Chief Nursing Officer
CFO: Crystal Betts, Chief Financial Officer
CIO: Mark Griffiths, Director Management Information Systems
CHR: Jayne O'Flanagan, Director Human Resources
Web address: www.tfhd.com
Control: Hospital district or authority, Government, nonfederal **Service:** General Medical and Surgical

Staffed Beds: 6

LAS VEGAS—Clark County

☒ **AMG SPECIALTY HOSPITAL – LAS VEGAS (292007)**, 4015 Mcleod Drive, Zip 89121–4305; tel. 702/433–2200, (Data for 245 days) **A**10 **F**1 29 85 130 148 **P**5 **S** AMG Integrated Healthcare Management, Lafayette, LA
Primary Contact: William Fox, Chief Executive Officer
CMO: Anthony Pollard, D.O., Chief Medical Officer
Web address: www.amgihm.com/locations/#map_top
Control: Corporation, Investor–owned, for–profit **Service:** Long–Term Acute Care hospital

Staffed Beds: 24 Admissions: 93 Census: 10 Outpatient Visits: 0 Births: 0 Total Expense ($000): 4211 Payroll Expense ($000): 2101 Personnel: 90

☐ **CENTENNIAL HILLS HOSPITAL MEDICAL CENTER (290054)**, 6900 North Durango Drive, Zip 89149–4409; tel. 702/835–9700, (Nonreporting) **A**1 10 **S** Universal Health Services, Inc., King of Prussia, PA
Primary Contact: Sajit Pullarkat, Chief Executive Officer and Managing Director
Web address: www.centennialhillshospital.com
Control: Corporation, Investor–owned, for–profit **Service:** General Medical and Surgical

Staffed Beds: 171

☒ **COMPLEX CARE HOSPITAL AT TENAYA (292006)**, 2500 North Tenaya, Zip 89128–0482; tel. 702/562–2021, (Nonreporting) **A**1 10 **S** LifeCare Management Services, Plano, TX
Primary Contact: Michael R. Shaw, Chief Executive Officer
COO: Paul D'Ambrosio, Chief Operating Officer
CFO: Anna Rich, Chief Financial Officer
CMO: C. Dean Milne, D.O., Medical Director
CIO: Lynn Tunson, Manager Medical Records
CHR: Belinda McGraw, Director Human Resources
CNO: Robin Wolf, Chief Nursing Officer
Web address: www.lifecare–hospitals.com
Control: Corporation, Investor–owned, for–profit **Service:** Long–Term Acute Care hospital

Staffed Beds: 70

☐ **DESERT SPRINGS HOSPITAL MEDICAL CENTER (290022)**, 2075 East Flamingo Road, Zip 89119–5121; tel. 702/733–8800, (Nonreporting) **A**1 10 **S** Universal Health Services, Inc., King of Prussia, PA
Primary Contact: Jeremy Bradshaw, Chief Executive Officer
CFO: George Wiley, Chief Financial Officer
CMO: Golam Choudhury, Chief of Staff
CIO: Alan Woratschek, System Director of Information Services
CNO: Elena McNutt, Chief Nursing Officer
Web address: www.desertspringshospital.com
Control: Corporation, Investor–owned, for–profit **Service:** General Medical and Surgical

Staffed Beds: 346

DESERT WILLOW TREATMENT CENTER, 6171 West Charleston Boulevard, Zip 89146–1126; tel. 702/486–8900 **A**3 5 **F**29 98 99 106 **P**6
Primary Contact: Linda Santangelo, Ph.D., Director
Control: State–Government, nonfederal **Service:** Children's hospital psychiatric

Staffed Beds: 58 Admissions: 283 Census: 44 Outpatient Visits: 0 Births: 0 Total Expense ($000): 8897 Payroll Expense ($000): 6767 Personnel: 103

HARMON MEDICAL AND REHABILITATION HOSPITAL (290042), 2170 East Harmon Avenue, Zip 89119–7840; tel. 702/794–0100, (Nonreporting) **A**10 **S** Fundamental Long Term Care Holdings, LLC, Sparks Glencoe, MD
Primary Contact: Bonnie Essex Hillegass, Chief Executive Officer
Control: Corporation, Investor–owned, for–profit **Service:** Rehabilitation

Staffed Beds: 118

☒ **HEALTHSOUTH DESERT CANYON REHABILITATION HOSPITAL (293033)**, 9175 West Oquendo Road, Zip 89148–1234; tel. 702/252–7342 **A**1 10 **F**3 29 75 77 78 79 86 91 93 95 96 132 **S** HEALTHSOUTH Corporation, Birmingham, AL
Primary Contact: Andrea Davis, Chief Executive Officer
CMO: Bevins Chue, M.D., Medical Director
CNO: Timothy Murphy, R.N., Chief Nursing Officer
Web address: www.healthsouthdesertcanyon.com
Control: Corporation, Investor–owned, for–profit **Service:** Rehabilitation

Staffed Beds: 50 Admissions: 1186 Census: 39 Outpatient Visits: 3455 Births: 0

NV

HEALTHSOUTH REHABILITATION HOSPITAL–LAS VEGAS (293026), 1250 South Valley View Boulevard, Zip 89102–1861; tel. 702/877–8898, (Nonreporting) **A**1 10 **S** HEALTHSOUTH Corporation, Birmingham, AL
Primary Contact: Michael Ward, Chief Executive Officer
CFO: Daniel Lai, Controller
CMO: John D. Reneau, Medical Director
CHR: Debra Tafoya, Director Human Resources
CNO: Susan Ramirez, Chief Nursing Officer
Web address: www.healthsouthlasvegas.com
Control: Corporation, Investor–owned, for–profit **Service:** Rehabilitation

Staffed Beds: 79

HORIZON SPECIALTY HOSPITAL (292003), 640 Desert Lane, Zip 89106–4207; tel. 702/382–3155, (Nonreporting) **A**1 10 **S** Fundamental Long Term Care Holdings, LLC, Sparks Glencoe, MD
Primary Contact: Darrin Cook, Chief Executive Officer and Administrator
CFO: Darnell Bennett, Director Finance
CMO: Syed Rahman, M.D., Chief of Staff
CIO: Azena Ansi, Manager Health Information Management
CHR: Melvin Layugan, Director Human Resources
Web address: www.horizonspecialtyhosp.com/
Control: Corporation, Investor–owned, for–profit **Service:** Long–Term Acute Care hospital

Staffed Beds: 49

KINDRED HOSPITAL LAS VEGAS–SAHARA (292002), 5110 West Sahara Avenue, Zip 89146–3406; tel. 702/871–1418, (Includes KINDRED HOSPITAL–FLAMINGO, 2250 East Flamingo Road, Zip 89119; tel. 702/871–1418), (Nonreporting) **A**1 10 **S** Kindred Healthcare, Louisville, KY
Primary Contact: Doug McCoy, Chief Executive Officer
CFO: William Lysaght, Chief Financial Officer
CMO: Paul Stewart, M.D., Medical Director
CHR: Jim Sturgeon, Area Director Human Resources
Web address: www.kindredhospitallvs.com/
Control: Corporation, Investor–owned, for–profit **Service:** Long–Term Acute Care hospital

Staffed Beds: 238

MONTEVISTA HOSPITAL (294009), 5900 West Rochelle Avenue, Zip 89103–3327; tel. 702/364–1111 **A**1 10 **F**4 5 29 30 32 34 35 38 44 56 57 58 68 98 99 100 101 102 103 104 105 106 **P**5 **S** Strategic Behavioral Health, LLC, Memphis, TN
Primary Contact: Richard Failla, Chief Executive Officer
CMO: William Bauer, M.D., Medical Director
CHR: Carol Nelson, Director Human Resources
Web address: www.montevistahospital.com
Control: Corporation, Investor–owned, for–profit **Service:** Psychiatric

Staffed Beds: 162 Admissions: 3943 Census: 114 Outpatient Visits: 16580 Births: 0 Total Expense ($000): 22864 Payroll Expense ($000): 12649 Personnel: 199

MOUNTAINVIEW HOSPITAL (290039), 3100 North Tenaya Way, Zip 89128–0436; tel. 702/255–5000, (Nonreporting) **A**1 3 5 10 **S** HCA, Nashville, TN
Primary Contact: Chris Mowan, Chief Executive Officer
CFO: Lana Arad, Chief Financial Officer
CMO: Jack Collier, M.D., Chief of Staff
CHR: Robert Nettles, Director Human Resources
CNO: Natalie Ransom, Chief Nursing Officer
Web address: www.mountainview–hospital.com
Control: Corporation, Investor–owned, for–profit **Service:** General Medical and Surgical

Staffed Beds: 340

RED ROCK BEHAVIORAL HOSPITAL (294008), 5975 West Twain Avenue, Zip 89103–1237; tel. 702/214–8099 **A**1 10 **F**5 29 56 98 99 102 103 105 106 **P**5 **S** Strategic Behavioral Health, LLC, Memphis, TN
Primary Contact: Richard Failla, Chief Executive Officer
Web address: www.redrockhospital.com
Control: Corporation, Investor–owned, for–profit **Service:** Psychiatric

Staffed Beds: 21 Admissions: 513 Census: 17 Outpatient Visits: 0 Births: 0 Personnel: 24

SOUTHERN HILLS HOSPITAL AND MEDICAL CENTER (290047), 9300 West Sunset Road, Zip 89148–4844; tel. 702/880–2100 **A**1 10 **F**3 13 15 18 20 22 29 30 31 34 40 44 45 49 50 51 56 57 59 60 65 68 70 72 74 75 76 77 78 79 81 84 85 87 98 102 103 104 107 108 110 111 114 115 119 126 130 135 146 147 148 **S** HCA, Nashville, TN
Primary Contact: Adam Rudd, Chief Executive Officer
CFO: Jennifer Le, Chief Financial Officer
CMO: Eric Ramos, M.D., Division Chief Medical Officer
CIO: Joe Grandiosi, Director Information Technology
CHR: Brian Wood, Director Human Resources
CNO: Maura Wright, Chief Nursing Officer
Web address: www.southernhillshospital.com
Control: Corporation, Investor–owned, for–profit **Service:** General Medical and Surgical

Staffed Beds: 134 Admissions: 8718 Census: 104 Outpatient Visits: 44268 Births: 1557 Total Expense ($000): 144595 Payroll Expense ($000): 52968 Personnel: 662

SOUTHERN NEVADA ADULT MENTAL HEALTH SERVICES (294002), 6161 West Charleston Boulevard, Zip 89146–1126; tel. 702/486–6000 **A**1 3 5 10 **F**29 34 98 106 135
Primary Contact: Chelsea Szklany, Hospital Administrator
Web address: www.mhds.state.nv.us
Control: State–Government, nonfederal **Service:** Psychiatric

Staffed Beds: 190 Admissions: 2696 Census: 212 Outpatient Visits: 0 Births: 0 Total Expense ($000): 77724 Payroll Expense ($000): 32714 Personnel: 595

SPRING MOUNTAIN SAHARA (294010), 5460 West Sahara, Zip 89146–3307; tel. 702/216–8900 **A**1 10 **F**29 56 64 98 103 104 130 **S** Universal Health Services, Inc., King of Prussia, PA
Primary Contact: Darryl S. Dubroca, Chief Executive Officer and Managing Director
Web address: www.springmountainsahara.com
Control: Corporation, Investor–owned, for–profit **Service:** Psychiatric

Staffed Beds: 30 Admissions: 755 Census: 22 Outpatient Visits: 1850 Births: 0 Total Expense ($000): 5962 Payroll Expense ($000): 2792 Personnel: 53

SPRING MOUNTAIN TREATMENT CENTER (294011), 7000 West Spring Mountain Road, Zip 89117–3816; tel. 702/873–2400 **A**1 10 **F**29 98 99 105 130 **S** Universal Health Services, Inc., King of Prussia, PA
Primary Contact: C. Alan Eaks, Chief Executive Officer and Managing Director
Web address: www.springmountaintreatmentcenter.com/
Control: Corporation, Investor–owned, for–profit **Service:** Psychiatric

Staffed Beds: 110 Admissions: 4202 Census: 80 Outpatient Visits: 1796 Births: 0 Total Expense ($000): 17791 Payroll Expense ($000): 8093 Personnel: 158

SPRING VALLEY HOSPITAL MEDICAL CENTER (290046), 5400 South Rainbow Boulevard, Zip 89118–1859; tel. 702/853–3000, (Nonreporting) **A**1 3 10 **S** Universal Health Services, Inc., King of Prussia, PA
Primary Contact: Leonard Freehof, Chief Executive Officer and Managing Director
COO: Matthew Wheelus, Chief Operating Officer
CFO: Carl Caley, Chief Financial Officer
CMO: S. Daniel, M.D., Chief Medical Officer
CHR: Angelique Ford, Administrator Human Resources
CNO: Margaret Covelli, R.N., Chief Nursing Officer
Web address: www.springvalleyhospital.com
Control: Corporation, Investor–owned, for–profit **Service:** General Medical and Surgical

Staffed Beds: 169

ST. ROSE DOMINICAN HOSPITALS – SAN MARTIN CAMPUS (290053), 8280 West Warm Springs Road, Zip 89113–3612; tel. 702/492–8000 **A**1 10 **F**3 8 13 15 18 19 20 22 24 26 28 29 30 31 34 35 38 40 44 45 47 49 50 57 59 61 62 63 64 68 70 73 74 75 76 77 78 79 80 81 83 84 85 86 87 93 102 107 108 110 111 115 119 126 130 131 132 135 146 147 148 **S** Dignity Health, San Francisco, CA
Primary Contact: Lawrence Barnard, President and Chief Executive Officer
CFO: Dev Ramsamy, Chief Financial Officer
CMO: Robert Pretzlaff, M.D., Chief Medical Officer
CIO: Russ Patterson, Site Manager Information Technology
CHR: Linda Gerstenberger, Vice President Human Resources
CNO: Katherine Raymond, Chief Nursing Officer
Web address: www.strosehospitals.org
Control: Church–operated, Nongovernment, not–for profit **Service:** General Medical and Surgical

Staffed Beds: 147 Admissions: 6791 Census: 90 Outpatient Visits: 37853 Births: 1020 Total Expense ($000): 183070 Payroll Expense ($000): 66184 Personnel: 699

NV

☐ **SUMMERLIN HOSPITAL MEDICAL CENTER (290041)**, 657 Town Center Drive, Zip 89144–6367; tel. 702/233–7000, (Nonreporting) **A**1 10 **S** Universal Health Services, Inc., King of Prussia, PA
Primary Contact: Robert S. Freymuller, Chief Executive Officer
Web address: www.summerlinhospital.com
Control: Corporation, Investor–owned, for–profit **Service:** General Medical and Surgical

Staffed Beds: 148

✠ △ **SUNRISE HOSPITAL AND MEDICAL CENTER (290003)**, 3186 Maryland Parkway, Zip 89109–2306, Mailing Address: P.O. Box 98530, Zip 89193; tel. 702/731–8000, (Includes SUNRISE CHILDREN'S HOSPITAL) **A**1 2 3 5 7 10 **F**3 11 12 13 15 17 18 19 20 21 22 23 24 25 26 27 28 29 30 31 32 34 35 39 40 41 43 44 45 46 49 50 51 57 58 59 60 64 65 68 70 72 74 75 76 77 78 79 81 82 84 85 87 88 89 90 91 92 96 100 107 108 110 111 114 115 116 117 118 119 124 126 130 132 135 146 147 148 **S** HCA, Nashville, TN
Primary Contact: Todd Sklamberg, President
CFO: Daniel Perritt, Chief Financial Officer
CMO: Katherine Keeley, M.D., Chief of Staff
CIO: Alan Burt, Director Information Services
Web address: www.sunrisehospital.com
Control: Corporation, Investor–owned, for–profit **Service:** General Medical and Surgical

Staffed Beds: 668 Admissions: 32492 Census: 543 Outpatient Visits: 197558 Births: 5000 Total Expense ($000): 534886 Payroll Expense ($000): 223273 Personnel: 2721

✠ **UNIVERSITY MEDICAL CENTER (290007)**, 1800 West Charleston Boulevard, Zip 89102–2386; tel. 702/383–2000, (Includes CHILDREN'S HOSPITAL OF NEVADA AT UMC, 800 Hope Place, Zip 89106; tel. 702/383–2000), (Nonreporting) **A**1 2 3 5 10
Primary Contact: Mason VanHouweling, Chief Executive Officer
COO: Kurt Houser, Chief Operating Officer
CFO: Stephanie Merrill, Chief Financial Officer
CIO: Ernie McKinley, Chief Information Officer
CHR: John Espinoza, Chief Human Resources Officer
CNO: Debra Fox, Chief Nursing Officer
Web address: www.umcsn.com
Control: County–Government, nonfederal **Service:** General Medical and Surgical

Staffed Beds: 541

☐ **VALLEY HOSPITAL MEDICAL CENTER (290021)**, 620 Shadow Lane, Zip 89106–4119; tel. 702/388–4000, (Nonreporting) **A**1 3 10 **S** Universal Health Services, Inc., King of Prussia, PA
Primary Contact: Elaine Glaser, Chief Executive Officer
CFO: Betsy A. Sponsler, Chief Financial Officer
CMO: Dost Wattoo, M.D., Chief of Staff
CIO: Tom Schoenig, Regional Director Information Services
CHR: Dana Thorne, Administrator Human Resources
Web address: www.valleyhospital.net
Control: Corporation, Investor–owned, for–profit **Service:** General Medical and Surgical

Staffed Beds: 365

LOVELOCK—Pershing County

★ **PERSHING GENERAL HOSPITAL (291304)**, 855 Sixth Street, Zip 89419, Mailing Address: P.O. Box 661, Zip 89419–0661; tel. 775/273–2621, (Nonreporting) **A**10 18
Primary Contact: Patty Bianchi, Chief Executive Officer
CFO: Marjorie Skinner, Director Finance
CMO: Yousri Gadallah, M.D., Chief Medical Officer
CIO: Jim Weeldreyer, Manager Information Technology
CHR: Cynthia Hixenbaugh, Director Human Resources
Web address: www.pershinghospital.org
Control: Hospital district or authority, Government, nonfederal **Service:** General Medical and Surgical

Staffed Beds: 38

MESQUITE—Clark County

✠ **MESA VIEW REGIONAL HOSPITAL (291307)**, 1299 Bertha Howe Avenue, Zip 89027–7500; tel. 702/346–8040 **A**1 10 18 **F**3 11 13 15 18 29 30 34 35 40 45 46 51 56 57 59 64 70 75 76 79 81 85 87 107 108 110 111 114 119 130 132 133 135 146 147 148 **P**7 **S** Quorum Health, Brentwood, TN
Primary Contact: Patricia Holden, Chief Executive Officer
CFO: Mitchell Fransen, Chief Financial Officer
CHR: Steve Siegrist, Director of Human Resources
CNO: Nancy K. Seck, Chief Nursing Officer
Web address: www.mesaviewhospital.com
Control: Corporation, Investor–owned, for–profit **Service:** General Medical and Surgical

Staffed Beds: 25 Admissions: 724 Census: 6 Outpatient Visits: 30952 Births: 107 Total Expense ($000): 22504 Payroll Expense ($000): 9616 Personnel: 171

NELLIS AFB—Clark County

✠ **MIKE O'CALLAGHAN FEDERAL HOSPITAL**, 4700 Las Vegas Boulevard North, Suite 2419, Zip 89191–6600; tel. 702/653–2000, (Nonreporting) **A**1 3 5 **S** Department of the Air Force, Washington, DC
Primary Contact: Colonel Christian Benjamin, USAF, MC, Commander
COO: Colonel Linnes L. Chester, USAF, Administrator
CFO: Major Kari Turkal–Barrett, Flight Commander Resource Management Officer
CMO: Lieutenant Colonel Markham Brown, M.D., Chief Medical Staff
CIO: Major Kevin Seeley, Chief Information Officer
Web address: www.lasvegas.va.gov/
Control: Air Force, Government, federal **Service:** General Medical and Surgical

Staffed Beds: 46

NORTH LAS VEGAS—Clark County

★ ◇ **NORTH VISTA HOSPITAL (290005)**, 1409 East Lake Mead Boulevard, Zip 89030–7197; tel. 702/649–7711, (Nonreporting) **A**10 21 **S** Prime Healthcare Services, Ontario, CA
Primary Contact: Vincenzo Variale, Chief Executive Officer
CFO: Peter S. Miller, Chief Financial Officer
CHR: Abayomi Fibiyi, Chief Human Resources Officer
CNO: Joanna Young, R.N., Chief Nursing Officer
Web address: www.northvistahospital.com
Control: Corporation, Investor–owned, for–profit **Service:** General Medical and Surgical

Staffed Beds: 177

✠ **VETERANS AFFAIRS SOUTHERN NEVADA HEALTHCARE SYSTEM**, 6900 North Pecos Road, Zip 89086–4400; tel. 702/791–9000 **A**1 5 **F**3 5 8 11 12 15 18 20 22 28 29 30 31 33 34 35 36 38 39 40 44 45 47 48 50 51 54 56 57 58 59 60 61 64 68 70 74 75 77 78 79 81 82 84 85 86 87 91 92 93 94 95 96 97 98 100 101 102 103 104 105 107 108 110 111 114 115 116 117 118 119 127 129 130 131 132 135 143 146 147 148 **S** Department of Veterans Affairs, Washington, DC
Primary Contact: Peggy W. Kearns, MS, FACHE, Executive Director
CFO: Richard O. Hays, Chief Fiscal Service
CMO: Ramanujam Komanduri, M.D., Chief of Staff
Web address: www.lasvegas.va.gov/
Control: Veterans Affairs, Government, federal **Service:** General Medical and Surgical

Staffed Beds: 90 Admissions: 5266 Census: 79 Outpatient Visits: 797804 Births: 0 Total Expense ($000): 601140 Payroll Expense ($000): 244423 Personnel: 1602

PAHRUMP—Nye County

★ **DESERT VIEW HOSPITAL (291311)**, 360 South Lola Lane, Zip 89048–0884; tel. 775/751–7500 **A**10 18 **F**3 15 18 29 34 40 41 44 45 46 57 59 64 65 66 68 77 79 81 82 83 84 85 86 87 93 107 108 110 111 115 119 130 132 133 135 147 148 **S** Rural Health Group, Nephi, UT
Primary Contact: Susa Davila, Chief Executive Officer
CFO: Ryan Eggleston, Chief Financial Officer
CMO: Fredric Siegel, M.D., Chief of Staff
CIO: Chad Andres, Chief Information Officer
CHR: Lisa Doty, Manager Human Resources
CNO: Markeeta Araujo, Chief Nursing Officer
Web address: www.desertviewhospital.com
Control: Corporation, Investor–owned, for–profit **Service:** General Medical and Surgical

Staffed Beds: 25 Admissions: 1401 Census: 12 Outpatient Visits: 38780 Births: 0

DESERT VIEW REGIONAL MEDICAL CENTER See Desert View Hospital

RENO—Washoe County

✠ **RENOWN REGIONAL MEDICAL CENTER (290001)**, 1155 Mill Street, Zip 89502–1576; tel. 775/982–4100, (Includes RENOWN CHILDREN'S HOSPITAL, 1155 Mill Street, tel. 775/982–5437) **A**1 2 3 5 10 **F**3 5 11 13 15 17 18 19 20 21 22 23 24 25 26 27 28 29 30 31 32 34 35 40 41 43 45 49 54 56 57 58 59 61 62 63 64 65 66 68 70 72 73 74 75 76 77 78 79 80 81 84 85 86 87 88 89 92 99 100 101 102 103 104 105 107 108 111 114 115 118 119 120 121 123 124 126 130 131 132 135 146 148 **S** Renown Health, Reno, NV
Primary Contact: Erik Olson, Chief Executive Officer
COO: Sy Johnson, Executive Vice President, Chief Operating Officer
CFO: Sam King, Chief Financial Officer
CMO: Charles Johnson, M.D., Chief of Staff
CIO: Charles Scully, Chief Information Officer
CHR: Michelle Sanchez–Bickley, Vice President Human Resources
Web address: www.renown.org
Control: Other not–for–profit (including NFP Corporation) **Service:** General Medical and Surgical

Staffed Beds: 643 Admissions: 27003 Census: 400 Outpatient Visits: 467483 Births: 4060 Total Expense ($000): 514701 Payroll Expense ($000): 172154 Personnel: 3297

★ △ **RENOWN REHABILITATION HOSPITAL**, 1495 Mill Street, Zip 89502–1479; tel. 775/982–3500 **A**3 5 7 **F**29 54 77 82 90 93 95 96 143 148 **S** Renown Health, Reno, NV
Primary Contact: Chris Nicholas, Chief Executive Officer
CFO: Dawn Ahner, Chief Financial Officer
CIO: Ronald Fuschillo, Chief Information Officer
CHR: Michelle Sanchez–Bickley, Vice President Human Resources
CNO: Melodie Osborn, Chief Nursing Officer
Web address: www.renown.org
Control: Other not–for–profit (including NFP Corporation) **Service:** Rehabilitation

Staffed Beds: 62 Admissions: 879 Census: 37 Outpatient Visits: 21315 Births: 0 Total Expense ($000): 20759 Payroll Expense ($000): 10362 Personnel: 267

✠ **RENOWN SOUTH MEADOWS MEDICAL CENTER (290049)**, 10101 Double R Boulevard, Zip 89521–5931; tel. 775/982–7000 **A**1 3 5 10 **F**8 10 12 29 30 35 39 40 46 49 68 70 74 75 79 81 82 84 85 87 93 97 107 108 111 119 125 130 131 146 **S** Renown Health, Reno, NV
Primary Contact: Gregory E. Boyer, Interim Administrator
COO: Sy Johnson, Executive Vice President, Chief Operating Officer
CFO: Gina Nelson, Chief Financial Officer
CMO: Dennis Rochier, Chief Medical Officer
CIO: Ronald Fuschillo, Chief Information Officer
CHR: Michelle Sanchez–Bickley, Vice President Human Resources
CNO: Melodie Osborn, Chief Nursing Officer
Web address: www.renown.org
Control: Other not–for–profit (including NFP Corporation) **Service:** General Medical and Surgical

Staffed Beds: 76 Admissions: 2896 Census: 24 Outpatient Visits: 66987 Births: 0 Total Expense ($000): 64300 Payroll Expense ($000): 22874 Personnel: 596

✠ **SAINT MARY'S REGIONAL MEDICAL CENTER (290009)**, 235 West Sixth Street, Zip 89503–4548; tel. 775/770–3000 **A**1 2 3 5 10 **F**3 11 12 13 15 17 18 20 22 24 26 28 29 30 31 34 35 36 40 45 46 47 49 50 51 53 54 56 57 59 62 63 64 65 68 70 72 74 75 76 77 78 79 81 82 84 85 86 87 89 91 92 93 94 95 96 97 107 108 110 111 114 115 119 120 121 123 124 126 129 130 132 143 144 146 147 148 **S** Prime Healthcare Services, Ontario, CA
Primary Contact: Helen Lidholm, Chief Executive Officer
CFO: John R. Deakyne, Chief Financial Officer
CIO: Cindy Mullins, Director Information Technology
CHR: David Milovich, Vice President Human Resources
Web address: www.saintmarysreno.org
Control: Corporation, Investor–owned, for–profit **Service:** General Medical and Surgical

Staffed Beds: 293 Admissions: 15408 Census: 164 Outpatient Visits: 141930 Births: 2168 Total Expense ($000): 293897 Payroll Expense ($000): 101249 Personnel: 1516

✠ **VETERANS AFFAIRS SIERRA NEVADA HEALTH CARE SYSTEM**, 975 Kirman Avenue, Zip 89502–0993; tel. 775/786–7200, (Total facility includes 60 beds in nursing home–type unit) **A**1 3 5 **F**1 3 5 18 20 22 29 30 31 34 35 36 38 39 40 44 45 46 47 49 50 54 56 57 58 59 60 61 62 63 64 65 66 68 70 74 75 77 78 79 81 82 83 84 85 86 87 91 92 93 94 96 97 98 100 101 102 103 104 107 108 111 114 115 119 127 129 130 132 135 143 144 146 147 148 **P**6 **S** Department of Veterans Affairs, Washington, DC
Primary Contact: Lisa M. Howard, Director
COO: Lisa M. Howard, Associate Director
CFO: Kelly Manson, Chief Financial Officer
CMO: Steven Brilliant, M.D., Chief of Staff
CIO: Jack Smith, Acting Chief Information Resources Management Service
CHR: Debbie Jenkins, Chief Human Resources Management Service
CNO: Rachel Crossley, R.N., Chief Patient Care Services
Web address: www.reno.va.gov/
Control: Veterans Affairs, Government, federal **Service:** General Medical and Surgical

Staffed Beds: 124 Admissions: 3380 Census: 104 Outpatient Visits: 448715 Births: 0 Total Expense ($000): 287398 Payroll Expense ($000): 98894 Personnel: 1338

☐ **WEST HILLS HOSPITAL (294003)**, 1240 East Ninth Street, Zip 89512–2964; tel. 775/323–0478, (Nonreporting) **A**1 10 **S** Universal Health Services, Inc., King of Prussia, PA
Primary Contact: Allison Zednicek, Chief Executive Officer
CMO: Philip Rich, M.D., Chief Medical Officer
CHR: Don Gay, Director Human Resources
Web address: www.westhillshospital.net
Control: Corporation, Investor–owned, for–profit **Service:** Psychiatric

Staffed Beds: 190

★ **WILLOW SPRINGS CENTER**, 690 Edison Way, Zip 89502–4135; tel. 775/858–3303, (Nonreporting) **A**3 5
Primary Contact: Duane Runyan, Chief Executive Officer and Managing Director
CMO: Dana Arlien, M.D., Chief Medical Officer
CNO: Sam McCord, Chief Nursing Officer
Web address: www.willowspringscenter.com
Control: Corporation, Investor–owned, for–profit **Service:** Children's hospital psychiatric

Staffed Beds: 116

SPARKS—Washoe County

☐ **NORTHERN NEVADA ADULT MENTAL HEALTH SERVICES (294000)**, 480 Galletti Way, Zip 89431–5564; tel. 775/688–2001 **A**1 3 5 10 **F**29 50 98 103 104 130
Primary Contact: Cody Phinney, Administrator
CFO: Elizabeth O'Brien, Chief Financial Officer
CIO: Lois Repass, Quality Assurance Specialist and Coordinator Performance Improvement
Web address: www.mhds.state.nv.us/
Control: State–Government, nonfederal **Service:** Psychiatric

Staffed Beds: 30 Admissions: 1330 Census: 25 Outpatient Visits: 0 Births: 0 Total Expense ($000): 18185 Payroll Expense ($000): 12469 Personnel: 241

☐ **NORTHERN NEVADA MEDICAL CENTER (290032)**, 2375 East Prater Way, Zip 89434–9641; tel. 775/331–7000, (Nonreporting) **A**1 10 **S** Universal Health Services, Inc., King of Prussia, PA
Primary Contact: Alan C. Olive, Chief Executive Officer
COO: Tiffany Coury, Chief Operating Officer
CFO: Ryan Heit, Chief Financial Officer
CHR: Patricia Downs, Director Human Resources
CNO: Carla Adams, Chief Nursing Officer
Web address: www.nnmc.com
Control: Corporation, Investor–owned, for–profit **Service:** General Medical and Surgical

Staffed Beds: 108

✠ **TAHOE PACIFIC HOSPITALS (292004)**, 2375 East Prater Way, Zip 89434; tel. 775/355–5600, (Includes TAHOE PACIFIC HOSPITALS – WEST, 235 West Sixth Street, 5th Floor, Reno, Zip 89503–4548) **A**1 10 **F**1 3 29 35 75 148 **P**8 **S** LifeCare Management Services, Plano, TX
Primary Contact: Matt Archer, Chief Executive Officer
COO: Theresa Fegan, R.N., Chief Clinical Officer
CFO: Nena Swenson, Financial Manager
CMO: T. Brian Callister, M.D., Chief Medical Officer
CIO: Kaylene Reeves, Director
CHR: Nelson Coy, Director Human Resources
Web address: www.lifecare–hospitals.com
Control: Corporation, Investor–owned, for–profit **Service:** Long–Term Acute Care hospital

Staffed Beds: 60 Admissions: 474 Census: 40 Outpatient Visits: 0 Births: 0 Total Expense ($000): 22779 Payroll Expense ($000): 10834 Personnel: 163

WINNEMUCCA—Humboldt County

★ **HUMBOLDT GENERAL HOSPITAL (291308)**, 118 East Haskell Street,
Zip 89445–3299; tel. 775/623–5222, (Total facility includes 63 beds in nursing
home–type unit) **A**3 10 18 **F**3 6 11 13 15 28 29 30 31 35 40 43 45 50 53 57
59 62 63 64 68 75 76 77 78 79 81 82 85 86 90 93 99 100 103 107 110
111 114 118 119 127 128 129 130 131 132 133 135 146 147 148
Primary Contact: James G. Parrish, FACHE, Chief Executive Officer
CFO: Sandi Lehman, Chief Financial Officer
CMO: Brad Granath, M.D., Chief of Staff
CHR: Rose Marie Green, Director Human Resources
CNO: Darlene Bryan, R.N., Chief Nursing Officer
Web address: www.hghospital.org
Control: Church–operated, Nongovernment, not–for profit **Service:** General
Medical and Surgical

Staffed Beds: 88 **Admissions:** 572 **Census:** 62 **Outpatient Visits:** 71624
Births: 61 **Total Expense ($000):** 31150 **Payroll Expense ($000):** 14322
Personnel: 229

YERINGTON—Lyon County

SOUTH LYON MEDICAL CENTER (290002), 213 South Whitacre,
Zip 89447–2561, Mailing Address: P.O. Box 940, Zip 89447–0940;
tel. 775/463–2301, (Nonreporting) **A**10 20
Primary Contact: Toni A. Inserra, Interim Administrator
Web address: www.southlyonmedicalcenter.org
Control: Other not–for–profit (including NFP Corporation) **Service:** General
Medical and Surgical

Staffed Beds: 63

NV

NEW HAMPSHIRE

BERLIN—Coos County

ANDROSCOGGIN VALLEY HOSPITAL (301310), 59 Page Hill Road,
Zip 03570–3531; tel. 603/752–2200 **A**10 18 **F**3 8 11 12 13 15 28 29 30 34
40 41 43 45 47 57 59 61 64 70 74 75 77 79 81 82 85 92 93 102 107 108
110 114 119 129 130 131 132 133 146 147 **P**6
Primary Contact: Michael Peterson, FACHE, President
CFO: Jeremy Roberge, Director Reimbursement
CMO: Keith M. Shute, M.D., Senior Vice President Medical Affairs and Clinical
Services
CIO: Linda M. Laperle, Vice President Administrative Services
CHR: James A. Wheeler, Vice President Human Relations and Community
Development
Web address: www.avhnh.org
Control: Other not–for–profit (including NFP Corporation) **Service:** General
Medical and Surgical

Staffed Beds: 25 **Admissions:** 1459 **Census:** 16 **Outpatient Visits:** 71777
Births: 100 **Total Expense ($000):** 54965 **Payroll Expense ($000):** 23113
Personnel: 286

CLAREMONT—Sullivan County

VALLEY REGIONAL HOSPITAL (301308), 243 Elm Street, Zip 03743–4921;
tel. 603/542–7771 **A**1 10 18 **F**2 3 11 14 15 28 29 34 35 38 40 43 45 49 50
51 54 57 59 62 63 64 68 70 75 77 79 81 83 84 85 87 93 97 107 108 110
114 118 119 130 132 133 135 144 146 147 148 **P**6
Primary Contact: Peter J. Wright, FACHE, Chief Executive Officer
CFO: Jean Shaw, Chief Financial Officer
CMO: Oliver Herfort, M.D., Chief Medical Officer
CIO: Patricia Witthaus, Director Information Services
CHR: Cheryl Cavanaugh, Senior Director Human Resources
CNO: Lynne Gagnon, Chief Nursing Officer
Web address: www.vrh.org
Control: Other not–for–profit (including NFP Corporation) **Service:** General
Medical and Surgical

Staffed Beds: 25 **Admissions:** 786 **Census:** 11 **Outpatient Visits:** 69392
Births: 0 **Total Expense ($000):** 40264 **Payroll Expense ($000):** 16803
Personnel: 290

COLEBROOK—Coos County

UPPER CONNECTICUT VALLEY HOSPITAL (301300), 181 Corliss·Lane,
Zip 03576–3207; tel. 603/237–4971 **A**10 18 **F**3 15 29 31 34 35 40 45 50 56
57 59 64 67 68 75 77 81 85 93 102 107 110 114 119 128 130 133 144
146 147 148 **P**6
Primary Contact: Scott Colby, President
CFO: Celeste Pitts, Chief Financial Officer
CMO: Nicole Paier–Mullan, M.D., Medical Director
CIO: Heather Leighton, Director, Revenue Cycle and Privacy Officer
CHR: Heidi L. Saari, Director, Human Resources
CNO: Laurie Cotnoir, Director Nursing and Quality
Web address: www.ucvh.org
Control: Other not–for–profit (including NFP Corporation) **Service:** General
Medical and Surgical

Staffed Beds: 16 **Admissions:** 397 **Census:** 6 **Outpatient Visits:** 17900
Total Expense ($000): 15641 **Payroll Expense ($000):** 6420 **Personnel:** 91

CONCORD—Merrimack County

★ ◇ **CONCORD HOSPITAL (300001)**, 250 Pleasant Street, Zip 03301–2598;
tel. 603/225–2711 **A**2 3 5 10 21 **F**3 8 12 13 14 15 17 18 20 22 24 26 28 29
30 31 33 34 35 36 37 38 39 40 42 43 44 45 46 49 50 51 53 54 55 56 57
58 59 61 64 65 66 68 69 70 71 74 75 76 77 78 79 80 81 82 83 84 85 86
87 89 93 97 98 99 100 101 102 103 104 105 107 108 110 111 114 115
118 119 120 121 123 126 129 130 131 132 134 135 144 145 146 147
148 **P**6
Primary Contact: Robert P. Steigmeyer, President and Chief Executive Officer
COO: Timothy P. Jones, Chief Operating Officer
CFO: Bruce R. Burns, Chief Financial Officer
CMO: David F. Green, M.D., Chief Medical Officer
CIO: Deane Morrison, Chief Information Officer
CHR: Robin A. Moore, Vice President Human Resources
CNO: Diane Wood–Allen, MS, Chief Nursing Officer
Web address: www.concordhospital.org
Control: Other not–for–profit (including NFP Corporation) **Service:** General
Medical and Surgical

Staffed Beds: 237 **Admissions:** 12400 **Census:** 155 **Outpatient Visits:**
712369 **Births:** 1294 **Total Expense ($000):** 400572 **Payroll Expense**
($000): 192365 **Personnel:** 2873

HEALTHSOUTH REHABILITATION HOSPITAL (303027), 254 Pleasant Street,
Zip 03301–2508; tel. 603/226–9800, (Nonreporting) **A**1 10 **S** HEALTHSOUTH
Corporation, Birmingham, AL
Primary Contact: Catherine Devaney, Chief Executive Officer
CFO: Diana Lachapelle, Controller
CMO: Muhammad Salmanullah, Chief Medical Director
CHR: Myra Nixon, Director Human Resources
CNO: Joseph Adamski, Chief Nursing Officer
Web address: www.healthsouthrehabconcordnh.com
Control: Corporation, Investor–owned, for–profit **Service:** Rehabilitation

Staffed Beds: 50

☐ **NEW HAMPSHIRE HOSPITAL (304000)**, 36 Clinton Street, Zip 03301–2359;
tel. 603/271–5300 **A**1 3 10 **F**3 29 30 39 56 57 68 74 75 86 87 91 98 99
101 103 130 135 146 **P**4 6
Primary Contact: Robert J. MacLeod, Chief Executive Officer
COO: Geoffrey C. Souther, Chief Operating Officer
CFO: Jamie Dall, Chief Financial Officer
CMO: David G. Folks, M.D., Chief Medical Officer
CIO: David Levesque, Director, Information Systems
CHR: Mark Bussiere, Administrator Human Resources
CNO: Roberta A. Vitale–Nolen, Administrator, Patient Care Services
Web address: www.dhhs.state.nh.us./dhhs/default.htm
Control: State–Government, nonfederal **Service:** Psychiatric

Staffed Beds: 158 **Admissions:** 2009 **Census:** 156 **Outpatient Visits:** 0
Births: 0 **Total Expense ($000):** 54119 **Payroll Expense ($000):** 27743
Personnel: 527

DERRY—Rockingham County

PARKLAND MEDICAL CENTER (300017), One Parkland Drive,
Zip 03038–2750; tel. 603/432–1500, (Nonreporting) **A**1 2 10 **S** HCA,
Nashville, TN
Primary Contact: Jeff Scionti, Interim Chief Executive Officer
COO: Jeff Scionti, Chief Operating Officer
CFO: Jacob Wisemann, Chief Financial Officer
CMO: Edward Yourtee, M.D., Chief Medical Officer
CIO: Brad George, Director Information Systems
CHR: Molly Lahti, Director Human Resources
CNO: Eileen Keefe, Chief Nursing Officer
Web address: www.parklandmedicalcenter.com
Control: Corporation, Investor–owned, for–profit **Service:** General Medical and
Surgical

Staffed Beds: 82

DOVER—Strafford County

WENTWORTH–DOUGLASS HOSPITAL (300018), 789 Central Avenue,
Zip 03820; tel. 603/742–5252 **A**1 2 10 **F**3 8 13 17 18 19 20 22 26 28 29 30
31 32 34 35 36 39 40 41 42 43 44 45 46 47 48 49 50 51 54 55 57 58 59
61 62 63 64 65 68 70 73 74 75 76 77 78 79 81 82 84 85 86 87 89 92 93
94 96 97 100 101 104 107 108 110 111 114 115 118 119 120 121 123
124 126 129 130 131 132 134 135 143 144 145 146 147 148 **P**6 8
Primary Contact: Gregory J. Walker, Chief Executive Officer
COO: Daniel N. Dunn, Vice President Operations
CFO: Peter Walcek, Vice President Finance
CMO: Paul Cass, D.O., Chief Medical & Clinical Integration Officer
CIO: Jeffrey Pollock, Chief Information Officer
CHR: Erin Flanigan, Vice President Human Resources
CNO: Sheila Woolley, R.N., Vice President, Patient Care Services
Web address: www.wdhospital.com
Control: Other not–for–profit (including NFP Corporation) **Service:** General
Medical and Surgical

Staffed Beds: 114 **Admissions:** 6269 **Census:** 74 **Outpatient Visits:** 285477
Births: 1167 **Total Expense ($000):** 240086 **Payroll Expense ($000):**
95898 **Personnel:** 1427

NH

Many Facility Codes have changed. Please refer to the AHA Guide Code Chart. © 2016 AHA Guide

EXETER—Rockingham County

★ ◇ **EXETER HOSPITAL (300023)**, 5 Alumni Drive, Zip 03833–2128;
tel. 603/778–7311 **A**2 10 19 21 **F**3 8 13 14 15 18 20 22 26 28 29 30 31 32
34 35 36 37 38 40 44 45 46 47 48 49 50 51 52 54 55 57 58 59 64 70 74
75 76 77 78 79 80 81 84 85 86 87 89 93 107 108 110 111 114 117 118
119 120 121 123 124 129 130 131 132 135 143 144 145 146 147 148
Primary Contact: Kevin J. Callahan, President and Chief Executive Officer
CFO: Kevin J. O'Leary, Senior Vice President and Chief Financial Officer
CMO: Richard Hollister, President of Medical Staff
CIO: David Briden, Chief Information Officer
CHR: Christopher M. Callahan, Vice President Human Resources
CNO: Susan Burns–Tisdale, Senior Vice President Clinical Operations, Interim CNO
Web address: www.ehr.org
Control: Other not–for–profit (including NFP Corporation) **Service:** General
Medical and Surgical

Staffed Beds: 99 **Admissions:** 4892 **Census:** 54 **Outpatient Visits:** 193880
Births: 652 **Total Expense ($000):** 178538 **Payroll Expense ($000):** 67585
Personnel: 1206

FRANKLIN—Merrimack County

★ ◇ **FRANKLIN REGIONAL HOSPITAL (301306)**, 15 Aiken Avenue,
Zip 03235–1299; tel. 603/934–2060 **A**10 18 21 **F**3 11 15 18 29 30 34 35 36
39 40 44 45 46 47 48 49 50 57 58 59 61 64 65 66 68 70 74 75 77 78 79
81 82 83 84 85 86 87 93 97 98 99 100 101 102 103 107 110 119 127 128
130 131 132 133 135 146 147 148 **P**4 6 **S** LRGHealthcare, Laconia, NH
Primary Contact: Kevin Donovan, Chief Executive Officer
CFO: Henry D. Lipman, Senior Vice President, Financial Strategy and External
Relations
CMO: Peter Doane, M.D., Chief Medical Officer
CIO: Kevin Irish, Chief Information Officer
CHR: Cass Walker, Vice President Administrative & Support Services
CNO: Jacqueline Dawe, R.N., Chief Nursing Officer
Web address: www.lrgh.org
Control: Other not–for–profit (including NFP Corporation) **Service:** General
Medical and Surgical

Staffed Beds: 35 **Admissions:** 1196 **Census:** 21 **Outpatient Visits:** 49967
Births: 0 **Total Expense ($000):** 40816 **Payroll Expense ($000):** 20793
Personnel: 198

GREENFIELD—Hillsborough County

CROTCHED MOUNTAIN REHABILITATION CENTER, 1 Verney Drive,
Zip 03047–5000; tel. 603/547–3311, (Nonreporting)
Primary Contact: Michael Coughlin, Chief Executive Officer
COO: Michael Redmond, Senior Vice President and Chief Operating Officer
CFO: Thomas Zubricki, Vice President Finance, Chief Financial Officer
CMO: W. Carl Cooley, M.D., Chief Medical Officer
CIO: Jerry Hunter, Vice President, Information Technology
CHR: Lorrie Rudis, Vice President, Human Resources
Web address: www.cmf.org
Control: Other not–for–profit (including NFP Corporation) **Service:** Rehabilitation

Staffed Beds: 181

HAMPSTEAD—Rockingham County

☐ **HAMPSTEAD HOSPITAL (304001)**, 218 East Road, Zip 03841–2305;
tel. 603/329–5311, (Nonreporting) **A**1 10
Primary Contact: Phillip J. Kubiak, President
COO: Cynthia A. Gove, Chief Operating Officer
CFO: Cherie Clough–Berry, Vice President, Finance
CMO: Michael Knight, M.D., Medical Director
CIO: Sandra J. Lucia, Director Health Information and Corporate Compliance
Officer
CHR: Lisa M. Ryan, Coordinator Human Resources
CNO: Julie D'Apollo, R.N., Director of Nursing
Web address: www.hampsteadhospital.com
Control: Corporation, Investor–owned, for–profit **Service:** Psychiatric

Staffed Beds: 60

KEENE—Cheshire County

⊠ **CHESHIRE MEDICAL CENTER (300019)**, 580 Court Street, Zip 03431–1718;
tel. 603/354–5400 **A**1 2 3 10 **F**3 12 13 15 18 28 29 30 31 34 35 36 38 40
41 43 44 45 46 49 50 54 55 56 58 59 61 64 65 68 70 74 75 76 77 78 79
81 82 84 85 86 87 89 90 91 92 93 94 96 97 98 99 100 102 104 107 108
110 111 115 118 119 121 123 129 130 131 132 133 135 144 146 147
148 **P**6
Primary Contact: Don Caruso, M.D., Chief Executive Officer and President
CFO: Robert K. Cochrane, Interim Vice President, Finance
CMO: Don Caruso, M.D., Chief Medical Officer
CIO: Peter Malloy, Chief Information Officer
CHR: Julie Green, Vice President Human Resources
CNO: Cynthia Coughlin, MS, Chief Nursing Officer
Web address: www.cheshire–med.com
Control: Other not–for–profit (including NFP Corporation) **Service:** General
Medical and Surgical

Staffed Beds: 116 **Admissions:** 3667 **Census:** 54 **Outpatient Visits:** 494679
Births: 448 **Total Expense ($000):** 156824 **Payroll Expense ($000):** 55659
Personnel: 1134

LACONIA—Belknap County

★ ◇ **LAKES REGION GENERAL HOSPITAL (300005)**, 80 Highland Street,
Zip 03246–3298; tel. 603/524–3211 **A**10 21 **F**3 8 11 12 13 15 18 28 29 30
31 32 34 35 36 37 39 40 43 44 45 46 47 48 49 50 53 54 57 58 59 60
61 64 65 66 68 70 74 75 76 77 78 79 81 82 84 85 86 87 93 97 98 99 100
101 102 103 107 108 110 114 118 119 129 130 131 132 133 135 144 146
147 148 **P**4 6 **S** LRGHealthcare, Laconia, NH
Primary Contact: Kevin Donovan, Chief Executive Officer
CFO: Henry D. Lipman, Senior Vice President, Financial Strategy and External
Relations
CMO: Peter Doane, M.D., Chief Medical Officer
CIO: Kevin Irish, Chief Information Officer
CHR: Cass Walker, Vice President Administrative & Support Services
CNO: Jacqueline Dawe, R.N., Chief Nursing Officer
Web address: www.lrgh.org
Control: Other not–for–profit (including NFP Corporation) **Service:** General
Medical and Surgical

Staffed Beds: 88 **Admissions:** 4614 **Census:** 65 **Outpatient Visits:** 222029
Births: 352 **Total Expense ($000):** 189460 **Payroll Expense ($000):** 89347
Personnel: 976

LANCASTER—Coos County

★ **WEEKS MEDICAL CENTER (301303)**, 173 Middle Street, Zip 03584–3508;
tel. 603/788–4911 **A**10 18 **F**3 11 15 18 28 29 31 32 34 35 36 40 45 50 51
56 57 59 61 62 63 64 65 66 68 70 75 77 78 79 81 85 87 91 92 93 94 97
100 104 107 108 110 111 114 116 117 118 119 127 130 131 132 133 134
135 146 147 148 **P**6
Primary Contact: Michael Lee, President
CMO: Lars Nielson, M.D., Chief Medical Officer
CIO: Darrell Bodnar, Director Information
CHR: Linda Rexford, Director Human Resources
CNO: Donna Walker, Chief Nurse Executive
Web address: www.weeksmedical.org
Control: Other not–for–profit (including NFP Corporation) **Service:** General
Medical and Surgical

Staffed Beds: 25 **Admissions:** 832 **Census:** 10 **Outpatient Visits:** 84485
Births: 0 **Total Expense ($000):** 42062 **Payroll Expense ($000):** 22820
Personnel: 292

LEBANON—Grafton County

★ **ALICE PECK DAY MEMORIAL HOSPITAL (301305)**, 10 Alice Peck Day Drive,
Zip 03766–2650; tel. 603/448–3121 **A**10 18 **F**3 11 13 15 29 34 35 36 37 39
40 41 45 47 50 51 54 56 57 59 63 64 65 66 67 75 76 77 79 81 82 83 84
85 93 97 107 110 113 114 115 116 117 119 128 129 130 131 133 135
145 146 147 148 **P**5 6
Primary Contact: Susan E. Mooney, M.D., MS, President and Chief Executive
Officer
COO: J. Todd Miller, Vice President and Chief Operating Officer
CFO: Evalie M. Crosby, CPA, Vice President Finance and Chief Financial Officer
CMO: Randy Lea, M.D., Vice President and Chief Medical Officer
CIO: Kristin Kneisel, Interim Director, Information Services
CHR: Brenda Blair, Vice President Human Resources
CNO: Beverley A. Rankin, R.N., Vice President & Chief Nursing Officer
Web address: www.alicepeckday.org
Control: Other not–for–profit (including NFP Corporation) **Service:** General
Medical and Surgical

Staffed Beds: 25 **Admissions:** 1288 **Census:** 14 **Outpatient Visits:** 110643
Births: 295 **Total Expense ($000):** 61390 **Payroll Expense ($000):** 33656
Personnel: 418

NH

Hospital, Medicare Provider Number, Address, Telephone, Approval, Facility, and Physician Codes, Health Care System

★ American Hospital Association (AHA) membership ☐ The Joint Commission accreditation ◯ Healthcare Facilities Accreditation Program ◇ DNV Healthcare Inc. accreditation ⇧ Center for Improvement in Healthcare Quality Accreditation △ Commission on Accreditation of Rehabilitation Facilities (CARF) accreditation

✠ **DARTMOUTH–HITCHCOCK MEDICAL CENTER (300003)**, One Medical Center Drive, Zip 03756–0001; tel. 603/650–5000, (Includes CHILDREN'S HOSPITAL AT DARTMOUTH, One Medical Center Drive, Zip 03756; tel. 603/650–5000) **A**1 3 5 8 10 **F**3 5 6 7 8 9 11 12 13 14 15 17 18 19 20 21 22 23 24 25 26 27 28 29 30 31 32 34 35 36 37 38 39 40 41 43 44 45 46 47 48 49 50 51 52 53 54 55 56 57 58 59 60 61 63 64 65 66 68 70 71 72 74 75 76 77 78 79 80 81 82 84 85 86 87 88 89 91 92 93 94 96 97 98 99 100 101 102 103 104 105 107 108 110 111 112 114 115 116 117 118 119 120 121 123 124 126 129 130 131 132 134 135 136 138 141 142 143 145 146 147 148 **P**6
Primary Contact: James Weinstein, D.O., MS, President and Chief Executive Officer
COO: Daniel Jantzen, Senior Vice President and Chief Operating Officer
CFO: Daniel Jantzen, Chief Financial Officer
CMO: Edward J. Merrens, M.D., Medical Director
CIO: Terrence Carroll, Ph.D., Vice President, Information Services
CHR: John S. Malanowski, Chief Human Resources Officer
CNO: Gay L. Landstrom, Ph.D., Chief Nursing Officer
Web address: www.hitchcock.org
Control: Other not–for–profit (including NFP Corporation) **Service:** General Medical and Surgical

Staffed Beds: 417 **Admissions:** 19479 **Census:** 320 **Outpatient Visits:** 878361 **Births:** 1107 **Total Expense ($000):** 1126180 **Payroll Expense ($000):** 538987 **Personnel:** 6110

LITTLETON—Grafton County

★ **LITTLETON REGIONAL HOSPITAL (301302)**, 600 Saint Johnsbury Road, Zip 03561–3442; tel. 603/444–9000 **A**10 18 **F**3 11 13 15 18 26 28 29 31 32 34 35 36 38 40 43 44 45 50 56 57 59 64 65 67 70 74 75 76 77 78 79 81 84 85 86 87 89 90 92 93 96 97 100 104 107 108 110 111 114 115 118 119 127 128 129 130 131 133 143 146 147 148 **P**6
Primary Contact: Nick Braccino, Interim President
CFO: Robert L. Fotter, Chief Financial Officer
CIO: Scott Vachon, Director Information Technology
CHR: Georgene Novak, Director Human Resources
CNO: Linda Gilmore, Chief Nursing Officer/Chief Administrative Officer
Web address: www.littletonhospital.org
Control: Other not–for–profit (including NFP Corporation) **Service:** General Medical and Surgical

Staffed Beds: 25 **Admissions:** 1623 **Census:** 15 **Outpatient Visits:** 54217 **Births:** 359 **Total Expense ($000):** 86731 **Payroll Expense ($000):** 35660 **Personnel:** 409

MANCHESTER—Hillsborough County

✠ **CATHOLIC MEDICAL CENTER (300034)**, 100 McGregor Street, Zip 03102–3770; tel. 603/668–3545 **A**1 2 3 10 **F**3 9 12 15 18 20 22 24 26 28 29 30 31 32 34 35 36 37 38 39 40 41 43 44 46 47 48 49 50 53 57 58 59 60 61 63 64 65 66 70 71 73 74 75 76 77 78 79 80 81 82 84 85 86 87 90 92 93 96 100 102 104 107 108 110 111 114 115 118 119 124 126 129 130 131 132 134 135 143 144 146 147 148 **P**6
Primary Contact: Joseph Pepe, M.D., President and Chief Executive Officer
COO: Alexander J. Walker, Executive Vice President Operations and Strategic Development
CFO: Edward L. Dudley, III, Executive Vice President and Chief Financial Officer
CMO: William H. Goodman, Vice President Medical Affairs, Chief Medical Officer
CIO: Thomas Della Flora, Vice President and Chief Information Officer
CHR: Merryll Rosenfeld, Vice President, Human Resources
CNO: Robert A. Duhaime, R.N., Senior Vice President Clinical Operations and Chief Nursing Officer
Web address: www.catholicmedicalcenter.org
Control: Other not–for–profit (including NFP Corporation) **Service:** General Medical and Surgical

Staffed Beds: 240 **Admissions:** 10566 **Census:** 152 **Outpatient Visits:** 168670 **Births:** 1028 **Total Expense ($000):** 303432 **Payroll Expense ($000):** 133248 **Personnel:** 1545

✠ **ELLIOT HOSPITAL (300012)**, One Elliot Way, Zip 03103–3502; tel. 603/669–5300 **A**1 2 3 10 **F**3 8 9 12 13 15 18 20 22 26 28 29 30 31 32 34 35 36 37 38 39 40 41 42 43 44 45 46 47 48 49 50 51 53 54 55 56 57 59 62 64 65 68 70 72 74 75 76 77 78 79 81 82 83 84 85 86 87 88 89 91 93 97 98 99 100 101 102 103 104 107 108 110 111 114 115 118 119 120 121 123 124 126 129 130 131 132 134 135 144 146 147 148 **P**6
Primary Contact: Gary Muller, Interim Chief Executive Officer
COO: Rick Phelps, M.D., President and Chief Operating Officer
CFO: Richard Elwell, Senior Vice President and Chief Financial Officer
CMO: Greg Baxter, M.D., Senior Vice President Medical Affairs and Chief Medical Officer
CIO: Denise Purington, Vice President and Chief Information Officer
CHR: Catherine Bardier, Vice President, Human Resources
Web address: www.elliothospital.org
Control: Other not–for–profit (including NFP Corporation) **Service:** General Medical and Surgical

Staffed Beds: 266 **Admissions:** 12794 **Census:** 176 **Outpatient Visits:** 521248 **Births:** 2032 **Total Expense ($000):** 361260 **Payroll Expense ($000):** 132284 **Personnel:** 2922

★ **MANCHESTER VETERANS AFFAIRS MEDICAL CENTER**, 718 Smyth Road, Zip 03104–4098; tel. 603/624–4366, (Nonreporting) **A**5 **S** Department of Veterans Affairs, Washington, DC
Primary Contact: Danielle Ocker, R.N., Director
COO: Richard T. Rose, Associate Director
CFO: Frank Ryan, Chief Financial Officer
CMO: Andrew Breuder, M.D., Chief of Staff
CIO: John Foote, Chief Information Officer
CHR: Mary Ellen Kenney, Chief Human Services
Web address: www.manchester.va.gov/
Control: Veterans Affairs, Government, federal **Service:** Rehabilitation

Staffed Beds: 90

VETERANS AFFAIRS MEDICAL CENTER See Manchester Veterans Affairs Medical Center

NASHUA—Hillsborough County

★ ◇ **SOUTHERN NEW HAMPSHIRE MEDICAL CENTER (300020)**, 8 Prospect Street, Zip 03060–3925, Mailing Address: P.O. Box 2014, Zip 03061–2014; tel. 603/577–2000 **A**2 3 5 10 21 **F**3 11 13 15 18 20 22 26 28 29 30 31 34 35 40 42 43 45 49 50 51 52 57 59 61 65 68 70 72 74 75 76 77 78 79 81 84 85 86 87 89 93 96 98 100 102 104 105 107 110 111 115 118 119 126 129 130 131 132 135 143 146 147 148 **P**6
Primary Contact: Michael S. Rose, President and Chief Executive Officer
COO: Tate Curti, Senior Vice President and Chief Operating Officer
CFO: Paul Trainor, Chief Financial Officer
CMO: Kenneth Howe, Chief Medical Officer
CIO: Andrew Watt, M.D., Vice President, Chief Information Officer and Chief Medical Information Officer
CHR: Jacqueline Wooley, Vice President
CNO: Cheryl Gagne, Vice President and Chief Nursing Officer
Web address: www.snhhs.org
Control: Other not–for–profit (including NFP Corporation) **Service:** General Medical and Surgical

Staffed Beds: 166 **Admissions:** 7909 **Census:** 94 **Outpatient Visits:** 228065 **Births:** 1218 **Total Expense ($000):** 183534 **Payroll Expense ($000):** 87987 **Personnel:** 1471

★ △ ◇ **ST. JOSEPH HOSPITAL (300011)**, 172 Kinsley Street, Zip 03060–3648; tel. 603/882–3000, (Nonreporting) **A**2 7 10 21 **S** Covenant Health, Tewksbury, MA
Primary Contact: Richard Boehler, M.D., President and Chief Executive Officer
COO: Pam Duchene, R.N., Vice President Patient Care Services
CFO: Richard Plamondon, Vice President Finance and Chief Financial Officer
CIO: Keith A. Choinka, Vice President Information Systems and Chief Information Officer
CHR: Jacqueline Woolley, Vice President Human Resources
Web address: www.stjosephhospital.com
Control: Other not–for–profit (including NFP Corporation) **Service:** General Medical and Surgical

Staffed Beds: 126

NEW LONDON—Merrimack County

★ **NEW LONDON HOSPITAL (301304)**, 273 County Road, Zip 03257–5736; tel. 603/526–2911, (Total facility includes 58 beds in nursing home–type unit) **A**3 10 18 **F**3 7 11 15 18 29 30 31 32 34 40 41 45 50 51 54 56 57 59 64 67 70 74 75 77 78 79 81 82 84 85 87 89 93 94 97 99 100 102 104 107 110 111 114 119 127 128 130 131 133 134 146 147 148 **P**6
Primary Contact: Bruce King, President and Chief Executive Officer
CFO: Donald Griffin, CPA, Chief Financial Officer
CMO: James M. Murphy, M.D., Chief Medical Officer Regional Development and Outpatient Services
CIO: David Foss, Chief Information Officer
CHR: Shari Bostwick, Director Human Resources
CNO: Sally K. Patton, R.N., Chief Nursing Officer
Web address: www.newlondonhospital.org
Control: Other not–for–profit (including NFP Corporation) **Service:** General Medical and Surgical

Staffed Beds: 83 **Admissions:** 998 **Census:** 58 **Outpatient Visits:** 124472 **Births:** 0 **Total Expense ($000):** 59743 **Payroll Expense ($000):** 27562 **Personnel:** 430

NH

Many Facility Codes have changed. Please refer to the AHA Guide Code Chart. © 2016 AHA Guide

NORTH CONWAY—Carroll County

★ **MEMORIAL HOSPITAL (301307)**, 3073 White Mountain Highway, Zip 03860–7101; tel. 603/356–5461, (Total facility includes 45 beds in nursing home–type unit) **A**10 18 **F**3 11 13 15 28 29 30 31 34 35 36 40 45 50 51 57 59 64 67 68 70 75 76 77 78 79 81 82 84 85 86 87 90 94 96 97 100 101 103 104 105 107 110 115 119 128 129 130 131 132 133 144 146 147 **P**6 **S** MaineHealth, Portland, ME
Primary Contact: Scott McKinnon, President and Chief Executive Officer
CFO: Diane Maheux, Vice President Finance
CMO: Ray Rabideau, M.D., Senior Vice President and Chief Medical Officer
CIO: Curtis Kerbs, Regional Chief Information Officer
CHR: Melanie Sleime, Director Human Resources
CNO: Ethnee Garner, R.N., Vice President Patient Care Services
Web address: www.memorialhospitalnh.org
Control: Other not–for–profit (including NFP Corporation) **Service:** General Medical and Surgical

Staffed Beds: 70 Admissions: 1631 **Census:** 58 **Outpatient Visits:** 54736 **Births:** 260 **Total Expense ($000):** 65694 **Payroll Expense ($000):** 26278 **Personnel:** 389

PETERBOROUGH—Hillsborough County

★ **MONADNOCK COMMUNITY HOSPITAL (301309)**, 452 Old Street Road, Zip 03458–1295; tel. 603/924–7191 **A**5 10 18 **F**3 11 13 15 28 29 30 31 34 35 36 40 41 44 45 50 53 57 59 64 65 70 74 75 76 77 78 79 81 82 85 86 89 91 92 93 97 99 100 101 102 103 104 107 110 114 118 119 127 130 131 132 133 134 135 146 147 148 **P**6
Primary Contact: Cynthia McGuire, FACHE, President and Chief Executive Officer
CFO: Richard Scheinblum, Chief Financial Officer
CMO: Michael Lindberg, M.D., Chief Medical Officer
CIO: Peter A. Johnson, Interim Chief Information Officer
CHR: John Sansone, Director Human Resources
CNO: Vicki Loughery, R.N., Chief Nursing Officer
Web address: www.monadnockhospital.org
Control: Other not–for–profit (including NFP Corporation) **Service:** General Medical and Surgical

Staffed Beds: 25 Admissions: 1474 **Census:** 13 **Outpatient Visits:** 77373 **Births:** 298 **Total Expense ($000):** 75700 **Payroll Expense ($000):** 31996 **Personnel:** 449

PLYMOUTH—Grafton County

★ **SPEARE MEMORIAL HOSPITAL (301311)**, 16 Hospital Road, Zip 03264–1199; tel. 603/536–1120 **A**10 18 **F**3 13 15 28 29 30 31 32 34 35 40 45 53 54 57 59 64 70 75 76 77 78 79 81 84 85 93 94 97 107 110 111 113 114 119 127 129 130 131 132 133 146 147 148 **P**8
Primary Contact: Michelle McEwen, President and Chief Executive Officer
CFO: Thomas Lenkowski, Chief Financial Officer
CMO: Joseph Ebner, M.D., Chief Medical Officer
CIO: Michael Cosgrave, Director, Information System
CHR: Laurie Bolognani, Human Resources Officer
CNO: Kristine Hering, R.N., Chief Nursing Officer
Web address: www.spearehospital.com
Control: Other not–for–profit (including NFP Corporation) **Service:** General Medical and Surgical

Staffed Beds: 25 Admissions: 1344 **Census:** 15 **Outpatient Visits:** 46721 **Births:** 396 **Total Expense ($000):** 50780 **Payroll Expense ($000):** 23677 **Personnel:** 381

PORTSMOUTH—Rockingham County

⊠ **PORTSMOUTH REGIONAL HOSPITAL (300029)**, 333 Borthwick Avenue, Zip 03801–7128; tel. 603/436–5110, (Nonreporting) **A**1 2 10 **S** HCA, Nashville, TN
Primary Contact: Dean Carucci, Chief Executive Officer
COO: Stuart Hemming, Chief Operating Officer
CFO: Richard Senger, Chief Financial Officer
CMO: Tim Pike, M.D., Chief Medical Officer
CIO: Ed Sovetskhy, Director Information Services
CHR: Jackie Brayton, Vice President Human Resources
Web address: www.portsmouthhospital.com
Control: Corporation, Investor–owned, for–profit **Service:** General Medical and Surgical

Staffed Beds: 165

ROCHESTER—Strafford County

★ **FRISBIE MEMORIAL HOSPITAL (300014)**, 11 Whitehall Road, Zip 03867–3297; tel. 603/332–5211 **A**10 **F**3 7 11 13 17 18 20 21 28 29 31 32 34 35 40 45 46 49 50 56 57 59 64 68 70 75 77 78 79 81 82 83 86 87 93 97 98 103 104 105 107 111 115 117 118 119 129 130 132 135 146 147 **P**5 8
Primary Contact: John A. Marzinzik, President and Chief Executive Officer
CFO: Nick Samilo, Vice President Finance and Chief Financial Officer
CMO: Jocelyn Caple, M.D., Chief Medical Officer
CHR: Christi Green, R.N., Vice President, Human Resources
CNO: Amy Dumont, R.N., Chief Clinical Officer and Vice President Patient Care Services
Web address: www.frisbiehospital.com
Control: Other not–for–profit (including NFP Corporation) **Service:** General Medical and Surgical

Staffed Beds: 92 Admissions: 3290 **Census:** 43 **Outpatient Visits:** 127440 **Births:** 365 **Total Expense ($000):** 134115 **Payroll Expense ($000):** 57258 **Personnel:** 835

SALEM—Rockingham County

☐ △ **NORTHEAST REHABILITATION HOSPITAL (303026)**, 70 Butler Street, Zip 03079–3925; tel. 603/893–2900 **A**1 7 10 **F**29 30 62 68 82 87 90 91 93 96 131 133 147 148
Primary Contact: John F. Prochilo, Chief Executive Officer and Administrator
COO: Robert Kotsonis, Chief Operating Officer
CFO: Charles Champagne, Chief Financial Officer
CMO: A. Deniz Ozel, M.D., Chief Medical Director
CHR: Shirley G. Lussier, Vice President Human Resources
CNO: Helene Thibodeau, R.N., Vice President Patient Care Services
Web address: www.northeastrehab.com
Control: Corporation, Investor–owned, for–profit **Service:** Rehabilitation

Staffed Beds: 135 Admissions: 3266 **Census:** 106 **Outpatient Visits:** 191283 **Births:** 0 **Total Expense ($000):** 76160 **Payroll Expense ($000):** 41722 **Personnel:** 636

WOLFEBORO—Carroll County

★ **HUGGINS HOSPITAL (301312)**, 240 South Main Street, Zip 03894–4455, Mailing Address: P.O. Box 912, Zip 03894–0912; tel. 603/569–7500 **A**10 18 **F**2 3 10 15 28 29 34 35 36 40 45 50 53 57 59 64 65 68 70 75 79 81 85 86 87 93 96 97 107 108 110 115 119 130 131 132 133 146 147 148 **P**6
Primary Contact: Jeremy Roberge, President and Chief Executive Officer
CFO: Jeremy Roberge, Chief Financial Officer
CMO: John Boornazian, M.D., Chief Medical Officer
CIO: Pam McGovern, Director Technology
CHR: Laura Stauss, Director of Human Resources
Web address: www.hugginshospital.org
Control: Other not–for–profit (including NFP Corporation) **Service:** General Medical and Surgical

Staffed Beds: 25 Admissions: 890 **Census:** 11 **Outpatient Visits:** 76232 **Births:** 0 **Total Expense ($000):** 53259 **Payroll Expense ($000):** 22897 **Personnel:** 338

WOODSVILLE—Grafton County

★ **COTTAGE HOSPITAL (301301)**, 90 Swiftwater Road, Zip 03785–1421, Mailing Address: P.O. Box 2001, Zip 03785–2001; tel. 603/747–9000 **A**10 18 **F**3 11 15 18 28 29 30 31 34 35 40 43 46 49 50 59 64 65 67 68 70 74 75 77 78 79 81 82 84 85 87 89 93 97 107 111 114 119 127 128 130 132 133 135 146 147 148
Primary Contact: Maria Ryan, Ph.D., Chief Executive Officer
COO: Lori Hughes, R.N., Chief Nursing Officer, Vice President Operations and Patient Care Services
CFO: Steven L. Plant, Chief Financial Officer
CIO: Rick Fredrick, Director Information Technology
CNO: Lori Hughes, R.N., Chief Nursing Officer, Vice President Operations & Patient Care Services
Web address: www.cottagehospital.org
Control: Other not–for–profit (including NFP Corporation) **Service:** General Medical and Surgical

Staffed Beds: 25 Admissions: 503 **Census:** 6 **Outpatient Visits:** 40865 **Births:** 0 **Total Expense ($000):** 27912 **Payroll Expense ($000):** 12811 **Personnel:** 215

NH

Hospital, Medicare Provider Number, Address, Telephone, Approval, Facility, and Physician Codes, Health Care System

★ American Hospital Association (AHA) membership
☐ The Joint Commission accreditation
○ Healthcare Facilities Accreditation Program
◇ DNV Healthcare Inc. accreditation
⇑ Center for Improvement in Healthcare Quality Accreditation
△ Commission on Accreditation of Rehabilitation Facilities (CARF) accreditation

NEW JERSEY

ATLANTIC CITY—Atlantic County

★ ◇ **ACUITY SPECIALTY HOSPITAL OF NEW JERSEY (312023)**, 1925 Pacific Avenue, 7th Floor, Zip 08401–6713; tel. 609/441–2122, (Nonreporting) **A**10 21 **S** AcuityHealthcare, LP, Charlotte, NC
Primary Contact: Monica Titus, President and Chief Executive Officer
CFO: Cheryl Lambert, Chief Financial Officer
CHR: Maria Ciro, Director Human Resources
CNO: Kathleen Kerstetter, R.N., Chief Clinical Officer
Web address: www.acuityhealthcare.net
Control: Corporation, Investor–owned, for–profit **Service:** Long–Term Acute Care hospital

Staffed Beds: 30

✠ **ATLANTICARE REGIONAL MEDICAL CENTER (310064)**, 1925 Pacific Avenue, Zip 08401–6713; tel. 609/441–8994, (Includes ATLANTICARE REGIONAL MEDICAL CENTER–MAINLAND DIVISION, Jimmie Leeds Road, Pomona, Zip 08240; tel. 609/652–1000), (Data for 273 days) **A**1 2 3 10 **F**3 7 11 12 13 15 17 18 20 22 24 26 29 30 31 34 35 36 37 38 40 41 42 43 45 46 47 48 49 50 54 57 58 59 60 61 64 66 68 70 71 72 73 74 75 78 79 81 82 83 84 85 86 87 93 97 98 99 100 102 103 104 105 106 107 108 110 111 114 115 116 117 118 119 120 121 123 124 126 130 132 135 143 146 147 148 **P**6 **S** Geisinger Health System, Danville, PA
Primary Contact: Lori Herndon, R.N., President and Chief Executive Officer
CFO: Walter Greiner, Chief Financial Officer
CMO: Marilouise Vendetti, M.D., Chief Medical Officer
CIO: Christopher A. Scanzera, Vice President and Chief Information Officer
CHR: Richard Lovering, Corporate Vice President Human Resources and Organizational Development
CNO: Robyn Begley, R.N., Chief Nursing Officer
Web address: www.atlanticare.org
Control: Other not–for–profit (including NFP Corporation) **Service:** General Medical and Surgical

Staffed Beds: 530 **Admissions:** 21548 **Census:** 352 **Outpatient Visits:** 236704 **Births:** 1493 **Total Expense ($000):** 492311 **Payroll Expense ($000):** 204384 **Personnel:** 3050

BAYONNE—Hudson County

✠ **BAYONNE MEDICAL CENTER (310025)**, 29th Street & Avenue E., Zip 07002–4699; tel. 201/858–5000, (Nonreporting) **A**1 2 10 12 13 **S** CarePoint Health, Jersey City, NJ
Primary Contact: Jeffrey M. Mandler, Chief Executive Officer
COO: Catherine Shull Fernald, MSN, Chief Operating Officer – Bayonne Medical Center
CFO: Gary Bryant, Chief Financial Officer
CMO: Vijayant Singh, M.D., Chief Medical Officer
CIO: Joel Taylor, Chief Information Officer
CHR: Jennifer Dobin, Executive Vice President Human Resources
Web address: www.carepointhealth.org
Control: Corporation, Investor–owned, for–profit **Service:** General Medical and Surgical

Staffed Beds: 205

BELLE MEAD—Somerset County

✠ **CARRIER CLINIC (314012)**, 252 County Route 601, Zip 08502–0147, Mailing Address: P.O. Box 147, Zip 08502–0147; tel. 908/281–1000, (Nonreporting) **A**1 3 5 10
Primary Contact: Donald J. Parker, President and Chief Executive Officer
CFO: Randolph Jacobson, Chief Financial Officer
CMO: Umesh Mehta, M.D., Interim Chief Medical Officer
CIO: Peter Schwartz, Director of Information Systems
CHR: Trish Toole, Vice President Administrative Services
CNO: Carol Kosztyo, R.N., Vice President, Patient Care Services
Web address: www.carrierclinic.org
Control: Other not–for–profit (including NFP Corporation) **Service:** Psychiatric

Staffed Beds: 270

EAST MOUNTAIN HOSPITAL (314026), 252 County Route 601, Zip 08502; tel. 908/281–1500, (Nonreporting) **A**10
Primary Contact: Michael Voorhees, MS, Executive Director
CFO: Randolph Jacobson, Chief Financial Officer
CMO: Bohdan Cehelyk, M.D., Chief Medical Officer
CIO: Peter Schwartz, Director Information Systems
CHR: Patricia Toole, Vice President Human Resources
CNO: Deborah Charette, Director of Nursing
Web address: www.eastmountainhospital.com
Control: Corporation, Investor–owned, for–profit **Service:** Psychiatric

Staffed Beds: 16

BELLEVILLE—Essex County

✠ **CLARA MAASS MEDICAL CENTER (310009)**, One Clara Maass Drive, Zip 07109–3557; tel. 973/450–2000 **A**1 2 3 5 10 **F**3 4 8 11 12 13 15 16 17 18 19 20 22 28 29 30 31 34 35 36 38 39 40 41 44 45 47 49 50 51 53 55 56 57 58 59 60 63 64 65 66 67 68 70 71 72 73 74 75 76 77 78 79 81 82 83 84 85 86 87 88 89 90 91 92 93 96 98 101 102 103 107 108 110 114 119 120 121 123 124 126 128 129 130 131 132 135 143 146 147 148 **P**6 **S** RWJBarnabas Health, West Orange, NJ
Primary Contact: Mary Ellen Clyne, MSN, Ph.D., R.N., President and Chief Executive Officer
CFO: Nik Alexiades, Chief Financial Officer
CMO: Frank Mazzarella, M.D., Chief Medical Officer
CIO: Michael McTigue, Chief Information Officer
CHR: Jim Rolek, Chief Human Resources Officer, Vice President
CNO: Lea Rodriguez, R.N., Chief Nursing Officer, Vice President Patient Care Services
Web address: www.barnabashealth.org/hospitals/clara_maass/index.html
Control: Other not–for–profit (including NFP Corporation) **Service:** General Medical and Surgical

Staffed Beds: 469 **Admissions:** 15234 **Census:** 208 **Outpatient Visits:** 135609 **Births:** 1295 **Total Expense ($000):** 248025 **Payroll Expense ($000):** 106241 **Personnel:** 1417

BERKELEY HEIGHTS—Union County

CORNERSTONE BEHAVIORAL HEALTH HOSPITAL OF UNION COUNTY (314027), 40 Watchung Way, Zip 07922–2600; tel. 908/771–5700, (Nonreporting)
Primary Contact: Michael Flemming, Administrator
Control: County–Government, nonfederal **Service:** Psychiatric

Staffed Beds: 44

★ **RUNNELLS CENTER FOR REHABILITATION AND HEALTHCARE (315009)**, 40 Watchung Way, Zip 07922–2618; tel. 908/771–5700, (Nonreporting) **A**10
Primary Contact: Josh Bamberger, Administrator
CFO: Michael Drummond, Chief Financial Officer
CMO: Raymond Lanza, D.O., Medical Director
CHR: Greg Hardoby, Director Personnel
CNO: Patricia Spina, R.N., Director of Nursing
Web address: www.ucnj.org/runnells
Control: Corporation, Investor–owned, for–profit **Service:** Other specialty

Staffed Beds: 344

BLACKWOOD—Camden County

NORTHBROOK BEHAVIORAL HEALTH HOSPITAL (314018), 425 Woodbury Turnersville Road, Zip 08012–2960; tel. 856/374–6500, (Nonreporting)
Primary Contact: Barbara Loughrey, Administrator
Web address: www.northbrookbhh.com
Control: Corporation, Investor–owned, for–profit **Service:** Psychiatric

Staffed Beds: 153

BOONTON TOWNSHIP—Morris County

SAINT CLARE'S HOSPITAL/BOONTON TOWNSHIP See Saint Clare's Health System, Denville

BRICK—Ocean County

✠ △ **SHORE REHABILITATION INSTITUTE (313033)**, 425 Jack Martin Boulevard, Zip 08724–7732; tel. 732/836–4500, (Nonreporting) **A**1 7 10 **S** Hackensack Meridian Health, Edison, NJ
Primary Contact: Marci Gietter, Interim Executive Director
CFO: Richard C. Smith, Senior Vice President Finance
CMO: Lisa Luciano, D.O., Medical Director
CNO: Maria Clohsey, Director of Nursing
Web address: www.shorerehabilitationinstitute.com
Control: Other not–for–profit (including NFP Corporation) **Service:** Rehabilitation

Staffed Beds: 40

Many Facility Codes have changed. Please refer to the AHA Guide Code Chart.

© 2016 AHA Guide

NJ

BRICK TOWNSHIP—Ocean County

☒ **OCEAN MEDICAL CENTER (310052)**, 425 Jack Martin Boulevard,
Zip 08724–7732; tel. 732/840–2200 **A**1 2 10 **F**3 11 12 13 15 18 20 22 28
29 30 31 32 34 35 36 38 39 40 41 42 43 44 45 46 47 48 49 50 54 55 56
57 59 60 63 64 65 66 68 70 73 74 75 76 77 78 79 80 81 82 84 85 86 87
92 93 94 96 100 101 102 103 107 108 110 111 114 115 116 117 118 119
120 121 123 124 126 129 130 131 132 134 135 144 146 147 148 **P**6 7
S Hackensack Meridian Health, Edison, NJ
Primary Contact: Dean Q. Lin, FACHE, President
COO: Regina Foley, R.N., Vice President Nursing and Operations
CFO: Robert Palermo, Vice President Finance
CMO: James Clarke, M.D., Vice President Medical Affairs and Clinical
Effectiveness
CIO: Rebecca Weber, Senior Vice President and Chief Information Officer
CHR: Sherrie String, Senior Vice President Human Resources
Web address: www.meridianhealth.com
Control: Other not–for–profit (including NFP Corporation) **Service:** General
Medical and Surgical

Staffed Beds: 271 **Admissions:** 13918 **Census:** 194 **Outpatient Visits:**
178049 **Births:** 968 **Total Expense ($000):** 259157 **Payroll Expense**
($000): 109700 **Personnel:** 1408

BRIDGETON—Cumberland County

BRIDGETON HEALTH CENTER See Inspira Medical Center–Vineland, Vineland

BROWNS MILLS—Burlington County

☐ **DEBORAH HEART AND LUNG CENTER (310031)**, 200 Trenton Road,
Zip 08015–1705; tel. 609/893–6611, (Nonreporting) **A**1 3 5 10 13
Primary Contact: Joseph Chirichella, President and Chief Executive Officer
COO: Joseph Manni, Vice President Operations Chief Operating Officer
CFO: R. Grant Leidy, Vice President Finance
CMO: Lynn McGrath, M.D., Vice President Medical Affairs
CHR: James Carlino, Vice President Human Resources
CNO: Rita Zenna, R.N., Vice President Patient Care Services
Web address: www.deborah.org
Control: Other not–for–profit (including NFP Corporation) **Service:** Other specialty

Staffed Beds: 89

CAMDEN—Camden County

☒ **COOPER UNIVERSITY HEALTH CARE (310014)**, One Cooper Plaza,
Zip 08103–1489; tel. 856/342–2000, (Includes CHILDEN'S REGIONAL HOSPITAL
AT COOPER, Three Cooper Plaza, Zip 08103; tel. 800/826–6737) **A**1 2 3 5 8 10
F3 8 11 12 13 15 17 18 19 20 22 24 26 29 30 31 32 34 35 36 37 39 40 41
42 43 44 45 46 47 48 49 50 51 52 54 55 56 57 58 59 60 61 64 65 66 68
70 72 73 74 75 76 78 79 80 81 82 84 85 86 87 88 89 92 93 96 97 98 99
100 101 102 103 104 107 108 110 111 114 115 117 118 119 120 121 123
124 126 129 130 131 132 135 144 146 147 148 **P**6
Primary Contact: Adrienne Kirby, President and Chief Executive Officer
CFO: Douglas E. Shirley, Senior Executive Vice President and Chief Financial
Officer
CMO: Anthony J. Mazzarelli, JD, Senior Executive Vice President Chief Physician
Executive
CIO: Stephanie Conners, Senior Executive Vice President Chief Operating Officer
and Chief Nursing Officer
CHR: Elizabeth Green, Chief Human Resources Officer
Web address: www.cooperhealth.org
Control: Other not–for–profit (including NFP Corporation) **Service:** General
Medical and Surgical

Staffed Beds: 493 **Admissions:** 27765 **Census:** 406 **Outpatient Visits:**
334238 **Births:** 2238 **Total Expense ($000):** 751961 **Payroll Expense**
($000): 270650 **Personnel:** 6012

☒ △ **OUR LADY OF LOURDES MEDICAL CENTER (310029)**, 1600 Haddon
Avenue, Zip 08103–3117; tel. 856/757–3500 **A**1 2 3 7 10 **F**3 7 11 12 13 15
17 18 20 22 24 26 28 29 30 31 32 34 35 36 37 38 40 44 46 47 49 50 55
56 57 58 59 60 61 64 65 66 68 70 72 73 74 75 76 78 79 81 82 84 85 86
87 89 90 95 96 100 107 108 110 111 114 115 118 119 126 130 132 134
135 138 139 142 146 147 148 **P**8 **S** Trinity Health, Livonia, MI
Primary Contact: Alexander J. Hatala, FACHE, President and Chief Executive
Officer
COO: Mark Nessel, Chief Operating Officer
CFO: Michael Hammond, Chief Financial Officer
CMO: Alan R. Pope, M.D., Chief Medical Officer
CIO: Maureen Hetu, Chief Information Officer
CHR: Jennifer L. Moughan, Chief Human Resources Officer
CNO: Audrey Jadczak, R.N., Vice President Chief Nursing Officer
Web address: www.lourdesnet.org
Control: Other not–for–profit (including NFP Corporation) **Service:** General
Medical and Surgical

Staffed Beds: 350 **Admissions:** 12322 **Census:** 175 **Outpatient Visits:**
146939 **Births:** 1046 **Total Expense ($000):** 280172 **Payroll Expense**
($000): 98220 **Personnel:** 2019

CAPE MAY COURT HOUSE—Cape May County

☒ **CAPE REGIONAL MEDICAL CENTER (310011)**, Two Stone Harbor Boulevard,
Zip 08210–9990; tel. 609/463–2000 **A**1 2 10 **F**3 8 11 12 13 15 18 20 28 29
30 31 34 35 40 44 45 46 49 50 53 57 59 64 70 74 75 76 77 78 79 81 82
84 85 86 87 89 91 93 97 107 111 114 118 119 120 121 123 124 129 130
132 135 143 146 148
Primary Contact: Joanne Carrocino, FACHE, President and Chief Executive Officer
CFO: Mark Gill, Vice President Finance and Chief Financial Officer
CMO: Andrea C.S. McCoy, M.D., Chief Medical Officer
CIO: Richard Wheatley, Chief Information Officer
CHR: Byron Hunter, Vice President Human Resources
CNO: Deborah Baehser, Vice President Patient Care Services
Web address: www.caperegional.com
Control: Other not–for–profit (including NFP Corporation) **Service:** General
Medical and Surgical

Staffed Beds: 180 **Admissions:** 6883 **Census:** 76 **Outpatient Visits:** 184090
Births: 455 **Total Expense ($000):** 114944 **Payroll Expense ($000):** 50046
Personnel: 818

CEDAR GROVE—Essex County

☐ **ESSEX COUNTY HOSPITAL CENTER (314020)**, 204 Grove Avenue,
Zip 07009–1436; tel. 973/571–2800, (Nonreporting) **A**1 10
Primary Contact: Frank J. Del Gaudio, Director and Chief Executive Officer
CFO: Jacqueline Campoverde, Business Manager
CMO: Bolivar Pascual, M.D., Medical Director
CIO: Anthony C. Greco, Compliance Officer
CHR: Marlon Brown, Human Resources
Web address: www.essexcountynj.org
Control: County–Government, nonfederal **Service:** Psychiatric

Staffed Beds: 180

CHERRY HILL—Camden County

☒ ○ **KENNEDY HEALTH SYSTEM (310086)**, 2201 Chapel Avenue West,
Zip 08002–2048; tel. 856/488–6500, (Includes KENNEDY UNIVERSITY HOSPITAL
– STRATFORD, 18 East Laurel Road, Stratford, Zip 08084; tel. 609/346–6000;
KENNEDY UNIVERSITY HOSPITAL – WASHINGTON TOWNSHIP, 435
Hurffville–Cross Keys Road, Turnersville, Zip 08012; tel. 609/582–2500) **A**1 2 10
11 **F**3 5 7 8 11 12 13 15 18 20 22 29 30 31 32 34 35 38 39 40 41 44 46
49 50 54 55 56 57 59 60 61 62 64 65 66 68 70 72 73 74 75 76 77 78 79
81 82 84 85 86 87 89 93 97 98 99 100 101 102 103 104 105 107 108 110
111 114 115 117 118 119 120 121 123 126 129 130 131 132 134 143 146
147 148
Primary Contact: Joseph W. Devine, FACHE, President and Chief Executive Officer
CFO: Glenn Zirbser, Senior Vice President Finance and Chief Financial Officer
CMO: David Condoluci, M.D., Senior Vice President and Chief Medical Officer
CIO: Thomas Balcavage, Vice President Information Systems and Chief Information
Officer Technology
CHR: Anneliese McMenamin, Vice President Human Resources
CNO: Helene M. Burns, MSN, Chief Nursing Executive
Web address: www.kennedyhealth.org
Control: Other not–for–profit (including NFP Corporation) **Service:** General
Medical and Surgical

Staffed Beds: 527 **Admissions:** 25770 **Census:** 327 **Outpatient Visits:**
455123 **Births:** 1035 **Total Expense ($000):** 488160 **Payroll Expense**
($000): 205501 **Personnel:** 3633

KENNEDY MEMORIAL HOSPITALS–UNIVERSITY MEDICAL CENTER See
Kennedy Health System

NJ

CHESTER—Morris County

KESSLER INSTITUTE FOR REHABILITATION See Kessler Institute for Rehabilitation, West Orange

DENVILLE—Morris County

✠ **SAINT CLARE'S HEALTH SYSTEM (310050)**, 25 Pocono Road, Zip 07834–2954; tel. 973/625–6000, (Includes SAINT CLARE'S HEALTH CENTER AT SUSSEX, 20 Walnut Street, Sussex, Zip 07461; tel. 973/702–2200; SAINT CLARE'S HOSPITAL/BOONTON TOWNSHIP, 130 Powerville Road, Boonton Township, Zip 07005; tel. 973/316–1800; SAINT CLARE'S HOSPITAL/DENVILLE, 25 Pocono Road, Zip 07834; tel. 973/625–6000; SAINT CLARE'S HOSPITAL/DOVER, 400 West Blackwell Street, Dover, Zip 07801–3311; tel. 973/989–3000), (Nonreporting) **A**1 2 10 **S** Prime Healthcare Services, Ontario, CA
Primary Contact: Brian Finestein, Chief Executive Officer
COO: Joe Nolan, Chief Operating Officer
CFO: Dianne Halford, Chief Financial Officer
CMO: Alma Ratcliffe, M.D., Executive Vice President Medical Staff and Business Development
CIO: Tero Caamano, Director Information Technology
CHR: Kay Bryant, Executive Director Human Resources
Web address: www.saintclares.org
Control: Church–operated, Nongovernment, not–for profit **Service:** General Medical and Surgical

Staffed Beds: 478

SAINT CLARE'S HOSPITAL/DENVILLE See Saint Clare's Health System

DOVER—Morris County

✠ **KINDRED HOSPITAL–NEW JERSEY MORRIS COUNTY (312020)**, 400 West Blackwell Street, Zip 07801–2525; tel. 973/537–3818, (Includes KINDRED HOSPITAL NEW JERSEY – RAHWAY, 865 Stone Street, Rahway, Zip 07065; tel. 732/453–2950; Michele S. Basile, Chief Executive Officer; KINDRED HOSPITAL NEW JERSEY – WAYNE, 224 Hamburg Turnpike, Wayne, Zip 07470; tel. 973/636–7200; Alice M. O'Connor, Chief Executive Officer), (Nonreporting) **A**1 10 **S** Kindred Healthcare, Louisville, KY
Primary Contact: Michael Pizzano, Chief Executive Officer
CFO: David Davis, Senior Vice President Finance
CHR: Jeff Jasnoff, Senior Vice President Human Resources
Web address: www.khmorriscounty.com/
Control: Corporation, Investor–owned, for–profit **Service:** Long–Term Acute Care hospital

Staffed Beds: 117

EAST ORANGE—Essex County

☐ **EAST ORANGE GENERAL HOSPITAL (310083)**, 300 Central Avenue, Zip 07018–2897; tel. 973/672–8400, (Nonreporting) **A**1 10
Primary Contact: Otis L. Story, Sr., President and Chief Executive Officer
CMO: Valentine Burroughs, M.D., Chief Medical Officer
CIO: Thomas Ciccarelli, Chief Information Officer
CHR: Chester Banks, Director Human Resources
Web address: www.evh.org
Control: Other not–for–profit (including NFP Corporation) **Service:** General Medical and Surgical

Staffed Beds: 190

✠ △ **VETERANS AFFAIRS NEW JERSEY HEALTH CARE SYSTEM**, 385 Tremont Avenue, Zip 07018–1095; tel. 973/676–1000, (Includes EAST ORANGE DIVISION, 385 Tremont Avenue, tel. 973/676–1000; LYONS DIVISION, 151 Knollcroft Road, Lyons, Zip 07939–9998; tel. 908/647–0180), (Nonreporting) **A**1 2 3 5 7 **S** Department of Veterans Affairs, Washington, DC
Primary Contact: Mara Davis, Interim Director
CFO: Tyrone Taylor, Chief Financial Officer
CMO: Steven L. Lieberman, M.D., Chief of Staff
CIO: Kamesha Scarlett, Chief Information Resource Management
CHR: Nancy Hamilton, Chief Human and Learning Resources
CNO: Patrick J. Troy, R.N., Associate Director Patient Care Services
Web address: www.newjersey.va.gov/
Control: Veterans Affairs, Government, federal **Service:** Other specialty

Staffed Beds: 439

EDISON—Middlesex County

★ △ **JFK JOHNSON REHABILITATION INSTITUTE**, 65 James Street, Zip 08818; tel. 732/321–7050 **A**7 **F**3 9 28 29 30 35 36 50 53 54 64 82 90 91 92 93 94 96 130 131 132 143 **P**6 **S** JFK Health, Edison, NJ
Primary Contact: Anthony Cuzzola, Vice President Administrator
Web address: www.njrehab.org
Control: Other not–for–profit (including NFP Corporation) **Service:** Rehabilitation

Staffed Beds: 94 **Admissions:** 2022 **Census:** 75 **Outpatient Visits:** 111199 **Births:** 0 **Total Expense ($000):** 69275 **Payroll Expense ($000):** 45154 **Personnel:** 642

✠ **JFK MEDICAL CENTER (310108)**, 65 James Street, Zip 08818; tel. 732/321–7000 **A**1 2 3 10 **F**3 5 7 8 11 12 13 14 15 17 18 20 22 26 28 29 30 31 34 35 37 38 39 40 41 42 45 46 47 49 50 51 53 54 56 57 58 59 60 61 63 64 66 68 69 70 73 74 75 76 77 78 79 81 82 83 84 85 86 87 89 91 92 93 94 96 97 100 101 102 104 107 108 110 111 113 114 115 116 117 118 119 120 121 124 126 129 130 131 132 135 141 143 144 145 146 147 148 **P**5 6 7 **S** JFK Health, Edison, NJ
Primary Contact: Raymond F. Fredericks, President and CEO
COO: Scott Gebhard, Executive VP and Chief Operating Officer
CFO: Richard C. Smith, Senior Vice President and Chief Financial Officer
CMO: William F. Oser, M.D., Senior Vice President and Chief Medical Officer
CIO: Indranil Ganguly, Vice President and Chief Information Officer
CHR: Shirley Higgins Bowers, Senior Vice President Human Resources
CNO: James Lindquist, R.N., Chief Nursing Officer
Web address: www.jfkmc.org
Control: Other not–for–profit (including NFP Corporation) **Service:** General Medical and Surgical

Staffed Beds: 334 **Admissions:** 17564 **Census:** 236 **Outpatient Visits:** 185051 **Births:** 2264 **Total Expense ($000):** 394505 **Payroll Expense ($000):** 184715 **Personnel:** 2874

ELIZABETH—Union County

✠ **TRINITAS REGIONAL MEDICAL CENTER (310027)**, 225 Williamson Street, Zip 07202–3625; tel. 908/994–5000, (Includes TRINITAS HOSPITAL, 225 Williamson Street, Zip 07207; tel. 908/994–5000; Gary S. Horan, FACHE, President and Chief Executive Officer; TRINITAS REGIONAL MEDICAL CENTER – NEW POINT CAMPUS, 655 East Jersey Street, Zip 07206; tel. 908/994–5000; Gary S. Horan, FACHE, President and Chief Executive Officer), (Total facility includes 124 beds in nursing home–type unit) **A**1 2 3 5 10 13 **F**3 5 7 8 11 12 13 15 17 18 20 22 28 29 30 32 34 35 36 38 40 44 45 46 48 49 53 56 57 58 59 60 61 64 65 66 68 70 73 74 75 76 77 78 79 81 82 84 85 86 87 91 93 97 98 99 100 101 102 103 104 105 106 107 108 110 111 114 118 119 120 121 123 124 126 128 129 130 132 134 135 141 143 146 147 **P**6
Primary Contact: Gary S. Horan, FACHE, President and Chief Executive Officer
CFO: Karen Lumpp, Senior Vice President and Chief Financial Officer
CMO: William McHugh, M.D., Medical Director and Chief Medical Officer
CIO: Judy Comitto, Vice President Information Services and Chief Information Officer
CHR: Glenn Nacion, Vice President Human Resources
CNO: Mary McTigue, Vice President Patient Care Services and Chief Nursing Officer
Web address: www.trinitasrmc.com
Control: Other not–for–profit (including NFP Corporation) **Service:** General Medical and Surgical

Staffed Beds: 461 **Admissions:** 14985 **Census:** 382 **Outpatient Visits:** 438863 **Births:** 2089 **Total Expense ($000):** 291188 **Payroll Expense ($000):** 135324 **Personnel:** 2335

ELMER—Salem County

★ ◇ **INSPIRA MEDICAL CENTER–ELMER (310069)**, 501 West Front Street, Zip 08318–2101; tel. 856/363–1000 **A**10 21 **F**3 8 11 12 13 15 18 20 28 29 30 34 38 40 42 44 50 57 59 64 68 70 74 75 76 77 78 79 81 82 85 86 87 89 93 107 108 110 111 119 130 131 132 134 146 147 148 **S** Inspira Health Network, Mullica Hill, NJ
Primary Contact: John A. DiAngelo, President and Chief Executive Officer
COO: David Yhlen, Chief Operating Officer
CFO: Thomas Baldosaro, Chief Financial Officer
CMO: Steven C. Linn, M.D., Chief Medical Officer
CIO: Thomas Pacek, Vice President Information Systems and Chief Information Officer
CHR: Erich Florentine, Chief People Officer
CNO: Elizabeth Sheridan, Chief Operating Officer and Chief Nursing Executive
Web address: www.inspirahealthnetwork.org/?id=5281&sid=1
Control: Other not–for–profit (including NFP Corporation) **Service:** General Medical and Surgical

Staffed Beds: 88 **Admissions:** 3240 **Census:** 32 **Outpatient Visits:** 55153 **Births:** 286 **Total Expense ($000):** 57179 **Payroll Expense ($000):** 25732 **Personnel:** 285

Many Facility Codes have changed. Please refer to the AHA Guide Code Chart.

NJ

ENGLEWOOD—Bergen County

✶ **ENGLEWOOD HOSPITAL AND MEDICAL CENTER (310045)**, 350 Engle Street, Zip 07631–1898; tel. 201/894–3000 **A**1 2 3 5 10 **F**3 7 8 9 11 12 13 15 17 18 19 20 22 24 26 28 29 30 31 32 34 35 36 37 38 40 41 44 45 46 47 48 49 50 51 52 53 54 55 56 57 58 59 60 61 64 65 68 70 72 73 74 75 76 77 78 79 80 81 82 83 84 85 86 87 89 91 92 93 94 96 97 98 99 100 101 102 103 104 105 106 107 108 110 111 114 115 116 117 118 119 120 121 123 124 126 129 130 131 132 133 134 135 143 144 145 146 147 148 **P**3 4 6 7 8
Primary Contact: Warren Geller, President and Chief Executive Officer
CFO: Anthony T. Orlando, Senior Vice President Finance
CMO: Michael Harris, M.D., Chief Medical Officer
CIO: Dimitri Cruz, Vice President Information Technology
CHR: Patricia Wilson, Senior Vice President Human Resources
CNO: MaryAnn Donohue–Ryan, Senior Vice President Patient Care Services
Web address: www.englewoodhealth.org
Control: Other not–for–profit (including NFP Corporation) **Service:** General Medical and Surgical

Staffed Beds: 274 **Admissions:** 15196 **Census:** 205 **Outpatient Visits:** 934512 **Births:** 2560 **Total Expense ($000):** 477294 **Payroll Expense ($000):** 143302 **Personnel:** 2315

FLEMINGTON—Hunterdon County

✶ **HUNTERDON MEDICAL CENTER (310005)**, 2100 Wescott Drive, Zip 08822–4604; tel. 908/788–6100 **A**1 2 3 5 10 13 **F**3 4 5 8 11 12 13 14 15 18 20 22 28 29 30 31 32 34 35 38 40 45 46 47 48 49 53 54 55 56 57 58 59 60 61 62 64 65 68 70 71 73 74 75 76 77 78 79 81 82 83 84 85 86 87 89 91 92 93 94 97 98 99 100 101 102 103 104 105 106 107 108 110 114 115 118 119 121 123 126 127 129 130 131 132 134 135 144 146 147 148
Primary Contact: Robert P. Wise, President and Chief Executive Officer
COO: Lawrence N. Grand, MS, Chief Operating Officer
CFO: Gail Kosyla, Chief Financial Officer
CMO: Robert P. Wise, Vice President, Medical Affairs
CIO: Daniel Morreale, Chief Information Officer
CHR: Violet Kocsis, Chief Human Resources Officer
CNO: Patricia Steingall, MS, Vice President, Patient Care Services
Web address: www.hunterdonhealthcare.org
Control: Other not–for–profit (including NFP Corporation) **Service:** General Medical and Surgical

Staffed Beds: 178 **Admissions:** 8281 **Census:** 96 **Outpatient Visits:** 685105 **Births:** 887 **Total Expense ($000):** 268787 **Payroll Expense ($000):** 132970 **Personnel:** 1908

FREEHOLD—Monmouth County

✶ **CENTRASTATE HEALTHCARE SYSTEM (310111)**, 901 West Main Street, Zip 07728–2549; tel. 732/431–2000 **A**1 2 3 5 10 **F**3 11 12 13 15 18 19 20 28 29 30 31 32 34 35 36 37 38 40 41 45 46 49 56 57 58 59 61 64 65 66 70 73 74 75 76 77 78 79 81 82 84 86 87 89 92 93 97 98 100 101 102 107 108 110 114 118 119 120 121 123 124 126 129 130 131 132 134 135 144 146 147 148 **P**1 6
Primary Contact: John Gribbin, FACHE, President and Chief Executive Officer
COO: Thomas W. Scott, Senior Vice President and Chief Operating Officer
CFO: John Dellocono, Senior Vice President and Chief Financial Officer
CMO: Jack H. Dworkin, M.D., Vice President Medical Affairs and Chief Medical Officer
CIO: John Ulett, Vice President and Chief Information Officer
CHR: Fran Keane, Vice President Human Resources
CNO: Linda W. Geisler, R.N., Vice President Patient Services
Web address: www.centrastate.com
Control: Other not–for–profit (including NFP Corporation) **Service:** General Medical and Surgical

Staffed Beds: 283 **Admissions:** 14232 **Census:** 170 **Outpatient Visits:** 264073 **Births:** 1368 **Total Expense ($000):** 252783 **Payroll Expense ($000):** 109568 **Personnel:** 1510

HACKENSACK—Bergen County

✶ **HACKENSACK UNIVERSITY MEDICAL CENTER (310001)**, 30 Prospect Avenue, Zip 07601–1914; tel. 201/996–2000, (Includes THE JOSEPH M. SANZARI CHILDREN'S HOSPITAL, 30 Prospect Avenue, tel. 201/996–2000) **A**1 2 3 5 8 10 **F**2 3 4 5 6 7 8 9 10 11 12 13 14 15 16 19 20 21 22 24 26 27 28 29 30 31 32 33 34 35 36 37 38 39 40 41 42 43 44 45 46 47 48 49 50 51 52 53 54 55 56 57 58 59 60 61 63 64 65 66 68 69 70 71 72 73 74 75 76 77 78 79 80 81 82 84 85 86 87 88 89 90 91 92 93 94 96 97 98 99 100 101 102 103 104 105 107 108 109 110 111 112 113 114 115 116 117 118 119 120 121 123 124 126 129 130 131 132 134 135 136 138 141 142 143 144 145 146 147 148 **P**1 5 6 **S** Hackensack Meridian Health, Edison, NJ
Primary Contact: Ihor S. Sawczuk, M.D., President
CFO: Robert Glenning, Executive Vice President Finance and Chief Financial Officer
CMO: Peter A. Gross, M.D., Senior Vice President and Chief Medical Officer
CHR: Nancy R. Corcoran, Senior Vice President Human Resources and Quality Service
Web address: www.hackensackumc.org
Control: Other not–for–profit (including NFP Corporation) **Service:** General Medical and Surgical

Staffed Beds: 711 **Admissions:** 70407 **Census:** 587 **Outpatient Visits:** 2920421 **Births:** 6349 **Total Expense ($000):** 1523422 **Payroll Expense ($000):** 675470 **Personnel:** 7536

HACKETTSTOWN—Warren County

✶ **HACKETTSTOWN MEDICAL CENTER (310115)**, 651 Willow Grove Street, Zip 07840–1799; tel. 908/852–5100 **A**1 10 **F**3 5 7 11 12 13 15 18 19 26 28 29 30 31 34 35 40 41 45 46 49 50 51 53 56 57 59 60 68 70 74 75 76 77 78 79 81 82 85 86 87 93 97 107 108 110 114 116 117 119 121 129 130 131 132 135 143 146 147 148 **P**6 **S** Atlantic Health System, Morristown, NJ
Primary Contact: Jason C. Coe, President
COO: Stella Visaggio, Chief Operating Officer
CFO: Robert Peterson, Chief Financial Officer
CMO: Kenneth Janowski, M.D., Chief Medical Officer
CIO: Dorothy Cox, Manager Information Systems
CHR: Jeanne Jepson, Director Human Resources
CNO: Linda Ambacher, Interim Chief Nursing Officer
Web address: www.hrmcnj.org
Control: Other not–for–profit (including NFP Corporation) **Service:** General Medical and Surgical

Staffed Beds: 103 **Admissions:** 3542 **Census:** 45 **Outpatient Visits:** 56196 **Births:** 360 **Total Expense ($000):** 92885 **Payroll Expense ($000):** 38480 **Personnel:** 851

HAMILTON—Mercer County

✶ **ROBERT WOOD JOHNSON UNIVERSITY HOSPITAL AT HAMILTON (310110)**, One Hamilton Health Place, Zip 08690–3599; tel. 609/586–7900 **A**1 2 3 5 10 **F**3 8 9 11 12 15 17 18 22 26 29 30 31 32 34 35 36 37 39 40 41 44 46 47 48 49 50 51 53 54 55 56 57 58 59 60 61 63 64 65 66 68 69 70 71 74 75 77 78 79 81 82 84 85 86 87 92 93 96 97 100 102 103 107 108 110 111 114 115 116 117 118 119 120 121 123 124 126 129 130 131 132 134 135 143 144 145 146 147 148 **P**5 6 **S** RWJBarnabas Health, West Orange, NJ
Primary Contact: Richard Freeman, President and Chief Executive Officer
COO: Barbara H. Smith, Senior Vice President & Chief Operating Officer
CFO: James M. Maher, Senior Vice President and Chief Financial Officer
CMO: Ronald Ryder, D.O., President of the Medical Staff
CNO: Lisa Breza, R.N., Vice President and Chief Nursing Officer
Web address: www.rwjhamilton.org
Control: Other not–for–profit (including NFP Corporation) **Service:** General Medical and Surgical

Staffed Beds: 164 **Admissions:** 9042 **Census:** 125 **Outpatient Visits:** 116338 **Births:** 47 **Total Expense ($000):** 184333 **Payroll Expense ($000):** 70782 **Personnel:** 1032

HAMMONTON—Camden County

☐ **ANCORA PSYCHIATRIC HOSPITAL (314005)**, 301 Spring Garden Road, Zip 08037–9699; tel. 609/561–1700 **A**1 10 **F**30 39 56 68 75 87 97 98 130 135 143 146 **P**6 **S** Division of Mental Health and Addiction Services, Department of Human Services, State of New Jersey, Trenton, NJ
Primary Contact: John Lubitsky, Chief Executive Officer
CFO: John Holmes, Business Manager
CMO: David Roat, D.O., Medical Director
CIO: Charlene Ruberti, Director Information Technology Development
CHR: Alfred Filipini, Manager Human Resources
CNO: Catherine Jones, Chief Nursing Officer
Web address: www.state.nj.us/humanservices/dmhs/oshm/aph/
Control: State–Government, nonfederal **Service:** Psychiatric

Staffed Beds: 450 **Admissions:** 471 **Census:** 353 **Outpatient Visits:** 0 **Births:** 0 **Personnel:** 1616

NJ

Hospital, Medicare Provider Number, Address, Telephone, Approval, Facility, and Physician Codes, Health Care System

★ American Hospital Association (AHA) membership
☐ The Joint Commission accreditation
○ Healthcare Facilities Accreditation Program
◇ DNV Healthcare Inc. accreditation
⇑ Center for Improvement in Healthcare Quality Accreditation
△ Commission on Accreditation of Rehabilitation Facilities (CARF) accreditation

HOBOKEN—Hudson County

☒ **HOBOKEN UNIVERSITY MEDICAL CENTER (310040)**, 308 Willow Avenue, Zip 07030–3889; tel. 201/418–1000, (Nonreporting) **A**1 3 5 10 **S** CarePoint Health, Jersey City, NJ
Primary Contact: Ann P. Logan, R.N., Ph.D., Chief Operating Officer
COO: Ann P. Logan, R.N., Chief Operating Officer
CFO: Vincent Riccitelli, Vice President Finance
CMO: Meika Roberson, M.D., Chief Medical Officer
CIO: Joel Taylor, Chief Information Officer
CHR: Roberto Gonzalez, Executive Director Human Resources
CNO: Neena S. Philip, R.N., Assistant Vice President Nursing
Web address: www.hobokenumc.com
Control: Corporation, Investor–owned, for–profit **Service:** General Medical and Surgical

Staffed Beds: 204

HOLMDEL—Monmouth County

☒ **BAYSHORE COMMUNITY HOSPITAL (310112)**, 727 North Beers Street, Zip 07733–1598; tel. 732/739–5900 **A**1 2 10 **F**3 11 12 15 18 20 22 28 29 30 31 32 34 35 36 38 39 40 41 43 44 45 46 49 50 51 54 55 56 57 58 59 60 61 63 64 65 66 68 69 70 71 74 75 77 78 79 80 81 82 84 85 86 87 92 93 94 96 97 100 101 102 103 107 108 110 111 114 116 117 118 119 129 130 131 132 134 135 144 146 147 148 **P**6 7 **S** Hackensack Meridian Health, Edison, NJ
Primary Contact: Timothy J. Hogan, FACHE, Regional President
COO: Anthony Cava, Chief Operating Officer
CFO: Joseph M. Lemaire, Executive Vice President Finance and Partner Company Operations
CMO: Ian Leber, M.D., Chief Medical Officer
CIO: Rebecca Weber, Senior Vice President and Chief Information Officer
CHR: Sherrie String, Senior Vice President Human Resources
CNO: Linda Walsh, R.N., Vice President Chief Nursing Executive
Web address: www.bchs.com
Control: Other not–for–profit (including NFP Corporation) **Service:** General Medical and Surgical

Staffed Beds: 142 **Admissions:** 7088 **Census:** 104 **Outpatient Visits:** 83236 **Births:** 0 **Total Expense ($000):** 128923 **Payroll Expense ($000):** 56182 **Personnel:** 806

JERSEY CITY—Hudson County

☒ **CAREPOINT HEALTH –CHRIST HOSPITAL (310016)**, 176 Palisade Avenue, Zip 07306–1196, Mailing Address: 176 Palisades Avenue, Zip 07306–1196; tel. 201/795–8200, (Nonreporting) **A**1 3 10 12 13 **S** CarePoint Health, Jersey City, NJ
Primary Contact: Marie Theresa Duffy, Chief Operating Officer
COO: Marie Theresa Duffy, Chief Operating Officer
CFO: Gary Bryant, Executive Vice President and Chief Financial Officer
CMO: William Holubek, M.D., Chief Medical Officer
CHR: Josiane Deroncerey, Director Human Resources
CNO: Denise Cimmino, MSN, Assistant Vice President, Nursing and Patient Care Services
Web address: www.carepointhealth.org
Control: Other not–for–profit (including NFP Corporation) **Service:** General Medical and Surgical

Staffed Beds: 376

★ ◇ **JERSEY CITY MEDICAL CENTER (310074)**, 355 Grand Street, Zip 07302–4321; tel. 201/915–2000 **A**3 5 10 13 21 **F**3 5 7 11 12 13 15 17 18 20 22 24 26 29 30 31 34 35 38 39 40 41 43 45 46 47 48 49 50 54 55 56 57 59 60 61 64 65 66 68 70 71 72 73 74 75 76 77 78 79 81 82 84 85 87 89 91 92 93 96 97 98 99 100 101 102 104 105 106 107 108 110 111 112 114 115 119 130 132 135 143 144 146 147 148 **S** RWJBarnabas Health, West Orange, NJ
Primary Contact: Joseph F. Scott, FACHE, President and Chief Executive Officer
COO: Michael Prilutsky, Chief Operating Officer
CFO: Paul R. Goldberg, Chief Financial Officer
CMO: Kenneth Garay, M.D., Chief Medical Officer
CIO: Stephen Li, Vice President Management Information Systems
CHR: Mary Cataudella, Corporate Director Human Resources
Web address: www.barnabashealth.org/Jersey–City–Medical–Center.aspx
Control: Other not–for–profit (including NFP Corporation) **Service:** General Medical and Surgical

Staffed Beds: 316 **Admissions:** 15185 **Census:** 225 **Outpatient Visits:** 259088 **Births:** 2314 **Total Expense ($000):** 367866 **Payroll Expense ($000):** 197232 **Personnel:** 2140

LAKEWOOD—Ocean County

☒ **MONMOUTH MEDICAL CENTER, SOUTHERN CAMPUS (310084)**, 600 River Avenue, Zip 08701–5237; tel. 732/363–1900 **A**1 2 10 **F**3 11 15 18 28 29 30 31 34 35 36 38 40 41 43 44 50 56 57 58 59 60 61 64 68 70 74 75 77 78 79 81 82 86 87 93 96 98 100 101 102 103 107 108 110 111 114 117 119 130 131 132 133 134 146 148 **P**6 **S** RWJBarnabas Health, West Orange, NJ
Primary Contact: Frank J. Vozos, M.D., FACS, President and Chief Executive Officer, Barnabas Health Behavioral Health Center
CFO: James Alexander, Regional Assistant Vice President, Financial Services
CMO: Todd Phillips, M.D., Chief Medical Officer
CIO: Ray Duarte, Director, Information Technology and Services
CHR: Michele Schweers, Vice President and Chief Human Resources Officer
CNO: Judy Colorado, R.N., Chief Nursing Officer
Web address: www.barnabashealth.org/monmouth–medical–center–southern–campus.aspx
Control: Other not–for–profit (including NFP Corporation) **Service:** General Medical and Surgical

Staffed Beds: 124 **Admissions:** 5749 **Census:** 94 **Outpatient Visits:** 81210 **Births:** 0 **Total Expense ($000):** 107354 **Payroll Expense ($000):** 42892 **Personnel:** 631

☐ **SPECIALTY HOSPITAL OF CENTRAL JERSEY (312017)**, 600 River Avenue, 4 West, Zip 08701–5237; tel. 732/942–3588, (Nonreporting) **A**1 10
Primary Contact: Violeta Peters, R.N., Chief Executive Officer
CFO: Kristin Prentiss, Chief Financial Officer
CMO: Howard Lebowitz, M.D., Chief Medical Officer
CHR: Mary Pat Napolitano, Director Human Resources
CNO: Judy Boccellato, R.N., Chief Nursing Officer
Web address: www.acutecarehs.com
Control: Corporation, Investor–owned, for–profit **Service:** Long–Term Acute Care hospital

Staffed Beds: 50

LAWRENCEVILLE—Mercer County

☒ **ST. LAWRENCE REHABILITATION CENTER (313027)**, 2381 Lawrenceville Road, Zip 08648–2025; tel. 609/896–9500, (Total facility includes 60 beds in nursing home–type unit) **A**1 10 **F**29 30 34 35 57 64 68 90 91 93 96 108 119 128 130 132 143 146 148
Primary Contact: Darlene S. Hanley, R.N., FACHE, President and Chief Executive Officer
COO: Shirley Pukala, R.N., Assistant Administrator Operations
CFO: Thomas W. Boyle, Chief Financial Officer
CMO: Kevin McGuigan, M.D., Medical Director
CIO: Joseph Castronuevo, Director Information Management
CHR: John Levi, Director Human Resources
CNO: Janet Machulsky, RN, BSN, Director of Nursing
Web address: www.slrc.org
Control: Church–operated, Nongovernment, not–for profit **Service:** Rehabilitation

Staffed Beds: 120 **Admissions:** 2416 **Census:** 98 **Outpatient Visits:** 20550 **Births:** 0 **Total Expense ($000):** 35497 **Payroll Expense ($000):** 20117 **Personnel:** 330

LIVINGSTON—Essex County

☒ **SAINT BARNABAS MEDICAL CENTER (310076)**, 94 Old Short Hills Road, Zip 07039–5672; tel. 973/322–5000 **A**1 2 3 5 8 10 13 **F**3 8 11 12 13 16 17 18 19 20 22 24 26 28 29 30 31 32 34 35 36 37 38 39 40 41 44 45 46 47 48 49 50 53 54 55 56 57 58 59 60 61 62 63 64 65 66 68 69 70 71 72 73 74 75 76 77 78 79 81 82 84 85 86 87 88 89 91 92 93 94 96 97 100 102 103 107 108 111 114 115 118 119 120 121 123 124 126 129 130 131 132 134 135 138 141 142 146 147 148 **P**7 **S** RWJBarnabas Health, West Orange, NJ
Primary Contact: Stephen P. Zieniewicz, FACHE, President and Chief Executive Officer
COO: Patrick Ahearn, Chief Operating Officer and Senior Vice President
CFO: Richard Davis, Chief Financial Officer
CMO: Gregory Rokosz, D.O., Senior Vice President Medical and Academic Affairs
CIO: Michael McTigue, Chief Information Officer
CHR: Arnold D. Manzo, Vice President Human Resources
CNO: Jennifer A. O'Neill, R.N., Chief Nursing Officer, Vice President Patient Care Services
Web address: www.barnabashealth.org/hospitals/saint_barnabas/index.html
Control: Other not–for–profit (including NFP Corporation) **Service:** General Medical and Surgical

Staffed Beds: 545 **Admissions:** 32940 **Census:** 405 **Outpatient Visits:** 274187 **Births:** 5803 **Total Expense ($000):** 668159 **Payroll Expense ($000):** 235924 **Personnel:** 3244

NJ

Many Facility Codes have changed. Please refer to the AHA Guide Code Chart. © 2016 AHA Guide

LONG BRANCH—Monmouth County

☒ **MONMOUTH MEDICAL CENTER, LONG BRANCH CAMPUS (310075)**, 300 Second Avenue, Zip 07740–6303; tel. 732/222–5200, (Includes CHILDREN'S HOSPITAL AT MONMOUTH MEDICAL CENTER, 300 Second Avenue, tel. 732/222–5200) **A**1 2 3 5 8 10 **F**3 5 8 9 11 12 13 14 15 17 18 19 20 22 28 29 30 31 32 34 35 38 39 40 41 44 45 46 47 48 49 50 51 52 53 54 55 56 57 58 59 60 61 64 65 66 68 69 70 72 73 74 75 76 77 78 79 81 82 83 84 85 86 87 88 89 97 98 99 100 101 102 103 104 105 106 107 108 109 110 111 114 115 116 119 120 121 123 124 126 129 130 131 132 133 134 135 143 144 145 146 147 148 **S** RWJBarnabas Health, West Orange, NJ
Primary Contact: Bill Arnold, President and Chief Executive Officer
CMO: Eric Burkett, M.D., Vice President Medical Affairs
CIO: Chris Butler, Chief Information Officer
CHR: Richard Kiernan, Vice President Human Resources
CNO: Diann Johnston, R.N., Vice President of Patient Care Services
Web address: www.barnabashealth.org/hospitals/monmouth_medical/index.html
Control: Other not–for–profit (including NFP Corporation) **Service:** General Medical and Surgical

Staffed Beds: 305 **Admissions:** 16415 **Census:** 209 **Outpatient Visits:** 243450 **Births:** 5073 **Total Expense ($000):** 366499 **Payroll Expense ($000):** 134425 **Personnel:** 1836

LYONS—Somerset County

LYONS DIVISION See Veterans Affairs New Jersey Health Care System, East Orange

MANAHAWKIN—Ocean County

☒ **SOUTHERN OCEAN MEDICAL CENTER (310113)**, 1140 Route 72 West, Zip 08050–2499; tel. 609/597–6011, (Total facility includes 20 beds in nursing home–type unit) **A**1 2 10 **F**3 11 12 13 15 18 20 28 29 30 31 32 34 35 36 38 39 40 41 43 44 45 46 48 49 50 51 54 55 56 57 58 59 60 61 63 64 65 66 68 70 71 74 75 76 77 78 79 80 81 82 84 85 86 87 92 93 94 96 97 100 101 102 103 107 108 110 111 114 115 116 117 118 119 120 121 123 128 129 130 131 132 134 135 144 145 146 147 148 **P**6 7 **S** Hackensack Meridian Health, Edison, NJ
Primary Contact: Joseph P. Coyle, President and Chief Executive Officer
COO: Kim Frazee, R.N., Vice President Physician and Business Development
CFO: Joseph M. Lemaire, Executive Vice President
CMO: Theodore Zaleski, M.D., Vice President Clinical Effectiveness
CIO: Rebecca Weber, Senior Vice President and Chief Information Officer
CHR: Susan Tillman–Taylor, Manager Human Resources
CNO: Donna Ciufo, R.N., Vice President and Chief Nurse Executive
Web address: www.soch.com
Control: Other not–for–profit (including NFP Corporation) **Service:** General Medical and Surgical

Staffed Beds: 153 **Admissions:** 7099 **Census:** 93 **Outpatient Visits:** 101284 **Births:** 360 **Total Expense ($000):** 143824 **Payroll Expense ($000):** 56390 **Personnel:** 770

MARLTON—Burlington County

☒ △ **MARLTON REHABILITATION HOSPITAL (313032)**, 92 Brick Road, Zip 08053–2177; tel. 856/988–8778 **A**1 7 10 **F**34 50 57 59 64 68 75 77 85 87 90 91 92 93 130 132 148 **P**8 **S** Vibra Healthcare, Mechanicsburg, PA
Primary Contact: Phyllis J. Schlichtmann, Chief Executive Officer
CFO: Stuart Moss, Chief Financial Officer
CMO: Kenneth Wu, M.D., Medical Director
CHR: Joanne Cernava, Director Human Resources
CNO: Chris Kreeley, Director Nursing
Web address: www.marltonrehab.com
Control: Corporation, Investor–owned, for–profit **Service:** Rehabilitation

Staffed Beds: 61 **Admissions:** 1683 **Census:** 54 **Outpatient Visits:** 15852 **Births:** 0 **Total Expense ($000):** 24413 **Payroll Expense ($000):** 11587 **Personnel:** 172

☒ **VIRTUA MARLTON**, 90 Brick Road, Zip 08053–2177; tel. 856/355–6000 **A**1 2 3 5 **F**3 20 22 26 29 31 40 45 46 47 49 56 60 64 68 70 75 77 78 79 81 82 84 85 87 91 92 107 108 111 114 115 118 119 130 141 146 **S** Virtua Health, Marlton, NJ
Primary Contact: Matthew Zuino, Senior Vice President Hospital Services
CFO: Robert Segin, Executive Vice President & Chief Financial Officer
CMO: John Matsinger, D.O., Chief Medical Officer
CIO: Thomas Gordon, Chief Information Officer
CHR: Rhonda R. Jordan, Chief Human Resources Officer
CNO: Tracy Carlino, R.N., Chief Nursing Officer
Web address: www.virtua.org
Control: Other not–for–profit (including NFP Corporation) **Service:** General Medical and Surgical

Staffed Beds: 189 **Admissions:** 9271 **Census:** 123 **Outpatient Visits:** 49648 **Births:** 0 **Total Expense ($000):** 167520 **Payroll Expense ($000):** 54923 **Personnel:** 668

☐ **WEISMAN CHILDREN'S REHABILITATION HOSPITAL (313302)**, 92 Brick Road 3rd Floor, Zip 08053–2177; tel. 856/489–4520, (Nonreporting) **A**1 10
Primary Contact: Michael Rosiak, Chief Operating Officer
COO: Michael Rosiak, Chief Operating Officer
CMO: Connie Domingo, M.D., Medical Director
CIO: Darren Pedersen, Coordinator Information Technology
CHR: Jill Koerner, Manager Employee Relations
CNO: Daniel William Pfeffer, Chief Nurse Executive
Web address: www.weismanchildrens.com
Control: Corporation, Investor–owned, for–profit **Service:** Children's rehabilitation

Staffed Beds: 24

MONTCLAIR—Essex County

☒ **HACKENSACK UNIVERSITY MEDICAL CENTER MOUNTAINSIDE (310054)**, 1 Bay Avenue, Zip 07042–4898; tel. 973/429–6000 **A**1 2 3 5 10 **F**3 8 12 13 14 15 18 20 22 26 28 29 30 31 34 35 38 39 40 42 43 44 45 46 48 49 50 51 52 53 54 55 56 57 59 60 66 67 68 70 73 74 75 76 77 78 79 81 82 84 85 86 87 91 93 94 97 98 102 103 104 105 107 108 109 110 111 114 115 116 117 118 119 120 121 124 128 129 130 131 132 134 135 144 145 146 147 148 **P**5 **S** LHP Hospital Group, Plano, TX
Primary Contact: John A. Fromhold, FACHE, Chief Executive Officer
CFO: Al Aboud, CPA, Chief Financial Officer
CMO: Theresa Soroko, M.D., Chief Medical Officer
CIO: Max Siu, Chief Information Officer
CHR: Fran Corridon, Vice President Human Resources and Shared Services
CNO: Debbie Regen, R.N., Chief Nursing Officer
Web address: www.mountainsidenow.com
Control: Partnership, Investor–owned, for–profit **Service:** General Medical and Surgical

Staffed Beds: 218 **Admissions:** 11266 **Census:** 133 **Outpatient Visits:** 105661 **Births:** 1508 **Total Expense ($000):** 205355 **Payroll Expense ($000):** 85650 **Personnel:** 1370

MORRIS PLAINS—Morris County

☐ **GREYSTONE PARK PSYCHIATRIC HOSPITAL (314016)**, 59 Koch Avenue, Zip 07950–4400; tel. 973/538–1800 **A**1 3 5 10 **F**29 30 39 68 75 77 86 87 97 98 103 130 135 146 **P**6 **S** Division of Mental Health and Addiction Services, Department of Human Services, State of New Jersey, Trenton, NJ
Primary Contact: Janet J. Monroe, R.N., Chief Executive Officer
COO: Ross Friedman, Chief Operating Officer
CFO: Jack Frey, Acting Business Manager
CMO: Cherry Monroy–Miller, M.D., Acting Medical Director
CIO: David Saleem, Director Information Technology
CHR: James Frey, Jr., Acting Manager Human Resources
CNO: Doreen Sperber–Weiss, Ph.D., Chief Nursing Officer
Web address: www.state.nj.us/humanservices/dmhs/oshm/gpph/
Control: State–Government, nonfederal **Service:** Psychiatric

Staffed Beds: 542 **Admissions:** 571 **Census:** 534 **Outpatient Visits:** 0 **Births:** 0 **Total Expense ($000):** 115803 **Payroll Expense ($000):** 73388 **Personnel:** 1414

MORRISTOWN—Morris County

☒ **MORRISTOWN MEDICAL CENTER (310015)**, 100 Madison Avenue, Zip 07960–6136; tel. 973/971–5000, (Includes REHABILITATION INSTITUTE AT THE MOUNT KEMBLE DIVISION ; GORYEB CHILDREN'S HOSPITAL, 100 Madison Avenue, tel. 800/247–9580), (Total facility includes 40 beds in nursing home–type unit) **A**1 2 3 5 8 10 13 **F**3 5 6 7 8 9 11 12 13 14 15 17 18 19 20 22 24 26 28 29 30 31 32 33 34 35 36 37 38 39 40 41 43 44 45 46 47 48 49 50 51 52 53 54 55 56 57 58 59 60 61 62 63 64 65 66 68 69 70 71 72 73 74 75 76 77 78 79 81 82 83 84 85 86 87 88 89 90 91 92 93 94 95 96 97 98 99 100 101 102 103 104 105 107 108 110 111 114 115 116 117 118 119 120 121 123 126 128 129 130 131 132 134 135 141 143 144 145 146 147 148 **P**2 3 5 6 **S** Atlantic Health System, Morristown, NJ
Primary Contact: Trish O'Keefe, Ph.D., R.N., President
CFO: Joseph D'Auria, Director Finance
CMO: Louis Brusco, M.D., Chief Medical Officer
CNO: Carol S. Jones, MSN, Interim Chief Nursing Officer
Web address: www.atlantichealth.org/Morristown/
Control: Other not–for–profit (including NFP Corporation) **Service:** General Medical and Surgical

Staffed Beds: 702 **Admissions:** 37527 **Census:** 571 **Outpatient Visits:** 465110 **Births:** 4455 **Total Expense ($000):** 1147919 **Payroll Expense ($000):** 470394 **Personnel:** 5725

NJ

MOUNT HOLLY—Burlington County

☒ **VIRTUA MEMORIAL (310057)**, 175 Madison Avenue, Zip 08060–2099; tel. 609/267–0700 **A**1 3 5 10 **F**3 11 12 13 15 18 20 22 28 29 30 31 40 41 45 46 48 49 56 60 70 73 74 75 76 77 78 79 81 82 85 86 87 89 92 93 98 102 105 107 108 110 111 114 115 118 119 120 121 123 126 129 130 143 146 147 **S** Virtua Health, Marlton, NJ
Primary Contact: Matthew Zuino, Senior Vice President Hospital Services
CFO: Robert Segin, Chief Financial Officer
CMO: James P. Dwyer, D.O., Executive Vice President and Chief Medical Officer
CHR: E. D. Dunn, Vice President Human Resources
Web address: www.virtua.org
Control: Other not–for–profit (including NFP Corporation) **Service:** General Medical and Surgical

Staffed Beds: 334 **Admissions:** 17781 **Census:** 222 **Outpatient Visits:** 181629 **Births:** 2307 **Total Expense ($000):** 290494 **Payroll Expense ($000):** 97903 **Personnel:** 1293

VIRTUA MEMORIAL HOSPITAL BURLINGTON COUNTY See Virtua Memorial

NEPTUNE—Monmouth County

☒ **JERSEY SHORE UNIVERSITY MEDICAL CENTER (310073)**, 1945 Route 33, Zip 07754–0397; tel. 732/775–5500, (Includes K. HOVNANIAN CHILDREN'S HOSPITAL, 1945 State Route 33, Zip 07753–4859; tel. 800/560–9990) **A**1 2 3 5 8 10 13 **F**3 5 11 12 13 17 18 19 20 22 24 26 28 29 30 31 32 34 35 36 38 39 40 41 43 44 45 46 47 48 49 50 52 54 55 56 57 58 59 60 61 63 64 65 66 68 70 71 72 73 74 75 76 77 78 79 80 81 82 84 85 86 87 88 89 92 93 94 96 97 98 99 100 101 102 103 104 105 107 108 111 114 115 116 117 118 119 120 121 123 126 129 130 131 132 134 135 144 145 146 147 148 **P**6 7 **S** Hackensack Meridian Health, Edison, NJ
Primary Contact: Kenneth N. Sable, M.D., President
COO: Robert H. Adams, Vice President Operations
CFO: John Gantner, Executive Vice President Finance and Partner Company Operations
CMO: David Kountz, M.D., Senior Vice President Medical Affairs
CIO: Rebecca Weber, Senior Vice President and Chief Information Officer
Web address: www.meridianhealth.com
Control: Other not–for–profit (including NFP Corporation) **Service:** General Medical and Surgical

Staffed Beds: 554 **Admissions:** 24576 **Census:** 370 **Outpatient Visits:** 210675 **Births:** 2011 **Total Expense ($000):** 617794 **Payroll Expense ($000):** 237435 **Personnel:** 3044

NEW BRUNSWICK—Middlesex County

☐ **CHILDREN'S SPECIALIZED HOSPITAL–PSE&G (313300)**, 200 Somerset Street, Zip 08901–1942; tel. 732/258–7000, (Includes CHILDREN'S SPECIALIZED HOSPITAL, 200 Somerset Street, tel. 732/258–7134; Warren E. Moore, President and Chief Executive Officer), (Total facility includes 72 beds in nursing home–type unit) **A**1 3 5 10 **F**29 32 35 54 64 65 74 75 77 79 90 91 93 94 97 99 104 130 146 **S** RWJBarnabas Health, West Orange, NJ
Primary Contact: Warren E. Moore, President and Chief Executive Officer
COO: Charles Chianese, Vice President Chief Operating Office
CFO: Joseph J. Dobosh, Jr., Vice President and Chief Financial Officer
CMO: Christopher Haines, D.O., Vice President Chief Medical Officer
CIO: Charles Chianese, Vice President Chief Operating Officer
CHR: William Dwyer, Vice President Chief Human Resources Officer
CNO: Bonnie Baloga–Altieri, Ph.D., Vice President Patient Care Services and Chief Nursing Officer
Web address: www.childrens–specialized.org
Control: Other not–for–profit (including NFP Corporation) **Service:** Children's rehabilitation

Staffed Beds: 140 **Admissions:** 617 **Census:** 129 **Births:** 0 **Total Expense ($000):** 131435 **Payroll Expense ($000):** 76363 **Personnel:** 984

☒ **ROBERT WOOD JOHNSON UNIVERSITY HOSPITAL (310038)**, 1 Robert Wood Johnson Place, Zip 08901–1928; tel. 732/828–3000, (Includes BRISTOL–MYERS SQUIBB CHILDREN'S HOSPITAL, One Robert Wood Johnson Place, Zip 08901, Mailing Address: P.O. Box 2601, Zip 08903–2601; tel. 732/828–3000) **A**1 2 3 5 8 10 **F**3 6 7 8 9 11 12 13 14 15 17 18 19 20 22 24 26 28 29 30 31 32 34 35 36 37 38 39 40 41 42 43 44 45 46 47 48 49 50 51 52 53 54 55 56 57 58 59 60 61 62 63 64 65 66 68 70 71 72 73 74 75 76 77 78 79 81 82 83 84 85 86 87 88 89 91 92 93 94 96 97 99 100 102 104 107 108 109 110 111 112 113 114 115 116 117 118 119 120 121 122 123 124 126 129 130 131 132 134 135 136 137 138 141 142 143 146 147 148 **P**3 6 7 **S** RWJBarnabas Health, West Orange, NJ
Primary Contact: Michael A. Antoniades, President and Chief Executive Officer
COO: Jessie Lee Tucker, III, Ph.D., Senior Vice President and Chief Operating Officer
CFO: Brian M. Reilly, Chief Financial Officer
CMO: Joshua M. Bershad, M.D., Senior Vice President Medical Affairs and Chief Medical Officer
CIO: Robert G. Irwin, Vice President Information Systems
CHR: Martin S. Everhart, Senior Vice President Human Resources
CNO: Lori Colineri, MSN, Senior Vice President Nursing and Chief Nursing Officer
Web address: www.rwjuh.edu
Control: Other not–for–profit (including NFP Corporation) **Service:** General Medical and Surgical

Staffed Beds: 610 **Admissions:** 34845 **Census:** 539 **Outpatient Visits:** 254753 **Births:** 2462 **Total Expense ($000):** 952468 **Payroll Expense ($000):** 350720 **Personnel:** 4534

☒ **SAINT PETER'S UNIVERSITY HOSPITAL (310070)**, 254 Easton Avenue, Zip 08901–1780; tel. 732/745–8600, (Includes THE CHILDREN'S HOSPITAL AT SAINT PETER'S UNIVERSITY, 254 Easton Avenue, Zip 08901–1766; tel. 732/565–5437) **A**1 2 3 5 8 10 **F**2 3 12 13 15 17 18 19 20 22 26 27 29 30 31 32 34 35 37 38 39 40 41 44 45 46 49 50 51 54 55 56 57 58 59 60 61 63 64 65 66 68 70 71 72 73 74 75 76 77 78 79 81 82 83 84 85 86 87 88 89 91 92 93 94 96 97 99 100 101 102 103 104 105 107 108 110 111 113 114 115 118 119 120 121 123 124 126 129 130 131 132 134 135 143 145 146 147 148 **P**3 6
Primary Contact: Ronald C. Rak, JD, Chief Executive Officer
CFO: Garrick J. Stoldt, Vice President and Chief Financial Officer
CMO: Anthony Passannante, Jr., M.D., Vice President, Chief Medical Officer and Co–Chief Quality Officer
CIO: Frank DiSanzo, Vice President and Chief Information Officer and Chief Strategy Officer
CHR: Susan Ballestero, Vice President and Chief Human Resources Officer
CNO: Elizabeth Wise, R.N., Chief Nursing Officer and Vice President, Patient Care Services
Web address: www.saintpetersuh.com
Control: Church–operated, Nongovernment, not–for profit **Service:** General Medical and Surgical

Staffed Beds: 348 **Admissions:** 17995 **Census:** 227 **Outpatient Visits:** 385864 **Births:** 5415 **Total Expense ($000):** 417792 **Payroll Expense ($000):** 197298 **Personnel:** 2530

NEWARK—Essex County

◇ **COLUMBUS HOSPITAL LTACH (312024)**, 495 North Thirteenth Street, Zip 07107–1317; tel. 973/587–7777, (Nonreporting) **A**10 21
Primary Contact: Richard Lipsky, Chairman and Chief Executive Officer
COO: Peter Callaghan, President and Chief Operating Officer
CFO: Alexey Gololobov, Chief Financial Officer
CHR: Patrice Ricciardi, Director Human Resources
CNO: Arthur Kharonov, Vice President Nursing
Web address: www.columbusltach.org
Control: Corporation, Investor–owned, for–profit **Service:** Long–Term Acute Care hospital

Staffed Beds: 66

☒ **NEWARK BETH ISRAEL MEDICAL CENTER (310002)**, 201 Lyons Avenue, Zip 07112–2027; tel. 973/926–7000, (Includes CHILDREN'S HOSPITAL OF NEW JERSEY, 201 Lyons Avenue, tel. 973/926–7000; Darrell K. Terry, Sr., Interim President and Chief Executive Officer) **A**1 2 3 5 8 10 12 13 **F**3 15 17 18 19 20 21 22 23 24 25 26 27 28 29 30 31 32 34 35 43 44 45 46 47 48 49 50 51 53 55 56 57 58 59 60 61 63 64 65 66 68 70 71 72 73 74 75 76 77 78 79 81 82 84 85 86 87 88 89 92 93 94 97 98 99 100 101 102 103 104 105 107 108 109 110 111 114 115 117 118 119 120 121 123 126 129 130 131 132 137 140 141 143 145 146 147 148 **P**8 **S** RWJBarnabas Health, West Orange, NJ
Primary Contact: Darrell K. Terry, Sr., Interim President and Chief Executive Officer
COO: Darrell K. Terry, Sr., Senior Vice President Operations
CFO: Douglas A. Zehner, Chief Financial Officer
CMO: Jeremias Murillo, M.D., Chief Medical Officer
CHR: Zach Lipner, Vice President Human Resources
CNO: Mary Fuhro, Chief Nursing Officer
Web address: www.barnabashealth.org/hospitals/newark_beth_israel/index.html
Control: Other not–for–profit (including NFP Corporation) **Service:** General Medical and Surgical

Staffed Beds: 338 **Admissions:** 18839 **Census:** 355 **Outpatient Visits:** 296280 **Births:** 3047 **Total Expense ($000):** 563819 **Payroll Expense ($000):** 247745 **Personnel:** 3067

NJ

Many Facility Codes have changed. Please refer to the AHA Guide Code Chart. © 2016 AHA Guide

⊞ **SAINT MICHAEL'S MEDICAL CENTER (310096)**, 111 Central Avenue, Zip 07102–1909; tel. 973/877–5350 **A**1 2 3 5 10 13 **F**3 5 12 15 17 18 20 22 24 26 29 30 31 34 35 37 40 45 47 49 50 57 58 59 61 64 66 68 70 71 74 75 77 78 79 81 85 87 97 98 100 107 108 110 111 114 115 119 121 123 126 130 132 143 147 148 **S** Prime Healthcare Services, Ontario, CA
Primary Contact: Robert C. Iannaccone, Chief Executive Officer
COO: Dennis Pettigrew, Chief Operating Officer
CFO: Dennis Pettigrew, Chief Financial Officer
CMO: Joseph DePasquale, M.D., Interim Chief Medical Officer
CIO: Tom Addington, Chief Information Officer
CHR: Dennis Sparks, Vice President Human Resources
CNO: Johanna Magner, Interim Chief Nursing Officer
Web address: www.smmcnj.org
Control: Church–operated, Nongovernment, not–for profit **Service:** General Medical and Surgical

Staffed Beds: 162 **Admissions:** 7362 **Census:** 100 **Outpatient Visits:** 105173 **Births:** 0 **Total Expense ($000):** 222233 **Payroll Expense ($000):** 81756 **Personnel:** 1140

⊞ **UNIVERSITY HOSPITAL (310119)**, 150 Bergen Street, Zip 07103–2496; tel. 973/972–4300 **A**1 2 3 5 10 **F**3 7 8 11 15 17 18 20 22 24 26 28 29 30 31 32 34 35 37 38 39 40 41 43 44 45 46 47 48 49 50 54 55 57 58 59 60 61 64 65 66 68 70 71 72 73 74 75 76 77 78 79 80 81 82 84 85 86 87 88 89 92 93 96 97 98 100 102 107 108 110 111 114 118 119 120 121 123 124 126 130 131 132 134 135 139 141 142 145 146 147 148 **P**5
Primary Contact: John N. Kastanis, FACHE, President and Chief Executive Officer
COO: Nancy Hamstra, Chief Operating Officer
CFO: Thomas M. Daly, CPA, Chief Financial Officer
CMO: Suzanne Atkin, M.D., Chief Medical Officer
CIO: Richard Tunnell, Chief Information Officer
CHR: Gerard Garcia, Chief Human Resource Officer
CNO: Carl Kirton, Ph.D., Chief Nursing Officer
Web address: www.uhnj.org
Control: State–Government, nonfederal **Service:** General Medical and Surgical

Staffed Beds: 531 **Admissions:** 14871 **Census:** 257 **Outpatient Visits:** 249926 **Births:** 1555 **Total Expense ($000):** 616144 **Payroll Expense ($000):** 304253 **Personnel:** 3513

NEWTON—Sussex County

⊞ **NEWTON MEDICAL CENTER (310028)**, 175 High Street, Zip 07860–1004; tel. 973/383–2121 **A**1 2 10 **F**3 5 6 8 9 11 12 13 14 15 18 19 20 28 30 31 32 34 35 38 39 40 41 44 45 47 49 50 53 54 56 57 58 59 60 61 62 64 65 66 68 69 70 71 73 74 75 76 77 78 79 81 82 84 85 86 87 91 92 93 94 95 96 97 98 99 100 101 102 103 104 105 106 107 108 109 110 111 114 118 119 129 130 131 132 134 135 143 144 146 147 148 **P**6 **S** Atlantic Health System, Morristown, NJ
Primary Contact: Joseph DiPaolo, FACHE, President
CFO: Kevin Lenahan, Director Corporate Accounting, Budgets, Grants and Reimbursements
CMO: David Lazarus, M.D., Medical Director Clinical Affairs
CIO: Linda Reed, Vice President Information Systems and Chief Information Officer
CHR: Andrew L. Kovach, Vice President Human Resources and Chief Administrative Officer
Web address: www.atlantichealth.org/newton/
Control: Other not–for–profit (including NFP Corporation) **Service:** General Medical and Surgical

Staffed Beds: 148 **Admissions:** 7529 **Census:** 92 **Outpatient Visits:** 112761 **Births:** 446 **Total Expense ($000):** 145810 **Payroll Expense ($000):** 69042 **Personnel:** 901

NORTH BERGEN—Hudson County

⊞ **HACKENSACKUMC PALISADES (310003)**, 7600 River Road, Zip 07047–6217; tel. 201/854–5000 **A**1 3 5 10 12 13 **F**3 7 8 11 12 13 15 18 20 28 29 30 34 35 38 40 43 45 49 50 56 57 68 70 73 74 75 76 77 78 79 81 82 84 85 86 87 89 92 93 102 104 107 110 111 114 115 119 129 130 132 143 145 146 147 148 **S** Hackensack Meridian Health, Edison, NJ
Primary Contact: Bruce J. Markowitz, President and Chief Executive Officer
COO: David J. Berkowitz, Vice President and Chief Operating Officer
CFO: John Calandriello, Vice President and Chief Financial Officer
CMO: Suresh Raina, M.D., Vice President Medical Staff and Chief Medical Officer
CIO: Albert Porco, Director Management Information Systems
CHR: Donna Cahill, Vice President Human Resources
CNO: Ruben D. Fernandez, R.N., Vice President and Chief Nursing Officer
Web address: www.palisadesmedical.org
Control: Other not–for–profit (including NFP Corporation) **Service:** General Medical and Surgical

Staffed Beds: 228 **Admissions:** 9280 **Census:** 118 **Outpatient Visits:** 100145 **Births:** 1236 **Total Expense ($000):** 162474 **Payroll Expense ($000):** 71916 **Personnel:** 882

PARAMUS—Bergen County

☐ **BERGEN REGIONAL MEDICAL CENTER (310058)**, 230 East Ridgewood Avenue, Zip 07652–4142; tel. 201/967–4000, (Nonreporting) **A**1 3 10
Primary Contact: Susan Mendelowitz, R.N., FACHE, President, Administrator and Chief Operating Officer
COO: Susan Mendelowitz, R.N., Executive Vice President and Chief Operating Officer
CFO: Connie Magdangal, Executive Vice President and Chief Financial Officer
CMO: Robert M. Harris, M.D., President Medical and Dental Staff
CIO: Ronald Li, Vice President Management Information Systems
CHR: Guy Mennonna, Senior Vice President Human Resources
Web address: www.bergenregional.com
Control: County–Government, nonfederal **Service:** Psychiatric

Staffed Beds: 432

PASSAIC—Passaic County

⊞ **ST. MARY'S GENERAL HOSPITAL (310006)**, 350 Boulevard, Zip 07055–2840; tel. 973/365–4300, (Nonreporting) **A**1 10 **S** Prime Healthcare Services, Ontario, CA
Primary Contact: Edward Condit, President and Chief Executive Officer
CFO: Nicholas Lanza, Controller
CMO: Ronald Poblete, M.D., President Medical and Dental Staff
CHR: Cathy Lynch–Kilic, Vice President Human Resources
Web address: www.smh–passaic.org
Control: Other not–for–profit (including NFP Corporation) **Service:** General Medical and Surgical

Staffed Beds: 269

PATERSON—Passaic County

★ ◇ **ST. JOSEPH'S HEALTHCARE SYSTEM (310019)**, 703 Main Street, Zip 07503–2691; tel. 973/754–2000, (Includes ST. JOSEPH'S CHILDREN'S HOSPITAL, 703 Main Street, Zip 07503–2621; tel. 973/754–2500; Kevin J. Slavin, FACHE, President and Chief Executive Officer; ST. JOSEPH'S WAYNE HOSPITAL, 224 Hamburg Turnpike, Wayne, Zip 07470–2100; tel. 973/942–6900; Daniel B. Kline, Vice President, Site Administrator), (Nonreporting) **A**2 3 5 10 13 21
Primary Contact: Kevin J. Slavin, FACHE, President and Chief Executive Officer
COO: Lisa Brady, Senior Vice President and Chief Operating Officer
CFO: David Alexander, Senior Vice President and Chief Financial Officer
CMO: James Labagnara, M.D., Vice President Medical Affairs
CIO: Linda Reed, Vice President and Chief Information Officer
CHR: John P. Bruno, Vice President Human Resources
CNO: Judy Padula, MSN, Vice President Patient Care Services and Chief Nursing Officer
Web address: www.stjosephshealth.org
Control: Church–operated, Nongovernment, not–for profit **Service:** General Medical and Surgical

Staffed Beds: 700

PEAPACK—Somerset County

☐ **MATHENY MEDICAL AND EDUCATIONAL CENTER (312014)**, (Medically complex developmental disabilities), 65 Highland Avenue, Zip 07977, Mailing Address: P.O. Box 339, Zip 07977–0339; tel. 908/234–0011 **A**1 5 10 **F**2 29 30 32 35 38 39 44 50 58 64 68 75 77 79 86 87 91 93 94 96 97 99 100 104 130 132 143 146 **P**6
Primary Contact: Kendell R. Sprott, M.D., JD, Chief Executive Officer
COO: Christopher King, Director Operations and Administrative Services
CFO: Wayne Guberman, Director Finance
CMO: Gary E. Eddey, M.D., Medical Director
CIO: Ron Daniel, Manager Information Systems
CHR: Nancy Petrillo, Director Human Resources
Web address: www.matheny.org
Control: Other not–for–profit (including NFP Corporation) **Service:** Other specialty

Staffed Beds: 101 **Admissions:** 1 **Census:** 98 **Outpatient Visits:** 1137 **Births:** 0 **Total Expense ($000):** 48277 **Payroll Expense ($000):** 29152 **Personnel:** 474

NJ

Hospital, Medicare Provider Number, Address, Telephone, Approval, Facility, and Physician Codes, Health Care System
★ American Hospital Association (AHA) membership ○ Healthcare Facilities Accreditation Program ⇑ Center for Improvement in Healthcare Quality Accreditation ☐ The Joint Commission accreditation ◇ DNV Healthcare Inc. accreditation △ Commission on Accreditation of Rehabilitation Facilities (CARF) accreditation

PENNINGTON—Mercer County

☒ **CAPITAL HEALTH MEDICAL CENTER–HOPEWELL (310044)**, 1 Capital Way, Zip 08534–2520; tel. 609/303–4000 **A**1 2 5 10 **F**3 7 8 11 12 13 15 18 19 20 22 28 29 30 31 32 34 35 36 39 40 41 44 45 46 47 48 49 50 51 52 55 57 58 59 60 61 65 68 70 72 73 74 75 76 78 79 81 82 84 85 86 87 89 90 93 94 96 97 107 108 109 110 111 112 114 115 117 118 119 120 121 123 124 126 130 132 135 143 145 146 147 148 **S** Capital Health, Trenton, NJ
Primary Contact: Al Maghazehe, Ph.D., FACHE, President and Chief Executive Officer
CFO: Shane Fleming, Chief Financial Officer
CMO: Eugene McMahon, Senior Vice President and Chief Medical Officer
CIO: Eugene Grochala, Vice President Information Systems
CHR: Scott Clemmensen, Vice President Human Resources and Leadership Enhancement
CNO: Margaret Reiter, Chief Nursing Officer
Web address: www.capitalhealth.org
Control: Other not–for–profit (including NFP Corporation) **Service:** General Medical and Surgical

Staffed Beds: 215 Admissions: 15350 Census: 175 Outpatient Visits: 149554 Births: 3357 Personnel: 1457

PERTH AMBOY—Middlesex County

☐ **CARE ONE AT RARITAN BAY MEDICAL CENTER (312018)**, 530 New Brunswick Avenue, Zip 08861–3654; tel. 732/324–6090, (Nonreporting) **A**1 10
Primary Contact: Sharon Bready, R.N., Chief Executive Officer
CFO: Richard Burguillos, Chief Financial Officer
Web address: www.care-one.com
Control: Corporation, Investor–owned, for–profit **Service:** Long–Term Acute Care hospital

Staffed Beds: 30

☒ **RARITAN BAY MEDICAL CENTER (310039)**, 530 New Brunswick Avenue, Zip 08861–3654; tel. 732/442–3700, (Includes OLD BRIDGE DIVISION, One Hospital Plaza, Old Bridge, Zip 08857; tel. 732/360–1000; PERTH AMBOY DIVISION, 530 New Brunswick Avenue, Zip 08861–3685; tel. 732/442–3700) **A**1 3 5 10 **F**3 4 5 7 8 11 12 18 20 22 29 30 31 32 34 35 36 38 39 40 43 45 46 47 48 49 50 51 54 56 57 58 59 60 61 64 65 66 68 70 73 74 75 76 77 78 79 80 81 82 85 86 87 89 92 93 94 96 97 98 100 101 102 103 104 107 108 110 111 114 115 116 117 118 119 120 130 131 132 143 144 146 147 148 **P**6 **S** Hackensack Meridian Health, Edison, NJ
Primary Contact: Michael R. D'Agnes, FACHE, President and Chief Executive Officer
COO: Vincent Costantino, Vice President Operations and Human Resources
CFO: Thomas Shanahan, Chief Financial Officer and Senior Vice President
CMO: Michael Ciencewicki, M.D., Vice President Medical Affairs
CHR: Vincent Costantino, Vice President Operations and Human Resources
Web address: www.rbmc.org
Control: Other not–for–profit (including NFP Corporation) **Service:** General Medical and Surgical

Staffed Beds: 276 Admissions: 12590 Census: 176 Outpatient Visits: 138925 Births: 1193 Total Expense ($000): 237610 Payroll Expense ($000): 108804 Personnel: 1737

PHILLIPSBURG—Warren County

☐ **ST. LUKE'S HOSPITAL – WARREN CAMPUS (310060)**, 185 Roseberry Street, Zip 08865–1690; tel. 908/859–6700 **A**1 2 3 5 10 13 **F**2 3 8 11 15 18 20 28 29 30 31 34 35 39 40 45 48 49 53 56 59 61 64 65 66 68 70 74 75 77 78 79 81 82 85 86 87 91 92 93 97 100 102 103 104 106 107 108 110 111 114 118 119 124 129 130 131 132 134 146 147 148 **S** St. Luke's University Health Network, Bethlehem, PA
Primary Contact: Scott R. Wolfe, CPA, President
COO: Alice Wilson, FACHE, Vice President Administration
CMO: Edward Gilkey, M.D., Vice President Medical Affairs
CHR: Morgan G. Mahl, Director Human Resources
CNO: Gail Newton, R.N., Vice President Patient Care Services
Web address: www.slhn.org
Control: Other not–for–profit (including NFP Corporation) **Service:** General Medical and Surgical

Staffed Beds: 94 Admissions: 4161 Census: 55 Outpatient Visits: 113373 Births: 0 Total Expense ($000): 95808 Payroll Expense ($000): 41362 Personnel: 544

PISCATAWAY—Middlesex County

UNIVERSITY BEHAVIORAL HEALTHCARE (314011), 671 Hoes Lane West, Zip 08854–8021; tel. 732/235–5900, (Nonreporting) **A**3 5 10
Primary Contact: Rosemarie Rosati, Interim President and Chief Executive Officer
COO: Rosemarie Rosati, Chief Operating Officer
CFO: Alan Weinkrantz, Chief Financial Officer, Finance
CMO: Theresa Miskimen, M.D., Vice President Medical Services
CIO: Adam Levinson, Associate Director, Information Services
CNO: Michele A. Miller, R.N., Vice President, Acute and Nursing Services
Web address: www.ubhc.rutgers.edu
Control: State–Government, nonfederal **Service:** Psychiatric

Staffed Beds: 48

PLAINSBORO—Middlesex County

UNIVERSITY MEDICAL CENTER AT PRINCETON See University Medical Center of Princeton at Plainsboro

☒ **UNIVERSITY MEDICAL CENTER OF PRINCETON AT PLAINSBORO (310010)**, One Plainsboro Road, Zip 08536–1913; tel. 609/853–7100, (Includes ACUTE GENERAL HOSPITAL, MERWICK UNIT–EXTENDED CARE AND REHABILITATION, PRINCETON HOUSE UNIT–COMMUNITY MENTAL HEALTH AND SUBSTANCE ABUSE) **A**1 2 3 5 10 **F**3 4 5 8 11 12 13 14 15 18 19 20 22 26 28 29 30 31 32 34 35 36 38 39 40 41 45 46 47 48 49 50 51 53 54 55 56 57 58 59 60 61 62 63 64 65 66 68 70 73 74 75 76 77 78 79 81 82 84 85 86 87 89 90 91 92 93 96 97 98 99 100 101 102 103 104 105 107 108 110 111 114 115 116 117 118 119 120 121 123 124 126 129 130 131 132 134 135 143 145 146 147 148 **P**6
Primary Contact: Barry S. Rabner, President and Chief Executive Officer, Princeton Healthcare System
COO: James Demetriades, Vice President, Operations
CMO: Donald Denny, M.D., Senior Vice President, Medical Affairs
CIO: Anne Searle, Chief Information Officer
CHR: Marcia M. Telthorster, M.Ed, CCP, Vice President Human Resources
CNO: Barbara Christiano, Vice President, Patient Care Services and Chief Nursing Officer
Web address: www.princetonhcs.org
Control: Other not–for–profit (including NFP Corporation) **Service:** General Medical and Surgical

Staffed Beds: 355 Admissions: 17677 Census: 268 Outpatient Visits: 481815 Births: 2401 Total Expense ($000): 401250 Payroll Expense ($000): 147149 Personnel: 2587

POMONA—Atlantic County

ATLANTICARE REGIONAL MEDICAL CENTER–MAINLAND DIVISION See AtlantiCare Regional Medical Center, Atlantic City

☒ △ **BACHARACH INSTITUTE FOR REHABILITATION (313030)**, 61 West Jimmie Leeds Road, Zip 08240–9102, Mailing Address: P.O. Box 723, Zip 08240–0723; tel. 609/652–7000, (Nonreporting) **A**1 7 10
Primary Contact: Richard J. Kathrins, Ph.D., President and Chief Executive Officer
CFO: Jeanne Vuksta, Chief Financial Officer
CMO: Craig Anmuth, M.D., Medical Director
CIO: Jeff Rees, Director Information Systems
CHR: Diane Croshaw, Vice President Human Resources
Web address: www.bacharach.org
Control: Other not–for–profit (including NFP Corporation) **Service:** Rehabilitation

Staffed Beds: 80

POMPTON PLAINS—Morris County

☒ **CHILTON MEDICAL CENTER (310017)**, 97 West Parkway, Zip 07444–1696; tel. 973/831–5000 **A**1 2 10 **F**3 7 8 11 12 13 15 18 20 22 28 29 30 31 32 34 35 36 38 40 41 44 45 47 49 50 54 55 56 57 58 59 60 62 63 64 65 66 68 70 73 74 75 76 77 78 79 81 82 84 85 86 87 89 93 97 102 107 108 110 111 114 115 116 117 118 119 120 121 123 126 129 130 131 132 135 143 146 147 148 **P**3 6 **S** Atlantic Health System, Morristown, NJ
Primary Contact: Stephanie L. Bloom, FACHE, President
COO: Thomas Scott, Chief Operating Officer
CFO: Michael Richetti, Chief Financial Officer
CMO: Charles Ross, M.D., Vice President Medical Affairs
CIO: Karen S. Smith, Director Information Services
CHR: Julia McGovern, Vice President Human Resources
Web address: www.chiltonmemorial.org
Control: Other not–for–profit (including NFP Corporation) **Service:** General Medical and Surgical

Staffed Beds: 199 Admissions: 9494 Census: 128 Outpatient Visits: 125256 Births: 772 Total Expense ($000): 191466 Payroll Expense ($000): 87385 Personnel: 1131

RAHWAY—Union County

KINDRED HOSPITAL NEW JERSEY – RAHWAY See Kindred Hospital–New Jersey Morris County, Dover

☒ **ROBERT WOOD JOHNSON UNIVERSITY HOSPITAL RAHWAY (310024)**, 865 Stone Street, Zip 07065–2797; tel. 732/381–4200 **A**1 10 **F**3 11 15 17 20 29 30 31 34 35 38 40 46 47 49 50 53 56 57 59 64 65 68 70 74 75 77 78 79 81 82 86 87 93 97 100 101 102 107 108 111 117 118 119 129 130 132 134 143 144 146 147 148 **S** RWJBarnabas Health, West Orange, NJ
Primary Contact: Kirk C. Tice, President and Chief Executive Officer
CFO: Peter Bihuniak, Vice President Finance
CMO: Juan Baez, M.D., President Medical Staff
CIO: Denine Izzi, Senior Director Information Technology
CHR: Barbara M. Mullery, Vice President Administration
CNO: Ann Marie Shears, Vice President Patient Care Services
Web address: www.rwjuhr.com
Control: Other not–for–profit (including NFP Corporation) **Service:** General Medical and Surgical

Staffed Beds: 123 Admissions: 5454 Census: 75 Outpatient Visits: 71045 Births: 0 Total Expense ($000): 112283 Payroll Expense ($000): 44755 Personnel: 702

NJ

Many Facility Codes have changed. Please refer to the AHA Guide Code Chart.
© 2016 AHA Guide

RED BANK—Monmouth County

⊠ △ **RIVERVIEW MEDICAL CENTER (310034)**, 1 Riverview Plaza,
Zip 07701–1864; tel. 732/741–2700 **A**1 2 7 10 **F**3 5 11 13 15 18 20 22 28
29 30 31 32 34 35 36 37 38 39 40 41 43 44 45 46 47 49 50 51 54 55 56
57 58 59 60 61 63 64 65 66 68 70 71 73 74 75 76 77 78 79 80 81 82 84
85 86 87 90 91 92 93 94 96 97 98 99 100 101 102 103 104 105 107 108
110 111 114 115 116 117 118 119 120 121 123 124 126 130 131 132 134
135 144 146 147 148 **P**6 7 **S** Hackensack Meridian Health, Edison, NJ
Primary Contact: Timothy J. Hogan, FACHE, Regional President
COO: Kelly O'Brien, Chief Operating Officer
CFO: Joseph M. Lemaire, Executive Vice President Finance
CMO: Joseph Reichman, M.D., Vice President Medical Affairs and Clinical
Effectiveness
CIO: Rebecca Weber, Senior Vice President Information Technology
CHR: Sherrie String, Senior Vice President Human Resources
CNO: Kathy McKean, M.P.H., Vice President, Chief Nursing Executive
Web address: www.riverviewmedicalcenter.com
Control: Other not–for–profit (including NFP Corporation) **Service:** General
Medical and Surgical

Staffed Beds: 281 **Admissions:** 12752 **Census:** 183 **Outpatient Visits:**
135998 **Births:** 1384 **Total Expense ($000):** 240500 **Payroll Expense
($000):** 102156 **Personnel:** 1288

RIDGEWOOD—Bergen County

⊠ **VALLEY HOSPITAL (310012)**, 223 North Van Dien Avenue, Zip 07450–2726;
tel. 201/447–8000 **A**1 2 3 5 10 **F**3 8 11 12 13 15 17 18 19 20 22 24 26 27
28 29 30 31 32 34 35 36 37 38 40 41 44 45 46 47 48 49 50 51 52 53 54
55 56 57 58 59 60 61 64 65 66 68 69 70 71 72 73 74 75 76 77 78 79 80
81 82 84 85 86 87 88 89 91 92 93 94 96 97 99 100 101 102 103 107 108
109 110 111 112 114 115 116 117 118 119 120 121 123 124 126 129 130
131 132 134 135 141 143 145 146 147 148 **P**6
Primary Contact: Audrey Meyers, President and Chief Executive Officer
COO: Peter Diestel, Senior Vice President and Chief Operating Officer
CFO: Richard Keenan, Senior Vice President Finance and Chief Financial Officer
CMO: Joseph Yallowitz, M.D., Vice President Medical Affairs
CIO: Eric R. Carey, Vice President Information Systems and Chief Information
Officer
CHR: Jose Balderrama, Vice President Human Resources
CNO: Ann Marie Leichman, R.N., Vice President Patient Care Services and Chief
Nursing Officer
Web address: www.valleyhealth.com
Control: Other not–for–profit (including NFP Corporation) **Service:** General
Medical and Surgical

Staffed Beds: 446 **Admissions:** 28244 **Census:** 307 **Outpatient Visits:**
290548 **Births:** 3384 **Total Expense ($000):** 548699 **Payroll Expense
($000):** 234938 **Personnel:** 3095

ROCHELLE PARK—Bergen County

⊠ **SELECT SPECIALTY HOSPITAL–NORTHEAST NEW JERSEY (312019)**, 96
Parkway, Zip 07662–4200; tel. 201/221–2358, (Nonreporting) **A**1 10 **S** Select
Medical Corporation, Mechanicsburg, PA
Primary Contact: Barbara E. Hannan, MS, R.N., Chief Executive Officer
Web address: www.selectspecialtyhospitals.com/company/locations/
northeastnewjersey.aspx
Control: Corporation, Investor–owned, for–profit **Service:** Long–Term Acute Care
hospital

Staffed Beds: 62

SADDLE BROOK—Bergen County

KESSLER INSTITUTE FOR REHABILITATION See Kessler Institute for
Rehabilitation, West Orange

SALEM—Salem County

⊠ **MEMORIAL HOSPITAL OF SALEM COUNTY (310091)**, 310 Woodstown Road,
Zip 08079–2080; tel. 856/935–1000, (Nonreporting) **A**1 10 **S** Community Health
Systems, Inc., Franklin, TN
Primary Contact: Ryan Jensen, Chief Executive Officer
CFO: Donald Bevers, Chief Financial Officer
CIO: Brian McCarthy, Director Information Systems
CHR: Victoria A. Bates, Director Human Resources
CNO: Patricia A. Scherle, Chief Nursing Officer
Web address: www.salemhospitalnj.org
Control: Corporation, Investor–owned, for–profit **Service:** General Medical and
Surgical

Staffed Beds: 110

SECAUCUS—Hudson County

LIBERTYHEALTH–MEADOWLANDS HOSPITAL MEDICAL CENTER See
Meadowlands Hospital Medical Center

◇ **MEADOWLANDS HOSPITAL MEDICAL CENTER (310118)**, 55 Meadowlands
Parkway, Zip 07094–2977; tel. 201/392–3100, (Nonreporting) **A**10 12 13 21
Primary Contact: Felicia Karsos, R.N., President and Chief Executive Officer
COO: Lynn McVey, Chief Operating Officer
CMO: Michael Sciarra, M.D., Chief Medical Officer
CHR: Elizabeth Garrity, Director Human Resources
CNO: Felicia Karsos, R.N., Chief Nursing Officer
Web address: www.meadowlandshospital.org
Control: Partnership, Investor–owned, for–profit **Service:** General Medical and
Surgical

Staffed Beds: 230

SOMERS POINT—Atlantic County

☐ **SHORE MEDICAL CENTER (310047)**, 100 Medical Center Way, Zip 08244;
tel. 609/653–3500, (Nonreporting) **A**1 2 10
Primary Contact: Ronald W. Johnson, FACHE, President and Chief Executive
Officer
COO: Linda S. Kenwood, R.N., Chief Nursing Officer and Chief Operating Officer
CFO: James T. Foley, CPA, Vice President and Chief Financial Officer
CMO: Jeanne M. Rowe, M.D., Chief Medical Officer
CIO: Fred Banner, Chief Information Officer
CHR: Alan L. Beatty, Vice President Human Resources
CNO: Linda S. Kenwood, R.N., Chief Nursing Officer and Chief Operating Officer
Web address: www.shoremedicalcenter.org
Control: Other not–for–profit (including NFP Corporation) **Service:** General
Medical and Surgical

Staffed Beds: 198

SOMERVILLE—Somerset County

⊠ **ROBERT WOOD JOHNSON UNIVERSITY HOSPITAL SOMERSET (310048)**,
110 Rehill Avenue, Zip 08876–2598; tel. 908/685–2200 **A**1 2 3 5 10 **F**3 4 5 7
8 11 12 13 14 15 18 20 22 26 28 29 30 31 34 35 38 40 44 45 46 47 48 49
50 51 52 56 57 58 59 60 61 62 63 64 65 66 68 70 71 73 74 75 76 77 78
79 81 82 83 84 85 86 87 91 92 93 94 97 98 99 100 101 102 103 104 105
107 108 110 111 114 115 116 117 118 119 120 121 123 124 126 129 130
131 132 134 135 143 144 146 147 148 **P**3 5 **S** RWJBarnabas Health, West
Orange, NJ
Primary Contact: Michael A. Antoniades, President and Chief Executive Officer
COO: Patrick Delaney, Administrative Director, Operations
CFO: Kenneth Wright, Chief Financial Officer
CMO: Salvatore Moffa, M.D., Vice President, Medical Affairs and Chief Medical
Officer
CIO: Jordan Ruch, Vice President and Chief Information Officer
CHR: Anastasia Jacobs, Chief Human Resources Officer
CNO: Lynn Kearney, Vice President, Nursing
Web address: www.rwjuh.edu
Control: Other not–for–profit (including NFP Corporation) **Service:** General
Medical and Surgical

Staffed Beds: 250 **Admissions:** 13333 **Census:** 181 **Outpatient Visits:**
186730 **Births:** 786 **Total Expense ($000):** 278481 **Payroll Expense
($000):** 109492 **Personnel:** 1738

STRATFORD—Camden County

KENNEDY UNIVERSITY HOSPITAL – STRATFORD See Kennedy Health System,
Cherry Hill

SUMMIT—Union County

⊠ **OVERLOOK MEDICAL CENTER (310051)**, 99 Beauvoir Avenue,
Zip 07901–3533; tel. 908/522–2000 **A**1 2 3 5 8 10 13 **F**3 5 6 7 8 9 11 12 13
14 15 17 18 19 20 22 28 29 30 31 32 34 35 36 37 38 39 40 41 42 44 45
46 47 48 49 50 51 52 53 54 55 56 57 58 59 60 61 62 63 64 65 66 68 69
70 71 72 74 75 76 77 78 79 81 82 83 84 85 86 87 89 91 92 93 94 95 96
97 98 99 100 101 102 103 104 105 107 108 110 111 113 114 115 116
117 118 119 120 121 123 124 126 129 130 131 132 134 135 143 144 145
146 147 148 **P**3 5 6 **S** Atlantic Health System, Morristown, NJ
Primary Contact: Alan R. Lieber, President
CFO: Kevin Lenahan, Vice President Finance and Chief Financial Officer
CMO: John R. Audett, M.D., Medical Director Clinical Affairs
CIO: Elizabeth Lindsay–Wood, Interim Chief Information Officer
CNO: Mary Patricia Sullivan, R.N., Chief Nursing Officer
Web address: www.atlantichealth.org/Overlook
Control: Other not–for–profit (including NFP Corporation) **Service:** General
Medical and Surgical

Staffed Beds: 320 **Admissions:** 22324 **Census:** 285 **Outpatient Visits:**
285442 **Births:** 2482 **Total Expense ($000):** 662059 **Payroll Expense
($000):** 302776 **Personnel:** 3618

NJ

Hospital, Medicare Provider Number, Address, Telephone, Approval, Facility, and Physician Codes, Health Care System

★ American Hospital Association (AHA) membership
☐ The Joint Commission accreditation
○ Healthcare Facilities Accreditation Program
◇ DNV Healthcare Inc. accreditation
⇑ Center for Improvement in Healthcare Quality Accreditation
△ Commission on Accreditation of Rehabilitation Facilities (CARF) accreditation

☐ **SUMMIT OAKS HOSPITAL (314001)**, 19 Prospect Street, Zip 07901–2530; tel. 908/522–7000, (Nonreporting) **A**1 10 **S** Universal Health Services, Inc., King of Prussia, PA
Primary Contact: Oana Radu, Chief Executive Officer
Web address: www.summitoakshospital.com/
Control: Corporation, Investor–owned, for–profit **Service:** Psychiatric

Staffed Beds: 90

SUSSEX—Sussex County

SAINT CLARE'S HEALTH CENTER AT SUSSEX See Saint Clare's Health System, Denville

TEANECK—Bergen County

HOLY NAME HOSPITAL See Holy Name Medical Center

✠ **HOLY NAME MEDICAL CENTER (310008)**, 718 Teaneck Road, Zip 07666–4281; tel. 201/833–3000 **A**1 2 5 10 **F**2 3 7 8 11 12 13 15 18 19 20 22 28 29 30 31 32 34 35 36 37 38 39 40 41 44 45 46 47 48 49 50 51 53 54 55 56 57 58 59 60 62 63 64 65 66 68 70 71 73 74 75 76 77 78 79 80 81 82 83 84 85 86 87 89 90 91 92 93 94 96 97 98 100 101 102 103 107 108 110 111 114 115 116 117 118 119 120 121 123 124 126 129 130 131 132 133 135 143 144 145 146 147 148 **P**3 4 6 7
Primary Contact: Michael Maron, President and Chief Executive Officer
CFO: Ryan Kennedy, Chief Financial Officer
CMO: Adam D. Jarrett, M.D., Executive Vice President and Chief Medical Officer
CIO: Michael Skvarenina, Assistant Vice President Information Systems
CHR: April Rodgers, Vice President, Human Resources
CNO: Sheryl A. Slonim, Executive Vice President and Chief Nursing Officer
Web address: www.holyname.org
Control: Other not–for–profit (including NFP Corporation) **Service:** General Medical and Surgical

Staffed Beds: 318 **Admissions:** 19711 **Census:** 223 **Outpatient Visits:** 326850 **Births:** 1302 **Total Expense ($000):** 318366 **Payroll Expense ($000):** 139677 **Personnel:** 2486

TINTON FALLS—Monmouth County

★ **HEALTHSOUTH REHABILITATION HOSPITAL OF TINTON FALLS (313035)**, 2 Centre Plaza, Zip 07724–9744; tel. 732/460–5320, (Nonreporting) **A**10 **S** HEALTHSOUTH Corporation, Birmingham, AL
Primary Contact: Suji Thomas, RN, MSN, Chief Executive Officer
CFO: Lynne Traister, Controller
CMO: Todd Cooperman, M.D., Medical Director
CHR: Anita Saum, Director Human Resources
Web address: www.rehabnj.com
Control: Corporation, Investor–owned, for–profit **Service:** Rehabilitation

Staffed Beds: 60

TOMS RIVER—Ocean County

✠ **BARNABAS HEALTH BEHAVIORAL HEALTH CENTER (314022)**, 1691 Highway 9, Zip 08754; tel. 732/914–1688, (Nonreporting) **A**1 10 **S** RWJBarnabas Health, West Orange, NJ
Primary Contact: Deanna Sperling, President and Chief Executive Officer
Web address: www.barnabashealth.org/hospitals/psychiatric/index.html
Control: Other not–for–profit (including NFP Corporation) **Service:** Psychiatric

Staffed Beds: 40

✠ **COMMUNITY MEDICAL CENTER (310041)**, 99 Route 37 West, Zip 08755–6423; tel. 732/557–8000 **A**1 2 3 10 **F**3 11 13 15 18 20 22 28 29 30 31 32 34 35 36 38 40 41 43 44 46 47 48 49 50 54 55 56 57 58 59 60 61 62 63 64 68 69 70 73 74 75 76 77 78 79 81 82 84 85 86 87 89 92 93 96 100 107 108 109 110 111 114 115 118 119 120 121 123 124 126 129 130 131 132 133 134 143 146 147 148 **S** RWJBarnabas Health, West Orange, NJ
Primary Contact: Michael Mimoso, FACHE, President and Chief Executive Officer
CFO: Thomas Percello, Chief Financial Officer
CMO: Yeshavanth Nayak, M.D., Interim Chief Medical Officer
CIO: Shaun Fitzsimmons, Director Information Technology Services
CHR: Vanessa Smith, Chief Human Resources Officer
CNO: Jane O'Rourke, Vice President, Patient Care Services and Chief Nursing Officer
Web address: www.barnabashealth.org/hospitals/community_medical/index.html
Control: Other not–for–profit (including NFP Corporation) **Service:** General Medical and Surgical

Staffed Beds: 357 **Admissions:** 22836 **Census:** 303 **Outpatient Visits:** 273654 **Births:** 2357 **Total Expense ($000):** 304428 **Payroll Expense ($000):** 129067 **Personnel:** 1806

✠ **HEALTHSOUTH REHABILITATION HOSPITAL OF TOMS RIVER (313029)**, 14 Hospital Drive, Zip 08755–6470; tel. 732/244–3100, (Nonreporting) **A**1 10 **S** HEALTHSOUTH Corporation, Birmingham, AL
Primary Contact: Patricia Ostaszewski, MS, Chief Executive Officer
COO: Patricia Ostaszewski, MS, Chief Executive Officer
CFO: Janet Turso, Controller
CMO: Carol Sonatore, D.O., Medical Director
CIO: Coleen Rossi, Director Quality Services
CHR: Lori Munyan, Director, Human Resources
CNO: Susan Castor, Chief Nursing Officer
Web address: www.rehabnjtomsriver.com/
Control: Corporation, Investor–owned, for–profit **Service:** Rehabilitation

Staffed Beds: 92

SAINT BARNABAS BEHAVIORAL HEALTH CENTER See Barnabas Health Behavioral Health Center

TRENTON—Mercer County

✠ **CAPITAL HEALTH REGIONAL MEDICAL CENTER (310092)**, 750 Brunswick Avenue, Zip 08638–4143; tel. 609/394–6000 **A**1 3 5 10 **F**3 11 15 18 29 30 34 35 40 43 44 45 46 47 48 50 54 57 58 59 60 61 64 65 66 68 70 74 75 77 78 79 81 82 84 85 87 89 93 96 97 98 100 101 102 107 109 111 112 114 115 118 119 129 130 132 135 143 145 146 148 **P**6 **S** Capital Health, Trenton, NJ
Primary Contact: Al Maghazehe, Ph.D., FACHE, President and Chief Executive Officer
CFO: Shane Fleming, Chief Financial Officer
CMO: Eugene McMahon, Senior Vice President and Chief Medical Officer
CIO: Eugene Grochala, Vice President Information Systems
CHR: Scott Clemmensen, Vice President Human Resources and Leadership Enhancement
CNO: Eileen M. Horton, Senior Vice President, Administration
Web address: www.capitalhealth.org
Control: Other not–for–profit (including NFP Corporation) **Service:** General Medical and Surgical

Staffed Beds: 204 **Admissions:** 8915 **Census:** 149 **Outpatient Visits:** 153482 **Births:** 9 **Personnel:** 1425

✠ **ST. FRANCIS MEDICAL CENTER (310021)**, 601 Hamilton Avenue, Zip 08629–1986; tel. 609/599–5000 **A**1 3 10 **F**2 3 11 12 15 17 18 20 22 29 30 31 35 40 45 46 48 49 50 56 57 58 59 60 61 64 65 66 69 70 71 74 75 78 79 81 82 85 86 87 92 93 97 98 99 100 101 102 103 104 105 107 108 110 111 114 115 118 119 121 123 124 126 129 130 132 135 143 144 146 147 148 **P**5 6 **S** Trinity Health, Livonia, MI
Primary Contact: Vincent Costantino, Chief Administrative Officer
CFO: Mark Kelly, Vice President Finance
CMO: C. James Romano, M.D., Chief Medical Officer
CIO: Richard Dowgun, Chief Information Officer
CHR: Laura James, Director Human Resources
CNO: Mary Anne Suttles, Chief Nursing Officer
Web address: www.stfrancismedical.com
Control: Church–operated, Nongovernment, not–for profit **Service:** General Medical and Surgical

Staffed Beds: 142 **Admissions:** 4777 **Census:** 67

☐ **TRENTON PSYCHIATRIC HOSPITAL (314013)**, Route 29 and Sullivan Way, Zip 08628–3425, Mailing Address: P.O. Box 7500, West Trenton, Zip 08628–0500; tel. 609/633–1500, (Nonreporting) **A**1 3 10 **S** Division of Mental Health and Addiction Services, Department of Human Services, State of New Jersey, Trenton, NJ
Primary Contact: Teresa A. McQuaide, Chief Executive Officer
COO: Christopher Morrison, Deputy Chief Executive Officer
CFO: Joseph Canale, Business Manager
CMO: Lawrence Rossi, M.D., Clinical Director
CIO: Scott Eustace, Director Health Information Technology
CHR: Marybeth Longo, Manager Human Resources
CNO: Colleen Birkhofer, Chief Nursing Officer
Web address: www.state.nj.us/humanservices/dmhs/oshm/tph/
Control: State–Government, nonfederal **Service:** Psychiatric

Staffed Beds: 431

TURNERSVILLE—Camden County

KENNEDY UNIVERSITY HOSPITAL – WASHINGTON TOWNSHIP See Kennedy Health System, Cherry Hill

VINELAND—Cumberland County

✠ **HEALTHSOUTH REHABILITATION HOSPITAL OF VINELAND (313036)**, 1237 West Sherman Avenue, Zip 08360–6920; tel. 856/696–7100 **A**1 10 **F**29 30 59 90 103 130 132 148 **S** HEALTHSOUTH Corporation, Birmingham, AL
Primary Contact: Tammy Feuer, Chief Executive Officer
CMO: Eugenio Rocksmith, M.D., Medical Director
CHR: Dawn Pearson, Director Human Resources
Web address: www.healthsouthvineland.com
Control: Corporation, Investor–owned, for–profit **Service:** Rehabilitation

Staffed Beds: 41 **Admissions:** 969 **Census:** 35 **Outpatient Visits:** 0 **Births:** 0 **Total Expense ($000):** 12113 **Payroll Expense ($000):** 7444 **Personnel:** 127

Many Facility Codes have changed. Please refer to the AHA Guide Code Chart. © 2016 AHA Guide

NJ

★ ◇ **INSPIRA MEDICAL CENTER–VINELAND (310032)**, 1505 West Sherman Avenue, Zip 08360–6912; tel. 856/641–8000, (Includes BRIDGETON HEALTH CENTER, 333 Irving Avenue, Bridgeton, Zip 08302–2100; tel. 856/575–4500) **A**2 3 10 12 13 21 **F**3 8 11 12 13 15 17 18 20 28 29 30 34 35 37 38 40 41 42 44 49 50 54 57 59 60 64 68 70 72 73 74 75 76 77 78 79 81 82 85 86 87 89 93 98 99 100 101 102 103 104 105 107 108 110 111 114 115 118 119 120 121 123 126 130 131 132 134 144 146 147 148 **P**8 **S** Inspira Health Network, Mullica Hill, NJ
Primary Contact: John A. DiAngelo, President and Chief Executive Officer
COO: Elizabeth Sheridan, Chief Operating Officer and Chief Nursing Executive
CFO: Thomas Baldosaro, Chief Financial Officer
CMO: Steven C. Linn, M.D., Chief Medical Officer
CIO: Thomas Pacek, Vice President Information Systems and Chief Information Officer
CHR: Erich Florentine, Chief People Officer
CNO: Elizabeth Sheridan, Chief Operating Officer and Chief Nursing Executive
Web address: www.inspirahealthnetwork.org/?id=5280&sid=1
Control: Other not–for–profit (including NFP Corporation) **Service:** General Medical and Surgical

Staffed Beds: 335 Admissions: 17800 **Census:** 227 **Outpatient Visits:** 272577 **Births:** 1920 **Total Expense ($000):** 339517 **Payroll Expense ($000):** 140172 **Personnel:** 1504

VOORHEES—Camden County

✠ **VIRTUA VOORHEES (310022)**, 100 Bowman Drive, Zip 08043–9612; tel. 856/325–3000, (Includes VOORHEES PEDIATRIC FACILITY, 1304 Laurel Oak Road, Zip 08043–4310; tel. 888/873–5437) **A**1 3 5 10 **F**3 11 13 29 30 31 34 35 40 41 45 46 48 49 50 55 58 59 64 66 68 70 72 73 74 75 76 78 79 81 82 86 87 88 89 90 92 93 107 108 111 115 116 117 119 126 129 130 143 145 146 147 **S** Virtua Health, Marlton, NJ
Primary Contact: Matthew Zuino, Senior Vice President Hospital Services
COO: Michael S. Kotzen, Vice President and Chief Operating Officer
CFO: Robert Rosvold, Director Finance
CMO: James P. Dwyer, D.O., Executive Vice President and Chief Medical Officer
CIO: Alfred Campanella, Chief Information Officer
Web address: www.virtua.org
Control: Other not–for–profit (including NFP Corporation) **Service:** General Medical and Surgical

Staffed Beds: 398 Admissions: 24544 **Census:** 294 **Outpatient Visits:** 284304 **Births:** 4609 **Total Expense ($000):** 510918 **Payroll Expense ($000):** 152228 **Personnel:** 1990

WAYNE—Passaic County

KINDRED HOSPITAL NEW JERSEY – WAYNE See Kindred Hospital–New Jersey Morris County, Dover

WEST ORANGE—Essex County

✠ △ **KESSLER INSTITUTE FOR REHABILITATION (313025)**, 1199 Pleasant Valley Way, Zip 07052–1424; tel. 973/731–3600, (Includes KESSLER INSTITUTE FOR REHABILITATION, 201 Pleasant Hill Road, Chester, Zip 07930–2141; tel. 973/252–6300; Sue Kida, Chief Executive Officer; KESSLER INSTITUTE FOR REHABILITATION, 300 Market Street, Saddle Brook, Zip 07663–5309; tel. 201/368–6000; Philip J. Driscoll, Jr., Chief Executive Officer; KESSLER INSTITUTE FOR REHABILITATION, 1199 Pleasant Valley Way, tel. 973/731–3600; Bonnie Evans, Chief Executive Officer; (Nonreporting) **A**1 3 5 7 10 **S** Select Medical Corporation, Mechanicsburg, PA
Primary Contact: Sue Kida, President
CMO: Bruce M. Gans, M.D., Executive Vice President and Chief Medical Officer
CHR: Ken Caldera, Director Human Resources
Web address: www.kessler–rehab.com
Control: Corporation, Investor–owned, for–profit **Service:** Rehabilitation

Staffed Beds: 336

KESSLER INSTITUTE FOR REHABILITATION See Kessler Institute for Rehabilitation

WESTAMPTON—Burlington County

☐ **HAMPTON BEHAVIORAL HEALTH CENTER (314021)**, 650 Rancocas Road, Zip 08060–5613; tel. 609/267–7000, (Nonreporting) **A**1 10 **S** Universal Health Services, Inc., King of Prussia, PA
Primary Contact: Craig Hilton, Chief Executive Officer
COO: Joanne Wijaya, Chief Operating Officer
CMO: Charles Trigiani, D.O., Medical Director
CHR: Lori DeCelis, Director Human Resources
CNO: Kathleena Cohen, R.N., Director of Nursing
Web address: www.hamptonhospital.com
Control: Corporation, Investor–owned, for–profit **Service:** Psychiatric

Staffed Beds: 110

WESTWOOD—Bergen County

✠ **HACKENSACK UNIVERSITY MEDICAL CENTER AT PASCACK VALLEY (310130)**, 250 Old Hook Road, Zip 07675–3123; tel. 201/383–1035 **A**1 **F**3 12 13 15 18 20 28 29 30 34 35 40 44 45 46 47 49 50 51 57 59 60 64 68 70 72 74 76 77 78 79 81 82 85 87 93 107 108 110 111 115 119 129 130 135 146 147 148 **S** LHP Hospital Group, Plano, TX
Primary Contact: Emily L. Holliman, Chief Executive Officer
COO: Colleen Smorra, Assistant Administrator
CFO: Jason Pritchard, Chief Financial Officer
CMO: George Lin, M.D., Physician Advisor
CIO: Anthony Teri, Director Information Technology
CHR: Theodora Carter, Administrative Director Human Resources
CNO: Susan Giordano, R.N., Chief Nursing Officer
Web address: www.hackensackumcpv.com/
Control: Partnership, Investor–owned, for–profit **Service:** General Medical and Surgical

Staffed Beds: 128 Admissions: 3994 **Census:** 45 **Outpatient Visits:** 22363 **Births:** 632 **Total Expense ($000):** 91195 **Payroll Expense ($000):** 30290 **Personnel:** 478

WILLINGBORO—Burlington County

✠ **LOURDES MEDICAL CENTER OF BURLINGTON COUNTY (310061)**, 218–A Sunset Road, Zip 08046–1162; tel. 609/835–2900 **A**1 2 10 **F**3 7 11 12 15 17 18 29 30 31 34 35 36 38 40 42 44 45 46 47 49 50 55 56 57 59 60 61 64 66 68 70 74 75 78 79 81 82 85 86 87 93 98 100 107 108 109 110 111 114 118 119 129 130 132 135 146 147 148 **P**8 **S** Trinity Health, Livonia, MI
Primary Contact: Mark Nessel, Executive Vice President and Chief Operating Officer
CFO: Michael Hammond, Chief Financial Officer
CMO: Alan R. Pope, M.D., Vice President, Medical Affairs
CIO: Mike Elfert, Director Information Services
CNO: Audrey Jadczak, R.N., Vice President/Chief Nursing Officer
Web address: www.lourdesnet.org
Control: Other not–for–profit (including NFP Corporation) **Service:** General Medical and Surgical

Staffed Beds: 169 Admissions: 5848 **Census:** 83 **Outpatient Visits:** 123612 **Births:** 0 **Total Expense ($000):** 113771 **Payroll Expense ($000):** 43449 **Personnel:** 535

✠ **LOURDES SPECIALTY HOSPITAL OF SOUTHERN NEW JERSEY (312022)**, 220 Sunset Road, Zip 08046–1110; tel. 609/835–3650 **A**1 10 **F**1 3 29 60 75 77 85 87 91 100 107 111 119 130 132 148 **S** AcuityHealthcare, LP, Charlotte, NC
Primary Contact: Cheri Cowperthwait, R.N., Chief Executive Officer
CFO: James Weinstein, Chief Financial Officer
CHR: Lisa M. Sinnott, Director Human Resources
CNO: Kim Fetterolf, R.N., Chief Clinical Officer
Web address: www.lshnj.com
Control: Corporation, Investor–owned, for–profit **Service:** Long–Term Acute Care hospital

Staffed Beds: 53 Admissions: 533 **Census:** 46 **Outpatient Visits:** 0 **Births:** 0 **Total Expense ($000):** 31879 **Payroll Expense ($000):** 14266 **Personnel:** 199

WOODBURY—Gloucester County

★ ◇ **INSPIRA MEDICAL CENTER–WOODBURY (310081)**, 509 North Broad Street, Zip 08096–1697; tel. 856/845–0100 **A**3 5 10 21 **F**3 5 11 13 15 17 18 20 22 26 28 29 30 31 34 35 38 40 41 45 46 47 48 49 50 56 57 58 59 62 64 66 67 70 73 74 75 77 78 79 80 81 85 86 87 91 92 93 96 97 98 99 100 101 102 104 105 107 110 111 119 129 130 131 132 133 135 144 146 147 148 **P**4 6 7 **S** Inspira Health Network, Mullica Hill, NJ
Primary Contact: John A. DiAngelo, President and Chief Executive Officer
COO: Patrick B. Nolan, Chief Operating Officer
CIO: Robert Mizia, Director Information Systems and Chief Information Officer
CHR: Robert Manestrina, Vice President Human Resources
CNO: Gina Mumolie, Senior Vice President and Chief Nurse Executive
Web address: www.inspirahealthnetwork.org/?id=5282&sid=1
Control: Other not–for–profit (including NFP Corporation) **Service:** General Medical and Surgical

Staffed Beds: 261 Admissions: 9597 **Census:** 121 **Outpatient Visits:** 130976 **Births:** 999 **Total Expense ($000):** 178605 **Payroll Expense ($000):** 81380 **Personnel:** 1039

NJ

✠ **CHRISTIAN HEALTH CARE CENTER (314019)**, 301 Sicomac Avenue,
Zip 07481–2194; tel. 201/848–5200, (Total facility includes 254 beds in nursing
home–type unit) **A**1 10 **F**2 6 10 29 30 34 35 50 56 57 59 63 64 69 83 86 87
90 96 98 99 101 103 104 105 125 128 130 132 143 146 148 **P**6
Primary Contact: Douglas A. Struyk, President and Chief Executive Officer
COO: Steve Dumke, FACHE, Executive Vice President and Chief Operating Officer
CFO: Kevin Stagg, Executive Vice President Finance and Chief Financial Officer
CMO: Howard Gilman, M.D., Medical Executive
CIO: Jennifer D'Angelo, Vice President Information Services
CHR: Bob Zierold, Senior Vice President Human Resources
CNO: Marianne Guerriero, Nurse Executive
Web address: www.chccnj.org
Control: Other not–for–profit (including NFP Corporation) **Service:** Psychiatric

Staffed Beds: 530 **Admissions:** 2025 **Census:** 499 **Outpatient Visits:** 55446
Births: 0 **Total Expense ($000):** 75387 **Payroll Expense ($000):** 43826
Personnel: 722

NJ

NEW MEXICO

ACOMA— County

☐ **ACOMA–CANONCITO–LAGUNA HOSPITAL (320070)**, 80B Veterans Boulevard, Zip 87034, Mailing Address: P.O. Box 130, San Fidel, Zip 87049–0130; tel. 505/552–5300, (Nonreporting) **A**1 10 **S** U. S. Indian Health Service, Rockville, MD
Primary Contact: William Thorne, Jr., Chief Executive Officer
Web address: www.ihs.gov/albuquerque/index.cfm?module=dsp_abq_acoma_
canoncito_laguna
Control: PHS, Indian Service, Government, federal **Service:** General Medical and Surgical

Staffed Beds: 25

ALAMOGORDO—Otero County

★ ◇ **GERALD CHAMPION REGIONAL MEDICAL CENTER (320004)**, 2669 North Scenic Drive, Zip 88310–8799; tel. 575/439–6100 **A**3 10 13 20 21 **F**3 8 11 12 13 18 29 30 31 34 35 38 40 43 44 45 50 51 56 57 58 59 60 64 70 74 75 76 77 78 79 81 82 85 86 87 90 92 96 97 98 100 101 102 103 104 107 108 111 114 115 119 129 130 131 132 145 146 147 148 **P**8
Primary Contact: Robert J. Heckert, Jr., Chief Executive Officer
CFO: Morgan Hay, Chief Financial Officer
CMO: Arthur Austin, M.D., Vice President Medical Affairs
CIO: Ana Castro, Director Information Services and Clinical Information Services
CHR: Karen O'Brien, Director Human Resources
CNO: Catherine A. Rhyne, M.P.H., Chief Nursing Officer
Web address: www.gcrmc.org
Control: Other not–for–profit (including NFP Corporation) **Service:** General Medical and Surgical

Staffed Beds: 99 **Admissions:** 4092 **Census:** 50 **Outpatient Visits:** 98591 **Births:** 519 **Total Expense ($000):** 109418 **Payroll Expense ($000):** 38562 **Personnel:** 707

ALBUQUERQUE—Bernalillo County

☐ **AMG SPECIALTY HOSPITAL–ALBUQUERQUE (322003)**, 235 Elm Street N.E., Zip 87102–3672; tel. 505/842–5550, (Nonreporting) **A**1 10 **S** AMG Integrated Healthcare Management, Lafayette, LA
Primary Contact: Susan Morgan, Chief Clinical Officer
CFO: Julie Lenzo, Director Business Office
CMO: Jeffrey Ross, M.D., Medical Director
CHR: Robin Stendel–Freels, Coordinator Human Resources
Web address: www.amgalbuquerque.com/
Control: Partnership, Investor–owned, for–profit **Service:** Long–Term Acute Care hospital

Staffed Beds: 24

☐ **HAVEN BEHAVIORAL SENIOR CARE OF ALBUQUERQUE (324013)**, 5400 Gibson Boulevard S.E., 4th Floor, Zip 87108–4729; tel. 505/254–4500, (Nonreporting) **A**1 10
Primary Contact: Sheila McDermott–Lord, Chief Executive Officer
Web address: www.https://albuquerque.havenbehavioral.com/
Control: Corporation, Investor–owned, for–profit **Service:** Psychiatric

Staffed Beds: 32

⊠ **HEALTHSOUTH REHABILITATION HOSPITAL (323027)**, 7000 Jefferson Street N.E., Zip 87109–4313; tel. 505/344–9478 **A**1 10 **F**28 29 34 35 56 57 59 60 62 64 74 75 77 79 90 91 93 94 95 96 130 132 143 148 **S** HEALTHSOUTH Corporation, Birmingham, AL
Primary Contact: David S. Nevill, Chief Executive Officer
CFO: Byron Aten, Controller
CMO: Angela Walker, M.D., Medical Director
CHR: Kristen Hernandez, Director Human Resources
CNO: Veronica Gadomski, R.N., Chief Nursing Officer
Web address: www.healthsouthnewmexico.com
Control: Corporation, Investor–owned, for–profit **Service:** Rehabilitation

Staffed Beds: 87 **Admissions:** 1652 **Census:** 59 **Outpatient Visits:** 8377 **Total Expense ($000):** 21665 **Payroll Expense ($000):** 11816 **Personnel:** 195

⊠ **KINDRED HOSPITAL–ALBUQUERQUE (322002)**, 700 High Street N.E., Zip 87102–2565; tel. 505/242–4444 **A**1 10 **F**1 3 16 29 30 67 70 75 80 90 91 98 107 130 135 148 **S** Kindred Healthcare, Louisville, KY
Primary Contact: Bud Schawl, Chief Executive Officer
CFO: Margaret Wantland, Chief Financial Officer
CMO: Jeffrey Dorf, M.D., Medical Director
CHR: Donald Whitney, Director Human Resources
CNO: Gary Gum, R.N., Chief Nursing Officer
Web address: www.kindredalbuquerque.com/
Control: Corporation, Investor–owned, for–profit **Service:** General Medical and Surgical

Staffed Beds: 61 **Admissions:** 482 **Census:** 45 **Births:** 0

★ ◇ **LOVELACE MEDICAL CENTER (320009)**, 601 Martin Luther King Avenue N.E., Zip 87102–3619; tel. 505/727–8000, (Includes HEART HOSPITAL OF NEW MEXICO, 504 Elm Street, Zip 87102; tel. 505/724–2000; Ronald C. Winger, President), (Nonreporting) **A**3 5 10 21 **S** Ardent Health Services, Nashville, TN
Primary Contact: Troy Greer, Chief Executive Officer
CHR: Helen V. Nielsen, Director Human Resources
CNO: Laurie S. Bigham, R.N., Chief Nursing Officer
Web address: www.lovelace.com/albuquerque–hospital/lovelace–medical–center#.
UDZ1laDhf48
Control: Corporation, Investor–owned, for–profit **Service:** General Medical and Surgical

Staffed Beds: 263

★ △ **LOVELACE REHABILITATION HOSPITAL (323028)**, 505 Elm Street N.E., Zip 87102–2500; tel. 505/727–4700 **A**3 5 7 10 **F**3 29 30 90 143 148 **S** Ardent Health Services, Nashville, TN
Primary Contact: Derrick Jones, Chief Executive Officer
CFO: Andrea Solin, Chief Financial Officer
CHR: Helen V. Nielsen, Director Human Resources
CNO: Cynthia Rankin, Chief Nursing Officer
Web address: www.lovelace.com
Control: Corporation, Investor–owned, for–profit **Service:** Rehabilitation

Staffed Beds: 62 **Admissions:** 971 **Census:** 37 **Births:** 0

★ ◇ **LOVELACE WESTSIDE HOSPITAL (320074)**, 10501 Golf Course Road N.W., Zip 87114–5000, Mailing Address: P.O. Box 25555, Zip 87125–0555; tel. 505/727–8000 **A**3 5 10 21 **F**3 12 13 15 29 30 34 39 40 41 49 51 57 59 68 70 75 76 79 81 85 93 107 110 111 115 119 130 133 135 146 148 **S** Ardent Health Services, Nashville, TN
Primary Contact: Farron Sneed, FACHE, Chief Executive Officer
COO: Nancye Cole, R.N., Chief Operating Officer
CFO: Andrea Solin, Chief Financial Officer
CNO: Nancye Cole, R.N., Chief Nursing Officer and Chief Operating Officer
Web address: www.lovelace.com/albuquerque–hospital/lovelace–westside–
hospital#.UDZ1t6Dhf48
Control: Corporation, Investor–owned, for–profit **Service:** General Medical and Surgical

Staffed Beds: 80 **Admissions:** 2629 **Census:** 22 **Outpatient Visits:** 30989 **Births:** 328 **Total Expense ($000):** 49252 **Payroll Expense ($000):** 18315 **Personnel:** 288

★ ◇ **LOVELACE WOMEN'S HOSPITAL (320017)**, 4701 Montgomery Boulevard N.E., Zip 87109–1251, Mailing Address: P.O. Box 25555, Zip 87125–0555; tel. 505/727–7800 **A**3 5 10 21 **F**8 11 13 15 29 34 35 40 43 46 49 57 59 64 70 72 73 76 78 79 81 85 89 91 93 107 108 110 111 114 115 116 117 119 126 130 132 146 147 **S** Ardent Health Services, Nashville, TN
Primary Contact: Sheri Milone, Chief Executive Officer and Administrator
COO: Janelle Raborn, Chief Operating Officer
CFO: Joseph Sereno, Chief Financial Officer
CHR: Carol Shelton, Director Human Resources
Web address: www.lovelace.com/albuquerque–hospital/lovelace–womens–
hospital#.UDZ17KDhf48
Control: Corporation, Investor–owned, for–profit **Service:** General Medical and Surgical

Staffed Beds: 78 **Admissions:** 9359 **Census:** 89

NM

Hospital, Medicare Provider Number, Address, Telephone, Approval, Facility, and Physician Codes, Health Care System

★ American Hospital Association (AHA) membership ○ Healthcare Facilities Accreditation Program ⇑ Center for Improvement in Healthcare Quality Accreditation
☐ The Joint Commission accreditation ◇ DNV Healthcare Inc. accreditation △ Commission on Accreditation of Rehabilitation Facilities (CARF) accreditation

✠ △ **NEW MEXICO VETERANS AFFAIRS HEALTH CARE SYSTEM – RAYMOND G. MURPHY MEDICAL CENTER**, 1501 San Pedro S.E., Zip 87108–5153; tel. 505/265–1711 **A**1 2 3 5 7 8 **F**3 4 5 8 12 15 17 18 20 22 24 26 28 29 30 31 34 35 38 39 40 44 45 46 47 48 49 50 54 56 57 58 59 60 61 62 63 65 68 70 74 75 77 78 79 80 81 82 83 84 85 86 87 90 91 92 93 94 96 97 98 100 101 102 103 104 105 106 107 110 111 112 113 119 126 127 129 130 132 135 143 144 146 147 148 **S** Department of Veterans Affairs, Washington, DC
Primary Contact: Andrew Welch, Director
CFO: Michael McNeill, Chief Financial Management
CMO: Meghan Gerety, M.D., Chief of Staff
CIO: Ronald Ferrell, Chief Information Officer
CHR: Melvin Hooker, Chief Human Resources
Web address: www.albuquerque.va.gov/
Control: Veterans Affairs, Government, federal **Service:** General Medical and Surgical

Staffed Beds: 203 **Admissions:** 5460 **Census:** 58 **Outpatient Visits:** 680063 **Births:** 0

✠ **PRESBYTERIAN HOSPITAL (320021)**, 1100 Central Avenue S.E., Zip 87106–4934, Mailing Address: P.O. Box 26666, Zip 87125–6666; tel. 505/841–1234, (Includes PRESBYTERIAN KASEMAN HOSPITAL, 8300 Constitution Avenue N.E., Zip 87110–7624, Mailing Address: P.O. Box 26666, Zip 87125–6666; tel. 505/291–2000; Doyle Boykin, R.N., MSN, Administrator; PRESBYTERIAN RUST MEDICAL CENTER, 2400 Unser Boulevard S.E., Rio Rancho, Zip 87124–4740; tel. 505/253–7878; Jeff McBee, Administrator) **A**1 2 3 5 10 **F**3 7 8 11 12 13 14 15 17 18 19 20 21 22 23 24 25 26 27 29 30 31 35 38 40 44 45 46 47 48 49 50 51 54 56 57 59 60 62 63 64 65 67 68 70 72 74 75 76 77 78 79 81 82 83 84 85 86 87 88 89 91 92 93 96 97 98 99 100 101 102 103 104 105 107 108 110 111 113 114 115 117 118 119 120 121 123 124 126 128 129 130 131 132 133 134 138 142 144 145 146 147 148 **P**6 **S** Presbyterian Healthcare Services, Albuquerque, NM
Primary Contact: Sandra C. Podley, Administrator
COO: Paul Briggs, Executive Vice President and Chief Operating Officer
CFO: Dale Maxwell, Executive Vice President and Chief Financial Officer
CMO: Jayne McCormick, M.D., Chief Medical Officer CDS
CIO: Lee Marley, VP/Information Services Chief Application Officer
CHR: Lee Patchell, Lead Human Resources Business Partner
CNO: Ann L. Wright, R.N., Assistant Central Delivery System CNO
Web address: www.phs.org
Control: Other not–for–profit (including NFP Corporation) **Service:** General Medical and Surgical

Staffed Beds: 638 **Admissions:** 39276 **Census:** 542 **Outpatient Visits:** 1974800 **Births:** 4798 **Total Expense ($000):** 1098819 **Payroll Expense ($000):** 456297 **Personnel:** 6044

TURQUOISE LODGE HOSPITAL, 5901 Zuni Road S.E., Zip 87108–3073; tel. 505/841–8978 **F**4 5 **P**6
Primary Contact: Shauna Hartley, Administrator
CFO: Juliette Aragon, Finance Director
CIO: Eric Gurule, Chief Information Officer
CHR: Mario Lechuga, Director Human Resources
CNO: Debra Jane Green, R.N., Director of Nursing
Web address: www.health.state.nm.us
Control: State–Government, nonfederal **Service:** Alcoholism and other chemical dependency

Staffed Beds: 52 **Admissions:** 771 **Census:** 39 **Outpatient Visits:** 0 **Births:** 0

✠ **UNIVERSITY OF NEW MEXICO HOSPITALS (320001)**, 2211 Lomas Boulevard N.E., Zip 87106–2745; tel. 505/272–2111, (Includes CARRIE TINGLEY HOSPITAL, 1127 University Boulevard N.E., Zip 87102–1715; tel. 505/272–5200; Crystal E. Frantz, MSN, R.N., Executive Director; MENTAL HEALTH CENTER, 2600 Marble N.E., Zip 87131–2600; tel. 505/272–2800; UNIVERSITY OF NEW MEXICO CHILDREN'S PSYCHIATRIC HOSPITAL, 1001 Yale Boulevard N.E., Zip 87131–3830; tel. 505/272–2890; UNM CHILDREN'S HOSPITAL, 2211 Lomas Boulevard, N.E., tel. 505/272–2111) **A**1 2 3 5 8 10 **F**3 8 9 11 13 15 16 18 19 20 21 23 24 25 26 27 29 30 31 33 34 35 38 40 41 43 44 45 46 47 48 49 50 51 54 56 57 59 60 61 63 64 65 68 70 72 73 74 75 76 77 78 79 81 82 83 84 85 86 87 88 89 90 92 93 94 95 96 97 107 108 109 110 111 114 115 116 117 118 119 121 123 126 129 130 131 132 135 136 138 144 146 147 148 **S** University of New Mexico Hospitals, Albuquerque, NM
Primary Contact: Stephen W. McKernan, Chief Executive Officer
COO: Paul F. Herzog, Chief Operating Officer
CFO: Ella Watt, Chief Financial Officer
CMO: Robert Katz, M.D., Vice President Clinical Affairs
CIO: Ron Margolis, Chief Information Officer
CHR: Jim Pendergast, Administrator Human Resources
Web address: www.unm.edu
Control: State–Government, nonfederal **Service:** General Medical and Surgical

Staffed Beds: 537 **Admissions:** 25504 **Census:** 426 **Outpatient Visits:** 637355 **Births:** 2979 **Total Expense ($000):** 991424 **Payroll Expense ($000):** 341532 **Personnel:** 5908

☐ **UNM SANDOVAL REGIONAL MEDICAL CENTER (320089)**, MSC09 5300 1 University of New Mexico, Zip 87131, Mailing Address: 3001 Broadmoor Boulevard N.E., Rio Rancho, Zip 87144–2100; tel. 505/994–7000 **A**1 3 5 10 **F**3 7 15 29 30 35 40 43 45 46 47 48 49 50 70 79 80 81 85 86 87 93 97 98 103 107 108 110 111 114 115 119 126 129 130 143 146 147 **P**8 **S** University of New Mexico Hospitals, Albuquerque, NM
Primary Contact: Jamie A. Silva-Steele, R.N., President and Chief Executive Officer
CFO: Darlene Fernandez, Chief Financial Officer
CMO: J. Anthony Ogburn, M.D., Chief Medical Officer
CIO: Matthew Braun, Executive Director Information Systems
CHR: Correen Bales, Executive Director Human Resources
CNO: Pamela Demarest, R.N., Chief Nursing Officer
Web address: www.hospitals.unm.edu/
Control: Other not–for–profit (including NFP Corporation) **Service:** General Medical and Surgical

Staffed Beds: 72 **Admissions:** 3292 **Census:** 42 **Outpatient Visits:** 50205 **Births:** 0 **Total Expense ($000):** 86805 **Payroll Expense ($000):** 29004 **Personnel:** 457

ARTESIA—Eddy County

★ **ARTESIA GENERAL HOSPITAL (320030)**, 702 North 13th Street, Zip 88210–1199; tel. 575/748–3333, (Nonreporting) **A**10 20
Primary Contact: Kenneth W. Randall, Chief Executive Officer
CFO: Carl Hollingsworth, Chief Financial Officer
CMO: Joe Salgado, M.D., Chief of Staff
CHR: Bruce Hinshaw, Director Human Resources
CNO: Wendi Hulett, Chief Nursing Officer
Web address: www.artesiageneral.com
Control: Other not–for–profit (including NFP Corporation) **Service:** General Medical and Surgical

Staffed Beds: 30

CARLSBAD—Eddy County

✠ **CARLSBAD MEDICAL CENTER (320063)**, 2430 West Pierce Street, Zip 88220–3597; tel. 575/887–4100 **A**1 10 **F**3 13 14 15 17 18 20 22 26 29 30 34 35 40 41 43 45 46 47 48 54 56 57 59 64 65 70 73 74 76 77 78 79 81 83 85 87 89 90 93 94 96 97 107 108 110 111 114 119 120 121 122 123 128 129 135 141 146 147 148 **S** Community Health Systems, Inc., Franklin, TN
Primary Contact: Cathy Hibbs, Chief Executive Officer
CFO: Craig Morse, Chief Financial Officer
CIO: Thomas Motejzik, Director Information Systems
CNO: Connie Shofner, Chief Nursing Officer
Web address: www.carlsbadmedicalcenter.com
Control: Corporation, Investor–owned, for–profit **Service:** General Medical and Surgical

Staffed Beds: 130 **Admissions:** 2804 **Census:** 33 **Outpatient Visits:** 65967 **Births:** 430 **Total Expense ($000):** 49663 **Payroll Expense ($000):** 19217 **Personnel:** 343

CLAYTON—Union County

★ **UNION COUNTY GENERAL HOSPITAL (321304)**, 300 Wilson Street, Zip 88415–3304, Mailing Address: P.O. Box 489, Zip 88415–0489; tel. 575/374–2585 **A**10 18 **F**3 11 13 29 31 35 40 45 50 57 59 62 64 65 68 70 76 77 81 82 85 87 89 93 97 102 107 114 119 129 130 133 144 145 148 **S** Community Hospital Corporation, Plano, TX
Primary Contact: Jerry Wiesner, Chief Executive Officer
CFO: Alexander B. Altman, III, Chief Financial Officer
CMO: Daniel Radunsky, M.D., Medical Staff President
CIO: Kelsey Lawrence, Manager Information Technology
CHR: Jill Swagerty, Director Human Resources
CNO: Stacye Bradley, R.N., Chief Nursing Officer
Web address: www.ucgh.net/
Control: Other not–for–profit (including NFP Corporation) **Service:** General Medical and Surgical

Staffed Beds: 21 **Admissions:** 321 **Census:** 3

CLOVIS—Curry County

✠ **PLAINS REGIONAL MEDICAL CENTER (320022)**, 2100 Martin Luther King Boulevard, Zip 88101–9412, Mailing Address: P.O. Box 1688, Zip 88102–1688; tel. 575/769–2141 **A**1 10 **F**3 8 11 13 15 20 28 29 30 31 35 39 40 45 47 48 50 51 53 57 58 61 62 63 64 65 68 69 70 75 76 77 78 79 81 84 85 87 89 93 97 107 108 110 111 112 114 115 116 119 120 121 123 129 130 135 146 147 148 **P**6 **S** Presbyterian Healthcare Services, Albuquerque, NM
Primary Contact: Vincent B. DiFranco, Chief Executive Officer
CMO: Brian Willmon, M.D., Medical Director
CHR: Cindy Duncan, Manager Human Resources
CNO: Terri A. Marney, R.N., Director of Nursing
Web address: www.phs.org
Control: Other not–for–profit (including NFP Corporation) **Service:** General Medical and Surgical

Staffed Beds: 59 **Admissions:** 4351 **Census:** 33 **Outpatient Visits:** 181728 **Births:** 1193 **Total Expense ($000):** 89968 **Payroll Expense ($000):** 30822 **Personnel:** 485

CROWNPOINT—McKinley County

★ **U. S. PUBLIC HEALTH SERVICE INDIAN HOSPITAL (320062)**, Route 9 and State Road 371, Zip 87313, Mailing Address: P.O. Box 358, Zip 87313–0358; tel. 505/786–5291, (Nonreporting) **A**10 **S** U. S. Indian Health Service, Rockville, MD
Primary Contact: Anslem Roanhorse, Chief Executive Officer
CFO: Darlene Kirk, Manager Finance
CMO: John Johnson, M.D., Clinical Director
CIO: Jimmy Burbank, Chief Information Officer
CHR: Christina Bitsilly, Human Resource Specialist
CNO: Alex Daniels, Chief Nurse Executive
Web address: www.ihs.gov
Control: PHS, Indian Service, Government, federal **Service:** General Medical and Surgical

Staffed Beds: 12	

DEMING—Luna County

✖ **MIMBRES MEMORIAL HOSPITAL (321309)**, 900 West Ash Street, Zip 88030–4098, Mailing Address: P.O. Box 710, Zip 88031–0710; tel. 575/546–5800, (Nonreporting) **A**1 10 18 **S** Quorum Health, Brentwood, TN
Primary Contact: Kelly Duke, Chief Executive Officer
CFO: Trisha Smith, Chief Financial Officer
CHR: Johanna Gramer, Director Human Resources
CNO: Joy Harrell, R.N., Chief Nursing Officer
Web address: www.mimbresmemorial.com
Control: Corporation, Investor–owned, for–profit **Service:** General Medical and Surgical

Staffed Beds: 75	

ESPANOLA—Rio Arriba County

✖ **PRESBYTERIAN ESPANOLA HOSPITAL (320011)**, 1010 Spruce Street, Zip 87532–2746; tel. 505/753–7111 **A**1 10 20 **F**3 7 8 11 13 15 29 30 32 34 35 40 45 50 51 53 57 59 62 64 68 70 75 76 79 81 85 93 107 108 110 114 115 118 119 129 130 146 **P**6 **S** Presbyterian Healthcare Services, Albuquerque, NM
Primary Contact: Brenda Romero, Administrator
CFO: Lupe Lucero, Manager Business Office
CMO: Fernando Bayardo, M.D., Chief Medical Officer
CHR: Joshua Griffith, Manager Human Resources
CNO: Nancy Santiesteban, Director Patient Care Services
Web address: www.phs.org
Control: Other not–for–profit (including NFP Corporation) **Service:** General Medical and Surgical

Staffed Beds: 42 **Admissions:** 2464 **Census:** 25 **Outpatient Visits:** 141667 **Births:** 295 **Total Expense ($000):** 62983 **Payroll Expense ($000):** 29826 **Personnel:** 306	

FARMINGTON—San Juan County

✖ ◇ **SAN JUAN REGIONAL MEDICAL CENTER (320005)**, 801 West Maple Street, Zip 87401–5630; tel. 505/609–2000, (Includes SAN JUAN REGIONAL MEDICAL CENTER REHABILITATION HOSPITAL, 525 South Schwartz Avenue, Zip 87401–5955; tel. 505/609–2625; Jeff Egbert, Interim President and Chief Executive Officer) **A**1 2 10 21 **F**3 7 8 11 13 15 18 20 22 26 28 29 30 31 32 34 35 39 40 42 43 47 48 49 50 53 54 57 59 60 64 65 68 70 74 75 76 78 79 81 82 85 86 87 89 90 93 96 97 98 99 100 102 107 108 111 112 114 115 118 119 121 130 132 135 143 144 146 148 **P**5 6
Primary Contact: Jeff Bourgeois, President and Chief Executive Officer
COO: John Buffington, Chief Operating Officer
CFO: Karen Miller, Chief Financial Officer
CMO: Melania Yeats, M.D., Chief Medical Officer
CIO: Sheri Rawlings, Chief Information Officer
CHR: Elizabeth Volkerding, Director Workforce Excellence
CNO: Suzanne E. Smith, R.N., Chief Nursing Officer
Web address: www.sanjuanregional.com
Control: Other not–for–profit (including NFP Corporation) **Service:** General Medical and Surgical

Staffed Beds: 198 **Admissions:** 9788 **Census:** 123 **Outpatient Visits:** 752422 **Births:** 1300 **Total Expense ($000):** 267730 **Payroll Expense ($000):** 124015 **Personnel:** 1884	

GALLUP—Mckinley County

✖ **GALLUP INDIAN MEDICAL CENTER (320061)**, 516 East Nizhoni Boulevard, Zip 87301–5748, Mailing Address: P.O. Box 1337, Zip 87305–1337; tel. 505/722–1000 **A**1 5 10 **F**5 8 13 15 18 29 34 36 39 40 43 50 59 61 64 65 66 70 74 75 76 77 79 81 83 84 85 87 89 91 93 97 99 100 104 107 115 119 130 135 144 146 147 148 **S** U. S. Indian Health Service, Rockville, MD
Primary Contact: Vida J. Khow, Chief Executive Officer
CFO: Agnes Kee, Financial Manager
CMO: Douglas G. Peter, M.D., Chief Medical Officer
CIO: Adrian C. Haven, Site Manager
CHR: Karen Lee, Director Human Resources
CNO: Selva Thompson, R.N., Chief Nurse Executive
Web address: www.ihs.gov/navajo/index.cfm?module=nao_hcc_gallup
Control: PHS, Indian Service, Government, federal **Service:** General Medical and Surgical

Staffed Beds: 58 **Admissions:** 3070 **Census:** 36 **Outpatient Visits:** 255029 **Births:** 521	

✖ **REHOBOTH MCKINLEY CHRISTIAN HEALTH CARE SERVICES (320038)**, 1901 Red Rock Drive, Zip 87301–5683; tel. 505/863–7000 **A**1 10 20 **F**3 4 5 11 13 15 28 29 30 32 34 35 40 45 50 57 59 62 63 64 65 68 70 74 75 76 77 79 81 82 84 85 86 87 89 93 104 107 108 110 111 115 118 119 129 130 132 133 135 **P**8
Primary Contact: David Conejo, Chief Executive Officer
COO: William Kiefer, Chief Operating Officer
CFO: John McMullin, Chief Financial Officer
CMO: Samuel MacBride, M.D., Chief Medical Officer
CIO: David Odom, Chief Information Officer
CHR: Susan Macias, Chief Human Resources Officer
CNO: William Kiefer, Chief Nursing Officer
Web address: www.rmch.org
Control: Other not–for–profit (including NFP Corporation) **Service:** General Medical and Surgical

Staffed Beds: 80 **Admissions:** 2473 **Census:** 21 **Outpatient Visits:** 121036 **Births:** 385 **Total Expense ($000):** 54849 **Payroll Expense ($000):** 22339 **Personnel:** 400	

GRANTS—Cibola County

✖ **CIBOLA GENERAL HOSPITAL (321308)**, 1016 East Roosevelt Avenue, Zip 87020–2118; tel. 505/287–4446 **A**1 10 18 **F**3 13 15 29 30 34 40 45 46 50 56 57 59 64 65 66 68 70 75 76 77 81 85 93 97 107 110 115 119 129 130 133 135 147 148
Primary Contact: Thomas Whelan, Chief Executive Officer
CFO: Jeff Rimel, Chief Financial Officer
CMO: Janice Shipley, M.D., Chief Medical Officer
CIO: Rick Smith, Director Information Services
CHR: Sheila Cox, Director Human Resources
CNO: Glenna Losito, R.N., Chief Nursing Officer
Web address: www.cibolahospital.com
Control: Other not–for–profit (including NFP Corporation) **Service:** General Medical and Surgical

Staffed Beds: 25 **Admissions:** 951 **Census:** 9 **Births:** 215	

HOBBS—Lea County

✖ **LEA REGIONAL MEDICAL CENTER (320065)**, 5419 North Lovington Highway, Zip 88240–9125, Mailing Address: P.O. Box 3000, Zip 88241–9501; tel. 575/492–5000, (Nonreporting) **A**1 10 **S** Community Health Systems, Inc., Franklin, TN
Primary Contact: Timothy Thornell, FACHE, Chief Executive Officer
CFO: Jorge Latibeaudiere, Chief Financial Officer
CMO: Naishadh Mankad, M.D., Chief of Staff
CIO: Terry Purcell, Director Information Services
CHR: Laurie Russell, Director Human Resources
CNO: Patrick A. Dunn, R.N., Chief Nursing Officer
Web address: www.learegionalmedical.com
Control: Corporation, Investor–owned, for–profit **Service:** General Medical and Surgical

Staffed Beds: 195	

LAS CRUCES—Dona Ana County

☐ **ADVANCED CARE HOSPITAL OF SOUTHERN NEW MEXICO (322004)**, 4451 East Lohman Avenue, Zip 88011–8267; tel. 575/521–6600, (Nonreporting) **A**1 10 **S** Ernest Health, Inc., Albuquerque, NM
Primary Contact: Claudia Saiz, Chief Operating Officer
Web address: www.achsnm.ernesthealth.com
Control: Corporation, Investor–owned, for–profit **Service:** Long–Term Acute Care hospital

Staffed Beds: 40	

NM

✠ **MEMORIAL MEDICAL CENTER (320018)**, 2450 South Telshor Boulevard,
Zip 88011–5076; tel. 575/522–8641 **A**1 2 3 10 13 **F**3 8 11 13 15 17 18 20
22 24 26 28 29 30 31 35 39 40 44 45 49 50 51 54 57 59 60 61 62 64 65
68 70 72 74 75 76 78 79 81 85 89 93 97 98 102 103 107 108 111 114 115
118 119 121 122 123 124 130 132 135 147 148 **S** LifePoint Health,
Brentwood, TN
Primary Contact: John Harris, Chief Executive Officer
COO: Steven T. Ruwoldt, Chief Operating Officer
CFO: Raymond Grenier, Chief Financial Officer
CMO: Bruce San Filippo, M.D., Chief Medical Officer
CHR: Laura Pierce, Director Human Resources
CNO: Ann Debooy, R.N., Chief Nursing Officer
Web address: www.mmclc.org
Control: Corporation, Investor–owned, for–profit **Service:** General Medical and
Surgical

Staffed Beds: 224 **Admissions:** 9498 **Census:** 109

✠ **MESILLA VALLEY HOSPITAL (324010)**, 3751 Del Rey Boulevard,
Zip 88012–8526; tel. 575/382–3500 **A**1 10 **F**87 98 99 100 101 103 106
S Universal Health Services, Inc., King of Prussia, PA
Primary Contact: Diana Schultz, Chief Executive Officer
CFO: Dana McRimmon, Chief Financial Officer
CMO: Arthur L. Ramirez, M.D., Medical Director
CIO: Rebecca Mumpower, Director Marketing
CHR: Linda Moya, Director Human Resources
CNO: Veronica Hughes, Chief Nursing Officer
Web address: www.mesillavalleyhospital.com
Control: Corporation, Investor–owned, for–profit **Service:** Psychiatric

Staffed Beds: 120 **Admissions:** 2663 **Census:** 90 **Outpatient Visits:** 0
Births: 0

✠ **MOUNTAINVIEW REGIONAL MEDICAL CENTER (320085)**, 4311 East Lohman
Avenue, Zip 88011–8255; tel. 575/556–7600, (Nonreporting) **A**1 10 12 13
S Community Health Systems, Inc., Franklin, TN
Primary Contact: Denten Park, Chief Executive Officer
COO: Warren Yehl, Chief Operating Officer
CFO: Nathan Crabdree, Chief Financial Officer
CIO: Donald Harlow, Director of Information Services
CHR: Delilah Doss, Director, Human Resources
CNO: Gayle Nash, R.N., Chief Nursing Officer
Web address: www.mountainviewregional.com
Control: Corporation, Investor–owned, for–profit **Service:** General Medical and
Surgical

Staffed Beds: 142

✠ **REHABILITATION HOSPITAL OF SOUTHERN NEW MEXICO (323032)**, 4441
East Lohman Avenue, Zip 88011–8267; tel. 575/521–6400, (Nonreporting) **A**1
10 **S** Ernest Health, Inc., Albuquerque, NM
Primary Contact: Sabrina Martin, Chief Executive Officer
CFO: Elizabeth Striplin, Chief Financial Officer
CMO: Kimberly Encapera, M.D., Medical Director
CIO: Ricky Molina, Director Marketing and Business Development
CHR: Yolanda Mendoza, Director Human Resources
CNO: Carole Carson, Director of Nursing Operations
Web address: www.rhsnm.ernesthealth.com
Control: Corporation, Investor–owned, for–profit **Service:** Rehabilitation

Staffed Beds: 40

LAS VEGAS—San Miguel County

✠ **ALTA VISTA REGIONAL HOSPITAL (320003)**, 104 Legion Drive,
Zip 87701–4804; tel. 505/426–3500, (Nonreporting) **A**1 10 20 **S** Quorum
Health, Brentwood, TN
Primary Contact: R. Chris Wolf, Chief Executive Officer
CMO: Nancy Wright, M.D., Chief Medical Staff
CIO: Laird Thornton, Director Information Systems
CHR: Michael Freeman, Director Human Resources
CNO: Rhonda Clark, Interim Chief Nursing Officer
Web address: www.altavistaregionalhospital.com
Control: Corporation, Investor–owned, for–profit **Service:** General Medical and
Surgical

Staffed Beds: 54

☐ **NEW MEXICO BEHAVIORAL HEALTH INSTITUTE AT LAS VEGAS**, 3695 Hot
Springs Boulevard, Zip 87701–9549; tel. 505/454–2100, (Nonreporting) **A**1
Primary Contact: Frances Tweed, Executive Director and Administrator
COO: Charles Jaramillo, Chief Operating Officer
CFO: Darlene Martinez, Director Finance
Web address: www.health.state.nm.us
Control: State–Government, nonfederal **Service:** Psychiatric

Staffed Beds: 257

LOS ALAMOS—Los Alamos County

✠ **LOS ALAMOS MEDICAL CENTER (320033)**, 3917 West Road,
Zip 87544–2293; tel. 505/661–9500 **A**1 10 20 **F**8 11 13 15 28 29 30 31 34
35 40 41 45 50 52 55 57 59 64 65 67 68 70 73 75 76 78 79 81 82 85 87
89 92 93 107 108 110 111 114 115 116 117 118 119 124 130 146 147
148 **P**8 **S** LifePoint Health, Brentwood, TN
Primary Contact: John Whiteside, Interim Chief Executive Officer
CFO: Steve Weingart, Chief Financial Officer
CMO: Barbara Van Eeckhout, M.D., Chief of Staff
CIO: Kevin Vigil, Director Information Systems
CHR: Jacqueline Carroll, Director Human Resources
CNO: Tracie Stratton, Chief Nursing Officer
Web address: www.losalamosmedicalcenter.com
Control: Corporation, Investor–owned, for–profit **Service:** General Medical and
Surgical

Staffed Beds: 38 **Admissions:** 926 **Census:** 7 **Outpatient Visits:** 59183
Births: 213 **Total Expense ($000):** 39208 **Payroll Expense ($000):** 12053
Personnel: 262

LOVINGTON—Lea County

★ ◇ **NOR-LEA GENERAL HOSPITAL (321305)**, 1600 North Main Avenue,
Zip 88260–2871; tel. 575/396–6611 **A**10 18 21 **F**3 9 15 18 26 28 29 30 31
32 34 35 39 40 43 45 46 49 50 51 54 57 59 64 65 66 68 74 75 77 78 81
82 89 92 93 97 100 101 102 103 104 107 108 110 111 115 119 127 129
130 132 133 135 147 148 **P**6
Primary Contact: David B. Shaw, Chief Executive Officer and Administrator
COO: Dan Hamilton, Chief Operating Officer
CFO: Allyson Roberts, CPA, Chief Financial Officer
CMO: Ronald Hopkins, D.O., Chief of Staff
CIO: Brent Kelley, Director Information Technology
CHR: Angela Carrejo, Director Human Resources
CNO: Marcia Patterson, Chief Nursing Officer
Web address: www.norlea.org/
Control: Hospital district or authority, Government, nonfederal **Service:** General
Medical and Surgical

Staffed Beds: 18 **Admissions:** 502 **Census:** 3 **Outpatient Visits:** 185248
Births: 0 **Total Expense ($000):** 56913 **Payroll Expense ($000):** 22030
Personnel: 395

MESCALERO—Otero County

☐ **MESCALERO PUBLIC HEALTH SERVICE INDIAN HOSPITAL (320058)**, 318
Abalone Loop, Zip 88340, Mailing Address: Box 210, Zip 88340–0210;
tel. 505/464–3801, (Nonreporting) **A**1 10 **S** U. S. Indian Health Service,
Rockville, MD
Primary Contact: Dorlynn Simmons, Chief Executive Officer
CFO: Rainey Enjady, Administrative Officer
CIO: Kathy Murphy, Site Manager
Web address: www.ihs.gov
Control: Public Health Service, Government, federal **Service:** General Medical
and Surgical

Staffed Beds: 13

PORTALES—Roosevelt County

◇ **ROOSEVELT GENERAL HOSPITAL (320084)**, 42121 U.S. Highway 70,
Zip 88130, Mailing Address: P.O. Box 868, Zip 88130–0868;
tel. 575/359–1800, (Nonreporting) **A**10 21
Primary Contact: Larry E. Leaming, Ph.D., FACHE, Chief Executive Officer
CFO: Eva Steven, Chief Financial Officer
CMO: Les Donaldson, M.D., Chief of Staff
CHR: Cindy Duncan, Director Human Resources
Web address: www.myrgh.org
Control: Hospital district or authority, Government, nonfederal **Service:** General
Medical and Surgical

Staffed Beds: 22

RATON—Colfax County

★ **MINERS' COLFAX MEDICAL CENTER (321307)**, 200 Hospital Drive,
Zip 87740–2099; tel. 575/445–7700, (Includes MINERS' HOSPITAL OF NEW
MEXICO, Hospital Drive, Zip 87740, Mailing Address: Box 1067, Zip 87740;
tel. 505/445–2741) **A**10 18 **F**11 13 15 18 34 40 45 46 50 53 54 56 57 58
59 65 70 71 75 76 77 78 81 82 85 86 87 97 107 115 119 127 129 130 132
133 135 146 147 148
Primary Contact: Shawn Lerch, Chief Executive Officer
CFO: Albino Martinez, Director Budget and Finance
CIO: Richard Laner, Jr., Manager Information Systems
CHR: Jamie Johnson, Director Human Resources
Web address: www.minershosp.com
Control: State–Government, nonfederal **Service:** General Medical and Surgical

Staffed Beds: 25 **Admissions:** 658 **Census:** 5 **Outpatient Visits:** 9285
Births: 120 **Total Expense ($000):** 21120 **Payroll Expense ($000):** 10000

NM

Many Facility Codes have changed. Please refer to the AHA Guide Code Chart. © 2016 AHA Guide

ROSWELL—Chaves County

✠ **EASTERN NEW MEXICO MEDICAL CENTER (320006)**, 405 West Country Club Road, Zip 88201–5209; tel. 575/622–8170, (Nonreporting) **A**1 3 10 19 **S** Community Health Systems, Inc., Franklin, TN
Primary Contact: Rodney Schumacher, Interim Chief Executive Officer
COO: Warren Yehl, Chief Operating Officer
CFO: Leanne Hacker, Chief Financial Officer
CMO: Richard Pinon, Chief Medical Officer
CIO: Deepak Surl, Chief Information Officer
CHR: Sheila Nunez, Director Human Resources
CNO: Kathy Williams, Chief Nursing Officer
Web address: www.enmmc.com
Control: Corporation, Investor–owned, for–profit **Service:** General Medical and Surgical

Staffed Beds: 149

★ **LOVELACE REGIONAL HOSPITAL – ROSWELL (320086)**, 117 East 19th Street, Zip 88201–5151; tel. 575/627–7000 **A**10 13 **F**3 13 17 18 22 29 34 40 42 45 57 59 70 76 79 81 82 85 89 90 91 93 111 119 130 146 147 **P**6 7 **S** Ardent Health Services, Nashville, TN
Primary Contact: Dawn M. Tschabrun, R.N., Chief Executive Officer
CNO: Kristin Trotter, Chief Nursing Officer
Web address: www.lovelace.com
Control: Corporation, Investor–owned, for–profit **Service:** General Medical and Surgical

Staffed Beds: 26 **Admissions:** 2184 **Census:** 16 **Outpatient Visits:** 50562 **Births:** 975 **Total Expense ($000):** 35608 **Payroll Expense ($000):** 11580 **Personnel:** 194

☐ **NEW MEXICO REHABILITATION CENTER (323026)**, 72 Gail Harris Street, Zip 88203–8116; tel. 575/347–3400, (Includes PECOS VALLEY LODGE, 31 Gail Harris Avenue, Zip 88201; tel. 505/347–5491), (Nonreporting) **A**1 10
Primary Contact: Bradley McGrath, Administrator
CFO: Janie Davies, Chief Financial Officer
CMO: Stephen Dorman, M.D., Chief Medical Officer
CIO: Dennis Hoefs, Manager Information Technology
CHR: Teresa Casarez, Director Human Resources
Control: State–Government, nonfederal **Service:** Rehabilitation

Staffed Beds: 41

RUIDOSO—Lincoln County

✠ **LINCOLN COUNTY MEDICAL CENTER (321306)**, 211 Sudderth Drive, Zip 88345–6043, Mailing Address: P.O. Box 8000, Zip 88355–8000; tel. 575/257–8200 **A**1 10 18 **F**7 11 13 15 29 30 34 35 39 40 45 46 53 56 57 59 64 68 70 76 77 81 85 87 91 93 107 110 111 115 119 127 130 132 135 144 146 148 **P**6 **S** Presbyterian Healthcare Services, Albuquerque, NM
Primary Contact: Todd Oberheu, Administrator
CFO: Dudley McCauley, Controller
CMO: Gary Jackson, D.O., Medical Director
CHR: Susanne Johnston, Manager Human Resources
Web address: www.phs.org
Control: Other not–for–profit (including NFP Corporation) **Service:** General Medical and Surgical

Staffed Beds: 25 **Admissions:** 1468 **Census:** 12 **Outpatient Visits:** 84377 **Births:** 358 **Total Expense ($000):** 40266 **Payroll Expense ($000):** 17377 **Personnel:** 235

SANTA FE—Santa Fe County

✠ △ **CHRISTUS ST. VINCENT REGIONAL MEDICAL CENTER (320002)**, 455 St. Michael's Drive, Zip 87505–7663, Mailing Address: P.O. Box 2107, Zip 87505; tel. 505/983–3361, (Includes CHRISTUS ST. VINCENT PHYSICIANS MEDICAL CENTER, 2990 Rodeo Park Drive East, Zip 87505; tel. 505/428–5400; J. Alex Valdez, JD, President and Chief Executive Officer) **A**1 2 3 7 10 20 **F**8 12 13 15 17 18 19 20 21 22 24 26 28 29 30 31 32 34 35 36 37 38 39 40 41 43 45 46 47 48 49 50 51 53 54 56 57 64 65 66 68 70 73 74 75 76 77 78 79 81 82 83 84 85 86 87 88 89 90 91 92 93 97 98 100 101 102 103 104 107 108 109 110 111 112 113 114 115 116 117 118 119 120 121 122 124 126 129 130 131 132 135 143 144 146 147 148 **S** CHRISTUS Health, Irving, TX
Primary Contact: Patrick Brian Carrier, President and Chief Executive Officer
COO: Jason Adams, Chief Operating Officer
CFO: Bob Moon, Chief Financial Officer
CMO: John C. Beeson, M.D., Chief Medical Officer
CIO: Ron Dekeyzer, Regional Director Information Systems
CHR: Pearl Mohnkern, Vice President and Director Human Resources
Web address: www.stvin.org
Control: Other not–for–profit (including NFP Corporation) **Service:** General Medical and Surgical

Staffed Beds: 268 **Admissions:** 11625 **Census:** 133 **Outpatient Visits:** 140909 **Births:** 1196 **Total Expense ($000):** 357452 **Payroll Expense ($000):** 132509 **Personnel:** 1686

☐ **PHS SANTA FE INDIAN HOSPITAL (320057)**, 1700 Cerrillos Road, Zip 87505–3554; tel. 505/988–9821, (Nonreporting) **A**1 5 10 **S** U. S. Indian Health Service, Rockville, MD
Primary Contact: Leslie Dye, Chief Executive Officer
CMO: Bret Smoker, M.D., Clinical Director
CIO: Vernita Jones, Site Manager
Control: Public Health Service, Government, federal **Service:** General Medical and Surgical

Staffed Beds: 4

SANTA ROSA—Guadalupe County

★ **GUADALUPE COUNTY HOSPITAL (320067)**, 117 Camino de Vida, Zip 88435–2267; tel. 575/472–3417 **A**10 20 **F**3 29 34 35 40 50 57 59 64 65 81 82 87 107 114 119 130 148 **P**5
Primary Contact: Christina Campos, Administrator
CFO: Bret Goebel, Finance Officer
CMO: Randal Brown, M.D., Chief of Staff
CIO: Emilio Campos, Manager Information Technology
CHR: Colleen Gallegos, Director Human Resources
CNO: Mandelyn Cordova, R.N., Director of Nurses
Web address: www.gchnm.org
Control: County–Government, nonfederal **Service:** General Medical and Surgical

Staffed Beds: 10 **Admissions:** 223 **Census:** 2 **Outpatient Visits:** 7293 **Births:** 0 **Total Expense ($000):** 9058 **Payroll Expense ($000):** 1799 **Personnel:** 41

SANTA TERESA—Dona Ana County

☐ **PEAK BEHAVIORAL HEALTH SERVICES (324012)**, 5065 McNutt Road, Zip 88008–9442; tel. 575/589–3000, (Nonreporting) **A**1 10 **S** Strategic Behavioral Health, LLC, Memphis, TN
Primary Contact: Jose Santos-Roheu, Chief Executive Officer
COO: Doug Ginn, Executive Vice President Operations
CFO: Espie Herrara, Chief Financial Officer
CHR: Norma Oaxaca, Director Human Resources
Web address: www.peakbehavioral.com/
Control: Corporation, Investor–owned, for–profit **Service:** Psychiatric

Staffed Beds: 120

SHIPROCK—San Juan County

✠ **NORTHERN NAVAJO MEDICAL CENTER (320059)**, Highway 491 North, Zip 87420–0160, Mailing Address: P.O. Box 160, Zip 87420–0160; tel. 505/368–6001 **A**1 10 **F**2 3 8 13 15 29 30 32 34 35 36 38 39 40 44 45 48 50 51 53 57 59 61 62 63 64 65 68 70 74 75 76 77 79 81 82 83 84 85 86 87 89 93 97 99 100 101 102 103 104 105 107 110 115 119 127 130 131 132 134 135 144 147 148 **S** U. S. Indian Health Service, Rockville, MD
Primary Contact: Fannessa Comer, Chief Executive Officer
CFO: Shawn Morgan, Finance Officer
CMO: Ira Salom, M.D., Clinical Director
CIO: Roland Chapman, Chief Information Officer
CHR: Gloria Redhorse–Charley, Director Human Resources
CNO: Lavenia Diswood, R.N., Chief Nurse Executive
Web address: www.ihs.gov/
Control: PHS, Indian Service, Government, federal **Service:** General Medical and Surgical

Staffed Beds: 68 **Admissions:** 1900 **Census:** 20 **Outpatient Visits:** 305936 **Births:** 449

SILVER CITY—Grant County

✠ **GILA REGIONAL MEDICAL CENTER (320016)**, 1313 East 32nd Street, Zip 88061–7251; tel. 575/538–4000 **A**1 3 10 20 **F**3 7 11 13 15 30 31 35 37 40 41 45 50 51 53 57 59 62 63 64 70 73 75 76 78 79 81 85 87 89 93 98 102 103 107 108 111 115 119 120 121 123 129 130 132 148
Primary Contact: Brian Cunningham, Chief Executive Officer
CFO: Craig Stewart, Chief Financial Officer
CIO: David Furnas, Chief Information Officer
CHR: Barbara Barela, Director Human Resources
CNO: Patricia Sheyka, Chief Nursing Officer
Web address: www.grmc.org
Control: County–Government, nonfederal **Service:** General Medical and Surgical

Staffed Beds: 68 **Admissions:** 2764 **Census:** 23

NM

SOCORRO—Socorro County

☒ **SOCORRO GENERAL HOSPITAL (321301)**, 1202 Highway 60 West,
Zip 87801–3914, Mailing Address: P.O. Box 1009, Zip 87801–1009;
tel. 575/835–1140 **A**1 10 18 **F**3 8 11 13 15 29 30 34 35 40 45 57 59 62 63
64 65 68 75 77 81 83 85 91 93 100 103 107 114 130 132 133 134 135
146 147 **P**6 **S** Presbyterian Healthcare Services, Albuquerque, NM
Primary Contact: Veronica Pound, R.N., Administrator
CFO: Scott Shannon, Director Finance
CMO: Darla Bejnar, M.D., Chief Medical Officer
CHR: Pam Miller–Balfour, Director Human Resources
CNO: Veronica Pound, R.N., Interim Administrator and Director of Patient Care
Web address: www.phs.org
Control: Other not–for–profit (including NFP Corporation) **Service:** General
Medical and Surgical

Staffed Beds: 18 **Admissions:** 571 **Census:** 4 **Outpatient Visits:** 65771
Births: 142 **Total Expense ($000):** 27296 **Payroll Expense ($000):** 13536
Personnel: 169

TAOS—Taos County

★ ◇ **HOLY CROSS HOSPITAL (320013)**, 1397 Weimer Road,
Zip 87571–6253; tel. 575/758–8883 **A**3 10 20 21 **F**3 11 13 15 18 29 30 32
34 35 36 40 45 46 50 59 64 68 75 76 79 80 81 85 86 87 89 90 91 93 97
100 102 107 110 114 115 118 119 130 132 145 146 147 148 **P**6 8
Primary Contact: William D. Patten, Jr., Chief Executive Officer
CFO: Steve Rozenboom, Chief Financial Officer
CHR: Brian Chew, Human Resources Officer
CNO: Mary Anna Abeyta, R.N., Chief Nursing Officer
Web address: www.taoshospital.org
Control: Other not–for–profit (including NFP Corporation) **Service:** General
Medical and Surgical

Staffed Beds: 29 **Admissions:** 1618 **Census:** 15 **Outpatient Visits:** 70252
Births: 237 **Total Expense ($000):** 48505 **Payroll Expense ($000):** 19686
Personnel: 609

TRUTH OR CONSEQUENCES—Sierra County

★ **SIERRA VISTA HOSPITAL (321300)**, 800 East Ninth Avenue, Zip 87901–1961;
tel. 575/894–2111 **A**10 18 **F**7 11 15 16 30 34 40 54 57 59 65 67 93 99 102
104 107 110 127 128 130 133
Primary Contact: Michael P. Zimmerman, Chief Executive Officer
CFO: Bret Gobel, Chief Financial Officer
CMO: James F. Malcolmson, M.D., Chief of Staff
CIO: Dan Morrell, Manager Information Systems
CHR: Mindee Holguin, Manager Human Resources
CNO: Palmer Greene, R.N., Chief Nursing Officer
Web address: www.svhnm.org
Control: City–County, Government, nonfederal **Service:** General Medical and
Surgical

Staffed Beds: 15 **Admissions:** 758 **Census:** 8 **Outpatient Visits:** 12654

TUCUMCARI—Quay County

★ **DR. DAN C. TRIGG MEMORIAL HOSPITAL (321302)**, 301 East Miel De Luna
Avenue, Zip 88401–3810, Mailing Address: P.O. Box 608, Zip 88401–0608;
tel. 575/461–7000 **A**10 18 **F**11 15 29 35 38 40 45 59 62 63 64 65 68 81 85
87 97 104 107 110 114 119 130 133 135 146 148 **P**6 **S** Presbyterian
Healthcare Services, Albuquerque, NM
Primary Contact: Donald Weidemann, Administrator
CMO: Darrell Willis, M.D., Chief of Staff
CNO: Vickie Gutierrez, Director of Patient Care
Web address: www.phs.org
Control: Other not–for–profit (including NFP Corporation) **Service:** General
Medical and Surgical

Staffed Beds: 10 **Admissions:** 242 **Census:** 2 **Outpatient Visits:** 35376
Births: 0 **Total Expense ($000):** 20799 **Payroll Expense ($000):** 5556
Personnel: 86

ZUNI—McKinley County

☐ **U. S. PUBLIC HEALTH SERVICE INDIAN HOSPITAL (320060)**, Route 301
North B. Street, Zip 87327, Mailing Address: P.O. Box 467, Zip 87327–0467;
tel. 505/782–4431, (Nonreporting) **A**1 10 **S** U. S. Indian Health Service,
Rockville, MD
Primary Contact: Jean Othole, Chief Executive Officer
CFO: Clyde Yatsattie, Administrative Officer
CMO: David Kessler, M.D., Clinical Director
CHR: Cynthia Tsalate, Human Resource Specialist
Web address: www.ihs.gov
Control: PHS, Indian Service, Government, federal **Service:** General Medical and
Surgical

Staffed Beds: 32

NM

Many Facility Codes have changed. Please refer to the AHA Guide Code Chart.

NEW YORK

ALBANY—Albany County

☐ **ALBANY MEDICAL CENTER (330013)**, 43 New Scotland Avenue,
Zip 12208–3478; tel. 518/262–3125, (Includes ALBANY MEDICAL CENTER
SOUTH–CLINICAL CAMPUS, 25 Hackett Boulevard, Zip 12208–3499;
tel. 518/242–1200; Timothy W. Duffy, General Director) **A**1 2 3 5 8 10 19 **F**3 6
7 8 11 12 13 15 17 18 19 20 21 22 23 24 25 26 27 28 29 30 31 32 34 35
36 38 39 40 41 43 44 45 46 47 49 50 51 52 53 54 55 56 57 58 59 60 61
64 65 68 70 72 73 74 75 76 77 78 79 81 82 85 86 87 88 89 90 92 93 96
98 100 102 103 104 105 107 108 109 110 111 114 115 116 117 118 119
120 121 123 124 126 130 131 132 135 138 142 145 146 148
Primary Contact: James J. Barba, President and Chief Executive Officer
COO: Bernadette R. Pedlow, Senior Vice President Business and Chief Operating
Officer
CFO: Frances Spreer–Albert, Chief Financial Officer and Executive Vice President
CMO: Dennis McKenna, M.D., Interim Vice President Medical Affairs
CIO: George Hickman, Executive Vice President and Chief Information Officer
CHR: Catherine Halakan, Senior Vice President
Web address: www.amc.edu
Control: Other not–for–profit (including NFP Corporation) **Service:** General
Medical and Surgical

> **Staffed Beds:** 731 **Admissions:** 34965 **Census:** 601 **Outpatient Visits:**
> 395398 **Births:** 2093 **Total Expense ($000):** 860548 **Payroll Expense**
> **($000):** 282362 **Personnel:** 5894

★ **ALBANY MEMORIAL HOSPITAL (330003)**, 600 Northern Boulevard,
Zip 12204–1083; tel. 518/471–3221 **A**10 **F**8 15 29 30 31 40 45 46 49 50 57
59 60 63 68 70 77 81 84 85 87 93 107 111 119 130 146 147 148 **S** Trinity
Health, Livonia, MI
Primary Contact: Virginia L. Golden, Chief Executive Officer
CFO: Lori Santos, Vice President Finance
CMO: Robert Cella, M.D., Chief Medical Officer
CHR: Judy Gray, Vice President Human Resources
Web address: www.nehealth.com
Control: Other not–for–profit (including NFP Corporation) **Service:** General
Medical and Surgical

> **Staffed Beds:** 74 **Admissions:** 2910 **Census:** 40 **Outpatient Visits:** 167425
> **Births:** 0 **Total Expense ($000):** 91562 **Payroll Expense ($000):** 37865
> **Personnel:** 518

⊠ △ **ALBANY STRATTON VETERANS AFFAIRS MEDICAL CENTER**, 113
Holland Avenue, Zip 12208–3473; tel. 518/626–5000, (Total facility includes 50
beds in nursing home–type unit) **A**1 2 3 5 7 8 **F**2 3 4 5 15 17 18 20 22 28 29
30 31 34 35 39 40 44 45 46 47 49 50 54 55 56 57 58 59 60 61 62 63 64
65 68 70 74 75 77 78 79 81 82 83 84 85 86 87 91 92 93 94 97 98 100
102 103 104 105 106 107 108 110 111 115 117 118 119 120 121 122 126
127 128 129 130 132 135 143 146 147 148 **S** Department of Veterans Affairs,
Washington, DC
Primary Contact: Deborah Spath, Interim Director
CFO: Gerard Scorzelli, Chief Financial Officer
CMO: Lourdes Irizarry, M.D., Chief of Staff
CIO: Ron Diaz, Manager Operations
CHR: Kenneth Kio, Manager Human Resources
CNO: Deborah Spath, R.N., Associate Director Patient and Nurses Services
Web address: www.albany.va.gov/
Control: Veterans Affairs, Government, federal **Service:** General Medical and
Surgical

> **Staffed Beds:** 155 **Admissions:** 2775 **Census:** 88 **Outpatient Visits:** 398765
> **Births:** 0 **Total Expense ($000):** 254076 **Payroll Expense ($000):** 142232
> **Personnel:** 1304

☐ **CAPITAL DISTRICT PSYCHIATRIC CENTER (334046)**, 75 New Scotland
Avenue, Zip 12208–3474; tel. 518/549–6000, (Nonreporting) **A**1 3 5 10 **S** New
York State Office of Mental Health, Albany, NY
Primary Contact: William Dickson, Executive Director
COO: Catherine McGregor, Deputy Director Facility and Administrative Services
CMO: Kren K. Shriver, M.D., Clinical Director
CNO: Charlene Puorto, Chief Nursing Officer
Web address: www.omh.ny.gov/omhweb/facilities/cdpc/facility.htm
Control: State–Government, nonfederal **Service:** Psychiatric

> **Staffed Beds:** 200

⊠ **ST. PETER'S HOSPITAL (330057)**, 315 South Manning Boulevard,
Zip 12208–1789; tel. 518/525–1550 **A**1 2 3 5 10 19 **F**4 5 8 11 12 13 15 17
18 19 20 21 22 23 24 26 27 28 29 30 31 34 35 36 37 38 39 40 45 46 47
48 49 50 51 53 54 56 57 59 60 61 62 63 64 65 66 68 69 70 71 72 73 74
75 76 77 78 79 81 82 84 85 86 87 89 92 93 97 107 108 109 110 111 114
115 116 117 118 119 120 121 123 124 126 129 130 132 133 135 143 145
146 147 148 **P**6 **S** Trinity Health, Livonia, MI
Primary Contact: Virginia L. Golden, Chief Executive Officer
CFO: Lori Santos, Chief Financial Officer
CMO: Robert Cella, M.D., Chief Medical Officer
CHR: Judy Gray, Vice President Human Resources
CNO: Jane O'Rourke, R.N., Chief Nursing Officer, Vice President Operations
Web address: www.sphcs.org
Control: Church–operated, Nongovernment, not–for profit **Service:** General
Medical and Surgical

> **Staffed Beds:** 442 **Admissions:** 25586 **Census:** 369 **Outpatient Visits:**
> 522024 **Births:** 2792 **Total Expense ($000):** 91562 **Personnel:** 2924

ALEXANDRIA BAY—Jefferson County

★ **RIVER HOSPITAL (331309)**, 4 Fuller Street, Zip 13607–1316;
tel. 315/482–2511, (Nonreporting) **A**10 18
Primary Contact: Ben Moore, III, President and Chief Executive Officer
COO: William Connor, Assistant Administrator and Director Human Resources
CFO: Traci Mintonye, Chief Financial Officer
CMO: Prasad Yitta, M.D., Medical Director
CIO: John Smithers, Network Specialist
CHR: William Connor, Assistant Administrator and Director Human Resources
CNO: Ann Narrow, Director of Nursing
Web address: www.riverhospital.org
Control: Other not–for–profit (including NFP Corporation) **Service:** General
Medical and Surgical

> **Staffed Beds:** 11

AMITYVILLE—Suffolk County

☐ **BRUNSWICK PSYCH CENTER (334026)**, 81 Louden Avenue,
Zip 11701–2736; tel. 631/789–7421 **A**1 10 **F**98 99 100 101 102 103 130
132 135
Primary Contact: Amarjit Singh, M.D., President and Chief Executive Officer
Control: Corporation, Investor–owned, for–profit **Service:** Psychiatric

> **Staffed Beds:** 124 **Admissions:** 1977 **Census:** 85 **Outpatient Visits:** 0
> **Births:** 0 **Total Expense ($000):** 23394 **Payroll Expense ($000):** 11852
> **Personnel:** 169

⊠ **SOUTH OAKS HOSPITAL (334027)**, 400 Sunrise Highway, Zip 11701–2508;
tel. 631/264–4000 **A**1 10 **F**4 5 50 53 68 98 99 103 104 105 135 **P**5 6
S Northwell Health, New Hyde Park, NY
Primary Contact: Patricia Porter, Executive Director
CMO: Tina Walch, M.D., Medical Director
CHR: Irene Calvin, Vice President Human Resources
Web address: www.longislandhome.org
Control: Other not–for–profit (including NFP Corporation) **Service:** Psychiatric

> **Staffed Beds:** 258 **Admissions:** 5536 **Census:** 143 **Outpatient Visits:** 87512
> **Births:** 0 **Total Expense ($000):** 62704 **Payroll Expense ($000):** 38078
> **Personnel:** 714

AMSTERDAM—Montgomery County

ST. MARY'S HEALTHCARE See St. Mary's Healthcare

NY

Hospital, Medicare Provider Number, Address, Telephone, Approval, Facility, and Physician Codes, Health Care System

★ American Hospital Association (AHA) membership   ○ Healthcare Facilities Accreditation Program   ⇑ Center for Improvement in Healthcare Quality Accreditation
☐ The Joint Commission accreditation   ◇ DNV Healthcare Inc. accreditation   △ Commission on Accreditation of Rehabilitation Facilities (CARF) accreditation

✠ **ST. MARY'S HEALTHCARE (330047)**, 427 Guy Park Avenue, Zip 12010–1054; tel. 518/842–1900, (Includes ST. MARY'S HEALTHCARE, 427 Guy Park Avenue, tel. 518/842–1900; Victor Giulianelli, FACHE, President and Chief Executive Officer), (Total facility includes 160 beds in nursing home–type unit) **A**1 10 **F**2 3 4 5 8 11 13 15 17 28 29 30 31 34 35 36 38 40 45 46 49 50 51 54 56 57 59 60 61 65 66 68 70 71 74 75 76 77 78 79 81 84 85 86 87 89 90 93 94 96 97 98 99 100 101 102 103 104 105 106 107 108 110 111 115 118 119 126 127 128 130 131 132 135 144 145 146 147 **S** Ascension Health, Saint Louis, MO
Primary Contact: Victor Giulianelli, FACHE, President and Chief Executive Officer
COO: Scott Bruce, Vice President Operations
CFO: Rick Henze, Chief Financial Officer
CMO: William Mayer, M.D., Vice President Medical Staff Services
CIO: Leigh Chiuminetta, Interim Chief Information Officer
CHR: Albert Turo, Vice President Human Resources
CNO: Michele M. Walsh, Chief Nursing Officer
Web address: www.smha.org
Control: Other not–for–profit (including NFP Corporation) **Service:** General Medical and Surgical

Staffed Beds: 290 **Admissions:** 6926 **Census:** 252 **Outpatient Visits:** 420053 **Births:** 483 **Total Expense ($000):** 155871 **Payroll Expense ($000):** 81895 **Personnel:** 1437

AUBURN—Cayuga County

✠ **AUBURN COMMUNITY HOSPITAL (330235)**, 17 Lansing Street, Zip 13021–1943; tel. 315/255–7011, (Total facility includes 80 beds in nursing home–type unit) **A**1 10 20 **F**1 3 12 13 15 18 26 28 29 30 31 34 35 40 45 50 51 53 54 55 57 59 64 70 76 78 79 81 82 85 89 93 97 98 103 107 108 110 111 115 119 124 129 130 132 135 144 146 147
Primary Contact: Scott A. Berlucchi, FACHE, President and Chief Executive Officer
CFO: Jason Lesch, Chief Financial Officer
CMO: John A. Riccio, M.D., Chief Medical Officer
CIO: Chris Ryan, Chief Information Officer
CHR: Linda Daly, Vice President Human Resources
CNO: Tammy Sunderlin, Director of Nursing
Web address: www.auburnhospital.org
Control: Other not–for–profit (including NFP Corporation) **Service:** General Medical and Surgical

Staffed Beds: 179 **Admissions:** 5326 **Census:** 139 **Outpatient Visits:** 146436 **Births:** 394 **Total Expense ($000):** 109919 **Payroll Expense ($000):** 54853 **Personnel:** 743

BATAVIA—Genesee County

✠ **UNITED MEMORIAL MEDICAL CENTER (330073)**, 127 North Street, Zip 14020–1631; tel. 585/343–6030, (Includes UNITED MEMORIAL MEDICAL CENTER–BANK STREET, 127 North Street, Zip 14020–2260; tel. 716/343–3131; UNITED MEMORIAL MEDICAL CENTER–NORTH STREET, 16 Banks Street, Zip 14020–1697; tel. 585/343–6030) **A**1 10 13 **F**3 4 8 13 15 17 18 28 29 30 31 34 35 40 43 49 50 54 57 59 64 65 68 70 75 76 77 78 79 81 82 84 85 86 87 89 93 97 107 111 114 115 119 120 121 122 127 129 130 131 132 135 144 146 147 148 **P**5 **S** Rochester Regional Health, Rochester, NY
Primary Contact: Daniel P. Ireland, FACHE, President
CFO: Robert Chiavetta, Vice President Finance
CMO: Michael Merrill, M.D., Interim Vice President Medical Affairs
CIO: Kurt Calman, Chief Information Officer
CHR: Sonja Gonyea, Director Human Resources
CNO: Mary Beth Bowen, R.N., Vice President Nursing and Chief Nursing Officer
Web address: www.ummc.org
Control: Other not–for–profit (including NFP Corporation) **Service:** General Medical and Surgical

Staffed Beds: 131 **Admissions:** 3637 **Census:** 50 **Outpatient Visits:** 238733 **Births:** 635 **Total Expense ($000):** 89520 **Payroll Expense ($000):** 36871 **Personnel:** 642

★ **VETERANS AFFAIRS WESTERN NEW YORK HEALTHCARE SYSTEM–BATAVIA DIVISION**, 222 Richmond Avenue, Zip 14020–1288; tel. 585/297–1000, (Nonreporting) **A**5 **S** Department of Veterans Affairs, Washington, DC
Primary Contact: Brian G. Stiller, Director Medical Center
Web address: www.buffalo.va.gov/batavia.asp
Control: Veterans Affairs, Government, federal **Service:** General Medical and Surgical

Staffed Beds: 128

BATH—Steuben County

✠ **BATH VETERANS AFFAIRS MEDICAL CENTER**, 76 Veterans Avenue, Zip 14810–0842; tel. 607/664–4000, (Total facility includes 94 beds in nursing home–type unit) **A**1 **F**3 4 5 7 11 12 18 29 30 33 34 35 36 38 39 44 50 53 54 56 57 59 61 62 63 64 65 66 68 71 74 75 77 79 82 83 84 86 87 90 91 93 94 97 100 101 103 104 107 119 127 128 129 130 132 133 135 143 144 146 147 148 **P**6 **S** Department of Veterans Affairs, Washington, DC
Primary Contact: Michael J. Swartz, FACHE, Medical Center Director
COO: David Krueger, Associate Director
CFO: Jill Haynes, Financial Coach
CMO: Felipe Diaz, M.D., Chief of Staff
CIO: Karen Clancy, Manager Information Systems Operations
CHR: Susan DeSalvo, Manager Human Resources
Web address: www.bath.va.gov
Control: Veterans Affairs, Government, federal **Service:** General Medical and Surgical

Staffed Beds: 274 **Admissions:** 1355 **Census:** 236 **Outpatient Visits:** 175000 **Births:** 0 **Total Expense ($000):** 97641 **Payroll Expense ($000):** 64599 **Personnel:** 740

◇ **IRA DAVENPORT MEMORIAL HOSPITAL (330144)**, 7571 State Route 54, Zip 14810–9590; tel. 607/776–8500, (Total facility includes 120 beds in nursing home–type unit) **A**10 21 **F**2 8 11 14 15 28 29 30 34 35 40 42 45 50 55 57 59 64 65 68 75 79 81 87 91 93 107 110 111 115 119 128 129 130 135 146 **S** Arnot Health, Elmira, NY
Primary Contact: Richard Cleland, FACHE, Site Administrator
CFO: Ronald J. Kintz, Chief Financial Officer
CMO: Dennis O'Connor, M.D., Medical Director
CIO: Gregg Martin, Chief Information Officer
CHR: Brian K. Forrest, Director Human Resources
CNO: Linda Donley, Vice President Operations
Web address: www.arnothealth.org
Control: Other not–for–profit (including NFP Corporation) **Service:** General Medical and Surgical

Staffed Beds: 132 **Admissions:** 945 **Census:** 116 **Total Expense ($000):** 24010 **Payroll Expense ($000):** 9928

BAY SHORE—Suffolk County

✠ △ **SOUTHSIDE HOSPITAL (330043)**, 301 East Main Street, Zip 11706–8458; tel. 631/968–3000 **A**1 2 3 5 7 10 **F**3 8 11 13 15 17 18 19 20 22 24 26 28 29 30 31 32 34 35 36 38 40 41 43 44 45 46 49 50 54 55 56 57 58 59 60 61 62 63 64 65 66 68 70 73 74 75 76 77 78 79 80 81 82 84 85 86 87 89 90 93 96 97 100 101 102 103 107 108 110 111 115 118 119 121 123 126 129 130 131 132 135 145 146 147 148 **P**5 6 **S** Northwell Health, New Hyde Park, NY
Primary Contact: Donna Moravick, R.N., MSN, Executive Director
CFO: Robert Power, Associate Executive Director Finance
CMO: Jay Enden, M.D., Medical Director
CIO: Lowney Mincy, Director Information Services
CHR: Anne J. Barrett, Associate Executive Director Human Resources
Web address: www.southsidehospital.org
Control: Other not–for–profit (including NFP Corporation) **Service:** General Medical and Surgical

Staffed Beds: 287 **Admissions:** 18605 **Census:** 255 **Outpatient Visits:** 153302 **Births:** 2472 **Total Expense ($000):** 487170 **Payroll Expense ($000):** 244159 **Personnel:** 2357

BELLEROSE—Queens County, See New York City

BETHPAGE—Nassau County

☐ **ST. JOSEPH HOSPITAL (330332)**, 4295 Hempstead Turnpike, Zip 11714–5769; tel. 516/579–6000 **A**1 10 **F**3 8 15 17 18 29 30 34 35 39 40 45 46 49 50 51 56 57 59 60 64 65 68 69 70 74 75 79 81 85 86 87 93 107 108 110 111 114 119 127 128 133 135 141 146 148 **S** Catholic Health Services of Long Island, Rockville Centre, NY
Primary Contact: Ronald Steimel, Executive Vice President and Chief Administrative Officer
CFO: John Morahan, Vice President Finance
CMO: Howard Sussman, M.D., Chief Medical Officer
CHR: Peter Chiacchiaro, Vice President Human Resources
CNO: Barbara Gibbons, Vice President Patient Care Services
Web address: www.stjosephhospital.chsli.org
Control: Other not–for–profit (including NFP Corporation) **Service:** General Medical and Surgical

Staffed Beds: 128 **Admissions:** 6158 **Census:** 92 **Outpatient Visits:** 44636 **Births:** 0 **Total Expense ($000):** 109406 **Payroll Expense ($000):** 47386 **Personnel:** 656

BINGHAMTON—Broome County

BINGHAMTON GENERAL HOSPITAL See United Health Services Hospitals–Binghamton

☐ **GREATER BINGHAMTON HEALTH CENTER (334012)**, 425 Robinson Street, Zip 13904–1735; tel. 607/724–1391, (Nonreporting) **A**1 10 **S** New York State Office of Mental Health, Albany, NY
Primary Contact: Mark Stephany, Executive Director
CFO: Cherry Randall, Business Officer
CHR: Renee O'Brien, Director Human Resources
Web address: www.omh.ny.gov/omhweb/facilities/bipc/facility.htm
Control: State–Government, nonfederal **Service:** Psychiatric

Staffed Beds: 115

☒ **OUR LADY OF LOURDES MEMORIAL HOSPITAL, INC. (330011)**, 169 Riverside Drive, Zip 13905–4246; tel. 607/798–5111 **A**1 2 10 13 **F**3 11 12 13 15 18 19 28 29 30 31 32 34 35 36 39 40 44 45 46 47 49 50 51 53 54 56 57 59 60 62 63 64 65 66 68 70 71 74 75 76 77 78 79 81 84 85 86 87 89 93 97 99 100 101 103 104 107 108 110 111 114 115 118 119 120 121 123 124 126 127 129 130 131 132 134 135 143 144 145 146 147 148 **P**6 **S** Ascension Health, Saint Louis, MO
Primary Contact: Kathryn Connerton, President and Chief Executive Officer
COO: Linda Miller, R.N., Senior Vice President Operations and Chief Nursing Officer
CFO: Sean Mills, Chief Financial Officer
CMO: Lisa Harris, M.D., Senior Vice President Medical Affairs
CIO: Thomas Ellerson, Chief Information Officer
CHR: Mary Hughs, Chief Human Resources Officer
CNO: Linda Miller, R.N., Senior Vice President Operations and Chief Nursing Officer
Web address: www.lourdes.com
Control: Church–operated, Nongovernment, not–for profit **Service:** General Medical and Surgical

Staffed Beds: 154 **Admissions:** 10429 **Census:** 121 **Outpatient Visits:** 1540469 **Births:** 1115 **Total Expense ($000):** 297175 **Payroll Expense ($000):** 126574 **Personnel:** 1740

UNITED HEALTH SERVICES HOSPITALS–BINGHAMTON (330394), 10–42 Mitchell Avenue, Zip 13903–1678; tel. 607/763–6000, (Includes BINGHAMTON GENERAL HOSPITAL, 10–42 Mitchell Avenue, Zip 13903; tel. 607/762–2200; Matthew J. Salanger, President and Chief Executive Officer; WILSON MEMORIAL REGIONAL MEDICAL CENTER, 33–57 Harrison Street, Johnson City, Zip 13790; tel. 607/763–6000; Matthew J. Salanger, President and Chief Executive Officer) **A**8 10 **F**1 3 4 5 8 11 12 13 15 17 18 20 22 24 26 28 29 30 31 32 33 34 35 38 39 40 43 45 46 49 50 51 54 56 57 58 59 61 64 65 68 70 72 74 75 76 77 78 79 81 82 84 85 86 87 89 90 92 93 96 97 98 99 100 101 102 103 104 105 107 108 110 114 115 118 119 120 121 123 124 127 129 130 131 132 135 144 145 146 147 148 **P**3 **S** United Health Services, Binghamton, NY
Primary Contact: Matthew J. Salanger, President and Chief Executive Officer
COO: John Carrigg, Executive Vice President and Chief Operating Officer
CFO: David MacDougall, Chief Financial Officer
CMO: Rajesh J. Dave', M.D., Executive Vice President and Chief Medical Officer
CIO: Susan Carman, Chief Information Officer
CHR: Michael McNally, Vice President Human Resources
CNO: E. Kay Boland, R.N., Vice President and Chief Nursing Officer
Web address: www.uhs.net
Control: Other not–for–profit (including NFP Corporation) **Service:** General Medical and Surgical

Staffed Beds: 466 **Admissions:** 18166 **Census:** 282 **Outpatient Visits:** 1015785 **Births:** 1179 **Total Expense ($000):** 560604 **Payroll Expense ($000):** 200305 **Personnel:** 3743

BRENTWOOD—Suffolk County

☐ **PILGRIM PSYCHIATRIC CENTER (334013)**, 998 Crooked Hill Road, Zip 11717–1019; tel. 631/761–3500, (Nonreporting) **A**1 10 **S** New York State Office of Mental Health, Albany, NY
Primary Contact: Kathy O'Keefe, Executive Director
CFO: Florence Corwin, Director for Administration
CMO: Inderjit Singh, M.D., Clinical Director
CIO: Douglas Cargonara, Ph.D., Chief Information Officer
CHR: Florence Corwin, Director Administration
Web address: www.omh.ny.gov/omhweb/facilities/pgpc/facility.htm
Control: State–Government, nonfederal **Service:** Psychiatric

Staffed Beds: 569

BRONX—Bronx County, See New York City

BRONXVILLE—Westchester County

☒ **NEW YORK–PRESBYTERIAN/LAWRENCE HOSPITAL (330061)**, 55 Palmer Avenue, Zip 10708–3403; tel. 914/787–1000 **A**1 2 5 10 **F**3 7 12 13 14 15 17 18 20 22 28 29 30 31 34 35 36 40 41 45 46 47 48 49 50 51 55 56 59 60 62 63 64 68 70 72 73 74 75 77 78 79 81 82 83 84 85 87 88 89 93 96 100 107 108 110 111 114 115 119 126 129 130 131 132 135 144 145 148 **P**4 **S** New York Presbyterian Regional Hospital Network, New York, NY
Primary Contact: Michael Fosina, M.P.H., FACHE, President
COO: James Y. Lee, Executive Vice President and Chief Operating Officer
CFO: Murray Askinazi, Senior Vice President and Chief Financial Officer
CMO: Werner Roeder, M.D., Vice President Medical Affairs
CHR: Tom Mastroianni, Vice President Human Resources
Web address: www.lawrencehealth.org
Control: Other not–for–profit (including NFP Corporation) **Service:** General Medical and Surgical

Staffed Beds: 205 **Admissions:** 10281 **Census:** 136 **Outpatient Visits:** 179831 **Births:** 1347 **Total Expense ($000):** 219677 **Payroll Expense ($000):** 91156 **Personnel:** 929

BROOKLYN—Kings County, See New York City

BUFFALO—Erie County

BRYLIN HOSPITALS (334022), 1263 Delaware Avenue, Zip 14209–2402; tel. 716/886–8200, (Nonreporting) **A**10
Primary Contact: Eric D. Pleskow, President and Chief Executive Officer
CFO: E. Paul Hettich, Chief Financial Officer
CMO: Maria Cartagena, M.D., Chief Medical Officer
CIO: Pawel Wieczorek, Director Information Technology
CHR: Jacquelyn Bixler, Vice President Human Resources
Web address: www.brylin.com
Control: Corporation, Investor–owned, for–profit **Service:** Psychiatric

Staffed Beds: 88

☐ **BUFFALO PSYCHIATRIC CENTER (334052)**, 400 Forest Avenue, Zip 14213–1298; tel. 716/885–2261, (Nonreporting) **A**1 3 5 10 **S** New York State Office of Mental Health, Albany, NY
Primary Contact: Thomas Dodson, Executive Director
COO: Celia Spacone, M.D., Director Operations
CFO: Pamela Esposito, Director Administration
CMO: Jeffery Grace, M.D., Clinical Director
CIO: Anne Buchheit, Coordinator Mental Health Local Information Systems
CHR: Charles Siewert, Director Human Resources
CNO: Susan Fallis, Chief Nursing Officer
Web address: www.omh.ny.gov
Control: State–Government, nonfederal **Service:** Psychiatric

Staffed Beds: 240

☒ △ **ERIE COUNTY MEDICAL CENTER (330219)**, 462 Grider Street, Zip 14215–3098; tel. 716/898–3000, (Total facility includes 390 beds in nursing home–type unit) **A**1 3 5 7 10 **F**3 4 5 8 12 15 16 17 18 20 22 24 26 27 29 30 31 33 34 35 38 39 40 43 45 50 53 54 56 57 58 59 60 61 62 63 64 65 66 67 68 70 71 74 75 77 78 79 81 82 83 84 85 87 90 91 93 94 96 97 98 99 100 101 102 103 104 105 107 110 111 115 119 128 130 131 132 138 146 148 **P**6 7
Primary Contact: Thomas J. Quatroche, Jr., Chief Executive Officer
CFO: Michael Sammarco, M.D., Chief Financial Officer
CMO: Brian Murray, M.D., Medical Director
CIO: Leslie Feidt, Chief Information Officer
CHR: Kathleen O'Hara, Vice President Human Resources
CNO: Karen Ziemianski, R.N., Senior Vice President Nursing
Web address: www.ecmc.edu
Control: Hospital district or authority, Government, nonfederal **Service:** General Medical and Surgical

Staffed Beds: 881 **Admissions:** 18990 **Census:** 786 **Outpatient Visits:** 305737 **Births:** 0 **Total Expense ($000):** 552157 **Payroll Expense ($000):** 202137 **Personnel:** 3004

NY

Hospital, Medicare Provider Number, Address, Telephone, Approval, Facility, and Physician Codes, Health Care System

★ American Hospital Association (AHA) membership   ◯ Healthcare Facilities Accreditation Program   ⇑ Center for Improvement in Healthcare Quality Accreditation
☐ The Joint Commission accreditation   ◇ DNV Healthcare Inc. accreditation   △ Commission on Accreditation of Rehabilitation Facilities (CARF) accreditation

△ ◇ **KALEIDA HEALTH (330005)**, 100 High Street, Zip 14203–1154;
tel. 716/859–5600, (Includes DE GRAFF MEMORIAL HOSPITAL, 445 Tremont
Street, North Tonawanda, Zip 14120–0750, Mailing Address: P.O. Box 0750,
Zip 14120–0750; tel. 716/694–4500; Tamara Owen, President; MILLARD
FILLMORE SUBURBAN HOSPITAL, 1540 Maple Road, Williamsville, Zip 14221;
tel. 716/688–3100; WOMEN AND CHILDREN'S HOSPITAL, 219 Bryant Street,
Zip 14222–2099; tel. 716/878–7000; Cheryl Klass, President), (Total facility
includes 380 beds in nursing home–type unit) **A**3 5 7 10 21 **F**1 2 3 6 8 9 11 12
13 15 17 18 19 20 21 22 24 26 27 28 29 30 31 32 34 35 36 37 38 39 40
41 43 44 45 46 47 48 49 50 51 54 55 56 57 58 59 60 61 62 63 64 65 66
67 68 70 71 72 73 74 75 76 77 78 79 80 81 82 83 84 85 86 87 88 89 90
91 92 93 94 96 97 99 100 101 102 103 104 105 107 108 109 110 111 114
115 118 119 120 124 126 128 130 131 132 134 135 136 143 146 147 148
P2 4 5 6 7
Primary Contact: Jody Lomeo, Chief Executive Officer
CFO: Joseph Kessler, Executive Vice President and Chief Financial Officer
CMO: Margaret Paroski, M.D., Executive Vice President and Chief Medical Officer
CIO: Francis Meyer, Vice President Information Systems Technology
Web address: www.kaleidahealth.org
Control: Other not–for–profit (including NFP Corporation) **Service:** General
Medical and Surgical

Staffed Beds: 1368 **Admissions:** 49383 **Census:** 1065 **Outpatient Visits:**
782101 **Births:** 5487 **Total Expense ($000):** 1274430 **Payroll Expense
($000):** 550011 **Personnel:** 7870

⊠ **MERCY HOSPITAL (330279)**, 565 Abbott Road, Zip 14220–2095;
tel. 716/826–7000, (Total facility includes 84 beds in nursing home–type unit) **A**1
3 5 10 **F**3 8 13 15 17 18 20 22 24 26 29 30 31 34 35 39 40 41 42 45 46
48 49 50 54 57 59 60 64 65 70 72 74 75 76 77 78 79 81 84 85 87 89 90
92 93 96 97 104 107 108 110 111 114 115 118 119 126 128 129 130 131
132 146 147 148 **P**5 6 **S** Catholic Health System, Buffalo, NY
Primary Contact: Charles J. Urlaub, President and Chief Executive Officer
COO: Eddie Bratko, Chief Operating Officer
CFO: James H. Dunlop, Jr., CPA, Senior Vice President Finance and Chief Financial
Officer
CMO: Timothy Gabryel, M.D., Vice President Medical Affairs and Medical Director
CIO: Michael Galang, M.D., Chief Information Officer
CHR: Joseph A. Scrivo, Jr., Director Human Resources
CNO: Shari McDonald, Vice President Patient Care Services
Web address: www.chsbuffalo.org
Control: Church–operated, Nongovernment, not–for profit **Service:** General
Medical and Surgical

Staffed Beds: 438 **Admissions:** 18139 **Census:** 348 **Outpatient Visits:**
318999 **Births:** 2448 **Total Expense ($000):** 397176 **Payroll Expense
($000):** 162030 **Personnel:** 1955

☐ **ROSWELL PARK CANCER INSTITUTE (330354)**, Elm and Carlton Streets,
Zip 14263–0001; tel. 716/845–2300 **A**1 2 3 5 8 10 **F**3 8 14 15 29 30 31 32
34 35 38 39 44 45 46 47 49 50 55 56 57 58 59 64 65 66 67 70 74 75 77
78 80 81 82 84 85 86 87 89 90 93 94 96 97 98 100 104 107 108 110 111
112 114 115 116 117 118 119 120 121 123 124 126 130 132 135 136 141
145 146 147 148 **P**6
Primary Contact: Candace Johnson, Ph.D., President and Chief Executive Officer
COO: Victor A. Filadora, II, M.D., Chief Clinical Services
CFO: Gregory McDonald, Vice President Finance and Chief Financial Officer
CMO: Boris Kuvshinoff, II, M.D., Chief Medical Officer
CIO: Kerry Kerlin, Chief Information Officer
CNO: Margarita Frances Coyne, MS, Interim Chief Nursing Officer
Web address: www.roswellpark.org
Control: Hospital district or authority, Government, nonfederal **Service:** Cancer

Staffed Beds: 133 **Admissions:** 4442 **Census:** 104 **Outpatient Visits:**
201490 **Births:** 0 **Total Expense ($000):** 673162 **Payroll Expense ($000):**
246304 **Personnel:** 2923

⊠ **SISTERS OF CHARITY HOSPITAL OF BUFFALO (330078)**, 2157 Main Street,
Zip 14214–2692; tel. 716/862–1000, (Includes ST. JOSEPH HOSPITAL, 2605
Harlem Road, Cheektowaga, Zip 14225–4097; tel. 716/891–2400), (Total facility
includes 80 beds in nursing home–type unit) **A**1 2 3 5 10 12 13 **F**2 3 5 8 12 13
15 17 18 28 29 30 31 34 35 39 40 45 46 47 49 50 57 59 60 62 64 65 68
70 72 73 74 75 76 77 78 79 81 84 85 87 90 93 96 97 107 108 110 111
114 115 118 119 126 128 129 130 131 146 147 148 **P**5 6 **S** Catholic Health
System, Buffalo, NY
Primary Contact: Peter U. Bergmann, President and Chief Executive Officer
COO: Matthew Hamp, Chief Operating Officer
CFO: James H. Dunlop, Jr., CPA, Chief Financial Officer
CMO: Nady Shehata, M.D., Vice President Medical Affairs
CIO: Michael Galang, M.D., Chief Information Officer
CHR: David DeLorenzo, Senior Director Human Resources
CNO: Mary E. Dillon, MS, Vice President Patient Care Services
Web address: www.chsbuffalo.org
Control: Church–operated, Nongovernment, not–for profit **Service:** General
Medical and Surgical

Staffed Beds: 467 **Admissions:** 15133 **Census:** 295 **Outpatient Visits:**
702685 **Births:** 3480 **Total Expense ($000):** 323554 **Payroll Expense
($000):** 144053 **Personnel:** 1941

⊠ **VETERANS AFFAIRS WESTERN NEW YORK HEALTHCARE
SYSTEM–BUFFALO DIVISION**, 3495 Bailey Avenue, Zip 14215–1129;
tel. 716/834–9200, (Nonreporting) **A**1 2 3 5 8 **S** Department of Veterans Affairs,
Washington, DC
Primary Contact: Brian G. Stiller, Director Medical Center
CFO: Susan Gage, Financial Manager
CMO: Ali El–Solh, M.D., Interim Chief of Staff
CIO: Margaret Senker, Chief Information Officer
Web address: www.buffalo.va.gov/index.asp
Control: Veterans Affairs, Government, federal **Service:** General Medical and
Surgical

Staffed Beds: 113

WOMEN AND CHILDREN'S HOSPITAL See KALEIDA Health

CALLICOON—Sullivan County

GROVER M. HERMANN HOSPITAL (331303), 8881 Route 97, Zip 12723;
tel. 845/887–5530 **A**10 18 **F**3 11 15 29 30 34 35 40 50 57 59 64 65 68 75
85 97 107 130 132 133 146 **S** Greater Hudson Valley Health System,
Middletown, NY
Primary Contact: Rolland Bojo, R.N., Administrator
Web address: www.crmcny.org
Control: Other not–for–profit (including NFP Corporation) **Service:** General
Medical and Surgical

Staffed Beds: 25 **Admissions:** 126 **Census:** 3 **Outpatient Visits:** 13019
Total Expense ($000): 4353 **Payroll Expense ($000):** 2408 **Personnel:** 33

CANANDAIGUA—Ontario County

★ **CANANDAIGUA VETERANS AFFAIRS MEDICAL CENTER**, 400 Fort Hill Avenue,
Zip 14424–1159; tel. 585/394–2000, (Nonreporting) **A**3 5 **S** Department of
Veterans Affairs, Washington, DC
Primary Contact: Michael J. Swartz, FACHE, Medical Center Director
CMO: Robert Babcock, M.D., Chief of Staff
CIO: Bob Corrado, Chief Information Officer
Web address: www.canandaigua.va.gov/
Control: Veterans Affairs, Government, federal **Service:** Psychiatric

Staffed Beds: 196

⊠ **F. F. THOMPSON HOSPITAL (330074)**, 350 Parrish Street, Zip 14424–1731;
tel. 585/396–6000, (Total facility includes 188 beds in nursing home–type unit)
A1 10 **F**1 3 4 8 11 13 15 16 17 18 28 29 30 32 33 34 35 38 40 43 44 45
46 49 50 54 57 59 64 67 68 70 72 75 76 77 79 80 81 83 84 85 86 87 88
89 90 93 95 96 97 98 107 108 110 111 115 118 119 126 128 129 130 131
132 135 144 145 146 147 148 **S** University of Rochester Medical Center,
Rochester, NY
Primary Contact: Michael Stapleton, President and Chief Executive Officer
COO: Kurt Koczent, Executive Vice President and Chief Operating Officer
CFO: Mark Prunoske, Chief Financial Officer and Senior Vice President Finance
CMO: David Baum, M.D., Senior Vice President Medical Services
CIO: Mark Halladay, Director Information Services
CHR: Jennifer DeVault, Vice President Associate Services
CNO: Hazel Robertshaw, R.N., Chief Nursing Officer, Vice President Patient
Services
Web address: www.thompsonhealth.com
Control: Other not–for–profit (including NFP Corporation) **Service:** General
Medical and Surgical

Staffed Beds: 264 **Admissions:** 5630 **Census:** 234 **Outpatient Visits:**
214097 **Births:** 657 **Total Expense ($000):** 131378 **Payroll Expense
($000):** 61049 **Personnel:** 1053

THOMPSON HEALTH See F. F. Thompson Hospital

CARMEL—Putnam County

ARMS ACRES, 75 Seminary Hill Road, Zip 10512–1921;
tel. 845/225–3400, (Nonreporting)
Primary Contact: Patrice Wallace–Moore, Chief Executive Officer and Executive
Director
CFO: Jason Burczeuski, Controller
CMO: Fred Hesse, M.D., Medical Director
CIO: Dolores Watson, Director Health Information Management
CHR: Kim Halpin, Director Human Resources
CNO: Barbara Klein, R.N., Director of Nursing
Web address: www.armsacres.com
Control: Corporation, Investor–owned, for–profit **Service:** Alcoholism and other
chemical dependency

Staffed Beds: 146

Many Facility Codes have changed. Please refer to the AHA Guide Code Chart. © 2016 AHA Guide

☐ **PUTNAM HOSPITAL CENTER (330273)**, 670 Stoneleigh Avenue, Zip 10512–3997; tel. 845/279–5711 **A**1 2 10 **F**3 8 12 13 15 18 28 29 30 31 34 35 37 38 40 41 45 46 49 55 56 57 59 61 64 65 68 70 74 75 76 77 78 79 81 82 83 84 85 87 89 91 92 93 94 98 100 101 102 103 104 105 107 108 110 111 114 118 119 120 121 126 129 130 131 132 143 146 **P**6 **S** Health Quest Systems, Inc., LaGrangeville, NY
Primary Contact: Peter Kelly, President
CFO: Joseph Hart, Director Finance and Support Services
CNO: Luanne Convery, Vice President Patient Care Services
Web address: www.healthquest.org/carmel/putnam–hospital–center.aspx
Control: Other not–for–profit (including NFP Corporation) **Service:** General Medical and Surgical

Staffed Beds: 164 **Admissions:** 6427 **Census:** 80 **Outpatient Visits:** 199577 **Births:** 407 **Total Expense ($000):** 151976 **Payroll Expense ($000):** 50055 **Personnel:** 611

CARTHAGE—Jefferson County

✠ **CARTHAGE AREA HOSPITAL (331318)**, 1001 West Street, Zip 13619–9703; tel. 315/493–1000, (Nonreporting) **A**1 10 18
Primary Contact: Richard Duvall, Chief Executive Officer
CFO: Donald Schnackel, Chief Financial Officer
CMO: Mirza Ashraf, M.D., Medical Director
CIO: Joe Virkler, Chief Information Officer
CHR: Cathy Siedlecki, Director Human Resources
CNO: Susan Kellogg, Administrator Patient Care Services
Web address: www.carthagehospital.com
Control: Other not–for–profit (including NFP Corporation) **Service:** General Medical and Surgical

Staffed Beds: 55

CATSKILL—Greene County

KAATERSKILL CARE See Columbia Memorial Hospital, Hudson

CLIFTON SPRINGS—Ontario County

★ ◇ **CLIFTON SPRINGS HOSPITAL AND CLINIC (330265)**, 2 Coulter Road, Zip 14432–1189; tel. 315/462–9561, (Total facility includes 108 beds in nursing home–type unit) **A**10 21 **F**4 5 11 15 28 29 30 31 34 35 36 38 40 45 48 49 50 51 57 59 60 64 65 68 70 75 77 78 79 81 82 87 93 97 98 100 102 104 107 110 111 115 116 117 119 124 128 130 132 146 148 **P**5 6 **S** Rochester Regional Health, Rochester, NY
Primary Contact: Dustin Riccio, M.D., President
CFO: Sharon Kelley, Chief Financial Officer
CIO: Joel Majauskas, Chief Information Officer
CHR: Kathy Babb, Manager Human Resources
CNO: Donna P. Smith, R.N., Vice President Chief Operating Officer and Chief Nursing Officer
Web address: www.cliftonspringshospital.org
Control: Other not–for–profit (including NFP Corporation) **Service:** General Medical and Surgical

Staffed Beds: 214 **Admissions:** 2771 **Census:** 151 **Outpatient Visits:** 72635 **Births:** 0 **Total Expense ($000):** 59902 **Payroll Expense ($000):** 27595 **Personnel:** 523

COBLESKILL—Schoharie County

✠ **COBLESKILL REGIONAL HOSPITAL (330268)**, 178 Grandview Drive, Zip 12043–5144; tel. 518/254–3456, (Nonreporting) **A**1 10 20 **S** Bassett Healthcare Network, Cooperstown, NY
Primary Contact: Eric H. Stein, FACHE, President and Chief Executive Officer
CFO: Leanna Jensen, Vice President Finance and Chief Financial Officer
CMO: Roy Korn, M.D., Medical Director
CIO: Bridgette West, Director Patient Access Services
CHR: Christine Pirri, SHRM–SCP, Vice President, Human Resources, Education and Volunteer Services
CNO: Susan Oakes Ferrucci, MS, Vice President Patient Services and Chief Nursing Officer
Web address: www.cobleskillhospital.org
Control: Other not–for–profit (including NFP Corporation) **Service:** General Medical and Surgical

Staffed Beds: 40

COOPERSTOWN—Otsego County

✠ **BASSETT MEDICAL CENTER (330136)**, One Atwell Road, Zip 13326–1394; tel. 607/547–3100, (Nonreporting) **A**1 2 3 5 8 10 **S** Bassett Healthcare Network, Cooperstown, NY
Primary Contact: Vance Brown, M.D., President and Chief Executive Officer
COO: Andrew R. Manzer, Chief Operating Officer
CFO: Michael A. Tengeres, Corporate Vice President and Chief Financial Officer
CMO: William W. LeCates, M.D., Medical Director
CIO: Scott C. Groom, Vice President Information Services and Chief Information Officer
CHR: Sara Z. Albright, Vice President Human Resources
CNO: Judi Brendle, Vice President Clinical Support and Chief Nursing Officer
Web address: www.bassett.org
Control: Other not–for–profit (including NFP Corporation) **Service:** General Medical and Surgical

Staffed Beds: 164

CORNING—Steuben County

✠ **GUTHRIE CORNING HOSPITAL (330277)**, One Guthrie Drive, Zip 14830–3696; tel. 607/937–7200, (Nonreporting) **A**1 10 **S** Guthrie Clinic, Sayre, PA
Primary Contact: Garrett W. Hoover, FACHE, President
CFO: Francis M. Macafee, Vice President Finance and Chief Financial Officer
CMO: Chris Wentzel, M.D., Interim Medical Director
CHR: Laura Manning, Administrative Director
CNO: Deb Raupers, MSN, Chief Nursing Officer
Web address: www.corninghospital.com
Control: Other not–for–profit (including NFP Corporation) **Service:** General Medical and Surgical

Staffed Beds: 82

CORNWALL—Orange County

ST. LUKE'S CORNWALL HOSPITAL – CORNWALL CAMPUS See St. Luke's Cornwall Hospital, Newburgh

CORTLAND—Cortland County

✠ **CORTLAND REGIONAL MEDICAL CENTER (330175)**, 134 Homer Avenue, Zip 13045–1206; tel. 607/756–3500, (Total facility includes 82 beds in nursing home–type unit) **A**1 10 20 **F**2 3 8 11 13 15 18 28 29 30 31 34 35 40 44 45 49 50 54 56 57 59 62 64 70 75 76 77 78 79 81 82 85 86 87 91 93 96 98 100 102 103 107 108 110 111 114 115 118 119 128 130 131 132 133 135 144 146 147 148 **P**6
Primary Contact: Mark Webster, President and Chief Executive Officer
COO: Tracy Gates, Vice President Operations and Chief Operating Officer
CFO: Denise Wrinn, Vice President Finance and Chief Financial Officer
CMO: Roger Scott, D.O., Vice President Medical Affairs and Chief Medical Officer
CIO: Robert J. Duthe, Director Information Systems and Chief Information Officer
CNO: Mary Wright, Vice President Nursing Services and Chief Nursing Officer
Web address: www.cortlandregional.org
Control: Other not–for–profit (including NFP Corporation) **Service:** General Medical and Surgical

Staffed Beds: 184 **Admissions:** 4043 **Census:** 121 **Outpatient Visits:** 131329 **Births:** 431 **Total Expense ($000):** 85349 **Payroll Expense ($000):** 37908 **Personnel:** 680

CORTLANDT MANOR—Westchester County

☐ **NEW YORK–PRESBYTERIAN/HUDSON VALLEY HOSPITAL (330267)**, 1980 Crompond Road, Zip 10567–4182; tel. 914/737–9000, (Nonreporting) **A**1 10 **S** New York Presbyterian Regional Hospital Network, New York, NY
Primary Contact: Stacey Petrower, President
COO: Deborah Neuendorf, Vice President Administration
CFO: Mark Webster, Vice President Finance
CMO: William Higgins, M.D., Vice President Medical Affairs
CIO: Bud Sorbello, Director Management Information Systems
CHR: Jeane L. Costella, Vice President
CNO: Kathleen Webster, R.N., Vice President Patient Services
Web address: www.hvhc.org
Control: Other not–for–profit (including NFP Corporation) **Service:** General Medical and Surgical

Staffed Beds: 128

CUBA—Allegany County

CUBA MEMORIAL HOSPITAL (331301), 140 West Main Street, Zip 14727–1398; tel. 585/968–2000, (Nonreporting) **A**10 18
Primary Contact: Andrew Boser, Chief Executive Officer
CFO: Jack Ormond, Chief Financial Officer
Web address: www.cubamemorialhospital.com
Control: Other not–for–profit (including NFP Corporation) **Service:** General Medical and Surgical

Staffed Beds: 81

NY

DANSVILLE—Livingston County

✠ **NICHOLAS H. NOYES MEMORIAL HOSPITAL (330238)**, 111 Clara Barton Street, Zip 14437–9503; tel. 585/335–6001 **A**1 10 **F**3 8 11 13 15 29 31 32 34 35 40 45 47 49 50 51 54 57 59 60 64 68 70 75 76 79 81 82 84 85 93 99 100 102 104 107 108 110 115 119 130 131 132 133 144 146 **P**5
Primary Contact: Amy Pollard, R.N., President and Chief Executive Officer
CFO: Jay T. Maslyn, Chief Financial Officer
CMO: Douglas Mayhle, M.D., Medical Director
CIO: John Dorak, Chief Information Officer
CNO: Tamara West, R.N., Vice President Patient Care
Web address: www.noyes–health.org
Control: Other not–for–profit (including NFP Corporation) **Service:** General Medical and Surgical

Staffed Beds: 40 **Admissions:** 1536 **Census:** 17 **Outpatient Visits:** 183782 **Births:** 353 **Personnel:** 403

DELHI—Delaware County

✠ **O'CONNOR HOSPITAL (331305)**, 460 Andes Road, State Route 28, Zip 13753–7407; tel. 607/746–0300 **A**1 10 18 **F**15 29 34 35 40 45 46 50 56 57 59 64 65 75 77 79 81 85 86 87 91 92 93 96 107 110 119 130 131 132 133 135 147 **S** Bassett Healthcare Network, Cooperstown, NY
Primary Contact: Carlton Rule, M.D., Chief Executive Officer
CFO: Sue E. Andrews, Chief Financial Officer
CMO: Peter L. Sosnow, Medical Director
CHR: Barbara Green, Director Human Resources
CNO: Debra Neale, R.N., Chief Nursing Officer
Web address: www.bassett.org
Control: Other not–for–profit (including NFP Corporation) **Service:** General Medical and Surgical

Staffed Beds: 16 **Admissions:** 279 **Census:** 6 **Outpatient Visits:** 30936 **Births:** 0 **Total Expense ($000):** 21186 **Payroll Expense ($000):** 7264

DIX HILLS—Suffolk County

☐ **SAGAMORE CHILDREN'S PSYCHIATRIC CENTER**, 197 Half Hollow Road, Zip 11746–5861; tel. 631/370–1700, (Nonreporting) **A**1 **S** New York State Office of Mental Health, Albany, NY
Primary Contact: Kathy O'Keefe, Interim Executive Director
COO: Cathy Stein, Chief Inpatient Services
CFO: Jane Alexander, Director Facility Administrative Services
CIO: Bryan Doherty, Management Information Technology Services I
CHR: Nancy Angell, Associate Administrator Personnel
CNO: Sandra King, Chief Nursing Officer
Web address: www.omh.ny.gov
Control: State–Government, nonfederal **Service:** Children's hospital psychiatric

Staffed Beds: 69

DUNKIRK—Chautauqua County

◇ **BROOKS MEMORIAL HOSPITAL (330229)**, 529 Central Avenue, Zip 14048–2599; tel. 716/366–1111, (Nonreporting) **A**10 21
Primary Contact: Mary E. LaRowe, FACHE, President and Chief Executive Officer
CFO: Jeffrey H. Morgan, Vice President Finance and Chief Financial Officer
CIO: Kevin Kimball, Director Information Technology
CHR: Tracie Luther, Director of Labor Relations and Human Relations
CNO: Jodi Witherell, Vice President Patient Care and Quality
Web address: www.brookshospital.org
Control: Other not–for–profit (including NFP Corporation) **Service:** General Medical and Surgical

Staffed Beds: 65

EAST MEADOW—Nassau County

✠ **NASSAU UNIVERSITY MEDICAL CENTER (330027)**, 2201 Hempstead Turnpike, Zip 11554–1859; tel. 516/572–0123, (Nonreporting) **A**1 3 5 10 12 13
Primary Contact: Victor Politi, M.D., President and Chief Executive Officer
COO: Harold E. McDonald, Deputy Executive Director and Senior Vice President Administration
CFO: John P. Maher, Executive Vice President and Chief Financial Officer
CMO: Victor Scarmato, M.D., Acting Medical Director
CIO: Farooq Ajmal, Vice President and Chief Information Officer
CHR: Maureen Roarty, Executive Vice President Human Resources
CNO: Kathy Skarka, MSN, Executive Vice President Patient Care Services
Web address: www.nuhealth.net
Control: Hospital district or authority, Government, nonfederal **Service:** General Medical and Surgical

Staffed Beds: 1119

ELIZABETHTOWN—Essex County

✠ **THE UNIVERSITY OF VERMONT HEALTH NETWORK ELIZABETHTOWN COMMUNITY HOSPITAL (331302)**, 75 Park Street, Zip 12932, Mailing Address: P.O. Box 277, Zip 12932–0277; tel. 518/873–6377, (Nonreporting) **A**1 10 18
Primary Contact: John R. Remillard, Interim Chief Executive Officer
COO: Matthew Nolan, Chief Operating Officer
CFO: Alan Chardavoyne, Chief Financial Officer
CMO: Rob DeMuro, M.D., Chief Medical Officer
CIO: Darrin Goodrow, Chief Information Officer
CHR: Michelle Meachem, Director Human Resources
CNO: Julie Tromblee, R.N., Chief Nursing Officer
Web address: www.ech.org
Control: Other not–for–profit (including NFP Corporation) **Service:** General Medical and Surgical

Staffed Beds: 25

ELLENVILLE—Ulster County

★ **ELLENVILLE REGIONAL HOSPITAL (331310)**, 10 Healthy Way, Zip 12428–5612; tel. 845/647–6400 **A**10 18 **F**8 11 15 18 28 29 30 31 35 36 40 45 48 50 57 58 60 65 68 77 79 81 82 85 93 107 110 111 115 119 125 132 133 147 148
Primary Contact: Steven L. Kelley, President and Chief Executive Officer
CFO: Patricia Gavis, Chief Financial Officer
CMO: Walter Sperling, M.D., Medical Director
CHR: Deborah Briggs, Vice President Human Resources, Marketing, Volunteer Services and Community Relations
CNO: Ann Marie Guntlow, Chief Nursing Officer
Web address: www.ellenvilleregional.org
Control: Other not–for–profit (including NFP Corporation) **Service:** General Medical and Surgical

Staffed Beds: 25 **Admissions:** 424 **Census:** 12 **Births:** 0 **Total Expense ($000):** 15903 **Payroll Expense ($000):** 8186 **Personnel:** 140

ELMHURST—Queens County, See New York City

ELMIRA—Chemung County

★ ◇ **ARNOT OGDEN MEDICAL CENTER (330090)**, 600 Roe Avenue, Zip 14905–1629; tel. 607/737–4100 **A**2 10 12 13 21 **F**11 12 15 17 18 20 22 24 26 28 29 30 31 35 40 45 46 48 49 50 51 53 54 56 57 59 60 61 65 68 70 72 73 74 75 77 78 79 81 87 91 93 97 100 103 106 107 110 111 115 116 119 129 130 131 132 135 143 144 146 147 148 **S** Arnot Health, Elmira, NY
Primary Contact: Kerry Watson, Interim President and Chief Operating Officer
CFO: Ronald J. Kintz, Vice President and Treasurer
CMO: William Huffner, M.D., Vice President Medical Affairs
CIO: Gregg Martin, Manager Management Information Systems
CHR: Brian K. Forrest, Director Human Resources
CNO: Mary M. Vosburgh, R.N., Vice President Nursing and Chief Nursing Officer
Web address: www.aomc.org
Control: Other not–for–profit (including NFP Corporation) **Service:** General Medical and Surgical

Staffed Beds: 244 **Admissions:** 11235 **Census:** 135 **Outpatient Visits:** 339112 **Births:** 1410 **Total Expense ($000):** 297218 **Payroll Expense ($000):** 151731

☐ **ELMIRA PSYCHIATRIC CENTER (334045)**, 100 Washington Street, Zip 14901–2898; tel. 607/737–4739 **A**1 10 **F**29 35 38 54 64 71 98 99 101 104 106 132 **P**6 **S** New York State Office of Mental Health, Albany, NY
Primary Contact: Mark Stephany, Executive Director
COO: Karen Patterson, Deputy Director Operations
CFO: J. Paul Bedzyk, Deputy Director Administration
CMO: Kurt Hahn, M.D., Acting Clinical Director
CIO: Jeremy Newcomer, Director Information Services
CHR: Patricia Santulli, Director Human Resources
CNO: Pam Seeley, Chief Nursing Officer
Web address: www.omh.ny.gov/omhweb/facilities/elpc/facility.htm
Control: State–Government, nonfederal **Service:** Psychiatric

Staffed Beds: 100 **Admissions:** 295 **Census:** 117 **Outpatient Visits:** 47548 **Births:** 0 **Total Expense ($000):** 32330 **Personnel:** 366

◇ **ST. JOSEPH'S HOSPITAL (330108)**, 555 St. Joseph's Boulevard, Zip 14901–3223; tel. 607/733–6541, (Includes TWIN TIERS REHABILITATION CENTER), (Nonreporting) **A**10 21 **S** Arnot Health, Elmira, NY
Primary Contact: Kerry Watson, Interim President and Chief Operating Officer
CFO: Ronald J. Kintz, Senior Vice President Finance and Chief Financial Officer
CMO: William Huffner, M.D., Chief Medical Officer and Senior Vice President Medical Affairs
CIO: Gregg Martin, Chief Information Officer
CHR: Brian K. Forrest, Vice President Human Resources
CNO: Mary M. Vosburgh, R.N., Vice President Nursing and Chief Nursing Officer
Web address: www.stjosephs.org
Control: Other not–for–profit (including NFP Corporation) **Service:** General Medical and Surgical

Staffed Beds: 250

Many Facility Codes have changed. Please refer to the AHA Guide Code Chart. © 2016 AHA Guide

FAR ROCKAWAY—Queens County, See New York City

FLUSHING—Queens County, See New York City

FOREST HILLS—Queens County, See New York City

FRESH MEADOWS—Queens County

CORNERSTONE OF MEDICAL ARTS CENTER HOSPITAL, 159–05 Union Turnpike, Zip 11366–1950; tel. 212/755–0200, (Nonreporting)
Primary Contact: Thomas C. Puzo, President and Chief Executive Officer
CFO: Jeff OniFather, Chief Financial Officer
CMO: Sami Kaddouri, M.D., Medical Director
CHR: Gloria Burtch, Director Human Resources
Web address: www.cornerstoneny.com
Control: Corporation, Investor–owned, for–profit **Service:** Alcoholism and other chemical dependency

Staffed Beds: 162

GENEVA—Ontario County

✠ **GENEVA GENERAL HOSPITAL (330058)**, 196 North Street, Zip 14456–1694; tel. 315/787–4000 **A**1 3 10 **F**3 8 11 13 15 17 18 28 29 30 31 32 34 35 40 45 50 54 57 59 60 61 64 66 69 70 74 75 76 77 79 81 85 86 87 90 92 93 96 97 107 108 110 111 115 118 119 129 130 131 132 135 146 147 **P**6 **S** Finger Lakes Health, Geneva, NY
Primary Contact: Jose Acevedo, M.D., President and Chief Executive Officer
COO: Frank Korich, Senior Vice President, Operations
CFO: Pamela Johnson, Treasurer and Chief Financial Officer
CMO: Jason Feinberg, M.D., Vice President Medical Affairs and Chief Medical Officer
CIO: Guy W. Mosher, III, Manager Information Systems
CHR: Patrick R. Boyle, Vice President Human Resources
CNO: Eileen Gage, R.N., Vice President Nursing
Web address: www.flhealth.org
Control: Other not–for–profit (including NFP Corporation) **Service:** General Medical and Surgical

Staffed Beds: 132 Admissions: 3864 Census: 51 Outpatient Visits: 455172 Births: 0 Total Expense ($000): 87083 Payroll Expense ($000): 46726 Personnel: 788

GLEN COVE—Nassau County

✠ **GLEN COVE HOSPITAL (330181)**, 101 St. Andrews Lane, Zip 11542–2254; tel. 516/674–7300 **A**1 2 3 5 10 **F**3 8 9 11 15 17 18 28 29 30 31 32 33 34 35 36 38 39 40 43 45 46 47 48 49 50 54 55 56 57 58 59 60 61 63 64 65 66 68 69 70 74 75 77 78 79 81 82 84 85 86 87 90 91 92 93 94 96 97 100 102 103 104 107 108 110 111 115 118 119 121 130 131 132 135 143 146 147 **P**5 6 **S** Northwell Health, New Hyde Park, NY
Primary Contact: Susan Kwiatek, R.N., Executive Director
COO: Michele Frankel, Associate Executive Director Finance
CFO: Michele Frankel, Associate Executive Director Finance
CMO: Barbara Barnett, M.D., Medical Director
CHR: Thomas Salvo, Associate Executive Director Human Resources
CNO: Cathy Sheerin, R.N., Director Patient Care Services
Web address: www.northshorelij.com
Control: Other not–for–profit (including NFP Corporation) **Service:** General Medical and Surgical

Staffed Beds: 140 Admissions: 4242 Census: 81 Outpatient Visits: 78741 Births: 0 Total Expense ($000): 135334 Payroll Expense ($000): 74435 Personnel: 697

GLEN OAKS—Queens County, See New York City

GLENS FALLS—Warren County

✠ **GLENS FALLS HOSPITAL (330191)**, 100 Park Street, Zip 12801–4413; tel. 518/926–1000 **A**1 2 5 10 **F**3 5 8 11 13 15 17 18 20 22 26 28 29 30 31 32 34 35 40 43 44 45 46 47 49 50 53 54 57 59 60 64 68 70 71 73 74 75 76 77 78 79 81 82 84 85 86 87 89 90 92 93 96 97 98 99 100 102 103 104 105 107 108 110 114 115 118 119 120 121 123 124 126 127 129 130 132 135 144 145 146 147 148 **P**6
Primary Contact: Dianne Shugrue, President and Chief Executive Officer
COO: Paul Scimeca, Senior Vice President Operations and Chief Operating Officer
CFO: Mitchell Amado, Senior Vice President Finance and Chief Financial Officer
CMO: Robert W. Pringle, M.D., Vice President Medical Affairs and Chief Medical Officer
CIO: John Kelleher, Vice President Information Technology and Chief Information Officer
CHR: Kyle Brock, Vice President Human Resources
CNO: Donna Kirker NEA–BC, R.N., Vice President Patient Services and Chief Nursing Officer
Web address: www.glensfallshospital.org
Control: Other not–for–profit (including NFP Corporation) **Service:** General Medical and Surgical

Staffed Beds: 275 Admissions: 13163 Census: 197 Outpatient Visits: 728613 Births: 1232 Total Expense ($000): 332074 Payroll Expense ($000): 149713 Personnel: 2206

GLENVILLE—Schenectady County

CONIFER PARK, 79 Glenridge Road, Zip 12302–4523; tel. 518/399–6446, (Nonreporting)
Primary Contact: Jeanne Gluchowski, Executive Director
COO: Jeanne Gluchowski, Executive Director
CFO: Jason Burczeuski, Controller
CMO: John Melbourne, M.D., Medical Director
CIO: Amy Kentera, Chief Information Officer
CHR: Maureen Fowler, Director Human Resources
Web address: www.libertymgt.com
Control: Corporation, Investor–owned, for–profit **Service:** Alcoholism and other chemical dependency

Staffed Beds: 225

GLOVERSVILLE—Fulton County

★ ◇ **NATHAN LITTAUER HOSPITAL AND NURSING HOME (330276)**, 99 East State Street, Zip 12078–1203; tel. 518/725–8621, (Total facility includes 84 beds in nursing home–type unit) **A**5 10 21 **F**3 8 11 13 15 18 28 29 30 31 32 34 35 36 37 40 45 50 53 54 57 59 61 64 65 70 74 75 76 77 78 79 81 82 85 86 87 89 93 97 107 108 110 115 118 119 128 130 131 132 135 145 146 147 **P**6
Primary Contact: Laurence E. Kelly, President and Chief Executive Officer
CFO: Michael Ostrander, Chief Financial Officer
CMO: Frederick Goldberg, M.D., Vice President Medical Affairs and Chief Medical Officer
CIO: Martin Brown, Vice President Information Services and Chief Information Officer
CHR: Lana Wydra, Vice President Human Resources
CNO: Stephanie Fishel, Vice President Patient Care Services and Chief Nursing Officer
Web address: www.nlh.org
Control: Other not–for–profit (including NFP Corporation) **Service:** General Medical and Surgical

Staffed Beds: 158 Admissions: 2709 Census: 109 Outpatient Visits: 246013 Births: 358 Total Expense ($000): 94276 Payroll Expense ($000): 47943 Personnel: 784

GOUVERNEUR—St. Lawrence County

★ ◇ **GOUVERNEUR HOSPITAL (331315)**, 77 West Barney Street, Zip 13642–1040; tel. 315/287–1000 **A**10 18 21 **F**3 8 11 15 29 34 40 45 57 59 64 75 81 85 87 89 93 107 108 111 114 119 129 130 133 **P**6 **S** St. Lawrence Health System, Potsdam, NY
Primary Contact: Marlinda L. LaValley, Chief Executive Officer
CFO: Richard T. Lang, Chief Financial Officer
CMO: George Dodds, M.D., Medical Director
CHR: Suzan McDermott, Director, Human Resources
CNO: Jennifer Shaver, Director of Nursing
Web address: www.gvnrhospital.org
Control: Other not–for–profit (including NFP Corporation) **Service:** General Medical and Surgical

Staffed Beds: 25 Admissions: 417 Census: 5 Outpatient Visits: 50722 Births: 0 Total Expense ($000): 17468 Payroll Expense ($000): 7644 Personnel: 185

NY

Hospital, Medicare Provider Number, Address, Telephone, Approval, Facility, and Physician Codes, Health Care System

★ American Hospital Association (AHA) membership
☐ The Joint Commission accreditation
○ Healthcare Facilities Accreditation Program
◇ DNV Healthcare Inc. accreditation
⇑ Center for Improvement in Healthcare Quality Accreditation
△ Commission on Accreditation of Rehabilitation Facilities (CARF) accreditation

GREENPORT—Suffolk County

☒ **EASTERN LONG ISLAND HOSPITAL (330088)**, 201 Manor Place,
Zip 11944–1298; tel. 631/477–1000 **A**1 10 **F**3 4 17 18 28 29 34 38 40 45
47 49 53 56 59 64 65 68 70 74 78 79 81 82 85 93 97 98 100 102 103 106
107 110 111 119 130 135 146
Primary Contact: Paul J. Connor, III, President and Chief Executive Officer
CFO: Robert A. Ragona, Senior Vice President Finance and Chief Financial Officer
CMO: Lloyd Simon, M.D., Medical Director
CIO: Dan Scotto, Director Information Technology
CHR: Frank Dumont, Assistant Vice President Human Resources and Corporate
Compliance
CNO: D. Patricia Pispisa, Executive Vice President Patient Care Services
Web address: www.elih.org
Control: Other not–for–profit (including NFP Corporation) **Service:** General
Medical and Surgical

Staffed Beds: 90 **Admissions:** 2581 **Census:** 48 **Outpatient Visits:** 43397
Births: 0 **Total Expense ($000):** 49152 **Payroll Expense ($000):** 22143
Personnel: 318

HAMILTON—Madison County

☒ **COMMUNITY MEMORIAL HOSPITAL (331316)**, 150 Broad Street,
Zip 13346–9518; tel. 315/824–1100 **A**1 10 18 **F**11 18 29 34 40 45 52 53 64
65 75 79 81 85 93 97 107 110 111 119 127 130 133 135 144
Primary Contact: Sean Fadale, President and Chief Executive Officer
CFO: Christopher W. Graham, Chief Financial Officer
CMO: Robert Delorme, Vice President Medical Affairs
CHR: Jennifer Montana, Manager Human Resources
CNO: Denise Hummer, R.N., Vice President Administrative Services
Web address: www.communitymemorial.org
Control: Other not–for–profit (including NFP Corporation) **Service:** General
Medical and Surgical

Staffed Beds: 72 **Admissions:** 1516 **Census:** 10 **Outpatient Visits:** 199347
Births: 0 **Total Expense ($000):** 40578 **Payroll Expense ($000):** 14881
Personnel: 252

HARRIS—Sullivan County

☒ **CATSKILL REGIONAL MEDICAL CENTER (330386)**, 68 Harris Bushville Road,
Zip 12742–5030, Mailing Address: P.O. Box 800, Zip 12742–0800;
tel. 845/794–3300, (Total facility includes 64 beds in nursing home–type unit) **A**1
10 **F**2 3 8 11 12 13 15 17 18 28 29 30 31 34 35 38 40 45 50 51 56 57 59 64 65
66 68 70 75 76 78 79 81 85 86 87 89 93 96 97 98 99 100 101 102 103
104 107 108 111 115 119 127 128 130 132 135 146 147 148 **S** Greater
Hudson Valley Health System, Middletown, NY
Primary Contact: Gerard Galarneau, M.D., Chief Executive Officer and Chief
Medical Officer
CFO: Frank Hemeon, Interim Chief Financial Officer
CMO: Gerard Galarneau, M.D., Chief Executive Officer and Chief Medical Officer
CIO: John Lynch, Vice President Chief Information Officer
CNO: Rolland Bojo, R.N., Chief Nursing Officer, Administrator Patient Care and
Services
Web address: www.crmcny.org
Control: Other not–for–profit (including NFP Corporation) **Service:** General
Medical and Surgical

Staffed Beds: 165 **Admissions:** 3895 **Census:** 113 **Outpatient Visits:** 84443
Births: 601 **Total Expense ($000):** 80779 **Payroll Expense ($000):** 33034
Personnel: 738

HOLLISWOOD—Queens County, See New York City

HORNELL—Steuben County

☒ **ST. JAMES MERCY HOSPITAL (330151)**, 411 Canisteo Street,
Zip 14843–2197; tel. 607/324–8000, (Nonreporting) **A**1 10 20 **S** Trinity Health,
Livonia, MI
Primary Contact: Jennifer Sullivan, President and Chief Executive Officer
CFO: Stan Konopko, Chief Financial Officer
CMO: John Carroll, M.D., Chief Medical Officer
CIO: Jason Soles, Manager Information Systems
CHR: Jennifer Spike, Director Human Resources
CNO: Kathleen Brodbeck, MSN, RN–B, Chief Nursing Officer
Web address: www.stjamesmercy.org
Control: Other not–for–profit (including NFP Corporation) **Service:** General
Medical and Surgical

Staffed Beds: 222

HUDSON—Columbia County

★ **COLUMBIA MEMORIAL HOSPITAL (330094)**, 71 Prospect Avenue,
Zip 12534–2907; tel. 518/828–7601, (Includes KAATERSKILL CARE, 161
Jefferson Heights, Catskill, Zip 12414; tel. 518/943–6363) **A**10 19 **F**8 11 13 18
29 32 34 35 39 40 43 45 49 50 54 59 61 64 68 70 71 75 76 77 79 81 82
87 89 97 98 100 102 103 104 105 107 108 110 111 114 115 119 125 127
130 131 144 146 147
Primary Contact: Jay P. Cahalan, Chief Executive Officer
COO: Karen Tassey, FACHE, Chief Operating Officer
CFO: Bryan Mahoney, Chief Financial Officer
CMO: Lawrence Perl, M.D., Chief Medical Officer
CIO: Bonnie Ratliff, Chief Information Officer
Web address: www.columbiamemorialhealth.org
Control: Other not–for–profit (including NFP Corporation) **Service:** General
Medical and Surgical

Staffed Beds: 192 **Admissions:** 5800 **Census:** 91 **Outpatient Visits:** 443000
Births: 420 **Total Expense ($000):** 152100 **Payroll Expense ($000):** 76850
Personnel: 1210

HUNTINGTON—Suffolk County

☒ **HUNTINGTON HOSPITAL (330045)**, 270 Park Avenue, Zip 11743–2799;
tel. 631/351–2200 **A**1 2 3 10 **F**3 8 11 12 13 15 17 20 22 26 29 30 31 34 35
36 38 40 41 43 44 45 49 50 51 53 54 55 56 57 58 59 60 63 64 65 66 68
69 70 73 74 75 78 79 81 82 84 85 86 87 89 91 93 97 98 100 101 102 103
107 108 110 111 114 115 118 119 126 130 132 135 146 147 148 **P**5 6
S Northwell Health, New Hyde Park, NY
Primary Contact: Gerard Brogan, Jr., M.D., Executive Director
CFO: Michael Fagan, Chief Financial Officer
CMO: Michael Grosso, M.D., Senior Vice President Medical Affairs
CIO: Linda Fischer, Director Information Services
CHR: Donna Cice, Vice President Human Resources
CNO: Susan Knoepffler, R.N., Vice President Nursing
Web address: www.hunthosp.org
Control: Other not–for–profit (including NFP Corporation) **Service:** General
Medical and Surgical

Staffed Beds: 290 **Admissions:** 15448 **Census:** 203 **Outpatient Visits:**
115723 **Births:** 1423 **Total Expense ($000):** 372552 **Payroll Expense**
($000): 180723 **Personnel:** 1710

IRVING—Chautauqua County

◇ **TLC HEALTH NETWORK – LAKE SHORE HOSPITAL**, 845 Route 5 and 20,
Zip 14081–9716; tel. 716/951–7000, (Nonreporting) **A**21
Primary Contact: John P. Galati, Chief Executive Officer
CFO: John Eichner, Vice President Finance
CMO: James Wild, M.D., Medical Director
CIO: Raymond Manning, Director Information Technology
CHR: Shannon Bobseine, Manager Human Resources
CNO: Patricia Dole, Vice President Patient Care Services
Web address: www.tlchealth.org
Control: Other not–for–profit (including NFP Corporation) **Service:** General
Medical and Surgical

Staffed Beds: 220

ITHACA—Tompkins County

☒ **CAYUGA MEDICAL CENTER AT ITHACA (330307)**, 101 Dates Drive,
Zip 14850–1342; tel. 607/274–4011 **A**1 2 5 10 **F**3 8 12 13 15 18 20 22 28
29 30 31 34 35 38 40 41 45 48 49 50 51 54 57 59 61 64 68 70 72 74 75
76 77 78 79 81 82 84 85 86 87 90 92 93 98 99 100 101 102 103 107 108
110 111 114 115 116 117 118 119 121 129 130 131 132 133 135 144 145
146 147 148 **P**6
Primary Contact: John Rudd, President and Chief Executive Officer
CFO: John Collett, Vice President and Chief Financial Officer
CMO: David M. Evelyn, M.D., Vice President Medical Affairs
CIO: Brett Mello, Chief Information Officer
CHR: Brian Forrestt, Vice President Human Resources
CNO: Deb Raupers, MSN, Vice President Patient Services and Chief Nursing
Officer
Web address: www.cayugamed.org
Control: Other not–for–profit (including NFP Corporation) **Service:** General
Medical and Surgical

Staffed Beds: 193 **Admissions:** 6392 **Census:** 83 **Outpatient Visits:** 260893
Births: 894 **Total Expense ($000):** 181676 **Payroll Expense ($000):** 67217
Personnel: 1277

JACKSON HEIGHTS—Queens County, See New York City

JAMAICA—Queens County, See New York City

Many Facility Codes have changed. Please refer to the AHA Guide Code Chart. © 2016 AHA Guide

JAMESTOWN—Chautauqua County

⊠ **WOMAN'S CHRISTIAN ASSOCIATION HOSPITAL (330239)**, 207 Foote Avenue, Zip 14701–7077, Mailing Address: P.O. Box 840, Zip 14702–0840; tel. 716/487–0141 **A**1 2 10 **F**4 5 8 11 12 13 15 18 19 20 28 29 31 32 34 35 40 45 46 57 59 63 64 68 69 70 74 75 77 78 79 81 82 83 84 85 86 87 90 92 93 94 96 98 99 100 101 102 103 104 107 108 110 111 117 119 121 126 129 130 131 132 135 141 146 147 148
Primary Contact: Betsy T. Wright, President and Chief Executive Officer
CMO: Marlene Garone, M.D., Vice President Medical Affairs and Medical Director
CIO: Keith Robison, Chief Information Officer
CHR: Karen Bohall, Director Human Resources
Web address: www.wcahospital.org
Control: Other not-for-profit (including NFP Corporation) **Service:** General Medical and Surgical

Staffed Beds: 197 **Admissions:** 6307 **Census:** 93 **Outpatient Visits:** 275301 **Births:** 685 **Total Expense ($000):** 104899 **Payroll Expense ($000):** 40778 **Personnel:** 906

JOHNSON CITY—Broome County

WILSON MEMORIAL REGIONAL MEDICAL CENTER See United Health Services Hospitals–Binghamton, Binghamton

KATONAH—Westchester County

⊠ **FOUR WINDS HOSPITAL (334002)**, 800 Cross River Road, Zip 10536–3549; tel. 914/763–8151, (Nonreporting) **A**1 10
Primary Contact: Martin A. Buccolo, Ph.D., Chief Executive Officer
COO: Moira Morrissey, Chief Operating Officer and General Counsel
CFO: Barry S. Weinstein, Chief Financial Officer
CMO: Jonathan Bauman, M.D., Chief Medical Officer
CIO: Barry S. Weinstein, Chief Financial Officer
CHR: Susan Cusano, Director Human Resources
Web address: www.fourwindshospital.com
Control: Partnership, Investor–owned, for–profit **Service:** Psychiatric

Staffed Beds: 181

KENMORE—Erie County

⊠ **KENMORE MERCY HOSPITAL (330102)**, 2950 Elmwood Avenue, Zip 14217–1390, Mailing Address: 2950 Elmwood Avenue, Room 4024, Zip 14217–1390; tel. 716/447–6100, (Total facility includes 160 beds in nursing home–type unit) **A**1 10 **F**3 11 15 17 18 29 30 31 34 35 37 40 49 50 57 59 60 64 65 66 68 70 74 75 77 78 79 81 83 84 85 87 90 93 96 97 107 108 110 111 114 115 118 119 126 128 129 130 131 146 147 148 **P**5 6 **S** Catholic Health System, Buffalo, NY
Primary Contact: James M. Millard, President and Chief Executive Officer
COO: Walter Ludwig, Chief Operating Officer
CFO: James H. Dunlop, Jr., CPA, Executive Vice President and Chief Financial Officer
CMO: James Fitzpatrick, M.D., Vice President Medical Affairs
CHR: Laura Cianflone, Director Human Resources
CNO: Cheryl Hayes, Vice President Patient Care Services
Web address: www.chsbuffalo.org
Control: Church–operated, Nongovernment, not–for profit **Service:** General Medical and Surgical

Staffed Beds: 288 **Admissions:** 9414 **Census:** 226 **Outpatient Visits:** 129095 **Births:** 0 **Total Expense ($000):** 167953 **Payroll Expense ($000):** 69999 **Personnel:** 985

KINGSTON—Ulster County

BENEDICTINE HOSPITAL See Health Alliance Hospital – Mary's Avenue Campus

◇ **HEALTH ALLIANCE HOSPITAL – BROADWAY CAMPUS (330004)**, 396 Broadway, Zip 12401–4692; tel. 845/331–3131 **A**10 19 21 **F**3 8 11 13 18 20 28 29 30 31 34 35 36 40 45 49 50 63 64 68 70 74 75 76 77 78 79 81 83 84 85 86 87 92 93 102 107 108 111 114 115 119 130 131 132 135 146 148 **S** WMCHealth, Valhalla, NY
Primary Contact: David Scarpino, President and Chief Executive Officer
COO: Robert Seidman, Chief Operating Officer
CFO: Steven J. Haas, Chief Financial Officer
CMO: Frank Ehrlich, M.D., Chief Medical Officer
CIO: John Finch, Vice President Information Services
CHR: Greg M. Howard, Director Human Resource
Web address: www.hahv.org
Control: Other not-for-profit (including NFP Corporation) **Service:** General Medical and Surgical

Staffed Beds: 150 **Admissions:** 7781 **Census:** 101 **Outpatient Visits:** 117955 **Births:** 339 **Total Expense ($000):** 116320 **Payroll Expense ($000):** 44720 **Personnel:** 801

◇ **HEALTH ALLIANCE HOSPITAL – MARY'S AVENUE CAMPUS (330224)**, 105 Marys Avenue, Zip 12401–5894; tel. 845/338–2500 **A**2 10 19 21 **F**3 4 8 11 15 18 20 29 30 31 34 35 36 50 54 56 57 59 63 64 66 68 70 74 75 78 79 81 83 84 85 86 87 90 98 105 107 108 110 114 119 120 121 123 129 130 131 132 146 147 148 **P**7 **S** WMCHealth, Valhalla, NY
Primary Contact: David Scarpino, President and Chief Executive Officer
COO: Robert Seidman, Chief Operating Officer
CFO: Steven J. Haas, Chief Financial Officer
CMO: Frank Ehrlich, M.D., Chief Medical Officer
CIO: John Finch, Chief Information and Community Officer
CHR: Greg M. Howard, Vice President Human Resources
Web address: www.hahv.org
Control: Other not-for-profit (including NFP Corporation) **Service:** General Medical and Surgical

Staffed Beds: 120 **Admissions:** 3090 **Census:** 59 **Outpatient Visits:** 24188 **Births:** 0 **Total Expense ($000):** 64540 **Payroll Expense ($000):** 21324 **Personnel:** 524

KINGSTON HOSPITAL See Health Alliance Hospital – Broadway Campus

LEWISTON—Niagara County

⊠ **MOUNT ST. MARY'S HOSPITAL AND HEALTH CENTER (330188)**, 5300 Military Road, Zip 14092–1903; tel. 716/297–4800 **A**1 10 **F**3 4 13 15 17 18 28 29 30 34 35 40 41 49 50 54 57 59 60 64 65 66 68 70 74 75 76 77 79 81 84 85 87 89 90 92 93 97 107 108 110 111 114 115 119 130 132 135 143 146 147 148 **P**5 **S** Catholic Health System, Buffalo, NY
Primary Contact: Gary C. Tucker, President and Chief Executive Officer
CFO: Stephen Franko, Vice President Finance and Chief Financial Officer
CMO: Domonic F. Falsetti, M.D., Chief of Staff and Medical Director
CHR: Deborah J. Serafin, Vice President Human Resources
CNO: Barbara A. Bucci, R.N., Vice President Patient Care and Chief Nursing Officer
Web address: www.msmh.org
Control: Church–operated, Nongovernment, not–for profit **Service:** General Medical and Surgical

Staffed Beds: 127 **Admissions:** 4957 **Census:** 71 **Outpatient Visits:** 162263 **Births:** 426 **Total Expense ($000):** 94803 **Payroll Expense ($000):** 47488 **Personnel:** 707

LITTLE FALLS—Herkimer County

★ **LITTLE FALLS HOSPITAL (331311)**, 140 Burwell Street, Zip 13365–1725; tel. 315/823–1000 **A**10 18 **F**3 8 15 18 29 30 34 35 40 45 46 53 54 59 64 65 68 77 81 82 85 86 87 91 92 93 94 97 107 108 110 111 112 115 119 130 131 133 135 **S** Bassett Healthcare Network, Cooperstown, NY
Primary Contact: Michael L. Ogden, President and Chief Executive Officer
CFO: James Vielkind, Chief Financial Officer
CMO: Mark Winther, M.D., Medical Director
CIO: Duane Merry, Chief Information Officer
CHR: Marlene Little, Senior Director
CNO: Heidi Camardello, Vice President Patient Care Services and Chief Nursing Officer
Web address: www.bassett.org
Control: Other not-for-profit (including NFP Corporation) **Service:** General Medical and Surgical

Staffed Beds: 25 **Admissions:** 747 **Census:** 8 **Outpatient Visits:** 48299 **Births:** 0

LITTLE NECK—Queens County, See New York City

LOCKPORT—Niagara County

★ **EASTERN NIAGARA HOSPITAL (330163)**, 521 East Avenue, Zip 14094–3299; tel. 716/514–5700, (Includes EASTERN NIAGARA HOSPITAL LOCKPORT, 521 East Avenue, tel. 716/514–5700; EASTERN NIAGARA HOSPITAL NEWFANE, 2600 William Street, Newfane, Zip 14108–1093; tel. 716/778–5111) **A**10 13 **F**3 4 13 15 18 19 28 29 30 31 34 40 42 45 46 47 48 49 50 51 54 57 59 60 63 65 68 70 74 75 76 77 79 81 82 83 84 85 87 89 93 94 98 99 100 102 107 108 110 111 115 118 119 126 130 132 135 144 146 147 148
Primary Contact: Clare A. Haar, Chief Executive Officer
COO: David J. Di Bacco, Chief Operating Officer
CFO: Michael F. Ickowski, Chief Financial Officer
CMO: Bruce J. Cusenz, M.D., Medical Director
CHR: Joseph Farrauto, Director Human Resources
CNO: Mary Beth Campo, MS, Director of Nursing
Web address: www.enhs.org
Control: Other not-for-profit (including NFP Corporation) **Service:** General Medical and Surgical

Staffed Beds: 140 **Admissions:** 4413 **Census:** 80 **Outpatient Visits:** 244100 **Births:** 361 **Total Expense ($000):** 67209 **Payroll Expense ($000):** 28203 **Personnel:** 531

NY

Hospital, Medicare Provider Number, Address, Telephone, Approval, Facility, and Physician Codes, Health Care System

★ American Hospital Association (AHA) membership
□ The Joint Commission accreditation
○ Healthcare Facilities Accreditation Program
◇ DNV Healthcare Inc. accreditation
⇑ Center for Improvement in Healthcare Quality Accreditation
△ Commission on Accreditation of Rehabilitation Facilities (CARF) accreditation

© 2016 AHA Guide   *Many Facility Codes have changed. Please refer to the AHA Guide Code Chart.*   Hospitals **A441**

LONG ISLAND CITY—Queens County, See New York City

LOWVILLE—Lewis County

⊠ **LEWIS COUNTY GENERAL HOSPITAL (331317)**, 7785 North State Street, Zip 13367–1297; tel. 315/376–5200, (Total facility includes 160 beds in nursing home–type unit) **A**1 10 18 **F**2 3 6 8 11 13 15 29 30 34 40 45 50 54 56 57 59 62 63 70 75 76 77 78 79 81 82 84 85 86 87 91 93 96 97 107 108 110 111 115 119 124 127 129 130 131 132 133 143 146 147 148 **P**6 8
Primary Contact: Michael Prince, Interim Chief Executive Officer
CFO: Jeffrey Hellinger, Interim Chief Financial Officer
CMO: Catherine Williams, M.D., Medical Director
CIO: Rob Uttendorfsky, Director Information Management
CHR: James Swords, Director Human Resources
CNO: Jennifer Shaver, Director of Nursing
Web address: www.lcgh.net
Control: County–Government, nonfederal **Service:** General Medical and Surgical

Staffed Beds: 185 **Admissions:** 1251 **Census:** 154 **Outpatient Visits:** 135781 **Births:** 285 **Total Expense ($000):** 73206 **Payroll Expense ($000):** 26865 **Personnel:** 587

MALONE—Franklin County

⊠ **THE UNIVERSITY OF VERMONT HEALTH NETWORK – ALICE HYDE MEDICAL CENTER (330084)**, 133 Park Street, Zip 12953–1243, Mailing Address: P.O. Box 729, Zip 12953–0729; tel. 518/483–3000, (Total facility includes 135 beds in nursing home–type unit) **A**1 10 20 **F**3 11 13 15 17 18 28 29 31 34 36 39 40 45 50 57 59 64 68 70 75 76 77 78 79 81 82 84 85 86 87 90 93 96 97 107 108 110 111 115 117 119 121 127 128 129 130 131 132 135 144 146 148 **P**6
Primary Contact: Douglas F. DiVello, President and Chief Executive Officer
COO: Matthew Jones, Senior Director Support Services and Facilities
CFO: Sean Curtin, Chief Financial Officer
CMO: William Latreille, M.D., Chief Medical Officer
CIO: Darrin Goodrow, Chief Information Officer
CHR: Emily Campbell, Senior Director Human Resources
CNO: Julie Marshall, Chief Nursing Officer
Web address: www.UVMHealth.org/AHMC
Control: Other not–for–profit (including NFP Corporation) **Service:** General Medical and Surgical

Staffed Beds: 225 **Admissions:** 2240 **Census:** 131 **Outpatient Visits:** 185114 **Births:** 240 **Total Expense ($000):** 81115 **Payroll Expense ($000):** 39677 **Personnel:** 581

MANHASSET—Nassau County

⊠ **NORTH SHORE UNIVERSITY HOSPITAL (330106)**, 300 Community Drive, Zip 11030–3816; tel. 516/562–0100 **A**1 2 3 5 8 10 **F**3 6 7 8 9 11 12 13 14 15 17 18 20 22 24 26 28 29 30 31 34 35 36 37 38 39 40 41 43 44 45 46 47 48 49 50 51 52 54 55 56 57 58 59 60 61 62 63 64 65 66 68 69 70 71 72 73 74 75 76 77 78 79 80 81 82 83 84 85 86 87 91 92 93 94 97 98 99 100 101 102 103 104 107 108 109 110 111 112 114 115 116 117 118 119 120 121 123 124 126 129 130 131 132 134 135 136 138 141 142 143 144 145 146 147 148 **P**5 6 **S** Northwell Health, New Hyde Park, NY
Primary Contact: Alessandro Bellucci, M.D., Executive Director
CFO: Frank Rizzo, Chief Financial Officer, Central Region
CMO: Michael Gitman, M.D., Medical Director
CIO: Nympha Meindel, R.N., Chief Information Officer
CHR: Debra Bierman, Associate Executive Director Human Resources
CNO: Kerri Scanlon, MSN, Chief Nursing Officer
Web address: www.northshorelij.com
Control: Other not–for–profit (including NFP Corporation) **Service:** General Medical and Surgical

Staffed Beds: 764 **Admissions:** 47034 **Census:** 742 **Outpatient Visits:** 865757 **Births:** 6645 **Total Expense ($000):** 1940630 **Payroll Expense ($000):** 962004 **Personnel:** 10111

MANHATTAN—New York County, See New York City

MARCY—Oneida County

☐ **CENTRAL NEW YORK PSYCHIATRIC CENTER**, 9005 Old River Road, Zip 13403–3000, Mailing Address: P.O. Box 300, Zip 13403–0300; tel. 315/765–3600, (Nonreporting) **A**1 **S** New York State Office of Mental Health, Albany, NY
Primary Contact: Maureen Bosco, Executive Director
Web address: www.omh.ny.gov
Control: State–Government, nonfederal **Service:** Psychiatric

Staffed Beds: 226

MARGARETVILLE—Delaware County

◇ **MARGARETVILLE HOSPITAL (331304)**, 42084 State Highway 28, Zip 12455–2820; tel. 845/586–2631, (Nonreporting) **A**10 18 21 **S** WMCHealth, Valhalla, NY
Primary Contact: Sandra A. Horan, Executive Director
CHR: Linda Mead, Director Human Resources
Web address: www.margaretvillehospital.org
Control: Other not–for–profit (including NFP Corporation) **Service:** General Medical and Surgical

Staffed Beds: 15

MASSENA—St. Lawrence County

☐ **MASSENA MEMORIAL HOSPITAL (330223)**, One Hospital Drive, Zip 13662–1097; tel. 315/764–1711, (Nonreporting) **A**1 10 20
Primary Contact: Robert G. Wolleben, Chief Executive Officer
CFO: Patrick M. Facteau, Chief Financial Officer
CMO: Nimesh Desai, M.D., Medical Director
CIO: Jana Grose, Chief Information Officer
CHR: Jonnie Dorothy, Senior Director Human Resources
CNO: Ralene North, Chief Nurse Executive
Web address: www.massenahospital.org
Control: City–Government, nonfederal **Service:** General Medical and Surgical

Staffed Beds: 50

MEDINA—Orleans County

★ △ ◇ **MEDINA MEMORIAL HOSPITAL (331319)**, 200 Ohio Street, Zip 14103–1095; tel. 585/798–2000, (Total facility includes 30 beds in nursing home–type unit) **A**7 10 18 24 26 29 34 35 40 45 46 50 51 53 54 57 59 60 62 64 68 70 75 77 79 81 85 86 87 90 91 92 93 96 97 107 108 110 111 115 118 119 128 129 130 132 133 135 144 146 148
Primary Contact: Wendy Jacobson, President and Chief Executive Officer
CFO: David Britton, Interim Chief Financial Officer
CMO: Joseph Misiti, M.D., President Medical Staff
CHR: Mary Williams, Director Human Resources
Web address: www.medinamemorial.org
Control: Other not–for–profit (including NFP Corporation) **Service:** General Medical and Surgical

Staffed Beds: 64 **Admissions:** 1272 **Census:** 47 **Outpatient Visits:** 53073 **Births:** 0 **Total Expense ($000):** 32469 **Payroll Expense ($000):** 15709 **Personnel:** 309

MIDDLETOWN—Orange County

⊠ △ **ORANGE REGIONAL MEDICAL CENTER (330126)**, 707 East Main Street, Zip 10940–2650; tel. 845/333–1000 **A**1 2 7 10 12 13 **F**3 5 8 11 12 13 15 17 18 19 20 22 26 28 29 30 31 34 35 40 41 49 51 54 55 57 59 60 64 68 70 72 74 75 76 77 78 79 81 82 83 84 85 86 87 89 90 93 96 98 99 100 101 102 103 104 105 107 108 110 111 114 115 117 118 119 121 123 124 126 129 130 132 135 144 146 147 148 **S** Greater Hudson Valley Health System, Middletown, NY
Primary Contact: Scott Batulis, President and Chief Executive Officer
COO: Timothy P. Selz, Vice President
CFO: Mitch Amodo, Vice President and Chief Financial Officer
CMO: James Oxley, D.O., Vice President Medical Affairs
CIO: Shafiq Rab, Chief Information Officer
CHR: Deborah Carr, Vice President Human Resources
Web address: www.ormc.org
Control: Other not–for–profit (including NFP Corporation) **Service:** General Medical and Surgical

Staffed Beds: 301 **Admissions:** 23098 **Census:** 293 **Outpatient Visits:** 746992 **Births:** 1746 **Total Expense ($000):** 409569 **Payroll Expense ($000):** 146282 **Personnel:** 1482

MINEOLA—Nassau County

⊠ **WINTHROP–UNIVERSITY HOSPITAL (330167)**, 259 First Street, Zip 11501–3957; tel. 516/663–0333, (Includes CHILDREN'S MEDICAL CENTER, 259 First Street, tel. 516/663–0333) **A**1 2 3 5 8 10 **F**3 5 6 8 9 11 12 13 14 15 17 18 19 20 22 24 26 28 29 30 31 32 34 35 36 37 38 39 40 41 43 44 45 46 47 48 49 50 51 53 54 55 56 57 58 59 60 61 64 65 66 68 69 70 71 72 73 74 75 76 77 78 79 81 82 84 85 86 87 88 89 92 93 94 97 99 100 101 102 103 104 107 108 110 111 113 114 115 116 117 118 119 120 121 123 124 126 129 130 131 132 134 135 141 142 144 145 146 147 148 **P**5 6 7 8
Primary Contact: John F. Collins, President and Chief Executive Officer
COO: Garry Schwall, Chief Operating Officer
CFO: Palmira Cataliotti, Senior Vice President, Chief Financial Officer and Treasurer
CMO: Michael Ammazzalorso, M.D., Chief Medical Officer
CIO: Nicholas Casabona, Chief Information Officer
CHR: Stacey Pfeffer, Senior Vice President Human Resources
CNO: Valerie Terzano, MSN, Senior Vice President Nursing
Web address: www.winthrop.org
Control: Other not–for–profit (including NFP Corporation) **Service:** General Medical and Surgical

Staffed Beds: 511 **Admissions:** 30865 **Census:** 442 **Outpatient Visits:** 415381 **Births:** 5086 **Total Expense ($000):** 1237317 **Payroll Expense ($000):** 628204 **Personnel:** 7530

NY

Many Facility Codes have changed. Please refer to the AHA Guide Code Chart.   © 2016 AHA Guide

MONTOUR FALLS—Schuyler County

☒ **SCHUYLER HOSPITAL (331313)**, 220 Steuben Street, Zip 14865–9709; tel. 607/535–7121, (Total facility includes 120 beds in nursing home–type unit) **A**1 10 18 **F**3 11 14 15 29 30 34 35 40 45 59 64 70 75 77 81 82 85 87 91 92 93 94 97 107 110 111 114 119 128 129 130 133 135 146 **P**6
Primary Contact: James B. Watson, President
CMO: Michael Eisman, M.D., Medical Director
CHR: Troy Preston, Director Human Resources
Web address: www.schuylerhospital.org
Control: Other not–for–profit (including NFP Corporation) **Service:** General Medical and Surgical

> **Staffed Beds:** 145 **Admissions:** 923 **Census:** 130 **Outpatient Visits:** 48414 **Births:** 0 **Total Expense ($000):** 32856 **Payroll Expense ($000):** 17591 **Personnel:** 314

MONTROSE—Westchester County

☒ **VETERANS AFFAIRS HUDSON VALLEY HEALTH CARE SYSTEM**, 2094 Albany Post Road, Zip 10548–1454, Mailing Address: P.O. Box 100, Zip 10548–0100; tel. 914/737–4400, (Includes VETERAN AFFAIRS HUDSON VALLEY HEALTH CARE SYSTEM–CASTLE POINT CAMPUS, 41 Castle Point Road, Wappingers, Zip 12590; tel. 914/831–2000; VETERANS AFFAIRS HUDSON VALLEY HEALTH CARE SYSTEM–MONTROSE CAMPUS, 2094 Albany Post Road, Zip 10548; tel. 914/737–4400), (Nonreporting) **A**1 3 5 **S** Department of Veterans Affairs, Washington, DC
Primary Contact: Margaret B. Caplan, Director
COO: John M. Grady, Associate Director
CFO: John Walsh, Chief Fiscal Services
CMO: Joanne J. Malina, M.D., Chief of Staff
CIO: Thomas Rooney, Chief Information Resource Management
CHR: Dardanella Russell, Chief Human Resources Management Service
Web address: www.hudsonvalley.va.gov/
Control: Veterans Affairs, Government, federal **Service:** Psychiatric

> **Staffed Beds:** 383

MOUNT KISCO—Westchester County

☒ **NORTHERN WESTCHESTER HOSPITAL (330162)**, 400 East Main Street, Zip 10549–3477, Mailing Address: 400 East Main Street, G–02, Zip 10549–3477; tel. 914/666–1200 **A**1 2 10 **F**3 8 12 13 15 17 18 28 29 30 31 32 34 35 36 37 40 43 46 47 48 49 50 51 54 55 56 57 59 60 61 64 65 68 70 72 73 74 75 76 78 79 81 82 84 85 86 87 89 91 92 93 97 98 99 100 101 102 103 107 108 109 110 111 114 115 118 119 120 121 123 124 126 129 130 131 132 135 146 147 148 **P**5 6 **S** Northwell Health, New Hyde Park, NY
Primary Contact: Joel Seligman, President and Chief Executive Officer
CFO: John Partenza, Vice President and Treasurer
CMO: Marla Koroly, M.D., Chief Medical Officer and Senior Vice President Medical Affairs
CIO: Sue Prince, Director Information Systems
CHR: Kerry Flynn Barrett, Vice President Human Resources
CNO: Lauraine Szekely, R.N., Senior Vice President, Patient Care
Web address: www.nwhc.net
Control: Other not–for–profit (including NFP Corporation) **Service:** General Medical and Surgical

> **Staffed Beds:** 195 **Admissions:** 9118 **Census:** 120 **Outpatient Visits:** 139524 **Births:** 1637 **Total Expense ($000):** 241891 **Payroll Expense ($000):** 102626 **Personnel:** 1335

MOUNT VERNON—Westchester County

☐ **MONTEFIORE MOUNT VERNON (330086)**, 12 North Seventh Avenue, Zip 10550–2098; tel. 914/664–8000 **A**1 3 5 10 **F**3 14 15 18 29 30 31 34 35 40 45 50 59 60 61 64 65 66 68 74 75 77 78 79 81 84 85 86 87 92 93 97 98 100 102 104 107 110 111 114 119 130 146 147 **P**5 **S** Montefiore Health System, Bronx, NY
Primary Contact: Jaccel Kouns, R.N., MS, Vice President and Executive Director
CFO: Albert M. Farina, Chief Financial Officer
CMO: Gary Ishkanian, M.D., Vice President Medical Affairs
CIO: Barbara Cooke, Director Health Information Systems
CHR: Dennis H. Ashley, Vice President Human Resources
Web address: www.montefiorehealthsystem.org/landing.cfm?id=17
Control: Other not–for–profit (including NFP Corporation) **Service:** General Medical and Surgical

> **Staffed Beds:** 65 **Admissions:** 3243 **Census:** 66 **Outpatient Visits:** 141546 **Births:** 0 **Total Expense ($000):** 83216 **Payroll Expense ($000):** 38112 **Personnel:** 569

NEW HAMPTON—Orange County

☐ **MID–HUDSON FORENSIC PSYCHIATRIC CENTER (334061)**, Route 17M, Zip 10958, Mailing Address: P.O. Box 158, Zip 10958–0158; tel. 845/374–8700 **A**1 10 **F**39 68 77 87 98 106 130 **S** New York State Office of Mental Health, Albany, NY
Primary Contact: Joseph Freebern, Executive Director
COO: Kristin Orlando, Director Operations
Web address: www.omh.ny.gov
Control: State–Government, nonfederal **Service:** Psychiatric

> **Staffed Beds:** 169 **Admissions:** 298 **Census:** 265 **Outpatient Visits:** 0 **Births:** 0

NEW HYDE PARK—Queens County, See New York City

NEW ROCHELLE—Westchester County

☒ **MONTEFIORE NEW ROCHELLE (330184)**, 16 Guion Place, Zip 10801–5502; tel. 914/632–5000, (Total facility includes 150 beds in nursing home–type unit) **A**1 2 3 5 10 **F**2 3 8 11 12 13 15 18 28 29 30 31 32 34 35 37 40 45 50 55 64 65 66 68 70 73 74 75 76 77 78 79 81 82 84 85 86 87 89 90 92 93 97 100 107 108 110 114 119 128 130 132 146 **P**5 **S** Montefiore Health System, Bronx, NY
Primary Contact: Anthony Alfano, Vice President Executive Director
COO: John P. Mamangakis, Senior Vice President
CFO: Albert M. Farina, Senior Vice President and Chief Financial Officer
CMO: Richard Barone, M.D., Medical Director
CIO: Barbara Cooke, Director Health Information Systems
CHR: Dennis H. Ashley, Vice President Human Resources
CNO: Pamela M. Dupuis, R.N., Senior Vice President Patient Care Services
Web address: www.montefiorehealthsystem.org
Control: Other not–for–profit (including NFP Corporation) **Service:** General Medical and Surgical

> **Staffed Beds:** 255 **Admissions:** 7574 **Census:** 224 **Outpatient Visits:** 96060 **Births:** 1090 **Total Expense ($000):** 189740 **Payroll Expense ($000):** 91064 **Personnel:** 1314

NEW YORK (Includes all hospitals located within the five boroughs)
BRONX - Bronx County (Mailing Address - Bronx)
BROOKLYN - Kings County (Mailing Address - Brooklyn)
MANHATTAN - New York County (Mailing Address - New York)
QUEENS - Queens County (Mailing Addresses - Bellerose, Elmhurst, Far Rockaway, Flushing, Forest Hills, Glen Oaks, Holliswood, Jackson Heights, Jamaica, Little Neck, Long Island City, New Hyde Park, and Queens Village)
RICHMOND VALLEY - Richmond County (Mailing Address - Staten Island)
BETH ISRAEL MEDICAL CENTER See Mount Sinai Beth Israel

BETH ISRAEL MEDICAL CENTER–KINGS HIGHWAY DIVISION See Mount Sinai Beth Israel Brooklyn

☐ **BRONX PSYCHIATRIC CENTER (334053)**, 1500 Waters Place, Bronx, Zip 10461–2796; tel. 718/931–0600, (Nonreporting) **A**1 3 5 10 **S** New York State Office of Mental Health, Albany, NY
Primary Contact: Anita Daniels, Director
CFO: Robert Erway, Director for Administration
Web address: www.omh.ny.gov
Control: State–Government, nonfederal **Service:** Psychiatric

> **Staffed Beds:** 450

NY

☒ **BRONX–LEBANON HOSPITAL CENTER HEALTH CARE SYSTEM (330009)**, 1276 Fulton Avenue, Bronx, Zip 10456–3499; tel. 718/590–1800, (Includes BRONX–LEBANON SPECIAL CARE CENTER, 1265 Fulton Avenue, Zip 10465; tel. 718/579–7000; Octavio Marin, Vice President Long Term Care and Ambulatory Care Services; CONCOURSE DIVISION, 1650 Grand Concourse, Zip 10457, Mailing Address: 1276 Fulton Avenue, Zip 10456–3402; tel. 718/590–1800; Miguel A. Fuentes, Jr., President and Chief Executive Officer; FULTON DIVISION, 1276 Fulton Avenue, Zip 10456, Mailing Address: 1650 Grand Concourse, Zip 10457–7606; tel. 718/590–1800; Miguel A. Fuentes, Jr., President and Chief Executive Officer; HIGHBRIDGE WOODYCREST CENTER, 936 Woodycrest Avenue, Zip 10452; tel. 718/579–8875; Leonardo Vicent, III, Executive Director), (Total facility includes 330 beds in nursing home–type unit) **A**1 3 5 10 **F**1 2 3 4 5 8 9 11 12 13 15 17 18 19 20 21 22 26 28 29 30 31 32 33 34 35 37 38 39 40 44 45 46 47 48 49 50 51 52 57 58 59 60 61 64 65 66 67 68 70 71 72 73 74 75 76 77 78 79 80 81 82 83 84 85 86 87 88 89 91 92 93 94 96 97 98 99 100 101 102 103 104 105 106 107 108 109 110 111 113 114 115 119 123 126 128 129 130 131 132 133 134 135 143 144 145 146 147 148 **P**6
Primary Contact: Miguel A. Fuentes, Jr., President and Chief Executive Officer
CFO: Victor DeMarco, Chief Financial Officer
CMO: Milton A. Gumbs, M.D., Vice President and Medical Director
CIO: Ivan Durbak, Chief Information Officer
CHR: Selena Griffin–Mahon, Assistant Vice President Human Resources
CNO: Patricia Cahill, R.N., Vice President, Patient Care Services and Chief Nursing Officer
Web address: www.bronxcare.org
Control: Other not–for–profit (including NFP Corporation) **Service:** General Medical and Surgical

Staffed Beds: 972 **Admissions:** 31936 **Census:** 784 **Outpatient Visits:** 1165447 **Births:** 2263 **Total Expense ($000):** 793643 **Payroll Expense ($000):** 380239 **Personnel:** 4203

☐ **BROOKDALE HOSPITAL MEDICAL CENTER (330233)**, 125 Worth Street, 4th Floor Suite 418, Zip 10013, Mailing Address: One Brookdale Plaza, Brooklyn, Zip 11212–3139; tel. 718/240–5000, (Nonreporting) **A**1 3 5 10
Primary Contact: Mark Toney, President and Chief Executive Officer
CFO: James Porter, Chief Financial Officer
CMO: Estevan Garcia, M.D., Chief Medical Officer
CIO: David Reitzel, Chief Information Officer
CHR: Margaret M. Brubaker, Senior Vice President Human Resources
Web address: www.brookdalehospital.org
Control: Other not–for–profit (including NFP Corporation) **Service:** General Medical and Surgical

Staffed Beds: 789

☐ **BROOKLYN HOSPITAL CENTER (330056)**, 121 DeKalb Avenue, Brooklyn, Zip 11201–5425; tel. 718/250–8000 **A**1 3 5 10 **F**3 4 7 8 12 13 15 17 18 19 20 26 29 30 31 32 34 35 39 40 41 45 46 47 48 49 50 52 54 55 56 57 58 59 60 61 63 64 65 68 70 72 74 75 76 77 78 79 81 82 83 84 85 86 87 88 89 90 93 94 97 100 101 103 107 109 110 111 112 114 115 116 117 119 120 121 122 123 129 130 131 132 133 134 135 143 144 145 146 147 148
Primary Contact: Gary G. Terrinoni, President and Chief Executive Officer
COO: John Gupta, Executive Vice President and Chief Operating Officer
CIO: Irene Farrelly, Vice President and Chief Information Officer
CHR: Ira Warm, Senior Vice President Human Resources
Web address: www.tbh.org
Control: Other not–for–profit (including NFP Corporation) **Service:** General Medical and Surgical

Staffed Beds: 302 **Admissions:** 15062 **Census:** 240 **Outpatient Visits:** 344463 **Births:** 2131 **Total Expense ($000):** 407654 **Payroll Expense ($000):** 212660 **Personnel:** 4736

☒ **CALVARY HOSPITAL (332006)**, 1740 Eastchester Road, Bronx, Zip 10461–2392; tel. 718/863–6900 **A**1 3 5 10 **F**1 29 30 35 39 62 63 64 68 74 76 82 84 87 119 121 130 132 134 146 148 **P**6
Primary Contact: Frank A. Calamari, President and Chief Executive Officer
COO: Richard J. Kutilek, Chief Operating Officer
CFO: Andrew Greco, Chief Financial Officer
CMO: Michael J. Brescia, M.D., Executive Medical Director
CIO: Patrick Martin, Director Information Systems
CHR: Michael T. Troncone, Chief Human Resources Officer
CNO: Margaret Pelkowski, R.N., Vice President Patient Care Services
Web address: www.calvaryhospital.org
Control: Church–operated, Nongovernment, not–for profit **Service:** Long–Term Acute Care hospital

Staffed Beds: 225 **Admissions:** 3045 **Census:** 209 **Outpatient Visits:** 106966 **Births:** 0 **Total Expense ($000):** 120286 **Payroll Expense ($000):** 63478 **Personnel:** 894

COLER–GOLDWATER SPECIALTY HOSPITAL AND NURSING FACILITY See NYC Health + Hospitals / Carter

CONCOURSE DIVISION See Bronx–Lebanon Hospital Center Health Care System, Bronx

☐ **CREEDMOOR PSYCHIATRIC CENTER (334004)**, 79–25 Winchester Boulevard, Jamaica, Zip 11427–2128; tel. 718/264–3600 **A**1 10 **F**29 30 34 38 39 53 54 59 75 86 98 101 103 106 130 132 135 **S** New York State Office of Mental Health, Albany, NY
Primary Contact: Ann Marie Barbarotta, Executive Director
CFO: Viodelda Ho–Shing, Deputy Director Administration
CIO: Ed Yunusov, Chief Information Officer
CHR: Adrienne Jones, Director Human Resources
CNO: Marie S. Jean–Louis, R.N., Chief Nursing Officer
Web address: www.omh.ny.gov
Control: State–Government, nonfederal **Service:** Psychiatric

Staffed Beds: 380 **Admissions:** 326 **Census:** 317 **Outpatient Visits:** 88600 **Births:** 0 **Total Expense ($000):** 153957 **Personnel:** 946

☒ **FLUSHING HOSPITAL MEDICAL CENTER (330193)**, 4500 Parsons Boulevard, Flushing, Zip 11355–2205; tel. 718/670–5000 **A**1 3 5 10 **F**3 4 5 7 8 12 13 15 17 18 19 29 30 31 32 34 35 36 39 40 41 45 49 50 51 55 56 57 59 60 61 64 65 68 70 71 72 73 74 75 76 77 78 79 81 82 84 85 87 89 91 92 93 97 98 100 101 103 104 107 110 111 114 119 126 128 130 132 135 146 147 148 **P**5 **S** MediSys Health Network, Jamaica, NY
Primary Contact: Bruce J. Flanz, President and Chief Executive Officer
COO: Robert V. Levine, Executive Vice President and Chief Operating Officer
CFO: Mounir F. Doss, Executive Vice President and Chief Financial Officer
CMO: Siamack Nemazie, M.D., Medical Director, Patient Safety Officer
CIO: Tony Gatto, Director Management Information Systems
CHR: Sheila Garvey, Vice President Human Resources
Web address: www.flushinghospital.org
Control: Other not–for–profit (including NFP Corporation) **Service:** General Medical and Surgical

Staffed Beds: 299 **Admissions:** 15142 **Census:** 233 **Outpatient Visits:** 153903 **Births:** 2882 **Total Expense ($000):** 258379 **Payroll Expense ($000):** 119454 **Personnel:** 1678

FULTON DIVISION See Bronx–Lebanon Hospital Center Health Care System, Bronx

☐ **GRACIE SQUARE HOSPITAL (334048)**, 420 East 76th Street, Zip 10021–3396; tel. 212/988–4400, (Nonreporting) **A**1 10
Primary Contact: David Wyman, President and Chief Executive Officer
Web address: www.nygsh.org
Control: Other not–for–profit (including NFP Corporation) **Service:** Psychiatric

Staffed Beds: 157

HENRY J. CARTER SPECIALTY HOSPITAL & NURSING FACILITY See NYC Health + Hospitals / Carter

☒ **HOSPITAL FOR SPECIAL SURGERY (330270)**, 535 East 70th Street, Zip 10021–4898, Mailing Address: 535 East 70th Street, Belaire 10–08, Zip 10021–4898; tel. 212/606–1000 **A**1 3 5 8 10 **F**3 8 9 29 30 32 33 34 35 36 37 38 43 44 50 53 54 56 57 58 59 64 66 68 70 74 75 77 79 80 81 82 84 85 86 87 89 92 93 94 97 100 107 109 111 114 115 116 117 118 119 121 123 126 130 131 132 134 141 142 146 147 148 **P**8
Primary Contact: Louis A. Shapiro, President and Chief Executive Officer
COO: Lisa Goldstein, Executive Vice President and Chief Operating Officer
CFO: Stacey Malakoff, Executive Vice President and Chief Financial Officer
CMO: Todd Albert, M.D., Surgeon–in–Chief and Medical Director
CIO: Jamie Nelson, Vice President and Chief Information Officer
CHR: Bruce Slawitsky, Vice President Human Resources
CNO: Stephanie J. Goldberg, MSN, Senior Vice President and Chief Nursing Officer
Web address: www.hss.edu
Control: Other not–for–profit (including NFP Corporation) **Service:** Orthopedic

Staffed Beds: 209 **Admissions:** 15580 **Census:** 147 **Outpatient Visits:** 411385 **Births:** 0 **Total Expense ($000):** 896559 **Payroll Expense ($000):** 387836 **Personnel:** 4167

☐ **INTERFAITH MEDICAL CENTER (330397)**, 1545 Atlantic Avenue, Brooklyn, Zip 11213–1122; tel. 718/613–4000, (Nonreporting) **A**1 3 5 10
Primary Contact: LaRay Brown, President and Chief Executive Officer
CMO: Jochanan Weisenfreund, M.D., Senior Vice President Academic and Medical Affairs
CIO: Mark Lederman, Chief Information Officer
CHR: Venra Mathurin, Vice President Human Resources
Web address: www.interfaithmedical.com
Control: Other not–for–profit (including NFP Corporation) **Service:** General Medical and Surgical

Staffed Beds: 277

JACK D WEILER HOSPITAL OF ALBERT EINSTEIN COLLEGE OF MEDICINE See Montefiore Medical Center, Bronx

NY

☒ **JAMAICA HOSPITAL MEDICAL CENTER (330014)**, 8900 Van Wyck Expressway, Jamaica, Zip 11418–2832; tel. 718/206–6000, (Total facility includes 228 beds in nursing home–type unit) **A**1 3 5 10 13 **F**1 3 7 11 13 15 17 18 19 20 22 26 29 30 31 32 34 35 36 38 39 40 41 43 44 45 49 50 52 53 54 55 56 57 58 59 60 61 62 64 65 66 68 70 71 72 73 74 75 76 77 78 79 81 82 83 84 85 86 87 89 90 92 93 94 96 97 98 99 100 101 102 103 104 107 108 110 111 114 115 118 119 128 129 130 131 132 134 135 143 144 146 147 **P**5 7 8 **S** MediSys Health Network, Jamaica, NY
Primary Contact: Bruce J. Flanz, President and Chief Executive Officer
COO: William Lynch, Executive Vice President and Chief Operating Officer
CFO: Mounir F. Doss, Executive Vice President and Chief Financial Officer
CMO: Antonietta Morisco, M.D., Medical Director, Chairman Anesthesiology
CIO: Sami Boshut, Chief Information Officer
CHR: Trina Cornet, JD, Vice President Human Resources
CNO: Kathleen Scher, Ed.D., Chief Nursing Officer
Web address: www.Jamaicahospital.org
Control: Other not–for–profit (including NFP Corporation) **Service:** General Medical and Surgical

Staffed Beds: 668 **Admissions:** 23341 **Census:** 550 **Outpatient Visits:** 400708 **Births:** 2362 **Total Expense ($000):** 652430 **Payroll Expense ($000):** 246878 **Personnel:** 3358

☒ △ **JAMES J. PETERS VETERANS AFFAIRS MEDICAL CENTER**, 130 West Kingsbridge Road, Bronx, Zip 10468–3904; tel. 718/584–9000, (Total facility includes 80 beds in nursing home–type unit) **A**1 2 3 5 7 8 **F**3 8 9 11 12 17 18 29 30 31 33 34 35 36 38 39 40 43 44 45 46 47 48 49 50 51 53 54 56 57 58 59 60 61 62 63 64 65 66 68 70 71 74 75 77 78 79 80 81 82 83 84 85 86 87 90 91 92 93 94 95 96 97 98 100 101 102 103 104 107 108 109 111 113 114 115 118 119 120 121 122 123 126 129 130 131 132 135 143 146 147 148 **S** Department of Veterans Affairs, Washington, DC
Primary Contact: Erik Langhoff, M.D., Ph.D., Director
CFO: Gregory Angelo, Chief Fiscal Program
CMO: Clive Rosendorff, M.D., Chief Medical Program
CIO: Linda Bund, Chief Information Officer and Director Education
CHR: Peter Tinker, Chief Human Resources Officer
CNO: Kathleen Capitulo, Ph.D., Chief Nurse Executive
Web address: www.bronx.va.gov/
Control: Veterans Affairs, Government, federal **Service:** General Medical and Surgical

Staffed Beds: 325 **Admissions:** 3770 **Census:** 101 **Outpatient Visits:** 513994 **Births:** 0 **Total Expense ($000):** 296626 **Payroll Expense ($000):** 142632 **Personnel:** 1986

☐ **KINGSBORO PSYCHIATRIC CENTER (334063)**, 681 Clarkson Avenue, Brooklyn, Zip 11203–2125; tel. 718/221–7395, (Nonreporting) **A**1 3 5 10 **S** New York State Office of Mental Health, Albany, NY
Primary Contact: Deborah Parchment, Executive Director
CFO: Yinusa Awolowo, Business Officer
CMO: Jeffery Lucey, M.D., Clinical Director
CIO: George Gavora, Director Program Evaluation
CHR: Vera Thompson, Director Human Resources
CNO: Deborah Denigris, Chief Nursing Officer
Web address: www.omh.ny.gov/omhweb/facilities/kbpc/facility/htm
Control: State–Government, nonfederal **Service:** Psychiatric

Staffed Beds: 290

☐ △ **KINGSBROOK JEWISH MEDICAL CENTER (330201)**, 585 Schenectady Avenue, Brooklyn, Zip 11203–1891; tel. 718/604–5000, (Total facility includes 466 beds in nursing home–type unit) **A**1 3 5 7 10 **F**3 8 14 15 17 18 28 29 30 31 34 35 39 40 45 46 48 49 50 54 56 57 59 65 68 70 74 75 77 78 79 80 81 82 84 85 87 90 91 92 93 94 96 97 98 100 101 103 104 107 108 110 111 115 119 128 130 131 135 143 146 147 148 **P**6
Primary Contact: Linda Brady, M.D., President and Chief Executive Officer
COO: Robert Dubicki, Executive Vice President and Chief Operating Officer
CFO: John Schmitt, Senior Vice President and Chief Financial Officer
CMO: Sibte Burney, M.D., Senior Vice President Medical Affairs and Chief Medical Officer
CIO: Daniel Morreale, Vice President and Chief Information Officer
CHR: John McKeon, Vice President Human Resources
CNO: Jane Lederer, R.N., Vice President and Chief Nursing Officer
Web address: www.kingsbrook.org
Control: Other not–for–profit (including NFP Corporation) **Service:** General Medical and Surgical

Staffed Beds: 740 **Admissions:** 8983 **Census:** 630 **Outpatient Visits:** 132882 **Births:** 0 **Total Expense ($000):** 283454 **Payroll Expense ($000):** 139538 **Personnel:** 1893

☒ **LENOX HILL HOSPITAL (330119)**, 100 East 77th Street, Zip 10075–1850; tel. 212/434–2000, (Includes MANHATTAN EYE, EAR AND THROAT HOSPITAL, 210 East 64th Street, Zip 10021–9885; tel. 212/838–9200; Philip P. Rosenthal, Executive Director) **A**1 3 5 8 10 **F**3 7 8 9 11 12 13 14 15 17 18 20 22 24 26 29 30 31 32 34 35 36 37 39 40 42 43 44 45 46 47 48 49 50 51 52 54 55 56 57 58 59 60 61 62 63 64 65 66 68 70 72 74 75 76 77 78 79 81 82 84 85 86 87 89 91 92 93 94 97 98 99 100 101 102 103 104 107 108 110 111 115 116 117 118 119 120 121 123 124 126 130 131 132 135 141 143 146 147 148 **P**5 6 **S** Northwell Health, New Hyde Park, NY
Primary Contact: Dennis Connors, Executive Director
CMO: Marc L. Napp, M.D., Vice President Medical Affairs
CIO: Beth Dituro, Divisional Chief Information Officer
Web address: www.lenoxhillhospital.org
Control: Other not–for–profit (including NFP Corporation) **Service:** General Medical and Surgical

Staffed Beds: 441 **Admissions:** 28449 **Census:** 341 **Outpatient Visits:** 237666 **Births:** 4305 **Total Expense ($000):** 1030349 **Payroll Expense ($000):** 491207 **Personnel:** 4098

☒ **LONG ISLAND JEWISH MEDICAL CENTER (330195)**, 270–05 76th Avenue, New Hyde Park, Zip 11040–1496; tel. 718/470–7000, (Includes LONG ISLAND JEWISH FOREST HILLS, 102–01 66th Road, Forest Hills, Zip 11375–2029; tel. 718/830–4000; Susan Browning, Executive Director; LONG ISLAND JEWISH VALLEY STREAM, 900 Franklin Avenue, Valley Stream, Zip 11580–2190; tel. 516/256–6000; Stephen Bello, Executive Director; MANHASSET AMBULATORY CARE PAVILION, 1554 Northern Boulevard, Manhasset, Zip 11030; tel. 516/365–2070; STEVEN AND ALEXANDRA COHEN CHILDREN'S MEDICAL CENTER OF NEW YORK, 270–05 76th Avenue, Zip 11040; tel. 718/470–3000; ZUCKER HILLSIDE HOSPITAL, 75–59 263rd Street, Glen Oaks, Zip 11004; tel. 718/470–8000) **A**1 2 3 5 8 10 13 **F**2 3 5 6 7 8 9 11 12 13 14 15 17 18 19 20 21 22 23 24 25 26 27 28 29 30 31 32 34 35 38 39 40 41 42 43 44 45 46 47 48 49 50 51 52 53 54 55 56 57 58 59 60 61 62 63 64 65 66 68 70 72 73 74 75 76 77 78 79 80 81 82 84 85 86 87 88 89 92 93 97 98 99 100 101 102 103 104 105 106 107 108 109 110 111 114 115 116 117 118 119 120 121 123 124 126 129 130 131 132 134 135 136 141 142 143 144 145 146 147 148 **P**5 6 **S** Northwell Health, New Hyde Park, NY
Primary Contact: Michael Goldberg, Executive Director
CIO: John Bosco, Senior Vice President and Chief Information Officer
CHR: Ronald W. Stone, Regional Chief Human Resource Officer
Web address: www.lij.edu
Control: Other not–for–profit (including NFP Corporation) **Service:** General Medical and Surgical

Staffed Beds: 900 **Admissions:** 52171 **Census:** 814 **Outpatient Visits:** 845147 **Births:** 8187 **Total Expense ($000):** 1832746 **Payroll Expense ($000):** 895307 **Personnel:** 9756

☒ **MAIMONIDES MEDICAL CENTER (330194)**, 4802 Tenth Avenue, Brooklyn, Zip 11219–2916; tel. 718/283–6000, (Includes MAIMONIDES INFANTS AND CHILDREN'S HOSPITAL OF BROOKLYN, 4802 Tenth Avenue, tel. 718/283–6000) **A**1 2 3 5 8 10 12 13 **F**2 3 7 8 9 11 12 13 14 15 17 18 19 20 22 24 26 28 29 30 31 32 34 35 38 39 40 41 44 45 46 47 48 49 50 51 52 54 55 56 57 58 59 60 61 64 65 66 68 70 72 73 74 75 76 77 78 79 81 82 84 85 86 87 88 89 91 92 93 96 97 98 99 100 101 102 103 104 107 108 110 111 114 115 117 118 119 120 121 123 124 126 129 130 131 132 135 145 146 147 148 **P**5 6
Primary Contact: Kenneth Gibbs, President and Chief Executive Officer
COO: Mark McDougle, Executive Vice President and Chief Operating Officer
CFO: Robert Naldi, Chief Financial Officer
CMO: Samuel Kopel, M.D., Medical Director
CIO: Walter Fahey, Chief Information Officer
Web address: www.maimonidesmed.org/
Control: Other not–for–profit (including NFP Corporation) **Service:** General Medical and Surgical

Staffed Beds: 575 **Admissions:** 35230 **Census:** 539 **Outpatient Visits:** 508185 **Births:** 8621 **Total Expense ($000):** 1095366 **Payroll Expense ($000):** 537452 **Personnel:** 5504

☐ **MANHATTAN PSYCHIATRIC CENTER–WARD'S ISLAND (334054)**, 600 East 125th Street, Zip 10035–6000; tel. 646/672–6767, (Nonreporting) **A**1 3 5 10 **S** New York State Office of Mental Health, Albany, NY
Primary Contact: Vincent Miccoli, Executive Director
Web address: www.omh.ny.gov
Control: State–Government, nonfederal **Service:** Psychiatric

Staffed Beds: 745

NY

Hospital, Medicare Provider Number, Address, Telephone, Approval, Facility, and Physician Codes, Health Care System

★ American Hospital Association (AHA) membership ○ Healthcare Facilities Accreditation Program ⇑ Center for Improvement in Healthcare Quality Accreditation
☐ The Joint Commission accreditation ◇ DNV Healthcare Inc. accreditation △ Commission on Accreditation of Rehabilitation Facilities (CARF) accreditation

✠ **MEMORIAL SLOAN–KETTERING CANCER CENTER (330154)**, 1275 York Avenue, Zip 10065–6007; tel. 212/639–2000 **A**1 2 3 5 8 10 **F**3 8 11 14 15 29 31 32 34 35 36 37 39 44 45 46 47 48 49 50 54 55 56 57 58 59 60 61 64 66 68 70 74 75 77 78 79 81 82 84 85 86 87 88 89 92 93 94 96 99 100 103 104 107 108 110 111 112 114 115 117 118 119 120 121 123 124 126 130 132 135 136 142 143 144 145 146 147 148 **P**6
Primary Contact: Craig B. Thompson, M.D., President and Chief Executive Officer
COO: Ned Groves, Executive Vice President and Administrator
CFO: Michael Gutnick, Executive Vice President and Chief Financial Officer
CMO: Jose Baselga, M.D., Physician–in–Chief
CIO: Patricia Skarulis, Senior Vice President and Chief Information Systems Officer
CHR: Kerry Bessey, Senior Vice President and Chief Human Resources Officer
CNO: Elizabeth Nelkin McCormick, MSN, Senior Vice President and Chief Nursing Officer
Web address: www.mskcc.org
Control: Other not–for–profit (including NFP Corporation) **Service:** Cancer

Staffed Beds: 473 **Admissions:** 22467 **Census:** 416 **Outpatient Visits:** 1515200 **Births:** 0 **Total Expense ($000):** 2670739 **Payroll Expense ($000):** 1101359 **Personnel:** 14608

✠ **MONTEFIORE MEDICAL CENTER (330059)**, 111 East 210th Street, Bronx, Zip 10467–2401; tel. 718/920–4321, (Includes CHILDREN'S HOSPITAL OF MONTEFIORE, 3415 Bainbridge Avenue, Zip 10467–2403; tel. 718/741–2426; JACK D WEILER HOSPITAL OF ALBERT EINSTEIN COLLEGE OF MEDICINE, 1825 Eastchester Road, Zip 10461–2373; tel. 718/904–2000; MONTEFIORE MEDICAL CENTER – NORTH DIVISION, 600 East 233rd Street, Zip 10466–2697; tel. 718/920–9000) **A**1 2 3 5 8 10 **F**3 5 6 7 8 9 12 13 14 15 17 18 19 20 21 22 23 24 25 26 27 28 29 30 31 32 34 35 36 37 38 39 40 41 42 44 45 46 47 48 49 50 51 52 54 55 56 57 58 59 60 61 62 63 64 65 66 68 70 71 72 73 74 75 76 77 78 79 80 81 82 83 84 85 86 87 88 89 90 92 93 94 97 98 99 100 101 102 103 104 107 108 110 111 114 115 118 119 120 121 123 124 126 129 130 131 132 134 135 136 137 138 139 141 142 143 144 145 146 147 148 **P**5 6 **S** Montefiore Health System, Bronx, NY
Primary Contact: Steven M. Safyer, M.D., President and Chief Executive Officer
COO: Philip O. Ozuah, M.D., Executive Vice President and Chief Operating Officer
CFO: Colleen M. Blye, Executive Vice President and Chief Financial Officer
CMO: Gary Kalkut, M.D., Senior Vice President and Chief Medical Officer
CIO: Jack Wolf, Vice President Information Systems
Web address: www.montefiore.org
Control: Other not–for–profit (including NFP Corporation) **Service:** General Medical and Surgical

Staffed Beds: 1498 **Admissions:** 87702 **Census:** 1341 **Outpatient Visits:** 1546343 **Births:** 5721 **Total Expense ($000):** 3704886 **Payroll Expense ($000):** 1666288 **Personnel:** 19853

MORGAN STANLEY CHILDREN'S HOSPITAL OF NEW YORK–PRESBYTERIAN See New York–Presbyterian Hospital

✠ **MOUNT SINAI BETH ISRAEL (330169)**, First Avenue and 16th Street, Zip 10003–3803; tel. 212/420–2000, (Includes MOUNT SINAI BETH ISRAEL BROOKLYN, 3201 Kings Highway, Brooklyn, Zip 11234; tel. 718/252–3000; Lin H. Mo, M.P.H., President) **A**1 2 3 5 8 10 **F**3 4 5 7 8 9 11 13 14 15 17 18 19 20 22 24 26 28 29 30 31 32 33 34 35 36 38 39 40 41 43 44 45 48 49 50 51 52 54 55 56 57 58 59 60 61 62 63 64 65 66 68 70 72 74 75 76 77 78 79 80 81 82 83 84 85 86 87 88 89 90 92 93 94 96 97 98 99 100 101 102 103 104 107 108 110 111 114 115 117 118 119 120 121 123 124 126 129 130 131 132 134 135 141 143 144 145 146 147 148 **P**5 6 7 **S** Mount Sinai Health System, New York, NY
Primary Contact: Susan Somerville, R.N., President
COO: Kevin Molloy, Senior Vice President and Chief Operating Officer
CFO: Donald Scanlon, Chief Corporate Services, Mount Sinai Health System
CMO: Jeremy Boal, M.D., Executive Vice President and Chief Medical Officer
CIO: Kumar Chatani, Senior Vice President and Chief Information Officer Mount Sinai Health System
CHR: Jane Maksoud, R.N., Senior Vice President Human Resources and Labor Relations, Mount Sinai Health System
CNO: Mary Walsh, R.N., Vice President Patient Care Services and Chief Nursing Officer
Web address: www.bethisraelny.org
Control: Other not–for–profit (including NFP Corporation) **Service:** General Medical and Surgical

Staffed Beds: 1028 **Admissions:** 42204 **Census:** 656 **Outpatient Visits:** 528347 **Births:** 3351 **Total Expense ($000):** 1406096 **Payroll Expense ($000):** 624158 **Personnel:** 7489

✠ △ **MOUNT SINAI HOSPITAL (330024)**, One Gustave L. Levy Place, Zip 10029–0310; tel. 212/241–6500, (Includes KRAVIS CHILDREN'S HOSPITAL, 1184 Fifth Avenue, Zip 10029–6503, Mailing Address: One Gustave L. Levy Place, Zip 10029–0312; tel. 212/241–9500; MOUNT SINAI QUEENS, 25–10 30th Avenue, Long Island City, Zip 11102–2448; tel. 718/932–1000; Caryn A. Schwab, Executive Director) **A**1 2 3 5 7 8 10 **F**1 3 4 6 7 8 9 11 12 13 14 15 17 18 19 20 21 22 23 24 25 26 27 28 29 30 31 32 34 35 36 37 38 39 40 41 43 44 45 46 47 48 49 50 51 52 54 55 56 57 58 59 60 61 63 64 65 66 67 68 70 71 72 73 74 75 76 77 78 79 80 81 82 83 84 85 86 87 88 89 90 91 92 93 94 95 96 97 98 99 100 101 102 103 104 105 107 108 110 111 114 115 116 117 118 119 120 121 123 124 126 128 129 130 131 132 134 135 136 137 138 139 141 142 143 144 145 146 147 148 **P**5 6 7 **S** Mount Sinai Health System, New York, NY
Primary Contact: David L. Reich, M.D., President and Chief Operating Officer
COO: David L. Reich, M.D., President and Chief Operating Officer
CFO: Donald Scanlon, Chief Financial Officer
CMO: Vicki LoPachin, M.D., Chief Medical Officer
CIO: Kumar Chatani, Senior Vice President and Chief Information Officer Mount Sinai Health System
CHR: Jane Maksoud, R.N., Senior Vice President Human Resources and Labor Relations
Web address: www.mountsinai.org
Control: Other not–for–profit (including NFP Corporation) **Service:** General Medical and Surgical

Staffed Beds: 1175 **Admissions:** 59459 **Census:** 985 **Outpatient Visits:** 870632 **Births:** 7751 **Total Expense ($000):** 2021865 **Payroll Expense ($000):** 773306 **Personnel:** 9286

MOUNT SINAI ROOSEVELT HOSPITAL See Mount Sinai St. Luke's – Roosevelt

✠ **MOUNT SINAI ST. LUKE'S – ROOSEVELT (330046)**, 1111 Amsterdam Avenue, Zip 10025–1716; tel. 212/523–4000, (Includes MOUNT SINAI ROOSEVELT HOSPITAL, 1000 Tenth Avenue, Zip 10019; tel. 212/523–4000; Evan Flatow, M.D., President) **A**1 2 3 5 8 10 **F**3 4 5 6 7 8 11 12 13 14 15 17 18 20 22 24 26 29 30 31 32 34 35 38 39 40 41 43 44 46 49 50 51 52 54 55 56 57 58 59 60 61 62 63 64 65 66 68 70 72 74 75 76 77 78 79 81 82 83 84 85 86 87 90 92 93 94 96 97 98 99 100 101 102 103 104 107 108 110 111 114 115 119 120 121 123 124 126 130 131 132 134 135 143 144 145 146 147 148 **P**5 6 7 **S** Mount Sinai Health System, New York, NY
Primary Contact: Arthur A. Gianelli, M.P.H., President
COO: Kevin Molloy, Senior Vice President and Chief Operating Officer
CFO: Donald Scanlon, Chief Corporate Services, Mount Sinai Health System
CMO: Jeremy Boal, M.D., Executive Vice President and Chief Medical Officer
CIO: Kumar Chatani, Chief Information Officer, Mount Sinai Health System
CHR: Jane Maksoud, R.N., Senior Vice President Human Resources and Labor Relations, Mount Sinai Health System
CNO: Mary Walsh, R.N., Vice President Patient Care Services and Chief Nursing Officer
Web address: www.stlukeshospitalnyc.org
Control: Other not–for–profit (including NFP Corporation) **Service:** General Medical and Surgical

Staffed Beds: 671 **Admissions:** 33869 **Census:** 548 **Outpatient Visits:** 604431 **Births:** 5450 **Total Expense ($000):** 1095259 **Payroll Expense ($000):** 534439 **Personnel:** 5537

☐ **NEW YORK CITY CHILDREN'S CENTER**, 74–03 Commonwealth Boulevard, Jamaica, Zip 11426–1890; tel. 718/264–4506, (Includes BRONX CHILDREN'S PSYCHIATRIC CENTER, 1000 Waters Place, Bronx, Zip 10461–2799; tel. 718/239–3600; BROOKLYN CHILDREN'S PSYCHIATRIC CENTER, 1819 Bergen Street, Brooklyn, Zip 11233–4513; tel. 718/221–4500), (Nonreporting) **A**1 **S** New York State Office of Mental Health, Albany, NY
Primary Contact: Anita Daniels, Executive Director
CMO: David M. Rube, M.D., Clinical Director
CIO: Ed Yunusov, Coordinator Facility Information Center
Web address: www.omh.ny.gov/omhweb/facilities/nyccc/
Control: State–Government, nonfederal **Service:** Children's hospital psychiatric

Staffed Beds: 84

☐ **NEW YORK COMMUNITY HOSPITAL (330019)**, 2525 Kings Highway, Brooklyn, Zip 11229–1705; tel. 718/692–5300, (Nonreporting) **A**1 5 10
Primary Contact: Barry Stern, President and Chief Executive Officer
COO: Una E. Morrissey, R.N., Senior Vice President Chief Operating Officer and Chief Nursing Officer
CFO: Leonardo Tamburello, Divisional Chief Financial Officer
CMO: Herbert Rader, M.D., Advisor for Medical Affairs
CIO: Edward B. Stolyar, D.O., Director Management Information Systems
CHR: Carlos Ortiz, Vice President Human Resources
CNO: Una E. Morrissey, R.N., Senior Vice President Chief Operating Officer and Chief Nursing Officer
Web address: www.nych.com
Control: Other not–for–profit (including NFP Corporation) **Service:** General Medical and Surgical

Staffed Beds: 127

Many Facility Codes have changed. Please refer to the AHA Guide Code Chart. © 2016 AHA Guide

NY

⊠ **NEW YORK EYE AND EAR INFIRMARY OF MOUNT SINAI (330100)**, 310 East 14th Street, Zip 10003–4201; tel. 212/979–4000 **A**1 3 5 8 10 **F**3 11 29 30 34 35 44 50 54 57 58 59 64 66 68 74 81 82 85 86 87 91 92 93 94 97 107 114 119 129 130 132 146 **S** Mount Sinai Health System, New York, NY
Primary Contact: James Tsai, M.D., President
COO: Allan Fine, Chief Operating Officer
CFO: Donald Scanlon, Chief Corporate Services, Mount Sinai Health System
CMO: Jeremy Boal, M.D., Executive Vice President and Chief Medical Officer
CIO: Kumar Chatani, Chief Information Officer, Mount Sinai Health System
CHR: Jane Maksoud, R.N., Senior Vice President Human Resources and Labor Relations, Mount Sinai Health System
CNO: Sonja Tennaro, Ed.D., Senior Vice President Clinical Operations
Web address: www.nyee.edu
Control: Other not–for–profit (including NFP Corporation) **Service:** Eye, ear, nose, and throat

Staffed Beds: 32 **Admissions:** 409 **Census:** 3 **Outpatient Visits:** 112820 **Births:** 0 **Total Expense ($000):** 173180 **Payroll Expense ($000):** 83404 **Personnel:** 970

⊠ **NEW YORK METHODIST HOSPITAL (330236)**, 506 Sixth Street, Brooklyn, Zip 11215–3609; tel. 718/780–3000 **A**1 2 3 5 8 10 **F**3 6 8 9 11 12 13 15 17 18 19 20 22 24 26 29 30 31 32 33 34 35 36 39 40 41 43 44 45 46 47 48 49 50 51 52 54 55 56 57 58 59 60 61 64 65 66 68 70 72 73 74 75 76 77 78 79 81 82 83 84 85 87 88 89 90 91 92 93 95 96 97 98 99 102 103 104 107 108 109 110 111 112 114 115 118 119 120 121 123 124 126 129 130 131 132 144 145 146 147 148 **P**4 5 6 7
Primary Contact: Mark J. Mundy, President and Chief Executive Officer
COO: Lauren Yedvab, Chief Operating Officer
CFO: Michael Fagan, Senior Vice President Finance
CMO: Steven Silber, M.D., Senior Vice President Medical Affairs
CIO: Rick Plisko, Director information Systems
CHR: Dennis Buchanan, Vice President Human Resources
CNO: Rebecca L. Flood, R.N., Senior Vice President Nursing
Web address: www.nym.org
Control: Other not–for–profit (including NFP Corporation) **Service:** General Medical and Surgical

Staffed Beds: 591 **Admissions:** 37322 **Census:** 539 **Outpatient Visits:** 533547 **Births:** 5726 **Total Expense ($000):** 839591 **Payroll Expense ($000):** 325796 **Personnel:** 4133

☐ **NEW YORK STATE PSYCHIATRIC INSTITUTE (334009)**, 1051 Riverside Drive, Zip 10032–1007; tel. 212/543–5000, (Nonreporting) **A**1 3 5 10 **S** New York State Office of Mental Health, Albany, NY
Primary Contact: Jeffrey A. Lieberman, M.D., Executive Director
COO: Janelle Dierkens, Chief Administration Officer
CFO: Jonathan Segal, Chief Financial Officer
CMO: David Lowenthal, M.D., Clinical Director
CIO: Joseph Grun, Chief Information Officer
CHR: Rebecca Dechabert, Acting Director Personnel
Web address: www.nyspi.org
Control: State–Government, nonfederal **Service:** Psychiatric

Staffed Beds: 58

⊠ △ **NEW YORK–PRESBYTERIAN HOSPITAL (330101)**, 525 East 68th Street, Zip 10065–4870; tel. 212/746–5454, (Includes MORGAN STANLEY CHILDREN'S HOSPITAL OF NEW YORK–PRESBYTERIAN, 3959 Broadway, Zip 10032–3784; tel. 212/305–2500; NEW YORK PRESBYTERIAN LOWER MANHATTAN HOSPITAL, 170 William Street, Zip 10038–2649; tel. 212/312–5000; Robert E. Kelly, M.D., President; NEW YORK–PRESBYTERIAN HOSPITAL, WESTCHESTER DIVISION, 21 Bloomingdale Road, White Plains, Zip 10605; tel. 914/682–9100; NEW YORK–PRESBYTERIAN HOSPITAL/WEILL CORNELL MEDICAL CENTER, 525 East 68th Street, Zip 10021–4885; tel. 212/746–5454; NEW YORK–PRESBYTERIAN/COLUMBIA UNIVERSITY MEDICAL CENTER, 161 Fort Washington Avenue, Zip 10032; tel. 212/305–2500; PAYNE WHITNEY PSYCHIATRIC CLINIC, 525 East 68th Street, Zip 10021; tel. 212/746–3800; PHYLLIS AND DAVID KOMANSKY CENTER FOR CHILDREN'S HEALTH, 525 East 68th Street, tel. 212/746–5454; THE ALLEN PAVILION, 5141 Broadway, Zip 10032; tel. 212/932–5000) **A**1 2 3 5 8 10 **F**3 4 5 6 7 9 11 12 13 14 15 16 17 18 19 20 21 22 23 24 25 26 27 28 29 30 31 32 34 35 36 37 38 39 40 41 43 44 45 46 47 48 49 50 51 52 53 54 55 56 57 58 59 60 63 64 65 66 68 69 70 71 72 73 74 75 76 77 78 79 80 81 82 84 85 86 87 88 89 90 91 92 93 94 96 97 98 99 100 101 102 103 104 105 107 108 110 111 112 114 115 116 117 118 119 120 121 123 124 126 129 130 131 132 134 135 136 137 138 139 140 141 142 143 144 145 146 147 148 **S** New York Presbyterian Regional Hospital Network, New York, NY
Primary Contact: Steven J. Corwin, M.D., President and Chief Executive Officer
CFO: Phyllis R. Lantos, Executive Vice President, Corporate Chief Financial Officer and Treasurer
CMO: Laura Forese, M.D., Executive Vice President and Chief Medical Officer
CIO: Aurelia Boyer, Senior Vice President and Chief Information Officer
CHR: G. Thomas Ferguson, Senior Vice President and Chief Human Resources Officer
Web address: www.nyp.org
Control: Other not–for–profit (including NFP Corporation) **Service:** General Medical and Surgical

Staffed Beds: 2381 **Admissions:** 108964 **Census:** 1956 **Outpatient Visits:** 2150080 **Births:** 14846 **Total Expense ($000):** 4544595 **Payroll Expense ($000):** 2170025 **Personnel:** 21480

☐ **NEW YORK–PRESBYTERIAN/QUEENS (330055)**, 56–45 Main Street, Flushing, Zip 11355–5045; tel. 718/670–1231 **A**1 2 3 5 10 **F**3 7 11 12 13 14 15 17 18 19 20 22 24 26 28 29 30 31 32 34 35 37 39 40 41 43 44 45 46 47 49 50 51 52 54 55 56 57 58 59 60 61 64 65 66 68 70 71 72 73 74 75 76 77 78 79 80 81 82 83 84 85 86 87 89 91 92 93 96 97 100 101 107 108 110 111 114 115 116 117 118 119 120 121 123 126 130 131 132 143 145 146 147 148 **P**4 7 **S** New York Presbyterian Regional Hospital Network, New York, NY
Primary Contact: Jaclyn Mucaria, President and Chief Executive Officer
COO: John E. Sciortino, Senior Vice President and Chief Operating Officer
CFO: Kevin J. Ward, Vice President and Chief Financial Officer
CMO: Stephen Rimar, M.D., Senior Vice President Medical Affairs
CIO: Thomas Kemp, Chief Information Officer
CHR: Lorraine Orlando, Vice President Human Resources
Web address: www.nyhq.org
Control: Other not–for–profit (including NFP Corporation) **Service:** General Medical and Surgical

Staffed Beds: 519 **Admissions:** 27071 **Census:** 424 **Outpatient Visits:** 502326 **Births:** 4330 **Total Expense ($000):** 731998 **Payroll Expense ($000):** 345713 **Personnel:** 3656

⊠ **NYC HEALTH + HOSPITALS / BELLEVUE (330204)**, 462 First Avenue, Zip 10016–9198; tel. 212/562–4141 **A**1 3 5 10 **F**3 4 5 8 11 12 13 15 17 18 19 20 22 24 26 28 29 30 31 34 35 36 38 39 40 41 43 44 45 46 48 49 50 52 55 56 57 58 59 61 64 65 66 68 70 71 72 73 74 75 76 77 78 79 81 82 84 85 86 87 88 89 90 91 92 93 94 96 97 98 99 100 101 102 103 104 105 107 108 110 111 114 115 118 119 130 132 134 135 144 146 147 148 **S** NYC Health + Hospitals, New York, NY
Primary Contact: William Hicks, Interim Executive Director
COO: Michael Rawlings, Interim Chief Operating Officer
CFO: Jay Weinmann, Chief Financial Officer
CMO: Nate Link, M.D., Medical Director
CIO: Tonguc Yaman, Deputy Chief Information Officer
CHR: Howard Kritz, Director Human Resources
CNO: Kim K. Mendez, Ed.D., Chief Nurse Officer
Web address: www.nyc.gov/bellevue
Control: City–Government, nonfederal **Service:** General Medical and Surgical

Staffed Beds: 827 **Admissions:** 29189 **Census:** 646 **Outpatient Visits:** 594767 **Births:** 1506 **Total Expense ($000):** 887435 **Payroll Expense ($000):** 315687 **Personnel:** 4744

NY

Hospital, Medicare Provider Number, Address, Telephone, Approval, Facility, and Physician Codes, Health Care System

★ American Hospital Association (AHA) membership   ○ Healthcare Facilities Accreditation Program   ⇑ Center for Improvement in Healthcare Quality Accreditation
☐ The Joint Commission accreditation   ◇ DNV Healthcare Inc. accreditation   △ Commission on Accreditation of Rehabilitation Facilities (CARF) accreditation

☒ **NYC HEALTH + HOSPITALS / CARTER (332008)**, 1752 Park Avenue, Zip 10035; tel. 646/686–0000, (Includes COLER REHABILITATION AND NURSING CARE CENTER, 900 Main Street, Zip 10044; tel. 212/848–6300; Robert K. Hughes, Chief Executive Officer; HENRY J. CARTER SPECIALTY HOSPITAL & NURSING FACILITY, 1752 Park Avenue, tel. 646/686–0000; Floyd R. Long, Chief Executive Officer), (Total facility includes 164 beds in nursing home–type unit) **A**1 3 10 **F**1 3 11 28 29 30 39 56 58 68 74 75 77 79 84 85 87 100 103 107 114 119 128 130 132 135 146 148 **P**4 **S** NYC Health + Hospitals, New York, NY
Primary Contact: Floyd R. Long, Chief Executive Officer
CFO: Manuela Brito, Chief Financial Officer
CMO: Yolanda Bruno, M.D., Medical Director
CIO: Steve ONeill, Chief Information Officer
CHR: Howard Kritz, Senior Associate Executive Director
CNO: Stanlee Richards, Chief Nurse Executive
Web address: www.coler–goldwater.org
Control: City–Government, nonfederal **Service:** Long–Term Acute Care hospital

Staffed Beds: 365 Admissions: 562 Census: 311 Outpatient Visits: 0 Births: 0 Total Expense ($000): 150675 Payroll Expense ($000): 55243 Personnel: 835

☒ **NYC HEALTH + HOSPITALS / CONEY ISLAND (330196)**, 2601 Ocean Parkway, Brooklyn, Zip 11235–7795; tel. 718/616–3000 **A**1 3 5 10 12 13 **F**3 4 5 8 9 11 13 15 16 17 18 20 26 29 30 31 32 34 35 36 38 39 40 41 44 45 50 51 54 55 56 57 58 59 60 61 64 65 66 68 70 71 73 74 75 76 77 78 79 81 82 83 84 85 87 89 90 91 92 93 94 96 97 98 99 100 102 103 104 107 108 110 111 114 115 118 119 129 130 132 134 135 143 146 147 148 **S** NYC Health + Hospitals, New York, NY
Primary Contact: Anthony Rajkumar, Chief Executive Officer
COO: Mei Kong, Chief Operating Officer
CMO: Wehbeh Wehbeh, M.D., Chief Medical Officer
CIO: Robert Kee, Chief Information Officer
CHR: Andrew Campbell, Associate Executive Director
CNO: Patricia Ruiz, Chief Nursing Officer
Web address: www.nyc.gov/html/hhc/html/facilities/coneyisland.shtml
Control: City–Government, nonfederal **Service:** General Medical and Surgical

Staffed Beds: 371 Admissions: 15169 Census: 315 Outpatient Visits: 330848 Births: 1226 Total Expense ($000): 454131 Payroll Expense ($000): 179208 Personnel: 3115

☒ **NYC HEALTH + HOSPITALS / ELMHURST (330128)**, 79–01 Broadway, Elmhurst, Zip 11373–1329; tel. 718/334–4000 **A**1 2 3 5 10 **F**3 5 8 9 13 14 15 17 18 20 22 26 29 30 31 32 34 35 38 40 41 43 44 45 49 50 51 53 54 55 56 57 58 59 60 61 64 65 66 68 70 72 73 74 75 76 77 78 79 81 82 83 84 85 86 87 89 90 92 93 96 97 98 99 100 101 102 103 104 105 107 108 110 111 115 119 121 126 130 131 132 134 135 143 146 147 **P**6 **S** NYC Health + Hospitals, New York, NY
Primary Contact: Israel Rocha, Chief Executive Officer
COO: Wayne Zimmermann, Chief Operating Officer
CMO: Jasmin Moshirpur, M.D., Dean and Medical Director
CIO: Vincent Smith, Chief Information Officer
CHR: Jeannith Michelen, Associate Executive Director
CNO: Joann Bernadette Gull, Chief Nursing Officer
Web address: www.nyc.gov/html/hhc/ehc/html/home/home.shtml
Control: City–Government, nonfederal **Service:** General Medical and Surgical

Staffed Beds: 525 Admissions: 20526 Census: 439 Outpatient Visits: 660503 Births: 3159 Total Expense ($000): 652700 Payroll Expense ($000): 239845 Personnel: 3212

☒ △ **NYC HEALTH + HOSPITALS / HARLEM (330240)**, 506 Lenox Avenue, Zip 10037–1802; tel. 212/939–1000, (Includes HARLEM GENERAL CARE UNIT AND HARLEM PSYCHIATRIC UNIT) **A**1 3 5 7 10 **F**3 4 5 8 11 12 13 15 16 17 18 19 20 29 30 32 34 35 38 39 40 41 43 44 45 48 49 50 51 53 57 58 59 60 64 65 68 70 71 72 73 74 75 76 77 79 81 82 84 85 86 87 88 89 90 93 94 96 97 98 99 100 101 102 103 104 107 108 110 111 114 115 118 119 130 132 134 135 141 144 146 147 148 **S** NYC Health + Hospitals, New York, NY
Primary Contact: Ebone' Carrington, Interim Executive Director
COO: Ebone' Carrington, Chief Operating Officer
Web address: www.nyc.gov/html/hhc/harlem
Control: City–Government, nonfederal **Service:** General Medical and Surgical

Staffed Beds: 272 Admissions: 11193 Census: 192 Outpatient Visits: 309414 Births: 908 Total Expense ($000): 469970 Payroll Expense ($000): 161087 Personnel: 2307

☒ **NYC HEALTH + HOSPITALS / JACOBI (330127)**, 1400 Pelham Parkway South, Bronx, Zip 10461–1197; tel. 718/918–5000 **A**1 3 5 10 **F**3 4 5 8 11 12 13 15 16 17 18 20 26 29 30 31 32 34 35 38 39 40 41 43 44 45 46 47 49 50 51 55 56 57 58 59 60 61 62 64 65 66 70 72 73 74 75 76 77 78 79 80 81 82 84 85 87 88 89 90 92 93 94 96 97 98 99 100 101 102 103 104 107 108 110 111 117 119 130 131 132 134 135 144 146 147 148 **P**6 **S** NYC Health + Hospitals, New York, NY
Primary Contact: John Morley, M.D., Acting Executive Director
COO: Christopher Mastromanno, Chief Operating Officer
CFO: Kathy Garramone, Chief Financial Officer
CMO: John Morley, M.D., Chief Medical Officer
CIO: Md Alam, Chief Information Officer
CHR: Jamie Grecco, Chief Human Resource Executive
CNO: Suzanne Pennacchio, Chief Nursing Officer
Web address: www.nyc.gov/hhc/jacobi/home.html
Control: City–Government, nonfederal **Service:** General Medical and Surgical

Staffed Beds: 457 Admissions: 19051 Census: 347 Outpatient Visits: 437581 Births: 2304 Total Expense ($000): 732249 Payroll Expense ($000): 261854 Personnel: 3557

☒ **NYC HEALTH + HOSPITALS / KINGS COUNTY (330202)**, 451 Clarkson Avenue, Brooklyn, Zip 11203–2097; tel. 718/245–3131 **A**1 2 3 5 10 **F**3 4 5 8 9 11 12 13 15 17 18 19 20 24 26 28 29 30 31 32 34 35 38 39 40 41 43 45 46 47 49 50 51 52 53 56 57 58 59 60 61 64 65 66 68 70 71 72 73 74 75 76 77 78 79 81 82 84 85 86 87 88 89 90 91 92 93 94 97 98 99 100 101 102 103 104 105 106 107 108 110 111 114 115 116 119 120 121 123 129 130 131 132 134 135 143 144 145 146 147 148 **P**6 **S** NYC Health + Hospitals, New York, NY
Primary Contact: Ernest Baptiste, Executive Director
COO: Robert R. Miller, II, Chief Operating Officer
CFO: Julian John, Chief Financial Officer
CMO: Ghassan Jamaleddine, M.D., Medical Director
CIO: Dino Civan, Chief Information Officer
CHR: Michelle Emmons, Associate Executive Director
CNO: Opal Sinclair–Chung, R.N., Chief Nursing Officer, Deputy Executive Director
Web address: www.nyc.gov/html/hhc/kchc/html/home/home.shtml
Control: City–Government, nonfederal **Service:** General Medical and Surgical

Staffed Beds: 599 Admissions: 24174 Census: 512 Outpatient Visits: 699087 Births: 2187 Total Expense ($000): 827703 Payroll Expense ($000): 395035 Personnel: 5575

☒ **NYC HEALTH + HOSPITALS / LINCOLN (330080)**, 234 East 149th Street, Bronx, Zip 10451–5504, Mailing Address: 234 East 149th Street, Room 923, Zip 10451–5504; tel. 718/579–5700 **A**1 2 3 5 10 **F**3 5 8 11 13 15 18 19 29 30 31 32 34 35 38 39 40 41 43 45 50 55 56 57 58 59 60 61 64 65 66 68 70 71 72 73 74 75 76 77 78 79 81 82 84 85 86 87 88 89 93 97 98 99 100 101 102 103 104 107 108 110 111 114 115 119 121 123 130 132 134 135 143 144 146 147 148 **P**4 **S** NYC Health + Hospitals, New York, NY
Primary Contact: Milton Nunez, Executive Director
CFO: Caswell Samms, Network Chief Financial Officer
CMO: Melissa Schori, M.D., Medical Director
CIO: Maricar Barrameda, Chief Information Officer
CHR: Jeannith Michelen, Senior Associate Executive Director
Web address: www.nyc.gov/html/hhc/lincoln/
Control: City–Government, nonfederal **Service:** General Medical and Surgical

Staffed Beds: 355 Admissions: 20563 Census: 289 Outpatient Visits: 551544 Births: 2226 Total Expense ($000): 565871 Payroll Expense ($000): 221553 Personnel: 3353

☒ **NYC HEALTH + HOSPITALS / METROPOLITAN (330199)**, 1901 First Avenue, Zip 10029–7404; tel. 212/423–6262, (Includes METROPOLITAN GENERAL CARE UNIT, METROPOLITAN DRUG DETOXIFICATION AND METROPOLITAN PSYCHIATRIC UNIT) **A**1 3 5 10 **F**3 4 8 9 11 13 15 17 18 28 29 30 31 32 34 35 38 39 40 41 43 44 45 46 48 49 50 51 54 55 56 57 58 59 60 61 64 65 66 68 70 72 73 74 75 76 77 78 79 81 82 84 85 86 87 89 90 92 93 94 96 97 98 99 100 101 102 103 104 107 108 110 111 114 119 130 131 132 134 135 144 146 147 148 **S** NYC Health + Hospitals, New York, NY
Primary Contact: Alina Moran, Chief Executive Officer
COO: William Norberto Wang, M.D., Chief Operating Officer
CFO: Tracy V. Green, Chief Financial Officer
CMO: John T. Pellicone, M.D., Chief Medical Officer
CIO: Md Alam, Chief Information Officer
CHR: April Alexander, Director Human Resources
CNO: Noreen Brennan, Chief Nursing Officer
Web address: www.nyc.gov/html/hhc/mhc/html/home/home.shtml
Control: City–Government, nonfederal **Service:** General Medical and Surgical

Staffed Beds: 317 Admissions: 11760 Census: 209 Outpatient Visits: 399745 Births: 1016 Total Expense ($000): 362791 Payroll Expense ($000): 142920 Personnel: 2019

✠ **NYC HEALTH + HOSPITALS / NORTH CENTRAL BRONX (330385)**, 3424 Kossuth Avenue, Bronx, Zip 10467–2489; tel. 718/519–3500 **A**1 3 5 10 **F**3 5 8 11 12 13 15 18 28 29 30 32 34 35 38 39 40 41 43 44 45 46 48 50 51 55 56 57 58 59 60 61 64 65 66 68 70 72 73 74 75 76 77 78 79 80 81 82 84 85 87 92 93 94 96 97 98 99 100 101 102 103 104 105 107 108 110 111 115 119 130 131 132 135 144 146 147 148 **P**6 **S** NYC Health + Hospitals, New York, NY
Primary Contact: Maureen Pode, Co–Interim Executive Director
COO: Sheldon McLeod, Chief Operating Officer
CFO: Kathy Garramone, Chief Financial Officer
CMO: Joseph Skarzynski, M.D., Medical Director
CIO: Diane Carr, Chief Information Officer
CHR: Dolores Leite, Chief Human Resource Executive
CNO: Elizabeth Gerdts, Chief Nursing Officer
Web address: www.nyc.gov/html/hhc/ncbh/html/home/home.shtml
Control: City–Government, nonfedeal **Service:** General Medical and Surgical

Staffed Beds: 207 **Admissions:** 6168 **Census:** 111 **Outpatient Visits:** 212927 **Births:** 699 **Total Expense ($000):** 211946 **Payroll Expense ($000):** 75898 **Personnel:** 1173

✠ **NYC HEALTH + HOSPITALS / QUEENS (330231)**, 82–68 164th Street, Jamaica, Zip 11432–1104; tel. 718/883–3000 **A**1 2 3 5 10 **F**3 5 8 11 13 14 15 18 29 30 31 32 34 35 38 39 40 45 50 53 54 56 57 59 61 64 68 70 72 73 76 77 78 79 81 83 84 85 87 90 93 97 98 99 100 102 103 104 105 107 111 115 116 119 121 129 130 134 135 146 147 **P**6 **S** NYC Health + Hospitals, New York, NY
Primary Contact: Dona Green, Chief Operating Officer
COO: Dona Green, Chief Operating Officer
CFO: Brian Stacey, Chief Financial Officer
CMO: Jasmin Moshirpur, M.D., Chief Medical Officer
CIO: Vincent Smith, Chief Information Officer
CHR: Jeannith Michelen, Senior Associate Executive Director
CNO: Joan Gabriele, Deputy Executive Director
Web address: www.nyc.gov/html/hhc/qhc/html/home/home.shtml
Control: City–Government, nonfederal **Service:** General Medical and Surgical

Staffed Beds: 259 **Admissions:** 12757 **Census:** 210 **Outpatient Visits:** 420876 **Total Expense ($000):** 434976 **Payroll Expense ($000):** 149554 **Personnel:** 1980

✠ **NYC HEALTH + HOSPITALS / WOODHULL (330396)**, 760 Broadway, Brooklyn, Zip 11206–5383; tel. 718/963–8000 **A**1 3 5 10 **F**3 4 5 11 13 15 18 19 29 30 31 32 34 35 36 38 39 40 41 43 44 45 46 49 50 54 55 58 60 61 62 64 65 68 70 71 72 73 74 75 76 77 78 79 81 82 84 87 89 91 92 93 94 97 98 99 100 102 103 104 107 108 110 111 115 118 119 130 131 132 135 143 145 146 147 148 **P**6 **S** NYC Health + Hospitals, New York, NY
Primary Contact: Gregory Calliste, Ph.D., FACHE, Chief Executive Officer
COO: Eve Borzon, R.N., Chief Operating Officer
CFO: Erika Soiman, CPA, Chief Financial Officer
CMO: Edward Fishkin, M.D., Medical Director
CHR: Irma Suarez, Deputy Executive Director
CNO: Angela Imelda Edwards, R.N., Chief Nurse Executive
Web address: www.nyc.gov/html/hhc
Control: City–County, Government, nonfederal **Service:** General Medical and Surgical

Staffed Beds: 323 **Admissions:** 11980 **Census:** 244 **Outpatient Visits:** 486636 **Births:** 1639 **Total Expense ($000):** 467048 **Payroll Expense ($000):** 175880 **Personnel:** 2594

NYU HOSPITAL FOR JOINT DISEASES See NYU Langone Medical Center's Hospital for Joint Diseases

✠ △ **NYU LANGONE MEDICAL CENTER (330214)**, 550 First Avenue, Zip 10016–6402; tel. 212/263–7300, (Includes HASSENFELD CHILDRENS HOSPITAL OF NEW YORK AT NYU LANGONE MEDICAL CENTER, 550 First Avenue, Zip 10016–6401; tel. 212/263–7300; NYU LANGONE MEDICAL CENTER'S HOSPITAL FOR JOINT DISEASES, 301 East 17th Street, Zip 10003–3890; tel. 212/598–6000; David A. Dibner, FACHE, Senior Vice President Hospital Operations and Musculoskeletal Strategic Areas; NYU LUTHERAN (NYU HOSPITALS CENTER), 150 55th Street, Brooklyn, Zip 11220–2559; tel. 718/630–7000; Robert I. Grossman, M.D., Chief Executive Officer; RUSK INSTITUTE AT NYU–HJD, 301 E. 17th ST, Zip 10003–3804; tel. 212/598–6000; David A. Dibner, FACHE, Senior Vice President Hospital Operations and Muscuoloskeltal Strategic Areas) **A**1 2 3 5 7 8 10 **F**3 5 6 8 9 11 12 13 14 15 17 18 19 20 21 22 23 24 25 26 27 28 29 30 31 32 33 34 35 36 37 38 39 40 41 42 43 44 45 46 47 48 49 50 51 52 53 54 55 56 57 58 59 60 61 63 64 65 66 68 70 73 74 75 76 77 78 79 80 81 82 84 85 86 87 88 89 90 91 92 93 95 96 97 98 99 100 101 102 103 104 107 108 110 111 113 114 115 116 117 118 119 120 121 123 124 126 129 130 131 132 134 135 136 138 139 141 142 145 146 147 148 **P**5 6
Primary Contact: Robert I. Grossman, M.D., Chief Executive Officer
COO: Robert Press, M.D., Senior Vice President, Vice Dean and Chief Hospital Operations
CFO: Michael Burke, Senior Vice President and Corporate Chief Financial Officer
CMO: Fritz Francois, M.D., Chief Medical Officer
CIO: Nader Mherabi, Senior Vice President and Vice Dean, Chief Information Officer
CHR: Nancy Sanchez, Senior Vice President and Vice Dean Human Resources
CNO: Kimberly S. Glassman, Ph.D., Chief Nursing Officer
Web address: www.nyumedicalcenter.org
Control: Other not–for–profit (including NFP Corporation) **Service:** General Medical and Surgical

Staffed Beds: 718 **Admissions:** 34732 **Census:** 484 **Outpatient Visits:** 919211 **Births:** 5886 **Total Expense ($000):** 2415551 **Payroll Expense ($000):** 795591 **Personnel:** 10322

PAYNE WHITNEY PSYCHIATRIC CLINIC See New York–Presbyterian Hospital

QUEENS CHILDREN'S PSYCHIATRIC CENTER See New York City Children's Center

✠ **RICHMOND UNIVERSITY MEDICAL CENTER (330028)**, 355 Bard Avenue, Staten Island, Zip 10310–1664; tel. 718/818–1234, (Nonreporting) **A**1 2 3 5 10
Primary Contact: Daniel J. Messina, Ph.D., FACHE, President and Chief Executive Officer
CMO: Edward Arsura, M.D., Chief Medical Officer
CHR: Patricia Caldari, Vice President
Web address: www.rumcsi.org
Control: Other not–for–profit (including NFP Corporation) **Service:** General Medical and Surgical

Staffed Beds: 386

☐ **ROCKEFELLER UNIVERSITY HOSPITAL (330387)**, (Clinical Research), 1230 York Avenue, Zip 10065–6399; tel. 212/327–8000 **A**1 10 **F**34 50 57 58 75 77 87 130
Primary Contact: James G. Krueger, M.D., Ph.D., Chief Executive Officer
CMO: Barbara O'Sullivan, M.D., Medical Director
Web address: www.rucares.org
Control: State–Government, nonfederal **Service:** Other specialty

Staffed Beds: 17 **Admissions:** 132 **Census:** 1 **Outpatient Visits:** 5461 **Births:** 0

ROOSEVELT HOSPITAL See Mount Sinai Roosevelt Hospital

☐ **SOUTH BEACH PSYCHIATRIC CENTER (334043)**, 777 Seaview Avenue, Staten Island, Zip 10305–3409; tel. 718/667–2300, (Nonreporting) **A**1 3 10 **S** New York State Office of Mental Health, Albany, NY
Primary Contact: Rosanne Gaylor, M.D., Acting Executive Director
CHR: George Bouquio, Director Human Resources
Web address: www.omh.ny.gov/omhweb/facilities/sbpc/facility.htm
Control: State–Government, nonfederal **Service:** Psychiatric

Staffed Beds: 340

✠ **ST. BARNABAS HOSPITAL (330399)**, 183rd Street & Third Avenue, Bronx, Zip 10457–9998; tel. 718/960–9000, (Nonreporting) **A**1 3 5 10 12 13
Primary Contact: David A. Perlstein, M.D., President and Chief Executive Officer
COO: Len Walsh, Executive Vice President and Chief Operating Officer
CFO: Todd Gorlewski, Senior Vice President and Chief Financial Officer
CIO: Jitendra Barmecha, M.D., Senior Vice President and Chief Information Officer
CHR: Marc Wolf, Assistant Vice President Human Resources
CNO: Denise Richardson, R.N., Senior Vice President and Chief Nursing Officer
Web address: www.sbhny.org
Control: Other not–for–profit (including NFP Corporation) **Service:** General Medical and Surgical

Staffed Beds: 660

NY

☐ **ST. JOHN'S EPISCOPAL HOSPITAL–SOUTH SHORE (330395)**, 327 Beach 19th Street, Far Rockaway, Zip 11691–4423; tel. 718/869–7000 **A**1 3 5 10 12 13 **F**3 12 13 15 17 18 19 29 30 31 32 34 35 38 40 41 45 49 50 54 55 56 57 59 60 61 64 65 68 70 73 74 75 76 77 78 79 81 82 84 85 87 89 92 93 97 98 99 100 101 102 103 104 107 108 110 111 114 118 119 130 132 134 135 141 146 148
Primary Contact: Gerard W. Walsh, Chief Executive Officer
COO: Patrick L. Sullivan, Chief Operating Officer
CFO: Kathleen Garcia, Controller
CMO: Raymond Pastore, M.D., Chief Medical Officer
CIO: Michael J. Piro, Chief Information Officer
CHR: Roger Franco, Director Human Resources
Web address: www.ehs.org
Control: State–Government, nonfederal **Service:** General Medical and Surgical

Staffed Beds: 241 **Admissions:** 8278 **Census:** 160 **Outpatient Visits:** 117446 **Births:** 683 **Total Expense ($000):** 193226 **Payroll Expense ($000):** 94718

✖ △ **STATEN ISLAND UNIVERSITY HOSPITAL (330160)**, 475 Seaview Avenue, Staten Island, Zip 10305–3436; tel. 718/226–9000 **A**1 2 3 5 7 8 10 **N**4 5 7 8 11 12 13 14 15 16 17 18 19 20 22 24 26 28 29 30 31 32 34 35 36 38 39 40 41 43 44 45 46 47 48 49 50 51 52 54 55 56 57 58 59 60 61 63 64 65 66 68 70 71 72 73 74 75 76 77 78 79 81 82 84 85 86 87 88 89 90 92 93 95 96 97 98 100 101 102 103 104 105 107 108 110 111 114 115 116 117 118 119 121 123 124 126 129 130 131 132 134 135 145 146 147 148 **P**5 6 **S** Northwell Health, New Hyde Park, NY
Primary Contact: Donna Proske, MS, R.N., Executive Director
CFO: Thomas Reca, Sr., Deputy Executive Director and Chief Financial Officer
CMO: Theodore Maniatis, M.D., Medical Director
CIO: Kathy Kania, Chief Information Officer
CHR: Margaret DiAlto, Regional Chief Human Resource Officer
CNO: Dian I. Johnson, MSN, Chief Nurse Executive
Web address: www.siuh.edu
Control: Other not–for–profit (including NFP Corporation) **Service:** General Medical and Surgical

Staffed Beds: 663 **Admissions:** 39422 **Census:** 581 **Outpatient Visits:** 937825 **Births:** 2939 **Total Expense ($000):** 814057 **Payroll Expense ($000):** 367958 **Personnel:** 4950

STEVEN AND ALEXANDRA COHEN CHILDREN'S MEDICAL CENTER OF NEW YORK See Long Island Jewish Medical Center, New Hyde Park

✖ **SUNY DOWNSTATE MEDICAL CENTER UNIVERSITY HOSPITAL (330350)**, 450 Clarkson Avenue, Brooklyn, Zip 11203–2012, Mailing Address: 450 Clarkson Avenue, MSC#75, Zip 11203–2012; tel. 718/270–1000, (Includes UNIVERSITY HOSPITAL OF BROOKLYN AT LONG ISLAND COLLEGE HOSPITAL, 339 Hicks Street, Zip 11201–5509; tel. 718/780–1000; George P. Caralis, Interim Chief Executive Officer) **A**1 3 5 8 10 **F**7 8 13 14 15 17 18 19 20 21 22 23 24 25 26 27 28 29 30 31 32 34 35 36 37 38 39 40 41 42 44 45 46 47 48 49 50 51 52 53 54 55 56 57 58 59 60 61 64 65 66 68 70 72 73 74 75 76 77 78 79 80 81 82 84 86 87 88 89 90 91 92 93 94 97 104 107 108 111 112 114 115 116 117 118 119 120 121 122 123 124 126 129 130 131 132 138 143 144 146 147
Primary Contact: William P. Walsh, Senior Vice President Hospital Affairs and Managing Director
COO: Patricia A. Winston, FACHE, Vice President, Chief Administrative Officer and Chief Operating Officer
CFO: Richard B. Miller, Ph.D., Vice President Hospital Affairs and Chief Financial Officer
CMO: Michael Lucchesi, M.D., Chief Medical Officer; Chair, Emergency Medicine
CIO: Dilip Nath, Sc.D., Associate Chief Information Officer
CHR: Maria Silas, Manager Human Resources
CNO: Margaret G. Jackson, R.N., Vice President Patient Care Services and Chief Nursing Officer
Web address: www.downstate.edu
Control: State–Government, nonfederal **Service:** General Medical and Surgical

Staffed Beds: 342 **Admissions:** 13318 **Census:** 217 **Outpatient Visits:** 324817 **Births:** 1010 **Total Expense ($000):** 549469 **Payroll Expense ($000):** 246723 **Personnel:** 2691

TERENCE CARDINAL COOKE HEALTH CARE CENTER (332022), 1249 Fifth Avenue, Zip 10029–4413; tel. 212/360–1000, (Nonreporting) **A**10
Primary Contact: Mitch Marsh, Interim Executive Director
COO: Neil Pollack, Senior Administrator
CFO: Ann Marie Covone, Senior Vice President and Chief Financial Officer
CMO: Anthony Lechich, M.D., Chief Medical Officer
CIO: Mitze Amoroso, Chief Information Officer
CHR: Hugo A. Pizarro, Vice President Human Resources
CNO: Monica McGibbon, Chief Nursing Officer
Web address: www.tcchcc.org/
Control: Church–operated, Nongovernment, not–for profit **Service:** Long–Term Acute Care hospital

Staffed Beds: 28

THE ALLEN PAVILION See New York–Presbyterian Hospital

VETERANS AFFAIRS MEDICAL CENTER See James J. Peters Veterans Affairs Medical Center

✖ **VETERANS AFFAIRS NEW YORK HARBOR HEALTHCARE SYSTEM**, 800 Poly Place, Brooklyn, Zip 11209–7104; tel. 718/630–3500, (Includes VETERANS AFFAIRS NEW YORK HARBOR HEALTHCARE SYSTEM – MANHATTAN CAMPUS, 423 East 23rd Street, New York, Zip 10010–5050; tel. 212/686–7500), (Nonreporting) **A**1 2 3 5 **S** Department of Veterans Affairs, Washington, DC
Primary Contact: Martina A. Parauda, Director
CFO: Daniel Downey, Chief Fiscal Service
CIO: Maria Schay, Chief Information Officer
Web address: www.nyharbor.va.gov
Control: Veterans Affairs, Government, federal **Service:** General Medical and Surgical

Staffed Beds: 476

☐ **WYCKOFF HEIGHTS MEDICAL CENTER (330221)**, 374 Stockholm Street, Brooklyn, Zip 11237–4006; tel. 718/963–7272 **A**1 3 5 10 12 13 **F**3 7 8 9 12 13 15 18 19 20 26 29 30 31 34 35 39 40 41 44 45 50 54 56 57 61 64 65 68 70 72 73 74 75 76 78 79 81 82 85 86 87 89 90 92 93 94 97 102 107 108 109 110 111 114 115 118 119 120 121 123 124 130 132 134 143 146 147 148
Primary Contact: Ramon J. Rodriguez, President and Chief Executive Officer
COO: David Rock, Executive Vice President and Chief Operating Officer
CFO: Frank A. Vutrano, Chief Financial Officer
CMO: Gustavo Del Toro, M.D., Chief Medical Officer
CIO: Jebashini Jesurasa, Vice President, Chief Information Technology Officer
CHR: Margaret E. Cornelius, Vice President Human Resources
CNO: Catherine A. Gallogly–Simon, R.N., Chief Nursing Officer
Web address: www.wyckoffhospital.org
Control: Other not–for–profit (including NFP Corporation) **Service:** General Medical and Surgical

Staffed Beds: 276 **Admissions:** 12591 **Census:** 149 **Outpatient Visits:** 232202 **Births:** 1368 **Total Expense ($000):** 297720 **Payroll Expense ($000):** 126727 **Personnel:** 2022

ZUCKER HILLSIDE HOSPITAL See Long Island Jewish Medical Center, New Hyde Park

NEWARK—Wayne County

✖ **NEWARK–WAYNE COMMUNITY HOSPITAL (330030)**, 1200 Driving Park Avenue, Zip 14513–1057, Mailing Address: P.O. Box 111, Zip 14513–0111; tel. 315/332–2022, (Total facility includes 180 beds in nursing home–type unit) **A**1 10 **F**2 3 6 8 11 13 15 28 29 30 34 35 38 40 44 50 54 55 56 57 59 61 64 68 70 74 75 76 77 79 80 81 85 86 87 90 93 97 98 100 102 103 107 110 111 114 118 119 126 128 130 131 132 135 143 146 147 148 **P**5 7 **S** Rochester Regional Health, Rochester, NY
Primary Contact: Dustin Riccio, M.D., President Eastern Region
CFO: Tom Crilly, Executive Vice President, Chief Financial Officer
CMO: Robert Mayo, M.D., Executive Vice President, Chief Medical Officer
CIO: John Glynn, Executive Vice President, Chief Information Officer
CHR: Janine Schue, Executive Vice President, Chief Human Resources Officer
CNO: Theresa Glessner, Vice President, Chief Nursing Officer
Web address: www.rochesterregional.org
Control: Other not–for–profit (including NFP Corporation) **Service:** General Medical and Surgical

Staffed Beds: 280 **Admissions:** 5591 **Census:** 233 **Outpatient Visits:** 176318 **Births:** 713 **Total Expense ($000):** 95003 **Payroll Expense ($000):** 43501 **Personnel:** 775

NEWBURGH—Orange County

✖ **ST. LUKE'S CORNWALL HOSPITAL (330264)**, 70 Dubois Street, Zip 12550–4851; tel. 845/561–4400, (Includes ST. LUKE'S CORNWALL HOSPITAL – CORNWALL CAMPUS, 19 Laurel Avenue, Cornwall, Zip 12518–1499; tel. 845/534–7711; ST. LUKE'S CORNWALL HOSPITAL – NEWBURGH CAMPUS, 70 Dubois Street, Zip 12550–4898; tel. 845/561–4400; Joan Cusack–McGuirk, Interim President and Chief Executive Officer) **A**1 2 10 **F**3 11 12 13 15 18 20 22 26 28 29 31 34 35 37 40 42 43 46 49 51 54 57 59 60 61 64 70 72 74 75 76 77 78 79 81 82 84 85 86 87 89 93 100 102 107 108 110 114 115 118 119 120 121 123 124 126 129 130 131 132 146 147
Primary Contact: Joan Cusack–McGuirk, Interim President and Chief Executive Officer
CFO: Thomas Gibney, Senior Vice President and Chief Financial Officer
CMO: Christine Jelalian, M.D., Medical Director
CIO: Dwayne Simmons, Interim Chief Information Officer
CHR: Daniel Bengyak, Vice President, Human Resources
CNO: Margaret Deyo–Allers, Vice President, Chief Nursing Officer
Web address: www.stlukescornwallhospital.org
Control: Other not–for–profit (including NFP Corporation) **Service:** General Medical and Surgical

Staffed Beds: 128 **Admissions:** 10378 **Census:** 124 **Outpatient Visits:** 155024 **Births:** 783 **Total Expense ($000):** 184508 **Payroll Expense ($000):** 67709 **Personnel:** 868

NIAGARA FALLS—Niagara County

○ **NIAGARA FALLS MEMORIAL MEDICAL CENTER (330065)**, 621 Tenth Street, Zip 14301–1813, Mailing Address: P.O. Box 708, Zip 14302–0708; tel. 716/278–4000, (Nonreporting) **A**3 5 10 11 13
Primary Contact: Joseph A. Ruffolo, President and Chief Executive Officer
CMO: Fatma Patel, M.D., Vice President Medical Affairs
CIO: Diane Martin–Pratt, Director Information Systems
Web address: www.nfmmc.org
Control: Other not–for–profit (including NFP Corporation) **Service:** General Medical and Surgical

Staffed Beds: 288

NORTH TONAWANDA—Niagara County

DE GRAFF MEMORIAL HOSPITAL See KALEIDA Health, Buffalo

NORTHPORT—Suffolk County

⊠ △ **NORTHPORT VETERANS AFFAIRS MEDICAL CENTER**, 79 Middleville Road, Zip 11768–2200; tel. 631/261–4400, (Total facility includes 170 beds in nursing home–type unit) **A**1 2 3 5 7 **F**3 5 8 20 29 30 31 33 34 35 36 38 39 40 44 45 46 47 49 50 51 53 54 56 57 58 59 60 61 62 63 64 65 68 70 71 74 75 77 78 79 81 82 83 84 85 86 87 90 91 92 93 94 95 96 97 98 100 101 102 103 104 105 106 107 108 111 114 116 117 118 119 120 121 123 127 128 129 130 132 133 135 144 146 147 148 **S** Department of Veterans Affairs, Washington, DC
Primary Contact: Philip C. Moschitta, Director
COO: Maria Favale, FACHE, Associate Director
CFO: Mary Pat Hessman, Chief Fiscal
CMO: Edward Mack, M.D., Chief of Staff
CIO: Robert Ziskin, Chief Information Officer
CHR: Wilmino Sainbert, Chief Human Resources Management Service
Web address: www.northport.va.gov/index.asp
Control: Veterans Affairs, Government, federal **Service:** General Medical and Surgical

Staffed Beds: 502 **Admissions:** 3840 **Census:** 217 **Outpatient Visits:** 606632 **Births:** 0 **Personnel:** 1887

NORWICH—Chenango County

★ ○ **UHS CHENANGO MEMORIAL HOSPITAL (330033)**, 179 North Broad Street, Zip 13815–1097; tel. 607/337–4111, (Total facility includes 80 beds in nursing home–type unit) **A**10 11 **F**3 8 11 13 15 17 18 29 32 34 35 38 39 40 45 47 50 54 56 57 59 61 64 65 68 70 75 77 79 81 82 85 86 87 93 97 107 108 110 111 115 119 127 128 130 132 133 146 147 148 **P**6 **S** United Health Services, Binghamton, NY
Primary Contact: Drake M. Lamen, President, Chief Executive Officer and Chief Medical Officer
COO: Christina A. Kisacky, Vice President, Operations
CFO: Peggy Swartwood, Assistant Vice President, Finance and Controller
CIO: Richard Stone, Manager, Technical Services
CHR: Anne L. English, Director Human Resources
CNO: David Finney, R.N., Vice President Nursing
Web address: www.uhs.net/cmh
Control: Other not–for–profit (including NFP Corporation) **Service:** General Medical and Surgical

Staffed Beds: 138 **Admissions:** 1574 **Census:** 85 **Outpatient Visits:** 258780 **Births:** 249 **Total Expense ($000):** 66866 **Payroll Expense ($000):** 19712 **Personnel:** 422

NYACK—Rockland County

□ **NYACK HOSPITAL (330104)**, 160 North Midland Avenue, Zip 10960–1998; tel. 845/348–2000 **A**1 2 5 10 **F**4 5 8 11 12 13 14 15 17 29 30 31 34 40 43 45 46 62 64 70 73 75 76 77 78 79 81 82 83 84 85 86 87 89 93 94 98 99 102 103 107 108 111 118 119 129 130 135 146 148
Primary Contact: Mark Geller, M.D., President and Chief Executive Officer
COO: John Volanto, Vice President, Chief Operating Officer
CFO: John Burke, Chief Financial Officer
CMO: Anthony Matejicka, D.O., Vice President, Chief Medical Officer
CHR: Mary K. Shinick, Vice President Human Resources
CNO: Renee Mauriello, Vice President, Chief Nursing Officer
Web address: www.nyackhospital.org
Control: Other not–for–profit (including NFP Corporation) **Service:** General Medical and Surgical

Staffed Beds: 245 **Admissions:** 11724 **Census:** 171 **Outpatient Visits:** 162441 **Births:** 1806 **Total Expense ($000):** 229195 **Personnel:** 1338

OCEANSIDE—Nassau County

⊠ **SOUTH NASSAU COMMUNITIES HOSPITAL (330198)**, One Healthy Way, Zip 11572–1551; tel. 516/632–3000 **A**1 2 3 5 10 12 13 **F**3 5 11 12 13 15 17 18 20 22 26 28 29 30 31 34 35 37 38 40 43 44 45 46 47 49 50 54 55 56 57 58 59 60 62 64 66 68 69 70 73 74 75 76 77 78 79 81 82 83 84 85 87 89 91 92 93 97 98 99 100 102 103 104 105 107 108 109 110 111 114 115 118 119 120 121 123 124 126 128 129 130 131 132 135 144 145 146 148 **P**8
Primary Contact: Richard J. Murphy, President and Chief Executive Officer
CFO: Mark A. Bogen, Senior Vice President and Chief Financial Officer
CMO: Adhi Sharma, M.D., Chief Medical Officer
CIO: John Mertz, Chief Information Officer
CHR: Paul Giordano, Vice President Human Resources
CNO: Sue Penque, R.N., Senior Vice President and Chief Nursing Officer
Web address: www.southnassau.org
Control: Other not–for–profit (including NFP Corporation) **Service:** General Medical and Surgical

Staffed Beds: 363 **Admissions:** 20696 **Census:** 320 **Outpatient Visits:** 347381 **Births:** 2078 **Total Expense ($000):** 472664 **Payroll Expense ($000):** 225041 **Personnel:** 2723

OGDENSBURG—St. Lawrence County

★ ◇ **CLAXTON–HEPBURN MEDICAL CENTER (330211)**, 214 King Street, Zip 13669–1142; tel. 315/393–3600, (Nonreporting) **A**2 10 20 21
Primary Contact: Nathan Howell, President and Chief Executive Officer
COO: Vicki Perrine, FACHE, Chief Operating Officer
CFO: Kelley Tiernan, Chief Financial Officer
CIO: James Flood, Director Information Systems
CHR: Lou–Ann McNally, Executive Director Human Resources and Staff Development
CNO: David Ferris, Chief Nursing Officer and Vice President Patient Care Services
Web address: www.claxtonhepburn.org
Control: Other not–for–profit (including NFP Corporation) **Service:** General Medical and Surgical

Staffed Beds: 130

□ **ST. LAWRENCE PSYCHIATRIC CENTER (334003)**, 1 Chimney Point Drive, Zip 13669–2291; tel. 315/541–2001, (Nonreporting) **A**1 10 **S** New York State Office of Mental Health, Albany, NY
Primary Contact: Timothy Farrell, Executive Director
CMO: Harishankar Sanghi, M.D., Clinical Director
CHR: Rosie Turnbull, Director Human Resources
Web address: www.omh.ny.gov/omhweb/facilities/slpc/facility.htm
Control: State–Government, nonfederal **Service:** Psychiatric

Staffed Beds: 146

OLEAN—Cattaraugus County

⊠ **OLEAN GENERAL HOSPITAL (330103)**, 515 Main Street, Zip 14760–1513; tel. 716/373–2600 **A**1 3 5 10 19 **F**3 8 11 13 15 17 18 20 22 28 29 30 31 34 35 38 39 40 45 46 47 48 49 50 51 54 57 58 59 60 61 62 64 65 70 71 74 75 76 77 78 79 81 82 83 84 85 86 87 89 91 92 93 94 96 97 98 100 101 102 103 107 108 109 110 111 114 115 116 117 118 119 120 121 123 127 129 130 131 132 133 134 135 143 144 145 146 147 148 **P**6 8 **S** Upper Allegheny Health System, Olean, NY
Primary Contact: Timothy J. Finan, FACHE, President and Chief Executive Officer
COO: Jeff S. Zewe, R.N., Senior Vice President, Chief Operating Officer
CFO: Richard G. Braun, Jr., CPA, Senior Vice President and Chief Financial Officer
CMO: William Mills, M.D., Senior Vice President Quality and Professional Affairs
CIO: Jason Yaworsky, Senior Vice President Information Systems and Chief Information Officer
CHR: Timothy M. McNamara, Senior Vice President Human Resources
Web address: www.ogh.org
Control: Other not–for–profit (including NFP Corporation) **Service:** General Medical and Surgical

Staffed Beds: 186 **Admissions:** 5874 **Census:** 82 **Outpatient Visits:** 254569 **Births:** 738 **Total Expense ($000):** 112623 **Payroll Expense ($000):** 43926 **Personnel:** 831

NY

ONEIDA—Madison County

☒ **ONEIDA HEALTHCARE (330115)**, 321 Genesee Street, Zip 13421–2611; tel. 315/363–6000, (Total facility includes 140 beds in nursing home–type unit) **A**1 10 **F**3 11 13 15 18 29 34 40 45 49 50 54 57 59 64 65 68 70 74 75 76 77 79 81 85 86 87 89 92 93 97 107 108 111 115 117 118 119 126 128 129 130 135 146 **P**6
Primary Contact: Gene Morreale, President and Chief Executive Officer
COO: Mary Parry, Vice President Operations and Chief Operating Officer
CFO: John D. Milligan, Vice President Finance and Chief Financial Officer
CMO: Dan J. Vick, M.D., Vice President of Medical Affairs and Chief Medical Officer
CIO: Mary McGuirl, Director Information Systems
CHR: Michael Fifield, Vice President Human Resources
CNO: Janis Kohlbrenner, R.N., Vice President Clinical Services and Chief Nursing Officer
Web address: www.oneidahealthcare.org
Control: Other not–for–profit (including NFP Corporation) **Service:** General Medical and Surgical

Staffed Beds: 211 **Admissions:** 3228 **Census:** 177 **Outpatient Visits:** 188067 **Births:** 494 **Total Expense ($000):** 93083 **Payroll Expense ($000):** 43585 **Personnel:** 781

ONEONTA—Otsego County

★ ◇ **AURELIA OSBORN FOX MEMORIAL HOSPITAL (330085)**, 1 Norton Avenue, Zip 13820–2629; tel. 607/432–2000, (Total facility includes 131 beds in nursing home–type unit) **A**10 21 **F**2 3 11 13 15 26 28 29 30 34 35 39 40 45 46 47 48 51 53 54 56 57 59 64 65 68 75 76 77 81 85 86 87 93 96 97 104 107 108 110 111 115 118 119 120 121 123 128 129 130 146 147 **P**6 **S** Bassett Healthcare Network, Cooperstown, NY
Primary Contact: Jeff Joyner, President
CFO: Mark J. Wright, Vice President Finance
CMO: Benjamin Friedell, Vice President Medical Affairs
CHR: Jennie Gliha, Vice President Human Resources and Clinical Services
CNO: Robbin Scobie, Vice President Nursing
Web address: www.bassett.org/ao–fox–hospital/
Control: Other not–for–profit (including NFP Corporation) **Service:** General Medical and Surgical

Staffed Beds: 191 **Admissions:** 2652 **Census:** 159 **Outpatient Visits:** 180810 **Births:** 228 **Total Expense ($000):** 79155 **Payroll Expense ($000):** 33144 **Personnel:** 687

ORANGEBURG—Rockland County

☐ **ROCKLAND CHILDREN'S PSYCHIATRIC CENTER**, 599 Convent Road, Zip 10962–1162; tel. 845/359–7400, (Nonreporting) **A**1 3 5 **S** New York State Office of Mental Health, Albany, NY
Primary Contact: Christopher Tavella, Acting Executive Director
COO: Kenneth Perrotte, Director Operations
CFO: Peter Gorey, Administrative Coordinator
CMO: Sadhana Sardana, M.D., Clinical Director
CIO: Mary Pivonka, Director Quality Management
Web address: www.omh.ny.gov/
Control: State–Government, nonfederal **Service:** Children's hospital psychiatric

Staffed Beds: 54

☐ **ROCKLAND PSYCHIATRIC CENTER (334015)**, 140 Old Orangeburg Road, Zip 10962–1157; tel. 845/359–1000, (Nonreporting) **A**1 3 5 10 **S** New York State Office of Mental Health, Albany, NY
Primary Contact: Christopher Tavella, Executive Director
Web address: www.omh.ny.gov/
Control: State–Government, nonfederal **Service:** Psychiatric

Staffed Beds: 525

OSSINING—Westchester County

OSSINING CORRECTIONAL FACILITIES HOSPITAL, 354 Hunter Street, Zip 10562–5498; tel. 914/941–0108, (Nonreporting)
Primary Contact: Riza Ferdous, Health Services Director
Control: State–Government, nonfederal **Service:** Hospital unit of an institution (prison hospital, college infirmary, etc.)

Staffed Beds: 25

OSWEGO—Oswego County

☒ **OSWEGO HOSPITAL (330218)**, 110 West Sixth Street, Zip 13126–2507; tel. 315/349–5511 **A**1 10 20 **F**2 3 11 13 15 17 18 29 34 37 38 40 41 45 49 50 51 57 59 62 70 75 76 77 79 81 85 86 87 89 93 97 98 99 100 101 102 104 107 108 110 111 114 115 119 124 130 131 132 135 144 146 **P**6
Primary Contact: Charles Gijanto, President and Chief Executive Officer
COO: Allison A.N. Duggan, FACS, Chief Operating Officer
CFO: Eric Campbell, Chief Financial Officer
CMO: Renato Mandanas, M.D., Chief Medical Officer
CIO: Barry W. Ryle, Chief Information Officer
CHR: James E. Marco, Jr., Interim Vice President, Human Resources
CNO: Valerie Favata, R.N., Chief Nursing Officer
Web address: www.oswegohealth.org
Control: Other not–for–profit (including NFP Corporation) **Service:** General Medical and Surgical

Staffed Beds: 109 **Admissions:** 4210 **Census:** 61 **Outpatient Visits:** 335969 **Births:** 522 **Total Expense ($000):** 108157 **Payroll Expense ($000):** 52436 **Personnel:** 891

PATCHOGUE—Suffolk County

★ ◇ **BROOKHAVEN MEMORIAL HOSPITAL MEDICAL CENTER (330141)**, 101 Hospital Road, Zip 11772–4897; tel. 631/714–2941 **A**10 12 13 21 **F**12 15 17 18 20 22 24 26 28 29 30 31 34 35 40 43 45 46 47 49 50 51 54 57 59 60 62 63 64 66 68 70 74 75 78 79 80 81 82 83 84 85 89 97 98 99 100 102 103 104 107 110 111 114 115 116 117 119 129 130 131 132 135 146 147 148 **P**6
Primary Contact: Richard T. Margulis, President and Chief Executive Officer
COO: Ron Stephenson, Chief Operating Officer
CFO: Brenda Farrell, Vice President Finance
CMO: Nejat Zeyneloglu, Vice President and Chief Quality Medical Officer
CIO: Joseph Wood, Vice President and Chief Information Officer
CHR: Susan C. Hever, Director Human Resources
Web address: www.bmhmc.org
Control: Other not–for–profit (including NFP Corporation) **Service:** General Medical and Surgical

Staffed Beds: 242 **Admissions:** 12696 **Census:** 221 **Outpatient Visits:** 185436 **Births:** 0 **Total Expense ($000):** 262025 **Payroll Expense ($000):** 120183 **Personnel:** 1771

PENN YAN—Yates County

SOLDIERS AND SAILORS MEMORIAL HOSPITAL OF YATES COUNTY (331314), 418 North Main Street, Zip 14527–1085; tel. 315/531–2000 **A**10 18 **F**2 3 11 15 18 28 29 34 35 38 40 45 54 56 57 59 64 65 66 68 70 75 81 87 93 97 98 100 101 102 103 104 107 110 114 119 128 130 132 133 135 146 147 **P**6 **S** Finger Lakes Health, Geneva, NY
Primary Contact: Jose Acevedo, M.D., President and Chief Executive Officer
COO: Lina Brennan, Site Administrator
CFO: Pamela Johnson, Treasurer and Chief Financial Officer
CMO: Jason Feinberg, M.D., Vice President Medical Affairs and Chief Medical Officer
CIO: Guy W. Mosher, III, Manager Information Systems
CHR: Patrick R. Boyle, Vice President Human Resources
CNO: Eileen Gage, R.N., Vice President Nursing
Web address: www.flhealth.org
Control: Other not–for–profit (including NFP Corporation) **Service:** General Medical and Surgical

Staffed Beds: 186 **Admissions:** 928 **Census:** 153 **Outpatient Visits:** 155699 **Births:** 0 **Total Expense ($000):** 28192 **Payroll Expense ($000):** 16238 **Personnel:** 341

PLAINVIEW—Nassau County

☒ **PLAINVIEW HOSPITAL (330331)**, 888 Old Country Road, Zip 11803–4978; tel. 516/719–3000 **A**1 2 10 12 13 **F**3 8 9 15 17 18 29 30 31 34 35 36 38 40 43 44 45 46 49 50 51 57 58 59 60 63 64 65 68 69 70 71 74 75 78 79 81 84 85 86 87 97 100 101 102 107 108 110 111 114 115 119 130 132 135 146 148 **P**5 6 **S** Northwell Health, New Hyde Park, NY
Primary Contact: Michael Fener, Executive Director
CMO: Alan Mensch, M.D., Senior Vice President Medical Affairs
CIO: Nicholas O'Connor, Vice President and Chief Information Officer
Web address: www.northshorelij.com
Control: Other not–for–profit (including NFP Corporation) **Service:** General Medical and Surgical

Staffed Beds: 189 **Admissions:** 8506 **Census:** 116 **Outpatient Visits:** 58723 **Births:** 0 **Total Expense ($000):** 198525 **Payroll Expense ($000):** 98406 **Personnel:** 1090

NY

Many Facility Codes have changed. Please refer to the AHA Guide Code Chart. © 2016 AHA Guide

PLATTSBURGH—Clinton County

⊠ **THE UNIVERSITY OF VERMONT HEALTH NETWORK–CHAMPLAIN VALLEY PHYSICIANS HOSPITAL (330250)**, 75 Beekman Street, Zip 12901–1438; tel. 518/561–2000, (Total facility includes 54 beds in nursing home–type unit) **A**1 2 10 **F**3 7 8 11 13 14 15 18 20 22 26 28 29 30 31 34 35 36 38 40 41 43 45 46 49 50 53 56 58 59 64 68 70 76 77 78 79 81 83 84 85 87 89 93 94 96 98 99 102 107 108 110 111 114 115 116 117 118 119 120 121 123 126 128 130 132 143 144 145 146 147 148 **P**6
Primary Contact: Stephens M. Mundy, President and Chief Executive Officer
COO: Michelle Lebeau, Senior Vice President, Chief Operating Officer, Chief Nursing Officer
CFO: Joyce Rafferty, Vice President Finance
CMO: Kent Hall, M.D., Vice President and Chief Medical Officer
CIO: Wouter Rietsema, M.D., Chief Quality and Information Officer
CHR: Dean Civitello, Vice President, Human Resources, Public Relations and Development
CNO: Michelle Lebeau, Senior Vice President, Chief Operating Officer, Chief Nursing Officer
Web address: www.UVMHealth.org/CVPH
Control: Other not–for–profit (including NFP Corporation) **Service:** General Medical and Surgical

Staffed Beds: 247 **Admissions:** 9460 **Census:** 236 **Outpatient Visits:** 351537 **Births:** 939 **Total Expense ($000):** 295604 **Payroll Expense ($000):** 146914 **Personnel:** 1941

PORT JEFFERSON—Suffolk County

⊠ **JOHN T. MATHER MEMORIAL HOSPITAL (330185)**, 75 North Country Road, Zip 11777–2190; tel. 631/473–1320 **A**1 2 3 10 **F**5 8 11 12 14 15 17 18 29 34 35 36 37 38 40 44 45 46 47 54 55 56 57 59 60 64 65 69 70 74 75 77 78 79 81 82 84 85 86 87 91 93 98 99 100 101 102 103 104 105 107 108 110 111 114 115 118 119 120 124 126 129 130 132 146 147 148 **P**6
Primary Contact: Kenneth D. Roberts, President
COO: Kevin J. Murray, Senior Vice President
CFO: Joseph Wisnoski, Vice President Finance and Chief Financial Officer
CMO: Joan Faro, M.D., Chief Medical Officer
CIO: Thomas Heiman, Vice President Information Services and Chief Information Officer
CHR: Diane Marotta, Vice President Human Resources
CNO: Marie Mulligan, R.N., Vice President Nursing
Web address: www.matherhospital.com
Control: Other not–for–profit (including NFP Corporation) **Service:** General Medical and Surgical

Staffed Beds: 248 **Admissions:** 11518 **Census:** 192 **Outpatient Visits:** 164822 **Births:** 0 **Total Expense ($000):** 312331 **Payroll Expense ($000):** 148667 **Personnel:** 2020

☐ △ **ST. CHARLES HOSPITAL (330246)**, 200 Belle Terre Road, Zip 11777–1928; tel. 631/474–6000 **A**1 2 3 7 10 **F**3 4 5 8 11 12 13 15 17 28 29 30 31 32 34 35 37 39 40 41 44 45 46 48 50 54 57 58 59 64 65 66 68 69 70 72 73 74 75 76 77 78 79 80 81 82 84 85 86 87 89 90 91 92 93 96 97 107 110 111 115 119 126 129 130 132 134 135 136 141 142 146 **S** Catholic Health Services of Long Island, Rockville Centre, NY
Primary Contact: James O'Connor, Executive Vice President and Chief Administrative Officer
COO: Ronald Weingartner, Vice President Administration
CFO: Kathleen Vasil, Vice President Finance
CMO: Michael Sauter, M.D., Chief Medical Officer
CIO: Felix Pabon–Ramirez, Chief Information Officer
CNO: Nicolette Fiore–Lopez, R.N., Chief Nursing Officer
Web address: www.stcharleshospital.chsli.org
Control: Church–operated, Nongovernment, not–for profit **Service:** General Medical and Surgical

Staffed Beds: 243 **Admissions:** 9799 **Census:** 175 **Outpatient Visits:** 199534 **Births:** 1485 **Total Expense ($000):** 226464 **Payroll Expense ($000):** 115086 **Personnel:** 1219

PORT JERVIS—Orange County

⊠ **BON SECOURS COMMUNITY HOSPITAL (330135)**, 160 East Main Street, Zip 12771–2245, Mailing Address: P.O. Box 1014, Zip 12771–0268; tel. 845/858–7000, (Total facility includes 46 beds in nursing home–type unit) **A**1 10 **F**3 4 12 15 17 18 29 30 31 34 35 36 40 49 50 57 59 66 68 70 75 77 78 79 81 84 85 87 91 93 94 97 98 100 102 107 108 119 128 129 130 146 147 148 **S** WMCHealth, Valhalla, NY
Primary Contact: Jeff Reilly, Administrator
COO: Gaynor Rosenstein, Vice President Operations
CMO: Jeffrey Auerbach, D.O., Medical Director
CHR: Kim Hirkaler, Director Human Resources
Web address: www.bonsecourscommunityhosp.org
Control: Church–operated, Nongovernment, not–for profit **Service:** General Medical and Surgical

Staffed Beds: 143 **Admissions:** 4041 **Census:** 58 **Outpatient Visits:** 84898 **Births:** 0 **Total Expense ($000):** 76858 **Payroll Expense ($000):** 28047

POTSDAM—St. Lawrence County

★ ◇ **CANTON–POTSDAM HOSPITAL (330197)**, 50 Leroy Street, Zip 13676–1799; tel. 315/265–3300 **A**10 20 21 **F**3 4 5 11 13 15 18 26 28 29 30 31 34 36 38 40 43 51 54 57 58 59 64 65 68 75 76 77 78 79 81 82 85 86 87 92 93 95 96 97 99 100 101 102 104 107 108 110 111 115 116 117 118 119 120 121 123 127 129 130 131 132 133 135 144 145 146 147 148 **P**5 **S** St. Lawrence Health System, Potsdam, NY
Primary Contact: David B. Acker, FACHE, President and CEO
CFO: Richard Jacobs, Vice President Finance and Chief Financial Officer
CMO: Robert T. Rogers, II, M.D., Medical Director
CIO: Jorge C. Grillo, Chief Information Officer
CHR: Darlene Lewis, Vice President Human Resources
CNO: Marie T. Martin, Chief Nursing Officer Vice President Patient Care Services
Web address: www.cphospital.org
Control: Other not–for–profit (including NFP Corporation) **Service:** General Medical and Surgical

Staffed Beds: 87 **Admissions:** 4765 **Census:** 63 **Outpatient Visits:** 287465 **Births:** 520 **Total Expense ($000):** 146454 **Payroll Expense ($000):** 74976 **Personnel:** 989

POUGHKEEPSIE—Dutchess County

☐ **VASSAR BROTHERS MEDICAL CENTER (330023)**, 45 Reade Place, Zip 12601–3947; tel. 845/454–8500 **A**1 2 10 **F**3 8 11 12 13 15 17 18 20 22 24 26 28 29 30 31 34 35 36 37 40 44 45 46 47 48 49 50 51 54 55 57 58 59 60 68 70 72 73 74 75 76 77 78 79 81 82 84 85 86 87 89 92 93 97 99 100 107 108 109 110 111 114 115 117 118 119 120 121 123 124 126 129 130 131 132 135 146 147 148 **S** Health Quest Systems, Inc., LaGrangeville, NY
Primary Contact: Ann McMackin, President
CFO: Tony Perugino, Director Finance
CMO: Michael Doyle, M.D., Vice President Medical Affairs
CNO: Loretta Bogolin, MSN, Chief Nursing Officer and Vice President Care Services
Web address: www.health–quest.org
Control: Other not–for–profit (including NFP Corporation) **Service:** General Medical and Surgical

Staffed Beds: 365 **Admissions:** 19545 **Census:** 269 **Outpatient Visits:** 315235 **Births:** 2165 **Total Expense ($000):** 457566 **Payroll Expense ($000):** 138281 **Personnel:** 1733

QUEENS—Queens County, See New York City

QUEENS VILLAGE—Queens County, See New York City

RHINEBECK—Dutchess County

☐ △ **NORTHERN DUTCHESS HOSPITAL (330049)**, 6511 Springbrook Avenue, Zip 12572–3709, Mailing Address: P.O. Box 5002, Zip 12572–5002; tel. 845/876–3001 **A**1 7 10 **F**3 11 13 15 18 28 29 34 35 36 37 40 45 50 53 56 64 68 70 74 75 76 77 78 79 81 82 84 85 87 90 93 100 107 108 110 111 115 118 119 125 126 129 130 146 147 148 **S** Health Quest Systems, Inc., LaGrangeville, NY
Primary Contact: Denise George, R.N., President
CFO: Alan Mossoff, Director Finance
CMO: John Sabia, M.D., Vice President Medical Affairs
CNO: Pamela Rhodes, R.N., Vice President Patient Care Services and Chief Nursing Officer
Web address: www.health–quest.org/home_nd.cfm?id=9
Control: Other not–for–profit (including NFP Corporation) **Service:** General Medical and Surgical

Staffed Beds: 68 **Admissions:** 3502 **Census:** 45 **Outpatient Visits:** 18913 **Births:** 964 **Total Expense ($000):** 80199 **Payroll Expense ($000):** 27652 **Personnel:** 415

RICHMOND VALLEY—Richmond County, See New York City

NY

Hospital, Medicare Provider Number, Address, Telephone, Approval, Facility, and Physician Codes, Health Care System

★ American Hospital Association (AHA) membership
☐ The Joint Commission accreditation
○ Healthcare Facilities Accreditation Program
◇ DNV Healthcare Inc. accreditation
⇑ Center for Improvement in Healthcare Quality Accreditation
△ Commission on Accreditation of Rehabilitation Facilities (CARF) accreditation

RIVERHEAD—Suffolk County

⊠ **PECONIC BAY MEDICAL CENTER (330107)**, 1300 Roanoke Avenue, Zip 11901–2031; tel. 631/548–6000 **A**1 3 10 12 13 **F**3 7 8 11 12 13 15 18 29 30 31 34 35 40 45 46 47 49 50 54 57 59 60 61 62 64 68 70 74 75 77 78 79 80 81 82 84 85 86 87 91 92 93 94 96 97 107 108 110 111 115 118 119 126 130 131 132 143 146 147 148 **P**6 7 **S** Northwell Health, New Hyde Park, NY
Primary Contact: Andrew J. Mitchell, President and Chief Executive Officer
COO: Ronald McManus, Senior Vice President Clinical Services and Business Entities
CFO: Michael F. O'Donnell, CPA, Chief Financial Officer
CMO: Richard Kubiak, M.D., Vice President Medical Affairs
CIO: Arthur Crowe, Director Information Systems
CHR: Monica Chestnut–Rauls, Vice President Human Resources
CNO: Gerard Zunno, R.N., Vice President Patient Care Services
Web address: www.pbmchealth.org
Control: Other not–for–profit (including NFP Corporation) **Service:** General Medical and Surgical

Staffed Beds: 176 **Admissions:** 8558 **Census:** 140 **Outpatient Visits:** 102679 **Births:** 336 **Total Expense ($000):** 161817 **Payroll Expense ($000):** 63778 **Personnel:** 881

ROCHESTER—Monroe County

⊠ **HIGHLAND HOSPITAL (330164)**, 1000 South Avenue, Zip 14620–2733; tel. 585/473–2200 **A**1 3 5 10 19 **F**3 12 13 15 18 24 29 30 31 34 35 37 40 44 45 46 47 49 50 54 56 57 58 59 63 64 65 66 68 70 74 75 76 77 78 79 81 82 83 84 85 86 87 91 97 100 107 108 110 111 114 115 118 119 120 121 123 126 130 132 134 135 141 145 146 147 148 **P**5 6 **S** University of Rochester Medical Center, Rochester, NY
Primary Contact: Steven I. Goldstein, President and Chief Executive Officer
COO: Cindy Becker, Vice President and Chief Operating Officer
CFO: Adam Anolik, Chief Financial Officer
CMO: Raymond Mayewski, M.D., Chief Medical Officer
CIO: D. Jerome Powell, M.D., Chief Information Officer
CHR: Amy Taney, Chief Human Resource Officer
CNO: Tommye Hinton, R.N., Chief Nursing Officer
Web address: www.stronghealth.com
Control: Other not–for–profit (including NFP Corporation) **Service:** General Medical and Surgical

Staffed Beds: 261 **Admissions:** 15973 **Census:** 201 **Outpatient Visits:** 373097 **Births:** 3135 **Total Expense ($000):** 315410 **Payroll Expense ($000):** 147325 **Personnel:** 2170

⊠ **ROCHESTER GENERAL HOSPITAL (330125)**, 1425 Portland Avenue, Zip 14621–3099; tel. 585/922–4000 **A**1 2 3 5 10 **F**3 5 8 9 11 12 13 14 15 17 18 20 22 24 26 28 29 30 31 32 34 35 36 38 39 40 41 44 45 47 49 50 51 53 54 55 56 57 58 59 60 61 63 64 65 66 70 73 74 75 76 77 78 79 80 81 82 84 85 86 87 89 90 92 93 96 97 98 99 100 101 102 103 104 107 108 110 111 114 115 116 117 118 119 120 121 123 124 126 130 131 132 134 135 145 146 147 148 **P**5 7 **S** Rochester Regional Health, Rochester, NY
Primary Contact: Nancy Tinsley, President
CMO: Robert Mayo, M.D., Chief Medical Officer
CIO: John Glynn, Chief Information Officer
CHR: Janine Schue, Senior Vice President Human Resources
CNO: Cheryl Sheridan, R.N., Senior Vice President Patient Care Services
Web address: www.rochestergeneral.org
Control: Other not–for–profit (including NFP Corporation) **Service:** General Medical and Surgical

Staffed Beds: 520 **Admissions:** 28834 **Census:** 429 **Outpatient Visits:** 1634482 **Births:** 2308 **Total Expense ($000):** 901347 **Payroll Expense ($000):** 418433 **Personnel:** 5802

☐ **ROCHESTER PSYCHIATRIC CENTER (334020)**, 1111 Elmwood Avenue, Zip 14620–3005; tel. 585/241–1200, (Nonreporting) **A**1 3 5 10 **S** New York State Office of Mental Health, Albany, NY
Primary Contact: Philip Griffin, Director of Operations
COO: Joseph Coffey, Director Facility Administration
CFO: Rosanne Minnis, Business Officer
CMO: Laurence Guttmacher, M.D., Clinical Director
CIO: Lori Hintz, Coordinator Information Systems
CHR: Colomba Misseritti, Director Human Resources
CNO: Christopher Kirisits, Chief Nursing Officer
Web address: www.omh.ny.gov/omhweb/facilities/ropc/facility.htm
Control: State–Government, nonfederal **Service:** Psychiatric

Staffed Beds: 180

⊠ △ **STRONG MEMORIAL HOSPITAL OF THE UNIVERSITY OF ROCHESTER (330285)**, 601 Elmwood Avenue, Zip 14642–0002, Mailing Address: 601 Elmwood Avenue, Box 612, Zip 14642–0002; tel. 585/275–2100, (Includes GOLISANO CHILDREN'S HOSPITAL, 601 Elmwood Avenue, Zip 14610; tel. 585/275–2182) **A**1 2 3 5 7 8 10 19 **F**3 5 6 8 9 11 12 13 14 15 16 17 18 19 20 21 22 23 24 25 26 27 28 29 30 31 32 33 34 35 36 38 39 40 41 42 43 44 45 46 47 48 49 50 51 52 53 54 55 56 57 58 59 61 63 64 65 66 68 70 71 72 73 74 75 76 77 78 79 81 82 83 84 85 86 87 88 89 90 91 92 93 94 95 96 97 98 99 100 101 102 103 104 105 107 108 110 111 114 115 116 117 118 119 120 121 123 124 126 127 129 130 131 132 134 135 136 137 138 139 141 142 143 144 145 146 147 148 **P**6 **S** University of Rochester Medical Center, Rochester, NY
Primary Contact: Steven I. Goldstein, President and Chief Executive Officer
COO: Kathleen M. Parrinello, Ph.D., Chief Operating Officer
CFO: Leonard J. Shute, Chief Financial Officer
CMO: Raymond Mayewski, M.D., Chief Medical Officer
CIO: D. Jerome Powell, M.D., Chief Information Officer
CHR: Charles J. Murphy, Associate Vice President Human Resources
Web address: www.urmc.rochester.edu
Control: Other not–for–profit (including NFP Corporation) **Service:** General Medical and Surgical

Staffed Beds: 818 **Admissions:** 36343 **Census:** 768 **Outpatient Visits:** 1447433 **Births:** 2798 **Total Expense ($000):** 1329865 **Payroll Expense ($000):** 538733 **Personnel:** 10096

⊠ **UNITY HOSPITAL (330226)**, 1555 Long Pond Road, Zip 14626–4182; tel. 585/723–7000, (Total facility includes 120 beds in nursing home–type unit) **A**1 2 3 5 10 **F**3 4 5 13 15 18 20 22 26 28 29 30 31 33 34 35 38 39 40 44 45 46 47 48 49 50 52 55 56 57 59 60 61 63 64 65 66 67 70 71 73 74 75 76 77 78 79 81 82 84 85 86 87 90 91 92 93 96 97 98 100 102 104 107 108 118 119 126 128 129 130 131 132 134 141 144 146 147 148 **P**6 **S** Rochester Regional Health, Rochester, NY
Primary Contact: Douglas Stewart, PsyD, President
COO: Stewart C. Putnam, Executive Vice President and Chief Operating Officer
CFO: Tom Crilly, Executive Vice President and Chief Financial Officer
CMO: James Haley, M.D., Senior Vice President and Chief Medical Officer
CIO: John Glynn, Senior Vice President and Chief Information Officer
CHR: Maryalice Keller, Vice President Brand and Talent Management
CNO: Jane McCormack, R.N., Vice President, Chief Nursing Officer and Nursing and Patient Care Services
Web address: www.unityhealth.org
Control: Other not–for–profit (including NFP Corporation) **Service:** General Medical and Surgical

Staffed Beds: 487 **Admissions:** 16462 **Census:** 371 **Outpatient Visits:** 1157813 **Births:** 1531 **Total Expense ($000):** 446667 **Payroll Expense ($000):** 216311 **Personnel:** 3520

ROCKVILLE CENTRE—Nassau County

☐ **MERCY MEDICAL CENTER (330259)**, 1000 North Village Avenue, Zip 11570–1000; tel. 516/705–2525 **A**1 2 3 10 13 **F**3 8 12 13 15 20 26 29 30 31 34 35 37 38 40 41 43 45 46 48 49 50 51 56 57 58 59 60 64 65 66 68 70 72 74 75 76 77 78 79 81 82 84 85 87 90 92 93 94 96 97 98 100 102 103 104 105 107 108 110 111 115 116 117 119 130 131 132 135 141 142 143 146 147 148 **P**5 **S** Catholic Health Services of Long Island, Rockville Centre, NY
Primary Contact: Ronald Steimel, Executive Vice President and Chief Administrative Officer
CFO: William C. Armstrong, Senior Vice President and Chief Financial Officer
CMO: John Reilly, M.D., Vice President Medical Affairs and Chief Medical Officer
CIO: Marcy Dunn, Vice President Information Services and Chief Information Officer
CHR: Allison Cianciotto Croyle, Vice President of Human Resources
CNO: Beth Vlahavas, R.N., Vice President Patient Care Services and Chief Nursing Officer
Web address: www.mercymedicalcenter.chsli.org
Control: Church–operated, Nongovernment, not–for profit **Service:** General Medical and Surgical

Staffed Beds: 191 **Admissions:** 10378 **Census:** 188 **Outpatient Visits:** 119000 **Births:** 1136 **Total Expense ($000):** 207571 **Payroll Expense ($000):** 96833 **Personnel:** 1084

Many Facility Codes have changed. Please refer to the AHA Guide Code Chart.

NY

ROME—Oneida County

★ ○ **ROME MEMORIAL HOSPITAL (330215)**, 1500 North James Street, Zip 13440–2844; tel. 315/338–7000, (Total facility includes 82 beds in nursing home–type unit) **A**10 11 **F**3 5 8 11 13 15 17 18 26 28 29 30 34 40 41 45 47 48 49 50 54 56 57 59 64 68 70 74 76 77 78 79 80 81 85 86 87 89 93 98 100 101 102 103 104 107 108 109 110 111 112 113 114 115 116 117 119 120 121 122 123 124 128 129 130 132 135 143 144 146 147 148
Primary Contact: David W. Lundquist, President and Chief Executive Officer
CFO: Dewey R. Rowlands, Vice President and Chief Financial Officer
CMO: Ankur Desai, Interim Chief Medical officer
CIO: Bruce Peterson, Chief Information Officer
CHR: Regina Chambers, Vice President Human Resource
CNO: Durinda Durr, Vice President Clinical Services and Chief Nursing Officer
Web address: www.romehospital.org
Control: Other not–for–profit (including NFP Corporation) **Service:** General Medical and Surgical

Staffed Beds: 203 **Admissions:** 3797 **Census:** 118 **Outpatient Visits:** 167311 **Births:** 547 **Total Expense ($000):** 79324 **Payroll Expense ($000):** 37404 **Personnel:** 652

ROSLYN—Nassau County

⊠ **ST. FRANCIS HOSPITAL, THE HEART CENTER (330182)**, 100 Port Washington Boulevard, Zip 11576–1353; tel. 516/562–6000 **A**1 3 10 **F**3 7 11 12 15 17 18 19 20 21 22 23 24 26 27 28 29 30 31 34 35 36 37 38 39 40 43 44 45 46 47 49 50 53 54 55 56 57 58 59 60 61 62 63 64 65 66 68 70 71 72 74 75 77 78 79 81 82 83 84 85 86 87 88 89 93 94 97 100 102 107 108 109 110 111 114 115 116 117 118 119 120 121 123 124 126 130 131 132 135 141 145 146 147 148 **P**6 **S** Catholic Health Services of Long Island, Rockville Centre, NY
Primary Contact: Ruth Hennessey, Executive Vice President and Chief Administrative Officer
CFO: William C. Armstrong, Vice President and Chief Financial Officer
CMO: Jack Soterakis, M.D., Executive Vice President Medical Affairs
CIO: Marcy Dunn, Vice President Information Services and Chief Information Officer
CHR: Barbara Fierro, Director, Human Resources
CNO: Ann S. Cella, R.N., Senior Vice President, Patient Care Services
Web address: www.stfrancisheartcenter.com/index.html
Control: Church–operated, Nongovernment, not–for profit **Service:** General Medical and Surgical

Staffed Beds: 306 **Admissions:** 15763 **Census:** 277 **Outpatient Visits:** 195133 **Births:** 0 **Total Expense ($000):** 613886 **Payroll Expense ($000):** 284815 **Personnel:** 2962

SARANAC LAKE—Franklin County

★ ○ **ADIRONDACK MEDICAL CENTER (330079)**, 2233 State Route 86, Zip 12983–5644, Mailing Address: P.O. Box 471, Zip 12983–0471; tel. 518/891–4141, (Total facility includes 155 beds in nursing home–type unit) **A**5 10 11 **F**3 8 9 12 13 15 18 28 29 30 31 34 35 37 38 39 40 41 42 43 45 46 49 50 53 54 56 57 59 60 64 70 71 74 75 76 77 78 79 81 82 84 85 86 89 90 92 93 94 97 98 102 103 104 107 108 110 111 114 116 119 127 128 129 130 131 132 135 146 147 148 **P**6 **S** HealthTech Management Services, Brentwood, TN
Primary Contact: Sylvia Getman, President and Chief Executive Officer
COO: Patti Hammond, Chief Operating Officer
CFO: Tristan Glanville, Chief Financial Officer
CMO: Anthony Dowidowicz, Chief Medical Officer
CHR: Michael D. Lee, Chief Human Resources Officer
CNO: Linda McClarigan, R.N., Chief Nursing Officer
Web address: www.adirondackhealth.org
Control: Other not–for–profit (including NFP Corporation) **Service:** General Medical and Surgical

Staffed Beds: 200 **Admissions:** 2408 **Census:** 154 **Outpatient Visits:** 130868 **Births:** 183 **Total Expense ($000):** 97286 **Payroll Expense ($000):** 46263 **Personnel:** 774

SARATOGA SPRINGS—Saratoga County

☐ **FOUR WINDS HOSPITAL (334049)**, 30 Crescent Avenue, Zip 12866–5142; tel. 518/584–3600 **A**1 10 **F**98 99 100 101 102 103 104 105
Primary Contact: Samuel A. Bastien, IV, Ph.D., Chief Executive Officer
CFO: Juanita Wheeler–Moore, Director Financial Services
CMO: Kevin P. Martin, M.D., Chief Medical Officer
CIO: Susan Snowdon, Director Information Technology
CHR: Susan M. Kirchner, Director Human Resources
CNO: James Colamaria, Director of Nursing
Web address: www.fourwindshospital.com
Control: Corporation, Investor–owned, for–profit **Service:** Psychiatric

Staffed Beds: 88 **Admissions:** 2787 **Census:** 86 **Personnel:** 303

⊠ **SARATOGA HOSPITAL (330222)**, 211 Church Street, Zip 12866–1003; tel. 518/587–3222, (Total facility includes 36 beds in nursing home–type unit) **A**1 2 5 10 **F**3 8 11 12 13 15 18 20 22 26 28 29 30 31 34 35 37 40 42 44 46 47 49 50 54 57 59 60 64 66 68 70 74 75 76 77 78 79 81 82 84 85 87 92 93 96 97 98 100 101 102 104 105 107 108 110 111 114 117 119 120 121 126 127 128 129 130 131 132 133 141 143 144 146 147 **P**6
Primary Contact: Angelo G. Calbone, President and Chief Executive Officer
CFO: Gary Foster, Vice President and Chief Financial Officer
CMO: Richard Falivena, D.O., Vice President and Chief Medical Officer
CIO: John Mangona, Vice President, Chief Information Officer and Compliance Officer
CHR: Jeffrey M. Methven, Vice President Ambulatory Services and Chief Human Resources Officer
CNO: Mary Jo LaPosta, Ph.D., Senior Vice President Patient Care and Organizational Excellence
Web address: www.saratogacare.org
Control: Other not–for–profit (including NFP Corporation) **Service:** General Medical and Surgical

Staffed Beds: 207 **Admissions:** 9129 **Census:** 164 **Outpatient Visits:** 213039 **Births:** 729

SCHENECTADY—Schenectady County

⊠ **ELLIS HOSPITAL (330153)**, 1101 Nott Street, Zip 12308–2425; tel. 518/243–4000, (Includes BELLEVUE WOMAN'S CARE CENTER, 2210 Troy Road, Zip 12309–4797; tel. 518/346–9400; ELLIS HOSPITAL HEALTH CENTER, 600 McClellan Street, Zip 12304–1090; tel. 518/382–2000), (Total facility includes 82 beds in nursing home–type unit) **A**1 3 5 10 13 **F**5 7 12 13 14 15 17 18 20 22 24 26 28 29 30 31 32 34 35 36 37 38 39 40 41 42 43 44 45 46 48 49 50 54 56 57 58 59 60 61 62 64 65 66 68 70 72 74 75 76 77 78 79 81 83 84 86 87 89 90 91 93 97 98 99 100 101 102 103 104 105 107 108 110 111 114 115 119 120 121 122 123 126 128 129 130 132 134 143 144 146 147 148
Primary Contact: Paul A. Milton, Acting President and Chief Executive Officer
COO: Paul A. Milton, Executive Vice President and Chief Operating Officer
CFO: Daniel Rinaldi, Chief Financial Officer
CMO: David Liebers, M.D., Chief Medical Officer and Vice President Medical Affairs
CIO: Ron McKinnon, Chief Information Officer
CHR: Joseph Giansante, Vice President Human Resources
Web address: www.ellismedicine.org
Control: Other not–for–profit (including NFP Corporation) **Service:** General Medical and Surgical

Staffed Beds: 436 **Admissions:** 18071 **Census:** 321 **Births:** 2756 **Total Expense ($000):** 390153 **Payroll Expense ($000):** 194375 **Personnel:** 2887

ELLIS HOSPITAL HEALTH CENTER See Ellis Hospital

ELLIS HOSPITAL MCCLELLAN CAMPUS See Ellis Hospital Health Center

⊠ △ **SUNNYVIEW REHABILITATION HOSPITAL (330406)**, 1270 Belmont Avenue, Zip 12308–2104; tel. 518/382–4500 **A**1 3 5 7 10 **F**3 28 29 53 56 57 59 64 74 79 90 93 94 95 119 130 132 135 **P**5 **S** Trinity Health, Livonia, MI
Primary Contact: Edward Eisenman, Chief Executive Officer
CFO: Kristin Signor, Director Finance
CMO: Lynne T. Nicolson, M.D., Medical Director
CIO: Patrick Clark, Manager Information Technology
CHR: Meghan Glowa, Director Human Resources
Web address: www.sunnyview.org
Control: Other not–for–profit (including NFP Corporation) **Service:** Rehabilitation

Staffed Beds: 115 **Admissions:** 2297 **Census:** 86 **Outpatient Visits:** 78227 **Births:** 0 **Total Expense ($000):** 49603 **Payroll Expense ($000):** 27577 **Personnel:** 547

SLEEPY HOLLOW—Westchester County

⊠ **PHELPS MEMORIAL HOSPITAL CENTER (330261)**, 701 North Broadway, Zip 10591–1020; tel. 914/366–3000 **A**1 2 3 5 10 **F**3 4 5 8 9 11 13 14 15 17 18 28 29 30 34 35 37 39 40 45 46 47 48 49 50 53 55 56 57 58 59 60 61 63 64 65 68 70 74 75 76 77 78 79 81 82 84 85 86 87 89 90 91 92 93 94 96 97 98 100 101 102 103 104 107 108 110 111 114 115 118 119 129 130 131 132 135 141 143 145 146 147 148 **P**5 6 **S** Northwell Health, New Hyde Park, NY
Primary Contact: Daniel Blum, President
CFO: Vincent DeSantis, Vice President Finance
CHR: Jussi Maijala, Vice President, Human Resources
CNO: Mary McDermott, MS, Senior Vice President Patient Care Services and Chief Nursing Officer
Web address: www.phelpshospital.org
Control: Other not–for–profit (including NFP Corporation) **Service:** General Medical and Surgical

Staffed Beds: 158 **Admissions:** 7054 **Census:** 135 **Outpatient Visits:** 238190 **Births:** 921 **Total Expense ($000):** 238274 **Payroll Expense ($000):** 124633 **Personnel:** 1368

NY

Hospital, Medicare Provider Number, Address, Telephone, Approval, Facility, and Physician Codes, Health Care System		
★ American Hospital Association (AHA) membership	○ Healthcare Facilities Accreditation Program	⇑ Center for Improvement in Healthcare Quality Accreditation
☐ The Joint Commission accreditation	◇ DNV Healthcare Inc. accreditation	△ Commission on Accreditation of Rehabilitation Facilities (CARF) accreditation

SMITHTOWN—Suffolk County

☐ **ST. CATHERINE OF SIENA MEDICAL CENTER (330401)**, 50 Route 25–A, Zip 11787–1348; tel. 631/862–3000, (Nonreporting) **A**1 10 **S** Catholic Health Services of Long Island, Rockville Centre, NY
Primary Contact: Paul J. Rowland, Executive Vice President and Chief Administrative Officer
CFO: Dan Macksood, Regional Vice President and Chief Financial Officer
CHR: Danielle A. Robbins, Vice President Human Resources
Web address: www.stcatherines.chsli.org/
Control: Other not–for–profit (including NFP Corporation) **Service:** General Medical and Surgical

Staffed Beds: 535

SOUTHAMPTON—Suffolk County

⊠ **SOUTHAMPTON HOSPITAL (330340)**, 240 Meeting House Lane, Zip 11968–5090; tel. 631/726–8200 **A**1 3 10 12 13 **F**3 12 13 15 18 28 29 30 31 32 34 35 36 37 39 40 44 45 46 47 49 50 51 53 54 55 56 57 59 60 61 63 64 65 68 70 74 75 76 77 78 79 81 82 84 85 87 89 93 97 100 107 108 110 111 112 115 119 130 131 132 135 144 145 146 147 148 **P**6
Primary Contact: Robert S. Chaloner, President and Chief Executive Officer
COO: Frederic Weinbaum, M.D., Executive Vice President Operations and Chief Medical Officer
CFO: Chris Schulteis, Vice President/Chief Financial Officer
CMO: Frederic Weinbaum, M.D., Executive Vice President Operations and Chief Medical Officer
CIO: Jim Maul, Chief Information Officer and Director Information Services
CNO: Patricia Darcey, R.N., Vice President/Chief Nursing Officer
Web address: www.southamptonhospital.org
Control: Other not–for–profit (including NFP Corporation) **Service:** General Medical and Surgical

Staffed Beds: 80 Admissions: 5124 Census: 50 Outpatient Visits: 815489 Births: 776 Total Expense ($000): 145396 Payroll Expense ($000): 67133 Personnel: 877

SPRINGVILLE—Erie County

BERTRAND CHAFFEE HOSPITAL (330111), 224 East Main Street, Zip 14141–1497; tel. 716/592–2871, (Nonreporting) **A**10
Primary Contact: Nils Gunnersen, Administrator
CMO: J. Matthew Baker, M.D., President Medical Staff
CHR: Mary Beth Brown, Director Human Resources
Web address: www.chaffeehospitalandhome.com
Control: Other not–for–profit (including NFP Corporation) **Service:** General Medical and Surgical

Staffed Beds: 24

STAR LAKE—St. Lawrence County

★ **CLIFTON–FINE HOSPITAL (331307)**, 1014 Oswegatchie Trail, Zip 13690–3143; tel. 315/848–3351, (Nonreporting) **A**10 18
Primary Contact: Robert L. Seamon, Chief Executive Officer
CFO: Nancy Russell, Chief Financial Officer
CMO: David Welch, M.D., Medical Director
CIO: Devin Rice, Director Information Systems
CNO: Michelle Bristol, Director of Nursing
Web address: www.cliftonfinehospital.org
Control: Other not–for–profit (including NFP Corporation) **Service:** General Medical and Surgical

Staffed Beds: 20

STATEN ISLAND—Richmond County, See New York City

STONY BROOK—Suffolk County

⊠ **STONY BROOK UNIVERSITY HOSPITAL (330393)**, State University of New York, Zip 11794–8410; tel. 631/444–1077, (Includes STONY BROOK CHILDREN'S HOSPITAL, 100 Nicolls Road, Zip 11794–0001; tel. 631/444–4000) **A**1 2 3 5 8 10 **F**3 6 7 8 9 11 12 13 14 15 16 17 18 19 20 22 24 26 28 29 30 31 32 34 35 36 38 39 40 41 43 44 45 46 47 48 49 50 51 52 53 54 55 56 57 58 59 60 61 63 64 65 66 68 70 72 73 74 75 76 77 78 79 81 82 84 85 86 87 88 89 91 92 93 94 96 97 98 99 100 101 102 103 104 105 107 108 110 111 114 115 116 117 118 119 120 121 122 123 124 126 129 130 131 132 134 135 136 138 141 143 145 146 147 148 **P**1 6
Primary Contact: L. Reuven Pasternak, M.D., M.P.H., Vice President for Health System and Chief Executive Officer
COO: Carol Gomes, FACHE, Chief Operating Officer
CFO: Gary E. Bie, CPA, Chief Financial Officer
CMO: Joseph H. Laver, M.D., Chief Medical Officer
CIO: Jim Murry, Chief Information Officer
CHR: Luis de Onis, Interim Chief Human Resources Officer
CNO: Mary Ann T. Donohue, Ph.D., Chief Patient Care Services Officer
Web address: www.stonybrookmedicalcenter.org
Control: State–Government, nonfederal **Service:** General Medical and Surgical

Staffed Beds: 603 Admissions: 33891 Census: 542 Outpatient Visits: 393950 Births: 3390 Total Expense ($000): 1125055 Payroll Expense ($000): 478248 Personnel: 5325

SUFFERN—Rockland County

⊠ **GOOD SAMARITAN REGIONAL MEDICAL CENTER (330158)**, 255 Lafayette Avenue, Zip 10901–4869; tel. 845/368–5000, (Nonreporting) **A**1 2 10 **S** WMCHealth, Valhalla, NY
Primary Contact: Mary Leahy, M.D., Chief Executive Officer
COO: Gerry Durney, Chief Operating Officer
CMO: Rodney W. Williams, M.D., Vice President Medical Affairs
CIO: Deborah K. Marshall, Vice President Public Relations
CHR: Pamela Tarulli, Senior Vice President Human Resources
Web address: www.goodsamhosp.org
Control: Other not–for–profit (including NFP Corporation) **Service:** General Medical and Surgical

Staffed Beds: 308

SYOSSET—Nassau County

★ **SYOSSET HOSPITAL**, 221 Jericho Turnpike, Zip 11791–4515; tel. 516/496–6500 **A**3 **F**3 8 12 15 18 29 30 31 34 35 36 38 40 43 44 45 50 57 58 59 60 62 63 64 65 68 70 74 78 79 81 82 84 85 87 97 98 100 101 102 107 108 114 119 126 130 132 135 146 **P**5 6 **S** Northwell Health, New Hyde Park, NY
Primary Contact: Michael Fener, Executive Director
COO: Mark J. Solazzo, Regional Chief Operating Officer
CFO: Richard Reilly, Deputy Executive Director
CMO: Randolph DiLorenzo, M.D., Medical Director
CHR: Andrew S. Goldberg, Associate Executive Director
Web address: www.northshorelij.com
Control: Other not–for–profit (including NFP Corporation) **Service:** General Medical and Surgical

Staffed Beds: 75 Admissions: 3857 Census: 56 Outpatient Visits: 63648 Births: 0 Total Expense ($000): 173883 Payroll Expense ($000): 90415 Personnel: 732

SYRACUSE—Onondaga County

COMMUNITY–GENERAL HOSPITAL OF GREATER SYRACUSE See Upstate University Hospital at Community General

★ ◇ **CROUSE HOSPITAL (330203)**, 736 Irving Avenue, Zip 13210–1690; tel. 315/470–7111 **A**3 5 10 21 **F**3 4 5 8 11 12 13 15 18 19 20 21 22 23 26 27 29 31 34 35 36 37 40 49 50 53 59 60 70 72 74 75 76 77 78 79 81 84 86 87 89 93 96 107 108 110 112 114 115 116 117 118 119 126 129 130 131 132 135 144 145 146 147 148
Primary Contact: Kimberly Boynton, President and Chief Executive Officer
CFO: Kelli Harris, Chief Financial Officer
CMO: Seth Kronenberg, M.D., Chief Medical Officer
CIO: Kim Rose, Chief Information Technology
CHR: John Bergemann, Director Human Resources
CNO: Betty O'Connor, Chief Nursing Officer
Web address: www.crouse.org
Control: Other not–for–profit (including NFP Corporation) **Service:** General Medical and Surgical

Staffed Beds: 501 Admissions: 20165 Census: 315 Outpatient Visits: 413860 Births: 3897 Total Expense ($000): 420933 Payroll Expense ($000): 172245 Personnel: 2020

☐ **RICHARD H. HUTCHINGS PSYCHIATRIC CENTER (334001)**, 620 Madison Street, Zip 13210–2319; tel. 315/426–3632, (Nonreporting) **A**1 3 5 10 **S** New York State Office of Mental Health, Albany, NY
Primary Contact: Colleen A. Sawyer, R.N., MSN, Executive Director
COO: David Peppel, Director Operations
CFO: Robert Stapleton, Director Administration
CMO: Mark Cattalani, M.D., Clinical Director
CIO: Neil Nemi, Administrator Facility Information Center
CHR: Katherine Herron, Director Human Resources
Web address: www.omh.ny.gov
Control: State–Government, nonfederal **Service:** Psychiatric

Staffed Beds: 131

★ ◇ **ST. JOSEPH'S HOSPITAL HEALTH CENTER (330140)**, 301 Prospect Avenue, Zip 13203–1807; tel. 315/448–5111 **A**3 5 10 21 **F**2 3 5 8 11 12 13 14 15 17 18 20 22 24 26 28 29 30 31 34 35 36 37 38 40 45 46 47 48 49 50 51 54 56 57 58 59 60 62 64 65 66 68 70 71 72 73 74 75 76 77 78 79 81 82 83 84 85 87 92 93 94 97 98 99 100 101 102 103 104 106 107 108 110 111 114 115 119 126 129 130 131 132 135 144 145 146 147 148 **S** Trinity Health, Livonia, MI
Primary Contact: Kathryn H. Ruscitto, President
COO: Mary W. Brown, Senior Vice President Operations
CFO: Meredith Price, Vice President Fiscal Services and Chief Financial Officer
CMO: Sandra Sulik, M.D., Vice President Medical Affairs
CIO: Charles Fennell, Vice President Information Management
CHR: Sallie Biittner, Vice President Human Resources
CNO: AnneMarie Czyz, R.N., Senior Vice President Operations, Chief Operating Officer and Chief Nursing Officer
Web address: www.sjhsyr.org
Control: Other not–for–profit (including NFP Corporation) **Service:** General Medical and Surgical

Staffed Beds: 431 Admissions: 25824 Census: 374 Outpatient Visits: 601355 Births: 1839 Personnel: 3650

⊠ △ **SYRACUSE VETERANS AFFAIRS MEDICAL CENTER**, 800 Irving Avenue, Zip 13210–2716; tel. 315/425–4400, (Nonreporting) **A**1 3 5 7 8 **S** Department of Veterans Affairs, Washington, DC
Primary Contact: James Cody, Director
CFO: Deborah Angell, Chief Financial Officer
CMO: Syed Asif Ali, M.D., Chief of Staff
CIO: James Stenson, Chief Information Officer
CHR: Mark Antinelli, Manager Human Resources
CNO: Cheryl Czajkowski, Associate Director Patient and Nursing Services
Web address: www.syracuse.va.gov/
Control: Veterans Affairs, Government, federal **Service:** General Medical and Surgical

Staffed Beds: 161

★ ◇ **UPSTATE UNIVERSITY HOSPITAL (330241)**, 750 East Adams Street, Zip 13210–2342; tel. 315/464–5540, (Includes GOLISANO CHILDREN'S HOSPITAL, 750 East Adams Street, tel. 315/464–4570; UPSTATE UNIVERSITY HOSPITAL AT COMMUNITY GENERAL, 4900 Broad Road, Zip 13215–2293; tel. 315/492–5011) **A**2 8 10 21 **F**3 5 6 9 12 13 15 16 17 18 19 20 21 22 23 24 25 26 27 28 29 30 31 34 35 36 37 38 39 40 41 43 44 45 46 47 48 49 50 51 52 53 54 55 56 57 58 59 61 64 65 66 68 70 74 76 78 79 81 82 84 85 86 87 88 89 90 92 93 95 96 97 98 99 100 101 102 104 107 108 109 110 111 112 114 115 118 119 120 121 123 124 126 128 129 130 131 132 135 136 138 141 142 145 146 147 148 **P**4
Primary Contact: John B. McCabe, M.D., Chief Executive Officer
CFO: Stuart M. Wright, CPA, Chief Financial Officer
CMO: Anthony Weiss, M.D., Medical Director
CIO: Terry Wagner, Chief Information Officer
CHR: Eric Frost, Associate Vice President Human Resources
CNO: Nancy E. Page, MS, Interim Chief Nursing Officer
Web address: www.upstate.edu/hospital
Control: State–Government, nonfederal **Service:** General Medical and Surgical

Staffed Beds: 625 **Admissions:** 29060 **Census:** 479 **Outpatient Visits:** 667762 **Births:** 1129 **Total Expense ($000):** 917108 **Payroll Expense ($000):** 322153 **Personnel:** 4962

VETERANS AFFAIRS MEDICAL CENTER See Syracuse Veterans Affairs Medical Center

TICONDEROGA—Essex County

★ **MOSES LUDINGTON HOSPITAL (331306)**, 1019 Wicker Street, Zip 12883–1097; tel. 518/585–2831 **A**10 18 **F**15 40 50 53 57 59 68 71 93 107 114 119 133
Primary Contact: John R. Remillard, Interim Chief Executive Officer
CFO: Alan Chardavoyne, Chief Financial Officer
CIO: Darrin Goodrow, Chief Information Officer
CHR: Tamara Evens, Director Human Resources
Web address: www.interlakeshealth.com
Control: Other not–for–profit (including NFP Corporation) **Service:** General Medical and Surgical

Staffed Beds: 15 **Admissions:** 144 **Census:** 1 **Births:** 0 **Total Expense ($000):** 10953 **Payroll Expense ($000):** 4854 **Personnel:** 101

TROY—Rensselaer County

★ **SAMARITAN HOSPITAL (330180)**, 2215 Burdett Avenue, Zip 12180–2475; tel. 518/271–3300, (Nonreporting) **A**10 **S** Trinity Health, Livonia, MI
Primary Contact: Norman E. Dascher, Jr., Chief Executive Officer
CFO: Daniel A. Kochie, CPA, Chief Financial Officer
CMO: Daniel C. Silverman, M.D., Chief Medical Officer, Acute Care Troy
CIO: Karen LeBlanc, Director, Applications
CNO: Jacqueline Priore, Chief Nursing Officer
Web address: www.nehealth.com
Control: Other not–for–profit (including NFP Corporation) **Service:** General Medical and Surgical

Staffed Beds: 134

★ **ST. MARY'S HOSPITAL (330232)**, 1300 Massachusetts Avenue, Zip 12180–1695; tel. 518/268–5000, (Includes SETON HEALTH SYSTEM–ST. MARY'S HOSPITAL, 1300 Massachusetts Avenue, Zip 12180; tel. 518/272–5000), (Nonreporting) **A**10 **S** Trinity Health, Livonia, MI
Primary Contact: Norman E. Dascher, Jr., Chief Executive Officer
CFO: Daniel A. Kochie, CPA, Chief Financial Officer
CMO: Daniel C. Silverman, M.D., Chief Medical Officer
CHR: Barbara McCandless, Vice President Human Resources
CNO: Carol Crucetti, R.N., Chief Nursing Officer
Web address: www.setonhealth.org
Control: Other not–for–profit (including NFP Corporation) **Service:** General Medical and Surgical

Staffed Beds: 173

★ △ ◇ **FAXTON ST. LUKE'S HEALTHCARE (330044)**, 1656 Champlin Avenue, Zip 13502–4830, Mailing Address: P.O. Box 479, Zip 13503–0479; tel. 315/624–6000, (Includes FAXTON CAMPUS, 1676 Sunset Avenue, Zip 13502–5475; tel. 315/624–6000; ST. LUKE'S CAMPUS, 1656 Champlin Avenue, Mailing Address: P.O. Box 479, Zip 13503–0479; tel. 315/624–6000) **A**2 3 7 10 21 **F**2 3 11 12 13 15 17 28 29 30 31 34 35 36 39 40 45 46 47 48 49 50 51 53 54 56 57 58 59 60 62 64 65 66 68 70 73 74 75 76 77 78 79 80 81 84 85 86 87 89 90 92 93 97 98 102 103 104 107 108 110 114 115 116 117 118 119 120 121 123 124 127 130 131 132 135 141 143 144 146 147 148 **P**6
Primary Contact: Scott H. Perra, FACHE, President and Chief Executive Officer
COO: Robert Scholefield, MS, Executive Vice President and Chief Operating Officer
CFO: Louis Aiello, Senior Vice President and Chief Financial Officer
CMO: Michael F. Trevisani, M.D., Senior Vice President and Chief Medical Officer
CIO: John Lynch, Vice President and Chief Information Officer
CHR: Jack Davis, Vice President Human Resources
CNO: Patricia A. Roach, Senior Vice President and Chief Nursing Officer
Web address: www.mvhealthsystem.org
Control: Other not–for–profit (including NFP Corporation) **Service:** General Medical and Surgical

Staffed Beds: 278 **Admissions:** 14129 **Census:** 203 **Outpatient Visits:** 447809 **Births:** 1939 **Total Expense ($000):** 275471 **Payroll Expense ($000):** 129016 **Personnel:** 2188

☐ **MOHAWK VALLEY PSYCHIATRIC CENTER (334021)**, 1400 Noyes Street, Zip 13502–3854; tel. 315/738–3800, (Nonreporting) **A**1 10 **S** New York State Office of Mental Health, Albany, NY
Primary Contact: Colleen A. Sawyer, R.N., MSN, Executive Director
Web address: www.omh.ny.gov/omhweb/facilities/mvpc/facility.htm
Control: State–Government, nonfederal **Service:** Psychiatric

Staffed Beds: 614

★ ◇ **ST. ELIZABETH MEDICAL CENTER (330245)**, 2209 Genesee Street, Zip 13501–5999; tel. 315/798–8100 **A**3 10 13 21 **F**3 11 15 17 18 20 22 24 26 29 30 31 34 36 37 40 43 45 50 54 57 58 59 61 62 65 66 68 70 74 75 77 78 79 80 81 84 85 87 89 92 93 97 98 102 103 107 108 114 115 119 126 127 129 130 131 132 135 141 146 147 148 **P**6 **S** Sisters of Saint Francis, Syracuse, NY
Primary Contact: Scott H. Perra, FACHE, Chief Executive Officer
COO: Robert Scholefield, MS, Chief Operating Officer
CFO: Louis Aiello, Chief Financial Officer
CMO: Albert D'Accurzio, M.D., Medical Director
CIO: Robert Gillette, Chief Information Officer
CHR: Patrick Buckley, Vice President Human Resources
CNO: Varinya Sheppard, R.N., Chief Nursing Officer
Web address: www.stemc.org
Control: Church–operated, Nongovernment, not–for profit **Service:** General Medical and Surgical

Staffed Beds: 181 **Admissions:** 10412 **Census:** 149 **Outpatient Visits:** 473290 **Births:** 0 **Total Expense ($000):** 209138 **Payroll Expense ($000):** 101721 **Personnel:** 1647

ST. LUKE'S CAMPUS See Faxton St. Luke's Healthcare

⊠ **BLYTHEDALE CHILDREN'S HOSPITAL (333301)**, 95 Bradhurst Avenue, Zip 10595–1697; tel. 914/592–7555, (Nonreporting) **A**1 10
Primary Contact: Larry L. Levine, President and Chief Executive Officer
COO: Maureen Desimone, Chief Operating Officer
CFO: John Canning, Chief Financial Officer
CMO: Joelle Mast, Ph.D., Chief Medical Officer
CHR: Ronald Gallo, Director Human Resources
Web address: www.blythedale.org
Control: Other not–for–profit (including NFP Corporation) **Service:** Children's rehabilitation

Staffed Beds: 92

NY

Hospital, Medicare Provider Number, Address, Telephone, Approval, Facility, and Physician Codes, Health Care System

★ American Hospital Association (AHA) membership
☐ The Joint Commission accreditation
◯ Healthcare Facilities Accreditation Program
◇ DNV Healthcare Inc. accreditation
⇑ Center for Improvement in Healthcare Quality Accreditation
△ Commission on Accreditation of Rehabilitation Facilities (CARF) accreditation

◇ **WESTCHESTER MEDICAL CENTER (330234)**, 100 Woods Road,
Zip 10595–1530; tel. 914/493–7000, (Includes MARIA FARERI CHILDREN'S
HOSPITAL, 100 Woods Road, Zip 10595–1652; tel. 866/962–7337; MIDHUDSON
REGIONAL HOSPITAL OF WESTCHESTER MEDICAL CENTER, 241 North Road,
Poughkeepsie, Zip 12601–1154; tel. 845/483–5000; Paul S. Hochenberg,
Executive Director) **A**2 3 5 8 10 21 **F**3 4 5 8 12 13 14 15 16 17 18 19 20 21
22 23 24 25 26 27 28 29 30 31 32 34 35 36 37 38 39 40 41 43 44 45 46
47 48 49 50 51 52 54 55 56 57 58 59 60 61 62 64 65 66 68 70 71 72 73
74 75 76 77 78 79 80 81 82 84 85 86 87 88 89 90 91 92 93 94 97 98 99
100 101 102 103 104 107 108 110 111 114 115 116 117 118 119 120 121
123 124 126 129 130 131 132 134 135 136 137 138 139 141 142 145 146
147 148 **P**6 **S** WMCHealth, Valhalla, NY
Primary Contact: Michael D. Israel, President and Chief Executive Officer
COO: Gary F. Brudnicki, Senior Executive Vice President, Chief Operating Officer
and Chief Financial Officer
CFO: Gary F. Brudnicki, Senior Executive Vice President, Chief Operating Officer
and Chief Financial Officer
CMO: Renee Garrick, M.D., Executive Medical Director
CIO: John Moustakakis, Senior Vice President Information Systems and Chief
Information Officer
CHR: Jordy Rabinowitz, Senior Vice President Human Resources Operations
CNO: Patricia A. Wrobbel, Senior Vice President and Chief Nurse Executive
Web address: www.wmchealth.org
Control: Hospital district or authority, Government, nonfederal **Service:** General
Medical and Surgical

Staffed Beds: 895 **Admissions:** 27903 **Census:** 656 **Outpatient Visits:**
109557 **Births:** 918 **Total Expense ($000):** 1103859 **Payroll Expense**
($000): 295283 **Personnel:** 4369

WALTON—Delaware County

UHS DELAWARE VALLEY HOSPITAL (331312), 1 Titus Place,
Zip 13856–1498; tel. 607/865–2100 **A**10 18 **F**3 4 5 11 15 18 28 29 34 35
40 45 50 57 59 64 75 77 85 87 89 93 97 107 110 114 119 130 133 146
147 148 **S** United Health Services, Binghamton, NY
Primary Contact: Paul Summers, President and Chief Executive Officer
CFO: Paul Summers, Chief Financial Officer
CMO: John Giannone, M.D., Chief Medical Officer
CIO: James Armstrong, Manager Information Technology
CHR: Paul Summers, Chief Human Resources Officer
CNO: Victoria Conkling, Vice President Patient Care Services and Chief Nursing
Officer
Web address: www.uhs.net/locations/
Control: Other not–for–profit (including NFP Corporation) **Service:** General
Medical and Surgical

Staffed Beds: 25 **Admissions:** 582 **Census:** 11 **Outpatient Visits:** 151693
Births: 0 **Total Expense ($000):** 19767 **Payroll Expense ($000):** 6789
Personnel: 163

WAPPINGERS—Dutchess County

**VETERAN AFFAIRS HUDSON VALLEY HEALTH CARE SYSTEM–CASTLE
POINT CAMPUS** See Veterans Affairs Hudson Valley Health Care System,
Montrose

WARSAW—Wyoming County

□ **WYOMING COUNTY COMMUNITY HOSPITAL (330008)**, 400 North Main
Street, Zip 14569–1025; tel. 585/786–2233, (Nonreporting) **A**1 10 20
Primary Contact: Donald T. Eichenauer, Chief Executive Officer
COO: Michael Corcimiglia, Chief Operating Officer
CFO: James T. Cullen, III, Director Finance
CMO: Bilal Ahmed, M.D., Medical Director
CIO: Jane Beechler, Director Healthcare Information Systems
CHR: Peter J. Bendyna, Director Human Resources
CNO: Connie Almeter, Director of Nursing
Web address: www.wcchs.net
Control: County–Government, nonfederal **Service:** General Medical and Surgical

Staffed Beds: 75

WARWICK—Orange County

✠ **ST. ANTHONY COMMUNITY HOSPITAL (330205)**, 15 Maple Avenue,
Zip 10990–1028; tel. 845/986–2276 **A**1 10 **F**3 13 15 29 30 31 40 45 46 49
54 68 70 74 75 76 77 78 79 81 82 84 85 87 93 107 110 111 115 116 117
129 130 132 146 147 148 **S** WMCHealth, Valhalla, NY
Primary Contact: Jeff Reilly, Chief Operating Officer
Web address: www.stanthonycommunityhosp.org
Control: Other not–for–profit (including NFP Corporation) **Service:** General
Medical and Surgical

Staffed Beds: 60 **Admissions:** 2343 **Census:** 25 **Outpatient Visits:** 41050
Births: 336 **Total Expense ($000):** 54943 **Payroll Expense ($000):** 19935
Personnel: 244

WATERTOWN—Jefferson County

✠ **SAMARITAN MEDICAL CENTER (330157)**, 830 Washington Street,
Zip 13601–4034; tel. 315/785–4000 **A**1 10 12 13 20 **F**3 5 8 13 15 18 20 29
30 31 35 40 49 51 57 60 64 68 70 73 74 75 76 77 78 79 81 82 87 89 90
93 97 98 99 100 102 103 104 107 108 111 114 116 119 120 121 126 127
129 130 135 146 147 148 **P**6
Primary Contact: Thomas H. Carman, President and Chief Executive Officer
CFO: Sean Mills, Chief Financial Officer
CMO: Mario Victoria, M.D., Vice President, Medical Affairs
CIO: M. Andrew Short, Vice President Information Services
CHR: Thomas Shatraw, Director Human Resources
CNO: Kimberly Thibert, R.N., Vice President Patient Care Services and Chief
Nursing Officer
Web address: www.samaritanhealth.com
Control: Other not–for–profit (including NFP Corporation) **Service:** General
Medical and Surgical

Staffed Beds: 210 **Admissions:** 8699 **Census:** 136 **Outpatient Visits:**
271067 **Births:** 1232 **Total Expense ($000):** 201268 **Payroll Expense**
($000): 90350 **Personnel:** 1369

WELLSVILLE—Allegany County

✠ **JONES MEMORIAL HOSPITAL (330096)**, 191 North Main Street,
Zip 14895–1150, Mailing Address: P.O. Box 72, Zip 14895–0072;
tel. 585/593–1100 **A**1 10 20 **F**3 8 11 13 15 17 28 29 30 31 34 35 36 40 43
50 57 59 61 64 68 70 75 76 77 78 79 81 85 89 93 97 107 110 114 119
129 131 132 133 146 147
Primary Contact: Eva Benedict, R.N., President and Chief Executive Officer
CFO: James Helms, Vice President Finance
CMO: William Coch, M.D., Medical Director
CIO: James Helms, Vice President Finance
CHR: Brenda Sobeck, Director of Human Resources
CNO: Donna Bliven, Vice President Patient Care Services and Chief Nursing
Officer
Web address: www.jmhny.org
Control: Other not–for–profit (including NFP Corporation) **Service:** General
Medical and Surgical

Staffed Beds: 33 **Admissions:** 1686 **Census:** 18 **Outpatient Visits:** 129613
Births: 409 **Total Expense ($000):** 38061 **Payroll Expense ($000):** 17874
Personnel: 344

WEST HAVERSTRAW—Rockland County

□ △ **HELEN HAYES HOSPITAL (330405)**, Route 9W, Zip 10993–1127;
tel. 845/786–4000, (Nonreporting) **A**1 5 7 10
Primary Contact: Edmund Coletti, Chief Executive Officer
COO: Kathleen Martucci, Chief Operating Officer
CFO: Lori A. Meszler, Chief Financial Officer
CIO: Virgil Ennis, Chief Information Officer
CHR: Patrick J. Ryan, Chief Human Resources Officer
Web address: www.helenhayeshospital.org
Control: State–Government, nonfederal **Service:** Rehabilitation

Staffed Beds: 155

WEST ISLIP—Suffolk County

✠ **GOOD SAMARITAN HOSPITAL MEDICAL CENTER (330286)**, 1000 Montauk
Highway, Zip 11795–4927; tel. 631/376–3000, (Total facility includes 100 beds
in nursing home–type unit) **A**1 2 3 5 10 12 13 **F**3 8 11 12 13 15 17 18 19 20
22 24 26 28 29 30 31 32 34 35 40 41 43 45 46 47 48 49 50 54 55 56 57
59 64 65 66 68 70 72 73 74 75 76 77 78 79 81 82 84 85 86 87 88 89 91
93 94 96 97 99 100 102 107 108 110 111 114 115 117 118 119 120 121
123 124 126 128 129 130 131 132 146 147 **P**1 5 6 7 8 **S** Catholic Health
Services of Long Island, Rockville Centre, NY
Primary Contact: Nancy B. Simmons, Executive Vice President and Chief
Administrative Officer
CFO: Dan Macksood, Regional Senior Vice President and Chief Financial Officer
CMO: Jerome Weiner, M.D., Senior Vice President Medical Affairs
CIO: Marcy Dunn, Vice President Information Services and Chief Information
Officer
CHR: Lori Spina, Vice President Human Resources
Web address: www.good–samaritan–hospital.org
Control: Church–operated, Nongovernment, not–for profit **Service:** General
Medical and Surgical

Staffed Beds: 537 **Admissions:** 24708 **Census:** 463 **Outpatient Visits:**
218224 **Births:** 2723 **Total Expense ($000):** 613952 **Payroll Expense**
($000): 276508 **Personnel:** 3229

NY

Many Facility Codes have changed. Please refer to the AHA Guide Code Chart.   © 2016 AHA Guide

WEST POINT—Orange County

⊞ **KELLER ARMY COMMUNITY HOSPITAL**, 900 Washington Road,
Zip 10996–1197, Mailing Address: U.S. Military Academy, Building 900,
Zip 10996–1197; tel. 845/938–5169 **A**1 3 5 **F**3 5 7 8 29 34 40 44 45 50 54
57 59 64 65 68 75 76 77 79 81 85 86 87 89 97 99 100 101 102 104 107
110 111 115 131 132 135 141 146 **P**6 **S** Department of the Army, Office of
the Surgeon General, Falls Church, VA
Primary Contact: Colonel Brian S. Burlingame, Commanding Officer
CIO: Patrick McGuinness, Chief Information Management
CHR: Margaret Greco, Chief Human Resources
Web address: www.kach.amedd.army.mil/SitePages/Home.aspx
Control: Army, Government, federal **Service:** General Medical and Surgical

Staffed Beds: 20 **Admissions:** 800 **Census:** 4 **Outpatient Visits:** 126200
Births: 142 **Personnel:** 547

WEST SENECA—Erie County

☐ **WESTERN NEW YORK CHILDREN'S PSYCHIATRIC CENTER**, 1010 East and
West Road, Zip 14224–3602; tel. 716/677–7000 **A**1 3 5 **F**34 54 64 98 99 100
101 104 130 132 134 135 142 **S** New York State Office of Mental Health,
Albany, NY
Primary Contact: Kathe Hayes, Executive Director
COO: David Privett, Deputy Director
CMO: Patrick Stein, M.D., Clinical Director
CIO: Dan Hrubiak, Associate Computer Program Analyst
CHR: Charles Siewert, Director Human Resources
Web address: www.omh.ny.gov
Control: State–Government, nonfederal **Service:** Children's hospital psychiatric

Staffed Beds: 46 **Admissions:** 172 **Census:** 47 **Outpatient Visits:** 172
Births: 0 **Personnel:** 182

WESTFIELD—Chautauqua County

★ **WESTFIELD MEMORIAL HOSPITAL (330166)**, 189 East Main Street,
Zip 14787–1195; tel. 716/326–4921 **A**10 **F**3 8 11 14 15 28 29 34 35 40 45
59 68 75 79 81 93 107 110 114 119 129 135 148 **S** Allegheny Health
Network, Pittsburgh, PA
Primary Contact: Scott Whalen, Ph.D., FACHE, President and Chief Executive
Officer
COO: Patricia Ballman, Director
CFO: Tina Gowen, System Controller
CMO: Russell Elwell, M.D., Medical Director
CIO: Cindy Harper, Manager Patient Data
Web address: www.wmhinc.org
Control: Other not–for–profit (including NFP Corporation) **Service:** General
Medical and Surgical

Staffed Beds: 4 **Admissions:** 18 **Census:** 1 **Outpatient Visits:** 22694 **Births:**
0 **Total Expense ($000):** 9782 **Payroll Expense ($000):** 4102 **Personnel:**
77

WHITE PLAINS—Westchester County

⊞ △ **BURKE REHABILITATION HOSPITAL (330404)**, 785 Mamaroneck Avenue,
Zip 10605–2523; tel. 914/597–2500 **A**1 3 5 7 10 **F**11 28 29 30 34 35 53 54
57 58 59 74 75 87 90 92 93 94 95 96 100 104 130 131 132 133 146
Primary Contact: Mary Beth Walsh, M.D., Chief Executive Officer
COO: Brian M. Swift, Senior Administrator Plant Operations
CFO: John Stewart, Director Finance
CMO: Mary Beth Walsh, M.D., Chief Executive Officer
CIO: Cathy Dwyer, Senior Administrator Information Systems
CHR: Annette Bucci, Senior Administrator Human Resources
CNO: Marie Spencer, Chief Nursing Officer and Senior Administrator
Web address: www.burke.org
Control: Other not–for–profit (including NFP Corporation) **Service:** Rehabilitation

Staffed Beds: 150 **Admissions:** 2500 **Census:** 118 **Outpatient Visits:**
115136 **Births:** 0 **Total Expense ($000):** 82538 **Payroll Expense ($000):**
44464 **Personnel:** 347

NEW YORK–PRESBYTERIAN HOSPITAL, WESTCHESTER DIVISION See New
York–Presbyterian Hospital, New York

⊞ **WHITE PLAINS HOSPITAL CENTER (330304)**, 41 East Post Road,
Zip 10601–4699; tel. 914/681–0600 **A**1 2 3 5 10 **F**3 11 12 13 14 15 17 18
20 22 26 29 30 31 32 34 35 36 40 41 44 45 46 47 49 50 51 54 55 56 57
58 59 60 61 63 64 65 66 68 70 72 73 74 75 77 78 79 81 82 83 84 85 86
87 92 93 97 99 100 101 102 104 107 108 110 111 115 116 117 118 119
120 121 122 123 126 129 130 131 132 135 144 145 146 147 148 **P**5 6
Primary Contact: Susan Fox, President and Chief Executive Officer
COO: Edward F. Leonard, Executive Vice President and Chief Operating Officer
CFO: Joseph Guarracino, Senior Vice President and Chief Financial Officer
CMO: Michael Palumbo, M.D., Executive Vice President and Medical Director
CIO: Elizabeth King, Director
CHR: John Sanchez, Vice President Human Resources
CNO: Leigh McMahon, MS, Senior Vice President Patient Care Services and Chief
Nursing Officer
Web address: www.wphospital.org
Control: Other not–for–profit (including NFP Corporation) **Service:** General
Medical and Surgical

Staffed Beds: 292 **Admissions:** 15048 **Census:** 184 **Outpatient Visits:**
388256 **Births:** 1856 **Total Expense ($000):** 439563 **Payroll Expense
($000):** 223227 **Personnel:** 2302

WILLIAMSVILLE—Erie County

MILLARD FILLMORE SUBURBAN HOSPITAL See KALEIDA Health, Buffalo

YONKERS—Westchester County

ANDRUS PAVILION See St. John's Riverside Hospital

⊞ **SAINT JOSEPH'S MEDICAL CENTER (330006)**, 127 South Broadway,
Zip 10701–4006; tel. 914/378–7000, (Total facility includes 200 beds in nursing
home–type unit) **A**1 3 5 10 **F**2 3 4 5 8 11 15 18 29 30 31 34 35 38 39 40 45
47 48 49 54 56 57 58 59 60 61 62 64 68 70 74 75 77 78 79 81 82 85 87
89 93 94 97 98 99 100 101 102 103 104 105 106 107 108 110 111 115
118 119 120 130 132 134 135 143 144 146 **P**5 8
Primary Contact: Michael J. Spicer, President and Chief Executive Officer
COO: Frances Casola, Senior Vice President Operations
CFO: Frank Hagan, Senior Vice President Finance
CMO: James Neuendorf, M.D., Medical Director
CIO: Deborah Di Bernardo, Chief Information Officer
CHR: Dean Civitello, Vice President Human Resources
CNO: Margaret M. Cusumano, R.N., Vice President Patient Care Services and
Chief Nursing Officer
Web address: www.saintjosephs.org
Control: Other not–for–profit (including NFP Corporation) **Service:** General
Medical and Surgical

Staffed Beds: 483 **Admissions:** 8460 **Census:** 416 **Outpatient Visits:**
1070944 **Births:** 0 **Total Expense ($000):** 272100 **Payroll Expense ($000):**
116009 **Personnel:** 1693

☐ **ST. JOHN'S RIVERSIDE HOSPITAL (330208)**, 967 North Broadway,
Zip 10701–1399; tel. 914/964–4444, (Includes ANDRUS PAVILION, 967 North
Broadway, tel. 914/964–4444; ST. JOHN'S RIVERSIDE HOSPITAL – PARK CARE
PAVILION, Two Park Avenue, Zip 10703–3497; tel. 914/964–7300; ST. JOHN'S
RIVERSIDE HOSPITAL – DOBBS FERRY PAVILION, 128 Ashford Avenue, Dobbs
Ferry, Zip 10522–1896; tel. 914/693–0700) **A**1 2 3 10 **F**3 4 5 8 11 12 13 15
17 18 29 30 31 34 35 36 37 40 41 45 48 49 50 51 55 57 59 60 61 66 68
70 73 74 75 76 77 78 79 80 81 82 84 85 87 93 97 107 108 110 111 113
114 115 119 123 124 126 129 130 132 135 143 146 147 148 **P**7
Primary Contact: Ronald J. Corti, President and Chief Executive Officer
COO: Lynn M. Nelson, R.N., Chief Nursing Officer and Chief Operating Officer
CFO: Dennis M. Keane, Vice President Finance and Chief Financial Officer
CMO: Paul Antonecchia, M.D., Vice President Medical Affairs and Chief Medical
Officer
CIO: Peter Weidner, Director Information Technology
CHR: Marc Leff, Vice President Human Resources
CNO: Lynn M. Nelson, R.N., Chief Nursing Officer and Chief Operating Officer
Web address: www.riversidehealth.org
Control: Other not–for–profit (including NFP Corporation) **Service:** General
Medical and Surgical

Staffed Beds: 309 **Admissions:** 18173 **Census:** 253 **Outpatient Visits:**
213238 **Births:** 1328 **Total Expense ($000):** 250078 **Payroll Expense
($000):** 111670 **Personnel:** 1443

NY

Hospital, Medicare Provider Number, Address, Telephone, Approval, Facility, and Physician Codes, Health Care System

★ American Hospital Association (AHA) membership   ○ Healthcare Facilities Accreditation Program   ⇑ Center for Improvement in Healthcare Quality Accreditation
☐ The Joint Commission accreditation   ◇ DNV Healthcare Inc. accreditation   △ Commission on Accreditation of Rehabilitation Facilities (CARF) accreditation

NORTH CAROLINA

AHOSKIE—Hertford County

⊠ **VIDANT ROANOKE–CHOWAN HOSPITAL (340099)**, 500 South Academy Street, Zip 27910–3261, Mailing Address: P.O. Box 1385, Zip 27910–1385; tel. 252/209–3000 **A**1 10 20 **F**3 11 13 15 28 29 30 31 34 35 40 43 44 45 53 56 57 59 64 68 70 75 76 77 78 79 81 82 85 86 87 89 92 98 100 101 102 103 107 108 110 111 114 119 121 123 129 130 132 146 148 **S** Vidant Health, Greenville, NC
Primary Contact: Susan S. Lassiter, FACHE, President and Chief Executive Officer
CFO: Jon Graham, Chief Financial Officer
CMO: Jeff Severa, D.O., Chief of Staff
CHR: Debbie Sisler, Director Human Resources
CNO: Susan Mitchell, Vice President Patient Care Services
Web address: www.vidanthealth.com
Control: Other not–for–profit (including NFP Corporation) **Service:** General Medical and Surgical

Staffed Beds: 70 **Admissions:** 4280 **Census:** 54 **Outpatient Visits:** 66954 **Births:** 340 **Total Expense ($000):** 67651 **Payroll Expense ($000):** 25302 **Personnel:** 578

ALBEMARLE—Stanly County

⊠ **STANLY REGIONAL MEDICAL CENTER (340119)**, 301 Yadkin Street, Zip 28001–3441, Mailing Address: P.O. Box 1489, Zip 28002–1489; tel. 704/984–4000 **A**1 2 10 **F**3 11 12 13 15 18 20 28 29 30 34 35 39 40 45 46 49 57 59 60 61 62 63 64 68 70 74 75 76 77 79 81 82 85 86 89 93 98 100 101 102 103 107 108 110 111 114 115 119 120 121 123 129 130 131 132 146 147 148 **S** Carolinas Healthcare System, Charlotte, NC
Primary Contact: Alfred P. Taylor, President and Chief Executive Officer
COO: Brian Freeman, Vice President of Operations
CFO: Nick Samilo, Vice President Fiscal Services and Chief Financial Officer
CMO: Paul D'Amico, M.D., Chief of Staff
CIO: Brian Freeman, Vice President of Operations
CNO: Judy Doran, R.N., Vice President of Hospital Services and Chief Nurse Executive
Web address: www.stanly.org
Control: Hospital district or authority, Government, nonfederal **Service:** General Medical and Surgical

Staffed Beds: 94 **Admissions:** 4056 **Census:** 42 **Outpatient Visits:** 85252 **Births:** 646 **Total Expense ($000):** 95479 **Payroll Expense ($000):** 37888 **Personnel:** 514

ASHEBORO—Randolph County

⊠ **RANDOLPH HOSPITAL (340123)**, 364 White Oak Street, Zip 27203–5400, Mailing Address: P.O. Box 1048, Zip 27204–1048; tel. 336/625–5151 **A**1 2 10 **F**3 8 13 15 18 28 29 30 31 34 35 37 40 45 48 49 50 53 56 57 58 59 61 62 64 68 70 74 75 76 77 78 79 80 81 83 84 85 86 87 89 91 92 93 94 96 97 107 109 110 111 114 115 119 120 121 123 130 131 132 143 146 148 **P**6 **S** Carolinas Healthcare System, Charlotte, NC
Primary Contact: Steven E. Eblin, Chief Executive Officer / President
CMO: Charles West, M.D., Chief Medical Officer
CIO: Angela Burgess, Chief Information Officer
Web address: www.randolphhospital.org
Control: Other not–for–profit (including NFP Corporation) **Service:** General Medical and Surgical

Staffed Beds: 101 **Admissions:** 5413 **Census:** 52 **Outpatient Visits:** 133661 **Births:** 770 **Total Expense ($000):** 95888 **Payroll Expense ($000):** 41532 **Personnel:** 923

ASHEVILLE—Buncombe County

★ **ASHEVILLE SPECIALTY HOSPITAL (342017)**, 428 Biltmore Avenue, 4th Floor, Zip 28801–4502; tel. 828/213–5400 **A**3 10 **F**1 3 29 30 36 77 85 91 130 148 **S** Mission Health System, Asheville, NC
Primary Contact: Robert C. Desotelle, President and Chief Executive Officer
COO: Michelle Stillman, Director of Care Management
CMO: Joseph Aiello, M.D., Chief of Staff
CIO: Dorothy L. Porter, Director of Compliance/Risk/Quality
CHR: Jennifer Calloway, Human Resources Coordinator
CNO: Wanda Miller, R.N., Director of Clinical Services
Web address: www.missionhospitals.org/acute–care
Control: Partnership, Investor–owned, for–profit **Service:** Long–Term Acute Care hospital

Staffed Beds: 34 **Admissions:** 339 **Census:** 27 **Outpatient Visits:** 0 **Births:** 0 **Total Expense ($000):** 14049 **Payroll Expense ($000):** 6306 **Personnel:** 109

⊠ △ **CAREPARTNERS HEALTH SERVICES (343025)**, 68 Sweeten Creek Road, Zip 28803–2318, Mailing Address: P.O. Box 15025, Zip 28813–0025; tel. 828/277–4800, (Nonreporting) **A**1 7 10 **S** Mission Health System, Asheville, NC
Primary Contact: Tracy Buchanan, Chief Executive Officer and President
CFO: Gregg Dixon, CPA, Chief Financial Officer
CMO: Michael Parmer, Chief Medical Officer
CIO: Jennifer Scott, Director of Informatics
CHR: Katy Pless, Director of Human Resources
CNO: Cathleen Adams, Chief Nursing Officer
Web address: www.carepartners.org
Control: Other not–for–profit (including NFP Corporation) **Service:** Rehabilitation

Staffed Beds: 80

⊠ **CHARLES GEORGE VETERANS AFFAIRS MEDICAL CENTER**, 1100 Tunnel Road, Zip 28805–2087; tel. 828/298–7911, (Total facility includes 85 beds in nursing home–type unit) **A**1 3 5 **F**3 4 5 12 18 20 22 24 26 28 29 30 31 34 35 36 38 39 40 45 49 50 56 57 58 59 61 62 63 64 65 68 70 74 75 77 78 79 81 82 83 84 85 86 87 91 92 93 94 97 98 100 101 102 103 104 107 108 111 114 115 119 128 130 132 135 145 146 147 148 **P**3 6 8 **S** Department of Veterans Affairs, Washington, DC
Primary Contact: Cynthia Breyfogle, FACHE, Director
CFO: Margaret Wilkes, Chief Fiscal Officer
CMO: Webster Carl Bazemore, M.D., Interim Chief of Staff
CIO: Carla McLendon, Director Information Resource Management Services
CHR: James Sitlinger, Chief Human Resources Management
CNO: David Przestrzelski, Associate Director, Patient Care Services and Chief Nursing Executive
Web address: www.asheville.va.gov/
Control: Veterans Affairs, Government, federal **Service:** General Medical and Surgical

Staffed Beds: 257 **Admissions:** 4770 **Census:** 116 **Outpatient Visits:** 457988 **Births:** 0 **Total Expense ($000):** 313160 **Payroll Expense ($000):** 142127 **Personnel:** 1794

⊠ **MISSION HOSPITAL (340002)**, 509 Biltmore Avenue, Zip 28801–4690; tel. 828/213–1111, (Includes MISSION CHILDREN'S HOSPITAL, 509 Biltmore Avenue, Zip 28801–4601; tel. 828/213–1111; MISSION HOSPITAL, 509 Biltmore Avenue, tel. 828/213–1111; Jill Hoggard Green, Ph.D., R.N., President; MISSION HOSPITAL – ST. JOSEPH'S CAMPUS, 428 Biltmore Avenue, Zip 28801–9839; tel. 828/213–1111) **A**1 2 3 5 10 **F**3 7 8 11 12 13 15 17 18 19 20 22 24 26 28 29 30 31 32 34 35 36 37 39 40 43 44 45 46 47 48 49 50 51 53 54 55 56 57 58 59 60 61 64 65 68 70 71 72 73 74 75 76 77 78 79 80 81 82 84 85 86 87 88 89 91 92 93 95 96 97 98 99 100 101 102 103 104 105 107 108 110 111 114 115 116 117 118 119 120 121 123 124 126 129 130 131 132 134 135 141 142 143 146 147 148 **S** Mission Health System, Asheville, NC
Primary Contact: Jill Hoggard Green, Ph.D., R.N., President
COO: Amanda Hoggard, President and Chief Operating Officer
CFO: Paul L. McDowell, Deputy Chief Financial Officer
CMO: William Hathaway, M.D., Chief Medical Officer
CIO: Jon Brown, Chief Information Officer
CHR: Sheila M. Meadows, Chief Human Resources Officer
CNO: Karen M. Olsen, R.N., Chief Nursing Officer
Web address: www.mission–health.org
Control: Other not–for–profit (including NFP Corporation) **Service:** General Medical and Surgical

Staffed Beds: 763 **Admissions:** 38084 **Census:** 558 **Outpatient Visits:** 544172 **Births:** 4105 **Total Expense ($000):** 981612 **Payroll Expense ($000):** 291093 **Personnel:** 6131

BLACK MOUNTAIN—Buncombe County

JULIAN F. KEITH ALCOHOL AND DRUG ABUSE TREATMENT CENTER (344023), 201 Tabernacle Road, Zip 28711–2599; tel. 828/669–3400, (Nonreporting) **A**10
Primary Contact: W. Douglas Baker, Director
CFO: Jackie Maurer, Fiscal Officer
CMO: Anthony Burnett, M.D., Medical Director
CHR: Faye Hamlin, Manager Human Resources
Web address: www.jfkadatc.net
Control: State–Government, nonfederal **Service:** Alcoholism and other chemical dependency

Staffed Beds: 80

Many Facility Codes have changed. Please refer to the AHA Guide Code Chart.

© 2016 AHA Guide

NC

BOLIVIA—Brunswick County

⊞ **NOVANT HEALTH BRUNSWICK MEDICAL CENTER (340158)**, 240 Hospital Drive N.E., Zip 28422–8346; tel. 910/721–1000 **A**1 10 **F**3 11 13 15 18 26 28 29 30 34 35 40 45 46 57 59 64 70 71 75 76 79 80 81 82 85 87 93 107 108 110 111 114 118 119 126 130 132 135 141 145 146 147 148 **S** Novant Health, Winston Salem, NC
Primary Contact: Shelbourn Stevens, President
CFO: Joan Thomas, Chief Financial Officer
CMO: Robert Hassler, M.D., Director Medical Affairs
CIO: Pamela Parrish, Director Information Systems
Web address: www.brunswicknovant.org
Control: Other not–for–profit (including NFP Corporation) **Service:** General Medical and Surgical

Staffed Beds: 53 **Admissions:** 4484 **Census:** 45 **Outpatient Visits:** 110301 **Births:** 466 **Total Expense ($000):** 84454 **Payroll Expense ($000):** 23989 **Personnel:** 429

BOONE—Watauga County

⊞ **WATAUGA MEDICAL CENTER (340051)**, 336 Deerfield Road, Zip 28607–5008, Mailing Address: P.O. Box 2600, Zip 28607–2600; tel. 828/262–4100 **A**1 2 10 **F**3 5 13 15 17 18 20 22 26 28 29 30 31 32 34 35 38 40 44 45 46 47 48 49 50 53 54 57 59 64 70 73 75 76 77 78 81 82 84 85 86 87 91 92 93 96 107 108 110 111 114 115 118 119 120 121 122 123 124 129 130 131 132 135 144 145 146 147 148 **P**6 **S** Appalachian Regional Healthcare System, Boone, NC
Primary Contact: Richard G. Sparks, Chief Executive Officer
CFO: Kevin B. May, Chief Financial Officer
CMO: Herman A. Godwin, Jr., M.D., Senior Vice President and Medical Director
CIO: Mike Quinto, Chief Information Officer
CHR: Amy J. Crabbe, Senior Vice President Human Resources
Web address: www.https://apprhs.org/contact–us
Control: Other not–for–profit (including NFP Corporation) **Service:** General Medical and Surgical

Staffed Beds: 99 **Admissions:** 4015 **Census:** 39 **Outpatient Visits:** 124157 **Births:** 516 **Total Expense ($000):** 119189 **Payroll Expense ($000):** 38046 **Personnel:** 581

BREVARD—Transylvania County

⊞ **TRANSYLVANIA REGIONAL HOSPITAL (341319)**, 260 Hospital Drive, Zip 28712–3378; tel. 828/884–9111, (Total facility includes 10 beds in nursing home–type unit) **A**1 10 18 **F**3 11 13 15 28 29 30 31 35 40 45 49 53 56 64 70 78 79 80 81 97 107 108 110 111 114 119 128 130 131 133 146 147 **P**6 **S** Mission Health System, Asheville, NC
Primary Contact: Melina Arrowood, Interim President and Chief Nursing Officer
CFO: Theresa M. Parker, Regional Finance Director
CMO: Mark Lemel, Chief of Staff
CIO: Ed Coye, Director Information Technology
CHR: Susan Stevens, Human Resources Strategic Business Partner
CNO: Melina Arrowood, Interim President and Chief Nursing Officer
Web address: www.trhospital.org
Control: Other not–for–profit (including NFP Corporation) **Service:** General Medical and Surgical

Staffed Beds: 30 **Admissions:** 1635 **Census:** 15 **Outpatient Visits:** 103414 **Births:** 64 **Total Expense ($000):** 62718 **Payroll Expense ($000):** 24057 **Personnel:** 377

BRYSON CITY—Swain County

★ **SWAIN COMMUNITY HOSPITAL (341305)**, 45 Plateau Street, Zip 28713–4200; tel. 828/488–2155 **A**10 18 **F**8 11 15 29 30 35 40 44 57 59 62 63 68 75 77 81 82 84 85 91 93 103 107 119 130 133 146 148 **S** Duke LifePoint Healthcare, Brentwood, TN
Primary Contact: Steve Heatherly, Chief Executive Officer
CMO: David Zimmerman, M.D., Chief of Staff
Web address: www.westcare.org
Control: Corporation, Investor–owned, for–profit **Service:** General Medical and Surgical

Staffed Beds: 25 **Admissions:** 479 **Census:** 5 **Outpatient Visits:** 30467 **Births:** 0 **Total Expense ($000):** 15913 **Payroll Expense ($000):** 5818 **Personnel:** 80

BURGAW—Pender County

⊞ **PENDER MEMORIAL HOSPITAL (341307)**, 507 East Freemont Street, Zip 28425–5131; tel. 910/259–5451, (Total facility includes 43 beds in nursing home–type unit) **A**1 10 18 **F**3 11 15 29 34 35 40 45 54 56 57 59 62 64 81 85 87 93 96 107 110 114 119 128 130 133 143 146 148 **S** New Hanover Regional Medical Center, Wilmington, NC
Primary Contact: Ruth Glaser, President
CFO: Morrison Hall, Chief Financial Officer
CMO: Heather Davis, M.D., Chief of Staff
CIO: Ashley Hernandez, Chief Information Technology Officer
CHR: Lori McKoy, Business Partner
CNO: Cynthia Faulkner, R.N., Chief Nursing Executive
Web address: www.pendermemorial.org
Control: County–Government, nonfederal **Service:** General Medical and Surgical

Staffed Beds: 68 **Admissions:** 728 **Census:** 46 **Outpatient Visits:** 24511 **Births:** 0 **Total Expense ($000):** 21386 **Payroll Expense ($000):** 7124 **Personnel:** 157

BURLINGTON—Alamance County

⊞ **ALAMANCE REGIONAL MEDICAL CENTER (340070)**, 1240 Huffman Mill Road, Zip 27215–8700, Mailing Address: P.O. Box 202, Zip 27216–0202; tel. 336/538–7000 **A**1 2 10 **F**3 8 9 12 13 15 18 20 22 24 26 28 29 30 31 32 34 35 36 38 39 40 44 45 46 47 49 50 53 54 56 57 58 59 60 64 66 68 70 73 74 75 76 77 78 79 81 82 84 85 86 87 89 91 93 94 96 97 98 100 101 102 103 107 108 110 111 114 117 118 119 120 121 123 126 130 131 132 135 144 145 146 147 148 **P**6 **S** Carolinas Healthcare System, Charlotte, NC
Primary Contact: Preston W. Hammock, President and Chief Executive Officer
COO: Preston W. Hammock, President and Chief Operating Officer
CFO: Rex Street, Senior Vice President and Chief Financial Officer
CMO: Andrew Lamb, M.D., Chief of Staff
CIO: Terri Andrews, Director Information Technology
CNO: Theresa M. Brodrick, R.N., Chief Nursing Officer
Web address: www.armc.com
Control: Other not–for–profit (including NFP Corporation) **Service:** General Medical and Surgical

Staffed Beds: 218 **Admissions:** 10523 **Census:** 127 **Outpatient Visits:** 117856 **Births:** 1281 **Total Expense ($000):** 239206 **Payroll Expense ($000):** 74275 **Personnel:** 1768

BUTNER—Granville County

☐ **CENTRAL REGIONAL HOSPITAL (344004)**, 300 Veazey Road, Zip 27509–1668; tel. 919/764–2000, (Nonreporting) **A**1 3 5 10
Primary Contact: Walter Edwin Beal, Chief Executive Officer
COO: Cliff Hood, Chief Operating Officer
CMO: Stephen Oxley, M.D., Chief Medical Officer
CIO: Joe Thurber, Director Information Technology
CHR: Katherine Williamson, Director of Human Resources
CNO: Diana Holmes, Chief Nursing Officer
Control: State–Government, nonfederal **Service:** Psychiatric

Staffed Beds: 382

CAMP LEJEUNE—Onslow County

⊞ **NAVAL HOSPITAL CAMP LEJEUNE**, 100 Brewster Boulevard, Zip 28547–2538, Mailing Address: P.O. Box 10100, Zip 28547–0100; tel. 910/450–4300, (Nonreporting) **A**1 3 5 **S** Bureau of Medicine and Surgery, Department of the Navy, Falls Church, VA
Primary Contact: Captain Rick Freedman, Commanding Officer
Web address: www.med.navy.mil/sites/nhcl/Pages/default.aspx
Control: Navy, Government, federal **Service:** General Medical and Surgical

Staffed Beds: 117

Hospital, Medicare Provider Number, Address, Telephone, Approval, Facility, and Physician Codes, Health Care System

★ American Hospital Association (AHA) membership
☐ The Joint Commission accreditation
○ Healthcare Facilities Accreditation Program
◇ DNV Healthcare Inc. accreditation
⇑ Center for Improvement in Healthcare Quality Accreditation
△ Commission on Accreditation of Rehabilitation Facilities (CARF) accreditation

NC

CARY—Wake County

⊞ **WAKEMED CARY HOSPITAL (340173)**, 1900 Kildaire Farm Road,
Zip 27518–6616; tel. 919/350–8000 **A**1 10 **F**3 7 12 13 15 18 20 28 29 30
31 35 40 42 44 45 46 48 49 50 54 61 64 68 70 73 74 75 76 77 79 81 82
85 86 92 107 110 111 114 115 118 119 126 129 130 132 146 147 **P**6
S WakeMed Health & Hospitals, Raleigh, NC
Primary Contact: Donald R. Gintzig, President and Chief Executive Officer
COO: Denise Wilder Warren, R.N., Executive Vice President and Chief Operating
Officer
CMO: West Paul, M.D., Senior Vice President, Chief Quality and Medical Staff
Officer
CIO: Denton Arledge, Vice President and Chief Information Officer
CHR: Jeanene R. Martin, M.P.H., Senior Vice President Human Resources and
Chief People Officer
CNO: Cindy Boily, MSN, Senior Vice President and Chief Nursing Officer
Web address: www.wakemed.org
Control: Other not–for–profit (including NFP Corporation) **Service:** General
Medical and Surgical

Staffed Beds: 156 **Admissions:** 10238 **Census:** 118 **Outpatient Visits:**
259847 **Births:** 2276 **Total Expense ($000):** 174688 **Payroll Expense**
($000): 61206 **Personnel:** 1053

CHAPEL HILL—Orange County

⊞ △ **UNIVERSITY OF NORTH CAROLINA HOSPITALS (340061)**, 101 Manning
Drive, Zip 27514–4220; tel. 984/974–1000, (Includes NORTH CAROLINA
CHILDREN'S AND WOMEN'S HOSPITAL ; N.C. WOMEN'S HOSPITAL, 101 Manning
Drive, tel. 984/974–1000; NORTH CAROLINA CHILDREN'S HOSPITAL, 101
Manning Drive, tel. 984/974–1000; NORTH CAROLINA NEUROSCIENCES
HOSPITAL, University Campus, Zip 27514; tel. 984/974–1000; UNC HEALTH
CARE HILLSBOROUGH CAMPUS, 430 Waterstone Drive, Hillsborough,
Zip 27278–9078; tel. 984/974–1000; Gary L. Park, Chief Executive Officer; UNC
LINEBERGER COMPREHENSIVE CANCER CENTER, 450 West Drive,
Zip 27599–5020; tel. 919/966–3036) **A**1 2 3 5 7 8 10 **F**3 4 5 7 8 9 11 12 13
14 15 16 17 18 19 20 21 22 23 24 25 26 27 28 29 30 31 32 34 35 36 37
38 39 40 41 43 44 45 46 47 48 49 50 52 53 54 55 56 57 58 59 60 61 62
63 64 65 66 68 70 72 73 74 75 76 77 78 79 80 81 82 84 85 86 87 88 89
90 91 92 93 96 97 98 99 100 101 102 103 104 105 106 107 108 110 111
114 115 116 117 118 119 120 121 123 124 126 129 130 131 132 134 135
136 137 138 139 140 141 142 143 144 145 146 147 148 **S** UNC Health
Care, Chapel Hill, NC
Primary Contact: Gary L. Park, President
COO: Brian Goldstein, M.D., Executive Vice President and Chief Operating Officer
CFO: Christopher Ellington, Executive Vice President and Chief Financial Officer
CMO: Tony Lindsey, M.D., Chief of Staff
CIO: Tracy Parham
CHR: Bill Rotella, System Vice President, Human Resources
CNO: Catherine Madigan, Chief Nursing Officer
Web address: www.unchealthcare.org
Control: State–Government, nonfederal **Service:** General Medical and Surgical

Staffed Beds: 866 **Admissions:** 37883 **Census:** 671 **Outpatient Visits:**
965521 **Births:** 3624 **Total Expense ($000):** 1242432 **Payroll Expense**
($000): 463633 **Personnel:** 8506

CHARLOTTE—Mecklenburg County

⊞ **CAROLINAS CONTINUECARE HOSPITAL AT PINEVILLE (342015)**, 10648
Park Road, Zip 28210; tel. 704/667–8050, (Data for 273 days) **A**1 5 10 **F**1 3
29 34 35 59 65 68 74 75 77 79 82 84 85 91 130 146 148 **P**5 **S** Community
Hospital Corporation, Plano, TX
Primary Contact: Daniel C. Dunmyer, Chief Executive Officer
CFO: Joanne Tyo, Chief Financial Officer
CMO: Joseph Lang, M.D., Chief of Staff
CHR: Doug Gallagher, Director Human Resources
CNO: Teshia Davis, Chief Clinical Officer
Web address: www.cshnc.com
Control: Other not–for–profit (including NFP Corporation) **Service:** Long–Term
Acute Care hospital

Staffed Beds: 40 **Admissions:** 343 **Census:** 34 **Outpatient Visits:** 0 **Births:**
0 **Total Expense ($000):** 15026 **Payroll Expense ($000):** 6350 **Personnel:**
161

CAROLINAS CONTINUECARE HOSPITAL AT UNIVERSITY (340189), 8800
North Tryon Street, Zip 28262–3300; tel. 704/863–8300, (Nonreporting)
S Community Hospital Corporation, Plano, TX
Primary Contact: Derek Murzyn, Chief Executive Officer
Web address: www.continuecare.org/charlotte//
Control: Other not–for–profit (including NFP Corporation) **Service:** Long–Term
Acute Care hospital

Staffed Beds: 35

⊞ △ **CAROLINAS HEALTHCARE SYSTEM PINEVILLE (340098)**, 10628 Park
Road, Zip 28210–8407; tel. 704/543–2000 **A**1 2 3 7 10 **F**3 13 17 18 20 22
24 26 28 29 30 40 42 45 49 50 64 70 72 74 75 76 77 79 81 82 84 86 87
90 91 92 93 100 107 111 112 114 115 119 126 129 130 132 146 147 148
S Carolinas Healthcare System, Charlotte, NC
Primary Contact: Christopher R. Hummer, President
Web address: www.carolinashealthcare.org/pineville
Control: Hospital district or authority, Government, nonfederal **Service:** General
Medical and Surgical

Staffed Beds: 229 **Admissions:** 15265 **Census:** 184 **Outpatient Visits:**
167520 **Births:** 2475 **Total Expense ($000):** 269403 **Payroll Expense**
($000): 89443 **Personnel:** 1356

⊞ △ **CAROLINAS MEDICAL CENTER (340113)**, 1000 Blythe Boulevard,
Zip 28203–5871, Mailing Address: P.O. Box 32861, Zip 28232–2861;
tel. 704/355–2000, (Includes CAROLINAS MEDICAL CENTER–MERCY, 2001 Vail
Avenue, Zip 28207–1289; tel. 704/304–5000; Scott Jones, Vice President and
Facility Executive; LEVINE CHILDREN'S HOSPITAL, 1000 Blythe Boulevard,
Zip 28203; tel. 704/381–2000) **A**1 2 3 5 7 8 10 **F**3 4 5 6 7 8 12 13 15 17 18
19 20 21 22 23 24 25 26 27 28 29 30 31 32 34 35 36 37 38 39 40 41 42
43 44 45 46 47 48 49 50 52 54 55 56 57 58 59 60 61 62 64 65 66 68 70
71 72 73 74 75 76 77 78 79 80 81 82 83 84 85 86 87 88 89 90 93 96 97
98 99 100 101 102 103 104 105 107 111 114 115 116 117 118 119 120
121 123 124 126 129 130 131 132 134 135 136 137 138 139 141 142 143
145 146 147 148 **P**6 **S** Carolinas Healthcare System, Charlotte, NC
Primary Contact: Spencer Lilly, President
CFO: Greg A. Gombar, Chief Financial Officer
CMO: Roger A. Ray, M.D., Executive Vice President and Chief Medical Officer
CIO: Craig D. Richardville, Senior Vice President and Chief Information Officer
CHR: Debra Plousha–Moore, Senior Vice President Human Resources
Web address: www.carolinashealthcare.org/cmc
Control: Hospital district or authority, Government, nonfederal **Service:** General
Medical and Surgical

Staffed Beds: 1132 **Admissions:** 61788 **Census:** 958 **Outpatient Visits:**
951430 **Births:** 7023 **Total Expense ($000):** 2117221 **Payroll Expense**
($000): 567468 **Personnel:** 14476

⊞ **CAROLINAS MEDICAL CENTER–UNIVERSITY (340166)**, 8800 North Tryon
Street, Zip 28262–3300, Mailing Address: P.O. Box 560727, Zip 28256–0727;
tel. 704/863–6000 **A**1 2 10 22 **F**3 8 13 15 18 20 26 29 30 31 34 40 42 43
44 45 46 49 50 51 57 59 60 64 65 68 70 72 74 75 76 78 79 81 82 84 85
86 87 93 107 111 114 115 118 119 126 129 130 145 146 148 **S** Carolinas
Healthcare System, Charlotte, NC
Primary Contact: William H. Leonard, President
CFO: Greg A. Gombar, Chief Financial Officer
CIO: John Knox, Senior Vice President and Chief Information Officer
Web address: www.carolinashealthcare.org/university
Control: Hospital district or authority, Government, nonfederal **Service:** General
Medical and Surgical

Staffed Beds: 100 **Admissions:** 6049 **Census:** 61 **Outpatient Visits:** 146891
Births: 1560 **Total Expense ($000):** 140888 **Payroll Expense ($000):**
48468 **Personnel:** 716

⊞ △ **CAROLINAS REHABILITATION (343026)**, 1100 Blythe Boulevard,
Zip 28203–5864; tel. 704/355–4300 **A**1 7 10 **F**3 11 29 30 31 64 74 77 79
82 90 91 93 95 129 130 131 132 146 **P**1 **S** Carolinas Healthcare System,
Charlotte, NC
Primary Contact: Robert G. Larrison, Jr., President
CFO: William Hopkins, Director Finance
CMO: William Bockenek, M.D., Chief Medical Officer
CIO: Craig D. Richardville, Chief Information Officer
CHR: Deonca Leach, Director, Human Resources
CNO: Susan Chase, Vice President
Web address: www.carolinashealthcare.org/rehabilitation
Control: Other not–for–profit (including NFP Corporation) **Service:** Rehabilitation

Staffed Beds: 157 **Admissions:** 2749 **Census:** 126 **Outpatient Visits:** 78664
Births: 0 **Total Expense ($000):** 89898 **Payroll Expense ($000):** 38219
Personnel: 688

★ **NOVANT HEALTH CHARLOTTE ORTHOPAEDIC HOSPITAL (340153)**, 1901
Randolph Road, Zip 28207–1195; tel. 704/316–2000, (Total facility includes 16
beds in nursing home–type unit) **A**10 **F**3 11 29 30 37 44 50 51 64 75 79 81 82
86 87 107 111 114 118 119 128 130 131 132 141 146 **S** Novant Health,
Winston Salem, NC
Primary Contact: Jason Bernd, Vice President
CFO: Tammy Geist, Chief Financial Officer
CIO: Shelia Cook, Director Information Systems
CNO: Maurice Wilson, Director of Nursing
Web address: www.novanthealth.org
Control: Other not–for–profit (including NFP Corporation) **Service:** Orthopedic

Staffed Beds: 33 **Admissions:** 3324 **Census:** 29 **Outpatient Visits:** 21303
Births: 0 **Total Expense ($000):** 87834 **Payroll Expense ($000):** 18228
Personnel: 359

NC

✸ **NOVANT HEALTH PRESBYTERIAN MEDICAL CENTER (340053)**, 200 Hawthorne Lane, Zip 28204–2528, Mailing Address: P.O. Box 33549, Zip 28233–3549; tel. 704/384–4000, (Includes PRESBYTERIAN HEMBY CHILDREN'S HOSPITAL, 200 Hawthorne Lane, Zip 28204–2515; tel. 704/384–5134) **A**1 2 3 10 **F**3 5 11 12 13 15 17 18 19 20 22 24 26 28 29 30 31 32 34 35 36 38 40 41 45 46 47 48 49 54 55 56 57 58 59 60 61 63 64 65 67 70 71 72 74 75 76 77 78 79 81 82 84 85 86 87 88 89 91 92 93 98 99 100 101 102 103 104 105 107 108 110 111 114 115 116 117 118 119 120 121 124 126 129 130 132 135 141 142 145 146 147 148 **P**6 **S** Novant Health, Winston Salem, NC
Primary Contact: Paula Vincent, MSN, President and Chief Operating Officer
CFO: Melissa Masterton, Vice President
CMO: Thomas Zweng, M.D., Executive Vice President Medical Affairs
CIO: David B. Garrett, Senior Vice President Information Technology
CHR: Janet Smith–Hill, Senior Vice President Human Resources
CNO: Michael Vaccaro, Chief Nursing Officer
Web address: www.novanthealth.org
Control: Other not–for–profit (including NFP Corporation) **Service:** General Medical and Surgical

Staffed Beds: 419 **Admissions:** 27017 **Census:** 389 **Outpatient Visits:** 426404 **Births:** 5100 **Total Expense ($000):** 637620 **Payroll Expense ($000):** 169870 **Personnel:** 2920

PRESBYTERIAN HOSPITAL See Novant Health Presbyterian Medical Center

PRESBYTERIAN–ORTHOPAEDIC HOSPITAL See Novant Health Charlotte Orthopaedic Hospital

STRATEGIC BEHAVIORAL HEALTH – CHARLOTTE, 1715 Sharon Road West, Zip 28210–5663; tel. 704/944–0650, (Nonreporting) **S** Strategic Behavioral Health, LLC, Memphis, TN
Primary Contact: Mercy Estevez, Chief Executive Officer
Web address: www.sbccharlotte.com/
Control: Corporation, Investor–owned, for–profit **Service:** Children's hospital psychiatric

Staffed Beds: 60

CHEROKEE—Swain County

✸ **CHEROKEE INDIAN HOSPITAL (340156)**, 1 Hospital Road, Zip 28719; tel. 828/497–9163, (Nonreporting) **A**1 10
Primary Contact: Casey Cooper, Chief Executive Officer
COO: Beth Greene, Chief Operating Officer
CFO: Chrissy Arch, Chief Financial Officer
CMO: Michael E. Toedt, M.D., Director Clinical Services
CIO: Anthony Taylor, Manager Information Technology
Control: Other not–for–profit (including NFP Corporation) **Service:** General Medical and Surgical

Staffed Beds: 15

CLINTON—Sampson County

✸ **SAMPSON REGIONAL MEDICAL CENTER (340024)**, 607 Beaman Street, Zip 28328–2697, Mailing Address: P.O. Box 260, Zip 28329–0260; tel. 910/592–8511 **A**1 10 12 13 **F**14 15 34 35 40 45 46 47 50 51 53 57 59 62 64 68 75 77 79 81 82 85 86 91 93 107 111 114 119 130 132 133 144 146 148
Primary Contact: Shawn Howerton, M.D., Chief Executive Officer and President, Medical Staff
COO: Geraldine H. Shipp, Director of Risk Management
CFO: Jerry Heinzman, Senior Vice President and Chief Financial Officer
CMO: Shawn Howerton, M.D., Chief Executive Officer and President, Medical Staff
CIO: Kelly Lucas, Chief Information Officer
CHR: Michael W. Gilpin, Vice President Human Resources
CNO: Allison H. Taylor, R.N., Chief Nursing Officer and Vice President Clinical Services
Web address: www.sampsonrmc.org
Control: County–Government, nonfederal **Service:** General Medical and Surgical

Staffed Beds: 105 **Admissions:** 3233 **Census:** 38 **Outpatient Visits:** 76059 **Births:** 455 **Total Expense ($000):** 60036 **Payroll Expense ($000):** 23459 **Personnel:** 545

CLYDE—Haywood County

✸ **HAYWOOD REGIONAL MEDICAL CENTER (340184)**, 262 Leroy George Drive, Zip 28721–7430; tel. 828/456–7311 **A**1 10 **F**3 11 13 15 18 20 28 29 30 31 34 35 38 40 44 45 46 50 51 53 54 57 59 62 63 64 65 68 70 71 74 75 76 77 78 79 81 82 84 85 86 87 93 98 100 101 102 107 108 111 114 118 119 129 130 131 132 144 146 147 148 **P**8 **S** Duke LifePoint Healthcare, Brentwood, TN
Primary Contact: Rod Harkleroad, R.N., Chief Executive Officer
COO: Teresa Reynolds, Chief Operating Officer
CFO: Rose Coyne, Interim CFO
CMO: Tyson Smith, M.D., Chief Medical Officer
CIO: Greg Copen, Chief Information Officer
CHR: Janet Millsaps, Vice President Human Resources
Web address: www.haymed.org
Control: Corporation, Investor–owned, for–profit **Service:** General Medical and Surgical

Staffed Beds: 146 **Admissions:** 5144 **Census:** 55 **Outpatient Visits:** 254033 **Births:** 268 **Total Expense ($000):** 86446 **Payroll Expense ($000):** 30804 **Personnel:** 870

COLUMBUS—Polk County

✸ **ST. LUKE'S HOSPITAL (341322)**, 101 Hospital Drive, Zip 28722–6418; tel. 828/894–3311 **A**1 10 18 **F**3 11 15 29 30 34 35 40 45 56 57 59 64 70 75 77 79 81 85 87 91 93 98 103 104 107 108 115 119 130 133 135 146 **P**6 **S** Carolinas Healthcare System, Charlotte, NC
Primary Contact: James B. Bross, President
CFO: Elizabeth Presnell, Assistant Vice President of Finance
CMO: James Holleman, M.D., Chief of Staff
CIO: Nick Whichard, Chief Information Officer
CHR: Amy Norville, Vice President Support Services
CNO: Cathy Moore, Chief Nursing Officer
Web address: www.saintlukeshospital.com
Control: Other not–for–profit (including NFP Corporation) **Service:** General Medical and Surgical

Staffed Beds: 35 **Admissions:** 1557 **Census:** 21 **Outpatient Visits:** 22182 **Total Expense ($000):** 29043 **Payroll Expense ($000):** 11782 **Personnel:** 270

CONCORD—Cabarrus County

✸ **CAROLINAS HEALTHCARE SYSTEM NORTHEAST (340001)**, 920 Church Street North, Zip 28025–2983; tel. 704/403–3000 **A**1 2 10 **F**3 5 6 8 9 11 12 13 15 17 18 20 22 24 26 28 29 30 32 34 36 37 38 40 42 43 44 45 46 49 50 51 53 55 56 57 58 59 60 61 64 65 68 70 71 72 73 74 75 76 78 79 81 82 84 85 86 87 88 89 93 97 98 99 100 102 103 104 105 107 108 111 114 115 116 117 118 119 121 123 124 126 129 130 131 132 135 145 146 147 148 **P**6 **S** Carolinas Healthcare System, Charlotte, NC
Primary Contact: Phyllis A. Wingate, FACHE, President
COO: Bill Hubbard, Vice President, Operations
CFO: Rodney Ball, Vice President Finance
CMO: Dan Hagler, M.D., Vice President and Chief Medical Officer
CIO: Lisa Sykes, Manager, Information Services
CHR: Lesley Chambless, Assistant Vice President Workforce Relations
CNO: Kate Grew, MSN, Vice President/Chief Nurse Executive
Web address: www.carolinashealthcare.org/northeast
Control: Hospital district or authority, Government, nonfederal **Service:** General Medical and Surgical

Staffed Beds: 455 **Admissions:** 22838 **Census:** 286 **Outpatient Visits:** 365165 **Births:** 2847 **Total Expense ($000):** 429603 **Payroll Expense ($000):** 149801 **Personnel:** 2520

DANBURY—Stokes County

★ ◇ **PIONEER COMMUNITY HOSPITAL OF STOKES (341317)**, 1570 Highway 8 and 89 North, Zip 27016, Mailing Address: P.O. Box 10, Zip 27016–0010; tel. 336/593–2831, (Nonreporting) **A**10 18 21 **S** Pioneer Health Services, Magee, MS
Primary Contact: Pamela P. Tillman, R.N., Chief Executive Officer
COO: Tim Fontaine, Chief Operating Officer
CFO: Julie Gieger, Chief Financial Officer
CMO: Samuel C. Newsome, M.D., Chief of Staff
CIO: Jack York, Chief Information Officer
CHR: Lashaunda Lash, Manager Human Resources
CNO: Jane Pantano, R.N., Chief Nursing Officer
Web address: www.pchstokes.com
Control: Corporation, Investor–owned, for–profit **Service:** General Medical and Surgical

Staffed Beds: 65

Hospital, Medicare Provider Number, Address, Telephone, Approval, Facility, and Physician Codes, Health Care System

★ American Hospital Association (AHA) membership
☐ The Joint Commission accreditation
◯ Healthcare Facilities Accreditation Program
◇ DNV Healthcare Inc. accreditation
⇧ Center for Improvement in Healthcare Quality Accreditation
△ Commission on Accreditation of Rehabilitation Facilities (CARF) accreditation

NC

DUNN—Harnett County

☐ **HARNETT HEALTH SYSTEM (340071)**, 800 Tilghman Drive, Zip 28334–5599, Mailing Address: P.O. Box 1706, Zip 28335–1706; tel. 910/892–1000, (Includes CENTRAL HARTNETT HOSPITAL, 215 Brightwater Drive, Lillington, Zip 27546; tel. 910/892–1000) **A**1 10 12 13 **F**3 11 13 15 18 28 29 30 34 35 39 40 45 50 56 57 59 70 73 75 76 77 79 81 85 86 87 89 92 93 96 102 107 108 110 111 114 118 119 129 130 135 146 148 **S** Cape Fear Valley Health System, Fayetteville, NC
Primary Contact: Kevin Jackson, Interim Chief Executive Officer
COO: Kenneth E. Bryan, FACHE, President and Chief Executive Officer
CFO: Lynn Lambert, Chief Financial Officer
CIO: Tim Krieger, Director Information Systems
CHR: Sondra Davis, Vice President Human Resources & System Development
CNO: Vicki Allen, R.N., Vice President Patient Care Services and Chief Nursing Officer
Web address: www.myharnetthealth.org/
Control: Other not–for–profit (including NFP Corporation) **Service:** General Medical and Surgical

Staffed Beds: 96 **Admissions:** 6320 **Census:** 68 **Outpatient Visits:** 117806 **Births:** 599 **Total Expense ($000):** 98781 **Payroll Expense ($000):** 40357 **Personnel:** 727

DURHAM—Durham County

☒ **DUKE REGIONAL HOSPITAL (340155)**, 3643 North Roxboro Street, Zip 27704–2763; tel. 919/470–4000 **A**1 3 5 10 **F**3 8 11 12 13 15 17 18 20 22 24 26 29 30 31 34 35 40 44 45 47 48 50 51 57 58 59 60 64 66 68 70 73 74 75 76 77 78 79 80 81 82 84 85 86 87 90 93 96 98 100 102 107 108 110 111 115 118 119 120 121 123 124 126 130 131 132 146 147 148 **P**6 **S** Duke University Health System, Durham, NC
Primary Contact: Kathleen B. Galbraith, FACHE, President
COO: A. Mitch Babb, Vice President, Operations
CFO: Jonathan B. Hoy, Chief Financial Officer
CMO: Barbara Griffith, M.D., Chief Medical Officer
CIO: Terry Mears, Director Information Systems
CHR: Dexter Nolley, Chief Human Resources Officer
CNO: Victoria K. Orto, R.N., Chief Nursing and Patient Care Services Officer
Web address: www.dukehealth.org
Control: Other not–for–profit (including NFP Corporation) **Service:** General Medical and Surgical

Staffed Beds: 208 **Admissions:** 16060 **Census:** 208 **Outpatient Visits:** 114108 **Births:** 2358 **Total Expense ($000):** 286028 **Payroll Expense ($000):** 124241 **Personnel:** 1884

☒ **DUKE UNIVERSITY HOSPITAL (340030)**, 2301 Erwin Road, Zip 27705–4699, Mailing Address: P.O. Box 3814, Zip 27710–3708; tel. 919/684–8111, (Includes DUKE CHILDREN'S HOSPITAL & HEALTH CENTER, 2301 Erwin Road, Zip 27710–0001, Mailing Address: PO Box 3708, Zip 27702; tel. 919/684–8111) **A**1 2 3 5 8 10 **F**3 5 6 7 8 9 11 12 13 15 17 18 19 20 21 22 23 24 25 26 27 28 29 30 31 32 34 35 36 37 39 40 41 43 44 45 46 47 48 49 50 52 53 54 55 56 57 58 59 60 61 63 64 65 66 68 70 72 73 74 75 76 77 78 79 80 81 82 84 85 86 87 88 89 91 92 93 94 96 97 98 99 100 101 102 103 104 107 108 110 111 112 114 115 116 117 118 119 120 121 123 124 126 127 129 130 131 132 134 135 136 137 138 139 140 141 142 145 146 147 148 **P**6 **S** Duke University Health System, Durham, NC
Primary Contact: Kevin W. Sowers, R.N., MSN, President
COO: Carolyn Carpenter, Chief Operating Officer
CFO: Sabrina Olsen, Chief Financial Officer
CMO: Lisa C. Pickett, M.D., Chief Medical Officer
CIO: Jeffrey Ferranti, M.D., Chief Information Officer
CHR: Deborah Page, Chief Human Resources Officer
CNO: Mary Ann Fuchs, R.N., Vice President Patient Care and System Chief Nurse Executive
Web address: www.dukehealth.org
Control: Other not–for–profit (including NFP Corporation) **Service:** General Medical and Surgical

Staffed Beds: 905 **Admissions:** 40326 **Census:** 750 **Outpatient Visits:** 1063837 **Births:** 3127 **Total Expense ($000):** 2056429 **Payroll Expense ($000):** 658197 **Personnel:** 10200

DURHAM REGIONAL HOSPITAL See Duke Regional Hospital

☒ **DURHAM VETERANS AFFAIRS MEDICAL CENTER**, 508 Fulton Street, Zip 27705–3897; tel. 919/286–0411, (Nonreporting) **A**1 3 5 8 **S** Department of Veterans Affairs, Washington, DC
Primary Contact: DeAnne Seekins, Director
COO: Sara Haigh, Associate Director
CFO: David Kuboushek, Chief, Fiscal Service
CMO: John D. Shelburne, M.D., Chief of Staff
CIO: Toby Dickerson, Chief Information Resources Management Services
CHR: Jerry Freeman, Chief, Human Resources Management Services
CNO: Gregory S. Eagerton, Ph.D., Nurse Executive
Web address: www.durham.va.gov/
Control: Veterans Affairs, Government, federal **Service:** General Medical and Surgical

Staffed Beds: 265

☐ **NORTH CAROLINA SPECIALTY HOSPITAL (340049)**, 3916 Ben Franklin Boulevard, Zip 27704–2383, Mailing Address: PO Box 15819, Zip 27704–2383; tel. 919/956–9300 **A**1 10 **F**3 29 30 51 64 79 81 82 85 86 87 107 119 126 130 131 148 **S** National Surgical Healthcare, Chicago, IL
Primary Contact: Randi L. Shults, Chief Executive Officer
CFO: Bill Wilson, Chief Financial Officer
CMO: Thomas Dimmig, M.D., Medical Director
CHR: Maggie Glenn, Director Human Resources
CNO: John Medlin, Chief Nursing Officer
Web address: www.ncspecialty.com
Control: Partnership, Investor–owned, for–profit **Service:** Surgical

Staffed Beds: 18 **Admissions:** 1568 **Census:** 9 **Outpatient Visits:** 8257 **Births:** 0 **Total Expense ($000):** 36592 **Payroll Expense ($000):** 10878 **Personnel:** 196

☒ **SELECT SPECIALTY HOSPITAL–DURHAM (342018)**, 3643 North Roxboro Road, 6th Floor, Zip 27704–2702; tel. 919/470–9137, (Nonreporting) **A**1 10 **S** Select Medical Corporation, Mechanicsburg, PA
Primary Contact: Theresa Hunkins, R.N., Chief Executive Officer
Web address: www.selectspecialtyhospitals.com/company/locations/durham.aspx
Control: Corporation, Investor–owned, for–profit **Service:** Long–Term Acute Care hospital

Staffed Beds: 30

EDEN—Rockingham County

★ ◇ **MOREHEAD MEMORIAL HOSPITAL (340060)**, 117 East King's Highway, Zip 27288–5201; tel. 336/623–9711, (Total facility includes 121 beds in nursing home–type unit) **A**2 10 21 **F**3 11 13 15 18 26 29 30 34 35 40 45 47 48 49 50 57 59 64 68 70 74 76 77 78 79 81 82 85 87 89 90 93 97 107 108 110 111 114 118 119 122 123 128 129 130 132 135 143 144 146 147 148 **P**6 **S** Novant Health, Winston Salem, NC
Primary Contact: Dana Weston, Chief Executive Officer
CFO: Robert G. Hetrick, Vice President Finance and Chief Financial Officer
CHR: Tom Stevens, Director Personnel
Web address: www.morehead.org
Control: Other not–for–profit (including NFP Corporation) **Service:** General Medical and Surgical

Staffed Beds: 188 **Admissions:** 3390 **Census:** 135 **Outpatient Visits:** 167856 **Births:** 518 **Total Expense ($000):** 81102 **Payroll Expense ($000):** 33586 **Personnel:** 540

EDENTON—Chowan County

☒ **VIDANT CHOWAN HOSPITAL (341318)**, 211 Virginia Road, Zip 27932–9668, Mailing Address: P.O. Box 629, Zip 27932–0629; tel. 252/482–8451 **A**1 3 10 18 **F**3 11 13 15 18 19 28 29 30 31 34 35 40 45 46 56 57 59 64 70 74 75 76 77 78 79 81 82 85 89 93 107 108 110 111 114 119 130 132 146 147 148 **S** Vidant Health, Greenville, NC
Primary Contact: Jeffrey Sackrison, President
CFO: Brian Harvill, Vice President Financial Services
CMO: William Hope, IV, Chief of Medical Staff
CIO: Brian White, Director Strategic Operations
CHR: Nicole Spell, Director Human Resources
CNO: Cindy Coker, Vice President, Patient Care Services
Web address: www.vidanthealth.com
Control: Other not–for–profit (including NFP Corporation) **Service:** General Medical and Surgical

Staffed Beds: 19 **Admissions:** 1383 **Census:** 13 **Outpatient Visits:** 41901 **Births:** 198 **Total Expense ($000):** 40999 **Payroll Expense ($000):** 16757 **Personnel:** 300

ELIZABETH CITY—Pasquotank County

★ ◇ **SENTARA ALBEMARLE MEDICAL CENTER (340109)**, 1144 North Road Street, Zip 27909–3473, Mailing Address: P.O. Box 1587, Zip 27906–1587; tel. 252/335–0531 **A**10 21 **F**3 11 13 15 17 18 20 22 28 29 30 31 34 35 36 37 38 39 40 41 44 45 46 47 48 49 50 51 53 54 55 56 57 58 59 60 61 64 65 68 70 74 75 76 77 78 79 81 84 85 86 87 91 92 93 94 96 97 100 102 103 107 108 110 111 114 116 117 118 119 121 126 129 130 131 132 135 142 144 146 147 148 **P**6 **S** Sentara Healthcare, Norfolk, VA
Primary Contact: Coleen F. Santa Ana, President
CFO: Craig Lewis, Chief Financial Officer
CMO: Charles Nicholson, Vice President, Medical Affairs
CHR: Deborah Ferguson, Director, Human Resources
CNO: Jaime Carroll, R.N., Vice President Nursing
Web address: www.albemarlehealth.org
Control: Other not–for–profit (including NFP Corporation) **Service:** General Medical and Surgical

Staffed Beds: 83 **Admissions:** 5228 **Census:** 57 **Outpatient Visits:** 134921 **Births:** 603 **Total Expense ($000):** 93185 **Payroll Expense ($000):** 35608 **Personnel:** 706

ELIZABETHTOWN—Bladen County

BLADEN COUNTY HOSPITAL See Cape Fear Valley – Bladen County Hospital

✠ **CAPE FEAR VALLEY – BLADEN COUNTY HOSPITAL (341315)**, 501 South Poplar Street, Zip 28337–9375, Mailing Address: P.O. Box 398, Zip 28337–0398; tel. 910/862–5100 **A**1 10 18 **F**3 11 13 14 15 28 29 30 34 35 40 45 50 54 59 64 68 70 76 77 81 90 91 93 97 107 114 119 129 133 135 144 146 147 **P**6 **S** Cape Fear Valley Health System, Fayetteville, NC
Primary Contact: Daniel R. Weatherly, Interim Chief Executive Officer
CFO: Sandra Williams, Chief Financial Officer
CMO: Pearly Graham Hoskins, M.D., President Medical Staff
CIO: Craig Kellum, Director Management Information Systems
CHR: Ginger Parks, Director Human Resources
Web address: www.bchn.org
Control: Other not–for–profit (including NFP Corporation) **Service:** General Medical and Surgical

> **Staffed Beds:** 25 **Admissions:** 878 **Census:** 9 **Outpatient Visits:** 36963 **Births:** 194 **Total Expense ($000):** 34928 **Payroll Expense ($000):** 19027 **Personnel:** 292

ELKIN—Surry County

✠ **HUGH CHATHAM MEMORIAL HOSPITAL (340097)**, 180 Parkwood Drive, Zip 28621–2430, Mailing Address: P.O. Box 560, Zip 28621–0560; tel. 336/527–7000 **A**1 10 **F**3 11 13 15 28 29 30 34 40 45 49 53 57 59 62 64 70 76 79 81 85 87 91 93 96 97 107 108 110 111 114 118 119 120 121 125 127 130 131 132 133 135 144 146 147 148 **P**6 **S** Alliant Management Services, Louisville, KY
Primary Contact: Paul Hammes, Chief Executive Officer
COO: Mary Blackburn, Vice President Operations and Chief Practice Officer
CFO: Donald E. Trippel, Chief Financial Officer
CMO: Dominick Carbone, M.D., Chief of Staff
CIO: Lee Powe, Director Management Information Systems
CHR: Kathy Poteate, Interim Director Human Resources
CNO: Paula Moore, R.N., Chief Clinical Officer
Web address: www.hughchatham.org
Control: Other not–for–profit (including NFP Corporation) **Service:** General Medical and Surgical

> **Staffed Beds:** 81 **Admissions:** 4464 **Census:** 44 **Outpatient Visits:** 69643 **Births:** 575 **Total Expense ($000):** 64263 **Payroll Expense ($000):** 21770 **Personnel:** 665

FAYETTEVILLE—Cumberland County

✠ △ **CAPE FEAR VALLEY MEDICAL CENTER (340028)**, 1638 Owen Drive, Zip 28304–3431, Mailing Address: P.O. Box 2000, Zip 28302–2000; tel. 910/615–4000, (Includes SOUTHEASTERN REGIONAL REHABILITATION CENTER ; BEHAVIORAL HEALTH CARE OF CAPE FEAR VALLEY HEALTH SYSTEM, 711 Executive Place, Zip 28301; tel. 910/615–3700; CAPE FEAR VALLEY REHABILITATION CENTER, 1638 Owen Drive, Zip 28304; tel. 910/615–4000) **A**1 2 3 5 7 10 12 13 **F**3 4 5 7 12 13 14 15 17 18 20 22 24 26 28 29 30 31 34 35 38 39 40 41 43 44 46 49 53 54 55 56 57 59 61 64 65 68 70 72 73 74 75 76 77 78 79 81 82 84 85 86 87 88 89 90 91 92 93 96 97 98 99 100 101 102 103 104 105 106 107 108 109 110 111 114 115 116 117 118 119 120 121 122 123 124 126 127 129 130 132 135 143 144 146 147 148 **P**6 **S** Cape Fear Valley Health System, Fayetteville, NC
Primary Contact: Michael Nagowski, Chief Executive Officer
COO: Daniel R. Weatherly, Chief Operating Officer
CFO: Sandra Williams, Chief Financial Officer
CMO: Samuel A. Fleishman, M.D., Chief Medical Officer
CIO: Phillip E. Wood, Jr., Chief Information Officer
CHR: William B. Pryor, Chief Human Resources Officer
CNO: Deborah Marshburn, R.N., Chief Nursing Executive
Web address: www.capefearvalley.com
Control: Other not–for–profit (including NFP Corporation) **Service:** General Medical and Surgical

> **Staffed Beds:** 592 **Admissions:** 30150 **Census:** 447 **Outpatient Visits:** 425695 **Births:** 4595 **Total Expense ($000):** 632430 **Payroll Expense ($000):** 294934 **Personnel:** 4641

✠ **FAYETTEVILLE VETERANS AFFAIRS MEDICAL CENTER**, 2300 Ramsey Street, Zip 28301–3899; tel. 910/488–2120, (Nonreporting) **A**1 3 5 **S** Department of Veterans Affairs, Washington, DC
Primary Contact: Elizabeth Goolsby, Director
COO: James Galkowski, Associate Director for Operations
CFO: Patrick Bullard, Chief Financial Officer
CMO: Greg Antoine, M.D., Chief of Staff
CIO: Kenneth Williams, Chief Information Officer
CHR: Joseph Whaley, Chief, Human Resources Management Service
CNO: Joyce Alexander–Hines, R.N., Associate Director, Patient Care Services
Web address: www.fayettevillenc.va.gov
Control: Veterans Affairs, Government, federal **Service:** General Medical and Surgical

> **Staffed Beds:** 58

□ **HIGHSMITH–RAINEY SPECIALTY HOSPITAL (342014)**, 150 Robeson Street, Zip 28301–5570; tel. 910/615–1000 **A**1 10 **F**1 3 11 29 30 35 39 50 51 58 68 70 81 85 107 114 119 130 144 146 148 **P**6 **S** Cape Fear Valley Health System, Fayetteville, NC
Primary Contact: Kevin Jackson, On Site Administrator
Web address: www.capefearvalley.com
Control: Other not–for–profit (including NFP Corporation) **Service:** Long–Term Acute Care hospital

> **Staffed Beds:** 60 **Admissions:** 336 **Census:** 48 **Outpatient Visits:** 35868 **Births:** 0 **Total Expense ($000):** 34677 **Payroll Expense ($000):** 19400 **Personnel:** 312

VETERANS AFFAIRS MEDICAL CENTER See Fayetteville Veterans Affairs Medical Center

FORT BRAGG—Cumberland County

✠ **WOMACK ARMY MEDICAL CENTER**, Normandy Drive, Zip 28307–5000; tel. 910/907–6000, (Nonreporting) **A**1 3 5 **S** Department of the Army, Office of the Surgeon General, Falls Church, VA
Primary Contact: Colonel Ronald Stephens, Commander
CIO: Mary Peters, Chief Information Officer
Web address: www.wamc.amedd.army.mil/
Control: Army, Government, federal **Service:** General Medical and Surgical

> **Staffed Beds:** 156

FRANKLIN—Macon County

✠ **ANGEL MEDICAL CENTER (341326)**, 120 Riverview Street, Zip 28734–2612, Mailing Address: P.O. Box 1209, Zip 28744–0569; tel. 828/524–8411 **A**1 10 18 **F**3 11 13 15 18 28 29 30 31 34 35 40 44 45 47 49 50 54 57 59 64 70 76 77 78 79 81 85 86 87 93 96 97 107 108 110 111 114 119 127 130 131 132 133 135 144 146 147 148 **P**6 **S** Mission Health System, Asheville, NC
Primary Contact: Karen S. Gorby, R.N., MSN, FACHE, President and Chief Nursing Officer
COO: Martin Wadewitz, Chief Operations Officer/ Vice President, Operations
CFO: George Kimbro, Vice President Finance
CIO: Ed Coye, Director Information Technology Mission Health System Hospitals
CHR: Teresa Mallonee, Director Human Resources
Web address: www.angelmed.org
Control: Other not–for–profit (including NFP Corporation) **Service:** General Medical and Surgical

> **Staffed Beds:** 43 **Admissions:** 1805 **Census:** 18 **Outpatient Visits:** 98525 **Births:** 388 **Total Expense ($000):** 57256 **Payroll Expense ($000):** 17284 **Personnel:** 298

GARNER—Wake County

□ **STRATEGIC BEHAVIORAL HEALTH – RALEIGH (344028)**, 3200 Waterfield Drive, Zip 27529–7727; tel. 919/800–4400, (Nonreporting) **A**1 10 **S** Strategic Behavioral Health, LLC, Memphis, TN
Primary Contact: Matt Doyle, Chief Executive Officer
CMO: Karen Miles, M.D., Medical Director
CHR: Christina Meeker, Director Human Resources
CNO: Shawanna Royal, R.N., Director Nursing
Web address: www.sbcraleigh.com/
Control: Corporation, Investor–owned, for–profit **Service:** Children's hospital psychiatric

> **Staffed Beds:** 50

GASTONIA—Gaston County

✠ **CAROMONT REGIONAL MEDICAL CENTER (340032)**, 2525 Court Drive, Zip 28054–2140, Mailing Address: P.O. Box 1747, Zip 28053–1747; tel. 704/834–2000 **A**1 2 10 **F**3 13 15 17 18 20 22 24 26 28 29 30 31 34 35 40 42 43 44 45 49 50 53 54 55 57 58 59 60 64 68 70 71 72 73 74 75 76 78 79 81 82 84 87 89 91 92 93 94 96 98 99 100 101 104 107 110 111 114 115 116 117 118 119 120 121 123 124 126 129 130 131 132 135 146 147 148
Primary Contact: Douglas R. Luckett, President and Chief Executive Officer
COO: Kathleen Besson, Executive Vice President and Chief Operating Officer
CFO: David O'Connor, Executive Vice President and Chief Financial Officer
CMO: Todd Davis, M.D., Vice President Medical Affairs, Patient Safety Officer
CIO: Mike Johnson, Vice President, Chief Information Officer
CHR: Elizabeth McCraw, Vice President, Human Resources
CNO: Scott E. Wells, MSN, Vice President Patient Care Services
Web address: www.caromont.org
Control: Other not–for–profit (including NFP Corporation) **Service:** General Medical and Surgical

> **Staffed Beds:** 423 **Admissions:** 20064 **Census:** 248 **Outpatient Visits:** 358677 **Births:** 2248 **Total Expense ($000):** 347972 **Payroll Expense ($000):** 140230 **Personnel:** 2831

GASTON MEMORIAL HOSPITAL See CaroMont Regional Medical Center

GOLDSBORO—Wayne County

☐ **CHERRY HOSPITAL (344026)**, 201 Stevens Mill Road, Zip 27530–1057; tel. 919/731–3200 **A**1 3 10 **F**30 39 98 99 103 108 130 143 146
Primary Contact: J. Luckey Welsh, Jr., Chief Executive Officer
CFO: Susie Sherrod Sanders, Budget Officer
CMO: Jim Mayo, M.D., Clinical Director
CIO: Mike Letchworth, Manager Information Systems
CHR: Carol Thornton, Director Human Resources
CNO: Cherie Custer, Chief Nursing Officer
Web address: www.cherryhospital.org
Control: State–Government, nonfederal **Service:** Psychiatric

Staffed Beds: 197 **Admissions:** 675 **Census:** 178 **Outpatient Visits:** 676 **Births:** 0 **Total Expense ($000):** 80370 **Payroll Expense ($000):** 48694 **Personnel:** 970

⊞ **WAYNE MEMORIAL HOSPITAL (340010)**, 2700 Wayne Memorial Drive, Zip 27534–9494, Mailing Address: P.O. Box 8001, Zip 27533–8001; tel. 919/736–1110 **A**1 3 10 **F**3 8 13 15 18 20 22 28 29 30 31 34 35 39 40 47 49 50 57 58 59 60 64 65 68 70 71 73 74 76 77 78 79 80 81 85 86 89 92 93 96 98 100 101 102 103 107 108 110 111 114 118 119 126 129 130 132 134 135 142 143 145 146 147 148 **P**6 **S** UNC Health Care, Chapel Hill, NC
Primary Contact: Robert A. Enders, Jr., Interim President and Chief Executive Officer
COO: Thomas A. Bradshaw, Vice President Operations
CFO: Rebecca W. Craig, Vice President and Chief Financial Officer
CIO: Lori Cole, Director Information Technology
CHR: Richard K. Rogers, FACHE, Vice President Human Resources
CNO: Shirley S. Harkey, FACHE, R.N., Vice President, Patient Services
Web address: www.waynehealth.org
Control: Other not–for–profit (including NFP Corporation) **Service:** General Medical and Surgical

Staffed Beds: 274 **Admissions:** 10250 **Census:** 130 **Outpatient Visits:** 242259 **Births:** 1355 **Total Expense ($000):** 211719 **Payroll Expense ($000):** 81806 **Personnel:** 1583

GREENSBORO—Guilford County

⊞ **KINDRED HOSPITAL–GREENSBORO (342012)**, 2401 Southside Boulevard, Zip 27406–3311; tel. 336/271–2800, (Nonreporting) **A**1 10 **S** Kindred Healthcare, Louisville, KY
Primary Contact: Christopher Haynes, Chief Executive Officer
CMO: Percy E. Jones, M.D., Chief of Staff
CIO: Little Shuford, Manager Medical Information
CHR: Michele Roberts, Hospital Recruiter
Web address: www.khgreensboro.com
Control: Corporation, Investor–owned, for–profit **Service:** Long–Term Acute Care hospital

Staffed Beds: 124

⊞ △ **MOSES H. CONE MEMORIAL HOSPITAL (340091)**, 1200 North Elm Street, Zip 27401–1020; tel. 336/832–7000, (Includes ANNIE PENN HOSPITAL, 618 South Main Street, Reidsville, Zip 27320–5094; tel. 336/951–4000; Mickey Foster, President; BEHAVIORAL HEALTH CENTER, 700 Walter Reed Drive, Zip 27403–1129; tel. 336/832–9600; Debbie Green, R.N., MSN, President; CONE HEALTH, 1200 North Elm Street, Zip 27401; tel. 336/832–7000; Judith A. Schanel, R.N., MSN, FACHE, Chief Operating Officer; WESLEY LONG COMMUNITY HOSPITAL, 501 North Elam Avenue, Zip 27403; tel. 336/832–1000; Paul A. Jeffrey, President; WOMEN'S HOSPITAL OF GREENSBORO, 801 Green Valley Road, Zip 27408; tel. 336/832–6500), (Total facility includes 92 beds in nursing home–type unit) **A**1 2 3 5 7 10 **F**3 5 7 8 11 12 13 15 17 19 20 22 24 26 28 29 30 31 32 34 35 36 37 39 40 41 42 43 44 45 46 47 49 50 54 55 56 57 58 59 60 61 63 64 66 68 70 72 74 75 76 77 78 79 80 81 82 83 84 85 86 87 88 89 90 92 93 95 96 97 98 99 100 101 102 103 104 107 108 110 111 114 115 117 118 119 120 121 123 124 126 128 129 130 131 132 134 135 144 145 146 147 148 **P**8 **S** Carolinas Healthcare System, Charlotte, NC
Primary Contact: Mickey Foster, President
COO: Terry Akin, President and Chief Operating Officer
CFO: Jeffrey Jones, Chief Financial Officer
CMO: William Bowman, M.D., Vice President Medical Affairs
CIO: Steve Horsley, Vice President and Chief Information Officer
CHR: Noel F. Burt, Ph.D., Chief Human Resources Officer
CNO: Theresa M. Brodrick, R.N., Executive Vice President and Chief Nursing Officer
Web address: www.conehealth.com/locations/moses-cone-hospital/
Control: Other not–for–profit (including NFP Corporation) **Service:** General Medical and Surgical

Staffed Beds: 954 **Admissions:** 51303 **Census:** 670 **Outpatient Visits:** 866766 **Births:** 6120 **Total Expense ($000):** 1167029 **Payroll Expense ($000):** 421646 **Personnel:** 8316

⊞ **SELECT SPECIALTY HOSPITAL–GREENSBORO (342020)**, 1200 North Elm Street, 5th Floor, Zip 27401–1004; tel. 336/832–8571, (Nonreporting) **A**1 10 **S** Select Medical Corporation, Mechanicsburg, PA
Primary Contact: Deana Knight, Chief Executive Officer
CHR: Karen Tracey, Chief Human Resources
CNO: Robin Clark, Chief Nursing Officer
Web address: www.selectspecialtyhospitals.com/company/locations/greensboro.aspx
Control: Corporation, Investor–owned, for–profit **Service:** Long–Term Acute Care hospital

Staffed Beds: 30

GREENVILLE—Pitt County

PITT COUNTY MEMORIAL HOSPITAL See Vidant Medical Center

⊞ △ **VIDANT MEDICAL CENTER (340040)**, 2100 Stantonsburg Road, Zip 27834–2818, Mailing Address: P.O. Box 6028, Zip 27835–6028; tel. 252/847–4100, (Includes JAMES AND CONNIE MAYNARD CHILDREN'S HOSPITAL, 2101 Stantonsburg Road, Zip 27834–2817; tel. 252/847–5712; UNIVERSITY HEALTH SYSTEMS CHILDREN'S HOSPITAL, 2100 Stantonsburg Road, Mailing Address: PO Box 6028, Zip 27835–6028; tel. 252/847–4100) **A**1 2 3 5 7 8 10 **F**3 7 12 13 14 17 18 19 20 21 22 23 24 25 26 27 28 29 30 31 34 35 38 40 41 42 43 44 45 46 47 48 49 50 51 52 55 56 57 58 59 60 61 64 65 68 70 72 75 76 77 78 79 80 81 82 83 84 85 86 87 88 89 90 92 93 94 95 96 97 98 100 101 102 103 104 107 108 111 114 115 116 117 118 119 124 126 129 130 131 132 134 135 138 139 143 145 146 147 148 **P**6 **S** Vidant Health, Greenville, NC
Primary Contact: William Brian Floyd, President
CFO: David S. Hughes, Chief Financial Officer
CMO: Paul Shackelford, M.D., Chief Medical Officer
CIO: Donnette Herring, Chief Information Officer
CHR: Tyree Walker, Chief Human Resources Officer
CNO: Linda D. Hofler, Ph.D., Senior Vice President, Nurse Executive
Web address: www.https://www.vidanthealth.com/
Control: Other not–for–profit (including NFP Corporation) **Service:** General Medical and Surgical

Staffed Beds: 909 **Admissions:** 38925 **Census:** 677 **Outpatient Visits:** 297087 **Births:** 3690 **Total Expense ($000):** 974709 **Payroll Expense ($000):** 340219 **Personnel:** 6047

WALTER B. JONES ALCOHOL AND DRUG ABUSE TREATMENT CENTER (344024), 2577 West Fifth Street, Zip 27834–7813; tel. 252/830–3426, (Nonreporting) **A**10
Primary Contact: Ben Gregory, Director
CFO: Jo Ann Whitfield, Business Officer
CMO: Sonya Longest, M.D., Clinical Director
CNO: Cecelia Karas, Director of Nursing
Web address: www.ncdhhs.gov
Control: State–Government, nonfederal **Service:** Alcoholism and other chemical dependency

Staffed Beds: 80

HAMLET—Richmond County

⊞ **SANDHILLS REGIONAL MEDICAL CENTER (340106)**, 1000 West Hamlet Avenue, Zip 28345–4522, Mailing Address: P.O. Box 1109, Zip 28345–1109; tel. 910/205–8000, (Nonreporting) **A**1 10 **S** Quorum Health, Brentwood, TN
Primary Contact: David Clay, Chief Executive Officer
CFO: Patrick Sloan, Chief Financial Officer
CMO: Charlita Mangrum, M.D., Chief of Staff
CIO: Regina Yingling, Supervisor
CHR: Della Connor, Director Human Resource
CNO: Brenda Ewing, Chief Nursing Officer
Web address: www.sandhillsregional.com
Control: Corporation, Investor–owned, for–profit **Service:** General Medical and Surgical

Staffed Beds: 64

HENDERSON—Vance County

⊞ **MARIA PARHAM MEDICAL CENTER (340132)**, 566 Ruin Creek Road, Zip 27536–2927; tel. 252/438–4143 **A**1 2 3 10 **F**3 11 13 15 18 20 28 29 30 31 34 35 39 40 44 45 46 48 49 50 54 57 59 60 62 64 68 70 74 75 76 77 78 79 80 81 82 85 86 87 90 91 92 93 94 96 97 107 108 110 111 114 118 119 120 121 123 129 130 131 132 135 146 147 148 **P**6 **S** Duke LifePoint Healthcare, Brentwood, TN
Primary Contact: Bert Beard, Chief Executive Officer
CFO: Jim Chatman, Chief Financial Officer
CIO: Randy Williams, Director Management Information Systems
Web address: www.mariaparham.com
Control: Partnership, Investor–owned, for–profit **Service:** General Medical and Surgical

Staffed Beds: 102 **Admissions:** 5362 **Census:** 64 **Outpatient Visits:** 133734 **Births:** 567 **Total Expense ($000):** 87553 **Payroll Expense ($000):** 29384

Many Facility Codes have changed. Please refer to the AHA Guide Code Chart. © 2016 AHA Guide

HENDERSONVILLE—Henderson County

★ ◇ **MARGARET R. PARDEE MEMORIAL HOSPITAL (340017)**, 800 North Justice Street, Zip 28791–3410; tel. 828/696–1000 **A**2 3 10 21 **F**3 4 5 11 13 15 18 22 28 29 30 31 34 35 36 38 39 40 44 45 46 47 48 49 50 54 56 57 58 59 62 63 65 68 69 70 74 75 76 77 78 79 81 82 85 86 87 89 93 94 97 98 100 101 102 103 104 107 108 110 111 114 115 118 119 120 121 123 129 130 131 132 135 143 144 146 147 148 **P**6 **S** UNC Health Care, Chapel Hill, NC
Primary Contact: James M. Kirby, II, President and Chief Executive Officer
CFO: Alan House, Chief Financial Officer
CMO: Robert Kiskaddon, M.D., Chief Medical Officer
CHR: Hope Reynolds, Executive Director Human Resources and Support Services
CNO: Denise Lucas, R.N., Vice President Clinical Services and Chief Nursing Officer
Web address: www.pardeehospital.org
Control: County–Government, nonfederal **Service:** General Medical and Surgical

Staffed Beds: 138 **Admissions:** 7561 **Census:** 80 **Outpatient Visits:** 242514 **Births:** 310 **Total Expense ($000):** 165036 **Payroll Expense ($000):** 63415 **Personnel:** 1065

⊠ ○ **PARK RIDGE HEALTH (340023)**, 100 Hospital Drive, Zip 28792–5272; tel. 828/684–8501 **A**1 2 10 11 19 **F**3 11 13 15 18 26 28 29 30 31 32 34 35 39 40 45 46 47 48 49 50 54 57 59 62 65 68 70 71 74 75 76 77 78 79 80 81 82 85 87 93 94 97 98 101 102 103 104 105 107 108 110 111 114 115 119 129 130 131 132 135 142 146 147 148 **P**6 **S** Adventist Health System Sunbelt Health Care Corporation, Altamonte Springs, FL
Primary Contact: Jimm Bunch, President and Chief Executive Officer
CFO: Wendi Barber, Vice President Finance and Chief Financial Officer
CMO: Carlo Mainardi, M.D., Vice President Medical Affairs and Chief Medical Officer
CIO: Lee Strickland, Regional Director Information Technology
CHR: Sharon J. Campbell, Director, Human Resources
CNO: Craig Lindsey, R.N., Vice President Clinical Services/Chief Nursing Officer
Web address: www.parkridgehealth.org
Control: Other not–for–profit (including NFP Corporation) **Service:** General Medical and Surgical

Staffed Beds: 95 **Admissions:** 4125 **Census:** 53 **Outpatient Visits:** 368320 **Births:** 621 **Total Expense ($000):** 157142 **Payroll Expense ($000):** 64569 **Personnel:** 1136

HICKORY—Catawba County

⊠ △ **CATAWBA VALLEY MEDICAL CENTER (340143)**, 810 Fairgrove Church Road S.E., Zip 28602–9643; tel. 828/326–3000 **A**1 2 5 7 10 **F**3 5 11 12 13 15 18 20 22 26 28 29 30 31 33 34 35 39 40 44 45 49 50 51 53 54 56 57 58 59 61 64 65 68 70 71 73 74 75 77 78 79 81 84 85 86 87 90 91 92 93 96 97 98 100 101 102 103 104 107 108 109 110 111 114 115 117 118 119 120 121 122 123 124 126 129 130 131 132 135 143 144 145 146 147 148 **P**3 8
Primary Contact: J. Anthony Rose, President and Chief Executive Officer
COO: Edward L. Beard, R.N., Chief Operating Officer and Chief Nursing Officer
CFO: David J. Boone, Senior Vice President, Finance
CMO: Andrew Chesson, Chief Medical Officer
CIO: Tim Blanchat, Chief Information Officer
CHR: Phyllis M. Johnston, Vice President
CNO: Edward L. Beard, R.N., Chief Operating Officer and Chief Nursing Officer
Web address: www.catawbavalleymc.org
Control: County–Government, nonfederal **Service:** General Medical and Surgical

Staffed Beds: 250 **Admissions:** 10137 **Census:** 130 **Outpatient Visits:** 221577 **Births:** 2071 **Total Expense ($000):** 220984 **Payroll Expense ($000):** 97760 **Personnel:** 1420

⊠ **FRYE REGIONAL MEDICAL CENTER (340116)**, 420 North Center Street, Zip 28601–5049; tel. 828/322–6070, (Includes FRYE REGIONAL MEDICAL CENTER–SOUTH CAMPUS, One Third Avenue N.W., Zip 28601, Mailing Address: P.O. Box 369, Zip 28603; tel. 704/315–5777) **A**1 2 10 **F**3 11 12 13 15 17 18 20 22 24 26 28 29 30 31 34 35 37 40 44 45 46 49 54 57 59 64 70 72 74 75 76 77 78 79 81 82 85 86 87 89 90 93 96 98 101 103 107 108 110 111 114 115 119 126 128 129 130 131 132 144 146 147 148 **P**6 **S** Duke LifePoint Healthcare, Brentwood, TN
Primary Contact: Garfield Atchison, Chief Executive Officer
COO: Rich Ellis, Chief Operating Officer
CMO: Frank C. Smeeks, M.D., Chief Medical Officer
CHR: Elizabeth Elich, Vice President Human Resources
Web address: www.fryemedctr.com
Control: Corporation, Investor–owned, for–profit **Service:** General Medical and Surgical

Staffed Beds: 256 **Admissions:** 10599 **Census:** 157 **Outpatient Visits:** 139848 **Births:** 382 **Personnel:** 1344

HIGH POINT—Guilford County

⊠ △ **HIGH POINT REGIONAL HEALTH SYSTEM (340004)**, 601 North Elm Street, Zip 27262–4398, Mailing Address: P.O. Box HP–5, Zip 27261–1899; tel. 336/878–6000 **A**1 2 7 10 **F**3 4 5 7 8 11 12 13 15 17 18 20 22 24 26 28 29 30 31 34 35 38 39 40 44 45 47 48 49 50 51 52 53 54 55 57 58 59 60 61 62 64 66 68 70 71 73 74 75 76 77 78 79 80 81 82 84 85 86 87 90 91 92 93 96 97 98 100 101 102 103 104 105 107 108 109 110 111 114 115 116 117 118 119 120 121 123 124 126 129 130 131 132 135 144 145 146 147 148 **P**6 **S** UNC Health Care, Chapel Hill, NC
Primary Contact: Ernest L. Bovio, Jr., Chief Executive Officer
COO: Gregory W. Taylor, M.D., Vice President and Chief Operating Officer
CFO: Kimberly Crews, Vice President Finance and Chief Financial Officer
CMO: L. Dale Williams, M.D., Vice President and Chief Medical Director
CIO: Nancy Waters, Interim Chief Information Officer
CHR: Katherine Burns, Vice President Human Resources
CNO: Tammi Erving–Mengel, R.N., Vice President, Chief Nursing Officer
Web address: www.highpointregional.com
Control: Other not–for–profit (including NFP Corporation) **Service:** General Medical and Surgical

Staffed Beds: 335 **Admissions:** 15712 **Census:** 188 **Outpatient Visits:** 243046 **Births:** 1551 **Total Expense ($000):** 226751 **Payroll Expense ($000):** 84889 **Personnel:** 1597

HIGHLANDS—Macon County

⊠ **HIGHLANDS–CASHIERS HOSPITAL (341316)**, 190 Hospital Drive, Zip 28741–7600, Mailing Address: P.O. Drawer 190, Zip 28741–0190; tel. 828/526–1200, (Total facility includes 80 beds in nursing home–type unit) **A**1 10 18 **F**3 11 15 28 29 30 34 35 40 45 46 47 48 53 56 57 59 64 65 74 75 77 79 91 97 107 108 110 111 113 119 128 130 133 146 **P**6 **S** Mission Health System, Asheville, NC
Primary Contact: Christina Derosa, Ph.D., Interim Chief Executive Officer and Chief Nursing Officer
CFO: Lena Cochran, Director of Finance
CHR: Ruby Rowland, Strategic Partner
CNO: Cindy Pierson, Clinical Services Manager
Web address: www.hchospital.org
Control: Other not–for–profit (including NFP Corporation) **Service:** General Medical and Surgical

Staffed Beds: 104 **Admissions:** 401 **Census:** 69 **Outpatient Visits:** 30690 **Births:** 0 **Total Expense ($000):** 21630 **Payroll Expense ($000):** 8287 **Personnel:** 181

HUNTERSVILLE—Mecklenburg County

⊠ **NOVANT HEALTH HUNTERSVILLE MEDICAL CENTER (340183)**, 10030 Gilead Road, Zip 28078–7545, Mailing Address: P.O. Box 3508, Zip 28070–3508; tel. 704/316–4000 **A**1 2 10 13 **F**8 11 12 13 15 18 26 28 29 30 31 34 35 40 45 49 50 53 55 56 57 59 64 67 68 70 72 74 75 76 77 78 79 81 82 85 86 87 93 100 107 108 110 111 114 115 118 119 120 126 129 130 132 135 141 146 147 **S** Novant Health, Winston Salem, NC
Primary Contact: Mike Riley, President
CFO: Jason Yanni, Senior Financial Analyst
CMO: David Cook, M.D., Chief Medical Officer
CIO: Richard B. McKnight, Senior Vice President and Chief Information Officer
CHR: Tracy Craig, Director Human Resources
Web address: www.novanthealth.org
Control: Other not–for–profit (including NFP Corporation) **Service:** General Medical and Surgical

Staffed Beds: 78 **Admissions:** 6824 **Census:** 66 **Outpatient Visits:** 129993 **Births:** 1411 **Total Expense ($000):** 112723 **Payroll Expense ($000):** 32572 **Personnel:** 540

JACKSONVILLE—Onslow County

☐ **BRYNN MARR HOSPITAL (344016)**, 192 Village Drive, Zip 28546–7299; tel. 910/577–1400, (Nonreporting) **A**1 10 **S** Universal Health Services, Inc., King of Prussia, PA
Primary Contact: Jay Kortemeyer, Chief Executive Officer
CFO: David Warmerdam, Chief Financial Officer
CMO: Ashraf Mikhail, M.D., Medical Director
CIO: Amy Black, Risk Manager/PI Director
CHR: Jennifer Gier, Director Human Resources
CNO: Sheila Maraan, Director of Nursing
Web address: www.brynnmarr.org
Control: Corporation, Investor–owned, for–profit **Service:** Psychiatric

Staffed Beds: 99

Hospital, Medicare Provider Number, Address, Telephone, Approval, Facility, and Physician Codes, Health Care System

★ American Hospital Association (AHA) membership
☐ The Joint Commission accreditation
○ Healthcare Facilities Accreditation Program
◇ DNV Healthcare Inc. accreditation
⇑ Center for Improvement in Healthcare Quality Accreditation
△ Commission on Accreditation of Rehabilitation Facilities (CARF) accreditation

NC

✠ **ONSLOW MEMORIAL HOSPITAL (340042)**, 317 Western Boulevard, Zip 28546–6379, Mailing Address: P.O. Box 1358, Zip 28541–1358; tel. 910/577–2345 **A**1 2 10 20 **F**3 8 11 13 15 19 20 28 29 34 35 40 45 46 47 48 49 54 57 59 60 64 68 70 72 73 75 76 77 79 81 82 84 85 86 87 89 93 96 107 108 110 111 117 118 119 126 129 131 132 135 146 147 148 **P**8
Primary Contact: Penney Burlingame Deal, FACHE, R.N., Chief Executive Officer
CFO: Roy Smith, Chief Financial Officer
CMO: Scott Johnston, Chief of Staff
CHR: Taylor Flowers, Director Human Resources
CNO: Regina Lanier, R.N., Senior Vice President and Chief Nursing Officer
Web address: www.onslow.org
Control: Hospital district or authority, Government, nonfederal **Service:** General Medical and Surgical

Staffed Beds: 149 **Admissions:** 7093 **Census:** 82 **Outpatient Visits:** 137421 **Births:** 1704 **Total Expense ($000):** 130646 **Payroll Expense ($000):** 49484 **Personnel:** 881

JEFFERSON—Ashe County

✠ **ASHE MEMORIAL HOSPITAL (341325)**, 200 Hospital Avenue, Zip 28640–9244; tel. 336/846–7101 **A**1 10 18 **F**3 11 13 15 28 30 34 35 40 45 48 56 57 59 64 75 76 78 79 80 81 85 86 89 93 102 107 108 110 111 114 118 119 127 130 132 133 135 141 142 146 147 **S** Novant Health, Winston Salem, NC
Primary Contact: Laura Lambeth, Chief Executive Officer
COO: Joe Thore, Chief Operating Officer
CFO: Charles Wright, Chief Financial Officer
CMO: David Factor, M.D., Chief of Staff
CIO: William Baldwin, Chief Information Officer
CHR: Teresa Patrick, Human Resources Director
CNO: Sara Houser, Chief Nursing Officer
Web address: www.ashememorial.org
Control: Other not–for–profit (including NFP Corporation) **Service:** General Medical and Surgical

Staffed Beds: 25 **Admissions:** 1340 **Census:** 13 **Outpatient Visits:** 56334 **Births:** 143 **Total Expense ($000):** 27048 **Payroll Expense ($000):** 11788 **Personnel:** 256

KENANSVILLE—Duplin County

✠ **VIDANT DUPLIN HOSPITAL (340120)**, 401 North Main Street, Zip 28349–8801, Mailing Address: P.O. Box 278, Zip 28349–0278; tel. 910/296–0941 **A**1 10 **F**3 11 13 15 18 19 29 30 31 34 35 39 40 45 56 57 59 68 70 75 76 77 78 79 81 91 93 97 98 101 102 103 107 108 110 111 115 119 129 130 131 135 146 147 **S** Vidant Health, Greenville, NC
Primary Contact: Jay Briley, President
COO: Matthew Gitzinger, Director of Operations
CFO: Lucinda Crawford, Vice President Financial Services
CMO: Dyrek Miller, M.D., Chief Medical Staff
CIO: Lucinda Crawford, Vice President Financial Services
CHR: Pansy Chase, Director Human Resources
CNO: Sue O. Taylor, Vice President Nursing
Web address: www.vidanthealth.com
Control: Other not–for–profit (including NFP Corporation) **Service:** General Medical and Surgical

Staffed Beds: 48 **Admissions:** 3263 **Census:** 46 **Outpatient Visits:** 45359 **Births:** 479 **Total Expense ($000):** 47300 **Payroll Expense ($000):** 18103 **Personnel:** 359

KINGS MOUNTAIN—Cleveland County

CAROLINAS CONTINUECARE HOSPITAL AT KINGS MOUNTAIN (342019), 706 West King Street, 2nd Floor, Zip 28086–2708, Mailing Address: P.O. Box 159, Zip 28086–0159; tel. 980/487–5520 **F**1 3 29 34 35 59 86 87 130 135 148 **P**5 **S** Community Hospital Corporation, Plano, TX
Primary Contact: Denise R. Murray, Chief Executive Officer
CFO: Lisa Young, CPA, Chief Financial Officer
Web address: www.continuecare.org/kings–mountain/
Control: Other not–for–profit (including NFP Corporation) **Service:** Long–Term Acute Care hospital

Staffed Beds: 28 **Admissions:** 245 **Census:** 19 **Outpatient Visits:** 0 **Births:** 0 **Total Expense ($000):** 8934 **Payroll Expense ($000):** 3638 **Personnel:** 69

✠ **KINGS MOUNTAIN HOSPITAL (340037)**, 706 West King Street, Zip 28086–2708; tel. 980/487–5000 **A**1 10 **F**3 4 15 29 30 34 40 45 49 59 70 79 81 82 85 93 98 107 110 111 115 119 130 133 146 148 **S** Carolinas Healthcare System, Charlotte, NC
Primary Contact: Brian Gwyn, President and Chief Executive Officer
CFO: Terry Edwards, Controller
CHR: Debra Kale, Director Human Resources
Web address: www.clevelandregional.org/kings–mountain–hospital.html
Control: Hospital district or authority, Government, nonfederal **Service:** General Medical and Surgical

Staffed Beds: 59 **Admissions:** 2811 **Census:** 35 **Outpatient Visits:** 55036 **Births:** 0 **Total Expense ($000):** 33621 **Payroll Expense ($000):** 14005 **Personnel:** 253

KINSTON—Lenoir County

✠ **UNC LENOIR HEALTHCARE (340027)**, 100 Airport Road, Zip 28501–1634, Mailing Address: P.O. Box 1678, Zip 28503–1678; tel. 252/522–7000 **A**1 10 **F**3 8 11 13 18 20 22 28 29 30 31 34 35 38 40 43 45 47 48 49 50 53 56 57 59 60 61 64 65 68 70 75 76 77 78 79 81 82 85 86 87 89 90 93 102 107 108 111 114 115 118 119 120 121 129 130 132 134 135 143 145 146 148 **S** UNC Health Care, Chapel Hill, NC
Primary Contact: Gary E. Black, President and Chief Executive Officer
CFO: Sarah Mayo, Vice President Financial Services
CMO: Alan Kirollos, M.D., President Medical Staff
CIO: Karl Vanderstouw, Vice President Information Systems
CHR: Jim Dobbins, Vice President Human Resources
CNO: Laurel Molloy, Vice President Nursing and Rehab Services
Web address: www.lenoirmemorial.org
Control: Other not–for–profit (including NFP Corporation) **Service:** General Medical and Surgical

Staffed Beds: 155 **Admissions:** 5361 **Census:** 76 **Outpatient Visits:** 85774 **Births:** 425 **Total Expense ($000):** 98919 **Payroll Expense ($000):** 41234 **Personnel:** 839

LAURINBURG—Scotland County

✠ **SCOTLAND HEALTH CARE SYSTEM (340008)**, 500 Lauchwood Drive, Zip 28352–5599; tel. 910/291–7000 **A**1 2 3 10 **F**3 11 13 15 18 28 29 31 34 37 40 45 54 57 59 64 66 70 71 73 74 75 76 77 78 79 81 85 86 87 89 90 92 93 96 97 107 110 111 114 115 119 120 121 123 127 130 132 135 143 144 145 146 147 148 **S** Carolinas Healthcare System, Charlotte, NC
Primary Contact: Gregory C. Wood, President and Chief Executive Officer
CFO: Matthew Pracht, Vice President Finance
CMO: Cheryl Davis, M.D., Chief Medical Officer
CIO: Gary Liuzzo, Director Information Systems
CHR: Ann Locklear, Vice President, Human Resources
CNO: Camille Utter, R.N., Chief Nursing Officer
Web address: www.scotlandhealth.org
Control: Other not–for–profit (including NFP Corporation) **Service:** General Medical and Surgical

Staffed Beds: 104 **Admissions:** 5178 **Census:** 53 **Outpatient Visits:** 131628 **Births:** 675 **Total Expense ($000):** 112226 **Payroll Expense ($000):** 39838 **Personnel:** 943

LELAND—Brunswick County

☐ **STRATEGIC BEHAVIORAL HEALTH – WILMINGTON (344030)**, 2050 Mercantile Drive, Zip 28451–4053; tel. 910/371–2500, (Nonreporting) **A**1 10 **S** Strategic Behavioral Health, LLC, Memphis, TN
Primary Contact: Daniel Kern, Chief Executive Officer
CHR: Kelly Pace, Director Human Resource
CNO: Brooke Cook, Director of Nursing
Web address: www.sbcwilmington.com/
Control: Corporation, Investor–owned, for–profit **Service:** Children's hospital psychiatric

Staffed Beds: 92

LENOIR—Caldwell County

✠ **CALDWELL MEMORIAL HOSPITAL (340041)**, 321 Mulberry Street S.W., Zip 28645–5720, Mailing Address: P.O. Box 1890, Zip 28645–1890; tel. 828/757–5100 **A**1 10 **F**3 8 11 13 15 18 20 22 29 31 34 35 37 40 45 46 48 49 50 53 54 55 57 59 64 65 70 75 77 78 79 81 82 85 86 87 93 97 107 108 109 110 111 114 119 120 121 122 123 129 132 135 144 145 146 147 148 **P**6 **S** UNC Health Care, Chapel Hill, NC
Primary Contact: Laura J. Easton, R.N., President and Chief Executive Officer
COO: Rebecca T. Smith, Chief Operating Officer and Vice President
CMO: John Powell, M.D., Chief Medical Officer
CIO: Deborah Purcell, Director of Information Technology
CHR: Rebecca T. Smith, Vice President and Chief Operating Officer
Web address: www.caldwellmemorial.org
Control: Other not–for–profit (including NFP Corporation) **Service:** General Medical and Surgical

Staffed Beds: 82 **Admissions:** 3744 **Census:** 48 **Outpatient Visits:** 84572 **Births:** 354 **Total Expense ($000):** 110344 **Payroll Expense ($000):** 45279 **Personnel:** 856

LEXINGTON—Davidson County

LEXINGTON MEMORIAL HOSPITAL See Wake Forest Baptist Health–Lexington Medical Center

NC

Many Facility Codes have changed. Please refer to the AHA Guide Code Chart. © 2016 AHA Guide

⊞ **WAKE FOREST BAPTIST HEALTH–LEXINGTON MEDICAL CENTER (340096)**, 250 Hospital Drive, Zip 27292–6728, Mailing Address: P.O. Box 1817, Zip 27293–1817; tel. 336/248–5161 **A**1 3 10 **F**3 13 15 18 28 29 30 31 34 35 39 40 45 46 50 57 58 59 61 64 65 68 70 74 75 76 78 79 81 82 85 87 91 92 93 97 102 107 108 110 111 115 119 120 121 123 129 130 131 146 147 148 **S** Wake Forest Baptist Health, Winston–Salem, NC
Primary Contact: William B. James, FACHE, President
CFO: Danny Squires, Vice President and Chief Financial Officer
CMO: Raghava Nagaraj, Chief Medical Officer
CIO: Dee Emon, R.N., Chief Information Officer
CNO: Clyde A. Bristow, III, MSN, Senior Director Nursing and Clinical Services, Chief Nursing Officer
Web address: www.lexington.wakehealth.edu
Control: Other not–for–profit (including NFP Corporation) **Service:** General Medical and Surgical

Staffed Beds: 76 **Admissions:** 3321 **Census:** 27 **Outpatient Visits:** 104668 **Births:** 464 **Total Expense ($000):** 64050 **Payroll Expense ($000):** 26088 **Personnel:** 513

LINCOLNTON—Lincoln County

⊞ **CAROLINAS HEALTHCARE SYSTEM LINCOLN (340145)**, 433 McAlister Road, Zip 28092–4147, Mailing Address: PO Box 677, Zip 28093–0677; tel. 980/212–2000 **A**1 10 **F**3 8 11 13 15 18 28 29 30 31 34 40 44 45 50 51 57 59 64 68 70 73 74 75 76 77 78 79 81 82 84 85 87 91 93 94 96 107 108 111 114 115 118 119 129 130 131 132 135 146 148 **S** Carolinas Healthcare System, Charlotte, NC
Primary Contact: Peter W. Acker, President and Chief Executive Officer
COO: Teresa C. Watson, Vice President Administration
CFO: Jarrett L. Morris, Controller
CMO: Vineet Goel, Chief Medical Officer
CIO: Jarrett L. Morris, Controller and Chief Information Officer
CHR: Lesley Chambless, Assistant Vice President Human Resources
CNO: Elaine S. Haynes, R.N., Vice President Patient Services and Chief Nursing Executive
Web address: www.carolinashealthcare.org/lincoln
Control: Hospital district or authority, Government, nonfederal **Service:** General Medical and Surgical

Staffed Beds: 101 **Admissions:** 4671 **Census:** 50 **Outpatient Visits:** 96256 **Births:** 441 **Total Expense ($000):** 94839 **Payroll Expense ($000):** 31014 **Personnel:** 514

LUMBERTON—Robeson County

⊞ **SOUTHEASTERN HEALTH (340050)**, 300 West 27th Street, Zip 28358–3075, Mailing Address: P.O. Box 1408, Zip 28359–1408; tel. 910/671–5000, (Total facility includes 115 beds in nursing home–type unit) **A**1 2 10 12 13 **F**3 5 7 8 9 12 13 15 17 18 20 22 24 28 29 30 31 34 35 37 40 45 48 49 50 53 54 57 59 60 61 62 63 64 67 68 70 71 72 73 74 75 76 77 78 79 80 81 82 83 84 85 87 89 92 93 98 102 103 107 108 111 112 113 114 115 118 119 120 121 126 127 128 129 130 131 132 135 143 144 146 147 148 **P**6
Primary Contact: Joann Anderson, President and Chief Executive Officer
CFO: C. Thomas Johnson, III, Vice President Finance and Chief Financial Officer
CMO: Barry Williamson, President Medical Staff
CIO: Eric Harper, Chief Information Officer
CHR: Susan Hayes, Director Human Resources
CNO: Renae Taylor, Chief Nursing Officer
Web address: www.srmc.org
Control: Other not–for–profit (including NFP Corporation) **Service:** General Medical and Surgical

Staffed Beds: 380 **Admissions:** 15217 **Census:** 294 **Outpatient Visits:** 496757 **Births:** 1400 **Total Expense ($000):** 303851 **Payroll Expense ($000):** 122530 **Personnel:** 2277

MARION—Mcdowell County

⊞ **MCDOWELL HOSPITAL (340087)**, 430 Rankin Drive, Zip 28752–6568, Mailing Address: P.O. Box 730, Zip 28752–0730; tel. 828/659–5000 **A**1 10 **F**3 13 15 28 29 30 31 34 35 39 40 45 54 57 59 64 65 70 76 77 78 79 81 82 85 87 91 93 97 107 108 110 111 115 119 129 130 131 132 135 144 146 147 148 **S** Mission Health System, Asheville, NC
Primary Contact: Carol C. Wolfenbarger, FACHE, MSN, President and Chief Executive Officer
CFO: Clint Stewart, Regional Director of Finance East
CMO: Rex Henderson, M.D., Chief of Staff
CIO: Pam Blevins, R.N., Director Information Technology Member Hospitals Mission
CHR: Tonya Revels, Senior Strategic Business Partner
CNO: Kathy Hefner, Chief Nursing Officer
Web address: www.mission–health.org
Control: Other not–for–profit (including NFP Corporation) **Service:** General Medical and Surgical

Staffed Beds: 49 **Admissions:** 1971 **Census:** 20 **Outpatient Visits:** 162726 **Births:** 201 **Total Expense ($000):** 51975 **Payroll Expense ($000):** 15120 **Personnel:** 407

MATTHEWS—Mecklenburg County

⊞ **NOVANT HEALTH MATTHEWS MEDICAL CENTER (340171)**, 1500 Matthews Township Parkway, Zip 28105–4656; tel. 704/384–6500 **A**1 2 10 **F**3 11 12 13 15 18 20 22 26 28 29 30 31 34 35 36 40 45 49 56 57 59 64 67 70 73 75 76 77 78 79 81 82 84 85 86 87 92 93 107 110 111 114 115 118 119 126 129 130 132 141 144 145 146 147 148 **S** Novant Health, Winston Salem, NC
Primary Contact: Roland R. Bibeau, FACHE, President
COO: Amy Vance, Executive Vice President and Chief Operating Officer
CFO: Greg Klein, Senior Director Finance
CMO: Thomas Zweng, M.D., Senior Vice President Medical Affairs
CIO: David B. Garrett, Chief Information Officer
CHR: Susan Kennedy, Manager Human Resources
Web address: www.https://www.novanthealth.org
Control: Other not–for–profit (including NFP Corporation) **Service:** General Medical and Surgical

Staffed Beds: 111 **Admissions:** 10029 **Census:** 104 **Outpatient Visits:** 179171 **Births:** 2009 **Total Expense ($000):** 139159 **Payroll Expense ($000):** 43423 **Personnel:** 659

MOCKSVILLE—Davie County

★ **WAKE FOREST BAPTIST HEALTH–DAVIE MEDICAL CENTER (341313)**, 223 Hospital Street, Zip 27028–2038, Mailing Address: 329 NC Highway 801 North, Bermuda Run, Zip 27006; tel. 336/998–1300 **A**10 **F**3 15 28 29 30 34 35 40 50 57 59 64 68 74 75 77 79 81 85 87 93 107 115 119 129 130 131 133 146 **S** Wake Forest Baptist Health, Winston–Salem, NC
Primary Contact: Chad J. Brown, M.P.H., President
CFO: Danny Squires, Chief Financial Officer
CMO: Bret Nicks, M.D., Chief Medical Officer and Chief of Staff
CIO: Dee Emon, R.N., Vice President and Chief Information Officer
CHR: Lisa Moncus, Human Resources Business Partner
CNO: Susan T. Bachmeier, MSN, Chief Nursing Officer
Web address: www.wakehealth.edu/Davie–Medical–Center
Control: Other not–for–profit (including NFP Corporation) **Service:** General Medical and Surgical

Staffed Beds: 25 **Admissions:** 221 **Census:** 15 **Outpatient Visits:** 40168 **Births:** 0 **Total Expense ($000):** 29261 **Payroll Expense ($000):** 7952 **Personnel:** 172

MONROE—Union County

⊞ **CAROLINAS HEALTHCARE SYSTEM UNION (340130)**, 600 Hospital Drive, Zip 28112–6000, Mailing Address: P.O. Box 5003, Zip 28111–5003; tel. 980/993–3100, (Total facility includes 70 beds in nursing home–type unit) **A**1 2 3 10 **F**3 4 5 8 11 13 18 20 22 26 27 28 29 30 31 34 35 39 40 42 45 49 53 56 57 59 64 66 67 70 73 74 75 76 77 78 79 81 82 83 84 85 86 87 89 93 97 107 108 111 114 115 117 118 119 120 121 123 128 129 130 132 135 146 147 148 **S** Carolinas Healthcare System, Charlotte, NC
Primary Contact: Michael Lutes, President
COO: Dave Anderson, FACHE, Vice President Administration
CFO: John G. Moore, Vice President and Chief Financial Officer
CMO: Craig M. Slater, M.D., Chief Medical Officer
CIO: Lisa Sykes, Director Information Services
CHR: Rhonda McFarland, Director Human Resources
CNO: Denise White, MSN, Chief Nurse Executive
Web address: www.carolinashealthcare.org/union
Control: Hospital district or authority, Government, nonfederal **Service:** General Medical and Surgical

Staffed Beds: 224 **Admissions:** 9015 **Census:** 155 **Outpatient Visits:** 161365 **Births:** 1119 **Total Expense ($000):** 180687 **Payroll Expense ($000):** 58653 **Personnel:** 982

Hospital, Medicare Provider Number, Address, Telephone, Approval, Facility, and Physician Codes, Health Care System

★ American Hospital Association (AHA) membership
□ The Joint Commission accreditation
○ Healthcare Facilities Accreditation Program
◇ DNV Healthcare Inc. accreditation
⇑ Center for Improvement in Healthcare Quality Accreditation
△ Commission on Accreditation of Rehabilitation Facilities (CARF) accreditation

NC

MOORESVILLE—Iredell County

⊠ **LAKE NORMAN REGIONAL MEDICAL CENTER (340129)**, 171 Fairview Road, Zip 28117–9500, Mailing Address: P.O. Box 3250, Zip 28117–3250; tel. 704/660–4000 **A**1 2 10 19 **F**3 8 11 12 13 15 18 20 29 30 31 34 35 37 40 41 45 46 47 48 49 50 51 56 57 59 60 61 62 64 65 68 70 72 73 74 75 76 77 78 79 81 82 84 85 86 87 93 96 97 100 107 108 110 111 114 115 116 117 118 119 129 130 131 132 135 145 146 147 148 **P**8 **S** Community Health Systems, Inc., Franklin, TN
Primary Contact: Stephen L. Midkiff, Chief Executive Officer
COO: Matthew Banks, Chief Operating Officer
CFO: Claire Polk, Chief Financial Officer
CHR: Stephanie Williams, Market Director Human Resources
CNO: Marie Marks, Chief Nursing Officer
Web address: www.lnrmc.com
Control: Corporation, Investor–owned, for–profit **Service:** General Medical and Surgical

Staffed Beds: 123 **Admissions:** 4640 **Census:** 44 **Outpatient Visits:** 71687 **Births:** 850

MOREHEAD CITY—Carteret County

⊠ **CARTERET HEALTH CARE (340142)**, 3500 Arendell Street, Zip 28557–2901, Mailing Address: P.O. Box 1619, Zip 28557–1619; tel. 252/499–6000 **A**1 2 10 **F**3 7 11 12 13 15 18 28 29 30 31 34 35 37 40 45 46 54 57 59 62 63 64 65 68 70 74 75 76 77 78 79 81 82 84 85 86 87 89 91 93 97 107 108 110 111 114 115 118 119 120 130 132 135 143 145 146 148
Primary Contact: Richard A. Brvenik, FACHE, President
CFO: Joanie King, Chief Financial Officer
CIO: Kyle Marek, Manager Information Services
CHR: Elizabeth Beswick, Vice President Human Resources and Public Relations
Web address: www.carterethealth.org
Control: County–Government, nonfederal **Service:** General Medical and Surgical

Staffed Beds: 99 **Admissions:** 5497 **Census:** 66 **Outpatient Visits:** 159099 **Births:** 738 **Total Expense ($000):** 127782 **Payroll Expense ($000):** 52709 **Personnel:** 860

MORGANTON—Burke County

☐ **BROUGHTON HOSPITAL (344025)**, 1000 South Sterling Street, Zip 28655–3999; tel. 828/433–2111 **A**1 5 10 **F**3 30 39 53 56 59 65 75 77 86 87 91 92 98 99 100 101 102 103 130 132 135 146
Primary Contact: Vivian Streater, Co–Acting Chief Executive Officer
CFO: Bea Tullis, Chief Financial Officer and Budget Officer
CMO: George Krebs, M.D., Chief Medical Officer
CIO: Darin Kiracofe, Director Information Resource Management
CHR: Jean Buchanan, Director Human Resources
CNO: Vivian Streater, Chief Nursing Officer and Co–Acting Chief Executive Officer
Web address: www.ncdhhs.gov/dsohf/broughton
Control: State–Government, nonfederal **Service:** Psychiatric

Staffed Beds: 297 **Admissions:** 554 **Census:** 271 **Outpatient Visits:** 0 **Births:** 0 **Total Expense ($000):** 94620 **Payroll Expense ($000):** 54794 **Personnel:** 1190

⊠ **CAROLINAS HEALTHCARE SYSTEM BLUE RIDGE (340075)**, 2201 South Sterling Street, Zip 28655–4058; tel. 828/580–5000, (Includes GRACE HOSPITAL, 2201 South Sterling Street, tel. 828/580–5000; VALDESE GENERAL HOSPITAL, 720 Malcolm Boulevard, Valdese, Zip 28690–2872, Mailing Address: P.O. Box 700, Zip 28690–0700; tel. 828/874–2251) **A**1 2 10 **F**3 13 15 18 20 22 28 29 30 31 34 35 40 42 45 49 50 53 57 59 64 68 69 70 71 72 76 77 78 81 82 85 86 87 93 96 97 98 107 108 110 111 114 115 119 120 121 123 130 131 132 146 147 148 **S** Carolinas Healthcare System, Charlotte, NC
Primary Contact: Kathy C. Bailey, Ph.D., FACHE, President and Chief Executive Officer
CFO: Robert G. Fritts, Chief Financial Officer and Senior Vice President
CMO: Joe Mazzola, D.O., Senior Vice President Medical Affairs and Chief Medical Officer
CHR: Thomas Eure, Vice President Administration
CNO: Susan E. Brown, R.N., Senior Vice President, Chief Nursing Officer
Web address: www.blueridgehealth.org
Control: Other not–for–profit (including NFP Corporation) **Service:** General Medical and Surgical

Staffed Beds: 154 **Admissions:** 8575 **Census:** 97 **Outpatient Visits:** 170357 **Births:** 887 **Total Expense ($000):** 190020 **Payroll Expense ($000):** 64787 **Personnel:** 1285

MOUNT AIRY—Surry County

⊠ **NORTHERN HOSPITAL OF SURRY COUNTY (340003)**, 830 Rockford Street, Zip 27030–5365, Mailing Address: P.O. Box 1101, Zip 27030–1101; tel. 336/719–7000, (Total facility includes 33 beds in nursing home–type unit) **A**1 10 **F**3 13 15 18 29 30 31 34 35 40 45 50 51 53 54 56 57 59 64 65 67 70 75 76 77 79 80 81 82 85 86 87 89 102 107 108 110 111 114 115 118 119 128 130 131 132 133 135 145 146 147 **P**6 **S** QHR, Brentwood, TN
Primary Contact: Ned Hill, President and Chief Executive Officer
CFO: Andrea Hickling, Vice President Finance and Chief Financial Officer
CMO: William Lawing, Chief of Medical Staff
CIO: Rodney Bond, Director Information Technology
CHR: Julia Nelson, Vice President Human Resources
CNO: Robin Hodgin, R.N., Vice President Patient Services and Chief Nursing Officer
Web address: www.northernhospital.com
Control: Hospital district or authority, Government, nonfederal **Service:** General Medical and Surgical

Staffed Beds: 108 **Admissions:** 3832 **Census:** 66 **Outpatient Visits:** 114690 **Births:** 374 **Total Expense ($000):** 80678 **Payroll Expense ($000):** 33111 **Personnel:** 654

MURPHY—Cherokee County

⊠ **MURPHY MEDICAL CENTER (340160)**, 3990 U.S. Highway 64 East Alt, Zip 28906–7917; tel. 828/837–8161, (Nonreporting) **A**1 10 18 **S** Carolinas Healthcare System, Charlotte, NC
Primary Contact: Michael Stevenson, Chief Executive Officer
COO: Toni Lovingood, Chief Operating Officer
CFO: Steve Gilgen, Chief Financial Officer
CMO: Jeffrey H. Martin, M.D., Chief of Staff
CIO: Connie Stalcup, Manager Information Systems
CHR: Russ Paine, Human Resources Officer
CNO: Teresa Bowleg, R.N., Chief Nursing Officer
Web address: www.murphymedical.org
Control: Other not–for–profit (including NFP Corporation) **Service:** General Medical and Surgical

Staffed Beds: 191

NAGS HEAD—Dare County

⊠ **THE OUTER BANKS HOSPITAL (341324)**, 4800 South Croatan Highway, Zip 27959–9704; tel. 252/449–4511 **A**1 10 18 **F**3 13 15 29 30 31 34 35 36 38 40 45 50 51 54 57 59 64 65 68 71 75 77 78 79 81 82 84 85 87 93 100 107 108 109 110 111 115 118 119 120 121 124 129 130 133 135 141 144 146 147 **S** Vidant Health, Greenville, NC
Primary Contact: Ronald A. Sloan, FACHE, President
CFO: Todd Warlitner, Vice President Business Operations
CMO: Roger Lever, M.D., President Medical Staff
CHR: Mary Kelley, Director Human Resources
CNO: Marcia Bryant, R.N., Vice President, Clinical Operations
Web address: www.theouterbankshospital.com
Control: Other not–for–profit (including NFP Corporation) **Service:** General Medical and Surgical

Staffed Beds: 21 **Admissions:** 1201 **Census:** 8 **Outpatient Visits:** 39939 **Births:** 379 **Total Expense ($000):** 51655 **Payroll Expense ($000):** 15313 **Personnel:** 284

NEW BERN—Craven County

⊠ △ **CAROLINAEAST HEALTH SYSTEM (340131)**, 2000 Neuse Boulevard, Zip 28560–3499, Mailing Address: P.O. Box 12157, Zip 28561–2157; tel. 252/633–8111 **A**1 2 7 10 **F**3 7 8 11 13 15 17 18 20 22 24 26 28 29 30 31 34 35 40 42 45 47 48 49 54 57 59 61 62 64 67 70 74 75 76 77 78 79 81 85 87 89 90 91 92 93 94 96 98 100 101 102 103 104 105 107 108 110 111 113 114 115 116 117 118 119 120 121 123 126 129 130 132 135 143 146 147 148 **P**6
Primary Contact: G. Raymond Leggett, III, President and Chief Executive Officer
CFO: Tammy M. Sherron, Vice President Finance
CMO: Ronald B. May, M.D., Vice President Medical Affairs
CIO: Ronald B. May, M.D., Vice President Medical Affairs
CHR: Bruce A. Martin, Vice President Human Resources
CNO: Rosanne Leahy, Vice President Nursing Services
Web address: www.carolinaeasthealth.com
Control: Hospital district or authority, Government, nonfederal **Service:** General Medical and Surgical

Staffed Beds: 218 **Admissions:** 12035 **Census:** 161 **Outpatient Visits:** 173451 **Births:** 1232 **Total Expense ($000):** 241058 **Payroll Expense ($000):** 89611 **Personnel:** 1541

Many Facility Codes have changed. Please refer to the AHA Guide Code Chart. © 2016 AHA Guide

NEWLAND—Avery County

⊞ **CHARLES A. CANNON MEMORIAL HOSPITAL (341323)**, 434 Hospital Drive, Zip 28646, Mailing Address: P.O. Box 767, Linville, Zip 28646–0767; tel. 828/737–7000 **A**1 10 18 **F**3 11 15 28 29 30 38 40 45 64 70 81 85 91 93 98 100 102 104 107 110 115 119 130 133 135 146 **S** Appalachian Regional Healthcare System, Boone, NC
Primary Contact: Carmen Lacey, MSN, R.N., President
CFO: Kevin B. May, System Director Finance
CMO: Thomas M. Haizlip, Jr., M.D., Chief of Staff
CIO: Nathan White, Chief Information Officer
CHR: Amy J. Crabbe, Vice President People Services
CNO: Carmen Lacey, MSN, President and Director of Patient Care Services
Web address: www.https://apprhs.org/locations/cannon–memorial–hospital
Control: Other not–for–profit (including NFP Corporation) **Service:** General Medical and Surgical

Staffed Beds: 35 **Admissions:** 1596 **Census:** 18 **Outpatient Visits:** 26547 **Births:** 101 **Total Expense ($000):** 23568 **Payroll Expense ($000):** 9375 **Personnel:** 181

NORTH WILKESBORO—Wilkes County

⊞ **WILKES REGIONAL MEDICAL CENTER (340064)**, 1370 West D Street, Zip 28659–3506, Mailing Address: P.O. Box 609, Zip 28659–0609; tel. 336/651–8100, (Total facility includes 10 beds in nursing home–type unit) **A**1 10 **F**3 11 13 15 18 29 30 34 35 40 45 57 59 60 64 67 68 70 74 76 77 79 81 82 85 87 92 93 107 108 110 111 114 115 119 124 128 130 146 **S** Carolinas Healthcare System, Charlotte, NC
Primary Contact: J. Gene Faile, Chief Executive Officer and President
CFO: Barry Wald, Chief Financial Officer
CMO: Richard Barber, M.D., Chief Medical Officer
CIO: William Hofman, Manager Information Technology
CHR: Vanya Baker, Director
CNO: Sandy Sheppard, Vice President Patient Services
Web address: www.wilkesregional.com/
Control: City–Government, nonfederal **Service:** General Medical and Surgical

Staffed Beds: 91 **Admissions:** 4302 **Census:** 49 **Outpatient Visits:** 104762 **Births:** 430 **Total Expense ($000):** 72171 **Payroll Expense ($000):** 27430 **Personnel:** 640

OXFORD—Granville County

⊞ **GRANVILLE HEALTH SYSTEM (340127)**, 1010 College Street, Zip 27565–2507, Mailing Address: P.O. Box 947, Zip 27565–0947; tel. 919/690–3000, (Total facility includes 80 beds in nursing home–type unit) **A**1 3 10 **F**2 3 7 11 13 15 18 19 29 30 31 34 35 38 39 40 45 50 54 55 56 57 59 64 66 70 75 76 77 78 79 81 82 85 86 93 99 100 101 103 104 107 108 110 111 118 119 124 127 128 129 130 132 133 143 144 146 147 148 **P**3 6 8
Primary Contact: L. Lee Isley, FACHE, Ph.D., Chief Executive Officer
COO: Cristina Rigsbee Carroll, Chief Operating Officer
CFO: Jeffery Armstrong, CPA, Chief Financial Officer
CMO: Richard Pacca, Chief Medical Staff
CIO: Geoff Tanthorey, Director Information Systems
CHR: Scott Thomas, Administrative Director Human Resources and Communications
CNO: Bill Hughes, Chief Nursing Officer
Web address: www.ghshospital.org
Control: County–Government, nonfederal **Service:** General Medical and Surgical

Staffed Beds: 142 **Admissions:** 2473 **Census:** 89 **Outpatient Visits:** 49783 **Births:** 301 **Total Expense ($000):** 58229 **Payroll Expense ($000):** 26019 **Personnel:** 528

PINEHURST—Moore County

⊞ △ **FIRSTHEALTH MOORE REGIONAL HOSPITAL (340115)**, 155 Memorial Drive, Zip 28374–8710, Mailing Address: P.O. Box 3000, Zip 28374–3000; tel. 910/715–1000 **A**1 2 7 10 13 19 **F**3 4 5 11 12 13 15 17 18 20 22 24 26 28 29 30 31 34 35 40 44 45 46 47 48 49 50 51 53 54 55 56 57 58 59 60 64 65 68 70 72 74 75 76 77 78 79 81 82 86 87 89 90 91 93 96 98 99 100 101 102 103 104 105 107 108 111 114 115 118 119 121 124 126 129 130 132 134 135 143 146 147 148 **S** FirstHealth of the Carolinas, Pinehurst, NC
Primary Contact: David J. Kilarski, FACHE, Chief Executive Officer
COO: Brian Canfield, Chief Operating Officer
CFO: Lynn S. DeJaco, Chief Financial Officer
CMO: John F. Krahnert, M.D., Chief Medical Officer
CIO: David B. Dillehunt, Chief Information Officer
CHR: Daniel F. Biediger, Vice President Human Resources
CNO: Karen Robeano, R.N., Chief Nursing Officer and Vice President Patient Care Services
Web address: www.firsthealth.org
Control: Other not–for–profit (including NFP Corporation) **Service:** General Medical and Surgical

Staffed Beds: 371 **Admissions:** 20820 **Census:** 272 **Outpatient Visits:** 190228 **Births:** 1930 **Total Expense ($000):** 381178 **Payroll Expense ($000):** 140892 **Personnel:** 3283

PLYMOUTH—Washington County

◇ **WASHINGTON COUNTY HOSPITAL (341314)**, 958 U.S. Highway 64 East, Zip 27962–9591; tel. 252/793–4135, (Nonreporting) **A**10 18 21 **S** Rural Community Hospitals of America, Kansas City, MO
Primary Contact: Cameron Highsmith, Chief Executive Officer
CMO: Robert Venable, M.D., Chief Medical Staff
CIO: Christina Craft, Director Information Systems
CNO: Kimberly Manning, Chief Nursing Officer
Control: County–Government, nonfederal **Service:** General Medical and Surgical

Staffed Beds: 25

RAEFORD—Hoke County

HOKE HOSPITAL (340188), 210 Medical Pavilion Drive, Zip 28376–9111; tel. 910/904–8000, (Nonreporting) **S** Cape Fear Valley Health System, Fayetteville, NC
Primary Contact: Roxie Wells, President
Web address: www.capefearvalley.com
Control: County–Government, nonfederal **Service:** General Medical and Surgical

Staffed Beds: 41

RALEIGH—Wake County

CENTRAL PRISON HOSPITAL, 1300 Western Boulevard, Zip 27606–2148; tel. 919/743–2440, (Nonreporting)
Primary Contact: Dean Doering, Chief Executive Officer
CMO: Olushola Metiko, M.D., Medical Director
CHR: Bruce McKinney, Business Officer, Administrative Services
CNO: Cindy J. McLean, R.N., Director of Nursing
Web address: www.https://www.ncdps.gov/index2.cfm?a=
000003,002240,002381,002252
Control: State–Government, nonfederal **Service:** Hospital unit of an institution (prison hospital, college infimary, etc.)

Staffed Beds: 230

⊞ **DUKE RALEIGH HOSPITAL (340073)**, 3400 Wake Forest Road, Zip 27609–7373; tel. 919/954–3000 **A**1 2 3 10 **F**3 11 12 15 18 20 22 26 28 29 30 31 34 35 36 39 40 44 45 46 47 49 50 51 53 55 57 58 59 60 64 68 70 74 75 77 78 79 80 81 82 84 85 87 92 93 94 96 100 101 102 103 104 107 108 110 111 115 117 118 119 120 121 123 126 129 130 131 132 146 148 **P**6 **S** Duke University Health System, Durham, NC
Primary Contact: David Zaas, M.D., Chief Executive Officer
CMO: Ted Kunstling, M.D., Chief Medical Officer
CIO: Janis Curtis, Interim Director Information Technology
CHR: Donald K. Barnes, Chief Human Resources Officer
Web address: www.dukehealthraleigh.org
Control: Other not–for–profit (including NFP Corporation) **Service:** General Medical and Surgical

Staffed Beds: 148 **Admissions:** 8204 **Census:** 96 **Outpatient Visits:** 172839 **Births:** 0 **Total Expense ($000):** 307961 **Payroll Expense ($000):** 78887 **Personnel:** 1353

NC

☐ **HOLLY HILL HOSPITAL (344014)**, 3019 Falstaff Road, Zip 27610–1812; tel. 919/250–7000 **A**1 10 **F**4 5 29 38 56 68 87 98 99 103 105 **S** Universal Health Services, Inc., King of Prussia, PA
Primary Contact: Michael S. McDonald, Jr., Chief Executive Officer
CFO: Ron Howard, Chief Financial Officer
CMO: Thomas Cornwall, M.D., Medical Director
CHR: Ebuni McFall–Roberts, Director Human Resources
CNO: Michael Hartley, MS, Chief Nursing Officer
Web address: www.hollyhillhospital.com
Control: Corporation, Investor–owned, for–profit **Service:** Psychiatric

Staffed Beds: 200 **Admissions:** 7493 **Census:** 183 **Outpatient Visits:** 5259 **Births:** 0 **Total Expense ($000):** 39848 **Payroll Expense ($000):** 17322 **Personnel:** 430

LARRY B. ZIEVERINK, SR. ALCOHOLISM TREATMENT CENTER, 3000 Falstaff Road, Zip 27610–1897; tel. 919/250–1500, (Nonreporting)
Primary Contact: Martin D. Woodward, Director Acute Care Services
COO: Martin D. Woodward, Director Acute Care Services
CFO: Paul Gross, Human Services and Finance Officer
CMO: Enrique Lopez, M.D., Medical Director
CIO: Wil A. Glenn, Director Communications
Web address: www.wakegov.com/county/family/atc
Control: County–Government, nonfederal **Service:** Alcoholism and other chemical dependency

Staffed Beds: 16

✠ **UNC REX HEALTHCARE (340114)**, 4420 Lake Boone Trail, Zip 27607–6599; tel. 919/784–3100, (Total facility includes 227 beds in nursing home–type unit) **A**1 2 3 5 10 **F**3 7 8 11 12 13 14 15 17 18 20 22 24 26 28 29 30 31 34 35 36 40 44 45 46 47 48 49 50 53 54 56 57 58 59 60 62 64 65 66 68 70 71 72 73 74 75 76 77 78 79 81 82 84 85 86 87 89 92 93 96 97 100 102 107 108 110 111 114 115 116 117 118 119 120 121 123 126 128 129 130 131 132 135 142 143 144 145 146 147 148 **P**6 **S** UNC Health Care, Chapel Hill, NC
Primary Contact: Steve W. Burriss, Ph.D., President
COO: Sue Sandberg, R.N., Chief Operating Officer
CFO: Jeff LeGay, Interim Chief Financial Officer
CMO: Linda H. Butler, M.D., Chief Medical Officer
CIO: Tracy Parham, Health Care System Chief Information Officer
CHR: Bill Rotella, System Vice President, Human Resources
CNO: Colonel Joel Ray, MSN, Vice President and Chief Nursing Officer
Web address: www.rexhealth.com
Control: Other not–for–profit (including NFP Corporation) **Service:** General Medical and Surgical

Staffed Beds: 660 **Admissions:** 27993 **Census:** 523 **Outpatient Visits:** 779537 **Births:** 5484 **Total Expense ($000):** 812770 **Payroll Expense ($000):** 331104 **Personnel:** 5031

✠ △ **WAKEMED RALEIGH CAMPUS (340069)**, 3000 New Bern Avenue, Zip 27610–1295; tel. 919/350–8000, (Includes WAKEMED NORTH FAMILY HEALTH AND WOMEN'S HOSPITAL, 10000 Falls Of Neuse Road, Zip 27614–7838; tel. 919/350–8000; Sherri De Shazo, R.N., Vice President and Administrator, WakeMed North Family Health and Women's Hospital) **A**1 3 5 7 10 **F**3 7 8 12 13 15 17 18 20 22 24 26 28 29 30 31 32 34 35 37 38 40 41 42 43 44 45 46 48 49 50 53 54 56 57 58 59 60 61 62 64 65 66 68 70 71 72 73 74 75 76 77 78 79 80 81 85 86 87 88 89 90 92 93 95 96 97 107 110 111 114 115 118 119 126 130 131 132 135 143 144 146 147 148 **P**6 **S** WakeMed Health & Hospitals, Raleigh, NC
Primary Contact: Donald R. Gintzig, President and Chief Executive Officer
COO: Denise Wilder Warren, R.N., Executive Vice President and Chief Operating Officer
CMO: West Paul, M.D., Senior Vice President and Chief Quality and Medical Staff Officer
CIO: Denton Arledge, Vice President and Chief Information Officer
CHR: Jeanene R. Martin, M.P.H., Senior Vice President Human Resources
CNO: Cindy Boily, MSN, Senior Vice President and Chief Nursing Officer
Web address: www.wakemed.org
Control: Other not–for–profit (including NFP Corporation) **Service:** General Medical and Surgical

Staffed Beds: 681 **Admissions:** 31481 **Census:** 510 **Outpatient Visits:** 1369797 **Births:** 5351 **Total Expense ($000):** 924530 **Payroll Expense ($000):** 482899 **Personnel:** 6836

REIDSVILLE—Rockingham County

ANNIE PENN HOSPITAL See Moses H. Cone Memorial Hospital, Greensboro

NC

ROANOKE RAPIDS—Halifax County

✠ **HALIFAX REGIONAL MEDICAL CENTER (340151)**, 250 Smith Church Road, Zip 27870–4914, Mailing Address: P.O. Box 1089, Zip 27870–1089; tel. 252/535–8011 **A**1 10 20 **F**3 11 13 15 18 20 29 31 34 35 40 45 50 57 59 64 65 68 70 76 77 78 79 81 82 85 86 87 91 93 98 100 101 102 103 106 107 108 110 111 114 119 124 127 129 130 132 146 147 148 **S** Novant Health, Winston Salem, NC
Primary Contact: William Mahone, President and Chief Executive Officer
CFO: Sherry Jensen, Chief Financial Officer
CIO: Robert Gordon, Manager Information Systems
CHR: Thomas Mastroianni, Administrative Director of Human Resources
CNO: Karen Daniels, MSN, Chief Nursing Officer
Web address: www.halifaxmedicalcenter.org
Control: Other not–for–profit (including NFP Corporation) **Service:** General Medical and Surgical

Staffed Beds: 142 **Admissions:** 5566 **Census:** 72 **Outpatient Visits:** 72860 **Births:** 579 **Total Expense ($000):** 79936 **Payroll Expense ($000):** 32178 **Personnel:** 743

ROCKINGHAM—Richmond County

★ **FIRSTHEALTH RICHMOND MEMORIAL HOSPITAL (340035)**, 925 Long Drive, Zip 28379–4835; tel. 910/417–3000, (Nonreporting) **S** FirstHealth of the Carolinas, Pinehurst, NC
Primary Contact: John J. Jackson, President
COO: Allison G. Duckworth, R.N., Chief Operating Officer and Chief Nursing Officer
CFO: John D. Price, Chief Financial Officer
CMO: Matthew Vreeland, M.D., Chief Medical Officer
Web address: www.firsthealth.org
Control: Other not–for–profit (including NFP Corporation) **Service:** General Medical and Surgical

Staffed Beds: 91

ROCKY MOUNT—Nash County

✠ **LIFECARE HOSPITALS OF NORTH CAROLINA (342013)**, 1051 Noell Lane, Zip 27804–1761; tel. 252/451–2300, (Nonreporting) **A**1 10 **S** LifeCare Management Services, Plano, TX
Primary Contact: Robyn Perkerson, R.N., Administrator
COO: Robyn Perkerson, R.N., Administrator
CMO: Daniel Crocker, M.D., Chief Medical Officer
CHR: Vicky Goode, Director Human Resources
CNO: Brandee Chappell, Director of Nursing
Web address: www.lifecare–hospitals.com
Control: Corporation, Investor–owned, for–profit **Service:** Long–Term Acute Care hospital

Staffed Beds: 41

✠ **NASH HEALTH CARE SYSTEMS (340147)**, 2460 Curtis Ellis Drive, Zip 27804–2237; tel. 252/962–8000, (Data for 181 days) **A**1 2 10 **F**3 4 11 12 13 15 18 20 22 28 29 30 31 34 35 38 40 41 44 45 48 49 50 54 55 57 59 60 63 64 70 73 74 75 76 77 78 79 80 81 82 84 85 86 87 89 90 93 96 98 100 101 102 107 108 110 111 114 115 117 118 119 120 121 123 126 129 130 131 132 135 146 147 148 **P**6 **S** UNC Health Care, Chapel Hill, NC
Primary Contact: Larry H. Chewning, III, President and Chief Executive Officer
COO: Brad Weisner, Executive Vice President and Chief Operating Officer
CMO: Meera Kelley, M.D., Senior Vice President and Chief Medical Officer
CHR: Cam Blalock, Senior Vice President Corporate Services
CNO: Leslie Hall, R.N., Senior Vice President–Chief Nursing Officer
Web address: www.nhcs.org
Control: Hospital district or authority, Government, nonfederal **Service:** General Medical and Surgical

Staffed Beds: 303 **Admissions:** 6000 **Census:** 186 **Outpatient Visits:** 87626 **Births:** 482 **Total Expense ($000):** 111799 **Payroll Expense ($000):** 44407 **Personnel:** 1563

ROXBORO—Person County

✠ **PERSON MEMORIAL HOSPITAL (340159)**, 615 Ridge Road, Zip 27573–4629; tel. 336/599–2121, (Total facility includes 60 beds in nursing home–type unit) **A**1 10 **F**3 11 15 18 28 29 34 40 45 57 59 64 70 75 77 79 81 85 87 93 96 97 107 108 110 111 114 119 128 130 132 146 **P**6 **S** Duke LifePoint Healthcare, Brentwood, TN
Primary Contact: David Ziolkowski, Chief Executive Officer
CFO: Jessi Ayers, Chief Financial Officer
CIO: Rhonda M. Elliott, Director Information Technology and Meaningful Use
CHR: Mary Barksdale, Director Human Resources
CNO: Lynn Peoples, Interim Chief Nursing Officer
Web address: www.personhospital.com
Control: Partnership, Investor–owned, for–profit **Service:** General Medical and Surgical

Staffed Beds: 106 **Admissions:** 1252 **Census:** 61 **Outpatient Visits:** 25551 **Births:** 0 **Total Expense ($000):** 27100 **Payroll Expense ($000):** 8981 **Personnel:** 243

Many Facility Codes have changed. Please refer to the AHA Guide Code Chart.   © 2016 AHA Guide

RUTHERFORDTON—Rutherford County

⊞ **RUTHERFORD REGIONAL HEALTH SYSTEM (340013)**, 288 South Ridgecrest Avenue, Zip 28139–2838; tel. 828/286–5000 **A**1 2 10 19 **F**3 11 13 15 18 20 28 29 30 31 34 35 40 45 48 49 50 57 59 62 64 70 74 75 76 77 78 79 81 82 85 86 87 89 93 97 98 100 101 102 104 106 107 108 110 111 114 115 118 119 130 131 132 135 146 147 **S** Duke LifePoint Healthcare, Brentwood, TN
Primary Contact: James Atkins, PharmD, Chief Executive Officer
COO: John Domansky, Vice President Operations
CFO: Jeff Rush, Chief Financial Officer
CIO: Tommy Finley, Chief Information Officer
CHR: Robin B. Callas, R.N., Vice President Human Resources
Web address: www.rutherfordhosp.org
Control: Partnership, Investor–owned, for–profit **Service:** General Medical and Surgical

Staffed Beds: 112 **Admissions:** 4500 **Census:** 51 **Outpatient Visits:** 84232 **Births:** 541 **Total Expense ($000):** 79602 **Payroll Expense ($000):** 35358 **Personnel:** 638

SALISBURY—Rowan County

⊞ **NOVANT HEALTH ROWAN MEDICAL CENTER (340015)**, 612 Mocksville Avenue, Zip 28144–2799; tel. 704/210–5000 **A**1 2 10 19 **F**3 8 11 12 13 15 18 20 22 26 28 29 30 31 32 34 35 37 39 40 44 45 49 50 53 56 57 59 60 64 65 68 70 71 73 74 75 76 77 78 79 81 84 85 86 87 90 91 92 93 94 98 100 102 103 107 108 110 111 114 115 119 120 121 123 124 126 130 131 132 135 141 142 146 147 148 **S** Novant Health, Winston Salem, NC
Primary Contact: Dari Caldwell, R.N., Ph.D., FACHE, President and Chief Operating Officer
COO: Dari Caldwell, R.N., President and Chief Operating Officer
CMO: Thomas F. Trahey, M.D., Vice President Medical Affairs
CNO: Cora Greene, Chief Nursing Officer
Web address: www.https://www.novanthealth.org/rowan–medical–center.aspx
Control: Other not–for–profit (including NFP Corporation) **Service:** General Medical and Surgical

Staffed Beds: 147 **Admissions:** 9755 **Census:** 137 **Outpatient Visits:** 117988 **Births:** 727 **Total Expense ($000):** 178869 **Payroll Expense ($000):** 57865 **Personnel:** 899

VETERANS AFFAIRS MEDICAL CENTER See W. G. (Bill) Heffner Veterans Affairs Medical Center

⊞ **W. G. (BILL) HEFFNER VETERANS AFFAIRS MEDICAL CENTER**, 1601 Brenner Avenue, Zip 28144–2559; tel. 704/638–9000, (Nonreporting) **A**1 3 5 **S** Department of Veterans Affairs, Washington, DC
Primary Contact: Kaye Green, FACHE, Director
CFO: Steve Patil, Chief Financial Officer
CIO: Deborah Gunn, Chief Information Officer
CHR: Sandra Fischer, Director Human Resources
Web address: www.salisbury.va.gov
Control: Veterans Affairs, Government, federal **Service:** Psychiatric

Staffed Beds: 171

SANFORD—Lee County

⊞ **CENTRAL CAROLINA HOSPITAL (340020)**, 1135 Carthage Street, Zip 27330–4162; tel. 919/774–2100 **A**1 10 **F**3 7 8 11 13 15 20 22 28 29 30 34 40 45 47 49 50 57 59 60 65 68 70 72 74 75 76 79 81 84 85 87 92 93 97 98 107 108 110 111 115 118 119 126 129 130 132 135 146 147 148 **S** Duke LifePoint Healthcare, Brentwood, TN
Primary Contact: John Maxwell, Chief Executive Officer
CFO: Debbie Kyzar, Chief Financial Officer
CIO: Jimmy Whitaker, Director Information Systems
CHR: Deanna Lamb, Director Human Resources
CNO: Mary Florit, Interim Chief Nursing Officer
Web address: www.centralcarolinahosp.com
Control: Corporation, Investor–owned, for–profit **Service:** General Medical and Surgical

Staffed Beds: 137 **Admissions:** 4853 **Census:** 45 **Outpatient Visits:** 72150 **Births:** 826 **Total Expense ($000):** 69513 **Payroll Expense ($000):** 28024 **Personnel:** 603

SCOTLAND NECK—Halifax County

★ **OUR COMMUNITY HOSPITAL (341302)**, 921 Junior High Road, Zip 27874–0405, Mailing Address: Box 405, Zip 27874–0405; tel. 252/826–4144, (Nonreporting) **A**10 18
Primary Contact: Thomas K. Majure, Administrator
CFO: Sarah Diversi, Chief Financial Officer
CMO: Cornelius Artis, M.D., Chief Medical Officer
CIO: Dana Mobley, Chief Information Officer
CNO: Claudia Giddings, R.N., Chief Nursing Officer
Web address: www.och–bltc.org
Control: Other not–for–profit (including NFP Corporation) **Service:** General Medical and Surgical

Staffed Beds: 75

SHELBY—Cleveland County

⊞ **CLEVELAND REGIONAL MEDICAL CENTER (340021)**, 201 East Grover Street, Zip 28150–3917; tel. 980/487–3000 **A**1 2 10 19 **F**3 8 13 15 18 20 28 29 30 31 32 34 35 39 40 43 45 47 48 49 50 51 56 57 59 64 65 70 74 75 76 77 78 79 80 81 85 86 87 89 93 102 107 108 110 111 114 115 118 119 121 123 126 130 131 132 135 143 145 146 147 148 **S** Carolinas Healthcare System, Charlotte, NC
Primary Contact: Brian Gwyn, President and Chief Executive Officer
COO: Brian Gwyn, President Chief Operating Officer
CFO: Christine M. Martin, Vice President and Chief Financial Officer
CMO: Charles M. Tomlinson, M.D., Chief Medical Officer
CIO: Craig D. Richardville, Chief Information Officer
CHR: Debra Kale, Vice President Human Resources
CNO: Veronica Poole–Adams, R.N., Vice President, Chief Operating Officer and Chief Nursing Executive
Web address: www.clevelandregional.org
Control: Hospital district or authority, Government, nonfederal **Service:** General Medical and Surgical

Staffed Beds: 173 **Admissions:** 7172 **Census:** 75 **Outpatient Visits:** 138992 **Births:** 1023 **Total Expense ($000):** 142285 **Payroll Expense ($000):** 51133 **Personnel:** 944

SILER CITY—Chatham County

⊞ **CHATHAM HOSPITAL (341311)**, 475 Progress Boulevard, Zip 27344–6787, Mailing Address: P.O. Box 649, Zip 27344–0649; tel. 919/799–4000 **A**1 10 18 **F**3 15 18 26 28 29 30 34 35 39 40 45 46 57 59 68 70 75 77 81 85 92 93 107 110 111 114 119 130 133 135 **S** UNC Health Care, Chapel Hill, NC
Primary Contact: Robert A. Enders, Jr., President
CMO: Raghid Bitar, Chief of Medical Staff
CIO: Janice Fraley, IT Entity Director – Information Services Division
CHR: Jodie Sartor Solow, Director Human Resources
CNO: Tammy Needham, Chief Nursing Officer
Web address: www.chathamhospital.org
Control: Other not–for–profit (including NFP Corporation) **Service:** General Medical and Surgical

Staffed Beds: 25 **Admissions:** 954 **Census:** 14 **Outpatient Visits:** 38400 **Births:** 3 **Total Expense ($000):** 30528 **Payroll Expense ($000):** 9636 **Personnel:** 192

SMITHFIELD—Johnston County

⊞ **JOHNSTON HEALTH (340090)**, 509 North Bright Leaf Boulevard, Zip 27577–4407, Mailing Address: P.O. Box 1376, Zip 27577–1376; tel. 919/934–8171 **A**1 2 10 **F**3 11 13 15 17 18 20 22 26 28 29 30 31 32 34 35 40 42 45 49 50 53 57 59 61 62 63 64 66 68 70 73 74 75 76 79 81 85 86 87 89 92 93 97 98 100 107 108 110 111 115 119 120 121 126 130 132 144 146 147 148 **S** UNC Health Care, Chapel Hill, NC
Primary Contact: Charles W. Elliott, Jr., Chief Executive Officer
COO: Ruth Marler, Chief Nursing Officer and Chief Operating Officer
CFO: Edward A. Klein, Chief Financial Officer
CIO: Teresa Chappell, Chief Information Officer
CHR: Timothy A. Hays, Vice President Human Resources
CNO: Ruth Marler, Chief Nursing Officer and Chief Operating Officer
Web address: www.johnstonhealth.org
Control: Hospital district or authority, Government, nonfederal **Service:** General Medical and Surgical

Staffed Beds: 145 **Admissions:** 9569 **Census:** 111 **Outpatient Visits:** 157422 **Births:** 1390 **Total Expense ($000):** 171860 **Payroll Expense ($000):** 70505 **Personnel:** 1257

Hospital, Medicare Provider Number, Address, Telephone, Approval, Facility, and Physician Codes, Health Care System

★ American Hospital Association (AHA) membership
□ The Joint Commission accreditation
○ Healthcare Facilities Accreditation Program
◇ DNV Healthcare Inc. accreditation
⇧ Center for Improvement in Healthcare Quality Accreditation
△ Commission on Accreditation of Rehabilitation Facilities (CARF) accreditation

NC

SOUTHPORT—Brunswick County

✠ **J. ARTHUR DOSHER MEMORIAL HOSPITAL (341327)**, 924 North Howe Street, Zip 28461–3099; tel. 910/457–3800, (Total facility includes 57 beds in nursing home–type unit) **A**1 10 18 **F**3 15 28 30 34 35 40 45 47 50 54 57 59 64 68 75 77 79 81 91 93 97 107 110 111 114 115 118 119 127 128 129 130 131 132 133 144 146 148 **P**6
Primary Contact: Thomas R. Siemers, Chief Executive Officer
COO: Carol Northup, R.N., Chief Nursing Officer and Chief Operating Officer
CFO: Daniel J. Porter, Senior Vice President and Chief Financial Officer
CIO: Susan Shomaker, Director Information Management Systems
CHR: Deanna Parker, Director Human Relations
CNO: Carol Northup, R.N., Chief Nursing Officer and Chief Operating Officer
Web address: www.dosher.org
Control: Hospital district or authority, Government, nonfederal **Service:** General Medical and Surgical

> **Staffed Beds:** 89 **Admissions:** 932 **Census:** 45 **Outpatient Visits:** 60480 **Births:** 0 **Total Expense ($000):** 40741 **Payroll Expense ($000):** 15874 **Personnel:** 287

SPARTA—Alleghany County

✠ **ALLEGHANY MEMORIAL HOSPITAL (341320)**, 233 Doctors Street, Zip 28675–9247; tel. 336/372–5511 **A**1 10 18 **F**3 15 18 28 29 30 34 35 40 43 45 59 64 67 77 78 79 81 82 87 90 93 97 107 111 114 119 129 130 131 133 135 146 **S** Alliant Management Services, Louisville, KY
Primary Contact: Craig James, President
CFO: Brett Liverman, Chief Financial Officer
CMO: Joe Arocha, Chief of Staff
CIO: Darlene Keith, Chief Information Systems
CHR: Courtney Bennett, Human Resource Manager
CNO: Wendy Orton, Chief Nursing Officer
Web address: www.amhsparta.org
Control: Other not–for–profit (including NFP Corporation) **Service:** General Medical and Surgical

> **Staffed Beds:** 25 **Admissions:** 461 **Census:** 5 **Outpatient Visits:** 27660 **Births:** 0 **Total Expense ($000):** 12210 **Payroll Expense ($000):** 5244 **Personnel:** 141

SPRUCE PINE—Mitchell County

✠ **BLUE RIDGE REGIONAL HOSPITAL (340011)**, 125 Hospital Drive, Zip 28777–3035; tel. 828/765–4201, (Includes BLUE RIDGE MEDICAL CENTER – YANCEY CAMPUS, 800 Medical Campus Drive, Burnsville, Zip 28714–9010; tel. 828/682–0200) **A**1 10 18 **F**3 13 15 17 28 29 30 31 32 34 35 40 43 45 46 50 53 54 57 59 64 66 70 75 76 77 78 79 81 82 85 87 90 93 96 97 107 108 111 114 118 119 127 128 129 130 131 132 135 146 147 148 **P**6 **S** Mission Health System, Asheville, NC
Primary Contact: Rebecca W. Carter, MSN, R.N., FACHE, Chief Executive Officer and Chief Nursing Officer
CFO: Clint Stewart, Chief Financial Officer
CMO: Jennifer Larson, M.D., Chief of Staff
CIO: Pam Blevins, R.N., Director, Clinical Informatics
CNO: Rebecca W. Carter, MSN, Chief Executive Officer and Chief Nursing Officer
Web address: www.spchospital.org
Control: Other not–for–profit (including NFP Corporation) **Service:** General Medical and Surgical

> **Staffed Beds:** 42 **Admissions:** 1440 **Census:** 11 **Outpatient Visits:** 102726 **Births:** 127 **Total Expense ($000):** 40249 **Payroll Expense ($000):** 11233 **Personnel:** 265

STATESVILLE—Iredell County

✠ **DAVIS REGIONAL MEDICAL CENTER (340144)**, 218 Old Mocksville Road, Zip 28625–1930, Mailing Address: P.O. Box 1823, Zip 28687–1823; tel. 704/873–0281, (Nonreporting) **A**1 10 19 **S** Community Health Systems, Inc., Franklin, TN
Primary Contact: William Chad French, Chief Executive Officer
CFO: Hugh Tobin, Chief Financial Officer
CMO: John Allan, Chief of Staff
CIO: Janie Stikeleather, Director Marketing and Community Relations
CHR: Christine McKenzie, Director Human Resources
CNO: Janice S. Martin, R.N., Chief Nursing Officer
Web address: www.davisregional.com
Control: Corporation, Investor–owned, for–profit **Service:** General Medical and Surgical

> **Staffed Beds:** 130

IREDELL HEALTH SYSTEM (340039)

✠ **IREDELL HEALTH SYSTEM (340039)**, 557 Brookdale Drive, Zip 28677–4107, Mailing Address: P.O. Box 1828, Zip 28687–1828; tel. 704/873–5661, (Total facility includes 48 beds in nursing home–type unit) **A**1 2 10 **F**3 11 13 15 17 18 20 22 28 29 30 31 32 34 35 40 41 45 47 49 50 56 57 58 59 60 62 64 68 70 74 75 76 77 78 79 81 82 85 86 87 89 91 93 97 107 108 111 114 115 117 118 119 120 121 123 127 128 129 130 132 135 146 147 148 **P**6
Primary Contact: Ed Rush, President and Chief Executive Officer
COO: John Snow, Vice President Ancillary and Support Services
CFO: Skip Smith, Vice President Finance
CMO: Carla Pence, President Medical Staff
CIO: Kyle Smith, Director Information Systems
CHR: John Green, Vice President Professional Services and Facility Planning
CNO: Becky Quate, Vice President Nursing and Patient Care Services
Web address: www.iredellhealth.org
Control: Other not–for–profit (including NFP Corporation) **Service:** General Medical and Surgical

> **Staffed Beds:** 203 **Admissions:** 8100 **Census:** 121 **Outpatient Visits:** 127613 **Births:** 773 **Total Expense ($000):** 150087 **Payroll Expense ($000):** 67244 **Personnel:** 1012

SYLVA—Jackson County

✠ **HARRIS REGIONAL HOSPITAL (340016)**, 68 Hospital Road, Zip 28779–2722; tel. 828/586–7000 **A**1 10 **F**3 7 8 11 13 15 28 29 30 31 34 35 40 46 50 54 62 63 64 68 70 72 75 76 77 78 79 81 82 84 85 86 87 89 93 107 108 110 111 114 119 120 121 129 130 131 135 143 144 146 147 148 **S** Duke LifePoint Healthcare, Brentwood, TN
Primary Contact: Steve Heatherly, Chief Executive Officer
CHR: Janet Millsaps, Chief Human Resources Officer
Web address: www.westcare.org
Control: Corporation, Investor–owned, for–profit **Service:** General Medical and Surgical

> **Staffed Beds:** 86 **Admissions:** 3645 **Census:** 37 **Outpatient Visits:** 120757 **Births:** 464 **Total Expense ($000):** 62538 **Payroll Expense ($000):** 23191 **Personnel:** 756

TARBORO—Edgecombe County

✠ △ **VIDANT EDGECOMBE HOSPITAL (340107)**, 111 Hospital Drive, Zip 27886–2011; tel. 252/641–7700 **A**1 2 3 7 10 **F**3 11 13 15 18 28 29 30 31 34 35 40 45 50 57 59 70 73 75 76 78 79 81 82 85 87 89 90 92 93 96 107 110 111 119 127 130 131 132 135 145 146 **S** Vidant Health, Greenville, NC
Primary Contact: Wendell H. Baker, Jr., President
CFO: Charles Alford, Vice President Financial Services
CMO: Barry Bunn, M.D., Chief of Staff
CHR: David Prafka, Ed.D., Director of Human Resources
CNO: Patrick Heins, Vice President Patient Care Services
Web address: www.https://www.vidanthealth.com/edgecombe/default.aspx
Control: Other not–for–profit (including NFP Corporation) **Service:** General Medical and Surgical

> **Staffed Beds:** 94 **Admissions:** 3852 **Census:** 45 **Outpatient Visits:** 73188 **Births:** 496 **Total Expense ($000):** 69305 **Payroll Expense ($000):** 23946 **Personnel:** 499

THOMASVILLE—Davidson County

✠ ◇ **NOVANT HEALTH THOMASVILLE MEDICAL CENTER (340085)**, 207 Old Lexington Road, Zip 27360–3428, Mailing Address: P.O. Box 789, Zip 27361–0789; tel. 336/472–2000 **A**1 3 10 21 **F**3 8 13 15 18 20 28 29 30 34 35 40 45 47 48 50 56 57 59 64 70 74 76 77 78 79 81 82 83 84 85 86 87 91 98 103 104 107 108 111 114 117 118 119 124 126 129 130 131 132 135 141 144 146 147 148 **S** Novant Health, Winston Salem, NC
Primary Contact: Kathie A. Johnson, R.N., MS, Ph.D., Chief Executive Officer
CNO: Christina Grabus, R.N., Chief Nursing Officer
Web address: www.thomasvillemedicalcenter.org
Control: Other not–for–profit (including NFP Corporation) **Service:** General Medical and Surgical

> **Staffed Beds:** 80 **Admissions:** 4277 **Census:** 72 **Outpatient Visits:** 111006 **Births:** 727 **Total Expense ($000):** 78599 **Payroll Expense ($000):** 27349 **Personnel:** 450

TROY—Montgomery County

✠ **FIRSTHEALTH MONTGOMERY MEMORIAL HOSPITAL (341303)**, 520 Allen Street, Zip 27371–2802; tel. 910/571–5000 **A**1 10 18 **F**3 11 15 29 30 40 45 47 49 59 64 81 85 87 93 97 107 110 114 119 127 129 133 135 146 **S** FirstHealth of the Carolinas, Pinehurst, NC
Primary Contact: Beth Walker, R.N., President
CFO: Bryan Hawkins, Controller
CIO: David B. Dillehunt, Chief Information Officer
CHR: Tina H. Thompson, Coordinator Human Resources
CNO: Pam Gaddy, Director, Patient Care Services and Chief Nursing Officer
Web address: www.firsthealth.org
Control: Other not–for–profit (including NFP Corporation) **Service:** General Medical and Surgical

> **Staffed Beds:** 25 **Admissions:** 281 **Census:** 2 **Outpatient Visits:** 20936 **Births:** 0 **Total Expense ($000):** 11816 **Payroll Expense ($000):** 5750 **Personnel:** 107

NC

WADESBORO—Anson County

☒ **CAROLINAS HEALTHCARE SYSTEM ANSON (340084)**, 2301 U.S Highway 74 West, Zip 28170; tel. 704/994–4500 **A**1 10 **F**11 15 28 29 34 35 40 57 59 62 64 71 77 81 86 87 93 97 107 110 114 119 130 131 132 135 145 146 **S** Carolinas Healthcare System, Charlotte, NC
Primary Contact: Michael Lutes, President
CFO: Jeff Griffin, Assistant Vice President Finance
CMO: Edward Blasko, Chief of Staff
CIO: Lisa Sykes, IS/Communications Director
CHR: Rhonda McFarland, Director Human Resources
CNO: Denise White, MSN, Chief Nurse Executive
Web address: www.carolinashealthcare.org/anson
Control: Hospital district or authority, Government, nonfederal **Service:** General Medical and Surgical

Staffed Beds: 15 **Admissions:** 190 **Census:** 1 **Outpatient Visits:** 31131
Births: 0 **Total Expense ($000):** 16267 **Payroll Expense ($000):** 6116
Personnel: 111

WASHINGTON—Beaufort County

BEAUFORT COUNTY HOSPITAL See Vidant Beaufort Hospital

☒ **VIDANT BEAUFORT HOSPITAL (340186)**, 628 East 12th Street, Zip 27889–3409; tel. 252/975–4100 **A**1 10 **F**3 5 9 13 15 26 27 28 29 30 31 34 35 36 38 40 49 53 57 59 64 65 69 70 75 76 77 78 79 81 82 85 86 87 93 97 98 99 100 101 102 104 107 108 109 111 115 118 119 129 130 132 135 143 144 145 146 **S** Vidant Health, Greenville, NC
Primary Contact: Harvey Case, President
CFO: Charles Alford, Vice President Finance
CMO: Paul Garcia, Chief of Staff
CHR: Jenny Brown, Human Resources Director
CNO: Lou Montana–Rhodes, Vice President of Patient Care Services
Web address: www.vidanthealth.com
Control: Hospital district or authority, Government, nonfederal **Service:** General Medical and Surgical

Staffed Beds: 79 **Admissions:** 3060 **Census:** 45 **Outpatient Visits:** 54926
Births: 313 **Total Expense ($000):** 62762 **Payroll Expense ($000):** 20860
Personnel: 454

WHITEVILLE—Columbus County

☒ **COLUMBUS REGIONAL HEALTHCARE SYSTEM (340068)**, 500 Jefferson Street, Zip 28472–3634; tel. 910/642–8011 **A**1 10 19 **F**11 13 15 18 20 22 28 29 30 31 34 35 40 45 46 47 48 49 50 55 57 59 60 65 68 70 71 74 75 76 77 78 79 81 86 87 89 91 92 93 94 97 107 110 111 112 114 119 120 126 129 130 132 135 146 147 148 **P**5 7 **S** Carolinas Healthcare System, Charlotte, NC
Primary Contact: Carla Hollis, President and Chief Executive Officer
CFO: Carl Biber, Chief Financial Officer
CMO: Samuel N. Wheatley, Chief Medical Officer
CIO: Lisa Ward, Director Management Information Systems
CHR: Andrea West, MS, Vice President of Human Resources
CNO: Terri Veneziano, Interim Chief Nursing Officer
Web address: www.crhealthcare.org/
Control: Other not–for–profit (including NFP Corporation) **Service:** General Medical and Surgical

Staffed Beds: 85 **Admissions:** 4247 **Census:** 54 **Outpatient Visits:** 120895
Births: 410 **Total Expense ($000):** 72289 **Payroll Expense ($000):** 25402
Personnel: 495

WILLIAMSTON—Martin County

☒ **MARTIN GENERAL HOSPITAL (340133)**, 310 South McCaskey Road, Zip 27892–2150, Mailing Address: P.O. Box 1128, Zip 27892–1128; tel. 252/809–6300, (Nonreporting) **A**1 10 **S** Quorum Health, Brentwood, TN
Primary Contact: Taffy J. Arias, Chief Executive Officer
CFO: John Jacobson, Chief Financial Officer
CIO: James Griffin, Manager Information Systems
CHR: Rebecca Edwards, Director Human Resources
CNO: Gregory Hornick, MSN, Chief Nursing Officer
Web address: www.martingeneral.com
Control: Corporation, Investor–owned, for–profit **Service:** General Medical and Surgical

Staffed Beds: 49

WILMINGTON—New Hanover County

☒ △ **NEW HANOVER REGIONAL MEDICAL CENTER (340141)**, 2131 South 17th Street, Zip 28401–7483, Mailing Address: P.O. Box 9000, Zip 28402–9000; tel. 910/343–7000, (Includes CAPE FEAR HOSPITAL, 5301 Wrightsville Avenue, Zip 28403–6599; tel. 910/452–8100) **A**1 2 3 5 7 10 13 20 **F**3 7 8 11 12 13 15 17 18 20 22 24 26 28 29 30 31 34 35 36 37 39 40 42 43 44 45 46 47 48 49 50 53 54 56 57 58 59 60 61 64 65 66 68 70 72 73 74 75 76 77 78 79 80 81 82 84 85 86 87 88 89 90 92 93 94 96 97 98 100 101 102 103 107 108 110 111 114 115 117 118 119 121 123 126 130 131 132 135 144 146 147 148 **S** New Hanover Regional Medical Center, Wilmington, NC
Primary Contact: John H. Gizdic, President and Chief Operating Officer
COO: John H. Gizdic, President and Chief Operating Officer
CFO: Edwin J. Ollie, Executive Vice President and Chief Financial Officer
CMO: Sam Spicer, M.D., Vice President Medical Affairs
CIO: Avery Cloud, Vice President and Chief Information Officer
CHR: Keith A. Strawn, Vice President Human Resources
CNO: Mary Ellen Bonczek, R.N., Chief Nursing Executive
Web address: www.nhrmc.org
Control: County–Government, nonfederal **Service:** General Medical and Surgical

Staffed Beds: 692 **Admissions:** 39565 **Census:** 536 **Outpatient Visits:** 376983 **Births:** 4186 **Total Expense ($000):** 729469 **Payroll Expense ($000):** 288996 **Personnel:** 4599

WILMINGTON TREATMENT CENTER (340168), 2520 Troy Drive, Zip 28401–7643; tel. 910/762–2727, (Nonreporting) **A**10 **S** CRC Health Group, Inc., Cupertino, CA
Primary Contact: Robert Pitts, Executive Director
COO: Paige Bottom, Director Operations
CFO: Virginia Powell, Director Finance
CMO: Patrick Martin, M.D., Medical Director
Web address: www.wilmtreatment.com
Control: Corporation, Investor–owned, for–profit **Service:** Alcoholism and other chemical dependency

Staffed Beds: 44

WILSON—Wilson County

TRIANGLE EAST NURSING CARE CENTER See WilMed Nursing Care Center

☒ **WILSON MEDICAL CENTER (340126)**, 1705 Tarboro Street, S.W., Zip 27893–3428; tel. 252/399–8040, (Nonreporting) **A**1 2 10 19 **S** Duke LifePoint Healthcare, Brentwood, TN
Primary Contact: William E. Caldwell, Jr., Chief Executive Officer
CMO: Rick Guarino, M.D., Vice President Medical Affairs
CIO: Brian Dietrick, Director Information Systems
CHR: Denise O'Hara, Vice President Human Resources
Web address: www.wilmed.org
Control: Other not–for–profit (including NFP Corporation) **Service:** General Medical and Surgical

Staffed Beds: 206

WINDSOR—Bertie County

☒ **VIDANT BERTIE HOSPITAL (341304)**, 1403 South King Street, Zip 27983–9666, Mailing Address: P.O. Box 40, Zip 27983–0040; tel. 252/794–6600 **A**1 10 18 **F**3 15 29 30 34 35 40 45 46 47 48 49 57 59 64 77 79 81 82 93 94 97 107 110 114 119 127 132 135 146 148 **S** Vidant Health, Greenville, NC
Primary Contact: Jeffrey Sackrison, President
CFO: Brian Harvill, Vice President Financial Services
CMO: William Ballance, Chief of Medical Staff
CIO: Brian White, Director Strategic Planning
CHR: Nicole Spell, Director Human Resources
CNO: Silvia Rose, Director Patient Care Services
Web address: www.vidanthealth.com
Control: Other not–for–profit (including NFP Corporation) **Service:** General Medical and Surgical

Staffed Beds: 6 **Admissions:** 430 **Census:** 4 **Outpatient Visits:** 25004
Births: 0 **Total Expense ($000):** 17691 **Payroll Expense ($000):** 6062
Personnel: 98

WINSTON SALEM—Forsyth County

BRENNER CHILDREN'S HOSPITAL & HEALTH SERVICES See Wake Forest Baptist Medical Center, Winston–Salem

WINSTON–SALEM—Forsyth County

MEDICAL PARK HOSPITAL See Novant Health Medical Park Hospital

---

Hospital, Medicare Provider Number, Address, Telephone, Approval, Facility, and Physician Codes, Health Care System

★ American Hospital Association (AHA) membership   ○ Healthcare Facilities Accreditation Program   ⇑ Center for Improvement in Healthcare Quality Accreditation
□ The Joint Commission accreditation   ◇ DNV Healthcare Inc. accreditation   △ Commission on Accreditation of Rehabilitation Facilities (CARF) accreditation

NC

✠ △ **NOVANT HEALTH FORSYTH MEDICAL CENTER (340014)**, 3333 Silas Creek Parkway, Zip 27103–3090; tel. 336/718–5000, (Includes KERNERSVILLE MEDICAL CENTER, 2911750 Kernersville Medical Parkway, Kernersville, Zip 27284–2932, Mailing Address: 1750 Kernersville Medical Parkway, Zip 27284–2932; tel. 336/564–4000; Chad Setliff, President and Chief Operating Officer) **A**1 2 3 5 7 10 **F**3 5 8 9 12 13 14 15 17 18 20 22 24 26 28 29 30 31 32 34 35 37 38 40 42 45 46 49 50 53 54 56 57 58 59 60 61 64 65 66 67 70 71 72 74 75 76 77 78 79 80 81 82 83 84 85 86 87 89 90 93 98 100 101 102 103 104 105 107 108 109 111 112 114 115 116 117 118 119 120 121 123 124 126 129 130 131 132 135 141 143 146 147 148 **P**6 **S** Novant Health, Winston Salem, NC
Primary Contact: Sean M. Sanz, Chief Executive Officer
CMO: Elms Allen, M.D., Senior Vice President Medical Affairs
CIO: David B. Garrett, Chief Information Officer
CHR: Janet Smith–Hill, Senior Vice President Human Resources
Web address: www.forsythmedicalcenter.org
Control: Other not–for–profit (including NFP Corporation) **Service:** General Medical and Surgical

Staffed Beds: 706 **Admissions:** 42676 **Census:** 655 **Outpatient Visits:** 424804 **Births:** 6181 **Total Expense ($000):** 775107 **Payroll Expense ($000):** 233504 **Personnel:** 3805

✠ **NOVANT HEALTH MEDICAL PARK HOSPITAL (340148)**, 1950 South Hawthorne Road, Zip 27103–3993; tel. 336/718–0600 **A**1 2 10 **F**3 29 35 39 62 64 74 78 79 81 85 126 130 131 141 146 **S** Novant Health, Winston Salem, NC
Primary Contact: Kirsten Royster, Chief Executive Officer
CMO: Elms Allen, M.D., Senior Vice President Medical Affairs
CHR: Vasilia Perimenis, Vice President Human Resources
Web address: www.novanthealth.org
Control: Other not–for–profit (including NFP Corporation) **Service:** General Medical and Surgical

Staffed Beds: 14 **Admissions:** 929 **Census:** 10 **Outpatient Visits:** 34386 **Births:** 0 **Total Expense ($000):** 56203 **Payroll Expense ($000):** 11992 **Personnel:** 201

☐ **OLD VINEYARD BEHAVIORAL HEALTH SERVICES (344007)**, 3637 Old Vineyard Road, Zip 27104–4842; tel. 336/794–3550 **A**1 10 **F**29 50 75 87 98 99 101 102 103 104 105 130 **S** Universal Health Services, Inc., King of Prussia, PA
Primary Contact: Kevin Patton, Chief Executive Officer
CFO: Ernest C. Priddy, III, Chief Financial Officer
CMO: Raj Thotakura, M.D., Medical Director
CHR: Jackie Pennino, Director Human Resources
CNO: Susan Evans, Chief Nursing Officer
Web address: www.oldvineyardbhs.com
Control: Corporation, Investor–owned, for–profit **Service:** Psychiatric

Staffed Beds: 104 **Admissions:** 3804 **Census:** 98 **Outpatient Visits:** 3849 **Births:** 0 **Total Expense ($000):** 19706 **Payroll Expense ($000):** 9841 **Personnel:** 163

✠ **SELECT SPECIALTY HOSPITAL–WINSTON–SALEM (342016)**, 3333 Silas Creek Parkway, 6th Floor, Zip 27103–3013; tel. 336/718–6300, (Nonreporting) **A**1 10 **S** Select Medical Corporation, Mechanicsburg, PA
Primary Contact: Leslie Deane, Chief Executive Officer
CHR: Sherry Meacham, Coordinator Human Resources
Web address: www.selectspecialtyhospitals.com/company/locations/winston–salem.aspx
Control: Corporation, Investor–owned, for–profit **Service:** Long–Term Acute Care hospital

Staffed Beds: 42

✠ △ **WAKE FOREST BAPTIST MEDICAL CENTER (340047)**, Medical Center Boulevard, Zip 27157–0001; tel. 336/716–2011, (Includes BRENNER CHILDREN'S HOSPITAL & HEALTH SERVICES, Medical Center Boulevard, Winston Salem, Zip 27157, Mailing Address: One Medical Center Boulevard, Zip 27157; tel. 336/716–2255) **A**1 2 3 5 7 8 10 **F**3 5 6 7 8 9 11 12 15 16 17 18 19 20 21 22 23 24 25 26 27 28 29 30 31 32 34 35 36 37 38 39 40 41 43 44 45 46 47 48 49 50 52 53 54 55 56 57 58 59 60 61 62 64 65 66 67 68 70 71 72 73 74 75 77 78 79 80 81 82 84 85 86 87 88 89 90 92 93 96 97 98 99 100 101 102 103 104 107 108 110 111 113 114 115 116 117 118 119 120 121 123 124 126 129 130 131 132 133 134 135 136 137 138 141 142 143 144 145 146 147 148 **P**6 7 **S** Wake Forest Baptist Health, Winston–Salem, NC
Primary Contact: John D. McConnell, M.D., Chief Executive Officer
CMO: Russell M. Howerton, M.D., Chief Medical Officer
CIO: Chad Eckes, Vice President Information Services and Chief Information Officer
CHR: Cheryl Locke, Vice President and Chief Human Resource Officer
Web address: www.wakehealth.edu
Control: Other not–for–profit (including NFP Corporation) **Service:** General Medical and Surgical

Staffed Beds: 787 **Admissions:** 40251 **Census:** 656 **Outpatient Visits:** 902054 **Births:** 9 **Total Expense ($000):** 1310782 **Payroll Expense ($000):** 473722 **Personnel:** 8080

NC

NORTH DAKOTA

ASHLEY—Mcintosh County

★ **ASHLEY MEDICAL CENTER (351322)**, 612 North Center Avenue,
Zip 58413–7013, Mailing Address: P.O. Box 450, Zip 58413–0450;
tel. 701/288–3433, (Nonreporting) **A**10 18
Primary Contact: Jerry Lepp, Chief Executive Officer
CMO: Udom Tinsa, M.D., Medical Director
Web address: www.amctoday.org
Control: Other not–for–profit (including NFP Corporation) **Service:** General
Medical and Surgical

Staffed Beds: 64

BELCOURT—Rolette County

☐ ◇ **INDIAN HEALTH SERVICE – QUENTIN N. BURDICK MEMORIAL HEALTH
CARE FACILITY (350063)**, 1300 Hospital Loop, Zip 58316, Mailing Address:
P.O. Box 160, Zip 58316–0160; tel. 701/477–6111 **A**1 3 5 10 21 **F**3 29 34 38
39 40 41 45 48 50 54 56 57 59 61 62 64 65 75 77 81 82 83 85 86 87 93
96 97 99 100 101 102 103 104 107 108 110 114 119 130 132 135 143
144 145 146 147 148 **S** U. S. Indian Health Service, Rockville, MD
Primary Contact: Shelly Harris, Chief Executive Officer
CFO: Deland Davis, Chief Financial Officer
CMO: Vernon Azure, Clinical Director
CIO: Chance Wilkie, Information Technology Specialist
CHR: Donna Belgarde, Human Resources Specialist
CNO: Lynelle Hunt, Director of Nursing
Web address: www.ihs.gov
Control: PHS, Indian Service, Government, federal **Service:** General Medical and
Surgical

Staffed Beds: 27 **Admissions:** 473 **Census:** 6 **Outpatient Visits:** 177629
Births: 151 **Total Expense ($000):** 50991 **Payroll Expense ($000):** 20331
Personnel: 285

BISMARCK—Burleigh County

⊞ △ **CHI ST. ALEXIUS HEALTH (350002)**, 900 East Broadway,
Zip 58501–4586, Mailing Address: P.O. Box 5510, Zip 58506–5510;
tel. 701/530–7000, (Total facility includes 19 beds in nursing home–type unit) **A**1
2 3 5 7 10 **F**3 8 9 11 12 13 15 17 18 19 20 21 22 23 24 25 26 28 29 30 32
34 35 38 40 43 49 53 56 57 58 59 60 62 63 64 68 70 72 74 75 76 77 78
79 81 82 85 86 87 88 89 90 91 92 93 94 95 97 98 99 100 101 102 103
104 105 106 107 110 111 114 117 119 128 129 130 131 132 135 146 147
148 **P**8 **S** Catholic Health Initiatives, Englewood, CO
Primary Contact: Kurt Schley, Market Chief Executive Officer
CFO: Susan Sisk, Chief Financial Officer
CMO: Shiraz Hyder, M.D., Director Medical Affairs
CIO: Todd Bortke, Director Information Systems
CHR: Tom Gregg, Vice President Human Resources
CNO: Rosanne Schmidt, R.N., Chief Nursing Officer
Web address: www.st.alexius.org
Control: Church–operated, Nongovernment, not–for profit **Service:** General
Medical and Surgical

Staffed Beds: 271 **Admissions:** 10368 **Census:** 138 **Outpatient Visits:**
286346 **Births:** 1625 **Total Expense ($000):** 304059 **Payroll Expense
($000):** 160102 **Personnel:** 2193

⊞ △ **SANFORD BISMARCK (350015)**, 300 North Seventh Street,
Zip 58501–4439, Mailing Address: P.O. Box 5525, Zip 58506–5525;
tel. 701/323–6000 **A**1 2 3 5 7 10 19 **F**3 7 9 11 12 13 15 17 18 20 22 24 26
28 29 30 31 32 33 34 35 36 37 38 40 43 44 45 48 49 50 51 52 53 54 56
57 58 59 60 61 62 63 64 68 69 70 72 73 74 75 77 78 79 81 82 85 86 87
88 89 90 91 92 93 96 97 98 99 100 101 102 103 104 105 107 108 110
111 114 115 116 117 118 119 128 129 130 131 132 135 138 144 146
147 148 **P**6 **S** Sanford Health, Sioux Falls, SD
Primary Contact: Craig Lambrecht, M.D., President
COO: Al Hurley, Clinic Chief Operating Officer
CFO: Kirk Cristy, Chief Financial Officer
CMO: Chris Meeker, M.D., Chief Medical Officer
CHR: Scott D. Boehm, Executive Vice President Human Resources and Facilities
CNO: Jan Kamphuis, Ph.D., Executive Vice President and Chief Nurse Executive
Web address: www.bismarck.sanfordhealth.org/
Control: Other not–for–profit (including NFP Corporation) **Service:** General
Medical and Surgical

Staffed Beds: 208 **Admissions:** 11224 **Census:** 139 **Outpatient Visits:**
211291 **Births:** 1089 **Total Expense ($000):** 397109 **Payroll Expense
($000):** 118498 **Personnel:** 2440

SANFORD HEALTH See Sanford Bismarck

BOTTINEAU—Bottineau County

ST. ANDREW'S HEALTH CENTER (351307), 316 Ohmer Street,
Zip 58318–1045; tel. 701/228–9300 **A**5 10 18 **F**3 15 28 29 30 34 35 40 43
57 59 81 93 107 108 110 125 127 130 132 133 143 144 146 **P**5 **S** Sisters
of Mary of the Presentation Health System, Fargo, ND
Primary Contact: Jodi Atkinson, President and Chief Executive Officer
CFO: Sean Rinkenberger, Chief Financial Officer
CMO: Jessica Skjolden, M.D., Chief of Staff
CHR: Brenda Arneson, Administrative Assistant
CNO: Karla Spence, Director of Nursing
Web address: www.standrewshealth.com
Control: Church–operated, Nongovernment, not–for profit **Service:** General
Medical and Surgical

Staffed Beds: 25 **Admissions:** 114 **Census:** 20 **Outpatient Visits:** 8500
Births: 0 **Total Expense ($000):** 8232 **Payroll Expense ($000):** 3370
Personnel: 95

BOWMAN—Bowman County

SOUTHWEST HEALTHCARE SERVICES (351313), 802 2nd Street Northwest,
Zip 58623–4483, Mailing Address: P.O. Drawer C, Zip 58623;
tel. 701/523–5265, (Nonreporting) **A**10 18
Primary Contact: Becky Hansen, Chief Executive Officer
CFO: Becky Hansen, Chief Financial Officer
Web address: www.swhealthcare.net
Control: Other not–for–profit (including NFP Corporation) **Service:** General
Medical and Surgical

Staffed Beds: 89

CANDO—Towner County

★ **TOWNER COUNTY MEDICAL CENTER (351331)**, State Highway 281 North,
Zip 58324, Mailing Address: P.O. Box 688, Zip 58324–0688;
tel. 701/968–4411, (Total facility includes 35 beds in nursing home–type unit) **A**5
10 18 **F**29 31 32 33 34 35 40 41 45 50 53 56 57 59 64 65 67 75 78 81 85
86 87 91 92 93 97 107 110 114 127 128 129 130 133 135 147 148
Primary Contact: Ben Bucher, Chief Executive Officer
CFO: Tammy Larson, Chief Financial Officer
CMO: Russ Petty, M.D., Chief of Staff
CIO: David Fite, Director Information Technology
CHR: Pat Klingenberg, Director Human Resources
Web address: www.tcmedcenter.org
Control: Other not–for–profit (including NFP Corporation) **Service:** General
Medical and Surgical

Staffed Beds: 55 **Admissions:** 190 **Census:** 32 **Outpatient Visits:** 11000
Births: 0 **Personnel:** 120

CARRINGTON—Foster County

★ **CHI ST ALEXIUS HEALTH CARRINGTON MEDICAL CENTER (351318)**, 800
North Fourth Street, Zip 58421–1217, Mailing Address: P.O. Box 461,
Zip 58421–0461; tel. 701/652–3141 **A**5 10 18 **F**7 11 15 28 30 34 40 45 46
75 81 87 107 108 110 114 119 124 127 133 143 146 **P**6 **S** Catholic Health
Initiatives, Englewood, CO
Primary Contact: Mariann Doeling, R.N., President
COO: Brenda Rask, Vice President Operations
CFO: Kurt Sargent, CPA, Vice President, Operational Finance
CIO: Keith Stauffer, Regional Chief Information Officer
CHR: Carol Risovi, Human Resources
CNO: Jodi Lynn Hovdenes, Vice President of Patient Care
Web address: www.carringtonhealthcenter.org
Control: Other not–for–profit (including NFP Corporation) **Service:** General
Medical and Surgical

Staffed Beds: 25 **Admissions:** 330 **Census:** 2 **Outpatient Visits:** 21254
Births: 0 **Total Expense ($000):** 13589 **Payroll Expense ($000):** 3876
Personnel: 99

Hospital, Medicare Provider Number, Address, Telephone, Approval, Facility, and Physician Codes, Health Care System

★ American Hospital Association (AHA) membership ◯ Healthcare Facilities Accreditation Program ⇑ Center for Improvement in Healthcare Quality Accreditation
☐ The Joint Commission accreditation ◇ DNV Healthcare Inc. accreditation △ Commission on Accreditation of Rehabilitation Facilities (CARF) accreditation

CAVALIER—Pembina County

★ **PEMBINA COUNTY MEMORIAL HOSPITAL AND WEDGEWOOD MANOR (351319)**, 301 Mountain Street East, Zip 58220–4015, Mailing Address: P.O. Box 380, Zip 58220–0380; tel. 701/265–8461, (Total facility includes 50 beds in nursing home–type unit) **A**5 10 18 **F**2 3 28 29 31 40 42 43 45 56 59 65 68 78 81 82 84 87 93 97 107 114 119 127 128 130 131 132 133 135 146 **P**5
Primary Contact: Everett A. Butler, Interim Chief Executive Officer
CMO: K. S. Sumra, M.D., Chief of Staff
CIO: Robert Heidt, Director Information Systems
Web address: www.cavalierhospital.com
Control: Other not–for–profit (including NFP Corporation) **Service:** General Medical and Surgical

Staffed Beds: 70 **Admissions:** 460 **Census:** 38 **Outpatient Visits:** 19844 **Births:** 0 **Total Expense ($000):** 12385 **Payroll Expense ($000):** 5417 **Personnel:** 152

COOPERSTOWN—Griggs County

COOPERSTOWN MEDICAL CENTER (351306), 1200 Roberts Avenue, Zip 58425–7101; tel. 701/797–2221, (Nonreporting) **A**10 18
Primary Contact: Nikki Johnson, Interim Chief Executive Officer
CMO: Jeffrey Peterson, M.D., Medical Director
CHR: Pamela VenHuizen, Chief Human Resources Officer
Web address: www.coopermc.com
Control: Other not–for–profit (including NFP Corporation) **Service:** General Medical and Surgical

Staffed Beds: 10

CROSBY—Divide County

★ **ST. LUKE'S MEDICAL CENTER (351325)**, 702 First Street Southwest, Zip 58730–3329, Mailing Address: P.O. Box 10, Zip 58730–0010; tel. 701/965–6384 **A**10 18 **F**1 35 40 59 67 81 90 128 133 **P**6
Primary Contact: Cody Barnhart, Chief Executive Officer
Web address: www.dcstlukes.org/
Control: Other not–for–profit (including NFP Corporation) **Service:** General Medical and Surgical

Staffed Beds: 15 **Admissions:** 87 **Census:** 1 **Outpatient Visits:** 1356 **Births:** 0 **Total Expense ($000):** 10077 **Payroll Expense ($000):** 5367 **Personnel:** 75

DEVILS LAKE—Ramsey County

✠ **CHI ST. ALEXIUS HEALTH DEVILS LAKE HOSPITAL (351333)**, 1031 Seventh Street N.E., Zip 58301–2798; tel. 701/662–2131 **A**1 5 10 18 **F**3 11 13 28 29 30 34 35 40 43 45 50 57 70 75 76 81 87 93 107 108 111 114 119 130 133 146 148 **S** Catholic Health Initiatives, Englewood, CO
Primary Contact: Andrew Lankowicz, FACHE, President
CFO: Kurt Sargent, CPA, Vice President Operational Finance
CMO: Richard Johnson, M.D., Chief of Medical Staff
CHR: Bonnie Mattern, Director Human Resources
CNO: Aaron Johnson, Vice President Patient Care Services and Chief Nursing Officer
Web address: www.mercyhospitaldl.com
Control: Other not–for–profit (including NFP Corporation) **Service:** General Medical and Surgical

Staffed Beds: 25 **Admissions:** 821 **Census:** 11 **Outpatient Visits:** 20109 **Births:** 319 **Total Expense ($000):** 20387 **Payroll Expense ($000):** 8456 **Personnel:** 130

DICKINSON—Stark County

✠ **ST. JOSEPH'S HOSPITAL AND HEALTH CENTER (351336)**, 2500 Fairway Street, Zip 58601–4399; tel. 701/456–4000 **A**1 5 10 18 **F**3 8 11 13 15 28 29 30 34 35 40 53 57 59 64 70 75 76 79 81 84 85 86 87 89 97 107 108 111 114 119 127 129 130 132 133 146 **S** Catholic Health Initiatives, Englewood, CO
Primary Contact: Reed Reyman, President
CFO: Stephanie Franken, Vice President Operational Finance
CHR: Denise Lutz, Chief Human Resources Officer
CNO: DeeAnna Opstedahl, R.N., Vice President Patient Care Services
Web address: www.stjoeshospital.org
Control: Church–operated, Nongovernment, not–for profit **Service:** General Medical and Surgical

Staffed Beds: 25 **Admissions:** 1889 **Census:** 16 **Outpatient Visits:** 48734 **Births:** 693 **Total Expense ($000):** 64542 **Payroll Expense ($000):** 26322 **Personnel:** 280

ELGIN—Grant County

JACOBSON MEMORIAL HOSPITAL CARE CENTER (351314), 601 East Street North, Zip 58533–7105, Mailing Address: P.O. Box 367, Zip 58533–0367; tel. 701/584–2792 **A**10 18 **F**1 4 16 17 28 34 40 41 43 56 59 67 70 71 72 73 80 88 89 90 93 97 98 102 107 119 127 128 130 131 133 146 148
Primary Contact: Theo Stoller, Chief Executive Officer
CFO: Scott Ostenson, Chief Financial Officer
CMO: Deepak Goyal, M.D., Chief of Staff
CHR: Rynae Golke, Director Human Resources
CNO: Connie Gustafson, Director of Nursing
Web address: www.jacobsonhospital.org
Control: Other not–for–profit (including NFP Corporation) **Service:** Long–Term Acute Care hospital

Staffed Beds: 25 **Admissions:** 235 **Census:** 21 **Outpatient Visits:** 8017 **Births:** 0 **Total Expense ($000):** 6274 **Payroll Expense ($000):** 2355 **Personnel:** 65

FARGO—Cass County

✠ **ESSENTIA HEALTH FARGO (350070)**, 3000 32nd Avenue South, Zip 58103–6132; tel. 701/364–8000 **A**1 2 5 10 **F**3 9 11 12 13 15 17 18 20 22 24 25 26 28 29 30 31 32 33 34 35 38 40 41 43 44 45 46 47 48 49 50 51 56 57 58 59 60 61 64 65 70 72 74 75 76 77 78 79 81 82 83 84 85 86 87 89 91 92 93 97 107 108 109 110 111 112 113 114 115 116 117 118 119 120 121 122 123 124 126 129 130 131 132 135 144 145 146 147 148 **S** Essentia Health, Duluth, MN
Primary Contact: Timothy Sayler, Chief Operating Officer
COO: Timothy Sayler, Chief Operating Officer
CFO: Dennis Fuhrman, Vice President Finance
CMO: Michael Briggs, M.D., Chief Medical Officer
CIO: Ken Gilles, Chief Information Officer
CHR: Keith Wahlund, Vice President Human Resources
Web address: www.essentiahealth.com
Control: Other not–for–profit (including NFP Corporation) **Service:** General Medical and Surgical

Staffed Beds: 117 **Admissions:** 8093 **Census:** 95 **Outpatient Visits:** 130671 **Births:** 1476 **Total Expense ($000):** 311919 **Payroll Expense ($000):** 140169 **Personnel:** 1653

✠ **FARGO VETERANS AFFAIRS HEALTH CARE SYSTEM**, 2101 Elm Street North, Zip 58102–2498; tel. 701/232–3241, (Nonreporting) **A**1 3 5 **S** Department of Veterans Affairs, Washington, DC
Primary Contact: Lavonne Liversage, Director
COO: Dale DeKrey, MS, Associate Director Operations and Resources
CFO: Roger Sayler, Finance Officer
CMO: J. Brian Hancock, M.D., Chief of Staff
CIO: Raymond Nelson, Acting Chief Information Resource Management
CHR: Jason Wells, Chief Human Resources Management Service
CNO: Julie Bruhn, R.N., Associate Director Patient Care and Nurse Executive
Web address: www.fargo.va.gov/
Control: Veterans Affairs, Government, federal **Service:** General Medical and Surgical

Staffed Beds: 77

INNOVIS HEALTH See Essentia Health Fargo

KINDRED HOSPITAL FARGO See Vibra Hospital of Fargo

MERITCARE MEDICAL CENTER See Sanford Medical Center Fargo

✠ **PRAIRIE ST. JOHN'S (354004)**, 510 4th Street South, Zip 58103–1914; tel. 701/476–7200, (Nonreporting) **A**1 10 **S** Universal Health Services, Inc., King of Prussia, PA
Primary Contact: Jeff Herman, Chief Executive Officer
COO: Jennifer Faul, Chief Operating Officer
CFO: Tom Eide, Chief Financial Officer
CMO: Eduardo Meza, M.D., Medical Director
CHR: Michelle A. Parkinson, Director Human Resources
CNO: Jacki Toppen, Director of Nursing
Web address: www.prairie–stjohns.com
Control: Partnership, Investor–owned, for–profit **Service:** Psychiatric

Staffed Beds: 94

Many Facility Codes have changed. Please refer to the AHA Guide Code Chart. © 2016 AHA Guide

✉ △ **SANFORD MEDICAL CENTER FARGO (350011)**, 801 Broadway North, Zip 58122–3641; tel. 701/234–2000, (Includes SANFORD SOUTH UNIVERSITY, 1720 South University Drive, Zip 58103–4994; tel. 701/234–2000; Paul F. Richard, Executive Vice President) **A**1 2 3 5 7 8 10 19 **F**3 7 8 9 11 12 13 15 17 18 19 20 21 22 23 24 25 26 27 28 29 30 31 32 33 34 35 36 37 38 39 40 43 44 45 46 47 48 49 50 51 52 53 54 55 56 57 58 59 60 61 62 63 64 65 68 70 71 72 73 74 75 76 78 79 80 81 82 83 84 85 86 87 88 89 90 91 92 93 94 96 97 98 99 100 101 102 103 104 105 107 111 112 114 115 116 117 118 119 120 121 123 124 126 129 130 131 132 135 138 141 142 143 144 145 146 147 148 **P**6 **S** Sanford Health, Sioux Falls, SD
Primary Contact: Paul F. Richard, Executive Vice President
COO: Ellen Cooke, Chief Operating Officer
CFO: Tiffany Lawrence, Vice President of Finance
CMO: Douglas Griffin, M.D., Vice President Medical Officer
CIO: Arlyn Broekhuis, Chief Information Officer
CHR: Bill Gassen, Chief Human Resource Officer
CNO: Roberta Young, Vice President Nursing
Web address: www.sanfordhealth.org
Control: Other not–for–profit (including NFP Corporation) **Service:** General Medical and Surgical

Staffed Beds: 473 **Admissions:** 22743 **Census:** 341 **Outpatient Visits:** 435910 **Births:** 2634 **Total Expense ($000):** 861830 **Payroll Expense ($000):** 226740 **Personnel:** 3960

VETERANS AFFAIRS HEALTH CARE SYSTEM See Fargo Veterans Affairs Health Care System

✉ **VIBRA HOSPITAL OF FARGO (352004)**, 1720 University Drive South, Zip 58103–4940; tel. 701/241–9099, (Nonreporting) **A**1 10 **S** Vibra Healthcare, Mechanicsburg, PA
Primary Contact: Custer Huseby, Chief Executive Officer
Web address: www.vhfargo.com
Control: Corporation, Investor–owned, for–profit **Service:** Long–Term Acute Care hospital

Staffed Beds: 31

FORT YATES—Sioux County

◇ **STANDING ROCK SERVICE UNIT, FORT YATES HOSPITAL, INDIAN HEALTH SERVICE, DHHS (350064)**, 10 North River Road, Zip 58538, Mailing Address: P.O. Box J, Zip 58538; tel. 701/854–3831, (Nonreporting) **A**5 10 21 **S** U. S. Indian Health Service, Rockville, MD
Primary Contact: Jana Gipp, Chief Executive Officer
CFO: Byron Wilcox, Chief Financial Management Officer
CMO: Sara Jumping Eagle, Clinical Director
CNO: Joelle Keepseagle, Director of Nursing
Web address: www.ihs.gov
Control: PHS, Indian Service, Government, federal **Service:** General Medical and Surgical

Staffed Beds: 12

GARRISON—Mclean County

★ **GARRISON MEMORIAL HOSPITAL (351303)**, 407 Third Avenue S.E., Zip 58540–7235; tel. 701/463–2275, (Nonreporting) **A**5 10 18 **S** Catholic Health Initiatives, Englewood, CO
Primary Contact: Tod Graeber, Administrator
CMO: Vern Harchenko, M.D., Chief of Staff
CNO: Beth Hetletved, Director of Nurses
Web address: www.garrisonmh.com
Control: Other not–for–profit (including NFP Corporation) **Service:** General Medical and Surgical

Staffed Beds: 50

GRAFTON—Walsh County

★ **UNITY MEDICAL CENTER (351320)**, 164 West 13th Street, Zip 58237–1896; tel. 701/352–1620, (Nonreporting) **A**5 10 18
Primary Contact: Alan O'Neil, Chief Executive Officer
CFO: Rachel Ray, Chief Financial Officer
Web address: www.unitymedcenter.com
Control: Other not–for–profit (including NFP Corporation) **Service:** General Medical and Surgical

Staffed Beds: 14

GRAND FORKS—Grand Forks County

✉ △ **ALTRU HEALTH SYSTEM (350019)**, 1200 South Columbia Road, Zip 58201–4036, Mailing Address: P.O. Box 6002, Zip 58206–6002; tel. 701/780–5000, (Includes ALTRU HOSPITAL, 1200 South Columbia Road, Zip 58201, Mailing Address: PO Box 6002, Zip 58206–6002; tel. 701/780–5000; David R. Molmen, M.P.H., Chief Executive Officer; ALTRU REHABILITATION CENTER, 1300 South Columbia Road, Zip 58201; tel. 701/780–2311; David R. Molmen, M.P.H., Chief Executive Officer) **A**1 2 3 5 7 10 20 **F**3 7 8 11 12 13 14 15 18 20 22 24 26 28 29 30 31 32 33 34 35 36 37 38 40 43 44 45 48 49 50 52 53 55 56 57 58 59 60 61 62 63 64 65 68 69 70 71 72 74 75 77 78 79 81 82 83 84 85 86 87 90 91 92 93 94 96 97 98 99 100 101 102 103 104 105 107 108 110 111 114 115 117 119 121 123 124 125 129 130 131 132 135 143 144 145 146 147 148 **P**6
Primary Contact: David R. Molmen, M.P.H., Chief Executive Officer
COO: Brad Wehe, Chief Operating Officer
CFO: Dwight Thompson, Chief Financial Officer
CMO: Colleen Swank, Chief Medical Officer
CIO: Mark Waind, Chief Information Officer
CHR: Kellee J. Fisk, Chief People Officer
CNO: Margaret M. Reed, R.N., Chief Nursing Officer
Web address: www.altru.org
Control: Other not–for–profit (including NFP Corporation) **Service:** General Medical and Surgical

Staffed Beds: 299 **Admissions:** 13079 **Census:** 177 **Outpatient Visits:** 795834 **Births:** 1772 **Total Expense ($000):** 505179 **Payroll Expense ($000):** 266974 **Personnel:** 3282

◇ **RICHARD P. STADTER PSYCHIATRIC CENTER (354005)**, 1451 44th Avenue South Unit A., Zip 58201–3434; tel. 701/772–2500, (Nonreporting) **A**10 21
Primary Contact: Bonnie Peterson, Chief Executive Officer
CFO: Michelle Currie, Chief Financial Officer
CMO: Thomas Peterson, M.D., President
CHR: Amanda Altendorf, Chief Human Resources and Quality Management
Web address: www.stadtercenter.com
Control: Corporation, Investor–owned, for–profit **Service:** Psychiatric

Staffed Beds: 71

HARVEY—Wells County

★ **ST. ALOISIUS MEDICAL CENTER (351327)**, 325 East Brewster Street, Zip 58341–1653; tel. 701/324–4651, (Total facility includes 92 beds in nursing home–type unit) **A**5 10 18 **F**15 28 30 40 45 53 56 57 59 77 81 93 107 110 114 125 128 130 131 132 133 146 147 **S** Sisters of Mary of the Presentation Health System, Fargo, ND
Primary Contact: Gregory LaFrancois, President and Chief Executive Officer
CFO: Sandra Teubner, Chief Financial Officer
Web address: www.staloisius.com
Control: Church–operated, Nongovernment, not–for profit **Service:** General Medical and Surgical

Staffed Beds: 117 **Admissions:** 288 **Census:** 91 **Outpatient Visits:** 7611 **Births:** 0 **Total Expense ($000):** 14100 **Payroll Expense ($000):** 6102 **Personnel:** 160

HAZEN—Mercer County

★ **SAKAKAWEA MEDICAL CENTER (351310)**, 510 Eighth Avenue N.E., Zip 58545–4637; tel. 701/748–2225, (Nonreporting) **A**5 10 18
Primary Contact: Darrold Bertsch, Chief Executive Officer
CFO: Renae Snyder, Chief Financial Officer
CHR: Laurie Miller, Administrative Assistant
CNO: Marcie Schulz, Director Patient Care
Web address: www.sakmedcenter.com
Control: Other not–for–profit (including NFP Corporation) **Service:** General Medical and Surgical

Staffed Beds: 18

HETTINGER—Adams County

WEST RIVER REGIONAL MEDICAL CENTER (351330), 1000 Highway 12, Zip 58639–7530; tel. 701/567–4561, (Nonreporting) **A**3 5 10 18
Primary Contact: Matthew Shahan, Chief Executive Officer
CFO: Nathan Stadheim, Chief Financial Officer
CMO: Jennifer Shefield, M.D., Chief of Staff
CIO: Julia Gochenour, Manager Information Systems
CHR: Tera Fried, Manager Human Resources
CNO: Barbara Stadheim, Chief Nursing Officer
Web address: www.wrhs.com
Control: Other not–for–profit (including NFP Corporation) **Service:** General Medical and Surgical

Staffed Beds: 25

Hospital, Medicare Provider Number, Address, Telephone, Approval, Facility, and Physician Codes, Health Care System

★ American Hospital Association (AHA) membership ○ Healthcare Facilities Accreditation Program ⇧ Center for Improvement in Healthcare Quality Accreditation
☐ The Joint Commission accreditation ◇ DNV Healthcare Inc. accreditation △ Commission on Accreditation of Rehabilitation Facilities (CARF) accreditation

HILLSBORO—Traill County

★ **SANFORD HILLSBORO MEDICAL CENTER (351329)**, 12 Third Street S.E., Zip 58045–4840, Mailing Address: P.O. Box 609, Zip 58045–0609; tel. 701/636–3200, (Total facility includes 36 beds in nursing home–type unit) **A**5 10 18 **F**7 10 11 34 35 40 64 65 68 75 93 97 103 125 128 130 131 133 143 146 148 **P**6 **S** Sanford Health, Sioux Falls, SD
Primary Contact: Jac McTaggart, Chief Executive Officer
CFO: Scott Awalt, Chief Financial Officer
CMO: Charles J. Breen, M.D., Medical Director
CHR: Jenny Jacobson, Manager Human Resources
Web address: www.hillsboromedicalcenter.com
Control: Other not–for–profit (including NFP Corporation) **Service:** General Medical and Surgical

Staffed Beds: 52 **Admissions:** 223 **Census:** 39 **Outpatient Visits:** 14578 **Births:** 0 **Total Expense ($000):** 8645 **Payroll Expense ($000):** 3532 **Personnel:** 73

JAMESTOWN—Stutsman County

⊞ **JAMESTOWN REGIONAL MEDICAL CENTER (351335)**, 2422 20th Street S.W., Zip 58401–6201; tel. 701/252–1050 **A**1 5 10 18 **F**1 3 4 11 13 15 16 17 28 29 31 34 35 40 43 45 50 53 57 59 62 63 64 67 70 72 73 75 76 77 79 80 81 82 84 85 86 87 88 89 90 93 98 107 108 110 111 115 118 119 128 130 131 132 133 135 146 148
Primary Contact: K. C. DeBoer, President and Chief Executive Officer
COO: Ricki Ramlo, Chief Operating Officer and Vice President Operations
CFO: Brandon Vaughan, Chief Financial Officer and Vice President Finance
CMO: Derek Brickner, President Medical Staff
CIO: Jeff Gunkel, Chief Information Officer
CHR: Ricki Ramlo, Vice President Human Resources
CNO: Trisha Jungels, R.N., Chief Nursing Officer and Vice President Clinical Services
Web address: www.jamestownhospital.com
Control: Other not–for–profit (including NFP Corporation) **Service:** General Medical and Surgical

Staffed Beds: 25 **Admissions:** 2145 **Census:** 12 **Outpatient Visits:** 40084 **Births:** 335 **Total Expense ($000):** 41738 **Payroll Expense ($000):** 16027 **Personnel:** 283

☐ **NORTH DAKOTA STATE HOSPITAL (354003)**, 2605 Circle Drive S.E., Zip 58401–6905; tel. 701/253–3964 **A**1 5 10 **F**1 4 38 56 98 100 101 102 103 105 106 130 132 135 143 146
Primary Contact: Rosalie Etherington, Superintendent and Chief Executive Officer
COO: Ken Schulz, Chief Operating Officer
CMO: Eduardo Yabut, M.D., Medical Director
CIO: Amy Shape, Information Technology
CHR: Lyle Grove, Human Resources Director
CNO: Leah Schulz, Director of Nursing
Web address: www.nd.gov/
Control: State–Government, nonfederal **Service:** Psychiatric

Staffed Beds: 100 **Admissions:** 875 **Census:** 86 **Outpatient Visits:** 0 **Births:** 0

KENMARE—Ward County

★ **KENMARE COMMUNITY HOSPITAL (351305)**, 317 First Avenue N.W., Zip 58746–7104, Mailing Address: P.O. Box 697, Zip 58746–0697; tel. 701/385–4296, (Nonreporting) **A**10 18
Primary Contact: Danielle Alsadon, Clinic/Hospital Manager
COO: Bev Heninger, Director of Nursing
CFO: Dennis Empey, Chief Financial Officer
CMO: Buki Oni, M.D., Chief Medical Officer
CIO: David Wanner, Director Information Technology
CHR: Ranae Ehlke, Administrative Secretary and Coordinator Risk Management and Human Resources
CNO: Bev Heninger, Director of Nursing
Web address: www.kenmarend.net/hospital.htm
Control: Corporation, Investor–owned, for–profit **Service:** General Medical and Surgical

Staffed Beds: 25

LANGDON—Cavalier County

★ **CAVALIER COUNTY MEMORIAL HOSPITAL AND CLINICS (351323)**, 909 Second Street, Zip 58249–2407; tel. 701/256–6100, (Nonreporting) **A**5 10 18
Primary Contact: Christopher B. Wyatt, Chief Executive Officer
COO: Darla Roder, Chief Operating Officer
CFO: Marcus Lewis, Chief Financial Officer
CMO: Suresh Patel, M.D., Chief Medical Officer
CHR: Nicole Walker, Human Resource Officer
CNO: Jamie Nienhuis, Chief Nursing Officer
Web address: www.cavaliercountyhospital.com
Control: Other not–for–profit (including NFP Corporation) **Service:** General Medical and Surgical

Staffed Beds: 20

LINTON—Emmons County

LINTON HOSPITAL (351328), 518 North Broadway, Zip 58552–7308, Mailing Address: P.O. Box 850, Zip 58552–0850; tel. 701/254–4511, (Nonreporting) **A**5 10 18
Primary Contact: Robert O. Black, Chief Executive Officer
CMO: John Knecht, Chief Medical Staff
CHR: Sue Meidinger, Manager Business Office
Web address: www.lintonhospital.com
Control: Other not–for–profit (including NFP Corporation) **Service:** General Medical and Surgical

Staffed Beds: 14

LISBON—Ransom County

★ **CHI LISBON HEALTH (351311)**, 905 Main Street, Zip 58054–4334, Mailing Address: P.O. Box 353, Zip 58054–0353; tel. 701/683–6400 **A**5 10 18 **F**3 15 28 29 30 31 34 40 56 57 59 67 78 79 81 82 85 87 93 119 128 130 133 **S** Catholic Health Initiatives, Englewood, CO
Primary Contact: Peggy Reinke, R.N., Administrator
COO: Sheri Heinisch, Compliance Officer
CFO: Amber Stowman, Controller
CHR: Janet Froemke, Human Resources Officer
Web address: www.lisbonhospital.com
Control: Church–operated, Nongovernment, not–for profit **Service:** General Medical and Surgical

Staffed Beds: 25 **Admissions:** 200 **Census:** 5 **Outpatient Visits:** 11283 **Births:** 0 **Total Expense ($000):** 10510 **Payroll Expense ($000):** 3654 **Personnel:** 63

MANDAN—Morton County

TRIUMPH HOSPITAL – CENTRAL DAKOTAS See Vibra Hospital of Central Dakotas

⊞ **VIBRA HOSPITAL OF CENTRAL DAKOTAS (352005)**, 1000 18th Street N.W., Zip 58554–1612; tel. 701/667–2000, (Nonreporting) **A**1 10 **S** Vibra Healthcare, Mechanicsburg, PA
Primary Contact: Glynda Troyo–Sauviac, Chief Executive Officer
Web address: www.vhcentraldakotas.com
Control: Corporation, Investor–owned, for–profit **Service:** Long–Term Acute Care hospital

Staffed Beds: 41

MAYVILLE—Traill County

MERITCARE MAYVILLE UNION HOSPITAL See Sanford Mayville Medical Center

★ **SANFORD MAYVILLE MEDICAL CENTER (351309)**, 42 Sixth Avenue S.E., Zip 58257–1598; tel. 701/786–3800 **A**5 10 18 **F**7 40 43 45 50 65 77 81 93 97 107 119 128 129 130 133 **P**6 **S** Sanford Health, Sioux Falls, SD
Primary Contact: Roger Baier, Chief Executive Officer
CFO: Shauna Slabik, Chief Financial Officer
CMO: Jane Ostlig, Chief Medical Officer
Web address: www.unionhospital.com
Control: Other not–for–profit (including NFP Corporation) **Service:** General Medical and Surgical

Staffed Beds: 18 **Admissions:** 244 **Census:** 3 **Outpatient Visits:** 20871 **Births:** 0 **Total Expense ($000):** 8445 **Payroll Expense ($000):** 3307 **Personnel:** 65

MCVILLE—Nelson County

NELSON COUNTY HEALTH SYSTEM (351308), 200 Main Street, Zip 58254, Mailing Address: P.O. Box 367, Zip 58254–0367; tel. 701/322–4328, (Total facility includes 39 beds in nursing home–type unit) **A**10 18 **F**40 127 128 133
Primary Contact: Bruce D. Bowersox, Chief Executive Officer
CFO: Steve Forde, Chief Financial Officer
CMO: Erling Martinson, M.D., Medical Director
Web address: www.nelsoncountyhealthsystem.org
Control: Other not–for–profit (including NFP Corporation) **Service:** General Medical and Surgical

Staffed Beds: 58 **Admissions:** 44 **Census:** 37 **Outpatient Visits:** 673 **Births:** 0 **Total Expense ($000):** 5501 **Payroll Expense ($000):** 2542 **Personnel:** 53

Many Facility Codes have changed. Please refer to the AHA Guide Code Chart. © 2016 AHA Guide

MINOT—Ward County

✉ △ **TRINITY HEALTH (350006)**, One Burdick Expressway West,
Zip 58701–4406, Mailing Address: P.O. Box 5020, Zip 58702–5020;
tel. 701/857–5766, (Includes TRINITY HOSPITAL–ST. JOSEPH'S, 407 3rd Street
S.E., Zip 58702–5001; tel. 701/857–2000), (Total facility includes 230 beds in
nursing home–type unit) **A**1 2 3 5 7 10 **F**3 4 5 7 8 11 13 15 17 18 20 22 24
28 29 30 31 34 35 38 40 43 45 46 49 50 54 55 56 57 58 59 60 62 63 64
65 68 70 72 73 74 75 76 77 78 79 80 81 82 85 86 87 89 90 91 92 93 94
96 97 98 99 100 101 102 103 104 105 107 108 110 111 114 115 116 117
118 119 120 121 124 126 127 128 129 130 131 132 133 143 144 146 147
148 **P**8
Primary Contact: John M. Kutch, President
CFO: Dennis Empey, Chief Financial Officer
CIO: David Wanner, Chief Information Officer
CHR: Paul Simonson, Vice President
Web address: www.trinityhealth.org
Control: Other not–for–profit (including NFP Corporation) **Service:** General
Medical and Surgical

Staffed Beds: 630 **Admissions:** 10420 **Census:** 326 **Outpatient Visits:**
196711 **Births:** 1716 **Total Expense ($000):** 405216 **Payroll Expense
($000):** 194958 **Personnel:** 1380

NORTHWOOD—Grand Forks County

★ **NORTHWOOD DEACONESS HEALTH CENTER (351312)**, 4 North Park Street,
Zip 58267–4102, Mailing Address: P.O. Box 190, Zip 58267–0190;
tel. 701/587–6060, (Nonreporting) **A**5 10 18 **S** Sanford Health, Sioux Falls, SD
Primary Contact: Pete Antonson, Chief Executive Officer
CMO: Jon Berg, M.D., Chief of Staff
CIO: Chad Peterson, Chief Information Officer
Web address: www.ndhc.net
Control: Church–operated, Nongovernment, not–for profit **Service:** General
Medical and Surgical

Staffed Beds: 73

OAKES—Dickey County

★ **CHI OAKES HOSPITAL (351315)**, 1200 North Seventh Street,
Zip 58474–2502; tel. 701/742–3291, (Nonreporting) **A**5 10 18 **S** Catholic Health
Initiatives, Englewood, CO
Primary Contact: Becki Thompson, President
CFO: Bethany Smith, Director of Finance
CMO: Katie O'Brien–Paradis, M.D., Chief Medical Officer
CHR: Julie Entzminger, Manager Human Resources
CNO: Kimberly A. Ketterling, R.N., Vice President of Nursing
Web address: www.oakeshospital.com
Control: Other not–for–profit (including NFP Corporation) **Service:** General
Medical and Surgical

Staffed Beds: 20

PARK RIVER—Walsh County

★ **FIRST CARE HEALTH CENTER (351326)**, 115 Vivian Street, Zip 58270–4540,
Mailing Address: PO Box I., Zip 58270–0708; tel. 701/284–7500 **A**5 10 18 **F**11
15 28 29 30 31 34 35 40 45 50 59 64 65 68 77 81 93 104 107 110 111
114 119 127 130 133 135 **P**6
Primary Contact: Louise Dryburgh, Chief Executive Officer
CFO: Layne Ensrude, Chief Financial Officer
CMO: Joel Johnson, M.D., Chief Medical Staff
CNO: Lori Seim, R.N., Director Nursing Services
Web address: www.firstcarehc.com
Control: Other not–for–profit (including NFP Corporation) **Service:** General
Medical and Surgical

Staffed Beds: 14 **Admissions:** 365 **Census:** 7 **Outpatient Visits:** 29670
Births: 0 **Total Expense ($000):** 10308 **Payroll Expense ($000):** 3801
Personnel: 78

ROLLA—Rolette County

PRESENTATION MEDICAL CENTER (351316), 213 Second Avenue N.E.,
Zip 58367–7153, Mailing Address: P.O. Box 759, Zip 58367–0759;
tel. 701/477–3161 **A**5 10 18 **F**11 15 18 28 29 30 31 34 40 41 43 45 57 59
63 64 66 81 87 93 97 107 110 114 115 119 127 129 133 135 146 **P**6
S Sisters of Mary of the Presentation Health System, Fargo, ND
Primary Contact: Mark Kerr, Chief Executive Officer
CFO: Paula Wilkie, Chief Financial Officer
CMO: Roy Cordy, M.D., President Medical Staff
CHR: Tara Okerson, Director Human Resources
Web address: www.pmc–rolla.com
Control: Church–operated, Nongovernment, not–for profit **Service:** General
Medical and Surgical

Staffed Beds: 25 **Admissions:** 144 **Census:** 1 **Outpatient Visits:** 8794
Births: 0 **Total Expense ($000):** 9291 **Payroll Expense ($000):** 3811
Personnel: 81

RUGBY—Pierce County

★ **HEART OF AMERICA MEDICAL CENTER (351332)**, 800 Main Avenue South,
Zip 58368–2198; tel. 701/776–5261, (Nonreporting) **A**5 10 18
Primary Contact: Patrick J. Branco, Chief Executive Officer
CFO: Bonnie Kuehnemund, Comptroller
CIO: Jeremy Schonebery, Director Information Technology
Web address: www.hamc.com
Control: Other not–for–profit (including NFP Corporation) **Service:** General
Medical and Surgical

Staffed Beds: 20

STANLEY—Mountrail County

★ **MOUNTRAIL COUNTY MEDICAL CENTER (351301)**, 615 6th Street S.E.,
Zip 58784–4444, Mailing Address: P.O. Box 399, Zip 58784–0399;
tel. 701/628–2424, (Nonreporting) **A**10 18
Primary Contact: Rockford Zastoupil, Administrator
CFO: Susan Weston, CPA, Chief Financial Officer
CMO: Marla Longmuir, M.D., Chief Medical Officer
CIO: Kathy Janssen, Director Medical Records
CHR: Alisha McMahon, Director Human Resources
CNO: Belinda Moen, R.N., Interim Director of Nursing
Web address: www.stanleyhealth.org
Control: Other not–for–profit (including NFP Corporation) **Service:** General
Medical and Surgical

Staffed Beds: 11

TIOGA—Williams County

★ **TIOGA MEDICAL CENTER (351300)**, 810 North Welo Street, Zip 58852–7157,
Mailing Address: P.O. Box 159, Zip 58852–0159; tel. 701/664–3305,
(Nonreporting) **A**3 5 10 18
Primary Contact: Randall K. Pederson, Chief Executive Officer
CMO: Swami P. Gade, M.D., Medical Director
CHR: Mary Ann Holm, Office Clerk
Web address: www.tiogahealth.org
Control: Other not–for–profit (including NFP Corporation) **Service:** General
Medical and Surgical

Staffed Beds: 55

TURTLE LAKE—McLean County

★ **COMMUNITY MEMORIAL HOSPITAL (351304)**, 220 Fifth Avenue,
Zip 58575–4005, Mailing Address: P.O. Box 280, Zip 58575–0280;
tel. 701/448–2331, (Nonreporting) **A**10 18 **S** Catholic Health Initiatives,
Englewood, CO
Primary Contact: Tod Graeber, Administrator
CFO: Janet Kurle, Chief Financial Officer
CNO: Jason Landenberger, Director of Nursing
Web address: www.wrtc.com/cullum/hospital
Control: Other not–for–profit (including NFP Corporation) **Service:** General
Medical and Surgical

Staffed Beds: 25

Hospital, Medicare Provider Number, Address, Telephone, Approval, Facility, and Physician Codes, Health Care System

★ American Hospital Association (AHA) membership
□ The Joint Commission accreditation
○ Healthcare Facilities Accreditation Program
◇ DNV Healthcare Inc. accreditation
⇑ Center for Improvement in Healthcare Quality Accreditation
△ Commission on Accreditation of Rehabilitation Facilities (CARF) accreditation

VALLEY CITY—Barnes County

★ **CHI MERCY HEALTH (351324)**, 570 Chautauqua Boulevard, Zip 58072–3199; tel. 701/845–6400 **A**10 18 **F**29 30 34 40 45 48 50 75 77 81 82 91 93 107 108 111 119 129 130 133 146 **S** Catholic Health Initiatives, Englewood, CO
Primary Contact: Keith E. Heuser, President
CFO: Cyndee Thormodson, Vice President, Operational Finance
CHR: Sheri Sweere, Division Director Human Resources
Web address: www.mercyhospitalvalleycity.org
Control: Church–operated, Nongovernment, not–for profit **Service:** General Medical and Surgical

Staffed Beds: 19 **Admissions:** 412 **Census:** 10 **Outpatient Visits:** 14103 **Births:** 0 **Total Expense ($000):** 13507 **Payroll Expense ($000):** 4242

WATFORD CITY—Mckenzie County

★ **MCKENZIE COUNTY HEALTHCARE SYSTEM (351302)**, 516 North Main Street, Zip 58854–7310; tel. 701/842–3000 **A**10 18 **F**3 11 28 29 34 40 43 45 50 57 59 64 67 81 85 93 94 97 107 114 119 127 128 129 131 133 146
Primary Contact: Daniel R. Kelly, Chief Executive Officer
COO: Michael Curtis, Chief Administrative Officer
CFO: Kenneth Cox, Interim Chief Financial Officer
CMO: Gary Ramage, M.D., Chief Medical Officer
CIO: Karn Pederson, Manager Health Information Management
CHR: Amy Gonzales, Director of Human Resources
CNO: Cheryl Faulkner, Director of Nursing
Web address: www.mckenziehealth.com
Control: Other not–for–profit (including NFP Corporation) **Service:** General Medical and Surgical

Staffed Beds: 24 **Admissions:** 119 **Census:** 1 **Outpatient Visits:** 14763 **Births:** 0 **Total Expense ($000):** 15556 **Payroll Expense ($000):** 6273 **Personnel:** 99

WILLISTON—Williams County

⊠ **MERCY MEDICAL CENTER (351334)**, 1301 15th Avenue West, Zip 58801–3896; tel. 701/774–7400 **A**1 3 10 18 **F**3 28 29 30 31 34 35 40 45 47 50 51 56 59 64 65 70 74 75 76 77 78 79 81 82 85 87 91 93 97 102 107 108 110 111 114 118 119 120 121 123 124 129 130 132 133 135 141 142 146 147 148 **S** Catholic Health Initiatives, Englewood, CO
Primary Contact: Matthew Grimshaw, President
CMO: Brett Vibeto, M.D., Chief of Staff
CIO: Jeff Rust, Information Technology Systems Site Manager
CHR: Dan Bjerknes, Director Human Resources
CNO: Lori Hahn, Vice President Nursing Services
Web address: www.mercy–williston.org
Control: Church–operated, Nongovernment, not–for profit **Service:** General Medical and Surgical

Staffed Beds: 25 **Admissions:** 1942 **Census:** 12 **Outpatient Visits:** 76492 **Births:** 883 **Total Expense ($000):** 75521 **Payroll Expense ($000):** 36103 **Personnel:** 371

WISHEK—Mcintosh County

★ **WISHEK COMMUNITY HOSPITAL AND CLINICS (351321)**, 1007 Fourth Avenue South, Zip 58495–7527, Mailing Address: P.O. Box 647, Zip 58495–0647; tel. 701/452–2326 **A**5 10 18 **F**3 7 11 15 17 18 28 29 30 32 34 35 36 40 42 44 50 53 56 57 59 60 64 65 68 75 81 83 87 91 92 93 97 107 114 127 128 130 131 133 143 146 147 **P**3 6
Primary Contact: Beverly Vilhauer, Chief Executive Officer
CFO: Megan Rath, Chief Financial Officer
CMO: Joseph Thirumalareddy, M.D., Chief of Staff
CIO: Kari Buchholz, Director Health Information Management
CHR: Shar Bauer, Executive Secretary
Web address: www.wishekhospital.com
Control: Other not–for–profit (including NFP Corporation) **Service:** General Medical and Surgical

Staffed Beds: 19 **Admissions:** 202 **Census:** 2 **Outpatient Visits:** 9618 **Births:** 0 **Total Expense ($000):** 7247 **Payroll Expense ($000):** 2821 **Personnel:** 76

Many Facility Codes have changed. Please refer to the AHA Guide Code Chart.

© 2016 AHA Guide

OHIO

AKRON—Summit County

⊞ **AKRON CHILDREN'S HOSPITAL (363303)**, One Perkins Square,
Zip 44308–1063; tel. 330/543–1000 **A**1 2 3 5 8 10 **F**3 7 11 13 16 18 19 20
21 22 23 25 26 27 29 30 31 32 33 34 35 36 38 39 40 41 42 43 44 48 50
54 55 57 58 59 60 61 62 63 64 65 66 68 72 73 74 75 77 78 79 81 82 84
85 86 87 88 89 91 92 93 94 96 97 98 99 100 101 102 104 105 107 108
111 112 114 115 116 117 118 119 129 130 131 132 134 135 136 141 143
144 146 148 **P**6
Primary Contact: William H. Considine, President
COO: Grace Wakulchik, R.N., Chief Operating Officer
CFO: Michael Trainer, Chief Financial Officer
CMO: Robert McGregor, M.D., Chief Medical Officer
CHR: Walt Schwoeble, Vice President Human Resources
CNO: Lisa Aurilio, R.N., Vice President Patient Services and Chief Nursing Officer
Web address: www.akronchildrens.org
Control: Other not–for–profit (including NFP Corporation) **Service:** Children's general

> **Staffed Beds:** 407 **Admissions:** 10382 **Census:** 202 **Outpatient Visits:**
> 917456 **Births:** 0 **Total Expense ($000):** 693005 **Payroll Expense ($000):**
> 339871 **Personnel:** 4670

⊞ **AKRON GENERAL MEDICAL CENTER (360027)**, 1 Akron General Avenue,
Zip 44307–2433; tel. 330/344–6000 **A**1 2 3 5 8 10 **F**3 5 8 11 12 13 14 15
17 18 20 22 24 26 28 29 30 31 32 34 35 36 37 38 40 42 43 44 45 46 47
48 49 50 51 52 53 54 55 56 57 58 59 60 61 62 63 64 65 66 68 70 71 72
74 75 78 79 81 82 84 85 86 87 91 92 93 94 96 97 98 100 101 102 103
104 105 107 108 110 111 112 114 115 118 119 120 121 123 124 126 129
130 131 132 134 135 138 144 145 146 147 148 **P**6 8 **S** Cleveland Clinic
Health System, Cleveland, OH
Primary Contact: Alan Papa, President
CFO: Dave Frigo, Vice President Financial Planning and Treasury
CMO: David Peter, M.D., Senior Vice President Medical Affairs and Chief Medical Director
CIO: David Fiser, Vice President and Chief Information Officer
CHR: Don Corpora, Executive Vice President and Chief Human Resources Officer
CNO: Cherie M. Guster, R.N., Senior Vice President and Chief Nursing Officer
Web address: www.akrongeneral.org
Control: Other not–for–profit (including NFP Corporation) **Service:** General Medical and Surgical

> **Staffed Beds:** 417 **Admissions:** 22793 **Census:** 273 **Outpatient Visits:**
> 614129 **Births:** 3031 **Total Expense ($000):** 485747 **Payroll Expense ($000):** 192540 **Personnel:** 2756

⊞ **SELECT SPECIALTY HOSPITAL–AKRON (362027)**, 200 East Market Street,
Zip 44308–2015; tel. 330/761–7500, (Nonreporting) **A**1 10 **S** Select Medical
Corporation, Mechanicsburg, PA
Primary Contact: Sonda Burns, Chief Executive Officer
Web address: www.selectspecialtyhospitals.com/company/locations/akron.aspx
Control: Corporation, Investor–owned, for–profit **Service:** Long–Term Acute Care hospital

> **Staffed Beds:** 60

SUMMA AKRON CITY HOSPITAL See Summa Health System

⊞ **SUMMA HEALTH SYSTEM (360020)**, 525 East Market Street,
Zip 44304–1619; tel. 330/375–3000, (Includes SUMMA AKRON CITY HOSPITAL,
525 East Market Street, Zip 44309–2090, Mailing Address: P.O. Box 2090,
Zip 44309–2090; tel. 330/375–3000; SUMMA HEALTH SYSTEM BARBERTON
HOSPITAL, 155 Fifth Street N.E., Barberton, Zip 44203–3332;
tel. 330/615–3000; Jason Niehaus, Senior Vice President Operations and
Administrator; SUMMA SAINT THOMAS HOSPITAL, 444 North Main Street,
Zip 44310; tel. 330/375–3000) **A**1 2 3 5 8 10 13 **F**3 4 5 6 8 11 12 13 15 17
18 20 22 24 26 28 29 30 31 33 34 35 36 38 39 40 42 43 44 45 46 49 50
51 52 53 54 56 57 58 59 60 61 62 63 64 65 66 68 70 71 74 75 76 77 78
79 80 81 82 83 84 85 86 87 92 93 96 97 98 100 101 102 103 104 105 107
108 110 111 114 115 116 117 118 119 120 121 123 124 126 129 130 131
132 133 135 144 146 147 148 **P**6 8 **S** Summa Health, Akron, OH
Primary Contact: Thomas Malone, M.D., President and Chief Executive Officer
COO: Robert Harrigan, President, Summa Hospitals
CMO: Erik N. Steele, D.O., Senior Vice President and Chief Medical Officer
CIO: Greg Kall, Chief Information Officer
CHR: Kyle Klawitter, Vice President Human Resources
Web address: www.summahealth.org
Control: Other not–for–profit (including NFP Corporation) **Service:** General Medical and Surgical

> **Staffed Beds:** 717 **Admissions:** 37286 **Census:** 464 **Outpatient Visits:**
> 511696 **Births:** 3700 **Total Expense ($000):** 880209 **Payroll Expense ($000):** 254386 **Personnel:** 4970

☐ △ **SUMMA REHAB HOSPITAL (363035)**, 29 North Adams Street,
Zip 44304–1641; tel. 330/572–7300 **A**1 7 10 **F**3 29 30 75 90 91 96 132 146
148 **S** Summa Health, Akron, OH
Primary Contact: Cheryl Henthorn, Chief Executive Officer
Web address: www.summarehabhospital.com/
Control: Partnership, Investor–owned, for–profit **Service:** Rehabilitation

> **Staffed Beds:** 60 **Admissions:** 2008 **Census:** 52 **Outpatient Visits:** 0 **Births:**
> 0 **Total Expense ($000):** 19487 **Payroll Expense ($000):** 9371 **Personnel:**
> 181

SUMMA SAINT THOMAS HOSPITAL See Summa Health System

ALLIANCE—Stark County

○ **ALLIANCE COMMUNITY HOSPITAL (360131)**, 200 East State Street,
Zip 44601–4936; tel. 330/596–6000, (Total facility includes 78 beds in nursing
home–type unit) **A**2 5 10 11 **F**3 8 11 13 15 28 29 30 31 34 35 36 40 45 49
50 51 56 57 59 60 62 63 64 68 69 70 74 75 76 77 79 81 82 84 85 86 87
90 93 96 98 103 107 108 110 111 114 115 118 119 120 121 128 129 130
132 135 143 146 147 148 **P**5 7 8
Primary Contact: Stanley W. Jonas, Chief Executive Officer
COO: Dale W. Wells, Chief Financial and Operating Officer
CFO: Dale W. Wells, Chief Financial and Operating Officer
CMO: Ashraf Ahmed, M.D., Senior Vice President Physician and Hospital Services
CIO: David W. Shroades, Vice President Technology Services
CHR: Nicole L. Russ, Director Colleague Relations
CNO: Amy Antonacci, MSN, Vice President Nursing Services
Web address: www.achosp.org
Control: Other not–for–profit (including NFP Corporation) **Service:** General Medical and Surgical

> **Staffed Beds:** 202 **Admissions:** 3337 **Census:** 106 **Outpatient Visits:**
> 171462 **Births:** 388 **Total Expense ($000):** 87715 **Payroll Expense ($000):**
> 39586 **Personnel:** 790

AMHERST—Lorain County

☐ **SPECIALTY HOSPITAL OF LORAIN (362025)**, 254 Cleveland Avenue,
Zip 44001–1620; tel. 440/988–6260, (Nonreporting) **A**1 10
Primary Contact: Rajive Khanna, Chief Executive Officer
COO: Susan Adams, Chief Nursing Officer and Chief Operating Officer
CNO: Susan Adams, Chief Nursing Officer and Chief Operating Officer
Control: Other not–for–profit (including NFP Corporation) **Service:** Long–Term Acute Care hospital

> **Staffed Beds:** 30

ARCHBOLD—Fulton County

ARCHBOLD HOSPITAL See Community Hospitals and Wellness Centers, Bryan

---

Hospital, Medicare Provider Number, Address, Telephone, Approval, Facility, and Physician Codes, Health Care System

★ American Hospital Association (AHA) membership
☐ The Joint Commission accreditation
○ Healthcare Facilities Accreditation Program
◇ DNV Healthcare Inc. accreditation
⇑ Center for Improvement in Healthcare Quality Accreditation
△ Commission on Accreditation of Rehabilitation Facilities (CARF) accreditation

OH

ASHLAND—Ashland County

✠ **UNIVERSITY HOSPITALS SAMARITAN MEDICAL CENTER (360002)**, 1025 Center Street, Zip 44805–4011; tel. 419/289–0491 **A**1 5 10 **F**11 13 15 18 20 28 29 30 31 34 35 40 45 50 51 56 59 62 64 68 75 77 78 79 81 82 86 87 93 96 107 111 114 119 129 130 131 132 135 146 147 148 **S** University Hospitals, Cleveland, OH
Primary Contact: Danny L. Boggs, President and Chief Executive Officer
CFO: Mary Griest, Vice President Finance and Chief Financial Officer
CMO: Philip Myers, M.D., Vice President Medical Affairs
CIO: Kathleen Metcalf, Chief Information Officer
CHR: Alyce Legg, Vice President Human Resources
CNO: Karin Schwan, Chief Nursing Officer, Vice President Patient Care Services
Web address: www.samaritanhospital.org
Control: Other not–for–profit (including NFP Corporation) **Service:** General Medical and Surgical

Staffed Beds: 49 **Admissions:** 2453 **Census:** 18 **Outpatient Visits:** 129382
Births: 404

ASHTABULA—Ashtabula County

✠ **ASHTABULA COUNTY MEDICAL CENTER (360125)**, 2420 Lake Avenue, Zip 44004–4954; tel. 440/997–2262, (Total facility includes 15 beds in nursing home–type unit) **A**1 5 10 20 **F**3 11 13 15 18 19 20 26 28 29 30 31 34 40 44 45 49 51 53 54 57 59 61 62 63 64 68 70 74 76 78 79 81 82 85 87 89 92 93 97 98 100 102 103 104 107 108 110 111 114 116 117 118 119 128 129 130 131 132 135 144 146 147 148 **P**4 6 7 8
Primary Contact: Michael J. Habowski, President and Chief Executive Officer
COO: Lewis Hutchison, Vice President Operations and Quality
CFO: Donald L. Kepner, Chief Financial Officer
CMO: Jude Cauwenberg, M.D., Chief of Staff
CIO: Jared Swiger, Director Information Systems
CHR: Jonathan Forbes, Director Human Resources
CNO: Ken Frame, Chief Nursing Officer
Web address: www.acmchealth.org
Control: Other not–for–profit (including NFP Corporation) **Service:** General Medical and Surgical

Staffed Beds: 151 **Admissions:** 5592 **Census:** 68 **Outpatient Visits:** 253956
Births: 378 **Total Expense ($000):** 116895 **Payroll Expense ($000):** 53733
Personnel: 828

ATHENS—Athens County

☐ **APPALACHIAN BEHAVIORAL HEALTHCARE (364015)**, 100 Hospital Drive, Zip 45701–2301; tel. 740/594–5000, (Nonreporting) **A**1 10 **S** Ohio Department of Mental Health, Columbus, OH
Primary Contact: Jane E. Krason, R.N., Chief Executive Officer
CMO: Mark F. McGee, M.D., Chief Clinical Officer
CHR: Amy Grover, Director
Web address: www.mh.state.oh.us
Control: State–Government, nonfederal **Service:** Psychiatric

Staffed Beds: 224

✠ **O'BLENESS MEMORIAL HOSPITAL (360014)**, 55 Hospital Drive, Zip 45701–2302; tel. 740/593–5551, (Nonreporting) **A**1 10 12 13 **S** OhioHealth, Columbus, OH
Primary Contact: Mark R. Seckinger, President
CFO: Robert Melaragno, Vice President Finance
CIO: Kristine Barr, Vice President Communication Services
CHR: Sandie Leasure, Senior Vice President Human Resources
CNO: Sandy Wood, MSN, Vice President Patient Services and Chief Nursing Officer
Web address: www.obleness.org
Control: Other not–for–profit (including NFP Corporation) **Service:** General Medical and Surgical

Staffed Beds: 64

AVON—Lorain County

★ **CLEVELAND CLINIC REHABILITATION HOSPITAL**, 33355 Health Campus Boulevard, Zip 44011; tel. 440/937–9099, (Nonreporting) **S** Select Medical Corporation, Mechanicsburg, PA
Primary Contact: Sam Bayoumy, Chief Executive Officer
Web address: www.my.clevelandclinic.org
Control: Partnership, Investor–owned, for–profit **Service:** Rehabilitation

Staffed Beds: 60

UH AVON REHABILITATION HOSPITAL, 37900 Chester Road, Zip 44011–1044; tel. 440/695–7100, (Nonreporting) **S** Kindred Healthcare, Louisville, KY
Primary Contact: Andrew Goldfrach, Chief Executive Officer
CFO: Jason DiGuilio, Controller
CHR: Abby Hoag, Director, Human Resources
CNO: Katie Kasper, Chief Clinical Officer
Web address: www.uhhospitals.org/uh–avon–rehabilitation–hospital
Control: Corporation, Investor–owned, for–profit **Service:** Rehabilitation

Staffed Beds: 50

BARNESVILLE—Belmont County

✠ **BARNESVILLE HOSPITAL (361321)**, 639 West Main Street, Zip 43713–1039; Mailing Address: P.O. Box 309, Zip 43713–0309; tel. 740/425–3941 **A**1 10 18 **F**3 11 15 17 28 29 30 32 34 35 39 40 41 45 50 57 59 64 65 69 70 74 75 77 78 79 81 85 86 87 89 90 91 93 107 108 110 114 119 128 129 130 132 133 135 145 146 **P**6
Primary Contact: David D. Phillips, Chief Executive Officer and Administrator
CFO: Willie Cooper–Lohr, Chief Financial Officer
CMO: David J. Hilliard, D.O., Chief of Staff
CHR: Beth K. Brill, Senior Director Human Resources
CNO: Cynthia Touvelle, R.N., Senior Director Care Management and Chief Nursing Officer
Web address: www.barnesvillehospital.com
Control: Other not–for–profit (including NFP Corporation) **Service:** General Medical and Surgical

Staffed Beds: 25 **Admissions:** 829 **Census:** 9 **Outpatient Visits:** 33584
Births: 0 **Total Expense ($000):** 20164 **Payroll Expense ($000):** 8105
Personnel: 178

BATAVIA—Clermont County

✠ **MERCY HEALTH – CLERMONT HOSPITAL (360236)**, 3000 Hospital Drive, Zip 45103–1921; tel. 513/732–8200, (Nonreporting) **A**1 2 3 10 **S** Mercy Health, Cincinnati, OH
Primary Contact: Jeff Graham, Market Leader and President
CFO: Philip Wheeler, Director Finance
CMO: Parma Hariharan, M.D., Chief of Staff
CHR: Angie Ferrell, Director Human Resources
CNO: Gayle Heintzelman, R.N., Site Administrator and Chief Nursing Officer
Web address: www.e–mercy.com
Control: Other not–for–profit (including NFP Corporation) **Service:** General Medical and Surgical

Staffed Beds: 119

BEACHWOOD—Cuyahoga County

UH REHABILITATION HOSPITAL, 23333 Harvard Road, Zip 44122–6232; tel. 216/593–2200, (Nonreporting) **S** Kindred Healthcare, Louisville, KY
Primary Contact: Mirza Baig, M.D., Medical Director
Web address: www.uhhospitals.org
Control: Corporation, Investor–owned, for–profit **Service:** Rehabilitation

Staffed Beds: 50

✠ **UNIVERSITY HOSPITALS AHUJA MEDICAL CENTER (360359)**, 3999 Richmond Road, Zip 44122–6046; tel. 216/593–5500 **A**1 3 10 **F**3 5 15 18 20 22 24 26 28 29 30 34 35 36 40 41 42 45 46 47 48 50 51 56 57 59 60 61 65 68 70 74 75 77 79 80 81 82 85 87 91 93 107 108 109 110 111 115 119 126 130 131 144 145 146 148 **P**8 **S** University Hospitals, Cleveland, OH
Primary Contact: Susan V. Juris, President
Web address: www.uhhospitals.org/ahuja/tabid/7051/uhahujamedicalcenter.aspx
Control: Other not–for–profit (including NFP Corporation) **Service:** General Medical and Surgical

Staffed Beds: 138 **Admissions:** 9179 **Census:** 99 **Outpatient Visits:** 160377
Births: 0 **Total Expense ($000):** 159526 **Payroll Expense ($000):** 51301
Personnel: 934

BEAVERCREEK—Greene County

★ ○ **SOIN MEDICAL CENTER (360360)**, 3535 Pentagon Boulevard, Zip 45431–1705; tel. 937/702–4000 **A**2 10 11 **F**3 11 13 18 20 22 29 30 31 34 35 38 39 40 43 44 45 46 47 48 49 50 51 53 56 57 59 61 64 66 70 73 74 75 76 77 78 79 81 82 85 86 87 102 107 108 111 114 115 116 117 118 119 126 130 132 135 146 148 **S** Kettering Health Network, Dayton, OH
Primary Contact: Rick A. Dodds, President
COO: Ron D. Connovich, Chief Financial Officer and Chief Operating Officer
CFO: Ron D. Connovich, Chief Financial Officer and Chief Operating Officer
CMO: David Small, M.D., Chief Medical Officer
CIO: Andy Lehman, Vice President Information Systems
CNO: Belinda Mallett, R.N., Vice President, Patient Care and Clinical Services
Web address: www.khnetwork.org/soin
Control: Church–operated, Nongovernment, not–for profit **Service:** General Medical and Surgical

Staffed Beds: 101 **Admissions:** 5367 **Census:** 49 **Outpatient Visits:** 65948
Births: 566 **Total Expense ($000):** 139160 **Payroll Expense ($000):** 51033
Personnel: 705

BELLAIRE—Belmont County

☐ **BELMONT COMMUNITY HOSPITAL (360153)**, 4697 Harrison Street, Zip 43906–1338, Mailing Address: P.O. Box 653, Zip 43906–0653; tel. 740/671–1200, (Nonreporting) **A**1 10
Primary Contact: John DeBlasis, Vice President
CFO: James B. Murdy, Chief Financial Officer
CMO: Jeffrey A. Patey, M.D., Chief of Staff
CHR: Serge Gentile, Director Human Resources
Web address: www.wheelinghospital.org/facilities/bch/
Control: Other not–for–profit (including NFP Corporation) **Service:** General Medical and Surgical

Staffed Beds: 66

Many Facility Codes have changed. Please refer to the AHA Guide Code Chart. © 2016 AHA Guide

BELLEFONTAINE—Logan County

★ ◇ **MARY RUTAN HOSPITAL (360197)**, 205 Palmer Avenue,
Zip 43311–2281; tel. 937/592–4015 **A**3 5 10 20 21 **F**3 11 12 13 14 15 18
20 28 29 30 31 32 34 40 50 51 54 57 59 64 66 68 70 74 75 76 77 79 81
82 85 86 87 89 107 108 110 111 115 119 129 130 132 133 135 146 147
Primary Contact: Mandy C. Goble, President and Chief Executive Officer
CFO: Steven Brown, Vice President Fiscal Affairs
CMO: Grant Varian, M.D., Medical Director
CIO: Robert Reynolds, Director Information Systems
CHR: Vickie L. Crumley, Vice President Human Resources
CNO: Frank Gliha, Vice President of Patient Care
Web address: www.maryrutan.org
Control: Other not–for–profit (including NFP Corporation) **Service:** General
Medical and Surgical

Staffed Beds: 46 **Admissions:** 1630 **Census:** 16 **Outpatient Visits:** 97691
Births: 377 **Total Expense ($000):** 88669 **Payroll Expense ($000):** 35946
Personnel: 562

BELLEVUE—Sandusky County

⊞ **BELLEVUE HOSPITAL (360107)**, 1400 West Main Street, Zip 44811–9088,
Mailing Address: P.O. Box 8004, Zip 44811–8004; tel. 419/483–4040 **A**1 5 10
F3 13 15 28 29 30 31 34 35 40 41 45 46 50 53 56 57 59 61 68 70 74 75
76 77 79 81 82 85 89 93 107 110 111 114 118 119 127 129 130 131 132
133 135 143 144 146 147 **P**8
Primary Contact: Michael Winthrop, President
CFO: Timothy Buit, Executive Vice President and Chief Financial Officer
CMO: Donald Smith, President Medical Staff
CIO: Kim Stults, Director, Information Systems
CHR: Lisa M. Sartain, Vice President, Human Resources
CNO: Sara Brokaw, Vice President Patient Care Services
Web address: www.bellevuehospital.com
Control: Other not–for–profit (including NFP Corporation) **Service:** General
Medical and Surgical

Staffed Beds: 50 **Admissions:** 1413 **Census:** 11 **Outpatient Visits:** 85105
Births: 409 **Total Expense ($000):** 46658 **Payroll Expense ($000):** 16921
Personnel: 347

BLUFFTON—Allen County

★ **BLUFFTON HOSPITAL (361322)**, 139 Garau Street, Zip 45817–1027;
tel. 419/358–9010 **A**10 18 **F**11 13 15 18 29 40 45 54 57 59 63 64 70 76 77
79 81 82 83 84 91 93 107 110 114 119 127 130 133 146 148 **S** Blanchard
Valley Health System, Findlay, OH
Primary Contact: Christine Keller, Chief Administrative Officer
CFO: David Cytlak, Vice President Finance
CMO: William H. Kose, M.D., Vice President Quality and Medical Affairs
CIO: David Cytlak, Vice President Finance
CHR: Ryan Fisher, Director Human Resources
CNO: Barbara J. Pasztor, R.N., Vice President Nursing and Patient Care Services
Web address: www.bvhealthsystem.org/
Control: Other not–for–profit (including NFP Corporation) **Service:** General
Medical and Surgical

Staffed Beds: 25 **Admissions:** 284 **Census:** 2 **Outpatient Visits:** 40773
Births: 206 **Total Expense ($000):** 12313 **Payroll Expense ($000):** 8337
Personnel: 116

BOARDMAN—Mahoning County

MAHONING VALLEY HOSPITAL See Vibra Hospital of Mahoning Valley

⊞ **MERCY HEALTH – ST. ELIZABETH BOARDMAN HOSPITAL (360276)**, 8401
Market Street, Zip 44512–6777; tel. 330/729–2929 **A**1 10 13 **F**3 11 13 15
18 29 30 31 34 35 37 40 45 46 49 50 59 60 68 70 74 75 76 77 78 79 81
84 87 93 107 108 110 111 114 115 116 117 118 119 120 121 123 129
130 131 146 147 148 **S** Mercy Health, Cincinnati, OH
Primary Contact: Eugenia Aubel, President
CFO: Matthew Love, Senior Vice President Finance
CMO: Heath Dorion, Physican Administrator
CIO: Maureen Kordupel, Director Information Technology Relationship Manager
CHR: Molly Seals, System Vice President, Human Resources Program Delivery
and Youngstown Market
CNO: Stacie Call, Chief Nursing Officer
Web address: www.ehealthconnection.com/regions/youngstown/content/show_
facility.asp?facility_id=190
Control: Church–operated, Nongovernment, not–for profit **Service:** General
Medical and Surgical

Staffed Beds: 193 **Admissions:** 12961 **Census:** 137 **Outpatient Visits:**
111298 **Births:** 2519 **Total Expense ($000):** 144704 **Payroll Expense
($000):** 44340 **Personnel:** 711

⊞ **SELECT SPECIALTY HOSPITAL – BOARDMAN (360363)**, 8401 Market
Street, 7 South, Zip 44512–6725; tel. 330/729–1750, (Nonreporting) **A**1 10
S Select Medical Corporation, Mechanicsburg, PA
Primary Contact: Jodi Costello, Chief Executive Officer
Control: Corporation, Investor–owned, for–profit **Service:** Long–Term Acute Care
hospital

Staffed Beds: 56

⊞ **VIBRA HOSPITAL OF MAHONING VALLEY (362023)**, 8049 South Avenue,
Zip 44512–6154; tel. 330/726–5000, (Includes VIBRA HOSPITAL OF MAHONING
VALLEY–TRUMBULL CAMPUS, 1350 East Market Street, 9th Floor, Warren,
Zip 44483–6608; tel. 330/675–5555; Nathan Mast, Chief Executive Officer) **A**1
10 **F**1 3 29 30 130 148 **S** Vibra Healthcare, Mechanicsburg, PA
Primary Contact: Nathan Mast, Chief Executive Officer
CMO: Lawrence Goldstein, M.D., Chief Medical Officer
Web address: www.vhmvalley.com
Control: Corporation, Investor–owned, for–profit **Service:** Long–Term Acute Care
hospital

Staffed Beds: 42 **Admissions:** 488 **Census:** 27 **Outpatient Visits:** 0 **Births:**
0 **Total Expense ($000):** 15786 **Payroll Expense ($000):** 5132 **Personnel:**
121

BOWLING GREEN—Wood County

⊞ **WOOD COUNTY HOSPITAL (360029)**, 950 West Wooster Street,
Zip 43402–2603; tel. 419/354–8900 **A**1 3 5 10 **F**3 11 12 13 15 17 18 28 29
30 31 32 34 35 40 44 45 50 57 59 64 65 68 69 70 74 75 76 77 78 79 81
82 85 87 89 93 107 108 110 111 114 115 118 119 120 121 123 124 129
130 131 132 135 144 146 147 148 **P**6 8
Primary Contact: Stanley R. Korducki, President
CFO: Karol Bortel, Vice President Financial Services
CMO: Shawn Stansbery, M.D., Chief of Staff
CIO: Joanne White, Chief Information Officer
CHR: Michael Ford, Vice President Patient Services
CNO: Sandra Beidelschies, MSN, Vice President Patient Services
Web address: www.woodcountyhospital.org
Control: Other not–for–profit (including NFP Corporation) **Service:** General
Medical and Surgical

Staffed Beds: 102 **Admissions:** 2906 **Census:** 26 **Outpatient Visits:** 102008
Births: 350 **Total Expense ($000):** 82345 **Payroll Expense ($000):** 30614
Personnel: 637

BRYAN—Williams County

☐ **COMMUNITY HOSPITALS AND WELLNESS CENTERS (360121)**, 433 West
High Street, Zip 43506–1679; tel. 419/636–1131, (Includes ARCHBOLD
HOSPITAL, 121 Westfield Drive, Archbold, Zip 43502; tel. 419/445–4415;
BRYAN HOSPITAL, 433 West High Street, Zip 43506; tel. 419/636–1131;
MONTPELIER HOSPITAL, 909 East Snyder Avenue, Montpelier, Zip 43543;
tel. 419/485–3154), (Nonreporting) **A**1 2 5 10
Primary Contact: Philip L. Ennen, Vice President and Chief Executive Officer
CFO: Leroy P. Feather, Vice President Finance
CIO: Greg Slattery, Vice President Information
CHR: Mary Ann Potts, Director Personnel
Web address: www.chwchospital.com
Control: Other not–for–profit (including NFP Corporation) **Service:** General
Medical and Surgical

Staffed Beds: 113

BUCYRUS—Crawford County

★ ◇ **BUCYRUS COMMUNITY HOSPITAL (361316)**, 629 North Sandusky
Avenue, Zip 44820–1821; tel. 419/562–4677, (Nonreporting) **A**5 10 18 21
S Avita Health System, Galion, OH
Primary Contact: Jerome Morasko, Chief Executive Officer
COO: Andy Daniels, Chief Operating Officer
CMO: Michael A. Johnson, M.D., Chief of Staff
CIO: Joann Riedlinger, Vice President Nursing and Manager Information Systems
CHR: Jeanne Perkins, Vice President Nursing and Interim Manager Human
Resources
Web address: www.bchonline.org
Control: Other not–for–profit (including NFP Corporation) **Service:** General
Medical and Surgical

Staffed Beds: 25

Hospital, Medicare Provider Number, Address, Telephone, Approval, Facility, and Physician Codes, Health Care System

★ American Hospital Association (AHA) membership   ◯ Healthcare Facilities Accreditation Program   ⇑ Center for Improvement in Healthcare Quality Accreditation
☐ The Joint Commission accreditation   ◇ DNV Healthcare Inc. accreditation   △ Commission on Accreditation of Rehabilitation Facilities (CARF) accreditation

CADIZ—Harrison County

⊠ **HARRISON COMMUNITY HOSPITAL (361311)**, 951 East Market Street, Zip 43907–9799; tel. 740/942–4631 **A**1 10 18 **F**7 11 15 18 28 29 30 31 34 35 40 45 47 50 51 53 57 59 62 64 65 68 75 77 78 79 81 82 85 86 87 93 97 107 108 110 111 114 119 129 130 132 133 135 143 146 147 148
Primary Contact: Clifford K. Harmon, Chief Executive Officer
CFO: Donald Huelskamp, Interim Chief Financial Officer
CMO: Siripurapu Prasad, Chief of Staff
CIO: Will Combs, Director Information Technology
CHR: Peter Giordano, Senior Director Human Resources
CNO: Janis Olinski, R.N., Vice President Clinical Services
Web address: www.harrisoncommunity.com
Control: Other not–for–profit (including NFP Corporation) **Service:** General Medical and Surgical

Staffed Beds: 25 **Admissions:** 327 **Census:** 4 **Outpatient Visits:** 32769 **Births:** 0 **Total Expense ($000):** 20009 **Payroll Expense ($000):** 7103 **Personnel:** 161

CAMBRIDGE—Guernsey County

⊠ **SOUTHEASTERN OHIO REGIONAL MEDICAL CENTER (360203)**, 1341 North Clark Street, Zip 43725–9614, Mailing Address: P.O. Box 610, Zip 43725–0610; tel. 740/439–8000 **A**1 2 10 20 **F**3 7 11 13 15 18 20 28 29 30 31 32 34 35 40 43 46 48 49 50 51 57 59 60 62 63 64 65 66 70 75 77 78 79 81 82 83 84 85 86 87 91 93 96 97 107 108 110 111 114 116 118 119 129 130 131 132 135 144 146 147 148 **P**6 8
Primary Contact: Raymond M. Chorey, President and Chief Executive Officer
CFO: Timothy R. Evancho, Chief Financial Officer
CMO: E. Edwin Conaway, M.D., Vice President Medical Affairs and Chief Medical Officer
CIO: Kevin Ludwigsen, Chief Information Officer
CHR: Steven Michael Brooks, Vice President Human Resources
CNO: Angela S. Long, Vice President Clinical Services and Chief Nursing Officer
Web address: www.seormc.org
Control: Other not–for–profit (including NFP Corporation) **Service:** General Medical and Surgical

Staffed Beds: 95 **Admissions:** 3609 **Census:** 32 **Outpatient Visits:** 91711 **Births:** 435 **Total Expense ($000):** 87645 **Payroll Expense ($000):** 31276 **Personnel:** 660

CANAL WINCHESTER—Fairfield County

☐ **DILEY RIDGE MEDICAL CENTER (360358)**, 7911 Diley Road, Zip 43110–9653; tel. 614/838–7911 **A**1 10 **F**3 15 29 30 35 40 50 54 64 68 85 87 107 110 111 114 119 130 147
Primary Contact: Jodi Wilson, President and Chief Operating Officer
COO: Jodi Wilson, President and Chief Operating Officer
Web address: www.dileyridgemedicalcenter.com
Control: Other not–for–profit (including NFP Corporation) **Service:** General Medical and Surgical

Staffed Beds: 10 **Admissions:** 25 **Census:** 1 **Outpatient Visits:** 59497 **Births:** 0 **Total Expense ($000):** 13378 **Payroll Expense ($000):** 4694 **Personnel:** 78

CANTON—Stark County

⊠ △ **AULTMAN HOSPITAL (360084)**, 2600 Sixth Street S.W., Zip 44710–1702; tel. 330/452–9911, (Includes AULTMAN HOSPITAL PEDIATRIC SERVICES, 2600 Sixth Street, S.W., tel. 330/363–5455), (Total facility includes 60 beds in nursing home–type unit) **A**1 2 3 5 7 10 **F**3 7 8 11 12 13 14 15 17 18 20 22 24 26 28 29 30 31 34 35 39 40 43 44 45 48 49 50 51 53 54 55 56 57 58 59 60 61 62 63 64 68 70 71 72 74 75 76 77 78 79 81 82 83 84 85 86 87 89 90 93 96 97 98 102 103 104 105 106 107 108 109 110 111 114 117 118 119 120 121 123 127 128 129 130 131 132 133 134 135 143 144 145 146 147 148 **P**6 **S** Aultman Health Foundation, Canton, OH
Primary Contact: Edward J. Roth, III, President and Chief Executive Officer
CFO: Mark Wright, Vice President
CMO: Allison Oprandi, M.D., Chief Medical Officer
CIO: Liz Getz, Chief Information Officer
CHR: Sue Olivera, Vice President
CNO: Anne Gunther, DNP, R.N., Chief Nursing Officer
Web address: www.aultman.com
Control: Other not–for–profit (including NFP Corporation) **Service:** General Medical and Surgical

Staffed Beds: 532 **Admissions:** 22448 **Census:** 332 **Outpatient Visits:** 463385 **Births:** 2426 **Total Expense ($000):** 435783 **Payroll Expense ($000):** 173853 **Personnel:** 3468

☐ **AULTMAN SPECIALTY HOSPITAL (362032)**, 2600 Sixth Street, S.W., Zip 44710–1702; tel. 330/363–4000, (Nonreporting) **A**1 10 **S** Aultman Health Foundation, Canton, OH
Primary Contact: Terry Regula, Chief Executive Officer
CFO: Mark Wright, Chief Financial Officer
CMO: George Kefalas, Chief Medical Officer
Web address: www.aultman.org
Control: Other not–for–profit (including NFP Corporation) **Service:** Long–Term Acute Care hospital

Staffed Beds: 30

⊠ △ **MERCY MEDICAL CENTER (360070)**, 1320 Mercy Drive N.W., Zip 44708–2641; tel. 330/489–1000 **A**1 2 3 5 7 10 **F**3 11 13 15 17 18 20 22 24 26 28 29 30 34 35 39 40 43 44 46 48 49 50 51 53 54 57 58 59 60 61 62 63 64 66 68 70 72 74 75 76 77 78 79 80 81 82 84 85 86 87 89 90 91 92 93 96 97 107 108 110 111 114 115 116 117 118 119 120 121 123 124 126 129 130 131 132 135 144 146 147 148 **P**6 7 **S** Sisters of Charity Health System, Cleveland, OH
Primary Contact: Thomas E. Cecconi, President and Chief Executive Officer
COO: David D. Cemate, FACHE, Senior Vice President and Chief Operating Officer
CFO: David K. Stewart, Senior Vice President and Chief Financial Officer
CMO: David Gormsen, D.O., Vice President and Chief Medical Officer
CIO: Trevor Clere, Director Information Technology
CHR: Patti Bresnahan, Director Human Resources
CNO: Barbara Yingling, R.N., Vice President Patient Care Services and Chief Nursing Officer
Web address: www.cantonmercy.org
Control: Other not–for–profit (including NFP Corporation) **Service:** General Medical and Surgical

Staffed Beds: 329 **Admissions:** 14357 **Census:** 196 **Outpatient Visits:** 625190 **Births:** 1697 **Total Expense ($000):** 309151 **Payroll Expense ($000):** 129058 **Personnel:** 2048

⊠ **SELECT SPECIALTY HOSPITAL–CANTON (362016)**, 1320 Mercy Drive N.W., 6th Floor, Zip 44708–2614; tel. 330/489–8189, (Nonreporting) **A**1 10 **S** Select Medical Corporation, Mechanicsburg, PA
Primary Contact: Dawne Wheeler, Chief Executive Officer
Web address: www.selectspecialtyhospitals.com/company/locations/canton.aspx
Control: Corporation, Investor–owned, for–profit **Service:** Long–Term Acute Care hospital

Staffed Beds: 30

CHARDON—Geauga County

☐ **HEATHERHILL CARE COMMUNITIES (362014)**, 12340 Bass Lake Road, Zip 44024–8327; tel. 440/285–4040, (Nonreporting) **A**1 10
Primary Contact: Jim Homa, Chief Executive Officer
COO: Lisa Deering, Administrator
CFO: Valerie Love, Manager Business Office
CMO: Beejadi Makunda, M.D., Chief Medical Officer
CHR: Pam McCall, Director Human Resources
CNO: Alice Harvey, Director of Nursing
Web address: www.heatherhill.com
Control: Other not–for–profit (including NFP Corporation) **Service:** Long–Term Acute Care hospital

Staffed Beds: 214

⊠ **UNIVERSITY HOSPITALS GEAUGA MEDICAL CENTER (360192)**, 13207 Ravenna Road, Zip 44024–7032; tel. 440/269–6000 **A**1 2 3 10 **F**3 8 11 12 13 15 18 20 22 26 28 29 30 31 32 34 35 36 38 39 40 41 43 44 47 49 50 51 54 56 57 58 59 60 62 63 64 65 68 70 74 75 77 78 79 81 82 84 85 86 87 91 92 93 96 97 98 100 101 102 103 107 108 109 110 111 114 115 116 117 118 119 120 121 123 124 129 130 131 132 134 135 143 145 146 147 148 **P**8 **S** University Hospitals, Cleveland, OH
Primary Contact: M. Steven Jones, President
COO: M. Steven Jones, President
CFO: Paul Amantea, Director Finance
CMO: David Kosnosky, M.D., Chief Medical Officer
CIO: Lou Ciraldo, Information Services Representative
CHR: Danialle Lynce, Manager Human Resources
CNO: Peggy A. Kuhar, R.N., Chief Nursing Officer
Web address: www.uhhospitals.org/geauga/
Control: Other not–for–profit (including NFP Corporation) **Service:** General Medical and Surgical

Staffed Beds: 142 **Admissions:** 7958 **Census:** 90 **Outpatient Visits:** 138991 **Births:** 1028 **Total Expense ($000):** 127822 **Payroll Expense ($000):** 43206 **Personnel:** 782

CHILLICOTHE—Ross County

⊠ **ADENA MEDICAL CENTER (360159)**, 272 Hospital Road, Zip 45601–9031; tel. 740/779–7500 **A**1 2 5 10 12 13 19 **F**3 5 8 13 15 18 20 22 24 26 28 29 30 31 32 34 35 38 40 41 45 46 48 49 50 54 57 59 62 63 64 66 70 73 74 75 76 77 78 79 81 82 83 84 85 87 89 91 93 96 97 98 99 100 101 102 103 104 107 108 114 115 119 120 121 123 126 127 129 130 131 132 133 135 144 146 147 148 **P**6 **S** Adena Health System, Chillicothe, OH
Primary Contact: Mark H. Shuter, President and Chief Executive Officer
COO: Eric Cecava, Chief Operating Officer
CFO: Robert Rosenberger, Chief Financial Officer
CMO: John Fortney, M.D., Senior System Medical Advisor
CIO: Linn Weimer, Chief Information Officer
CHR: Jay Justice, Chief Human Resource Officer
Web address: www.adena.org
Control: Other not–for–profit (including NFP Corporation) **Service:** General Medical and Surgical

Staffed Beds: 214 **Admissions:** 10148 **Census:** 108 **Outpatient Visits:** 671041 **Births:** 1049 **Total Expense ($000):** 416759 **Payroll Expense ($000):** 195457 **Personnel:** 2514

⊠ **CHILLICOTHE VETERANS AFFAIRS MEDICAL CENTER**, 17273 State Route 104, Zip 45601–9718; tel. 740/773–1141, (Nonreporting) **A**1 5 **S** Department of Veterans Affairs, Washington, DC
Primary Contact: Keith Sullivan, Director
CFO: Rick Deckard, Chief Fiscal Service
CMO: Deborah Meesig, M.D., Chief of Staff
CIO: William Gawler, Chief Information Officer
CHR: Angela Young, Human Resources Officer
Web address: www.chillicothe.va.gov/
Control: Veterans Affairs, Government, federal **Service:** Psychiatric

Staffed Beds: 297

VETERANS AFFAIRS MEDICAL CENTER See Chillicothe Veterans Affairs Medical Center

CINCINNATI—Hamilton County

⊠ **BETHESDA NORTH HOSPITAL (360179)**, 10500 Montgomery Road, Zip 45242–4402; tel. 513/865–1111, (Includes BETHESDA BUTLER HOSPITAL, 3125 Hamilton Mason Road, Hamilton, Zip 45011–5307; tel. 513/894–8888; Chuck Brown, Administrator) **A**1 3 5 10 **F**1 3 4 5 8 9 11 12 13 15 16 17 18 20 22 24 26 28 29 30 31 34 35 36 37 38 39 40 41 42 43 44 45 46 47 48 49 50 53 54 55 56 57 58 59 61 63 64 65 66 67 68 70 71 72 73 74 75 76 77 78 79 80 81 82 84 85 86 87 88 89 90 91 92 93 94 96 97 98 99 100 101 102 103 104 107 108 110 111 114 115 116 117 118 119 120 121 123 124 126 128 129 130 131 132 134 135 141 143 144 145 146 147 148 **P**1 6 8
Primary Contact: Barbara Boyne, Executive Director, Operations
COO: Jenny Oliphant, Executive Vice President and Chief Operating Officer
CFO: Michael Crofton, Senior Vice President and Chief Financial Officer
CMO: Georges Feghali, M.D., Senior Vice President Quality and Chief Medical Officer
CIO: Rick Moore, Chief Information Officer
CHR: Walter L. McLarty, Chief Human Resources Officer
CNO: Mary Irvin, R.N., Senior Vice President and Chief Nursing Officer
Web address: www.trihealth.com
Control: Other not–for–profit (including NFP Corporation) **Service:** General Medical and Surgical

Staffed Beds: 367 Admissions: 23223 Census: 271 Outpatient Visits: 341581 Births: 4165 Total Expense ($000): 485874 Payroll Expense ($000): 168508 Personnel: 3119

BRIDGEWELL HOSPITAL OF CINCINNATI (364046), 5500 Verulam Avenue, Zip 45213–2448; tel. 513/531–6444, (Nonreporting) **A**10
Primary Contact: Glenna Coffey, R.N., Chief Operating Officer
CNO: Doug Eppley, Director of Nursing
Web address: www.bridgewellhospitals.com
Control: Corporation, Investor–owned, for–profit **Service:** Psychiatric

Staffed Beds: 48

☐ △ **CHRIST HOSPITAL (360163)**, 2139 Auburn Avenue, Zip 45219–2906; tel. 513/585–2000 **A**1 2 3 5 7 10 **F**1 3 6 8 9 11 12 13 15 17 18 20 22 24 26 28 29 30 31 34 35 36 37 38 39 40 44 45 46 47 48 49 50 51 53 54 55 56 57 58 59 60 61 64 65 66 68 70 73 74 75 76 77 78 79 80 81 82 83 84 85 86 87 90 92 93 94 96 97 98 99 100 101 102 103 104 107 108 109 110 111 114 115 116 117 118 119 120 121 123 124 126 129 130 131 132 135 136 138 141 143 144 145 146 147 148 **P**6
Primary Contact: Michael Keating, President and Chief Executive Officer
COO: Victor DiPilla, Vice President and Chief Business Development Officer
CMO: Bernard B. Gawne, M.D., Vice President and Chief Medical Officer
CIO: Alex Vaillancourt, Chief Information Officer
CHR: Rick Tolson, Chief Administrative Officer and Chief Human Resources Officer
CNO: Deborah Marie Hayes, R.N., Chief Hospital Officer and Chief Nursing Officer
Web address: www.thechristhospital.com
Control: Other not–for–profit (including NFP Corporation) **Service:** General Medical and Surgical

Staffed Beds: 513 Admissions: 23134 Census: 284 Outpatient Visits: 505992 Births: 3227 Total Expense ($000): 597380 Payroll Expense ($000): 208677 Personnel: 3466

⊠ △ **CINCINNATI CHILDREN'S HOSPITAL MEDICAL CENTER (363300)**, 3333 Burnet Avenue MLC 8006, Zip 45229–3039, Mailing Address: 3333 Burnet Avenue, Zip 45229–3039; tel. 513/636–4200, (Includes DIVISION OF ADOLESCENT MEDICINE, CINCINNATI CENTER FOR DEVELOPMENTAL DISORDERS, AND CONVALESCENT HOSPITAL FOR CHILDREN ; CHILDREN'S HOSPITAL, Elland and Bethesda Avenues, Zip 45229) **A**1 2 3 5 7 8 10 **F**3 7 9 11 12 17 18 19 20 21 22 23 24 25 26 27 28 29 30 31 32 34 35 36 37 38 39 40 41 42 43 44 45 46 48 49 50 51 54 55 57 58 59 60 61 62 63 64 65 66 68 72 74 75 76 77 78 79 81 82 84 85 86 87 88 89 90 91 92 93 94 95 96 97 98 99 100 101 102 104 105 106 107 108 111 112 115 117 118 119 120 126 129 130 131 132 134 135 136 137 138 139 140 141 142 144 146 148 **P**1
Primary Contact: Michael Fisher, President and Chief Executive Officer
CFO: Scott J. Hamlin, Chief Financial Officer
CIO: Marianne Speight, Vice President Information System and Chief Information Officer
Web address: www.cincinnatichildrens.org
Control: Other not–for–profit (including NFP Corporation) **Service:** Children's general

Staffed Beds: 589 Admissions: 19427 Census: 411 Outpatient Visits: 1235772 Births: 9 Total Expense ($000): 1996846 Payroll Expense ($000): 1031542 Personnel: 12899

⊠ **CINCINNATI VETERANS AFFAIRS MEDICAL CENTER**, 3200 Vine Street, Zip 45220–2288; tel. 513/475–6300, (Nonreporting) **A**1 2 3 5 **S** Department of Veterans Affairs, Washington, DC
Primary Contact: Glenn A. Costie, FACHE, Interim Director
COO: David Ninneman, Associate Director
CFO: Sandra Selvidge, Chief Fiscal Service
CIO: Vique Caro, Chief Information Officer
CHR: Sandra Stenger, Acting Chief Human Resources
CNO: Katheryn Cook, R.N., Nurse Executive
Web address: www.cincinnati.va.gov/
Control: Veterans Affairs, Government, federal **Service:** General Medical and Surgical

Staffed Beds: 268

⊠ **DANIEL DRAKE CENTER FOR POST ACUTE CARE (362004)**, 151 West Galbraith Road, Zip 45216–1015; tel. 513/418–2500, (Nonreporting) **A**1 3 5 10 **S** UC Health, Cincinnati, OH
Primary Contact: Amy Schroyer, Vice President Administration and Senior Site Executive
CFO: Duane Pifko, Interim Director Financial Services
Web address: www.uchealth.com/danieldrakecenter/
Control: Other not–for–profit (including NFP Corporation) **Service:** Long–Term Acute Care hospital

Staffed Beds: 202

⊠ △ **GOOD SAMARITAN HOSPITAL (360134)**, 375 Dixmyth Avenue, Zip 45220–2489; tel. 513/862–1400 **A**1 2 3 5 7 8 10 **F**3 5 6 9 11 12 13 15 17 18 20 22 24 26 28 29 30 31 34 35 36 37 38 39 40 41 42 44 45 46 47 48 49 50 53 54 55 56 57 58 59 61 63 64 65 66 68 70 71 72 74 75 76 77 78 79 81 82 84 85 86 87 90 91 92 93 94 96 97 98 99 100 101 102 103 104 105 107 108 110 111 114 115 116 117 118 119 120 121 123 124 126 129 130 131 132 134 135 141 143 144 145 146 147 148 **P**1 6 8 **S** Catholic Health Initiatives, Englewood, CO
Primary Contact: Jamie Easterling, Executive Director, Operations
COO: Gerald P. Oliphant, Executive Vice President and Chief Operating Officer
CFO: Michael Crofton, Chief Financial Officer
CMO: Georges Feghali, M.D., Senior Vice President Quality and Chief Medical Officer
CIO: Rick Moore, Chief Information Officer
CHR: Walter L. McLarty, Chief Human Resources Officer
Web address: www.trihealth.com
Control: Church–operated, Nongovernment, not–for profit **Service:** General Medical and Surgical

Staffed Beds: 504 Admissions: 23357 Census: 337 Outpatient Visits: 268199 Births: 5791 Total Expense ($000): 525195 Payroll Expense ($000): 180246 Personnel: 2822

⊠ **HEALTHSOUTH REHABILITATION HOSPITAL AT DRAKE (363034)**, 151 West Galbraith Road, Zip 45216–1015; tel. 513/418–5600 **A**1 10 **F**29 31 34 35 56 74 90 91 92 130 148 **S** HEALTHSOUTH Corporation, Birmingham, AL
Primary Contact: Brad Kennedy, Chief Executive Officer
CFO: Scott Corder, Controller
CMO: Mark Goddard, M.D., Medical Director
CHR: Jason Sparks, Director, Human Resources
CNO: Kathy McNally, Chief Nursing Officer
Web address: www.healthsouthatdrake.com
Control: Corporation, Investor–owned, for–profit **Service:** Rehabilitation

Staffed Beds: 60 Admissions: 1306 Census: 52 Outpatient Visits: 0 Births: 0 Total Expense ($000): 16359 Payroll Expense ($000): 9308 Personnel: 157

Hospital, Medicare Provider Number, Address, Telephone, Approval, Facility, and Physician Codes, Health Care System

★ American Hospital Association (AHA) membership ☐ The Joint Commission accreditation ○ Healthcare Facilities Accreditation Program ◇ DNV Healthcare Inc. accreditation ⇑ Center for Improvement in Healthcare Quality Accreditation △ Commission on Accreditation of Rehabilitation Facilities (CARF) accreditation

OH

☒ **MERCY HEALTH – ANDERSON HOSPITAL (360001)**, 7500 State Road, Zip 45255–2492; tel. 513/624–4500, (Nonreporting) **A**1 2 3 10 **S** Mercy Health, Cincinnati, OH
Primary Contact: Jeff Graham, Market Leader and President
COO: Katherine Edrington, R.N., Administrator
CFO: Patrick A. Kowalski, Chief Financial Officer
CMO: Leonard M. Randolph, Jr., M.D., Senior Vice President and Chief Medical Officer
CIO: Matt Eversole, Regional Vice President Information Services
CHR: Angie Ferrell, Director Human Resources
Web address: www.e–mercy.com
Control: Other not–for–profit (including NFP Corporation) **Service:** General Medical and Surgical

Staffed Beds: 188

☒ **MERCY HEALTH – WEST HOSPITAL (360234)**, 3300 Mercy Health Boulevard, Zip 45211; tel. 513/215–5000, (Nonreporting) **A**1 2 10 **S** Mercy Health, Cincinnati, OH
Primary Contact: Michael Kramer, Chief Executive Officer
COO: Jason Asic, Chief Operating Officer
CFO: Kyle Klein, Assistant Chief Financial Officer
CMO: Creighton Wright, M.D., Vice President Medical Administration
CHR: Bridget Mentzel, Director Human Resources
CNO: Stephanie Meade, R.N., Chief Nursing Officer
Web address: www.e–mercy.com/west–hospital
Control: Other not–for–profit (including NFP Corporation) **Service:** General Medical and Surgical

Staffed Beds: 250

☒ **SELECT SPECIALTY HOSPITAL – CINCINNATI NORTH (362034)**, 10500 Montgomery Road, Zip 45242–4402; tel. 513/865–5300, (Nonreporting) **A**1 10 **S** Select Medical Corporation, Mechanicsburg, PA
Primary Contact: Susan Glen, Chief Executive Officer
CMO: Sunil Dama, M.D., Medical Director
CHR: Elizabeth M. Wilson, Coordinator Human Resources
Web address: www.cincinnatinorth.selectspecialtyhospitals.com/
Control: Corporation, Investor–owned, for–profit **Service:** Long–Term Acute Care hospital

Staffed Beds: 25

☒ **SELECT SPECIALTY HOSPITAL–CINCINNATI (362019)**, 375 Dixmyth Avenue, 15th Floor, Zip 45220–2475; tel. 513/872–4444 **A**1 10 **F**1 29 75 77 85 86 87 91 130 **P**5 **S** Select Medical Corporation, Mechanicsburg, PA
Primary Contact: Curtis Ohashi, Chief Executive Officer
CMO: Brian Boster, M.D., Medical Director
CNO: Bobbi Schmidt, Chief Nursing Officer
Web address: www.selectspecialtyhospitals.com/company/locations/cincinnati.aspx
Control: Corporation, Investor–owned, for–profit **Service:** Long–Term Acute Care hospital

Staffed Beds: 36 **Admissions:** 328 **Census:** 29 **Outpatient Visits:** 0 **Births:** 0

☐ **SHRINERS HOSPITALS FOR CHILDREN–CINCINNATI BURNS HOSPITAL (363308)**, 3229 Burnet Avenue, Zip 45229–3095; tel. 513/872–6000, (Nonreporting) **A**1 10 **S** Shriners Hospitals for Children, Tampa, FL
Primary Contact: Mark D. Shugarman, Administrator
CFO: Susan Harris, Director Fiscal Services
CMO: Petra Warner, Interim Chief of Staff
CIO: David Brian, Chief Information Officer
CHR: Debra A. Felder, Director Human Resources
Web address: www.shrinershospitalsforchildren.org/Hospitals/Locations/Cincinnati.aspx
Control: Other not–for–profit (including NFP Corporation) **Service:** Children's other specialty

Staffed Beds: 30

☒ **SUMMIT BEHAVIORAL HEALTHCARE (364035)**, 1101 Summit Road, Zip 45237–2652; tel. 513/948–3600, (Nonreporting) **A**1 10 **S** Ohio Department of Mental Health, Columbus, OH
Primary Contact: Elizabeth Banks, Chief Executive Officer
COO: Steven Burns, Director Fiscal Services
CFO: Steven Burns, Director Fiscal Services
CMO: Patrick McCullough, M.D., Chief Medical Services
CIO: Eric Bradley, Director Computer Information Services
CHR: Bobbie Carrelli, Director Human Resources
CNO: Kathy A. Smith, MSN, Nurse Executive
Web address: www.mh.state.oh.us/
Control: State–Government, nonfederal **Service:** Psychiatric

Staffed Beds: 291

☒ **THE JEWISH HOSPITAL – MERCY HEALTH (360016)**, 4777 East Galbraith Road, Zip 45236–2725; tel. 513/686–3000, (Nonreporting) **A**1 2 3 5 10 **S** Mercy Health, Cincinnati, OH
Primary Contact: Patricia Davis–Hagens, R.N., Central Market Leader and President
COO: Jack Hill, Chief Operating Officer and Administrator
Web address: www.jewishhospitalcincinnati.com/
Control: Other not–for–profit (including NFP Corporation) **Service:** General Medical and Surgical

Staffed Beds: 209

☐ **TRIHEALTH EVENDALE HOSPITAL (360362)**, 3155 Glendale Milford Road, Zip 45241–3134; tel. 513/454–2222 **A**1 2 10 **F**3 8 29 34 35 44 46 50 57 59 64 68 70 75 79 81 82 85 86 87 107 111 115 119 130 131 143 146 **P**1 6 8
Primary Contact: Kelvin Hanger, Chief Executive Officer
CFO: Michael Crofton, Chief Financial Officer
Web address: www.evendalemedical.com
Control: Other not–for–profit (including NFP Corporation) **Service:** Surgical

Staffed Beds: 18 **Admissions:** 587 **Census:** 3 **Outpatient Visits:** 31363 **Births:** 0 **Total Expense ($000):** 45724 **Payroll Expense ($000):** 13753 **Personnel:** 191

☒ **UNIVERSITY OF CINCINNATI MEDICAL CENTER (360003)**, 234 Goodman Street, Zip 45219–2316; tel. 513/584–1000 **A**1 2 3 5 8 10 **F**3 7 9 11 12 13 15 16 17 18 20 22 24 26 29 30 31 34 35 36 37 38 39 40 41 43 44 45 46 47 48 49 50 51 53 54 55 56 57 58 59 60 61 63 64 66 68 70 71 72 73 74 75 76 77 78 79 80 81 82 84 85 86 87 91 92 97 98 100 101 102 103 104 107 108 110 111 112 114 115 116 117 118 119 120 121 123 124 126 129 130 131 132 134 135 136 138 139 141 142 145 146 147 148 **P**6 **S** UC Health, Cincinnati, OH
Primary Contact: Jennifer Jackson, R.N., MSN, Chief Administrative Officer, Chief Nursing Officer and Vice President
CFO: Matthew Nealon, Vice President, Chief Financial Officer
CMO: Bill Hurford, Chief Medical Officer
CIO: Jay Brown, Vice President and Chief Information Officer
CHR: Clarence Pauley, Senior Vice President and Chief Human Resources Officer
CNO: Jennifer Jackson, R.N., Vice President and Chief Nursing Officer
Web address: www.uchealth.com/university–of–cincinnati–medical–center/
Control: Other not–for–profit (including NFP Corporation) **Service:** General Medical and Surgical

Staffed Beds: 607 **Admissions:** 27009 **Census:** 418 **Outpatient Visits:** 455572 **Births:** 2499 **Total Expense ($000):** 836473 **Payroll Expense ($000):** 257884 **Personnel:** 4452

VETERANS AFFAIRS MEDICAL CENTER See Cincinnati Veterans Affairs Medical Center

CIRCLEVILLE—Pickaway County

☒ **BERGER HEALTH SYSTEM (360170)**, 600 North Pickaway Street, Zip 43113–1447; tel. 740/474–2126 **A**1 5 10 **F**3 13 15 18 20 28 29 30 31 34 35 40 45 46 50 54 59 63 64 70 76 77 78 81 85 87 92 93 96 107 108 110 111 115 119 124 129 130 131 132 135 146 148
Primary Contact: Tim A. Colburn, President and Chief Executive Officer
CFO: Richard Filler, Chief Financial Officer
CMO: Jill Barno, M.D., Chief Medical Officer
CIO: Andy Chileski, Chief Information Officer and Vice President Facilities
CHR: Richard Filler, Chief Human Resource Officer
CNO: Kristin Day Gardner, Chief Nursing Officer
Web address: www.bergerhealth.com
Control: City–County, Government, nonfederal **Service:** General Medical and Surgical

Staffed Beds: 56 **Admissions:** 1940 **Census:** 17 **Outpatient Visits:** 105259 **Births:** 381 **Total Expense ($000):** 62874 **Payroll Expense ($000):** 22017 **Personnel:** 410

CLEVELAND—Cuyahoga County

☒ **CLEVELAND CLINIC (360180)**, 9500 Euclid Avenue, Zip 44195–5108; tel. 216/444–2200, (Includes CLEVELAND CLINIC CHILDREN'S HOSPITAL, 9500 Euclid Avenue, Zip 44103; tel. 800/223–2273) **A**1 3 5 8 10 **F**3 6 7 8 9 12 13 14 15 17 18 19 20 21 22 23 24 25 26 27 28 29 30 31 32 33 34 35 36 37 38 39 40 42 44 45 46 47 48 49 50 51 52 53 54 55 56 57 58 59 60 61 62 63 64 65 66 68 70 71 72 74 75 76 77 78 79 80 81 82 83 84 85 86 87 88 89 90 91 92 93 94 96 97 100 101 103 104 107 108 109 110 111 112 113 114 115 116 117 118 119 120 121 123 124 126 129 130 131 132 134 135 136 137 138 139 140 141 142 143 144 145 146 147 148 **P**6 **S** Cleveland Clinic Health System, Cleveland, OH
Primary Contact: Delos Cosgrove, M.D., President and Chief Executive Officer
CFO: Steven Glass, Chief Financial Officer
CMO: Joseph Hahn, M.D., Chief of Staff
CIO: C. Martin Harris, M.D., Chief Information Officer
CNO: Katherine Hancock, R.N., Executive Chief Nursing Officer
Web address: www.clevelandclinic.org
Control: Other not–for–profit (including NFP Corporation) **Service:** General Medical and Surgical

Staffed Beds: 1280 **Admissions:** 53765 **Census:** 1013 **Outpatient Visits:** 5633024 **Births:** 173 **Total Expense ($000):** 4722292 **Payroll Expense ($000):** 2367209 **Personnel:** 27829

Many Facility Codes have changed. Please refer to the AHA Guide Code Chart.   © 2016 AHA Guide

☒ △ **CLEVELAND CLINIC CHILDREN'S HOSPITAL FOR REHABILITATION (363304)**, 2801 Martin Luther King Jr. Drive, Zip 44104–3865; tel. 216/448–6400 **A**1 3 7 10 **F**28 29 30 32 34 35 36 44 50 60 68 74 75 79 80 82 86 90 91 93 94 96 99 100 130 131 132 143 146 148 **S** Cleveland Clinic Health System, Cleveland, OH
Primary Contact: Michael J. McHugh, M.D., Medical Director
COO: Alec G. Kulik, Administrator
CFO: Debra Nyikes, Director Finance and Chief Financial Officer
CMO: Roberta Bauer, M.D., Acting Chair Medical Staff
CIO: C. Martin Harris, M.D., Chief Information Officer
CHR: Jan Hlahol, Manager Human Resources
Web address: www.my.clevelandclinic.org/childrens–hospital/default.aspx
Control: Other not–for–profit (including NFP Corporation) **Service:** Children's rehabilitation

Staffed Beds: 25 **Admissions:** 196 **Census:** 13 **Outpatient Visits:** 82215 **Births:** 0 **Total Expense ($000):** 39239 **Payroll Expense ($000):** 22623 **Personnel:** 371

☒ **CLEVELAND CLINIC FAIRVIEW HOSPITAL (360077)**, 18101 Lorain Avenue, Zip 44111–5656; tel. 216/476–7000 **A**1 2 3 5 10 13 **F**3 8 12 13 15 17 18 19 20 22 24 26 28 29 30 31 34 35 36 40 41 43 45 46 47 49 50 51 53 55 57 58 59 60 64 68 69 70 71 72 73 74 75 76 78 79 81 82 85 86 87 89 92 93 97 98 99 100 107 108 110 111 114 115 117 118 119 120 121 123 124 126 130 131 132 135 146 147 148 **S** Cleveland Clinic Health System, Cleveland, OH
Primary Contact: Neil Smith, D.O., President
COO: John C. Mills, Senior Vice President Operations
CFO: Ankit Chhabra, Director Finance
CMO: Brent Burkey, M.D., Chief Medical Officer
CIO: C. Martin Harris, M.D., Chief Information Officer
CHR: Ann Beatty, Director Human Resources
CNO: Deborah C. Small, R.N., Vice President Patient Care Services and Chief Nursing Officer
Web address: www.fairviewhospital.org
Control: Other not–for–profit (including NFP Corporation) **Service:** General Medical and Surgical

Staffed Beds: 454 **Admissions:** 22569 **Census:** 268 **Outpatient Visits:** 241815 **Births:** 4669 **Total Expense ($000):** 361086 **Payroll Expense ($000):** 133543 **Personnel:** 2215

☐ **GRACE HOSPITAL (362015)**, 2307 West 14th Street, Zip 44113–3698; tel. 216/687–1500, (Nonreporting) **A**1 10
Primary Contact: Rajive Khanna, Chief Executive Officer
COO: Rajive Khanna, Chief Executive Officer
CFO: Michelle Hennis, Administrative Director Financial Services
CMO: John Nickels, M.D., President Medical Staff
CNO: Barbara Moran, R.N., Director Patient Care Services and Chief Nursing Officer
Web address: www.gracehospital.org
Control: Other not–for–profit (including NFP Corporation) **Service:** Long–Term Acute Care hospital

Staffed Beds: 87

☒ **HILLCREST HOSPITAL (360230)**, 6780 Mayfield Road, Zip 44124–2203; tel. 440/312–4500 **A**1 2 3 10 **F**3 11 12 13 15 17 18 20 22 24 26 28 29 30 31 34 35 36 37 38 40 41 43 46 49 50 51 53 54 55 56 57 59 60 64 65 68 69 70 72 74 75 76 77 78 79 81 82 84 85 86 87 89 93 97 100 107 108 110 111 114 115 116 117 118 119 120 121 126 129 130 131 132 135 143 145 146 147 148 **S** Cleveland Clinic Health System, Cleveland, OH
Primary Contact: Brian J. Harte, M.D., President
Web address: www.hillcresthospital.org
Control: Other not–for–profit (including NFP Corporation) **Service:** General Medical and Surgical

Staffed Beds: 453 **Admissions:** 23154 **Census:** 309 **Outpatient Visits:** 238801 **Births:** 4440 **Total Expense ($000):** 355956 **Payroll Expense ($000):** 125148 **Personnel:** 2053

★ **SELECT SPECIALTY HOSPITAL CLEVELAND–GATEWAY (362026)**, 2351 East 22nd Street, 7th Floor, Zip 44115–3111; tel. 216/363–2671, (Includes SELECT SPECIALTY HOSPITAL CLEVELAND FAIRHILL, 11900 Fairhill Road, Zip 44120–1062; tel. 216/983–8030; Steve Jakubcanin, Executive Director), (Nonreporting) **A**3 10 **S** Kindred Healthcare, Louisville, KY
Primary Contact: Cheryl G. Gentry, Interim Chief Executive Officer
Web address: www.kindredgateway.com
Control: Corporation, Investor–owned, for–profit **Service:** Long–Term Acute Care hospital

Staffed Beds: 153

KINDRED HOSPITAL OF CLEVELAND See Kindred Hospital Cleveland–Gateway

☒ △ **LOUIS STOKES CLEVELAND VETERANS AFFAIRS MEDICAL CENTER**, 10701 East Boulevard, Zip 44106–1702; tel. 216/791–3800, (Nonreporting) **A**1 2 3 5 7 8 **S** Department of Veterans Affairs, Washington, DC
Primary Contact: Susan Fuehrer, Director
CFO: Michael Pappas, Chief Fiscal Service Officer
CMO: Murray Altose, M.D., Chief of Staff
CIO: Steve Gaj, Facility Chief Information Officer
CHR: Charles Franks, Chief Human Resources
CNO: Innette Mary Sarduy, M.P.H., Associate Director Patient Care Services and Nurse Executive
Web address: www.cleveland.va.gov/
Control: Veterans Affairs, Government, federal **Service:** General Medical and Surgical

Staffed Beds: 585

☒ **LUTHERAN HOSPITAL (360087)**, 1730 West 25th Street, Zip 44113–3170; tel. 216/696–4300 **A**1 3 10 **F**3 4 5 15 29 30 34 35 37 40 50 56 57 58 59 60 64 65 70 74 75 77 79 81 85 86 87 93 98 99 103 104 105 107 110 111 114 130 131 132 143 146 148 **S** Cleveland Clinic Health System, Cleveland, OH
Primary Contact: Donald Malone, M.D., President
COO: Matthew Mattner, Chief Operating Officer
CFO: Don Urbancsik, Director Finance
CMO: Ronald Golovan, M.D., Vice President Medical Operations
CIO: C. Martin Harris, M.D., Chief Information Officer
CHR: Ron Robinson, Business Partner
CNO: Janet Schuster, R.N., Chief Nursing Officer
Web address: www.lutheranhospital.org
Control: Other not–for–profit (including NFP Corporation) **Service:** General Medical and Surgical

Staffed Beds: 198 **Admissions:** 7880 **Census:** 100 **Outpatient Visits:** 60473 **Births:** 0 **Total Expense ($000):** 92298 **Payroll Expense ($000):** 38792 **Personnel:** 614

☒ △ **METROHEALTH MEDICAL CENTER (360059)**, 2500 MetroHealth Drive, Zip 44109–1998; tel. 216/778–7800, (Total facility includes 140 beds in nursing home–type unit) **A**1 2 3 5 7 8 10 13 **F**3 5 6 7 8 9 11 12 13 15 16 18 19 20 22 24 26 27 28 29 30 31 32 34 35 36 38 39 40 43 44 45 46 47 48 49 50 51 52 53 54 55 56 57 58 59 60 61 63 64 65 66 68 70 71 72 74 75 76 77 78 79 80 81 82 83 84 85 86 87 88 89 90 91 92 93 94 95 96 97 98 99 100 101 102 103 104 105 107 108 110 111 114 115 116 117 118 119 120 121 123 124 126 128 129 130 131 132 134 135 143 144 146 147 148 **P**6
Primary Contact: Akram Boutros, M.D., FACHE, President and Chief Executive Officer
COO: Daniel Lewis, Executive Vice President and Chief Operating Officer
CFO: Craig Richmond, Senior Vice President and Chief Financial Officer
CMO: Alfred Connors, M.D., Executive Vice President and Chief Quality Officer and Interim Chief Medical Officer
CIO: Don Reichert, Vice President Associate Chief Information Officer
CHR: Debbie Warman, Vice President Human Resources
CNO: Melissa Kline, Chief Nursing Officer
Web address: www.metrohealth.org
Control: County–Government, nonfederal **Service:** General Medical and Surgical

Staffed Beds: 737 **Admissions:** 25164 **Census:** 507 **Outpatient Visits:** 1174039 **Births:** 3013 **Total Expense ($000):** 903928 **Payroll Expense ($000):** 499194 **Personnel:** 5958

☐ **ST. VINCENT CHARITY MEDICAL CENTER (360037)**, 2351 East 22nd Street, Zip 44115–3111; tel. 216/861–6200, (Nonreporting) **A**1 2 3 5 10 **S** Sisters of Charity Health System, Cleveland, OH
Primary Contact: David F. Perse, M.D., President and Chief Executive Officer
COO: Joan Ross, Senior Vice President and Chief Operating Officer
CFO: John Rusnaczyk, Senior Vice President and Chief Financial Officer
CMO: Joseph A. Sopko, M.D., Chief Medical Officer
CIO: Robin Stursa, Chief Information Officer
CHR: Ted Monczewski, Vice President Human Resources
CNO: Beverly Lozar, Chief Nursing Executive
Web address: www.stvincentcharity.com/
Control: Other not–for–profit (including NFP Corporation) **Service:** General Medical and Surgical

Staffed Beds: 214

✠ **UH REGIONAL HOSPITALS (360075)**, 27100 Chardon Road, Zip 44143–1116; tel. 440/585–6500, (Includes UNIVERSITY HOSPITALS BEDFORD MEDICAL CENTER, 44 Blaine Avenue, Zip 44146–2709; tel. 440/735–3900; UNIVERSITY HOSPITALS RICHMOND MEDICAL CENTER, 27100 Chardon Road, tel. 440/585–6500) **A**1 3 10 12 13 **F**8 14 15 20 29 34 35 40 50 57 59 60 65 66 68 70 75 77 79 81 82 84 86 87 89 91 92 93 96 97 105 106 107 108 109 110 111 114 116 117 118 119 129 130 131 132 133 135 143 146 147 148 **P**8 **S** University Hospitals, Cleveland, OH
Primary Contact: Brian Monter, MSN, R.N., President
CFO: Scott Platz, Director Finance
CMO: Rosemary Leeming, M.D., Chief Medical Officer
CHR: Stephanie W. Neonakis, Manager Human Resources
CNO: Michelle Giltner, Interim Chief Nursing Officer
Web address: www.uhhospitals.org
Control: Other not–for–profit (including NFP Corporation) **Service:** General Medical and Surgical

Staffed Beds: 101 **Admissions:** 4684 **Census:** 54 **Outpatient Visits:** 132695 **Births:** 0 **Total Expense ($000):** 106517 **Payroll Expense ($000):** 41246 **Personnel:** 788

✠ **UNIVERSITY HOSPITALS CLEVELAND MEDICAL CENTER (360137)**, 11100 Euclid Avenue, Zip 44106–1716; tel. 216/844–1000, (Includes ALFRED AND NORMA LERNER TOWER, BOLWELL HEALTH CENTER, HANNA PAVILION, LAKESIDE HOSPITAL, SAMUEL MATHER PAVILION ; HANNA HOUSE SKILLED NURSING FACILITY, 11100 Euclid Avenue, Zip 44106; RAINBOW BABIES AND CHILDREN'S HOSPITAL, 2101 Adelbert Road, Zip 44106–2624; tel. 216/844–3911; Patricia DePompei, President; UNIVERSITY MACDONALD WOMEN'S HOSPITAL, 2101 Adelbert Road, Zip 44106–2624; tel. 216/844–3911; Patricia DePompei, President), (Total facility includes 38 beds in nursing home–type unit) **A**1 2 3 5 8 10 **F**3 5 6 8 9 11 12 13 14 15 17 18 19 20 21 22 23 24 25 26 27 28 29 30 31 32 34 35 36 37 38 39 40 41 42 43 44 45 46 47 48 49 50 51 52 53 54 55 56 57 58 59 60 61 62 64 65 66 68 70 71 72 73 74 75 76 77 78 79 80 81 82 83 84 85 86 87 88 89 91 92 93 94 96 97 98 99 100 101 102 103 104 105 107 108 109 110 111 112 114 115 116 117 118 119 120 121 123 124 126 128 129 130 131 132 133 134 135 136 137 138 139 140 141 142 143 144 145 146 147 148 **P**6 7 **S** University Hospitals, Cleveland, OH
Primary Contact: Daniel I. Simon, M.D., President
COO: Ron Dziedzicki, R.N., Chief Operating Officer
CFO: Sonia Salvino, Vice President Finance
CMO: Michael Anderson, M.D., Chief Medical Officer
CIO: Sue Schade, Interim Chief Information Officer
CHR: Julie Chester, Vice President Human Resources
CNO: Jean Blake, Chief Nursing Officer
Web address: www.UHhospitals.org
Control: Other not–for–profit (including NFP Corporation) **Service:** General Medical and Surgical

Staffed Beds: 814 **Admissions:** 42329 **Census:** 663 **Outpatient Visits:** 493419 **Births:** 4006 **Total Expense ($000):** 1313525 **Payroll Expense ($000):** 456527 **Personnel:** 8666

VETERANS AFFAIRS MEDICAL CENTER See Louis Stokes Cleveland Veterans Affairs Medical Center

COLDWATER—Mercer County

✠ **MERCER HEALTH (360058)**, 800 West Main Street, Zip 45828–1698; tel. 419/678–2341 **A**1 10 **F**3 7 11 12 13 15 18 28 29 30 31 34 35 40 44 45 47 50 51 54 57 59 61 62 64 65 70 75 76 77 78 79 81 82 85 87 92 93 94 97 107 108 110 111 114 118 119 130 131 132 133 134 135 143 144 145 146 147 148 **P**3
Primary Contact: Lisa R. Klenke, R.N., Chief Executive Officer
CFO: George Boyles, Senior Vice President of Finance and Chief Financial Officer
CMO: James Reichert, Chief Medical Officer
CIO: DeWayne Marsee, Director Information Systems
CHR: Jon Dingledine, Senior Director Human Resources and Support Services
CNO: Cindy Liette, Vice President Patient Care Services
Web address: www.mercer–health.com
Control: Hospital district or authority, Government, nonfederal **Service:** General Medical and Surgical

Staffed Beds: 60 **Admissions:** 1860 **Census:** 13 **Outpatient Visits:** 132442 **Births:** 337 **Total Expense ($000):** 48318 **Payroll Expense ($000):** 16696 **Personnel:** 403

COLUMBUS—Franklin County

✠ **JAMES CANCER HOSPITAL AND SOLOVE RESEARCH INSTITUTE (360242)**, 460 West Tenth Avenue, Zip 43210–1240; tel. 614/293–3300 **A**1 3 5 10 **F**3 15 29 30 31 32 34 35 36 37 38 39 44 46 47 48 49 50 52 54 55 57 58 59 61 64 66 68 70 71 74 75 77 78 79 81 82 84 85 86 87 93 97 100 107 108 110 111 112 114 115 116 117 118 119 120 121 123 124 126 130 132 134 135 136 141 143 144 145 146 147 148 **P**6 **S** Ohio State University Health System, Columbus, OH
Primary Contact: Michael Caligiuri, Chief Executive Officer
COO: Jeff Walker, Chief Operating Officer
CFO: Bell Julian, Associate Executive Director and Chief Financial Officer
CIO: Michael Townsend, Chief Information Officer
CHR: Jill Hannah, Director Human Resources
CNO: Kris M. Kipp, Executive Director, Patient Services and Chief Nursing Officer
Web address: www.jamesline.com
Control: State–Government, nonfederal **Service:** Cancer

Staffed Beds: 304 **Admissions:** 12653 **Census:** 235 **Outpatient Visits:** 359253 **Births:** 0 **Total Expense ($000):** 806519 **Payroll Expense ($000):** 189349 **Personnel:** 3941

✠ △ **MOUNT CARMEL (360035)**, 793 West State Street, Zip 43222–1551; tel. 614/234–5000, (Includes MOUNT CARMEL EAST HOSPITAL, 6001 East Broad Street, Zip 43213; tel. 614/234–6000; Brinsley Lewis, FACHE, President; MOUNT CARMEL WEST HOSPITAL, 793 West State Street, Zip 43222; tel. 614/234–5000) **A**1 2 3 5 7 10 **F**3 11 12 13 15 17 18 20 22 24 26 28 29 30 31 34 35 37 40 42 43 44 45 46 47 48 49 50 51 54 55 57 58 59 61 63 64 65 66 68 70 72 74 75 76 77 78 79 81 82 83 84 85 86 87 90 91 92 93 96 97 98 100 101 102 103 104 107 108 109 110 111 114 115 116 117 118 119 120 121 123 124 126 130 131 132 144 145 146 147 148 **P**6 8 **S** Trinity Health, Livonia, MI
Primary Contact: Sean McKibben, President and Chief Operating Officer
COO: Mary R. Trimmer, Interim Chief Operating Officer
CFO: Keith T. Coleman, Chief Financial Officer
Web address: www.mountcarmelhealth.com
Control: Church–operated, Nongovernment, not–for profit **Service:** General Medical and Surgical

Staffed Beds: 747 **Admissions:** 38266 **Census:** 471 **Outpatient Visits:** 394077 **Births:** 3766 **Total Expense ($000):** 672000 **Payroll Expense ($000):** 233364 **Personnel:** 4068

✠ △ **NATIONWIDE CHILDREN'S HOSPITAL (363305)**, 700 Children's Drive, Zip 43205–2664; tel. 614/722–2000 **A**1 3 5 7 10 **F**3 7 8 12 16 17 18 19 20 21 22 23 24 25 26 27 28 29 30 31 32 34 35 36 38 39 40 41 43 44 45 47 48 50 51 52 53 54 55 57 58 59 60 61 62 63 64 65 66 68 71 72 74 75 77 78 79 81 82 83 84 85 86 87 88 89 90 92 93 94 96 97 98 99 100 101 102 104 105 107 108 111 112 114 115 116 117 118 119 126 127 129 130 131 132 133 134 135 136 137 138 140 141 143 144 145 146 148 **P**8
Primary Contact: Steve Allen, M.D., Chief Executive Officer
COO: Rick Miller, President and Chief Operating Officer
CFO: Tim Robinson, Executive Vice President, Chief Financial and Administrative Officer and Treasurer
CMO: Richard Brilli, M.D., Chief Medical Officer
CIO: Denise Zabawski, Vice President Information Services and Chief Information Officer
Web address: www.nationwidechildrens.org
Control: Other not–for–profit (including NFP Corporation) **Service:** Children's general

Staffed Beds: 610 **Admissions:** 18250 **Census:** 429 **Outpatient Visits:** 1185244 **Births:** 0 **Total Expense ($000):** 1067842 **Payroll Expense ($000):** 471501 **Personnel:** 7807

□ **OHIO HOSPITAL FOR PSYCHIATRY (364041)**, 880 Greenlawn Avenue, Zip 43223–2616; tel. 614/449–9664, (Nonreporting) **A**1 10 **S** Acadia Healthcare Company, Inc., Franklin, TN
Primary Contact: Stanley Frank, Chief Executive Officer
COO: Shannon Robbins, Chief Operating Officer
CFO: Steve Snyder, Chief Financial Officer
CMO: Richard Nockowitz, M.D., Medical Director
CNO: Jayne Zink, Director of Nursing
Web address: www.ohiohospitalforpsychiatry.com/
Control: Corporation, Investor–owned, for–profit **Service:** Children's hospital psychiatric

Staffed Beds: 90

Many Facility Codes have changed. Please refer to the AHA Guide Code Chart. © 2016 AHA Guide

⊠ △ **OHIO STATE UNIVERSITY WEXNER MEDICAL CENTER (360085)**, 370 West 9th Avenue, Zip 43210–1238; tel. 614/293–8000, (Includes OHIO STATE UNIVERSITY HOSPITALS EAST, 1492 East Broad Street, Zip 43205–1546; tel. 614/257–3000) **A**1 3 5 7 8 10 **F**3 4 5 6 8 9 11 12 13 15 16 17 18 20 22 24 26 28 29 30 31 33 34 35 36 37 38 39 40 43 44 45 46 47 48 49 50 51 52 53 54 55 56 57 58 59 60 61 64 65 66 68 70 72 73 74 75 76 77 78 79 80 81 82 84 85 86 87 90 91 92 93 94 95 96 97 98 99 100 101 102 103 104 105 107 108 110 111 112 113 114 115 118 119 126 129 130 131 132 134 135 137 138 139 140 141 142 143 144 145 146 147 148 **P**6 **S** Ohio State University Health System, Columbus, OH
Primary Contact: Sheldon Retchin, M.D., Chief Executive Officer
COO: David P. McQuaid, FACHE, Chief Operating Officer
CMO: Andrew Thomas, M.D., Chief Medical Officer
CIO: Phyllis Teater, Chief Information Officer
CHR: Kim Shumate, Human Resources Officer
CNO: Mary G. Nash, Ph.D., Chief Nursing Officer
Web address: www.medicalcenter.osu.edu
Control: State–Government, nonfederal **Service:** General Medical and Surgical

Staffed Beds: 963 **Admissions:** 45558 **Census:** 745 **Outpatient Visits:** 1304899 **Births:** 4882 **Total Expense ($000):** 1371365 **Payroll Expense ($000):** 408081 **Personnel:** 10100

⊠ ○ **OHIOHEALTH DOCTORS HOSPITAL (360152)**, 5100 West Broad Street, Zip 43228–1607; tel. 614/544–1000 **A**1 2 3 5 10 11 12 13 **F**3 13 15 17 18 20 22 24 26 28 29 30 31 34 35 36 40 45 46 47 48 49 50 57 58 59 64 65 66 68 70 72 74 75 76 77 78 79 81 85 87 92 93 97 100 107 109 110 111 114 115 116 117 119 120 121 123 126 130 131 135 145 146 147 148 **P**1 3 5 **S** OhioHealth, Columbus, OH
Primary Contact: Michael L. Reichfield, President
CFO: Troy Hammett, Vice President and Chief Financial Officer
CMO: Dean Colwell, D.O., Vice President Medical Affairs
CIO: Michael Krouse, Chief Information Officer
CHR: David Sullivan, Director Human Resources
Web address: www.ohiohealth.com
Control: Church–operated, Nongovernment, not–for profit **Service:** General Medical and Surgical

Staffed Beds: 176 **Admissions:** 8956 **Census:** 95 **Outpatient Visits:** 247147 **Births:** 973 **Total Expense ($000):** 197633 **Payroll Expense ($000):** 87455 **Personnel:** 1260

⊠ **OHIOHEALTH GRANT MEDICAL CENTER (360017)**, 111 South Grant Avenue, Zip 43215–1898; tel. 614/566–9000 **A**1 2 3 5 8 10 **F**3 7 8 9 11 13 15 17 18 20 22 24 26 28 29 30 31 34 35 36 37 40 42 43 45 46 47 48 49 50 53 54 56 57 58 59 60 61 64 66 67 68 70 72 74 75 76 78 79 81 82 83 84 85 86 87 97 100 102 107 108 109 110 111 114 115 116 117 119 120 121 123 124 126 129 130 131 132 135 143 144 146 147 148 **P**1 3 5 **S** OhioHealth, Columbus, OH
Primary Contact: Michael Lawson, President and Chief Operating Officer
COO: Kevin Lutz, DPM, Chief Operating Officer, Grant
CFO: Heather Brandon, Vice President of Finance, Grant
CMO: Michael Ezzie, Director of Medical Education and Interim Vice President of Medical Affairs
CIO: Michael Krouse, Chief Information Officer
CHR: Qiana Williams, Director, Human Resource Business Partner, Grant
CNO: Sharon Neenan, Interim Chief Nursing Officer, Grant
Web address: www.ohiohealth.com
Control: Church–operated, Nongovernment, not–for profit **Service:** General Medical and Surgical

Staffed Beds: 434 **Admissions:** 20632 **Census:** 263 **Outpatient Visits:** 95055 **Births:** 2556 **Total Expense ($000):** 482817 **Payroll Expense ($000):** 192732 **Personnel:** 2895

⊠ **OHIOHEALTH REHABILITATION HOSPITAL (363037)**, 1087 Dennison Avenue, 4th Floor, Zip 43201–3201; tel. 614/484–9600, (Nonreporting) **A**1 10 **S** Select Medical Corporation, Mechanicsburg, PA
Primary Contact: Eric Yap, Chief Executive Officer
CFO: Ted Bolcavage, Vice President Division Controller, Inpatient
CMO: Lisa Lombard, Chief Medical Officer
CHR: Josette Alexander, Director, Human Resources
CNO: Graydon Todd Auckerman, Chief Nursing Officer
Web address: www.ohiohealth–rehab.com
Control: Partnership, Investor–owned, for–profit **Service:** Rehabilitation

Staffed Beds: 44

⊠ **OHIOHEALTH RIVERSIDE METHODIST HOSPITAL (360006)**, 3535 Olentangy River Road, Zip 43214–3998; tel. 614/566–5000 **A**1 2 3 5 8 10 **F**3 5 7 8 11 12 13 14 15 17 18 20 21 22 24 26 28 29 30 31 33 34 35 36 37 38 39 40 43 44 45 46 47 48 49 50 51 53 54 55 56 57 58 59 60 61 62 63 64 65 66 68 69 70 71 72 74 75 76 77 78 79 80 81 82 83 84 85 86 87 90 91 92 93 94 96 97 98 100 102 103 104 105 107 108 110 111 114 115 116 117 118 119 120 121 123 124 126 129 130 132 135 143 144 145 146 147 148 **P**1 3 5 **S** OhioHealth, Columbus, OH
Primary Contact: Brian Jepson, President
COO: Elizabeth Brill, M.D., Chief Operating Officer
CFO: Peter Bury, Vice President Finance
CMO: Thomas Harmon, M.D., Vice President Medical Affairs
CIO: Michael Krouse, Chief Information Officer
CHR: Shereen Solaiman, Vice President Human Resources
CNO: Lisa Gossett, MSN, Chief Nursing Officer
Web address: www.ohiohealth.com
Control: Church–operated, Nongovernment, not–for profit **Service:** General Medical and Surgical

Staffed Beds: 817 **Admissions:** 44442 **Census:** 518 **Outpatient Visits:** 802465 **Births:** 6256 **Total Expense ($000):** 928223 **Payroll Expense ($000):** 376004 **Personnel:** 6289

⊠ **REGENCY HOSPITAL OF COLUMBUS (362037)**, 1430 South High Street, Zip 43207–1045; tel. 614/456–0300, (Includes SELECT SPECIALTY HOSPITAL – COLUMBUS EAST, 1492 East Broad Street, 6th Floor, Zip 43205–1546; tel. 614/685–1703; Lisa J. Pettrey, MSN, R.N., Interim Chief Executive Officer), (Nonreporting) **A**1 10 **S** Select Medical Corporation, Mechanicsburg, PA
Primary Contact: Lisa J. Pettrey, MSN, R.N., Chief Executive Officer
Web address: www.regencyhospital.com/
Control: Corporation, Investor–owned, for–profit **Service:** Long–Term Acute Care hospital

Staffed Beds: 43

⊠ **SELECT SPECIALTY HOSPITAL–COLUMBUS (362022)**, 1087 Dennison Avenue, Zip 43201–3201; tel. 614/458–9000, (Includes SELECT SPECIALTY HOSPITAL–COLUMBUS, MOUNT CARMEL CAMPUS, 793 West State Street, Zip 43222–1551; tel. 614/234–0950), (Nonreporting) **A**1 10 **S** Select Medical Corporation, Mechanicsburg, PA
Primary Contact: Patrick Tuer, Chief Executive Officer
CMO: Victoria Ruff, M.D., Medical Director
CHR: Charles Pankowski, Manager Human Resources
Web address: www.selectspecialtyhospitals.com/company/locations/columbus.aspx
Control: Corporation, Investor–owned, for–profit **Service:** Long–Term Acute Care hospital

Staffed Beds: 186

SELECT SPECIALTY HOSPITAL–COLUMBUS, MOUNT CARMEL CAMPUS See Select Specialty Hospital–Columbus

☐ **TWIN VALLEY BEHAVIORAL HEALTHCARE (364007)**, 2200 West Broad Street, Zip 43223–1297; tel. 614/752–0333, (Nonreporting) **A**1 10 **S** Ohio Department of Mental Health, Columbus, OH
Primary Contact: Veronica Lofton, Acting Chief Executive Officer
COO: David Blahnik, Chief Operating Officer
CFO: Tracy Gladen, Chief Financial Officer
CMO: R. Alan Freeland, M.D., Chief Clinical Officer
CIO: Missy McGarvey, Chief Information Officer
CHR: Marcia McKeen, Director Human Resources
CNO: Michael Breakwell, R.N., Nurse Executive
Web address: www.mh.state.oh.us/ibhs/bhos/tvbh.html
Control: State–Government, nonfederal **Service:** Psychiatric

Staffed Beds: 228

CONCORD TOWNSHIP—Lake County

⊠ **LAKE HEALTH (360098)**, 7590 Auburn Road, Zip 44077–9176; tel. 440/953–9600, (Includes TRIPOINT MEDICAL CENTER, 7590 Auburn Road, Zip 44077; Cynthia Moore–Hardy, FACHE, President and Chief Executive Officer), (Nonreporting) **A**1 10
Primary Contact: Cynthia Moore–Hardy, FACHE, President and Chief Executive Officer
CFO: Robert B. Tracz, CPA, Senior Vice President and Chief Financial Officer
CMO: John Baniewicz, M.D., Chief Medical Officer
CIO: Gerald Peters, Vice President Information Technologies and Chief Information Officer
CHR: Craig J. Ghidotti, Vice President Human Resources
CNO: Mary L. Ogrinc, R.N., Chief Nursing Officer, Senior Vice President Patient Care Services
Web address: www.lakehealth.org
Control: Other not–for–profit (including NFP Corporation) **Service:** General Medical and Surgical

Staffed Beds: 357

Hospital, Medicare Provider Number, Address, Telephone, Approval, Facility, and Physician Codes, Health Care System

★ American Hospital Association (AHA) membership ○ Healthcare Facilities Accreditation Program ⇑ Center for Improvement in Healthcare Quality Accreditation
☐ The Joint Commission accreditation ◇ DNV Healthcare Inc. accreditation △ Commission on Accreditation of Rehabilitation Facilities (CARF) accreditation

OH

CONNEAUT—Ashtabula County

✠ UNIVERSITY HOSPITALS CONNEAUT MEDICAL CENTER (361308), 158 West Main Road, Zip 44030–2039; tel. 440/593–1131 **A**1 10 18 **F**3 7 11 15 18 28 29 31 34 35 37 40 45 56 57 59 64 68 70 75 77 78 79 81 82 85 86 87 93 107 110 111 115 119 130 132 133 135 143 144 146 147 148 **P**8 **S** University Hospitals, Cleveland, OH
Primary Contact: M. Steven Jones, President
COO: Karen McNeil, Chief Operating Officer
CFO: Lara Eggleston, Finance Manager
CMO: Abirammy Sundaramoorthy, M.D., Chief Medical Officer
CIO: Kirsten Hale, Coordinator Health Information Services
CHR: Danialle Lynce, Business Partner Human Resources
CNO: Ashley Fertig, Chief Nursing Officer
Web address: www.uhhospitals.org
Control: Other not–for–profit (including NFP Corporation) **Service:** General Medical and Surgical

Staffed Beds: 25 **Admissions:** 618 **Census:** 6 **Outpatient Visits:** 34511 **Births:** 0 **Total Expense ($000):** 26728 **Payroll Expense ($000):** 9551 **Personnel:** 227

COSHOCTON—Coshocton County

☐ COSHOCTON COUNTY MEMORIAL HOSPITAL (360109), 1460 Orange Street, Zip 43812–2229, Mailing Address: P.O. Box 1330, Zip 43812–6330; tel. 740/622–6411, (Nonreporting) **A**1 5 10 20
Primary Contact: Lorri Wildi, Interim Chief Executive Officer
CFO: Robin Nichols, Chief Financial Officer
CMO: Tammy S. Alverson, M.D., Chief of Staff
CIO: Seth Peterson, Director Information Services
CHR: Rick Davis, Chief Operating Officer and Support Services
Web address: www.ccmh.com
Control: Other not–for–profit (including NFP Corporation) **Service:** General Medical and Surgical

Staffed Beds: 56

CUYAHOGA FALLS—Summit County

CUYAHOGA FALLS GENERAL HOSPITAL See Summa Western Reserve Hospital

✠ △ EDWIN SHAW REHAB (360241), 330 Broadway Street East, Zip 44221–3312; tel. 330/436–0910 **A**1 5 7 10 **F**5 29 34 35 57 90 93 130 135 146 **S** Cleveland Clinic Health System, Cleveland, OH
Primary Contact: Alan Papa, President and Chief Operating Officer
CFO: Dave Frigo, Chief Financial Officer
CMO: Anthony Hayek, D.O., Medical Director
CHR: Heather Saus, Human Resource Generalist
Web address: www.edwinshaw.com
Control: Other not–for–profit (including NFP Corporation) **Service:** Rehabilitation

Staffed Beds: 35 **Admissions:** 713 **Census:** 27 **Outpatient Visits:** 0 **Births:** 0 **Total Expense ($000):** 15771 **Payroll Expense ($000):** 8867 **Personnel:** 184

○ SUMMA WESTERN RESERVE HOSPITAL (360150), 1900 23rd Street, Zip 44223–1499; tel. 330/971–7000 **A**10 11 13 **F**3 8 11 18 26 29 30 31 32 33 34 35 36 38 40 44 45 47 49 50 51 54 57 59 60 63 64 65 66 68 70 74 75 77 78 79 81 82 84 85 86 87 93 94 96 97 107 108 111 114 115 119 129 130 132 135 144 146 148 **P**6 8 **S** Summa Health, Akron, OH
Primary Contact: Robert Kent, D.O., President and Chief Executive Officer
CFO: Jill Hiner, Vice President and Chief Financial Officer
CMO: Charles Feunning, M.D., President Medical Staff
CHR: Heather Milicevic, Director Human Resources
Web address: www.westernreservehospital.org
Control: Partnership, Investor–owned, for–profit **Service:** General Medical and Surgical

Staffed Beds: 72 **Admissions:** 3686 **Census:** 41 **Outpatient Visits:** 130016 **Births:** 0 **Total Expense ($000):** 109484 **Payroll Expense ($000):** 37454 **Personnel:** 752

DAYTON—Montgomery County

☐ ACCESS HOSPITAL DAYTON (364050), 2611 Wayne Avenue, Zip 45420–1833; tel. 937/256–7802, (Nonreporting) **A**1 10
Primary Contact: Belinda Stevens, Chief Executive Officer
Web address: www.accesshospital.com/
Control: Corporation, Investor–owned, for–profit **Service:** Psychiatric

Staffed Beds: 28

☐ CHILDREN'S MEDICAL CENTER (363306), One Children's Plaza, Zip 45404–1815; tel. 937/641–3000 **A**1 2 3 5 10 **F**3 7 11 19 21 29 30 31 32 34 35 39 40 41 43 44 45 50 54 55 57 58 59 60 61 62 63 64 65 66 68 72 74 75 77 78 79 81 82 84 85 86 87 88 89 93 97 100 104 107 111 115 119 129 130 131 132 134 135 144 146 **P**6
Primary Contact: Deborah A. Feldman, President and Chief Executive Officer
COO: Matthew P. Graybill, Chief Operating Officer
CFO: Chris Bergman, Chief Financial Officer
CMO: Adam Mezoff, M.D., Vice President and Chief Medical Officer
CIO: Beth Fredette, Chief Information Officer
Web address: www.childrensdayton.org
Control: Other not–for–profit (including NFP Corporation) **Service:** Children's general

Staffed Beds: 133 **Admissions:** 6321 **Census:** 78 **Outpatient Visits:** 292746 **Births:** 0 **Total Expense ($000):** 226167 **Payroll Expense ($000):** 91342 **Personnel:** 1714

✠ △ DAYTON VETERANS AFFAIRS MEDICAL CENTER, 4100 West Third Street, Zip 45428–9000; tel. 937/268–6511, (Nonreporting) **A**1 3 5 7 8 **S** Department of Veterans Affairs, Washington, DC
Primary Contact: Glenn A. Costie, FACHE, Director
COO: Mark Murdock, Associate Director
CFO: Shannon Rappach, Chief Fiscal Services
CMO: James Hardy, D.O., Chief of Staff
CIO: Susan Sherer, Chief Information Resource Management
CHR: Rolanda Watkins, Chief Human Resources Management Service
CNO: Anna Jones Monnett, MS, Associate Director Patient Care Services
Web address: www.dayton.va.gov/
Control: Veterans Affairs, Government, federal **Service:** General Medical and Surgical

Staffed Beds: 471

✠ GOOD SAMARITAN HOSPITAL (360052), 2222 Philadelphia Drive, Zip 45406–1813; tel. 937/734–2612 **A**1 2 3 5 10 **F**3 11 13 15 17 18 20 22 24 26 28 29 30 31 36 37 39 40 42 44 45 46 49 50 53 54 56 58 60 61 64 66 70 73 74 75 76 77 78 79 80 81 82 83 85 86 87 92 93 97 100 101 102 107 108 110 111 114 115 118 119 126 129 130 131 132 145 146 148 **P**6 **S** Premier Health, Dayton, OH
Primary Contact: Eloise Broner, President and Chief Executive Officer
COO: Mary E. Garman, MS, Chief Operating Officer
CMO: Daniel L. Schoulties, M.D., Vice President Medical Affairs
CHR: Barbara A. Johnson, Vice President Human Resources
CNO: Christie Gray, Chief Nursing Officer
Web address: www.goodsamdayton.org
Control: Church–operated, Nongovernment, not–for profit **Service:** General Medical and Surgical

Staffed Beds: 346 **Admissions:** 12588 **Census:** 147 **Outpatient Visits:** 261270 **Births:** 909 **Total Expense ($000):** 338732 **Payroll Expense ($000):** 131543 **Personnel:** 2222

★ ○ GRANDVIEW MEDICAL CENTER (360133), 405 West Grand Avenue, Zip 45405–4796; tel. 937/723–3200, (Includes SOUTHVIEW MEDICAL CENTER, 1997 Miamisburg–Centerville Road, Zip 45459–3800; tel. 937/439–6000; Rebecca Lewis, Senior Vice President, Administrator) **A**2 3 10 11 12 13 **F**3 11 12 13 15 18 20 22 24 28 29 30 31 34 35 36 38 39 40 42 43 44 45 47 48 49 50 51 53 54 56 57 58 59 60 61 64 65 66 68 70 73 74 75 76 77 78 79 81 82 85 86 87 93 96 97 98 100 101 102 103 104 105 107 108 110 111 114 115 116 117 118 119 120 121 123 124 129 130 131 132 135 141 144 145 146 147 148 **S** Kettering Health Network, Dayton, OH
Primary Contact: Russell J. Wetherell, President
CFO: Luis Chanaga, Chief Financial Officer
CMO: Paul Martin, Chief Medical Officer
CIO: Andy Lehman, Senior Vice President Technology and Analytics
CHR: Keith Jenkins, Director, Human Resources
CNO: Ronda Brandstater, Vice President Patient Care
Web address: www.ketteringhealth.org/grandview/
Control: Church–operated, Nongovernment, not–for profit **Service:** General Medical and Surgical

Staffed Beds: 277 **Admissions:** 11285 **Census:** 140 **Outpatient Visits:** 371087 **Births:** 1673 **Total Expense ($000):** 430593 **Payroll Expense ($000):** 165880 **Personnel:** 1654

☐ HAVEN BEHAVIORAL SENIOR CARE OF DAYTON (364048), One Elizabeth Place, 4th Floor Southwest Tower, Zip 45417–3445; tel. 937/234–0100 **A**1 10 **F**6 56 98 103 130 **S** Haven Behavioral Healthcare, Nashville, TN
Primary Contact: Keith Kuhn, Chief Executive Officer
CMO: Amita Patel, M.D., Medical Director
CNO: Cheryl Meyer, MSN, Director of Nursing
Web address: www.havenbehavioraldayton.com/
Control: Corporation, Investor–owned, for–profit **Service:** Psychiatric

Staffed Beds: 32 **Admissions:** 775 **Census:** 27 **Outpatient Visits:** 0 **Births:** 0 **Total Expense ($000):** 7229 **Payroll Expense ($000):** 3712

⊠ **HEALTHSOUTH REHABILITATION HOSPITAL OF DAYTON (363033)**, One Elizabeth Place, Zip 45417–3445; tel. 937/424–8200 **A**1 10 **F**29 90 96 148 **S** HEALTHSOUTH Corporation, Birmingham, AL
Primary Contact: Brad Kennedy, Chief Executive Officer
Web address: www.reliantdayton.com
Control: Partnership, Investor–owned, for–profit **Service:** Rehabilitation

Staffed Beds: 50 **Admissions:** 479 **Census:** 20 **Outpatient Visits:** 0 **Births:** 0 **Total Expense ($000):** 7314 **Payroll Expense ($000):** 3041 **Personnel:** 53

⊠ **KINDRED HOSPITAL–DAYTON (362033)**, 707 South Edwin C. Moses Boulevard, Zip 45417–3462; tel. 937/222–5963, (Nonreporting) **A**1 10 **S** Kindred Healthcare, Louisville, KY
Primary Contact: Lynn Schoen, Chief Executive Officer
CMO: Felipe Rubio, M.D., Medical Director
Web address: www.khdayton.com
Control: Corporation, Investor–owned, for–profit **Service:** Long–Term Acute Care hospital

Staffed Beds: 67

⊠ △ **MIAMI VALLEY HOSPITAL (360051)**, One Wyoming Street, Zip 45409–2793; tel. 937/208–8000, (Includes MIAMI VALLEY HOSPITAL SOUTH, 2400 Miami Valley Drive, Centerville, Zip 45459–4774; tel. 937/438–2400) **A**1 2 3 5 7 10 **F**3 5 7 12 13 14 20 22 24 26 28 29 30 31 34 35 37 39 40 42 43 44 45 46 47 48 49 50 53 54 55 56 57 58 59 60 61 64 68 70 72 73 74 75 76 77 78 79 81 82 84 85 86 87 90 91 92 93 95 96 98 100 101 102 103 104 107 108 110 111 114 115 117 118 119 120 121 123 126 129 130 131 132 134 135 136 141 143 145 146 147 148 **P**8 **S** Premier Health, Dayton, OH
Primary Contact: Mark S. Shaker, President and Chief Executive Officer
COO: Mikki Clancy, Chief Operating Officer
CFO: Thomas M. Duncan, Executive Vice President and Chief Financial Officer
CMO: Mark Williams, M.D., Vice President and Chief Medical Officer
CIO: Gary Ginter, System Vice President and Chief Information Officer
CHR: Barbara A. Johnson, Vice President Human Resources
CNO: Jolyn M. Angus, R.N., Chief Nursing Officer
Web address: www.miamivalleyhospital.org
Control: Other not–for–profit (including NFP Corporation) **Service:** General Medical and Surgical

Staffed Beds: 845 **Admissions:** 27563 **Census:** 388 **Outpatient Visits:** 306597 **Births:** 5142 **Total Expense ($000):** 807838 **Payroll Expense ($000):** 305058 **Personnel:** 5418

☐ **THE MEDICAL CENTER AT ELIZABETH PLACE (360274)**, One Elizabeth Place, Zip 45417–3445; tel. 937/660–3100, (Nonreporting) **A**1 10
Primary Contact: Alexander M. Rintoul, Chief Executive Officer
Web address: www.regentsurgicalhealth.com/Partner+Centers/Medical+Center+at+Elizabeth+Place
Control: Partnership, Investor–owned, for–profit **Service:** General Medical and Surgical

Staffed Beds: 26

VETERANS AFFAIRS MEDICAL CENTER See Dayton Veterans Affairs Medical Center

DEFIANCE—Defiance County

⊠ **MERCY HOSPITAL OF DEFIANCE (360270)**, 1404 East Second Street, Zip 43512–2440; tel. 419/782–8444, (Nonreporting) **A**1 10 **S** Mercy Health, Cincinnati, OH
Primary Contact: B. Lynn Detterman, President and Chief Executive Officer
COO: Kerry Knuth, Chief Operating Officer
CFO: James Puffenberger, Vice President and Chief Financial Officer
CMO: Jeffrey Pruitt, M.D., Chief of Staff
CHR: Susan Pscodna, Director Human Resources
CNO: Sonya Selhorst, R.N., Administrator and Chief Nursing Officer
Web address: www.ehealthconnection.com/regions/toledo/
Control: Partnership, Investor–owned, for–profit **Service:** General Medical and Surgical

Staffed Beds: 23

⊠ **PROMEDICA DEFIANCE REGIONAL HOSPITAL (361328)**, 1200 Ralston Avenue, Zip 43512–1396; tel. 419/783–6955 **A**1 5 10 18 **F**3 11 13 15 18 20 28 31 32 34 40 43 57 59 64 66 68 70 75 76 77 78 79 81 82 85 86 87 93 98 100 101 102 103 104 105 107 108 110 111 114 118 119 129 130 132 135 144 146 147 148 **S** ProMedica Health System, Toledo, OH
Primary Contact: Darrin Arquette, President
CFO: Ken Swint, Director Finance
CMO: Stanislaw Dajczak, M.D., Chief of Staff
CIO: Patricia Swint, Director Information Management Systems
CHR: Carrie Miller, Director Human Resources
Web address: www.promedica.org
Control: Other not–for–profit (including NFP Corporation) **Service:** General Medical and Surgical

Staffed Beds: 35 **Admissions:** 2208 **Census:** 18 **Outpatient Visits:** 99164 **Births:** 560 **Total Expense ($000):** 52504 **Payroll Expense ($000):** 14988 **Personnel:** 254

DELAWARE—Delaware County

⊠ **OHIOHEALTH GRADY MEMORIAL HOSPITAL (360210)**, 561 West Central Avenue, Zip 43015–1410; tel. 740/615–1000 **A**1 2 10 **F**3 13 15 18 20 26 28 29 30 31 34 35 40 45 46 48 50 54 57 58 59 60 63 64 66 68 70 75 76 77 78 79 81 82 85 86 87 92 93 96 97 102 107 108 109 110 111 114 119 124 129 130 131 132 134 135 146 147 148 **P**1 3 5 **S** OhioHealth, Columbus, OH
Primary Contact: Steve Bunyard, President
COO: Anna Hensley, Chief Operating Officer
CFO: David Hensel, Director Financial Operations
CMO: Barbara Evert, M.D., Vice President Medical Affairs
CIO: Michael Krouse, Chief Information Officer Information Services
CHR: Victoria L. Matlack, Director and Human Resources Business Partner
CNO: Elizabeth Anne Biegler, R.N., Chief Nursing Officer
Web address: www.ohiohealth.com
Control: Church–operated, Nongovernment, not–for profit **Service:** General Medical and Surgical

Staffed Beds: 59 **Admissions:** 2553 **Census:** 24 **Outpatient Visits:** 109110 **Births:** 229 **Total Expense ($000):** 75652 **Payroll Expense ($000):** 31216 **Personnel:** 498

DENNISON—Tuscarawas County

☐ **TEN LAKES CENTER (364042)**, 819 North First Street, 3rd Floor, Zip 44621–1003; tel. 740/922–7499 **A**1 10 **F**98 102 103 105 130 143 **P**6 **S** Acadia Healthcare Company, Inc., Franklin, TN
Primary Contact: Debra C. Gardner, R.N., MSN, Administrator
Web address: www.tenlakescenter.com/
Control: Corporation, Investor–owned, for–profit **Service:** Psychiatric

Staffed Beds: 16 **Admissions:** 346 **Census:** 14 **Outpatient Visits:** 2789 **Births:** 0 **Total Expense ($000):** 3859 **Payroll Expense ($000):** 1935

⊠ **TRINITY HOSPITAL TWIN CITY (361302)**, 819 North First Street, Zip 44621–1098; tel. 740/922–2800 **A**1 10 18 **F**11 15 18 19 28 29 30 34 35 40 45 50 57 59 64 70 75 77 81 85 86 87 89 93 97 107 114 119 127 128 129 130 132 133 146 147 148 **P**4 **S** Catholic Health Initiatives, Englewood, CO
Primary Contact: Joseph J. Mitchell, President
CMO: Tim McKnight, M.D., Chief of Staff
CHR: Bianca Love, Assistant Administrator Human Resources
CNO: Teresa Gagliardi, R.N., Chief Nursing Officer
Web address: www.trinitytwincity.org
Control: Church–operated, Nongovernment, not–for profit **Service:** General Medical and Surgical

Staffed Beds: 12 **Admissions:** 354 **Census:** 4 **Outpatient Visits:** 44352 **Births:** 0 **Total Expense ($000):** 23284 **Payroll Expense ($000):** 10695 **Personnel:** 219

DOVER—Tuscarawas County

★ ◇ **UNION HOSPITAL (360010)**, 659 Boulevard, Zip 44622–2077; tel. 330/343–3311 **A**10 19 21 **F**3 8 11 13 15 18 28 29 34 35 40 50 53 54 57 59 62 64 70 74 75 76 77 79 80 81 82 85 86 90 91 93 105 107 108 110 111 115 119 124 129 130 131 132 135 144 146 148 **P**6
Primary Contact: Bruce James, Chief Executive Officer
CFO: Eugene A. Thorn, III, Vice President Finance and Chief Financial Officer
CMO: Todd Meyerhoefer, M.D., Vice President Medical Affairs
CIO: David Baumgardner, Director Information Management
CHR: Darwin K. Smith, Vice President Human Resources
CNO: Diana Boyd, Vice President Nursing
Web address: www.unionhospital.org
Control: Other not–for–profit (including NFP Corporation) **Service:** General Medical and Surgical

Staffed Beds: 149 **Admissions:** 4944 **Census:** 52 **Outpatient Visits:** 261397 **Births:** 684 **Total Expense ($000):** 112086 **Payroll Expense ($000):** 48298 **Personnel:** 994

Hospital, Medicare Provider Number, Address, Telephone, Approval, Facility, and Physician Codes, Health Care System

★ American Hospital Association (AHA) membership ○ Healthcare Facilities Accreditation Program ⇑ Center for Improvement in Healthcare Quality Accreditation
☐ The Joint Commission accreditation ◇ DNV Healthcare Inc. accreditation △ Commission on Accreditation of Rehabilitation Facilities (CARF) accreditation

OH

DUBLIN—Franklin County

☐ **DUBLIN SPRINGS (364049)**, 7625 Hospital Drive, Zip 43016–9649; tel. 614/717–1800, (Nonreporting) **A**1 10
Primary Contact: Garry W. Hoyes, Chief Executive Officer
COO: Merissa McKinstry, Chief Operating Officer
CFO: Alexis Barbour, Director Finance
CMO: Mark Blair, M.D., Medical Director
CHR: Tam Wisler, Director Human Resources
CNO: Melissa Patton, MSN, Director of Nursing
Web address: www.dublinsprings.com/
Control: Corporation, Investor–owned, for–profit **Service:** Psychiatric

Staffed Beds: 72

⊞ **OHIOHEALTH DUBLIN METHODIST HOSPITAL (360348)**, 7500 Hospital Drive, Zip 43016–8518; tel. 614/544–8000 **A**1 10 **F**3 13 15 18 20 22 28 29 34 40 45 46 57 59 62 68 70 76 77 79 81 82 85 87 97 107 110 111 115 119 126 129 130 131 132 135 144 146 147 148 **P**1 3 5 **S** OhioHealth, Columbus, OH
Primary Contact: Steve Bunyard, President
COO: Anna Hensley, Chief Operating Officer
CFO: Keely Pummel, Director, Financial Operations
CMO: Barbara Evert, M.D., Vice President Medical Affairs
CIO: Michael Krouse, Senior Vice President Chief Information Officer
CHR: Victoria L. Matlack, Director and Human Resources Business Partner
CNO: Elizabeth Anne Biegler, R.N., Chief Nursing Officer
Web address: www.ohiohealth.com
Control: Church–operated, Nongovernment, not–for profit **Service:** General Medical and Surgical

Staffed Beds: 107 Admissions: 6466 Census: 47 Outpatient Visits: 114897 Births: 2220 Total Expense ($000): 141771 Payroll Expense ($000): 50601 Personnel: 798

EAST LIVERPOOL—Columbiana County

⊞ **EAST LIVERPOOL CITY HOSPITAL (360096)**, 425 West Fifth Street, Zip 43920–2498; tel. 330/385–7200 **A**1 10 13 **F**3 11 15 18 28 29 30 31 34 35 39 40 41 44 50 51 53 54 56 57 59 60 64 65 66 70 75 77 78 79 81 85 86 87 93 97 98 100 101 102 103 107 110 111 115 118 119 130 131 132 135 146 147 148 **P**6 **S** Prime Healthcare Services, Ontario, CA
Primary Contact: Keith Richardson, President and Chief Executive Officer
CFO: Kyle Johnson, Vice President Finance
CMO: Steve LaTulippe, President Medical Staff
CIO: Frank Mader, Director Information Services
CHR: Teri Pasco, Director Human Resources
CNO: Stacie Call, R.N., Vice President Patient Care and Chief Nursing Officer
Web address: www.elch.org
Control: Other not–for–profit (including NFP Corporation) **Service:** General Medical and Surgical

Staffed Beds: 109 Admissions: 4083 Census: 125 Outpatient Visits: 108011 Births: 0 Personnel: 156

ELYRIA—Lorain County

⊞ **UNIVERSITY HOSPITALS ELYRIA MEDICAL CENTER (360145)**, 630 East River Street, Zip 44035–5902; tel. 440/329–7500 **A**1 2 10 13 **F**3 11 12 13 15 17 18 20 22 24 26 28 29 30 31 32 34 35 36 37 40 41 42 44 45 46 49 50 53 54 57 59 60 62 64 68 70 73 74 75 76 77 78 79 81 82 85 86 87 89 91 92 93 94 98 100 102 107 108 110 111 114 115 116 117 118 119 126 129 130 131 132 133 135 146 147 148 **P**8 **S** University Hospitals, Cleveland, OH
Primary Contact: Charlotte Wray, MSN, President
CFO: David A. Cook, Vice President and Chief Financial Officer
CHR: Daniel Miller, Vice President Human Resources
CNO: Sandra Jean Kantelas, Chief Nursing Officer
Web address: www.emh–healthcare.org
Control: Other not–for–profit (including NFP Corporation) **Service:** General Medical and Surgical

Staffed Beds: 237 Admissions: 10868 Census: 127 Outpatient Visits: 262222 Births: 905 Total Expense ($000): 195575 Payroll Expense ($000): 73449 Personnel: 1435

EUCLID—Cuyahoga County

⊞ △ **EUCLID HOSPITAL (360082)**, 18901 Lake Shore Boulevard, Zip 44119–1090; tel. 216/531–9000, (Total facility includes 40 beds in nursing home–type unit) **A**1 3 7 10 **F**3 15 17 18 26 28 29 30 34 35 39 40 45 47 50 51 56 57 59 60 64 70 74 75 77 79 81 82 85 87 90 91 93 94 96 98 100 102 103 107 108 111 114 118 119 128 130 131 146 148 **S** Cleveland Clinic Health System, Cleveland, OH
Primary Contact: Daniel Napierkowski, M.D., President
COO: Rich Lea, Vice President Operations
CFO: Don Urbancsik, Director Finance
CMO: John Bertsch, M.D., Chief of Staff
CHR: Gloria Donnelly, Director Human Resources
CNO: Dawn A. Bailey, R.N., Vice President Nursing and Chief Nursing Officer
Web address: www.euclidhospital.org
Control: Other not–for–profit (including NFP Corporation) **Service:** General Medical and Surgical

Staffed Beds: 221 Admissions: 7264 Census: 134 Outpatient Visits: 103594 Births: 0 Total Expense ($000): 108643 Payroll Expense ($000): 45815 Personnel: 691

FAIRFIELD—Butler County

⊞ △ **MERCY HEALTH – FAIRFIELD HOSPITAL (360056)**, 3000 Mack Road, Zip 45014–5335; tel. 513/870–7000, (Nonreporting) **A**1 2 3 7 10 **S** Mercy Health, Cincinnati, OH
Primary Contact: Thomas S. Urban, Market Leader and President
COO: Justin Krueger, Chief Operating Officer
CFO: Robin Yon, Site Finance Director
CMO: John Kennedy, M.D., Vice President Medical Affairs
CIO: Yousuf Ahmad, Divisional Senior Vice President and Chief Network Transformation Officer
CHR: Maggie Lund, Divisional Senior Vice President Human Resources
Web address: www.e–mercy.com
Control: Other not–for–profit (including NFP Corporation) **Service:** General Medical and Surgical

Staffed Beds: 236

FINDLAY—Hancock County

⊞ **BLANCHARD VALLEY HOSPITAL (360095)**, 1900 South Main Street, Zip 45840–1214; tel. 419/423–4500, (Includes BLANCHARD VALLEY HOSPITAL, 1900 South Main Street, Zip 45840; tel. 419/423–4500) **A**1 2 3 5 10 19 **F**3 7 8 11 13 15 17 18 20 22 24 26 28 29 30 31 34 35 40 41 42 43 44 45 48 49 50 54 55 57 58 59 60 64 65 68 70 73 74 76 77 78 79 81 82 83 84 85 86 87 91 93 96 97 98 101 103 104 107 108 110 111 114 115 117 118 119 120 121 124 126 129 130 131 132 135 146 147 148 **P**5 **S** Blanchard Valley Health System, Findlay, OH
Primary Contact: Scott C. Malaney, President and Chief Executive Officer
CFO: David Cytlak, Chief Financial Officer
CMO: William H. Kose, M.D., Chief Quality Officer
CIO: David Cytlak, Chief Financial Officer
CHR: Ryan Fisher, Director of Human Resources
CNO: Barbara J. Pasztor, R.N., Vice President Patient Care Services and Chief Nursing Officer
Web address: www.bvhealthsystem.org
Control: Other not–for–profit (including NFP Corporation) **Service:** General Medical and Surgical

Staffed Beds: 159 Admissions: 7343 Census: 69 Outpatient Visits: 235563 Births: 1392 Total Expense ($000): 176879 Payroll Expense ($000): 77529 Personnel: 1264

FOSTORIA—Hancock County

⊞ **PROMEDICA FOSTORIA COMMUNITY HOSPITAL (361318)**, 501 Van Buren Street, Zip 44830–1534, Mailing Address: P.O. Box 907, Zip 44830–0907; tel. 419/435–7734 **A**1 5 10 18 **F**3 11 15 28 31 34 35 40 45 46 55 57 59 60 62 64 66 68 70 75 78 79 81 82 85 86 87 89 93 94 96 97 104 107 108 110 111 115 117 118 119 128 129 130 131 132 133 135 144 146 **P**7 **S** ProMedica Health System, Toledo, OH
Primary Contact: Holly L. Bristoll, President
COO: Tom Borer, Vice President Operations
CFO: Ken Swint, Vice President Finance and Chief Financial Officer
CMO: Terrence Fondessy, M.D., Vice President Medical Affairs
CIO: Rose Ann Laureto, Chief Information Officer
CNO: Paula Grieb, R.N., Chief Nursing Officer
Web address: www.promedica.org
Control: Other not–for–profit (including NFP Corporation) **Service:** General Medical and Surgical

Staffed Beds: 25 Admissions: 689 Census: 6 Outpatient Visits: 56009 Births: 0 Total Expense ($000): 35047 Payroll Expense ($000): 8698 Personnel: 164

Many Facility Codes have changed. Please refer to the AHA Guide Code Chart. © 2016 AHA Guide

FREMONT—Sandusky County

☒ **PROMEDICA MEMORIAL HOSPITAL (360156)**, 715 South Taft Avenue, Zip 43420–3237; tel. 419/332–7321 **A**1 10 **F**3 7 11 13 14 15 18 19 28 29 30 34 35 38 40 44 45 46 47 48 50 51 53 56 57 59 61 64 65 69 70 74 75 76 77 79 80 81 82 84 85 86 87 89 91 92 93 96 97 107 108 110 111 114 115 119 129 130 131 132 135 141 142 143 146 147 148 **P**1 5 6
S ProMedica Health System, Toledo, OH
Primary Contact: Pamela Jensen, FACHE, President
CFO: David Brewer, Chief Financial Officer
CHR: Warrenette Parthemore, Director Human Resources
CNO: Jodi Rucker, Chief Nursing Officer
Web address: www.promedica.org
Control: Other not–for–profit (including NFP Corporation) **Service:** General Medical and Surgical

Staffed Beds: 49 **Admissions:** 1239 **Census:** 12 **Outpatient Visits:** 82495 **Births:** 290 **Total Expense ($000):** 62788 **Payroll Expense ($000):** 18382 **Personnel:** 348

GAHANNA—Franklin County

THE WOODS AT PARKSIDE (360247), 349 Olde Ridenour Road, Zip 43230–2528; tel. 614/471–2552, (Nonreporting) **A**10
Primary Contact: Harry Nguyen, Medical Director
Web address: www.thewoodsatparkside.com
Control: Partnership, Investor–owned, for–profit **Service:** Alcoholism and other chemical dependency

Staffed Beds: 50

GALION—Crawford County

★ ◇ **GALION COMMUNITY HOSPITAL (361325)**, 269 Portland Way South, Zip 44833–2399; tel. 419/468–4841, (Nonreporting) **A**10 18 21 **S** Avita Health System, Galion, OH
Primary Contact: Jerome Morasko, President and Chief Executive Officer
CIO: Andy Daniels, Vice President Non–Clinical Operations and Information Systems
CHR: Traci L. Oswald, Vice President Human Resources
Web address: www.avitahs.org
Control: Other not–for–profit (including NFP Corporation) **Service:** General Medical and Surgical

Staffed Beds: 35

GALLIPOLIS—Gallia County

☐ △ **HOLZER MEDICAL CENTER (360054)**, 100 Jackson Pike, Zip 45631–1563; tel. 740/446–5000, (Nonreporting) **A**1 2 3 5 7 10 13 19
Primary Contact: Christopher T. Meyer, D.O., Chief Executive Officer and Chairman of the Board of Governors
CFO: Kenneth G. Payne, Chief Financial Officer
CMO: John Viall, M.D., Vice President Medical Affairs
CIO: John Allen, Chief Information Officer
CHR: Lisa B. Halley, Vice President Human Resources
Web address: www.holzer.org
Control: Other not–for–profit (including NFP Corporation) **Service:** General Medical and Surgical

Staffed Beds: 181

GARFIELD HEIGHTS—Cuyahoga County

☒ **MARYMOUNT HOSPITAL (360143)**, 12300 McCracken Road, Zip 44125–2975; tel. 216/581–0500 **A**1 2 3 10 **F**3 7 8 11 15 18 28 29 30 31 34 35 38 39 40 42 44 50 51 53 56 59 60 62 63 64 65 68 70 74 75 77 78 79 81 82 85 86 87 92 93 96 97 98 100 102 103 104 107 108 110 111 114 116 118 119 124 129 130 131 132 135 143 146 147 148
S Cleveland Clinic Health System, Cleveland, OH
Primary Contact: Richard Parker, M.D., President
COO: Mark Nussbaum, Vice President Operations
CFO: Mike Stilgenbauer, Director Finance
CMO: Douglas Kohler, M.D., Vice President Medical Operations
CIO: Ralph A. Cagna, Director Information Technology Operations, Cleveland Clinic Health System South Market
CHR: Judith Santora, Human Resources Business Partner
CNO: Barbara Zinner, Chief Nursing Officer
Web address: www.marymount.org
Control: Other not–for–profit (including NFP Corporation) **Service:** General Medical and Surgical

Staffed Beds: 286 **Admissions:** 9335 **Census:** 137 **Outpatient Visits:** 116894 **Births:** 0 **Total Expense ($000):** 155248 **Payroll Expense ($000):** 56525 **Personnel:** 987

GENEVA—Ashtabula County

☒ **UNIVERSITY HOSPITALS GENEVA MEDICAL CENTER (361307)**, 870 West Main Street, Zip 44041–1295; tel. 440/466–1141 **A**1 10 18 **F**3 5 7 11 15 18 29 34 35 40 46 51 56 57 59 60 64 68 70 75 77 78 79 80 81 82 85 86 87 91 93 107 110 111 115 116 119 129 130 132 133 135 143 146 147 148 **P**8 **S** University Hospitals, Cleveland, OH
Primary Contact: M. Steven Jones, President
COO: Karen McNeil, Chief Operating Officer
CFO: Lara Eggleston, Finance Manager
CMO: Amitabh Goel, M.D., Chief Medical Officer
CIO: Kirsten Hale, Coordinator Health Informations Systems and Coding
CHR: Danialle Lynce, Business Partner Human Resources
CNO: Ashley Fertig, Chief Nursing Officer
Web address: www.uhhs.com
Control: Other not–for–profit (including NFP Corporation) **Service:** General Medical and Surgical

Staffed Beds: 25 **Admissions:** 1311 **Census:** 16 **Outpatient Visits:** 64129 **Births:** 0 **Total Expense ($000):** 36382 **Payroll Expense ($000):** 12942 **Personnel:** 223

GREEN SPRINGS—Sandusky County

☐ **ELMWOOD HEALTHCARE CENTER AT THE SPRINGS (362007)**, 401 North Broadway, Zip 44836–9653; tel. 419/639–2626, (Nonreporting) **A**1 10
Primary Contact: Kathy Hunt, Chief Executive Officer
CFO: Douglas Morris, Chief Financial Officer
CMO: John Yuhas, D.O., Medical Director
CHR: Joan E. Schmidt, Director Human Resources
Web address: www.sfhcc.org
Control: Other not–for–profit (including NFP Corporation) **Service:** Long–Term Acute Care hospital

Staffed Beds: 186

GREENFIELD—Highland County

☐ △ **ADENA GREENFIELD MEDICAL CENTER (361304)**, 550 Mirabeau Street, Zip 45123–1617; tel. 937/981–9400, (Nonreporting) **A**1 7 10 18 **S** Adena Health System, Chillicothe, OH
Primary Contact: Kathy Dye, Interim Administrator
CFO: Ralph W. Sorrell, Sr., Chief Financial Officer
CIO: Marcus Bost, Director Information Services and Chief Information Officer
CHR: Brandt Lippert, Vice President Human Resources
Web address: www.adena.org
Control: Other not–for–profit (including NFP Corporation) **Service:** General Medical and Surgical

Staffed Beds: 25

GREENVILLE—Darke County

★ ○ **WAYNE HOSPITAL (360044)**, 835 Sweitzer Street, Zip 45331–1077; tel. 937/548–1141 **A**2 10 11 **F**3 8 11 13 15 28 29 30 31 34 35 39 40 41 45 57 59 64 65 70 75 76 78 79 81 82 84 85 86 89 93 107 108 110 111 114 118 119 129 130 131 132 135 141 146 147 148 **P**1
Primary Contact: Wayne G. Deschambeau, President and Chief Executive Officer
COO: Jeffrey R. Subler, Vice President Support Services
CFO: Dennis Lockard, Vice President Fiscal Services and Chief Financial Officer
CMO: Tom Brown, M.D., President Medical Staff
CIO: Shelton Monger, Director Information Technology
CHR: Peggy Schwartz, Vice President Human Resources
CNO: Kimberlee Freeman, R.N., Vice President Patient Care Services and Chief Nursing Officer
Web address: www.waynehealthcare.org
Control: Other not–for–profit (including NFP Corporation) **Service:** General Medical and Surgical

Staffed Beds: 63 **Admissions:** 1896 **Census:** 16 **Outpatient Visits:** 81051 **Births:** 258 **Total Expense ($000):** 51689 **Payroll Expense ($000):** 17739 **Personnel:** 374

Hospital, Medicare Provider Number, Address, Telephone, Approval, Facility, and Physician Codes, Health Care System

★ American Hospital Association (AHA) membership   ○ Healthcare Facilities Accreditation Program   ⇑ Center for Improvement in Healthcare Quality Accreditation
☐ The Joint Commission accreditation   ◇ DNV Healthcare Inc. accreditation   △ Commission on Accreditation of Rehabilitation Facilities (CARF) accreditation

OH

HAMILTON—Butler County

★ ○ **FORT HAMILTON HOSPITAL (360132)**, 630 Eaton Avenue,
Zip 45013–2770; tel. 513/867–2000 **A**2 10 11 **F**3 11 13 15 18 20 22 24 28
29 30 31 34 35 40 45 46 49 50 53 54 59 60 64 68 70 73 74 75 76 78 79
81 82 85 86 87 93 98 99 100 105 107 108 110 111 114 115 116 117 119
120 121 124 129 130 131 135 144 146 147 148 **S** Kettering Health Network,
Dayton, OH
Primary Contact: Michael Mewhirter, President
CMO: Marcus Romanello, Chief Medical Officer
CIO: Andy Lehman, Senior Vice President Technology and Analytics
CHR: Joseph Geigle, Director Human Resources
CNO: Carol Appelgeet, MSN, Vice President and Chief Nursing Officer
Web address: www.khnetwork.org/forthamilton
Control: Church–operated, Nongovernment, not–for profit **Service:** General
Medical and Surgical

Staffed Beds: 166 **Admissions:** 8601 **Census:** 97 **Outpatient Visits:** 115565
Births: 669 **Total Expense ($000):** 157462 **Payroll Expense ($000):** 68313
Personnel: 922

HICKSVILLE—Defiance County

☐ **COMMUNITY MEMORIAL HOSPITAL (361301)**, 208 North Columbus Street,
Zip 43526–1299; tel. 419/542–6692, (Nonreporting) **A**1 10 18
Primary Contact: Michelle Waggoner, Chief Executive Officer
CFO: Steve Caryer, Chief Financial Officer
CNO: Jane Zachrich, Chief Nursing Officer
Web address: www.cmhosp.com
Control: Hospital district or authority, Government, nonfederal **Service:** General
Medical and Surgical

Staffed Beds: 25

HILLSBORO—Highland County

⊠ **HIGHLAND DISTRICT HOSPITAL (361332)**, 1275 North High Street,
Zip 45133–8273; tel. 937/393–6100 **A**1 10 18 **F**3 11 13 15 29 30 31 34 35
40 45 47 49 50 57 59 62 64 74 76 77 78 79 81 85 86 87 92 93 94 96 98
103 107 110 111 115 118 119 127 130 131 132 133 135 146 148 **P**3
Primary Contact: Randal P. Lennartz, CPA, President and Chief Executive Officer
COO: Timothy Parry, R.N., Chief Operating Officer
CMO: Ron Zile, M.D., Chief of Staff
CIO: Tim Bogard, Manager Information Technology
CHR: Melanie Wymer, Director Human Resources
CNO: Pam Barnett, R.N., Director of Nursing
Web address: www.hdh.org
Control: Hospital district or authority, Government, nonfederal **Service:** General
Medical and Surgical

Staffed Beds: 25 **Admissions:** 1975 **Census:** 18 **Outpatient Visits:** 61352
Births: 282 **Total Expense ($000):** 37828 **Payroll Expense ($000):** 15092
Personnel: 313

JACKSON—Jackson County

☐ **HOLZER MEDICAL CENTER – JACKSON (361320)**, 500 Burlington Road,
Zip 45640–9360; tel. 740/288–4625, (Nonreporting) **A**1 10 18
Primary Contact: Christopher T. Meyer, D.O., Chief Executive Officer and
Chairman of the Board of Governors
CFO: Kevin Yeager, Vice President Fiscal Services
CMO: Nimal Dutla, M.D., Chief Medical Staff
CHR: Sandy Carlisle, Manager Human Resources
Web address: www.holzer.org
Control: Other not–for–profit (including NFP Corporation) **Service:** General
Medical and Surgical

Staffed Beds: 24

KENTON—Hardin County

⊠ **OHIOHEALTH HARDIN MEMORIAL HOSPITAL (361315)**, 921 East Franklin
Street, Zip 43326–2099; tel. 419/673–0761 **A**1 10 18 **F**11 15 29 30 34 40 45
57 59 61 75 77 78 79 81 86 87 93 97 102 107 108 110 111 114 116 119
129 130 131 132 133 146 147 **S** OhioHealth, Columbus, OH
Primary Contact: Ron Snyder, Chief Operating Officer
Web address: www.hardinmemorial.org
Control: Other not–for–profit (including NFP Corporation) **Service:** General
Medical and Surgical

Staffed Beds: 25 **Admissions:** 636 **Census:** 7 **Outpatient Visits:** 60358
Births: 0 **Total Expense ($000):** 21824 **Payroll Expense ($000):** 9069
Personnel: 185

KETTERING—Montgomery County

★ ○ △ **KETTERING MEDICAL CENTER (360079)**, 3535 Southern Boulevard,
Zip 45429–1221; tel. 937/298–4331 **A**2 3 5 7 8 10 11 **F**3 8 11 13 15 17 18
20 22 24 26 28 29 30 31 34 35 36 37 38 39 40 43 44 45 46 47 48 49 50
51 52 53 54 55 56 57 58 59 60 61 64 65 66 68 70 71 72 74 75 77 78 79
81 82 84 85 86 87 90 91 92 93 96 97 102 107 108 110 111 114 115 116
117 118 119 120 121 123 124 126 129 130 131 132 135 141 145 146 147
148 **S** Kettering Health Network, Dayton, OH
Primary Contact: Roy G. Chew, Ph.D., President
CFO: Steven Chavez, Vice President Finance and Operations
CMO: Robert T. Smith, M.D., Chief Medical Officer
CIO: Andy Lehman, Senior Vice President Technology and Analytics
CHR: Derek Morgan, Vice President Human Resources
CNO: Brenda Kuhn, Ph.D., Chief Nursing Officer
Web address: www.ketteringhealth.org/kettering
Control: Church–operated, Nongovernment, not–for profit **Service:** General
Medical and Surgical

Staffed Beds: 395 **Admissions:** 20674 **Census:** 255 **Outpatient Visits:**
264938 **Births:** 2483 **Total Expense ($000):** 625161 **Payroll Expense**
($000): 251838 **Personnel:** 2814

LANCASTER—Fairfield County

⊠ △ **FAIRFIELD MEDICAL CENTER (360072)**, 401 North Ewing Street,
Zip 43130–3371; tel. 740/687–8000 **A**1 2 3 5 7 10 13 **F**3 8 11 12 13 15 18
20 22 24 26 28 29 30 31 34 35 38 40 44 45 48 49 50 53 54 57 59 64 70
74 75 76 77 78 79 81 82 83 84 85 87 89 93 96 97 98 102 104 107 108
110 111 114 115 118 119 129 130 131 132 135 145 146 147 148
Primary Contact: John R. Janoso, Chief Executive Officer
CFO: Sky Gettys, Chief Financial Officer
CMO: Terrence Welsh, Chief Medical Administrator
CIO: Martha Buckley, Chief Medical Informatics Officer
CHR: Debra L. Palmer, MS, Chief Human Resources Officer and Corporate
Compliance Officer
CNO: Helen Harding, Chief Nursing Officer
Web address: www.fmchealth.org
Control: Other not–for–profit (including NFP Corporation) **Service:** General
Medical and Surgical

Staffed Beds: 222 **Admissions:** 9159 **Census:** 93 **Outpatient Visits:** 266994
Births: 948 **Total Expense ($000):** 230234 **Payroll Expense ($000):** 86452
Personnel: 1807

LIMA—Allen County

⊠ **INSTITUTE FOR ORTHOPAEDIC SURGERY (360263)**, 801 Medical Drive,
Suite B., Zip 45804–4030; tel. 419/224–7586, (Nonreporting) **A**1 10 **S** Mercy
Health, Cincinnati, OH
Primary Contact: Mark McDonald, M.D., President and Chief Executive Officer
CMO: Mark McDonald, M.D., President and Chief Executive Officer
CHR: Pat Farmer, Coordinator Human Resources and Safety Officer
Web address: www.ioshospital.com
Control: Partnership, Investor–owned, for–profit **Service:** Orthopedic

Staffed Beds: 3

⊠ **KINDRED HOSPITAL LIMA (362020)**, 730 West Market Street, 6th Floor,
Zip 45801–4602; tel. 419/224–1888, (Nonreporting) **A**1 10 **S** Kindred
Healthcare, Louisville, KY
Primary Contact: Susan Krinke, Chief Executive Officer
Web address: www.khlima.com
Control: Corporation, Investor–owned, for–profit **Service:** Long–Term Acute Care
hospital

Staffed Beds: 26

⊠ △ **LIMA MEMORIAL HEALTH SYSTEM (360009)**, 1001 Bellefontaine
Avenue, Zip 45804–2899; tel. 419/228–3335, (Total facility includes 17 beds in
nursing home–type unit) **A**1 2 7 10 **F**3 11 13 15 17 18 20 22 24 28 29 30 31
34 35 36 40 41 43 45 46·47 48 49 50 51 54 57 59 60 62 63 64 68 70 73
74 75 76 77 78 79 81 82 84 85 86 89 90 93 96 107 108 110 111 114 115
119 121 126 130 131 132 135 146 147 148 **P**8
Primary Contact: Michael D. Swick, President and Chief Executive Officer
COO: Robert Armstrong, Senior Vice President and Chief Operating Officer
CFO: John Fischbach, Vice President of Finance, Chief Financial Officer
CMO: Kha H. Tran, M.D., Vice President Medical Affairs
CIO: KC Williams, Director, MIS Operations
CHR: Denise G. Kiraly, Director, Human Resources and Organization Development
CNO: Ann–Marie J. Pohl, R.N., Vice President and Chief Nursing Officer
Web address: www.limamemorial.org
Control: Other not–for–profit (including NFP Corporation) **Service:** General
Medical and Surgical

Staffed Beds: 217 **Admissions:** 6256 **Census:** 76 **Outpatient Visits:** 264839
Births: 578 **Total Expense ($000):** 160210 **Payroll Expense ($000):** 59230
Personnel: 1212

Many Facility Codes have changed. Please refer to the AHA Guide Code Chart. © 2016 AHA Guide

OAKWOOD CORRECTIONAL FACILITY, 3200 North West Street, Zip 45801–2000; tel. 419/225–8052, (Nonreporting)
Primary Contact: Ed Sheldon, Warden and Chief Executive Officer
CFO: Thomas Ferry, Business Administrator
CHR: Glenda Turner, Director Personnel
Web address: www.drc.state.oh.us/public/ocf.htm
Control: State–Government, nonfederal **Service:** Psychiatric

Staffed Beds: 61

✠ △ **ST. RITA'S MEDICAL CENTER (360066)**, 730 West Market Street, Zip 45801–4602; tel. 419/227–3361 **A**1 2 7 10 **F**3 4 5 7 8 11 12 13 15 17 18 20 22 24 26 28 29 30 31 32 34 35 36 38 39 40 41 42 43 45 46 47 48 49 50 53 54 56 57 58 59 60 61 62 63 64 65 66 68 70 72 73 74 75 76 77 78 79 81 82 84 85 86 87 89 90 91 92 93 96 98 102 103 104 105 107 108 110 111 112 114 115 116 117 118 119 120 121 123 124 126 128 129 130 131 132 135 143 144 146 147 148 **P**6 8 **S** Mercy Health, Cincinnati, OH
Primary Contact: Robert O. Baxter, Regional CEO, Lima
COO: Ronda Lehman, PharmD, Chief Operating Officer, SRPS
CFO: Tim Rieger, Chief Financial Officer
CMO: Kevin Casey, M.D., Chief Clinical Officer
CHR: Will Cason, Vice President Human Resources
CNO: Jodi Pahl, Chief Nurse Executive
Web address: www.stritas.org
Control: Church–operated, Nongovernment, not–for profit **Service:** General Medical and Surgical

Staffed Beds: 415 Admissions: 20142 Census: 194 Outpatient Visits: 430754 Births: 1813 Total Expense ($000): 335724 Payroll Expense ($000): 96651 Personnel: 2058

TRIUMPH HOSPITAL LIMA See Kindred Hospital Lima

LODI—Medina County

✠ **LODI COMMUNITY HOSPITAL (361303)**, 225 Elyria Street, Zip 44254–1096; tel. 330/948–1222 **A**1 10 18 **F**3 11 15 18 26 28 29 30 34 35 40 44 45 57 59 64 65 75 77 78 79 81 82 91 93 96 97 107 111 114 119 129 130 132 133 135 146 147 **P**6 **S** Cleveland Clinic Health System, Cleveland, OH
Primary Contact: Alan Papa, President and Chief Operating Officer
COO: Dana Kocsis, Vice President Nursing and Operations
CFO: Dave Frigo, Director Finance and Controller
CMO: David Peter, M.D., Senior Vice President Medical Affairs and Chief Medical Officer
CIO: Robb Baldauf, Coordinator Information Systems
CHR: Lynn Moraca, Director Human Resources
CNO: Dana Kocsis, Vice President, Nursing and Operations
Web address: www.lodihospital.org
Control: Other not–for–profit (including NFP Corporation) **Service:** General Medical and Surgical

Staffed Beds: 20 Admissions: 257 Census: 6 Outpatient Visits: 36727 Births: 0 Total Expense ($000): 13790 Payroll Expense ($000): 6204 Personnel: 105

LOGAN—Hocking County

✠ **HOCKING VALLEY COMMUNITY HOSPITAL (361330)**, 601 State Route 664 North, Zip 43138–8541, Mailing Address: P.O. Box 966, Zip 43138–0966; tel. 740/380–8000 **A**1 10 18 **F**3 8 11 15 28 29 31 34 40 56 57 59 64 70 75 77 78 79 81 82 85 86 87 93 98 103 107 111 114 118 119 129 130 133 135 144 146 147 148 **P**1
Primary Contact: Julie Stuck, R.N., Chief Executive Officer
CFO: Julie E. Grow, Chief Financial Officer
CMO: Duane Mast, M.D., Medical Director
CIO: John Burgess, Director Information Services
CHR: Robert F. Schmidt, Director Human Resources
CNO: Janelle Hicks, R.N., Vice President Patient Services
Web address: www.hvch.org
Control: County–Government, nonfederal **Service:** General Medical and Surgical

Staffed Beds: 35 Admissions: 1195 Census: 19 Outpatient Visits: 76747 Births: 0 Total Expense ($000): 33478 Payroll Expense ($000): 12433 Personnel: 273

LONDON—Madison County

✠ **MADISON HEALTH (360189)**, 210 North Main Street, Zip 43140–1115; tel. 740/845–7000 **A**1 10 **F**3 11 13 15 18 29 31 34 35 40 45 50 53 57 64 68 70 75 76 77 78 79 81 85 87 89 93 97 107 108 110 111 114 118 119 129 130 131 132 146 147
Primary Contact: Dana E. Engle, Chief Executive Officer
CFO: Michael Browning, Chief Financial Officer
CMO: Bernard Oppong, D.O., Chief of Staff
CIO: Dennis Vogt, Director Information Technology
CHR: Becky Rozell, Chief Human Resources Officer
CNO: Jennifer Piccione, Chief Nursing and Clinical Services Officer
Web address: www.madison–health.com
Control: Other not–for–profit (including NFP Corporation) **Service:** General Medical and Surgical

Staffed Beds: 55 Admissions: 1277 Census: 12 Outpatient Visits: 42031 Births: 250 Total Expense ($000): 36787 Payroll Expense ($000): 14160 Personnel: 304

LORAIN—Lorain County

✠ △ **MERCY REGIONAL MEDICAL CENTER (360172)**, 3700 Kolbe Road, Zip 44053–1697; tel. 440/960–4000 **A**1 2 7 10 **F**8 11 13 15 18 20 22 24 26 28 29 30 31 32 34 35 36 38 39 40 41 46 50 53 54 56 57 58 59 61 62 63 64 65 66 68 70 71 74 75 76 77 78 79 81 82 84 85 86 87 90 93 96 97 98 100 101 102 103 104 105 107 111 114 115 116 119 120 121 129 130 131 132 135 143 146 147 148 **P**8 **S** Mercy Health, Cincinnati, OH
Primary Contact: Edwin M. Oley, President and Chief Executive Officer
COO: Robert Tonkinson, Chief Operating Officer and Chief Financial Officer
CFO: Robert Tonkinson, Chief Operating Officer and Chief Financial Officer
CMO: Sam El–Dalati, M.D., Chief Medical Officer
CHR: JC Fischer, Director Human Resources
CNO: Catherine Walsh, Interim Nursing Executive
Web address: www.community–health–partners.com
Control: Church–operated, Nongovernment, not–for profit **Service:** General Medical and Surgical

Staffed Beds: 259 Admissions: 12269 Census: 154 Outpatient Visits: 371680 Births: 742 Total Expense ($000): 187648 Payroll Expense ($000): 61719 Personnel: 1249

MANSFIELD—Richland County

✠ **KINDRED HOSPITAL OF CENTRAL OHIO (362021)**, 335 Glessner Avenue, 5th Floor, Zip 44903–2269; tel. 419/526–0777 **A**1 10 **F**1 3 29 148 **P**7 **S** Kindred Healthcare, Louisville, KY
Primary Contact: Jeffrey Paul Weier, Chief Executive Officer
Web address: www.khcentralohio.com/
Control: Corporation, Investor–owned, for–profit **Service:** Long–Term Acute Care hospital

Staffed Beds: 33 Admissions: 309 Census: 23 Outpatient Visits: 0 Births: 0 Personnel: 99

MEDCENTRAL – MANSFIELD HOSPITAL See OhioHealth MedCentral Mansfield Hospital

✠ **OHIOHEALTH MEDCENTRAL MANSFIELD HOSPITAL (360118)**, 335 Glessner Avenue, Zip 44903–2265; tel. 419/526–8000, (Includes MANSFIELD HOSPITAL, 335 Glessner Avenue, tel. 419/526–8000) **A**1 2 5 10 **F**3 5 8 11 13 15 17 18 20 22 24 26 28 29 30 31 32 34 35 38 39 40 43 44 45 46 47 48 49 50 51 53 54 55 56 57 58 59 61 62 63 64 65 68 70 73 74 75 76 77 78 79 81 82 83 84 85 86 87 89 90 92 93 96 98 99 100 101 102 103 104 105 107 108 110 111 114 115 116 117 118 119 120 121 122 123 124 126 129 130 131 132 133 135 144 146 147 148 **S** OhioHealth, Columbus, OH
Primary Contact: Jean Halpin, President
CFO: Michael Bichimer, Acting Vice President of Finance
CMO: Terry Weston, M.D., Vice President Physician Services
CIO: Cindy Sheets, Vice President Information Systems and Chief Information Officer
CHR: Beth Hildreth, Vice President Human Resources
CNO: Pam Crawford, R.N., Vice President of Nursing and Chief Nursing Officer
Web address: www.medcentral.org
Control: Other not–for–profit (including NFP Corporation) **Service:** General Medical and Surgical

Staffed Beds: 235 Admissions: 11430 Census: 143 Outpatient Visits: 270208 Births: 950 Personnel: 1937

Hospital, Medicare Provider Number, Address, Telephone, Approval, Facility, and Physician Codes, Health Care System

★ American Hospital Association (AHA) membership
□ The Joint Commission accreditation
○ Healthcare Facilities Accreditation Program
◇ DNV Healthcare Inc. accreditation
⇑ Center for Improvement in Healthcare Quality Accreditation
△ Commission on Accreditation of Rehabilitation Facilities (CARF) accreditation

OH

MARIETTA—Washington County

★ ○ **MARIETTA MEMORIAL HOSPITAL (360147)**, 401 Matthew Street, Zip 45750–1699; tel. 740/374–1400, (Nonreporting) **A**2 5 10 11 13 **S** Memorial Health System, Marietta, OH
Primary Contact: J. Scott Cantley, President and Chief Executive Officer
CFO: Eric L. Young, Vice President Finance and Chief Financial Officer
CMO: Matthew Macatol, M.D., President Medical Staff
CIO: Andy Altenburger, Chief Information Officer
CHR: Dee Ann Gehlauf, Senior Vice President Business and Organization Development
Web address: www.mhsystem.org
Control: Other not–for–profit (including NFP Corporation) **Service:** General Medical and Surgical

Staffed Beds: 152

★ △ **SELBY GENERAL HOSPITAL (361319)**, 1106 Colegate Drive, Zip 45750–1323; tel. 740/568–2000 **A**7 10 18 **F**3 11 29 40 41 45 68 69 74 77 79 81 85 87 89 90 91 92 97 100 107 114 116 117 119 130 133 135 146 **S** Memorial Health System, Marietta, OH
Primary Contact: Stephen Smith, President
CFO: Eric L. Young, Chief Financial Officer
CMO: David Spears, D.O., Chief of Staff
CHR: Tricia A. Engfehr, Chief Human Resources
CNO: Misti Spencer, Director Inpatient Services
Web address: www.selbygeneral.org
Control: Other not–for–profit (including NFP Corporation) **Service:** General Medical and Surgical

Staffed Beds: 35 **Admissions:** 1044 **Census:** 9 **Outpatient Visits:** 25388 **Births:** 0 **Total Expense ($000):** 30477 **Payroll Expense ($000):** 10147 **Personnel:** 165

MARION—Marion County

✖ **OHIOHEALTH MARION GENERAL HOSPITAL (360011)**, 1000 McKinley Park Drive, Zip 43302–6397; tel. 740/383–8400 **A**1 2 10 19 **F**3 8 13 15 18 20 22 24 26 28 29 30 31 35 40 53 54 57 59 60 62 63 64 68 70 72 73 74 75 76 77 78 79 81 82 87 89 91 93 94 98 104 105 107 111 114 116 119 126 129 130 132 135 146 147 148 **S** OhioHealth, Columbus, OH
Primary Contact: Bruce P. Hagen, President
CMO: Julie Tome, M.D., Vice President North Central Region Medical Affairs
CIO: Chris King, Director Information Services
CHR: Gianna Ferrarotti, Director Human Resources North Region
Web address: www.ohiohealth.com/mariongeneral
Control: Other not–for–profit (including NFP Corporation) **Service:** General Medical and Surgical

Staffed Beds: 170 **Admissions:** 7604 **Census:** 75 **Outpatient Visits:** 240610 **Births:** 948 **Total Expense ($000):** 171681 **Payroll Expense ($000):** 64938

MARTINS FERRY—Belmont County

☐ **EAST OHIO REGIONAL HOSPITAL (360080)**, 90 North Fourth Street, Zip 43935–1648; tel. 740/633–1100, (Total facility includes 50 beds in nursing home–type unit) **A**1 10 **F**3 8 11 13 15 20 28 29 30 31 34 35 37 40 43 44 45 53 57 59 64 68 70 74 75 77 79 81 82 85 87 107 108 110 111 114 115 118 119 128 129 130 131 132 133 135 146 148 **P**6 **S** Ohio Valley Health Services and Education Corporation, Wheeling, WV
Primary Contact: Michael J. Caruso, President and Chief Executive Officer
COO: Bernie Albertini, Chief Administrative Officer
CFO: Lisa M. Simon, Senior Vice President Chief Financial Officer
CIO: Lisa M. Simon, Senior Vice President Chief Financial Officer
CHR: Robert Wright, Senior Human Resource Advisor
CNO: Christine Kerwood, Chief Nursing Officer
Web address: www.ovmc–eorh.com
Control: Other not–for–profit (including NFP Corporation) **Service:** General Medical and Surgical

Staffed Beds: 139 **Admissions:** 2949 **Census:** 68 **Outpatient Visits:** 136922 **Births:** 191 **Total Expense ($000):** 67404 **Payroll Expense ($000):** 24227 **Personnel:** 491

MARYSVILLE—Union County

★ ◇ **MEMORIAL HEALTH (360092)**, 500 London Avenue, Zip 43040–1594; tel. 937/644–6115 **A**5 10 21 **F**3 8 11 13 15 18 20 22 28 29 30 31 32 34 35 40 45 48 49 50 51 53 54 57 59 62 69 74 75 76 77 78 79 80 81 82 85 86 87 91 92 93 96 107 108 110 111 114 115 118 119 120 129 130 131 132 135 144 145 146 148 **P**6
Primary Contact: Olas A. Hubbs, III, FACHE, President and Chief Executive Officer
COO: Laurie A. Whittington, Chief Operating Officer
CFO: Jeffrey Ehlers, Chief Financial Officer
CMO: Matthew Hazelbaker, M.D., President Medical Staff
CIO: Carl Zani, Chief Technology Officer
CHR: Larry C. Schleeter, Chief Human Resources Officer
CNO: Robin Slattman, Chief Nursing Officer
Web address: www.memorialhosp.org
Control: County–Government, nonfederal **Service:** General Medical and Surgical

Staffed Beds: 74 **Admissions:** 1547 **Census:** 12 **Outpatient Visits:** 265668 **Births:** 585 **Total Expense ($000):** 87298 **Payroll Expense ($000):** 34307 **Personnel:** 517

MASON—Warren County

☐ **LINDNER CENTER OF HOPE (364044)**, 4075 Old Western Row Road, Zip 45040–3104; tel. 513/536–0311, (Nonreporting) **A**1 10
Primary Contact: Paul Keck, M.D., President and Chief Executive Officer
COO: Brian Owens, Chief Operating Officer
CFO: David McAdams, Chief Financial Officer
CIO: Cliff McClintick, Chief Information Officer
CHR: Debbie A. Strawser, Director Human Resources
Web address: www.lindnercenterofhope.org
Control: Other not–for–profit (including NFP Corporation) **Service:** Psychiatric

Staffed Beds: 48

MASSILLON—Stark County

★ ○ **AFFINITY MEDICAL CENTER (360151)**, 875 Eighth Street N.E., Zip 44646–8503, Mailing Address: P.O. Box 4805, Zip 44648–0805; tel. 330/832–8761, (Nonreporting) **A**10 11 13 **S** Quorum Health, Brentwood, TN
Primary Contact: Ronald L. Bierman, Chief Executive Officer
CFO: James Hutchinson, CPA, Chief Financial Officer
Web address: www.affinitymedicalcenter.com
Control: Corporation, Investor–owned, for–profit **Service:** General Medical and Surgical

Staffed Beds: 112

☐ **HEARTLAND BEHAVIORAL HEALTHCARE (364031)**, 3000 Erie Stree South, Zip 44646–7993, Mailing Address: 3000 Erie Street South, Zip 44646–7976; tel. 330/833–3135 **A**1 5 10 **F**98 101 102 **S** Ohio Department of Mental Health, Columbus, OH
Primary Contact: Jeffrey Sims, Chief Executive Officer
CFO: Patricia Eddleman, Fiscal Officer
CMO: Steven Thomson, M.D., Medical Director
CIO: Robert Hobart, Director Management Information Systems
CHR: Jerald Wilhite, Administrator Human Resources
Web address: www.mh.state.oh.us/ibhs/bhos/hoh.html
Control: State–Government, nonfederal **Service:** Psychiatric

Staffed Beds: 152 **Admissions:** 1294 **Census:** 138 **Outpatient Visits:** 0 **Births:** 0

MAUMEE—Lucas County

☐ **ARROWHEAD BEHAVIORAL HEALTH HOSPITAL (364036)**, 1725 Timber Line Road, Zip 43537–4015; tel. 419/891–9333 **A**1 10 **F**4 5 35 57 71 82 86 87 97 98 101 102 103 104 105 106 130 132 135 **P**5 **S** Universal Health Services, Inc., King of Prussia, PA
Primary Contact: Joseph Denicola, Chief Executive Officer and Managing Director
CFO: Allison Duncan, Chief Financial Officer
CMO: Kenneth Adler, M.D., Medical Director
CIO: Peggy Montgomery, Director Medical Records
CHR: Dawn Bosworth, Director Human Resources
CNO: Anita Zych, Director of Nursing
Web address: www.arrowheadbehavioral.com
Control: Corporation, Investor–owned, for–profit **Service:** Alcoholism and other chemical dependency

Staffed Beds: 48 **Admissions:** 1853 **Census:** 29 **Outpatient Visits:** 0 **Births:** 0 **Total Expense ($000):** 6656 **Payroll Expense ($000):** 3630 **Personnel:** 39

★ ◇ **PROMEDICA ST. LUKE'S HOSPITAL (360090)**, 5901 Monclova Road, Zip 43537–1899; tel. 419/893–5911 **A**2 3 5 10 21 **F**3 8 11 13 15 17 18 20 22 24 26 28 29 30 31 34 35 40 45 46 48 49 57 59 64 68 70 74 76 77 78 79 81 82 85 86 87 89 92 93 100 107 108 111 114 115 118 119 126 129 130 131 132 143 145 146 147 148 **S** ProMedica Health System, Toledo, OH
Primary Contact: Daniel L. Wakeman, President
CMO: Stephen Bazeley, M.D., Vice President Medical Affairs
CIO: Patricia Swint, Director Information Technology
CHR: Connie Sessler, Director Human Resources
CNO: Jill A. Trosin, R.N., Vice President Patient Care Services, Chief Nursing Officer
Web address: www.stlukeshospital.com
Control: Other not–for–profit (including NFP Corporation) **Service:** General Medical and Surgical

Staffed Beds: 172 **Admissions:** 11126 **Census:** 114 **Outpatient Visits:** 196754 **Births:** 876 **Total Expense ($000):** 174229 **Payroll Expense ($000):** 58143 **Personnel:** 1029

Many Facility Codes have changed. Please refer to the AHA Guide Code Chart. © 2016 AHA Guide

MEDINA—Medina County

✠ **CLEVELAND CLINIC, MEDINA HOSPITAL (360091)**, 1000 East Washington Street, Zip 44256–2170; tel. 330/725–1000 **A**1 2 5 10 **F**3 7 8 13 15 18 20 28 29 30 31 34 35 40 47 49 50 51 57 59 60 64 70 74 75 76 77 78 79 81 82 85 86 93 96 107 111 114 117 119 129 130 131 132 133 135 146 147 148 **S** Cleveland Clinic Health System, Cleveland, OH
Primary Contact: Thomas Tulisiak, M.D., President
COO: Vicky Snyder, Chief Operating Officer
CFO: Becky Molnar, Director of Finance
CMO: Richard K. Shewbridge, M.D., Vice President Medical Operations
CIO: Frank Longley, Business Partner Information Technology
CHR: Tracie Curtis, Business Partner Human Resources
CNO: Mary Kennedy, R.N., Chief Nursing Officer
Web address: www.medinahospital.org
Control: Other not–for–profit (including NFP Corporation) **Service:** General Medical and Surgical

Staffed Beds: 136 **Admissions:** 6522 **Census:** 71 **Outpatient Visits:** 97581 **Births:** 888 **Total Expense ($000):** 105081 **Payroll Expense ($000):** 37917 **Personnel:** 638

MIAMISBURG—Montgomery County

✠ **LIFECARE HOSPITAL OF DAYTON (362028)**, 4000 Miamisburg–Centerville Road, Zip 45342–7615; tel. 937/384–8300, (Nonreporting) **A**1 10 **S** LifeCare Management Services, Plano, TX
Primary Contact: William Bryant, Chief Executive Officer
CMO: Richard Gregg, M.D., Medical Director
CHR: Pam Fannin, Coordinator Human Resources
Web address: www.lifecare–hospitals.com
Control: Corporation, Investor–owned, for–profit **Service:** Long–Term Acute Care hospital

Staffed Beds: 44

★ ○ **SYCAMORE MEDICAL CENTER (360239)**, 4000 Miamisburg–Centerville Road, Zip 45342–7615; tel. 937/866–0551 **A**10 11 **F**3 11 12 15 18 20 28 29 30 31 34 35 36 38 40 42 44 45 47 48 49 50 53 54 56 57 58 59 60 61 64 65 66 68 70 74 75 77 78 79 81 82 84 85 86 87 91 92 93 97 98 99 100 101 102 103 104 105 107 108 110 111 114 115 118 119 129 130 131 132 134 135 141 145 146 148 **S** Kettering Health Network, Dayton, OH
Primary Contact: Walter Sackett, President
CFO: Steven Chavez, Vice President Finance and Operations
CMO: Robert T. Smith, M.D., Chief Medical Officer
CIO: Andy Lehman, Senior Vice President Technology and Analytics
CHR: Derek Morgan, Vice President Human Resources
CNO: Brenda Kuhn, Ph.D., Chief Nursing Officer
Web address: www.khnetwork.org/sycamore
Control: Church–operated, Nongovernment, not–for profit **Service:** General Medical and Surgical

Staffed Beds: 168 **Admissions:** 8448 **Census:** 94 **Outpatient Visits:** 139220 **Births:** 0 **Total Expense ($000):** 163661 **Payroll Expense ($000):** 69171 **Personnel:** 676

MIDDLE POINT—Van Wert County

☐ **RIDGEVIEW BEHAVIORAL HOSPITAL (364047)**, 17872 Lincoln Highway, Zip 45863–9700; tel. 419/968–2950, (Nonreporting) **A**1 10
Primary Contact: Pat Tracy, Administrator
Web address: www.ridgeviewhospital.net/
Control: Corporation, Investor–owned, for–profit **Service:** Psychiatric

Staffed Beds: 40

MIDDLEBURG HEIGHTS—Cuyahoga County

☐ **SOUTHWEST GENERAL HEALTH CENTER (360155)**, 18697 Bagley Road, Zip 44130–3497; tel. 440/816–8000 **A**1 2 3 5 10 **F**3 5 7 11 13 15 18 20 22 24 26 28 29 30 31 32 34 35 36 37 38 39 40 42 43 44 45 49 50 51 53 54 56 57 59 60 62 63 64 65 68 70 74 75 76 77 78 79 81 82 84 85 86 87 90 92 93 94 98 99 100 101 102 103 104 105 107 108 110 111 114 115 118 119 120 121 123 126 128 129 130 131 132 134 135 143 146 147 148 **P**6
Primary Contact: William A. Young, Jr., President and Chief Executive Officer
COO: Bradley W. Rauh, Vice President, Chief Operating Officer
CFO: Mary Ann Freas, Senior Vice President and Chief Financial Officer
CMO: Marilyn McNamara, M.D., Chief Medical Officer
CIO: Alec Williams, Chief Information Officer
CHR: Judy Murphy, Vice President Human Resources
CNO: Martha F. Bauschka, R.N., Vice President and Chief Nursing Officer
Web address: www.swgeneral.com
Control: Other not–for–profit (including NFP Corporation) **Service:** General Medical and Surgical

Staffed Beds: 293 **Admissions:** 15170 **Census:** 185 **Outpatient Visits:** 417132 **Births:** 1024 **Total Expense ($000):** 292675 **Payroll Expense ($000):** 109863 **Personnel:** 1967

MIDDLETOWN—Warren County

✠ △ **ATRIUM MEDICAL CENTER (360076)**, One Medical Center Drive, Zip 45005–1066; tel. 513/424–2111 **A**1 2 3 7 10 **F**3 8 11 13 15 17 18 20 22 24 26 28 29 30 31 32 34 35 40 41 42 43 44 45 46 47 48 49 50 54 56 57 59 61 64 65 68 70 71 73 74 75 76 77 78 79 80 81 82 84 85 86 87 90 92 93 94 96 98 100 101 102 103 107 108 110 111 114 115 116 117 118 119 126 130 131 132 135 145 146 147 148 **S** Premier Health, Dayton, OH
Primary Contact: Carol Turner, President and Chief Executive Officer
COO: Michael Uhl, Chief Operating Officer
CFO: Lisa Gibbs, Vice President, Finance
CMO: Jeff Hoffman, M.D., Chief Medical Officer
CHR: Ted Ripperger, Administrative Director Human Resources
CNO: Marquita Turner, Chief Nursing Officer
Web address: www.PremierHealth.com
Control: Other not–for–profit (including NFP Corporation) **Service:** General Medical and Surgical

Staffed Beds: 302 **Admissions:** 9992 **Census:** 102 **Outpatient Visits:** 112415 **Births:** 857 **Total Expense ($000):** 231175 **Payroll Expense ($000):** 88893 **Personnel:** 1423

MILLERSBURG—Holmes County

POMERENE HOSPITAL (360148), 981 Wooster Road, Zip 44654–1094; tel. 330/763–2001 **A**10 22 **F**3 11 13 15 18 29 30 34 35 40 45 50 53 55 57 59 68 70 75 76 79 81 85 86 87 89 93 107 108 110 115 119 127 130 131 132 135 143 144 146 **P**7
Primary Contact: Tony Snyder, Administrator and Chief Executive Officer
CFO: Jason Justus, Vice President Finance and Chief Financial Officer
CMO: Yasser Omran, M.D., President Medical Staff
CIO: Mark Jacobs, Director Information Services
CHR: Kim Croft, R.N., Executive Director Human Resources
CNO: Nicole Kolacz, Vice President Patient Services
Web address: www.pomerenehospital.org
Control: County–Government, nonfederal **Service:** General Medical and Surgical

Staffed Beds: 41 **Admissions:** 1556 **Census:** 14 **Outpatient Visits:** 44731 **Births:** 587 **Total Expense ($000):** 28365 **Payroll Expense ($000):** 11685 **Personnel:** 225

MONTPELIER—Williams County

COMMUNITY HOSPITALS AND WELLNESS CENTERS–MONTPELIER (361327), 909 East Snyder Avenue, Zip 43543–1251; tel. 419/385–3154, (Nonreporting) **A**10 18
Primary Contact: Philip L. Ennen, President and Chief Executive Officer
Web address: www.chwchospital.com
Control: Corporation, Investor–owned, for–profit **Service:** General Medical and Surgical

Staffed Beds: 35

MONTPELIER HOSPITAL See Community Hospitals and Wellness Centers, Bryan

MOUNT GILEAD—Morrow County

✠ **MORROW COUNTY HOSPITAL (361313)**, 651 West Marion Road, Zip 43338–1027; tel. 419/946–5015, (Nonreporting) **A**1 5 10 18 **S** OhioHealth, Columbus, OH
Primary Contact: Chad J. Miller, President and Chief Executive Officer
CFO: Joe Schueler, Chief Financial Officer
Web address: www.morrowcountyhospital.com
Control: County–Government, nonfederal **Service:** General Medical and Surgical

Staffed Beds: 23

MOUNT VERNON—Knox County

✠ **KNOX COMMUNITY HOSPITAL (360040)**, 1330 Coshocton Road, Zip 43050–1495; tel. 740/393–9000 **A**1 2 10 20 **F**3 5 11 13 15 18 20 22 26 28 29 30 31 32 34 35 36 38 40 44 45 48 50 51 53 57 59 64 69 70 75 76 77 78 79 81 82 83 84 85 86 87 93 94 96 97 107 108 110 111 114 115 116 117 118 119 120 121 129 130 131 132 134 144 146 147 **P**6 **S** QHR, Brentwood, TN
Primary Contact: Bruce D. White, Chief Executive Officer
COO: Bruce M. Behner, Chief Operating Officer
CFO: Michael Ambrosiani, Chief Financial Officer
CMO: Jeffrey Northup, D.O., Chief Medical Officer
CIO: Kwi Holland, Vice President Information Services
CHR: Lisa Bragg, Vice President Human Resources
CNO: James Middleton, MSN, Chief Nursing Officer
Web address: www.knoxcommhosp.org
Control: Other not–for–profit (including NFP Corporation) **Service:** General Medical and Surgical

Staffed Beds: 65 **Admissions:** 3047 **Census:** 27 **Outpatient Visits:** 155995 **Births:** 407 **Total Expense ($000):** 129240 **Payroll Expense ($000):** 57856 **Personnel:** 854

OH

NAPOLEON—Henry County

★ ◇ **HENRY COUNTY HOSPITAL (361309)**, 1600 East Riverview Avenue, Zip 43545–9399; tel. 419/592–4015 **A**5 10 18 21 **F**3 5 11 13 15 28 29 30 31 34 35 36 40 45 50 53 57 59 64 65 68 70 75 76 77 78 79 81 82 85 86 87 93 99 100 101 104 107 108 110 114 119 130 132 133 135 146
Primary Contact: Kimberly Hupp Bordenkircher, Chief Executive Officer
CFO: Diane Walther, Controller
CIO: William Grimm, Chief Information Officer
CHR: Jennifer A. Fisher, Manager Human Resources
CNO: Patricia Frank, Chief Nursing Officer
Web address: www.henrycountyhospital.org
Control: Other not–for–profit (including NFP Corporation) **Service:** General Medical and Surgical

Staffed Beds: 25 **Admissions:** 820 **Census:** 10 **Outpatient Visits:** 64073
Births: 106 **Total Expense ($000):** 28290 **Payroll Expense ($000):** 11363
Personnel: 210

NEW ALBANY—Franklin County

✦ **MOUNT CARMEL NEW ALBANY SURGICAL HOSPITAL (360266)**, 7333 Smith's Mill Road, Zip 43054–9291; tel. 614/775–6600 **A**1 10 **F**3 29 34 35 44 57 58 59 64 65 68 74 75 79 81 85 86 87 107 111 114 119 146 **P**6 8 **S** Trinity Health, Livonia, MI
Primary Contact: Diane Doucette, R.N., President
Web address: www.mountcarmelhealth.com
Control: Church–operated, Nongovernment, not–for profit **Service:** Surgical

Staffed Beds: 60 **Admissions:** 4375 **Census:** 20 **Outpatient Visits:** 13709
Births: 0 **Total Expense ($000):** 82920 **Payroll Expense ($000):** 13908
Personnel: 228

NEWARK—Licking County

☐ **LICKING MEMORIAL HOSPITAL (360218)**, 1320 West Main Street, Zip 43055–3699; tel. 740/348–4000 **A**1 2 10 **F**3 4 5 13 15 18 20 22 28 29 30 31 32 34 35 40 41 45 46 48 49 50 53 57 59 62 64 65 68 70 74 75 76 77 78 79 81 82 84 85 86 87 89 90 92 93 97 98 100 101 102 104 106 107 108 110 111 114 115 118 119 130 132 135 144 146 147 148 **P**6
Primary Contact: Robert A. Montagnese, President and Chief Executive Officer
CFO: Cindy Webster, Vice President Financial Services
CMO: Craig Cairns, M.D., Vice President Medical Affairs
CIO: Sallie Arnett, Vice President Information Systems
CHR: Anne Peterson, Vice President Human Resources and Support Services
Web address: www.lmhealth.org
Control: Other not–for–profit (including NFP Corporation) **Service:** General Medical and Surgical

Staffed Beds: 199 **Admissions:** 8054 **Census:** 78 **Outpatient Visits:** 318899
Births: 1090 **Total Expense ($000):** 163888 **Payroll Expense ($000):** 66452 **Personnel:** 1424

✦ **SELECT SPECIALTY HOSPITAL OF SOUTHEAST OHIO (362031)**, 2000 Tamarack Road, Zip 43055; tel. 740/588–7888, (Nonreporting) **A**1 10 **S** Select Medical Corporation, Mechanicsburg, PA
Primary Contact: Linda Supplee, Chief Executive Officer
CMO: Armand Bermudez, M.D., Medical Director
CHR: Jacqueline Nezbeth, Human Resources Officer
CNO: Taryn Vierling, Chief Nursing Officer
Web address: www.selectspecialtyhospitals.com/company/locations/zanesville.aspx
Control: Corporation, Investor–owned, for–profit **Service:** Long–Term Acute Care hospital

Staffed Beds: 35

NORTHFIELD—Summit County

☐ **NORTHCOAST BEHAVIORAL HEALTHCARE (364011)**, 1756 Sagamore Road, Zip 44067–1086; tel. 330/467–7131 **A**1 3 10 **F**30 53 65 75 77 98 106 130 135 **S** Ohio Department of Mental Health, Columbus, OH
Primary Contact: Douglas W. Kern, Chief Executive Officer
CIO: Karl Donenwirth, Vice President Information Services
Web address: www.mha.ohio.gov
Control: State–Government, nonfederal **Service:** Psychiatric

Staffed Beds: 260 **Admissions:** 1649 **Census:** 219 **Outpatient Visits:** 0
Births: 0 **Total Expense ($000):** 46295 **Payroll Expense ($000):** 25679
Personnel: 419

NORWALK—Huron County

★ ○ **FISHER–TITUS MEDICAL CENTER (360065)**, 272 Benedict Avenue, Zip 44857–2374; tel. 419/668–8101, (Total facility includes 69 beds in nursing home–type unit) **A**2 5 10 11 19 **F**3 10 11 13 15 18 20 28 29 31 34 35 36 39 40 43 45 49 50 51 54 56 57 58 59 62 64 68 70 74 75 76 77 78 79 81 82 85 86 87 92 93 94 96 97 107 108 110 111 115 118 119 126 128 129 130 131 132 135 143 146 147 148 **P**2 6 7
Primary Contact: Lorna Strayer, President and Chief Executive Officer
COO: Lorna Strayer, Executive Vice President
CFO: Duane L. Woods, Jr., Chief Financial Officer
CMO: Shankar Kurra, M.D., Senior Vice President Medical Affairs
CIO: John Britton, Vice President Information Services
CHR: Phillip Annarino, Vice President Human Resources
CNO: Suzanne Inglis, MSN, Senior Vice President Nursing Services
Web address: www.fisher–titus.org
Control: Other not–for–profit (including NFP Corporation) **Service:** General Medical and Surgical

Staffed Beds: 147 **Admissions:** 3921 **Census:** 98 **Outpatient Visits:** 174903
Births: 614 **Total Expense ($000):** 111884 **Payroll Expense ($000):** 46757
Personnel: 810

OBERLIN—Lorain County

✦ **MERCY ALLEN HOSPITAL (361306)**, 200 West Lorain Street, Zip 44074–1077; tel. 440/775–1211, (Nonreporting) **A**1 10 18 **S** Mercy Health, Cincinnati, OH
Primary Contact: Joseph Sober, President
COO: Robert Tonkinson, Chief Operating Officer and Chief Financial Officer
CFO: Robert Tonkinson, Chief Operating Officer and Chief Financial Officer
CMO: Vamsee Amirneni, M.D., Chief of Staff
CNO: Catherine Walsh, Interim Chief Nursing Officer
Web address: www.mercyonline.org/mercy_allen_hospital.aspx
Control: Other not–for–profit (including NFP Corporation) **Service:** General Medical and Surgical

Staffed Beds: 25

OREGON—Lucas County

✦ △ **MERCY HEALTH – ST. CHARLES HOSPITAL (360081)**, 2600 Navarre Avenue, Zip 43616–3297; tel. 419/696–7200 **A**1 2 3 7 10 **F**3 11 13 15 18 28 29 30 31 34 35 40 43 44 46 48 49 51 56 57 59 60 64 66 68 70 74 75 76 77 78 79 81 82 85 86 87 90 91 92 93 97 98 100 102 103 104 105 107 108 110 111 114 115 118 119 120 121 123 126 129 130 132 135 146 147 148 **P**8 **S** Mercy Health, Cincinnati, OH
Primary Contact: Jeffrey Dempsey, President and Chief Operating Officer
COO: Jeffrey Dempsey, President and Chief Executive Officer
CFO: Mark Thompson, Market Chief Financial Officer Northern Region and Chief Financial Officer
CMO: Riaz Chaudhry, M.D., Chief Medical Officer
CIO: Rebecca S. Sykes, Senior Vice President Resource Management, Chief Information Officer
CHR: Maggie A. Lund, System Vice President Human Resource Market and Labor
CNO: Craig Albers, Vice President Patient Care and Chief Nursing Officer
Web address: www.mercyweb.org
Control: Church–operated, Nongovernment, not–for profit **Service:** General Medical and Surgical

Staffed Beds: 257 **Admissions:** 9641 **Census:** 140 **Outpatient Visits:** 174092 **Births:** 524 **Personnel:** 977

✦ **PROMEDICA BAY PARK HOSPITAL (360259)**, 2801 Bay Park Drive, Zip 43616–4920; tel. 419/690–7900 **A**1 10 **F**3 11 13 15 18 28 29 30 31 34 35 40 49 50 54 57 58 59 64 68 70 75 76 77 78 79 81 82 85 86 92 93 97 107 108 110 111 114 118 119 124 126 129 130 131 132 134 135 146 147 148 **S** ProMedica Health System, Toledo, OH
Primary Contact: Holly L. Bristoll, President
COO: Darrell Wachowiak, Associate Vice President Operations
CFO: Scott Fought, Vice President Finance
CMO: David Lindstrom, M.D., Vice President Medical Affairs
CIO: Rose Ann Laureto, Corporate Vice President Information Resources
CHR: Kara Zimmerly, Manager Human Resources
CNO: Paula Grieb, R.N., Vice President Patient Care Service and Chief Nursing Officer
Web address: www.promedica.org
Control: Other not–for–profit (including NFP Corporation) **Service:** General Medical and Surgical

Staffed Beds: 77 **Admissions:** 3205 **Census:** 34 **Outpatient Visits:** 99251
Births: 527 **Total Expense ($000):** 76092 **Payroll Expense ($000):** 23292
Personnel: 360

ST. CHARLES MERCY HOSPITAL See Mercy Health – St. Charles Hospital

Many Facility Codes have changed. Please refer to the AHA Guide Code Chart. © 2016 AHA Guide

ORRVILLE—Wayne County

✠ **AULTMAN ORRVILLE HOSPITAL (361323)**, 832 South Main Street,
Zip 44667–2208; tel. 330/682–3010 **A**1 10 18 **F**7 8 11 13 14 15 28 29 30
34 35 40 45 50 51 53 55 57 59 68 70 75 76 77 81 82 85 86 87 93 108
110 111 115 118 119 129 130 131 132 133 135 143 146 147 **S** Aultman
Health Foundation, Canton, OH
Primary Contact: Marchelle Suppan, DPM, President and Chief Executive Officer
CFO: Adam Luntz, Chief Financial Officer
CIO: Vince Logozzo, Director Information Technology
CHR: Jennifer Kessel, Assistant Vice President, Operations and Human Resources
CNO: Angela McGee, Vice President Nursing Services
Web address: www.aultmanorrville.org
Control: Other not–for–profit (including NFP Corporation) **Service:** General
Medical and Surgical

Staffed Beds: 25 **Admissions:** 774 **Census:** 5 **Outpatient Visits:** 36204
Births: 434 **Total Expense ($000):** 22363 **Payroll Expense ($000):** 8622
Personnel: 181

OXFORD—Butler County

★ ○ **MCCULLOUGH–HYDE MEMORIAL HOSPITAL/TRIHEALTH (360046)**,
110 North Poplar Street, Zip 45056–1292; tel. 513/523–2111, (Nonreporting)
A2 10 11
Primary Contact: Bryan D. Hehemann, President and Chief Executive Officer
CFO: John R. Clements, Chief Financial Officer
CMO: Amy Spivey, Chief Medical Officer
CIO: Kathy Dickman, Director Information Technology
CHR: Sharon Hancock, Chief Human Resources Officer
CNO: Pamela Collins, Vice President Chief Patient Services Officer
Web address: www.mhmh.org
Control: Other not–for–profit (including NFP Corporation) **Service:** General
Medical and Surgical

Staffed Beds: 45

PARMA—Cuyahoga County

✠ △ **UNIVERSITY HOSPITALS PARMA MEDICAL CENTER (360041)**, 7007
Powers Boulevard, Zip 44129–5495; tel. 440/743–3000, (Total facility includes
10 beds in nursing home–type unit) **A**1 2 7 10 13 **F**2 3 10 11 12 13 15 17 18
20 22 24 26 28 29 30 31 34 35 36 40 44 45 49 50 51 53 55 56 57 58 59
62 63 64 65 68 69 70 71 74 75 76 77 78 79 81 82 85 86 87 90 93 96 98
100 101 103 107 108 111 114 115 116 117 118 119 120 121 126 128 130
131 132 135 143 146 147 148 **P**6 8 **S** University Hospitals, Cleveland, OH
Primary Contact: Kristi M. Sink, Interim President
COO: Kristi M. Sink, Chief Operating Officer
CMO: Christopher Loyke, Chief Medical Officer
CHR: Daniel Miller, Human Resources Business Partner
Web address: www.uhhospitals.org/parma
Control: Other not–for–profit (including NFP Corporation) **Service:** General
Medical and Surgical

Staffed Beds: 254 **Admissions:** 10724 **Census:** 129 **Outpatient Visits:**
244259 **Births:** 629 **Total Expense ($000):** 181627 **Payroll Expense
($000):** 68306 **Personnel:** 1352

PAULDING—Paulding County

☐ **PAULDING COUNTY HOSPITAL (361300)**, 1035 West Wayne Street,
Zip 45879–1544; tel. 419/399–4080, (Nonreporting) **A**1 10 18
Primary Contact: Randy Ruge, Chief Executive Officer
COO: Randy Ruge, Chief Operating Officer
CFO: Rob Goshia, Chief Financial Officer
CMO: Wendell J. Spangler, M.D., Chief of Staff
CIO: Dan Kaufman, Director Information Services
CHR: Melanie Rittenour, Director Human Resources
Web address: www.pauldingcountyhospital.com
Control: County–Government, nonfederal **Service:** General Medical and Surgical

Staffed Beds: 25

PORT CLINTON—Ottawa County

✠ **MAGRUDER MEMORIAL HOSPITAL (361314)**, 615 Fulton Street,
Zip 43452–2001; tel. 419/734–3131 **A**1 5 10 18 **F**3 11 15 18 28 29 31 34
35 40 44 45 46 48 50 53 57 59 64 65 70 75 77 78 79 81 82 85 86 87 89
93 107 108 110 115 118 119 129 130 131 132 133 135 146 147 148 **P**6 8
Primary Contact: J. Todd Almendinger, President and Chief Executive Officer
COO: Nick Marsico, Vice President and Chief Operating Officer
CFO: Ronald Weiner, Vice President Finance and Chief Financial Officer
CMO: Barry Cover, M.D., Medical Director
CIO: Charles Dellick, Director Information Technology
CHR: Jason Kraus, Director Human Resources
Web address: www.magruderhospital.com
Control: Other not–for–profit (including NFP Corporation) **Service:** General
Medical and Surgical

Staffed Beds: 25 **Admissions:** 613 **Census:** 5 **Outpatient Visits:** 92166
Births: 0 **Total Expense ($000):** 52001 **Payroll Expense ($000):** 19696
Personnel: 358

PORTSMOUTH—Scioto County

KING'S DAUGHTERS MEDICAL CENTER OHIO (360361), 2001 Scioto Trail,
Zip 45662–2845; tel. 740/991–4000, (Nonreporting)
Primary Contact: Kim Grooms, Administrator
Web address: www.kdmcohio.com/
Control: Other not–for–profit (including NFP Corporation) **Service:** Long–Term
Acute Care hospital

Staffed Beds: 10

✠ △ **SOUTHERN OHIO MEDICAL CENTER (360008)**, 1805 27th Street,
Zip 45662–2640; tel. 740/356–5000 **A**1 2 5 7 10 13 **F**3 11 13 15 17 18 20
22 24 26 28 29 30 31 34 35 37 38 40 41 44 45 46 47 48 49 50 53 54 57
59 62 63 64 65 68 70 74 75 76 77 78 79 81 84 85 86 87 89 90 92 97 98
100 101 102 103 104 107 108 109 110 111 114 115 116 117 118 119 120
121 122 123 124 129 130 131 132 135 144 145 146 **P**3
Primary Contact: Randal M. Arnett, President and Chief Executive Officer
CFO: Dean Wray, Vice President Finance
CMO: Kendall Stewart, M.D., Chief Medical Officer
CIO: Brent Richard, Administrative Director Information Systems
CHR: Vicki Noel, Vice President Human Resources
CNO: Claudia L. Burchett, R.N., Vice President of Patient Services
Web address: www.somc.org
Control: Other not–for–profit (including NFP Corporation) **Service:** General
Medical and Surgical

Staffed Beds: 248 **Admissions:** 11671 **Census:** 162 **Outpatient Visits:**
388846 **Births:** 1133 **Total Expense ($000):** 278748 **Payroll Expense
($000):** 105731 **Personnel:** 2117

PROCTORVILLE—Lawrence County

☐ **THREE GABLES SURGERY CENTER (360261)**, 5897 County Road 107,
Zip 45669–8852, Mailing Address: P.O. Box 490, Zip 45669–0490;
tel. 740/886–9911, (Nonreporting) **A**1 10
Primary Contact: Tony Aluise, Chief Executive Officer
Web address: www.threegablessurgery.com
Control: Partnership, Investor–owned, for–profit **Service:** Surgical

Staffed Beds: 8

RAVENNA—Portage County

✠ **UH PORTAGE MEDICAL CENTER (360078)**, 6847 North Chestnut Street,
Zip 44266–3929, Mailing Address: P.O. Box 1204, Zip 44266–1204;
tel. 330/297–0811 **A**1 2 3 5 10 **F**3 13 15 18 20 22 26 28 29 30 31 34 35 36
40 42 43 45 46 47 48 49 50 51 56 57 59 60 61 62 63 64 65 68 70 74 75
76 77 79 81 82 85 87 91 93 97 107 108 109 110 111 115 116 119 120
126 129 131 132 135 144 145 146 147 148 **P**8 **S** University Hospitals,
Cleveland, OH
Primary Contact: M. Steven Jones, President
CFO: Jen Hahn, Finance Manager
CMO: Benjamin Prestegaard, Chief Medical Officer
CIO: Rhonda Smith, Applications Support Manager
CHR: Neil Everett, Vice President Human Resources
CNO: Linda Breedlove, Vice President of Patient Care Services and Chief Nursing
Officer
Web address: www.uhportage.org
Control: Other not–for–profit (including NFP Corporation) **Service:** General
Medical and Surgical

Staffed Beds: 117 **Admissions:** 5333 **Census:** 63 **Outpatient Visits:** 116613
Births: 633 **Total Expense ($000):** 115606 **Payroll Expense ($000):** 47517
Personnel: 823

Hospital, Medicare Provider Number, Address, Telephone, Approval, Facility, and Physician Codes, Health Care System

★ American Hospital Association (AHA) membership
☐ The Joint Commission accreditation
○ Healthcare Facilities Accreditation Program
◇ DNV Healthcare Inc. accreditation
⇑ Center for Improvement in Healthcare Quality Accreditation
△ Commission on Accreditation of Rehabilitation Facilities (CARF) accreditation

OH

ROCK CREEK—Ashtabula County

GLENBEIGH HOSPITAL AND OUTPATIENT CENTERS (360245), 2863 Route 45, Zip 44084, Mailing Address: P.O. Box 298, Zip 44084–0298; tel. 440/563–3400 **A**10 **F**4 5 29 30 34 36 53 54 57 75 86 87 100 130 132 135
Primary Contact: Patricia Weston–Hall, Chief Executive Officer
CFO: Phil Pawlowski, Chief Financial Officer
CIO: Linda Advey, Manager Information Systems
CHR: Shirley Deary, Director Human Resources
Web address: www.glenbeigh.com
Control: Other not–for–profit (including NFP Corporation) **Service:** Alcoholism and other chemical dependency

Staffed Beds: 114 **Admissions:** 3179 **Census:** 80 **Outpatient Visits:** 94519
Births: 0 **Total Expense ($000):** 19638 **Payroll Expense ($000):** 9779
Personnel: 248

SAINT MARYS—Auglaize County

◇ **JOINT TOWNSHIP DISTRICT MEMORIAL HOSPITAL (360032)**, 200 St. Clair Street, Zip 45885–2400; tel. 419/394–3335, (Total facility includes 13 beds in nursing home–type unit) **A**10 21 **F**3 7 8 11 12 13 15 28 29 30 32 34 35 36 40 41 45 47 51 53 57 59 62 63 64 70 74 75 76 77 79 81 82 83 84 85 87 90 93 107 108 110 115 119 124 128 129 130 131 132 143 144 146 147 148
Primary Contact: Kevin W. Harlan, President
CFO: Jeffrey W. Vossler, Chief Financial Officer
CIO: Joshua Miller, Director Information Systems
CHR: Art Swain, Vice President Support Services
CNO: Debra McKee, R.N., Chief Clinical Officer and Chief Nursing Officer
Web address: www.grandlakehealth.org
Control: Other not–for–profit (including NFP Corporation) **Service:** General Medical and Surgical

Staffed Beds: 53 **Admissions:** 1284 **Census:** 16 **Outpatient Visits:** 78610
Births: 276 **Total Expense ($000):** 63220 **Payroll Expense ($000):** 18917
Personnel: 454

SALEM—Columbiana County

✠ **SALEM REGIONAL MEDICAL CENTER (360185)**, 1995 East State Street, Zip 44460–2423; tel. 330/332–1551, (Total facility includes 15 beds in nursing home–type unit) **A**1 5 10 **F**3 8 13 15 18 29 30 31 34 35 40 45 48 49 51 54 57 59 64 70 74 75 76 77 78 79 81 82 85 86 87 93 100 104 105 107 108 109 110 111 114 115 116 117 118 119 128 129 130 132 144 145 146 148 **P**6
Primary Contact: Anita Hackstedde, M.D., President and Chief Executive Officer
COO: Keith Meredith, Chief Operating Officer
CFO: Mike Giangardella, Vice President Finance and Administration
CMO: Anita Hackstedde, M.D., Vice President Medical Affairs
CIO: Mark L'Italien, Director Information Services
CHR: Barb Hirst, R.N., Vice President Human Resources and Chief Nursing Officer
CNO: Barb Hirst, R.N., Vice President Human Resources and Chief Nursing Officer
Web address: www.salemregional.com
Control: Other not–for–profit (including NFP Corporation) **Service:** General Medical and Surgical

Staffed Beds: 116 **Admissions:** 5427 **Census:** 63 **Outpatient Visits:** 130657
Births: 452 **Total Expense ($000):** 99700 **Payroll Expense ($000):** 38244
Personnel: 779

SANDUSKY—Erie County

○ **FIRELANDS REGIONAL HEALTH SYSTEM (360025)**, 1111 Hayes Avenue, Zip 44870–3323; tel. 419/557–7400, (Includes FIRELANDS REGIONAL MEDICAL CENTER – MAIN CAMPUS, 1111 Hayes Avenue, Zip 44870; tel. 419/557–7400; FIRELANDS REGIONAL MEDICAL CENTER SOUTH CAMPUS, 1912 Hayes Avenue, Zip 44870–4736; tel. 419/557–7000) **A**2 10 11 12 13 19 **F**3 5 8 11 13 15 18 20 22 24 28 29 31 34 35 36 38 40 43 45 46 48 49 50 51 54 57 58 59 60 62 64 68 70 74 75 76 77 78 79 80 81 82 85 86 87 89 90 92 93 96 98 99 100 101 102 103 104 105 107 108 110 111 115 117 118 119 120 121 123 124 129 130 131 132 135 143 145 146 147 148 **P**8
Primary Contact: Martin Tursky, President and Chief Executive Officer
CFO: Daniel J. Moncher, Vice President and Chief Financial Officer
CMO: Brenda Violette, M.D., Director Medical Staff
CIO: Robert Ayres, Director Information Systems
CHR: James Sennish, Vice President Human Resources
Web address: www.firelands.com
Control: Other not–for–profit (including NFP Corporation) **Service:** General Medical and Surgical

Staffed Beds: 236 **Admissions:** 8865 **Census:** 122 **Outpatient Visits:** 318840 **Births:** 752 **Total Expense ($000):** 220767 **Payroll Expense ($000):** 90128 **Personnel:** 1657

SEAMAN—Adams County

✠ **ADAMS COUNTY REGIONAL MEDICAL CENTER (361326)**, 230 Medical Center Drive, Zip 45679–8002; tel. 937/386–3400 **A**1 10 18 **F**3 15 28 29 30 31 34 40 45 49 50 53 57 59 62 64 65 75 77 78 79 81 82 85 86 93 107 110 111 115 116 119 129 130 132 133 148
Primary Contact: Roland D. Gee, Interim Chief Executive Officer
CFO: Pete Dagenbach, Chief Financial Officer
CHR: Heather Hoop, Human Resources Generalist
CNO: Sharon Ashley, MSN, Chief Nursing Officer
Web address: www.acrmc.com
Control: County–Government, nonfederal **Service:** General Medical and Surgical

Staffed Beds: 25 **Admissions:** 823 **Census:** 8 **Outpatient Visits:** 48181
Births: 0 **Total Expense ($000):** 23165 **Payroll Expense ($000):** 7831
Personnel: 207

SHELBY—Richland County

★ **OHIOHEALTH MEDCENTRAL SHELBY HOSPITAL (361324)**, 199 West Main Street, Zip 44875–1490; tel. 419/342–5015 **A**10 18 **F**3 11 13 15 18 29 30 31 34 35 40 57 59 64 68 69 70 75 76 78 79 81 93 107 108 110 115 118 119 130 133 146 **S** OhioHealth, Columbus, OH
Primary Contact: Jean Halpin, President
CNO: Trish DelGreco, Director of Nursing
Web address: www.medcentral.org/body.cfm?id=153
Control: Other not–for–profit (including NFP Corporation) **Service:** General Medical and Surgical

Staffed Beds: 25 **Admissions:** 1016 **Census:** 10 **Outpatient Visits:** 33579
Births: 166 **Personnel:** 178

SIDNEY—Shelby County

★ ○ **WILSON MEMORIAL HOSPITAL (360013)**, 915 West Michigan Street, Zip 45365–2491; tel. 937/498–2311 **A**10 11 **F**3 11 13 15 20 28 29 30 34 40 45 49 56 57 59 62 63 64 68 70 75 76 77 79 81 82 85 86 87 89 93 97 98 103 107 108 111 115 118 119 129 130 131 132 135 144 146 147 **P**6
Primary Contact: Mark J. Dooley, Chief Executive Officer
COO: Craig Lannoye, Vice President Operations
CFO: Julie Covault, Vice President Finance
CMO: Robert J. McDevitt, M.D., Chief of Staff
CIO: Larry Meyers, Chief Information Officer
CHR: John Eve, Vice President Human Resources and Education
CNO: Linda Maurer, Vice President Patient Care Services
Web address: www.wilsonhospital.com
Control: Other not–for–profit (including NFP Corporation) **Service:** General Medical and Surgical

Staffed Beds: 71 **Admissions:** 2503 **Census:** 28 **Outpatient Visits:** 202731
Births: 720 **Total Expense ($000):** 75872 **Payroll Expense ($000):** 28286
Personnel: 707

SPRINGFIELD—Clark County

☐ **MENTAL HEALTH SERVICES FOR CLARK AND MADISON COUNTIES (364040)**, 474 North Yellow Springs Street, Zip 45504–2463; tel. 937/399–9500, (Nonreporting) **A**1 10
Primary Contact: Curt Gillespie, Chief Executive Officer
Web address: www.mhscc.org
Control: County–Government, nonfederal **Service:** Psychiatric

Staffed Beds: 16

☐ **OHIO VALLEY SURGICAL HOSPITAL (360355)**, 100 West Main Street, Zip 45502–1312; tel. 937/521–3900, (Nonreporting) **A**1 10
Primary Contact: Steve Eisentrager, President
CFO: Amanda martin, Manager Human Resources
CMO: Thales Pavlatos, Medical Director
CIO: Jonathan Bisdorf, Director Information Technology
CNO: Beth Lizza, Chief Nursing Officer
Web address: www.ovsurgical.com/
Control: Partnership, Investor–owned, for–profit **Service:** Surgical

Staffed Beds: 24

⊠ **SPRINGFIELD REGIONAL MEDICAL CENTER (360086)**, 100 Medical Center Drive, Zip 45504–2687; tel. 937/523–1000 **A**1 2 10 **F**3 5 8 11 12 13 15 17 18 20 22 24 26 28 29 30 31 34 35 37 40 45 49 51 53 59 61 63 64 68 70 74 75 76 77 78 79 81 82 83 84 85 86 87 89 90 93 107 108 110 111 114 115 118 119 120 121 126 129 130 131 132 135 146 147 148 **P**6 **S** Mercy Health, Cincinnati, OH
Primary Contact: Paul C. Hiltz, FACHE, Market President and Chief Executive Officer
COO: Gary Hagens, Chief Operating Officer and Chief Medical Officer
CFO: William J. Kusnierz, Vice President and Chief Financial Officer
CMO: Gary Hagens, Chief Operating Officer and Chief Medical Officer
CIO: Denise Craven, Director Information Systems Relationship Management
CHR: Steven E. Kile, Director Human Resources
CNO: Sherry Nelson, JD, Chief Nursing Officer
Web address: www.community-mercy.org
Control: Church–operated, Nongovernment, not–for profit **Service:** General Medical and Surgical

Staffed Beds: 259 **Admissions:** 13896 **Census:** 174 **Outpatient Visits:** 291078 **Births:** 1244 **Total Expense ($000):** 211447 **Payroll Expense ($000):** 64385

STEUBENVILLE—Jefferson County

⊠ **ACUITY SPECIALTY HOSPITALS OHIO VALLEY (362035)**, 380 Summit Avenue, 3rd Floor, Zip 43952–2667; tel. 740/283–7600, (Includes ACUITY SPECIALTY HOSPITALS OHIO VALLEY AT BELMONT, 4697 Harrison Street, Bellaire, Zip 43906–1338; tel. 740/671–2086) **A**1 10 **F**1 3 29 34 57 77 85 91 148 **S** AcuityHealthcare, LP, Charlotte, NC
Primary Contact: Judy K. Weaver, MS, Chief Executive Officer
Web address: www.acuityhealthcare.net
Control: Partnership, Investor–owned, for–profit **Service:** Long–Term Acute Care hospital

Staffed Beds: 65 **Admissions:** 846 **Census:** 61 **Outpatient Visits:** 0 **Births:** 0 **Total Expense ($000):** 33959 **Payroll Expense ($000):** 12825 **Personnel:** 203

LIFE LINE HOSPITAL (362039), 200 School Street, Zip 43953–9610; tel. 740/346–2600, (Nonreporting) **A**10
Primary Contact: Patricia Cross, Chief Executive Officer
Web address: www.llhospital.com
Control: Partnership, Investor–owned, for–profit **Service:** Long–Term Acute Care hospital

Staffed Beds: 36

⊠ **TRINITY HEALTH SYSTEM (360211)**, 380 Summit Avenue, Zip 43952–2699; tel. 740/283–7000, (Includes TRINITY MEDICAL CENTER EAST, 380 Summit Avenue, tel. 740/283–7000; TRINITY MEDICAL CENTER WEST, 4000 Johnson Road, Zip 43952–2393; tel. 740/264–8000) **A**1 2 10 13 **F**3 4 5 12 13 15 17 18 20 22 24 26 28 29 30 31 32 33 34 35 38 40 46 47 48 49 51 54 56 57 59 62 64 65 70 74 75 76 77 78 79 81 82 85 86 87 89 90 91 92 93 94 96 97 98 99 100 101 102 103 104 105 107 108 110 111 114 115 117 118 119 120 121 123 126 128 129 130 131 132 135 144 146 147 148 **P**6 **S** Catholic Health Initiatives, Englewood, CO
Primary Contact: Joseph M. Tasse, FACHE, Interim Chief Executive Officer
COO: JoAnn M. Mulrooney, R.N., Chief Operating Officer
CFO: Dave Werkin, Vice President Finance and Chief Financial Officer
CMO: Gray Goncz, Vice President of Medical Affairs
CIO: Tom Kiger, Director Information Systems
CHR: Lewis C. Musso, Vice President Human Resources
Web address: www.trinityhealth.com
Control: Other not–for–profit (including NFP Corporation) **Service:** General Medical and Surgical

Staffed Beds: 312 **Admissions:** 11096 **Census:** 178 **Outpatient Visits:** 277865 **Births:** 585 **Total Expense ($000):** 233241 **Payroll Expense ($000):** 85474 **Personnel:** 1609

SYLVANIA—Lucas County

⊠ △ **PROMEDICA FLOWER HOSPITAL (360074)**, 5200 Harroun Road, Zip 43560–2196; tel. 419/824–1444 **A**1 2 3 5 7 10 **F**3 11 12 13 15 18 28 29 30 31 34 36 38 40 47 48 49 50 54 57 59 64 65 67 68 70 75 76 77 78 79 81 82 84 85 86 87 90 91 92 93 96 97 98 100 101 102 103 107 108 109 110 111 114 116 117 118 119 120 121 123 124 126 129 130 131 132 146 147 **S** ProMedica Health System, Toledo, OH
Primary Contact: Neeraj Kanwal, M.D., President
CFO: Michael Browning, Chief Financial Officer
CMO: John Evanoff, M.D., Vice President Medical Affairs
CIO: Lori Johnston, Chief Information Officer
CHR: Karen Strauss, Chief Human Resources Officer
CNO: Maurine Weis, MSN, Vice President Nursing and Chief Nursing Officer
Web address: www.promedica.org
Control: Other not–for–profit (including NFP Corporation) **Service:** General Medical and Surgical

Staffed Beds: 273 **Admissions:** 10972 **Census:** 158 **Outpatient Visits:** 185722 **Births:** 877 **Total Expense ($000):** 212632 **Payroll Expense ($000):** 69574 **Personnel:** 1024

⊠ **REGENCY HOSPITAL OF TOLEDO (362036)**, 5220 Alexis Road, Zip 43560–2504; tel. 419/318–5700, (Nonreporting) **A**1 3 5 10 **S** Select Medical Corporation, Mechanicsburg, PA
Primary Contact: Brett Johnson, Chief Executive Officer
Web address: www.regencyhospital.com
Control: Corporation, Investor–owned, for–profit **Service:** Long–Term Acute Care hospital

Staffed Beds: 45

TIFFIN—Seneca County

⊠ **MERCY TIFFIN HOSPITAL (360089)**, 45 St. Lawrence Drive, Zip 44883–8310; tel. 419/455–7000 **A**1 2 10 **F**3 12 13 15 18 19 20 28 29 30 31 34 35 36 40 46 49 50 51 56 57 59 62 64 66 68 70 74 75 76 77 78 79 81 82 83 84 85 86 87 89 93 97 107 108 110 111 115 118 119 129 130 133 134 135 145 146 147 148 **S** Mercy Health, Cincinnati, OH
Primary Contact: B. Lynn Detterman, President and Chief Executive Officer
CFO: Cynthia Dennison, Assistant Chief Financial Officer 3
CMO: Steven Bruhl, Chief Medical Officer
CHR: Diana Olson, Director Human Resources
CNO: Anne Zimmerman, Senior Director Patient Care Services and Chief Nursing Officer
Web address: www.mercyweb.org
Control: Church–operated, Nongovernment, not–for profit **Service:** General Medical and Surgical

Staffed Beds: 51 **Admissions:** 1975 **Census:** 19 **Outpatient Visits:** 82910 **Births:** 269 **Total Expense ($000):** 55029 **Payroll Expense ($000):** 12487 **Personnel:** 312

TOLEDO—Lucas County

☐ **ADVANCED SPECIALTY HOSPITAL OF TOLEDO (362038)**, 1015 Garden Lake Parkway, Zip 43614–2779; tel. 419/381–0037, (Nonreporting) **A**1 3 10
Primary Contact: Kim Burkholder–McNutt, Chief Executive Officer
CFO: Troy Holmes, Director Finance
CMO: B. Sarroui, M.D., Chief of Staff
CHR: Lauren Avigdor, Director Human Resources
CNO: Bridgett Mitchell, Chief Clinical Officer
Web address: www.advancedspecialtyhospitals.com
Control: Corporation, Investor–owned, for–profit **Service:** Long–Term Acute Care hospital

Staffed Beds: 25

⊠ **MERCY ST. ANNE HOSPITAL (360262)**, 3404 West Sylvania Avenue, Zip 43623–4467; tel. 419/407–2663 **A**1 2 10 **F**3 8 15 18 20 22 24 28 29 30 31 34 35 36 38 40 42 45 56 57 59 64 65 68 70 74 75 78 79 81 82 84 85 86 87 92 107 108 110 111 115 118 119 120 121 123 126 129 130 132 135 146 147 **P**8 **S** Mercy Health, Cincinnati, OH
Primary Contact: Bradley J. Bertke, President and Chief Ooperating Officer
CFO: Michael Whipple, Chief Financial Officer
CMO: Herbert Stockard, M.D., Chief Medical Officer
CIO: Rebecca S. Sykes, Chief Information Officer
CNO: Barb Dianda–Martin, Chief Nursing Officer
Web address: www.mercyweb.org
Control: Church–operated, Nongovernment, not–for profit **Service:** General Medical and Surgical

Staffed Beds: 96 **Admissions:** 4881 **Census:** 51 **Outpatient Visits:** 225604 **Births:** 0 **Personnel:** 523

OH

✠ **MERCY ST. VINCENT MEDICAL CENTER (360112)**, 2213 Cherry Street, Zip 43608–2691; tel. 419/251–3232, (Includes MERCY CHILDREN'S HOSPITAL, 2213 Cherry Street, tel. 419/251–8000) **A**1 2 3 5 10 13 **F**3 7 8 11 12 13 15 16 18 19 20 21 22 23 24 25 26 29 30 31 32 34 35 37 38 39 40 41 42 43 44 45 46 48 49 50 51 53 54 55 56 57 58 59 60 61 64 65 66 68 70 72 74 75 77 78 79 81 82 83 84 85 86 87 88 92 93 97 98 107 108 110 111 114 115 118 119 126 129 130 131 132 134 135 146 147 148 **P**8 **S** Mercy Health, Cincinnati, OH
Primary Contact: Kerry Tirman, Chief Executive Officer
COO: Kerry Tirman, President and Chief Operating Officer
CMO: Thomas Welch, M.D., Chief Medical Officer
CHR: Gary George, Senior Vice President Human Resources
CNO: Barbara Martin, Chief Nursing Officer
Web address: www.mercyweb.org
Control: Church–operated, Nongovernment, not–for profit **Service:** General Medical and Surgical

Staffed Beds: 381 Admissions: 16874 Census: 203 Outpatient Visits: 221647 Births: 1072 Personnel: 2548

☐ **NORTHWEST OHIO PSYCHIATRIC HOSPITAL (364014)**, 930 Detroit Avenue, Zip 43614–2701; tel. 419/381–1881, (Nonreporting) **A**1 3 10 **S** Ohio Department of Mental Health, Columbus, OH
Primary Contact: Tamara Junge, Chief Executive Officer
CMO: Thomas Osinowo, M.D., Chief Clinical Officer
CIO: Michael Carter, Administrator Information Technology
CHR: Lois Mason–Williams, Director of Human Resources
CNO: Deb Duris, Director of Nursing
Web address: www.mh.state.oh.us/
Control: State–Government, nonfederal **Service:** Psychiatric

Staffed Beds: 114

✠ **PROMEDICA TOLEDO HOSPITAL (360068)**, 2142 North Cove Boulevard, Zip 43606–3896; tel. 419/291–4000, (Includes PROMEDICA WILDWOOD ORTHOPAEDIC AND SPINE HOSPITAL, 2901 North Reynolds Road, Zip 43615; tel. 419/578–7700; Holly L. Bristoll, President; TOLEDO CHILDREN'S HOSPITAL, 2142 North Cove Boulevard, Zip 43606), (Total facility includes 35 beds in nursing home–type unit) **A**1 2 3 5 10 13 **F**3 7 8 11 12 13 15 17 18 20 22 24 26 29 30 31 32 34 36 38 40 48 49 50 51 53 54 55 57 58 59 60 64 65 67 68 70 72 74 75 76 77 78 79 81 82 84 85 86 87 88 89 91 92 93 94 96 97 98 99 100 101 102 104 105 107 108 111 114 115 118 119 126 128 129 130 131 132 134 135 143 144 146 147 148 **S** ProMedica Health System, Toledo, OH
Primary Contact: Arturo Polizzi, President
CMO: Khurram Kamran, M.D., Vice President Medical Affairs
CIO: Rose Ann Laureto, Chief Information Officer
CHR: Arturo Polizzi, Chief Human Resources Officer
Web address: www.promedica.org
Control: Other not–for–profit (including NFP Corporation) **Service:** General Medical and Surgical

Staffed Beds: 609 Admissions: 31863 Census: 442 Outpatient Visits: 747600 Births: 3658 Total Expense ($000): 796615 Payroll Expense ($000): 239436 Personnel: 4118

✠ △ **THE UNIVERSITY OF TOLEDO MEDICAL CENTER (360048)**, 3000 Arlington Avenue, Zip 43614–2595; tel. 419/383–4000 **A**1 2 3 5 7 8 10 **F**3 8 11 15 17 18 20 22 24 26 28 29 30 31 32 34 35 36 39 44 45 46 47 48 49 50 51 53 54 55 56 57 58 59 60 61 64 65 68 70 74 75 77 78 79 81 82 84 85 86 87 90 91 92 93 94 96 97 98 99 100 101 102 104 105 107 108 110 111 114 115 116 117 118 119 120 121 123 124 126 129 130 131 132 134 135 138 146 147 148
Primary Contact: Daniel Barbee, Interim Chief Executive Officer
CMO: Linda Speer, M.D., Interim Chief Medical Officer
CIO: William McCreary, Vice President and Chief Information Officer
CHR: Jovita Thomas–Williams, Associate Vice President Human Resources
CNO: Moneca Smith, Chief Nursing Offcer
Web address: www.utoledo.edu
Control: State–Government, nonfederal **Service:** General Medical and Surgical

Staffed Beds: 249 Admissions: 11390 Census: 178 Outpatient Visits: 292139 Births: 0 Total Expense ($000): 299946 Payroll Expense ($000): 117611 Personnel: 2370

TROY—Miami County

✠ △ **UPPER VALLEY MEDICAL CENTER (360174)**, 3130 North County Road 25A, Zip 45373–1309; tel. 937/440–4000, (Nonreporting) **A**1 2 5 7 10 **S** Premier Health, Dayton, OH
Primary Contact: Rebecca Rice, FACHE, Chief Executive Officer
CFO: Tim Snider, Senior Vice President for Finance
CMO: Jennifer Hauler, D.O., Chief Medical Officer
CIO: James Kaiser, Site Director Information Technology
CHR: Kathy Boerger, Director Human Resources
CNO: Terry Fry, R.N., Chief Nursing Officer
Web address: www.uvmc.com
Control: Other not–for–profit (including NFP Corporation) **Service:** General Medical and Surgical

Staffed Beds: 449

UPPER SANDUSKY—Wyandot County

★ **WYANDOT MEMORIAL HOSPITAL (361329)**, 885 North Sandusky Avenue, Zip 43351–1098; tel. 419/294–4991 **A**10 18 **F**3 11 13 15 17 18 28 29 31 34 35 40 45 46 53 57 59 64 65 74 75 76 77 78 79 81 82 85 86 87 89 92 93 97 107 108 110 111 115 116 117 118 119 129 130 132 133 135 144 146 148 **P**6
Primary Contact: Joseph A. D'Ettorre, Chief Executive Officer
COO: Ty Shaull, Chief Operating Officer
CFO: Alan H. Yeates, Vice President Fiscal Services
CHR: Vickie Underwood, Director Human Resources
CNO: Marty Gray, R.N., Director of Nursing
Web address: www.wyandotmemorial.org
Control: Hospital district or authority, Government, nonfederal **Service:** General Medical and Surgical

Staffed Beds: 25 Admissions: 949 Census: 13 Outpatient Visits: 62174 Births: 124 Total Expense ($000): 40258 Payroll Expense ($000): 13872 Personnel: 222

URBANA—Champaign County

★ **MERCY MEMORIAL HOSPITAL (361312)**, 904 Scioto Street, Zip 43078–2200; tel. 937/653–5231 **A**10 18 **F**3 5 8 11 15 28 29 30 34 35 40 45 50 59 63 64 70 75 77 79 81 84 85 93 107 108 110 111 114 119 130 133 135 146 148 **P**6 **S** Mercy Health, Cincinnati, OH
Primary Contact: Paul C. Hiltz, FACHE, President and Market Leader
Web address: www.health–partners.org
Control: Church–operated, Nongovernment, not–for profit **Service:** General Medical and Surgical

Staffed Beds: 25 Admissions: 946 Census: 8 Outpatient Visits: 85886 Births: 0 Total Expense ($000): 21292 Payroll Expense ($000): 7175

VAN WERT—Van Wert County

✠ **VAN WERT COUNTY HOSPITAL (360071)**, 1250 South Washington Street, Zip 45891–2599; tel. 419/238–2390 **A**1 5 10 **F**8 13 15 28 29 34 35 40 48 50 53 54 57 59 62 64 70 76 77 79 81 85 87 89 91 93 107 108 113 119 127 129 130 135 146 **P**7 8
Primary Contact: James W. Pope, FACHE, President and Chief Executive Officer
CFO: Michael T. Holliday, Vice President Fiscal and Administrative Services
CMO: Charles Hoehn, President, Medical Staff
CIO: Brett Taylor, Manager Information
CNO: Shelia Kay Brokenshire, Vice President of Nursing
Web address: www.vanwerthospital.org
Control: Other not–for–profit (including NFP Corporation) **Service:** General Medical and Surgical

Staffed Beds: 69 Admissions: 868 Census: 8 Outpatient Visits: 122276 Births: 138 Total Expense ($000): 37949 Payroll Expense ($000): 10729 Personnel: 276

WARREN—Trumbull County

✠ △ **HILLSIDE REHABILITATION HOSPITAL (363026)**, 8747 Squires Lane N.E., Zip 44484–1649; tel. 330/841–3700, (Nonreporting) **A**1 5 7 10 **S** Community Health Systems, Inc., Franklin, TN
Primary Contact: Linda Case, Administrator
CFO: Anthony Seminaro, Chief Financial Officer
CMO: Joseph Cerimele, D.O., Medical Director
CIO: Barry Fitts, Chief Information Officer
CHR: Jody Roman, Chief Human Resource Officer
CNO: Susan Joy, Chief Nursing Officer
Web address: www.valleycareofohio.net
Control: Corporation, Investor–owned, for–profit **Service:** Rehabilitation

Staffed Beds: 65

✠ **MERCY HEALTH – ST. JOSEPH WARREN HOSPITAL (360161)**, 667 Eastland Avenue S.E., Zip 44484–4531; tel. 330/841–4000 **A**1 2 10 13 **F**3 5 8 11 12 13 14 15 28 29 30 31 34 35 37 40 41 42 43 45 46 49 50 51 54 58 59 64 66 67 68 70 74 75 76 77 78 79 81 82 84 85 87 89 92 93 102 107 108 110 111 114 115 116 117 118 119 120 121 123 126 129 130 135 144 146 147 148 **S** Mercy Health, Cincinnati, OH
Primary Contact: Kathy Cook, FACHE, MSN, President
COO: Donald E. Koenig, Jr., Chief Operating Officer
CFO: Matthew Love, Chief Financial Officer
CMO: Nicholas Kreatsoulas, Vice President Medical Affairs
Web address: www.hmpartners.org
Control: Church–operated, Nongovernment, not–for profit **Service:** General Medical and Surgical

Staffed Beds: 141 Admissions: 8036 Census: 94 Outpatient Visits: 191509 Births: 833 Total Expense ($000): 143288 Payroll Expense ($000): 41824 Personnel: 623

Many Facility Codes have changed. Please refer to the AHA Guide Code Chart.
© 2016 AHA Guide

✠ **TRUMBULL MEMORIAL HOSPITAL (360055)**, 1350 East Market Street, Zip 44483–6628; tel. 330/841–9011, (Nonreporting) **A**1 2 5 10 **S** Community Health Systems, Inc., Franklin, TN
Primary Contact: John Walsh, Chief Executive Officer
COO: Jay De Los Reyes, Chief Operating Officer
CMO: Thomas L. James, M.D., Chief Medical Officer
CIO: Barry Fitts, Chief Information Officer
CHR: Robert Sincich, Vice President Human Resources
CNO: Melissa Bennett, Chief Nursing Officer
Web address: www.vchs.net
Control: Corporation, Investor–owned, for–profit **Service:** General Medical and Surgical

Staffed Beds: 292

WARRENSVILLE HEIGHTS—Cuyahoga County

✠ **REGENCY HOSPITAL CLEVELAND EAST (362029)**, 4200 Interchange Corporate Center Road, Zip 44128–5631; tel. 216/910–3800, (Includes REGENCY HOSPITAL OF CLEVELAND – WEST, 6990 Engle Road, Middleburg Heights, Zip 44130–3420; tel. 440/202–4200; Timothy Rolsen, Chief Executive Officer), (Nonreporting) **A**1 10 **S** Select Medical Corporation, Mechanicsburg, PA
Primary Contact: Thomas Knoske, Chief Executive Officer
Web address: www.regencyhospital.com/
Control: Corporation, Investor–owned, for–profit **Service:** Long–Term Acute Care hospital

Staffed Beds: 132

✠ **SOUTH POINTE HOSPITAL (360144)**, 20000 Harvard Road, Zip 44122–6805; tel. 216/491–6000 **A**1 2 10 13 **F**15 18 28 29 30 31 34 35 36 38 39 40 42 44 50 51 54 55 56 57 58 59 60 61 64 65 66 68 70 74 75 77 78 79 81 82 84 85 86 87 92 93 97 100 102 107 108 110 111 114 117 119 130 131 132 135 143 144 146 148 **S** Cleveland Clinic Health System, Cleveland, OH
Primary Contact: Robert S. Juhasz, D.O., President
COO: Andrea Jacobs, Chief Operating Officer
CFO: Lindsay Bird, Director Finance
CMO: Arun Gupta, M.D., Vice President Medical Affairs
CIO: Ralph A. Cagna, Director Information Technology
CHR: Doris A. Zajec, Director Human Resources
Web address: www.southpointehospital.org
Control: Other not–for–profit (including NFP Corporation) **Service:** General Medical and Surgical

Staffed Beds: 175 Admissions: 7046 Census: 93 Outpatient Visits: 118061 Births: 0 Total Expense ($000): 120869 Payroll Expense ($000): 48680 Personnel: 803

WASHINGTON COURT HOUSE—Fayette County

✠ **FAYETTE COUNTY MEMORIAL HOSPITAL (361331)**, 1430 Columbus Avenue, Zip 43160–1791; tel. 740/335–1210, (Nonreporting) **A**1 10 18
Primary Contact: Jane Bissel, Interim Chief Executive Officer
COO: Lenora Fitton, D.O., Chief of Staff
CFO: Jane Bissel, Chief Financial Officer
CIO: Bruce Denen, Manager Data Processing
CHR: Earlene Christensen, Director Human Resources
CNO: Beverly Hughes, R.N., Vice President Nursing
Web address: www.fcmh.org
Control: County–Government, nonfederal **Service:** General Medical and Surgical

Staffed Beds: 25

WAUSEON—Fulton County

✠ **FULTON COUNTY HEALTH CENTER (361333)**, 725 South Shoop Avenue, Zip 43567–1701; tel. 419/335–2015, (Total facility includes 71 beds in nursing home–type unit) **A**1 2 5 10 18 **F**3 8 11 12 13 15 18 26 28 29 31 34 40 53 57 59 67 69 70 75 76 77 78 79 81 87 89 93 98 101 102 103 104 105 107 108 111 115 118 119 128 129 130 131 132 135 146 148
Primary Contact: Patti Finn, Chief Executive Officer
COO: Patti Finn, Chief Executive Officer
CFO: Jenee Seibert, Director Finance
CIO: Larry Hefflinger, Director Information Systems
CHR: Kristy Snyder, Director Human Resources
CNO: Tiffany Siegel, Director of Nursing
Web address: www.fultoncountyhealthcenter.org
Control: Other not–for–profit (including NFP Corporation) **Service:** General Medical and Surgical

Staffed Beds: 106 Admissions: 1599 Census: 80 Outpatient Visits: 186920 Births: 228 Total Expense ($000): 62251 Payroll Expense ($000): 23026 Personnel: 666

WAVERLY—Pike County

ADENA PIKE MEDICAL CENTER (361334), 100 Dawn Lane, Zip 45690–9138; tel. 740/947–2186 **A**10 18 **F**3 18 28 29 30 34 35 40 41 45 50 54 57 59 79 81 93 107 108 114 118 119 130 131 133 135 146 **P**6 **S** Adena Health System, Chillicothe, OH
Primary Contact: David M. Zanni, Associate Administrator
COO: Tina Perko, Vice President Operations
CFO: Sharon Novak, CPA, Vice President Finance
CHR: Berna Brock, Vice President Human Resources
Web address: www.pikecommunityhospital.org
Control: Other not–for–profit (including NFP Corporation) **Service:** General Medical and Surgical

Staffed Beds: 24 Admissions: 526 Census: 7 Outpatient Visits: 35507 Births: 0 Total Expense ($000): 17814 Payroll Expense ($000): 6995 Personnel: 131

WEST CHESTER—Butler County

☐ **BECKETT SPRINGS (364051)**, 8614 Shepherd Farm Drive, Zip 45069; tel. 513/942–9500, (Nonreporting) **A**1 10
Primary Contact: Phil Sheridan, Chief Executive Officer
Web address: www.springstone.com/hospitals.stmhl
Control: Corporation, Investor–owned, for–profit **Service:** Psychiatric

Staffed Beds: 48

✠ **WEST CHESTER HOSPITAL (360354)**, 7700 University Drive, Zip 45069–2505; tel. 513/298–3000, (Includes WEST CHESTER HOSPITAL SURGICAL CENTER, 7750 University Court, Zip 45069; tel. 513/475–8300; Tom G. Daskalakis, Chief Administrative Officer) **A**1 3 10 **F**3 9 12 13 15 18 20 22 26 29 30 31 34 35 37 38 40 41 43 44 45 46 47 48 49 50 51 54 57 58 59 60 61 63 64 68 70 71 73 74 75 76 77 78 79 80 81 82 84 85 86 87 91 92 100 107 108 110 111 114 115 116 117 119 126 129 130 131 132 135 141 145 146 147 148 **P**6 **S** UC Health, Cincinnati, OH
Primary Contact: Tom G. Daskalakis, Chief Administrative Officer
CFO: Karen Shadowens, Director Finance and Chief Financial Officer
CIO: Jay Brown, Senior Vice President, Chief Information Officer
CHR: Jack Talbot, Director, Human Resources
CNO: Patrick Baker, R.N., Vice President, Chief Nursing Officer
Web address: www.uchealth.com/westchesterhospital
Control: Other not–for–profit (including NFP Corporation) **Service:** General Medical and Surgical

Staffed Beds: 182 Admissions: 8264 Census: 89 Outpatient Visits: 197272 Births: 59 Total Expense ($000): 177179 Payroll Expense ($000): 52119 Personnel: 927

WESTERVILLE—Franklin County

✠ **MOUNT CARMEL ST. ANN'S (360012)**, 500 South Cleveland Avenue, Zip 43081–8998; tel. 614/898–4000 **A**1 2 3 5 10 **F**3 11 13 15 18 20 22 24 26 28 29 30 31 34 35 37 40 44 45 47 48 49 50 51 54 55 57 58 59 61 63 64 65 66 68 70 74 75 76 77 78 79 81 83 84 85 86 87 91 93 97 100 101 102 107 108 109 110 111 114 115 116 118 119 120 121 123 124 126 130 131 132 145 146 147 148 **P**6 8 **S** Trinity Health, Livonia, MI
Primary Contact: Roger Spoelman, Interim President and Chief Executive Officer
Web address: www.mountcarmelhealth.com
Control: Church–operated, Nongovernment, not–for profit **Service:** General Medical and Surgical

Staffed Beds: 281 Admissions: 21101 Census: 174 Outpatient Visits: 175615 Births: 4409 Total Expense ($000): 263977 Payroll Expense ($000): 93289 Personnel: 1518

WESTLAKE—Cuyahoga County

✠ **ST. JOHN MEDICAL CENTER (360123)**, 29000 Center Ridge Road, Zip 44145–5293; tel. 440/835–8000 **A**1 2 3 10 13 **F**3 8 13 15 17 18 20 22 24 26 28 29 30 31 34 35 39 40 43 44 45 46 47 49 50 51 54 56 57 59 64 65 68 70 71 74 75 76 78 79 80 81 82 84 85 86 87 89 92 93 100 107 108 110 114 115 119 130 132 143 144 146 147 148 **P**4 **S** University Hospitals, Cleveland, OH
Primary Contact: Robert G. David, President
CFO: Allen R. Tracy, Senior Vice President and Chief Financial Officer
CMO: Michael Dobrovich, M.D., Chief Medical Officer
CIO: James H. Carroll, Chief Information Officer
CHR: Gary Lazroff, Vice President Human Resources
Web address: www.sjws.net
Control: Other not–for–profit (including NFP Corporation) **Service:** General Medical and Surgical

Staffed Beds: 191 Admissions: 9392 Census: 93 Outpatient Visits: 164847 Births: 790 Total Expense ($000): 146246 Payroll Expense ($000): 58873 Personnel: 975

ST. JOHN WEST SHORE HOSPITAL See St. John Medical Center

Hospital, Medicare Provider Number, Address, Telephone, Approval, Facility, and Physician Codes, Health Care System

★ American Hospital Association (AHA) membership
☐ The Joint Commission accreditation
○ Healthcare Facilities Accreditation Program
◇ DNV Healthcare Inc. accreditation
⇑ Center for Improvement in Healthcare Quality Accreditation
△ Commission on Accreditation of Rehabilitation Facilities (CARF) accreditation

OH

WILLARD—Huron County

⊠ **MERCY HEALTH – WILLARD HOSPITAL (361310)**, 1100 Neal Zick Road, Zip 44890–9287; tel. 419/964–5000 **A**1 10 18 **F**3 5 7 15 18 28 29 30 31 34 35 40 46 57 59 68 70 74 75 77 78 79 81 84 85 87 89 93 107 111 114 119 129 130 131 132 133 135 143 145 146 147 **S** Mercy Health, Cincinnati, OH
Primary Contact: B. Lynn Detterman, President and Chief Executive Officer
CMO: Christopher Bohach, DPM, Chief of Staff
CHR: Diana Olson, Chief Human Resources Officer
CNO: Pamela Napier, MSN, Chief Nursing Officer
Web address: www.mercyweb.org
Control: Church–operated, Nongovernment, not–for profit **Service:** General Medical and Surgical

Staffed Beds: 20 **Admissions:** 609 **Census:** 7 **Outpatient Visits:** 38362 **Births:** 0 **Total Expense ($000):** 25134 **Payroll Expense ($000):** 7051 **Personnel:** 152

WILLOUGHBY—Lake County

☐ **WINDSOR–LAURELWOOD CENTER FOR BEHAVIORAL MEDICINE (364029)**, 35900 Euclid Avenue, Zip 44094–4648; tel. 440/953–3000 **A**1 10 **F**4 5 64 98 99 100 101 103 104 105 130 132 143 **P**5 6 **S** Universal Health Services, Inc., King of Prussia, PA
Primary Contact: Ric McAllister, Chief Executive Officer
COO: Brenda Bailey, Assistant Administrator
CFO: Robin Stough, Chief Financial Officer
CMO: Leonard Barley, M.D., Chief Medical Officer
CIO: Cory Wheatcraft, Information Technology and Purchasing Officer
CHR: Pam Connell, Manager Human Resources
CNO: Debra Schaefer, Chief Nursing Officer
Web address: www.windsorlaurelwood.com
Control: Corporation, Investor–owned, for–profit **Service:** Psychiatric

Staffed Beds: 159 **Admissions:** 5125 **Census:** 130 **Outpatient Visits:** 11687 **Births:** 0 **Total Expense ($000):** 32031 **Payroll Expense ($000):** 12613 **Personnel:** 228

WILMINGTON—Clinton County

☐ **CLINTON MEMORIAL HOSPITAL (360175)**, 610 West Main Street, Zip 45177–2125; tel. 937/382–6611 **A**1 2 3 5 10 **F**3 13 15 18 20 29 30 31 34 40 41 44 45 50 51 57 59 62 64 70 74 75 76 78 79 81 85 87 93 96 107 108 110 111 114 115 119 120 121 130 146 148 **P**6 **S** RCCH HealthCare Partners, Brentwood, TN
Primary Contact: Gregory A. Nielsen, FACHE, Chief Executive Officer
CFO: Bradley Boggus, Chief Financial Officer
CIO: Ray Doherty, Director Information Technology
CHR: Jan Blair, Director Human Resources
CNO: Sheila Martin, Chief Nursing Officer
Web address: www.cmhregional.com
Control: Corporation, Investor–owned, for–profit **Service:** General Medical and Surgical

Staffed Beds: 119 **Admissions:** 2387 **Census:** 21 **Outpatient Visits:** 372611 **Births:** 542 **Total Expense ($000):** 65995 **Payroll Expense ($000):** 23262 **Personnel:** 564

WOOSTER—Wayne County

☐ △ **WOOSTER COMMUNITY HOSPITAL (360036)**, 1761 Beall Avenue, Zip 44691–2342; tel. 330/263–8100, (Nonreporting) **A**1 2 5 7 10 19 **S** QHR, Brentwood, TN
Primary Contact: William E. Sheron, Chief Executive Officer
Web address: www.woosterhospital.org
Control: City–Government, nonfederal **Service:** General Medical and Surgical

Staffed Beds: 150

WRIGHT–PATTERSON AFB—Greene County

⊠ **WRIGHT PATTERSON MEDICAL CENTER**, 4881 Sugar Maple Drive, Zip 45433–5529; tel. 937/257–9144, (Nonreporting) **A**1 2 3 5 **S** Department of the Air Force, Washington, DC
Primary Contact: Colonel Brent J. Erickson, Administrator
COO: Colonel Brent J. Erickson, Administrator
CFO: Major Kelly Lesnick, Resource Manager Flight Commander
CMO: Gregory Sweitzer, Chief Medical Officer
CIO: John Beighle, Flight Chief Medical Information Systems
CHR: Hubert Chatman, Chief Civilian Personnel
CNO: Colonel Daniel Gerke, Chief Nursing Officer
Web address: www.wpafb.af.mil/units/wpmc/
Control: Air Force, Government, federal **Service:** General Medical and Surgical

Staffed Beds: 52

XENIA—Greene County

★ ○ **GREENE MEMORIAL HOSPITAL (360026)**, 1141 North Monroe Drive, Zip 45385–1600; tel. 937/352–2000 **A**2 3 5 10 11 **F**3 11 15 18 28 29 30 31 34 35 38 39 40 43 44 45 46 48 50 51 53 54 56 57 59 61 64 68 70 74 75 77 78 79 81 82 85 86 87 91 93 96 102 107 108 110 111 114 118 119 127 129 130 132 135 146 148 **S** Kettering Health Network, Dayton, OH
Primary Contact: Rick A. Dodds, President
CFO: Ron D. Connovich, Chief Financial Officer
CMO: David Small, M.D., Chief Medical Officer
CIO: Andy Lehman, Senior Vice President Technology & Analytics
CHR: Jeff Jones, Director Human Resources
CNO: Brenda Kuhn, Ph.D., Chief Nursing Officer
Web address: www.ketteringhealth.org/greene
Control: Church–operated, Nongovernment, not–for profit **Service:** General Medical and Surgical

Staffed Beds: 49 **Admissions:** 2134 **Census:** 21 **Outpatient Visits:** 96302 **Births:** 0 **Total Expense ($000):** 61172 **Payroll Expense ($000):** 25852 **Personnel:** 332

YOUNGSTOWN—Trumbull County

☐ **BELMONT PINES HOSPITAL (364038)**, 615 Churchill–Hubbard Road, Zip 44505–1379; tel. 330/759–2700, (Nonreporting) **A**1 10 **S** Universal Health Services, Inc., King of Prussia, PA
Primary Contact: Lisa Cocca, Chief Executive Officer
CFO: Robin Stough, Chief Financial Officer
CMO: Phillip Maiden, M.D., Medical Director
Web address: www.belmontpines.com
Control: Corporation, Investor–owned, for–profit **Service:** Psychiatric

Staffed Beds: 46

⊠ △ **MERCY HEALTH – ST. ELIZABETH YOUNGSTOWN HOSPITAL (360064)**, 1044 Belmont Avenue, Zip 44504–1096, Mailing Address: P.O. Box 1790, Zip 44501–1790; tel. 330/746–7211 **A**1 2 3 5 7 10 **F**1 3 7 8 11 14 15 17 18 20 22 24 26 28 29 30 31 34 35 37 39 40 42 43 44 45 46 49 50 51 53 54 56 57 58 59 60 61 64 66 68 70 71 74 75 77 78 79 81 82 84 85 86 87 88 89 90 92 93 96 97 98 100 101 102 103 104 105 107 110 111 114 115 116 117 118 119 120 121 123 126 129 130 131 132 135 143 146 147 148 **S** Mercy Health, Cincinnati, OH
Primary Contact: Donald E. Kline, President and Chief Executive Officer
COO: Donald E. Koenig, Jr., Executive Vice President and Regional Chief Operating Officer, President, St. Elizabeth Youngstown Hospital
CFO: Matthew Love, Senior Vice President Finance
CMO: Nicholas Kreatsoulas, Senior Vice President and Chief Medical Officer and Chief Quality Officer
CIO: Maureen Kordupel, Director Relationship Manager
CHR: Molly Seals, System Vice President, HR Program Delivery
CNO: Catherine L. Tolbert, FACHE, Chief Nursing Officer
Web address: www.mercy.com
Control: Church–operated, Nongovernment, not–for profit **Service:** General Medical and Surgical

Staffed Beds: 379 **Admissions:** 16911 **Census:** 244 **Outpatient Visits:** 284465 **Births:** 0 **Total Expense ($000):** 308718 **Payroll Expense ($000):** 93983 **Personnel:** 1752

⊠ **NORTHSIDE MEDICAL CENTER (360141)**, 500 Gypsy Lane, Zip 44504–1315; tel. 330/884–1000, (Includes NORTHSIDE MEDICAL CENTER, 500 Gypsy Lane, Zip 44501–0240; tel. 330/747–1444), (Nonreporting) **A**1 2 3 5 10 **S** Community Health Systems, Inc., Franklin, TN
Primary Contact: K. Robert Bauer, Jr., Interim Chief Executive Officer
CMO: Jay Osborne, M.D., Senior Vice President Medical Affairs
CHR: Lavern H. Carrera, Senior Vice President Human Resources
Web address: www.northsidemedicalcenter.net
Control: Corporation, Investor–owned, for–profit **Service:** General Medical and Surgical

Staffed Beds: 373

NORTHSIDE MEDICAL CENTER See Northside Medical Center

⊠ **SELECT SPECIALTY HOSPITAL–YOUNGSTOWN (262024)**, 1044 Belmont Avenue, Zip 44504–1006; tel. 330/480–2349, (Includes SELECT SPECIALTY HOSPITAL–YOUNGSTOWN, BOARDMAN CAMPUS, 667 Eastland Avenue S.E., Warren, Zip 44484–4503; tel. 330/729–1700), (Nonreporting) **A**1 10 **S** Select Medical Corporation, Mechanicsburg, PA
Primary Contact: Jodi Costello, Chief Executive Officer
Web address: www.selectspecialtyhospitals.com/company/locations/youngstown.aspx
Control: Corporation, Investor–owned, for–profit **Service:** Long–Term Acute Care hospital

Staffed Beds: 51

☐ **SURGICAL HOSPITAL AT SOUTHWOODS (360352)**, 7630 Southern Boulevard, Zip 44512–5633; tel. 330/729–8000, (Nonreporting) **A**1 3 10
Primary Contact: Ed Muransky, Owner
Web address: www.surgeryatsouthwoods.com/
Control: Individual, Investor–owned, for–profit **Service:** Surgical

Staffed Beds: 12

Many Facility Codes have changed. Please refer to the AHA Guide Code Chart. © 2016 AHA Guide

ZANESVILLE—Muskingum County

★ ○ **GENESIS HEALTHCARE SYSTEM (360039)**, 2951 Maple Avenue,
Zip 43701–1406; tel. 740/454–5000, (Includes BETHESDA HOSPITAL, 2951
Maple Avenue, Zip 43701–1465; tel. 614/454–4000; GOOD SAMARITAN
MEDICAL AND REHABILITATION CENTER, 800 Forest Avenue, Zip 43701–2881;
tel. 614/454–5000) **A**2 5 10 11 **F**3 5 8 9 11 13 15 17 18 20 22 24 26 28 29
30 31 32 34 35 40 43 44 45 46 47 48 50 51 54 57 58 59 60 63 64 65 68
70 73 74 75 76 77 78 79 81 82 84 85 86 87 89 91 92 93 94 96 98 99 100
101 102 103 104 105 107 108 109 110 111 114 115 116 117 118 119 120
121 123 124 126 129 130 131 132 135 144 146 147 148 **P**6 8 **S** Franciscan
Sisters of Christian Charity Sponsored Ministries, Inc., Manitowoc, WI
Primary Contact: Matthew J. Perry, President and Chief Executive Officer
COO: Richard S. Helsper, Chief Operating Officer
CFO: Paul Masterson, Chief Financial Officer
CMO: Dan Scheerer, M.D., Chief Medical Officer
CIO: Edmund J. Romito, Chief Information Officer
CHR: Dianna LeVeck, Chief Human Resources Officer
CNO: Abby Nguyen, R.N., Chief Nursing Officer
Web address: www.genesishcs.org
Control: Other not–for–profit (including NFP Corporation) **Service:** General
Medical and Surgical

Staffed Beds: 321 **Admissions:** 14514 **Census:** 160 **Outpatient Visits:**
443859 **Births:** 1558 **Total Expense ($000):** 331592 **Payroll Expense
($000):** 121066 **Personnel:** 2581

OKLAHOMA

ADA—Pontotoc County

CHICKASAW NATION MEDICAL CENTER (370180), 1921 Stonecipher Drive, Zip 74820–3439; tel. 580/436–3980 **A**1 10 13 **F**3 5 7 8 13 15 18 29 30 34 38 39 40 43 45 50 53 54 57 58 59 60 61 64 65 66 68 69 70 75 76 79 81 82 85 86 87 89 91 92 93 97 99 100 104 107 110 111 115 119 127 130 132 135 143 144 146 147 148
Primary Contact: Judy Goforth Parker, Ph.D., Secretary of Health
CFO: Marty Wafford, Executive Officer of Support and Programs
CMO: Richard McClain, M.D., Chief Medical Officer
CIO: Desiree Traylor, Chief Information Officer
CHR: Jalinda Kelley, Secretary of Interior Services
CNO: Jerod Waters, Chief Nursing Officer
Web address: www.chickasaw.net
Control: PHS, Indian Service, Government, federal **Service:** General Medical and Surgical

Staffed Beds: **72** Admissions: **4295** Census: **34** Outpatient Visits: **577171** Births: **834** Total Expense ($000): **191482** Payroll Expense ($000): **80020** Personnel: **537**

MERCY HOSPITAL ADA (370020), 430 North Monte Vista, Zip 74820–4610; tel. 580/332–2323 **A**1 2 3 10 **F**3 7 11 13 15 18 29 30 31 34 35 40 43 44 45 49 50 59 64 68 69 70 72 75 76 77 78 79 81 82 85 86 87 89 90 93 98 100 101 102 103 107 108 110 111 114 116 117 119 120 121 124 127 129 130 131 132 133 146 148 **P**6 **S** Mercy Health, Chesterfield, MO
Primary Contact: Lori Wightman, R.N., MSN, FACHE, Chief Executive Officer
COO: Daniel J. Coats, Vice President Operations
CFO: Mary Garber, Vice President Finance
CMO: Imtiaz Ahmed, Chief of Staff
CHR: Katrina Godfrey, Director Human Resources
CNO: Karen Sweeney, MSN, Vice President, Chief Nursing Officer
Web address: www.mercy.net/ada
Control: Church–operated, Nongovernment, not–for profit **Service:** General Medical and Surgical

Staffed Beds: **156** Admissions: **3422** Census: **52** Outpatient Visits: **90834** Births: **530** Total Expense ($000): **74041** Payroll Expense ($000): **31762** Personnel: **658**

ROLLING HILLS HOSPITAL (374016), 1000 Rolling Hills Lane, Zip 74820–9415; tel. 580/436–3600 **A**1 10 **F**98 103 104 **S** Acadia Healthcare Company, Inc., Franklin, TN
Primary Contact: Anthony Guild, Chief Executive Officer
CMO: Robert Morton, M.D., Medical Director
CIO: Sherry Barnes, Director Health Information and Quality Management
CHR: Timothy Blackwell, Manager Human Resources
Web address: www.rollinghillshospital.com
Control: Corporation, Investor–owned, for–profit **Service:** Psychiatric

Staffed Beds: **60** Admissions: **1425** Census: **76** Outpatient Visits: **0** Births: **0** Total Expense ($000): **12766** Payroll Expense ($000): **7119**

ALTUS—Jackson County

JACKSON COUNTY MEMORIAL HOSPITAL (370022), 1200 East Pecan Street, Zip 73521–6192, Mailing Address: P.O. Box 8190, Zip 73522–8190; tel. 580/379–5000 **A**1 3 10 **F**3 10 11 13 15 29 30 34 35 40 43 45 49 56 57 59 62 63 64 65 70 75 76 77 79 81 85 86 87 93 100 101 103 104 107 110 111 114 119 129 130 132 133 135 145 146 147 148 **P**6
Primary Contact: Steve L. Hartgraves, President and Chief Executive Officer
COO: Jim King, Executive Vice President and Chief Operating Officer
CFO: Nancy Davidson, Senior Vice President and Chief Financial Officer
CMO: Gregory D. Pickett, M.D., Chief of Staff
CIO: Dena Daniel, Director Information Systems
CHR: Richard Pope, Vice President Human Resources
CNO: Kay Bolding, R.N., Vice President Patient Care Services and Chief Nursing Officer
Web address: www.jcmh.com
Control: Hospital district or authority, Government, nonfederal **Service:** General Medical and Surgical

Staffed Beds: **69** Admissions: **2782** Census: **28** Outpatient Visits: **143088** Births: **442** Total Expense ($000): **64496** Payroll Expense ($000): **31646** Personnel: **637**

ALVA—Woods County

SHARE MEDICAL CENTER (370080), 800 Share Drive, Zip 73717–3618, Mailing Address: P.O. Box 727, Zip 73717–0727; tel. 580/327–2800, (Total facility includes 65 beds in nursing home–type unit) **A**10 20 **F**3 15 29 30 34 40 45 57 59 63 64 65 67 69 81 85 87 93 97 100 104 107 110 119 129 130 133 146 148
Primary Contact: Kandice K. Allen, R.N., Chief Executive Officer
CFO: Kevin O'Brien, Chief Financial Officer
CMO: Elizabeth Kinzic, M.D., Chief of Staff
CIO: Alan Vaughan, Director Information Technology
CHR: Mary Herold, Director Human Resources
CNO: Regina Wilson, R.N., Director of Nursing
Web address: www.smcok.com
Control: Hospital district or authority, Government, nonfederal **Service:** General Medical and Surgical

Staffed Beds: **90** Admissions: **314** Census: **53** Outpatient Visits: **23289** Births: **0** Total Expense ($000): **13019** Payroll Expense ($000): **5511** Personnel: **138**

ANADARKO—Caddo County

PHYSICIANS' HOSPITAL IN ANADARKO (371314), 1002 Central Boulevard East, Zip 73005–4496; tel. 405/247–2551 **A**10 18 **F**3 8 11 29 30 35 40 41 45 47 57 64 65 77 81 82 85 89 90 93 107 114 128 130 133 146 **S** Southern Plains Medical Group, Oklahoma City, OK
Primary Contact: Travis A. Villani, FACHE, Chief Executive Officer and Administrator
Web address: www.anadarkohospital.com
Control: Other not–for–profit (including NFP Corporation) **Service:** General Medical and Surgical

Staffed Beds: **25** Admissions: **204** Census: **7** Outpatient Visits: **9305** Births: **1** Total Expense ($000): **28776** Payroll Expense ($000): **5493** Personnel: **66**

ANTLERS—Pushmataha County

PUSHMATAHA HOSPITAL & HOME HEALTH (370083), 510 East Main Street, Zip 74523–3262, Mailing Address: P.O. Box 518, Zip 74523–0518; tel. 580/298–3341, (Nonreporting) **A**10
Primary Contact: Paul Reano, Chief Executive Officer
COO: Nick Rowland, Chief Operating Officer
CFO: Rory Ward, Chief Financial Officer
CMO: G. Wayne Flatt, D.O., Chief Medical Director
CHR: Paula Schalski, Director Human Resources
CNO: Marla Barnes, Director of Nursing
Web address: www.pushhospital.com
Control: State–Government, nonfederal **Service:** General Medical and Surgical

Staffed Beds: **25**

ARDMORE—Carter County

MERCY HOSPITAL ARDMORE (370047), 1011 14th Avenue N.W., Zip 73401–1828; tel. 580/223–5400 **A**1 10 **F**3 11 13 15 18 20 22 28 29 30 31 34 35 40 43 44 45 47 49 50 53 57 59 62 64 68 70 74 75 76 78 79 81 82 83 84 85 86 87 89 90 93 98 103 107 108 110 111 114 117 118 119 120 121 123 126 129 130 146 148 **P**6 **S** Mercy Health, Chesterfield, MO
Primary Contact: Daryle Voss, FACHE, President
CFO: Karen Hendren, Vice President of Finance and Operations
CMO: Pam Kimbrough, M.D., Vice President Medical Affairs
CHR: Melinda Sharum, Director of Human Resources
CNO: Debra Pender, R.N., Vice President of Nursing
Web address: www.mercyok.net
Control: Church–operated, Nongovernment, not–for profit **Service:** General Medical and Surgical

Staffed Beds: **187** Admissions: **7039** Census: **83** Outpatient Visits: **112594** Births: **911** Total Expense ($000): **124426** Payroll Expense ($000): **40599** Personnel: **866**

Many Facility Codes have changed. Please refer to the AHA Guide Code Chart. © 2016 AHA Guide

ATOKA—Atoka County

ATOKA COUNTY MEDICAL CENTER (371300), 1590 West Liberty Road,
Zip 74525–1621, Mailing Address: PO Box 1107, Zip 74525–1621;
tel. 580/889–3333, (Nonreporting) **A**10 18
Primary Contact: Traci Walker, Chief Executive Officer
COO: Traci Walker, Chief Operating Officer
CFO: Rory Ward, Chief Financial Officer
CMO: Ted Rowland, Chief of Medical Staff
CIO: Owetha Wilson, Chief Information Officer
CHR: Paula Schalski, Director Human Resources
CNO: Ronda Thomas, Chief Nursing Officer
Web address: www.atokamedicalcenter.org
Control: Hospital district or authority, Government, nonfederal **Service:** General
Medical and Surgical

Staffed Beds: 25

BARTLESVILLE—Washington County

★ ◇ **JANE PHILLIPS MEMORIAL MEDICAL CENTER (370018)**, 3500 East
Frank Phillips Boulevard, Zip 74006–2411; tel. 918/333–7200 **A**3 5 10 21 **F**3 8
11 13 15 17 18 20 22 24 28 29 30 31 34 35 40 43 46 49 50 51 53 57 58
59 60 61 62 64 68 70 74 75 76 77 78 79 81 82 84 85 86 87 90 92 93 96
98 102 103 107 111 114 115 116 117 118 119 121 123 127 129 130 131
135 143 145 146 147 148 **P**4 **S** Ascension Health, Saint Louis, MO
Primary Contact: Mike Moore, President and Chief Operating Officer
CFO: James Brasel, Chief Financial Officer
CMO: Paul McQuillen, M.D., Chief Medical Officer
CIO: Rob Poole, Director
CHR: Jennifer Workman, Director Human Resources
CNO: Angie Bidleman, Chief Nursing Officer
Web address: www.jpmc.org
Control: Church–operated, Nongovernment, not–for profit **Service:** General
Medical and Surgical

Staffed Beds: 119 **Admissions:** 4704 **Census:** 49 **Outpatient Visits:** 82373
Births: 685 **Total Expense ($000):** 98924 **Payroll Expense ($000):** 37146
Personnel: 800

BEAVER—Beaver County

BEAVER COUNTY MEMORIAL HOSPITAL (371322), 212 East Eighth Street,
Zip 73932, Mailing Address: P.O. Box 640, Zip 73932–0640;
tel. 580/625–4551, (Nonreporting) **A**10 18
Primary Contact: Alissa Schlessman, Administrator
CMO: Gary Mathews, M.D., Medical Doctor
CHR: Karla Leisher, Business Office Manager
CNO: Stacey Perry, Director of Nursing
Web address: www.beavercountyhospitalauthority.com
Control: Hospital district or authority, Government, nonfederal **Service:** General
Medical and Surgical

Staffed Beds: 24

BETHANY—Oklahoma County

△ **THE CHILDREN'S CENTER REHABILITATION HOSPITAL (373302)**, 6800
N.W. 39th Expressway, Zip 73008–2513; tel. 405/789–6711 **A**5 7 10 **F**1 29 30
35 39 53 58 59 68 74 75 79 84 87 90 91 93 96 107 130 146 148 **P**6
Primary Contact: Albert Gray, Chief Executive Officer
Web address: www.tccokc.org
Control: Other not–for–profit (including NFP Corporation) **Service:** Children's
general

Staffed Beds: 120 **Admissions:** 138 **Census:** 98 **Outpatient Visits:** 9279
Births: 0 **Total Expense ($000):** 32795 **Payroll Expense ($000):** 19799
Personnel: 461

BLACKWELL—Kay County

⊠ **ALLIANCEHEALTH BLACKWELL (370030)**, 710 South 13th Street,
Zip 74631–3700; tel. 580/363–2311 **A**1 10 **F**3 15 29 30 34 40 57 59 64 65
79 81 93 107 108 111 119 128 129 133 146 **P**5 6 **S** Community Health
Systems, Inc., Franklin, TN
Primary Contact: Andrew Wachtel, Chief Executive Officer
CFO: Sheryl Schmidtberger, Chief Financial Officer
CMO: Samuel Hague, M.D., Chief of Staff
CHR: Karen Ware, Director Human Resources
Web address: www.integris–health.com
Control: Corporation, Investor–owned, for–profit **Service:** General Medical and
Surgical

Staffed Beds: 49 **Admissions:** 472 **Census:** 5 **Outpatient Visits:** 13425
Total Expense ($000): 7828 **Payroll Expense ($000):** 3142 **Personnel:** 71

BOISE CITY—Cimarron County

CIMARRON MEMORIAL HOSPITAL (371307), 100 South Ellis Street,
Zip 73933, Mailing Address: P.O. Box 1059, Zip 73933–1059;
tel. 580/544–2501, (Nonreporting) **A**10 18
Primary Contact: Tim Beard, Chief Executive Officer
CFO: John Dolan, Chief Financial Officer
CIO: Tim Beard, Director, Information Technology
CNO: Barbara Carter, Chief Nursing Officer
Web address: www.cimarronmemorialhospital.org
Control: County–Government, nonfederal **Service:** General Medical and Surgical

Staffed Beds: 25

BRISTOW—Creek County

BRISTOW MEDICAL CENTER (370041), 700 West 7th Avenue, Suite 6,
Zip 74010–2302; tel. 918/367–2215, (Nonreporting) **A**10
Primary Contact: Jan Winter–Clark, Chief Executive Officer
CFO: Robin Van Vickle, Chief Financial Officer
Web address: www.bristowmedcenter.com
Control: Corporation, Investor–owned, for–profit **Service:** General Medical and
Surgical

Staffed Beds: 30

BROKEN ARROW—Tulsa County

★ **ST. JOHN BROKEN ARROW (370235)**, 1000 West Boise Circle,
Zip 74012–4900; tel. 918/994–8100 **A**10 **F**3 8 11 14 15 18 29 30 34 35 37
40 43 45 50 57 59 64 65 68 74 79 81 84 85 87 93 94 107 108 110 111
114 115 119 130 132 135 143 146 **P**1 5 **S** Ascension Health, Saint Louis, MO
Primary Contact: David L. Phillips, Chief Executive Officer
CFO: Michael R. Nevins, Chief Financial Officer
CMO: Todd Hoffman, M.D., Medical Director
CNO: Dwan Borens, Director of Nursing
Web address: www.stjohnbrokenarrow.com
Control: Church–operated, Nongovernment, not–for profit **Service:** General
Medical and Surgical

Staffed Beds: 44 **Admissions:** 2691 **Census:** 18 **Outpatient Visits:** 89244
Births: 0 **Total Expense ($000):** 54362 **Payroll Expense ($000):** 13155
Personnel: 251

BUFFALO—Harper County

★ **HARPER COUNTY COMMUNITY HOSPITAL (371324)**, Highway 64 North,
Zip 73834, Mailing Address: P.O. Box 60, Zip 73834–0060; tel. 580/735–2555,
(Nonreporting) **A**10 18
Primary Contact: Georganna Buss, Chief Executive Officer
COO: Pam Dodd, Chief Operating Officer
CFO: Lisa Oakley, Chief Financial Officer
CNO: Melissa Madrid, R.N., Chief Nursing Officer
Web address: www.hcchospital.com/
Control: County–Government, nonfederal **Service:** General Medical and Surgical

Staffed Beds: 16

CARNEGIE—Caddo County

CARNEGIE TRI–COUNTY MUNICIPAL HOSPITAL (371334), 102 North
Broadway, Zip 73015, Mailing Address: P.O. Box 97, Zip 73015–0097;
tel. 580/654–1050, (Nonreporting) **A**10 18
Primary Contact: Doris Brown, Chief Executive Officer and Administrator
Web address: www.carnegiehospital.org/
Control: City–Government, nonfederal **Service:** General Medical and Surgical

Staffed Beds: 19

CHEYENNE—Roger Mills County

★ **ROGER MILLS MEMORIAL HOSPITAL (371303)**, 501 South L.L. Males,
Zip 73628, Mailing Address: P.O. Box 219, Zip 73628; tel. 580/497–3336 **A**10
18 **F**3 7 34 40 57 59 64 65 93 107 115 133
Primary Contact: Cynthia Duncan, Chief Executive Officer
Web address: www.rogermillsmemorialhospital.com/
Control: Hospital district or authority, Government, nonfederal **Service:** General
Medical and Surgical

Staffed Beds: 15 **Admissions:** 19 **Census:** 1 **Outpatient Visits:** 3553 **Births:**
0

Hospital, Medicare Provider Number, Address, Telephone, Approval, Facility, and Physician Codes, Health Care System

★ American Hospital Association (AHA) membership
□ The Joint Commission accreditation
○ Healthcare Facilities Accreditation Program
◇ DNV Healthcare Inc. accreditation
⇑ Center for Improvement in Healthcare Quality Accreditation
△ Commission on Accreditation of Rehabilitation Facilities (CARF) accreditation

OK

CHICKASHA—Grady County

★ **GRADY MEMORIAL HOSPITAL (370054)**, 2220 West Iowa Avenue, Zip 73018–2738; tel. 405/224–2300 **A**10 **F**3 8 11 13 15 17 29 30 34 35 40 43 45 57 59 65 66 70 73 76 77 79 81 82 85 87 89 91 93 107 110 111 115 119 127 128 130 131 132 133 144 146 147 **P**6
Primary Contact: Warren K. Spellman, Chief Executive Officer
CFO: Jackie McAdoo, Chief Financial Officer
CMO: Mitch Coppedge, M.D., Chief Medical Officer
CIO: Sylvia Ho, Director Health Information Systems
CHR: Rebel Rutledge, Director Human Resources
CNO: Cathy Groseclose, Vice President Patient Care Services
Web address: www.gradymem.org
Control: Hospital district or authority, Government, nonfederal **Service:** General Medical and Surgical

Staffed Beds: 49 **Admissions:** 1448 **Census:** 14 **Outpatient Visits:** 60801 **Births:** 170 **Total Expense ($000):** 41787 **Payroll Expense ($000):** 21105 **Personnel:** 314

CLAREMORE—Rogers County

☐ **CLAREMORE INDIAN HOSPITAL (370173)**, 101 South Moore Avenue, Zip 74017–5091; tel. 918/342–6200, (Nonreporting) **A**1 10 **S** U. S. Indian Health Service, Rockville, MD
Primary Contact: George Valliere, Chief Executive Officer
CFO: LaLana Spears, Supervisor Accounting
CIO: David Ponder, Information Technology Officer
CHR: Quinn Proctor, Director Human Resources
CNO: Tamara Wampler, Chief Nursing Executive
Web address: www.ihs.gov
Control: PHS, Indian Service, Government, federal **Service:** General Medical and Surgical

Staffed Beds: 44

★ ◇ **HILLCREST HOSPITAL CLAREMORE (370039)**, 1202 North Muskogee Place, Zip 74017–3036; tel. 918/341–2556 **A**10 21 **F**3 6 11 13 15 18 20 22 26 28 29 30 34 35 37 40 45 49 51 59 64 70 74 76 77 79 81 82 85 86 87 93 98 103 107 108 110 111 119 126 129 130 131 133 135 145 146 147 148 **P**6 **S** Ardent Health Services, Nashville, TN
Primary Contact: David Chaussard, Chief Executive Officer
CFO: Brandon Bullard, Chief Financial Officer
CIO: Celeste Rodden, Chief Information Officer
CHR: Pat Goad, Director Human Resources
CNO: Randy Walker, Chief Nursing Officer
Web address: www.hillcrestclaremore.com
Control: Corporation, Investor–owned, for–profit **Service:** General Medical and Surgical

Staffed Beds: 67 **Admissions:** 2963 **Census:** 33 **Outpatient Visits:** 41223 **Births:** 643 **Total Expense ($000):** 44018 **Payroll Expense ($000):** 15991 **Personnel:** 296

CLEVELAND—Pawnee County

★ **CLEVELAND AREA HOSPITAL (371320)**, 1401 West Pawnee Street, Zip 74020–3019; tel. 918/358–2501 **A**10 18 **F**1 15 29 34 35 40 43 55 57 59 64 71 75 77 81 86 87 89 90 91 92 93 97 102 103 107 119 128 130 133 **P**6
Primary Contact: Edred Benton, Chief Executive Officer and Chief Operating Officer
COO: Edred Benton, Chief Executive Officer and Chief Operating Officer
CMO: Jason Sims, M.D., Chief Medical Officer
CHR: Sherry Brown, Director Human Resources
Web address: www.clevelandareahospital.com
Control: Hospital district or authority, Government, nonfederal **Service:** General Medical and Surgical

Staffed Beds: 14 **Admissions:** 147 **Census:** 3 **Outpatient Visits:** 14758 **Births:** 0 **Total Expense ($000):** 11930 **Payroll Expense ($000):** 6083 **Personnel:** 101

CLINTON—Custer County

✠ **ALLIANCEHEALTH CLINTON (370029)**, 100 North 30th Street, Zip 73601–3117, Mailing Address: P.O. Box 1569, Zip 73601–1569; tel. 580/323–2363 **A**1 10 **F**3 11 13 29 30 31 34 35 40 45 50 59 68 70 75 76 77 78 79 81 90 91 93 97 107 108 111 119 129 130 131 133 146 147 148 **P**6 **S** Community Health Systems, Inc., Franklin, TN
Primary Contact: Cameron Lewis, Chief Executive Officer
CFO: Jay Johnson, Chief Financial Officer
CHR: Julie Graumann, Director
CNO: Kimberly Todd, Chief Nursing Officer
Web address: www.alliancehealthclinton.com
Control: Corporation, Investor–owned, for–profit **Service:** General Medical and Surgical

Staffed Beds: 49 **Admissions:** 1168 **Census:** 11 **Outpatient Visits:** 32143 **Births:** 295

COALGATE—Coal County

★ **COAL COUNTY GENERAL HOSPITAL (371319)**, 6 North Covington Street, Zip 74538–2002, Mailing Address: P.O. Box 326, Zip 74538–0326; tel. 580/927–2327 **A**10 18 **F**40 41 57 64 68 107 114 119 133
Primary Contact: Billy Johnson, Chief Executive Officer
CFO: Diane Downard, Chief Financial Officer
CMO: R.J Helton, D.O., Chief of Staff
CIO: Matt Balliett, Chief Information Officer
CHR: Cyndie Martin, Director
CNO: Farra Ybarra, R.N., Chief Nursing Officer
Web address: www.hillcrest.com
Control: Hospital district or authority, Government, nonfederal **Service:** General Medical and Surgical

Staffed Beds: 20 **Admissions:** 894 **Census:** 10 **Births:** 0 **Total Expense ($000):** 4899 **Payroll Expense ($000):** 2029 **Personnel:** 70

CORDELL—Washita County

★ **CORDELL MEMORIAL HOSPITAL (371325)**, 1220 North Glenn English Street, Zip 73632–2010; tel. 580/832–3339 **A**10 18 **F**40 57 59 107 128 133
Primary Contact: Landon Hise, Chief Executive Officer
CFO: Sue Kelley, Chief Financial Officer
Control: City–Government, nonfederal **Service:** General Medical and Surgical

Staffed Beds: 14 **Admissions:** 168 **Census:** 2 **Outpatient Visits:** 5594 **Births:** 0

CUSHING—Payne County

★ **HILLCREST HOSPITAL CUSHING (370099)**, 1027 East Cherry Street, Zip 74023–4101, Mailing Address: P.O. Box 1409, Zip 74023–1409; tel. 918/225–2915 **A**10 **F**11 13 15 18 29 30 31 34 35 40 43 44 45 46 50 51 56 57 59 64 65 66 68 70 71 75 81 82 86 87 93 94 97 98 100 101 102 103 106 107 110 111 114 115 119 129 130 131 143 145 146 147 148 **S** Ardent Health Services, Nashville, TN
Primary Contact: Kevin Hawk, Chief Executive Officer
CFO: Joseph Mendoza, Chief Financial Officer
CHR: Bethany Leininger, Manager Human Resource
CNO: Tina Petersen, Chief Nursing Officer
Web address: www.hillcrestcushing.com/
Control: Corporation, Investor–owned, for–profit **Service:** General Medical and Surgical

Staffed Beds: 99 **Admissions:** 1969 **Census:** 23 **Outpatient Visits:** 18993 **Births:** 220 **Total Expense ($000):** 24048 **Payroll Expense ($000):** 9116 **Personnel:** 191

DRUMRIGHT—Creek County

DRUMRIGHT REGIONAL HOSPITAL (371331), 610 West Bypass, Zip 74030–5957; tel. 918/382–2300 **A**10 18 **F**3 29 40 45 56 59 64 65 68 77 81 85 91 92 93 103 107 111 114 119 127 128 129 130 132 133 **P**6 **S** Rural Community Hospitals of America, Kansas City, MO
Primary Contact: William Holland, Chief Executive Officer
CFO: Mark Conrath, Chief Financial Officer
Web address: www.drumrighthospital.com/
Control: Corporation, Investor–owned, for–profit **Service:** General Medical and Surgical

Staffed Beds: 15 **Admissions:** 461 **Census:** 5 **Outpatient Visits:** 12633 **Births:** 0

DUNCAN—Stephens County

✠ **DUNCAN REGIONAL HOSPITAL (370023)**, 1407 North Whisenant Drive, Zip 73533–1650, Mailing Address: P.O. Box 2000, Zip 73534–2000; tel. 580/252–5300, (Total facility includes 16 beds in nursing home–type unit) **A**1 5 10 20 **F**3 11 13 15 18 28 29 30 34 35 40 43 45 50 57 59 62 63 64 70 75 76 77 79 81 85 86 87 89 90 93 96 98 103 104 107 108 110 111 114 115 119 128 129 130 131 132 141 142 143 145 146 147 148
Primary Contact: Jay R. Johnson, FACHE, President and Chief Executive Officer
CFO: Douglas R. Volinski, Vice President and Chief Financial Officer
CIO: Roger Neal, Vice President Operations
CHR: Mark Rhoades, Vice President and Chief Human Resources Officer
CNO: Cindy Rauh, R.N., Vice President and Chief Nursing Officer
Web address: www.duncanregional.com
Control: Other not–for–profit (including NFP Corporation) **Service:** General Medical and Surgical

Staffed Beds: 117 **Admissions:** 4113 **Census:** 54 **Outpatient Visits:** 155241 **Births:** 546 **Total Expense ($000):** 93109 **Payroll Expense ($000):** 42319 **Personnel:** 856

Many Facility Codes have changed. Please refer to the AHA Guide Code Chart. © 2016 AHA Guide

DURANT—Bryan County

⊞ **ALLIANCEHEALTH DURANT (370014)**, 1800 University Boulevard, Zip 74701–3006, Mailing Address: P.O. Box 1207, Zip 74702–1207; tel. 580/924–3080 **A**1 5 10 13 19 **F**3 11 13 15 17 18 20 28 29 39 40 43 45 50 51 59 70 74 75 76 79 80 81 85 86 89 107 108 110 111 115 118 119 126 129 130 135 145 146 147 148 **P**8 **S** Community Health Systems, Inc., Franklin, TN
Primary Contact: Jeffrey S. Tarrant, FACHE, Chief Executive Officer
CFO: Cindy Rios, Chief Financial Officer
CMO: Kevin Gordon, M.D., Chief of Staff
CIO: Katy Stinson, Director Information Services
Web address: www.alliancehealthdurant.com/
Control: Corporation, Investor–owned, for–profit **Service:** General Medical and Surgical

Staffed Beds: 148 **Admissions:** 5548 **Census:** 53 **Outpatient Visits:** 60019 **Births:** 957 **Personnel:** 386

EDMOND—Oklahoma County

☐ **AMG SPECIALTY HOSPITAL–EDMOND (372005)**, 1100 East Ninth Street, Zip 73034–5755; tel. 405/341–8150, (Nonreporting) **A**1 10 **S** AMG Integrated Healthcare Management, Lafayette, LA
Primary Contact: Ricky Higdon, Chief Executive Officer
CFO: Rowena Davidson, Manager Business Office
CMO: Brian Levy, M.D., Medical Director
CHR: Pam Grimes, Director Human Resources
Web address: www.amgedmond.com/
Control: Corporation, Investor–owned, for–profit **Service:** Long–Term Acute Care hospital

Staffed Beds: 37

EDMOND MEDICAL CENTER See OU Medical Center Edmond

⊞ **INTEGRIS HEALTH EDMOND (370236)**, 4801 Integris Parkway, Zip 73034–8864; tel. 405/657–3000 **A**1 10 **F**3 8 11 13 15 18 20 22 29 30 34 35 40 43 45 46 47 49 53 57 59 60 64 68 70 74 76 77 79 81 82 85 87 93 100 102 107 108 110 111 115 119 130 131 132 135 146 147 148 **P**6 7 **S** INTEGRIS Health, Oklahoma City, OK
Primary Contact: Avilla Williams, MS, President
CNO: Angela K. Kamermayer, MS, Chief Nursing Officer
Web address: www.integrisok.com/edmond
Control: Other not–for–profit (including NFP Corporation) **Service:** General Medical and Surgical

Staffed Beds: 40 **Admissions:** 2064 **Census:** 19 **Outpatient Visits:** 29254 **Births:** 537 **Total Expense ($000):** 44141 **Payroll Expense ($000):** 13146 **Personnel:** 188

OU MEDICAL CENTER EDMOND See OU Medical Center, Oklahoma City

★ **SUMMIT MEDICAL CENTER (370225)**, 1800 South Renaissance Boulevard, Zip 73013–3023; tel. 405/359–2400 **A**10 **F**3 12 29 40 41 45 54 64 70 75 79 81 82 85 107 111 119 127 129 148
Primary Contact: Curtis Summers, Chief Executive Officer
Web address: www.summitmedcenter.com/
Control: Individual, Investor–owned, for–profit **Service:** General Medical and Surgical

Staffed Beds: 9 **Admissions:** 263 **Census:** 2 **Outpatient Visits:** 21619 **Births:** 0 **Total Expense ($000):** 39030 **Payroll Expense ($000):** 7612 **Personnel:** 224

EL RENO—Canadian County

★ **MERCY HOSPITAL EL RENO (370011)**, 2115 Parkview Drive, Zip 73036–2199, Mailing Address: P.O. Box 129, Zip 73036–0129; tel. 405/262–2640 **A**3 10 **F**3 7 11 29 30 34 35 40 43 44 45 46 50 57 62 64 68 77 79 81 82 85 93 107 111 114 119 129 130 132 146 148 **P**6 **S** Mercy Health, Chesterfield, MO
Primary Contact: Doug Danker, Administrator
CMO: Michael Dean Sullivan, M.D., Chief of Staff
CIO: Karen Heldreth, Director Data Processing
CHR: Wendy Ward, Director Human Resources
Web address: www.mercyok.net
Control: Church–operated, Nongovernment, not–for profit **Service:** General Medical and Surgical

Staffed Beds: 48 **Admissions:** 431 **Census:** 4 **Outpatient Visits:** 23928 **Births:** 0 **Total Expense ($000):** 12349 **Payroll Expense ($000):** 6796 **Personnel:** 129

PARKVIEW HOSPITAL See Mercy Hospital El Reno

ELK CITY—Beckham County

⊞ **GREAT PLAINS REGIONAL MEDICAL CENTER (370019)**, 1801 West Third Street, Zip 73644–5145, Mailing Address: P.O. Box 2339, Zip 73648–2339; tel. 580/821–5300 **A**1 3 10 **F**3 11 13 15 18 20 22 26 29 30 31 34 35 40 43 47 50 51 56 57 59 62 64 68 70 75 76 77 78 79 81 82 85 87 89 91 93 96 98 100 101 102 103 107 108 110 111 115 118 119 120 121 123 129 130 131 132 133 135 146 147 148
Primary Contact: Corey Lively, Chief Executive Officer
COO: Misty Carter, Director Human Resources and Chief Operating Officer
CFO: Monica Scott, Chief Financial Officer
CMO: Joe Coker, M.D., Chief of Staff
CIO: Terry Price, Director Information Technology
CHR: Misty Carter, Vice President Human Resources and Ancillary Services
CNO: Gwen Fuchs, R.N., Director Perioperative Services and Interim Chief Nursing Officer
Web address: www.gprmc–ok.com
Control: Other not–for–profit (including NFP Corporation) **Service:** General Medical and Surgical

Staffed Beds: 46 **Admissions:** 1895 **Census:** 19 **Outpatient Visits:** 54259 **Births:** 391 **Total Expense ($000):** 47976 **Payroll Expense ($000):** 16205 **Personnel:** 378

ENID—Garfield County

INTEGRIS BASS BEHAVIORAL HEALTH SYSTEM See Integris Bass Meadowlake

⊞ **INTEGRIS BASS BAPTIST HEALTH CENTER (370016)**, 600 South Monroe Street, Zip 73701–7211, Mailing Address: P.O. Box 3168, Zip 73702–3168; tel. 580/233–2300 **A**1 10 13 19 **F**3 11 13 15 17 18 20 22 24 28 29 30 31 35 40 43 45 49 57 62 68 70 74 75 76 77 78 79 81 85 98 99 103 107 108 111 114 117 118 119 120 121 127 128 129 132 144 146 147 148 **S** INTEGRIS Health, Oklahoma City, OK
Primary Contact: Edward Herrman, R.N., FACHE, President
CFO: Duane Miller, Chief Financial Officer
CNO: Cynthia Leathers, R.N., Chief Nursing Officer
Web address: www.integris–health.com
Control: Other not–for–profit (including NFP Corporation) **Service:** General Medical and Surgical

Staffed Beds: 167 **Admissions:** 4844 **Census:** 87 **Personnel:** 511

☐ **INTEGRIS BASS PAVILION (372016)**, 401 South Third Street, Zip 73701–5737; tel. 580/249–4260 **A**1 10 **F**1 11 29 30 40 43 68 75 77 82 85 93 132 146 148
Primary Contact: Edward Herrman, R.N., FACHE, President
CFO: Duane Miller, Chief Financial Officer
CHR: Stacy Froese, Regional Director Human Resources
CNO: Cynthia Leathers, R.N., Chief Nursing Officer
Web address: www.integris–health.com/integris/en–us/locations/bass–enid
Control: Other not–for–profit (including NFP Corporation) **Service:** Long–Term Acute Care hospital

Staffed Beds: 24 **Admissions:** 128 **Census:** 9 **Outpatient Visits:** 0 **Births:** 0 **Personnel:** 49

☐ △ **ST. MARY'S REGIONAL MEDICAL CENTER (370026)**, 305 South Fifth Street, Zip 73701–5899, Mailing Address: P.O. Box 232, Zip 73702–0232; tel. 580/233–6100 **A**1 7 10 **F**3 11 13 15 18 20 22 26 28 29 30 31 34 35 37 39 40 43 45 49 51 53 54 56 57 59 60 64 68 69 70 73 74 75 76 77 78 79 80 81 82 85 86 87 90 91 92 93 96 98 100 101 102 107 108 110 111 114 115 118 119 129 130 131 132 135 146 147 **P**6 **S** Universal Health Services, Inc., King of Prussia, PA
Primary Contact: Stanley D. Tatum, FACHE, Chief Executive Officer
COO: Krista Roberts, Chief Operating Officer
CFO: David Jamin, Chief Financial Officer
CMO: Michael Pontious, M.D., Chief of Staff
CIO: Tracy Andersen, Chief Information Officer
CHR: David Camp, Director Human Resources
CNO: Douglas W. Coffey, R.N., Chief Nursing Officer
Web address: www.stmarysregional.com
Control: Corporation, Investor–owned, for–profit **Service:** General Medical and Surgical

Staffed Beds: 164 **Admissions:** 4185 **Census:** 56 **Outpatient Visits:** 71780 **Births:** 357 **Total Expense ($000):** 76137 **Payroll Expense ($000):** 30069 **Personnel:** 470

Hospital, Medicare Provider Number, Address, Telephone, Approval, Facility, and Physician Codes, Health Care System

★ American Hospital Association (AHA) membership
☐ The Joint Commission accreditation
○ Healthcare Facilities Accreditation Program
◇ DNV Healthcare Inc. accreditation
⇑ Center for Improvement in Healthcare Quality Accreditation
△ Commission on Accreditation of Rehabilitation Facilities (CARF) accreditation

OK

FAIRFAX—Osage County

FAIRFAX COMMUNITY HOSPITAL (371318), 40 Hospital Road,
Zip 74637–5084; tel. 918/642–3291 **A**10 18 **F**3 29 40 45 57 77 93 107 117
129 133 **S** Rural Community Hospitals of America, Kansas City, MO
Primary Contact: Tina Steele, Chief Executive Officer and Chief Financial Officer
COO: Linda Thompson, Chief Operating Officer
CFO: Tina Steele, Chief Executive Officer and Chief Financial Officer
CMO: Arman Janloo, M.D., Chief Medical Staff
CIO: Lisa Drymon, Manager
CHR: Sharon Binkley, Director Human Resources
Control: Corporation, Investor–owned, for-profit **Service:** General Medical and
Surgical

Staffed Beds: 15 **Admissions:** 195 **Census:** 3 **Outpatient Visits:** 5967
Births: 0 **Total Expense ($000):** 5698 **Payroll Expense ($000):** 2878
Personnel: 46

FAIRFAX MEMORIAL HOSPITAL See Fairfax Community Hospital

FAIRVIEW—Major County

FAIRVIEW REGIONAL MEDICAL CENTER (371329), 523 East State Road,
Zip 73737–1453, Mailing Address: P.O. Box 548, Zip 73737–0548;
tel. 580/227–3721 **A**10 18 **F**3 24 34 35 40 43 45 57 59 64 65 68 69 75 77
81 82 84 85 91 93 107 114 127 128 130 131 132 133 135 146 **P**5 6
Primary Contact: Roger Knak, Administrator
CMO: Solomon Ali, M.D., Chief of Staff
CIO: Bob Maynard, Chief Information Officer
CHR: Elisabeth Hughes, Director Human Resources and Community Relations
CNO: Tamara Eitzen, Chief Nursing Officer
Web address: www.fairviewregionalmedicalcenter.com
Control: Hospital district or authority, Government, nonfederal **Service:** General
Medical and Surgical

Staffed Beds: 25 **Admissions:** 229 **Census:** 3 **Outpatient Visits:** 10024
Births: 0 **Total Expense ($000):** 7328 **Payroll Expense ($000):** 2755
Personnel: 60

FORT SILL—Comanche County

☒ **REYNOLDS ARMY COMMUNITY HOSPITAL**, 4301 Wilson Street,
Zip 73503–4472; tel. 580/558–3000, (Nonreporting) **A**1 3 5 **S** Department of
the Army, Office of the Surgeon General, Falls Church, VA
Primary Contact: Colonel Kenneth Lemons, Commander
COO: Lieutenant Jennifer R. House, Chief Operations and Readiness
CFO: Lieutenant Colonel David Rollins, Chief Resource Management Division
CMO: Lieutenant Colonel Timothy Switaj, Deputy Commander for Clinical Services
CIO: Russell Seymour, Chief Information Management Division
CHR: Jacqueline V. Jones, Chief Civilian Personnel Branch
CNO: Lieutenant Colonel Richard A. Behr, Deputy Commander for Health Services
Web address: www.rach.sill.amedd.army.mil
Control: Army, Government, federal **Service:** General Medical and Surgical

Staffed Beds: 24

FORT SUPPLY— County

NORTHWEST CENTER FOR BEHAVIORAL HEALTH (374001), 1 Mi East
Highway 270, Zip 73841; tel. 580/766–2311 **A**10 **F**98 104 106 130 135 **P**6
S Oklahoma Department of Mental Health and Substance Abuse Services,
Oklahoma City, OK
Primary Contact: Trudy Hoffman, Executive Director
Web address: www.ncbhok.org/
Control: State–Government, nonfederal **Service:** Psychiatric

Staffed Beds: 24 **Admissions:** 518 **Census:** 17 **Outpatient Visits:** 69495
Births: 0 **Total Expense ($000):** 13289 **Payroll Expense ($000):** 6734
Personnel: 183

GROVE—Delaware County

☒ **INTEGRIS GROVE HOSPITAL (370113)**, 1001 East 18th Street,
Zip 74344–2907; tel. 918/786–2243 **A**1 10 20 **F**3 7 11 13 15 18 20 22 29
30 34 35 40 54 57 59 62 64 69 73 81 85 93 107 110 111 115 119 125
146 147 **S** INTEGRIS Health, Oklahoma City, OK
Primary Contact: Tim Bowen, President
CFO: Valerie Reeves, Chief Financial Officer
CMO: Kyle Schauf, M.D., President Medical Staff
CNO: Jonas Rabel, Vice President and Chief Nursing Officer
Web address: www.integris-health.com
Control: Other not–for–profit (including NFP Corporation) **Service:** General
Medical and Surgical

Staffed Beds: 58 **Admissions:** 2105 **Census:** 17 **Outpatient Visits:** 43545
Births: 332 **Total Expense ($000):** 44108 **Payroll Expense ($000):** 12235
Personnel: 209

GUTHRIE—Logan County

★ **MERCY HOSPITAL LOGAN COUNTY (371317)**, 200 South Academy Road,
Zip 73044–8727, Mailing Address: P.O. Box 1017, Zip 73044–1017;
tel. 405/282–6700 **A**10 18 **F**3 15 29 30 34 35 40 43 44 45 50 57 59 68 69
75 77 79 81 85 93 97 107 110 111 114 119 127 129 130 131 133 144 146
148 **P**6 **S** Mercy Health, Chesterfield, MO
Primary Contact: Joshua Tucker, Administrator
CMO: Jignesh Veragiwala, Chief of Staff
CHR: Mary Jo Messelt, Senior Human Resources Manager
CNO: Kim Williams, R.N., Director of Nursing
Web address: www.mercy.net
Control: Church–operated, Nongovernment, not–for profit **Service:** General
Medical and Surgical

Staffed Beds: 25 **Admissions:** 691 **Census:** 10 **Outpatient Visits:** 46218
Births: 0 **Total Expense ($000):** 18161 **Payroll Expense ($000):** 10347
Personnel: 158

GUYMON—Texas County

★ **MEMORIAL HOSPITAL OF TEXAS COUNTY (370138)**, 520 Medical Drive,
Zip 73942–4438; tel. 580/338–6515 **A**10 20 **F**3 11 13 15 29 34 40 43 45 57
59 64 65 68 70 75 76 81 85 89 107 108 110 111 114 119 133 135 146
147 **P**6
Primary Contact: Troy Zinn, Chief Executive Officer
CFO: Michele Reust, Controller
CIO: Sheldon Spence, Director of Revenue Cycle, IT
CHR: Sarah Wagner, Human Resources Officer
CNO: Dondie Rodgers, Interim Chief Nursing Officer
Web address: www.mhtcguymon.org
Control: County–Government, nonfederal **Service:** General Medical and Surgical

Staffed Beds: 14 **Admissions:** 684 **Census:** 5 **Outpatient Visits:** 31302
Births: 225 **Total Expense ($000):** 15187 **Payroll Expense ($000):** 5839
Personnel: 149

HEALDTON—Carter County

★ **MERCY HOSPITAL HEALDTON (371310)**, 918 South 8th Street,
Zip 73438–0928, Mailing Address: P.O. Box 928, Zip 73438–0928;
tel. 580/229–0701 **A**10 18 **F**3 40 43 44 57 64 68 107 114 127
133 146 **P**6 **S** Mercy Health, Chesterfield, MO
Primary Contact: Jeremy A. Jones, Administrator
CMO: Mark Newey, D.O., Chief of Staff
CHR: Melinda Sharum, Director Human Resources
Web address: www.mercyok.com
Control: Church–operated, Nongovernment, not–for profit **Service:** General
Medical and Surgical

Staffed Beds: 22 **Admissions:** 218 **Census:** 6 **Outpatient Visits:** 10957
Births: 0 **Total Expense ($000):** 5852 **Payroll Expense ($000):** 3222
Personnel: 60

HENRYETTA—Okmulgee County

★ **HILLCREST HOSPITAL HENRYETTA (370183)**, 2401 West Main Street,
Zip 74437–3893, Mailing Address: P.O. Box 1269, Zip 74437–1269;
tel. 918/650–1100 **A**10 **F**3 15 18 29 40 45 54 56 64 65 79 81 85 87 93 98
102 103 107 110 111 114 119 129 130 131 133 143 147 148 **P**6 **S** Ardent
Health Services, Nashville, TN
Primary Contact: Dee Renshaw, Chief Executive Officer
CFO: Joseph Mendoza, Chief Financial Officer
CNO: April Secor, R.N., Chief Nursing Officer
Web address: www.hillcresthenryetta.com/
Control: Corporation, Investor–owned, for–profit **Service:** General Medical and
Surgical

Staffed Beds: 41 **Admissions:** 996 **Census:** 17 **Outpatient Visits:** 12028
Births: 0 **Total Expense ($000):** 15270 **Payroll Expense ($000):** 5874
Personnel: 120

HOBART—Kiowa County

★ **ELKVIEW GENERAL HOSPITAL (370153)**, 429 West Elm Street,
Zip 73651–1615; tel. 580/726–1900 **A**10 20 **F**3 15 28 29 31 34 35 40 45 56
59 62 79 81 85 89 93 107 108 110 111 115 118 119 129 133 146 148 **P**6
Primary Contact: Lisa Hart, Chief Executive Officer
COO: Harold Moad, Chief Operating Officer
CFO: Amy Harmon, Chief Financial Officer
CMO: Julie Schaufele, M.D., Medical Director
CIO: Dennis Tarver, Director Information Technology
CHR: Sharon Moad, Human Resources Director Health Information Management
CNO: Debbie Norman, MSN, Chief Nursing Officer
Web address: www.elkviewhospital.com
Control: Hospital district or authority, Government, nonfederal **Service:** General
Medical and Surgical

Staffed Beds: 38 **Admissions:** 989 **Census:** 9 **Outpatient Visits:** 10075
Births: 3 **Total Expense ($000):** 12757 **Payroll Expense ($000):** 6853
Personnel: 155

Many Facility Codes have changed. Please refer to the AHA Guide Code Chart. © 2016 AHA Guide

HOLDENVILLE—Hughes County

★ **HOLDENVILLE GENERAL HOSPITAL (371321)**, 100 McDougal Drive,
Zip 74848–2822; tel. 405/379–4200 **A**10 18 **F**3 11 29 30 34 40 45 57 59 64
65 79 81 93 97 107 111 115 119 127 128 133 135 146 148
Primary Contact: Roberta Jeffrey, Chief Executive Officer
CFO: Drew Johnson, Chief Financial Officer
CMO: Tom Osborn, D.O., Chief Medical Staff
CIO: Mike Combs, Manager Information Technology
CHR: Heather Heard, Director Human Resources
CNO: Jackie Smith, R.N., Chief Nursing Officer
Web address: www.holdenvillegeneral.org
Control: City–Government, nonfederal **Service:** General Medical and Surgical

Staffed Beds: 25 **Admissions:** 435 **Census:** 6 **Outpatient Visits:** 40898
Births: 0 **Total Expense ($000):** 11583 **Payroll Expense ($000):** 5543
Personnel: 123

HOLLIS—Harmon County

HARMON MEMORIAL HOSPITAL (370036), 400 East Chestnut Street,
Zip 73550–2030, Mailing Address: P.O. Box 791, Zip 73550–0791;
tel. 580/688–3363, (Nonreporting) **A**10 20
Primary Contact: Sheila Lewis, Administrator
CFO: Willie Mae Copeland, Chief Financial Officer
CMO: Akram Abraham, M.D., Chief of Staff
CHR: Abbey Welch, Director Human Resources
Control: Hospital district or authority, Government, nonfederal **Service:** General
Medical and Surgical

Staffed Beds: 31

HUGO—Choctaw County

CHOCTAW MEMORIAL HOSPITAL (370100), 1405 East Kirk Street,
Zip 74743–3603; tel. 580/317–9500, (Nonreporting) **A**10
Primary Contact: Marcia O'Connor, Chief Executive Officer
CIO: Andy Richmond, Director Information Technology
CHR: Darlene Galyon, Director Human Resources
Web address: www.choctawmemorial.com
Control: Hospital district or authority, Government, nonfederal **Service:** General
Medical and Surgical

Staffed Beds: 32

LANE FROST HEALTH AND REHABILITATION CENTER (372017), 2815 East
Jackson Street, Zip 74743–4250; tel. 580/326–9200, (Nonreporting) **A**10
Primary Contact: Robert F. Berry, Chief Executive Officer
Web address: www.lanefrosthealth.com/
Control: Other not–for–profit (including NFP Corporation) **Service:** Long–Term
Acute Care hospital

Staffed Beds: 30

IDABEL—McCurtain County

MCCURTAIN MEMORIAL HOSPITAL (370048), 1301 Lincoln Road,
Zip 74745–7341; tel. 580/286–7623 **A**10 20 **F**3 11 13 15 28 29 34 40 45 49
53 59 62 64 70 75 76 81 87 93 98 103 107 110 111 114 119 130 132 148
P6 8
Primary Contact: Jahni Tapley, JD, Interim Chief Executive Officer
CFO: Ray B. Whitmore, Chief Financial Officer
CMO: Michael C. West, M.D., Chief of Staff
CIO: Dana A. Stowell, Chief Information Officer
CNO: Pam Johnson, R.N., Chief Nursing Officer
Web address: www.mmhok.com
Control: Other not–for–profit (including NFP Corporation) **Service:** General
Medical and Surgical

Staffed Beds: 77 **Admissions:** 1115 **Census:** 11 **Outpatient Visits:** 29323
Births: 254 **Total Expense ($000):** 16392 **Payroll Expense ($000):** 8540
Personnel: 193

KINGFISHER—Kingfisher County

★ **MERCY HOSPITAL KINGFISHER (371313)**, 1000 Kingfisher Regional Hospital
Drive, Zip 73750–3528, Mailing Address: P.O. Box 59, Zip 73750–0059;
tel. 405/375–3141 **A**10 18 **F**3 11 15 29 30 34 35 40 43 45 50 64 68 75 77
79 81 85 87 93 107 110 111 114 119 129 132 133 146 148 **P**6 **S** Mercy
Health, Chesterfield, MO
Primary Contact: Brian Denton, Administrator
CMO: Brett Krablin, M.D., Chief of Staff
CIO: Chad Kliewer, Information Technology Specialist
CHR: Carolyn Bjerke, Director Human Resources
CNO: Hannah Powell, Chief Nursing Officer
Web address: www.kingfisherhospital.com
Control: Church–operated, Nongovernment, not–for profit **Service:** General
Medical and Surgical

Staffed Beds: 25 **Admissions:** 389 **Census:** 6 **Outpatient Visits:** 18676
Births: 0 **Total Expense ($000):** 11820 **Payroll Expense ($000):** 5769
Personnel: 108

LAWTON—Comanche County

▣ △ **COMANCHE COUNTY MEMORIAL HOSPITAL (370056)**, 3401 West Gore
Boulevard, Zip 73505–6332, Mailing Address: P.O. Box 129, Zip 73502–0129;
tel. 580/355–8620, (Total facility includes 132 beds in nursing home–type unit)
A1 2 3 5 7 10 13 **F**3 6 7 8 11 12 13 15 17 18 20 22 24 26 28 29 30 32
34 35 40 43 45 46 47 48 49 50 51 54 56 57 58 59 62 63 64 65 66 68 70
72 74 75 76 77 78 79 80 81 82 84 85 86 89 90 91 92 93 96 97 98 103
104 107 108 110 111 114 115 116 117 118 119 120 121 123 124 127 128
129 130 131 132 134 135 143 146 147 148 **P**6
Primary Contact: Brent Smith, Chief Executive Officer
CFO: George Kruger, CPA, Chief Financial Officer
CMO: Scott Michener, M.D., Chief Medical Officer
CIO: James Wellman, Senior Director Information Services
CHR: Donna Wade, Senior Director Human Resources
CNO: Chris Ward, Chief Nursing Officer
Web address: www.ccmhonline.com
Control: Hospital district or authority, Government, nonfederal **Service:** General
Medical and Surgical

Staffed Beds: 389 **Admissions:** 9530 **Census:** 240 **Outpatient Visits:**
178793 **Births:** 1181 **Total Expense ($000):** 233056 **Payroll Expense
($000):** 95810 **Personnel:** 1519

JIM TALIAFERRO COMMUNITY MENTAL HEALTH (374008), 602 S.W. 38th
Street, Zip 73505; tel. 580/248–5780 **A**10 **F**4 5 29 34 35 36 38 44 53 59 64
66 68 71 87 98 99 100 101 102 103 104 106 130 134
Primary Contact: Brenda Ototivo, Executive Director
Web address: www.odmhsas.org
Control: State–Government, nonfederal **Service:** Psychiatric

Staffed Beds: 22 **Admissions:** 528 **Census:** 10 **Births:** 0 **Total Expense
($000):** 9024 **Payroll Expense ($000):** 5549 **Personnel:** 137

☐ **LAWTON INDIAN HOSPITAL (370170)**, 1515 Lawrie Tatum Road,
Zip 73507–3099; tel. 580/353–0350, (Nonreporting) **A**1 10 **S** U. S. Indian Health
Service, Rockville, MD
Primary Contact: Greg Ketcher, Administrator
COO: John Bear, Hospital Administrator Officer and Supervisor Human Resources
CFO: Sarabeth Sahmaunt, Supervisory Accountant
CMO: Richard Chadek, M.D., Clinical Director
CIO: William R. Harris, Chief Information Officer
CHR: John Bear, Hospital Administrator Officer and Supervisor Human Resources
CNO: Lenora Littledeer, R.N., Director of Nursing
Web address: www.ihs.gov
Control: PHS, Indian Service, Government, federal **Service:** General Medical and
Surgical

Staffed Beds: 26

☐ △ **SOUTHWESTERN MEDICAL CENTER (370097)**, 5602 S.W. Lee
Boulevard, Zip 73505–9635; tel. 580/531–4700 **A**1 3 5 7 10 **F**3 8 13 29 30
34 38 40 41 43 45 47 49 50 51 57 59 60 64 65 67 68 70 74 76 77 78 79
81 85 87 89 90 91 92 93 98 99 100 101 102 104 106 107 108 111 114
118 119 120 121 122 123 124 127 129 130 131 133 135 146 147 148 **P**6
S RCCH HealthCare Partners, Brentwood, TN
Primary Contact: Stephen O. Hyde, FACHE, Chief Executive Officer
CFO: Wayne Colson, Chief Financial Officer
CMO: Aryan Kadivar, M.D., Chief Medical Officer
CIO: Kent Lewis, Director Information Services
CHR: Danny Hale, Director Human Resources
CNO: Jayne Thomas, Chief Nursing Officer
Web address: www.swmconline.com
Control: Corporation, Investor–owned, for–profit **Service:** General Medical and
Surgical

Staffed Beds: 178 **Admissions:** 4501 **Census:** 91 **Outpatient Visits:** 54330
Births: 493 **Total Expense ($000):** 68281 **Payroll Expense ($000):** 23195
Personnel: 463

Hospital, Medicare Provider Number, Address, Telephone, Approval, Facility, and Physician Codes, Health Care System

★ American Hospital Association (AHA) membership
☐ The Joint Commission accreditation
◯ Healthcare Facilities Accreditation Program
◇ DNV Healthcare Inc. accreditation
⇑ Center for Improvement in Healthcare Quality Accreditation
△ Commission on Accreditation of Rehabilitation Facilities (CARF) accreditation

OK

LINDSAY—Garvin County

LINDSAY MUNICIPAL HOSPITAL (370214), Highway 19 West, Zip 73052, Mailing Address: P.O. Box 888, Zip 73052–0888; tel. 405/756–1404 **A**10 **F**29 30 40 45 59 64 65 68 75 79 81 82 83 84 86 87 93 100 101 107 114 119 148 **P**6
Primary Contact: Jeff Walraven, Chief Executive Officer
Control: Hospital district or authority, Government, nonfederal **Service:** Hospital unit of an institution (prison hospital, college infirmary, etc.)

Staffed Beds: 26 **Admissions:** 1024 **Census:** 17 **Outpatient Visits:** 6600 **Births:** 0

MADILL—Marshall County

✚ **ALLIANCEHEALTH MADILL (371326)**, 901 South Fifth Avenue, Zip 73446–3640, Mailing Address: P.O. Box 827, Zip 73446–0827; tel. 580/795–3384 **A**1 10 18 **F**3 11 29 30 34 35 40 45 49 59 64 81 87 93 107 114 119 127 130 133 135 146 **P**5 **S** Community Health Systems, Inc., Franklin, TN
Primary Contact: Minnie Burkhardt, Chief Executive Officer
CFO: Thomas Briggs, Chief Financial Officer
CMO: Heidi Haislip, M.D., Chief of Staff
CHR: D.J. Shawn, Director Human Resources
CNO: Carol Wright, Chief Nursing Officer
Web address: www.myalliancehealth.com
Control: Corporation, Investor–owned, for–profit **Service:** General Medical and Surgical

Staffed Beds: 21 **Admissions:** 408 **Census:** 5 **Births:** 0

MANGUM—Greer County

QUARTZ MOUNTAIN MEDICAL CENTER (371330), One Wickersham Drive, Zip 73554–9116, Mailing Address: P.O. Box 280, Zip 73554–0280; tel. 580/782–3353 **A**10 18 **F**29 40 41 45 57 68 81 82 85 93 107 111 114 119 127 128 133 148 **P**6
Primary Contact: Kevin Owens, Chief Executive Officer
COO: Danny Avery, Chief Financial Officer and Chief Operating Officer
CIO: Gregg Burnam, Chief Information Officer and Manager Business Office
Web address: www.qmhealth.org/
Control: Individual, Investor–owned, for–profit **Service:** General Medical and Surgical

Staffed Beds: 25 **Admissions:** 303 **Census:** 3 **Outpatient Visits:** 10000 **Births:** 0

MARIETTA—Love County

★ **MERCY HEALTH LOVE COUNTY (371306)**, 300 Wanda Street, Zip 73448–1200; tel. 580/276–3347 **A**10 18 **F**3 7 29 34 40 43 44 50 57 59 77 107 114 119 127 133 135 146 148 **P**6 **S** Mercy Health, Chesterfield, MO
Primary Contact: Richard Barker, Administrator
CMO: J. T. O'Connor, M.D., Medical Director
CIO: Connie Graham, Public Information Officer
Web address: www.mercyhealthlovecounty.com
Control: Church–operated, Nongovernment, not–for profit **Service:** General Medical and Surgical

Staffed Beds: 25 **Admissions:** 225 **Census:** 6 **Births:** 0 **Total Expense ($000):** 14497 **Payroll Expense ($000):** 7976 **Personnel:** 140

MCALESTER—Pittsburg County

CARL ALBERT COMMUNITY MENTAL HEALTH CENTER (374006), 1101 East Monroe Avenue, Zip 74501–4826; tel. 918/426–7800 **A**10 **F**5 29 35 38 98 99 100 101 102 103 104 130 132 135 146
Primary Contact: Debbie Moran, Executive Director
CFO: Konnie Taylor, Chief Financial Officer
CMO: William Mings, M.D., Medical Director
CHR: Judy Allen, Human Resource Specialist
Web address: www.odmhsas.org
Control: State–Government, nonfederal **Service:** Psychiatric

Staffed Beds: 15 **Admissions:** 379 **Census:** 13 **Outpatient Visits:** 41480 **Births:** 0 **Total Expense ($000):** 10637 **Payroll Expense ($000):** 5273 **Personnel:** 133

★ △ ◇ **MCALESTER REGIONAL HEALTH CENTER (370034)**, One East Clark Bass Boulevard, Zip 74501–4267, Mailing Address: P.O. Box 1228, Zip 74502–1228; tel. 918/426–1800 **A**7 10 13 21 **F**3 10 11 13 15 18 20 22 26 29 30 34 35 40 43 45 49 50 51 53 54 56 57 59 61 62 64 66 68 69 70 75 76 77 79 81 82 85 86 87 90 91 92 93 100 108 109 110 111 114 115 116 117 118 119 125 127 128 129 130 131 132 135 144 146 147 148 **P**6
Primary Contact: David N. Keith, FACHE, President and Chief Executive Officer
CFO: Darryl Linnington, Chief Financial Officer
CIO: Jason Bray, Chief Information Officer
CHR: Scott Lowe, Director Human Resource
CNO: Kimberly Dawn Stout, Chief Nursing Officer
Web address: www.mrhcok.com
Control: City–Government, nonfederal **Service:** General Medical and Surgical

Staffed Beds: 191 **Admissions:** 4287 **Census:** 53 **Outpatient Visits:** 88089 **Births:** 436 **Total Expense ($000):** 77497 **Payroll Expense ($000):** 33974 **Personnel:** 662

MIAMI—Ottawa County

✚ **INTEGRIS MIAMI HOSPITAL (370004)**, 200 Second Street S.W., Zip 74354–6830; tel. 918/542–6611 **A**1 10 20 **F**7 8 11 13 15 18 20 22 26 28 29 30 34 35 40 45 51 57 59 62 63 70 75 76 77 79 81 85 89 93 98 100 103 104 107 108 110 111 114 115 119 125 129 130 131 132 135 144 146 147 148 **S** INTEGRIS Health, Oklahoma City, OK
Primary Contact: Jordan Cash, President
CFO: Valerie Reeves, Chief Financial Officer
CMO: Elaine Mader, M.D., Chief of Staff
CHR: Jamil Haynes, Regional Director Human Resources
CNO: Lisa Halstead, Chief Nursing Officer
Web address: www.integris–health.com
Control: Other not–for–profit (including NFP Corporation) **Service:** General Medical and Surgical

Staffed Beds: 84 **Admissions:** 2265 **Census:** 26 **Outpatient Visits:** 47351 **Births:** 388 **Total Expense ($000):** 46431 **Payroll Expense ($000):** 15188 **Personnel:** 265

★ **WILLOW CREST HOSPITAL (374017)**, 130 A Street S.W., Zip 74354–6800; tel. 918/542–1836 **A**10 **F**29 75 98 99 101 102 106 130 **P**6
Primary Contact: Anne G. Anthony, FACHE, President and Chief Executive Officer
COO: Steven Goodman, Chief Operating Officer
CFO: Cindy Bell, Director Finance
CMO: Mark Elkington, M.D., Chief Medical Officer
CIO: Steven Goodman, Chief Operating Officer
CHR: Kathy Henderson, Director Human Resources
CNO: Kassi Davis, Director Patient Care Services
Web address: www.willowcresthospital.com
Control: Corporation, Investor–owned, for–profit **Service:** Children's hospital psychiatric

Staffed Beds: 75 **Admissions:** 661 **Census:** 47 **Outpatient Visits:** 0 **Births:** 0 **Total Expense ($000):** 8506 **Payroll Expense ($000):** 5145 **Personnel:** 130

MIDWEST CITY—Oklahoma County

✚ **ALLIANCEHEALTH MIDWEST (370094)**, 2825 Parklawn Drive, Zip 73110–4258; tel. 405/610–4411 **A**1 3 5 10 **F**3 7 8 11 13 14 15 17 18 20 22 26 29 30 31 34 40 43 45 46 49 50 57 59 64 70 74 76 77 78 79 80 81 85 86 87 89 91 93 98 100 101 102 103 107 108 110 111 114 115 119 126 130 132 135 143 146 147 **S** Community Health Systems, Inc., Franklin, TN
Primary Contact: Damon Brown, Chief Executive Officer
COO: Lisa Ellis, Chief Operating Officer
CFO: Brandon Bullard, Chief Financial Officer
CMO: Rockey Talley, M.D., Chief Medical Officer
CHR: Michael Ward Hartley, Director Human Resources
CNO: Gloria Alicia Ceballos, MSN, Chief Nursing Officer
Web address: www.alliancehealthmidwest.com
Control: Corporation, Investor–owned, for–profit **Service:** General Medical and Surgical

Staffed Beds: 255 **Admissions:** 9029 **Census:** 115 **Outpatient Visits:** 98193 **Births:** 558 **Total Expense ($000):** 119881 **Payroll Expense ($000):** 41954 **Personnel:** 706

✚ **MIDWEST CITY SPECIALTY HOSPITAL (372012)**, 8210 National Avenue, Zip 73110–8518; tel. 405/739–0800, (Nonreporting) **A**1 10 **S** Concord Healthcare Group, Lakewood, NJ
Primary Contact: Bobby Snyder, Chief Executive Officer
CFO: Veronica Scott, Business Office Manager
CHR: Anna Emamghoraishi, Human Resources
CNO: Jason Farris, Chief Nursing Officer
Web address: www.midwestcityspecialtyhospital.com/
Control: Corporation, Investor–owned, for–profit **Service:** Long–Term Acute Care hospital

Staffed Beds: 31

MOORE—Cleveland County

NORMAN REGIONAL MOORE See Norman Regional Health System, Norman

MUSKOGEE—Muskogee County

CORNERSTONE HOSPITAL OF OKLAHOMA–MUSKOGEE (372022), 351 South 40th Street, Zip 74401–4916; tel. 918/682–6161, (Includes CORNERSTONE HOSPITAL OF OKLAHOMA–BROKEN ARROW, 1000 West Boise Circle, Third Floor, Broken Arrow, Zip 74012–4900, Mailing Address: 1000 West Boise Circle, Zip 74012–4900; tel. 918/994–8300; Craig Koele, Chief Executive Officer) **A**10 22 **F**1 29 40 60 148 **S** Cornerstone Healthcare Group, Dallas, TX
Primary Contact: Craig Koele, Chief Executive Officer
CMO: Jeremiah Rutherford, Chief Medical Officer
Web address: www.chghospitals.com/muskogee/
Control: Partnership, Investor–owned, for–profit **Service:** Children's Long–Term Acute Care

Staffed Beds: 41 **Admissions:** 530 **Census:** 38 **Outpatient Visits:** 0 **Births:** 0 **Personnel:** 298

Many Facility Codes have changed. Please refer to the AHA Guide Code Chart.

© 2016 AHA Guide

OK

⊞ **EASTAR HEALTH SYSTEM (370025)**, 300 Rockefeller Drive, Zip 74401–5081; tel. 918/682–5501, (Includes EASTAR HEALTH SYSTEM, EAST CAMPUS, 2900 North Main Street, Zip 74401–4078; tel. 918/687–7777) **A**1 2 10 19 **F**3 8 11 13 15 18 20 22 29 30 31 34 35 37 38 40 41 43 44 45 46 47 48 49 50 51 53 56 57 59 64 65 70 73 74 75 76 78 79 81 82 85 86 87 89 90 92 96 98 100 101 102 103 107 108 110 111 114 115 119 120 121 123 130 131 135 146 147 148 **S** RCCH HealthCare Partners, Brentwood, TN
Primary Contact: Anthony R. Young, Chief Executive Officer
COO: Tony Capuano, Chief Operating Officer
CFO: Scott Bailey, Chief Financial Officer
CMO: Jay Gregory, M.D., Chief Medical Officer
CIO: James Tolbert, Director Information Systems
CHR: Bill Peterson, Director Human Resources
CNO: James Wells, R.N., Chief Nursing Officer
Web address: www.eastarhealth.com
Control: Corporation, Investor–owned, for–profit **Service:** General Medical and Surgical

Staffed Beds: 222 **Admissions:** 9157 **Census:** 128 **Outpatient Visits:** 80233 **Births:** 755 **Total Expense ($000):** 122686 **Payroll Expense ($000):** 42519 **Personnel:** 866

EASTAR HEALTH SYSTEM, EAST CAMPUS See EASTAR Health System

⊞ △ **JACK C. MONTGOMERY VETERANS AFFAIRS MEDICAL CENTER**, 1011 Honor Heights Drive, Zip 74401–1318; tel. 918/577–3000, (Nonreporting) **A**1 2 3 5 7 **S** Department of Veterans Affairs, Washington, DC
Primary Contact: Mark E. Morgan, Medical Center Director
CFO: Dwight Beal, Chief Fiscal Services
CMO: Thomas D. Schneider, D.O., Chief of Staff
CIO: Mark E. Carr, Chief Information Resource Management
CNO: Bonnie Pierce, MSN, Associate Director for Patient Care Services
Web address: www.muskogee.va.gov
Control: Veterans Affairs, Government, federal **Service:** General Medical and Surgical

Staffed Beds: 99

MUSKOGEE REGIONAL MEDICAL CENTER See EASTAR Health System

NORMAN—Cleveland County

☐ **GRIFFIN MEMORIAL HOSPITAL (374000)**, 900 East Main Street, Zip 73071–5305, Mailing Address: P.O. Box 151, Zip 73070–0151; tel. 405/573–6600 **A**1 3 5 10 **F**4 98 102 103 130 132 135 **P**6 **S** Oklahoma Department of Mental Health and Substance Abuse Services, Oklahoma City, OK
Primary Contact: Lori Jordan, Executive Director
CFO: Cheryl Cupps, Director Finance
CMO: Clayton Morris, Medical Director
CNO: Mike Abla, Director of Nursing
Web address: www.odmhsas.org
Control: State–Government, nonfederal **Service:** Psychiatric

Staffed Beds: 120 **Admissions:** 1231 **Census:** 114 **Outpatient Visits:** 594 **Births:** 0 **Total Expense ($000):** 24586 **Payroll Expense ($000):** 12403 **Personnel:** 332

J. D. MCCARTY CENTER FOR CHILDREN WITH DEVELOPMENTAL DISABILITIES (373300), 2002 East Robinson, Zip 73071–7420; tel. 405/307–2800 **A**10 **F**3 29 35 64 65 75 77 87 90 91 93 119 130 134 135 146
Primary Contact: Vicki Kuerstersteffen, Chief Executive Officer
CFO: Erik Paulson, Director of Finance
CMO: Thomas Thurston, M.D., Medical Director
CIO: Jeffery Setzer, Administrator Information Systems
CHR: Tina Martinez, Director Human Resources
Web address: www.jdmc.org
Control: State–Government, nonfederal **Service:** Children's rehabilitation

Staffed Beds: 36 **Admissions:** 208 **Census:** 33 **Outpatient Visits:** 11523 **Births:** 0 **Total Expense ($000):** 22943 **Payroll Expense ($000):** 9123 **Personnel:** 229

⊞ △ **NORMAN REGIONAL HEALTH SYSTEM (370008)**, 3300 HealthPlex Parkway, Zip 73072, Mailing Address: P.O. Box 1308, Zip 73070–1308; tel. 405/515–1000, (Includes NORMAN REGIONAL HOSPITAL, 901 North Porter Street, Zip 73071–6482, Mailing Address: P.O. Box 1308, Zip 73070–1308; tel. 405/307–1000; Richie Splitt, FACHE, President and Chief Executive Office; NORMAN REGIONAL MOORE, 700 South Telephone Road, Moore, Zip 73160; tel. 405/793–9355; Richie Splitt, FACHE, President and Chief Executive Officer) **A**1 7 10 13 **F**3 7 11 12 13 15 17 18 20 22 24 28 29 30 31 32 34 35 36 37 39 40 42 43 44 45 47 48 49 50 53 54 55 56 57 58 59 63 64 65 69 70 72 74 75 76 77 78 79 80 81 82 83 84 85 86 87 89 90 93 94 96 97 98 100 101 102 103 104 107 110 111 114 115 117 118 119 120 123 126 127 129 130 131 132 135 143 145 146 147 148 **P**5 6 8
Primary Contact: Richie Splitt, FACHE, Interim President and Chief Executive Officer
COO: Greg Terrell, Senior Vice President and Chief Operating Officer
CFO: Ken Hopkins, Vice President Finance and Chief Financial Officer
CMO: Aaron Boyd, M.D., Chief Medical Officer
CIO: John Meharg, Director Health Information Technology
CHR: Jim Beyer, Director Human Resources
CNO: Nancy Brown, R.N., Vice President Patient Care Services and Chief Nursing Officer
Web address: www.normanregional.com
Control: Hospital district or authority, Government, nonfederal **Service:** General Medical and Surgical

Staffed Beds: 387 **Admissions:** 15838 **Census:** 195 **Outpatient Visits:** 357870 **Births:** 2728 **Total Expense ($000):** 348772 **Payroll Expense ($000):** 156724 **Personnel:** 2524

NOWATA—Nowata County

★ **JANE PHILLIPS NOWATA HEALTH CENTER (371305)**, 237 South Locust Street, Zip 74048–3660; tel. 918/273–3102 **A**10 18 **F**3 29 30 34 35 40 50 57 64 68 107 114 119 128 133 146 **P**5 **S** Ascension Health, Saint Louis, MO
Primary Contact: Jason McCauley, Administrator
CMO: David Caughell, M.D., Chief of Staff
Web address: www.jpmc.org
Control: Church–operated, Nongovernment, not–for profit **Service:** General Medical and Surgical

Staffed Beds: 15 **Admissions:** 152 **Census:** 4 **Outpatient Visits:** 6110 **Births:** 0 **Total Expense ($000):** 4057 **Payroll Expense ($000):** 2265 **Personnel:** 44

OKEENE—Blaine County

★ **OKEENE MUNICIPAL HOSPITAL (371327)**, 207 East F Street, Zip 73763–9441, Mailing Address: P.O. Box 489, Zip 73763–0489; tel. 580/822–4417 **A**10 18 **F**3 29 34 40 50 59 64 65 68 81 85 93 97 107 130 132 133 135 **P**6
Primary Contact: Shelly Dunham, Chief Executive Officer
COO: Tammi Jantzen, Chief Operating Officer
CFO: Sandra Lamle, Chief Financial Officer
CMO: Michael R. Talley, M.D., Chief of Staff
CHR: Barbara Creps, Director Human Resources and Accounting
CNO: Tamara Fischer, Chief Nursing Officer
Web address: www.okeenehospital.com
Control: Hospital district or authority, Government, nonfederal **Service:** General Medical and Surgical

Staffed Beds: 17 **Admissions:** 163 **Census:** 4 **Outpatient Visits:** 20926 **Births:** 0 **Total Expense ($000):** 6395 **Payroll Expense ($000):** 2673 **Personnel:** 56

OKEMAH—Okfuskee County

★ ◇ **CREEK NATION COMMUNITY HOSPITAL (371333)**, 309 North 14th Street, Zip 74859–2028; tel. 918/623–1424, (Nonreporting) **A**10 18 21
Primary Contact: Sheryl Sharber–Howell, Administrator
COO: Rhonda Beaver, Chief Operating Officer
CFO: Tyler McIntosh, Chief Financial Officer
CMO: Lawrence Vark, M.D., Chief Medical Officer
CIO: Robert Coffee, Chief Information Officer
CHR: Russell B. Torbett, Director Human Resources
CNO: Annette James, R.N., Chief Nursing Officer
Web address: www.creekhealth.org
Control: Other not–for–profit (including NFP Corporation) **Service:** General Medical and Surgical

Staffed Beds: 18

OK

OKLAHOMA CITY—Oklahoma County

✖ △ **ALLIANCEHEALTH DEACONESS (370032)**, 5501 North Portland Avenue, Zip 73112–2099; tel. 405/604–6000 **A**1 2 3 5 7 10 **F**3 8 11 13 15 17 18 20 22 24 28 29 30 31 34 35 40 41 43 45 46 47 49 50 56 57 59 60 70 72 74 75 78 79 80 81 83 84 85 86 87 90 93 97 102 107 108 109 110 111 114 119 120 126 129 130 132 135 146 147 148 **P**8 **S** Community Health Systems, Inc., Franklin, TN
Primary Contact: Devon Hyde, Chief Executive Officer
COO: Brett Kirkham, Chief Operating Officer
CIO: Don Bandy, Director Information Technology
CHR: Ellen Gifford, Director Human Resources
CNO: Jayne Thomas, Chief Nursing Officer
Web address: www.deaconessokc.com
Control: Partnership, Investor–owned, for–profit **Service:** General Medical and Surgical

Staffed Beds: 238 Admissions: 5418 Census: 71 Outpatient Visits: 65848 Births: 745 Total Expense ($000): 102008 Payroll Expense ($000): 36723 Personnel: 815

☐ **CEDAR RIDGE HOSPITAL (374023)**, 6501 N.E. 50th Street, Zip 73141–9118; tel. 405/605–6111 **A**1 10 **F**98 99 102 103 106 130 **P**6 **S** Universal Health Services, Inc., King of Prussia, PA
Primary Contact: Rob Lake, Interim Chief Executive Officer
Web address: www.cedarridgebhs.com
Control: Corporation, Investor–owned, for–profit **Service:** Psychiatric

Staffed Beds: 116 Admissions: 2482 Census: 43 Outpatient Visits: 0 Births: 0 Total Expense ($000): 13304 Payroll Expense ($000): 7041 Personnel: 117

CHILDREN'S HOSPITAL OF OKLAHOMA See OU Medical Center

◇ **COMMUNITY HOSPITAL (370203)**, 3100 S.W. 89th Street, Zip 73159–7900; tel. 405/378–3755, (Nonreporting) **A**10 21
Primary Contact: Debbie Kearns, Chief Executive Officer
Web address: www.communityhospitalokc.com
Control: Corporation, Investor–owned, for–profit **Service:** Surgical

Staffed Beds: 40

EVERETT TOWER See OU Medical Center

✖ △ **INTEGRIS BAPTIST MEDICAL CENTER (370028)**, 3300 N.W. Expressway, Zip 73112–4418; tel. 405/949–3011, (Includes INTEGRIS MENTAL HEALTH SYSTEM–SPENCER, 2601 North Spencer Road, Spencer, Zip 73084–3699, Mailing Address: P.O. Box 11137, Oklahoma City, Zip 73136–0137; tel. 405/717–9800) **A**1 2 3 5 7 10 **F**3 8 11 12 13 15 16 17 18 20 22 24 26 28 29 30 31 32 34 35 36 38 39 40 43 44 45 46 49 50 51 52 53 54 55 57 58 59 60 62 63 64 68 70 71 72 74 75 76 77 78 79 80 81 82 84 85 86 87 88 89 90 92 93 96 97 98 99 100 101 102 104 105 106 107 108 109 110 111 114 115 116 118 119 120 121 123 124 126 129 130 131 132 133 134 135 137 138 139 140 141 142 143 146 147 148 **P**6 7 **S** INTEGRIS Health, Oklahoma City, OK
Primary Contact: Chris Hammes, FACHE, Interim President
CFO: David R. Hadley, Managing Director and Chief Financial Officer
CMO: James P. White, M.D., Chief Medical Officer
CIO: John Delano, Vice President Chief Information Officer
CHR: Jason L. Eliot, Vice President Human Resources
CNO: Joni R. Tiller, R.N., Chief Nursing Officer
Web address: www.integrisok.com
Control: Other not–for–profit (including NFP Corporation) **Service:** General Medical and Surgical

Staffed Beds: 587 Admissions: 22380 Census: 415 Outpatient Visits: 161821 Births: 2838 Total Expense ($000): 810918 Payroll Expense ($000): 181867 Personnel: 2126

✖ △ **INTEGRIS SOUTHWEST MEDICAL CENTER (370106)**, 4401 South Western, Zip 73109–3413; tel. 405/636–7000 **A**1 2 3 7 10 13 **F**3 11 13 15 18 20 22 24 26 28 29 30 31 34 35 40 43 44 45 47 49 50 57 58 59 60 64 68 70 74 75 77 78 79 80 81 82 85 86 87 90 91 92 93 95 96 97 98 100 102 103 107 108 110 111 114 115 118 119 120 121 123 124 129 130 131 132 133 135 143 146 147 148 **S** INTEGRIS Health, Oklahoma City, OK
Primary Contact: Chris Hammes, FACHE, Interim President
CFO: Errol Mitchell, Vice President
CMO: Son Nguyen, M.D., President of Medical Staff
CIO: John Delano, Vice President and Chief Information Officer
CHR: Lynn Ketch, Director
CNO: Marva Harrison, R.N., Vice President and Chief Nursing Officer
Web address: www.integris–health.com
Control: Other not–for–profit (including NFP Corporation) **Service:** General Medical and Surgical

Staffed Beds: 352 Admissions: 11994 Census: 203 Outpatient Visits: 132629 Births: 1295 Total Expense ($000): 235289 Payroll Expense ($000): 73265 Personnel: 1187

✖ **KINDRED HOSPITAL– OKLAHOMA CITY (372004)**, 1407 North Robinson Avenue, Zip 73103–4823; tel. 405/232–8000, (Includes KINDRED HOSPITAL–OKLAHOMA CITY SOUTH, 2129 S.W. 59th Street, Zip 73119; tel. 405/713–5955), (Nonreporting) **A**1 3 5 10 **S** Kindred Healthcare, Louisville, KY
Primary Contact: William Patton, Chief Executive Officer
Web address: www.kindredoklahoma.com
Control: Corporation, Investor–owned, for–profit **Service:** Long–Term Acute Care hospital

Staffed Beds: 93

✖ **LAKESIDE WOMEN'S HOSPITAL (370199)**, 11200 North Portland Avenue, Zip 73120–5045; tel. 405/936–1500 **A**1 10 **F**3 12 13 15 30 35 40 45 59 64 73 81 85 87 110 119 126 132 147 **P**6 **S** INTEGRIS Health, Oklahoma City, OK
Primary Contact: Kelley Brewer, R.N., MSN, President
CFO: Darla McCallister, Chief Financial Officer
CMO: Margaret Hall, M.D., Chief Medical Officer
Web address: www.lakeside–wh.net
Control: Corporation, Investor–owned, for–profit **Service:** Obstetrics and gynecology

Staffed Beds: 23 Admissions: 1564 Census: 10 Outpatient Visits: 4584 Births: 1437 Total Expense ($000): 21159 Payroll Expense ($000): 8013 Personnel: 114

MCBRIDE CLINIC ORTHOPEDIC HOSPITAL (370222), 9600 Broadway Extension, Zip 73114–7408; tel. 405/486–2100 **A**3 5 10 **F**3 29 34 40 64 68 77 79 81 82 85 86 87 107 111 114 119 130 131 146 **P**2 6
Primary Contact: Mark Galliart, Chief Executive Officer
CFO: Greg Gisler, Chief Financial Officer
CNO: Krista Reyna, Chief Nursing Officer
Web address: www.mcboh.com
Control: Corporation, Investor–owned, for–profit **Service:** Orthopedic

Staffed Beds: 60 Admissions: 3510 Census: 29 Outpatient Visits: 154318 Births: 0 Total Expense ($000): 122419 Payroll Expense ($000): 50265 Personnel: 677

✖ **MERCY HOSPITAL OKLAHOMA CITY (370013)**, 4300 West Memorial Road, Zip 73120–8362; tel. 405/755–1515 **A**1 2 5 10 **F**3 11 13 15 28 29 30 31 32 34 35 40 43 44 45 46 47 48 49 50 53 55 57 58 59 60 61 62 63 64 65 68 69 70 72 74 75 76 77 78 79 81 82 83 84 85 86 87 89 90 91 92 93 94 96 100 101 107 108 110 111 114 115 117 118 119 120 121 124 126 129 130 131 132 134 135 143 146 147 148 **P**6 **S** Mercy Health, Chesterfield, MO
Primary Contact: Jim Gebhart, Jr., FACHE, President
COO: Aaron Steffens, Chief Operating Officer
CFO: Jon Vitiello, Chief Financial Officer
CMO: Mark Johnson, M.D., Chief Medical Officer
CIO: Ellen Stephens, Vice President Information Services
CHR: Becky J. Payton, Vice President Human Resources
Web address: www.mercyok.net
Control: Church–operated, Nongovernment, not–for profit **Service:** General Medical and Surgical

Staffed Beds: 369 Admissions: 15172 Census: 214 Outpatient Visits: 294375 Births: 3141 Total Expense ($000): 377213 Payroll Expense ($000): 117044 Personnel: 2422

☐ △ **MERCY REHABILITATION HOSPITAL OKLAHOMA CITY (373033)**, 5401 West Memorial Road, Zip 73142–2026; tel. 405/752–3935 **A**1 7 10 **F**3 29 30 87 90 91 96 130 148
Primary Contact: Sharon Smeltzer, Chief Executive Officer
Control: Partnership, Investor–owned, for–profit **Service:** Rehabilitation

Staffed Beds: 50 Admissions: 1091 Census: 38 Outpatient Visits: 0 Births: 0 Total Expense ($000): 15271 Payroll Expense ($000): 7352 Personnel: 176

◇ **NORTHWEST SURGICAL HOSPITAL (370192)**, 9204 North May Avenue, Zip 73120–4419; tel. 405/848–1918, (Nonreporting) **A**10 21
Primary Contact: Debbie Kearns, Chief Executive Officer
CFO: Cindy Thompson, Chief Financial Officer
CMO: Jimmy Conway, M.D., President Medical Staff
Web address: www.nwsurgicalokc.com/
Control: Corporation, Investor–owned, for–profit **Service:** Orthopedic

Staffed Beds: 9

✖ **OKLAHOMA CENTER FOR ORTHOPEDIC AND MULTI–SPECIALTY SURGERY (370212)**, 8100 South Walker, Suite C., Zip 73139–9402, Mailing Address: P.O. Box 890609, Zip 73189–0609; tel. 405/602–6500 **A**1 10 **F**3 8 12 29 34 35 39 40 45 47 48 54 57 59 64 74 79 81 82 85 86 93 94 97 107 111 129 131 148 **P**6 **S** United Surgical Partners International, Addison, TX
Primary Contact: Mike Kimzey, Chief Executive Officer and Administrator
COO: Jeff Bibb, Chief Operating Officer
CFO: Amy Taylor, Chief Financial Officer
CHR: Sherry Wagner, Director Human Resources
CNO: Jolena Wyer, R.N., Chief Nursing Officer
Web address: www.ocomhospital.com
Control: Partnership, Investor–owned, for–profit **Service:** Orthopedic

Staffed Beds: 14 Admissions: 750 Census: 5 Outpatient Visits: 40815 Births: 0 Total Expense ($000): 51213 Payroll Expense ($000): 14694 Personnel: 247

Many Facility Codes have changed. Please refer to the AHA Guide Code Chart. © 2016 AHA Guide

⊠ △ **OKLAHOMA CITY VETERANS AFFAIRS MEDICAL CENTER**, 921 N.E. 13th Street, Zip 73104–5028; tel. 405/456–1000, (Nonreporting) **A**1 2 3 5 7 8 **S** Department of Veterans Affairs, Washington, DC
Primary Contact: Wade Vlosich, Director
CFO: Michele Pipgrass, Chief Fiscal Service
CMO: Mark Huycke, M.D., Chief of Staff
CIO: David Buckley, Acting Chief Information Management Services
CHR: Kyle Inhofe, Chief Human Resources Officer
CNO: Donna Delise, Associate Director Patient Care Services
Web address: www.oklahoma.va.gov
Control: Veterans Affairs, Government, federal **Service:** General Medical and Surgical

Staffed Beds: 192

◇ **OKLAHOMA HEART HOSPITAL (370215)**, 4050 West Memorial Road, Zip 73120–8382; tel. 405/608–3200 **A**10 21 **F**17 18 20 22 24 26 28 29 30 34 35 40 50 59 64 68 74 75 81 85 86 87 100 102 107 108 111 114 115 116 117 118 119 126 127 130 135 146 **P**3 6
Primary Contact: John Harvey, M.D., President and Chief Executive Officer
COO: Peggy Tipton, Chief Operating Officer and Chief Nursing Officer
CFO: Carol Walker, Chief Financial Officer
CMO: John Harvey, M.D., President and Chief Executive Officer
CIO: Michelle Mullins, Chief Information Officer
CHR: Katherine Wynn, Director Human Resource
Web address: www.okheart.com
Control: Corporation, Investor–owned, for–profit **Service:** Heart

Staffed Beds: 99 **Admissions:** 6981 **Census:** 76 **Outpatient Visits:** 246397 **Births:** 0 **Total Expense ($000):** 196896 **Payroll Expense ($000):** 78962 **Personnel:** 1574

◇ **OKLAHOMA HEART HOSPITAL SOUTH CAMPUS (370234)**, 5200 East I–240 Service Road, Zip 73135; tel. 405/628–6000 **A**10 21 **F**17 18 20 22 24 26 28 29 30 34 35 40 50 53 59 64 66 68 74 75 81 82 85 87 100 107 111 115 116 117 118 119 126 130 135 146 **P**3 6
Primary Contact: John Harvey, M.D., President and Chief Executive Officer
Web address: www.okheart.com
Control: Corporation, Investor–owned, for–profit **Service:** Heart

Staffed Beds: 46 **Admissions:** 4448 **Census:** 45 **Outpatient Visits:** 50993 **Births:** 0 **Total Expense ($000):** 108267 **Payroll Expense ($000):** 38749 **Personnel:** 496

◇ **OKLAHOMA SPINE HOSPITAL (370206)**, 14101 Parkway Commons Drive, Zip 73134–6012; tel. 405/749–2700, (Nonreporting) **A**10 21
Primary Contact: Kevin Blaylock, Chief Executive Officer
Web address: www.oklahomaspine.com
Control: Corporation, Investor–owned, for–profit **Service:** Surgical

Staffed Beds: 12

ONECORE HEALTH (370220), 1044 S.W. 44th Street, Suite 516, Zip 73109–3609; tel. 405/631–3085 **A**10 **F**3 15 40 54 59 64 79 81 82 85 86 87 107 110 111 114 119
Primary Contact: Steve Hockert, Chief Executive Officer
CMO: Joel L. Frazier, M.D., Medical Director
CNO: Teresa Carter, Vice President Patient Care Services
Web address: www.onecorehealth.com
Control: Corporation, Investor–owned, for–profit **Service:** Orthopedic

Staffed Beds: 8 **Admissions:** 249 **Census:** 2 **Outpatient Visits:** 7117 **Births:** 0 **Total Expense ($000):** 12218 **Payroll Expense ($000):** 3039 **Personnel:** 67

⊠ **OU MEDICAL CENTER (370093)**, 1200 Everett Drive, Zip 73104–5047, Mailing Address: P.O. Box 26307, Zip 73126–0307; tel. 405/271–3636, (Includes CHILDREN'S HOSPITAL OF OKLAHOMA, 940 N.E. 13th Street, Zip 73104, Mailing Address: P.O. Box 26307, Zip 73126; tel. 405/271–6165; EVERETT TOWER, 1200 Everett Drive, Zip 73104; tel. 405/271–4700; OU MEDICAL CENTER EDMOND, 1 South Bryant Avenue, Edmond, Zip 73034–6309; tel. 405/341–6100; PRESBYTERIAN TOWER, 700 N.E. 13th Street, Zip 73104–5070; tel. 405/271–5100) **A**1 2 3 5 8 10 **F**3 8 11 12 13 15 17 18 19 20 21 22 23 24 25 26 27 28 29 30 31 32 34 35 37 38 39 40 41 42 43 45 46 47 48 49 50 51 52 55 56 57 58 59 60 61 63 64 65 66 68 70 71 72 74 75 76 77 78 79 81 82 84 85 86 87 88 89 91 92 93 94 96 97 98 99 100 102 103 105 107 108 110 111 114 115 116 117 118 119 120 121 123 124 126 129 130 131 132 135 136 138 139 142 145 146 147 148 **S** HCA, Nashville, TN
Primary Contact: Charles Spicer, President and Chief Executive Officer
COO: Kristina Wallace, R.N., Chief Operating Officer
CFO: Mike Reese, Chief Financial Officer
CMO: Curt Steinhart, M.D., Chief Medical Officer
CIO: Larry Forsyth, Director Information Services
CHR: Jed M. Liuzza, Chief Human Resources Officer
Web address: www.oumedicine.com/oumedicalcenter
Control: Corporation, Investor–owned, for–profit **Service:** General Medical and Surgical

Staffed Beds: 724 **Admissions:** 35090 **Census:** 583 **Outpatient Visits:** 339022 **Births:** 4841 **Total Expense ($000):** 818976 **Payroll Expense ($000):** 226809 **Personnel:** 3333

PRESBYTERIAN TOWER See OU Medical Center

⊠ **SELECT SPECIALTY HOSPITAL–OKLAHOMA CITY (372009)**, 3524 N.W. 56th Street, Zip 73112–4518; tel. 405/606–6700 **A**1 10 **F**1 3 12 29 40 74 75 79 87 107 119 130 148 **S** Select Medical Corporation, Mechanicsburg, PA
Primary Contact: Connie Strickland, Chief Executive Officer
Web address: www.selectspecialtyhospitals.com/company/locations/oklahomacity.aspx
Control: Corporation, Investor–owned, for–profit **Service:** Long–Term Acute Care hospital

Staffed Beds: 72 **Admissions:** 878 **Census:** 65 **Outpatient Visits:** 0 **Births:** 0 **Total Expense ($000):** 31360 **Payroll Expense ($000):** 13713 **Personnel:** 232

⊠ △ **ST. ANTHONY HOSPITAL (370037)**, 1000 North Lee Street, Zip 73102–1080, Mailing Address: P.O. Box 205, Zip 73101–0205; tel. 405/272–7000, (Includes BONE AND JOINT HOSPITAL, 1111 North Dewey Avenue, Zip 73103–2609; tel. 405/272–9671; Tammy Powell, President) **A**1 2 3 5 7 10 12 13 **F**3 4 5 7 8 11 12 13 15 17 18 20 22 24 26 28 29 30 31 34 35 36 37 40 42 43 45 46 47 48 49 50 54 56 57 59 64 67 70 71 74 76 77 78 79 81 82 84 85 86 87 89 90 91 92 93 96 97 98 99 100 101 102 103 104 105 106 107 108 110 111 114 115 117 118 119 120 121 123 124 126 127 129 130 131 132 136 144 146 147 148 **S** SSM Health, Saint Louis, MO
Primary Contact: Tammy Powell, FACHE, M.P.H., President
COO: Marti Jourden, FACHE, Chief Quality Officer
CFO: Shasta Manuel, Executive Director Finance
CMO: Kersey Winfree, M.D., Chief Medical Officer
CIO: Kevin Olson, Director Information Systems
CHR: Cynthia Brundise, Vice President Human Resources
Web address: www.saintsok.com
Control: Church–operated, Nongovernment, not–for profit **Service:** General Medical and Surgical

Staffed Beds: 579 **Admissions:** 21935 **Census:** 432 **Outpatient Visits:** 329590 **Births:** 1264 **Total Expense ($000):** 462964 **Payroll Expense ($000):** 152687 **Personnel:** 2350

☐ **SURGICAL HOSPITAL OF OKLAHOMA (370201)**, 100 S.E. 59th Street, Zip 73129–3616; tel. 405/634–9300 **A**1 10 **F**3 40 81 111 129
Primary Contact: Phil Ross, Chief Executive Officer
Web address: www.sh-ok.com/
Control: Partnership, Investor–owned, for–profit **Service:** General Medical and Surgical

Staffed Beds: 12 **Admissions:** 141 **Census:** 1 **Outpatient Visits:** 5022 **Births:** 0 **Total Expense ($000):** 11561 **Payroll Expense ($000):** 3523 **Personnel:** 69

OK

✠ **VALIR REHABILITATION HOSPITAL (373025)**, 700 N.W. Seventh Street, Zip 73102–1212; tel. 405/236–3131 **A**1 10 **F**3 28 29 30 34 40 50 53 54 56 57 59 64 77 82 85 86 87 90 91 93 96 100 130 131 132 135 143 148 **P**1
Primary Contact: Stacy Smith, R.N., Chief Executive Officer
COO: Ginger Castleberry, Corporate Risk Manager, Quality and Patient Safety
CFO: Scott Brown, Chief Financial Officer
CMO: Tonya Washburn, M.D., Medical Director
CIO: Mark Dickey, Director Business Development
CHR: Bill Turner, Vice President Human Resources
Web address: www.valir.com
Control: Partnership, Investor–owned, for–profit **Service:** Rehabilitation

Staffed Beds: 45 Admissions: 1035 Census: 31 Outpatient Visits: 4200
Births: 0

VETERANS AFFAIRS MEDICAL CENTER See Oklahoma City Veterans Affairs Medical Center

OKMULGEE—Okmulgee County

GEORGE NIGH REHABILITATION CENTER See Muscogee Creek Nation Physical Rehabilitation Center

★ **MUSCOGEE CREEK NATION MEDICAL CENTER (370057)**, 1401 Morris Drive, Zip 74447–6429, Mailing Address: P.O. Box 1038, Zip 74447–1038; tel. 918/756–4233 **A**10 **F**7 11 15 29 34 40 43 50 56 57 59 62 68 81 83 85 87 89 92 93 98 103 107 108 111 115 119 128 130 133 146 **P**6
Primary Contact: Sheridan Pickering, Chief Executive Officer
CFO: John W. Crawford, Chief Financial Officer
CMO: Michael Sandlin, M.D., Chief of Staff
CHR: Stacey R. Burton, Director Human Resources
Web address: www.okmulgeehospital.com
Control: PHS, Indian Service, Government, federal **Service:** General Medical and Surgical

Staffed Beds: 45 Admissions: 674 Census: 10 Outpatient Visits: 27566
Births: 0 Total Expense ($000): 31788 Payroll Expense ($000): 11070
Personnel: 214

MUSCOGEE CREEK NATION PHYSICAL REHABILITATION CENTER (372023), 900 East Airport Road, Zip 74447–9082, Mailing Address: P.O. Box 1118, Zip 74447–1118; tel. 918/756–9211, (Total facility includes 8 beds in nursing home–type unit) **A**10 **F**1 28 29 56 82 90 93 94 96 128 130 135 143 146 148 **P**5
Primary Contact: Gala McBee, Administrator
CFO: Djogan Djogan, Chief Financial Officer
CHR: DeNaye S. Atwell, Manager Human Resources
Web address: www.gnrc.ouhsc.edu/
Control: PHS, Indian Service, Government, federal **Service:** Rehabilitation

Staffed Beds: 38 Admissions: 135 Census: 5 Outpatient Visits: 3726
Births: 0 Total Expense ($000): 8828 Payroll Expense ($000): 4214
Personnel: 111

OWASSO—Tulsa County

★ **BAILEY MEDICAL CENTER (370228)**, 10502 North 110th East Avenue, Zip 74055–6655; tel. 918/376–8000 **A**10 **F**3 12 13 15 18 29 34 40 45 51 57 70 76 79 81 94 107 108 110 111 115 119 129 132 146 147 **S** Ardent Health Services, Nashville, TN
Primary Contact: Keith Mason, Chief Executive Officer
CFO: Brandon Bullard, Chief Financial Officer
CHR: Tandy Groves, Coordinator Human Resources
Web address: www.baileymedicalcenter.com
Control: Corporation, Investor–owned, for–profit **Service:** General Medical and Surgical

Staffed Beds: 37 Admissions: 1391 Census: 9 Outpatient Visits: 30970
Births: 413 Total Expense ($000): 31428 Payroll Expense ($000): 10938
Personnel: 179

★ **ST. JOHN OWASSO (370227)**, 12451 East 100th Street North, Zip 74055–4600; tel. 918/274–5000 **A**10 **F**3 11 13 15 18 29 30 34 35 40 43 45 57 59 64 68 76 79 81 85 87 93 107 108 110 111 114 115 119 130 131 132 146 **P**5 6 **S** Ascension Health, Saint Louis, MO
Primary Contact: David L. Phillips, President and Chief Executive Officer
CFO: Michael R. Nevins, Chief Financial Officer
CMO: Tim Hepner, M.D., Medical Director
CIO: Mike Reeves, Chief Information Officer
CNO: Dan Hall, R.N., Director of Nursing
Web address: www.stjohnowasso.com
Control: Church–operated, Nongovernment, not–for profit **Service:** General Medical and Surgical

Staffed Beds: 45 Admissions: 1836 Census: 9 Outpatient Visits: 60896
Births: 441 Total Expense ($000): 30813 Payroll Expense ($000): 10316
Personnel: 186

PAULS VALLEY—Garvin County

★ **PAULS VALLEY GENERAL HOSPITAL (370156)**, 100 Valley Drive, Zip 73075–6613, Mailing Address: P.O. Box 368, Zip 73075–0368; tel. 405/238–5501 **A**10 20 **F**3 7 10 11 15 29 30 40 57 59 63 64 65 77 81 82 84 87 93 107 117 119 129 130 132 133 146 147 148 **P**3
Primary Contact: Nathan Staggs, Chief Executive Officer
CFO: Dale Semar, Controller
CIO: Rusty Weaver, Manager Information Technology
CHR: Stephanie Dancer, Manager Human Resources
CNO: Kari Howard, Interim Director of Nursing
Web address: www.pvgh.net
Control: City–Government, nonfederal **Service:** General Medical and Surgical

Staffed Beds: 53 Admissions: 449 Census: 6 Outpatient Visits: 18300
Births: 0 Total Expense ($000): 14495 Payroll Expense ($000): 6845
Personnel: 158

PAWHUSKA—Osage County

★ **PAWHUSKA HOSPITAL (371309)**, 1101 East 15th Street, Zip 74056–1920; tel. 918/287–3232, (Nonreporting) **A**10 18
Primary Contact: Godwin Feh, Interim Administrator
CMO: Mike Priest, M.D., Chief of Staff
Control: City–Government, nonfederal **Service:** General Medical and Surgical

Staffed Beds: 27

PERRY—Noble County

★ ◇ **PERRY MEMORIAL HOSPITAL (370139)**, 501 North 14th Street, Zip 73077–5099; tel. 580/336–3541 **A**10 20 21 **F**3 15 28 29 40 45 59 62 64 65 79 81 85 93 97 107 111 114 133 146 148 **P**6 **S** QHR, Brentwood, TN
Primary Contact: Daniel Odegaard, FACHE, Chief Executive Officer
CFO: Courtney Kozikuski, Chief Financial Officer
CMO: Michael Hartwig, M.D., Chief of Staff
CIO: Randy Taylor, Chief Information Technology Officer
CHR: Deb Ellis, Director Human Resources
CNO: Jeannie Carey, R.N., Director Patient Care
Web address: www.pmh–ok.org
Control: Hospital district or authority, Government, nonfederal **Service:** General Medical and Surgical

Staffed Beds: 26 Admissions: 380 Census: 5 Outpatient Visits: 25248
Births: 0 Total Expense ($000): 8404 Payroll Expense ($000): 4091
Personnel: 106

PONCA CITY—Kay County

✠ **ALLIANCEHEALTH PONCA CITY (370006)**, 1900 North 14th Street, Zip 74601–2099; tel. 580/765–3321 **A**1 10 19 **F**3 13 15 18 20 28 29 30 34 35 40 43 46 53 56 57 59 64 65 66 68 69 70 74 75 77 78 79 81 82 85 90 91 93 97 107 108 110 111 115 118 119 129 130 131 132 133 145 146 147 148 **P**6 **S** Community Health Systems, Inc., Franklin, TN
Primary Contact: Christopher Mendoza, Chief Executive Officer
CFO: Sheryl Schmidtberger, Chief Financial Officer
CIO: William Gazaway, Information Technology Security Officer
CHR: Calvin Hodges, Director Human Resources
CNO: Jeanne Stara, R.N., Chief Nursing Officer
Web address: www.AllianceHealthPoncaCity.com
Control: Corporation, Investor–owned, for–profit **Service:** General Medical and Surgical

Staffed Beds: 74 Admissions: 2654 Census: 24 Outpatient Visits: 59809
Births: 555 Total Expense ($000): 51795 Payroll Expense ($000): 21605
Personnel: 358

POTEAU—Le Flore County

★ ◇ **EASTERN OKLAHOMA MEDICAL CENTER (370040)**, 105 Wall Street, Zip 74953–4433, Mailing Address: P.O. Box 1148, Zip 74953–1148; tel. 918/647–8161 **A**10 21 **F**3 11 13 15 29 30 34 40 43 45 46 47 50 57 64 68 70 76 81 85 87 89 98 100 103 105 107 108 110 111 115 119 127 129 133 145 **P**6
Primary Contact: Michael J. Carter, Chief Executive Officer
CFO: Nancy Frier, Chief Financial Officer
CMO: Dennis Carter, M.D., Chief of Staff
CIO: Michael C. Huggins, Administrator Network System
Web address: www.eomchospital.com
Control: County–Government, nonfederal **Service:** General Medical and Surgical

Staffed Beds: 45 Admissions: 1116 Census: 14 Outpatient Visits: 25252
Births: 1 Total Expense ($000): 17411 Payroll Expense ($000): 7504
Personnel: 169

OK

PRAGUE—Lincoln County

PRAGUE COMMUNITY HOSPITAL (371301), 1322 Klabzuba Avenue,
Zip 74864–9005, Mailing Address: P.O. Box S., Zip 74864–1090;
tel. 405/567–4922 **A**10 18 **F**28 34 40 43 45 55 57 59 64 65 68 79 81 93 97
107 111 119 127 128 130 133 148 **P**6 **S** Rural Community Hospitals of
America, Kansas City, MO
Primary Contact: Randy Simmons, Chief Executive Officer
CFO: Doug Erickson, Chief Financial Officer
CMO: Darryl Jackson, D.O., Chief of Staff
CIO: Rhonda Whitnum, Director Health Improvement Management
CHR: Angie Brezny, Director Human Resources
Web address: www.praguehospital.com
Control: Corporation, Investor–owned, for–profit **Service:** General Medical and
Surgical

Staffed Beds: 15 **Admissions:** 101 **Census:** 2 **Outpatient Visits:** 18675
Births: 0 **Total Expense ($000):** 4811 **Payroll Expense ($000):** 3332
Personnel: 55

PRYOR—Mayes County

⊞ **ALLIANCEHEALTH PRYOR (370015)**, 111 North Bailey Street,
Zip 74361–4201, Mailing Address: P.O. Box 278, Zip 74362–0278;
tel. 918/825–1600, (Nonreporting) **A**1 10 **S** Community Health Systems, Inc.,
Franklin, TN
Primary Contact: Douglas K. Weaver, FACHE, President
CMO: Jason Joice, M.D., Chief Medical Staff
CHR: Pamela A. Guthrie, Chief Human Resources Officer
CNO: Mary Ozment, Chief Nursing Officer
Web address: www.integrismayescounty.com
Control: Partnership, Investor–owned, for–profit **Service:** General Medical and
Surgical

Staffed Beds: 24

PURCELL—Mcclain County

PURCELL MUNICIPAL HOSPITAL (370158), 1500 North Green Avenue,
Zip 73080–1699, Mailing Address: P.O. Box 511, Zip 73080–0511;
tel. 405/527–6524 **A**10 **F**3 11 15 18 29 30 34 35 40 45 48 57 59 64 65 68
75 79 81 82 86 87 89 110 114 119 127 130 132 133 148 **P**4 6
Primary Contact: Kem Scully, Chief Executive Officer
COO: Lisa Roberts, Chief Operating Officer
CFO: Jennifer Warren, Chief Financial Officer
CMO: Heather Lynch, M.D., Chief of Staff
CIO: Jennifer Coates, Coordinator Information Technology
CHR: Tara Selfridge, Manager Human Resources
Web address: www.purcellhospital.com
Control: City–Government, nonfederal **Service:** General Medical and Surgical

Staffed Beds: 28 **Admissions:** 645 **Census:** 6 **Outpatient Visits:** 46527
Births: 0 **Total Expense ($000):** 12387 **Payroll Expense ($000):** 5587
Personnel: 130

SALLISAW—Sequoyah County

SEQUOYAH MEMORIAL HOSPITAL (370112), 213 East Redwood Street,
Zip 74955–2811, Mailing Address: P.O. Box 505, Zip 74955–0505;
tel. 918/774–1100 **A**10 **F**3 8 11 14 15 18 29 30 32 34 35 40 43 45 49 50
57 59 62 63 64 65 77 81 84 86 87 91 93 107 111 114 115 119 128 129
130 132 133 146 147 148 **P**5
Primary Contact: Debra R. Knoke, Chief Executive Officer
COO: Debra R. Knoke, Chief Executive Officer
CFO: Glenn Click, Chief Financial Officer
CMO: William E. Wood, M.D., Chief of Staff
CIO: Gary McClanahan, Chief Information Officer
Web address: www.sequoyahmemorial.com/home.php
Control: Hospital district or authority, Government, nonfederal **Service:** General
Medical and Surgical

Staffed Beds: 26 **Admissions:** 1184 **Census:** 10 **Outpatient Visits:** 19344
Births: 0 **Total Expense ($000):** 15704 **Payroll Expense ($000):** 7570
Personnel: 180

SAPULPA—Creek County

★ **ST. JOHN SAPULPA (371312)**, 519 South Division Street, Zip 74066–4501,
Mailing Address: P.O. Box 1368, Zip 74067–1368; tel. 918/224–4280 **A**10 18
F3 8 11 14 29 30 34 35 40 45 57 59 64 68 79 81 85 86 87 107 111 119
128 130 132 133 135 143 146 147 **P**5 6 **S** Ascension Health, Saint Louis, MO
Primary Contact: David L. Phillips, Chief Executive Officer
CFO: John W. Crawford, Chief Financial Officer
CMO: Jason Lepak, M.D., Medical Director
CNO: Kelly Johnson, R.N., Chief Nursing Officer
Web address: www.sjmc.org
Control: Church–operated, Nongovernment, not–for profit **Service:** General
Medical and Surgical

Staffed Beds: 25 **Admissions:** 852 **Census:** 13 **Outpatient Visits:** 36335
Births: 0 **Total Expense ($000):** 23251 **Payroll Expense ($000):** 7469
Personnel: 145

SEILING—Dewey County

★ **SEILING MUNICIPAL HOSPITAL (371332)**, Highway 60 N.E., Zip 73663,
Mailing Address: P.O. Box 720, Zip 73663–0720; tel. 580/922–7361,
(Nonreporting) **A**10 18 **S** Mercy Health, Chesterfield, MO
Primary Contact: Jennifer Coons, Acting Chief Executive Officer
CFO: Nancy Freed, Chief Financial Officer
CMO: Kenneth Duffy, M.D., Medical Director
CHR: Sandy Landreth, Director Human Resources
Web address: www.seilinghospital.com
Control: City–Government, nonfederal **Service:** General Medical and Surgical

Staffed Beds: 18

SEMINOLE—Seminole County

⊞ **ALLIANCEHEALTH SEMINOLE (370229)**, 2401 Wrangler Boulevard,
Zip 74868–1917; tel. 405/303–4000, (Nonreporting) **A**1 10 **S** Community Health
Systems, Inc., Franklin, TN
Primary Contact: Adam Bracks, Chief Executive Officer
CMO: Nikki Chawla, M.D., Medical Director
CHR: Lori Friend, Human Resources Director
CNO: Barbara Lewis, Chief Nursing Officer
Web address: www.hma.com
Control: Partnership, Investor–owned, for–profit **Service:** General Medical and
Surgical

Staffed Beds: 32

SHATTUCK—Ellis County

★ **NEWMAN MEMORIAL HOSPITAL (370007)**, 905 South Main Street,
Zip 73858–9205; tel. 580/938–2551 **A**10 20 **F**3 40 45 81 82 107 114
Primary Contact: Davis S. Wanger, Chief Executive Officer
CFO: Kellcie Skinner, Controller
CMO: Danna Stuart, M.D., Chief Medical Officer
CIO: Robert Neal, Manager Information Technology Services
CNO: Rylee Casper, R.N., Chief Nursing Officer
Web address: www.newmanmemorialhospital.org
Control: City–Government, nonfederal **Service:** General Medical and Surgical

Staffed Beds: 15 **Admissions:** 202 **Census:** 2 **Outpatient Visits:** 37660
Births: 0 **Total Expense ($000):** 8724 **Payroll Expense ($000):** 3327

SHAWNEE—Pottawatomie County

CORNERSTONE HOSPITAL OF OKLAHOMA–SHAWNEE (372019), 1900
Gordon Cooper Drive, 2nd Floor, Zip 74801–8603, Mailing Address: P.O. Box
1245, Zip 74802–1245; tel. 405/395–5800, (Nonreporting) **A**10 **S** Cornerstone
Healthcare Group, Dallas, TX
Primary Contact: Elizabeth Waytula, Chief Executive Officer
COO: Cindy Linck, Chief Nursing Officer
CMO: Rakesh Shrivastava, M.D., Chief Medical Officer
Web address: www.chghospitals.com/shawnee/
Control: Corporation, Investor–owned, for–profit **Service:** Long–Term Acute Care
hospital

Staffed Beds: 34

Hospital, Medicare Provider Number, Address, Telephone, Approval, Facility, and Physician Codes, Health Care System

★ American Hospital Association (AHA) membership
□ The Joint Commission accreditation
○ Healthcare Facilities Accreditation Program
◇ DNV Healthcare Inc. accreditation
⇑ Center for Improvement in Healthcare Quality Accreditation
△ Commission on Accreditation of Rehabilitation Facilities (CARF) accreditation

✠ **ST. ANTHONY SHAWNEE HOSPITAL (370149)**, 1102 West Macarthur ST, Zip 74804–1744, Mailing Address: 1102 West MacArthur Street, Zip 74804–1744; tel. 405/273–2270 **A**1 10 19 **F**3 11 13 15 18 20 22 29 30 31 34 35 40 43 45 50 57 59 60 64 65 68 69 70 75 76 77 78 79 81 82 87 94 107 110 111 114 119 121 123 129 130 131 132 135 144 146 147 148 **P**6 **S** SSM Health, Saint Louis, MO
Primary Contact: Charles E. Skillings, President and Chief Executive Officer
COO: Angela Mohr, R.N., Vice President Nursing and Chief Operating Officer
CFO: Jennifer Pierce, Administrative Director of Finance
CMO: Gaynell Anderson, M.D., Medical Director
CHR: Michael Spears, Human Resource Leader
CNO: Angela Mohr, R.N., Vice President Nursing and Chief Operating Officer
Web address: www.stanthonyshawnee.com
Control: Other not–for–profit (including NFP Corporation) **Service:** General Medical and Surgical

Staffed Beds: 76 **Admissions:** 3837 **Census:** 33 **Outpatient Visits:** 106937 **Births:** 834 **Total Expense ($000):** 72308 **Payroll Expense ($000):** 24960 **Personnel:** 430

UNITY HEALTH CENTER See St. Anthony Shawnee Hospital

SPENCER—Oklahoma County

INTEGRIS MENTAL HEALTH SYSTEM–SPENCER See Integris Baptist Medical Center, Oklahoma City

STIGLER—Haskell County

HASKELL COUNTY COMMUNITY HOSPITAL (371335), 401 Northwest H Street, Zip 74462–1625; tel. 918/967–4682, (Nonreporting) **A**10 18 **S** Rural Community Hospitals of America, Kansas City, MO
Primary Contact: Donald E. Buchanan, Interim Chief Executive Officer
CMO: Stephen Woodson, D.O., Chief of Staff
CIO: Steve Hurst, Information Technology Specialist
Web address: www.haskellhospital.com
Control: Corporation, Investor–owned, for–profit **Service:** General Medical and Surgical

Staffed Beds: 32

HASKELL COUNTY HEALTHCARE SYSTEM See Haskell County Community Hospital

STILLWATER—Payne County

★ ◇ **STILLWATER MEDICAL CENTER (370049)**, 1323 West Sixth Avenue, Zip 74074–4399, Mailing Address: P.O. Box 2408, Zip 74076–2408; tel. 405/372–1480 **A**3 5 10 21 **F**3 8 11 13 15 18 20 22 28 29 31 34 35 39 40 43 45 46 47 48 49 50 51 53 54 57 59 62 63 64 65 68 69 70 74 75 76 78 79 81 82 85 87 90 91 93 94 97 107 108 110 111 115 117 119 126 129 130 131 132 135 144 146 147 148 **P**5 6
Primary Contact: Denise Webber, President and Chief Executive Officer
CFO: Alan Lovelace, Vice President and Chief Financial Officer
CMO: Steve Cummings, M.D., Chief of Medical Staff
CIO: Chris Roark, Chief Information Officer
CHR: Keith Hufnagel, Director Human Resources
CNO: Elizabeth Michael, R.N., Vice President Patient Care Services and Chief Nursing Officer
Web address: www.stillwater–medical.org
Control: Hospital district or authority, Government, nonfederal **Service:** General Medical and Surgical

Staffed Beds: 87 **Admissions:** 3944 **Census:** 42 **Outpatient Visits:** 119507 **Births:** 911 **Total Expense ($000):** 141433 **Payroll Expense ($000):** 59619 **Personnel:** 1030

STILWELL—Adair County

MEMORIAL HOSPITAL (370178), 1401 West Locust, Zip 74960–3275, Mailing Address: P.O. Box 272, Zip 74960–0272; tel. 918/696–3101 **A**10 **F**11 13 15 29 30 32 34 40 43 45 47 49 54 56 57 59 62 65 68 74 75 76 77 79 81 85 86 87 91 92 93 100 101 104 107 111 114 119 129 131 132 133 135 146 147 148
Primary Contact: Alan L. Adams, President
Web address: www.stilwellmemorialhospital.com
Control: Other not–for–profit (including NFP Corporation) **Service:** General Medical and Surgical

Staffed Beds: 34 **Admissions:** 1727 **Census:** 15

STROUD—Lincoln County

STROUD REGIONAL MEDICAL CENTER (371316), Highway 66 West, Zip 74079, Mailing Address: P.O. Box 530, Zip 74079–0530; tel. 918/968–3571 **A**10 18 **F**3 8 11 29 30 34 35 40 41 43 45 57 59 64 68 77 81 89 93 107 114 119 128 130 133 135 143 146 148 **P**5 **S** Southern Plains Medical Group, Oklahoma City, OK
Primary Contact: Larry Troxell, Administrator
CFO: Richard E. Rentsch, President
CMO: Ken Darvin, M.D., Chief of Staff
CIO: Donna Buchanan, Director Nursing
CHR: Leannette Raffety, Administrative Generalist
Web address: www.stroudhospital.com/
Control: Other not–for–profit (including NFP Corporation) **Service:** General Medical and Surgical

Staffed Beds: 25 **Admissions:** 138 **Census:** 2

SULPHUR—Murray County

★ **ARBUCKLE MEMORIAL HOSPITAL (371328)**, 2011 West Broadway Street, Zip 73086–4221; tel. 580/622–2161 **A**10 18 **F**3 11 29 32 40 45 56 57 81 87 93 107 119 133 135 148 **P**6 **S** Mercy Health, Chesterfield, MO
Primary Contact: Darin Farrell, Chief Executive Officer
CFO: Denise Welch, Chief Financial Officer
CMO: Ryan Oden, D.O., Chief of Staff
CIO: Tiffany Sands, Manager Health Information
CHR: Sallie Tomlinson, Manager Human Resources
CNO: Sarah Freehill, Chief Nursing Officer
Web address: www.arbucklehospital.com/
Control: County–Government, nonfederal **Service:** General Medical and Surgical

Staffed Beds: 13 **Admissions:** 559 **Census:** 12 **Outpatient Visits:** 24936 **Total Expense ($000):** 14033 **Payroll Expense ($000):** 7411 **Personnel:** 116

TAHLEQUAH—Cherokee County

★ ◇ **CHEROKEE NATION W.W. HASTINGS INDIAN HOSPITAL (370171)**, 100 South Bliss Avenue, Zip 74464–2512; tel. 918/458–3100, (Nonreporting) **A**10 21 **S** U. S. Indian Health Service, Rockville, MD
Primary Contact: Brian Hail, Chief Executive Officer
COO: Mitchell Thornbrugh, Administrative Officer
CMO: Douglas Nolan, M.D., Medical Director
CIO: Mitchell Thornbrugh, Acting Chief Information Officer
CNO: Valerie J. Rogers, Director of Nursing
Web address: www.cherokee.org
Control: PHS, Indian Service, Government, federal **Service:** General Medical and Surgical

Staffed Beds: 58

★ **NORTHEASTERN HEALTH SYSTEM (370089)**, 1400 East Downing Street, Zip 74464–3324, Mailing Address: P.O. Box 1008, Zip 74465–1008; tel. 918/456–0641 **A**10 13 20 **F**3 7 11 13 15 17 18 20 22 24 28 29 30 31 34 35 39 40 43 45 46 47 49 51 57 59 60 64 68 70 75 76 77 78 79 80 81 82 85 87 89 90 93 97 98 103 107 108 110 111 114 115 116 117 118 119 120 121 123 129 130 135 144 146 147 148 **P**6
Primary Contact: James Berry, Executive Vice President and Administrator
COO: Mark McCroskey, Vice President Operations
CFO: Julie Ward, Vice President Finance
CIO: Julie Ward, Vice President Finance
CHR: Phyllis Smith, Vice President Human Resources
CNO: Donna Dallis, R.N., Vice President Patient Care
Web address: www.nhs–ok.org/
Control: City–Government, nonfederal **Service:** General Medical and Surgical

Staffed Beds: 90 **Admissions:** 3437 **Census:** 43 **Outpatient Visits:** 141847 **Births:** 278 **Total Expense ($000):** 95647 **Payroll Expense ($000):** 30509 **Personnel:** 728

TALIHINA—Latimer County

✠ **CHOCTAW NATION HEALTH CARE CENTER (370172)**, One Choctaw Way, Zip 74571–2022; tel. 918/567–7000 **A**1 10 13 **F**3 4 5 7 12 13 15 18 29 34 35 38 39 40 45 50 53 54 56 57 58 59 64 65 68 71 74 75 76 79 81 87 89 91 93 97 107 110 111 119 127 129 130 135 141 142 143 144 146 147 148
Primary Contact: Todd Hallmark, Chief Executive Officer
COO: Todd Hallmark, Chief Operating Officer
CMO: Jason Hill, M.D., Chief Medical Officer
CIO: Dwane Sorrells, Chief Information Officer
CHR: Jami Beckwith, Director Human Resources
CNO: Lisa Isaac, Chief Nursing Officer
Web address: www.cnhsa.com
Control: PHS, Indian Service, Government, federal **Service:** General Medical and Surgical

Staffed Beds: 44 **Admissions:** 1433 **Census:** 11 **Outpatient Visits:** 223893 **Births:** 529 **Personnel:** 1673

Many Facility Codes have changed. Please refer to the AHA Guide Code Chart. © 2016 AHA Guide

TISHOMINGO—Johnston County

JOHNSTON MEMORIAL HOSPITAL See Mercy Hospital Tishomingo

★ **MERCY HOSPITAL TISHOMINGO (371304)**, 1000 South Byrd Street, Zip 73460–3299; tel. 580/371–2327 **A**10 18 **F**3 29 40 43 44 108 133 **S** Mercy Health, Chesterfield, MO
Primary Contact: Gary Sharum, Administrator
CFO: Lisa Dowling, Manager Finance
CHR: Arlita Hummelke, Manager Human Resources
Web address: www.mercy.net/
Control: Church–operated, Nongovernment, not–for profit **Service:** General Medical and Surgical

Staffed Beds: 25 **Admissions:** 259 **Census:** 5 **Outpatient Visits:** 5068
Births: 0 **Total Expense ($000):** 5665 **Payroll Expense ($000):** 3114
Personnel: 56

TULSA—Tulsa County

AMG SPECIALTY HOSPITAL–TULSA (372011), 2408 East 81st Street, Suite 2800, Zip 74104–6510; tel. 918/710–3620, (Includes CONTINUOUS CARE CENTERS OF OKLAHOMA, 744 West Ninth Street, 9th Floor, Zip 74127; tel. 918/599–4604) **A**10 **F**1 3 29 30 35 75 77 85 87 91 100 130 148 **S** AMG Integrated Healthcare Management, Lafayette, LA
Primary Contact: Elizabeth Rees, Chief Executive Officer
COO: Mike Harris, Chief Operating Officer
CFO: Basil Wyatt, Chief Financial Officer
CMO: Mark Myers, M.D., Chief Medical Officer
CIO: Dana Jetton, Chief Information Officer
CHR: Donna Nagel, Director Human Resources
Web address: www.amgoftulsa.com/
Control: Corporation, Investor–owned, for–profit **Service:** Long–Term Acute Care hospital

Staffed Beds: 40 **Admissions:** 343 **Census:** 24 **Outpatient Visits:** 0 **Births:** 0 **Total Expense ($000):** 11104 **Payroll Expense ($000):** 5440 **Personnel:** 100

△ **BROOKHAVEN HOSPITAL (374012)**, 201 South Garnett Road, Zip 74128–1805; tel. 918/438–4257 **A**7 10 **F**4 5 29 30 38 74 75 77 98 104 106 130 132
Primary Contact: Rolf B. Gainer, M.D., Chief Executive Officer and Administrator
CFO: Kenneth Pierce, Chief Financial Officer
CMO: Mark Gage, D.O., Medical Director
CHR: Heather Dudley, Director Administrative Services
CNO: Matt Maxey, R.N., Director of Nursing
Web address: www.brookhavenhospital.com
Control: Corporation, Investor–owned, for–profit **Service:** Psychiatric

Staffed Beds: 64 **Admissions:** 1166 **Census:** 51 **Outpatient Visits:** 3625
Births: 0 **Total Expense ($000):** 11325 **Payroll Expense ($000):** 6267
Personnel: 162

CONTINUOUS CARE CENTERS OF TULSA See AMG Specialty Hospital–Tulsa

✳ ◇ **HILLCREST HOSPITAL – SOUTH (370202)**, 8801 South 101st East Avenue, Zip 74133–5716; tel. 918/294–4000 **A**1 10 21 **F**3 13 15 18 20 22 24 26 28 29 34 40 43 47 49 51 64 70 76 79 81 85 86 87 91 93 97 107 108 110 111 114 115 119 126 129 130 131 145 146 147 148 **S** Ardent Health Services, Nashville, TN
Primary Contact: Lynn M. Mergen, Chief Executive Officer
COO: Matthew Morgan, Associate Administrator
CFO: James Washecka, Chief Financial Officer
CMO: David L. Pohl, M.D., Chief of Staff
CIO: David Graser, Vice President and Chief Information Officer
CHR: Rachel Steward, Director Human Resources
CNO: Dava Baldridge, R.N., Chief Nursing Officer
Web address: www.southcresthospital.com
Control: Corporation, Investor–owned, for–profit **Service:** General Medical and Surgical

Staffed Beds: 160 **Admissions:** 7609 **Census:** 94 **Outpatient Visits:** 87050
Births: 1407 **Total Expense ($000):** 121250 **Payroll Expense ($000):** 39494 **Personnel:** 590

★ ◇ **HILLCREST MEDICAL CENTER (370001)**, 1120 South Utica Avenue, Zip 74104–4090; tel. 918/579–1000 **A**3 5 10 21 **F**3 11 13 15 16 17 18 20 22 24 26 28 29 30 31 34 37 40 43 45 46 47 48 49 50 51 53 55 57 58 59 60 64 68 70 72 74 75 76 78 79 80 81 83 84 85 86 87 90 93 98 100 107 108 110 111 114 115 116 117 118 119 120 121 123 124 126 129 130 131 135 145 146 147 148 **S** Ardent Health Services, Nashville, TN
Primary Contact: Kevin J. Gross, FACHE, President and Chief Executive Officer
COO: Brian Connor, FACHE, Chief Operating Officer
CFO: Donald Baker, CPA, Chief Financial Officer
CMO: Jennifer Clark, M.D., Chief Quality Officer and Chief Medical Officer
CIO: Richard Gomez, Assistant Vice President Information Technology Division
CHR: Donald Morris, Vice President Human Resources
CNO: Danny Hardman, FACHE, Chief Nursing Officer
Web address: www.hillcrestmedicalcenter.com
Control: Corporation, Investor–owned, for–profit **Service:** General Medical and Surgical

Staffed Beds: 508 **Admissions:** 23220 **Census:** 322 **Outpatient Visits:** 183112 **Births:** 2950 **Total Expense ($000):** 421579 **Payroll Expense ($000):** 121830 **Personnel:** 1985

✦ **LAUREATE PSYCHIATRIC CLINIC AND HOSPITAL (374020)**, 6655 South Yale Avenue, Zip 74136–3329; tel. 918/481–4000 **A**1 3 5 10 **F**4 5 40 98 99 100 101 102 103 104 105 106 146 **P**6 **S** Saint Francis Health System, Tulsa, OK
Primary Contact: William Schloss, Senior Vice President, Administrator
CFO: Eric Schick, Senior Vice President, Chief Administrative Officer and Chief Financial Officer
CMO: Mark I. Frost, M.D., Senior Vice President Medical Affairs
CNO: Lynn A. Sund, Senior Vice President, Administrator and Chief Nursing Executive
Web address: www.laureate.com
Control: Other not–for–profit (including NFP Corporation) **Service:** Psychiatric

Staffed Beds: 75 **Admissions:** 2941 **Census:** 68 **Outpatient Visits:** 62032
Births: 0 **Total Expense ($000):** 33046 **Payroll Expense ($000):** 19002
Personnel: 359

MEADOWBROOK SPECIALTY HOSPITAL OF TULSA See Post Acute Medical Specialty Hospital of Tulsa

◯ **OKLAHOMA STATE UNIVERSITY MEDICAL CENTER (370078)**, 744 West Ninth Street, Zip 74127–9020; tel. 918/599–1000 **A**10 11 12 13 **F**3 8 13 15 18 20 22 24 26 28 29 30 31 34 35 40 43 45 47 49 50 53 56 57 58 59 61 64 65 68 70 71 72 74 75 76 77 78 79 81 84 85 87 92 93 96 97 100 104 107 108 110 111 115 116 117 119 129 130 131 135 146 147 148 **P**6 8
Primary Contact: Rhett Stover, Chief Executive Officer
COO: Jeff Stroup, Chief Operating Officer
CFO: Sara Bradley, Chief Financial Officer
CMO: Damon Baker, D.O., Chief Medical Officer
CIO: Heidi Holmes, Chief Information Officer
CNO: Joy Upshaw, Chief Nursing Officer
Web address: www.osumc.net
Control: Hospital district or authority, Government, nonfederal **Service:** General Medical and Surgical

Staffed Beds: 191 **Admissions:** 6600 **Census:** 92 **Outpatient Visits:** 72500
Births: 475

OKLAHOMA SURGICAL HOSPITAL (370210), 2408 East 81st Street, Suite 300, Zip 74137–4215; tel. 918/477–5000 **A**3 5 10 **F**3 12 29 30 34 35 40 41 44 45 49 50 51 58 64 65 68 74 75 77 79 81 82 85 86 87 93 94 107 108 111 114 119 126 130 131 **P**2
Primary Contact: Rick Ferguson, Chief Executive Officer
CFO: Dub Cleland, Chief Financial Officer
Web address: www.oklahomasurgicalhospital.com
Control: Partnership, Investor–owned, for–profit **Service:** Surgical

Staffed Beds: 49 **Admissions:** 3857 **Census:** 24 **Outpatient Visits:** 27581
Births: 0 **Total Expense ($000):** 86289 **Payroll Expense ($000):** 18913
Personnel: 383

PARKSIDE PSYCHIATRIC HOSPITAL AND CLINIC (374021), 1620 East 12th Street, Zip 74120–5407; tel. 918/582–2131 **A**3 5 10 **F**3 5 35 38 59 98 99 102 103 104 105 106 146
Primary Contact: Debra Moore, Chief Executive Officer
CFO: Saunya Moore, Chief Financial Officer
CMO: Marvin Jin, M.D., Medical Director
CIO: Joe Vitali, Director Information Technology
CHR: David Patterson, Director Human Resources
Web address: www.parksideinc.org
Control: Other not–for–profit (including NFP Corporation) **Service:** Psychiatric

Staffed Beds: 60 **Admissions:** 1844 **Census:** 59 **Outpatient Visits:** 20900
Births: 0 **Total Expense ($000):** 13279 **Payroll Expense ($000):** 7853
Personnel: 179

Hospital, Medicare Provider Number, Address, Telephone, Approval, Facility, and Physician Codes, Health Care System

★ American Hospital Association (AHA) membership
☐ The Joint Commission accreditation
◯ Healthcare Facilities Accreditation Program
◇ DNV Healthcare Inc. accreditation
⇑ Center for Improvement in Healthcare Quality Accreditation
△ Commission on Accreditation of Rehabilitation Facilities (CARF) accreditation

OK

○ **PINNACLE SPECIALTY HOSPITAL (370233)**, 2408 East 81st Street, Suite 600, Zip 74137–4200; tel. 918/392–2780, (Nonreporting) **A**10 11
Primary Contact: Vicki Schaff, Chief Executive Officer and Chief Operating Officer
CFO: Marc Cravens, Chief Financial Officer
CHR: Roberta Wagle, Director Human Resources
CNO: Jill Voelkel, Chief Nursing Officer
Web address: www.pinnaclespecialtyhospital.com/
Control: Partnership, Investor–owned, for–profit **Service:** General Medical and Surgical

Staffed Beds: 4

⊠ **POST ACUTE MEDICAL SPECIALTY HOSPITAL OF TULSA (372018)**, 3219 South 79th East Avenue, Zip 74145–1343; tel. 918/663–8183 **A**1 10 **F**1 3 29 40 60 68 70 75 87 94 100 107 108 114 130 143 148 **S** Post Acute Medical, LLC, Enola, PA
Primary Contact: Lee A. Simpson, Jr., Chief Executive Officer
CFO: Lee A. Simpson, Jr., Chief Executive Officer
Web address: www.postacutetulsa.com
Control: Corporation, Investor–owned, for–profit **Service:** Long–Term Acute Care hospital

Staffed Beds: 60 **Admissions:** 485 **Census:** 34 **Outpatient Visits:** 5 **Births:** 0 **Total Expense ($000):** 14596 **Payroll Expense ($000):** 6237 **Personnel:** 144

SAINT FRANCIS HEART HOSPITAL See Saint Francis Hospital

⊠ ◇ **SAINT FRANCIS HOSPITAL (370091)**, 6161 South Yale Avenue, Zip 74136–1902; tel. 918/494–2200, (Includes CHILDREN'S HOSPITAL AT SAINT FRANCIS, 6161 South Yale Avenue, tel. 918/502–6714; Shannon M. Filosa, Executive Director Women's and Children; SAINT FRANCIS HEART HOSPITAL, 6151 South Yale Avenue, tel. 918/494–1817; Douglas Williams, Vice President, Saint Francis Heart Hospital) **A**1 2 3 5 10 21 **F**3 7 8 11 12 13 15 17 18 19 20 21 22 23 24 25 26 27 28 29 30 31 32 35 37 39 40 41 43 44 45 46 47 48 49 50 51 54 55 56 57 58 59 60 61 64 66 68 70 72 73 74 75 76 77 78 79 80 81 82 83 84 85 86 87 88 89 90 92 93 107 108 110 111 114 115 116 117 118 119 120 121 123 124 126 129 130 131 132 135 136 138 141 146 148 **P**6 **S** Saint Francis Health System, Tulsa, OK
Primary Contact: Lynn A. Sund, Senior Vice President, Chief Nurse Executive, Saint Francis Health System and Administrator, Saint F
COO: Barry L. Steichen, Executive Vice President and Chief Operating Officer, Saint Francis Health System
CFO: Eric Schick, Senior Vice President and Chief Financial Officer, Saint Francis Health System
CMO: Mark I. Frost, M.D., Senior Vice President Medical Affairs, Saint Francis Health System
CIO: Meridith Coburn, Vice President Information Services
CNO: Lynn A. Sund, Senior Vice President, Chief Nurse Executive, Saint Francis Health System and Administrator, Saint Francis Hospital
Web address: www.saintfrancis.com
Control: Other not–for–profit (including NFP Corporation) **Service:** General Medical and Surgical

Staffed Beds: 841 **Admissions:** 43284 **Census:** 586 **Outpatient Visits:** 372739 **Births:** 4138 **Total Expense ($000):** 745499 **Payroll Expense ($000):** 279594 **Personnel:** 5224

⊠ **SAINT FRANCIS HOSPITAL SOUTH (370218)**, 10501 East 91St. Streeet, Zip 74133–5790; tel. 918/307–6010 **A**1 10 **F**11 13 15 18 20 22 26 29 30 34 35 37 39 40 44 48 49 50 51 57 58 60 61 64 68 70 72 75 76 79 80 81 82 85 87 107 108 110 111 114 115 118 119 130 146 148 **P**6 **S** Saint Francis Health System, Tulsa, OK
Primary Contact: David S. Weil, Senior Vice President and Administrator
COO: Barry L. Steichen, Executive Vice President and Chief Operating Officer
CFO: Eric Schick, Chief Financial Officer
CMO: Mark I. Frost, M.D., Senior Vice President Medical Affairs
CIO: Meridith Coburn, Vice President, Information Systems
CHR: Amy B. Adams, Executive Director Human Resources
CNO: Lynn A. Sund, Chief Nursing Executive
Web address: www.saintfrancis.com/south/
Control: Other not–for–profit (including NFP Corporation) **Service:** General Medical and Surgical

Staffed Beds: 84 **Admissions:** 4429 **Census:** 44 **Outpatient Visits:** 71190 **Births:** 1295 **Total Expense ($000):** 68552 **Payroll Expense ($000):** 26074 **Personnel:** 425

⊠ **SELECT SPECIALTY HOSPITAL–TULSA MIDTOWN (372007)**, 1125 South Trenton Avenue, 3rd Floor, Zip 74120–5418; tel. 918/579–7300 **A**1 10 **F**1 3 29 75 85 87 130 148 **S** Select Medical Corporation, Mechanicsburg, PA
Primary Contact: Beth Cullum, Interim Chief Executive Officer
CMO: E. Joe Schelbar, M.D., Medical Director
CNO: Connie Ryan, Chief Nursing Officer
Web address: www.tulsa.selectspecialtyhospitals.com/
Control: Corporation, Investor–owned, for–profit **Service:** Long–Term Acute Care hospital

Staffed Beds: 56 **Admissions:** 382 **Census:** 26 **Outpatient Visits:** 0 **Births:** 0 **Total Expense ($000):** 14269 **Payroll Expense ($000):** 6507 **Personnel:** 83

☐ **SHADOW MOUNTAIN BEHAVIORAL HEALTH SYSTEM**, 6262 South Sheridan Road, Zip 74133–4055; tel. 918/492–8200 **A**1 3 5 **F**40 41 54 64 98 99 101 102 104 106 **P**6 **S** Universal Health Services, Inc., King of Prussia, PA
Primary Contact: Mike Kistler, Chief Executive Officer
CFO: Kirt Penrod, Chief Financial Officer
CMO: K. Michael Saliba, M.D., Medical Director
CHR: Jordan Cooke, Director Human Resources
Web address: www.shadowmountainbhs.com
Control: Corporation, Investor–owned, for–profit **Service:** Children's hospital psychiatric

Staffed Beds: 238 **Admissions:** 2703 **Census:** 195 **Outpatient Visits:** 24448 **Births:** 0 **Total Expense ($000):** 34718 **Payroll Expense ($000):** 13525 **Personnel:** 360

☐ **SOUTHWESTERN REGIONAL MEDICAL CENTER (370190)**, 10109 East 79th Street, Zip 74133–4564; tel. 918/286–5000 **A**1 2 3 5 10 **F**3 11 15 29 30 31 34 35 36 40 44 45 46 47 49 53 55 57 58 59 64 67 70 75 77 78 80 81 82 84 85 87 93 97 100 104 107 108 110 111 114 116 117 118 119 120 121 123 124 126 130 132 135 136 143 145 146 148 **P**6 **S** Cancer Treatment Centers of America, Schaumburg, IL
Primary Contact: Richard Haldeman, President and Chief Executive Officer
COO: Jay Foley, Chief Operating Officer
CFO: David Hedges, Chief Financial Officer
CMO: Daniel Nader, D.O., Chief of Staff
CIO: Craig Olson, Director Information Technology
CHR: Ryan Crawford, Director Talent
CNO: Denise Geuder, Vice President Patient Care Service and Chief Nursing Officer
Web address: www.cancercenter.com
Control: Corporation, Investor–owned, for–profit **Service:** Cancer

Staffed Beds: 40 **Admissions:** 796 **Census:** 16 **Outpatient Visits:** 56189 **Births:** 0

⊠ **ST. JOHN MEDICAL CENTER (370114)**, 1923 South Utica Avenue, Zip 74104–6502; tel. 918/744–2345 **A**1 2 3 5 10 **F**3 8 9 11 12 13 14 15 17 18 19 20 22 24 26 28 29 30 31 34 35 37 39 40 43 45 46 47 48 49 50 51 53 54 56 57 58 59 60 61 62 63 64 65 66 68 70 72 73 74 75 76 77 78 79 80 81 82 83 84 85 86 87 88 89 90 92 93 94 96 97 100 104 107 108 110 111 114 115 116 117 118 119 120 121 123 124 126 129 130 131 132 135 138 141 143 145 146 147 148 **P**1 5 **S** Ascension Health, Saint Louis, MO
Primary Contact: Jeffrey D. Nowlin, President and Chief Operating Officer
COO: Jeffrey D. Nowlin, President and Chief Operating Officer
CFO: Wayne Walthall, Vice President and Chief Financial Officer
CMO: William Allred, M.D., Vice President Medical Affairs
CIO: Mike Reeves, Vice President
CHR: John Page Bachman, Corporate Vice President
CNO: Pamela Kiser, R.N., Chief Nursing Executive and Vice President of Nursing
Web address: www.sjmc.org
Control: Church–operated, Nongovernment, not–for profit **Service:** General Medical and Surgical

Staffed Beds: 546 **Admissions:** 28900 **Census:** 435 **Outpatient Visits:** 249436 **Births:** 2153 **Total Expense ($000):** 496539 **Payroll Expense ($000):** 159872 **Personnel:** 2591

⊠ **TULSA SPINE AND SPECIALTY HOSPITAL (370216)**, 6901 South Olympia Avenue, Zip 74132–1843; tel. 918/388–5701, (Nonreporting) **A**1 10
Primary Contact: Terry L. Woodbeck, Administrator
CFO: Thom Biby, Chief Financial Officer
CMO: David Fell, M.D., Chief Medical Officer
Web address: www.tulsaspinehospital.com
Control: Corporation, Investor–owned, for–profit **Service:** General Medical and Surgical

Staffed Beds: 21

VINITA—Craig County

★ **CRAIG GENERAL HOSPITAL (370065)**, 735 North Foreman Street, Zip 74301–1418, Mailing Address: P.O. Box 326, Zip 74301–0326; tel. 918/256–7551 **A**10 20 **F**3 11 13 15 29 30 34 35 40 53 55 56 57 59 64 65 75 76 77 81 85 89 97 98 100 101 103 104 105 106 107 108 110 111 115 119 127 128 130 132 133 135 146 147 148
Primary Contact: Herbert Crum, Jr., Chief Executive Officer
CMO: Ed Allensworth, M.D., Medical Director
CHR: Darlene R. Nolte, Chief Human Resource Officer
CNO: Ann Carr, R.N., Chief Nursing Officer
Web address: www.craiggeneralhospital.com
Control: Hospital district or authority, Government, nonfederal **Service:** General Medical and Surgical

Staffed Beds: 55 **Admissions:** 1274 **Census:** 22 **Outpatient Visits:** 34360 **Births:** 55 **Total Expense ($000):** 28213 **Payroll Expense ($000):** 10903 **Personnel:** 252

OKLAHOMA FORENSIC CENTER, 24800 South 4420 Road, Zip 74301–5544, Mailing Address: P.O. Box 69, Zip 74301–0069; tel. 918/256–7841, (Nonreporting) **S** Oklahoma Department of Mental Health and Substance Abuse Services, Oklahoma City, OK
Primary Contact: Kevan Finley, Chief Executive Officer
CFO: Miriam Harris, Director Finance
CMO: Satwant Tandon, M.D., Director of Clinical Services
CIO: Kevin Marble, Director Information Technology
CHR: Julie Jacobs, Director Human Resources
CNO: Glenda Satterwhite, Director of Nursing
Web address: www.odmhsas.org
Control: State–Government, nonfederal **Service:** Psychiatric

Staffed Beds: 200

WAGONER—Wagoner County

WAGONER COMMUNITY HOSPITAL (370166), 1200 West Cherokee Street, Zip 74467–4624, Mailing Address: P.O. Box 407, Zip 74477–0407; tel. 918/485–5514 **A**10 **F**3 11 15 28 29 30 34 39 40 41 45 50 51 57 59 64 65 68 70 75 79 81 82 85 87 89 98 102 107 108 110 111 114 119 130 131 135 146 148
Primary Contact: Jimmy Leopard, FACHE, Chief Executive Officer
COO: Louise Dodson, R.N., Chief Operating Officer and Chief Nursing Officer
CFO: Rebecca Sharp, Chief Financial Officer
CMO: Casey Hanna, M.D., Chief of Staff
CIO: Jim Riley, Director Information Technology
CHR: Barnetta Pofahl, Director Human Resources
CNO: Louise Dodson, R.N., Chief Nursing Officer
Web address: www.wagonerhospital.com
Control: Hospital district or authority, Government, nonfederal **Service:** General Medical and Surgical

Staffed Beds: 100 Admissions: 2570 Census: 34 Outpatient Visits: 25320
Births: 0 Total Expense ($000): 23069 Payroll Expense ($000): 9807
Personnel: 194

WATONGA—Blaine County

★ **MERCY HOSPITAL WATONGA (371302)**, 500 North Clarence Nash Boulevard, Zip 73772–2845, Mailing Address: P.O. Box 370, Zip 73772–0370; tel. 580/623–7211 **A**10 18 **F**3 11 29 30 34 40 43 50 57 59 64 68 75 85 87 93 107 114 119 130 132 133 135 **P**6 **S** Mercy Health, Chesterfield, MO
Primary Contact: Bobby Stitt, R.N., Administrator
CFO: Patricia Dianne Robertson, Chief Financial Officer
CHR: Mary Jo Messelt, Manager Human Resources
Web address: www.mercy.net/watongaok/practice/mercy–hospital–watonga
Control: Church–operated, Nongovernment, not–for profit **Service:** General Medical and Surgical

Staffed Beds: 17 Admissions: 180 Census: 2 Outpatient Visits: 10058
Births: 0 Total Expense ($000): 6041 Payroll Expense ($000): 3422
Personnel: 56

WAURIKA—Jefferson County

★ **JEFFERSON COUNTY HOSPITAL (371311)**, Highway 70 and 81, Zip 73573–3075, Mailing Address: P.O. Box 90, Zip 73573–0090; tel. 580/228–2344 **A**10 18 **F**11 40 43 64 93 107 119 127 129 133 146 **P**6
Primary Contact: Richard Gillespie, Chief Executive Officer
CFO: Richard Tallon, Chief Financial Officer
CMO: Rob Linzman, D.O., Chief of Staff
CIO: Nikki McGahey, Information Officer
Web address: www.jeffersoncountyhospital.net
Control: Hospital district or authority, Government, nonfederal **Service:** General Medical and Surgical

Staffed Beds: 25 Admissions: 139 Census: 2 Outpatient Visits: 9452
Births: 0 Total Expense ($000): 3345 Payroll Expense ($000): 1604
Personnel: 39

WEATHERFORD—Custer County

★ **WEATHERFORD REGIONAL HOSPITAL (371323)**, 3701 East Main Street, Zip 73096–3309; tel. 580/772–5551 **A**10 18 **F**3 11 13 15 29 34 40 43 45 64 68 75 76 77 81 86 87 93 107 108 110 111 115 119 130 133 135 144 146 147 148 **P**6 7
Primary Contact: Debbie Howe, Chief Executive Officer
CFO: Stephanie Helton, Chief Financial Officer
CMO: Jonathan Ray Long, M.D., Chief of Staff
CIO: Amy Outhier, Director Health Information Management
CHR: Tawnya Paden, Director Human Resources
CNO: Delvin Mast, R.N., Director of Nursing
Web address: www.weatherfordhospital.com
Control: Hospital district or authority, Government, nonfederal **Service:** General Medical and Surgical

Staffed Beds: 22 Admissions: 674 Census: 7 Outpatient Visits: 56306
Births: 149 Total Expense ($000): 18641 Payroll Expense ($000): 7192
Personnel: 164

WILBURTON—Latimer County

LATIMER COUNTY GENERAL HOSPITAL (370072), 806 Highway 2 North, Zip 74578–3698; tel. 918/465–2391, (Nonreporting) **A**10
Primary Contact: Shawn Howard, Administrator
CMO: Richard Valbuena, M.D., Medical Director
CHR: Rachel Chinnock, Chief Human Resources Officer
Web address: www.lcghok.com/
Control: County–Government, nonfederal **Service:** General Medical and Surgical

Staffed Beds: 33

WOODWARD—Woodward County

⊞ **ALLIANCEHEALTH WOODWARD (370002)**, 900 17th Street, Zip 73801–2448; tel. 580/256–5511 **A**1 10 **F**13 15 29 30 31 32 34 35 40 43 45 50 57 59 64 68 69 70 75 76 77 79 81 85 93 107 108 110 111 115 119 124 127 129 130 131 133 135 146 **S** Community Health Systems, Inc., Franklin, TN
Primary Contact: David Wallace, Chief Executive Officer
CFO: Tom Earley, Chief Financial Officer
CIO: Larry Churchill, Director Information Services
CHR: Melinda Brock, Director Human Resources
CNO: Kimberly N. Arnold, R.N., Chief Nursing Officer and Interim Chief Quality Officer
Web address: www.woodwardhospital.com
Control: Corporation, Investor–owned, for–profit **Service:** General Medical and Surgical

Staffed Beds: 40 Admissions: 1636 Census: 14

YUKON—Canadian County

⊞ **INTEGRIS CANADIAN VALLEY HOSPITAL (370211)**, 1201 Health Center Parkway, Zip 73099–6381; tel. 405/717–6800 **A**1 10 **F**3 11 13 15 29 30 34 40 45 46 49 52 57 59 60 64 68 70 76 79 81 87 93 107 108 110 111 115 118 119 130 135 145 146 148 **P**8 **S** INTEGRIS Health, Oklahoma City, OK
Primary Contact: Rex Van Meter, President
COO: Cindy White, CPA, Vice President of Operations
CFO: Errol Mitchell, Chief Financial Officer
CHR: Lynn Ketch, Human Resources Recruiter Generalist
CNO: Teresa Gray, Chief Nursing Officer and Assistant Vice President
Web address: www.integris–health.com
Control: Other not–for–profit (including NFP Corporation) **Service:** General Medical and Surgical

Staffed Beds: 75 Admissions: 2352 Census: 20 Outpatient Visits: 48748
Births: 746 Total Expense ($000): 49982 Payroll Expense ($000): 15608
Personnel: 235

Hospital, Medicare Provider Number, Address, Telephone, Approval, Facility, and Physician Codes, Health Care System

★ American Hospital Association (AHA) membership
□ The Joint Commission accreditation
○ Healthcare Facilities Accreditation Program
◇ DNV Healthcare Inc. accreditation
⇑ Center for Improvement in Healthcare Quality Accreditation
△ Commission on Accreditation of Rehabilitation Facilities (CARF) accreditation

OREGON

ALBANY—Linn County

★ ◇ **SAMARITAN ALBANY GENERAL HOSPITAL (380022)**, 1046 Sixth Avenue, S.W., Zip 97321–1999; tel. 541/812–4000 **A**10 21 **F**3 5 11 13 15 18 28 29 30 31 34 35 36 37 40 43 45 47 49 53 54 57 59 61 63 64 67 68 70 73 74 76 77 78 79 81 83 84 85 86 87 89 92 93 97 104 107 108 110 111 114 116 117 119 129 130 131 132 135 144 145 146 147 148 **P**6 **S** Samaritan Health Services, Corvallis, OR
Primary Contact: David G. Triebes, Chief Executive Officer
CFO: Daniel B. Smith, Vice President Finance
Web address: www.samhealth.org
Control: Other not–for–profit (including NFP Corporation) **Service:** General Medical and Surgical

Staffed Beds: 70 **Admissions:** 2937 **Census:** 25 **Outpatient Visits:** 302219 **Births:** 599 **Total Expense ($000):** 174356 **Payroll Expense ($000):** 70345 **Personnel:** 789

ASHLAND—Jackson County

★ ◇ **ASANTE ASHLAND COMMUNITY HOSPITAL (380005)**, 280 Maple Street, Zip 97520–1593; tel. 541/201–4000 **A**10 21 **F**3 11 13 15 29 30 34 35 36 40 43 48 49 50 57 59 62 63 64 65 70 75 76 79 81 82 84 85 86 87 93 97 107 110 114 119 130 132 145 146 147 148 **P**6 **S** Asante Health System, Medford, OR
Primary Contact: Sheila Clough, Chief Executive Officer
CFO: Patrick Hocking, Chief Financial Officer
CMO: Bill Steinsick, M.D., Chief Medical Staff
CIO: Mark Hetz, Chief Information Officer
CHR: Gregg Edwards, Vice President Human Resources
CNO: Susan Montgomery, Chief Nursing Officer
Web address: www.ashlandhospital.org
Control: Other not–for–profit (including NFP Corporation) **Service:** General Medical and Surgical

Staffed Beds: 36 **Admissions:** 1306 **Census:** 12 **Outpatient Visits:** 71555 **Births:** 269 **Total Expense ($000):** 50484 **Payroll Expense ($000):** 18541 **Personnel:** 264

ASTORIA—Clatsop County

★ **COLUMBIA MEMORIAL HOSPITAL (381320)**, 2111 Exchange Street, Zip 97103–3329; tel. 503/325–4321 **A**10 18 **F**3 8 11 13 15 18 19 28 29 30 31 34 35 36 40 43 44 46 50 51 57 58 59 62 63 64 68 70 75 76 77 78 79 81 85 86 87 89 91 93 97 107 108 110 111 114 115 119 130 131 132 133 134 135 143 144 146 147 148 **P**5 6 8
Primary Contact: Erik Thorsen, Chief Executive Officer
CFO: Stephanie D. Brenden, Vice President Finance
CMO: Bruce Bobek, President Professional Staff
CIO: Galina Gandy, Vice President Information Technology
CHR: Lucy G. Dupree, Director Human Resources
CNO: Trece Gurrad, Vice President Patient Care Services
Web address: www.columbiamemorial.org
Control: Other not–for–profit (including NFP Corporation) **Service:** General Medical and Surgical

Staffed Beds: 25 **Admissions:** 1789 **Census:** 13 **Outpatient Visits:** 173799 **Births:** 301 **Total Expense ($000):** 88969 **Payroll Expense ($000):** 36554 **Personnel:** 492

BAKER CITY—Baker County

✠ **SAINT ALPHONSUS MEDICAL CENTER – BAKER CITY (381315)**, 3325 Pocahontas Road, Zip 97814–1464; tel. 541/523–6461 **A**1 10 18 **F**3 11 13 15 29 31 34 35 36 37 40 43 44 45 50 57 59 66 70 75 76 77 79 81 82 83 85 91 93 97 107 110 115 119 127 128 129 131 133 143 144 146 147 148 **P**6 **S** Trinity Health, Livonia, MI
Primary Contact: H. Ray Gibbons, FACHE, Chief Executive Officer
CFO: Robert D. Wehling, Interim Chief Financial Officer
CHR: Jerry Nickell, Vice President Human Resource and Mission
Web address: www.saintalphonsus.org/bakercity
Control: Other not–for–profit (including NFP Corporation) **Service:** General Medical and Surgical

Staffed Beds: 25 **Admissions:** 632 **Census:** 14 **Outpatient Visits:** 50359 **Births:** 122 **Total Expense ($000):** 32048 **Payroll Expense ($000):** 14779 **Personnel:** 187

ST. ELIZABETH HEALTH SERVICES See Saint Alphonsus Medical Center – Baker City

BANDON—Coos County

★ **SOUTHERN COOS HOSPITAL AND HEALTH CENTER (381304)**, 900 11th Street S.E., Zip 97411–9114; tel. 541/347–2426 **A**10 18 **F**3 11 15 34 35 40 45 50 57 59 64 65 68 75 81 82 85 87 97 107 110 114 119 130 132 133 135 148 **P**6
Primary Contact: Jim A. Wathen, Interim Chief Executive Officer
CFO: Robin Triplett, Chief Financial Officer
CIO: Mandy Calvert, Director Information Systems
CHR: Cyndy Vollmer, Director Human Resources
Web address: www.southerncoos.org
Control: Hospital district or authority, Government, nonfederal **Service:** General Medical and Surgical

Staffed Beds: 19 **Admissions:** 351 **Census:** 3 **Outpatient Visits:** 18338 **Births:** 0 **Total Expense ($000):** 16809 **Payroll Expense ($000):** 6692 **Personnel:** 120

BEND—Deschutes County

✠ **ST. CHARLES BEND (380047)**, 2500 N.E. Neff Road, Zip 97701–6015; tel. 541/382–4321 **A**1 2 3 5 10 19 **F**3 8 11 12 13 14 15 18 19 20 21 22 24 26 28 29 30 31 34 35 36 37 38 40 42 43 44 45 46 47 49 50 51 54 57 58 59 60 62 63 64 65 67 70 72 74 75 77 78 79 81 82 84 85 86 87 90 91 92 93 97 98 99 100 101 102 104 107 108 111 112 114 115 119 120 121 122 124 126 129 130 132 135 142 144 146 147 148 **P**6 **S** St. Charles Health System, Inc., Bend, OR
Primary Contact: Joseph Sluka, Chief Executive Officer
CFO: Jennifer Welander, CPA, Senior Vice President Finance and Chief Financial Officer
CMO: Jeffrey Absalon, M.D., Chief Physician Officer
CIO: Jerimiah Brickhouse, Chief Information Officer
CHR: Rebecca Berry, Vice President Human Resources
CNO: Karen Reed, R.N., Chief Nursing Officer
Web address: www.stcharleshealthcare.org
Control: Other not–for–profit (including NFP Corporation) **Service:** General Medical and Surgical

Staffed Beds: 261 **Admissions:** 15708 **Census:** 174 **Outpatient Visits:** 118978 **Births:** 1723 **Total Expense ($000):** 361584 **Payroll Expense ($000):** 164382 **Personnel:** 2281

BURNS—Harney County

★ **HARNEY DISTRICT HOSPITAL (381307)**, 557 West Washington Street, Zip 97720–1497; tel. 541/573–7281 **A**3 10 18 **F**3 7 13 15 29 31 34 35 40 43 45 47 53 57 59 64 65 70 75 76 78 81 82 85 86 93 107 111 114 119 127 129 131 132 133 135 146 **P**6
Primary Contact: Dan Grigg, Chief Executive Officer
CFO: Catherine White, Chief Financial Officer
CMO: Sarah Laiosa, M.D., Chief Medical Staff
CIO: Tanya Strong, Manager Information Technology
CHR: Sammie Masterson, Director Human Resources
CNO: Deana Altman, Interim Chief Nursing Officer
Web address: www.harneydh.com
Control: Hospital district or authority, Government, nonfederal **Service:** General Medical and Surgical

Staffed Beds: 20 **Admissions:** 381 **Census:** 4 **Outpatient Visits:** 33649 **Births:** 55 **Total Expense ($000):** 21800 **Payroll Expense ($000):** 9842 **Personnel:** 141

CLACKAMAS—Clackamas County

✠ **KAISER PERMANENTE SUNNYSIDE MEDICAL CENTER (380091)**, 10180 S.E. Sunnyside Road, Zip 97015–8970; tel. 503/652–2880 **A**1 2 3 5 10 **F**3 11 12 13 15 17 18 20 22 24 26 29 30 31 34 35 40 45 46 47 49 51 60 61 64 65 68 70 72 74 75 76 77 78 79 81 84 85 86 87 93 94 97 102 107 108 110 111 114 115 118 119 130 135 141 146 147 148 **P**6 **S** Kaiser Foundation Hospitals, Oakland, CA
Primary Contact: Justin N. Evander, Administrator and Chief Operating Officer
CFO: Justin N. Evander, Chief Financial Officer
CMO: Richard Hunt, M.D., Chief Operating Officer
CIO: Mark A. Burmester, Vice President Strategy and Communications
CHR: Rich Smith, Vice President Human Resources
CNO: Lauren M. Bridge, R.N., Chief Nursing Officer
Web address: www.kaiserpermanente.org
Control: Other not–for–profit (including NFP Corporation) **Service:** General Medical and Surgical

Staffed Beds: 302 **Admissions:** 19783 **Census:** 181 **Outpatient Visits:** 70090 **Births:** 2382 **Total Expense ($000):** 369836 **Payroll Expense ($000):** 148523 **Personnel:** 2032

OR

COOS BAY—Coos County

☒ **BAY AREA HOSPITAL (380090)**, 1775 Thompson Road, Zip 97420–2198; tel. 541/269–8111 **A**1 2 3 5 10 **F**3 11 12 13 15 18 20 22 26 28 29 31 34 35 40 43 45 46 48 50 51 57 59 62 68 70 73 74 75 76 77 78 79 81 82 84 85 89 91 92 93 98 99 100 101 102 104 107 108 110 111 115 118 119 120 121 123 126 129 130 132 135 142 146 147 148
Primary Contact: Paul Janke, FACHE, President and Chief Executive Officer
COO: Ben Pfau, Chief Facility and Information Officer
CFO: Sam Patterson, Chief Financial Officer
CIO: Bob Adams, Director Information Services
CHR: Suzie Q. McDaniel, Chief Human Resource Officer
CNO: Lori L. Krenos, R.N., Chief Nursing Officer
Web address: www.bayareahospital.org
Control: Hospital district or authority, Government, nonfederal **Service:** General Medical and Surgical

Staffed Beds: 139 Admissions: 5876 Census: 63 Outpatient Visits: 83297 Births: 671 Total Expense ($000): 144529 Payroll Expense ($000): 63251 Personnel: 870

COQUILLE—Coos County

★ **COQUILLE VALLEY HOSPITAL (381312)**, 940 East Fifth Street, Zip 97423–1699; tel. 541/396–3101 **A**10 18 **F**3 8 11 15 17 29 34 35 40 43 45 50 57 59 62 64 67 70 75 79 81 82 85 86 87 97 107 110 111 114 118 119 128 132 133 135 148 **P**6
Primary Contact: Jim Basch, Interim Chief Executive Officer
CFO: Jim Basch, Chief Financial Officer
CMO: James Sinnott, M.D., Chief Medical Staff
CIO: Curt Carpenter, Manager Information Technology
CHR: Monte Johnston, Manager Human Resources
Web address: www.cvhospital.org
Control: Hospital district or authority, Government, nonfederal **Service:** General Medical and Surgical

Staffed Beds: 17 Admissions: 694 Census: 7 Outpatient Visits: 21882 Births: 0 Total Expense ($000): 25465 Payroll Expense ($000): 11624 Personnel: 204

CORVALLIS—Benton County

★ ◇ **GOOD SAMARITAN REGIONAL MEDICAL CENTER (380014)**, 3600 N.W. Samaritan Drive, Zip 97330–3737, Mailing Address: P.O. Box 1068, Zip 97339–1068; tel. 541/768–5111 **A**2 10 12 13 19 21 **F**3 11 12 13 15 17 18 20 22 24 26 28 29 30 31 34 35 36 37 40 43 46 47 49 53 54 56 57 58 59 61 62 64 68 70 73 74 76 77 78 79 81 82 84 85 86 87 89 92 93 97 98 99 100 101 102 103 104 107 108 110 111 114 115 116 117 118 119 120 121 123 124 126 129 130 131 132 135 144 146 147 148 **P**6 **S** Samaritan Health Services, Corvallis, OR
Primary Contact: Becky A. Pape, R.N., Chief Executive Officer
CFO: Daniel B. Smith, Vice President Finance
CIO: Bob Power, Vice President Information Services
CHR: Doug Boysen, Chief Legal Counsel and Vice President Human Resources
CNO: William Howden, Vice President Nursing
Web address: www.samhealth.org
Control: Other not–for–profit (including NFP Corporation) **Service:** General Medical and Surgical

Staffed Beds: 165 Admissions: 9451 Census: 119 Outpatient Visits: 403726 Births: 1068 Total Expense ($000): 362169 Payroll Expense ($000): 146408 Personnel: 1659

COTTAGE GROVE—Lane County

★ **PEACEHEALTH COTTAGE GROVE COMMUNITY MEDICAL CENTER (381301)**, 1515 Village Drive, Zip 97424–9700; tel. 541/942–0511 **A**10 18 **F**3 11 15 29 30 32 34 35 38 40 44 50 59 64 65 66 68 75 91 93 97 102 107 110 115 119 127 130 132 133 146 148 **P**1 6 **S** PeaceHealth, Vancouver, WA
Primary Contact: Tim Herrmann, R.N., Administrator
Web address: www.peacehealth.org
Control: Church–operated, Nongovernment, not–for profit **Service:** General Medical and Surgical

Staffed Beds: 14 Admissions: 407 Census: 3 Outpatient Visits: 37165 Births: 0 Total Expense ($000): 29153 Payroll Expense ($000): 11125 Personnel: 114

DALLAS—Polk County

SALEM HEALTH WEST VALLEY (381308), 525 S.E. Washington Street, Zip 97338–2834, Mailing Address: P.O. Box 378, Zip 97338–0378; tel. 503/623–8301 **A**10 18 **F**3 15 35 40 50 59 64 75 79 81 85 93 97 107 108 110 111 114 119 131 132 133 143 146 148 **P**6 **S** Salem Health, Salem, OR
Primary Contact: Bruce C. Rodgers, Chief Administrative Officer
CFO: James Parr, Chief Financial Officer
CMO: Ralph Yates, D.O., Chief Medical Officer
CHR: Laurie C. Barr, Vice President Human Resources
CNO: Sarah Horn, Chief Nursing Officer
Web address: www.salemhealth.org/wvh/
Control: Other not–for–profit (including NFP Corporation) **Service:** General Medical and Surgical

Staffed Beds: 6 Admissions: 186 Census: 1 Outpatient Visits: 70584 Births: 0 Total Expense ($000): 22309 Payroll Expense ($000): 10824 Personnel: 117

ENTERPRISE—Wallowa County

★ **WALLOWA MEMORIAL HOSPITAL (381306)**, 601 Medical Parkway, Zip 97828–5124; tel. 541/426–3111 **A**3 5 10 18 **F**3 4 7 11 13 15 16 17 29 30 31 34 35 40 43 45 46 56 57 59 62 64 67 68 70 72 73 75 76 78 79 80 81 82 85 87 88 89 90 93 97 98 102 107 110 115 119 127 128 131 132 133 134 135 143 145 148 **P**6
Primary Contact: Larry Davy, Chief Executive Officer
CFO: Joe Wanner, Chief Financial Officer
CMO: Keith DeYoung, M.D., Chief Medical Staff
CIO: John Straughan, Director Information Technology
CHR: Linda Childers, Director Human Resources
CNO: Jenni Word, R.N., Chief Nursing Officer
Web address: www.wchcd.org
Control: Hospital district or authority, Government, nonfederal **Service:** General Medical and Surgical

Staffed Beds: 25 Admissions: 489 Census: 7 Outpatient Visits: 20513 Births: 45 Total Expense ($000): 17648 Payroll Expense ($000): 7226 Personnel: 133

EUGENE—Lane County

★ △ ◇ **PEACEHEALTH SACRED HEART MEDICAL CENTER UNIVERSITY DISTRICT (380033)**, 1255 Hilyard Street, Zip 97401–3700, Mailing Address: P.O. Box 10905, Zip 97440–2905; tel. 541/686–7300 **A**7 10 21 **F**3 29 30 40 43 56 62 63 68 90 93 98 102 105 107 115 130 133 146 148 **P**6 **S** PeaceHealth, Vancouver, WA
Primary Contact: Mary Anne McMurren, FACHE, Chief Administrative Officer
CFO: Wendy Apland, Interim Chief Financial Officer
CMO: Bill Moshofsky, M.D., Chief of Staff
CIO: Donn McMillan, Chief Information Officer
CHR: Craig Mills, Vice President Human Resources
Web address: www.peacehealth.org
Control: Church–operated, Nongovernment, not–for profit **Service:** General Medical and Surgical

Staffed Beds: 104 Admissions: 2750 Census: 61 Outpatient Visits: 108940 Births: 0 Total Expense ($000): 104851 Payroll Expense ($000): 43020 Personnel: 392

FLORENCE—Lane County

★ ◇ **PEACEHEALTH PEACE HARBOR MEDICAL CENTER (381316)**, 400 Ninth Street, Zip 97439–7398; tel. 541/997–8412 **A**10 18 21 **F**1 3 4 8 11 13 15 16 17 28 29 30 34 35 40 43 45 50 57 59 62 63 64 65 66 67 68 70 72 73 75 76 77 79 80 81 85 87 88 89 90 91 93 97 98 100 102 107 108 110 111 114 115 116 117 118 119 128 130 132 133 135 143 146 147 148 **P**6 **S** PeaceHealth, Vancouver, WA
Primary Contact: Rick Yecny, Chief Executive Officer and Chief Mission Officer
CMO: Ron Shearer, M.D., Regional Medical Director
CIO: Ginni Boughal, Director Health Information and Information Technology
CHR: Don Bourland, Vice President Human Resources
Web address: www.peacehealth.org
Control: Church–operated, Nongovernment, not–for profit **Service:** General Medical and Surgical

Staffed Beds: 21 Admissions: 1053 Census: 9 Outpatient Visits: 100306 Births: 78 Total Expense ($000): 73126 Payroll Expense ($000): 32339 Personnel: 208

FOREST GROVE—Washington County

TUALITY FOREST GROVE HOSPITAL See Tuality Healthcare, Hillsboro

---

Hospital, Medicare Provider Number, Address, Telephone, Approval, Facility, and Physician Codes, Health Care System

★ American Hospital Association (AHA) membership
☐ The Joint Commission accreditation
◯ Healthcare Facilities Accreditation Program
◇ DNV Healthcare Inc. accreditation
⇑ Center for Improvement in Healthcare Quality Accreditation
△ Commission on Accreditation of Rehabilitation Facilities (CARF) accreditation

OR

GOLD BEACH—Curry County

★ ◇ **CURRY GENERAL HOSPITAL (381322)**, 94220 Fourth Street,
Zip 97444–7756; tel. 541/247–3000 **A**10 18 21 **F**3 8 10 11 13 15 28 29 34
40 43 50 54 59 64 70 75 76 79 81 82 85 89 97 107 114 119 127 128 133
135 144 147 148 **P**6
Primary Contact: Virginia Razo, Chief Executive Officer
CFO: Carl Gerlach, Chief Financial Officer
CMO: Reginald Williams, M.D., Medical Staff President
CIO: Kristina Martin, Chief Information Officer
CHR: Terri Tomberlin, Human Resources Director
CNO: Barbara A. Hannon, R.N., Interim Chief Nursing Officer and Chief Clinical
Officer
Web address: www.curryhealthnetwork.com
Control: Hospital district or authority, Government, nonfederal **Service:** General
Medical and Surgical

Staffed Beds: 16 **Admissions:** 518 **Census:** 6 **Outpatient Visits:** 85275
Births: 27 **Total Expense ($000):** 33009 **Payroll Expense ($000):** 17328
Personnel: 264

GRANTS PASS—Josephine County

★ ◇ **ASANTE THREE RIVERS MEDICAL CENTER (380002)**, 500 S.W. Ramsey
Avenue, Zip 97527–5554; tel. 541/472–7000 **A**3 10 21 **F**11 13 15 29 30 31
34 35 40 43 45 46 50 57 59 64 65 70 75 76 78 81 87 93 102 107 108 110
111 118 119 122 130 132 143 146 147 148 **P**6 **S** Asante Health System,
Medford, OR
Primary Contact: Win Howard, Chief Executive Officer
COO: David Kinyon, Vice President of Operations and Outpatient Services
CFO: Patrick Hocking, Chief Financial Officer
CMO: Eric Loeliger, Vice President of Medical Affairs
CIO: Mark Hetz, Chief Information Officer
CHR: Gregg Edwards, Chief People Officer
CNO: Nancy Greer, R.N., Vice President Nursing
Web address: www.asante.org/trmc/
Control: Other not–for–profit (including NFP Corporation) **Service:** General
Medical and Surgical

Staffed Beds: 111 **Admissions:** 7141 **Census:** 63 **Outpatient Visits:** 256398
Births: 756 **Total Expense ($000):** 140850 **Payroll Expense ($000):** 53580
Personnel: 865

GRESHAM—Multnomah County

⊞ **LEGACY MOUNT HOOD MEDICAL CENTER (380025)**, 24800 S.E. Stark,
Zip 97030–3378; tel. 503/667–1122 **A**1 2 10 **F**3 11 13 15 18 20 26 28 29
30 31 32 34 35 38 40 44 45 46 48 49 50 51 57 59 60 64 68 70 74 75 76
77 78 79 81 85 86 87 93 100 101 102 107 108 110 111 114 115 118 119
120 121 123 126 129 130 132 146 147 148 **P**6 **S** Legacy Health,
Portland, OR
Primary Contact: Gretchen Nichols, R.N., Chief Administrative Officer
COO: Michael Newcomb, D.O., Senior Vice President and Chief Operating Officer
CFO: Linda Hoff, Senior Vice President and Chief Financial Officer
CMO: Lewis Low, M.D., Chief Medical Officer
CIO: John Jay Kenagy, Ph.D., Senior Vice President and Chief Information Officer
CHR: Sonja Steves, Senior Vice President Human Resources
CNO: Marcia Soderling, R.N., Hospital Nurse Executive
Web address: www.legacyhealth.org
Control: Other not–for–profit (including NFP Corporation) **Service:** General
Medical and Surgical

Staffed Beds: 91 **Admissions:** 5952 **Census:** 60 **Outpatient Visits:** 111637
Births: 969 **Total Expense ($000):** 120992 **Payroll Expense ($000):** 47592
Personnel: 542

HEPPNER—Morrow County

PIONEER MEMORIAL HOSPITAL (381310), 564 East Pioneer Drive,
Zip 97836–7318, Mailing Address: P.O. Box 9, Zip 97836–0009;
tel. 541/676–9133 **A**10 18 **F**3 7 17 34 35 40 45 50 57 59 62 63 64 66 68
69 75 97 107 119 127 133 143 147 148 **P**6
Primary Contact: Robert Housee, FACHE, Chief Executive Officer
CFO: Nicole Mahoney, Chief Financial Officer
CIO: Shawn Cutsforth, Information Systems Officer
CHR: Patti Allstott, Administrative Coordinator Human Resources and Grant Writer
Web address: www.morrowcountyhealthdistrict.org
Control: Hospital district or authority, Government, nonfederal **Service:** General
Medical and Surgical

Staffed Beds: 21 **Admissions:** 91 **Census:** 7 **Outpatient Visits:** 5562 **Births:**
0 **Total Expense ($000):** 9442 **Payroll Expense ($000):** 4957 **Personnel:**
65

HERMISTON—Umatilla County

★ ◇ **GOOD SHEPHERD HEALTH CARE SYSTEM (381325)**, 610 N.W. 11th
Street, Zip 97838–6601; tel. 541/667–3400 **A**10 18 21 **F**3 11 13 15 28 29 30
34 35 37 40 43 45 46 50 53 57 59 62 63 64 65 68 70 75 76 77 78 79 81
82 84 85 86 89 97 107 108 110 111 114 115 119 126 127 130 131 132
133 135 141 143 146 147 148 **P**3 4 7
Primary Contact: Dennis E. Burke, President and Chief Executive Officer
COO: Jim Schlenker, Chief Operating Officer
CFO: Jan D. Peter, Vice President Fiscal Services and Chief Financial Officer
CMO: Gary Trupp, President Medical Staff
CIO: Rob Rizk, Director Information Technology
CHR: Kelly B. Sanders, Vice President Human Resources
CNO: Theresa Brock, Vice President Nursing
Web address: www.gshealth.org
Control: Other not–for–profit (including NFP Corporation) **Service:** General
Medical and Surgical

Staffed Beds: 25 **Admissions:** 1832 **Census:** 13 **Outpatient Visits:** 61394
Births: 425 **Total Expense ($000):** 66933 **Payroll Expense ($000):** 30484
Personnel: 525

HILLSBORO—Washington County

⊞ **KAISER FOUNDATION HOSPITAL WESTSIDE MEDICAL CENTER (380103)**,
2875 N.W. Stucki Avenue, Zip 97124–5806; tel. 971/310–1000 **A**1 10 **F**3 13
15 29 30 31 34 35 40 45 46 47 49 51 60 61 64 65 68 70 74 75 76 77 79
81 84 85 86 87 93 96 97 102 107 108 110 111 114 115 118 119 126 130
135 141 146 147 148 **P**6 **S** Kaiser Foundation Hospitals, Oakland, CA
Primary Contact: Brantley Dettmer, Hospital Administrator and Chief Operating
Officer
CFO: Brantley Dettmer, Finance Director
CMO: Carol Unitan, M.D., Chief Medical Officer
CIO: Charles Stearns, Area Information Officer
CHR: Rich Smith, Vice President Human Resources
Web address: www.kp.org
Control: Other not–for–profit (including NFP Corporation) **Service:** General
Medical and Surgical

Staffed Beds: 122 **Admissions:** 9128 **Census:** 65 **Outpatient Visits:** 33360
Births: 1399 **Total Expense ($000):** 154922 **Payroll Expense ($000):**
63527 **Personnel:** 855

⊞ **TUALITY HEALTHCARE (380021)**, 335 S.E. Eighth Avenue, Zip 97123–4246;
tel. 503/681–1111, (Includes TUALITY COMMUNITY HOSPITAL, 335 S.E. Eighth
Avenue, Zip 97123, Mailing Address: P.O. Box 309, Zip 97123;
tel. 503/681–1111; Manuel S. Berman, FACHE, President and Chief Executive
Officer; TUALITY FOREST GROVE HOSPITAL, 1809 Maple Street, Forest Grove,
Zip 97116–1995; tel. 503/357–2173; Manuel S. Berman, FACHE, President and
Chief Executive Officer) **A**1 5 10 **F**3 11 13 15 17 18 20 22 24 26 28 29 30 31
32 34 35 36 37 40 44 45 47 49 50 53 54 56 57 59 62 64 68 70 71 74 75
76 77 78 79 80 81 82 85 86 87 92 93 97 98 100 103 104 107 108 110 111
114 115 118 119 129 130 131 132 135 143 144 145 146 147 148 **P**1 6
Primary Contact: Manuel S. Berman, FACHE, President and Chief Executive Officer
COO: Steven P. Krautscheid, Ancillary Services Administrator
CFO: Tim Fleischmann, Chief Financial Officer
CMO: Stuart Currie, Chief Medical Officer
CIO: Sonney Sapra, Director Information Systems and Chief Information Officer
CHR: Cheryl Gebhart, Chief Human Resources Officer
CNO: Eunice A. Rech, MSN, Chief Clinical Officer and Administrator of Quality
Services
Web address: www.tuality.org
Control: Other not–for–profit (including NFP Corporation) **Service:** General
Medical and Surgical

Staffed Beds: 148 **Admissions:** 4144 **Census:** 51 **Outpatient Visits:** 243618
Births: 741 **Total Expense ($000):** 174870 **Payroll Expense ($000):** 85070
Personnel: 1114

HOOD RIVER—Hood River County

⊞ **PROVIDENCE HOOD RIVER MEMORIAL HOSPITAL (381318)**, 810 12th
Street, Zip 97031–1587, Mailing Address: P.O. Box 149, Zip 97031–0055;
tel. 541/386–3911 **A**1 3 10 18 **F**2 3 5 8 9 10 11 12 13 15 28 29 30 31 34
35 36 40 43 45 47 48 53 54 56 57 59 60 64 65 68 70 71 75 76 77 79 81
85 86 89 92 97 99 100 101 102 104 107 108 110 111 114 118 119 125
129 132 133 134 135 143 146 147 148 **P**6 **S** Providence St. Joseph Health,
Renton, WA
Primary Contact: Jeanie Vieira, Chief Executive Officer
CHR: Jami McCaslin, Director Human Resources
Web address: www.providence.org/hoodriver
Control: Church–operated, Nongovernment, not–for profit **Service:** General
Medical and Surgical

Staffed Beds: 25 **Admissions:** 1574 **Census:** 10 **Outpatient Visits:** 158644
Births: 436 **Total Expense ($000):** 84026 **Payroll Expense ($000):** 27255
Personnel: 405

OR

JOHN DAY—Grant County

★ **BLUE MOUNTAIN HOSPITAL (381305)**, 170 Ford Road, Zip 97845–2009; tel. 541/575–1311, (Total facility includes 29 beds in nursing home–type unit) **A**3 5 10 18 **F**2 3 7 11 13 15 30 31 34 35 36 40 41 43 45 50 56 57 59 62 63 64 67 68 70 75 76 81 82 86 87 89 93 97 107 110 111 114 119 127 128 130 131 132 133 135 143 144 145 146 148 **P**6 **S** HealthTech Management Services, Brentwood, TN
Primary Contact: Randall L. Mee, FACHE, Chief Executive Officer
CFO: Carl J. Flanagan, Chief Financial Officer
CMO: Keith Thomas, M.D., Chief of Staff
CIO: Sean Tsao, Director Information Technology
CHR: Verlene Davis, Director Human Resources
CNO: Les McLeod, Director of Nursing Services
Web address: www.bluemountainhospital.org
Control: Hospital district or authority, Government, nonfederal **Service:** General Medical and Surgical

> **Staffed Beds:** 45 **Admissions:** 332 **Census:** 25 **Outpatient Visits:** 26091
> **Births:** 49 **Total Expense ($000):** 20091 **Payroll Expense ($000):** 10355
> **Personnel:** 153

KLAMATH FALLS—Klamath County

★ ◇ **SKY LAKES MEDICAL CENTER (380050)**, 2865 Daggett Avenue, Zip 97601–1106; tel. 541/882–6311 **A**2 3 5 10 21 **F**3 8 11 13 15 18 20 22 29 30 31 34 35 37 40 43 44 45 46 47 48 50 51 53 54 56 57 59 61 62 64 68 70 71 75 76 77 78 79 81 84 85 86 87 92 93 94 96 97 100 102 107 108 110 111 114 115 116 117 118 119 120 121 123 130 131 132 134 135 141 142 143 144 145 146 148 **P**6
Primary Contact: Paul R. Stewart, President and Chief Executive Officer
CFO: Richard Rico, Vice President and Chief Financial Officer
CMO: Grant Niskanen, M.D., Vice President Medical Affairs
CHR: Don York, Vice President and Chief Human Resource Officer
CNO: Annette E. Cole, R.N., Vice President and Chief Nursing Officer
Web address: www.skylakes.org
Control: Other not–for–profit (including NFP Corporation) **Service:** General Medical and Surgical

> **Staffed Beds:** 105 **Admissions:** 5010 **Census:** 55 **Outpatient Visits:** 382724
> **Births:** 796 **Total Expense ($000):** 200187 **Payroll Expense ($000):** 76796
> **Personnel:** 1131

LA GRANDE—Union County

⌧ **GRANDE RONDE HOSPITAL (381321)**, 900 Sunset Drive, Zip 97850–1387, Mailing Address: P.O. Box 3290, Zip 97850–7290; tel. 541/963–8421 **A**1 10 18 **F**3 8 11 13 15 17 29 30 31 34 35 37 39 40 41 43 44 45 50 53 54 57 59 62 63 64 66 70 74 75 76 78 79 81 82 84 85 86 87 89 92 93 96 97 107 108 110 111 114 118 119 128 129 130 131 132 133 135 144 146 147 148 **P**6
Primary Contact: James A. Mattes, President and Chief Executive Officer
CFO: Wade Weis, Chief Financial Officer and Senior Director Finance
CMO: Aaron Spracklen, M.D., Professional Staff President
CIO: Parhez Sattar, Senior Director Information Technology
CHR: Kristi Puckett, Director Human Resources
Web address: www.grh.org
Control: Other not–for–profit (including NFP Corporation) **Service:** General Medical and Surgical

> **Staffed Beds:** 25 **Admissions:** 1527 **Census:** 12 **Outpatient Visits:** 109084
> **Births:** 244 **Total Expense ($000):** 71479 **Payroll Expense ($000):** 39806
> **Personnel:** 520

LAKEVIEW—Lake County

★ **LAKE DISTRICT HOSPITAL (381309)**, 700 South J Street, Zip 97630–1679; tel. 541/947–2114, (Total facility includes 22 beds in nursing home–type unit) **A**5 10 18 **F**3 13 15 18 29 30 31 34 35 40 45 46 57 59 62 63 64 67 68 76 78 81 82 84 85 87 90 93 107 111 114 119 127 128 129 130 132 133 135 146 148 **P**6
Primary Contact: Charles B. Tveit, Chief Executive Officer
CFO: Cheryl J. Cornwell, Chief Financial Officer
CMO: Stephen Hussey, M.D., Chief of Staff
CIO: Steven Vance, Information Technology Director
CHR: Lesley Hanson, Director Human Resources
CNO: Teresa Squires, R.N., Chief Nursing Officer
Web address: www.lakehealthdistrict.org
Control: Hospital district or authority, Government, nonfederal **Service:** General Medical and Surgical

> **Staffed Beds:** 46 **Admissions:** 546 **Census:** 27 **Outpatient Visits:** 29536
> **Births:** 66 **Total Expense ($000):** 21609 **Payroll Expense ($000):** 9004
> **Personnel:** 191

LEBANON—Linn County

★ ◇ **SAMARITAN LEBANON COMMUNITY HOSPITAL (381323)**, 525 North Santiam Highway, Zip 97355–4363, Mailing Address: P.O. Box 739, Zip 97355–0739; tel. 541/258–2101 **A**10 18 21 **F**3 10 11 13 15 28 29 30 31 34 35 40 43 44 45 46 47 53 59 64 68 70 75 76 78 79 81 85 86 87 89 92 93 97 107 108 110 111 114 116 117 118 119 125 130 131 132 135 144 146 147 148 **P**6 **S** Samaritan Health Services, Corvallis, OR
Primary Contact: Marty Cahill, Chief Executive Officer
CFO: Daniel B. Smith, Vice President Finance
CMO: Alan Blake, M.D., President Medical Staff
CIO: Robert Power, Vice President Information Services
CHR: Connie Erwin, Manager
CNO: Wendie Wunderwald, R.N., Vice President Patient Care Services
Web address: www.samhealth.org
Control: Other not–for–profit (including NFP Corporation) **Service:** General Medical and Surgical

> **Staffed Beds:** 25 **Admissions:** 1722 **Census:** 16 **Outpatient Visits:** 222664
> **Births:** 318 **Total Expense ($000):** 103181 **Payroll Expense ($000):** 45197
> **Personnel:** 568

LINCOLN CITY—Lincoln County

★ ◇ **SAMARITAN NORTH LINCOLN HOSPITAL (381302)**, 3043 N.E. 28th Street, Zip 97367–4518, Mailing Address: P.O. Box 767, Zip 97367–0767; tel. 541/994–3661 **A**10 18 21 **F**3 8 11 13 15 26 29 30 31 34 35 40 44 45 51 57 58 59 62 63 64 68 70 71 75 76 77 78 79 81 85 86 87 93 97 107 108 110 111 115 116 117 118 119 127 130 132 133 135 144 146 147 148 **P**6 **S** Samaritan Health Services, Corvallis, OR
Primary Contact: Lesley Ogden, M.D., Chief Executive Officer
CFO: Kathryn Doksum, Director Finance
CMO: Raj Baman, D.O., President Medical Staff
CHR: Gina Tapp, Director Human Resources
CNO: Virginia Riffle, Vice President Patient Care Services
Web address: www.samhealth.org
Control: Other not–for–profit (including NFP Corporation) **Service:** General Medical and Surgical

> **Staffed Beds:** 25 **Admissions:** 1079 **Census:** 10 **Outpatient Visits:** 95448
> **Births:** 143 **Total Expense ($000):** 54846 **Payroll Expense ($000):** 26809
> **Personnel:** 276

MADRAS—Jefferson County

★ **ST. CHARLES MADRAS (381324)**, 470 N.E. A Street, Zip 97741–1844; tel. 541/475–3882 **A**10 18 **F**3 13 15 29 30 34 35 40 43 45 50 57 59 62 63 64 67 68 70 75 76 77 79 80 81 85 87 89 90 98 107 110 115 119 128 132 133 135 146 **P**6 **S** St. Charles Health System, Inc., Bend, OR
Primary Contact: John Bishop, President
CHR: JoDee Tittle, Director Community and Human Resources
Web address: www.mvhd.org
Control: Other not–for–profit (including NFP Corporation) **Service:** General Medical and Surgical

> **Staffed Beds:** 22 **Admissions:** 693 **Census:** 7 **Outpatient Visits:** 23055
> **Births:** 94 **Total Expense ($000):** 24246 **Payroll Expense ($000):** 15462
> **Personnel:** 170

MCMINNVILLE—Yamhill County

☐ **WILLAMETTE VALLEY MEDICAL CENTER (380071)**, 2700 S.E. Stratus Avenue, Zip 97128–6255; tel. 503/472–6131 **A**1 2 10 **F**3 11 12 13 15 18 20 24 26 27 28 29 30 31 34 35 40 41 43 45 46 48 50 51 56 57 58 59 60 64 65 70 74 75 76 77 78 79 81 82 84 85 86 87 91 92 93 98 103 107 108 110 111 114 115 119 120 123 124 130 131 132 135 146 147 148 **P**6 **S** RCCH HealthCare Partners, Brentwood, TN
Primary Contact: Peter A. Hofstetter, Chief Executive Officer
CFO: Meredith Nelson, Chief Financial Officer
CIO: Diane Farrow, Manager Information Technology and Systems
CHR: Lisa Clark, Director Human Resources
CNO: Connie Pullen, R.N., Chief Nursing Officer
Web address: www.wvmcweb.com
Control: Corporation, Investor–owned, for–profit **Service:** General Medical and Surgical

> **Staffed Beds:** 88 **Admissions:** 3355 **Census:** 35 **Outpatient Visits:** 116603
> **Births:** 514 **Total Expense ($000):** 73032 **Payroll Expense ($000):** 29905
> **Personnel:** 500

Hospital, Medicare Provider Number, Address, Telephone, Approval, Facility, and Physician Codes, Health Care System

★ American Hospital Association (AHA) membership   ◯ Healthcare Facilities Accreditation Program   ⇑ Center for Improvement in Healthcare Quality Accreditation
☐ The Joint Commission accreditation   ◇ DNV Healthcare Inc. accreditation   △ Commission on Accreditation of Rehabilitation Facilities (CARF) accreditation

OR

MEDFORD—Jackson County

★ ◇ **ASANTE ROGUE REGIONAL MEDICAL CENTER (380018)**, 2825 East Barnett Road, Zip 97504–8332; tel. 541/789–7000 **A**2 3 10 21 **F**11 12 13 15 17 18 20 22 24 26 28 29 30 31 32 34 35 37 40 43 45 46 50 51 57 58 59 60 63 64 65 70 72 74 75 76 78 79 81 82 85 86 87 89 90 93 94 97 98 100 102 107 108 110 111 112 115 119 120 121 122 126 129 130 132 143 146 147 148 **P**6 **S** Asante Health System, Medford, OR
Primary Contact: Scott A. Kelly, Chief Executive Officer
COO: Kristi Blackhurst, Interim Vice President Operations
CFO: Patrick Hocking, Chief Financial Officer
CMO: Jamie Grebosky, M.D., Vice President of Medical Affairs
CIO: Mark Hetz, Chief Information Officer
CHR: Gregg Edwards, Chief People Officer
Web address: www.asante.org
Control: Other not–for–profit (including NFP Corporation) **Service:** General Medical and Surgical

Staffed Beds: 320 **Admissions:** 17228 **Census:** 229 **Outpatient Visits:** 407186 **Births:** 1718 **Total Expense ($000):** 406552 **Payroll Expense ($000):** 133245 **Personnel:** 2135

⊠ **PROVIDENCE MEDFORD MEDICAL CENTER (380075)**, 1111 Crater Lake Avenue, Zip 97504–6241; tel. 541/732–5000 **A**1 2 10 **F**3 11 13 15 17 18 20 22 28 29 30 31 32 34 35 40 43 45 46 50 51 55 56 57 59 61 62 63 64 68 70 74 75 76 77 78 79 81 82 84 85 86 87 90 91 92 93 96 97 102 107 110 114 115 118 119 120 121 123 124 126 129 130 132 143 146 147 148 **P**6 **S** Providence St. Joseph Health, Renton, WA
Primary Contact: Cindy Mayo, R.N., FACHE, Chief Executive Officer
COO: Chris Pizzi, Chief Operating Officer and Chief Financial Officer
CFO: Chris Pizzi, Chief Operating Officer and Chief Financial Officer
CHR: Julie Levison, Director Human Resources
CNO: Sherri Steele, Chief Nursing Officer
Web address: www.providence.org
Control: Church–operated, Nongovernment, not–for profit **Service:** General Medical and Surgical

Staffed Beds: 142 **Admissions:** 6508 **Census:** 76 **Outpatient Visits:** 338753 **Births:** 426 **Total Expense ($000):** 207776 **Payroll Expense ($000):** 59553 **Personnel:** 906

MILWAUKIE—Clackamas County

⊠ **PROVIDENCE MILWAUKIE HOSPITAL (380082)**, 10150 S.E. 32nd Avenue, Zip 97222–6516; tel. 503/513–8300 **A**1 3 5 10 **F**3 15 18 29 30 34 35 36 39 40 44 45 46 50 53 54 57 59 63 64 68 70 71 74 75 77 79 81 82 84 85 87 89 91 92 93 97 100 102 105 107 108 110 111 114 115 119 129 130 131 132 133 135 146 147 148 **P**6 **S** Providence St. Joseph Health, Renton, WA
Primary Contact: Keith Hyde, Chief Executive
COO: Sherri Paris, Chief Operating Officer
CFO: Sheila Waldron, Finance Manager
CHR: Julie Smith, Senior Human Resources Strategic Partner
CNO: Lisa Halvorsen, Chief Nurse Executive
Web address: www.providence.org
Control: Church–operated, Nongovernment, not–for profit **Service:** General Medical and Surgical

Staffed Beds: 51 **Admissions:** 2914 **Census:** 25 **Outpatient Visits:** 254088 **Births:** 0 **Total Expense ($000):** 99521 **Payroll Expense ($000):** 29671 **Personnel:** 391

NEWBERG—Yamhill County

⊠ **PROVIDENCE NEWBERG MEDICAL CENTER (380037)**, 1001 Providence Drive, Zip 97132–7485; tel. 503/537–1555 **A**1 10 **F**3 11 13 15 18 20 29 30 34 35 40 45 49 50 57 59 60 64 68 70 75 76 77 79 81 85 87 93 100 107 108 110 111 114 118 119 129 130 132 135 146 147 148 **P**6 **S** Providence St. Joseph Health, Renton, WA
Primary Contact: Lorinda Van Zanten, MSN, Chief Executive Officer
CFO: Jack R. Sumner, Assistant Administrator Finance
CMO: George Weghorst, M.D., Chief Medical Officer
CIO: Laureen O'Brien, Chief Information Officer
CHR: Cheryl Gebhart, Director Human Resources Providence Health Plan and Providence Medical Group
Web address: www.phsor.org
Control: Church–operated, Nongovernment, not–for profit **Service:** General Medical and Surgical

Staffed Beds: 40 **Admissions:** 2775 **Census:** 24 **Outpatient Visits:** 233421 **Births:** 525 **Total Expense ($000):** 96091 **Payroll Expense ($000):** 28683 **Personnel:** 401

NEWPORT—Lincoln County

★ ◇ **SAMARITAN PACIFIC COMMUNITIES HOSPITAL (381314)**, 930 S.W. Abbey Street, Zip 97365–4820, Mailing Address: P.O. Box 945, Zip 97365–0072; tel. 541/265–2244 **A**10 18 21 **F**3 8 11 13 15 28 29 30 31 34 35 40 44 45 47 54 62 63 64 68 70 75 76 77 78 79 81 85 87 89 92 93 97 107 110 111 114 119 127 129 130 132 133 135 144 146 147 148 **P**6 **S** Samaritan Health Services, Corvallis, OR
Primary Contact: David C. Bigelow, PharmD, Chief Executive Officer
CFO: Daniel B. Smith, Chief Financial Officer
CIO: Robert Power, Chief Information Officer
CHR: Gina Tapp, Director Human Resources
CNO: Lorie Williams, R.N., Vice President Nursing
Web address: www.samhealth.org
Control: Other not–for–profit (including NFP Corporation) **Service:** General Medical and Surgical

Staffed Beds: 25 **Admissions:** 1309 **Census:** 11 **Outpatient Visits:** 145701 **Births:** 171 **Total Expense ($000):** 81087 **Payroll Expense ($000):** 36326 **Personnel:** 391

ONTARIO—Malheur County

HOLY ROSARY MEDICAL CENTER See Saint Alphonsus Medical Center – Ontario

⊠ **SAINT ALPHONSUS MEDICAL CENTER – ONTARIO (380052)**, 351 S.W. Ninth Street, Zip 97914–2693; tel. 541/881–7000 **A**1 3 5 10 20 **F**3 11 13 15 29 30 31 32 34 35 40 43 44 45 46 50 54 56 57 59 64 65 66 68 70 75 76 77 78 79 81 82 85 87 93 97 107 108 110 114 118 119 129 130 131 132 135 142 144 146 147 148 **P**6 **S** Trinity Health, Livonia, MI
Primary Contact: Karl Keeler, Chief Executive Officer
COO: Ken Hart, Vice President Operations
CFO: Lannie Checketts, Vice President Finance and Operations
CMO: Paul Gering, M.D., Vice President Medical Affairs
CHR: Stefanie Thiel, Senior Human Resources Business Partner
CNO: Dina Ellwanger, R.N., Chief Nursing Officer
Web address: www.saintalphonsus.org/ontario
Control: Church–operated, Nongovernment, not–for profit **Service:** General Medical and Surgical

Staffed Beds: 49 **Admissions:** 2584 **Census:** 20 **Outpatient Visits:** 70357 **Births:** 520 **Total Expense ($000):** 62018 **Payroll Expense ($000):** 23691 **Personnel:** 401

OREGON CITY—Clackamas County

⊠ **PROVIDENCE WILLAMETTE FALLS MEDICAL CENTER (380038)**, 1500 Division Street, Zip 97045–1597; tel. 503/656–1631 **A**1 10 **F**13 15 29 30 34 35 36 40 44 45 46 50 53 54 57 59 63 64 68 70 74 75 76 77 78 79 81 82 84 85 87 89 91 92 93 97 98 100 107 108 111 114 119 130 131 132 133 135 146 147 **P**6 **S** Providence St. Joseph Health, Renton, WA
Primary Contact: Russ Reinhard, Chief Executive
COO: Patricia A. Markesino, FACHE, Chief Nurse Executive and Chief Operating Officer
CFO: Elizabeth Sublette, Director Finance
CMO: James Watkins, M.D., President Medical Staff
CHR: Joann M. Pfister, Director Human Resources
CNO: Jessica Bailey-Oetker, Director Quality and Medical Staff
Web address: www.providence.org/pwfmc
Control: Church–operated, Nongovernment, not–for profit **Service:** General Medical and Surgical

Staffed Beds: 111 **Admissions:** 5122 **Census:** 49 **Outpatient Visits:** 164299 **Births:** 1052 **Total Expense ($000):** 123683 **Payroll Expense ($000):** 38187 **Personnel:** 484

PENDLETON—Umatilla County

⊠ **CHI ST. ANTHONY HOSPITAL (381319)**, 2801 St. Anthony Way, Zip 97801–3800; tel. 541/276–5121 **A**1 10 18 **F**3 11 13 15 18 29 30 31 35 40 43 45 50 51 53 54 57 59 62 63 64 65 68 70 75 76 77 78 79 81 85 86 87 91 93 97 107 108 110 111 114 119 127 129 130 131 132 133 134 135 146 147 **P**6 **S** Catholic Health Initiatives, Englewood, CO
Primary Contact: Harold S. Geller, Chief Executive Officer
CMO: Malcolm Townsley, M.D., Chief of Staff
CHR: Janeen K. Reding, Director Human Resources
Web address: www.sahpendleton.org
Control: Church–operated, Nongovernment, not–for profit **Service:** General Medical and Surgical

Staffed Beds: 25 **Admissions:** 1448 **Census:** 12 **Outpatient Visits:** 72384 **Births:** 366 **Total Expense ($000):** 60240 **Payroll Expense ($000):** 21691 **Personnel:** 273

PORTLAND—Multnomah County

☒ **ADVENTIST MEDICAL CENTER–PORTLAND (380060)**, 10123 S.E. Market Street, Zip 97216–2599; tel. 503/257–2500 **A**1 2 10 **F**3 9 11 13 15 17 18 20 22 24 26 28 29 30 31 34 35 36 37 40 44 45 46 49 54 57 58 59 64 70 71 74 75 76 77 78 79 81 82 84 85 86 93 97 98 100 102 107 108 110 111 114 115 118 119 120 121 123 126 129 130 131 132 135 144 146 147 148 **P**6 7 **S** Adventist Health, Roseville, CA
Primary Contact: David Russell, President and Chief Executive Officer
CFO: V. Mark Perry, Chief Financial Officer
CMO: Wesley E. Rippey, M.D., Chief Medical Officer
CHR: Shane Voshell, Director Human Resources
CNO: Ellen Tryon, R.N., Chief Nursing Officer
Web address: www.adventisthealthnw.com
Control: Church–operated, Nongovernment, not–for profit **Service:** General Medical and Surgical

Staffed Beds: 242 Admissions: 10251 Census: 113 Outpatient Visits: 364147 Births: 1060 Total Expense ($000): 341762 Payroll Expense ($000): 132199 Personnel: 1591

☐ **CEDAR HILLS HOSPITAL (384012)**, 10300 S.W. Eastridge Street, Zip 97225–5004; tel. 503/944–5000, (Nonreporting) **A**1 10 **S** Universal Health Services, Inc., King of Prussia, PA
Primary Contact: Elizabeth Hutter, Chief Executive Officer
Web address: www.cedarhillshospital.com
Control: Corporation, Investor–owned, for–profit **Service:** Psychiatric

Staffed Beds: 78

GOOD SAMARITAN HOSPITAL AND MEDICAL CENTER See Legacy Good Samaritan Hospital and Medical Center

☒ △ ◇ **LEGACY EMANUEL HOSPITAL AND HEALTH CENTER (380007)**, 2801 North Gantenbein Avenue, Zip 97227–1674; tel. 503/413–2200, (Includes RANDALL CHILDREN'S HOSPITAL, 2801 North Gantenbein Avenue, Zip 97227–1623; tel. 503/413–2200) **A**1 2 3 5 7 10 21 **F**3 7 11 13 15 16 17 18 19 20 21 22 23 24 25 26 27 29 30 31 32 34 35 38 39 40 41 43 44 45 46 47 49 50 51 54 55 56 57 59 60 61 64 65 66 68 70 72 74 75 76 77 78 79 80 81 83 84 85 86 87 88 89 93 97 98 99 100 101 102 107 108 110 111 112 114 115 118 119 126 127 129 130 131 132 135 144 146 147 148 **P**6 **S** Legacy Health, Portland, OR
Primary Contact: Lori Morgan, M.D., Chief Administrative Officer
CHR: Sonja Steves, Senior Vice President Human Resources and Marketing
Web address: www.legacyhealth.org
Control: Other not–for–profit (including NFP Corporation) **Service:** General Medical and Surgical

Staffed Beds: 427 Admissions: 17779 Census: 285 Outpatient Visits: 294083 Births: 2040 Total Expense ($000): 683316 Payroll Expense ($000): 317821 Personnel: 2848

☒ **LEGACY GOOD SAMARITAN HOSPITAL AND MEDICAL CENTER (380017)**, 1015 N.W. 22nd Avenue, Zip 97210–3099; tel. 503/413–7711, (Includes GOOD SAMARITAN HOSPITAL AND MEDICAL CENTER, 1015 N.W. 22nd Avenue, Zip 97210; tel. 503/229–7711; REHABILITATION INSTITUTE OF OREGON, 2010 N.W. Kearney Street, Zip 97209; tel. 503/226–3774) **A**1 2 3 5 10 **F**3 8 11 12 15 18 20 22 24 26 28 29 30 31 34 35 38 40 44 45 46 47 48 49 50 51 55 56 57 58 59 60 61 64 65 68 70 74 75 76 77 78 79 80 81 82 83 84 85 86 87 90 91 93 94 96 97 98 100 101 102 103 107 108 110 111 114 115 116 117 118 119 120 121 123 124 126 129 130 132 135 138 142 143 145 146 147 148 **P**6 **S** Legacy Health, Portland, OR
Primary Contact: Jonathan Avery, Chief Administrative Officer
CIO: C. Matthew Calais, Senior Vice President and Chief Information Officer
CHR: Sonja Steves, Vice President Marketing
CNO: Cindy Evans, R.N., Chief Nursing Officer
Web address: www.legacyhealth.org
Control: Other not–for–profit (including NFP Corporation) **Service:** General Medical and Surgical

Staffed Beds: 247 Admissions: 10634 Census: 144 Outpatient Visits: 162798 Births: 1130 Total Expense ($000): 293126 Payroll Expense ($000): 109904 Personnel: 1271

☒ **OHSU HOSPITAL (380009)**, 3181 S.W. Sam Jackson Park Road, Zip 97239–3098; tel. 503/494–8311, (Includes DOERNBECHER CHILDREN'S HOSPITAL, 700 S.W. Campus Drive, Zip 97239; tel. 503/494–8811; Timothy Goldfarb, Interim Chief Executive Officer) **A**1 2 3 5 8 10 **F**3 5 6 7 8 9 12 13 15 17 18 19 20 21 22 23 24 25 26 27 28 29 30 31 32 34 35 36 37 38 39 40 41 43 44 45 46 47 48 49 50 51 52 53 54 55 56 57 58 59 60 61 64 66 68 70 71 72 74 75 76 77 78 79 81 82 84 85 86 87 88 89 92 93 95 96 97 98 100 103 104 107 108 110 111 112 114 115 116 117 118 119 120 121 123 124 126 127 129 130 131 132 134 135 136 137 138 139 141 145 146 147 148 **P**1
Primary Contact: Timothy Goldfarb, Interim Chief Executive Officer
COO: Cynthia M. Grueber, Senior Vice President and Chief Operating Officer
CFO: Diana Gernhart, Senior Vice President and Hospital Chief Financial Officer
CMO: Charles M. Kilo, M.D., Vice President and Chief Medical Officer
CIO: Bridget Barnes, Vice President and Chief Information Officer
CHR: Dan Forbes, Vice President Human Resources
CNO: Dana Bjarnason, R.N., Vice President and Chief Nursing Officer
Web address: www.ohsu.edu
Control: Hospital district or authority, Government, nonfederal **Service:** General Medical and Surgical

Staffed Beds: 564 Admissions: 29244 Census: 466 Outpatient Visits: 811510 Births: 2457 Total Expense ($000): 1406235 Payroll Expense ($000): 478459 Personnel: 6959

☒ **PORTLAND VETERANS AFFAIRS MEDICAL CENTER**, 3710 S.W. U.S. Veterans Hospital Road, Zip 97239–2964, Mailing Address: P.O. Box 1034, Zip 97207–1034; tel. 503/220–8262, (Nonreporting) **A**1 2 3 5 8 **S** Department of Veterans Affairs, Washington, DC
Primary Contact: Michael W. Fisher, Director
CFO: Annette Barkema, Chief Financial Officer
CMO: Thomas Anderson, M.D., Chief of Staff
CIO: James Horner, Chief Information Officer
CHR: Melody Mikutowski, Chief Human Resources Management
Web address: www.portland.va.gov/
Control: Veterans Affairs, Government, federal **Service:** General Medical and Surgical

Staffed Beds: 303

☒ **PROVIDENCE PORTLAND MEDICAL CENTER (380061)**, 4805 N.E. Glisan Street, Zip 97213–2933; tel. 503/215–5526 **A**1 2 3 5 10 **F**3 4 5 9 13 15 17 18 20 22 24 26 27 29 30 31 34 35 36 37 38 40 44 45 46 49 50 51 53 54 56 57 58 59 60 61 62 63 64 65 66 68 70 72 73 74 76 77 78 79 81 82 84 85 86 87 89 90 92 93 97 98 99 100 102 103 104 105 107 108 109 110 111 114 116 117 118 119 121 123 124 126 129 130 131 132 133 135 136 137 145 146 147 148 **P**6 **S** Providence St. Joseph Health, Renton, WA
Primary Contact: Paul Gaden, Chief Executive Officer
COO: Krista Farnham, Chief Operating Officer
CFO: Eric Olson, Chief Financial Officer
CMO: Robert Wells, M.D., Chief Medical Officer
CIO: Mark Premo, Senior Director HC Intelligence
CHR: Jeannie Mikulic, Director Human Resources
CNO: Mary T. McFadden, MSN, Chief Nurse Executive
Web address: www.providence.org
Control: Church–operated, Nongovernment, not–for profit **Service:** General Medical and Surgical

Staffed Beds: 417 Admissions: 23456 Census: 309 Outpatient Visits: 1309818 Births: 2662 Total Expense ($000): 758176 Payroll Expense ($000): 215018 Personnel: 2746

☒ **PROVIDENCE ST. VINCENT MEDICAL CENTER (380004)**, 9205 S.W. Barnes Road, Zip 97225–6661; tel. 503/216–1234, (Includes CHILDREN AT PROVIDENCE ST. VINCENT, 9205 S.W. Barnes Road, Zip 97225–6603; tel. 503/216–4400) **A**1 2 3 5 10 **F**3 5 13 15 17 18 20 22 24 26 28 29 30 31 34 35 36 37 38 40 41 44 45 46 47 48 49 50 51 53 54 56 57 58 59 60 61 64 65 70 72 74 75 76 77 78 79 81 82 83 84 85 86 87 88 89 91 92 93 97 98 100 102 103 104 105 107 108 109 110 111 112 114 115 116 117 118 119 120 121 123 126 129 130 131 132 133 135 146 147 148 **P**6 **S** Providence St. Joseph Health, Renton, WA
Primary Contact: Janice Burger, Chief Executive
COO: Nancy Roberts, Chief Operating Officer
CFO: Scott Pfister, Director Finance
Web address: www.providence.org/portland/hospitals
Control: Church–operated, Nongovernment, not–for profit **Service:** General Medical and Surgical

Staffed Beds: 552 Admissions: 26377 Census: 324 Outpatient Visits: 827727 Births: 3999 Total Expense ($000): 776179 Payroll Expense ($000): 213766 Personnel: 2746

REHABILITATION INSTITUTE OF OREGON See Legacy Good Samaritan Hospital and Medical Center

---

Hospital, Medicare Provider Number, Address, Telephone, Approval, Facility, and Physician Codes, Health Care System

★ American Hospital Association (AHA) membership
☐ The Joint Commission accreditation
○ Healthcare Facilities Accreditation Program
◇ DNV Healthcare Inc. accreditation
⇑ Center for Improvement in Healthcare Quality Accreditation
△ Commission on Accreditation of Rehabilitation Facilities (CARF) accreditation

OR

☐ **SHRINERS HOSPITALS FOR CHILDREN–PORTLAND (383300)**, 3101 S.W. Sam Jackson Park Road, Zip 97239–3009; tel. 503/241–5090 **A**1 3 5 10 **F**3 29 34 35 37 50 53 58 64 68 75 77 79 81 85 86 87 89 91 93 94 130 131 132 134 146 148 **P**6 **S** Shriners Hospitals for Children, Tampa, FL
Primary Contact: J. Craig Patchin, Administrator
CFO: Mark Knudsen, Director Fiscal Services
CMO: Michael Aiona, M.D., Chief of Staff
CIO: Carl Montante, Director Information Systems and Information Technology
CHR: Rhonda Smith, Director Human Resources
CNO: Suzanne Diers, R.N., Director Patient Care Services
Web address: www.shrinershospitalsforchildren.org/Hospitals/Locations/Portland. aspx
Control: Other not–for–profit (including NFP Corporation) **Service:** Children's general

Staffed Beds: 12 **Admissions:** 327 **Census:** 5 **Outpatient Visits:** 11653 **Births:** 0 **Total Expense ($000):** 36993 **Payroll Expense ($000):** 18551 **Personnel:** 237

VETERANS AFFAIRS MEDICAL CENTER See Portland Veterans Affairs Medical Center

☒ **VIBRA SPECIALTY HOSPITAL OF PORTLAND (382004)**, 10300 N.E. Hancock Street, Zip 97220–3831; tel. 503/257–5500, (Nonreporting) **A**1 10 **S** Vibra Healthcare, Mechanicsburg, PA
Primary Contact: David Tupper, Chief Executive Officer
CFO: Stephanie Lawrence, Chief Financial Officer
CMO: Cynthia Wallace, M.D., Medical Director
CIO: Marie Roof, Executive Vice President Information Systems
CHR: Kellie Bernert–Yap, Director Human Resources
CNO: Susan E. Brooker, R.N., Chief Clinical Officer
Web address: www.vshportland.com
Control: Corporation, Investor–owned, for–profit **Service:** Long–Term Acute Care hospital

Staffed Beds: 68

PRINEVILLE—Crook County

★ **ST. CHARLES PRINEVILLE (381313)**, 1201 N.E. Elm Street, Zip 97754–1206; tel. 541/447–6254 **A**10 18 **F**3 11 15 29 30 34 35 40 43 45 50 59 64 65 68 70 75 77 79 81 82 84 85 86 87 93 97 100 107 110 115 119 127 128 130 132 133 135 146 **P**6 **S** St. Charles Health System, Inc., Bend, OR
Primary Contact: John Bishop, President
CFO: Karen Shepard, Senior Vice President and Chief Financial Officer
CMO: Michel Boileau, M.D., Chief Clinical Officer
CHR: Rebecca Berry, Senior Director Human Resources
Web address: www.stcharleshealthcare.org
Control: Other not–for–profit (including NFP Corporation) **Service:** General Medical and Surgical

Staffed Beds: 16 **Admissions:** 651 **Census:** 6 **Outpatient Visits:** 33782 **Births:** 0 **Total Expense ($000):** 22613 **Payroll Expense ($000):** 13947 **Personnel:** 174

REDMOND—Deschutes County

☒ **ST. CHARLES REDMOND (380040)**, 1253 N.W. Canal Boulevard, Zip 97756–1395; tel. 541/548–8131 **A**1 10 20 **F**3 11 13 28 29 30 34 40 43 45 47 51 54 57 59 62 63 64 68 70 75 76 79 81 82 84 85 93 97 107 108 114 119 130 132 135 146 148 **P**6 **S** St. Charles Health System, Inc., Bend, OR
Primary Contact: Joseph Sluka, Chief Executive Officer
CFO: Jennifer Welander, CPA, Senior Vice President Finance and Chief Financial Officer
CMO: Jeffrey Absalon, M.D., Chief Physician Officer
CIO: Jerimiah Brickhouse, Chief Information Officer
CHR: Rebecca Berry, Vice President Human Resources
CNO: Karen Reed, R.N., Chief Nursing Officer
Web address: www.stcharleshealthcare.org
Control: Other not–for–profit (including NFP Corporation) **Service:** General Medical and Surgical

Staffed Beds: 48 **Admissions:** 2574 **Census:** 21 **Outpatient Visits:** 52751 **Births:** 463 **Total Expense ($000):** 65728 **Payroll Expense ($000):** 39472 **Personnel:** 405

REEDSPORT—Douglas County

LOWER UMPQUA HOSPITAL DISTRICT (381311), 600 Ranch Road, Zip 97467–1795; tel. 541/271–2171 **A**10 18 **F**3 7 11 15 29 34 35 40 43 45 46 50 57 64 70 75 77 79 81 82 85 87 93 97 107 108 115 119 127 130 132 133 144 148 **P**6
Primary Contact: Sylvia Tommasino, Interim Administrator
CMO: Ronald Vail, M.D., Chief of Staff
CIO: Timothy Picou, Manager Information Technology
Web address: www.lowerumpquahospital.com
Control: Hospital district or authority, Government, nonfederal **Service:** General Medical and Surgical

Staffed Beds: 20 **Admissions:** 346 **Census:** 5 **Outpatient Visits:** 18247 **Births:** 0 **Total Expense ($000):** 24552 **Payroll Expense ($000):** 10290 **Personnel:** 146

ROSEBURG—Douglas County

☒ **MERCY MEDICAL CENTER (380027)**, 2700 Stewart Parkway, Zip 97471–1281; tel. 541/673–0611 **A**1 10 **F**3 8 11 13 15 17 18 19 20 21 22 23 24 25 26 27 28 29 30 31 32 34 35 37 38 40 43 44 45 46 47 48 49 50 51 54 56 57 59 60 61 62 63 64 65 68 70 74 75 76 77 78 79 81 82 84 85 86 87 89 93 96 102 107 108 110 111 114 115 118 119 129 130 132 135 143 146 147 148 **S** Catholic Health Initiatives, Englewood, CO
Primary Contact: Kelly C. Morgan, President and Chief Executive Officer
COO: Debbie Boswell, Chief Operating Officer and Chief Nursing Officer
CFO: Doug Klebe, Vice President Operational Finance
CMO: Jason Gray, M.D., Chief Medical Officer
CIO: Kathleen Nickel, Director Communications
CHR: Debora Lightcap, Director Human Resources
CNO: Debbie Boswell, Chief Operating Officer and Chief Nursing Officer
Web address: www.mercyrose.org
Control: Church–operated, Nongovernment, not–for profit **Service:** General Medical and Surgical

Staffed Beds: 141 **Admissions:** 7124 **Census:** 74 **Outpatient Visits:** 379579 **Births:** 916 **Total Expense ($000):** 164323 **Payroll Expense ($000):** 56842 **Personnel:** 761

☒ **VETERANS AFFAIRS ROSEBURG HEALTHCARE SYSTEM**, 913 N.W. Garden Valley Boulevard, Zip 97471–6513; tel. 541/440–1000, (Nonreporting) **A**1 **S** Department of Veterans Affairs, Washington, DC
Primary Contact: Carol Bogedain, FACHE, Director
COO: Steven Broskey, Associate Director
CHR: Larry Mentzer, Chief Human Resources Officer
CNO: Tracy Weistreich, Ph.D., Associate Director Patient Care Services/Nurse Executive
Web address: www.roseburg.va.gov/
Control: Veterans Affairs, Government, federal **Service:** General Medical and Surgical

Staffed Beds: 88

SALEM—Marion County

☐ **OREGON STATE HOSPITAL (384008)**, 2600 Center Street N.E., Zip 97301–2682; tel. 503/945–2870, (Nonreporting) **A**1 3 5 10
Primary Contact: Greg Roberts, Superintendent
Web address: www.oregon.gov/dhs/mentalhealth/osh/main.shtml
Control: State–Government, nonfederal **Service:** Psychiatric

Staffed Beds: 638

☒ **SALEM HOSPITAL (380051)**, 890 Oak Street S.E., Zip 97301–3959, Mailing Address: P.O. Box 14001, Zip 97309–5014; tel. 503/561–5200, (Includes PSYCHIATRIC MEDICINE CENTER, 1127 Oak Street S.E., Zip 97301, Mailing Address: P.O. Box 14001, Zip 97309–5014; REGIONAL REHABILITATION CENTER, 2561 Center Street N.E., Zip 97301, Mailing Address: P.O. Box 14001, Zip 97309–5014; tel. 503/370–5986) **A**1 2 5 10 **F**3 11 12 13 15 17 18 19 20 22 24 26 28 29 30 31 34 35 36 37 38 40 43 45 46 47 48 49 50 53 54 55 56 57 58 59 64 67 68 70 72 74 75 76 77 78 79 81 84 85 86 87 89 90 91 92 93 94 95 96 97 98 99 100 102 103 104 105 106 107 108 109 110 111 112 113 114 115 116 117 118 119 120 121 122 123 124 126 129 130 131 132 135 145 146 147 148 **P**6 **S** Salem Health, Salem, OR
Primary Contact: Cheryl R. Nester Wolfe, President and Chief Executive Officer
COO: Bahaa Wanly, Interim Chief Operating Officer
CFO: James Parr, Chief Financial Officer
CMO: Ralph Yates, D.O., Chief Medical Officer
CIO: Leah Mitchell, R.N., Interim Chief Information Officer
CHR: Laurie C. Barr, Vice President Human Resources
CNO: Sarah Horn, Chief Nursing Officer
Web address: www.salemhealth.org
Control: Other not–for–profit (including NFP Corporation) **Service:** General Medical and Surgical

Staffed Beds: 441 **Admissions:** 25260 **Census:** 317 **Outpatient Visits:** 382243 **Births:** 3271 **Total Expense ($000):** 618438 **Payroll Expense ($000):** 271770 **Personnel:** 3502

SEASIDE—Clatsop County

☒ **PROVIDENCE SEASIDE HOSPITAL (381303)**, 725 South Wahanna Road, Zip 97138–7735; tel. 503/717–7000 **A**1 10 18 **F**3 12 13 15 18 29 30 31 32 34 35 40 45 46 56 57 59 61 64 65 66 70 75 76 77 78 79 81 82 83 84 85 86 87 91 92 93 97 107 108 110 111 114 119 127 130 132 133 135 143 146 147 148 **P**6 **S** Providence St. Joseph Health, Renton, WA
Primary Contact: Kendall Sawa, R.N., Chief Executive Officer
COO: Debbie Glass, Interim Chief Operating Officer
CFO: Pamela Cooper, Director Finance
CMO: Susan Heineck, M.D., President Professional Staff
CHR: Theresa Osburne, Human Resources Strategic Partners
CNO: Janiece Zauner, Chief Nursing Officer
Web address: www.providence.org
Control: Church–operated, Nongovernment, not–for profit **Service:** General Medical and Surgical

Staffed Beds: 25 **Admissions:** 1007 **Census:** 9 **Outpatient Visits:** 136980 **Births:** 119 **Total Expense ($000):** 61460 **Payroll Expense ($000):** 24556 **Personnel:** 328

Many Facility Codes have changed. Please refer to the AHA Guide Code Chart. © 2016 AHA Guide

OR

SILVERTON—Marion County

✠ **LEGACY SILVERTON MEDICAL CENTER (380029)**, 342 Fairview Street, Zip 97381–1993; tel. 503/873–1500 **A**1 10 **F**3 11 13 15 20 26 28 29 30 34 35 40 43 47 50 54 57 59 64 65 66 70 75 76 77 79 81 85 86 87 89 102 104 107 108 110 111 114 115 119 124 127 130 131 132 133 135 143 144 146 147 148 **P**4 8
Primary Contact: Sarah Fronza, Interim President and Chief Executive Officer
COO: Karen Brady, Chief Operating Officer, Chief Nursing Officer and Chief Information Officer
CFO: Daniel Jessup, Chief Financial Officer
CMO: Joseph Huang, M.D., Chief Medical and Quality Officer
CIO: Karen Brady, Chief Operating Officer, Chief Nursing Officer and Chief Information Officer
CHR: Natalie Britton, Director Human Resources
CNO: Karen Brady, Chief Operating Officer, Chief Nursing Officer and Chief Information Officer
Web address: www.silvertonhealth.org
Control: Other not–for–profit (including NFP Corporation) **Service:** General Medical and Surgical

Staffed Beds: 48 **Admissions:** 2976 **Census:** 21 **Outpatient Visits:** 122082 **Births:** 1504 **Total Expense ($000):** 127764 **Payroll Expense ($000):** 54618 **Personnel:** 731

SPRINGFIELD—Lane County

✠ **MCKENZIE–WILLAMETTE MEDICAL CENTER (380020)**, 1460 G Street, Zip 97477–4197; tel. 541/726–4400 **A**1 10 **F**3 11 13 17 18 20 22 24 26 28 29 30 31 34 35 39 40 41 43 45 46 47 49 50 57 59 70 73 76 78 79 81 82 85 87 89 93 107 108 111 115 118 119 126 129 130 132 146 147 148 **P**6 **S** Quorum Health, Brentwood, TN
Primary Contact: Chad Campbell, Chief Executive Officer
CFO: Rosanne Devault, Chief Financial Officer
CIO: David Blomquist, Director Information Technology
CHR: Megan A. O'Leary, Vice President Human Resources and Rehabilitation Services
Web address: www.mckweb.com
Control: Corporation, Investor–owned, for–profit **Service:** General Medical and Surgical

Staffed Beds: 113 **Admissions:** 7604 **Census:** 68 **Outpatient Visits:** 92104 **Births:** 995 **Total Expense ($000):** 138198 **Payroll Expense ($000):** 50874 **Personnel:** 623

★ ◇ **PEACEHEALTH SACRED HEART MEDICAL CENTER AT RIVERBEND (380102)**, 3333 Riverbend Drive, Zip 97477–8800; tel. 541/222–7300 **A**10 21 **F**3 11 12 13 19 20 21 22 24 26 28 29 30 31 37 38 40 43 45 46 47 49 51 57 60 64 68 70 72 74 75 76 78 79 81 84 85 89 93 102 107 108 111 115 118 119 124 126 129 130 146 148 **P**6 **S** PeaceHealth, Vancouver, WA
Primary Contact: Rand O'Leary, FACHE, Chief Executive, Oregon Network
COO: Shannon Surber, Chief Operating Officer
CFO: Wendy Apland, Regional Vice President of Finance/Chief Financial Officer
CHR: Marie F. Stehmer, Senior Director of Human Resources
CNO: Louella Freeman, MSN, Chief Nursing Officer
Web address: www.peacehealth.org
Control: Church–operated, Nongovernment, not–for profit **Service:** General Medical and Surgical

Staffed Beds: 379 **Admissions:** 23964 **Census:** 296 **Outpatient Visits:** 106377 **Births:** 2907 **Total Expense ($000):** 522035 **Payroll Expense ($000):** 175822 **Personnel:** 2291

STAYTON—Marion County

✠ **SANTIAM HOSPITAL (380056)**, 1401 North 10th Avenue, Zip 97383–1399; tel. 503/769–2175 **A**1 10 **F**3 7 11 13 15 16 29 30 40 41 43 50 65 70 73 76 80 81 85 87 88 89 90 107 111 115 119 128 130 133 135 143 **P**8
Primary Contact: Terry L. Fletchall, President and Chief Executive Officer
COO: Maggie Hudson, Chief Financial and Operations Officer
CFO: Rachael Seeder, Controller
CMO: Amy Sutkus, M.D., Medical Staff President
CIO: Trace Jacobs, Director Information Technology
CNO: Janet Dow, R.N., Chief Nursing Officer
Web address: www.santiamhospital.org
Control: Other not–for–profit (including NFP Corporation) **Service:** General Medical and Surgical

Staffed Beds: 40 **Admissions:** 1034 **Census:** 9 **Outpatient Visits:** 40692 **Births:** 83 **Total Expense ($000):** 41094 **Payroll Expense ($000):** 18763 **Personnel:** 265

THE DALLES—Wasco County

✠ △ **MID–COLUMBIA MEDICAL CENTER (380001)**, 1700 East 19th Street, Zip 97058–3317; tel. 541/296–1111 **A**1 2 7 10 **F**3 11 13 15 18 20 28 29 30 31 32 34 35 36 40 41 43 45 46 50 53 57 59 62 65 66 68 70 75 76 77 78 79 81 82 83 84 86 87 89 90 91 92 93 99 100 101 104 107 108 110 111 114 118 119 120 121 123 127 129 130 131 132 133 135 146 147 148 **P**6
Primary Contact: Duane Francis, President and Chief Executive Officer
CFO: Don Arbon, Vice President Finance
CMO: Judy Richardson, M.D., President Medical Staff
CIO: Erick Larson, Vice President and Chief Information Officer
CHR: Christine Espy, Division Director
CNO: Regina P. Rose, R.N., Vice President Nursing Services
Web address: www.mcmc.net
Control: Other not–for–profit (including NFP Corporation) **Service:** General Medical and Surgical

Staffed Beds: 43 **Admissions:** 2390 **Census:** 19 **Outpatient Visits:** 121018 **Births:** 317 **Total Expense ($000):** 93880 **Payroll Expense ($000):** 44635 **Personnel:** 528

TILLAMOOK—Tillamook County

✠ **TILLAMOOK REGIONAL MEDICAL CENTER (381317)**, 1000 Third Street, Zip 97141–3430; tel. 503/842–4444 **A**1 10 18 **F**2 3 7 13 15 17 18 29 30 31 33 34 35 40 43 45 50 57 59 64 65 68 75 76 77 78 79 81 82 85 87 93 94 97 102 107 108 110 111 115 119 127 129 130 132 133 134 135 144 146 147 148 **P**6 **S** Adventist Health, Roseville, CA
Primary Contact: David Butler, President and Chief Executive Officer
CFO: Walt Larson, Vice President Finance
CMO: Mark Bowman, M.D., President Medical Staff
CNO: Kathy Saxon, R.N., Vice President Patient Care Services
Web address: www.tillamookregionalmc.com
Control: Church–operated, Nongovernment, not–for profit **Service:** General Medical and Surgical

Staffed Beds: 25 **Admissions:** 1282 **Census:** 11 **Outpatient Visits:** 128283 **Births:** 183 **Total Expense ($000):** 71317 **Payroll Expense ($000):** 30279 **Personnel:** 390

TUALATIN—Clackamas County

✠ **LEGACY MERIDIAN PARK MEDICAL CENTER (380089)**, 19300 S.W. 65th Avenue, Zip 97062–9741; tel. 503/692–1212 **A**1 2 10 **F**3 11 13 15 18 20 22 28 29 30 31 32 34 35 38 40 44 45 46 49 50 51 56 57 59 60 64 68 70 74 75 76 77 78 79 80 81 85 86 87 91 93 97 107 108 110 111 114 115 116 117 118 119 120 121 126 129 130 132 145 146 147 148 **P**6 **S** Legacy Health, Portland, OR
Primary Contact: Allyson Anderson, Chief Administrative Officer
COO: Michael Newcomb, D.O., Senior Vice President and Chief Operating Officer
CMO: Lewis Low, M.D., Senior Vice President and Chief Medical Officer
CIO: John Jay Kenagy, Ph.D., Senior Vice President and Chief Information Officer
CHR: Sonja Steves, Vice President Human Resources and Marketing
CNO: Carol Bradley, MSN, Senior Vice President and Chief Nursing Officer
Web address: www.legacyhealth.org
Control: Other not–for–profit (including NFP Corporation) **Service:** General Medical and Surgical

Staffed Beds: 130 **Admissions:** 8931 **Census:** 81 **Outpatient Visits:** 165633 **Births:** 1130 **Total Expense ($000):** 182741 **Payroll Expense ($000):** 66685 **Personnel:** 765

Hospital, Medicare Provider Number, Address, Telephone, Approval, Facility, and Physician Codes, Health Care System

★ American Hospital Association (AHA) membership
□ The Joint Commission accreditation
○ Healthcare Facilities Accreditation Program
◇ DNV Healthcare Inc. accreditation
⇑ Center for Improvement in Healthcare Quality Accreditation
△ Commission on Accreditation of Rehabilitation Facilities (CARF) accreditation

PENNSYLVANIA

ABINGTON—Montgomery County

⊞ **ABINGTON HOSPITAL (390231)**, 1200 Old York Road, Zip 19001–3720;
tel. 215/481–2000 **A**1 2 3 5 10 13 **F**3 6 8 9 11 12 13 15 17 18 20 22 24 26
28 29 30 31 32 34 35 36 37 38 39 40 43 44 45 46 47 48 49 50 52 53 54
55 56 57 58 59 61 62 63 64 65 66 70 72 73 74 75 76 77 78 79 80 81
82 84 85 86 87 89 90 91 92 93 94 96 97 98 99 100 101 102 103 104 107
108 110 111 114 115 118 119 120 121 123 124 126 129 130 131 132 135
144 145 146 147 148 **P**6 **S** Jefferson Health, Radnor, PA
Primary Contact: Margaret M. McGoldrick, President
CFO: Michael Walsh, Senior Vice President Finance and Chief Financial Officer
CMO: John J. Kelly, M.D., Chief of Staff
CIO: Colleen Saul, Executive Director Information Services and Technology
CHR: Meghan Patton, Vice President Human Resources
CNO: Theresa Reilly, MSN, Senior Vice President Patient Services and Chief
Nursing Officer
Web address: www.abingtonhealth.org
Control: Other not–for–profit (including NFP Corporation) **Service:** General
Medical and Surgical

Staffed Beds: 618 **Admissions:** 28412 **Census:** 354 **Outpatient Visits:**
534689 **Births:** 4699 **Total Expense ($000):** 692602 **Payroll Expense**
($000): 327703 **Personnel:** 3956

ALLENTOWN—Lehigh County

☐ △ **GOOD SHEPHERD REHABILITATION HOSPITAL (393035)**, 850 South 5th
Street, Zip 18103–3308; tel. 610/776–3299 **A**1 3 5 7 10 **F**28 29 30 32 34 35
36 53 54 56 57 58 59 64 65 66 68 74 75 82 86 87 90 91 93 94 95 100
106 107 111 119 130 131 132 143 146 147 148 **P**1 **S** Good Shepherd
Rehabilitation Network, Allentown, PA
Primary Contact: John Kristel, President and Chief Executive Officer
CFO: Ronald J. Petula, Chief Financial Officer
Web address: www.goodshepherdrehab.org
Control: Other not–for–profit (including NFP Corporation) **Service:** Rehabilitation

Staffed Beds: 106 **Admissions:** 1637 **Census:** 79 **Outpatient Visits:** 225206
Births: 0 **Total Expense ($000):** 84932 **Payroll Expense ($000):** 35442
Personnel: 890

⊞ **LEHIGH VALLEY HOSPITAL (390133)**, 1200 South Cedar Crest Boulevard,
Zip 18103–6248, Mailing Address: P.O. Box 689, Zip 18105–1556;
tel. 610/402–8000, (Includes LEHIGH VALLEY HEALTH NETWORK PEDITATRICS,
1200 South Cedar Crest Boulevard, Zip 18103–6202, Mailing Address: P.O. Box
689, Zip 18105; tel. 484/862–3131) **A**1 2 3 5 8 10 **F**3 6 7 8 12 13 15 16 17
18 19 20 22 24 26 28 29 30 31 32 33 34 35 36 37 38 39 40 43 44 45
46 47 48 49 50 51 53 54 55 56 57 58 59 60 61 62 63 64 65 66 70 71 72
74 76 77 78 79 80 81 82 84 85 86 87 88 89 90 92 93 96 97 98 99 100
101 102 104 105 106 107 108 110 114 115 116 117 118 119 120 121 123
124 126 128 129 130 131 132 134 135 138 141 142 143 144 145 146 147
148 **P**5 6 8 **S** Lehigh Valley Health Network, Allentown, PA
Primary Contact: Brian A. Nester, President and Chief Executive Officer
COO: Terry Ann Capuano, R.N., Chief Operating Officer
CFO: Edward O'Dea, Executive Vice President and Chief Financial Officer
CMO: Thomas V. Whalen, M.D., Chief Medical Officer
CIO: Michael N. Minear, Senior Vice President and Chief Information Officer
CHR: Deborah A. Patrick, Senior Vice President Human Resources
CNO: Marie Kim Jordan, R.N., Senior Vice President and Chief Nursing Officer
Web address: www.lvhn.org
Control: Other not–for–profit (including NFP Corporation) **Service:** General
Medical and Surgical

Staffed Beds: 833 **Admissions:** 42926 **Census:** 647 **Outpatient Visits:**
460156 **Births:** 4352 **Total Expense ($000):** 1238290 **Payroll Expense**
($000): 409640 **Personnel:** 6984

☐ △ **SACRED HEART HOSPITAL (390197)**, 421 West Chew Street,
Zip 18102–3490; tel. 610/776–4500, (Total facility includes 22 beds in nursing
home–type unit) **A**1 3 5 7 10 **F**3 11 12 13 15 18 20 22 24 28 29 30 31 32 34
35 38 39 40 43 45 46 47 49 50 56 57 59 61 64 66 68 74 75 76 77 78 79
80 81 82 84 85 87 91 92 93 97 98 100 101 102 103 107 108 110 111 115
117 118 119 121 128 129 130 132 135 143 146 147 148 **P**8
Primary Contact: John L. Nespoli, Chief Executive Officer
CMO: Farrokh Sadr, M.D., Chief Medical Officer
CIO: Tracy Burkhart, Vice President Information Services
CHR: Joseph Mikitka, Vice President Human Resources
Web address: www.shh.org
Control: Other not–for–profit (including NFP Corporation) **Service:** General
Medical and Surgical

Staffed Beds: 131 **Admissions:** 5040 **Census:** 110 **Outpatient Visits:**
158645 **Births:** 303 **Total Expense ($000):** 97510 **Payroll Expense ($000):**
34851 **Personnel:** 810

ST LUKE'S HOSPITAL – ALLENTOWN CAMPUS See St. Luke's University
Hospital – Bethlehem Campus, Bethlehem

☐ **SURGICAL SPECIALTY CENTER AT COORDINATED HEALTH (390321)**,
1503 North Cedar Crest Boulevard, Zip 18104–2302; tel. 610/861–8080,
(Nonreporting) **A**1 10
Primary Contact: Emil Dilorio, M.D., Chief Executive Officer
Web address: www.coordinatedhealth.com
Control: Other not–for–profit (including NFP Corporation) **Service:** Surgical

Staffed Beds: 20

ALTOONA—Blair County

ALTOONA REGIONAL HEALTH SYSTEM See UPMC Altoona

⊞ **HEALTHSOUTH REHABILITATION HOSPITAL OF ALTOONA (393040)**, 2005
Valley View Boulevard, Zip 16602–4598; tel. 814/944–3535 **A**1 10 **F**28 29 30 34
64 74 75 82 90 91 93 94 96 130 131 **P**5 **S** HEALTHSOUTH Corporation,
Birmingham, AL
Primary Contact: Scott Filler, Chief Executive Officer
CFO: George Berger, Controller
CMO: Rakesh Patel, D.O., Medical Director
CIO: Kathleen Edwards, Manager Information Systems Operation
CHR: Christine Filer, Director Human Resources
CNO: Mary Gen Boyles, Chief Nursing Officer
Web address: www.healthsouthaltoona.com
Control: Corporation, Investor–owned, for–profit **Service:** Rehabilitation

Staffed Beds: 80 **Admissions:** 1836 **Census:** 70 **Births:** 0

⊞ **JAMES E. VAN ZANDT VETERANS AFFAIRS MEDICAL CENTER**, 2907
Pleasant Valley Boulevard, Zip 16602–4305; tel. 877/626–2500, (Nonreporting)
A1 **S** Department of Veterans Affairs, Washington, DC
Primary Contact: Judy A. Hayman, Ph.D., Acting Director
CFO: Carl Parrish, Chief Fiscal Service
CMO: Santha Kurian, M.D., Chief of Staff
CIO: Michael Hynoski, Chief Information Resource Management
CHR: Gina Dunio, Chief Human Resources
Web address: www.altoona.va.gov/
Control: Veterans Affairs, Government, federal **Service:** General Medical and
Surgical

Staffed Beds: 68

⊞ **UPMC ALTOONA (390073)**, 620 Howard Avenue, Zip 16601–4804;
tel. 814/889–2011 **A**1 2 3 5 10 12 13 **F**3 5 8 11 12 13 15 18 20 22 24 26
28 29 30 31 34 35 37 38 39 40 43 44 45 47 48 49 50 51 54 56 57 59 60
61 63 64 65 66 68 70 73 74 75 77 78 79 81 83 84 85 86 87 91 92 93 97
98 100 101 102 103 107 108 110 111 114 115 117 118 119 120 121 123
126 129 130 131 132 135 146 147 148 **S** UPMC, Pittsburgh, PA
Primary Contact: Gerald Murray, President
COO: Ron McConnell, Chief Operating Officer
CFO: Betsy Kreuz, Chief Financial Officer
CMO: Linnane Batzel, M.D., Senior Vice President Quality and Medical Affairs and
Chief Medical Officer
CIO: Dale Fuller, Vice President and Chief Information Officer
CHR: Michelle A. Speck, Vice President Human Resources
CNO: Chris Rickens, R.N., Senior Vice President and Chief Nursing Officer
Web address: www.altoonaregional.org
Control: Other not–for–profit (including NFP Corporation) **Service:** General
Medical and Surgical

Staffed Beds: 380 **Admissions:** 17732 **Census:** 227 **Outpatient Visits:**
371925 **Births:** 884 **Total Expense ($000):** 448397 **Payroll Expense**
($000): 198370 **Personnel:** 1961

AMBLER—Montgomery County

☐ **HORSHAM CLINIC (394034)**, 722 East Butler Pike, Zip 19002–2310;
tel. 215/643–7800, (Nonreporting) **A**1 3 5 10 **S** Universal Health Services, Inc.,
King of Prussia, PA
Primary Contact: Phyllis Weisfield, Chief Executive Officer and Managing Director
CFO: Christian Owen, Chief Operating Officer
CMO: James B. Congdon, M.D., Medical Director
CIO: Suzanne Scholz, Director Medical Records
CHR: Kathleen Nichelson, Director Human Resources
CNO: Calvin Litka, R.N., Director of Nursing
Web address: www.horshamclinic.com
Control: Individual, Investor–owned, for–profit **Service:** Psychiatric

Staffed Beds: 138

Many Facility Codes have changed. Please refer to the AHA Guide Code Chart. © 2016 AHA Guide

BEAVER—Beaver County

☐ **HERITAGE VALLEY HEALTH SYSTEM (390036)**, 1000 Dutch Ridge Road,
Zip 15009–9727; tel. 724/728–7000 **A**1 3 10 13 **F**3 11 13 14 15 18 20 22
24 26 28 29 30 32 34 35 38 40 46 49 50 53 54 55 57 59 60 64 66 70 73
74 75 76 77 78 79 81 82 84 85 86 89 90 92 93 96 97 98 100 101 102 103
104 107 108 110 111 115 116 118 119 120 121 129 130 131 132 135 145
147 148 **P**6 **S** Heritage Valley Health System, Beaver, PA
Primary Contact: Norman F. Mitry, President and Chief Executive Officer
CFO: Bryan J. Randall, Vice President Finance and Chief Financial Officer
CMO: John Cinicola, M.D., Chief Medical Officer
CIO: David Carleton, Chief Information Officer
CHR: Bruce Edwards, Vice President Human Resources
CNO: Marcia L. Ferrero, MS, Chief Nursing Officer
Web address: www.heritagevalley.org
Control: Other not–for–profit (including NFP Corporation) **Service:** General
Medical and Surgical

Staffed Beds: 271 **Admissions:** 13691 **Census:** 168 **Births:** 1107

☒ **CURAHEALTH HERITAGE VALLEY (392043)**, 1000 Dutch Ridge Road,
Zip 15009–9727; tel. 724/773–8480, (Nonreporting) **A**1 10
Primary Contact: Jennifer Sullivan, Chief Executive Officer
CFO: Kevin Varley, Chief Financial Officer
CMO: Jeffrey Erukhimou, M.D., Medical Director
Control: Corporation, Investor–owned, for–profit **Service:** Long–Term Acute Care
hospital

Staffed Beds: 35

BENSALEM—Bucks County

LIVENGRIN FOUNDATION, 4833 Hulmeville Road, Zip 19020–3099;
tel. 215/638–5200, (Nonreporting)
Primary Contact: Richard M. Pine, President and Chief Executive Officer
CFO: James D. Flis, Chief Financial Officer
CMO: William J. Lorman, Ph.D., Clinical Director
CIO: William Miller, Coordinator Management Information Systems
Web address: www.livengrin.org
Control: Other not–for–profit (including NFP Corporation) **Service:** Alcoholism and
other chemical dependency

Staffed Beds: 76

☐ **ROTHMAN SPECIALTY HOSPITAL (390322)**, 3300 Tillman Drive,
Zip 19020–2071; tel. 215/244–7400 **A**1 3 10 **F**29 79 81 82 85 89 141 146
Primary Contact: Kelly Doyle, Chief Executive Officer
Web address: www.rothmanspecialtyhospital.com/
Control: Partnership, Investor–owned, for–profit **Service:** Surgical

Staffed Beds: 24 **Admissions:** 1658 **Census:** 5 **Outpatient Visits:** 2176
Births: 0

BERWICK—Columbia County

☒ **BERWICK HOSPITAL CENTER (390072)**, 701 East 16th Street,
Zip 18603–2397; tel. 570/759–5000, (Nonreporting) **A**1 10 **S** Community Health
Systems, Inc., Franklin, TN
Primary Contact: Diane Ljungquist, R.N., MS, Chief Executive Officer
COO: Chad Kramer, Chief Operating Officer
CFO: Whitney Holloway, Chief Financial Officer
CMO: M. Joseph John, M.D., Chief of Staff
CIO: Jeff Leslie, Director Information Technology
CHR: Jackie Ridall, Director Human Resources
CNO: Doreen Kolojejechick, Chief Nursing Officer
Web address: www.berwick–hospital.com
Control: Corporation, Investor–owned, for–profit **Service:** General Medical and
Surgical

Staffed Beds: 341

BETHLEHEM—Northampton County

☐ **COORDINATED HEALTH–BETHLEHEM (390314)**, 2310 Highland Avenue,
Zip 18020–8920, Mailing Address: 2300 Highland Avenue, Zip 18020;
tel. 610/861–8080 **A**1 10 **F**3 29 34 65 68 79 81 82 85 119 130 131
141 148
Primary Contact: Mark Holtz, Chief Operating Officer
Web address: www.coordinatedhealth.com
Control: Corporation, Investor–owned, for–profit **Service:** Orthopedic

Staffed Beds: 20 **Admissions:** 1137 **Census:** 7 **Outpatient Visits:** 6790
Births: 0 **Total Expense ($000):** 28687 **Payroll Expense ($000):** 5568
Personnel: 121

☒ △ **GOOD SHEPHERD SPECIALTY HOSPITAL (392033)**, 2545 Schoenersville
Road, 3rd Floor, Zip 18017–7300; tel. 484/884–5051 **A**1 7 10 **F**1 3 29 30 36
77 85 87 91 95 130 148 **P**5 **S** Good Shepherd Rehabilitation Network,
Allentown, PA
Primary Contact: Greg Wuchter, R.N., MSN, Administrator
CFO: Ronald J. Petula, Chief Financial Officer
CIO: Michael Cirba, Chief Information Officer
CHR: Kristen Melan, Director Human Resources Administration
CNO: Samuel Miranda, Jr., Chief Nursing Officer
Web address: www.goodshepherdrehab.org
Control: Other not–for–profit (including NFP Corporation) **Service:** Long–Term
Acute Care hospital

Staffed Beds: 32 **Admissions:** 393 **Census:** 29 **Outpatient Visits:** 0 **Births:**
0 **Total Expense ($000):** 15682 **Payroll Expense ($000):** 5505 **Personnel:**
87

☒ **LEHIGH VALLEY HOSPITAL–MUHLENBERG (390263)**, 2545 Schoenersville
Road, Zip 18017–7300; tel. 484/884–2200 **A**1 2 3 10 12 13 **F**3 7 11 12 15
17 18 20 22 24 26 28 29 30 31 34 35 36 37 38 39 40 44 45 46 49 50 51
53 54 57 58 59 60 62 63 64 65 68 70 74 77 78 79 80 81 82 84 85 86 87
92 93 97 100 102 105 107 108 110 111 115 118 119 120 121 123 124
126 129 130 131 132 134 135 141 143 146 148 **P**5 6 8 **S** Lehigh Valley
Health Network, Allentown, PA
Primary Contact: Brian A. Nester, President and Chief Executive Officer
COO: Terry Ann Capuano, R.N., Chief Operating Officer
CFO: Edward O'Dea, Executive Vice President and Chief Financial Officer
CMO: Thomas V. Whalen, M.D., Executive Vice President and Chief Medical Officer
CIO: Michael N. Minear, Senior Vice President and Chief Information Officer
CHR: Deborah A. Patrick, Senior Vice President Human Resources
CNO: Marie Kim Jordan, R.N., Senior Vice President, Chief Nursing Officer
Web address: www.lvhn.org
Control: Other not–for–profit (including NFP Corporation) **Service:** General
Medical and Surgical

Staffed Beds: 168 **Admissions:** 9670 **Census:** 133 **Outpatient Visits:**
179436 **Births:** 0 **Total Expense ($000):** 209751 **Payroll Expense ($000):**
75100 **Personnel:** 1236

☐ △ **ST. LUKE'S UNIVERSITY HOSPITAL – BETHLEHEM CAMPUS (390049)**,
801 Ostrum Street, Zip 18015–1065; tel. 484/526–4000, (Includes ST LUKE'S
HOSPITAL – ALLENTOWN CAMPUS, 1736 Hamilton Street, Allentown,
Zip 18104–5656; tel. 610/628–8300) **A**1 2 3 7 8 10 12 13 **F**3 9 11 12 13 15
17 18 19 20 22 24 26 27 28 29 30 31 32 34 35 36 37 38 39 40 42 43 44
45 46 47 48 49 50 51 52 53 54 55 56 57 58 59 60 61 62 63 64 65 66 68 70
71 72 73 74 75 76 77 78 79 81 82 84 85 86 87 89 90 92 93 96 97 98 99
100 101 102 103 104 105 107 108 109 110 111 115 117 118 119 120 121
123 124 126 129 130 131 132 134 135 144 145 146 147 148 **P**6 8 **S** St.
Luke's University Health Network, Bethlehem, PA
Primary Contact: Carol Kuplen, R.N., MSN, President and Chief Executive Officer
CFO: Tom Lichtenwalner, Vice President Finance
CMO: Jeffrey Jahre, M.D., Vice President Medical and Academic Affairs
CIO: Chad Brisendine, Chief Information Officer
CHR: Robert Zimmel, Senior Vice President Human Resources
Web address: www.slhn–lehighvalley.org
Control: Other not–for–profit (including NFP Corporation) **Service:** General
Medical and Surgical

Staffed Beds: 540 **Admissions:** 27426 **Census:** 358 **Outpatient Visits:**
625629 **Births:** 3566 **Total Expense ($000):** 558833 **Payroll Expense
($000):** 231207 **Personnel:** 4380

BLOOMSBURG—Columbia County

★ **GEISINGER–BLOOMSBURG HOSPITAL (390003)**, 549 Fair Street,
Zip 17815–1419; tel. 570/387–2100, (Nonreporting) **A**3 10 **S** Geisinger Health
System, Danville, PA
Primary Contact: Lissa Bryan–Smith, Chief Administrative Officer
COO: Joseph M. DeVito, Vice President Finance and Chief Operating Officer
CFO: Joseph M. DeVito, Vice President Finance and Chief Operating Officer
CMO: James Joseph, M.D., President Medical Staff
CIO: Thomas Wray, Director Information
CHR: Mary Lenzini Howe, Vice President Human Resources
Web address: www.bloomhealth.net
Control: Other not–for–profit (including NFP Corporation) **Service:** General
Medical and Surgical

Staffed Beds: 72

Hospital, Medicare Provider Number, Address, Telephone, Approval, Facility, and Physician Codes, Health Care System

★ American Hospital Association (AHA) membership   ○ Healthcare Facilities Accreditation Program   ⇑ Center for Improvement in Healthcare Quality Accreditation
☐ The Joint Commission accreditation   ◇ DNV Healthcare Inc. accreditation   △ Commission on Accreditation of Rehabilitation Facilities (CARF) accreditation

BRADFORD—Mckean County

☐ **BRADFORD REGIONAL MEDICAL CENTER (390118)**, 116 Interstate Parkway, Zip 16701–1036; tel. 814/368–4143, (Total facility includes 95 beds in nursing home–type unit) **A**1 10 **F**3 5 11 13 15 18 20 28 29 30 31 34 35 38 39 40 45 47 49 50 53 54 56 57 59 64 65 70 75 76 77 78 79 81 82 83 84 85 86 87 93 94 96 97 98 100 101 102 103 104 105 107 108 110 111 114 117 118 119 127 128 129 130 131 132 135 146 147 148 **P**6 8 **S** Upper Allegheny Health System, Olean, NY
Primary Contact: Timothy J. Finan, FACHE, President and Chief Executive Officer
COO: Jeff S. Zewe, R.N., Chief Operating Officer
CFO: Richard G. Braun, Jr., CPA, Senior Vice President and Chief Financial Officer
CMO: William Mills, M.D., Senior Vice President Quality and Professional Affairs
CIO: Jason Yaworsky, Chief Information Officer
CHR: Timothy M. McNamara, Senior Vice President Human Resources
Web address: www.brmc.com
Control: Other not–for–profit (including NFP Corporation) **Service:** General Medical and Surgical

Staffed Beds: 182 **Admissions:** 2683 **Census:** 122 **Outpatient Visits:** 134021 **Births:** 241 **Total Expense ($000):** 63836 **Payroll Expense ($000):** 26288 **Personnel:** 494

BRISTOL—Bucks County

✠ **LOWER BUCKS HOSPITAL (390070)**, 501 Bath Road, Zip 19007–3190; tel. 215/785–9200 **A**1 10 13 **F**3 17 18 20 22 24 26 28 29 30 31 34 35 38 40 45 50 51 57 59 60 62 68 70 74 75 77 78 79 81 85 89 91 92 93 97 98 102 103 107 108 111 114 115 119 129 130 133 146 147 148 **S** Prime Healthcare Services, Ontario, CA
Primary Contact: Linda J. Grass, Chief Executive Officer
COO: Matt Shelak, Chief Operating Officer
CFO: Courtney Coffman, Chief Financial Officer
CMO: Sanjay Bhatia, Chief Medical Officer
CIO: Steve Kane, Director Information Technology
CNO: Pat Bain, Chief Nursing Officer
Web address: www.lowerbuckshosp.com
Control: Corporation, Investor–owned, for–profit **Service:** General Medical and Surgical

Staffed Beds: 104 **Admissions:** 5409 **Census:** 60 **Births:** 0 **Personnel:** 731

BROOKVILLE—Jefferson County

PENN HIGHLANDS BROOKVILLE (391312), 100 Hospital Road, Zip 15825–1367; tel. 814/849–2312 **A**10 18 **F**3 11 15 18 28 29 30 34 35 39 40 45 46 57 59 62 64 65 75 77 81 82 85 86 93 98 102 103 104 107 108 110 114 118 129 130 131 132 133 145 146
Primary Contact: Julie Peer, President
CFO: Jessica Park, Director Accounting
CMO: Timothy Pendleton, M.D., President Medical Staff
CIO: Thomas Johnson, Director Information Systems
CHR: Rebecca Edwards, Chief Human Resources Officer
CNO: Debra A. Thomas, Vice President of Patient Care Services and Chief Nursing Officer
Web address: www.phhealthcare.org/
Control: Other not–for–profit (including NFP Corporation) **Service:** General Medical and Surgical

Staffed Beds: 35 **Admissions:** 984 **Census:** 16 **Outpatient Visits:** 78760 **Births:** 0 **Total Expense ($000):** 25411 **Payroll Expense ($000):** 10608 **Personnel:** 208

BRYN MAWR—Montgomery County

✠ **BRYN MAWR HOSPITAL (390139)**, 130 South Bryn Mawr Avenue, Zip 19010–3160; tel. 484/337–3000 **A**1 2 3 5 10 13 **F**3 5 11 12 13 15 17 18 20 22 24 26 28 29 30 31 34 35 36 37 38 39 40 41 44 45 46 48 49 50 54 55 56 57 58 59 63 64 65 70 72 74 75 76 78 79 80 81 82 84 85 86 87 89 92 97 98 99 100 101 102 103 104 105 107 108 110 111 114 115 118 119 120 124 126 129 130 131 134 135 141 146 147 148 **S** Main Line Health
Primary Contact: Andrea F. Gilbert, FACHE, President
COO: Andrea F. Gilbert, FACHE, President
CFO: Michael J. Buongiorno, Executive Vice President Finance and Chief Financial Officer
CMO: Andrew J. Norton, M.D., Chief Medical Officer
CIO: Karen A. Thomas, Vice President and Chief Information Officer
CHR: Terry Dougherty, Director Human Resources
CNO: Barbara A. Wadsworth, MSN, Chief Nursing Officer
Web address: www.brynmawrhospital.org
Control: Other not–for–profit (including NFP Corporation) **Service:** General Medical and Surgical

Staffed Beds: 319 **Admissions:** 14696 **Census:** 168 **Outpatient Visits:** 255353 **Births:** 1600 **Total Expense ($000):** 301658 **Payroll Expense ($000):** 101885 **Personnel:** 1496

BUTLER—Butler County

★ **BUTLER HEALTH SYSTEM (390168)**, 1 Hospital Way, Zip 16001–4697; tel. 724/283–6666, (Total facility includes 25 beds in nursing home–type unit) **A**2 10 **F**3 4 5 12 13 15 18 20 22 24 26 28 29 31 32 35 40 45 57 59 70 74 76 77 79 81 82 85 87 93 97 98 100 103 107 108 111 114 118 119 128 129 130 132 135 146 147 148 **P**6
Primary Contact: Ken DeFurio, President and Chief Executive Officer
COO: Stephanie Roskovski, Chief Operating Officer
CFO: Anne Krebs, Chief Financial Officer
CMO: John C. Reefer, M.D., Director
CIO: Thomas McGill, Chief Information Officer
CHR: Thomas A. Genevro, Vice President Human Resources
CNO: Karen A. Allen, R.N., Chief Nursing Officer
Web address: www.butlerhealthsystem.org
Control: Other not–for–profit (including NFP Corporation) **Service:** General Medical and Surgical

Staffed Beds: 288 **Admissions:** 11813 **Census:** 167 **Outpatient Visits:** 502705 **Births:** 830 **Total Expense ($000):** 213204 **Payroll Expense ($000):** 81171 **Personnel:** 1456

CAMP HILL—Cumberland County

✠ **HOLY SPIRIT – A GEISINGER AFFILIATE (390004)**, 503 North 21st Street, Zip 17011–2204; tel. 717/763–2100 **A**1 10 **F**3 8 11 12 13 14 15 17 18 20 22 24 26 28 29 30 31 34 35 37 38 40 44 46 49 50 54 57 58 59 61 62 63 64 65 70 72 73 74 75 76 77 78 79 80 81 82 84 85 86 87 98 99 100 101 102 103 104 105 107 108 110 111 114 115 118 119 124 126 129 130 132 134 135 145 146 147 148
Primary Contact: Kyle C. Snyder, Chief Administrative Officer
COO: Richard Schaffner, Senior Vice President and Chief Operating Officer
CFO: Manuel J. Evans, Senior Vice President Finance and Chief Financial Officer
CMO: Joseph Torchia, M.D., Senior Vice President Medical Affairs and Chief Medical Officer
CIO: Edith Dees, Vice President Information Services and Chief Information Officer
CHR: William Shartle, Senior Vice President Human Resources
CNO: Lisa F. Torchia MSN, RN, NEA–BC, MSN, Vice President and Chief Nursing Officer
Web address: www.hsh.org
Control: Other not–for–profit (including NFP Corporation) **Service:** General Medical and Surgical

Staffed Beds: 294 **Admissions:** 11026 **Census:** 156 **Births:** 1189

✠ **SELECT SPECIALTY HOSPITAL–CENTRAL PENNSYLVANIA (392039)**, 503 North 21st Street, 5th Floor, Zip 17011–2204; tel. 717/972–4575, (Includes SELECT SPECIALTY HOSPITAL–HARRISBURG, 2501 NorthThird Street, Landis Building, Harrisburg, Zip 17110–1904; tel. 717/724–6605; SELECT SPECIALTY HOSPITAL–YORK, 1001 South George Street, York, Zip 17403–3676; tel. 717/851–2661; Marcia Medlin, Chief Executive Officer) **A**1 10 **F**1 3 5 12 28 29 30 31 34 38 39 45 46 47 48 49 50 57 63 74 75 78 79 82 84 87 100 107 108 109 110 111 112 113 114 115 116 117 118 119 130 133 **S** Select Medical Corporation, Mechanicsburg, PA
Primary Contact: John E. Simodejka, Chief Executive Officer
Web address: www.camphill.selectspecialtyhospitals.com/
Control: Corporation, Investor–owned, for–profit **Service:** Long–Term Acute Care hospital

Staffed Beds: 92 **Admissions:** 987 **Census:** 72 **Births:** 0

STATE CORRECTIONAL INSTITUTION AT CAMP HILL, 2500 Lisburn Road, Zip 17011–8005, Mailing Address: P.O. Box 200, Zip 17001–0200; tel. 717/737–4531, (Nonreporting)
Primary Contact: Beth Herb, Administrator
Web address: www.cor.state.pa.us/
Control: State–Government, nonfederal **Service:** Hospital unit of an institution (prison hospital, college infirmary, etc.)

Staffed Beds: 34

CANONSBURG—Washington County

✠ **CANONSBURG HOSPITAL (390160)**, 100 Medical Boulevard, Zip 15317–9762; tel. 724/745–6100 **A**1 10 **F**3 7 11 15 16 17 29 30 34 35 40 44 45 46 47 48 49 50 51 55 57 59 60 64 70 72 74 75 76 78 79 80 81 85 86 87 88 89 90 91 92 93 98 107 108 111 114 118 119 129 130 132 135 146 **S** Allegheny Health Network, Pittsburgh, PA
Primary Contact: David Goldberg, Interim President and Chief Executive Officer
CMO: Thomas B. Corkery, D.O., Chief Medical Officer
CIO: David Vincent, Director Information Systems
CHR: Martha L. Clister, Director Human Resources
Web address: www.wpahs.org
Control: Other not–for–profit (including NFP Corporation) **Service:** General Medical and Surgical

Staffed Beds: 104 **Admissions:** 2611 **Census:** 32 **Outpatient Visits:** 64130 **Births:** 0 **Total Expense ($000):** 48185 **Payroll Expense ($000):** 15951 **Personnel:** 311

PA

Many Facility Codes have changed. Please refer to the AHA Guide Code Chart. © 2016 AHA Guide

CARLISLE—Cumberland County

⊞ **CARLISLE REGIONAL MEDICAL CENTER (390058)**, 361 Alexander Spring Road, Zip 17015–6940; tel. 717/249–1212 **A**1 10 **F**3 8 11 12 13 14 15 18 20 29 30 31 34 38 40 45 46 47 48 49 50 51 53 56 57 59 60 64 65 68 70 73 74 75 76 78 79 81 82 85 86 87 90 91 92 93 94 107 108 109 110 111 112 114 115 116 117 119 120 121 123 124 126 129 130 132 141 142 146 147 148 **P**5 **S** Community Health Systems, Inc., Franklin, TN
Primary Contact: David P. Steitz, Chief Executive Officer
CFO: Mark Reyngoudt, Chief Financial Officer
CMO: Ivan' Sola', President Medical Staff
CIO: Sherry Aby, Director Information Management
CHR: Sylvia Rockwood, Director Human Resources
CNO: Ann M. Spade, Chief Nursing Executive
Web address: www.carlislermc.com/default.aspx
Control: Corporation, Investor–owned, for–profit **Service:** General Medical and Surgical

Staffed Beds: 65 **Admissions:** 4200 **Census:** 43 **Outpatient Visits:** 115383 **Births:** 435 **Total Expense ($000):** 101733 **Payroll Expense ($000):** 32300 **Personnel:** 518

CENTRE HALL—Centre County

⊞ **MEADOWS PSYCHIATRIC CENTER (394040)**, 132 The Meadows Drive, Zip 16828–9231; tel. 814/364–2161 **A**1 10 **F**29 38 98 99 103 **S** Universal Health Services, Inc., King of Prussia, PA
Primary Contact: Ann Wayne, Interim Chief Executive Officer and Managing Director
CFO: David Witt, Chief Financial Officer
CMO: Craig Richman, M.D., Medical Director
CHR: Mary Jane Schreffler, Director Human Resources
CNO: Dana Thies, Director of Nursing
Web address: www.themeadows.net
Control: Corporation, Investor–owned, for–profit **Service:** Psychiatric

Staffed Beds: 107 **Admissions:** 2626 **Census:** 97 **Outpatient Visits:** 2852 **Births:** 0 **Personnel:** 209

CHAMBERSBURG—Franklin County

⊞ **CHAMBERSBURG HOSPITAL (390151)**, 112 North Seventh Street, Zip 17201–1720; tel. 717/267–3000 **A**1 2 3 5 10 19 **F**3 11 12 13 15 17 18 20 22 28 29 30 31 34 35 39 40 44 45 49 50 54 56 57 58 59 61 64 65 68 70 74 75 76 77 79 81 85 86 87 90 91 93 94 98 100 102 103 104 107 108 110 111 114 115 118 119 126 129 130 131 132 135 146 147 148 **P**8 **S** Summit Health, Chambersburg, PA
Primary Contact: Patrick W. O'Donnell, CPA, President and Chief Executive Officer
COO: John P. Massimilla, FACHE, Vice President Administration and Chief Operating Officer
CFO: Kimberly Rzomp, Vice President and Chief Financial Officer
CMO: Thomas Anderson, M.D., Vice President Medical Affairs
CIO: Michele Zeigler, Vice President and Chief Information Officer
CHR: Cathy A. Puhl, Vice President Human Resources
CNO: Sherri Stahl, R.N., Senior Vice President for Hospital Services
Web address: www.summithealth.org
Control: Other not–for–profit (including NFP Corporation) **Service:** General Medical and Surgical

Staffed Beds: 248 **Admissions:** 12638 **Census:** 144 **Outpatient Visits:** 333190 **Births:** 1320 **Total Expense ($000):** 253408 **Payroll Expense ($000):** 103197 **Personnel:** 1467

CLARION—Clarion County

★ ○ **CLARION HOSPITAL (390093)**, One Hospital Drive, Zip 16214–8501; tel. 814/226–9500 **A**10 11 12 13 **F**3 7 11 13 15 29 30 31 35 40 48 49 51 57 59 64 70 76 77 78 79 81 82 84 85 90 107 108 111 115 119 129 130 132 133 135 145 146 148 **S** QHR, Brentwood, TN
Primary Contact: Byron Quinton, Chief Executive Officer
CFO: Vincent M. Lamorella, Chief Financial Officer
CMO: Janice Semeyn, D.O., President, Medical Staff
CIO: James Confer, Manager Information Systems
CHR: Brooke Divins, Manager Human Resources
CNO: Leslie Walters, MSN, Chief Nursing Officer
Web address: www.clarionhospital.org
Control: Other not–for–profit (including NFP Corporation) **Service:** General Medical and Surgical

Staffed Beds: 66 **Admissions:** 1856 **Census:** 19 **Outpatient Visits:** 160907 **Births:** 132 **Total Expense ($000):** 52051 **Payroll Expense ($000):** 18356 **Personnel:** 482

☐ **CLARION PSYCHIATRIC CENTER (394043)**, 2 Hospital Drive, Zip 16214–8502; tel. 814/226–9545 **A**1 10 **F**98 99 101 102 105 **P**6 **S** Universal Health Services, Inc., King of Prussia, PA
Primary Contact: Michael Post, Chief Executive Officer
CFO: Shelly Rhoades, Chief Financial Officer
CMO: Jeffrey Moll, M.D., Medical Director
CHR: Dianne C. Bilunka, Director Human Resources
CNO: Rhonda Massa, Director of Nursing
Web address: www.clarioncenter.com
Control: Individual, Investor–owned, for–profit **Service:** Psychiatric

Staffed Beds: 74 **Admissions:** 1921 **Census:** 69 **Outpatient Visits:** 0 **Births:** 0

CLARKS SUMMIT—Lackawanna County

CLARKS SUMMIT STATE HOSPITAL (394012), 1451 Hillside Drive, Zip 18411–9504; tel. 570/586–2011 **A**10 **F**29 39 57 77 91 98 130 135 143 146 **P**6
Primary Contact: Monica Bradbury, Chief Executive Officer
COO: Gordon Weber, Chief Operating Officer
CMO: David Waibel, M.D., Medical Director
CHR: William Abda, Chief Human Resources Officer
Web address: www.dpw.state.pa.us/
Control: State–Government, nonfederal **Service:** Psychiatric

Staffed Beds: 210 **Admissions:** 84 **Census:** 200 **Total Expense ($000):** 53535 **Payroll Expense ($000):** 23010 **Personnel:** 422

CLEARFIELD—Clearfield County

PENN HIGHLANDS CLEARFIELD (390052), 809 Turnpike Avenue, Zip 16830–1232, Mailing Address: P.O. Box 992, Zip 16830–0992; tel. 814/765–5341 **A**10 **F**3 8 11 14 15 18 28 29 30 32 34 40 45 50 57 59 62 63 68 75 77 79 81 82 84 85 86 87 93 97 98 103 104 107 108 110 111 115 118 119 129 130 131 132 133 146 148
Primary Contact: Gary Macioce, President
CFO: William Cain, Controller
CMO: Kevin L. Tyler, M.D., President Medical Staff
CHR: James G. Glade, Director Human Resources
CNO: Kathy Bedger, Chief Nursing Officer
Web address: www.phhealthcare.org
Control: Other not–for–profit (including NFP Corporation) **Service:** General Medical and Surgical

Staffed Beds: 50 **Admissions:** 2005 **Census:** 26 **Outpatient Visits:** 24304 **Births:** 0 **Total Expense ($000):** 52647 **Payroll Expense ($000):** 20699 **Personnel:** 320

COALDALE—Schuylkill County

☐ **ST. LUKE'S HOSPITAL – MINERS CAMPUS (390183)**, 360 West Ruddle Street, Zip 18218–1027; tel. 570/645–2131, (Total facility includes 48 beds in nursing home–type unit) **A**1 10 **F**3 15 18 28 29 31 34 35 40 43 45 46 49 50 51 53 54 56 57 59 60 64 65 68 70 75 77 78 79 81 85 86 93 107 108 110 111 115 118 119 127 128 129 130 131 132 145 146 148 **P**6 8 **S** St. Luke's University Health Network, Bethlehem, PA
Primary Contact: William E. Moyer, President
COO: Joel Fagerstrom, Executive Vice President and Chief Operating Officer
CFO: Michele Levitz, Director Finance
CMO: Glenn Freed, D.O., Medical Director
CIO: Chad Brisendine, Vice President and Chief Information Officer
CHR: Susan Van Why, Director Human Resources
CNO: Kimberly Sargent, Vice President Patient Services
Web address: www.slhn.org
Control: Other not–for–profit (including NFP Corporation) **Service:** General Medical and Surgical

Staffed Beds: 92 **Admissions:** 2002 **Census:** 65 **Outpatient Visits:** 83761 **Births:** 0 **Total Expense ($000):** 46263 **Payroll Expense ($000):** 20168 **Personnel:** 364

COATESVILLE—Chester County

⊞ **BRANDYWINE HOSPITAL (390076)**, 201 Reeceville Road, Zip 19320–1536; tel. 610/383–8000 **A**1 10 **F**3 12 15 17 18 20 22 24 26 28 29 31 34 35 40 45 46 50 51 54 56 59 60 62 64 69 70 74 75 77 78 79 81 82 92 93 98 103 104 106 107 108 110 111 114 115 116 117 119 126 129 132 146 147 148 **S** Community Health Systems, Inc., Franklin, TN
Primary Contact: W. Jeffrey Hunt, Chief Executive Officer
COO: Jill Tillman, Assistant Chief Executive Officer
CFO: Jay Graham, Interim Chief Financial Officer
Web address: www.brandywinehospital.com
Control: Corporation, Investor–owned, for–profit **Service:** General Medical and Surgical

Staffed Beds: 169 **Admissions:** 6319 **Census:** 92 **Births:** 0

| Hospital, Medicare Provider Number, Address, Telephone, Approval, Facility, and Physician Codes, Health Care System |

★ American Hospital Association (AHA) membership
☐ The Joint Commission accreditation
○ Healthcare Facilities Accreditation Program
◇ DNV Healthcare Inc. accreditation
⇑ Center for Improvement in Healthcare Quality Accreditation
△ Commission on Accreditation of Rehabilitation Facilities (CARF) accreditation

© 2016 AHA Guide   *Many Facility Codes have changed. Please refer to the AHA Guide Code Chart.*   Hospitals **A535**

✠ **COATESVILLE VETERANS AFFAIRS MEDICAL CENTER**, 1400 Black Horse Hill Road, Zip 19320–2040; tel. 610/384–7711, (Nonreporting) **A**1 3 5
S Department of Veterans Affairs, Washington, DC
Primary Contact: Gary W. Devansky, Director
CFO: Tony Wolfgang, Chief Financial Officer
CMO: Sheila Chellappa, M.D., Chief of Staff
CIO: Ryan McGettigan, Chief Information Officer
CHR: Andrew Sutton, Chief Human Resources Officer
CNO: Nancy A. Schmid, R.N., Associate Director Patient Care Services
Web address: www.coatesville.va.gov/
Control: Veterans Affairs, Government, federal **Service:** Alcoholism and other chemical dependency

Staffed Beds: 118	

VETERANS AFFAIRS MEDICAL CENTER See Coatesville Veterans Affairs Medical Center

CONNELLSVILLE—Fayette County

HIGHLANDS HOSPITAL (390184), 401 East Murphy Avenue, Zip 15425–2700; tel. 724/628–1500 **A**10 **F**3 11 15 26 27 29 30 34 35 39 40 44 45 46 49 50 53 54 56 57 59 61 64 65 70 74 75 77 79 81 82 85 86 87 89 97 98 99 100 102 103 107 108 111 115 119 129 130 132 143 146
Primary Contact: Michelle P. Cunningham, Chief Executive Officer
CFO: John Andursky, Chief Financial Officer
CMO: Richard Grimaldi, President Medical Staff
CIO: John Andursky, Chief Financial Officer
CHR: Mary June Krosoff, Chief Human Resources Officer
CNO: Tammy Donaldson, Director of Nursing
Web address: www.highlandshospital.org
Control: Other not–for–profit (including NFP Corporation) **Service:** General Medical and Surgical

Staffed Beds: 64 **Admissions:** 2371 **Census:** 28 **Outpatient Visits:** 60073 **Births:** 0 **Total Expense ($000):** 23714 **Payroll Expense ($000):** 10687 **Personnel:** 272

CORRY—Erie County

CORRY MEMORIAL HOSPITAL (391308), 965 Shamrock Lane, Zip 16407; tel. 814/664–4641, (Nonreporting) **A**10 18
Primary Contact: Barbara Nichols, R.N., President and Chief Executive Officer
CFO: Michael Heller, Chief Financial Officer
CMO: Paul McGeehan, M.D., Chief Medical Staff
CIO: Andrew Jackman, Director Information Technology
CHR: Sharon Kimmy, Coordinator Human Resources
Web address: www.corryhospital.com
Control: Other not–for–profit (including NFP Corporation) **Service:** General Medical and Surgical

Staffed Beds: 25

COUDERSPORT—Potter County

✠ **COLE MEMORIAL (391313)**, 1001 East Second Street, Zip 16915–8161; tel. 814/274–9300, (Total facility includes 49 beds in nursing home–type unit) **A**1 10 18 **F**3 10 13 15 28 29 30 31 35 39 40 45 49 53 57 59 62 63 64 68 70 76 77 78 79 81 82 85 87 92 93 98 103 107 108 110 111 115 119 121 127 128 129 130 131 132 133 146 147 148 **P**6
Primary Contact: Edward C. Pitchford, President and Chief Executive Officer
CFO: Ron Rapp, Controller
CMO: Brenda Wahlers, M.D., Chief of Staff
CIO: Janice Walters, Executive Director, Revenue Systems and Information Technology
CHR: James Evens, Executive Director Human Resources
Web address: www.colememorial.org/
Control: Other not–for–profit (including NFP Corporation) **Service:** General Medical and Surgical

Staffed Beds: 84 **Admissions:** 1933 **Census:** 65 **Outpatient Visits:** 228829 **Births:** 201 **Total Expense ($000):** 80619 **Payroll Expense ($000):** 28669 **Personnel:** 506

CRANBERRY—Butler County

UPMC PASSAVANT CRANBERRY See UPMC Passavant, Pittsburgh

DANVILLE—Montour County

DANVILLE STATE HOSPITAL (394004), 200 State Hospital Drive, Zip 17821–9198; tel. 570/271–4500 **A**3 10 **F**30 39 65 75 77 98 106 130 135 146 **P**6
Primary Contact: Theresa Long, Chief Executive Officer
COO: Thomas J. Burk, Chief Operating Officer
CFO: Patricia Riegert, Director Fiscal Services
CMO: Vikrant Mittal, M.D., Chief Medical Officer
CHR: Thomas J. Burk, Chief Operating Officer
CNO: Brenda Lahout, Chief Nurse Executive
Web address: www.dpw.state.pa.us/foradults/statehospitals/danvillestatehospital/index.htm
Control: State–Government, nonfederal **Service:** Psychiatric

Staffed Beds: 168 **Admissions:** 74 **Census:** 166 **Outpatient Visits:** 0 **Births:** 0 **Total Expense ($000):** 41878 **Payroll Expense ($000):** 19634 **Personnel:** 378

✠ **GEISINGER HEALTHSOUTH REHABILITATION HOSPITAL (393047)**, 2 Rehab Lane, Zip 17821–8498; tel. 570/271–6733, (Nonreporting) **A**1 10
S HEALTHSOUTH Corporation, Birmingham, AL
Primary Contact: Lorie Dillon, Chief Executive Officer
CFO: Sally Shipierski, Controller
CMO: Greg Burke, M.D., Medical Director
CHR: Christian Shirley, Director Human Resources
Web address: www.geisingerhealthsouth.com
Control: Corporation, Investor–owned, for–profit **Service:** Rehabilitation

Staffed Beds: 42

✠ **GEISINGER MEDICAL CENTER (390006)**, 100 North Academy Avenue, Zip 17822–2201; tel. 570/271–6211, (Includes GEISINGER–SHAMOKIN AREA COMMUNITY HOSPITAL, 4200 Hospital Road, Coal Township, Zip 17866–9697; tel. 570/644–4200; Sam Balukoff, Interim Administrator), (Nonreporting) **A**1 2 3 5 8 10 13 19 **S** Geisinger Health System, Danville, PA
Primary Contact: Thomas P. Sokola, Chief Administrative Officer
CFO: Kevin F. Brennan, CPA, Executive Vice President and Chief Financial Officer
CMO: Albert Bothe, Jr., M.D., Chief Medical Officer
CIO: Frank Richards, Chief Information Officer
CHR: Amy Brayford, Chief Human Resources Officer
CNO: Susan M. Hallick, R.N., Executive Vice President and Chief Nursing Officer
Web address: www.geisinger.org
Control: Other not–for–profit (including NFP Corporation) **Service:** General Medical and Surgical

Staffed Beds: 545

✠ **SELECT SPECIALTY HOSPITAL–DANVILLE (392047)**, 100 North Academy Avenue, 3rd Floor, Zip 17822–3050; tel. 570/214–9653, (Nonreporting) **A**1 10
S Select Medical Corporation, Mechanicsburg, PA
Primary Contact: Brian Mann, Chief Executive Officer
Web address: www.selectspecialtyhospitals.com/company/locations/danville.aspx
Control: Corporation, Investor–owned, for–profit **Service:** Long–Term Acute Care hospital

Staffed Beds: 30

DARBY—Delaware County

✠ △ **MERCY FITZGERALD HOSPITAL (390156)**, 1500 Lansdowne Avenue, Zip 19023–1200; tel. 610/237–4000, (Includes MERCY FITZGERALD HOSPITAL, 1500 South Lansdowne Avenue, Zip 19023; tel. 610/237–4000; MERCY PHILADELPHIA HOSPITAL, 501 South 54th Street, Philadelphia, Zip 19143; tel. 215/748–9000; Susan Cusack, Executive Director) **A**1 2 3 5 7 10 12 13 **F**3 4 11 12 15 18 20 22 24 26 28 29 30 31 34 35 38 40 45 46 49 50 51 54 55 57 58 59 61 64 65 66 70 75 77 78 79 81 82 85 86 87 90 91 92 93 97 98 100 101 102 103 107 108 110 111 114 115 118 119 120 121 123 124 130 132 135 145 146 147 148 **S** Trinity Health, Livonia, MI
Primary Contact: Susan Cusack, Executive Director
COO: Ruth Thomas, Chief Operating Officer
CFO: Don Snenk, Chief Financial Officer
CMO: Jeff Komins, M.D., Chief Medical Officer
CIO: Jeff Byda, Vice President Information Technology
Web address: www.mercyhealth.org
Control: Other not–for–profit (including NFP Corporation) **Service:** General Medical and Surgical

Staffed Beds: 366 **Admissions:** 17397 **Census:** 223 **Outpatient Visits:** 230498 **Births:** 0 **Total Expense ($000):** 310272 **Payroll Expense ($000):** 115482 **Personnel:** 1783

DOWNINGTOWN—Chester County

ST. JOHN VIANNEY HOSPITAL, 151 Woodbine Road, Zip 19335–3057; tel. 610/269–2600 **F**4 29 30 75 98 106 **P**5
Primary Contact: David Shellenberger, Chief Operating Officer
CMO: James MacFadyen, M.D., Medical Director
Web address: www.sjvcenter.org
Control: Church–operated, Nongovernment, not–for profit **Service:** Psychiatric

Staffed Beds: 47 **Admissions:** 133 **Census:** 41 **Outpatient Visits:** 0 **Births:** 0 **Total Expense ($000):** 7307 **Payroll Expense ($000):** 3963 **Personnel:** 64

Many Facility Codes have changed. Please refer to the AHA Guide Code Chart. © 2016 AHA Guide

PA

DOYLESTOWN—Bucks County

☒ △ **DOYLESTOWN HOSPITAL (390203)**, 595 West State Street,
Zip 18901–2597; tel. 215/345–2200 **A**1 2 3 5 7 10 **F**3 8 10 13 15 17 18 20
22 24 26 28 29 30 31 32 34 35 40 45 46 49 50 51 54 56 57 58 59 62 63
64 70 73 74 75 76 77 78 79 81 85 86 87 89 92 93 94 96 107 108 110 111
114 115 118 119 124 126 130 131 132 141 146 147 **P**2 8
Primary Contact: James L. Brexler, President and Chief Executive Officer
COO: Eleanor Wilson, R.N., Vice President and Chief Operating Officer
CFO: Daniel Upton, Vice President and Chief Financial Officer
CMO: Scott S. Levy, M.D., Vice President and Chief Medical Officer
CIO: Richard Lang, Ed.D., Vice President and Chief Information Officer
CHR: Barbara Hebel, Vice President Human Resources
CNO: Patricia A. Stover, Administrator Nursing
Web address: www.dh.org
Control: Other not–for–profit (including NFP Corporation) **Service:** General
Medical and Surgical

Staffed Beds: 232 **Admissions:** 12149 **Census:** 137 **Outpatient Visits:**
294665 **Births:** 1148 **Total Expense ($000):** 237653 **Payroll Expense
($000):** 97743 **Personnel:** 1839

☐ **FOUNDATIONS BEHAVIORAL HEALTH (394038)**, 833 East Butler Avenue,
Zip 18901–2280; tel. 215/345–0444 **A**1 10 **F**98 99 100 101 102 105 106
S Universal Health Services, Inc., King of Prussia, PA
Primary Contact: Robert Weinhold, Chief Executive Officer
Web address: www.fbh.com
Control: Corporation, Investor–owned, for–profit **Service:** Children's hospital
psychiatric

Staffed Beds: 58 **Admissions:** 1154 **Census:** 47 **Outpatient Visits:** 0 **Births:**
0

DREXEL HILL—Delaware County

☒ **DELAWARE COUNTY MEMORIAL HOSPITAL (390081)**, 501 North Lansdowne
Avenue, Zip 19026–1114; tel. 610/284–8100 **A**1 2 3 5 10 **F**3 7 8 9 11 12 13
15 17 18 29 30 31 34 35 36 40 44 45 46 47 50 51 54 55 56 57 59 60 61
62 63 64 65 66 68 72 74 75 76 77 78 79 81 82 84 85 86 87 90 92 93 94
96 97 100 107 108 109 110 111 114 115 116 117 118 119 120 121 123
124 129 130 131 132 134 135 143 146 147 148 **P**6 **S** Crozer–Keystone
Health System, Springfield, PA
Primary Contact: Robert Haffey, R.N., President
CFO: Richard I. Bennett, Senior Vice President and Chief Financial Officer
CMO: Seth Malin, M.D., President Medical and Dental Staff
CIO: Robert E. Wilson, Vice President and Chief Information Officer
Web address: www.crozer.org
Control: Other not–for–profit (including NFP Corporation) **Service:** General
Medical and Surgical

Staffed Beds: 168 **Admissions:** 7478 **Census:** 96 **Outpatient Visits:** 105233
Births: 1386 **Total Expense ($000):** 167785 **Payroll Expense ($000):**
61252 **Personnel:** 775

DUBOIS—Clearfield County

☐ **PENN HIGHLANDS DUBOIS (390086)**, 100 Hospital Avenue, Zip 15801–1440,
Mailing Address: P.O. Box 447, Zip 15801–0447; tel. 814/371–2200 **A**1 2 10
19 **F**5 11 13 15 17 18 19 20 22 24 26 27 28 29 30 31 34 35 40 49 51 54
55 57 58 59 62 63 64 70 72 74 76 77 78 79 81 82 85 89 90 93 97 98 99
104 107 108 111 115 116 117 119 120 121 122 129 130 131 132 133 135
146 147 148
Primary Contact: John Sutika, President
CFO: Brian S. Kline, Vice President and Chief Financial Officer
CMO: Gary Dugan, M.D., Vice President Medical Affairs
CHR: Robert J. McKee, Vice President Human Resources
Web address: www.drmc.org
Control: Other not–for–profit (including NFP Corporation) **Service:** General
Medical and Surgical

Staffed Beds: 219 **Admissions:** 9240 **Census:** 111 **Births:** 1190

EAGLEVILLE—Montgomery County

★ **EAGLEVILLE HOSPITAL (390278)**, 100 Eagleville Road, Zip 19403–1829,
Mailing Address: P.O. Box 45, Zip 19408–0045; tel. 610/539–6000 **A**5 10 **F**4
29 34 35 50 61 68 75 86 98 100 101 103 130 132 134 143 146 147 **P**6
Primary Contact: Maureen King Pollock, Chief Executive Officer
COO: Lois Chepak, R.N., Chief Clinical Officer
CFO: Alfred P. Salvitti, Chief Financial Officer
CMO: Robert Wilson, D.O., Director Medical Services
CIO: Richard R. Mitchell, Director Information Technology
CHR: Zoe Yousaitis, Director Human Resources
Web address: www.eaglevillehospital.org
Control: Other not–for–profit (including NFP Corporation) **Service:** Alcoholism and
other chemical dependency

Staffed Beds: 83 **Admissions:** 2734 **Census:** 53 **Outpatient Visits:** 0 **Births:**
0

EAST NORRITON—Montgomery County

☐ **EINSTEIN MEDICAL CENTER MONTGOMERY (390329)**, 559 West
Germantown Pike, Zip 19403–4250; tel. 484/622–1000 **A**1 2 3 10 **F**3 11 12 13
15 18 20 22 24 26 29 30 31 34 35 40 45 46 49 55 57 59 62 63 64 68 70
72 74 75 76 78 79 80 81 82 84 85 87 92 100 107 108 110 111 115 117
119 120 121 123 126 129 130 131 132 135 146 147 **S** Einstein Healthcare
Network, Philadelphia, PA
Primary Contact: Beth Duffy, Chief Operating Officer
COO: Beth Duffy, Chief Operating Officer
CFO: David Ertel, Chief Financial Officer
CMO: Robert Czincila, D.O., Medical Staff President
CIO: Brenda West, Assistant Vice President, Information Services
CHR: Lynne R. Kornblatt, Chief Human Resources Officer
CNO: AnnMarie Papa, R.N., Vice President and Chief Nursing Officer
Control: Other not–for–profit (including NFP Corporation) **Service:** General
Medical and Surgical

Staffed Beds: 171 **Admissions:** 9231 **Census:** 106 **Outpatient Visits:**
196871 **Births:** 1905 **Total Expense ($000):** 233148 **Payroll Expense
($000):** 62873 **Personnel:** 1073

EAST STROUDSBURG—Monroe County

☐ △ **POCONO MEDICAL CENTER (390201)**, 206 East Brown Street,
Zip 18301–3006; tel. 570/421–4000 **A**1 2 7 10 **F**3 11 12 13 14 15 17 18 20
22 24 26 28 29 30 31 32 34 35 36 38 39 40 43 45 47 48 49 50 54 55 56
57 59 61 64 65 66 70 72 74 75 76 77 78 79 81 82 84 85 86 87 89 92 97
98 100 101 102 103 107 108 110 111 114 115 116 117 118 119 120 121
123 124 126 130 132 134 135 144 146 147 148 **P**6 7
Primary Contact: Jeffrey Snyder, Chief Executive Officer
CFO: Michael Wilk, Senior President Financial Services and Chief Financial Officer
CMO: William K. Cors, M.D., Vice President and Chief Medical Quality Officer
CIO: Ferd Feola, Chief Information Officer
CHR: Lynn M. Lansdowne, Vice President Human Resources
Web address: www.pmchealthsystem.org
Control: Other not–for–profit (including NFP Corporation) **Service:** General
Medical and Surgical

Staffed Beds: 235 **Admissions:** 11199 **Census:** 130 **Births:** 1028

EASTON—Northampton County

☒ **EASTON HOSPITAL (390162)**, 250 South 21st Street, Zip 18042–3892;
tel. 610/250–4000 **A**1 2 3 5 10 **F**3 12 13 15 17 18 20 22 24 26 28 29 30 31
34 35 45 46 47 48 49 50 51 56 57 58 59 60 64 67 70 72 76 78 79 81 82
85 87 89 90 98 103 107 108 109 110 111 114 115 116 117 118 119 120
121 124 126 129 130 132 135 146 148 **S** Community Health Systems, Inc.,
Franklin, TN
Primary Contact: John A. Zidansek, Chief Executive Officer
CFO: Steven Clark, Chief Financial Officer
CMO: Roman Tuma, Chief Medical Officer
CIO: Don Lutz, Director Information Technology
CHR: Tanya Segal, Director
CNO: Karen Vadyak, Chief Nursing Officer
Web address: www.easton–hospital.com
Control: Corporation, Investor–owned, for–profit **Service:** General Medical and
Surgical

Staffed Beds: 196 **Admissions:** 7113 **Census:** 89 **Outpatient Visits:** 246121
Births: 405 **Total Expense ($000):** 164695 **Payroll Expense ($000):** 62777

☐ **ST. LUKE'S HOSPITAL – ANDERSON CAMPUS (390326)**, 1872 Riverside
Circle, Zip 18045–5669; tel. 484/503–3000 **A**1 2 3 10 **F**3 11 15 18 20 22 24
26 29 30 31 34 35 38 40 44 45 49 50 51 53 54 55 57 59 60 63 64 68
70 74 75 77 78 79 81 82 84 85 86 87 93 96 102 107 108 110 111 115 118
119 120 121 123 124 130 132 144 145 146 **P**6 8 **S** St. Luke's University
Health Network, Bethlehem, PA
Primary Contact: Edward Nawrocki, President
CMO: Justin P. Psaila, M.D., Vice President Medical Affairs
CNO: Darla Frack, RN, R.N., Vice President, Patient Services
Web address: www.mystlukesonline.org
Control: Other not–for–profit (including NFP Corporation) **Service:** General
Medical and Surgical

Staffed Beds: 108 **Admissions:** 6033 **Census:** 64 **Outpatient Visits:** 170743
Births: 0 **Total Expense ($000):** 125634 **Payroll Expense ($000):** 40898
Personnel: 594

Hospital, Medicare Provider Number, Address, Telephone, Approval, Facility, and Physician Codes, Health Care System

★ American Hospital Association (AHA) membership ○ Healthcare Facilities Accreditation Program ⇑ Center for Improvement in Healthcare Quality Accreditation
☐ The Joint Commission accreditation ◇ DNV Healthcare Inc. accreditation △ Commission on Accreditation of Rehabilitation Facilities (CARF) accreditation

PA

ELLWOOD CITY—Lawrence County

ELLWOOD CITY HOSPITAL (390008), 724 Pershing Street, Zip 16117–1474; tel. 724/752–0081, (Nonreporting) **A**10
Primary Contact: Carolyn Izzo, President and Chief Executive Officer
CFO: Christopher M. Little, Vice President and Chief Financial Officer
CIO: Connie Cunningham, Chief Information Officer
CHR: Paul Landman, Director Human Resources
CNO: Della Stabryla, Director of Nursing
Web address: www.TheEllwoodCityHospital.org
Control: Other not–for–profit (including NFP Corporation) **Service:** General Medical and Surgical

Staffed Beds: 95

EPHRATA—Lancaster County

WELLSPAN EPHRATA COMMUNITY HOSPITAL (390225), 169 Martin Avenue, Zip 17522–1724, Mailing Address: P.O. Box 1002, Zip 17522–1002; tel. 717/733–0311 **A**1 2 10 **F**3 12 13 15 18 20 28 29 30 31 34 35 36 40 45 49 50 51 54 57 59 60 61 62 64 69 70 72 74 75 76 77 78 79 80 81 82 85 87 89 90 91 97 98 99 100 101 102 103 107 108 110 111 114 115 116 117 118 119 120 121 129 130 131 132 135 144 146 147 148 **P**6 8 **S** WellSpan Health, York, PA
CFO: David Kreider, Controller
CMO: Mark Jacobson, D.O., Vice President Medical Affairs
CIO: Leon John Jabour, Regional Chief Information Officer
CHR: Jana Salaki, Regional Director Human Resources
CNO: Marcia A. Hansen, R.N., Vice President Operations and Chief Nursing Officer
Web address: www.wellspan.org
Control: Other not–for–profit (including NFP Corporation) **Service:** General Medical and Surgical

Staffed Beds: 130 **Admissions:** 6029 **Census:** 69 **Outpatient Visits:** 297707 **Births:** 829 **Total Expense ($000):** 181822 **Payroll Expense ($000):** 64355 **Personnel:** 1055

ERIE—Erie County

ERIE VETERANS AFFAIRS MEDICAL CENTER, 135 East 38th Street, Zip 16504–1559; tel. 814/860–2576, (Nonreporting) **A**1 **S** Department of Veterans Affairs, Washington, DC
Primary Contact: John Gennaro, FACHE, Director
CFO: Joann Pritchard, Chief Financial Officer
CMO: Anthony Behm, D.O., Chief of Staff
CIO: Jonathan Seale, Chief Information Officer
CHR: Lynn Nies, Human Resources Officer
CNO: Dorene M. Sommers, Associate Director Patient Care Services
Web address: www.erie.va.gov/
Control: Veterans Affairs, Government, federal **Service:** General Medical and Surgical

Staffed Beds: 78

HAMOT MEDICAL CENTER See UPMC Hamot

HEALTHSOUTH REHABILITATION HOSPITAL OF ERIE (393046), 143 East Second Street, Zip 16507–1501; tel. 814/878–1200 **A**1 10 **F**29 34 90 91 95 96 132 **S** HEALTHSOUTH Corporation, Birmingham, AL
Primary Contact: John Papalia, Chief Executive Officer
CFO: Lori Gibbens, Controller
CMO: Douglas Grisier, D.O., Medical Director
CIO: Sharon Zielinski, Manager Health Information
CHR: William Robinson, Director Human Resources
CNO: Evelyn Armstrong, Chief Nursing Officer
Web address: www.healthsoutherie.com
Control: Corporation, Investor–owned, for–profit **Service:** Rehabilitation

Staffed Beds: 100 **Admissions:** 1318 **Census:** 45 **Outpatient Visits:** 0 **Births:** 0

MILLCREEK COMMUNITY HOSPITAL (390198), 5515 Peach Street, Zip 16509–2695; tel. 814/864–4031, (Nonreporting) **A**10 11 12 13
Primary Contact: Mary L. Eckert, President and Chief Executive Officer
CFO: Richard P. Olinger, Chief Financial Officer
CMO: James Y. Lin, D.O., Chief of Staff
CIO: Cheryl Girardier, Director Information Technology
CHR: Polly Momeyer, Manager Human Resources
CNO: Katie Agresti, R.N., Director Patient Care Services
Web address: www.millcreekcommunityhospital.com
Control: Other not–for–profit (including NFP Corporation) **Service:** General Medical and Surgical

Staffed Beds: 168

SAINT VINCENT HOSPITAL (390009), 232 West 25th Street, Zip 16544–0002; tel. 814/452–5000 **A**1 2 3 5 10 12 13 **F**3 8 11 12 13 15 17 18 20 22 24 26 28 29 30 31 34 35 36 38 39 40 42 44 46 47 48 49 50 51 53 54 56 57 58 59 60 61 64 65 68 70 71 72 74 75 76 77 78 79 80 81 82 83 85 86 87 89 90 92 93 94 96 98 100 101 102 103 107 108 110 111 114 115 116 117 118 119 126 129 130 132 135 146 147 148 **P**6 **S** Allegheny Health Network, Pittsburgh, PA
Primary Contact: Scott Whalen, Ph.D., FACHE, President and Chief Executive Officer
CFO: Al Mansfield, Chief Financial Officer
CMO: Chris Clark, M.D., Senior Vice President Medical Affairs and Chief Medical Officer
CIO: Richard B. Ong, Chief Information Officer
CHR: Johnie M. Atkinson, Chief Human Resources Officer
CNO: Maureen C. Chadwick, R.N., Chief Nursing Officer
Web address: www.svhs.org
Control: Other not–for–profit (including NFP Corporation) **Service:** General Medical and Surgical

Staffed Beds: 400 **Admissions:** 14044 **Census:** 178 **Outpatient Visits:** 197499 **Births:** 1020 **Total Expense ($000):** 256299 **Payroll Expense ($000):** 79889 **Personnel:** 1715

SELECT SPECIALTY HOSPITAL–ERIE (392037), 252 West 11th Street, Zip 16501–1702; tel. 814/874–5300, (Nonreporting) **A**1 10 **S** Select Medical Corporation, Mechanicsburg, PA
Primary Contact: Thomas Fucci, FACHE, Chief Executive Officer
CNO: Keith Christiansen, Chief Nursing Officer
Web address: www.erie.selectspecialtyhospitals.com/
Control: Corporation, Investor–owned, for–profit **Service:** Long–Term Acute Care hospital

Staffed Beds: 50

UPMC HAMOT (390063), 201 State Street, Zip 16550–0002; tel. 814/877–6000 **A**1 2 3 5 8 10 13 **F**3 9 11 12 13 15 17 18 20 22 24 26 28 29 30 31 34 35 36 37 38 39 40 43 44 45 46 47 48 49 50 51 56 57 58 59 60 61 62 63 64 65 66 68 70 72 74 75 76 77 78 79 80 81 82 84 85 86 87 89 92 93 96 97 99 100 101 102 103 104 106 107 108 109 110 111 114 115 118 119 124 126 129 130 131 132 134 135 141 146 147 148 **P**6 **S** UPMC, Pittsburgh, PA
Primary Contact: V. James Fiorenzo, President
COO: David Gibbons, Executive Vice President and Chief Operating Officer
CFO: Stephen M. Danch, Chief Financial Officer
CMO: Richard Long, M.D., Chief Medical Officer
CIO: Lisa D. McChesney, R.N., Senior Director Information Systems
CHR: Brian Durniok, Vice President Human Resources
CNO: James E. Donnelly, Chief Nursing Officer and Vice President Patient Care Services
Web address: www.hamot.org
Control: Other not–for–profit (including NFP Corporation) **Service:** General Medical and Surgical

Staffed Beds: 317 **Admissions:** 19698 **Census:** 242 **Outpatient Visits:** 207181 **Births:** 2019 **Total Expense ($000):** 338397 **Payroll Expense ($000):** 99817 **Personnel:** 1992

VETERANS AFFAIRS MEDICAL CENTER See Erie Veterans Affairs Medical Center

EVERETT—Bedford County

UPMC BEDFORD MEMORIAL (390117), 10455 Lincoln Highway, Zip 15537–7046; tel. 814/623–6161 **A**1 10 20 **F**3 8 11 13 15 18 28 29 30 31 34 35 36 39 40 41 45 50 51 56 57 59 61 64 65 68 70 74 75 76 77 78 79 81 85 86 87 89 93 97 102 104 107 108 110 111 114 119 129 130 131 132 133 135 146 147 **P**6 **S** UPMC, Pittsburgh, PA
Primary Contact: Gerald Murray, President
CFO: Mario Wilfong, Vice President Finance and Administration
CIO: Mark Wiley, Manager Information Systems Development
CHR: Michelle A. Speck, Vice President Human Resources
CNO: Paula Thomas, R.N., Vice President Patient Services
Web address: www.upmcbedfordmemorial.com
Control: Other not–for–profit (including NFP Corporation) **Service:** General Medical and Surgical

Staffed Beds: 27 **Admissions:** 1658 **Census:** 12 **Outpatient Visits:** 113169 **Births:** 304 **Total Expense ($000):** 56762 **Payroll Expense ($000):** 14630 **Personnel:** 268

FARRELL—Mercer County

SHENANGO VALLEY CAMPUS See UPMC Horizon, Greenville

☐ ○ **UPMC HORIZON (390178)**, 110 North Main Street, Zip 16125–1726,
Mailing Address: 2200 Memorial Drive, Farrell, Zip 16121–1357;
tel. 724/588–2100, (Includes GREENVILLE CAMPUS, 110 North Main Street,
Zip 16125–1795; tel. 724/588–2100; SHENANGO VALLEY CAMPUS, 2200
Memorial Drive, Farrell, Zip 16121–1398; tel. 724/981–3500) **A**1 2 10 11 13 **F**3
11 12 13 15 18 20 26 28 29 30 31 32 34 35 39 40 43 44 45 46 49 50 53
54 56 57 59 61 64 65 68 70 73 74 75 76 77 78 79 81 82 85 86 87 90 92
97 107 108 110 111 115 118 119 121 123 129 130 131 132 133 135 146
147 148 **S** UPMC, Pittsburgh, PA
Primary Contact: Donald R. Owrey, President
CFO: David Shulik, Vice President and Chief Financial Officer
CMO: Samuel Daisley, D.O., Vice President Medical Affairs
CHR: Connie Mayle, Vice President Administrative Services
Web address: www.upmc.com
Control: Other not–for–profit (including NFP Corporation) **Service:** General
Medical and Surgical

Staffed Beds: 121 **Admissions:** 6376 **Census:** 74 **Outpatient Visits:** 222405
Births: 1010 **Total Expense ($000):** 157652 **Payroll Expense ($000):**
39130 **Personnel:** 701

FORT WASHINGTON—Montgomery County

☐ **BROOKE GLEN BEHAVIORAL HOSPITAL (394049)**, 7170 Lafayette Avenue,
Zip 19034–2301; tel. 215/641–5300, (Nonreporting) **A**1 3 5 10 **S** Universal
Health Services, Inc., King of Prussia, PA
Primary Contact: Neil Callahan, Chief Executive Officer
COO: William R. Mason, Chief Operating Officer
CFO: Robert Zagerman, Chief Financial Officer
CMO: Chand Nair, M.D., Medical Director
CHR: Dawn Kownacki, Director Human Resources
Web address: www.brookeglenhospital.com
Control: Corporation, Investor–owned, for–profit **Service:** Psychiatric

Staffed Beds: 146

GETTYSBURG—Adams County

✠ **WELLSPAN GETTYSBURG HOSPITAL (390065)**, 147 Gettys Street,
Zip 17325–2534; tel. 717/334–2121 **A**1 3 10 **F**3 8 11 13 15 18 20 26 28 29
30 31 35 40 45 46 49 50 51 54 56 59 60 64 65 68 70 74 75 76 78 79 81
82 84 85 87 89 92 93 102 107 108 110 111 114 117 118 119 120 121 123
129 130 131 132 134 135 146 147 148 **S** WellSpan Health, York, PA
Primary Contact: Jane E. Hyde, President
COO: Joseph H. Edgar, Senior Vice President Operations
CMO: Charles Marley, D.O., Vice President Medical Affairs
CIO: Robin Kimple, Director Information Services
CHR: Kim Brister, Director Human Resources
Web address: www.wellspan.org
Control: Other not–for–profit (including NFP Corporation) **Service:** General
Medical and Surgical

Staffed Beds: 76 **Admissions:** 4140 **Census:** 45 **Outpatient Visits:** 189442
Births: 519 **Total Expense ($000):** 139382 **Payroll Expense ($000):** 39937
Personnel: 647

GREENSBURG—Westmoreland County

☐ **EXCELA HEALTH WESTMORELAND HOSPITAL (390145)**, 532 West
Pittsburgh Street, Zip 15601–2282; tel. 724/832–4000 **A**1 3 10 **F**3 5 8 11 12
13 15 17 18 20 22 24 26 28 29 30 31 34 35 38 40 44 45 46 48 49 50 51
54 56 57 59 61 64 65 68 70 73 74 75 76 77 78 79 81 82 84 85 86 87 89
90 92 93 96 98 100 102 103 104 105 107 108 110 111 114 115 118 119
126 129 130 131 132 134 135 143 146 147 148 **S** Excela Health,
Greensburg, PA
Primary Contact: Ronald H. Ott, President
COO: Michael D. Busch, Executive Vice President and Chief Operating Officer
CFO: Jeffrey T. Curry, Executive Vice President and Chief Financial Officer
CMO: Jerome Granato, M.D., Senior Vice President and Chief Medical Officer
CIO: David Gawaluck, Vice President and Chief Information Officer
CHR: John Caverno, Chief Human Resources Officer
CNO: Helen K. Burns, Ph.D., Senior Vice President and Chief Nursing Officer
Web address: www.excelahealth.org
Control: Other not–for–profit (including NFP Corporation) **Service:** General
Medical and Surgical

Staffed Beds: 270 **Admissions:** 15749 **Census:** 202 **Outpatient Visits:**
417872 **Births:** 1637 **Total Expense ($000):** 218354 **Payroll Expense
($000):** 94617 **Personnel:** 1655

GROVE CITY—Mercer County

GROVE CITY MEDICAL CENTER (390266), 631 North Broad Street Extension,
Zip 16127–4603; tel. 724/450–7000, (Total facility includes 20 beds in nursing
home–type unit) **A**10 **F**3 15 20 26 28 29 31 34 35 40 45 46 49 51 57 59 64
70 75 78 79 81 82 87 91 92 93 107 108 110 111 115 117 119 128 129
130 132 146 148 **P**6
Primary Contact: Robert Jackson, Jr., Chief Executive Officer
CFO: David Poland, Vice President Finance
CMO: Daniel Ferguson, Chief of Staff
CIO: Philip Swartwood, Director Information Systems
CHR: Donald Henley, Vice President Human Resources and Social Services
CNO: Anthony Bono, Chief Nursing Officer
Web address: www.gcmcpa.org
Control: Other not–for–profit (including NFP Corporation) **Service:** General
Medical and Surgical

Staffed Beds: 55 **Admissions:** 1932 **Census:** 31 **Outpatient Visits:** 97670
Births: 0 **Total Expense ($000):** 43498 **Payroll Expense ($000):** 16788
Personnel: 384

HANOVER—York County

✠ **HANOVER HOSPITAL (390233)**, 300 Highland Avenue, Zip 17331–2297;
tel. 717/316–3711 **A**1 10 **F**3 11 13 15 18 20 22 28 29 30 31 34 35 36 40
44 45 49 50 53 54 57 59 61 62 64 65 75 76 77 78 81 84 85 86 87 89 93
94 96 107 108 110 111 115 118 119 129 130 131 132 134 135 144 146
147 148
Primary Contact: Michael W. Gaskins, Interim President and Chief Executive
Officer
COO: Michael A. Hockenberry, Senior Vice President and Chief Operating Officer
CFO: Donna L. Muller, Interim Chief Financial Officer
CMO: Michael H. Ader, M.D., Vice President Medical Affairs
CIO: William C. Tandy, Chief Information Officer
CHR: Christine Miller, General Counsel and Vice President Human Resources
CNO: M. Patricia Saunders, R.N., Vice President Nursing
Web address: www.hanoverhospital.org
Control: Other not–for–profit (including NFP Corporation) **Service:** General
Medical and Surgical

Staffed Beds: 93 **Admissions:** 5701 **Census:** 62 **Outpatient Visits:** 217825
Births: 551 **Total Expense ($000):** 139155 **Payroll Expense ($000):** 54776
Personnel: 943

HARRISBURG—Dauphin County

✠ **HELEN M. SIMPSON REHABILITATION HOSPITAL**, 4300 Londonderry Road,
Zip 17109–5317; tel. 717/920–4300, (Nonreporting) **A**1 **S** Select Medical
Corporation, Mechanicsburg, PA
Primary Contact: Melissa Gillis, Chief Executive Officer
Control: Corporation, Investor–owned, for–profit **Service:** Rehabilitation

Staffed Beds: 55

✠ **PENNSYLVANIA PSYCHIATRIC INSTITUTE (394051)**, 2501 North Third
Street, Zip 17110–1904; tel. 717/782–6420 **A**1 3 5 10 **F**34 35 50 56 57 59
64 87 98 99 103 104 105 130 132 143 146
Primary Contact: William Daly, Chief Executive Officer
CFO: Robert Fotter, Chief Financial Officer
CHR: Wanda Geesey, Director Human Resources
CNO: Teresa Terry–Williams, Chief Nursing Officer
Web address: www.ppimhs.org/
Control: Other not–for–profit (including NFP Corporation) **Service:** Psychiatric

Staffed Beds: 80 **Admissions:** 1910 **Census:** 52 **Births:** 0

PA

Hospital, Medicare Provider Number, Address, Telephone, Approval, Facility, and Physician Codes, Health Care System

★ American Hospital Association (AHA) membership ○ Healthcare Facilities Accreditation Program ⇑ Center for Improvement in Healthcare Quality Accreditation
☐ The Joint Commission accreditation ◇ DNV Healthcare Inc. accreditation △ Commission on Accreditation of Rehabilitation Facilities (CARF) accreditation

PA

☐ **PINNACLE HEALTH SYSTEM (390067)**, 111 South Front Street, Zip 17101–2010, Mailing Address: P.O. Box 8700, Zip 17105–8700; tel. 717/231–8900, (Includes PINNACLEHEALTH AT COMMUNITY GENERAL OSTEOPATHIC HOSPITAL, 4300 Londonderry Road, Zip 17109–5397, Mailing Address: P.O. Box 3000, Zip 17105–3000; tel. 717/652–3000; PINNACLEHEALTH AT HARRISBURG HOSPITAL, 111 South Front Street, Zip 17101–2099; tel. 717/782–3131; PINNACLEHEALTH WEST SHORE HOSPITAL, 1995 Technology Parkway, Mechanicsburg, Zip 17050–8522; tel. 717/791–2600) **A**1 2 3 5 10 12 13 **F**3 7 8 11 12 13 14 15 17 18 19 20 22 24 26 27 28 29 30 31 32 34 35 36 37 38 40 44 45 46 47 48 49 50 52 53 54 55 56 57 58 59 60 61 64 65 66 68 70 72 74 75 76 77 78 79 81 82 84 85 86 87 89 91 93 97 100 101 102 103 104 107 108 109 110 111 114 115 116 117 118 119 120 121 123 124 126 129 130 131 132 134 138 141 142 143 144 146 147 148
Primary Contact: Michael A. Young, FACHE, President and Chief Executive Officer
COO: Philip Guarneschelli, Senior Vice President and Chief Operating Officer
CFO: William H. Pugh, Senior Vice President Corporate Finance and Chief Financial Officer
CMO: Nirmal Joshi, M.D., Senior Vice President Medical Affairs and Chief Medical Officer
CIO: Deborah Cancilla, Senior Vice President, Information Services and Chief Information Officer
CHR: Ann H. Gormley, Senior Vice President Human Resources
CNO: Susan Comp, R.N., Senior Vice President and Chief Nursing Officer
Web address: www.pinnaclehealth.org
Control: Other not–for–profit (including NFP Corporation) **Service:** General Medical and Surgical

Staffed Beds: 628 **Admissions:** 33829 **Census:** 439 **Outpatient Visits:** 832586 **Births:** 4073 **Total Expense ($000):** 764987 **Payroll Expense ($000):** 257544 **Personnel:** 5139

PINNACLEHEALTH AT COMMUNITY GENERAL OSTEOPATHIC HOSPITAL See Pinnacle Health System

SELECT SPECIALTY HOSPITAL–HARRISBURG See Select Specialty Hospital–Central Pennsylvania, Camp Hill

HASTINGS—Cambria County

★ **CONEMAUGH MINERS MEDICAL CENTER (390130)**, 290 Haida Avenue, Zip 16646–5610, Mailing Address: P.O. Box 689, Zip 16646–0689; tel. 814/247–3100 **A**10 20 **F**3 15 18 29 30 31 35 36 40 45 48 56 57 59 64 70 75 78 79 81 86 92 93 96 97 107 108 110 119 129 130 133 144 146 148 **P**8 **S** Duke LifePoint Healthcare, Brentwood, TN
Primary Contact: William R. Crowe, President
CFO: Linda Fanale, Chief Financial Officer
CMO: Susan Williams, M.D., Chief Medical Officer
CIO: Joe Dado, Chief Information Officer
CHR: Brent J. Mallek, Chief Human Resource Officer
CNO: Anna Anna, R.N., Chief Nursing Officer
Web address: www.conemaugh.org
Control: Corporation, Investor–owned, for–profit **Service:** General Medical and Surgical

Staffed Beds: 30 **Admissions:** 403 **Census:** 5 **Outpatient Visits:** 51152 **Births:** 1 **Total Expense ($000):** 17047 **Payroll Expense ($000):** 5314 **Personnel:** 116

HAZLETON—Luzerne County

★ ◇ **LEHIGH VALLEY HOSPITAL – HAZLETON (390185)**, 700 East Broad Street, Zip 18201–6897; tel. 570/501–4000 **A**10 11 **F**3 8 11 12 13 15 18 28 29 30 31 33 34 35 40 43 50 53 54 57 59 60 62 64 68 69 70 75 76 77 78 79 81 82 85 86 87 89 90 93 107 108 110 111 114 118 119 124 129 130 131 132 135 143 144 146 147 148 **P**6 **S** Lehigh Valley Health Network, Allentown, PA
Primary Contact: John R. Fletcher, President
CFO: William Bauer, Vice President Finance and Chief Financial Officer
CMO: Anthony Valente, M.D., Vice President Medical Affairs
CIO: Carl Shoener, Chief Information Officer
Web address: www.lvhn.org/hazleton/
Control: Other not–for–profit (including NFP Corporation) **Service:** General Medical and Surgical

Staffed Beds: 120 **Admissions:** 6734 **Census:** 83 **Outpatient Visits:** 160795 **Births:** 673 **Total Expense ($000):** 101112 **Payroll Expense ($000):** 42207 **Personnel:** 763

HERSHEY—Dauphin County

✉ **PENN STATE MILTON S. HERSHEY MEDICAL CENTER (390256)**, 500 University Drive, Zip 17033–2360, Mailing Address: P.O. Box 850, Zip 17033–0850; tel. 717/531–8323, (Includes PENN STATE CHILDREN'S HOSPITAL, 500 University Drive, tel. 717/531–8521) **A**1 2 3 5 8 10 **F**3 5 6 7 8 9 11 12 13 14 15 17 18 19 20 21 22 23 24 25 26 27 28 29 30 31 32 34 35 36 37 38 40 41 43 44 45 46 47 48 49 50 51 52 53 54 55 56 57 58 59 60 61 64 65 66 68 70 71 72 73 74 75 76 77 78 79 80 81 82 84 85 86 87 88 89 91 92 93 95 96 97 99 100 101 102 103 104 105 106 107 108 109 110 111 114 115 116 117 118 119 120 121 123 124 126 129 130 131 132 134 135 136 137 138 139 141 142 143 144 145 146 147 148 **P**6 **S** Penn State Hershey Health System, Hershey, PA
Primary Contact: A. Craig Hillemeier, M.D., Chief Executive Officer
COO: Robin D. Wittenstein, Ed.D., Director and Chief Operating Officer
CFO: Stephen M. Massini, Chief Financial Officer
CMO: Thomas Tracy, Jr., Chief Medical Officer
CIO: Rod Dykehouse, Chief Information Officer
CHR: Jane Mannon, Interim Chief Human Resources Officer
CNO: Judy N. Himes, Interim Chief Nursing Officer
Web address: www.pennstatehershey.org/
Control: Other not–for–profit (including NFP Corporation) **Service:** General Medical and Surgical

Staffed Beds: 539 **Admissions:** 26934 **Census:** 440 **Outpatient Visits:** 999019 **Births:** 1901 **Total Expense ($000):** 1214077 **Payroll Expense ($000):** 417999 **Personnel:** 8832

HONESDALE—Wayne County

★ ◇ **WAYNE MEMORIAL HOSPITAL (390125)**, 601 Park Street, Zip 18431–1498; tel. 570/253–8100 **A**10 21 **F**3 11 13 15 18 28 29 30 31 34 35 36 37 39 40 45 46 48 49 50 51 53 54 56 57 59 61 62 63 64 65 75 76 77 78 79 81 86 90 92 93 99 100 101 102 103 104 107 108 110 111 115 116 117 119 124 129 130 131 132 133 134 135 146 147 148
Primary Contact: David L. Hoff, Chief Executive Officer
COO: John Conte, Director Facility Services and Real Estate
CFO: Michael J. Clifford, Director Finance
CMO: William Dewar, M.D., Chief of Staff
CIO: Tom Hoffman, Manager Information Systems
CHR: Elizabeth McDonald, Director Human Resources
CNO: Jim Pettinato, Director Patient Care Services
Web address: www.wmh.org
Control: Other not–for–profit (including NFP Corporation) **Service:** General Medical and Surgical

Staffed Beds: 87 **Admissions:** 3409 **Census:** 48 **Outpatient Visits:** 154565 **Births:** 465 **Total Expense ($000):** 75043 **Payroll Expense ($000):** 31322 **Personnel:** 591

HUMMELSTOWN—Dauphin County

✉ △ **PENN STATE HERSHEY REHABILITATION HOSPITAL (393053)**, 1135 Old West Chocolate Avenue, Zip 17036; tel. 717/832–2600, (Nonreporting) **A**1 3 7 10 **S** Select Medical Corporation, Mechanicsburg, PA
Primary Contact: Scott Guevin, Chief Executive Officer
CMO: Brenda Mallory, M.D., Medical Director
Web address: www.psh–rehab.com
Control: Corporation, Investor–owned, for–profit **Service:** Rehabilitation

Staffed Beds: 32

HUNTINGDON—Huntingdon County

✉ **J. C. BLAIR MEMORIAL HOSPITAL (390056)**, 1225 Warm Springs Avenue, Zip 16652–2398; tel. 814/643–2290 **A**1 10 20 **F**3 11 13 15 18 28 29 34 35 40 45 50 53 55 57 59 64 68 70 75 76 77 79 81 85 86 87 89 96 98 100 102 103 107 108 110 111 114 116 117 118 119 129 130 132 133 135 146 147 148
Primary Contact: Jason F. Hawkins, President and Chief Executive Officer
COO: Adam Dimm, Vice President Operations and Chief Operating Officer
CFO: Deborah A. Shughart, Vice President and Chief Financial Officer
CMO: James Hayden, M.D., Chief Medical Officer
CIO: Armen Arakelian, Chief Information Officer
CHR: Susan Hess, Director Human Ressources
CNO: Joye Gingrich, Director Patient Care Services and Chief Nursing Officer
Web address: www.jcblair.org
Control: Other not–for–profit (including NFP Corporation) **Service:** General Medical and Surgical

Staffed Beds: 70 **Admissions:** 2070 **Census:** 22 **Outpatient Visits:** 113286 **Births:** 215 **Total Expense ($000):** 43748 **Payroll Expense ($000):** 20965 **Personnel:** 348

Many Facility Codes have changed. Please refer to the AHA Guide Code Chart.

© 2016 AHA Guide

INDIANA—Indiana County

★ **INDIANA REGIONAL MEDICAL CENTER (390173)**, 835 Hospital Road, Zip 15701–3629, Mailing Address: P.O. Box 788, Zip 15701–0788; tel. 724/357–7000 **A**2 10 20 22 **F**3 11 15 18 20 28 29 31 34 35 40 44 45 46 47 49 53 56 57 59 64 65 70 71 74 75 76 77 78 79 81 82 83 84 85 87 89 90 98 102 103 107 108 111 114 115 118 119 120 121 123 124 129 130 132 144 146 147 148
Primary Contact: Stephen A. Wolfe, President and Chief Executive Officer
COO: Dominic Paccapaniccia, Chief Operating Officer
CFO: Robert Gongaware, Senior Vice President Finance
CMO: Bruce A. Bush, M.D., Senior Vice President Medical Affairs
CIO: Sam Norton, Interim Chief Information Officer
CHR: James W. Kinneer, Vice President Organizational Development
CNO: Cindy L. Virgil, MSN, Senior Vice President Patient Care Services
Web address: www.indianarmc.org
Control: Other not–for–profit (including NFP Corporation) **Service:** General Medical and Surgical

Staffed Beds: 164 **Admissions:** 7272 **Census:** 89 **Outpatient Visits:** 254411 **Births:** 543 **Total Expense ($000):** 137765 **Payroll Expense ($000):** 62869 **Personnel:** 865

JEFFERSON HILLS—Allegheny County

☒ **JEFFERSON HOSPITAL (390265)**, 565 Coal Valley Road, Zip 15025–3703, Mailing Address: Box 18119, Pittsburgh, Zip 15236–0119; tel. 412/469–5000 **A**1 3 10 **F**3 8 11 12 13 15 18 20 22 24 26 28 29 30 31 34 35 40 44 45 46 47 48 49 51 54 57 59 60 64 70 73 74 75 76 78 79 81 84 85 86 87 89 90 93 98 100 104 107 110 111 114 115 116 117 118 119 126 129 130 132 146 147 148 **P**2 6 **S** Allegheny Health Network, Pittsburgh, PA
Primary Contact: Louise Urban, R.N., President and Chief Executive Officer
CMO: Richard F. Collins, M.D., Executive Vice President and Chief Medical Officer
CIO: James Witenske, Chief Information Officer
Web address: www.jeffersonregional.com
Control: Other not–for–profit (including NFP Corporation) **Service:** General Medical and Surgical

Staffed Beds: 341 **Admissions:** 14802 **Census:** 181 **Outpatient Visits:** 681649 **Births:** 777 **Total Expense ($000):** 301155 **Payroll Expense ($000):** 112146 **Personnel:** 1569

JERSEY SHORE—Lycoming County

☒ **JERSEY SHORE HOSPITAL (391300)**, 1020 Thompson Street, Zip 17740–1794; tel. 570/398–0100 **A**1 10 18 **F**3 15 18 28 29 30 34 35 40 45 46 47 48 50 57 59 75 77 79 81 82 85 93 107 108 109 110 111 115 119 129 130 133 135 144 145 **S** QHR, Brentwood, TN
Primary Contact: David A. Shannon, President and Chief Executive Officer
CFO: Mark Rice, CPA, Chief Financial Officer
CMO: Stephen Goykovich, D.O., Chief Medical Officer
CIO: Christine Haas, Chief Information Officer
CHR: Joan Rounsley, Director Human Resources
CNO: Paulette Nish, Chief Nursing Officer
Web address: www.jsh.org
Control: Other not–for–profit (including NFP Corporation) **Service:** General Medical and Surgical

Staffed Beds: 25 **Admissions:** 843 **Census:** 9 **Outpatient Visits:** 83502 **Births:** 0 **Total Expense ($000):** 26948 **Payroll Expense ($000):** 12032 **Personnel:** 242

JOHNSTOWN—Cambria County

☒ △ **CONEMAUGH MEMORIAL MEDICAL CENTER (390110)**, 1086 Franklin Street, Zip 15905–4398; tel. 814/534–9000, (Includes MEMORIAL MEDICAL CENTER – LEE CAMPUS, 320 Main Street, Zip 15901–1601; tel. 814/533–0123) **A**1 3 7 10 12 13 **F**3 5 8 12 13 14 15 17 18 20 22 24 26 28 29 30 31 32 34 35 40 42 43 44 45 46 49 50 51 53 54 55 56 57 59 61 63 64 68 70 72 74 75 76 77 78 79 81 82 83 84 85 86 87 89 90 92 93 97 98 99 100 101 103 104 107 108 110 111 114 115 118 119 126 129 130 131 132 134 135 144 145 146 147 148 **S** Duke LifePoint Healthcare, Brentwood, TN
Primary Contact: Steven E. Tucker, President
COO: Steven E. Tucker, President
CMO: Susan Williams, M.D., Chief Medical Officer
CIO: Joe Dado, Chief Information Officer
CHR: Brent J. Mallek, Chief Human Resources Officer
CNO: Claudia Rager, R.N., Vice President Patient Care Services
Web address: www.conemaugh.org
Control: Corporation, Investor–owned, for–profit **Service:** General Medical and Surgical

Staffed Beds: 539 **Admissions:** 21517 **Census:** 330 **Outpatient Visits:** 468314 **Births:** 1534 **Total Expense ($000):** 384315 **Payroll Expense ($000):** 161288 **Personnel:** 3099

MEMORIAL MEDICAL CENTER – LEE CAMPUS See Conemaugh Memorial Medical Center

☒ **SELECT SPECIALTY HOSPITAL–JOHNSTOWN (392031)**, 320 Main Street, 3rd Floor, Zip 15901–1601; tel. 814/534–7300, (Nonreporting) **A**1 10 **S** Select Medical Corporation, Mechanicsburg, PA
Primary Contact: Kelly Blake, Chief Executive Officer
CMO: Gary Davidson, M.D., Medical Director
Web address: www.selectspecialtyhospitals.com/company/locations/johnstown.aspx
Control: Corporation, Investor–owned, for–profit **Service:** Long–Term Acute Care hospital

Staffed Beds: 39

KANE—Mckean County

KANE COMMUNITY HOSPITAL (390104), 4372 Route 6, Zip 16735–3060; tel. 814/837–8585 **A**10 20 **F**3 11 15 17 18 28 29 30 34 35 40 41 45 46 50 53 57 59 62 64 65 70 75 77 79 81 82 85 89 91 93 107 108 110 111 114 118 119 128 129 130 132 133 135 145 146 147 **P**4
Primary Contact: J. Gary Rhodes, FACHE, Chief Executive Officer
CFO: Angela Hadzega, Chief Financial Officer
CMO: Linda Rettger, M.D., President Medical Staff
CIO: Deano Cherry, Chief Information Officer
CHR: Marsha Keller, Director Human Resources
CNO: Pam Bray, Director of Nursing and Director Inpatient Services
Web address: www.kanehosp.com
Control: Other not–for–profit (including NFP Corporation) **Service:** General Medical and Surgical

Staffed Beds: 31 **Admissions:** 637 **Census:** 7 **Outpatient Visits:** 76397 **Births:** 0 **Total Expense ($000):** 22035 **Payroll Expense ($000):** 10792 **Personnel:** 187

KINGSTON—Luzerne County

☒ **FIRST HOSPITAL WYOMING VALLEY (394039)**, 562 Wyoming Avenue, Zip 18704–3721; tel. 570/552–3900 **A**1 10 **F**42 98 99 103 105 130 **P**6 **S** Community Health Systems, Inc., Franklin, TN
Primary Contact: Ron Ziobro, Interim Chief Executive Officer
COO: Gene Boylan, Interim Chief Operating Officer
CFO: Kelly Knorr, Chief Financial Officer
CMO: David Liskov, M.D., Medical Director
CNO: Rhonda Moffitt Sod, Chief Nursing Officer
Web address: www.commonwealthhealth.net/locations/first–hospital
Control: Corporation, Investor–owned, for–profit **Service:** Psychiatric

Staffed Beds: 127 **Admissions:** 4332 **Census:** 109 **Outpatient Visits:** 0 **Births:** 0 **Personnel:** 112

KITTANNING—Armstrong County

◇ **ACMH HOSPITAL (390163)**, One Nolte Drive, Zip 16201–7111; tel. 724/543–8500 **A**2 10 19 21 **F**3 11 13 15 17 18 20 22 26 28 29 30 34 35 40 45 49 59 70 74 75 76 77 78 79 81 82 85 90 93 98 102 103 107 108 110 111 112 114 119 120 127 128 129 130 131 132 135 136 141 142 146 148
Primary Contact: John I. Lewis, President and Chief Executive Officer
CFO: Patrick Burns, Vice President Finance
CMO: Harold Altman, M.D., Chief Medical Officer
CIO: Dianne Emminger, Vice President Information Services
CHR: Anne Remaley, Vice President Human Resources
Web address: www.acmh.org
Control: Other not–for–profit (including NFP Corporation) **Service:** General Medical and Surgical

Staffed Beds: 165 **Admissions:** 5235 **Census:** 70 **Outpatient Visits:** 256139 **Births:** 514 **Total Expense ($000):** 98143 **Payroll Expense ($000):** 43811 **Personnel:** 593

Hospital, Medicare Provider Number, Address, Telephone, Approval, Facility, and Physician Codes, Health Care System

★ American Hospital Association (AHA) membership
□ The Joint Commission accreditation
○ Healthcare Facilities Accreditation Program
◇ DNV Healthcare Inc. accreditation
⇑ Center for Improvement in Healthcare Quality Accreditation
△ Commission on Accreditation of Rehabilitation Facilities (CARF) accreditation

PA

PA

LANCASTER—Lancaster County

☒ **LANCASTER GENERAL HOSPITAL (390100)**, 555 North Duke Street, Zip 17602–2250; tel. 717/544–5511 **A**1 2 3 5 10 **F**3 7 11 12 13 14 15 17 18 19 20 22 24 26 28 29 30 31 32 34 35 36 39 40 43 44 45 46 47 49 50 54 55 56 57 58 59 60 61 64 65 66 68 70 72 73 74 75 76 77 78 79 80 81 82 84 85 86 87 89 91 92 93 94 96 97 98 100 102 103 104 107 108 110 112 114 115 117 118 119 120 121 123 124 126 129 130 132 135 141 145 146 147 148 **P**6 **S** University of Pennsylvania Health System, Philadelphia, PA
Primary Contact: Jan L. Bergen, President and Chief Executive Officer
CFO: Dennis Roemer, Executive Vice President and Chief Financial Officer
CMO: Lee M. Duke, II, M.D., Senior Vice President and Chief Physician Executive
CIO: Gary Davidson, Senior Vice President and Chief Information Officer
CHR: Regina Mingle, Senior Vice President and Chief Leadership Officer
CNO: Lanyce Roldan, Interim Chief Nursing Officer
Web address: www.lancastergeneralhealth.org
Control: Other not-for-profit (including NFP Corporation) **Service:** General Medical and Surgical

Staffed Beds: 630 **Admissions:** 32656 **Census:** 404 **Outpatient Visits:** 1523990 **Births:** 4342 **Total Expense ($000):** 825107 **Payroll Expense ($000):** 337441 **Personnel:** 4881

☒ **LANCASTER REGIONAL MEDICAL CENTER (390061)**, 250 College Avenue, Zip 17603–3363, Mailing Address: P.O. Box 3434, Zip 17604–3434; tel. 717/291–8211 **A**1 10 **F**3 15 18 20 22 24 26 28 29 30 31 34 35 37 40 45 46 47 48 49 50 51 56 57 59 64 68 70 74 75 77 78 79 81 82 84 85 87 90 91 92 93 96 98 100 101 102 103 107 108 110 111 114 121 126 129 130 131 135 146 **S** Community Health Systems, Inc., Franklin, TN
Primary Contact: Brooks Turkel, Chief Executive Officer
CFO: Mike Johnson, Chief Financial Officer
CMO: N. A. Mastropietro, M.D., Medical Director
CHR: Brian Hoffman, Director Human Resources
CNO: Michelle Reaser, R.N., Chief Nursing Executive
Web address: www.lancasterregional.com
Control: Corporation, Investor-owned, for-profit **Service:** General Medical and Surgical

Staffed Beds: 150 **Admissions:** 4269 **Census:** 66 **Births:** 0

☐ **LANCASTER REHABILITATION HOSPITAL (393054)**, 675 Good Drive, Zip 17601–2426; tel. 717/406–3000, (Nonreporting) **A**1 10
Primary Contact: Tammy L. Ober, Chief Executive Officer
CFO: David Stark, Chief Financial Officer
CHR: Lisa Andrews, Director Human Resources
Web address: www.lancastergeneral.org
Control: Corporation, Investor-owned, for-profit **Service:** Rehabilitation

Staffed Beds: 10

LANGHORNE—Bucks County

☐ **BARIX CLINICS OF PENNSYLVANIA (390302)**, 280 Middletown Boulevard, Zip 19047–1816; tel. 267/572–3100, (Nonreporting) **A**1 10
Primary Contact: Tony Adams, President
Web address: www.barixclinics.com
Control: Partnership, Investor-owned, for-profit **Service:** Surgical

Staffed Beds: 40

BUCKS COUNTY CAMPUS See Aria – Jefferson Health, Philadelphia

☒ **ST. MARY MEDICAL CENTER (390258)**, 1201 Langhorne–Newtown Road, Zip 19047–1201; tel. 215/710–2000 **A**1 2 10 **F**2 7 12 15 17 18 20 22 24 26 28 29 30 31 32 34 35 36 40 41 43 53 55 56 57 58 59 64 66 70 72 74 75 76 77 78 79 81 82 84 86 87 89 90 91 92 93 94 107 108 110 111 114 115 116 117 118 119 120 121 123 124 126 129 130 132 135 146 147 148 **S** Trinity Health, Livonia, MI
Primary Contact: James L. Woodward, President and Chief Executive Officer
COO: Jeffrey N. Yarmel, Chief Operating Officer
CFO: Daniel Confalone, Chief Financial Officer and Vice President Finance
CMO: Deirdre Donaghy, M.D., Vice President Medical Affairs
CIO: Bonnie Buehler, Chief Information Officer
CHR: Mary Sweeney, Vice President Colleague Services and Development
CNO: Sharon Brown, R.N., Vice President Patient Care and Chief Nursing Officer
Web address: www.stmaryhealthcare.org
Control: Church-operated, Nongovernment, not-for profit **Service:** General Medical and Surgical

Staffed Beds: 307 **Admissions:** 21595 **Census:** 240 **Outpatient Visits:** 319539 **Births:** 2347 **Total Expense ($000):** 384258 **Payroll Expense ($000):** 152897 **Personnel:** 2216

LANSDALE—Montgomery County

☒ **ABINGTON–LANSDALE HOSPITAL JEFFERSON HEALTH (390012)**, 100 Medical Campus Drive, Zip 19446–1200; tel. 215/368–2100 **A**1 10 **F**2 3 11 15 18 28 29 30 32 34 35 40 44 45 49 50 54 56 57 59 63 64 65 68 70 74 75 77 78 79 81 82 84 85 86 87 90 93 96 97 107 111 114 115 119 129 130 131 132 146 147 148 **P**6 **S** Jefferson Health, Radnor, PA
Primary Contact: Gary R. Candia, Ph.D., FACHE, Chief Administrative Officer
COO: Katie Farrell, Chief Operating Officer
CFO: Michael Walsh, Senior Vice President Finance and Chief Financial Officer
CMO: Michel Taupin, M.D., Chief Medical Officer
CIO: Alison Ferren, Vice President Information Technology and Chief Information Officer
CHR: Meghan Patton, Vice President Human Resources
CNO: Kelly Cummings, Chief Nursing Officer
Web address: www.abingtonhealth.org/find–a–location/abington–lansdale–hospital/#.V5dyVVL9yk4
Control: Other not-for-profit (including NFP Corporation) **Service:** General Medical and Surgical

Staffed Beds: 140 **Admissions:** 5627 **Census:** 57 **Outpatient Visits:** 76008 **Births:** 0 **Total Expense ($000):** 76254 **Payroll Expense ($000):** 29102 **Personnel:** 335

LATROBE—Westmoreland County

☐ **EXCELA LATROBE AREA HOSPITAL (390219)**, One Mellon Way, Zip 15650–1096; tel. 724/537–1000 **A**1 2 3 5 10 13 **F**3 7 8 12 15 18 28 29 30 34 35 40 44 45 48 49 50 51 54 57 59 64 65 68 70 74 75 77 78 79 81 82 85 86 87 92 93 96 97 98 99 100 101 102 104 107 108 110 111 114 115 117 118 119 126 130 132 134 135 143 146 147 **P**6 **S** Excela Health, Greensburg, PA
Primary Contact: Michael D. Busch, Executive Vice President and Chief Operating Officer
COO: Michael D. Busch, Executive Vice President and Chief Operating Officer
CMO: Carol J. Fox, M.D., Senior Vice President and Chief Medical Officer
CIO: David Gawaluck, Vice President and Chief Information Officer
CHR: Laurie English, Senior Vice President and Chief Human Resource Officer
CNO: Helen K. Burns, Ph.D., Senior Vice President and Chief Nursing Officer
Web address: www.excelahealth.org
Control: Other not-for-profit (including NFP Corporation) **Service:** General Medical and Surgical

Staffed Beds: 114 **Admissions:** 6832 **Census:** 74 **Outpatient Visits:** 307277 **Births:** 0 **Total Expense ($000):** 116375 **Payroll Expense ($000):** 38124 **Personnel:** 737

☒ **SELECT SPECIALTY HOSPITAL–LAUREL HIGHLANDS (392036)**, One Mellon Way, 3rd Floor, Zip 15650–1197; tel. 724/539–3230, (Nonreporting) **A**1 10 **S** Select Medical Corporation, Mechanicsburg, PA
Primary Contact: Laurie Kozorosky, Chief Executive Officer
Web address: www.selectspecialtyhospitals.com/company/locations/laurelhighlands.aspx
Control: Corporation, Investor-owned, for-profit **Service:** Long–Term Acute Care hospital

Staffed Beds: 40

LEBANON—Lebanon County

☒ **LEBANON VETERANS AFFAIRS MEDICAL CENTER**, 1700 South Lincoln Avenue, Zip 17042–7529; tel. 717/272–6621, (Nonreporting) **A**1 2 3 5 **S** Department of Veterans Affairs, Washington, DC
Primary Contact: Robert W. Callahan, Jr., Director
CFO: Geoffrey Smith, Chief Financial Officer
CMO: Kanan Chatterjee, M.D., Chief of Staff
CIO: Andru Ditzler, Chief Information Officer
CHR: Cindy Shiner, Manager Human Resources
Web address: www.lebanon.va.gov
Control: Veterans Affairs, Government, federal **Service:** General Medical and Surgical

Staffed Beds: 213

VETERANS AFFAIRS MEDICAL CENTER See Lebanon Veterans Affairs Medical Center

Many Facility Codes have changed. Please refer to the AHA Guide Code Chart.

© 2016 AHA Guide

✠ **WELLSPAN GOOD SAMARITAN HOSPITAL (390066)**, Fourth and Walnut Streets, Zip 17042–1281, Mailing Address: P.O. Box 1281, Zip 17042–1281; tel. 717/270–7500, (Total facility includes 19 beds in nursing home–type unit) **A**1 3 5 10 13 **F**3 8 11 13 14 15 17 18 20 22 24 26 28 29 30 31 34 35 40 45 49 50 51 57 59 62 63 64 67 68 70 74 75 76 77 78 79 80 81 82 85 87 89 90 91 92 93 94 96 97 107 110 111 114 115 116 117 118 119 120 121 124 126 129 130 132 135 145 146 148 **P**8 **S** WellSpan Health, York, PA
Primary Contact: Thomas R. Harlow, FACHE, President
COO: Kimberly Feeman, Senior Vice President and Chief Operating Officer
CMO: Robert D. Shaver, M.D., Vice President Medical Affairs
CIO: Leon John Jabour, Regional Chief Information Officer
CHR: Denise M. Garman, Director Human Resources
CNO: Jacquelyn M. Gould, MS, Vice President Patient Care Services and Chief Nursing Officer
Web address: www.gshleb.org
Control: Other not–for–profit (including NFP Corporation) **Service:** General Medical and Surgical

Staffed Beds: 151 **Admissions:** 7746 **Census:** 102 **Outpatient Visits:** 273091 **Births:** 800 **Total Expense ($000):** 170694 **Payroll Expense ($000):** 59701 **Personnel:** 1248

LEHIGHTON—Carbon County

✠ △ **BLUE MOUNTAIN HOSPITAL (390194)**, 211 North 12th Street, Zip 18235–1138; tel. 610/377–1300, (Total facility includes 91 beds in nursing home–type unit) **A**1 7 10 **F**3 11 13 14 15 17 18 20 22 24 26 28 29 30 34 35 40 50 57 59 62 64 65 68 70 74 75 77 79 81 82 85 87 90 93 94 97 98 102 107 111 114 116 117 119 124 128 130 132 133 135 146 147 148 **S** Blue Mountain Health System, Lehighton, PA
Primary Contact: Andrew E. Harris, Chief Executive Officer
CFO: Andrea Andrae, Chief Financial Officer
CMO: Dennis Kondash, D.O., Vice President Medical Affairs
CIO: Steve Kinkaid, Director Information Systems
CHR: Terrance J. Purcell, Vice President Support Services and Ambulatory Care
CNO: Dorothy Patzek, Vice President Nursing
Web address: www.blmtn.org
Control: Other not–for–profit (including NFP Corporation) **Service:** General Medical and Surgical

Staffed Beds: 183 **Admissions:** 3426 **Census:** 137 **Outpatient Visits:** 66787 **Births:** 0 **Total Expense ($000):** 60091 **Payroll Expense ($000):** 26252 **Personnel:** 574

LEWISBURG—Union County

◇ **EVANGELICAL COMMUNITY HOSPITAL (390013)**, One Hospital Drive, Zip 17837–9350; tel. 570/522–2000 **A**10 19 21 **F**3 8 11 12 13 15 18 20 22 28 29 30 31 34 35 40 43 45 49 50 51 53 54 57 59 63 64 65 68 74 75 76 77 78 79 81 82 84 85 86 87 89 90 93 94 96 107 108 110 111 114 115 116 117 118 119 129 130 131 132 135 144 146 148 **P**7
Primary Contact: Kendra A. Aucker, President and Chief Executive Officer
COO: Kendra A. Aucker, Vice President Operations
CFO: Jim Stopper, CPA, Chief Financial Officer
CMO: J. Lawrence Ginsburg, M.D., Vice President Medical Affairs
CIO: Dale Moyer, Vice President Information Systems
CHR: Angela Hummel, Vice President Human Resources
CNO: Paul E. Tarves, R.N., Vice President Nursing Services
Web address: www.evanhospital.com
Control: Other not–for–profit (including NFP Corporation) **Service:** General Medical and Surgical

Staffed Beds: 132 **Admissions:** 5426 **Census:** 48 **Outpatient Visits:** 287435 **Births:** 957 **Total Expense ($000):** 148707 **Payroll Expense ($000):** 61906 **Personnel:** 1416

U. S. PENITENTIARY INFIRMARY, Route 7, Zip 17837–9303; tel. 570/523–1251, (Nonreporting)
Primary Contact: Steve Brown, Health Services Director
Control: Department of Justice, Government, federal **Service:** Hospital unit of an institution (prison hospital, college infimary, etc.)

Staffed Beds: 17

LEWISTOWN—Mifflin County

✠ **GEISINGER–LEWISTOWN HOSPITAL (390048)**, 400 Highland Avenue, Zip 17044–1198; tel. 717/248–5411 **A**1 2 10 **F**3 11 12 13 15 17 18 19 28 29 30 31 34 35 40 50 51 57 59 64 68 70 71 74 75 76 78 79 81 82 85 86 89 97 98 100 101 102 103 107 108 110 111 114 116 117 118 119 121 124 129 130 132 135 146 147 148 **P**6 **S** Geisinger Health System, Danville, PA
Primary Contact: Kay A. Hamilton, R.N., MS, Chief Administrative Officer
COO: Kirk E. Thomas, Vice President Operations
CFO: Kristy Hine, Associate Vice President Finance
CMO: Michael T. Hegstrom, M.D., Chief Medical Officer
CIO: Ronald M. Cowan, Vice President Information Systems
CHR: N. Sue Reinke, Vice President Human Resources
CNO: Christine W. Mathews, R.N., Vice President Nursing Services
Web address: www.geisinger.org
Control: Other not–for–profit (including NFP Corporation) **Service:** General Medical and Surgical

Staffed Beds: 123 **Admissions:** 4930 **Census:** 53 **Births:** 585

LITITZ—Lancaster County

✠ **HEART OF LANCASTER REGIONAL MEDICAL CENTER (390068)**, 1500 Highlands Drive, Zip 17543–7694; tel. 717/625–5000 **A**1 10 13 **F**3 12 13 15 18 29 30 31 34 35 44 45 47 49 50 57 59 60 64 68 70 72 74 75 76 77 79 81 82 85 87 89 107 108 110 111 115 119 126 130 146 147 148 **S** Community Health Systems, Inc., Franklin, TN
Primary Contact: Deborah J. Willwerth, R.N., MSN, Chief Executive Officer
CIO: David Fisher, Director Information Systems
Web address: www.heartoflancaster.com
Control: Corporation, Investor–owned, for–profit **Service:** General Medical and Surgical

Staffed Beds: 148 **Admissions:** 2723 **Census:** 30 **Births:** 1052

LOCK HAVEN—Clinton County

✠ **LOCK HAVEN HOSPITAL (390071)**, 24 Cree Drive, Zip 17745–2699; tel. 570/893–5000, (Total facility includes 64 beds in nursing home–type unit) **A**1 10 **F**1 3 11 13 15 18 19 29 30 34 35 40 41 45 50 54 56 57 59 64 65 67 68 70 75 76 77 81 82 85 89 90 93 96 97 107 108 110 111 114 118 119 127 128 130 132 133 146 147 **S** Quorum Health, Brentwood, TN
Primary Contact: Steven T. Davis, Chief Executive Officer
CFO: Jennifer Lesher, Chief Financial Officer
CMO: Rajesh Patel, M.D., Chief of Staff
CIO: Judy Chapman, Interim Director Information Systems
CHR: Courtney Kunes, Director Human Resources
Web address: www.lockhavenhospital.com
Control: Corporation, Investor–owned, for–profit **Service:** General Medical and Surgical

Staffed Beds: 84 **Admissions:** 1291 **Census:** 63 **Outpatient Visits:** 34697 **Births:** 137 **Total Expense ($000):** 32343 **Payroll Expense ($000):** 13290 **Personnel:** 254

MALVERN—Chester County

✠ △ **BRYN MAWR REHABILITATION HOSPITAL (393025)**, 414 Paoli Pike, Zip 19355–3300, Mailing Address: P.O. Box 3007, Zip 19355–0707; tel. 484/596–5400 **A**1 3 7 10 **F**3 11 28 29 30 34 35 36 44 50 65 71 75 82 86 87 90 91 92 93 95 96 119 130 131 132 143 146 **P**5 **S** Main Line Health
Primary Contact: Donna Phillips, President
CFO: Dave Schmotzer, Chief Financial Officer
CMO: John Kraus, M.D., Chief Medical Officer
CIO: Karen A. Thomas, Chief Information Officer
Web address: www.brynmawrrehab.org
Control: Other not–for–profit (including NFP Corporation) **Service:** Rehabilitation

Staffed Beds: 148 **Admissions:** 2331 **Census:** 100 **Outpatient Visits:** 71796 **Births:** 0 **Total Expense ($000):** 66459 **Payroll Expense ($000):** 35149 **Personnel:** 520

DEVEREUX CHILDREN'S BEHAVIORAL HEALTH CENTER, 655 Sugartown Road, Zip 19355–3303, Mailing Address: 655 Sugartown Road, Zip 19355–3303; tel. 800/345–1292 **F**29 98 99 106 **P**6 **S** Devereux, Villanova, PA
Primary Contact: David E. Woodward, Executive Director
CFO: Tim Evans, Assistant Financial Director
CMO: Jacquelyn Zavodnick, M.D., Medical Director
CIO: MaryLou Hettinger, Director Quality Management
CHR: Sean Maher, Director Human Resources
CNO: Deanna Reiss, Hospital Director of Nursing
Web address: www.devereux.org
Control: Other not–for–profit (including NFP Corporation) **Service:** Children's hospital psychiatric

Staffed Beds: 49 **Admissions:** 587 **Census:** 31 **Outpatient Visits:** 0 **Births:** 0

PA

MALVERN INSTITUTE, 940 King Road, Zip 19355–3166; tel. 610/647–0330, (Nonreporting)
Primary Contact: Scott Weisenberger, Chief Executive Officer
CFO: Janet Corley, Accountant
Web address: www.malverninstitute.com
Control: Corporation, Investor–owned, for–profit **Service:** Alcoholism and other chemical dependency

Staffed Beds: 40

MC CONNELLSBURG—Fulton County

★ **FULTON COUNTY MEDICAL CENTER (391303)**, 214 Peach Orchard Road, Zip 17233–8559; tel. 717/485–3155, (Total facility includes 67 beds in nursing home–type unit) **A**10 18 **F**3 11 12 15 18 28 29 30 34 35 40 50 57 59 62 64 70 75 77 78 79 81 87 91 93 97 107 108 111 115 118 119 128 129 130 132 133 135 146 147 148
Primary Contact: Jason F. Hawkins, President and Chief Executive Officer
COO: William Buterbaugh, Director Support Services
CFO: Deborah A. Shughart, Vice President and Chief Financial Officer
CMO: Sharon E. Martin, M.D., President Medical Staff
CIO: Armen Arakelian, Chief Information Officer
CHR: Cheryl Rose, Human Resources Director
Web address: www.fcmcpa.org
Control: Other not–for–profit (including NFP Corporation) **Service:** General Medical and Surgical

Staffed Beds: 88 **Admissions:** 852 **Census:** 75 **Outpatient Visits:** 60559 **Births:** 0 **Total Expense ($000):** 43372 **Payroll Expense ($000):** 20879 **Personnel:** 336

MCKEES ROCKS—Allegheny County

⊞ **OHIO VALLEY HOSPITAL (390157)**, 25 Heckel Road, Zip 15136–1694; tel. 412/777–6161 **A**1 10 **F**3 10 15 18 20 29 30 40 45 46 49 51 59 65 70 74 75 77 79 81 82 85 87 90 92 93 98 103 107 108 111 118 119 126 129 130 143 146 148 **P**6
Primary Contact: David W. Scott, President and Chief Executive Officer
CFO: Jack Nelson, Vice President Finance and Chief Financial Officer
CHR: Erin J. Frohnhofer, Vice President Human Resources
CNO: Paulette Bingham, Director Nursing Services
Web address: www.ohiovalleyhospital.org
Control: Other not–for–profit (including NFP Corporation) **Service:** General Medical and Surgical

Staffed Beds: 138 **Admissions:** 3680 **Census:** 63 **Outpatient Visits:** 106870 **Births:** 0 **Total Expense ($000):** 61035 **Payroll Expense ($000):** 21405 **Personnel:** 438

MCKEESPORT—Allegheny County

⊞ **SELECT SPECIALTY HOSPITAL–MCKEESPORT (392045)**, 1500 Fifth Avenue, 6th Floor, Zip 15132–2422; tel. 412/664–2900 **A**1 10 **F**1 3 91 92 97 130 148 **S** Select Medical Corporation, Mechanicsburg, PA
Primary Contact: Angela Merryman, Chief Executive Officer
Web address: www.mckeesport.selectspecialtyhospitals.com/
Control: Corporation, Investor–owned, for–profit **Service:** Long–Term Acute Care hospital

Staffed Beds: 30 **Admissions:** 249 **Census:** 19 **Outpatient Visits:** 0 **Births:** 0

☐ **UPMC MCKEESPORT (390002)**, 1500 Fifth Avenue, Zip 15132–2422; tel. 412/664–2000, (Total facility includes 24 beds in nursing home–type unit) **A**1 3 5 10 13 **F**3 8 11 15 18 20 22 28 29 30 31 32 34 35 37 40 46 49 50 54 56 57 59 60 61 62 64 65 66 70 74 75 77 78 79 81 84 85 86 87 90 96 97 98 100 101 102 103 107 111 114 115 118 119 121 128 130 131 132 135 143 146 148 **P**6 **S** UPMC, Pittsburgh, PA
Primary Contact: Mark Sevco, President
COO: Amy Bush, Vice President Operations
CFO: Christopher Stockhausen, Chief Financial Officer
CMO: R. Curtis Waligura, D.O., Vice President Medical Affairs, Chief Medical Officer
CIO: Terri Keeling, Vice President Information Systems
CHR: Kelli Reale, Vice President Human Resources
CNO: Leeanna McKibben, R.N., Vice President Patient Services and Chief Nursing Officer
Web address: www.mckeesport.upmc.com
Control: Other not–for–profit (including NFP Corporation) **Service:** General Medical and Surgical

Staffed Beds: 184 **Admissions:** 7562 **Census:** 129 **Outpatient Visits:** 125623 **Births:** 0 **Total Expense ($000):** 138373 **Payroll Expense ($000):** 42583 **Personnel:** 684

MEADOWBROOK—Montgomery County

◇ **HOLY REDEEMER HOSPITAL (390097)**, 1648 Huntingdon Pike, Zip 19046–8001; tel. 215/947–3000, (Total facility includes 21 beds in nursing home–type unit) **A**2 3 5 10 21 **F**3 13 15 17 18 20 22 29 30 31 32 34 35 36 39 40 41 44 45 46 49 50 51 53 54 55 56 57 58 59 61 62 63 64 68 69 70 72 74 75 76 77 78 79 81 82 84 85 86 87 92 93 96 98 100 103 104 107 108 109 110 114 115 116 117 118 119 120 121 123 128 129 130 131 132 135 141 143 146 147 148
Primary Contact: Michael B. Laign, President and Chief Executive Officer
CFO: Russell R. Wagner, Executive Vice President and Chief Financial Officer
CMO: Henry D. Unger, M.D., Senior Vice President and Chief Medical Officer
CIO: Donald F. Friel, Executive Vice President
CHR: Joseph J. Cassidy, Vice President and Chief Human Resources Officer
CNO: Anne Catino, R.N., Vice President and Chief Nursing Officer
Web address: www.holyredeemer.com
Control: Other not–for–profit (including NFP Corporation) **Service:** General Medical and Surgical

Staffed Beds: 230 **Admissions:** 10908 **Census:** 147 **Outpatient Visits:** 309508 **Births:** 2588 **Total Expense ($000):** 175422 **Payroll Expense ($000):** 70234 **Personnel:** 1280

MEADVILLE—Crawford County

★ ◇ **MEADVILLE MEDICAL CENTER (390113)**, 751 Liberty Street, Zip 16335–2559; tel. 814/333–5000, (Total facility includes 32 beds in nursing home–type unit) **A**2 10 12 13 21 **F**3 4 5 11 13 15 18 20 22 28 29 30 31 35 36 38 40 45 46 49 53 57 59 63 64 70 75 76 77 78 79 81 82 84 85 86 87 89 90 91 93 98 99 103 107 110 111 114 115 118 119 120 128 129 130 131 132 146 147 148 **P**6 7 **S** Meadville Medical Center, Meadville, PA
Primary Contact: Philip E. Pandolph, FACHE, Chief Executive Officer
CFO: Renato Suntay, Chief Financial Officer
CMO: Denise Johnson, M.D., Medical Director
CIO: Young Vu, Chief Information Officer
CHR: Greg Maras, Vice President Human Resources
CNO: David Shaffer, MSN, Chief Nurse Executive
Web address: www.mmchs.org
Control: Other not–for–profit (including NFP Corporation) **Service:** General Medical and Surgical

Staffed Beds: 210 **Admissions:** 7040 **Census:** 107 **Outpatient Visits:** 234773 **Births:** 584 **Total Expense ($000):** 160780 **Payroll Expense ($000):** 64068 **Personnel:** 1137

MECHANICSBURG—Cumberland County

HEALTHSOUTH REGIONAL SPECIALTY HOSPITAL See LifeCare Hospitals of Mechanicsburg

⊞ **HEALTHSOUTH REHABILITATION HOSPITAL OF MECHANICSBURG (393031)**, 175 Lancaster Boulevard, Zip 17055–3562; tel. 717/691–3700 **A**1 10 **F**28 29 34 54 57 59 64 68 75 77 79 82 90 91 92 93 94 95 96 130 132 146 148 **S** HEALTHSOUTH Corporation, Birmingham, AL
Primary Contact: Mark Freeburn, Chief Executive Officer
CMO: Michael Lupinacci, M.D., Medical Director
CHR: David Staskin, Director Human Resources
Web address: www.healthsouthpa.com
Control: Corporation, Investor–owned, for–profit **Service:** Rehabilitation

Staffed Beds: 75 **Admissions:** 1398 **Census:** 48 **Births:** 0

⊞ **LIFECARE HOSPITALS OF MECHANICSBURG (392038)**, 4950 Wilson Lane, Zip 17055–4442; tel. 717/697–7706 **A**1 10 **F**1 3 29 60 77 91 **P**5 **S** LifeCare Management Services, Plano, TX
Primary Contact: Mary Ellen Kable, Chief Executive Officer
CFO: Trisha Niemuth, Director of Finance
CMO: Michael Gluck, M.D., Medical Director
CHR: Jennifer Rashford, Manager Human Resources
CNO: Alicia Kuntz, Nurse Manager
Web address: www.lifecare-hospitals.com/hospital.php?id=20
Control: Corporation, Investor–owned, for–profit **Service:** Long–Term Acute Care hospital

Staffed Beds: 68 **Admissions:** 314 **Census:** 21 **Outpatient Visits:** 0 **Births:** 0

Many Facility Codes have changed. Please refer to the AHA Guide Code Chart.

MEDIA—Delaware County

⊠ **RIDDLE HOSPITAL (390222)**, 1068 West Baltimore Pike, Zip 19063–5177; tel. 484/227–9400, (Total facility includes 23 beds in nursing home–type unit) **A**1 2 3 10 **F**3 7 11 13 15 18 20 22 26 28 29 30 31 34 35 36 37 38 40 41 44 45 46 49 50 53 54 55 56 57 58 59 63 64 65 70 72 74 75 76 78 79 80 81 82 84 85 86 87 92 97 100 102 103 107 108 110 111 114 115 118 119 120 124 128 129 130 131 132 135 141 143 145 146 147 148 **S** Main Line Health
Primary Contact: Gary L. Perecko, President
COO: Jeshahnton Essex, Vice President of Administration
CFO: Ed McKillip, Director of Finance
CMO: David Thomas, President Medical Staff
CHR: Mary Louise Ciciretti, Director Human Resources
CNO: Rosemary H. Wurster, Vice President Patient Care Services
Web address: www.riddlehospital.org
Control: Other not–for–profit (including NFP Corporation) **Service:** General Medical and Surgical

Staffed Beds: 227 **Admissions:** 10544 **Census:** 133 **Outpatient Visits:** 147637 **Births:** 1013 **Total Expense ($000):** 171879 **Payroll Expense ($000):** 63827 **Personnel:** 923

RIDDLE MEMORIAL HOSPITAL See Riddle Hospital

MEYERSDALE—Somerset County

★ **CONEMAUGH MEYERSDALE MEDICAL CENTER (391302)**, 200 Hospital Drive, Zip 15552–1249; tel. 814/634–5911 **A**10 18 **F**29 34 40 64 75 81 107 114 119 127 130 132 133 146 148 **S** Duke LifePoint Healthcare, Brentwood, TN
Primary Contact: Heather Smith, President
CMO: Dwayne Platt, M.D., Chief Medical Officer
Web address: www.conemaugh.org
Control: Corporation, Investor–owned, for–profit **Service:** General Medical and Surgical

Staffed Beds: 20 **Admissions:** 320 **Census:** 5 **Outpatient Visits:** 44988 **Births:** 0 **Total Expense ($000):** 14081 **Payroll Expense ($000):** 4820 **Personnel:** 106

MONONGAHELA—Washington County

⊠ **MONONGAHELA VALLEY HOSPITAL (390147)**, 1163 Country Club Road, Zip 15063–1095; tel. 724/258–1000 **A**1 2 10 **F**3 8 9 11 12 15 17 18 20 22 28 29 30 31 32 34 35 40 45 48 49 50 51 54 55 56 57 59 61 64 68 70 74 75 77 78 79 80 81 82 85 86 87 89 90 92 93 96 98 100 101 102 103 107 108 110 115 118 119 120 121 123 124 125 132 134 135 144 146 147 148 **P**7 8
Primary Contact: Louis J. Panza, Jr., President and Chief Executive Officer
COO: Patrick J. Alberts, Senior Vice President and Chief Operating Officer
CFO: Daniel F. Simmons, Senior Vice President and Treasurer
CMO: Walter R. Cox, M.D., President Medical Staff
CIO: Thomas Lamb, Director Information Systems
CHR: Louis Goodman, Senior Vice President Human Resources
CNO: Mary Lou Murt, R.N., Senior Vice President Nursing
Web address: www.monvalleyhospital.com
Control: Other not–for–profit (including NFP Corporation) **Service:** General Medical and Surgical

Staffed Beds: 210 **Admissions:** 7968 **Census:** 113 **Outpatient Visits:** 294137 **Births:** 0 **Total Expense ($000):** 131704 **Payroll Expense ($000):** 54149 **Personnel:** 1061

MONROEVILLE—Allegheny County

⊠ **FORBES HOSPITAL (390267)**, 2570 Haymaker Road, Zip 15146–3513; tel. 412/858–2000 **A**1 2 3 5 10 **F**3 7 8 11 13 15 17 18 20 22 24 26 28 29 30 31 34 35 36 38 40 43 44 45 46 49 50 54 55 57 58 59 63 64 65 70 73 74 75 76 77 78 79 80 81 82 84 85 86 87 89 90 96 98 100 101 102 103 107 108 110 111 115 119 120 121 123 126 130 132 135 146 147 148 **P**6 **S** Allegheny Health Network, Pittsburgh, PA
Primary Contact: Mark Rubino, M.D., President
CFO: Tom Hipkiss, Vice President Finance
CMO: Mark Rubino, M.D., Chief Medical Officer
CIO: Sharon Lewis, Director Information Systems
CHR: Georgia Redding, Director Human Resources
CNO: Amber Egyud, Vice President Chief Nursing Officer
Web address: www.ahn.org
Control: Other not–for–profit (including NFP Corporation) **Service:** General Medical and Surgical

Staffed Beds: 329 **Admissions:** 13533 **Census:** 187 **Outpatient Visits:** 127176 **Births:** 924 **Total Expense ($000):** 199353 **Payroll Expense ($000):** 66979 **Personnel:** 1212

HEALTHSOUTH HOSPITAL OF PITTSBURGH See LifeCare Hospitals of Pittsburgh – Monroeville

⊠ **LIFECARE HOSPITALS OF PITTSBURGH – MONROEVILLE (392041)**, 2380 McGinley Road, Zip 15146–4400; tel. 412/856–2400, (Nonreporting) **A**1 10 **S** LifeCare Management Services, Plano, TX
Primary Contact: James Novak, Interim Chief Executive Officer
CMO: Robert Crossey, D.O., Chief Medical Officer
CHR: Chelsea Webber, Director Human Resources
Web address: www.lifecare–hospitals.com/hospital.php?id=8
Control: Corporation, Investor–owned, for–profit **Service:** Long–Term Acute Care hospital

Staffed Beds: 87

UPMC EAST (390328), 2775 Mosside Boulevard, Zip 15146–2760; tel. 412/357–3000 **A**10 **F**3 18 20 22 26 28 29 30 31 34 35 40 45 46 49 50 57 59 60 62 64 68 70 74 75 77 78 79 81 84 85 87 90 92 96 100 107 108 111 115 119 120 121 122 123 130 132 135 146 148 **S** UPMC, Pittsburgh, PA
Primary Contact: Mark Sevco, President
CNO: Tamra Minton, R.N., Vice President Patient Care Services and Chief Nursing Officer
Web address: www.upmc.com/locations/hospitals/east/Pages/default.aspx
Control: Other not–for–profit (including NFP Corporation) **Service:** General Medical and Surgical

Staffed Beds: 155 **Admissions:** 7138 **Census:** 100 **Outpatient Visits:** 80306 **Births:** 0 **Total Expense ($000):** 125760 **Payroll Expense ($000):** 37573 **Personnel:** 616

WESTERN PENNSYLVANIA HOSPITAL – FORBES REGIONAL CAMPUS See Forbes Hospital

MONTROSE—Susquehanna County

ENDLESS MOUNTAIN HEALTH SYSTEMS (391306), 25 Grow Avenue, Zip 18801–1106, Mailing Address: 100 Hospital Drive, Zip 18801–1106; tel. 570/278–3801 **A**10 18 **F**3 15 34 40 44 45 50 53 57 59 64 65 77 79 81 85 93 107 110 111 114 119 130 132 133 135 146 **P**4
Primary Contact: Rexford Catlin, Chief Executive Officer
CIO: Gary Passmore, Chief Information Officer
CHR: Paula Anderson, Administrative Director Human Resources
Web address: www.endlesscare.org
Control: Other not–for–profit (including NFP Corporation) **Service:** General Medical and Surgical

Staffed Beds: 25 **Admissions:** 960 **Census:** 10 **Births:** 0

MOUNT GRETNA—Lebanon County

⊠ **PHILHAVEN (394020)**, 283 South Butler Road, Zip 17064–6085, Mailing Address: P.O. Box 550, Zip 17064–0550; tel. 717/273–8871 **A**1 10 **F**30 98 99 100 101 102 103 104 105 106 130 146 **P**6
Primary Contact: Phil Hess, Chief Executive Officer
COO: Phil Hess, Chief Executive Officer
CFO: Matt Rogers, Chief Financial Officer
CMO: Francis D. Sparrow, M.D., Medical Director
CIO: Lori Nolt, Director Information Technology
CHR: Denis Orthaus, Director Human Resources
CNO: Heidi McMullan, R.N., Chief Nursing Officer
Web address: www.philhaven.org
Control: Church–operated, Nongovernment, not–for profit **Service:** Psychiatric

Staffed Beds: 103 **Admissions:** 2382 **Census:** 96 **Outpatient Visits:** 132351 **Births:** 0 **Total Expense ($000):** 59985 **Payroll Expense ($000):** 41212 **Personnel:** 928

MOUNT PLEASANT—Westmoreland County

☐ **EXCELA FRICK HOSPITAL (390217)**, 508 South Church Street, Zip 15666–1790; tel. 724/547–1500 **A**1 3 10 **F**3 8 12 15 28 29 30 34 35 40 45 49 51 57 59 64 65 68 70 75 77 78 79 81 85 86 87 93 96 107 108 110 111 114 118 119 129 130 132 135 143 146 148 **S** Excela Health, Greensburg, PA
Primary Contact: Ronald H. Ott, President
COO: Michael D. Busch, Executive Vice President and Chief Operating Officer
CFO: Jeffrey T. Curry, Executive Vice President and Chief Financial Officer
CMO: Jerome Granato, M.D., Senior Vice President and Chief Medical Officer
CIO: David Gawaluck, Vice President and Chief Information Officer
CHR: John Caverno, Chief Human Resources Officer
CNO: Helen K. Burns, Ph.D., Senior Vice President and Chief Nursing Officer
Web address: www.excelahealth.org/PatientsandVisitors/HospitalsFacilities/Hospitals/Frick.aspx
Control: Other not–for–profit (including NFP Corporation) **Service:** General Medical and Surgical

Staffed Beds: 33 **Admissions:** 2361 **Census:** 26 **Outpatient Visits:** 129200 **Births:** 0 **Total Expense ($000):** 38374 **Payroll Expense ($000):** 14151 **Personnel:** 235

PA

Hospital, Medicare Provider Number, Address, Telephone, Approval, Facility, and Physician Codes, Health Care System

★ American Hospital Association (AHA) membership   ○ Healthcare Facilities Accreditation Program   ⇑ Center for Improvement in Healthcare Quality Accreditation
☐ The Joint Commission accreditation   ◇ DNV Healthcare Inc. accreditation   △ Commission on Accreditation of Rehabilitation Facilities (CARF) accreditation

---

MUNCY—Lycoming County

★ **MUNCY VALLEY HOSPITAL (391301)**, 215 East Water Street,
Zip 17756–8700; tel. 570/546–8282, (Total facility includes 136 beds in nursing home–type unit) **A**3 10 18 **F**6 11 34 40 44 50 56 57 59 64 68 81 86 87 93 107 108 119 128 130 133 144 146 **P**7 **S** Susquehanna Health System, Williamsport, PA
Primary Contact: Ronald J. Reynolds, Vice President East Lycoming Operations and Chief Administrative Officer
CFO: Eric D. Pohjala, Executive Vice President and Chief Financial Officer
CIO: Timothy E. Schoener, Chief Information Officer
CHR: Christine A. Ballard, Vice President Human Resources
CNO: C. Cynthia Whipple, Director of Nursing
Web address: www.susquehannahealth.org
Control: Other not–for–profit (including NFP Corporation) **Service:** General Medical and Surgical

Staffed Beds: 156 **Admissions:** 788 **Census:** 138 **Outpatient Visits:** 28695 **Births:** 0 **Total Expense ($000):** 45380 **Payroll Expense ($000):** 13387 **Personnel:** 305

NATRONA HEIGHTS—Allegheny County

⊞ **ALLEGHENY VALLEY HOSPITAL (390032)**, 1301 Carlisle Street,
Zip 15065–1152; tel. 724/224–5100 **A**1 2 3 10 **F**3 11 15 17 18 24 29 30 31 34 35 38 39 40 44 45 47 50 51 54 56 57 58 59 63 64 65 68 70 74 75 77 78 79 80 81 84 85 86 87 92 93 96 98 100 101 102 103 107 108 111 114 117 118 119 120 121 123 126 129 130 132 135 143 144 146 147 148 **S** Allegheny Health Network, Pittsburgh, PA
Primary Contact: William Englert, Chief Executive Officer
CFO: James A. Kanuch, Vice President Finance
CMO: Thomas McClure, M.D., Vice President Medical Affairs and Chief Medical Officer
CIO: Linda Fergus, Manager Information Technology
CHR: Cindy Moser, Director Human Resources
Web address: www.wpahs.org
Control: Other not–for–profit (including NFP Corporation) **Service:** General Medical and Surgical

Staffed Beds: 228 **Admissions:** 5634 **Census:** 76 **Outpatient Visits:** 196629 **Births:** 0 **Total Expense ($000):** 106353 **Payroll Expense ($000):** 36381 **Personnel:** 704

NEW CASTLE—Lawrence County

☐ **JAMESON HOSPITAL (390016)**, 1211 Wilmington Avenue, Zip 16105–2516; tel. 724/658–9001, (Total facility includes 20 beds in nursing home–type unit) **A**1 10 19 **F**3 8 11 13 15 18 20 22 28 29 30 32 34 35 40 41 45 46 49 57 59 63 64 65 70 74 75 76 77 79 81 82 85 86 90 92 93 96 98 100 101 102 103 105 107 108 110 111 114 115 119 128 129 130 146 147 **S** UPMC, Pittsburgh, PA
Primary Contact: Douglas Danko, President and Chief Executive Officer
CFO: James Aubel, Chief Financial Officer
CMO: Robert McGann, M.D., President Medical Staff
CIO: Frank Divito, Manager Information Systems
CHR: Neil A. Chessin, Vice President
CNO: Barbara Bernardi, R.N., Nurse Executive
Web address: www.jamesonhealth.org
Control: Other not–for–profit (including NFP Corporation) **Service:** General Medical and Surgical

Staffed Beds: 238 **Admissions:** 7306 **Census:** 104 **Outpatient Visits:** 311648 **Births:** 304 **Total Expense ($000):** 110616 **Payroll Expense ($000):** 44997 **Personnel:** 971

NORRISTOWN—Montgomery County

☐ **MONTGOMERY COUNTY EMERGENCY SERVICE (394033)**, 50 Beech Drive, Zip 19403–5421; tel. 610/279–6100 **A**1 10 **F**4 5 7 29 35 38 50 64 98 99 100 101 102 103 104 130 **P**6
Primary Contact: William Myers, Chief Executive Officer
CMO: Deepraj Singh, M.D., Medical Director
CHR: Byanka Meacham, Director Human Resources
CNO: Naomi Finkel, Nurse Executive
Web address: www.mces.org
Control: Other not–for–profit (including NFP Corporation) **Service:** Psychiatric

Staffed Beds: 81 **Admissions:** 2136 **Census:** 56 **Outpatient Visits:** 2648 **Births:** 0 **Total Expense ($000):** 17465 **Payroll Expense ($000):** 10963 **Personnel:** 192

NORRISTOWN STATE HOSPITAL (394001), 1001 Sterigere Street, Zip 19401–5300; tel. 610/270–1000 **A**3 10 **F**30 35 38 39 53 59 65 75 98 101 103 130 146 **P**6
Primary Contact: Edna I. McCutcheon, Chief Executive Officer
COO: Gary Raisner, Chief Operating Officer
CMO: Mia Marcovici, M.D., Chief Medical Officer
CHR: Richard Szczurowski, Director Human Resources
CNO: Taryn Mason–Jones, Chief Nurse Executive
Control: State–Government, nonfederal **Service:** Psychiatric

Staffed Beds: 266 **Admissions:** 98 **Census:** 258 **Outpatient Visits:** 126 **Births:** 0 **Total Expense ($000):** 71276 **Payroll Expense ($000):** 37137 **Personnel:** 554

⊞ **SUBURBAN COMMUNITY HOSPITAL (390116)**, 2701 DeKalb Pike, Zip 19401–1820; tel. 610/278–2000 **A**1 2 10 12 13 **F**3 12 15 18 28 29 30 31 34 40 45 46 50 54 56 57 59 64 70 74 75 77 78 79 81 82 85 87 93 96 98 103 107 108 110 111 114 115 118 119 120 121 126 129 130 132 135 146 147 **S** Prime Healthcare Services, Ontario, CA
Primary Contact: Peter J. Adamo, Chief Executive Officer
COO: Joseph Schofield, Chief Operating Officer
CFO: Joseph Marino, Chief Financial Officer
CMO: Andrea D. Pedano, D.O., Chief Medical Officer
CIO: Jason Wayne, Network Administrator
CHR: Gretchen Pendleton, Director Human Resources
CNO: Mary Ellen Rauner, R.N., Chief Nursing Officer
Web address: www.suburbanhosp.org
Control: Church–operated, Nongovernment, not–for profit **Service:** General Medical and Surgical

Staffed Beds: 126 **Admissions:** 4237 **Census:** 53 **Births:** 0

☐ **VALLEY FORGE MEDICAL CENTER AND HOSPITAL (390272)**, 1033 West Germantown Pike, Zip 19403–3905; tel. 610/539–8500 **A**1 10 **F**3 4 29 61 68 75 82 100 130 132 148 **P**6
Primary Contact: Marian W. Colcher, President and Chief Executive Officer
CFO: Gregg Y. Slocum, Chief Financial Officer
CMO: Robert E. Colcher, M.D., Medical Director
CHR: Frederick D. Jackes, Assistant Administrator and Director Human Resources
Web address: www.vfmc.net
Control: Corporation, Investor–owned, for–profit **Service:** Alcoholism and other chemical dependency

Staffed Beds: 50 **Admissions:** 2370 **Census:** 45 **Outpatient Visits:** 0 **Births:** 0 **Total Expense ($000):** 14051 **Payroll Expense ($000):** 9051 **Personnel:** 155

OAKDALE—Allegheny County

⊞ **CURAHEALTH PITTSBURGH (392028)**, 7777 Steubenville Pike, Zip 15071–3409; tel. 412/494–5500, (Nonreporting) **A**1 10
Primary Contact: Janie Rosenberger–Slampack, Market Chief Executive Officer
CFO: Kevin Varley, Chief Financial Officer
CMO: Ravi Alagar, M.D., Medical Director
Control: Corporation, Investor–owned, for–profit **Service:** Long–Term Acute Care hospital

Staffed Beds: 63

OREFIELD—Lehigh County

KIDSPEACE CHILDREN'S HOSPITAL, 5300 Kids Peace Drive, Zip 18069–2044; tel. 610/799–7900 **F**29 39 59 98 99 100 101 105 130
Primary Contact: William R. Isemann, President and Chief Executive Officer
CFO: Michael Callan, Executive Vice President and Chief Financial Officer
CMO: Matthew Koval, M.D., Vice President Medical Affairs
CIO: Joan Lesko, Director Technical Support and Services
CHR: Sheila Rulli, Director Human Resources
CNO: Tamara Wasilick, Director Operations
Web address: www.kidspeace.org
Control: Other not–for–profit (including NFP Corporation) **Service:** Children's hospital psychiatric

Staffed Beds: 112 **Admissions:** 2186 **Census:** 91 **Outpatient Visits:** 0 **Births:** 0

PALMERTON—Carbon County

⊞ **PALMERTON HOSPITAL (390019)**, 135 Lafayette Avenue, Zip 18071–1596; tel. 610/826–3141 **A**1 10 **F**2 3 11 12 15 28 29 34 35 40 44 46 47 49 50 56 57 59 64 65 68 70 74 75 77 79 81 86 87 92 93 97 98 102 103 107 108 110 119 129 130 132 135 146 **S** Blue Mountain Health System, Lehighton, PA
Primary Contact: Andrew E. Harris, Chief Executive Officer
CFO: Andrea Andrae, Chief Financial Officer
CMO: Dennis Kondash, D.O., Vice President Medical Affairs
CIO: Steve Kinkaid, Director Information Systems
CHR: Terrance J. Purcell, Vice President Ambulatory Care and Support Services
Web address: www.ghmh.org/content/palmertoncampus.htm
Control: Other not–for–profit (including NFP Corporation) **Service:** General Medical and Surgical

Staffed Beds: 67 **Admissions:** 2011 **Census:** 35 **Outpatient Visits:** 40812 **Births:** 0 **Total Expense ($000):** 30048 **Payroll Expense ($000):** 12937 **Personnel:** 284

PAOLI—Chester County

✦ **PAOLI HOSPITAL (390153)**, 255 West Lancaster Avenue, Zip 19301–1763; tel. 484/565–1000 **A**1 2 3 10 **F**3 5 11 13 15 18 20 22 24 26 28 29 30 31 32 34 35 36 38 39 40 41 43 44 45 46 47 48 49 50 54 55 56 57 59 63 64 65 70 72 74 75 76 78 79 80 81 82 84 85 86 87 92 97 99 100 101 102 103 104 105 107 108 110 111 114 115 118 119 120 121 123 124 126 129 130 131 132 134 135 141 144 146 147 148 **S** Main Line Health
Primary Contact: James Paradis, President
CFO: John Doyle, Vice President Finance
CMO: Andrew J. Norton, M.D., Chief Medical Officer
CIO: Karen A. Thomas, Vice President and Chief Information Officer
CHR: Deborah Fedora, Director Human Resources
Web address: www.mainlinehealth.org
Control: Other not–for–profit (including NFP Corporation) **Service:** General Medical and Surgical

Staffed Beds: 231 Admissions: 14136 Census: 140 Outpatient Visits: 293384 Births: 2222 Total Expense ($000): 251124 Payroll Expense ($000): 81463 Personnel: 1149

PHILADELPHIA—Philadelphia County

ALBERT EINSTEIN MEDICAL CENTER See Einstein Medical Center Philadelphia

✦ △ **ARIA – JEFFERSON HEALTH (390115)**, 10800 Knights Road, Zip 19114–4200; tel. 215/612–4101, (Includes BUCKS COUNTY CAMPUS, 380 North Oxford Valley Road, Langhorne, Zip 19047–8399; tel. 215/949–5000; FRANKFORD CAMPUS, Frankford Avenue and Wakeling Street, Zip 19124; tel. 215/831–2000) **A**1 3 5 7 10 13 **F**3 5 11 12 14 17 18 20 22 24 26 28 29 30 31 32 34 35 36 39 40 43 44 45 46 48 49 53 54 57 59 61 62 64 65 66 68 69 70 74 75 77 78 79 80 81 82 85 86 87 100 101 102 103 104 107 108 110 114 115 116 117 118 119 120 121 123 124 126 127 129 130 131 132 135 143 144 145 146 147 148 **P**6 **S** Jefferson Health, Radnor, PA
Primary Contact: Kathleen Kinslow, Ed.D., Chief Executive Officer
COO: Sandra Gomberg, Chief Operating Officer
CFO: William Degnan, Vice President Finance
CMO: Stanton Segal, M.D., Chief Medical Officer
CIO: Dan Walsh, Chief Information Officer
CHR: Dorinda Carolina, Chief Human Resources Officer
CNO: Michelle E. Conley, R.N., Chief Nursing Officer
Web address: www.ariahealth.org
Control: Other not–for–profit (including NFP Corporation) **Service:** General Medical and Surgical

Staffed Beds: 480 Admissions: 23705 Census: 294 Outpatient Visits: 302416 Births: 0 Total Expense ($000): 439187 Payroll Expense ($000): 172257 Personnel: 2691

☐ **BELMONT BEHAVIORAL HOSPITAL (394023)**, 4200 Monument Road, Zip 19131–1625; tel. 215/877–2000 **A**1 3 5 10 **F**5 29 34 35 58 86 87 98 99 103 104 105 130 146 **P**6 **S** Acadia Healthcare Company, Inc., Franklin, TN
Primary Contact: Mark Schor, Chief Executive Officer
CFO: Guy Romaniello, Director Fiscal Services
CMO: Richard Jaffe, M.D., Medical Director
CHR: Jenna Pacini, Human Resources Specialist
CNO: Nona Fain, Ph.D., Director of Nursing
Web address: www.einstein.edu/locations/belmont–behavioral–health/
Control: Other not–for–profit (including NFP Corporation) **Service:** Psychiatric

Staffed Beds: 147 Admissions: 3704 Census: 130 Outpatient Visits: 68716 Births: 0 Total Expense ($000): 40005 Payroll Expense ($000): 25151

✦ **CHESTNUT HILL HOSPITAL (390026)**, 8835 Germantown Avenue, Zip 19118–2718; tel. 215/248–8200, (Nonreporting) **A**1 3 5 10 **S** Community Health Systems, Inc., Franklin, TN
Primary Contact: John D. Cacciamani, M.D., Chief Executive Officer
CFO: Marc Costner, Chief Financial Officer
CMO: John Scanlon, DPM, Chief Medical Officer
CHR: Marilyn DiCicco, Director Human Resources
CNO: Teresa M. Kelly, MSN, Chief Nursing Officer
Web address: www.chhealthsystem.com
Control: Corporation, Investor–owned, for–profit **Service:** General Medical and Surgical

Staffed Beds: 135

☐ **CHILDREN'S HOSPITAL OF PHILADELPHIA (393303)**, 3401 Civic Center Boulevard, Zip 19104–4319; tel. 215/590–1000 **A**1 3 5 8 10 **F**3 7 8 11 12 13 17 18 19 20 21 22 23 24 25 26 27 28 29 30 31 32 34 35 37 38 39 40 41 43 44 45 46 48 50 53 54 55 57 58 59 60 61 62 64 65 66 68 71 72 74 75 76 77 78 79 81 82 83 84 85 86 87 88 89 90 91 92 93 95 96 97 99 100 101 102 104 107 108 111 112 113 114 115 116 117 118 119 126 129 130 131 132 133 136 137 138 139 140 141 142 143 144 146 148 **P**6
Primary Contact: Madeline Bell, President and Chief Executive Officer
COO: Douglas G. Hock, Executive Vice President and Chief Operating Officer
CFO: Thomas Todorow, Chief Financial Officer and Executive Vice President
CMO: Jan Boswinkel, M.D., Vice President Medical Operations and Chief Safety Officer
CHR: Robert Croner, Senior Vice President and Chief Human Resources Officer
CNO: Paula M. Agosto, R.N., Senior Vice President and Chief Nursing Officer
Web address: www.chop.edu
Control: Other not–for–profit (including NFP Corporation) **Service:** Children's general

Staffed Beds: 520 Admissions: 29065 Census: 445 Outpatient Visits: 1259581 Births: 410 Total Expense ($000): 1763846 Payroll Expense ($000): 799657 Personnel: 10410

☐ **EASTERN REGIONAL MEDICAL CENTER (390312)**, 1331 East Wyoming Avenue, Zip 19124–3808; tel. 800/615–3055 **A**1 2 10 **F**3 15 29 30 31 33 34 35 36 45 46 47 48 49 50 55 56 57 58 59 64 65 68 70 75 78 79 80 81 82 85 86 87 91 93 96 97 100 101 104 107 108 110 111 116 118 119 120 121 123 124 126 129 130 132 135 136 143 144 146 147 148 **P**6 **S** Cancer Treatment Centers of America, Schaumburg, IL
Primary Contact: John McNeil, President and Chief Executive Officer
CFO: Steve Rusinko, Chief Financial Officer
CMO: Steven B. Standiford, M.D., Chief of Staff
CIO: Kristin Darby, Chief Information Officer
CHR: Ronald Gilg, Assistant Vice President Talent
CNO: Nancy Hesse, R.N., Senior Vice President Patient Care Services
Web address: www.cancercenter.com
Control: Corporation, Investor–owned, for–profit **Service:** Cancer

Staffed Beds: 74 Admissions: 1127 Census: 24 Births: 0

☐ **EINSTEIN MEDICAL CENTER PHILADELPHIA (390142)**, 5501 Old York Road, Zip 19141–3098; tel. 215/456–7890, (Includes EINSTEIN MEDICAL CENTER ELKINS PARK, 60 Township Line Road, Elkins Park, Zip 19027–2220; tel. 215/663–6000; Barry R. Freedman, President and Chief Executive Officer), (Total facility includes 47 beds in nursing home–type unit) **A**1 2 3 5 8 10 13 **F**3 11 12 13 15 17 18 20 22 24 26 28 29 30 31 32 34 35 36 37 38 39 40 41 43 44 45 46 48 49 51 54 55 56 57 58 59 60 61 64 65 66 68 70 72 73 74 75 76 77 78 79 81 82 84 85 86 87 90 97 98 100 101 102 103 104 106 107 108 110 111 114 115 119 120 121 124 126 128 129 130 131 132 134 138 139 143 145 146 147 148 **P**6 **S** Einstein Healthcare Network, Philadelphia, PA
Primary Contact: Barry R. Freedman, President and Chief Executive Officer
COO: Ruth Lefton, Chief Operating Officer
CFO: Gerard Blaney, Vice President Finance and Interim Chief Financial Officer
CMO: Steven Sivak, M.D., Chief Medical Officer, Einstein Physicians Philadelphia
CIO: Brenda West, Vice President, Information Services and Interim Chief Information Officer
CHR: Lynne R. Kornblatt, Chief Human Resources Officer
CNO: Jill Stunkard, R.N., Associate Chief Nurse Executive and Interim Chief Nursing Officer
Web address: www.einstein.edu
Control: Other not–for–profit (including NFP Corporation) **Service:** General Medical and Surgical

Staffed Beds: 488 Admissions: 26341 Census: 486 Outpatient Visits: 541008 Births: 2977 Total Expense ($000): 721756 Payroll Expense ($000): 311476 Personnel: 5290

☐ **FAIRMOUNT BEHAVIORAL HEALTH SYSTEM (394027)**, 561 Fairthorne Avenue, Zip 19128–2499; tel. 215/487–4000 **A**1 10 **F**4 98 99 102 105 130 **P**6 **S** Universal Health Services, Inc., King of Prussia, PA
Primary Contact: Lisa M. McConlogue, MSN, Ph.D., Chief Executive Officer and Managing Director
CFO: Anthony Tortella, Chief Financial Officer
CMO: Silvia Gratz, D.O., Chief Medical Officer
CIO: Anthony Tortella, Chief Financial Officer
CHR: Theresa Mahoney, Director Human Resources
Web address: www.fairmountbhs.com
Control: Corporation, Investor–owned, for–profit **Service:** Psychiatric

Staffed Beds: 235 Admissions: 6204 Census: 222 Outpatient Visits: 8496 Births: 0

PA

⊞ **FOX CHASE CANCER CENTER–AMERICAN ONCOLOGIC HOSPITAL (390196)**, 333 Cottman Avenue, Zip 19111–2434; tel. 215/728–6900 **A**1 2 3 5 10 **F**3 11 15 29 30 31 34 35 36 45 46 47 49 50 55 57 58 59 60 61 64 68 70 71 75 77 78 79 81 82 84 85 86 87 93 100 104 107 108 109 110 111 114 115 116 117 118 119 120 121 123 124 126 130 132 135 136 144 145 146 147 148 **P**6 **S** Temple University Health System, Philadelphia, PA
Primary Contact: Richard Fisher, President and Chief Executive Officer
COO: Judith Lynn Bachman, Chief Operating Officer
CFO: Anthony J. Diasio, Chief Financial Officer
CMO: James Helstrom, Chief Medical Officer
CIO: Michael Sweeney, Chief Information Officer
CNO: Anne Jadwin, Chief Nursing Officer
Web address: www.fccc.org
Control: Other not–for–profit (including NFP Corporation) **Service:** Cancer

Staffed Beds: 65 **Admissions:** 4180 **Census:** 61 **Outpatient Visits:** 99869 **Births:** 0 **Total Expense ($000):** 256276 **Payroll Expense ($000):** 73722 **Personnel:** 1370

☐ **FRIENDS HOSPITAL (394008)**, 4641 Roosevelt Boulevard, Zip 19124–2343; tel. 215/831–4600 **A**1 3 5 10 **F**30 68 87 98 99 101 102 103 130 132 **P**1 **S** Universal Health Services, Inc., King of Prussia, PA
Primary Contact: R. John Repique, R.N., Chief Executive Officer
COO: Diane Carugati, Chief Operating Officer
CFO: Michael Terwilliger, Chief Financial Officer
CMO: Marc Rothman, M.D., Medical Director
CIO: John Healy, Manager Information Technology
CHR: Paul Cavanaugh, Director Human Resources
Web address: www.friendshospital.com
Control: Corporation, Investor–owned, for–profit **Service:** Psychiatric

Staffed Beds: 192 **Admissions:** 5744 **Census:** 176 **Births:** 0

⊞ **GOOD SHEPHERD PENN PARTNERS SPECIALTY HOSPITAL AT RITTENHOUSE (392050)**, 1800 Lombard Street, Zip 19146–1414; tel. 877/969–7342, (Nonreporting) **A**1 10
Primary Contact: Laura Porter, Executive Director
CFO: Ronald J. Petula, Vice President Finance
CMO: Michael Grippi, M.D., Chief Medical Officer
CHR: Jana Romano, Manager Human Resources
CNO: Lawanda Goehring, MSN, Chief Nursing Officer
Web address: www.phillyrehab.com
Control: Partnership, Investor–owned, for–profit **Service:** Long–Term Acute Care hospital

Staffed Beds: 38

⊞ **HAHNEMANN UNIVERSITY HOSPITAL (390290)**, Broad and Vine Streets, Zip 19102–1192; tel. 215/762–7000 **A**1 2 3 5 8 10 **F**3 12 13 14 15 17 18 20 22 24 26 28 29 31 34 35 40 43 45 46 48 49 50 51 58 59 60 61 65 68 70 72 74 75 76 78 79 80 81 82 85 92 94 95 96 97 98 100 101 102 103 105 107 108 109 110 111 112 113 114 115 116 117 118 119 120 121 123 124 126 130 132 135 136 137 138 139 147 148 **P**6 **S** TENET Healthcare Corporation, Dallas, TX
Primary Contact: Michael P. Halter, Chief Executive Officer
COO: James B. Burke, Chief Operating Officer
CFO: Richard Imbimbo, Chief Financial Officer
CMO: George Amrom, M.D., Vice President Medical Affairs
CIO: Tom Nataloni, Senior Director Information Technology
CHR: Steven Simmons, Chief Human Resources Officer
CNO: Rosemary Dunn, R.N., Chief Nursing Officer
Web address: www.hahnemannhospital.com
Control: Corporation, Investor–owned, for–profit **Service:** General Medical and Surgical

Staffed Beds: 496 **Admissions:** 17566 **Census:** 260 **Outpatient Visits:** 117080 **Births:** 1996 **Personnel:** 2425

⊞ △ **HOSPITAL OF THE UNIVERSITY OF PENNSYLVANIA (390111)**, 3400 Spruce Street, Zip 19104–4206; tel. 215/662–4000, (Includes SCHEIE EYE INSTITUTE OF THE HOSPITAL OF THE UNIVERSITY OF PENNSYLVANIA, 3400 Civic Center Boulevard FL 3, Zip 19104–5127; tel. 215/662–8100; Sheara Hollin, Chief Operating Officer) **A**1 2 3 5 7 8 10 **F**3 6 7 9 11 12 13 14 15 17 18 19 20 21 22 23 24 25 26 27 29 30 31 34 35 36 37 38 39 40 44 45 46 47 48 49 50 51 52 54 55 56 57 58 59 60 61 62 63 64 65 66 68 70 71 72 73 74 75 76 77 78 80 81 82 84 85 86 87 90 91 92 93 94 95 96 97 99 100 101 102 103 104 107 108 110 111 115 117 118 119 121 122 123 126 130 131 132 134 135 136 137 138 139 140 141 142 145 146 147 148 **P**6 **S** University of Pennsylvania Health System, Philadelphia, PA
Primary Contact: Garry L. Scheib, Chief Executive Officer
COO: Carolyn Jackson, Chief Operating Officer
CFO: Joseph M. Huber, Chief Financial Officer
CMO: Patrick J. Brennan, M.D., Senior Vice President and Chief Medical Officer
CIO: Michael Restuccia, Chief Information Officer
CHR: Denise Mariotti, Chief Human Resource Officer
CNO: Regina Cunningham, Ph.D., Chief Nurse Executive
Web address: www.pennmedicine.org
Control: Other not–for–profit (including NFP Corporation) **Service:** General Medical and Surgical

Staffed Beds: 789 **Admissions:** 34653 **Census:** 681 **Outpatient Visits:** 1594132 **Births:** 4253 **Total Expense ($000):** 2219016 **Payroll Expense ($000):** 882191 **Personnel:** 13310

⊞ **JEANES HOSPITAL (390080)**, 7600 Central Avenue, Zip 19111–2499; tel. 215/728–2000 **A**1 3 5 10 **F**3 11 12 15 17 18 20 22 24 26 28 29 30 31 34 35 43 44 45 49 50 56 57 59 60 61 62 65 68 70 74 75 77 78 79 81 82 84 85 86 87 91 92 93 96 107 108 110 111 114 115 118 119 129 130 132 135 146 147 148 **S** Temple University Health System, Philadelphia, PA
Primary Contact: Marc P. Hurowitz, D.O., President and Chief Executive Officer
COO: Judith Lynn Bachman, Chief Operating Officer
CFO: Ray Lefton, Chief Financial Officer
CMO: Rebecca Armbruster, M.D., Chief Medical Officer
CIO: Michael Sweeney, Chief Informatics Officer
CHR: Beverly Sherbondy, Assistant Vice President, Human Resources
CNO: Denise Anne Lavery Frasca, MSN, Vice President Patient Care Services and Chief Nursing Officer
Web address: www.jeanes.com
Control: Other not–for–profit (including NFP Corporation) **Service:** General Medical and Surgical

Staffed Beds: 146 **Admissions:** 7679 **Census:** 89 **Outpatient Visits:** 132390 **Births:** 0 **Total Expense ($000):** 147509 **Payroll Expense ($000):** 58834 **Personnel:** 930

☐ **KENSINGTON HOSPITAL (390025)**, 136 West Diamond Street, Zip 19122–1721; tel. 215/426–8100, (Nonreporting) **A**1 10
Primary Contact: Eileen Hause, Chief Executive Officer
CFO: Kenneth Biddle, Controller
CMO: Luis F. Vera, M.D., Medical Director
CHR: Maria Dimichele, Administrative Assistant
CNO: Aleyamma John, R.N., Director of Nursing
Control: State–Government, nonfederal **Service:** General Medical and Surgical

Staffed Beds: 33

⊞ **KINDRED HOSPITAL SOUTH PHILADELPHIA (392046)**, 1930 South Broad Street, Zip 19145–2328; tel. 267/570–5200, (Nonreporting) **A**1 10 **S** Kindred Healthcare, Louisville, KY
Primary Contact: Deborah Karn, Chief Executive Officer
COO: Diane K. White, MSN, Chief Clinical Officer
CFO: Kevin Varley, Chief Financial Officer
CMO: James Dovnarsky, M.D., Director Pulmonary Medical
CHR: Amy Cain, District Director Human Resources
CNO: Diane K. White, MSN, Chief Clinical Officer
Web address: www.khsouthphilly.com
Control: Corporation, Investor–owned, for–profit **Service:** Long–Term Acute Care hospital

Staffed Beds: 58

⊞ **KINDRED HOSPITAL–PHILADELPHIA (392027)**, 6129 Palmetto Street, Zip 19111–5729; tel. 215/722–8555, (Includes KINDRED HOSPITAL PHILADELPHIA – HAVERTOWN, 2000 Old West Chester Pike, Havertown, Zip 19083–2712; tel. 610/536–2100; Margaret M. Murphy, Chief Executive Officer) **A**1 10 **F**1 3 29 70 75 77 84 87 130 148 **S** Kindred Healthcare, Louisville, KY
Primary Contact: Sandra Larson, R.N., MSN, Chief Executive Officer
COO: Sandra Collins, Chief Clinical Officer
CFO: Thomas A. McMullen, Chief Financial Officer
Web address: www.kindredphila.com/
Control: Corporation, Investor–owned, for–profit **Service:** Long–Term Acute Care hospital

Staffed Beds: 57 **Admissions:** 332 **Census:** 27 **Outpatient Visits:** 0 **Births:** 0

☐ **KIRKBRIDE CENTER (394007)**, 111 North 49th Street, Zip 19139–2718; tel. 215/471–2600, (Nonreporting) **A**1 10
Primary Contact: Marlene Douglas–Walsh, Chief Executive Officer
Web address: www.kirkbridecenter.com
Control: Partnership, Investor–owned, for–profit **Service:** Psychiatric

Staffed Beds: 205

⊞ △ **MAGEE REHABILITATION HOSPITAL (393038)**, 1513 Race Street, Zip 19102–1177; tel. 215/587–3000 **A**1 3 5 7 10 **F**2 29 30 34 35 50 60 64 68 74 75 77 79 82 86 90 91 92 93 94 95 96 130 132 146 148 **P**6
Primary Contact: Jack A. Carroll, Ph.D., President and Chief Executive Officer
CFO: Patricia A. Underwood, Chief Financial Officer
CMO: Guy Fried, M.D., Chief Medical Officer
CIO: Travis Gathright, Chief Information and Corporate Compliance Officer
CHR: Scott Agostini, Director
Web address: www.mageerehab.org
Control: Other not–for–profit (including NFP Corporation) **Service:** Rehabilitation

Staffed Beds: 96 **Admissions:** 961 **Census:** 69 **Outpatient Visits:** 62224 **Births:** 0 **Total Expense ($000):** 60986 **Payroll Expense ($000):** 34099 **Personnel:** 526

MERCY PHILADELPHIA HOSPITAL See Mercy Fitzgerald Hospital, Darby

METHODIST HOSPITAL See Thomas Jefferson University Hospitals

Many Facility Codes have changed. Please refer to the AHA Guide Code Chart. © 2016 AHA Guide

⊠ △ **NAZARETH HOSPITAL (390204)**, 2601 Holme Avenue, Zip 19152–2096; tel. 215/335–6000, (Total facility includes 26 beds in nursing home–type unit) **A**1 3 7 10 **F**3 12 15 18 20 22 29 30 31 34 35 37 39 40 45 46 49 50 53 56 57 58 59 64 65 70 74 75 77 78 79 80 81 82 84 85 86 87 90 93 97 100 107 108 110 111 114 115 117 118 119 120 121 128 130 131 132 135 146 147 148 **P**7 **S** Trinity Health, Livonia, MI
Primary Contact: Nancy Cherone, Executive Director and Administrator
CFO: David Wajda, Chief Financial Officer
CMO: Mathew Matthew, M.D., Chief Medical Officer
CIO: Terry O'Neil, Chief Information Technology
CHR: Kathleen M. Pries, Director Human Resources
CNO: Michael Beshel, R.N., Vice President Patient Care and Chief Nursing Officer
Web address: www.nazarethhospital.org
Control: Other not–for–profit (including NFP Corporation) **Service:** General Medical and Surgical

Staffed Beds: 141 **Admissions:** 8133 **Census:** 115 **Outpatient Visits:** 135107 **Births:** 0 **Total Expense ($000):** 141932 **Payroll Expense ($000):** 56897 **Personnel:** 964

NORTH PHILADELPHIA HEALTH SYSTEM (390132), 1524 West Girard Avenue, Zip 19130–1613; tel. 215/787–9000, (Includes GIRARD MEDICAL CENTER, Girard Avenue at Eighth Street, Zip 19122; tel. 215/787–2000; George J. Walmsley, III, CPA, President and Chief Executive Officer), (Nonreporting) **A**3 10
Primary Contact: George J. Walmsley, III, CPA, President and Chief Executive Officer
CFO: Ronald Kaplan, Chief Financial Officer
CIO: Tony Iero, Director Management Information Systems
CHR: James Gloner, Senior Vice President
Web address: www.nphs.com
Control: Other not–for–profit (including NFP Corporation) **Service:** General Medical and Surgical

Staffed Beds: 315

⊠ **PENN PRESBYTERIAN MEDICAL CENTER (390223)**, 51 North 39th Street, Zip 19104–2699; tel. 215/662–8000, (Total facility includes 26 beds in nursing home–type unit) **A**1 2 3 5 10 **F**3 4 5 7 8 9 10 11 12 15 17 18 20 22 24 26 29 30 31 32 34 35 36 37 38 39 40 43 44 45 46 49 50 51 52 54 56 57 58 59 60 61 62 63 64 65 66 68 70 74 75 77 78 79 81 82 84 85 86 87 92 94 96 97 98 100 101 104 107 108 110 111 114 115 118 119 126 128 130 131 132 134 135 141 142 146 147 148 **P**6 **S** University of Pennsylvania Health System, Philadelphia, PA
Primary Contact: Michele M. Volpe, Chief Executive Officer
COO: Robert J. Russell, Associate Executive Director Operations
CFO: Anthony Zumpano, Chief Financial Officer
CMO: Kevin Fosnocht, M.D., Chief Medical Officer and Associate Executive Director
CIO: Theresa Hiltunen, Entity Information Officer
CHR: Margorie Michele, Chief Human Resources Officer
CNO: James R. Ballinghoff, MSN, Chief Nursing Officer and Associate Executive Director
Web address: www.pennmedicine.org/pmc/
Control: Other not–for–profit (including NFP Corporation) **Service:** General Medical and Surgical

Staffed Beds: 354 **Admissions:** 15388 **Census:** 226 **Outpatient Visits:** 216352 **Births:** 0 **Total Expense ($000):** 442092 **Payroll Expense ($000):** 186629 **Personnel:** 2170

⊠ **PENNSYLVANIA HOSPITAL (390226)**, 800 Spruce Street, Zip 19107–6192; tel. 215/829–3000 **A**1 2 3 5 10 13 **F**3 7 8 11 12 15 17 18 20 22 24 26 29 30 31 34 35 36 37 38 39 40 44 45 46 49 50 51 52 54 55 56 57 58 59 60 61 62 63 64 68 70 72 74 75 76 77 78 79 80 81 82 84 85 86 87 92 97 98 99 100 101 102 103 104 107 108 110 111 114 115 116 117 118 119 120 121 123 124 126 129 130 131 132 134 135 141 142 145 146 147 148 **P**6 **S** University of Pennsylvania Health System, Philadelphia, PA
Primary Contact: Theresa M. Larivee, Chief Executive Officer
CFO: Frank Anastasi, Chief Financial Officer
CMO: Daniel Feinberg, M.D., Chief Medical Officer
CIO: Kwon Lee, Chief Information Officer
CNO: Mary Margaret Del Guidice, R.N., Chief Nursing Officer
Web address: www.pahosp.com
Control: Other not–for–profit (including NFP Corporation) **Service:** General Medical and Surgical

Staffed Beds: 397 **Admissions:** 19621 **Census:** 271 **Outpatient Visits:** 286864 **Births:** 5044 **Total Expense ($000):** 558188 **Payroll Expense ($000):** 181385 **Personnel:** 2341

⊠ △ **PHILADELPHIA VETERANS AFFAIRS MEDICAL CENTER**, 3900 Woodland Avenue, Zip 19104–4594; tel. 215/823–5800, (Nonreporting) **A**1 2 3 5 7 8 **S** Department of Veterans Affairs, Washington, DC
Primary Contact: Daniel Hendee, Director
COO: Jeffrey Beiler, Associate Director
CFO: Graciela McDaniel, Chief Financial Officer
CMO: Dave Oslin, M.D., Chief of Staff
CIO: Adrienne Ficchi, Vice President Information Management
CHR: Gerald Morelli, Director Human Resources
Web address: www.philadelphia.va.gov/
Control: Veterans Affairs, Government, federal **Service:** General Medical and Surgical

Staffed Beds: 280

⊠ **ROXBOROUGH MEMORIAL HOSPITAL (390304)**, 5800 Ridge Avenue, Zip 19128–1737; tel. 215/483–9900 **A**1 10 **F**3 15 18 24 29 31 34 40 44 49 50 56 57 59 65 68 70 74 77 78 79 81 82 84 85 90 93 96 98 103 104 107 108 110 111 116 119 129 130 143 146 148 **S** Prime Healthcare Services, Ontario, CA
Primary Contact: Peter J. Adamo, Chief Executive Officer
CFO: Thomas Reinboth, Chief Financial Officer
CHR: Michael Henrici, Associate Administrator
Web address: www.roxboroughmemorial.com
Control: Corporation, Investor–owned, for–profit **Service:** General Medical and Surgical

Staffed Beds: 140 **Admissions:** 4313 **Census:** 60 **Births:** 0

⊠ **SHRINERS HOSPITALS FOR CHILDREN–PHILADELPHIA (393309)**, 3551 North Broad Street, Zip 19140–4160; tel. 215/430–4000 **A**1 3 5 10 **F**29 35 57 58 64 65 68 74 75 77 79 81 82 85 88 89 91 92 93 94 95 96 119 130 132 133 143 146 **S** Shriners Hospitals for Children, Tampa, FL
Primary Contact: Ed Myers, Administrator
CFO: Mario Salvati, Director Fiscal Services
CMO: Scott Kozin, M.D., Chief of Staff
CHR: Megan Hauser, Director Human Resources
CNO: Cindy Max, Chief Nursing Officer
Web address: www.shrinershospitalsforchildren.org/Hospitals/Locations/Philadelphia.aspx
Control: Other not–for–profit (including NFP Corporation) **Service:** Children's orthopedic

Staffed Beds: 39 **Admissions:** 500 **Census:** 10 **Outpatient Visits:** 11611 **Births:** 0 **Personnel:** 295

⊠ **ST. CHRISTOPHER'S HOSPITAL FOR CHILDREN (393307)**, 3601 A. Street, Zip 19134–1043; tel. 215/427–5000 **A**1 3 5 8 10 **F**1 3 4 7 16 17 19 21 23 25 27 29 30 31 32 34 35 39 40 41 43 44 48 49 50 54 55 58 59 60 61 64 67 68 70 71 72 73 74 75 76 77 78 79 80 81 82 83 84 87 88 89 90 93 97 98 99 100 101 102 107 111 119 128 129 130 131 132 134 136 138 143 144 146 **P**6 **S** TENET Healthcare Corporation, Dallas, TX
Primary Contact: J. Mark McLoone, FACHE, Chief Executive Officer
COO: Maria Scenna, Chief Operating Officer
CFO: George Rizzuto, CPA, Chief Financial Officer
CMO: Barbara Hoffman, M.D., Chief Medical Officer
CIO: Robert Taylor, Director Information Services
CHR: Stephen W. Krouse, Chief Human Resource Officer
CNO: Heidi Baur, R.N., Chief Nursing Officer
Web address: www.stchristophershospital.com
Control: Corporation, Investor–owned, for–profit **Service:** Children's general

Staffed Beds: 181 **Admissions:** 9147 **Census:** 114 **Outpatient Visits:** 140465 **Births:** 0

Hospital, Medicare Provider Number, Address, Telephone, Approval, Facility, and Physician Codes, Health Care System		
★ American Hospital Association (AHA) membership	○ Healthcare Facilities Accreditation Program	⇑ Center for Improvement in Healthcare Quality Accreditation
□ The Joint Commission accreditation	◇ DNV Healthcare Inc. accreditation	△ Commission on Accreditation of Rehabilitation Facilities (CARF) accreditation

PA

⊞ **TEMPLE UNIVERSITY HOSPITAL (390027)**, 3401 North Broad Street, Zip 19140–5103; tel. 215/707–2000, (Includes TEMPLE UNIVERSITY HOSPITAL – EPISCOPAL DIVISION, 100 East Lehigh Avenue, Zip 19125–1098; tel. 215/427–7000; Kathleen Barron, Executive Director) **A**1 2 3 5 8 10 **F**3 8 11 12 13 14 15 16 17 18 20 22 24 26 28 29 30 31 34 35 37 38 40 41 43 44 45 46 47 48 49 50 53 54 55 56 57 58 59 60 61 64 68 70 72 73 74 75 76 77 78 79 80 81 82 83 84 85 86 87 90 92 93 94 96 97 98 100 101 102 104 107 108 109 110 111 112 114 115 118 119 120 121 123 124 126 129 130 131 132 135 136 137 138 139 140 141 142 146 147 148 **S** Temple University Health System, Philadelphia, PA
Primary Contact: Verdi Disesa, M.D., President and Chief Executive Officer
COO: Rosemary Nolan, R.N., Chief Operating Officer
CFO: Gerald P. Oetzel, Chief Financial Officer
CMO: Herbert Cushing, M.D., Chief Medical Officer
CIO: David Kamowski, Vice President and Chief Information Officer
CHR: John Lasky, Jr., Vice President, Chief Human Resources Officer
CNO: Elizabeth J. Craig, MSN, Chief Nursing Officer and Vice President Patient Services
Web address: www.tuh.templehealth.org/content/default.htm
Control: Other not–for–profit (including NFP Corporation) **Service:** General Medical and Surgical

> **Staffed Beds:** 701 **Admissions:** 35473 **Census:** 534 **Outpatient Visits:** 336979 **Births:** 2942 **Total Expense ($000):** 916581 **Payroll Expense ($000):** 319917 **Personnel:** 4392

⊞ △ **THOMAS JEFFERSON UNIVERSITY HOSPITALS (390174)**, 111 South 11th Street, Zip 19107–5084; tel. 215/955–6000, (Includes METHODIST HOSPITAL, 2301 South Broad Street, Zip 19148; tel. 215/952–9000; Richard Webster, R.N., President) **A**1 2 3 5 7 8 10 **F**3 5 6 7 8 9 11 12 13 14 15 17 18 20 22 24 26 28 29 30 31 34 35 36 37 38 39 40 43 44 45 46 47 48 49 50 51 52 53 54 55 56 57 58 59 61 64 65 66 68 70 72 74 75 76 77 78 79 80 81 82 84 85 86 87 89 92 93 94 96 97 98 100 101 102 103 104 107 108 109 110 111 114 115 118 119 120 121 123 124 126 129 130 131 132 134 135 136 137 138 139 141 142 144 145 146 147 148 **P**2 6 8 **S** Jefferson Health, Radnor, PA
Primary Contact: Richard Webster, R.N., President
CFO: Neil Lubarsky, Senior Vice President, Finance and Chief Financial Officer
CMO: Anne Docimo, M.D., Executive Vice President and Chief Medical Officer, Jefferson Health
CIO: Praveen Chopra, Executive Vice President and Chief Information and Transformative Innovative Environment Officer
CHR: Jeffrey Stevens, Senior Vice President and Chief Human Resource Officer
CNO: Mary Ann McGinley, Ph.D., Senior Vice President, Patient Services and Chief Nursing Officer
Web address: www.jefferson.edu
Control: Other not–for–profit (including NFP Corporation) **Service:** General Medical and Surgical

> **Staffed Beds:** 893 **Admissions:** 44294 **Census:** 650 **Outpatient Visits:** 468815 **Births:** 1942 **Total Expense ($000):** 1505596 **Payroll Expense ($000):** 470883 **Personnel:** 7677

TRIUMPH HOSPITAL PHILADELPHIA See Kindred Hospital South Philadelphia

VETERANS AFFAIRS MEDICAL CENTER See Philadelphia Veterans Affairs Medical Center

PHOENIXVILLE—Chester County

⊞ △ **PHOENIXVILLE HOSPITAL (390127)**, 140 Nutt Road, Zip 19460–3900, Mailing Address: P.O. Box 3001, Zip 19460–0916; tel. 610/983–1000 **A**1 2 7 10 **F**3 8 13 15 17 18 20 22 24 26 28 29 31 32 34 35 36 38 39 40 45 49 50 51 55 56 57 59 61 64 68 69 70 72 74 75 76 77 78 79 81 82 85 86 87 93 102 107 108 111 114 115 117 118 119 126 130 132 134 135 146 147 **S** Community Health Systems, Inc., Franklin, TN
Primary Contact: Stephen M. Tullman, Chief Executive Officer
CFO: David Paulosky, Chief Financial Officer
CMO: David Stepansky, M.D., Chief Medical Officer
CIO: Terry Murphy, Director Information Services
CHR: Denise Chiolo, Chief Human Resources Officer
CNO: Sarah Strzelecki, Ed.D., Chief Nursing Officer
Web address: www.phoenixvillehospital.com
Control: Corporation, Investor–owned, for–profit **Service:** General Medical and Surgical

> **Staffed Beds:** 127 **Admissions:** 6891 **Census:** 87 **Outpatient Visits:** 99871 **Births:** 686 **Total Expense ($000):** 157896 **Payroll Expense ($000):** 48447 **Personnel:** 753

PITTSBURGH—Allegheny County

⊞ **ALLEGHENY GENERAL HOSPITAL (390050)**, 320 East North Avenue, Zip 15212–4756; tel. 412/359–3131 **A**1 2 3 5 8 10 12 13 **F**3 7 8 9 11 12 15 17 18 19 20 22 24 26 28 29 30 31 32 34 35 36 38 39 40 43 44 45 46 47 48 49 50 51 53 54 55 57 58 59 61 63 64 65 66 68 70 74 75 77 78 79 80 81 82 84 85 86 87 89 92 93 94 96 97 99 100 101 102 103 104 105 107 108 110 111 114 115 116 117 118 119 120 121 123 124 126 129 130 131 132 134 135 137 138 139 142 143 145 146 148 **P**6 **S** Allegheny Health Network, Pittsburgh, PA
Primary Contact: Jeffrey Cohen, M.D., President
COO: Duke Rupert, Chief Operating Officer
CFO: Richard W. Fries, Vice President Finance
CMO: Tony Farah, M.D., President Medical Staff
CIO: John Foley, Chief Information Officer
Web address: www.wpahs.org/locations/allegheny–general–hospital
Control: Other not–for–profit (including NFP Corporation) **Service:** General Medical and Surgical

> **Staffed Beds:** 381 **Admissions:** 23939 **Census:** 348 **Outpatient Visits:** 339486 **Births:** 0 **Total Expense ($000):** 663031 **Payroll Expense ($000):** 182883 **Personnel:** 3550

☐ **CHILDREN'S HOSPITAL OF PITTSBURGH OF UPMC (393302)**, One Children's Hospital Drive, Zip 15224–1334; tel. 412/692–5325 **A**1 3 5 10 **F**3 8 12 17 19 21 22 23 24 25 27 28 29 30 31 32 34 35 39 40 41 43 45 46 48 49 50 53 54 55 57 59 60 64 66 68 71 72 74 75 77 78 79 81 82 84 86 87 88 89 90 91 92 93 97 100 107 108 109 111 114 115 116 117 118 119 120 121 123 124 126 129 130 131 132 134 135 136 137 138 139 140 141 142 143 144 146 **S** UPMC, Pittsburgh, PA
Primary Contact: Christopher A. Gessner, President
COO: Christopher A. Gessner, President
CFO: Nicholas J. Barcellona, Chief Financial Officer
CMO: Steven G. Docimo, M.D., Chief Medical Officer
CIO: Srinivasan Suresh, M.D., Chief Medical Information Officer
CHR: Rhonda Larimore, Vice President, Human Resources
CNO: Diane Hupp, R.N., Chief Nursing Officer and Vice President, Patient Care Services
Web address: www.chp.edu
Control: Other not–for–profit (including NFP Corporation) **Service:** Children's general

> **Staffed Beds:** 305 **Admissions:** 12432 **Census:** 225 **Outpatient Visits:** 312984 **Births:** 0 **Total Expense ($000):** 575673 **Payroll Expense ($000):** 150725 **Personnel:** 2670

EYE AND EAR HOSPITAL OF PITTSBURGH See UPMC Presbyterian Shadyside

⊞ **HEALTHSOUTH HARMARVILLE REHABILITATION HOSPITAL (393027)**, Guys Run Road, Zip 15238–0460, Mailing Address: P.O. Box 11460, Zip 15238–0460; tel. 412/828–1300 **A**1 10 **F**29 62 64 75 77 79 86 90 93 95 96 132 148 **S** HEALTHSOUTH Corporation, Birmingham, AL
Primary Contact: Mark Van Volkenburg, Chief Executive Officer
CFO: Daniel A. Vrana, Controller
CMO: Thomas Franz, M.D., Medical Director
CHR: Eric Larson, Director Human Resources
Web address: www.healthsouthharmarville.com
Control: Corporation, Investor–owned, for–profit **Service:** Rehabilitation

> **Staffed Beds:** 162 **Admissions:** 1644 **Census:** 71 **Outpatient Visits:** 13290 **Births:** 0 **Total Expense ($000):** 24908 **Payroll Expense ($000):** 13850 **Personnel:** 239

⊞ **LIFECARE HOSPITALS OF PITTSBURGH (392024)**, 225 Penn Avenue, Zip 15221–2148; tel. 412/247–2424, (Includes LIFECARE HOSPITALS OF PITTSBURGH – SUBURBAN CAMPUS, 100 South Jackson Avenue, 4th Floor, Zip 15202–3428), (Nonreporting) **A**1 10 **S** LifeCare Management Services, Plano, TX
Primary Contact: James Novak, Interim Chief Executive Officer
CFO: Nikki Aykul, Manager Business Office
CMO: Steven Sotos, M.D., President Medical Staff
CIO: George Fitzgerald, Regional Director Information Systems
CHR: Robin Arslanpay, Director Human Resources
Web address: www.lifecare–hospitals.com
Control: Corporation, Investor–owned, for–profit **Service:** Long–Term Acute Care hospital

> **Staffed Beds:** 236

Many Facility Codes have changed. Please refer to the AHA Guide Code Chart. © 2016 AHA Guide

⊞ MAGEE–WOMENS HOSPITAL OF UPMC (390114), 300 Halket Street, Zip 15213–3108; tel. 412/641–1000, (Total facility includes 20 beds in nursing home–type unit) **A**1 2 3 5 10 **F**3 11 12 13 15 29 30 31 34 43 44 45 46 49 52 54 55 56 57 58 59 64 65 66 68 70 72 74 75 76 78 79 80 81 82 84 85 86 87 97 107 108 110 111 115 119 120 121 123 126 128 130 131 132 134 135 146 147 148 **S** UPMC, Pittsburgh, PA
Primary Contact: Leslie C. Davis, President
COO: Lou Baverso, Vice President Operations
CFO: Eileen Simmons, Chief Financial Officer
CMO: Dennis English, M.D., Vice President Medical Affairs
CIO: Harun Rashid, Chief Information Officer
CHR: Rhonda Larimore, Vice President Human Resources
CNO: Maribeth McLaughlin, R.N., Vice President Patient Care Services
Web address: www.magee.edu
Control: Other not–for–profit (including NFP Corporation) **Service:** Obstetrics and gynecology

Staffed Beds: 321 Admissions: 20128 Census: 242 Outpatient Visits: 588624 Births: 8426 Total Expense ($000): 794805 Payroll Expense ($000): 134028 Personnel: 2109

⊞ SELECT SPECIALTY HOSPITAL–PITTSBURGH/UPMC (392044), 200 Lothrop Street, E824, Zip 15213–2536; tel. 412/586–9800 **A**1 10 **F**1 3 29 36 65 85 86 87 91 148 **S** Select Medical Corporation, Mechanicsburg, PA
Primary Contact: John St. Leger, Chief Executive Officer
CMO: Michael Donahue, M.D., Medical Director
CHR: Prudence Sloan, Coordinator Human Resources
CNO: Eli Babich, Chief Nursing Officer
Web address: www.selectspecialtyhospitals.com/company/locations/pittsburghupmc.aspx
Control: Corporation, Investor–owned, for–profit **Service:** Long–Term Acute Care hospital

Staffed Beds: 32 Admissions: 293 Census: 27 Outpatient Visits: 0 Births: 0

☐ SOUTHWOOD PSYCHIATRIC HOSPITAL, 2575 Boyce Plaza Road, Zip 15241–3925; tel. 412/257–2290, (Nonreporting) **A**1 **S** Acadia Healthcare Company, Inc., Franklin, TN
Primary Contact: Stephen J. Quigley, Chief Executive Officer
CFO: Frank Urban, Chief Financial Officer
CMO: Allan W. Clark, M.D., Medical Director
CHR: Erin J. Frohnhofer, Director Human Resources
Web address: www.southwoodhospital.com
Control: Corporation, Investor–owned, for–profit **Service:** Children's hospital psychiatric

Staffed Beds: 112

⊞ ST. CLAIR HOSPITAL (390228), 1000 Bower Hill Road, Zip 15243–1873; tel. 412/942–4000 **A**1 2 3 10 **F**3 8 13 15 17 18 20 22 24 26 28 29 30 31 34 35 37 40 45 46 49 51 53 54 56 60 64 67 70 73 74 75 76 77 78 79 81 82 84 85 86 87 89 90 91 92 93 96 98 100 102 103 104 105 107 108 111 114 115 119 126 129 130 131 132 135 143 144 146 147 148
Primary Contact: James M. Collins, President and Chief Executive Officer
COO: Michael J. Flanagan, Senior Vice President and Chief Operating Officer
CFO: Richard C. Chesnos, Senior Vice President Finance and Chief Financial Officer
CMO: G. Alan Yeasted, M.D., Senior Vice President and Chief Medical Officer
CIO: Richard Schaeffer, Vice President Information Systems and Chief Information Officer
CHR: Andrea Kalina, Vice President External Affairs and Chief Human Resources Officer
CNO: Joan Massella, Administrative Vice President and Chief Nursing Officer
Web address: www.stclair.org
Control: Other not–for–profit (including NFP Corporation) **Service:** General Medical and Surgical

Staffed Beds: 303 Admissions: 16359 Census: 196 Outpatient Visits: 322459 Births: 1346 Total Expense ($000): 249250 Payroll Expense ($000): 96558 Personnel: 1973

★ THE CHILDREN'S HOME OF PITTSBURGH (393304), 5324 Penn Avenue, Zip 15224–1733; tel. 412/441–4884 **A**10 **F**19 63 77 83 86 89 132 146
Primary Contact: Pamela R. Schanwald, Chief Executive Officer
COO: Kimberly Reblock, M.D., Chief Operating Officer
CFO: Kimberly A. Phillips, Chief Financial Officer
CMO: Frederick C. Sherman, M.D., Chief Medical Officer
Web address: www.childrenshomepgh.org
Control: Other not–for–profit (including NFP Corporation) **Service:** Children's general

Staffed Beds: 30 Admissions: 374 Census: 20 Outpatient Visits: 0 Births: 0

★ △ THE CHILDREN'S INSTITUTE OF PITTSBURGH (393308), 1405 Shady Avenue, Zip 15217–1350; tel. 412/420–2400 **A**7 10 **F**3 29 30 34 54 58 59 64 74 75 79 82 85 86 87 90 91 93 96 97 98 99 100 104 107 130 131 132 146 148 **P**6
Primary Contact: David K. Miles, President and Chief Executive Officer
COO: Stacey Vaccaro, Chief Operating Officer
CFO: John Jubas, Vice President Finance
CMO: Matthew Masiello, M.D., Chief Medical Officer
CIO: Sharon Dorogy, Chief Information Officer
CHR: Linda M. Allen, Vice President Human Resources
Web address: www.amazingkids.org
Control: Other not–for–profit (including NFP Corporation) **Service:** Children's rehabilitation

Staffed Beds: 62 Admissions: 272 Census: 21 Outpatient Visits: 56785 Births: 0 Total Expense ($000): 26809 Payroll Expense ($000): 15807 Personnel: 306

☐ △ UPMC MERCY (390028), 1400 Locust Street, Zip 15219–5166; tel. 412/232–8111 **A**1 3 5 7 10 12 13 **F**3 4 8 13 15 16 17 19 20 22 24 26 28 29 30 31 32 34 35 36 39 40 43 44 45 49 50 51 54 57 58 59 60 61 64 65 66 68 70 72 74 75 76 77 78 79 81 82 85 86 87 90 91 92 93 94 95 96 97 98 101 102 107 108 111 115 116 118 119 126 129 130 141 142 146 147 148 **P**6 **S** UPMC, Pittsburgh, PA
Primary Contact: Michael A. Grace, President
COO: Julie Hecker, Vice President, Operations
CFO: Eileen Simmons, Chief Financial Officer, UPMC Hospital Network
CIO: Kevin Conway, Chief Information Officer
CHR: Tracey Stange Kolo, Vice President, Human Resources
CNO: Leeanna McKibben, R.N., Vice President Patient Services and Chief Nursing Officer
Web address: www.upmc.com/HospitalsFacilities/HFHome/Hospitals/Mercy/
Control: Other not–for–profit (including NFP Corporation) **Service:** General Medical and Surgical

Staffed Beds: 482 Admissions: 20158 Census: 343 Outpatient Visits: 186884 Births: 1102 Total Expense ($000): 389872 Payroll Expense ($000): 123711 Personnel: 2328

UPMC MONTEFIORE See UPMC Presbyterian Shadyside

☐ UPMC PASSAVANT (390107), 9100 Babcock Boulevard, Zip 15237–5815; tel. 412/748–6700, (Includes UPMC PASSAVANT CRANBERRY, One St. Francis Way, Cranberry, Zip 16066; tel. 724/772–5300; Teresa G. Petrick, President) **A**1 2 5 10 **F**3 8 11 15 17 18 20 22 24 26 28 29 30 31 34 35 40 45 46 47 48 49 51 54 56 57 58 59 64 68 70 74 75 77 78 79 81 82 84 85 86 87 90 92 96 100 107 108 109 110 111 114 115 116 117 118 119 120 121 123 126 129 130 132 143 146 147 148 **S** UPMC, Pittsburgh, PA
Primary Contact: David T. Martin, President
CFO: Thomas M. Newman, Chief Financial Officer
CMO: James W. Boyle, M.D., Chief Medical Officer
CNO: Susan E. Hoolahan, R.N., Vice President Patient Care Services and Chief Nursing Officer
Web address: www.upmc.edu/passavant
Control: Other not–for–profit (including NFP Corporation) **Service:** General Medical and Surgical

Staffed Beds: 328 Admissions: 16121 Census: 226 Outpatient Visits: 288328 Births: 0 Total Expense ($000): 351235 Payroll Expense ($000): 91287 Personnel: 1566

☐ UPMC PRESBYTERIAN SHADYSIDE (390164), 200 Lothrop Street, Zip 15213–2536; tel. 412/647–2345, (Includes EYE AND EAR HOSPITAL OF PITTSBURGH, 200 Lothrop Street, Zip 15213–2592; tel. 412/647–2345; UPMC MONTEFIORE, 3459 Fifth Avenue, Zip 15213; tel. 412/647–2345; John Innocenti, Sr., President and Chief Executive Officer; UPMC PRESBYTERIAN HOSPITAL, 200 Lothrop Street, Zip 15213; tel. 412/647–2345; UPMC SHADYSIDE, 5230 Centre Avenue, Zip 15232–1381; tel. 412/623–2121; WESTERN PSYCHIATRIC INSTITUTE AND CLINIC, 3811 O'Hara Street, Zip 15213–2593; tel. 412/624–2100), (Total facility includes 30 beds in nursing home–type unit) **A**1 2 5 8 10 12 13 **F**2 3 5 6 7 8 9 11 12 14 15 17 18 19 20 22 24 25 26 28 29 30 31 32 33 34 35 36 37 38 39 40 43 44 45 46 47 48 49 50 51 52 53 54 55 56 57 58 59 60 61 62 63 64 65 66 68 69 70 71 74 75 77 78 79 81 82 83 84 85 86 87 90 91 92 93 94 97 98 99 100 101 102 103 104 105 106 107 108 109 110 111 112 113 114 115 116 117 118 119 120 121 123 124 126 128 129 130 131 132 134 135 136 137 138 139 140 141 142 143 144 145 146 147 148 **P**6 **S** UPMC, Pittsburgh, PA
Primary Contact: John Innocenti, Sr., President and Chief Executive Officer
CFO: Eileen Simmons, Chief Financial Officer
CMO: Margaret Reidy, M.D., Vice President Medical Affairs
CHR: Kathryn Devine, Vice President Human Resources
CNO: Holly Lorenz, R.N., Chief Nurse Executive
Web address: www.upmc.edu
Control: Other not–for–profit (including NFP Corporation) **Service:** General Medical and Surgical

Staffed Beds: 1482 Admissions: 59960 Census: 1207 Outpatient Visits: 1023660 Births: 0 Total Expense ($000): 1963266 Payroll Expense ($000): 494248 Personnel: 11081

PA

☐ **UPMC ST. MARGARET (390102)**, 815 Freeport Road, Zip 15215–3301; tel. 412/784–4000 **A**1 2 3 5 10 13 **F**3 6 8 9 11 15 18 20 29 30 31 34 35 40 44 45 46 49 50 51 54 56 57 58 59 60 61 63 64 65 68 70 74 75 77 78 79 81 82 84 85 86 87 90 96 97 102 103 104 107 108 111 114 115 118 119 120 121 123 129 130 131 132 134 135 146 **S** UPMC, Pittsburgh, PA
Primary Contact: David J. Patton, President
COO: Merle Taylor, Vice President Operations
CFO: Thomas M. Newman, Vice President Finance
CMO: John Lagnese, M.D., Vice President Medical Affairs
CIO: Charles M. Rudek, Chief Information Officer
CHR: Tracey Stange Kolo, Vice President Human Resources
CNO: Mary C. Barkhymer, R.N., Vice President Patient Care Services and Chief Nursing Officer
Web address: www.upmc.com/locations/hospitals/st–margaret/Pages/default.aspx
Control: Other not–for–profit (including NFP Corporation) **Service:** General Medical and Surgical

Staffed Beds: 226 **Admissions:** 12784 **Census:** 176 **Outpatient Visits:** 166862 **Births:** 0 **Total Expense ($000):** 241110 **Payroll Expense ($000):** 63086 **Personnel:** 1038

☒ △ **VETERANS AFFAIRS PITTSBURGH HEALTHCARE SYSTEM**, University Drive, Zip 15240–1001; tel. 866/482–7488, (Includes VETERANS AFFAIRS MEDICAL CENTER, 7180 Highland Drive, Zip 15206–1297; tel. 412/365–4900; VETERANS AFFAIRS MEDICAL CENTER, University Drive C, tel. 412/688–6000), (Total facility includes 325 beds in nursing home–type unit) **A**1 2 3 5 7 8 **F**2 3 4 5 11 12 15 18 20 22 24 26 28 29 30 31 33 34 35 36 37 38 39 40 44 46 47 48 49 50 52 53 54 56 57 58 59 60 61 62 63 64 65 67 68 70 71 74 75 77 78 79 80 81 82 83 84 85 86 87 90 92 93 94 96 97 98 100 101 102 103 104 106 107 108 111 114 115 116 117 118 119 126 127 128 129 130 132 135 138 139 143 146 147 148 **P**6 **S** Department of Veterans Affairs, Washington, DC
Primary Contact: Karin L. McGraw, MSN, FACHE, Director
CFO: Charles Thilges, Chief Financial Officer
CMO: Ali Sonel, M.D., Chief of Staff
CIO: John Kovac, Facility Chief Information Officer
CHR: Amber Mesoras, Chief Human Resources Officer
CNO: Ira Richmond, Associate Director Patient Care Services
Web address: www.pittsburgh.va.gov/
Control: Veterans Affairs, Government, federal **Service:** General Medical and Surgical

Staffed Beds: 549 **Admissions:** 9918 **Census:** 408 **Outpatient Visits:** 706270 **Births:** 0 **Total Expense ($000):** 667589 **Payroll Expense ($000):** 268636 **Personnel:** 3563

☒ **WEST PENN HOSPITAL (390090)**, 4800 Friendship Avenue, Zip 15224–1722; tel. 412/578–5000 **A**1 2 3 5 10 13 **F**3 8 11 12 13 15 16 17 18 20 22 24 26 29 30 31 34 35 37 39 40 43 45 46 47 48 49 50 51 52 53 54 55 56 57 58 59 64 65 68 70 72 74 75 76 77 78 79 80 81 82 84 85 86 87 89 90 91 92 96 97 100 102 107 108 110 111 114 115 116 117 118 119 120 121 123 124 129 130 131 132 135 136 141 145 146 147 148 **P**6 **S** Allegheny Health Network, Pittsburgh, PA
Primary Contact: Ronald J. Andro, President and Chief Executive Officer
CFO: James A. Kanuch, Vice President Finance
CMO: I. William Goldfarb, Chief Medical Officer
CIO: Jacqueline Dailey, Chief Information Officer
CHR: Sally Carozza, Director Human Resources
CNO: Paula A. Lacher, MSN, Chief Nursing Officer
Web address: www.wpahs.org
Control: Other not–for–profit (including NFP Corporation) **Service:** General Medical and Surgical

Staffed Beds: 317 **Admissions:** 11241 **Census:** 159 **Outpatient Visits:** 107050 **Births:** 3740 **Total Expense ($000):** 323725 **Payroll Expense ($000):** 81554 **Personnel:** 1420

WESTERN PSYCHIATRIC INSTITUTE AND CLINIC See UPMC Presbyterian Shadyside

PLEASANT GAP—Centre County

☒ **HEALTHSOUTH NITTANY VALLEY REHABILITATION HOSPITAL (393039)**, 550 West College Avenue, Zip 16823–7401; tel. 814/359–3421 **A**1 10 **F**29 34 44 59 60 64 90 93 148 **S** HEALTHSOUTH Corporation, Birmingham, AL
Primary Contact: Susan Hartman, Chief Executive Officer
CFO: Alan M. Phillips, Controller
CMO: Richard Allatt, M.D., Medical Director
CHR: Michelle Katz, Director Human Resources
CNO: Susan Evans, Chief Nursing Officer
Web address: www.nittanyvalleyrehab.com
Control: Corporation, Investor–owned, for–profit **Service:** Rehabilitation

Staffed Beds: 73 **Admissions:** 1317 **Census:** 44 **Births:** 0

POTTSTOWN—Montgomery County

☒ **POTTSTOWN MEMORIAL MEDICAL CENTER (390123)**, 1600 East High Street, Zip 19464–5093; tel. 610/327–7000 **A**1 2 10 **F**3 7 12 13 15 18 29 30 31 34 35 38 40 44 45 48 49 50 51 54 57 59 64 68 70 74 75 76 77 78 79 80 81 82 85 89 92 93 96 97 98 100 103 107 108 110 111 117 119 120 121 123 124 131 132 135 146 147 148 **P**6 **S** Community Health Systems, Inc., Franklin, TN
Primary Contact: Rich Newell, Chief Executive Officer
CFO: Debbie Konarski, Interim Chief Financial Officer
CMO: Richard F. Saylor, M.D., Chief Medical Officer
CIO: Ron Peterson, Chief Information Officer
CHR: Ruta Ore, Director Human Resources
Web address: www.pottstownmemorial.com
Control: Corporation, Investor–owned, for–profit **Service:** General Medical and Surgical

Staffed Beds: 232 **Admissions:** 8887 **Census:** 108 **Outpatient Visits:** 84814 **Births:** 489 **Total Expense ($000):** 136632 **Payroll Expense ($000):** 50740 **Personnel:** 817

POTTSVILLE—Schuylkill County

☒ △ **SCHUYLKILL MEDICAL CENTER – SCHUYLKILL EAST NORWEGIAN STREET (390031)**, 700 East Norwegian Street, Zip 17901–2710; tel. 570/621–4000 **A**1 7 10 **F**3 5 11 15 18 29 30 31 34 40 45 49 56 57 59 64 70 74 75 77 78 79 81 85 86 90 93 98 100 103 107 108 109 110 115 117 118 119 130 132 135 146 147 148 **P**6 **S** Schuylkill Health System, Pottsville, PA
Primary Contact: William Reppy, President
CFO: Diane Boris, Vice President and Chief Financial Officer
CIO: Tina Zanis, Director Information Technology
CHR: Martin Treasure, Director Human Resources
CNO: Darnell F. Furer, MS, Vice President of Patient Care Services
Web address: www.schuylkillhealth.com
Control: Other not–for–profit (including NFP Corporation) **Service:** General Medical and Surgical

Staffed Beds: 109 **Admissions:** 3726 **Census:** 59 **Outpatient Visits:** 101329 **Births:** 0 **Total Expense ($000):** 56681 **Payroll Expense ($000):** 25563 **Personnel:** 453

☒ **SCHUYLKILL MEDICAL CENTER – SCHUYLKILL SOUTH JACKSON STREET (390030)**, 420 South Jackson Street, Zip 17901–3625; tel. 570/621–5000 **A**1 10 19 **F**3 11 13 15 18 19 28 29 30 32 34 35 38 40 45 49 51 56 57 59 62 64 70 74 75 76 77 78 79 81 82 85 86 89 92 93 96 98 99 100 101 102 107 108 110 111 115 118 119 124 126 129 130 132 146 147 **P**6 **S** Schuylkill Health System, Pottsville, PA
Primary Contact: William Reppy, President
CFO: Diane Boris, Chief Financial Officer
CIO: Tina Zanis, Director Information Systems
CHR: Martin Treasure, Director Human Resources
CNO: Darnell F. Furer, MS, Vice President Patient Care Services and Chief Nursing Officer
Web address: www.schuylkillhealth.com
Control: Other not–for–profit (including NFP Corporation) **Service:** General Medical and Surgical

Staffed Beds: 179 **Admissions:** 5472 **Census:** 76 **Outpatient Visits:** 109322 **Births:** 765 **Total Expense ($000):** 85258 **Payroll Expense ($000):** 39109 **Personnel:** 649

PUNXSUTAWNEY—Jefferson County

PUNXSUTAWNEY AREA HOSPITAL (390199), 81 Hillcrest Drive, Zip 15767–2616; tel. 814/938–1800 **A**10 20 **F**3 13 15 26 29 30 34 35 40 44 45 46 48 50 51 57 59 62 64 70 74 75 76 77 78 79 81 82 85 86 87 92 93 96 100 104 107 108 110 111 115 118 119 127 130 132 133 146 147 148 **P**6
Primary Contact: Daniel D. Blough, Jr., Chief Executive Officer
CFO: Jack Sisk, Chief Financial Officer
CMO: Dajani Zuhd, M.D., President Medical Staff
CIO: Chuck States, Director Information Systems
CHR: Barbara Kostok, Manager Human Resources
CNO: Paula Spack, R.N., Vice President Nursing
Web address: www.pah.org
Control: Other not–for–profit (including NFP Corporation) **Service:** General Medical and Surgical

Staffed Beds: 45 **Admissions:** 1566 **Census:** 19 **Outpatient Visits:** 70359 **Births:** 146 **Total Expense ($000):** 33465 **Payroll Expense ($000):** 16411 **Personnel:** 346

PA

QUAKERTOWN—Bucks County

☐ **ST. LUKE'S HOSPITAL – QUAKERTOWN CAMPUS (390035)**, 1021 Park Avenue, Zip 18951–1573; tel. 215/538–4500 **A**1 2 10 **F**3 15 18 28 29 30 31 34 35 38 40 44 45 49 50 51 54 56 57 59 64 65 68 69 70 74 75 77 78 79 81 82 85 86 87 92 93 98 100 102 103 107 108 109 110 111 115 118 119 129 130 131 132 135 146 148 **P**6 8 **S** St. Luke's University Health Network, Bethlehem, PA
Primary Contact: Edward Nawrocki, President
CFO: Theresa Corrado, Director Finance
CMO: Thomas Filipowicz, M.D., Medical Director
CIO: Chad Brisendine, Chief Information Officer
CHR: Shelley Maley, Director Human Resources
Web address: www.slhhn.org
Control: Other not–for–profit (including NFP Corporation) **Service:** General Medical and Surgical

Staffed Beds: 57 **Admissions:** 2845 **Census:** 37 **Outpatient Visits:** 75724 **Births:** 0 **Total Expense ($000):** 55914 **Payroll Expense ($000):** 22287 **Personnel:** 291

READING—Berks County

☐ **HAVEN BEHAVIORAL HOSPITAL OF EASTERN PENNSYLVANIA (394052)**, 145 North 6th Street, 3rd Floor, Zip 19601–3096; tel. 610/406–4340, (Nonreporting) **A**1 10 **S** Haven Behavioral Healthcare, Nashville, TN
Primary Contact: Bryan W. Lett, Chief Executive Officer
CMO: Mark Putnam, M.D., Medical Director
CHR: Kathy Copenhaver, Director Human Resources
Web address: www.https://havenbehavioral.com/
Control: Corporation, Investor–owned, for–profit **Service:** Psychiatric

Staffed Beds: 48

✠ **HEALTHSOUTH READING REHABILITATION HOSPITAL (393026)**, 1623 Morgantown Road, Zip 19607–9455; tel. 610/796–6000, (Nonreporting) **A**1 10 **S** HEALTHSOUTH Corporation, Birmingham, AL
Primary Contact: Amy Teal, Chief Executive Officer
CFO: Jason Pulaski, Controller
CMO: Patti Brown, M.D., Medical Director
CHR: Edward Werner, Director Human Resources
CNO: Margaret Montgomery, Chief Nursing Officer
Web address: www.healthsouthreading.com
Control: Corporation, Investor–owned, for–profit **Service:** Rehabilitation

Staffed Beds: 60

✠ **PENN STATE HEALTH ST. JOSEPH (390096)**, 2500 Bernville Road, Zip 19605–9453, Mailing Address: P.O. Box 316, Zip 19603–0316; tel. 610/378–2000, (Includes ST. JOSEPH MEDICAL CENTER–DOWNTOWN READING, 145 North Sixth Street, Zip 19601, Mailing Address: P.O. Box 316, Zip 19603–0316; tel. 610/378–2000; John R. Morahan, President and Chief Executive Officer) **A**1 2 10 12 13 **F**1 3 4 13 15 16 17 18 20 22 24 26 28 29 30 31 32 34 35 39 40 44 45 46 49 50 51 53 54 57 58 59 64 66 67 68 70 72 73 74 75 76 77 78 79 80 81 82 84 85 87 88 89 90 93 97 98 107 108 111 113 114 115 116 117 118 119 120 121 128 130 131 132 135 144 146 147 148 **P**1 6 **S** Penn State Hershey Health System, Hershey, PA
Primary Contact: John R. Morahan, President and Chief Executive Officer
CFO: Lim David, Vice President Finance and Chief Financial Officer
CMO: Gary Lattin, M.D., Vice President, Medical Affairs
CIO: Amanda Klopp, Director, Innovation and Clinical Integration
CHR: Scott Mengle, Vice President Human Resources
CNO: Sharon Strohecker, R.N., Vice President Clinical Operations and Chief Nursing Officer
Web address: www.thefutureofhealthcare.org
Control: Church–operated, Nongovernment, not–for profit **Service:** General Medical and Surgical

Staffed Beds: 180 **Admissions:** 7645 **Census:** 92 **Outpatient Visits:** 259133 **Births:** 760 **Total Expense ($000):** 234389 **Payroll Expense ($000):** 59679 **Personnel:** 1440

RENOVO—Clinton County

★ **BUCKTAIL MEDICAL CENTER (391304)**, 1001 Pine Street, Zip 17764–1620; tel. 570/923–1000, (Nonreporting) **A**10 18
Primary Contact: Timothy Reeves, Administrator
CFO: Wendy Janerella, Controller
CMO: Alvin Berlot, M.D., Medical Director
Web address: www.bucktailmed.org
Control: Other not–for–profit (including NFP Corporation) **Service:** General Medical and Surgical

Staffed Beds: 64

RIDLEY PARK—Delaware County

TAYLOR HOSPITAL See Crozer–Chester Medical Center, Upland

ROARING SPRING—Blair County

✠ **NASON HOSPITAL (390062)**, 105 Nason Drive, Zip 16673–1202; tel. 814/224–2141 **A**1 10 **F**3 11 13 15 18 19 29 30 34 35 40 45 57 59 62 63 64 65 70 74 75 76 77 79 81 85 86 92 107 108 110 111 114 119 124 130 146 147 148 **S** LifePoint Health, Brentwood, TN
Primary Contact: Timothy Harclerode, Chief Executive Officer
CFO: Kimberly Semelsberger, CPA, Chief Financial Officer
CHR: Lorie Smith, Director Human Resources
Web address: www.nasonhospital.com
Control: Corporation, Investor–owned, for–profit **Service:** General Medical and Surgical

Staffed Beds: 45 **Admissions:** 1861 **Census:** 16 **Outpatient Visits:** 99678 **Births:** 408 **Total Expense ($000):** 35183 **Payroll Expense ($000):** 13814 **Personnel:** 268

ROYERSFORD—Montgomery County

◇ **PHYSICIANS CARE SURGICAL HOSPITAL (390324)**, 454 Enterprise Drive, Zip 19468–1200; tel. 610/495–3330 **A**10 21 **F**3 8 29 65 81
Primary Contact: Christopher Doyle, Chief Executive Officer
Web address: www.phycarehospital.com
Control: Corporation, Investor–owned, for–profit **Service:** Surgical

Staffed Beds: 12 **Admissions:** 891 **Census:** 4 **Outpatient Visits:** 5096 **Births:** 0 **Personnel:** 91

SAINT MARYS—Elk County

PENN HIGHLANDS ELK (390154), 763 Johnsonburg Road, Zip 15857–3498; tel. 814/788–8000, (Total facility includes 138 beds in nursing home–type unit) **A**10 20 **F**1 2 3 4 6 8 11 13 15 16 17 28 29 30 34 35 40 44 45 56 57 59 62 63 67 70 72 73 75 76 77 79 80 81 82 84 85 86 87 88 89 90 93 98 100 103 107 108 110 111 115 118 119 128 129 130 131 132 133 135 144 146 147 148
Primary Contact: Rose Campbell, R.N., President
CFO: Laurie MacDonald, Vice President Finance
CMO: David Johe, M.D., President Medical Staff
CIO: Mary Ann Schwabenbauer, Director Information Technology
CHR: Seanna D'Amore, Director Human Resources
Web address: www.phhealthcare.org
Control: Other not–for–profit (including NFP Corporation) **Service:** General Medical and Surgical

Staffed Beds: 218 **Admissions:** 2641 **Census:** 154 **Outpatient Visits:** 153853 **Births:** 180 **Total Expense ($000):** 59349 **Payroll Expense ($000):** 25666 **Personnel:** 525

SAYRE—Bradford County

✠ **ROBERT PACKER HOSPITAL (390079)**, 1 Guthrie Square, Zip 18840–1698; tel. 570/888–6666 **A**1 2 3 5 10 12 13 19 **F**3 11 12 13 15 17 18 20 22 24 26 28 29 30 31 34 37 38 40 43 45 46 47 48 49 50 51 57 58 59 60 61 64 70 73 74 75 76 78 79 81 82 84 85 86 87 89 92 93 98 99 100 101 102 103 105 107 108 110 111 114 115 116 117 118 119 120 121 123 126 129 130 132 141 142 145 146 148 **S** Guthrie Clinic, Sayre, PA
Primary Contact: Marie T. Droege, President
CFO: Scott Silvestri, Chief Financial Officer, Hospital Financial Operations
CMO: Brian Fillipo, M.D., Chief Medical Officer
CIO: Burt Robles, Vice President Information Services
CHR: Frank Pinkosky, Senior Vice President
CNO: Catherine Mohr, R.N., Chief Nursing Officer
Web address: www.https://www.guthrie.org/location/robert–packer–hospital
Control: Other not–for–profit (including NFP Corporation) **Service:** General Medical and Surgical

Staffed Beds: 254 **Admissions:** 14053 **Census:** 180 **Outpatient Visits:** 172393 **Births:** 909 **Total Expense ($000):** 263425 **Payroll Expense ($000):** 79413 **Personnel:** 1357

PA

Hospital, Medicare Provider Number, Address, Telephone, Approval, Facility, and Physician Codes, Health Care System

★ American Hospital Association (AHA) membership
☐ The Joint Commission accreditation
○ Healthcare Facilities Accreditation Program
◇ DNV Healthcare Inc. accreditation
⇑ Center for Improvement in Healthcare Quality Accreditation
△ Commission on Accreditation of Rehabilitation Facilities (CARF) accreditation

PA

SCRANTON—Lackawanna County

□ △ **ALLIED SERVICES REHABILITATION HOSPITAL (393030)**, 475 Morgan Highway, Zip 18508–2605, Mailing Address: P.O. Box 1103, Zip 18501–1103; tel. 570/348–1300 **A**1 7 10 **F**11 29 34 53 56 59 64 74 75 77 78 79 86 87 90 91 93 94 96 130 143 146
Primary Contact: Karen Kearney, Vice President Inpatient Rehabilitation Services
CFO: Michael Avvisato, Senior Vice President and Chief Financial Officer
CMO: Gregory Basting, M.D., Vice President Medical Affairs
CIO: John Regula, Chief Information Officer
CHR: Judy P. Oprisko, Vice President
CNO: Jeana Sluck, R.N., Executive Director Nursing Clinical Inpatient Departments
Web address: www.allied–services.org
Control: Other not–for–profit (including NFP Corporation) **Service:** Rehabilitation

Staffed Beds: 117 **Admissions:** 1937 **Census:** 55 **Births:** 0

COMMUNITY MEDICAL CENTER HEALTHCARE SYSTEM See Geisinger–Community Medical Center

☒ **GEISINGER–COMMUNITY MEDICAL CENTER (390001)**, 1800 Mulberry Street, Zip 18510–2369; tel. 570/703–8000 **A**1 3 5 10 **F**89 98 **S** Geisinger Health System, Danville, PA
Primary Contact: David T. Feinberg, M.D., Chief Executive Officer
CFO: Edward Chabalowski, Chief Financial Officer
CMO: Anthony Aquilina, D.O., Chief Medical Officer
CHR: Lois Wolfe, Director Human Resources
Web address: www.geisinger.org/for–patients/locations–directions/gcmc/
Control: Other not–for–profit (including NFP Corporation) **Service:** General Medical and Surgical

Staffed Beds: 270 **Admissions:** 12036 **Census:** 159 **Outpatient Visits:** 59604 **Births:** 0 **Total Expense ($000):** 181947 **Payroll Expense ($000):** 71614

MERCY HOSPITAL OF SCRANTON See Regional Hospital of Scranton

☒ △ **MOSES TAYLOR HOSPITAL (390119)**, 700 Quincy Avenue, Zip 18510–1724; tel. 570/770–5000 **A**1 3 5 7 10 **F**3 7 13 15 18 29 30 31 34 40 45 49 51 56 57 59 60 61 62 64 65 66 68 70 72 74 75 77 78 79 81 85 86 87 93 98 103 107 108 110 111 114 119 124 129 130 132 135 146 147 **P**6 **S** Community Health Systems, Inc., Franklin, TN
Primary Contact: Justin Davis, Chief Executive Officer
CFO: Thomas Bisignani, Chief Financial Officer
CMO: Mary Sewatsky, M.D., Chief Medical Officer
CHR: Elizabeth Leo, Chief Human Resources Officer
CNO: Patricia Seliga, R.N., Chief Nursing Officer
Web address: www.mth.org
Control: Corporation, Investor–owned, for–profit **Service:** General Medical and Surgical

Staffed Beds: 214 **Admissions:** 9441 **Census:** 122 **Outpatient Visits:** 167756 **Births:** 2506 **Total Expense ($000):** 137594 **Payroll Expense ($000):** 43106 **Personnel:** 789

☒ △ **REGIONAL HOSPITAL OF SCRANTON (390237)**, 746 Jefferson Avenue, Zip 18510–1624; tel. 570/348–7100 **A**1 2 3 5 7 10 12 **F**7 8 11 12 15 17 18 20 22 24 26 28 29 30 31 34 35 39 40 44 45 46 47 48 49 50 51 53 54 57 58 59 60 61 63 64 65 66 68 70 74 75 77 78 79 81 85 86 87 91 92 93 97 107 108 109 110 111 112 113 114 115 116 117 118 119 120 121 122 123 124 126 130 132 143 144 145 146 147 148 **P**6 **S** Community Health Systems, Inc., Franklin, TN
Primary Contact: Justin Davis, Chief Executive Officer
CFO: Stephen Franko, Vice President Finance and Chief Financial Officer
CMO: Anthony Yanni, M.D., Vice President Medical Affairs
CIO: Jorge Coronel, Chief Information Officer
Web address: www.regionalhospitalofscranton.net
Control: Corporation, Investor–owned, for–profit **Service:** General Medical and Surgical

Staffed Beds: 186 **Admissions:** 8680 **Census:** 122 **Outpatient Visits:** 102661 **Births:** 0 **Total Expense ($000):** 155781 **Payroll Expense ($000):** 48435 **Personnel:** 818

SELLERSVILLE—Bucks County

☒ **GRAND VIEW HEALTH (390057)**, 700 Lawn Avenue, Zip 18960–1548, Mailing Address: P.O. Box 902, Zip 18960–0902; tel. 215/453–4000 **A**1 2 10 **F**3 7 11 12 13 15 18 28 29 32 34 35 37 40 44 45 46 47 48 49 50 51 54 56 57 58 59 61 62 63 64 65 66 68 70 71 72 74 75 76 77 78 79 81 84 85 86 87 89 90 93 96 97 107 108 110 111 114 115 117 118 119 120 121 123 130 131 132 135 141 143 146 147 148 **P**6
Primary Contact: Jean M. Keeler, President and Chief Executive Officer
COO: J. Mark Horne, Senior Vice President, Ambulatory Services and Chief Operating Officer
CFO: Michael Keen, Senior Vice President and Chief Financial Officer
CMO: Jane Ferry, M.D., Vice President Medical Affairs
CIO: Jane Doll Loveless, Vice President, Chief Information Officer
CNO: Kathleen Burkey, R.N., Vice President, Patient Care Service and Chief Nursing Officer
Web address: www.gvh.org
Control: Other not–for–profit (including NFP Corporation) **Service:** General Medical and Surgical

Staffed Beds: 194 **Admissions:** 8274 **Census:** 102 **Outpatient Visits:** 320221 **Births:** 1300 **Total Expense ($000):** 183553 **Payroll Expense ($000):** 96888 **Personnel:** 1454

SENECA—Venango County

□ **UPMC NORTHWEST (390091)**, 100 Fairfield Drive, Zip 16346–2130; tel. 814/676–7600, (Total facility includes 16 beds in nursing home–type unit) **A**1 2 10 19 **F**3 11 13 15 18 20 28 29 31 34 35 40 44 45 46 47 50 56 57 59 63 64 65 68 70 74 75 76 77 78 79 81 84 85 86 87 89 90 93 96 98 100 101 102 103 107 108 110 111 114 115 118 119 121 128 130 131 132 135 141 142 146 147 148 **S** UPMC, Pittsburgh, PA
Primary Contact: David Gibbons, President
COO: Brian Durniok, Vice President Operations
CFO: Bradley Dinger, Financial Representative
CMO: David McCandless, Vice President Medical Affairs
CHR: Brian Durniok, Vice President Human Resources
CNO: Daniel Shearn, R.N., Vice President Patient Services and Chief Nursing Officer
Web address: www.upmc.com/locations/hospitals/northwest/Pages/default.aspx
Control: Other not–for–profit (including NFP Corporation) **Service:** General Medical and Surgical

Staffed Beds: 128 **Admissions:** 6493 **Census:** 89 **Outpatient Visits:** 135919 **Births:** 612 **Total Expense ($000):** 103308 **Payroll Expense ($000):** 27919 **Personnel:** 557

SEWICKLEY—Allegheny County

☒ **HEALTHSOUTH REHABILITATION HOSPITAL OF SEWICKLEY (393045)**, 303 Camp Meeting Road, Zip 15143–8322; tel. 412/741–9500 **A**1 10 **F**29 34 56 57 59 60 64 65 74 75 87 90 91 92 93 95 96 100 132 146 148 **S** HEALTHSOUTH Corporation, Birmingham, AL
Primary Contact: Leah Laffey, R.N., Chief Executive Officer
CFO: Daniel A. Vrana, Area Controller
CMO: Shelana Gibbs–McElvy, M.D., Medical Director
CIO: Jamie Smith, Supervisor Health Information Management Systems
CHR: Melissa Coleman, Director Human Resources
CNO: Christie Ryan, Chief Nursing Officer
Web address: www.healthsouthsewickley.com
Control: Corporation, Investor–owned, for–profit **Service:** Rehabilitation

Staffed Beds: 44 **Admissions:** 880 **Census:** 36 **Outpatient Visits:** 4124 **Births:** 0 **Total Expense ($000):** 11946 **Payroll Expense ($000):** 6026 **Personnel:** 104

□ **SEWICKLEY VALLEY HOSPITAL, (A DIVISION OF VALLEY MEDICAL FACILITIES) (390037)**, 720 Blackburn Road, Zip 15143–1459; tel. 412/741–6600 **A**1 10 **F**3 8 11 12 13 14 15 18 20 28 29 30 32 34 35 38 40 46 49 50 53 54 55 57 59 60 64 70 74 75 76 77 78 79 81 82 84 85 86 90 92 93 96 97 98 100 101 102 103 104 107 108 109 110 111 115 118 119 120 121 126 129 130 132 135 145 **P**6 **S** Heritage Valley Health System, Beaver, PA
Primary Contact: Norman F. Mitry, President and Chief Executive Officer
CFO: Bryan J. Randall, Vice President Finance and Chief Financial Officer
CMO: John Cinicola, M.D., Chief Medical Officer
CIO: David Carleton, Chief Information Officer
CHR: Bruce Edwards, Vice President Human Resources
CNO: Linda Homyk, Chief Nursing Officer
Web address: www.heritagevalley.org
Control: Other not–for–profit (including NFP Corporation) **Service:** General Medical and Surgical

Staffed Beds: 179 **Admissions:** 8279 **Census:** 94 **Births:** 752

Many Facility Codes have changed. Please refer to the AHA Guide Code Chart.

SHARON—Mercer County

✠ **SHARON REGIONAL HEALTH SYSTEM (390211)**, 740 East State Street, Zip 16146–3395; tel. 724/983–3911, (Nonreporting) **A**1 10 **S** Community Health Systems, Inc., Franklin, TN
Primary Contact: Jason Roeback, Chief Executive Officer
CFO: Jeffrey Chrobak, Vice President Finance and Chief Financial Officer
CHR: John Davidson, Vice President Human Resources
Web address: www.sharonregional.com
Control: Corporation, Investor–owned, for–profit **Service:** General Medical and Surgical

Staffed Beds: 256

SHICKSHINNY—Luzerne County

CLEAR BROOK LODGE, 890 Bethel Road, Zip 18655;
tel. 570/864–3116, (Nonreporting)
Primary Contact: Nicholas Colangelo, Ph.D., Chief Executive Officer
Web address: www.clearbrookinc.com
Control: Other not–for–profit (including NFP Corporation) **Service:** Alcoholism and other chemical dependency

Staffed Beds: 65

SHIPPENSBURG—Franklin County

☐ **ROXBURY TREATMENT CENTER (394050)**, 601 Roxbury Road, Zip 17257–9302; tel. 800/648–4673, (Nonreporting) **A**1 10 **S** Universal Health Services, Inc., King of Prussia, PA
Primary Contact: Shauna Mogerman, Chief Executive Officer
Web address: www.roxburyhospital.com
Control: Corporation, Investor–owned, for–profit **Service:** Psychiatric

Staffed Beds: 94

SOMERSET—Somerset County

★ **SOMERSET HOSPITAL (390039)**, 225 South Center Avenue, Zip 15501–2088; tel. 814/443–5000 **A**10 20 **F**3 8 11 13 15 17 18 20 22 26 28 29 30 32 34 35 40 45 47 49 50 53 57 59 62 63 64 68 74 76 77 79 80 81 82 85 86 87 89 93 97 98 99 100 103 104 107 108 111 115 119 129 130 131 132 133 135 141 146 147 148
Primary Contact: Craig M. Saylor, Interim CEO
COO: Andy Rush, Senior Vice President and Chief Operating Officer
CFO: Matthew Kociola, Senior Vice President and Chief Financial Officer
CIO: Jonathan Bauer, Director Information Systems
CHR: Mark P. Frick, Senior Vice President Human Resources
CNO: Suellen Lichtenfels, Vice President and Chief Nursing Officer
Web address: www.somersethospital.com
Control: Other not–for–profit (including NFP Corporation) **Service:** General Medical and Surgical

Staffed Beds: 111 **Admissions:** 3349 **Census:** 43 **Outpatient Visits:** 138857 **Births:** 343 **Total Expense ($000):** 65522 **Payroll Expense ($000):** 25827 **Personnel:** 581

SPRINGFIELD—Delaware County

SPRINGFIELD HOSPITAL See Crozer–Chester Medical Center, Upland

STATE COLLEGE—Centre County

✠ **MOUNT NITTANY MEDICAL CENTER (390268)**, 1800 East Park Avenue, Zip 16803–6797; tel. 814/231–7000 **A**1 2 3 5 10 **F**3 7 8 13 15 17 20 22 26 28 29 30 31 35 40 49 51 57 59 64 68 70 73 74 75 76 77 78 79 80 81 82 85 87 89 93 98 100 101 102 107 108 111 114 115 118 119 121 126 129 130 132 135 143 146 148
Primary Contact: Steven E. Brown, FACHE, President and Chief Executive Officer
CFO: Randy E. Tewksbury, Senior Vice President Finance and Chief Financial Officer
CMO: Jeffrey Ratner, M.D., Senior Vice President Medical Affairs
CIO: Wayne Thompson, Executive Vice President and Chief Information Officer
CHR: Jerry Dittmann, Vice President Human Resources
CNO: Janet Schachtner, R.N., Senior Vice President, Patient Care Services
Web address: www.mountnittany.org
Control: Other not–for–profit (including NFP Corporation) **Service:** General Medical and Surgical

Staffed Beds: 207 **Admissions:** 13145 **Census:** 140 **Outpatient Visits:** 299770 **Births:** 1444 **Total Expense ($000):** 351632 **Payroll Expense ($000):** 155679 **Personnel:** 1437

SUNBURY—Northumberland County

✠ **SUNBURY COMMUNITY HOSPITAL AND OUTPATIENT CENTER (390084)**, 350 North Eleventh Street, Zip 17801–1611; tel. 570/286–3333, (Nonreporting) **A**1 10 **S** Quorum Health, Brentwood, TN
Primary Contact: Robert D. Williams, Chief Executive Officer
CFO: James J. Pachucki, Jr., Chief Financial Officer
CMO: Charles C. Pagana, M.D., Chief Medical Officer
CIO: Fax Rector, III, Director Information Technology
CHR: Talia Beatty, Director Human Resources
CNO: Catharine L. Keister, Chief Nursing Officer
Web address: www.sunburyhospital.com
Control: Other not–for–profit (including NFP Corporation) **Service:** General Medical and Surgical

Staffed Beds: 76

SUSQUEHANNA—Susquehanna County

BARNES–KASSON COUNTY HOSPITAL (391309), 2872 Turnpike Street, Zip 18847–2771; tel. 570/853–3135, (Nonreporting) **A**10 18
Primary Contact: Sara F. Adornato, Executive Director
CFO: Kelli R. Kane, Director of Finance
CMO: Pravinchandra Patel, M.D., Chief Medical Officer
CIO: Eric Detwiler, Director Information Technology
Web address: www.barnes–kasson.org
Control: Other not–for–profit (including NFP Corporation) **Service:** General Medical and Surgical

Staffed Beds: 83

TITUSVILLE—Crawford County

TITUSVILLE AREA HOSPITAL (391314), 406 West Oak Street, Zip 16354–1404; tel. 814/827–1851, (Nonreporting) **A**10 18 **S** Meadville Medical Center, Meadville, PA
Primary Contact: Lee Clinton, FACHE, Chief Executive Officer
CFO: Jill Neely, Chief Financial Officer
CMO: William Sonnenberg, M.D., President Medical Staff
CIO: Karen Humes, Chief Information Officer
CHR: Jeffrey Saintz, Vice President Human Resources
CNO: Brenda Burnett, Vice President Patient Care Services and Chief Nursing Officer
Web address: www.titusvillehospital.org
Control: Other not–for–profit (including NFP Corporation) **Service:** General Medical and Surgical

Staffed Beds: 50

TORRANCE—Westmoreland County

TORRANCE STATE HOSPITAL (394026), Torrance Road, Zip 15779–0111, Mailing Address: P.O. Box 111, Zip 15779–0111; tel. 724/459–8000 **A**10 **F**39 75 98 130 135 143 146 147 148
Primary Contact: Edna I. McCutcheon, Chief Executive Officer
COO: R. Brad Snyder, Chief Operating Officer
CFO: Michael Yahner, Chief Financial Officer
CMO: Herbert G. Chissell, M.D., Chief Medical Officer
Web address: www.dpw.state.pa.us
Control: State–Government, nonfederal **Service:** Psychiatric

Staffed Beds: 328 **Admissions:** 273 **Census:** 324 **Outpatient Visits:** 0 **Births:** 0

TOWANDA—Bradford County

★ **GUTHRIE TOWANDA MEMORIAL HOSPITAL (390236)**, 91 Hospital Drive, Zip 18848–9702; tel. 570/265–2191, (Nonreporting) **A**10 **S** Guthrie Clinic, Sayre, PA
Primary Contact: Staci Covey, R.N., MS, President
CMO: Joseph Cama, M.D., President Medical Staff
CIO: Karen Brown, Manager Information Technology
CHR: Linda Berry, Vice President Human Resources
CNO: Lynn Dibble, Vice President Patient Care Services
Web address: www.memorialhospital.org
Control: Other not–for–profit (including NFP Corporation) **Service:** General Medical and Surgical

Staffed Beds: 203

TRANSFER—Mercer County

EDGEWOOD SURGICAL HOSPITAL (390307), 239 Edgewood Drive Extension, Zip 16154–1817; tel. 724/646–0400, (Nonreporting) **A**10
Primary Contact: Lloyd Scarrow, FACHE, Chief Executive Officer
Web address: www.edgewoodsurgical.com
Control: Corporation, Investor–owned, for–profit **Service:** Surgical

Staffed Beds: 10

Hospital, Medicare Provider Number, Address, Telephone, Approval, Facility, and Physician Codes, Health Care System

★ American Hospital Association (AHA) membership
☐ The Joint Commission accreditation
○ Healthcare Facilities Accreditation Program
◇ DNV Healthcare Inc. accreditation
⇧ Center for Improvement in Healthcare Quality Accreditation
△ Commission on Accreditation of Rehabilitation Facilities (CARF) accreditation

PA

TROY—Bradford County

★ **TROY COMMUNITY HOSPITAL (391305)**, 275 Guthrie Drive, Zip 16947;
tel. 570/297–2121 **A**10 18 **F**3 11 15 28 30 34 40 45 50 57 64 75 81 82 85
87 93 96 107 110 111 119 129 130 133 135 146 148 **S** Guthrie Clinic,
Sayre, PA
Primary Contact: Staci Covey, R.N., MS, President
CFO: Bernie Smith, Chief Financial Officer
CMO: Vance A. Good, M.D., Chief Medical Staff
CIO: Dale Swingle, Vice President Information Services
CHR: Frank Pinkosky, Executive Vice President
CNO: Lori Barnett, R.N., Chief Nursing Officer
Web address: www.guthrie.org
Control: Other not–for–profit (including NFP Corporation) **Service:** General
Medical and Surgical

Staffed Beds: 25 **Admissions:** 980 **Census:** 18 **Outpatient Visits:** 30866
Births: 0 **Total Expense ($000):** 18551 **Payroll Expense ($000):** 5690
Personnel: 117

TUNKHANNOCK— County

✉ **TYLER MEMORIAL HOSPITAL (390192)**, 5950 State Route 6,
Zip 18657–7905; tel. 570/836–2161 **A**1 10 **F**15 18 20 22 24 26 28 29 30 31
34 35 40 50 54 56 58 60 62 64 70 75 77 78 79 81 82 86 87 89 92 93 107
108 110 111 119 120 121 129 130 133 146 147 148 **S** Community Health
Systems, Inc., Franklin, TN
Primary Contact: Ann Marie Stevens, R.N., Chief Executive Officer
CFO: Robert Stiekes, Chief Financial Officer
CMO: Terrance Chilson, Chief of Staff
CNO: Patricia Casals, MSN, Chief Nursing Officer
Web address: www.tylermemorialhospital.net
Control: Corporation, Investor–owned, for–profit **Service:** General Medical and
Surgical

Staffed Beds: 44 **Admissions:** 649 **Census:** 6 **Births:** 2

TYRONE—Blair County

TYRONE HOSPITAL (391307), 187 Hospital Drive, Zip 16686–1808;
tel. 814/684–1255 **A**10 18 **F**3 15 40 75 77 79 81 82 93 107 119 130
133 146
Primary Contact: Joseph J. Peluso, Chief Executive Officer
CFO: Todd Dieffenbach, Chief Financial Officer
CMO: Kelly Biggs, M.D., Chief Medical Officer
CHR: Rosemary Jorden Best, Director Human Resources
CNO: Sharon Fisher, R.N., Chief Nursing Officer
Web address: www.tyronehospital.org
Control: Other not–for–profit (including NFP Corporation) **Service:** General
Medical and Surgical

Staffed Beds: 25 **Admissions:** 734 **Census:** 5 **Births:** 0

UNIONTOWN—Fayette County

✉ **UNIONTOWN HOSPITAL (390041)**, 500 West Berkeley Street,
Zip 15401–5596; tel. 724/430–5000 **A**1 10 **F**11 12 13 15 18 20 22 26 28 29
30 34 35 40 45 49 51 54 57 59 64 70 73 74 75 77 78 79 81 84 90 92 93
95 96 102 107 108 110 111 114 115 118 119 130 132 135 146 148
Primary Contact: Steven P. Handy, CPA, Chief Executive Officer
CHR: James Proud, Vice President Human Resources and Marketing
CNO: Betty Ann Rock, Vice President Nursing and Chief Nursing Officer
Web address: www.uniontownhospital.com
Control: Other not–for–profit (including NFP Corporation) **Service:** General
Medical and Surgical

Staffed Beds: 140 **Admissions:** 8714 **Census:** 93 **Outpatient Visits:** 218402
Births: 960 **Total Expense ($000):** 118653 **Payroll Expense ($000):** 43488
Personnel: 979

UPLAND—Delaware County

✉ **CROZER–CHESTER MEDICAL CENTER (390180)**, One Medical Center
Boulevard, Zip 19013–3995; tel. 610/447–2000, (Includes SPRINGFIELD
HOSPITAL, 190 West Sproul Road, Springfield, Zip 19064–2097;
tel. 610/328–8700; TAYLOR HOSPITAL, 175 East Chester Pike, Ridley Park,
Zip 19078–2212; tel. 610/595–6000) **A**1 2 3 5 10 12 13 **F**2 3 5 6 7 8 11 12
13 14 15 16 17 18 20 22 24 26 28 29 30 31 32 34 35 36 37 38 40 41 42
43 44 45 46 47 48 49 50 51 52 54 55 56 57 58 59 61 62 63 64 65 66 68
70 72 74 75 77 78 79 81 82 83 84 85 86 87 89 90 92 93 94 96 97 98 99
100 101 102 103 104 105 107 108 109 110 111 114 115 116 117 118 119
120 121 123 124 126 129 130 131 132 134 135 138 143 145 146 147 148
P6 **S** Crozer–Keystone Health System, Springfield, PA
Primary Contact: Patrick J. Gavin, President
CMO: Sat Arora, M.D., President Medical and Dental Staff
CIO: Robert E. Wilson, Vice President and Chief Information Officer
Web address: www.crozer.org
Control: Other not–for–profit (including NFP Corporation) **Service:** General
Medical and Surgical

Staffed Beds: 384 **Admissions:** 18927 **Census:** 260 **Outpatient Visits:**
412532 **Births:** 1507 **Total Expense ($000):** 514873 **Payroll Expense**
($000): 189231 **Personnel:** 2433

WARREN—Warren County

WARREN GENERAL HOSPITAL (390146), Two Crescent Park West,
Zip 16365–0068, Mailing Address: P.O. Box 68, Zip 16365–0068;
tel. 814/723–4973 **A**10 **F**11 13 15 28 29 30 31 34 35 39 40 44 45 47 50 51
57 59 62 63 64 75 77 78 79 81 84 85 86 87 92 93 96 97 99 100 103 107
108 110 111 114 117 119 120 121 130 131 133 144 146 **P**6
Primary Contact: Richard Allen, Chief Executive Officer
COO: Randy California, Chief Operating Officer
CFO: Julie Jacobs, Chief Financial Officer
CMO: John Maljovec, M.D., Medical Director
CIO: Helen Rosequist, Manager Information Systems
CHR: Matthew Franklin, Director Human Resources
CNO: Joe Akif, Chief Clinical Officer and Chief Nursing Officer
Web address: www.wgh.org
Control: Other not–for–profit (including NFP Corporation) **Service:** General
Medical and Surgical

Staffed Beds: 87 **Admissions:** 3079 **Census:** 37 **Births:** 362

WARREN STATE HOSPITAL (394016), 33 Main Drive, Zip 16365–5001;
tel. 814/723–5500 **A**10 **F**4 39 50 56 75 77 82 98 100 101 103 128 130 132
135 143 146 **P**6
Primary Contact: Charlotte M. Uber, Chief Executive Officer
COO: Ronnie Cropper, Chief Operating Officer
CFO: Terry Crambes, Manager Finance
CMO: Asha Prabhu, M.D., Chief Medical Officer
CIO: Karen Byler, Information Technology Generalist
CHR: Nancy Saullo, Director Human Resources
CNO: Sara Flasher, Chief Nurse Executive
Web address: www.dpw.pa.gov
Control: State–Government, nonfederal **Service:** Psychiatric

Staffed Beds: 162 **Admissions:** 83 **Census:** 152 **Outpatient Visits:** 0 **Births:**
0 **Total Expense ($000):** 46103 **Payroll Expense ($000):** 20440
Personnel: 396

WASHINGTON—Washington County

☐ **ADVANCED SURGICAL HOSPITAL (390323)**, 100 Trich Drive Suite 1,
Zip 15301–5990; tel. 724/884–0710 **A**1 10 **F**64 77 79 81 82 93 111 129
Primary Contact: Anne S. Hast, R.N., Chief Executive Officer
CFO: Diane Hritz, Chief Financial Officer
CNO: Anne S. Hast, R.N., Director of Nursing
Web address: www.ashospital.net
Control: Partnership, Investor–owned, for–profit **Service:** Orthopedic

Staffed Beds: 14 **Admissions:** 567 **Census:** 4 **Births:** 0

✉ **WASHINGTON HOSPITAL (390042)**, 155 Wilson Avenue, Zip 15301–3398;
tel. 724/225–7000 **A**1 3 5 10 13 **F**3 5 11 12 13 15 18 20 22 24 26 28 29 30
31 32 34 35 36 38 39 40 45 46 48 50 51 54 56 57 59 60 61 63 64 65 70
74 75 76 77 78 79 81 82 83 84 85 86 89 90 91 92 93 94 96 97 98 100
101 102 103 107 108 110 111 114 115 118 119 126 127 130 131 132 134
135 146 147 148 **P**1 7 **S** Washington Health System, Washington, PA
Primary Contact: Gary B. Weinstein, President and Chief Executive Officer
COO: Brook Ward, Executive Vice President
CFO: Alisa Rucker, Vice President Finance and Chief Financial Officer
CMO: Paul T. Cullen, M.D., Vice President Medical Affairs
CIO: Rodney Louk, Vice President Information Systems
CHR: Barbara A. McCullough, Vice President Human Resources
CNO: Karen A. Bray, R.N., Vice President Patient Care Services
Web address: www.washingtonhospital.org
Control: Other not–for–profit (including NFP Corporation) **Service:** General
Medical and Surgical

Staffed Beds: 251 **Admissions:** 11573 **Census:** 140 **Outpatient Visits:**
687483 **Births:** 955 **Total Expense ($000):** 218290 **Payroll Expense**
($000): 98312 **Personnel:** 1513

WAYNESBORO—Franklin County

✉ **WAYNESBORO HOSPITAL (390138)**, 501 East Main Street, Zip 17268–2394;
tel. 717/765–4000 **A**1 10 **F**3 11 13 15 29 30 34 40 44 45 49 50 54 56 57
59 61 64 65 68 74 75 76 77 79 81 85 86 87 91 93 94 100 107 108 110
111 115 118 119 129 130 131 132 133 135 146 147 148 **P**8 **S** Summit
Health, Chambersburg, PA
Primary Contact: Melissa Dubrow, Chief Operating Officer
COO: Melissa Dubrow, Vice President and Chief Operating Officer
CFO: Kimberly Rzomp, Vice President Finance
CMO: Thomas Anderson, M.D., Vice President Medical Affairs
CIO: Michele Zeigler, Vice President Information Services
CHR: Jennifer Knight, Manager Human Resources
CNO: Jill Keller, R.N., Vice President for Nursing Services, Quality and Risk
Management
Web address: www.summithealth.org
Control: Other not–for–profit (including NFP Corporation) **Service:** General
Medical and Surgical

Staffed Beds: 56 **Admissions:** 2643 **Census:** 22 **Outpatient Visits:** 98481
Births: 395 **Total Expense ($000):** 52741 **Payroll Expense ($000):** 24588
Personnel: 387

Many Facility Codes have changed. Please refer to the AHA Guide Code Chart. © 2016 AHA Guide

WAYNESBURG—Greene County

⊞ **WASHINGTON HEALTH SYSTEM GREENE (390150)**, 350 Bonar Avenue, Zip 15370–1608; tel. 724/627–3101 **A**1 10 **F**5 11 18 29 30 34 35 40 44 45 50 51 57 59 62 64 75 77 81 85 87 98 103 104 107 108 110 111 114 119 130 133 135 146 148 **P**6 **S** Washington Health System, Washington, PA
Primary Contact: Terry Wiltrout, President
COO: Janel Mudry, Chief Operating Officer
CMO: Jamie Boris, M.D., President Medical Staff
CIO: Leslie Hayhurst, Director Information Systems
CHR: Patricia Marshall, Assistant Administrator Human Resources
Web address: www.southwestregionalmedical.com/
Control: Other not–for–profit (including NFP Corporation) **Service:** General Medical and Surgical

Staffed Beds: 49 **Admissions:** 1743 **Census:** 25 **Outpatient Visits:** 59408 **Births:** 0 **Total Expense ($000):** 27819 **Payroll Expense ($000):** 12199 **Personnel:** 359

WELLSBORO—Tioga County

⊞ **SOLDIERS AND SAILORS MEMORIAL HOSPITAL (390043)**, 32–36 Central Avenue, Zip 16901–1899; tel. 570/724–1631 **A**1 10 20 **F**3 11 13 15 17 28 31 34 40 48 49 64 65 70 75 76 78 79 81 85 93 104 107 108 110 111 115 118 119 129 130 146 **P**7 **S** Susquehanna Health System, Williamsport, PA
Primary Contact: Janie Hilfiger, President
CFO: Eric Pohjala, Chief Financial Officer
CMO: Walter Laibinis, M.D., Chief Medical Officer
CIO: Timothy E. Schoener, Senior Vice President and Chief Information Officer
CHR: Christine A. Ballard, Vice President Human Resources
CNO: Matt Romania, Director of Nursing
Web address: www.susquehannahealth.org
Control: Other not–for–profit (including NFP Corporation) **Service:** General Medical and Surgical

Staffed Beds: 67 **Admissions:** 1903 **Census:** 19 **Outpatient Visits:** 106643 **Births:** 306 **Total Expense ($000):** 58403 **Payroll Expense ($000):** 21524 **Personnel:** 433

WERNERSVILLE—Berks County

WERNERSVILLE STATE HOSPITAL (394014), Route 422, Zip 19565–0300, Mailing Address: P.O. Box 300, Zip 19565–0300; tel. 610/678–3411 **A**10 **F**30 39 75 77 98 103 130 135 146
Primary Contact: Andrea Kepler, Chief Executive Officer
COO: Cheryl Benson, Chief Operating Officer
CMO: Dale K. Adair, M.D., Chief Medical Officer
CIO: William Edwards, Information Technology Generalist
CHR: Melvin McMinn, Director Human Resources
Web address: www.dpw.state.pa.us/
Control: State–Government, nonfederal **Service:** Psychiatric

Staffed Beds: 266 **Admissions:** 64 **Census:** 250 **Outpatient Visits:** 0 **Births:** 0 **Total Expense ($000):** 64592 **Payroll Expense ($000):** 31223 **Personnel:** 535

WEST CHESTER—Chester County

⊞ **LIFECARE HOSPITALS OF CHESTER COUNTY (392048)**, 400 East Marshall Street, Zip 19380–5412; tel. 484/826–0400 **A**1 10 **F**1 77 79 130 148 **P**5 **S** LifeCare Management Services, Plano, TX
Primary Contact: Garrett Arneson, Chief Executive Officer
CMO: Raj Patel, M.D., Medical Director
CHR: Evan Ganley, Manager Human Resources
CNO: Bonnie Barclay, Chief Nursing Officer
Web address: www.lifecare–hospitals.com
Control: Corporation, Investor–owned, for–profit **Service:** Long–Term Acute Care hospital

Staffed Beds: 39 **Admissions:** 338 **Census:** 24 **Outpatient Visits:** 0 **Births:** 0

⊞ **PENN MEDICINE CHESTER COUNTY HOSPITAL (390179)**, 701 East Marshall Street, Zip 19380–4412; tel. 610/431–5000 **A**1 2 3 5 10 **F**3 11 13 15 17 18 20 22 24 26 28 29 30 31 34 35 36 39 40 44 45 46 49 50 51 54 55 57 58 59 60 62 63 64 68 70 72 73 74 75 76 77 78 79 81 82 84 85 86 87 89 91 93 107 108 110 111 114 115 116 117 119 120 121 126 130 131 132 135 146 147 148 **S** University of Pennsylvania Health System, Philadelphia, PA
Primary Contact: Michael J. Duncan, President and Chief Executive Officer
COO: Michael Barber, Chief Operating Officer
CFO: Kenneth E. Flickinger, Chief Financial Officer
CMO: Richard D. Donze, D.O., Senior Vice President Medical Affairs
CIO: Karen Pinsky, M.D., Chief Medical Information Officer
CHR: Jacqueline Felicetti, Chief Human Resource Officer
CNO: Angela R. Coladonato DNP, RN, NEA–BC, MSN, Chief Nursing Officer
Web address: www.chestercountyhospital.org
Control: Other not–for–profit (including NFP Corporation) **Service:** General Medical and Surgical

Staffed Beds: 211 **Admissions:** 13521 **Census:** 149 **Outpatient Visits:** 249055 **Births:** 2609 **Total Expense ($000):** 272203 **Payroll Expense ($000):** 113023 **Personnel:** 1733

WEST GROVE—Chester County

⊞ **JENNERSVILLE REGIONAL HOSPITAL (390220)**, 1015 West Baltimore Pike, Zip 19390–9459; tel. 610/869–1000 **A**1 2 10 **F**3 13 15 18 29 35 40 45 49 50 51 57 59 70 74 75 76 79 81 82 85 87 92 93 107 108 110 111 115 119 129 130 131 132 133 146 147 **P**6 **S** Community Health Systems, Inc., Franklin, TN
Primary Contact: Andrew Guz, Chief Executive Officer
CFO: Tracey Claxton, Chief Financial Officer
CMO: Tracy Carmellini, M.D., Chief of Staff
CHR: Debra Basquill, Director Human Resources
CNO: David Schmidt, R.N., Chief Nursing Officer
Web address: www.jennersville.com
Control: Corporation, Investor–owned, for–profit **Service:** General Medical and Surgical

Staffed Beds: 63 **Admissions:** 3211 **Census:** 30 **Births:** 352

WEST READING—Berks County

⊞ △ **READING HOSPITAL (390044)**, Sixth Avenue and Spruce Street, Zip 19611–1428, Mailing Address: P.O. Box 16052, Zip 19612–6052; tel. 610/988–8000 **A**1 2 3 5 7 8 10 12 13 **F**3 5 8 11 12 13 15 18 20 22 24 26 28 29 30 31 32 34 35 37 40 41 42 43 44 45 46 48 49 50 51 54 58 59 60 61 62 64 65 66 68 70 72 73 74 75 76 77 78 79 81 82 84 85 86 87 89 90 92 93 94 96 97 98 99 100 101 102 103 104 105 106 107 108 110 111 114 115 116 117 118 119 120 121 123 124 125 126 128 129 130 131 132 135 144 146 147 148 **P**6 8
Primary Contact: Clinton Matthews, President and Chief Executive Officer
CFO: Richard W. Jones, Chief Financial Officer
CMO: M. Joseph Grennan, Jr., M.D., Senior Vice President and Chief Medical Officer
CIO: Jayashree Raman, Vice President and Chief Information Officer
CNO: Mary Christine Agnew, R.N., Vice President and Chief Nursing Officer
Web address: www.readinghospital.org
Control: Other not–for–profit (including NFP Corporation) **Service:** General Medical and Surgical

Staffed Beds: 679 **Admissions:** 31071 **Census:** 454 **Outpatient Visits:** 973282 **Births:** 3599 **Total Expense ($000):** 782783 **Payroll Expense ($000):** 315476 **Personnel:** 4653

WILKES BARRE—Luzerne County

⊞ **GEISINGER WYOMING VALLEY MEDICAL CENTER (390270)**, 1000 East Mountain Boulevard, Zip 18711–0027; tel. 570/808–7300, (Nonreporting) **A**1 2 3 5 10 13 **S** Geisinger Health System, Danville, PA
Primary Contact: Ronald R. Beer, FACHE, Vice President, Clinical Operations
CFO: Thomas A. Bielecki, Chief Financial Officer
CMO: Steven Pierdon, M.D., Executive Vice President and Chief Medical Officer
CIO: Frank Richards, Chief Information Officer
CHR: Margaret Heffers, Assistant Vice President Human Resources
Web address: www.geisinger.org
Control: Other not–for–profit (including NFP Corporation) **Service:** General Medical and Surgical

Staffed Beds: 238

PA

Hospital, Medicare Provider Number, Address, Telephone, Approval, Facility, and Physician Codes, Health Care System

★ American Hospital Association (AHA) membership
□ The Joint Commission accreditation
○ Healthcare Facilities Accreditation Program
◇ DNV Healthcare Inc. accreditation
⇑ Center for Improvement in Healthcare Quality Accreditation
△ Commission on Accreditation of Rehabilitation Facilities (CARF) accreditation

PA

WILKES–BARRE—Luzerne County

☐ △ **JOHN HEINZ INSTITUTE OF REHABILITATION MEDICINE (393036)**, 150 Mundy Street, Zip 18702–6830; tel. 570/826–3800, (Total facility includes 21 beds in nursing home–type unit) **A**1 7 10 **F**3 11 29 30 32 35 54 57 59 62 64 68 75 77 82 86 90 91 92 93 130 131 132 143 146 148
Primary Contact: Karen Kearney, Vice President Inpatient Rehabilitation Services
CFO: Mike Avvisato, Vice President and Chief Financial Officer
CMO: Gregory Basting, M.D., Vice President Medical Affairs
CIO: John Regula, Chief Information Officer
CHR: Judy P. Oprisko, Vice President Human Resources
CNO: Maria Berlyn, Assistant Vice President Nursing Services
Web address: www.allied–services.org
Control: Other not–for–profit (including NFP Corporation) **Service:** Rehabilitation

Staffed Beds: 71 **Admissions:** 1431 **Census:** 50 **Births:** 0

VETERANS AFFAIRS MEDICAL CENTER See Wilkes–Barre Veterans Affairs Medical Center

★ △ **WILKES–BARRE GENERAL HOSPITAL (390137)**, 575 North River Street, Zip 18764–0001; tel. 570/829–8111, (Includes WILKES–BARRE GENERAL HOSPITAL, 575 North River Street, Zip 18764; tel. 570/829–8111) **A**2 3 5 7 10 **F**3 8 12 13 15 17 18 20 22 24 26 28 29 30 31 34 37 40 44 45 46 48 49 50 51 53 54 56 57 59 61 64 66 70 73 74 75 76 78 79 81 82 83 84 85 86 87 89 90 91 92 93 96 107 108 110 111 112 114 115 116 117 118 119 126 129 130 132 145 146 147 148 **S** Community Health Systems, Inc., Franklin, TN
Primary Contact: Cornelio R. Catena, President and Chief Executive Officer
COO: Robert P. Hoffman, Vice President and Director Patient Care Services
CFO: Maggie Koehler, Senior Vice President and Chief Financial Officer
CMO: Ragupathy Veluswamy, M.D., Vice President Medical Affairs
CIO: Chris Galanda, Chief Information Officer
CHR: James Carmody, Vice President Human Resources
Web address: www.wvhc.org
Control: Corporation, Investor–owned, for–profit **Service:** General Medical and Surgical

Staffed Beds: 374 **Admissions:** 14537 **Census:** 204 **Outpatient Visits:** 525785 **Births:** 1149 **Total Expense ($000):** 272349 **Payroll Expense ($000):** 84019 **Personnel:** 1609

⌧ **WILKES–BARRE VETERANS AFFAIRS MEDICAL CENTER**, 1111 East End Boulevard, Zip 18711–0030; tel. 570/824–3521, (Nonreporting) **A**1 2 3 5 **S** Department of Veterans Affairs, Washington, DC
Primary Contact: Michael Adelman, M.D., Medical Center Director
COO: Joesph P. Sharon, Associate Director
CFO: Donald E. Foote, Fiscal Officer
CMO: Mirza Z. Ali, M.D., Chief of Staff
CIO: David Longmore, Chief Information Officer
CHR: Dawn P. DeMorrow, Chief Human Resources Service
Web address: www.va.gov/vamcwb
Control: Veterans Affairs, Government, federal **Service:** General Medical and Surgical

Staffed Beds: 158

WYOMING VALLEY HEALTH CARE SYSTEM See Wilkes–Barre General Hospital

WILLIAMSPORT—Lycoming County

★ **DIVINE PROVIDENCE HOSPITAL (394048)**, 1100 Grampian Boulevard, Zip 17701–1995; tel. 570/326–8000 **A**3 10 **F**10 11 15 31 35 38 44 50 51 53 54 55 56 59 62 63 64 68 75 77 78 79 81 82 83 84 86 87 93 98 99 100 103 108 110 111 115 120 121 129 130 131 132 134 146 147 148 **P**7 **S** Susquehanna Health System, Williamsport, PA
Primary Contact: Robert E. Kane, President
COO: Neil G. Armstrong, FACHE, Vice President and Chief Operating Officer
Web address: www.susquehannahealth.org
Control: Other not–for–profit (including NFP Corporation) **Service:** Psychiatric

Staffed Beds: 31 **Admissions:** 663 **Census:** 17 **Outpatient Visits:** 306241 **Births:** 0 **Total Expense ($000):** 85321 **Payroll Expense ($000):** 22327 **Personnel:** 233

WILLIAMSPORT HOSPITAL AND MEDICAL CENTER See Williamsport Regional Medical Center

⌧ **WILLIAMSPORT REGIONAL MEDICAL CENTER (390045)**, 700 High Street, Zip 17701–3100; tel. 570/321–1000 **A**1 2 5 10 13 **F**3 7 9 11 12 13 15 17 18 20 22 24 26 28 29 30 32 34 35 37 38 40 44 45 46 47 48 49 50 51 52 53 54 56 57 58 59 60 61 65 68 70 73 74 75 76 77 79 81 85 86 87 89 90 91 92 93 94 96 97 107 108 110 111 114 115 116 117 118 119 120 121 123 124 126 130 132 134 135 143 144 146 147 **P**7 **S** Susquehanna Health System, Williamsport, PA
Primary Contact: Jan E. Fisher, Executive Vice President, Chief Operating Officer and Chief Administrative Officer
COO: Jan E. Fisher, Executive Vice President, Chief Operating Officer and Chief Administrative Officer
CFO: Eric D. Pohjala, Executive Vice President and Chief Financial Officer
CIO: Timothy E. Schoener, Vice President and Chief Information Officer
CHR: Christine A. Ballard, Vice President Human Resources
CNO: Lori A. Beucler, MSN, RN, BS–NE, FACHE, R.N., Vice President and Chief Nursing Officer
Web address: www.susquehannahealth.org
Control: Other not–for–profit (including NFP Corporation) **Service:** General Medical and Surgical

Staffed Beds: 220 **Admissions:** 11362 **Census:** 132 **Outpatient Visits:** 89229 **Births:** 1191 **Total Expense ($000):** 292838 **Payroll Expense ($000):** 97665 **Personnel:** 1332

WINDBER—Somerset County

★ **CHAN SOON–SHIONG MEDICAL CENTER (390112)**, 600 Somerset Avenue, Zip 15963–1331; tel. 814/467–3000 **A**10 **F**3 11 12 15 18 28 29 30 34 35 36 40 45 53 55 56 57 58 59 62 63 70 75 79 81 83 84 85 93 107 110 111 114 117 118 119 129 130 131 132 135 146 147
Primary Contact: Thomas M. Kurtz, President and Chief Executive Officer
CFO: Richard Sukenik, CPA, Vice President Finance and Chief Financial Officer
CMO: Kim Marley, M.D., Chief Medical Officer
CIO: Renee Adams, Director Information Technology
CHR: Jamie Brock, Director Human Resources
CNO: Michelle Hamula, Director of Nursing and Quality
Web address: www.windbercare.org
Control: Other not–for–profit (including NFP Corporation) **Service:** General Medical and Surgical

Staffed Beds: 45 **Admissions:** 1111 **Census:** 9 **Outpatient Visits:** 102264 **Births:** 0 **Total Expense ($000):** 44367 **Payroll Expense ($000):** 16953 **Personnel:** 346

WYNNEWOOD—Montgomery County

LANKENAU HOSPITAL See Lankenau Medical Center

⌧ **LANKENAU MEDICAL CENTER (390195)**, 100 Lancaster Avenue West, Zip 19096–3411; tel. 484/476–2000, (Total facility includes 22 beds in nursing home–type unit) **A**1 2 3 5 8 10 12 13 **F**3 11 13 15 17 18 20 22 24 26 28 29 30 31 32 34 35 36 37 38 39 40 41 43 44 45 46 47 48 49 50 54 55 56 57 58 59 63 64 65 66 70 72 73 74 75 76 78 79 81 82 84 85 86 87 92 97 100 102 103 107 108 110 111 114 115 119 120 121 124 126 128 129 130 131 132 135 138 141 143 146 148 **S** Main Line Health
Primary Contact: Phillip D. Robinson, President
COO: John Schwarz, Vice President Administration
CFO: Michael J. Buongiorno, Vice President Finance
CMO: Robert Benz, M.D., Chief Medical Officer
CIO: Karen A. Thomas, Acting Vice President and Chief Information Officer
CHR: Paul Yakulis, MS, Senior Vice President Human Resources
CNO: Margaret Iacobacci, Vice President Patient Care
Web address: www.mainlinehealth.org
Control: Other not–for–profit (including NFP Corporation) **Service:** General Medical and Surgical

Staffed Beds: 353 **Admissions:** 18099 **Census:** 244 **Outpatient Visits:** 319910 **Births:** 2847 **Total Expense ($000):** 426559 **Payroll Expense ($000):** 129408 **Personnel:** 2365

WYOMISSING—Berks County

⌧ **SURGICAL INSTITUTE OF READING (390316)**, 2752 Century Boulevard, Zip 19610–3345; tel. 610/378–8800 **A**1 10 **F**8 29 45 68 79 81 82 85 86 107 114
Primary Contact: Debbie Beissel, Chief Executive Officer
CFO: Cheryl Peterson, Business Office Manager
CHR: Megan Schaffer, Administrative Assistant
Web address: www.sireading.com
Control: Partnership, Investor–owned, for–profit **Service:** Surgical

Staffed Beds: 15 **Admissions:** 742 **Census:** 4 **Outpatient Visits:** 13275 **Births:** 0 **Total Expense ($000):** 23583 **Payroll Expense ($000):** 6032 **Personnel:** 158

Many Facility Codes have changed. Please refer to the AHA Guide Code Chart. © 2016 AHA Guide

YORK—York County

✠ **HEALTHSOUTH REHABILITATION HOSPITAL OF YORK (393037)**, 1850 Normandie Drive, Zip 17408–1534; tel. 717/767–6941, (Nonreporting) **A**1 10
S HEALTHSOUTH Corporation, Birmingham, AL
Primary Contact: Steven Alwine, Chief Executive Officer
CFO: Joyce Henry, Controller
CMO: Bruce Sicilia, M.D., Medical Director
CIO: Laura Emig, Director Marketing Operations
CHR: Bradley Teahl, Director Human Resources
CNO: Julie Scott, Chief Nursing Officer
Web address: www.healthsouthyork.com
Control: Corporation, Investor–owned, for–profit **Service:** Rehabilitation

Staffed Beds: 90

★ ○ **MEMORIAL HOSPITAL (390101)**, 325 South Belmont Street,
Zip 17403–2609, Mailing Address: P.O. Box 15118, Zip 17405–7118;
tel. 717/843–8623 **A**10 11 13 **F**3 7 8 13 15 18 20 22 26 29 30 31 34 35 40
45 47 48 49 50 51 54 56 57 58 59 60 64 65 66 68 70 75 76 77 78 79 81
84 85 93 97 107 108 111 116 117 118 119 126 129 130 132 135 146 147
P6 **S** Community Health Systems, Inc., Franklin, TN
Primary Contact: Sally J. Dixon, Chief Executive Officer
CIO: James Mahoney, Chief Information Officer
CHR: Corey Hudak, Director Human Resources
CNO: Susan Gordon, R.N., Chief Nursing Officer
Web address: www.mhyork.org
Control: Other not–for–profit (including NFP Corporation) **Service:** General
Medical and Surgical

Staffed Beds: 100 Admissions: 4690 Census: 45 Births: 561

✠ **OSS ORTHOPAEDIC HOSPITAL (390325)**, 1861 Powder Mill Road,
Zip 17402–4723; tel. 717/718–2000 **A**1 3 10 **F**3 29 34 62 64 79 81 82 85
86 87 92 94 107 111 114 119 130 131 135 144 148 **P**1 2 6
Primary Contact: Joseph Alhadeff, M.D., President and Chief Executive Officer
COO: Michael Enriquez, Chief Operating Officer
CFO: Dale Bushey, Chief Financial Officer
CMO: Gracia Etienne, M.D., President Medical Staff
CIO: Tricia Wolf, Director Information Technology
CHR: Maureen M. Putnam, Director Human Resources
CNO: Debra Garton, R.N., Chief Nursing Officer
Web address: www.osshealth.com
Control: Partnership, Investor–owned, for–profit **Service:** Orthopedic

Staffed Beds: 30 Admissions: 1538 Census: 10 Births: 0

SELECT SPECIALTY HOSPITAL–YORK See Select Specialty Hospital–Central
Pennsylvania, Camp Hill

✠ △ **WELLSPAN YORK HOSPITAL (390046)**, 1001 South George Street,
Zip 17403–3645; tel. 717/851–2345, (Includes WELLSPAN SURGERY AND
REHABILLITATION HOSPITAL, 55 Monument Road, Zip 17403–5023;
tel. 717/812–6100; Barbara Yarrish, R.N., President) **A**1 2 3 5 7 8 10 12 13 **F**3
7 11 12 13 14 15 17 18 20 22 24 26 28 29 30 31 34 35 39 40 43 44 45 46
48 49 50 54 55 56 57 58 59 60 61 64 65 66 68 70 72 74 75 76 77 78 79
81 82 84 85 86 87 89 92 93 96 97 98 100 101 102 103 104 107 108 110
111 114 115 117 118 119 120 121 123 124 126 129 130 131 132 135 146
147 148 **S** WellSpan Health, York, PA
Primary Contact: Keith D. Noll, President
COO: Raymond Rosen, FACHE, Vice President Operations
CFO: Michael F. O'Connor, Senior Vice President Finance
CMO: Peter M. Hartmann, M.D., Vice President Medical Affairs
CIO: R. Hal Baker, M.D., Vice President and Chief Information Officer
CHR: Robert J. Batory, Vice President Human Resources
CNO: Astrid Davis, R.N., Chief Nursing Officer
Web address: www.wellspan.org
Control: Other not–for–profit (including NFP Corporation) **Service:** General
Medical and Surgical

Staffed Beds: 556 Admissions: 29912 Census: 424 Births: 3155

PA

Hospital, Medicare Provider Number, Address, Telephone, Approval, Facility, and Physician Codes, Health Care System

★ American Hospital Association (AHA) membership ○ Healthcare Facilities Accreditation Program ⇑ Center for Improvement in Healthcare Quality Accreditation
□ The Joint Commission accreditation ◇ DNV Healthcare Inc. accreditation △ Commission on Accreditation of Rehabilitation Facilities (CARF) accreditation

© 2016 AHA Guide *Many Facility Codes have changed. Please refer to the AHA Guide Code Chart.* Hospitals **A559**

RHODE ISLAND

CRANSTON—Providence County

☐ **ELEANOR SLATER HOSPITAL (412001)**, 111 Howard Avenue, Zip 02920–0269, Mailing Address: P.O. Box 8269, Zip 02920–0269; tel. 401/462–3085, (Nonreporting) **A**1 3 10
Primary Contact: Paul J. Despres, Chief Executive Officer
CMO: Charlene Tate, M.D., Chief Medical Staff and Clinical Services
Web address: www.bhddh.ri.gov/esh/
Control: State–Government, nonfederal **Service:** Long–Term Acute Care hospital

Staffed Beds: 495

EAST PROVIDENCE—Providence County

☐ **EMMA PENDLETON BRADLEY HOSPITAL (414003)**, 1011 Veterans Memorial Parkway, Zip 02915–5099; tel. 401/432–1000 **A**1 3 5 10 **F**3 29 34 35 38 57 58 62 64 68 77 86 87 98 99 100 101 104 105 106 130 132 134 **S** Lifespan Corporation, Providence, RI
Primary Contact: Daniel J. Wall, President and Chief Executive Officer
CFO: Mamie Wakefield, Vice President Finance and Chief Financial Officer
CMO: Henry T. Sachs, III, M.D., Medical Director
CIO: Carole Cotter, Senior Vice President and Chief Information Officer
CHR: Rob Duval, Chief Human Resources Officer
CNO: Vareen O'Keefe Domaleski, MS, Vice Patient Care Services and Chief Nursing Officer
Web address: www.lifespan.org
Control: Other not–for–profit (including NFP Corporation) **Service:** Children's hospital psychiatric

Staffed Beds: 60 **Admissions:** 1417 **Census:** 58 **Outpatient Visits:** 11807 **Births:** 0 **Total Expense ($000):** 65686 **Payroll Expense ($000):** 36225 **Personnel:** 541

NEWPORT—Newport County

☐ △ **NEWPORT HOSPITAL (410006)**, 11 Friendship Street, Zip 02840–2299; tel. 401/846–6400 **A**1 2 3 7 10 **F**3 8 11 13 15 18 28 29 30 31 34 35 40 45 49 50 51 53 54 56 57 59 60 64 68 70 74 75 76 77 78 79 81 82 85 86 87 89 90 91 92 93 96 97 98 99 100 102 103 104 105 107 108 110 111 114 118 119 129 130 132 135 141 143 146 147 148 **S** Lifespan Corporation, Providence, RI
Primary Contact: Crista F. Durand, President
CFO: Frank J. Byrne, Vice President Finance
CMO: Thomas E. McGue, M.D., Vice President Medical Affairs and Chief Medical Officer
CHR: Barbara J. Arcangeli, Vice President Human Resources
CNO: Cathy E. Duquette, Ph.D., Vice President Nursing and Chief Nursing Officer
Web address: www.newporthospital.org
Control: Other not–for–profit (including NFP Corporation) **Service:** General Medical and Surgical

Staffed Beds: 119 **Admissions:** 4521 **Census:** 60 **Outpatient Visits:** 72116 **Births:** 406 **Total Expense ($000):** 100723 **Payroll Expense ($000):** 44593 **Personnel:** 608

NORTH PROVIDENCE—Providence County

☐ △ **ST. JOSEPH HEALTH SERVICES OF RHODE ISLAND (410005)**, 200 High Service Avenue, Zip 02904–5199; tel. 401/456–3000, (Includes OUR LADY OF FATIMA HOSPITAL, John J. Holiver, CEO, 200 High Service Avenue, Zip 02904; tel. 401/456–3000; Thomas Hughes, President; ST. JOSEPH HOSPITAL FOR SPECIALTY CARE, 21 Peace Street, Providence, Zip 02907; tel. 401/456–3000), (Nonreporting) **A**1 2 7 10 **S** CharterCare Health Partners, Providence, RI
Primary Contact: Thomas Hughes, President
CFO: Michael E. Conklin, Jr., Chief Financial Officer
CIO: Susan Cerrone Abely, Chief Information Officer
CHR: Darlene Souza, Vice President
CNO: Patricia A. Nadle, R.N., Chief Nursing Officer
Web address: www.saintjosephri.com
Control: Other not–for–profit (including NFP Corporation) **Service:** General Medical and Surgical

Staffed Beds: 125

NORTH SMITHFIELD—Providence County

LANDMARK MEDICAL CENTER–FOGARTY UNIT See Landmark Medical Center, Woonsocket

✠ **REHABILITATION HOSPITAL OF RHODE ISLAND (413025)**, 116 Eddie Dowling Highway, Zip 02896–7327; tel. 401/766–0800, (Nonreporting) **A**1 10 **S** Prime Healthcare Services, Ontario, CA
Primary Contact: Richard Charest, Chief Executive Officer
COO: Demetra Ouellette, Chief Operating Officer
CFO: Thomas Klessens, Chief Financial Officer
CMO: Khin Yin, Medical Director
CIO: Vincent Larosa, Director of Information Technology Services
CHR: Gail Gosselin, Director Human Resources
CNO: Kathy Keeling, Director of Nursing
Web address: www.rhri.net
Control: Corporation, Investor–owned, for–profit **Service:** Rehabilitation

Staffed Beds: 70

PAWTUCKET—Providence County

✠ △ **MEMORIAL HOSPITAL OF RHODE ISLAND (410001)**, 111 Brewster Street, Zip 02860–4499; tel. 401/729–2000, (Nonreporting) **A**1 2 3 5 7 8 10 **S** Care New England Health System, Providence, RI
Primary Contact: Michael Dacey, MD, Interim Chief Operating Officer and Chief Medical Officer
CFO: James M. Burke, Senior Vice President Finance
CMO: Joseph Diaz, M.D., Chief Medical Officer
CHR: Lisa D. Pratt, Vice President Human Resources
CNO: Eileen Dobbing, R.N., Senior Vice President for Patient Care Services
Web address: www.mhri.org
Control: Other not–for–profit (including NFP Corporation) **Service:** General Medical and Surgical

Staffed Beds: 150

PROVIDENCE—Providence County

✠ **BUTLER HOSPITAL (414000)**, 345 Blackstone Boulevard, Zip 02906–4829; tel. 401/455–6200, (Nonreporting) **A**1 3 5 10 **S** Care New England Health System, Providence, RI
Primary Contact: Lawrence Price, M.D., President and Chief Operating Officer
COO: Lawrence Price, M.D., President and Chief Operating Officer
CFO: Bonnie Baker, Vice President Finance and Chief Financial Officer
CMO: James Sullivan, M.D., Chief Medical Officer
CIO: Summa Gaddam, Chief Information Officer
CHR: Timothy Bigelow, Director Human Resources
CNO: Mary Leveillee, Senior Vice President Patient Care Services and Chief Nursing Officer
Web address: www.butler.org
Control: Other not–for–profit (including NFP Corporation) **Service:** Psychiatric

Staffed Beds: 143

☐ **MIRIAM HOSPITAL (410012)**, 164 Summit Avenue, Zip 02906–2853; tel. 401/793–2500 **A**1 2 3 5 8 10 **F**3 8 11 12 15 18 20 22 26 28 29 30 31 34 35 40 44 45 46 49 50 53 54 56 57 58 59 60 61 64 65 66 67 68 70 74 75 77 78 79 81 82 84 85 87 92 93 97 100 103 107 108 110 111 114 115 118 119 126 130 132 135 143 146 147 148 **P**3 5 6 **S** Lifespan Corporation, Providence, RI
Primary Contact: Arthur J. Sampson, FACHE, President
COO: Maria Ducharme, R.N., Senior Vice President Patient Care Services and Chief Nursing Officer
CFO: Mamie Wakefield, Chief Financial Officer
CMO: R. William Corwin, M.D., Vice President and Chief Medical Officer
CIO: Carole Cotter, Vice President and Chief Information Officer
CHR: Nancy McMahon, Vice President Human Resources
Web address: www.lifespan.org
Control: Other not–for–profit (including NFP Corporation) **Service:** General Medical and Surgical

Staffed Beds: 247 **Admissions:** 16690 **Census:** 185 **Outpatient Visits:** 188632 **Births:** 0 **Total Expense ($000):** 418741 **Payroll Expense ($000):** 181128 **Personnel:** 2312

✠ **PROVIDENCE VETERANS AFFAIRS MEDICAL CENTER**, 830 Chalkstone Avenue, Zip 02908–4799; tel. 401/273–7100 **A**1 2 3 5 **F**3 5 8 12 18 29 30 31 35 37 38 39 40 44 45 46 47 48 49 50 51 53 54 55 56 57 58 59 60 61 62 63 64 65 68 70 74 75 77 78 79 81 82 84 85 86 87 91 92 93 94 97 98 100 101 102 103 104 107 108 111 114 115 118 119 126 130 132 135 143 144 145 146 147 148 **S** Department of Veterans Affairs, Washington, DC
Primary Contact: Susan MacKenzie, Director
COO: Erin Clare Sears, Associate Director of Operations
CMO: Satish C. Sharma, M.D., Chief of Staff
Web address: www.providence.va.gov/
Control: Veterans Affairs, Government, federal **Service:** General Medical and Surgical

Staffed Beds: 73 **Admissions:** 3305 **Census:** 47 **Outpatient Visits:** 439038 **Births:** 0 **Total Expense ($000):** 262173 **Personnel:** 1431

☐ **RHODE ISLAND HOSPITAL (410007)**, 593 Eddy Street, Zip 02903–4900; tel. 401/444–4000, (Includes HASBRO CHILDREN'S HOSPITAL, 593 Eddy Street, Zip 02903–4923; tel. 401/444–4000) **A**1 2 3 5 8 10 **F**3 6 7 8 11 15 16 17 18 19 20 21 22 23 24 26 29 30 31 33 34 35 38 39 40 41 43 44 45 46 47 48 49 50 51 53 54 55 56 57 58 59 60 61 64 65 66 67 68 70 74 75 77 78 79 81 82 84 85 86 87 88 89 90 92 93 94 97 98 99 100 101 102 103 104 105 107 108 110 111 114 115 116 117 118 119 121 124 128 129 130 131 132 133 134 135 138 142 143 145 146 147 148 **P**3 5 6 **S** Lifespan Corporation, Providence, RI
Primary Contact: Margaret Vanbref, MD, President and Chief Executive Officer
COO: Fredrick Macri, Executive Vice President
CFO: Mamie Wakefield, Senior Vice President and Chief Financial Officer
CMO: John B. Murphy, M.D., Vice President Medical Affairs and Chief Medical Officer
CIO: Carole Cotter, Senior Vice President and Chief Information Officer
CHR: Louis J. Sperling, Vice President Human Resources
Web address: www.rhodeislandhospital.org/
Control: Other not–for–profit (including NFP Corporation) **Service:** General Medical and Surgical

Staffed Beds: 650 **Admissions:** 35372 **Census:** 526 **Outpatient Visits:** 459704 **Births:** 0 **Total Expense ($000):** 1183063 **Payroll Expense ($000):** 518545 **Personnel:** 5890

☒ **ROGER WILLIAMS MEDICAL CENTER (410004)**, 825 Chalkstone Avenue, Zip 02908–4735; tel. 401/456–2000, (Nonreporting) **A**1 2 3 5 8 10 **S** CharterCare Health Partners, Providence, RI
Primary Contact: Kimberly O'Connell, President
CFO: Addy Kane, Chief Financial Officer
CMO: Elaine Jones, M.D., President Medical Staff
CIO: Susan Cerrone Abely, Vice President and Chief Information Officer
Web address: www.rwmc.com
Control: Other not–for–profit (including NFP Corporation) **Service:** General Medical and Surgical

Staffed Beds: 86

ST. JOSEPH HOSPITAL FOR SPECIALTY CARE See St. Joseph Health Services of Rhode Island, North Providence

VETERANS AFFAIRS MEDICAL CENTER See Providence Veterans Affairs Medical Center

☒ **WOMEN & INFANTS HOSPITAL OF RHODE ISLAND (410010)**, 101 Dudley Street, Zip 02905–2499; tel. 401/274–1100 **A**1 2 3 5 8 10 **F**3 5 11 13 15 29 30 31 33 34 35 36 38 40 44 45 50 52 54 55 57 58 59 63 64 65 66 68 71 72 74 75 76 77 78 81 82 84 85 86 87 93 97 100 101 102 104 105 107 110 111 114 119 126 130 132 134 135 143 146 147 **P**5 6 8 **S** Care New England Health System, Providence, RI
Primary Contact: Mark R. Marcantano, President and Chief Operating Officer
COO: Mark R. Marcantano, President and Chief Operating Officer
CFO: Robert W. Pacheco, Vice President Finance
CMO: Raymond Powrie, M.D., Senior Vice President Quality and Clinical Effectiveness
CHR: Paul F. Heffernan, Vice President Human Resources
CNO: Angelleen Peters–Lewis, R.N., System Chief Nursing Officer
Web address: www.womenandinfants.org
Control: Other not–for–profit (including NFP Corporation) **Service:** Obstetrics and gynecology

Staffed Beds: 247 **Admissions:** 11689 **Census:** 152 **Outpatient Visits:** 340043 **Births:** 8948 **Total Expense ($000):** 480237 **Payroll Expense ($000):** 189988 **Personnel:** 1947

☐ **SOUTH COUNTY HOSPITAL (410008)**, 100 Kenyon Avenue, Zip 02879–4299; tel. 401/782–8000 **A**1 2 10 **F**3 13 15 18 20 28 29 30 31 34 35 36 37 40 44 45 46 47 49 50 51 53 54 56 57 59 60 61 64 65 68 70 74 77 78 79 81 85 86 87 103 107 108 110 111 114 119 126 129 130 131 135 141 146 **P**6
Primary Contact: Louis R. Giancola, President and Chief Executive Officer
CFO: Thomas Breen, Vice President and Chief Financial Officer
CMO: John Russell Corcoran, Vice President Medical Affairs
CIO: Gary Croteau, Assistant Vice President and Chief Information Officer
CHR: Maggie Thomas, Vice President Human Resources and Practice Management
CNO: Anne Schmidt, Vice President of Patient Care Services and Chief Nursing Officer
Web address: www.schospital.com
Control: Other not–for–profit (including NFP Corporation) **Service:** General Medical and Surgical

Staffed Beds: 85 **Admissions:** 4490 **Census:** 45 **Outpatient Visits:** 194246 **Births:** 632 **Total Expense ($000):** 145608 **Payroll Expense ($000):** 62173 **Personnel:** 756

☒ △ **KENT COUNTY MEMORIAL HOSPITAL (410009)**, 455 Tollgate Road, Zip 02886–2770; tel. 401/737–7000 **A**1 2 3 5 7 10 13 **F**3 8 11 12 13 15 17 18 20 22 26 29 30 31 34 35 36 40 44 45 46 47 48 49 50 51 56 57 58 59 60 61 63 64 65 68 70 73 74 75 76 77 78 79 81 82 84 85 86 87 90 93 94 96 98 100 102 103 105 107 108 110 111 115 119 126 129 130 131 132 143 146 147 148 **P**8 **S** Care New England Health System, Providence, RI
Primary Contact: Michael J. Dacey, M.D., President and Chief Operating Officer
COO: Michael J. Dacey, M.D., President and Chief Operating Officer
CFO: James M. Burke, Vice President Finance, Chief Nursing Executive Medical Surgical Hospitals
CMO: Joseph W. Spinale, D.O., Senior Vice President and Chief Medical Officer
CIO: Sumalatha Gaddam, Senior Vice President and Chief Information Officer
CHR: Marilyn J. Walsh, Vice President Human Resources
CNO: Rebecca Burke, R.N., Senior Vice President and Chief Nursing Officer
Web address: www.kentri.org
Control: Other not–for–profit (including NFP Corporation) **Service:** General Medical and Surgical

Staffed Beds: 318 **Admissions:** 14560 **Census:** 215 **Outpatient Visits:** 209486 **Births:** 838 **Total Expense ($000):** 338401 **Payroll Expense ($000):** 138698 **Personnel:** 1511

★ ◇ **WESTERLY HOSPITAL (410013)**, 25 Wells Street, Zip 02891–2934; tel. 401/596–6000, (Nonreporting) **A**2 10 21 **S** L+M Healthcare, New London, CT
Primary Contact: Bruce D. Cummings, President and Chief Executive Officer
COO: Daniel Rissi, Vice President, Chief Medical and Clinical Operations
CFO: Seth Van Essendelft, Vice President and Chief Financial Officer
CMO: Daniel Rissi, M.D., Vice President, Chief Medical and Clinical Operations
CIO: Kimberly Kalajainen, Vice President, Operations and Information Technology, Chief Information Officer
CHR: Donna Epps, Vice President, Chief Human Resource Officer
CNO: Lauren Williams, MS, Vice President Patient Care Services and Chief Nursing Officer
Web address: www.westerlyhospital.org
Control: Other not–for–profit (including NFP Corporation) **Service:** General Medical and Surgical

Staffed Beds: 100

☒ **LANDMARK MEDICAL CENTER (410011)**, 115 Cass Avenue, Zip 02895–4731; tel. 401/769–4100, (Includes LANDMARK MEDICAL CENTER–FOGARTY UNIT, Eddie Dowling Highway, North Smithfield, Zip 02896; Mailing Address: Woonsocket, tel. 401/766–0800; LANDMARK MEDICAL CENTER–WOONSOCKET UNIT, 115 Cass Avenue, Zip 02895; tel. 401/769–4100) **A**1 2 10 **F**3 8 13 15 17 18 20 22 26 28 29 30 31 34 35 38 40 44 45 46 47 48 49 50 51 54 56 57 59 60 61 64 65 68 70 74 75 76 77 78 79 81 82 83 84 85 86 87 97 98 100 102 103 107 108 109 110 111 114 118 119 126 129 130 131 132 133 135 143 144 146 147 148 **P**5 6 **S** Prime Healthcare Services, Ontario, CA
Primary Contact: Richard Charest, President & Chief Executive Officer
CFO: Thomas Klessens, Chief Financial Officer
CMO: Glenn Fort, Chief Medical Officer
CIO: Vincent Larosa, Director of Information Systems
CHR: Gail Gosselin, Director Human Resources
CNO: Carol Conley, Chief Nursing Officer
Web address: www.landmarkmedcenter.com
Control: Individual, Investor–owned, for–profit **Service:** General Medical and Surgical

Staffed Beds: 140 **Admissions:** 6596 **Census:** 84 **Outpatient Visits:** 141749 **Births:** 200 **Total Expense ($000):** 190234 **Payroll Expense ($000):** 50362 **Personnel:** 761

RI

Hospital, Medicare Provider Number, Address, Telephone, Approval, Facility, and Physician Codes, Health Care System

★ American Hospital Association (AHA) membership
☐ The Joint Commission accreditation
◯ Healthcare Facilities Accreditation Program
◇ DNV Healthcare Inc. accreditation
⇑ Center for Improvement in Healthcare Quality Accreditation
△ Commission on Accreditation of Rehabilitation Facilities (CARF) accreditation

SOUTH CAROLINA

ABBEVILLE—Abbeville County

★ ◇ **ABBEVILLE AREA MEDICAL CENTER (421301)**, 420 Thomson Circle, Zip 29620–5656, Mailing Address: P.O. Box 887, Zip 29620–0887; tel. 864/366–5011 **A**10 18 21 **F**3 15 17 29 30 35 40 51 53 54 56 57 59 62 64 67 70 74 75 77 79 81 85 87 89 90 93 103 107 108 110 114 119 127 128 129 130 132 133 135 146 147 148 **P**5 **S** QHR, Brentwood, TN
Primary Contact: Howard D. Turner, Chief Executive Officer
CFO: Timothy Wren, Chief Financial Officer
CMO: Christopher Ceraldi, M.D., Chief of Staff
CIO: Tim Stewart, Chief Information Officer
CHR: Alice Rigney, Chief Human Resources Officer
CNO: Ernest Shock, Chief Nursing Officer
Web address: www.abbevilleareamc.com
Control: County–Government, nonfederal **Service:** General Medical and Surgical

Staffed Beds: 25 Admissions: 665 Census: 8 Outpatient Visits: 30497
Births: 0 Total Expense ($000): 39154 Payroll Expense ($000): 17517
Personnel: 349

AIKEN—Aiken County

☐ **AIKEN REGIONAL MEDICAL CENTERS (420082)**, 302 University Parkway, Zip 29801–6302; tel. 803/641–5000, (Includes AURORA PAVILION, 655 Medical Park Drive, Zip 29801; tel. 803/641–5900) **A**1 3 5 10 **F**3 4 5 11 12 15 18 20 22 24 29 30 31 34 35 40 46 49 56 57 58 59 64 70 73 74 76 77 78 79 80 81 85 86 87 89 98 99 100 101 102 103 104 105 107 108 110 111 114 115 119 121 123 129 130 131 132 135 146 147 148 **S** Universal Health Services, Inc., King of Prussia, PA
Primary Contact: Vance V. Reynolds, FACHE, CPA, Chief Executive Officer
Web address: www.aikenregional.com
Control: Corporation, Investor–owned, for–profit **Service:** General Medical and Surgical

Staffed Beds: 271 Admissions: 11773 Census: 162 Outpatient Visits: 135719 Births: 1132 Total Expense ($000): 153405 Payroll Expense ($000): 51715 Personnel: 818

ANDERSON—Anderson County

✠ **ANMED HEALTH MEDICAL CENTER (420027)**, 800 North Fant Street, Zip 29621–5793; tel. 864/512–1000, (Includes ANMED HEALTH WOMEN'S AND CHILDREN'S HOSPITAL, 2000 East Greenville Street, Zip 29621; tel. 864/512–1000; William T. Manson, III, Chief Executive Officer) **A**1 2 3 5 10 **F**3 4 5 8 11 12 13 14 15 17 18 20 22 24 28 29 30 31 34 35 37 39 40 43 45 46 48 49 50 51 53 54 56 57 58 59 60 61 62 64 65 68 70 71 73 74 75 76 77 78 79 81 84 85 86 87 89 90 91 97 98 100 101 102 103 104 105 107 108 110 111 114 117 118 119 121 123 126 127 129 130 131 132 135 144 146 147 148 **S** AnMed Health, Anderson, SC
Primary Contact: William T. Manson, III, Chief Executive Officer
CFO: Christine Pearson, Vice President Finance and Chief Financial Officer
CMO: Mike Tillirson, D.O., Executive Vice President and Chief Medical Officer
CIO: Marty Stewart, Director Information Services
CHR: Richard Walter Grooms, Jr., Chief Human Resources Officer
CNO: Tina M. Jury, MSN, Executive Vice President Hospital Operations and Chief Nursing Officer
Web address: www.anmedhealth.org
Control: Other not–for–profit (including NFP Corporation) **Service:** General Medical and Surgical

Staffed Beds: 400 Admissions: 19067 Census: 257 Outpatient Visits: 862228 Births: 1825 Total Expense ($000): 488106 Payroll Expense ($000): 191353 Personnel: 3823

✠ **ANMED HEALTH REHABILITATION HOSPITAL (423029)**, 1 Spring Back Way, Zip 29621–2676; tel. 864/716–2600 **A**1 10 **F**3 29 30 56 74 75 79 90 91 93 94 95 96 **S** HEALTHSOUTH Corporation, Birmingham, AL
Primary Contact: Michele M. Skripps, R.N., Chief Executive Officer
CFO: Julie Saylors, Controller
CMO: William Vogentiz, M.D., Medical Director
CHR: Tara Myers, Director Human Resources
CNO: Carmella Burton, Chief Nursing Officer
Web address: www.anmedrehab.com
Control: Corporation, Investor–owned, for–profit **Service:** Rehabilitation

Staffed Beds: 45 Admissions: 1453 Census: 50 Births: 0 Total Expense ($000): 14169 Payroll Expense ($000): 8368 Personnel: 190

☐ **PATRICK B. HARRIS PSYCHIATRIC HOSPITAL (424011)**, 130 Highway 252, Zip 29621–5054; tel. 864/231–2600 **A**1 3 5 10 **F**98 100 101 102 103 106 130 143 146
Primary Contact: John Fletcher, Chief Executive Officer
Web address: www.patrickbharris.com/
Control: State–Government, nonfederal **Service:** Psychiatric

Staffed Beds: 121 Admissions: 777 Census: 111 Outpatient Visits: 0 Births: 0 Personnel: 295

BEAUFORT—Beaufort County

✠ **BEAUFORT MEMORIAL HOSPITAL (420067)**, 955 Ribaut Road, Zip 29902–5441; tel. 843/522–5200 **A**1 2 10 **F**3 11 12 13 15 18 20 22 28 29 30 31 32 34 35 40 43 45 49 50 51 53 54 57 59 60 64 65 69 70 71 73 74 75 76 77 78 79 81 85 86 87 89 90 93 94 97 98 100 101 102 103 104 107 108 111 114 115 117 119 120 121 126 127 130 132 134 135 145 146 147 148
Primary Contact: Edmond Russell Baxley, III, President and Chief Executive Officer
CFO: Jeffrey L. White, Senior Vice President and Chief Financial Officer
CMO: Kurt Gambla, D.O., Chief Medical Officer
CIO: Edward Ricks, Vice President and Chief Information Officer
CHR: Doug Douglas, Interim Vice President Human Resources
CNO: Karen Carroll, MSN, Vice President and Chief Nursing Officer
Web address: www.bmhsc.org
Control: County–Government, nonfederal **Service:** General Medical and Surgical

Staffed Beds: 197 Admissions: 9545 Census: 124

✠ **NAVAL HOSPITAL BEAUFORT**, 1 Pinckney Boulevard, Zip 29902–6122; tel. 843/228–5301, (Nonreporting) **A**1 5 **S** Bureau of Medicine and Surgery, Department of the Navy, Falls Church, VA
Primary Contact: Lieutenant Commander Willie Brown, Director Administration
Web address: www.med.navy.mil/sites/nhbeaufort/Pages/Welcome_Page.aspx
Control: Navy, Government, federal **Service:** General Medical and Surgical

Staffed Beds: 20

CAMDEN—Kershaw County

✠ **KERSHAWHEALTH (420048)**, 1315 Roberts Street, Zip 29020–3737, Mailing Address: P.O. Box 7003, Zip 29021–7003; tel. 803/432–4311, (Nonreporting) **A**1 10 **S** RCCH HealthCare Partners, Brentwood, TN
Primary Contact: Terry Gunn, FACHE, Chief Executive Officer
COO: Mike Bunch, Executive Vice President, Chief Operating Officer and Chief Financial Officer
CMO: Tallulah Holmstrom, Chief Medical Officer
CIO: Diane Arrants, Chief Information Officer
CHR: Angela F. Nettles, Director Human Resources
Web address: www.kershawhealth.com
Control: County–Government, nonfederal **Service:** General Medical and Surgical

Staffed Beds: 215

CHARLESTON—Charleston County

✠ **BON SECOURS ST. FRANCIS HOSPITAL (420065)**, 2095 Henry Tecklenburg Drive, Zip 29414–5733; tel. 843/402–1000 **A**1 10 **F**3 7 12 13 14 15 20 28 29 30 31 34 35 40 45 46 47 48 49 50 51 56 57 59 60 64 68 70 73 74 75 76 77 78 79 80 81 82 84 85 86 87 89 93 94 100 102 107 108 110 111 114 115 117 118 119 120 121 123 130 131 132 145 146 147 148 **S** Carolinas Healthcare System, Charlotte, NC
Primary Contact: Allen P. Carroll, Senior Vice President and Chief Executive Officer
CFO: Bret Johnson, Chief Financial Officer
CMO: Steven D. Shapiro, M.D., Chief Medical Officer
CIO: Michael Taylor, Chief Information Officer
CNO: Pennie Peralta, R.N., VP, Nursing & Chief Nursing Officer
Web address: www.rsfh.com/
Control: Other not–for–profit (including NFP Corporation) **Service:** General Medical and Surgical

Staffed Beds: 172 Admissions: 9193 Census: 93 Outpatient Visits: 162983 Births: 2620 Total Expense ($000): 169728 Payroll Expense ($000): 53152 Personnel: 1039

✠ **HEALTHSOUTH REHABILITATION HOSPITAL OF CHARLESTON (423027)**, 9181 Medcom Street, Zip 29406–9168; tel. 843/820–7777 **A**1 10 **F**90 93 94 **S** HEALTHSOUTH Corporation, Birmingham, AL
Primary Contact: Troy Powell, Chief Executive Officer
CFO: Beckye Lariviere, Controller
CMO: William Livesay, Jr., D.O., Medical Director
CHR: Donna White, Director Human Resources
Web address: www.healthsouthcharleston.com
Control: Corporation, Investor–owned, for–profit **Service:** Rehabilitation

Staffed Beds: 49 Admissions: 1087 Census: 40 Outpatient Visits: 6239 Births: 0 Total Expense ($000): 16864 Payroll Expense ($000): 7417 Personnel: 124

Many Facility Codes have changed. Please refer to the AHA Guide Code Chart.

⊞ **MUSC MEDICAL CENTER OF MEDICAL UNIVERSITY OF SOUTH CAROLINA (420004)**, 169 Ashley Avenue, Zip 29425–8905; tel. 843/792-2300, (Includes CHILDREN'S HOSPITAL OF SOUTH CAROLINA AT MUSC, 171 Ashley Avenue, Zip 29425–8908; tel. 843/792-1414; Patrick J. Cawley, M.D., Chief Executive Officer, MUSC Health and Vice President for Health Affairs, University) **A**1 2 3 5 8 10 **F**3 4 5 6 7 8 9 11 12 13 14 15 16 17 18 19 20 21 22 23 24 25 26 27 28 29 30 31 32 34 35 37 38 39 40 41 43 44 45 46 47 48 49 50 51 52 53 54 55 56 57 58 59 60 61 64 65 66 67 68 70 71 72 73 74 75 76 77 78 79 80 81 82 84 85 86 87 88 89 91 92 93 94 97 98 99 100 101 102 103 104 105 107 108 109 110 111 114 115 116 117 118 119 120 121 123 124 126 129 130 131 132 134 135 136 137 138 139 140 141 142 144 145 146 147 148
Primary Contact: Patrick J. Cawley, M.D., Chief Executive Officer, MUSC Health and Vice President for Health Affairs, University
COO: Matthew Wain, Chief Operating Officer
CFO: Stephen Hargett, Administrator Finance and Support Services
CMO: Daniel Handel, M.D., Chief Medical Officer
CIO: Michael Caputo, Chief Information Officer
CHR: Darrick Paul, Chief People Officer
CNO: Jerry A. Mansfield, Ph.D., Executive Chief Nursing Officer & Chief Patient Experience Officer
Web address: www.muschealth.com
Control: State–Government, nonfederal **Service:** General Medical and Surgical

Staffed Beds: 722 **Admissions:** 34459 **Census:** 655 **Outpatient Visits:** 1040230 **Births:** 2738 **Personnel:** 6776

☐ **PALMETTO LOWCOUNTRY BEHAVIORAL HEALTH (424006)**, 2777 Speissegger Drive, Zip 29405–8229; tel. 843/747-5830 **A**1 10 **F**4 5 64 98 99 102 103 104 105 **S** Universal Health Services, Inc., King of Prussia, PA
Primary Contact: Clint Hanger, Chief Executive Officer
CFO: Stan Markowski, Chief Financial Officer
CMO: Steven Lopez, M.D., Chief Medical Officer
CHR: Sheila Simpson, Vice President Human Resources
CNO: Jo Good, Director of Nursing
Web address: www.palmettobehavioralhealth.com
Control: Corporation, Investor–owned, for–profit **Service:** Psychiatric

Staffed Beds: 100 **Admissions:** 2827 **Census:** 63 **Outpatient Visits:** 5736 **Births:** 0 **Total Expense ($000):** 16107 **Payroll Expense ($000):** 7426

⊞ **RALPH H. JOHNSON VETERANS AFFAIRS MEDICAL CENTER**, 109 Bee Street, Zip 29401–5799; tel. 843/577-5011, (Nonreporting) **A**1 2 3 5 8 **S** Department of Veterans Affairs, Washington, DC
Primary Contact: Scott R. Isaacks, FACHE, Director and Chief Executive Officer
COO: Pamela Crowell, Associate Director and Chief Operating Officer
CFO: Cassandra Helfer, Chief Financial Officer
CMO: Florence N. Hutchison, M.D., Chief of Staff
CIO: LaBon Hardy, Chief Information Officer
CHR: Renae A. Jacobson, Human Resources Officer
CNO: Garett E. Schreier, R.N., Associate Director, Nursing and Patient Care Services
Web address: www.charleston.va.gov/
Control: Veterans Affairs, Government, federal **Service:** General Medical and Surgical

Staffed Beds: 98

⊞ △ **ROPER ST. FRANCIS (420087)**, 316 Calhoun Street, Zip 29401–1125; tel. 843/724-2000 **A**1 2 3 5 7 10 **F**3 7 8 9 14 15 17 18 20 22 24 26 28 29 30 31 34 35 37 40 42 43 45 49 50 51 53 54 55 56 57 58 59 60 61 62 63 64 65 67 68 69 70 74 75 77 78 79 80 81 82 84 85 86 87 90 92 93 94 95 96 102 107 108 110 111 114 115 118 119 120 121 123 124 126 129 130 131 132 135 136 143 146 147 148 **S** Carolinas Healthcare System, Charlotte, NC
Primary Contact: Matthew J. Severance, FACHE, Chief Executive Officer
CFO: Bret Johnson, Chief Financial Officer
CMO: Steven D. Shapiro, M.D., Vice President Medical Affairs
CIO: Melinda H. Cardell, Interim Vice President and Chief Information Officer
CHR: Melanie Stith, Vice President Human Resources
CNO: Carolyn Viall Donohue, MSN, Vice President Nursing
Web address: www.rsfh.com/
Control: Other not–for–profit (including NFP Corporation) **Service:** General Medical and Surgical

Staffed Beds: 298 **Admissions:** 13206 **Census:** 199 **Outpatient Visits:** 211263 **Births:** 0 **Total Expense ($000):** 333664 **Payroll Expense ($000):** 97684 **Personnel:** 1951

⊞ **TRIDENT MEDICAL CENTER (420079)**, 9330 Medical Plaza Drive, Zip 29406–9195; tel. 843/797-7000, (Includes MONCKS CORNER MEDICAL CENTER, 401 North Live Oak Drive, Highway 17A, Moncks Corner, Zip 29461–5603; tel. 843/761-8721; SUMMERVILLE MEDICAL CENTER, 295 Midland Parkway, Summerville, Zip 29485–8104; tel. 843/832-5000) **A**1 2 3 5 10 **F**3 8 12 13 15 16 18 20 22 24 26 28 29 30 31 34 35 40 41 42 43 45 46 47 48 49 50 54 55 56 57 59 60 61 64 70 72 73 74 75 76 77 78 79 80 81 84 85 86 87 88 89 90 93 94 98 100 102 105 107 108 110 111 114 115 116 117 118 119 120 121 123 126 128 130 131 132 135 145 146 147 148 **S** HCA, Nashville, TN
Primary Contact: Todd Gallati, FACHE, President and Chief Executive Officer
CFO: Teresa Finch, Chief Financial Officer
CIO: Susan Murray, Director Information Services
CHR: Joe B. Hill, Jr., Vice President Human Resources
Web address: www.tridenthealthsystem.com
Control: Corporation, Investor–owned, for–profit **Service:** General Medical and Surgical

Staffed Beds: 421 **Admissions:** 23734 **Census:** 282 **Outpatient Visits:** 338372 **Births:** 2708 **Personnel:** 1882

CHERAW—Chesterfield County

⊞ **MCLEOD HEALTH CHERAW (420062)**, 711 Chesterfield Highway, Zip 29520–7002; tel. 843/537-7881, (Data for 101 days) **A**1 10 **F**3 13 15 18 28 29 30 34 35 40 45 56 57 59 68 70 76 79 80 81 85 86 87 89 90 102 107 108 114 118 119 130 132 135 **P**3 **S** McLeod Health, Florence, SC
Primary Contact: Mib Scoggins, Chief Executive Officer
CFO: Louis Anderson, Chief Financial Officer
CMO: David Bersinger, M.D., Chief of Staff
CIO: Jim Spencer, Director Information System
Web address: www.chesterfieldgeneral.com
Control: Other not–for–profit (including NFP Corporation) **Service:** General Medical and Surgical

Staffed Beds: 55 **Admissions:** 474 **Census:** 16 **Outpatient Visits:** 8004 **Births:** 65 **Total Expense ($000):** 9521 **Payroll Expense ($000):** 3035 **Personnel:** 118

CHESTER—Chester County

⊞ **CHESTER REGIONAL MEDICAL CENTER (420019)**, 1 Medical Park Drive, Zip 29706–9769; tel. 803/581-3151 **A**1 10 **F**15 28 29 34 35 40 50 56 57 59 70 75 77 79 81 85 86 87 89 90 94 107 108 110 111 119 128 129 130 131 132 135 **S** Community Health Systems, Inc., Franklin, TN
Primary Contact: Page H. Vaughan, Chief Executive Officer
CFO: Tracey Claxton, Chief Financial Officer
CMO: Terry Dodge, M.D., Chief of Staff
CIO: Shaw Laird, Chief Information Officer
CHR: Karen Chapman, Director Human Resources
CNO: Betty Griffin, Interim Chief Nursing Officer
Web address: www.chesterregional.com
Control: Corporation, Investor–owned, for–profit **Service:** General Medical and Surgical

Staffed Beds: 36 **Admissions:** 1121 **Census:** 9 **Births:** 0 **Personnel:** 227

CLINTON—Laurens County

⊞ **GREENVILLE HEALTH SYSTEM – LAURENS COUNTY MEMORIAL HOSPITAL (420038)**, 22725 Highway 76 East, Zip 29325–7527, Mailing Address: P.O. Drawer 976, Zip 29325–0976; tel. 864/833-9100, (Includes GHS – LAURENS COUNTY MEMORIAL HOSPITAL, 22725 Highway 76 E., Mailing Address: PO Box 976, Zip 29325–0976; tel. 803/833-9100), (Total facility includes 10 beds in nursing home–type unit) **A**1 5 10 20 **F**3 13 15 18 28 30 40 45 46 59 70 76 79 80 81 87 89 107 108 110 114 115 119 128 132 147 **P**6 **S** Greenville Health System, Greenville, SC
Primary Contact: Richard E. D'Alberto, FACHE, Campus President
CFO: Todd Walker, Director Operations
CMO: Vincent Green, Medical Director
CIO: Gina Driggers, Manager Information Technology
CHR: Cathy M. Rogers, Manager Human Resources
CNO: Kay Swisher, Chief Nursing Officer
Web address: www.ghs.org/laurens
Control: Hospital district or authority, Government, nonfederal **Service:** General Medical and Surgical

Staffed Beds: 67 **Admissions:** 2920 **Census:** 38 **Outpatient Visits:** 71814 **Births:** 343 **Total Expense ($000):** 66092 **Payroll Expense ($000):** 18382 **Personnel:** 342

WHITTEN CENTER, Highway 76 East, Zip 29325, Mailing Address: P.O. Box 239, Zip 29325–0239; tel. 864/833-2733, (Nonreporting)
Primary Contact: Wes Leonard, Chief Executive Officer
Control: State–Government, nonfederal **Service:** Intellectual disabilities

Staffed Beds: 22

SC

Hospital, Medicare Provider Number, Address, Telephone, Approval, Facility, and Physician Codes, Health Care System

★ American Hospital Association (AHA) membership ○ Healthcare Facilities Accreditation Program ⇑ Center for Improvement in Healthcare Quality Accreditation
☐ The Joint Commission accreditation ◇ DNV Healthcare Inc. accreditation △ Commission on Accreditation of Rehabilitation Facilities (CARF) accreditation

COLUMBIA—Richland County

CONTINUECARE HOSPITAL AT PALMETTO HEALTH BAPTIST (422006), Taylor at Marion Street, Zip 29220, Mailing Address: PO BOX 11069, Zip 29211–1069; tel. 803/296–3757, (Nonreporting) **A**10 **S** Community Hospital Corporation, Plano, TX
Primary Contact: Larkin Virden, Interim Chief Executive Officer
Web address: www.continuecare.org/palmetto//
Control: Other not–for–profit (including NFP Corporation) **Service:** Long–Term Acute Care hospital

Staffed Beds: 35

EARLE E. MORRIS ALCOHOL AND DRUG TREATMENT CENTER, 610 Faison Drive, Zip 29203–3218; tel. 803/935–7100 **F**4 29 39 53 61 67 74 75 87 98 130 132 146
Primary Contact: George McConnell, Director
Web address: www.state.sc.us/dmh/morris_village/
Control: State–Government, nonfederal **Service:** Alcoholism and other chemical dependency

Staffed Beds: 96 **Admissions:** 1320 **Census:** 93 **Outpatient Visits:** 0 **Births:** 0 **Personnel:** 176

G. WERBER BRYAN PSYCHIATRIC HOSPITAL (424005), 220 Faison Drive, Zip 29203–3210; tel. 803/935–7146 **A**1 3 10 **F**1 4 30 50 74 75 97 98 101 103 128 130 132 135 146
Primary Contact: Harvey Miller, Director
COO: Jaclyn Upfield, Chief Operating Officer
CIO: Sam Livingston, Information Resource Consultant
CHR: Kim Church, Manager Human Resources
Web address: www.scdmh.org
Control: State–Government, nonfederal **Service:** Psychiatric

Staffed Beds: 165 **Admissions:** 244 **Census:** 140 **Personnel:** 424

HEALTHSOUTH REHABILITATION HOSPITAL OF COLUMBIA (423025), 2935 Colonial Drive, Zip 29203–6811; tel. 803/254–7777 **A**1 10 **F**29 50 53 60 64 77 90 91 92 93 94 95 96 97 119 **S** HEALTHSOUTH Corporation, Birmingham, AL
Primary Contact: Catherine Landis, R.N., Chief Executive Officer
CFO: Jessica Burriss, Chief Financial Officer
CMO: Devin Troyer, M.D., Medical Director
CHR: Luanne Burton, Director Human Resources
CNO: April Brooks, Chief Nursing Officer
Web address: www.healthsouthcolumbia.com
Control: Corporation, Investor–owned, for–profit **Service:** Rehabilitation

Staffed Beds: 96 **Admissions:** 1766 **Census:** 65 **Births:** 0 **Total Expense ($000):** 20078 **Payroll Expense ($000):** 11319 **Personnel:** 212

PALMETTO HEALTH BAPTIST (420086), Taylor at Marion Street, Zip 29220–0001; tel. 803/296–5010, (Total facility includes 22 beds in nursing home–type unit) **A**1 2 3 5 10 **F**1 3 5 11 12 13 15 18 20 29 30 31 34 35 40 45 47 48 49 51 54 57 59 61 62 63 64 68 70 71 72 73 74 75 76 77 78 79 80 81 82 84 85 86 87 89 90 93 94 98 99 100 101 102 103 104 105 107 108 110 111 112 114 115 116 117 118 119 124 128 130 132 145 146 147 148 **S** Palmetto Health, Columbia, SC
Primary Contact: Gregory B. Gattman, Acute Care Executive
COO: James M. Bridges, Executive Vice President and Chief Operating Officer
CFO: Paul K. Duane, Chief Financial Officer and Office of Health Reform
CMO: Mark J. Mayson, M.D., Medical Director
CIO: Michelle Edwards, Executive Vice President Information Technology
CHR: Trip Gregory, Senior Vice President Human Resources
Web address: www.palmettohealth.org
Control: Other not–for–profit (including NFP Corporation) **Service:** General Medical and Surgical

Staffed Beds: 429 **Admissions:** 19031 **Census:** 250 **Outpatient Visits:** 200261 **Births:** 3008 **Total Expense ($000):** 289348 **Payroll Expense ($000):** 119708 **Personnel:** 2061

PALMETTO HEALTH BAPTIST PARKRIDGE (420106), 400 Palmetto Health Parkway, Zip 29212–1760, Mailing Address: P.O. BOX 2266, Zip 29202–2266; tel. 803/907–7000 **A**1 10 **F**3 8 13 15 29 30 31 34 35 40 45 46 50 55 57 59 64 68 70 75 76 77 78 79 81 86 87 89 90 93 94 107 110 111 119 130 132 143 144 146 147 **S** Palmetto Health, Columbia, SC
Primary Contact: Sarah Kirby, R.N., MSN, FACHE, Chief Executive Officer
Web address: www.palmettohealth.org
Control: Other not–for–profit (including NFP Corporation) **Service:** General Medical and Surgical

Staffed Beds: 68 **Admissions:** 3917 **Census:** 43 **Outpatient Visits:** 71878 **Births:** 558 **Total Expense ($000):** 99463 **Payroll Expense ($000):** 33006 **Personnel:** 590

PALMETTO HEALTH RICHLAND (420018), Five Richland Medical Park Drive, Zip 29203–6897; tel. 803/434–7000, (Includes PALMETTO HEALTH CHILDREN'S HOSPITAL, Five Richland Medical Park Drive, Zip 29203–6863; tel. 803/434–6882) **A**1 2 3 5 8 10 **F**1 2 3 4 5 11 13 15 17 18 20 22 24 28 29 30 31 32 34 35 39 40 41 43 45 46 50 54 55 56 57 58 59 60 61 64 68 70 72 73 74 75 76 77 78 79 81 86 87 88 89 90 93 94 98 99 100 101 102 103 104 105 107 108 110 111 114 115 118 119 121 126 128 129 130 131 132 134 135 143 146 147 148 **S** Palmetto Health, Columbia, SC
Primary Contact: Jay Hamm, R.N., FACHE, Chief Acute Care Executive
CFO: Paul K. Duane, Chief Financial Officer and Office of Health Reform
CMO: Eric Brown, M.D., Physician Executive
CNO: Carole A. Siegfried, MSN, Campus Nurse Executive
Web address: www.palmettohealth.org
Control: Other not–for–profit (including NFP Corporation) **Service:** General Medical and Surgical

Staffed Beds: 708 **Admissions:** 31341 **Census:** 548 **Outpatient Visits:** 495505 **Births:** 2424 **Total Expense ($000):** 700164 **Payroll Expense ($000):** 274237 **Personnel:** 4785

PROVIDENCE HOSPITAL (420026), 2435 Forest Drive, Zip 29204–2098; tel. 803/865–4500, (Includes PROVIDENCE HOSPITAL NORTHEAST, 120 Gateway Corporate Boulevard, Zip 29203–9611; tel. 803/865–4500; Ryan Hall, Vice President) **A**10 21 **F**3 8 11 17 18 20 22 24 26 28 29 30 34 35 38 40 44 45 49 50 53 54 56 57 58 59 61 63 64 68 70 74 75 77 79 80 81 83 84 85 86 87 90 92 93 94 100 107 108 111 114 115 118 119 129 130 131 132 141 146 147 148 **P**5 **S** LifePoint Health, Brentwood, TN
Primary Contact: Terrence Kessler, Interim President and Chief Executive Officer
COO: W. Carl Martin, Chief Operating Officer
CFO: Pamela Gallagher, Chief Financial Officer
CMO: Wayne Sribnick, M.D., Senior Vice President and Chief Medical Officer
CIO: Lib Cumbee, Director Information Systems
CHR: Justin A. Lofurno, Director Human Resources
Web address: www.sistersofcharityhealth.org/health–care/providence–hospitals/
Control: Church–operated, Nongovernment, not–for profit **Service:** General Medical and Surgical

Staffed Beds: 247 **Admissions:** 9882 **Census:** 125 **Outpatient Visits:** 109893 **Births:** 0 **Total Expense ($000):** 222912 **Payroll Expense ($000):** 66938 **Personnel:** 1200

PROVIDENCE HOSPITAL NORTHEAST See Providence Hospital

SOUTH CAROLINA DEPARTMENT OF CORRECTIONS HOSPITAL, 4344 Broad River Road, Zip 29210–4098; tel. 803/896–8567, (Nonreporting)
Primary Contact: John Solomon, M.D., Director
Web address: www.doc.sc.gov/
Control: State–Government, nonfederal **Service:** Hospital unit of an institution (prison hospital, college infirmary, etc.)

Staffed Beds: 70

WILLIAM S. HALL PSYCHIATRIC INSTITUTE (424003), 1800 Colonial Drive, Zip 29203–6827; tel. 803/898–1693 **A**1 3 5 10 **F**1 4 30 74 75 98 99 104 128 130 146
Primary Contact: Angela Forand, Director
COO: Doug Glover, Controller
CFO: Doug Glover, Controller
CMO: Phyllis Bryant–Mobley, M.D., Director Medical Services
CIO: Mesa Foard, Director Information technology
CHR: Kim Church, Manager Human Resources
Web address: www.scdmh.org
Control: State–Government, nonfederal **Service:** Psychiatric

Staffed Beds: 38 **Admissions:** 474 **Census:** 30 **Personnel:** 231

WM. JENNINGS BRYAN DORN VETERANS AFFAIRS MEDICAL CENTER, 6439 Garners Ferry Road, Zip 29209–1639; tel. 803/776–4000, (Nonreporting) **A**1 2 3 5 7 **S** Department of Veterans Affairs, Washington, DC
Primary Contact: Timothy McMurry, Director
COO: David Omura, Associate Director
CMO: Bernard L. DeKoning, M.D., Chief of Staff
CIO: Steve Chalphant, Director Information Management Service Line
CHR: Phyllis Jones, Chief Human Resources
CNO: Ruth W. Mustard, R.N., Associate Director Nursing and Patient Services
Web address: www.columbiasc.va.gov/
Control: Veterans Affairs, Government, federal **Service:** General Medical and Surgical

Staffed Beds: 216

Many Facility Codes have changed. Please refer to the AHA Guide Code Chart. © 2016 AHA Guide

CONWAY—Horry County

★ ◇ **CONWAY MEDICAL CENTER (420049)**, 300 Singleton Ridge Road,
Zip 29526–9142, Mailing Address: P.O. Box 829, Zip 29528–0829;
tel. 843/347–7111, (Total facility includes 88 beds in nursing home–type unit)
A10 21 **F**1 3 8 11 12 13 15 18 20 26 28 29 30 34 35 40 43 45 46 49 50 51
57 59 60 61 68 70 71 73 75 76 77 79 81 83 84 85 86 87 89 90 93 94 100
102 107 108 110 111 114 115 118 119 128 129 130 132 135 145 146
147 148
Primary Contact: Philip A. Clayton, President and Chief Executive Officer
CFO: Bret A. Barr, Executive Vice President and Chief Financial Officer
CMO: Paul McKinley Richardson, Jr., Vice President, Medical Affairs
CIO: David Crutchfield, Vice President, Information Services & Chief Information
Officer
CHR: Matthew J. Securro, Vice President, Human Resources
CNO: Tony L. Minshew, Vice President, Patient Care Services
Web address: www.conwaymedicalcenter.com
Control: Other not–for–profit (including NFP Corporation) **Service:** General
Medical and Surgical

Staffed Beds: 287 **Admissions:** 9112 **Census:** 175 **Outpatient Visits:**
123069 **Births:** 1406 **Total Expense ($000):** 144919 **Payroll Expense**
($000): 52819 **Personnel:** 1044

☐ **LIGHTHOUSE CARE CENTER OF CONWAY (424002)**, 152 Waccamaw
Medical Park Drive, Zip 29526–8901; tel. 843/347–8871 **A**1 10 **F**4 98 101 102
103 106 130 **S** Universal Health Services, Inc., King of Prussia, PA
Primary Contact: Thomas L. Ryba, Chief Executive Officer
CFO: Gabrielle Gale, Chief Financial Officer
CMO: Adedapo Oduwole, M.D., Medical Director
CIO: Gabrielle Gale, Chief Financial Officer
CHR: Lois Woodall, Director Human Resources
Web address: www.lighthousecarecenterofconway.com/
Control: Corporation, Investor–owned, for–profit **Service:** Psychiatric

Staffed Beds: 78 **Admissions:** 2783 **Census:** 65 **Outpatient Visits:** 0 **Births:**
0 **Personnel:** 178

DARLINGTON—Darlington County

☐ **MCLEOD MEDICAL CENTER–DARLINGTON (420057)**, 701 Cashua Ferry
Road, Zip 29532–8488, Mailing Address: P.O. Box 1859, Zip 29540;
tel. 843/395–1100 **A**1 10 **F**1 3 4 15 34 35 38 56 57 59 61 64 67 68 77 85
90 93 94 97 98 100 101 103 104 107 110 114 119 127 128 130 135 147
148 **P**3 **S** McLeod Health, Florence, SC
Primary Contact: Tim Smoak, Administrator
Web address: www.mcleodhealth.org
Control: Other not–for–profit (including NFP Corporation) **Service:** General
Medical and Surgical

Staffed Beds: 72 **Admissions:** 1196 **Census:** 38 **Outpatient Visits:** 8560
Births: 0 **Total Expense ($000):** 12602 **Payroll Expense ($000):** 6339
Personnel: 116

DILLON—Dillon County

☐ **MCLEOD MEDICAL CENTER DILLON (420005)**, 301 East Jackson Street,
Zip 29536–2509, Mailing Address: P.O. Box 1327, Zip 29536–1327;
tel. 843/774–4111 **A**1 10 **F**3 11 13 15 28 29 30 34 35 40 50 57 59 64 68
70 75 76 79 81 82 85 87 89 90 94 107 111 114 119 130 132 134 135 146
147 148 **P**3 **S** McLeod Health, Florence, SC
Primary Contact: Joan Ervin, FACHE, Administrator
CFO: Fulton Ervin, Senior Vice President and Chief Financial Officer
CMO: Walter B. Blum, M.D., Chief of Staff
CIO: Jenean Blackmon, Assistant Vice President and Chief Information Officer
CHR: Cynthia Causey, Associate Administrator Human and Mission Services
Web address: www.mcleodhealth.org
Control: Other not–for–profit (including NFP Corporation) **Service:** General
Medical and Surgical

Staffed Beds: 58 **Admissions:** 2665 **Census:** 23 **Outpatient Visits:** 70990
Births: 276 **Total Expense ($000):** 41745 **Payroll Expense ($000):** 17517
Personnel: 298

EASLEY—Pickens County

✠ **BAPTIST EASLEY HOSPITAL (420015)**, 200 Fleetwood Drive,
Zip 29640–2022, Mailing Address: P.O. Box 2129, Zip 29641–2129;
tel. 864/442–7200 **A**1 5 10 **F**3 11 13 15 20 28 29 30 34 35 39 40 56 57 59
64 70 76 79 81 85 86 87 89 107 108 111 114 115 119 124 130 132
146 147
Primary Contact: Todd Walker, Campus President
CFO: Kathleen Stapleton, Chief Financial Officer
CIO: Cynthia Ellenburg, Director Health Information Services
CHR: Richard B. Posey, Director Human Resources
CNO: Mary Ann Hunter, Director Nursing Services
Web address: www.baptisteasley.org
Control: Other not–for–profit (including NFP Corporation) **Service:** General
Medical and Surgical

Staffed Beds: 89 **Admissions:** 3664 **Census:** 42 **Outpatient Visits:** 106272
Births: 435 **Total Expense ($000):** 76575 **Payroll Expense ($000):** 27017
Personnel: 732

EDGEFIELD—Edgefield County

★ **EDGEFIELD COUNTY HOSPITAL (421304)**, 300 Ridge Medical Plaza,
Zip 29824–4525, Mailing Address: PO Box 590, Zip 29824–4525;
tel. 803/637–3174 **A**10 18 **F**3 28 29 34 35 40 45 59 65 68 77 79 81 84 90
93 94 107 115 119 127 128 130 133 146 **P**1
Primary Contact: Carlos Milanes, Chief Executive Officer
CFO: Lori Jacobs, Chief Financial Officer
CMO: W. Hugh Morgan, M.D., Chief Medical Staff
CIO: Juli Corley, Chief Information Officer
CHR: Theresa Stover, Chief Human Resource Officer
CNO: Cheryl Faust, Chief Nursing Officer
Web address: www.myech.org
Control: County–Government, nonfederal **Service:** General Medical and Surgical

Staffed Beds: 25 **Admissions:** 337 **Census:** 3 **Outpatient Visits:** 14644
Births: 0 **Personnel:** 176

FAIRFAX—Allendale County

★ **ALLENDALE COUNTY HOSPITAL (421300)**, 1787 Allendale Fairfax Highway,
Zip 29827–9133, Mailing Address: P.O. Box 218, Zip 29827–0218;
tel. 803/632–3311, (Nonreporting) **A**10 18
Primary Contact: Lari Gooding, Chief Executive Officer
Web address: www.achospital.org
Control: County–Government, nonfederal **Service:** General Medical and Surgical

Staffed Beds: 69

FLORENCE—Florence County

✠ △ **CAROLINAS HOSPITAL SYSTEM (420091)**, 805 Pamplico Highway,
Zip 29505–6050, Mailing Address: P.O. Box 100550, Zip 29502–0550;
tel. 843/674–5000 **A**1 7 10 **F**4 5 6 8 13 15 17 18 20 22 24 26 28 29 30 31
34 35 40 41 43 45 53 56 57 58 59 60 63 64 67 70 72 73 76 77 78 79 81
87 88 89 90 94 107 110 111 114 115 116 117 119 121 128 129 132 135
145 146 147 148 **S** Community Health Systems, Inc., Franklin, TN
Primary Contact: Darcy Craven, Chief Executive Officer
CFO: Loren Rials, Chief Financial Officer
CMO: Kevin Shea, M.D., Chief of Staff
CIO: Lynn Northcutt, Chief Information Officer
CHR: Donna Damico, Director Human Resources
Web address: www.carolinashospital.com
Control: Corporation, Investor–owned, for–profit **Service:** General Medical and
Surgical

Staffed Beds: 416 **Admissions:** 12681 **Census:** 180 **Births:** 694 **Total**
Expense ($000): 184129 **Payroll Expense ($000):** 58165

✠ **HEALTHSOUTH REHABILITATION HOSPITAL OF FLORENCE (423026)**, 900
East Cheves Street, Zip 29506–2704; tel. 843/679–9000 **A**1 10 **F**29 90 95 96
132 148 **S** HEALTHSOUTH Corporation, Birmingham, AL
Primary Contact: Jill Strawn, Chief Executive Officer
CFO: Robert Wheeler, Controller
CMO: Adora Matthews, M.D., Medical Director
CHR: Susan Trantham, Director Human Resources
Web address: www.healthsouthflorence.com
Control: Corporation, Investor–owned, for–profit **Service:** Rehabilitation

Staffed Beds: 88 **Admissions:** 1127 **Census:** 42 **Outpatient Visits:** 0 **Births:**
0 **Total Expense ($000):** 13755 **Payroll Expense ($000):** 7494 **Personnel:**
156

SC

Hospital, Medicare Provider Number, Address, Telephone, Approval, Facility, and Physician Codes, Health Care System

★ American Hospital Association (AHA) membership
☐ The Joint Commission accreditation
◯ Healthcare Facilities Accreditation Program
◇ DNV Healthcare Inc. accreditation
⇑ Center for Improvement in Healthcare Quality Accreditation
△ Commission on Accreditation of Rehabilitation Facilities (CARF) accreditation

✠ **MCLEOD REGIONAL MEDICAL CENTER (420051)**, 555 East Cheves Street, Zip 29506–2617, Mailing Address: P.O. Box 100551, Zip 29502–0551; tel. 843/777–2000 **A**1 2 3 5 10 **F**3 7 8 11 13 15 17 18 20 22 24 26 28 29 30 31 32 34 35 39 40 43 44 45 46 47 48 49 50 51 53 54 56 57 58 59 60 61 62 63 64 66 67 68 70 71 72 73 74 75 76 77 78 79 80 81 82 84 85 86 87 88 89 90 92 94 96 97 100 102 107 108 110 111 112 114 115 116 117 118 119 120 121 124 126 129 130 131 132 135 143 145 146 147 148 **P**3 **S** McLeod Health, Florence, SC
Primary Contact: Robert L. Colones, President and Chief Executive Officer
COO: Ron Boring, Senior Vice President and Chief Operating Officer
CFO: Fulton Ervin, Chief Financial Officer
CMO: Alva W. Whitehead, M.D., Vice President Medical Services
CIO: Jenean Blackmon, Associate Vice President and Chief Information Officer
CHR: Jeannette Glenn, Vice President Human Resources, Education and Training
Web address: www.mcleodhealth.org
Control: Other not–for–profit (including NFP Corporation) **Service:** General Medical and Surgical

Staffed Beds: 493 **Admissions:** 25844 **Census:** 388 **Outpatient Visits:** 195977 **Births:** 2205 **Total Expense ($000):** 546764 **Payroll Expense ($000):** 190120 **Personnel:** 3276

✠ **REGENCY HOSPITAL OF FLORENCE (422007)**, 121 East Cedar Street, 4th Floor, Zip 29506–2576; tel. 843/661–3471 **A**1 10 **F**1 3 29 34 35 57 58 70 77 80 85 90 100 130 148 **S** Select Medical Corporation, Mechanicsburg, PA
Primary Contact: Amy Metz, Chief Executive Officer
CMO: Stephen Dersch, M.D., President Medical Staff
CHR: Tina Stokes, Manager Human Resources
Web address: www.regencyhospital.com
Control: Corporation, Investor–owned, for–profit **Service:** Long–Term Acute Care hospital

Staffed Beds: 40 **Admissions:** 499 **Census:** 35 **Outpatient Visits:** 0 **Births:** 0 **Personnel:** 108

FORT JACKSON—Richland County

✠ **MONCRIEF ARMY COMMUNITY HOSPITAL**, 4500 Stuart Street, Zip 29207–5700; tel. 803/751–2160, (Nonreporting) **A**1 3 5 **S** Department of the Army, Office of the Surgeon General, Falls Church, VA
Primary Contact: Colonel Traci Crawford, R.N., Commander
Web address: www.moncrief.amedd.army.mil
Control: Army, Government, federal **Service:** General Medical and Surgical

Staffed Beds: 60

GAFFNEY—Cherokee County

✠ **MARY BLACK HEALTH SYSTEM – GAFFNEY (420043)**, 1530 North Limestone Street, Zip 29340–4738; tel. 864/487–4271 **A**1 10 **F**3 11 13 15 18 19 29 34 35 40 45 46 51 57 59 64 65 67 70 75 76 79 81 82 85 86 87 89 107 108 110 111 113 119 129 130 131 132 135 145 146 147 148 **S** Community Health Systems, Inc., Franklin, TN
Primary Contact: Joshua Self, Chief Executive Officer
COO: Leslie Glover, Director Operations
CMO: Frank Phillips, M.D., Chief of Staff
CIO: Richard Bledsoe, Director Information Systems
CHR: Connie Gibson, R.N., Director Human Resources
CNO: Brian Nunn, R.N., Chief Nursing Officer
Web address: www.upstatecarolina.org
Control: Corporation, Investor–owned, for–profit **Service:** General Medical and Surgical

Staffed Beds: 125 **Admissions:** 2114 **Census:** 25 **Outpatient Visits:** 54554 **Births:** 240 **Personnel:** 263

GEORGETOWN—Georgetown County

✠ **TIDELANDS GEORGETOWN MEMORIAL HOSPITAL (420020)**, 606 Black River Road, Zip 29440–3368, Mailing Address: Drawer 421718, Zip 29442–4203; tel. 843/527–7000 **A**1 3 5 10 19 **F**3 8 11 12 13 15 17 18 20 22 26 28 29 30 31 32 34 45 50 51 53 54 56 57 61 64 65 68 70 73 74 75 76 77 78 79 81 82 84 85 86 87 89 90 93 94 97 100 102 107 108 110 111 115 118 119 130 131 132 135 146 147 148 **S** QHR, Brentwood, TN
Primary Contact: Gayle L. Resetar, Chief Operating Officer
COO: Gayle L. Resetar, Vice President and Chief Operating Officer
CFO: Terry L. Kiser, Vice President and Chief Financial Officer
CIO: Frank Scafidi, Vice President and Chief Information Officer
CHR: James F. Harper, Senior Vice President and Chief Human Resources Officer
Web address: www.georgetownhospitalsystem.org
Control: Other not–for–profit (including NFP Corporation) **Service:** General Medical and Surgical

Staffed Beds: 136 **Admissions:** 4172 **Census:** 46 **Outpatient Visits:** 180964 **Births:** 299 **Total Expense ($000):** 132182 **Payroll Expense ($000):** 47328 **Personnel:** 771

GREENVILLE—Greenville County

✠ △ **BON SECOURS ST. FRANCIS HEALTH SYSTEM (420023)**, One St. Francis Drive, Zip 29601–3207; tel. 864/255–1000, (Includes ST. FRANCIS EASTSIDE, 125 Commonwealth Drive, Zip 29615–4812; tel. 864/675–4000) **A**1 2 7 10 **F**3 8 12 13 14 15 17 18 20 22 24 26 29 30 31 34 35 36 39 40 44 45 46 47 48 49 50 51 53 54 55 57 58 59 60 61 62 63 64 66 68 69 70 71 73 74 75 76 77 78 79 80 81 82 83 84 85 86 87 89 90 94 96 97 107 108 110 111 114 115 118 119 124 126 129 130 132 135 136 141 146 147 **P**6 **S** Bon Secours Health System, Inc., Marriottsville, MD
Primary Contact: Craig McCoy, Chief Executive Officer
COO: Daniel Duggan, Chief Operating Officer
CFO: Ronnie Hyatt, Senior Vice President Finance and Chief Financial Officer
CMO: Saria Saccoio, M.D., Chief Medical Officer
CIO: Rita Hooker, Administrative Director Information Services
CHR: Fernando Fleites, Senior Vice President Human Resources
CNO: Teri Ficicchy, R.N., Chief Nursing Officer
Web address: www.stfrancishealth.org
Control: Other not–for–profit (including NFP Corporation) **Service:** General Medical and Surgical

Staffed Beds: 394 **Admissions:** 17860 **Census:** 214 **Outpatient Visits:** 195610 **Births:** 2318 **Total Expense ($000):** 382019 **Payroll Expense ($000):** 129087 **Personnel:** 2326

✠ △ **GHS GREENVILLE MEMORIAL HOSPITAL (420078)**, 701 Grove Road, Zip 29605–4295; tel. 864/455–7000, (Includes GHS CHILDREN'S HOSPITAL, 701 Grove Road, Zip 29605–5611; tel. 864/455–7000; MARSHALL I. PICKENS HOSPITAL, 701 Grove Road, Zip 29605–5601; tel. 864/455–8988; ROGER C. PEACE REHABILITATION HOSPITAL, 701 Grove Road, tel. 864/455–7000), (Total facility includes 15 beds in nursing home–type unit) **A**1 2 3 5 7 8 10 **F**1 3 4 5 11 13 15 17 18 19 20 22 24 26 27 29 30 31 34 35 36 38 39 40 41 43 44 45 46 47 48 49 50 52 53 54 56 57 58 59 61 64 65 66 68 70 72 73 74 75 76 77 78 79 81 82 83 84 85 86 87 88 89 90 92 93 94 96 97 98 99 100 101 102 103 104 105 106 107 110 111 114 115 116 117 118 119 120 121 124 126 128 129 130 132 134 135 136 141 142 145 146 147 148 **P**6 **S** Greenville Health System, Greenville, SC
Primary Contact: Paul F. Johnson, President
COO: Greg Rusnak, Executive Vice President and Chief Operating Officer
CFO: Terri Newsom, Vice President of Finance and Chief Financial Officer
CMO: Angelo Sinopoli, M.D., Vice President Clinical Integration and Chief Medical Officer
CIO: Rich Rogers, Vice President Information Services
CHR: Doug Dorman, Vice President Human Resources
CNO: Michelle T. Smith, R.N., Vice President Nursing Chief Nursing Officer Chief Experience Officer
Web address: www.ghs.org
Control: Other not–for–profit (including NFP Corporation) **Service:** General Medical and Surgical

Staffed Beds: 742 **Admissions:** 36407 **Census:** 610 **Outpatient Visits:** 267074 **Births:** 5657 **Total Expense ($000):** 798867 **Payroll Expense ($000):** 230509 **Personnel:** 6390

✠ **PATEWOOD MEMORIAL HOSPITAL (420102)**, 175 Patewood Drive, Zip 29615–3570; tel. 864/797–1000 **A**1 5 10 **F**3 11 29 30 37 45 50 64 74 77 79 80 81 85 130 135 146 **P**6 **S** Greenville Health System, Greenville, SC
Primary Contact: Beverly J. Haines, R.N., President
Web address: www.ghs.org/patewood
Control: Other not–for–profit (including NFP Corporation) **Service:** Surgical

Staffed Beds: 72 **Admissions:** 1288 **Census:** 6 **Outpatient Visits:** 6207 **Births:** 0 **Total Expense ($000):** 40747 **Payroll Expense ($000):** 10170 **Personnel:** 170

✠ **REGENCY HOSPITAL OF GREENVILLE (422009)**, One St. Francis Drive, 4th Floor, Zip 29601–3955; tel. 864/255–1438 **A**1 10 **F**3 29 60 75 77 85 97 **S** Select Medical Corporation, Mechanicsburg, PA
Primary Contact: Paige Beauregard, Chief Executive Officer
Web address: www.regencyhospital.com
Control: Corporation, Investor–owned, for–profit **Service:** Long–Term Acute Care hospital

Staffed Beds: 32 **Admissions:** 353 **Census:** 26 **Outpatient Visits:** 0 **Births:** 0 **Personnel:** 151

☐ **SHRINERS HOSPITALS FOR CHILDREN–GREENVILLE (423300)**, 950 West Faris Road, Zip 29605–4277; tel. 864/271–3444 **A**1 3 5 10 **F**59 64 68 75 77 79 81 85 87 89 90 93 94 130 131 146 148 **P**6 **S** Shriners Hospitals for Children, Tampa, FL
Primary Contact: Randall R. Romberger, Administrator
CFO: John Conti, Director Finance
CMO: J. Michael Wattenbarger, M.D., Chief of Staff
CHR: Willis E. Tisdale, Director Human Resources
CNO: Allison Leigh Windas, Director of Patient Care Services
Web address: www.greenvilleshrinershospital.org
Control: Other not–for–profit (including NFP Corporation) **Service:** Children's orthopedic

Staffed Beds: 15 **Admissions:** 245 **Census:** 2 **Outpatient Visits:** 16900 **Births:** 0 **Total Expense ($000):** 24042 **Payroll Expense ($000):** 11079 **Personnel:** 171

SC

Many Facility Codes have changed. Please refer to the AHA Guide Code Chart.   © 2016 AHA Guide

GREENWOOD—Greenwood County

☐ **GREENWOOD REGIONAL REHABILITATION HOSPITAL (423030)**, 1530 Parkway, Zip 29646–4027; tel. 864/330–9070, (Total facility includes 7 beds in nursing home–type unit) **A**1 10 **F**3 29 75 90 128 130 132 143 148 **S** Ernest Health, Inc., Albuquerque, NM
Primary Contact: Kristin Manske, Chief Executive Officer
CFO: Charity Walker, Controller and Regional Business Officer Manager
CMO: Cam Monda, D.O., Medical Director
CNO: Teresa Nabors, Director of Nursing
Web address: www.grrh.ernesthealth.com
Control: Corporation, Investor–owned, for–profit **Service:** Rehabilitation

Staffed Beds: 49 **Admissions:** 1059 **Census:** 38 **Outpatient Visits:** 0 **Births:** 0 **Personnel:** 94

★ ◇ **SELF REGIONAL HEALTHCARE (420071)**, 1325 Spring Street, Zip 29646–3860; tel. 864/725–4111 **A**2 3 5 10 21 **F**3 8 11 13 15 17 18 20 22 24 26 28 29 30 31 32 34 35 39 40 43 45 51 53 57 58 59 60 62 64 68 70 72 73 74 75 76 77 78 79 80 81 82 86 87 89 90 93 94 97 98 102 103 104 107 108 110 111 114 115 117 119 120 121 123 124 129 130 131 132 134 135 144 146 147 148 **P**5 8
Primary Contact: James A. Pfeiffer, FACHE, President and Chief Executive Officer
CFO: Timothy Evans, Vice President and Chief Financial Officer
CMO: F Gregory Mappin, M.D., Vice President Medical Affairs and Chief Medical Officer
CIO: Andy Hartung, Director Information Systems
CHR: Michael Dixon, Director Human Resources
CNO: Linda Russell, Vice President and Chief Nursing Officer
Web address: www.selfregional.org
Control: County–Government, nonfederal **Service:** General Medical and Surgical

Staffed Beds: 326 **Admissions:** 11764 **Census:** 155 **Outpatient Visits:** 281122 **Births:** 1418 **Total Expense ($000):** 289043 **Payroll Expense ($000):** 97747 **Personnel:** 2168

GREER—Greenville County

☐ **CAROLINA CENTER FOR BEHAVIORAL HEALTH (424010)**, 2700 East Phillips Road, Zip 29650–4816; tel. 864/235–2335 **A**1 10 **F**4 98 99 100 101 102 103 104 105 **S** Universal Health Services, Inc., King of Prussia, PA
Primary Contact: John Willingham, Chief Executive Officer and Managing Director
COO: Greg Schlangen, R.N., Chief Operating Officer
CFO: James P. Boynton, Jr., Chief Financial Officer
CMO: Gergana Dimitrova, M.D., Medical Director
CHR: George Hammett, Director Human Resources
CNO: Jennifer Daigle, R.N., Director of Nursing and Utilization Review
Web address: www.thecarolinacenter.com
Control: Corporation, Investor–owned, for–profit **Service:** Psychiatric

Staffed Beds: 130 **Admissions:** 3904 **Census:** 110 **Outpatient Visits:** 0 **Births:** 0 **Personnel:** 281

✖ **GHS GREER MEMORIAL HOSPITAL (420033)**, 830 South Buncombe Road, Zip 29650–2400; tel. 864/797–8000, (Includes ROGER HUNTINGTON NURSING CENTER) **A**1 5 10 **F**3 11 13 15 18 28 29 30 34 35 40 44 47 49 50 57 59 61 64 65 68 70 76 77 79 81 82 85 86 87 89 94 107 110 111 114 119 129 130 146 147 **P**6 **S** Greenville Health System, Greenville, SC
Primary Contact: John F. Mansure, FACHE, President
Web address: www.ghs.org
Control: Other not–for–profit (including NFP Corporation) **Service:** General Medical and Surgical

Staffed Beds: 70 **Admissions:** 3619 **Census:** 30 **Outpatient Visits:** 108400 **Births:** 673 **Total Expense ($000):** 76609 **Payroll Expense ($000):** 24658 **Personnel:** 397

★ ◇ **PELHAM MEDICAL CENTER (420103)**, 250 Westmoreland Road, Zip 29651–9013; tel. 864/530–6000 **A**10 21 **F**3 11 15 18 20 26 29 30 34 35 37 40 45 49 50 54 57 59 64 68 70 74 75 77 79 81 82 84 85 86 87 90 94 107 108 110 111 114 115 118 119 130 146 **S** Spartanburg Regional Healthcare System, Spartanburg, SC
Primary Contact: Anthony Kouskolekas, FACHE, President
CNO: Connie Spykerman, Chief Nursing Officer
Web address: www.pelhammedicalcenter.com
Control: Hospital district or authority, Government, nonfederal **Service:** General Medical and Surgical

Staffed Beds: 46 **Admissions:** 2484 **Census:** 26 **Outpatient Visits:** 49590 **Births:** 0 **Total Expense ($000):** 59625 **Payroll Expense ($000):** 18883 **Personnel:** 668

HARDEEVILLE—Jasper County

✖ **COASTAL CAROLINA HOSPITAL (420101)**, 1000 Medical Center Drive, Zip 29927–3446; tel. 843/784–8000 **A**1 10 **F**3 11 13 15 28 29 30 34 35 40 45 46 47 48 49 51 57 59 60 64 70 74 75 76 77 79 81 85 89 90 93 94 107 108 110 111 115 119 126 127 130 132 135 146 147 148 **S** TENET Healthcare Corporation, Dallas, TX
Primary Contact: Joel C. Taylor, Interim Chief Executive Officer
CFO: Ronald J. Groteluschen, Chief Financial Officer
CIO: Cheryl Grant, Director Information Systems
CHR: Darlene E. Nester, Market Chief Human Resources Officer
CNO: Patricia A. Feilmeier, Interim Chief Nursing Officer
Web address: www.coastalhospital.com
Control: Corporation, Investor–owned, for–profit **Service:** General Medical and Surgical

Staffed Beds: 35 **Admissions:** 2756 **Census:** 24 **Outpatient Visits:** 46438 **Births:** 711 **Total Expense ($000):** 42628 **Payroll Expense ($000):** 13817 **Personnel:** 259

HARTSVILLE—Darlington County

✖ **CAROLINA PINES REGIONAL MEDICAL CENTER (420010)**, 1304 West Bobo Newsom Highway, Zip 29550–4710; tel. 843/339–2100 **A**1 10 **F**3 11 13 15 20 28 29 30 34 35 40 43 46 49 57 64 70 73 75 76 79 81 82 85 86 87 89 90 93 107 108 110 111 114 115 118 119 129 130 131 132 135 146 147 148 **S** RCCH HealthCare Partners, Brentwood, TN
Primary Contact: J. Timothy Browne, FACHE, Chief Executive Officer
COO: Susan C. Shugart, Chief Operating Officer
CFO: Rodney VanDonkelaar, Chief Financial Officer
CMO: Tallulah Holmstrom, Chief Medical Officer
CIO: Denise Barefoot, Director of Information Technology
CHR: Charlotte Adams, Director of Human Resources
CNO: Danny Wharton, Chief Nursing Officer
Web address: www.cprmc.com
Control: Corporation, Investor–owned, for–profit **Service:** General Medical and Surgical

Staffed Beds: 120 **Admissions:** 4604 **Census:** 44 **Outpatient Visits:** 96117 **Births:** 553 **Total Expense ($000):** 74565 **Payroll Expense ($000):** 26297 **Personnel:** 452

HILTON HEAD ISLAND—Beaufort County

✖ **HILTON HEAD HOSPITAL (420080)**, 25 Hospital Center Boulevard, Zip 29926–2738; tel. 843/681–6122 **A**1 10 20 **F**3 11 13 15 17 18 20 22 24 26 28 29 30 34 35 37 40 45 46 48 49 50 51 53 54 57 59 60 61 64 65 68 70 74 76 77 78 79 81 85 86 89 94 96 107 108 110 111 114 115 119 130 131 132 135 146 147 148 **S** TENET Healthcare Corporation, Dallas, TX
Primary Contact: Jeremy L. Clark, Market Chief Executive Officer
CFO: Cassie Ball, Chief Financial Officer
CMO: Glenn Neil Love, M.D., Medical Director
CIO: Stephen Brendler, Director Information Systems
CHR: Darlene E. Nester, Chief Human Resources Officer
Web address: www.hiltonheadregional.com
Control: Partnership, Investor–owned, for–profit **Service:** General Medical and Surgical

Staffed Beds: 93 **Admissions:** 5868 **Census:** 62 **Outpatient Visits:** 66187 **Births:** 558 **Total Expense ($000):** 96776 **Payroll Expense ($000):** 26443 **Personnel:** 471

LAKE CITY—Florence County

★ **LAKE CITY COMMUNITY HOSPITAL (420066)**, 258 North Ron McNair Boulevard, Zip 29560–2462, Mailing Address: P.O. Box 1479, Zip 29560–1479; tel. 843/374–2036 **A**10 **F**3 11 15 28 29 34 35 40 50 56 57 59 61 64 65 69 75 77 79 81 85 86 87 93 94 107 108 110 111 113 114 119 127 130 132 144 146
Primary Contact: Mary Duke, Interim Chief Executive Officer
CFO: Henry McCutcheon, Jr., Chief Financial Officer
CMO: Stephen Askins, M.D., Chief of Staff
CIO: David Moon, Jr., Director Information Systems
CHR: Anne Poston, Director of Human Resources/Compliance
CNO: Renate Browder, R.N., Director of Nursing
Web address: www.lcchospital.org
Control: Hospital district or authority, Government, nonfederal **Service:** General Medical and Surgical

Staffed Beds: 26 **Admissions:** 839 **Census:** 11 **Outpatient Visits:** 42628 **Births:** 0 **Total Expense ($000):** 15532 **Payroll Expense ($000):** 7205 **Personnel:** 198

SC

Hospital, Medicare Provider Number, Address, Telephone, Approval, Facility, and Physician Codes, Health Care System

★ American Hospital Association (AHA) membership   ○ Healthcare Facilities Accreditation Program   ⇑ Center for Improvement in Healthcare Quality Accreditation
☐ The Joint Commission accreditation   ◇ DNV Healthcare Inc. accreditation   △ Commission on Accreditation of Rehabilitation Facilities (CARF) accreditation

---

LANCASTER—Lancaster County

☐ **REBOUND BEHAVIORAL HEALTH**, 134 East Rebound Road, Zip 29720–7712; tel. 877/914–1876, (Nonreporting) **A**1 **S** Acadia Healthcare Company, Inc., Franklin, TN
Primary Contact: George G. Boykin, Chief Executive Officer
Web address: www.reboundbehavioralhealth.com
Control: Corporation, Investor–owned, for–profit **Service:** Psychiatric

Staffed Beds: 42

☒ **SPRINGS MEMORIAL HOSPITAL (420036)**, 800 West Meeting Street, Zip 29720–2298; tel. 803/286–1214 **A**1 5 10 **F**3 8 11 13 15 17 18 20 29 30 31 34 35 40 47 48 49 51 57 59 60 62 63 64 68 70 72 73 74 75 76 78 79 80 81 85 89 90 93 94 98 107 108 110 111 114 115 118 119 128 129 130 132 135 146 147 148 **S** Community Health Systems, Inc., Franklin, TN
Primary Contact: Janice Dabney, Chief Executive Officer
CFO: Holt Smith, Chief Financial Officer
CMO: Douglas Tiedt, M.D., Chief of Staff
CIO: Chrys Steele, Director Information Systems
CHR: Trent Elmore, Director Human Resources
CNO: Karen Martin, Chief Nursing Officer
Web address: www.springsmemorial.com
Control: Corporation, Investor–owned, for–profit **Service:** General Medical and Surgical

Staffed Beds: 162 Admissions: 5783 Census: 70 Outpatient Visits: 78722 Births: 681 Total Expense ($000): 97606 Payroll Expense ($000): 30407 Personnel: 641

LORIS—Horry County

☐ **MCLEOD LORIS SEACOAST HOSPITAL (420105)**, 3655 Mitchell Street, Zip 29569–2827; tel. 843/716–7000, (Includes MCLEOD SEACOAST, 4000 Highway 9 East, Little River, Zip 29566–7833; tel. 843/390–8100) **A**1 10 **F**3 11 13 15 17 18 20 28 29 30 31 32 34 35 40 44 50 53 57 58 59 60 64 68 70 74 75 76 77 78 79 81 82 85 86 87 89 90 94 96 107 108 110 111 115 118 119 130 131 132 134 135 143 146 148 **P**3 **S** McLeod Health, Florence, SC
Primary Contact: Edward D. Tinsley, III, Chief Executive Officer
COO: Arnold Green, Senior Vice President and Chief Operating Officer
CFO: Fred O. Todd, Senior Vice President Finance
CMO: James N. Craigie, M.D., Vice President Medical Affairs
CHR: Teresa Pougnaud, Vice President Human Resources
Web address: www.mcleodhealth.org
Control: Other not–for–profit (including NFP Corporation) **Service:** General Medical and Surgical

Staffed Beds: 155 Admissions: 4812 Census: 51 Outpatient Visits: 103233 Births: 452 Total Expense ($000): 100896 Payroll Expense ($000): 36503 Personnel: 344

MANNING—Clarendon County

★ ◇ **MCLEOD HEALTH CLARENDON (420069)**, 10 Hospital Street, Zip 29102–3153, Mailing Address: P.O. Box 550, Zip 29102–0550; tel. 803/433–3000 **A**10 21 **F**3 7 11 13 15 18 26 28 29 34 35 39 40 45 50 51 53 54 56 57 59 62 64 65 67 70 75 76 77 79 81 85 87 89 90 91 93 94 96 97 107 108 110 111 114 119 127 128 129 130 132 133 135 143 146 147 148 **S** McLeod Health, Florence, SC
Primary Contact: Deborah Locklair, FACHE, Administrator
COO: Paul Schumacher, Chief Operating Officer
CFO: John Shaughnessy, Chief Financial Officer
CMO: Catherine Rabon, M.D., Chief Medical Officer
CIO: Pat Kolb, Manager Information Technology
CHR: Gail A. Richbourg, Director Human Resources
CNO: Natalie Davis, R.N., Interim Chief Nursing Officer
Web address: www.clarendonhealth.com
Control: Hospital district or authority, Government, nonfederal **Service:** General Medical and Surgical

Staffed Beds: 48 Admissions: 2493 Census: 33 Outpatient Visits: 135818 Births: 417 Total Expense ($000): 46560 Payroll Expense ($000): 21061 Personnel: 801

MOUNT PLEASANT—Charleston County

☒ **EAST COOPER MEDICAL CENTER (420089)**, 2000 Hospital Drive, Zip 29464–3764; tel. 843/881–0100 **A**1 3 5 10 **F**3 13 15 18 29 31 34 35 40 43 46 51 57 59 60 64 68 70 73 74 75 76 77 78 79 80 81 82 84 85 86 90 92 93 94 100 102 107 108 110 111 114 115 119 126 129 130 131 132 135 146 147 148 **S** TENET Healthcare Corporation, Dallas, TX
Primary Contact: Jason P. Alexander, FACHE, Chief Executive Officer
COO: Ramona Pickens, Chief Operating Officer
CFO: Patrick C. Bolander, Chief Financial Officer
CMO: William Stroud, M.D., Physician Advisor
CIO: Michael Foster, Director Information Systems
CHR: Tracy Hunter, Chief Human Resources Officer
CNO: Terri Harris, R.N., Chief Nursing Officer
Web address: www.eastcoopermedctr.com
Control: Corporation, Investor–owned, for–profit **Service:** General Medical and Surgical

Staffed Beds: 140 Admissions: 5321 Census: 43 Outpatient Visits: 53967 Births: 1476 Total Expense ($000): 112805 Payroll Expense ($000): 28019 Personnel: 436

EAST COOPER REGIONAL MEDICAL CENTER See East Cooper Medical Center

☒ **ROPER ST. FRANCIS MOUNT PLEASANT HOSPITAL (420104)**, 3500 Highway 17 North, Zip 29466–9123, Mailing Address: 3500 North Highway 17, Zip 29466–9123; tel. 843/606–7000 **A**1 10 **F**3 7 13 15 29 30 34 40 45 54 59 68 70 75 76 79 81 84 85 86 87 89 94 102 107 108 110 111 115 118 119 129 143 146 147 148 **S** Carolinas Healthcare System, Charlotte, NC
Primary Contact: Anthony Jackson, Chief Executive Officer
CFO: Bret Johnson, Chief Financial Officer
CMO: Steven D. Shapiro, M.D., Chief Medical Officer
CIO: Melinda H. Cardell, Interim Chief Information Officer
CHR: Melanie Stith, Vice President Human Resources
CNO: Tavia Buck, Chief Nursing Officer
Web address: www.rsfh.com/mount–pleasant–hospital
Control: Other not–for–profit (including NFP Corporation) **Service:** General Medical and Surgical

Staffed Beds: 50 Admissions: 1640 Census: 14 Outpatient Visits: 42810 Births: 498 Total Expense ($000): 55047 Payroll Expense ($000): 13340 Personnel: 295

MT. PLEASANT—Mt. Pleasant County

KINDRED HOSPITAL–CHARLESTON See Vibra Hospital of Charleston

☒ **VIBRA HOSPITAL OF CHARLESTON (422005)**, 1200 Hospital Drive, Zip 29464; tel. 843/375–4000, (Nonreporting) **A**1 10 **S** Vibra Healthcare, Mechanicsburg, PA
Primary Contact: Peter Miller, Chief Executive Officer
CFO: Julia Smith, Chief Financial Officer
CMO: Athena Beldecos, M.D., Medical Director
CHR: Julia Taylor, Area Director Human Resources
Web address: www.vhcharleston.com
Control: Corporation, Investor–owned, for–profit **Service:** Long–Term Acute Care hospital

Staffed Beds: 94

MULLINS—Marion County

☒ **CAROLINAS HOSPITAL SYSTEM MARION (420055)**, 2829 East Highway 76, Zip 29574–6035, Mailing Address: P.O. Drawer 1150, Marion, Zip 29571–1150; tel. 843/431–2000, (Total facility includes 92 beds in nursing home–type unit) **A**1 10 **F**1 3 13 15 28 29 34 40 45 46 53 57 59 67 70 75 76 77 79 81 82 85 86 89 90 94 107 111 119 128 129 130 131 133 146 148 **S** Community Health Systems, Inc., Franklin, TN
Primary Contact: Parkes Coggins, Chief Executive Officer
CFO: Christopher Green, Chief Financial Officer
CMO: Alvin Abinsay, M.D., Chief Medical Staff
CIO: Charlie Grantham, Manager Information Systems
CHR: Kay White, Director Human Resources and Diversity
Web address: www.carolinashospitalmarion.com
Control: Corporation, Investor–owned, for–profit **Service:** General Medical and Surgical

Staffed Beds: 216 Admissions: 2634 Census: 117 Outpatient Visits: 46114 Births: 261 Personnel: 269

MARION COUNTY MEDICAL CENTER See Carolinas Hospital System Marion

MURRELLS INLET—Georgetown County

☒ △ **TIDELANDS WACCAMAW COMMUNITY HOSPITAL (420098)**, 4070 Highway 17 Bypass, Zip 29576–5033, Mailing Address: P.O. Drawer 3350, Zip 29576–2673; tel. 843/652–1000 **A**1 2 7 10 **F**3 8 11 13 15 17 18 28 29 30 31 32 35 37 39 40 45 50 51 56 60 61 64 65 68 70 73 74 75 76 77 78 79 81 82 84 85 86 87 89 90 93 94 96 97 100 102 107 108 110 111 114 115 118 119 130 131 146 147 148 **S** QHR, Brentwood, TN
Primary Contact: Gayle L. Resetar, Chief Operating Officer
CFO: Terry L. Kiser, Chief Financial Officer
CIO: Frank Scafidi, Chief Information Officer
Web address: www.tidelandshealth.org
Control: Other not–for–profit (including NFP Corporation) **Service:** General Medical and Surgical

Staffed Beds: 169 Admissions: 7924 Census: 110 Outpatient Visits: 118524 Births: 577 Total Expense ($000): 140013 Payroll Expense ($000): 34761 Personnel: 627

MYRTLE BEACH—Horry County

☒ **GRAND STRAND REGIONAL MEDICAL CENTER (420085)**, 809 82nd Parkway, Zip 29572–4607; tel. 843/692–1000 **A**1 2 3 10 19 **F**3 11 13 15 17 18 20 22 24 26 28 29 30 31 34 35 37 39 40 42 43 46 47 49 50 54 56 57 59 60 64 70 73 74 75 76 77 78 79 81 82 85 86 87 88 89 90 107 108 110 111 114 115 118 119 126 130 132 135 146 147 **S** HCA, Nashville, TN
Primary Contact: Mark E. Sims, Chief Executive Officer
CFO: Turner Wortham, Chief Financial Officer
Web address: www.grandstrandmed.com
Control: Corporation, Investor–owned, for–profit **Service:** General Medical and Surgical

Staffed Beds: 303 Admissions: 17567 Census: 225 Outpatient Visits: 172498 Births: 956 Personnel: 1248

Many Facility Codes have changed. Please refer to the AHA Guide Code Chart. © 2016 AHA Guide

SC

NEWBERRY—Newberry County

☒ **NEWBERRY COUNTY MEMORIAL HOSPITAL (420053)**, 2669 Kinard Street,
Zip 29108–2911, Mailing Address: P.O. Box 497, Zip 29108–0497;
tel. 803/276–7570 **A**1 10 20 **F**3 7 11 13 15 17 28 29 30 31 32 34 35 40 45
47 49 53 56 57 59 64 68 70 75 76 77 78 79 81 82 85 86 87 89 90 93 94
103 104 107 108 109 110 111 114 129 130 133 135 143 146 147 148
P6 **S** QHR, Brentwood, TN
Primary Contact: Bruce A. Baldwin, Chief Executive Officer
CFO: Mike Reynolds, Chief Financial Officer
CMO: Mark Davis, M.D., Chief of Staff
CIO: David Wolff, Director Information Technology
CHR: Dyan Bowman, Director Human Resources
Web address: www.newberryhospital.org
Control: County–Government, nonfederal **Service:** General Medical and Surgical

Staffed Beds: 52 **Admissions:** 1921 **Census:** 22 **Outpatient Visits:** 41693
Births: 298 **Total Expense ($000):** 49505 **Payroll Expense ($000):** 18241
Personnel: 393

ORANGEBURG—Orangeburg County

☒ **REGIONAL MEDICAL CENTER (420068)**, 3000 St. Matthews Road,
Zip 29118–1442; tel. 803/395–2200 **A**1 2 10 13 **F**3 11 12 13 14 15 17 18
20 28 29 30 31 32 34 35 39 40 44 45 46 47 48 49 50 53 57 58 59 60 61
62 64 65 68 70 71 73 74 75 76 77 78 79 81 82 84 85 86 87 89 90 93 94
97 98 100 101 102 103 107 108 110 111 114 115 119 121 127 129 130
131 132 134 135 144 146 147 148 **S** QHR, Brentwood, TN
Primary Contact: Thomas C. Dandridge, President and Chief Executive Officer
CFO: Liza Porterfield, Chief Financial Officer
CIO: James Albin, Chief Information Officer
CHR: Howard Harris, Vice President Human Resources
CNO: Mickey Whisenhunt, Interim Chief Nursing Officer
Web address: www.trmchealth.org
Control: County–Government, nonfederal **Service:** General Medical and Surgical

Staffed Beds: 286 **Admissions:** 10939 **Census:** 146 **Outpatient Visits:**
218745 **Births:** 987 **Total Expense ($000):** 222932 **Payroll Expense
($000):** 97983 **Personnel:** 1212

☐ **WILLIAM J. MCCORD ADOLESCENT TREATMENT FACILITY (424013)**, 910
Cook Road, Zip 29118–2124, Mailing Address: P.O. Box 1166, Zip 29116–1166;
tel. 803/534–2328 **A**1 10 **F**4 5 29 34 38 57 61 98 99 130 132 134 135
Primary Contact: Michael Dennis, Director
CFO: Laura Murdaugh, Finance Director
CMO: Dorothy Kendall, Medical Director
CNO: Linda Mitchum, Director of Nursing
Web address: www.tccada.com
Control: Other not–for–profit (including NFP Corporation) **Service:** Alcoholism and
other chemical dependency

Staffed Beds: 15 **Admissions:** 115 **Census:** 11 **Outpatient Visits:** 0 **Births:**
0 **Total Expense ($000):** 2170 **Payroll Expense ($000):** 1118 **Personnel:**
23

PICKENS—Pickens County

★ ◇ **CANNON MEMORIAL HOSPITAL (420011)**, 123 West G. Acker Drive,
Zip 29671–2739, Mailing Address: P.O. Box 188, Zip 29671–0188;
tel. 864/878–4791 **A**10 21 **F**3 11 15 29 34 40 50 51 53 56 57 59 61 64 65
70 75 79 81 85 94 97 107 108 110 111 114 119 127 130 135 146 **P**8
S Carolinas Healthcare System, Charlotte, NC
Primary Contact: Norman G. Rentz, President and Chief Executive Officer
CFO: Will Grant, Chief Financial Officer
CMO: Daniel J. Dahlhausen, M.D., President of Medical Staff/Chief Medical Officer
CIO: Robert Furr, Director Information Services
CHR: Lisa G. Bryant, Director Human Resources
CNO: Donna K. Anderson, R.N., Chief Nursing Officer
Web address: www.cannonhospital.org
Control: Other not–for–profit (including NFP Corporation) **Service:** General
Medical and Surgical

Staffed Beds: 35 **Admissions:** 969 **Census:** 10 **Outpatient Visits:** 46070
Births: 0 **Total Expense ($000):** 22626 **Payroll Expense ($000):** 10003
Personnel: 274

ROCK HILL—York County

☒ **HEALTHSOUTH REHABILITATION HOSPITAL OF ROCK HILL (423028)**, 1795
Dr. Frank Gaston Boulevard, Zip 29732–1190; tel. 803/326–3500,
(Nonreporting) **A**1 10 **S** HEALTHSOUTH Corporation, Birmingham, AL
Primary Contact: Deanna Martin, Chief Executive Officer
Web address: www.healthsouthrockhill.com
Control: Corporation, Investor–owned, for–profit **Service:** Rehabilitation

Staffed Beds: 50

☒ **PIEDMONT MEDICAL CENTER (420002)**, 222 Herlong Avenue, Zip 29732;
tel. 803/329–1234 **A**1 2 10 **F**3 7 11 12 13 15 17 18 20 22 24 26 28 29 30
31 34 35 40 43 45 49 50 57 59 60 64 70 72 73 74 75 76 77 78 79 81 82
85 86 89 90 91 93 98 100 102 107 108 110 111 114 115 118 119 126 130
132 135 146 147 148 **S** TENET Healthcare Corporation, Dallas, TX
Primary Contact: Bradley S. Talbert, FACHE, Chief Executive Officer
COO: Christina E. Oh, Chief Operating Officer
CFO: Alice W. Rigdon, Chief Financial Officer
CMO: Phil Perry, M.D., Regional Chief Medical Officer
CIO: Joel Dean, Director Information Services
CHR: Elizabeth Elich, Vice President Human Resources
CNO: Patricia Ann LeCroy, MSN, Interim Chief Nursing Officer
Web address: www.piedmontmedicalcenter.com
Control: Corporation, Investor–owned, for–profit **Service:** General Medical and
Surgical

Staffed Beds: 280 **Admissions:** 13991 **Census:** 172 **Outpatient Visits:**
142842 **Births:** 1638 **Total Expense ($000):** 211021 **Payroll Expense
($000):** 71215 **Personnel:** 1571

SENECA—Oconee County

☒ **OCONEE MEMORIAL HOSPITAL (420009)**, 298 Memorial Drive,
Zip 29672–9499; tel. 864/882–3351, (Includes LILA DOYLE NURSING CARE
FACILITY), (Total facility includes 120 beds in nursing home–type unit) **A**1 3 5 10
20 **F**3 7 11 13 15 17 18 20 28 29 30 31 34 35 39 40 54 56 57 59 61 62 63
64 67 70 74 75 76 77 78 79 81 82 84 85 86 87 89 90 94 97 107 108 114
119 128 130 132 135 143 146 **P**6 **S** Greenville Health System, Greenville, SC
Primary Contact: Hunter Kome, Campus President
CMO: Conrad K. Shuler, M.D., Chief Medical Officer
CIO: Jay Hansen, Director Information Services
CNO: Patricia Smith, Chief Nursing Officer
Web address: www.oconeemed.org
Control: Hospital district or authority, Government, nonfederal **Service:** General
Medical and Surgical

Staffed Beds: 252 **Admissions:** 6050 **Census:** 173 **Outpatient Visits:**
106396 **Births:** 515 **Personnel:** 772

SIMPSONVILLE—Greenville County

☒ **GHS HILLCREST MEMORIAL HOSPITAL (420037)**, 729 S.E. Main Street,
Zip 29681–3280; tel. 864/454–6100 **A**1 5 10 **F**3 11 12 15 18 29 34 35 40
44 45 50 57 58 59 61 64 68 70 79 81 85 86 90 107 110 111 114 119 129
130 132 135 146 **P**6 **S** Greenville Health System, Greenville, SC
Primary Contact: Eric Bour, M.D., FACS, President
Web address: www.ghs.org
Control: Other not–for–profit (including NFP Corporation) **Service:** General
Medical and Surgical

Staffed Beds: 43 **Admissions:** 1996 **Census:** 17 **Outpatient Visits:** 63891
Births: 0 **Total Expense ($000):** 54834 **Payroll Expense ($000):** 16309
Personnel: 253

SPARTANBURG—Spartanburg County

☒ △ **MARY BLACK HEALTH SYSTEM–SPARTANBURG (420083)**, 1700 Skylyn
Drive, Zip 29307–1061, Mailing Address: P.O. Box 3217, Zip 29304–3217;
tel. 864/573–3000 **A**1 3 5 7 10 **F**3 11 13 15 18 20 29 30 31 34 35 40 45 47
50 51 56 57 59 60 64 68 70 73 74 76 77 78 79 81 85 89 90 93 94 96 98
102 103 107 108 110 111 114 115 119 126 129 130 135 146 147 148
S Community Health Systems, Inc., Franklin, TN
Primary Contact: Sean T. Dardeau, FACHE, Chief Executive Officer
COO: Daniel McKinney, Chief Operating Officer
CFO: Richard A. Meyer, Chief Financial Officer
CMO: Howard Bean, M.D., Chief Medical Officer
CIO: John O'Donnell, Director of Information Technology Services
CHR: Lee Ann Roque, Director of Human Resources
CNO: Chanda Flynn, R.N., Chief Nursing Officer
Web address: www.maryblackhealthsystem.com
Control: Corporation, Investor–owned, for–profit **Service:** General Medical and
Surgical

Staffed Beds: 181 **Admissions:** 6329 **Census:** 77 **Outpatient Visits:** 107079
Births: 810 **Total Expense ($000):** 112754 **Payroll Expense ($000):** 39150
Personnel: 934

SC

Hospital, Medicare Provider Number, Address, Telephone, Approval, Facility, and Physician Codes, Health Care System

★ American Hospital Association (AHA) membership ◯ Healthcare Facilities Accreditation Program ⇑ Center for Improvement in Healthcare Quality Accreditation
☐ The Joint Commission accreditation ◇ DNV Healthcare Inc. accreditation △ Commission on Accreditation of Rehabilitation Facilities (CARF) accreditation

⊞ **SPARTANBURG HOSPITAL FOR RESTORATIVE CARE (422004)**, 389 Serpentine Drive, Zip 29303–3026; tel. 864/560–3280, (Total facility includes 25 beds in nursing home–type unit) **A**1 10 **F**1 29 30 31 35 57 59 60 68 70 75 77 79 82 84 85 87 90 119 128 130 148 **S** Spartanburg Regional Healthcare System, Spartanburg, SC
Primary Contact: Anita M. Butler, Chief Executive Officer
Web address: www.srhs.com
Control: Hospital district or authority, Government, nonfederal **Service:** Long–Term Acute Care hospital

Staffed Beds: 116 **Admissions:** 788 **Census:** 43 **Outpatient Visits:** 0 **Births:** 0 **Total Expense ($000):** 20369 **Payroll Expense ($000):** 11384 **Personnel:** 205

★ **SPARTANBURG MEDICAL CENTER (420007)**, 101 East Wood Street, Zip 29303–3040; tel. 864/560–6000 **A**2 3 5 10 13 **F**3 7 11 12 13 15 17 18 20 22 24 26 28 29 30 31 34 35 36 37 38 39 40 43 45 46 47 48 49 50 53 54 56 57 58 59 60 61 62 63 64 65 66 68 70 71 72 73 74 75 76 77 78 79 81 82 83 84 85 86 87 88 89 90 94 97 98 99 100 101 102 103 104 105 107 108 110 111 114 115 117 118 119 120 123 124 126 129 130 131 132 135 143 144 145 146 147 148 **S** Spartanburg Regional Healthcare System, Spartanburg, SC
Primary Contact: J. Philip Feisal, President and Chief Executive Officer
COO: Mark Aycock, Chief Operating Officer
CFO: Kenneth Meinke, Senior Vice President Administrative Services, Finance and Chief Financial Officer
CMO: Charles Morrow, M.D., Chief Medical Officer
CIO: Harold Moore, Chief Information Technology Officer
CHR: Kathy Sinclair, Vice President Human Resources
CNO: Susan Duggar, R.N., Vice President Nursing
Web address: www.spartanburgregional.com
Control: Hospital district or authority, Government, nonfederal **Service:** General Medical and Surgical

Staffed Beds: 514 **Admissions:** 34876 **Census:** 432 **Outpatient Visits:** 370525 **Births:** 2754 **Total Expense ($000):** 540185 **Payroll Expense ($000):** 211982 **Personnel:** 4110

SUMTER—Sumter County

⊞ **PALMETTO HEALTH TUOMEY (420070)**, 129 North Washington Street, Zip 29150–4983; tel. 803/774–9000, (Total facility includes 18 beds in nursing home–type unit) **A**1 10 19 **F**1 3 13 15 20 28 29 30 31 32 34 35 40 48 49 50 51 54 56 59 60 62 63 64 68 70 71 73 75 76 77 78 79 81 84 85 86 87 89 90 94 102 107 108 110 111 114 117 119 121 128 129 130 131 132 135 146 147 148 **P**6 **S** Palmetto Health, Columbia, SC
Primary Contact: Michelle Logan–Owens, Acting Chief Executive Officer
CFO: Mark Lovell, Vice President and Chief Financial Officer
CMO: Gene Dickerson, M.D., Vice President Medical Affairs
CIO: Cheryl Martin, Chief Information Officer
CHR: Letitia Pringle–Miller, Administrative Director
CNO: Terrie Carlton, R.N., Vice President & Chief Nursing Officer
Web address: www.tuomey.com
Control: Other not–for–profit (including NFP Corporation) **Service:** General Medical and Surgical

Staffed Beds: 238 **Admissions:** 6760 **Census:** 157 **Outpatient Visits:** 131859 **Births:** 1370 **Total Expense ($000):** 196437 **Payroll Expense ($000):** 80551 **Personnel:** 1384

TRAVELERS REST—Greenville County

⊞ △ **NORTH GREENVILLE HOSPITAL (422008)**, 807 North Main Street, Zip 29690–1551; tel. 864/455–9206 **A**1 5 7 10 **F**1 3 15 29 30 34 35 40 44 50 64 68 75 79 85 86 87 107 110 111 114 119 130 146 148 **P**6
Primary Contact: Adrienne Talbert, Interim Administrator
CMO: Amy Treece, M.D., Medical Director
CHR: Carol Bish, Human Resources Coordinator
CNO: Marian Lorraine McVey, Chief Nursing Officer
Web address: www.ghs.org
Control: Other not–for–profit (including NFP Corporation) **Service:** Long–Term Acute Care hospital

Staffed Beds: 28 **Admissions:** 226 **Census:** 21 **Outpatient Visits:** 27008 **Births:** 0 **Total Expense ($000):** 28677 **Payroll Expense ($000):** 9148 **Personnel:** 156

☐ **SPRINGBROOK BEHAVIORAL HEALTH SYSTEM (424007)**, One Havenwood Lane, Zip 29690–9447, Mailing Address: P.O. Box 1005, Zip 29690–1005; tel. 864/834–8013, (Total facility includes 68 beds in nursing home–type unit) **A**1 10 **F**98 99 104 106
Primary Contact: Mike Rowley, Chief Executive Officer
COO: Mary Ann Bennett, R.N., Chief Operating Officer and Chief Nursing Officer
CFO: Bart Bennett, Chief Financial Officer
CMO: Mathew Fisher, M.D., Medical Director
CIO: Bart Bennett, Chief Information Technology Officer
CHR: Teresa Lipscomb, Director Human Resources
CNO: Mary Ann Bennett, R.N., Chief Operating Officer and Chief Nursing Officer
Web address: www.springbrookbehavioral.com
Control: Corporation, Investor–owned, for–profit **Service:** Psychiatric

Staffed Beds: 112 **Admissions:** 1081 **Census:** 92 **Outpatient Visits:** 0 **Births:** 0 **Personnel:** 250

UNION—Union County

◇ **UNION MEDICAL CENTER (420039)**, 322 West South Street, Zip 29379–2857, Mailing Address: P.O. Box 789, Zip 29379–0789; tel. 864/301–2000 **A**10 21 **F**1 3 7 13 15 29 30 34 35 40 57 59 64 69 70 75 76 81 89 107 111 115 119 129 130 133 135 146 147 **S** Spartanburg Regional Healthcare System, Spartanburg, SC
Primary Contact: Paul R. Newhouse, President
CFO: Cindy L. Gault, Chief Financial Officer
CHR: Angie Benfield, Human Resources Generalist
CNO: Beth Lawson, Chief Nursing Officer
Web address: www.https://www.spartanburgregional.com/locations/union–medical–center/
Control: Hospital district or authority, Government, nonfederal **Service:** General Medical and Surgical

Staffed Beds: 50 **Admissions:** 1574 **Census:** 17 **Outpatient Visits:** 27988 **Births:** 91 **Personnel:** 231

VARNVILLE—Hampton County

★ **HAMPTON REGIONAL MEDICAL CENTER (420072)**, 503 Carolina Avenue West, Zip 29944–4735, Mailing Address: P.O. Box 338, Zip 29944–0338; tel. 803/943–2771 **A**10 20 **F**15 17 18 24 28 29 31 34 40 59 65 67 70 75 78 79 81 90 93 94 102 107 108 110 111 115 119 127 128 129 133 146
Primary Contact: Dave H. Hamill, President and Chief Executive Officer
Web address: www.hamptonregional.com
Control: Other not–for–profit (including NFP Corporation) **Service:** General Medical and Surgical

Staffed Beds: 32 **Admissions:** 628 **Census:** 7 **Outpatient Visits:** 24780 **Births:** 3 **Total Expense ($000):** 19005 **Payroll Expense ($000):** 7639 **Personnel:** 125

WALTERBORO—Colleton County

⊞ **COLLETON MEDICAL CENTER (420030)**, 501 Robertson Boulevard, Zip 29488–5714; tel. 843/782–2000 **A**1 10 20 **F**3 11 13 15 18 26 29 30 32 34 35 36 40 41 45 47 49 56 57 59 60 64 65 68 70 75 76 77 79 81 82 85 86 87 89 90 93 94 96 98 102 107 108 110 111 114 115 119 129 130 131 132 146 147 148 **P**5 **S** HCA, Nashville, TN
Primary Contact: Brad Griffin, Chief Executive Officer
CFO: Jimmy O. Hiott, III, Chief Financial Officer
CMO: Kim Rakes–Stephens, M.D., Chief Medical Staff
CIO: Damien Noble, Director Information Technology and System
CHR: Wendy Glass, Director Human Resources
CNO: Anna Jonason, Ph.D., Chief Nursing Officer
Web address: www.colletonmedical.com
Control: Corporation, Investor–owned, for–profit **Service:** General Medical and Surgical

Staffed Beds: 131 **Admissions:** 5166 **Census:** 67 **Outpatient Visits:** 70909 **Births:** 316 **Total Expense ($000):** 61188 **Payroll Expense ($000):** 22363 **Personnel:** 360

WEST COLUMBIA—Lexington County

★ ◇ **LEXINGTON MEDICAL CENTER (420073)**, 2720 Sunset Boulevard, Zip 29169–4810; tel. 803/791–2000 **A**2 3 10 21 **F**3 8 11 12 13 15 18 20 22 24 26 28 29 30 31 32 34 35 38 39 40 43 44 45 48 49 50 53 54 57 58 59 60 61 64 68 70 72 73 74 75 76 77 78 79 80 81 82 85 86 87 89 90 92 93 94 107 108 110 111 114 115 118 119 120 121 123 126 127 129 130 131 132 135 141 142 144 145 146 147 148 **P**6
Primary Contact: Tod Augsburger, President and Chief Executive Officer
COO: Tod Augsburger, Senior Vice President and Chief Operating Officer
CFO: Melinda Kruzner, Chief Financial Officer
CMO: Brent Powers, M.D., Vice President/Chief Medical Officer
CIO: Kathleen R. Herald, Vice President and Chief Information Officer
CHR: Kathy A. Howell, Vice President Human Resources
CNO: Cindy Rohman, R.N., Vice President/Chief Nursing Officer
Web address: www.lexmed.com
Control: Hospital district or authority, Government, nonfederal **Service:** General Medical and Surgical

Staffed Beds: 434 **Admissions:** 26548 **Census:** 351 **Outpatient Visits:** 310076 **Births:** 3674 **Total Expense ($000):** 493826 **Payroll Expense ($000):** 192922 **Personnel:** 3413

☐ **THREE RIVERS BEHAVIORAL HEALTH (424008)**, 2900 Sunset Boulevard, Zip 29169–3422; tel. 803/796–9911, (Total facility includes 20 beds in nursing home–type unit) **A**1 10 **F**4 5 35 98 99 100 101 103 104 105 106 **S** Universal Health Services, Inc., King of Prussia, PA
Primary Contact: Nannette M. Lewis, Chief Executive Officer
CFO: Christopher Jensen, Chief Financial Officer
CMO: Christina Lynn, M.D., Medical Director
CHR: Nita Sundberg, Director Human Resources
CNO: Lilly Wing, Chief Nursing Officer
Web address: www.threeriversbehavioral.org
Control: Corporation, Investor–owned, for–profit **Service:** Psychiatric

Staffed Beds: 118 **Admissions:** 2874 **Census:** 92 **Births:** 0 **Total Expense ($000):** 20128 **Payroll Expense ($000):** 9249 **Personnel:** 171

SC

WINNSBORO—Fairfield County

☐ **FAIRFIELD MEMORIAL HOSPITAL (421302)**, 102 U.S. Highway 321 By–Pass N., Zip 29180–9251, Mailing Address: P.O. Box 620, Zip 29180–0620; tel. 803/635–5548, (Total facility includes 15 beds in nursing home–type unit) **A**1 5 10 18 **F**3 11 15 18 28 29 30 34 35 40 50 56 57 59 62 63 64 65 68 75 77 79 86 87 90 94 102 107 110 111 114 119 127 128 129 130 132 133 135 146 148
Primary Contact: Suzanne C. Doscher, Chief Executive Officer
COO: Darlene Hines
CFO: Timothy Mitchell, Chief Financial Officer
CMO: Roger A. Gaddy, Jr., Chief Medical Officer
CIO: Donnie Doherty, Director Information Systems
CHR: Kristi Godwin, Interim Human Resource Director
CNO: Starr Connor, Chief Nursing Officer
Web address: www.fairfieldmemorial.com
Control: County–Government, nonfederal **Service:** General Medical and Surgical

Staffed Beds: 40 **Admissions:** 391 **Census:** 16 **Outpatient Visits:** 19614 **Births:** 0 **Personnel:** 168

SC

Hospital, Medicare Provider Number, Address, Telephone, Approval, Facility, and Physician Codes, Health Care System

★ American Hospital Association (AHA) membership   ◯ Healthcare Facilities Accreditation Program   ⇑ Center for Improvement in Healthcare Quality Accreditation
☐ The Joint Commission accreditation   ◇ DNV Healthcare Inc. accreditation   △ Commission on Accreditation of Rehabilitation Facilities (CARF) accreditation

SOUTH DAKOTA

ABERDEEN—Brown County

★ **AVERA ST. LUKE'S HOSPITAL (430014)**, 305 South State Street,
Zip 57401–4527; tel. 605/622–5000, (Total facility includes 137 beds in nursing
home–type unit) **A**2 10 19 **F**2 3 5 7 10 11 13 15 17 18 20 22 28 29 30 31 32
34 35 36 39 40 43 45 46 47 48 50 56 57 59 60 61 64 70 71 74 75 76 77
78 79 81 82 84 85 86 87 89 91 92 93 96 97 98 99 100 101 102 103 104
107 108 110 111 114 115 118 119 120 121 123 125 127 128 129 130 131
132 133 135 144 146 147 148 **P**6 **S** Avera Health, Sioux Falls, SD
Primary Contact: Todd Forkel, President and Chief Executive Officer
CFO: Geoff Durst, Vice President Finance
CMO: Shahid Chaudhary, M.D., Chief Medical Officer
CIO: Julie Kusler, Manager Information Services
CHR: Tracy L. Olson, Human Resource Officer
CNO: Jan Patterson, Chief Nursing Officer
Web address: www.avera.org/st–lukes–hospital/
Control: Church–operated, Nongovernment, not–for profit **Service:** General
Medical and Surgical

> **Staffed Beds:** 222 **Admissions:** 4488 **Census:** 177 **Outpatient Visits:**
> 196922 **Births:** 520 **Total Expense ($000):** 175569 **Payroll Expense**
> **($000):** 84818 **Personnel:** 1306

DAKOTA PLAINS SURGICAL CENTER (430092), 701 8th Avenue N.W., Suite
C., Zip 57401–1865; tel. 605/225–3300, (Nonreporting) **A**10
Primary Contact: Charles Livingston, Administrator
Control: Corporation, Investor–owned, for–profit **Service:** Surgical

> **Staffed Beds:** 15

★ **SANFORD ABERDEEN MEDICAL CENTER (430097)**, 2905 3rd Avenue S.E.,
Zip 57401–5420; tel. 605/626–4200, (Nonreporting) **A**10 **S** Sanford Health,
Sioux Falls, SD
Primary Contact: Ashley M. Erickson, Chief Executive Officer
CFO: Jeffrey Poppen, Chief Financial Officer
CMO: Samuel Nyamu, M.D., Chief Medical Officer
CHR: Katie Palmer, Manager Human Resources
CNO: Kila Legrand, Chief Nursing Officer
Web address: www.sanfordaberdeen.org/
Control: Other not–for–profit (including NFP Corporation) **Service:** General
Medical and Surgical

> **Staffed Beds:** 16

ARMOUR—Douglas County

DOUGLAS COUNTY MEMORIAL HOSPITAL (431305), 708 Eighth Street,
Zip 57313–2102; tel. 605/724–2159, (Nonreporting) **A**10 18
Primary Contact: Heath Brouwer, Administrator
CFO: Dorothy Spease, Manager Business Office
Web address: www.dcmhsd.org
Control: Other not–for–profit (including NFP Corporation) **Service:** General
Medical and Surgical

> **Staffed Beds:** 11

BOWDLE— County

★ **BOWDLE HOSPITAL (431318)**, 8001 West Fifth Street, Zip 57428, Mailing
Address: P.O. Box 556, Zip 57428–0556; tel. 605/285–6146, (Nonreporting)
A10 18
Primary Contact: Sandy Schlechter, Chief Executive Officer
CFO: Brooke Heilman, Chief Financial Officer
CMO: John Ottenbacher, Chief of Staff
CNO: Bobbi Noess, Director of Nursing
Web address: www.bowdlehc.com
Control: City–Government, nonfederal **Service:** General Medical and Surgical

> **Staffed Beds:** 50

BRITTON—Marshall County

★ **MARSHALL COUNTY HEALTHCARE CENTER AVERA (431312)**, 413 Ninth
Street, Zip 57430–2274; tel. 605/448–2253, (Nonreporting) **A**10 18 **S** Avera
Health, Sioux Falls, SD
Primary Contact: Nick Fosness, Chief Executive Officer
Web address: www.avera.org
Control: Other not–for–profit (including NFP Corporation) **Service:** General
Medical and Surgical

> **Staffed Beds:** 18

BROOKINGS—Brookings County

★ **BROOKINGS HEALTH SYSTEM (430008)**, 300 22nd Avenue,
Zip 57006–2496; tel. 605/696–9000, (Total facility includes 79 beds in nursing
home–type unit) **A**10 20 **F**3 7 8 11 13 28 29 30 31 32 34 40 41 43 45 51 53
57 59 62 63 64 65 69 70 74 75 76 79 81 82 85 87 89 92 93 102 107 111
114 118 119 125 126 127 128 129 130 133 135 146 147 148
Primary Contact: Jason R. Merkley, Chief Executive Officer
CFO: Steve Lindemann, Chief Financial Officer
CMO: Shelby Eischens, Chief Medical Officer
CHR: September Bessler, Director, Human Resources
CNO: Tammy Hillestad, Chief Nursing Officer
Web address: www.brookingshealth.org
Control: City–Government, nonfederal **Service:** General Medical and Surgical

> **Staffed Beds:** 128 **Admissions:** 1435 **Census:** 90 **Outpatient Visits:** 63239
> **Births:** 341 **Total Expense ($000):** 53562 **Payroll Expense ($000):** 25900
> **Personnel:** 280

BURKE—Gregory County

★ **COMMUNITY MEMORIAL HOSPITAL (431309)**, 809 Jackson Street,
Zip 57523–2065, Mailing Address: P.O. Box 319, Zip 57523–0319;
tel. 605/775–2621 **A**10 18 **F**11 14 15 26 28 29 31 35 **S** Sanford Health, Sioux
Falls, SD
Primary Contact: Mistie Sachtjen, Chief Executive Officer
CMO: Megan Smith, M.D., Chief Medical Staff
CHR: Tami Lyon, Director Human Resources
Web address: www.sanfordhealth.org
Control: Other not–for–profit (including NFP Corporation) **Service:** General
Medical and Surgical

> **Staffed Beds:** 16 **Admissions:** 213 **Census:** 4 **Outpatient Visits:** 2966
> **Births:** 0 **Total Expense ($000):** 2867 **Payroll Expense ($000):** 1931
> **Personnel:** 57

CANTON—Lincoln County

★ **SANFORD CANTON–INWOOD MEDICAL CENTER (431333)**, 440 North
Hiawatha Drive, Zip 57013–5800; tel. 605/764–1400 **A**10 18 **F**7 10 15 28 40
45 59 71 77 81 93 107 130 133 **S** Sanford Health, Sioux Falls, SD
Primary Contact: Scott C. Larson, Chief Executive Officer
CFO: Paul Gerhart, Chief Financial Officer
Web address: www.sanfordcantoninwood.org
Control: Other not–for–profit (including NFP Corporation) **Service:** General
Medical and Surgical

> **Staffed Beds:** 11 **Admissions:** 152 **Census:** 2 **Outpatient Visits:** 18856
> **Births:** 0 **Total Expense ($000):** 6742 **Payroll Expense ($000):** 2867
> **Personnel:** 75

CHAMBERLAIN—Brule County

★ **SANFORD CHAMBERLAIN MEDICAL CENTER (431329)**, 300 South Byron
Boulevard, Zip 57325–9741; tel. 605/234–5511, (Total facility includes 44 beds
in nursing home–type unit) **A**10 18 **F**3 8 13 15 18 19 28 29 31 34 35 40 43 50
57 59 68 70 75 76 77 78 81 85 86 87 89 93 100 101 102 104 107 110 114
119 130 131 132 133 148 **P**6 **S** Sanford Health, Sioux Falls, SD
Primary Contact: Erica Peterson, Chief Executive Officer
COO: Paul Miller, Director of Operations
CFO: Erica Peterson, Chief Executive Officer and Chief Financial Officer
CMO: Lacey Olson, M.D., Chief Medical Staff
CHR: Dorothy Hieb, Director Human Resources
CNO: Sarah Talbott, Chief Nursing Officer
Web address: www.sanfordchamberlain.org
Control: Other not–for–profit (including NFP Corporation) **Service:** General
Medical and Surgical

> **Staffed Beds:** 69 **Admissions:** 633 **Census:** 49 **Outpatient Visits:** 29156
> **Births:** 99 **Total Expense ($000):** 19947 **Payroll Expense ($000):** 9061
> **Personnel:** 166

SANFORD MID DAKOTA MEDICAL CENTER See Sanford Chamberlain Medical
Center

SD

Many Facility Codes have changed. Please refer to the AHA Guide Code Chart.
© 2016 AHA Guide

CLEAR LAKE—Deuel County

★ **SANFORD CLEAR LAKE MEDICAL CENTER (431307)**, 701 Third Avenue South, Zip 57226–2016; tel. 605/874–2141 **A**10 18 **F**3 28 29 34 35 40 43 45 50 53 57 59 62 64 65 68 81 86 87 92 97 107 115 119 127 128 133 135 144 147 148 **P**6 **S** Sanford Health, Sioux Falls, SD
Primary Contact: Lori Sisk, R.N., Chief Executive Officer
CFO: Allison Nelson, Chief Financial Officer
CMO: Terrance Smith, M.D., Chairman Medical Staff
CNO: Stephanie Dobbs, Chief Nursing Officer
Web address: www.sanforddeuelcounty.org
Control: Other not–for–profit (including NFP Corporation) **Service:** General Medical and Surgical

Staffed Beds: 10 **Admissions:** 226 **Census:** 3 **Outpatient Visits:** 15814 **Births:** 0 **Total Expense ($000):** 5888 **Payroll Expense ($000):** 2827 **Personnel:** 64

CUSTER—Custer County

★ **CUSTER REGIONAL HOSPITAL (431323)**, 1039 Montgomery Street, Zip 57730–1397; tel. 605/673–2229, (Nonreporting) **A**10 18 **S** Regional Health, Rapid City, SD
Primary Contact: Veronica Schmidt, President
Web address: www.regionalhealth.com
Control: Other not–for–profit (including NFP Corporation) **Service:** General Medical and Surgical

Staffed Beds: 87

DAKOTA DUNES—Union County

SIOUXLAND SURGERY CENTER (430089), 600 North Sioux Point Road, Zip 57049–5000; tel. 605/232–3332, (Nonreporting) **A**10
Primary Contact: Greg Miner, Administrator
Web address: www.siouxlandsurg.com/
Control: Corporation, Investor–owned, for–profit **Service:** Surgical

Staffed Beds: 40

DE SMET—Kingsbury County

★ **AVERA DE SMET MEMORIAL HOSPITAL (431332)**, 306 Prairie Avenue S.W., Zip 57231–2285, Mailing Address: P.O. Box 160, Zip 57231–0160; tel. 605/854–3329 **A**10 18 **F**3 15 28 34 35 40 59 68 93 133 **P**6 **S** Avera Health, Sioux Falls, SD
Primary Contact: Janice Schardin, R.N., MS, Administrator and Chief Executive Officer
Web address: www.desmetmemorial.org
Control: Other not–for–profit (including NFP Corporation) **Service:** General Medical and Surgical

Staffed Beds: 6 **Admissions:** 74 **Census:** 1 **Outpatient Visits:** 10901 **Births:** 0 **Total Expense ($000):** 3772 **Payroll Expense ($000):** 1631 **Personnel:** 26

DEADWOOD—Lawrence County

★ **LEAD–DEADWOOD REGIONAL HOSPITAL (431320)**, 61 Charles Street, Zip 57732–1303; tel. 605/717–6000 **A**10 18 **F**3 7 15 28 29 30 34 40 43 45 59 64 68 69 70 75 77 81 85 87 93 107 114 119 132 133 148 **S** Regional Health, Rapid City, SD
Primary Contact: Mark C. Schmidt, President
CMO: Elizabeth Sayler, M.D., Chief of Staff
CHR: Kathryn L. Shockey, Director Human Resources
Web address: www.regionalhealth.com
Control: State–Government, nonfederal **Service:** General Medical and Surgical

Staffed Beds: 7 **Admissions:** 253 **Census:** 6 **Outpatient Visits:** 10944 **Births:** 0 **Total Expense ($000):** 8111 **Payroll Expense ($000):** 4461 **Personnel:** 83

DELL RAPIDS—Minnehaha County

AVERA DELLS AREA HEALTH CENTER See Avera Dells Area Hospital

★ **AVERA DELLS AREA HOSPITAL (431331)**, 909 North Iowa Avenue, Zip 57022–1231; tel. 605/428–5431 **A**10 18 **F**3 11 15 18 28 34 35 40 45 53 57 59 64 65 75 81 86 92 93 94 97 107 110 128 132 133 146 148 **P**6 **S** Avera Health, Sioux Falls, SD
Primary Contact: Scott James Hargens, Interim Administrator & Chief Executive Officer
CFO: Kory Holt, Division Controller Network Operations
CMO: Demetre Skliris, Chief Medical Officer
CIO: Val Witham, Director of Health Information
CHR: Amy Aukes, Regional Manager of Human Resources
CNO: Karla Carstensen, Director Patient Care
Web address: www.avera.org/dell–rapids/
Control: Other not–for–profit (including NFP Corporation) **Service:** General Medical and Surgical

Staffed Beds: 23 **Admissions:** 207 **Census:** 2 **Outpatient Visits:** 18166 **Births:** 0 **Total Expense ($000):** 5068 **Payroll Expense ($000):** 2141 **Personnel:** 52

EAGLE BUTTE—Dewey County

◇ **U. S. PUBLIC HEALTH SERVICE INDIAN HOSPITAL (430083)**, 317 Main Street, Zip 57625–1012, Mailing Address: P.O. Box 1012, Zip 57625–1012; tel. 605/964–7724 **A**10 21 **F**3 7 13 29 40 50 64 65 66 68 75 82 86 91 93 96 97 107 111 114 119 135 148 **P**6 **S** U. S. Indian Health Service, Rockville, MD
Primary Contact: Charles Fisher, Chief Executive Officer
CFO: Lisa Deal, Budget Analyst
Web address: www.ihs.gov
Control: PHS, Indian Service, Government, federal **Service:** General Medical and Surgical

Staffed Beds: 8 **Admissions:** 302 **Census:** 4 **Outpatient Visits:** 83056 **Births:** 37 **Total Expense ($000):** 25379 **Payroll Expense ($000):** 10087 **Personnel:** 212

EUREKA—Mcpherson County

★ **EUREKA COMMUNITY HEALTH SERVICES AVERA (431308)**, 410 Ninth Street, Zip 57437–2182, Mailing Address: P.O. Box 517, Zip 57437–0517; tel. 605/284–2661 **A**10 18 **F**10 28 34 35 40 41 45 59 62 65 81 93 133 **P**5 **S** Avera Health, Sioux Falls, SD
Primary Contact: Carmen Weber, Administrator
CFO: Joyce Schwingler, Chief Financial Officer
Web address: www.avera.org
Control: Other not–for–profit (including NFP Corporation) **Service:** General Medical and Surgical

Staffed Beds: 6 **Admissions:** 86 **Census:** 1 **Outpatient Visits:** 5905 **Births:** 0 **Total Expense ($000):** 2210 **Payroll Expense ($000):** 949 **Personnel:** 27

FAULKTON—Faulk County

FAULKTON AREA MEDICAL CENTER (431301), 1300 Oak Street, Zip 57438–2149, Mailing Address: P.O. Box 100, Zip 57438–0100; tel. 605/598–6263, (Nonreporting) **A**10 18
Primary Contact: Jay A. Jahnig, Chief Executive Officer
COO: Jay A. Jahnig, Chief Executive Officer
CFO: Susan Miller, Financial Administrator
CMO: K. A. Bartholomew, M.D., Medical Director
CIO: Cheryl Bue, Health Information Transcriptionist
CHR: Blythe Smith, Administrative Assistant
CNO: Shannon Stuwe, Director of Nursing
Web address: www.faulktonmedical.org
Control: Other not–for–profit (including NFP Corporation) **Service:** General Medical and Surgical

Staffed Beds: 12

FLANDREAU—Moody County

★ **AVERA FLANDREAU HOSPITAL (431310)**, 214 North Prairie Street, Zip 57028–1243; tel. 605/997–2433 **A**10 18 **F**28 34 35 40 45 57 59 64 65 75 81 86 92 93 97 107 127 128 132 133 146 148 **P**6 **S** Avera Health, Sioux Falls, SD
Primary Contact: Scott Hargens, Interim Administrator and Chief Executive Officer
CFO: Kory Holt, Assistant Vice President for Financial Integration
CMO: Scott Peterson, M.D., President Medical Staff
CIO: Val Witham, Director Health Information
CHR: Amy Aukes, Human Resources Analyst
Web address: www.avera.org/flandreau–medical/
Control: Other not–for–profit (including NFP Corporation) **Service:** General Medical and Surgical

Staffed Beds: 18 **Admissions:** 115 **Census:** 1 **Outpatient Visits:** 13909 **Births:** 0 **Total Expense ($000):** 5279 **Payroll Expense ($000):** 2058 **Personnel:** 49

SD

Hospital, Medicare Provider Number, Address, Telephone, Approval, Facility, and Physician Codes, Health Care System

★ American Hospital Association (AHA) membership   ○ Healthcare Facilities Accreditation Program   ⇑ Center for Improvement in Healthcare Quality Accreditation
□ The Joint Commission accreditation   ◇ DNV Healthcare Inc. accreditation   △ Commission on Accreditation of Rehabilitation Facilities (CARF) accreditation

---

AVERA FLANDREAU MEDICAL CENTER See Avera Flandreau Hospital

FORT MEADE—Meade County

⊞ **VETERANS AFFAIRS BLACK HILLS HEALTH CARE SYSTEM**, 113 Comanche Road, Zip 57741–1099; tel. 605/347–2511, (Includes VETERANS AFFAIRS MEDICAL CENTER HOT SPRINGS CAMPUS, 500 North Fifth Street, Hot Springs, Zip 57747; tel. 605/745–2052), (Nonreporting) **A**1 5 **S** Department of Veterans Affairs, Washington, DC
Primary Contact: Sandra Horsman, Director
CFO: Joseph Ferris, Chief Financial Officer
CHR: Denis Sullivan, Chief Human Resources Management
Web address: www.blackhills.va.gov/
Control: Veterans Affairs, Government, federal **Service:** General Medical and Surgical

Staffed Beds: 308

FREEMAN—Hutchinson County

★ **FREEMAN REGIONAL HEALTH SERVICES (431313)**, 510 East Eighth Street, Zip 57029–2086, Mailing Address: P.O. Box 370, Zip 57029–0370; tel. 605/925–4000, (Total facility includes 56 beds in nursing home–type unit) **A**10 18 **F**2 3 6 11 15 28 30 34 35 40 43 45 49 54 56 57 59 64 65 68 69 70 75 77 79 81 82 86 93 97 107 114 119 125 127 128 130 132 133 146 **P**6
Primary Contact: Nicholas R. Brandner, Chief Executive Officer
CFO: Mark Miller, Chief Financial Officer
Web address: www.freemanregional.com
Control: Other not–for–profit (including NFP Corporation) **Service:** General Medical and Surgical

Staffed Beds: 81 Admissions: 225 Census: 57 Outpatient Visits: 10916 Births: 0 Total Expense ($000): 9941 Payroll Expense ($000): 4369 Personnel: 122

GETTYSBURG—Potter County

★ **AVERA GETTYSBURG HOSPITAL (431302)**, 606 East Garfield Avenue, Zip 57442–1398; tel. 605/765–2480, (Nonreporting) **A**10 18 **S** Avera Health, Sioux Falls, SD
Primary Contact: Robert L. Sheckler, Administrator
Web address: www.avera.org/st–marys–pierre/gettysburg–hospital/
Control: Other not–for–profit (including NFP Corporation) **Service:** General Medical and Surgical

Staffed Beds: 60

GREGORY—Gregory County

★ **AVERA GREGORY HOSPITAL (431338)**, 400 Park Avenue, Zip 57533–1302, Mailing Address: P.O. Box 408, Zip 57533–0408; tel. 605/835–8394, (Nonreporting) **A**10 18 **S** Avera Health, Sioux Falls, SD
Primary Contact: Anthony Timanus, Chief Executive Officer
CFO: Trish Keiser, Comptroller
CMO: Rich Kafka, M.D., Chief Medical Officer
CIO: Justin Keegan, Director Support Services
CHR: Carol Postulka, Administrative Coordinator
Web address: www.gregoryhealthcare.org
Control: Other not–for–profit (including NFP Corporation) **Service:** General Medical and Surgical

Staffed Beds: 67

HOT SPRINGS—Fall River County

★ **FALL RIVER HOSPITAL (431322)**, 1201 Highway 71 South, Zip 57747–8800; tel. 605/745–3159, (Includes CASTLE MANOR), (Total facility includes 48 beds in nursing home–type unit) **A**10 18 **F**3 28 34 40 43 45 56 57 59 64 65 74 77 81 93 99 100 101 102 103 104 107 111 114 119 127 128 129 130 131 133 146 148 **P**6
Primary Contact: Tricia Uhlir, Chief Executive Officer
CFO: Jesse Naze, Chief Financial Officer
CMO: Rodney Larson, M.D., Medical Director
CIO: Dustin Kleinsasser, Information Technology and BioMed
CHR: Cindy Trent, Manager Personnel
Web address: www.frhssd.org
Control: Other not–for–profit (including NFP Corporation) **Service:** General Medical and Surgical

Staffed Beds: 73 Admissions: 387 Census: 54 Outpatient Visits: 22273 Births: 0 Total Expense ($000): 16753 Payroll Expense ($000): 7702 Personnel: 163

VETERANS AFFAIRS MEDICAL CENTER HOT SPRINGS CAMPUS See Veterans Affairs Black Hills Health Care System, Fort Meade

HURON—Beadle County

★ **HURON REGIONAL MEDICAL CENTER (431335)**, 172 Fourth Street S.E., Zip 57350–2590; tel. 605/353–6200 **A**10 18 **F**3 11 13 14 15 28 29 31 34 35 40 41 43 45 57 59 60 62 63 64 68 70 75 77 78 79 81 85 86 93 102 107 108 110 111 115 118 119 130 132 133 146 148 **P**6 **S** QHR, Brentwood, TN
Primary Contact: David Dick, Chief Executive Officer
CFO: Marcia Zwanziger, Vice President Finance
CMO: Bill Miner, M.D., Chief of Staff
CHR: Rhonda Hanson, Director Human Resources
CNO: Gail Robeson, Vice President Patient Services
Web address: www.huronregional.org
Control: Other not–for–profit (including NFP Corporation) **Service:** General Medical and Surgical

Staffed Beds: 25 Admissions: 1219 Census: 12 Outpatient Visits: 62864 Births: 330 Total Expense ($000): 31106 Payroll Expense ($000): 14688 Personnel: 233

MADISON—Lake County

★ **MADISON COMMUNITY HOSPITAL (431300)**, 917 North Washington Avenue, Zip 57042–1696; tel. 605/256–6551 **A**10 18 **F**7 11 13 15 28 31 34 35 40 41 43 57 59 62 64 70 75 76 77 81 82 85 87 89 93 97 107 110 111 114 119 129 132 133 135 143 144 145 146 148 **P**6
Primary Contact: Tamara Miller, R.N., Administrator
CFO: Teresa Mallett, Chief Financial Officer
CNO: Charlotte Charles, Director Acute Patient Services
Web address: www.madisonhospital.com
Control: Other not–for–profit (including NFP Corporation) **Service:** General Medical and Surgical

Staffed Beds: 25 Admissions: 415 Census: 6 Outpatient Visits: 27466 Births: 5 Total Expense ($000): 17564 Payroll Expense ($000): 9690 Personnel: 216

MARTIN—Bennett County

BENNETT COUNTY HOSPITAL AND NURSING HOME (431314), 102 Major Allen Street, Zip 57551–6005, Mailing Address: P.O. Box 70, Zip 57551–0070; tel. 605/685–6622, (Total facility includes 42 beds in nursing home–type unit) **A**10 18 **F**7 28 34 40 50 53 57 59 62 65 66 67 68 77 84 93 107 130 133 143
Primary Contact: Ethel Frein, Chief Executive Officer
CFO: Jean Kirk, Chief Financial Officer
CMO: Peter Knowles–Smith, M.D., Medical Director
CIO: Jean Kirk, Chief Financial Officer
CHR: T. J. Porter, Director Human Resources
Web address: www.bennettcountyhospital.com/
Control: Other not–for–profit (including NFP Corporation) **Service:** General Medical and Surgical

Staffed Beds: 56 Admissions: 141 Census: 40 Outpatient Visits: 48252 Births: 1 Total Expense ($000): 7059 Payroll Expense ($000): 3235 Personnel: 99

MILBANK—Grant County

★ **MILBANK AREA HOSPITAL AVERA (431326)**, 901 East Virgil Avenue, Zip 57252–2124; tel. 605/432–4538, (Includes ST. WILLIAM HOME FOR THE AGED), (Nonreporting) **A**10 18 **S** Avera Health, Sioux Falls, SD
Primary Contact: Natalie Gauer, Administrator
CMO: Kevin Bjordahl, M.D., Chief Medical Officer
CHR: Mona Schafer, Regional Manager Human Resources
Web address: www.averamilbank.org
Control: Other not–for–profit (including NFP Corporation) **Service:** General Medical and Surgical

Staffed Beds: 25

MILLER—Hand County

★ **AVERA HAND COUNTY MEMORIAL HOSPITAL (431337)**, 300 West Fifth Street, Zip 57362–1238; tel. 605/853–2421 **A**10 18 **F**3 8 11 15 17 28 29 34 35 40 43 45 46 50 53 57 59 64 77 79 81 86 87 93 107 114 119 128 129 132 133 146 148 **S** Avera Health, Sioux Falls, SD
Primary Contact: Bryan Breitling, Administrator
CFO: Debbie Pullman, Director Finance
CMO: Steve Schroeder, M.D., Chief of Staff
CIO: Janice Purrington, Coordinator Medical Records
CNO: Teresa E. Fanning, Director of Patient Care
Web address: www.avera.org
Control: Other not–for–profit (including NFP Corporation) **Service:** General Medical and Surgical

Staffed Beds: 9 Admissions: 269 Census: 3 Outpatient Visits: 16624 Births: 0 Total Expense ($000): 6788 Payroll Expense ($000): 3180 Personnel: 61

SD

Many Facility Codes have changed. Please refer to the AHA Guide Code Chart. © 2016 AHA Guide

MITCHELL—Davison County

☒ **AVERA QUEEN OF PEACE HOSPITAL (430013)**, 525 North Foster, Zip 57301–2999; tel. 605/995–2000, (Total facility includes 109 beds in nursing home–type unit) **A**1 2 10 **F**3 10 13 15 28 29 30 31 34 40 43 45 48 50 51 53 54 57 59 64 69 70 71 75 76 77 78 79 81 82 84 85 86 89 93 94 96 104 107 108 110 111 114 117 118 119 121 123 127 128 129 130 131 132 133 135 144 146 147 148 **P**6 **S** Avera Health, Sioux Falls, SD
Primary Contact: Thomas A. Clark, Regional President and Chief Executive Officer
CFO: Will Flett, Vice President Finance and Chief Financial Officer
CMO: David Balt, D.O., Chief Medical Officer
CIO: Jim Hanson, Director Information Systems
CHR: Rita Lemon, Director Human Resources
CNO: Rochelle Reider, Vice President Patient Care
Web address: www.averaqueenofpeace.org
Control: Church–operated, Nongovernment, not–for profit **Service:** General Medical and Surgical

Staffed Beds: 176 **Admissions:** 2649 **Census:** 131 **Outpatient Visits:** 130769 **Births:** 472 **Total Expense ($000):** 89352 **Payroll Expense ($000):** 40337 **Personnel:** 384

MOBRIDGE—Walworth County

★ **MOBRIDGE REGIONAL HOSPITAL (431325)**, 1401 Tenth Avenue West, Zip 57601–1106, Mailing Address: P.O. Box 580, Zip 57601–0580; tel. 605/845–3692 **A**10 18 **F**3 7 10 11 13 15 17 28 32 34 35 40 43 45 50 56 57 59 62 64 65 67 70 76 81 89 93 94 97 107 108 110 114 119 125 127 128 129 130 131 132 133 147 148 **P**6
Primary Contact: Angelia K. Svihovec, Chief Executive Officer
COO: Beth Jensen, Director Clinic Operations
CFO: Renae Tisdall, Chief Financial Officer
CMO: Travis Henderson, M.D., Chief of Staff
CIO: Lynn Schott, Director Information Technology
CHR: Keri Wientjes, Director Human Resources
CNO: Kristi Voller, Director of Nursing
Web address: www.mobridgehospital.org
Control: Other not–for–profit (including NFP Corporation) **Service:** General Medical and Surgical

Staffed Beds: 25 **Admissions:** 692 **Census:** 7 **Outpatient Visits:** 50905 **Births:** 57 **Total Expense ($000):** 18277 **Payroll Expense ($000):** 8308 **Personnel:** 171

PARKSTON—Hutchinson County

★ **AVERA ST. BENEDICT HEALTH CENTER (431330)**, 401 West Glynn Drive, Zip 57366–9605; tel. 605/928–3311, (Total facility includes 74 beds in nursing home–type unit) **A**10 18 **F**2 3 8 10 13 15 28 29 30 31 32 34 35 38 40 45 53 56 57 59 62 64 65 69 75 76 81 82 83 85 86 87 89 107 110 111 115 116 119 128 129 130 131 132 133 135 146 148 **P**6 **S** Avera Health, Sioux Falls, SD
Primary Contact: Gale N. Walker, President and Chief Executive Officer
CFO: Rita Blasius, Assistant Administrator and Chief Financial Officer
CMO: Antoinette VanderPol, Chief of Staff
CIO: Adam Popp, Director Information Systems
CHR: Phyllis Ehler, Director Human Resources
CNO: Denise Muntefering, Vice President Patient Care Services
Web address: www.averastbenedict.org
Control: Church–operated, Nongovernment, not–for profit **Service:** General Medical and Surgical

Staffed Beds: 99 **Admissions:** 569 **Census:** 81 **Outpatient Visits:** 21252 **Births:** 35 **Total Expense ($000):** 19047 **Payroll Expense ($000):** 9799 **Personnel:** 170

PHILIP—Haakon County

HANS P. PETERSON MEMORIAL HOSPITAL See Philip Health Services

★ **PHILIP HEALTH SERVICES (431319)**, 503 West Pine Street, Zip 57567–3300, Mailing Address: P.O. Box 790, Zip 57567–0790; tel. 605/859–2511, (Total facility includes 30 beds in nursing home–type unit) **A**10 18 **F**10 11 40 43 57 59 62 85 93 107 114 119 125 127 128 130 131 133 148 **P**6 **S** Regional Health, Rapid City, SD
Primary Contact: Kent Olson, Administrator and Chief Executive Officer
Control: Other not–for–profit (including NFP Corporation) **Service:** General Medical and Surgical

Staffed Beds: 48 **Admissions:** 160 **Census:** 42 **Outpatient Visits:** 11400 **Births:** 1 **Total Expense ($000):** 9516 **Payroll Expense ($000):** 5374 **Personnel:** 146

PIERRE—Hughes County

☒ **AVERA ST. MARY'S HOSPITAL (430015)**, 801 East Sioux Avenue, Zip 57501–3323; tel. 605/224–3100, (Total facility includes 70 beds in nursing home–type unit) **A**1 10 20 **F**2 8 11 13 15 28 29 30 31 34 38 40 43 45 54 59 60 64 65 68 70 76 128 **S** Avera Health, Sioux Falls, SD
Primary Contact: Todd Forkel, Interim Chief Executive Officer
CFO: Tom Wagner, Interim Vice President Finance
CMO: Denise Hanisch, M.D., Chief of Staff
CIO: Jamie Raske, Information Technology Lead
CHR: Paul Marso, Vice President Human Resources
Web address: www.avera.org/st-marys-pierre/
Control: Other not–for–profit (including NFP Corporation) **Service:** General Medical and Surgical

Staffed Beds: 110 **Admissions:** 1500 **Census:** 79 **Outpatient Visits:** 70000 **Births:** 390

PINE RIDGE—Shannon County

◇ **U. S. PUBLIC HEALTH SERVICE INDIAN HOSPITAL (430081)**, East Highway 18, Zip 57770, Mailing Address: P.O. Box 1201, Zip 57770–1201; tel. 605/867–5131, (Nonreporting) **A**10 21 **S** U. S. Indian Health Service, Rockville, MD
Primary Contact: Ellen Davis, Service Unit Director
CFO: Sophia Conny, Deputy Administrative Officer
CMO: Jan Colton, M.D., Acting Clinical Director
CHR: Annabelle Blackbear, Human Resources Specialist
Web address: www.ihs.gov
Control: Public Health Service, Government, federal **Service:** General Medical and Surgical

Staffed Beds: 45

PLATTE—Charles Mix County

★ **PLATTE HEALTH CENTER AVERA (431306)**, 601 East Seventh, Zip 57369–2123, Mailing Address: P.O. Box 200, Zip 57369–0200; tel. 605/337–3364, (Nonreporting) **A**10 18 **S** Avera Health, Sioux Falls, SD
Primary Contact: Mark Burket, Chief Executive Officer
CFO: Jerry Hoffman, Chief Financial Officer
Web address: www.phcavera.org
Control: Other not–for–profit (including NFP Corporation) **Service:** General Medical and Surgical

Staffed Beds: 65

RAPID CITY—Pennington County

BLACK HILLS SURGERY CENTER (430091), 216 Anamaria Drive, Zip 57701–7366, Mailing Address: 1868 Lombardy Drive, Zip 57703–4130; tel. 605/721–4900, (Nonreporting) **A**10
Primary Contact: Franklin Shobe, Administrator and Chief Executive Officer
Web address: www.bhsc.com
Control: Partnership, Investor–owned, for–profit **Service:** Surgical

Staffed Beds: 26

◇ **INDIAN HEALTH SERVICE HOSPITAL (430082)**, 3200 Canyon Lake Drive, Zip 57702–8197; tel. 605/355–2280, (Nonreporting) **A**10 21 **S** U. S. Indian Health Service, Rockville, MD
Primary Contact: Kevin J. Stiffarm, Chief Executive Officer
Web address: www.ihs.gov
Control: PHS, Indian Service, Government, federal **Service:** General Medical and Surgical

Staffed Beds: 9

☒ **RAPID CITY REGIONAL HOSPITAL (430077)**, 353 Fairmont Boulevard, Zip 57701–7393, Mailing Address: P.O. Box 6000, Zip 57709–6000; tel. 605/755–1000, (Nonreporting) **A**1 3 5 10 **S** Regional Health, Rapid City, SD
Primary Contact: Dennis C. Millirons, FACHE, Interim President
CFO: Mark Thompson, Vice President Financial Services
CMO: David Houser, M.D., Vice President Medical Affairs
CIO: Richard Latuchie, Vice President Business Development
CHR: Maureen Henson, Vice President Human Resources
Web address: www.regionalhealth.com
Control: Other not–for–profit (including NFP Corporation) **Service:** General Medical and Surgical

Staffed Beds: 408

SAME DAY SURGERY CENTER (430093), 651 Cathedral Drive, Zip 57701–7368; tel. 605/755–9900, (Nonreporting) **A**10
Primary Contact: Doris Fritts, R.N., Executive Director
Web address: www.samedaysurgerycenter.com
Control: Corporation, Investor–owned, for–profit **Service:** Surgical

Staffed Beds: 8

SD

Hospital, Medicare Provider Number, Address, Telephone, Approval, Facility, and Physician Codes, Health Care System

★ American Hospital Association (AHA) membership	○ Healthcare Facilities Accreditation Program	⇑ Center for Improvement in Healthcare Quality Accreditation
□ The Joint Commission accreditation	◇ DNV Healthcare Inc. accreditation	△ Commission on Accreditation of Rehabilitation Facilities (CARF) accreditation

REDFIELD—Spink County

COMMUNITY MEMORIAL HOSPITAL (431316), 110 West Tenth Avenue, Zip 57469–1520, Mailing Address: P.O. Box 420, Zip 57469–0420; tel. 605/472–1110, (Nonreporting) **A**10 18
Primary Contact: Michael O'Keefe, Interim Chief Executive Officer
CFO: William Boyer, Chief Financial Officer
CHR: Rhonda Stroh, Chief Human Resources Officer
CNO: Julene J. Cass, R.N., Director of Nursing
Web address: www.redfield-sd.com/hospital.html
Control: City–Government, nonfederal **Service:** General Medical and Surgical

Staffed Beds: 23

ROSEBUD—Todd County

◇ **U. S. PUBLIC HEALTH SERVICE INDIAN HOSPITAL (430084)**, Highway 18, Soldier Creek Road, Zip 57570; tel. 605/747–2231, (Nonreporting) **A**10 21 **S** U. S. Indian Health Service, Rockville, MD
Primary Contact: Kathey Wilson, Acting Chief Executive Officer
COO: Romeo Vivit, Chief Surgeon
CMO: Valerie Parker, M.D., Clinical Director
CHR: Michelle Zephier, Human Resource Specialist
Web address: www.ihs.gov
Control: PHS, Indian Service, Government, federal **Service:** General Medical and Surgical

Staffed Beds: 35

SCOTLAND—Bon Homme County

★ **LANDMANN–JUNGMAN MEMORIAL HOSPITAL AVERA (431317)**, 600 Billars Street, Zip 57059–2026; tel. 605/583–2226 **A**10 18 **F**28 40 41 91 93 107 128 133 **P**6 **S** Avera Health, Sioux Falls, SD
Primary Contact: Darcy Permann, Interim Chief Executive Officer
CFO: Darcy Permann, Manager Business Office
Web address: www.ljmh.org
Control: Other not–for–profit (including NFP Corporation) **Service:** General Medical and Surgical

Staffed Beds: 17 Admissions: 41 Census: 1 Outpatient Visits: 2533 Births: 0 Total Expense ($000): 3967 Payroll Expense ($000): 1779

SIOUX FALLS—Lincoln County

☐ **AVERA HEART HOSPITAL OF SOUTH DAKOTA (430095)**, 4500 West 69th Street, Zip 57108–8148; tel. 605/977–7000 **A**1 5 10 **F**3 11 17 18 20 22 24 26 28 29 30 34 35 40 43 45 57 59 68 71 74 75 79 80 81 84 85 87 89 107 114 115 119 130 132 135 146 148 **P**2 **S** Avera Health, Sioux Falls, SD
Primary Contact: Jon Soderholm, President
CFO: Jean White, Vice President Finance
Web address: www.avera.org/heart–hospital
Control: Corporation, Investor–owned, for–profit **Service:** Heart

Staffed Beds: 53 Admissions: 2230 Census: 25 Outpatient Visits: 56980 Births: 0 Total Expense ($000): 86416 Payroll Expense ($000): 25949 Personnel: 449

⊞ △ **AVERA MCKENNAN HOSPITAL AND UNIVERSITY HEALTH CENTER (430016)**, 1325 South Cliff Avenue, Zip 57105–1007, Mailing Address: P.O. Box 5045, Zip 57117–5045; tel. 605/322–8000, (Includes AVERA BEHAVIORAL HEALTH CENTER, 440 West 69th Street, Zip 57108; tel. 605/322–4065; Steve Lindquist, Assistant Vice President, Behavioral Health; AVERA CHILDREN'S HOSPITAL, 1325 South Cliff Avenue, Zip 57105–1016, Mailing Address: PO Box 5045, Zip 57117–5045; tel. 605/322–5437), (Total facility includes 90 beds in nursing home–type unit) **A**1 2 3 5 7 10 **F**3 5 7 10 11 12 13 15 18 19 20 21 22 23 24 29 30 31 32 34 35 36 38 39 40 41 43 44 46 49 50 53 54 55 56 57 58 59 60 61 63 64 65 66 67 68 70 71 72 74 75 76 77 78 79 81 82 84 85 86 87 88 89 90 92 93 94 96 97 98 99 100 101 102 103 104 105 107 108 110 111 114 115 116 117 118 119 120 121 123 124 125 126 128 129 130 131 132 134 135 136 138 141 142 143 144 145 146 147 148 **P**6 **S** Avera Health, Sioux Falls, SD
Primary Contact: David Kapaska, D.O., Regional President and Chief Executive Officer
COO: Judy Blauwet, M.P.H., Senior Vice President Operations and Chief Nursing Officer
CFO: Julie Norton, Chief Financial Officer
CMO: Michael Elliott, M.D., Chief Medical Officer and Senior Vice President of Medical Affairs
CIO: Kristin Gross, Director Information Technology Center
CHR: Lynne D. Hagen, Human Resources Officer
CNO: Judy Blauwet, M.P.H., Senior Vice President of Hospital Operations and Chief Nursing Officer
Web address: www.averamckennan.org
Control: Church–operated, Nongovernment, not–for profit **Service:** General Medical and Surgical

Staffed Beds: 415 Admissions: 21481 Census: 400 Outpatient Visits: 266085 Births: 2193 Total Expense ($000): 761695 Payroll Expense ($000): 327312 Personnel: 4119

CHILDRENS CARE HOSPITAL AND SCHOOL (433300), 2501 West 26th Street, Zip 57105–2498; tel. 605/782–2300, (Nonreporting) **A**10
Primary Contact: David A. Timpe, Interim President and Chief Executive Officer
CFO: John Clark, Chief Financial Officer
CMO: Christiane Maroun, M.D., Chief of Staff
CHR: Tiffany Reilly, Director Human Resources
Web address: www.cchs.org
Control: Other not–for–profit (including NFP Corporation) **Service:** Children's rehabilitation

Staffed Beds: 114

⊞ △ **SANFORD USD MEDICAL CENTER (430027)**, 1305 West 18th Street, Zip 57105–0496, Mailing Address: P.O. Box 5039, Zip 57117–5039; tel. 605/333–1000, (Includes SANFORD CHILDREN'S HOSPITAL, 1600 West 22nd Street, Zip 57105, Mailing Address: PO Box 5039, Zip 57117–5039; tel. 605/333–1000) **A**1 2 3 5 7 8 10 **F**3 7 8 9 11 12 13 14 15 17 18 19 20 21 22 23 24 25 26 27 28 29 30 31 32 34 35 36 37 38 40 43 44 45 46 48 49 50 51 52 53 54 55 56 57 58 59 60 61 63 64 65 68 70 71 72 73 74 75 76 77 78 79 80 81 82 83 84 85 86 87 88 89 90 91 92 93 94 96 97 99 100 101 103 104 105 107 108 110 111 114 115 116 117 118 119 120 121 123 124 126 129 130 131 132 134 135 138 141 142 143 146 147 148 **P**6 **S** Sanford Health, Sioux Falls, SD
Primary Contact: Paul A. Hanson, FACHE, President
COO: Brad J. Schipper, Chief Operating Officer
CFO: Merrilee Schultz, Chief Finance
CIO: Arlyn Broekhuis, Vice President and Chief Information Officer
CHR: Evan Burkett, Chief Human Resource Officer
Web address: www.sanfordhealth.org
Control: Other not–for–profit (including NFP Corporation) **Service:** General Medical and Surgical

Staffed Beds: 483 Admissions: 23323 Census: 291 Outpatient Visits: 500170 Births: 3111 Total Expense ($000): 763984 Payroll Expense ($000): 243628 Personnel: 4954

⊞ **SELECT SPECIALTY HOSPITAL–SIOUX FALLS (432002)**, 1305 West 18th Street, Zip 57105–0401; tel. 605/312–9500, (Nonreporting) **A**1 10 **S** Select Medical Corporation, Mechanicsburg, PA
Primary Contact: Carol Ulmer, Chief Executive Officer
CNO: Dawn Anderson, Chief Nursing Officer
Web address: www.selectspecialtyhospitals.com/company/locations/siouxfalls.aspx
Control: Corporation, Investor–owned, for–profit **Service:** Long–Term Acute Care hospital

Staffed Beds: 24

SIOUX FALLS SPECIALTY HOSPITAL (430090), 910 East 20th Street, Zip 57105–1012; tel. 605/334–6730, (Nonreporting) **A**10
Primary Contact: R. Blake Curd, M.D., Chief Executive Officer
CFO: Kyle Goldammer, Chief Financial Officer
Web address: www.sfsurgical.com
Control: Partnership, Investor–owned, for–profit **Service:** Surgical

Staffed Beds: 35

⊞ **SIOUX FALLS VETERANS AFFAIRS HEALTH CARE SYSTEM**, 2501 West 22nd Street, Zip 57105–1305, Mailing Address: P.O. Box 5046, Zip 57117–5046; tel. 605/336–3230, (Total facility includes 58 beds in nursing home–type unit) **A**1 3 5 8 **F**5 8 18 29 30 31 33 34 35 36 38 39 40 45 46 50 53 54 56 57 58 59 60 62 63 64 65 68 70 71 74 75 77 78 79 81 82 84 85 86 87 91 92 93 94 97 98 100 101 102 103 104 107 111 118 119 127 130 131 132 135 143 146 147 148 **S** Department of Veterans Affairs, Washington, DC
Primary Contact: Darwin Goodspeed, Director
COO: Sara Ackert, Associate Director
CFO: Daniel Hubbard, Chief Financial Officer
CMO: John M. Wempe, M.D., Chief of Staff
CIO: Eric Heiser, Chief Information Resource Management
CHR: Betsy Geiver, Chief Human Resources Officer
CNO: Barbara Teal, R.N., Associate Director Patient Care Services and Nurse Executive
Web address: www.siouxfalls.va.gov
Control: Veterans Affairs, Government, federal **Service:** General Medical and Surgical

Staffed Beds: 92 Admissions: 2442 Census: 77 Outpatient Visits: 299811 Births: 0 Total Expense ($000): 85927 Payroll Expense ($000): 59286 Personnel: 1169

SISSETON—Roberts County

★ **COTEAU DES PRAIRIES HOSPITAL (431339)**, 205 Orchard Drive, Zip 57262–2398; tel. 605/698–7647, (Nonreporting) **A**10 18
Primary Contact: Michael F. Coyle, Chief Executive Officer
CFO: Larry Moen, Chief Financial Officer
CMO: David Staub, M.D., Chief of Staff
CIO: Cheryl Kaufman, Information Technology Technician
CHR: Leslie Hendrickson, Director Human Resources
CNO: Brenda Bostrom, Director of Nursing
Web address: www.cdphospital.com
Control: Other not–for–profit (including NFP Corporation) **Service:** General Medical and Surgical

Staffed Beds: 25

SD

SPEARFISH—Lawrence County

★ **SPEARFISH REGIONAL HOSPITAL (430048)**, 1440 North Main Street, Zip 57783–1504; tel. 605/644–4000, (Includes SPEARFISH REGIONAL SURGERY CENTER, 1316 N. 10th Street, Zip 57783–1530, Mailing Address: 1316 North 10th Street, Zip 57783–1530; tel. 605/642–3113; Larry W. Veitz, President) **A**10 20 **F**3 11 13 15 28 29 31 34 40 57 59 62 63 70 75 79 81 82 84 85 93 97 107 108 110 111 114 119 127 129 130 131 132 135 144 146 147 148 **P**6 **S** Regional Health, Rapid City, SD
Primary Contact: Larry W. Veitz, President
CFO: Marcia Olson, Director Finance and Controller
CMO: Christopher Gasbarre, D.O., Community Medical Director
CIO: Richard Latuchie, Chief Information Officer
CHR: Patsy Aiken, Coordinator Human Resource
CNO: Suzanne Campbell, Director Patient Services
Web address: www.regionalhealth.com/Our–Locations/Regional–Hospitals/Spearfish–Regional–Hospital.aspx
Control: Other not–for–profit (including NFP Corporation) **Service:** General Medical and Surgical

Staffed Beds: 35 **Admissions:** 1424 **Census:** 10 **Outpatient Visits:** 48901 **Births:** 426 **Total Expense ($000):** 40676 **Payroll Expense ($000):** 17055 **Personnel:** 420

STURGIS—Meade County

★ **STURGIS REGIONAL HOSPITAL (431321)**, 949 Harmon Street, Zip 57785–2452; tel. 605/720–2400, (Nonreporting) **A**10 18 **S** Regional Health, Rapid City, SD
Primary Contact: Mark Schulte, FACHE, President
CFO: Jodie Mitchell, Facility Financial Director
CMO: Constance Stock, M.D., Chief Medical Officer
CHR: Ginger Chord, Coordinator Human Resources
CNO: Rikki Plaggemeyer, Director Acute Care Nursing
Web address: www.regionalhealth.com/Our–Locations/Regional–Hospitals/Sturgis–Regional–Hospital.aspx
Control: Other not–for–profit (including NFP Corporation) **Service:** General Medical and Surgical

Staffed Beds: 109

TYNDALL—Bon Homme County

★ **ST. MICHAEL'S HOSPITAL AVERA (431327)**, 410 West 16th Avenue, Zip 57066–2318; tel. 605/589–2152 **A**10 18 **F**3 15 28 31 34 40 43 45 53 57 59 64 65 67 70 75 77 81 86 89 92 93 94 107 110 114 119 127 128 129 131 133 148 **P**6 **S** Avera Health, Sioux Falls, SD
Primary Contact: Carol Deurmier, Chief Executive Officer
CFO: Lisa Ronke, Director Finance
CMO: Melvin Wallinga, M.D., Medical Director
Web address: www.stmichaels–bhfp.org
Control: Church–operated, Nongovernment, not–for profit **Service:** General Medical and Surgical

Staffed Beds: 25 **Admissions:** 217 **Census:** 6 **Outpatient Visits:** 11004 **Births:** 0 **Total Expense ($000):** 7863 **Payroll Expense ($000):** 3160 **Personnel:** 61

VERMILLION—Clay County

★ **SANFORD VERMILLION MEDICAL CENTER (431336)**, 20 South Plum Street, Zip 57069–3346; tel. 605/677–3500, (Total facility includes 66 beds in nursing home–type unit) **A**10 18 **F**15 28 29 31 34 35 40 43 45 57 59 67 76 81 91 92 93 97 107 110 114 116 119 125 129 130 131 132 133 135 **P**8 **S** Sanford Health, Sioux Falls, SD
Primary Contact: Timothy J. Tracy, Chief Executive Officer
CFO: Valerie Osterberg, Chief Financial Officer
CMO: Roy Mortinsen, M.D., Chief of Staff
CIO: Mary C. Merrigan, Manager Public Relations
CHR: Cindy Benzel, Manager Human Resources
CNO: Jeff Berens, MS, Chief Nursing Officer
Web address: www.sanfordvermillion.org
Control: Other not–for–profit (including NFP Corporation) **Service:** General Medical and Surgical

Staffed Beds: 114 **Admissions:** 477 **Census:** 70 **Outpatient Visits:** 40092 **Births:** 82 **Total Expense ($000):** 16620 **Payroll Expense ($000):** 7269 **Personnel:** 181

VIBORG—Turner County

★ **PIONEER MEMORIAL HOSPITAL AND HEALTH SERVICES (431328)**, 315 North Washington Street, Zip 57070–2002, Mailing Address: P.O. Box 368, Zip 57070–0368; tel. 605/326–5161, (Total facility includes 52 beds in nursing home–type unit) **A**10 18 **F**6 10 15 28 30 34 40 43 45 53 56 57 59 63 65 69 75 79 81 87 97 107 111 119 125 127 128 130 132 133 **P**6 **S** Sanford Health, Sioux Falls, SD
Primary Contact: Thomas V. Richter, Chief Executive Officer
CFO: Anne Christiansen, Chief Financial Officer
CMO: Syed Shah, M.D., Chief of Staff
Web address: www.pioneermemorial.org
Control: Other not–for–profit (including NFP Corporation) **Service:** General Medical and Surgical

Staffed Beds: 64 **Admissions:** 180 **Census:** 52 **Outpatient Visits:** 28776 **Births:** 0 **Total Expense ($000):** 11904 **Payroll Expense ($000):** 6621 **Personnel:** 145

WAGNER—Charles Mix County

★ **WAGNER COMMUNITY MEMORIAL HOSPITAL AVERA (431315)**, 513 Third Street S.W., Zip 57380–9675, Mailing Address: P.O. Box 280, Zip 57380–0280; tel. 605/384–3611 **A**10 18 **F**3 11 15 17 18 28 31 34 40 43 45 57 59 64 67 70 72 75 77 81 93 97 107 110 114 119 128 130 133 148 **P**6 **S** Avera Health, Sioux Falls, SD
Primary Contact: Bryan Slaba, Chief Executive Officer
CFO: Lisa Weisser, Supervisor Finance
CHR: Marcia Podzimek, Chief Human Resources Officer
Web address: www.avera.org/wagnerhospital
Control: Other not–for–profit (including NFP Corporation) **Service:** General Medical and Surgical

Staffed Beds: 20 **Admissions:** 185 **Census:** 1 **Outpatient Visits:** 8057 **Births:** 0 **Total Expense ($000):** 8060 **Payroll Expense ($000):** 3167 **Personnel:** 71

WATERTOWN—Codington County

★ **PRAIRIE LAKES HEALTHCARE SYSTEM (430005)**, 401 9th Avenue N.W., Zip 57201–1548, Mailing Address: P.O. Box 1210, Zip 57201–6210; tel. 605/882–7000, (Nonreporting) **A**10 20
Primary Contact: Jill Fuller, R.N., President and Chief Executive Officer
COO: Traci Rabine, Vice President Clinic Operations
CFO: Adam Paul, Chief Financial Officer
CMO: Daniel Flaherty, M.D., Chief Medical Staff
CHR: Nathan Lake, Vice President Human Resources
CNO: Shelly Turbak, R.N., Chief Nursing Officer
Web address: www.prairielakes.com
Control: Other not–for–profit (including NFP Corporation) **Service:** General Medical and Surgical

Staffed Beds: 81

WEBSTER—Day County

★ **SANFORD WEBSTER MEDICAL CENTER (431311)**, 1401 West 1st Street, Zip 57274–1054, Mailing Address: P.O. Box 489, Zip 57274–0489; tel. 605/345–3336 **A**10 18 **F**15 28 29 34 35 40 43 57 59 63 64 71 77 81 86 87 91 93 97 107 111 114 119 127 128 130 131 133 148 **S** Sanford Health, Sioux Falls, SD
Primary Contact: Isaac Gerdes, Chief Executive Officer
CFO: Sheryl L. Pappas, Chief Financial Officer
Web address: www.sanfordhealth.org
Control: Other not–for–profit (including NFP Corporation) **Service:** General Medical and Surgical

Staffed Beds: 20 **Admissions:** 204 **Census:** 2 **Outpatient Visits:** 16510 **Births:** 0 **Total Expense ($000):** 7155 **Payroll Expense ($000):** 3220 **Personnel:** 56

WESSINGTON SPRINGS—Jerauld County

★ **AVERA WESKOTA MEMORIAL HOSPITAL (431324)**, 604 First Street N.E., Zip 57382–2166; tel. 605/539–1201 **A**10 18 **F**3 15 28 31 34 35 40 53 57 59 64 75 77 81 85 93 107 114 119 128 130 131 132 133 **P**5 **S** Avera Health, Sioux Falls, SD
Primary Contact: Gaea Blue, R.N., Administrator and Chief Executive Officer
CFO: Linda Jager, Director Finance
CMO: Thomas Dean, M.D., Chief of Staff
CNO: JoAnn Hettinger, R.N., Director of Patient Care Services
Web address: www.averaweskota.org
Control: Other not–for–profit (including NFP Corporation) **Service:** General Medical and Surgical

Staffed Beds: 23 **Admissions:** 141 **Census:** 2 **Outpatient Visits:** 4883 **Births:** 0 **Total Expense ($000):** 3807 **Payroll Expense ($000):** 1546 **Personnel:** 24

SD

Hospital, Medicare Provider Number, Address, Telephone, Approval, Facility, and Physician Codes, Health Care System

★ American Hospital Association (AHA) membership
□ The Joint Commission accreditation
○ Healthcare Facilities Accreditation Program
◇ DNV Healthcare Inc. accreditation
⇑ Center for Improvement in Healthcare Quality Accreditation
△ Commission on Accreditation of Rehabilitation Facilities (CARF) accreditation

WINNER—Tripp County

★ **WINNER REGIONAL HEALTHCARE CENTER (431334)**, 745 East Eighth
Street, Zip 57580–2631; tel. 605/842–7100, (Total facility includes 79 beds in
nursing home–type unit) **A**10 18 **F**1 4 11 13 15 16 17 28 29 31 34 35 40 43
47 56 57 59 62 64 65 67 68 70 72 73 76 79 80 81 85 88 89 90 91 97 107
108 127 128 129 131 132 133 148 **P**3 **S** Sanford Health, Sioux Falls, SD
Primary Contact: Kevin Coffey, Chief Executive Officer
COO: Debra K. Davis, Director of Operations
CFO: Phil Husher, Chief Financial Officer
CMO: Tony L. Berg, M.D., Chief of Staff
CIO: Gary Burrus, Director Information Technology
CHR: Susan Hughes, Interim Director Human Resources
CNO: Julie Hennebold, R.N., Interim Chief Nursing Officer
Web address: www.winnerregional.org
Control: Other not–for–profit (including NFP Corporation) **Service:** General
Medical and Surgical

Staffed Beds: 104 **Admissions:** 693 **Census:** 83 **Outpatient Visits:** 10884
Births: 175 **Total Expense ($000):** 20994 **Payroll Expense ($000):** 6967
Personnel: 187

YANKTON—Yankton County

✠ **AVERA SACRED HEART HOSPITAL (430012)**, 501 Summit Avenue,
Zip 57078–3855; tel. 605/668–8000, (Total facility includes 187 beds in nursing
home–type unit) **A**1 2 5 10 **F**2 3 6 8 10 13 15 18 20 28 29 30 31 34 35 39
40 43 45 46 47 48 53 57 59 60 62 63 64 70 71 73 76 77 78 79 81 82 84
85 86 87 89 91 93 96 100 103 104 107 108 110 111 114 115 118 119 120
121 127 128 129 130 132 133 146 147 148 **S** Avera Health, Sioux Falls, SD
Primary Contact: Douglas R. Ekeren, Regional President and Chief Executive
Officer
CFO: Jamie Schaefer, Vice President Finance
CIO: Kathy Quinlivan, Director Management Information Systems
CHR: Jane E. Miller, Human Resources Officer
CNO: Lindsay Flannery, R.N., Vice President Patient Care Services
Web address: www.averasacredheart.com
Control: Church–operated, Nongovernment, not–for profit **Service:** General
Medical and Surgical

Staffed Beds: 293 **Admissions:** 3722 **Census:** 217 **Outpatient Visits:** 85574
Births: 643 **Total Expense ($000):** 95367 **Payroll Expense ($000):** 38184
Personnel: 643

LEWIS AND CLARK SPECIALTY HOSPITAL (430096), 2601 Fox Run Parkway,
Zip 57078–5341; tel. 605/665–5100, (Nonreporting) **A**10
Primary Contact: Michelle J. Jordan, Administrator
CFO: Terry Steichen, Business Officer
CHR: Elizabeth Steichen, Human Resources
Web address: www.lewisandclarkspecialty.com
Control: Corporation, Investor–owned, for–profit **Service:** Surgical

Staffed Beds: 6

Many Facility Codes have changed. Please refer to the AHA Guide Code Chart. © 2016 AHA Guide

TENNESSEE

ASHLAND CITY—Cheatham County

★ **TRISTAR ASHLAND CITY MEDICAL CENTER (441311)**, 313 North Main Street, Zip 37015–1347; tel. 615/792–3030, (Nonreporting) **A**10 18 **S** HCA, Nashville, TN
Primary Contact: Darrell White, R.N., Administrator and Chief Nursing Officer
COO: Brian Marger, Chief Operating Officer
CFO: Joe Bowman, Chief Financial Officer
CMO: Divya Shroff, Chief Medical Officer
CIO: David Archer, Director Information Systems
CNO: Darrell White, R.N., Administrator and Chief Nursing Officer
Web address: www.tristarashlandcity.com/
Control: Corporation, Investor–owned, for–profit **Service:** General Medical and Surgical

Staffed Beds: 12

ATHENS—Mcminn County

⊞ **STARR REGIONAL MEDICAL CENTER (440068)**, 1114 West Madison Avenue, Zip 37303–4150, Mailing Address: P.O. Box 250, Zip 37371–0250; tel. 423/745–1411, (Nonreporting) **A**1 3 5 10 **S** LifePoint Health, Brentwood, TN
Primary Contact: Mark Nichols, FACHE, Chief Executive Officer
COO: Michael Herr, Chief Operating Officer
CFO: David Alley, Chief Financial Officer
CNO: Teresa Reynolds, Interim Chief Nursing Officer
Web address: www.starrregional.com
Control: Corporation, Investor–owned, for–profit **Service:** General Medical and Surgical

Staffed Beds: 63

BARTLETT—Shelby County

⊞ **SAINT FRANCIS HOSPITAL–BARTLETT (440228)**, 2986 Kate Bond Road, Zip 38133–4003; tel. 901/820–7000 **A**1 10 **F**3 11 13 15 18 20 22 29 30 31 34 35 38 39 40 44 45 47 48 49 50 54 57 59 60 61 63 64 68 70 72 74 75 76 77 78 79 81 84 85 86 87 93 107 108 110 111 114 115 119 126 130 131 141 142 146 147 148 **P**5 **S** TENET Healthcare Corporation, Dallas, TX
Primary Contact: Christopher Locke, Chief Executive Officer
COO: Gwen Bonner, Chief Operating Officer
CFO: Tina Kovacs, Chief Financial Officer
CMO: David Schwartz, M.D., Chief Medical Officer
CIO: Mark Lawrence, Director Information Systems
CHR: Adrienne Huntley, Chief Human Resources Officer
CNO: Kris Cherry, Ph.D., Chief Nursing Officer
Web address: www.saintfrancisbartlett.com
Control: Corporation, Investor–owned, for–profit **Service:** General Medical and Surgical

Staffed Beds: 156 Admissions: 7201 Census: 93 Outpatient Visits: 71928 Births: 621 Total Expense ($000): 112045 Payroll Expense ($000): 33785 Personnel: 541

BOLIVAR—Hardeman County

⊞ **BOLIVAR GENERAL HOSPITAL (440181)**, 650 Nuckolls Road, Zip 38008–1532, Mailing Address: PO Box 509, Zip 38008–0509; tel. 731/658–3100 **A**1 10 **F**3 15 29 30 35 40 44 45 57 59 64 75 81 87 93 107 119 130 132 133 146 **S** West Tennessee Healthcare, Jackson, TN
Primary Contact: Ruby Kirby, Administrator
CFO: Terry Swindell, Controller
CMO: Felix Nnaji, Chief Medical Staff
CNO: Angela Lacy, Director of Nursing
Web address: www.wth.net
Control: Hospital district or authority, Government, nonfederal **Service:** General Medical and Surgical

Staffed Beds: 21 Admissions: 283 Census: 2 Outpatient Visits: 15432 Births: 0 Total Expense ($000): 6361 Payroll Expense ($000): 2662 Personnel: 59

☐ **WESTERN MENTAL HEALTH INSTITUTE (444008)**, 11100 Old Highway 64, West, Zip 38008–1554; tel. 731/228–2000, (Nonreporting) **A**1 10
Primary Contact: Roger Pursley, Chief Executive Officer
CFO: Richard Taylor, Chief Financial Officer
CMO: Doug King, M.D., Director Clinical Services
CIO: Earl Bates, Director Information Technology
CHR: Barry Young, Director Human Resources
Control: State–Government, nonfederal **Service:** Psychiatric

Staffed Beds: 247

BRISTOL—Sullivan County

⊞ **SELECT SPECIALTY HOSPITAL–TRI CITIES (442016)**, One Medical Park Boulevard, 5th Floor, Zip 37620–8964; tel. 423/844–5900, (Nonreporting) **A**1 10 **S** Select Medical Corporation, Mechanicsburg, PA
Primary Contact: Jeffrey Radford, Chief Executive Officer
CMO: John Byers, M.D., Medical Director
CHR: William G. Ison, Human Resources Manager
CNO: Valerie Anderson, Chief Nursing Officer
Web address: www.tricities.selectspecialtyhospitals.com/
Control: Corporation, Investor–owned, for–profit **Service:** Long–Term Acute Care hospital

Staffed Beds: 33

⊞ **WELLMONT BRISTOL REGIONAL MEDICAL CENTER (440012)**, 1 Medical Park Boulevard, Zip 37620–7430; tel. 423/844–1121 **A**1 2 3 5 10 **F**3 8 11 13 15 17 18 20 22 24 28 29 30 31 34 35 37 38 39 40 43 44 45 46 47 49 51 54 56 57 58 59 60 61 63 64 70 73 74 75 76 77 78 79 81 82 83 84 85 86 87 91 92 93 94 96 97 98 100 101 102 103 104 106 107 108 110 111 114 115 118 119 120 121 123 124 126 129 130 131 132 135 144 145 146 147 148 **P**1 6 **S** Wellmont Health System, Kingsport, TN
Primary Contact: Greg Neal, FACHE, Chief Executive Officer
COO: Christopher Brian Hobson, Chief Operating Officer
CFO: Dale Poe, Vice President and Chief Financial Officer, Hospital Division
CMO: Chad Couch, Chief Medical Officer
CIO: Martha O'Regan Chill, Interim Chief Information Officer
CHR: Hamlin J. Wilson, Senior Vice President Human Resources
CNO: Timothy Craig Anderson, Jr., Chief Nursing Officer
Web address: www.wellmont.org
Control: Other not–for–profit (including NFP Corporation) **Service:** General Medical and Surgical

Staffed Beds: 288 Admissions: 12977 Census: 157 Outpatient Visits: 126488 Births: 881 Total Expense ($000): 226404 Payroll Expense ($000): 57561 Personnel: 1479

CAMDEN—Benton County

⊞ **CAMDEN GENERAL HOSPITAL (441316)**, 175 Hospital Drive, Zip 38320–1617; tel. 731/584–6135 **A**1 10 18 **F**3 15 29 30 35 40 44 57 59 64 75 79 81 85 87 93 107 111 119 130 132 133 146 **S** West Tennessee Healthcare, Jackson, TN
Primary Contact: Betty Haskins, Interim Administrator
COO: James E. Ross, Chief Operating Officer
CFO: Terry Swindell, Chief Financial Officer
CMO: Jon R. Winter, D.O., Chief of Staff
CIO: Jeff Frieling, Vice President Information Systems
CHR: Barry Phillips, Executive Director Human Resources
Web address: www.wth.net
Control: Hospital district or authority, Government, nonfederal **Service:** General Medical and Surgical

Staffed Beds: 25 Admissions: 305 Census: 4 Outpatient Visits: 12270 Births: 0 Total Expense ($000): 6743 Payroll Expense ($000): 2754 Personnel: 70

CARTHAGE—Smith County

⊞ **RIVERVIEW REGIONAL MEDICAL CENTER (441307)**, 158 Hospital Drive, Zip 37030–1096; tel. 615/735–1560, (Nonreporting) **A**1 10 18 **S** LifePoint Health, Brentwood, TN
Primary Contact: Michael Herman, Chief Executive Officer
CHR: Gina Anderson, Human Resources Officer
CNO: Patricia Anderson, Chief Nursing Officer
Web address: www.myriverviewmedical.com/
Control: Corporation, Investor–owned, for–profit **Service:** General Medical and Surgical

Staffed Beds: 35

TN

Hospital, Medicare Provider Number, Address, Telephone, Approval, Facility, and Physician Codes, Health Care System

★ American Hospital Association (AHA) membership   ○ Healthcare Facilities Accreditation Program   ⇑ Center for Improvement in Healthcare Quality Accreditation
☐ The Joint Commission accreditation   ◇ DNV Healthcare Inc. accreditation   △ Commission on Accreditation of Rehabilitation Facilities (CARF) accreditation

---

CELINA—Clay County

☐ **CUMBERLAND RIVER HOSPITAL (440141)**, 100 Old Jefferson Street,
Zip 38551–4040, Mailing Address: P. O. Box 427, Zip 38551–0427;
tel. 931/243–3581, (Nonreporting) **A**1 10
Primary Contact: Patricia Strong, Interim Chief Executive Officer
CFO: Patricia Strong, Chief Financial Officer
CMO: Harry Horne, D.O., Chief of Staff
CIO: Margie Boone, Registered Health Information Technician
CHR: Angel Lewis, Senior Vice President
CNO: Patsy Marinich, Chief Nursing Officer
Web address: www.cumberlandriverhospital.com
Control: Corporation, Investor–owned, for–profit **Service:** General Medical and
Surgical

Staffed Beds: 34

CENTERVILLE—Hickman County

⊞ **SAINT THOMAS HICKMAN HOSPITAL (441300)**, 135 East Swan Street,
Zip 37033–1417; tel. 931/729–4271, (Total facility includes 40 beds in nursing
home–type unit) **A**1 10 18 **F**3 29 30 34 35 40 41 45 56 57 59 62 64 65 67 77
81 86 87 89 90 91 93 104 107 119 127 128 130 133 135 148 **P**6
S Ascension Health, Saint Louis, MO
Primary Contact: Jack M. Keller, Chief Executive Officer
COO: Robin Crowell, Chief Nursing Officer and Chief Operating Officer
CFO: Bailey Pratt, Chief Financial Officer
CMO: Zachary Hutchens, M.D., Chief Medical Officer
CHR: Patty Matney, Human Resources Consultant
CNO: Robin Crowell, Chief Nursing Officer and Chief Operating Officer
Web address: www.sths.com/hickman
Control: Other not–for–profit (including NFP Corporation) **Service:** General
Medical and Surgical

Staffed Beds: 65 **Admissions:** 127 **Census:** 37 **Outpatient Visits:** 11302
Births: 0 **Total Expense ($000):** 14989 **Payroll Expense ($000):** 6196
Personnel: 73

CHATTANOOGA—Hamilton County

⊞ **CHI MEMORIAL (440091)**, 2525 De Sales Avenue, Zip 37404–1161;
tel. 423/495–2525, (Includes MEMORIAL HOSPITAL HIXSON, 2051 Hamill Road,
Hixson, Zip 37343–4026; tel. 423/495–7100; Larry P. Schumacher, R.N., MSN,
Chief Executive Officer) **A**1 2 3 10 **F**3 7 8 11 12 15 17 18 20 22 24 26 28 29
30 31 34 35 36 40 43 44 45 46 47 48 49 50 54 55 56 57 58 59 60 61 64
67 68 70 71 74 75 77 78 79 81 82 84 85 86 87 93 107 108 110 111 114
115 116 117 118 119 120 121 124 126 129 130 132 135 145 146 147 148
P3 6 7 8 **S** Catholic Health Initiatives, Englewood, CO
Primary Contact: Larry P. Schumacher, R.N., MSN, Chief Executive Officer
COO: Janelle Reilly, Chief Operating Officer
CFO: Troy Hammett, Chief Financial Officer
CMO: Helen Kuroki, Senior Vice President and Chief Medical Officer
CHR: Brad W. Pope, Vice President Human Resources
CNO: Rhonda Poulson, Chief Nursing Officer and Vice President of Clinical
Operations
Web address: www.memorial.org
Control: Church–operated, Nongovernment, not–for profit **Service:** General
Medical and Surgical

Staffed Beds: 405 **Admissions:** 24442 **Census:** 317 **Outpatient Visits:**
347394 **Total Expense ($000):** 488172 **Payroll Expense ($000):** 135518
Personnel: 2282

⊞ **ERLANGER MEDICAL CENTER (440104)**, 975 East Third Street,
Zip 37403–2147; tel. 423/778–7000, (Includes ERLANGER EAST HOSPITAL,
1755 Gunbarrel Road, Zip 37421; tel. 423/778–8700; Phillip E. Jackson, Vice
President & CEO; ERLANGER NORTH HOSPITAL, 632 Morrison Springs Road,
Zip 37415; tel. 615/778–3300; Phillip E. Jackson, Vice President and CEO; T. C.
THOMPSON CHILDREN'S HOSPITAL, 910 Blackford Street, Zip 37403;
tel. 615/778–6011; Donald Mueller, Vice President and CEO; WILLIE D. MILLER
EYE CENTER, 975 East Third Street, Zip 37403; tel. 615/778–6011) **A**1 2 3 5 8
10 **F**3 5 6 9 11 12 13 14 15 16 17 18 19 20 21 22 23 24 25 26 27 28
29 30 31 32 34 35 36 37 38 39 40 41 42 43 44 45 46 47 48 49 50 51 52
53 54 55 56 57 58 59 60 61 62 63 64 65 66 67 68 70 71 72 73 74 75 76
77 78 79 80 81 82 83 84 85 86 87 88 89 91 92 93 94 96 97 98 99 100
101 102 103 104 105 107 108 109 110 111 112 114 115 116 117 118 119
120 121 123 124 126 127 129 130 131 132 133 134 135 138 141 142 143
144 145 146 147 148 **P**2 4 6 7 **S** Erlanger Health System, Chattanooga, TN
Primary Contact: Kevin M. Spiegel, Chief Executive Officer
COO: Robert M. Brooks, FACHE, Executive Vice President, Chief Operating Officer
CFO: J. Britton Tabor, Executive Vice President, Chief Financial Officer
CMO: William L. Jackson, Jr., M.D., Executive Vice President, Chief Medical Officer
CIO: David Peterson, Senior Vice President, Chief Technology Officer
CHR: Floyd Chasse, Vice President Human Resources
CNO: Janice C. Keys, FACHE, Senior Vice President, Chief Nurse Executive
Web address: www.erlanger.org
Control: Hospital district or authority, Government, nonfederal **Service:** General
Medical and Surgical

Staffed Beds: 585 **Admissions:** 32931 **Census:** 430 **Outpatient Visits:**
446219 **Births:** 5343 **Total Expense ($000):** 630381 **Payroll Expense
($000):** 258649 **Personnel:** 5102

ERLANGER WOMEN'S EAST HOSPITAL See Erlanger East Hospital

⊞ **HEALTHSOUTH CHATTANOOGA REHABILITATION HOSPITAL (443032)**,
2412 McCallie Avenue, Zip 37404–3398; tel. 423/698–0221 **A**1 10 **F**29 34 90
92 95 96 101 103 130 132 148 **S** HEALTHSOUTH Corporation, Birmingham, AL
Primary Contact: Scott Rowe, Chief Executive Officer
COO: Scott Rowe, Chief Executive Officer
CFO: Karen Klassen, Controller
CMO: Amjad Munir, M.D., Medical Director
CIO: Denise Smith, Director Health Information
CHR: Rebekah McNair, Director Human Resources
CNO: Cinthia Campbell, Chief Nursing Officer
Web address: www.healthsouthchattanooga.com
Control: Corporation, Investor–owned, for–profit **Service:** Rehabilitation

Staffed Beds: 69 **Admissions:** 1157 **Census:** 40

⊞ **KINDRED HOSPITAL–CHATTANOOGA (442007)**, 709 Walnut Street,
Zip 37402–1916; tel. 423/266–7721, (Nonreporting) **A**1 10 **S** Kindred
Healthcare, Louisville, KY
Primary Contact: Steve Patterson, Chief Executive Officer
COO: Rick Rheinheimer, Chief Clinical Officer
CFO: Julia Smith, Chief Financial Officer
CMO: Randy Heisser, M.D., Medical Director
CHR: Kellie McCampbell, Coordinator Human Resources
CNO: Gigi Johnson, Chief Nursing Officer
Web address: www.kindredchattanooga.com/
Control: Corporation, Investor–owned, for–profit **Service:** Long–Term Acute Care
hospital

Staffed Beds: 44

☐ **MOCCASIN BEND MENTAL HEALTH INSTITUTE (444002)**, 100 Moccasin
Bend Road, Zip 37405–4415; tel. 423/265–2271 **A**1 10 **F**3 98 102 103
130 135
Primary Contact: Mary C. Young, Chief Executive Officer
CFO: Sylvia Harris, Fiscal Director
CMO: Terry R. Holmes, M.D., Clinical Director
CIO: Mickey Williams, Manager Information Technology
CHR: Cynthia Honeycutt, Director Human Resources
CNO: Charlynne Parson, Nurse Executive
Web address: www.state.tn.us/mental/mhs/mbhmhi/moc.htm
Control: State–Government, nonfederal **Service:** Psychiatric

Staffed Beds: 150 **Admissions:** 3442 **Census:** 136 **Outpatient Visits:** 0
Births: 0 **Total Expense ($000):** 35192 **Payroll Expense ($000):** 17396
Personnel: 442

⊞ **PARKRIDGE MEDICAL CENTER (440156)**, 2333 McCallie Avenue,
Zip 37404–3258; tel. 423/698–6061, (Includes EAST RIDGE HOSPITAL, 941
Spring Creek Road, East Ridge, Zip 37412, Mailing Address: P.O. Box 91229,
Zip 37412–6229; tel. 423/855–3500; Jarrett B. Millsaps, Jr., FACHE, Chief
Executive Officer; PARKRIDGE EAST HOSPITAL, 941 Spring Creek Road,
Zip 37412–3909; tel. 423/894–7870; Jarrett B. Millsaps, Jr., FACHE, Chief
Executive Officer; PARKRIDGE VALLEY CHILD AND ADOLESCENT CAMPUS, 2200
Morris Hill Road, Zip 37421; tel. 423/894–4220; Melissa Arkin, Chief Executive
Officer; PARKRIDGE WEST HOSPITAL, 1000 Highway 28, Jasper,
Zip 37347–3638; tel. 423/837–9500; Shirley K. Scarlatti, Associate Chief
Nursing Officer) **A**1 2 3 5 10 **F**1 3 4 5 13 15 16 17 18 20 22 24 25 28 29 30
31 39 40 45 46 49 50 51 55 56 57 58 59 60 67 70 72 73 75 76 77 78 79
80 81 85 88 89 90 93 98 99 103 104 105 106 107 108 110 111 114 115
119 120 121 124 126 128 129 130 131 132 146 148 **S** HCA, Nashville, TN
Primary Contact: Darrell W. Moore, Chief Executive Officer
COO: Jim L. Coleman, Jr., Chief Operating Officer
CFO: Tom Jackson, Chief Financial Officer
CMO: Gary Lanham, Chief Medical Officer
CIO: David Cornelius, Director Information Systems
CHR: Carole Hoffman, Vice President
CNO: Jerri C. Underwood, R.N., Chief Nursing Officer
Web address: www.parkridgemedicalcenter.com
Control: Corporation, Investor–owned, for–profit **Service:** General Medical and
Surgical

Staffed Beds: 472 **Admissions:** 17011 **Census:** 311 **Outpatient Visits:**
168492 **Births:** 2004 **Total Expense ($000):** 245882 **Payroll Expense
($000):** 93130 **Personnel:** 1336

⊞ △ **SISKIN HOSPITAL FOR PHYSICAL REHABILITATION (443025)**, One
Siskin Plaza, Zip 37403–1306; tel. 423/634–1200, (Total facility includes 109
beds in nursing home–type unit) **A**1 7 10 **F**3 29 34 35 53 64 74 77 87 90 91
93 95 128 130 132 146 148 **P**4
Primary Contact: Carol Sim, President and Chief Executive Officer
CFO: Carol Arnhart, Vice President Finance and Chief Financial Officer
CMO: David N. Bowers, M.D., Medical Director
CIO: Shane Pilcher, Administrative Director Information Systems
CHR: Kristi Delaney, Director, Human Resources
CNO: Tracy Collings Reed, Vice President Patient Care Services, Chief Nursing
Officer
Web address: www.siskinrehab.org
Control: Other not–for–profit (including NFP Corporation) **Service:** Rehabilitation

Staffed Beds: 177 **Admissions:** 3647 **Census:** 177 **Outpatient Visits:** 29957
Births: 0 **Total Expense ($000):** 39422 **Payroll Expense ($000):** 22616
Personnel: 516

T. C. THOMPSON CHILDREN'S HOSPITAL See Erlanger Medical Center

Many Facility Codes have changed. Please refer to the AHA Guide Code Chart.

© 2016 AHA Guide

TN

CLARKSVILLE—Montgomery County

BEHAVIORAL HEALTHCARE CENTER AT CLARKSVILLE (444019), 930 Professional Park Drive, Zip 37040–5136; tel. 931/538–6420, (Nonreporting) **A**10 **S** Tennessee Health Management, Parsons, TN
Primary Contact: Jennifer Robinson, Administrator
CMO: Michael McGhee, M.D., Medical Director
CNO: Chrissy Myers, R.N., Director of Nursing
Web address: www.bhcclarksville.com
Control: Partnership, Investor–owned, for–profit **Service:** Psychiatric

Staffed Beds: 26

⊞ **TENNOVA HEALTHCARE–CLARKSVILLE (440035)**, 651 Dunlop Lane, Zip 37040–5015, Mailing Address: P.O. Box 31629, Zip 37040–0028; tel. 931/502–1000, (Nonreporting) **A**1 10 **S** Community Health Systems, Inc., Franklin, TN
Primary Contact: Alex Villa, Chief Executive Officer
COO: Shawn Molsberger, Chief Operating Officer
CFO: George Sprinkel, Chief Financial Officer
CMO: Thomas L. Ely, D.O., Chief Medical Officer
CIO: Scott Greene, Chief Information Officer
CHR: Liza Edmunds, Director Human Resources
CNO: Faye Perry, Chief Nursing Officer
Web address: www.tennova.com/
Control: Partnership, Investor–owned, for–profit **Service:** General Medical and Surgical

Staffed Beds: 247

CLEVELAND—Bradley County

⊞ **TENNOVA HEALTHCARE – CLEVELAND (440185)**, 2305 Chambliss Avenue N.W., Zip 37311–3847, Mailing Address: P.O. Box 3060, Zip 37320–3060; tel. 423/559–6000, (Includes SKYRIDGE MEDICAL CENTER – WESTSIDE CAMPUS, 2800 Westside Drive N.W., Zip 37312–3599; tel. 423/339–4100; R. Coleman Foss, Chief Executive Officer) **A**1 3 5 10 **F**3 5 13 15 18 20 22 28 29 30 31 34 35 36 39 40 44 45 49 50 51 60 68 70 73 75 76 77 78 79 81 82 85 87 89 93 98 104 105 107 108 110 111 114 115 118 119 124 129 135 146 148 **S** Community Health Systems, Inc., Franklin, TN
Primary Contact: R. Coleman Foss, Chief Executive Officer
COO: Bernadette De Prez, Chief Operating Officer
CFO: H. Wes Griffith, Chief Financial Officer
CMO: William F. Johnson, Chief Medical Officer
CHR: Kristine Godfrey, Director Human Resources
Web address: www.skyridgemedicalcenter.net
Control: Corporation, Investor–owned, for–profit **Service:** General Medical and Surgical

Staffed Beds: 208 Admissions: 8382 Census: 99 Outpatient Visits: 97759 Births: 1036 Total Expense ($000): 124638 Payroll Expense ($000): 42579 Personnel: 843

COLLIERVILLE—Shelby County

★ **BAPTIST MEMORIAL HOSPITAL–COLLIERVILLE (440217)**, 1500 West Poplar Avenue, Zip 38017–0601; tel. 901/861–9400 **A**5 **F**3 7 8 12 15 18 19 20 21 22 23 24 25 26 27 28 29 30 31 32 34 35 36 37 38 40 41 45 46 47 48 49 52 53 54 55 56 57 58 59 60 61 62 63 64 65 66 68 70 71 74 75 77 78 79 81 82 83 84 85 86 87 92 93 96 107 108 109 110 111 112 113 114 115 116 117 118 119 120 121 123 124 126 129 130 132 135 136 137 143 144 145 146 147 148 **S** Baptist Memorial Health Care Corporation, Memphis, TN
Primary Contact: Lindsay Stencel, Chief Administrative Officer
CFO: Terri Seago, Chief Financial Officer
CIO: Doug Reiselt, Vice President and Chief Information Officer
CHR: Brenda Johnson, Director Human Resources
CNO: Denise Ferguson, Chief Nursing Officer
Web address: www.baptistonline.org/collierville/
Control: Other not–for–profit (including NFP Corporation) **Service:** General Medical and Surgical

Staffed Beds: 61 Admissions: 2888 Census: 23 Outpatient Visits: 30172 Births: 0 Total Expense ($000): 52115 Payroll Expense ($000): 17097 Personnel: 277

COLUMBIA—Maury County

⊞ **BEHAVIORAL HEALTHCARE CENTER AT COLUMBIA (440230)**, 1400 Rosewood Drive, Zip 38401–4878; tel. 931/388–6573 **A**10 **F**29 34 38 56 98 103 130 **S** Tennessee Health Management, Parsons, TN
Primary Contact: Paula Chennault, Administrator
CMO: Rodney Poling, M.D., Medical Director
CHR: Pam Brown, Human Resources Manager
CNO: Sheila Ridner, R.N., Director of Nursing
Web address: www.thmgt.com/locations/behavioral–healthcare–center–at–columbia
Control: Corporation, Investor–owned, for–profit **Service:** Psychiatric

Staffed Beds: 16 Admissions: 283 Census: 10 Outpatient Visits: 0 Births: 0 Total Expense ($000): 2936 Payroll Expense ($000): 1398 Personnel: 44

⊞ **MAURY REGIONAL HOSPITAL (440073)**, 1224 Trotwood Avenue, Zip 38401–4802; tel. 931/381–1111, (Total facility includes 17 beds in nursing home–type unit) **A**1 2 10 19 **F**7 8 11 13 15 17 18 20 22 24 28 29 30 31 34 35 40 44 45 46 48 50 54 57 59 60 62 64 66 68 70 73 74 75 76 77 78 79 80 81 84 85 86 87 93 97 107 108 110 111 114 116 117 118 119 120 121 123 124 128 129 130 131 132 135 144 146 147 148 **S** Maury Regional Health System, Columbia, TN
Primary Contact: H. Alan Watson, FACHE, Chief Executive Officer
COO: Paul Betz, FACHE, Chief Operating Officer and Senior Vice President
CFO: Nick Swift, Chief Financial Officer
CMO: Chris Edwards, M.D., Chief Medical Officer
CIO: Jim Parcel, Director Information Technology
CHR: Kaye Brewer, Vice President Human Resources
CNO: Deborah Lumpkins, MSN, Chief Nursing Officer
Web address: www.mauryregional.com
Control: County–Government, nonfederal **Service:** General Medical and Surgical

Staffed Beds: 211 Admissions: 12785 Census: 131 Outpatient Visits: 217663 Births: 1492 Total Expense ($000): 242116 Payroll Expense ($000): 95061 Personnel: 2120

COOKEVILLE—Putnam County

⊞ **COOKEVILLE REGIONAL MEDICAL CENTER (440059)**, 1 Medical Center Boulevard, Zip 38501–4294; tel. 931/783–2000 **A**1 2 10 19 **F**3 8 11 12 13 15 17 18 20 22 24 26 28 29 30 31 34 35 40 44 45 49 50 51 54 57 59 62 64 65 68 70 73 74 75 76 77 78 79 81 85 86 87 89 90 93 96 107 108 110 111 114 115 117 118 119 120 121 123 126 129 130 132 135 146 147 148 **P**7
Primary Contact: Paul Korth, Chief Executive Officer
COO: Scott Williams, Chief Operating Officer
CFO: Paul Korth, Chief Financial Officer
CMO: Jeffrey J. Gleason, M.D., Chief Medical Officer
CIO: Les Bernstein, Chief Information Officer
CHR: Angel Lewis, Senior Vice President Administration
CNO: Linda Crawford, R.N., Chief Nursing Officer
Web address: www.crmchealth.org
Control: Hospital district or authority, Government, nonfederal **Service:** General Medical and Surgical

Staffed Beds: 243 Admissions: 13242 Census: 156 Outpatient Visits: 200878 Births: 1544 Total Expense ($000): 220790 Payroll Expense ($000): 88258 Personnel: 1668

◇ **TEN BROECK TENNESSEE TREATMENT FACILITY (444022)**, 1 Medical Center Boulevard, 5 West, Zip 38501; tel. 931/783–2570, (Nonreporting) **A**10 21 **S** United Medical Corporation, Windermere, FL
Primary Contact: Kelly Tripp, Chief Executive Officer
CFO: David Corddry, Chief Financial Officer
CMO: Glenn T. Webb, M.D., Medical Director
CHR: Glenda Guy, Director, Health Information Management
CNO: Annasue Collins, Chief Nursing Officer
Web address: www.tenbroeck.com
Control: Corporation, Investor–owned, for–profit **Service:** General Medical and Surgical

Staffed Beds: 36

TN

Hospital, Medicare Provider Number, Address, Telephone, Approval, Facility, and Physician Codes, Health Care System

★ American Hospital Association (AHA) membership
□ The Joint Commission accreditation
○ Healthcare Facilities Accreditation Program
◇ DNV Healthcare Inc. accreditation
⇑ Center for Improvement in Healthcare Quality Accreditation
△ Commission on Accreditation of Rehabilitation Facilities (CARF) accreditation

© 2016 AHA Guide   *Many Facility Codes have changed. Please refer to the AHA Guide Code Chart.*   Hospitals **A581**

COPPERHILL—Polk County

☐ **COPPER BASIN MEDICAL CENTER (441315)**, 144 Medical Center Drive,
Zip 37317–5005, Mailing Address: P.O. Box 990, Zip 37317–0990;
tel. 423/496–5511, (Nonreporting) **A**1 10 18
Primary Contact: Anna Clark, Interim Chief Executive Officer
COO: Anna Clark, Chief Operating Officer
CMO: Allen Uhlik, M.D., Chief of Staff
CIO: Florence Tichenor, Director Information Technology
CHR: Kathy Pack, Manager Human Resources
CNO: Sonya Standridge, Chief Nursing Officer
Web address: www.copperbasin.org
Control: Other not–for–profit (including NFP Corporation) **Service:** General
Medical and Surgical

Staffed Beds: 25

COVINGTON—Tipton County

☒ **BAPTIST MEMORIAL HOSPITAL–TIPTON (440131)**, 1995 Highway 51 South,
Zip 38019–3635; tel. 901/476–2621 **A**1 10 **F**3 11 15 29 30 31 34 35 40 45
55 57 58 59 65 70 74 75 76 77 78 79 81 85 87 89 93 100 107 108 110
111 114 115 119 120 121 129 130 135 146 148 **P**6 **S** Baptist Memorial
Health Care Corporation, Memphis, TN
Primary Contact: Samuel Lynd, Administrator and Chief Executive Officer
CFO: Monique Hart, Chief Financial Officer
CMO: Kenneth Afenya, M.D., Chief of Staff
CHR: Myra Cousar, Director Human Resources
CNO: Cheryl Furdge Berry, Chief Nursing Officer
Web address: www.baptistonline.org/tipton/
Control: Other not–for–profit (including NFP Corporation) **Service:** General
Medical and Surgical

Staffed Beds: 44 **Admissions:** 1283 **Census:** 9 **Outpatient Visits:** 44315
Births: 428 **Total Expense ($000):** 75030 **Payroll Expense ($000):** 15117
Personnel: 223

CROSSVILLE—Cumberland County

☒ **CUMBERLAND MEDICAL CENTER (440009)**, 421 South Main Street,
Zip 38555–5031; tel. 931/484–9511 **A**1 2 10 20 **F**3 11 13 15 18 20 22 28
29 30 31 34 35 40 45 47 48 49 51 53 57 59 68 70 74 75 76 77 78 79 81
82 85 86 87 93 107 108 110 111 114 119 120 121 129 130 132 135 146
147 148 **P**6 **S** Covenant Health, Knoxville, TN
Primary Contact: David V. Bunch, President and Chief Administrative Officer
CFO: April VonAchen, Chief Financial Officer and Vice President Financial Services
CIO: Joe Lowe, Director Management Information Systems
CHR: Charles Sexton, Manager Human Resources
CNO: Rebecca Foster, MSN, Chief Nursing Officer
Web address: www.cmchealthcare.org
Control: Other not–for–profit (including NFP Corporation) **Service:** General
Medical and Surgical

Staffed Beds: 97 **Admissions:** 5157 **Census:** 55 **Outpatient Visits:** 90129
Births: 678 **Total Expense ($000):** 74277 **Payroll Expense ($000):** 29666
Personnel: 658

DAYTON—Rhea County

☒ **RHEA MEDICAL CENTER (441310)**, 9400 Rhea County Highway,
Zip 37321–7922; tel. 423/775–1121 **A**1 10 18 **F**3 15 28 29 34 35 40 45 47
50 59 75 77 80 81 85 107 110 111 114 119 128 133 146 **S** QHR,
Brentwood, TN
Primary Contact: Kennedy L. Croom, Jr., Administrator and Chief Executive Officer
CFO: Harv Sanders, Chief Financial Officer
CMO: Michael Prostko, M.D., Chief of Staff
CHR: Peri Meadows, Director Human Resources
Web address: www.rheamedical.com
Control: County–Government, nonfederal **Service:** General Medical and Surgical

Staffed Beds: 25 **Admissions:** 1196 **Census:** 11 **Outpatient Visits:** 42458
Births: 0 **Total Expense ($000):** 18062 **Payroll Expense ($000):** 7822
Personnel: 171

DICKSON—Dickson County

☒ **TRISTAR HORIZON MEDICAL CENTER (440046)**, 111 Highway 70 East,
Zip 37055–2080; tel. 615/446–0446, (Nonreporting) **A**1 2 10 **S** HCA,
Nashville, TN
Primary Contact: Dustin Greene, Chief Executive Officer
CFO: Clarence Gray, Chief Financial Officer
CIO: Rick Stoker, Director Management Information Systems
CHR: Sheila Kight, Director Human Resources
CNO: Gina Bullington, Chief Nursing Officer
Web address: www.horizonmedicalcenter.com
Control: Corporation, Investor–owned, for–profit **Service:** General Medical and
Surgical

Staffed Beds: 130

DYERSBURG—Dyer County

☒ **TENNOVA HEALTHCARE DYERSBURG REGIONAL MEDICAL CENTER
(440072)**, 400 East Tickle Street, Zip 38024–3120; tel. 731/285–2410 **A**1 10
20 **F**3 7 8 13 15 18 20 29 39 40 45 46 47 48 49 50 51 57 59 60 70 74 75
76 79 81 82 85 87 89 91 92 93 97 107 108 109 110 111 112 113 114 115
119 120 121 127 129 130 131 133 145 146 147 **P**4 5 6 **S** Community Health
Systems, Inc., Franklin, TN
Primary Contact: Reba Celsor, Chief Executive Officer
CFO: Meredith Malone, Chief Financial Officer
CMO: Darren Johnson, M.D., Chief of Staff
CIO: Russ Shephard, Senior Systems Analyst
CHR: Beverly Ray, Director Human Resources
Web address: www.dyersburgregionalmc.com
Control: Corporation, Investor–owned, for–profit **Service:** General Medical and
Surgical

Staffed Beds: 120 **Admissions:** 4252 **Census:** 37 **Outpatient Visits:** 69186
Births: 519

EAST RIDGE—Hamilton County

EAST RIDGE HOSPITAL See Parkridge Medical Center, Chattanooga

ELIZABETHTON—Carter County

☐ **SYCAMORE SHOALS HOSPITAL (440018)**, 1501 West Elk Avenue,
Zip 37643–2874; tel. 423/542–1300 **A**1 10 **F**3 11 15 18 29 30 34 35 40 44
45 48 49 50 53 54 56 57 62 63 64 68 70 75 77 78 79 81 85 87 93 98 103
107 110 111 115 118 119 130 132 135 146 147 148 **S** Mountain States
Health Alliance, Johnson City, TN
Primary Contact: Dwayne Taylor, Chief Executive Officer
COO: Melanie Stanton, R.N., Chief Nursing Officer
CFO: Chase Wilson, Chief Financial Officer
CMO: Morris H. Seligman, M.D., Chief Medical Officer and Chief Medical
Information Officer
CIO: Paul Merrywell, Chief Information Officer
CHR: Sharon Sheppard, Manager Human Resources
Web address: www.msha.com
Control: Other not–for–profit (including NFP Corporation) **Service:** General
Medical and Surgical

Staffed Beds: 121 **Admissions:** 3716 **Census:** 45 **Outpatient Visits:** 62471
Births: 0 **Total Expense ($000):** 39273 **Payroll Expense ($000):** 16929
Personnel: 317

ERIN—Houston County

☒ **HOUSTON COUNTY COMMUNITY HOSPITAL (440232)**, 5001 East Main
Street, Zip 37061–4115, Mailing Address: P.O. Box 489, Zip 37061–0489;
tel. 931/289–4211, (Nonreporting) **A**1 10
Primary Contact: Scott Bradley, Interim Chief Executive Officer
CFO: Shannon Allison, Chief Financial Officer
CMO: Erin Chambers, M.D., Chief Medical Officer
Web address: www.pcmc–erintn.com/
Control: County–Government, nonfederal **Service:** General Medical and Surgical

Staffed Beds: 25

ERWIN—Unicoi County

☒ **UNICOI COUNTY MEMORIAL HOSPITAL (440001)**, 100 Greenway Circle,
Zip 37650–2196, Mailing Address: P.O. Box 802, Zip 37650–0802;
tel. 423/743–3141, (Total facility includes 46 beds in nursing home–type unit) **A**1
10 **F**11 15 29 30 34 35 40 45 62 64 67 70 75 77 79 81 85 87 107 110 111
115 130 131 146
Primary Contact: Eric Carroll, Chief Executive Officer
CFO: Toni Buchanan, Chief Financial Officer
CMO: Jose Picaza, M.D., Chief of Staff
CIO: Maggie Tipton, Chief Information Officer
CHR: Susan Broyles, Director Human Resources and Safety
CNO: Melanie Stanton, R.N., Chief Nursing Officer
Web address: www.msha.com
Control: Other not–for–profit (including NFP Corporation) **Service:** General
Medical and Surgical

Staffed Beds: 94 **Admissions:** 720 **Census:** 51 **Outpatient Visits:** 27027
Births: 0 **Total Expense ($000):** 15090 **Payroll Expense ($000):** 5839
Personnel: 122

TN

Many Facility Codes have changed. Please refer to the AHA Guide Code Chart.
© 2016 AHA Guide

FAYETTEVILLE—Lincoln County

☒ **LINCOLN COUNTY HEALTH SYSTEM (440102)**, 106 Medical Center Boulevard, Zip 37334–2684; tel. 931/438–1100, (Total facility includes 264 beds in nursing home–type unit) **A**1 10 **F**3 7 10 11 13 15 18 29 30 34 35 40 45 50 53 56 57 59 62 63 64 67 68 70 74 75 76 77 79 81 85 93 98 103 104 107 108 110 111 114 118 119 128 129 132 135 143 146 148 **P**6
Primary Contact: John R. Harding, Chief Executive Officer
CFO: Bailey Pratt, Interim Chief Financial Officer
CMO: Richard Cline, D.O., Chief of Staff
CHR: Wendy Nogler, Director Human Resources
CNO: Vicky Groce, Chief Nursing Officer
Web address: www.lchealthsystem.com
Control: County–Government, nonfederal **Service:** General Medical and Surgical

Staffed Beds: 313 **Admissions:** 2230 **Census:** 202 **Outpatient Visits:** 57238 **Births:** 254 **Total Expense ($000):** 40273 **Payroll Expense ($000):** 18464 **Personnel:** 456

FRANKLIN—Williamson County

☐ **HEALTHSOUTH REHABILITATION HOSPITAL OF FRANKLIN** 1000 Physicians Way, Franklin, TN 37067–1471; tel. 615/721–4000; S HEALTHSOUTH Corporation
Primary Contact: Scott Peterson, Chief Executive Officer
CMO: Scott Craig, Medical Director
Control: Corporation, Investor-owned, for-profit **Service:** Rehabilitation

Staffed Beds: 40

☐ **ROLLING HILLS HOSPITAL (444007)**, 2014 Quail Hollow Circle, Zip 37067–5967; tel. 615/628–5700, (Nonreporting) **A**1 10 **S** Universal Health Services, Inc., King of Prussia, PA
Primary Contact: Jim Spruyt, Chief Executive Officer
CFO: Chris Leonard, Chief Financial Officer
CMO: James Hart, M.D., Medical Director
CHR: Lisa Hodge, Manager, Human Resources
CNO: Laurel Roberts, R.N., Chief Nursing Officer
Web address: www.RollingHillsHospital.org/
Control: Corporation, Investor–owned, for–profit **Service:** Psychiatric

Staffed Beds: 80

☐ **WILLIAMSON MEDICAL CENTER (440029)**, 4321 Carothers Parkway, Zip 37067–8542; tel. 615/435–5000 **A**1 2 10 **F**3 7 11 13 15 17 18 20 22 28 29 30 31 34 35 40 43 45 49 50 54 57 59 64 67 68 70 72 74 75 76 78 79 80 81 85 86 87 93 97 102 107 108 110 111 114 115 118 119 124 126 129 130 132 135 146 148 **P**6 8
Primary Contact: Donald Webb, Chief Executive Officer
COO: Julie Miller, Chief Operating Officer
CMO: Starling C. Evins, M.D., Chief of Staff
CIO: Steve Dycus, Director Marketing and Public Relations
CHR: Phyllis Molyneux, Associate Administrator Human Resources and Education
Web address: www.williamsonmedicalcenter.org
Control: County–Government, nonfederal **Service:** General Medical and Surgical

Staffed Beds: 185 **Admissions:** 8824 **Census:** 89 **Outpatient Visits:** 104326 **Births:** 1752 **Total Expense ($000):** 162756 **Payroll Expense ($000):** 66368 **Personnel:** 1088

GALLATIN—Sumner County

☒ **SUMNER REGIONAL MEDICAL CENTER (440003)**, 555 Hartsville Pike, Zip 37066–2400, Mailing Address: P.O. Box 1558, Zip 37066–1558; tel. 615/452–4210, (Nonreporting) **A**1 2 3 10 **S** LifePoint Health, Brentwood, TN
Primary Contact: Susan M. Peach, R.N., Chief Executive Officer
CIO: Vickie Carter, Information Systems Director
CNO: Anne Melton, Chief Nursing Officer
Web address: www.mysumnermedical.com
Control: Corporation, Investor–owned, for–profit **Service:** General Medical and Surgical

Staffed Beds: 155

GERMANTOWN—Shelby County

☐ **BAPTIST MEMORIAL REHABILITATION HOSPITAL (443034)**, 1240 South Germantown Road, Zip 38138–2226; tel. 901/275–3300 **A**1 10 **F**3 90 **S** Baptist Memorial Health Care Corporation, Memphis, TN
Primary Contact: Christopher L. Bariola, Chief Executive Officer
CFO: Carlos Mendoza, Controller
CHR: Stacie Schroeppel, Director of Human Resources
CNO: Donna Hale, Director of Nursing
Web address: www.baptistrehab.com
Control: Hospital district or authority, Government, nonfederal **Service:** Rehabilitation

Staffed Beds: 49 **Admissions:** 1176 **Census:** 36 **Outpatient Visits:** 0 **Births:** 0

METHODIST LE BONHEUR GERMANTOWN HOSPITAL See Methodist Healthcare Memphis Hospitals, Memphis

GREENEVILLE—Greene County

☒ **LAUGHLIN MEMORIAL HOSPITAL (440025)**, 1420 Tusculum Boulevard, Zip 37745–5825; tel. 423/787–5000, (Total facility includes 81 beds in nursing home–type unit) **A**1 2 10 19 **F**3 11 12 13 15 18 20 28 29 31 34 35 37 40 45 46 49 50 56 57 59 62 64 68 70 73 74 75 76 77 78 79 81 85 86 87 89 93 97 107 108 110 111 114 115 118 119 120 121 123 128 129 130 131 132 134 135 146 147 148 **P**6
Primary Contact: Charles H. Whitfield, Jr., President and Chief Executive Officer
CFO: Mark Compton, Chief Financial Officer
CMO: Mark Patterson, M.D., Chief Medical Officer
CIO: Eric L. Garrison, Chief Information Officer
CHR: Robert R. Roark, Director Human Resources
CNO: Brenda Cannon, R.N., Director of Nursing
Web address: www.laughlinmemorial.org
Control: Other not–for–profit (including NFP Corporation) **Service:** General Medical and Surgical

Staffed Beds: 143 **Admissions:** 3412 **Census:** 112 **Outpatient Visits:** 96584 **Births:** 220 **Total Expense ($000):** 74585 **Payroll Expense ($000):** 32871 **Personnel:** 721

☒ **TAKOMA REGIONAL HOSPITAL (440050)**, 401 Takoma Avenue, Zip 37743–4647; tel. 423/639–3151, (Nonreporting) **A**1 10
Primary Contact: Dennis Kiley, Interim Chief Executive Officer
CFO: Steven Miller, Chief Financial Officer
CMO: Daniel Lewis, Chief Medical Officer
CHR: Jack Lister, Director Human Resources
CNO: Tammy Albright, Chief Nursing Officer
Web address: www.takoma.org
Control: Church–operated, Nongovernment, not–for profit **Service:** General Medical and Surgical

Staffed Beds: 100

HARRIMAN—Roane County

☒ **ROANE MEDICAL CENTER (440031)**, 8045 Roane Medical Center Drive, Zip 37748–8333; tel. 865/316–1000 **A**1 10 **F**3 11 15 18 20 28 29 30 40 45 57 59 68 70 77 79 81 85 93 107 108 110 111 119 129 130 136 141 142 146 **S** Covenant Health, Knoxville, TN
Primary Contact: Gaye Jolly, FACHE, President/Chief Administrative Officer
COO: Jason B. Pilant, Chief Operating Officer
CFO: Julie Utterback, Chief Financial Officer
CMO: Mark Browne, M.D., Chief Medical Officer
CIO: Mike Ward, Senior Vice President Chief Information Officer
CHR: Randall Carr, Director Human Resources
CNO: Carolyn Shipley, Chief Nursing Officer
Web address: www.roanemedical.com
Control: Other not–for–profit (including NFP Corporation) **Service:** General Medical and Surgical

Staffed Beds: 36 **Admissions:** 2603 **Census:** 28 **Outpatient Visits:** 64230 **Births:** 0 **Total Expense ($000):** 35112 **Payroll Expense ($000):** 12378 **Personnel:** 231

TN

Hospital, Medicare Provider Number, Address, Telephone, Approval, Facility, and Physician Codes, Health Care System

★ American Hospital Association (AHA) membership
☐ The Joint Commission accreditation
○ Healthcare Facilities Accreditation Program
◇ DNV Healthcare Inc. accreditation
⇑ Center for Improvement in Healthcare Quality Accreditation
△ Commission on Accreditation of Rehabilitation Facilities (CARF) accreditation

HARTSVILLE—Trousdale County

✠ **TROUSDALE MEDICAL CENTER (441301)**, 500 Church Street, Zip 37074–1744; tel. 615/374–2221, (Nonreporting) **A**1 10 18 **S** LifePoint Health, Brentwood, TN
Primary Contact: Michael Herman, Chief Executive Officer
COO: William D. Mize, Chief Operating Officer
CFO: David Wilhoite, CPA, Senior Vice President Finance and Chief Financial Officer
CIO: David Young, Senior Vice President Planning and Technology
CHR: Amy Overstreet, Director Human Resources
Web address: www.mytrousdalemedical.com
Control: Corporation, Investor–owned, for–profit **Service:** General Medical and Surgical

Staffed Beds: 25

HENDERSONVILLE—Sumner County

✠ **TRISTAR HENDERSONVILLE MEDICAL CENTER (440194)**, 355 New Shackle Island Road, Zip 37075–2479; tel. 615/338–1000, (Nonreporting) **A**1 10 **S** HCA, Nashville, TN
Primary Contact: Regina Bartlett, Chief Executive Officer
COO: Cory Darling, Chief Operating Officer
CFO: Jon Baker, Chief Financial Officer
CMO: Jason Thurman, Chief of Staff
CIO: Hal Schultheis, Director Information Systems
CNO: Lisa Gann, R.N., Chief Nursing Officer
Web address: www.hendersonvillemedicalcenter.com
Control: Corporation, Investor–owned, for–profit **Service:** General Medical and Surgical

Staffed Beds: 81

HERMITAGE—Davidson County

✠ **TRISTAR SUMMIT MEDICAL CENTER (440150)**, 5655 Frist Boulevard, Zip 37076–2053; tel. 615/316–3000 **A**1 2 10 **F**3 11 13 15 18 20 22 26 28 29 30 31 34 35 37 38 39 40 43 45 46 47 48 49 50 56 57 61 64 70 72 74 75 76 77 78 79 80 81 82 85 87 89 90 93 96 97 100 107 108 110 111 114 115 118 119 121 123 124 126 129 130 131 135 145 146 147 148 **P**6 **S** HCA, Nashville, TN
Primary Contact: Jeffrey T. Whitehorn, Chief Executive Officer
COO: Greg Caples, Chief Operating Officer
CFO: Bryan Shephard, Chief Financial Officer
CIO: Joel Bain, Director Information Services
CHR: Emily Dye, Vice President Human Resources
CNO: Mary Ann Angle, R.N., Chief Nursing Officer
Web address: www.summitmedctr.com
Control: Corporation, Investor–owned, for–profit **Service:** General Medical and Surgical

Staffed Beds: 196 **Admissions:** 10598 **Census:** 125 **Outpatient Visits:** 125539 **Births:** 1187 **Total Expense ($000):** 134849 **Payroll Expense ($000):** 51546 **Personnel:** 803

HUNTINGDON—Carroll County

✠ **BAPTIST MEMORIAL HOSPITAL–HUNTINGDON (440016)**, 631 R.B. Wilson Drive, Zip 38344–1727; tel. 731/986–4461 **A**1 10 **F**3 7 15 18 28 29 30 34 35 40 44 50 56 57 59 61 62 63 64 65 68 70 75 77 81 85 86 87 93 98 102 103 107 111 115 118 119 130 132 133 135 145 146 148 **S** Baptist Memorial Health Care Corporation, Memphis, TN
Primary Contact: Susan M. Breeden, Administrator and Chief Executive Officer
CFO: Sharron Holland, Chief Financial Officer
CHR: Kim King, Director Human Resources and Public Relations
CNO: Kimberly Sanders, Chief Nursing Officer
Web address: www.baptistonline.org/huntingdon/
Control: Other not–for–profit (including NFP Corporation) **Service:** General Medical and Surgical

Staffed Beds: 35 **Admissions:** 865 **Census:** 15 **Outpatient Visits:** 14559 **Births:** 0 **Total Expense ($000):** 18422 **Payroll Expense ($000):** 7051 **Personnel:** 142

JACKSON—Madison County

✠ △ **JACKSON–MADISON COUNTY GENERAL HOSPITAL (440002)**, 620 Skyline Drive, Zip 38301–3923; tel. 731/541–5000 **A**1 2 3 5 7 10 19 **F**3 7 8 11 13 15 17 18 20 22 24 26 28 29 30 31 34 35 40 44 45 46 47 48 49 51 53 55 56 57 58 59 60 63 64 65 68 70 72 74 75 76 77 78 79 80 81 82 83 84 85 86 87 89 90 92 93 94 96 97 107 108 109 110 111 112 114 115 116 117 118 119 120 121 124 126 129 130 131 132 135 145 146 147 148 **P**5 8 **S** West Tennessee Healthcare, Jackson, TN
Primary Contact: James E. Ross, Interim Chief Executive Officer
COO: James E. Ross, Vice President and Chief Operating Officer
CFO: Jeff Blankenship, CPA, Vice President and Chief Financial Officer
CMO: David Roberts, M.D., Chief Medical Officer
CIO: Jeff Frieling, Vice President and Chief Information Officer
CHR: Wendie Carlson, Chief Human Resources Officer
CNO: Tina Prescott, Vice President, Hospital Services
Web address: www.wth.org
Control: Hospital district or authority, Government, nonfederal **Service:** General Medical and Surgical

Staffed Beds: 635 **Admissions:** 27430 **Census:** 441 **Outpatient Visits:** 199906 **Births:** 3941 **Total Expense ($000):** 553710 **Payroll Expense ($000):** 205074 **Personnel:** 4141

★ **PATHWAYS OF TENNESSEE (444010)**, 238 Summar Drive, Zip 38301–3906; tel. 731/541–8200 **A**10 **F**4 5 29 35 38 44 57 59 98 99 100 101 102 103 104 132 134 **S** West Tennessee Healthcare, Jackson, TN
Primary Contact: Pam Henson, Executive Director
CFO: Jeff Blankenship, CPA, Chief Financial Officer
CMO: Kevin Turner, M.D., Medical Director
CIO: Jeff Frieling, Chief Information Officer
CHR: Wendy Carlson, Director Human Resources
CNO: Angela Hensley, Director of Nursing
Web address: www.wth.net/pathways
Control: Hospital district or authority, Government, nonfederal **Service:** Psychiatric

Staffed Beds: 25 **Admissions:** 753 **Census:** 9 **Outpatient Visits:** 114148 **Births:** 0 **Total Expense ($000):** 16032 **Payroll Expense ($000):** 8673 **Personnel:** 199

✠ **TENNOVA HEALTHCARE REGIONAL HOSPITAL OF JACKSON (440189)**, 367 Hospital Boulevard, Zip 38305–2080; tel. 731/661–2000, (Nonreporting) **A**1 3 10 **S** Community Health Systems, Inc., Franklin, TN
Primary Contact: Charles F. Miller, Chief Executive Officer
CFO: Richard Read, Chief Financial Officer
CMO: Michael Saridakis, M.D., Physician Adviser
CIO: Jimmy Anderson, Director of Information Systems
CHR: Barbara Euler, Director Human Resources
CNO: Jan Zimmer, R.N., Chief Nursing Officer
Web address: www.regionalhospitaljackson.com/Pages/Home.aspx
Control: Corporation, Investor–owned, for–profit **Service:** General Medical and Surgical

Staffed Beds: 134

JAMESTOWN—Fentress County

✠ **TENNOVA HEALTHCARE–JAMESTOWN (440083)**, 436 Central Avenue W., Zip 38556–3031, Mailing Address: P.O. Box 1500, Zip 38556–1500; tel. 931/879–8171, (Nonreporting) **A**1 10 20 **S** Community Health Systems, Inc., Franklin, TN
Primary Contact: Lynette Pritchett, Chief Executive Officer
CMO: Mark Hendrixson, M.D., Chief Medical Officer
CIO: Rick Smith, Director Information Systems
CHR: Shelia Russell, Director Human Resources
Web address: www.jamestownregional.org
Control: Corporation, Investor–owned, for–profit **Service:** General Medical and Surgical

Staffed Beds: 85

JEFFERSON CITY—Jefferson County

ST. MARY'S JEFFERSON MEMORIAL HOSPITAL See Tennova Healthcare–Jefferson Memorial Hospital

✠ **TENNOVA HEALTHCARE–JEFFERSON MEMORIAL HOSPITAL (440056)**, 110 Hospital Drive, Zip 37760–5281; tel. 865/471–2500, (Nonreporting) **A**1 10 **S** Community Health Systems, Inc., Franklin, TN
Primary Contact: Colin McRae, Chief Executive Officer
CFO: Roseann M. Devault, Chief Financial Officer
CMO: Richard Carter, M.D., Chief of Staff
Web address: www.tennova.com/
Control: Corporation, Investor–owned, for–profit **Service:** General Medical and Surgical

Staffed Beds: 54

TN

JELLICO—Campbell County

⊞ **JELLICO COMMUNITY HOSPITAL (440180)**, 188 Hospital Lane, Zip 37762–4400; tel. 423/784–7252, (Nonreporting) **A**1 10 **S** Community Hospital Corporation, Plano, TX
Primary Contact: Kim Dowell, R.N., Chief Executive Officer
COO: Pamela Hodge, R.N., Chief Nursing Officer and Coordinator Performance Improvement
CFO: Evelyn Ghulum, Chief Financial Officer
CMO: Gregory Wilkens, M.D., Chief of Staff
CIO: Derek Brown, Chief Information Officer
CHR: Vince Vannett, Director Human Resources
Web address: www.jellicohospital.com
Control: Other not–for–profit (including NFP Corporation) **Service:** General Medical and Surgical

Staffed Beds: 31

JOHNSON CITY—Washington County

⊞ **FRANKLIN WOODS COMMUNITY HOSPITAL (440184)**, 300 MedTech Parkway, Zip 37604–2277; tel. 423/302–1000, (Total facility includes 34 beds in nursing home–type unit) **A**1 3 10 **F**3 11 13 29 30 34 35 40 44 45 50 51 56 59 68 70 74 75 76 77 81 85 86 87 91 97 100 107 108 111 114 115 118 119 126 128 130 143 146 147 148 **S** Mountain States Health Alliance, Johnson City, TN
Primary Contact: Lindy P. White, Chief Executive Officer
CFO: Bradley Logan, Chief Financial Officer
CHR: Brooke Graham, Human Resources Manager
CNO: Rhonda Mann, Chief Nursing Officer
Web address: www.msha.com
Control: Other not–for–profit (including NFP Corporation) **Service:** General Medical and Surgical

Staffed Beds: 80 **Admissions:** 5323 **Census:** 50 **Outpatient Visits:** 47435 **Births:** 1201 **Total Expense ($000):** 65117 **Payroll Expense ($000):** 20987 **Personnel:** 428

⊞ **JOHNSON CITY MEDICAL CENTER (440063)**, 400 North State of Franklin Road, Zip 37604–6094; tel. 423/431–6111, (Includes NISWONGER CHILDREN'S HOSPITAL, 400 North State Of Franklin Road, Zip 37604–6035; tel. 423/431–6111; Lisa Carter, Chief Executive Officer; WOODRIDGE HOSPITAL, 403 State of Franklin Road, Zip 37604–6034; tel. 423/431–7111; Lindy P. White, Chief Executive Officer) **A**1 2 3 5 8 10 **F**3 4 5 7 11 12 13 15 17 18 19 20 21 22 24 26 27 28 29 30 31 32 34 35 38 39 40 41 43 44 45 46 47 48 49 50 51 52 53 54 55 56 57 58 59 60 61 62 63 64 68 70 72 74 75 76 77 78 79 81 82 85 86 87 88 89 91 93 97 98 99 100 101 102 103 104 105 107 108 110 111 114 115 117 118 119 120 121 123 124 129 130 131 132 134 135 143 146 147 148 **S** Mountain States Health Alliance, Johnson City, TN
Primary Contact: Melody Trimble, Chief Executive Officer
COO: Tony Benton, Chief Operating Officer
CFO: Richard Boone, Chief Financial Officer
CMO: Clay Runnels, Vice President Chief Medical Officer Washington County
CHR: Barry Tourigny, Human Resources Director
CNO: Dru Malcolm, Vice President and Chief Nursing Officer
Web address: www.msha.com
Control: Other not–for–profit (including NFP Corporation) **Service:** General Medical and Surgical

Staffed Beds: 585 **Admissions:** 29482 **Census:** 427 **Outpatient Visits:** 269696 **Births:** 1400 **Total Expense ($000):** 397255 **Payroll Expense ($000):** 127360 **Personnel:** 2360

NORTH SIDE HOSPITAL See Franklin Woods Community Hospital

⊞ △ **QUILLEN REHABILITATION HOSPITAL (443033)**, 2511 Wesley Street, Zip 37601–1723; tel. 423/952–1700 **A**1 7 10 **F**29 75 77 90 91 132 148 **S** HEALTHSOUTH Corporation, Birmingham, AL
Primary Contact: Brian Luff, Chief Executive Officer
CFO: Debbie Wyse, Controller
CHR: Penny Lawson, Human Resource Director
CNO: Lynn Langan, Chief Nursing Officer
Web address: www.quillenrehabilitationhospital.com/
Control: Corporation, Investor–owned, for–profit **Service:** Rehabilitation

Staffed Beds: 26 **Admissions:** 579 **Census:** 21 **Outpatient Visits:** 0 **Births:** 0 **Total Expense ($000):** 8667 **Payroll Expense ($000):** 4291 **Personnel:** 80

KINGSPORT—Sullivan County

⊞ **HEALTHSOUTH REHABILITATION HOSPITAL (443027)**, 113 Cassel Drive, Zip 37660–3775; tel. 423/246–7240, (Nonreporting) **A**1 10 **S** HEALTHSOUTH Corporation, Birmingham, AL
Primary Contact: Troy Clark, Chief Executive Officer
CFO: Natalie Tilson, Controller
CMO: James P. Little, M.D., Medical Director
CIO: Natalie Tilson, Controller
CHR: Joyce Jones, Director Human Resources
CNO: Debra Smith, Chief Nursing Officer
Web address: www.healthsouthkingsport.com
Control: Corporation, Investor–owned, for–profit **Service:** Rehabilitation

Staffed Beds: 50

☐ **INDIAN PATH MEDICAL CENTER (440176)**, 2000 Brookside Drive, Zip 37660–4627; tel. 423/857–7000, (Total facility includes 22 beds in nursing home–type unit) **A**1 3 10 **F**3 8 11 13 15 18 20 22 26 28 29 30 34 35 40 45 46 47 49 50 51 57 59 60 64 65 68 70 73 74 75 76 77 78 79 81 85 86 87 91 97 107 108 110 111 114 115 116 117 118 119 121 123 128 129 130 132 135 146 147 **S** Mountain States Health Alliance, Johnson City, TN
Primary Contact: Monty E. McLaurin, President and Chief Executive Officer
CFO: Steven Sawyer, Chief Financial Officer
CMO: Mark Wilkinson, M.D., Chief Medical Officer
CIO: Jackson Dale, Site Manager Information Systems
CHR: Kevin M. Smith, Director Human Resources
CNO: Susan Fannon, Chief Nursing Officer
Web address: www.msha.com
Control: Other not–for–profit (including NFP Corporation) **Service:** General Medical and Surgical

Staffed Beds: 239 **Admissions:** 6061 **Census:** 74 **Outpatient Visits:** 118858 **Births:** 716 **Total Expense ($000):** 86351 **Payroll Expense ($000):** 31200 **Personnel:** 555

⊞ **WELLMONT HOLSTON VALLEY MEDICAL CENTER (440017)**, 130 West Ravine Street, Zip 37660–3837, Mailing Address: P.O. Box 238, Zip 37662–0238; tel. 423/224–4000 **A**1 2 3 5 10 13 19 **F**3 11 12 13 15 17 18 19 20 22 24 26 28 29 30 31 34 35 40 41 43 45 46 47 48 49 50 51 54 55 57 58 59 60 61 64 65 70 72 74 75 76 77 78 79 81 82 83 84 85 87 88 89 92 93 107 108 110 114 115 118 119 120 121 122 123 126 129 130 131 132 135 146 147 148 **S** Wellmont Health System, Kingsport, TN
Primary Contact: Tim Attebery, Chief Executive Officer
COO: Fred L. Pelle, FACHE, Chief Operating Officer
CFO: Dale Poe, Vice President Finance and Operations
CMO: Daniel Carlson, M.D., Chief Medical Officer
CIO: Will Showalter, Senior Vice President Information Technology
CHR: Hamlin J. Wilson, Senior Vice President Human Resources
CNO: Kathy Campbell, Interim Chief Nursing Officer
Web address: www.wellmont.org
Control: Other not–for–profit (including NFP Corporation) **Service:** General Medical and Surgical

Staffed Beds: 345 **Admissions:** 16568 **Census:** 210 **Outpatient Visits:** 162252 **Births:** 1073 **Total Expense ($000):** 319571 **Payroll Expense ($000):** 77664

KNOXVILLE—Knox County

☐ **EAST TENNESSEE CHILDREN'S HOSPITAL (443303)**, 2018 Clinch Avenue, Zip 37916–2393, Mailing Address: P.O. Box 15010, Zip 37901–5010; tel. 865/541–8000, (Nonreporting) **A**1 3 5 10
Primary Contact: Keith D. Goodwin, President and Chief Executive Officer
COO: Rudolph McKinley, Jr., Vice President Operations and Chief Operating Officer
CFO: Zane Goodrich, Vice President Finance
CMO: Joe Childs, M.D., Vice President Medical Services
CIO: John Hanks, Director Information Systems
CHR: Sue Wilburn, Vice President Human Resources and Organizational Development
CNO: Laura P. Barnes, MSN, Vice President Patient Care Services and Chief Nursing Officer
Web address: www.etch.com
Control: Other not–for–profit (including NFP Corporation) **Service:** Children's general

Staffed Beds: 152

Hospital, Medicare Provider Number, Address, Telephone, Approval, Facility, and Physician Codes, Health Care System

★ American Hospital Association (AHA) membership   ○ Healthcare Facilities Accreditation Program   ⇑ Center for Improvement in Healthcare Quality Accreditation
☐ The Joint Commission accreditation   ◇ DNV Healthcare Inc. accreditation   △ Commission on Accreditation of Rehabilitation Facilities (CARF) accreditation

TN

✠ △ **FORT SANDERS REGIONAL MEDICAL CENTER (440125)**, 1901 West
Clinch Avenue, Zip 37916–2307; tel. 865/541–1111, (Total facility includes 24
beds in nursing home–type unit) **A**1 2 7 10 **F**3 11 12 13 15 17 18 20 22 24 26
28 29 30 31 34 35 40 45 46 48 49 50 51 54 55 57 58 59 60 61 64 68
74 75 76 77 78 79 80 81 84 85 86 87 90 91 92 93 94 96 100 102 107 108
110 111 114 115 116 117 118 119 120 121 123 124 126 128 129 130 131
132 136 141 142 146 147 148 **S** Covenant Health, Knoxville, TN
Primary Contact: Keith Altshuler, President and Chief Administrative Officer
Web address: www.covenanthealth.com
Control: Other not–for–profit (including NFP Corporation) **Service:** General
Medical and Surgical

Staffed Beds: 402 Admissions: 16299 Census: 239 Outpatient Visits:
239692 **Births:** 2594 **Total Expense ($000):** 277519 **Payroll Expense**
($000): 87967 **Personnel:** 1530

MERCY MEDICAL CENTER WEST See Tennova Turkey Creek Medical Center

✠ **PARKWEST MEDICAL CENTER (440173)**, 9352 Park West Boulevard,
Zip 37923–4325, Mailing Address: P.O. Box 22993, Zip 37933–0993;
tel. 865/373–1000 **A**1 2 10 **F**3 13 15 17 18 20 22 24 26 28 29 30 31 34 35
37 40 45 46 47 48 49 50 51 56 58 60 64 68 70 74 75 76 77 78 79 80 81
84 85 87 92 93 98 103 107 108 110 111 115 116 117 118 119 120 121
123 124 126 129 130 131 132 135 141 142 146 147 148 **S** Covenant Health,
Knoxville, TN
Primary Contact: Rick Lassiter, President and Chief Administrative Officer
COO: Emlyn Cobble, Vice President and Chief Support Officer
CFO: Scott Hamilton, Vice President and Chief Financial Officer
CHR: Randall Carr, Director Human Resources
CNO: Diane Oliver, R.N., Chief Nursing Officer
Web address: www.yesparkwest.com
Control: Other not–for–profit (including NFP Corporation) **Service:** General
Medical and Surgical

Staffed Beds: 297 Admissions: 16311 Census: 211 Outpatient Visits:
184607 **Births:** 1650 **Total Expense ($000):** 240164 **Payroll Expense**
($000): 76758 **Personnel:** 1416

✠ **SELECT SPECIALTY HOSPITAL–KNOXVILLE (442012)**, 1901 Clinch Avenue,
4th Floor North, Zip 37916–2307; tel. 865/541–2615, (Nonreporting) **A**1 10
S Select Medical Corporation, Mechanicsburg, PA
Primary Contact: Rita Wilder, Chief Executive Officer
CFO: David Elledge, Controller
CMO: Jano Janoyan, M.D., Medical Director
CHR: Christina Blanton, Administrative Assistant and Human Resources
Coordinator
CNO: Danielle Connolly Robbins, Chief Nursing Officer
Web address: www.knoxville.selectspecialtyhospitals.com/
Control: Corporation, Investor–owned, for–profit **Service:** Long–Term Acute Care
hospital

Staffed Beds: 35

✠ △ **TENNOVA PHYSICIANS REGIONAL MEDICAL CENTER (440120)**, 900
East Oak Hill Avenue, Zip 37917–4556; tel. 865/545–8000, (Includes TENNOVA
NORTH KNOXVILLE MEDICAL CENTER, 7565 Dannaher Way, Powell,
Zip 37849–4029; tel. 865/859–7000; Clyde Wood, Chief Executive Officer;
TENNOVA TURKEY CREEK MEDICAL CENTER, 10820 Parkside Drive,
Zip 37934–1956; tel. 865/218–7092; Ben Youree, Chief Executive Officer;
TENNOVA TURKEY CREEK MEDICAL CENTER, 10820 Parkside Drive,
Zip 37922–1956; tel. 865/218–7090) **A**1 2 7 10 **F**8 13 15 18 20 22 24 26 28
29 30 31 34 35 40 49 51 53 54 56 57 59 60 61 62 63 64 70 73 74 75 76
77 78 79 80 81 82 84 85 86 87 90 92 93 96 98 100 102 103 104 105 107
108 110 111 114 115 117 118 119 120 121 123 124 126 128 129 130 131
132 146 147 **S** Community Health Systems, Inc., Franklin, TN
Primary Contact: Neil Heatherly, Interim Chief Executive Officer
CFO: Rhonda Maynard, Chief Financial Officer
CIO: Tom Lakins, Director Information Systems
CHR: Sarah M. Laboranti, Interim Director Human Resources
Web address: www.hma.com/content/physicians–regional–medical–center
Control: Corporation, Investor–owned, for–profit **Service:** General Medical and
Surgical

Staffed Beds: 220 Admissions: 14530 Census: 209 Outpatient Visits:
178560 **Births:** 1503 **Total Expense ($000):** 209528 **Payroll Expense**
($000): 58880 **Personnel:** 1017

✠ **UNIVERSITY OF TENNESSEE MEDICAL CENTER (440015)**, 1924 Alcoa
Highway, Zip 37920–6900; tel. 865/305–9000 **A**1 2 3 5 8 10 **F**3 6 8 9 11 12
13 15 17 18 20 22 24 26 28 29 30 31 34 35 36 39 40 41 43 44 45 46 47
48 49 50 51 53 54 55 56 57 58 59 60 61 64 65 70 71 72 74 75 76 77 78
79 81 82 84 85 86 87 88 91 92 93 94 96 97 100 102 103 107 108 109 110
111 114 115 116 117 118 119 120 121 123 124 126 129 130 131 132 135
138 141 142 144 145 146 147 148 **P**5 6
Primary Contact: Joseph Landsman, President and Chief Executive Officer
COO: David Hall, Senior Vice President and Chief Operating Officer
CFO: Thomas Fisher, Senior Vice President and Chief Financial Officer
CMO: Jerry Epps, M.D., Senior Vice President and Chief Medical Officer
CIO: Michael Saad, Vice President and Chief Information Officer
CHR: Betty Gissel, Vice President Human Resources
CNO: Janell Cecil, R.N., Senior Vice President and Chief Nursing Officer
Web address: www.utmedicalcenter.org
Control: Other not–for–profit (including NFP Corporation) **Service:** General
Medical and Surgical

Staffed Beds: 583 Admissions: 27734 Census: 448 Outpatient Visits:
265817 **Births:** 3340 **Total Expense ($000):** 743667 **Payroll Expense**
($000): 262667 **Personnel:** 3598

LA FOLLETTE—Campbell County

✠ **TENNOVA HEALTHCARE–LAFOLLETTE MEDICAL CENTER (440033)**, 923
East Central Avenue, Zip 37766–2768, Mailing Address: P.O. Box 1301,
Zip 37766–1301; tel. 423/907–1200, (Nonreporting) **A**1 10 20 **S** Community
Health Systems, Inc., Franklin, TN
Primary Contact: Mark Cain, Chief Executive Officer
COO: Sara Heatherly–Lloyd, Chief Operating Officer
CMO: Jan Robbins, M.D., Chief of Staff
CIO: Dillon Ward, Management Information Systems Specialist
CHR: Bess Stout, Director Human Resources
CNO: Kathy R. Myers, MS, Chief Nursing Officer
Web address: www.tennova.com
Control: Corporation, Investor–owned, for–profit **Service:** General Medical and
Surgical

Staffed Beds: 164

LAFAYETTE—Macon County

★ ◇ **MACON COUNTY GENERAL HOSPITAL (441305)**, 204 Medical Drive,
Zip 37083–1799, Mailing Address: P.O. Box 378, Zip 37083–0378;
tel. 615/666–2147 **A**10 18 21 **F**29 34 35 40 45 57 77 81 93 107 110 111
115 119 128 130 132 133 146 **S** QHR, Brentwood, TN
Primary Contact: Dennis A. Wolford, FACHE, Chief Executive Officer
CFO: Thomas J. Kidd, Assistant Administrator and Chief Financial Officer
Web address: www.mcgh.net
Control: Other not–for–profit (including NFP Corporation) **Service:** General
Medical and Surgical

Staffed Beds: 25 Admissions: 854 Census: 10 Outpatient Visits: 28903
Births: 0 **Total Expense ($000):** 11269 **Payroll Expense ($000):** 5186
Personnel: 117

LAWRENCEBURG—Lawrence County

✠ **SOUTHERN TENNESSEE REGIONAL HEALTH SYSTEM–LAWRENCEBURG**
(440175), 1607 South Locust Avenue, Zip 38464–4011, Mailing Address: P.O.
Box 847, Zip 38464–0847; tel. 931/762–6571, (Nonreporting) **A**1 10
S LifePoint Health, Brentwood, TN
Primary Contact: Jeff Noblin, FACHE, Chief Executive Officer
CFO: Kristie Taylor, Chief Financial Officer
CIO: Jason Weaver, Director Information Systems
CHR: Robert Augustin, Director Human Resources
CNO: Carrie Rogers, Chief Nursing Officer
Web address: www.crocketthospital.com
Control: Corporation, Investor–owned, for–profit **Service:** General Medical and
Surgical

Staffed Beds: 99

LEBANON—Wilson County

✠ **TENNOVA HEALTHCARE–LEBANON (440193)**, 1411 Baddour Parkway,
Zip 37087–2513; tel. 615/444–8262, (Includes TENNOVA
HEALTHCARE–LEBANON MCFARLAND CAMPUS, 500 Park Avenue,
Zip 37087–3720; tel. 615/449–0500), (Nonreporting) **A**1 5 10 **S** Community
Health Systems, Inc., Franklin, TN
Primary Contact: Matthew T. Caldwell, Chief Executive Officer
CMO: Andrew Jordan, M.D., Chief of Staff
CIO: Adrian Fung, Director Information Systems
Web address: www.universitymedicalcenter.com
Control: Corporation, Investor–owned, for–profit **Service:** General Medical and
Surgical

Staffed Beds: 245

TN

LENOIR CITY—Loudon County

☒ **FORT LOUDOUN MEDICAL CENTER (440110)**, 550 Fort Loudoun Medical Center Drive, Zip 37772–5673; tel. 865/271–6000 **A**1 10 **F**3 15 18 28 29 30 34 35 40 50 57 59 68 70 77 79 81 85 93 102 107 108 110 111 114 118 119 130 135 146 148 **S** Covenant Health, Knoxville, TN
Primary Contact: Jeffrey Feike, President and Chief Administrative Officer
CNO: Teresa Fisher, R.N., Chief Nursing Officer
Web address: www.covenanthealth.com
Control: Other not–for–profit (including NFP Corporation) **Service:** General Medical and Surgical

Staffed Beds: 30 **Admissions:** 2026 **Census:** 22 **Outpatient Visits:** 68067 **Births:** 0 **Total Expense ($000):** 27140 **Payroll Expense ($000):** 11118 **Personnel:** 205

LEWISBURG—Marshall County

☒ **MARSHALL MEDICAL CENTER (441309)**, 1080 North Ellington Parkway, Zip 37091–2227, Mailing Address: P.O. Box 1609, Zip 37091–1609; tel. 931/359–6241 **A**1 10 18 **F**3 11 15 29 30 34 40 45 50 56 57 59 68 75 77 81 85 86 92 93 104 107 108 110 111 114 119 129 131 132 133 135 146 **S** Maury Regional Health System, Columbia, TN
Primary Contact: Phyllis Brown, Chief Executive Officer
CFO: Kyle Jones, Controller
CMO: Tim Nash, M.D., Chief of Staff
CHR: Jeff M. Pierce, Manager Human Resources
CNO: Karen Martin, R.N., Chief Nursing Officer
Web address: www.mauryregional.com
Control: County–Government, nonfederal **Service:** General Medical and Surgical

Staffed Beds: 12 **Admissions:** 442 **Census:** 4 **Outpatient Visits:** 35634 **Births:** 0 **Total Expense ($000):** 14791 **Payroll Expense ($000):** 6555 **Personnel:** 133

LEXINGTON—Henderson County

☒ **HENDERSON COUNTY COMMUNITY HOSPITAL (440008)**, 200 West Church Street, Zip 38351–2038; tel. 731/968–3646, (Nonreporting) **A**1 10 **S** Quorum Health, Brentwood, TN
Primary Contact: Pamela W. Roberts, Chief Executive Officer
CFO: John Bostwick, Interim Chief Financial Officer
CHR: Linda Durham, Director Human Resources
CNO: Charlene Morgan, Chief Nursing Officer
Web address: www.hendersoncchospital.com
Control: Corporation, Investor–owned, for–profit **Service:** General Medical and Surgical

Staffed Beds: 36

LINDEN—Perry County

PERRY COMMUNITY HOSPITAL (440040), 2718 Squirrel Hollow Drive, Zip 37096–3526; tel. 931/589–2121, (Nonreporting) **A**10
Primary Contact: John B. Avery, III, Administrator
Control: Other not–for–profit (including NFP Corporation) **Service:** General Medical and Surgical

Staffed Beds: 53

LIVINGSTON—Overton County

☒ **LIVINGSTON REGIONAL HOSPITAL (440187)**, 315 Oak Street, Zip 38570–1728, Mailing Address: P.O. Box 550, Zip 38570–0550; tel. 931/823–5611, (Nonreporting) **A**1 10 **S** LifePoint Health, Brentwood, TN
Primary Contact: Timothy W. McGill, Chief Executive Officer
CMO: Donnie Huff, M.D., Chief Medical Officer
CIO: Mark Hambridge, Director Information Systems
CNO: Colleen Tuck, Chief Nursing Officer
Web address: www.MyLivingstonHospital.com
Control: Corporation, Investor–owned, for–profit **Service:** General Medical and Surgical

Staffed Beds: 114

LOUISVILLE—Blount County

★ **PENINSULA HOSPITAL**, 2347 Jones Bend Road, Zip 37777–5213, Mailing Address: P.O. Box 2000, Zip 37777–2000; tel. 865/970–9800 **F**4 5 29 30 34 35 38 50 64 68 98 99 101 104 130 **P**6
Primary Contact: Elizabeth P. Clary, R.N., Vice President Behavioral Health
COO: Todd Roberts, Manager Business Operations
CFO: Scott Hamilton, Chief Financial Officer
CMO: Reggie Raman, M.D., Medical Director
CIO: Shelby Bowers, Director Marketing and Public Relations
CHR: Anita Rivera, Director Human Resources
CNO: Heather Jett, Director Patient Care Services
Web address: www.peninsula–hospital.org
Control: Other not–for–profit (including NFP Corporation) **Service:** Psychiatric

Staffed Beds: 137 **Admissions:** 4947 **Census:** 85 **Outpatient Visits:** 79018 **Births:** 0 **Total Expense ($000):** 31004 **Payroll Expense ($000):** 15705 **Personnel:** 310

MADISON—Davidson County

★ **TRISTAR SKYLINE MADISON CAMPUS (440135)**, 500 Hospital Drive, Zip 37115–5032; tel. 615/769–5000, (Nonreporting) **S** HCA, Nashville, TN
Primary Contact: Steve Otto, Chief Executive Officer
COO: Jill Howard, R.N., Chief Operating Officer
CFO: Michael Morrison, Chief Financial Officer
CMO: Sunil Kaza, M.D., President Medical Staff
CIO: Troy Sypien, Director Information Technology and Systems
CHR: Robert A. Hooper, Director Human Resources
CNO: Laurie Turner, Chief Nursing Officer
Web address: www.skylinemadison.com
Control: Corporation, Investor–owned, for–profit **Service:** General Medical and Surgical

Staffed Beds: 284

MANCHESTER—Coffee County

UNITY MEDICAL CENTER (440007), 1001 McArthur Drive, Zip 37355–2455, Mailing Address: P.O. Box 1079, Zip 37349–1079; tel. 931/728–3586, (Nonreporting) **A**10
Primary Contact: Martha McCormick, Chief Executive Officer
CFO: Pam Jernigan, Chief Financial Officer
CMO: James Van Winkle, M.D., Chief of Staff
CIO: Matt Burks, Director Information Technology
CHR: Sherry Holt, Director Human Resources
CNO: Stephanie Byars, Chief Nursing Officer
Web address: www.urmchealthcare.com
Control: Corporation, Investor–owned, for–profit **Service:** General Medical and Surgical

Staffed Beds: 36

MARTIN—Weakley County

BEHAVIORAL HEALTHCARE CENTER AT MARTIN (444005), 458 Hannings Lane, Zip 38237–3308; tel. 731/588–2830, (Nonreporting) **A**10 **S** Tennessee Health Management, Parsons, TN
Primary Contact: Carrie Brawley, Administrator
Web address: www.tnhealthmanagement.com/BHC/martin/
Control: Partnership, Investor–owned, for–profit **Service:** Psychiatric

Staffed Beds: 16

☒ **HEALTHSOUTH CANE CREEK REHABILITATION HOSPITAL (443030)**, 180 Mount Pelia Road, Zip 38237–3812; tel. 731/587–4231 **A**1 10 **F**3 29 56 75 82 90 91 94 95 96 130 132 135 143 148 **S** HEALTHSOUTH Corporation, Birmingham, AL
Primary Contact: Rick Johnson, Chief Executive Officer
CFO: Bethany Smith, Controller
CMO: Belinda Merritt, M.D., Medical Director
CIO: Jan Trowhill, Director Health Information Management Systems
CHR: Sharon Shihady, Director Human Resources
CNO: Lindsey Rotger, Chief Nursing Officer
Web address: www.healthsouthcanecreek.com
Control: Corporation, Investor–owned, for–profit **Service:** Rehabilitation

Staffed Beds: 40 **Admissions:** 784 **Census:** 28 **Outpatient Visits:** 0 **Births:** 0

Hospital, Medicare Provider Number, Address, Telephone, Approval, Facility, and Physician Codes, Health Care System

★ American Hospital Association (AHA) membership   ○ Healthcare Facilities Accreditation Program   ⇑ Center for Improvement in Healthcare Quality Accreditation
□ The Joint Commission accreditation   ◇ DNV Healthcare Inc. accreditation   △ Commission on Accreditation of Rehabilitation Facilities (CARF) accreditation

✠ **TENNOVA HEALTHCARE VOLUNTEER COMMUNITY HOSPITAL (440061)**, 161 Mount Pelia Road, Zip 38237–3811; tel. 731/587–4261, (Nonreporting) **A**1 10 **S** Community Health Systems, Inc., Franklin, TN
Primary Contact: Darrell Blaylock, Chief Executive Officer
CFO: Jason Draper, Chief Financial Officer
CMO: Elizabeth Lund, M.D., Chief of Staff
CHR: Tammie Bell, Director Human Resources
CNO: Donna Barfield, Chief Nursing Officer
Web address: www.volunteercommunityhospital.com
Control: Corporation, Investor–owned, for–profit **Service:** General Medical and Surgical

Staffed Beds: 65

MARYVILLE—Blount County

✠ **BLOUNT MEMORIAL HOSPITAL (440011)**, 907 East Lamar Alexander Parkway, Zip 37804–5016; tel. 865/983–7211, (Total facility includes 76 beds in nursing home–type unit) **A**1 2 10 **F**3 4 10 11 12 13 15 17 18 20 22 26 28 29 30 31 32 35 38 40 43 45 46 48 49 53 54 56 57 59 62 63 64 66 67 70 74 75 76 77 78 79 80 81 84 85 86 87 90 93 96 97 98 99 100 101 102 103 104 105 107 108 110 111 115 117 118 119 120 121 122 123 125 126 128 129 130 131 132 134 135 144 146 147 148 **P**6
Primary Contact: Don Heinemann, Administrator and Chief Executive Officer
CFO: Jonathan Smith, Assistant Administrator and Chief Financial Officer
CMO: G. Harold Naramore, M.D., Chief Medical Officer and In house Legal Counsel
CIO: Clay Puckett, Assistant Administrator and Chief Information Officer
CHR: Chris Wilkes, MS, Director Human Resources
CNO: Sonya Newman, R.N., Chief Nursing Officer
Web address: www.blountmemorial.org
Control: County–Government, nonfederal **Service:** General Medical and Surgical

Staffed Beds: 314 **Admissions:** 12207 **Census:** 194 **Outpatient Visits:** 280421 **Births:** 724 **Total Expense ($000):** 232689 **Payroll Expense ($000):** 111533 **Personnel:** 1901

MC MINNVILLE—Warren County

✠ **SAINT THOMAS RIVER PARK HOSPITAL (440151)**, 1559 Sparta Street, Zip 37110–1316; tel. 931/815–4000, (Nonreporting) **A**1 10 **S** Ascension Health, Saint Louis, MO
Primary Contact: Dale Humphrey, Chief Executive Officer
COO: Joseph Mazzo, Chief Operating Officer
CFO: Christina Patterson, Chief Financial Officer
CMO: Randal D. Rampp, M.D., Chief Medical Officer
CIO: Jeff Johnson, Director Information Systems
CHR: Deeann Johnson, Director Human Resources
Web address: www.riverparkhospital.com
Control: Other not–for–profit (including NFP Corporation) **Service:** General Medical and Surgical

Staffed Beds: 85

MCKENZIE—Carroll County

✠ **MCKENZIE REGIONAL HOSPITAL (440182)**, 161 Hospital Drive, Zip 38201–1636; tel. 731/352–5344 **A**1 10 **F**3 13 29 34 40 45 53 57 59 64 76 81 85 89 93 107 110 111 114 115 119 131 133 146 **S** Quorum Health, Brentwood, TN
Primary Contact: Michael Morrical, Chief Executive Officer
CFO: Kevin Harvey, Chief Financial Officer
CHR: Tammie Bell, Director Human Resources
CNO: Penny V. Kirby, MSN, Chief Nursing Officer
Web address: www.mckenzieregionalhospital.com
Control: Corporation, Investor–owned, for–profit **Service:** General Medical and Surgical

Staffed Beds: 35 **Admissions:** 943 **Census:** 7 **Outpatient Visits:** 22013 **Births:** 395 **Total Expense ($000):** 17279 **Payroll Expense ($000):** 5769 **Personnel:** 113

MEMPHIS—Shelby County

✠ **BAPTIST MEMORIAL HOSPITAL – MEMPHIS (440048)**, 6019 Walnut Grove Road, Zip 38120–2173; tel. 901/226–5000 **A**1 2 3 5 10 **F**3 6 8 12 17 18 19 20 21 22 24 26 28 29 30 31 34 35 36 37 40 41 45 46 47 48 49 53 54 56 57 58 59 63 64 65 68 70 74 75 77 78 79 80 81 82 84 85 86 87 91 92 93 107 108 109 111 112 114 115 116 117 118 119 120 121 123 124 126 130 132 135 136 137 143 146 148 **S** Baptist Memorial Health Care Corporation, Memphis, TN
Primary Contact: Dana Dye, R.N., Vice President, Administrator and Chief Executive Officer
CFO: Cyndi Pittman, Chief Financial Officer
CMO: Christian C. Patrick, M.D., Chief Medical Officer
CIO: Doug Reiselt, Vice President and Chief Information Officer
CHR: Jerry Barbaree, Director Human Resources
Web address: www.baptistonline.org/memphis/
Control: Other not–for–profit (including NFP Corporation) **Service:** General Medical and Surgical

Staffed Beds: 555 **Admissions:** 25843 **Census:** 442 **Outpatient Visits:** 117374 **Births:** 0 **Total Expense ($000):** 500652 **Payroll Expense ($000):** 150307 **Personnel:** 2597

★ **BAPTIST MEMORIAL HOSPITAL FOR WOMEN (440222)**, 6225 Humphreys Boulevard, Zip 38120–2373; tel. 901/227–9000 **A**3 **F**3 7 8 12 13 15 18 19 20 21 22 23 24 25 26 27 28 29 30 31 32 34 35 36 37 38 41 45 46 47 48 49 52 53 54 55 56 57 58 59 60 61 64 65 66 68 70 71 72 73 74 75 76 77 78 79 81 82 83 84 85 86 87 89 92 93 96 107 108 109 110 111 112 113 114 115 116 117 118 119 120 121 123 124 126 129 130 132 135 136 137 143 144 145 146 147 148 **S** Baptist Memorial Health Care Corporation, Memphis, TN
Primary Contact: Kevin R. Hammeran, Chief Executive Officer and Administrator
CFO: Margaret Williams, Chief Financial Officer
CMO: Judi Carney, M.D., President Medical Staff
CIO: Melissa Nelson, Assistant Administrator
CHR: Karen Ingram, Director Human Resources
CNO: Carol Thetford, Chief Nursing Officer
Web address: www.baptistonline.org/womens/
Control: Other not–for–profit (including NFP Corporation) **Service:** Obstetrics and gynecology

Staffed Beds: 140 **Admissions:** 6655 **Census:** 74 **Outpatient Visits:** 46256 **Births:** 4897 **Total Expense ($000):** 98476 **Payroll Expense ($000):** 34079 **Personnel:** 551

✠ **BAPTIST MEMORIAL RESTORATIVE CARE HOSPITAL (442010)**, 6019 Walnut Grove Road, Zip 38120–2113; tel. 901/226–4200 **A**1 10 **F**1 3 16 17 29 67 68 70 72 73 75 80 88 89 90 98 128 130 148 **S** Baptist Memorial Health Care Corporation, Memphis, TN
Primary Contact: Janice Hill, R.N., Administrator
Web address: www.baptistonline.org/restorative–care/
Control: Other not–for–profit (including NFP Corporation) **Service:** Long–Term Acute Care hospital

Staffed Beds: 30 **Admissions:** 242 **Census:** 22 **Outpatient Visits:** 0 **Births:** 0 **Total Expense ($000):** 16044 **Payroll Expense ($000):** 4754 **Personnel:** 72

CRESTWYN BEHAVIORAL HEALTH, 9485 Crestwyn Hills Cove, Zip 38125–8515; tel. 877/241–1359, (Nonreporting) **S** Acadia Healthcare Company, Inc., Franklin, TN
Web address: www.crestwynbh.com
Control: Corporation, Investor–owned, for–profit **Service:** Psychiatric

Staffed Beds: 60

☐ **DELTA MEDICAL CENTER (440159)**, 3000 Getwell Road, Zip 38118–2299; tel. 901/369–8100 **A**1 10 **F**4 5 8 15 18 29 30 38 40 45 56 57 60 81 82 90 98 103 104 105 107 111 114 119 129 130 143 147 148 **S** Acadia Healthcare Company, Inc., Franklin, TN
Primary Contact: Phil Willcoxon, Chief Executive Officer
CFO: Mike Reynolds, Chief Financial Officer
CMO: David Richardson, M.D., Chief of Staff
CIO: Patrick Duffee, Director Medical Information Systems
CHR: Karyn Erickson, Director Human Resources
CNO: Donna Lanier, R.N., Chief Nursing Officer
Web address: www.deltamedcenter.com
Control: Corporation, Investor–owned, for–profit **Service:** Psychiatric

Staffed Beds: 179 **Admissions:** 4091 **Census:** 117 **Outpatient Visits:** 49150 **Births:** 1 **Total Expense ($000):** 47909 **Payroll Expense ($000):** 23190 **Personnel:** 459

✠ **HEALTHSOUTH REHABILITATION HOSPITAL MEMPHIS–NORTH (443031)**, 4100 Austin Peay Highway, Zip 38128–2502; tel. 901/213–5400 **A**1 10 **F**3 28 29 34 35 57 59 75 77 82 87 90 91 95 96 130 132 135 148 **S** HEALTHSOUTH Corporation, Birmingham, AL
Primary Contact: Adam Yoe, Chief Executive Officer
CFO: Thaddeus Williams, Controller
CMO: Donald Sullivan, M.D., Medical Director
CHR: Adrienne Huntley, Director Human Resources
CNO: Charlotte Boyce, Chief Nursing Officer
Web address: www.healthsouthnorthmemphis.com
Control: Corporation, Investor–owned, for–profit **Service:** Rehabilitation

Staffed Beds: 50 **Admissions:** 1096 **Census:** 38 **Outpatient Visits:** 0 **Births:** 0 **Total Expense ($000):** 12315 **Payroll Expense ($000):** 6084 **Personnel:** 102

✠ **HEALTHSOUTH REHABILITATION HOSPITAL OF MEMPHIS (443029)**, 1282 Union Avenue, Zip 38104–3414; tel. 901/722–2000 **A**1 3 5 10 **F**3 28 29 30 34 60 68 75 90 91 93 96 130 148 **S** HEALTHSOUTH Corporation, Birmingham, AL
Primary Contact: Kevin Spears, Chief Executive Officer
CFO: Eric Gray, Chief Financial Officer
CMO: Jonathan D. Ellen, M.D., Medical Director
CHR: Sandra Milburn, Director Human Resources
CNO: Jennifer Ferrell, Chief Nursing Officer
Web address: www.healthsouthmemphis.com
Control: Partnership, Investor–owned, for–profit **Service:** Rehabilitation

Staffed Beds: 72 **Admissions:** 1353 **Census:** 48 **Outpatient Visits:** 5845 **Births:** 0 **Total Expense ($000):** 16749 **Payroll Expense ($000):** 8532 **Personnel:** 175

Many Facility Codes have changed. Please refer to the AHA Guide Code Chart. © 2016 AHA Guide

TN

LAKESIDE BEHAVIORAL HEALTH SYSTEM (444004), 2911 Brunswick Road, Zip 38133–4199; tel. 901/377–4700 **A**1 3 5 10 **F**4 5 34 38 54 56 98 99 100 101 102 103 104 105 106 130 132 **S** Universal Health Services, Inc., King of Prussia, PA
Primary Contact: Joy Golden, Chief Executive Officer
CFO: Thomas Joyner, Chief Financial Officer
CMO: C. Hal Brunt, M.D., Medical Director
CIO: Jacob Arnett, Chief Information Technology Officer
CHR: Stacie Schroeppel, Director Human Resources
CNO: Lisa Weaver, Nurse Executive
Web address: www.lakesidebhs.com
Control: Corporation, Investor–owned, for–profit **Service:** Psychiatric

Staffed Beds: 319 **Admissions:** 8378 **Census:** 233 **Outpatient Visits:** 21119 **Births:** 0 **Total Expense ($000):** 39488 **Payroll Expense ($000):** 20402 **Personnel:** 485

LE BONHEUR CHILDREN'S HOSPITAL See Methodist Healthcare Memphis Hospitals

MEMPHIS MENTAL HEALTH INSTITUTE (444001), 951 Court Avenue, Zip 38103–2813, Mailing Address: P.O. Box 40966, Zip 38174–0966; tel. 901/577–1800 **A**1 3 5 10 **F**86 87 98 101 130 **P**6
Primary Contact: Lisa Daniel, Chief Executive Officer
CFO: Donny Hornsby, Director Fiscal Services
CHR: Claudette Seymour, Director Personnel
Web address: www.tn.gov/mental/mhs/mhs2.html
Control: State–Government, nonfederal **Service:** Psychiatric

Staffed Beds: 55 **Admissions:** 1547 **Census:** 47 **Outpatient Visits:** 0 **Births:** 0 **Total Expense ($000):** 14364 **Payroll Expense ($000):** 8542 **Personnel:** 176

△ **MEMPHIS VETERANS AFFAIRS MEDICAL CENTER**, 1030 Jefferson Avenue, Zip 38104–2193; tel. 901/523–8990, (Nonreporting) **A**1 3 5 7 8 **S** Department of Veterans Affairs, Washington, DC
Primary Contact: C. Diane Knight, M.D., Director and Chief Executive Officer
CFO: Kristi Depperman, Chief Financial Officer
CMO: Christopher Marino, M.D., Chief of Staff
CIO: Robert Page, III, Chief Information and Technology Officer
CHR: Natalie Brown, Chief Human Resources Management Services
CNO: Karen Gillette, Associate Director Patient Care Services
Web address: www.memphis.va.gov/
Control: Veterans Affairs, Government, federal **Service:** General Medical and Surgical

Staffed Beds: 262

METHODIST HEALTHCARE MEMPHIS HOSPITALS (440049), 1265 Union Avenue, Zip 38104–3415; tel. 901/516–7000, (Includes LE BONHEUR CHILDREN'S HOSPITAL, 50 North Dunlap Street, Zip 38103; tel. 901/287–5437; Meri Armour, Chief Executive Officer; METHODIST HEALTHCARE–NORTH HOSPITAL, 3960 New Covington Pike, Zip 38128; tel. 901/384–5389; Gyasi Chisley, Chief Executive Officer; METHODIST HEALTHCARE–SOUTH HOSPITAL, 1300 Wesley Drive, Zip 38116; tel. 901/516–3081; James L. Robinson, III, PsyD, Chief Executive Officer; METHODIST LE BONHEUR GERMANTOWN HOSPITAL, 7691 Poplar Avenue, Germantown, Zip 38138; tel. 901/516–6000; William A. Kenley, Chief Executive Officer) **A**1 2 3 5 8 10 **F**3 7 8 9 11 12 13 15 17 18 19 20 21 22 23 24 25 26 27 28 29 30 31 32 34 35 37 38 39 40 41 43 44 45 46 47 48 49 50 54 55 56 57 58 59 60 61 64 65 68 70 71 72 73 74 75 76 78 79 80 81 82 84 85 86 87 88 89 92 93 94 96 97 98 99 100 101 102 103 104 105 107 108 110 111 112 113 114 115 117 118 119 120 121 123 126 129 130 131 132 134 135 136 138 139 141 142 143 144 146 147 148 **P**5 6 8 **S** Methodist Le Bonheur Healthcare, Memphis, TN
Primary Contact: Michael O. Ugwueke, President and Chief Executive Officer
COO: James R. Carter, Jr., Chief Operating Officer
CFO: Chris J. McLean, Chief Financial Officer
CMO: Robin Womeodu, M.D., Chief Medical Officer
CIO: Andy Fowler, Senior Vice President Information Systems
CHR: Carol Ross–Spang, Senior Vice President
Web address: www.methodisthealth.org
Control: Other not–for–profit (including NFP Corporation) **Service:** General Medical and Surgical

Staffed Beds: 1397 **Admissions:** 62624 **Census:** 957 **Outpatient Visits:** 621847 **Births:** 5642 **Total Expense ($000):** 1456088 **Payroll Expense ($000):** 462179 **Personnel:** 7347

REGIONAL ONE HEALTH (440152), 877 Jefferson Avenue, Zip 38103–2897; tel. 901/545–7100, (Nonreporting) **A**1 3 5 8 10
Primary Contact: Reginald W. Coopwood, M.D., President and Chief Executive Officer
COO: Rob Sumter, Executive Vice President and Chief Operating Officer
CFO: Rick Wagers, Senior Executive Vice President and Chief Financial Officer
CIO: Rob Sumter, Executive Vice President and Chief Operation Officer
CHR: Sarah Colley, Senior Vice President Human Resources
CNO: Pam Castleman, MSN, Chief Nursing Officer
Web address: www.regionalonehealth.org
Control: Other not–for–profit (including NFP Corporation) **Service:** General Medical and Surgical

Staffed Beds: 325

REGIONAL ONE HEALTH EXTENDED CARE HOSPITAL, 890 Madison Avenue, Turner Tower, Zip 38103–3409; tel. 901/515–3000 **F**1 16 28 148 **P**3
Primary Contact: Mark Kelly, Administrator
CNO: Paula Harrell, Chief Nursing Officer
Web address: www.regionalonehealth.org/extended–care–hospital/
Control: Other not–for–profit (including NFP Corporation) **Service:** Long–Term Acute Care hospital

Staffed Beds: 21 **Admissions:** 196 **Census:** 20 **Outpatient Visits:** 0 **Births:** 0

SAINT FRANCIS HOSPITAL (440183), 5959 Park Avenue, Zip 38119–5198, Mailing Address: P.O. Box 171808, Zip 38187–1808; tel. 901/765–1000 **A**1 2 3 5 10 **F**3 8 11 12 13 15 17 18 20 22 24 26 28 29 30 31 34 35 38 39 40 44 45 46 47 48 49 50 51 54 56 57 58 59 64 68 70 72 74 75 76 77 78 79 81 82 84 85 86 87 90 93 96 97 98 99 100 101 102 103 104 107 108 110 111 114 115 118 119 121 123 124 126 129 130 131 132 143 146 147 148 **S** TENET Healthcare Corporation, Dallas, TX
Primary Contact: Audrey Gregory, R.N., MSN, Chief Executive Officer
CFO: Steven Frantz, Chief Financial Officer
CMO: David Schwartz, M.D., Chief Medical Officer
CIO: Keith Scarbrough, Chief Information Officer
CHR: Keith Stanhill, Chief Human Resources Officer
CNO: Terri L. Stewart, R.N., Chief Nursing Officer
Web address: www.saintfrancishosp.com
Control: Corporation, Investor–owned, for–profit **Service:** General Medical and Surgical

Staffed Beds: 511 **Admissions:** 15819 **Census:** 231 **Outpatient Visits:** 123576 **Births:** 1342 **Total Expense ($000):** 264301 **Payroll Expense ($000):** 73863 **Personnel:** 1388

SELECT SPECIALTY HOSPITAL–MEMPHIS (442014), 5959 Park Avenue, 12th Floor, Zip 38119–5200; tel. 901/765–1245, (Nonreporting) **A**1 10 **S** Select Medical Corporation, Mechanicsburg, PA
Primary Contact: Marcia Taylor, Chief Executive Officer
Web address: www.selectspecialtyhospitals.com/company/locations/memphis.aspx
Control: Corporation, Investor–owned, for–profit **Service:** Long–Term Acute Care hospital

Staffed Beds: 39

ST. JUDE CHILDREN'S RESEARCH HOSPITAL (443302), 262 Danny Thomas Place, Zip 38105–3678; tel. 901/595–3300, (Nonreporting) **A**1 3 5 10
Primary Contact: James R. Downing, M.D., Chief Executive Officer
COO: Mary Anna Quinn, Executive Vice President, Chief Administrative Officer
CFO: Patricia Keel, Senior Vice President and Chief Financial Officer
CMO: Patricia Flynn, Interim Chief Medical Officer
CIO: Darrin Keith Perry, Chief Information Officer and Senior Vice President
CHR: Dana Bottenfield, Vice President Human Resources
CNO: Pam Dotson, Senior Vice President and Chief Nursing Officer
Web address: www.stjude.org
Control: Other not–for–profit (including NFP Corporation) **Service:** Children's other specialty

Staffed Beds: 56

VETERANS AFFAIRS MEDICAL CENTER See Memphis Veterans Affairs Medical Center

TN

MILAN—Gibson County

☒ **MILAN GENERAL HOSPITAL (440060)**, 4039 Highland Street,
Zip 38358–3483; tel. 731/686–1591 **A**1 10 **F**3 15 29 30 35 40 44 45 57 59
64 68 70 81 85 87 107 110 114 119 130 132 133 146 **S** West Tennessee
Healthcare, Jackson, TN
Primary Contact: Sherry Scruggs, Administrator
CMO: Joe Appleton, M.D., Chief of Surgery
CNO: Carolyn Drake, Director of Nursing
Web address: www.wth.org
Control: Hospital district or authority, Government, nonfederal **Service:** General
Medical and Surgical

Staffed Beds: 28 Admissions: 561 Census: 7 Outpatient Visits: 13776
Births: 1 **Total Expense ($000):** 9079 **Payroll Expense ($000):** 3680
Personnel: 80

MORRISTOWN—Hamblen County

☒ **LAKEWAY REGIONAL HOSPITAL (440067)**, 726 McFarland Street,
Zip 37814–3990; tel. 423/586–2302, (Nonreporting) **A**1 10 19 **S** Community
Health Systems, Inc., Franklin, TN
Primary Contact: Steve Simpson, Chief Executive Officer
CMO: Paul Cardali, M.D., Chief of Staff
CHR: Deirdre Helton, Director Human Resources
Web address: www.tennova.com
Control: Corporation, Investor–owned, for–profit **Service:** General Medical and
Surgical

Staffed Beds: 135

☒ **MORRISTOWN–HAMBLEN HEALTHCARE SYSTEM (440030)**, 908 West
Fourth North Street, Zip 37814–3894, Mailing Address: P.O. Box 1178,
Zip 37816–1178; tel. 423/492–9000 **A**1 5 10 **F**3 11 13 15 18 20 22 26 28
29 30 31 34 35 40 45 46 47 49 50 51 56 57 59 60 64 68 74 76 78 79 80
81 85 93 98 102 103 107 108 110 111 114 115 117 118 119 121 123 129
141 142 146 147 148 **S** Covenant Health, Knoxville, TN
Primary Contact: Gordon Lintz, Chief Administrative Officer
CFO: Amy Herndon, Chief Finance Officer
CIO: Mike Ward, Chief Information Officer
CNO: Wilma Hart–Flynn, MSN, Chief Nursing Officer
Web address: www.morristownhamblen.com
Control: Other not–for–profit (including NFP Corporation) **Service:** General
Medical and Surgical

Staffed Beds: 131 Admissions: 6094 Census: 65 Outpatient Visits: 101599
Births: 1019 **Total Expense ($000):** 75851 **Payroll Expense ($000):** 28013
Personnel: 519

MOUNTAIN CITY—Johnson County

JOHNSON COUNTY COMMUNITY HOSPITAL (441304), 1901 South Shady
Street, Zip 37683–2271; tel. 423/727–1100 **A**5 10 18 **F**3 15 18 28 30 34 35
40 44 50 57 62 64 68 87 93 97 104 107 108 110 111 114 119 127
S Mountain States Health Alliance, Johnson City, TN
Primary Contact: Chastity Trivette, Chief Executive Officer
CNO: Helen Pardue, Interim Chief Nursing Officer
Web address: www.msha.com
Control: Other not–for–profit (including NFP Corporation) **Service:** General
Medical and Surgical

Staffed Beds: 2 Admissions: 22 Census: 1 Outpatient Visits: 41334 Births:
0 **Total Expense ($000):** 8059 **Payroll Expense ($000):** 3862 **Personnel:**
62

MOUNTAIN HOME— County

☒ **JAMES H. QUILLEN VETERANS AFFAIRS MEDICAL CENTER**, Corner of
Lamont & Veterans Way, Zip 37684, Mailing Address: P.O. Box 4000,
Zip 37684–4000; tel. 423/926–1171, (Nonreporting) **A**1 2 3 5 **S** Department of
Veterans Affairs, Washington, DC
Primary Contact: Daniel B. Snyder, FACHE, Acting Director
CFO: Sandra Nash, Chief Fiscal Service
CMO: David Hecht, M.D., Chief of Staff
CIO: Karen Perry, Chief Information Resource Management Services
CHR: John Henderson, Chief Human Resources Management
CNO: Linda M. McConnell, R.N., Associate Medical Center Director Patient Care
Services
Web address: www.mountainhome.va.gov/
Control: Veterans Affairs, Government, federal **Service:** General Medical and
Surgical

Staffed Beds: 98

MURFREESBORO—Rutherford County

ALVIN C. YORK CAMPUS See Tennessee Valley Healthcare System, Nashville

☒ **SAINT THOMAS RUTHERFORD HOSPITAL (440053)**, 1700 Medical Center
Parkway, Zip 37129–2245; tel. 615/396–4100, (Nonreporting) **A**1 2 3 5 10
S Ascension Health, Saint Louis, MO
Primary Contact: Gordon B. Ferguson, President and Chief Executive Officer
COO: Elizabeth Lemons, Chief Operating Officer
CFO: Larry Spratlin, Chief Financial Officer
CMO: Scott Corlew, M.D., Chief Medical Officer
CHR: Carol Bragdon, Director Human Resources
CNO: Stacey Beaven, R.N., Chief Nursing Officer
Web address: www.mtmc.org
Control: Other not–for–profit (including NFP Corporation) **Service:** General
Medical and Surgical

Staffed Beds: 286

☐ **TRUSTPOINT HOSPITAL (440231)**, 1009 North Thompson Lane,
Zip 37129–4351; tel. 615/867–1111 **A**1 10 **F**29 34 38 56 57 64 77 90 91 93
98 100 101 102 103 104 105 130 132 **P**6 **S** Acadia Healthcare Company, Inc.,
Franklin, TN
Primary Contact: Jeffrey Woods, Chief Executive Officer
Web address: www.trustpointhospital.com
Control: Corporation, Investor–owned, for–profit **Service:** General Medical and
Surgical

Staffed Beds: 101 Admissions: 1800 Census: 35 Outpatient Visits: 3647
Births: 0

NASHVILLE—Davidson County

CENTENNIAL MEDICAL CENTER See TriStar Centennial Medical Center

☒ **CURAHEALTH NASHVILLE (442006)**, 1412 County Hospital Road,
Zip 37218–3007; tel. 615/687–2600, (Nonreporting) **A**1 10
Primary Contact: William P. Macri, Chief Executive Officer
CFO: Philip L. Jones, Chief Financial Officer
CMO: Clyde Heflin, M.D., Chief Medical Officer
CNO: Tom Rone, Chief Clinical Officer
Control: Corporation, Investor–owned, for–profit **Service:** Long–Term Acute Care
hospital

Staffed Beds: 58

☐ **MIDDLE TENNESSEE MENTAL HEALTH INSTITUTE (444014)**, 221 Stewarts
Ferry Pike, Zip 37214–3325; tel. 615/902–7535 **A**1 3 5 10 **F**3 29 30 75 98
101 102 103 106 130
Primary Contact: Rob Cotterman, Chief Executive Officer
CFO: Mark Stanley, Director Fiscal Services
CMO: Mohammad S. Jahan, M.D., Clinical Director
CHR: Margie Dunn, Director Human Resources
Web address: www.tn.gov/mental/mhs/mhs2.html
Control: State–Government, nonfederal **Service:** Psychiatric

Staffed Beds: 207 Admissions: 3702 Census: 181 Outpatient Visits: 0
Births: 0 **Total Expense ($000):** 45648 **Payroll Expense ($000):** 24845
Personnel: 491

MONROE CARELL JR. CHILDREN'S HOSPITAL AT VANDERBILT See
Vanderbilt University Medical Center

☐ **NASHVILLE GENERAL HOSPITAL (440111)**, 1818 Albion Street,
Zip 37208–2918; tel. 615/341–4000, (Nonreporting) **A**1 2 3 5 10
Primary Contact: Joseph Webb, Chief Executive Officer
CFO: Robert Lonis, Interim Chief Financial Officer
CMO: Chike Nzerue, M.D., Chief Medical Officer
CIO: Chris Whorley, Chief Information Officer
CHR: Diana Wohlfardt, Director Human Resources
CNO: Leonora Collins, Chief Nursing Officer
Web address: www.nashvilleha.org
Control: City–County, Government, nonfederal **Service:** General Medical and
Surgical

Staffed Beds: 116

☒ **SAINT THOMAS HOSPITAL FOR SPINAL SURGERY (440218)**, 2011 Murphy
Avenue, Suite 400, Zip 37203–2065; tel. 615/341–7500, (Nonreporting) **A**1 10
S Ascension Health, Saint Louis, MO
Primary Contact: Kathy Watson, R.N., Administrator and Chief Nursing Officer
CFO: Angie Crow, Director Finance
CMO: Carl Hampf, M.D., Chief Medical Officer
Web address: www.hospitalforspinalsurgery.com
Control: Partnership, Investor–owned, for–profit **Service:** General Medical and
Surgical

Staffed Beds: 23

Many Facility Codes have changed. Please refer to the AHA Guide Code Chart. © 2016 AHA Guide

☒ **SAINT THOMAS MIDTOWN HOSPITAL (440133)**, 2000 Church Street, Zip 37236–0002; tel. 615/284–5555, (Nonreporting) **A**1 2 3 5 10 **S** Ascension Health, Saint Louis, MO
Primary Contact: Don King, Chief Executive Officer
COO: Renee A. Kessler, Chief Operating Officer
CFO: Carrie Teaford, Vice President Finance
CMO: William Thompson, M.D., Chief Medical Officer
CIO: Jim Drew, Chief Information Officer
CHR: Martha Underwood, Chief Human Resources Officer
Web address: www.sths.com
Control: Other not–for–profit (including NFP Corporation) **Service:** General Medical and Surgical

Staffed Beds: 425

☒ **SAINT THOMAS WEST HOSPITAL (440082)**, 4220 Harding Road, Zip 37205–2095, Mailing Address: P.O. Box 380, Zip 37202–0380; tel. 615/222–2111, (Nonreporting) **A**1 2 3 5 10 **S** Ascension Health, Saint Louis, MO
Primary Contact: Don King, Chief Executive Officer
CFO: Lisa Davis, Vice President Finance
CMO: Dale Batchelor, M.D., Chief Medical Officer
CHR: Bud Wood, Chief Human Resources Officer
CNO: Jennifer Elliott, Chief Nursing Officer
Web address: www.stthomas.org
Control: Other not–for–profit (including NFP Corporation) **Service:** General Medical and Surgical

Staffed Beds: 395

☒ **SELECT SPECIALTY HOSPITAL–NASHVILLE (442011)**, 2000 Hayes Street, Zip 37203–2318; tel. 615/284–4599, (Nonreporting) **A**1 10 **S** Select Medical Corporation, Mechanicsburg, PA
Primary Contact: Jennifer Causey, Chief Executive Officer
CNO: Karen Cagle, Chief Nursing Officer
Web address: www.selectspecialtyhospitals.com/company/locations/nashville.aspx
Control: Corporation, Investor–owned, for–profit **Service:** Long–Term Acute Care hospital

Staffed Beds: 47

☒ **TENNESSEE VALLEY HEALTHCARE SYSTEM**, 1310 24th Avenue South, Zip 37212–2637; tel. 615/327–4751, (Includes ALVIN C. YORK CAMPUS, 3400 Lebanon Pike, Murfreesboro, Zip 37129–1236; tel. 615/867–6000; NASHVILLE CAMPUS, 1310 24th Avenue South, tel. 615/327–4751), (Nonreporting) **A**1 2 3 5 8 **S** Department of Veterans Affairs, Washington, DC
Primary Contact: Suzanne L. Jene, Interim Executive Director
COO: Suzanne L. Jene, Chief Operating Officer
CFO: Lynn Menthcoast, Chief Fiscal Service
CMO: Roger Jones, M.D., Interim Chief of Staff
CIO: Paul Mardy, Chief Information Technology Officer
CHR: Shirley F. Pettite, Chief Human Resources Officer
CNO: Janice M. Cobb, R.N., Chief Nursing Officer
Web address: www.tennesseevalley.va.gov
Control: Veterans Affairs, Government, federal **Service:** General Medical and Surgical

Staffed Beds: 546

☒ **TRISTAR CENTENNIAL MEDICAL CENTER (440161)**, 2300 Patterson Street, Zip 37203–1528; tel. 615/342–1000, (Includes TRISTAR CENTENNIAL WOMEN'S & CHILDREN'S, 2221 Murphy Avenue, Zip 37203; tel. 615/342–1000), (Nonreporting) **A**1 2 3 5 10 **S** HCA, Nashville, TN
Primary Contact: Heather J. Rohan, Chief Executive Officer
COO: Micki J. Slingerland, Chief Operating Officer
CFO: David A. Summers, Chief Financial Officer
CHR: Jennifer Burden, Human Resources Director
Web address: www.tristarcentennial.com
Control: Corporation, Investor–owned, for–profit **Service:** General Medical and Surgical

Staffed Beds: 650

☒ △ **TRISTAR SKYLINE MEDICAL CENTER (440006)**, 3441 Dickerson Pike, Zip 37207–2539; tel. 615/769–2000, (Nonreporting) **A**1 2 3 5 7 10 **S** HCA, Nashville, TN
Primary Contact: Steve Otto, Chief Executive Officer
CFO: Michael Morrison, Chief Financial Officer
CMO: Sunil Kaza, M.D., President Medical Staff
CIO: Troy Sypien, Director Information Technology and Systems
CHR: Robert A. Hooper, Director Human Resources
CNO: Laurie Turner, Chief Nursing Officer
Web address: www.skylinemedicalcenter.com
Control: Corporation, Investor–owned, for–profit **Service:** General Medical and Surgical

Staffed Beds: 295

☒ **TRISTAR SOUTHERN HILLS MEDICAL CENTER (440197)**, 391 Wallace Road, Zip 37211–4859; tel. 615/781–4000, (Nonreporting) **A**1 2 10 **S** HCA, Nashville, TN
Primary Contact: Thomas H. Ozburn, Chief Executive Officer
COO: Richard Tumlin, Chief Operating Officer
CFO: John Porada, Chief Financial Officer
CIO: Ronnie Gannon, Director Information Services
CHR: Gary Briggs, Vice President Human Resources
CNO: Chris Staigl, Chief Nursing Officer
Web address: www.tristarsouthernhills.com
Control: Corporation, Investor–owned, for–profit **Service:** General Medical and Surgical

Staffed Beds: 101

VANDERBILT PSYCHIATRIC HOSPITAL See Vanderbilt University Medical Center

☒ **VANDERBILT STALLWORTH REHABILITATION HOSPITAL (443028)**, 2201 Childrens Way, Zip 37212–3165; tel. 615/320–7600, (Nonreporting) **A**1 3 5 10 **S** HEALTHSOUTH Corporation, Birmingham, AL
Primary Contact: Armando Colombo, Chief Executive Officer
CFO: Christine Campbell, Controller
CMO: Jeffery Johns, M.D., Medical Director
CHR: Ruth Beasley, Director Human Resources
CNO: Karen Lasher, Chief Nursing Officer
Web address: www.vanderbiltstallworthrehab.com
Control: Corporation, Investor–owned, for–profit **Service:** Rehabilitation

Staffed Beds: 80

☒ **VANDERBILT UNIVERSITY MEDICAL CENTER (440039)**, 1211 22nd Avenue North, Zip 37232–2102; tel. 615/322–5000, (Includes MONROE CARELL JR. CHILDREN'S HOSPITAL AT VANDERBILT, 2200 Children's Way, Zip 37232; tel. 615/936–1000; Luke Gregory, Chief Executive Officer; VANDERBILT PSYCHIATRIC HOSPITAL, 1601 23rd Avenue South, Zip 37212–3198; tel. 615/320–7770) **A**1 2 3 5 8 10 **F**2 3 4 5 6 7 8 9 11 12 13 15 16 17 18 19 20 21 22 23 24 25 26 27 28 29 30 31 32 34 35 36 37 38 39 40 41 43 44 45 46 47 48 49 50 51 52 53 54 55 56 57 58 59 60 61 62 64 65 66 68 70 72 74 75 76 77 78 79 80 81 82 83 84 85 86 87 88 89 91 92 93 94 96 97 98 99 100 101 102 103 104 105 107 108 109 110 111 114 115 116 117 118 119 120 121 123 124 126 129 130 131 132 134 135 136 137 138 139 140 141 142 143 144 146 147 148 **P**2 6 **S** Vanderbilt Health, Nashville, TN
Primary Contact: Mitch Edgeworth, Chief Executive Officer
CFO: Cecelia B. Moore, CPA, Associate Vice Chancellor Finance
CMO: Paul Sternberg, M.D., Professor and Chairman
CIO: William Stead, Associate Vice Chancellor Health Affairs, Director Informatics Center and Chief Strategy and Information Officer
CHR: Traci Nordberg, Chief Human Resources Officer
CNO: Pam Jones, MSN, Associate Hospital Director and Chief Nursing Officer
Web address: www.mc.vanderbilt.edu
Control: Other not–for–profit (including NFP Corporation) **Service:** General Medical and Surgical

Staffed Beds: 1000 Admissions: 59026 Census: 861 Outpatient Visits: 2071530 Births: 4598 Total Expense ($000): 2009183 Payroll Expense ($000): 688624 Personnel: 11377

VETERANS AFFAIRS TENNESSEE VALLEY HEALTHCARE SYSTEM See Tennessee Valley Healthcare System

NEWPORT—Cocke County

BAPTIST HOSPITAL OF COCKE COUNTY See Tennova Newport Medical Center

☒ **TENNOVA NEWPORT MEDICAL CENTER (440153)**, 435 Second Street, Zip 37821–3799; tel. 423/625–2200, (Nonreporting) **A**1 10 **S** Community Health Systems, Inc., Franklin, TN
Primary Contact: Trevor Castaneda, Chief Executive Officer
CFO: Jon Richards, Chief Financial Officer
CMO: Larry Mathers, M.D., Chief of Staff
CNO: Tonia Hale, Chief Nursing Officer
Web address: www.tennova.com
Control: Corporation, Investor–owned, for–profit **Service:** General Medical and Surgical

Staffed Beds: 47

TN

Hospitals, U.S. / TENNESSEE

OAK RIDGE—Anderson County

METHODIST MEDICAL CENTER OF OAK RIDGE (440034), 990 Oak Ridge Turnpike, Zip 37830–6976, Mailing Address: P.O. Box 2529, Zip 37831–2529; tel. 865/835–1000 **A**1 2 3 10 **F**3 11 13 15 17 18 20 22 24 26 28 29 30 31 34 35 37 40 45 46 47 48 49 50 51 54 57 58 59 60 64 68 70 74 75 76 77 78 79 80 81 84 85 86 87 92 102 107 108 110 111 114 115 118 119 120 121 123 124 126 129 130 132 135 141 142 146 148 **S** Covenant Health, Knoxville, TN
Primary Contact: Jeremy Biggs, Chief Executive Officer
COO: Connie Martin, Vice President and Chief Support Officer
CFO: Rick Carringer, Vice President and Chief Financial Officer
CMO: Mark Browne, M.D., Covenant Health, Senior Vice President and Chief Medical Officer
CIO: Mike Ward, Covenant Health, Senior Vice President and Chief Information Officer
CHR: Rick Akens, Director Human Resources and Labor Relations
CNO: Sue Harris, Vice President and Chief Nursing Officer
Web address: www.mmcoakridge.com
Control: Other not–for–profit (including NFP Corporation) **Service:** General Medical and Surgical

Staffed Beds: 210 **Admissions:** 10881 **Census:** 132 **Outpatient Visits:** 171070 **Births:** 544 **Total Expense ($000):** 155654 **Payroll Expense ($000):** 54143 **Personnel:** 884

RIDGEVIEW PSYCHIATRIC HOSPITAL AND CENTER (444003), 240 West Tyrone Road, Zip 37830–6571; tel. 865/482–1076, (Nonreporting) **A**10
Primary Contact: Brian Buuck, Chief Executive Officer
CFO: Mary Claire Duff, CPA, Chief Financial Officer
CMO: Renu Bhateja, M.D., President Medical Staff
CHR: Julie M. Wright, Director Human Resources
Web address: www.ridgeviewresources.com
Control: Other not–for–profit (including NFP Corporation) **Service:** Psychiatric

Staffed Beds: 20

PARIS—Henry County

HENRY COUNTY MEDICAL CENTER (440132), 301 Tyson Avenue, Zip 38242–4544, Mailing Address: P.O. Box 1030, Zip 38242–1030; tel. 731/642–1220, (Total facility includes 150 beds in nursing home–type unit) **A**1 10 **F**3 7 8 11 13 15 18 26 28 29 30 31 32 34 35 37 40 44 50 51 53 54 57 59 62 63 64 65 67 68 70 71 76 77 78 79 81 82 85 86 87 89 93 98 102 103 107 108 110 111 114 118 119 121 126 128 129 130 131 132 133 135 146 148 **P**6 7
Primary Contact: Thomas H. Gee, Administrator
CFO: Lisa Casteel, Assistant Administrator and Chief Financial Officer
CIO: Pam Ridley, Director Information Systems
CHR: Edwin L. Ledden, Assistant Administrator and Director Human Resources
CNO: Cynthia Whitaker, Chief Nursing Officer
Web address: www.hcmc–tn.org
Control: Hospital district or authority, Government, nonfederal **Service:** General Medical and Surgical

Staffed Beds: 251 **Admissions:** 3857 **Census:** 131 **Outpatient Visits:** 80304 **Births:** 305 **Total Expense ($000):** 75910 **Payroll Expense ($000):** 32340 **Personnel:** 687

PARSONS—Decatur County

DECATUR COUNTY GENERAL HOSPITAL (440070), 969 Tennessee Avenue South, Zip 38363–3700, Mailing Address: P.O. Box 250, Zip 38363–0250; tel. 731/847–3031, (Nonreporting) **A**1 10
Primary Contact: Scott Barber, Chief Executive Officer
CFO: Donna Hayes, Controller
CMO: Tom Hamilton, M.D., Chief of Staff
CHR: Shelley Bartholomew, Director Human Resources
Web address: www.dcgh.org
Control: County–Government, nonfederal **Service:** General Medical and Surgical

Staffed Beds: 40

PIKEVILLE—Bledsoe County

ERLANGER BLEDSOE HOSPITAL (441306), 71 Wheeler Avenue, Zip 37367, Mailing Address: P.O. Box 699, Zip 37367–0699; tel. 423/447–2112 **A**10 18 **F**3 11 15 18 28 29 30 34 35 38 40 41 42 44 50 54 56 57 59 61 63 64 65 66 68 75 82 84 86 87 92 93 96 97 102 103 107 110 114 119 127 130 131 133 135 144 146 147 148 **P**6 **S** Erlanger Health System, Chattanooga, TN
Primary Contact: Stephanie Boynton, Administrator
CMO: Arturo L. Quito, M.D., Chief of Staff
CIO: Debbie Rains, Coordinator Health Information Management
CHR: Patsy Brown, Site Coordinator Human Resources
Web address: www.erlanger.org
Control: Hospital district or authority, Government, nonfederal **Service:** General Medical and Surgical

Staffed Beds: 25 **Admissions:** 293 **Census:** 5 **Outpatient Visits:** 24277 **Births:** 0 **Total Expense ($000):** 11875 **Payroll Expense ($000):** 4842 **Personnel:** 96

POWELL—Knox County

MERCY MEDICAL CENTER NORTH See Tennova North Knoxville Medical Center

SELECT SPECIALTY HOSPITAL–NORTH KNOXVILLE (442015), 7557B Dannaher Drive, Suite 145, Zip 37849–3568; tel. 865/512–2450, (Nonreporting) **A**1 10 **S** Select Medical Corporation, Mechanicsburg, PA
Primary Contact: Steve Plumlee, Chief Executive Officer
CFO: David Elledge, Controller
CMO: Jeff Summers, M.D., Medical Director
CIO: Steve Plumlee, Chief Executive Officer
CHR: Mallory Wilson, Administrative Assistant and Human Resources Coordinator
CNO: Nancy Johnson, Chief Nursing Officer
Web address: www.northknoxville.selectspecialtyhospitals.com/
Control: Corporation, Investor–owned, for–profit **Service:** Long–Term Acute Care hospital

Staffed Beds: 33

PULASKI—Giles County

SOUTHERN TENNESSEE REGIONAL HEALTH SYSTEM–PULASKI (440020), 1265 East College Street, Zip 38478–4541; tel. 931/363–7531 **A**1 10 **F**3 13 15 17 28 29 30 34 40 41 45 50 56 57 59 64 68 70 74 75 76 77 79 81 85 86 89 91 93 98 103 107 110 111 114 119 129 130 133 146 148 **S** LifePoint Health, Brentwood, TN
Primary Contact: James H. Edmondson, Chief Executive Officer
CFO: Donald Gavin, Chief Financial Officer
CMO: J. Michael Windland, M.D., Chief of Staff
CIO: Mitzi Foster, Director Information Services
CHR: Jane Petty, Director Human Resources
CNO: Sherry Sands, R.N., Chief Nursing Officer
Web address: www.hillsidehospital.com
Control: Corporation, Investor–owned, for–profit **Service:** General Medical and Surgical

Staffed Beds: 42 **Admissions:** 1601 **Census:** 19 **Outpatient Visits:** 17605 **Births:** 101 **Total Expense ($000):** 25960 **Payroll Expense ($000):** 10284 **Personnel:** 181

RIPLEY—Lauderdale County

LAUDERDALE COMMUNITY HOSPITAL (441314), 326 Asbury Avenue, Zip 38063–5577; tel. 731/221–2200, (Nonreporting) **A**10 18 21 **S** Rural Community Hospitals of America, Kansas City, MO
Primary Contact: Michael G. Layfield, Interim Chief Executive Officer
CFO: T J Sheehan, Chief Financial Officer
CMO: Syed A. Zaidi, M.D., Chief of Staff
CIO: Jim Vaden, Director Information Systems
CHR: Joan W. Simpson, Manager Human Resources
CNO: Michelle Simpson, Chief Nursing Officer and Quality Leader
Web address: www.lauderdalehospital.com/
Control: Corporation, Investor–owned, for–profit **Service:** General Medical and Surgical

Staffed Beds: 25

ROGERSVILLE—Hawkins County

WELLMONT HAWKINS COUNTY MEMORIAL HOSPITAL (440032), 851 Locust Street, Zip 37857–2407, Mailing Address: P.O. Box 130, Zip 37857–0130; tel. 423/921–7000 **A**1 5 10 **F**3 11 15 29 30 31 34 40 45 50 57 59 64 75 77 78 80 81 82 85 87 93 97 107 108 110 118 119 129 130 133 135 146 **S** Wellmont Health System, Kingsport, TN
Primary Contact: Rebecca Beck, President
CFO: Dale Poe, Vice President and Chief Financial Officer
CHR: Robin Poteete, Manager Human Resources
Web address: www.wellmont.org
Control: Other not–for–profit (including NFP Corporation) **Service:** General Medical and Surgical

Staffed Beds: 50 **Admissions:** 1016 **Census:** 9 **Outpatient Visits:** 34752 **Births:** 0 **Total Expense ($000):** 52589 **Payroll Expense ($000):** 6392 **Personnel:** 162

SAVANNAH—Hardin County

HARDIN MEDICAL CENTER (440109), 935 Wayne Road, Zip 38372–1904; tel. 731/926–8000, (Total facility includes 73 beds in nursing home–type unit) **A**10 21 **F**2 3 7 11 13 15 18 19 28 29 31 34 40 45 57 59 65 69 75 76 77 78 79 80 81 89 93 107 110 111 115 119 124 128 129 130 133 144 148 **P**6
Primary Contact: Nicholas P. Lewis, Chief Executive Officer
CFO: Leigh Ann Hughes, Chief Financial Officer
CMO: Gilbert M. Thayer, M.D., Chief Medical Staff
CIO: Jacob Bomar, Director Information Technology
CNO: Jesse Wint, Director of Nursing
Web address: www.hardinmedicalcenter.org
Control: County–Government, nonfederal **Service:** General Medical and Surgical

Staffed Beds: 122 **Admissions:** 1791 **Census:** 85 **Outpatient Visits:** 60850 **Births:** 328 **Total Expense ($000):** 37464 **Payroll Expense ($000):** 17049 **Personnel:** 405

Many Facility Codes have changed. Please refer to the AHA Guide Code Chart. © 2016 AHA Guide

SEVIERVILLE—Sevier County

✠ **LECONTE MEDICAL CENTER (440081)**, 742 Middle Creek Road,
Zip 37862–5019, Mailing Address: P.O. Box 8005, Zip 37864–8005;
tel. 865/446–7000, (Total facility includes 54 beds in nursing home–type unit) **A**1
5 10 **F**3 11 13 15 18 20 28 29 30 31 34 35 40 45 50 51 53 57 59 61 64 67
68 70 75 76 77 78 79 81 85 87 93 107 110 111 114 115 116 119 120 121
123 124 128 129 130 131 135 146 147 **S** Covenant Health, Knoxville, TN
Primary Contact: Jennifer Hanson, MS, R.N., President and Chief Administrative
Officer
COO: Rick Carringer, Vice President Finance and Support Services
CFO: Rick Carringer, Vice President Finance and Support Services
CMO: Stephen Dill, M.D., Chief of Staff
CIO: Amanda Paletz, Director Marketing and Public Relations
CHR: Derek Winkle, Director Human Resources
Web address: www.lecontemedicalcenter.com
Control: Other not–for–profit (including NFP Corporation) **Service:** General
Medical and Surgical

Staffed Beds: 129 **Admissions:** 4927 **Census:** 87 **Outpatient Visits:** 131481
Births: 995 **Total Expense ($000):** 71466 **Payroll Expense ($000):** 25054
Personnel: 459

SEWANEE—Franklin County

SOUTHERN TENNESSEE REGIONAL HEALTH SYSTEM–SEWANEE See
Southern Tennessee Regional Health System–Winchester, Winchester

SHELBYVILLE—Bedford County

✠ **TENNOVA HEALTHCARE–SHELBYVILLE (440137)**, 2835 Highway 231 North,
Zip 37160–7327; tel. 931/685–5433 **A**1 10 **F**3 12 13 15 17 18 29 34 40 45
47 57 59 60 64 70 76 79 81 85 87 89 93 96 102 107 108 110 111 115 119
124 130 131 132 145 146 148 **S** Community Health Systems, Inc., Franklin, TN
Primary Contact: Bill Rich, Chief Executive Officer
CFO: Mitchell Frank, Chief Financial Officer
CIO: Jonathon Willis, Director Information Services
CHR: Brian Woods, Director Human Resources
CNO: Vickie Vaughn, Chief Nursing Officer
Web address: www.heritagemedicalcenter.com
Control: Corporation, Investor–owned, for–profit **Service:** General Medical and
Surgical

Staffed Beds: 52 **Admissions:** 1594 **Census:** 16 **Outpatient Visits:** 42072
Births: 1 **Total Expense ($000):** 25690 **Payroll Expense ($000):** 10224
Personnel: 198

SMITHVILLE—Dekalb County

✠ **SAINT THOMAS DEKALB HOSPITAL (440148)**, 520 West Main Street,
Zip 37166–1138, Mailing Address: P.O. Box 640, Zip 37166–0640;
tel. 615/215–5000, (Nonreporting) **A**1 10 **S** Ascension Health, Saint Louis, MO
Primary Contact: Craig Norris, Interim Chief Executive Officer
CFO: Alan Sharp, Chief Financial Officer
CMO: Kimberly Collins, M.D., Chief of Staff
CNO: Nancy A. Trapp, MSN, Director of Nursing
Web address: www.dekalbcommunityhospital.com
Control: Other not–for–profit (including NFP Corporation) **Service:** General
Medical and Surgical

Staffed Beds: 71

SMYRNA—Rutherford County

✠ **TRISTAR STONECREST MEDICAL CENTER (440227)**, 200 StoneCrest
Boulevard, Zip 37167–6810; tel. 615/768–2000, (Nonreporting) **A**1 2 10 **S** HCA,
Nashville, TN
Primary Contact: Louis Caputo, Chief Executive Officer
COO: Andrew Tyrer, Chief Operating Officer
CFO: Joseph E. Bowman, Chief Financial Officer
CMO: William Mayfield, M.D., Chief of Staff
CHR: Cynthia Adams, Vice President Human Resources
CNO: Ruth Willard, Chief Nursing Officer
Web address: www.stonecrestmedical.com
Control: Corporation, Investor–owned, for–profit **Service:** General Medical and
Surgical

Staffed Beds: 101

SNEEDVILLE—Hancock County

★ **WELLMONT HANCOCK COUNTY HOSPITAL (441313)**, 1519 Main Street,
Zip 37869–3657; tel. 423/733–5000 **A**10 18 **F**3 29 30 34 40 50 57 59 85 87
107 108 118 119 133 135 **S** Wellmont Health System, Kingsport, TN
Primary Contact: Rebecca Beck, President
COO: Eric Deaton, Executive Vice President, Chief Operating Officer and
Corporate Operating
CFO: Regina Day, Director of Finance
CIO: Martha O'Regan Chill, Interim Chief Information Officer
CHR: Robin Poteete, Manager Human Resources
CNO: Phyllis Dossett, Director of Clinical Services
Web address: www.wellmont.org/Hospitals/Hancock–County–Hospital.aspx
Control: Other not–for–profit (including NFP Corporation) **Service:** General
Medical and Surgical

Staffed Beds: 10 **Admissions:** 224 **Census:** 2 **Outpatient Visits:** 6098
Births: 0 **Total Expense ($000):** 5706 **Payroll Expense ($000):** 1719
Personnel: 36

SPARTA—White County

✠ **SAINT THOMAS HIGHLANDS HOSPITAL (440192)**, 401 Sewell Road,
Zip 38583–1299; tel. 931/738–9211, (Nonreporting) **A**1 10 **S** Ascension Health,
Saint Louis, MO
Primary Contact: Craig Norris, Interim Chief Executive Officer
CFO: Rodney VanDonkelaar, Chief Financial Officer
CMO: Robert Knowles, M.D., Chief of Staff
CIO: Glenn Wade, Director Information Systems
CHR: Kent Frisbee, Director Human Resources
CNO: Gearline Copeland, R.N., Chief Nursing Officer
Web address: www.whitecountyhospital.com
Control: Other not–for–profit (including NFP Corporation) **Service:** General
Medical and Surgical

Staffed Beds: 60

SPRINGFIELD—Robertson County

✠ **NORTHCREST MEDICAL CENTER (440065)**, 100 North Crest Drive,
Zip 37172–3961; tel. 615/384–2411, (Nonreporting) **A**1 10
Primary Contact: Randy Davis, Chief Executive Officer
CFO: Kim Pridgen, Chief Financial Officer
CHR: Kimberly Walker, Director of Human Resources
CNO: Angie Beard, Chief Nursing Officer
Web address: www.northcrest.com
Control: Other not–for–profit (including NFP Corporation) **Service:** General
Medical and Surgical

Staffed Beds: 80

SWEETWATER—Monroe County

✠ **SWEETWATER HOSPITAL (440084)**, 304 Wright Street, Zip 37874–2823;
tel. 865/213–8200, (Nonreporting) **A**1 10
Primary Contact: Scott Bowman, Administrator
CFO: Debbie Thompson, Chief Financial Officer
CMO: David Norris, Chief Medical Staff
CIO: Tony Sharp, Supervisor Information System
CHR: Lucretia Allen, Director Human Resources
CNO: Andrea Henry, Director of Nursing
Web address: www.sweetwaterhospital.org
Control: Other not–for–profit (including NFP Corporation) **Service:** General
Medical and Surgical

Staffed Beds: 59

TAZEWELL—Claiborne County

✠ **CLAIBORNE MEDICAL CENTER (440057)**, 1850 Old Knoxville Road,
Zip 37879–3625; tel. 423/626–4211, (Total facility includes 99 beds in nursing
home–type unit) **A**1 10 20 **F**7 15 18 28 29 30 34 40 57 70 77 81 93 107 110
111 115 119 128 130 146 147 **S** Covenant Health, Knoxville, TN
Primary Contact: Patricia P. Ketterman, R.N., President and Chief Administrative
Officer
CFO: Tracee McFarland, Chief Financial Officer
CHR: Susan Stone, Director Human Resources
Web address: www.claibornehospital.org
Control: Other not–for–profit (including NFP Corporation) **Service:** General
Medical and Surgical

Staffed Beds: 132 **Admissions:** 1698 **Census:** 88 **Outpatient Visits:** 42735
Births: 0 **Total Expense ($000):** 28951 **Payroll Expense ($000):** 14520
Personnel: 331

TN

Hospital, Medicare Provider Number, Address, Telephone, Approval, Facility, and Physician Codes, Health Care System

★ American Hospital Association (AHA) membership ○ Healthcare Facilities Accreditation Program ⇑ Center for Improvement in Healthcare Quality Accreditation
□ The Joint Commission accreditation ◇ DNV Healthcare Inc. accreditation △ Commission on Accreditation of Rehabilitation Facilities (CARF) accreditation

TULLAHOMA—Coffee County

☒ **TENNOVA HEALTHCARE–HARTON (440144)**, 1801 North Jackson Street, Zip 37388–8259; tel. 931/393–3000 **A**1 10 19 **F**3 11 13 15 18 20 22 26 28 29 30 31 34 35 39 40 41 48 50 57 59 60 62 64 70 74 75 76 77 78 79 81 82 85 87 89 92 93 94 97 102 107 108 110 111 114 115 119 124 129 130 131 132 135 146 147 148 **S** Community Health Systems, Inc., Franklin, TN
Primary Contact: Kenneth James, Chief Executive Officer
CFO: Shaun Adams, Chief Financial Officer
CMO: John D. Crabtree, M.D., Chief of Staff
CIO: Donald Cooper, Director Information Systems
CHR: Lenore Blackwell, Director Human Resources
Web address: www.hartonmedicalcenter.com
Control: Corporation, Investor–owned, for–profit **Service:** General Medical and Surgical

Staffed Beds: 135 **Admissions:** 4757 **Census:** 56 **Outpatient Visits:** 1728 **Births:** 698 **Total Expense ($000):** 63481 **Payroll Expense ($000):** 24049 **Personnel:** 398

UNION CITY—Obion County

☒ **BAPTIST MEMORIAL HOSPITAL–UNION CITY (440130)**, 1201 Bishop Street, Zip 38261–5403, Mailing Address: P.O. Box 310, Zip 38281–0310; tel. 731/885–2410 **A**1 10 **F**7 11 13 15 18 20 26 28 29 30 34 35 40 45 48 50 51 53 57 59 63 64 70 75 76 79 80 81 82 84 85 86 87 89 91 93 107 108 109 110 111 115 118 119 124 130 132 135 146 **P**3 **S** Baptist Memorial Health Care Corporation, Memphis, TN
Primary Contact: Barry Bondurant, Administrator and Chief Executive Officer
CFO: Mike Perryman, Chief Financial Officer
CMO: Kofi Nuako, M.D., President Medical Staff
CIO: David Mercer, Coordinator Information Systems
CHR: Nicky Thomas, Director Human Resources
CNO: Lori Brown, Chief Nursing Officer
Web address: www.baptistonline.org/union–city/
Control: Other not–for–profit (including NFP Corporation) **Service:** General Medical and Surgical

Staffed Beds: 65 **Admissions:** 2052 **Census:** 18 **Outpatient Visits:** 46740 **Births:** 279 **Total Expense ($000):** 43399 **Payroll Expense ($000):** 14925 **Personnel:** 277

WAVERLY—Humphreys County

THREE RIVERS HOSPITAL (441303), 451 Highway 13 South, Zip 37185–2109, Mailing Address: P.O. Box 437, Zip 37185–0437; tel. 931/296–4203 **A**10 18 **F**3 8 15 29 34 40 59 68 74 81 91 93 94 97 103 107 110 114 119 130 133
Primary Contact: Freda Russell, R.N., Chief Executive Officer and Chief Nursing Officer
CFO: Sandra Patrick, Chief Financial Officer
CMO: George Mathai, M.D., Chief of Staff
CIO: Joe Hildreth, Director Information Technology
CHR: Linda Rawlings, Director Human Resources and Personnel
CNO: Freda Russell, R.N., Chief Executive Officer and Chief Nursing Officer
Web address: www.threerivershospital.org
Control: Other not–for–profit (including NFP Corporation) **Service:** General Medical and Surgical

Staffed Beds: 25 **Admissions:** 454 **Census:** 7 **Outpatient Visits:** 23747 **Births:** 0 **Total Expense ($000):** 8380 **Payroll Expense ($000):** 3896 **Personnel:** 110

WAYNESBORO—Wayne County

☒ **WAYNE MEDICAL CENTER (440010)**, 103 J. V. Mangubat Drive, Zip 38485–2440, Mailing Address: P.O. Box 580, Zip 38485–0580; tel. 931/722–5411, (Nonreporting) **A**1 10 20 **S** Maury Regional Health System, Columbia, TN
Primary Contact: Teresa Grimmett, Chief Executive Officer
CMO: Harish Veeramachaneni, M.D., Chief of Staff
CHR: Jeff M. Pierce, Manager Human Resources
Web address: www.mauryregional.com
Control: Other not–for–profit (including NFP Corporation) **Service:** General Medical and Surgical

Staffed Beds: 78

WINCHESTER—Franklin County

☒ **SOUTHERN TENNESSEE REGIONAL HEALTH SYSTEM–WINCHESTER (440058)**, 185 Hospital Road, Zip 37398–2404; tel. 931/967–8200, (Includes SOUTHERN TENNESSEE REGIONAL HEALTH SYSTEM–SEWANEE, 1260 University Avenue, Sewanee, Zip 37375–2303; tel. 931/598–5691; Ralph Underwood, Administrator), (Nonreporting) **A**1 10 **S** LifePoint Health, Brentwood, TN
Primary Contact: Rob Followell, Chief Executive Officer
CFO: Steve Moore, Chief Financial Officer
CIO: James Payne, Director Information Systems
CHR: Linda Tipps, Director Human Resources
Web address: www.southerntennessee.com
Control: Corporation, Investor–owned, for–profit **Service:** General Medical and Surgical

Staffed Beds: 188

WOODBURY—Cannon County

☒ **SAINT THOMAS STONES RIVER HOSPITAL (440200)**, 324 Doolittle Road, Zip 37190–1139; tel. 615/563–4001, (Nonreporting) **A**1 10 **S** Ascension Health, Saint Louis, MO
Primary Contact: Craig Norris, Interim Chief Executive Officer
CFO: Alan Sharp, Chief Financial Officer
CMO: James Spurlock, D.O., Chief of Staff
CNO: Emily Elrod, R.N., Director of Nursing
Web address: www.stonesriverhospital.com
Control: Other not–for–profit (including NFP Corporation) **Service:** General Medical and Surgical

Staffed Beds: 60

TEXAS

ABILENE—Taylor County

⊞ **ABILENE BEHAVIORAL HEALTH (454098)**, 4225 Woods Place, Zip 79602–7991, Mailing Address: P.O. Box 5559, Zip 79608–5559; tel. 325/698–6600 **A**1 10 **F**4 5 29 54 56 64 87 98 99 101 102 103 104 105 106 130 135 143 **S** Acadia Healthcare Company, Inc., Franklin, TN
Primary Contact: Anthony Guild, Chief Executive Officer
Web address: www.abilenebehavioralhealth.com/
Control: Corporation, Investor–owned, for–profit **Service:** Psychiatric

Staffed Beds: 92 **Admissions:** 1608 **Census:** 40 **Outpatient Visits:** 3358 **Births:** 0 **Total Expense ($000):** 10390 **Payroll Expense ($000):** 5235 **Personnel:** 110

⊞ **ABILENE REGIONAL MEDICAL CENTER (450558)**, 6250 U.S. Highway 83, Zip 79606–5299; tel. 325/428–1000, (Total facility includes 25 beds in nursing home–type unit) **A**1 10 19 **F**8 11 13 15 17 18 20 22 24 26 28 29 30 31 34 35 40 41 43 45 46 49 50 53 56 57 59 64 68 70 72 75 76 77 78 79 81 85 86 87 89 91 93 107 108 110 111 114 115 118 119 126 128 130 132 135 146 147 148 **P**3 **S** Community Health Systems, Inc., Franklin, TN
Primary Contact: Michael D. Murphy, Chief Executive Officer
COO: Matthew van Leeuwe, Chief Operating Officer
CFO: Ron Bennett, Chief Financial Officer
CMO: Tim Bumann, D.O., Chief of Staff
CIO: Dennis Newquist, Director Information Systems
CHR: John J. Jeziorske, Director Human Resources
CNO: Jessica Kiehle, R.N., Chief Nursing Officer
Web address: www.abileneregional.com
Control: Partnership, Investor–owned, for–profit **Service:** General Medical and Surgical

Staffed Beds: 205 **Admissions:** 6565 **Census:** 78 **Outpatient Visits:** 83467 **Births:** 1463 **Total Expense ($000):** 91570 **Payroll Expense ($000):** 36454 **Personnel:** 643

ACADIA ABILENE HOSPITAL See Abilene Behavioral Health

★ **CONTINUECARE HOSPITAL AT HENDRICK MEDICAL CENTER (452029)**, 1900 Pine Street, Zip 79601–2432; tel. 325/670–6251 **A**10 **F**1 3 29 34 35 68 85 87 148 **S** Community Hospital Corporation, Plano, TX
Primary Contact: Thomas P. Harlan, Chief Executive Officer
CFO: Lisa Young, CPA, Chief Financial Officer
CHR: Laurie Fields, Director Human Resources
CNO: Sherry Hendricksen, R.N., Chief Nursing Officer
Web address: www.continuecare.org/hendrick/
Control: Other not–for–profit (including NFP Corporation) **Service:** Long–Term Acute Care hospital

Staffed Beds: 19 **Admissions:** 199 **Census:** 15 **Outpatient Visits:** 0 **Births:** 0 **Total Expense ($000):** 6556 **Payroll Expense ($000):** 3214 **Personnel:** 51

⊞ **HEALTHSOUTH REHABILITATION HOSPITAL – ABILENE (673039)**, 6401 Directors Parkway, Zip 79606–5869; tel. 325/691–1600, (Data for 92 days) **A**1 10 **F**3 29 77 90 96 130 148 **S** HEALTHSOUTH Corporation, Birmingham, AL
Primary Contact: Joe Roberson, Chief Executive Officer
Web address: www.reliantabilene.com
Control: Partnership, Investor–owned, for–profit **Service:** Rehabilitation

Staffed Beds: 30 **Admissions:** 131 **Census:** 15 **Outpatient Visits:** 0 **Births:** 0 **Total Expense ($000):** 1657 **Payroll Expense ($000):** 785 **Personnel:** 56

⊞ **HENDRICK HEALTH SYSTEM (450229)**, 1900 Pine Street, Zip 79601–2432; tel. 325/670–2000, (Total facility includes 20 beds in nursing home–type unit) **A**1 10 **F**3 11 12 13 14 15 17 18 20 22 24 26 28 29 30 31 32 34 35 36 39 40 43 44 45 48 49 50 51 53 56 57 59 60 61 62 64 68 70 73 74 75 76 77 78 79 80 81 84 85 86 87 89 93 107 102 107 108 110 111 114 115 118 119 121 123 128 129 130 131 132 135 143 146 147 148 **P**6 8
Primary Contact: Tim Lancaster, FACHE, President and Chief Executive Officer
CFO: Jeremy Tyler Walker, Vice President and Chief Financial Officer
CIO: Duane Donaway, Director Information Technology
CHR: Susan Wade, Vice President
CNO: Susie Cassle, R.N., Vice President Nursing Services
Web address: www.ehendrick.org
Control: Church–operated, Nongovernment, not–for profit **Service:** General Medical and Surgical

Staffed Beds: 409 **Admissions:** 15402 **Census:** 252 **Outpatient Visits:** 271678 **Births:** 1324 **Total Expense ($000):** 313117 **Payroll Expense ($000):** 106660 **Personnel:** 2350

□ **OCEANS BEHAVIORAL HOSPITAL ABILENE (454122)**, 6401 Directors Parkway, Suite 200, Zip 79606–5869; tel. 325/691–0030 **A**1 10 **F**29 35 98 100 101 103 104 130 **P**6 **S** Oceans Healthcare, Lake Charles, LA
Primary Contact: Stacy Sanford, Chief Executive Officer
Web address: www.oceansabilene.com
Control: Corporation, Investor–owned, for–profit **Service:** Psychiatric

Staffed Beds: 35 **Admissions:** 603 **Census:** 23 **Outpatient Visits:** 5522 **Births:** 0 **Total Expense ($000):** 5317 **Payroll Expense ($000):** 2530 **Personnel:** 71

ADDISON—Dallas County

◇ **METHODIST HOSPITAL FOR SURGERY (670073)**, 17101 North Dallas Parkway, Zip 75001–7103; tel. 469/248–3900 **A**10 21 **F**3 29 30 35 40 64 70 81 93 107 111 119 130 146 148
Primary Contact: Daniel L. Gideon, FACHE, President
CFO: Kelly Hayes, Chief Financial Officer
CMO: Robert Fischer, M.D., Medical Director
CHR: Erik Leopard, Manager Human Resource
CNO: Patti Griffith, R.N., Chief Nursing Officer
Web address: www.methodisthospitalforsurgery.com/
Control: Corporation, Investor–owned, for–profit **Service:** Surgical

Staffed Beds: 32 **Admissions:** 2446 **Census:** 17 **Outpatient Visits:** 29710 **Births:** 0 **Total Expense ($000):** 111717 **Payroll Expense ($000):** 14831 **Personnel:** 231

ALICE—Jim Wells County

⊞ **CHRISTUS SPOHN HOSPITAL ALICE (450828)**, 2500 East Main Street, Zip 78332–4169; tel. 361/661–8000 **A**1 10 20 **F**3 11 13 15 18 20 22 28 29 30 35 39 40 43 45 46 50 57 59 64 68 70 75 76 77 78 79 81 85 86 87 89 91 93 97 98 102 103 107 108 111 115 119 127 130 146 147 148 **P**8 **S** CHRISTUS Health, Irving, TX
Primary Contact: David LaMonte, Interim President
COO: Steven G. Daniel, Senior Vice President and Chief Operating Officer
CFO: Michael Guajardo, Director Finance
CMO: Jerry Liles, D.O.
CHR: Mindy Soliz, Director Human Resources
CNO: Margot Rios, R.N., Chief Nursing Officer
Web address: www.christusspohn.org/locations_alice.htm
Control: Church–operated, Nongovernment, not–for profit **Service:** General Medical and Surgical

Staffed Beds: 73 **Admissions:** 3017 **Census:** 32 **Outpatient Visits:** 51881 **Births:** 417 **Total Expense ($000):** 42980 **Payroll Expense ($000):** 15368 **Personnel:** 221

ALLEN—Collin County

⊞ **POST ACUTE/WARM SPRINGS REHABILITATION HOSPITAL OF ALLEN (673025)**, 1001 Raintree Circle, Zip 75013–4912; tel. 972/908–2015 **A**1 10 **F**3 28 29 30 34 40 56 59 60 74 75 79 87 90 91 94 96 100 130 132 148 **S** Post Acute Medical, LLC, Enola, PA
Primary Contact: Bill Kaupas, Chief Executive Officer
Web address: www.warmsprings.org
Control: Partnership, Investor–owned, for–profit **Service:** Rehabilitation

Staffed Beds: 39 **Admissions:** 867 **Census:** 27 **Outpatient Visits:** 0 **Births:** 0 **Total Expense ($000):** 12486 **Payroll Expense ($000):** 6028 **Personnel:** 106

⊞ **TEXAS HEALTH PRESBYTERIAN HOSPITAL ALLEN (450840)**, 1105 Central Expressway North, Suite 140, Zip 75013–6103; tel. 972/747–1000 **A**1 10 **F**3 13 15 18 20 28 29 30 34 35 38 40 43 45 47 49 51 54 55 57 59 64 65 70 73 74 75 76 78 79 81 89 93 107 110 111 114 115 118 119 126 129 130 132 135 146 147 148 **S** Texas Health Resources, Arlington, TX
Primary Contact: Jared Shelton, Chief Executive Officer
COO: Crispin P. Hocate, Professional and Support Services Officer
CFO: Lisa Gildon, Group Financial Officer
CMO: Bob Schwab, M.D., Chief Medical Officer
CHR: Sharon Chisholm, Entity Human Resource Officer
Web address: www.texashealth.org
Control: Other not–for–profit (including NFP Corporation) **Service:** General Medical and Surgical

Staffed Beds: 48 **Admissions:** 3147 **Census:** 27 **Outpatient Visits:** 41881 **Births:** 581 **Total Expense ($000):** 72851 **Payroll Expense ($000):** 26966 **Personnel:** 298

Hospital, Medicare Provider Number, Address, Telephone, Approval, Facility, and Physician Codes, Health Care System

★ American Hospital Association (AHA) membership
□ The Joint Commission accreditation
○ Healthcare Facilities Accreditation Program
◇ DNV Healthcare Inc. accreditation
⇑ Center for Improvement in Healthcare Quality Accreditation
△ Commission on Accreditation of Rehabilitation Facilities (CARF) accreditation

ALPINE—Brewster County

BIG BEND REGIONAL MEDICAL CENTER (451378), 2600 Highway 118 North, Zip 79830–2002; tel. 432/837–3447 **A**1 3 10 18 **F**3 13 29 30 34 35 40 43 45 49 57 59 64 68 70 75 76 77 81 85 93 107 119 132 133 146 147 148 **P**6 **S** Quorum Health, Brentwood, TN
Primary Contact: Matthew van Leeuwe, Interim Chief Executive Officer
CFO: Diane Moore, Chief Financial Officer
CNO: Keith Ellison, Chief Nursing Officer
Web address: www.bigbendhealthcare.com
Control: Corporation, Investor–owned, for–profit **Service:** General Medical and Surgical

Staffed Beds: 25 **Admissions:** 773 **Census:** 6 **Outpatient Visits:** 12551 **Births:** 182 **Total Expense ($000):** 21193 **Payroll Expense ($000):** 6408 **Personnel:** 115

ALVIN—Brazoria County

ALVIN DIAGNOSTIC AND URGENT CARE CENTER See Clear Lake Regional Medical Center, Webster

AMARILLO—Potter County

AMARILLO VETERANS AFFAIRS HEALTH CARE SYSTEM, 6010 West Amarillo Boulevard, Zip 79106–1992; tel. 806/355–9703, (Nonreporting) **A**1 2 3 5 **S** Department of Veterans Affairs, Washington, DC
Primary Contact: Colonel Michael L. Kiefer, Director
COO: Lance Robinson, Associate Director
CIO: Modesto Baca, Chief Information Officer
CHR: Ken Creamer, Chief Human Resource
Web address: www.amarillo.va.gov/
Control: Veterans Affairs, Government, federal **Service:** General Medical and Surgical

Staffed Beds: 55

BSA HOSPITAL, LLC (450231), 1600 Wallace Boulevard, Zip 79106–1799; tel. 806/212–2000 **A**2 3 5 10 21 **F**3 7 8 11 13 15 17 18 20 22 24 26 28 29 30 31 34 40 45 46 48 49 51 53 54 57 58 59 62 67 70 71 72 74 75 76 77 78 79 81 82 84 85 86 87 88 89 90 91 93 96 107 108 110 111 114 115 117 119 121 123 124 125 126 129 130 135 146 147 148 **S** Ardent Health Services, Nashville, TN
Primary Contact: Bob Williams, President and Chief Executive Officer
COO: Michael Cruz, Senior Vice President Operations
CFO: Lorenzo Olivarez, Senior Vice President and Chief Financial Officer
CMO: Mike Lamanteer, M.D., Senior Vice President Medical Affairs
CIO: Lewis Brown, Director Information Technology
CHR: Cheryl L. Jones, Vice President Human Resources and Organizational Development
CNO: Belinda D. Gibson, R.N., Senior Vice President Patient Services
Web address: www.bsahs.org
Control: Corporation, Investor–owned, for–profit **Service:** General Medical and Surgical

Staffed Beds: 318 **Admissions:** 20245 **Census:** 257 **Outpatient Visits:** 162154 **Births:** 2098 **Total Expense ($000):** 320025 **Payroll Expense ($000):** 119896 **Personnel:** 1954

KINDRED HOSPITAL–AMARILLO See Vibra Hospital of Amarillo

KINDRED REHABILITATION HOSPITAL AMARILLO See Vibra Rehabilitation Hospital of Amarillo

NORTHWEST TEXAS HEALTHCARE SYSTEM (450209), 1501 South Coulter Avenue, Zip 79106–1770, Mailing Address: P.O. Box 1110, Zip 79105–1110; tel. 806/354–1000, (Includes NORTHWEST CHILDREN'S HOSPITAL, 1501 South Coulter Street, tel. 806/354–1000; NORTHWEST PAVILION, 7201 Evans, Zip 79106, Mailing Address: P.O. Box 1110, Zip 79105–1110; tel. 806/354–1000) **A**1 2 3 5 10 **F**3 4 5 8 11 12 13 15 17 18 20 22 24 26 28 29 30 31 32 34 35 37 38 39 40 43 44 45 46 48 49 50 54 56 57 59 60 61 64 65 66 68 70 72 74 75 76 77 78 79 80 81 82 84 85 86 87 88 89 90 92 93 94 96 97 98 99 100 101 102 103 104 105 107 108 110 111 115 118 119 126 130 132 135 144 146 147 148 **P**6 **S** Universal Health Services, Inc., King of Prussia, PA
Primary Contact: Mark W. Crawford, Chief Executive Officer
COO: John McDonald, Chief Operating Officer
CFO: Gene Winters, Chief Financial Officer
CMO: Brian Weis, M.D., Chief Medical Officer
CIO: Bach Nguyen, Director Information Systems
CHR: Samuel Lynn, Director Human Resources
Web address: www.nwtexashealthcare.com
Control: Corporation, Investor–owned, for–profit **Service:** General Medical and Surgical

Staffed Beds: 437 **Admissions:** 17571 **Census:** 239 **Outpatient Visits:** 207365 **Births:** 2441 **Total Expense ($000):** 264811 **Payroll Expense ($000):** 86310 **Personnel:** 1611

NORTHWEST TEXAS SURGERY CENTER (450796), 3501 South Soncy Road Suite 118, Zip 79119–6405; tel. 806/359–7999, (Nonreporting) **A**10
Primary Contact: Mark W. Crawford, Chief Executive Officer
Control: Corporation, Investor–owned, for–profit **Service:** Surgical

Staffed Beds: 4

PHYSICIANS SURGICAL HOSPITAL – PANHANDLE CAMPUS, 7100 West 9th Avenue, Zip 79106–1704; tel. 806/212–0247, (Nonreporting) **S** Ardent Health Services, Nashville, TN
Primary Contact: Brad McCall, JD, Chief Executive Officer
CFO: Austin Jones, CPA, Chief Financial Officer
CMO: Robert Crabtree, M.D., Chief of Staff and Medical Director
CNO: Debbie Inman, Chief Nursing Officer
Web address: www.physurg.com/
Control: Partnership, Investor–owned, for–profit **Service:** General Medical and Surgical

Staffed Beds: 11

PHYSICIANS SURGICAL HOSPITAL – QUAIL CREEK (450875), 6819 Plum Creek, Zip 79124–1602; tel. 806/354–6100 **A**10 **F**3 29 30 40 44 68 75 79 81 82 85 89 130 135 **S** Ardent Health Services, Nashville, TN
Primary Contact: Brad McCall, JD, Chief Executive Officer
CFO: Austin Jones, CPA, Chief Financial Officer
CMO: Robert Crabtree, M.D., Chief of Staff and Medical Director
CNO: Debbie Inman, Chief Nursing Officer
Web address: www.physurg.com
Control: Partnership, Investor–owned, for–profit **Service:** Surgical

Staffed Beds: 41 **Admissions:** 1897 **Census:** 11 **Outpatient Visits:** 13659 **Births:** 0 **Total Expense ($000):** 42429 **Payroll Expense ($000):** 11086 **Personnel:** 178

PLUM CREEK SPECIALTY HOSPITAL (452066), 5601 Plum Creek Drive, Zip 79124–1801; tel. 806/351–1000, (Data for 275 days) **A**1 10 **F**1 3 29 40 60 75 85 148 **S** Concord Healthcare Group, Lakewood, NJ
Primary Contact: Bobby Snyder, Interim Chief Executive Officer
Web address: www.plumcreekspecialtyhosp.com/
Control: Corporation, Investor–owned, for–profit **Service:** Long–Term Acute Care hospital

Staffed Beds: 47 **Admissions:** 118 **Census:** 14 **Outpatient Visits:** 0 **Births:** 0 **Total Expense ($000):** 4639 **Payroll Expense ($000):** 1880 **Personnel:** 43

SPECIALTY HOSPITAL AT PLUM CREEK See Plum Creek Specialty Hospital

VIBRA HOSPITAL OF AMARILLO (452060), 7501 Wallace Boulevard, Zip 79124–2150; tel. 806/467–7000 **A**1 10 **F**1 3 29 45 46 50 56 59 60 61 70 74 75 77 79 82 84 85 86 87 91 96 107 114 130 148 **S** Vibra Healthcare, Mechanicsburg, PA
Primary Contact: Jerry Jasper, Chief Executive Officer
CFO: Carlene Wright, Chief Financial Officer
CMO: Pablo Rodrigues, M.D., Medical Director
CNO: Melany McCarty, R.N., Chief Clinical Officer
Web address: www.vhamarillo.com
Control: Corporation, Investor–owned, for–profit **Service:** Long–Term Acute Care hospital

Staffed Beds: 72 **Admissions:** 746 **Census:** 56 **Outpatient Visits:** 0 **Births:** 0 **Total Expense ($000):** 18061 **Payroll Expense ($000):** 10168 **Personnel:** 223

VIBRA REHABILITATION HOSPITAL OF AMARILLO (453096), 7200 West 9th Avenue, Zip 79106–1703; tel. 806/468–2900 **A**1 7 10 **F**3 28 29 56 75 77 82 87 90 91 96 107 130 143 148 **S** Vibra Healthcare, Mechanicsburg, PA
Primary Contact: Jerry Jasper, Chief Executive Officer
Web address: www.vrhamarillo.com
Control: Corporation, Investor–owned, for–profit **Service:** Rehabilitation

Staffed Beds: 44 **Admissions:** 730 **Census:** 22 **Outpatient Visits:** 0 **Births:** 0 **Total Expense ($000):** 7672 **Payroll Expense ($000):** 5165 **Personnel:** 98

ANAHUAC—Chambers County

CHAMBERS COUNTY PUBLIC HOSPITAL DISTRICT NO. 1 (451320), 200 Hospital Drive, Zip 77514, Mailing Address: P.O. Box 398, Zip 77514–0398; tel. 409/267–3143 **A**10 18 **F**3 8 11 29 34 35 40 43 45 47 50 53 54 56 57 59 64 70 81 86 93 107 111 114 119 128 130 133 **P**3
Primary Contact: Steven Gularte, Chief Executive Officer
CFO: Peggy Hamilton, Chief Financial Officer
CMO: Anthony Capili, M.D., Chief of Staff
CNO: Christi Morris, Director of Nursing
Web address: www.chambershealth.org
Control: Hospital district or authority, Government, nonfederal **Service:** General Medical and Surgical

Staffed Beds: 14 **Admissions:** 140 **Census:** 1 **Outpatient Visits:** 14432 **Births:** 0 **Total Expense ($000):** 19565 **Payroll Expense ($000):** 5813 **Personnel:** 104

Many Facility Codes have changed. Please refer to the AHA Guide Code Chart.

© 2016 AHA Guide

ANDREWS—Andrews County

★ ◇ **PERMIAN REGIONAL MEDICAL CENTER (450144)**, Northeast By–Pass, Zip 79714, Mailing Address: P.O. Box 2108, Zip 79714–2108; tel. 432/523–2200 **A**10 20 21 **F**3 11 13 15 29 34 35 36 38 40 43 44 50 53 56 57 59 62 63 64 65 68 70 73 75 76 77 81 82 84 85 86 87 89 93 97 107 108 110 111 115 119 127 129 130 131 132 133 135 145 146 148 **P**6
Primary Contact: Russell Tippin, Chief Executive Officer and Administrator
CFO: Sandra Cox, Controller
CIO: Dan Smart, Chief Information Management Officer
CHR: Pam McCormick, Director Human Resources
Web address: www.permianregional.com
Control: Hospital district or authority, Government, nonfederal **Service:** General Medical and Surgical

Staffed Beds: 44 Admissions: 767 Census: 4 Outpatient Visits: 29398 **Births: 347 Total Expense ($000):** 43148 **Payroll Expense ($000):** 20388 **Personnel:** 248

ANSON—Jones County

ANSON GENERAL HOSPITAL (450078), 101 Avenue J, Zip 79501–2198; tel. 325/823–3231 **A**10 **F**7 11 29 40 75 77 81 93 107 127 133 **P**8
Primary Contact: Joe Duerr, Chief Executive Officer
CIO: Lynna B. Cox, Director Health Information Services
Control: City–Government, nonfederal **Service:** General Medical and Surgical

Staffed Beds: 30 Admissions: 325 Census: 9 Outpatient Visits: 9467 **Births: 0 Total Expense ($000):** 7711 **Payroll Expense ($000):** 3852 **Personnel:** 85

ARANSAS PASS—San Patricio County

CARE REGIONAL MEDICAL CENTER (450605), 1711 West Wheeler Avenue, Zip 78336–4536; tel. 361/758–8585 **A**10 **F**3 11 15 18 29 34 35 40 44 45 50 56 57 59 64 65 68 70 75 77 78 79 81 85 86 87 93 97 98 101 102 103 107 108 114 119 130 132 133 146 148 **P**7
Primary Contact: Sunil Reddy, Chief Executive Officer
CMO: Salim Surani, M.D., Chief of Staff
CIO: Greg Palmer, Administrator Information Technology Network
CHR: Kerry L. Upton, Administrative Director Human Resources
CNO: Christal Burns, R.N., Chief Nursing Officer
Web address: www.crmctx.com
Control: Corporation, Investor–owned, for–profit **Service:** General Medical and Surgical

Staffed Beds: 54 Admissions: 738 Census: 12 Outpatient Visits: 26150 **Births: 0 Total Expense ($000):** 15560 **Payroll Expense ($000):** 7162 **Personnel:** 184

NORTH BAY HOSPITAL See Care Regional Medical Center

ARLINGTON—Tarrant County

ARLINGTON REHABILITATION HOSPITAL See Kindred Rehabilitation Hospital Arlington

☐ **BAYLOR ORTHOPEDIC AND SPINE HOSPITAL AT ARLINGTON (670067)**, 707 Highlander Boulevard, Zip 76015–4319; tel. 817/583–7100 **A**1 10 **F**3 29 40 65 75 79 81 82 85 107 111 114
Primary Contact: Allan Beck, Chief Executive Officer
Web address: www.baylorarlington.com/
Control: Partnership, Investor–owned, for–profit **Service:** Orthopedic

Staffed Beds: 24 Admissions: 1383 Census: 8 Outpatient Visits: 10506 **Births: 0 Total Expense ($000):** 48618 **Payroll Expense ($000):** 8733 **Personnel:** 110

✠ **HEALTHSOUTH REHABILITATION HOSPITAL OF ARLINGTON (453040)**, 3200 Matlock Road, Zip 76015–2911; tel. 817/468–4000 **A**1 10 **F**3 29 74 75 77 79 90 91 94 95 96 130 148 **S** HEALTHSOUTH Corporation, Birmingham, AL
Primary Contact: Sheril Appel, Chief Executive Officer
CFO: Kathy Dickerson, Chief Financial Officer
CMO: Todd Daniels, M.D., Medical Director
CHR: Nancy Rosiles, Director Human Resources
CNO: David Jones, Chief Nursing Officer
Web address: www.healthsoutharlington.com
Control: Corporation, Investor–owned, for–profit **Service:** Rehabilitation

Staffed Beds: 85 Admissions: 1905 Census: 65 Outpatient Visits: 0 **Births: 0 Total Expense ($000):** 26331 **Payroll Expense ($000):** 13417 **Personnel:** 231

✠ **KINDRED HOSPITAL TARRANT COUNTY–ARLINGTON (452028)**, 1000 North Cooper Street, Zip 76011–5540; tel. 817/548–3400 **A**1 10 **F**1 3 29 30 40 56 57 77 80 82 93 130 148 **S** Kindred Healthcare, Louisville, KY
Primary Contact: Christina Richard, Market Chief Executive Officer
CFO: Jennifer Penland, Controller
CMO: Bernard A. McGowen, M.D., Medical Director
Web address: www.kindredhospitalarl.com/
Control: Corporation, Investor–owned, for–profit **Service:** Long–Term Acute Care hospital

Staffed Beds: 68 Admissions: 512 Census: 40 Outpatient Visits: 2051 **Births: 0 Total Expense ($000):** 17672 **Payroll Expense ($000):** 8418 **Personnel:** 143

✠ **KINDRED REHABILITATION HOSPITAL ARLINGTON (453094)**, 2601 West Randol Mill Road, #101, Zip 76012–4289; tel. 817/804–4400 **A**1 10 **F**3 29 34 35 57 74 75 86 87 90 94 96 130 132 146 148
Primary Contact: Amy Hoffner, Administrator
CFO: Jared Griffin, Controller
CMO: Albert Ramirez, M.D., Medical Director
CNO: Layo Orekoya, Director of Nursing, Clinical Services
Web address: www.khrehabarlington.com
Control: Corporation, Investor–owned, for–profit **Service:** Rehabilitation

Staffed Beds: 24 Admissions: 598 Census: 19 Outpatient Visits: 0 **Births:** 0 **Total Expense ($000):** 8371 **Payroll Expense ($000):** 3974 **Personnel:** 69

✠ **MEDICAL CENTER ARLINGTON (450675)**, 3301 Matlock Road, Zip 76015–2908; tel. 817/465–3241 **A**1 2 3 10 **F**3 11 12 13 15 17 18 20 22 24 26 28 29 31 34 35 39 40 41 42 43 45 46 47 48 49 50 57 59 64 70 72 73 74 75 76 78 79 81 82 84 85 86 87 92 93 107 108 110 111 114 115 119 126 130 131 132 135 145 146 147 148 **S** HCA, Nashville, TN
Primary Contact: Winston Borland, FACHE, President and Chief Executive Officer
COO: Ben Coogan, Chief Operating Officer
CFO: Jeff Ardemagni, Chief Financial Officer
CMO: Edwin Duppstadt, M.D., Chief Medical Officer
CIO: Craig Santangelo, Director Information Services
CHR: Jennifer C. Morris, Vice President Human Resources
Web address: www.medicalcenterarlington.com
Control: Partnership, Investor–owned, for–profit **Service:** General Medical and Surgical

Staffed Beds: 265 Admissions: 14925 Census: 205 Outpatient Visits: 112778 **Births: 4331 Total Expense ($000):** 192090 **Payroll Expense ($000):** 73196 **Personnel:** 1040

☐ **MILLWOOD HOSPITAL (454012)**, 1011 North Cooper Street, Zip 76011–5517; tel. 817/261–3121 **A**1 10 **F**4 5 29 30 35 54 56 71 75 87 98 99 100 101 102 103 104 105 130 132 **S** Universal Health Services, Inc., King of Prussia, PA
Primary Contact: Dwight A. Lacy, Chief Executive Officer
CFO: Jeff Epperson, Chief Financial Officer
CMO: Robert Bennett, M.D., Medical Director
CIO: William Jackson, Director Medical Records
CHR: Betty Nuru, Director Human Resources
CNO: Nancy Stewart, Chief Nursing Officer
Web address: www.millwoodhospital.com
Control: Partnership, Investor–owned, for–profit **Service:** Psychiatric

Staffed Beds: 122 Admissions: 3667 Census: 88 Outpatient Visits: 23686 **Births: 0 Total Expense ($000):** 25716 **Payroll Expense ($000):** 11653 **Personnel:** 197

☐ **SUNDANCE HOSPITAL (454113)**, 7000 U.S. Highway 287 South, Zip 76001; tel. 817/583–8080 **A**1 10 **F**4 98 99 101 102 103
Primary Contact: Drew Carleton, Chief Executive Officer
Web address: www.sundancehealthcare.com/arlington/
Control: Corporation, Investor–owned, for–profit **Service:** Psychiatric

Staffed Beds: 116 Admissions: 3619 Census: 84 Outpatient Visits: 0 **Births: 0 Total Expense ($000):** 13160 **Payroll Expense ($000):** 7446 **Personnel:** 164

TX

Hospital, Medicare Provider Number, Address, Telephone, Approval, Facility, and Physician Codes, Health Care System

★ American Hospital Association (AHA) membership ○ Healthcare Facilities Accreditation Program ⇑ Center for Improvement in Healthcare Quality Accreditation
☐ The Joint Commission accreditation ◇ DNV Healthcare Inc. accreditation △ Commission on Accreditation of Rehabilitation Facilities (CARF) accreditation

⊠ **TEXAS HEALTH ARLINGTON MEMORIAL HOSPITAL (450064)**, 800 West Randol Mill Road, Zip 76012–2503; tel. 817/548–6100 **A**1 2 10 **F**3 11 12 13 15 18 26 28 29 30 31 34 35 37 40 45 46 47 48 49 51 53 54 57 59 60 63 64 65 66 68 70 72 74 75 76 77 78 79 80 81 82 85 86 87 93 98 99 100 101 102 103 104 105 107 108 110 111 114 115 118 119 120 123 124 126 130 131 132 135 136 141 142 145 146 147 148 **S** Texas Health Resources, Arlington, TX
Primary Contact: Blake Kretz, President
COO: Sandra L. Harris, R.N., Senior Vice President and Chief Operating Officer
CMO: Robert N. Cluck, M.D., Vice President and Medical Director
CHR: Yvonne Kyler, Director Human Resources
Web address: www.arlingtonmemorial.org
Control: Other not–for–profit (including NFP Corporation) **Service:** General Medical and Surgical

Staffed Beds: 290 **Admissions:** 13496 **Census:** 191 **Outpatient Visits:** 105102 **Births:** 1997 **Total Expense ($000):** 246107 **Payroll Expense ($000):** 105037 **Personnel:** 1384

☐ **TEXAS HEALTH HEART & VASCULAR HOSPITAL ARLINGTON (670071)**, 811 Wright Street, Zip 76012–4708; tel. 817/960–3500 **A**1 10 **F**3 17 18 20 22 24 26 29 30 60 64 65 68 81 85
Primary Contact: Sherri Emerson, Chief Nursing Officer and Chief Operating Officer
CFO: Kay Mason, Chief Financial Officer
CMO: William Nesbitt, M.D., President Medical Staff
CHR: Yvonne Kyler, Director Human Resources
Web address: www.texashealthheartandvascular.org/
Control: Partnership, Investor–owned, for–profit **Service:** Heart

Staffed Beds: 32 **Admissions:** 1228 **Census:** 15 **Outpatient Visits:** 2472 **Births:** 0 **Total Expense ($000):** 41941 **Payroll Expense ($000):** 8760 **Personnel:** 109

TEXAS REHABILITATION HOSPITAL OF ARLINGTON (673060), 900 West Arbrook Boulevard, Zip 76015; tel. 682/304–6000, (Data for 177 days) **F**3 28 29 34 35 60 65 75 90 91 96 97 130 132 135 148
Primary Contact: John Reel, Chief Executive Officer
CFO: Donna Colson, Controller
CMO: Camelia Mitchell, M.D., Medical Director
CHR: Christopher Burns, Director Human Resources
CNO: Tonia Torregrossa, Chief Nursing Officer
Web address: www.texasrehabarlington.com
Control: Partnership, Investor–owned, for–profit **Service:** Rehabilitation

Staffed Beds: 40 **Admissions:** 293 **Census:** 17 **Outpatient Visits:** 0 **Births:** 0 **Total Expense ($000):** 5152 **Payroll Expense ($000):** 2571 **Personnel:** 116

⊠ **USMD HOSPITAL AT ARLINGTON (450872)**, 801 West Interstate 20, Zip 76017–5851; tel. 817/472–3400 **A**1 10 **F**3 12 29 34 35 36 39 40 45 46 49 50 51 57 59 64 70 74 75 78 79 81 82 85 87 107 108 111 114 115 119 124 126 132 **S** USMD Health System, Irving, TX
Primary Contact: Marcia Crim, R.N., MSN, Chief Executive Officer
CFO: Andrew Summers, Chief Financial Officer
CMO: M. Patrick Collini, M.D., President Medical Staff
CIO: Bob Rick, Vice President Information Technology
CHR: Bernardo Valle, Vice President Human Resources
CNO: Marcia Crim, R.N., Chief Nursing Officer and Chief Executive Officer
Web address: www.usmdarlington.com
Control: Partnership, Investor–owned, for–profit **Service:** General Medical and Surgical

Staffed Beds: 34 **Admissions:** 1824 **Census:** 15 **Outpatient Visits:** 32852 **Births:** 0 **Total Expense ($000):** 78984 **Payroll Expense ($000):** 16675 **Personnel:** 318

ASPERMONT—Stonewall County

STONEWALL MEMORIAL HOSPITAL (451318), 821 North Broadway, Zip 79502–2029, Mailing Address: P.O. Box C, Zip 79502–0902; tel. 940/989–3551 **A**10 18 **F**3 29 34 35 40 41 56 57 59 64 93 97 103 107 114 119 127 128 133 148 **P**5
Primary Contact: Andy Kolb, Chief Executive Officer
COO: Billie Carter, Chief Operating Officer and Assistant Administrator
CFO: Andy Kolb, Chief Executive Officer
CMO: Frederic K. Passmann, M.D., Chief of Staff
CIO: Billie Carter, Chief Operating Officer and Assistant Administrator
CHR: Andy Kolb, Chief Executive Officer
CNO: Jan Harris, R.N., Director of Nursing
Web address: www.smhdhealth.org/
Control: Hospital district or authority, Government, nonfederal **Service:** General Medical and Surgical

Staffed Beds: 12 **Admissions:** 155 **Census:** 2 **Outpatient Visits:** 3691 **Births:** 0 **Total Expense ($000):** 9200 **Payroll Expense ($000):** 4213 **Personnel:** 54

ATHENS—Henderson County

⊠ **EAST TEXAS MEDICAL CENTER ATHENS (450389)**, 2000 South Palestine Street, Zip 75751–5610; tel. 903/676–1000 **A**1 10 **F**3 11 13 15 18 20 29 34 40 42 43 45 49 50 70 74 76 79 81 85 89 107 108 110 111 114 115 118 119 127 130 132 146 **S** East Texas Medical Center Regional Healthcare System, Tyler, TX
Primary Contact: Patrick L. Wallace, Administrator
CFO: David A. Travis, Chief Financial Officer
CHR: Jennifer Rummel, Director Human Resources
CNO: Kevin M. Jablonski, Chief Nursing Officer
Web address: www.etmc.org
Control: Other not–for–profit (including NFP Corporation) **Service:** General Medical and Surgical

Staffed Beds: 127 **Admissions:** 5274 **Census:** 51 **Outpatient Visits:** 88513 **Births:** 877 **Total Expense ($000):** 69645 **Payroll Expense ($000):** 23801 **Personnel:** 420

AUBREY—Denton County

★ ◇ **BAYLOR EMERGENCY MEDICAL CENTER AT AUBREY (670062)**, 26791 Highway 380, Zip 76227; tel. 972/347–2525, (Includes BAYLOR EMERGENCY MEDICAL CENTER MURPHY, 511 FM 544, Suite 100, Plano, Zip 75094; tel. 214/294–6150; Kyle Kirkpatrick, Chief Executive Officer; BAYLOR EMERGENCY MEDICAL CENTERS – COLLEYVILLE, 5500 Colleyville Boulevard, Colleyville, Zip 76034–5835; tel. 214/294–6350; Kyle Kirkpatrick, Chief Executive Officer; BAYLOR EMERGENCY MEDICAL CENTERS – KELLER, 620 South Main Street, Suite 100, Keller, Zip 76248–4960; tel. 214/294–6100; Kyle Kirkpatrick, Chief Executive Officer) **A**10 21 **F**3 29 40 75 87 107 119 **P**5 **S** Emerus, The Woodlands, TX
Primary Contact: Kyle Kirkpatrick, Chief Executive Officer
CFO: Michael Rzendzian, Chief Financial Officer
CMO: Amynah Kara, M.D., Chief Medical Officer
CIO: Trang Dawson, Chief Information Officer
CHR: Larry Guillory, Chief Human Resources Officer
CNO: Daniel Baas, R.N., Chief Nursing Officer
Web address: www.bemcataubrey.com
Control: Partnership, Investor–owned, for–profit **Service:** General Medical and Surgical

Staffed Beds: 32 **Admissions:** 227 **Census:** 1 **Outpatient Visits:** 33845 **Births:** 0 **Total Expense ($000):** 24892 **Payroll Expense ($000):** 7821 **Personnel:** 143

AUSTIN—Travis County

☐ **ARISE AUSTIN MEDICAL CENTER (450871)**, 3003 Bee Caves Road, Zip 78746–5542; tel. 512/314–3800 **A**1 10 **F**29 40 59 64 65 68 70 75 79 81 82 85 91 107 111 114 119 126 148
Primary Contact: Shawn G. Strash, Chief Executive Officer
CFO: Lawrence Oldham, Chief Financial Officer
CMO: Robert Wills, M.D., Chief Medical Officer
CHR: Marilyn Jennings, Director Human Resources
Web address: www.austinsurgicalhospital.com
Control: Corporation, Investor–owned, for–profit **Service:** Orthopedic

Staffed Beds: 23 **Admissions:** 970 **Census:** 7 **Outpatient Visits:** 5756 **Births:** 0 **Total Expense ($000):** 43230 **Payroll Expense ($000):** 9713 **Personnel:** 158

☐ **AUSTIN LAKES HOSPITAL (454069)**, 1025 East 32nd Street, Zip 78705–2714; tel. 512/544–5253 **A**1 5 10 **F**98 103 104 105 130 **S** Universal Health Services, Inc., King of Prussia, PA
Primary Contact: Rick Buckelew, Chief Executive Officer
CFO: Greg Wysocki, Chief Financial Officer
CMO: Shiva Lam, M.D., Executive Medical Director
CHR: Dan Smith, Director Human Resources
CNO: Barbara Powers, R.N., Chief Nursing Officer
Web address: www.austinlakeshospital.com
Control: Corporation, Investor–owned, for–profit **Service:** Psychiatric

Staffed Beds: 58 **Admissions:** 2388 **Census:** 51 **Outpatient Visits:** 7747 **Births:** 0 **Total Expense ($000):** 11396 **Payroll Expense ($000):** 6451 **Personnel:** 122

☐ **AUSTIN OAKS HOSPITAL (454121)**, 1407 West Stassney Lane, Zip 78745–2947; tel. 512/440–4800 **A**1 10 **F**29 38 64 98 99 100 101 103 104 105 130 **S** Universal Health Services, Inc., King of Prussia, PA
Primary Contact: Steve Kelly, Interim Chief Executive Officer
Web address: www.austinoakshospital.com
Control: Partnership, Investor–owned, for–profit **Service:** Psychiatric

Staffed Beds: 80 **Admissions:** 2212 **Census:** 48 **Outpatient Visits:** 4363 **Births:** 0 **Total Expense ($000):** 11762 **Payroll Expense ($000):** 6145 **Personnel:** 123

TX

Many Facility Codes have changed. Please refer to the AHA Guide Code Chart.
© 2016 AHA Guide

☐ **AUSTIN STATE HOSPITAL (454084)**, 4110 Guadalupe Street, Zip 78751–4296; tel. 512/452–0381 **A**1 3 5 10 **F**29 30 39 50 56 59 65 68 75 82 86 98 99 101 103 130 132 143 146 **P**1 **S** Texas Department of State Health Services, Austin, TX
Primary Contact: Cathy Nottebart, Interim Superintendent
CMO: Ross Taylor, M.D., Clinical Director
CIO: Cindy Reed, Director Community Relations
Web address: www.dshs.state.tx.us/mhhospitals/austinsh/default.shtm
Control: State–Government, nonfederal **Service:** Psychiatric

Staffed Beds: 299 **Admissions:** 1633 **Census:** 260 **Outpatient Visits:** 0
Births: 0 **Total Expense ($000):** 88097 **Payroll Expense ($000):** 38244
Personnel: 826

✠ **CENTRAL TEXAS REHABILITATION HOSPITAL (673027)**, 700 West 45th Street, Zip 78751–2800; tel. 512/407–2111 **A**1 3 5 10 **F**3 29 59 74 79 82 90 91 96 130 132 148
Primary Contact: A. Jay Rimovsky, Chief Executive Officer
CFO: Tracey Allen, Controller
CMO: Mary Ann Gonzales, M.D., Medical Director
CIO: Peggy Barrett, R.N., Chief Information Officer
CHR: Liza Cuero, Coordinator Human Resources
CNO: Kerry Radcliffe, JD, Chief Nursing Officer
Web address: www.khrehabcentraltexas.com/
Control: Partnership, Investor–owned, for–profit **Service:** Rehabilitation

Staffed Beds: 50 **Admissions:** 1001 **Census:** 38 **Outpatient Visits:** 0 **Births:**
0 **Total Expense ($000):** 14642 **Payroll Expense ($000):** 8661 **Personnel:**
120

☐ **CORNERSTONE HOSPITAL OF AUSTIN (452034)**, 4207 Burnet Road, Zip 78756–3396; tel. 512/706–1900, (Includes CORNERSTONE HOSPITAL OF AUSTIN, 1005 East 32nd Street, Zip 78705; tel. 512/867–5822; Edward J. Sherwood, M.D., Chief Executive Officer; CORNERSTONE HOSPITAL OF ROUND ROCK, 4681 College Park Drive, Round Rock, Zip 78665; tel. 512/533–2525; Edward L. Dyer, Chief Executive Officer) **A**1 10 **F**1 3 29 30 45 70 75 77 87 91 148 **S** Cornerstone Healthcare Group, Dallas, TX
Primary Contact: Scott Galliardt, MSN, R.N., Chief Executive Officer
CMO: David F. Pohl, M.D., Chief of Staff
Web address: www.chghospitals.com/austin/
Control: Corporation, Investor–owned, for–profit **Service:** Long–Term Acute Care hospital

Staffed Beds: 118 **Admissions:** 768 **Census:** 62 **Outpatient Visits:** 0 **Births:**
0 **Total Expense ($000):** 31620 **Payroll Expense ($000):** 12680
Personnel: 187

CROSS CREEK HOSPITAL (454133), 8402 Cross Park Drive, Zip 78754; tel. 512/215–3900, (Nonreporting) **S** Acadia Healthcare Company, Inc., Franklin, TN
Primary Contact: Jennifer Miller, Chief Executive Officer
Web address: www.cornerstonehealthcaregroup.com
Control: Corporation, Investor–owned, for–profit **Service:** Psychiatric

Staffed Beds: 90

✠ **DELL CHILDREN'S MEDICAL CENTER OF CENTRAL TEXAS (453310)**, 4900 Mueller Boulevard, Zip 78723–3079; tel. 512/324–0000 **A**1 2 3 5 10 **F**3 11 19 21 23 25 27 29 30 31 32 34 35 39 40 41 43 44 46 49 50 53 54 58 59 61 64 65 68 71 72 74 75 77 78 79 80 81 82 83 84 85 86 87 88 89 93 99 100 101 104 107 108 111 112 114 115 116 126 129 130 131 132 135 143 146 148 **P**3 8 **S** Ascension Health, Saint Louis, MO
Primary Contact: Mark W. Shen, M.D., President and Chief Executive Officer
Web address: www.dellchildrens.net
Control: Church–operated, Nongovernment, not–for profit **Service:** Children's general

Staffed Beds: 248 **Admissions:** 10096 **Census:** 117 **Outpatient Visits:**
317627 **Births:** 0 **Total Expense ($000):** 365619 **Payroll Expense ($000):**
157008 **Personnel:** 2433

✠ **HEALTHSOUTH REHABILITATION HOSPITAL – AUSTIN (673054)**, 330 West Ben White Boulevard, Zip 78704; tel. 512/730–4800, (Data for 92 days) **A**1 10 **F**3 29 68 75 77 86 87 90 91 94 96 130 148 **S** HEALTHSOUTH Corporation, Birmingham, AL
Primary Contact: Jack Boggess, Chief Executive Officer
CNO: Vidette J. Forbes, R.N., Chief Nursing Officer and Chief Operating Officer
Web address: www.reliantaustin.com
Control: Corporation, Investor–owned, for–profit **Service:** Rehabilitation

Staffed Beds: 60 **Admissions:** 133 **Census:** 13 **Outpatient Visits:** 0 **Births:**
0 **Total Expense ($000):** 2411 **Payroll Expense ($000):** 670 **Personnel:** 54

✠ **HEALTHSOUTH REHABILITATION HOSPITAL OF AUSTIN (453044)**, 1215 Red River Street, Zip 78701–1921; tel. 512/474–5700 **A**1 10 **F**3 29 56 62 74 75 77 79 86 87 90 91 130 132 143 148 **P**5 **S** HEALTHSOUTH Corporation, Birmingham, AL
Primary Contact: Brad Dinsmore, Interim Chief Executive Officer
CFO: Pamela McLaughlin, Chief Financial Officer
CMO: Johnny Shane Ross, Executive Medical Director
Web address: www.healthsouthaustin.com
Control: Corporation, Investor–owned, for–profit **Service:** Rehabilitation

Staffed Beds: 40 **Admissions:** 890 **Census:** 33 **Outpatient Visits:** 6675
Births: 0 **Total Expense ($000):** 16816 **Payroll Expense ($000):** 7361
Personnel: 129

☐ **NORTHWEST HILLS SURGICAL HOSPITAL (450808)**, 6818 Austin Center Boulevard, Suite 100, Zip 78731–3199; tel. 512/346–1994 **A**1 5 10 **F**3 40 45 64 75 79 81
Primary Contact: Scott Cullen, Chief Executive Officer
CFO: Jenny Salome, Chief Financial Officer and Assistant Administrator
Web address: www.northwesthillssurgical.com
Control: Partnership, Investor–owned, for–profit **Service:** General Medical and Surgical

Staffed Beds: 8 **Admissions:** 470 **Census:** 2 **Outpatient Visits:** 7749 **Births:**
0 **Total Expense ($000):** 26480 **Payroll Expense ($000):** 5362 **Personnel:**
91

✠ ◇ **SETON MEDICAL CENTER AUSTIN (450056)**, 1201 West 38th Street, Zip 78705–1006; tel. 512/324–1000 **A**1 2 3 5 10 21 **F**3 11 12 13 15 18 20 22 24 26 28 29 30 31 34 35 40 43 44 45 46 49 50 51 57 58 59 60 61 64 68 70 72 74 75 76 77 78 79 80 81 82 84 85 86 87 93 107 108 111 114 115 119 126 130 131 132 135 137 145 146 147 148 **P**3 8 **S** Ascension Health, Saint Louis, MO
Primary Contact: Katherine Henderson, President
COO: Tad Hatton, Vice President Chief Operating Officer
CFO: Robert Scott Herndon, Vice President Chief Financial Officer
CMO: David W. Martin, M.D., Vice President Chief Medical Officer
CIO: Mike Minks, Chief Information Officer VI
CHR: Joe Canales, Vice President Human Resources
CNO: Elizabeth Steger, FACHE, Chief Nursing Officer
Web address: www.seton.net/locations/smc/
Control: Church–operated, Nongovernment, not–for profit **Service:** General Medical and Surgical

Staffed Beds: 422 **Admissions:** 20845 **Census:** 282 **Outpatient Visits:**
84110 **Births:** 4324 **Total Expense ($000):** 448525 **Payroll Expense
($000):** 127522 **Personnel:** 2505

✠ **SETON NORTHWEST HOSPITAL (450867)**, 11113 Research Boulevard, Zip 78759–5236; tel. 512/324–6000 **A**1 2 3 5 10 **F**3 11 12 13 15 18 29 30 31 34 35 36 37 40 43 44 45 47 49 50 51 57 59 64 68 70 73 74 75 76 77 78 79 80 81 85 86 87 93 107 111 114 119 130 131 132 135 146 148 **P**3 8 **S** Ascension Health, Saint Louis, MO
Primary Contact: Karen Litterer, R.N., MSN, Administrator and Chief Operating Officer
COO: Karen Litterer, R.N., Administrator and Chief Operating Officer
CFO: Douglas D. Waite, Chief Financial Officer
CMO: Ed LeBlanc, M.D., Vice President Medical Affairs
CIO: Gerry Lewis, Chief Information Officer
CHR: Trennis Jones, Senior Vice President and Chief Administrative Officer
Web address: www.seton.net
Control: Church–operated, Nongovernment, not–for profit **Service:** General Medical and Surgical

Staffed Beds: 74 **Admissions:** 5556 **Census:** 49 **Outpatient Visits:** 51502
Births: 1487 **Total Expense ($000):** 88586 **Payroll Expense ($000):** 32735
Personnel: 465

✠ **SETON SHOAL CREEK HOSPITAL (454029)**, 3501 Mills Avenue, Zip 78731–6391; tel. 512/324–2000 **A**1 3 5 10 **F**4 5 29 30 34 68 70 72 73 80 86 87 88 89 90 98 99 100 101 103 104 130 132 135 146 **P**3 8 **S** Ascension Health, Saint Louis, MO
Primary Contact: William Henricks, Ph.D., Vice President and Chief Operating Officer
COO: William Henricks, Ph.D., Vice President and Chief Operating Officer
CFO: Robert Scott Herndon, Chief Financial Officer
CMO: Amy E. Walton, M.D., Chief Medical Officer
CIO: Mike Minks, Chief Information Officer
CHR: Joe Canales, Director Human Resources
CNO: Debra T. Hernandez, Chief Nursing Officer
Web address: www.seton.net
Control: Church–operated, Nongovernment, not–for profit **Service:** Psychiatric

Staffed Beds: 94 **Admissions:** 3762 **Census:** 60 **Outpatient Visits:** 23224
Births: 0 **Total Expense ($000):** 30097 **Payroll Expense ($000):** 15292
Personnel: 230

TX

Hospital, Medicare Provider Number, Address, Telephone, Approval, Facility, and Physician Codes, Health Care System

★ American Hospital Association (AHA) membership ◯ Healthcare Facilities Accreditation Program ⇑ Center for Improvement in Healthcare Quality Accreditation
☐ The Joint Commission accreditation ◇ DNV Healthcare Inc. accreditation △ Commission on Accreditation of Rehabilitation Facilities (CARF) accreditation

SETON SOUTHWEST HOSPITAL (450865), 7900 F. M. 1826,
Zip 78737–1407; tel. 512/324–9000 **A**1 10 **F**3 11 13 15 28 29 30 34 35 36
40 43 44 45 57 59 64 68 71 72 75 76 79 81 85 87 93 107 110 111 115
119 130 131 132 135 146 147 **P**3 8 **S** Ascension Health, Saint Louis, MO
Primary Contact: Mary Faria, FACHE, Ph.D., Vice President and Chief Operating
Officer
Web address: www.seton.net
Control: Church–operated, Nongovernment, not–for profit **Service:** General
Medical and Surgical

Staffed Beds: 33 **Admissions:** 1090 **Census:** 9 **Outpatient Visits:** 30459
Births: 830 **Total Expense ($000):** 31291 **Payroll Expense ($000):** 11594
Personnel: 144

◇ **ST. DAVID'S MEDICAL CENTER (450431)**, 919 East 32nd Street,
Zip 78705–2709, Mailing Address: P.O. Box 4039, Zip 78765–4039;
tel. 512/476–7111, (Includes HEART HOSPITAL OF AUSTIN, 3801 North Lamar
Boulevard, Zip 78756–4080; tel. 512/407–7000; David Laird, Chief Executive
Officer; ST. DAVID'S GEORGETOWN HOSPITAL, 2000 Scenic Drive, Georgetown,
Zip 78626–7726; tel. 512/943–3000; Hugh Brown, Chief Executive Officer; ST.
DAVID'S REHABILITATION, 1005 East 32nd Street, Zip 78705–2713,
Mailing Address: P.O. Box 4270, Zip 78765–4270; tel. 512/544–5100; Diane
Owens, Assistant Administrator) **A**1 2 3 5 10 21 **F**3 11 12 13 15 17 18 20 22
24 26 28 29 30 31 34 35 36 37 39 40 43 45 46 47 48 52 53 56 57 58 59
61 64 68 70 72 73 74 75 76 77 78 79 81 85 86 87 90 93 95 96 107 108
109 110 111 114 115 116 119 126 130 131 132 135 146 147 148 **P**3 6 8
S HCA, Nashville, TN
Primary Contact: Donald H. Wilkerson, Chief Executive Officer
COO: David Shimp, Chief Operating Officer
CFO: Julie Perez, Chief Financial Officer
CMO: John Marietta, M.D., Chief Medical Officer
CIO: Richard Lear, Director Information Systems
CHR: Julie Hajek, Director Human Resources
Web address: www.stdavids.com
Control: Other not–for–profit (including NFP Corporation) **Service:** General
Medical and Surgical

Staffed Beds: 555 **Admissions:** 26006 **Census:** 394 **Outpatient Visits:**
225317 **Births:** 5486 **Total Expense ($000):** 466391 **Payroll Expense
($000):** 156632 **Personnel:** 2635

ST. DAVID'S NORTH AUSTIN MEDICAL CENTER (450809), 12221 North
MoPac Expressway, Zip 78758–2496; tel. 512/901–1000 **A**1 2 3 10 **F**3 12 13
15 18 20 22 24 26 28 29 30 31 34 35 37 40 41 42 43 45 47 49 53 54 58
59 64 70 72 73 74 75 76 77 78 79 81 85 86 87 88 89 90 93 107 108 110
111 114 115 118 119 126 129 130 132 138 144 145 146 147 148 **P**3 6 8
S HCA, Nashville, TN
Primary Contact: Allen Harrison, Chief Executive Officer
COO: Sheri Dube, Chief Operating Officer
CFO: Natalie Pack, Chief Financial Officer
CMO: Kenneth W. Mitchell, M.D., Medical Director
CIO: Marshall Pearson, Director Management Information Systems
CHR: Laura Light, Director Human Resources
Web address: www.northaustin.com
Control: Other not–for–profit (including NFP Corporation) **Service:** General
Medical and Surgical

Staffed Beds: 378 **Admissions:** 19791 **Census:** 273 **Outpatient Visits:**
154566 **Births:** 6570 **Total Expense ($000):** 261737 **Payroll Expense
($000):** 91058 **Personnel:** 1467

ST. DAVID'S SOUTH AUSTIN MEDICAL CENTER (450713), 901 West Ben
White Boulevard, Zip 78704–6903; tel. 512/447–2211 **A**1 2 3 5 10 **F**11 12 13
15 17 18 20 22 24 26 28 29 30 31 34 35 37 40 42 43 45 46 48 49 54 56
59 60 64 70 73 74 75 76 77 78 79 80 81 82 84 85 87 93 107 108 110 111
114 115 119 124 126 129 130 132 136 144 145 146 147 148 **P**3 6 8
S HCA, Nashville, TN
Primary Contact: Todd E. Steward, FACHE, Chief Executive Officer
CFO: Wesley D. Fountain, Chief Financial Officer
CMO: Albert Gros, M.D., Chief Medical Officer
CIO: Richard Lear, Director Information Systems
CHR: Lisa Talbot, Director Human Resources
CNO: Sally A. Gillam, R.N., Chief Nursing Officer
Web address: www.southaustinmc.com
Control: Other not–for–profit (including NFP Corporation) **Service:** General
Medical and Surgical

Staffed Beds: 270 **Admissions:** 15996 **Census:** 213 **Outpatient Visits:**
146214 **Births:** 1654 **Total Expense ($000):** 208864 **Payroll Expense
($000):** 73152 **Personnel:** 1213

TEXAS NEUROREHAB CENTER (452038), 1106 West Dittmar Road, Building
9, Zip 78745–6328, Mailing Address: P.O. Box 150459, Zip 78715–0459;
tel. 512/444–4835 **A**1 10 **F**1 3 29 54 74 75 77 79 93 108 130 148 **P**5
S Universal Health Services, Inc., King of Prussia, PA
Primary Contact: Edgar E. Prettyman, PsyD, Chief Executive Officer
COO: Janet Bitner, Chief Operating Officer
CFO: Omar Correa, Chief Financial Officer
CMO: James Boysen, M.D., Executive Medical Director
CHR: Colleen Lewis, Director Human Resources
Web address: www.texasneurorehab.com
Control: Partnership, Investor–owned, for–profit **Service:** Long–Term Acute Care
hospital

Staffed Beds: 47 **Admissions:** 441 **Census:** 37 **Outpatient Visits:** 6991
Births: 0 **Total Expense ($000):** 11834 **Payroll Expense ($000):** 6958
Personnel: 274

☐ **TEXAS STAR RECOVERY (454111)**, 1106 West Dittmar Road,
Zip 78745–6328; tel. 512/462–6729, (Nonreporting) **A**1 10
Primary Contact: William Loving, M.D., Medical Director
Web address: www.texasstarrecovery.com
Control: Partnership, Investor–owned, for–profit **Service:** Psychiatric

Staffed Beds: 28

THE HOSPITAL AT WESTLAKE MEDICAL CENTER (670006), 5656 Bee
Caves Road, Suite M302, Zip 78746–5280; tel. 512/327–0000 **A**10 **F**3 18 20
22 26 29 37 39 40 45 51 53 58 59 64 68 70 75 77 79 81 82 85 93 96 107
108 111 114 118 119 129 130 131 135 148
Primary Contact: Robin Allen, Chief Executive Officer
CFO: Devon Culbert, Controller
CMO: Tom Burns, M.D., Chief of Staff
CHR: Kellie Bryson, Director Human Resources
Web address: www.westlakemedical.com
Control: Partnership, Investor–owned, for–profit **Service:** General Medical and
Surgical

Staffed Beds: 23 **Admissions:** 1067 **Census:** 7 **Outpatient Visits:** 9832
Births: 0 **Total Expense ($000):** 41099 **Payroll Expense ($000):** 10573
Personnel: 191

◇ **UNIVERSITY MEDICAL CENTER AT BRACKENRIDGE (450124)**, 601
East 15th Street, Zip 78701–1996; tel. 512/324–7000 **A**1 2 3 5 10 21 **F**3 11
13 15 18 20 22 24 26 29 30 31 34 35 37 39 40 43 44 45 47 49 55 57 58
59 60 64 65 66 68 70 71 72 74 75 76 77 78 79 81 82 84 85 87 93 97 102
104 107 108 110 111 114 119 124 130 132 135 143 146 148 **P**3
8 **S** Ascension Health, Saint Louis, MO
Primary Contact: Christann Vasquez, President
CFO: Robert Scott Herndon, Chief Financial Officer
CMO: Tom Caven, M.D., Vice President Medical Affairs
CIO: Mike Minks, Vice President
CHR: Joe Canales, Vice President Human Resources
Web address: www.seton.net
Control: Church–operated, Nongovernment, not–for profit **Service:** General
Medical and Surgical

Staffed Beds: 208 **Admissions:** 12633 **Census:** 172 **Outpatient Visits:**
613234 **Births:** 999 **Total Expense ($000):** 623800 **Payroll Expense
($000):** 221723 **Personnel:** 3070

AZLE—Tarrant County

TEXAS HEALTH HARRIS METHODIST HOSPITAL AZLE (450419), 108 Denver
Trail, Zip 76020–3614; tel. 817/444–8600 **A**1 10 **F**3 11 15 18 29 30 34 35
40 43 45 56 57 59 64 70 75 77 79 81 85 93 107 110 114 119 130 135 146
147 148 **S** Texas Health Resources, Arlington, TX
Primary Contact: Bob S. Ellzey, FACHE, President
CFO: Brian Blessing, Chief Financial Officer
CMO: Judy Laviolette, M.D., Chief Medical Officer
CIO: Patricia Johnston, Vice President Information Services
CHR: Lance Waring, Director Human Resources
CNO: Valarie Gilbert, R.N., Chief Nursing Officer
Web address: www.texashealth.org/Azle
Control: Other not–for–profit (including NFP Corporation) **Service:** General
Medical and Surgical

Staffed Beds: 31 **Admissions:** 1522 **Census:** 13 **Outpatient Visits:** 31554
Births: 0 **Total Expense ($000):** 32898 **Payroll Expense ($000):** 14686
Personnel: 206

TX

BALLINGER—Runnels County

★ **BALLINGER MEMORIAL HOSPITAL (451310)**, 608 Avenue B,
Zip 76821–2499, Mailing Address: P.O. Box 617, Zip 76821–0617;
tel. 325/365–2531, (Total facility includes 135 beds in nursing home–type unit)
A10 18 **F**3 7 11 29 34 40 43 53 64 65 68 77 93 107 114 119 127 128 130
133 **P**5
Primary Contact: Rhett D. Fricke, Chief Executive Officer
CFO: Josilyn Peterson, Chief Financial Officer
CHR: Roselyn Hudgens, Director Human Resources
Web address: www.ballingerhospital.org
Control: Hospital district or authority, Government, nonfederal **Service:** General
Medical and Surgical

Staffed Beds: 151 **Admissions:** 109 **Census:** 85 **Outpatient Visits:** 17201
Births: 0 **Total Expense ($000):** 12335 **Payroll Expense ($000):** 3322
Personnel: 79

BAY CITY—Matagorda County

✠ **MATAGORDA REGIONAL MEDICAL CENTER (450465)**, 104 7th Street,
Zip 77414–4853; tel. 979/245–6383 **A**1 10 20 **F**3 11 13 15 18 20 22 28 29
30 32 34 38 39 40 43 45 46 47 50 51 53 56 57 59 64 65 66 68 70 75 76
77 79 81 82 85 86 89 93 98 103 107 108 110 111 114 119 130 132 135
146 147 148 **S** QHR, Brentwood, TN
Primary Contact: Steven L. Smith, Chief Executive Officer
CFO: Bryan Prochnow, Chief Financial Officer
CIO: Beverly Trombatore, R.N., Director Managed Information Systems
CHR: Cindy Krebs, District Director Human Resources
CNO: Mike Lee, R.N., Chief Nursing Officer
Web address: www.matagordaregional.org
Control: Hospital district or authority, Government, nonfederal **Service:** General
Medical and Surgical

Staffed Beds: 58 **Admissions:** 2176 **Census:** 26 **Outpatient Visits:** 57216
Births: 498 **Total Expense ($000):** 59313 **Payroll Expense ($000):** 20145
Personnel: 294

BAYTOWN—Harris County

★ ◇ **HOUSTON METHODIST SAN JACINTO HOSPITAL (450424)**, 4401 Garth
Road, Zip 77521–2122; tel. 281/420–8600, (Includes HOUSTON METHODIST
SAN JACINTO HOSPITAL – ALEXANDER, 1700 James Bowie Drive,
Zip 77520–3386; tel. 281/420–6100; David P. Bernard, FACHE, Chief Executive
Officer), (Total facility includes 30 beds in nursing home–type unit) **A**2 3 10 21 **F**3
8 11 12 13 15 18 20 22 24 26 28 29 30 31 34 35 38 40 41 44 48 49 50 51
53 57 59 61 64 65 68 70 71 73 74 75 76 77 78 79 81 82 85 86 87 90 91
93 96 97 98 102 103 107 108 110 111 114 115 116 117 118 119 120 121
123 126 128 129 130 132 145 146 147 148 **S** Houston Methodist,
Houston, TX
Primary Contact: David P. Bernard, FACHE, Chief Executive Officer
CFO: Jonathan Sturgis, Chief Financial Officer
CMO: Klaus Thaler, FACS, Chief Medical Officer
CHR: Sherri Davis–Sampson, Director Human Resources
CNO: Rebecca Chalupa, MSN, Chief Nursing Officer
Web address: www.houstonmethodist.org
Control: Other not–for–profit (including NFP Corporation) **Service:** General
Medical and Surgical

Staffed Beds: 275 **Admissions:** 13184 **Census:** 180 **Outpatient Visits:**
126216 **Births:** 1641 **Total Expense ($000):** 226146 **Payroll Expense
($000):** 86577 **Personnel:** 1362

BEAUMONT—Jefferson County

★ **BAPTIST HOSPITALS OF SOUTHEAST TEXAS (450346)**, 3080 College Street,
Zip 77701–4689, Mailing Address: P.O. Box 1591, Zip 77704–1591;
tel. 409/212–5000, (Includes BAPTIST HOSPITALS OF SOUTHEAST TEXAS
FANNIN BEHAVIORAL HEALTH CENTER, 3250 Fannin Street, Zip 77701;
tel. 409/212–7000; David N. Parmer, Chief Executive Officer) **A**2 10 22 **F**3 4 5
11 12 13 15 17 18 20 22 24 26 28 29 30 31 34 35 37 40 41 42 43 45 49
51 55 57 59 60 64 70 72 73 74 75 76 77 78 79 81 82 85 86 87 88 89 90
93 96 98 99 100 101 102 103 104 105 107 108 110 111 114 115 117 118
119 120 121 123 124 130 132 135 144 146 147 **P**6 **S** Community Hospital
Corporation, Plano, TX
Primary Contact: David N. Parmer, Chief Executive Officer
COO: Patrick Shannon, Chief Operating Officer
CFO: Gary Troutman, CPA, Chief Financial Officer
CMO: Shariq Ahmad, M.D., Chief of Staff
CIO: William Toon, Chief Information Officer
CHR: Hannah Schiesler, Interim Assistant Director Human Resources
CNO: Karen Tomsu, MSN, Chief Nursing Officer
Web address: www.bhset.net
Control: Other not–for–profit (including NFP Corporation) **Service:** General
Medical and Surgical

Staffed Beds: 355 **Admissions:** 16113 **Census:** 198 **Outpatient Visits:**
150031 **Births:** 1537 **Total Expense ($000):** 223853 **Payroll Expense
($000):** 84453 **Personnel:** 1658

✠ **CHRISTUS DUBUIS HOSPITAL OF BEAUMONT (452042)**, 2830 Calder
Avenue, 4th Floor, Zip 77702–1809; tel. 409/899–8154 **A**1 10 **F**1 3 18 29 30
31 35 130 148 **S** CHRISTUS Health, Irving, TX
Primary Contact: Terry W. Kepler, Administrator
Web address: www.christusdubuis.org/BeaumontandPortArthurSystem–
CHRISTUSDubuisHospitalofBeaumont
Control: Church–operated, Nongovernment, not–for profit **Service:** Long–Term
Acute Care hospital

Staffed Beds: 51 **Admissions:** 560 **Census:** 39 **Outpatient Visits:** 0 **Births:**
0 **Total Expense ($000):** 16518 **Payroll Expense ($000):** 6364 **Personnel:**
100

✠ **CHRISTUS SOUTHEAST TEXAS HOSPITAL (450034)**, 2830 Calder Avenue,
Zip 77702–1809, Mailing Address: P.O. Box 5405, Zip 77726–5405;
tel. 409/892–7171, (Includes CHRISTUS SOUTHEAST TEXAS HOSPITAL–ST.
MARY, 3600 Gates Boulevard, Port Arthur, Zip 77642–3601, Mailing Address:
P.O. Box 3696, Zip 77643–3696; tel. 409/985–7431; Wayne Moore,
Administrator) **A**1 2 3 10 **F**3 11 12 13 15 17 18 20 22 24 26 28 29 30 31 34
35 36 38 40 43 44 45 46 49 50 51 54 57 59 60 63 64 70 72 74 75 76 77
78 79 81 82 84 85 86 87 88 89 93 94 107 108 111 114 118 119 124 126
130 131 132 144 146 147 148 **P**8 **S** CHRISTUS Health, Irving, TX
Primary Contact: Paul Trevino, Chief Executive Officer
CFO: Shawn Adams, Chief Financial Officer
CMO: Rick Tyler, M.D., Vice President Medical Affairs
CIO: Robert Jacobs, Regional Director Information Management
CHR: Charles Foster, Regional Director Human Resources
Web address: www.christushospital.org
Control: Church–operated, Nongovernment, not–for profit **Service:** General
Medical and Surgical

Staffed Beds: 425 **Admissions:** 17429 **Census:** 197 **Outpatient Visits:**
386690 **Births:** 2357 **Total Expense ($000):** 339987 **Payroll Expense
($000):** 104503 **Personnel:** 1652

**CHRISTUS SOUTHEAST TEXAS ORTHOPEDIC SPECIALTY CENTER
(670007)**, 3650 Laurel Street, Zip 77707–2216; tel. 409/838–0346,
(Nonreporting) **A**10
Primary Contact: Duane N. Hill, Chief Executive Officer
Web address: www.orthodoc.aaos.org/bbji/
Control: Partnership, Investor–owned, for–profit **Service:** General Medical and
Surgical

Staffed Beds: 6

HARBOR HOSPITAL OF SOUTHEAST TEXAS (452093), 860 South 8th Street,
Zip 77701–4626; tel. 409/840–3200, (Data for 105 days) **A**10 **F**1 3 29 30 35
45 85 130 148
Primary Contact: Ronald Hunt, Chief Executive Officer
Web address: www.hhsetx.com
Control: Partnership, Investor–owned, for–profit **Service:** Long–Term Acute Care
hospital

Staffed Beds: 30 **Admissions:** 139 **Census:** 28 **Outpatient Visits:** 0 **Births:**
0 **Total Expense ($000):** 6517 **Payroll Expense ($000):** 1393 **Personnel:**
50

✠ **HEALTHSOUTH REHABILITATION HOSPITAL OF BEAUMONT (453048)**,
3340 Plaza 10 Boulevard, Zip 77707–2551; tel. 409/835–0835 **A**1 10 **F**3 28
29 30 62 64 74 75 77 79 87 90 91 93 95 96 131 132 148 **S** HEALTHSOUTH
Corporation, Birmingham, AL
Primary Contact: H. J. Gaspard, Chief Executive Officer
CFO: David Pipkins, Controller
CMO: Linda C. Smith, M.D., Medical Director
CHR: Joanna Donica, Director Human Resource
CNO: Barbara Morris, R.N., Chief Nursing Officer
Web address: www.healthsouthbeaumont.com
Control: Corporation, Investor–owned, for–profit **Service:** Rehabilitation

Staffed Beds: 61 **Admissions:** 721 **Census:** 25 **Outpatient Visits:** 2916
Births: 0 **Total Expense ($000):** 11742 **Payroll Expense ($000):** 6037
Personnel: 118

☐ **MEDICAL CENTER OF SOUTHEAST TEXAS**, 6025 Metropolitan Drive,
Zip 77706–2407; tel. 409/617–7700, (Nonreporting) **A**1 **S** IASIS Healthcare,
Franklin, TN
Primary Contact: Becky Ames, Chief Executive Officer
Web address: www.medicalcentersetexas.com/
Control: Other not–for–profit (including NFP Corporation) **Service:** Surgical

Staffed Beds: 17

MEMORIAL HERMANN BAPTIST FANNIN BEHAVIORAL HEALTH CENTER
See Baptist Hospitals of Southeast Texas Fannin Behavioral Health Center

BEDFORD—Tarrant County

⊠ **HEALTHSOUTH REHABILITATION HOSPITAL – MID–CITIES (673044)**, 2304 State Highway 121, Zip 76021–5985; tel. 817/684–2000, (Data for 91 days) **A**1 10 **F**3 29 90 96 148 **S** HEALTHSOUTH Corporation, Birmingham, AL
Primary Contact: Robert M. Smart, Chief Executive Officer
CFO: Mary Mwaniki, Chief Financial Officer
CMO: Toni Willis, M.D., Medical Director
CHR: Christie Moore, Director Human Resources
Web address: www.relianthcp.com
Control: Partnership, Investor–owned, for–profit **Service:** Rehabilitation

Staffed Beds: 60 **Admissions:** 321 **Census:** 36 **Outpatient Visits:** 0 **Births:** 0 **Total Expense ($000):** 3803 **Payroll Expense ($000):** 1757 **Personnel:** 126

⊠ **TEXAS HEALTH HARRIS METHODIST HOSPITAL HURST–EULESS–BEDFORD (450639)**, 1600 Hospital Parkway, Zip 76022–6913, Mailing Address: P.O. Box 669, Zip 76095–0669; tel. 817/685–4000, (Includes TEXAS HEALTH SPRINGWOOD, 1608 Hospital Parkway, Zip 76022; tel. 817/355–7700; Ramona Osburn, Senior Vice President, Texas Health Resources Behavioral Health) **A**1 2 10 **F**9 11 12 13 15 18 20 22 24 26 28 29 30 31 34 35 40 43 47 49 50 53 60 64 70 72 74 75 76 78 79 80 81 82 86 87 93 107 108 111 114 118 119 126 130 131 132 134 135 146 147 148 **S** Texas Health Resources, Arlington, TX
Primary Contact: Deborah Paganelli, President
COO: Alice Landers, Administrative Director Operations
CFO: Jaime James, Entity Finance Officer
CMO: Susann Land, M.D., Chief Medical Officer
CHR: Lee Mulvey, Human Resource Officer
CNO: Debra Grant, R.N., Chief Nursing Officer
Web address: www.texashealth.org
Control: Other not–for–profit (including NFP Corporation) **Service:** General Medical and Surgical

Staffed Beds: 202 **Admissions:** 14658 **Census:** 178 **Outpatient Visits:** 81564 **Births:** 2144 **Total Expense ($000):** 237017 **Payroll Expense ($000):** 97145 **Personnel:** 1314

BEEVILLE—Bee County

⊠ **CHRISTUS SPOHN HOSPITAL BEEVILLE (450082)**, 1500 East Houston Street, Zip 78102–5312; tel. 361/354–2000 **A**1 10 20 **F**3 11 13 15 29 30 32 34 35 40 43 45 50 53 57 59 63 64 70 75 76 77 79 81 85 87 93 97 107 108 111 114 115 119 127 130 146 147 148 **P**8 **S** CHRISTUS Health, Irving, TX
Primary Contact: Nathan Tudor, Vice President and Chief Executive Officer
Web address: www.christusspohn.org
Control: Church–operated, Nongovernment, not–for profit **Service:** General Medical and Surgical

Staffed Beds: 49 **Admissions:** 2108 **Census:** 18 **Outpatient Visits:** 41564 **Births:** 288 **Total Expense ($000):** 31007 **Payroll Expense ($000):** 11322 **Personnel:** 154

BELLAIRE—Harris County

◇ **FIRST SURGICAL HOSPITAL**, 4801 Bissonnet, Zip 77401–4028; tel. 713/275–1111 **A**10 21 **F**3 12 29 40 48 49 64 65 79 81 82 85 107 111 119 126 130
Primary Contact: David Kreye, Chief Executive Officer
Web address: www.firststreethospital.com
Control: Other not–for–profit (including NFP Corporation) **Service:** Surgical

Staffed Beds: 19 **Admissions:** 709 **Census:** 4 **Outpatient Visits:** 2200 **Births:** 0 **Total Expense ($000):** 65977 **Payroll Expense ($000):** 10099 **Personnel:** 139

☐ **MEMORIAL HERMANN ORTHOPEDIC AND SPINE HOSPITAL (670012)**, 5410 West Loop South, Zip 77401–2103; tel. 713/314–4500, (Nonreporting) **A**1 3 5 10 **S** Memorial Hermann Health System, Houston, TX
Primary Contact: Andrew Knizley, Chief Executive Officer
CMO: L. V. Ansell, M.D., Medical Director
Web address: www.memorialhermann.org/
Control: Partnership, Investor–owned, for–profit **Service:** General Medical and Surgical

Staffed Beds: 64

BELLVILLE—Austin County

BELLVILLE GENERAL HOSPITAL See Bellville St. Joseph Health Center

⊠ **BELLVILLE ST. JOSEPH HEALTH CENTER (450253)**, 44 North Cummings Street, Zip 77418–1347, Mailing Address: P.O. Box 977, Zip 77418–0977; tel. 979/413–7400, (Data for 181 days) **A**1 10 **F**3 11 15 29 34 40 43 45 50 53 57 59 64 65 68 75 81 93 107 110 111 114 119 130 133 146 **S** Catholic Health Initiatives, Englewood, CO
Primary Contact: Reed Edmundson, Chief Executive Officer
CMO: Christophe Gay, M.D., Chief of Staff
CHR: Jacqueline McEuen, Coordinator Human Resources
Web address: www.st–joseph.org/body.cfm?id=773
Control: Other not–for–profit (including NFP Corporation) **Service:** General Medical and Surgical

Staffed Beds: 23 **Admissions:** 70 **Census:** 2 **Outpatient Visits:** 8909 **Births:** 0 **Total Expense ($000):** 5816 **Payroll Expense ($000):** 2224 **Personnel:** 77

BELTON—Bell County

☐ **CEDAR CREST HOSPITAL AND RESIDENTIAL TREATMENT CENTER (454114)**, 3500 I–35 South, Zip 76513; tel. 254/939–2100 **A**1 10 **F**4 29 34 35 59 68 86 87 98 99 100 101 102 103 104 105 106 130 143 **P**4
Primary Contact: Rob Marsh, Chief Executive Officer
CFO: Melissa West, Chief Financial Officer
CMO: Daniel C. Mathews, M.D., Medical Director
CIO: Cesar Osario, Specialist Information Technology
CHR: Tracy McHaney, Director Human Resources
CNO: Donna Berry, Interim Director of Nursing Services
Web address: www.cedarcresthospital.com
Control: Corporation, Investor–owned, for–profit **Service:** Psychiatric

Staffed Beds: 88 **Admissions:** 3006 **Census:** 59 **Outpatient Visits:** 2292 **Births:** 0 **Total Expense ($000):** 10300 **Payroll Expense ($000):** 5106 **Personnel:** 152

BIG LAKE—Reagan County

★ **REAGAN MEMORIAL HOSPITAL (451301)**, 805 North Main Street, Zip 76932–3999; tel. 325/884–2561 **A**10 18 **F**3 40 43 53 57 89 93 107 114 115 128 130 133 143 **P**5
Primary Contact: Kyle Rockwall, Chief Executive Officer
CMO: Joseph Sudolcan, M.D., Medical Director
Control: Hospital district or authority, Government, nonfederal **Service:** General Medical and Surgical

Staffed Beds: 7 **Admissions:** 17 **Census:** 1 **Outpatient Visits:** 4261 **Births:** 0 **Total Expense ($000):** 8403 **Payroll Expense ($000):** 2614 **Personnel:** 38

BIG SPRING—Howard County

☐ **BIG SPRING STATE HOSPITAL (454000)**, 1901 North Highway 87, Zip 79720–0283; tel. 432/267–8216 **A**1 3 5 10 **F**3 30 39 50 56 59 61 68 75 77 86 87 97 98 101 103 106 130 132 135 146 **P**6 **S** Texas Department of State Health Services, Austin, TX
Primary Contact: Lorie Dunnam, Superintendent
CFO: Adrienne Bides, Assistant Chief Financial Officer and Budget Analyst
CMO: Guido Spangher, M.D., Clinical Director
CIO: Elizabeth Correa, Director Information Management
CHR: Traci Phillips, Assistant Superintendent
CNO: Stormy Ward, Chief Nurse Executive
Web address: www.dshs.state.tx.us/mhhospitals/BigSpringSH/default.shtm
Control: State–Government, nonfederal **Service:** Psychiatric

Staffed Beds: 200 **Admissions:** 475 **Census:** 181 **Outpatient Visits:** 0 **Births:** 0 **Total Expense ($000):** 58054 **Payroll Expense ($000):** 22745 **Personnel:** 558

⊠ **SCENIC MOUNTAIN MEDICAL CENTER (450653)**, 1601 West 11th Place, Zip 79720–4198; tel. 432/263–1211 **A**1 10 20 **F**3 8 11 13 15 18 20 22 29 30 34 35 39 40 43 47 50 51 57 59 64 65 68 69 70 75 76 77 79 81 85 87 89 93 107 108 110 111 114 119 129 130 133 146 147 148 **P**6 **S** Quorum Health, Brentwood, TN
Primary Contact: Emma Krabill, Chief Executive Officer
CFO: Rodger W. Bowen, M.P.H., Chief Financial Officer
CMO: Keith Ledford, M.D., Chief of Staff
CIO: Gene Mills, Director Information Technology
CHR: Deborah Elder, Director Human Resources
CNO: Judy Roever, MSN, Chief Nursing Officer
Web address: www.smmccares.com
Control: Corporation, Investor–owned, for–profit **Service:** General Medical and Surgical

Staffed Beds: 75 **Admissions:** 2165 **Census:** 20 **Outpatient Visits:** 29568 **Births:** 262 **Total Expense ($000):** 43731 **Payroll Expense ($000):** 12850 **Personnel:** 209

Many Facility Codes have changed. Please refer to the AHA Guide Code Chart. © 2016 AHA Guide

★ **WEST TEXAS VETERANS AFFAIRS HEALTH CARE SYSTEM**, 300 Veterans Boulevard, Zip 79720–5500; Mailing Address: Big Springs, tel. 432/263–7361, (Nonreporting) **A**3 5 **S** Department of Veterans Affairs, Washington, DC
Primary Contact: Colonel Michael L. Kiefer, Director
CFO: Ray Olivas, Chief Fiscal Service
CMO: Martin Schnier, D.O., Chief of Staff
CIO: Mike McKinley, Information Security Officer
CHR: Anna Osborne, Chief Human Resources Management Service
Web address: www.bigspring.va.gov/about/
Control: Veterans Affairs, Government, federal **Service:** General Medical and Surgical

Staffed Beds: 149

BONHAM—Fannin County

SAM RAYBURN MEMORIAL VETERANS CENTER See Veterans Affairs North Texas Health Care System, Dallas

TMC BONHAM HOSPITAL (451370), 504 Lipscomb Street, Zip 75418–4028; tel. 903/583–8585 **A**10 18 **F**3 11 15 28 29 30 34 35 40 46 50 57 59 64 65 70 75 81 87 93 107 108 110 111 118 119 130 133 135
Primary Contact: Harley Smith, Chief Executive Officer
CFO: Jay Hodges, Chief Financial Officer
CMO: Michael Brown, D.O., Chief of Staff
CIO: Jack Farguson, Director Information Technology
CHR: Brenda Bagley, Director Human Resources
CNO: William Kiefer, Chief Nursing Officer
Web address: www.redriverregional.com/
Control: Hospital district or authority, Government, nonfederal **Service:** General Medical and Surgical

Staffed Beds: 25 **Admissions:** 748 **Census:** 10 **Outpatient Visits:** 15472 **Births:** 0 **Total Expense ($000):** 18558 **Payroll Expense ($000):** 7221 **Personnel:** 164

BORGER—Hutchinson County

GOLDEN PLAINS COMMUNITY HOSPITAL (451369), 100 Medical Drive, Zip 79007–7579; tel. 806/467–5700 **A**10 18 **F**11 13 15 29 30 34 35 40 43 45 50 54 57 59 62 64 65 66 68 70 75 76 77 79 81 85 86 87 89 93 107 108 115 119 127 130 131 132 133 146 147 148 **P**6
Primary Contact: Don Bates, Chief Executive Officer
COO: Melody Henderson, R.N., Chief Operating Officer and Chief Nursing Officer
CFO: Dina Hermes, Chief Financial Officer
CMO: Wilson Landers, Chief of Staff
CHR: Sally Mason, Director Human Resources
Web address: www.goldenplains.org
Control: Corporation, Investor–owned, for–profit **Service:** General Medical and Surgical

Staffed Beds: 25 **Admissions:** 915 **Census:** 8 **Outpatient Visits:** 48455 **Births:** 298 **Total Expense ($000):** 26269 **Payroll Expense ($000):** 7746 **Personnel:** 191

BRADY—Mcculloch County

HEART OF TEXAS MEMORIAL HOSPITAL (451348), 2008 Nine Road, Zip 76825–7210, Mailing Address: P.O. Box 1150, Zip 76825–1150; tel. 325/597–2901 **A**10 18 **F**15 28 40 43 45 64 81 93 107 111 114 119 127 133 **P**4
Primary Contact: Tim Jones, Chief Executive Officer
CFO: Brad Burnett, Chief Financial Officer
CMO: Pete Castro, D.O., Chief of Staff
Web address: www.bradyhospital.com/
Control: Other not–for–profit (including NFP Corporation) **Service:** General Medical and Surgical

Staffed Beds: 25 **Admissions:** 316 **Census:** 3 **Outpatient Visits:** 15153 **Births:** 0 **Total Expense ($000):** 13738 **Payroll Expense ($000):** 4081 **Personnel:** 102

BRECKENRIDGE—Stephens County

STEPHENS MEMORIAL HOSPITAL (450498), 200 South Geneva Street, Zip 76424–4799; tel. 254/559–2242 **A**10 20 **F**3 7 8 11 15 28 30 34 35 40 43 45 50 53 56 57 59 63 64 68 69 81 85 87 89 93 97 103 107 114 130 133 146 **P**6
Primary Contact: Matthew Kempton, Chief Executive Officer and Administrator
CFO: Samuel Grant, Chief Financial Officer
CMO: Cynthia Perry, M.D., Chief of Staff
CIO: Bobby Thompson, Director Information Technology
CHR: Michelle Funderburg, Director Human Resources
CNO: Alicia Whitt, R.N., Chief Nursing Officer
Web address: www.smhtx.com
Control: County–Government, nonfederal **Service:** General Medical and Surgical

Staffed Beds: 22 **Admissions:** 366 **Census:** 4 **Outpatient Visits:** 14181 **Births:** 0 **Total Expense ($000):** 11176 **Payroll Expense ($000):** 5323 **Personnel:** 127

BRENHAM—Washington County

⊞ **SCOTT & WHITE HOSPITAL – BRENHAM (450187)**, 700 Medical Parkway, Zip 77833–5498; tel. 979/337–5000 **A**1 10 **F**3 11 13 15 18 29 30 34 35 38 40 43 50 57 59 63 65 68 70 75 76 79 80 81 82 85 87 93 97 102 107 119 130 132 133 135 146 147 **S** Baylor Scott & White Health, Dallas, TX
Primary Contact: John R. Hughson, Vice President Operations
CFO: Jane Wellmann, Chief Financial Officer
CMO: Michael Schlabach, M.D., Chief Medical Officer
CIO: Sharon Schwartz, Director Medical Records
CHR: Virginia Counts, Manager Human Resources
Web address: www.swbrenham.org
Control: Other not–for–profit (including NFP Corporation) **Service:** General Medical and Surgical

Staffed Beds: 53 **Admissions:** 1324 **Census:** 13 **Outpatient Visits:** 38231 **Births:** 379 **Total Expense ($000):** 28959 **Payroll Expense ($000):** 13381 **Personnel:** 168

BROWNFIELD—Terry County

★ **BROWNFIELD REGIONAL MEDICAL CENTER (450399)**, 705 East Felt Street, Zip 79316–3439; tel. 806/637–3551 **A**10 20 **F**3 7 13 28 29 30 34 40 43 45 50 57 59 62 64 65 68 75 76 80 81 85 86 87 89 90 93 97 102 107 119 127 130 135 148 **P**4
Primary Contact: Mike Click, R.N., Administrator
CFO: Grady Paul Gafford, Chief Financial Officer
CIO: Sheryl Holcombe, Administrative Assistant
CHR: Kelly Barnett, Human Resource Officer
CNO: Yvonne Schue, R.N., Chief Nursing Officer
Web address: www.brownfield–rmc.org
Control: Hospital district or authority, Government, nonfederal **Service:** General Medical and Surgical

Staffed Beds: 26 **Admissions:** 602 **Census:** 6 **Outpatient Visits:** 46568 **Births:** 122 **Total Expense ($000):** 16845 **Payroll Expense ($000):** 8071 **Personnel:** 187

BROWNSVILLE—Cameron County

☐ **SOUTH TEXAS REHABILITATION HOSPITAL (453092)**, 425 East Alton Gloor Boulevard, Zip 78526–3361; tel. 956/554–6000 **A**1 10 **F**3 28 29 34 35 59 64 75 77 86 87 90 93 94 96 130 132 148 **P**6 **S** Ernest Health, Inc., Albuquerque, NM
Primary Contact: Leo Garza, Chief Executive Officer
CFO: Ernest Nash, Chief Financial Officer
CMO: Christopher Wilson, M.D., Inpatient Medical Director
CIO: Deborah Alcocer, Chief Information Officer
CHR: Tony Rodriguez, Director Human Resources
CNO: Aaron Cepeda, Director Nursing Operations
Web address: www.strh.ernesthealth.com
Control: Partnership, Investor–owned, for–profit **Service:** Rehabilitation

Staffed Beds: 40 **Admissions:** 825 **Census:** 32 **Outpatient Visits:** 4186 **Births:** 0 **Total Expense ($000):** 14346 **Payroll Expense ($000):** 6594 **Personnel:** 140

TX

Hospital, Medicare Provider Number, Address, Telephone, Approval, Facility, and Physician Codes, Health Care System

★ American Hospital Association (AHA) membership　　○ Healthcare Facilities Accreditation Program　　⇑ Center for Improvement in Healthcare Quality Accreditation
☐ The Joint Commission accreditation　　◇ DNV Healthcare Inc. accreditation　　△ Commission on Accreditation of Rehabilitation Facilities (CARF) accreditation

TX

★ **VALLEY BAPTIST MEDICAL CENTER–BROWNSVILLE (450028)**, 1040 West Jefferson Street, Zip 78520–6338, Mailing Address: P.O. Box 3590, Zip 78523–3590; tel. 956/698–5400, (Total facility includes 11 beds in nursing home–type unit) **A**5 10 **F**3 11 12 13 15 18 20 22 24 26 28 29 30 34 35 37 39 40 43 44 45 49 50 54 56 57 59 60 63 64 65 70 72 74 75 76 77 79 81 82 84 85 86 87 89 93 98 100 101 102 103 104 105 106 107 109 110 111 112 114 115 119 126 128 129 130 132 146 147 148 **S** TENET Healthcare Corporation, Dallas, TX
Primary Contact: Leslie Bingham, Senior Vice President and Chief Executive Officer
COO: Marisa Aguilar, Chief Operating Officer
CFO: Harvey Torres, Chief Financial Officer
CMO: Jose L. Ayala, M.D., Chief Medical Officer
CIO: Mary Garrido, Vice President and Regional Chief Information Officer
CHR: Irma L. Pye, Chief Human Resource Officer
CNO: Aniceta Mendoza, R.N., Chief Nursing Officer
Web address: www.valleybaptist.net/brownsville/index.htm
Control: Corporation, Investor–owned, for–profit **Service:** General Medical and Surgical

Staffed Beds: 262 **Admissions:** 11378 **Census:** 144 **Outpatient Visits:** 74916 **Births:** 2192 **Total Expense ($000):** 122740 **Payroll Expense ($000):** 48399 **Personnel:** 818

⊞ **VALLEY REGIONAL MEDICAL CENTER (450662)**, 100A Alton Gloor Boulevard, Zip 78526–3354, Mailing Address: P.O. Box 3710, Zip 78523–3710; tel. 956/350–7101 **A**1 10 **F**3 11 13 15 18 20 22 24 26 29 30 31 32 34 35 40 43 44 45 47 49 50 53 57 59 60 61 64 65 68 70 72 73 74 75 76 77 78 79 81 82 84 85 86 87 89 93 107 108 110 111 115 118 119 124 130 132 135 146 147 148 **P**7 **S** HCA, Nashville, TN
Primary Contact: Art Garza, Chief Executive Officer
COO: Steven C. Hoelscher, Chief Operating Officer
CFO: Marcia Patterson, Chief Financial Officer
CIO: Carlos Leal, Director Information Technology
CHR: Vicky Kahl, Director Human Resources
Web address: www.valleyregionalmedicalcenter.com
Control: Partnership, Investor–owned, for–profit **Service:** General Medical and Surgical

Staffed Beds: 214 **Admissions:** 9196 **Census:** 153 **Outpatient Visits:** 71391 **Births:** 2553 **Total Expense ($000):** 127551 **Payroll Expense ($000):** 55148 **Personnel:** 707

BROWNWOOD—Brown County

⊞ **BROWNWOOD REGIONAL MEDICAL CENTER (450587)**, 1501 Burnet Road, Zip 76801–8520, Mailing Address: P.O. Box 760, Zip 76804–0760; tel. 325/646–8541, (Total facility includes 20 beds in nursing home–type unit) **A**1 10 20 **F**3 11 13 15 18 28 29 30 31 34 35 39 40 45 48 49 50 51 53 54 56 57 59 63 64 68 70 74 75 76 77 78 79 81 82 85 86 87 93 97 98 103 107 108 111 114 119 120 121 123 128 129 130 132 146 147 148 **P**3 8 **S** Community Health Systems, Inc., Franklin, TN
Primary Contact: Claude E. Chip"" Camp, III, FACHE, Chief Executive Officer
COO: Grant Magness, Assistant Chief Executive Officer
CFO: Joseph Wooldridge, Chief Financial Officer
CMO: Sammy Horton, Chief of Staff
CIO: Jay Smith, Director Information Systems
CHR: Mikeana Bailey, Director Human Resources
CNO: Alicia R. Kayga, R.N., Chief Nursing Officer
Web address: www.brmc–cares.com
Control: Partnership, Investor–owned, for–profit **Service:** General Medical and Surgical

Staffed Beds: 188 **Admissions:** 3593 **Census:** 41 **Outpatient Visits:** 68663 **Births:** 657 **Total Expense ($000):** 62342 **Payroll Expense ($000):** 22455 **Personnel:** 552

BRYAN—Brazos County

⊞ **ST. JOSEPH REGIONAL HEALTH CENTER (450011)**, 2801 Franciscan Drive, Zip 77802–2599; tel. 979/776–3777, (Data for 181 days) **A**1 2 3 5 10 **F**3 7 11 12 13 15 17 18 20 22 24 28 29 30 31 32 34 35 37 40 42 43 44 45 46 48 49 50 53 54 57 59 64 65 68 70 74 75 76 77 78 79 80 81 82 84 85 86 87 89 90 93 96 107 110 111 114 118 119 123 124 126 127 129 130 131 132 135 143 144 146 148 **S** Catholic Health Initiatives, Englewood, CO
Primary Contact: Rick D. Napper, Market President
CFO: Lisa McNair, CPA, Senior Vice President and Chief Financial Officer
CIO: John Phillips, Vice President Information Services
CHR: Michael G. Costa, Vice President Human Resources
Web address: www.st–joseph.org
Control: Church–operated, Nongovernment, not–for profit **Service:** General Medical and Surgical

Staffed Beds: 228 **Admissions:** 6974 **Census:** 163 **Outpatient Visits:** 125053 **Births:** 697 **Total Expense ($000):** 123810 **Payroll Expense ($000):** 45083 **Personnel:** 1577

☐ **THE PHYSICIANS CENTRE HOSPITAL (450834)**, 3131 University Drive East, Zip 77802–3473; tel. 979/731–3100 **A**1 10 **F**3 12 15 29 34 35 40 44 45 50 51 59 64 68 74 75 77 79 81 82 85 86 87 89 107 111 114 119 130 131 132 135
Primary Contact: Kori Rich, Chief Executive Officer
CFO: Paul Tannos, Chief Financial Officer
CMO: Barry Solcher, M.D., Chief of Staff
CIO: Shawn Clark, Director Information Systems
CHR: LeeAnn Ford, Director Human Resources and Imaging
CNO: Robert Raymond Lemay, R.N., Chief Nursing Officer
Web address: www.thephysicianscentre.com
Control: Corporation, Investor–owned, for–profit **Service:** Surgical

Staffed Beds: 16 **Admissions:** 348 **Census:** 2 **Outpatient Visits:** 7744 **Births:** 0 **Total Expense ($000):** 15890 **Payroll Expense ($000):** 3974 **Personnel:** 95

BURLESON—Tarrant County

BAYLOR EMERGENCY MEDICAL CENTERS – BURLESON (670107), 12500 South Freeway Suite 100, Zip 76028–7128; tel. 214/294–6250, (Includes BAYLOR EMERGENCY MEDICAL CENTERS – MANSFIELD, 1776 U.S. 287, Suite 100, Mansfield, Zip 76063; tel. 214/294–6300; Kyle Kirkpatrick, Chief Executive Officer), (Nonreporting) **S** Emerus, The Woodlands, TX
Primary Contact: Kyle Kirkpatrick, Chief Executive Officer
Web address: www.bayloremc.com/burleson
Control: Partnership, Investor–owned, for–profit **Service:** General Medical and Surgical

Staffed Beds: 8

⊞ **TEXAS HEALTH HUGULEY HOSPITAL FORT WORTH SOUTH (450677)**, 11801 South Freeway, Zip 76028–7021, Mailing Address: P.O. Box 6337, Fort Worth, Zip 76115–0337; tel. 817/293–9110 **A**1 10 **F**3 5 8 11 13 15 17 18 20 22 24 26 28 29 30 31 32 34 35 38 40 41 43 45 46 48 49 51 54 56 57 59 60 64 65 68 70 71 74 75 76 77 78 79 80 81 84 85 86 87 89 91 93 98 100 101 102 103 104 107 108 110 111 114 118 119 126 130 132 135 146 147 148 **S** Adventist Health System Sunbelt Health Care Corporation, Altamonte Springs, FL
Primary Contact: Kenneth A. Finch, President and Chief Executive Officer
CFO: Penny Johnson, Chief Financial Officer
CMO: Edward Laue, M.D., Chief Medical Officer
CIO: Thomas Schoenig, Regional Chief Information Officer
CHR: Laura Shepherd, Director Human Resources
CNO: Tammy Collier, R.N., Vice President Patient Services
Web address: www.TexasHealthHuguley.org
Control: Church–operated, Nongovernment, not–for profit **Service:** General Medical and Surgical

Staffed Beds: 197 **Admissions:** 10100 **Census:** 116 **Outpatient Visits:** 127228 **Births:** 1240 **Total Expense ($000):** 165816 **Payroll Expense ($000):** 67229 **Personnel:** 1255

BURNET—Burnet County

⊞ **SETON HIGHLAND LAKES (451365)**, 3201 South Water Street, Zip 78611–4510, Mailing Address: P.O. Box 1219, Zip 78611–7219; tel. 512/715–3000 **A**1 3 10 18 **F**3 11 15 18 28 29 30 34 35 40 43 44 50 57 59 62 63 64 65 66 68 70 71 74 75 77 78 79 81 82 84 85 86 87 91 92 93 97 107 110 111 115 119 127 130 132 133 135 146 148 **P**3 8 **S** Ascension Health, Saint Louis, MO
Primary Contact: Karen Litterer, R.N., MSN, Administrator and Chief Operating Officer
COO: Karen Litterer, R.N., Administrator and Chief Operating Officer
CFO: Douglas D. Waite, Senior Vice President and Chief Financial Officer
CIO: Gerry Lewis, Chief Information Officer
Web address: www.seton.net
Control: Church–operated, Nongovernment, not–for profit **Service:** General Medical and Surgical

Staffed Beds: 19 **Admissions:** 1145 **Census:** 11 **Outpatient Visits:** 105051 **Births:** 0 **Total Expense ($000):** 46949 **Payroll Expense ($000):** 15457 **Personnel:** 260

CALDWELL—Burleson County

⊞ **BURLESON ST. JOSEPH HEALTH CENTER (451305)**, 1101 Woodson Drive, Zip 77836–1052, Mailing Address: P.O. Box 360, Zip 77836–0360; tel. 979/567–3245, (Data for 181 days) **A**1 10 18 **F**3 7 11 28 29 30 34 35 40 43 57 59 64 93 119 130 133 135 143 **S** Catholic Health Initiatives, Englewood, CO
Primary Contact: Brian Stanford, Administrator
CFO: Daniel Goggin, Senior Vice President and Chief Financial Officer
CMO: Scott Chennault, M.D., Chief of Staff
CHR: Michael G. Costa, Vice President Human Resources
Web address: www.st–joseph.org/
Control: Church–operated, Nongovernment, not–for profit **Service:** General Medical and Surgical

Staffed Beds: 19 **Admissions:** 107 **Census:** 5 **Outpatient Visits:** 11142 **Births:** 0 **Total Expense ($000):** 5297 **Payroll Expense ($000):** 2434 **Personnel:** 64

CAMERON—Milam County

◇ **LITTLE RIVER CAMERON HOSPITAL (670094)**, 806 North Crockett Avenue, Zip 76520–2553; tel. 254/605–1300 **A**21 **F**3 8 40 41 97 107 114 119
Primary Contact: Troy Zinn, Chief Executive Officer
Web address: www.lrhealthcare.com/cameronhospital
Control: Partnership, Investor–owned, for–profit **Service:** General Medical and Surgical

Staffed Beds: 10 **Admissions:** 39 **Census:** 1 **Outpatient Visits:** 1829 **Births:** 0 **Total Expense ($000):** 21833 **Payroll Expense ($000):** 5407 **Personnel:** 176

CANADIAN—Hemphill County

HEMPHILL COUNTY HOSPITAL (450578), 1020 South Fourth Street, Zip 79014–3315; tel. 806/323–6422, (Total facility includes 42 beds in nursing home–type unit) **A**10 20 **F**2 7 29 35 40 45 56 57 62 63 64 68 69 87 89 93 97 102 107 108 130 133 146 148
Primary Contact: Christy Francis, Chief Executive Officer
COO: Patrick Murfee, Chief Operating Officer
CFO: Bob Ericson, Chief Financial Officer
CMO: G. Anthony Cook, M.D., Medical Director
CIO: Brian Goza, Chief Information Officer
CHR: David Troublefield, Chief Communications Officer
CNO: Debra Sappenfield, R.N., Chief Nursing Officer
Web address: www.hchdst.org
Control: Hospital district or authority, Government, nonfederal **Service:** General Medical and Surgical

Staffed Beds: 61 **Admissions:** 265 **Census:** 27 **Outpatient Visits:** 13844 **Births:** 0 **Total Expense ($000):** 12327 **Payroll Expense ($000):** 5309 **Personnel:** 90

CARRIZO SPRINGS—Dimmit County

★ **DIMMIT REGIONAL HOSPITAL (450620)**, 704 Hospital Drive, Zip 78834–3836, Mailing Address: P.O. Box 1016, Zip 78834–7016; tel. 830/876–2424 **A**10 20 **F**11 13 40 43 45 57 62 64 70 76 81 89 93 107 115 119 144
Primary Contact: James E. Buckner, Jr., FACHE, Chief Executive Officer
CFO: Alma Melendez, Controller
Web address: www.dcmhospital.org
Control: Other not–for–profit (including NFP Corporation) **Service:** General Medical and Surgical

Staffed Beds: 35 **Admissions:** 742 **Census:** 10 **Outpatient Visits:** 20561 **Births:** 236 **Total Expense ($000):** 16590 **Payroll Expense ($000):** 7393 **Personnel:** 178

CARROLLTON—Denton County

☒ **BAYLOR SCOTT & WHITE MEDICAL CENTER – CARROLLTON (450730)**, 4343 North Josey Lane, Zip 75010–4691; tel. 972/394–1010 **A**1 2 10 **F**3 11 12 13 15 18 20 22 29 30 31 35 40 45 46 47 48 49 50 51 59 60 66 70 72 74 76 78 79 80 81 84 85 93 107 111 114 115 119 126 129 130 132 146 147 148 **S** Baylor Scott & White Health, Dallas, TX
Primary Contact: Michael Sanborn, FACHE, MS, President
CFO: James McNatt, Chief Financial Officer
CMO: Matthew Smith, M.D., Vice President Medical Affairs and Chief Medical Officer
CIO: Paul Ratcliff, Director Information Services
CHR: Erica Calime, Director Human Resources
CNO: Barbara Vaughn, R.N., Chief Nursing Officer
Web address: www.baylorhealth.com
Control: Other not–for–profit (including NFP Corporation) **Service:** General Medical and Surgical

Staffed Beds: 124 **Admissions:** 6102 **Census:** 77 **Outpatient Visits:** 60310 **Births:** 1287 **Total Expense ($000):** 140767 **Payroll Expense ($000):** 48782 **Personnel:** 537

☐ **CARROLLTON SPRINGS (454119)**, 2225 Parker Road, Zip 75010–4711; tel. 972/242–4114 **A**1 10 **F**4 98 102 103 104 105
Primary Contact: Lance Folske, Chief Executive Officer
Web address: www.carrolltonsprings.com
Control: Corporation, Investor–owned, for–profit **Service:** Psychiatric

Staffed Beds: 45 **Admissions:** 1631 **Census:** 41 **Outpatient Visits:** 12907 **Births:** 0 **Total Expense ($000):** 10705 **Payroll Expense ($000):** 6735 **Personnel:** 141

FIRST TEXAS HOSPITAL, 1401 East Trinity Mills Road, Zip 75006; tel. 972/810–0700, (Nonreporting)
Primary Contact: Terri Shovald, Chief Executive Officer
Web address: www.firsttexashospital.com/
Control: Corporation, Investor–owned, for–profit **Service:** General Medical and Surgical

Staffed Beds: 50

☒ **SELECT SPECIALTY HOSPITAL–DALLAS (452022)**, 2329 West Parker Road, Zip 75010–4713 **A**1 10 **F**1 3 29 56 74 75 77 85 91 107 114 119 130 135 148 **S** Select Medical Corporation, Mechanicsburg, PA
Primary Contact: Holly Powell, Chief Executive Officer
Web address: www.firsttexashospital.com/
Control: Corporation, Investor–owned, for–profit **Service:** Long–Term Acute Care hospital

Staffed Beds: 60 **Admissions:** 420 **Census:** 35 **Outpatient Visits:** 0 **Births:** 0 **Total Expense ($000):** 20706 **Payroll Expense ($000):** 9272 **Personnel:** 162

CARTHAGE—Panola County

☒ **EAST TEXAS MEDICAL CENTER CARTHAGE (450210)**, 409 Cottage Road, Zip 75633–1466; tel. 903/693–3841 **A**1 10 20 **F**3 8 11 15 28 29 30 34 35 40 43 45 50 57 59 64 65 75 81 85 107 108 110 111 115 119 127 129 145 146 **S** East Texas Medical Center Regional Healthcare System, Tyler, TX
Primary Contact: Gary Mikeal Hudson, Administrator
COO: Gary Mikeal Hudson, Administrator
CFO: Phillip A. Caron, Chief Financial Officer
CMO: Salah Almohammed, Chief of Staff
CIO: Renee Lawhorn, Director Medical Records
CHR: Amber Cox, Director Human Resources
CNO: Judy Peterson, R.N., Chief Nursing Officer
Web address: www.etmc.org
Control: Other not–for–profit (including NFP Corporation) **Service:** General Medical and Surgical

Staffed Beds: 25 **Admissions:** 761 **Census:** 6 **Outpatient Visits:** 68893 **Births:** 0 **Total Expense ($000):** 19682 **Payroll Expense ($000):** 6608 **Personnel:** 133

CEDAR PARK—Williamson County

★ ◇ **BAYLOR SCOTT & WHITE EMERGENCY HOSPITAL– CEDAR PARK (670087)**, 900 East Whitestone Boulevard, Zip 78613–9093; tel. 512/684–4911 **A**10 21 **F**3 29 40 75 87 107 119 **P**5
Primary Contact: John Wood, Regional Chief Executive Officer
Web address: www.sweh.org
Control: Partnership, Investor–owned, for–profit **Service:** General Medical and Surgical

Staffed Beds: 8 **Admissions:** 28 **Census:** 1 **Outpatient Visits:** 10024 **Births:** 0 **Total Expense ($000):** 5238 **Payroll Expense ($000):** 1813 **Personnel:** 42

☒ **CEDAR PARK REGIONAL MEDICAL CENTER (670043)**, 1401 Medical Parkway, Zip 78613–7763; tel. 512/528–7000 **A**1 5 10 **F**3 12 13 15 18 20 22 28 29 34 35 40 43 45 46 47 49 50 54 57 59 64 70 73 74 75 76 77 78 79 81 82 85 87 89 93 107 108 110 111 114 115 118 119 126 129 130 132 135 146 147 148 **S** Community Health Systems, Inc., Franklin, TN
Primary Contact: Brad D. Holland, Chief Executive Officer
COO: Curt M. Junkins, Chief Operating Officer
CFO: Erich Wallschlaeger, Chief Financial Officer
CIO: Brad Hoar, Director Information and Technology
CHR: Jeffery Ward, Director Human Resources
CNO: Krista Baty, R.N., Chief Nursing Officer
Web address: www.cedarparkregional.com
Control: Corporation, Investor–owned, for–profit **Service:** General Medical and Surgical

Staffed Beds: 93 **Admissions:** 4141 **Census:** 41 **Outpatient Visits:** 49773 **Births:** 1060 **Total Expense ($000):** 80523 **Payroll Expense ($000):** 27108 **Personnel:** 518

TX

| Hospital, Medicare Provider Number, Address, Telephone, Approval, Facility, and Physician Codes, Health Care System |
★ American Hospital Association (AHA) membership ○ Healthcare Facilities Accreditation Program ⇑ Center for Improvement in Healthcare Quality Accreditation
☐ The Joint Commission accreditation ◇ DNV Healthcare Inc. accreditation △ Commission on Accreditation of Rehabilitation Facilities (CARF) accreditation

CHILDRESS—Childress County

★ **CHILDRESS REGIONAL MEDICAL CENTER (450369)**, Highway 83 North, Zip 79201–5800, Mailing Address: P.O. Box 1030, Zip 79201–1030; tel. 940/937–6371 **A**10 20 **F**3 7 8 13 15 29 31 32 34 35 40 43 45 50 56 57 59 60 61 62 63 64 65 66 68 77 78 79 81 84 91 92 93 107 111 114 119 127 129 130 133 **P**6
Primary Contact: John Henderson, Chief Executive Officer
COO: Holly Holcomb, R.N., Chief Operating Officer
CFO: Kathy McLain, Chief Financial Officer
CMO: Dustin Pratt, M.D., Chief of Staff
CIO: Holly Holcomb, R.N., Chie Operating Officer
CHR: Gayle Cannon, Director Human Resources
CNO: Sulynn Mester, R.N., Chief Nursing Officer
Web address: www.childresshospital.com
Control: Hospital district or authority, Government, nonfederal **Service:** General Medical and Surgical

Staffed Beds: 35 **Admissions:** 934 **Census:** 7 **Outpatient Visits:** 166519 **Births:** 183 **Total Expense ($000):** 28627 **Payroll Expense ($000):** 14366 **Personnel:** 232

CHILLICOTHE—Hardeman County

CHILLICOTHE HOSPITAL DISTRICT (451326), 303 Avenue I, Zip 79225, Mailing Address: P.O. Box 370, Zip 79225–0370; tel. 940/852–5131 **A**10 18 **F**29 34 40 43 45 57 59 69 81 89 132 133 **P**5
Primary Contact: Linda Hall, Administrator and Chief Executive Officer
COO: Linda Hall, Administrator and Chief Executive Officer
CFO: Linda Hall, Administrator and Chief Executive Officer
CMO: Sherry L. Wolf, M.D., Chief of Medical Staff
CIO: Kathy Busby, Medical Record Technician
CHR: Linda Hall, Administrator and Chief Executive Officer
CNO: Stormy Smith, Chief Nursing Officer
Web address: www.chillhd.org
Control: Hospital district or authority, Government, nonfederal **Service:** General Medical and Surgical

Staffed Beds: 13 **Admissions:** 28 **Census:** 1 **Outpatient Visits:** 5940 **Births:** 0 **Total Expense ($000):** 2525 **Payroll Expense ($000):** 1048 **Personnel:** 23

CLEBURNE—Johnson County

✖ **TEXAS HEALTH HARRIS METHODIST HOSPITAL CLEBURNE (450148)**, 201 Walls Drive, Zip 76033–4007; tel. 817/641–2551 **A**1 10 **F**3 11 13 15 18 29 30 32 34 35 40 43 44 47 48 50 57 59 64 65 66 68 70 75 76 77 79 81 85 89 93 107 108 110 114 119 124 126 129 130 146 148 **P**6 **S** Texas Health Resources, Arlington, TX
Primary Contact: Lorrie Normand, R.N., Interim Chief Executive Officer and Chief Nursing Officer
CFO: Shelly Miland, Group Finance Officer
CMO: Judy Laviolette, M.D., Chief Medical Officer
CIO: Brenda Taylor, Director Information Systems
CHR: Marsha Adams, Interim Director Human Resources
CNO: Lorrie Normand, R.N., Interim Chief Executive Officer and Chief Nursing Officer
Web address: www.texashealth.org
Control: Other not–for–profit (including NFP Corporation) **Service:** General Medical and Surgical

Staffed Beds: 85 **Admissions:** 4348 **Census:** 41 **Outpatient Visits:** 45738 **Births:** 684 **Total Expense ($000):** 66642 **Payroll Expense ($000):** 26572 **Personnel:** 283

CLIFTON—Bosque County

★ ◇ **GOODALL–WITCHER HOSPITAL AUTHORITY (450052)**, 101 South Avenue T, Zip 76634–1897, Mailing Address: P.O. Box 549, Zip 76634–0549; tel. 254/675–8322 **A**10 20 21 **F**3 11 13 15 28 29 30 34 35 36 40 43 45 50 53 57 59 62 64 65 68 76 77 81 93 107 108 114 119 127 130 133 146 147 148 **P**3
Primary Contact: Adam Willmann, President and Chief Executive Officer
CFO: Vicki Gloff, Chief Financial Officer
CMO: Kevin Blanton, D.O., Chief of Staff
CHR: Jennie Oldham, Director Human Resources
CNO: Donna Nichols, R.N., Chief Nursing Officer
Web address: www.gwhf.org
Control: Hospital district or authority, Government, nonfederal **Service:** General Medical and Surgical

Staffed Beds: 25 **Admissions:** 550 **Census:** 9 **Outpatient Visits:** 40858 **Births:** 72 **Total Expense ($000):** 18334 **Payroll Expense ($000):** 7437 **Personnel:** 181

COLEMAN—Coleman County

COLEMAN COUNTY MEDICAL CENTER (451347), 310 South Pecos Street, Zip 76834–4159; tel. 325/625–2135 **A**10 18 **F**3 11 13 28 29 32 34 35 40 43 45 57 59 64 65 66 68 75 77 81 84 93 97 107 114 127 133 134 **S** Preferred Management Corporation, Shawnee, OK
Primary Contact: Michael W. Pruitt, Administrator and Chief Executive Officer
CMO: Paul Reynolds, M.D., Medical Director
CIO: Harvey Ramirez, Chief Information Officer
CHR: Sue Titsworth, Director Human Resources
CNO: Melissa Ereman, R.N., Chief Nursing Officer
Web address: www.colemantexas.org/hospital.html
Control: Corporation, Investor–owned, for–profit **Service:** General Medical and Surgical

Staffed Beds: 25 **Admissions:** 552 **Census:** 8 **Outpatient Visits:** 24548 **Births:** 25 **Total Expense ($000):** 10005 **Payroll Expense ($000):** 4484 **Personnel:** 112

COLLEGE STATION—Brazos County

✖ **COLLEGE STATION MEDICAL CENTER (450299)**, 1604 Rock Prairie Road, Zip 77845–8345; tel. 979/764–5100 **A**1 3 5 10 19 **F**3 11 13 15 18 20 22 24 26 28 29 30 31 34 40 43 45 46 49 53 57 61 70 72 74 76 77 78 79 81 82 84 85 87 89 90 91 93 107 108 111 113 115 118 119 126 127 129 130 131 132 135 146 147 148 **P**7 **S** Community Health Systems, Inc., Franklin, TN
Primary Contact: Leslie Paul Luke, Interim Chief Executive Officer
COO: Vicky Cha Bridier, Chief Operating Officer
CFO: Ken Pannell, Chief Financial Officer
CIO: Daphane Hartman, Director Information Systems
CHR: Sharon Bond, Director Human Resources
CNO: Sherri Welch, R.N., Chief Nursing Officer
Web address: www.csmedcenter.com
Control: Corporation, Investor–owned, for–profit **Service:** General Medical and Surgical

Staffed Beds: 148 **Admissions:** 4780 **Census:** 67 **Outpatient Visits:** 53229 **Births:** 1306 **Total Expense ($000):** 93412 **Payroll Expense ($000):** 30092 **Personnel:** 489

☐ **ROCK PRAIRIE BEHAVIORAL HEALTH (454125)**, 3550 Normand Drive, Zip 77845–6399; tel. 979/703–8848 **A**1 10 **F**98 99 100 101 102 103 105 130 135 **S** Strategic Behavioral Health, LLC, Memphis, TN
Primary Contact: Jackie St. Germain, Chief Executive Officer
CFO: Doug Smith, Chief Financial Officer
CMO: Jason Boley, M.D., Medical Director
CHR: MaxAnne Jones, Director Human Resources
Control: Partnership, Investor–owned, for–profit **Service:** Psychiatric

Staffed Beds: 72 **Admissions:** 1907 **Census:** 46 **Outpatient Visits:** 3678 **Births:** 0 **Total Expense ($000):** 10393 **Payroll Expense ($000):** 5429 **Personnel:** 135

✖ **SCOTT & WHITE HOSPITAL – COLLEGE STATION (670088)**, 700 Scott & White Drive, Zip 77845; tel. 979/207–0100 **A**1 5 10 **F**2 3 11 13 15 17 18 20 22 24 26 29 30 31 32 34 35 38 40 41 45 46 47 48 49 50 51 56 57 59 61 65 67 68 70 72 73 74 75 76 77 78 79 81 82 84 85 86 87 89 93 94 102 107 108 110 111 114 115 116 119 124 126 129 130 131 132 135 145 146 147 148 **S** Baylor Scott & White Health, Dallas, TX
Primary Contact: Jason Jennings, Chief Executive Officer
Web address: www.sw.org/location/college–station–hospital
Control: Other not–for–profit (including NFP Corporation) **Service:** General Medical and Surgical

Staffed Beds: 119 **Admissions:** 4861 **Census:** 49 **Outpatient Visits:** 220825 **Births:** 1170 **Total Expense ($000):** 113005 **Payroll Expense ($000):** 36910 **Personnel:** 837

COLORADO CITY—Mitchell County

★ **MITCHELL COUNTY HOSPITAL (451342)**, 997 West Interstate 20, Zip 79512–2685; tel. 325/728–3431 **A**10 18 **F**3 7 11 28 29 34 35 40 43 45 50 53 57 59 64 65 68 71 81 86 87 93 107 108 109 114 119 127 133 135 146 **P**6
Primary Contact: Robbie Dewberry, Chief Executive Officer
CFO: Joe Wright, Chief Financial Officer
CMO: Dee A. Roach, M.D., Chief of Staff
CIO: Randy Myers, Chief Information Officer, Information Technology
CHR: Deana Overton, Director Human Resources
CNO: Donna Goebel, M.D., Chief Nursing Officer
Web address: www.mitchellcountyhospital.com
Control: Hospital district or authority, Government, nonfederal **Service:** General Medical and Surgical

Staffed Beds: 25 **Admissions:** 492 **Census:** 7 **Outpatient Visits:** 33455 **Births:** 0 **Total Expense ($000):** 21727 **Payroll Expense ($000):** 10525 **Personnel:** 208

Many Facility Codes have changed. Please refer to the AHA Guide Code Chart.
© 2016 AHA Guide

COLUMBUS—Colorado County

COLUMBUS COMMUNITY HOSPITAL (450370), 110 Shult Drive,
Zip 78934–3010; tel. 979/732–2371 **A**3 5 10 20 **F**11 13 15 29 35 40 43 57
68 76 79 81 107 110 111 114 119 127 130 133 135
Primary Contact: James Vanek, Chief Executive Officer
CFO: Regina Wicke, Chief Financial Officer
CMO: Jorge Duchicela, M.D., Chief of Staff
CIO: Ashley Mathis, Privacy Officer
CHR: Janie Hammonds, Human Resources Officer
CNO: Jeno Hargrove, R.N., Director of Nursing
Web address: www.columbusch.com
Control: Other not–for–profit (including NFP Corporation) **Service:** General
Medical and Surgical

Staffed Beds: 40 **Admissions:** 1316 **Census:** 14 **Outpatient Visits:** 78443
Births: 227 **Total Expense ($000):** 27115 **Payroll Expense ($000):** 8314
Personnel: 146

COMANCHE—Comanche County

★ **COMANCHE COUNTY MEDICAL CENTER (451382)**, 10201 Highway 16
North, Zip 76442–4462; tel. 254/879–4900 **A**10 18 **F**3 11 15 28 29 30 34 35
40 43 45 50 53 57 59 64 65 68 70 75 77 79 81 85 86 87 93 97 107 108
110 111 115 119 127 129 130 131 133 145 146 147 148
Primary Contact: David Freshour, Chief Executive Officer
CFO: David Freshour, Chief Financial Officer
CMO: Guyle Donham, M.D., Chief of Staff
CIO: Ismelda Garza, Director Information Systems
CHR: Karen DeLavan, Interim Director Human Resources
CNO: Colleen Jedlicka, R.N., Chief Nursing Officer
Web address: www.comanchecmc.org
Control: Other not–for–profit (including NFP Corporation) **Service:** General
Medical and Surgical

Staffed Beds: 23 **Admissions:** 755 **Census:** 9 **Outpatient Visits:** 54553
Births: 0 **Total Expense ($000):** 21205 **Payroll Expense ($000):** 6641
Personnel: 172

CONROE—Montgomery County

✠ **ASPIRE HOSPITAL (454112)**, 2006 South Loop 336 West, Suite 500,
Zip 77304–3315; tel. 936/647–3500 **A**1 10 **F**3 34 54 56 57 59 78 79 87 93
96 98 103 104 105 107 108 111 112 113 114 115 118 119 120 121 123
124 129 130 131 147 **P**6
Primary Contact: Kostas Gotsoulias, Interim Chief Executive Officer
CFO: Bob Gray, Chief Financial Officer
CIO: John Heemann, Vice President and Chief Information Officer
CHR: Angela Walker, Manager Human Resources
CNO: Troy Ryder, Director of Nursing
Web address: www.aspirehospital.com
Control: Partnership, Investor–owned, for–profit **Service:** Psychiatric

Staffed Beds: 28 **Admissions:** 699 **Census:** 18 **Outpatient Visits:** 11632
Births: 0 **Total Expense ($000):** 9446 **Payroll Expense ($000):** 4564
Personnel: 62

☐ **CHG CORNERSTONE HOSPITAL CONROE (452107)**, 1500 Grand Lake Drive,
Zip 77304–2891; tel. 936/523–1800 **A**1 10 **F**1 3 29 40 74 75 77 79 85 86
87 91 119 148 **S** Cornerstone Healthcare Group, Dallas, TX
Primary Contact: Suzanne Kretschmer, Chief Executive Officer
Web address: www.chghospitals.com/conroe/
Control: Partnership, Investor–owned, for–profit **Service:** Long–Term Acute Care
hospital

Staffed Beds: 41 **Admissions:** 514 **Census:** 35 **Outpatient Visits:** 0 **Births:**
0 **Total Expense ($000):** 12785 **Payroll Expense ($000):** 6633 **Personnel:**
127

✠ **CONROE REGIONAL MEDICAL CENTER (450222)**, 504 Medical Boulevard,
Zip 77304, Mailing Address: P.O. Box 1538, Zip 77305–1538;
tel. 936/539–1111 **A**1 3 10 13 **F**3 11 12 13 15 17 18 20 22 24 26 28 29 31
34 35 40 41 43 45 46 53 54 57 59 64 68 70 72 73 74 75 76 78 79 81 82
85 86 89 90 91 93 107 108 111 114 115 118 119 121 124 129 130 132
135 146 147 148 **S** HCA, Nashville, TN
Primary Contact: Matt Davis, Chief Executive Officer
COO: Reed Hammond, Chief Operating Officer
CFO: Thomas A. Holt, Chief Financial Officer
CMO: Mujtaba Ali–Khan, D.O., Chief Medical Officer
CIO: Jeremy Fuller, Director Information Systems
CHR: Diana Howell, Director Human Resources
Web address: www.conroeregional.com/
Control: Partnership, Investor–owned, for–profit **Service:** General Medical and
Surgical

Staffed Beds: 301 **Admissions:** 15945 **Census:** 223 **Outpatient Visits:**
127963 **Births:** 1380 **Total Expense ($000):** 205453 **Payroll Expense**
($000): 73878 **Personnel:** 1002

✠ **HEALTHSOUTH REHABILITATION HOSPITAL THE WOODLANDS (453059)**,
18550 'IH' 45 South, Zip 77384; tel. 281/364–2000 **A**1 10 **F**3 28 29 34 35 44
57 59 62 65 68 74 75 77 79 82 86 87 90 91 95 96 130 132 148
S HEALTHSOUTH Corporation, Birmingham, AL
Primary Contact: Jeff Crawford, Chief Executive Officer
CMO: Ben Agana, M.D., Medical Director
CHR: Valerie Wells, Manager Human Resources
Web address: www.healthsouththewoodlands.com
Control: Corporation, Investor–owned, for–profit **Service:** Rehabilitation

Staffed Beds: 84 **Admissions:** 1178 **Census:** 37 **Outpatient Visits:** 4121
Births: 0 **Total Expense ($000):** 17189 **Payroll Expense ($000):** 8598
Personnel: 122

CORINTH—Denton County

ATRIUM MEDICAL CENTER OF CORINTH (452111), 3305 Corinth Parkway,
Zip 76208–5380; tel. 940/270–4100 **A**10 **F**1 3 28 29 40 45 47 60 64 68 70
75 77 81 86 87 96 107 111 114 119 148 **P**2
Primary Contact: Barbara Callaghan, Interim Chief Executive Officer
COO: Kathy Mason, Chief Operating Officer
CFO: Anbu Nachimuthu, Chief Financial Officer
CMO: Jalil Kahn, M.D., Chief of Staff
CIO: Wendy Keller, Director Health Information Management
CHR: Melissa Dovel, Manager Human Resources
CNO: Michelle Gray, Nurse Executive
Web address: www.atriumhealthcare.net
Control: Corporation, Investor–owned, for–profit **Service:** Long–Term Acute Care
hospital

Staffed Beds: 60 **Admissions:** 323 **Census:** 22 **Outpatient Visits:** 4291
Births: 0 **Total Expense ($000):** 19737 **Payroll Expense ($000):** 7452
Personnel: 165

CORPUS CHRISTI—Nueces County

✠ **CHRISTUS SPOHN HOSPITAL CORPUS CHRISTI MEMORIAL (450046)**,
2606 Hospital Boulevard, Zip 78405–1804, Mailing Address: P.O. Box 5280,
Zip 78405; tel. 361/902–4000, (Includes CHRISTUS SPOHN HOSPITAL CORPUS
CHRISTI SHORELINE, 600 Elizabeth Street, Zip 78404–2235;
tel. 361/881–3000; Kelly Elkins, President; CHRISTUS SPOHN HOSPITAL
CORPUS CHRISTUS SOUTH, 5950 Saratoga, Zip 78414–4100;
tel. 361/985–5000), (Total facility includes 22 beds in nursing home–type unit)
A1 2 3 5 10 **F**3 8 11 13 15 17 18 20 22 24 26 28 29 30 34 35 37 38 39 40
43 45 46 47 48 49 50 51 53 54 56 57 58 59 60 64 66 67 68 70 72 74 75
76 77 78 79 81 85 86 87 90 93 96 97 98 99 100 101 102 103 107 108 111
114 115 118 119 120 121 123 126 127 128 130 146 147 148 **P**8
S CHRISTUS Health, Irving, TX
Primary Contact: Pamela Robertson, President and Chief Executive Officer
CFO: Brower Pam, Chief Financial Officer
CMO: Charles T. Volk, M.D., Regional Chief Medical Officer
CHR: Mary LaFrancois, Vice President Human Resources
CNO: Jennifer Gentry, R.N., Chief Nursing Officer
Web address: www.christusspohn.org
Control: Church–operated, Nongovernment, not–for profit **Service:** General
Medical and Surgical

Staffed Beds: 576 **Admissions:** 31023 **Census:** 466 **Outpatient Visits:**
269765 **Births:** 2632 **Total Expense ($000):** 534179 **Payroll Expense**
($000): 175086 **Personnel:** 2987

✠ **CORPUS CHRISTI MEDICAL CENTER (450788)**, 3315 South Alameda Street,
Zip 78411–1883, Mailing Address: P.O. Box 8991, Zip 78468–8991;
tel. 361/761–1400, (Includes BAYVIEW BEHAVIORAL HOSPITAL, 6629 Wooldridge
Road, Zip 78414; tel. 361/986–9444; CORPUS CHRISTI MEDICAL CENTER BAY
AREA, 7101 South Padre Island Drive, Zip 78412–4999; tel. 361/985–1200) **A**1
10 13 **F**3 4 5 11 12 13 15 17 18 20 22 24 26 28 29 31 34 35 37 38 40 42
44 47 49 50 53 57 58 59 64 68 70 72 73 74 75 76 77 78 79 81 82 85 86
87 90 93 97 98 99 100 101 102 103 104 105 107 108 110 111 114 115
118 119 120 121 123 124 126 130 131 132 146 147 148 **P**3 8 **S** HCA,
Nashville, TN
Primary Contact: Jay Woodall, Chief Executive Officer
CFO: Chris Nicosia, Chief Financial Officer
CMO: Lawrence Brenner, M.D., Chief of Staff
CIO: Bryan Brown, Director Information Services and Technology
CHR: Michael Conwill, Director Human Resources
CNO: Kathleen A. Rubano, MSN, Chief Nursing Officer
Web address: www.ccmedicalcenter.com
Control: Partnership, Investor–owned, for–profit **Service:** General Medical and
Surgical

Staffed Beds: 416 **Admissions:** 19648 **Census:** 262 **Outpatient Visits:**
128308 **Births:** 4719 **Total Expense ($000):** 271416 **Payroll Expense**
($000): 88487 **Personnel:** 1610

TX

✠ △ **DRISCOLL CHILDREN'S HOSPITAL (453301)**, 3533 South Alameda Street, Zip 78411–1785, Mailing Address: P.O. Box 6530, Zip 78466–6530; tel. 361/694–5000 **A**1 3 5 7 10 **F**3 7 11 12 19 21 23 25 27 29 30 31 32 34 35 38 39 40 41 43 49 50 54 55 57 58 59 60 61 64 65 68 72 74 75 77 78 79 81 82 85 86 87 88 89 92 93 97 99 104 107 108 111 115 118 119 130 132 134 138 143 144 146 148
Primary Contact: Steve Woerner, President and Chief Executive Officer
COO: Donna Quinn, Vice President Operations and Quality
CFO: Eric Hamon, Chief Financial Officer
CIO: Miguel Perez, Director Information Systems
CHR: Bill Larsen, Vice President Human Resources
Web address: www.driscollchildrens.org
Control: Other not–for–profit (including NFP Corporation) **Service:** Children's general

Staffed Beds: 162 Admissions: 4222 Census: 78 Outpatient Visits: 165909 Births: 0 Total Expense ($000): 238675 Payroll Expense ($000): 90493 Personnel: 1981

KINDRED HOSPITAL–CORPUS CHRISTI See Post Acute Medical Specialty Hospital of Corpus Christi – South

✠ **POST ACUTE MEDICAL SPECIALTY HOSPITAL OF CORPUS CHRISTI – NORTH (452086)**, 600 Elizabeth Street, 3rd Floor, Zip 78404–2235; tel. 361/881–3223, (Data for 184 days) **A**1 10 **F**1 3 29 75 85 87 91 148 **P**5 **S** Post Acute Medical, LLC, Enola, PA
Primary Contact: Hector Bernal, Chief Executive Officer
Web address: www.postacutemedical.com/our–facilities/hospitals/post–acute–medical–specialty–hospital–corpus–christi/
Control: Corporation, Investor–owned, for–profit **Service:** Long–Term Acute Care hospital

Staffed Beds: 22 Admissions: 129 Census: 20 Outpatient Visits: 0 Births: 0 Total Expense ($000): 4739 Payroll Expense ($000): 1859 Personnel: 61

✠ **POST ACUTE MEDICAL SPECIALTY HOSPITAL OF CORPUS CHRISTI – SOUTH (452092)**, 6226 Saratoga Boulevard, Zip 78414–3421; tel. 361/986–1600 **A**1 10 **F**1 3 29 30 34 35 45 57 59 60 74 75 77 79 82 85 86 87 107 130 148 **S** Post Acute Medical, LLC, Enola, PA
Primary Contact: Michael L. Pierce, Chief Executive Officer
CFO: Eva De La Paz, Chief Financial Officer
CHR: Kasey Parkey, Coordinator Payroll and Benefits
Web address: www.postacutemedical.com
Control: Corporation, Investor–owned, for–profit **Service:** Long–Term Acute Care hospital

Staffed Beds: 74 Admissions: 557 Census: 41 Outpatient Visits: 0 Total Expense ($000): 20640 Payroll Expense ($000): 8761 Personnel: 162

☐ **SOUTH TEXAS SURGICAL HOSPITAL (670061)**, 6130 Parkway Drive, Zip 78414–2455; tel. 361/993–2000 **A**1 10 **F**3 29 40 45 54 64 68 75 79 81 82 85 119 126 130 **S** National Surgical Healthcare, Chicago, IL
Primary Contact: James Murphy, Chief Executive Officer
CFO: Julie Wittwer, Chief Financial Officer
CMO: Michael Mintz, M.D., Chief Medical Officer
CHR: Lory Beth Smith, Manager Human Resource
CNO: Jan O'Donnell, Chief Nursing Officer
Web address: www.southtexassurgicalhospital.com
Control: Partnership, Investor–owned, for–profit **Service:** Surgical

Staffed Beds: 20 Admissions: 942 Census: 8 Outpatient Visits: 9111 Births: 0 Total Expense ($000): 27047 Payroll Expense ($000): 6584 Personnel: 149

CORSICANA—Navarro County

✠ **NAVARRO REGIONAL HOSPITAL (450447)**, 3201 West State Highway 22, Zip 75110–2469; tel. 903/654–6800 **A**1 10 19 **F**3 11 13 15 18 28 29 30 34 35 39 40 43 45 47 49 50 51 57 60 64 68 70 75 76 79 81 82 85 93 107 108 110 111 114 115 119 129 132 135 146 148 **P**7 **S** Community Health Systems, Inc., Franklin, TN
Primary Contact: Michael K. Stewart, Chief Executive Officer
CFO: Shea C. Brock, Chief Financial Officer
CIO: Bryan Chilton, Director Information Systems
CHR: Melodee Pugh, Director Human Resources
CNO: Dona E. Townsend, Chief Nursing Officer
Web address: www.navarrohospital.com
Control: Partnership, Investor–owned, for–profit **Service:** General Medical and Surgical

Staffed Beds: 148 Admissions: 2547 Census: 22 Outpatient Visits: 49341 Births: 553 Total Expense ($000): 40389 Payroll Expense ($000): 14647 Personnel: 251

CRANE—Crane County

★ **CRANE MEMORIAL HOSPITAL (451353)**, 1310 South Alford Street, Zip 79731–3899; tel. 432/558–3555 **A**10 18 **F**3 29 32 34 40 57 59 64 65 68 75 81 86 97 107 114 119 127 133 145 147 148 **P**2 6
Primary Contact: Dianne Yeager, Chief Executive Officer
CFO: Daniel Ibarra, Chief Financial Officer
CMO: Sixta Gumato, M.D., Chief Medical Officer
CHR: Becky Esparza, Human Resources
CNO: Pat Touchstone, Chief Nursing Officer
Web address: www.cranememorial.org
Control: Hospital district or authority, Government, nonfederal **Service:** General Medical and Surgical

Staffed Beds: 10 Admissions: 100 Census: 1 Outpatient Visits: 10302 Births: 0 Total Expense ($000): 6595 Payroll Expense ($000): 2703 Personnel: 49

CROCKETT—Houston County

★ **HOUSTON COUNTY MEDICAL CENTER (450580)**, 1100 Loop 304 East, Zip 75835–1810; tel. 936/546–3862, (Data for 122 days) **A**3 5 10 20 22 **F**3 11 13 15 28 29 32 35 40 46 50 54 57 58 59 61 64 70 75 76 81 87 93 97 107 108 111 114 118 119 127 129 146 **P**7
Primary Contact: Robert D. Torres, Interim Administrator
CFO: Richard V. Wallace, Chief Financial Officer
CIO: Norman Moore, Director Information Services
CNO: Marilyn Walker, R.N., Chief Nursing Officer
Web address: www.hcmctx.com
Control: Other not–for–profit (including NFP Corporation) **Service:** General Medical and Surgical

Staffed Beds: 46 Admissions: 204 Census: 5 Outpatient Visits: 5542 Births: 47 Total Expense ($000): 5279 Payroll Expense ($000): 1962 Personnel: 121

CROSBYTON—Crosby County

CROSBYTON CLINIC HOSPITAL (451345), 710 West Main Street, Zip 79322–2143; tel. 806/675–2382 **A**10 18 **F**7 10 29 34 40 50 57 59 63 64 68 87 93 119 127 130 133 148 **P**6
Primary Contact: Debra Miller, Administrator
CFO: Cherie Parkhill, Chief Financial Officer
CMO: Steve B. Alley, M.D., Chief of Staff
CHR: Janie Cantu, Director Human Resources
CNO: Freda Bartlett, Director of Nursing
Web address: www.crosbytonclinichospital.com
Control: Other not–for–profit (including NFP Corporation) **Service:** General Medical and Surgical

Staffed Beds: 25 Admissions: 188 Census: 2 Outpatient Visits: 17229 Births: 0 Total Expense ($000): 6256 Payroll Expense ($000): 2633 Personnel: 74

CUERO—Dewitt County

★ **CUERO COMMUNITY HOSPITAL (450597)**, 2550 North Esplanade Street, Zip 77954–4716; tel. 361/275–6191 **A**10 **F**3 7 11 13 15 29 34 40 43 45 57 59 62 64 68 70 75 76 77 79 81 85 86 93 103 107 108 111 115 118 119 127 129 130 131 **P**6
Primary Contact: Lynn Falcone, Chief Executive Officer
CFO: Greg Pritchett, Chief Financial Officer
CMO: Michael McLeod, M.D., Chief Medical Officer
CIO: Arthur Mueller, Director Management Information Systems
CHR: Wanda S. Kolodziejcyk, Director Human Resources
CNO: Judith Krupala, R.N., Chief Nursing Officer
Web address: www.cuerohospital.org
Control: Hospital district or authority, Government, nonfederal **Service:** General Medical and Surgical

Staffed Beds: 29 Admissions: 908 Census: 9 Outpatient Visits: 113131 Births: 109 Total Expense ($000): 32619 Payroll Expense ($000): 13933 Personnel: 363

CYPRESS—Harris County

☐ **LONE STAR BEHAVIORAL HEALTH (454118)**, 16303 Grant Road, Zip 77429–1253; tel. 281/516–6200 **A**1 10 **F**40 98 104 105 **P**5
Primary Contact: Nathan Daniel Ingram, Chief Executive Officer and Owner
Web address: www.lonestarbehavioralhealth.com
Control: Partnership, Investor–owned, for–profit **Service:** Psychiatric

Staffed Beds: 24 Admissions: 562 Census: 13 Outpatient Visits: 35515 Births: 0 Total Expense ($000): 6200 Payroll Expense ($000): 3811 Personnel: 78

Many Facility Codes have changed. Please refer to the AHA Guide Code Chart. © 2016 AHA Guide

TX

NORTH CYPRESS MEDICAL CENTER (670024), 21214 Northwest Freeway, Zip 77429–3373; tel. 832/912–3500 **A**1 10 **F**3 4 5 8 12 15 17 18 19 20 22 24 26 28 29 31 34 35 37 39 40 41 42 44 45 54 55 56 57 58 59 60 61 64 65 67 70 74 75 77 78 79 80 81 82 84 85 86 87 89 90 91 92 93 96 97 107 108 109 110 111 114 115 116 117 118 119 120 121 123 124 126 129 130 131 132 135 141 142 144 146 148
Primary Contact: Robert Behar, M.D., Chief Executive Officer
Web address: www.ncmc–hospital.com
Control: Partnership, Investor–owned, for–profit **Service:** General Medical and Surgical

Staffed Beds: 139 **Admissions:** 9593 **Census:** 117 **Outpatient Visits:** 207473 **Births:** 0 **Total Expense ($000):** 222321 **Payroll Expense ($000):** 75403 **Personnel:** 1348

DALHART—Hartley County

COON MEMORIAL HOSPITAL (451331), 1411 Denver Avenue, Zip 79022–4809, Mailing Address: P.O. Box 2014, Zip 79022–6014; tel. 806/244–4571 **A**10 18 **F**3 7 10 11 13 30 34 35 40 43 45 50 53 57 59 62 63 64 65 68 69 71 76 77 79 81 82 83 85 87 93 97 103 107 114 119 125 127 131 133 143 144 146 148 **P**5
Primary Contact: Leroy Schaffner, Chief Executive Officer
CFO: Donny Pettit, Chief Financial Officer
CMO: Randy Herring, M.D., Chief of Staff
CIO: Anthony Lovato, Director Information Technology
CHR: Dee Dawn McCormick, Director Personnel and Human Resources
Web address: www.coonmemorial.org
Control: Hospital district or authority, Government, nonfederal **Service:** General Medical and Surgical

Staffed Beds: 21 **Admissions:** 406 **Census:** 3 **Outpatient Visits:** 21179 **Births:** 153 **Total Expense ($000):** 27819 **Payroll Expense ($000):** 9503 **Personnel:** 186

DALLAS—Dallas County

BAYLOR INSTITUTE FOR REHABILITATION (453036), 909 North Washington Avenue, Zip 75246–1520; tel. 214/820–9300 **A**1 10 **F**3 29 30 34 35 44 62 64 65 68 74 75 77 85 86 87 90 92 93 94 95 96 130 131 132 135 143 148 **S** Baylor Scott & White Health, Dallas, TX
Primary Contact: Fabian Polo, Chief Executive Officer
CMO: Amy Wilson, M.D., Medical Director
CHR: Karen Hill, Director Human Resources
CNO: Beth Hudson, Chief Nursing Officer
Web address: www.baylorhealth.com/PhysiciansLocations/BIR/Pages/Default.aspx
Control: Partnership, Investor–owned, for–profit **Service:** Rehabilitation

Staffed Beds: 89 **Admissions:** 1535 **Census:** 81 **Outpatient Visits:** 143 **Births:** 0 **Total Expense ($000):** 67676 **Payroll Expense ($000):** 40326 **Personnel:** 268

BAYLOR JACK AND JANE HAMILTON HEART AND VASCULAR HOSPITAL (450851), 621 North Hall Street, Suite 150, Zip 75226–1339; tel. 214/820–0600 **A**1 5 10 **F**3 18 20 22 26 28 29 30 34 35 44 50 57 58 59 64 68 75 77 81 85 86 87 93 96 107 115 119 130 131 132 135 146
Primary Contact: Nancy Vish, Ph.D., R.N., President
CFO: Julius Wicke, III, Vice President Finance and Hospital Financial Officer
CMO: Kevin Wheelan, M.D., Medical Director
CHR: Kim Krause, Director Human Resources
Web address: www.baylorhearthospital.com
Control: Partnership, Investor–owned, for–profit **Service:** General Medical and Surgical

Staffed Beds: 54 **Admissions:** 2261 **Census:** 23 **Outpatient Visits:** 30600 **Births:** 0 **Total Expense ($000):** 105117 **Payroll Expense ($000):** 29310 **Personnel:** 318

BAYLOR MEDICAL CENTER AT UPTOWN (450422), 2727 East Lemmon Avenue, Zip 75204–2895; tel. 214/443–3000 **A**1 3 5 10 **F**29 40 68 77 79 81 82 85 107 111 **P**4 **S** United Surgical Partners International, Addison, TX
Primary Contact: Jon Duckert, Chief Executive Officer
CFO: Colene Fielding, Manager Business Office
CMO: Mark Armstrong, M.D., Medical Director
CIO: Javier Vela, Director Information Technology
CHR: Emalie Sanchez, Director Human Resources
CNO: Verette Neeb, R.N., Chief Nursing Officer
Web address: www.bmcuptown.com
Control: Partnership, Investor–owned, for–profit **Service:** Surgical

Staffed Beds: 24 **Admissions:** 1153 **Census:** 5 **Outpatient Visits:** 10249 **Births:** 0 **Total Expense ($000):** 49132 **Payroll Expense ($000):** 9946 **Personnel:** 175

BAYLOR SCOTT & WHITE MEDICAL CENTER – WHITE ROCK (450678), 9440 Poppy Drive, Zip 75218–3694; tel. 214/324–6100 **A**1 10 **F**3 11 12 13 15 17 18 20 22 24 26 28 29 30 31 34 35 37 40 42 45 47 49 50 51 53 56 57 59 64 70 72 73 74 75 76 77 78 79 81 85 93 107 108 110 111 114 115 119 120 124 126 129 130 132 135 144 146 147 148 **S** TENET Healthcare Corporation, Dallas, TX
Primary Contact: Jaikumar Krishnaswamy, Chief Executive Officer
COO: Jorge Trevino, Chief Operations Officer
CFO: Drew Shea, Chief Financial Officer
CMO: William Jones, II, M.D., Chief Medical Officer
CHR: Lorinnsa Bridges–Kee, Chief Human Resources Officer
CNO: Cheryl Nail, R.N., Chief Nursing Officer
Web address: www.BaylorScottandWhite.com/WhiteRock
Control: Partnership, Investor–owned, for–profit **Service:** General Medical and Surgical

Staffed Beds: 151 **Admissions:** 7628 **Census:** 85 **Outpatient Visits:** 66940 **Births:** 1242 **Total Expense ($000):** 112517 **Payroll Expense ($000):** 39760 **Personnel:** 643

BAYLOR UNIVERSITY MEDICAL CENTER (450021), 3500 Gaston Avenue, Zip 75246–2088; tel. 214/820–0111, (Includes A. WEBB ROBERTS HOSPITAL, 3500 Gaston Avenue, Zip 75246–2017; ERIK AND MARGARET JONSSON HOSPITAL, 3500 Gaston Avenue, Zip 75246–2017; GEORGE W. TRUETT MEMORIAL HOSPITAL, 3500 Gaston Avenue, Zip 75246; KARL AND ESTHER HOBLITZELLE MEMORIAL HOSPITAL, 3500 Gaston Avenue, Zip 75246) **A**1 2 3 5 8 10 21 **F**3 6 11 12 13 14 15 17 18 20 22 24 26 28 29 30 31 34 35 36 37 38 39 40 43 44 45 46 47 48 49 50 51 54 55 56 57 58 59 60 61 63 64 65 68 70 71 72 74 75 76 77 78 79 80 81 82 84 85 86 87 91 92 94 96 97 102 107 108 110 111 112 114 115 116 117 118 119 121 123 126 129 130 132 135 136 137 138 139 140 141 142 143 145 146 147 148 **S** Baylor Scott & White Health, Dallas, TX
Primary Contact: John B. McWhorter, III, President
COO: Doug Lawson, Chief Operating Officer
CFO: Jay Whitfield, Chief Financial Officer
CMO: Brad Lembcke, M.D., Vice President Medical Staff Affairs
CHR: Julie Strittmatter, Director Human Resources
CNO: Claudia Wilder, R.N., Chief Nursing Executive
Web address: www.baylorhealth.com/PhysiciansLocations/Dallas/Pages/Default.aspx
Control: Other not–for–profit (including NFP Corporation) **Service:** General Medical and Surgical

Staffed Beds: 893 **Admissions:** 35703 **Census:** 641 **Outpatient Visits:** 241134 **Births:** 4660 **Total Expense ($000):** 981456 **Payroll Expense ($000):** 318040 **Personnel:** 3613

CHILDREN'S HEALTH SYSTEM OF TEXAS (453302), 1935 Medical District Drive, Zip 75235; tel. 214/456–7000 **A**1 3 5 8 10 **F**3 7 8 11 12 17 19 21 23 25 27 29 30 31 32 35 38 39 40 41 43 44 45 46 47 48 49 50 51 54 55 57 58 59 60 61 62 64 65 66 68 72 74 75 77 78 79 81 82 84 85 86 87 88 89 91 92 93 94 97 98 99 100 101 102 104 105 106 107 108 111 114 116 117 118 119 126 127 129 130 131 132 134 136 137 138 139 140 141 142 143 144 145 146 148
Primary Contact: Christopher J. Durovich, President and Chief Executive Officer
COO: David T. Berry, President, System Clinical Operations
CFO: David Eager, Senior Vice President and Chief Financial Officer
CMO: W. Robert Morrow, M.D., Executive Vice President and Chief Medical Officer
CIO: Pamela Arora, Senior Vice President Information Systems
CHR: Kim Besse, Senior Vice President and Chief Human Resource Officer
CNO: Mary Stowe, Senior Vice President and Chief Nursing Officer
Web address: www.childrens.com
Control: Other not–for–profit (including NFP Corporation) **Service:** Children's general

Staffed Beds: 408 **Admissions:** 24204 **Census:** 251 **Outpatient Visits:** 472863 **Births:** 0

DALLAS MEDICAL CENTER (450379), Seven Medical Parkway, Zip 75234–7823, Mailing Address: P.O. Box 819094, Zip 75381–9094; tel. 972/247–1000 **A**1 10 **F**3 12 13 15 18 20 22 26 29 34 40 44 45 49 56 57 59 68 70 74 75 76 77 78 79 81 82 83 86 93 97 107 108 111 114 116 119 130 131 132 141 142 146 147 148 **S** Prime Healthcare Services, Ontario, CA
Primary Contact: J. T. Barnhart, Chief Executive Officer
CFO: Nicholas Geer, Chief Financial Officer
CIO: Mary Jo Tallant–Ball, Director Health Information Systems
CHR: Sheila K. Richards, Human Resources Director
CNO: Dawn Beljin, R.N., Chief Nursing Officer
Web address: www.dallasmedcenter.com
Control: Corporation, Investor–owned, for–profit **Service:** General Medical and Surgical

Staffed Beds: 83 **Admissions:** 4194 **Census:** 39 **Outpatient Visits:** 45113 **Births:** 830 **Total Expense ($000):** 92549 **Payroll Expense ($000):** 29012 **Personnel:** 491

TX

Hospital, Medicare Provider Number, Address, Telephone, Approval, Facility, and Physician Codes, Health Care System

★ American Hospital Association (AHA) membership
□ The Joint Commission accreditation
○ Healthcare Facilities Accreditation Program
◇ DNV Healthcare Inc. accreditation
⇑ Center for Improvement in Healthcare Quality Accreditation
△ Commission on Accreditation of Rehabilitation Facilities (CARF) accreditation

FIRST BAPTIST MEDICAL CENTER, 8111 Meadow Road, Zip 75231; tel. 469/329–3700, (Nonreporting)
Primary Contact: Kane Dawson, Chief Executive Officer
Web address: www.fbmcdallas.com
Control: Other not–for–profit (including NFP Corporation) **Service:** Surgical

Staffed Beds: 25

✠ **GREEN OAKS HOSPITAL (454094)**, 7808 Clodus Fields Drive, Zip 75251–2206; tel. 972/991–9504 **A**1 5 10 **F**4 5 29 54 87 98 99 102 103 104 105 130 132 **P**5 **S** HCA, Nashville, TN
Primary Contact: Thomas M. Collins, President, Chairman and Chief Executive Officer
COO: Pam Whitley, R.N., Chief Operating Officer and Chief Nursing Officer
CMO: Joel Holiner, M.D., Executive Medical Director
CIO: Richard Fontenault, Director Information Systems
CHR: Kevin Adkins, Director Human Resources
CNO: Pam Whitley, R.N., Chief Nursing Officer and Chief Operating Officer
Web address: www.greenoakspsych.com
Control: Corporation, Investor–owned, for–profit **Service:** Psychiatric

Staffed Beds: 124 Admissions: 4720 Census: 123 Outpatient Visits: 35832 Births: 0 Total Expense ($000): 44222 Payroll Expense ($000): 20800 Personnel: 343

✠ **HEALTHSOUTH REHABILITATION HOSPITAL – DALLAS (673043)**, 7930 Northaven Road, Zip 75230–3331; tel. 214/706–8200, (Data for 92 days) **A**1 10 **F**3 29 90 96 130 148 **S** HEALTHSOUTH Corporation, Birmingham, AL
Primary Contact: Daniel MacNicol, Chief Executive Officer
CFO: Elizabeth Robertson, Area Controller
CMO: Anna Freed–Sigurdsson, M.D., Medical Director
CHR: Lindsay Battles, Director Human Resources
CNO: Janice McFadden, MSN, Chief Nursing Officer
Web address: www.healthsouthdallas.com
Control: Corporation, Investor–owned, for–profit **Service:** Rehabilitation

Staffed Beds: 60 Admissions: 262 Census: 31 Outpatient Visits: 0 Births: 0 Total Expense ($000): 3320 Payroll Expense ($000): 1387 Personnel: 103

✠ **KINDRED HOSPITAL DALLAS CENTRAL (452108)**, 8050 Meadows Road, Zip 75231–3406; tel. 469/232–6500 **A**1 10 **F**1 3 29 75 77 85 87 96 107 114 148 **P**8 **S** Kindred Healthcare, Louisville, KY
Primary Contact: Kyron Kooken, Administrator
CFO: Joni Gonzalez, Controller
CNO: Jackie Gordon, Chief Clinical Officer
Web address: www.khdallascentral.com/
Control: Corporation, Investor–owned, for–profit **Service:** Long–Term Acute Care hospital

Staffed Beds: 60 Admissions: 578 Census: 47 Outpatient Visits: 340 Births: 0 Total Expense ($000): 26686 Payroll Expense ($000): 9432 Personnel: 143

KINDRED HOSPITAL DALLAS–WALNUT HILL See Kindred Hospital–Dallas

✠ **KINDRED HOSPITAL–DALLAS (452015)**, 9525 Greenville Avenue, Zip 75243–4116; tel. 214/355–2600, **A**1 10 **F**1 3 29 70 107 114 130 148 **S** Kindred Healthcare, Louisville, KY
Primary Contact: James Mendez, Chief Executive Officer
CFO: Jean McDowell, Chief Financial Officer
Web address: www.khdallas.com
Control: Corporation, Investor–owned, for–profit **Service:** Long–Term Acute Care hospital

Staffed Beds: 50 Admissions: 488 Census: 39 Outpatient Visits: 0 Total Expense ($000): 22444 Payroll Expense ($000): 7909 Personnel: 158

✠ **KINDRED HOSPITAL–WHITE ROCK (452071)**, 9440 Poppy Drive, 5th Floor, Zip 75218–3652; tel. 214/324–6562 **A**1 10 **F**1 29 85 86 87 130 148 **S** Kindred Healthcare, Louisville, KY
Primary Contact: Kelly Bailey, Chief Executive Officer and Administrator
COO: Kim Chipman, Chief Clinical Officer
CFO: Jennifer Penland, Controller
CMO: Mark Ferris, M.D., Medical Director
CNO: Brenda Perez, R.N., Chief Clinical Officer
Web address: www.khwhiterock.com
Control: Corporation, Investor–owned, for–profit **Service:** Long–Term Acute Care hospital

Staffed Beds: 25 Admissions: 254 Census: 17 Outpatient Visits: 0 Births: 0 Total Expense ($000): 9312 Payroll Expense ($000): 3797 Personnel: 63

TX

✠ **LIFECARE HOSPITALS OF DALLAS (452044)**, 1950 Record Crossing Road, Zip 75235–6223; tel. 214/640–9600 **A**1 10 **F**1 3 29 75 91 107 114 115 119 130 148 **S** LifeCare Management Services, Plano, TX
Primary Contact: Christy Carver, R.N., Chief Executive Officer
CFO: Amie Gratch, Director Financial Services
CMO: Jonathan Weissler, M.D., Chief Medical Officer
CHR: Linzie Riley, Interim Human Resource Manager
CNO: Kathy Mason, R.N., Chief Nursing Officer
Web address: www.lifecare–hospitals.com/hospital/dallas
Control: Corporation, Investor–owned, for–profit **Service:** Long–Term Acute Care hospital

Staffed Beds: 60 Admissions: 509 Census: 38 Outpatient Visits: 0 Births: 0 Total Expense ($000): 22423 Payroll Expense ($000): 9740 Personnel: 162

LIFECARE HOSPITALS OF NORTH TEXAS See LifeCare Hospitals of Dallas

MARY SHIELS HOSPITAL See Baylor Medical Center at Uptown

✠ ◇ **MEDICAL CITY DALLAS HOSPITAL (450647)**, 7777 Forest Lane, Zip 75230–2598; tel. 972/566–7000, (Includes MEDICAL CITY CHILDREN'S HOSPITAL, 7777 Forest Lane, Zip 75230–2505; tel. 972/566–7000; Keith Zimmerman, Chief Executive Officer) **A**1 2 3 5 10 21 **F**3 8 11 12 13 15 17 18 19 20 21 22 23 24 25 26 27 28 29 30 31 34 35 37 40 41 42 43 44 45 46 47 49 50 51 55 56 57 58 59 60 63 64 65 68 70 72 73 74 75 76 77 78 79 81 82 84 85 86 87 88 89 93 97 105 107 108 110 111 114 115 116 117 118 119 126 129 130 132 135 136 137 138 141 142 143 144 146 147 148 **P**6 **S** HCA, Nashville, TN
Primary Contact: Chris Mowan, Chief Executive Officer
CFO: Mark Atchley, Vice President and Chief Financial Officer
CMO: Mark Hebert, M.D., President Medical Staff
CIO: Troy Sypien, Director Information Technology and Systems
CHR: Jenifer K. Tertel, Director Human Resources
Web address: www.medicalcityhospital.com
Control: Corporation, Investor–owned, for–profit **Service:** General Medical and Surgical

Staffed Beds: 561 Admissions: 25604 Census: 416 Outpatient Visits: 169220 Births: 3625 Total Expense ($000): 508377 Payroll Expense ($000): 182722 Personnel: 2135

✠ **METHODIST CHARLTON MEDICAL CENTER (450723)**, 3500 West Wheatland Road, Zip 75237–3460, Mailing Address: P.O. Box 225357, Zip 75222–5357; tel. 214/947–7777 **A**1 3 10 13 **F**3 11 13 15 18 20 22 24 28 29 30 31 34 35 40 45 46 47 49 50 53 58 59 60 64 66 70 74 76 78 79 81 82 84 85 86 87 97 107 108 110 111 114 115 118 119 126 130 131 132 146 148 **P**1 7 **S** Methodist Health System, Dallas, TX
Primary Contact: Fran Laukaitis, R.N., President
COO: Pamela Stoyanoff, Executive Vice President and Chief Operating Officer
CFO: Michael J. Schaefer, Executive Vice President and Chief Financial Officer
CIO: Pamela McNutt, Vice President Information Systems
CHR: Cheryl Flynn, Senior Vice President Chief Human Resources Officer
Web address: www.methodisthealthsystem.org/charlton
Control: Other not–for–profit (including NFP Corporation) **Service:** General Medical and Surgical

Staffed Beds: 290 Admissions: 13281 Census: 179 Outpatient Visits: 156224 Births: 2076 Total Expense ($000): 225129 Payroll Expense ($000): 105211 Personnel: 1289

✠ **METHODIST DALLAS MEDICAL CENTER (450051)**, 1441 North Beckley Avenue, Zip 75203–1201, Mailing Address: P.O. Box 655999, Zip 75265–5999; tel. 214/947–8181 **A**1 2 3 5 8 10 **F**3 11 12 13 15 18 20 22 24 26 28 29 30 31 34 35 37 40 43 45 46 47 48 49 50 53 54 58 59 60 64 66 68 70 72 74 76 78 79 81 82 84 85 87 92 93 97 107 108 110 111 118 119 126 130 132 138 139 142 146 148 **P**1 7 **S** Methodist Health System, Dallas, TX
Primary Contact: David D. Clark, FACHE, President
COO: Pamela Stoyanoff, Executive Vice President and Chief Operating Officer
CFO: Randy Walker, Vice President
CIO: Pamela McNutt, Senior Vice President and Chief Information Officer
CHR: Jackie Middleton, Vice President Human Resources
Web address: www.methodisthealthsystem.org/Dallas
Control: Other not–for–profit (including NFP Corporation) **Service:** General Medical and Surgical

Staffed Beds: 432 Admissions: 15601 Census: 244 Outpatient Visits: 160683 Births: 3389 Total Expense ($000): 404369 Payroll Expense ($000): 159129 Personnel: 1988

☐ **METHODIST REHABILITATION HOSPITAL (673031)**, 3020 West Wheatland Road, Zip 75237–3537; tel. 972/708–8600 **A**1 10 **F**29 30 60 90 91 93 96
Primary Contact: Shari Moore, Chief Executive Officer
CFO: Darline Kennemer, Controller
Web address: www.methodist–rehab.com
Control: Partnership, Investor–owned, for–profit **Service:** Rehabilitation

Staffed Beds: 40 Admissions: 1018 Census: 34 Outpatient Visits: 9584 Births: 0 Total Expense ($000): 15549 Payroll Expense ($000): 8530 Personnel: 156

Many Facility Codes have changed. Please refer to the AHA Guide Code Chart. © 2016 AHA Guide

☐ **NORTH CENTRAL SURGICAL CENTER (670049)**, 9301 North Central Expressway, Suite 100, Zip 75231–0802; tel. 214/265–2810 **A**1 10 **F**3 40 45 79 81 82 85 91 93 107 111 115 119
Primary Contact: Thanh Tran, Chief Executive Officer
CMO: Stuart Simon, M.D., Medical Director
CNO: Katherine Martinez, Chief Nursing Officer
Web address: www.northcentralsurgical.com
Control: Partnership, Investor–owned, for–profit **Service:** Surgical

Staffed Beds: 24 **Admissions:** 1248 **Census:** 8 **Outpatient Visits:** 19438 **Births:** 0 **Total Expense ($000):** 67345 **Payroll Expense ($000):** 15219 **Personnel:** 265

★ **OUR CHILDREN'S HOUSE (453308)**, 1208 North Hall Street, Zip 75204; tel. 214/820–9838 **A**3 5 10 **F**29 30 35 39 81 89 93 129 130 132 146
Primary Contact: David T. Berry, President, Children's Health Clinical Operations
CMO: Andrew Gelfand, M.D., Medical Director
CHR: Stacie Roberts, Coordinator Human Resources
CNO: Kelli Terpstra, R.N., Chief Nursing Officer
Web address: www.https://www.childrens.com/och
Control: Other not–for–profit (including NFP Corporation) **Service:** Children's general

Staffed Beds: 32 **Admissions:** 376 **Census:** 23 **Outpatient Visits:** 105680 **Births:** 0 **Total Expense ($000):** 35592 **Payroll Expense ($000):** 18467

⌧ **PARKLAND HEALTH & HOSPITAL SYSTEM (450015)**, 5200 Harry Hines Boulevard, Zip 75235–7708; tel. 214/590–8000, (Total facility includes 1645 beds in nursing home–type unit) **A**1 2 3 5 8 10 **F**3 8 9 11 12 13 15 16 17 18 20 22 26 28 29 30 31 34 35 37 38 39 40 43 46 47 48 49 50 51 54 55 56 57 58 59 60 61 64 65 66 67 68 70 71 72 74 75 76 77 78 79 81 82 83 84 85 86 87 90 91 92 93 94 97 98 99 100 101 102 103 104 105 107 108 110 111 115 116 117 118 119 128 129 130 131 132 134 135 138 141 144 146 147 148 **P**1
Primary Contact: Fred Cerise, M.D., Chief Executive Officer
COO: David S. Lopez, FACHE, Executive Vice President and Chief Operating Officer
CIO: Fernando Martinez, Senior Vice President and Chief Information Officer
CNO: Mary K. Eagen, R.N., Executive Vice President, Chief Nursing Officer
Web address: www.parklandhospital.com
Control: Hospital district or authority, Government, nonfederal **Service:** General Medical and Surgical

Staffed Beds: 2574 **Admissions:** 38886 **Census:** 929 **Outpatient Visits:** 1221437 **Births:** 9238 **Total Expense ($000):** 1531457 **Payroll Expense ($000):** 730750 **Personnel:** 11026

☐ **PINE CREEK MEDICAL CENTER (450894)**, 9032 Harry Hines Boulevard, Zip 75235–1720; tel. 214/231–2273 **A**1 10 **F**3 12 18 24 29 30 34 40 42 45 49 51 64 79 81 82 85 93 107 111 114
Primary Contact: Corazon Ramirez, M.D., Chief Executive Officer
CFO: Michael Conroy, Chief Financial Officer
CIO: Kevin Carney, Senior Information Systems Analyst
Web address: www.pinecreekmedicalcenter.com
Control: Partnership, Investor–owned, for–profit **Service:** Surgical

Staffed Beds: 15 **Admissions:** 1365 **Census:** 8 **Outpatient Visits:** 6576 **Births:** 0 **Total Expense ($000):** 65730 **Payroll Expense ($000):** 9571 **Personnel:** 164

☐ **PROMISE HOSPITAL OF DALLAS (452067)**, 7955 Harry Hines Boulevard, Zip 75235–3305; tel. 214/637–0000 **A**1 10 **F**1 3 29 30 40 64 75 77 91 148 **S** Promise Healthcare, Boca Raton, FL
Primary Contact: Louis P. Bradley, Jr., Chief Executive Officer
CFO: Diana B. Smith, Chief Financial Officer
CMO: Gary E. Goff, M.D., Medical Director
CHR: Ginger Davenport, Director Human Resources
Web address: www.promise–dallas.com/
Control: Corporation, Investor–owned, for–profit **Service:** Long–Term Acute Care hospital

Staffed Beds: 62 **Admissions:** 309 **Census:** 30 **Outpatient Visits:** 1650 **Births:** 0 **Total Expense ($000):** 15444 **Payroll Expense ($000):** 7021 **Personnel:** 79

★ **SELECT SPECIALTY HOSPITAL – DALLAS DOWNTOWN**, 3500 Gaston Avenue, Floors 3&4 Jonnson, Zip 75246–2017; tel. 469/801–4500 **F**1 3 29 77 85 86 87 91 96 148 **S** Select Medical Corporation, Mechanicsburg, PA
Primary Contact: Melody Nagel, Chief Executive Officer
Web address: www.dallasdowntown.selectspecialtyhospitals.com/
Control: Corporation, Investor–owned, for–profit **Service:** Long–Term Acute Care hospital

Staffed Beds: 46 **Admissions:** 221 **Census:** 16 **Outpatient Visits:** 0 **Births:** 0 **Total Expense ($000):** 10975 **Payroll Expense ($000):** 5180 **Personnel:** 94

⌧ **SELECT SPECIALTY HOSPITAL–SOUTH DALLAS (452078)**, 3500 West Wheatland Road, 4th Floor, Zip 75237–3460; tel. 972/780–6500 **A**1 10 **F**1 3 29 85 130 148 **S** Select Medical Corporation, Mechanicsburg, PA
Primary Contact: Robert Dickens, Chief Executive Officer
Web address: www.selectspecialtyhospitals.com/company/locations/southdallas.aspx
Control: Corporation, Investor–owned, for–profit **Service:** Long–Term Acute Care hospital

Staffed Beds: 69 **Admissions:** 534 **Census:** 38 **Outpatient Visits:** 0 **Births:** 0 **Total Expense ($000):** 22298 **Payroll Expense ($000):** 8721 **Personnel:** 131

⌧ △ **TEXAS HEALTH PRESBYTERIAN HOSPITAL DALLAS (450462)**, 8200 Walnut Hill Lane, Zip 75231–4426; tel. 214/345–6789 **A**1 2 3 5 7 10 **F**3 5 11 12 13 15 18 20 22 24 26 28 29 30 31 32 34 35 36 37 38 40 44 45 46 47 49 50 51 52 53 54 56 57 58 59 60 61 64 65 66 68 70 72 74 75 76 77 78 79 81 84 85 86 87 90 91 92 93 94 95 96 97 98 100 101 102 103 104 105 107 108 110 111 112 114 115 118 119 124 126 129 131 132 135 141 143 144 146 147 148 **P**6 **S** Texas Health Resources, Arlington, TX
Primary Contact: James Berg, FACHE, President
CFO: Brian Craft, Group Finance Officer
CMO: Aurora Estevez, M.D., Chief Medical Officer
CIO: Tammy Phillips, Director, Information Systems
CHR: Stacy Miller, Entity Human Resources Officer
CNO: Cole Edmonson, R.N., Vice President and Chief Nursing Officer
Web address: www.texashealth.org
Control: Other not–for–profit (including NFP Corporation) **Service:** General Medical and Surgical

Staffed Beds: 611 **Admissions:** 26369 **Census:** 401 **Outpatient Visits:** 338006 **Births:** 5303 **Total Expense ($000):** 589241 **Payroll Expense ($000):** 204716 **Personnel:** 2681

TEXAS HOSPITAL FOR ADVANCED MEDICINE See Dallas Medical Center

☐ **TEXAS INSTITUTE FOR SURGERY AT TEXAS HEALTH PRESBYTERIAN DALLAS (450889)**, 7115 Greenville Avenue, Suite 100, Zip 75231–5100; tel. 214/647–5300 **A**1 10 **F**40 51 64 79 81 82 107 114 115 119
Primary Contact: David Helfer, FACHE, President
CFO: John S. Croley, Vice President Business Operations
CMO: Presley Mock, M.D., Chief of Staff
CHR: Jennifer Cherrnay Levy, Director Human Resources
CNO: Tammy Jarvis, Vice President Clinical Services and Chief Nursing Officer
Web address: www.texasinstituteforsurgery.com
Control: Partnership, Investor–owned, for–profit **Service:** General Medical and Surgical

Staffed Beds: 9 **Admissions:** 440 **Census:** 2 **Outpatient Visits:** 10967 **Births:** 0 **Total Expense ($000):** 49743 **Payroll Expense ($000):** 12065 **Personnel:** 162

⌧ **TEXAS SCOTTISH RITE HOSPITAL FOR CHILDREN (453314)**, 2222 Welborn Street, Zip 75219–3924, Mailing Address: P.O. Box 190567, Zip 75219–0567; tel. 214/559–5000 **A**1 3 5 10 **F**3 9 11 29 34 35 50 53 54 58 68 74 75 77 79 81 82 85 86 87 89 92 94 107 111 115 119 130 131 132 146 148 **P**6
Primary Contact: Robert L. Walker, President and Chief Executive Officer
CFO: William R. Huston, Senior Vice President and Chief Financial Officer
CMO: Daniel J. Sucato, M.D., Chief of Staff
CIO: Les Clonch, Chief Information Officer
CHR: Connie Wright, Vice President Human Resources
CNO: Debbie A. Sayles, R.N., Vice President and Chief Nursing Officer
Web address: www.tsrhc.org
Control: Other not–for–profit (including NFP Corporation) **Service:** Children's orthopedic

Staffed Beds: 52 **Admissions:** 689 **Census:** 13 **Outpatient Visits:** 39798 **Births:** 0 **Total Expense ($000):** 158344 **Payroll Expense ($000):** 76695 **Personnel:** 908

☐ **TIMBERLAWN MENTAL HEALTH SYSTEM (454081)**, 4600 Samuell Boulevard, Zip 75228–6800; tel. 214/381–7181 **A**1 5 10 **F**4 5 54 56 59 64 87 98 99 100 101 102 103 104 105 130 132 143 **S** Universal Health Services, Inc., King of Prussia, PA
Primary Contact: Shelah Adams, Chief Executive Officer
COO: Rick Paczkowski, Chief Operating Officer
CFO: Lori Verbeke, Chief Financial Officer
CMO: John Pascoe, M.D., Executive Medical Director
CIO: Twila Ragar–Thomas, Director Health Information Management and Quality Improvement
CHR: Winnie Boehnke, Director Human Resources
CNO: Paula Hirschberg, R.N., Director of Nursing
Web address: www.timberlawn.com
Control: Corporation, Investor–owned, for–profit **Service:** Psychiatric

Staffed Beds: 19 **Admissions:** 3263 **Census:** 64 **Outpatient Visits:** 10814 **Births:** 0 **Total Expense ($000):** 23937 **Payroll Expense ($000):** 9913 **Personnel:** 47

TX

Hospital, Medicare Provider Number, Address, Telephone, Approval, Facility, and Physician Codes, Health Care System		
★ American Hospital Association (AHA) membership	○ Healthcare Facilities Accreditation Program	⇑ Center for Improvement in Healthcare Quality Accreditation
☐ The Joint Commission accreditation	◇ DNV Healthcare Inc. accreditation	△ Commission on Accreditation of Rehabilitation Facilities (CARF) accreditation

⊠ **UNIVERSITY OF TEXAS SOUTHWESTERN MEDICAL CENTER (450766)**, 5323 Harry Hines Boulevard, Zip 75390–9265; tel. 214/648–3111, (Includes UNIVERSITY OF TEXAS SOUTHWESTERN MEDICAL CENTER – ZALE LIPSHY, 5151 Harry Hines Boulevard, tel. 214/645–8300; Daniel Podolsky, M.D., President) **A**1 2 3 5 8 10 **F**3 6 7 8 9 11 12 13 15 17 18 20 22 24 26 28 29 30 31 34 35 36 38 39 40 44 45 46 47 48 51 53 54 55 56 57 58 59 60 61 62 64 65 68 70 71 72 74 75 76 77 78 79 80 81 82 84 85 86 87 90 91 92 93 94 95 96 97 98 99 100 101 102 103 104 107 108 109 110 111 114 115 116 117 118 119 120 121 123 124 126 129 130 131 132 135 136 137 138 139 140 141 142 143 145 146 147 148 **P**4 6
Primary Contact: John Warner, M.D., Chief Executive Officer
COO: Becky McCulley, Chief Operations Officer
CFO: Elizabeth S. Ward, Chief Financial Officer
CMO: John Warner, M.D., Chief Executive Officer, Interim Chief Medical Officer
CIO: Mark Rauschuber, Associate Vice President, Chief Information Officer
CHR: Ivan Thompson, Vice President, Chief Human Resource Officer
CNO: Susan Hernandez, Chief Nurse Executive
Web address: www.utsouthwestern.edu
Control: State–Government, nonfederal **Service:** General Medical and Surgical

Staffed Beds: 546 **Admissions:** 23132 **Census:** 394 **Outpatient Visits:** 387290 **Births:** 1778 **Total Expense ($000):** 938357 **Payroll Expense ($000):** 375747 **Personnel:** 6062

⊠ △ **VETERANS AFFAIRS NORTH TEXAS HEALTH CARE SYSTEM**, 4500 South Lancaster Road, Zip 75216–7167; tel. 214/742–8387, (Includes SAM RAYBURN MEMORIAL VETERANS UNIT, 1201 East Ninth Street, Bonham, Zip 75418–4091; tel. 903/583–2111; Angela Nix, Administrator), (Nonreporting) **A**1 2 3 5 7 **S** Department of Veterans Affairs, Washington, DC
Primary Contact: Jeffrey Milligan, Director
CFO: Garry Martin, Chief Fiscal
CIO: Lucy Rogers, Chief Information Resource Management Systems
Web address: www.northtexas.va.gov/
Control: Veterans Affairs, Government, federal **Service:** General Medical and Surgical

Staffed Beds: 875

☐ **WALNUT HILL MEDICAL CENTER (670092)**, 7502 Greenville Avenue, Zip 75231–3802; tel. 972/863–6000 **A**1 10 **F**3 15 18 20 22 24 26 29 34 40 45 47 49 57 58 59 60 64 70 74 75 77 79 81 84 85 87 92 97 102 107 108 110 111 114 119 129 130 145 148
Primary Contact: Cory Countryman, Chief Executive Officer
Web address: www.walnuthillmc.com
Control: Partnership, Investor–owned, for–profit **Service:** General Medical and Surgical

Staffed Beds: 52 **Admissions:** 2109 **Census:** 23 **Outpatient Visits:** 12448 **Births:** 0 **Total Expense ($000):** 117293 **Payroll Expense ($000):** 21892 **Personnel:** 304

WILLIAM P. CLEMENTS, JR. UNIVERSITY HOSPITAL (450044), 6201 Harry Hines Boulevard, Zip 75235–5202; tel. 214/633–5555, (Nonreporting) **A**5
Primary Contact: Daniel Podolsky, M.D., President
Web address: www.utswmedicine.org/hospitals-clinics/clements/about/faqs/
Control: State–Government, nonfederal **Service:** General Medical and Surgical

Staffed Beds: 460

DECATUR—Wise County

⊠ **WISE REGIONAL HEALTH SYSTEM (450271)**, 609 Medical Center Drive, Zip 76234–3836; tel. 940/627–5921, (Includes PARKWAY SURGICAL & CARDIOVASCULAR HOSPITAL, 3200 North Tarrant Parkway, Fort Worth, Zip 76177–8611; tel. 817/502–7300; WISE REGIONAL HEALTH SYSTEM – BRIDGEPORT CAMPUS, 1905 Doctors Hospital Drive, Bridgeport, Zip 76426–2260; tel. 940/683–0300; WISE REGIONAL HEALTH SYSTEM, EAST CAMPUS DECATUR, 609 Medical Center Drive, tel. 940/627–5921; WISE REGIONAL HEALTH SYSTEM, WEST CAMPUS DECATUR, 2000 South Fm 51, Zip 76234–3702; tel. 940/627–5921) **A**1 2 10 **F**3 11 12 13 15 18 20 22 24 26 28 29 30 31 32 34 40 43 45 47 49 51 53 54 56 57 59 60 64 70 74 75 76 77 78 79 81 85 87 89 90 93 96 97 98 103 104 107 108 110 111 114 115 116 118 119 129 130 131 132 135 144 147 148
Primary Contact: Stephen M. Summers, CPA, FACHE, Administrator and Chief Executive Officer
COO: Leon Fuqua, Chief Operating Officer
CFO: Jim Eaton, Chief Financial Officer
CMO: Jason Schuh, M.D., Chief of Staff
CIO: Joe Arispe, Director Information Systems
CHR: Mike McQuiston, Administrative Director Human Resources
CNO: Sue Sewell, Chief Nursing Officer
Web address: www.wiseregional.com
Control: Hospital district or authority, Government, nonfederal **Service:** General Medical and Surgical

Staffed Beds: 145 **Admissions:** 5281 **Census:** 69 **Outpatient Visits:** 274206 **Births:** 702 **Total Expense ($000):** 288561 **Payroll Expense ($000):** 71092 **Personnel:** 1316

DEL RIO—Val Verde County

⊠ **VAL VERDE REGIONAL MEDICAL CENTER (450154)**, 801 Bedell Avenue, Zip 78840–4112, Mailing Address: 801 North Bedell Avenue, Zip 78840–4112; tel. 830/775–8566 **A**1 10 20 22 **F**3 7 11 13 15 18 20 29 30 34 35 40 43 46 48 54 57 59 63 73 75 76 77 79 81 82 84 85 87 89 93 96 107 108 110 111 114 119 129 131 132 133 146 147
Primary Contact: Xochy Hurtado, FACHE, Chief Executive Officer
CFO: Eddie Read, Interim Chief Financial Officer
CMO: Mohamed Shafiu, M.D., Chief of Staff
CIO: Val King, Chief Information Officer
CHR: Leigh Ann Qualia, Director Human Resources
CNO: Kathy Fletcher, R.N., Interim Chief Nursing Officer
Web address: www.vvrmc.org
Control: Hospital district or authority, Government, nonfederal **Service:** General Medical and Surgical

Staffed Beds: 80 **Admissions:** 2495 **Census:** 23 **Outpatient Visits:** 58815 **Births:** 991 **Total Expense ($000):** 54402 **Payroll Expense ($000):** 21614 **Personnel:** 455

DENISON—Grayson County

☐ **TEXOMA MEDICAL CENTER (450324)**, 5016 South U.S. Highway 75, Zip 75020–4584, Mailing Address: P.O. Box 890, Zip 75021–0890; tel. 903/416–4000, (Includes TMC BEHAVIORAL HEALTH CENTER, 2601 North Cornerstone Drive, Sherman, Zip 75092–2551; tel. 903/416–3000; Jennifer Wiggins, Chief Executive Officer) **A**1 10 13 **F**3 11 12 13 15 17 18 20 22 24 28 29 30 31 34 35 40 43 45 46 47 48 49 50 53 54 57 59 62 64 70 74 75 76 77 78 79 80 81 85 86 87 89 90 91 93 96 98 100 101 102 103 104 105 107 108 110 111 115 119 129 130 132 144 145 146 147 148 **S** Universal Health Services, Inc., King of Prussia, PA
Primary Contact: Ronald T. Seal, Chief Executive Officer
CFO: Gerard Hebert, Chief Financial Officer
CMO: Robert Sanders, M.D., Chief Medical Officer
CIO: Lisa Engle, Director Information Technology
CHR: Bill Heinzmann, Director Human Resources
CNO: Andrea Brenn, R.N., Chief Nursing Officer
Web address: www.texomamedicalcenter.net
Control: Corporation, Investor–owned, for–profit **Service:** General Medical and Surgical

Staffed Beds: 326 **Admissions:** 14085 **Census:** 190 **Outpatient Visits:** 124276 **Births:** 1153 **Total Expense ($000):** 205005 **Payroll Expense ($000):** 83720 **Personnel:** 1660

DENTON—Denton County

⊠ **DENTON REGIONAL MEDICAL CENTER (450634)**, 3535 South 1–35 East, Zip 76210; tel. 940/384–3535 **A**1 3 10 **F**3 13 15 18 20 22 24 26 28 29 30 34 35 40 43 45 46 47 49 50 57 59 64 69 70 73 74 75 76 77 79 81 82 84 85 86 87 93 107 108 110 111 114 115 118 119 126 130 132 144 146 147 148 **S** HCA, Nashville, TN
Primary Contact: Steven Edgar, President and Chief Executive Officer
COO: Jeffrey T. Lawrence, Chief Operating Officer
CFO: Todd Gibson, Chief Financial Officer
CMO: Stanley Evans, M.D., Chief of Staff
CHR: Stacey Bravo, Vice President Human Resources
CNO: Nicki Roderman, Chief Nursing Officer
Web address: www.dentonregional.com
Control: Partnership, Investor–owned, for–profit **Service:** General Medical and Surgical

Staffed Beds: 185 **Admissions:** 9220 **Census:** 126 **Outpatient Visits:** 91434 **Births:** 501 **Total Expense ($000):** 143530 **Payroll Expense ($000):** 51673 **Personnel:** 758

☐ **INTEGRITY TRANSITIONAL HOSPITAL (452109)**, 2813 South Mayhill Road, Zip 76208–5910; tel. 940/320–2300 **A**1 10 **F**1 3 29 77 80 81 82 84 86 87 91 130 148
Primary Contact: Israel Navarro, Chief Executive Officer
CNO: Michele Andrews, Chief Clinical Officer
Web address: www.ithcare.com
Control: Partnership, Investor–owned, for–profit **Service:** Long–Term Acute Care hospital

Staffed Beds: 44 **Admissions:** 240 **Census:** 16 **Outpatient Visits:** 2350 **Births:** 0 **Total Expense ($000):** 44562 **Personnel:** 123

⊠ **MAYHILL HOSPITAL (670010)**, 2809 South Mayhill Road, Zip 76208–5910; tel. 940/239–3000 **A**1 10 **F**4 5 29 40 56 82 98 101 102 103 104 105 130 **S** Universal Health Services, Inc., King of Prussia, PA
Primary Contact: Adam Vincent, Chief Executive Officer
CFO: Emmy Adams, Chief Financial Officer
CMO: Asad Islam, M.D., Chief Medical Officer
CIO: Kyle Murphy, Director Information Technology
CHR: Patricia Gloria–Barraza, Coordinator Human Resources
Web address: www.mayhillhospital.com
Control: Partnership, Investor–owned, for–profit **Service:** Psychiatric

Staffed Beds: 59 **Admissions:** 1723 **Census:** 40 **Outpatient Visits:** 2008 **Births:** 0 **Total Expense ($000):** 9288 **Payroll Expense ($000):** 4707 **Personnel:** 99

Many Facility Codes have changed. Please refer to the AHA Guide Code Chart. © 2016 AHA Guide

TX

⊠ **SELECT REHABILITATION HOSPITAL OF DENTON (673036)**, 2620 Scripture Street, Zip 76201–4315; tel. 940/297–6500 **A**1 10 **F**3 29 40 60 64 68 74 75 77 79 86 87 90 93 96 132 135 148 **P**6 **S** Select Medical Corporation, Mechanicsburg, PA
Primary Contact: Michelle Powell, Chief Executive Officer
CFO: Doug Selsor, Director Finance
CHR: Patsy Martin, Manager Human Resources
CNO: Lee Ann Elliott, R.N., Director of Nursing
Web address: www.selectrehab–denton.com/
Control: Partnership, Investor–owned, for–profit **Service:** Rehabilitation

Staffed Beds: 44 **Admissions:** 929 **Census:** 31 **Outpatient Visits:** 10272 **Births:** 0 **Total Expense ($000):** 14952 **Payroll Expense ($000):** 8342 **Personnel:** 99

⊠ **TEXAS HEALTH PRESBYTERIAN HOSPITAL DENTON (450743)**, 3000 North I–35, Zip 76201–5119; tel. 940/898–7000 **A**1 10 **F**3 11 12 13 15 17 18 20 22 24 26 28 29 30 31 34 35 40 45 46 47 48 49 57 59 65 66 70 72 74 75 76 78 79 81 82 83 84 85 86 89 93 107 108 110 111 114 115 118 119 126 129 130 132 135 145 146 147 148 **S** Texas Health Resources, Arlington, TX
Primary Contact: Jeff Reecer, FACHE, Chief Executive Officer
CFO: David B. Meltzer, Chief Financial Officer
CMO: Timothy Harris, M.D., Chief Quality Officer
CIO: Melissa Smart, Communication ad Public Relations Specialist
CHR: Kathy Hardcastle, Director Human Resources
CNO: Deborah Bostic, R.N., Chief Nursing Officer
Web address: www.dentonhospital.com
Control: Other not–for–profit (including NFP Corporation) **Service:** General Medical and Surgical

Staffed Beds: 208 **Admissions:** 10090 **Census:** 123 **Outpatient Visits:** 67904 **Births:** 2218 **Total Expense ($000):** 177882 **Payroll Expense ($000):** 66772 **Personnel:** 908

★ ◇ **THE HEART HOSPITAL BAYLOR DENTON (450893)**, 2801 South Mayhill Road, Zip 76208–5910; tel. 940/220–0600 **A**10 21 **F**3 17 18 20 22 24 26 28 29 30 34 40 54 57 59 64 75 81 84 85 86 87 91 92 93 97 107 108 111 112 114 115 116 117 118 119 120 121 123 124 126 130 137 146 147
Primary Contact: Mark Valentine, President
COO: Bradley Morgan, Vice President of Operations
Web address: www.https://denton.thehearthospitalbaylor.com
Control: Partnership, Investor–owned, for–profit **Service:** Heart

Staffed Beds: 22 **Admissions:** 290 **Census:** 3 **Outpatient Visits:** 4489 **Births:** 0 **Total Expense ($000):** 32018 **Payroll Expense ($000):** 10747 **Personnel:** 111

⊠ **UNIVERSITY BEHAVIORAL HEALTH OF DENTON (454104)**, 2026 West University Drive, Zip 76201–0644; tel. 940/320–8100 **A**1 10 **F**4 5 34 68 98 99 100 101 102 104 105 **S** Universal Health Services, Inc., King of Prussia, PA
Primary Contact: Samantha Castle, Chief Executive Officer
CFO: Ed Sopiarz, Chief Financial Officer
CMO: Atique Khan, M.D., Medical Director
CIO: Marsh Smith, Manager Health Information
CHR: Dorie Atherton, Manager Human Resources
CNO: Vicki Stoker, Chief Nursing Officer
Web address: www.ubhdenton.com
Control: Partnership, Investor–owned, for–profit **Service:** Psychiatric

Staffed Beds: 104 **Admissions:** 2781 **Census:** 69 **Outpatient Visits:** 10692 **Births:** 0 **Total Expense ($000):** 21900 **Payroll Expense ($000):** 9656 **Personnel:** 189

DENVER CITY—Yoakum County

★ **YOAKUM COUNTY HOSPITAL (451308)**, 412 Mustang Avenue, Zip 79323–2762, Mailing Address: P.O. Box 1130, Zip 79323–1130; tel. 806/592–2121 **A**10 18 **F**3 11 13 28 34 35 40 43 50 53 57 59 60 62 64 76 81 87 89 93 107 114 119 127 129 133 **P**6
Primary Contact: Jerry Osburn, Chief Executive Officer
CFO: Suann Parrish, Chief Financial Officer
CMO: Dan Khan, M.D., Chief Medical Officer
CIO: Todd Carrillo, Chief Information Officer
CHR: Teresa Howard, Manager Human Resources
Web address: www.ych.us
Control: County–Government, nonfederal **Service:** General Medical and Surgical

Staffed Beds: 22 **Admissions:** 647 **Census:** 7 **Outpatient Visits:** 51742 **Births:** 247 **Total Expense ($000):** 24654 **Payroll Expense ($000):** 8294 **Personnel:** 183

DESOTO—Dallas County

☐ **DALLAS BEHAVIORAL HEALTHCARE HOSPITAL**, 800 Kirnwood Drive, Zip 75115–2000; tel. 855/982–0897 **A**1 **F**4 5 56 87 98 99 100 101 103 104 105 130 **S** Signature Healthcare Services, Corona, CA
Primary Contact: Selene Q. Hammon, Chief Executive Officer
CMO: Rahim Haqqani, M.D., Medical Director
CIO: Rhonda Nash, Director Health Information Management
CHR: Henry In, Director Human Resources
CNO: Susie Edler, R.N., Chief Nursing Officer
Web address: www.dallasbehavioral.com
Control: Individual, Investor–owned, for–profit **Service:** Psychiatric

Staffed Beds: 116 **Admissions:** 1893 **Census:** 41 **Outpatient Visits:** 3269 **Births:** 0 **Total Expense ($000):** 20959 **Payroll Expense ($000):** 6807 **Personnel:** 150

☐ **HICKORY TRAIL HOSPITAL (454065)**, 2000 Old Hickory Trail, Zip 75115–2242; tel. 972/298–7323 **A**1 10 **F**4 5 29 38 98 99 100 101 103 104 105 130 **S** Universal Health Services, Inc., King of Prussia, PA
Primary Contact: Kay McKennery, Interim Chief Executive Officer
CFO: Terri Logsdon, Chief Financial Officer
CMO: Manoochehr Khatami, M.D., Medical Director
CHR: Sarah Warren, Coordinator Human Resources
Web address: www.hickorytrail.com
Control: Corporation, Investor–owned, for–profit **Service:** Psychiatric

Staffed Beds: 86 **Admissions:** 3113 **Census:** 61 **Outpatient Visits:** 6813 **Births:** 0 **Total Expense ($000):** 17421 **Payroll Expense ($000):** 8481 **Personnel:** 183

⊠ **VIBRA SPECIALTY HOSPITAL AT DESOTO (452097)**, 2700 Walker Way, Zip 75115–2088; tel. 972/298–1100 **A**1 10 **F**1 3 29 70 75 77 87 91 107 130 148 **S** Vibra Healthcare, Mechanicsburg, PA
Primary Contact: Thomas Alexander, Chief Executive Officer
CFO: Donald Trimble, CPA, Chief Financial Officer
CMO: Ed Dominguez, President Medical Staff
CHR: Tim Lozier, Director Human Resources
CNO: Mae C. Weathersby, R.N., Chief Clinical Officer
Web address: www.vshdesoto.com
Control: Corporation, Investor–owned, for–profit **Service:** Long–Term Acute Care hospital

Staffed Beds: 40 **Admissions:** 454 **Census:** 30 **Outpatient Visits:** 0 **Births:** 0 **Total Expense ($000):** 17555 **Payroll Expense ($000):** 7789 **Personnel:** 135

DILLEY—Frio County

☐ **NIX COMMUNITY GENERAL HOSPITAL (670089)**, 230 West Miller, Zip 78017–3818; tel. 830/965–2003 **A**1 10 **F**34 35 40 57 97 107 127
Primary Contact: Allen Tinker, Administrator
CFO: Lester Surrock, Chief Financial Officer
CNO: Amy Lieck, Chief Nursing Officer
Web address: www.nixhealth.com/home/facilities/nix–community–general–hospital?headerbar=2
Control: Corporation, Investor–owned, for–profit **Service:** General Medical and Surgical

Staffed Beds: 10 **Admissions:** 66 **Census:** 1 **Outpatient Visits:** 9142 **Births:** 0 **Total Expense ($000):** 4439 **Payroll Expense ($000):** 1750 **Personnel:** 81

DIMMITT—Castro County

★ **PLAINS MEMORIAL HOSPITAL (451350)**, 310 West Halsell Street, Zip 79027–1846, Mailing Address: P.O. Box 278, Zip 79027–0278; tel. 806/647–2191 **A**10 18 **F**3 7 32 34 35 40 43 53 57 59 64 65 69 75 77 85 86 87 93 97 107 114 115 119 127 130 133 135 **P**6
Primary Contact: Linda Rasor, R.N., Chief Executive Officer
CFO: Terri Martinez, Chief Financial Officer
CMO: Gary R. Hardee, M.D., Medical Director
CIO: Terry Young, Chief Information Officer
CHR: Debbie Underwood, Manager Human Resources
CNO: Renee Castillo, Chief Nursing Officer
Web address: www.plainsmemorial.com
Control: Hospital district or authority, Government, nonfederal **Service:** General Medical and Surgical

Staffed Beds: 17 **Admissions:** 180 **Census:** 4 **Outpatient Visits:** 25104 **Births:** 0 **Total Expense ($000):** 10127 **Payroll Expense ($000):** 4217 **Personnel:** 100

TX

Hospital, Medicare Provider Number, Address, Telephone, Approval, Facility, and Physician Codes, Health Care System

★ American Hospital Association (AHA) membership
☐ The Joint Commission accreditation
◯ Healthcare Facilities Accreditation Program
◇ DNV Healthcare Inc. accreditation
⇑ Center for Improvement in Healthcare Quality Accreditation
△ Commission on Accreditation of Rehabilitation Facilities (CARF) accreditation

DUMAS—Moore County

☐ **MOORE COUNTY HOSPITAL DISTRICT (450221)**, 224 East Second Street, Zip 79029–3808; tel. 806/935–7171 **A**1 10 20 **F**3 7 11 13 15 28 34 35 40 43 46 50 51 57 59 62 63 70 75 79 81 85 86 91 93 107 110 111 115 119 130 131 132 133 135 146 147 148
Primary Contact: Jeff Turner, FACHE, Chief Executive Officer
COO: Yvonne Blue, Chief Operations Officer
CFO: John E. Bailey, Chief Financial Officer
CHR: Ashleigh Wiswell, Director Human Resources
CNO: Stacey Cropley, M.D., Chief Nursing Officer
Web address: www.mchd.net
Control: Hospital district or authority, Government, nonfederal **Service:** General Medical and Surgical

Staffed Beds: 47 **Admissions:** 1010 **Census:** 8 **Outpatient Visits:** 36587 **Births:** 334 **Total Expense ($000):** 35821 **Payroll Expense ($000):** 14458 **Personnel:** 389

EAGLE LAKE—Colorado County

★ **RICE MEDICAL CENTER (451312)**, 600 South Austin Road, Zip 77434–3298, Mailing Address: P.O. Box 277, Zip 77434–0277; tel. 979/234–5571 **A**10 18 **F**3 11 13 15 29 34 40 43 57 59 64 65 70 75 76 77 79 81 107 119 127 133 **P**6
Primary Contact: James D. Janek, Chief Executive Officer
CFO: Brian Mc Bride, Chief Financial Officer
CMO: Russell Thomas, M.D., Chief of Staff
CHR: Velma Loya, Administrative Human Resource Coordinator
CNO: Susan Hernandez, R.N., Chief Nursing Officer
Web address: www.ricemedicalcenter.net/
Control: Corporation, Investor–owned, for–profit **Service:** General Medical and Surgical

Staffed Beds: 15 **Admissions:** 266 **Census:** 3 **Outpatient Visits:** 32446 **Births:** 42 **Total Expense ($000):** 12833 **Payroll Expense ($000):** 3562 **Personnel:** 97

EAGLE PASS—Maverick County

☐ **FORT DUNCAN REGIONAL MEDICAL CENTER (450092)**, 3333 North Foster Maldonado Boulevard, Zip 78852–5893; tel. 830/773–5321 **A**1 10 20 **F**3 11 13 15 18 20 22 29 40 43 45 57 60 65 68 70 75 76 77 79 81 85 89 90 91 93 107 108 110 111 114 118 119 129 130 146 147 148 **S** Universal Health Services, Inc., King of Prussia, PA
Primary Contact: Eladio Montalvo, Chief Executive Officer
COO: Alan Gonzalez, Chief Operating Officer
CFO: Joel Morales, Chief Financial Officer
CMO: Ruben de los Santos, M.D., Chief Medical Officer
CIO: Jose Elias, Director Information Technology
CHR: Daisy Rodriquez, Director Human Resources
CNO: Scott Lethi, R.N., Chief Nursing Officer
Web address: www.fortduncanmedicalcenter.com
Control: Partnership, Investor–owned, for–profit **Service:** General Medical and Surgical

Staffed Beds: 101 **Admissions:** 4734 **Census:** 55 **Outpatient Visits:** 45869 **Births:** 1265 **Total Expense ($000):** 51487 **Payroll Expense ($000):** 21642 **Personnel:** 374

EASTLAND—Eastland County

EASTLAND MEMORIAL HOSPITAL (450411), 304 South Daugherty Street, Zip 76448–2609, Mailing Address: P.O. Box 897, Zip 76448–0897; tel. 254/629–2601 **A**10 20 **F**7 11 15 28 30 34 40 43 45 49 50 53 56 57 59 64 65 68 75 81 85 86 87 93 107 111 114 119 128 129 130 131 133 146 148
Primary Contact: Ted Matthews, Chief Executive Officer
CFO: Jamie Hayden, Chief Financial Officer
CHR: Leisha Hodges, Human Resources Officer
Web address: www.eastlandmemorial.com
Control: Hospital district or authority, Government, nonfederal **Service:** General Medical and Surgical

Staffed Beds: 36 **Admissions:** 596 **Census:** 7 **Outpatient Visits:** 21208 **Births:** 2 **Total Expense ($000):** 12435 **Payroll Expense ($000):** 5488 **Personnel:** 136

EDEN—Concho County

CONCHO COUNTY HOSPITAL (451325), 614 Eaker Street, Zip 76837–0359, Mailing Address: P.O. Box 987, Zip 76837–0987; tel. 325/869–5911 **A**10 18 **F**3 34 40 43 50 53 59 77 87 107 133 146
Primary Contact: Dudley R. White, Administrator and Chief Executive Officer
CFO: Melanie Lozano, Chief Financial Officer
CNO: Toby Lehn, Director of Nurses
Web address: www.conchocountyhospital.com
Control: Hospital district or authority, Government, nonfederal **Service:** General Medical and Surgical

Staffed Beds: 16 **Admissions:** 126 **Census:** 1 **Outpatient Visits:** 4662 **Births:** 0 **Total Expense ($000):** 7224 **Payroll Expense ($000):** 2737 **Personnel:** 51

EDINBURG—Hidalgo County

⊠ **CORNERSTONE REGIONAL HOSPITAL (450825)**, 2302 Cornerstone Boulevard, Zip 78539–8471; tel. 956/618–4444 **A**1 10 **F**3 8 29 34 35 37 39 40 45 46 47 51 57 59 74 79 81 82 85 119 126 145 **S** Universal Health Services, Inc., King of Prussia, PA
Primary Contact: Roxanna M. Godinez, Chief Executive Officer
CFO: Janie Alvarez, Accounting Director
CMO: Omar Gomez, M.D., Chief of Staff
CHR: Erika Betancourt, Coordinator Human Resources
CNO: Roxanne Reyes, Director of Nursing
Web address: www.cornerstoneregional.com
Control: Partnership, Investor–owned, for–profit **Service:** General Medical and Surgical

Staffed Beds: 14 **Admissions:** 552 **Census:** 3 **Outpatient Visits:** 2841 **Births:** 0 **Total Expense ($000):** 12920 **Payroll Expense ($000):** 3496 **Personnel:** 78

☐ **DOCTOR'S HOSPITAL AT RENAISSANCE (450869)**, 5501 South McColl Road, Zip 78539–9152; tel. 956/362–7360 **A**1 2 3 5 10 **F**3 8 9 11 12 13 15 17 18 19 20 22 24 26 28 29 30 31 34 35 38 39 40 41 43 45 46 47 48 49 50 51 52 53 54 55 56 57 58 59 60 64 65 66 68 70 71 72 73 74 75 76 77 78 79 80 81 82 83 84 85 86 87 88 89 90 91 92 93 96 97 98 99 100 101 102 103 104 105 107 108 109 110 111 112 113 114 115 116 117 118 119 120 121 123 124 126 130 131 132 135 139 144 145 146 147 148 **P**3 8
Primary Contact: Carlos Cardenas, M.D., Chief Administrative Officer
COO: Marissa Castaneda, Chief Operating Officer and Director Marketing
CFO: Susan S. Turley, Chief Financial Officer
Web address: www.dhr–rgv.com
Control: Partnership, Investor–owned, for–profit **Service:** General Medical and Surgical

Staffed Beds: 513 **Admissions:** 32704 **Census:** 404 **Outpatient Visits:** 255864 **Births:** 9089 **Total Expense ($000):** 408525 **Payroll Expense ($000):** 169062 **Personnel:** 3926

☐ **SOUTH TEXAS HEALTH SYSTEM (450119)**, 1102 West Trenton Road, Zip 78539–9105; tel. 956/388–6000, (Includes EDINBURG CHILDREN'S HOSPITAL, 1400 West Trenton Road, Zip 78539; tel. 956/388–8000; EDINBURG REGIONAL MEDICAL CENTER, 1102 West Trenton Road, Zip 78539–6199; tel. 956/388–6000; MCALLEN HEART HOSPITAL, 1900 South D. Street, McAllen, Zip 78503; tel. 956/994–2000; Dan Caldwell, Chief Executive Officer; MCALLEN MEDICAL CENTER, 301 West Expressway 83, McAllen, Zip 78503–3045; tel. 956/632–4000; Todd Mann, Chief Executive Officer; SOUTH TEXAS BEHAVIORAL HEALTH CENTER, 2101 West Trenton Road, Zip 78539; tel. 956/388–1300; Joe Rodriguez, Chief Executive Officer) **A**1 3 10 **F**3 4 5 11 12 13 15 17 18 19 20 22 24 26 29 30 31 34 35 38 40 41 42 43 45 47 48 49 50 53 56 57 58 59 60 64 68 70 72 74 75 76 77 78 79 81 85 86 87 88 89 90 96 97 98 99 100 101 102 103 104 107 108 110 111 114 115 119 126 129 130 132 135 138 146 148 **P**6 **S** Universal Health Services, Inc., King of Prussia, PA
Primary Contact: Jennifer Garza, Chief Executive Officer
COO: Jerome M. Brooks, Chief Operating Officer
CFO: Carlos Guajardo, Chief Financial Officer
CMO: Yuri Bermudez, M.D., Chief of Staff
CIO: Rosie L. Mendiola–Balderas, Director Information Systems
CHR: Patricia Mcclelland, Director Human Resources
CNO: Catherine Domian, R.N., Chief Nursing Officer
Web address: www.southtexashealthsystem.com
Control: Partnership, Investor–owned, for–profit **Service:** General Medical and Surgical

Staffed Beds: 788 **Admissions:** 24904 **Census:** 344 **Outpatient Visits:** 168300 **Births:** 1666 **Total Expense ($000):** 315933 **Payroll Expense ($000):** 121961 **Personnel:** 2167

EDNA—Jackson County

★ **JACKSON COUNTY HOSPITAL DISTRICT (451363)**, 1013 South Wells Street, Zip 77957–4098; tel. 361/782–7800 **A**10 18 **F**3 7 15 29 34 35 40 43 44 45 50 53 57 59 62 64 65 68 75 81 87 97 102 107 110 114 119 127 130 133 143 146 **P**8
Primary Contact: Bill Jones, Chief Executive Officer
CFO: Lance Smiga, Chief Financial Officer
CMO: Francisco Ortiz, M.D., Chief of Staff
CIO: Jeff Prukop, Director Professional Services
CHR: Donna Coleman, Coordinator Human Resources
CNO: Tammy Zajicek, Director of Nursing
Web address: www.jchd.org
Control: Hospital district or authority, Government, nonfederal **Service:** General Medical and Surgical

Staffed Beds: 17 **Admissions:** 181 **Census:** 3 **Outpatient Visits:** 16917 **Births:** 0 **Total Expense ($000):** 20394 **Payroll Expense ($000):** 6867 **Personnel:** 143

TX

Many Facility Codes have changed. Please refer to the AHA Guide Code Chart.

EL CAMPO—Wharton County

EL CAMPO MEMORIAL HOSPITAL (450694), 303 Sandy Corner Road, Zip 77437–9535; tel. 979/543–6251 **A**10 **F**3 11 15 29 34 35 40 43 45 56 57 59 60 64 68 70 77 79 81 85 86 93 97 107 108 110 111 114 119 127 129 130 131 132 148 **P**6
Primary Contact: Tisha Zalman, Chief Executive Officer
CFO: Laurie Harvey, Controller
CMO: Brooke Dorotik, M.D., Chief of Medical Staff
CIO: Bill Eller, Director Information Technology
CHR: Ginger Andreas, Coordinator Personnel and Credentialing
CNO: Desiree Cernoch, Director of Nurses
Web address: www.ecmh.org
Control: Other not–for–profit (including NFP Corporation) **Service:** General Medical and Surgical

Staffed Beds: 25 **Admissions:** 423 **Census:** 5 **Outpatient Visits:** 52823
Births: 0 **Total Expense ($000):** 18586 **Payroll Expense ($000):** 6996
Personnel: 134

EL PASO—El Paso County

EAST EL PASO PHYSICIANS MEDICAL CENTER See Foundation Surgical Hospital of El Paso

EL PASO BEHAVIORAL HEALTH SYSTEM (454109), 1900 Denver Avenue, Zip 79902–3008; tel. 915/544–4000 **A**1 3 5 10 **F**4 5 56 57 75 86 87 98 99 101 102 103 104 105 130 **S** Universal Health Services, Inc., King of Prussia, PA
Primary Contact: David W. Morris, Chief Executive Officer
CFO: Phillip Sosa, Chief Financial Officer
CMO: Arthur L. Ramirez, M.D., Medical Director
CIO: Victor Torres, Information Technology Specialist Administrator
CHR: Brenda Holguin, Manager Human Resources
CNO: Susan Brown, Chief Nursing Officer
Web address: www.ubhelpaso.com/
Control: Corporation, Investor–owned, for–profit **Service:** Psychiatric

Staffed Beds: 163 **Admissions:** 5924 **Census:** 141 **Outpatient Visits:** 31445
Births: 0 **Total Expense ($000):** 25555 **Payroll Expense ($000):** 14538
Personnel: 342

EL PASO CHILDREN'S HOSPITAL (453313), 4845 Alameda Avenue, Zip 79905–2705; tel. 915/242–8614 **A**1 3 5 10 **F**3 11 29 31 40 41 44 45 46 47 48 49 50 58 64 65 72 73 74 75 78 81 85 86 87 88 89 93 96 111 119 130 146 148 **P**6
Primary Contact: George Caralis, Interim Chief Executive Officer
COO: Ellen Pitcher, Chief Nursing Officer and Chief Operating Officer
CFO: Omar Bernal, Controller
CMO: Bradley Fuhrman, M.D., Physician in Chief
CIO: Janina Prada, Director Information Technology
CHR: Marina Estrada, Director Human Resources
CNO: Ellen Pitcher, Chief Nursing Officer and Chief Operating Officer
Web address: www.elpasochildrens.org
Control: Other not–for–profit (including NFP Corporation) **Service:** Children's general

Staffed Beds: 122 **Admissions:** 3918 **Census:** 60 **Outpatient Visits:** 41655
Births: 0 **Total Expense ($000):** 101135 **Payroll Expense ($000):** 26774
Personnel: 488

EL PASO LTAC HOSPITAL (452103), 1221 North Cotton Street, 3rd Floor, Zip 79902–3015; tel. 915/546–5822 **A**10 **F**1 3 7 29 30 34 57 60 75 77 82 84 85 86 87 91 100 103 119 130 148
Primary Contact: Jose Huerta, Chief Executive Officer
CNO: Skylier Blake, R.N., Director of Nursing
Web address: www.epltachospital.com/
Control: Partnership, Investor–owned, for–profit **Service:** Long–Term Acute Care hospital

Staffed Beds: 33 **Admissions:** 239 **Census:** 16 **Outpatient Visits:** 0 **Births:** 0 **Total Expense ($000):** 7766 **Payroll Expense ($000):** 2921 **Personnel:** 82

EL PASO PSYCHIATRIC CENTER (454100), 4615 Alameda Avenue, Zip 79905–2702; tel. 915/532–2202 **A**1 3 5 10 **F**29 98 99 103 130 135 **P**6 **S** Texas Department of State Health Services, Austin, TX
Primary Contact: Zulema Carrillo, Superintendent
CFO: David Osterhout, Assistant Superintendent and Chief Financial Officer
CMO: Nicolas Baida–Fragoso, M.D., Clinical Director
CNO: Raul D. Luna, Chief Nurse Executive
Web address: www.dshs.state.tx.us/mhhospitals/ElPasoPC/default.shtm
Control: State–Government, nonfederal **Service:** Psychiatric

Staffed Beds: 74 **Admissions:** 870 **Census:** 66 **Outpatient Visits:** 0 **Births:** 0 **Total Expense ($000):** 31088 **Payroll Expense ($000):** 10406
Personnel: 250

EL PASO SPECIALTY HOSPITAL (450845), 1755 Curie Drive, Zip 79902–2919; tel. 915/544–3636 **A**1 3 10 **F**3 29 34 35 40 59 64 68 75 79 81 82 85 86 87 107 111 115 130 131 148 **S** National Surgical Healthcare, Chicago, IL
Primary Contact: James Wilcox, Chief Executive Officer
CFO: Greg Watters, Chief Financial Officer
CMO: David Mansfield, M.D., Chief of Staff
CNO: Anne Harvey, MSN, Chief Nursing Officer
Web address: www.elpasospecialtyhospital.com
Control: Partnership, Investor–owned, for–profit **Service:** Orthopedic

Staffed Beds: 27 **Admissions:** 792 **Census:** 5 **Outpatient Visits:** 21873
Births: 0 **Total Expense ($000):** 31846 **Payroll Expense ($000):** 8485
Personnel: 173

FOUNDATION SURGICAL HOSPITAL OF EL PASO (450877), 1416 George Dieter Drive, Zip 79936–7601; tel. 915/598–4240 **A**3 10 11 **F**3 29 40 45 49 79 81 82 85 86 93 107 111 114 119 **S** Foundation Surgical Hospital Affiliates, Oklahoma City, OK
Primary Contact: Don Burris, Chief Executive Officer
COO: Marta Contreras, Chief Nursing Officer and Chief Operating Officer
CIO: Louie Aguilera, Director Information Technology
CHR: Grace Beltran, Director Human Resources
CNO: Marta Contreras, Chief Nursing Officer and Chief Operating Officer
Web address: www.physiciansmedcenter.com
Control: Partnership, Investor–owned, for–profit **Service:** Surgical

Staffed Beds: 20 **Admissions:** 1031 **Census:** 5 **Outpatient Visits:** 71722
Births: 0 **Total Expense ($000):** 68108 **Payroll Expense ($000):** 7940
Personnel: 194

HIGHLANDS REHABILITATION HOSPITAL (453086), 1395 George Dieter Drive, Zip 79936–7410; tel. 915/298–7222 **A**1 7 10 **F**3 29 30 34 57 59 64 74 75 79 86 87 90 93 96 100 130 132 143 146 148 **S** Vibra Healthcare, Mechanicsburg, PA
Primary Contact: Mariaelena Carmona, Chief Executive Officer
CHR: Janet Straughan, Manager Human Resources
CNO: Oscar Mendizabal, Chief Nursing Officer
Web address: www.vrhhighlands.com/
Control: Partnership, Investor–owned, for–profit **Service:** Rehabilitation

Staffed Beds: 41 **Admissions:** 767 **Census:** 26 **Outpatient Visits:** 4802
Births: 0 **Total Expense ($000):** 13056 **Payroll Expense ($000):** 5832
Personnel: 104

KINDRED HOSPITAL EL PASO (452079), 1740 Curie Drive, Zip 79902–2901; tel. 915/351–9044 **A**1 10 **F**1 3 29 30 34 75 77 87 130 148 **S** Kindred Healthcare, Louisville, KY
CFO: Melissa Campa, Controller
CMO: Edward Juarez, M.D., Chief Medical Officer
CHR: Laura Anchondo, Administrator Human Resources
Web address: www.khelpaso.com
Control: Corporation, Investor–owned, for–profit **Service:** Long–Term Acute Care hospital

Staffed Beds: 72 **Admissions:** 576 **Census:** 42 **Outpatient Visits:** 687
Births: 0 **Total Expense ($000):** 17810 **Payroll Expense ($000):** 8215
Personnel: 115

LAS PALMAS MEDICAL CENTER (450107), 1801 North Oregon Street, Zip 79902–3591; tel. 915/521–1200, (Includes DEL SOL MEDICAL CENTER, 10301 West Gateway Boulevard, Zip 79925–7798; tel. 915/595–9000; Gary Purushotham, Interim Chief Executive Officer; LAS PALMAS REHABILITATION HOSPITAL, 300 Waymore Drive, Zip 79902–1628; tel. 915/577–2600; Don Karl, Interim Chief Executive Officer) **A**1 3 5 7 10 **F**3 8 11 12 13 15 17 18 19 20 22 24 26 27 28 29 30 31 34 35 37 38 39 40 41 42 43 45 46 47 48 49 50 51 53 54 56 57 58 59 60 64 68 70 72 73 74 75 76 77 78 79 81 82 85 86 87 88 89 90 91 92 93 96 103 107 108 110 111 112 114 115 119 120 121 122 124 126 127 129 130 132 134 135 136 138 143 144 145 146 147 148 **S** HCA, Nashville, TN
Primary Contact: Don Karl, Interim Chief Executive Officer
COO: Don Karl, Chief Operating Officer
CNO: Jerry Gonzalez, Interim Chief Nursing Officer
Web address: www.laspalmashealth.com
Control: Partnership, Investor–owned, for–profit **Service:** General Medical and Surgical

Staffed Beds: 570 **Admissions:** 27773 **Census:** 384 **Outpatient Visits:** 220550 **Births:** 5095 **Total Expense ($000):** 348539 **Payroll Expense ($000):** 140264 **Personnel:** 2274

TX

Hospital, Medicare Provider Number, Address, Telephone, Approval, Facility, and Physician Codes, Health Care System

★ American Hospital Association (AHA) membership   ○ Healthcare Facilities Accreditation Program   ⇑ Center for Improvement in Healthcare Quality Accreditation
□ The Joint Commission accreditation   ◇ DNV Healthcare Inc. accreditation   △ Commission on Accreditation of Rehabilitation Facilities (CARF) accreditation

☐ **MESA HILLS SPECIALTY HOSPITAL (452035)**, 2311 North Oregon Street, 5th Floor, Zip 79902–3216; tel. 915/545–1823, (Data for 275 days) **A**1 10 **F**1 3 29 54 61 64 65 68 74 75 77 82 85 86 87 97 130 143 148 **P**8 **S** Concord Healthcare Group, Lakewood, NJ
Primary Contact: Jose Huerta, Chief Executive Officer
COO: Elena Pino, Chief Operating Officer and Chief Nursing Officer
CFO: Priscilla Carter, Chief Financial Officer
Web address: www.mesahillsspecialtyhospital.com/mesa_hills/index.aspx
Control: Corporation, Investor–owned, for–profit **Service:** Children's Long–Term Acute Care

> **Staffed Beds:** 32 **Admissions:** 251 **Census:** 18 **Outpatient Visits:** 0 **Births:** 0 **Total Expense ($000):** 4991 **Payroll Expense ($000):** 2112 **Personnel:** 111

✠ **THE HOSPITALS OF PROVIDENCE EAST CAMPUS (670047)**, 3280 Joe Battle Boulevard, Zip 79938–2622; tel. 915/832–2000 **A**1 2 5 10 **F**3 13 15 18 20 22 26 29 30 31 34 35 37 40 41 45 46 47 49 50 57 59 60 63 64 68 70 72 73 74 75 76 77 78 79 81 83 84 85 86 87 89 93 107 108 110 111 115 119 126 130 134 146 147 148 **P**4 **S** TENET Healthcare Corporation, Dallas, TX
Primary Contact: Nicholas R. Tejeda, FACHE, Chief Executive Officer
COO: Lauren Morton, Chief Operating Officer
Web address: www.sphn.com
Control: Individual, Investor–owned, for–profit **Service:** General Medical and Surgical

> **Staffed Beds:** 182 **Admissions:** 11102 **Census:** 120 **Outpatient Visits:** 95196 **Births:** 2304 **Total Expense ($000):** 147163 **Payroll Expense ($000):** 46379 **Personnel:** 815

✠ **THE HOSPITALS OF PROVIDENCE MEMORIAL CAMPUS (450002)**, 2001 North Oregon Street, Zip 79902–3368; tel. 915/577–6625, (Includes PROVIDENCE CHILDREN'S HOSPITAL, 2001 North Oregon Street, Zip 79902–3320; tel. 915/577–7746; Sally A. Hurt–Deitch, FACHE, R.N., Market Chief Executive Officer) **A**1 2 10 **F**3 11 12 13 14 15 17 18 19 20 21 22 23 24 25 28 29 31 32 34 35 40 41 42 43 45 46 49 50 51 54 56 57 59 63 64 65 67 70 72 73 74 75 76 77 78 79 81 84 85 86 87 88 89 91 92 93 98 103 107 108 110 111 114 118 119 126 129 130 132 134 145 146 147 148 **S** TENET Healthcare Corporation, Dallas, TX
Primary Contact: Sally A. Hurt–Deitch, FACHE, R.N., Market Chief Executive Officer
COO: Roddex Barlow, Chief Operating Officer
CFO: Charles Handley, Chief Financial Officer
CMO: Enrique Martinez, M.D., Chief Medical Officer
CIO: Ray Davis, Administrative Director
CHR: Stephanie S. Talley, Market Chief Human Resource Officer
CNO: Karen Fowler, MSN, Chief Nursing Officer
Web address: www.thehospitalsofprovidence.com
Control: Partnership, Investor–owned, for–profit **Service:** General Medical and Surgical

> **Staffed Beds:** 409 **Admissions:** 17093 **Census:** 209 **Outpatient Visits:** 145920 **Births:** 3164 **Total Expense ($000):** 236788 **Payroll Expense ($000):** 78192 **Personnel:** 1378

✠ **THE HOSPITALS OF PROVIDENCE SIERRA CAMPUS (450668)**, 1625 Medical Center Drive, Zip 79902–5005; tel. 915/747–4000 **A**1 2 5 10 **F**3 17 18 20 22 24 26 29 30 34 37 40 42 43 45 46 48 49 50 54 57 58 59 60 61 64 65 68 69 70 72 74 75 76 77 78 79 81 82 85 86 90 96 97 107 108 110 111 114 115 118 119 120 124 126 130 132 134 144 145 146 147 148 **P**1 **S** TENET Healthcare Corporation, Dallas, TX
Primary Contact: Monica Vargas–Mahar, FACHE, Chief Executive Officer
COO: Benson Chacko, Chief Operating Officer
CFO: Victoria Gonzalez, Chief Financial Officer
CIO: Ray Davis, Administrative Director Information Systems
CHR: Stephanie S. Talley, Chief Human Resource Officer
CNO: Erik Cazares, Chief Nursing Officer
Web address: www.thehospitalsofprovidence.com
Control: Corporation, Investor–owned, for–profit **Service:** General Medical and Surgical

> **Staffed Beds:** 225 **Admissions:** 10273 **Census:** 143 **Outpatient Visits:** 105118 **Births:** 1346 **Total Expense ($000):** 158197 **Payroll Expense ($000):** 50638 **Personnel:** 762

TRIUMPH HOSPITAL EL PASO See Kindred Hospital El Paso

☒ **UNIVERSITY MEDICAL CENTER OF EL PASO (450024)**, 4815 Alameda Avenue, Zip 79905–2794, Mailing Address: P.O. Box 20009, Zip 79998–0009; tel. 915/544–1200 **A**1 2 3 5 10 **F**3 8 11 13 15 17 18 20 22 24 26 28 29 30 31 34 35 37 40 43 44 47 48 49 50 51 53 54 56 57 59 60 61 64 65 68 70 74 75 76 77 78 79 81 82 85 86 87 91 92 93 94 96 97 100 102 107 108 110 111 112 113 114 115 118 119 126 127 130 131 134 143 144 145 146 147 148 **P**6
Primary Contact: Jacob Cintron, FACHE, President and Chief Executive Officer
COO: Maria Zampini, Chief Operating Officer
CFO: Michael Nunez, Chief Financial Officer
CMO: Carmela Morales, M.D., Chief of Staff
CIO: Janina Prada, Director Information Services
CHR: Janice M. Harris, Director Human Resources
CNO: Diana Fancher, Chief Nursing Officer
Web address: www.thomasoncares.org
Control: Hospital district or authority, Government, nonfederal **Service:** General Medical and Surgical

> **Staffed Beds:** 261 **Admissions:** 15106 **Census:** 181 **Outpatient Visits:** 752387 **Births:** 3572 **Total Expense ($000):** 556666 **Payroll Expense ($000):** 135427 **Personnel:** 2447

☒ **WILLIAM BEAUMONT ARMY MEDICAL CENTER**, 5005 North Piedras Street, Zip 79920–5001; tel. 915/742–2121, (Nonreporting) **A**1 2 3 5 **S** Department of the Army, Office of the Surgeon General, Falls Church, VA
Primary Contact: Colonel Michael S. Heimall, Commander
CIO: Major Rion Koon, Chief Information Management Division
Web address: www.wbamc.amedd.army.mil
Control: Army, Government, federal **Service:** General Medical and Surgical

> **Staffed Beds:** 209

ELDORADO—Schleicher County

★ **SCHLEICHER COUNTY MEDICAL CENTER (451304)**, 102 North U.S. Highway 277, Zip 76936–4010; tel. 325/853–2507 **A**10 18 **F**34 40 57 59 64 65 66 68 87 93 107 127 133 **S** Preferred Management Corporation, Shawnee, OK
Primary Contact: Paul Burke, Administrator
CFO: Larry Stephens, Chief Financial Officer
CMO: Gordy Day, M.D., Medical Director
CHR: Beverly Minor, Chief Human Resources
Web address: www.scmc.us
Control: Corporation, Investor–owned, for–profit **Service:** General Medical and Surgical

> **Staffed Beds:** 14 **Admissions:** 102 **Census:** 1 **Outpatient Visits:** 7755 **Births:** 0 **Total Expense ($000):** 4442 **Payroll Expense ($000):** 1966 **Personnel:** 48

ELECTRA—Wichita County

★ **ELECTRA MEMORIAL HOSPITAL (451343)**, 1207 South Bailey Street, Zip 76360–3221, Mailing Address: P.O. Box 1112, Zip 76360–1112; tel. 940/495–3981 **A**10 18 **F**3 7 11 28 32 34 40 43 45 53 59 62 64 65 66 75 77 82 86 93 97 107 114 119 127 129 130 131 133 144 148
Primary Contact: Rebecca J. McCain, Chief Executive Officer
CFO: Ginnie Holmes, Chief Financial Officer
CIO: Brandon Huffstutler, Chief Information Officer
CNO: Kim Gilbert, R.N., Chief Nursing Officer
Web address: www.electrahospital.com
Control: Hospital district or authority, Government, nonfederal **Service:** General Medical and Surgical

> **Staffed Beds:** 19 **Admissions:** 502 **Census:** 7 **Outpatient Visits:** 20360 **Births:** 0 **Total Expense ($000):** 14842 **Payroll Expense ($000):** 7761 **Personnel:** 116

ENNIS—Ellis County

☒ **ENNIS REGIONAL MEDICAL CENTER (450833)**, 2201 West Lampasas Street, Zip 75119–5644; tel. 972/875–0900 **A**1 10 **F**3 11 13 15 18 29 30 34 35 40 43 45 50 51 57 59 64 65 70 75 76 77 79 81 82 85 93 107 108 110 111 115 119 146 **S** LifePoint Health, Brentwood, TN
Primary Contact: Alan Daugherty, Chief Executive Officer
CFO: Jack Wilcox, Chief Financial Officer
CMO: Raymond W. Blair, Jr., M.D., Chief of Staff
CHR: Selena Cryer, Director Human Resources
CNO: Edwina A. Miner, R.N., Chief Nursing Officer
Web address: www.ennisregional.com
Control: Partnership, Investor–owned, for–profit **Service:** General Medical and Surgical

> **Staffed Beds:** 58 **Admissions:** 1422 **Census:** 11 **Outpatient Visits:** 30088 **Births:** 489 **Total Expense ($000):** 24431 **Payroll Expense ($000):** 9459 **Personnel:** 167

TX

FAIRFIELD—Freestone County

★ **EAST TEXAS MEDICAL CENTER FAIRFIELD (450658)**, 125 Newman Street, Zip 75840–1499; tel. 903/389–2121 **A**10 20 **F**15 28 34 40 43 45 50 57 59 68 75 81 82 107 110 115 119 127 130 132 **P**7
Primary Contact: Ruth Cook, Administrator
CFO: David A. Travis, Chief Financial Officer
CMO: Darryl White, M.D., Chief of Staff
CHR: Jennifer Rummel, Director Human Resources
CNO: Tonya Basque, Chief Nursing Officer
Web address: www.etmc.org
Control: Other not–for–profit (including NFP Corporation) **Service:** General Medical and Surgical

Staffed Beds: 37 **Admissions:** 463 **Census:** 4 **Outpatient Visits:** 43349 **Births:** 0 **Total Expense ($000):** 12747 **Payroll Expense ($000):** 3664 **Personnel:** 81

FLORESVILLE—Wilson County

CONNALLY MEMORIAL MEDICAL CENTER (450108), 499 10th Street, Zip 78114–3175; tel. 830/393–1300 **A**10 **F**3 15 18 29 34 35 40 43 45 47 49 54 57 59 62 64 70 75 81 82 85 86 87 107 108 110 111 114 119 130 132 133 144 146 148 **P**4 6
Primary Contact: Brian D. Burnside, FACHE, Chief Executive Officer
COO: Bob Gillespie, Chief Operating Officer
CFO: Jamie Jacoby, Chief Financial Officer
CMO: Wade Krause, M.D., Chief Medical Officer
CIO: Jamie Jacoby, Information Technology Officer
CHR: Jamie Jacoby, Director Human Resources
CNO: Sue Tackitt, Chief Nursing Officer
Web address: www.connallymmc.org
Control: Hospital district or authority, Government, nonfederal **Service:** General Medical and Surgical

Staffed Beds: 26 **Admissions:** 1007 **Census:** 10 **Outpatient Visits:** 95668 **Births:** 2 **Total Expense ($000):** 32529 **Payroll Expense ($000):** 11244 **Personnel:** 247

FLOWER MOUND—Denton County

◇ **CONTINUUM REHABILITATION HOSPITAL OF NORTH TEXAS (673047)**, 3100 Peters Colony Road, Zip 75022–2949; tel. 214/513–0310, (Nonreporting) **A**10 21
Primary Contact: Gina Tomaseski, Chief Executive Officer
Web address: www.continuumhs.com
Control: Corporation, Investor–owned, for–profit **Service:** Rehabilitation

Staffed Beds: 41

□ **TEXAS HEALTH PRESBYTERIAN HOSPITAL FLOWER MOUND (670068)**, 4400 Long Prairie Road, Zip 75028–1892; tel. 469/322–7000 **A**1 10 **F**3 12 13 15 17 18 20 29 30 31 34 40 45 49 57 59 70 72 73 75 76 77 78 79 81 82 85 87 93 107 108 110 111 114 115 119 126 130 146 147
Primary Contact: Spencer Turner, President
COO: Shelley R. Tobey, R.N., Chief Operating Officer and Chief Nursing Officer
CFO: Tom Howard, Chief Financial Officer
CHR: Nicole Schweigert, Director Human Resources
CNO: Shelley R. Tobey, R.N., Chief Operating Officer and Chief Nursing Officer
Web address: www.texashealthflowermound.com/
Control: Partnership, Investor–owned, for–profit **Service:** General Medical and Surgical

Staffed Beds: 92 **Admissions:** 5426 **Census:** 54 **Outpatient Visits:** 33464 **Births:** 1601 **Total Expense ($000):** 104592 **Payroll Expense ($000):** 35496 **Personnel:** 700

FORT HOOD—Bell County

⊞ **CARL R. DARNALL ARMY MEDICAL CENTER**, 36000 Darnall Loop, Zip 76544–5095; tel. 254/288–8000, (Nonreporting) **A**1 2 3 5 **S** Department of the Army, Office of the Surgeon General, Falls Church, VA
Primary Contact: Colonel Mark W. Thompson, M.D., Commanding Officer
CMO: Colonel Carolyn Tiffany, Deputy Commander Clinical Service
CHR: Charles Burton, Chief Human Resources
Web address: www.crdamc.amedd.army.mil
Control: Army, Government, federal **Service:** General Medical and Surgical

Staffed Beds: 109

FORT SAM HOUSTON—Bexar County

⊞ **BROOKE ARMY MEDICAL CENTER**, 3851 Roger Brookes Drive, Zip 78234–4501; tel. 210/916–4141, (Nonreporting) **A**1 2 3 5 **S** Department of the Army, Office of the Surgeon General, Falls Church, VA
Primary Contact: Colonel Evan Renz, Chief Executive Officer
CMO: Colonel Joseph P. Chozinski, M.D., Deputy Commander Clinical Services
CIO: Lieutenant Colonel David Broyhill, Chief Information Management
CHR: Rose Juarez, Chief Civilian Personnel Branch
CNO: Colonel Sheri Howell, Deputy Commander Nursing
Web address: www.bamc.amedd.army.mil
Control: Army, Government, federal **Service:** General Medical and Surgical

Staffed Beds: 226

FORT STOCKTON—Pecos County

★ **PECOS COUNTY MEMORIAL HOSPITAL (450178)**, 387 West I. H–10, Zip 79735–8912, Mailing Address: P.O. Box 1648, Zip 79735–1648; tel. 432/336–2004 **A**10 20 **F**3 11 13 28 29 30 32 34 35 40 43 53 57 59 62 63 64 65 75 76 81 93 107 111 119 127 129 130 146 148 **P**5 6
Primary Contact: James E. Koulovatos, Chief Executive Officer
CFO: Anthony Ortiz, Chief Financial Officer
CMO: Subodh Mallik, M.D., Chief of Staff
CHR: Malissa Trevino, Director Human Resources
CNO: Gina Kalka, R.N., Chief Nursing Officer
Web address: www.pcmhfs.com
Control: County–Government, nonfederal **Service:** General Medical and Surgical

Staffed Beds: 31 **Admissions:** 1286 **Census:** 11 **Outpatient Visits:** 84244 **Births:** 156 **Total Expense ($000):** 29957 **Payroll Expense ($000):** 15625 **Personnel:** 251

FORT WORTH—Tarrant County

⊞ **BAYLOR ALL SAINTS MEDICAL CENTER AT FORT WORTH (450137)**, 1400 Eighth Avenue, Zip 76104–4192; tel. 817/926–2544 **A**1 2 3 5 10 **F**3 11 12 13 17 18 24 26 28 29 30 31 34 35 38 40 43 45 46 47 49 53 55 59 64 70 72 73 74 75 76 77 78 79 80 81 82 84 86 87 90 96 97 100 101 102 103 104 105 107 108 111 114 115 119 124 126 130 131 132 138 139 142 146 147 148 **S** Baylor Scott & White Health, Dallas, TX
Primary Contact: Janice Whitmire, Interim President
COO: Janice L. Walker, R.N., Chief Operating Officer
CFO: Lucy Catala, Vice President Finance
CMO: Dahlia Hassani, Vice President of Medical Affairs
CIO: Sandy Vaughn, Director Information Services
CHR: Tracy Stanford, Director Human Resources
Web address: www.baylorhealth.com/PhysiciansLocations/AllSaints/Pages/Default.aspx
Control: Other not–for–profit (including NFP Corporation) **Service:** General Medical and Surgical

Staffed Beds: 373 **Admissions:** 17728 **Census:** 231 **Outpatient Visits:** 71035 **Births:** 5577 **Total Expense ($000):** 307708 **Payroll Expense ($000):** 115135 **Personnel:** 1296

⊞ **BAYLOR INSTITUTE FOR REHABILITATION AT FORT WORTH (673035)**, 6601 Harris Parkway, Zip 76132–6108 **A**1 10 **F**3 28 29 30 64 75 90 93 130 **S** Select Medical Corporation, Mechanicsburg, PA
Primary Contact: Jeffrey D. Thompson, Chief Executive Officer
CMO: Ade Adedokun, M.D., Medical Director
CHR: Lenae Romack, Manager Human Resources
CNO: Fred J. Andrews, Director of Nursing and Ancillary Services
Web address: www.baylorhealth.com/PhysiciansLocations/BIR/Pages/Default.aspx
Control: Partnership, Investor–owned, for–profit **Service:** Rehabilitation

Staffed Beds: 42 **Admissions:** 993 **Census:** 31 **Outpatient Visits:** 3244 **Births:** 0 **Total Expense ($000):** 16372 **Payroll Expense ($000):** 7944 **Personnel:** 123

□ **BAYLOR SURGICAL HOSPITAL AT FORT WORTH (450880)**, 1800 Park Place Avenue, Zip 76110–1302; tel. 682/703–5600 **A**1 10 **F**3 8 29 40 43 51 54 64 70 79 81 82 85 87 107 111 119
Primary Contact: Paul Debona, Chief Executive Officer
CFO: Jane Mathis, Chief Financial Officer
CMO: Bruce Bollinger, M.D., Medical Director
CNO: Stacie Merrill, Chief Nursing Officer
Web address: www.mcsh–hospital.com
Control: Partnership, Investor–owned, for–profit **Service:** Surgical

Staffed Beds: 30 **Admissions:** 1203 **Census:** 8 **Outpatient Visits:** 10347 **Births:** 0 **Total Expense ($000):** 71858 **Payroll Expense ($000):** 12883 **Personnel:** 206

TX

✠ **COOK CHILDREN'S MEDICAL CENTER (453300)**, 801 Seventh Avenue, Zip 76104–2796; tel. 682/885–4000 **A**1 3 5 10 **F**3 7 8 17 19 21 23 25 27 29 30 31 32 34 35 38 39 40 41 43 44 45 50 54 55 57 58 59 60 61 64 68 72 74 75 77 78 79 80 81 82 83 84 85 86 87 88 89 90 91 92 93 97 98 99 100 101 102 104 105 106 107 108 111 112 113 114 118 119 129 130 131 132 134 136 138 143 144 146 148 **P**6
Primary Contact: Rick W. Merrill, System President and Chief Executive Officer
CFO: Stephen Kimmel, Chief Financial Officer
CMO: James C. Cunningham, M.D., Chief Medical Officer
CIO: Theresa Meadows, Chief Information Officer
CNO: Teresa J. Clark, R.N., Chief Nursing Officer
Web address: www.cookchildrens.org
Control: Other not-for-profit (including NFP Corporation) **Service:** Children's general

Staffed Beds: 363 **Admissions:** 10337 **Census:** 197 **Outpatient Visits:** 329777 **Births:** 0 **Total Expense ($000):** 668520 **Payroll Expense ($000):** 226223 **Personnel:** 3486

✠ **HEALTHSOUTH CITY VIEW REHABILITATION HOSPITAL (453042)**, 6701 Oakmont Boulevard, Zip 76132–2957; tel. 817/370–4700 **A**1 10 **F**3 29 62 77 90 91 94 95 96 118 130 148 **S** HEALTHSOUTH Corporation, Birmingham, AL
Primary Contact: Janell Briscoe, Chief Executive Officer
Web address: www.healthsouthcityview.com
Control: Corporation, Investor-owned, for-profit **Service:** Rehabilitation

Staffed Beds: 62 **Admissions:** 1303 **Census:** 44 **Outpatient Visits:** 2362 **Births:** 0 **Total Expense ($000):** 15733 **Payroll Expense ($000):** 8886 **Personnel:** 145

✠ **HEALTHSOUTH REHABILITATION HOSPITAL OF FORT WORTH (453041)**, 1212 West Lancaster Avenue, Zip 76102–4510; tel. 817/870–2336 **A**1 10 **F**3 29 30 60 68 74 75 77 79 86 90 91 95 96 130 131 148 **S** HEALTHSOUTH Corporation, Birmingham, AL
Primary Contact: Janell Briscoe, Chief Executive Officer
CFO: Sherry Hapney, Chief Financial Officer
CMO: Patrick Donovan, M.D., Director Medical Staff
CHR: Tara Kleas, Director Human Resources
Web address: www.healthsouthfortworth.com
Control: Corporation, Investor-owned, for-profit **Service:** Rehabilitation

Staffed Beds: 60 **Admissions:** 1226 **Census:** 42 **Outpatient Visits:** 0 **Births:** 0 **Total Expense ($000):** 13979 **Payroll Expense ($000):** 8117 **Personnel:** 141

JOHN PETER SMITH HOSPITAL See JPS Health Network

✠ **JPS HEALTH NETWORK (450039)**, 1500 South Main Street, Zip 76104–4917; tel. 817/921–3431, (Includes JOHN PETER SMITH HOSPITAL, 1500 South Main Street, Zip 76104; tel. 817/921–3431; TRINITY SPRINGS PAVILION, 1500 South Main Street, tel. 817/927–3636; Lily Wong, Director Psychiatry), (Total facility includes 15 beds in nursing home–type unit) **A**1 2 3 5 8 10 **F**3 8 11 13 15 17 18 20 22 24 26 28 29 30 31 32 34 35 36 37 38 39 40 43 44 45 47 49 50 54 55 56 57 58 59 60 61 64 65 66 68 70 72 74 75 76 77 78 79 80 81 82 84 85 86 87 89 91 92 93 97 98 99 100 101 102 103 104 105 107 108 110 111 114 115 118 119 120 121 123 124 126 128 130 131 132 134 135 142 143 144 146 147 148
Primary Contact: Robert Earley, President and Chief Executive Officer
CFO: Alan Townsend, Interim Chief Financial Officer
CIO: Melinda Custin, Chief Information Officer
CHR: Nikki Sumpter, Senior Vice President Human Resources
CNO: Wanda V. Peebles, Chief Nursing Officer
Web address: www.jpshealthnet.org
Control: Hospital district or authority, Government, nonfederal **Service:** General Medical and Surgical

Staffed Beds: 517 **Admissions:** 25557 **Census:** 388 **Outpatient Visits:** 1168056 **Births:** 4698 **Total Expense ($000):** 799152 **Payroll Expense ($000):** 325400 **Personnel:** 5446

✠ **KINDRED HOSPITAL–FORT WORTH (452088)**, 815 Eighth Avenue, Zip 76104–2609; tel. 817/332–4812, (Includes KINDRED HOSPITAL TARRANT COUNTY–FORT WORTH SOUTHWEST, 7800 Oakmont Boulevard, Zip 76132–4299; tel. 817/346–0094; Anna Rojas, Chief Executive Officer) **A**1 10 **F**3 29 46 48 60 70 77 79 82 85 107 114 130 148 **S** Kindred Healthcare, Louisville, KY
Primary Contact: Matthew Malinak, Chief Executive Officer
CFO: Susan Popp, Controller
CMO: Stuart McDonald, M.D., President Medical Staff
CIO: Norma Warner, Area Director Health Information Management
CHR: Nicole Newpower, Coordinator Human Resources
Web address: www.kindredfortworth.com/
Control: Corporation, Investor-owned, for-profit **Service:** Long–Term Acute Care hospital

Staffed Beds: 54 **Admissions:** 655 **Census:** 42 **Outpatient Visits:** 0 **Births:** 0 **Total Expense ($000):** 18023 **Payroll Expense ($000):** 8621 **Personnel:** 135

★ **MEDICAL CENTER ALLIANCE**, 3101 North Tarrant Parkway, Zip 76177; tel. 817/639–1000, (Data for 316 days) **F**3 11 12 13 15 18 20 22 24 26 29 30 34 35 40 45 47 48 49 50 56 57 59 64 70 72 74 75 76 79 81 82 85 86 87 92 107 108 110 111 114 119 126 130 132 135 145 146 147 148 **S** HCA, Nashville, TN
Primary Contact: Glenn Wallace, Chief Executive Officer
Web address: www.baylorhealth.com/PhysiciansLocations/BIR/Pages/Default.aspx
Control: Corporation, Investor-owned, for-profit **Service:** General Medical and Surgical

Staffed Beds: 55 **Admissions:** 1536 **Census:** 15 **Outpatient Visits:** 21915 **Births:** 552 **Total Expense ($000):** 45946 **Payroll Expense ($000):** 16320 **Personnel:** 172

☐ **MESA SPRINGS (454124)**, 5560 Mesa Springs Drive, Zip 76123; tel. 817/292–4600 **A**1 10 **F**5 29 54 98 99 101 103 104 105
Primary Contact: Barbara Schmidt, Chief Executive Officer
CFO: Kent Ashley, Chief Financial Officer
CMO: Stewart Keller, M.D., Medical Director
CHR: Jill Housand, Director Human Resources
CNO: Ana Ramirez, Director of Nursing
Web address: www.springstone.com/hospitals.stmhl
Control: Corporation, Investor-owned, for-profit **Service:** Psychiatric

Staffed Beds: 72 **Admissions:** 1933 **Census:** 44 **Outpatient Visits:** 16813 **Births:** 0 **Total Expense ($000):** 12525 **Payroll Expense ($000):** 7391 **Personnel:** 173

OCEANS BEHAVIORAL HOSPITAL FORT WORTH, 6200 Overton Ridge Boulevard, Zip 76132–3614; tel. 817/361–1991 **F**29 35 64 98 100 101 103 104 **S** Oceans Healthcare, Lake Charles, LA
Primary Contact: Scott Blakeley, Acting Administrator
Web address: www.oceanshealthcare.com
Control: Corporation, Investor-owned, for-profit **Service:** Psychiatric

Staffed Beds: 48 **Admissions:** 896 **Census:** 33 **Outpatient Visits:** 3376 **Births:** 0 **Total Expense ($000):** 7765 **Payroll Expense ($000):** 3551 **Personnel:** 69

✠ **PLAZA MEDICAL CENTER OF FORT WORTH (450672)**, 900 Eighth Avenue, Zip 76104–3902; tel. 817/336–2100 **A**1 2 3 10 13 **F**3 11 12 17 18 20 22 24 26 28 29 30 31 34 35 40 42 45 46 48 49 53 56 58 64 67 70 74 77 78 79 81 85 87 91 93 107 108 111 114 115 119 130 138 145 146 148 **P**8 **S** HCA, Nashville, TN
Primary Contact: Clay Franklin, Chief Executive Officer
COO: Gregory Haralson, Chief Operating Officer
CFO: Elia Stokes, Chief Financial Officer
CMO: Amir Malik, M.D., Cardiologist
CIO: Kelley Fredrickson, Director Information Services
CHR: Cyndi Roberts, Director Human Resources
Web address: www.plazamedicalcenter.com
Control: Partnership, Investor-owned, for-profit **Service:** General Medical and Surgical

Staffed Beds: 212 **Admissions:** 9634 **Census:** 142 **Outpatient Visits:** 47086 **Births:** 0 **Total Expense ($000):** 185024 **Payroll Expense ($000):** 57648 **Personnel:** 762

✠ **TEXAS HEALTH HARRIS METHODIST HOSPITAL ALLIANCE (670085)**, 10864 Texas Health Trail, Zip 76244–4897; tel. 682/212–2000 **A**1 10 **F**3 11 12 13 15 18 20 29 30 34 35 40 45 46 48 49 57 59 64 70 72 74 75 76 77 79 81 82 85 86 91 93 107 108 110 111 113 114 115 118 119 130 131 132 135 145 146 147 148 **S** Texas Health Resources, Arlington, TX
Primary Contact: Clint Abernathy, President and Chief Operating Officer
Web address: www.https://www.texashealth.org/alliance/Pages/default.aspx
Control: Other not-for-profit (including NFP Corporation) **Service:** General Medical and Surgical

Staffed Beds: 74 **Admissions:** 5035 **Census:** 46 **Outpatient Visits:** 37840 **Births:** 1527 **Total Expense ($000):** 82395 **Payroll Expense ($000):** 31807 **Personnel:** 388

✠ △ **TEXAS HEALTH HARRIS METHODIST HOSPITAL FORT WORTH (450135)**, 1301 Pennsylvania Avenue, Zip 76104–2122; tel. 817/250–2000 **A**1 2 5 7 10 **F**3 8 12 15 17 18 20 22 24 26 28 29 30 31 34 35 36 40 42 43 45 46 47 48 49 53 54 56 57 58 59 60 61 64 65 68 70 71 72 74 75 76 77 78 79 81 82 83 84 85 86 87 91 92 93 94 95 96 107 108 110 111 112 114 115 116 117 118 119 120 126 130 131 132 135 138 146 147 148 **S** Texas Health Resources, Arlington, TX
Primary Contact: Lillie Biggins, RN, R.N., President
CFO: Shelly Miland, Group Financial Officer
CMO: Joseph Prosser, M.D., Chief Medical Officer
CHR: Joseph Condon, Entity Human Resources Officer
CNO: Elaine Nelson, R.N., Chief Nursing Officer
Web address: www.texashealth.org
Control: Other not-for-profit (including NFP Corporation) **Service:** General Medical and Surgical

Staffed Beds: 639 **Admissions:** 34359 **Census:** 506 **Outpatient Visits:** 156952 **Births:** 3487 **Total Expense ($000):** 671888 **Payroll Expense ($000):** 268983 **Personnel:** 4082

TX

⊠ **TEXAS HEALTH HARRIS METHODIST HOSPITAL SOUTHWEST FORT WORTH (450779)**, 6100 Harris Parkway, Zip 76132–4199; tel. 817/433–5000 **A**1 2 10 **F**3 11 13 15 18 20 29 30 31 34 35 36 37 40 45 46 47 48 49 50 57 59 64 67 68 70 72 75 76 77 78 79 80 81 84 85 86 87 93 102 107 110 111 114 115 119 126 130 131 146 147 **S** Texas Health Resources, Arlington, TX
Primary Contact: Joseph DeLeon, President
CFO: Charlotte Ward, Entity Financial Officer
CMO: Mark Montgomery, M.D., Chief Medical Officer
CHR: Leanna W. Nalley, Director Human Resources
CNO: Mary Robinson, Chief Nursing Officer and Vice President Patient Care Services
Web address: www.texashealth.org
Control: Other not–for–profit (including NFP Corporation) **Service:** General Medical and Surgical

Staffed Beds: 199 **Admissions:** 14158 **Census:** 139 **Outpatient Visits:** 95229 **Births:** 3075 **Total Expense ($000):** 224197 **Payroll Expense ($000):** 73225 **Personnel:** 952

⊠ **TEXAS HEALTH SPECIALTY HOSPITAL (452018)**, 1301 Pennsylvania Avenue, 4th Floor, Zip 76104–2190; tel. 817/250–5500 **A**1 10 **F**1 3 42 44 87 130 148 **S** Texas Health Resources, Arlington, TX
Primary Contact: Cheryl Mobley, FACHE, President
CFO: Shelly Miland, Chief Financial Officer
CMO: Michael Thornsberry, M.D., Chief Medical Officer
CHR: Joseph Condon, Director Human Resources
CNO: Pam Duffey, MSN, Chief Nursing Officer
Web address: www.texashealth.org
Control: Church–operated, Nongovernment, not–for profit **Service:** Long–Term Acute Care hospital

Staffed Beds: 10 **Admissions:** 97 **Census:** 8 **Outpatient Visits:** 0 **Births:** 0 **Total Expense ($000):** 7029 **Payroll Expense ($000):** 3125 **Personnel:** 38

☐ △ **TEXAS REHABILITATION HOSPITAL OF FORT WORTH (673048)**, 425 Alabama Avenue, Zip 76104–1022; tel. 817/820–3400 **A**1 7 10 **F**3 29 74 79 90 91 96 130 132 148 **S** Kindred Healthcare, Louisville, KY
Primary Contact: Russell Bailey, Chief Executive Officer
Web address: www.texasrehabhospital.com/
Control: Corporation, Investor–owned, for–profit **Service:** Rehabilitation

Staffed Beds: 66 **Admissions:** 1384 **Census:** 51 **Outpatient Visits:** 0 **Births:** 0 **Total Expense ($000):** 19416 **Payroll Expense ($000):** 9032 **Personnel:** 164

☐ **USMD HOSPITAL AT FORT WORTH (670046)**, 5900 Altamesa Boulevard, Zip 76132–5473; tel. 817/433–9100 **A**1 10 **F**3 29 39 40 51 64 68 81 85 89 107 114 119 130 **S** USMD Health System, Irving, TX
Primary Contact: Stephanie Atkins–Guidry, Administrator and Chief Nursing Officer
CHR: Michelle Speck, Senior Vice President Human Resources
CNO: Stephanie Atkins–Guidry, Administrator and Chief Nursing Officer
Web address: www.usmdfortworth.com/
Control: Partnership, Investor–owned, for–profit **Service:** Surgical

Staffed Beds: 8 **Admissions:** 163 **Census:** 1 **Outpatient Visits:** 5929 **Births:** 0 **Total Expense ($000):** 22453 **Payroll Expense ($000):** 4734 **Personnel:** 104

FREDERICKSBURG—Gillespie County

⊠ **HILL COUNTRY MEMORIAL HOSPITAL (450604)**, 1020 South State Highway 16, Zip 78624–4471, Mailing Address: P.O. Box 835, Zip 78624–0835; tel. 830/997–4353 **A**1 10 **F**3 11 13 15 18 20 28 29 30 31 32 34 35 37 40 43 45 49 50 51 53 57 59 62 63 64 68 70 74 75 76 77 78 79 81 82 84 85 86 87 90 93 96 107 108 110 111 114 115 119 124 129 130 131 132 135 144 146 148 **P**8
Primary Contact: Jayne E. Pope, R.N., FACHE, Chief Executive Officer
COO: Mike Reno, Chief Operating Officer
CFO: Mark Jones, Chief Financial Officer
CMO: James R. Partin, M.D., Chief Medical Director
CIO: Holly Schmidt, Chief Information Officer
CHR: Alysha Metzger, Director Human Resources
CNO: Maureen Polivka, Chief Nursing Officer
Web address: www.hcmhs.org
Control: Other not–for–profit (including NFP Corporation) **Service:** General Medical and Surgical

Staffed Beds: 57 **Admissions:** 2695 **Census:** 22 **Outpatient Visits:** 84460 **Births:** 476 **Total Expense ($000):** 71479 **Payroll Expense ($000):** 28194 **Personnel:** 479

FRIONA—Parmer County

PARMER COUNTY COMMUNITY HOSPITAL See Parmer Medical Center

★ **PARMER MEDICAL CENTER (451300)**, 1307 Cleveland Street, Zip 79035–1121; tel. 806/250–2754 **A**10 18 **F**11 30 34 35 40 43 57 64 75 77 89 93 107 119 127 130 133 148 **S** Preferred Management Corporation, Shawnee, OK
Primary Contact: Gayla Quillin, Administrator
Web address: www.parmermedicalcenter.com
Control: Other not–for–profit (including NFP Corporation) **Service:** General Medical and Surgical

Staffed Beds: 15 **Admissions:** 205 **Census:** 4 **Outpatient Visits:** 12317 **Births:** 0 **Total Expense ($000):** 10610 **Payroll Expense ($000):** 4468 **Personnel:** 100

FRISCO—Collin County

⊠ **BAYLOR INSTITUTE FOR REHABILITATION AT FRISCO (673046)**, 2990 Legacy Drive, Zip 75034–6066; tel. 469/888–5100 **A**1 10 **F**3 29 30 34 64 75 90 91 92 93 96 130 132 148 **S** Select Medical Corporation, Mechanicsburg, PA
Primary Contact: Ryan Seymour, Chief Executive Officer
Web address: www.baylorhealth.com/bir
Control: Partnership, Investor–owned, for–profit **Service:** Rehabilitation

Staffed Beds: 44 **Admissions:** 854 **Census:** 27 **Outpatient Visits:** 7998 **Births:** 0 **Total Expense ($000):** 16390 **Payroll Expense ($000):** 7648 **Personnel:** 104

☐ **BAYLOR MEDICAL CENTER AT FRISCO (450853)**, 5601 Warren Parkway, Zip 75034–4069; tel. 214/407–5000 **A**1 3 5 10 **F**3 13 29 34 40 51 54 57 64 68 72 74 75 76 79 81 85 87 107 111 114 119 126 129 144 **S** United Surgical Partners International, Addison, TX
Primary Contact: William A. Keaton, Chief Executive Officer
COO: Kevin Coats, Chief Operating Officer and Chief Financial Officer
CFO: Kevin Coats, Chief Financial Officer
CMO: Jimmy Laferney, M.D., Vice President Medical Staff Affairs
CIO: Rick Barry, Director Information Systems
CHR: Margaret Garcia, Manager Human Resources
CNO: Randi Elliott MSN, Chief Nursing Officer
Web address: www.bmcf.com
Control: Partnership, Investor–owned, for–profit **Service:** Surgical

Staffed Beds: 68 **Admissions:** 4761 **Census:** 38 **Outpatient Visits:** 25354 **Births:** 2593 **Total Expense ($000):** 130307 **Payroll Expense ($000):** 43486 **Personnel:** 527

⊠ **CENTENNIAL MEDICAL CENTER (450885)**, 12505 Lebanon Road, Zip 75035–8298; tel. 972/963–3333 **A**1 10 **F**3 8 13 15 18 20 22 24 29 30 34 35 40 45 46 47 48 49 50 51 57 59 64 65 70 72 74 75 76 78 79 81 82 85 86 89 92 93 107 108 110 111 114 115 119 124 126 130 131 144 146 147 148 **S** TENET Healthcare Corporation, Dallas, TX
Primary Contact: Joe D. Thomason, Chief Executive Officer
CFO: Blaise Bondi, Chief Financial Officer
CMO: Robert S. Hendler, M.D., Regional Chief Medical Officer
CIO: Dianne Yarborough, Director of Information Technology
CHR: Stephanie S. Talley, Director Human Resources
CNO: Calee Travis, R.N., Chief Nursing Officer
Web address: www.centennialmedcenter.com
Control: Corporation, Investor–owned, for–profit **Service:** General Medical and Surgical

Staffed Beds: 106 **Admissions:** 3803 **Census:** 43 **Outpatient Visits:** 34996 **Births:** 714 **Total Expense ($000):** 85117 **Payroll Expense ($000):** 29150 **Personnel:** 355

☐ **HAVEN BEHAVIORAL HOSPITAL OF FRISCO**, 5680 Frisco Square Boulevard, Suite 3000, Zip 75034–3300; tel. 469/353–2219 **A**1 **F**98 102 130
Primary Contact: William W. Brattvet, Chief Executive Officer
Web address: www.frisco.havenbehavioral.com/
Control: Corporation, Investor–owned, for–profit **Service:** Psychiatric

Staffed Beds: 24 **Admissions:** 349 **Census:** 13 **Outpatient Visits:** 0 **Births:** 0 **Total Expense ($000):** 6691 **Payroll Expense ($000):** 3001 **Personnel:** 54

TX

Hospital, Medicare Provider Number, Address, Telephone, Approval, Facility, and Physician Codes, Health Care System

★ American Hospital Association (AHA) membership ☐ The Joint Commission accreditation ○ Healthcare Facilities Accreditation Program ◇ DNV Healthcare Inc. accreditation ⇑ Center for Improvement in Healthcare Quality Accreditation △ Commission on Accreditation of Rehabilitation Facilities (CARF) accreditation

GAINESVILLE—Cooke County

NORTH TEXAS MEDICAL CENTER (450090), 1900 Hospital Boulevard, Zip 76240–2002; tel. 940/665–1751 **A**10 20 **F**3 11 13 15 28 29 34 35 40 43 45 50 59 60 62 64 68 70 75 76 77 79 81 82 85 87 93 107 108 110 111 115 118 119 127 130 132 133 146 147 **P**5 6
Primary Contact: Ramin Roufeh, Interim Chief Executive Officer
CFO: Melissa Walker, CPA, Chief Financial Officer
CHR: Teresa Westover, Director Human Resources
CNO: Audimarie Hayes, R.N., Chief Nursing Officer
Web address: www.ntmconline.net
Control: Hospital district or authority, Government, nonfederal **Service:** General Medical and Surgical

Staffed Beds: 48 **Admissions:** 1306 **Census:** 13 **Outpatient Visits:** 61393 **Births:** 341 **Total Expense ($000):** 37621 **Payroll Expense ($000):** 13442 **Personnel:** 297

GALVESTON—Galveston County

SHRINERS HOSPITALS FOR CHILDREN–GALVESTON (453311), (Burn Care), 815 Market Street, Zip 77550–2725; tel. 409/770–6600 **A**1 3 5 10 **F**3 11 16 29 30 32 34 35 50 64 68 75 77 81 82 85 86 93 99 100 101 104 119 130 132 146 148 **S** Shriners Hospitals for Children, Tampa, FL
Primary Contact: Mary Jaco, Administrator
CFO: Michael B. Schimming, Chief Financial Services
CMO: David N. Herndon, M.D., Chief of Staff
CIO: Michael Lyons, Regional Director Information Services
CHR: Robert A. Magee, Director Human Resources
CNO: Angel Martinez, RN, BSN, R.N., Director Patient Care Services
Web address: www.shrinershospitalsforchildren.org/Hospitals/Locations/Galveston.aspx
Control: Other not-for-profit (including NFP Corporation) **Service:** Children's other specialty

Staffed Beds: 15 **Admissions:** 187 **Census:** 9 **Outpatient Visits:** 10205 **Births:** 0 **Total Expense ($000):** 34725 **Payroll Expense ($000):** 13027 **Personnel:** 217

⊞ **UNIVERSITY OF TEXAS MEDICAL BRANCH (450018)**, 301 University Boulevard, Zip 77555–0128; tel. 409/772–1011, (Includes ANGLETON DANBURY CAMPUS, 132 East Hospital Drive, Angleton, Zip 77515–4112; tel. 979/849–7721; Donna K. Sollenberger, Executive Vice President and Chief Executive Officer) **A**1 2 3 5 10 **F**3 8 11 12 13 14 15 16 17 18 19 20 22 24 26 28 29 30 31 34 35 36 38 39 40 41 43 44 45 46 49 50 51 53 54 55 56 57 58 59 60 61 64 65 66 68 70 71 72 73 74 75 76 77 78 79 81 82 84 85 86 87 88 89 92 93 94 96 97 99 100 101 102 103 104 107 108 110 111 114 115 117 118 119 120 121 123 124 126 129 130 131 132 134 135 137 138 141 142 144 145 146 147 148 **P**6 **S** University of Texas System, Austin, TX
Primary Contact: Donna K. Sollenberger, Executive Vice President and Chief Executive Officer
COO: Deborah A. McGrew, Vice President and Chief Operating Officer
CFO: Cheryl A. Sadro, Executive Vice President Chief Business and Finance Officer
CMO: Selwyn O. Rogers, M.D., Vice President and Chief Medical Officer
CIO: Todd Leach, Vice President and Chief Information Officer
CHR: Ronald McKinley, Ph.D., Vice President Human Resources and Employee Services
CNO: David R. Marshall, JD, Chief Nursing and Patient Care Services Officer
Web address: www.utmb.edu
Control: State–Government, nonfederal **Service:** General Medical and Surgical

Staffed Beds: 562 **Admissions:** 26420 **Census:** 366 **Outpatient Visits:** 943490 **Births:** 6298 **Total Expense ($000):** 806382 **Payroll Expense ($000):** 293804 **Personnel:** 4136

GARLAND—Dallas County

⊞ **BAYLOR MEDICAL CENTER AT GARLAND (450280)**, 2300 Marie Curie Drive, Zip 75042–5706; tel. 972/487–5000 **A**1 2 3 5 10 **F**3 11 15 18 20 22 24 26 28 29 30 31 34 35 40 45 47 49 50 54 57 59 60 64 65 66 70 74 75 78 79 81 82 84 86 87 107 108 110 111 114 118 119 126 129 130 132 135 145 146 148 **S** Baylor Scott & White Health, Dallas, TX
Primary Contact: Thomas J. Trenary, President
COO: Janice L. Walker, R.N., Chief Nursing Officer and Chief Operating Officer
CFO: Robert Knowlton, Vice President and Chief Financial Officer
CMO: Steven Arze, M.D., Chief Medical Officer and Vice President Medical Affairs
CIO: Michael Larsen, Director Information Systems
CHR: Laura Settles, Director Human Resources
CNO: Janice L. Walker, R.N., Chief Nursing Officer and Chief Operating Officer
Web address: www.baylorhealth.com/PhysiciansLocations/Garland/Pages/Default.aspx
Control: Other not-for-profit (including NFP Corporation) **Service:** General Medical and Surgical

Staffed Beds: 112 **Admissions:** 7823 **Census:** 95 **Outpatient Visits:** 94600 **Births:** 0 **Total Expense ($000):** 159162 **Payroll Expense ($000):** 56896 **Personnel:** 644

⊞ **SELECT SPECIALTY HOSPITAL – DALLAS GARLAND (452120)**, 2300 Marie Curie Drive, Floors 3E and 3W, Zip 75042–5706; tel. 469/440–5800 **A**1 **F**1 3 29 77 85 86 87 91 130 148 **S** Select Medical Corporation, Mechanicsburg, PA
Primary Contact: Ron Norris, Chief Executive Officer
Web address: www.dallasgarland.selectspecialtyhospitals.com/
Control: Corporation, Investor–owned, for–profit **Service:** Long–Term Acute Care hospital

Staffed Beds: 40 **Admissions:** 179 **Census:** 12 **Outpatient Visits:** 0 **Births:** 0 **Total Expense ($000):** 7407 **Payroll Expense ($000):** 4068 **Personnel:** 93

GATESVILLE—Coryell County

☐ **CORYELL MEMORIAL HOSPITAL (451379)**, 1507 West Main Street, Zip 76528–1098; tel. 254/865–8251 **A**1 10 18 **F**3 7 10 11 15 18 20 28 34 40 43 45 50 57 58 59 61 62 64 65 70 74 79 81 82 84 87 93 97 102 104 107 108 110 111 115 119 125 127 129 130 133 146 **P**6
Primary Contact: David Byrom, Chief Executive Officer
COO: David Byrom, Chief Executive Officer
CFO: Carol Jones, Controller and Manager Business Office
CMO: Diedra Wuenschel, D.O., President Medical Staff
CIO: Mike Huckabee, Network Administrator
CHR: Paula Smithhart, Director Human Resources
CNO: Jeanne Griffith, Chief Nursing Officer
Web address: www.cmhos.org
Control: Hospital district or authority, Government, nonfederal **Service:** General Medical and Surgical

Staffed Beds: 25 **Admissions:** 971 **Census:** 12 **Outpatient Visits:** 70485 **Births:** 0 **Total Expense ($000):** 37465 **Payroll Expense ($000):** 13545 **Personnel:** 379

GEORGETOWN—Williamson County

☐ **GEORGETOWN BEHAVIORAL HEALTH INSTITUTE**, 3101 South Austin Avenue, Zip 78626–7541; tel. 512/819–1100 **A**1 **F**4 5 29 56 98 99 102 103 104 105 130 132 135 **S** Signature Healthcare Services, Corona, CA
Primary Contact: Joseph R. Rodriguez, Chief Executive Officer
CFO: Shelli Surcouf, Chief Financial Officer
CHR: Kristi Hynes, Director Human Resources
CNO: Nini Perry, Chief Nursing Officer
Web address: www.georgetownbehavioral.co
Control: Corporation, Investor–owned, for–profit **Service:** Psychiatric

Staffed Beds: 50 **Admissions:** 1713 **Census:** 34 **Outpatient Visits:** 1686 **Births:** 0 **Total Expense ($000):** 13318 **Payroll Expense ($000):** 6132 **Personnel:** 188

★ **ROCK SPRINGS, LLC**, 700 Southeast Inner Loop, Zip 78626; tel. 512/819–9400 **F**98 100 102 104 105
Primary Contact: Jamie Molbert, Chief Executive Officer
COO: Lisa Margraves, Chief Operating Officer, Director Clinical Services
CFO: Jason Guzak, Chief Financial Officer
CMO: Tiffany Thomure, M.D., Medical Director
CHR: Sharon McMurray, Director, Human Resources
CNO: Harriet Moore, R.N., Director of Nursing
Web address: www.rockspringshealth.com/
Control: Corporation, Investor–owned, for–profit **Service:** Psychiatric

Staffed Beds: 72 **Admissions:** 1730 **Census:** 38 **Outpatient Visits:** 3986 **Births:** 0 **Total Expense ($000):** 13151 **Payroll Expense ($000):** 6001 **Personnel:** 128

GLEN ROSE—Somervell County

☐ **GLEN ROSE MEDICAL CENTER (450451)**, 1021 Holden Street, Zip 76043–4937, Mailing Address: P.O. Box 2099, Zip 76043–2099; tel. 254/897–2215 **A**1 10 **F**2 15 29 34 40 43 45 48 51 56 57 59 65 81 93 103 104 107 108 110 111 119 129 130 132 133 143 146 **P**7
Primary Contact: Ray Reynolds, Chief Executive Officer
CFO: Michael Honea, Chief Financial Officer
CHR: Ladonna Green, Director Human Resources
CNO: Laura Hodnett, Interim Chief Nursing Officer
Web address: www.glenrosemedicalcenter.com
Control: Hospital district or authority, Government, nonfederal **Service:** General Medical and Surgical

Staffed Beds: 16 **Admissions:** 552 **Census:** 5 **Outpatient Visits:** 22207 **Births:** 2 **Total Expense ($000):** 16137 **Payroll Expense ($000):** 5994 **Personnel:** 161

TX

Many Facility Codes have changed. Please refer to the AHA Guide Code Chart.
© 2016 AHA Guide

GONZALES—Gonzales County

★ **MEMORIAL HOSPITAL (450235)**, 1110 Sarah Dewitt Drive, Zip 78629–3311, Mailing Address: P.O. Box 587, Zip 78629–0587; tel. 830/672–7581 **A**10 **F**3 11 13 15 29 34 35 38 40 43 53 57 59 62 64 65 68 70 75 76 77 81 85 87 93 97 107 110 111 115 119 127 129 130 132 148 **S** QHR, Brentwood, TN
Primary Contact: Charles Norris, Chief Executive Officer
CFO: Patty Stewart, Chief Financial Officer
CMO: Commie Hisey, D.O., Chief of Staff
CHR: Joni Leland, Director Human Resources
CNO: Valerie Hohenshell, Director of Clinical Services
Web address: www.gonzaleshealthcare.com
Control: Hospital district or authority, Government, nonfederal **Service:** General Medical and Surgical

Staffed Beds: 33 **Admissions:** 717 **Census:** 6 **Outpatient Visits:** 79417 **Births:** 176 **Total Expense ($000):** 39128 **Payroll Expense ($000):** 10730 **Personnel:** 248

GRAHAM—Young County

★ **GRAHAM REGIONAL MEDICAL CENTER (450085)**, 1301 Montgomery Road, Zip 76450–4240, Mailing Address: P.O. Box 1390, Zip 76450–1390; tel. 940/549–3400 **A**10 20 **F**3 7 11 13 15 28 29 40 43 45 50 53 57 59 62 63 75 76 77 79 81 85 93 104 107 111 115 119 127 130 133 135
Primary Contact: Shane Kernell, Chief Executive Officer
CIO: Jeff Clark, Director Information Systems
CHR: Judy Guinn, Chief Human Resources Officer
Web address: www.grahamrmc.com
Control: Hospital district or authority, Government, nonfederal **Service:** General Medical and Surgical

Staffed Beds: 25 **Admissions:** 831 **Census:** 7 **Outpatient Visits:** 66070 **Births:** 216 **Total Expense ($000):** 25911 **Payroll Expense ($000):** 8921 **Personnel:** 195

GRANBURY—Hood County

⊞ **LAKE GRANBURY MEDICAL CENTER (450596)**, 1310 Paluxy Road, Zip 76048–5655; tel. 817/573–2273 **A**1 10 **F**3 8 11 12 13 15 18 20 22 26 28 29 30 34 37 40 43 45 49 53 57 59 64 68 70 74 75 76 77 79 81 82 85 86 93 107 108 110 111 114 118 119 126 129 133 135 146 147 **S** Community Health Systems, Inc., Franklin, TN
Primary Contact: Derrick Cuenca, Chief Executive Officer
CFO: Noe Gutierrez, Chief Financial Officer
CIO: Kevin Myers, Director Information Systems
CHR: Brooke Montoya, Director Human Resources
CNO: Abigail Kendall, Chief Nursing Officer
Web address: www.lakegranburymedicalcenter.com
Control: Corporation, Investor–owned, for–profit **Service:** General Medical and Surgical

Staffed Beds: 73 **Admissions:** 2795 **Census:** 25 **Outpatient Visits:** 66817 **Births:** 550 **Total Expense ($000):** 66348 **Payroll Expense ($000):** 20986 **Personnel:** 355

GRAND PRAIRIE—Dallas County

◇ **TEXAS GENERAL HOSPITAL (670083)**, 2709 Hospital Boulevard, Zip 75051–1017; tel. 469/999–0000 **A**10 21 **F**3 18 20 22 29 34 40 45 46 48 50 57 59 64 70 74 75 79 81 82 85 107 108 111 115 119 148
Primary Contact: Suleman Hashmi, President and Chief Executive Officer
Web address: www.texasgeneralhospital.com
Control: Partnership, Investor–owned, for–profit **Service:** General Medical and Surgical

Staffed Beds: 41 **Admissions:** 429 **Census:** 3 **Outpatient Visits:** 12837 **Births:** 0 **Personnel:** 158

GRAND SALINE—Van Zandt County

TEXAS GENERAL HOSPITAL – VAN ZANDT REGIONAL MEDICAL CENTER, 707 North Waldrip Street, Zip 75140–1555; tel. 903/717–3300, (Data for 261 days) **A**20 **F**3 34 35 40 45 46 47 57 75 77 81 87 107 114 119 148
Primary Contact: Faraz Hashmi, Chief Executive Officer
Control: Partnership, Investor–owned, for–profit **Service:** General Medical and Surgical

Staffed Beds: 52 **Admissions:** 3 **Census:** 1 **Outpatient Visits:** 1383 **Births:** 0 **Personnel:** 26

GRAPEVINE—Tarrant County

⊞ **BAYLOR REGIONAL MEDICAL CENTER AT GRAPEVINE (450563)**, 1650 West College Street, Zip 76051–3565; tel. 817/481–1588 **A**1 2 3 10 **F**3 11 12 13 15 18 20 22 24 26 28 29 30 31 34 35 40 45 46 47 48 49 56 57 59 61 64 65 70 72 74 75 76 77 78 79 80 81 82 84 86 87 107 108 110 111 114 115 119 126 130 131 132 135 145 146 147 **S** Baylor Scott & White Health, Dallas, TX
Primary Contact: Steven R. Newton, President
CFO: Terri Foster, Hospital Finance Officer
CMO: Ron Jensen, D.O., Chief Medical Officer and Vice President
CIO: Sandy Vaughn, Director Information Systems
CHR: Donna Stark, Director Human Resources
CNO: Beth P. Beckman, R.N., Chief Nursing Officer
Web address: www.https://www.baylorhealth.com/PhysiciansLocations/Grapevine/Pages/Default.aspx
Control: Other not–for–profit (including NFP Corporation) **Service:** General Medical and Surgical

Staffed Beds: 244 **Admissions:** 11424 **Census:** 140 **Outpatient Visits:** 62860 **Births:** 2517 **Total Expense ($000):** 192019 **Payroll Expense ($000):** 68311 **Personnel:** 773

☐ **ETHICUS HOSPITAL – GRAPEVINE (452110)**, 4201 William D. Tate Avenue, Zip 76051–5736; tel. 817/288–1300 **A**1 10 **F**1 3 29 40 64 74 75 77 87 93 96 107 119 130 148
Primary Contact: Roger T. Jenkins, Chief Executive Officer
Web address: www.ethicusgrapevine.com
Control: Partnership, Investor–owned, for–profit **Service:** Long–Term Acute Care hospital

Staffed Beds: 24 **Admissions:** 391 **Census:** 29 **Outpatient Visits:** 13 **Births:** 0 **Total Expense ($000):** 19770 **Payroll Expense ($000):** 7951 **Personnel:** 121

GREENVILLE—Hunt County

⊞ **GLEN OAKS HOSPITAL (454050)**, 301 Division Street, Zip 75401–4101; tel. 903/454–6000 **A**1 10 **F**4 5 29 34 35 40 50 75 86 87 98 99 100 101 102 103 104 105 132 135 **S** Universal Health Services, Inc., King of Prussia, PA
Primary Contact: Jennifer Dedrick, Chief Executive Officer
CFO: Lowell K. Hudson, Chief Financial Officer
CHR: Joe Carson, Director Human Resources
Web address: www.glenoakshospital.com
Control: Corporation, Investor–owned, for–profit **Service:** Psychiatric

Staffed Beds: 54 **Admissions:** 1882 **Census:** 33 **Outpatient Visits:** 2588 **Births:** 0 **Total Expense ($000):** 8770 **Payroll Expense ($000):** 4201 **Personnel:** 94

⊞ **HUNT REGIONAL MEDICAL CENTER (450352)**, 4215 Joe Ramsey Boulevard, Zip 75401–7899, Mailing Address: P.O. Box 1059, Zip 75403–1059; tel. 903/408–5000 **A**1 10 **F**3 11 12 13 15 20 28 29 30 34 37 40 42 43 44 45 46 49 50 53 56 57 59 62 64 65 68 70 71 72 73 74 75 76 77 78 79 81 82 84 85 86 87 90 91 92 93 94 96 98 102 103 104 107 108 110 111 114 115 118 119 120 121 123 129 130 132 135 141 143 144 146 147 148 **P**1 6 **S** Hunt Regional Healthcare, Greenville, TX
Primary Contact: Richard Carter, District Chief Executive Officer
COO: Michael R. Klepin, Administrator
CFO: Lee Boles, Assistant Administrator and Chief Financial Officer
CMO: James H. Sandin, M.D., Assistant Administrator Medical Affairs
CIO: Richard Montanye, Director Information Systems
CHR: John Heatherly, Assistant Administrator Support Services
CNO: Deborah Clack, Chief Nursing Officer
Web address: www.huntregional.org
Control: Hospital district or authority, Government, nonfederal **Service:** General Medical and Surgical

Staffed Beds: 206 **Admissions:** 6383 **Census:** 92 **Outpatient Visits:** 113921 **Births:** 992 **Total Expense ($000):** 125246 **Payroll Expense ($000):** 49484 **Personnel:** 946

TX

Hospital, Medicare Provider Number, Address, Telephone, Approval, Facility, and Physician Codes, Health Care System

★ American Hospital Association (AHA) membership ○ Healthcare Facilities Accreditation Program ⇑ Center for Improvement in Healthcare Quality Accreditation
☐ The Joint Commission accreditation ◇ DNV Healthcare Inc. accreditation △ Commission on Accreditation of Rehabilitation Facilities (CARF) accreditation

GROESBECK—Limestone County

LIMESTONE MEDICAL CENTER (451303), 701 McClintic Drive,
Zip 76642–2128; tel. 254/729–3281 **A**10 18 **F**3 7 11 28 32 34 35 40 41 43
45 57 64 65 75 77 84 85 90 93 96 97 104 107 114 127 129 130 133 135
146 148
Primary Contact: Larry Price, Chief Executive Officer
CFO: Michael F. Williams, Chief Financial Officer
CMO: Larry C. Hughes, M.D., Chief Medical Staff
CIO: Byong Lee, Chief Information Officer
CHR: Jean Koester, Manager Human Resources
CNO: Jean Wragge, Chief Nursing Officer
Web address: www.lmchospital.com
Control: Hospital district or authority, Government, nonfederal **Service:** General
Medical and Surgical

> **Staffed Beds:** 20 **Admissions:** 389 **Census:** 6 **Outpatient Visits:** 17368
> **Births:** 0 **Total Expense ($000):** 18365 **Payroll Expense ($000):** 7475
> **Personnel:** 191

HALLETTSVILLE—Lavaca County

LAVACA MEDICAL CENTER (451376), 1400 North Texana Street,
Zip 77964–2099; tel. 361/798–3671 **A**10 18 **F**3 11 15 18 29 34 40 41 43 45
47 53 56 57 59 64 65 68 75 77 81 85 86 87 93 107 108 110 111 114 118
119 127 133 135 146 148
Primary Contact: Stephen Bowen, Administrator
Control: Hospital district or authority, Government, nonfederal **Service:** General
Medical and Surgical

> **Staffed Beds:** 25 **Admissions:** 558 **Census:** 7 **Outpatient Visits:** 43015
> **Births:** 0 **Total Expense ($000):** 17408 **Payroll Expense ($000):** 5784
> **Personnel:** 144

HAMILTON—Hamilton County

★ ◇ **HAMILTON GENERAL HOSPITAL (450754)**, 400 North Brown Street,
Zip 76531–1518; tel. 254/386–1600 **A**10 20 21 **F**3 7 11 15 28 29 34 40 43
44 45 50 53 56 57 59 64 68 79 80 81 82 85 86 93 97 103 104 107 110
114 127 130 132
Primary Contact: Grady A. Hooper, Chief Executive Officer
CMO: James R. Lee, M.D., Chief of Staff
CIO: Chad Reinert, Chief Information Officer
CHR: Keela Payne, Director Human Resources
CNO: Debra Martin, Chief Nursing Officer
Web address: www.hamiltonhospital.org
Control: Hospital district or authority, Government, nonfederal **Service:** General
Medical and Surgical

> **Staffed Beds:** 42 **Admissions:** 1309 **Census:** 14 **Outpatient Visits:** 71792
> **Births:** 0 **Total Expense ($000):** 23153 **Payroll Expense ($000):** 9899
> **Personnel:** 236

HAMLIN—Jones County

HAMLIN MEMORIAL HOSPITAL (450243), 632 Northwest Second Street,
Zip 79520–3831, Mailing Address: P.O. Box 400, Zip 79520–0400;
tel. 325/576–3646 **A**10 **F**3 7 11 18 28 29 35 40 43 64 68 69 107 114 127
133 135 146 148 **P**5
Primary Contact: Clay Vogel, Chief Executive Officer
CMO: Krishna Sunkavalle, M.D., Chief Medical Officer
Control: Hospital district or authority, Government, nonfederal **Service:** General
Medical and Surgical

> **Staffed Beds:** 23 **Admissions:** 169 **Census:** 2 **Outpatient Visits:** 3630
> **Births:** 0 **Total Expense ($000):** 3163 **Payroll Expense ($000):** 1627
> **Personnel:** 46

HARKER HEIGHTS—Bell County

⊞ **SETON MEDICAL CENTER HARKER HEIGHTS (670080)**, 850 West Central
Texas Expressway, Zip 76548–1890; tel. 254/690–0900 **A**1 10 **F**3 13 15 18
20 22 26 28 29 30 34 35 40 43 45 50 51 57 59 60 62 63 66 70 74 75 76
79 81 91 107 108 110 111 115 119 129 130 146 147 148 **P**3 **S** LHP
Hospital Group, Plano, TX
Primary Contact: Matt T. Maxfield, FACHE, Chief Executive Officer
CFO: John K. Sharp, Chief Financial Officer
CHR: Mona Tucker, Director Human Resources
CNO: Pamela Craig, R.N., Chief Nursing Officer
Web address: www.setonharkerheights.net
Control: Partnership, Investor–owned, for–profit **Service:** General Medical and
Surgical

> **Staffed Beds:** 83 **Admissions:** 3760 **Census:** 30 **Outpatient Visits:** 72910
> **Births:** 960 **Total Expense ($000):** 71258 **Payroll Expense ($000):** 23044
> **Personnel:** 341

HARLINGEN—Cameron County

⊞ **HARLINGEN MEDICAL CENTER (450855)**, 5501 South Expressway 77,
Zip 78550–3213; tel. 956/365–1000 **A**1 3 5 10 **F**3 12 13 15 17 18 20 22 24
29 30 40 43 49 50 51 57 59 64 68 70 74 75 76 79 81 85 86 107 108 110
111 114 115 118 119 129 130 146 147 148 **S** Prime Healthcare Services,
Ontario, CA
Primary Contact: Brenda Ivory, Chief Executive Officer
CFO: David Glassburn, Vice President Finance and Chief Financial Officer
CMO: Elizabeth Juarez, M.D., Chief Medical Officer
CHR: Emmett Craig, Director Human Resources
CNO: Deborah Meeks, Chief Nursing Officer
Web address: www.harlingenmedicalcenter.com
Control: Partnership, Investor–owned, for–profit **Service:** General Medical and
Surgical

> **Staffed Beds:** 88 **Admissions:** 5275 **Census:** 57 **Outpatient Visits:** 55286
> **Births:** 793 **Total Expense ($000):** 98825 **Payroll Expense ($000):** 31257
> **Personnel:** 500

☐ **RIO GRANDE STATE CENTER/SOUTH TEXAS HEALTH CARE SYSTEM
(454088)**, 1401 South Rangerville Road, Zip 78552–7638; tel. 956/364–8000,
(Includes RIO GRANDE STATE CENTER, 1401 South Rangerville Road,
tel. 956/364–8000; SOUTH TEXAS HEALTH CARE SYSTEM, 1401 Rangerville
Road, Zip 78552–7609; tel. 956/364–8000) **A**1 3 5 10 **F**30 53 54 57 65 66
68 75 87 97 98 101 107 119 130 132 135 143 146 147 **P**6 **S** Texas
Department of State Health Services, Austin, TX
Primary Contact: Sonia Hernandez–Keeble, Superintendent
CFO: Tom Garza, Director Fiscal and Support
CMO: David Moron, M.D., Clinical Director
CIO: Blas Ortiz, Jr., Assistant Superintendent and Public Information Officer
CHR: Irma Garcia, Job Coordinator
CNO: Maia Baker, MSN, Chief Nurse Executive
Web address: www.dshs.state.tx.us/mhhospitals/RioGrandeSC/default.shtm
Control: State–Government, nonfederal **Service:** Psychiatric

> **Staffed Beds:** 55 **Admissions:** 762 **Census:** 52 **Births:** 0 **Total Expense
> ($000):** 38568 **Payroll Expense ($000):** 8952 **Personnel:** 270

SOLARA HOSPITAL HARLINGEN (452101), 508 Victoria Lane,
Zip 78550–3225; tel. 956/425–9600, (Includes SOLARA HOSPITAL –
BROWNSVILLE CAMPUS, 333 Lorenaly Drive, Brownsville, Zip 78526–4333;
tel. 956/546–0808) **A**10 22 **F**1 29 30 35 40 57 70 75 85 86 130 148
S Cornerstone Healthcare Group, Dallas, TX
Primary Contact: Cary L. Montalvo, Chief Executive Officer
CFO: Kurt Schultz, Chief Financial Officer
CHR: Dan Perkins, Vice President of Human Resources
CNO: Nesa Caldwell, Chief Nursing Officer
Web address: www.chghospitals.com/harlingen/
Control: Partnership, Investor–owned, for–profit **Service:** Long–Term Acute Care
hospital

> **Staffed Beds:** 82 **Admissions:** 813 **Census:** 55 **Outpatient Visits:** 0 **Births:**
> 0 **Total Expense ($000):** 23391 **Payroll Expense ($000):** 10271
> **Personnel:** 177

⊞ **VALLEY BAPTIST MEDICAL CENTER–HARLINGEN (450033)**, 2101 Pease
Street, Zip 78550–8307, Mailing Address: P.O. Drawer 2588, Zip 78551–2588;
tel. 956/389–1100 **A**1 3 5 10 **F**3 11 13 14 15 17 18 20 22 24 26 28 29
30 31 34 35 39 40 43 44 45 46 47 48 49 50 54 56 57 59 60 63 64 65 68
70 71 72 73 74 75 76 77 78 79 80 81 82 84 85 86 87 88 89 90 91 92 93
94 100 103 104 107 108 110 111 112 114 115 119 126 129 130 132 144
146 147 148 **S** TENET Healthcare Corporation, Dallas, TX
Primary Contact: Manuel Vela, President and Chief Executive Officer
COO: Daniel Listi, Chief Operating Officer
CFO: Marco Rodriguez, Chief Financial Officer
CHR: Irma L. Pye, Senior Vice President and Chief Human Resource Officer
CNO: Stephen Hill, Vice President and Chief Nursing Officer
Web address: www.valleybaptist.net/harlingen/index.htm
Control: Corporation, Investor–owned, for–profit **Service:** General Medical and
Surgical

> **Staffed Beds:** 416 **Admissions:** 16145 **Census:** 213 **Outpatient Visits:**
> 118296 **Births:** 2394 **Total Expense ($000):** 235400 **Payroll Expense
> ($000):** 79336 **Personnel:** 1316

HASKELL—Haskell County

HASKELL MEMORIAL HOSPITAL (451341), 1 North Avenue N,
Zip 79521–5499, Mailing Address: P.O. Box 1117, Zip 79521–1117;
tel. 940/864–2621 **A**10 18 **F**11 28 29 34 35 40 53 54 57 59 64 68 75 77 86
87 93 97 107 119 130 131 133 146 **P**1
Primary Contact: Fran McCown, Administrator
CHR: Emily Moore, Director Human Resources and Information Technology
CNO: Teri Turner, Chief Nursing Officer
Control: Hospital district or authority, Government, nonfederal **Service:** General
Medical and Surgical

> **Staffed Beds:** 15 **Admissions:** 232 **Census:** 3 **Outpatient Visits:** 17145
> **Births:** 0 **Total Expense ($000):** 6787 **Payroll Expense ($000):** 2852
> **Personnel:** 84

Many Facility Codes have changed. Please refer to the AHA Guide Code Chart.   © 2016 AHA Guide

TX

HEMPHILL—Sabine County

☐ **SABINE COUNTY HOSPITAL (451361)**, 2301 Worth Street, Zip 75948–7216, Mailing Address: P.O. Box 750, Zip 75948–0750; tel. 409/787–3300 **A**1 10 18 **F**3 29 34 35 40 43 50 57 59 64 65 68 75 93 107 114 119 127 133 **S** Preferred Management Corporation, Shawnee, OK
Primary Contact: Jerry Howell, Administrator
COO: Mike Easley, Vice President and Chief Operating Officer
CFO: Larry Stephens, Chief Financial Officer
CMO: Vera Luther, M.D., Chief of Staff
CIO: Margaret Moore, Director Business Office
CHR: Laura Simpson, Director Human Resources
CNO: Margie Watson, MSN, RN–B, Chief Nursing Officer
Web address: www.sabinecountyhospital.com/
Control: Corporation, Investor–owned, for–profit **Service:** General Medical and Surgical

Staffed Beds: 25 **Admissions:** 295 **Census:** 3 **Outpatient Visits:** 19752 **Births:** 0 **Total Expense ($000):** 8545 **Payroll Expense ($000):** 3455 **Personnel:** 84

HENDERSON—Rusk County

✖ **EAST TEXAS MEDICAL CENTER HENDERSON (450475)**, 300 Wilson Street, Zip 75652–5956; tel. 903/657–7541 **A**1 10 **F**3 8 11 13 15 18 28 29 30 34 35 37 40 43 45 50 57 59 64 65 76 79 81 85 107 108 110 111 115 119 127 129 133 135 145 146 147 148 **S** East Texas Medical Center Regional Healthcare System, Tyler, TX
Primary Contact: Mark Leitner, Administrator
CFO: Phillip A. Caron, Chief Financial Officer
CHR: William Henry, Director Human Resources
CNO: Donna K. Stanley, R.N., Chief Nursing Officer
Web address: www.etmc.org/etmchenderson/
Control: Other not–for–profit (including NFP Corporation) **Service:** General Medical and Surgical

Staffed Beds: 41 **Admissions:** 1442 **Census:** 11 **Outpatient Visits:** 55790 **Births:** 232 **Total Expense ($000):** 29081 **Payroll Expense ($000):** 7866 **Personnel:** 134

HENRIETTA—Clay County

CLAY COUNTY MEMORIAL HOSPITAL (451362), 310 West South Street, Zip 76365–3346; tel. 940/538–5621 **A**10 18 **F**7 8 11 28 34 35 40 50 53 57 62 68 80 81 90 93 107 111 119 130 132 133 144 148 **P**5
Primary Contact: Jeff Huskey, Chief Executive Officer and Administrator
CFO: Debra Haehn, Chief Financial Officer
CMO: Lexi Mitchell Sanchez, D.O., Chief of Staff
CHR: Linda Burleson, Administrative Secretary
CNO: Kelley McMillion, Chief Nursing Officer
Web address: www.ccmhospital.com
Control: County–Government, nonfederal **Service:** General Medical and Surgical

Staffed Beds: 25 **Admissions:** 187 **Census:** 3 **Outpatient Visits:** 7124 **Total Expense ($000):** 7574 **Payroll Expense ($000):** 2970 **Personnel:** 74

HEREFORD—Deaf Smith County

HEREFORD REGIONAL MEDICAL CENTER (450155), 540 West 15th Street, Zip 79045–2820; tel. 806/364–2141 **A**10 **F**3 7 11 13 15 29 35 40 43 50 57 59 62 65 70 76 77 81 85 93 107 111 114 119 127 130 133 147 **P**5
Primary Contact: Greg Reinart, Chief Executive Officer
COO: Meri Killingsworth, Chief Operating Officer
CNO: Anthony T. Jerina, Chief Nursing Officer
Web address: www.dschd.org/
Control: Hospital district or authority, Government, nonfederal **Service:** General Medical and Surgical

Staffed Beds: 39 **Admissions:** 824 **Census:** 8 **Outpatient Visits:** 70432 **Births:** 348 **Total Expense ($000):** 25686 **Payroll Expense ($000):** 7531 **Personnel:** 172

HILLSBORO—Hill County

✖ **HILL REGIONAL HOSPITAL (450192)**, 101 Circle Drive, Zip 76645–2670; tel. 254/580–8500 **A**1 10 **F**3 13 15 17 18 19 29 34 35 40 43 45 50 57 59 64 65 68 70 75 76 77 78 79 81 86 87 88 89 93 107 114 118 119 133 146 147 **S** Community Health Systems, Inc., Franklin, TN
Primary Contact: Michael J. Ellis, FACHE, Chief Executive Officer
CFO: Judy Culp, Chief Financial Officer
CHR: Becky Hale, Director Human Resources
Web address: www.chs.net
Control: Corporation, Investor–owned, for–profit **Service:** General Medical and Surgical

Staffed Beds: 66 **Admissions:** 1122 **Census:** 9 **Outpatient Visits:** 21807 **Births:** 207 **Total Expense ($000):** 29788 **Payroll Expense ($000):** 8165 **Personnel:** 147

HONDO—Medina County

MEDINA COMMUNITY HOSPITAL See Medina Regional Hospital

MEDINA REGIONAL HOSPITAL (451330), 3100 Avenue E., Zip 78861–3599; tel. 830/426–7700 **A**10 18 **F**3 11 13 15 29 34 35 40 43 45 50 57 59 64 76 81 87 93 97 107 111 114 119 127 133 146 **P**4
Primary Contact: Janice Simons, FACHE, Chief Executive Officer
CFO: Kevin Frosch, Chief Financial Officer
CMO: Matthew Windrow, M.D., Chief of Staff
CIO: Ken Gallegos, Director Support Services and Information Technology
CHR: Sharon Garcia, Human Resources Representative
CNO: Rebecca Hinojoza, Chief Nursing Officer
Web address: www.medinahospital.net
Control: Hospital district or authority, Government, nonfederal **Service:** General Medical and Surgical

Staffed Beds: 25 **Admissions:** 800 **Census:** 9 **Outpatient Visits:** 101775 **Births:** 151 **Total Expense ($000):** 23804 **Payroll Expense ($000):** 9200 **Personnel:** 216

HOUSTON—Harris County

AD HOSPITAL EAST (670102), 12950 East Freeway, Zip 77015–5710; tel. 713/330–3887, (Nonreporting)
Primary Contact: Robert A. Turner, Chief Executive Officer
Control: Other not–for–profit (including NFP Corporation) **Service:** General Medical and Surgical

Staffed Beds: 25

☐ **ADVANCED DIAGNOSTICS HOSPITAL (670203)**, 12950 East Freeway, Zip 77015–5710; tel. 713/330–3887, (Nonreporting) **A**1
Primary Contact: Steve Winnett, Chief Executive Officer
CFO: Carol Files, Chief Financial Officer
CMO: Ian Reynolds, Chief Medical Officer
CIO: Yobi Kasper, Chief Information Officer
CHR: Gabby Myers, Human Resources Director
CNO: David Gonzalez, Chief Clinical Officer
Control: Individual, Investor–owned, for–profit **Service:** Surgical

Staffed Beds: 4

★ ◇ **BAYLOR ST. LUKE'S MEDICAL CENTER (450193)**, 6720 Bertner Avenue, Zip 77030–2697, Mailing Address: P.O. Box 20269, Zip 77225–0269; tel. 832/355–1000 **A**2 3 5 8 10 21 **F**3 8 11 14 15 17 18 20 22 24 26 28 29 30 31 34 35 36 39 40 42 44 45 46 47 48 49 50 51 54 56 57 58 59 60 61 64 65 66 68 70 71 74 75 77 78 79 80 81 82 84 85 86 87 90 91 92 96 97 100 107 108 110 111 114 115 116 117 118 119 120 121 123 124 126 129 130 132 135 137 138 139 140 145 146 147 148 **P**5 6 **S** Catholic Health Initiatives, Englewood, CO
Primary Contact: Michael H. Covert, FACHE, Chief Executive Officer
CFO: William Brosius, Vice President and Chief Financial Officer
CIO: James Albin, Chief Information Officer
CHR: Susan Bailey–Newell, Vice President Human Resources
Web address: www.stlukestexas.com
Control: Church–operated, Nongovernment, not–for profit **Service:** General Medical and Surgical

Staffed Beds: 640 **Admissions:** 24557 **Census:** 489 **Outpatient Visits:** 254422 **Births:** 0 **Total Expense ($000):** 823892 **Payroll Expense ($000):** 275988 **Personnel:** 3568

✖ **BAYLOR ST. LUKE'S MEDICAL CENTER MCNAIR CAMPUS**, One Baylor Plaza, BCM 100, Zip 77030–3411; tel. 713/798–4951, (Nonreporting) **A**1 **S** Catholic Health Initiatives, Englewood, CO
Primary Contact: Michael H. Covert, FACHE, Chief Executive Officer
Web address: www.bcm.edu
Control: Other not–for–profit (including NFP Corporation) **Service:** General Medical and Surgical

Staffed Beds: 256

☐ **BEHAVIORAL HOSPITAL OF BELLAIRE (454107)**, 5314 Dashwood Drive, Zip 77081–4603; tel. 713/600–9500 **A**1 10 **F**4 5 29 98 99 100 101 103 104 105 130 **S** Universal Health Services, Inc., King of Prussia, PA
Primary Contact: Ethan Permenter, Chief Executive Officer
Web address: www.bhbhospital.com
Control: Corporation, Investor–owned, for–profit **Service:** Psychiatric

Staffed Beds: 114 **Admissions:** 3518 **Census:** 83 **Outpatient Visits:** 3054 **Births:** 0 **Total Expense ($000):** 16198 **Payroll Expense ($000):** 9596 **Personnel:** 194

TX

Hospital, Medicare Provider Number, Address, Telephone, Approval, Facility, and Physician Codes, Health Care System

★ American Hospital Association (AHA) membership
☐ The Joint Commission accreditation
○ Healthcare Facilities Accreditation Program
◇ DNV Healthcare Inc. accreditation
⇑ Center for Improvement in Healthcare Quality Accreditation
△ Commission on Accreditation of Rehabilitation Facilities (CARF) accreditation

CORNERSTONE HOSPITAL–MEDICAL CENTER OF HOUSTON (452055),
2001 Hermann Drive, Zip 77004; tel. 832/649–6200 **A**10 22 **F**1 3 29 31 70 77
85 86 87 119 130 148 **S** Cornerstone Healthcare Group, Dallas, TX
Primary Contact: Michael Higginbotham, Chief Executive Officer
Web address: www.chghospitals.com
Control: Corporation, Investor–owned, for–profit **Service:** Long–Term Acute Care
hospital

Staffed Beds: 35 **Admissions:** 338 **Census:** 24 **Outpatient Visits:** 0 **Births:**
0 **Total Expense ($000):** 11679 **Payroll Expense ($000):** 5741 **Personnel:**
104

☐ **CYPRESS CREEK HOSPITAL (454108)**, 17750 Cali Drive, Zip 77090–2700;
tel. 281/586–7600 **A**1 10 **F**4 5 29 30 64 87 98 99 100 102 104 105 130
132 **S** Universal Health Services, Inc., King of Prussia, PA
Primary Contact: Brian Brooker, Chief Executive Officer
CFO: Leslie Stuart, Chief Financial Officer
CMO: Marshall Lucas, M.D., Medical Director
CIO: James Harmon, Information Technology
CHR: Brenda Dominguez, Director Human Resources
CNO: Michael Smith, Director of Nursing
Web address: www.cypresscreekhospital.com
Control: Corporation, Investor–owned, for–profit **Service:** Psychiatric

Staffed Beds: 96 **Admissions:** 3821 **Census:** 87 **Outpatient Visits:** 8751
Births: 0 **Total Expense ($000):** 21279 **Payroll Expense ($000):** 10369
Personnel: 193

✠ **CYPRESS FAIRBANKS MEDICAL CENTER (450716)**, 10655 Steepletop Drive,
Zip 77065–4297; tel. 281/890–4285 **A**1 10 **F**3 11 12 13 15 18 20 22 24 29
30 31 34 35 40 42 43 45 46 47 49 50 53 57 59 64 65 70 72 74 75 76 77
78 79 81 82 85 87 89 93 107 108 110 111 114 115 119 120 121 124 129
130 132 144 145 146 147 148 **P**8 **S** TENET Healthcare Corporation, Dallas, TX
Primary Contact: Terry J. Wheeler, Chief Executive Officer
CFO: James Wright, M.D., Chief Financial Officer
CMO: Arturo Bravo, M.D., Chief of Staff
CIO: Donna Cain, Director Information Systems Department
CHR: Linda Creswell, Director Human Resource
CNO: Lisa D. Cox, R.N., Chief Nursing Officer
Web address: www.cyfairhospital.com
Control: Corporation, Investor–owned, for–profit **Service:** General Medical and
Surgical

Staffed Beds: 160 **Admissions:** 9331 **Census:** 95 **Outpatient Visits:** 129708
Births: 3641 **Total Expense ($000):** 144309 **Payroll Expense ($000):**
56237 **Personnel:** 773

DUBUIS HOSPITAL OF HOUSTON See Cornerstone Hospital–Medical Center of
Houston

★ △ ◇ **HARRIS HEALTH SYSTEM (450289)**, 2525 Holly Hall Street,
Zip 77054–4108, Mailing Address: P.O. Box 66769, Zip 77266–6769;
tel. 713/566–6403, (Includes BEN TAUB GENERAL HOSPITAL, 1504 Taub Loop,
Zip 77030; tel. 713/873–2300; LYNDON B JOHNSON GENERAL HOSPITAL, 5656
Kelley, Zip 77026; tel. 713/566–5000; QUENTIN MEASE HOSPITAL, 3601 North
MacGregor, Zip 77004; tel. 713/873–3700; Jeffrey Webster, Administrator),
(Total facility includes 24 beds in nursing home–type unit) **A**2 3 5 7 10 21 **F**3 5 7
8 13 15 17 18 20 22 24 26 29 30 31 32 34 35 39 40 41 43 45 46 49 50 51
54 55 56 57 58 59 60 61 64 65 68 70 71 72 73 74 75 76 77 78 79 81 82
84 87 89 90 91 92 93 94 97 98 99 100 101 102 103 104 107 110 111 112
114 115 118 119 120 121 124 128 129 130 132 134 135 143 144 145 146
147 148 **P**6
Primary Contact: George V. Masi, Chief Executive Officer
CFO: Michael Norby, Chief Financial Officer
CMO: Fred Sutton, M.D., Chief Medical Officer
CIO: Tim Tindle, Chief Information Officer
CHR: Diane Poirot, Vice President Human Resources
CNO: Elizabeth Cloyd, R.N., Chief Nurse Executive and Executive Vice President
Web address: www.hchdonline.com
Control: Hospital district or authority, Government, nonfederal **Service:** General
Medical and Surgical

Staffed Beds: 796 **Admissions:** 38634 **Census:** 577 **Outpatient Visits:**
1941653 **Births:** 6683 **Total Expense ($000):** 1298173 **Payroll Expense
($000):** 529241 **Personnel:** 7428

◇ **HEALTHBRIDGE CHILDREN'S HOSPITAL OF HOUSTON (453309)**, 2929
Woodland Park Drive, Zip 77082–2687; tel. 281/293–7774 **A**10 21 **F**3 29 74
75 79 85 87 89 93 100 130 146 148 **S** Nexus Health Systems, Houston, TX
Primary Contact: Tony Bonilla, Chief Executive Officer
CMO: Robert Yetman, M.D., Medical Director
CHR: Guy Murdock, Vice President Human Resources
Web address: www.healthbridgehouston.com/
Control: Partnership, Investor–owned, for–profit **Service:** Children's general

Staffed Beds: 37 **Admissions:** 249 **Census:** 28 **Outpatient Visits:** 117
Births: 0 **Total Expense ($000):** 15970 **Payroll Expense ($000):** 7509
Personnel: 115

✠ **HEALTHSOUTH REHABILITATION HOSPITAL OF CYPRESS (673050)**, 13031
Wortham Center Drive, Zip 77065–5662; tel. 832/280–2500 **A**1 10 **F**3 29 34
57 62 64 75 77 87 90 91 93 95 96 130 132 146 148 **S** HEALTHSOUTH
Corporation, Birmingham, AL
Primary Contact: Sheila A. Bollier, Chief Executive Officer
CFO: Melissa Haddox, Controller
CMO: Ignazio LaChina, M.D., Medical Director
CHR: Keisha Pittman, Director Human Resources
CNO: Roshonda Henry, Chief Nursing Officer
Web address: www.healthsouthcypress.com
Control: Corporation, Investor–owned, for–profit **Service:** Rehabilitation

Staffed Beds: 60 **Admissions:** 1415 **Census:** 50 **Outpatient Visits:** 5571
Births: 0 **Total Expense ($000):** 16247 **Payroll Expense ($000):** 10335
Personnel: 161

✠ **HEALTHSOUTH REHABILITATION HOSPITAL THE VINTAGE (673052)**, 20180
Chasewood Park Drive, Zip 77070–1436; tel. 281/205–5100, (Data for 92 days)
A1 10 **F**3 29 65 90 91 96 130 148 **S** HEALTHSOUTH Corporation,
Birmingham, AL
Primary Contact: Jeff Crawford, Chief Executive Officer
CNO: Stanley F. Kiebzak, R.N., Chief Nursing Officer
Web address: www.reliantnwhouston.com
Control: Corporation, Investor–owned, for–profit **Service:** Rehabilitation

Staffed Beds: 60 **Admissions:** 262 **Census:** 32 **Outpatient Visits:** 1188
Births: 0 **Total Expense ($000):** 3441 **Payroll Expense ($000):** 1563
Personnel: 107

☐ **HERMANN DRIVE SURGICAL HOSPITAL**, 2001 Hermann Drive,
Zip 77004–7643; tel. 713/285–5500 **A**1 **F**3 12 29 40 45 46 68 81 85 86
107 114
Primary Contact: Mac Davidson, Chief Executive Officer
Web address: www.nobilishealth.com/our–facilities/houston/
Control: Corporation, Investor–owned, for–profit **Service:** Surgical

Staffed Beds: 25 **Admissions:** 588 **Census:** 2 **Outpatient Visits:** 1323
Births: 0 **Total Expense ($000):** 15602 **Payroll Expense ($000):** 7063
Personnel: 60

◇ **HOPEBRIDGE HOSPITAL (670072)**, 5556 Gasmer Drive, Zip 77035–4502;
tel. 713/422–2625 **A**10 21 **F**3 29 35 38 64 68 98 99 100 101 103 104 105
130 **P**5
Primary Contact: Tim C. Simmons, Chief Executive Officer
Control: Corporation, Investor–owned, for–profit **Service:** Psychiatric

Staffed Beds: 85 **Admissions:** 2364 **Census:** 55 **Outpatient Visits:** 35197
Births: 0 **Total Expense ($000):** 16264 **Payroll Expense ($000):** 9139
Personnel: 149

★ △ ◇ **HOUSTON METHODIST HOSPITAL (450358)**, 6565 Fannin Street,
D200, Zip 77030–2707; tel. 713/790–3311, (Total facility includes 18 beds in
nursing home–type unit) **A**2 3 5 7 8 10 21 **F**3 6 8 9 11 12 13 14 15 17 18 20
22 24 26 28 29 30 31 34 35 36 37 38 39 40 41 42 44 45 46 47 48 49 50
51 53 54 55 58 59 60 61 62 63 64 65 66 68 70 72 73 74 75 76 77
78 79 80 81 82 84 85 86 87 90 91 92 93 95 96 97 98 100 101 103 104
107 108 110 111 114 115 116 117 118 119 120 121 123 124 126 128 129
130 131 132 135 136 137 138 139 140 141 142 145 146 147 148 **P**6
S Houston Methodist, Houston, TX
Primary Contact: Roberta Schwartz, Ph.D., Executive Vice President
CMO: Dirk Sostman, M.D., Executive Vice President, Chief Medical Officer and
Chief Academic Officer
CIO: Timothy L. Thompson, Sr., Senior Vice President and Chief Information
Officer
CHR: Lauren P. Rykert, Senior Vice President
Web address: www.methodisthealth.com
Control: Other not–for–profit (including NFP Corporation) **Service:** General
Medical and Surgical

Staffed Beds: 861 **Admissions:** 36720 **Census:** 677 **Outpatient Visits:**
398933 **Births:** 1026 **Total Expense ($000):** 1496077 **Payroll Expense
($000):** 415499 **Personnel:** 7518

★ ◇ **HOUSTON METHODIST WEST HOSPITAL (670077)**, 18500 Katy
Freeway, Zip 77094–1110; tel. 832/522–1000 **A**3 10 21 **F**3 13 15 18 20 22
24 26 28 29 30 34 35 36 39 40 44 45 49 50 51 53 54 57 59 61 63
64 68 70 73 74 75 76 77 78 79 81 82 85 87 93 107 108 109 110 111 114
115 117 119 120 121 123 124 126 130 131 132 135 146 147 148 **P**6
S Houston Methodist, Houston, TX
Primary Contact: Wayne M. Voss, Chief Executive Officer
COO: Peyton Elliott, Vice President Operations
CNO: Victoria Brownewell, Chief Nursing Officer
Web address: www.methodisthealth.com
Control: Other not–for–profit (including NFP Corporation) **Service:** General
Medical and Surgical

Staffed Beds: 193 **Admissions:** 11743 **Census:** 119 **Outpatient Visits:**
129301 **Births:** 2912 **Total Expense ($000):** 220754 **Payroll Expense
($000):** 80794 **Personnel:** 1361

Many Facility Codes have changed. Please refer to the AHA Guide Code Chart. © 2016 AHA Guide

TX

★ ◇ **HOUSTON METHODIST WILLOWBROOK HOSPITAL (450844)**, 18220 Tomball Parkway, Zip 77070–4347; tel. 281/477–1000 **A**3 10 21 **F**3 8 11 12 13 15 17 18 20 22 24 26 28 29 30 31 34 35 36 37 40 42 44 45 49 53 57 59 64 65 70 72 73 74 75 76 77 78 79 81 85 86 87 93 97 102 107 108 110 111 112 115 119 120 121 123 126 130 131 132 135 146 147 **P**6 **S** Houston Methodist, Houston, TX
Primary Contact: Keith Barber, CPA, Chief Executive Officer
CHR: Sherene Thompson, Director Human Resources
CNO: Nancy C. Keenan, R.N., Senior Vice President and Chief Nursing Officer
Web address: www.houstonmethodist.org/locations/willowbrook/
Control: Other not–for–profit (including NFP Corporation) **Service:** General Medical and Surgical

Staffed Beds: 276 **Admissions:** 16639 **Census:** 190 **Outpatient Visits:** 159495 **Births:** 3433 **Total Expense ($000):** 289684 **Payroll Expense ($000):** 103423 **Personnel:** 1656

⊠ **HOUSTON NORTHWEST MEDICAL CENTER (450638)**, 710 FM 1960 Road West, Zip 77090–3402; tel. 281/440–1000 **A**1 2 3 5 10 **F**3 11 12 13 15 18 20 22 24 26 28 29 30 31 34 35 40 43 45 46 49 50 57 59 64 65 70 72 74 75 76 77 78 79 81 82 84 85 86 87 89 91 92 93 96 102 107 108 109 110 111 114 115 117 118 119 126 129 130 132 135 144 146 147 148 **S** TENET Healthcare Corporation, Dallas, TX
Primary Contact: Timothy Puthoff, Chief Executive Officer
COO: Juan Fresquez, Chief Operating Officer
CFO: Bryan Forry, Chief Financial Officer
CIO: Ed Roberson, Director Information Systems
CHR: Melanie R. Webb, Director Human Resources
CNO: Cindy Henning, R.N., Chief Nursing Officer
Web address: www.hnmc.com
Control: Partnership, Investor–owned, for–profit **Service:** General Medical and Surgical

Staffed Beds: 339 **Admissions:** 16209 **Census:** 190 **Outpatient Visits:** 149749 **Births:** 4473 **Total Expense ($000):** 262678 **Payroll Expense ($000):** 91106 **Personnel:** 1336

☐ **INTRACARE NORTH HOSPITAL (454083)**, 1120 Cypress Station Drive, Zip 77090–3031; tel. 281/893–7200 **A**1 10 **F**5 98 99 100 101 103 104 105
Primary Contact: Terry Scovill, Chief Executive Officer
CFO: Fred Chan, Chief Financial Officer
CMO: Javier Ruiz, M.D., Medical Director
Web address: www.intracare.org
Control: Other not–for–profit (including NFP Corporation) **Service:** Psychiatric

Staffed Beds: 86 **Admissions:** 2316 **Census:** 53 **Outpatient Visits:** 57151 **Births:** 0 **Total Expense ($000):** 17926 **Payroll Expense ($000):** 7979 **Personnel:** 183

⊠ **KINDRED HOSPITAL HOUSTON MEDICAL CENTER (452023)**, 6441 Main Street, Zip 77030–1596; tel. 713/790–0500 **A**1 3 5 10 **F**1 3 29 30 70 75 77 85 107 130 148 **S** Kindred Healthcare, Louisville, KY
Primary Contact: Robert Stein, Chief Executive Officer
CFO: Sara Langlitz, Controller
Web address: www.khhouston.com/
Control: Corporation, Investor–owned, for–profit **Service:** Long–Term Acute Care hospital

Staffed Beds: 105 **Admissions:** 929 **Census:** 85 **Outpatient Visits:** 0 **Births:** 0 **Total Expense ($000):** 43077 **Payroll Expense ($000):** 19996 **Personnel:** 319

⊠ **KINDRED HOSPITAL–HOUSTON NORTHWEST (452039)**, 11297 Fallbrook Drive, Zip 77065–4292; tel. 281/897–8114, (Includes KINDRED HOSPITAL–BAY AREA, 4801 East Sam Houston Parkway South, Pasadena, Zip 77505–3955; tel. 281/991–5463; Aleen D. Arabit, Chief Executive Officer) **A**1 10 **F**1 3 29 49 57 64 70 77 85 87 107 114 130 148 **P**5 **S** Kindred Healthcare, Louisville, KY
Primary Contact: Aleen Arabit, Chief Executive Officer
Web address: www.khhoustonnw.com/
Control: Corporation, Investor–owned, for–profit **Service:** Long–Term Acute Care hospital

Staffed Beds: 84 **Admissions:** 667 **Census:** 46 **Outpatient Visits:** 387 **Births:** 0 **Total Expense ($000):** 28357 **Payroll Expense ($000):** 10160 **Personnel:** 140

LYNDON B JOHNSON GENERAL HOSPITAL See Harris Health System

⊠ **MEMORIAL HERMANN – TEXAS MEDICAL CENTER (450068)**, 6411 Fannin Street, Zip 77030–1501; tel. 713/704–4000, (Includes CHILDREN'S MEMORIAL HERMANN HOSPITAL, 6411 Fannin, Zip 77030; tel. 713/704–5437), (Total facility includes 8 beds in nursing home–type unit) **A**1 2 3 5 8 10 **F**3 7 12 15 16 17 18 19 20 21 22 23 24 25 26 27 31 32 34 35 36 37 40 41 43 44 45 46 47 48 49 50 51 55 56 57 58 59 60 61 64 68 70 72 73 74 75 76 77 78 79 81 82 84 85 86 87 88 89 90 91 92 93 96 100 102 107 108 109 110 111 113 114 115 116 118 119 120 121 123 124 126 128 129 130 131 132 135 137 138 139 141 142 146 147 148 **P**5 6 **S** Memorial Hermann Health System, Houston, TX
Primary Contact: Brian Dean, FACHE, Chief Executive Officer
COO: Tom Flanagan, Chief Operating Officer
CFO: William Pack, Chief Financial Officer
CMO: Jeffrey Katz, M.D., Chief Medical Officer
CIO: David Bradshaw, Chief Information Officer
CHR: Vivian Kardow, Chief Human Resources Officer
Web address: www.mhhs.org
Control: Other not–for–profit (including NFP Corporation) **Service:** General Medical and Surgical

Staffed Beds: 973 **Admissions:** 37658 **Census:** 699 **Outpatient Visits:** 225776 **Births:** 5035 **Total Expense ($000):** 1276716 **Payroll Expense ($000):** 373764 **Personnel:** 4939

⊠ **MEMORIAL HERMANN GREATER HEIGHTS HOSPITAL (450184)**, 1635 North Loop West, Zip 77008–1532; tel. 713/867–3380, (Includes MEMORIAL HERMANN PEARLAND MEDICAL CENTER, 16100 South Freeway, Pearland, Zip 77584–1895; tel. 713/413–5000; Mario J. Garner, Ed.D., FACHE, Chief Executive Officer; MEMORIAL HERMANN SOUTHEAST HOSPITAL, 11800 Astoria Boulevard, Zip 77089–6041; tel. 281/929–6100; Kyle Price, Interim Chief Executive Officer; MEMORIAL HERMANN SOUTHWEST HOSPITAL, 7600 Beechnut, Zip 77074–1850; tel. 713/456–5000; Gary Kerr, Chief Executive Officer; MEMORIAL HERMANN THE WOODLANDS HOSPITAL, 9250 Pinecroft Drive, The Woodlands, Zip 77380–3225; tel. 281/364–2300) **A**1 2 3 5 10 **F**3 13 15 17 18 20 22 24 26 28 29 30 31 34 35 40 41 43 44 45 46 49 50 51 56 57 58 59 60 64 68 70 72 73 74 75 76 77 78 79 80 81 82 84 85 86 87 89 90 91 92 93 96 107 108 109 110 111 114 115 116 117 118 119 126 129 130 132 135 146 147 148 **P**5 6 **S** Memorial Hermann Health System, Houston, TX
Primary Contact: Susan Jadlowski, MSN, R.N., Chief Executive Officer
COO: Wesley Tidwell, Chief Operating Officer
CFO: James R. Shallock, Chief Financial Officer
CMO: Maurice Leibman, M.D., Chief Medical Officer
CIO: David Bradshaw, Chief Information Officer
CNO: Melody Ford Dickerson, Chief Nursing Officer
Web address: www.mhbh.org
Control: Other not–for–profit (including NFP Corporation) **Service:** General Medical and Surgical

Staffed Beds: 1275 **Admissions:** 61090 **Census:** 796 **Outpatient Visits:** 568891 **Births:** 11355 **Total Expense ($000):** 1126843 **Payroll Expense ($000):** 380600 **Personnel:** 4906

⊠ **MEMORIAL HERMANN MEMORIAL CITY MEDICAL CENTER (450610)**, 921 Gessner Road, Zip 77024–2501; tel. 713/242–3000 **A**1 2 3 5 10 **F**3 12 13 15 18 20 22 24 26 28 29 30 31 34 35 37 40 41 43 45 46 49 51 56 57 59 60 65 70 72 74 75 76 77 78 79 80 81 82 84 85 87 89 107 108 110 111 114 115 117 118 119 120 121 123 124 126 129 130 131 132 135 146 147 148 **P**5 6 **S** Memorial Hermann Health System, Houston, TX
Primary Contact: Paul O'Sullivan, FACHE, Chief Executive Officer
COO: Allen Tseng, Chief Operations Officer
CFO: Lisa Kendler, Chief Financial Officer
CMO: Harold Gottlieb, M.D., Chief Medical Officer
CIO: David Bradshaw, Chief Information, Planning and Marketing Officer
CHR: Suzanne S. Meier, System Director, Compensation and Human Resources Technology
CNO: Dan Kelly, R.N., Chief Nursing Officer
Web address: www.memorialhermann.org
Control: Other not–for–profit (including NFP Corporation) **Service:** General Medical and Surgical

Staffed Beds: 382 **Admissions:** 21559 **Census:** 251 **Outpatient Visits:** 205081 **Births:** 3591 **Total Expense ($000):** 430069 **Payroll Expense ($000):** 116553 **Personnel:** 1581

MEMORIAL HERMANN SOUTHEAST HOSPITAL See Memorial Hermann Greater Heights Hospital

MEMORIAL HERMANN SOUTHWEST HOSPITAL See Memorial Hermann Greater Heights Hospital

TX

Hospital, Medicare Provider Number, Address, Telephone, Approval, Facility, and Physician Codes, Health Care System

★ American Hospital Association (AHA) membership   ◯ Healthcare Facilities Accreditation Program   ⇑ Center for Improvement in Healthcare Quality Accreditation
☐ The Joint Commission accreditation   ◇ DNV Healthcare Inc. accreditation   △ Commission on Accreditation of Rehabilitation Facilities (CARF) accreditation

☐ **MENNINGER CLINIC**, 12301 Main Street, Zip 77035–6207; tel. 713/275–5000 **A**1 3 5 **F**30 35 74 98 99 101 104 106 130 132
Primary Contact: C. Edward Coffey, M.D., President, Chief Executive Officer and Chief of Staff
CFO: Tony Gaglio, CPA, Senior Vice President and Chief Financial Officer
CMO: Ed Poa, M.D., Chief Inpatient Services
CIO: M. Justin Coffey, Vice President and Chief Information Officer, Medical Director Center for Brain Stimulation
CHR: Andrea Preisinger, Director Human Resources
CNO: Avni Cirpili, Senior Vice President, Chief Nursing Officer
Web address: www.menningerclinic.com
Control: Other not–for–profit (including NFP Corporation) **Service:** Psychiatric

Staffed Beds: 102 **Admissions:** 783 **Census:** 85 **Outpatient Visits:** 2522 **Births:** 0 **Total Expense ($000):** 58950 **Payroll Expense ($000):** 24324 **Personnel:** 362

METHODIST WEST HOUSTON HOSPITAL See Houston Methodist West Hospital

METHODIST WILLOWBROOK HOSPITAL See Houston Methodist Willowbrook Hospital

✠ △ **MICHAEL E. DEBAKEY VETERANS AFFAIRS MEDICAL CENTER**, 2002 Holcombe Boulevard, Zip 77030–4298; tel. 713/791–1414, (Nonreporting) **A**1 2 3 5 7 8 **S** Department of Veterans Affairs, Washington, DC
Primary Contact: Adam C. Walmus, FACHE, Director
COO: Christopher Sandles, Associate Director
CFO: Alisa Cooper, Manager Financial Resources
CMO: Jagadeesh S. Kalavar, M.D., Chief of Staff
CIO: Kevin Lenamond, Information Management Service Line Executive
CHR: Mark Muhammad, Manager Human Resources
CNO: Kelly Ann Irving, MSN, RN–B, Associate Director for Patient Care Services
Web address: www.houston.va.gov
Control: Veterans Affairs, Government, federal **Service:** General Medical and Surgical

Staffed Beds: 479

✠ **PARK PLAZA HOSPITAL (450659)**, 1313 Hermann Drive, Zip 77004–7092; tel. 713/527–5000 **A**1 2 3 10 **F**3 12 15 18 20 22 29 31 34 35 40 45 49 50 56 57 59 70 74 78 79 81 85 92 107 108 110 111 114 115 118 119 120 121 123 129 130 132 146 147 148 **S** TENET Healthcare Corporation, Dallas, TX
Primary Contact: Steven D. Patonai, Interim Chief Executive Officer
COO: Mary Jo Goodman, Chief Operating Officer
CMO: Robert Brown, M.D., Chief Medical Officer
CIO: Terry Janis, Assistant Vice President
CHR: Melanie R. Webb, Chief Human Resources Officer
CNO: Martha M. Smith, R.N., Chief Nursing Officer
Web address: www.parkplazahospital.com
Control: Partnership, Investor–owned, for–profit **Service:** General Medical and Surgical

Staffed Beds: 139 **Admissions:** 3723 **Census:** 62 **Outpatient Visits:** 34417 **Births:** 0 **Total Expense ($000):** 86949 **Payroll Expense ($000):** 28838 **Personnel:** 444

☐ **PINE VALLEY SPECIALTY HOSPITAL (452043)**, 6160 South Loop East, Zip 77087–1010; tel. 713/640–2400 **A**1 10 **F**1 3 29 75 77 85 87 130 148 **S** Concord Healthcare Group, Lakewood, NJ
Primary Contact: Brent Hanson, Chief Executive Officer
CFO: Betty Priestley, Manager Business Office
CMO: Alfred Louis, M.D., Chief Medical Staff
CHR: Laura Garza, Director Human Resources
Web address: www.promise–houston.com
Control: Corporation, Investor–owned, for–profit **Service:** Long–Term Acute Care hospital

Staffed Beds: 35 **Admissions:** 274 **Census:** 22 **Outpatient Visits:** 0 **Births:** 0 **Total Expense ($000):** 12814 **Payroll Expense ($000):** 6061 **Personnel:** 57

✠ **PLAZA SPECIALTY HOSPITAL (452046)**, 1300 Binz Street, Zip 77004–7016; tel. 713/285–1000 **A**1 10 **F**1 3 70 85 87 **P**8 **S** TENET Healthcare Corporation, Dallas, TX
Primary Contact: Richard Andrew Pletz, Chief Executive Officer
CFO: Charles Handley, Chief Financial Officer
CMO: Wasae S. Tabibi, M.D., President Medical Staff
CIO: Steve Peacock, Assistant Vice President
Web address: www.plazaspecialtyhospital.com
Control: Corporation, Investor–owned, for–profit **Service:** Long–Term Acute Care hospital

Staffed Beds: 46 **Admissions:** 321 **Census:** 34 **Outpatient Visits:** 0 **Births:** 0 **Total Expense ($000):** 26348 **Payroll Expense ($000):** 7866 **Personnel:** 84

☐ **SCA HOUSTON HOSPITAL FOR SPECIALIZED SURGERY (450797)**, 5445 La Branch Street, Zip 77004–6835; tel. 713/528–6800 **A**1 3 10 **F**3 8 40 42 45 54 64 79 81 82 85 107 111 113 119
Primary Contact: Gary Williams, Administrator
CFO: Deborah Jones, Controller
Web address: www.scasurgery.com
Control: Partnership, Investor–owned, for–profit **Service:** Surgical

Staffed Beds: 7 **Admissions:** 198 **Census:** 1 **Outpatient Visits:** 11866 **Births:** 0 **Total Expense ($000):** 13087 **Payroll Expense ($000):** 4376 **Personnel:** 70

★ **SELECT SPECIALTY HOSPITAL–HOUSTON MEDICAL CENTER (452049)**, 2130 West Holcombe, Zip 77030–1502; tel. 713/218–2300, (Nonreporting) **A**5 **S** Select Medical Corporation, Mechanicsburg, PA
Primary Contact: Michael A. Anaya, FACHE, Chief Executive Officer
Web address: www.selectmedicalcorp.com
Control: Corporation, Investor–owned, for–profit **Service:** Long–Term Acute Care hospital

Staffed Beds: 34

☐ **SHRINERS HOSPITALS FOR CHILDREN–HOUSTON (453312)**, 6977 Main Street, Zip 77030–3701; tel. 713/797–1616 **A**1 3 5 10 **F**3 29 30 35 50 59 64 68 74 75 77 79 81 86 87 89 93 94 96 130 131 132 134 143 146 148 **P**6 **S** Shriners Hospitals for Children, Tampa, FL
Primary Contact: Cathy Moniaci, MS, R.N., Administrator
COO: Cathy Moniaci, MS, Administrator
CFO: Michael B. Schimming, Director Fiscal Services
CMO: Douglas A. Barnes, M.D., Chief of Staff
CHR: Robert A. Magee, Director Human Resources
CNO: Jeannie Keith, Director Patient Care Services and Nurse Executive
Web address: www.shrinershospitalsforchildren.org/Locations/houston
Control: Other not–for–profit (including NFP Corporation) **Service:** Children's orthopedic

Staffed Beds: 40 **Admissions:** 507 **Census:** 13 **Outpatient Visits:** 10525 **Births:** 0 **Total Expense ($000):** 27258 **Payroll Expense ($000):** 14394 **Personnel:** 172

◇ **ST. JOSEPH MEDICAL CENTER (450035)**, 1401 St. Joseph Parkway, Zip 77002–8301; tel. 713/757–1000, (Total facility includes 18 beds in nursing home–type unit) **A**3 5 10 21 **F**3 11 12 13 15 18 20 22 24 26 29 30 31 34 35 40 42 43 45 49 50 51 53 58 59 60 64 68 70 72 74 75 76 77 78 79 81 82 84 85 86 87 90 93 94 97 98 101 102 103 104 105 107 108 110 111 114 115 116 117 118 119 121 123 124 126 128 129 130 131 132 135 143 144 146 147 148 **P**8 **S** IASIS Healthcare, Franklin, TN
Primary Contact: Bryanie W. Swilley, Jr., Interim Chief Executive Officer
COO: Laura Fortin, R.N., Chief Operating Officer
CIO: Robin Bryan, Chief Information Officer and Compliance Officer
CHR: Kris Clatanoff, Director Human Resources
Web address: www.sjmctx.com
Control: Partnership, Investor–owned, for–profit **Service:** General Medical and Surgical

Staffed Beds: 374 **Admissions:** 15759 **Census:** 228 **Outpatient Visits:** 107769 **Births:** 4918 **Total Expense ($000):** 223735 **Payroll Expense ($000):** 91527 **Personnel:** 1270

★ ◇ **ST. LUKE'S HOSPITAL – THE VINTAGE HOSPITAL (670075)**, 20171 Chasewood Park Drive, Zip 77070–1437; tel. 832/534–5000 **A**10 21 **F**3 11 12 13 15 18 20 22 24 26 29 30 34 35 40 45 49 50 57 59 60 64 68 70 72 75 76 77 79 81 82 85 87 107 108 110 111 114 115 118 119 130 146 147 **P**5 **S** Catholic Health Initiatives, Englewood, CO
Primary Contact: Roland Cruickshank, President
Web address: www.stlukesvintage.com/
Control: Church–operated, Nongovernment, not–for profit **Service:** General Medical and Surgical

Staffed Beds: 78 **Admissions:** 3347 **Census:** 41 **Outpatient Visits:** 25033 **Total Expense ($000):** 80675 **Payroll Expense ($000):** 22933

☐ △ **TEXAS CHILDREN'S HOSPITAL (453304)**, 6621 Fannin Street, Zip 77030–2399, Mailing Address: Box 300630, Zip 77230–0630; tel. 832/824–1000, (Includes TEXAS CHILDREN'S HOSPITAL WEST CAMPUS, 18200 Katy Freeway, Zip 77094–1285; tel. 832/227–1000) **A**1 3 5 7 8 10 **F**3 7 11 12 13 17 19 21 23 25 27 29 30 31 32 34 35 38 39 40 41 43 48 49 50 52 54 55 57 58 59 60 61 64 65 68 71 72 73 74 75 76 77 78 79 80 81 84 85 86 87 88 89 90 92 93 94 95 96 97 99 100 101 104 107 108 111 114 115 116 117 118 119 126 129 130 131 132 134 136 137 138 139 140 143 144 146 147 148
Primary Contact: Mark A. Wallace, FACHE, President and Chief Executive Officer
CFO: Benjamin B. Melson, CPA, Executive Vice President and Chief Financial Officer
CMO: Mark W. Kline, M.D., Physician in Chief
CHR: Linda W. Aldred, Senior Vice President
Web address: www.texaschildrenshospital.org
Control: Other not–for–profit (including NFP Corporation) **Service:** Children's general

Staffed Beds: 651 **Admissions:** 30002 **Census:** 545 **Outpatient Visits:** 1081328 **Births:** 6009 **Total Expense ($000):** 1619167 **Payroll Expense ($000):** 614886 **Personnel:** 6467

⊠ **TEXAS ORTHOPEDIC HOSPITAL (450804)**, 7401 South Main Street, Zip 77030–4509; tel. 713/799–8600 **A**1 3 5 10 **F**3 29 30 40 59 64 68 70 79 81 82 85 86 87 93 94 97 107 111 115 119 146 **S** HCA, Nashville, TN
Primary Contact: Eric Becker, Chief Executive Officer
CFO: Virgil Winslow, Chief Financial Officer
CMO: Gregory Stocks, M.D., Chief of Staff
CNO: Troy Sarver, R.N., Chief Nursing Officer
Web address: www.texasorthopedic.com
Control: Partnership, Investor–owned, for–profit **Service:** Orthopedic

> **Staffed Beds:** 49 **Admissions:** 3502 **Census:** 24 **Outpatient Visits:** 34955
> **Births:** 0 **Total Expense ($000):** 77991 **Payroll Expense ($000):** 24361
> **Personnel:** 375

THE METHODIST HOSPITAL See Houston Methodist Hospital

⊠ △ **TIRR MEMORIAL HERMANN (453025)**, 1333 Moursund Street, Zip 77030–3405; tel. 713/799–5000 **A**1 2 3 5 7 10 **F**11 29 30 34 35 44 50 52 54 58 59 60 64 68 74 75 77 79 82 86 87 90 91 93 95 96 97 100 104 107 114 119 129 130 131 132 146 148 **P**5 6 **S** Memorial Hermann Health System, Houston, TX
Primary Contact: Carl E. Josehart, Chief Executive Officer
COO: Mary Ann Euliarte, R.N., Chief Operating Officer and Chief Nursing Officer
CFO: Wayne Gordon, Chief Financial Officer
CMO: Gerard E. Francisco, M.D., Chief Medical Officer
CIO: Gina Tripp, Director Information Systems
CHR: Vivian Kardow, Chief Human Resources Officer
CNO: Mary Ann Euliarte, R.N., Chief Operating Officer and Chief Nursing Officer
Web address: www.memorialhermann.org/locations/tirr.html
Control: Other not–for–profit (including NFP Corporation) **Service:** Rehabilitation

> **Staffed Beds:** 134 **Admissions:** 1264 **Census:** 94 **Outpatient Visits:** 22312
> **Births:** 0 **Total Expense ($000):** 99302 **Payroll Expense ($000):** 47684
> **Personnel:** 712

☐ **TOPS SURGICAL SPECIALTY HOSPITAL (450774)**, 17080 Red Oak Drive, Zip 77090–2602; tel. 281/539–2900 **A**1 10 **F**3 15 29 40 45 51 79 81 82 107 119 **S** United Surgical Partners International, Addison, TX
Primary Contact: Samuel H. Rossmann, Chief Executive Officer
CFO: Daniel Smith, Chief Financial Officer
CMO: Thomas Barton, M.D., Medical Director
CIO: Maud Jones, Manager Medical Records
CHR: Ashley Monzingo, Human Resources, Accounts Payable and Payroll
CNO: Andrea Wappelhorst, Chief Nursing Officer
Web address: www.tops–hospital.com
Control: Partnership, Investor–owned, for–profit **Service:** Surgical

> **Staffed Beds:** 15 **Admissions:** 727 **Census:** 4 **Outpatient Visits:** 48580
> **Births:** 0 **Total Expense ($000):** 32781 **Payroll Expense ($000):** 8874
> **Personnel:** 166

TRIUMPH HOSPITAL NORTHWEST See Kindred Hospital Spring

UNITED MEMORIAL MEDICAL CARE (450803), 510 West Tidwell Road, Zip 77091–4399; tel. 713/691–1111, (Includes DOCTORS HOSPITAL PARKWAY, 233 West Parker Road, Zip 77076–2999; tel. 281/765–2600) **A**10 22 **F**22 29 40 43 50 64 68 70 75 79 81 92 107 114 119 130 148
Primary Contact: Farida Moeen, M.D., Chief Executive Officer
COO: Farida Moeen, M.D., Chief Executive Officer
CFO: Theresa Eatherly, Chief Financial Officer
CMO: Cesar Ortega, M.D., Chief of Staff
CIO: Dell Davis, Director Information Systems
CHR: Carolyn Washington, Director of Human Resources
Web address: www.ummc.care/
Control: Partnership, Investor–owned, for–profit **Service:** General Medical and Surgical

> **Staffed Beds:** 42 **Admissions:** 1519 **Census:** 23 **Outpatient Visits:** 11611
> **Births:** 0 **Total Expense ($000):** 23112 **Payroll Expense ($000):** 8948
> **Personnel:** 178

☐ **UNIVERSITY GENERAL HOSPITAL (670019)**, 7501 Fannin Street, Zip 77054–1938; tel. 713/375–7000 **A**1 10 **F**3 8 12 18 20 22 29 31 40 45 47 49 54 57 59 67 70 75 79 81 82 85 86 107 108 111 114 119 130 132 148
Primary Contact: Harmonee Vice, Chief Executive Officer
Web address: www.ughospital.com
Control: Partnership, Investor–owned, for–profit **Service:** General Medical and Surgical

> **Staffed Beds:** 69 **Admissions:** 9155 **Census:** 34 **Outpatient Visits:** 996
> **Total Expense ($000):** 59009 **Payroll Expense ($000):** 22931 **Personnel:** 297

★ **UNIVERSITY OF TEXAS HARRIS COUNTY PSYCHIATRIC CENTER (454076)**, 2800 South MacGregor Way, Zip 77021–1000, Mailing Address: P.O. Box 20249, Zip 77225–0249; tel. 713/741–7870 **A**5 10 **F**29 30 34 35 57 58 68 75 86 87 98 99 100 101 103 106 130 146 **P**6 **S** University of Texas System, Austin, TX
Primary Contact: Jair C. Soares, M.D., Executive Director
COO: Stephen Glazier, Chief Operating Officer
CFO: Lois K. Pierson, Chief Financial Officer
CMO: R. Andrew Harper, M.D., Medical Director
CHR: Jill Strutton, Director Personnel Systems
CNO: Margaret Pung, R.N., Chief Nursing Officer
Web address: www.hcpc.uth.tmc.edu
Control: State–Government, nonfederal **Service:** Psychiatric

> **Staffed Beds:** 208 **Admissions:** 8807 **Census:** 184 **Outpatient Visits:** 0
> **Births:** 0 **Total Expense ($000):** 50268 **Payroll Expense ($000):** 31786
> **Personnel:** 511

⊠ **UNIVERSITY OF TEXAS M.D. ANDERSON CANCER CENTER (450076)**, 1515 Holcombe Boulevard, Unit 1491, Zip 77030–4000; tel. 713/792–2121 **A**1 2 3 5 8 10 **F**3 8 11 14 15 18 20 22 26 29 30 31 32 34 35 36 37 38 39 40 41 44 45 46 47 49 50 54 55 57 58 59 63 64 66 68 70 71 74 75 77 78 79 80 81 82 83 84 85 86 87 88 89 91 92 93 96 97 99 100 101 102 103 104 107 108 110 111 112 114 115 117 118 119 120 121 122 123 124 126 129 130 132 134 135 136 141 145 146 147 148 **P**6 **S** University of Texas System, Austin, TX
Primary Contact: Ronald A. DePinho, M.D., President
CMO: Thomas Buchholz, M.D., Physician–in–Chief and Executive Vice President
CIO: Chris Belmont, Chief Information Officer and Vice President
CHR: Shibu Varghese, Vice President Human Resources
CNO: Barbara L. Summers, Ph.D., Vice President Nursing Practice and Chief Nursing Officer
Web address: www.mdanderson.org
Control: State–Government, nonfederal **Service:** Cancer

> **Staffed Beds:** 665 **Admissions:** 28167 **Census:** 555 **Outpatient Visits:** 1440684 **Births:** 0 **Total Expense ($000):** 4040940 **Payroll Expense ($000):** 1776415 **Personnel:** 20237

⊠ **WEST HOUSTON MEDICAL CENTER (450644)**, 12141 Richmond Avenue, Zip 77082–2499; tel. 281/558–3444 **A**1 10 **F**3 11 12 13 15 18 20 22 24 26 28 29 30 31 40 42 45 46 47 48 49 50 51 56 57 59 60 64 70 73 74 75 76 77 78 79 80 81 82 85 90 93 96 98 102 103 107 110 111 115 116 117 118 119 121 124 126 129 130 132 145 146 147 148 **S** HCA, Nashville, TN
Primary Contact: Todd Caliva, Chief Executive Officer
COO: Philip Morris, Chief Operating Officer
CFO: Stanley K. Nord, Chief Financial Officer
CMO: Magdy Rizk, M.D., Chief of Staff
CIO: Sergio Almeida, Director Information Systems
CHR: Carol Melville, Director Human Resources
Web address: www.westhoustonmedical.com
Control: Partnership, Investor–owned, for–profit **Service:** General Medical and Surgical

> **Staffed Beds:** 264 **Admissions:** 13257 **Census:** 207 **Outpatient Visits:** 105357 **Births:** 3196 **Total Expense ($000):** 197237 **Payroll Expense ($000):** 82493 **Personnel:** 1107

☐ **WEST OAKS HOSPITAL (454026)**, 6500 Hornwood Drive, Zip 77074–5095; tel. 713/995–0909 **A**1 3 5 10 **F**5 29 54 56 64 68 98 99 100 101 103 104 105 132 **S** Universal Health Services, Inc., King of Prussia, PA
Primary Contact: Mandy Westerman, Chief Executive Officer
CFO: Rob Tyler, Chief Financial Officer
CMO: Vernon Walling, M.D., Executive Medical Director
CIO: James Harmon, Network Administrator
CHR: Janice Webster, Director Human Resources
CNO: Israel Ahaine, Chief Nursing Officer
Web address: www.westoakshospital.com
Control: Corporation, Investor–owned, for–profit **Service:** Psychiatric

> **Staffed Beds:** 144 **Admissions:** 5471 **Census:** 111 **Outpatient Visits:** 19219
> **Births:** 0 **Total Expense ($000):** 24395 **Payroll Expense ($000):** 14536
> **Personnel:** 262

★ **WESTSIDE SURGICAL HOSPITAL**, 4200 Twelve Oaks Drive, Zip 77027; tel. 713/621–5010 **F**3 15 29 34 35 40 45 64 75 79 81 82 85 86 107 110 119 126 132 147
Primary Contact: Angie Kauffman, R.N., MSN, Chief Executive Officer
Control: Corporation, Investor–owned, for–profit **Service:** Surgical

> **Staffed Beds:** 12 **Admissions:** 144 **Census:** 3 **Outpatient Visits:** 2446
> **Births:** 0 **Total Expense ($000):** 27649 **Payroll Expense ($000):** 6663
> **Personnel:** 98

TX

Hospital, Medicare Provider Number, Address, Telephone, Approval, Facility, and Physician Codes, Health Care System

★ American Hospital Association (AHA) membership   ◯ Healthcare Facilities Accreditation Program   ⇑ Center for Improvement in Healthcare Quality Accreditation
☐ The Joint Commission accreditation   ◇ DNV Healthcare Inc. accreditation   △ Commission on Accreditation of Rehabilitation Facilities (CARF) accreditation

✠ **WOMAN'S HOSPITAL OF TEXAS (450674)**, 7600 Fannin Street,
Zip 77054–1906; tel. 713/790–1234 **A**1 3 5 10 **F**7 8 13 15 19 29 30 34 35
40 41 45 46 53 55 58 64 65 68 70 71 72 73 75 76 77 81 85 86 87 88 89
90 91 93 107 108 110 111 118 119 126 130 132 146 147 **S** HCA,
Nashville, TN
Primary Contact: Ashley McClellan, Chief Executive Officer
COO: Eric Evans, Chief Operating Officer
CFO: Scott Bentley, Chief Financial Officer
CMO: Eberhard Lotze, M.D., Chief Medical Officer
CIO: Emily Le, Director Information Technology and Services
CHR: Arnita Crawford, Director Human Resources
CNO: Holley Tyler, R.N., Chief Nursing Officer
Web address: www.womanshospital.com
Control: Partnership, Investor–owned, for–profit **Service:** Obstetrics and
gynecology

> **Staffed Beds:** 345 **Admissions:** 16690 **Census:** 248 **Outpatient Visits:**
> 64070 **Births:** 11324 **Total Expense ($000):** 253087 **Payroll Expense**
> **($000):** 103578 **Personnel:** 1432

HUMBLE—Harris County

✠ **HEALTHSOUTH REHABILITATION HOSPITAL OF HUMBLE, LLC (453029)**,
19002 McKay Drive, Zip 77338–5701; tel. 281/446–6148 **A**1 10 **F**29 56 75 77
82 86 87 90 91 92 95 96 130 132 143 148 **P**5 **S** HEALTHSOUTH Corporation,
Birmingham, AL
Primary Contact: Angela L. Simmons, Chief Executive Officer
CFO: Sheila Shepard, Controller
CMO: Emile Mathurin, Jr., M.D., Medical Director
CHR: Christy Dixon, Chief Human Resources Officer
CNO: Christie Griffin–Jones, R.N., Chief Nursing Officer
Web address: www.healthsouthhumble.com
Control: Corporation, Investor–owned, for–profit **Service:** Rehabilitation

> **Staffed Beds:** 60 **Admissions:** 1036 **Census:** 36 **Outpatient Visits:** 0 **Births:**
> 0 **Total Expense ($000):** 10869 **Payroll Expense ($000):** 7975 **Personnel:**
> 119

✠ **ICON HOSPITAL (452112)**, 19211 McKay Boulevard, Zip 77338–5502;
tel. 281/883–5500 **A**1 10 **F**1 3 29 40 45 64 75 77 82 85 107 114 119 130
146 148
Primary Contact: Kenya Fair, Chief Executive Officer
Web address: www.iconhospitalonline.com/
Control: Partnership, Investor–owned, for–profit **Service:** Long–Term Acute Care
hospital

> **Staffed Beds:** 32 **Admissions:** 448 **Census:** 30 **Outpatient Visits:** 440
> **Births:** 0 **Total Expense ($000):** 18632 **Payroll Expense ($000):** 8554
> **Personnel:** 130

✠ **KINDRED REHABILITATION HOSPITAL NORTHEAST HOUSTON (673051)**,
18839 McKay Boulevard, Zip 77338–5721; tel. 281/964–6600 **A**1 10 **F**3 29 64
77 90 91 93 130 148
Primary Contact: Tracy Wilson, Chief Executive Officer
CFO: Cheryl Csepke, Controller
CMO: Helen Schilling, M.D., Medical Director
CHR: Stephanie Williams, Coordinator Human Resources
CNO: Albert J. Chapple, R.N., Chief Clinical Officer
Web address: www.khrehabnortheasthouston.com
Control: Corporation, Investor–owned, for–profit **Service:** Rehabilitation

> **Staffed Beds:** 46 **Admissions:** 683 **Census:** 26 **Outpatient Visits:** 1238
> **Births:** 0 **Total Expense ($000):** 13917 **Payroll Expense ($000):** 6314
> **Personnel:** 105

✠ **MEMORIAL HERMANN NORTHEAST (450684)**, 18951 North Memorial Drive,
Zip 77338–4297; tel. 281/540–7700 **A**1 2 3 5 10 **F**3 11 13 15 18 20 22 24
26 29 30 31 34 35 40 42 45 46 49 53 54 57 59 64 65 68 70 72 73 74 75
76 77 78 79 80 81 85 86 87 93 100 107 108 109 110 111 114 115 119
120 121 123 126 129 130 131 132 135 146 147 148 **P**5 6 **S** Memorial
Hermann Health System, Houston, TX
Primary Contact: Heath Rushing, Chief Executive Officer
COO: Heath Rushing, Chief Executive Officer
CFO: Rebecca Tucker, Chief Financial Officer
CMO: Susan Curling, M.D., Chief Medical Officer
CHR: Monica Baisden, Director Human Resources
CNO: Linda Stephens, R.N., Chief Nursing Officer
Web address: www.memorialhermann.org/locations/northeast/
Control: Other not–for–profit (including NFP Corporation) **Service:** General
Medical and Surgical

> **Staffed Beds:** 218 **Admissions:** 11741 **Census:** 155 **Outpatient Visits:**
> 123424 **Births:** 1376 **Total Expense ($000):** 209909 **Payroll Expense**
> **($000):** 73769 **Personnel:** 917

HUNTSVILLE—Walker County

✠ **HUNTSVILLE MEMORIAL HOSPITAL (450347)**, 110 Memorial Hospital Drive,
Zip 77340–4940, Mailing Address: P.O. Box 4001, Zip 77342–4001;
tel. 936/291–3411 **A**1 10 **F**3 8 11 12 13 15 18 20 22 26 28 29 32 34 35 39
40 42 43 45 46 47 49 50 53 54 57 59 63 64 65 66 67 68 70 71 74 75 76
77 79 81 82 85 86 87 89 90 91 92 93 96 97 102 107 108 110 111 114 115
118 119 127 130 131 132 135 146 147 148
Primary Contact: Shannon Brown, Chief Executive Officer
CFO: Guy Gyros, Chief Financial Officer
CIO: Raul Velez, Director Information Systems
CHR: Brenda Ray, Director Human Resources
CNO: Sheila Ard, Chief Nursing Officer
Web address: www.huntsvillememorial.com
Control: Other not–for–profit (including NFP Corporation) **Service:** General
Medical and Surgical

> **Staffed Beds:** 98 **Admissions:** 4558 **Census:** 55 **Outpatient Visits:** 98598
> **Births:** 470 **Total Expense ($000):** 80912 **Payroll Expense ($000):** 31033
> **Personnel:** 506

HURST—Tarrant County

✠ **COOK CHILDREN'S NORTHEAST HOSPITAL (670045)**, 6316 Precinct Line
Road, Zip 76054–2766; tel. 817/605–2500 **A**1 10 **F**3 40 41 45 48 64 68 79
81 85 89 107 111 114 119 144
Primary Contact: Kyllan Cody, FACHE, Chief Executive Officer
CMO: Christopher Mann, M.D., Medical Director
CHR: Laurie Stanley, Manager Human Resources
CNO: Jan Milligan, Chief Nursing Officer
Web address: www.cookchildrens.org/northeasthospital/Pages/default.aspx
Control: Corporation, Investor–owned, for–profit **Service:** Children's general

> **Staffed Beds:** 3 **Admissions:** 3 **Census:** 1 **Outpatient Visits:** 45855 **Births:**
> 0 **Total Expense ($000):** 26852 **Payroll Expense ($000):** 9974 **Personnel:**
> 163

IRAAN—Pecos County

IRAAN GENERAL HOSPITAL (451307), 600 349 North, Zip 79744, Mailing
Address: P.O. Box 665, Zip 79744–0665; tel. 432/639–2871 **A**10 18 **F**28 40
43 56 57 59 64 65 75 86 93 104 107 119 127 130 133
Primary Contact: Teresa Callahan, R.N., MSN, Chief Executive Officer
CFO: Tami Burks, Chief Fiscal Services
CMO: Robert W. Garcia, M.D., Chief Medical Officer
CHR: Cathy Tucker, Director Human Resources
Web address: www.igh–hospital.com
Control: Hospital district or authority, Government, nonfederal **Service:** General
Medical and Surgical

> **Staffed Beds:** 14 **Admissions:** 86 **Census:** 2 **Outpatient Visits:** 7764 **Births:**
> 0 **Total Expense ($000):** 8953 **Payroll Expense ($000):** 3518 **Personnel:**
> 58

IRVING—Dallas County

✠ **BAYLOR MEDICAL CENTER AT IRVING (450079)**, 1901 North MacArthur
Boulevard, Zip 75061–2220; tel. 972/579–8100 **A**1 2 3 5 10 **F**3 8 11 13 15
17 18 20 22 24 26 28 29 30 31 34 35 40 45 46 47 49 54 55 57 58 59 64
65 66 70 73 74 75 76 77 78 79 80 81 82 84 85 86 87 90 93 94 98 100
107 108 110 111 114 115 116 117 118 119 120 121 122 126 129 130 141
143 146 147 148 **S** Baylor Scott & White Health, Dallas, TX
Primary Contact: Cindy K. Schamp, President
COO: Brenda K. Blain, FACHE, Chief Nursing Officer and Chief Operating Officer
CMO: Jeffrey Embrey, M.D., Vice President Medical Affairs
CIO: Catherine Shisler, Director Information Services
CHR: Donna Stark, Director Human Resources
CNO: Brenda K. Blain, FACHE, Chief Nursing Officer and Chief Operating Officer
Web address: www.baylorhealth.com/PhysiciansLocations/Irving/Pages/Default.
aspx
Control: Other not–for–profit (including NFP Corporation) **Service:** General
Medical and Surgical

> **Staffed Beds:** 220 **Admissions:** 11494 **Census:** 148 **Outpatient Visits:**
> 98769 **Births:** 2299 **Total Expense ($000):** 214636 **Payroll Expense**
> **($000):** 75978 **Personnel:** 841

☐ **BAYLOR SURGICAL HOSPITAL AT LAS COLINAS (450874)**, 400 West
Interstate 635, Zip 75063; tel. 972/868–4000 **A**1 10 **F**3 29 30 40 51 81 85 99
100 101 102 103 107 111 119 130 **S** United Surgical Partners International,
Addison, TX
Primary Contact: Deonna Unell, Chief Executive Officer
CFO: Gabrielle Holland, Chief Financial Officer
CMO: Scott McGraw, M.D., Medical Director
Web address: www.baylorhealth.com/About/Community/Assessments/West/ICSH/
Pages/Default.aspx
Control: Partnership, Investor–owned, for–profit **Service:** General Medical and
Surgical

> **Staffed Beds:** 12 **Admissions:** 732 **Census:** 4 **Outpatient Visits:** 8409
> **Births:** 0 **Total Expense ($000):** 44365 **Payroll Expense ($000):** 8539
> **Personnel:** 143

TX

Many Facility Codes have changed. Please refer to the AHA Guide Code Chart.

⊠ **LAS COLINAS MEDICAL CENTER (450822)**, 6800 North MacArthur Boulevard, Zip 75039–2422; tel. 972/969–2000 **A**1 10 **F**3 8 13 15 18 20 22 24 29 30 31 34 35 37 40 45 46 47 48 49 50 57 59 60 64 68 70 72 74 75 76 77 78 79 81 87 93 100 102 107 108 110 111 114 118 119 126 129 130 147 148 **S** HCA, Nashville, TN
Primary Contact: Daniela Decell, Chief Executive Officer
COO: Chip Zahn, Chief Operating Officer
CFO: Nick Galt, Chief Financial Officer
Web address: www.lascolinasmedical.com
Control: Corporation, Investor–owned, for–profit **Service:** General Medical and Surgical

Staffed Beds: 90 **Admissions:** 4795 **Census:** 48 **Outpatient Visits:** 53431 **Births:** 1399 **Total Expense ($000):** 75395 **Payroll Expense ($000):** 25741 **Personnel:** 407

JACKSBORO—Jack County

FAITH COMMUNITY HOSPITAL (450241), 215 Chisholm Trail, Zip 76458–1111; tel. 940/567–6633 **A**10 20 **F**7 11 28 34 35 40 43 57 59 77 81 93 107 114 119 127 130 133 **P**6
Primary Contact: Frank Beaman, Chief Executive Officer
COO: Kim Lee, Chief Operating Officer
CFO: Bonnie Blevins, R.N., Chief Financial Officer
CMO: Sushil Chokshi, M.D., Chief Medical Officer
CIO: Chris Russell, Chief Information Officer
CHR: Deborah White, Coordinator Human Resource
CNO: Joy Henry, R.N., Director Nurses
Web address: www.fchtexas.org
Control: Hospital district or authority, Government, nonfederal **Service:** General Medical and Surgical

Staffed Beds: 17 **Admissions:** 244 **Census:** 2 **Outpatient Visits:** 25723 **Births:** 45 **Total Expense ($000):** 9928 **Payroll Expense ($000):** 4330 **Personnel:** 111

JACKSONVILLE—Cherokee County

⊠ **CHRISTUS MOTHER FRANCES HOSPITAL – JACKSONVILLE (451319)**, 2026 South Jackson, Zip 75766–5822; tel. 903/541–4500 **A**1 10 18 **F**3 15 18 29 30 32 34 35 40 43 45 50 53 56 57 59 64 65 68 77 79 81 82 85 93 97 107 108 110 111 114 119 129 130 133 145 147 **P**5 6 7 8 **S** CHRISTUS Health, Irving, TX
Primary Contact: Anne Pileggi, Administrator and Associate Vice President
CFO: Elizabeth Pulliam, Chief Financial Officer
CMO: Jane Ragland, President Medical Staff
CIO: Jeff Pearson, Chief Information Officer
CHR: Marsha Ballard, Human Resources
CNO: Jamie Maddox, Chief Nursing Officer
Web address: www.tmfhs.org/jacksonville
Control: Other not–for–profit (including NFP Corporation) **Service:** General Medical and Surgical

Staffed Beds: 21 **Admissions:** 822 **Census:** 6 **Outpatient Visits:** 70449 **Births:** 0 **Total Expense ($000):** 29254 **Payroll Expense ($000):** 7878 **Personnel:** 162

⊠ **EAST TEXAS MEDICAL CENTER JACKSONVILLE (450194)**, 501 South Ragsdale Street, Zip 75766–2413; tel. 903/541–5000 **A**1 10 20 **F**3 8 11 13 15 18 26 29 34 35 39 40 43 45 50 57 59 64 65 70 75 76 79 81 82 85 97 107 108 110 111 115 119 127 129 145 146 147 148 **S** East Texas Medical Center Regional Healthcare System, Tyler, TX
Primary Contact: Jack R. Endres, FACHE, JD, Administrator
CFO: Jack A. Endres, FACHE, Chief Financial Officer
CMO: Todd Parrish, M.D., Chief of Staff
CHR: Elysia Epperson, Director Human Resources
CNO: Jana Bateman, R.N., Chief Nursing Officer
Web address: www.etmc.org
Control: Other not–for–profit (including NFP Corporation) **Service:** General Medical and Surgical

Staffed Beds: 38 **Admissions:** 1766 **Census:** 13 **Outpatient Visits:** 79116 **Births:** 478 **Total Expense ($000):** 32879 **Payroll Expense ($000):** 9655 **Personnel:** 175

JASPER—Jasper County

⊠ **CHRISTUS SOUTHEAST TEXAS JASPER MEMORIAL (450573)**, 1275 Marvin Hancock Drive, Zip 75951–4995; tel. 409/384–5461 **A**1 10 **F**3 11 13 15 29 30 34 40 43 50 51 57 59 64 70 76 77 79 81 82 89 107 111 119 127 130 135 146 **P**8 **S** CHRISTUS Health, Irving, TX
Primary Contact: Lance Beus, Administrator
COO: Mark Durand, Assistant Administrator Operations
CFO: Nikki Martin, Chief Financial Officer
CIO: Robert Jacobs, Regional Information Management Executive
CHR: Kay Powell, Director Human Resources
Web address: www.christusjasper.org
Control: Church–operated, Nongovernment, not–for profit **Service:** General Medical and Surgical

Staffed Beds: 40 **Admissions:** 1496 **Census:** 11 **Outpatient Visits:** 78925 **Births:** 334 **Total Expense ($000):** 25407 **Payroll Expense ($000):** 9808 **Personnel:** 143

JOURDANTON—Atascosa County

⊠ **SOUTH TEXAS REGIONAL MEDICAL CENTER (450165)**, 1905 Highway 97 East, Zip 78026–1504; tel. 830/769–3515 **A**1 10 20 **F**3 11 13 15 18 29 30 34 35 39 40 43 45 57 59 63 64 68 70 75 76 77 79 81 85 93 107 108 110 111 114 119 129 130 132 133 144 146 147 148 **P**6 **S** Community Health Systems, Inc., Franklin, TN
Primary Contact: John E. Ulbricht, Chief Executive Officer
CFO: Gary Redmon, Chief Financial Officer
CIO: Rita S. Castillo, R.N., Chief Quality Officer and Risk Management
Web address: www.strmc.com
Control: Corporation, Investor–owned, for–profit **Service:** General Medical and Surgical

Staffed Beds: 67 **Admissions:** 1610 **Census:** 15 **Outpatient Visits:** 33085 **Births:** 280 **Total Expense ($000):** 31912 **Payroll Expense ($000):** 11943 **Personnel:** 246

JUNCTION—Kimble County

KIMBLE HOSPITAL (451306), 349 Reid Road, Zip 76849–3049; tel. 325/446–3321 **A**10 18 **F**3 34 35 40 43 45 56 57 59 65 66 75 93 97 107 114 127 133 146 **S** Preferred Management Corporation, Shawnee, OK
Primary Contact: Jimmy D. Stuart, Administrator
COO: Teena Hagood, Chief Nursing Officer
CFO: Larry Stephens, Chief Financial Officer
CMO: Ben Udall, M.D., Chief of Staff
CIO: Anna Henry, Chief Information Officer
CHR: Hope Lamb, Manager Human Resources
Web address: www.kimblehospital.org/
Control: Corporation, Investor–owned, for–profit **Service:** General Medical and Surgical

Staffed Beds: 15 **Admissions:** 164 **Census:** 2 **Outpatient Visits:** 13803 **Births:** 0 **Total Expense ($000):** 6784 **Payroll Expense ($000):** 2940 **Personnel:** 70

KATY—Harris County

CHRISTUS ST. CATHERINE HOSPITAL See Houston Methodist St. Catherine Hospital

★ ◇ **HOUSTON METHODIST ST. CATHERINE HOSPITAL (450832)**, 701 Fry Road, Zip 77450–2255; tel. 281/599–5700 **A**10 21 **F**1 29 30 35 36 68 75 82 84 86 87 130 132 **S** Houston Methodist, Houston, TX
Primary Contact: Gary L. Kempf, R.N., Administrator
CFO: Nancy Brock, Chief Financial Officer
CHR: James A. Fitch, Director Human Resources
Web address: www.houstonmethodist.org/katy–st–catherine–hospital
Control: Other not–for–profit (including NFP Corporation) **Service:** Long–Term Acute Care hospital

Staffed Beds: 44 **Admissions:** 361 **Census:** 27 **Outpatient Visits:** 0 **Births:** 0 **Total Expense ($000):** 26782 **Payroll Expense ($000):** 9271 **Personnel:** 179

⊠ **MEMORIAL HERMANN KATY HOSPITAL (450847)**, 23900 Katy Freeway, Zip 77494–1323; tel. 281/644–7000 **A**1 2 3 5 10 **F**3 8 11 13 15 18 22 29 30 34 35 39 40 42 43 45 46 49 50 51 54 57 59 61 64 65 68 69 70 73 74 75 76 77 78 79 81 85 87 89 93 102 107 108 110 111 114 119 126 130 131 132 144 145 146 147 **P**1 5 6 **S** Memorial Hermann Health System, Houston, TX
Primary Contact: James Parisi, Chief Executive Officer
CFO: Linda Kulhanek, Chief Financial Officer
Web address: www.memorialhermann.org/locations/katy/
Control: Other not–for–profit (including NFP Corporation) **Service:** General Medical and Surgical

Staffed Beds: 142 **Admissions:** 9464 **Census:** 94 **Outpatient Visits:** 93110 **Births:** 2310 **Total Expense ($000):** 161032 **Payroll Expense ($000):** 56491 **Personnel:** 775

TX

Hospital, Medicare Provider Number, Address, Telephone, Approval, Facility, and Physician Codes, Health Care System

★ American Hospital Association (AHA) membership ○ Healthcare Facilities Accreditation Program ⇑ Center for Improvement in Healthcare Quality Accreditation
□ The Joint Commission accreditation ◇ DNV Healthcare Inc. accreditation △ Commission on Accreditation of Rehabilitation Facilities (CARF) accreditation

✠ **MEMORIAL HERMANN REHABILITATION HOSPITAL – KATY (673038)**,
21720 Kingsland Boulevard #102, Zip 77450–2550 **A**1 2 10 **F**3 29 30 64 79
90 92 93 107 111 114 119 129 130 131 148 **P**5 6 **S** Memorial Hermann
Health System, Houston, TX
Primary Contact: Carl E. Josehart, Chief Executive Officer
COO: Mary Ann Euliarte, R.N., Chief Operating Officer
CFO: Wayne Gordon, Chief Financial Officer
CMO: Shalin Patel, M.D., Chief Medical Officer
CIO: David Bradshaw, Chief Information Officer
CHR: Joyce Williams, Consultant Human Resources and Organizational
Development
CNO: Mary Ann Euliarte, R.N., Chief Nursing Officer
Web address: www.oceanskaty.com/
Control: Partnership, Investor–owned, for–profit **Service:** Rehabilitation

Staffed Beds: 35 Admissions: 565 Census: 23 Outpatient Visits: 12817
Births: 0 Total Expense ($000): 18797 Payroll Expense ($000): 7768
Personnel: 104

OCEANS BEHAVIORAL HOSPITAL KATY, 455 Park Grove Lane,
Zip 77450–1572; tel. 281/492–8888, (Data for 287 days) **F**29 35 64 98 100
101 103 104 **S** Oceans Healthcare, Lake Charles, LA
Primary Contact: Stuart Archer, Chief Executive Officer
Web address: www.oceanskaty.com/
Control: Corporation, Investor–owned, for–profit **Service:** Psychiatric

Staffed Beds: 48 Admissions: 345 Census: 15 Outpatient Visits: 3668
Births: 0 Total Expense ($000): 4612 Payroll Expense ($000): 2109
Personnel: 73

KAUFMAN—Kaufman County

✠ **TEXAS HEALTH PRESBYTERIAN HOSPITAL KAUFMAN (450292)**, 850 Ed
Hall Drive, Zip 75142–1861, Mailing Address: P.O. Box 1108, Zip 75142–5401;
tel. 972/932–7200 **A**1 10 **F**3 11 13 15 18 29 30 34 35 40 43 45 53 57 59
64 65 68 70 75 76 79 81 82 85 86 87 93 100 102 107 108 111 115 118
119 130 132 135 146 147 148 **P**5 **S** Texas Health Resources, Arlington, TX
Primary Contact: Patsy Youngs, President
CMO: Benjamin Bradshaw, M.D., President Medical Staff
CHR: Mark J. Rainey, Director Human Resources
CNO: Denise Claussen, R.N., Chief Nursing Officer
Web address: www.texashealth.org/Kaufman
Control: Other not–for–profit (including NFP Corporation) **Service:** General
Medical and Surgical

Staffed Beds: 68 Admissions: 2083 Census: 18 Outpatient Visits: 37644
Births: 252 Total Expense ($000): 35420 Payroll Expense ($000): 14767
Personnel: 186

KENEDY—Karnes County

★ **OTTO KAISER MEMORIAL HOSPITAL (451364)**, 3349 South Highway 181,
Zip 78119–5247; tel. 830/583–3401 **A**10 18 **F**3 11 15 29 30 34 40 45 46 53
57 59 62 64 68 77 81 93 107 111 114 119 133 135 148 **P**8
Primary Contact: David Lee, Chief Executive Officer
CIO: Joseph Wiatrek, Director Information Technology
CHR: Christina Benavides, Director Employee Services
CNO: Vincent Sowell, Chief Nursing Officer
Web address: www.okmh.org/
Control: Hospital district or authority, Government, nonfederal **Service:** General
Medical and Surgical

Staffed Beds: 25 Admissions: 296 Census: 4 Outpatient Visits: 25203
Births: 0 Total Expense ($000): 17780 Payroll Expense ($000): 7500
Personnel: 132

KERMIT—Winkler County

WINKLER COUNTY MEMORIAL HOSPITAL (451314), 821 Jeffee Drive,
Zip 79745–4696, Mailing Address: P.O. Box H., Zip 79745–6008;
tel. 432/586–5864 **A**10 18 **F**3 32 34 36 40 57 59 64 65 69 93 97 107 114
119 127 133
Primary Contact: Lorenzo Serrano, Chief Executive Officer
CFO: Wannah Hartley, Controller
CMO: K. Pham, M.D., Chief of Staff
CIO: Keith Palmer, Assistant Administrator
Control: County–Government, nonfederal **Service:** General Medical and Surgical

Staffed Beds: 19 Admissions: 198 Census: 2 Outpatient Visits: 6728
Births: 0 Total Expense ($000): 7738 Payroll Expense ($000): 3318
Personnel: 73

KERRVILLE—Kerr County

KERRVILLE DIVISION See South Texas Veterans Health Care System, San
Antonio

☐ **KERRVILLE STATE HOSPITAL (454014)**, 721 Thompson Drive,
Zip 78028–5154; tel. 830/896–2211 **A**1 3 5 10 **F**11 30 34 39 44 50 56 65
68 75 86 87 97 98 101 103 130 132 135 146 **S** Texas Department of State
Health Services, Austin, TX
Primary Contact: Leigh Ann Fitzpatrick, Superintendent
CFO: Laurie Harris, Chief Accountant
CMO: Matthew Faubion, M.D., Clinical Director
CNO: Amanda McDonald, MSN, Chief Nurse Executive
Web address: www.dshs.state.tx.us/mhhospitals/KerrvilleSH/default.shtm
Control: State–Government, nonfederal **Service:** Psychiatric

Staffed Beds: 202 Admissions: 64 Census: 203 Outpatient Visits: 0 Births:
0 Total Expense ($000): 36135 Payroll Expense ($000): 22486
Personnel: 549

✠ **PETERSON REGIONAL MEDICAL CENTER (450007)**, 551 Hill Country Drive,
Zip 78028–6085; tel. 830/896–4200 **A**1 10 **F**3 8 11 13 15 18 22 26 29
30 31 34 35 39 40 44 45 49 54 57 59 62 63 64 65 68 70 74 75 76 77 78
79 80 81 82 84 85 86 87 90 93 96 97 100 107 110 111 114 115 118 119
126 130 131 132 135 145 146 147 148 **P**1 6
Primary Contact: J. Patrick Murray, FACHE, President and Chief Executive Officer
COO: J. Stephen Pautler, FACHE, Chief Operating Officer
CFO: Lisa Medovich, Chief Financial Officer
CMO: Thomas Ducker, M.D., Chief of Staff
CIO: Richard Cruthirds, Director Information Systems
CHR: Buddy Volpe, Director Human Resources
CNO: Kaeli Dressler, R.N., Chief Nursing Officer
Web address: www.petersonrmc.com
Control: Other not–for–profit (including NFP Corporation) **Service:** General
Medical and Surgical

Staffed Beds: 124 Admissions: 4798 Census: 65 Outpatient Visits: 146111
Births: 482 Total Expense ($000): 109826 Payroll Expense ($000): 44215
Personnel: 826

KILGORE—Gregg County

★ ◇ **ALLEGIANCE SPECIALTY HOSPITAL OF KILGORE (450488)**, 1612
South Henderson Boulevard, Zip 75662–3594; tel. 903/984–3505 **A**10 21 **F**3
29 34 35 56 59 98 101 103 104 130 **S** Allegiance Health Management,
Shreveport, LA
Primary Contact: Karen Ross, Chief Executive Officer
CHR: Michelle Yarbrough, Coordinator Human Resources
CNO: Jackie McDonald, Chief Nursing Officer
Web address: www.ahmgt.com
Control: Corporation, Investor–owned, for–profit **Service:** Psychiatric

Staffed Beds: 60 Admissions: 324 Census: 12 Outpatient Visits: 14134
Births: 0 Total Expense ($000): 6999 Payroll Expense ($000): 3692
Personnel: 94

KILLEEN—Bell County

✠ **METROPLEX ADVENTIST HOSPITAL (450152)**, 2201 South Clear Creek Road,
Zip 76549–4110; tel. 254/526–7523 **A**1 3 10 **F**3 8 11 12 13 15 18 20 22 26
28 29 30 34 35 39 40 43 45 46 48 49 54 57 59 62 65 68 70 71 74 75 76
77 78 79 81 82 83 85 86 87 89 91 93 98 99 100 101 102 103 104 105 107
108 110 111 114 115 118 119 129 130 131 132 135 146 147 148 **P**8
S Adventist Health System Sunbelt Health Care Corporation, Altamonte
Springs, FL
Primary Contact: Carlyle L. E. Walton, FACHE, Chief Executive Officer
CFO: Penny Johnson, Chief Financial Officer
CMO: Frederick Barnett, M.D., Chief of Staff
CIO: Dale Koebnick, Director Management Information Systems and Patient
Access
CHR: Brenda Coley, Executive Director
Web address: www.mplex.org
Control: Church–operated, Nongovernment, not–for profit **Service:** General
Medical and Surgical

Staffed Beds: 177 Admissions: 6081 Census: 63 Outpatient Visits: 95763
Births: 1300 Total Expense ($000): 106569 Payroll Expense ($000):
41326 Personnel: 752

KINGSVILLE—Kleberg County

✠ **CHRISTUS SPOHN HOSPITAL KLEBERG (450163)**, 1311 General Cavazos
Boulevard, Zip 78363–7130; tel. 361/595–1661 **A**1 10 20 **F**3 11 13 15 28 29
30 34 35 40 43 53 54 57 59 64 65 70 75 76 77 79 81 85 86 87 89 93 102
108 110 111 119 130 146 **P**8 **S** CHRISTUS Health, Irving, TX
Primary Contact: David LeMonte, Vice President and Chief Operating Officer
CFO: Jessica Pena, Manager Finance
CHR: Mindy Soliz, Director Human Resource Strategy
Web address: www.christusspohn.org
Control: Church–operated, Nongovernment, not–for profit **Service:** General
Medical and Surgical

Staffed Beds: 50 Admissions: 3000 Census: 35 Outpatient Visits: 37013
Births: 310 Total Expense ($000): 37291 Payroll Expense ($000): 14339
Personnel: 203

Many Facility Codes have changed. Please refer to the AHA Guide Code Chart. © 2016 AHA Guide

TX

KINGWOOD—Montgomery County

⊠ **KINGWOOD MEDICAL CENTER (450775)**, 22999 U.S. Highway 59 North, Zip 77339; tel. 281/348–8000 **A**1 10 **F**3 13 15 18 19 20 22 24 26 28 29 31 34 35 40 41 42 45 46 47 49 57 58 59 70 72 74 76 78 79 81 85 86 87 89 90 96 107 108 109 110 111 112 114 115 119 126 129 130 132 146 147 **S** HCA, Nashville, TN
Primary Contact: Melinda Stephenson, Chief Executive Officer
COO: Megan Marietta, Chief Operating Officer
CFO: Daniel E. Davis, Chief Financial Officer
CMO: Eugene Ogrod, M.D., Chief Medical Officer
CNO: Kevin Manning, RN, Chief Nursing Officer
Web address: www.kingwoodmedical.com
Control: Corporation, Investor–owned, for–profit **Service:** General Medical and Surgical

Staffed Beds: 357 **Admissions:** 16962 **Census:** 245 **Outpatient Visits:** 108364 **Births:** 2758 **Total Expense ($000):** 204968 **Payroll Expense ($000):** 78572 **Personnel:** 904

☐ **KINGWOOD PINES HOSPITAL (454103)**, 2001 Ladbrook Drive, Zip 77339–3004; tel. 281/404–1001 **A**1 10 **F**4 5 75 86 87 98 99 101 102 103 104 105 130 132 **S** Universal Health Services, Inc., King of Prussia, PA
Primary Contact: James Burroughs, Chief Executive Officer
COO: Grey Mc Kellar, Chief Operating Officer and Director of Performance Improvement and Risk
CFO: Sharon Corum, Chief Financial Officer
CMO: Javier Ruiz, M.D., Medical Director
CNO: Kevin Manning, RN, Chief Nursing Officer
Web address: www.kingwoodpines.com
Control: Corporation, Investor–owned, for–profit **Service:** Psychiatric

Staffed Beds: 82 **Admissions:** 3895 **Census:** 92 **Outpatient Visits:** 3583 **Births:** 0 **Total Expense ($000):** 21694 **Payroll Expense ($000):** 10852 **Personnel:** 191

KINGWOOD SPECIALTY HOSPITAL See Memorial Hermann Surgical Hospital Kingwood

☐ **MEMORIAL HERMANN SURGICAL HOSPITAL KINGWOOD (670005)**, 300 Kingwood Medical Drive, Zip 77339–6400; tel. 281/312–4000 **A**1 10 **F**3 29 40 45 64 79 81 82 85 86 87 111
Primary Contact: Teal A. Holden, Chief Executive Officer
CFO: Jay Michael Gomez, Chief Financial Officer
CNO: Shawna Fugler, R.N., Chief Nursing Officer
Web address: www.memorialhermannkingwood.com
Control: Partnership, Investor–owned, for–profit **Service:** Surgical

Staffed Beds: 10 **Admissions:** 221 **Census:** 1 **Outpatient Visits:** 7513 **Births:** 0 **Total Expense ($000):** 21682 **Payroll Expense ($000):** 4889 **Personnel:** 86

KNOX CITY—Knox County

KNOX COUNTY HOSPITAL (450746), 701 South Fifth Street, Zip 79529–2107, Mailing Address: P.O. Box 608, Zip 79529–0608; tel. 940/657–3535 **A**10 20 **F**7 11 28 33 34 35 40 43 57 59 62 127 130 133 **P**6
Primary Contact: Stephen A. Kuehler, Administrator
CFO: Dan Offutt, Manager Finance
CMO: Kevin Finley, D.O., Chief of Staff
CIO: Tamelia Carter, Office Manager
CNO: Sheila Kuehler, R.N., Director of Nursing
Web address: www.knoxcountyhospital–texas.com
Control: Hospital district or authority, Government, nonfederal **Service:** General Medical and Surgical

Staffed Beds: 14 **Admissions:** 113 **Census:** 1 **Outpatient Visits:** 21923 **Births:** 0 **Total Expense ($000):** 6296 **Payroll Expense ($000):** 2574 **Personnel:** 65

KYLE—Hays County

⊠ **SETON MEDICAL CENTER HAYS (670056)**, 6001 Kyle Parkway, Zip 78640–6112, Mailing Address: 6001 Kyle Prkway, Zip 78640–6112; tel. 512/504–5000 **A**1 3 5 10 **F**3 11 13 15 18 20 22 24 28 29 30 31 34 35 40 43 44 45 46 49 50 57 60 65 68 70 72 74 75 76 77 78 79 81 82 85 87 107 108 110 111 114 115 118 119 129 130 131 135 146 148 **P**3 8 **S** Ascension Health, Saint Louis, MO
Primary Contact: Christopher L. Hartle, President
COO: Neal Kelley, Vice President and Chief Operating Officer
Web address: www.seton.net/locations/seton_medical_center_hays/
Control: Church–operated, Nongovernment, not–for profit **Service:** General Medical and Surgical

Staffed Beds: 112 **Admissions:** 6640 **Census:** 78 **Outpatient Visits:** 53109 **Births:** 931 **Total Expense ($000):** 116518 **Payroll Expense ($000):** 37215 **Personnel:** 637

LA GRANGE—Fayette County

★ **ST. MARK'S MEDICAL CENTER (670004)**, One St. Mark's Place, Zip 78945; tel. 979/242–2200 **A**3 5 10 **F**3 8 11 12 13 15 29 30 34 40 43 45 50 56 57 59 68 70 74 75 79 81 82 84 85 87 93 107 110 111 114 119 129 130 133 145 146 147 **P**6 **S** Community Hospital Corporation, Plano, TX
Primary Contact: Rick J. Montelongo, Chief Executive Officer
COO: Carol Drozd, Chief Operating Officer
CFO: Dennis Boyd, Chief Financial Officer
CMO: Russell Juno, M.D., Chief of Staff
CHR: Tammy Oehlke, Director Human Resources
Web address: www.smmctx.org
Control: Other not–for–profit (including NFP Corporation) **Service:** General Medical and Surgical

Staffed Beds: 65 **Admissions:** 1722 **Census:** 18 **Outpatient Visits:** 48670 **Births:** 293 **Total Expense ($000):** 29212 **Payroll Expense ($000):** 11974 **Personnel:** 185

LAKE JACKSON—Brazoria County

⊠ **CHI ST. LUKE'S HEALTH BRAZOSPORT (450072)**, 100 Medical Drive, Zip 77566–5674; tel. 979/297–4411 **A**1 10 **F**3 11 13 15 18 20 22 28 29 30 31 34 37 40 41 43 45 47 48 49 50 51 54 57 59 60 62 64 65 68 70 74 75 76 78 79 81 82 85 86 87 89 90 91 93 94 107 108 110 111 114 117 118 119 120 121 123 129 130 131 132 146 147 148 **P**8 **S** Catholic Health Initiatives, Englewood, CO
Primary Contact: Al Guevara, Jr., FACHE, President
CFO: Chuck Jeffress, Vice President Fiscal Services
CMO: Michael Gilliand, M.D., Chief of Staff
CIO: Todd Edwards, Director Information Management Systems
CHR: Christopher Calia, Vice President Human Resources
CNO: Shannon Haltom, Vice President, Patient Care Services
Web address: www.chistlukesbrazosport.org
Control: Other not–for–profit (including NFP Corporation) **Service:** General Medical and Surgical

Staffed Beds: 103 **Admissions:** 4478 **Census:** 47 **Outpatient Visits:** 136066 **Births:** 528 **Total Expense ($000):** 86629 **Payroll Expense ($000):** 32078 **Personnel:** 599

LAKEWAY—Travis County

⊠ **LAKEWAY REGIONAL MEDICAL CENTER (670079)**, 100 Medical Parkway, Zip 78738–5621; tel. 512/571–5000 **A**1 10 **F**3 13 15 17 18 20 22 29 30 34 38 40 45 46 49 50 54 57 59 60 64 69 70 72 74 75 76 78 79 81 82 85 86 87 91 92 93 107 108 110 111 115 116 117 118 119 130 135 146 147 148 **P**6
Primary Contact: Philippe Bochaton, Chief Executive Officer
COO: Lisa Hoffpauir, Chief Administrative Officer
CIO: Anthony Martinez, Director Information Technology
CHR: Amy D. Reeves, Director Human Resources
CNO: Denise Krajewski, Chief Nursing Officer
Web address: www.lakewayregional.com
Control: Corporation, Investor–owned, for–profit **Service:** General Medical and Surgical

Staffed Beds: 68 **Admissions:** 2550 **Census:** 25 **Outpatient Visits:** 25013 **Births:** 285 **Total Expense ($000):** 21407 **Payroll Expense ($000):** 20357 **Personnel:** 358

⊠ △ **VIBRA REHABILITATION HOSPITAL LAKE TRAVIS (673058)**, 2000 Medical Drive, Zip 78734–4200; tel. 512/263–4500 **A**1 7 **F**3 29 60 68 90 91 96 119 148 **S** Vibra Healthcare, Mechanicsburg, PA
Primary Contact: Deborah Hopps, Chief Executive Officer
CMO: Maria Elena Arizmendez, M.D., Medical Director
CHR: Debbie Belcher, Director Human Resource
CNO: Paul Bruce, Chief Nursing Officer
Web address: www.vrhlaketravis.com
Control: Corporation, Investor–owned, for–profit **Service:** Rehabilitation

Staffed Beds: 36 **Admissions:** 428 **Census:** 13 **Outpatient Visits:** 0 **Births:** 0 **Total Expense ($000):** 10283 **Payroll Expense ($000):** 3981 **Personnel:** 68

TX

Hospital, Medicare Provider Number, Address, Telephone, Approval, Facility, and Physician Codes, Health Care System

★ American Hospital Association (AHA) membership
☐ The Joint Commission accreditation
○ Healthcare Facilities Accreditation Program
◇ DNV Healthcare Inc. accreditation
⇑ Center for Improvement in Healthcare Quality Accreditation
△ Commission on Accreditation of Rehabilitation Facilities (CARF) accreditation

LAMESA—Dawson County

MEDICAL ARTS HOSPITAL (450489), 2200 North Bryan Avenue, Zip 79331–2451; tel. 806/872–2183 **A**10 20 **F**3 7 11 13 29 30 35 40 43 45 50 57 59 62 63 64 75 76 81 87 97 107 111 115 119 127 128 130 133 146 148 **P**6
Primary Contact: Letha Stokes, Chief Executive Officer
COO: Jo Beth Smith, Chief Operating Officer
CFO: Jeff Weaver, Chief Financial Officer
CMO: Michael Sprys, D.O., Chief of Staff
CHR: Traci Brown, Human Resources Generalist
CNO: Heidi Cobb, R.N., Chief Nursing Officer
Web address: www.medicalartshospital.org
Control: Hospital district or authority, Government, nonfederal **Service:** General Medical and Surgical

Staffed Beds: 22 **Admissions:** 357 **Census:** 3 **Outpatient Visits:** 79842 **Births:** 99 **Total Expense ($000):** 23438 **Payroll Expense ($000):** 8776 **Personnel:** 212

LAMPASAS—Lampasas County

⊠ **ROLLINS–BROOK COMMUNITY HOSPITAL (451323)**, 608 North Key Avenue, Zip 76550–1106, Mailing Address: P.O. Box 589, Zip 76550–0032; tel. 512/556–3682 **A**1 10 18 **F**3 8 15 29 35 40 43 45 46 61 81 85 87 93 97 107 110 111 114 119 130 131 133 146 **P**4 8 **S** Adventist Health System Sunbelt Health Care Corporation, Altamonte Springs, FL
Primary Contact: Carlyle L. E. Walton, FACHE, Chief Executive Officer
CFO: Robert Brock, Chief Financial Officer and Vice President
CMO: Don Daniels, M.D., Chief Medical Officer
CIO: Carl Elkins, Director Information Technology
CHR: Brenda Coley, Executive Director
CNO: Tammy Rodriguez, Vice President of Patient Care Services
Web address: www.mplex.org
Control: Church–operated, Nongovernment, not–for profit **Service:** General Medical and Surgical

Staffed Beds: 35 **Admissions:** 663 **Census:** 10 **Outpatient Visits:** 16274 **Births:** 0 **Total Expense ($000):** 14756 **Payroll Expense ($000):** 4503 **Personnel:** 85

LANCASTER—Dallas County

◇ **CRESCENT MEDICAL CENTER LANCASTER (670090)**, 2600 West Pleasant Run Road, Zip 75146–1114; tel. 972/230–8888 **A**10 21 **F**3 18 40 41 46 51 59 70 79 81 85 87 107 114 119 124 130 135 143 148
Primary Contact: Khalid Mahmood, M.D., President and Chairman
Web address: www.cmcl.us/
Control: Individual, Investor–owned, for–profit **Service:** General Medical and Surgical

Staffed Beds: 84 **Admissions:** 347 **Census:** 4 **Outpatient Visits:** 13859 **Births:** 0 **Total Expense ($000):** 15331 **Payroll Expense ($000):** 6846 **Personnel:** 115

LAREDO—Webb County

☐ **DOCTORS HOSPITAL OF LAREDO (450643)**, 10700 McPherson Road, Zip 78045–6268; tel. 956/523–2000 **A**1 2 10 **F**3 11 12 13 15 18 20 22 24 26 28 29 30 31 32 34 35 37 39 40 43 45 48 49 50 54 57 59 60 63 64 70 71 72 74 75 76 77 78 79 81 85 87 89 90 91 93 107 108 111 114 119 121 129 130 132 146 147 148 **P**5 7 **S** Universal Health Services, Inc., King of Prussia, PA
Primary Contact: James R. Resendez, Chief Executive Officer
COO: Raymond Ramos, FACHE, Chief Operating Officer
CFO: Faraz Khan, Chief Financial Officer
CMO: Santiago Gutierrez, M.D., Chief Medical Officer
CIO: Maribel Mata, Director Information Services
CHR: Roseann Figueroa, Director Human Resources
CNO: Daman Mott, MSN, Chief Nursing Officer
Web address: www.doctorshoslaredo.com
Control: Partnership, Investor–owned, for–profit **Service:** General Medical and Surgical

Staffed Beds: 183 **Admissions:** 8360 **Census:** 120 **Outpatient Visits:** 118722 **Births:** 2574 **Total Expense ($000):** 105391 **Payroll Expense ($000):** 42365 **Personnel:** 694

⊠ **LAREDO MEDICAL CENTER (450029)**, 1700 East Saunders Avenue, Zip 78041–5474, Mailing Address: P.O. Box 2068, Zip 78044–2068; tel. 956/796–5000, (Total facility includes 18 beds in nursing home–type unit) **A**1 10 13 **F**3 8 11 12 13 15 18 20 22 24 26 28 29 30 31 32 34 35 36 37 40 43 45 46 49 50 51 53 54 56 57 59 60 64 68 70 72 74 75 76 77 78 79 81 85 86 87 89 92 107 108 110 111 114 119 120 121 123 128 132 135 146 147 148 **S** Community Health Systems, Inc., Franklin, TN
Primary Contact: Enrique Gallegos, Chief Executive Officer
CIO: Joe Rivera, Chief Information Technology Officer
Web address: www.laredomedical.com
Control: Corporation, Investor–owned, for–profit **Service:** General Medical and Surgical

Staffed Beds: 326 **Admissions:** 14154 **Census:** 208 **Outpatient Visits:** 139331 **Births:** 3393 **Total Expense ($000):** 268610 **Payroll Expense ($000):** 55019 **Personnel:** 1086

LAREDO REHABILITATION HOSPITAL, 2005a East Bustamante Street, Zip 78041; tel. 956/764–8555, (Data for 353 days) **F**29 90 **S** Ernest Health, Inc., Albuquerque, NM
Primary Contact: Larisa Higgins, Administrator and Chief Operating Officer
Web address: www.lrh.ernesthealth.com
Control: Partnership, Investor–owned, for–profit **Service:** Rehabilitation

Staffed Beds: 20 **Admissions:** 284 **Census:** 12 **Outpatient Visits:** 0 **Births:** 0 **Total Expense ($000):** 5254 **Payroll Expense ($000):** 2685 **Personnel:** 52

☐ **LAREDO SPECIALTY HOSPITAL (452096)**, 2005 Bustamente Street, Zip 78041–5470; tel. 956/753–5353 **A**1 10 **F**1 3 29 30 75 85 91 96 130 148 **S** Ernest Health, Inc., Albuquerque, NM
Primary Contact: Mario Rodriguez, Chief Executive Officer
CFO: Robert Voss, Chief Financial Officer
CMO: Marisa Guerrero, Director Human Resources
Web address: www.lsh.ernesthealth.com
Control: Partnership, Investor–owned, for–profit **Service:** Long–Term Acute Care hospital

Staffed Beds: 40 **Admissions:** 472 **Census:** 34 **Outpatient Visits:** 0 **Births:** 0 **Total Expense ($000):** 19673 **Payroll Expense ($000):** 6906 **Personnel:** 136

LEAGUE CITY—Galveston County

☐ **DEVEREUX TEXAS TREATMENT NETWORK (454085)**, 1150 Devereux Drive, Zip 77573–2043; tel. 281/335–1000 **A**1 10 **F**4 29 32 35 38 53 54 59 64 75 86 87 98 99 101 104 106 130 132 134 **S** Devereux, Villanova, PA
Primary Contact: Pamela E. Helm, Executive Director
Web address: www.devereux.org
Control: Other not–for–profit (including NFP Corporation) **Service:** Children's hospital psychiatric

Staffed Beds: 36 **Admissions:** 29 **Census:** 43 **Outpatient Visits:** 179 **Births:** 0 **Total Expense ($000):** 7853 **Payroll Expense ($000):** 2793 **Personnel:** 58

LEVELLAND—Hockley County

★ **COVENANT HOSPITAL–LEVELLAND (450755)**, 1900 South College Avenue, Zip 79336–6508; tel. 806/894–4963 **A**10 **F**11 13 15 29 30 34 40 43 45 50 57 59 64 65 68 75 76 77 81 85 87 97 107 110 111 114 115 119 127 133 **P**6 **S** Providence St. Joseph Health, Renton, WA
Primary Contact: Bruce White, Administrator
CFO: Newman Wheeler, Chief Financial Officer and Chief Operating Officer
CMO: Harry Weaver, M.D., Chief of Staff
CIO: Kevin Elmore, Chief Information Officer
CHR: Tammy Franklin, Manager Personnel and Marketing
CNO: Connie Thomman, Director of Nursing
Web address: www.covenanthospitallevelland.com/
Control: Church–operated, Nongovernment, not–for profit **Service:** General Medical and Surgical

Staffed Beds: 26 **Admissions:** 848 **Census:** 7 **Outpatient Visits:** 34209 **Births:** 214 **Total Expense ($000):** 18826 **Payroll Expense ($000):** 7908 **Personnel:** 188

LEWISVILLE—Denton County

⊠ **MEDICAL CENTER OF LEWISVILLE (450669)**, 500 West Main, Zip 75057–3699; tel. 972/420–1000 **A**1 10 **F**3 13 15 18 20 22 24 26 28 29 30 31 34 35 40 42 43 46 49 50 56 57 59 68 70 72 74 75 76 78 79 81 85 87 89 90 93 96 107 108 110 111 114 118 119 129 130 131 132 135 146 147 148 **S** HCA, Nashville, TN
Primary Contact: LaSharndra Barbarin, Chief Executive Officer
CFO: Lisa Brodbeck, Chief Financial Officer
CIO: Shirley Archambeault, Chief Information Officer
CHR: Dara Biegert, Vice President Human Resources
CNO: Lynn O'Neill, R.N., Chief Nursing Officer
Web address: www.lewisvillemedical.com
Control: Corporation, Investor–owned, for–profit **Service:** General Medical and Surgical

Staffed Beds: 166 **Admissions:** 6804 **Census:** 89 **Outpatient Visits:** 80284 **Births:** 1487 **Total Expense ($000):** 134294 **Payroll Expense ($000):** 52417 **Personnel:** 626

LIBERTY—Liberty County

☐ **LIBERTY DAYTON REGIONAL MEDICAL CENTER (451375)**, 1353 North Travis, Zip 77575–3549; tel. 936/336–7316 **A**1 10 18 **F**3 29 40 45 64 89 107 114 119 127 130 133
Primary Contact: Matt Thornton, Chief Executive Officer
CFO: Hal Mayo, Chief Financial Officer
CMO: Don Callens, M.D., Chief Medical Officer
CNO: Cindy Griffin, Chief Nursing Officer
Web address: www.libertydaytonrmc.com
Control: Hospital district or authority, Government, nonfederal **Service:** General Medical and Surgical

Staffed Beds: 14 **Admissions:** 182 **Census:** 2 **Outpatient Visits:** 22393 **Births:** 0 **Total Expense ($000):** 8908 **Payroll Expense ($000):** 3960 **Personnel:** 84

Many Facility Codes have changed. Please refer to the AHA Guide Code Chart.
© 2016 AHA Guide

TX

LITTLEFIELD—Lamb County

★ **LAMB HEALTHCARE CENTER (450698)**, 1500 South Sunset,
Zip 79339–4899; tel. 806/385–6411 **A**10 20 **F**13 35 40 43 45 57 59 64 66
75 76 81 86 87 89 107 114 119 127 132 133 134 147 **P**6
Primary Contact: Cindy Klein, Chief Executive Officer
CMO: Isabel Molina, M.D., Chief Medical Officer
CHR: Joan Williams, Administrative Assistant/Human Resources
CNO: Stacie Styron, Chief Nursing Officer
Control: County–Government, nonfederal **Service:** General Medical and Surgical

Staffed Beds: 41 **Admissions:** 393 **Census:** 6 **Outpatient Visits:** 33931
Births: 84 **Total Expense ($000):** 11121 **Payroll Expense ($000):** 4400
Personnel: 126

LIVINGSTON—Polk County

⊠ **CHI ST. LUKE'S HEALTH MEMORIAL LIVINGSTON (450395)**, 1717 Highway
59 Bypass, Zip 77351–1257, Mailing Address: P.O. Box 1257, Zip 77351–0022;
tel. 936/329–8700 **A**1 10 **F**3 11 13 15 29 34 35 40 45 46 50 57 59 62 64
68 70 74 75 76 79 81 85 87 89 107 108 110 111 114 119 129 130 132
146 **S** Catholic Health Initiatives, Englewood, CO
Primary Contact: Randy Slack, Chief Executive Officer
CFO: Ken Miller, Chief Financial Officer
CMO: Shane Shaw, M.D., Chief of Staff
CIO: Mark Clifton, Interim Chief Financial Officer
CNO: Jacqueline Gordon, R.N., Chief Nursing Officer
Web address: www.memorialhealth.org
Control: Other not–for–profit (including NFP Corporation) **Service:** General
Medical and Surgical

Staffed Beds: 66 **Admissions:** 2096 **Census:** 19 **Outpatient Visits:** 58391
Births: 423 **Total Expense ($000):** 42259 **Payroll Expense ($000):** 17838
Personnel: 241

LLANO—Llano County

★ **SCOTT & WHITE HOSPITAL – LLANO (450219)**, 200 West Ollie Street,
Zip 78643–2628; tel. 325/247–5040 **A**10 20 **F**3 7 13 15 18 29 31 34 40 43
45 50 65 76 77 79 81 85 93 97 107 108 114 119 127 129 146 147 **S** Baylor
Scott & White Health, Dallas, TX
Primary Contact: Eric N. Looper, Chief Executive Officer, Hill County Region
COO: Linda Meredith, MSN, Chief Operating Officer
CFO: Jason Cole, Director Finance
CMO: Kim Russell, M.D., Chief of Staff
CIO: Rodney Lott, Director Management Information Systems and Facility
Operations
CHR: Pearl Oestreich, Director Human Resources
CNO: Reta Hunt, Director of Nursing
Web address: www.sw.org/location/llano–hospital
Control: Other not–for–profit (including NFP Corporation) **Service:** General
Medical and Surgical

Staffed Beds: 13 **Admissions:** 751 **Census:** 5 **Outpatient Visits:** 15929
Births: 222 **Total Expense ($000):** 55020 **Payroll Expense ($000):** 28129
Personnel: 240

LOCKNEY—Floyd County

★ **W. J. MANGOLD MEMORIAL HOSPITAL (451337)**, 320 North Main Street,
Zip 79241–0037, Mailing Address: Box 37, Zip 79241–0037;
tel. 806/652–3373 **A**10 18 **F**1 3 4 13 16 17 35 40 43 45 53 57 59 62 64 65
67 70 72 73 76 80 81 85 88 90 93 97 98 107 111 119 127 128 130 133
148 **P**4
Primary Contact: Larry Mullins, Chief Executive Officer and Administrator
CFO: Alyssa McCarter, Chief Financial Officer
CMO: Kevin T. Stennett, M.D., Chief of Staff
CIO: Sam Vanderbeek, Chief Information Officer
CNO: Billie Hendrix, R.N., Director of Nursing
Web address: www.mangoldmemorial.org
Control: Hospital district or authority, Government, nonfederal **Service:** General
Medical and Surgical

Staffed Beds: 25 **Admissions:** 451 **Census:** 5 **Outpatient Visits:** 27184
Births: 40 **Total Expense ($000):** 10778 **Payroll Expense ($000):** 4521
Personnel: 106

LONGVIEW—Gregg County

☐ **BEHAVIORAL HOSPITAL OF LONGVIEW (454105)**, 22 Bermuda Lane,
Zip 75605–2902; tel. 903/291–3456 **A**1 10 **F**98 100 105 130
Primary Contact: Andre Deshong, Administrator
Web address: www.longviewhospital.com
Control: Corporation, Investor–owned, for–profit **Service:** Psychiatric

Staffed Beds: 76 **Admissions:** 1225 **Census:** 47 **Outpatient Visits:** 0 **Births:**
0 **Total Expense ($000):** 10149 **Payroll Expense ($000):** 5339 **Personnel:**
132

⊠ △ **GOOD SHEPHERD MEDICAL CENTER (450037)**, 700 East Marshall
Avenue, Zip 75601–5580; tel. 903/315–2000 **A**1 3 7 10 **F**3 11 12 13 15 18
20 22 24 26 28 29 30 31 32 34 35 37 40 42 43 45 46 49 50 51 53 54 56
57 59 61 63 64 68 70 71 72 73 74 75 76 77 78 79 80 81 82 84 85 86 87
89 90 92 93 97 102 107 108 110 111 114 115 118 119 126 129 130 131
132 135 143 144 146 147 148 **S** Good Shepherd Health System, Longview, TX
Primary Contact: Steve Altmiller, President and Chief Executive Officer
CFO: Tim Pileggi, Interim Chief Financial Officer
CMO: Larry Verfurth, D.O., Chief Medical Officer and Senior Vice President
CIO: Chris Blakemore, Interim Chief Information Officer
CHR: Ginger Morrow, Executive Vice President Human Resources
CNO: Patti Bennett, Chief Nursing Officer and Senior Vice President
Web address: www.gsmc.org
Control: Other not–for–profit (including NFP Corporation) **Service:** General
Medical and Surgical

Staffed Beds: 393 **Admissions:** 15336 **Census:** 217 **Outpatient Visits:**
213650 **Births:** 2014 **Total Expense ($000):** 291769 **Payroll Expense
($000):** 94263 **Personnel:** 1358

⊠ **LONGVIEW REGIONAL MEDICAL CENTER (450702)**, 2901 North Fourth
Street, Zip 75605–5191, Mailing Address: P.O. Box 14000, Zip 75607–4000;
tel. 903/758–1818, (Total facility includes 15 beds in nursing home–type unit) **A**1
10 19 **F**3 8 11 12 13 15 18 20 22 24 26 28 29 30 31 34 35 37 39 40 43 45
46 47 49 50 57 59 61 64 65 67 70 72 74 75 76 77 78 79 81 85 86 87 89
91 93 107 108 110 111 114 115 118 119 120 126 128 130 146 148 **P**8
S Community Health Systems, Inc., Franklin, TN
Primary Contact: Casey Robertson, Chief Executive Officer
COO: Roy Finch, Chief Operating Officer
CFO: Todd Johnson, Chief Financial Officer
CMO: Kenneth McClure, M.D., Chief of Staff
CIO: Keith Jarvis, Director Information Systems
CHR: Terry Hardan, Director Human Resources
CNO: Stephanie Foster, MSN, Chief Nursing Officer
Web address: www.longviewregional.com
Control: Partnership, Investor–owned, for–profit **Service:** General Medical and
Surgical

Staffed Beds: 230 **Admissions:** 9052 **Census:** 105 **Outpatient Visits:** 84499
Births: 1871 **Total Expense ($000):** 141649 **Payroll Expense ($000):**
50931 **Personnel:** 873

☐ **OCEANS BEHAVIORAL HOSPITAL LONGVIEW (454117)**, 615 Clinic Drive,
Zip 75605–5172; tel. 903/212–3105 **A**1 10 **F**64 98 100 101 103 104 130
S Oceans Healthcare, Lake Charles, LA
Primary Contact: Lauren Weber, Administrator
Web address: www.oceanslongview.com/
Control: Corporation, Investor–owned, for–profit **Service:** Psychiatric

Staffed Beds: 24 **Admissions:** 456 **Census:** 17 **Outpatient Visits:** 13895
Births: 0 **Total Expense ($000):** 4724 **Payroll Expense ($000):** 2208
Personnel: 60

⊠ **SELECT SPECIALTY HOSPITAL–LONGVIEW (452087)**, 700 East Marshall
Avenue, 1st Floor, Zip 75601–5580; tel. 903/315–1100 **A**1 10 **F**1 3 28 29 75
77 85 91 92 130 148 **S** Select Medical Corporation, Mechanicsburg, PA
Primary Contact: Dennis Baker, Chief Executive Officer
Web address: www.selectspecialtyhospitals.com/company/locations/longview.
aspx
Control: Corporation, Investor–owned, for–profit **Service:** Long–Term Acute Care
hospital

Staffed Beds: 32 **Admissions:** 394 **Census:** 29 **Outpatient Visits:** 0 **Births:**
0 **Total Expense ($000):** 13462 **Payroll Expense ($000):** 6347 **Personnel:**
105

LUBBOCK—Lubbock County

⊠ **COVENANT CHILDREN'S HOSPITAL (453306)**, 4015 22nd Place, Zip 79410;
tel. 806/725–1011 **A**1 3 5 10 **F**3 19 21 23 25 27 30 31 32 40 41 43 50 59
72 73 81 89 **P**8 **S** Providence St. Joseph Health, Renton, WA
Primary Contact: Amy Thompson, M.D., Chief Executive Officer
COO: Clay Thomas, Chief Operating Officer
CMO: Scott Robins, M.D., Chief Medical Officer
CIO: Jim Reid, Vice President and Chief Information Officer
CHR: Rodney Cates, Senior Vice President Human Resources
Web address: www.covenanthealth.org/About–Us/Facilities/Childrens–Hospital.
aspx
Control: Other not–for–profit (including NFP Corporation) **Service:** Children's
general

Staffed Beds: 73 **Admissions:** 2429 **Census:** 45 **Outpatient Visits:** 32301
Births: 0 **Total Expense ($000):** 67251 **Payroll Expense ($000):** 19709
Personnel: 217

TX

Hospital, Medicare Provider Number, Address, Telephone, Approval, Facility, and Physician Codes, Health Care System

★ American Hospital Association (AHA) membership ○ Healthcare Facilities Accreditation Program ⇑ Center for Improvement in Healthcare Quality Accreditation
☐ The Joint Commission accreditation ◇ DNV Healthcare Inc. accreditation △ Commission on Accreditation of Rehabilitation Facilities (CARF) accreditation

✠ **COVENANT MEDICAL CENTER (450040)**, 3615 19th Street,
Zip 79410–1203, Mailing Address: P.O. Box 1201, Zip 79408–1201;
tel. 806/725–0000, (Includes COVENANT MEDICAL CENTER–LAKESIDE, 4000
24th Street, Zip 79410–1894; tel. 806/725–0000) **A**1 3 10 **F**7 8 15 17 18 19
20 22 23 26 27 28 30 34 35 37 39 40 43 46 47 48 49 50 51 53 54 55 57
58 59 60 61 63 64 65 68 70 71 74 75 76 77 78 79 80 81 82 83 84 85 86
87 90 91 92 93 94 96 98 102 105 107 108 109 111 114 115 116 117 119
120 121 123 129 130 131 132 135 143 144 146 147 148 **P**6 8 **S** Providence
St. Joseph Health, Renton, WA
Primary Contact: Walt Cathey, Chief Executive Officer
CFO: John A. Grigson, Vice President and Chief Financial Officer
CMO: Craig Rhyne, M.D., Chief Medical Officer
CIO: Troy Pratt, Information Technology Site Director
CHR: Chris Shaver, Vice President Human Resources
CNO: Karen Baggerly, Chief Nursing Officer and Vice President
Web address: www.covenanthealth.org
Control: Other not–for–profit (including NFP Corporation) **Service:** General
Medical and Surgical

Staffed Beds: 566 **Admissions:** 22414 **Census:** 326 **Outpatient Visits:** 334282 **Births:** 2553 **Total Expense ($000):** 518681 **Payroll Expense ($000):** 139572 **Personnel:** 2992	

COVENANT SPECIALTY HOSPITAL (452102), 3815 20th Street,
Zip 79410–1235; tel. 806/725–9200 **A**10 **F**1 3 29 30 31 60 63 68 75 77 78
79 87 119 130 143 148 **S** Covenant Health System, Lubbock, TX
Primary Contact: Julie Bell, Interim Chief Executive Officer and Chief Nursing
Officer
CFO: John Carigson, Chief Financial Officer
CMO: Naidu Chekuru, M.D., Chief Medical Officer
CHR: Chris Shaver, Vice President Human Resources
CNO: Julie Bell, Chief Nursing Officer
Web address: www.covenanthealth.org/view/Facilities/Specialty_Hospital
Control: Partnership, Investor–owned, for–profit **Service:** Long–Term Acute Care
hospital

Staffed Beds: 56 **Admissions:** 403 **Census:** 31 **Outpatient Visits:** 0 **Births:** 0 **Total Expense ($000):** 16321 **Payroll Expense ($000):** 6278 **Personnel:** 102	

✠ **GRACE MEDICAL CENTER (450162)**, 2412 50th Street, Zip 79412–2494;
tel. 806/788–4100 **A**1 3 10 **F**3 8 11 12 15 29 31 34 35 40 44 45 47 49 50
51 59 64 66 70 75 78 79 81 82 85 87 107 108 110 111 114 115 118 119
135 146
Primary Contact: Vanessa Reasoner, Chief Executive Officer
CMO: Howard Beck, M.D., Chief of Staff
CIO: Jason Derouen, Director Management Information Systems
CHR: Sally Charles, Coordinator Human Resources
Web address: www.gracehealthsystem.com
Control: Partnership, Investor–owned, for–profit **Service:** General Medical and
Surgical

Staffed Beds: 43 **Admissions:** 1068 **Census:** 8 **Outpatient Visits:** 87879 **Births:** 0 **Total Expense ($000):** 54099 **Payroll Expense ($000):** 10902 **Personnel:** 232	

LUBBOCK HEART & SURGICAL HOSPITAL (450876), 4810 North Loop 289,
Zip 79416–3025; tel. 806/687–7777 **A**3 5 10 **F**3 17 18 20 22 24 26 29 34
40 45 57 59 79 81 82 85 107 108 115 119 130 131 148
Primary Contact: Charley O. Trimble, Chief Executive Officer
Web address: www.lubbockhearthospital.com
Control: Partnership, Investor–owned, for–profit **Service:** Heart

Staffed Beds: 73 **Admissions:** 3087 **Census:** 32 **Outpatient Visits:** 86007 **Births:** 0 **Total Expense ($000):** 72138 **Payroll Expense ($000):** 20671 **Personnel:** 408	

☐ **SUNRISE CANYON HOSPITAL (454093)**, 1950 Aspen Avenue,
Zip 79404–1211, Mailing Address: P.O. Box 2828, Zip 79408–2828;
tel. 806/740–1420 **A**1 10 **F**29 35 38 53 61 86 98 101 103 130 132 135
Primary Contact: Leonard Valderaz, Administrator
CFO: Jerome Flores, Chief Financial Officer
CMO: Dana Butler, M.D., Medical Director
CIO: Wendy Potitadkul, Chief Information Officer
CHR: Barbara McCann, Director Human Resources
Web address: www.starcarelubbock.org
Control: Other not–for–profit (including NFP Corporation) **Service:** Psychiatric

Staffed Beds: 30 **Admissions:** 428 **Census:** 25 **Outpatient Visits:** 0 **Births:** 0 **Total Expense ($000):** 5576 **Payroll Expense ($000):** 2125 **Personnel:** 45	

☐ **TEXAS SPECIALTY HOSPITAL AT LUBBOCK (452116)**, 4302B Princeton
Street, Zip 79415–1304; tel. 806/723–8700 **A**1 10 **F**1 12 29 60 92 107 111
119 148 **S** Fundamental Long Term Care Holdings, LLC, Sparks Glencoe, MD
Primary Contact: Deanna Graves, Chief Executive Officer
CFO: Robert Stanley, Chief Financial Officer
CMO: Michael Ragain, M.D., Chief Medical Officer
CNO: Bernadette Hernandez, R.N., Chief Nursing Officer
Web address: www.texasspecialtylubbock.com/services.html
Control: Corporation, Investor–owned, for–profit **Service:** Long–Term Acute Care
hospital

Staffed Beds: 26 **Admissions:** 305 **Census:** 24 **Outpatient Visits:** 0 **Births:** 0 **Total Expense ($000):** 9916 **Payroll Expense ($000):** 4121 **Personnel:** 58	

☐ **TRUSTPOINT REHABILITATION HOSPITAL OF LUBBOCK (670050)**, 4302A
Princeton Street, Zip 79415–1304; tel. 806/749–2222 **A**1 3 5 10 **F**3 29 34 35
40 56 68 74 75 77 79 85 86 87 90 91 94 96 130 148 **S** Ernest Health, Inc.,
Albuquerque, NM
Primary Contact: Craig Bragg, Chief Executive Officer
CFO: Crystal Roach, Chief Financial Officer
CNO: John Parsons, R.N., Chief Nursing Officer
Web address: www.trustpointhospital.com/
Control: Partnership, Investor–owned, for–profit **Service:** Rehabilitation

Staffed Beds: 60 **Admissions:** 1010 **Census:** 49 **Outpatient Visits:** 0 **Births:** 0 **Total Expense ($000):** 18427 **Payroll Expense ($000):** 8187 **Personnel:** 199	

◇ **UNIVERSITY MEDICAL CENTER (450686)**, 602 Indiana Avenue,
Zip 79415–3364, Mailing Address: P.O. Box 5980, Zip 79408–5980;
tel. 806/775–8200 **A**2 3 5 8 10 21 **F**3 7 8 11 12 13 15 16 17 18 19 20 22
24 26 28 29 30 31 34 35 38 40 41 43 45 46 47 48 49 50 54 55 57 58 59
60 62 64 65 66 68 70 72 74 75 76 77 78 79 80 81 82 83 84 85 86 87 88
89 93 94 96 97 107 108 110 111 114 115 116 117 118 119 120 121 122
123 124 126 127 130 131 132 135 136 141 142 143 144 146 147 148
Primary Contact: David G. Allison, President and Chief Executive Officer
COO: Mark Funderburk, Executive Vice President and Administrator
CFO: Jeff Dane, Executive Vice President and Chief Financial Officer
CMO: Michael Ragain, M.D., Chief Medical Officer and Senior Vice President
CIO: Bill Eubanks, Senior Vice President and Chief Information Officer
CHR: Adrienne Cozart, Vice President Human Resources
CNO: Tammy J. Williams, R.N., Chief Nursing Officer and Senior Vice President
Web address: www.umchealthsystem.com
Control: Hospital district or authority, Government, nonfederal **Service:** General
Medical and Surgical

Staffed Beds: 446 **Admissions:** 29663 **Census:** 359 **Outpatient Visits:** 304851 **Births:** 3109 **Total Expense ($000):** 510352 **Payroll Expense ($000):** 180845 **Personnel:** 3052	

LUFKIN—Angelina County

★ **CHI ST. LUKE'S HEALTH MEMORIAL LUFKIN (450211)**, 1201 West Frank
Avenue, Zip 75904–3357, Mailing Address: P.O. Box 1447, Zip 75902–1447;
tel. 936/634–8111 **A**2 10 19 **F**3 11 12 15 16 17 18 19 20 21 22 23 24 26
28 29 30 31 34 35 37 38 40 44 45 46 47 48 49 50 51 56 57 59 60 61 62
63 64 68 70 71 74 75 76 77 78 79 81 82 83 84 85 86 87 90 91 92 93 97
100 101 102 107 108 110 111 112 114 115 116 117 119 121 126 129 130
132 135 143 144 146 147 148 **S** Catholic Health Initiatives, Englewood, CO
Primary Contact: Monte J. Bostwick, Market Chief Executive Officer
CFO: Kristi Gay, Chief Financial Officer
CHR: Tanya Tyler, Vice President Human Resources
Web address: www.memorialhealth.us/centers/lufkin
Control: Other not–for–profit (including NFP Corporation) **Service:** General
Medical and Surgical

Staffed Beds: 217 **Admissions:** 6668 **Census:** 95 **Outpatient Visits:** 83496 **Births:** 295 **Total Expense ($000):** 143522 **Payroll Expense ($000):** 37398 **Personnel:** 829	

★ **CHI ST. LUKE'S HEALTH MEMORIAL SPECIALTY HOSPITAL (452031)**, 1201
West Frank Avenue, Zip 75904–3357, Mailing Address: P.O. Box 1447,
Zip 75902–1447; tel. 936/639–7530 **A**10 **F**1 3 29 31 50 61 68 74 75 85 86
130 145 **S** Catholic Health Initiatives, Englewood, CO
Primary Contact: Leslie Leach, Administrator
CFO: Ken Miller, Chief Financial Officer
CMO: Karl Krohn, M.D., President Medical Staff
CNO: Brenda Broadway, Chief Nursing Officer
Web address: www.memorialhealth.org
Control: Other not–for–profit (including NFP Corporation) **Service:** Long–Term
Acute Care hospital

Staffed Beds: 20 **Admissions:** 247 **Census:** 18 **Outpatient Visits:** 0 **Births:** 0 **Total Expense ($000):** 9373 **Payroll Expense ($000):** 5725 **Personnel:** 52	

Many Facility Codes have changed. Please refer to the AHA Guide Code Chart.

TX

☐ **OCEANS BEHAVIORAL HOSPITAL LUFKIN (454123)**, 302 Gobblers Knob Road, Zip 75904–5419; tel. 936/632–2276 **A**1 10 **F**29 35 64 98 100 101 103 104 130 **S** Oceans Healthcare, Lake Charles, LA
Primary Contact: Frances Dick, Chief Executive Officer
Web address: www.oceanslufkin.com/
Control: Corporation, Investor–owned, for–profit **Service:** Psychiatric

Staffed Beds: 24 **Admissions:** 364 **Census:** 17 **Outpatient Visits:** 10054
Births: 0 **Total Expense ($000):** 4387 **Payroll Expense ($000):** 1950
Personnel: 46

☒ **WOODLAND HEIGHTS MEDICAL CENTER (450484)**, 505 South John Redditt Drive, Zip 75904–3157, Mailing Address: P.O. Box 150610, Zip 75904; tel. 936/634–8311, (Total facility includes 15 beds in nursing home–type unit) **A**1 10 19 **F**8 11 12 13 15 18 20 22 24 26 28 29 30 34 35 40 41 46 49 50 51 53 57 59 64 68 70 72 74 75 76 77 78 79 81 82 85 86 87 93 102 107 108 111 114 115 118 119 126 128 129 130 131 146 147 148 **S** Community Health Systems, Inc., Franklin, TN
Primary Contact: Kyle Swift, Chief Executive Officer
COO: Conner Hickey, Chief Operating Officer
CFO: William Whiddon, Chief Financial Officer
CMO: Imran Nazeer, M.D., Chief of Staff
CIO: Kalvin Buckley, Director Information Systems
CHR: Emilie Hobbs, Director Human Resources
CNO: Cathy L. Busbee, Chief Nursing Officer
Web address: www.woodlandheights.net
Control: Partnership, Investor–owned, for–profit **Service:** General Medical and Surgical

Staffed Beds: 115 **Admissions:** 5233 **Census:** 61 **Outpatient Visits:** 51766
Births: 1215 **Total Expense ($000):** 85669 **Payroll Expense ($000):** 30427
Personnel: 487

LULING—Caldwell County

☒ **POST ACUTE/WARM SPRINGS SPECIALTY HOSPITAL OF LULING (452062)**, 200 Memorial Drive, Zip 78648–3213; tel. 830/875–8400 **A**1 10 **F**1 3 29 53 64 93 96 130 133 148 **S** Post Acute Medical, LLC, Enola, PA
Primary Contact: Jana Kuykendall, Chief Executive Officer
Web address: www.warmsprings.org
Control: Partnership, Investor–owned, for–profit **Service:** Long–Term Acute Care hospital

Staffed Beds: 34 **Admissions:** 417 **Census:** 33 **Outpatient Visits:** 11089
Births: 0 **Total Expense ($000):** 14784 **Payroll Expense ($000):** 6548
Personnel: 155

☒ **SETON EDGAR B. DAVIS HOSPITAL (451371)**, 130 Hays Street, Zip 78648–3207; tel. 830/875–7000 **A**1 10 18 **F**3 11 15 18 29 30 35 40 43 44 45 50 56 68 71 75 77 78 79 81 84 85 87 93 97 103 107 110 111 114 119 127 130 133 135 143 146 **P**3 8 **S** Ascension Health, Saint Louis, MO
Primary Contact: Apryl Haynes, R.N., Vice President, Chief Operating Officer, Administrator
CFO: Thomas E. Gallagher, Chief Financial Officer
CMO: Arjun Mohandas, M.D., Chief of Staff
CIO: Mike Minks, Chief Information Officer
CHR: Joe Canales, Director Human Resources
CNO: Nikki Rivers, R.N., Regional Chief Nursing Officer, South Market
Web address: www.seton.net/locations/edgar_davis/
Control: Church–operated, Nongovernment, not–for profit **Service:** General Medical and Surgical

Staffed Beds: 25 **Admissions:** 701 **Census:** 8 **Outpatient Visits:** 62697
Births: 0 **Total Expense ($000):** 23690 **Payroll Expense ($000):** 9231
Personnel: 166

WARM SPRINGS SPECIALTY HOSPITAL OF LULING See Post Acute/Warm Springs Specialty Hospital of Luling

MADISONVILLE—Madison County

☒ **MADISON ST. JOSEPH HEALTH CENTER (451316)**, 100 West Cross Street, Zip 77864–2432, Mailing Address: Box 698, Zip 77864–0698; tel. 936/348–2631, (Data for 181 days) **A**1 10 18 **F**3 7 11 15 30 40 43 50 57 59 64 68 75 93 103 107 110 119 130 133 146 148 **S** Catholic Health Initiatives, Englewood, CO
Primary Contact: Reed Edmundson, Administrator
COO: Reed Edmundson, Administrator
CFO: Kris Smith, Controller
CMO: Grover Hubley, M.D., President Medical Staff
CIO: Maurita Turner, Team Leader Health Information Systems Services
CHR: Marybeth Murphy, Director Human Resources
CNO: Roxanne Hass, Director of Nursing
Web address: www.st–joseph.org
Control: Church–operated, Nongovernment, not–for profit **Service:** General Medical and Surgical

Staffed Beds: 25 **Admissions:** 127 **Census:** 6 **Outpatient Visits:** 9302
Births: 0 **Total Expense ($000):** 5193 **Payroll Expense ($000):** 2343
Personnel: 71

MANSFIELD—Tarrant County

☒ **KINDRED HOSPITAL–MANSFIELD (452019)**, 1802 Highway 157 North, Zip 76063–3923; tel. 817/473–6101 **A**1 10 **F**1 3 29 30 45 46 64 70 75 82 85 107 130 132 148 **S** Kindred Healthcare, Louisville, KY
Primary Contact: Jason Naranjo, Chief Executive Officer
CFO: Judy Baker, Chief Financial Officer
Web address: www.kindredmansfield.com
Control: Corporation, Investor–owned, for–profit **Service:** Long–Term Acute Care hospital

Staffed Beds: 55 **Admissions:** 469 **Census:** 31 **Outpatient Visits:** 275
Births: 0 **Total Expense ($000):** 15727 **Payroll Expense ($000):** 6516
Personnel: 100

☒ **METHODIST MANSFIELD MEDICAL CENTER (670023)**, 2700 East Broad Street, Zip 76063–5899; tel. 682/622–2000 **A**1 10 **F**3 11 13 15 18 20 22 24 29 30 31 34 35 37 44 45 46 48 49 50 58 59 60 64 68 70 74 76 78 79 81 82 85 87 93 97 107 108 110 111 115 118 119 126 130 132 146 148 **P**1 7 **S** Methodist Health System, Dallas, TX
Primary Contact: John E. Phillips, FACHE, President
CFO: Jary Ganske, Chief Financial Officer
CIO: Pamela McNutt, Senior Vice President and Chief Information Officer
CHR: Judy K. Laister, Director, Human Resources
CNO: Nora Frasier, R.N., Chief Nursing Officer
Web address: www.methodisthealthsystem.org/mansfield
Control: Other not–for–profit (including NFP Corporation) **Service:** General Medical and Surgical

Staffed Beds: 167 **Admissions:** 9947 **Census:** 118 **Outpatient Visits:** 82163
Births: 1926 **Total Expense ($000):** 139534 **Payroll Expense ($000):** 66408 **Personnel:** 716

MARBLE FALLS—Williamson County

★ **SCOTT & WHITE HOSPITAL – MARBLE FALLS**, 800 West Highway 71, Zip 78654; tel. 830/598–1204, (Nonreporting) **S** Baylor Scott & White Health, Dallas, TX
Primary Contact: Eric N. Looper, Chief Executive Officer
Web address: www.sw.org/location/marble–falls–hospital
Control: Other not–for–profit (including NFP Corporation) **Service:** General Medical and Surgical

Staffed Beds: 84

MARLIN—Falls County

★ **FALLS COMMUNITY HOSPITAL AND CLINIC (450348)**, 322 Coleman Street, Zip 76661–2358, Mailing Address: P.O. Box 60, Zip 76661–0060; tel. 254/803–3561 **A**10 20 **F**3 11 32 33 34 35 36 40 43 45 53 56 57 59 64 65 66 68 75 82 87 91 93 97 99 103 104 107 114 127 129 131 135 146 148
Primary Contact: Willis L. Reese, Administrator
COO: Becca Brewer, Chief Operations Officer
CFO: Willis L. Reese, Administrator
CMO: James Scott Crockett, M.D., Chief of Staff
CIO: Chris Smith, Chief Information Officer
CHR: Peggy Polster, Manager Personnel and Administrative Assistant
CNO: Tasha Burnett, Director of Nursing
Web address: www.fallshospital.com
Control: Other not–for–profit (including NFP Corporation) **Service:** General Medical and Surgical

Staffed Beds: 32 **Admissions:** 363 **Census:** 3 **Outpatient Visits:** 74020
Births: 0 **Total Expense ($000):** 19526 **Payroll Expense ($000):** 6270
Personnel: 183

TX

MARSHALL—Harrison County

☐ **GOOD SHEPHERD MEDICAL CENTER–MARSHALL (450032)**, 811 South Washington Avenue, Zip 75670–5336, Mailing Address: P.O. Box 1599, Zip 75671–1599; tel. 903/927–6000 **A**1 3 10 **F**3 11 13 15 18 28 29 30 34 35 40 43 49 50 53 54 57 59 60 64 65 68 70 75 77 79 80 81 86 87 89 90 93 97 102 103 107 110 115 119 129 130 131 132 145 146 147 148 **P**7 8 **S** Good Shepherd Health System, Longview, TX
Primary Contact: Russell J. Collier, FACHE, President and Chief Executive Officer
COO: Keith Creel, Vice President Operations
CFO: Tim Pileggi, Interim Chief Financial Officer
CMO: Larry Verfurth, D.O., Executive Vice President and Chief Medical Officer
CIO: Walter Grimes, Director Information Technology
CHR: Ginger Morrow, Executive Vice President Human Resources
CNO: Keith Kirbow, R.N., Vice President and Chief Nursing Officer
Web address: www.gsmcmarshall.org
Control: Other not–for–profit (including NFP Corporation) **Service:** General Medical and Surgical

Staffed Beds: 140 **Admissions:** 3971 **Census:** 40 **Outpatient Visits:** 187961 **Births:** 528 **Total Expense ($000):** 64421 **Payroll Expense ($000):** 22363 **Personnel:** 415

MCALLEN—Hidalgo County

LIFECARE HOSPITALS OF SOUTH TEXAS–MCALLEN See Lifecare Hospitals of South Texas–North McAllen

☒ **LIFECARE HOSPITALS OF SOUTH TEXAS–NORTH MCALLEN (452063)**, 5101 North Jackson, Zip 78504–6343; tel. 956/926–7000, (Includes LIFECARE HOSPITALS OF SOUTH TEXAS–MCALLEN, 2001 South M Street, Zip 78503; tel. 956/688–4300) **A**1 10 **F**1 3 29 57 75 77 85 87 148 **S** LifeCare Management Services, Plano, TX
Primary Contact: Angel Lozano, Chief Executive Officer
Web address: www.lifecare–hospitals.com/hospital/southtexas
Control: Corporation, Investor–owned, for–profit **Service:** Long–Term Acute Care hospital

Staffed Beds: 84 **Admissions:** 726 **Census:** 53 **Outpatient Visits:** 0 **Births:** 0 **Total Expense ($000):** 24342 **Payroll Expense ($000):** 10619 **Personnel:** 177

☒ **RIO GRANDE REGIONAL HOSPITAL (450711)**, 101 East Ridge Road, Zip 78503–1299; tel. 956/632–6000 **A**1 3 10 **F**3 8 11 12 13 15 18 19 20 21 22 23 24 25 26 27 29 30 31 34 35 39 40 42 43 45 46 49 50 54 56 57 59 60 64 66 68 70 71 72 73 74 75 76 78 79 81 85 87 88 89 93 107 108 110 111 114 118 119 126 130 132 146 147 148 **P**7 **S** HCA, Nashville, TN
Primary Contact: Cristina Rivera, Chief Executive Officer
CFO: William Saller, Chief Financial Officer
CHR: Marjorie Whittemore, Director Human Resources
Web address: www.riohealth.com
Control: Partnership, Investor–owned, for–profit **Service:** General Medical and Surgical

Staffed Beds: 320 **Admissions:** 14796 **Census:** 179 **Outpatient Visits:** 118061 **Births:** 2721 **Total Expense ($000):** 155671 **Payroll Expense ($000):** 64718 **Personnel:** 873

SOLARA HOSPITAL MCALLEN (452095), 301 West Expressway 83, 8th Floor, Zip 78503–3045; tel. 956/632–4880 **A**10 22 **F**1 3 29 30 56 57 70 75 77 85 86 87 91 130 148 **S** Cornerstone Healthcare Group, Dallas, TX
Primary Contact: Hari Namboodiri, Chief Executive Officer
Web address: www.chghospitals.com/mcallen/
Control: Corporation, Investor–owned, for–profit **Service:** Long–Term Acute Care hospital

Staffed Beds: 78 **Admissions:** 581 **Census:** 43 **Outpatient Visits:** 0 **Births:** 0 **Total Expense ($000):** 20048 **Payroll Expense ($000):** 8991 **Personnel:** 152

MCCAMEY—Upton County

★ **MCCAMEY COUNTY HOSPITAL DISTRICT (451309)**, 2500 Highway 305 South, Zip 79752, Mailing Address: P.O. Box 1200, Zip 79752–1200; tel. 432/652–8626, (Total facility includes 30 beds in nursing home–type unit) **A**10 18 **F**3 40 53 59 64 65 66 93 127 128 133
Primary Contact: Jaime Ramirez, Chief Executive Officer
COO: Tana Robertson, Chief Operating Officer
CFO: Jason J. Menefee, Chief Financial Officer
CMO: Ramon Domingo, M.D., Chief of Staff
CIO: Larry Rollins, Supervisor Information Technology
CHR: Judith Gulihur, Director Human Resources
CNO: Cheryl Roberts, Chief Nursing Officer
Web address: www.mccameyhospital.org
Control: Hospital district or authority, Government, nonfederal **Service:** General Medical and Surgical

Staffed Beds: 44 **Admissions:** 60 **Census:** 23 **Outpatient Visits:** 5686 **Births:** 0 **Total Expense ($000):** 10033 **Payroll Expense ($000):** 3821 **Personnel:** 79

MCKINNEY—Collin County

☒ **BAYLOR MEDICAL CENTER AT MCKINNEY (670082)**, 5252 West University Drive, Zip 75071–7822; tel. 469/764–1000 **A**1 5 10 **F**3 13 15 18 20 22 26 29 30 31 34 35 40 45 46 47 49 50 51 57 67 70 72 73 74 75 76 77 78 79 81 84 85 87 107 110 111 114 115 119 126 130 131 132 146 147 148 **S** Baylor Scott & White Health, Dallas, TX
Primary Contact: Scott Peek, FACHE, President
COO: Melissa Winter, R.N., Chief Operating Officer and Chief Nursing Officer
CFO: Steve Roussel, Chief Financial Officer
CMO: Jeff Kerr, M.D., Chief Medical Officer
CNO: Melissa Winter, R.N., Chief Operating Officer and Chief Nursing Officer
Web address: www.baylorhealth.com/PhysiciansLocations/McKinney/Pages/Default.aspx
Control: Other not–for–profit (including NFP Corporation) **Service:** General Medical and Surgical

Staffed Beds: 102 **Admissions:** 6772 **Census:** 72 **Outpatient Visits:** 47336 **Births:** 1870 **Total Expense ($000):** 133525 **Payroll Expense ($000):** 43682 **Personnel:** 502

☒ **MEDICAL CENTER OF MCKINNEY (450403)**, 4500 Medical Center Drive, Zip 75069–1650; tel. 972/547–8000, (Includes WYSONG CAMPUS, 130 South Central Expressway, Zip 75070; tel. 972/548–5300) **A**1 10 **F**3 4 11 13 18 20 22 24 26 28 29 30 34 37 40 42 43 45 49 50 56 57 59 60 64 68 70 72 74 75 76 77 78 79 81 82 85 87 90 91 92 93 94 96 97 98 102 103 107 108 109 111 114 115 119 126 130 131 132 146 147 148 **S** HCA, Nashville, TN
Primary Contact: Ernest C. Lynch, III, President and Chief Executive Officer
COO: William Windham, Chief Operating Officer
CFO: Aaron Rowe, Chief Financial Officer
CIO: Kevin Fletcher, Director Information Systems
CHR: Alayne Sewick, Vice President Human Resources
CNO: Cassidi Roberts, R.N., Chief Nursing Officer
Web address: www.medicalcenterofmckinney.com
Control: Partnership, Investor–owned, for–profit **Service:** General Medical and Surgical

Staffed Beds: 222 **Admissions:** 11407 **Census:** 165 **Outpatient Visits:** 72891 **Births:** 1152 **Total Expense ($000):** 128336 **Payroll Expense ($000):** 56382 **Personnel:** 793

☐ **METHODIST MCKINNEY HOSPITAL (670069)**, 8000 West Eldorado Parkway, Zip 75070–5940; tel. 972/569–2700 **A**1 10 **F**3 15 29 34 40 45 51 70 75 79 81 82 85 93 107 110 111 119 126 129 130 131
Primary Contact: Joseph Minissale, President
CFO: Mike Conroy, Chief Financial Officer
CIO: Sharon Stark, R.N., Manager Clinical Information Systems
CHR: Diana Hume, Manager Human Resources
CNO: Staci Jones, R.N., Chief Nursing Officer
Web address: www.methodistmckinneyhospital.com
Control: Partnership, Investor–owned, for–profit **Service:** Surgical

Staffed Beds: 21 **Admissions:** 832 **Census:** 6 **Outpatient Visits:** 35762 **Births:** 0 **Total Expense ($000):** 47552 **Payroll Expense ($000):** 8806 **Personnel:** 151

MESQUITE—Dallas County

☒ **DALLAS REGIONAL MEDICAL CENTER (450688)**, 1011 North Galloway Avenue, Zip 75149–2433; tel. 214/320–7000, (Data for 306 days) **A**1 10 **F**3 12 15 18 20 22 24 26 29 30 34 35 37 40 41 43 45 46 49 50 54 56 57 59 64 65 67 68 70 74 75 79 80 81 85 87 107 108 110 111 114 115 119 126 130 134 135 146 148 **S** Prime Healthcare Services, Ontario, CA
Primary Contact: Glenda Newby, Chief Executive Officer
CMO: Srinivas Gunukula, M.D., Chief of Staff
Web address: www.dallasregionalmedicalcenter.com
Control: Individual, Investor–owned, for–profit **Service:** General Medical and Surgical

Staffed Beds: 100 **Admissions:** 3575 **Census:** 52 **Outpatient Visits:** 50397 **Births:** 0 **Total Expense ($000):** 58746 **Payroll Expense ($000):** 24338 **Personnel:** 518

☐ **MESQUITE REHABILITATION INSTITUTE (673045)**, 1023 North Belt Line Road, Zip 75149–1788; tel. 972/216–2400 **A**1 10 **F**3 28 29 34 35 57 59 64 74 75 82 90 91 93 96 130 132 148 **S** Ernest Health, Inc., Albuquerque, NM
Primary Contact: Brian Abraham, Chief Executive Officer
Web address: www.mesquiterehab.ernesthealth.com/
Control: Corporation, Investor–owned, for–profit **Service:** Rehabilitation

Staffed Beds: 20 **Admissions:** 516 **Census:** 19 **Outpatient Visits:** 3039 **Births:** 0 **Total Expense ($000):** 6598 **Payroll Expense ($000):** 3988 **Personnel:** 52

☐ **MESQUITE SPECIALTY HOSPITAL (452100)**, 1024 North Galloway Avenue, Zip 75149–2434; tel. 972/216–2300 **A**1 10 **F**1 3 29 74 75 82 84 130 135 148 **S** Ernest Health, Inc., Albuquerque, NM
Primary Contact: Louis Bradley, Chief Executive Officer
Web address: www.msh.ernesthealth.com
Control: Partnership, Investor–owned, for–profit **Service:** Long–Term Acute Care hospital

Staffed Beds: 40 **Admissions:** 453 **Census:** 32 **Outpatient Visits:** 0 **Births:** 0 **Total Expense ($000):** 18194 **Payroll Expense ($000):** 7041 **Personnel:** 111

Many Facility Codes have changed. Please refer to the AHA Guide Code Chart. © 2016 AHA Guide

MEXIA—Limestone County

⊞ **PARKVIEW REGIONAL HOSPITAL (450400)**, 600 South Bonham,
Zip 76667–3603; tel. 254/562–5332 **A**1 10 20 **F**3 11 15 29 30 34 35 40 43
45 51 53 56 57 59 64 65 70 75 77 78 79 81 85 86 87 93 97 98 103 107
108 110 111 114 119 127 130 132 133 146 **P**5 6 **S** LifePoint Health,
Brentwood, TN
Primary Contact: Alan Daugherty, Chief Executive Officer
COO: R. Austin Wratchford, Chief Operating Officer
Web address: www.parkviewregional.com
Control: Partnership, Investor–owned, for–profit **Service:** General Medical and
Surgical

Staffed Beds: 58 **Admissions:** 580 **Census:** 7 **Outpatient Visits:** 22513
Births: 0 **Total Expense ($000):** 16134 **Payroll Expense ($000):** 7149
Personnel: 160

MIDLAND—Midland County

CONTINUECARE HOSPITAL AT MIDLAND MEMORIAL (670091), 4214
Andrews Highway, 3rd Floor, Zip 79703–4822; tel. 432/221–3044 **A**10 22 **F**1 3
29 34 35 79 85 87 148 **S** Community Hospital Corporation, Plano, TX
Primary Contact: Judith Schiros, Chief Executive Officer
Web address: www.continuecare.org/midland/
Control: Other not–for–profit (including NFP Corporation) **Service:** Long–Term
Acute Care hospital

Staffed Beds: 29 **Admissions:** 289 **Census:** 21 **Outpatient Visits:** 0 **Births:**
0 **Total Expense ($000):** 11085 **Payroll Expense ($000):** 5580 **Personnel:**
72

⊞ **HEALTHSOUTH REHABILITATION HOSPITAL MIDLAND–ODESSA (453057)**,
1800 Heritage Boulevard, Zip 79707–9750; tel. 432/520–1600 **A**1 10 **F**3 29 57
59 74 75 77 90 91 96 130 143 148 **S** HEALTHSOUTH Corporation,
Birmingham, AL
Primary Contact: Christopher Wortham, Chief Executive Officer
CFO: Vivian Irwin, Chief Financial Officer and Controller
CMO: Mark A. Fredrickson, M.D., Medical Director
CHR: Tina Parker, Director Human Resources
Web address: www.healthsouthmidland.com
Control: Corporation, Investor–owned, for–profit **Service:** Rehabilitation

Staffed Beds: 60 **Admissions:** 1296 **Census:** 49 **Outpatient Visits:** 1098
Births: 0 **Total Expense ($000):** 17242 **Payroll Expense ($000):** 11404
Personnel: 152

★ ◇ **MIDLAND MEMORIAL HOSPITAL (450133)**, 400 Rosalind Redfern Grover
Parkway, Zip 79701–6499; tel. 432/221–1111, (Includes MIDLAND MEMORIAL
HOSPITAL, 400 Rosalind Redfern Grover Parkway, Zip 79701–5846;
tel. 432/221–1111) **A**2 3 5 10 21 **F**3 8 11 12 13 15 17 18 20 22 24 26 28
29 30 32 34 35 37 40 43 45 49 50 56 57 59 61 64 68 70 73 74 75 76 77
78 79 81 82 83 84 85 86 87 88 89 93 97 107 108 111 114 115 116 117
118 119 124 126 129 130 131 132 135 145 146 147 148 **P**8
Primary Contact: Russell Meyers, President and Chief Executive Officer
COO: Robert L. Dent, R.N., Senior Vice President, Chief Operating Officer and
Chief Nursing Officer
CFO: Stephen Bowerman, Senior Vice President, Chief Financial Officer
CMO: Lawrence Wilson, M.D., Vice President, Chief Medical Officer
CIO: Taylor Weems, Vice President, Chief Information Officer
CHR: Roberta SoloRio, Vice President, Chief Human Resource Officer
Web address: www.midland–memorial.com
Control: Hospital district or authority, Government, nonfederal **Service:** General
Medical and Surgical

Staffed Beds: 257 **Admissions:** 12224 **Census:** 158 **Outpatient Visits:**
149630 **Births:** 2614 **Total Expense ($000):** 255617 **Payroll Expense
($000):** 99980 **Personnel:** 1707

☐ **OCEANS BEHAVIORAL HEALTH CENTER PERMIAN BASIN (454110)**, 3300
South FM 1788, Zip 79706–2601; tel. 432/561–5915 **A**1 3 10 **F**29 64 98 99
100 101 103 104 130 132 **P**6 **S** Oceans Healthcare, Lake Charles, LA
Primary Contact: Kristin Harris, Interim Chief Executive Officer
Web address: www.oceanspermianbasin.com/
Control: Corporation, Investor–owned, for–profit **Service:** Psychiatric

Staffed Beds: 58 **Admissions:** 1535 **Census:** 42 **Outpatient Visits:** 2254
Births: 0 **Total Expense ($000):** 9300 **Payroll Expense ($000):** 4584
Personnel: 93

MINERAL WELLS—Palo Pinto County

⊞ **PALO PINTO GENERAL HOSPITAL (450565)**, 400 S.W. 25th Avenue,
Zip 76067–8246; tel. 940/328–6403 **A**1 10 **F**11 13 15 17 18 28 29 32 34 40
43 45 46 51 53 54 57 59 62 63 64 65 66 68 69 71 74 75 76 77 79 81 84
86 87 91 93 107 108 110 111 114 119 127 129 130 131 133 135 146
147 **P**1
Primary Contact: Harris W. Brooks, Chief Executive Officer
CFO: Dee Waldow, Chief Financial Officer
CMO: George Thomas, M.D., Chief of Staff
CHR: Mary B. Braddock, Director Human Resources
CNO: James Fesser, Chief Nursing Officer
Web address: www.ppgh.com
Control: Hospital district or authority, Government, nonfederal **Service:** General
Medical and Surgical

Staffed Beds: 42 **Admissions:** 1705 **Census:** 18 **Outpatient Visits:** 88112
Births: 198 **Total Expense ($000):** 36295 **Payroll Expense ($000):** 15236
Personnel: 309

MISSION—Hidalgo County

⊞ △ **MISSION REGIONAL MEDICAL CENTER (450176)**, 900 South Bryan
Road, Zip 78572–6613; tel. 956/323–9103 **A**1 7 10 **F**3 11 12 13 15 18 20 22
29 30 31 34 35 40 43 45 46 49 50 51 57 59 60 64 65 66 68 70 72 74 75
76 77 79 81 85 87 89 90 93 96 107 108 110 111 115 119 130 132 146
147 148 **P**8
Primary Contact: Javier Iruegas, FACHE, Chief Executive Officer
COO: Carlos Trevino, Chief Operating Officer
CFO: Timothy J. McVey, Chief Financial Officer
CNO: Kennetha Foster, Chief Nursing Officer
Web address: www.missionrmc.org
Control: Other not–for–profit (including NFP Corporation) **Service:** General
Medical and Surgical

Staffed Beds: 256 **Admissions:** 9029 **Census:** 130 **Outpatient Visits:** 79038
Births: 2443 **Total Expense ($000):** 115014 **Payroll Expense ($000):**
53306 **Personnel:** 971

MONAHANS—Ward County

★ **WARD MEMORIAL HOSPITAL (451373)**, 406 South Gary Street,
Zip 79756–4798, Mailing Address: P.O. Box 40, Zip 79756–0040;
tel. 432/943–2511 **A**10 18 **F**3 40 43 45 64 65 66 81 82 89 93 107 114 119
127 131 133 148 **P**6
Primary Contact: Leticia Rodriguez, Chief Executive Officer
CFO: Alison Cooper, Chief Financial Officer
CMO: Htin Thaung, M.D., Chief Medical Officer
CIO: David Hargrave, Chief Information Officer
CHR: Corina Subia, Director Human Resources
CNO: Jason Harbin, Director of Nursing
Web address: www.wardmemorial.com
Control: County–Government, nonfederal **Service:** General Medical and Surgical

Staffed Beds: 25 **Admissions:** 255 **Census:** 2 **Outpatient Visits:** 58566
Births: 0 **Total Expense ($000):** 9666 **Payroll Expense ($000):** 5032
Personnel: 84

MORTON—Cochran County

COCHRAN MEMORIAL HOSPITAL (451366), 201 East Grant Street,
Zip 79346–3444; tel. 806/266–5565 **A**10 18 **F**34 40 57 59 65 127 **P**6
Primary Contact: Larry Turney, Administrator
CFO: Lynnette Whitten, Chief Financial Officer
CIO: David Turney, Chief Information Officer
CHR: Lynnette Whitten, Chief Financial Officer
Control: Hospital district or authority, Government, nonfederal **Service:** General
Medical and Surgical

Staffed Beds: 13 **Admissions:** 23 **Census:** 1 **Outpatient Visits:** 5648 **Births:**
0 **Total Expense ($000):** 3760 **Payroll Expense ($000):** 1800 **Personnel:**
47

TX

Hospital, Medicare Provider Number, Address, Telephone, Approval, Facility, and Physician Codes, Health Care System

★ American Hospital Association (AHA) membership   ◯ Healthcare Facilities Accreditation Program   ⇑ Center for Improvement in Healthcare Quality Accreditation
☐ The Joint Commission accreditation   ◇ DNV Healthcare Inc. accreditation   △ Commission on Accreditation of Rehabilitation Facilities (CARF) accreditation

MOUNT PLEASANT—Titus County

☐ **TITUS REGIONAL MEDICAL CENTER (450080)**, 2001 North Jefferson Avenue, Zip 75455–2398; tel. 903/577–6000, (Total facility includes 7 beds in nursing home–type unit) **A**1 10 19 **F**3 7 11 12 13 15 18 19 20 24 26 28 29 30 34 35 39 40 43 45 47 50 51 53 54 56 57 58 59 64 68 70 73 74 75 76 78 79 81 82 85 89 90 93 97 98 103 107 108 110 111 114 115 117 118 119 121 123 127 129 130 132 135 147 148
Primary Contact: John P. Allen, Chief Executive Officer
CFO: Terry Scoggin, Chief Financial Officer
CMO: Chris Burling, M.D., Chief of Staff
CIO: Kevin Harris, Director Information Systems
CHR: Tony Piazza, Director Human Resources
CNO: Carol Slider, Chief Nursing Officer
Web address: www.titusregional.com
Control: Hospital district or authority, Government, nonfederal **Service:** General Medical and Surgical

Staffed Beds: 64 **Admissions:** 4702 **Census:** 51 **Outpatient Visits:** 214416
Births: 1043 **Total Expense ($000):** 70104 **Payroll Expense ($000):** 25313
Personnel: 527

MUENSTER—Cooke County

MUENSTER MEMORIAL HOSPITAL (451335), 605 North Maple Street, Zip 76252–2424, Mailing Address: P.O. Box 370, Zip 76252–0370; tel. 940/759–2271 **A**10 18 **F**11 35 40 43 45 53 57 59 62 64 65 75 77 81 93 107 114 119 127 130 133 146 **P**8
Primary Contact: Brian Roland, Chief Executive Officer
CFO: Julie Williams, Chief Financial Officer
CNO: Tiffany Lutkenhaus, Chief Nursing Officer
Web address: www.muensterhospital.com
Control: Hospital district or authority, Government, nonfederal **Service:** General Medical and Surgical

Staffed Beds: 18 **Admissions:** 279 **Census:** 9 **Outpatient Visits:** 3280
Births: 0 **Total Expense ($000):** 10519 **Payroll Expense ($000):** 4546
Personnel: 91

MULESHOE—Bailey County

★ **MULESHOE AREA MEDICAL CENTER (451372)**, 708 South First Street, Zip 79347–3627; tel. 806/272–4524, (Data for 214 days) **A**10 18 **F**3 29 32 34 40 43 50 56 57 59 64 65 68 69 77 91 93 97 107 114 119 127 130 133
Primary Contact: Dennis Fleenor, R.N., Administrator
CMO: Bruce Purdy, M.D., Chief of Staff
CHR: Suzanne Nichols, Director Human Resources
Web address: www.mahdtx.org
Control: Corporation, Investor–owned, for–profit **Service:** General Medical and Surgical

Staffed Beds: 25 **Admissions:** 146 **Census:** 5 **Outpatient Visits:** 15464
Births: 0 **Total Expense ($000):** 5305 **Payroll Expense ($000):** 1964
Personnel: 95

NACOGDOCHES—Nacogdoches County

⊞ **NACOGDOCHES MEDICAL CENTER (450656)**, 4920 N.E. Stallings Drive, Zip 75965–1200; tel. 936/569–9481 **A**1 2 10 19 **F**3 13 15 17 18 20 22 24 26 29 30 31 34 35 40 42 45 46 49 50 51 54 56 57 59 64 65 68 70 74 75 76 77 78 79 81 82 84 85 86 87 89 93 96 97 100 102 107 108 110 111 114 115 118 119 120 121 122 123 126 129 130 131 132 135 141 146 147 **S** TENET Healthcare Corporation, Dallas, TX
Primary Contact: Jeff Patterson, Chief Executive Officer
COO: Philip Koovakada, Chief Operating Officer
CFO: Frank Malek, Chief Financial Officer
CMO: Charles Thompson, M.D., Chief Medical Officer
CIO: Teresa Simon, Director Information Systems
CHR: Teresa Farrell, Chief Human Resources Officer
CNO: Mario B. Estrella, Chief Nursing Officer
Web address: www.nacmedicalcenter.com
Control: Partnership, Investor–owned, for–profit **Service:** General Medical and Surgical

Staffed Beds: 109 **Admissions:** 3785 **Census:** 37 **Outpatient Visits:** 61974
Births: 566 **Total Expense ($000):** 59481 **Payroll Expense ($000):** 21466
Personnel: 349

☐ **NACOGDOCHES MEMORIAL HOSPITAL (450508)**, 1204 North Mound Street, Zip 75961–4061; tel. 936/564–4611 **A**1 10 19 **F**3 7 11 13 15 18 20 22 24 28 29 30 31 34 35 38 40 43 49 50 57 59 61 64 68 70 74 76 77 78 79 80 81 85 86 89 90 93 96 107 108 110 111 114 118 119 126 130 132 146 147 148 **P**8
Primary Contact: Scott Street, Chief Executive Officer
CFO: Jane Ann Bridges, Chief Financial Officer
CNO: Beth Knight, Chief Nursing Officer
Web address: www.nacmem.org
Control: Hospital district or authority, Government, nonfederal **Service:** General Medical and Surgical

Staffed Beds: 116 **Admissions:** 4512 **Census:** 66 **Outpatient Visits:** 68568
Births: 788 **Total Expense ($000):** 85094 **Payroll Expense ($000):** 32836
Personnel: 605

NASSAU BAY—Harris County

★ ◇ **HOUSTON METHODIST ST. JOHN HOSPITAL (450709)**, 18300 St. John Drive, Zip 77058–6302; tel. 281/333–5503 **A**2 3 5 10 21 **F**3 8 11 12 13 15 18 20 22 26 28 29 30 34 35 39 40 41 44 45 47 49 50 51 53 54 57 59 64 65 68 69 70 73 74 75 76 77 78 79 81 82 84 85 86 87 93 94 96 102 107 108 110 111 115 118 119 130 131 132 135 146 147 **S** Houston Methodist, Houston, TX
Primary Contact: Dan Newman, Chief Executive Officer
CFO: David A. Witt, Vice President Finances
CHR: Becky A. Merritt, Director Human Resources
Web address: www.houstonmethodist.org/st-john-clear-lake
Control: Other not-for-profit (including NFP Corporation) **Service:** General Medical and Surgical

Staffed Beds: 137 **Admissions:** 6050 **Census:** 67 **Outpatient Visits:** 131342
Births: 629 **Total Expense ($000):** 118194 **Payroll Expense ($000):** 47443
Personnel: 720

NAVASOTA—Grimes County

⊞ **GRIMES ST. JOSEPH HEALTH CENTER (451322)**, 210 South Judson Street, Zip 77868–3704; tel. 936/825–6585, (Data for 181 days) **A**1 10 18 **F**3 28 29 34 40 43 56 57 59 75 77 93 103 107 111 119 130 132 133 135 146 **S** Catholic Health Initiatives, Englewood, CO
Primary Contact: Reed Edmundson, Administrator
CFO: Daniel Goggin, Senior Vice President and Chief Financial Officer
CMO: Luke P. Scamardo, II, M.D., Chief of Staff
CIO: Mike Russo, Vice President Information Systems
CHR: Michael G. Costa, Director Human Resources
CNO: Cesar Lopez, R.N., Director of Nurses
Web address: www.st-joseph.org
Control: Church-operated, Nongovernment, not-for profit **Service:** General Medical and Surgical

Staffed Beds: 18 **Admissions:** 136 **Census:** 7 **Outpatient Visits:** 8832
Births: 0 **Total Expense ($000):** 5184 **Payroll Expense ($000):** 2521
Personnel: 99

NEDERLAND—Jefferson County

MID–JEFFERSON EXTENDED CARE HOSPITAL (452083), 2600 Highway 365, Zip 77627–6237; tel. 409/726–8700 **A**10 **F**1 3 29 30 34 35 40 70 74 75 77 79 85 130 148
Primary Contact: Mark Rice, Chief Executive Officer
COO: Wade K. Lester, Chief Nursing and Operations Officer
Web address: www.midjeffextendedcare.com/index.php
Control: Corporation, Investor–owned, for–profit **Service:** Long–Term Acute Care hospital

Staffed Beds: 48 **Admissions:** 624 **Census:** 43 **Outpatient Visits:** 0 **Births:** 0 **Total Expense ($000):** 17215 **Payroll Expense ($000):** 8223 **Personnel:** 167

NEW BRAUNFELS—Comal County

GULF STATES LONG TERM ACUTE CARE OF NEW BRAUNFELS See Post Acute/Warm Springs Specialty Hospital of New Braunfels

☐ **NEW BRAUNFELS REGIONAL REHABILITATION HOSPITAL (673049)**, 2041 Sundance Parkway, Zip 78130–2779; tel. 830/625–6700 **A**1 10 **F**29 34 57 64 90 91 93 130 132 148 **S** Ernest Health, Inc., Albuquerque, NM
Primary Contact: Jennifer Malatek, Chief Executive Officer
CFO: Sue Thomsen, Chief Financial Officer
CMO: Maria R. Lomba, Medical Director
CHR: Cheryl Smith, Manager Human Resources
CNO: Peggy Schmits, Director, Nursing Operations
Web address: www.nbrrh.ernesthealth.com
Control: Corporation, Investor–owned, for–profit **Service:** Rehabilitation

Staffed Beds: 40 **Admissions:** 726 **Census:** 29 **Outpatient Visits:** 5892
Births: 0 **Total Expense ($000):** 12691 **Payroll Expense ($000):** 5794
Personnel: 142

⊞ **POST ACUTE/WARM SPRINGS SPECIALTY HOSPITAL OF NEW BRAUNFELS (452106)**, 1445 Hanz Drive, Zip 78130–2567; tel. 830/627–7600 **A**1 10 **F**1 3 29 30 34 85 130 148 **S** Post Acute Medical, LLC, Enola, PA
Primary Contact: Shayne Goode, Administrator
Web address: www.warmsprings.org/locations/hos/h1/
Control: Partnership, Investor–owned, for–profit **Service:** Long–Term Acute Care hospital

Staffed Beds: 40 **Admissions:** 476 **Census:** 27 **Outpatient Visits:** 0 **Births:** 0 **Total Expense ($000):** 13537 **Payroll Expense ($000):** 5708 **Personnel:** 96

Many Facility Codes have changed. Please refer to the AHA Guide Code Chart. © 2016 AHA Guide

TX

✠ **RESOLUTE HEALTH (670098)**, 555 Creekside Crossing, Zip 78130–2594; tel. 830/500–6000 **A**1 10 **F**3 13 18 20 29 30 34 35 40 45 48 49 50 53 64 65 70 72 74 75 76 77 79 81 85 87 107 108 111 114 115 119 126 130 146 **P**8 **S** TENET Healthcare Corporation, Dallas, TX
Primary Contact: Matt Stone, Chief Executive Officer
Web address: www.resolutehealth.com
Control: Corporation, Investor–owned, for–profit **Service:** General Medical and Surgical

Staffed Beds: 54 **Admissions:** 3479 **Census:** 27 **Outpatient Visits:** 23689 **Births:** 632 **Total Expense ($000):** 76498 **Payroll Expense ($000):** 23199 **Personnel:** 393

NOCONA—Montague County

NOCONA GENERAL HOSPITAL (450641), 100 Park Road, Zip 76255–3616; tel. 940/825–3235 **A**10 **F**3 7 11 28 29 30 34 35 40 43 45 50 53 57 59 62 64 68 75 81 82 86 87 93 107 108 114 119 130 133 146 148 **P**5
Primary Contact: Lance Meekins, Chief Executive Officeer
CFO: Lance Meekins, Chief Executive Officer
CMO: Chance Dingler, M.D., Chief Medical Officer
CHR: Paula Monkres, Administrative Assistant and Director Human Resources
Web address: www.noconageneral.com/
Control: Hospital district or authority, Government, nonfederal **Service:** General Medical and Surgical

Staffed Beds: 25 **Admissions:** 426 **Census:** 6 **Outpatient Visits:** 5020 **Births:** 0 **Total Expense ($000):** 7386 **Payroll Expense ($000):** 3738 **Personnel:** 94

NORTH RICHLAND HILLS—Tarrant County

✠ **NORTH HILLS HOSPITAL (450087)**, 4401 Booth Calloway Road, Zip 76180–7399; tel. 817/255–1000 **A**1 10 **F**3 8 12 15 17 18 20 22 24 28 29 30 31 34 37 40 43 45 49 53 56 57 64 70 74 75 77 78 79 81 84 85 86 87 93 98 103 107 108 110 111 115 118 119 126 130 132 135 146 148 **P**3 6 **S** HCA, Nashville, TN
Primary Contact: Xavier Villarreal, FACHE, Chief Executive Officer
COO: Nancy L. Hill, R.N., Chief Operating Officer
CFO: Nick Galt, Chief Financial Officer
CMO: John McDonald, M.D., Chief Medical Officer
CIO: Jason Sims, Facility Information Security Officer
CHR: Cynthia Dang, Vice President Human Resources
CNO: Tracey Smithson, MSN, Chief Nursing Officer
Web address: www.northhillshospital.com
Control: Partnership, Investor–owned, for–profit **Service:** General Medical and Surgical

Staffed Beds: 164 **Admissions:** 6258 **Census:** 81 **Outpatient Visits:** 62204 **Births:** 41 **Total Expense ($000):** 106959 **Payroll Expense ($000):** 35441 **Personnel:** 599

ODESSA—Ector County

☐ **BASIN HEALTHCARE CENTER (670066)**, 900 East 4th Street, Zip 79761–5255; tel. 432/362–9900, (Nonreporting) **A**1 10
Primary Contact: Gail Knous, Interim Administrator
CMO: Richard Bartlett, M.D., Chief Medical Officer
CHR: Gail Knous, Chief Executive Officer and Chief Compliance Officer
Web address: www.bhcodessa.com/
Control: Partnership, Investor–owned, for–profit **Service:** General Medical and Surgical

Staffed Beds: 14

CONTINUECARE HOSPITAL AT MEDICAL CENTER (ODESSA) (67011), 500 West Fourth Street, 4th Floor, Zip 79761–5001; tel. 432/640–4380, (Nonreporting) **S** Community Hospital Corporation, Plano, TX
Primary Contact: Judith Schiros, Chief Executive Officer
Web address: www.continuecare.org/odessa//
Control: Other not–for–profit (including NFP Corporation) **Service:** Long–Term Acute Care hospital

Staffed Beds: 25

✠ **MEDICAL CENTER HEALTH SYSTEM (450132)**, 500 West Fourth Street, Zip 79761–5059, Mailing Address: P.O. Drawer 7239, Zip 79760–7239; tel. 432/640–4000 **A**1 2 3 5 8 10 **F**3 8 11 12 13 15 17 18 20 22 24 26 28 29 30 31 34 35 39 40 43 45 46 47 48 49 50 51 53 54 57 59 64 65 66 68 70 71 72 74 75 76 77 78 79 81 85 87 89 90 93 107 111 114 115 116 117 118 119 126 129 130 131 132 135 144 146 147 148 **P**6 8
Primary Contact: William W. Webster, FACHE, President and Chief Executive Officer
COO: Tony Ruiz, Senior Vice President, Chief Operating Officer
CFO: Jon Riggs, Senior Vice President, Chief Financial Officer
CMO: Arun Mathews, M.D., Chief Medical Officer (Acute)
CIO: Gary Barnes, Senior Vice President, Chief Information Officer
CHR: Robbi Banks, Vice President, Human Resources
CNO: Chad Dunavan, R.N., Vice President, Chief Nursing Officer
Web address: www.mchodessa.com
Control: Hospital district or authority, Government, nonfederal **Service:** General Medical and Surgical

Staffed Beds: 368 **Admissions:** 13462 **Census:** 203 **Outpatient Visits:** 361050 **Births:** 1723 **Total Expense ($000):** 264962 **Payroll Expense ($000):** 103299 **Personnel:** 1650

MEDICAL CENTER HOSPITAL See Medical Center Health System

◇ **ODESSA REGIONAL MEDICAL CENTER (450661)**, 520 East Sixth Street, Zip 79761–4565, Mailing Address: P.O. Box 4859, Zip 79760–4859; tel. 432/582–8000 **A**3 5 10 21 **F**3 12 13 15 17 18 20 22 23 24 25 29 34 35 40 43 46 49 50 51 52 55 57 59 60 64 72 74 75 79 80 81 82 85 86 87 89 90 91 107 108 111 115 119 124 130 132 146 147 148 **P**8 **S** IASIS Healthcare, Franklin, TN
Primary Contact: Stacey L. Gerig, Chief Executive Officer
CIO: Jimmy Diaz, Director Information Technology
CHR: Jill Sparkman, Director Human Resources
CNO: Levi Ross Stone, R.N., Chief Nursing Officer and Chief Operating Officer
Web address: www.odessaregionalmedicalcenter.com
Control: Partnership, Investor–owned, for–profit **Service:** General Medical and Surgical

Staffed Beds: 213 **Admissions:** 6007 **Census:** 84 **Outpatient Visits:** 44975 **Births:** 2671 **Total Expense ($000):** 108910 **Payroll Expense ($000):** 40007 **Personnel:** 623

OLNEY—Young County

★ **HAMILTON HOSPITAL (451354)**, 901 West Hamilton Street, Zip 76374–1725, Mailing Address: P.O. Box 158, Zip 76374–0158; tel. 940/564–5521 **A**10 18 **F**7 11 13 28 29 30 34 40 43 53 57 76 77 81 86 89 93 107 114 119 127 129 133 146 148
Primary Contact: Michael H. Huff, Chief Executive Officer
CFO: Coy Noles, Chief Financial Officer Consultant
CMO: Mark L. Mankins, M.D., Chief of Staff
CIO: Rick Oliver, Information Technology
CHR: Amy Moore, Human Resources
CNO: Samantha Isbell, R.N., Chief Nursing Officer
Web address: www.olneyhamiltonhospital.com
Control: Hospital district or authority, Government, nonfederal **Service:** General Medical and Surgical

Staffed Beds: 25 **Admissions:** 517 **Census:** 7 **Outpatient Visits:** 14034 **Births:** 39 **Total Expense ($000):** 13408 **Payroll Expense ($000):** 4848 **Personnel:** 130

PALACIOS—Matagorda County

PALACIOS COMMUNITY MEDICAL CENTER (451332), 311 Green Street, Zip 77465–3213; tel. 361/972–2511 **A**10 18 **F**29 34 40 41 50 54 57 59 64 65 87 91 93 97 107 119 127 133 146 148 **P**6
Primary Contact: Alden M. Vandeveer, Jr., FACHE, Chief Executive Officer
COO: Lisa Henderson, Chief Operating Officer
CFO: Claude Manning, Chief Financial Officer
CIO: Angela Yeager, Director Information Technology
CHR: Lisa Henderson, Chief Operations Officer
CNO: Susan Easter, Chief Nursing Officer
Web address: www.palacioshospital.net/
Control: Other not–for–profit (including NFP Corporation) **Service:** General Medical and Surgical

Staffed Beds: 17 **Admissions:** 162 **Census:** 3 **Outpatient Visits:** 13101 **Births:** 0 **Total Expense ($000):** 5690 **Payroll Expense ($000):** 3085 **Personnel:** 66

TX

Hospital, Medicare Provider Number, Address, Telephone, Approval, Facility, and Physician Codes, Health Care System

★ American Hospital Association (AHA) membership
☐ The Joint Commission accreditation
◯ Healthcare Facilities Accreditation Program
◇ DNV Healthcare Inc. accreditation
⇑ Center for Improvement in Healthcare Quality Accreditation
△ Commission on Accreditation of Rehabilitation Facilities (CARF) accreditation

PALESTINE—Anderson County

✠ **PALESTINE REGIONAL MEDICAL CENTER (453089)**, 2900 South Loop 256, Zip 75801–6958; tel. 903/731–1000, (Nonreporting) **A**1 **S** LifePoint Health, Brentwood, TN
Primary Contact: Richard Grogan, Interim Chief Executive Officer
CFO: Louis D. Ferguson, Chief Financial Officer
CIO: Rebecca Chou, Directory Information Systems
CHR: Rhonda Beard, Director Human Resources
CNO: Christi Watkins, R.N., Chief Operating Officer
Web address: www.palestineregional.com
Control: Corporation, Investor–owned, for–profit **Service:** Rehabilitation

Staffed Beds: 12

✠ **PALESTINE REGIONAL MEDICAL CENTER–EAST (450747)**, 2900 South Loop 256, Zip 75801–6958; tel. 903/731–1000 **A**1 10 **F**3 4 7 11 13 15 18 20 22 26 28 29 30 34 40 43 44 47 48 49 50 51 56 57 59 60 62 63 70 76 79 81 82 85 86 87 89 90 93 96 97 98 100 101 102 103 104 107 108 110 111 114 118 119 129 130 131 146 147 148 **S** LifePoint Health, Brentwood, TN
Primary Contact: Richard Grogan, Interim Chief Executive Officer
CFO: Louis D. Ferguson, Chief Financial Officer
CIO: Rebecca Chou, Director Information Systems
CHR: Rhonda Beard, Director Human Resources
Web address: www.palestineregional.com
Control: Partnership, Investor–owned, for–profit **Service:** General Medical and Surgical

Staffed Beds: 139 Admissions: 4796 Census: 51 Outpatient Visits: 85100 Births: 668 Total Expense ($000): 61845 Payroll Expense ($000): 28464 Personnel: 475

PAMPA—Gray County

✠ **PAMPA REGIONAL MEDICAL CENTER (450099)**, One Medical Plaza, Zip 79065; tel. 806/665–3721 **A**1 10 20 **F**3 11 12 13 15 18 20 22 29 30 34 40 43 45 46 47 48 49 50 51 52 54 56 57 58 59 60 61 63 64 65 66 68 70 75 76 77 79 81 83 84 85 86 87 91 92 93 96 97 98 100 101 103 104 105 107 108 110 111 114 115 119 130 132 134 135 146 147 148 **P**7 **S** Prime Healthcare Services, Ontario, CA
Primary Contact: Brad S. Morse, Chief Executive Officer
CFO: Paul Christenson, Chief Financial Officer
CMO: David Hampton, M.D., Chief Medical Staff
CIO: Joy Patton, Chief Information Services
CHR: Debbie Dixon, Director Human Resources
CNO: Catherine Kenney, Chief Nursing Officer
Web address: www.prmctx.com
Control: Other not–for–profit (including NFP Corporation) **Service:** General Medical and Surgical

Staffed Beds: 32 Admissions: 2030 Census: 21 Outpatient Visits: 37637 Births: 194 Total Expense ($000): 33626 Payroll Expense ($000): 12064 Personnel: 234

PARIS—Lamar County

★ **CHRISTUS CONTINUING CARE DBA DUBUIS HOSPITAL OF PARIS (452082)**, 820 Clarksville Street, 6th Floor, Zip 75460–6027; tel. 903/737–3600 **A**10 **F**1 3 29 30 85 148 **S** CHRISTUS Health, Irving, TX
Primary Contact: Kathie Reese, R.N., Regional Administrator and Chief Executive Officer
CFO: Michael Murray, Chief Financial Officer
CMO: Devabrata Ganguly, M.D., Medical Director
CNO: Janice Cochran, Director Patient Care
Web address: www.christusdubuis.org
Control: Church–operated, Nongovernment, not–for profit **Service:** Long–Term Acute Care hospital

Staffed Beds: 25 Admissions: 210 Census: 15 Outpatient Visits: 0 Births: 0 Total Expense ($000): 6240 Payroll Expense ($000): 2030 Personnel: 39

☐ **PARIS REGIONAL MEDICAL CENTER (450196)**, 865 Deshong Drive, Zip 75460–9313, Mailing Address: P.O. Box 9070, Zip 75461–9070; tel. 903/785–4521, (Includes PARIS REGIONAL MEDICAL CENTER, 865 Deshong Drive, Zip 75462–2097; tel. 903/785–4521; PARIS REGIONAL MEDICAL CENTER–SOUTH CAMPUS, 820 Clarksville Street, Zip 75460–9070, Mailing Address: P.O. Box 9070, Zip 75461–9070; tel. 903/785–4521) **A**1 10 19 **F**3 8 11 13 15 17 18 20 22 24 26 28 30 31 34 35 36 39 40 45 49 50 51 55 57 59 60 64 65 66 68 70 72 74 75 77 78 79 81 82 85 86 87 90 91 93 97 98 102 103 107 108 111 115 119 126 127 130 132 135 144 145 146 147 148 **P**5 **S** RCCH HealthCare Partners, Brentwood, TN
Primary Contact: Patti Monczewski, Interim Chief Executive Officer
COO: Patti Monczewski, Chief Operating Officer
CFO: Janet Montel, Chief Financial Officer
CMO: Richard Bercher, M.D., Chief Medical Officer
CHR: Cheryl Perry, Director Human Resources
CNO: Debra Taylor, Chief Nursing Officer
Web address: www.parisrmc.com
Control: Partnership, Investor–owned, for–profit **Service:** General Medical and Surgical

Staffed Beds: 173 Admissions: 7750 Census: 101 Outpatient Visits: 82364 Births: 774 Total Expense ($000): 108618 Payroll Expense ($000): 36919 Personnel: 808

PASADENA—Harris County

✠ **BAYSHORE MEDICAL CENTER (450097)**, 4000 Spencer Highway, Zip 77504–1202; tel. 713/359–2000, (Includes EAST HOUSTON REGIONAL MEDICAL CENTER, 13111 East Freeway, Houston, Zip 77015–5820; tel. 713/393–2000; Alice G. Adams, R.N., Chief Executive Officer) **A**1 2 3 10 **F**3 11 12 13 15 17 18 20 22 24 26 28 29 31 34 35 40 41 42 43 45 49 50 51 56 57 59 60 64 70 72 74 75 76 77 78 79 81 82 85 90 93 96 98 100 102 103 104 105 107 108 110 111 114 116 117 118 119 121 123 124 129 130 131 132 146 147 148 **S** HCA, Nashville, TN
Primary Contact: Jeanna Barnard, FACHE, Chief Executive Officer
CFO: John Armour, Chief Financial Officer
CIO: Clifford Ferguson, Director Information Technology and Systems
Web address: www.bayshoremedical.com
Control: Partnership, Investor–owned, for–profit **Service:** General Medical and Surgical

Staffed Beds: 461 Admissions: 22154 Census: 310 Outpatient Visits: 188662 Births: 4545 Total Expense ($000): 274845 Payroll Expense ($000): 113904 Personnel: 2152

★ ◇ **CHI ST. LUKE'S HEALTH – PATIENTS MEDICAL CENTER (670031)**, 4600 East Sam Houston Parkway South, Zip 77505–3948; tel. 713/948–7000 **A**10 21 **F**15 18 20 22 24 29 30 31 35 40 45 46 54 64 70 74 77 81 82 86 87 91 93 94 107 111 114 115 116 117 119 129 130 135 146 147 148 **S** Catholic Health Initiatives, Englewood, CO
Primary Contact: Steven Foster, Chief Executive Officer
Web address: www.stlukestexas.com
Control: Corporation, Investor–owned, for–profit **Service:** General Medical and Surgical

Staffed Beds: 61 Admissions: 4048 Census: 55 Outpatient Visits: 34526 Births: 0 Total Expense ($000): 70420 Payroll Expense ($000): 27322 Personnel: 412

PATIENTS MEDICAL CENTER See CHI St. Luke's Health – Patients Medical Center

◯ **SURGERY SPECIALTY HOSPITALS OF AMERICA (450831)**, 4301B Vista Road, Zip 77504; tel. 713/378–3000 **A**10 11 **F**3 12 29 40 45 68 70 75 79 81 82 107 109 111 114 119 132 135
Primary Contact: Eric Chan, M.D., Chief Executive Officer
COO: Hemant Khemka, Chief Operating Officer
CFO: Hemant Khemka, Chief Financial Officer
CMO: Xiao H. Li, M.D., Chief of Staff
CIO: Ringo Cheng, Director Chief Information Technology
Web address: www.surgeryspecialty.com/
Control: Partnership, Investor–owned, for–profit **Service:** General Medical and Surgical

Staffed Beds: 37 Admissions: 99 Census: 1 Outpatient Visits: 1884 Births: 0 Total Expense ($000): 14072 Payroll Expense ($000): 3557 Personnel: 81

PEARLAND—Brazoria County

✠ **PEARLAND MEDICAL CENTER**, 11100 Shadow Creek Parkway, Zip 77584–7285; tel. 713/770–7000, (Data for 332 days) **A**1 **F**3 13 15 18 20 22 26 29 31 34 35 37 40 41 45 49 50 51 57 59 60 68 73 74 75 77 78 79 81 82 85 86 87 107 108 110 111 114 119 126 130 143 146 148 **S** HCA, Nashville, TN
Primary Contact: David S. Wagner, Chief Executive Officer
Web address: www.pearlandmc.com
Control: Partnership, Investor–owned, for–profit **Service:** General Medical and Surgical

Staffed Beds: 33 Admissions: 1219 Census: 11 Outpatient Visits: 19902 Births: 66 Total Expense ($000): 46783 Payroll Expense ($000): 14154 Personnel: 234

PEARSALL—Frio County

★ **FRIO REGIONAL HOSPITAL (450293)**, 200 South I. H. 35, Zip 78061–3998; tel. 830/334–3617 **A**10 **F**3 8 15 29 34 35 40 43 45 53 57 59 62 64 68 77 81 87 107 114 119 130 133 148 **P**6
Primary Contact: Andrew G. Williams, Chief Executive Officer
CMO: Oscar Garza, M.D., Chief Medical Staff
CIO: Jacob Flores, Chief Information Officer
CHR: Nancy Ortiz, Director Human Resource and Marketing
CNO: Louisa Martinez, Director of Nursing
Web address: www.frioregionalhospital.com
Control: Other not–for–profit (including NFP Corporation) **Service:** General Medical and Surgical

Staffed Beds: 22 Admissions: 335 Census: 3 Outpatient Visits: 20199 Births: 132 Total Expense ($000): 13403 Payroll Expense ($000): 5431 Personnel: 116

TX

PECOS—Reeves County

REEVES COUNTY HOSPITAL (451377), 2323 Texas Street, Zip 79772–7338;
tel. 432/447–3551 **A**10 18 **F**3 11 13 35 40 43 57 60 64 68 70 81 87 93 107
110 114 119 127 130 131 133 146 147 148
Primary Contact: Brenda McKinney, Chief Executive Officer
CFO: Bomi Bharucha, Chief Financial Officer
CMO: W. J. Bang, M.D., Chief of Staff
CHR: Nadine Smith, Director Human Resources
CNO: Faye Lease, Director of Nursing
Web address: www.reevescountyhospital.com
Control: Hospital district or authority, Government, nonfederal **Service:** General
Medical and Surgical

Staffed Beds: 25 **Admissions:** 801 **Census:** 9 **Outpatient Visits:** 55984
Births: 143 **Total Expense ($000):** 22761 **Payroll Expense ($000):** 12419
Personnel: 209

PERRYTON—Ochiltree County

★ **OCHILTREE GENERAL HOSPITAL (451359)**, 3101 Garrett Drive,
Zip 79070–5323; tel. 806/435–3606 **A**10 18 **F**10 11 13 15 30 35 40 43 57
59 62 63 64 69 76 81 85 89 93 107 108 114 119 127 130 133 143 146
147 **P**1
Primary Contact: Robert A. Pascasio, FACHE, Administrator and Chief Executive
Officer
CFO: Debbie Blodgett, Director Fiscal Services
CIO: Dyan Harrison, Manager Health Information
CHR: Debbie Beck, Manager Human Resource and Payroll
Web address: www.ochiltreehospital.com
Control: Hospital district or authority, Government, nonfederal **Service:** General
Medical and Surgical

Staffed Beds: 25 **Admissions:** 506 **Census:** 7 **Outpatient Visits:** 35304
Births: 195 **Total Expense ($000):** 15655 **Payroll Expense ($000):** 6452
Personnel: 160

PITTSBURG—Camp County

★ **EAST TEXAS MEDICAL CENTER PITTSBURG (451367)**, 2701 Highway 271
North, Zip 75686–1032; tel. 903/946–5000 **A**10 18 **F**3 11 12 28 29 35 40 43
45 50 53 57 59 64 68 70 75 77 81 85 87 89 92 93 97 107 108 111 115
119 127 129 130 133 **P**6 **S** East Texas Medical Center Regional Healthcare
System, Tyler, TX
Primary Contact: James Warren Robicheaux, FACHE, Senior Administrator
CMO: W. R. Christensen, M.D., Chief of Staff
CIO: Paula Anthony, Vice President Information Services
CHR: Kathy Shelton, Director Human Resources
CNO: Casey Mayben, Chief Nursing Officer
Web address: www.etmc.org/newpittsburg.htm
Control: Other not–for–profit (including NFP Corporation) **Service:** General
Medical and Surgical

Staffed Beds: 25 **Admissions:** 934 **Census:** 10 **Outpatient Visits:** 100975
Births: 0 **Total Expense ($000):** 30010 **Payroll Expense ($000):** 9543
Personnel: 188

PLAINVIEW—Hale County

ALLEGIANCE BEHAVIORAL HEALTH CENTER OF PLAINVIEW (454101),
2601 Dimmit Road, Suite 400, Zip 79072–1833; tel. 806/296–9191 **A**10 **F**29
35 56 64 98 101 103 104 **S** Allegiance Health Management, Shreveport, LA
Primary Contact: Angie Alexander, Chief Executive Officer
COO: Don Cameron, Chief Operating Officer
CMO: Victor A. Gutierrez, M.D., Medical Director
CIO: Richard Merk, Executive Vice President
CHR: Richard Merk, Director Human Resources
Web address: www.ahmgt.com
Control: Corporation, Investor–owned, for–profit **Service:** Psychiatric

Staffed Beds: 20 **Admissions:** 288 **Census:** 11 **Outpatient Visits:** 26884
Births: 0 **Total Expense ($000):** 6808 **Payroll Expense ($000):** 2000
Personnel: 49

⊞ **COVENANT HOSPITAL PLAINVIEW (450539)**, 2601 Dimmitt Road,
Zip 79072–1833; tel. 806/296–5531 **A**1 3 10 20 **F**3 11 12 15 18 29 30
32 34 35 38 40 43 44 45 46 48 50 51 54 56 57 59 61 64 65 68 70 75
76 77 79 80 81 85 86 87 97 107 108 110 114 119 127 129 130 131 132
135 146 147 148 **S** Providence St. Joseph Health, Renton, WA
Primary Contact: Robert Copeland, Interim Chief Executive Officer
COO: Mike McNutt, Assistant Administrator
CFO: Cassie Mogg, Chief Financial Officer
CMO: Sergio Lara, M.D., Chief Medical Officer
CNO: Leslie Hackett, Chief Nursing Officer
Web address: www.covenantplainview.org
Control: Church–operated, Nongovernment, not–for profit **Service:** General
Medical and Surgical

Staffed Beds: 68 **Admissions:** 1858 **Census:** 15 **Outpatient Visits:** 81478
Births: 462 **Total Expense ($000):** 36058 **Payroll Expense ($000):** 12233
Personnel: 295

PLANO—Collin County

⊞ **BAYLOR REGIONAL MEDICAL CENTER AT PLANO (450890)**, 4700 Alliance
Boulevard, Zip 75093–5323; tel. 469/814–2000 **A**1 2 3 5 10 **F**3 12 15 29 30
31 34 35 40 45 46 47 49 54 57 59 64 70 74 75 77 78 79 80 81 82 84 85
86 87 107 108 110 111 114 118 119 126 130 131 132 135 145 146 147
148 **S** Baylor Scott & White Health, Dallas, TX
Primary Contact: Jerri Garison, R.N., President
COO: Joseph Brown, Vice President Operations
CFO: Deanne Kindered, Vice President Finance
CMO: John Marcucci, M.D., Vice President Medical Affairs
CHR: Kriss Gamez, Director Human Resources
Web address: www.baylorhealth.com/PhysiciansLocations/Plano/Pages/Default.
aspx
Control: Other not–for–profit (including NFP Corporation) **Service:** General
Medical and Surgical

Staffed Beds: 112 **Admissions:** 6216 **Census:** 88 **Outpatient Visits:** 53153
Births: 0 **Total Expense ($000):** 163390 **Payroll Expense ($000):** 55812
Personnel: 625

CHILDREN'S MEDICAL CENTER PLANO, 7601 Preston Road,
Zip 75024–3214; tel. 469/303–7000 **A**3 5 **F**88 89 98
Primary Contact: David T. Berry, President, Children's Health Clinical Operations
CIO: Pamela Arora, Senior Vice President and Chief Information Officer
CHR: Kim Besse, Senior Vice President and Chief Human Resource Officer
CNO: Mary Stowe, Senior Vice President and Chief Nursing Officer
Web address: www.https://www.childrens.com/location–landing/locations–and–
directions/childrens–health–plano
Control: Other not–for–profit (including NFP Corporation) **Service:** General
Medical and Surgical

Staffed Beds: 66 **Admissions:** 6085 **Census:** 27 **Outpatient Visits:** 147486
Births: 0

⊞ **HEALTHSOUTH PLANO REHABILITATION HOSPITAL (453047)**, 2800 West
15th Street, Zip 75075–7526; tel. 972/612–9000 **A**1 10 **F**34 57 59 90 93 95
96 130 132 148 **S** HEALTHSOUTH Corporation, Birmingham, AL
Primary Contact: Jennifer Lynn Brewer, Chief Executive Officer
CFO: Catrina Madkins, Controller and Chief Financial Officer
CMO: Omar Colon, M.D., Medical Director
Web address: www.healthsouthplano.com
Control: Corporation, Investor–owned, for–profit **Service:** Rehabilitation

Staffed Beds: 83 **Admissions:** 1639 **Census:** 52 **Outpatient Visits:** 9366
Births: 0 **Total Expense ($000):** 19967 **Payroll Expense ($000):** 11425
Personnel: 220

⊞ ◇ **MEDICAL CENTER OF PLANO (450651)**, 3901 West 15th Street,
Zip 75075–7738; tel. 972/596–6800, (Includes MEDICAL CENTER FRISCO, 5500
Frisco Square Boulevard, Frisco, Zip 75034–3305; tel. 214/618–0500; Charles
Gressle, Chief Executive Officer) **A**1 2 3 10 13 21 **F**3 12 13 15 16 18 19 20 22
24 26 28 29 30 31 34 35 40 42 43 45 46 47 48 49 51 54 55 57 58 59 60
64 70 72 74 75 76 78 79 81 82 84 85 86 87 90 91 93 107 108 110 111
112 114 115 117 118 119 124 126 130 132 135 145 146 147 148 **P**5
S HCA, Nashville, TN
Primary Contact: Charles Gressle, Chief Executive Officer
CFO: W. Patrick Whitmore, Chief Financial Officer
CMO: Ann Arnold, M.D., Medical Director
CIO: Michael Gfeller, Director Information Systems
CHR: Shanna Warren, Director Human Resources
Web address: www.medicalcenterplano.com
Control: Partnership, Investor–owned, for–profit **Service:** General Medical and
Surgical

Staffed Beds: 395 **Admissions:** 18467 **Census:** 291 **Outpatient Visits:**
137366 **Births:** 2545 **Total Expense ($000):** 327551 **Payroll Expense
($000):** 101960 **Personnel:** 1375

TX

Hospital, Medicare Provider Number, Address, Telephone, Approval, Facility, and Physician Codes, Health Care System

★ American Hospital Association (AHA) membership ○ Healthcare Facilities Accreditation Program ⇑ Center for Improvement in Healthcare Quality Accreditation
□ The Joint Commission accreditation ◇ DNV Healthcare Inc. accreditation △ Commission on Accreditation of Rehabilitation Facilities (CARF) accreditation

OCEANS BEHAVIORAL HOSPITAL PLANO, 4301 Mapleshade Lane, Zip 75093–0010; tel. 972/596–5445, (Nonreporting) **S** Oceans Healthcare, Lake Charles, LA
Primary Contact: Rick Harding, Administrator
Web address: www.oceansplano.com
Control: Corporation, Investor–owned, for–profit **Service:** Psychiatric

Staffed Beds: 25

☐ **PLANO SPECIALTY HOSPITAL (452054)**, 1621 Coit Road, Zip 75075–6141; tel. 972/758–5200 **A**1 10 **F**1 3 29 75 82 84 85 86 87 96 130 135 148 **S** Concord Healthcare Group, Lakewood, NJ
Primary Contact: Wayne Cook, Chief Executive Officer
CFO: Deanna Lankford, Business Office Manager
CHR: Robbie McCranie, Director Human Resources
Web address: www.specialtyhospital–plano.com
Control: Corporation, Investor–owned, for–profit **Service:** Long–Term Acute Care hospital

Staffed Beds: 43 Admissions: 286 Census: 17 Outpatient Visits: 0 Births: 0 Total Expense ($000): 6395 Payroll Expense ($000): 2582 Personnel: 57

☐ **PLANO SURGICAL HOSPITAL (673055)**, 2301 Marsh Lane, Zip 75093–8497; tel. 972/820–2600, (Data for 152 days) **A**1 10 **F**3 29 40 45 46 49 79 81 82 85 87 107 114
Primary Contact: Jay Lindsey, Chief Executive Officer
Web address: www.nobilishealth.com/our–facilities/dallas/
Control: Corporation, Investor–owned, for–profit **Service:** Surgical

Staffed Beds: 26 Admissions: 23 Census: 1 Outpatient Visits: 1148 Births: 0 Total Expense ($000): 17614 Payroll Expense ($000): 2204 Personnel: 101

☐ **TEXAS HEALTH CENTER FOR DIAGNOSTIC & SURGERY (450891)**, 6020 West Parker Road, Suite 100, Zip 75093–8171; tel. 972/403–2700 **A**1 2 10 **F**3 29 40 45 54 64 79 81 82 85 87 107 111 115 119 126 129
Primary Contact: Larry Robertson, President
CFO: Douglas Browning, Chief Financial Officer
CHR: Cookie Tedder, Human Resources Manager
CNO: Ellen Baldwin, R.N., Chief Nursing Officer
Web address: www.thcds.com
Control: Partnership, Investor–owned, for–profit **Service:** General Medical and Surgical

Staffed Beds: 18 Admissions: 675 Census: 4 Outpatient Visits: 16261 Births: 0 Total Expense ($000): 51116 Payroll Expense ($000): 12017 Personnel: 163

✠ **TEXAS HEALTH PRESBYTERIAN HOSPITAL PLANO (450771)**, 6200 West Parker Road, Zip 75093–8185; tel. 972/981–8000 **A**1 3 10 **F**3 12 13 15 18 20 22 24 26 28 29 30 31 32 34 35 37 38 40 43 44 45 46 49 50 52 54 55 57 58 59 60 64 65 68 70 72 74 75 76 77 78 79 81 84 85 86 87 89 93 98 107 108 110 111 114 115 118 119 126 130 131 132 134 135 141 145 146 147 148 **P**6 **S** Texas Health Resources, Arlington, TX
Primary Contact: Joshua Floren, President
CFO: Lisa Gildon, Vice President and Chief Financial Officer
CMO: Gwen Webster, M.D., President Medical Staff
CIO: Susan Anderson, Director Information Systems
CHR: Kelly K. Martin, Human Resource Officer
CNO: Raymond Kelly, R.N., Chief Nursing Officer
Web address: www.texashealth.org
Control: Other not–for–profit (including NFP Corporation) **Service:** General Medical and Surgical

Staffed Beds: 334 Admissions: 16508 Census: 217 Outpatient Visits: 98098 Births: 3952 Total Expense ($000): 308028 Payroll Expense ($000): 108823 Personnel: 1403

✠ **THE HEART HOSPITAL BAYLOR PLANO (670025)**, 1100 Allied Drive, Zip 75093–5348; tel. 469/814–3278 **A**1 5 10 **F**3 17 18 20 22 24 26 28 29 30 34 40 54 57 59 64 68 75 81 84 85 86 87 91 92 93 96 97 107 108 111 112 114 115 116 117 118 119 120 121 123 124 126 130 146 147
Primary Contact: Mark Valentine, President
CFO: Bryan Nichols, Chief Financial Officer
CMO: Trent Pettijohn, M.D., Chief Medical Officer
CIO: Nayan Patel, Director Information Systems
CHR: Kriss Gamez, Director Human Resources
CNO: Susan Moats, R.N., Vice President of Patient Care Services and Chief Nursing Officer
Web address: www.https://www.thehearthospitalbaylor.com
Control: Partnership, Investor–owned, for–profit **Service:** Heart

Staffed Beds: 116 Admissions: 4365 Census: 70 Outpatient Visits: 25062 Births: 0 Total Expense ($000): 194963 Payroll Expense ($000): 60186 Personnel: 676

PORT ARTHUR—Jefferson County

★ **CHRISTUS DUBUIS HOSPITAL OF PORT ARTHUR**, 3600 Gates Boulevard, 3rd Floor West, Zip 77642–3858; tel. 409/989–5300, (Nonreporting) **S** CHRISTUS Health, Irving, TX
Primary Contact: Terry W. Kepler, Administrator
Web address: www.christusdubuis.org/CHRISTUSDubuisHospitalofPortArthur
Control: Other not–for–profit (including NFP Corporation) **Service:** Long–Term Acute Care hospital

Staffed Beds: 15

DUBUIS HOSPITAL OF PORT ARTHUR See CHRISTUS Dubuis Hospital of Port Arthur

◇ **THE MEDICAL CENTER OF SOUTHEAST TEXAS (450518)**, 2555 Jimmy Johnson Boulevard, Zip 77640–2007; tel. 409/724–7389 **A**10 21 **F**3 8 11 12 13 15 17 18 20 22 24 28 29 30 34 35 40 43 44 45 47 49 50 56 57 59 64 72 74 76 77 78 79 81 82 85 86 87 89 90 91 92 93 94 98 101 102 103 104 105 107 108 110 111 114 115 119 121 129 130 132 135 146 147 148 **P**2 **S** IASIS Healthcare, Franklin, TN
Primary Contact: Richard Gonzalez, Chief Executive Officer
COO: Chris McMahon, Chief Operating Officer
CFO: Jason R. Miller, Chief Financial Officer
CMO: Don Duplan, M.D., Chief of Staff
CIO: Bryan Hebert, Director Information Systems
CHR: Carol Hebert, Director Human Resources
CNO: Heidi Wolf, R.N., Chief Nursing Officer
Web address: www.medicalcentersetexas.com
Control: Partnership, Investor–owned, for–profit **Service:** General Medical and Surgical

Staffed Beds: 168 Admissions: 8269 Census: 99 Outpatient Visits: 72037 Births: 1307 Total Expense ($000): 110598 Payroll Expense ($000): 41669 Personnel: 757

PORT LAVACA—Calhoun County

★ **MEMORIAL MEDICAL CENTER (451356)**, 815 North Virginia Street, Zip 77979–3025, Mailing Address: P.O. Box 25, Zip 77979–0025; tel. 361/552–6713 **A**10 18 **F**3 11 13 15 18 29 30 32 34 35 40 43 44 45 46 49 50 57 59 64 65 68 70 75 76 77 78 79 81 84 85 86 87 93 107 108 111 115 118 119 127 129 130 132 133 134 135 146 147 148
Primary Contact: Jason Anglin, Chief Executive Officer
COO: Roshanda Gray, Assistant Administrator
CMO: Jeannine Griffin, M.D., Chief of Staff
CIO: Adam Besio, Chief Information Officer
CNO: Erin R. Clevenger, Chief Nursing Officer and Director of Quality
Web address: www.mmcportlavaca.com
Control: County–Government, nonfederal **Service:** General Medical and Surgical

Staffed Beds: 25 Admissions: 1103 Census: 12 Outpatient Visits: 50445 Births: 121 Total Expense ($000): 24491 Payroll Expense ($000): 9484 Personnel: 199

QUANAH—Hardeman County

HARDEMAN COUNTY MEMORIAL HOSPITAL (451352), 402 Mercer Street, Zip 79252–4026, Mailing Address: P.O. Box 90, Zip 79252–0090; tel. 940/663–2795 **A**10 18 **F**28 29 30 34 40 43 50 56 59 62 63 64 75 77 87 93 100 101 103 104 107 127 130 133 147 **P**5
Primary Contact: Dave Clark, FACHE, Interim Chief Executive Officer
CFO: Tracy Betts, Chief Financial Officer
CMO: Kevin Lane, D.O., Chief of Staff
CNO: Dennis Thomas, Chief Nursing Officer
Web address: www.hcmhosp.com/
Control: Hospital district or authority, Government, nonfederal **Service:** General Medical and Surgical

Staffed Beds: 18 Admissions: 262 Census: 4 Outpatient Visits: 14704 Births: 0 Total Expense ($000): 6595 Payroll Expense ($000): 3352 Personnel: 79

QUITMAN—Wood County

★ **EAST TEXAS MEDICAL CENTER–QUITMAN (451380)**, 117 Winnsboro Street, Zip 75783–2144, Mailing Address: P.O. Box 1000, Zip 75783–1000; tel. 903/763–6300 **A**10 18 **F**3 11 15 29 30 35 40 43 45 50 57 59 64 65 68 79 81 85 87 107 108 110 111 115 119 127 129 130 133 **P**7 **S** East Texas Medical Center Regional Healthcare System, Tyler, TX
Primary Contact: Patrick Swindle, Administrator
CFO: Janet Andersen, Chief Financial Officer
CHR: William Henry, Director Human Resources
CNO: Allicia Settles, Chief Nursing Officer
Web address: www.etmc.org/etmcquitman/
Control: Other not–for–profit (including NFP Corporation) **Service:** General Medical and Surgical

Staffed Beds: 25 Admissions: 1023 Census: 11 Outpatient Visits: 46608 Births: 0 Total Expense ($000): 20880 Payroll Expense ($000): 6421 Personnel: 107

TX

Many Facility Codes have changed. Please refer to the AHA Guide Code Chart.
© 2016 AHA Guide

RANKIN—Upton County

★ **RANKIN COUNTY HOSPITAL DISTRICT (451329)**, 1105 Elizabeth Street, Zip 79778, Mailing Address: P.O. Box 327, Zip 79778–0327; tel. 432/693–2443 **A**10 18 **F**7 29 35 40 53 59 64 65 68 93 97 119 133
Primary Contact: Jim Horton, Chief Executive Officer
CFO: Tami Burks, Comptroller
CMO: Thomas J. Curvin, M.D., Chief of Staff
Web address: www.rankincountyhospital.com/
Control: Hospital district or authority, Government, nonfederal **Service:** General Medical and Surgical

Staffed Beds: 15 **Admissions:** 46 **Census:** 1 **Outpatient Visits:** 11287
Births: 0 **Total Expense ($000):** 9961 **Payroll Expense ($000):** 4355
Personnel: 71

REFUGIO—Refugio County

REFUGIO COUNTY MEMORIAL HOSPITAL (451317), 107 Swift Street, Zip 78377–2425; tel. 361/526–2321 **A**10 18 **F**3 7 29 40 43 57 61 64 75 81 86 87 93 97 107 119 127 133 **P**6
Primary Contact: Louis R. Willeke, Administrator
Web address: www.refugiohospital.com/
Control: Hospital district or authority, Government, nonfederal **Service:** General Medical and Surgical

Staffed Beds: 20 **Admissions:** 68 **Census:** 1 **Outpatient Visits:** 20667
Births: 0 **Total Expense ($000):** 14477 **Payroll Expense ($000):** 5359
Personnel: 144

RICHARDSON—Collin County

▣ **HEALTHSOUTH REHABILITATION HOSPITAL NORTH TEXAS (673029)**, 3351 Waterview Parkway, Zip 75080–1449; tel. 972/398–5700, (Data for 92 days) **A**1 10 **F**3 29 90 93 96 148 **S** HEALTHSOUTH Corporation, Birmingham, AL
Primary Contact: Jim Ransom, Chief Executive Officer
CFO: Nichole Dykes, Chief Financial Officer
CMO: Richard Jones, M.D., Medical Director
CNO: Pam Smith, Chief Nursing Officer
Web address: www.relianthcp.com
Control: Corporation, Investor–owned, for–profit **Service:** Rehabilitation

Staffed Beds: 50 **Admissions:** 291 **Census:** 37 **Outpatient Visits:** 858
Births: 0 **Total Expense ($000):** 3473 **Payroll Expense ($000):** 1770
Personnel: 102

▣ **METHODIST RICHARDSON MEDICAL CENTER (450537)**, 2831 East President George Bush Highway, Zip 75082–3561; tel. 469/204–1000 **A**1 2 10 **F**3 5 11 13 15 18 20 22 24 29 30 31 34 35 38 40 45 46 49 54 55 56 57 59 64 65 68 70 72 74 75 76 77 78 79 81 82 85 86 87 93 97 98 100 101 102 103 104 105 107 108 109 110 111 112 115 116 117 119 120 121 123 124 126 129 130 131 132 135 146 147 148 **P**1 7 **S** Methodist Health System, Dallas, TX
Primary Contact: E. Kenneth Hutchenrider, Jr., FACHE, President
COO: Robert Simpson, Vice President Operations
CFO: Amy Bodwell, Vice President Finance
CMO: Mark Smith, M.D., Chief Medical Officer
CIO: Pamela McNutt, Senior Vice President and Chief Information Officer
CHR: Chris Loyd, Director Human Resources
CNO: Irene T. Strejc, M.P.H., Vice President, Nursing
Web address: www.methodisthealthsystem.org/richardson
Control: Other not–for–profit (including NFP Corporation) **Service:** General Medical and Surgical

Staffed Beds: 249 **Admissions:** 9245 **Census:** 117 **Outpatient Visits:** 81318
Births: 1883 **Total Expense ($000):** 172433 **Payroll Expense ($000):** 67745 **Personnel:** 767

RICHMOND—Fort Bend County

□ △ **OAKBEND MEDICAL CENTER (450330)**, 1705 Jackson Street, Zip 77469–3289; tel. 281/341–3000, (Total facility includes 19 beds in nursing home–type unit) **A**1 3 7 10 **F**3 11 13 15 18 20 22 24 26 28 29 30 31 34 35 40 41 43 44 45 46 48 49 50 53 56 57 59 68 70 72 74 75 76 77 78 79 81 85 87 89 97 98 107 110 111 114 115 119 128 129 130 131 146 147 148 **P**6
Primary Contact: Joe Freudenberger, Chief Executive Officer
CFO: Rodney Lenfant, Chief Financial Officer
CMO: Douglas Thibodeaux, M.D., Chief Medical Officer
CIO: Tim McCarty, Chief Information Officer
CHR: Eileen Gamboa, Director Human Resources
Web address: www.oakbendmedcenter.org
Control: Hospital district or authority, Government, nonfederal **Service:** General Medical and Surgical

Staffed Beds: 188 **Admissions:** 6726 **Census:** 94 **Outpatient Visits:** 74769
Births: 1813 **Total Expense ($000):** 164625 **Payroll Expense ($000):** 44172 **Personnel:** 894

WESTPARK SPRINGS, 6902 South Peek Road, Zip 77407; tel. 832/532–8107, (Nonreporting)
Primary Contact: Jim Serratt, Chief Executive Officer
Web address: www.westparksprings.com/why–westpark–springs/
Control: Other not–for–profit (including NFP Corporation) **Service:** Psychiatric

Staffed Beds: 72

RIO GRANDE CITY—Starr County

★ **STARR COUNTY MEMORIAL HOSPITAL (450654)**, 2753 Hospital Court, Zip 78582–6859, Mailing Address: P.O. Box 78, Zip 78582–0078; tel. 956/487–5561, (Total facility includes 119 beds in nursing home–type unit) **A**10 20 **F**7 11 13 15 29 34 35 40 43 45 46 50 57 59 64 65 66 68 75 76 81 89 107 110 111 115 119 127 128 130 135 145 148 **P**5
Primary Contact: Thalia H. Munoz, R.N., MS, Chief Executive Officer
CFO: Rafael Olivares, Controller
CHR: Amaro Salinas, Assistant Administrator and Human Resource Officer
CNO: Mario Segura, Director of Nursing
Web address: www.starrcountyhospital.com
Control: Hospital district or authority, Government, nonfederal **Service:** General Medical and Surgical

Staffed Beds: 166 **Admissions:** 1225 **Census:** 121 **Outpatient Visits:** 34894
Births: 214 **Total Expense ($000):** 26511 **Payroll Expense ($000):** 13016
Personnel: 273

ROCKDALE—Milam County

◇ **ROCKDALE HOSPITAL (451357)**, 1700 Brazos Street, Zip 76567–2517, Mailing Address: Drawer 1010, Zip 76567–1010; tel. 512/446–4500 **A**10 18 21 **F**3 7 15 18 20 22 29 34 40 43 45 46 47 54 56 57 59 64 65 68 74 75 77 79 81 82 84 85 87 91 93 107 108 110 111 114 116 117 119 127 129 131 133 135 146 147 148
Primary Contact: Jeffrey Madison, FACHE, Chief Executive Officer
CMO: John Weed, III, M.D., Medical Director
CHR: Crystal Foley, Director Human Resources
Web address: www.lrhealthcare.com
Control: Partnership, Investor–owned, for–profit **Service:** General Medical and Surgical

Staffed Beds: 21 **Admissions:** 233 **Census:** 2 **Outpatient Visits:** 324594
Births: 0 **Total Expense ($000):** 106437 **Payroll Expense ($000):** 31549
Personnel: 645

ROCKWALL—Rockwall County

BAYLOR EMERGENCY MEDICAL CENTERS – ROCKWALL (670097), 1975 Alpha Drive Suite 100, Zip 75087–4951; tel. 214/294–6200, (Nonreporting) **S** Emerus, The Woodlands, TX
Primary Contact: Kyle Kirkpatrick, Chief Executive Officer
Web address: www.bayloremc.com/rockwall
Control: Partnership, Investor–owned, for–profit **Service:** General Medical and Surgical

Staffed Beds: 8

▣ **TEXAS HEALTH PRESBYTERIAN HOSPITAL OF ROCKWALL (670044)**, 3150 Horizon Road, Zip 75032–7805; tel. 469/698–1000 **A**1 3 10 **F**3 12 13 15 29 30 34 35 40 42 45 46 47 49 50 54 68 70 75 76 77 79 81 82 84 85 87 89 107 108 110 111 115 119 130 146 147 148
Primary Contact: Cynthia K. Paris, FACHE, R.N., President and Chief Executive Officer
CFO: Jason Linscott, CPA, Chief Financial Officer
CMO: Gary Bonacquisti, M.D., Chief Medical Officer
CNO: Tami Hawkins, R.N., Vice President Patient Care and Chief Nursing Officer
Web address: www.phrtexas.com
Control: Corporation, Investor–owned, for–profit **Service:** General Medical and Surgical

Staffed Beds: 50 **Admissions:** 4131 **Census:** 41 **Outpatient Visits:** 56126
Births: 602 **Total Expense ($000):** 97913 **Payroll Expense ($000):** 33838
Personnel: 498

Hospital, Medicare Provider Number, Address, Telephone, Approval, Facility, and Physician Codes, Health Care System

★ American Hospital Association (AHA) membership
□ The Joint Commission accreditation
◇ Healthcare Facilities Accreditation Program
◇ DNV Healthcare Inc. accreditation
⇑ Center for Improvement in Healthcare Quality Accreditation
△ Commission on Accreditation of Rehabilitation Facilities (CARF) accreditation

TX

ROTAN—Fisher County

FISHER COUNTY HOSPITAL DISTRICT (451313), 774 State Highway 70
North, Zip 79546–6918, Mailing Address: P.O. Drawer F, Zip 79546–4019;
tel. 325/735–2256 **A**10 18 **F**7 28 32 34 35 40 43 50 53 56 57 59 64 66 75
93 97 107 119 127 133 **P**6
Primary Contact: Leanne Martinez, Chief Executive Officer and Administrator
CFO: Debbie Hull, Chief Financial Officer
CMO: Joseph Lampley, D.O., Chief of Staff
CHR: Teresa Terry, Director Human Resource, Payroll
CNO: D'Linda Benham, Director of Nursing
Web address: www.fishercountyhospital.com
Control: Hospital district or authority, Government, nonfederal **Service:** General
Medical and Surgical

Staffed Beds: 13 **Admissions:** 149 **Census:** 3 **Outpatient Visits:** 20309
Births: 0 **Total Expense ($000):** 8394 **Payroll Expense ($000):** 3844
Personnel: 71

ROUND ROCK—Williamson County

✠ **HEALTHSOUTH REHABILITATION HOSPITAL ROUND ROCK (673032)**, 1400
Hester's Crossing, Zip 78681–8025; tel. 512/244–4400, (Total facility includes
25 beds in nursing home–type unit) (Data for 92 days) **A**1 10 **F**3 29 90 93 96
128 130 148 **S** HEALTHSOUTH Corporation, Birmingham, AL
Primary Contact: Jack Boggess, Chief Executive Officer
CFO: Joe Griffin, Controller
CHR: Amelia Leudecke, Director Human Resources
CNO: Stephanie Guerin, Chief Nursing Officer
Web address: www.healthsouthroundrock.com/
Control: Corporation, Investor–owned, for–profit **Service:** Rehabilitation

Staffed Beds: 75 **Admissions:** 403 **Census:** 56 **Outpatient Visits:** 1163
Births: 0 **Total Expense ($000):** 4931 **Payroll Expense ($000):** 2071
Personnel: 123

✠ **SCOTT & WHITE HOSPITAL AT ROUND ROCK (670034)**, 300 University
Boulevard, Zip 78665–1032; tel. 512/509–0100 **A**1 10 **F**3 11 13 15 18 19 20
22 24 26 28 29 30 31 34 35 40 43 45 46 47 49 50 51 52 54 55 56 57
58 59 60 62 63 64 65 68 74 75 76 77 78 79 81 82 84 85 87 91 92 93 97
99 100 101 103 104 107 108 110 111 114 115 116 119 121 130 131 132
133 135 143 146 147 148 **S** Baylor Scott & White Health, Dallas, TX
Primary Contact: Jay Fox, Chief Executive Officer
COO: Kevin E. Smith, Chief Operating Officer
CFO: Jason Cole, Senior Director Finance
CMO: Rob Watson, M.D., Chief Medical Officer
CIO: Matthew Chambers, Chief Information Officer
CHR: Mark A. Sherry, Director Human Resource
CNO: Leslie Gembol, MSN, Chief Nursing Officer
Web address: www.sw.org
Control: Other not–for–profit (including NFP Corporation) **Service:** General
Medical and Surgical

Staffed Beds: 101 **Admissions:** 5825 **Census:** 57 **Outpatient Visits:** 490196
Births: 544 **Total Expense ($000):** 157611 **Payroll Expense ($000):** 43323
Personnel: 890

✠ **SETON MEDICAL CENTER WILLIAMSON (670041)**, 201 Seton Parkway,
Zip 78665–8000; tel. 512/324–4000 **A**1 2 3 10 **F**3 11 12 13 15 18 20 22 24
26 28 29 30 31 34 35 37 40 43 44 45 46 49 50 51 53 54 57 58 59 60 64
68 70 72 74 75 76 77 78 79 81 82 83 84 86 87 93 96 107 108 110 111
114 115 119 124 126 130 131 132 135 146 147 148 **P**3 8 **S** Ascension
Health, Saint Louis, MO
Primary Contact: Christopher L. Hartle, President
CFO: Douglas D. Waite, Senior Vice President and Chief Financial Officer
CMO: Hugh V. Gilmore, M.D., Vice President Medical Affairs
CIO: Gerry Lewis, Chief Information Officer
CHR: Thomas Wilken, Vice President Human Resources
Web address: www.seton.net/williamson
Control: Church–operated, Nongovernment, not–for profit **Service:** General
Medical and Surgical

Staffed Beds: 143 **Admissions:** 6589 **Census:** 86 **Outpatient Visits:** 63237
Births: 35 **Total Expense ($000):** 148043 **Payroll Expense ($000):** 42535
Personnel: 681

✠ **ST. DAVID'S ROUND ROCK MEDICAL CENTER (450718)**, 2400 Round Rock
Avenue, Zip 78681–4097; tel. 512/341–1000 **A**1 2 5 10 **F**1 3 8 12 13 15 18
20 22 24 26 27 28 29 30 31 34 35 40 42 43 45 49 57 59 60 64 70 72 74
75 77 78 79 81 85 87 90 91 92 93 96 107 108 110 111 112 114 115 117
118 119 124 126 129 130 132 135 144 146 147 148 **P**3 6 8 **S** HCA,
Nashville, TN
Primary Contact: Deborah L. Ryle, Administrator and Chief Executive Officer
COO: Tad Hatton, Chief Operating Officer
CFO: Cindy Sexton, Chief Financial Officer
CHR: Amy Noak, Director Human Resources
Web address: www.stdavids.com
Control: Other not–for–profit (including NFP Corporation) **Service:** General
Medical and Surgical

Staffed Beds: 155 **Admissions:** 8486 **Census:** 105 **Outpatient Visits:** 71564
Births: 1872 **Total Expense ($000):** 134801 **Payroll Expense ($000):**
46590 **Personnel:** 729

ROWLETT—Rockwall County

✠ **LAKE POINTE MEDICAL CENTER (450742)**, 6800 Scenic Drive,
Zip 75088–4552, Mailing Address: P.O. Box 1550, Zip 75030–1550;
tel. 972/412–2273 **A**1 10 **F**3 12 13 15 18 20 22 24 28 29 30 34 35 40 42
45 46 49 50 53 54 57 59 60 64 65 70 72 73 74 75 76 77 78 79 81 82 85
86 87 93 107 108 110 111 114 115 118 119 120 121 126 129 130 131
132 144 146 147 148 **S** TENET Healthcare Corporation, Dallas, TX
Primary Contact: Brett D. Lee, Chief Executive Officer
COO: Deborah A. Moeller, R.N., Chief Operating Officer
CFO: Becky Speight, Chief Financial Officer
CMO: Larry Dencklau, D.O., Chief of Staff
CIO: Mark Slater, Director Information Systems
CHR: David Olmstead, Chief Human Resource Officer – Dallas Market
CNO: Patti Gilliano, Chief Nursing Officer
Web address: www.lakepointemedical.com
Control: Corporation, Investor–owned, for–profit **Service:** General Medical and
Surgical

Staffed Beds: 112 **Admissions:** 7490 **Census:** 71 **Outpatient Visits:** 114438
Births: 1787 **Total Expense ($000):** 121247 **Payroll Expense ($000):**
41876 **Personnel:** 585

RUSK—Cherokee County

☐ **RUSK STATE HOSPITAL (454009)**, 805 North Dickinson, Zip 75785–2333,
Mailing Address: P.O. Box 318, Zip 75785–0318; tel. 903/683–3421 **A**1 10 **F**3
30 39 44 50 68 75 86 87 98 103 106 130 135 146 148 **P**6 **S** Texas
Department of State Health Services, Austin, TX
Primary Contact: Brenda Slaton, Superintendent
COO: Lynda Roberson, Senior Program Director
CFO: Rhonda Transier, Financial Officer
CMO: Joe Bates, M.D., Clinical Director
CHR: Kendra Brown, Job Requisition Coordinator
Web address: www.dshs.state.tx.us/mhhospitals/RuskSH/default.shtm
Control: State–Government, nonfederal **Service:** Psychiatric

Staffed Beds: 325 **Admissions:** 565 **Census:** 313 **Outpatient Visits:** 0
Births: 0 **Total Expense ($000):** 58788 **Payroll Expense ($000):** 34586
Personnel: 1026

SAN ANGELO—Tom Green County

☐ **RIVER CREST HOSPITAL (454064)**, 1636 Hunters Glen Road,
Zip 76901–5016; tel. 325/949–5722 **A**1 10 **F**4 5 29 64 87 98 99 100 101
102 103 104 105 130 132 **S** Universal Health Services, Inc., King of Prussia, PA
Primary Contact: Chris Rupert, Interim Chief Executive Officer
CFO: Juana Giralt, Chief Financial Officer
CMO: Raymond Mays, M.D., Medical Director
CHR: Lydia Cardenas, Director Human Resources
CNO: Melissa Gabrielli, MSN, RN–B, Director of Nursing
Web address: www.rivercresthospital.com
Control: Corporation, Investor–owned, for–profit **Service:** Psychiatric

Staffed Beds: 80 **Admissions:** 3066 **Census:** 56 **Outpatient Visits:** 989
Births: 0 **Total Expense ($000):** 11584 **Payroll Expense ($000):** 5890
Personnel: 125

✠ **SAN ANGELO COMMUNITY MEDICAL CENTER (450340)**, 3501
Knickerbocker Road, Zip 76904–7698; tel. 325/949–9511 **A**1 10 **F**3 8 11 13
15 18 20 22 24 26 28 29 30 31 34 35 37 40 43 45 49 51 53 54 57 59 60
63 64 68 70 72 74 75 76 77 78 79 81 82 85 89 93 107 108 110 111 115
118 119 126 129 130 131 135 144 145 146 147 148 **P**8 **S** Community Health
Systems, Inc., Franklin, TN
Primary Contact: Jeremy Riney, Chief Executive Officer
CHR: Lisa Bibb, Director Human Resources
Web address: www.sacmc.com
Control: Partnership, Investor–owned, for–profit **Service:** General Medical and
Surgical

Staffed Beds: 131 **Admissions:** 4461 **Census:** 43 **Outpatient Visits:** 75889
Births: 963 **Total Expense ($000):** 77991 **Payroll Expense ($000):** 28344
Personnel: 506

Many Facility Codes have changed. Please refer to the AHA Guide Code Chart.

TX

★ **SHANNON MEDICAL CENTER (450571)**, 120 East Harris Street,
Zip 76903–5976, Mailing Address: P.O. Box 1879, Zip 76902–1879;
tel. 325/653–6741, (Includes SHANNON MEDICAL CENTER– ST. JOHN'S
CAMPUS, 2018 Pulliam Street, Zip 76905–5197; tel. 325/659–7100; Bryan
Horner, President and Chief Executive Officer), (Total facility includes 21 beds in
nursing home–type unit) **A**3 5 10 22 **F**3 7 8 11 13 15 18 20 22 24 26 28 29
30 31 32 34 35 37 38 40 43 45 47 48 49 50 51 53 54 56 57 58 59 60 61
62 64 68 70 71 72 73 74 75 76 77 78 79 80 81 82 84 85 86 87 89 90 92
93 94 96 98 100 101 102 103 107 108 110 111 114 115 117 119 128 130
132 145 146 147 148
Primary Contact: Bryan Horner, President and Chief Executive Officer
COO: Shane Plymell, Chief Operating Officer
CFO: Staci Wetz, Chief Financial Officer
CMO: Irvin Zeitler, D.O., Vice President Medical Affairs
CIO: Tom Perkins, Chief Information Officer
CHR: Teresa Morgan, Assistant Vice President Human Resources
CNO: Pamela Bradshaw, Chief Nursing Officer
Web address: www.shannonhealth.com
Control: Other not–for–profit (including NFP Corporation) **Service:** General
Medical and Surgical

Staffed Beds: 300 **Admissions:** 12535 **Census:** 172 **Outpatient Visits:**
109915 **Births:** 1227 **Total Expense ($000):** 231213 **Payroll Expense
($000):** 86442 **Personnel:** 1566

SAN ANTONIO—Bexar County

⊠ **ACUITY HOSPITAL OF SOUTH TEXAS (452040)**, 718 Lexington Avenue,
Zip 78212–4768; tel. 210/572–4600 **A**1 10 **F**1 3 29 45 75 85 87 91 107 119
148 **S** AcuityHealthcare, LP, Charlotte, NC
Primary Contact: Kris Karns, Ph.D., FACHE, Chief Executive Officer
CFO: Wayne Hegwood, Chief Financial Officer
CMO: Qasim Butt, M.D., Chief Medical Officer
CHR: Sheree Allstrom, Director Human Resources
CNO: Danny Fraley, Chief Clinical Officer
Web address: www.acuitysouthtexas.com
Control: Corporation, Investor–owned, for–profit **Service:** Long–Term Acute Care
hospital

Staffed Beds: 30 **Admissions:** 345 **Census:** 27 **Outpatient Visits:** 0 **Births:**
0 **Total Expense ($000):** 17131 **Payroll Expense ($000):** 7303 **Personnel:**
131

◇ **BAPTIST EMERGENCY HOSPITAL – THOUSAND OAKS (670078)**, 16088 San
Pedro, Zip 78232–2249; tel. 210/402–4092, (Includes BAPTIST EMERGENCY
HOSPITAL – HAUSMAN, 8230 North 1604 West, Zip 78249; tel. 210/572–8885;
David Mitchell, Chief Executive Officer; BAPTIST EMERGENCY HOSPITAL –
OVERLOOK, 25615 U.S. Highway 281 North, Zip 78258–7135;
tel. 210/572–2911; David Mitchell, Chief Executive Officer; BAPTIST EMERGENCY
HOSPITAL – SCHERTZ, 16977 Interstate 35 North, Schertz, Zip 78154–1466;
tel. 210/572–8400; David Mitchell, Chief Executive Officer; BAPTIST EMERGENCY
HOSPITAL – WESTOVER HILLS, 10811 Town Center Drive, Zip 78251–4585;
tel. 210/572–0911; David Mitchell, Chief Executive Officer) **A**10 21 **F**3 40 41 75
107 **P**5 **S** Emerus, The Woodlands, TX
Primary Contact: David Mitchell, Interim Chief Executive Officer
Web address: www.baptistemergencyhospital.com
Control: Corporation, Investor–owned, for–profit **Service:** General Medical and
Surgical

Staffed Beds: 42 **Admissions:** 625 **Census:** 3 **Outpatient Visits:** 75944
Births: 1 **Total Expense ($000):** 31636 **Payroll Expense ($000):** 11584
Personnel: 238

★ △ ◇ **BAPTIST MEDICAL CENTER (450058)**, 111 Dallas Street,
Zip 78205–1230; tel. 210/297–7000, (Includes MISSION TRAIL BAPTIST
HOSPITAL, 3333 Research Plaza, Zip 78235–5154; tel. 210/297–3000; Eric
Schmacker, President; NORTH CENTRAL BAPTIST HOSPITAL, 520 Madison Oak
Drive, Zip 78258–3912; tel. 210/297–4000; NORTHEAST BAPTIST HOSPITAL,
8811 Village Drive, Zip 78217–5440; tel. 210/297–2000; ST. LUKE'S BAPTIST
HOSPITAL, 7930 Floyd Curl Drive, Zip 78229–0100; tel. 210/297–5000; John E.
Knox, FACHE, Chief Executive Officer) **A**2 3 5 7 10 21 **F**3 4 11 12 13 14 15 16
17 18 19 20 22 24 26 28 29 30 31 35 37 38 40 41 42 43 44 45 46 47 50
54 55 56 57 59 60 64 65 68 70 72 73 74 75 76 77 78 79 80 81 82 85 86
87 88 89 90 91 92 93 95 96 98 101 102 103 107 108 111 114 115 116
117 119 124 126 129 130 132 135 145 146 147 148 **P**8 **S** TENET Healthcare
Corporation, Dallas, TX
Primary Contact: Jonathan Turton, FACHE, President and Chief Executive Officer
COO: Sandy Ethridge, Interim Chief Operating Officer
CFO: Linda Kirks, Chief Financial Officer
CMO: Richard Marple, M.D., Chief Medical Officer
CIO: Gary Davis, Vice President Information Systems
CHR: Sarah Spinharney, Senior Vice President
CNO: Nelson Tuazon, R.N., Chief Nursing Officer
Web address: www.baptisthealthsystem.com
Control: Partnership, Investor–owned, for–profit **Service:** General Medical and
Surgical

Staffed Beds: 1619 **Admissions:** 65258 **Census:** 793 **Outpatient Visits:**
288356 **Births:** 10920 **Total Expense ($000):** 789030 **Payroll Expense
($000):** 313897 **Personnel:** 5256

⊠ **CHRISTUS SANTA ROSA HEALTH SYSTEM (450237)**, 333 North Santa Rosa
Street, Zip 78207–3108; tel. 210/704–4184, (Includes CHILDREN'S HOSPITAL
OF SAN ANTONIO, 333 North Santa Rosa Street, Zip 78207; tel. 210/704–2011;
Elias Neujahr, Administrator; CHRISTUS SANTA ROSA HOSPITAL – ALAMO
HEIGHTS, 403 Treeline Park Building, Zip 78209–2042; tel. 216/704–2011; Ken
Haynes, Chief Executive Officer; CHRISTUS SANTA ROSA HOSPITAL – NEW
BRAUNFELS, 600 North Union Avenue, New Braunfels, Zip 78130–4191;
tel. 830/606–9111; Jim D. Wesson, Vice President and Administrator; CHRISTUS
SANTA ROSA–MEDICAL CENTER, 2827 Babcock Road, Zip 78229–4813;
tel. 210/705–6300; Asha S. Rodriguez, Interim Chief Executive Officer),
(Nonreporting) **A**1 3 5 10 **S** CHRISTUS Health, Irving, TX
Primary Contact: Ken Haynes, President and Chief Executive Officer
CFO: Shawn Barnett, Vice President and Chief Financial Officer
CMO: James C. Martin, M.D., Vice President and Chief Medical Officer
CHR: Crystal H. Kohanke, Group Vice President, Human Resources
CNO: Patty Toney, R.N., Chief Nurse Executive
Web address: www.christussantarosa.org
Control: Other not–for–profit (including NFP Corporation) **Service:** General
Medical and Surgical

Staffed Beds: 766

□ **CLARITY CHILD GUIDANCE CENTER**, 8535 Tom Slick, Zip 78229–3363;
tel. 210/616–0300 **A**1 3 5 **F**29 41 98 99 101 102 104 105 106 130
Primary Contact: Frederick W. Hines, President and Chief Executive Officer
CFO: Michael Bernick, Executive Vice President and Chief Financial Officer
CMO: Soad Michelson, M.D., Senior Medical Director
CHR: Gina Massey, Vice President Human Resources
CNO: Carol Carver, MSN, Vice President Patient Services
Web address: www.claritycgc.org
Control: Other not–for–profit (including NFP Corporation) **Service:** Children's
hospital psychiatric

Staffed Beds: 52 **Admissions:** 1740 **Census:** 48 **Outpatient Visits:** 19388
Births: 0 **Total Expense ($000):** 20715 **Payroll Expense ($000):** 12205
Personnel: 249

□ **CUMBERLAND SURGICAL HOSPITAL (670021)**, 5330 N. Loop 1604 W.,
Zip 78249; tel. 210/877–8000, (Nonreporting) **A**1 10 **S** Post Acute Medical,
LLC, Enola, PA
Primary Contact: Michelle Patino, Chief Executive Officer
COO: Leroy Bernal, Chief Operating Officer
CFO: Julie Churchill, Chief Financial Officer
CHR: Regina Woolridge, Director Human Resources
CNO: Adam Apolinar, Chief Clinical Officer
Control: Partnership, Investor–owned, for–profit **Service:** General Medical and
Surgical

Staffed Beds: 9

TX

TX

◇ **FOUNDATION SURGICAL HOSPITAL OF SAN ANTONIO (670054)**, 9522 Huebner Road, Zip 78240–1548; tel. 210/478–5400 **A**3 5 10 21 **F**3 12 29 30 35 37 40 44 45 51 53 68 74 75 77 79 81 85 86 87 107 114 119 129 130 132 135 148 **S** Foundation Surgical Hospital Affiliates, Oklahoma City, OK
Primary Contact: Blake W. Hubbard, FACHE, Chief Executive Officer
CNO: Beckie Leonard, R.N., Chief Nursing Officer
Web address: www.fshsanantonio.com/bariatric–foundation–surgical.html
Control: Corporation, Investor–owned, for–profit **Service:** Surgical

Staffed Beds: 20 **Admissions:** 1325 **Census:** 8 **Outpatient Visits:** 4613 **Births:** 0 **Total Expense ($000):** 32914 **Payroll Expense ($000):** 6396 **Personnel:** 94

✚ **HEALTHSOUTH REHABILITATION INSTITUTE OF SAN ANTONIO (453031)**, 9119 Cinnamon Hill, Zip 78240–5401; tel. 210/691–0737 **A**1 10 **F**29 62 90 91 96 130 132 148 **P**5 **S** HEALTHSOUTH Corporation, Birmingham, AL
Primary Contact: Scott Butcher, Chief Executive Officer
CFO: Larry Spriggs, Controller
CMO: Chaula Rana, M.D., Medical Director
CHR: Vanessa Tejada, Director Human Resources
Web address: www.hsriosa.com
Control: Corporation, Investor–owned, for–profit **Service:** Rehabilitation

Staffed Beds: 96 **Admissions:** 1172 **Census:** 55 **Outpatient Visits:** 1372 **Births:** 0 **Total Expense ($000):** 20308 **Payroll Expense ($000):** 10921 **Personnel:** 206

✚ **KINDRED HOSPITAL–SAN ANTONIO (452016)**, 3636 Medical Drive, Zip 78229–2183; tel. 210/616–0616 **A**1 10 **F**1 3 29 70 75 77 85 87 91 107 130 148 **S** Kindred Healthcare, Louisville, KY
Primary Contact: William Patton, Chief Executive Officer
CFO: Erin Russell, Controller
CMO: Charles Duncan, M.D., Medical Director
CHR: Stanley Richardson, Coordinator Human Resources and Payroll Benefits
Web address: www.khsanantonio.com/
Control: Corporation, Investor–owned, for–profit **Service:** Long–Term Acute Care hospital

Staffed Beds: 59 **Admissions:** 452 **Census:** 32 **Outpatient Visits:** 1 **Births:** 0 **Total Expense ($000):** 19856 **Payroll Expense ($000):** 7349 **Personnel:** 92

✚ **LAUREL RIDGE TREATMENT CENTER (454060)**, 17720 Corporate Woods Drive, Zip 78259–3500; tel. 210/491–9400 **A**1 3 10 **F**5 29 35 38 75 77 98 99 100 101 103 105 106 130 132 **S** Universal Health Services, Inc., King of Prussia, PA
Primary Contact: Jacob Cuellar, M.D., Chief Executive Officer
COO: Karla Ramirez, Chief Operating Officer
CFO: Linda Maenius, Chief Financial Officer
CMO: Benigno J. Fernandez, M.D., Executive Medical Director
CHR: Brenda Frederick, Director Human Resources
CNO: Kathy Rosetta, Chief Nursing Officer
Web address: www.laurelridgetc.com
Control: Partnership, Investor–owned, for–profit **Service:** Psychiatric

Staffed Beds: 208 **Admissions:** 7052 **Census:** 171 **Outpatient Visits:** 23079 **Births:** 0 **Total Expense ($000):** 48001 **Payroll Expense ($000):** 20200 **Personnel:** 379

✚ **LIFECARE HOSPITALS OF SAN ANTONIO (452059)**, 8902 Floyd Curl Drive, Zip 78240–1681; tel. 210/690–7000 **A**1 10 **F**1 3 29 45 75 77 85 86 87 96 97 107 114 130 148 **S** LifeCare Management Services, Plano, TX
Primary Contact: Randell G. Stokes, Chief Executive Officer
CMO: Randall C. Bell, M.D., Medical Director
CIO: Mike Wattenbarger, Chief Information Officer
Web address: www.lifecare–hospitals.com
Control: Corporation, Investor–owned, for–profit **Service:** Long–Term Acute Care hospital

Staffed Beds: 62 **Admissions:** 698 **Census:** 54 **Outpatient Visits:** 0 **Births:** 0 **Total Expense ($000):** 29169 **Payroll Expense ($000):** 13246 **Personnel:** 196

✚ **METHODIST AMBULATORY SURGERY HOSPITAL – NORTHWEST (450780)**, 9150 Huebner Road, Suite 100, Zip 78240–1545; tel. 210/575–5000 **A**1 10 **F**3 29 40 65 68 79 81 85 87 **P**8 **S** HCA, Nashville, TN
Primary Contact: Scott Davis, Chief Executive Officer
CFO: Tim Carr, Chief Financial Officer
CHR: Barry Burns, Vice President
CNO: Cathy Bump, R.N., Chief Nursing Officer
Web address: www.sahealth.com
Control: Partnership, Investor–owned, for–profit **Service:** Surgical

Staffed Beds: 23 **Admissions:** 451 **Census:** 3 **Outpatient Visits:** 6795 **Births:** 0 **Total Expense ($000):** 19766 **Payroll Expense ($000):** 6292 **Personnel:** 102

✚ **METHODIST HOSPITAL (450388)**, 7700 Floyd Curl Drive, Zip 78229–3993; tel. 210/575–4000, (Includes METHODIST CHILDREN'S HOSPITAL, 7700 Floyd Curl Drive, Zip 78229–3383; tel. 210/575–7000; Robert Lenza, Chief Executive Officer; METHODIST SPECIALTY AND TRANSPLANT HOSPITAL, 8026 Floyd Curl Drive, Zip 78229–3915; tel. 210/575–8090; Jeffrey Wilson, Chief Executive Officer; METHODIST TEXSAN HOSPITAL, 6700 IH–10 West, Zip 78201; tel. 210/736–6700; Scott Davis, Chief Executive Officer; METROPOLITAN METHODIST HOSPITAL, 1310 McCullough Avenue, Zip 78212–2617; tel. 210/757–2909; Gregory A. Seiler, Chief Executive Officer; NORTHEAST METHODIST HOSPITAL, 12412 Judson Road, Live Oak, Zip 78233–3255; tel. 210/757–5000; Michael D. Beaver, Chief Executive Officer) **A**1 2 3 5 10 **F**3 4 5 8 11 12 13 15 17 18 19 20 21 22 23 24 25 26 27 28 29 30 31 34 35 38 40 41 42 43 44 45 46 47 48 49 51 53 54 56 57 58 59 60 64 65 68 70 72 74 75 76 77 78 79 80 81 82 84 85 86 87 88 89 90 93 95 96 98 100 101 102 103 104 105 107 108 111 114 115 119 121 124 126 127 129 130 132 135 136 137 138 139 142 143 145 146 147 148 **P**7 **S** HCA, Nashville, TN
Primary Contact: Gay Nord, Chief Executive Officer
CFO: Nancy Meadows, Chief Financial Officer
CMO: Russell Woodward, M.D., Chief Medical Officer
CIO: Eddie Cuellar, Vice President Information Systems
CHR: Nancy Edgar, Vice President Human Resources
Web address: www.sahealth.com
Control: Partnership, Investor–owned, for–profit **Service:** General Medical and Surgical

Staffed Beds: 1593 **Admissions:** 79612 **Census:** 1175 **Outpatient Visits:** 467630 **Births:** 10026 **Total Expense ($000):** 1175197 **Payroll Expense ($000):** 435499 **Personnel:** 5793

✚ **METHODIST STONE OAK HOSPITAL (670055)**, 1139 East Sonterra Boulevard, Zip 78258–4347; tel. 210/638–2100 **A**1 3 5 10 **F**3 13 15 18 20 22 24 29 30 31 34 35 38 40 44 45 46 47 49 52 57 59 60 65 68 70 72 74 75 76 77 78 79 80 81 82 85 87 100 102 107 108 111 114 119 126 130 145 146 147 148 **S** HCA, Nashville, TN
Primary Contact: Marc Strode, Chief Executive Officer
COO: Candie Starr, Chief Operating Officer and Ethics and Compliance Officer
CFO: Gabriel Marrufo, Chief Financial Officer
CNO: Ann M. Winn, M.D., Chief Nursing Officer
Web address: www.sahealth.com/locations/methodist–stone–oak–hospital/
Control: Partnership, Investor–owned, for–profit **Service:** General Medical and Surgical

Staffed Beds: 140 **Admissions:** 11365 **Census:** 125 **Outpatient Visits:** 45749 **Births:** 2174 **Total Expense ($000):** 152671 **Payroll Expense ($000):** 42853 **Personnel:** 586

◇ **NIX HEALTH CARE SYSTEM (450130)**, 414 Navarro Street, Zip 78205–2516; tel. 210/271–1800 **A**3 5 10 21 **F**3 5 12 15 18 20 22 24 26 29 30 31 34 35 40 44 45 49 50 54 56 57 59 60 62 64 68 70 74 75 78 79 81 82 85 87 90 93 97 98 99 103 107 108 110 111 114 118 119 129 130 132 142 143 146 147 148
Primary Contact: Joseph Rafferty, Interim Chief Executive Officer
CFO: Lester Surrock, Chief Financial Officer
CMO: Dina Goytia–Leos, M.D., Chief of Staff
CIO: Adrian Dickreiter, Vice President Technology
CNO: Maria Rose Lopez, R.N., Chief of Nursing
Web address: www.nixhealth.com
Control: Corporation, Investor–owned, for–profit **Service:** General Medical and Surgical

Staffed Beds: 246 **Admissions:** 9348 **Census:** 170 **Outpatient Visits:** 85049 **Births:** 0 **Total Expense ($000):** 124774 **Payroll Expense ($000):** 45628 **Personnel:** 974

✚ **POST ACUTE/WARM SPRINGS REHABILITATION HOSPITAL OF SAN ANTONIO (453035)**, 5101 Medical Drive, Zip 78229–4801; tel. 210/616–0100, (Includes WARM SPRINGS REHABILITATION HOSPITAL OF THOUSAND OAKS, 14747 Jones Maltsberger Road, Zip 78247–3713; tel. 210/581–5300; Kasondra Kistner, R.N., Chief Executive Officer; WARM SPRINGS REHABILITATION HOSPITAL OF WESTOVER HILLS, 10323 State Highway 151, Zip 78251–4557; tel. 210/581–5306; Steve Flaherty, Chief Executive Officer), (Total facility includes 10 beds in nursing home–type unit) **A**1 3 5 10 **F**3 11 29 30 57 64 68 74 75 79 82 90 91 93 94 96 128 130 132 146 148 **S** Post Acute Medical, LLC, Enola, PA
Primary Contact: Debra Bormann, Chief Executive Officer
CMO: Alex Willingham, M.D., Medical Director
CIO: Rick Marek, Vice President Medical Information Systems
CHR: Waynea Finley, System Director Human Resources
Web address: www.postacutemedical.com/our–facilities/hospitals/warm–springs–rehabilitation–hospital–san–antonio/
Control: Partnership, Investor–owned, for–profit **Service:** Rehabilitation

Staffed Beds: 138 **Admissions:** 2641 **Census:** 94 **Outpatient Visits:** 29466 **Births:** 0 **Total Expense ($000):** 44707 **Payroll Expense ($000):** 23945 **Personnel:** 458

Many Facility Codes have changed. Please refer to the AHA Guide Code Chart. © 2016 AHA Guide

POST ACUTE/WARM SPRINGS SPECIALTY HOSPITAL OF SAN ANTONIO (452090), 7400 Barlite Boulevard, 2nd Floor, Zip 78224–1308; tel. 210/921–3550 **A**1 10 **F**1 3 29 30 148 **S** Post Acute Medical, LLC, Enola, PA
Primary Contact: James Asberry, Chief Executive Officer
CNO: Carrie Nims, Director of Nursing
Web address: www.postacutemedical.com
Control: Partnership, Investor–owned, for–profit **Service:** Long–Term Acute Care hospital

Staffed Beds: 26 Admissions: 190 Census: 15 Outpatient Visits: 0 Total Expense ($000): 8668 Payroll Expense ($000): 3706 Personnel: 68

SAN ANTONIO STATE HOSPITAL (454011), 6711 South New Braunfels, Suite 100, Zip 78223–3006; tel. 210/531–7711 **A**1 3 5 10 **F**30 39 53 56 57 59 68 75 77 86 87 91 98 99 100 101 103 106 130 132 135 146 **P**1 **S** Texas Department of State Health Services, Austin, TX
Primary Contact: Robert C. Arizpe, Superintendent
CFO: Janie Rabago, Chief Accountant
CMO: Terresa Stallworth, M.D., Clinical Director
CIO: Chris Stanush, Director Information Management
CHR: Renee Bourland, Human Resources Specialist
CNO: Maria DC Ostrander, R.N., Chief Nurse Executive
Web address: www.dshs.state.tx.us/mhhospitals/SanAntonioSH/default.shtm
Control: State–Government, nonfederal **Service:** Psychiatric

Staffed Beds: 302 Admissions: 1427 Census: 268 Outpatient Visits: 0 Births: 0 Total Expense ($000): 91820 Payroll Expense ($000): 36058 Personnel: 771

★ ○ **SELECT REHABILITATION HOSPITAL OF SAN ANTONIO (673040)**, 19126 Stonehue Road, Zip 78258–3490; tel. 210/482–3400 **A**10 11 **F**3 29 30 75 90 91 96 130 148
Primary Contact: Robert Ward, Chief Executive Officer
Web address: www.sanantonio–rehab.com/
Control: Partnership, Investor–owned, for–profit **Service:** Rehabilitation

Staffed Beds: 42 Admissions: 1009 Census: 38 Outpatient Visits: 0 Births: 0 Total Expense ($000): 16046 Payroll Expense ($000): 7651 Personnel: 139

KINDRED HOSPITAL SAN ANTONIO CENTRAL (452073), 111 Dallas Street, 4th Floor, Zip 78205–1201; tel. 210/297–7185 **A**1 10 **F**1 29 148 **P**8 **S** Select Medical Corporation, Mechanicsburg, PA
Primary Contact: Sean Stricker, Chief Executive Officer
Web address: www.selectspecialtyhospitals.com/company/locations/sanantonio.aspx
Control: Corporation, Investor–owned, for–profit **Service:** Long–Term Acute Care hospital

Staffed Beds: 44 Admissions: 426 Census: 33 Outpatient Visits: 0 Births: 0 Total Expense ($000): 18187 Payroll Expense ($000): 7480 Personnel: 132

SOUTH TEXAS SPINE AND SURGICAL HOSPITAL (450856), 18600 Hardy Oak Boulevard, Zip 78258–4206; tel. 210/507–4090 **A**1 3 5 10 **F**3 29 40 41 70 75 77 79 81 85 86 87 89 111 **S** National Surgical Healthcare, Chicago, IL
Primary Contact: Thomas Klawiter, Chief Executive Officer
CFO: Sylvia Garcia, Chief Accounting Officer
CHR: Sally Hall, Manager Human Resources
CNO: Jennifer West, R.N., Chief Nursing Officer
Web address: www.southtexassurgical.com
Control: Partnership, Investor–owned, for–profit **Service:** Orthopedic

Staffed Beds: 30 Admissions: 1058 Census: 7 Outpatient Visits: 4922 Births: 0 Total Expense ($000): 29437 Payroll Expense ($000): 6425 Personnel: 123

△ **SOUTH TEXAS VETERANS HEALTH CARE SYSTEM**, 7400 Merton Minter Boulevard, Zip 78229–4404; tel. 210/617–5300, (Includes KERRVILLE DIVISION, 3600 Memorial Boulevard, Kerrville, Zip 78028; tel. 210/896–2020; SAN ANTONIO DIVISION, 7400 Merton Minter Boulevard, Zip 78284–5799; tel. 210/617–5300), (Nonreporting) **A**1 3 5 7 8 **S** Department of Veterans Affairs, Washington, DC
Primary Contact: Robert M. Walton, Healthcare System Director
COO: Joe Perez, Associate Director
CFO: Eloisa Salazar, Chief Financial Officer
CMO: Julianne Flynn, M.D., Chief of Staff
CIO: Simon Willett, Director Administrative Operations
CHR: Jeffrey Young, Chief Human Resource Officer
CNO: Sharon Millican, Associate Director, Patient Care Services
Web address: www.southtexas.va.gov/
Control: Veterans Affairs, Government, federal **Service:** General Medical and Surgical

Staffed Beds: 838

◇ **SOUTHWEST GENERAL HOSPITAL (450697)**, 7400 Barlite Boulevard, Zip 78224–1399; tel. 210/921–2000 **A**10 21 **F**3 12 13 15 18 20 22 24 29 30 35 37 40 43 44 45 46 49 50 51 56 57 59 60 64 65 70 71 72 73 74 75 76 77 78 79 80 81 85 87 90 93 98 100 102 103 105 107 108 110 111 114 115 119 126 129 130 132 135 146 147 148 **S** IASIS Healthcare, Franklin, TN
Primary Contact: P. Craig Desmond, Chief Executive Officer
COO: Sarah Humme, MSN, Chief Operating Officer
CFO: Colin B. Brooks, Chief Financial Officer
CIO: Debbie Mora, Director
CHR: Christina Rivera, Director Human Resources
CNO: Sarah Humme, MSN, Chief Nursing Officer
Web address: www.swgeneralhospital.com
Control: Corporation, Investor–owned, for–profit **Service:** General Medical and Surgical

Staffed Beds: 253 Admissions: 9402 Census: 129 Outpatient Visits: 65440 Births: 1850 Total Expense ($000): 114535 Payroll Expense ($000): 45918 Personnel: 656

ST. LUKE'S BAPTIST HOSPITAL See Baptist Medical Center

TEXAS CENTER FOR INFECTIOUS DISEASE (452033), 2303 S.E. Military Drive, Zip 78223–3597; tel. 210/534–8857 **A**1 10 **F**1 3 29 30 50 53 54 61 64 68 75 87 130 132 135 143 146 **P**6 **S** Texas Department of State Health Services, Austin, TX
Primary Contact: James N. Elkins, FACHE, Director
CFO: Glenda Armstrong–Huff, Assistant Superintendent
CMO: David Griffith, M.D., Medical Director
CIO: Andre Avant, Facility Automation Manager
CHR: Gerald Shackelford, Staff Support Specialist
CNO: Rebecca Sanchez, R.N., Director of Nursing
Web address: www.dshs.state.tx.us/tcid/default.shtm
Control: State–Government, nonfederal **Service:** Tuberculosis and other respiratory diseases

Staffed Beds: 40 Admissions: 78 Census: 36 Outpatient Visits: 974 Births: 0 Total Expense ($000): 12221 Payroll Expense ($000): 6375 Personnel: 147

UNIVERSITY HEALTH SYSTEM (450213), 4502 Medical Drive, Zip 78229–4493; tel. 210/358–2000, (Includes UNIVERSITY HEALTH CENTER – DOWNTOWN, 4502 Medical Drive, tel. 210/358–3400; UNIVERSITY HOSPITAL, 4502 Medical Drive, tel. 210/358–4000; Edward Banos, Interim Chief Executive Officer) **A**1 2 3 5 8 10 **F**3 4 7 11 13 14 16 17 18 19 20 21 22 23 24 25 26 27 29 30 31 32 34 35 38 40 41 43 44 45 46 47 48 49 50 51 52 54 55 57 58 59 60 61 64 65 66 68 70 72 73 74 75 76 77 78 79 80 81 82 84 85 86 87 88 89 90 92 93 95 96 98 100 101 107 108 110 111 115 118 119 124 126 129 130 132 135 138 139 140 141 142 143 144 145 146 147 148
Primary Contact: George B. Hernandez, Jr., President and Chief Executive Officer
COO: Christann Vasquez, Executive Vice President and Chief Operating Officer
CFO: Peggy Deming, Executive Vice President and Chief Financial Officer
CMO: Bryan Alsip, M.D., Executive Vice President, Chief Medical Officer
CIO: Bill Phillips, Vice President Information Services
CHR: Theresa Scepanski, Vice President People and Organizational Development
CNO: Nancy L. Ray, R.N., Executive Vice President, Chief Nursing Executive
Web address: www.universityhealthsystem.com
Control: Hospital district or authority, Government, nonfederal **Service:** General Medical and Surgical

Staffed Beds: 456 Admissions: 26425 Census: 435 Outpatient Visits: 2269142 Births: 3184 Total Expense ($000): 1034136 Payroll Expense ($000): 383272 Personnel: 6836

SAN AUGUSTINE—San Augustine County

★ **CHI ST. LUKE'S HEALTH MEMORIAL SAN AUGUSTINE (451360)**, 511 East Hospital Street, Zip 75972–2121, Mailing Address: P.O. Box 658, Zip 75972–0658; tel. 936/275–3446 **A**10 18 **F**29 35 40 57 59 64 102 107 119 132 133 **S** Catholic Health Initiatives, Englewood, CO
Primary Contact: Darlene Williams, R.N., Administrator
CFO: Kristi Gay, Chief Financial Officer
Web address: www.memorialhealth.org
Control: Other not–for–profit (including NFP Corporation) **Service:** General Medical and Surgical

Staffed Beds: 9 Admissions: 318 Census: 3 Outpatient Visits: 11769 Births: 0 Total Expense ($000): 6057 Payroll Expense ($000): 3274 Personnel: 48

TX

SAN MARCOS—Hays County

✠ **CENTRAL TEXAS MEDICAL CENTER (450272)**, 1301 Wonder World Drive, Zip 78666–7544; tel. 512/353–8979 **A**1 10 **F**3 11 13 15 18 20 29 30 32 34 35 39 40 43 44 45 49 50 51 56 57 59 60 62 63 64 65 66 68 70 72 75 76 77 79 80 81 82 85 86 87 92 93 94 98 107 108 109 110 111 116 117 118 119 126 129 130 131 132 146 147 148 **P**6 8 **S** Adventist Health System Sunbelt Health Care Corporation, Altamonte Springs, FL
Primary Contact: Anthony Stahl, Chief Executive Officer
CFO: Jesse Sutton, Chief Financial Officer
CMO: Lee Johannsen, M.D., Chief Medical Officer
CHR: Debbie D. Cox, Administrative Director Human Resources
CNO: Elsie Graves, Chief Nursing Officer
Web address: www.ctmc.org
Control: Church–operated, Nongovernment, not–for profit **Service:** General Medical and Surgical

Staffed Beds: 111 **Admissions:** 4140 **Census:** 42 **Outpatient Visits:** 70598 **Births:** 832 **Total Expense ($000):** 92009 **Payroll Expense ($000):** 32564 **Personnel:** 571

OCEANS BEHAVIORAL HOSPITAL SAN MARCOS, 1106 North Interstate 35, Zip 78666–7030; tel. 512/353–0194, (Nonreporting) **S** Oceans Healthcare, Lake Charles, LA
Primary Contact: Clara Hollis, Administrator
Web address: www.oceanssanmarcos.com
Control: Corporation, Investor–owned, for–profit **Service:** Psychiatric

Staffed Beds: 25

SEGUIN—Guadalupe County

✠ **GUADALUPE REGIONAL MEDICAL CENTER (450104)**, 1215 East Court Street, Zip 78155–5189; tel. 830/379–2411 **A**1 10 **F**3 5 11 13 15 18 20 22 28 29 30 31 34 35 39 40 43 45 46 49 50 51 53 56 57 59 60 63 64 66 68 70 74 75 76 77 78 79 81 82 84 85 86 90 93 96 103 104 107 108 110 111 112 114 118 119 126 129 132 143 146 148 **P**1
Primary Contact: Robert Gerard Haynes, FACHE, Chief Executive Officer
COO: Sheri Williams, Chief Operating Officer
CFO: Penny Wallace, Chief Financial Officer
CMO: Robert Ryan, M.D., Chief Medical Officer
CIO: Steve Ratliff, Director Information Technology
CHR: Fay Bennett, Vice President Employee Services
CNO: Daphne Blake, R.N., Chief Nursing Officer
Web address: www.grmedcenter.com
Control: City–County, Government, nonfederal **Service:** General Medical and Surgical

Staffed Beds: 90 **Admissions:** 4269 **Census:** 42 **Outpatient Visits:** 138417 **Births:** 934 **Total Expense ($000):** 90860 **Payroll Expense ($000):** 33094 **Personnel:** 662

SEMINOLE—Gaines County

★ **MEMORIAL HOSPITAL (451358)**, 209 N.W. Eighth Street, Zip 79360–3447; tel. 432/758–5811 **A**10 18 **F**3 10 11 13 28 29 30 32 34 35 40 43 45 53 56 57 59 62 63 64 65 75 76 81 87 93 97 102 107 114 119 129 130 131 132 133 143 146 147 148
Primary Contact: Betsy Briscoe, Chief Executive Officer
COO: Heath Mitchell, Chief Operating Officer
CFO: Traci Anderson, Chief Financial Officer
CMO: Michael Watson, M.D., Chief of Staff
Web address: www.seminolehospitaldistrict.com
Control: Hospital district or authority, Government, nonfederal **Service:** General Medical and Surgical

Staffed Beds: 25 **Admissions:** 887 **Census:** 9 **Outpatient Visits:** 74061 **Births:** 361 **Total Expense ($000):** 33669 **Payroll Expense ($000):** 9167 **Personnel:** 218

SEYMOUR—Baylor County

SEYMOUR HOSPITAL (450586), 200 Stadium Drive, Zip 76380–2344; tel. 940/889–5572 **A**10 20 **F**3 7 8 11 13 14 28 29 34 36 40 43 45 50 53 56 57 59 62 64 65 66 68 70 75 76 81 85 86 87 89 93 94 100 102 103 104 107 119 127 130 133 135 146 147 148 **P**1
Primary Contact: Leslie Hardin, Chief Executive Officer and Chief Financial Officer
CFO: Leslie Hardin, Chief Executive Officer and Chief Financial Officer
CMO: Kory Lann Martin, M.D., Chief of Staff
CHR: Linda Moore, Manager Human Resources
CNO: Julie Smajstrla, Director Nursing
Web address: www.seymourhospital.com/
Control: Hospital district or authority, Government, nonfederal **Service:** General Medical and Surgical

Staffed Beds: 40 **Admissions:** 370 **Census:** 5 **Outpatient Visits:** 37546 **Births:** 37 **Total Expense ($000):** 28268 **Payroll Expense ($000):** 5386 **Personnel:** 118

SHAMROCK—Wheeler County

SHAMROCK GENERAL HOSPITAL (451340), 1000 South Main Street, Zip 79079–2896, Mailing Address: P. O. Box 511, Zip 79079–0511; tel. 806/256–2114 **A**10 18 **F**7 11 29 32 34 35 40 43 63 65 68 93 107 119 127 130 133 **P**4
Primary Contact: Wiley M. Fires, Administrator
CFO: Wiley M. Fires, Administrator
CHR: Cecille Williams, Assistant Administrator
CNO: Jeanne Crossland, Director of Nursing
Control: Hospital district or authority, Government, nonfederal **Service:** General Medical and Surgical

Staffed Beds: 13 **Admissions:** 93 **Census:** 2 **Outpatient Visits:** 11720 **Births:** 0 **Total Expense ($000):** 6630 **Payroll Expense ($000):** 3330 **Personnel:** 72

SHENANDOAH—Montgomery County

✠ **HEALTHSOUTH REHABILITATION HOSPITAL VISION PARK (673034)**, 117 Vision Park Boulevard, Zip 77384–3001; tel. 936/444–1700, (Data for 92 days) **A**1 10 **F**3 29 65 90 93 96 130 148 **S** HEALTHSOUTH Corporation, Birmingham, AL
Primary Contact: Jeff Crawford, Chief Executive Officer
CFO: Terri Weiss, Chief Financial Officer
Web address: www.healthsouthvisionpark.com/
Control: Partnership, Investor–owned, for–profit **Service:** Rehabilitation

Staffed Beds: 60 **Admissions:** 316 **Census:** 38 **Outpatient Visits:** 2615 **Births:** 0 **Total Expense ($000):** 4075 **Payroll Expense ($000):** 1902 **Personnel:** 110

◇ **NEXUS SPECIALTY HOSPITAL**, 123 Vision Park Boulevard, Zip 77384–3001; tel. 281/364–0317 **A**21 **F**1 3 70 74 75 77 82 84 85 91 92 93 100 101 107 119 130 132 135 148 **S** Nexus Health Systems, Houston, TX
Primary Contact: Mikael Simpson, Chief Executive Officer
CFO: Corey O'Connor, Vice President, Finance
CMO: Ather Siddiqi, M.D., Medical Director
CIO: Noe Salinas, Vice President Information Technology
CHR: Kevin McAndrews, Vice President Human Resources
Web address: www.nexusspecialty.com
Control: Partnership, Investor–owned, for–profit **Service:** Long–Term Acute Care hospital

Staffed Beds: 75 **Admissions:** 631 **Census:** 50 **Outpatient Visits:** 1823 **Births:** 0 **Total Expense ($000):** 28274 **Payroll Expense ($000):** 11460 **Personnel:** 175

SHERMAN—Grayson County

◇ **CARRUS REHABILITATION HOSPITAL (673041)**, 1810 West U.S. Highway 82, Suite 100, Zip 75092–7069; tel. 903/870–2600 **A**10 21 **F**3 29 40 41 44 65 74 75 77 79 85 86 87 90 91 96 130 **S** Carrus Hospitals, Sherman, TX
Primary Contact: Jon–Michael Rains, Chief Executive Officer
CFO: Michael Exline, Chief Financial Officer
CMO: Jose Matus, M.D., Director Medical
CIO: Gary Glenn, Director Information Technology
CHR: Charlene Shupert, Director Staff Services
CNO: Marie Johnson, Chief Nursing Officer
Web address: www.carrushospital.com
Control: Corporation, Investor–owned, for–profit **Service:** Rehabilitation

Staffed Beds: 24 **Admissions:** 594 **Census:** 21 **Outpatient Visits:** 0 **Births:** 0 **Total Expense ($000):** 8758 **Payroll Expense ($000):** 4554 **Personnel:** 79

◇ **CARRUS SPECIALTY HOSPITAL (452041)**, 1810 West U.S. Highway 82, Zip 75092–7069; tel. 903/870–2600 **A**10 21 **F**1 3 29 40 41 44 56 65 74 75 77 78 79 82 83 85 86 87 91 107 114 129 130 148 **S** Carrus Hospitals, Sherman, TX
Primary Contact: Jon–Michael Rains, Chief Executive Officer
CFO: Michael Exline, Chief Financial Officer
CMO: Nathan Watson, Jr., M.D., Chief of Staff
CIO: Gary Glenn, Director Information Technology
CHR: Charlene Shupert, Director Staff Services
CNO: Marie Johnson, Chief Nursing Officer
Web address: www.carrushospital.com
Control: Corporation, Investor–owned, for–profit **Service:** Long–Term Acute Care hospital

Staffed Beds: 16 **Admissions:** 214 **Census:** 15 **Outpatient Visits:** 1569 **Births:** 0 **Total Expense ($000):** 10486 **Payroll Expense ($000):** 4314 **Personnel:** 90

Many Facility Codes have changed. Please refer to the AHA Guide Code Chart.

© 2016 AHA Guide

TX

◇ **HERITAGE PARK SURGICAL HOSPITAL (670076)**, 3601 North Calais Street, Zip 75090–1785; tel. 903/870–0999 **A**10 21 **F**3 29 40 45 47 81 85 86 87 107 111 114 119 131 145 **S** Foundation Surgical Hospital Affiliates, Oklahoma City, OK
Primary Contact: Marc Devorsetz, Chief Executive Officer
CMO: Curtis Holbrook, M.D., Chief Medical Officer
CIO: Grant Hulsey, Director Information Technology
CHR: Terrie Langford, Director Human Resources
CNO: Teresa Dutton, R.N., Chief Nursing Officer
Web address: www.heritageparksurgicalhospital.com
Control: Partnership, Investor–owned, for–profit **Service:** General Medical and Surgical

Staffed Beds: 12 **Admissions:** 368 **Census:** 2 **Outpatient Visits:** 24460 **Births:** 0 **Total Expense ($000):** 33992 **Payroll Expense ($000):** 8755 **Personnel:** 190

WILSON N. JONES MEDICAL CENTER See Wilson N. Jones Regional Medical Center

☐ **WILSON N. JONES REGIONAL MEDICAL CENTER (450469)**, 500 North Highland Avenue, Zip 75092–7354; tel. 903/870–4611 **A**1 10 **F**3 11 13 15 17 18 20 22 24 26 28 29 30 35 40 41 43 45 53 54 56 57 58 59 61 64 70 74 76 77 78 79 81 84 86 87 93 96 98 100 103 106 107 108 111 118 119 129 130 132 146 147 148
Primary Contact: Kitty J. Richardson, Administrator
CFO: Mike Winter, CPA, Controller
CMO: Kenton Schrank, M.D., President Medical Staff
CIO: Prabhu Bollu, Director Information Technology
CHR: Tammy Dawn Johnson, Director Human Resources
CNO: Tonya Price, Chief Nursing Officer
Web address: www.wnj.org
Control: Corporation, Investor–owned, for–profit **Service:** General Medical and Surgical

Staffed Beds: 237 **Admissions:** 5933 **Census:** 72 **Outpatient Visits:** 40818 **Births:** 399 **Total Expense ($000):** 88846 **Payroll Expense ($000):** 28071 **Personnel:** 434

SMITHVILLE—Bastrop County

☒ **SETON SMITHVILLE REGIONAL HOSPITAL (450143)**, 800 East Highway 71, Zip 78957–1730; tel. 512/237–3214 **A**1 10 **F**3 11 15 29 30 34 40 43 53 57 62 64 68 77 79 81 85 87 93 107 110 111 114 119 146 148 **P**3 8 **S** Ascension Health, Saint Louis, MO
Primary Contact: Robbie G. Rabe, Interim Vice President and Senior Director of Nursing
CFO: Melissa Nordyke, Chief Financial Officer
CHR: Sara Rodriguez, Human Resources
CNO: Christine Laflamme, R.N., Chief Nursing Officer
Web address: www.seton.org
Control: Church–operated, Nongovernment, not–for profit **Service:** General Medical and Surgical

Staffed Beds: 10 **Admissions:** 274 **Census:** 3 **Outpatient Visits:** 28052 **Births:** 0 **Total Expense ($000):** 18930 **Payroll Expense ($000):** 7057 **Personnel:** 112

SNYDER—Scurry County

◇ **COGDELL MEMORIAL HOSPITAL (450073)**, 1700 Cogdell Boulevard, Zip 79549–6198; tel. 325/573–6374 **A**10 18 21 **F**8 11 13 15 18 19 29 30 34 40 43 45 46 47 48 49 50 53 56 57 59 62 64 65 68 75 76 77 79 81 85 86 87 91 92 93 97 107 108 111 115 119 127 130 131 132 133 145 146 147 148 **P**6
Primary Contact: Ella Raye Helms, Chief Executive Officer
CFO: John Everett, Chief Financial Officer
CMO: Robert Rakov, M.D., Chief Medical Officer
CHR: Linda Warren, Director Human Resources
Web address: www.cogdellhospital.com
Control: Hospital district or authority, Government, nonfederal **Service:** General Medical and Surgical

Staffed Beds: 25 **Admissions:** 583 **Census:** 5 **Outpatient Visits:** 64673 **Births:** 160 **Total Expense ($000):** 35421 **Payroll Expense ($000):** 12940 **Personnel:** 217

SONORA—Sutton County

★ **LILLIAN M. HUDSPETH MEMORIAL HOSPITAL (451324)**, 308 Hudspeth Avenue, Zip 76950–8003, Mailing Address: P.O. Box 455, Zip 76950–0455; tel. 325/387–2521 **A**10 18 **F**3 7 15 18 28 29 30 32 34 35 40 43 44 45 50 53 57 59 64 65 66 68 74 75 79 86 87 90 93 96 97 107 110 111 115 119 127 128 131 132 133 134 135 147 148
Primary Contact: John A. Graves, Chief Executive Officer
CFO: Michelle Schaefer, Chief Financial Officer
CMO: Kristy Edwards, M.D., Chief Medical Officer
CNO: Jon–Michael Parker, R.N., Chief Nursing Officer
Web address: www.sonora–hospital.org
Control: Hospital district or authority, Government, nonfederal **Service:** General Medical and Surgical

Staffed Beds: 12 **Admissions:** 154 **Census:** 1 **Outpatient Visits:** 9109 **Births:** 0 **Total Expense ($000):** 9728 **Payroll Expense ($000):** 4663 **Personnel:** 69

SOUTHLAKE—Tarrant County

○ **METHODIST SOUTHLAKE HOSPITAL**, 421 East State Highway 114, Zip 76092; tel. 817/865–4400, (Nonreporting) **A**11
Primary Contact: Julie A. Camp, R.N., Interim Chief Executive Officer
Web address: www.forestparksouthlake.com
Control: Corporation, Investor–owned, for–profit **Service:** General Medical and Surgical

Staffed Beds: 15

☐ **TEXAS HEALTH HARRIS METHODIST HOSPITAL SOUTHLAKE (450888)**, 1545 East Southlake Boulevard, Zip 76092–6422; tel. 817/748–8700 **A**1 10 **F**3 29 30 40 64 74 79 81 85 107 111 113 114 119 130 **P**2
Primary Contact: Traci Bernard, R.N., President, Chief Executive Officer and Chief Operating Officer
CFO: Mitchell Mulvehill, Group Financial Officer
CMO: David Taunton, M.D., Chief of Staff
CHR: Tasha Sledge, Director Human Resources
CNO: Debra Ennis, R.N., Vice President and Chief Nursing Officer
Web address: www.texashealthsouthlake.com
Control: Corporation, Investor–owned, for–profit **Service:** Surgical

Staffed Beds: 18 **Admissions:** 979 **Census:** 7 **Outpatient Visits:** 10403 **Births:** 0 **Total Expense ($000):** 48461 **Payroll Expense ($000):** 11335 **Personnel:** 146

SPEARMAN—Hansford County

★ **HANSFORD HOSPITAL (451344)**, 707 South Roland Street, Zip 79081–3441; tel. 806/659–2535 **A**10 18 **F**3 11 31 32 34 35 40 43 56 57 59 62 63 64 65 68 69 77 78 93 107 114 127 130 133 148 **P**6
Primary Contact: Jonathan D. Bailey, Chief Executive Officer and Administrator
CFO: Scott Beedy, Chief Financial Officer
CMO: Mark Garnett, M.D., Chief of Staff
CHR: Jackie Nelson, Director Human Resources
Web address: www.hchd.net
Control: Hospital district or authority, Government, nonfederal **Service:** General Medical and Surgical

Staffed Beds: 14 **Admissions:** 134 **Census:** 2 **Outpatient Visits:** 26716 **Births:** 0 **Total Expense ($000):** 10590 **Payroll Expense ($000):** 4114 **Personnel:** 102

STAFFORD—Fort Bend County

◇ **ATRIUM MEDICAL CENTER (452114)**, 11929 West Airport Boulevard, Zip 77477–2451; tel. 281/207–8200 **A**10 21 **F**1 3 18 26 28 29 45 46 56 59 60 64 65 68 70 74 77 82 83 85 90 91 107 114 119 130 146 148
Primary Contact: Ahmad Zaid, Chief Executive Officer
CFO: Ana Urbina, Chief Financial Officer
CMO: Shatish Patel, M.D., Chief Medical Officer
CNO: Ava Hearing, Chief Nursing Officer
Web address: www.atriummedicalcenter.com
Control: Partnership, Investor–owned, for–profit **Service:** Long–Term Acute Care hospital

Staffed Beds: 68 **Admissions:** 464 **Census:** 33 **Outpatient Visits:** 501 **Births:** 0 **Total Expense ($000):** 18436 **Payroll Expense ($000):** 7117 **Personnel:** 152

Hospital, Medicare Provider Number, Address, Telephone, Approval, Facility, and Physician Codes, Health Care System

★ American Hospital Association (AHA) membership
☐ The Joint Commission accreditation
○ Healthcare Facilities Accreditation Program
◇ DNV Healthcare Inc. accreditation
⇑ Center for Improvement in Healthcare Quality Accreditation
△ Commission on Accreditation of Rehabilitation Facilities (CARF) accreditation

TX

STAMFORD—Jones County

STAMFORD MEMORIAL HOSPITAL (450306), 1601 Columbia Street,
Zip 79553–6863, Mailing Address: P.O. Box 911, Zip 79553–0911;
tel. 325/773–2725 **A**10 **F**10 11 28 30 34 35 40 41 53 57 59 62 64 65 81 89
93 107 114 119 127 128 133 144 146 148 **P**4
Primary Contact: Richard G. DeFoore, FACHE, Chief Executive Officer
CFO: Elizabeth Miller, CPA, Chief Financial Officer
CMO: Douglas Kruckner, M.D., Medical Director
CHR: Cheryl Hertel, Coordinator Human Resources
CNO: Rickie Young, Chief Nursing Officer
Web address: www.stamfordhosp.com/
Control: Other not–for–profit (including NFP Corporation) **Service:** General
Medical and Surgical

Staffed Beds: 12 **Admissions:** 156 **Census:** 2 **Outpatient Visits:** 13193
Births: 0 **Total Expense ($000):** 8134 **Payroll Expense ($000):** 3416
Personnel: 80

STANTON—Martin County

MARTIN COUNTY HOSPITAL DISTRICT (451333), 600 Interstate 20E,
Zip 79782, Mailing Address: P.O. Box 640, Zip 79782–0640; tel. 432/607–3200
A10 18 **F**3 7 29 34 35 39 40 45 50 57 59 62 64 65 75 81 87 93 107 114
119 127 130 133 **P**6
Primary Contact: Paul McKinney, Chief Executive Officer
COO: Rance Ramsey, Chief Operating Officer
CFO: Michele Cathey, Interim Chief Financial officer
CIO: Freddy Oliveras, Chief Information Officer
CHR: Paula Dority, Director Human Resources
CNO: Brandi Avila, Chief Nursing Officer
Control: Hospital district or authority, Government, nonfederal **Service:** General
Medical and Surgical

Staffed Beds: 18 **Admissions:** 174 **Census:** 4 **Outpatient Visits:** 4562
Births: 2 **Total Expense ($000):** 15338 **Payroll Expense ($000):** 5526
Personnel: 144

STEPHENVILLE—Erath County

☒ **TEXAS HEALTH HARRIS METHODIST HOSPITAL STEPHENVILLE (450351)**,
411 North Belknap Street, Zip 76401–3415; tel. 254/965–1500 **A**1 10 20 **F**3
13 15 29 30 34 35 39 40 41 43 45 50 51 57 59 64 65 68 70 75 76 77 79
81 85 86 89 107 108 111 114 118 119 129 130 146 147 148 **P**6 **S** Texas
Health Resources, Arlington, TX
Primary Contact: Christopher Leu, President
CMO: Marilyn Brister, M.D., Chief of Staff
CHR: Kimberly Leondar, Director Human Resources
CNO: Cynthia L. McCarthy, MS, Chief Nursing Officer
Web address: www.texashealth.org/landing.cfm?id=108
Control: Other not–for–profit (including NFP Corporation) **Service:** General
Medical and Surgical

Staffed Beds: 54 **Admissions:** 1938 **Census:** 17 **Outpatient Visits:** 30363
Births: 375 **Total Expense ($000):** 40343 **Payroll Expense ($000):** 15924
Personnel: 179

SUGAR LAND—Fort Bend County

◇ **EMERUS HOSPITAL – SUGAR LAND (670058)**, 16000 Southwest Freeway,
Suite 100, Zip 77479–2674; tel. 281/277–0911 **A**10 21 **F**3 40 75 107 114
119 **P**5 **S** Emerus, The Woodlands, TX
Primary Contact: Mike Kohler, Chief Executive Officer
Web address: www.emerus.com
Control: Corporation, Investor–owned, for–profit **Service:** General Medical and
Surgical

Staffed Beds: 7 **Admissions:** 109 **Census:** 1 **Outpatient Visits:** 6897 **Births:**
0 **Total Expense ($000):** 5407 **Payroll Expense ($000):** 1824 **Personnel:**
28

☒ **HEALTHSOUTH SUGAR LAND REHABILITATION HOSPITAL (673042)**, 1325
Highway 6, Zip 77478–4906; tel. 281/276–7574 **A**1 10 **F**3 29 34 75 87 90 95
96 130 132 146 148 **S** HEALTHSOUTH Corporation, Birmingham, AL
Primary Contact: Nicholas Hardin, FACHE, Chief Executive Officer
CFO: Carol Neilson, CPA, Controller
CNO: Steve Midgett, R.N., Chief Nursing Officer
Web address: www.healthsouthsugarland.com
Control: Corporation, Investor–owned, for–profit **Service:** Rehabilitation

Staffed Beds: 50 **Admissions:** 1301 **Census:** 45 **Outpatient Visits:** 0 **Births:**
0 **Total Expense ($000):** 18671 **Payroll Expense ($000):** 9484 **Personnel:**
186

★ ◇ **HOUSTON METHODIST SUGAR LAND HOSPITAL (450820)**, 16655 S.W.
Freeway, Zip 77479–2329; tel. 281/274–7000 **A**2 3 10 21 **F**3 12 13 15 18 20
22 24 26 29 30 31 33 34 35 36 37 38 39 40 41 42 44 45 46 47 49 50 51
53 54 57 58 59 60 61 64 65 68 70 73 74 75 76 77 78 79 81 82 84 85 86
87 91 92 93 94 96 100 102 107 108 110 111 114 115 119 120 121 123
124 126 130 131 132 135 145 146 147 148 **P**6 **S** Houston Methodist,
Houston, TX
Primary Contact: Christopher Siebenaler, Chief Executive Officer
CFO: Lowell Stanton, Chief Financial Officer
CMO: Jeffrey Jackson, M.D., Medical Director
CHR: Luis Mario Garcia, Jr., Director Human Resources
Web address: www.methodisthealth.com
Control: Other not–for–profit (including NFP Corporation) **Service:** General
Medical and Surgical

Staffed Beds: 243 **Admissions:** 16003 **Census:** 188 **Outpatient Visits:**
192279 **Births:** 3358 **Total Expense ($000):** 314849 **Payroll Expense**
($000): 110761 **Personnel:** 1768

☒ **KINDRED HOSPITAL SUGAR LAND (452080)**, 1550 First Colony Boulevard,
Zip 77479–4000; tel. 281/275–6000 **A**1 10 **F**1 3 29 31 35 45 57 65 75 77
85 87 91 107 130 148 **S** Kindred Healthcare, Louisville, KY
Primary Contact: John D. Cross, Chief Executive Officer
CFO: Sara Rodriguez, Chief Financial Officer
CMO: Subodh Bhuchar, M.D., Chief of Staff
CIO: Feisal Ndomea, Director Case Management
CHR: Lupe Delgado, Coordinator Human Resources
CNO: Hala Alameddine, Chief Nursing Executive
Web address: www.khsugarland.com
Control: Corporation, Investor–owned, for–profit **Service:** Long–Term Acute Care
hospital

Staffed Beds: 171 **Admissions:** 1368 **Census:** 102 **Outpatient Visits:** 157
Births: 0 **Total Expense ($000):** 60039 **Payroll Expense ($000):** 20403
Personnel: 318

☒ **MEMORIAL HERMANN SUGAR LAND HOSPITAL (450848)**, 17500 West
Grand Parkway South, Zip 77479–2562; tel. 281/725–5000 **A**1 2 3 5 10 **F**3 8
11 13 15 18 20 22 29 30 34 35 36 37 40 41 43 44 45 46 47 48 49 50 51
55 56 57 59 60 64 68 70 72 74 75 76 77 78 79 81 82 85 86 87 89 91 92
93 97 107 108 109 110 111 112 114 117 119 126 129 130 135 146 147
148 **P**5 6 **S** Memorial Hermann Health System, Houston, TX
Primary Contact: Gregory Haralson, Chief Executive Officer
CFO: Lisa Kendler, Chief Financial Officer
CMO: William Riley, Jr., M.D., Chief of Staff
CHR: Robert Blake, Chief Human Resources Officer Southwest Market
Web address: www.memorialhermann.org
Control: Other not–for–profit (including NFP Corporation) **Service:** General
Medical and Surgical

Staffed Beds: 81 **Admissions:** 5459 **Census:** 54 **Outpatient Visits:** 86243
Births: 1344 **Total Expense ($000):** 118924 **Payroll Expense ($000):**
37549 **Personnel:** 503

☐ **MEMORIAL HERMANN SURGICAL HOSPITALG‰(FIRST COLONY (450860)**,
16906 Southwest Freeway, Zip 77479–2350; tel. 281/243–1000 **A**1 2 10 **F**3
29 40 48 50 79 81 85 87 107 111 114 119 **P**2 **S** Memorial Hermann Health
System, Houston, TX
Primary Contact: Daniel Smith, Chief Executive Officer
CFO: Raquel Hebert, Business Manager
CMO: Ken Thomson, M.D., Medical Director
Web address: www.memorialhermannfirstcolony.com
Control: Partnership, Investor–owned, for–profit **Service:** Surgical

Staffed Beds: 6 **Admissions:** 393 **Census:** 2 **Outpatient Visits:** 10578
Births: 0 **Total Expense ($000):** 28458 **Payroll Expense ($000):** 6185
Personnel: 120

METHODIST SUGAR LAND HOSPITAL See Houston Methodist Sugar Land
Hospital

★ ◇ **ST. LUKE'S SUGAR LAND HOSPITAL (670053)**, 1317 Lake Pointe
Parkway, Zip 77478–3997; tel. 281/637–7000 **A**10 21 **F**3 15 18 20 22 26 29
30 34 35 37 39 40 41 44 45 46 49 50 57 60 64 68 70 74 75 79 81 82 85
107 108 110 111 115 119 126 129 130 146 147 148 **P**5 **S** Catholic Health
Initiatives, Englewood, CO
Primary Contact: Robert A. Heifner, Chief Executive Officer
CFO: Bill Beauchamp, Chief Financial Officer
CNO: Wes Garrison
Web address: www.stlukessugarland.com
Control: Church–operated, Nongovernment, not–for profit **Service:** General
Medical and Surgical

Staffed Beds: 58 **Admissions:** 3082 **Census:** 41 **Outpatient Visits:** 23418
Births: 0 **Total Expense ($000):** 81301 **Payroll Expense ($000):** 30224
Personnel: 299

SUGAR LAND REHABILITATION HOSPITAL See HEALTHSOUTH Sugar Land
Rehabilitation Hospital

TRIUMPH HOSPITAL SOUTHWEST See Kindred Hospital Sugar Land

SULPHUR SPRINGS—Hopkins County

★ **CHRISTUS MOTHER FRANCES HOSPITAL – SULPHUR SPRINGS (450236)**, 115 Airport Road, Zip 75482–2105; tel. 903/885–7671 **A**10 **F**1 7 11 13 15 28 29 34 35 40 43 57 59 70 73 76 79 80 81 93 96 107 110 111 114 119 127 130 146 **P**6 **S** CHRISTUS Health, Irving, TX
Primary Contact: Paul Harvery, President and Chief Executive Officer
COO: Donna Geiken Wallace, Chief Operating Officer and Chief Financial Officer
CFO: Donna Geiken Wallace, Chief Operating Officer and Chief Financial Officer
CMO: Chris Gallagher, M.D., Chief Medical Officer
CHR: Donna Rudzik, Director Human Resources
CNO: Terri Bunch, R.N., Chief Nursing Officer
Web address: www.tmfhc.org/maps–and–locations/locations–profile/?id=72&searchId=8bcb329f–a152–e611–b37f–2c768a4e1b84&sort=11&page=1&pageSize=10
Control: Hospital district or authority, Government, nonfederal **Service:** General Medical and Surgical

Staffed Beds: 50 **Admissions:** 3350 **Census:** 32 **Outpatient Visits:** 68198 **Births:** 732 **Total Expense ($000):** 52456 **Payroll Expense ($000):** 19448 **Personnel:** 453

SUNNYVALE—Dallas County

⊞ **BAYLOR SCOTT & WHITE MEDICAL CENTER – SUNNYVALE (670060)**, 231 South Collins Road, Zip 75182–4624; tel. 972/892–3000 **A**1 10 **F**3 13 15 18 20 22 24 29 34 35 40 45 49 57 59 64 70 74 75 76 77 79 80 81 82 85 87 90 93 107 108 110 111 114 115 119 130 135 146 147 148 **P**2 **S** TENET Healthcare Corporation, Dallas, TX
Primary Contact: Collin LeMaistre, Chief Executive Officer
COO: Josiah De La Garza, Chief Operating Officer
CNO: Penny Range, Chief Nursing Officer
Web address: www.BaylorScottandWhite.com/Sunnyvale
Control: Partnership, Investor–owned, for–profit **Service:** General Medical and Surgical

Staffed Beds: 70 **Admissions:** 5364 **Census:** 53 **Outpatient Visits:** 38775 **Births:** 1290 **Total Expense ($000):** 75655 **Payroll Expense ($000):** 29427 **Personnel:** 347

SWEENY—Brazoria County

SWEENY COMMUNITY HOSPITAL (451311), 305 North McKinney Street, Zip 77480–2895; tel. 979/548–1500 **A**10 18 **F**3 7 10 11 15 29 34 35 40 43 45 53 56 57 59 65 69 70 75 81 85 93 103 104 107 110 114 119 130 132 133 143 145 148 **P**6
Primary Contact: William H. Barnes, FACHE, Administrator and Chief Executive Officer
CFO: Hong Wade, Chief Financial Officer
CMO: Enrique A. Leal, III, M.D., Chief of Staff
CIO: Stuart Butler, Director Information Technology
CHR: Rebecca McKay, Director Human Resources
Web address: www.sweenyhospital.org
Control: Hospital district or authority, Government, nonfederal **Service:** General Medical and Surgical

Staffed Beds: 14 **Admissions:** 223 **Census:** 2 **Outpatient Visits:** 16540 **Births:** 0 **Total Expense ($000):** 31263 **Payroll Expense ($000):** 7315 **Personnel:** 214

SWEETWATER—Nolan County

★ ◇ **ROLLING PLAINS MEMORIAL HOSPITAL (450055)**, 200 East Arizona Street, Zip 79556–7199, Mailing Address: P.O. Box 690, Zip 79556–0690; tel. 325/235–1701 **A**10 20 21 **F**3 11 13 15 28 29 34 40 43 45 53 57 59 62 70 76 77 79 81 85 89 91 93 107 108 114 119 130 133 135 146 148
Primary Contact: Donna Boatright, MSN, Chief Executive Officer
COO: Rhonda Guelker, Senior Director Finance
CFO: Rhonda Guelker, Senior Director Finance
CMO: Ronnie Dennis, Chief of Staff
CIO: Rhonda Guelker, Senior Director Finance
CHR: Ame Monroe, Director Human Resources
CNO: Rosa Best, Chief Nursing Officer
Web address: www.rpmh.net
Control: Hospital district or authority, Government, nonfederal **Service:** General Medical and Surgical

Staffed Beds: 52 **Admissions:** 1223 **Census:** 14 **Outpatient Visits:** 42888 **Births:** 216 **Total Expense ($000):** 25954 **Payroll Expense ($000):** 13029 **Personnel:** 245

TAHOKA—Lynn County

★ **LYNN COUNTY HOSPITAL DISTRICT (451351)**, 2600 Lockwood, Zip 79373–4118; tel. 806/998–4533 **A**10 18 **F**3 7 10 13 29 32 34 35 40 43 44 53 54 56 57 59 64 65 66 75 86 93 97 107 133 147 148 **P**5
Primary Contact: Jeff Barnhart, Chief Executive Officer
CFO: Steve Brock, Chief Financial Officer
CMO: Donald Freitag, M.D., Chief Medical Officer
CIO: Jim Brown, Director Information Technology
CHR: Jill Stone, Manager Human Resources
CNO: Angie Jalomo, Chief Nursing Officer
Web address: www.lchdhealthcare.org
Control: Hospital district or authority, Government, nonfederal **Service:** General Medical and Surgical

Staffed Beds: 24 **Admissions:** 152 **Census:** 1 **Outpatient Visits:** 8011 **Births:** 1 **Total Expense ($000):** 11907 **Payroll Expense ($000):** 4266 **Personnel:** 100

TAYLOR—Williamson County

JOHNS COMMUNITY HOSPITAL See Scott & White Hospital – Taylor

⊞ **SCOTT & WHITE HOSPITAL – TAYLOR (451374)**, 305 Mallard Lane, Zip 76574–1208; tel. 512/352–7611 **A**1 10 18 **F**3 18 29 34 35 40 43 45 50 56 57 59 62 64 65 68 75 77 81 82 85 87 91 92 93 97 107 108 111 119 127 129 130 132 133 135 146 148 **S** Baylor Scott & White Health, Dallas, TX
Primary Contact: Tim Tarbell, Director Operations
CIO: Tim Tarbell, Director Operations
Web address: www.swtaylor.org
Control: Other not–for–profit (including NFP Corporation) **Service:** General Medical and Surgical

Staffed Beds: 25 **Admissions:** 500 **Census:** 8 **Outpatient Visits:** 52844 **Births:** 0 **Total Expense ($000):** 18729 **Payroll Expense ($000):** 9822 **Personnel:** 111

TEMPLE—Bell County

CENTRAL TEXAS VETERANS AFFAIRS HEALTH CARE SYSTEM, OLIN E. TEAGUE VETERANS MEDICAL CENTER See Central Texas Veterans Health Care System

⊞ △ **CENTRAL TEXAS VETERANS HEALTH CARE SYSTEM**, 1901 Veterans Memorial Drive, Zip 76504–7493; tel. 254/778–4811, (Includes CENTRAL TEXAS VETERANS AFFAIRS HEALTH CARE SYSTEM, OLIN E. TEAGUE VETERANS MEDICAL CENTER, 1901 Veterans Memorial Drive, Zip 76504; tel. 254/778–4811; Russell E. Lloyd, Acting Director; CENTRAL TEXAS VETERANS HEALTH CARE SYSTEM, DORIS MILLER VETERANS MEDICAL CENTER, 4800 Memorial Drive, Waco, Zip 76711–1397; tel. 254/752–6581; Russell E. Lloyd, Acting Director), (Nonreporting) **A**1 2 3 5 7 8 **S** Department of Veterans Affairs, Washington, DC
Primary Contact: Russell E. Lloyd, Acting Director
COO: Andrew T. Garcia, Acting Associate Director
CFO: Rosey Anzures, Acting Chief Financial Officer
CMO: Olawale Fashina, M.D., Chief of Staff
CIO: Victor Vitolas, Acting Chief Information Technology Services
CHR: Mary P. Doerfler, Chief Human Resources Officer
CNO: Bryan W. Sisk, Associate Director Patient and Nursing Services
Web address: www.centraltexas.va.gov/
Control: Veterans Affairs, Government, federal **Service:** General Medical and Surgical

Staffed Beds: 1532

MCLANE CHILDREN'S HOSPITAL SCOTT & WHITE See Scott & White Memorial Hospital

★ **SCOTT & WHITE MEMORIAL HOSPITAL (450054)**, 2401 South 31st Street, Zip 76508–0002; tel. 254/724–2111, (Includes MCLANE CHILDREN'S HOSPITAL SCOTT & WHITE, 2401 South 31st Street, Zip 76508–0001; tel. 877/724–5437; John Boyd, III, M.D., Chief Executive Officer and Chief Medical Officer; MCLANE CHILDREN'S HOSPITAL SCOTT & WHITE, 1901 S.W. H. K. Dodgen Loop, Zip 76502–1896; tel. 254/771–8600; John Boyd, III, M.D., Chief Executive Officer), (Total facility includes 29 beds in nursing home–type unit) **A**1 2 3 5 8 10 **F**3 5 7 9 11 12 13 14 15 17 18 19 20 21 22 24 26 27 28 29 30 31 32 34 35 36 37 38 39 40 41 43 44 45 46 47 48 49 50 51 52 54 55 56 57 58 59 60 61 62 63 64 65 66 68 70 72 73 74 75 76 77 78 79 81 82 84 85 86 87 88 89 91 92 93 96 97 98 99 100 102 103 104 105 107 108 110 111 113 114 115 116 117 118 119 120 121 123 124 126 128 129 130 131 132 134 135 137 138 141 142 143 144 145 146 147 148 **S** Baylor Scott & White Health, Dallas, TX
Primary Contact: Shahin Motakef, FACHE, Chief Executive Officer
CFO: Alita Prosser, Chief Financial Officer
CMO: Stephen Sibbitt, M.D., Chief Medical Officer
CIO: Matthew Chambers, Chief Information Officer
CHR: Lorraine Bell, Vice President Operations Human Resources
CNO: Gerald W. Bryant, R.N., Chief Nursing Officer
Web address: www.sw.org/location/temple–hospital
Control: Other not–for–profit (including NFP Corporation) **Service:** General Medical and Surgical

Staffed Beds: 648 Admissions: 33529 Census: 456 Outpatient Visits: 1655182 **Births: 2725 Total Expense ($000): 757367 Payroll Expense ($000): 267239 Personnel: 5619**	

★ **SCOTT AND WHITE CONTINUING CARE HOSPITAL (452105)**, 546 North Kegley Road, Zip 76502–4069; tel. 254/215–0900 **A**10 **F**1 3 29 30 60 85 107 119 130 **S** Baylor Scott & White Health, Dallas, TX
Primary Contact: Kimberly K. Langston, R.N., Chief Executive Officer
CMO: David P. Ciceri, M.D., Chief Medical Officer
Web address: www.sw.org/location/temple–cch
Control: Other not–for–profit (including NFP Corporation) **Service:** Long–Term Acute Care hospital

Staffed Beds: 50 Admissions: 385 Census: 33 Outpatient Visits: 42 Births: 0 Total Expense ($000): 18669 Payroll Expense ($000): 7971 Personnel: 98	

TERRELL—Kaufman County

☐ **TERRELL STATE HOSPITAL (454006)**, 1200 East Brin Street, Zip 75160–2938, Mailing Address: P.O. Box 70, Zip 75160–9000; tel. 972/524–6452 **A**1 10 **F**30 34 39 57 68 75 86 87 98 99 100 101 103 130 132 135 146 **P**6 **S** Texas Department of State Health Services, Austin, TX
Primary Contact: Dorothy Floyd, Ph.D., Superintendent
CFO: Mike Verseckes, Financial Officer
CMO: Anthony Claxton, M.D., Clinical Director
CIO: Sims Anderson, Manager Facility Automation
Web address: www.dshs.state.tx.us/mhhospitals/terrellsh
Control: State–Government, nonfederal **Service:** Psychiatric

Staffed Beds: 288 Admissions: 2059 Census: 244 Outpatient Visits: 0 Births: 0 Total Expense ($000): 89524 Payroll Expense ($000): 36855 Personnel: 861	

TEXARKANA—Bowie County

★ **CHRISTUS ST. MICHAEL HEALTH SYSTEM (450801)**, 2600 St. Michael Drive, Zip 75503–5220; tel. 903/614–1000, (Includes CHRISTUS ST. MICHAEL HOSPITAL–ATLANTA, 1007 South William Street, Atlanta, Zip 75551–3245; tel. 903/799–3000; Thomas McKinney, Administrator) **A**1 2 10 **F**3 11 13 15 17 18 20 22 24 28 29 30 31 34 35 40 41 43 45 48 49 51 53 55 56 57 59 60 64 65 68 70 71 72 74 75 76 77 78 79 80 81 82 84 85 86 87 89 92 97 107 108 109 110 111 114 115 118 119 120 121 122 123 124 126 129 130 131 132 135 143 146 147 148 **P**8 **S** CHRISTUS Health, Irving, TX
Primary Contact: Chris Karam, President and Chief Executive Officer
COO: Jason Rounds, Chief Operating Officer and Administrator
CFO: Glen Boles, Vice President and Chief Financial Officer
CMO: Mike Finley, M.D., Chief Medical Officer
CIO: Alana Higgins, Regional Information Management Executive
CHR: Jennifer Wright, Vice President Regional Human Resources
CNO: Louise Thornell, Interim Chief Nursing Officer
Web address: www.christusstmichael.org
Control: Church–operated, Nongovernment, not–for profit **Service:** General Medical and Surgical

Staffed Beds: 355 Admissions: 14490 Census: 181 Outpatient Visits: 157832 **Births: 1534 Total Expense ($000): 239131 Payroll Expense ($000): 74549 Personnel: 1466**	

△ **CHRISTUS ST. MICHAEL REHABILITATION HOSPITAL (453065)**, 2400 St. Michael Drive, Zip 75503–2374; tel. 903/614–4000 **A**1 7 10 **F**3 11 18 28 29 30 34 35 57 59 65 68 75 77 79 82 87 90 93 96 132 135 143 148 **S** CHRISTUS Health, Irving, TX
Primary Contact: Aloma Gender, R.N., MSN, Administrator and Chief Nursing Officer
CFO: Glen Boles, Vice President and Chief Financial Officer
CMO: Richard Sharp, M.D., Medical Director
CIO: Alana Higgins, Regional Information Management Executive
CHR: Pam Kennedy, Director Human Resources
CNO: Aloma Gender, R.N., Administrator and Chief Nursing Officer
Web address: www.christusstmichael.org/rehab
Control: Church–operated, Nongovernment, not–for profit **Service:** Rehabilitation

Staffed Beds: 50 Admissions: 1159 Census: 34 Outpatient Visits: 11608 Births: 0 Total Expense ($000): 20597 Payroll Expense ($000): 9740 Personnel: 203	

★ **HEALTHSOUTH REHABILITATION HOSPITAL OF TEXARKANA (453053)**, 515 West 12th Street, Zip 75501–4416; tel. 903/735–5000 **A**1 10 **F**3 28 29 42 64 74 77 79 90 91 93 95 96 130 131 132 143 148 **P**5 **S** HEALTHSOUTH Corporation, Birmingham, AL
Primary Contact: Harlo McCall, Chief Executive Officer
CFO: Phylis Buck, Controller
CMO: Mark A. Wren, M.D., Medical Director
CHR: Ann R. Clapp, Director Human Resources
CNO: Lametria Griffie, Interim Chief Nursing Officer
Web address: www.healthsouthtexarkana.com
Control: Corporation, Investor–owned, for–profit **Service:** Rehabilitation

Staffed Beds: 60 Admissions: 1114 Census: 39 Outpatient Visits: 8370 Births: 0 Total Expense ($000): 14926 Payroll Expense ($000): 8185 Personnel: 151	

★ **POST ACUTE MEDICAL SPECIALTY HOSPITAL OF TEXARKANA – NORTH (452061)**, 2400 St. Michael Drive, 2nd Floor, Zip 75503–2372; tel. 903/614–7600 **A**1 10 **F**1 3 29 130 148 **S** Post Acute Medical, LLC, Enola, PA
Primary Contact: Benny Costello, Administrator
Web address: www.postacutemedical.com
Control: Corporation, Investor–owned, for–profit **Service:** Long–Term Acute Care hospital

Staffed Beds: 49 Admissions: 543 Census: 37 Outpatient Visits: 0 Births: 0 Total Expense ($000): 16711 Payroll Expense ($000): 5907 Personnel: 120	

☐ **WADLEY REGIONAL MEDICAL CENTER (450200)**, 1000 Pine Street, Zip 75501–5170; tel. 903/798–8000 **A**1 3 10 **F**3 11 13 15 18 20 22 24 28 29 30 31 34 35 40 43 45 49 50 56 57 59 60 64 65 70 71 73 74 75 76 77 78 79 81 85 86 87 89 98 103 107 108 110 111 114 115 119 126 130 146 147 148 **S** IASIS Healthcare, Franklin, TN
Primary Contact: Thomas D. Gilbert, FACHE, Chief Executive Officer
CFO: Bonny Sorensen, Chief Financial Officer
CIO: Matt Kesterson, Director Information Services
CHR: Debby Butler, Director Human Resources
CNO: Shelly Strayhorn, R.N., Chief Nursing Officer
Web address: www.wadleyhealth.com
Control: Corporation, Investor–owned, for–profit **Service:** General Medical and Surgical

Staffed Beds: 179 Admissions: 7324 Census: 86 Outpatient Visits: 80074 Births: 1178 Total Expense ($000): 92173 Payroll Expense ($000): 38529 Personnel: 652	

THE WOODLANDS—Montgomery County

MEMORIAL HERMANN THE WOODLANDS HOSPITAL See Memorial Hermann Greater Heights Hospital, Houston

NEXUS SPECIALTY HOSPITAL THE WOODLANDS (452057), 9182 Six Pines Drive, Zip 77380–3670; tel. 281/364–0317, (Nonreporting) **A**10
Primary Contact: Mikael Simpson, Chief Executive Officer
CFO: Corey O'Connor, Vice President, Finance
CMO: Ather Siddiqi, M.D., Medical Director
CIO: Noe Salinas, Vice President Information Technology
CHR: Kevin McAndrews, Vice President, Human Resources
Web address: www.nexusspecialty.com
Control: Partnership, Investor–owned, for–profit **Service:** Long–Term Acute Care hospital

Staffed Beds: 21	

Many Facility Codes have changed. Please refer to the AHA Guide Code Chart. © 2016 AHA Guide

TX

★ ◇ **ST. LUKE'S LAKESIDE HOSPITAL (670059)**, 17400 St. Luke's Way, Zip 77384–8036; tel. 936/266–9000 **A**10 21 **F**3 18 20 22 26 29 30 34 35 40 50 57 59 64 68 75 79 81 87 94 107 111 115 119 130 131 135 **P**5 **S** Catholic Health Initiatives, Englewood, CO
Primary Contact: David Argueta, Chief Executive Officer
CMO: Bruce Lachterman, M.D., Chief of Medical Staff
CIO: Paul Solverson, Chief Information Officer
CHR: Debra Roberts, Director of Human Resources
CNO: Diane Freeman, R.N., Assistant Vice President and Chief Nursing Officer
Web address: www.stlukeslakeside.com/
Control: Corporation, Investor–owned, for–profit **Service:** Surgical

Staffed Beds: 30 **Admissions:** 784 **Census:** 5 **Outpatient Visits:** 13920 **Births:** 0 **Total Expense ($000):** 38940 **Payroll Expense ($000):** 7928 **Personnel:** 135			

★ ◇ **ST. LUKE'S THE WOODLANDS HOSPITAL (450862)**, 17200 St. Luke's Way, Zip 77384–8007; tel. 936/266–2000 **A**10 21 **F**3 11 12 13 15 18 20 22 24 26 28 29 30 34 35 38 40 41 45 49 50 57 58 59 64 68 70 72 74 75 76 78 79 81 82 85 86 87 89 93 107 108 109 110 111 114 118 119 124 126 129 130 131 135 145 146 147 148 **P**5 **S** Catholic Health Initiatives, Englewood, CO
Primary Contact: David Argueta, Chief Executive Officer
CMO: Charles Sims, M.D., Chief of Staff
Web address: www.stlukeswoodlands.com
Control: Church–operated, Nongovernment, not–for profit **Service:** General Medical and Surgical

Staffed Beds: 192 **Admissions:** 11119 **Census:** 126 **Outpatient Visits:** 66754 **Births:** 2036 **Total Expense ($000):** 165455 **Payroll Expense ($000):** 69254 **Personnel:** 859	

★ **WOODLANDS SPECIALTY HOSPITAL**, 9182 Six Pines Drive, Zip 77380–3670, Mailing Address: 25540 I–45 North, Suite 100, Spring, Zip 77380–3670; tel. 281/602–8160, (Nonreporting)
Primary Contact: Nellie Kay, Chief Executive Officer
CFO: Virginia de Bond, Chief Financial Officer
Web address: www.woodlandsspecialtyhospital.com/
Control: Partnership, Investor–owned, for–profit **Service:** General Medical and Surgical

Staffed Beds: 6

THROCKMORTON—Throckmorton County

THROCKMORTON COUNTY MEMORIAL HOSPITAL (451339), 802 North Minter Street, Zip 76483–5357, Mailing Address: P.O. Box 729, Zip 76483–0729; tel. 940/849–2151 **A**10 18 **F**7 40 41 43 50 64 65 68 75 87 127 128 133 148 **P**5 6
Primary Contact: Kirby Gober, Chief Executive Officer
CFO: Cindy Parker, Chief Financial Officer and Director Human Resources
CMO: Ruth Ebangit, M.D., Chief of Staff and Medical Officer
CIO: Amber Myer, Director Medical Technology
CHR: Cindy Parker, Chief Financial Officer and Director Human Resources
CNO: Pam Stamm, Chief Nursing Officer
Web address: www.throckmortonhospital.com/index.html
Control: County–Government, nonfederal **Service:** General Medical and Surgical

Staffed Beds: 14 **Admissions:** 96 **Census:** 1 **Outpatient Visits:** 8447 **Births:** 0 **Total Expense ($000):** 3797 **Payroll Expense ($000):** 1526 **Personnel:** 38	

TOMBALL—Harris County

◇ **EMERUS COMMUNITY HOSPITAL (670095)**, 24429 State Highway 249, Zip 77375–8214; tel. 281/516–0911 **A**21 **F**3 40 75 107 114 119 **P**5 **S** Emerus, The Woodlands, TX
Primary Contact: Paula Gonzales, Administrator
Web address: www.emerus.com/tomball/
Control: Corporation, Investor–owned, for–profit **Service:** General Medical and Surgical

Staffed Beds: 8 **Admissions:** 71 **Census:** 1 **Outpatient Visits:** 6528 **Births:** 0 **Total Expense ($000):** 5657 **Payroll Expense ($000):** 1849 **Personnel:** 27	

⊞ **KINDRED HOSPITAL TOMBALL (452074)**, 505 Graham Drive, Zip 77375–3368; tel. 281/255–5600, (Includes KINDRED HOSPITAL SPRING, 205 Hollow Tree Lane, Houston, Zip 77090; tel. 832/249–2700; Tracy Kohler, Chief Executive Officer) **A**1 10 **F**1 3 18 29 30 31 42 49 64 70 74 75 78 79 84 85 86 87 93 94 107 119 130 **S** Kindred Healthcare, Louisville, KY
Primary Contact: Tracy Kohler, Chief Executive Officer
Web address: www.khtomball.com/
Control: Partnership, Investor–owned, for–profit **Service:** Long–Term Acute Care hospital

Staffed Beds: 75 **Admissions:** 1828 **Census:** 130 **Outpatient Visits:** 1457 **Births:** 0 **Total Expense ($000):** 81186 **Payroll Expense ($000):** 26834 **Personnel:** 405	

⊞ **TOMBALL REGIONAL MEDICAL CENTER (450670)**, 605 Holderrieth Street, Zip 77375–6445; tel. 281/401–7500, (Includes KINDRED HOSITAL THE HEIGHTS, 1800 West 26th Street, Houston, Zip 77008–1450; tel. 832/673–4200; William Elsesser, Chief Executive Officer) **A**1 10 **F**3 8 12 13 15 18 20 22 24 26 28 29 30 34 40 42 44 45 46 47 48 49 50 51 53 54 57 59 60 64 70 72 74 75 76 78 79 80 81 82 85 86 87 90 91 94 96 98 102 103 107 108 110 111 114 115 116 117 119 120 121 123 124 126 129 130 131 132 146 148 **P**6 **S** Community Health Systems, Inc., Franklin, TN
Primary Contact: Thomas W. Jackson, Chief Executive Officer
COO: Brett Kinman, Chief Operating Officer
CFO: Richard Ervin, Chief Financial Officer
CMO: Ian Glass, M.D., Chief Medical Officer
CIO: Marisa Smith, Director
CHR: Vanessa Anyaso, Chief Human Resources
Web address: www.tomballregionalmedicalcenter.com
Control: Corporation, Investor–owned, for–profit **Service:** General Medical and Surgical

Staffed Beds: 191 **Admissions:** 9745 **Census:** 133 **Outpatient Visits:** 70772 **Births:** 1053 **Total Expense ($000):** 166747 **Payroll Expense ($000):** 60442 **Personnel:** 861	

TRINITY—Trinity County

★ **EAST TEXAS MEDICAL CENTER TRINITY (450749)**, 317 Prospect Drive, Zip 75862–6202, Mailing Address: P.O. Box 3169, Zip 75862–3169; tel. 936/744–1100 **A**10 **F**11 29 40 43 64 97 107 114 115 119 127 146 **P**7 **S** East Texas Medical Center Regional Healthcare System, Tyler, TX
Primary Contact: Ruth Cook, Administrator
CFO: Jerry A. Dominguez, CPA, Chief Financial Officer
CMO: David Mandel, M.D., Chief of Staff
CHR: Kathy Turner, Director Human Resources
CNO: Roxann Langston, Chief Nursing Officer
Web address: www.etmc.org
Control: Other not–for–profit (including NFP Corporation) **Service:** General Medical and Surgical

Staffed Beds: 22 **Admissions:** 277 **Census:** 3 **Outpatient Visits:** 25639 **Births:** 0 **Total Expense ($000):** 8944 **Payroll Expense ($000):** 2743 **Personnel:** 60	

TROPHY CLUB—Denton County

☐ **BAYLOR MEDICAL CENTER AT TROPHY CLUB (450883)**, 2850 East State Highway 114, Zip 76262–5302; tel. 817/837–4600 **A**1 10 **F**3 12 29 40 64 70 75 79 81 85 87 107 111 114 119 141
Primary Contact: Melanie Chick, Chief Executive Officer
CFO: Jonathan Saunders, Chief Financial Officer
CMO: Mike Stanton, D.O., Medical Director
CIO: Scot Bradford, Chief Information Officer
CHR: Donna Irvin, Director Human Resources
CNO: Tina Huddleston, R.N., Chief Nursing Officer
Web address: www.baylortrophyclub.com
Control: Partnership, Investor–owned, for–profit **Service:** General Medical and Surgical

Staffed Beds: 22 **Admissions:** 721 **Census:** 5 **Outpatient Visits:** 7970 **Births:** 0 **Total Expense ($000):** 53164 **Payroll Expense ($000):** 9521 **Personnel:** 202	

TX

Hospital, Medicare Provider Number, Address, Telephone, Approval, Facility, and Physician Codes, Health Care System		
★ American Hospital Association (AHA) membership	◯ Healthcare Facilities Accreditation Program	⇑ Center for Improvement in Healthcare Quality Accreditation
☐ The Joint Commission accreditation	◇ DNV Healthcare Inc. accreditation	△ Commission on Accreditation of Rehabilitation Facilities (CARF) accreditation

TULIA—Swisher County

★ **SWISHER MEMORIAL HOSPITAL DISTRICT (451349)**, 539 Southeast Second, Zip 79088–2400, Mailing Address: P.O. Box 808, Zip 79088–0808; tel. 806/995–3581 **A**10 18 **F**3 7 10 11 29 34 35 40 43 50 53 57 59 62 64 65 68 77 93 107 114 127 129 130 133 **P**4
Primary Contact: Ryan Barnard, Chief Executive Officer
CFO: Connie Wilhelm, Chief Financial Officer
CIO: Brad Roberts, Network Administrator
Web address: www.swisherhospital.com
Control: Other not–for–profit (including NFP Corporation) **Service:** General Medical and Surgical

Staffed Beds: 20 **Admissions:** 236 **Census:** 2 **Outpatient Visits:** 23307 **Births:** 0 **Total Expense ($000):** 10766 **Payroll Expense ($000):** 4257 **Personnel:** 83

TYLER—Smith County

✠ **CHRISTUS MOTHER FRANCES HOSPITAL – TYLER (450102)**, 800 East Dawson Street, Zip 75701–2036; tel. 903/593–8441, (Includes LOUIS & PEACHES OWEN HEART HOSPITAL, 703 South Fleishel Avenue, Zip 75701–2015; tel. 903/606–3000; John McGreevy, Chief Executive Officer) **A**1 2 3 10 **F**3 7 8 11 12 13 15 17 18 19 20 22 24 26 28 29 30 31 32 34 37 40 43 45 46 47 48 49 50 51 53 54 55 59 60 64 66 68 70 72 73 74 75 76 77 78 79 80 81 82 83 84 85 86 87 89 93 107 108 110 111 114 115 118 119 124 126 127 129 130 131 132 134 144 146 147 148 **P**5 6 7 8 **S** CHRISTUS Health, Irving, TX
Primary Contact: John McGreevy, Chief Executive Officer
COO: Todd Hancock, Senior Vice President and Chief Operating Officer
CFO: Joyce Hester, CPA, Senior Vice President and Chief Financial Officer
CMO: Fadi Nasrallah, M.D., Vice President Medical Affairs
CIO: Jeff Pearson, Vice President and Chief Information Officer
CHR: Thomas Wilken, Senior Vice President and Chief Human Resources Officer
CNO: Robert Rose, R.N., Senior Vice President and System Chief Nursing Officer
Web address: www.tmfhc.org
Control: Other not–for–profit (including NFP Corporation) **Service:** General Medical and Surgical

Staffed Beds: 458 **Admissions:** 24482 **Census:** 301 **Outpatient Visits:** 572634 **Births:** 2700 **Total Expense ($000):** 509393 **Payroll Expense ($000):** 161004 **Personnel:** 3157

✠ **CHRISTUS TRINITY MOTHER FRANCES REHABILITATION HOSPITAL (453056)**, 3131 Troup Highway, Zip 75701–8352; tel. 903/510–7000 **A**1 10 **F**3 9 28 29 56 60 74 75 77 79 82 87 90 91 95 96 130 131 132 143 147 148 **S** HEALTHSOUTH Corporation, Birmingham, AL
Primary Contact: Sharla Anderson, Chief Executive Officer
CFO: Michael G. Treadway, Controller
CMO: Bradley Merritt, M.D., Medical Director
Web address: www.tmfrehabhospital.com
Control: Partnership, Investor–owned, for–profit **Service:** Rehabilitation

Staffed Beds: 74 **Admissions:** 1912 **Census:** 67 **Outpatient Visits:** 6678 **Births:** 0 **Total Expense ($000):** 19722 **Payroll Expense ($000):** 11360 **Personnel:** 181

✠ △ **EAST TEXAS MEDICAL CENTER REHABILITATION HOSPITAL (453072)**, 701 Olympic Plaza Circle, Zip 75701–1950, Mailing Address: P.O. Box 7530, Zip 75711–7530; tel. 903/596–3000 **A**1 7 10 **F**3 28 29 30 34 53 57 75 86 90 91 93 96 130 131 132 148 **S** East Texas Medical Center Regional Healthcare System, Tyler, TX
Primary Contact: Eddie L. Howard, Vice President and Chief Operating Officer
COO: Eddie L. Howard, Chief Operating Officer
CFO: James Blanton, Chief Financial Officer
CMO: Jerry Schwarzbach, M.D., Medical Director
CIO: Paula Anthony, Vice President Information Services
CHR: David L. Langston, Corporate Vice President Human Resources
CNO: Laurie Lehnhof-Watts, Assistant Administrator Patient Services
Web address: www.etmc.org
Control: Other not–for–profit (including NFP Corporation) **Service:** Rehabilitation

Staffed Beds: 49 **Admissions:** 925 **Census:** 32 **Outpatient Visits:** 74494 **Births:** 0 **Total Expense ($000):** 24900 **Payroll Expense ($000):** 11722 **Personnel:** 183

✠ **EAST TEXAS MEDICAL CENTER SPECIALTY HOSPITAL (452051)**, 1000 South Beckham, 5th Floor, Zip 75701–1908, Mailing Address: P.O. Box 7018, Zip 75711–7018; tel. 903/596–3600 **A**1 10 **F**1 3 29 30 75 84 130 148 **S** East Texas Medical Center Regional Healthcare System, Tyler, TX
Primary Contact: Eddie L. Howard, Vice President and Chief Operating Officer
CFO: James Blanton, Chief Financial Officer
CMO: J. David Johnson, M.D., Chief of Staff
CIO: Paula Anthony, Vice President Information Services
CHR: David L. Langston, Corporate Vice President Human Resources
CNO: Laurie Lehnhof-Watts, Assistant Administrator Risk Management Performance Improvement and Education
Web address: www.etmc.org
Control: Other not–for–profit (including NFP Corporation) **Service:** Long–Term Acute Care hospital

Staffed Beds: 36 **Admissions:** 334 **Census:** 29 **Outpatient Visits:** 0 **Births:** 0 **Total Expense ($000):** 14260 **Payroll Expense ($000):** 4717 **Personnel:** 69

✠ **EAST TEXAS MEDICAL CENTER TYLER (450083)**, 1000 South Beckham Street, Zip 75701–1908, Mailing Address: Box 6400, Zip 75711–6400; tel. 903/597–0351, (Includes EAST TEXAS MEDICAL CENTER BEHAVIORAL HEALTH CENTER, 4101 University Boulevard, Zip 75701–6600; tel. 903/566–8668; Jerry W. Echols, Administrator and Chief Executive Officer) **A**1 2 3 5 10 **F**3 5 8 11 12 13 15 17 18 20 22 24 25 26 28 29 30 31 34 35 37 38 40 42 43 44 45 46 47 48 49 51 56 58 59 60 61 64 65 68 70 71 72 73 74 75 76 78 79 80 81 82 84 85 86 87 89 93 98 99 100 101 102 103 104 105 107 110 111 115 117 118 119 120 121 123 124 126 129 130 132 138 141 145 146 147 148 **S** East Texas Medical Center Regional Healthcare System, Tyler, TX
Primary Contact: Robert B. Evans, Administrator and Chief Executive Officer
CFO: Byron Hale, Chief Financial Officer
CMO: John Andrews, M.D., Chief of Staff
CIO: Paula Anthony, Vice President Information Services
CHR: Mike Gray, Corporate Vice President Human Resources
CNO: Mariarose Kulma, R.N., Vice President Patient Services
Web address: www.etmc.org
Control: Other not–for–profit (including NFP Corporation) **Service:** General Medical and Surgical

Staffed Beds: 412 **Admissions:** 20283 **Census:** 284 **Outpatient Visits:** 131018 **Births:** 704 **Total Expense ($000):** 396654 **Payroll Expense ($000):** 131266 **Personnel:** 1905

✠ **TEXAS SPINE & JOINT HOSPITAL (450864)**, 1814 Roseland Boulevard, Suite 100, Zip 75701–4262; tel. 903/525–3300 **A**1 10 **F**8 29 39 40 77 79 81 82 85 107 111 114 119 144
Primary Contact: Tony Wahl, Chief Executive Officer
CFO: Greg Cummings, Chief Financial Officer
CMO: Kim Foreman, M.D., Chief of Staff
CNO: Deborah Pelton, R.N., Chief Nursing Officer
Web address: www.tsjh.org
Control: Partnership, Investor–owned, for–profit **Service:** Orthopedic

Staffed Beds: 18 **Admissions:** 2288 **Census:** 14 **Outpatient Visits:** 41822 **Births:** 0 **Total Expense ($000):** 73806 **Payroll Expense ($000):** 17162 **Personnel:** 305

★ **TYLER CONTINUECARE HOSPITAL (452091)**, 800 East Dawson, 4th Floor, Zip 75701–2036; tel. 903/531–4080 **A**10 **F**1 3 29 34 59 74 75 77 85 86 87 130 135 148 **P**4 **S** Community Hospital Corporation, Plano, TX
Primary Contact: Stephanie Hyde, R.N., MSN, Chief Executive Officer
Web address: www.continuecare.org
Control: Other not–for–profit (including NFP Corporation) **Service:** Long–Term Acute Care hospital

Staffed Beds: 51 **Admissions:** 598 **Census:** 44 **Outpatient Visits:** 0 **Births:** 0 **Total Expense ($000):** 23290 **Payroll Expense ($000):** 8579 **Personnel:** 122

✠ **UNIVERSITY OF TEXAS HEALTH NORTHEAST (450690)**, 11937 Highway 271, Zip 75708–3154; tel. 903/877–7777 **A**1 2 10 **F**3 8 11 15 18 20 22 24 26 28 29 30 31 32 34 35 40 45 46 47 49 50 53 55 56 57 58 59 64 65 68 70 71 75 77 78 79 81 84 85 86 87 93 94 97 98 101 102 103 104 105 106 107 108 110 111 114 115 116 117 118 120 121 122 123 124 129 130 132 135 143 146 147 148 **P**6 **S** University of Texas System, Austin, TX
Primary Contact: Kirk A. Calhoun, M.D., President
COO: Joe Woelkers, Executive Vice President and Chief Staff
CFO: Vernon Moore, Senior Vice President Chief Business and Finance
CMO: Steven Cox, M.D., Chief Medical Officer
CIO: Vernon Moore, Senior Vice President Chief Business and Finance
CHR: Jesse Gomez, Vice President Human Resources
CNO: Don Hunt, M.D., Vice President Patient Centered Care and Chief Nursing Officer
Web address: www.uthct.edu
Control: State–Government, nonfederal **Service:** General Medical and Surgical

Staffed Beds: 130 **Admissions:** 2228 **Census:** 38 **Outpatient Visits:** 260635 **Births:** 0 **Total Expense ($000):** 115517 **Payroll Expense ($000):** 55655 **Personnel:** 1159

UVALDE—Uvalde County

✠ **UVALDE MEMORIAL HOSPITAL (450177)**, 1025 Garner Field Road, Zip 78801–4809; tel. 830/278–6251 **A**1 10 20 **F**3 11 13 15 18 29 30 34 39 40 43 45 50 57 59 63 64 68 70 76 79 81 84 85 86 87 93 104 107 108 111 115 119 130 132 133 146 147 148 **P**3
Primary Contact: Thomas Nordwick, Chief Executive Officer
CFO: Valerie Lopez, CPA, Chief Financial Officer
CMO: Jared Reading, M.D., Chief of Staff
CIO: Blake Eaker, Interim Director Information Services
CHR: Charla Carter, Human Resource Officer
CNO: Adam Apolinar, Chief Nursing Officer
Web address: www.umhtx.org
Control: Hospital district or authority, Government, nonfederal **Service:** General Medical and Surgical

Staffed Beds: 48 **Admissions:** 1682 **Census:** 15 **Outpatient Visits:** 69845 **Births:** 454 **Total Expense ($000):** 122648 **Payroll Expense ($000):** 21935 **Personnel:** 411

TX

Many Facility Codes have changed. Please refer to the AHA Guide Code Chart. © 2016 AHA Guide

VAN HORN—Culberson County

CULBERSON HOSPITAL (451338), Eisenhower–Farm Market Road 2185, Zip 79855, Mailing Address: P.O. Box 609, Zip 79855–0609; tel. 432/283–2760 **A**10 18 **F**3 7 34 40 43 57 59 65 66 68 93 107 114 119 127 133 148 **P**6 **S** Preferred Management Corporation, Shawnee, OK
Primary Contact: Jonathon Voelkel, Administrator
CMO: John A. Thomas, M.D., Chief Medical Staff
Web address: www.culbersonhospital.org
Control: Corporation, Investor–owned, for–profit **Service:** General Medical and Surgical

Staffed Beds: 14 **Admissions:** 93 **Census:** 2 **Outpatient Visits:** 10803 **Births:** 0 **Total Expense ($000):** 5985 **Payroll Expense ($000):** 2533 **Personnel:** 65

VERNON—Wilbarger County

NORTH TEXAS STATE HOSPITAL, Highway 70 Northwest, Zip 76384, Mailing Address: P.O. Box 2231, Zip 76385–2231; tel. 940/552–9901 **F**11 30 34 39 44 50 56 57 68 75 86 87 96 97 98 99 103 130 132 135 146 **P**6 **S** Texas Department of State Health Services, Austin, TX
Primary Contact: James E. Smith, Superintendent
CFO: Robin Moreno, Financial Officer
CIO: Chad Hughes, Information Officer
Web address: www.online.dshs.state.tx.us/northtexassh/default.htm
Control: State–Government, nonfederal **Service:** Psychiatric

Staffed Beds: 640 **Admissions:** 1775 **Census:** 553 **Outpatient Visits:** 0 **Births:** 0 **Total Expense ($000):** 206024 **Payroll Expense ($000):** 74973 **Personnel:** 2051

WILBARGER GENERAL HOSPITAL (450584), 920 Hillcrest Drive, Zip 76384–3196; tel. 940/552–9351 **A**10 20 **F**3 11 15 29 34 35 40 43 45 54 56 57 60 62 75 81 85 86 87 93 98 101 104 107 111 115 119 124 130 132 133 143 146 148
Primary Contact: Claudia Eisenmann, Chief Executive Officer
CFO: Kim Fenter, Chief Financial Officer
CMO: Randall Schaffner, M.D., Chief of Staff and Medical Director
CIO: Ed Nary, Director Information Technology and Chief Compliance Officer
CHR: Cathie Bristo, Director Human Resources
CNO: Pam Akin, Interim Chief Nursing Officer
Web address: www.wghospital.com
Control: Hospital district or authority, Government, nonfederal **Service:** General Medical and Surgical

Staffed Beds: 27 **Admissions:** 527 **Census:** 6 **Outpatient Visits:** 12188 **Births:** 0 **Total Expense ($000):** 18887 **Payroll Expense ($000):** 7911 **Personnel:** 155

VICTORIA—Victoria County

★ ◇ **CITIZENS MEDICAL CENTER (450023)**, 2701 Hospital Drive, Zip 77901–5749; tel. 361/573–9181, (Total facility includes 20 beds in nursing home–type unit) **A**2 10 21 **F**3 11 12 13 15 18 20 22 24 28 29 30 31 34 35 38 40 41 42 43 45 49 50 51 53 54 56 57 59 62 64 65 70 72 74 75 76 77 78 79 81 82 85 86 87 89 93 94 97 102 107 108 109 110 111 113 114 115 116 117 118 119 120 121 124 126 128 129 130 131 132 135 146 147 148 **P**6
Primary Contact: Michael R. Olson, Chief Executive Officer
CFO: Carolyn Zafereo, Chief Accounting Officer
CMO: Daniel Cano, M.D., Chief Medical Officer
CIO: Russell Witte, Director Information Technology
CHR: Kathleen C. Mosmeyer, Director Human Resources
Web address: www.citizensmedicalcenter.org
Control: County–Government, nonfederal **Service:** General Medical and Surgical

Staffed Beds: 301 **Admissions:** 7427 **Census:** 104 **Outpatient Visits:** 149363 **Births:** 872 **Total Expense ($000):** 174951 **Payroll Expense ($000):** 61391 **Personnel:** 1022

⊞ **DETAR HEALTHCARE SYSTEM (450147)**, 506 East San Antonio Street, Zip 77901–6060, Mailing Address: P.O. Box 2089, Zip 77902–2089; tel. 361/575–7441, (Includes DETAR HOSPITAL NORTH, 101 Medical Drive, Zip 77904–3198; tel. 361/573–6100; William R. Blanchard, Chief Executive Officer) **A**1 3 10 **F**3 12 13 15 18 20 22 24 26 28 29 30 31 34 39 40 41 43 45 47 49 50 51 53 56 64 70 72 74 75 76 77 78 79 81 82 85 86 87 89 90 91 93 98 103 104 105 107 108 110 111 114 118 119 126 130 132 146 147 148 **P**3 5 **S** Community Health Systems, Inc., Franklin, TN
Primary Contact: William R. Blanchard, Chief Executive Officer
COO: George N. Parsley, Chief Operating Officer
CFO: Donald E. Hagan, Chief Financial Officer
CMO: Conde Nevin Anderson, M.D., Chief of Staff
CIO: Kim Tompkins, Director Information Services
CHR: Dwight Linton, Director Human Resources
CNO: Sammie Drehr, Chief Nursing Officer
Web address: www.detar.com
Control: Corporation, Investor–owned, for–profit **Service:** General Medical and Surgical

Staffed Beds: 245 **Admissions:** 9153 **Census:** 109 **Outpatient Visits:** 96119 **Births:** 1385 **Total Expense ($000):** 139426 **Payroll Expense ($000):** 51707 **Personnel:** 933

⊞ **POST ACUTE MEDICAL SPECIALTY HOSPITAL OF VICTORIA (452056)**, 506 East San Antonio Street, 3rd Floor, Zip 77901–6060; tel. 361/575–1445 **A**1 10 **F**1 3 29 30 31 82 85 86 87 97 130 148 **S** Post Acute Medical, LLC, Enola, PA
Primary Contact: Portlyn Brogger, Chief Executive Officer
CMO: Adam Burick, M.D., Chief Medical Officer
CHR: Waynea Finley, Manager Human Resources
CNO: Pamella Barrett, Director of Nursing
Web address: www.khvictoria.com
Control: Partnership, Investor–owned, for–profit **Service:** Long–Term Acute Care hospital

Staffed Beds: 23 **Admissions:** 335 **Census:** 22 **Outpatient Visits:** 0 **Births:** 0 **Total Expense ($000):** 11035 **Payroll Expense ($000):** 4501 **Personnel:** 76

⊞ **POST ACUTE/WARM SPRINGS SPECIALTY HOSPITAL OF VICTORIA (452094)**, 102 Medical Drive, Zip 77904–3101; tel. 361/576–6200 **A**1 10 **F**1 3 29 64 75 77 85 93 94 96 148 **S** Post Acute Medical, LLC, Enola, PA
Primary Contact: Portlyn Brogger, Chief Executive Officer
CMO: Adam Burick, M.D., Chief Medical Officer
CHR: Waynea Finley, Corporate Director Human Resources
CNO: Chris Reed, Director of Nursing
Web address: www.warmsprings.org
Control: Partnership, Investor–owned, for–profit **Service:** Long–Term Acute Care hospital

Staffed Beds: 26 **Admissions:** 364 **Census:** 24 **Outpatient Visits:** 9384 **Births:** 0 **Total Expense ($000):** 13687 **Payroll Expense ($000):** 5311 **Personnel:** 109

WACO—Mclennan County

⊞ **BAYLOR SCOTT & WHITE MEDICAL CENTER – HILLCREST (450101)**, 100 Hillcrest Medical Boulevard, Zip 76712–8897; tel. 254/202–2000, (Includes HILLCREST BAPTIST MEDICAL CENTER – HERRING AVENUE CAMPUS, 3000 HERRING AVENUE, ZIP 76708), (Total facility includes 20 beds in nursing home–type unit) **A**1 2 3 10 **F**3 11 13 15 18 20 22 24 26 28 29 30 31 34 40 43 44 46 49 50 53 54 57 58 59 60 61 63 64 70 72 74 75 76 78 79 81 82 84 85 86 87 89 90 93 96 107 108 110 111 115 118 119 120 121 123 128 129 130 131 132 135 145 146 148 **S** Baylor Scott & White Health, Dallas, TX
Primary Contact: Glenn A. Robinson, President
CFO: Richard Perkins, Chief Financial Officer
CMO: J. E. Morrison, M.D., Chief Medical Officer
CNO: Rebecca K. Hardie, Chief Nursing Officer
Web address: www.sw.org/hillcrest–medical–center
Control: Other not–for–profit (including NFP Corporation) **Service:** General Medical and Surgical

Staffed Beds: 275 **Admissions:** 13283 **Census:** 170 **Outpatient Visits:** 157364 **Births:** 2901 **Total Expense ($000):** 216901 **Payroll Expense ($000):** 79678 **Personnel:** 1292

CENTRAL TEXAS VETERANS HEALTH CARE SYSTEM, DORIS MILLER VETERANS MEDICAL CENTER See Central Texas Veterans Health Care System, Temple

TX

Hospital, Medicare Provider Number, Address, Telephone, Approval, Facility, and Physician Codes, Health Care System

★ American Hospital Association (AHA) membership ◯ Healthcare Facilities Accreditation Program ⇑ Center for Improvement in Healthcare Quality Accreditation
☐ The Joint Commission accreditation ◇ DNV Healthcare Inc. accreditation △ Commission on Accreditation of Rehabilitation Facilities (CARF) accreditation

---

✠ **PROVIDENCE HEALTHCARE NETWORK (450042)**, 6901 Medical Parkway, Zip 76712–7998, Mailing Address: P.O. Box 2589, Zip 76702–2589; tel. 254/751–4000, (Includes DEPAUL CENTER, 301 Londonderry Drive, Zip 76712; tel. 254/776–5970; Vicky Campbell, Vice President Mental Health and Support Services), (Nonreporting) **A**1 2 3 10 **S** Ascension Health, Saint Louis, MO
Primary Contact: Brett A. Esrock, President and Chief Executive Officer
COO: Steven Province, Senior Vice President and Chief Operating Officer
CFO: Karen K. Richardson, Senior Vice President and Chief Financial Officer
CMO: T. Marc Barrett, M.D., Senior Vice President and Chief Medical Officer
CIO: Jay Scherler, Vice President Finance and Chief Information Officer
CNO: Christine Courtney, R.N., Vice President and Chief Nursing Officer
Web address: www.providence.net
Control: Other not–for–profit (including NFP Corporation) **Service:** General Medical and Surgical

Staffed Beds: 620

WAXAHACHIE—Ellis County

✠ **BAYLOR SCOTT & WHITE MEDICAL CENTER AT WAXAHACHIE (450372)**, 2400 North I–35E, Zip 75165; tel. 469/843–4000 **A**1 2 3 10 **F**3 8 11 12 13 15 28 29 30 31 34 35 37 40 45 49 50 51 56 57 58 59 60 64 66 70 74 75 76 78 79 81 82 83 84 85 87 93 107 108 109 110 111 114 115 116 117 118 119 120 121 123 126 129 130 132 135 146 147 148 **S** Baylor Scott & White Health, Dallas, TX
Primary Contact: Christopher York, FACHE, President
COO: Cindy Murray, R.N., Chief Nursing Officer and Chief Operating Officer
CFO: Steve Roussel, Vice President Finance
CMO: Valerie Goman, M.D., President Medical Staff
CIO: Gary Beazley, Coordinator Information Systems
CHR: Marcos A. Ramirez, Human Resources Business Partner
Web address: www.baylorhealth.com/PhysiciansLocations/Waxahachie/Pages/Default.aspx
Control: Other not–for–profit (including NFP Corporation) **Service:** General Medical and Surgical

Staffed Beds: 86 **Admissions:** 4396 **Census:** 44 **Outpatient Visits:** 72655 **Births:** 212 **Total Expense ($000):** 94858 **Payroll Expense ($000):** 34838 **Personnel:** 433

WEATHERFORD—Parker County

✠ **WEATHERFORD REGIONAL MEDICAL CENTER (450203)**, 713 East Anderson Street, Zip 76086–5705; tel. 682/582–1000 **A**1 10 12 13 **F**3 8 13 15 17 18 20 22 28 29 34 35 40 43 48 49 51 57 59 60 68 70 74 75 76 77 79 81 82 85 91 93 98 103 107 110 111 114 115 119 130 131 132 133 135 146 148 **S** Community Health Systems, Inc., Franklin, TN
Primary Contact: David Orcutt, Chief Executive Officer
CFO: Nancy Cooke, Chief Financial Officer
CMO: Sanjeeb Shrestha, M.D., Chief Medical Staff
CIO: Brett Cates, Director Information Services
CNO: Donna Boone, MS, Chief Nursing Officer
Web address: www.weatherfordregional.com
Control: Corporation, Investor–owned, for–profit **Service:** General Medical and Surgical

Staffed Beds: 98 **Admissions:** 5457 **Census:** 55 **Outpatient Visits:** 79372 **Births:** 766 **Total Expense ($000):** 94505 **Payroll Expense ($000):** 27333 **Personnel:** 474

WEATHERFORD REHABILITATION HOSPITAL, 703 Eureka Street, Zip 76086–6547; tel. 682/803–0100, (Nonreporting)
Primary Contact: Cole E. Hatcher, Chief Executive Officer
Web address: www.weatherfordrehab.com
Control: Corporation, Investor–owned, for–profit **Service:** Rehabilitation

Staffed Beds: 26

WEBSTER—Harris County

☐ **BAY AREA REGIONAL MEDICAL CENTER (670096)**, 200 Blossom Street, Zip 77598–4204; tel. 281/525–7000 **A**1 **F**3 15 17 18 20 22 24 26 29 30 34 35 40 45 49 50 59 64 70 74 75 77 78 79 80 81 82 84 85 87 91 107 108 110 111 115 119 130 135 **P**4
Primary Contact: Timothy Schmidt, MS, Chief Executive Officer
COO: Benjamin Casmer, FACHE, Chief Operating Officer
CFO: Paul Hanson, Chief Financial Officer
CMO: Michael Lyons, Chief Medical Officer
CIO: Mark Albright, Chief Information Officer
CHR: Brad Horst, Vice President, Human Resources
CNO: Susan White, R.N., Chief Nursing Officer
Web address: www.barmc.us/
Control: Corporation, Investor–owned, for–profit **Service:** General Medical and Surgical

Staffed Beds: 94 **Admissions:** 4225 **Census:** 46 **Outpatient Visits:** 27373 **Births:** 0 **Total Expense ($000):** 142014 **Payroll Expense ($000):** 33778 **Personnel:** 494

✠ **CLEAR LAKE REGIONAL MEDICAL CENTER (450617)**, 500 Medical Center Boulevard, Zip 77598–4220; tel. 281/332–2511, (Includes ALVIN DIAGNOSTIC AND URGENT CARE CENTER, 301 Medic Lane, Alvin, Zip 77511–5597; tel. 281/331–6141; MAINLAND MEDICAL CENTER, 6801 E F Lowry Expressway, Texas City, Zip 77591; tel. 409/938–5000; Tripp Montalbo, Chief Executive Officer) **A**1 3 5 10 **F**3 11 13 15 17 18 20 22 24 26 28 29 30 31 34 35 40 41 42 43 44 45 46 47 49 50 51 54 56 57 59 60 64 70 72 73 74 75 76 77 78 79 81 85 86 87 88 89 90 93 94 96 98 100 101 103 104 105 107 108 110 111 114 115 119 124 126 129 130 132 135 146 147 148 **S** HCA, Nashville, TN
Primary Contact: Stephen K. Jones, Jr., FACHE, Chief Executive Officer
CFO: Jeff Sliwinski, Chief Financial Officer
CMO: Richard Marietta, M.D., Medical Director
CIO: Ley Samson, Director Management Information Systems
CHR: Brad Horst, Director Human Resources
Web address: www.clearlakermc.com
Control: Partnership, Investor–owned, for–profit **Service:** General Medical and Surgical

Staffed Beds: 683 **Admissions:** 29954 **Census:** 440 **Outpatient Visits:** 188880 **Births:** 4032 **Total Expense ($000):** 415101 **Payroll Expense ($000):** 175861 **Personnel:** 2240

CLEAR LAKE REHABILITATION HOSPITAL See Kindred Rehabilitation Hospital Clear Lake

☐ **CORNERSTONE HOSPITAL OF HOUSTON AT CLEARLAKE (452032)**, 709 Medical Center Boulevard, Zip 77598; tel. 281/332–3322, (Includes CORNERSTONE HOSPITAL OF HOUSTON – BELLAIRE, 5314 Dashwood, Houston, Zip 77081–4603; tel. 713/295–5300; Colin O'Sullivan, Interim Chief Executive Officer) **A**1 10 **F**1 3 29 30 44 50 56 75 82 85 86 87 130 148 **S** Cornerstone Healthcare Group, Dallas, TX
Primary Contact: Amy Stasney, Chief Executive Officer
COO: Brenda Lucero, Chief Clinical Officer
CFO: A. Shane Wells, Chief Financial Officer
CMO: Mark Barlow, M.D., Chief Medical Officer and President Medical Staff
CIO: Jerald Harris, Chief Information Officer
CHR: Yolanda Jacobs, Coordinator Human Resources
Web address: www.cornerstonehealthcaregroup.com
Control: Partnership, Investor–owned, for–profit **Service:** Long–Term Acute Care hospital

Staffed Beds: 148 **Admissions:** 1291 **Census:** 91 **Outpatient Visits:** 0 **Births:** 0 **Total Expense ($000):** 39007 **Payroll Expense ($000):** 19829 **Personnel:** 311

◇ **HOUSTON PHYSICIANS HOSPITAL (670008)**, 333 North Texas Avenue, Suite 100, Zip 77598–4966; tel. 281/557–5620 **A**10 21 **F**3 29 40 51 64 74 79 81 82 85 86 89 91 93 107 111 114 141
Primary Contact: Nicholas Crafts, Chief Executive Officer
Web address: www.houstonphysicianshospital.com
Control: Corporation, Investor–owned, for–profit **Service:** Surgical

Staffed Beds: 21 **Admissions:** 575 **Census:** 4 **Outpatient Visits:** 24919 **Births:** 0 **Total Expense ($000):** 36354 **Payroll Expense ($000):** 8919 **Personnel:** 164

✠ **KINDRED HOSPITAL CLEAR LAKE (452075)**, 350 Blossom Street, Zip 77598; tel. 281/316–7800, **A**1 **F**1 3 29 45 57 60 64 75 77 85 91 93 96 107 130 148 **S** Kindred Healthcare, Louisville, KY
Primary Contact: Mary Harbeson, R.N., Chief Executive Officer
Web address: www.khclearlake.com
Control: Corporation, Investor–owned, for–profit **Service:** Long–Term Acute Care hospital

Staffed Beds: 147 **Admissions:** 1387 **Census:** 99 **Outpatient Visits:** 3634 **Births:** 0 **Total Expense ($000):** 58788 **Payroll Expense ($000):** 20144 **Personnel:** 331

✠ **KINDRED REHABILITATION HOSPITAL CLEAR LAKE (453052)**, 655 East Medical Center Boulevard, Zip 77598–4328; tel. 281/286–1500 **A**1 10 **F**3 29 64 74 75 79 90 93 95 130 131 132 143 146 148
Primary Contact: Dale R. Mulder, Chief Executive Officer
CFO: Michael McFall, Chief Financial Officer
CMO: Michael Rosenblatt, M.D., Medical Director
CHR: Monica Little, Coordinator Human Resources
CNO: Kathy Hutchins–Otero, Chief Clinical Officer
Web address: www.khrehabclearlake.com/
Control: Corporation, Investor–owned, for–profit **Service:** Rehabilitation

Staffed Beds: 60 **Admissions:** 1031 **Census:** 38 **Outpatient Visits:** 6504 **Births:** 0 **Total Expense ($000):** 17663 **Payroll Expense ($000):** 7741 **Personnel:** 110

WEIMAR—Colorado County

WEIMAR MEDICAL CENTER (670114), 400 Youens Drive, Zip 78962–3680; tel. 979/725–8274, (Data for 184 days) **F**18 40 46 64 93 107 119 148
Primary Contact: Irving B. Sawyers, President
Control: Corporation, Investor–owned, for–profit **Service:** General Medical and Surgical

Staffed Beds: 38 **Admissions:** 70 **Census:** 2 **Outpatient Visits:** 600 **Births:** 0 **Total Expense ($000):** 2939 **Payroll Expense ($000):** 1453 **Personnel:** 48

TX

Many Facility Codes have changed. Please refer to the AHA Guide Code Chart.   © 2016 AHA Guide

WELLINGTON—Collingsworth County

COLLINGSWORTH GENERAL HOSPITAL (451355), 1013 15th Street,
Zip 79095–3703, Mailing Address: P.O. Box 1112, Zip 79095–1112;
tel. 806/447–2521 **A**10 18 **F**3 40 43 57 59 64 65 66 68 93 97 107 114 127
133 **S** Preferred Management Corporation, Shawnee, OK
Primary Contact: Candy Powell, Administrator
CFO: Larry Stephens, Chief Financial Officer
CMO: Wesley Nickens, M.D., Chief of Staff
CIO: Thomas T. Ng, Chief Information Officer
CHR: April Wright, Human Resources Officer
CNO: Vikki Barton, R.N., Chief Nursing Officer
Web address: www.collingsworthgeneral.net
Control: Corporation, Investor–owned, for–profit **Service:** General Medical and
Surgical

Staffed Beds: 13 **Admissions:** 144 **Census:** 3 **Outpatient Visits:** 10453
Births: 0 **Total Expense ($000):** 6396 **Payroll Expense ($000):** 2431
Personnel: 60

WESLACO—Hidalgo County

⊠ **KNAPP MEDICAL CENTER (450128)**, 1401 East Eighth Street,
Zip 78596–6640, Mailing Address: P.O. Box 1110, Zip 78599–1110;
tel. 956/968–8567, (Data for 184 days) **A**1 3 5 10 **F**3 8 11 12 13 15 20 22 29
30 31 34 35 39 40 43 44 46 49 50 51 56 57 59 60 63 64 70 73 74 75 76
77 78 79 81 82 84 85 86 87 89 93 107 108 110 111 114 115 119 130 131
132 134 135 143 146 147 148 **P**8 **S** Prime Healthcare Services, Ontario, CA
Primary Contact: Rene Lopez, Chief Executive Officer
CFO: Dinah L. Gonzalez, Chief Financial Officer
CIO: Teri Garza, Director Health Information Services
CHR: Emmett Craig, Chief Human Resources Officer
CNO: Anna Hinojosa, MSN, Interim Chief Nursing Officer
Web address: www.knappmed.org
Control: Other not–for–profit (including NFP Corporation) **Service:** General
Medical and Surgical

Staffed Beds: 192 **Admissions:** 4056 **Census:** 92 **Outpatient Visits:** 38039
Births: 878 **Total Expense ($000):** 53969 **Payroll Expense ($000):** 23157
Personnel: 767

△ **WESLACO REGIONAL REHABILITATION HOSPITAL (453091)**, 906 South
James Street, Zip 78596–9840; tel. 956/969–2222, (Data for 307 days) **A**7 10
F3 29 34 75 77 86 87 90 94 96 130 132 148 **P**6
Primary Contact: Jessie Smedley, Chief Executive Officer
COO: Corina Humphreys, Chief Operating Officer
CFO: Ernest Nash, Chief Financial Officer
CMO: Daisy Arce, President Medical Staff
CHR: Debbie Pemelton, Director Human Resources
CNO: Rita Mata–Guerrero, Director of Nursing
Web address: www.wrrh.ernesthealth.com
Control: Partnership, Investor–owned, for–profit **Service:** Rehabilitation

Staffed Beds: 32 **Admissions:** 382 **Census:** 17 **Outpatient Visits:** 0 **Births:**
0 **Total Expense ($000):** 8298 **Payroll Expense ($000):** 3370 **Personnel:**
94

WHARTON—Wharton County

☐ **GULF COAST MEDICAL CENTER (450214)**, 10141 Highway 59,
Zip 77488–3004; tel. 979/532–2500, (Nonreporting) **A**1 10 **S** Southwest
Healthcare System, Scottsdale, AZ
Primary Contact: Joy Janak, Interim Chief Executive Officer
COO: Joy Janak, Chief Operating Officer
CHR: Loretta M. Flynn, Consultant, Human Resources
CNO: Jennifer Monroe, Chief Nursing Officer
Web address: www.gulfcoastmedical.com
Control: Partnership, Investor–owned, for–profit **Service:** General Medical and
Surgical

Staffed Beds: 129

WHEELER—Wheeler County

PARKVIEW HOSPITAL (451334), 901 Sweetwater Street, Zip 79096–2421,
Mailing Address: P.O. Box 1030, Zip 79096–1030; tel. 806/826–5581 **A**10 18
F3 7 10 40 43 59 62 65 68 90 91 93 107 114 127 128 130 133 148
Primary Contact: Monica Kidd, R.N., MSN, Administrator
CFO: Jace Henderson, Chief Financial Officer
CMO: John P. Lavelle, M.D., Chief Medical Officer
CNO: Melisa Scales, Director of Nursing
Web address: www.parkviewhosp.org
Control: Hospital district or authority, Government, nonfederal **Service:** General
Medical and Surgical

Staffed Beds: 15 **Admissions:** 110 **Census:** 2 **Outpatient Visits:** 1491
Births: 0 **Total Expense ($000):** 7546 **Payroll Expense ($000):** 3382
Personnel: 78

WICHITA FALLS—Wichita County

⊠ **HEALTHSOUTH REHABILITATION HOSPITAL–WICHITA FALLS (453054)**,
3901 Armory Road, Zip 76302–2204; tel. 940/720–5700 **A**1 10 **F**3 28 29 44
50 53 62 64 68 74 75 77 79 82 86 87 90 91 92 93 95 96 132 143 146 148
S HEALTHSOUTH Corporation, Birmingham, AL
Primary Contact: Robbi Hudson, Chief Executive Officer
CFO: Tom Box, CPA, Chief Financial Officer
CMO: Virgil Frardo, M.D., Medical Director
CIO: Mary Walker, Manager Information Technology
CHR: Kathleen Pirtle, Director Human Resources
CNO: Karla Dwyer, R.N., Chief Nursing Officer
Web address: www.healthsouthwichitafalls.com
Control: Partnership, Investor–owned, for–profit **Service:** Rehabilitation

Staffed Beds: 63 **Admissions:** 1322 **Census:** 47 **Outpatient Visits:** 6931
Births: 0 **Total Expense ($000):** 15145 **Payroll Expense ($000):** 8838
Personnel: 172

☐ **KELL WEST REGIONAL HOSPITAL (450827)**, 5420 Kell West Boulevard,
Zip 76310–1610; tel. 940/692–5888 **A**1 10 **F**3 31 39 40 49 50 51 74 75 78
79 81 82 85 87 91 107 108 111 114 119 126 129 130
Primary Contact: Jerry Myers, M.D., Chief Executive Officer and Medical Director
CFO: Fran Lindemann, Director Finance
Web address: www.kellwest.com
Control: Partnership, Investor–owned, for–profit **Service:** General Medical and
Surgical

Staffed Beds: 41 **Admissions:** 1179 **Census:** 10 **Outpatient Visits:** 27261
Births: 0 **Total Expense ($000):** 29466 **Payroll Expense ($000):** 9610
Personnel: 254

☐ **NORTH TEXAS STATE HOSPITAL, WICHITA FALLS CAMPUS (454008)**,
6515 Lake Road, Zip 76308–5419, Mailing Address: Box 300, Zip 76307–0300;
tel. 940/692–1220, (Nonreporting) **A**1 10
Primary Contact: James E. Smith, Superintendent
CFO: Robin Moreno, Chief Financial Officer
CMO: Eulon Ross Taylor, Clinical Director
CIO: Chad Hughes, Chief Information Officer
Web address: www.online.dshs.state.tx.us/northtexassh/default.htm
Control: State–Government, nonfederal **Service:** Psychiatric

Staffed Beds: 381

☐ **PROMISE HOSPITAL OF WICHITA FALLS (452068)**, 1103 Grace Street,
Zip 76301–4414; tel. 940/720–6633 **A**1 10 **F**1 3 29 30 31 56 75 77 82 85
86 87 91 100 130 143 148 **P**8 **S** Promise Healthcare, Boca Raton, FL
Primary Contact: Michael L. McEachern, Chief Executive Officer
CFO: Debbie Herder, Controller
CMO: Robert McBroom, M.D., Medical Director
CIO: Gail McIlroy, Director Medical Records
CNO: Deanna Dowling, R.N., Chief Nursing Officer
Web address: www.promise–wichitafalls.com
Control: Corporation, Investor–owned, for–profit **Service:** Long–Term Acute Care
hospital

Staffed Beds: 31 **Admissions:** 292 **Census:** 19 **Outpatient Visits:** 0 **Births:**
0 **Total Expense ($000):** 8904 **Payroll Expense ($000):** 3985 **Personnel:**
72

☐ **RED RIVER HOSPITAL, LLC (454018)**, 1505 Eighth Street, Zip 76301–3106;
tel. 940/322–3171 **A**1 10 **F**4 5 29 38 50 86 87 98 99 100 101 102 103 104
105 106 130 135 143 **P**5 **S** Acadia Healthcare Company, Inc., Franklin, TN
Primary Contact: John B. Warburton, Chief Executive Officer
CFO: Bruce Porter, Chief Financial Officer
CMO: Harvey C. Martin, M.D., Medical Director
CIO: Fay Helton, Director Medical Records
CHR: Kimberley Pellegrin, Director, Human Resources
CNO: Glenda Lawrence, R.N., Chief Nursing Officer
Web address: www.redriverhospital.com
Control: Corporation, Investor–owned, for–profit **Service:** Psychiatric

Staffed Beds: 74 **Admissions:** 2125 **Census:** 63 **Outpatient Visits:** 5689
Births: 0 **Total Expense ($000):** 10378 **Payroll Expense ($000):** 5881
Personnel: 179

TX

Hospital, Medicare Provider Number, Address, Telephone, Approval, Facility, and Physician Codes, Health Care System

★ American Hospital Association (AHA) membership   ○ Healthcare Facilities Accreditation Program   ⇑ Center for Improvement in Healthcare Quality Accreditation
☐ The Joint Commission accreditation   ◇ DNV Healthcare Inc. accreditation   △ Commission on Accreditation of Rehabilitation Facilities (CARF) accreditation

✠ **UNITED REGIONAL HEALTH CARE SYSTEM (450010)**, 1600 11th Street, Zip 76301–4300; tel. 940/764–7000, (Includes UNITED REGIONAL HEALTH CARE SYSTEM–ELEVENTH STREET CAMPUS, 1600 11th Street, Zip 76301–9988; tel. 940/764–7000) **A**1 2 3 10 20 **F**3 11 12 13 15 17 18 20 21 22 24 26 28 29 30 31 32 34 35 37 39 40 43 44 45 46 47 48 49 50 51 53 57 59 60 61 64 65 68 70 73 74 75 76 77 78 79 80 81 82 84 85 86 87 89 92 93 102 107 110 111 114 115 116 117 118 119 126 130 131 132 134 146 147 148 **P**3
Primary Contact: Phyllis A. Cowling, CPA, President and Chief Executive Officer
COO: Nancy Townley, R.N., Senior Vice President Operations
CFO: Robert M. Pert, Vice President Finance and Chief Financial Officer
CMO: Lee Rodgers, M.D., Vice President Quality
CIO: Jerry Marshall, Director Information Services, Information Technology Security Officer
CHR: Kristi Faulkner, Vice President Organizational Growth
CNO: Jane Ritter, Vice President, Patient Care and Clinical Services
Web address: www.unitedregional.org
Control: Other not–for–profit (including NFP Corporation) **Service:** General Medical and Surgical

Staffed Beds: 286 **Admissions:** 14667 **Census:** 172 **Outpatient Visits:** 122722 **Births:** 2095 **Total Expense ($000):** 260670 **Payroll Expense ($000):** 105493 **Personnel:** 1827

WINNIE—Chambers County

RICELAND MEDICAL CENTER (451328), 538 Broadway, Zip 77665–7600; tel. 409/296–6000 **A**10 18 **F**3 29 34 40 59 65 81 105 107 119 127 133 146 **P**6
Primary Contact: Daniel Yancy, Chief Executive Officer
CFO: Julie Harris, Chief Financial Officer
CMO: Leonidas Andres, M.D., Chief of Staff
CHR: Anha Simon, Director Human Resources
Web address: www.energis.in/index.html
Control: Partnership, Investor–owned, for–profit **Service:** General Medical and Surgical

Staffed Beds: 25 **Admissions:** 364 **Census:** 3 **Outpatient Visits:** 37758 **Births:** 0 **Total Expense ($000):** 15760 **Payroll Expense ($000):** 5255 **Personnel:** 143

WINNSBORO—Wood County

✠ **CHRISTUS MOTHER FRANCES HOSPITAL – WINNSBORO (451381)**, 719 West Coke Road, Zip 75494–3011; tel. 903/342–5227 **A**1 10 18 **F**3 18 29 30 34 40 43 45 57 59 64 68 70 75 79 81 82 85 87 93 102 107 108 111 119 127 129 130 131 132 133 146 148 **P**5 6 7 8 **S** CHRISTUS Health, Irving, TX
Primary Contact: Janet E. Coates, R.N., President and Chief Executive Officer
CFO: Glenn Peltier, Chief Financial Officer
CNO: Kevin Jablonski, Chief Nursing Officer
Web address: www.tmfhs.org
Control: Other not–for–profit (including NFP Corporation) **Service:** General Medical and Surgical

Staffed Beds: 25 **Admissions:** 604 **Census:** 5 **Outpatient Visits:** 24418 **Births:** 0 **Total Expense ($000):** 17306 **Payroll Expense ($000):** 5080 **Personnel:** 91

TEXAS HEALTH PRESBYTERIAN HOSPITAL WINNSBORO See CHRISTUS Mother Frances Hospital – Winnsboro

WINTERS—Runnels County

★ **NORTH RUNNELS HOSPITAL (451315)**, 7821 State Highway 153, Zip 79567–7345, Mailing Address: P.O. Box 185, Zip 79567–0185; tel. 325/754–1317 **A**10 18 **F**7 11 40 57 59 62 65 66 68 97 107 119 127 133 **P**5
Primary Contact: Judy Espitia, Chief Executive Officer
CFO: Judy Espitia, Chief Financial Officer
CMO: Mark McKinnon, M.D., Chief of Staff
CHR: Judy Espitia, Chief Financial Officer
CNO: Bobbie Collom, Nursing Director
Control: Hospital district or authority, Government, nonfederal **Service:** General Medical and Surgical

Staffed Beds: 21 **Admissions:** 133 **Census:** 1 **Outpatient Visits:** 4822 **Births:** 0 **Total Expense ($000):** 5060 **Payroll Expense ($000):** 2508 **Personnel:** 54

WOODVILLE—Tyler County

★ **TYLER COUNTY HOSPITAL (450460)**, 1100 West Bluff Street, Zip 75979–4799, Mailing Address: P.O. Box 549, Zip 75979–0549; tel. 409/283–8141 **A**10 20 **F**3 11 30 35 40 43 57 59 64 107 114 119 127 146
Primary Contact: Sandra Gayle Wright, Chief Executive Officer
CFO: Scott Elton McCluskey, Chief Financial Officer
CMO: Paula Lajean Denson, M.D., President
CIO: Rachel Joy Haygood, Director Information Technology
CHR: Kenneth Lynn Jobe, Director Human Resources
CNO: Sondra Dianne Wilson RN, MSN,CEN, R.N., Assistant Administrator and Chief Nursing Officer
Web address: www.tchospital.us
Control: Hospital district or authority, Government, nonfederal **Service:** General Medical and Surgical

Staffed Beds: 25 **Admissions:** 534 **Census:** 5 **Outpatient Visits:** 25540 **Births:** 0 **Total Expense ($000):** 11406 **Payroll Expense ($000):** 4730 **Personnel:** 129

YOAKUM—Lavaca County

★ **YOAKUM COMMUNITY HOSPITAL (451346)**, 1200 Carl Ramert Drive, Zip 77995–4868; tel. 361/293–2321 **A**10 18 **F**3 11 13 15 29 34 35 40 43 56 57 59 64 70 76 79 81 85 86 93 107 108 111 114 119 129 132 133 134 146 148 **S** Community Hospital Corporation, Plano, TX
Primary Contact: Karen Barber, R.N., Chief Executive Officer
CFO: Robert Foret, Chief Financial Officer
CMO: Timothy Wagner, M.D., Chief Medical Staff
CIO: Barbara Vasek, Director Information Technology
CHR: Karen Roznovsky, Director Human Resources
CNO: Jennifer Franklin, R.N., Chief Clinical Officer
Web address: www.yoakumhospital.org
Control: Other not–for–profit (including NFP Corporation) **Service:** General Medical and Surgical

Staffed Beds: 25 **Admissions:** 977 **Census:** 12 **Outpatient Visits:** 21467 **Births:** 82 **Total Expense ($000):** 17797 **Payroll Expense ($000):** 7474 **Personnel:** 103

TX

UTAH

AMERICAN FORK—Utah County

☒ **AMERICAN FORK HOSPITAL (460023)**, 170 North 1100 East,
Zip 84003–2096; tel. 801/855–3300, (Nonreporting) **A**1 10 **S** Intermountain
Healthcare, Inc., Salt Lake City, UT
Primary Contact: Jason Wilson, Administrator and Chief Executive Officer
CMO: Paul H. Robinson, M.D., Medical Director
CIO: Mary Gathers, Manager Information Systems
CHR: Luke P. Morris, Regional Director Human Resources
CNO: Terri Lynn Hunter, R.N., Nurse Administrator
Web address: www.intermountainhealthcare.org
Control: Other not–for–profit (including NFP Corporation) **Service:** General
Medical and Surgical

Staffed Beds: 90

BEAVER—Beaver County

BEAVER VALLEY HOSPITAL (460035), 1109 North 100 West, Zip 84713,
Mailing Address: P.O. Box 1670, Zip 84713–1670; tel. 435/438–7100,
(Nonreporting) **A**10 20
Primary Contact: Craig Val Davidson, Chief Executive Officer and Administrator
Web address: www.bvhospital.com/
Control: City–Government, nonfederal **Service:** General Medical and Surgical

Staffed Beds: 49

BLANDING—San Juan County

☒ **BLUE MOUNTAIN HOSPITAL (461310)**, 802 South 200 West, Suite A.,
Zip 84511–3910; tel. 435/678–3993, (Nonreporting) **A**1 10 18
Primary Contact: Jeremy Lyman, Chief Executive Officer
CFO: Jimmy Johnson, Chief Financial Officer
CMO: Mahana Fisher, M.D., Medical Director
CIO: Anthony Torres, Manager Information Technology
CHR: Gail M. Northern, Director Human Resources
CNO: Derrill Kent Turek, R.N., Chief Nursing Officer
Web address: www.bmhutah.org/
Control: Other not–for–profit (including NFP Corporation) **Service:** General
Medical and Surgical

Staffed Beds: 11

BOUNTIFUL—Davis County

☒ **LAKEVIEW HOSPITAL (460042)**, 630 East Medical Drive, Zip 84010–4908;
tel. 801/299–2200 **A**1 10 13 **F**3 8 11 13 15 18 20 22 26 28 29 30 34 37 38
40 43 44 45 49 50 51 53 56 57 59 60 64 65 67 68 70 72 74 75 76 77 79
81 82 85 86 87 89 91 93 96 97 98 100 101 102 103 107 108 110 111 114
115 118 119 129 130 132 135 146 147 148 **P**6 **S** HCA, Nashville, TN
Primary Contact: Troy Wood, Chief Executive Officer
COO: Joe Mazzo, Chief Operating Officer
CFO: Wayne Dalton, Chief Financial Officer
CMO: Michael Hess, M.D., Chief Medical Officer
CIO: Mark Ellis, Director Information Technology
CHR: Julie Isom, Director Human Resources
CNO: Marilyn Mariani, R.N., Chief Nursing Officer
Web address: www.lakeviewhospital.com
Control: Corporation, Investor–owned, for–profit **Service:** General Medical and
Surgical

Staffed Beds: 119 **Admissions:** 3825 **Census:** 39 **Outpatient Visits:** 23905
Births: 529

SOUTH DAVIS COMMUNITY HOSPITAL (462003), 401 South 400 East,
Zip 84010–4933; tel. 801/295–2361, (Nonreporting) **A**10
Primary Contact: David Bland, Chief Executive Officer
CMO: Scott Southworth, M.D., Medical Director
CHR: Jamey Sulser, Director Human Resources
Web address: www.sdch.com
Control: Other not–for–profit (including NFP Corporation) **Service:** Long–Term
Acute Care hospital

Staffed Beds: 176

BRIGHAM CITY—Box Elder County

☒ **BRIGHAM CITY COMMUNITY HOSPITAL (460017)**, 950 South Medical Drive,
Zip 84302–4724; tel. 435/734–9471, (Nonreporting) **A**1 10 **S** HCA,
Nashville, TN
Primary Contact: Richard Spuhler, Chief Executive Officer
CMO: Joel Gardner, D.O., Chief Medical Officer
CIO: Steve Reichard, Manager Information Systems
CHR: Tracie Greene, Director Human Resources
CNO: Jerry Bushman, Chief Nursing Officer
Web address: www.brighamcityhospital.com
Control: Corporation, Investor–owned, for–profit **Service:** General Medical and
Surgical

Staffed Beds: 39

CEDAR CITY—Iron County

☒ **CEDAR CITY HOSPITAL (460007)**, 1303 North Main Street, Zip 84721–9746;
tel. 435/868–5000 **A**1 10 20 **F**8 11 13 15 18 28 29 31 34 35 40 45 46 57
65 70 74 75 76 78 79 81 86 89 107 110 111 114 119 130 146 147 148 **P**5
S Intermountain Healthcare, Inc., Salt Lake City, UT
Primary Contact: Eric Packer, Chief Executive Officer
CFO: Reed Sargent, Assistant Administrator Finance
Web address: www.https://intermountainhealthcare.org/locations/cedar–city–
hospital/
Control: Other not–for–profit (including NFP Corporation) **Service:** General
Medical and Surgical

Staffed Beds: 48 **Admissions:** 3783 **Census:** 22 **Outpatient Visits:** 38568
Births: 917

DELTA—Millard County

★ **DELTA COMMUNITY MEDICAL CENTER (461300)**, 126 South White Sage
Avenue, Zip 84624–8937; tel. 435/864–5591 **A**10 18 **F**3 8 11 13 15 29 31 34
38 40 41 42 43 45 54 57 59 64 68 71 75 76 81 82 86 87 89 102 107 111
119 128 133 144 145 146 **P**5 8 **S** Intermountain Healthcare, Inc., Salt Lake
City, UT
Primary Contact: Lenny Lyons, Administrator
CFO: Chris Thompson, Chief Financial Officer
Web address: www.ihc.com
Control: Other not–for–profit (including NFP Corporation) **Service:** General
Medical and Surgical

Staffed Beds: 18 **Admissions:** 276 **Census:** 2 **Outpatient Visits:** 19786
Births: 108 **Total Expense ($000):** 9133 **Payroll Expense ($000):** 2788
Personnel: 56

DRAPER—Salt Lake County

☒ **LONE PEAK HOSPITAL (460060)**, 1925 South State Street, Zip 84020;
tel. 801/545–8000 **A**1 10 **F**3 8 13 15 29 34 40 45 48 49 50 51 63 64 73 75
76 79 81 82 85 87 107 108 110 111 115 119 130 131 147 **S** HCA,
Nashville, TN
Primary Contact: Mark Meadows, Chief Executive Officer
Web address: www.lonepeakhospital.com
Control: Corporation, Investor–owned, for–profit **Service:** General Medical and
Surgical

Staffed Beds: 32 **Admissions:** 1468 **Census:** 10 **Outpatient Visits:** 27123
Births: 554 **Total Expense ($000):** 34631 **Payroll Expense ($000):** 10351
Personnel: 156

FILLMORE—Millard County

★ **FILLMORE COMMUNITY MEDICAL CENTER (461301)**, 674 South Highway
99, Zip 84631–5013; tel. 435/743–5591 **A**10 18 **F**3 8 11 13 15 29 31 34 38
40 41 50 56 57 59 62 63 64 67 68 75 76 81 82 86 87 89 93 107 110 119
128 133 145 146 147 148 **S** Intermountain Healthcare, Inc., Salt Lake City, UT
Primary Contact: Lenny Lyons, Administrator
CFO: Chris Thompson, Chief Financial Officer
Web address: www.ihc.com
Control: Other not–for–profit (including NFP Corporation) **Service:** General
Medical and Surgical

Staffed Beds: 19 **Admissions:** 251 **Census:** 11 **Outpatient Visits:** 11237
Births: 42 **Total Expense ($000):** 5341 **Payroll Expense ($000):** 2967
Personnel: 51

UT

GUNNISON—Sanpete County

★ **GUNNISON VALLEY HOSPITAL (461306)**, 64 East 100 North, Zip 84634,
Mailing Address: P.O. Box 759, Zip 84634–0759; tel. 435/528–7246, (Total
facility includes 99 beds in nursing home–type unit) **A**10 18 **F**7 11 13 15 18 34
35 39 40 45 56 57 59 62 63 64 65 79 81 82 85 97 100 102 107 115 119
129 130 133 135 146 147 148 **P**6
Primary Contact: Mark F. Dalley, Administrator
CFO: Brian Murray, Chief Financial Officer
CIO: Mike Ryan, Director of Information Services
CHR: Liz Brown, Manager Human Resources
CNO: Brenda Bartholomew, Chief Nursing Officer
Web address: www.gvhospital.org
Control: County–Government, nonfederal **Service:** General Medical and Surgical

**Staffed Beds: 124 Admissions: 790 Census: 91 Outpatient Visits: 28762
Births: 146 Total Expense ($000): 20766 Payroll Expense ($000): 5561
Personnel: 154**

HEBER CITY—Wasatch County

★ **HEBER VALLEY MEDICAL CENTER (461307)**, 1485 South Highway 40,
Zip 84032–3522; tel. 435/654–2500, (Nonreporting) **A**10 18 **S** Intermountain
Healthcare, Inc., Salt Lake City, UT
Primary Contact: Shawn Morrow, Administrator
CFO: Craig Mills, Chief Financial Officer
CMO: Stanton B. McDonald, M.D., Medical Director
CHR: Bruce Dent, Human Resources Director
CNO: Gayle Sturgis, R.N., Nurse Administrator
Web address: www.intermountainhealthcare.org
Control: Other not–for–profit (including NFP Corporation) **Service:** General
Medical and Surgical

Staffed Beds: 19

KANAB—Kane County

KANE COUNTY HOSPITAL (461309), 355 North Main Street,
Zip 84741–3260; tel. 435/644–5811, (Nonreporting) **A**10 18
Primary Contact: Sherrie Pandya, Administrator
CFO: Stephen Howells, Chief Financial Officer
CMO: Darin Ott, D.O., Chief of Staff
CHR: Laurali Noteman, Director Human Resources
CNO: Charlene Kelly, Chief Nursing Officer
Web address: www.kanecountyhospital.net
Control: Hospital district or authority, Government, nonfederal **Service:** General
Medical and Surgical

Staffed Beds: 25

LAYTON—Davis County

★ ◇ **DAVIS HOSPITAL AND MEDICAL CENTER (460041)**, 1600 West
Antelope Drive, Zip 84041–1142; tel. 801/807–1000 **A**3 10 21 **F**3 8 11 12 13
15 17 18 20 22 26 28 29 31 34 35 38 40 42 45 46 47 48 49 55 57 59 64
65 68 70 72 73 74 75 76 77 78 79 81 82 85 86 87 89 90 93 94 98 102
105 107 108 109 110 111 114 115 116 117 119 120 126 129 130 146 147
148 **S** IASIS Healthcare, Franklin, TN
Primary Contact: Michael E. Jensen, Chief Executive Officer
COO: Jared Spackman, Chief Operating Officer
CFO: Jared Spackman, Chief Financial Officer
CMO: Les Greenwood, President, Medical Staff
CIO: Shane Williams, Director Information Systems
CHR: Tara Cantrell, Director Human Resources
CNO: Chris Johnson, R.N., Chief Nursing Officer
Web address: www.davishospital.com
Control: Corporation, Investor–owned, for–profit **Service:** General Medical and
Surgical

**Staffed Beds: 200 Admissions: 6217 Census: 58 Outpatient Visits: 165915
Births: 1668 Personnel: 672**

LOGAN—Cache County

⌧ **LOGAN REGIONAL HOSPITAL (460015)**, 1400 North 500 East,
Zip 84341–2455; tel. 435/716–1000, (Total facility includes 11 beds in nursing
home–type unit) **A**1 10 **F**3 8 11 13 14 15 18 20 22 28 29 31 32 34 35 36 37
40 43 45 46 49 50 51 57 59 60 64 66 68 70 73 74 75 76 77 78 79 81 82
85 86 87 89 91 93 97 98 99 100 101 102 103 104 105 107 108 109 110
111 114 115 117 119 127 123 128 131 132 135 146 147 148 **P**6
S Intermountain Healthcare, Inc., Salt Lake City, UT
Primary Contact: Kyle A. Hansen, Chief Executive Officer
COO: Brandon McBride, Operations Officer
CFO: Alan Robinson, Chief Financial Officer
CMO: Todd A. Brown, M.D., Medical Director
CIO: Dave Felts, Chief Information Systems
CHR: Jolene Clonts, Director Human Resources
CNO: Neil C. Perkes, Operations Officer
Web address: www.loganregionalhospital.org
Control: Other not–for–profit (including NFP Corporation) **Service:** General
Medical and Surgical

**Staffed Beds: 139 Admissions: 7100 Census: 54 Outpatient Visits: 305435
Births: 2539 Total Expense ($000): 143440 Payroll Expense ($000):
46296 Personnel: 891**

MIDVALE—Salt Lake County

☐ **HIGHLAND RIDGE HOSPITAL**, 7309 South 180 West, Zip 84047–3769;
tel. 801/569–2153, (Nonreporting) **A**1 **S** Acadia Healthcare Company, Inc.,
Franklin, TN
Primary Contact: Robert Beatty, Chief Operating Officer
COO: Robert Beatty, Chief Operating Officer
CFO: Sheri Sorenson, Manager Business Office
CHR: Carol Cunningham, Administrative Assistant
Web address: www.highlandridgehospital.com
Control: Corporation, Investor–owned, for–profit **Service:** Psychiatric

Staffed Beds: 83

MILFORD—Beaver County

★ **MILFORD VALLEY MEMORIAL HOSPITAL (461305)**, 850 North Main Street,
Zip 84751–0640, Mailing Address: P.O. Box 640, Zip 84751–0640;
tel. 435/387–2411, (Nonreporting) **A**10 18
Primary Contact: Craig Val Davidson, Chief Executive Officer
Web address: www.bvhospital.com/directions–2.htm
Control: Hospital district or authority, Government, nonfederal **Service:** General
Medical and Surgical

Staffed Beds: 25

MOAB—Grand County

★ **MOAB REGIONAL HOSPITAL (461302)**, 450 West Williams Way,
Zip 84532–2065, Mailing Address: P.O. Box 998, Zip 84532–0998;
tel. 435/719–3500 **A**10 18 **F**3 13 15 29 30 31 34 35 40 43 45 57 59 63 64
65 66 68 75 76 79 81 82 85 86 89 90 97 107 110 111 114 115 119 130
131 132 133 144 148 **P**6
Primary Contact: Jennifer Sadoff, Chief Executive Officer
COO: Vicki Gigliotti, Chief Clinical Officer
CFO: Craig M. Daniels, Chief Financial Officer
CMO: Steven V. Rouzer, M.D., Chief Medical Officer
CIO: Mike Foster, Manager Information Systems
CHR: Katherine Sullivan, Director, Human Resources
Web address: www.mrhmoab.org
Control: Other not–for–profit (including NFP Corporation) **Service:** General
Medical and Surgical

**Staffed Beds: 17 Admissions: 598 Census: 6 Outpatient Visits: 16542
Births: 112 Total Expense ($000): 24049 Payroll Expense ($000): 9366
Personnel: 164**

MONTICELLO—San Juan County

SAN JUAN HOSPITAL (461308), 380 West 100 North, Zip 84535, Mailing
Address: P.O. Box 308, Zip 84535–0308; tel. 435/587–2116 **A**10 18 **F**3 13 15
29 31 32 34 35 40 41 45 56 59 64 65 66 68 76 79 81 82 107 110 119 127
128 133 **P**6
Primary Contact: Clayton Holt, Chief Executive Officer
CFO: Lyman Duncan, Chief Financial Officer
CMO: Kelly Jeppesen, Chief Medical Officer
CIO: Julie Bingham, IT Supervisor
CHR: Deana Dalton, Human Resources
CNO: Laurie Schafer, Chief Nursing Officer
Web address: www.sanjuanhealthservices.org/
Control: Hospital district or authority, Government, nonfederal **Service:** General
Medical and Surgical

**Staffed Beds: 25 Admissions: 243 Census: 2 Outpatient Visits: 6642
Births: 36 Total Expense ($000): 12754 Payroll Expense ($000): 4456
Personnel: 92**

MOUNT PLEASANT—Sanpete County

★ **SANPETE VALLEY HOSPITAL (461303)**, 1100 South Medical Drive,
Zip 84647–2222; tel. 435/462–2441, (Nonreporting) **A**10 18 **S** Intermountain
Healthcare, Inc., Salt Lake City, UT
Primary Contact: Aaron C. Wood, Chief Executive Officer and Administrator
COO: Kristina Skinner, Director Quality
CFO: Chris Thompson, Chief Financial Officer
CMO: David Krzymowski, M.D., Chief of Staff
CIO: Michael Ence, Computer Specialist
CHR: Brett Gray, Director Human Resource
CNO: Ryan Robison, Chief Nursing Officer
Web address: www.intermountainhealthcare.com
Control: Other not–for–profit (including NFP Corporation) **Service:** General
Medical and Surgical

Staffed Beds: 19

MURRAY—Salt Lake County

☐ △ **INTERMOUNTAIN MEDICAL CENTER (460010)**, 5121 South Cottonwood Street, Zip 84107–5701; tel. 801/507–7000 **A**1 2 3 5 7 10 **F**3 7 8 11 12 13 15 17 18 20 22 24 26 28 29 30 31 34 35 37 38 39 40 41 43 44 45 46 47 48 49 50 51 52 53 54 55 56 57 58 59 60 61 63 64 66 68 70 71 72 74 75 76 77 78 79 81 82 84 85 86 87 90 91 92 93 94 96 97 99 100 102 103 107 108 109 110 111 114 115 116 117 118 119 120 121 123 124 126 129 130 131 132 135 137 138 139 141 142 143 146 147 148 **S** Intermountain Healthcare, Inc., Salt Lake City, UT
Primary Contact: Moody Chisholm, Regional Vice President
COO: Kelly L. Duffin, Operations Officer
CFO: Royce Stephens, Director Finance
CMO: Mark Ott, M.D., Regional Chief Medical Director
CIO: David Baird, Director of Information Systems
CHR: Tiffiny J. Lipscomb, Manager Human Resources
CNO: Suzanne P. Anderson, Nurse Administrator
Web address: www.intermountainhealthcare.org
Control: Other not–for–profit (including NFP Corporation) **Service:** General Medical and Surgical

Staffed Beds: 468 **Admissions:** 26329 **Census:** 326 **Outpatient Visits:** 1143805 **Births:** 4967 **Total Expense ($000):** 760912 **Payroll Expense ($000):** 227839 **Personnel:** 3827

◇ **LANDMARK HOSPITAL OF SALT LAKE CITY (462006)**, 4252 South Birkhill Boulevard, Zip 84107–5715; tel. 801/268–5400, (Nonreporting) **A**10 21 **S** Landmark Hospitals, Cape Girardeau, MO
Primary Contact: Ken D'Amico, Chief Executive Officer
Web address: www.landmarkhospitals.com/utah.aspx
Control: Partnership, Investor–owned, for–profit **Service:** Long–Term Acute Care hospital

Staffed Beds: 38

✠ **THE ORTHOPEDIC SPECIALTY HOSPITAL (460049)**, 5848 South 300 East, Zip 84107–6121; tel. 801/314–4100 **A**1 10 **F**3 9 29 32 34 35 37 44 50 53 57 58 59 64 68 74 75 77 79 81 85 86 87 90 91 92 93 94 100 107 111 114 115 119 130 131 132 134 135 146 **S** Intermountain Healthcare, Inc., Salt Lake City, UT
Primary Contact: Barbara Ohm, Administrator
CFO: Sherlyn Lewis, Manager Finance
CMO: Jon Sundin, M.D., Medical Director
CIO: David Baird, Chief Information Officer
CHR: Tina Tasso, Manager Human Resources
Web address: www.intermountainhealthcare.org **Service:** Orthopedic
Control: Other not–for–profit (including NFP Corporation)

Staffed Beds: 40 **Admissions:** 1891 **Census:** 11 **Births:** 0 **Total Expense ($000):** 67861 **Payroll Expense ($000):** 18069 **Personnel:** 333

NEPHI—Juab County

★ **CENTRAL VALLEY MEDICAL CENTER (461304)**, 48 West 1500 North, Zip 84648–8900; tel. 435/623–3000 **A**10 18 **F**3 13 15 29 34 35 40 41 43 45 50 57 58 62 63 64 65 75 76 77 79 81 82 85 86 89 93 94 97 99 100 101 102 103 104 107 110 111 114 119 128 129 130 131 133 147 148 **P**6 **S** Rural Health Group, Nephi, UT
Primary Contact: Mark R. Stoddard, President
CFO: Brent Davis, Chief Financial Officer
CMO: Joel Holman, Chief of Staff
CIO: Ken Richens, Chief Information Officer
CHR: Brian Allsop, Director Human Resources
CNO: Randy Allinson, R.N., Patient Care Services Director
Web address: www.cvmed.net
Control: Other not–for–profit (including NFP Corporation) **Service:** General Medical and Surgical

Staffed Beds: 27 **Admissions:** 1075 **Census:** 11 **Outpatient Visits:** 30522 **Births:** 148 **Total Expense ($000):** 31229 **Payroll Expense ($000):** 9305 **Personnel:** 171

NORTH LOGAN—Cache County

✠ **CACHE VALLEY HOSPITAL (460054)**, 2380 North 400 East, Zip 84341–6000; tel. 435/713–9700 **A**1 10 **F**3 8 13 15 29 34 35 39 40 41 43 51 57 59 68 70 76 77 79 81 82 83 84 85 87 91 92 93 96 97 107 110 111 114 119 130 131 143 148 **P**6 **S** HCA, Nashville, TN
Primary Contact: John C. Worley, III, Chief Executive Officer
CFO: David S. Geary, Chief Financial Officer
CMO: Matt Welter, Chief Medical Officer
Web address: www.cachevalleyhospital.com/
Control: Corporation, Investor–owned, for–profit **Service:** General Medical and Surgical

Staffed Beds: 22 **Admissions:** 556 **Census:** 4 **Outpatient Visits:** 39506 **Births:** 15

OGDEN—Weber County

✠ **MCKAY–DEE HOSPITAL CENTER (460004)**, 4401 Harrison Boulevard, Zip 84403–3195; tel. 801/387–2800 **A**1 2 3 10 **F**3 8 11 12 13 15 17 18 20 22 24 26 28 29 30 31 34 35 38 39 40 43 44 45 46 49 50 51 53 54 55 57 58 59 60 61 64 65 66 67 68 70 72 74 75 76 77 78 79 81 82 84 85 86 87 89 90 91 93 97 98 99 100 101 102 104 105 107 108 110 111 114 115 116 117 118 119 120 121 123 126 129 130 131 132 134 135 146 147 148 **P**6 **S** Intermountain Healthcare, Inc., Salt Lake City, UT
Primary Contact: Michael A. Clark, Administrator
COO: Michael A. Clark, Chief Operating Officer
CFO: Doug Smith, Chief Financial Officer
CMO: Christine Nefcy, M.D., Chief Medical Officer
CIO: Mary Gathers, Director Information Systems
CHR: Lee Lorimer, IV, Regional Director Human Resources
CNO: Bonnie Jacklin, R.N., Chief Nursing Officer
Web address: www.mckay–dee.org
Control: Other not–for–profit (including NFP Corporation) **Service:** General Medical and Surgical

Staffed Beds: 312 **Admissions:** 18099 **Census:** 180 **Outpatient Visits:** 267195 **Births:** 4009 **Total Expense ($000):** 381581 **Payroll Expense ($000):** 124468 **Personnel:** 2200

✠ **OGDEN REGIONAL MEDICAL CENTER (460005)**, 5475 South 500 East, Zip 84405–6905; tel. 801/479–2111, (Nonreporting) **A**1 10 13 **S** HCA, Nashville, TN
Primary Contact: Mark B. Adams, Chief Executive Officer
COO: Brian Lines, Chief Operating Officer
CFO: Judd Taylor, Chief Financial Officer
CMO: Jeffrey Abel, M.D., Chief Medical Officer
CIO: Eric Peterson, Director
CHR: Chris Bissenden, Director Human Resources
CNO: Elizabeth B. Later, R.N., Chief Nursing Officer
Web address: www.ogdenregional.com
Control: Corporation, Investor–owned, for–profit **Service:** General Medical and Surgical

Staffed Beds: 167

OREM—Utah County

✠ **OREM COMMUNITY HOSPITAL (460043)**, 331 North 400 West, Zip 84057–1999; tel. 801/224–4080, (Nonreporting) **A**1 10 **S** Intermountain Healthcare, Inc., Salt Lake City, UT
Primary Contact: J. Francis Gibson, Administrator and Chief Executive Officer
CMO: Neil Whitaker, M.D., Chief Medical Director
CIO: Diane Rindlisbacher, Manager Information Systems
CHR: Pamela S. Niece, Director Human Resources
Web address: www.intermountainhealthcare.org
Control: Other not–for–profit (including NFP Corporation) **Service:** General Medical and Surgical

Staffed Beds: 18

☐ **PROVO CANYON BEHAVIORAL HOSPITAL (464014)**, 1350 East 750 North, Zip 84097–4345; tel. 801/852–2273, (Nonreporting) **A**1 10 **S** Universal Health Services, Inc., King of Prussia, PA
Primary Contact: Jeremy Cottle, Ph.D., Chief Executive Officer
CFO: Emmy Adams, Chief Financial Officer
CHR: Diann Decker, Chief Human Resource Officer
Web address: www.pcbh.com
Control: Corporation, Investor–owned, for–profit **Service:** Psychiatric

Staffed Beds: 80

✠ **TIMPANOGOS REGIONAL HOSPITAL (460052)**, 750 West 800 North, Zip 84057–3660; tel. 801/714–6000, (Nonreporting) **A**1 10 **S** HCA, Nashville, TN
Primary Contact: Kimball S. Anderson, FACHE, Chief Executive Officer
COO: Austin Lane Manning, Chief Operating Officer
CFO: Jody S. Dial, Chief Financial Officer
CMO: Randle L. Likes, M.D., Chief Medical Officer
CIO: Richard Neilson, Director of Information Services
CHR: Tim Black, Director Human Resources
CNO: Sandy Ewell, Chief Nursing Officer
Web address: www.timpanogosregionalhospital.com
Control: Corporation, Investor–owned, for–profit **Service:** General Medical and Surgical

Staffed Beds: 117

UT

Hospital, Medicare Provider Number, Address, Telephone, Approval, Facility, and Physician Codes, Health Care System

★ American Hospital Association (AHA) membership
☐ The Joint Commission accreditation
◯ Healthcare Facilities Accreditation Program
◇ DNV Healthcare Inc. accreditation
⇑ Center for Improvement in Healthcare Quality Accreditation
△ Commission on Accreditation of Rehabilitation Facilities (CARF) accreditation

PANGUITCH—Garfield County

★ **GARFIELD MEMORIAL HOSPITAL AND CLINICS (460033)**, 200 North 400
East, Zip 84759, Mailing Address: P.O. Box 389, Zip 84759–0389;
tel. 435/676–8811, (Total facility includes 27 beds in nursing home–type unit)
A10 20 **F**2 13 15 28 29 32 34 35 40 45 56 57 59 64 65 67 75 76 81 82 87
97 107 110 119 127 128 130 132 133 148 **P**6 **S** Intermountain
Healthcare, Inc., Salt Lake City, UT
Primary Contact: Alberto Vasquez, Administrator
CFO: Reed Sargent, Assistant Administrator Finance
Web address: www.ihc.com/hospitals/garfield
Control: Other not–for–profit (including NFP Corporation) **Service:** General
Medical and Surgical

Staffed Beds: 41 **Admissions:** 634 **Census:** 24 **Outpatient Visits:** 31883
Births: 22 **Total Expense ($000):** 10954 **Payroll Expense ($000):** 5611

PARK CITY—Summit County

⊞ **PARK CITY MEDICAL CENTER (460057)**, 900 Round Valley Drive,
Zip 84060–7552; tel. 435/658–7000 **A**1 10 **F**3 13 15 18 29 34 35 36 38 40
43 45 48 49 50 51 53 57 59 65 68 70 74 75 76 77 79 81 82 85 87 89 93
96 102 148 **P**6 **S** Intermountain Healthcare, Inc., Salt Lake City, UT
Primary Contact: Si William Hutt, Administrator
CFO: Lori Nielson, Regional Finance Director
CMO: Wain Allen, M.D., Medical Director
CHR: Christopher Saling, Manager Human Resources
CNO: Dan Davis, MSN, R.N., Nurse Administrator
Web address: www.intermountainhealthcare.org
Control: Other not–for–profit (including NFP Corporation) **Service:** General
Medical and Surgical

Staffed Beds: 37 **Admissions:** 1696 **Census:** 11 **Outpatient Visits:** 111666
Births: 318

PAYSON—Utah County

⊞ **MOUNTAIN VIEW HOSPITAL (460013)**, 1000 East 100 North,
Zip 84651–1600; tel. 801/465–7000, (Nonreporting) **A**1 10 **S** HCA,
Nashville, TN
Primary Contact: Kevin Johnson, Chief Executive Officer
COO: Ric Johnson, Associate Administrator
CFO: Steven R. Schramm, Chief Financial Officer
CMO: Jeffrey Wallentine, Chief of Staff
CIO: Cindy Mecham, Health Information Director
CHR: Wally Trotter, Director Human Resources
CNO: Lisa Taylor, Director of Nursing
Web address: www.mvhpayson.com
Control: Corporation, Investor–owned, for–profit **Service:** General Medical and
Surgical

Staffed Beds: 114

PRICE—Carbon County

⊞ **CASTLEVIEW HOSPITAL (460011)**, 300 North Hospital Drive,
Zip 84501–4200; tel. 435/637–4800 **A**1 10 20 **F**3 8 11 12 13 15 29 31 34
39 40 41 45 47 48 50 51 57 59 68 70 75 76 77 78 79 81 82 85 86 87 89
93 107 108 110 111 115 119 127 130 131 133 146 147 148 **S** LifePoint
Health, Brentwood, TN
Primary Contact: Mark Holyoak, Chief Executive Officer
CFO: Greg Cook, Chief Financial Officer
CMO: Scott Justesen, M.D., Chief of Staff
CIO: Fiore Wilson, Director Information Systems
CHR: Misty Birch, Director Human Resources
CNO: Terri Watkins, R.N., Chief Nursing Officer
Web address: www.castleviewhospital.net
Control: Corporation, Investor–owned, for–profit **Service:** General Medical and
Surgical

Staffed Beds: 49 **Admissions:** 1708 **Census:** 14 **Outpatient Visits:** 41277
Births: 335 **Total Expense ($000):** 34409 **Payroll Expense ($000):** 13816
Personnel: 350

PROVO—Utah County

☐ **UTAH STATE HOSPITAL (464001)**, 1300 East Center Street, Zip 84606–3554,
Mailing Address: P.O. Box 270, Zip 84603–0270; tel. 801/344–4400 **A**1 3 10
F30 34 56 75 77 86 87 91 98 99 100 101 103 130 135 143 146 **P**6
Primary Contact: Dallas Earnshaw, Superintendent
COO: Dallas Earnshaw, Superintendent
CFO: Robert Burton, Manager Finance
CMO: Madhu Gundlapalli, M.D., Clinical Director
CIO: Jill Hill, Director Information Technology
CHR: Devin Patrick, Manager Human Resources
CNO: Chris Metcalf, Director of Nursing
Web address: www.ush.utah.gov
Control: State–Government, nonfederal **Service:** Psychiatric

Staffed Beds: 329 **Admissions:** 341 **Census:** 297 **Outpatient Visits:** 0
Births: 0 **Total Expense ($000):** 56977 **Payroll Expense ($000):** 32679
Personnel: 745

⊞ △ **UTAH VALLEY REGIONAL MEDICAL CENTER (460001)**, 1034 North 500
West, Zip 84604–3337; tel. 801/357–7850 **A**1 2 3 7 10 **F**3 13 15 17 18 20
21 22 23 24 25 26 28 29 30 31 34 35 38 39 40 43 44 45 48 49 50 51 53
57 59 60 61 64 68 70 72 73 74 75 76 77 78 79 81 82 84 85 86 87 89 90
91 92 93 94 96 97 98 99 100 101 102 103 107 108 110 111 114 115 116
117 118 119 121 123 126 129 130 131 132 146 148 **S** Intermountain
Healthcare, Inc., Salt Lake City, UT
Primary Contact: Steve Smoot, Administrator
CFO: Rod Lisonbee, Chief Financial Officer
CIO: Mary Gathers, Director Information Systems
CHR: Luke P. Morris, Regional Director Human Resources
CNO: Lisa A. Paletta RN, MPA, NEA–BC, FACHE, R.N., Chief Nursing Officer
Web address: www.utahvalleyregional.org
Control: Other not–for–profit (including NFP Corporation) **Service:** General
Medical and Surgical

Staffed Beds: 344 **Admissions:** 18510 **Census:** 185 **Outpatient Visits:**
627385 **Births:** 3642 **Personnel:** 2685

☐ **UTAH VALLEY SPECIALTY HOSPITAL (462005)**, 306 River Bend Lane,
Zip 84604–5625; tel. 801/226–8880, (Nonreporting) **A**1 10 **S** Ernest Health,
Inc., Albuquerque, NM
Primary Contact: Ezra Segura, Chief Executive Officer
Web address: www.uvsh.ernesthealth.com
Control: Corporation, Investor–owned, for–profit **Service:** Long–Term Acute Care
hospital

Staffed Beds: 40

RICHFIELD—Sevier County

⊞ **SEVIER VALLEY MEDICAL CENTER (460026)**, 1000 North Main Street,
Zip 84701–1857; tel. 435/893–4100 **A**1 10 20 **F**3 8 13 15 29 31 34 40 41
43 59 62 65 68 75 76 78 79 81 89 107 108 110 111 114 129 146 147 148
P6 **S** Intermountain Healthcare, Inc., Salt Lake City, UT
Primary Contact: Gary E. Beck, Administrator
CFO: Chris Thompson, Chief Financial Officer
CMO: Justin Abbott, M.D., Medical Director
CHR: Katey Nelson, Director Human Resources
CNO: Cami Blackham, R.N., Nurse Administrator
Web address: www.sevierhospital.org
Control: Other not–for–profit (including NFP Corporation) **Service:** General
Medical and Surgical

Staffed Beds: 29 **Admissions:** 851 **Census:** 6 **Outpatient Visits:** 63181
Births: 201 **Total Expense ($000):** 28838 **Payroll Expense ($000):** 7530
Personnel: 165

RIVERTON—Salt Lake County

⊞ **RIVERTON HOSPITAL (460058)**, 3741 West 12600 South, Zip 84065–7215;
tel. 801/285–4000 **A**1 3 10 **F**3 13 15 29 30 31 34 35 39 40 41 44 45 46 47
48 49 50 51 57 59 64 68 70 73 75 76 77 78 79 81 85 86 87 89 91 93 94
97 107 108 110 111 114 115 118 119 129 130 131 146 147 148
S Intermountain Healthcare, Inc., Salt Lake City, UT
Primary Contact: Blair Kent, Administrator
CFO: Royce Stephens, Chief Financial Officer
CMO: David Haselton, Chief Medical Officer
CIO: Susan Hanks, Chief Information Officer
Web address: www.intermountainhealthcare.org/
Control: Other not–for–profit (including NFP Corporation) **Service:** General
Medical and Surgical

Staffed Beds: 92 **Admissions:** 5117 **Census:** 31 **Outpatient Visits:** 158917
Births: 2424 **Total Expense ($000):** 98055 **Payroll Expense ($000):** 26995
Personnel: 495

ROOSEVELT—Duchesne County

★ **UINTAH BASIN MEDICAL CENTER (460019)**, 250 West 300 North, 75–2,
Zip 84066–2336; tel. 435/722–6163, (Total facility includes 75 beds in nursing
home–type unit) **A**10 20 **F**6 7 11 13 15 17 35 40 43 45 50 52 53 54 57 59 60
62 63 70 73 74 75 76 77 79 81 82 84 85 87 89 93 107 108 110 111 115 119 127
128 129 130 131 132 135 146 147 148 **P**3
Primary Contact: James I. Marshall, President and Chief Executive Officer
CFO: Brent Hales, Chief Financial Officer
CMO: Gary B. White, M.D., Chief Medical Staff
CHR: Randall Bennett, Assistant Administrator
Web address: www.ubmc.org
Control: Other not–for–profit (including NFP Corporation) **Service:** General
Medical and Surgical

Staffed Beds: 124 **Admissions:** 2509 **Census:** 78 **Outpatient Visits:** 67113
Births: 704 **Total Expense ($000):** 73635 **Payroll Expense ($000):** 22893

Many Facility Codes have changed. Please refer to the AHA Guide Code Chart.
© 2016 AHA Guide

SAINT GEORGE—Washington County

☒ △ **DIXIE REGIONAL MEDICAL CENTER (460021)**, 1380 East Medical Center Drive, Zip 84790–2123; tel. 435/251–1000, (Includes DIXIE REGIONAL MEDICAL CENTER, 544 South 400 East, St. George, Zip 84770) **A**1 2 7 10 **F**3 11 12 13 15 18 19 20 21 22 23 24 25 28 29 31 34 35 38 40 43 45 46 50 53 54 57 59 64 67 68 70 72 74 75 76 77 78 79 80 81 82 83 84 85 89 90 93 98 102 107 108 110 111 114 115 117 119 120 121 127 129 130 131 132 135 146 147 148 **P**5 **S** Intermountain Healthcare, Inc., Salt Lake City, UT
Primary Contact: Terri Kane, Chief Executive Officer
CFO: Steven Vance, Chief Financial Officer
CMO: Steven Van Norman, M.D., Medical Director
CIO: Lance Bedingfield, Director Information Services
CHR: Vicki Wilson, Human Resources Director
CNO: Gary Cunningham, Chief Nursing Officer
Web address: www.intermountainhealthcare.org
Control: Other not–for–profit (including NFP Corporation) **Service:** General Medical and Surgical

Staffed Beds: 261 **Admissions:** 15958 **Census:** 159 **Outpatient Visits:** 551219 **Births:** 2317 **Total Expense ($000):** 420485 **Payroll Expense ($000):** 114497

SALT LAKE CITY—Salt Lake County

☒ **LDS HOSPITAL (460006)**, Eighth Avenue and C Street, Zip 84143–0001; tel. 801/408–1100 **A**1 2 3 5 10 **F**3 4 5 7 8 12 13 15 18 28 29 30 31 34 35 36 37 38 39 40 43 44 45 46 48 49 50 51 52 53 54 55 56 57 58 59 60 61 63 64 65 66 68 70 73 74 75 76 77 78 79 81 82 84 85 86 87 91 92 93 94 96 98 100 101 102 103 104 105 107 108 109 110 111 114 115 119 120 121 123 124 126 129 131 132 135 136 146 147 148 **S** Intermountain Healthcare, Inc., Salt Lake City, UT
Primary Contact: Jim Sheets, Chief Executive Officer and Administrator
CFO: Dan Brady, Chief Financial Officer
CMO: Kerry Fisher, M.D., Medical Director
CIO: David Baird, Chief Information Officer
CHR: Mollee Lamb, Manager Human Resources
CNO: Brandon Vonk, Nurse Administrator
Web address: www.intermountainhealthcare.org
Control: Other not–for–profit (including NFP Corporation) **Service:** General Medical and Surgical

Staffed Beds: 262 **Admissions:** 10298 **Census:** 120 **Births:** 2318 **Total Expense ($000):** 227570 **Payroll Expense ($000):** 65264 **Personnel:** 1189

☒ **MARIAN CENTER (464012)**, 451 East Bishop Federal Lane, Zip 84115–2357; tel. 801/487–7557 **A**1 10 **F**29 34 98 100 101 103 104 130 **P**8
Primary Contact: Bradley C. Albrechtsen, Chief Executive Officer and Administrator
Web address: www.stjosephvilla.com
Control: Corporation, Investor–owned, for–profit **Service:** Psychiatric

Staffed Beds: 14 **Admissions:** 192 **Census:** 9 **Outpatient Visits:** 2608 **Births:** 0 **Total Expense ($000):** 2453 **Payroll Expense ($000):** 1287 **Personnel:** 31

☐ △ **PRIMARY CHILDREN'S HOSPITAL (463301)**, 100 North Mario Capecchi Drive, Zip 84113–1100; tel. 801/662–1000 **A**1 3 5 7 10 **F**3 4 5 11 16 17 19 21 23 25 27 29 30 31 32 34 35 36 38 39 40 41 43 44 45 48 49 50 53 54 55 57 58 59 60 61 63 64 65 67 72 73 74 75 77 78 79 80 81 82 84 85 86 87 88 89 90 92 93 96 98 99 100 101 102 104 105 106 107 108 111 113 114 115 116 117 118 119 124 129 130 131 132 134 135 136 137 138 139 141 142 146 148 **S** Intermountain Healthcare, Inc., Salt Lake City, UT
Primary Contact: Katy Welkie, MBA, R.N., Chief Executive Officer
CFO: Jeremiah Radandt, Chief Financial Officer
CMO: Ed Clark, M.D., Chief Medical Officer
CIO: Joe Hales, Director Information Systems
CHR: Albert Bennett Buckworth, Human Resources Administrative Director
CNO: Judy Geiger, R.N., Chief Nursing Officer
Web address: www.intermountainhealthcare.org
Control: Other not–for–profit (including NFP Corporation) **Service:** Children's general

Staffed Beds: 289 **Admissions:** 13744 **Census:** 183 **Outpatient Visits:** 378731 **Births:** 0 **Total Expense ($000):** 433768 **Payroll Expense ($000):** 153306 **Personnel:** 2643

PROMISE HOSPITAL OF SALT LAKE (462004), 8 Avenue, C. Street, Zip 84143; tel. 801/408–7110 **A**10 **F**1 3 29 30 84 85 148 **P**8 **S** Promise Healthcare, Boca Raton, FL
Primary Contact: Wayne Kinsey, Chief Executive Officer
CMO: Geoff Harding, Chief Clinical Officer
Web address: www.promise–saltlake.com
Control: Individual, Investor–owned, for–profit **Service:** Long–Term Acute Care hospital

Staffed Beds: 41 **Admissions:** 403 **Census:** 32 **Outpatient Visits:** 0 **Births:** 0

☐ **SALT LAKE BEHAVIORAL HEALTH (464013)**, 3802 South 700 East, Zip 84106–1182; tel. 801/264–6000 **A**1 10 **F**4 5 29 30 50 56 75 82 98 102 103 104 130 132 **S** Universal Health Services, Inc., King of Prussia, PA
Primary Contact: Kreg Gillman, Chief Executive Officer
COO: Jim Hess, Chief Operations Officer
CFO: Nancy MacGregor, Chief Financial Officer
CMO: Monica Polk, Interim Medical Director
CHR: Robyn Holsten, Human Resources Director
CNO: Suzanne Nelson, RN, R.N., Director of Nursing
Web address: www.saltlakebehavioralhealth.com
Control: Corporation, Investor–owned, for–profit **Service:** Psychiatric

Staffed Beds: 118 **Admissions:** 2120 **Census:** 54 **Outpatient Visits:** 4895 **Births:** 0

★ ◇ **SALT LAKE REGIONAL MEDICAL CENTER (460003)**, 1050 East South Temple, Zip 84102–1507; tel. 801/350–4111, (Nonreporting) **A**3 5 10 21 **S** IASIS Healthcare, Franklin, TN
Primary Contact: Dale Johns, FACHE, Chief Executive Officer
COO: Scot Stevens, Assistant Administrator
CFO: Brian Ebright, Chief Financial Officer
CMO: Blake Johnson, M.D., Chief of Staff
CIO: Mark Runyan, Director Information Services
CHR: Carolyn Livingston, Director Human Resources
CNO: Terron Arbon, R.N., Chief Nursing Officer
Web address: www.saltlakeregional.com
Control: Corporation, Investor–owned, for–profit **Service:** General Medical and Surgical

Staffed Beds: 132

☐ **SHRINERS HOSPITALS FOR CHILDREN–SALT LAKE CITY (463302)**, Fairfax Road & Virginia Street, Zip 84103–4399; tel. 801/536–3500 **A**1 3 5 10 **F**3 8 29 32 50 57 58 59 64 67 74 75 77 79 81 89 90 91 93 94 119 128 130 131 143 146 **P**6 **S** Shriners Hospitals for Children, Tampa, FL
Primary Contact: Kevin Martin, M.P.H., R.N., Administrator
CFO: Heath Braby, Director Fiscal Services
CMO: Kristen Carroll, M.D., Chief of Staff
CIO: Mike Allen, Director Information Technology
CHR: Kris Goldman, Director Human Resources
CNO: Gail McGuill, R.N., Chief Nursing Officer and Administrative Director of Patient Care Services
Web address: www.shrinershospitalsforchildren.org/Hospitals/Locations/SaltLakeCity.aspx
Control: Other not–for–profit (including NFP Corporation) **Service:** Children's orthopedic

Staffed Beds: 45 **Admissions:** 220 **Census:** 3 **Outpatient Visits:** 10534 **Births:** 0 **Total Expense ($000):** 19814 **Payroll Expense ($000):** 11769 **Personnel:** 157

☒ **ST. MARK'S HOSPITAL (460047)**, 1200 East 3900 South, Zip 84124–1390; tel. 801/268–7111 **A**1 3 10 **F**3 5 8 11 12 13 15 17 18 20 22 24 26 28 29 30 31 34 35 36 38 40 42 43 45 46 49 50 51 53 55 56 57 58 59 60 64 65 67 70 72 73 74 75 76 77 78 79 81 82 84 85 86 87 90 91 92 98 102 107 108 110 111 115 118 119 124 126 128 129 130 132 135 145 146 147 148 **S** HCA, Nashville, TN
Primary Contact: Steven B. Bateman, Chief Executive Officer
CFO: Bryan McKinley, Chief Financial Officer
CMO: J. Eric Vanderhooft, M.D., President Medical Staff
CIO: Jesse Trujillo, Chief Information Officer
CHR: Robyn Opheikens, Assistant Administrator Human Resources
Web address: www.stmarkshospital.com
Control: Corporation, Investor–owned, for–profit **Service:** General Medical and Surgical

Staffed Beds: 277 **Admissions:** 14704 **Census:** 175 **Outpatient Visits:** 94762 **Births:** 2567

UT

Hospital, Medicare Provider Number, Address, Telephone, Approval, Facility, and Physician Codes, Health Care System

★ American Hospital Association (AHA) membership ◯ Healthcare Facilities Accreditation Program ⇑ Center for Improvement in Healthcare Quality Accreditation
☐ The Joint Commission accreditation ◇ DNV Healthcare Inc. accreditation △ Commission on Accreditation of Rehabilitation Facilities (CARF) accreditation

© 2016 AHA Guide   *Many Facility Codes have changed. Please refer to the AHA Guide Code Chart.*   Hospitals **A663**

★ △ ◇ **UNIVERSITY OF UTAH HEALTH CARE – HOSPITAL AND CLINICS (460009)**, 50 North Medical Drive, Zip 84132–0002; tel. 801/587–3572 **A**3 5 7 8 10 21 **F**3 5 6 7 8 9 11 12 13 15 16 17 18 20 22 24 26 28 29 30 31 34 35 36 37 38 39 40 42 43 44 45 46 47 48 49 50 51 52 53 54 55 56 57 58 59 60 61 64 65 68 70 71 72 73 74 75 76 77 78 79 80 81 82 83 84 85 86 87 90 91 92 93 94 95 96 97 98 99 100 101 102 103 104 105 106 107 108 109 110 111 112 113 114 115 116 117 118 119 120 121 123 124 126 129 130 131 132 134 135 136 137 138 139 140 141 142 143 144 146 147 148 **P**1
Primary Contact: Gordon Crabtree, Interim Chief Executive Officer
COO: Quinn McKenna, Chief Operating Officer
CFO: Gordon Crabtree, Chief Financial Officer
CMO: Thomas Miller, M.D., Medical Director
CIO: James Turnbull, Chief Information Officer
CHR: Dale A. Spartz, Chief Human Resources Officer
CNO: Margaret Pearce, R.N., Chief Nursing Officer
Web address: www.uuhsc.utah.edu
Control: State–Government, nonfederal **Service:** General Medical and Surgical

Staffed Beds: 528 **Admissions:** 25251 **Census:** 403 **Outpatient Visits:** 1715757 **Births:** 3984 **Total Expense ($000):** 1188508 **Payroll Expense ($000):** 404799 **Personnel:** 8784

◇ **UNIVERSITY OF UTAH NEUROPSYCHIATRIC INSTITUTE (464009)**, 501 South Chipeta Way, Zip 84108–1222; tel. 801/583–2500 **A**3 5 10 21 **F**4 5 30 34 35 38 54 58 64 68 75 87 98 99 100 101 103 104 105 106 130 132
Primary Contact: Ross Van Vranken, Executive Director
CFO: Becky Schaefer, Chief Financial Officer
CMO: James Ashworth, M.D., Medical Director
Web address: www.med.utah.edu/uni
Control: State–Government, nonfederal **Service:** Psychiatric

Staffed Beds: 140 **Admissions:** 4530 **Census:** 109 **Births:** 0 **Total Expense ($000):** 73218 **Payroll Expense ($000):** 28272 **Personnel:** 616

⊞ △ **VETERANS AFFAIRS SALT LAKE CITY HEALTH CARE SYSTEM**, 500 Foothill Drive, Zip 84148–0002; tel. 801/582–1565 **A**1 3 5 7 **F**3 4 5 8 12 18 20 22 24 28 29 30 34 35 36 38 39 40 44 45 46 47 48 49 50 53 54 55 56 57 58 59 60 61 62 63 64 65 70 71 74 75 77 78 79 81 82 83 84 85 86 87 90 92 93 94 96 97 98 100 101 102 103 104 105 106 107 108 109 111 114 115 116 117 118 119 126 127 129 130 132 133 135 137 143 144 146 147 148 **P**6 **S** Department of Veterans Affairs, Washington, DC
Primary Contact: Steven W. Young, Director
CFO: Val Martin, Director Financial Management Services Center
CMO: Ronald J. Gebhart, M.D., Chief of Staff
CIO: Lisa Leonelis, Chief Information Officer
CHR: Lisa Porter, Director Human Resources, Leadership and Education
Web address: www.saltlakecity.va.gov/
Control: Veterans Affairs, Government, federal **Service:** General Medical and Surgical

Staffed Beds: 121 **Admissions:** 4669 **Census:** 112 **Outpatient Visits:** 687393 **Births:** 0 **Personnel:** 2337

SANDY—Salt Lake County

⊞ **ALTA VIEW HOSPITAL (460044)**, 9660 South 1300 East, Zip 84094–3793; tel. 801/501–2600 **A**1 2 10 **F**3 8 12 13 15 29 30 31 34 35 38 39 40 44 45 46 47 48 49 50 51 53 54 56 57 59 64 68 70 75 76 77 78 79 81 85 86 87 92 93 102 107 108 110 111 115 119 129 130 131 132 135 146 147 **S** Intermountain Healthcare, Inc., Salt Lake City, UT
Primary Contact: Bryan L. Johnson, Administrator
CFO: Chris Hargis, Manager Finance
CHR: Leslie Bates, Manager Human Resources
Web address: www.intermountainhealthcare.org
Control: Other not–for–profit (including NFP Corporation) **Service:** General Medical and Surgical

Staffed Beds: 69 **Admissions:** 3322 **Census:** 22 **Outpatient Visits:** 261528 **Births:** 1171 **Total Expense ($000):** 90628 **Payroll Expense ($000):** 25298 **Personnel:** 429

⊞ **HEALTHSOUTH REHABILITATION HOSPITAL OF UTAH (463025)**, 8074 South 1300 East, Zip 84094–0743; tel. 801/561–3400, (Nonreporting) **A**1 10 **S** HEALTHSOUTH Corporation, Birmingham, AL
Primary Contact: Jeff Frandsen, Chief Executive Officer
CFO: Daren Woolstenhulme, Chief Financial Officer
CMO: Joseph VickRoy, M.D., Medical Director
CHR: Troy Jensen, Director Human Resources
Web address: www.healthsouthutah.com
Control: Corporation, Investor–owned, for–profit **Service:** Rehabilitation

Staffed Beds: 105

TOOELE—Tooele County

⊞ **MOUNTAIN WEST MEDICAL CENTER (460014)**, 2055 North Main Street, Zip 84074–9819; tel. 435/843–3600, (Nonreporting) **A**1 10 **S** Quorum Health, Brentwood, TN
Primary Contact: Philip Eaton, Interim Chief Executive Officer
CMO: James Antinori, M.D., Chief of Staff
CIO: Marc Taylor, IS Director
CHR: Matthew Flygare, Director Human Resources
CNO: Yvonne Nielson, Chief Nursing Officer, Director Quality Management and Regulatory Compliance
Web address: www.mountainwestmc.com
Control: Corporation, Investor–owned, for–profit **Service:** General Medical and Surgical

Staffed Beds: 44

TREMONTON—Box Elder County

★ **BEAR RIVER VALLEY HOSPITAL (460039)**, 905 North 1000 West, Zip 84337–2497; tel. 435/207–4500, (Nonreporting) **A**10 **S** Intermountain Healthcare, Inc., Salt Lake City, UT
Primary Contact: Ben Smalley, Chief Executive Officer
CHR: Joy Sadler, Director Human Resources
CNO: Penny Marshall, Chief Nursing Officer
Web address: www.https://intermountainhealthcare.org/locations/bear–river–valley–hospital/
Control: Other not–for–profit (including NFP Corporation) **Service:** General Medical and Surgical

Staffed Beds: 14

VERNAL—Uintah County

⊞ **ASHLEY REGIONAL MEDICAL CENTER (460030)**, 150 West 100 North, Zip 84078–2036; tel. 435/789–3342, (Nonreporting) **A**1 10 20 **S** LifePoint Health, Brentwood, TN
Primary Contact: Ben Cluff, Chief Executive Officer
CFO: Chad Labrum, Chief Financial Officer
CMO: Dennis Lewis, M.D., Chief of Staff
CIO: Mark Rich, Director Information Services
CHR: Deena Mansfield, Director Human Resources
CNO: Greg Gardiner, Chief Clinical Officer
Web address: www.ashleyregional.com
Control: Corporation, Investor–owned, for–profit **Service:** General Medical and Surgical

Staffed Beds: 39

WEST JORDAN—Salt Lake County

★ ◇ **JORDAN VALLEY MEDICAL CENTER (460051)**, 3580 West 9000 South, Zip 84088–8812; tel. 801/561–8888, (Includes MOUNTAIN POINT MEDICAL CENTER, 3000 North Triumph Boulevard, Lehii, Zip 84043; Mailing Address: Lehi, tel. 385/345–3000), (Nonreporting) **A**10 21 **S** IASIS Healthcare, Franklin, TN
Primary Contact: Steven Anderson, Chief Executive Officer
COO: Jon Butterfield, Chief Operating Officer
CFO: Kurt Shipley, Chief Financial Officer
CMO: B. Dee Allred, M.D., President Medical Staff
Web address: www.jordanvalleymc.com
Control: Partnership, Investor–owned, for–profit **Service:** General Medical and Surgical

Staffed Beds: 183

WEST VALLEY CITY—Salt Lake County

★ **JORDAN VALLEY MEDICAL CENTER WEST VALLEY CAMPUS**, 3460 South Pioneer Parkway, Zip 84120–2049; tel. 801/561–8888, (Nonreporting) **S** IASIS Healthcare, Franklin, TN
Primary Contact: Steven Anderson, Chief Executive Officer
COO: Jon Butterfield, Administrator and Chief Operating Officer
CFO: Steven Payne, Chief Financial Officer
CMO: Justin Parkinson, M.D., President Medical Staff
CIO: Mark Runyan, Director Information Systems
CHR: Rob Burnett, Director Human Resources
Web address: www.pioneervalleyhospital.com
Control: Corporation, Investor–owned, for–profit **Service:** General Medical and Surgical

Staffed Beds: 101

UT

Many Facility Codes have changed. Please refer to the AHA Guide Code Chart. © 2016 AHA Guide

VERMONT

BENNINGTON—Bennington County

☒ **SOUTHWESTERN VERMONT MEDICAL CENTER (470012)**, 100 Hospital Drive, Zip 05201–5004; tel. 802/442–6361, (Nonreporting) **A**1 2 10
Primary Contact: Thomas A. Dee, Chief Executive Officer
CFO: Stephen D. Majetich, CPA, Chief Financial Officer
CMO: Trey Dobson, M.D., Chief Medical Officer
CIO: Richard Ogilvie, Chief Information Officer
CHR: Rudolph D. Weaver, Vice President Human Resources
CNO: Carol Conroy, R.N., Chief Nursing Officer
Web address: www.svhealthcare.org
Control: Other not–for–profit (including NFP Corporation) **Service:** General Medical and Surgical

Staffed Beds: 77

BERLIN—Washington County

☒ **THE UNIVERSITY OF VERMONT HEALTH NETWORK CENTRAL VERMONT MEDICAL CENTER (470001)**, 130 Fisher Road, Zip 05602–9516, Mailing Address: P.O. Box 547, Barre, Zip 05641–0547; tel. 802/371–4100, (Total facility includes 153 beds in nursing home–type unit) **A**1 2 3 10 **F**3 11 12 13 15 18 28 29 30 31 34 35 36 40 44 45 46 48 49 50 51 53 54 59 61 63 64 65 68 70 71 74 75 76 77 78 79 81 84 85 86 87 92 93 94 96 97 98 99 100 102 103 104 107 108 110 111 114 115 119 120 121 123 128 130 131 132 135 141 143 146 147 148
Primary Contact: Judith C. Tartaglia, President and Chief Executive Officer
COO: Nancy Lothian, Chief Operating Officer and Chief Information Officer
CFO: Cheyenne Holland, Chief Financial Officer
CMO: Philip Brown, D.O., Vice President Medical Affairs
CHR: Robert Patterson, Vice President Human Resources and Rehabilitation Services
CNO: Karin Morrow, Chief Nursing Officer
Web address: www.cvmc.org/
Control: Other not–for–profit (including NFP Corporation) **Service:** General Medical and Surgical

Staffed Beds: 233 **Admissions:** 4179 **Census:** 169 **Outpatient Visits:** 313556 **Births:** 367 **Total Expense ($000):** 121009 **Payroll Expense ($000):** 63385 **Personnel:** 1329

BRATTLEBORO—Windham County

★ **BRATTLEBORO MEMORIAL HOSPITAL (470011)**, 17 Belmont Avenue, Zip 05301–3498; tel. 802/257–0341 **A**10 **F**3 11 13 15 18 28 29 30 31 34 35 39 40 45 49 50 51 53 55 57 59 64 68 70 74 75 76 77 78 79 81 85 87 93 107 108 110 111 115 118 119 130 131 132 135 146 147 148
Primary Contact: Steven R. Gordon, President and Chief Executive Officer
CFO: Michael Rogers, Vice President Fiscal Services
CMO: Kathleen McGraw, M.D., Chief Medical Officer
CIO: Jonathan Farina, Chief Information Officer
CHR: Robin R. Heald, Vice President Human Resources
CNO: Mary Urquhart, R.N., Vice President Patient Care
Web address: www.bmhvt.org
Control: Other not–for–profit (including NFP Corporation) **Service:** General Medical and Surgical

Staffed Beds: 42 **Admissions:** 1569 **Census:** 14 **Outpatient Visits:** 165075 **Births:** 359 **Total Expense ($000):** 76473 **Payroll Expense ($000):** 32493 **Personnel:** 387

☒ **BRATTLEBORO RETREAT (474001)**, Anna Marsh Lane, Zip 05301, Mailing Address: P.O. Box 803, Zip 05302–0803; tel. 802/257–7785 **A**1 5 10 **F**29 34 35 50 68 98 99 100 101 102 103 104 105 106 **P**6
Primary Contact: Louis Josephson, Ph.D., President and Chief Executive Officer
COO: Gerri Cote, Chief Operating Officer
CFO: Steven Monette, Chief Financial Officer
CMO: Frederick Engstrom, M.D., Chief Medical Officer
CHR: Jeffrey T. Corrigan, Vice President Human Resources
CNO: Linda J. Nagy, MSN, Chief Nursing Officer
Web address: www.brattlebororetreat.org
Control: Other not–for–profit (including NFP Corporation) **Service:** Psychiatric

Staffed Beds: 118 **Admissions:** 3946 **Census:** 107 **Outpatient Visits:** 34731 **Births:** 0 **Total Expense ($000):** 68826 **Payroll Expense ($000):** 43133 **Personnel:** 599

BURLINGTON—Chittenden County

☒ **THE UNIVERSITY OF VERMONT HEALTH NETWORK UNIVERSITY OF VERMONT MEDICAL CENTER (470003)**, 111 Colchester Avenue, Zip 05401–1473; tel. 802/847–0000, (Includes FANNY ALLEN CAMPUS, 101 College Parkway, Colchester, Zip 05446–3035; tel. 802/655–1234; MEDICAL CENTER HOSPITAL CAMPUS, Colchester Avenue, Zip 05401; tel. 802/847–2345; VERMONT CHILDREN'S HOSPITAL, 111 Colchester Avenue, tel. 802/847–0000) **A**1 2 3 5 8 10 **F**3 4 5 6 7 9 11 12 13 15 17 18 19 20 21 22 23 24 25 26 28 29 30 31 32 34 35 36 37 39 40 43 44 45 46 47 48 49 50 51 52 54 55 56 57 58 59 60 61 63 64 65 66 68 70 72 73 74 75 76 77 78 79 81 82 84 85 86 87 88 89 90 91 92 93 94 96 97 98 99 100 101 102 103 104 105 107 108 110 111 114 115 116 117 118 119 120 121 123 124 126 128 129 130 131 132 135 136 138 141 142 143 144 145 146 147 148 **P**6
Primary Contact: Eileen Whalen, R.N., President and Chief Operating Officer
CFO: Todd Keating, Chief Financial Officer
CMO: Stephen Leffler, Chief Medical Officer
CHR: Paul Macuga, Chief Human Resources Officer
Web address: www.fletcherallen.org
Control: Other not–for–profit (including NFP Corporation) **Service:** General Medical and Surgical

Staffed Beds: 426 **Admissions:** 18976 **Census:** 315 **Outpatient Visits:** 1419706 **Births:** 2245 **Total Expense ($000):** 1066269 **Payroll Expense ($000):** 517732 **Personnel:** 6546

MIDDLEBURY—Addison County

★ **PORTER MEDICAL CENTER (471307)**, 115 Porter Drive, Zip 05753–8423; tel. 802/388–4701 **A**10 18 **F**3 8 11 13 15 18 26 29 30 40 43 45 50 59 64 68 70 75 76 79 81 83 85 86 89 93 97 107 108 110 111 114 115 119 130 133 146 **P**6
Primary Contact: Fred Kniffin, M.D., Interim President and Chief Executive Officer
CFO: Steve Ciampa, Vice President Finance
CMO: Fred Kniffin, M.D., Chief Medical Officer
CIO: Rebecca Woods, Chief Information Officer
CHR: David Fuller, Director Human Resources
CNO: Lorraina Smith–Zuba, R.N., Chief Nursing Officer
Web address: www.portermedical.org
Control: Other not–for–profit (including NFP Corporation) **Service:** General Medical and Surgical

Staffed Beds: 25 **Admissions:** 1967 **Census:** 17

MORRISVILLE—Lamoille County

★ **COPLEY HOSPITAL (471305)**, 528 Washington Highway, Zip 05661–8973; tel. 802/888–8888 **A**10 18 **F**3 11 13 15 18 28 29 30 31 34 35 39 40 44 45 58 59 64 65 70 74 75 76 77 78 79 81 85 86 93 107 110 111 119 129 130 131 133 135 146 147
Primary Contact: Arthur Mathisen, FACHE, President and Chief Executive Officer
COO: Greg Ward, Vice President Support and Ancillary Services
CFO: Rassoul Rangaviz, Chief Financial Officer
CMO: Joel Silverstein, M.D., Chief Medical Officer
CIO: Randy Chesley, Director Information Technology
CHR: Amy Fitzgerald, Human Resources Manager
CNO: Lori Profota, R.N., Chief Nursing Officer
Web address: www.copleyvt.org
Control: Other not–for–profit (including NFP Corporation) **Service:** General Medical and Surgical

Staffed Beds: 25 **Admissions:** 1770 **Census:** 13 **Outpatient Visits:** 78767 **Births:** 210 **Total Expense ($000):** 60871 **Payroll Expense ($000):** 26973 **Personnel:** 342

VT

NEWPORT—Orleans County

★ **NORTH COUNTRY HOSPITAL AND HEALTH CENTER (471304)**, 189 Prouty
Drive, Zip 05855–9326; tel. 802/334–7331 **A**10 18 **F**11 13 15 28 29 30 31
34 35 40 45 53 70 74 75 76 77 78 79 81 82 84 85 89 93 107 108 110 111
114 118 119 127 129 130 131 133 135 146 148
Primary Contact: Claudio D. Fort, President and Chief Executive Officer
COO: Thomas Frank, Chief Operating Officer
CFO: Andre Bissonnette, Chief Financial Officer
CHR: William Perket, Vice President Human Resources
CNO: Avril Cochran, R.N., Vice President Patient Care Services
Web address: www.nchsi.org
Control: Other not–for–profit (including NFP Corporation) **Service:** General
Medical and Surgical

Staffed Beds: 25 **Admissions:** 1429 **Census:** 15 **Outpatient Visits:** 69362
Births: 229 **Total Expense ($000):** 78129 **Payroll Expense ($000):** 35949
Personnel: 483

RANDOLPH—Orange County

★ **GIFFORD MEDICAL CENTER (471301)**, 44 South Main Street,
Zip 05060–1381, Mailing Address: P.O. Box 2000, Zip 05060–2000;
tel. 802/728–7000, (Nonreporting) **A**2 10 18
Primary Contact: E. Berton Whitaker, FACHE, Interim Chief Executive Officer
CFO: Jeff Hebert, Interim Vice President Finance
CMO: Joshua Plavin, M.D., Medical Director Medicine Division
CIO: Sean Patrick, Director Information Systems
CHR: Janice Davis, Interim Director Human Resources
CNO: Linda Minsinger, Vice President Hospital Division
Web address: www.giffordmed.org
Control: Other not–for–profit (including NFP Corporation) **Service:** General
Medical and Surgical

Staffed Beds: 82

RUTLAND—Rutland County

☒ **RUTLAND REGIONAL MEDICAL CENTER (470005)**, 160 Allen Street,
Zip 05701–4595; tel. 802/775–7111 **A**1 2 10 **F**3 13 15 18 20 28 29 31 34
36 37 38 40 45 47 48 49 50 55 57 59 61 64 65 70 74 76 77 78 79 81 82
83 84 85 87 89 92 93 94 98 100 101 102 103 104 107 108 109 110 111
115 117 118 119 120 121 123 124 128 129 130 133 135 146 147 148
Primary Contact: Thomas W. Huebner, President
CFO: Ed Ogorzalek, Chief Financial Officer
CMO: Baxter C. Holland, M.D., Chief Medical Officer
CNO: Carol Egen, R.N., Chief Nursing Officer
Web address: www.rrmc.org
Control: Other not–for–profit (including NFP Corporation) **Service:** General
Medical and Surgical

Staffed Beds: 132 **Admissions:** 5206 **Census:** 79 **Outpatient Visits:** 233187
Births: 376 **Total Expense ($000):** 233197 **Payroll Expense ($000):**
108914 **Personnel:** 1351

SAINT ALBANS—Franklin County

☒ **NORTHWESTERN MEDICAL CENTER (470024)**, 133 Fairfield Street,
Zip 05478–1726; tel. 802/524–5911 **A**1 2 10 20 **F**5 11 13 15 28 29 30 32
34 35 36 37 38 40 43 44 45 50 51 57 58 59 63 64 65 69 75 77 78 79 81
82 84 85 86 87 93 96 97 107 108 110 111 114 119 130 131 132 133 134
135 143 144 146 147 148 **P**6 **S** QHR, Brentwood, TN
Primary Contact: Jill Berry Bowen, President and Chief Executive Officer
COO: Jane Catton, R.N., Chief Operating Officer and Chief Nursing Officer
CFO: Christopher Hickey, Chief Financial Officer
CMO: Lowery Sullivan, M.D., Chief Medical Officer
CIO: Joel Benware, Vice President Information Technology and Compliance
CHR: Thomas C. Conley, Vice President, Human Resources and Organizational
Development
CNO: Jane Catton, R.N., Chief Operating Officer and Chief Nursing Officer
Web address: www.northwesternmedicalcenter.org
Control: Other not–for–profit (including NFP Corporation) **Service:** General
Medical and Surgical

Staffed Beds: 55 **Admissions:** 2484 **Census:** 22 **Outpatient Visits:** 91553
Births: 438 **Total Expense ($000):** 92248 **Payroll Expense ($000):** 41573
Personnel: 630

SAINT JOHNSBURY—Caledonia County

★ **NORTHEASTERN VERMONT REGIONAL HOSPITAL (471303)**, 1315 Hospital
Drive, Zip 05819–9210, Mailing Address: PO Box 905, Zip 05819–0905;
tel. 802/748–8141, (Nonreporting) **A**10 18
Primary Contact: Paul R. Bengtson, Chief Executive Officer
CFO: Robert Hersey, Chief Financial Officer
CIO: Andrea Lott, Vice President Information Services
CHR: Betty Ann Gwatkin, Vice President Human Resources
CNO: Seleem Choudhury, R.N., Chief Nursing Officer
Web address: www.nvrh.org
Control: Other not–for–profit (including NFP Corporation) **Service:** General
Medical and Surgical

Staffed Beds: 25

SPRINGFIELD—Windsor County

★ **SPRINGFIELD HOSPITAL (471306)**, 25 Ridgewood Road, Zip 05156–3050,
Mailing Address: 25 Ridgewood Road, Zip 05156–3050; tel. 802/885–2151,
(Nonreporting) **A**10 18
Primary Contact: Timothy R. Ford, President and Chief Executive Officer
CFO: Scott Whittemore, Chief Financial Officer and Chief of Ancillary Services
CMO: Richard Marasa, M.D., President Medical Staff
CIO: Kyle Peoples, Director Technology Management Services
CHR: Janet Lyle, Chief Human Resources and Allied Health Services
CNO: Janet Sherer, Chief of Patient Care Services
Web address: www.springfieldmed.org
Control: Other not–for–profit (including NFP Corporation) **Service:** General
Medical and Surgical

Staffed Beds: 35

TOWNSHEND—Windham County

★ **GRACE COTTAGE HOSPITAL (471300)**, 185 Grafton Road, Zip 05353–0216,
Mailing Address: P.O. Box 216, Zip 05353–0216; tel. 802/365–7357 **A**10 18 **F**3
18 29 30 31 34 36 40 50 57 59 64 65 66 68 83 85 90 94 96 97 104 107
119 127 130 132 133 135 146 148
Primary Contact: Roger Allbee, Chief Executive Officer and Administrator
COO: Jeanne M. Fortier, R.N., Chief Nursing Officer and Interim Chief Operating
Officer
CFO: Stephen A. Brown, Chief Financial Officer
CMO: Timothy Shafer, M.D., Medical Director
CIO: Tony Marques, Director Information Systems
CHR: Christopher J. Lackney, Director Human Resources
CNO: Jeanne M. Fortier, R.N., Chief Nursing Officer and Interim Chief Operating
Officer
Web address: www.gracecottage.org
Control: Other not–for–profit (including NFP Corporation) **Service:** General
Medical and Surgical

Staffed Beds: 19 **Admissions:** 372 **Census:** 10 **Outpatient Visits:** 19070
Births: 0 **Total Expense ($000):** 22754 **Payroll Expense ($000):** 10259
Personnel: 148

WHITE RIVER JUNCTION—Windsor County

☒ **WHITE RIVER JUNCTION VETERANS AFFAIRS MEDICAL CENTER**, 215 North
Main Street, Zip 05009–0001; tel. 802/295–9363 **A**1 3 5 8 **F**3 5 8 9 12 18 26
28 29 30 31 33 34 35 36 38 39 40 44 45 46 47 48 49 50 53 54 55 56 57
58 59 60 61 63 64 65 70 74 75 77 78 79 81 82 83 84 85 86 87 89 91 93
94 97 98 100 101 102 103 104 105 106 107 108 111 115 116 117 118
119 127 130 131 132 135 141 143 144 146 147 148 **P**6 **S** Department of
Veterans Affairs, Washington, DC
Primary Contact: Al Montoya, Interim Medical Center Director
CFO: Joan Wilmot, Chief Finance Officer
CMO: M. Ganga Hematillake, M.D., Chief of Staff
CIO: Matthew Rafus, Chief Information Officer
CHR: Barbara Nadeau, Chief Human Resources Management Service
Web address: www.whiteriver.va.gov/
Control: Veterans Affairs, Government, federal **Service:** General Medical and
Surgical

Staffed Beds: 60 **Admissions:** 2426 **Census:** 39 **Outpatient Visits:** 281234
Births: 0

WINDSOR—Windsor County

★ △ **MT. ASCUTNEY HOSPITAL AND HEALTH CENTER (471302)**, 289
County Road, Zip 05089–9000; tel. 802/674–6711 **A**7 10 18 **F**3 8 10 11 15
28 29 30 31 32 34 35 36 40 41 44 45 49 50 54 56 57 59 63 64 65 66 68
69 70 71 75 77 78 79 81 82 84 85 86 87 90 91 92 93 94 95 96 97 99 100
104 107 110 111 114 119 125 129 130 132 133 134 135 143 146 148 **P**6
Primary Contact: Gay L. Landstrom, Ph.D., R.N., Interim Chief Executive Officer
COO: Paul Calandrella, Chief Operating Officer
CFO: David Sanville, Chief Financial Officer
CMO: Joseph Perras, Chief Medical Officer
CIO: Patti Strohla, Director of Clinical Information
CHR: Jean Martaniuk, Director Human Resources
CNO: Deanna Orfanidis, Interim Chief Nursing Officer
Web address: www.mtascutneyhospital.org
Control: Other not–for–profit (including NFP Corporation) **Service:** General
Medical and Surgical

Staffed Beds: 35 **Admissions:** 1088 **Census:** 27 **Outpatient Visits:** 75088
Births: 0 **Total Expense ($000):** 49105 **Payroll Expense ($000):** 23085
Personnel: 351

VT

Many Facility Codes have changed. Please refer to the AHA Guide Code Chart.   © 2016 AHA Guide

VIRGINIA

ABINGDON—Washington County

✠ **JOHNSTON MEMORIAL HOSPITAL (490053)**, 16000 Johnston Memorial Drive, Zip 24211–7659; tel. 276/258–1000 **A**1 2 10 13 **F**3 8 11 13 15 18 20 22 26 28 29 30 31 34 35 39 40 44 45 46 47 48 49 50 51 54 57 59 60 63 64 68 70 74 75 76 77 78 79 81 82 84 85 87 93 97 100 107 108 110 111 115 116 118 119 120 121 123 129 130 132 135 143 144 146 147 148 **S** Mountain States Health Alliance, Johnson City, TN
Primary Contact: Stan Hickson, FACHE, President and Chief Executive Officer
COO: Bryan Mullins, Chief Operating Officer
CFO: John Jeter, Assistant Administrator and Chief Financial Officer
CMO: Brian Condit, M.D., Chief Medical Officer
CIO: Jackson Dale, Director Management Information Services
CHR: Jackie G. Phipps, Director Human Resources
CNO: Nikki VanBuren, Chief Nursing Officer
Web address: www.jmh.org
Control: Other not–for–profit (including NFP Corporation) **Service:** General Medical and Surgical

Staffed Beds: 116 **Admissions:** 9009 **Census:** 81 **Outpatient Visits:** 153604 **Births:** 746 **Total Expense ($000):** 118324 **Payroll Expense ($000):** 34904 **Personnel:** 677

ALDIE—Loudoun County

✠ **HEALTHSOUTH REHABILITATION HOSPITAL OF NORTHERN VIRGINIA (493033)**, 24430 Millstream Drive, Zip 20105–3098; tel. 703/957–2000, (Nonreporting) **A**1 10 **S** HEALTHSOUTH Corporation, Birmingham, AL
Primary Contact: Jason Waibel, Interim Chief Executive Officer
Web address: www.healthsouthnorthernvirginia.com
Control: Corporation, Investor–owned, for–profit **Service:** Rehabilitation

Staffed Beds: 40

ALEXANDRIA—Alexandria City County

✠ **INOVA ALEXANDRIA HOSPITAL (490040)**, 4320 Seminary Road, Zip 22304–1535; tel. 703/504–3167 **A**1 2 5 10 **F**3 11 13 14 15 17 18 20 22 24 26 28 29 30 31 34 35 38 40 42 44 45 46 48 49 50 51 54 55 56 57 58 59 60 61 63 64 65 66 68 70 72 74 75 76 77 78 79 80 81 82 84 85 86 87 91 92 93 100 101 102 107 108 110 111 114 115 117 118 119 120 121 123 124 129 130 131 132 135 145 146 147 148 **P**6 **S** Inova Health System, Falls Church, VA
Primary Contact: Susan Carroll, Chief Executive Officer
CFO: Todd Lockcuff, Chief Financial Officer
CMO: William L. Jackson, Chief Medical Officer
CHR: Hugo Aguas, Vice President Human Resources
Web address: www.inova.org
Control: Other not–for–profit (including NFP Corporation) **Service:** General Medical and Surgical

Staffed Beds: 334 **Admissions:** 16773 **Census:** 209 **Outpatient Visits:** 179111 **Births:** 3619 **Total Expense ($000):** 289401 **Payroll Expense ($000):** 106594 **Personnel:** 1558

✠ **INOVA MOUNT VERNON HOSPITAL (490122)**, 2501 Parker's Lane, Zip 22306–3209; tel. 703/664–7000 **A**1 2 3 5 10 **F**3 4 5 11 14 15 18 26 28 29 30 31 34 35 37 38 39 40 42 44 45 48 49 50 51 53 54 55 57 58 59 60 61 63 64 65 66 68 70 74 75 77 78 79 80 81 82 84 85 86 87 90 91 92 93 94 96 98 100 101 102 103 104 105 107 108 110 111 114 115 118 119 130 131 132 135 145 146 147 148 **P**6 **S** Inova Health System, Falls Church, VA
Primary Contact: Deborah Addo–Samuels, Chief Executive Officer
CFO: Tammy Razmic, Associate Administrator Finance and Chief Financial Officer
CMO: Donald Brideau, M.D., Chief Medical Officer
CHR: Bev Sugar, Associate Administrator and Director Human Resources
Web address: www.inova.org
Control: Other not–for–profit (including NFP Corporation) **Service:** General Medical and Surgical

Staffed Beds: 237 **Admissions:** 8851 **Census:** 144 **Outpatient Visits:** 92628 **Births:** 0 **Total Expense ($000):** 180287 **Payroll Expense ($000):** 65413 **Personnel:** 806

ARLINGTON—Arlington County

CAPITAL HOSPICE (490129), 4715 15th Street North, Zip 22205–2640; tel. 703/538–2065, (Nonreporting) **A**3 10
Primary Contact: Malene S. Davis, R.N., President and Chief Executive Officer
CFO: David Schwind, Chief Financial Officer
CIO: Diane Rigsby, Chief Information Officer
Web address: www.capitalhospice.org
Control: Other not–for–profit (including NFP Corporation) **Service:** Other specialty

Staffed Beds: 15

✠ △ **VIRGINIA HOSPITAL CENTER – ARLINGTON (490050)**, 1701 North George Mason Drive, Zip 22205–3698; tel. 703/558–5000 **A**1 3 5 7 10 **F**3 4 5 8 11 12 13 15 17 18 20 22 24 26 28 29 30 31 34 35 37 38 40 45 46 47 48 49 50 51 54 57 59 60 61 64 65 66 68 70 72 73 74 75 76 77 78 79 81 84 85 86 87 89 90 91 92 93 94 95 96 97 98 100 102 103 104 105 107 110 111 114 115 116 117 118 119 120 121 123 124 126 129 130 132 135 144 145 146 147 148
Primary Contact: James B. Cole, Chief Executive Officer
COO: Carl Bahnlein, Executive Vice President and Chief Operating Officer
CFO: Robin Norman, Senior Vice President and Chief Financial Officer
CMO: Jeffrey P. DiLisi, Vice President and Chief Medical Officer
CIO: Russ McWey, M.D., Vice President and Chief Information Officer
CHR: Michael Malone, Vice President and Chief Human Resources Officer
CNO: Darlene Vrotsos, R.N., Senior Vice President and Chief Nursing Officer
Web address: www.virginiahospitalcenter.com
Control: Other not–for–profit (including NFP Corporation) **Service:** General Medical and Surgical

Staffed Beds: 357 **Admissions:** 22465 **Census:** 277 **Outpatient Visits:** 360267 **Births:** 5640 **Total Expense ($000):** 374376 **Payroll Expense ($000):** 148607 **Personnel:** 2823

BEDFORD—Bedford City County

✠ **BEDFORD MEMORIAL HOSPITAL (490088)**, 1613 Oakwood Street, Zip 24523–1213, Mailing Address: P.O. Box 688, Zip 24523–0688; tel. 540/586–2441, (Total facility includes 111 beds in nursing home–type unit) **A**1 10 **F**2 3 11 15 18 19 28 29 30 34 35 40 42 46 53 57 59 63 67 70 81 84 85 93 97 107 111 119 128 129 130 134 143 145 146 148 **P**6 **S** Centra Health, Inc., Lynchburg, VA
Primary Contact: Patti Jurkus, Chief Executive Officer
CFO: Donald E. Lorton, Executive Vice President
CMO: E. Allen Joslyn, M.D., Chief Medical Officer
Web address: www.bmhva.com
Control: Other not–for–profit (including NFP Corporation) **Service:** General Medical and Surgical

Staffed Beds: 144 **Admissions:** 1790 **Census:** 114 **Outpatient Visits:** 57231 **Births:** 0 **Total Expense ($000):** 38049 **Payroll Expense ($000):** 19087 **Personnel:** 320

BIG STONE GAP—Wise County

✠ **WELLMONT LONESOME PINE HOSPITAL (490114)**, 1990 Holton Avenue East, Zip 24219–3350; tel. 276/523–3111 **A**1 10 13 **F**3 11 15 29 30 31 34 40 45 49 50 57 59 76 77 78 79 80 81 82 85 87 89 93 107 108 110 111 118 119 120 121 129 130 135 146 148 **S** Wellmont Health System, Kingsport, TN
Primary Contact: Dale Clark, President
CFO: Regina Day, Executive Vice President of Finance
CMO: Michael Ketcham, President, Medical Staff
CHR: Bobby Collins, Director Human Resources
CNO: Cindy Stidham, Executive Director of Patient Care Services
Web address: www.wellmont.org
Control: Other not–for–profit (including NFP Corporation) **Service:** General Medical and Surgical

Staffed Beds: 30 **Admissions:** 1339 **Census:** 10 **Outpatient Visits:** 38611 **Births:** 292 **Total Expense ($000):** 39379 **Payroll Expense ($000):** 8236 **Personnel:** 198

VA

Hospital, Medicare Provider Number, Address, Telephone, Approval, Facility, and Physician Codes, Health Care System

★ American Hospital Association (AHA) membership
☐ The Joint Commission accreditation
○ Healthcare Facilities Accreditation Program
◇ DNV Healthcare Inc. accreditation
⇑ Center for Improvement in Healthcare Quality Accreditation
△ Commission on Accreditation of Rehabilitation Facilities (CARF) accreditation

VA

BLACKSBURG—Montgomery County

⊠ **LEWISGALE HOSPITAL MONTGOMERY (490110)**, 3700 South Main Street,
Zip 24060–7081, Mailing Address: P.O. Box 90004, Zip 24062–9004;
tel. 540/951–1111, (Nonreporting) **A**1 10 12 13 **S** HCA, Nashville, TN
Primary Contact: Alan J. Fabian, Chief Executive Officer
COO: Matt Mathias, Chief Operating Officer
CFO: Timothy W. Haasken, Chief Financial Officer
CIO: Diron Lane, Director Information Systems
CNO: Ellen Linkenhoker, Chief Nursing Officer
Web address: www.lewisgale.com
Control: Corporation, Investor–owned, for–profit **Service:** General Medical and
Surgical

Staffed Beds: 103

BRISTOL—Bristol City County

⊠ **REHABILITATION HOSPITAL OF SOUTHWEST VIRGINIA (493034)**, 103 North
Street, Zip 24201–3201; tel. 276/642–7900, (Nonreporting) **A**1 10
S HEALTHSOUTH Corporation, Birmingham, AL
Primary Contact: Georgeanne Cole, Chief Executive Officer
Web address: www.rehabilitationhospitalswvirginia.com
Control: Corporation, Investor–owned, for–profit **Service:** Rehabilitation

Staffed Beds: 25

BURKEVILLE—Nottoway County

PIEDMONT GERIATRIC HOSPITAL (490134), 5001 East Patrick Henry
Highway, Zip 23922–3460, Mailing Address: P.O. Box 427, Zip 23922–0427;
tel. 434/767–4401 **F**39 56 98 103 146 **P**1 **S** Virginia Department of Mental
Health, Richmond, VA
Primary Contact: Stephen M. Herrick, Ph.D., Director
CFO: James G. Ayers, Chief Financial Officer
CMO: Hugo Falcon, M.D., Director Medical Services
CHR: Michael Wimsatt, Director Human Resources
Web address: www.pgh.dmhmrsas.virginia.gov
Control: State–Government, nonfederal **Service:** Psychiatric

Staffed Beds: 135 **Admissions:** 50 **Census:** 114 **Outpatient Visits:** 0 **Births:**
0

CATAWBA—Roanoke County

☐ **CATAWBA HOSPITAL (490135)**, 5525 Catawba Hospital Drive,
Zip 24070–2115, Mailing Address: P.O. Box 200, Zip 24070–0200;
tel. 540/375–4200 **A**1 3 10 **F**29 30 35 38 39 44 50 68 75 77 98 103 130
146 **P**6 **S** Virginia Department of Mental Health, Richmond, VA
Primary Contact: Walton F. Mitchell, III, Director
COO: Charles Law, Ph.D., Chief Operating Officer
CFO: Cecil Hardin, CPA, Chief Financial Officer
CMO: Yad Jabbarpour, M.D., Chief of Staff
CIO: Charles Law, Ph.D., Chief Operating Officer
CHR: Patricia Ebbett, Chief Human Resources Officer
CNO: Vicky Fisher, Ph.D., Chief Nurse Executive
Web address: www.catawba.dbhds.virginia.gov
Control: State–Government, nonfederal **Service:** Psychiatric

Staffed Beds: 110 **Admissions:** 345 **Census:** 103 **Outpatient Visits:** 0
Births: 0 **Total Expense ($000):** 22518 **Payroll Expense ($000):** 12181
Personnel: 265

CHARLOTTESVILLE—Charlottesville City County

★ ◇ **MARTHA JEFFERSON HOSPITAL (490077)**, 500 Martha Jefferson Drive,
Zip 22911–4668; tel. 434/654–7000 **A**2 3 5 10 21 **F**3 8 11 12 13 15 18 20
22 26 28 29 30 31 34 35 36 40 41 42 44 45 46 47 48 49 50 54 55 56 57
58 59 61 64 65 66 68 70 74 75 76 77 78 79 81 82 84 85 86 87 91 92 93
94 97 107 108 110 111 114 115 116 117 118 119 120 121 123 124 129
130 131 132 134 135 141 145 146 147 **P**1 6 **S** Sentara Healthcare,
Norfolk, VA
Primary Contact: Jonathan S. Davis, FACHE, President
COO: Amy Black, R.N., Chief Operating Officer
CFO: J. Michael Burris, Vice President Corporate Services and Chief Financial
Officer
CMO: F. Michael Ashby, M.D., Vice President and Medical Director
CIO: Marijo Lecker, Vice President
CHR: Debbie Desmond, Director Human Resources
Web address: www.marthajefferson.org
Control: Other not–for–profit (including NFP Corporation) **Service:** General
Medical and Surgical

Staffed Beds: 158 **Admissions:** 9440 **Census:** 91 **Outpatient Visits:** 266182
Births: 1686 **Total Expense ($000):** 246130 **Payroll Expense ($000):**
107303 **Personnel:** 1641

⊠ △ **UNIVERSITY OF VIRGINIA MEDICAL CENTER (490009)**, 1215 Lee
Street, Zip 22908–0001, Mailing Address: P.O. Box 800809, Zip 22908–0809;
tel. 434/924–0211, (Includes UNIVERSITY OF VIRGINIA CHILDREN'S HOSPITAL,
1215 Lee Street, Zip 22908, Mailing Address: PO Box 800566, Zip 22908;
tel. 434/243–5500) **A**1 2 3 5 7 8 10 **F**3 4 5 6 7 8 9 11 12 13 15 16 17 18
19 20 21 22 23 24 25 26 27 28 29 30 31 32 34 35 36 37 38 39 40 41 43
44 45 46 47 48 49 50 51 52 54 55 56 57 58 59 60 61 62 63 64 65 66 68
69 70 71 72 73 74 75 76 77 78 79 80 81 82 83 84 85 86 87 88 89 90 91
92 93 94 97 98 99 100 101 102 103 104 107 108 110 111 112 114 115
116 117 118 119 120 121 123 124 126 129 130 131 132 134 135 136 137
138 139 140 141 142 143 145 146 147 148 **P**3 4 **S** UVA Health System,
Charlottesville, VA
Primary Contact: Pamela Sutton–Wallace, Chief Executive Officer
COO: James Amato, Interim Chief Operating Officer
CFO: Nick Mendyka, Chief Financial Officer
CMO: Chris A. Ghaemmaghami, M.D., Chief Medical Officer
CIO: Richard Skinner, Chief Information Technology Officer
CHR: John Boswell, Chief Human Resources Officer
CNO: Tina Mammone, Ph.D., Chief Nursing Officer
Web address: www.healthsystem.virginia.edu
Control: State–Government, nonfederal **Service:** General Medical and Surgical

Staffed Beds: 585 **Admissions:** 27920 **Census:** 457 **Outpatient Visits:**
1900697 **Births:** 1674 **Total Expense ($000):** 1341556 **Payroll Expense
($000):** 458453 **Personnel:** 7316

⊠ **UVA TRANSITIONAL CARE HOSPITAL (492011)**, 2965 Ivy Road (250 West),
Zip 22903–9330; tel. 434/924–7897 **A**1 10 **F**1 3 29 30 60 77 85 94 114 129
130 146 148 **P**3 4 **S** UVA Health System, Charlottesville, VA
Primary Contact: Michelle Hereford, Chief
Web address: www.uvahealth.com/services/transitional–care–hospital
Control: State–Government, nonfederal **Service:** Long–Term Acute Care hospital

Staffed Beds: 40 **Admissions:** 362 **Census:** 30 **Outpatient Visits:** 0 **Births:**
0 **Total Expense ($000):** 19595 **Payroll Expense ($000):** 7998 **Personnel:**
146

⊠ **UVA–HEALTHSOUTH REHABILITATION HOSPITAL (493029)**, 515 Ray C. Hunt
Drive, Zip 22903–2981; tel. 434/244–2000 **A**1 3 5 10 **F**28 29 30 34 54 57 59
64 74 75 77 90 91 93 94 96 131 148 **P**5 **S** HEALTHSOUTH Corporation,
Birmingham, AL
Primary Contact: Thomas J. Cook, Chief Executive Officer
CFO: Dianna Gomez, Chief Financial Officer
CMO: Alan Alfano, Medical Director
CIO: Michael Vanhoy, Director of Quality
CHR: Tonya Loving, Human Resources Director
CNO: Sherry Herring, Chief Nursing Officer
Web address: www.uvahealthsouth.com
Control: Corporation, Investor–owned, for–profit **Service:** Rehabilitation

Staffed Beds: 50 **Admissions:** 1317 **Census:** 43 **Outpatient Visits:** 28826
Births: 0 **Total Expense ($000):** 21309 **Payroll Expense ($000):** 13339
Personnel: 226

CHESAPEAKE—Chesapeake City County

★ ○ **CHESAPEAKE REGIONAL HEALTHCARE (490120)**, 736 Battlefield
Boulevard North, Zip 23320–4941, Mailing Address: P.O. Box 2028,
Zip 23327–2028; tel. 757/312–8121 **A**2 3 10 11 **F**3 6 10 11 12 13 15 18 20
22 24 26 28 29 30 31 34 35 37 40 44 45 46 49 50 53 54 57 58 59 61 62
63 64 65 66 68 69 70 71 73 74 75 76 77 78 79 81 83 84 85 86 87 89 91
93 100 101 102 103 107 108 110 111 114 115 118 119 120 121 123 126
129 130 132 135 141 142 143 146 147 148 **P**6 8
Primary Contact: Alton Stocks, M.D., Interim President and Chief Executive Officer
COO: Alton Stocks, M.D., Chief Operating Officer
CMO: Paul Brainstein, M.D., Interim Chief Medical Officer
CIO: Ken Deans, Chief Information Officer
CHR: Deborah L. Rosenburg, Vice President Human Resources
CNO: Elaine Griffiths, R.N., Chief Nursing Officer
Web address: www.chesapeakeregional.com
Control: Hospital district or authority, Government, nonfederal **Service:** General
Medical and Surgical

Staffed Beds: 310 **Admissions:** 15667 **Census:** 192 **Outpatient Visits:**
177952 **Births:** 2418 **Total Expense ($000):** 260733 **Payroll Expense
($000):** 96708 **Personnel:** 1716

Many Facility Codes have changed. Please refer to the AHA Guide Code Chart. © 2016 AHA Guide

CHRISTIANSBURG—Montgomery County

⊞ **CARILION NEW RIVER VALLEY MEDICAL CENTER (490042)**, 2900 Lamb Circle, Zip 24073–6344, Mailing Address: P.O. Box 5, Radford, Zip 24143–0005; tel. 540/731–2000, (Includes CARILION CLINIC SAINT ALBANS HOSPITAL, 2900 Lamb Circle, tel. 540/731–2000) **A**1 3 10 13 19 **F**3 5 12 13 15 18 20 22 26 28 29 30 31 34 35 36 40 43 45 47 48 49 50 51 53 57 59 60 62 63 64 68 70 74 75 76 77 79 81 82 84 85 86 87 89 91 92 93 96 98 99 102 103 104 105 107 108 110 111 114 115 118 119 126 129 130 131 135 146 147 148 **P**6 **S** Carilion Clinic, Roanoke, VA
Primary Contact: William Flattery, Vice President and Administrator Western Division
CFO: Rob Vaughan, Chief Financial Officer
CMO: Dennis Means, M.D., Vice President Medical Affairs
CIO: Daniel Borchi, Chief Information Officer
CHR: Patti Jurkus, Director Human Resources
Web address: www.carilionclinic.org/Carilion/cnrv
Control: Other not–for–profit (including NFP Corporation) **Service:** General Medical and Surgical

Staffed Beds: 82 **Admissions:** 8170 **Census:** 90 **Outpatient Visits:** 89382 **Births:** 1188 **Total Expense ($000):** 150260 **Payroll Expense ($000):** 55163 **Personnel:** 912

CLINTWOOD—Dickenson County

DICKENSON COMMUNITY HOSPITAL (491303), 312 Hospital Drive, Zip 24228, Mailing Address: P.O. Box 1440, Zip 24228–1440; tel. 276/926–0300 **A**10 18 **F**3 29 40 44 64 87 97 104 107 111 119 130 148 **S** Mountain States Health Alliance, Johnson City, TN
Primary Contact: Mark T. Leonard, Chief Executive Officer
CFO: Kevin Morrison, Chief Financial Officer
CMO: Erin Mullins, D.O., Chief Medical Staff
CHR: Valeri J. Colyer, Director Human Resources
CNO: Terri Roop, Director Patient Care Services
Web address: www.msha.com/dch
Control: Other not–for–profit (including NFP Corporation) **Service:** General Medical and Surgical

Staffed Beds: 1 **Admissions:** 2 **Census:** 1 **Outpatient Visits:** 23895 **Births:** 0 **Total Expense ($000):** 6982 **Payroll Expense ($000):** 2467 **Personnel:** 38

CULPEPER—Culpeper County

⊞ **NOVANT HEALTH UVA HEALTH SYSTEM CULPEPER MEDICAL CENTER (490019)**, 501 Sunset Lane, Zip 22701–3917, Mailing Address: P.O. Box 592, Zip 22701–0500; tel. 540/829–4100 **A**1 3 5 10 **F**3 7 8 11 13 15 18 29 30 31 34 35 36 37 40 45 50 54 57 59 64 70 74 75 76 77 78 79 81 85 87 89 91 93 107 108 110 111 114 115 119 120 121 123 130 132 135 143 146 148 **S** UVA Health System, Charlottesville, VA
Primary Contact: Greg Napps, Chief Executive Officer
COO: Greg Napps, Chief Executive Officer
CFO: David J. Plaviak, Interim Chief Financial Officer
CMO: Morton Chiles, M.D., Chief Medical Officer
CIO: Steven Speelman, Director Information Systems
CHR: Susan Edwards, Vice President Human Resources
Web address: www.culpeperhealth.org
Control: Other not–for–profit (including NFP Corporation) **Service:** General Medical and Surgical

Staffed Beds: 68 **Admissions:** 3245 **Census:** 33 **Outpatient Visits:** 77390 **Births:** 413 **Total Expense ($000):** 79126 **Payroll Expense ($000):** 30457 **Personnel:** 516

DANVILLE—Danville City County

⊞ **DANVILLE REGIONAL MEDICAL CENTER (490075)**, 142 South Main Street, Zip 24541–2922; tel. 434/799–2100, (Nonreporting) **A**1 2 10 12 13 **S** LifePoint Health, Brentwood, TN
Primary Contact: Alan Larson, Chief Executive Officer
CFO: Mark T. Anderson, Chief Financial Officer
CMO: James F. Starling, M.D., Chief Medical Officer
CIO: David Cartwright, Director Management Information Systems
Web address: www.danvilleregional.org
Control: Other not–for–profit (including NFP Corporation) **Service:** General Medical and Surgical

Staffed Beds: 250

SOUTHERN VIRGINIA MENTAL HEALTH INSTITUTE (494017), 382 Taylor Drive

☐ **SOUTHERN VIRGINIA MENTAL HEALTH INSTITUTE (494017)**, 382 Taylor Drive, Zip 24541–4023; tel. 434/799–6220 **A**1 10 **F**75 77 86 87 100 101 102 106 130 132 135 146 **P**6 **S** Virginia Department of Mental Health, Richmond, VA
Primary Contact: William Cook, Director
CFO: Wayne Peters, Administrator
CMO: Pravin Patel, M.D., Acting President and Chief Executive Officer
CIO: Larry Hays, Director Information Technology
CHR: Stephanie Haywood, Director Human Resources
CNO: Kathy M. Dodd, Director of Nursing
Web address: www.svmhi.dbhds.virginia.gov
Control: State–Government, nonfederal **Service:** Psychiatric

Staffed Beds: 72 **Admissions:** 282 **Census:** 59 **Outpatient Visits:** 0 **Births:** 0

EMPORIA—Emporia City County

⊞ **SOUTHERN VIRGINIA REGIONAL MEDICAL CENTER (490097)**, 727 North Main Street, Zip 23847–1274; tel. 434/348–4400 **A**1 10 **F**3 11 15 26 28 29 30 31 40 45 49 50 57 59 62 64 70 77 78 79 81 82 85 93 98 103 107 115 119 124 129 130 133 146 148 **S** Community Health Systems, Inc., Franklin, TN
Primary Contact: Matt Tavenner, Chief Executive Officer
CFO: Jim Porter, Chief Financial Officer
CMO: Fitzgerald Marcelin, M.D., Chief of Staff
CIO: Larry Gold, Vice President, Information Services
CHR: Becky Parrish, Director Human Resources
CNO: Linda Burnette, R.N., Chief Nursing Officer
Web address: www.svrmc.com
Control: Corporation, Investor–owned, for–profit **Service:** General Medical and Surgical

Staffed Beds: 80 **Admissions:** 1636 **Census:** 19 **Outpatient Visits:** 24024 **Births:** 0 **Total Expense ($000):** 31824 **Payroll Expense ($000):** 10884 **Personnel:** 213

FAIRFAX—Fairfax County

⊞ **INOVA FAIR OAKS HOSPITAL (490101)**, 3600 Joseph Siewick Drive, Zip 22033–1798; tel. 703/391–3600 **A**1 2 3 5 10 **F**3 11 12 13 14 15 18 29 30 31 32 34 35 37 38 39 40 44 45 47 48 49 50 51 54 55 57 58 59 60 61 63 64 65 66 68 69 70 72 74 75 76 77 78 79 80 81 82 84 85 86 87 89 91 92 93 100 101 102 107 108 110 111 114 115 118 119 120 121 123 126 129 130 131 132 135 145 146 147 148 **P**6 **S** Inova Health System, Falls Church, VA
Primary Contact: John L. Fitzgerald, Chief Executive Officer
CFO: Jerry Seager, Assistant Vice President and Chief Financial Officer
CMO: G. Michael Lynch, M.D., Chief Medical Officer
CIO: Marshall Ruffin, Chief Information Officer
CHR: Jeanne Robinson, Director Human Resources
Web address: www.inova.org
Control: Other not–for–profit (including NFP Corporation) **Service:** General Medical and Surgical

Staffed Beds: 196 **Admissions:** 13590 **Census:** 123 **Outpatient Visits:** 109150 **Births:** 3746 **Total Expense ($000):** 231102 **Payroll Expense ($000):** 71768 **Personnel:** 996

FALLS CHURCH—Fairfax County

⊞ **DOMINION HOSPITAL (494023)**, 2960 Sleepy Hollow Road, Zip 22044–2030; tel. 703/536–2000, (Nonreporting) **A**1 10 **S** HCA, Nashville, TN
Primary Contact: Lee Higginbotham, Chief Executive Officer
CFO: Edward R. Stojakovich, Chief Financial Officer
CMO: Gary Litovitz, M.D., Medical Director
CIO: Leslie Gilliam, Director Health Information Management
CHR: Lesley Channell, Vice President Human Resources
Web address: www.dominionhospital.com
Control: Corporation, Investor–owned, for–profit **Service:** Psychiatric

Staffed Beds: 100

VA

Hospital, Medicare Provider Number, Address, Telephone, Approval, Facility, and Physician Codes, Health Care System

★ American Hospital Association (AHA) membership
☐ The Joint Commission accreditation
○ Healthcare Facilities Accreditation Program
◇ DNV Healthcare Inc. accreditation
⇑ Center for Improvement in Healthcare Quality Accreditation
△ Commission on Accreditation of Rehabilitation Facilities (CARF) accreditation

☒ **INOVA FAIRFAX HOSPITAL (490063)**, 3300 Gallows Road, Zip 22042–3300; tel. 703/776–4001, (Includes INOVA FAIRFAX HOSPITAL FOR CHILDREN, 3300 Gallows Road, Zip 22042–3307; tel. 703/776–4002) **A**1 2 3 5 8 10 **F**3 4 5 6 8 9 11 12 13 14 15 17 18 19 20 21 22 23 24 25 26 27 28 29 30 31 32 34 35 36 38 39 40 41 42 43 44 45 46 47 48 49 50 51 54 55 56 57 58 59 60 61 63 64 65 68 69 70 71 72 74 75 76 77 78 79 80 81 82 83 84 85 86 87 88 89 91 92 93 94 96 97 98 99 100 101 102 103 104 105 107 108 109 110 111 114 115 118 119 120 121 123 124 126 129 130 131 132 134 135 136 137 138 140 141 142 145 146 147 148 **P**6 **S** Inova Health System, Falls Church, VA
Primary Contact: Patrick Christiansen, Ph.D., Chief Executive Officer
CFO: Ronald Ewald, Chief Financial Officer
CMO: Joseph Hallal, M.D., Chief Medical Officer
CIO: Geoffrey Brown, Vice President Information Systems
CHR: Ken Hull, Director Human Resources
Web address: www.inova.org
Control: Other not–for–profit (including NFP Corporation) **Service:** General Medical and Surgical

> **Staffed Beds:** 935 **Admissions:** 45646 **Census:** 669 **Outpatient Visits:** 293022 **Births:** 8600 **Total Expense ($000):** 1323110 **Payroll Expense ($000):** 489621 **Personnel:** 7639

☐ **NORTHERN VIRGINIA MENTAL HEALTH INSTITUTE (494010)**, 3302 Gallows Road, Zip 22042–3398; tel. 703/207–7110 **A**1 3 5 10 **F**29 30 97 98 101 106 130 132 **S** Virginia Department of Mental Health, Richmond, VA
Primary Contact: James R. Newton, Facility Director
CFO: John Poffenbarger, Director Fiscal Services
CMO: R. Maxilimien del Rio, M.D., Medical Director
CHR: Cynthia Lott, Director Human Resources
Web address: www.nvmhi.dmhmrsas.virginia.gov
Control: State–Government, nonfederal **Service:** Psychiatric

> **Staffed Beds:** 134 **Admissions:** 1059 **Census:** 122 **Outpatient Visits:** 0 **Births:** 0 **Total Expense ($000):** 31680 **Payroll Expense ($000):** 18098

FARMVILLE—Prince Edward County

☒ **CENTRA SOUTHSIDE COMMUNITY HOSPITAL (490090)**, 800 Oak Street, Zip 23901–1199; tel. 434/392–8811 **A**1 5 10 20 **F**3 11 13 15 28 29 30 34 35 40 44 45 49 50 57 59 62 63 64 70 74 75 76 77 79 81 82 85 86 87 89 93 107 108 110 111 115 118 119 129 130 132 133 146 147 148 **P**6 **S** Centra Health, Inc., Lynchburg, VA
Primary Contact: Thomas Angelo, Chief Executive Officer
Web address: www.sch.centrahealth.com/
Control: Other not–for–profit (including NFP Corporation) **Service:** General Medical and Surgical

> **Staffed Beds:** 86 **Admissions:** 3854 **Census:** 32 **Outpatient Visits:** 130321 **Births:** 395 **Total Expense ($000):** 74160 **Payroll Expense ($000):** 34719 **Personnel:** 500

SOUTHSIDE COMMUNITY HOSPITAL See Centra Southside Community Hospital

FISHERSVILLE—Augusta County

☒ **AUGUSTA HEALTH (490018)**, 78 Medical Center Drive, Zip 22939–2332, Mailing Address: P.O. Box 1000, Zip 22939–1000; tel. 540/932–4000 **A**1 2 3 10 **F**3 5 7 11 13 15 18 20 22 26 28 29 30 31 32 34 35 38 40 41 45 46 48 49 50 51 53 54 56 57 58 59 61 62 63 64 65 66 68 70 71 74 75 76 77 78 79 81 82 84 85 86 87 89 90 93 97 98 100 101 102 103 104 107 108 110 111 112 114 115 118 119 120 121 128 129 130 131 132 135 144 146 147 148 **P**6
Primary Contact: Mary N. Mannix, FACHE, President and Chief Executive Officer
CFO: John R. Heider, Vice President Finance
CMO: Fred Castello, M.D., Chief Medical Officer
CIO: Velma Carroll, Chief Information Officer
CHR: Sue Krzastek, Vice President Human Resources
Web address: www.augustahealth.com
Control: Other not–for–profit (including NFP Corporation) **Service:** General Medical and Surgical

> **Staffed Beds:** 224 **Admissions:** 11239 **Census:** 117 **Outpatient Visits:** 708958 **Births:** 1220 **Total Expense ($000):** 292971 **Payroll Expense ($000):** 121426 **Personnel:** 1916

WOODROW WILSON REHABILITATION CENTER, 243 Woodrow Wilson Avenue, Zip 22939, Mailing Address: P.O. Box 1500, Zip 22939–1500; tel. 540/332–7000, (Nonreporting)
Primary Contact: Richard Luck, Ed.D., Facility Director
COO: Richard Luck, Ed.D., Facility Director
CFO: Ernie Steidle, Chief Operating Officer
CMO: Mammen Mathew, M.D., Chief Rehabilitation Medicine
CIO: Keith Burt, Director Marketing
CHR: Debbie Mitchell, Director Human Resources
Web address: www.wwrc.net
Control: State–Government, nonfederal **Service:** Rehabilitation

> **Staffed Beds:** 30

FORT BELVOIR—Fairfax County

☒ **FORT BELVOIR COMMUNITY HOSPITAL**, 9300 Dewitt Loop, Zip 22060–5285; tel. 571/231–3224, (Nonreporting) **A**1 3 5 **S** Department of the Army, Office of the Surgeon General, Falls Church, VA
Primary Contact: Captain Jennifer Vedral–Baron, Commander
CMO: Lieutenant Colonel Mark D. Harris, Deputy Commander Clinical Services
CIO: Terrance Branch, Chief Information Management
Web address: www.fbch.capmed.mil/SitePages/Home.aspx
Control: Army, Government, federal **Service:** General Medical and Surgical

> **Staffed Beds:** 46

FRANKLIN—Franklin City County

☒ **SOUTHAMPTON MEMORIAL HOSPITAL (490092)**, 100 Fairview Drive, Zip 23851–1238, Mailing Address: P.O. Box 817, Zip 23851–0817; tel. 757/569–6100, (Nonreporting) **A**1 10 20 **S** Community Health Systems, Inc., Franklin, TN
Primary Contact: Kimberly W. Marks, Chief Executive Officer
CFO: Steve Ramey, Chief Financial Officer
CMO: Donald Bowling, M.D., Chief Medical Staff
CIO: Kristie Howell, System Information Technology Director
CHR: Loretha Ricks, Human Resources Supervisor
CNO: Laurie Ross, Chief Nursing Officer
Web address: www.smhfranklin.com
Control: Corporation, Investor–owned, for–profit **Service:** General Medical and Surgical

> **Staffed Beds:** 72

FREDERICKSBURG—Fredericksburg City County

☒ **HEALTHSOUTH REHABILITATION HOSPITAL OF FREDERICKSBURG (493032)**, 300 Park Hill Drive, Zip 22401–3387; tel. 540/368–7300, (Nonreporting) **A**1 10 **S** HEALTHSOUTH Corporation, Birmingham, AL
Primary Contact: Gary J. Herbek, Chief Executive Officer
Web address: www.fredericksburgrehabhospital.com
Control: Corporation, Investor–owned, for–profit **Service:** Rehabilitation

> **Staffed Beds:** 40

☒ **MARY WASHINGTON HOSPITAL (490022)**, 1001 Sam Perry Boulevard, Zip 22401–3354; tel. 540/741–1100 **A**1 2 3 5 10 **F**3 5 13 15 18 20 22 24 26 28 29 30 31 34 35 40 42 43 44 45 46 47 48 49 50 54 55 57 58 59 62 64 70 72 74 75 77 78 79 81 83 84 85 86 87 89 92 93 96 98 99 100 101 102 104 105 107 108 111 114 115 118 119 120 121 122 124 126 129 130 132 146 147 148 **P**8 **S** Mary Washington Healthcare, Fredericksburg, VA
Primary Contact: Michael P. McDermott, M.D., President and Chief Executive Officer
COO: Thomas Gettinger, Executive Vice President and Chief Operating Officer
CFO: Sean Barden, Executive Vice President and Chief Financial Officer
CMO: Rebecca Bigoney, Executive Vice President and Chief Medical Officer
CIO: Justin K. Box, Senior Vice President & Chief Information Officer
CHR: Kathryn S. Wall, Executive Vice President, Human Resources and Organizational Development
CNO: Eileen L. Dohmann, R.N., Senior Vice President and Chief Nursing Officer
Web address: www.marywashingtonhealthcare.com
Control: Other not–for–profit (including NFP Corporation) **Service:** General Medical and Surgical

> **Staffed Beds:** 437 **Admissions:** 21847 **Census:** 279 **Outpatient Visits:** 347676 **Births:** 2836 **Total Expense ($000):** 386943 **Payroll Expense ($000):** 118503 **Personnel:** 1617

SNOWDEN AT FREDERICKSBURG, 1200 Sam Perry Boulevard, Zip 22401–4456; tel. 540/741–3900, (Nonreporting)
Primary Contact: Charles Scercy, Corporate Director
Web address: www.marywashingtonhealthcare.com/locations/snowden–at–fredericksburg
Control: Other not–for–profit (including NFP Corporation) **Service:** Psychiatric

> **Staffed Beds:** 30

☒ **SPOTSYLVANIA REGIONAL MEDICAL CENTER (490141)**, 4600 Spotsylvania Parkway, Zip 22408–7762; tel. 540/498–4000, (Nonreporting) **A**1 10 **S** HCA, Nashville, TN
Primary Contact: Michael Clark, Chief Executive Officer
COO: Roberta Tinch, Chief Operations Officer
CFO: David McKnight, CPA, Chief Financial Officer
Web address: www.spotsrmc.com
Control: Corporation, Investor–owned, for–profit **Service:** General Medical and Surgical

> **Staffed Beds:** 100

VA

Many Facility Codes have changed. Please refer to the AHA Guide Code Chart. © 2016 AHA Guide

FRONT ROYAL—Warren County

☒ **WARREN MEMORIAL HOSPITAL (490033)**, 1000 North Shenandoah Avenue, Zip 22630–3598; tel. 540/636–0300, (Total facility includes 120 beds in nursing home–type unit) **A**1 3 10 13 **F**3 11 13 15 28 29 30 34 35 36 40 50 53 54 56 57 59 64 65 67 70 75 76 77 79 81 82 85 86 87 93 96 107 108 111 114 118 119 128 130 132 135 144 146 147 148 **P**6 **S** Valley Health System, Winchester, VA
Primary Contact: Floyd Heater, President and Chief Executive Officer
CFO: Phillip Graybeal, CPA, Chief Financial Officer
CMO: Robert Meltvedt, Jr., M.D., Vice President Medical Affairs
CNO: Terri Wright, Vice President and Chief Nursing Officer
Web address: www.valleyhealthlink.com/WMH
Control: Other not–for–profit (including NFP Corporation) **Service:** General Medical and Surgical

Staffed Beds: 166 **Admissions:** 2699 **Census:** 136 **Outpatient Visits:** 58030 **Births:** 352 **Total Expense ($000):** 55200 **Payroll Expense ($000):** 25012 **Personnel:** 418

GALAX—Galax City County

☒ **TWIN COUNTY REGIONAL HEALTHCARE (490115)**, 200 Hospital Drive, Zip 24333–2227; tel. 276/236–8181, (Nonreporting) **A**1 10 20 **S** Duke LifePoint Healthcare, Brentwood, TN
Primary Contact: Jon D. Applebaum, Chief Executive Officer
CFO: Marita Caldwell, Chief Financial Officer
CIO: Jack Roberts, Director Information Systems
CHR: Kristal Herrington, Senior Director, Human Resources
CNO: Agnes A. Smith, MSN, Chief Nursing Officer
Web address: www.tcrh.org
Control: Other not–for–profit (including NFP Corporation) **Service:** General Medical and Surgical

Staffed Beds: 141

GLOUCESTER—Gloucester County

☐ **RIVERSIDE WALTER REED HOSPITAL (490130)**, 7519 Hospital Drive, Zip 23061–4178, Mailing Address: P.O. Box 1130, Zip 23061–1130; tel. 804/693–8800 **A**1 2 3 10 **F**3 11 15 28 29 35 40 44 45 49 50 51 57 59 63 64 70 75 77 79 81 85 86 87 92 93 107 108 110 111 114 118 119 120 121 123 130 132 146 **P**6 **S** Riverside Health System, Newport News, VA
Primary Contact: Megan Kleckner, Vice President and Administrator
CHR: Tabetha Holt, Director of Human Resources
Web address: www.riversideonline.com
Control: Other not–for–profit (including NFP Corporation) **Service:** General Medical and Surgical

Staffed Beds: 28 **Admissions:** 2691 **Census:** 28 **Outpatient Visits:** 80340 **Births:** 0 **Total Expense ($000):** 60973 **Payroll Expense ($000):** 17913 **Personnel:** 315

GRUNDY—Buchanan County

☒ **BUCHANAN GENERAL HOSPITAL (490127)**, 1535 Slate Creek Road, Zip 24614–6974; tel. 276/935–1000 **A**1 10 20 **F**3 15 18 28 29 30 34 35 40 41 45 57 59 62 64 70 81 82 85 87 89 93 107 108 110 115 119 130 132 135 146 148
Primary Contact: Robert D. Ruchti, Chief Executive Officer
COO: Scott M. Pittman, Chief Operating Officer
CFO: Kim Boyd, Chief Financial Officer
CIO: Rita Ramey, Director Information Systems
CHR: Wanda Stiltner, Director Human Resources
CNO: Patty Dorton, Director of Nursing
Web address: www.bgh.org
Control: Other not–for–profit (including NFP Corporation) **Service:** General Medical and Surgical

Staffed Beds: 49 **Admissions:** 1150 **Census:** 14 **Outpatient Visits:** 45620 **Births:** 0 **Total Expense ($000):** 22581 **Payroll Expense ($000):** 8731 **Personnel:** 205

HAMPTON—Hampton City County

☒ **HAMPTON VETERANS AFFAIRS MEDICAL CENTER**, 100 Emancipation Drive, Zip 23667–0001; tel. 757/722–9961, (Nonreporting) **A**1 3 5 **S** Department of Veterans Affairs, Washington, DC
Primary Contact: Michael H. Dunfee, Director
COO: Lorraine B. Price, Associate Director
CFO: Terry Grew, Chief Business Office
CMO: Val Gibberman, M.D., Acting Chief of Staff
CIO: Cary Parks, Chief Information Resource Management
Web address: www.hampton.va.gov/
Control: Veterans Affairs, Government, federal **Service:** General Medical and Surgical

Staffed Beds: 395

★ ◇ **SENTARA CAREPLEX HOSPITAL (490093)**, 3000 Coliseum Drive, Zip 23666–5963; tel. 757/736–1000 **A**2 3 5 10 21 **F**3 8 11 12 15 18 20 22 26 28 29 30 31 34 35 36 37 38 39 40 41 42 44 45 46 47 48 49 50 54 55 56 57 58 59 60 61 62 63 64 65 68 70 74 75 77 78 79 81 82 84 85 86 87 91 92 93 94 96 97 100 102 107 108 110 111 114 118 119 120 121 123 126 129 130 131 132 135 141 144 146 147 148 **P**6 **S** Sentara Healthcare, Norfolk, VA
Primary Contact: Debra A. Flores, R.N., MS, President and Administrator
COO: Chet Hart, Vice President Operations
CFO: Cheryl Larner, Chief Financial Officer
CMO: Arthur Greene, M.D., Vice President Medical Affairs
CIO: Thomas Ewing, Director Information Technology
CHR: David Kidd, Manager Human Resources
Web address: www.sentara.com
Control: Other not–for–profit (including NFP Corporation) **Service:** General Medical and Surgical

Staffed Beds: 144 **Admissions:** 8469 **Census:** 108 **Outpatient Visits:** 433642 **Births:** 0 **Total Expense ($000):** 204754 **Payroll Expense ($000):** 82920 **Personnel:** 1303

☒ **U. S. AIR FORCE HOSPITAL**, 77 Nealy Avenue, Zip 23665–2040; tel. 757/764–6969, (Nonreporting) **A**1 **S** Department of the Air Force, Washington, DC
Primary Contact: Colonel Wayne M. Pritt, Commander
COO: Colonel Michael Dietz, Administrator
CFO: Major Steven Dadd, Flight Commander Resource Management
CMO: Colonel Paul Gourley, M.D., Chief Hospital Services
CIO: Major Merlinda Vergonio, Chief Information Management and Technology
CHR: Major Steven Dadd, Flight Commander Resource Management
CNO: Colonel Marlene Kerchenski, Chief Nurse
Web address: www.jble.af.mil
Control: Air Force, Government, federal **Service:** General Medical and Surgical

Staffed Beds: 65

HARRISONBURG—Harrisonburg City County

★ ◇ **SENTARA RMH MEDICAL CENTER (490004)**, 2010 Health Campus Drive, Zip 22801–3293; tel. 540/689–1000 **A**2 5 10 21 **F**3 5 8 11 12 13 15 17 18 20 21 24 26 28 29 30 31 32 34 35 36 40 41 44 45 46 47 48 49 50 53 54 55 56 57 59 62 63 64 65 66 68 70 71 73 74 76 77 78 79 81 82 84 85 86 87 89 93 97 98 100 102 104 105 107 108 110 111 114 115 116 117 118 119 120 121 129 130 131 132 135 141 144 145 146 147 148 **P**6 8 **S** Sentara Healthcare, Norfolk, VA
Primary Contact: James D. Krauss, President
COO: Richard L. Haushalter, Senior Vice President Operations and Chief Operating Officer
CFO: J. Michael Burris, Chief Financial Officer
CMO: Susan McDonald, Vice President, Medical Affairs
CNO: Donna S. Hahn, R.N., Vice President Acute Care and Chief Nurse Executive
Web address: www.rmhonline.com
Control: Other not–for–profit (including NFP Corporation) **Service:** General Medical and Surgical

Staffed Beds: 244 **Admissions:** 13482 **Census:** 136 **Outpatient Visits:** 430353 **Births:** 1750 **Total Expense ($000):** 362535 **Payroll Expense ($000):** 148039 **Personnel:** 2637

HAYMARKET—Prince William County

☒ **NOVANT HEALTH UVA HEALTH SYSTEM HAYMARKET MEDICAL CENTER (490144)**, 15225 Heathcote Boulevard, Zip 20155–4023, Mailing Address: 14535 John Marshall Highway, Gainesville, Zip 20155–4023; tel. 571/284–1000 **A**1 10 **F**3 8 11 13 15 18 29 30 34 35 37 40 44 45 46 47 49 50 56 57 58 59 60 63 64 65 70 74 75 76 78 79 81 84 85 87 93 97 100 102 107 108 110 111 114 119 130 131 132 135 141 146 147 **P**6 **S** Novant Health, Winston Salem, NC
Primary Contact: Don Sedgley, President
CNO: Jason Jenkins, Senior Director of Nursing
Web address: www.novanthealth.org
Control: Other not–for–profit (including NFP Corporation) **Service:** General Medical and Surgical

Staffed Beds: 18 **Admissions:** 2290 **Census:** 18 **Outpatient Visits:** 120309 **Births:** 562 **Total Expense ($000):** 52863 **Payroll Expense ($000):** 17979 **Personnel:** 247

VA

Hospital, Medicare Provider Number, Address, Telephone, Approval, Facility, and Physician Codes, Health Care System

★ American Hospital Association (AHA) membership   ○ Healthcare Facilities Accreditation Program   ⇑ Center for Improvement in Healthcare Quality Accreditation
☐ The Joint Commission accreditation   ◇ DNV Healthcare Inc. accreditation   △ Commission on Accreditation of Rehabilitation Facilities (CARF) accreditation

HOPEWELL—Hopewell City County

⊞ **JOHN RANDOLPH MEDICAL CENTER (490020)**, 411 West Randolph Road, Zip 23860–2938; tel. 804/541–1600, (Nonreporting) **A**1 2 10 **S** HCA, Nashville, TN
Primary Contact: Suzanne B. Jackson, FACHE, Chief Executive Officer
CFO: Chigger Bynum, Chief Financial Officer
CHR: MaDena DuChemin, Assistant Administrator Human Resources
Web address: www.johnrandolphmed.com
Control: Corporation, Investor–owned, for–profit **Service:** General Medical and Surgical

Staffed Beds: 118

HOT SPRINGS—Bath County

⊞ **BATH COMMUNITY HOSPITAL (491300)**, 83 Park Drive, Zip 24445–2788, Mailing Address: P.O. Box Z., Zip 24445–0750; tel. 540/839–7000, (Nonreporting) **A**1 10 18
Primary Contact: Kathy Landreth, Interim Chief Executive Officer
COO: Mitzi Grey, Chief Operating Officer
CMO: James Redington, M.D., Chief of Staff
CIO: Tracy Bartley, Manager Information Technology
CHR: Patricia Foutz, Director Human Resources
CNO: Kyna Moore, R.N., Director of Nursing
Web address: www.bcchospital.org
Control: Other not–for–profit (including NFP Corporation) **Service:** General Medical and Surgical

Staffed Beds: 25

KILMARNOCK—Lancaster County

⊞ **RAPPAHANNOCK GENERAL HOSPITAL (490123)**, 101 Harris Drive, Zip 22482–3880, Mailing Address: P.O. Box 1449, Zip 22482–1449; tel. 804/435–8000, (Nonreporting) **A**1 10 20 **S** Bon Secours Health System, Inc., Marriottsville, MD
Primary Contact: Mark M. Gordon, Chief Executive Officer
Web address: www.rgh–hospital.com
Control: Other not–for–profit (including NFP Corporation) **Service:** General Medical and Surgical

Staffed Beds: 76

LEBANON—Russell County

☐ **RUSSELL COUNTY MEDICAL CENTER (490002)**, 58 Carroll Street, Zip 24266, Mailing Address: P.O. Box 3600, Zip 24266–0200; tel. 276/883–8000 **A**1 10 **F**3 11 15 29 30 34 40 44 45 50 56 57 59 62 63 64 68 70 75 78 81 85 87 93 98 99 100 101 102 103 104 107 108 110 111 114 118 119 127 129 130 133 146 147 148 **S** Mountain States Health Alliance, Johnson City, TN
Primary Contact: Stephen K. Givens, Assistant Vice President and Administrator
CFO: John Jeter, Chief Financial Officer
CMO: Brian Condit, M.D., Vice President Chief Medical Officer, Virginia Operations Medical Staff Services
CHR: Beth Hill, Director Human Resources
CNO: Shannon Fullen–Roberts, Chief Nursing Officer
Web address: www.mountainstateshealth.com/rcmc
Control: Other not–for–profit (including NFP Corporation) **Service:** General Medical and Surgical

Staffed Beds: 78 Admissions: 1986 Census: 25 Outpatient Visits: 25776 Births: 0 Total Expense ($000): 21075 Payroll Expense ($000): 8050 Personnel: 159

LEESBURG—Loudoun County

⊞ **INOVA LOUDOUN HOSPITAL (490043)**, 44045 Riverside Parkway, Zip 20176–5101, Mailing Address: P.O. Box 6000, Zip 20177–0600; tel. 703/858–6000, (Total facility includes 100 beds in nursing home–type unit) **A**1 2 5 10 **F**3 5 11 13 14 15 18 20 22 26 28 29 30 31 34 35 37 38 39 40 41 42 44 45 48 49 50 54 55 57 58 59 60 61 63 64 65 66 67 68 70 71 72 74 75 76 77 78 79 80 81 82 84 85 86 87 89 91 92 93 96 98 100 101 102 103 104 105 107 108 110 111 114 115 118 119 120 121 123 126 128 130 131 132 135 145 146 147 148 **P**6 **S** Inova Health System, Falls Church, VA
Primary Contact: Patrick Walters, Chief Executive Officer
CFO: William Bane, Chief Financial Officer
CMO: Christopher Chiantella, M.D., Chief Medical Officer
CHR: Sarah Pavik, Director Human Resources and Guest Services
CNO: Elizabeth Dugan, Ph.D., Chief Nursing Officer
Web address: www.inova.org
Control: Other not–for–profit (including NFP Corporation) **Service:** General Medical and Surgical

Staffed Beds: 286 Admissions: 13294 Census: 222 Outpatient Visits: 141360 Births: 2795 Total Expense ($000): 248277 Payroll Expense ($000): 86314 Personnel: 1442

LEXINGTON—Lexington City County

⊞ **CARILION STONEWALL JACKSON HOSPITAL (491304)**, 1 Health Circle, Zip 24450–2492; tel. 540/458–3300 **A**1 10 18 **F**3 8 11 15 18 19 28 29 30 34 35 40 45 50 53 56 57 59 65 68 70 75 77 79 81 85 87 91 93 97 107 108 110 111 115 119 129 130 131 132 133 135 146 148 **P**6 **S** Carilion Clinic, Roanoke, VA
Primary Contact: Charles E. Carr, Vice President and Administrator
CMO: Lyle McClung, M.D., Chief of Staff
Web address: www.carilionclinic.org/Carilion/csjh
Control: Other not–for–profit (including NFP Corporation) **Service:** General Medical and Surgical

Staffed Beds: 15 Admissions: 1309 Census: 15 Outpatient Visits: 29818 Births: 0 Total Expense ($000): 28498 Payroll Expense ($000): 9885 Personnel: 194

LOW MOOR—Alleghany County

⊞ **LEWISGALE HOSPITAL ALLEGHANY (490126)**, One ARH Lane, Zip 24457, Mailing Address: P.O. Box 7, Zip 24457–0007; tel. 540/862–6011, (Nonreporting) **A**1 10 20 **S** HCA, Nashville, TN
Primary Contact: Charlotte C. Tyson, Chief Executive Officer
CMO: Michele Ballou, M.D., Chief Medical Staff
CIO: Jeffrey Steelman, Director Information Systems
CHR: Bernard M. Campbell, Administrator Human Resources
CNO: Robin Broughman, R.N., Chief Nursing Officer
Web address: www.alleghanyregional.com
Control: Corporation, Investor–owned, for–profit **Service:** General Medical and Surgical

Staffed Beds: 146

LURAY—Page County

⊞ **PAGE MEMORIAL HOSPITAL (491307)**, 200 Memorial Drive, Zip 22835–1005; tel. 540/743–4561 **A**1 10 18 **F**3 7 8 11 15 28 29 30 34 35 40 43 53 56 57 59 60 64 66 68 74 75 77 79 81 85 90 93 107 108 110 111 114 119 127 128 129 130 133 135 143 146 **P**2 **S** Valley Health System, Winchester, VA
Primary Contact: N. Travis Clark, President
CFO: Phillip Graybeal, CPA, Chief Financial Officer
Web address: www.valleyhealthlink.com/page
Control: Other not–for–profit (including NFP Corporation) **Service:** General Medical and Surgical

Staffed Beds: 25 Admissions: 738 Census: 12 Outpatient Visits: 81907 Births: 0 Total Expense ($000): 25016 Payroll Expense ($000): 13383 Personnel: 189

LYNCHBURG—Lynchburg City County

CENTRA HEALTH See Centra Lynchburg General Hospital

☐ **CENTRA LYNCHBURG GENERAL HOSPITAL (490021)**, 1920 Atherholt Road, Zip 24501–1104; tel. 434/200–4700, (Includes CENTRA VIRGINIA BAPTIST HOSPITAL, 3300 Rivermont Avenue, Zip 24503–2053; tel. 434/200–4000; LYNCHBURG GENERAL HOSPITAL, 1901 Tate Springs Road, Zip 24501–1167; tel. 434/200–3000), (Total facility includes 433 beds in nursing home–type unit) **A**1 2 3 5 10 20 **F**2 3 4 5 7 10 11 19 20 22 24 26 29 30 31 34 35 37 38 40 42 43 44 45 46 47 48 49 50 53 54 55 56 57 59 60 61 62 63 64 67 68 70 71 72 73 74 75 76 77 78 79 80 81 82 84 85 86 87 89 90 91 92 93 94 96 98 99 100 101 102 103 104 105 106 107 108 110 111 114 115 119 120 121 123 124 125 126 127 128 129 130 131 132 133 135 143 144 146 147 148 **P**7 **S** Centra Health, Inc., Lynchburg, VA
Primary Contact: E. W. Tibbs, President and Chief Executive Officer
CFO: Lewis C. Addison, Senior Vice President and Chief Financial Officer
CMO: Chalmers Nunn, M.D., Chief Medical Officer and Senior Vice President
CIO: Ben Clark, Vice President and Chief Information Officer
CHR: Jan Walker, Director Human Resources
Web address: www.centrahealth.com
Control: Other not–for–profit (including NFP Corporation) **Service:** General Medical and Surgical

Staffed Beds: 1045 Admissions: 29651 Census: 753 Outpatient Visits: 588281 Births: 2697 Total Expense ($000): 716612 Payroll Expense ($000): 316331 Personnel: 4916

CENTRA SPECIALTY HOSPITAL (492010), 3300 Rivermont Avenue, Zip 24503–2030; tel. 434/200–1799 **A**10 **F**1 3 29 31 68 75 82 85 100 130 148 **P**6
Primary Contact: Kay Bowling, Chief Executive Officer
Control: Other not–for–profit (including NFP Corporation) **Service:** Long–Term Acute Care hospital

Staffed Beds: 36 Admissions: 267 Census: 22 Outpatient Visits: 0 Births: 0 Total Expense ($000): 9782 Payroll Expense ($000): 4108 Personnel: 62

VA

Many Facility Codes have changed. Please refer to the AHA Guide Code Chart.
© 2016 AHA Guide

MADISON HEIGHTS—Amherst County

CENTRAL VIRGINIA TRAINING CENTER (490108), 210 East Colony Road, Zip 24572–2005, Mailing Address: P.O. Box 1098, Lynchburg, Zip 24505–1098; tel. 434/947–6326, (Nonreporting) **A**10 **S** Virginia Department of Mental Health, Richmond, VA
Primary Contact: Denise D. Micheletti, R.N., Director
COO: Denise D. Micheletti, R.N., Director
CFO: Charles Felmlee, Assistant Director Fiscal Services
CMO: Balraj Bawa, M.D., Assistant Director Medical Services
CHR: Burchkhard Blob, Manager Human Resources
Web address: www.cvtc.dmhmrsas.virginia.gov/
Control: State–Government, nonfederal **Service:** Intellectual disabilities

Staffed Beds: 1112

MANASSAS—Manassas City County

NOVANT HEALTH UVA HEALTH SYSTEM PRINCE WILLIAM MEDICAL CENTER (490045), 8700 Sudley Road, Zip 20110–4418, Mailing Address: P.O. Box 2610, Zip 20108–0867; tel. 703/369–8000 **A**1 2 3 10 **F**3 5 8 10 11 13 15 18 19 20 22 26 28 29 30 31 32 34 35 36 37 38 39 40 44 45 46 47 48 49 50 53 54 57 59 64 65 70 71 72 75 76 77 78 79 81 82 84 85 86 87 89 93 97 98 100 101 102 103 104 107 108 110 111 114 115 116 117 118 119 120 121 123 126 129 130 131 132 134 135 141 146 147 148 **P**6 **S** Novant Health, Winston Salem, NC
Primary Contact: Melissa Robson, President
COO: Bebe Holt, Vice President Chief Operating Officer
CMO: Doug Wall, M.D., Vice President Medical Affairs
CHR: Tracy Bowers, Director Human Resources
CNO: Bebe Holt, Vice President and Chief Nursing Officer
Web address: www.pwhs.org
Control: Other not–for–profit (including NFP Corporation) **Service:** General Medical and Surgical

Staffed Beds: 90 **Admissions:** 7613 **Census:** 83 **Outpatient Visits:** 241224 **Births:** 1461 **Total Expense ($000):** 154374 **Payroll Expense ($000):** 55508 **Personnel:** 919

MARION—Smyth County

SMYTH COUNTY COMMUNITY HOSPITAL (490038), 245 Medical Park Drive, Zip 24354, Mailing Address: P.O. Box 880, Zip 24354–0880; tel. 276/378–1000, (Total facility includes 109 beds in nursing home–type unit) **A**1 10 **F**2 3 11 15 18 28 29 30 31 34 35 40 45 50 51 54 57 59 62 64 67 68 70 75 77 78 79 81 85 87 90 93 97 107 110 111 115 118 119 128 129 130 131 132 133 135 146 147 148 **S** Mountain States Health Alliance, Johnson City, TN
Primary Contact: Stan Hickson, FACHE, President and Chief Executive Officer
CFO: John Jeter, Assistant Vice President and Chief Financial Officer
CHR: Sue Henderson, Human Resource Manager
CNO: Cathy L. Maine, MSN, RN–B, Chief Nursing Officer and Assistant Administrator
Web address: www.msha.com/scch
Control: Other not–for–profit (including NFP Corporation) **Service:** General Medical and Surgical

Staffed Beds: 153 **Admissions:** 1962 **Census:** 112 **Outpatient Visits:** 63020 **Births:** 0 **Total Expense ($000):** 37667 **Payroll Expense ($000):** 12928 **Personnel:** 293

SOUTHWESTERN VIRGINIA MENTAL HEALTH INSTITUTE (490105), 340 Bagley Circle, Zip 24354–3390; tel. 276/783–1200, (Nonreporting) **A**1 10 **S** Virginia Department of Mental Health, Richmond, VA
Primary Contact: Cynthia McClaskey, Ph.D., Director
CIO: Kim Ratliff, Director Health Information Management
Web address: www.swvmhi.dmhmrsas.virginia.gov/
Control: State–Government, nonfederal **Service:** Psychiatric

Staffed Beds: 266

MARTINSVILLE—Martinsville City County

MEMORIAL HOSPITAL (490079), 320 Hospital Drive, Zip 24112–1981, Mailing Address: P.O. Box 4788, Zip 24115–4788; tel. 276/666–7200 **A**1 2 10 19 **F**3 11 13 15 18 20 22 23 24 26 28 29 30 31 34 35 37 40 43 45 46 47 50 57 59 60 62 63 64 70 74 75 76 77 78 79 81 82 85 86 87 93 94 96 97 98 102 103 104 107 108 109 110 111 114 117 118 119 120 121 123 129 130 131 132 135 146 147 148 **P**6 7 **S** LifePoint Health, Brentwood, TN
Primary Contact: Michael Ehrat, Chief Executive Officer
CFO: Brandy Hanners, Chief Financial Officer
CIO: Jeff Butker, Chief Information Officer
CHR: Sherry Schofield, Director Human Resources
CNO: Michael Pittman, Chief Nursing Officer
Web address: www.martinsvillehospital.com
Control: Corporation, Investor–owned, for–profit **Service:** General Medical and Surgical

Staffed Beds: 150 **Admissions:** 5440 **Census:** 58 **Outpatient Visits:** 78864 **Births:** 403 **Total Expense ($000):** 92666 **Payroll Expense ($000):** 29521 **Personnel:** 784

MECHANICSVILLE—Hanover County

BON SECOURS MEMORIAL REGIONAL MEDICAL CENTER (490069), 8260 Atlee Road, Zip 23116–1844; tel. 804/764–6000, (Nonreporting) **A**1 2 3 5 10 **S** Bon Secours Health System, Inc., Marriottsville, MD
Primary Contact: Mark M. Gordon, Chief Executive Officer
COO: Gary A. Welch, Assistant to the Chief Executive Officer and Administrative Director Support Systems
CFO: Stephan F. Quiriconi, Vice President Finance
CMO: Sunil K. Sinha, M.D., Chief Medical Officer
CIO: Gwen Harding, Site Manager Information Systems
CHR: Rebecca Kamguia, Administrative Director Human Resources
CNO: Jill M. Kennedy, R.N., Vice President, Ambulatory Patient Care Services
Web address: www.bonsecours.com
Control: Other not–for–profit (including NFP Corporation) **Service:** General Medical and Surgical

Staffed Beds: 225

SHELTERING ARMS REHABILITATION HOSPITAL (493025), 8254 Atlee Road, Zip 23116–1844; tel. 804/764–1000 **A**1 3 10 **F**29 30 34 53 54 57 59 64 68 75 77 79 82 86 87 90 91 92 93 95 96 130 132 143 146 148 **P**6
Primary Contact: Mary A. Zweifel, President and Chief Executive Officer
CFO: James Litsinger, Vice President and Chief Financial Officer
CMO: Hillary Hawkins, M.D., Medical Director
CIO: Chris Sorenson, Chief Information Officer
CHR: Ellen B. Vance, Chief Human Resource Officer
CNO: Sandra Eyler, MS, Chief Nursing Officer
Web address: www.shelteringarms.com
Control: Other not–for–profit (including NFP Corporation) **Service:** Rehabilitation

Staffed Beds: 40 **Admissions:** 864 **Census:** 35 **Outpatient Visits:** 75090 **Births:** 0 **Total Expense ($000):** 37101 **Payroll Expense ($000):** 20695 **Personnel:** 163

MIDLOTHIAN—Chesterfield County

BON SECOURS ST. FRANCIS MEDICAL CENTER (490136), 13710 St. Francis Boulevard, Zip 23114–3267; tel. 804/594–7300 **A**1 2 3 5 10 **F**3 8 11 13 15 17 18 20 22 26 28 29 30 31 34 35 40 45 46 50 54 55 57 59 60 61 64 65 68 70 72 74 75 76 78 79 81 84 85 86 87 94 107 108 109 111 115 117 118 119 120 121 123 126 130 135 146 147 148 **S** Bon Secours Health System, Inc., Marriottsville, MD
Primary Contact: Chris Accashian, Chief Executive Officer
COO: Toni R. Ardabell, Chief Executive Officer, Bon Secours Virginia
CFO: Stephan F. Quiriconi, Vice President, Finance
CMO: John McCurley, M.D., Chief Medical Officer
CIO: Terri Spence, Vice President and Regional Chief Information Officer
CHR: James C. Godwin, Jr., Vice President, Human Resources
CNO: Barbara L. Gesme, MSN, Vice President Patient Care Services & Chief Nurse Executive
Web address: www.bonsecours.com/sfmc/default.asp
Control: Other not–for–profit (including NFP Corporation) **Service:** General Medical and Surgical

Staffed Beds: 124 **Admissions:** 9724 **Census:** 101

VA

☐ **SHELTERING ARMS HOSPITAL SOUTH (493030)**, 13700 St. Francis Boulevard, Suite 400, Zip 23114–3222; tel. 804/764–1000 **A**1 5 10 **F**29 30 34 53 54 57 59 64 75 77 79 82 86 87 90 91 92 93 95 96 130 132 143 146 148 **P**6
Primary Contact: Mary A. Zweifel, President and Chief Executive Officer
CFO: James Litsinger, President and Chief Financial Officer
CMO: Timothy Silver, M.D., Medical Director
CIO: Chris Sorenson, Chief Information Officer
CHR: Ellen B. Vance, Chief Human Resources Officer
CNO: Sandra Eyler, MS, Chief Nursing Officer
Web address: www.shelteringarms.com
Control: Other not–for–profit (including NFP Corporation) **Service:** Rehabilitation

Staffed Beds: 28 **Admissions:** 633 **Census:** 21 **Outpatient Visits:** 6743 **Births:** 0 **Total Expense ($000):** 11250 **Payroll Expense ($000):** 5491 **Personnel:** 78

NASSAWADOX—Northampton County

✠ **RIVERSIDE SHORE MEMORIAL HOSPITAL (490037)**, 9507 Hospital Avenue, Zip 23413–1821, Mailing Address: P.O. Box 17, Zip 23413–0017; tel. 757/414–8000 **A**1 2 3 10 20 **F**3 11 18 28 29 30 31 34 40 45 49 50 51 59 64 70 74 75 76 77 78 79 81 85 93 107 110 114 118 119 121 130 132 146 **P**6 **S** Riverside Health System, Newport News, VA
Primary Contact: John Peterman, Vice President and Administrator
CFO: W. William Austin, Jr., Senior Vice President Finance
CMO: David Jones, Service Chief
CHR: Nicole Miller, Director Human Resources
Web address: www.riversideonline.com
Control: Other not–for–profit (including NFP Corporation) **Service:** General Medical and Surgical

Staffed Beds: 29 **Admissions:** 2681 **Census:** 25 **Outpatient Visits:** 85480 **Births:** 387 **Total Expense ($000):** 60816 **Payroll Expense ($000):** 18412 **Personnel:** 300

SHORE MEMORIAL HOSPITAL See Riverside Shore Memorial Hospital

NEW KENT—New Kent County

☐ **CUMBERLAND HOSPITAL (493300)**, 9407 Cumberland Road, Zip 23124–2029; tel. 804/966–2242, (Nonreporting) **A**1 10 **S** Universal Health Services, Inc., King of Prussia, PA
Primary Contact: Patrice Gay Brooks, Chief Executive Officer
CFO: Joanne Rial, Chief Financial Officer
CMO: Daniel N. Davidow, M.D., Medical Director
CIO: Leslie Bowery, Director of Standards and Compliance
CHR: Kim Ivey, Director of Human Resources
CNO: Paula Roberts, Chief Nursing Officer
Web address: www.cumberlandhospital.com
Control: Corporation, Investor–owned, for–profit **Service:** Children's rehabilitation

Staffed Beds: 132

NEWPORT NEWS—Newport News City County

☐ **HAMPTON ROADS SPECIALTY HOSPITAL (492008)**, 245 Chesapeake Avenue, Zip 23607–6038; tel. 757/534–5000, (Nonreporting) **A**1 10 **S** Riverside Health System, Newport News, VA
Primary Contact: Courtney Detwiler, R.N., Administrator
Web address: www.hamptonroadsspecialtyhospital.com
Control: Other not–for–profit (including NFP Corporation) **Service:** Long–Term Acute Care hospital

Staffed Beds: 25

KEYSTONE NEWPORT NEWS, 17579 Warwick Boulevard, Zip 23603–1343; tel. 757/888–0400 **F**29 32 50 75 98 99 101 106 132 143
Primary Contact: Paul Kirkham, Chief Executive Officer
COO: Paul Kirkham, Chief Executive Officer
CFO: Joe Brooks, Chief Financial Officer
CMO: Avtar Dhillon, M.D., Medical Director
CIO: Gene Yelton, Director Support Services
CHR: Shawn Marston, Director Human Resources
CNO: Karen Bruce, Director of Nursing
Web address: www.newportnewsbhc.com/
Control: Corporation, Investor–owned, for–profit **Service:** Psychiatric

Staffed Beds: 132 **Admissions:** 432 **Census:** 101 **Outpatient Visits:** 0 **Births:** 0 **Total Expense ($000):** 16974 **Payroll Expense ($000):** 7908 **Personnel:** 201

✠ **MARY IMMACULATE HOSPITAL (490041)**, 2 Bernardine Drive, Zip 23602–4499; tel. 757/886–6000, (Includes ST. FRANCIS NURSING CENTER), (Total facility includes 115 beds in nursing home–type unit) **A**1 10 **F**3 5 11 12 13 15 18 20 22 24 26 28 29 30 31 32 34 35 36 37 38 40 44 45 46 50 51 57 59 61 63 64 67 68 70 71 73 74 75 76 77 78 79 81 82 84 85 86 87 91 93 102 107 108 111 114 118 119 130 131 132 143 145 146 147 148 **P**6 **S** Bon Secours Health System, Inc., Marriottsville, MD
Primary Contact: Darlene Stephenson, Chief Executive Officer
COO: Darlene Stephenson, Vice President Operations
CIO: Terri Spence, Vice President Information Services
CHR: Vickie Witcher Humphries, Vice President Human Resources
CNO: Jeffrey N. Doucette, R.N., Chief Nursing Officer
Web address: www.bonsecourshamptonroads.com
Control: Other not–for–profit (including NFP Corporation) **Service:** General Medical and Surgical

Staffed Beds: 238 **Admissions:** 8663 **Census:** 168 **Outpatient Visits:** 59334 **Births:** 1575 **Total Expense ($000):** 165250 **Payroll Expense ($000):** 46853 **Personnel:** 931

☐ **RIVERSIDE REGIONAL MEDICAL CENTER (490052)**, 500 J. Clyde Morris Boulevard, Zip 23601–1929; tel. 757/594–2000, (Includes RIVERSIDE PSYCHIATRIC INSTITUTE ; RIVERSIDE BEHAVIORAL HEALTH CENTER, 2244 Executive Drive, Hampton, Zip 23666–2430; tel. 757/827–1001; Debra Campbell, R.N., Administrator) **A**1 2 3 5 10 13 **F**3 4 8 11 12 13 15 18 20 22 24 26 28 30 31 36 38 40 43 44 45 49 50 51 54 56 58 60 64 70 72 74 75 76 77 78 79 81 82 84 85 86 87 91 93 94 96 98 99 102 106 107 108 110 111 114 115 116 117 118 119 120 121 123 124 126 129 130 131 132 141 143 146 148 **P**6 **S** Riverside Health System, Newport News, VA
Primary Contact: Michael J. Doucette, Senior Vice President and Administrator
COO: William B. Downey, Chief Operating Officer
CFO: Wade Broughman, Executive Vice President and Chief Financial Officer
CMO: Barry L. Gross, M.D., Executive Vice President and Chief Medical Officer
CIO: Dennis Loftis, Senior Vice President and Chief Information Officer
CHR: Sally Hartman, Senior Vice President
CNO: Candice R. Carroll, Nurse Executive
Web address: www.riverside–online.com
Control: Other not–for–profit (including NFP Corporation) **Service:** General Medical and Surgical

Staffed Beds: 312 **Admissions:** 20503 **Census:** 279 **Outpatient Visits:** 629432 **Births:** 2506 **Total Expense ($000):** 732913 **Payroll Expense ($000):** 189744 **Personnel:** 2120

✠ **RIVERSIDE REHABILITATION INSTITUTE (493027)**, 245 Chesapeake Avenue, Zip 23607–6038; tel. 757/928–8000 **A**1 5 10 **F**29 30 57 64 77 82 87 90 91 93 94 96 130 132 146 **P**6 **S** Riverside Health System, Newport News, VA
Primary Contact: Daniel Ballin, Administrator
COO: William B. Downey, President and Chief Executive Officer
CFO: Bill Austin, Senior Vice President of Finance
CMO: C. Renee Moss, M.D., Chief Medical Officer
CIO: Dennis Loftis, Senior Vice President of Information Systems
CHR: Rob Cuthrell, Director of Human Resources
CNO: Debbie Outlaw, R.N., Director Patient Care Services
Web address: www.riversideonline.com/rri/index.cfm
Control: Other not–for–profit (including NFP Corporation) **Service:** Rehabilitation

Staffed Beds: 30 **Admissions:** 721 **Census:** 30 **Outpatient Visits:** 14355 **Births:** 0 **Total Expense ($000):** 15495 **Payroll Expense ($000):** 7603 **Personnel:** 157

NORFOLK—Norfolk City County

✠ **BON SECOURS–DEPAUL MEDICAL CENTER (490011)**, 150 Kingsley Lane, Zip 23505–4650; tel. 757/889–5000, (Total facility includes 24 beds in nursing home–type unit) **A**1 2 3 5 10 **F**3 11 13 15 18 20 22 29 30 31 34 35 40 44 45 46 50 51 56 57 59 61 64 68 70 71 74 75 76 78 79 81 82 84 85 86 87 93 97 102 107 108 110 111 114 115 118 119 120 121 128 129 130 131 132 143 145 146 147 148 **P**6 **S** Bon Secours Health System, Inc., Marriottsville, MD
Primary Contact: John E. Barrett, III, Chief Executive Officer
CFO: Charmaine Rochester, Vice President Finance
CMO: Raymond McCue, M.D., Chief Medical Officer
CIO: Lynne Zultanky, Director Corporate Communications and Media Relations
CHR: Vickie Witcher Humphries, Vice President Human Resources
CNO: Michael J. Bratton, R.N., Chief Nurse Executive and Vice President Patient Care Services
Web address: www.bonsecourshamptonroads.com
Control: Other not–for–profit (including NFP Corporation) **Service:** General Medical and Surgical

Staffed Beds: 204 **Admissions:** 6864 **Census:** 90 **Outpatient Visits:** 179514 **Births:** 1418 **Total Expense ($000):** 187503 **Payroll Expense ($000):** 64489 **Personnel:** 1184

VA

☐ **CHILDREN'S HOSPITAL OF THE KING'S DAUGHTERS (493301)**, 601 Children's Lane, Zip 23507–1910; tel. 757/668–7000 **A**1 3 5 10 **F**3 7 8 9 12 16 17 19 21 23 25 27 29 30 31 32 34 35 39 40 41 44 45 48 49 50 54 55 57 58 59 60 61 64 65 66 68 72 73 74 75 77 78 79 80 81 82 84 85 86 87 88 89 90 91 92 93 94 97 99 100 102 107 111 115 118 119 129 130 131 132 134 138 144 145 146 148 **P**8
Primary Contact: James D. Dahling, President and Chief Executive Officer
COO: John P. Harding, Chief Operating Officer
CFO: Dennis Ryan, Senior Vice President and Chief Financial Officer
CMO: Chris Foley, Chief of Medicine
CIO: Deborah Barnes, Vice President and Chief Information Officer
CHR: Paul J. Morlock, FACHE, Vice President Human Resources and Occupational Health
CNO: Karen Mitchell, Vice President Patient Care Services
Web address: www.chkd.org
Control: Other not–for–profit (including NFP Corporation) **Service:** Children's general

Staffed Beds: 206 **Admissions:** 5064 **Census:** 124 **Outpatient Visits:** 230512 **Births:** 0 **Total Expense ($000):** 304672 **Payroll Expense ($000):** 126491 **Personnel:** 2232

HOSPITAL FOR EXTENDED RECOVERY (492007), 600 Gresham Drive, Suite 700, Zip 23507–1904; tel. 757/388–1700 **A**10 **F**1 3 18 20 22 28 29 30 31 34 35 39 57 59 60 74 77 78 79 82 84 85 87 97 103 107 108 109 111 116 117 118 119 126 130 143 148 **P**6
Primary Contact: Aimee Vergara, Chief Executive Officer
Control: Other not–for–profit (including NFP Corporation) **Service:** Long–Term Acute Care hospital

Staffed Beds: 25 **Admissions:** 174 **Census:** 15 **Outpatient Visits:** 0 **Births:** 0

☐ **KEMPSVILLE CENTER FOR BEHAVIORAL HEALTH**, 860 Kempsville Road, Zip 23502–3980; tel. 757/461–4565, (Nonreporting) **A**1
Primary Contact: Jaime Hernandez, Chief Executive Officer
Control: Corporation, Investor–owned, for–profit **Service:** Psychiatric

Staffed Beds: 77

LAKE TAYLOR TRANSITIONAL CARE HOSPITAL (492001), 1309 Kempsville Road, Zip 23502–2286; tel. 757/461–5001, (Total facility includes 192 beds in nursing home–type unit) **A**3 5 10 **F**1 28 29 30 34 35 39 56 59 60 61 63 65 67 74 75 77 82 84 96 119 128 130 143 146 148 **P**4
Primary Contact: Thomas J. Orsini, President and Chief Executive Officer
CFO: Robert W. Fogg, Director Finance
CMO: Kevin Murray, M.D., Director Medical Services
CIO: Mark Davis, Director Information Systems
CHR: LeeAnn Lowman, Director Human Resources
Web address: www.laketaylor.org
Control: City–Government, nonfederal **Service:** Long–Term Acute Care hospital

Staffed Beds: 284 **Admissions:** 1600 **Census:** 245 **Outpatient Visits:** 0 **Births:** 0

★ ◇ **SENTARA LEIGH HOSPITAL (490046)**, 830 Kempsville Road, Zip 23502–3920; tel. 757/261–6000 **A**2 3 5 10 21 **F**3 8 9 13 15 18 20 22 26 28 29 30 31 34 35 36 37 38 39 40 41 42 44 45 46 47 48 49 50 51 54 55 56 57 58 59 60 61 63 64 65 68 70 71 74 75 76 77 78 79 81 82 84 85 86 87 91 92 93 94 96 97 100 102 107 108 110 111 114 119 126 130 131 132 135 141 144 146 147 148 **P**6 **S** Sentara Healthcare, Norfolk, VA
Primary Contact: Teresa L. Edwards, President and Administrator
COO: Howard P. Kern, President and Chief Operating Officer
CFO: Robert Broermann, Senior Vice President and Chief Financial Officer
CMO: Terry Gilliland, M.D., Chief Medical Officer
CIO: Bert Reese, Chief Information Officer
CHR: Michael V. Taylor, Senior Vice President Human Resources
CNO: Genemarie McGee, R.N., Chief Nursing Officer
Web address: www.sentara.com
Control: Other not–for–profit (including NFP Corporation) **Service:** General Medical and Surgical

Staffed Beds: 250 **Admissions:** 14525 **Census:** 166 **Outpatient Visits:** 527887 **Births:** 1982 **Total Expense ($000):** 254089 **Payroll Expense ($000):** 99837 **Personnel:** 1642

★ ◇ **SENTARA NORFOLK GENERAL HOSPITAL (490007)**, 600 Gresham Drive, Zip 23507–1904; tel. 757/388–3000 **A**2 3 5 8 10 21 **F**3 7 11 12 13 15 16 17 18 20 22 24 28 29 30 31 34 35 36 37 38 39 40 41 43 44 45 46 47 48 49 50 51 52 54 56 57 58 59 60 61 63 64 65 66 68 70 71 74 75 76 77 78 79 81 82 84 85 86 87 90 91 93 94 96 97 98 100 101 102 103 107 108 109 110 111 114 115 116 117 118 119 120 121 123 124 126 129 130 131 132 135 136 137 138 141 142 144 146 147 148 **P**6 **S** Sentara Healthcare, Norfolk, VA
Primary Contact: Kurt T. Hofelich, President
CFO: Robert Broermann, Senior Vice President and Chief Financial Officer
CIO: Bert Reese, Chief Information Officer
Web address: www.sentara.com
Control: Other not–for–profit (including NFP Corporation) **Service:** General Medical and Surgical

Staffed Beds: 495 **Admissions:** 25715 **Census:** 426 **Outpatient Visits:** 1119932 **Births:** 2882 **Total Expense ($000):** 717025 **Payroll Expense ($000):** 239030 **Personnel:** 3908

NORTON—Norton City County

★ **MOUNTAIN VIEW REGIONAL MEDICAL CENTER (490027)**, 310 Third Street N.E., Zip 24273–1137; tel. 276/679–9100, (Total facility includes 44 beds in nursing home–type unit) **F**3 11 15 28 29 34 40 45 48 49 50 57 59 70 75 77 81 85 87 89 93 107 108 111 115 118 119 128 130 135 146 **S** Wellmont Health System, Kingsport, TN
Primary Contact: Dale Clark, President
CFO: Regina Day, Executive Director Finance
CMO: Michael Ketcham, Chief Medical Officer
CHR: Bobby Collins, Director Human Resources
CNO: Cindy Stidham, Executive Director of Patient Care
Web address: www.wellmont.org
Control: Other not–for–profit (including NFP Corporation) **Service:** General Medical and Surgical

Staffed Beds: 70 **Admissions:** 1281 **Census:** 37 **Outpatient Visits:** 34060 **Births:** 0 **Total Expense ($000):** 24334 **Payroll Expense ($000):** 6457 **Personnel:** 173

○ **NORTON COMMUNITY HOSPITAL (490001)**, 100 15th Street N.W., Zip 24273–1616; tel. 276/679–9600 **A**10 11 13 **F**3 11 13 15 18 28 29 30 34 35 40 44 45 51 53 57 62 63 64 68 70 75 76 77 79 81 82 87 90 91 93 107 108 110 111 115 116 117 118 119 129 130 131 133 135 146 147 148 **S** Mountain States Health Alliance, Johnson City, TN
Primary Contact: Mark T. Leonard, Chief Executive Officer
CFO: Stephen Sawyer, Chief Financial Officer
CMO: Allen Mullens, M.D., Chief Medical Staff
CIO: Judy Lawson, Director Information Services
CHR: Valeri J. Colyer, Director Human Resources
Web address: www.msha.com/nch
Control: Other not–for–profit (including NFP Corporation) **Service:** General Medical and Surgical

Staffed Beds: 129 **Admissions:** 3408 **Census:** 34 **Outpatient Visits:** 75476 **Births:** 249 **Total Expense ($000):** 47078 **Payroll Expense ($000):** 18688 **Personnel:** 401

PEARISBURG—Giles County

⊞ **CARILION GILES COMMUNITY HOSPITAL (491302)**, 159 Hartley Way, Zip 24134–2471; tel. 540/921–6000 **A**1 10 18 **F**3 11 15 18 28 29 34 35 36 40 45 50 53 57 59 64 65 68 70 75 77 79 81 85 86 87 91 93 96 107 108 110 111 115 118 119 130 133 135 146 147 148 **P**6 **S** Carilion Clinic, Roanoke, VA
Primary Contact: William Flattery, Vice President and Administrator Western Division
CMO: John Tamminen, M.D., President Medical Staff
CHR: Carrie Boggess, Human Resource Generalist
CNO: Veronica Stump, Director of Nursing
Web address: www.carilionclinic.org/Carilion/cgch
Control: Other not–for–profit (including NFP Corporation) **Service:** General Medical and Surgical

Staffed Beds: 17 **Admissions:** 1167 **Census:** 17 **Outpatient Visits:** 25326 **Births:** 0 **Total Expense ($000):** 27889 **Payroll Expense ($000):** 10258 **Personnel:** 193

VA

	Hospital, Medicare Provider Number, Address, Telephone, Approval, Facility, and Physician Codes, Health Care System	
★ American Hospital Association (AHA) membership	○ Healthcare Facilities Accreditation Program	⇑ Center for Improvement in Healthcare Quality Accreditation
☐ The Joint Commission accreditation	◇ DNV Healthcare Inc. accreditation	△ Commission on Accreditation of Rehabilitation Facilities (CARF) accreditation

PETERSBURG—Petersburg City County

☐ **CENTRAL STATE HOSPITAL**, 26317 West Washington Street, Zip 23803–2727, Mailing Address: P.O. Box 4030, Zip 23803–0030; tel. 804/524–7000 **A**1 **F**30 75 77 87 98 101 130 **S** Virginia Department of Mental Health, Richmond, VA
Primary Contact: Vicki Montgomery, Director and Chief Executive Officer
COO: Ann Bailey, Assistant Director Administration
CFO: Robert Kaufman, Director Financial Services
CMO: Ronald O. Forbes, M.D., Medical Director
CIO: Jonathan Baber, Director Information Technology
CHR: Tracy Salisbury, Regional Manager Human Resources
CNO: Eva Parham, R.N., Chief Nurse Executive
Web address: www.csh.dbhds.virginia.gov
Control: State–Government, nonfederal **Service:** Psychiatric

Staffed Beds: 277 **Admissions:** 620 **Census:** 223 **Outpatient Visits:** 0 **Births:** 0 **Total Expense ($000):** 63939 **Payroll Expense ($000):** 35737 **Personnel:** 912

✠ **HEALTHSOUTH REHABILITATION HOSPITAL OF PETERSBURG (493031)**, 95 Medical Park Boulevard, Zip 23805–9233; tel. 804/504–8100 **A**1 10 **F**28 29 34 35 59 68 75 82 90 91 97 130 132 135 143 148 **S** HEALTHSOUTH Corporation, Birmingham, AL
Primary Contact: Tracy Penn Turman, Chief Executive Officer
Web address: www.healthsouthpetersburg.com
Control: Corporation, Investor–owned, for–profit **Service:** Rehabilitation

Staffed Beds: 53 **Admissions:** 987 **Census:** 37 **Outpatient Visits:** 0 **Births:** 0

☐ **HIRAM W. DAVIS MEDICAL CENTER (490104)**, 26317 West Washington Street, Zip 23803–2727, Mailing Address: P.O. Box 4030, Zip 23803–0030; tel. 804/524–7344, (Nonreporting) **A**1 10 **S** Virginia Department of Mental Health, Richmond, VA
Primary Contact: Brenda Buenvenida, Director
CFO: Robert Kaufman, Fiscal Officer
CHR: Tracy Salisbury, Director Human Resources
Control: State–Government, nonfederal **Service:** Other specialty

Staffed Beds: 10

✠ **POPLAR SPRINGS HOSPITAL (494022)**, 350 Poplar Drive, Zip 23805–9367; tel. 804/733–6874, (Nonreporting) **A**1 10 **S** Universal Health Services, Inc., King of Prussia, PA
Primary Contact: Joseph Trapani, Chief Executive Officer
COO: Kate McBride, Chief Operating Officer
CFO: Bettie Hill, Chief Financial Officer
CMO: Thresa Simon, M.D., Medical Director
CHR: Morris Mitchell, Director Human Resources
Web address: www.poplarsprings.com
Control: Corporation, Investor–owned, for–profit **Service:** Psychiatric

Staffed Beds: 183

✠ **SOUTHSIDE REGIONAL MEDICAL CENTER (490067)**, 200 Medical Park Boulevard, Zip 23805–9274; tel. 804/765–5000 **A**1 2 3 10 **F**3 12 13 15 17 18 20 22 24 26 28 29 30 31 34 35 40 43 45 46 47 48 49 50 54 56 57 59 60 64 70 72 74 75 76 77 78 79 81 82 85 86 87 89 91 92 93 96 97 98 101 102 105 107 108 110 111 112 114 115 116 117 119 120 121 122 124 130 131 132 135 146 147 148 **P**6 **S** Community Health Systems, Inc., Franklin, TN
Primary Contact: Douglas J. Moyer, Chief Executive Officer
COO: Jerad Hanlon, Chief Operating Officer
CFO: Charles Coder, Chief Financial Officer
CMO: Boyd Wickizer, Jr., M.D., Chief Medical Officer
CIO: Eric Synnestvedt, Director Information Technology
CHR: Irene Buskey, Director Human Resources
CNO: Beverly Bzdek Smith, Chief Nursing Officer
Web address: www.srmconline.com
Control: Corporation, Investor–owned, for–profit **Service:** General Medical and Surgical

Staffed Beds: 300 **Admissions:** 13173 **Census:** 155 **Outpatient Visits:** 119276 **Births:** 1203 **Total Expense ($000):** 159401 **Payroll Expense ($000):** 67668 **Personnel:** 1155

PORTSMOUTH—Portsmouth City County

✠ **BON SECOURS MARYVIEW MEDICAL CENTER (490017)**, 3636 High Street, Zip 23707–3270; tel. 757/398–2200, (Total facility includes 120 beds in nursing home–type unit) **A**1 2 3 5 10 **F**3 4 5 11 12 13 15 17 18 20 22 24 26 28 29 30 31 34 35 36 37 38 40 42 44 45 46 50 51 54 57 59 61 62 63 64 66 67 68 70 71 73 74 75 76 77 78 79 81 82 84 85 86 87 90 91 93 96 97 98 99 100 101 102 103 104 105 106 107 108 110 111 114 115 118 119 121 126 128 129 130 131 132 134 135 143 145 146 147 **S** Bon Secours Health System, Inc., Marriottsville, MD
Primary Contact: Joseph M. Oddis, Chief Executive Officer
CFO: Ernest C. Padden, Chief Financial Officer
CMO: Warren Austin, M.D., Vice President Medical Affairs
CIO: Terri Spence, Chief Information Officer
CHR: Vickie Witcher Humphries, Director Human Resources
CNO: Leana Fox, MSN, Interim Chief Nurse Executive
Web address: www.bonsecourshamptonroads.com
Control: Other not–for–profit (including NFP Corporation) **Service:** General Medical and Surgical

Staffed Beds: 466 **Admissions:** 12456 **Census:** 277 **Outpatient Visits:** 415577 **Births:** 1029 **Total Expense ($000):** 341285 **Payroll Expense ($000):** 125968 **Personnel:** 2170

✠ **NAVAL MEDICAL CENTER**, 620 John Paul Jones Circle, Zip 23708–2197; tel. 757/953–1980, (Nonreporting) **A**1 2 3 5 **S** Bureau of Medicine and Surgery, Department of the Navy, Falls Church, VA
Primary Contact: Commander Matthew Case, MSC, USN, Director For Administration
CIO: Lieutenant Colonel Karen Albany, Chief Information Officer
Web address: www.nmcphc.med.navy.mil/
Control: Navy, Government, federal **Service:** General Medical and Surgical

Staffed Beds: 274

PULASKI—Pulaski County

✠ **LEWISGALE HOSPITAL PULASKI (490116)**, 2400 Lee Highway, Zip 24301–2326, Mailing Address: P.O. Box 759, Zip 24301–0759; tel. 540/994–8100, (Nonreporting) **A**1 2 10 **S** HCA, Nashville, TN
Primary Contact: Derek Vance, Chief Executive Officer
CFO: Jeff Kurcab, Chief Financial Officer
CMO: Karanita Ojomo, M.D., Chief of Staff
CIO: Diron Lane, Director Information Systems
CHR: Jana Beckner, Director Human Resources
CNO: Linda M. Shepherd, RN, BSN, Chief Nursing Officer
Web address: www.lewisgale.com/
Control: Corporation, Investor–owned, for–profit **Service:** General Medical and Surgical

Staffed Beds: 54

RESTON—Fairfax County

✠ **RESTON HOSPITAL CENTER (490107)**, 1850 Town Center Parkway, Zip 20190–3219; tel. 703/689–9000 **A**1 2 3 10 **F**3 8 12 13 14 15 18 20 22 26 29 30 34 35 37 39 40 41 44 45 46 47 48 49 50 51 53 54 55 57 58 59 60 63 64 65 68 69 70 72 74 75 76 77 78 79 81 82 84 85 87 89 91 93 94 96 97 107 108 110 111 114 115 117 118 119 120 121 123 124 126 127 130 131 132 135 145 146 147 148 **S** HCA, Nashville, TN
Primary Contact: John A. Deardorff, Chief Executive Officer
COO: Jane Raymond, Vice President and Chief Operating Officer
CFO: Edward R. Stojakovich, Chief Financial Officer
CMO: Walter R. Zolkiwsky, M.D., Chief Medical Officer
CIO: Paresh Shah, Director Information Systems
CHR: Lesley Channell, Vice President Human Resources
CNO: Cynthia Glover, R.N., Vice President and Chief Nursing Officer
Web address: www.restonhospital.com
Control: Corporation, Investor–owned, for–profit **Service:** General Medical and Surgical

Staffed Beds: 187 **Admissions:** 12957 **Census:** 142 **Outpatient Visits:** 113058 **Births:** 3767 **Total Expense ($000):** 221788 **Payroll Expense ($000):** 74435 **Personnel:** 885

VA

Many Facility Codes have changed. Please refer to the AHA Guide Code Chart. © 2016 AHA Guide

RICHLANDS—Tazewell County

☒ **CLINCH VALLEY MEDICAL CENTER (490060)**, 6801 Governor G. C. Peery Highway, Zip 24641–2194; tel. 276/596–6000, (Total facility includes 14 beds in nursing home–type unit) **A**1 10 **F**3 12 13 14 15 17 18 20 22 28 29 30 31 34 35 39 40 41 45 49 50 56 57 59 64 70 75 76 77 78 79 81 85 86 87 89 90 93 94 97 107 108 110 111 114 115 118 119 120 121 128 129 130 132 134 135 143 144 146 147 148 **S** LifePoint Health, Brentwood, TN
Primary Contact: Peter Mulkey, Chief Executive Officer
COO: Jennifer Coello, Chief Operating Officer
CFO: Jason Schmiedt, Chief Financial Officer
CMO: George Farrell, M.D., Chief Medical Officer
CIO: Chris Perkins, Director Information Services
CHR: John Knowles, Director Human Resources
CNO: Clint Kendall, R.N., Chief Nursing Officer
Web address: www.clinchvalleymedicalcenter.com
Control: Corporation, Investor–owned, for–profit **Service:** General Medical and Surgical

Staffed Beds: 111 **Admissions:** 4290 **Census:** 47 **Outpatient Visits:** 91043 **Births:** 333 **Personnel:** 427

RICHMOND—Henrico County

☒ **BON SECOURS ST. MARY'S HOSPITAL (490059)**, 5801 Bremo Road, Zip 23226–1907; tel. 804/285–2011, (Includes BON SECOURS ST. MARY'S CHILDREN'S SERVICES, 5801 Bremo Road, Zip 23226; tel. 804/285–2011) **A**1 2 3 5 10 **F**3 7 8 11 12 13 15 17 20 22 24 26 28 29 30 31 34 35 36 39 40 41 45 46 47 49 50 56 57 59 61 63 64 70 72 73 74 75 76 78 79 80 81 82 84 85 87 88 89 98 100 101 102 103 104 105 107 108 110 111 114 115 116 117 118 119 120 121 123 124 126 129 130 132 135 143 146 147 148 **P**6 **S** Bon Secours Health System, Inc., Marriottsville, MD
Primary Contact: Francine Barr, R.N., MS, Chief Executive Officer
COO: Francine Barr, R.N., Vice President and Chief Operating Officer
CFO: Stephan F. Quiriconi, Chief Financial Officer
CMO: Khiet Trinh, M.D., Chief Medical Officer
CIO: Terri Spence, Chief Information Officer
CHR: Kristin Crandall, Director Human Resources
Web address: www.bonsecours.com
Control: Church–operated, Nongovernment, not–for profit **Service:** General Medical and Surgical

Staffed Beds: 391 **Admissions:** 19956 **Census:** 263 **Outpatient Visits:** 163614 **Births:** 2177 **Total Expense ($000):** 505001 **Payroll Expense ($000):** 167113 **Personnel:** 2507

☒ **BON SECOURS–RICHMOND COMMUNITY HOSPITAL (490094)**, 1500 North 28th Street, Zip 23223–5396, Mailing Address: P.O. Box 27184, Zip 23261–7184; tel. 804/225–1700 **A**1 3 10 **F**3 11 15 18 20 22 24 26 28 29 30 31 34 35 38 40 41 44 45 46 50 57 59 60 64 68 70 74 75 78 81 84 85 86 87 98 100 103 104 105 107 108 111 115 118 119 130 145 146 148 **P**6 8 **S** Bon Secours Health System, Inc., Marriottsville, MD
Primary Contact: Mark M. Gordon, Chief Executive Officer
CIO: Jeff Burke, Chief Information Officer
CHR: Shelia White, Director Human Resources
Web address: www.bonsecours.com
Control: Other not–for–profit (including NFP Corporation) **Service:** General Medical and Surgical

Staffed Beds: 85 **Admissions:** 2788 **Census:** 36 **Outpatient Visits:** 31407 **Births:** 1

★ **CHILDREN'S HOSPITAL OF RICHMOND AT VCU–BROOK ROAD CAMPUS (493302)**, 2924 Brook Road, Zip 23220–1298; tel. 804/321–7474, (Nonreporting) **A**3 5 10 **S** VCU Health System, Richmond, VA
Primary Contact: Leslie G. Wyatt, Senior Vice President Children's Services and Executive Director
COO: Leslie G. Wyatt, Senior Vice President Children's Services and Executive Director
CFO: James A. Deyarmin, Controller
CMO: Eugene A. Monasterio, M.D., Medical Director
CIO: Tim Gibbs, Director of Information Technology, Information Security Officer
CNO: Sharon Darby, R.N., Vice President, Clinical Operations
Web address: www.chrichmond.org
Control: Other not–for–profit (including NFP Corporation) **Service:** Children's rehabilitation

Staffed Beds: 36

☒ ◇ **CHIPPENHAM HOSPITAL (490112)**, 7101 Jahnke Road, Zip 23225–4044; tel. 804/320–3911, (Includes CHIPPENHAM MEDICAL CENTER, 7101 Jahnke Road, Zip 23225; tel. 804/320–3911; JOHNSTON–WILLIS HOSPITAL, 1401 Johnston–Willis Drive, Zip 23235; tel. 804/330–2000; Brandon Haushalter, Chief Executive Officer) **A**1 2 3 5 10 21 **F**3 4 8 13 15 17 18 19 20 22 24 26 28 29 30 31 34 35 37 38 40 41 42 43 45 46 47 49 50 55 57 58 59 60 61 64 68 70 72 73 74 75 76 77 78 79 80 81 84 85 86 87 88 89 90 96 98 99 100 101 102 103 104 105 107 108 109 110 111 114 115 119 120 121 123 124 126 129 130 131 135 146 147 148 **S** HCA, Nashville, TN
Primary Contact: Tim McManus, President and Chief Executive Officer
COO: Jeremy Gray, Chief Operating Officer
CFO: Lynn Strader, Chief Financial Officer
CMO: Georgean DeBlois, M.D., Chairman Medical Staff
CIO: Tracy Hechler, Healthcare Director Information Services
CHR: Kris Lukish, Human Resources Officer
Web address: www.cjwmedical.com
Control: Corporation, Investor–owned, for–profit **Service:** General Medical and Surgical

Staffed Beds: 765 **Admissions:** 34962 **Census:** 494 **Outpatient Visits:** 294256 **Births:** 2707 **Personnel:** 2687

HALLMARK YOUTHCARE – RICHMOND, 12800 West Creek Parkway, Zip 23238–1116; tel. 804/784–2200 **F**98 99 101 106 **P**5
Primary Contact: Di Hayes, Chief Executive Officer
Web address: www.hallmarkyouthcare.org
Control: Partnership, Investor–owned, for–profit **Service:** Children's hospital psychiatric

Staffed Beds: 78 **Admissions:** 130 **Census:** 75 **Outpatient Visits:** 0 **Births:** 0 **Personnel:** 216

☒ **HEALTHSOUTH REHABILITATION HOSPITAL OF VIRGINIA (493028)**, 5700 Fitzhugh Avenue, Zip 23226–1800; tel. 804/288–5700, (Nonreporting) **A**1 10 **S** HEALTHSOUTH Corporation, Birmingham, AL
Primary Contact: David Cashwell, Chief Executive Officer
CMO: Roger Giordano, M.D., Medical Director
CIO: Faye Encke, Director Information Management
CHR: Tonya Ferguson, Director Human Resources
CNO: Michelle Anthony, Chief Nursing Officer
Web address: www.healthsouthrichmond.com
Control: Corporation, Investor–owned, for–profit **Service:** Rehabilitation

Staffed Beds: 40

☒ **HENRICO DOCTORS' HOSPITAL (490118)**, 1602 Skipwith Road, Zip 23229–5205; tel. 804/289–4500, (Includes HENRICO DOCTORS' HOSPITAL – FOREST, 1602 Skipwith Road, Zip 23229–5298; tel. 804/289–4500; HENRICO DOCTORS' HOSPITAL – PARHAM, 7700 East Parham Road, Zip 23294–4301; tel. 804/747–5600; William Wagnon, Chief Executive Officer; HENRICO DOCTORS' HOSPITAL – RETREAT CAMPUS, 2621 Grove Avenue, Zip 23220–4308; tel. 804/254–5100; William Wagnon, Chief Executive Officer) **A**1 2 10 **F**3 8 12 13 15 17 18 20 22 24 26 28 29 30 31 34 35 37 38 40 41 42 44 45 46 47 49 50 51 54 55 56 57 59 64 65 68 70 71 72 73 74 75 76 77 78 79 81 85 86 87 88 89 90 93 96 97 98 99 102 104 105 107 108 109 110 111 112 114 115 119 120 121 123 126 129 130 131 132 135 138 141 146 147 148 **S** HCA, Nashville, TN
Primary Contact: William Wagnon, Chief Executive Officer
COO: Lisa R. Valentine, Chief Operating Officer
CFO: Christopher Denton, Chief Financial Officer
CIO: Daniel Patton, Director Information Systems
CHR: Steven Burgess, Administrator Human Resources
Web address: www.henricodoctorshospital.com
Control: Corporation, Investor–owned, for–profit **Service:** General Medical and Surgical

Staffed Beds: 488 **Admissions:** 21070 **Census:** 305 **Outpatient Visits:** 143979 **Births:** 3638 **Total Expense ($000):** 391184 **Payroll Expense ($000):** 143595 **Personnel:** 2445

Hospital, Medicare Provider Number, Address, Telephone, Approval, Facility, and Physician Codes, Health Care System

★ American Hospital Association (AHA) membership
☐ The Joint Commission accreditation
◯ Healthcare Facilities Accreditation Program
◇ DNV Healthcare Inc. accreditation
⇑ Center for Improvement in Healthcare Quality Accreditation
△ Commission on Accreditation of Rehabilitation Facilities (CARF) accreditation

VA

⊞ △ **HUNTER HOLMES MCGUIRE VETERANS AFFAIRS MEDICAL CENTER–RICHMOND**, 1201 Broad Rock Boulevard, Zip 23249–0002; tel. 804/675–5000, (Total facility includes 98 beds in nursing home–type unit) **A**1 3 5 7 8 **F**3 4 5 8 9 15 17 18 20 22 24 26 28 29 30 31 34 35 36 38 39 40 44 45 46 47 48 49 50 51 53 54 56 57 58 59 60 61 62 63 64 65 66 70 71 74 75 77 78 79 81 82 83 84 85 86 87 90 91 92 93 94 95 96 97 98 100 102 103 104 106 107 108 110 111 115 117 118 119 120 121 124 126 127 128 129 130 131 132 135 137 141 143 144 145 146 147 148 **P**6 **S** Department of Veterans Affairs, Washington, DC
Primary Contact: John A. Brandecker, M.P.H., Director
COO: Alan Lombardo, Associate Director
CFO: Tanza Westry, Chief Financial Officer
CMO: Julie Beales, M.D., Chief of Staff
CIO: David Dahlstrand, Chief, OI&T
CHR: Adriana H. Hamilton, Chief Human Resources Officer
CNO: Marjorie Lyne, Associate Director for Patient Care Services
Web address: www.richmond.va.gov/
Control: Veterans Affairs, Government, federal **Service:** General Medical and Surgical

Staffed Beds: 381 Admissions: 7204 Census: 220 Outpatient Visits: 646277 Births: 0 Total Expense ($000): 594018 Payroll Expense ($000): 335053 Personnel: 3093

JOHNSTON–WILLIS HOSPITAL See Chippenham Hospital

KINDRED HOSPITAL RICHMOND See Vibra Hospital of Richmond

⊞ **VCU MEDICAL CENTER (490032)**, 1250 East Marshall Street, Zip 23298–5051, Mailing Address: P.O. Box 980510, Zip 23298–0510; tel. 804/828–9000, (Includes VCU HEALTH SYSTEM CHILDREN'S MEDICAL CENTER, 1001 East Marshall Street, Zip 23219–1918, Mailing Address: PO Box 980646, Zip 23298–0646; tel. 804/828–9602) **A**1 3 5 8 10 **F**2 3 5 6 8 9 11 12 13 15 16 17 18 19 20 21 22 23 24 25 26 27 28 29 30 31 32 34 35 36 37 38 39 40 41 43 44 45 46 47 48 49 50 51 52 54 55 56 57 58 59 60 61 62 64 65 66 68 70 72 73 74 75 76 78 79 80 81 82 83 84 85 86 87 88 89 90 92 93 95 96 97 98 99 100 101 102 103 104 107 108 109 110 111 114 115 116 117 118 119 120 121 123 124 126 129 130 131 132 134 135 136 137 138 139 141 142 143 145 146 147 148 **P**6 **S** VCU Health System, Richmond, VA
Primary Contact: John Duval, Chief Executive Officer
COO: Deborah W. Davis, Chief Operating Officer
CFO: Melinda Hancock, Chief Financial Officer
CMO: Ron Clark, M.D., Vice President Clinical Activities and Chief Medical Officer
CIO: Richard Pollack, Vice President Information Services
CHR: Maria Curran, Vice President Human Resources
CNO: Deb T. Zimmermann, R.N., Chief Nursing Officer and Vice President Patient Care Services
Web address: www.vcuhealth.org
Control: Hospital district or authority, Government, nonfederal **Service:** General Medical and Surgical

Staffed Beds: 786 Admissions: 33556 Census: 605 Outpatient Visits: 732827 Births: 2537 Total Expense ($000): 1194998 Payroll Expense ($000): 423072 Personnel: 7634

⊞ **VIBRA HOSPITAL OF RICHMOND (492009)**, 2220 Edward Holland Drive, Zip 23230–2519; tel. 804/678–7000 **A**1 10 **F**1 3 29 75 107 148 **P**6 **S** Vibra Healthcare, Mechanicsburg, PA
Primary Contact: Craig Johnson, Interim Chief Executive Officer
Web address: www.vhrichmond.com
Control: Corporation, Investor–owned, for–profit **Service:** Long–Term Acute Care hospital

Staffed Beds: 60 Admissions: 585 Census: 41 Outpatient Visits: 0 Births: 0

VA

ROANOKE—Roanoke County

⊞ **CARILION ROANOKE MEMORIAL HOSPITAL (490024)**, Belleview at Jefferson Street, Zip 24014, Mailing Address: P.O. Box 13367, Zip 24033–3367; tel. 540/981–7000, (Includes CARILION CLINIC CHILDREN'S HOSPITAL, 1906 Belleview Avenue, S.E., Zip 24014–1838; tel. 540/981–7000; CARILION ROANOKE COMMUNITY HOSPITAL, 101 Elm Avenue S.E., Zip 24013–2230, Mailing Address: P.O. Box 12946, Zip 24029–2946; tel. 540/985–8000; ROANOKE MEMORIAL REHABILITATION CENTER, South Jefferson and McClanahan Streets, Mailing Address: P.O. Box 13367, Zip 24033; tel. 703/342–4541) **A**1 2 3 5 8 10 13 **F**3 5 7 8 9 11 12 13 15 17 18 19 20 22 24 26 28 29 30 31 32 33 34 35 36 37 38 39 40 41 43 44 45 46 47 48 49 50 51 52 53 55 56 57 58 59 60 61 62 63 64 65 66 68 70 71 72 73 74 75 76 77 78 79 81 82 83 84 85 86 87 88 89 90 92 93 96 97 98 99 100 101 102 103 104 106 107 108 110 111 113 114 115 117 118 119 120 121 123 124 126 129 130 131 132 134 135 143 144 146 147 148 **P**6 **S** Carilion Clinic, Roanoke, VA
Primary Contact: Steven C. Arner, President
COO: Steven C. Arner, President
CFO: Donald B. Halliwill, Executive Vice President and Chief Financial Officer
CHR: Heather S. Shepardson, Vice President Human Resources
Web address: www.carilionclinic.org
Control: Other not–for–profit (including NFP Corporation) **Service:** General Medical and Surgical

Staffed Beds: 655 Admissions: 36489 Census: 544 Outpatient Visits: 251526 Births: 3136 Total Expense ($000): 1010973 Payroll Expense ($000): 454335 Personnel: 6137

ROCKY MOUNT—Franklin County

⊞ **CARILION FRANKLIN MEMORIAL HOSPITAL (490089)**, 180 Floyd Avenue, Zip 24151–1389; tel. 540/483–5277 **A**1 3 10 **F**3 11 15 18 28 29 30 34 35 40 45 50 53 59 62 63 68 70 75 81 84 85 91 93 96 107 110 115 119 130 132 135 146 **S** Carilion Clinic, Roanoke, VA
Primary Contact: William D. Jacobsen, Vice President and Administrator
COO: Steven C. Arner, Chief Operating Officer
CFO: Donald B. Halliwill, Chief Financial Officer
CMO: Patrice M. Weiss, Chief Medical Officer
CHR: Heather S. Shepardson, Chief Human Resource Officer
Web address: www.carilionclinic.org/Carilion/Franklin+Memorial+Hospital
Control: Other not–for–profit (including NFP Corporation) **Service:** General Medical and Surgical

Staffed Beds: 15 Admissions: 1452 Census: 14 Outpatient Visits: 38981 Births: 0 Total Expense ($000): 34089 Payroll Expense ($000): 13707 Personnel: 241

SALEM—Salem City County

⊞ **LEWIS–GALE MEDICAL CENTER (490048)**, 1900 Electric Road, Zip 24153–7494; tel. 540/776–4000, (Includes LEWIS–GALE PAVILION, 1902 Braeburn Drive, Zip 24153–7391; tel. 703/772–2800), (Nonreporting) **A**1 2 10 **S** HCA, Nashville, TN
Primary Contact: Jonathan L. Bartlett, Chief Executive Officer
COO: Michael Abbott, Chief Operating Officer
CFO: Angela D. Reynolds, Chief Financial Officer
CMO: Joseph Nelson, M.D., President Medical Staff
CIO: Beth Cole, Director Information Services
CHR: Dale Beaudoin, Vice President Human Resources
Web address: www.lewis–gale.com
Control: Corporation, Investor–owned, for–profit **Service:** General Medical and Surgical

Staffed Beds: 521

⊞ **SALEM VETERANS AFFAIRS MEDICAL CENTER**, 1970 Roanoke Boulevard, Zip 24153–6478; tel. 540/982–2463, (Nonreporting) **A**1 3 5 8 **S** Department of Veterans Affairs, Washington, DC
Primary Contact: Rebecca J. Stackhouse, Interim Director
CFO: Codie Walker, Chief Financial Officer
CMO: Anne Hutchins, M.D., Chief of Staff
CIO: Sharon Collins, Chief Information Officer
CHR: Brian Zeman, Chief Human Resources
CNO: Teresa England, R.N., Nurse Executive
Web address: www.salem.va.gov
Control: Veterans Affairs, Government, federal **Service:** General Medical and Surgical

Staffed Beds: 200

SOUTH BOSTON—Halifax County

★ ◇ **SENTARA HALIFAX REGIONAL HOSPITAL (490013)**, 2204 Wilborn Avenue, Zip 24592–1638; tel. 434/517–3100, (Total facility includes 341 beds in nursing home–type unit) **A**10 21 **F**3 11 13 14 15 17 18 20 28 29 30 31 34 35 38 39 40 41 44 45 46 47 48 50 51 56 57 59 60 61 62 63 64 65 68 70 74 75 76 77 78 79 81 82 84 85 86 87 89 92 93 94 96 97 100 101 102 103 104 107 108 110 111 114 115 116 117 118 119 127 128 129 130 131 132 135 146 147 148 **P**1 6 7 **S** Sentara Healthcare, Norfolk, VA
Primary Contact: Chris A. Lumsden, Chief Executive Officer
CFO: Stewart R. Nelson, Chief Financial Officer
CMO: Said Iskandar, M.D., Chief Medical Officer
CIO: William Zirkle, Manager Information Systems
CHR: Catherine Howard, Director Human Resources
CNO: Patricia F. Thomas, Chief Nursing Officer
Web address: www.hrhs.org
Control: Other not–for–profit (including NFP Corporation) **Service:** General Medical and Surgical

Staffed Beds: 413 Admissions: 4397 Census: 373 Outpatient Visits: 107212 Births: 444 Total Expense ($000): 124914 Payroll Expense ($000): 56927 Personnel: 585

SOUTH HILL—Mecklenburg County

☒ **VCU COMMUNITY MEMORIAL HOSPITAL (490098)**, 125 Buena Vista Circle, Zip 23970–1431, Mailing Address: P.O. Box 90, Zip 23970–0090; tel. 434/447–3151, (Total facility includes 110 beds in nursing home–type unit) **A**1 2 10 20 **F**3 11 15 18 28 29 30 31 34 35 40 45 46 49 50 53 54 56 59 62 63 64 65 70 74 75 77 78 79 81 82 84 85 86 87 93 96 97 107 108 110 111 115 117 118 119 127 128 130 131 132 133 135 146 147 148 **P**8 **S** VCU Health System, Richmond, VA
Primary Contact: W. Scott Burnette, Chief Executive Officer
CFO: Kenneth Libby, Vice President Finance
CMO: Manhal Saleeby, M.D., Chief of Staff
CIO: Brian Rock, Director of Information Systems
CHR: Maria Stephens, PHR, Director Human Resources, Education and Occupational Health and Wellness
CNO: Ursula N. Butts, FACHE, Vice President of Patient Care Services
Web address: www.cmh–sh.org
Control: Other not–for–profit (including NFP Corporation) **Service:** General Medical and Surgical

Staffed Beds: 178 **Admissions:** 3243 **Census:** 145 **Outpatient Visits:** 126536 **Births:** 0 **Total Expense ($000):** 78289 **Payroll Expense ($000):** 31423 **Personnel:** 625

STAFFORD—Stafford County

☒ **STAFFORD HOSPITAL (490140)**, 101 Hospital Center Boulevard, Zip 22554–6200; tel. 540/741–9000 **A**1 5 10 **F**3 13 15 18 20 22 26 29 30 31 34 35 40 44 45 46 47 48 49 50 54 57 58 59 64 70 73 74 75 77 78 79 81 84 85 86 87 92 93 96 102 107 108 110 111 115 118 119 120 121 122 129 130 132 146 148 **P**8 **S** Mary Washington Healthcare, Fredericksburg, VA
Primary Contact: Michael P. McDermott, M.D., President and Chief Executive Officer
COO: Thomas Gettinger, Executive Vice President and Chief Operating Officer
CFO: Sean Barden, Executive Vice President and Chief Financial Officer
CMO: Rebecca Bigoney, Executive Vice President and Chief Medical Officer
CIO: Justin K. Box, Senior Vice President and Chief Information Officer
CHR: Kathryn S. Wall, Executive Vice President Human Resources and Organizational Development
CNO: Eileen L. Dohmann, R.N., Senior Vice President and Chief Nursing Officer
Web address: www.mwhc.com
Control: Other not–for–profit (including NFP Corporation) **Service:** General Medical and Surgical

Staffed Beds: 100 **Admissions:** 4492 **Census:** 42 **Outpatient Visits:** 102979 **Births:** 1082 **Total Expense ($000):** 83930 **Payroll Expense ($000):** 24268 **Personnel:** 312

STAUNTON—Staunton City County

COMMONWEALTH CENTER FOR CHILDREN AND ADOLESCENTS, 1355 Richmond Road, Zip 24401–9146, Mailing Address: Box 4000, Zip 24402–4000; tel. 540/332–2100, (Nonreporting) **A**3 5 **S** Virginia Department of Mental Health, Richmond, VA
Primary Contact: William J. Tuell, MSN, Facility Director
Web address: www.ccca.dbhds.virginia.gov
Control: State–Government, nonfederal **Service:** Children's other specialty

Staffed Beds: 60

☐ **WESTERN STATE HOSPITAL (494021)**, 1301 Richmond Avenue, Zip 24401–9146, Mailing Address: P.O. Box 2500, Zip 24402–2500; tel. 540/332–8000 **A**1 3 5 10 **F**3 29 30 39 50 57 65 67 75 77 84 87 90 97 98 100 101 130 132 135 146 **S** Virginia Department of Mental Health, Richmond, VA
Primary Contact: Mary Clare Smith, M.D., Director
CFO: Jon Chapman, Fiscal Officer
CMO: Jonathan Anderson, Medical Director
CIO: Sharon Johnson, Director Health Information Management
CHR: Kimberly Harman, Regional Manager Human Resources
CNO: Diane Pavalonis, Chief Nurse Executive
Web address: www.dbhds.virginia.gov
Control: State–Government, nonfederal **Service:** Psychiatric

Staffed Beds: 246 **Admissions:** 786 **Census:** 227 **Outpatient Visits:** 0 **Births:** 0

STUART—Patrick County

★ ◇ **PIONEER COMMUNITY HOSPITAL OF PATRICK (491306)**, 18688 Jeb Stuart Highway, Zip 24171–1559; tel. 276/694–3151, (Nonreporting) **A**10 18 21 **S** Pioneer Health Services, Magee, MS
Primary Contact: Jeanette Filpi, Chief Executive Officer
CFO: Julie Gieger, Chief Financial Officer
CMO: Richard C. Cole, Chief of Staff
CIO: Jack York, Chief Information Officer
CHR: Paul Trussell, Vice President Human Resources
CNO: Gerald Grass, Chief Nursing Officer
Web address: www.pchpatrick.com
Control: Corporation, Investor–owned, for–profit **Service:** General Medical and Surgical

Staffed Beds: 25

SUFFOLK—Suffolk City County

★ ◇ **SENTARA OBICI HOSPITAL (490044)**, 2800 Godwin Boulevard, Zip 23434–8038; tel. 757/934–4000 **A**2 3 5 10 21 **F**3 8 11 13 15 18 20 22 28 29 30 31 34 35 36 37 38 39 40 41 42 44 45 47 49 50 54 56 57 58 59 60 61 63 64 65 68 70 71 73 74 75 77 78 79 81 82 84 85 86 87 91 92 93 96 97 98 100 107 108 110 111 114 115 118 119 120 121 126 128 129 130 131 132 135 141 142 144 146 147 148 **P**6 **S** Sentara Healthcare, Norfolk, VA
Primary Contact: Steve Julian, M.D., President
CFO: Mike Mounie, Director Finance
CMO: Steve Julian, M.D., Vice President Medical Affairs
CIO: Alice Oxton, Director Information Technology
CHR: Deborah Ferguson, Human Resources Consultant
Web address: www.sentara.com
Control: Other not–for–profit (including NFP Corporation) **Service:** General Medical and Surgical

Staffed Beds: 176 **Admissions:** 9349 **Census:** 108 **Outpatient Visits:** 352359 **Births:** 1352 **Total Expense ($000):** 172096 **Payroll Expense ($000):** 70689 **Personnel:** 1157

TAPPAHANNOCK—Essex County

☐ **RIVERSIDE TAPPAHANNOCK HOSPITAL (490084)**, 618 Hospital Road, Zip 22560–5000; tel. 804/443–3311 **A**1 10 20 **F**3 11 15 18 29 30 31 34 35 37 38 40 44 45 49 50 51 56 57 59 60 62 63 64 70 75 77 78 79 81 82 84 85 86 87 91 92 93 97 100 103 107 108 110 111 114 116 117 118 119 129 130 131 132 133 135 144 146 147 148 **P**6 **S** Riverside Health System, Newport News, VA
Primary Contact: Esther Desimini, Administrator
CFO: Jeri Sibley, Director Revenue Cycle
CMO: Randy Ferrance, M.D., President Medical Staff
CHR: Jaime Cook, Director Human Resources
Web address: www.riverside–online.com
Control: Other not–for–profit (including NFP Corporation) **Service:** General Medical and Surgical

Staffed Beds: 15 **Admissions:** 1602 **Census:** 14 **Outpatient Visits:** 63083 **Births:** 0 **Total Expense ($000):** 52641 **Payroll Expense ($000):** 14110 **Personnel:** 199

TAZEWELL—Tazewell County

☒ **CARILION TAZEWELL COMMUNITY HOSPITAL (490117)**, 141 Ben Bolt Avenue, Zip 24651–9700; tel. 276/988–8700 **A**1 10 **F**3 11 15 29 30 34 39 40 44 45 50 59 62 64 68 75 77 81 85 87 91 93 107 111 114 119 133 135 146 **S** Carilion Clinic, Roanoke, VA
Primary Contact: Kathren Dowdy, MSN, Regional Hospital Senior Director
CMO: Michael Rorrer, M.D., Chief of Staff
CHR: Carrie Boggess, Human Resources Generalist
CNO: Kathren Dowdy, MSN, Senior Director, Chief Executive Officer and Chief Nursing Officer
Web address: www.carilionclinic.org/Carilion/Carilion+Tazewell+Community+Hospital
Control: Other not–for–profit (including NFP Corporation) **Service:** General Medical and Surgical

Staffed Beds: 8 **Admissions:** 617 **Census:** 7 **Outpatient Visits:** 14966 **Births:** 0 **Total Expense ($000):** 14018 **Payroll Expense ($000):** 5292 **Personnel:** 100

VA

VIRGINIA BEACH—Virginia Beach City County

★ ◇ **SENTARA PRINCESS ANNE HOSPITAL (490119)**, 2025 Glenn Mitchell Drive, Zip 23456–0178; tel. 757/507–1000 **A**2 3 5 10 21 **F**3 8 11 13 15 18 20 22 26 28 29 30 31 34 35 36 37 38 39 40 41 44 45 46 47 49 50 54 55 56 57 58 59 60 61 63 64 65 68 70 71 72 73 74 75 76 77 78 79 81 82 84 85 86 87 91 92 93 94 96 97 100 102 110 111 113 114 115 118 119 126 129 130 131 132 135 141 144 146 147 148 **P**6 **S** Sentara Healthcare, Norfolk, VA
Primary Contact: Thomas B. Thames, M.D., President
COO: Howard P. Kern, Chief Operating Officer
CFO: Robert Broermann, Senior Vice President and Chief Financial Officer
CMO: Terry Gilliland, M.D., Senior Vice President and Chief Medical Officer
CIO: Bert Reese, Chief Information Officer
CHR: Michael V. Taylor, Vice President Human Resources
CNO: Grace Myers, MSN, Vice President, Nurse Executive
Web address: www.sentara.com
Control: Other not–for–profit (including NFP Corporation) **Service:** General Medical and Surgical

Staffed Beds: 160 **Admissions:** 11687 **Census:** 139 **Outpatient Visits:** 356710 **Births:** 2773 **Total Expense ($000):** 200464 **Payroll Expense ($000):** 64448 **Personnel:** 1379

★ ◇ **SENTARA VIRGINIA BEACH GENERAL HOSPITAL (490057)**, 1060 First Colonial Road, Zip 23454–3002; tel. 757/395–8000 **A**2 3 5 10 21 **F**3 11 15 17 18 20 22 24 26 28 29 30 31 34 36 37 38 39 40 41 42 43 44 45 46 47 48 49 50 51 53 54 55 56 57 58 59 60 61 63 64 65 68 70 71 74 75 77 78 79 81 82 84 85 86 87 90 92 93 94 96 97 98 100 101 102 103 107 108 109 110 111 114 115 118 119 120 121 123 126 129 130 131 132 135 141 142 144 146 147 148 **P**6 **S** Sentara Healthcare, Norfolk, VA
Primary Contact: Elwood Bernard Boone, III, FACHE, President
COO: Joanne Inman, Vice President Operations
CFO: Marley Nacey, Director Finance
CHR: Michelle Meekins, Manager Human Resources
CNO: Peggy Braun, R.N., Vice President Patient Care Services and Chief Nurse Executive
Web address: www.sentara.com
Control: Other not–for–profit (including NFP Corporation) **Service:** General Medical and Surgical

Staffed Beds: 259 **Admissions:** 13606 **Census:** 188 **Outpatient Visits:** 436248 **Births:** 0 **Total Expense ($000):** 247434 **Payroll Expense ($000):** 104163 **Personnel:** 1687

☐ **VIRGINIA BEACH PSYCHIATRIC CENTER (494025)**, 1100 First Colonial Road, Zip 23454–2403; tel. 757/496–6000 **A**1 10 **F**5 38 71 98 102 104 105 **S** Universal Health Services, Inc., King of Prussia, PA
Primary Contact: Dustin Davis, Chief Executive Officer
Web address: www.vbpcweb.com
Control: Corporation, Investor–owned, for–profit **Service:** Psychiatric

Staffed Beds: 100 **Admissions:** 4142 **Census:** 77 **Births:** 0

WARRENTON—Fauquier County

✉ △ **FAUQUIER HOSPITAL (490023)**, 500 Hospital Drive, Zip 20186–3099; tel. 540/316–5000, (Nonreporting) **A**1 3 5 7 10 **S** LifePoint Health, Brentwood, TN
Primary Contact: Rodger H. Baker, President and Chief Executive Officer
CFO: Lionel J. Phillips, Vice President Financial Services
CMO: Anhtai H. Nguyen, M.D., Vice President Medical Affairs and Chief Medical Officer
CIO: Donna Staton, Chief Information Officer
CHR: Katy Reeves, Vice President Human Resources
CNO: Linda Sharkey, R.N., Vice President Patient Care Services and Chief Nurse Executive
Web address: www.fauquierhospital.org
Control: Other not–for–profit (including NFP Corporation) **Service:** General Medical and Surgical

Staffed Beds: 86

WILLIAMSBURG—James City County

☐ **EASTERN STATE HOSPITAL (490109)**, 4601 Ironbound Road, Zip 23188–2652; tel. 757/253–5161 **A**1 3 5 10 **F**7 29 30 39 50 53 56 57 58 59 65 68 75 77 82 84 86 87 94 98 100 101 102 103 130 132 135 143 146 148 **S** Virginia Department of Mental Health, Richmond, VA
Primary Contact: John M. Favret, Director
CFO: E. Clifford Love, Director Fiscal Services
CMO: Guillermo Schrader, M.D., Acting Medical Director
CIO: Barbara Lambert, Director Healthcare Compliance
CHR: Edie Rogan, Manager Human Resources
Web address: www.esh.dmhmrsas.virginia.gov/
Control: State–Government, nonfederal **Service:** Psychiatric

Staffed Beds: 300 **Admissions:** 764 **Census:** 291 **Outpatient Visits:** 0 **Births:** 0

☐ **RIVERSIDE DOCTORS' HOSPITAL (490143)**, 1500 Commonwealth Avenue, Zip 23185–5229; tel. 757/585–2200 **A**1 10 21 **F**3 11 28 29 34 35 40 44 45 50 57 59 64 70 74 75 77 79 81 82 85 86 87 91 92 107 108 115 118 119 120 121 123 130 132 146 148 **P**6 **S** Riverside Health System, Newport News, VA
Primary Contact: Adria Vanhoosier, Administrator
CNO: Arlene Messina, R.N., Director of Nursing
Web address: www.riversideonline.com/rdhw
Control: Other not–for–profit (including NFP Corporation) **Service:** General Medical and Surgical

Staffed Beds: 13 **Admissions:** 1452 **Census:** 12 **Outpatient Visits:** 24874 **Births:** 0 **Total Expense ($000):** 39383 **Payroll Expense ($000):** 10752 **Personnel:** 220

★ ◇ **SENTARA WILLIAMSBURG REGIONAL MEDICAL CENTER (490066)**, 100 Sentara Circle, Zip 23188–5713; tel. 757/984–6000 **A**2 10 21 **F**3 8 11 13 15 18 20 22 28 29 30 31 34 35 36 37 39 40 41 43 44 45 46 47 48 49 50 51 54 55 56 57 58 59 60 61 63 64 65 68 70 74 75 76 77 78 79 81 82 84 85 86 87 89 90 91 92 93 94 96 97 100 102 103 107 108 110 111 114 115 116 117 118 119 129 130 131 132 135 141 144 146 147 148 **P**6 **S** Sentara Healthcare, Norfolk, VA
Primary Contact: David J. Masterson, President
CFO: Andreas Roehrle, Director Finance
CMO: Joe Robbins, M.D., Vice President Medical Affairs
CIO: Mike Freeman, Director Information Technology
CHR: Lois B. Demerich, Director Human Resources
CNO: Donna Wilmoth, Vice President Patient Care Services and Chief Nursing Officer
Web address: www.sentara.com
Control: Other not–for–profit (including NFP Corporation) **Service:** General Medical and Surgical

Staffed Beds: 145 **Admissions:** 6624 **Census:** 69 **Outpatient Visits:** 293840 **Births:** 940 **Total Expense ($000):** 141495 **Payroll Expense ($000):** 56662 **Personnel:** 729

☐ **THE PAVILION AT WILLIAMSBURG PLACE (494032)**, 5483 Mooretown Road, Zip 23188–2108; tel. 757/565–0106 **A**1 10 **F**29 98 103 **P**6
Primary Contact: Gary Williams, Executive Director
CNO: Vicki Smith, Director of Nursing
Web address: www.pavilionwp.com
Control: Corporation, Investor–owned, for–profit **Service:** Psychiatric

Staffed Beds: 57 **Admissions:** 1385 **Census:** 49 **Outpatient Visits:** 0 **Births:** 0

WINCHESTER—Winchester City County

✉ **WINCHESTER MEDICAL CENTER (490005)**, 1840 Amherst Street, Zip 22601–2808, Mailing Address: P.O. Box 3340, Zip 22604–2540; tel. 540/536–8000 **A**1 2 3 5 10 **F**3 5 11 12 13 15 17 18 20 22 24 26 28 29 30 31 32 34 35 38 39 40 41 43 44 45 47 49 50 51 54 56 57 58 59 61 62 64 65 68 70 71 72 74 75 76 77 78 79 80 81 82 84 85 86 87 89 90 91 92 93 97 98 100 101 102 103 107 108 110 111 114 115 116 117 118 119 120 121 123 124 129 130 131 132 135 136 146 147 148 **P**5 **S** Valley Health System, Winchester, VA
Primary Contact: Grady W. Philips, III, President
CFO: Robert Amos, Vice President and Chief Financial Officer
CMO: Nicolas Restrepo, M.D., Vice President Medical Affairs
CIO: Joan Roscoe, Chief Information Officer
CHR: Elizabeth Savage–Tracy, Vice President and Human Resources Officer
CNO: Anne Whiteside, Vice President Nursing
Web address: www.valleyhealthlink.com/WMC
Control: Other not–for–profit (including NFP Corporation) **Service:** General Medical and Surgical

Staffed Beds: 445 **Admissions:** 22385 **Census:** 317 **Outpatient Visits:** 343886 **Births:** 2217 **Total Expense ($000):** 498539 **Payroll Expense ($000):** 163057 **Personnel:** 2586

WOODBRIDGE—Prince William County

★ ◇ **SENTARA NORTHERN VIRGINIA MEDICAL CENTER (490113)**, 2300 Opitz Boulevard, Zip 22191–3399; tel. 703/523–1000 **A**2 10 21 **F**3 7 8 11 12 13 15 18 20 22 28 29 30 31 34 35 40 41 42 44 45 49 50 54 55 56 57 59 60 61 62 63 64 65 66 68 70 71 72 74 75 77 78 79 81 82 85 86 87 91 92 93 94 96 99 100 102 107 108 110 111 114 115 118 119 121 126 130 131 132 135 141 143 146 147 148 **P**6 **S** Sentara Healthcare, Norfolk, VA
Primary Contact: Stephen D. Porter, President
COO: Valerie E. Keane, FACHE, Vice President Operations
CMO: David M. Schwartz, D.O., Vice President, Medical Affairs
CIO: Thomas Ewing, Director Information Technology
CHR: Brett Willsie, Vice President Human Resources
CNO: Patricia Hill, Senior Director Nurse Executive
Web address: www.sentara.com/northernvirginia
Control: Other not–for–profit (including NFP Corporation) **Service:** General Medical and Surgical

Staffed Beds: 181 **Admissions:** 9929 **Census:** 110 **Outpatient Visits:** 349335 **Births:** 1662 **Total Expense ($000):** 203658 **Payroll Expense ($000):** 74430 **Personnel:** 1187

VA

Many Facility Codes have changed. Please refer to the AHA Guide Code Chart.
© 2016 AHA Guide

WOODSTOCK—Shenandoah County

⊠ **SHENANDOAH MEMORIAL HOSPITAL (491305)**, 759 South Main Street,
Zip 22664–1127; tel. 540/459–1100 **A**1 10 18 **F**3 11 15 28 29 30 35 40 45
50 53 57 59 64 65 68 69 70 75 77 79 81 82 87 92 93 97 107 108 110 114
118 119 130 132 133 135 146 148 **S** Valley Health System, Winchester, VA
Primary Contact: N. Travis Clark, President
CFO: Phillip Graybeal, CPA, Vice President, Finance
CMO: Greg Byrd, Vice President Medical Affairs
CIO: James Burton, Vice President and Chief Information Officer, Valley Health
CHR: Abbey Rembold, Manager, Human Resource Business Partnerships
CNO: Lisa Heishman, R.N., Vice President
Web address: www.valleyhealthlink.com/shenandoah
Control: Other not–for–profit (including NFP Corporation) **Service:** General
Medical and Surgical

Staffed Beds: 25 **Admissions:** 1532 **Census:** 16 **Outpatient Visits:** 60496
Births: 0 **Total Expense ($000):** 36767 **Payroll Expense ($000):** 16570

WYTHEVILLE—Wythe County

⊠ **WYTHE COUNTY COMMUNITY HOSPITAL (490111)**, 600 West Ridge Road,
Zip 24382–1099; tel. 276/228–0200 **A**1 2 10 20 **F**3 12 15 28 29 34 35 40
45 50 51 55 57 62 63 64 68 70 76 77 79 81 82 84 85 87 91 92 93 99 107
108 111 119 128 129 132 133 135 146 147 148 **P**6 **S** LifePoint Health,
Brentwood, TN
Primary Contact: Chad Melton, Chief Executive Officer
COO: Adam Martin, Chief Operating Officer
CFO: John D. White, Chief Financial Officer
CMO: George Farrell, M.D., Chief of Staff
CIO: Andrea Harless, Director Information Services
CHR: Kristie Walker, Director of Human Resources
CNO: Theresa Dix, R.N., Chief Nursing Officer
Web address: www.wcchcares.com
Control: Corporation, Investor–owned, for–profit **Service:** General Medical and
Surgical

Staffed Beds: 70 **Admissions:** 2129 **Census:** 23 **Outpatient Visits:** 39115
Births: 303 **Total Expense ($000):** 33712 **Payroll Expense ($000):** 14406
Personnel: 325

VA

Hospital, Medicare Provider Number, Address, Telephone, Approval, Facility, and Physician Codes, Health Care System

★ American Hospital Association (AHA) membership   ○ Healthcare Facilities Accreditation Program   ⇑ Center for Improvement in Healthcare Quality Accreditation
☐ The Joint Commission accreditation   ◇ DNV Healthcare Inc. accreditation   △ Commission on Accreditation of Rehabilitation Facilities (CARF) accreditation

WASHINGTON

ABERDEEN—Grays Harbor County

☐ **GRAYS HARBOR COMMUNITY HOSPITAL (500031)**, 915 Anderson Drive, Zip 98520–1097; tel. 360/532–8330 **A**1 10 20 **F**1 3 15 32 34 35 40 43 50 54 59 64 65 67 75 82 86 90 97 107 110 119 127 128 130 146
Primary Contact: Tom Jensen, Chief Executive Officer
COO: Larry Kahl, R.N., Chief Operating Officer
CFO: Joe Vessey, Chief Financial Officer
CMO: Anne Marie Wong, M.D., Chief Medical Officer
CIO: Brad Wallace, Director Information Services
CHR: Julie Feller, Executive Director Human Resources
CNO: Cynthia Walsh, Chief Nursing Officer
Web address: www.ghcares.org
Control: Other not–for–profit (including NFP Corporation) **Service:** General Medical and Surgical

Staffed Beds: 105 **Admissions:** 3166 **Census:** 28 **Births:** 517 **Total Expense ($000):** 100678 **Payroll Expense ($000):** 39813

ANACORTES—Skagit County

★ ◇ **ISLAND HOSPITAL (500007)**, 1211 24th Street, Zip 98221–2562; tel. 360/299–1300 **A**2 10 21 **F**3 8 11 13 15 28 29 30 31 34 35 40 43 45 50 53 57 59 62 64 70 75 76 77 78 79 81 82 85 86 89 93 96 97 99 100 104 107 108 110 111 114 115 116 119 127 129 130 132 134 135 144 146 147 148 **P**6
Primary Contact: Vincent Oliver, FACHE, Administrator
CFO: Elise Cutter, Chief Financial Officer
CIO: Tom Bluhm, Director Information Systems
CNO: Lois Pate, R.N., Chief Nursing Officer
Web address: www.islandhospital.org
Control: Hospital district or authority, Government, nonfederal **Service:** General Medical and Surgical

Staffed Beds: 43 **Admissions:** 3197 **Census:** 28 **Outpatient Visits:** 209449 **Births:** 436 **Total Expense ($000):** 94128 **Payroll Expense ($000):** 39616 **Personnel:** 581

ARLINGTON—Snohomish County

◇ **CASCADE VALLEY HOSPITAL AND CLINICS (500060)**, 330 South Stillaguamish Avenue, Zip 98223–1642; tel. 360/435–2133, (Nonreporting) **A**10 21 **S** Skagit Regional Health, Mount Vernon, WA
Primary Contact: Michael Liepman, Chief Executive Officer
CFO: Thomas Litaker, Regional Vice President and Chief Financial Officer
CMO: Peter Wolff, M.D., President Medical Staff
CIO: John Dwight, Regional Vice President and Chief Information Officer
CHR: Deborah Martin, Regional Vice President Human Resources
CNO: Michelle Sand, R.N., Vice President and Chief Nursing Officer
Web address: www.cascadevalley.org
Control: Hospital district or authority, Government, nonfederal **Service:** General Medical and Surgical

Staffed Beds: 48

AUBURN—King County

☐ △ **MULTICARE AUBURN MEDICAL CENTER (500015)**, 202 North Division, Plaza One, Zip 98001–4908; tel. 253/833–7711 **A**1 7 10 **F**3 13 18 20 22 28 29 30 34 35 40 41 43 45 49 51 57 64 65 68 70 73 74 75 76 77 79 81 84 85 87 93 96 98 102 103 107 108 111 114 115 119 126 129 130 132 135 146 148 **S** MultiCare Health System, Tacoma, WA
Primary Contact: Glenn Kasman, President and Market Leader
CFO: Anna Loomis, Senior Vice President Chief Financial Officer
CMO: Chad Krilich, M.D., Chief Med Officer–AMC/CMC
CHR: Kevin B. Dull, Senior Vice President Human Potential
CNO: Roseanna Bell, Chief Nurse Executive
Web address: www.https://www.multicare.org/auburn–medical–center/
Control: Other not–for–profit (including NFP Corporation) **Service:** General Medical and Surgical

Staffed Beds: 133 **Admissions:** 6742 **Census:** 99 **Outpatient Visits:** 63732 **Births:** 1198 **Total Expense ($000):** 156309 **Payroll Expense ($000):** 62026 **Personnel:** 672

BELLEVUE—King County

✠ **OVERLAKE MEDICAL CENTER (500051)**, 1035 116th Avenue N.E., Zip 98004–4604; tel. 425/688–5000 **A**1 2 10 **F**3 11 12 13 15 17 18 20 22 24 26 29 30 31 34 35 36 37 38 39 40 41 43 44 45 46 47 48 49 54 56 57 58 59 61 64 65 68 70 72 73 74 75 76 77 78 79 81 82 84 85 86 87 91 92 93 97 98 100 101 102 103 104 105 107 108 110 111 114 115 116 117 118 119 120 121 123 124 126 130 131 132 134 135 144 145 146 147 148 **P**6
Primary Contact: J. Michael Marsh, President and Chief Executive Officer
COO: Thomas DeBord, Chief Operating Officer
CFO: Gary McLaughlin, Executive Vice President and Chief Financial Officer
CMO: David Knoepfler, M.D., Chief Medical Officer
CHR: Lisa M. Brock, Chief Human Resource Officer
CNO: Julie Clayton, R.N., Chief Nursing Officer and Vice President Patient Care Services
Web address: www.overlakehospital.org
Control: Other not–for–profit (including NFP Corporation) **Service:** General Medical and Surgical

Staffed Beds: 282 **Admissions:** 18416 **Census:** 172 **Outpatient Visits:** 234187 **Births:** 3746 **Total Expense ($000):** 468693 **Payroll Expense ($000):** 192374 **Personnel:** 2039

BELLINGHAM—Whatcom County

★ △ ◇ **PEACEHEALTH ST. JOSEPH MEDICAL CENTER (500030)**, 2901 Squalicum Parkway, Zip 98225–1851; tel. 360/734–5400 **A**2 5 7 10 20 21 **F**2 3 13 17 18 20 22 24 26 28 29 30 31 34 35 40 41 43 45 46 47 48 49 50 51 56 57 58 59 63 64 65 70 74 75 76 77 78 79 81 84 85 86 87 89 90 92 93 94 96 97 98 106 107 108 109 114 115 118 119 120 121 123 129 130 131 132 135 141 146 148 **S** PeaceHealth, Vancouver, WA
Primary Contact: Dale Zender, President Hospital Services NW
COO: Stephen R. Omta, Chief Operating Officer
CFO: Carolyn Foster, Interim Executive Director and Chief Financial Officer
CMO: Chris Sprowl, M.D., Vice President
CIO: Kelly Lundy, Chief Information Officer
CHR: Cindy C. Klein, Vice President Human Resources
Web address: www.peacehealth.org
Control: Church–operated, Nongovernment, not–for profit **Service:** General Medical and Surgical

Staffed Beds: 253 **Admissions:** 15518 **Census:** 174 **Births:** 1845 **Total Expense ($000):** 460505 **Payroll Expense ($000):** 175436

ST. JOSEPH HOSPITAL See PeaceHealth St. Joseph Medical Center

BREMERTON—Kitsap County

✠ **HARRISON MEDICAL CENTER (500039)**, 2520 Cherry Avenue, Zip 98310–4229; tel. 360/744–3911 **A**1 2 10 **F**3 11 12 13 15 18 20 22 24 26 28 29 30 31 34 35 38 40 43 44 45 46 49 50 54 57 59 64 70 73 74 75 76 77 78 79 80 81 82 84 85 86 87 93 94 96 107 108 110 111 114 115 117 119 120 121 124 126 129 130 132 135 144 146 147 148 **S** Catholic Health Initiatives, Englewood, CO
Primary Contact: David W. Schultz, FACHE, President
CFO: Mike Fitzgerald, Chief Financial Officer
CMO: Michael Anderson, M.D., Senior Vice President Quality and Chief Medical Officer
CIO: Rand Strobel, Regional Chief Information Officer, Information Technology Services
CHR: Marie LaMarche, Executive Director, Human Resources, Organizational Development, Employee Health
CNO: Jeanell Rasmussen, R.N., Senior Vice President and Chief Nursing Officer
Web address: www.harrisonmedical.org
Control: Church–operated, Nongovernment, not–for profit **Service:** General Medical and Surgical

Staffed Beds: 262 **Admissions:** 13285 **Census:** 153 **Outpatient Visits:** 237217 **Births:** 1834 **Total Expense ($000):** 357275 **Payroll Expense ($000):** 128306 **Personnel:** 2185

✠ **NAVAL HOSPITAL BREMERTON**, One Boone Road, Zip 98312–1898; tel. 360/475–4000 **A**1 3 5 **F**3 5 8 12 13 15 18 29 30 32 33 34 35 38 39 45 50 53 54 57 59 64 65 74 75 76 77 79 81 85 86 87 92 93 97 99 100 101 104 107 108 110 111 114 115 119 130 131 132 134 135 143 144 146 147 **S** Bureau of Medicine and Surgery, Department of the Navy, Falls Church, VA
Primary Contact: Commander David Weiss, Commanding Officer
CFO: Judith Hogan, Comptroller and Director Resources and Logistics
CIO: Patrick Flaherty, Director Management Information
Web address: www.med.navy.mil/sites/nhbrem/Pages/default.aspx
Control: Navy, Government, federal **Service:** General Medical and Surgical

Staffed Beds: 23 **Admissions:** 1501 **Census:** 8 **Outpatient Visits:** 312935 **Births:** 713 **Personnel:** 1594

WA

Many Facility Codes have changed. Please refer to the AHA Guide Code Chart.   © 2016 AHA Guide

BREWSTER—Okanogan County

THREE RIVERS HOSPITAL (501324), 507 Hospital Way, Zip 98812–0577;
Mailing Address: P.O. Box 577, Zip 98812–0577; tel. 509/689–2517,
(Nonreporting) **A**10 18
Primary Contact: Scott Graham, Chief Executive Officer
CFO: Jennifer Munson, Chief Financial Officer
CMO: Gordon Tagge, M.D., President Medical Staff
CIO: Edgar Alejandro Arellano, Chief Information Technologist
CHR: Anita Fisk, Director Human Resources
CNO: Gretchen Aguilar, Director Patient Care and Chief Nursing Officer
Web address: www.threerivershospital.net
Control: Hospital district or authority, Government, nonfederal **Service:** General
Medical and Surgical

Staffed Beds: 20

BURIEN—King County

☒ △ **HIGHLINE MEDICAL CENTER (500011)**, 16251 Sylvester Road S.W.,
Zip 98166–3052; tel. 206/244–9970, (Includes HIGHLINE SPECIALTY CENTER,
12844 MILITARY ROAD FORK, TUKWILA, ZIP 98168; MARK BENEDUM,
ADMINISTRATOR) **A**1 2 7 10 **F**3 8 11 13 15 18 29 30 34 35 38 40 43 44 45
49 50 51 57 59 70 72 74 75 76 79 80 81 85 86 87 92 93 107 108 110 111
114 115 117 119 130 132 135 146 147 **S** Catholic Health Initiatives,
Englewood, CO
Primary Contact: Anthony McLean, President
CMO: Dennis De Leon, M.D., Associate Chief Medical Officer and Vice President
Medical Affairs
CHR: Grace M. Henley, Assistant Administrator Human Resources
CNO: Kim Baisch, R.N., Associate Vice President Patient Care Services
Web address: www.hchnet.org
Control: Church–operated, Nongovernment, not–for profit **Service:** General
Medical and Surgical

Staffed Beds: 128 **Admissions:** 7122 **Census:** 88 **Outpatient Visits:** 112839
Births: 888 **Total Expense ($000):** 174465 **Payroll Expense ($000):** 68804
Personnel: 1184

☐ **REGIONAL HOSPITAL FOR RESPIRATORY AND COMPLEX CARE (502001)**,
16251 Sylvester Road S.W., Zip 98166–3017; tel. 206/248–4548 **A**1 10 **F**1 29
30 44 50 75 85 87 130 135 148
Primary Contact: Anne McBride, Chief Executive Officer
CMO: Embra Roper, Chief Medical Officer
CHR: Valerie Albano, Director, Human Resources
CNO: Christi Sifri, Chief Nursing Executive
Web address: www.regionalhospital.org
Control: Church–operated, Nongovernment, not–for profit **Service:** Long–Term
Acute Care hospital

Staffed Beds: 26 **Admissions:** 186 **Census:** 20 **Outpatient Visits:** 0 **Births:**
0 **Total Expense ($000):** 16573 **Payroll Expense ($000):** 6913 **Personnel:**
94

CENTRALIA—Lewis County

☒ **PROVIDENCE CENTRALIA HOSPITAL (500019)**, 914 South Scheuber Road,
Zip 98531–9027; tel. 360/736–2803 **A**1 3 10 20 **F**3 8 11 13 15 30 31 34 35
40 43 45 47 51 57 58 59 64 68 70 75 76 77 78 79 80 81 82 83 84 85 86
87 93 107 108 110 111 114 115 116 117 118 119 120 121 123 124 130
131 132 146 148 **S** Providence St. Joseph Health, Renton, WA
Primary Contact: Medrice Coluccio, R.N., Southwest Region Chief Executive
CFO: Denise Marroni, Chief Financial Officer
CMO: Kevin Caserta, M.D., Chief Medical Officer
CIO: Kerry Miles, Site Director
CHR: Susan Meenk, Vice President Service Area
CNO: Michelle James, Regional Chief Nursing Officer
Web address: www.providence.org
Control: Church–operated, Nongovernment, not–for profit **Service:** General
Medical and Surgical

Staffed Beds: 91 **Admissions:** 5241 **Census:** 47 **Births:** 634

CHELAN—Chelan County

★ **LAKE CHELAN COMMUNITY HOSPITAL (501334)**, 503 East Highland Avenue,
Zip 98816–8631, Mailing Address: P.O. Box 908, Zip 98816–0908;
tel. 509/682–3300 **A**10 18 **F**5 7 8 11 13 15 29 30 32 34 35 36 38 40 41 43
44 45 50 56 57 59 63 64 65 66 68 71 74 75 76 77 79 80 81 84 85 86 87
91 92 93 94 96 97 99 100 101 102 103 104 106 107 108 110 111 119 127
130 131 132 133 134 135 143 144 146 147 **P**6
Primary Contact: Kevin Abel, Chief Executive Officer
COO: Brad Hankins, Chief Operating Quality Officer
CFO: Vickie Bodle, Chief Financial Officer
CMO: Ty Witt, M.D., Chief Medical Officer
CIO: Ross Hurd, Chief Information Officer
CHR: DeLynn K. Barnett, Director Human Resources
CNO: Carol Nunley Velasquez, R.N., Chief Nursing Officer
Web address: www.lakechelancommunityhospital.com
Control: Hospital district or authority, Government, nonfederal **Service:** General
Medical and Surgical

Staffed Beds: 25 **Admissions:** 735 **Census:** 15 **Outpatient Visits:** 27532
Births: 82 **Total Expense ($000):** 25489 **Payroll Expense ($000):** 15189
Personnel: 218

CHEWELAH—Stevens County

☒ **PROVIDENCE ST. JOSEPH'S HOSPITAL (501309)**, 500 East Webster Street,
Zip 99109–9523; tel. 509/935–8211, (Total facility includes 40 beds in nursing
home–type unit) **A**1 10 18 **F**3 8 10 11 15 29 30 34 35 40 43 44 45 57 59 65
75 79 81 82 84 87 91 93 107 114 119 128 133 146 148 **P**6 **S** Providence St.
Joseph Health, Renton, WA
Primary Contact: Ronald G. Rehn, Chief Executive Officer
CFO: Helen Andrus, Chief Financial Officer
CMO: Jeff Collins, Chief Medical Officer
CNO: Deborah Watson, R.N., Chief Nursing Officer
Web address: www.washington.providence.org/hospitals/st–josephs–hospital/
Control: Church–operated, Nongovernment, not–for profit **Service:** General
Medical and Surgical

Staffed Beds: 65 **Admissions:** 451 **Census:** 45 **Outpatient Visits:** 26593
Births: 0 **Total Expense ($000):** 14751 **Payroll Expense ($000):** 8807
Personnel: 143

CLARKSTON—Asotin County

★ ◇ **TRI–STATE MEMORIAL HOSPITAL (501332)**, 1221 Highland Avenue,
Zip 99403–2829, Mailing Address: P.O. Box 189, Zip 99403–0189;
tel. 509/758–5511 **A**10 18 21 **F**3 8 11 15 34 40 43 45 57 59 60 65 70 75
79 81 82 85 107 110 111 119 129 130 132 133 135 144 146 147 148 **P**6
Primary Contact: Donald Wee, Chief Executive Officer
CFO: Alex Town, Vice President Finance
CMO: Don Greggain, M.D., Physician Network Director
CIO: Joleen Carper, Vice President Quality and Risk
CHR: Regana Davis, Vice President Human Resources
CNO: Rhonda Mason, Vice President of Patient Care Services
Web address: www.tsmh.org
Control: Other not–for–profit (including NFP Corporation) **Service:** General
Medical and Surgical

Staffed Beds: 35 **Admissions:** 1200 **Census:** 11 **Outpatient Visits:** 264755
Births: 0

COLFAX—Whitman County

★ **WHITMAN HOSPITAL AND MEDICAL CENTER (501327)**, 1200 West Fairview
Street, Zip 99111–9579; tel. 509/397–3435 **A**10 18 **F**3 13 15 29 34 35 40 43
45 50 53 64 68 75 76 79 81 84 85 87 93 107 110 111 119 130 133 **P**6
S Providence St. Joseph Health, Renton, WA
Primary Contact: Hank Hanigan, MS, R.N., Chief Executive Officer
CFO: Hank Hanigan, MS, Interim Chief Financial Officer
CMO: Jeffrey Jones, Chief of Staff
CHR: Michelle Ellis, Director Human Resources
CNO: Sandy Fitzmaurice, MS, Interim Chief Nursing Officer
Web address: www.whitmanhospital.org
Control: Hospital district or authority, Government, nonfederal **Service:** General
Medical and Surgical

Staffed Beds: 25 **Admissions:** 534 **Census:** 5 **Outpatient Visits:** 15809
Births: 41 **Total Expense ($000):** 25357 **Payroll Expense ($000):** 10172
Personnel: 178

WA

COLVILLE—Stevens County

✠ **PROVIDENCE MOUNT CARMEL HOSPITAL (501326)**, 982 East Columbia Avenue, Zip 99114–3352; tel. 509/685–5100 **A**1 3 10 18 **F**3 11 13 15 29 30 34 40 43 44 45 57 59 64 70 75 76 77 79 81 82 84 85 86 87 93 107 108 115 118 119 123 129 131 132 133 135 146 148 **P**6 **S** Providence St. Joseph Health, Renton, WA
Primary Contact: Ronald G. Rehn, Chief Executive Officer
CFO: Helen Andrus, Chief Financial Officer
CNO: Deborah Watson, R.N., Chief Nursing Officer
Web address: www.mtcarmelhospital.org
Control: Church–operated, Nongovernment, not–for profit **Service:** General Medical and Surgical

Staffed Beds: 25 **Admissions:** 1160 **Census:** 13 **Outpatient Visits:** 71249 **Births:** 230 **Total Expense ($000):** 30403 **Payroll Expense ($000):** 14899 **Personnel:** 223

COUPEVILLE—Island County

★ **WHIDBEYHEALTH (501339)**, 101 North Main Street, Zip 98239–3413; tel. 360/678–5151, (Nonreporting) **A**2 10 18
Primary Contact: Geri Forbes, Chief Executive Officer
CMO: Gabe Barrio, M.D., Chief of Staff
CNO: Linda Stephens Gipson, MSN, Chief Nursing Officer
Web address: www.whidbeygen.org
Control: Hospital district or authority, Government, nonfederal **Service:** General Medical and Surgical

Staffed Beds: 25

DAVENPORT—Lincoln County

★ **LINCOLN HOSPITAL (501305)**, 10 Nicholls Street, Zip 99122–9729; tel. 509/725–7101, (Total facility includes 35 beds in nursing home–type unit) **A**10 18 **F**7 10 11 15 29 40 46 54 57 59 64 65 77 81 85 93 97 107 119 128 130 133 135 148
Primary Contact: Tyson Lacy, Chief Executive Officer and Superintendent
CFO: Tim O'Connell, Chief Financial Officer
CMO: Fred Reed, M.D., Chief of Staff
CIO: Elliott Donson, Chief Information Specialist
CHR: Becky Bailey, Director Human Resources
CNO: Jennifer Larmer, R.N., Chief Clinical Officer
Web address: www.lincolnhospital.org
Control: Hospital district or authority, Government, nonfederal **Service:** General Medical and Surgical

Staffed Beds: 60 **Admissions:** 474 **Census:** 13

DAYTON—Columbia County

COLUMBIA COUNTY HEALTH SYSTEM (501302), 1012 South Third Street, Zip 99328–1696; tel. 509/382–2531 **A**10 18 **F**3 11 34 35 40 43 50 57 59 64 65 68 75 77 85 87 93 97 107 111 127 130 132 133 135 143 146 148
Primary Contact: Shane McGuire, Chief Executive Officer
CFO: Lee H. Holter, Chief Financial Officer
CHR: Steven J. Stahl, Director Human Resources
CNO: Stephanie Carpenter, Director of Nursing Services
Web address: www.cchd–wa.org
Control: Hospital district or authority, Government, nonfederal **Service:** General Medical and Surgical

Staffed Beds: 59 **Admissions:** 156 **Census:** 35 **Outpatient Visits:** 9000 **Births:** 0

EDMONDS—Snohomish County

STEVENS HEALTHCARE See Swedish/Edmonds

✠ **SWEDISH/EDMONDS (500026)**, 21601 76th Avenue West, Zip 98026–7506; tel. 425/640–4000 **A**1 2 10 **F**2 3 11 13 15 18 20 22 28 29 30 31 34 35 38 40 41 43 45 49 56 59 60 61 64 65 68 70 73 74 75 76 77 78 79 81 82 84 85 87 92 93 96 98 100 101 102 103 104 105 107 108 111 114 118 119 124 129 130 131 132 135 141 146 147 148 **P**6 **S** Swedish Health Services, Seattle, WA
Primary Contact: Jennifer Graves, R.N., MS, Chief Executive
COO: Sarah Zabel, Vice President, Operations
CMO: Sandeep Sachdeva, M.D., Vice President Medical Affairs
CNO: Jean Doerge, R.N., Nurse Executive
Web address: www.swedish.org
Control: Other not–for–profit (including NFP Corporation) **Service:** General Medical and Surgical

Staffed Beds: 161 **Admissions:** 9509 **Census:** 116 **Outpatient Visits:** 159322 **Births:** 1166 **Total Expense ($000):** 258207 **Payroll Expense ($000):** 87322

ELLENSBURG—Kittitas County

★ **KITTITAS VALLEY HEALTHCARE (501333)**, 603 South Chestnut Street, Zip 98926–3875; tel. 509/962–7302, (Nonreporting) **A**3 10 18
Primary Contact: Julie Petersen, Interim Chief Executive Officer
COO: Catherine Bambrick, Chief Operating Officer
CFO: Libby Allgood, Chief Financial Officer
CMO: Don Solberg, M.D., Chief Medical Officer
CNO: Rhonda C. Holden, R.N., Chief Nursing Officer
Web address: www.kvhealthcare.org
Control: Hospital district or authority, Government, nonfederal **Service:** General Medical and Surgical

Staffed Beds: 25

ELMA—Grays Harbor County

SUMMIT PACIFIC MEDICAL CENTER (501304), 600 East Main Street, Zip 98541–9560; tel. 360/346–2222, (Nonreporting) **A**10 18
Primary Contact: Renee K. Jensen, Chief Executive Officer
COO: Tim G. O'Haver, Chief Operating Officer
CFO: William Callicoat, Chief Financial Officer
CMO: William Hurley, M.D., Chief Medical Officer
CIO: Jeff Painter, Manager Information Technology
CHR: Mindy Portchy, Manager Human Resources
CNO: Brenda West, R.N., Chief Nursing Officer
Web address: www.markreed.org
Control: Corporation, Investor–owned, for–profit **Service:** General Medical and Surgical

Staffed Beds: 6

ENUMCLAW—King County

★ **ST. ELIZABETH HOSPITAL (501335)**, 1455 Battersby Avenue, Zip 98022–3634, Mailing Address: P.O. Box 218, Zip 98022–0218; tel. 360/802–8800 **A**10 18 **F**3 13 15 18 29 30 34 35 38 40 44 45 50 57 64 70 74 75 76 79 81 85 87 107 108 110 111 115 119 130 135 146 **S** Catholic Health Initiatives, Englewood, CO
Primary Contact: Syd Bersante, R.N., President
COO: Joseph Wilczek, Chief Executive Officer
CFO: Philip Hjembo, Chief Financial Officer
CHR: Jerilyn Ray, Manager Human Resources
Web address: www.fhshealth.org
Control: Church–operated, Nongovernment, not–for profit **Service:** General Medical and Surgical

Staffed Beds: 25 **Admissions:** 1583 **Census:** 13 **Outpatient Visits:** 38155 **Births:** 310 **Total Expense ($000):** 44645 **Payroll Expense ($000):** 17518

EPHRATA—Grant County

★ **COLUMBIA BASIN HOSPITAL (501317)**, 200 Nat Washington Way, Zip 98823–1982; tel. 509/754–4631, (Total facility includes 12 beds in nursing home–type unit) **A**10 18 **F**3 10 11 34 40 50 54 56 57 59 64 68 75 87 93 96 97 107 119 127 130 133 135 143 146 148 **P**6
Primary Contact: Rosalinda Kibby, Superintendent and Administrator
CFO: Rhonda Handley, Chief Financial Officer
CMO: Lowell C. Allred, M.D., Chief of Staff
CHR: Suzanne Little, Human Resources Specialist
Web address: www.columbiabasinhospital.org
Control: Hospital district or authority, Government, nonfederal **Service:** General Medical and Surgical

Staffed Beds: 37 **Admissions:** 270 **Census:** 27 **Outpatient Visits:** 17904 **Births:** 0

EVERETT—Snohomish County

✠ △ **PROVIDENCE REGIONAL MEDICAL CENTER EVERETT (500014)**, 1321 Colby Avenue, Zip 98201–1665, Mailing Address: P.O. Box 1147, Zip 98206–1147; tel. 425/261–2000, (Includes PROVIDENCE EVERETT MEDICAL CENTER – COLBY CAMPUS, 1321 Colby Avenue, Zip 98206, Mailing Address: P.O. Box 1147, Zip 98206; tel. 425/261–2000; PROVIDENCE EVERETT MEDICAL CENTER – PACIFIC CAMPUS, Pacific and Nassau Streets, Zip 98201, Mailing Address: P.O. Box 1067, Zip 98206–1067; tel. 206/258–7123) **A**1 2 3 5 7 10 **F**3 4 5 8 11 12 13 15 17 18 20 22 24 26 28 29 30 31 32 34 35 36 38 40 43 44 45 46 47 48 49 50 53 54 55 56 57 58 59 61 64 65 66 68 70 72 73 74 75 76 77 78 79 80 81 82 84 85 86 87 89 90 93 94 96 97 100 107 108 109 110 111 114 115 116 117 118 119 120 121 123 124 126 129 130 131 132 135 144 145 146 147 148 **P**6 **S** Providence St. Joseph Health, Renton, WA
Primary Contact: Preston M. Simmons, FACHE, Chief Executive Officer
COO: Kim Williams, R.N., Chief Operating Officer
CFO: Sheri Feeney, Chief Financial Officer
CMO: Joanne Roberts, M.D., Chief Medical Officer
CIO: Matt Wonser, Director, Information Services
CHR: Lori A. Vocca, Vice President Human Resources
CNO: Barbara M. Hyland–Hill, R.N., Chief Nursing Officer
Web address: www.providence.org
Control: Church–operated, Nongovernment, not–for profit **Service:** General Medical and Surgical

Staffed Beds: 501 **Admissions:** 28603 **Census:** 371 **Outpatient Visits:** 478814 **Births:** 4578 **Total Expense ($000):** 524120 **Payroll Expense ($000):** 223099 **Personnel:** 2914

WA

Many Facility Codes have changed. Please refer to the AHA Guide Code Chart. © 2016 AHA Guide

FEDERAL WAY—King County

⊠ **ST. FRANCIS HOSPITAL (500141)**, 34515 Ninth Avenue South,
Zip 98003–6799; tel. 253/944–8100 **A**1 2 10 **F**3 8 11 12 13 15 18 20 22 29
30 34 35 38 40 43 44 45 49 50 51 57 59 64 70 73 74 75 76 77 78 79 80
81 85 86 87 92 93 107 108 110 111 114 117 119 126 129 130 132 135
146 147 **S** Catholic Health Initiatives, Englewood, CO
Primary Contact: Anthony McLean, President
CFO: Mike Fitzgerald, Chief Financial Officer
CIO: Rand Strobel, Regional Chief Information Officer
CHR: Les Soltis, Director – Human Resources
Web address: www.fhshealth.org
Control: Church–operated, Nongovernment, not–for profit **Service:** General
Medical and Surgical

Staffed Beds: 120 **Admissions:** 8568 **Census:** 89 **Outpatient Visits:** 162005
Births: 1267 **Total Expense ($000):** 187197 **Payroll Expense ($000):**
69281 **Personnel:** 1062

FORKS—Clallam County

◇ **FORKS COMMUNITY HOSPITAL (501325)**, 530 Bogachiel Way,
Zip 98331–9120; tel. 360/374–6271, (Total facility includes 20 beds in nursing
home–type unit) **A**10 18 21 **F**40 41 81 91 107 110 127 129 130 133
Primary Contact: Tim Cournyer, Administrator
CFO: Joe Bradick, Chief Financial Officer
CIO: Andrea Perkins–Peppers, Chief Information Officer
CHR: Cindy Paget, Chief Human Resources Officer
CNO: Laura Kripinski, Chief Nursing Officer
Web address: www.forkshospital.org
Control: Hospital district or authority, Government, nonfederal **Service:** General
Medical and Surgical

Staffed Beds: 45 **Admissions:** 373 **Census:** 22 **Outpatient Visits:** 6003
Births: 62 **Total Expense ($000):** 27161 **Payroll Expense ($000):** 12391
Personnel: 200

FRIDAY HARBOR—San Juan County

★ ◇ **PEACEHEALTH PEACE ISLAND MEDICAL CENTER (501340)**, 1117
Spring Street, Zip 98250–9782; tel. 360/378–2141 **A**10 18 21 **F**3 8 11 15 29 30
31 34 35 40 44 45 46 47 48 49 50 57 59 64 65 68 77 78 81 84 87 97 102
107 108 110 115 119 130 135 146 148 **S** PeaceHealth, Vancouver, WA
Primary Contact: Merry Ann Keane, Chief Administrative Officer
CFO: Carolyn Foster, Chief Financial Officer
CMO: Michael Sullivan, M.D., Medical Director Emergency Services
CHR: Lorraine Allison, Human Resource Partner
CNO: Sheryl Murphy, Chief Nursing Officer and Director of Clinical Services
Web address: www.peacehealth.org
Control: Other not–for–profit (including NFP Corporation) **Service:** General
Medical and Surgical

Staffed Beds: 10 **Admissions:** 85 **Census:** 1 **Outpatient Visits:** 11555
Births: 0 **Total Expense ($000):** 12759 **Payroll Expense ($000):** 5571

GIG HARBOR—Pierce County

⊠ **ST. ANTHONY HOSPITAL (500151)**, 11567 Canterwood Boulevard N.W.,
Zip 98332–5812; tel. 253/530–2000 **A**1 10 **F**3 11 12 15 18 20 29 30 31 34
38 40 44 45 49 50 51 57 59 60 64 70 74 75 78 79 81 85 87 92 93 107
108 110 111 114 115 119 129 130 132 135 146 147 **S** Catholic Health
Initiatives, Englewood, CO
Primary Contact: David W. Schultz, FACHE, President
Web address: www.fhshealth.org/
Control: Church–operated, Nongovernment, not–for profit **Service:** General
Medical and Surgical

Staffed Beds: 80 **Admissions:** 5341 **Census:** 62 **Outpatient Visits:** 70654
Births: 0 **Total Expense ($000):** 110955 **Payroll Expense ($000):** 39490
Personnel: 622

GOLDENDALE—Klickitat County

KLICKITAT VALLEY HEALTH (501316), 310 South Roosevelt Avenue,
Zip 98620–9201; tel. 509/773–4022 **A**3 10 18 **F**3 8 15 18 29 30 34 35 40
43 45 57 59 62 63 64 65 68 75 77 81 83 84 85 97 107 119 127 128 130
133 135 146 148
Primary Contact: Leslie Hiebert, Chief Executive Officer
CFO: Jamie Eldred, Controller
CMO: Rod Krehbiel, M.D., Chief of Staff
CIO: Jonathan Hatfield, Supervisor Information Technology
CHR: Herbert Hill, Director Human Resources
CNO: Gwen Cox, Director Nursing Services
Web address: www.kvhealth.net
Control: Hospital district or authority, Government, nonfederal **Service:** General
Medical and Surgical

Staffed Beds: 17 **Admissions:** 292 **Census:** 5 **Outpatient Visits:** 4849
Births: 0 **Total Expense ($000):** 20824 **Payroll Expense ($000):** 9831

GRAND COULEE—Grant County

COULEE COMMUNITY HOSPITAL See Coulee Medical Center

COULEE MEDICAL CENTER (501308), 411 Fortuyn Road, Zip 99133–8718;
tel. 509/633–1753, (Nonreporting) **A**10 18
Primary Contact: Jonathan Owens, Chief Executive Officer
CFO: Paul Babcock, Chief Financial Officer
CMO: Andrew Castrodale, M.D., Chief Medical Officer
CHR: Heather McCleary, Director Human Resources
Web address: www.cmccares.org
Control: Hospital district or authority, Government, nonfederal **Service:** General
Medical and Surgical

Staffed Beds: 25

ILWACO—Pacific County

★ **OCEAN BEACH HOSPITAL (501314)**, 174 First Avenue North,
Zip 98624–9137, Mailing Address: P.O. Box H., Zip 98624–0258;
tel. 360/642–3181 **A**10 18 **F**3 11 12 15 18 28 29 30 31 34 35 40 43 45 50
56 57 59 68 75 77 78 81 85 86 87 93 97 102 107 111 114 119 127 128
130 132 133 135 147 **P**6
Primary Contact: Larry Cohen, Interim Chief Executive Officer
CFO: Kathy Hubbard, Controller
CMO: Patty Malone, M.D., Chief Medical Officer
CIO: Julie P. Oakes, R.N., Manager Risk and Quality
CHR: Beth Whitton, Director Human Resources
CNO: Linda Kaino, Chief Nursing Officer
Web address: www.oceanbeachhospital.com
Control: Hospital district or authority, Government, nonfederal **Service:** General
Medical and Surgical

Staffed Beds: 15 **Admissions:** 371 **Census:** 4 **Outpatient Visits:** 32562
Births: 0 **Total Expense ($000):** 19892 **Payroll Expense ($000):** 9194
Personnel: 129

ISSAQUAH—King County

★ ◇ **SWEDISH/ISSAQUAH (500152)**, 751 N.E. Blakely Drive, Zip 98029–6201;
tel. 425/313–4000 **A**3 10 21 **F**3 12 13 15 18 20 22 29 30 31 34 35 37 38
40 41 45 48 49 50 56 57 58 59 60 61 64 65 68 70 73 74 75 76 77 78 79
81 82 85 86 87 89 92 93 96 97 102 107 108 110 111 114 115 119 126
129 130 131 132 134 135 141 143 146 147 148 **S** Swedish Health Services,
Seattle, WA
Primary Contact: Rayburn Lewis, M.D., Chief Executive
Web address: www.swedish.org/issaquah
Control: Other not–for–profit (including NFP Corporation) **Service:** General
Medical and Surgical

Staffed Beds: 49 **Admissions:** 6570 **Census:** 46 **Outpatient Visits:** 111988
Births: 1274 **Total Expense ($000):** 202562 **Payroll Expense ($000):**
52731

KENNEWICK—Benton County

⊠ **TRIOS HEALTH (500053)**, 900 South Auburn Street, Zip 99336–5621, Mailing
Address: P.O. Box 6128, Zip 99336–0128; tel. 509/586–6111 **A**1 2 10 13 **F**2
8 11 13 15 18 20 28 29 30 31 34 35 40 45 49 50 54 56 57 59 62 64 70 73
74 75 76 77 78 79 80 81 85 86 87 89 93 97 107 108 110 111 114 119 129
130 144 146 147
Primary Contact: Glen Marshall, Chief Executive Officer
CFO: Tony Sudduth, Chief Financial Officer
CIO: Michael Cloutier, Director Information Services
CHR: Russ Keefer, Chief Human Resources Officer
CNO: Diane M. Sanders, Chief Nursing Officer
Web address: www.trioshealth.org
Control: Hospital district or authority, Government, nonfederal **Service:** General
Medical and Surgical

Staffed Beds: 111 **Admissions:** 6558 **Census:** 55 **Births:** 1664 **Total
Expense ($000):** 191372 **Payroll Expense ($000):** 80455

KIRKLAND—King County

EVERGREEN HEALTHCARE See EvergreenHealth

WA

⊞ **EVERGREENHEALTH (500124)**, 12040 N.E. 128th Street, Zip 98034–3013; tel. 425/899–1000 **A**1 2 3 5 10 **F**3 8 11 12 13 15 18 20 22 28 29 30 34 35 37 38 40 42 43 44 45 46 49 50 51 54 55 56 57 58 59 62 63 64 65 68 70 71 72 73 74 75 76 78 79 80 81 82 84 85 86 87 89 90 91 92 93 94 95 96 97 100 102 103 107 108 110 111 114 115 119 120 121 123 124 126 129 130 131 132 134 135 144 146 147 148 **P**4 6
Primary Contact: Robert H. Malte, Chief Executive Officer
COO: Neil Johnson, Chief Operating Officer
CFO: Chrissy Yamada, CPA, Chief Financial Officer
CMO: Jeff Tomlin, M.D., Chief Medical and Quality Officer
CIO: Tom Martin, Chief Strategy and Information Officer
CHR: Bob Sampson, Vice President, Human Resources
CNO: Nancee Hofmeister, R.N., Chief Nursing Officer
Web address: www.evergreenhealth.com
Control: Hospital district or authority, Government, nonfederal **Service:** General Medical and Surgical

Staffed Beds: 278 **Admissions:** 15184 **Census:** 165 **Outpatient Visits:** 719867 **Births:** 4679 **Total Expense ($000):** 595439 **Payroll Expense ($000):** 303234 **Personnel:** 3371

⊞ **FAIRFAX BEHAVIORAL HEALTH (504002)**, 10200 N.E. 132nd Street, Zip 98034–2899; tel. 425/821–2000, (Includes FAIRFAX BEHAVIORAL HEALTH EVERETT, 916 Pacific Avenue, Everett, Zip 98201–4147; tel. 425/821–2000), (Nonreporting) **A**1 10 **S** Universal Health Services, Inc., King of Prussia, PA
Primary Contact: Ron Escarda, Chief Executive Officer
COO: Todd Thama, Chief Operating Officer
CFO: Pam Rhoads, Chief Financial Officer
CMO: Samir Aziz, M.D., Medical Director
CHR: Anne Schreiber, Manager Human Resources
Web address: www.fairfaxhospital.com
Control: Corporation, Investor–owned, for–profit **Service:** Psychiatric

Staffed Beds: 103

LAKEWOOD—Pierce County

⊞ △ **ST. CLARE HOSPITAL (500021)**, 11315 Bridgeport Way S.W., Zip 98499–3004; tel. 253/985–1711 **A**1 2 3 7 10 **F**3 8 18 29 30 31 34 35 38 40 44 45 49 50 51 57 59 64 70 74 75 77 78 79 80 81 82 85 86 87 92 93 107 108 111 114 119 129 130 132 135 146 **S** Catholic Health Initiatives, Englewood, CO
Primary Contact: Syd Bersante, R.N., President
CFO: Mike Fitzgerald, Chief Financial Officer
CIO: Bruce Elkington, Regional Chief Information Officer
CHR: David C. Lawson, Senior Vice President Human Resources
Web address: www.fhshealth.org
Control: Church–operated, Nongovernment, not–for profit **Service:** General Medical and Surgical

Staffed Beds: 104 **Admissions:** 6265 **Census:** 80 **Outpatient Visits:** 103619 **Births:** 0 **Total Expense ($000):** 128950 **Payroll Expense ($000):** 49718 **Personnel:** 769

LEAVENWORTH—Chelan County

★ **CASCADE MEDICAL CENTER (501313)**, 817 Commercial Street, Zip 98826–1316; tel. 509/548–5815 **A**5 10 18 **F**3 7 15 34 40 41 45 50 59 64 65 68 77 87 90 91 93 97 104 107 110 114 127 128 130 131 133 148 **P**6
Primary Contact: Diane Blake, Chief Executive Officer
COO: Amy Webb, Chief Operating Officer
CFO: Jim Hopkins, Chief Financial Officer
CMO: Karl Kranz, M.D., Chief of Staff
CIO: Charles Amstutz, Director of Information Technology
CHR: Reyne Boik, Director Human Resources
Web address: www.cascademedical.org
Control: Hospital district or authority, Government, nonfederal **Service:** Rehabilitation

Staffed Beds: 9 **Admissions:** 220 **Census:** 4 **Outpatient Visits:** 8000 **Births:** 0 **Total Expense ($000):** 14923 **Payroll Expense ($000):** 7855

LONGVIEW—Cowlitz County

⊞ ◇ **PEACEHEALTH ST. JOHN MEDICAL CENTER (500041)**, 1615 Delaware Street, Zip 98632–2367, Mailing Address: P.O. Box 3002, Zip 98632–0302; tel. 360/414–2000 **A**1 2 10 19 21 **F**5 11 13 15 18 20 22 26 28 29 30 31 32 33 34 35 38 40 43 45 46 49 50 51 56 57 59 60 61 63 64 65 68 70 71 74 75 76 77 78 79 80 81 82 84 85 93 94 96 97 98 99 100 101 102 104 107 108 109 111 114 115 117 119 120 121 129 130 144 145 146 147 148 **S** PeaceHealth, Vancouver, WA
Primary Contact: Kirk Raboin, Chief Administrative Officer
CFO: Ronald K. Benfield, Chief Financial Officer
CMO: Eleen Kirman, M.D., Chief Medical Officer
CHR: Kelley Frengle, Director, Human Resources
Web address: www.peacehealth.org
Control: Hospital district or authority, Government, nonfederal **Service:** General Medical and Surgical

Staffed Beds: 180 **Admissions:** 7473 **Census:** 82 **Births:** 878 **Total Expense ($000):** 255195 **Payroll Expense ($000):** 108106

MEDICAL LAKE—Spokane County

☐ **EASTERN STATE HOSPITAL (504004)**, Maple Street, Zip 99022–0045, Mailing Address: P.O. Box 800, Zip 99022–0800; tel. 509/565–4705, (Nonreporting) **A**1 3 10
Primary Contact: Dorothy Sawyer, Chief Executive Officer
COO: Ronda Kenney, Chief Operating Officer
CMO: Kamal Floura, M.D., Medical Director
CNO: Chet Roshetko, Chief Nursing Officer
Web address: www.dshs.wa.gov/mhsystems/esh.shtml
Control: State–Government, nonfederal **Service:** Psychiatric

Staffed Beds: 287

MONROE—Snohomish County

★ ◇ **EVERGREENHEALTH MONROE (500084)**, 14701 179th S.E., Zip 98272–1108, Mailing Address: P.O. Box 646, Zip 98272–0646; tel. 360/794–7497, (Nonreporting) **A**10 21
Primary Contact: Eric P. Jensen, Chief Executive Officer
CFO: Scott Olander, Chief Financial Officer
CMO: Jack Handley, M.D., Chief Medical Officer
CIO: John Gepford, Director Information Systems
CHR: Kathryn Rothberg, Director Human Resources
CNO: Debbie T. Brown, R.N., Chief Nursing Officer
Web address: www.evergreenhealthmonroe.com
Control: Hospital district or authority, Government, nonfederal **Service:** General Medical and Surgical

Staffed Beds: 68

MORTON—Lewis County

★ **MORTON GENERAL HOSPITAL (501319)**, 521 Adams Avenue, Zip 98356–9323, Mailing Address: P.O. Box 1138, Zip 98356–0019; tel. 360/496–5112 **A**10 18 **F**3 34 40 45 81 85 87 92 93 97 107 114 119 127 129 130 133 135 148
Primary Contact: Leianne Everett, Chief Executive Officer
CFO: Geoff Hamilton, Interim Chief Financial Officer
CIO: Randy Nielsen, Director Information Technology
CHR: Shannon Kelly, Director Human Resources
CNO: Heidi Anderson, Chief Nursing Officer
Web address: www.mortongeneral.org
Control: Hospital district or authority, Government, nonfederal **Service:** General Medical and Surgical

Staffed Beds: 25 **Admissions:** 213 **Census:** 2 **Outpatient Visits:** 5551 **Births:** 0 **Total Expense ($000):** 24045 **Payroll Expense ($000):** 11811

MOSES LAKE—Grant County

★ **SAMARITAN HEALTHCARE (500033)**, 801 East Wheeler Road, Zip 98837–1899; tel. 509/765–5606 **A**10 20 **F**3 8 13 15 29 34 35 40 43 45 50 57 59 64 65 68 75 76 79 80 81 86 87 93 97 107 108 110 111 115 118 119 127 130 132 135 144 146 147
Primary Contact: Theresa Sullivan, Chief Executive Officer
COO: Becky DeMers, R.N., Chief Operating Officer
CFO: Paul Ishizuka, Chief Financial Officer and Chief Operating Officer
CMO: Thomas Tuszynski, M.D., Chief of Staff
CHR: Lisa A. McDaniel, Chief Human Resources Officer
CNO: Kathryn E. Trumbull, R.N., Chief Nursing Officer and Vice President Patient Care Services
Web address: www.samaritanhealthcare.com
Control: Hospital district or authority, Government, nonfederal **Service:** General Medical and Surgical

Staffed Beds: 50 **Admissions:** 2818 **Census:** 22 **Births:** 1012 **Total Expense ($000):** 69618 **Payroll Expense ($000):** 32061 **Personnel:** 448

MOUNT VERNON—Skagit County

★ ◇ **SKAGIT REGIONAL HEALTH (500003)**, 1415 East Kincaid, Zip 98274–4126, Mailing Address: P.O. Box 1376, Zip 98273–1376; tel. 360/424–4111 **A**2 5 10 13 19 21 **F**11 13 18 20 22 26 28 29 30 31 32 34 35 36 40 41 43 44 45 47 48 49 50 51 57 58 59 60 62 63 64 65 68 70 73 74 77 78 79 80 81 82 84 85 86 87 93 97 98 100 102 103 107 108 111 114 115 116 117 118 120 121 123 124 127 129 130 144 146 147 148 **P**6 **S** Skagit Regional Health, Mount Vernon, WA
Primary Contact: Michael T. Liepman, Chief Executive Officer
CFO: Thomas Litaker, Regional Vice President and Chief Financial Officer
CMO: Jeffrey S. Gibbs, M.D., Regional Vice President Medical Affairs
CIO: John Dwight, Regional Vice President and Chief Information Officer
CHR: Deborah Martin, Regional Vice President Human Resources
CNO: Roxanne Olason, R.N., Vice President and Chief Nursing Officer
Web address: www.skagitregionalhealth.org
Control: Hospital district or authority, Government, nonfederal **Service:** General Medical and Surgical

Staffed Beds: 137 **Admissions:** 6651 **Census:** 79 **Outpatient Visits:** 563601 **Births:** 1116 **Total Expense ($000):** 297176 **Payroll Expense ($000):** 126356 **Personnel:** 2072

WA

Many Facility Codes have changed. Please refer to the AHA Guide Code Chart. © 2016 AHA Guide

NEWPORT—Pend Oreille County

NEWPORT HOSPITAL AND HEALTH SERVICES (501310), 714 West Pine Street, Zip 99156–9046; tel. 509/447–2441, (Total facility includes 50 beds in nursing home–type unit) **A**10 18 **F**8 10 11 13 15 32 34 40 41 50 57 59 64 75 76 77 79 81 82 87 89 93 97 107 111 114 119 127 128 130 133 146 147 148
Primary Contact: Thomas W. Wilbur, Chief Executive Officer and Superintendent
COO: Shelley Froehlich, R.N., Director Nursing Services
CMO: Clay Kersting, M.D., Chief Medical Staff
CIO: Walter Price, Director Information Technology
CHR: Joseph Clouse, Chief Administrative Officer
Web address: www.newporthospitalandhealth.org
Control: Hospital district or authority, Government, nonfederal **Service:** General Medical and Surgical

Staffed Beds: 70 **Admissions:** 611 **Census:** 54 **Outpatient Visits:** 47926
Births: 85 **Total Expense ($000):** 26447 **Payroll Expense ($000):** 14747

OAK HARBOR—Island County

NAVAL HOSPITAL OAK HARBOR, 3475 North Saratoga Street, Zip 98278–8800; tel. 360/257–9500, (Nonreporting) **A**1 **S** Bureau of Medicine and Surgery, Department of the Navy, Falls Church, VA
Primary Contact: Commander Frederick Joseph McDonald, Commanding Officer
COO: Lieutenant Michael Bowers, Interim Director for Administration
CFO: Lieutenant Matthew Martin, Director Resource Management
CMO: Lieutenant Commander Catherine Borja, M.D., Chairman Executive Committee Medical Staff
CIO: Gregory Carruth, Head Information Management
CHR: Lieutenant Michael Bowers, Head Human Resources
CNO: Captain Karen Pruett–Baer, Senior Nurse Executive
Web address: www.med.navy.mil/sites/nhoh/Pages/default.aspx
Control: Navy, Government, federal **Service:** General Medical and Surgical

Staffed Beds: 29

ODESSA—Lincoln County

★ **ODESSA MEMORIAL HEALTHCARE CENTER (501307)**, 502 East Amende Drive, Zip 99159–7003, Mailing Address: P.O. Box 368, Zip 99159–0368; tel. 509/982–2611, (Total facility includes 12 beds in nursing home–type unit) **A**10 18 **F**3 7 10 29 30 34 40 43 45 50 57 59 65 77 93 127 128 130 133
Primary Contact: Mo P. Sheldon, FACHE, Chief Executive Officer and Administrator
CFO: Annette Edwards, Chief Financial Officer
CMO: Linda J. Powel, M.D., Medical Director
CHR: Jodi J. Bailey, Human Resources Director
CNO: Megan Shepard, Director Clinical Services
Web address: www.omhc.org
Control: Hospital district or authority, Government, nonfederal **Service:** General Medical and Surgical

Staffed Beds: 25 **Admissions:** 65 **Census:** 34 **Births:** 0 **Total Expense ($000):** 7507 **Payroll Expense ($000):** 3438

OLYMPIA—Thurston County

☐ **CAPITAL MEDICAL CENTER (500139)**, 3900 Capital Mall Drive S.W., Zip 98502–5026, Mailing Address: P.O. Box 19002, Zip 98507–0013; tel. 360/754–5858 **A**1 10 **F**3 8 11 12 13 15 28 29 30 31 35 37 40 43 59 64 68 72 76 77 78 79 81 82 85 86 87 93 107 108 111 114 118 119 132 146 147 148 **S** RCCH HealthCare Partners, Brentwood, TN
Primary Contact: Jim Geist, Chief Executive Officer
CFO: Brian Anderson, Chief Financial Officer
CMO: Rojesh Sharangpani, M.D., Chief of Staff
CIO: Renee Crotty, Coordinator Marketing and Public Relations
CHR: Dana Vandewege, Director Human Resources
Web address: www.capitalmedical.com
Control: Partnership, Investor–owned, for–profit **Service:** General Medical and Surgical

Staffed Beds: 85 **Admissions:** 4549 **Census:** 39 **Births:** 681

PROVIDENCE ST. PETER HOSPITAL

△ **PROVIDENCE ST. PETER HOSPITAL (500024)**, 413 Lilly Road N.E., Zip 98506–5166; tel. 360/491–9480 **A**1 3 7 10 **F**3 5 11 13 15 17 18 20 22 24 26 28 29 30 31 34 35 38 40 43 44 45 46 47 48 49 50 51 53 56 57 58 59 60 61 64 70 73 74 75 76 77 78 79 80 81 82 83 84 85 86 87 89 90 92 93 96 98 99 100 101 102 104 105 107 108 111 114 115 118 119 124 126 129 130 131 132 135 143 144 145 146 147 148 **S** Providence St. Joseph Health, Renton, WA
Primary Contact: Medrice Coluccio, R.N., Chief Executive Officer
COO: Paul G. Wilkinson, Chief Operating Officer
CFO: Denise Marroni, Chief Financial Officer
CMO: Kevin Caserta, M.D., Chief Medical Officer
CIO: Kerry Miles, Chief Information Officer
CHR: Susan Meenk, Vice President Human Resources
CNO: Michelle James, Chief Nursing Officer
Web address: www.providence.org/swsa/facilities/st_peter_hospital
Control: Church–operated, Nongovernment, not–for profit **Service:** General Medical and Surgical

Staffed Beds: 347 **Admissions:** 19118 **Census:** 242 **Outpatient Visits:** 326629 **Births:** 2249 **Total Expense ($000):** 324308 **Payroll Expense ($000):** 148623 **Personnel:** 1937

OMAK—Okanogan County

MID–VALLEY HOSPITAL (501328), 810 Jasmine, Zip 98841–9578, Mailing Address: P.O. Box 793, Zip 98841–0793; tel. 509/826–1760 **A**5 10 18 **F**11 13 15 29 34 40 43 45 57 59 64 65 68 70 76 81 82 87 89 93 107 115 119 127 133 135
Primary Contact: Michael D. Billing, Administrator
CFO: Scott Attridge, Chief Financial Officer
CMO: Jennifer Thill, Chief of Staff
CIO: Ethan Harris, Manager Information Systems
CHR: Randy Coffell, Manager Human Resources
CNO: Rebecca Christoph, Director Nursing and Patient Care Services
Web address: www.mvhealth.org
Control: Hospital district or authority, Government, nonfederal **Service:** General Medical and Surgical

Staffed Beds: 30 **Admissions:** 976 **Census:** 7 **Births:** 227 **Total Expense ($000):** 31130 **Payroll Expense ($000):** 14419

OTHELLO—Adams County

★ **OTHELLO COMMUNITY HOSPITAL (501318)**, 315 North 14th Avenue, Zip 99344–1297; tel. 509/488–2636, (Nonreporting) **A**10 18
Primary Contact: Connie Agenbroad, Chief Executive Officer
CFO: Mark Bunch, Director Finance
CHR: Mindy Gonzales, Chief Human Resources Officer
CNO: Tina Bernsen, Chief Nursing Officer
Web address: www.othellocommunityhospital.org
Control: Hospital district or authority, Government, nonfederal **Service:** General Medical and Surgical

Staffed Beds: 25

PASCO—Franklin County

△ **LOURDES MEDICAL CENTER (501337)**, 520 North Fourth Avenue, Zip 99301–5257; tel. 509/547–7704 **A**1 7 10 18 **F**8 13 15 18 29 30 34 35 37 40 41 42 45 46 50 52 56 57 59 68 70 74 75 76 77 79 80 81 84 90 91 96 97 107 108 110 111 114 118 126 129 130 131 143 144 145 146 147 **S** Ascension Health, Saint Louis, MO
Primary Contact: John Serle, FACHE, President and Chief Executive Officer
CFO: Frank Becker, Chief Financial Officer
CMO: Venkataraman Sambasivan, M.D., Chief Medical Officer
CIO: Deb Carpenter, Director Information Technology
CHR: Barbara Blood, Executive Director Human Resources
CNO: Denise Clapp, Chief Nursing Officer
Web address: www.lourdeshealth.net
Control: Church–operated, Nongovernment, not–for profit **Service:** General Medical and Surgical

Staffed Beds: 53 **Admissions:** 1953 **Census:** 20 **Total Expense ($000):** 91157 **Payroll Expense ($000):** 29782

WA

Hospital, Medicare Provider Number, Address, Telephone, Approval, Facility, and Physician Codes, Health Care System

★ American Hospital Association (AHA) membership ☐ The Joint Commission accreditation ○ Healthcare Facilities Accreditation Program ◇ DNV Healthcare Inc. accreditation ⇑ Center for Improvement in Healthcare Quality Accreditation △ Commission on Accreditation of Rehabilitation Facilities (CARF) accreditation

© 2016 AHA Guide   *Many Facility Codes have changed. Please refer to the AHA Guide Code Chart.*   Hospitals **A687**

POMEROY—Garfield County

★ **GARFIELD COUNTY PUBLIC HOSPITAL DISTRICT (501301)**, 66 North 6th Street, Zip 99347–9705; tel. 509/843–1591, (Total facility includes 25 beds in nursing home–type unit) **A**10 18 **F**2 3 5 7 10 12 34 40 41 42 43 44 56 57 59 63 64 65 66 68 75 77 79 86 87 91 93 97 103 125 127 128 130 131 132 133 135 143 146 148 **P**5 6
Primary Contact: Jon D. Smiley, Interim Chief Executive Officer
CMO: Glenn Jefferson, Chief Medical Officer
CHR: Alicia Scharnhorst, Human Resources and Administrative Assistant
CNO: Barbara DeHerrera, Chief Nursing Officer
Web address: www.pomeroymd.com
Control: Hospital district or authority, Government, nonfederal **Service:** Long–Term Acute Care hospital

Staffed Beds: 40 **Admissions:** 57 **Census:** 23 **Outpatient Visits:** 8125 **Births:** 0 **Total Expense ($000):** 6679 **Payroll Expense ($000):** 3102

PORT ANGELES—Clallam County

★ ◇ **OLYMPIC MEDICAL CENTER (500072)**, 939 Caroline Street, Zip 98362–3997; tel. 360/417–7000 **A**2 5 10 21 **F**3 13 15 18 28 29 31 34 40 45 54 57 59 62 64 70 74 75 76 77 78 79 81 82 85 87 89 91 97 107 108 110 111 114 119 121 123 127 129 131 132 144 146 147 148 **P**4
Primary Contact: Eric Lewis, Chief Executive Officer
CFO: Darryl Wolfe, Chief Financial Officer
CMO: R. Scott Kennedy, M.D., Chief Medical Officer and Hospital Chief Operating Officer
CHR: Richard Newman, Chief Human Resources Officer
CNO: Lorraine Wall, Chief Nursing Officer
Web address: www.olympicmedical.org
Control: Hospital district or authority, Government, nonfederal **Service:** General Medical and Surgical

Staffed Beds: 67 **Admissions:** 4301 **Census:** 43 **Outpatient Visits:** 355210 **Births:** 466 **Total Expense ($000):** 152919 **Payroll Expense ($000):** 72160 **Personnel:** 1034

PORT TOWNSEND—Jefferson County

★ ◇ **JEFFERSON HEALTHCARE (501323)**, 834 Sheridan Street, Zip 98368–2443; tel. 360/385–2200 **A**10 18 21 **F**13 15 18 28 29 31 34 35 40 45 46 50 62 63 65 70 76 81 87 93 107 110 111 114 119 127 129 130 135 146 148
Primary Contact: Mike Glenn, Chief Executive Officer
COO: Paula Dowdle, Chief Operating Officer
CFO: Hilary Whittington, Chief Financial Officer
CMO: Joe Mattern, M.D., Chief Medical Officer
CHR: Heather Bailey, Chief Human Resources Officer
CNO: Joyce Cardinal, Chief Nursing Executive
Web address: www.jeffersonhealthcare.org
Control: Hospital district or authority, Government, nonfederal **Service:** General Medical and Surgical

Staffed Beds: 25 **Admissions:** 1440 **Census:** 12 **Births:** 125 **Total Expense ($000):** 78773 **Payroll Expense ($000):** 39148

PROSSER—Benton County

★ **PMH MEDICAL CENTER (501312)**, 723 Memorial Street, Zip 99350–1524; tel. 509/786–2222 **A**10 18 **F**3 7 11 12 13 15 29 34 35 37 40 41 43 44 45 50 52 53 54 57 59 65 68 75 76 77 79 81 82 85 87 89 91 93 97 107 108 110 119 127 128 130 131 132 133 135 143 146 148 **P**8
Primary Contact: Craig J. Marks, FACHE, Chief Executive Officer
CFO: Tim Cooper, Chief Financial Officer
CIO: Jim Zoesch, Information Technology Director
CNO: Marla Davis, Interim Chief Nursing Officer
Web address: www.pmhmedicalcenter.com/
Control: Hospital district or authority, Government, nonfederal **Service:** General Medical and Surgical

Staffed Beds: 25 **Admissions:** 1007 **Census:** 12 **Outpatient Visits:** 18967 **Births:** 26 **Total Expense ($000):** 41909 **Payroll Expense ($000):** 19574 **Personnel:** 142

PULLMAN—Whitman County

◇ **PULLMAN REGIONAL HOSPITAL (501331)**, 835 S.E. Bishop Boulevard, Zip 99163–5512; tel. 509/332–2541 **A**10 18 21 **F**3 13 15 28 29 30 34 35 36 37 38 40 43 44 45 47 50 51 53 55 57 59 64 68 70 74 75 76 77 78 79 81 86 87 89 93 98 101 102 104 105 107 108 110 111 114 118 119 126 129 130 131 132 133 144 146 **P**5 6 7
Primary Contact: Scott K. Adams, FACHE, Chief Executive Officer
CFO: Steven Febus, Chief Financial Officer
CMO: Gerald L. Early, M.D., Chief Medical Officer
CHR: Bernadette Berney, Director Human Resources
Web address: www.pullmanhospital.org
Control: Hospital district or authority, Government, nonfederal **Service:** General Medical and Surgical

Staffed Beds: 25 **Admissions:** 1400 **Census:** 10 **Outpatient Visits:** 77000 **Births:** 457

PUYALLUP—Pierce County

GOOD SAMARITAN COMMUNITY HEALTHCARE See MultiCare Good Samaritan Hospital

□ △ **MULTICARE GOOD SAMARITAN HOSPITAL (500079)**, 401 15th Avenue S.E., Zip 98372–3770, Mailing Address: P.O. Box 1247, Zip 98371–0192; tel. 253/697–4000 **A**1 2 3 7 10 13 **F**3 11 13 18 20 22 24 28 29 30 31 34 35 38 40 41 43 45 47 48 50 51 55 56 57 58 59 61 64 65 66 68 70 73 74 75 76 78 79 81 82 84 85 87 89 90 91 93 96 97 102 106 107 108 111 114 115 117 118 119 126 129 130 132 146 147 148 **S** MultiCare Health System, Tacoma, WA
Primary Contact: Glenn Kasman, President and Market Leader
COO: Christopher Bredeson, Chief Operating Officer
CFO: Anna Loomis, Senior Vice President Chief Financial Officer
CMO: Walter Fink, Chief Medical Officer
CHR: Kevin B. Dull, Senior Vice President Human Potential
CNO: Lucy Norris, Administrator Interim Chief Nursing Officer
Web address: www.multicare.org/good–samaritan–hospital/
Control: Other not–for–profit (including NFP Corporation) **Service:** General Medical and Surgical

Staffed Beds: 286 **Admissions:** 16709 **Census:** 214 **Outpatient Visits:** 140157 **Births:** 2356 **Total Expense ($000):** 409464 **Payroll Expense ($000):** 154546 **Personnel:** 1638

QUINCY—Grant County

★ **QUINCY VALLEY MEDICAL CENTER (501320)**, 908 10th Avenue S.W., Zip 98848–1376; tel. 509/787–3531, (Nonreporting) **A**10 18
Primary Contact: Jerry Hawley, Interim Chief Executive Officer
CFO: Dean Taplett, Controller
CMO: Mark Vance, M.D., Chief Medical Officer
CIO: Ruth Vance, Director Information Systems
CHR: Alene Walker, Director Human Resources
Web address: www.quincyhospital.org
Control: County–Government, nonfederal **Service:** General Medical and Surgical

Staffed Beds: 25

RENTON—King County

⊞ **UW MEDICINE/VALLEY MEDICAL CENTER (500088)**, 400 South 43rd Street, Zip 98055–5714, Mailing Address: P.O. Box 50010, Zip 98058–5010; tel. 425/228–3450 **A**1 2 3 5 10 **F**3 8 11 13 18 19 20 22 26 28 29 30 31 32 34 35 36 37 38 40 43 44 45 48 49 50 51 53 54 55 57 58 59 60 64 65 66 68 70 72 74 75 76 77 78 79 81 82 83 84 85 86 87 89 91 92 93 94 96 97 100 101 102 104 107 110 114 115 118 119 120 121 123 124 126 129 130 131 132 135 144 146 147 148 **P**6 **S** UW Medicine, Seattle, WA
Primary Contact: Richard D. Roodman, Chief Executive Officer
CFO: Larry Smith, Senior Vice President and Chief Financial Officer
CMO: Kathryn Beattie, M.D., Senior Vice President and Chief Medical Officer
CHR: Barbara Mitchell, Senior Vice President Marketing and Human Resources
CNO: Scott Alleman, Senior Vice President Patient Care Services and Chief Nursing Officer
Web address: www.valleymed.org
Control: Hospital district or authority, Government, nonfederal **Service:** General Medical and Surgical

Staffed Beds: 283 **Admissions:** 17174 **Census:** 180 **Outpatient Visits:** 560950 **Births:** 3776 **Total Expense ($000):** 523046 **Payroll Expense ($000):** 234262 **Personnel:** 2391

REPUBLIC—Ferry County

★ **FERRY COUNTY MEMORIAL HOSPITAL (501322)**, 36 Klondike Road, Zip 99166–9701; tel. 509/775–3333, (Nonreporting) **A**10 18
Primary Contact: Terali Stonehocker, Interim Chief Executive Officer
CFO: Kelly Leslie, Chief Financial Officer
CMO: Farhad H. Alrashedy, M.D., Chief Medical Officer
CIO: James Davidson, Director of Information Services
CHR: Michelle Loftis, Human Resources Officer
CNO: Thomas Durham, Chief Nursing Officer
Web address: www.fcphd.org
Control: Hospital district or authority, Government, nonfederal **Service:** General Medical and Surgical

Staffed Beds: 25

WA

Many Facility Codes have changed. Please refer to the AHA Guide Code Chart. © 2016 AHA Guide

RICHLAND—Benton County

⊠ △ **KADLEC REGIONAL MEDICAL CENTER (500058)**, 888 Swift Boulevard, Zip 99352–3514; tel. 509/946–4611 **A**1 2 3 7 10 **F**3 8 11 13 15 17 18 20 22 24 26 28 29 30 31 32 34 35 36 38 40 42 45 46 47 48 49 50 51 52 54 55 56 57 58 59 64 65 68 70 72 73 74 75 76 78 79 81 82 83 84 85 86 87 89 90 91 93 96 97 107 110 111 114 115 116 117 118 119 126 127 130 132 144 146 147 148 **S** Providence St. Joseph Health, Renton, WA
Primary Contact: Rand J. Wortman, President and Chief Executive Officer
COO: Rand J. Wortman, Chief Executive Officer
CFO: Spencer Harris, Senior Director Finance
CMO: Dale Hoekema, M.D., Vice President Medical Affairs and Chief Medical Officer
CIO: David Roach, Vice President Information Systems
CHR: Jeffrey A. Clark, Vice President Human Resources
CNO: Kirk Harper, R.N., Vice President, Nursing
Web address: www.kadlecmed.org
Control: Other not–for–profit (including NFP Corporation) **Service:** General Medical and Surgical

Staffed Beds: 254 Admissions: 15703 Census: 176 Outpatient Visits: 269894 Births: 2731 Total Expense ($000): 520248 Payroll Expense ($000): 225667

★ **LOURDES COUNSELING CENTER (504008)**, 1175 Carondelet Drive, Zip 99354–3300; tel. 509/943–9104 **A**10 **F**3 29 30 38 50 64 98 99 100 101 103 104 106 **S** Ascension Health, Saint Louis, MO
Primary Contact: Denise Clapp, Interim Executive Director
CFO: Frank Becker, Chief Financial Officer
CIO: Jared Fleming, Director, Information Services
CHR: Barbara Blood, Director Human Resources
CNO: Denise Clapp, Chief Nursing Officer
Web address: www.lourdeshealth.net
Control: Church–operated, Nongovernment, not–for profit **Service:** Psychiatric

Staffed Beds: 20 Admissions: 571 Census: 15 Births: 0

RITZVILLE—Adams County

★ **EAST ADAMS RURAL HEALTHCARE (501311)**, 903 South Adams Street, Zip 99169–2298; tel. 509/659–1200 **A**10 18 **F**7 40 43 57 65 82 84 93 97 107 127 133 143 148
Primary Contact: Gary Bostrom, Chief Executive Officer and Chief Financial Officer
COO: Dina McBride, Chief Operating Officer and Director Human Resources
CFO: Gary Bostrom, Chief Executive Officer and Chief Financial Officer
CMO: Charles Sackmann, M.D., Chief of Staff
CIO: Kellie Ottmar, Manager Information Services
CHR: Dina McBride, Chief Operating Officer and Director Human Resources
CNO: Brenda Herr, Chief Nursing Officer
Web address: www.earh.com
Control: Hospital district or authority, Government, nonfederal **Service:** General Medical and Surgical

Staffed Beds: 20 Admissions: 27 Census: 1

SEATTLE—King County

◇ **GROUP HEALTH COOPERATIVE CENTRAL HOSPITAL (500052)**, 201 16th Avenue East, Zip 98112–5226; tel. 206/326–3000, (Nonreporting) **A**3 5 10 21
Primary Contact: Carol M. Taylor, R.N., Regional Director Clinical Operations
Web address: www.https://www.ghc.org
Control: Corporation, Investor–owned, for–profit **Service:** General Medical and Surgical

Staffed Beds: 306

⊠ **KINDRED HOSPITAL SEATTLE–NORTHGATE (502002)**, 10631 8th Avenue N.E., Zip 98125–7213; tel. 206/364–2050, (Includes KINDRED HOSPITAL SEATTLE–FIRST HILL, 1334 Terry Avenue, Zip 98101–2747; tel. 206/682–2661) **A**1 10 **F**1 29 30 50 60 70 75 77 85 96 107 119 148 **S** Kindred Healthcare, Louisville, KY
Primary Contact: Jean Clark, Administrator
CFO: David Stob, Chief Financial Officer
Web address: www.kindredhospitalseattle.com/
Control: Corporation, Investor–owned, for–profit **Service:** General Medical and Surgical

Staffed Beds: 80 Admissions: 609 Census: 60 Births: 0

☐ **NAVOS (504009)**, 2600 S.W. Holden Street, Zip 98126–3505; tel. 206/933–7299 **A**1 10 **F**29 98 99 100 101 102 103 104
Primary Contact: David Johnson, Chief Executive Officer
COO: Cassie Undlin, Chief Operating Officer
CIO: Mary Sellers, Chief Information Officer
CHR: Karen White, Interim Vice President of Human Resources
CNO: Terry McInerney, Director of Nursing, Inpatient
Web address: www.navos.org
Control: Other not–for–profit (including NFP Corporation) **Service:** Psychiatric

Staffed Beds: 69 Admissions: 789 Census: 39 Births: 0

★ **SCHICK SHADEL HOSPITAL**, 12101 Ambaum Boulevard S.W., Zip 98146–2651, Mailing Address: P.O. Box 48149, Zip 98148–0149; tel. 206/244–8100 **F**4 130 132
Primary Contact: Philip Herink, Administrator
CFO: Troy Cherry, Chief Financial Officer
CMO: Kayyan Danbdala, M.D., Medical Director
CIO: Peter Vermulen, Director Information Technology
CHR: Elaine Oksendahl, Director Human Resources and Risk Management
Web address: www.schickshadel.com
Control: Corporation, Investor–owned, for–profit **Service:** Alcoholism and other chemical dependency

Staffed Beds: 55 Admissions: 1000 Census: 28 Outpatient Visits: 0 Births: 0 Total Expense ($000): 21231 Payroll Expense ($000): 11329

⊠ **SEATTLE CANCER CARE ALLIANCE (500138)**, 825 Eastlake Avenue East, Zip 98109–4405, Mailing Address: P.O. Box 19023, Zip 98109–1023; tel. 206/288–1400 **A**1 2 10 **F**3 15 30 31 34 35 39 50 55 57 59 64 68 75 78 80 82 84 86 87 93 107 108 110 111 114 115 116 117 119 120 121 123 124 130 132 135 136 142 143 146 147 148 **P**1
Primary Contact: Norm Hubbard, Executive Vice President
CFO: Jonathan Tingstad, Vice President and Chief Financial Officer
CMO: Marc Stewart, M.D., Vice President and Medical Director
CIO: David Ackerson, Chief Information Officer
CHR: Han Nachtrieb, Vice President Human Resources
Web address: www.seattlecca.org
Control: Other not–for–profit (including NFP Corporation) **Service:** Cancer

Staffed Beds: 20 Admissions: 587 Census: 16 Outpatient Visits: 76604 Births: 0 Total Expense ($000): 441543 Payroll Expense ($000): 85943 Personnel: 997

☐ △ ◇ **SEATTLE CHILDREN'S HOSPITAL (503300)**, 4800 Sand Point Way N.E., Zip 98105–3901, Mailing Address: P.O. Box 5371, Zip 98145–5005; tel. 206/987–2000 **A**1 2 3 5 7 8 10 21 **F**7 8 9 19 21 23 25 27 29 30 31 32 34 35 36 38 39 40 41 43 46 48 49 50 53 54 55 57 58 60 61 62 64 65 66 68 71 74 75 77 78 79 81 82 84 85 86 87 93 94 99 100 102 104 105 107 108 111 115 116 118 119 126 129 130 131 132 134 136 137 138 139 141 142 143 144 146 148
Primary Contact: Jeff Sperring, M.D., Chief Executive Officer
COO: Cindy Gazecki, Senior Vice President, Hospital Operations
CFO: Kelly Wallace, Senior Vice President and Chief Financial Officer
CMO: David Fisher, M.D., Senior Vice President and Chief Medical Officer
CIO: Wes Wright, Senior Vice President and Chief Information Officer
CHR: Steven Hurwitz, Senior Vice President Shared Services
CNO: Susan Heath, R.N., Senior Vice President and Chief Nursing Officer
Web address: www.seattlechildrens.org
Control: Other not–for–profit (including NFP Corporation) **Service:** Children's general

Staffed Beds: 316 Admissions: 15947 Census: 240 Births: 0

⊠ △ ◇ **SWEDISH MEDICAL CENTER–CHERRY HILL CAMPUS (500025)**, 500 17th Avenue, Zip 98122–5711; tel. 206/320–2000 **A**1 2 3 5 7 10 21 **F**3 8 11 17 18 20 21 22 23 24 26 27 28 29 30 31 34 35 37 38 40 41 45 46 53 57 58 59 60 61 64 65 68 74 75 77 78 79 80 81 82 85 87 90 91 92 93 97 98 100 101 102 107 108 109 111 118 119 124 126 129 130 131 132 135 141 143 146 148 **P**6 **S** Swedish Health Services, Seattle, WA
Primary Contact: June Altaras, R.N., Chief Executive Officer
CFO: Jeffrey Veilleux, Senior Vice President and Chief Financial Officer
CMO: John Vassall, M.D., Chief Medical Officer
CIO: Janice Newell, Chief Information Officer
Web address: www.swedish.org
Control: Other not–for–profit (including NFP Corporation) **Service:** General Medical and Surgical

Staffed Beds: 198 Admissions: 10055 Census: 153 Outpatient Visits: 156037 Total Expense ($000): 471091 Payroll Expense ($000): 124681

WA

Hospital, Medicare Provider Number, Address, Telephone, Approval, Facility, and Physician Codes, Health Care System

★ American Hospital Association (AHA) membership
☐ The Joint Commission accreditation
○ Healthcare Facilities Accreditation Program
◇ DNV Healthcare Inc. accreditation
⇑ Center for Improvement in Healthcare Quality Accreditation
△ Commission on Accreditation of Rehabilitation Facilities (CARF) accreditation

---

⊞ **SWEDISH MEDICAL CENTER–FIRST HILL (500027)**, 747 Broadway,
Zip 98122–4307; tel. 206/386–6000, (Includes SWEDISH MEDICAL
CENTER–BALLARD, 5300 Tallman Avenue N.W., Zip 98107–3932;
tel. 206/782–2700; Jennifer Graves, R.N., MS, Chief Executive) **A**1 2 3 5 10 **F**3
4 5 7 8 11 12 13 15 18 19 20 21 22 23 25 26 29 30 31 32 34 35 36 37 38
39 40 41 42 45 46 47 48 49 52 54 55 56 57 58 59 60 61 64 65 66 68 70
71 72 73 74 75 76 77 78 79 80 81 82 83 84 85 86 87 88 89 91 92 93 96
97 100 101 102 104 107 108 109 110 111 114 115 116 117 118 119 120
121 123 126 127 130 131 132 134 135 136 138 139 141 143 144 146 147
148 **P**6 **S** Swedish Health Services, Seattle, WA
Primary Contact: June Altaras, R.N., Chief Executive Officer
CFO: Jeffrey Veilleux, Executive Vice President and Chief Financial Officer
CMO: John Vassall, M.D., Chief Medical Officer
CIO: Janice Newell, Chief Information Officer
Web address: www.swedish.org
Control: Other not–for–profit (including NFP Corporation) **Service:** General
Medical and Surgical

Staffed Beds: 620 Admissions: 36750 Census: 427 Outpatient Visits:
648714 **Births:** 8316 **Total Expense ($000):** 1221793 **Payroll Expense**
($000): 375595

⊞ △ **UNIVERSITY OF WASHINGTON MEDICAL CENTER (500008)**, 1959 N.E.
Pacific Street, Zip 98195–6151; tel. 206/598–3300 **A**1 2 3 5 7 8 10 **F**3 8 9 11
12 13 15 17 18 20 22 24 26 29 31 32 34 35 36 40 44 45 46 47 48 49
50 52 54 55 56 57 58 59 60 61 64 65 68 70 72 74 75 76 77 78 79 81 82
84 85 86 87 90 91 92 93 94 95 97 98 100 101 102 103 104 107 110 111
114 115 116 117 118 119 120 121 123 124 126 130 131 132 136 137 138
139 140 141 142 144 145 146 147 148 **S** UW Medicine, Seattle, WA
Primary Contact: Geoff Austin, Interim Executive Director
CFO: Lori J. Mitchell, Chief Financial Officer
CMO: Tom Staiger, M.D., Medical Director
CHR: Jennifer J. Petritz, Director Human Resources
CNO: Grace E. Parker, R.N., Chief Nursing Officer
Web address: www.uwmedicine.org/uw–medical–center
Control: State–Government, nonfederal **Service:** General Medical and Surgical

Staffed Beds: 438 Admissions: 18092 Census: 346 Outpatient Visits:
332703 **Births:** 2043 **Total Expense ($000):** 1068755 **Payroll Expense**
($000): 342954 **Personnel:** 6526

⊞ △ **UW MEDICINE/HARBORVIEW MEDICAL CENTER (500064)**, 325 Ninth
Avenue, Zip 98104–2499, Mailing Address: P.O. Box 359717, Zip 98195–9717;
tel. 206/744–3000 **A**1 3 5 7 8 10 **F**3 6 16 17 20 22 26 29 30 31 32 34 35
36 37 38 40 41 43 45 46 47 48 50 56 58 59 60 61 64 65 66 68 70 72
73 74 75 77 78 79 80 81 82 84 85 86 87 88 89 90 91 92 93 94 96 97 98
100 101 102 103 104 105 107 108 111 114 115 118 119 124 129 130 131
132 135 146 147 148 **P**6 **S** UW Medicine, Seattle, WA
Primary Contact: Paul Hayes, R.N., Executive Director
CFO: Kera Dennis, Assistant Administrator, Finance
CMO: J. Richard Goss, M.D., Medical Director
CIO: James Fine, M.D., Chief Information Officer
CHR: Nicki McCraw, Assistant Vice President Human Resources
CNO: Darcy Jaffe, R.N., Chief Nursing Officer
Web address: www.uwmedicine.org/Patient–Care/Locations/HMC/Pages/default.
aspx
Control: County–Government, nonfederal **Service:** General Medical and Surgical

Staffed Beds: 413 Admissions: 17196 Census: 372 Outpatient Visits:
341992 **Births:** 0

⊞ **UW MEDICINE/NORTHWEST HOSPITAL & MEDICAL CENTER (500001)**,
1550 North 115th Street, Zip 98133–8401; tel. 206/364–0500 **A**1 2 3 5 10 **F**3
9 11 13 15 18 20 22 24 26 28 29 30 31 34 35 37 38 40 41 43 45 46 47 49
50 51 53 54 56 57 58 59 64 67 68 70 73 74 75 76 77 78 79 81 84 85 87
96 98 100 103 105 107 108 109 110 111 115 119 126 130 131 132 146
148 **P**6 **S** UW Medicine, Seattle, WA
Primary Contact: Adam Parcher, Interim Executive Director
CFO: Ketty Hsieh, Senior Director Finance
CMO: Greg Schroedl, M.D., Vice President, Medical and Chief Medical Officer
CIO: Eric Neil, Interim Chief Information Officer
CHR: Linda Olmstead, Director, Human Resources
CNO: Susan Manfredi, R.N., Vice President and Chief Nursing Officer
Web address: www.uwmedicine.org/Patient–Care/Locations/nwh/Pages/default.
aspx
Control: Other not–for–profit (including NFP Corporation) **Service:** General
Medical and Surgical

Staffed Beds: 176 Admissions: 9934 Census: 129 Births: 1223 Total
Expense ($000): 343919 **Payroll Expense ($000):** 134434

⊞ △ **VETERANS AFFAIRS PUGET SOUND HEALTH CARE SYSTEM**, 1660
South Columbian Way, Zip 98108–1597; tel. 206/762–1010, (Includes
VETERANS AFFAIRS PUGET SOUND HEALTH CARE SYSTEM–AMERICAN LAKE
DIVISION, 9600 Veterans Drive, Tacoma, Zip 98493–0003; tel. 253/582–8440),
(Nonreporting) **A**1 2 3 5 7 8 **S** Department of Veterans Affairs, Washington, DC
Primary Contact: Michael J. Murphy, FACHE, Director
CFO: Kenneth J. Hudson, Chief Financial Officer
CMO: Gordon Starkebaum, M.D., Chief of Staff
CIO: Glenn Zwinger, Manager Information Systems Services
Web address: www.pugetsound.va.gov/
Control: Veterans Affairs, Government, federal **Service:** General Medical and
Surgical

Staffed Beds: 358

★ △ **VIRGINIA MASON MEDICAL CENTER (500005)**, 1100 Ninth Avenue,
Zip 98101–2756, Mailing Address: P.O. Box 900, Zip 98111–0900;
tel. 206/223–6600, (Total facility includes 35 beds in nursing home–type unit) **A**2
3 5 7 10 **F**2 3 8 11 12 15 17 18 20 22 24 26 28 29 30 31 34 36 40 44 45
46 47 48 49 50 51 55 56 57 58 59 60 61 63 64 65 68 70 74 75 77 78 79
80 81 82 83 84 85 86 87 90 91 92 93 94 96 97 98 100 101 102 103 104
107 108 110 111 114 115 117 118 119 120 121 123 126 128 129 130 131
132 135 138 141 142 144 146 148 **P**6 **S** Virginia Mason Health System,
Seattle, WA
Primary Contact: Gary Kaplan, M.D., FACHE, Chairman and Chief Executive Officer
CFO: Craig Goodrich, Chief Financial Officer
CMO: Michael Glenn, M.D., Chief Medical Officer
CIO: Bill Poppy, Chief Information Officer
CHR: Kathy J. Shingleton, Ed.D., Vice President, Human Resources
CNO: Charleen Tachibana, R.N., Senior Vice President and Chief Nursing Officer
Web address: www.VirginiaMason.org
Control: Other not–for–profit (including NFP Corporation) **Service:** General
Medical and Surgical

Staffed Beds: 280 Admissions: 15517 Census: 237 Outpatient Visits:
892215 **Births:** 0 **Total Expense ($000):** 1018985 **Payroll Expense ($000):**
482025 **Personnel:** 4622

SEDRO–WOOLLEY—Skagit County

★ ◇ **PEACEHEALTH UNITED GENERAL MEDICAL CENTER (501329)**, 2000
Hospital Drive, Zip 98284–4327; tel. 360/856–6021 **A**2 10 18 21 **F**3 11 15 29
30 31 34 35 40 43 45 50 57 59 64 68 70 75 77 78 79 81 85 89 92 93 107
108 110 114 119 120 121 123 129 130 133 143 146 **P**6
S PeaceHealth, Vancouver, WA
Primary Contact: Christopher Johnston, Interim Chief Administrative Officer
CFO: Carolyn Haupt, Chief Financial Officer
CHR: Tracie Skrinde, Senior Human Resources Partner
Web address: www.peacehealth.org/united–general/Pages/default.aspx
Control: Church–operated, Nongovernment, not–for profit **Service:** General
Medical and Surgical

Staffed Beds: 25 Admissions: 668 Census: 6 Outpatient Visits: 39769
Births: 0 **Total Expense ($000):** 39615 **Payroll Expense ($000):** 14242
Personnel: 162

SHELTON—Mason County

⊞ **MASON GENERAL HOSPITAL (501336)**, 901 Mountain View Drive,
Zip 98584–4401, Mailing Address: P.O. Box 1668, Zip 98584–5001;
tel. 360/426–1611 **A**1 10 18 **F**11 13 15 29 30 40 57 68 70 75 79 81 83 85
107 110 130 132 147
Primary Contact: Eric Moll, Chief Executive Officer
COO: Eileen Branscome, Chief Operating Officer
CFO: Merle Brandt, Chief Financial Officer
CMO: Dean Gushee, M.D., Medical Director
CIO: Tom Hornburg, Director Information Systems
CHR: Claudia Hawley, Director Human Resources
Web address: www.masongeneral.com
Control: Hospital district or authority, Government, nonfederal **Service:** General
Medical and Surgical

Staffed Beds: 25 Admissions: 1594 Census: 14

SNOQUALMIE—King County

SNOQUALMIE VALLEY HOSPITAL DISTRICT (501338), 9801 Frontier Avenue
S.E., Zip 98065–9577; tel. 425/831–2300, (Nonreporting) **A**10 18
Primary Contact: Thomas Parker, Chief Executive Officer
CHR: Kimberly D. Washburn, Director Human Resources
Web address: www.snoqualmiehospital.org/
Control: Hospital district or authority, Government, nonfederal **Service:** General
Medical and Surgical

Staffed Beds: 18

SOUTH BEND—Pacific County

WILLAPA HARBOR HOSPITAL (501303), 800 Alder Street, Zip 98586–4900,
Mailing Address: P.O. Box 438, Zip 98586–0438; tel. 360/875–5526 **A**10 18 **F**3
8 11 15 34 35 40 41 45 46 50 81 85 87 92 97 107 110 113 119 127
133 145
Primary Contact: Carole Halsan, R.N., Chief Executive Officer
CFO: Terry Stone, Chief Financial Officer and Chief Information Officer
CIO: Terry Stone, Chief Financial Officer and Chief Information Officer
CHR: Krisy L. Funkhouser, Manager Human Resources
Web address: www.willapaharborhospital.com
Control: Hospital district or authority, Government, nonfederal **Service:** General
Medical and Surgical

Staffed Beds: 15 Admissions: 250 Census: 2 Total Expense ($000): 18638
Payroll Expense ($000): 9981

WA

Many Facility Codes have changed. Please refer to the AHA Guide Code Chart. © 2016 AHA Guide

SPOKANE—Spokane County

⊠ **DEACONESS HOSPITAL (500044)**, 800 West Fifth Avenue, Zip 99204–2803; Mailing Address: P.O. Box 248, Zip 99210–0248; tel. 509/458–5800 **A**1 2 3 10 **F**3 11 12 13 15 17 18 20 22 24 26 28 29 31 40 43 45 46 47 48 49 50 51 56 60 64 68 70 72 73 74 75 76 78 79 81 82 85 86 87 91 92 107 108 110 111 113 114 115 119 124 126 129 130 132 146 147 148 **S** Community Health Systems, Inc., Franklin, TN
Primary Contact: Maurine Cate, Chief Executive Officer
CFO: Rodney Higgins, Chief Financial Officer
CIO: Richard DeRoche, Manager Information Technology
CHR: Melinda Moore, Director Human Resources
CNO: Jennifer Petrik, Interim Chief Nursing Officer
Web address: www.deaconessspokane.com/Deaconess–Hospital/home.aspx
Control: Corporation, Investor–owned, for–profit **Service:** General Medical and Surgical

Staffed Beds: 352 **Admissions:** 11216 **Census:** 167 **Births:** 1450 **Total Expense ($000):** 264998 **Payroll Expense ($000):** 88254

⊠ **MANN–GRANDSTAFF VETERANS AFFAIRS MEDICAL CENTER**, 4815 North Assembly Street, Zip 99205–6197; tel. 509/434–7000, (Nonreporting) **A**1 3 5 **S** Department of Veterans Affairs, Washington, DC
Primary Contact: Ronald J. Johnson, Director
COO: Perry Klein, Chief Engineering
CFO: Michael Stuhlmiller, Chief Financial Officer
CIO: Rob Fortenberry, Chief Information Officer
CHR: Jacqueline Ross, Chief Human Resources Officer
CNO: Nancy Benton, Assistant Director Patient Care Services
Web address: www.spokane.va.gov/
Control: Veterans Affairs, Government, federal **Service:** General Medical and Surgical

Staffed Beds: 70

⊠ △ **PROVIDENCE HOLY FAMILY HOSPITAL (500077)**, 5633 North Lidgerwood Street, Zip 99208–1224; tel. 509/482–0111 **A**1 2 5 7 10 **F**3 4 8 11 12 13 15 16 17 18 20 22 24 26 28 29 31 34 35 37 38 39 40 41 43 45 46 47 48 49 50 53 56 57 58 59 60 61 64 68 70 73 74 75 76 77 78 79 80 81 82 84 85 86 87 89 92 100 107 108 129 130 131 132 135 143 145 146 147 148 **P**6 **S** Providence St. Joseph Health, Renton, WA
Primary Contact: Alex Jackson, Chief Executive
COO: Cathy J. Simchuk, Chief Operating Officer
CFO: Shelby Stokoe, Chief Financial Officer
CMO: Dean Martz, Chief Medical Officer
CIO: Mark Vogelsang, Director Information Services
CHR: Mark Smith, Director Human Resources
CNO: Sharon Hershman, R.N., Chief Nursing Officer
Web address: www.providence.org
Control: Church–operated, Nongovernment, not–for profit **Service:** General Medical and Surgical

Staffed Beds: 191 **Admissions:** 9208 **Census:** 100 **Outpatient Visits:** 201320 **Births:** 1298 **Total Expense ($000):** 148198 **Payroll Expense ($000):** 54731 **Personnel:** 805

⊠ **PROVIDENCE SACRED HEART MEDICAL CENTER & CHILDREN'S HOSPITAL (500054)**, 101 West Eighth Avenue, Zip 99204–2364, Mailing Address: P.O. Box 2555, Zip 99220–2555; tel. 509/474–3131, (Includes SACRED HEART CHILDREN'S HOSPITAL, 101 West Eight Avenue, Zip 99204–2307, Mailing Address: PO Box 2555, Zip 99220–2555; tel. 509/474–4841; Keith Georgeson, M.D., Chief Executive) **A**1 2 3 5 10 **F**3 8 13 15 17 18 19 20 21 22 23 24 25 26 27 28 29 30 31 35 36 37 40 41 43 45 46 47 48 56 58 60 64 70 72 73 74 75 76 77 78 79 81 82 83 84 85 86 87 88 89 92 98 99 100 101 102 103 104 105 106 107 108 109 110 111 112 114 115 118 119 120 121 123 124 126 130 132 136 137 138 141 142 145 146 147 148 **P**6 **S** Providence St. Joseph Health, Renton, WA
Primary Contact: Alex Jackson, Chief Executive
CFO: Shelby Stokoe, Senior Director Finance
CMO: Dean Martz, Chief Medical Officer
CHR: Mark Smith, Director Human Resources
CNO: Susan Stacey, Chief Nursing Officer
Web address: www.shmc.org
Control: Church–operated, Nongovernment, not–for profit **Service:** General Medical and Surgical

Staffed Beds: 672 **Admissions:** 29836 **Census:** 431 **Outpatient Visits:** 262260 **Births:** 3233 **Total Expense ($000):** 855826 **Payroll Expense ($000):** 268286 **Personnel:** 2883

☐ **SHRINERS HOSPITALS FOR CHILDREN–SPOKANE (503302)**, 911 West Fifth Avenue, Zip 99204–2901, Mailing Address: P.O. Box 2472, Zip 99210–2472; tel. 509/455–7844, (Nonreporting) **A**1 3 10 **S** Shriners Hospitals for Children, Tampa, FL
Primary Contact: Peter G. Brewer, Administrator
CFO: Monica Hickman, Director Fiscal Services
CMO: Glen Baird, M.D., Chief of Staff
CIO: Mike Allen, Director Information Services
CHR: Karen Mattern, Director of Human Resources
CNO: Lynda Vilanova, Director Patient Care Services
Web address: www.shrinershospitalsforchildren.org/Hospitals/Locations/Spokane.aspx
Control: Other not–for–profit (including NFP Corporation) **Service:** Children's orthopedic

Staffed Beds: 30

⊠ △ **ST. LUKE'S REHABILITATION INSTITUTE (503025)**, 711 South Cowley Street, Zip 99202–1388; tel. 509/473–6000 **A**1 7 10 **F**28 29 30 36 38 50 53 58 64 68 74 75 77 79 82 86 87 90 91 92 93 95 96 130 131 132 135 146 **P**6 **S** Providence St. Joseph Health, Renton, WA
Primary Contact: Nancy Webster, Chief Administrative Officer
COO: Ulrike Berzau, FACHE, Administrator
CFO: Helen Andrus, Chief Financial Officer
CMO: Stefan Humphries, M.D., Medical Director
CIO: Fred Galusha, Chief Information Officer
CHR: Staci Franz, Director Human Resources
CNO: Ginger Cohen, Chief Nurse Executive
Web address: www.st–lukes.org
Control: Other not–for–profit (including NFP Corporation) **Service:** Rehabilitation

Staffed Beds: 72 **Admissions:** 1350 **Census:** 49 **Outpatient Visits:** 70937 **Births:** 0 **Total Expense ($000):** 40423 **Payroll Expense ($000):** 24608 **Personnel:** 524

VETERANS AFFAIRS MEDICAL CENTER See Mann–Grandstaff Veterans Affairs Medical Center

SPOKANE VALLEY—Spokane County

⊠ **VALLEY HOSPITAL (500119)**, 12606 East Mission Avenue, Zip 99216–1090; tel. 509/924–6650 **A**1 2 3 10 **F**3 8 13 20 22 24 29 30 31 35 40 41 43 44 45 46 48 49 50 59 64 68 70 74 76 78 79 81 82 84 85 87 107 108 111 114 119 130 131 143 146 147 **S** Community Health Systems, Inc., Franklin, TN
Primary Contact: Gregory George Repetti, III, FACHE, Chief Executive Officer
COO: David Martin, Assistant Administrator
CFO: Justin Voelker, Chief Financial Officer
CIO: Brain Jones, Director of Information Technology
CHR: Jamie Caine, Director of Human Resources
CNO: Shannon S. Holland, R.N., Chief Nursing Officer
Web address: www.valleyhospital.org
Control: Corporation, Investor–owned, for–profit **Service:** General Medical and Surgical

Staffed Beds: 92 **Admissions:** 5512 **Census:** 56 **Outpatient Visits:** 54960 **Births:** 689 **Total Expense ($000):** 82318 **Payroll Expense ($000):** 41821 **Personnel:** 515

SUNNYSIDE—Yakima County

★ **SUNNYSIDE COMMUNITY HOSPITAL AND CLINICS (501330)**, 1016 Tacoma Avenue, Zip 98944–2263, Mailing Address: P.O. Box 719, Zip 98944–0719; tel. 509/837–1500, (Nonreporting) **A**10 18 **S** HealthTech Management Services, Brentwood, TN
Primary Contact: John Gallagher, Chief Executive Officer
CFO: Cary Rowan, Chief Financial Officer
CIO: John Andersen, Manager Information Systems
CHR: Elaina Wagner, Director Human Resources
CNO: Mary Beth Tubbs, Chief Nursing Officer
Web address: www.sunnysidehospital.com
Control: Other not–for–profit (including NFP Corporation) **Service:** General Medical and Surgical

Staffed Beds: 25

TACOMA—Pierce County

ALLENMORE HOSPITAL See MultiCare Tacoma General Hospital

⊠ **MADIGAN ARMY MEDICAL CENTER**, Fitzsimmons Drive, Building 9040, Zip 98431–1100; tel. 253/968–1110, (Nonreporting) **A**1 2 3 5 **S** Department of the Army, Office of the Surgeon General, Falls Church, VA
COO: Colonel R. Neal David, Administrator and Chief of Staff
CFO: Lieutenant Colonel Bryan Longmuir, Chief Resource Management
CIO: Lieutenant Colonel Andrew Smith, Chief Information Management
CHR: David Aiken, Chief Human Resources Officer
Web address: www.mamc.amedd.army.mil
Control: Army, Government, federal **Service:** General Medical and Surgical

Staffed Beds: 227

WA

⊞ **MULTICARE MARY BRIDGE CHILDREN'S HOSPITAL AND HEALTH CENTER (503301)**, 317 Martin Luther King Jr. Way, Zip 98405–4234, Mailing Address: P.O. Box 5299, Zip 98415–0299; tel. 253/403–1400 **A**1 5 10 **F**3 7 8 12 19 21 23 25 27 29 30 31 32 34 35 40 41 43 48 50 54 55 57 58 59 62 63 64 65 66 71 74 75 78 79 81 82 84 85 86 87 88 89 91 92 93 96 97 99 102 104 107 108 110 111 114 115 116 117 119 120 121 123 124 129 130 131 132 134 135 143 144 146 148 **S** MultiCare Health System, Tacoma, WA
Primary Contact: Linda Chen, President and Market Leader
COO: Jennifer Hamilton, COO – Mary Bridge
CFO: Anna Loomis, Senior Vice President Chief Financial Officer
CMO: Iain Asplin, Chief Medical Officer
CHR: Kevin B. Dull, Senior Vice PresidentHuman Potential
CNO: Diana Brovold, Chief Nurse Executive
Web address: www.multicare.org/marybridge
Control: Other not–for–profit (including NFP Corporation) **Service:** Children's general

Staffed Beds: 75 **Admissions:** 3889 **Census:** 38 **Outpatient Visits:** 122508 **Births:** 0 **Total Expense ($000):** 190974 **Payroll Expense ($000):** 67744 **Personnel:** 633

⊞ **MULTICARE TACOMA GENERAL HOSPITAL (500129)**, 315 Martin Luther King Jr. Way, Zip 98405–4234, Mailing Address: P.O. Box 5299, Zip 98415–0299; tel. 253/403–1000, (Includes ALLENMORE HOSPITAL, 1901 South Union Avenue, Zip 98405, Mailing Address: P.O. Box 11414, Zip 98411–0414; tel. 253/459–6633; Shelly Mullin, R.N., President Market Leader) **A**1 2 3 10 **F**3 8 13 17 18 20 22 24 26 28 29 30 31 35 36 40 42 43 45 46 47 48 49 50 51 54 55 57 58 59 64 70 71 72 73 74 75 76 78 79 80 81 82 84 85 87 93 102 107 108 109 111 114 115 116 117 119 120 121 123 124 126 129 130 131 132 135 146 147 148 **S** MultiCare Health System, Tacoma, WA
Primary Contact: Shelly Mullin, R.N., President and Market Leader
COO: Julia Truman, Chief Operating Officer
CFO: Anna Loomis, Senior Vice President,Chief Financial Officer
CHR: Kevin B. Dull, Senior Vice President, Human Potential
CNO: Anita Wolfe, Chief Nurse Executive
Web address: www.multicare.org
Control: Other not–for–profit (including NFP Corporation) **Service:** General Medical and Surgical

Staffed Beds: 366 **Admissions:** 17855 **Census:** 270 **Outpatient Visits:** 199674 **Births:** 3073 **Total Expense ($000):** 709250 **Payroll Expense ($000):** 252543 **Personnel:** 2434

⊞ △ **ST. JOSEPH MEDICAL CENTER (500108)**, 1717 South J Street, Zip 98405–3004, Mailing Address: P.O. Box 2197, Zip 98401–2197; tel. 253/426–4101 **A**1 2 3 7 10 **F**3 8 11 12 13 17 18 20 22 24 26 28 29 30 31 34 35 38 40 43 44 45 46 47 48 49 50 51 55 57 58 59 60 63 64 65 70 72 73 74 75 76 77 78 79 81 82 83 86 87 90 92 93 96 102 107 108 111 114 115 119 124 126 130 131 132 135 145 146 148 **S** Catholic Health Initiatives, Englewood, CO
Primary Contact: Tim O'Haver, Chief Operating Officer
CFO: Mike Fitzgerald, Chief Financial Officer
CIO: Rand Strobel, Vice President Information Technology and Compliance
CNO: Ruth Flint, Chief Nursing Officer
Web address: www.chifranciscan.org
Control: Church–operated, Nongovernment, not–for profit **Service:** General Medical and Surgical

Staffed Beds: 363 **Admissions:** 21776 **Census:** 302 **Outpatient Visits:** 278980 **Births:** 4140 **Total Expense ($000):** 583722 **Payroll Expense ($000):** 218602 **Personnel:** 3761

VETERANS AFFAIRS PUGET SOUND HEALTH CARE SYSTEM–AMERICAN LAKE DIVISION See Veterans Affairs Puget Sound Health Care System, Seattle

☐ **WESTERN STATE HOSPITAL (504003)**, 9601 Steilacom Boulevard S.W., Zip 98498–7213; tel. 253/582–8900, (Nonreporting) **A**1 5 10
Primary Contact: Cheryl Strange, Interim Chief Executive Officer
COO: David Holt, Chief Operating Officer
CFO: Sue Breen, Chief Financial Officer
CMO: James A. Polo, M.D., Chief Medical Officer
CHR: Lori Manning, Administrator Human Resources
CNO: Rae Simpson, R.N., Chief Nursing Officer
Web address: www.dshs.wa.gov/bhsia/division–state–hospitals/western–state–hospital
Control: State–Government, nonfederal **Service:** Psychiatric

Staffed Beds: 867

TONASKET—Okanogan County

★ **NORTH VALLEY HOSPITAL (501321)**, 203 South Western Avenue, Zip 98855–8803; tel. 509/486–2151, (Total facility includes 42 beds in nursing home–type unit) **A**10 18 **F**3 13 15 26 29 34 35 40 43 45 50 59 64 75 77 81 82 85 87 93 94 96 97 107 110 111 114 119 128 130 131 132 133 135 148
Primary Contact: Helen Veehasselt, Interim Chief Executive Officer
CFO: Helen Verhasselt, Chief Financial Officer
CMO: Paul Lacey, M.D., Chief Medical Staff
CIO: Kelly Cariker, Chief Information Officer
CHR: Jan Gonzales, Director Human Resources
Web address: www.nvhospital.org
Control: Hospital district or authority, Government, nonfederal **Service:** General Medical and Surgical

Staffed Beds: 67 **Admissions:** 615 **Census:** 46 **Births:** 106

TOPPENISH—Yakima County

⊞ **TOPPENISH COMMUNITY HOSPITAL (500037)**, 502 West Fourth Avenue, Zip 98948–1616, Mailing Address: P.O. Box 672, Zip 98948–0672; tel. 509/865–3105 **A**1 3 5 10 **F**3 13 15 18 20 28 29 30 34 35 40 43 45 46 50 57 59 68 70 76 79 89 107 111 114 119 133 135 **S** Community Health Systems, Inc., Franklin, TN
Primary Contact: Chris Mendoza, Interim Chief Executive Officer
CFO: Curtis Herrin, Chief Financial Officer
CHR: Rosa Solorzano, Interim Director Human Resources
Web address: www.toppenishhospital.com
Control: Corporation, Investor–owned, for–profit **Service:** General Medical and Surgical

Staffed Beds: 48 **Admissions:** 1553 **Census:** 10 **Births:** 432

TUKWILA—King County

⊞ **CASCADE BEHAVIORAL HOSPITAL (504011)**, 12844 Military Road South, Zip 98168–3045; tel. 206/244–0180, (Nonreporting) **A**1 3 10 **S** Acadia Healthcare Company, Inc., Franklin, TN
Primary Contact: Michael Uradnik, Chief Executive Officer
CFO: Gregg Terreson, Chief Financial Officer
CHR: Sherry Cochran, Manager Human Resources
Web address: www.cascadebh.com
Control: Corporation, Investor–owned, for–profit **Service:** Psychiatric

Staffed Beds: 63

VANCOUVER—Clark County

LEGACY SALMON CREEK HOSPITAL See Legacy Salmon Creek Medical Center

⊞ **LEGACY SALMON CREEK MEDICAL CENTER (500150)**, 2211 N.E. 139th Street, Zip 98686–2742; tel. 360/487–1000 **A**1 2 5 10 **F**3 11 13 15 18 20 26 28 29 30 31 32 34 35 38 39 40 44 45 46 47 50 51 57 59 60 65 68 70 72 74 75 76 77 78 79 80 81 82 84 85 87 93 96 97 101 107 108 110 111 114 116 117 118 119 120 121 126 129 130 132 146 147 148 **P**6 **S** Legacy Health, Portland, OR
Primary Contact: Bryce R. Helgerson, Chief Administrative Officer
COO: Michael Newcomb, D.O., Senior Vice President and Chief Operating Officer
CMO: Lewis Low, M.D., Senior Vice President and Chief Medical Officer
CHR: Sonja Steves, Senior Vice President Human Resources
CNO: Carol Bradley, MSN, Senior Vice President and Chief Nursing Officer
Web address: www.legacyhealth.org
Control: Other not–for–profit (including NFP Corporation) **Service:** General Medical and Surgical

Staffed Beds: 214 **Admissions:** 15239 **Census:** 149 **Outpatient Visits:** 226657 **Births:** 3325 **Total Expense ($000):** 254068 **Payroll Expense ($000):** 133840 **Personnel:** 1623

★ △ ◇ **PEACEHEALTH SOUTHWEST MEDICAL CENTER (500050)**, 400 N.E. Mother Joseph Place, Zip 98664–3200, Mailing Address: P.O. Box 1600, Zip 98668–1600; tel. 360/256–2000, (Includes VANCOUVER MEMORIAL CAMPUS, 3400 Main Street, Zip 98663; tel. 360/514–2000) **A**2 3 5 7 10 21 **F**3 11 12 13 15 17 18 20 24 26 28 29 30 31 34 35 40 43 44 45 46 49 50 51 54 57 58 59 60 61 62 63 64 65 68 70 72 74 75 76 77 78 79 81 82 84 85 86 87 89 90 92 93 96 97 98 100 101 102 103 104 105 107 108 109 110 111 113 114 115 116 119 120 121 122 124 126 129 130 131 132 135 144 145 146 147 148 **S** PeaceHealth, Vancouver, WA
Primary Contact: Nancy Steiger, FACHE, R.N., Chief Executive
COO: Wade Hunt, Chief Operating Officer
CFO: Ronald K. Benfield, Chief Financial Officer
CMO: Alden Roberts, M.D., Chief Medical Officer
CIO: Donn McMillan, Chief Information Officer
CHR: Kelley Frengle, Director, Human Resources
CNO: Cindy Davis, RN, BSN, MBA, NEA–BC, Chief Nursing Officer
Web address: www.peacehealth.org
Control: Other not–for–profit (including NFP Corporation) **Service:** General Medical and Surgical

Staffed Beds: 450 **Admissions:** 19378 **Census:** 244 **Births:** 2204 **Total Expense ($000):** 578198 **Payroll Expense ($000):** 184718

SOUTHWEST WASHINGTON MEDICAL CENTER See PeaceHealth Southwest Medical Center

WALLA WALLA—Walla Walla County

★ **JONATHAN M. WAINWRIGHT MEMORIAL VETERANS AFFAIRS MEDICAL CENTER**, 77 Wainwright Drive, Zip 99362–3994; tel. 509/525–5200, (Nonreporting) **S** Department of Veterans Affairs, Washington, DC
Primary Contact: Brian W. Westfield, MSN, Director
CFO: Debra Pearson, Chief Financial Officer
CMO: Charles Beleny, D.O., Chief of Staff
CIO: Gary Ramer, Manager Information Management
CHR: Mary C. Lee, Manager Human Resources
CNO: Diana Nelson, R.N., Associate Director for Patient Care Services/Nurse Executive
Web address: www.wallawalla.va.gov
Control: Veterans Affairs, Government, federal **Service:** General Medical and Surgical

Staffed Beds: 14

WA

Many Facility Codes have changed. Please refer to the AHA Guide Code Chart. © 2016 AHA Guide

✉ △ **PROVIDENCE ST. MARY MEDICAL CENTER (500002)**, 401 West Poplar Street, Zip 99362–2846, Mailing Address: P.O. Box 1477, Zip 99362–0312; tel. 509/525–3320 **A**1 2 7 10 19 **F**3 13 15 18 20 22 28 29 30 31 34 35 40 43 45 46 49 59 62 64 70 73 74 75 76 77 78 79 81 82 83 84 85 89 90 91 93 96 97 107 108 110 111 114 115 118 119 121 123 129 130 132 135 144 146 147 148 **P**6 **S** Providence St. Joseph Health, Renton, WA
Primary Contact: Steven A. Burdick, Chief Executive Officer
COO: Susan Blackburn, Chief Operating Officer
CMO: Tim Davidson, M.D., Chief Executive Physician Services
CIO: Martin Manny, Director, I.S.
CNO: Yvonne M. Strader, Chief Nursing Officer
Web address: www.washington.providence.org/hospitals/st-mary/
Control: Church–operated, Nongovernment, not–for profit **Service:** General Medical and Surgical

Staffed Beds: 105 **Admissions:** 4413 **Census:** 43 **Outpatient Visits:** 172572 **Births:** 564 **Total Expense ($000):** 151280 **Payroll Expense ($000):** 79500 **Personnel:** 871

STATE PENITENTIARY HOSPITAL, 1313 North 13th Street, Zip 99362–8817; tel. 509/525–3610, (Nonreporting)
Primary Contact: Karen Forest, Health Care Manager
Control: State–Government, nonfederal **Service:** Hospital unit of an institution (prison hospital, college infirmary, etc.)

Staffed Beds: 36

✉ **WALLA WALLA GENERAL HOSPITAL (500049)**, 1025 South Second Avenue, Zip 99362–4116, Mailing Address: P.O. Box 1398, Zip 99362–0309; tel. 509/525–0480 **A**1 10 **F**11 13 15 17 18 20 28 29 30 34 35 40 43 45 49 52 57 59 62 64 68 69 70 74 75 76 79 81 87 89 93 97 107 108 110 111 114 118 119 127 129 130 132 133 135 146 147 **S** Adventist Health, Roseville, CA
Primary Contact: Robert J. Beehler, Interim President and Chief Executive Officer
CFO: Don Welch, Chief Financial Officer
CMO: Tom Underhill, M.D., Chief Medical Officer
CIO: Dwight Morgan, Information Technology System Director
CHR: Candice Reece, Human Resources Director
CNO: Linda S. Givens, MSN, Chief Nursing Officer
Web address: www.wwgh.com
Control: Church–operated, Nongovernment, not–for profit **Service:** General Medical and Surgical

Staffed Beds: 38 **Admissions:** 1391 **Census:** 10 **Births:** 236

WENATCHEE—Chelan County

✉ **CONFLUENCE HEALTH/CENTRAL WASHINGTON HOSPITAL (500016)**, 1201 South Miller Street, Zip 98801–3201, Mailing Address: P.O. Box 1887, Zip 98807–1887; tel. 509/662–1511, (Total facility includes 22 beds in nursing home–type unit) **A**1 2 10 19 **F**3 13 17 18 20 22 24 26 28 29 30 31 34 35 40 43 45 46 47 49 50 62 63 64 68 69 70 73 74 75 76 78 79 81 84 85 86 89 91 93 94 95 107 111 114 115 119 127 128 130 146 148
Primary Contact: Peter Rutherford, M.D., Chief Executive Officer
COO: Vikki Noyes, Executive Vice President and Chief Operating Officer
CFO: John Doyle, Chief Financial Officer
CMO: Stuart Freed, M.D., Chief Medical Officer
CIO: Robert Pageler, Chief Information Officer
CHR: Jim Wood, Chief Administrative Officer
CNO: Tracey A. Kasnic, Senior Vice President Inpatient and Chief Nursing Officer
Web address: www.cwhs.com
Control: Other not–for–profit (including NFP Corporation) **Service:** General Medical and Surgical

Staffed Beds: 198 **Admissions:** 10957 **Census:** 133 **Outpatient Visits:** 143846 **Births:** 1883 **Total Expense ($000):** 279025 **Payroll Expense ($000):** 86998 **Personnel:** 1250

△ **CONFLUENCE HEALTH/WENATCHEE VALLEY HOSPITAL (500148)**, 820 North Chelan Avenue, Zip 98801–2028; tel. 509/663–8711, (Nonreporting) **A**2 7 10
Primary Contact: Peter Rutherford, M.D., Chief Executive Officer
COO: Kevin Gilbert, R.N., Vice President
CFO: John Doyle, Chief Financial Officer
CMO: Stuart Freed, M.D., Medical Director
CIO: Robert Pageler, Chief Information Officer
CHR: Jim Wood, Chief Human Resources Officer
CNO: Tracey A. Kasnic, Chief Nursing Officer
Web address: www.wvmedical.com
Control: Partnership, Investor–owned, for–profit **Service:** General Medical and Surgical

Staffed Beds: 20

WHITE SALMON—Klickitat County

SKYLINE HOSPITAL (501315), 211 Skyline Drive, Zip 98672–1918, Mailing Address: P.O. Box 99, Zip 98672–0099; tel. 509/493–1101 **A**10 18 **F**3 15 18 34 35 40 43 45 57 59 64 74 81 82 87 93 107 111 115 119 131 133 146 **P**6
Primary Contact: Robert P. Kimmes, Chief Executive Officer
CFO: Brenda Schneider, Chief Financial Officer
CMO: Christopher Samuels, Chief of Staff
CIO: Steve Opbroek, Manager Information Technology
CHR: Jessie Ramos, Manager Human Resources
CNO: Stefanie Boen, Chief Nursing Officer
Web address: www.skylinehospital.org
Control: Hospital district or authority, Government, nonfederal **Service:** General Medical and Surgical

Staffed Beds: 16 **Admissions:** 266 **Census:** 2 **Outpatient Visits:** 14721 **Births:** 0 **Total Expense ($000):** 17018 **Payroll Expense ($000):** 8324 **Personnel:** 124

YAKIMA—Yakima County

✉ △ **YAKIMA REGIONAL MEDICAL AND CARDIAC CENTER (500012)**, 110 South Ninth Avenue, Zip 98902–3315; tel. 509/575–5000 **A**1 2 7 10 **F**3 15 17 18 19 20 22 24 26 28 29 30 34 35 37 40 41 43 45 46 49 50 57 58 59 60 62 63 64 65 67 68 70 74 77 78 79 81 82 85 87 89 90 93 96 102 107 108 110 111 115 119 126 130 132 144 145 146 **S** Community Health Systems, Inc., Franklin, TN
Primary Contact: Bryan Braegger, Interim Chief Executive Officer
CMO: Dave Atteberry, M.D., Chief of Staff
CHR: Ralph L. Lundberg, Director Human Resources
Web address: www.yakimaregional.net
Control: Corporation, Investor–owned, for–profit **Service:** General Medical and Surgical

Staffed Beds: 167 **Admissions:** 4302 **Census:** 58 **Total Expense ($000):** 103155 **Payroll Expense ($000):** 37611

✉ **YAKIMA VALLEY MEMORIAL HOSPITAL (500036)**, 2811 Tieton Drive, Zip 98902–3761; tel. 509/575–8000 **A**1 2 3 5 10 **F**3 8 11 13 15 17 18 20 22 26 28 29 30 31 32 34 35 36 40 41 42 43 44 45 46 47 49 50 51 55 57 59 60 62 63 65 68 70 72 73 74 75 76 77 78 79 81 82 84 85 86 87 89 92 93 96 98 100 102 104 107 108 110 111 114 116 117 119 120 121 123 124 129 130 131 132 135 144 146 147 148 **P**4 6 7 **S** Virginia Mason Health System, Seattle, WA
Primary Contact: Russ Myers, Chief Executive Officer
COO: James Aberle, Vice President, Chief Operations Officer
CFO: Tim Reed, Vice President and Chief Financial Officer
CMO: Marty Brueggemann, Chief Medical Officer
CIO: Jeff Yamada, Vice President
CHR: Jolene R. Seda, Vice President People and Culture
CNO: Diane Patterson, Vice President, Chief Nursing Officer
Web address: www.yakimamemorial.org
Control: Other not–for–profit (including NFP Corporation) **Service:** General Medical and Surgical

Staffed Beds: 226 **Admissions:** 11958 **Census:** 122 **Outpatient Visits:** 427339 **Births:** 2768 **Total Expense ($000):** 347591 **Payroll Expense ($000):** 125491 **Personnel:** 2153

WA

Hospital, Medicare Provider Number, Address, Telephone, Approval, Facility, and Physician Codes, Health Care System

★ American Hospital Association (AHA) membership
□ The Joint Commission accreditation
○ Healthcare Facilities Accreditation Program
◇ DNV Healthcare Inc. accreditation
⇑ Center for Improvement in Healthcare Quality Accreditation
△ Commission on Accreditation of Rehabilitation Facilities (CARF) accreditation

WEST VIRGINIA

BECKLEY—Raleigh County

☐ **BECKLEY ARH HOSPITAL (510062)**, 306 Stanaford Road, Zip 25801–3142; tel. 304/255–3000 **A**1 10 **F**3 6 11 12 15 17 18 20 22 28 29 30 31 34 35 37 38 39 40 43 44 45 46 47 48 49 50 51 54 56 57 59 60 61 62 64 65 70 74 75 77 78 79 81 82 84 85 86 87 89 92 93 97 98 99 100 101 102 103 105 107 108 109 110 111 114 115 116 118 119 129 130 132 146 148 **P**6 **S** Appalachian Regional Healthcare, Inc., Lexington, KY
Primary Contact: Rocco K. Massey, Community Chief Executive Officer
CMO: Ahmad Khiami, Chief of Staff
CHR: Sue Thomas, Manager Human Resources
CNO: Angela Rivera, Chief Nursing Officer
Web address: www.arh.org
Control: Other not–for–profit (including NFP Corporation) **Service:** General Medical and Surgical

Staffed Beds: 170 **Admissions:** 6447 **Census:** 105 **Outpatient Visits:** 96044 **Births:** 0 **Total Expense ($000):** 88997 **Payroll Expense ($000):** 25864 **Personnel:** 613

☒ **BECKLEY VETERANS AFFAIRS MEDICAL CENTER**, 200 Veterans Avenue, Zip 25801–6499; tel. 304/255–2121 **A**1 **F**3 6 11 12 15 17 18 20 22 28 29 30 31 34 35 37 38 39 40 43 44 45 46 47 48 49 50 51 54 56 57 59 60 61 62 64 65 70 74 75 77 78 79 81 82 84 85 86 87 89 92 93 97 98 99 100 101 102 103 105 107 108 109 110 111 114 115 116 118 119 129 130 132 146 148 **P**6 **S** Department of Veterans Affairs, Washington, DC
Primary Contact: Daniel Bochicchio, M.D., Interim Director
CFO: Terry Massey, Chief Fiscal Services
CMO: John David Berryman, M.D., Chief of Staff
CIO: Sherry Gregg, Chief Information Technology Officer
CNO: Debra Lynn Legg, Associate Director Patient Care Services and Nurse Executive
Web address: www.beckley.va.gov/
Control: Other not–for–profit (including NFP Corporation) **Service:** General Medical and Surgical

Staffed Beds: 173 **Admissions:** 6447 **Census:** 105 **Outpatient Visits:** 96044 **Births:** 0 **Total Expense ($000):** 88997 **Payroll Expense ($000):** 25864 **Personnel:** 596

☒ **RALEIGH GENERAL HOSPITAL (510070)**, 1710 Harper Road, Zip 25801–3397; tel. 304/256–4100 **A**1 10 19 **F**3 13 15 17 18 20 22 29 30 31 34 35 40 43 45 49 50 57 59 60 64 70 74 75 76 78 79 81 85 87 89 107 108 110 111 114 115 117 119 126 130 132 146 147 **S** LifePoint Health, Brentwood, TN
Primary Contact: Harold L. Siglar, Interim Chief Executive Officer
CFO: Randy Harrison, Chief Financial Officer
CMO: Syed Siddiqi, M.D., President Medical Staff
CIO: Kevin Sexton, Director Information Systems
CHR: Chris T. Beebe, Director Human Resources
CNO: Alene Lewis, R.N., Chief Nursing Officer
Web address: www.raleighgeneral.com
Control: Corporation, Investor–owned, for–profit **Service:** General Medical and Surgical

Staffed Beds: 229 **Admissions:** 10354 **Census:** 129 **Outpatient Visits:** 108082 **Births:** 1146 **Total Expense ($000):** 134856 **Payroll Expense ($000):** 44239 **Personnel:** 797

BERKELEY SPRINGS—Morgan County

★ **WAR MEMORIAL HOSPITAL (511309)**, One Healthy Way, Zip 25411–7463; tel. 304/258–1234, (Total facility includes 16 beds in nursing home–type unit) **A**10 18 **F**3 11 15 28 29 30 34 35 40 45 50 53 54 57 59 64 65 77 79 81 85 86 93 97 107 119 129 130 133 **P**6 **S** Valley Health System, Winchester, VA
Primary Contact: Thomas S. Kluge, President
CFO: Kathryn Morales, Director of Finance
CMO: Gerald Bechamps, M.D., Vice President Medical Affairs
CHR: Abbey Rembold, Human Resources Senior Generalist
CNO: Heather Sigel, Director of Clinical Services
Web address: www.valleyhealthlink.com/war
Control: Other not–for–profit (including NFP Corporation) **Service:** General Medical and Surgical

Staffed Beds: 41 **Admissions:** 339 **Census:** 24 **Outpatient Visits:** 41485 **Births:** 0 **Total Expense ($000):** 19338 **Payroll Expense ($000):** 9007 **Personnel:** 156

BLUEFIELD—Mercer County

☒ **BLUEFIELD REGIONAL MEDICAL CENTER (510071)**, 500 Cherry Street, Zip 24701–3390; tel. 304/327–1100 **A**1 10 12 13 19 **F**3 8 13 15 18 20 22 28 29 31 34 40 43 45 46 47 49 50 56 57 59 60 64 68 70 74 75 76 78 79 81 86 89 96 107 108 110 111 115 118 119 121 124 126 127 129 130 132 144 146 147 **P**8 **S** Community Health Systems, Inc., Franklin, TN
Primary Contact: Derek W. Cimala, Interim Chief Executive Officer
COO: Michael Makosky, Chief Operating Officer
CMO: Joel Shor, M.D., Chief of Staff
CIO: Rose Lasker, Director Information Services
CHR: Sandee Cheynet, Vice President Administrative Services
Web address: www.bluefield.org
Control: Corporation, Investor–owned, for–profit **Service:** General Medical and Surgical

Staffed Beds: 92 **Admissions:** 3709 **Census:** 38 **Outpatient Visits:** 79300 **Births:** 505 **Total Expense ($000):** 82625 **Payroll Expense ($000):** 24478 **Personnel:** 430

BRIDGEPORT—Harrison County

☒ **UNITED HOSPITAL CENTER (510006)**, 327 Medical Park Drive, Zip 26330–9006; tel. 681/342–1000 **A**1 2 3 5 10 12 13 **F**3 5 11 13 15 17 18 20 22 28 29 30 31 34 36 38 40 43 45 46 47 49 50 51 54 57 58 59 60 62 63 64 65 68 70 74 75 76 77 78 79 81 82 84 85 86 87 89 93 97 98 99 100 101 102 103 104 107 108 109 110 111 114 115 116 117 118 119 120 121 123 126 128 129 130 131 132 146 148 **P**6 7 8 **S** West Virginia University Health System, Morgantown, WV
Primary Contact: Michael C. Tillman, President and Chief Executive Officer
COO: John Fernandez, Chief Operating Officer
CFO: Jim Rutkowski, Chief Financial Officer
CMO: Eric Radcliffe, M.D., Medical Director
CIO: Brian Cottrill, Chief Information Officer
CHR: Timothy M. Allen, Vice President Human Resources
CNO: Stephanie Smart, Chief Nursing Officer
Web address: www.thenewuhc.com
Control: Other not–for–profit (including NFP Corporation) **Service:** General Medical and Surgical

Staffed Beds: 264 **Admissions:** 12356 **Census:** 177 **Outpatient Visits:** 513964 **Births:** 1075 **Total Expense ($000):** 271144 **Payroll Expense ($000):** 108530 **Personnel:** 1862

BUCKEYE—Pocahontas County

★ **POCAHONTAS MEMORIAL HOSPITAL (511314)**, 150 Duncan Road, Zip 24924, Mailing Address: Rural Route 2, Box 52 W, Zip 24924; tel. 304/799–7400 **A**10 18 **F**3 7 11 29 30 34 35 40 43 50 56 57 59 64 65 68 75 77 86 93 97 107 119 127 130 132 133 135
Primary Contact: Barbara Lay, Chief Executive Officer
COO: Terry Wagner, R.N., Chief Operating Officer
CFO: Melissa Kane, Chief Financial Officer
CMO: Frank Puckett, M.D., Chief Medical Officer
CIO: Aaron Vaughan, Coordinator Information Systems
CHR: Katie Brown, Coordinator Human Resources
CNO: Kerrie Ridgeway, R.N., Chief Nursing Officer
Web address: www.pmhwv.org/
Control: County–Government, nonfederal **Service:** General Medical and Surgical

Staffed Beds: 24 **Admissions:** 238 **Census:** 3 **Outpatient Visits:** 15285 **Births:** 3 **Total Expense ($000):** 11490 **Payroll Expense ($000):** 7113 **Personnel:** 130

BUCKHANNON—Upshur County

☒ **ST. JOSEPH'S HOSPITAL OF BUCKHANNON (511321)**, 1 Amalia Drive, Zip 26201–2276; tel. 304/473–2000, (Total facility includes 20 beds in nursing home–type unit) **A**1 10 18 **F**3 11 13 15 18 28 29 30 31 34 35 40 43 44 45 50 57 59 64 65 70 75 76 79 81 83 84 85 87 89 107 110 115 119 128 129 130 132 133 135 144 146 147 **P**6 **S** West Virginia University Health System, Morgantown, WV
Primary Contact: Skip Gjolberg, FACHE, Administrator
CFO: Renee Hofer, Chief Financial Officer
CMO: Bartley Brown, D.O., Chief of Staff
CIO: Brian Williams, Web Services and Information Technology Manager
CHR: Anissa J. Hite Davis, Vice President Human Resources
CNO: Annamarie Chidester, R.N., Vice President, Patient Care Services
Web address: www.stj.net
Control: Other not–for–profit (including NFP Corporation) **Service:** General Medical and Surgical

Staffed Beds: 51 **Admissions:** 1187 **Census:** 25 **Outpatient Visits:** 98852 **Births:** 287 **Total Expense ($000):** 40781 **Payroll Expense ($000):** 19569 **Personnel:** 377

WV

Many Facility Codes have changed. Please refer to the AHA Guide Code Chart. © 2016 AHA Guide

CHARLESTON—Kanawha County

CAMC MEMORIAL HOSPITAL See Charleston Area Medical Center

CAMC WOMEN AND CHILDREN'S HOSPITAL See Charleston Area Medical Center

★ △ ◇ **CHARLESTON AREA MEDICAL CENTER (510022)**, 501 Morris Street, Zip 25301–1300, Mailing Address: P.O. Box 1547, Zip 25326–1547; tel. 304/388–5432, (Includes CAMC MEMORIAL HOSPITAL, 3200 MacCorkle Avenue S.E., Zip 25304; tel. 304/388–5973; Jeffrey L. Oskin, Vice President and Administrator; CAMC TEAYS VALLEY HOSPITAL, 1400 Hospital Drive, Hurricane, Zip 25526–9202; tel. 304/757–1700; Randall H. Hodges, FACHE, Vice President and Administrator; CAMC WOMEN AND CHILDREN'S HOSPITAL, 800 Pennsylvania Avenue, Zip 25302, Mailing Address: P.O. Box 6669, Zip 25362; tel. 304/388–5432; Andrew Weber, Vice President and Administrator; GENERAL HOSPITAL, 501 Morris Street, Zip 25301, Mailing Address: Box 1393, Zip 25325; tel. 304/388–5432; Michael D. Williams, Vice President and Administrator) **A**2 3 5 7 8 10 12 13 21 **F**3 8 11 12 13 15 17 18 19 20 22 24 26 28 29 30 31 32 34 35 38 40 41 43 44 45 46 47 48 49 50 51 52 54 55 56 57 59 60 61 64 65 68 70 72 74 75 76 77 78 79 81 82 84 85 86 88 89 90 92 93 94 96 97 98 99 100 101 102 103 104 107 108 110 111 114 115 116 117 118 119 120 121 123 124 126 129 130 131 132 134 135 138 141 143 144 145 146 147 148 **P**6
Primary Contact: David L. Ramsey, President and Chief Executive Officer
COO: Glenn Crotty, Jr., M.D., Executive Vice President and Chief Operating Officer
CFO: Larry C. Hudson, Executive Vice President and Chief Financial Officer
CMO: T. Pinckney McIlwain, M.D., Vice President and Chief Medical Officer
CIO: Eileen Clark, Vice President Information Services
CHR: Kristi Snyder, Vice President Human Resources
CNO: Ronald E. Moore, R.N., Vice President Professional Practice and Chief Nursing Officer
Web address: www.camc.org
Control: Other not–for–profit (including NFP Corporation) **Service:** General Medical and Surgical

Staffed Beds: 833 **Admissions:** 36439 **Census:** 543 **Outpatient Visits:** 639025 **Births:** 2657 **Total Expense ($000):** 952485 **Payroll Expense ($000):** 323687 **Personnel:** 6356

☐ **EYE AND EAR CLINIC OF CHARLESTON (510059)**, 1306 Kanawha Boulevard East, Zip 25301–3001, Mailing Address: P.O. Box 2271, Zip 25328–2271; tel. 304/343–4371 **A**1 10 **F**3 45 57 59 75 79 81 107 111 119 141
Primary Contact: Christina Arvon, Administrator and Chief Executive Officer
CMO: James W. Candill, M.D., President Medical Staff
Web address: www.eyeandearclinicwv.org
Control: Corporation, Investor–owned, for–profit **Service:** General Medical and Surgical

Staffed Beds: 6 **Admissions:** 166 **Census:** 1 **Outpatient Visits:** 10873 **Births:** 0 **Total Expense ($000):** 14447 **Payroll Expense ($000):** 4445 **Personnel:** 121

GENERAL HOSPITAL See Charleston Area Medical Center

✖ **HIGHLAND HOSPITAL (514001)**, 300 56th Street S.E., Zip 25304–2361, Mailing Address: P.O. Box 4107, Zip 25364–4107; tel. 304/926–1600 **A**1 10 **F**3 29 34 35 38 50 57 59 86 87 98 99 101 103 130
Primary Contact: Cynthia A. Persily, Ph.D., R.N., President and Chief Executive Officer
COO: Rick Rucker, Chief Operating Officer
CFO: Chris K. Miller, Chief Financial Officer
CMO: Kiran S. Devaraj, Chief Medical Officer and Chief Clinical Officer
CIO: Damon Carradine, Director Information Technology
CHR: Patrick Rawlings, Chief Human Resource Officer
CNO: Carla Hall, Director of Nursing
Web address: www.highlandhosp.com
Control: Other not–for–profit (including NFP Corporation) **Service:** Psychiatric

Staffed Beds: 80 **Admissions:** 2431 **Census:** 65 **Outpatient Visits:** 0 **Births:** 0 **Total Expense ($000):** 18781 **Payroll Expense ($000):** 9396 **Personnel:** 271

✖ **SAINT FRANCIS HOSPITAL (510031)**, 333 Laidley Street, Zip 25301–1628, Mailing Address: P.O. Box 471, Zip 25322–0471; tel. 304/347–6500, (Total facility includes 25 beds in nursing home–type unit) **A**1 10 **F**3 11 15 18 20 22 29 31 34 37 40 45 48 49 51 57 58 59 60 64 68 69 70 74 75 77 79 81 82 84 86 87 93 107 108 110 111 115 119 128 130 131 146 147 148 **S** Thomas Health System, Inc., South Charleston, WV
Primary Contact: Daniel Lauffer, FACHE, President and Chief Executive Officer
COO: Brian Ulery, Senior Vice President and Chief Operating Officer
CFO: Renee Cross, Senior Vice President and Chief Financial Officer
CMO: Matthew Upton, Chief Medical Officer and Chief Medical Information Officer
CIO: Jeremy Taylor, Director Information Services
CHR: Marybeth Smith, Director Human Resources
CNO: Rebecca Brannon, R.N., Senior Vice President and Chief Nursing Officer
Web address: www.stfrancishospital.com
Control: Other not–for–profit (including NFP Corporation) **Service:** General Medical and Surgical

Staffed Beds: 118 **Admissions:** 3295 **Census:** 43 **Outpatient Visits:** 96232 **Births:** 0 **Total Expense ($000):** 99285 **Payroll Expense ($000):** 30914 **Personnel:** 616

✖ **SELECT SPECIALTY HOSPITAL–CHARLESTON (512002)**, 333 Laidley Street, 3rd Floor East, Zip 25301–1614; tel. 304/720–7234 **A**1 10 **F**1 29 74 75 79 85 130 148 **S** Select Medical Corporation, Mechanicsburg, PA
Primary Contact: Frank Weber, Chief Executive Officer
CHR: Sabrina White, Coordinator Human Resources
Web address: www.selectspecialtyhospitals.com/company/locations/charleston.aspx
Control: Corporation, Investor–owned, for–profit **Service:** Long–Term Acute Care hospital

Staffed Beds: 32 **Admissions:** 424 **Census:** 31 **Outpatient Visits:** 0 **Births:** 0 **Total Expense ($000):** 17213 **Payroll Expense ($000):** 6368 **Personnel:** 109

CLARKSBURG—Harrison County

☐ **HIGHLAND–CLARKSBURG HOSPITAL (514011)**, 3 Hospital Plaza, Zip 26301–9316; tel. 304/969–3100 **A**1 10 **F**98 99
Primary Contact: James H. Dissen, Chief Executive Officer
COO: Michael Casdorph, Chief Operating Officer
CFO: Shelly Giaguinto, Chief Financial Officer
CMO: Marilou Patalinjug Tyner, M.D., Medical Director
CHR: Cynthia Drury, Coordinator Human Resources
CNO: Paula Herndon, R.N., Nurse Executive
Web address: www.highlandhosp.com
Control: Other not–for–profit (including NFP Corporation) **Service:** Psychiatric

Staffed Beds: 105 **Admissions:** 878 **Census:** 54 **Outpatient Visits:** 0 **Births:** 0 **Total Expense ($000):** 16971 **Payroll Expense ($000):** 8110 **Personnel:** 202

✖ **LOUIS A. JOHNSON VETERANS AFFAIRS MEDICAL CENTER**, 1 Medical Center Drive, Zip 26301–4199; tel. 304/623–3461, (Nonreporting) **A**1 2 3 5 **S** Department of Veterans Affairs, Washington, DC
Primary Contact: Glenn R. Snider, M.D., Interim Director
CMO: Glenn R. Snider, M.D., Chief of Staff
CIO: Michael Matthey, Facility Chief Information Officer
CHR: Ian Jacobs, Chief, Human Resource Management Service
Web address: www.clarksburg.va.gov
Control: Veterans Affairs, Government, federal **Service:** General Medical and Surgical

Staffed Beds: 71

ELKINS—Randolph County

✖ **DAVIS MEDICAL CENTER (510030)**, Gorman Avenue and Reed Street, Zip 26241, Mailing Address: P.O. Box 1484, Zip 26241–1484; tel. 304/636–3300 **A**1 2 10 20 **F**11 13 15 28 29 30 31 34 35 40 49 50 51 54 57 59 64 68 69 70 71 75 76 78 79 81 82 84 85 86 87 89 92 97 107 108 110 111 115 116 117 118 119 121 123 129 130 132 135 146 147 148 **P**8 **S** Davis Health System, Elkins, WV
Primary Contact: Vance Jackson, FACHE, Chief Executive Officer
COO: Greg Johnson, Vice President of Operations
CFO: Rebecca J. Hammer, Chief Financial Officer
CMO: Anne Banfield, Chief, Medical Staff
CIO: Steve Crowl, Director of Information Services
CHR: Jon Steen, Director Human Resources
CNO: Pamela Smithson, Vice President Nursing
Web address: www.davishealthsystem.com
Control: Other not–for–profit (including NFP Corporation) **Service:** General Medical and Surgical

Staffed Beds: 80 **Admissions:** 2835 **Census:** 27 **Outpatient Visits:** 155444 **Births:** 291 **Total Expense ($000):** 89697 **Payroll Expense ($000):** 40113 **Personnel:** 630

WV

FAIRMONT—Marion County

⊞ **FAIRMONT REGIONAL MEDICAL CENTER (510047)**, 1325 Locust Avenue, Zip 26554–1435; tel. 304/367–7100 **A**1 2 10 **F**3 11 12 13 14 15 18 20 28 29 30 31 34 35 38 39 40 41 43 44 45 46 47 48 49 50 51 53 54 56 57 59 60 62 64 65 68 69 70 75 76 77 78 81 84 85 86 87 89 91 92 93 98 100 102 103 104 107 108 110 111 114 115 118 119 130 132 135 145 146 147 148 **P**6
Primary Contact: Margaret C. Coster, R.N., MSN, President and Chief Executive Officer
CFO: Daniel Honerbrink, Vice President Finance and Chief Financial Officer
CMO: Wes Steele, M.D., Chief of Staff
CIO: Mike Wooddell, Director Information Services
CHR: Jim Harris, Vice President Human Resources
Web address: www.fghi.com
Control: Corporation, Investor–owned, for–profit **Service:** General Medical and Surgical

Staffed Beds: 144 **Admissions:** 5217 **Census:** 79 **Outpatient Visits:** 111665 **Births:** 227 **Total Expense ($000):** 69802 **Payroll Expense ($000):** 27989 **Personnel:** 596

GASSAWAY—Braxton County

BRAXTON COUNTY MEMORIAL HOSPITAL (511308), 100 Hoylman DR, Zip 26624–9318, Mailing Address: 100 Hoylman Drive, Zip 26624–9318; tel. 304/364–5156 **A**10 18 **F**3 8 11 15 30 32 34 35 40 43 45 57 59 62 64 75 81 97 107 108 114 127 130 133 146 147 **P**6
Primary Contact: Ben Vincent, FACHE, Chief Executive Officer
CFO: Kimber Knight, Chief Financial Officer
CMO: Russell L. Stewart, D.O., Chief Medical Officer
CNO: Julia Rose, R.N., Director of Nursing
Web address: www.braxtonmemorial.org
Control: Other not–for–profit (including NFP Corporation) **Service:** General Medical and Surgical

Staffed Beds: 25 **Admissions:** 292 **Census:** 3 **Outpatient Visits:** 45667 **Births:** 0 **Total Expense ($000):** 17121 **Payroll Expense ($000):** 7168 **Personnel:** 162

GLEN DALE—Marshall County

⊞ **REYNOLDS MEMORIAL HOSPITAL (510013)**, 800 Wheeling Avenue, Zip 26038–1697; tel. 304/845–3211, (Total facility includes 20 beds in nursing home–type unit) **A**1 10 **F**3 11 15 18 20 28 30 34 39 40 53 56 57 59 62 64 65 70 74 75 77 78 79 80 81 82 85 86 89 92 93 107 108 110 111 114 118 119 128 130 132 135 146 **P**8
Primary Contact: David F. Hess, M.D., Chief Executive Officer
COO: Kevin Britt, Chief Operating Officer
CFO: William Robert Hunt, Chief Financial Officer
CMO: David F. Hess, M.D., President Medical Staff
CIO: Warren Kelley, Chief Information Officer
CHR: R. Craig Madden, Director Employee Relations
CNO: Carol R. Miller, R.N., Chief Nursing Officer
Web address: www.reynoldsmemorial.com
Control: Other not–for–profit (including NFP Corporation) **Service:** General Medical and Surgical

Staffed Beds: 90 **Admissions:** 2041 **Census:** 38 **Outpatient Visits:** 91852 **Births:** 0 **Total Expense ($000):** 37664 **Payroll Expense ($000):** 18645 **Personnel:** 341

GRAFTON—Taylor County

GRAFTON CITY HOSPITAL (511307), 1 Hospital Plaza, Zip 26354–1283; tel. 304/265–0400, (Total facility includes 76 beds in nursing home–type unit) **A**10 18 **F**11 29 30 32 34 35 38 39 40 45 53 54 56 57 59 61 64 65 67 75 81 84 85 86 87 91 92 93 94 97 100 101 103 104 107 108 110 111 119 127 128 129 130 131 132 133 135 146 147 **P**6
Primary Contact: Patrick D. Shaw, Chief Executive Officer
CFO: Regina Pickens, Chief Financial Officer
CMO: David B. Bender, M.D., Chief Medical Staff
CIO: Jim Harris, Director Information Technology
CHR: Missey Kimbrew, Director Human Resources
CNO: Violet Shaw, R.N., Director of Nursing
Web address: www.graftonhospital.com
Control: City–Government, nonfederal **Service:** General Medical and Surgical

Staffed Beds: 101 **Admissions:** 585 **Census:** 72 **Outpatient Visits:** 35839 **Births:** 0 **Total Expense ($000):** 19426 **Payroll Expense ($000):** 10049 **Personnel:** 207

GRANTSVILLE—Calhoun County

★ **MINNIE HAMILTON HEALTHCARE CENTER (511303)**, 186 Hospital Drive, Zip 26147–7100; tel. 304/354–9244, (Total facility includes 24 beds in nursing home–type unit) **A**10 18 **F**7 11 15 28 29 30 32 34 35 36 39 40 41 43 44 50 53 56 57 59 61 64 65 66 68 75 82 84 86 87 93 97 99 101 107 108 119 127 130 132 133 134 135 143 144 146 147 148 **P**6
Primary Contact: Steve Whited, Chief Executive Officer
CFO: Kyle Pierson, Chief Financial Officer
CMO: Suresh Balasubramony, M.D., Chief Medical Officer
CIO: Brent Barr, Chief Information Officer
CHR: Sheila Gherke, Director Human Resources
CNO: Kim Houchin, Chief Nursing Officer
Web address: www.mhhcc.com
Control: Other not–for–profit (including NFP Corporation) **Service:** General Medical and Surgical

Staffed Beds: 42 **Admissions:** 284 **Census:** 4 **Outpatient Visits:** 60938 **Births:** 0 **Personnel:** 243

HINTON—Summers County

☐ **SUMMERS COUNTY ARH HOSPITAL (511310)**, Terrace Street, Zip 25951–2407, Mailing Address: Drawer 940, Zip 25951–0940; tel. 304/466–1000 **A**1 10 18 **F**11 15 28 29 32 34 35 40 43 44 50 54 57 59 62 64 65 71 77 81 82 85 86 87 93 97 107 110 114 119 127 130 133 146 147 148 **P**6 **S** Appalachian Regional Healthcare, Inc., Lexington, KY
Primary Contact: Wesley Dangerfield, Community Chief Executive Officer
CMO: Waheed Khan, M.D., President Medical Staff
CIO: Brent Styer, Chief Information Officer
CHR: Beth Elswick, Administrative Assistant
CNO: Sharon Milburn, Chief Nursing Officer
Web address: www.arh.org
Control: Other not–for–profit (including NFP Corporation) **Service:** General Medical and Surgical

Staffed Beds: 25 **Admissions:** 518 **Census:** 9 **Outpatient Visits:** 27446 **Births:** 0 **Total Expense ($000):** 13325 **Payroll Expense ($000):** 4746 **Personnel:** 112

HUNTINGTON—Cabell County

⊞ **CABELL HUNTINGTON HOSPITAL (510055)**, 1340 Hal Greer Boulevard, Zip 25701–0195; tel. 304/526–2000, (Includes HOOPS FAMILY CHILDREN'S HOSPITAL, 1340 Hal Greer Boulevard, Zip 25701–3800; tel. 304/526–2000), (Total facility includes 15 beds in nursing home–type unit) **A**1 2 3 5 8 10 **F**3 5 7 11 12 13 15 16 17 18 19 20 22 26 28 29 30 31 32 34 35 37 38 39 40 41 43 44 45 46 47 48 49 50 51 52 54 55 56 57 58 59 60 61 62 64 65 66 70 72 73 74 75 76 77 78 79 81 82 84 85 86 87 88 89 92 93 94 96 97 107 108 110 111 114 115 117 118 119 120 121 123 126 128 129 130 131 132 134 135 144 145 146 147 148
Primary Contact: Kevin N. Fowler, President and Chief Executive Officer
CFO: David M. Ward, Chief Financial Officer and Chief Acquisition Officer
CMO: Hoyt J. Burdick, M.D., Vice President Medical Affairs
CIO: Dennis Lee, Vice President and Chief Information Officer
CHR: Barry Tourigny, Vice President Human Resources and Organizational Development
CNO: Joy S. Pelfrey, R.N., Vice President and Chief Nursing Officer
Web address: www.cabellhuntington.org
Control: Other not–for–profit (including NFP Corporation) **Service:** General Medical and Surgical

Staffed Beds: 303 **Admissions:** 27810 **Census:** 269 **Outpatient Visits:** 568923 **Births:** 2835 **Total Expense ($000):** 470716 **Payroll Expense ($000):** 155251 **Personnel:** 2333

☐ **CORNERSTONE HOSPITAL OF HUNTINGTON (512003)**, 2900 First Avenue, Two East, Zip 25702–1241; tel. 304/399–2600 **A**1 10 **F**1 29 148 **S** Cornerstone Healthcare Group, Dallas, TX
Primary Contact: Cynthia Isaacs, Chief Executive Officer
CFO: Frank Carter, Chief Financial Officer
CMO: William Beam, M.D., Chief of Staff
Web address: www.chghospitals.com
Control: Corporation, Investor–owned, for–profit **Service:** Long–Term Acute Care hospital

Staffed Beds: 25 **Admissions:** 346 **Census:** 23 **Outpatient Visits:** 0 **Births:** 0 **Total Expense ($000):** 9781 **Payroll Expense ($000):** 4286 **Personnel:** 67

⊞ **HEALTHSOUTH HUNTINGTON REHABILITATION HOSPITAL (513028)**, 6900 West Country Club Drive, Zip 25705–2000; tel. 304/733–1060 **A**1 10 **F**29 34 59 90 95 96 148 **S** HEALTHSOUTH Corporation, Birmingham, AL
Primary Contact: Michael E. Zuliani, Chief Executive Officer
CHR: Jenny Overcash, Director Human Resources
CNO: Ann Evans, Chief Nursing Officer
Web address: www.healthsouthhuntington.com
Control: Corporation, Investor–owned, for–profit **Service:** Rehabilitation

Staffed Beds: 62 **Admissions:** 1305 **Census:** 46 **Outpatient Visits:** 0 **Births:** 0 **Total Expense ($000):** 14105 **Payroll Expense ($000):** 7357 **Personnel:** 155

Many Facility Codes have changed. Please refer to the AHA Guide Code Chart. © 2016 AHA Guide

⊠ **HUNTINGTON VETERANS AFFAIRS MEDICAL CENTER**, 1540 Spring Valley Drive, Zip 25704–9300; tel. 304/429–6741, (Nonreporting) **A**1 3 5 **S** Department of Veterans Affairs, Washington, DC
Primary Contact: Brian Nimmo, Director
CIO: Gary Henderson, Chief Information Resources Management Services
Web address: www.huntington.va.gov/
Control: Veterans Affairs, Government, federal **Service:** General Medical and Surgical

Staffed Beds: 80

☐ **MILDRED MITCHELL–BATEMAN HOSPITAL (514009)**, 1530 Norway Avenue, Zip 25705–1358, Mailing Address: P.O. Box 448, Zip 25709–0448; tel. 304/525–7801 **A**1 3 10 **F**3 4 11 30 86 87 97 98 103 106 130 135 143 146 **P**6
Primary Contact: Craig A. Richards, Chief Executive Officer
CFO: Lucille Gedies, Chief Financial Officer
CMO: Shahid Masood, M.D., Clinical Director
CIO: Elias Majdalani, Director Management Information Systems
CHR: Kieth Anne Worden, Director Human Resources
CNO: Patricia Hamilton, R.N., Director of Nursing
Web address: www.batemanhospital.org
Control: State–Government, nonfederal **Service:** Psychiatric

Staffed Beds: 110 **Admissions:** 510 **Census:** 107 **Outpatient Visits:** 0 **Births:** 0 **Total Expense ($000):** 39159 **Payroll Expense ($000):** 14944 **Personnel:** 419

☐ **RIVER PARK HOSPITAL (514008)**, 1230 Sixth Avenue, Zip 25701–2312, Mailing Address: P.O. Box 1875, Zip 25719–1875; tel. 304/526–9111 **A**1 3 10 **F**29 34 35 38 98 99 100 101 102 103 106 130 143 **P**4 5 6 **S** Universal Health Services, Inc., King of Prussia, PA
Primary Contact: Terry A. Stephens, Chief Executive Officer
CFO: Steve Kuhn, Chief Financial Officer
CMO: Mark A. Hughes, M.D., Medical Director
CIO: James Martin, Chief Information Officer
CHR: Mary Stratton, Director Human Resources
CNO: Charles Christopher Whitt, Chief Nursing Officer
Web address: www.riverparkhospital.net
Control: Corporation, Investor–owned, for–profit **Service:** Psychiatric

Staffed Beds: 175 **Admissions:** 1339 **Census:** 147 **Outpatient Visits:** 0 **Births:** 0 **Total Expense ($000):** 21678 **Payroll Expense ($000):** 12333 **Personnel:** 291

⊠ **ST. MARY'S MEDICAL CENTER (510007)**, 2900 First Avenue, Zip 25702–1272; tel. 304/526–1234, (Total facility includes 19 beds in nursing home–type unit) **A**1 2 3 10 **F**3 11 13 15 17 18 20 22 24 26 28 29 30 31 32 34 35 36 39 40 42 43 44 45 46 47 48 49 50 53 58 59 60 61 62 64 65 66 67 68 70 74 75 76 77 78 79 81 82 84 85 86 87 89 90 92 93 96 97 98 100 101 102 103 107 108 110 111 114 115 118 119 120 121 123 124 126 128 129 130 132 135 144 145 146 147 148 **P**8 **S** Pallottine Health Services, Huntington, WV
Primary Contact: Michael G. Sellards, President and Chief Executive Officer
COO: Todd Campbell, Senior Vice President and Chief Operating Officer
CFO: Angela Swearingen, Vice President Finance
CMO: Ernest Lee Taylor, M.D., Vice President Medical Affairs
CIO: David Wendell, Manager, Information Systems
CHR: Susan Beth Robinson, Vice President Human Resources
CNO: Elizabeth Bosley, R.N., Vice President Patient Services
Web address: www.st–marys.org
Control: Church–operated, Nongovernment, not–for profit **Service:** General Medical and Surgical

Staffed Beds: 393 **Admissions:** 16160 **Census:** 259 **Outpatient Visits:** 255047 **Births:** 347 **Total Expense ($000):** 363117 **Payroll Expense ($000):** 121761 **Personnel:** 2439

KEYSER—Mineral County

⊠ **POTOMAC VALLEY HOSPITAL (511315)**, 100 Pin Oak Lane, Zip 26726–5908; tel. 304/597–3500 **A**1 10 18 **F**3 15 18 28 29 30 34 35 40 44 45 50 57 59 63 64 68 70 71 75 79 81 85 86 87 93 107 108 110 111 112 114 119 127 130 132 133 135 146 **S** West Virginia University Health System, Morgantown, WV
Primary Contact: Linda K. Shroyer, Administrator
CFO: Marian Cardwell, Chief Financial Officer
CMO: Charles Bess, M.D., Medical Director
CIO: Micah Reel, Director of Bio–Med
CHR: Dianne Smith, Director Personnel and Human Resources
CNO: Mary Ann Billings, Director of Nursing
Web address: www.potomacvalleyhospital.org
Control: Other not–for–profit (including NFP Corporation) **Service:** General Medical and Surgical

Staffed Beds: 25 **Admissions:** 654 **Census:** 7 **Outpatient Visits:** 44708 **Births:** 0 **Total Expense ($000):** 20543 **Payroll Expense ($000):** 8496 **Personnel:** 223

KINGWOOD—Preston County

★ **PRESTON MEMORIAL HOSPITAL (511312)**, 150 Memorial Drive, Zip 26537–1495; tel. 304/329–1400 **A**10 18 **F**3 12 15 18 29 30 34 35 40 43 45 47 48 50 53 57 59 64 65 70 74 75 76 77 81 92 93 97 107 108 110 111 114 119 129 132 133 135 144 146 147 148 **P**6 **S** Monongalia Health System, Morgantown, WV
Primary Contact: Melissa Lockwood, Chief Executive Officer
CFO: Robert W. Milvet, Jr., Chief Financial Officer
CIO: Beth Horne, System Administrator Information Technology
CHR: Michele Batiste, Director Human Resources
Web address: www.prestonmemorial.org
Control: Other not–for–profit (including NFP Corporation) **Service:** General Medical and Surgical

Staffed Beds: 25 **Admissions:** 802 **Census:** 7 **Outpatient Visits:** 61698 **Births:** 0 **Total Expense ($000):** 29335 **Payroll Expense ($000):** 13275 **Personnel:** 253

LOGAN—Logan County

⊠ **LOGAN REGIONAL MEDICAL CENTER (510048)**, 20 Hospital Drive, Zip 25601–3452; tel. 304/831–1101 **A**1 10 20 **F**3 11 13 15 18 20 28 29 31 34 35 40 43 45 49 51 54 57 59 64 65 70 74 75 76 77 78 79 81 82 86 87 89 90 92 93 97 107 108 110 111 114 115 117 118 119 129 130 133 135 146 147 **P**6 **S** LifePoint Health, Brentwood, TN
Primary Contact: Kevin Zachary, Chief Executive Officer
COO: Simon Ratliff, Chief Operating Officer
CFO: Tim Matney, Chief Financial Officer
CMO: Kathy Harvey, D.O., Chief Medical Officer
CIO: Barry Hensley, Director Information Systems
CHR: Jessica Martin, Director Human Resources
CNO: Karen Barnes, Interim Chief Nursing Officer
Web address: www.loganregionalmedicalcenter.com
Control: Corporation, Investor–owned, for–profit **Service:** General Medical and Surgical

Staffed Beds: 129 **Admissions:** 4441 **Census:** 61 **Outpatient Visits:** 103172 **Births:** 256 **Total Expense ($000):** 79004 **Payroll Expense ($000):** 25715 **Personnel:** 628

MADISON—Boone County

⊠ **BOONE MEMORIAL HOSPITAL (511313)**, 701 Madison Avenue, Zip 25130–1699; tel. 304/369–1230 **A**1 10 18 **F**3 11 15 28 34 35 40 43 45 50 53 54 57 59 64 65 75 77 81 87 97 107 108 111 119 127 128 131 133 135 146 147
Primary Contact: Virgil Underwood, Chief Executive Officer
CFO: Randy Foxx, Chief Financial Officer
CMO: Ziad Chanaa, M.D., Chief of Staff
CIO: Susan Shreve, Executive Director Information Technology
CHR: Sheliah Cook, Director Human Resources
CNO: Teresa Meade, R.N., Chief Nursing Officer
Web address: www.bmh.org
Control: Other not–for–profit (including NFP Corporation) **Service:** General Medical and Surgical

Staffed Beds: 25 **Admissions:** 618 **Census:** 11 **Outpatient Visits:** 55028 **Births:** 0 **Total Expense ($000):** 24165 **Payroll Expense ($000):** 8326 **Personnel:** 193

MARTINSBURG—Berkeley County

⊠ **BERKELEY MEDICAL CENTER (510008)**, 2500 Hospital Drive, Zip 25401–3402; tel. 304/264–1000 **A**1 2 3 5 10 **F**3 11 12 13 15 17 18 20 22 28 29 30 31 34 35 38 40 43 44 45 47 49 51 53 57 59 62 64 70 72 74 75 76 77 78 79 81 82 85 86 87 89 92 93 98 102 103 107 108 110 111 115 118 119 124 129 130 131 132 135 143 144 145 146 147 148 **S** West Virginia University Health System, Morgantown, WV
Primary Contact: Anthony Zelenka, President and Chief Operating Officer
CFO: Kathleen Quinones, Interim Vice President Finance
CIO: Mark Combs, Interim Director System Information Technology
CHR: Michelle Thomas, Vice President Human Resources
CNO: Donna Clews, Ph.D., Vice President Patient Care Services
Web address: www.cityhospital.org
Control: Other not–for–profit (including NFP Corporation) **Service:** General Medical and Surgical

Staffed Beds: 195 **Admissions:** 8169 **Census:** 100 **Outpatient Visits:** 250663 **Births:** 995 **Total Expense ($000):** 173022 **Payroll Expense ($000):** 64222 **Personnel:** 1358

WV

Hospital, Medicare Provider Number, Address, Telephone, Approval, Facility, and Physician Codes, Health Care System

★ American Hospital Association (AHA) membership 　　○ Healthcare Facilities Accreditation Program 　　⇑ Center for Improvement in Healthcare Quality Accreditation
☐ The Joint Commission accreditation 　　◇ DNV Healthcare Inc. accreditation 　　△ Commission on Accreditation of Rehabilitation Facilities (CARF) accreditation

---

✠ **MARTINSBURG VETERANS AFFAIRS MEDICAL CENTER**, 510 Butler Avenue, Zip 25405–9990; tel. 304/263–0811, (Total facility includes 121 beds in nursing home–type unit) **A**1 3 5 **F**3 4 5 7 10 15 18 22 24 26 29 30 31 33 34 35 38 39 40 45 46 47 48 49 50 53 55 56 58 59 61 62 63 64 65 66 68 70 74 75 77 78 79 81 82 83 84 85 87 91 92 93 94 97 98 101 102 103 104 105 106 107 108 111 114 115 118 119 127 128 129 130 132 133 135 141 142 143 146 147 148 **S** Department of Veterans Affairs, Washington, DC
Primary Contact: Timothy J. Cooke, Medical Center Director and Chief Executive Officer
COO: Timothy J. Cooke, Medical Center Director and Chief Executive Officer
CMO: Jonathan Fierer, M.D., Chief of Staff
CIO: Mary Ann Creel, Chief Information Resource Management
CHR: Brenda Byrd–Pelaez, Chief Human Resources Management Office
CNO: Susan George, R.N., Associate Director Patient Care Services
Web address: www.martinsburg.va.gov/
Control: Veterans Affairs, Government, federal **Service:** General Medical and Surgical

> **Staffed Beds:** 495 **Admissions:** 4173 **Census:** 411 **Outpatient Visits:** 573876 **Births:** 0 **Total Expense ($000):** 312485 **Payroll Expense ($000):** 131811 **Personnel:** 1956

MONTGOMERY—Fayette County

✠ **MONTGOMERY GENERAL HOSPITAL (511318)**, 401 Sixth Avenue, Zip 25136–2116, Mailing Address: P.O. Box 270, Zip 25136–0270; tel. 304/442–5151, (Total facility includes 44 beds in nursing home–type unit) **A**1 10 18 **F**3 11 15 29 30 34 35 40 45 49 50 53 57 59 64 67 68 77 81 87 93 97 107 111 114 119 128 129 130 131 133 135 146 147 **P**6 8
Primary Contact: Vickie Gay, Chief Executive Officer
CFO: Sherri Murray, Chief Financial Officer
CMO: Traci Acklin, M.D., Chief of Staff
CIO: Denzil Blevins, Director Information Systems
CHR: Kelly D. Frye, Director Human Resources
Web address: www.mghwv.com
Control: Other not–for–profit (including NFP Corporation) **Service:** General Medical and Surgical

> **Staffed Beds:** 69 **Admissions:** 505 **Census:** 43 **Outpatient Visits:** 72687 **Births:** 0 **Total Expense ($000):** 21325 **Payroll Expense ($000):** 10726 **Personnel:** 224

MORGANTOWN—Monongalia County

CHESTNUT RIDGE HOSPITAL See West Virginia University Hospitals

✠ **HEALTHSOUTH MOUNTAINVIEW REGIONAL REHABILITATION HOSPITAL (513030)**, 1160 Van Voorhis Road, Zip 26505–3437; tel. 304/598–1100, (Nonreporting) **A**1 3 5 10 **S** HEALTHSOUTH Corporation, Birmingham, AL
Primary Contact: Lou Little, Chief Executive Officer
CFO: Jason Gizzi, Controller
CMO: Govind Patel, M.D., Medical Director
CIO: Robin Wherry, Risk Manager and Director Quality Assurance and Health Information Management
CHR: Shannon Hyde, Director Human Resources
CNO: Stacy Jones, Chief Nursing Officer
Web address: www.healthsouthmountainview.com
Control: Corporation, Investor–owned, for–profit **Service:** Rehabilitation

> **Staffed Beds:** 96

✠ **MONONGALIA GENERAL HOSPITAL (510024)**, 1200 J. D. Anderson Drive, Zip 26505–3486; tel. 304/598–1200 **A**1 2 3 10 19 **F**3 13 15 17 18 20 22 24 26 28 29 30 31 32 34 35 40 43 45 46 49 50 51 54 57 59 60 64 65 68 70 74 75 76 77 78 79 81 82 84 85 86 87 89 97 107 108 111 114 115 116 118 119 126 127 129 130 132 135 145 146 147 148 **P**6 8 **S** Monongalia Health System, Morgantown, WV
Primary Contact: Darryl L. Duncan, President and Chief Executive Officer
COO: Linda Neu Ollis, FACHE, Chief Operating Officer
CFO: Daris Rosencrance, Chief Financial Officer
CMO: Matthew P. Darmelio, Chief of Staff
CIO: Steve Carter, Chief Information Officer
CHR: Melissa Shreves, Director Human Resources
Web address: www.mongeneral.com
Control: Other not–for–profit (including NFP Corporation) **Service:** General Medical and Surgical

> **Staffed Beds:** 185 **Admissions:** 8065 **Census:** 100 **Outpatient Visits:** 290454 **Births:** 1168 **Total Expense ($000):** 236784 **Payroll Expense ($000):** 87457 **Personnel:** 1377

✠ **WEST VIRGINIA UNIVERSITY HOSPITALS (510001)**, 1 Medical Center Drive, Zip 26506–4749; tel. 304/598–4000, (Includes CHESTNUT RIDGE HOSPITAL, 930 Chestnut Ridge Road, Zip 26505–2854; tel. 304/293–4000; WEST VIRGINIA UNIVERSITY CHILDREN'S HOSPITAL, Medical Center Drive, Zip 26506–8111; tel. 800/982–6277) **A**1 3 5 8 10 19 **F**3 4 5 9 11 12 13 15 17 18 19 20 21 22 23 24 25 26 27 28 29 30 31 34 35 36 37 38 39 40 43 45 46 47 48 49 50 51 54 55 56 57 58 59 60 61 64 65 68 70 71 72 74 75 76 77 78 79 80 81 82 84 85 86 87 88 89 91 92 93 97 98 99 100 101 102 103 105 106 107 108 110 111 114 115 118 119 120 121 123 124 126 129 130 132 136 141 145 146 147 148 **P**6 **S** West Virginia University Health System, Morgantown, WV
Primary Contact: Albert Wright, PharmD, President and Chief Executive Officer
CFO: Mary Jo Shahan, Vice President and Chief Financial Officer
CMO: Michelle Nuss, M.D., Chief Medical Officer
CIO: Rich King, Vice President Information Technology
CHR: Charlotte Bennett, Vice President Human Resources
Web address: www.health.wvu.edu
Control: Other not–for–profit (including NFP Corporation) **Service:** General Medical and Surgical

> **Staffed Beds:** 524 **Admissions:** 27049 **Census:** 430 **Outpatient Visits:** 759312 **Births:** 1432 **Total Expense ($000):** 763874 **Payroll Expense ($000):** 268459 **Personnel:** 5229

NEW MARTINSVILLE—Wetzel County

✠ **WETZEL COUNTY HOSPITAL (510072)**, 3 East Benjamin Drive, Zip 26155–2758; tel. 304/455–8000 **A**1 10 20 **F**3 8 15 28 30 31 34 40 43 45 57 59 64 65 70 75 77 81 85 90 93 94 107 108 114 118 119 127 130 132 133 135 146 148 **P**6
Primary Contact: Brian K. Felici, Chief Executive Officer
CFO: Edwin Szewczyk, Chief Financial Officer
CMO: Donald A. Blum, M.D., Chief of Staff
CIO: Amy Frazier, Supervisor Management Information Systems
CHR: Sarah Boley, Director Human Resources
Web address: www.wetzelcountyhospital.com
Control: County–Government, nonfederal **Service:** General Medical and Surgical

> **Staffed Beds:** 44 **Admissions:** 617 **Census:** 8 **Outpatient Visits:** 85109 **Births:** 0 **Total Expense ($000):** 20903 **Payroll Expense ($000):** 8756 **Personnel:** 200

OAK HILL—Fayette County

✠ **PLATEAU MEDICAL CENTER (511317)**, 430 Main Street, Zip 25901–3455; tel. 304/469–8600 **A**1 10 18 **F**3 8 15 18 29 30 34 35 40 42 45 46 50 57 59 64 68 70 75 77 79 81 85 87 91 93 97 107 108 110 111 114 115 119 126 129 146 **S** Community Health Systems, Inc., Franklin, TN
Primary Contact: Derek W. Cimala, Interim Chief Executive Officer
COO: Michael Makosky, Chief Operating Officer
CFO: Heather Hylton, Chief Financial Officer
CMO: Jacob McNeel, D.O., Chief of Staff
CIO: Nick Stover, Director Information Systems
CHR: Tammie Chinn, Director Marketing and Public Relations
CNO: Randell Thompson, Chief Nursing Officer
Web address: www.plateaumedicalcenter.com
Control: Corporation, Investor–owned, for–profit **Service:** General Medical and Surgical

> **Staffed Beds:** 25 **Admissions:** 1264 **Census:** 12 **Outpatient Visits:** 31010 **Total Expense ($000):** 32788 **Payroll Expense ($000):** 13034 **Personnel:** 193

PARKERSBURG—Wood County

✠ **CAMDEN CLARK MEDICAL CENTER (510058)**, 800 Garfield Avenue, Zip 26101–5378, Mailing Address: P.O. Box 718, Zip 26102–0718; tel. 304/424–2111 **A**1 10 13 19 **F**1 3 7 8 11 12 13 15 17 18 20 22 24 28 29 30 31 34 35 40 43 45 50 51 53 54 57 58 59 64 65 66 67 68 70 74 75 76 78 79 81 84 85 86 87 89 92 97 98 100 101 102 107 108 110 111 114 115 116 117 118 119 120 121 123 124 128 129 130 132 133 135 146 147 148 **P**6 7 8 **S** West Virginia University Health System, Morgantown, WV
Primary Contact: David K. McClure, President and Chief Executive Officer
CFO: Carolyn Allen, Vice President and Chief Financial Officer
CMO: David Gnegy, M.D., Vice President of Medical Affairs
CIO: Josh Woods, Director Information Systems
CHR: Tom Heller, Vice President Operations and Human Resources
CNO: Tom L. Mars, R.N., Vice President Patient Care Services and Chief Nursing Officer
Web address: www.camdenclark.org
Control: Other not–for–profit (including NFP Corporation) **Service:** General Medical and Surgical

> **Staffed Beds:** 254 **Admissions:** 11560 **Census:** 130 **Outpatient Visits:** 296498 **Births:** 1441 **Total Expense ($000):** 229289 **Payroll Expense ($000):** 68490 **Personnel:** 1464

Many Facility Codes have changed. Please refer to the AHA Guide Code Chart. © 2016 AHA Guide

⊠ **HEALTHSOUTH WESTERN HILLS REGIONAL REHABILITATION HOSPITAL (513027)**, 3 Western Hills Drive, Zip 26105–8122; tel. 304/420–1300 **A**1 10 **F**29 64 90 93 94 96 130 148 **S** HEALTHSOUTH Corporation, Birmingham, AL
Primary Contact: Alvin R. Lawson, JD, FACHE, Chief Executive Officer
CFO: Jessica Walkup, Controller
CMO: Kalapala Rao, M.D., Medical Director
CHR: Julie Swanson, Coordinator Human Resources
CNO: Tonda Hockenberry, Chief Nursing Officer
Web address: www.healthsouthwesternhills.com
Control: Corporation, Investor–owned, for–profit **Service:** Rehabilitation

Staffed Beds: 40 **Admissions:** 1105 **Census:** 36 **Outpatient Visits:** 6211 **Births:** 0 **Total Expense ($000):** 14586 **Payroll Expense ($000):** 6176 **Personnel:** 105

PETERSBURG—Grant County

★ **GRANT MEMORIAL HOSPITAL (511316)**, 117 Hospital Drive, Zip 26847–9566, Mailing Address: P.O. Box 1019, Zip 26847–1019; tel. 304/257–1026, (Total facility includes 20 beds in nursing home–type unit) **A**10 18 **F**3 11 13 15 18 28 29 30 34 35 40 45 50 57 59 64 65 67 68 70 75 76 77 79 81 84 85 86 87 93 102 107 108 110 114 118 119 128 130 132 133 146 148
Primary Contact: Mary Beth Barr, R.N., Chief Executive Officer
CFO: Joe Barnes, Chief Financial Officer
CMO: Bruce W. Leslie, M.D., Chief of Staff
CIO: Derek Nesselrodt, Director Information Systems
CHR: Ronnie Arbaugh, Director Human Resources
CNO: Kimberly Linville, Chief Nursing Officer
Web address: www.grantmemorial.com
Control: County–Government, nonfederal **Service:** General Medical and Surgical

Staffed Beds: 45 **Admissions:** 1519 **Census:** 28 **Outpatient Visits:** 42962 **Births:** 217 **Total Expense ($000):** 32280 **Payroll Expense ($000):** 12741 **Personnel:** 303

PHILIPPI—Barbour County

★ **BROADDUS HOSPITAL (511300)**, 1 Healthcare Drive, Zip 26416–9405, Mailing Address: P.O. Box 930, Zip 26416–0930; tel. 304/457–1760, (Total facility includes 60 beds in nursing home–type unit) **A**10 18 **F**3 15 29 30 34 35 40 50 57 59 64 75 85 87 107 110 114 119 128 130 132 133 135 143 146 **P**8 **S** Davis Health System, Elkins, WV
Primary Contact: Jeffrey A. Powelson, Chief Executive Officer
COO: Dana L. Gould, Chief Operation Officer
CFO: Cathy Kalar, Chief Financial Officer
CHR: Penny D. Brown, Director of Human Resources
Web address: www.davishealthsystem.org/
Control: Other not–for–profit (including NFP Corporation) **Service:** General Medical and Surgical

Staffed Beds: 72 **Admissions:** 260 **Census:** 62 **Outpatient Visits:** 23634 **Births:** 0 **Total Expense ($000):** 15706 **Payroll Expense ($000):** 6844 **Personnel:** 159

POINT PLEASANT—Mason County

⊠ **PLEASANT VALLEY HOSPITAL (510012)**, 2520 Valley Drive, Zip 25550–2031; tel. 304/675–4340, (Total facility includes 100 beds in nursing home–type unit) **A**1 10 **F**3 11 16 18 28 29 30 31 34 40 43 48 50 53 56 57 59 62 63 68 70 74 75 76 77 78 79 81 85 86 87 89 93 107 108 110 111 114 115 118 119 128 129 130 131 132 143 144 146 147 148 **P**6
Primary Contact: Glen A. Washington, Chief Executive Officer
COO: William A. Barker, Jr., Vice President Administration
CFO: Richard Hogan, Chief Financial Officer
CMO: Agnes Enrico–Simon, M.D., President Medical Staff
CIO: Paula Brooker, Director Information Services
CHR: David A. Brown, Director Human Resources and Corporate Compliance
CNO: Amber Findley, Senior Director Nursing Services and NRC Administrator
Web address: www.pvalley.org
Control: Other not–for–profit (including NFP Corporation) **Service:** General Medical and Surgical

Staffed Beds: 201 **Admissions:** 1849 **Census:** 105 **Outpatient Visits:** 189129 **Births:** 141 **Total Expense ($000):** 63612 **Payroll Expense ($000):** 25115 **Personnel:** 631

PRINCETON—Mercer County

⊠ **HEALTHSOUTH SOUTHERN HILLS REHABILITATION HOSPITAL (513026)**, 120 Twelfth Street, Zip 24740–2352; tel. 304/487–8000 **A**1 10 **F**29 56 57 59 60 74 75 77 79 87 90 94 130 132 148 **S** HEALTHSOUTH Corporation, Birmingham, AL
Primary Contact: Robert Williams, R.N., Chief Executive Officer
CFO: Melinda Fanning, Chief Financial Officer and Controller
CMO: Robert Walker, M.D., Medical Director
CIO: Brian Bales, Director Plant Operations
CHR: Jan Thibodeau, Director Human Resources
CNO: Lisa Lester, Chief Nursing Officer
Web address: www.healthsouthsouthernhills.com
Control: Corporation, Investor–owned, for–profit **Service:** Rehabilitation

Staffed Beds: 45 **Admissions:** 952 **Census:** 30 **Outpatient Visits:** 0 **Births:** 0 **Personnel:** 103

⊠ **PRINCETON COMMUNITY HOSPITAL (510046)**, 122 12th Street, Zip 24740–2352, Mailing Address: P.O. Box 1369, Zip 24740–1369; tel. 304/487–7000 **A**1 2 10 19 **F**3 11 12 13 15 17 29 30 31 32 34 35 39 40 44 45 46 48 49 50 51 53 57 59 64 65 70 74 75 76 77 78 79 81 85 86 87 89 93 98 100 101 102 103 104 107 108 110 111 114 115 118 119 127 129 130 131 132 135 141 142 144 146 147 **P**1
Primary Contact: Jeffrey Lilley, CPA, Chief Executive Officer
CFO: Frank J. Sinicrope, Jr., Vice President Financial Services
CMO: Wesley Asbury, M.D., President Medical Staff
CIO: Stephen A. Curry, Director Information Services
CHR: Heather Poff, Director Human Resources
CNO: Rose Morgan, MS, Vice President Patient Care Services
Web address: www.pchonline.org
Control: City–Government, nonfederal **Service:** General Medical and Surgical

Staffed Beds: 210 **Admissions:** 8268 **Census:** 124 **Outpatient Visits:** 223482 **Births:** 732 **Total Expense ($000):** 125325 **Payroll Expense ($000):** 47812 **Personnel:** 1044

RANSON—Jefferson County

⊠ **JEFFERSON MEDICAL CENTER (511319)**, 300 South Preston Street, Zip 25438–1631; tel. 304/728–1600 **A**1 3 5 10 18 **F**3 11 13 15 29 30 34 35 38 40 43 44 45 57 59 64 70 74 75 77 79 81 82 85 86 87 92 93 107 108 110 111 115 118 119 129 130 132 133 135 146 148 **S** West Virginia University Health System, Morgantown, WV
Primary Contact: Anthony Zelenka, Chief Executive Officer
CFO: Kathleen Quinones, Interim Vice President Finance
CMO: David A. Baltierra, M.D., President Medical Staff
CIO: Mark Combs, Chief Information Security Officer
CNO: Linda Blanc, R.N., Administrative Director of Nursing
Web address: www.wvuniversityhealthcare.com/locations/Jefferson–Medical–Center.aspx
Control: Other not–for–profit (including NFP Corporation) **Service:** General Medical and Surgical

Staffed Beds: 25 **Admissions:** 1330 **Census:** 11 **Outpatient Visits:** 69764 **Births:** 257 **Total Expense ($000):** 42679 **Payroll Expense ($000):** 18438 **Personnel:** 332

RIPLEY—Jackson County

☐ **JACKSON GENERAL HOSPITAL (511320)**, 122 Pinnell Street, Zip 25271–9101, Mailing Address: P.O. Box 720, Zip 25271–0720; tel. 304/372–2731 **A**1 10 18 **F**3 11 15 29 30 34 35 40 43 50 57 59 64 68 75 79 81 85 93 107 114 119 127 132 133 **P**6
Primary Contact: Stephanie McCoy, President and Chief Executive Officer
CFO: Angela Frame, Chief Financial Officer
CMO: James G. Gaal, M.D., Chief of Medical Staff
CIO: John Manley, Director Information Systems
CHR: Jeffrey Tabor, Director Human Resources
Web address: www.jacksongeneral.com
Control: Other not–for–profit (including NFP Corporation) **Service:** General Medical and Surgical

Staffed Beds: 25 **Admissions:** 880 **Census:** 10 **Outpatient Visits:** 42145 **Births:** 0 **Total Expense ($000):** 23255 **Payroll Expense ($000):** 9950 **Personnel:** 234

WV

Hospital, Medicare Provider Number, Address, Telephone, Approval, Facility, and Physician Codes, Health Care System

★ American Hospital Association (AHA) membership   ◯ Healthcare Facilities Accreditation Program   ⇑ Center for Improvement in Healthcare Quality Accreditation
☐ The Joint Commission accreditation   ◇ DNV Healthcare Inc. accreditation   △ Commission on Accreditation of Rehabilitation Facilities (CARF) accreditation

ROMNEY—Hampshire County

☒ **HAMPSHIRE MEMORIAL HOSPITAL (511311)**, 363 Sunrise Boulevard, Zip 26757–4607; tel. 304/822–4561, (Total facility includes 30 beds in nursing home–type unit) **A**1 10 18 **F**3 15 29 30 40 45 54 59 64 65 71 77 79 81 85 93 97 107 119 127 128 129 130 133 148 **P**6 **S** Valley Health System, Winchester, VA
Primary Contact: Thomas S. Kluge, President
CFO: Kathryn Morales, Director of Finance
CMO: Gerald Bechamps, M.D., Vice President of Medical Affairs
CHR: Abbey Rembold, Human Resources Senior Generalist
CNO: Mary Sas, Director of Clinical Services
Web address: www.valleyhealthlink.com/hampshire
Control: Other not–for–profit (including NFP Corporation) **Service:** General Medical and Surgical

Staffed Beds: 44 **Admissions:** 466 **Census:** 36 **Outpatient Visits:** 47407
Births: 0 **Total Expense ($000):** 21310 **Payroll Expense ($000):** 8560
Personnel: 155

RONCEVERTE—Greenbrier County

★ ○ **GREENBRIER VALLEY MEDICAL CENTER (510002)**, 202 Maplewood Avenue, Zip 24970–1334, Mailing Address: P.O. Box 497, Zip 24970–0497; tel. 304/647–4411 **A**10 11 12 13 **F**13 15 18 20 29 31 34 40 45 49 51 57 59 60 68 70 75 76 78 79 81 86 87 89 107 108 110 111 114 116 119 120 129 133 135 146 148 **P**6 **S** Community Health Systems, Inc., Franklin, TN
Primary Contact: Robert Calhoun, Chief Executive Officer
CFO: Paige Adkins, Chief Financial Officer
CMO: John Johnson, M.D., Chief of Staff
CIO: Matt Turley, Interim Director Information Systems
CHR: Melissa Wickline, Director Marketing
CNO: Charlene Warren, R.N., Chief Nursing Officer
Web address: www.gvmc.com
Control: Corporation, Investor–owned, for–profit **Service:** General Medical and Surgical

Staffed Beds: 113 **Admissions:** 3749 **Census:** 43 **Outpatient Visits:** 57813
Births: 498 **Total Expense ($000):** 55665 **Payroll Expense ($000):** 20108
Personnel: 423

SISTERSVILLE—Tyler County

★ **SISTERSVILLE GENERAL HOSPITAL (511304)**, 314 South Wells Street, Zip 26175–1098; tel. 304/652–2611, (Nonreporting) **A**10 18
Primary Contact: John May, Chief Executive Officer
COO: Brandon Chadock, Director of Operations
CMO: Amanda Nichols, M.D., Chief of Staff
CIO: Casey Tuttle, Director Information Technology
CHR: Marissa Powell, Human Resources Director
CNO: Al Dawson, Director of Nursing
Web address: www.sistersvillehospital.com
Control: City–Government, nonfederal **Service:** General Medical and Surgical

Staffed Beds: 12

SOUTH CHARLESTON—Kanawha County

☒ **THOMAS MEMORIAL HOSPITAL (510029)**, 4605 MacCorkle Avenue S.W., Zip 25309–1398; tel. 304/766–3600 **A**1 3 5 10 **F**3 5 8 11 13 15 17 18 20 22 29 30 31 32 34 35 38 40 43 45 46 47 48 49 50 53 54 57 59 60 62 64 65 68 69 70 72 74 75 76 77 78 79 81 84 85 86 87 89 92 93 98 99 100 101 102 103 104 105 107 108 110 111 114 118 119 120 121 123 124 126 129 130 131 132 143 144 146 147 **S** Thomas Health System, Inc., South Charleston, WV
Primary Contact: Daniel Lauffer, FACHE, President and Chief Executive Officer
COO: Brian Ulery, Chief Operating Officer
CFO: Renee Cross, Chief Financial Officer
CMO: Matthew Upton, Chief Medical Information Officer
CHR: Marybeth Smith, Director Human Resources
CNO: Rebecca Brannon, R.N., Chief Nursing Officer
Web address: www.thomaswv.org
Control: Other not–for–profit (including NFP Corporation) **Service:** General Medical and Surgical

Staffed Beds: 215 **Admissions:** 8507 **Census:** 116 **Outpatient Visits:** 211820 **Births:** 1070 **Total Expense ($000):** 176801 **Payroll Expense ($000):** 57474 **Personnel:** 1064

SPENCER—Roane County

☒ **ROANE GENERAL HOSPITAL (511306)**, 200 Hospital Drive, Zip 25276–1050; tel. 304/927–4444, (Total facility includes 35 beds in nursing home–type unit) **A**1 10 18 **F**1 3 15 28 29 34 35 40 43 45 53 57 59 64 65 67 81 85 89 90 93 97 107 108 110 114 119 127 128 130 133 148 **P**6
Primary Contact: Douglas E. Bentz, Chief Executive Officer
CFO: Louise Ward, Vice President Financial and Support Services
CMO: Brent Watson, M.D., Chief Medical Staff
CIO: Tony Keaton, Director Information Systems
CHR: Jeff Beane, Director Human Resources
Web address: www.roanegeneralhospital.com
Control: Other not–for–profit (including NFP Corporation) **Service:** General Medical and Surgical

Staffed Beds: 60 **Admissions:** 409 **Census:** 42 **Outpatient Visits:** 39093
Births: 0 **Total Expense ($000):** 27286 **Payroll Expense ($000):** 12929
Personnel: 272

SUMMERSVILLE—Nicholas County

☒ **SUMMERSVILLE REGIONAL MEDICAL CENTER (510082)**, 400 Fairview Heights Road, Zip 26651–9308; tel. 304/872–2891, (Total facility includes 52 beds in nursing home–type unit) **A**1 10 20 **F**1 3 13 15 28 29 30 34 35 40 43 45 57 59 64 65 67 68 70 75 76 77 79 81 83 84 85 89 91 93 97 107 108 110 111 115 119 127 128 130 131 133 135 146 147 148
Primary Contact: Daniel M. Ayres, President and Chief Executive Officer
CFO: Brian Kelbaugh, Chief Financial Officer
CMO: Bandy Mullins, M.D., Chief of Staff
CIO: Mike Ellison, Information Systems Lead
CHR: David M. Henderson, Director Human Resources
CNO: Jennifer McCue, Director Patient Care
Web address: www.https://www.summersvilleregional.org/
Control: City–Government, nonfederal **Service:** General Medical and Surgical

Staffed Beds: 105 **Admissions:** 2006 **Census:** 71 **Outpatient Visits:** 118772
Births: 327 **Total Expense ($000):** 50462 **Payroll Expense ($000):** 25271
Personnel: 470

WEBSTER SPRINGS—Webster County

★ **WEBSTER COUNTY MEMORIAL HOSPITAL (511301)**, 324 Miller Mountain Drive, Zip 26288–1087, Mailing Address: P.O. Box 312, Zip 26288–0312; tel. 304/847–5682 **A**10 18 **F**7 15 28 30 34 35 40 57 59 64 75 82 87 93 97 107 114 119 127 130 133 135 146 147 148
Primary Contact: Robert M. Mace, M.D., Chief Executive Officer
CMO: Robert M. Mace, M.D., Chief of Staff
CIO: Margaret W. Short, Coordinator Information Technology
CHR: Michelle Holcomb, Human Resources
Web address: www.wcmhwv.org
Control: Other not–for–profit (including NFP Corporation) **Service:** General Medical and Surgical

Staffed Beds: 15 **Admissions:** 147 **Census:** 1 **Outpatient Visits:** 46656
Births: 0 **Total Expense ($000):** 16178 **Payroll Expense ($000):** 8251
Personnel: 138

WEIRTON—Brooke County

☒ **WEIRTON MEDICAL CENTER (510023)**, 601 Colliers Way, Zip 26062–5091; tel. 304/797–6000, (Total facility includes 33 beds in nursing home–type unit) **A**1 10 **F**3 5 9 11 13 15 17 18 20 22 29 30 32 34 35 37 39 40 41 43 45 46 47 48 49 50 51 53 54 56 61 62 64 68 70 74 75 76 77 78 79 81 82 85 86 89 90 92 93 96 97 99 100 101 102 103 104 107 108 110 111 114 115 116 118 119 124 126 128 129 130 131 132 135 143 145 146 147 148 **P**6
Primary Contact: John C. Frankovitch, President and Chief Executive Officer
COO: David S. Artman, Chief Operating Officer
CFO: Gene Trout, Chief Financial Officer
CMO: Eric Balzano, Chief of Staff
CIO: Dave Angalich, Director Information Services
CHR: Barbara Coalter, Director Human Resources
CNO: Denise P. Westwood, Chief Nursing Officer
Web address: www.weirtonmedical.com
Control: Other not–for–profit (including NFP Corporation) **Service:** General Medical and Surgical

Staffed Beds: 168 **Admissions:** 6210 **Census:** 97 **Outpatient Visits:** 330555
Births: 415 **Total Expense ($000):** 144354 **Payroll Expense ($000):** 61210
Personnel: 1118

Many Facility Codes have changed. Please refer to the AHA Guide Code Chart. © 2016 AHA Guide

WELCH—Mcdowell County

WELCH COMMUNITY HOSPITAL (510086), 454 McDowell Street, Zip 24801–2097; tel. 304/436–8461, (Total facility includes 59 beds in nursing home–type unit) **A**10 20 **F**3 13 15 29 35 40 45 50 57 59 64 65 66 67 68 70 75 76 81 86 87 97 107 110 114 119 127 130 135 146 147 148 **P**6
Primary Contact: Walter J. Garrett, Chief Executive Officer
COO: Heather Smith, Chief Operating Officer
CFO: Johnny Brant, Chief Financial Officer
CMO: Chandra Sharma, M.D., Chief of Staff
CHR: Diana Blankenship, Director Human Resources
CNO: Mark Simpson, Director of Nursing
Control: State–Government, nonfederal **Service:** General Medical and Surgical

Staffed Beds: 108 **Admissions:** 819 **Census:** 53 **Outpatient Visits:** 33140 **Births:** 66 **Total Expense ($000):** 32093 **Payroll Expense ($000):** 9787 **Personnel:** 312

WESTON—Lewis County

☒ **STONEWALL JACKSON MEMORIAL HOSPITAL (510038)**, 230 Hospital Plaza, Zip 26452–8558; tel. 304/269–8000 **A**1 10 **F**3 11 13 15 28 29 30 31 35 40 43 45 48 50 56 57 59 62 64 68 70 75 76 78 79 81 85 86 87 93 94 97 107 108 111 114 118 119 129 130 135 143 145 146 147 148 **P**6
Primary Contact: Avah Stalnaker, Chief Executive Officer
COO: Kevin P. Stalnaker, CPA, Assistant Chief Executive Officer
CFO: Crystal Frazier, Director of Financial Operations
CMO: William Kelley, Medical Staff President
CIO: Kay Butcher, Director Health Information Management
CHR: Rhonda M. Hager, Director Human Resources
CNO: Barbara Willis, Chief Nursing Officer and Chief Operating Officer
Web address: www.stonewallhospital.com
Control: Other not–for–profit (including NFP Corporation) **Service:** General Medical and Surgical

Staffed Beds: 70 **Admissions:** 1928 **Census:** 19 **Outpatient Visits:** 92406 **Births:** 232 **Total Expense ($000):** 46719 **Payroll Expense ($000):** 23105 **Personnel:** 414

☐ **WILLIAM R. SHARPE, JR. HOSPITAL (514010)**, 936 Sharpe Hospital Road, Zip 26452–8550; tel. 304/269–1210 **A**1 5 10 **F**11 30 53 56 75 86 87 98 100 101 103 130 132 143 146 **P**6
Primary Contact: Parker Haddix, Chief Executive Officer
COO: Terry L. Small, Assistant Chief Executive Officer
CFO: Robert J. Kimble, Chief Financial Officer
CIO: Pam Lewis, Chief Compliance Officer
CNO: Cheryl France, M.D., Chief Medical Officer
Web address: www.wvdhhr.org/sharpe
Control: State–Government, nonfederal **Service:** Psychiatric

Staffed Beds: 150 **Admissions:** 517 **Census:** 136 **Outpatient Visits:** 0 **Births:** 0 **Total Expense ($000):** 52356 **Payroll Expense ($000):** 14224 **Personnel:** 508

WHEELING—Ohio County

☐ ○ **OHIO VALLEY MEDICAL CENTER (510039)**, 2000 Eoff Street, Zip 26003–3870; tel. 304/234–0123 **A**1 2 10 11 12 13 19 **F**3 5 9 11 13 15 18 20 28 29 30 31 34 35 38 40 43 44 48 49 50 51 53 55 56 57 58 59 60 61 64 65 68 70 74 75 76 77 78 79 81 82 84 85 86 87 89 93 97 98 99 100 101 102 103 104 105 107 108 110 111 114 115 116 117 119 121 123 129 130 131 132 134 135 146 147 148 **P**6 **S** Ohio Valley Health Services and Education Corporation, Wheeling, WV
Primary Contact: Michael J. Caruso, President and Chief Executive Officer
COO: Kelly Bettem, Vice President, Ambulatory Services
CFO: Lisa M. Simon, Senior Vice President and Chief Financial Officer
CIO: Michael Martz, Chief Information Officer
CHR: Robert Wright, Senior Human Resource Advisor
CNO: Patsy George, R.N., Vice President and Chief Nursing Officer
Web address: www.ovmc-eorh.com
Control: Other not–for–profit (including NFP Corporation) **Service:** General Medical and Surgical

Staffed Beds: 189 **Admissions:** 5650 **Census:** 83 **Outpatient Visits:** 149384 **Births:** 409 **Total Expense ($000):** 111246 **Payroll Expense ($000):** 41525 **Personnel:** 880

★ **PETERSON HEALTHCARE AND REHABILITATION HOSPITAL (513025)**, Homestead Avenue, Zip 26003; tel. 304/234–0500, (Total facility includes 150 beds in nursing home–type unit) **A**10 **F**29 34 50 56 57 59 75 77 86 87 90 93 96 128 130 131 132 143 148
Primary Contact: Diane Miller, Administrator
CFO: Tammy Bortz, Director of Finance
CMO: William Mercer, M.D., Director
CIO: Hope Miller, Director of Medical Records
CHR: Spencer McIlvain, Director of Human Resources
CNO: Charlene Jones, Chief Nursing Officer
Web address: www.petersonrehabilitationhospital.com
Control: Corporation, Investor–owned, for–profit **Service:** Rehabilitation

Staffed Beds: 172 **Admissions:** 838 **Census:** 146 **Outpatient Visits:** 3116 **Births:** 0 **Total Expense ($000):** 19270 **Payroll Expense ($000):** 6013 **Personnel:** 139

☐ **WHEELING HOSPITAL (510050)**, 1 Medical Park, Zip 26003–6379; tel. 304/243–3000 **A**1 2 3 10 13 **F**3 9 11 13 15 17 18 20 22 24 26 28 29 30 31 32 34 35 36 40 43 44 45 46 49 50 53 54 57 58 59 61 62 64 65 66 67 68 70 73 74 75 76 77 78 79 81 82 84 85 86 87 89 90 92 93 96 97 98 99 100 107 108 110 111 114 115 118 119 120 121 123 128 129 130 131 132 135 143 146 147 148 **P**5
Primary Contact: Ronald L. Violi, Chief Executive Officer
CMO: Angelo Georges, M.D., President Medical and Dental Staff
CIO: David Rapp, Chief Information Officer
CHR: Kareen Simon, Vice President of Operations
CNO: Kathy Stahl, Chief Nursing Officer
Web address: www.wheelinghospital.org
Control: Other not–for–profit (including NFP Corporation) **Service:** General Medical and Surgical

Staffed Beds: 238 **Admissions:** 10163 **Census:** 122 **Outpatient Visits:** 600777 **Births:** 1176 **Total Expense ($000):** 274897 **Payroll Expense ($000):** 121077 **Personnel:** 1933

WILLIAMSON—Mingo County

☒ **WILLIAMSON MEMORIAL HOSPITAL (510077)**, 859 Alderson Street, Zip 25661–3215, Mailing Address: P.O. Box 1980, Zip 25661–1980; tel. 304/235–2500 **A**1 10 **F**3 15 18 26 28 29 30 34 40 49 50 51 57 59 61 65 70 74 75 76 77 79 81 87 91 93 107 108 114 119 130 131 135 **P**6 **S** Community Health Systems, Inc., Franklin, TN
Primary Contact: Cindy Segar-Miller, R.N., Chief Executive Officer
CFO: Robert Haralson, Chief Financial Officer
CMO: C. Donovan Beckett, Chief Medical Officer
CHR: Tammie Chinn, Chief Human Resource Officer
CNO: Justus Smith, Interim Chief Nursing Officer
Web address: www.williamsonmemorial.net
Control: Corporation, Investor–owned, for–profit **Service:** General Medical and Surgical

Staffed Beds: 76 **Admissions:** 1100 **Census:** 10 **Outpatient Visits:** 26769 **Births:** 6 **Total Expense ($000):** 19177 **Payroll Expense ($000):** 6610 **Personnel:** 137

WV

Hospital, Medicare Provider Number, Address, Telephone, Approval, Facility, and Physician Codes, Health Care System

★ American Hospital Association (AHA) membership
☐ The Joint Commission accreditation
○ Healthcare Facilities Accreditation Program
◇ DNV Healthcare Inc. accreditation
⇑ Center for Improvement in Healthcare Quality Accreditation
△ Commission on Accreditation of Rehabilitation Facilities (CARF) accreditation

WISCONSIN

AMERY—Polk County

★ **AMERY HOSPITAL AND CLINIC (521308)**, 265 Griffin Street East,
Zip 54001–1439; tel. 715/268–8000 **A**10 18 **F**3 6 11 13 15 18 28 29 31 33
34 35 36 38 40 44 45 50 53 54 56 57 59 64 65 68 74 75 76 77 78 80 81
82 85 86 87 89 92 93 97 98 100 103 104 107 108 110 111 115 119 127
130 131 132 133 135 143 144 145 146 148 **P**6 **S** HealthPartners,
Bloomington, MN
Primary Contact: Debra Rudquist, FACHE, President and Chief Executive Officer
CMO: James Quenan, M.D., Chief Medical Officer
CIO: Patrice P. Wolff, Director Management Information Systems
CHR: Joanne Jackson, Administrator Human Resources, Community Relations and
Quality Improvement
Web address: www.amerymedicalcenter.org
Control: Other not–for–profit (including NFP Corporation) **Service:** General
Medical and Surgical

> **Staffed Beds:** 11 **Admissions:** 1028 **Census:** 11 **Outpatient Visits:** 103165
> **Births:** 113 **Total Expense ($000):** 51511 **Payroll Expense ($000):** 28005
> **Personnel:** 305

ANTIGO—Langlade County

✣ **ASPIRUS LANGLADE HOSPITAL (521350)**, 112 East Fifth Avenue,
Zip 54409–2796; tel. 715/623–2331 **A**1 10 18 **F**2 3 5 6 9 10 11 12 13 15 28
29 30 31 34 35 36 40 43 50 53 54 56 57 59 60 61 63 64 65 68 69 70 75
76 77 78 79 81 82 84 85 86 87 89 92 93 96 97 99 100 101 103 104 107
108 110 111 115 118 119 121 127 129 130 131 132 133 144 146 147 148
S Aspirus, Inc., Wausau, WI
Primary Contact: David R. Schneider, Executive Director
CFO: Pat Tincher, Director Finance
CHR: Janelle K. Markgraf, Director Human Resources and Off Campus Services
CNO: Sherry Bunten, Director Patient Care Services
Web address: www.aspirus.org
Control: Church–operated, Nongovernment, not–for profit **Service:** General
Medical and Surgical

> **Staffed Beds:** 17 **Admissions:** 1224 **Census:** 11 **Outpatient Visits:** 114284
> **Births:** 240 **Total Expense ($000):** 86336 **Payroll Expense ($000):** 33562
> **Personnel:** 385

APPLETON—Outagamie County

☐ **APPLETON MEDICAL CENTER (520160)**, 1818 North Meade Street,
Zip 54911–3496; tel. 920/731–4101 **A**1 3 5 10 **F**4 9 11 13 15 17 20 22 24
28 29 34 36 40 43 51 53 55 56 60 64 69 70 75 76 78 80 81 82 86 87 88
89 93 107 108 111 116 118 119 130 144 147 **S** ThedaCare, Inc.,
Appleton, WI
Primary Contact: Brian Burmeister, Senior Vice President
CFO: Tim Olson, Senior Vice President Finance
CMO: Gregory L. Long, M.D., Chief Medical Officer
CIO: Keith Livingston, Senior Vice President and Chief Information Officer
CHR: Maureen Pistone, Senior Vice President Talent Development and Human
Resources
Web address: www.thedacare.org
Control: Other not–for–profit (including NFP Corporation) **Service:** General
Medical and Surgical

> **Staffed Beds:** 147 **Admissions:** 8287 **Census:** 92 **Outpatient Visits:** 122465
> **Births:** 1275 **Total Expense ($000):** 213516 **Payroll Expense ($000):**
> 85634 **Personnel:** 1145

✣ **ST. ELIZABETH HOSPITAL (520009)**, 1506 South Oneida Street,
Zip 54915–1305; tel. 920/738–2000 **A**1 2 3 5 10 **F**4 5 6 8 9 11 13 15 17 18
20 22 24 26 28 29 30 31 32 36 37 40 43 44 45 46 47 48 49 50 56 69 70
72 74 75 76 77 78 79 80 81 82 84 85 86 87 88 89 91 92 93 96 97 98 99
100 102 103 104 105 106 107 108 109 110 111 112 113 114 115 117 118
119 120 121 122 123 124 126 129 130 131 144 146 147 148 **S** Ascension
Health, Saint Louis, MO
Primary Contact: Monica Hilt, President and Chief Executive Officer
CFO: Jeff Badger, Chief Financial Officer
CMO: Lawrence Donatelle, M.D., Vice President Medical Affairs
CIO: Will Weider, Chief Information Officer
CHR: Vince Gallucci, Senior Vice President Human Resources
Web address: www.affinityhealth.org
Control: Church–operated, Nongovernment, not–for profit **Service:** General
Medical and Surgical

> **Staffed Beds:** 190 **Admissions:** 8348 **Census:** 98 **Outpatient Visits:** 216567
> **Births:** 1198 **Total Expense ($000):** 155496 **Payroll Expense ($000):**
> 66230 **Personnel:** 750

ASHLAND—Ashland County

✣ **MEMORIAL MEDICAL CENTER – ASHLAND (521359)**, 1615 Maple Lane,
Zip 54806–3689; tel. 715/685–5500 **A**1 10 18 **F**3 5 13 15 28 30 31 34 40
43 45 48 49 57 59 64 65 68 75 76 79 80 81 82 85 86 87 89 90 93 94 96
98 99 100 101 102 103 104 105 107 108 110 111 115 118 119 126 129
130 132 135 144 146 148
Primary Contact: Jason T. Douglas, Chief Executive Officer
COO: Karen Hansen, Vice President and Chief Operating Officer
CFO: Kent Dumonseau, Vice President Finance and Information Services
CIO: Todd Reynolds, Chief Information Officer
CHR: Diane Lulich, Director Human Resources
CNO: Kathryn Tuttle, R.N., Director of Nursing
Web address: www.ashlandmmc.com
Control: Other not–for–profit (including NFP Corporation) **Service:** General
Medical and Surgical

> **Staffed Beds:** 35 **Admissions:** 1883 **Census:** 16 **Outpatient Visits:** 14841
> **Births:** 213 **Total Expense ($000):** 52670 **Payroll Expense ($000):** 21978
> **Personnel:** 316

BALDWIN—St. Croix County

★ **BALDWIN AREA MEDICAL CENTER (521347)**, 730 10th Avenue,
Zip 54002–9416; tel. 715/684–3311 **A**10 18 **F**3 11 13 15 17 28 29 31 32 34
35 36 40 41 43 45 48 50 53 57 59 64 65 68 70 75 76 77 78 79 80 81 84
85 86 87 89 90 93 96 97 107 108 110 115 119 127 129 130 131 132 133
143 144 146 147 148
Primary Contact: Alison Page, Chief Executive Officer
CFO: Brian A. Lovdahl, Chief Financial Officer
CMO: Clint Semrau, Chief of Staff
CIO: Kendra Shaw, Chief Information Officer
CHR: Chris Riba, Director Human Resources
Web address: www.baldwinhospital.com
Control: Other not–for–profit (including NFP Corporation) **Service:** General
Medical and Surgical

> **Staffed Beds:** 25 **Admissions:** 452 **Census:** 5 **Outpatient Visits:** 34028
> **Births:** 52 **Total Expense ($000):** 32876 **Payroll Expense ($000):** 16742
> **Personnel:** 233

BARABOO—Sauk County

✣ **ST. CLARE HOSPITAL (520057)**, 707 14th Street, Zip 53913–1597;
tel. 608/356–1400 **A**1 3 5 10 **F**5 11 12 13 15 28 29 34 36 40 56 64 69 70
75 76 77 78 80 81 82 86 89 93 107 108 116 118 119 130 131 144 **S** SSM
Health, Saint Louis, MO
Primary Contact: Laura Jelle, President
CFO: Troy Walker, Director Finance
CMO: Maureen Murphy, M.D., Director of Medical Affairs
CIO: Heather Stephens, Director of Information Health Technology
CHR: Jason Stelzer, Director Human Resources
CNO: Ginger Selle, Vice President Patient Care Services
Web address: www.stclare.com
Control: Church–operated, Nongovernment, not–for profit **Service:** General
Medical and Surgical

> **Staffed Beds:** 60 **Admissions:** 1868 **Census:** 17 **Outpatient Visits:** 104481
> **Births:** 221 **Total Expense ($000):** 52061 **Payroll Expense ($000):** 20460
> **Personnel:** 289

BARRON—Barron County

☐ **MAYO CLINIC HEALTH SYSTEM – NORTHLAND IN BARRON (521315)**,
1222 Woodland Avenue, Zip 54812–1798; tel. 715/537–3186 **A**1 10 18 **F**3 6 8
13 15 18 28 29 30 31 32 34 35 36 40 43 44 45 53 54 56 57 59 60 63 64
65 69 75 76 77 78 79 80 81 82 84 85 86 87 89 90 93 97 100 104 107 110
115 118 130 131 132 133 135 144 145 146 147 148 **P**6 **S** Mayo Clinic,
Rochester, MN
Primary Contact: Maurita Sullivan, Vice President
COO: Karolyn Bartlett, Assistant Administrator
CFO: Paul Bammel, Vice President
CMO: Richard Nagler, M.D., Chief of Staff
CIO: Todd Muden, Section Head Information Management
CHR: Blythe Rinaldi, Vice President
CNO: Patricia Keller, MSN, Nurse Administrator
Web address: www.luthermidelfortnorthland.org
Control: Other not–for–profit (including NFP Corporation) **Service:** General
Medical and Surgical

> **Staffed Beds:** 15 **Admissions:** 881 **Census:** 27 **Outpatient Visits:** 56484
> **Births:** 108 **Total Expense ($000):** 54335 **Payroll Expense ($000):** 24108
> **Personnel:** 310

WI

Many Facility Codes have changed. Please refer to the AHA Guide Code Chart. © 2016 AHA Guide

BEAVER DAM—Dodge County

☒ **BEAVER DAM COMMUNITY HOSPITALS (520076)**, 707 South University Avenue, Zip 53916–3089; tel. 920/887–7181, (Total facility includes 115 beds in nursing home–type unit) **A**1 10 19 **F**3 6 8 10 11 13 15 17 28 29 30 31 34 36 37 40 41 43 44 45 47 51 53 56 57 59 62 63 64 65 69 70 74 75 76 77 78 79 80 81 82 85 86 87 89 93 96 97 107 108 110 111 114 115 118 119 128 129 130 131 132 135 143 144 146 147 148 **P**6
Primary Contact: Kimberly J. Miller, FACHE, Chief Executive Officer
COO: David Corso, Chief Operating Officer
CFO: Donna Hutchinson, Chief Financial Officer
CMO: Jason Smith, Chief Medical Officer
CHR: Melanie Bruins, Chief Talent Officer
CNO: Carolyn Catton, Interim Chief Patient Care Officer
Web address: www.bdch.com
Control: Other not–for–profit (including NFP Corporation) **Service:** General Medical and Surgical

Staffed Beds: 163 **Admissions:** 2115 **Census:** 112 **Outpatient Visits:** 94309 **Births:** 330 **Total Expense ($000):** 81628 **Payroll Expense ($000):** 29813 **Personnel:** 518

BELOIT—Rock County

☐ **BELOIT HEALTH SYSTEM (520100)**, 1969 West Hart Road, Zip 53511–2299; tel. 608/364–5011 **A**1 3 10 **F**5 6 9 10 11 12 13 15 17 20 22 24 26 28 29 36 40 43 51 53 54 56 60 62 70 75 76 77 78 80 81 82 86 87 89 93 99 100 101 102 103 104 108 111 116 118 119 130 131 144 147
Primary Contact: Timothy M. McKevett, President
CFO: William E. Groeper, Vice President Finance
CMO: Kenneth Klein, M.D., Vice President Medical Affairs
CHR: Thomas J. McCawley, Vice President
CNO: Doris Mulder, Vice President Nursing
Web address: www.beloithealthsystem.org
Control: Other not–for–profit (including NFP Corporation) **Service:** General Medical and Surgical

Staffed Beds: 103 **Admissions:** 3876 **Census:** 47 **Outpatient Visits:** 350096 **Births:** 480 **Total Expense ($000):** 194944 **Payroll Expense ($000):** 91991 **Personnel:** 1249

BERLIN—Green Lake County

☐ **BERLIN MEMORIAL HOSPITAL (521355)**, 225 Memorial Drive, Zip 54923–1295; tel. 920/361–1313, (Includes JULIETTE MANOR NURSING HOME, COMMUNITY CLINICS), (Total facility includes 54 beds in nursing home–type unit) **A**1 10 18 **F**10 11 13 15 17 28 29 34 40 43 51 53 54 56 62 69 70 75 76 77 78 80 81 82 86 87 88 89 93 107 108 111 116 119 125 128 130 131 144 147 **S** ThedaCare, Inc., Appleton, WI
Primary Contact: John Feeney, President and Chief Executive Officer
CFO: Thomas P. Krystowiak, Chief Financial Officer
Web address: www.chnwi.org
Control: Other not–for–profit (including NFP Corporation) **Service:** General Medical and Surgical

Staffed Beds: 75 **Admissions:** 1725 **Census:** 46 **Outpatient Visits:** 48628 **Births:** 148 **Total Expense ($000):** 64195 **Payroll Expense ($000):** 35074 **Personnel:** 332

BLACK RIVER FALLS—Jackson County

☐ **BLACK RIVER MEMORIAL HOSPITAL (521333)**, 711 West Adams Street, Zip 54615–9113; tel. 715/284–5361 **A**1 10 18 **F**3 11 13 29 30 34 35 40 48 50 53 56 57 62 63 69 75 76 77 81 84 86 87 89 93 107 111 112 115 116 117 118 119 129 130 131 132 133 135 144 146 148
Primary Contact: Mary Beth White–Jacobs, FACHE, R.N., President and Chief Executive Officer
COO: Holly Winn, FACHE, Chief Operating Officer
CFO: Robert Daley, CPA, Chief Financial Officer
CMO: Esteban Miller, Chief Medical Officer
CIO: Robert Daley, CPA, Vice President Fiscal and Information Technology Services
CNO: Melissa Bergerson, R.N., Chief Nursing Officer
Web address: www.brmh.net
Control: Other not–for–profit (including NFP Corporation) **Service:** General Medical and Surgical

Staffed Beds: 25 **Admissions:** 843 **Census:** 8 **Outpatient Visits:** 16895 **Births:** 168 **Total Expense ($000):** 40368 **Payroll Expense ($000):** 19839 **Personnel:** 285

BLOOMER—Chippewa County

☐ **MAYO CLINIC HEALTH SYSTEM – CHIPPEWA VALLEY IN BLOOMER (521314)**, 1501 Thompson Street, Zip 54724–1299; tel. 715/568–2000 **A**1 10 18 **F**3 8 15 18 28 29 30 32 34 35 40 43 44 45 53 54 57 59 63 64 65 75 77 78 80 81 84 85 86 87 90 93 96 97 107 110 115 119 130 132 133 135 144 146 147 148 **P**6 **S** Mayo Clinic, Rochester, MN
Primary Contact: Edward A. Wittrock, Vice President Regional System
Web address: www.bloomermedicalcenter.org
Control: Other not–for–profit (including NFP Corporation) **Service:** General Medical and Surgical

Staffed Beds: 19 **Admissions:** 466 **Census:** 19 **Outpatient Visits:** 48656 **Births:** 0 **Total Expense ($000):** 32915 **Payroll Expense ($000):** 16009 **Personnel:** 214

BOSCOBEL—Grant County

GUNDERSEN BOSCOBEL AREA HOSPITAL AND CLINICS (521344), 205 Parker Street, Zip 53805–1698; tel. 608/375–4112 **A**10 18 **F**3 4 8 11 15 28 29 31 34 35 38 40 43 53 56 57 59 62 64 70 72 78 79 80 81 82 85 86 87 88 89 90 93 97 98 108 110 118 119 127 130 131 133 135 144 148 **P**6
Primary Contact: David Hartberg, Chief Executive Officer
CFO: Melissa Uselman, Chief Financial Officer
CMO: Marilu Bintz, M.D., Chief of Staff
CIO: Tonia Midtlien, Information Systems Support Specialist
CHR: Jennifer Dax, Director Human Resources
CNO: Theresa Lynn Braudt, Chief Nursing Officer
Web address: www.gundersenhealth.org/boscobel
Control: Other not–for–profit (including NFP Corporation) **Service:** General Medical and Surgical

Staffed Beds: 8 **Admissions:** 247 **Census:** 2 **Outpatient Visits:** 26439 **Births:** 0 **Total Expense ($000):** 15636 **Payroll Expense ($000):** 4733 **Personnel:** 98

BROOKFIELD—Waukesha County

★ **WHEATON FRANCISCAN HEALTHCARE – ELMBROOK MEMORIAL (520170)**, 19333 West North Avenue, Zip 53045–4198; tel. 262/785–2000 **F**3 4 8 11 12 13 15 17 18 20 22 24 26 28 29 30 31 34 35 36 40 43 45 46 47 49 50 54 56 59 64 65 68 70 72 74 75 76 77 78 79 80 81 82 83 84 85 86 87 89 90 91 92 93 97 99 100 107 108 109 110 111 112 114 115 117 118 119 120 121 122 123 124 126 130 131 132 135 143 145 146 148 **P**6 **S** Ascension Health, Saint Louis, MO
Primary Contact: Debra K. Standridge, President
CFO: Michael Petitt, Director of Finance
CMO: Rita Hanson, M.D., Vice President Medical Affairs
CIO: Andrew Donovan, Director Information Technology
CHR: Christopher Morris, Director Human Resources
CNO: Sharon Baughman, R.N., Vice President Patient Services and Chief Nursing Officer
Web address: www.wfhealthcare.org
Control: Church–operated, Nongovernment, not–for profit **Service:** General Medical and Surgical

Staffed Beds: 120 **Admissions:** 4731 **Census:** 52 **Outpatient Visits:** 67927 **Births:** 490 **Total Expense ($000):** 104939 **Payroll Expense ($000):** 34817 **Personnel:** 358

BURLINGTON—Racine County

☒ **AURORA MEMORIAL HOSPITAL OF BURLINGTON (520059)**, 252 McHenry Street, Zip 53105–1828; tel. 262/767–6000 **A**1 2 10 **F**3 11 15 17 18 20 26 28 29 30 34 35 36 40 43 44 45 46 47 48 49 50 51 53 56 57 58 59 60 68 70 74 75 79 80 81 82 84 85 86 87 89 93 94 96 107 108 109 110 111 115 116 118 119 130 131 132 134 135 146 148 **P**6 **S** Aurora Health Care, Milwaukee, WI
Primary Contact: Lisa Just, President
CFO: Stuart Arnett, Vice President Finance and Chief Financial Officer
CIO: Jean Chase, Regional Manager Information Services
CHR: Gene Krauklis, Regional Vice President Human Resources
Web address: www.aurorahealthcare.org
Control: Other not–for–profit (including NFP Corporation) **Service:** General Medical and Surgical

Staffed Beds: 55 **Admissions:** 2370 **Census:** 21 **Outpatient Visits:** 75677 **Births:** 0 **Total Expense ($000):** 62868 **Payroll Expense ($000):** 21089 **Personnel:** 363

WI

Hospital, Medicare Provider Number, Address, Telephone, Approval, Facility, and Physician Codes, Health Care System

★ American Hospital Association (AHA) membership ○ Healthcare Facilities Accreditation Program ⇑ Center for Improvement in Healthcare Quality Accreditation
☐ The Joint Commission accreditation ◇ DNV Healthcare Inc. accreditation △ Commission on Accreditation of Rehabilitation Facilities (CARF) accreditation

---

CHILTON—Calumet County

☒ **CALUMET MEDICAL CENTER (521317)**, 614 Memorial Drive,
Zip 53014–1597; tel. 920/849–2386 **A**1 10 18 **F**3 7 11 15 28 29 34 35 40
42 43 45 54 56 57 59 64 65 75 77 78 79 80 81 82 85 86 87 89 92 93 97
107 110 114 119 127 129 130 131 132 133 144 145 146 148 **P**7
S Ascension Health, Saint Louis, MO
Primary Contact: Timothy Richman, President
CFO: Jeff Badger, Chief Financial Officer
CMO: Mark W. Kehrberg, M.D., Chief Medical Officer
CIO: Will Weider, Chief Information Officer
CHR: Beth O'laire, Manager Human Resources
Web address: www.affinityhealth.org
Control: Other not–for–profit (including NFP Corporation) **Service:** General
Medical and Surgical

Staffed Beds: 15 **Admissions:** 439 **Census:** 6 **Outpatient Visits:** 45113
Births: 0 **Total Expense ($000):** 21434 **Payroll Expense ($000):** 8964
Personnel: 103

CHIPPEWA FALLS—Chippewa County

☒ **HSHS ST. JOSEPH'S HOSPITAL (520017)**, 2661 County Highway I.,
Zip 54729–5407; tel. 715/723–1811 **A**1 10 **F**4 5 13 15 17 28 29 34 38 40
43 54 56 62 63 64 69 70 75 76 77 80 81 82 86 87 88 89 93 100 101 102
104 105 107 111 119 130 144 147 **P**6 **S** Hospital Sisters Health System,
Springfield, IL
Primary Contact: Joan M. Coffman, FACHE, President and Chief Executive Officer
CFO: David Nelson, FACHE, Divisional Chief Financial Officer
CIO: Kevin Groskreutz, Division Chief Information Officer, Ancillary Systems
CHR: Rick Tolson, Divisional Chief People Officer
CNO: Stella Clark, MSN, Chief Nursing Officer
Web address: www.stjoeschipfalls.com
Control: Other not–for–profit (including NFP Corporation) **Service:** General
Medical and Surgical

Staffed Beds: 126 **Admissions:** 3202 **Census:** 39 **Outpatient Visits:** 89512
Births: 375 **Total Expense ($000):** 67763 **Payroll Expense ($000):** 28431
Personnel: 372

COLUMBUS—Columbia County

☒ **COLUMBUS COMMUNITY HOSPITAL, INC. (521338)**, 1515 Park Avenue,
Zip 53925–2402; tel. 920/623–2200, (Nonreporting) **A**1 10 18
Primary Contact: John D. Russell, President and Chief Executive Officer
CFO: Phillip G. Roberts, Vice President Finance and Chief Financial Officer
CMO: Gary Galvin, Chief of the Medical Staff
CIO: Phillip G. Roberts, Vice President Finance and Chief Financial Officer
CHR: Ann Roundy, Vice President Employee Services
CNO: Jamie Hendrix, Vice President Patient Care Services
Web address: www.cch–inc.com
Control: Other not–for–profit (including NFP Corporation) **Service:** General
Medical and Surgical

Staffed Beds: 18

CUBA CITY—Grant County

SOUTHWEST HEALTH CENTER NURSING HOME See Southwest Health,
Platteville

CUDAHY—Milwaukee County

AURORA ST. LUKE'S SOUTH SHORE See Aurora St. Luke's Medical Center,
Milwaukee

CUMBERLAND—Barron County

☐ **CUMBERLAND MEMORIAL HOSPITAL (521353)**, 1110 Seventh Avenue,
Zip 54829–9138; tel. 715/822–2741, (Total facility includes 50 beds in nursing
home–type unit) **A**1 10 18 **F**11 13 28 29 34 40 43 53 55 56 75 76 77 78 81
82 86 87 89 93 107 125 128 130 131 144 **P**8
Primary Contact: Michael Gutsch, Chief Executive Officer
COO: Bob Lindberg, Chief Operating Officer
CFO: Angela Martens, Chief Financial Officer
CMO: Tom Lingen, M.D., Chief of Staff
CIO: Jason Morse, Director Information Technology
CHR: Hilary Butzler, Director Human Resources
Web address: www.cumberlandhealthcare.com
Control: Other not–for–profit (including NFP Corporation) **Service:** General
Medical and Surgical

Staffed Beds: 75 **Admissions:** 580 **Census:** 48 **Outpatient Visits:** 10667
Births: 49 **Total Expense ($000):** 22302 **Payroll Expense ($000):** 10380
Personnel: 173

DARLINGTON—Lafayette County

MEMORIAL HOSPITAL OF LAFAYETTE COUNTY (521312), 800 Clay Street,
Zip 53530–1228, Mailing Address: P.O. Box 70, Zip 53530–0070;
tel. 608/776–4466 **A**10 18 **F**1 11 15 28 29 34 40 43 54 56 64 75 76 80 81
82 86 89 90 93 102 105 107 111 116 119 130 131 144
Primary Contact: Julie Chikowski, Administrator
CFO: Marie Wamsley, Chief Financial Officer
Web address: www.memorialhospitaloflafayettecounty.org
Control: County–Government, nonfederal **Service:** General Medical and Surgical

Staffed Beds: 25 **Admissions:** 324 **Census:** 3 **Outpatient Visits:** 19999
Births: 11 **Total Expense ($000):** 13539 **Payroll Expense ($000):** 3880
Personnel: 89

DODGEVILLE—Iowa County

☒ **UPLAND HILLS HEALTH (521352)**, 800 Compassion Way, Zip 53533–1956,
Mailing Address: P.O. Box 800, Zip 53533–0800; tel. 608/930–8000, (Total
facility includes 44 beds in nursing home–type unit) **A**1 10 18 **F**3 8 11 13 15 17
28 29 32 33 34 35 36 40 43 44 45 50 53 54 56 57 59 62 63 64 67 70 75
76 77 78 79 80 81 82 85 86 87 88 89 90 93 97 107 110 111 115 119 127
128 129 130 131 132 133 144 146 147 148 **P**6
Primary Contact: Lisa W. Schnedler, FACHE, President and Chief Executive Officer
CFO: Karl Pustina, Vice President Finance
CIO: Karen Thuli, Coordinator Information Systems
CHR: Troy Marx, Director Human Resources
CNO: Lynn Hebgen, Vice President Nursing
Web address: www.uplandhillshealth.org
Control: Other not–for–profit (including NFP Corporation) **Service:** General
Medical and Surgical

Staffed Beds: 69 **Admissions:** 1294 **Census:** 50 **Outpatient Visits:** 58874
Births: 241 **Total Expense ($000):** 39679 **Payroll Expense ($000):** 17858
Personnel: 267

DURAND—Pepin County

★ **CHIPPEWA VALLEY HOSPITAL AND OAKVIEW CARE CENTER (521307)**,
1220 Third Avenue West, Zip 54736–1600, Mailing Address: P.O. Box 224,
Zip 54736–0224; tel. 715/672–4211 **A**10 18 **F**15 28 29 34 40 56 75 81 86
87 107 130 **S** Adventist Health System Sunbelt Health Care Corporation,
Altamonte Springs, FL
Primary Contact: Douglas R. Peterson, President and Chief Executive Officer
Web address: www.chippewavalleyhospital.com/
Control: Church–operated, Nongovernment, not–for profit **Service:** General
Medical and Surgical

Staffed Beds: 25 **Admissions:** 202 **Census:** 2 **Outpatient Visits:** 15240
Births: 0 **Total Expense ($000):** 16365 **Payroll Expense ($000):** 5791
Personnel: 88

EAGLE RIVER—Vilas County

★ **MINISTRY EAGLE RIVER MEMORIAL HOSPITAL (521300)**, 201 Hospital
Road, Zip 54521–8835; tel. 715/479–7411 **A**10 18 **F**3 11 15 28 29 30 35 40
45 47 50 57 59 64 68 75 80 81 82 84 85 86 87 89 93 107 110 111 115
119 130 133 146 148 **S** Ascension Health, Saint Louis, MO
Primary Contact: Sandra L. Anderson, President and Chief Executive Officer
COO: Laurie Oungst, Vice President, Operations
CFO: Jamon Lamers, Director Finance
CMO: Elmer Linboom, M.D., Medical Staff President
CIO: Howard Dobizl, Director Information Technology Services
CHR: Michelle Cornelius, Director Human Resources for Northern Region
CNO: Deborah Karow, R.N., Vice President Patient Care Services
Web address: www.ministryhealth.org
Control: Church–operated, Nongovernment, not–for profit **Service:** General
Medical and Surgical

Staffed Beds: 13 **Admissions:** 396 **Census:** 5 **Outpatient Visits:** 17622
Births: 0 **Total Expense ($000):** 14653 **Payroll Expense ($000):** 7657
Personnel: 109

EAU CLAIRE—Eau Claire County

☐ **MAYO CLINIC HEALTH SYSTEM IN EAU CLAIRE (520070)**, 1221 Whipple
Street, Zip 54703–5270, Mailing Address: P.O. Box 4105, Zip 54702–4105;
tel. 715/838–3311 **A**1 2 3 5 10 **F**3 4 5 8 11 13 15 17 18 20 22 24 26 28
29 30 31 32 34 35 36 37 40 43 44 45 46 48 49 53 55 56 57 58 59 60 63
64 65 70 71 72 74 75 76 78 79 80 81 82 83 84 85 86 87 89 90 92 93 96
97 98 99 100 101 102 103 104 105 107 108 110 111 115 118 119 120
121 124 126 129 130 132 135 144 145 146 147 148 **P**6 **S** Mayo Clinic,
Rochester, MN
Primary Contact: Randall L. Linton, M.D., President and Chief Executive Officer
COO: John M. Dickey, Chief Administrative Officer
CFO: Denise Mattison, Director Finance and Accounting Services
CMO: Robert C. Peck, M.D., Chief Medical Officer
CHR: Kenneth Lee, Division Chair, Human Resource Advisory
CNO: Pamela K. White, R.N., Chief Nursing Officer and Vice President
Web address: www.mhs.mayo.edu
Control: Other not–for–profit (including NFP Corporation) **Service:** General
Medical and Surgical

Staffed Beds: 185 **Admissions:** 9841 **Census:** 121 **Outpatient Visits:**
192622 **Births:** 1077 **Total Expense ($000):** 243179 **Payroll Expense
($000):** 93883 **Personnel:** 1464

WI

Many Facility Codes have changed. Please refer to the AHA Guide Code Chart.

© 2016 AHA Guide

☐ **OAKLEAF SURGICAL HOSPITAL (520196)**, 3802 West Oakwood Mall Drive, Zip 54701–3016; tel. 715/831–8130 **A**1 10 **F**3 37 45 47 48 51 64 75 79 80 81 82 85 107 114 119 130 145 148 **S** National Surgical Healthcare, Chicago, IL
Primary Contact: Anne Hargrave–Thomas, Chief Executive Officer
COO: Erma Radke, Director of Operations
CFO: Denise Freid–Scheppke, Chief Accounting Officer
CHR: Dorothy Conroy, Director Human Resources
CNO: Jacquelyn Maki, Chief Nursing Officer
Web address: www.oakleafmedical.com
Control: Corporation, Investor–owned, for–profit **Service:** General Medical and Surgical

Staffed Beds: 13 **Admissions:** 624 **Census:** 4 **Outpatient Visits:** 11814
Births: 0 **Total Expense ($000):** 43445 **Payroll Expense ($000):** 11856
Personnel: 166

☒ △ **SACRED HEART HOSPITAL (520013)**, 900 West Clairemont Avenue, Zip 54701–6122; tel. 715/717–4121 **A**1 2 3 5 7 10 **F**3 6 11 12 13 15 17 18 20 22 24 28 29 30 31 32 34 35 38 40 41 43 45 46 47 48 49 50 51 53 56 57 58 59 60 64 69 70 72 74 75 76 78 79 80 81 82 84 85 86 87 88 89 90 91 92 93 94 96 97 98 99 100 101 102 103 104 107 108 110 111 112 114 115 116 117 118 119 120 121 123 124 126 129 130 132 135 141 144 145 146 147 **P**6 **S** Hospital Sisters Health System, Springfield, IL
Primary Contact: Julie Manas, President and Chief Executive Officer
CFO: David Nelson, FACHE, Chief Financial Officer
CMO: Humayun Khan, M.D., Chief Medical Officer
CIO: Kevin Groskreutz, Chief Information Officer
CHR: Craig Brenholt, Division Director People Services
CNO: Amy L. Dwyer, R.N., Chief Nursing Officer
Web address: www.sacredhearteauclaire.org
Control: Other not–for–profit (including NFP Corporation) **Service:** General Medical and Surgical

Staffed Beds: 202 **Admissions:** 9520 **Census:** 123 **Outpatient Visits:** 116901 **Births:** 936 **Total Expense ($000):** 192198 **Payroll Expense ($000):** 70220 **Personnel:** 1079

EDGERTON—Rock County

☒ **EDGERTON HOSPITAL AND HEALTH SERVICES (521319)**, 11101 North Sherman Road, Zip 53534–9002; tel. 608/884–3441 **A**1 10 18 **F**3 8 11 15 18 28 34 40 41 43 44 45 48 49 59 64 65 75 77 81 85 86 90 92 93 97 107 108 110 111 115 119 129 130 132 133 134 135 144 146 148
Primary Contact: Jim Schultz, Chief Executive Officer
CFO: Charles Roader, Vice President Finance
CMO: Brian Stubitsch, M.D., Chief Medical Officer
CIO: JT Johrendt, Information Technology Network Specialist
CHR: Mark Kindschi, Director Human Resources
CNO: Sue Alwin–Popp, Chief Clinical Officer
Web address: www.edgertonhospital.com
Control: Other not–for–profit (including NFP Corporation) **Service:** General Medical and Surgical

Staffed Beds: 18 **Admissions:** 367 **Census:** 9 **Outpatient Visits:** 14231
Births: 0 **Total Expense ($000):** 21053 **Payroll Expense ($000):** 8911
Personnel: 119

ELKHORN—Walworth County

☒ △ **AURORA LAKELAND MEDICAL CENTER (520102)**, W3985 County Road NN, Zip 53121–4389; tel. 262/741–2000 **A**1 2 7 10 **F**3 11 13 15 17 18 29 30 31 34 35 36 40 43 44 45 46 47 48 49 50 51 56 57 58 59 60 64 68 70 74 75 76 78 79 80 81 82 84 85 86 87 89 90 93 94 96 100 107 108 110 111 115 116 118 119 129 130 131 132 135 146 148 **P**6 **S** Aurora Health Care, Milwaukee, WI
Primary Contact: Lisa Just, President
CFO: Stuart Arnett, Regional Vice President Finance
CMO: Greg Gerber, M.D., Chief Medical Officer
CIO: Jean Chase, Regional Manager Information Services
CHR: Gene Krauklis, Regional Vice President Human Resources
Web address: www.aurorahealthcare.org
Control: Other not–for–profit (including NFP Corporation) **Service:** General Medical and Surgical

Staffed Beds: 67 **Admissions:** 2796 **Census:** 27 **Outpatient Visits:** 73292
Births: 753 **Total Expense ($000):** 64942 **Payroll Expense ($000):** 19747
Personnel: 341

FOND DU LAC—Fond Du Lac County

☒ △ **AGNESIAN HEALTHCARE (520088)**, 430 East Division Street, Zip 54935–4560, Mailing Address: P.O. Box 385, Zip 54936–0385; tel. 920/929–2300 **A**1 2 7 10 20 **F**2 3 5 6 8 11 13 15 18 20 22 24 26 28 29 30 31 33 34 35 36 38 40 43 44 45 46 47 48 49 50 51 53 54 55 56 57 59 62 63 64 66 67 68 69 74 75 76 77 78 79 80 81 82 84 85 86 87 90 92 93 96 97 98 99 100 101 102 103 104 105 107 108 109 110 111 115 118 119 120 121 123 124 126 129 130 131 132 134 135 143 144 146 147 148 **P**3 6
Primary Contact: Steven N. Little, President and Chief Executive Officer
COO: James Mugan, Senior Vice President for Clinical Services and Chief Operating Officer
CFO: Bonnie Schmitz, Vice President and Chief Financial Officer
CMO: Derek Colmenares, M.D., Chief Medical Officer
CIO: Nancy Birschbach, Vice President and Chief Information Officer
CHR: Sue Edminster, Vice President Human Resources
Web address: www.agnesian.com
Control: Church–operated, Nongovernment, not–for profit **Service:** General Medical and Surgical

Staffed Beds: 160 **Admissions:** 6866 **Census:** 75 **Outpatient Visits:** 738716
Births: 799 **Total Expense ($000):** 324078 **Payroll Expense ($000):** 117886 **Personnel:** 1779

FOND DU LAC COUNTY MENTAL HEALTH CENTER (524025), 459 East First Street, Zip 54935–4599; tel. 920/929–3502 **A**10 **F**4 38 98 99 102 103 130 **P**6
Primary Contact: J.R. Musunuru, M.D., Executive Director
Web address: www.fdlco.wi.gov
Control: County–Government, nonfederal **Service:** Psychiatric

Staffed Beds: 25 **Admissions:** 977 **Census:** 14 **Outpatient Visits:** 574
Births: 0 **Total Expense ($000):** 3296 **Payroll Expense ($000):** 2172
Personnel: 46

FORT ATKINSON—Jefferson County

☒ **FORT HEALTHCARE (520071)**, 611 East Sherman Avenue, Zip 53538–1998; tel. 920/568–5000 **A**1 10 **F**3 11 12 13 15 28 29 34 35 40 47 48 50 53 55 56 57 59 68 75 76 77 79 80 81 85 86 87 89 90 93 94 96 107 108 110 111 115 118 119 124 129 130 132 135 144 145 146 147 **P**1 5
Primary Contact: Michael S. Wallace, President and Chief Executive Officer
CFO: James J. Nelson, Senior Vice President Finance and Strategic Planning
CMO: Thomas Nordland, Chief Medical Officer
CIO: Christopher Manakas, Chief Information Officer
CHR: Nancy Alstad, Director Human Resources
CNO: Renee Clark, R.N., Vice President Nursing Services and Performance Improvement
Web address: www.forthealthcare.com
Control: Other not–for–profit (including NFP Corporation) **Service:** General Medical and Surgical

Staffed Beds: 72 **Admissions:** 2095 **Census:** 16 **Outpatient Visits:** 281104
Births: 412 **Total Expense ($000):** 114237 **Payroll Expense ($000):** 36860
Personnel: 456

FRANKLIN—Milwaukee County

☒ **MIDWEST ORTHOPEDIC SPECIALTY HOSPITAL (520205)**, 10101 South 27th Street, 2nd Floor, Zip 53132–7209; tel. 414/817–5800 **A**1 3 5 10 **F**29 34 81 82 86 130 131 **S** Ascension Health, Saint Louis, MO
Primary Contact: Coreen Dicus–Johnson, President
CFO: Aaron Bridgeland, Director Finance
CMO: Daniel Guehlstorf, M.D., Chief of Staff
CIO: Gregory Smith, Senior Vice President and Chief Information Officer
CHR: Robert Bauer, Vice President Human Resources
CNO: Sheila Gansemer, R.N., Vice President Patient Care Services and Chief Nursing Officer
Web address: www.mymosh.com/
Control: Partnership, Investor–owned, for–profit **Service:** General Medical and Surgical

Staffed Beds: 16 **Admissions:** 1328 **Census:** 8 **Outpatient Visits:** 8008
Births: 0 **Total Expense ($000):** 40445 **Payroll Expense ($000):** 6751
Personnel: 101

WI

Hospital, Medicare Provider Number, Address, Telephone, Approval, Facility, and Physician Codes, Health Care System

★ American Hospital Association (AHA) membership ○ Healthcare Facilities Accreditation Program ⇑ Center for Improvement in Healthcare Quality Accreditation
☐ The Joint Commission accreditation ◇ DNV Healthcare Inc. accreditation △ Commission on Accreditation of Rehabilitation Facilities (CARF) accreditation

⊞ **WHEATON FRANCISCAN HEALTHCARE – FRANKLIN (520204)**, 10101 South 27th Street, Zip 53132–7209; tel. 414/325–4700 **A**1 10 **F**15 20 22 29 34 40 56 64 70 75 77 81 82 86 87 93 107 108 111 119 130 131 144 147 **S** Ascension Health, Saint Louis, MO
Primary Contact: Coreen Dicus–Johnson, President
CFO: Aaron Bridgeland, Director Finance
CMO: Michelle Graham, M.D., Vice President Medical Affairs
CIO: Gregory Smith, Senior Vice President and Chief Information Officer
CHR: Robert Bauer, Vice President Human Resources
CNO: Sheila Gansemer, R.N., Vice President Patient Care Services and Chief Nursing Officer
Web address: www.mywheaton.org/
Control: Church–operated, Nongovernment, not–for profit **Service:** General Medical and Surgical

Staffed Beds: 37 **Admissions:** 2230 **Census:** 26 **Outpatient Visits:** 86313 **Births:** 0 **Total Expense ($000):** 65630 **Payroll Expense ($000):** 24077 **Personnel:** 285

FRIENDSHIP—Adams County

MOUNDVIEW MEMORIAL HOSPITAL & CLINICS (521309), 402 West Lake Street, Zip 53934–9699, Mailing Address: P.O. Box 40, Zip 53934–0040; tel. 608/339–3331 **A**10 18 **F**6 11 15 28 29 34 36 40 53 56 64 77 81 82 86 87 93 107 108 111 119 130 131 144 **P**2 6
Primary Contact: Don Heinz, Interim Chief Executive Officer
Web address: www.moundview.org
Control: Other not–for–profit (including NFP Corporation) **Service:** General Medical and Surgical

Staffed Beds: 25 **Admissions:** 207 **Census:** 2 **Outpatient Visits:** 39541 **Births:** 0 **Total Expense ($000):** 14777 **Payroll Expense ($000):** 6482 **Personnel:** 116

GLENDALE—Milwaukee County

ORTHOPAEDIC HOSPITAL OF WISCONSIN – GLENDALE (520194), 475 West River Woods Parkway, Zip 53212–1081; tel. 414/961–6800 **A**10 **F**29 34 38 53 64 80 81 82 86 93 107 111 119 130 131
Primary Contact: Brian J. Cramer, Chief Executive Officer
CFO: Tom Swiderski, Chief Financial Officer
CMO: Rory Wright, M.D., President Medical Staff
CIO: Todd Heikkinen, Manager Sports Medicine and Rehabilitation Services
CNO: Nanette Johnson, Chief Nursing Officer
Web address: www.ohow.org
Control: Partnership, Investor–owned, for–profit **Service:** General Medical and Surgical

Staffed Beds: 30 **Admissions:** 1188 **Census:** 8 **Outpatient Visits:** 26821 **Births:** 0 **Total Expense ($000):** 35369 **Payroll Expense ($000):** 11281 **Personnel:** 179

GRAFTON—Ozaukee County

⊞ **AURORA MEDICAL CENTER GRAFTON (520207)**, 975 Port Washington Road, Zip 53024–9201; tel. 262/329–1000 **A**1 2 3 5 10 **F**3 6 8 13 15 17 18 20 22 24 26 28 29 30 31 36 37 40 43 44 45 46 48 49 50 51 53 54 56 60 64 65 68 69 70 71 72 74 75 76 78 79 80 81 82 85 86 87 89 90 92 93 94 96 107 108 110 111 114 115 116 117 119 120 123 126 130 131 135 146 148 **P**6 **S** Aurora Health Care, Milwaukee, WI
Primary Contact: Carrie Killoran, Interim President
CMO: Doug McManus, Chief Medical Officer
CNO: Terry Kabitzke–Groth, R.N., Vice President Nursing
Web address: www.aurorahealthcare.org
Control: Other not–for–profit (including NFP Corporation) **Service:** General Medical and Surgical

Staffed Beds: 127 **Admissions:** 7212 **Census:** 69 **Outpatient Visits:** 111088 **Births:** 905 **Total Expense ($000):** 172360 **Payroll Expense ($000):** 46611 **Personnel:** 784

GRANTSBURG—Burnett County

★ **BURNETT MEDICAL CENTER (521331)**, 257 West St. George Avenue, Zip 54840–7827; tel. 715/463–5353, (Total facility includes 50 beds in nursing home–type unit) **A**10 18 **F**2 3 11 15 28 29 30 31 34 35 40 43 45 56 57 59 64 68 75 76 77 78 80 81 84 86 87 89 90 93 97 107 115 127 128 130 131 132 133 135 144 148 **P**6
Primary Contact: Gordon Lewis, Chief Executive Officer
CFO: Charles J. Faught, Chief Financial Officer
CMO: Hans Rechsteiner, M.D., Chief of Staff
CIO: Andy Douglas, Manager Information Technology
CHR: Sandy Hinrichs, Director Human Resources
Web address: www.burnettmedicalcenter.com
Control: Other not–for–profit (including NFP Corporation) **Service:** General Medical and Surgical

Staffed Beds: 67 **Admissions:** 437 **Census:** 54 **Outpatient Visits:** 33372 **Births:** 41 **Total Expense ($000):** 14464 **Payroll Expense ($000):** 6977 **Personnel:** 137

GREEN BAY—Brown County

⊞ △ **AURORA BAYCARE MEDICAL CENTER (520193)**, 2845 Greenbrier Road, Zip 54311–6519, Mailing Address: P.O. Box 8900, Zip 54308–8900; tel. 920/288–8000 **A**1 2 7 10 **F**3 8 12 13 15 17 18 19 20 22 24 26 28 29 30 31 32 33 34 35 36 40 43 44 45 46 47 48 49 50 53 54 57 58 59 64 65 70 72 74 75 76 78 79 80 81 82 84 85 86 87 89 90 93 94 96 107 108 109 110 111 114 115 116 117 118 119 120 121 123 124 126 129 130 131 132 135 144 146 147 148 **P**6 **S** Aurora Health Care, Milwaukee, WI
Primary Contact: Daniel T. Meyer, President
COO: Daniel T. Meyer, President
CFO: Gwen Christensen, Vice President Finance
CMO: Gary Collins, M.D., Chief Medical Officer
CIO: Chuck Geurts, Manager Management Information Services
CHR: Elizabeth A. Kirby, Senior Director, Human Resource Business Partner
CNO: Heather Schroeder, R.N., Chief Nurse Executive and Vice President of Nursing
Web address: www.aurorabaycare.com
Control: Partnership, Investor–owned, for–profit **Service:** General Medical and Surgical

Staffed Beds: 167 **Admissions:** 8466 **Census:** 102 **Outpatient Visits:** 302339 **Births:** 1442 **Total Expense ($000):** 269886 **Payroll Expense ($000):** 85499 **Personnel:** 1252

★ ◇ **BELLIN MEMORIAL HOSPITAL (520049)**, 744 South Webster Avenue, Zip 54301–3581, Mailing Address: P.O. Box 23400, Zip 54305–3400; tel. 920/433–3500 **A**10 21 **F**3 12 13 15 17 18 20 22 24 26 28 29 30 31 36 37 40 41 42 43 44 45 46 47 48 49 51 53 54 62 64 68 71 74 75 76 77 78 79 80 81 82 83 84 85 86 87 89 90 91 92 96 97 106 107 108 110 111 115 116 118 119 126 129 130 131 144 146 148 **P**2 6
Primary Contact: George Kerwin, President
CFO: Jim Dietsche, Chief Financial Officer
CMO: Ed Millermaier, M.D., Chief Medical Officer
CIO: John Rocheleau, Vice President Business Support and Information Technology
CHR: Troy L. Koebke, Director Human Resources Management
CNO: Laura Hieb, R.N., Chief Nursing Officer
Web address: www.bellin.org
Control: Church–operated, Nongovernment, not–for profit **Service:** General Medical and Surgical

Staffed Beds: 167 **Admissions:** 8521 **Census:** 84 **Outpatient Visits:** 928220 **Births:** 1339 **Total Expense ($000):** 397737 **Payroll Expense ($000):** 177862 **Personnel:** 2300

◇ **BELLIN PSYCHIATRIC CENTER (524038)**, 301 East St. Joseph Street, Zip 54301, Mailing Address: P.O. Box 23725, Zip 54305–3725; tel. 920/433–3630 **A**10 21 **F**4 5 6 29 34 36 38 53 54 56 64 75 86 87 98 99 100 101 102 103 104 105 130 **P**2 6
Primary Contact: Sharla Baenen, MSN, R.N., President
COO: Chris Woleske, Chief Operating Officer
CFO: Kevin McGurk, Controller
CIO: Troy Schiesl, Director Information Services
CHR: Troy L. Koebke, Director Human Resources
CNO: Crystal Malakar, Team Leader Inpatient Nursing
Web address: www.bellin.org
Control: Church–operated, Nongovernment, not–for profit **Service:** Psychiatric

Staffed Beds: 53 **Admissions:** 1450 **Census:** 18 **Outpatient Visits:** 59168 **Births:** 0 **Total Expense ($000):** 16783 **Payroll Expense ($000):** 10817 **Personnel:** 127

BROWN COUNTY COMMUNITY TREATMENT CENTER (524014), 3150 Gershwin Drive, Zip 54311–5899; tel. 920/391–4700 **A**10 **F**98 102 106 130
Primary Contact: Roberta Morschauser, Administrator
CFO: Margaret Hoff, Account Manager
CMO: Yogesh Pareek, M.D., Clinical Director
CIO: Dawn LaPlant, Manager Health Information Management
CHR: Brent R. Miller, Manager Human Resources
Web address: www.co.brown.wi.us/
Control: County–Government, nonfederal **Service:** Psychiatric

Staffed Beds: 16 **Admissions:** 962 **Census:** 10 **Outpatient Visits:** 0 **Births:** 0 **Total Expense ($000):** 4269 **Payroll Expense ($000):** 2447 **Personnel:** 55

BROWN COUNTY HUMAN SERVICES MENTAL HEALTH CENTER See Brown County Community Treatment Center

Many Facility Codes have changed. Please refer to the AHA Guide Code Chart. © 2016 AHA Guide

WI

✠ **HSHS ST. VINCENT HOSPITAL (520075)**, 835 South Van Buren Street, Zip 54301–3526, Mailing Address: P.O. Box 13508, Zip 54307–3508; tel. 920/433–0111 **A**1 2 10 **F**3 9 11 12 13 15 17 18 20 22 24 29 30 31 34 35 36 40 43 44 45 49 50 51 56 57 58 59 60 62 64 65 68 70 72 74 75 76 77 78 79 80 81 83 84 85 86 87 88 89 90 91 92 94 96 107 108 110 111 114 115 116 117 118 119 120 121 123 124 126 129 130 132 135 143 144 146 147 148 **P**2 **S** Hospital Sisters Health System, Springfield, IL
Primary Contact: Therese B. Pandl, President and Chief Executive Officer
COO: Lawrence J. Connors, Chief Operating Officer
CFO: Greg Simia, Chief Financial Officer
CMO: Ken Johnson, Chief Physician Executive
CIO: Shane Miller, Chief Information Officer
CHR: Christine Jensema, Chief People Officer
CNO: Paula Hafeman, R.N., Chief Nurse Executive
Web address: www.stvincenthospital.org
Control: Church–operated, Nongovernment, not–for profit **Service:** General Medical and Surgical

Staffed Beds: 255 **Admissions:** 9995 **Census:** 135 **Outpatient Visits:** 130195 **Births:** 968 **Total Expense ($000):** 264637 **Payroll Expense ($000):** 83248 **Personnel:** 1346

✠ **ST. MARY'S HOSPITAL MEDICAL CENTER (520097)**, 1726 Shawano Avenue, Zip 54303–3282; tel. 920/498–4200 **A**1 2 10 **F**3 13 15 17 18 20 22 26 28 29 30 31 34 35 40 43 44 45 46 47 48 49 50 51 53 55 57 59 64 65 68 69 70 74 75 76 77 78 79 80 81 82 84 85 86 87 92 94 96 102 107 108 110 111 114 115 116 117 118 119 130 132 143 145 146 147 148 **P**2 **S** Hospital Sisters Health System, Springfield, IL
Primary Contact: Therese B. Pandl, President and Chief Executive Officer
COO: Lawrence J. Connors, Chief Operating Officer
CFO: Greg Simia, Chief Financial Officer
CMO: Ken Johnson, Chief Physician Executive
CIO: Shane Miller, Chief Information Officer
CHR: Christine Jensema, Chief People Officer
CNO: Paula Hafeman, R.N., Chief Nursing Officer
Web address: www.stmgb.org
Control: Church–operated, Nongovernment, not–for profit **Service:** General Medical and Surgical

Staffed Beds: 83 **Admissions:** 4174 **Census:** 35 **Outpatient Visits:** 105571 **Births:** 658 **Total Expense ($000):** 115813 **Payroll Expense ($000):** 34705

GREENFIELD—Milwaukee County

KINDRED HOSPITAL–MILWAUKEE See Post Acute Medical Specialty Hospital of Milwaukee

✠ **POST ACUTE MEDICAL SPECIALTY HOSPITAL OF MILWAUKEE (522004)**, 5017 South 110Th Street, Zip 53228–3131; tel. 414/427–8282 **A**1 10 **F**1 3 29 34 59 65 68 75 82 83 84 85 86 96 119 130 148 **S** Post Acute Medical, LLC, Enola, PA
Primary Contact: Christine Peterson, Chief Executive Officer
CMO: Alok Goyal, M.D., Medical Director
CNO: Dorie Petitt, Chief Nursing Officer
Web address: www.postacutemedical.com/
Control: Corporation, Investor–owned, for–profit **Service:** Long–Term Acute Care hospital

Staffed Beds: 56 **Admissions:** 401 **Census:** 26 **Outpatient Visits:** 0 **Births:** 0 **Total Expense ($000):** 17612 **Payroll Expense ($000):** 7751 **Personnel:** 113

HARTFORD—Washington County

✠ **AURORA MEDICAL CENTER IN WASHINGTON COUNTY (520038)**, 1032 East Sumner Street, Zip 53027–1698; tel. 262/673–2300 **A**1 2 10 **F**2 3 8 11 15 29 30 32 34 35 36 37 40 41 43 44 45 46 47 48 49 50 53 54 56 59 60 64 65 68 70 74 75 77 79 80 81 82 84 85 86 87 89 90 93 107 111 114 118 119 129 130 132 135 146 148 **P**6 **S** Aurora Health Care, Milwaukee, WI
Primary Contact: Carrie Killoran, Interim President
CIO: John Sipek, Supervisor Client Services
CNO: Terry Kabitzke–Groth, R.N., Chief Nursing Officer
Web address: www.aurorahealthcare.org
Control: Other not–for–profit (including NFP Corporation) **Service:** General Medical and Surgical

Staffed Beds: 35 **Admissions:** 1527 **Census:** 14 **Outpatient Visits:** 78557 **Births:** 0 **Total Expense ($000):** 51245 **Payroll Expense ($000):** 18684 **Personnel:** 281

HAYWARD—Sawyer County

★ **HAYWARD AREA MEMORIAL HOSPITAL AND NURSING HOME (521336)**, 11040 North State Road 77, Zip 54843–6391; tel. 715/934–4321, (Total facility includes 70 beds in nursing home–type unit) **A**10 18 **F**10 11 13 15 34 40 43 51 64 75 76 77 78 81 82 86 93 107 111 119 128 130
Primary Contact: Timothy M. Gullingsrud, Chief Executive Officer
COO: Brad Zeller, Vice President Operations
CFO: Kent Dumonseau, Vice President Finance and Information Services
CHR: Rose Gates, Director Human Resources
Web address: www.hamhnh.com
Control: Other not–for–profit (including NFP Corporation) **Service:** General Medical and Surgical

Staffed Beds: 75 **Admissions:** 846 **Census:** 73 **Outpatient Visits:** 22430 **Births:** 151 **Total Expense ($000):** 31024 **Payroll Expense ($000):** 13124 **Personnel:** 165

HILLSBORO—Vernon County

★ **GUNDERSEN ST. JOSEPH'S HOSPITAL AND CLINICS (521304)**, 400 Water Avenue, Zip 54634–9054, Mailing Address: P.O. Box 527, Zip 54634–0527; tel. 608/489–8000 **A**10 18 **F**15 29 34 40 43 53 54 56 64 69 75 77 80 81 82 86 87 89 90 93 99 100 101 103 104 107 108 130 131 144 147 **P**6
Primary Contact: Debra Smith, Chief Executive Officer
CFO: Robin Nelson, Chief Financial Officer
CMO: William Cooke, M.D., Chief of Staff
CIO: Danial Phetteplace, Director Information Technology
CHR: Kristie McCoic, Clinic Operations Officer and Director Human Resources
Web address: www.gundersenhealth.org/st-josephs
Control: Other not–for–profit (including NFP Corporation) **Service:** General Medical and Surgical

Staffed Beds: 14 **Admissions:** 255 **Census:** 3 **Outpatient Visits:** 33733 **Births:** 0 **Total Expense ($000):** 17165 **Payroll Expense ($000):** 6938 **Personnel:** 124

HUDSON—St. Croix County

☐ **HUDSON HOSPITAL AND CLINIC (521335)**, 405 Stageline Road, Zip 54016–7848; tel. 715/531–6000 **A**1 3 10 18 **F**3 5 8 13 15 18 19 26 28 29 30 31 32 34 35 36 38 40 43 44 45 46 50 53 56 57 59 64 68 74 75 76 77 78 79 80 81 85 86 87 89 93 94 96 97 107 110 111 115 117 119 129 130 132 133 135 143 146 148 **S** HealthPartners, Bloomington, MN
Primary Contact: Marian M. Furlong, R.N., FACHE, Chief Executive Officer
CFO: Douglas E. Johnson, Interim Vice President Operations and Chief Financial Officer
CMO: Paul Scott, M.D., Chief of Staff
CHR: Scott J. Allen, Director Human Resources
Web address: www.hudsonhospital.org
Control: Other not–for–profit (including NFP Corporation) **Service:** General Medical and Surgical

Staffed Beds: 24 **Admissions:** 1433 **Census:** 10 **Outpatient Visits:** 48652 **Births:** 581 **Total Expense ($000):** 54024 **Payroll Expense ($000):** 19872 **Personnel:** 254

JANESVILLE—Rock County

✠ **MERCY HOSPITAL AND TRAUMA CENTER (520066)**, 1000 Mineral Point Avenue, Zip 53548–2982, Mailing Address: P.O. Box 5003, Zip 53547–5003; tel. 608/756–6000, (Total facility includes 27 beds in nursing home–type unit) **A**1 2 10 **F**3 4 5 9 11 12 13 15 17 18 20 22 24 26 28 29 30 31 33 34 35 36 37 38 40 42 43 44 45 49 50 54 55 56 57 58 59 60 61 64 65 66 68 69 70 74 75 76 77 78 79 80 81 82 84 85 86 87 88 89 90 92 93 94 96 97 98 100 101 102 103 104 105 107 108 110 111 114 115 116 118 119 120 121 126 128 129 130 131 132 135 144 146 147 148 **P**6 **S** Mercy Health System, Janesville, WI
Primary Contact: Javon R. Bea, President and Chief Executive Officer
CFO: John Cook, Vice President and Chief Financial Officer
CMO: Mark L. Goelzer, M.D., Director Medical Affairs
CHR: Kathy Harris, Vice President
CNO: Sue Ripsch, Vice President and Chief Nursing Officer
Web address: www.mercyhealthsystem.org
Control: Other not–for–profit (including NFP Corporation) **Service:** General Medical and Surgical

Staffed Beds: 148 **Admissions:** 6894 **Census:** 99 **Outpatient Visits:** 1059829 **Births:** 846 **Total Expense ($000):** 396938 **Payroll Expense ($000):** 131536 **Personnel:** 1620

WI

Hospital, Medicare Provider Number, Address, Telephone, Approval, Facility, and Physician Codes, Health Care System

★ American Hospital Association (AHA) membership ◯ Healthcare Facilities Accreditation Program ⇑ Center for Improvement in Healthcare Quality Accreditation
☐ The Joint Commission accreditation ◇ DNV Healthcare Inc. accreditation △ Commission on Accreditation of Rehabilitation Facilities (CARF) accreditation

✠ **ST. MARY'S JANESVILLE HOSPITAL (520208)**, 3400 East Racine Steeet, Zip 53546–2344; tel. 608/373–8000 **A**1 10 **F**11 13 28 29 34 38 40 70 75 76 77 80 81 82 86 87 89 90 93 107 108 111 118 119 130 **S** SSM Health, Saint Louis, MO
Primary Contact: Kerry Swanson, President
Web address: www.stmarysjanesville.com
Control: Church–operated, Nongovernment, not–for profit **Service:** General Medical and Surgical

Staffed Beds: 50 **Admissions:** 2780 **Census:** 26 **Outpatient Visits:** 30540 **Births:** 455 **Total Expense ($000):** 57117 **Payroll Expense ($000):** 19497 **Personnel:** 307

KENOSHA—Kenosha County

✠ **AURORA MEDICAL CENTER (520189)**, 10400 75th Street, Zip 53142–7884; tel. 262/948–5600 **A**1 2 10 **F**3 8 11 13 15 17 18 19 20 28 29 30 31 34 35 36 40 43 44 45 46 47 48 49 50 51 54 57 59 60 64 68 70 74 75 76 79 80 81 82 84 85 86 87 89 93 94 96 100 107 108 110 111 114 115 116 117 118 119 120 121 123 129 130 131 132 135 146 148 **P**6 **S** Aurora Health Care, Milwaukee, WI
Primary Contact: Douglas E. Koch, Market President
COO: Linda A. Gump, Chief Clinical Services Officer
CFO: Laurie B. Yake, Vice President Finance
CMO: James Santarelli, M.D., President Medical Staff
CIO: Debora R. Chapdelaine, Manager Information Technology
CHR: Kellie Nelson, Director Human Resources
CNO: Donna F. Jamieson, Ph.D., Chief Nursing Officer
Web address: www.aurorahealthcare.org
Control: Other not–for–profit (including NFP Corporation) **Service:** General Medical and Surgical

Staffed Beds: 74 **Admissions:** 5167 **Census:** 48 **Outpatient Visits:** 176030 **Births:** 841 **Total Expense ($000):** 124172 **Payroll Expense ($000):** 37551 **Personnel:** 662

☐ **UNITED HOSPITAL SYSTEM–KENOSHA CAMPUS (520021)**, 6308 Eighth Avenue, Zip 53143–5082; tel. 262/656–2011 **A**1 2 10 **F**1 11 12 13 15 17 20 22 24 28 29 34 38 40 43 51 53 60 64 70 72 75 76 78 80 81 86 87 89 90 93 100 102 107 108 111 118 119 130 131 144 147 **P**6
Primary Contact: Richard O. Schmidt, Jr., President and Chief Executive Officer
Web address: www.unitedhospitalsystem.org/
Control: Other not–for–profit (including NFP Corporation) **Service:** General Medical and Surgical

Staffed Beds: 252 **Admissions:** 8528 **Census:** 100 **Outpatient Visits:** 335187 **Births:** 1061 **Total Expense ($000):** 269841 **Payroll Expense ($000):** 119647 **Personnel:** 1879

LA CROSSE—La Crosse County

✠ △ **GUNDERSEN HEALTH SYSTEM (520087)**, 1900 South Avenue, Zip 54601–5467; tel. 608/782–7300 **A**1 2 3 5 7 8 10 **F**2 3 4 5 6 9 11 13 15 18 19 20 22 24 28 29 30 31 32 34 35 36 38 40 43 45 46 47 48 49 50 51 52 54 55 56 59 61 64 68 72 74 78 79 80 81 82 83 85 86 87 88 89 90 91 92 93 94 96 97 98 99 100 101 102 103 104 105 106 107 108 109 110 111 114 115 116 117 118 119 120 121 123 124 126 129 130 131 134 144 145 146 147 148
Primary Contact: Scott W. Rathgaber, M.D., Chief Executive Officer and Board Chair
COO: Kathy Klock, R.N., Senior Vice President Clinical Operations and Human Resources
CFO: Dara Bartels, Chief Financial Officer
CMO: Greg Thompson, Chief Medical Officer
CIO: Deb Rislow, Chief Information Officer
CHR: Kathy Klock, R.N., Senior Vice President Clinical Operations and Human Resources
Web address: www.gundluth.org
Control: Other not–for–profit (including NFP Corporation) **Service:** General Medical and Surgical

Staffed Beds: 268 **Admissions:** 14303 **Census:** 181 **Outpatient Visits:** 647194 **Births:** 1500 **Total Expense ($000):** 806732 **Payroll Expense ($000):** 277681 **Personnel:** 2567

☐ **MAYO CLINIC HEALTH SYSTEM – FRANCISCAN HEALTHCARE IN LA CROSSE (520004)**, 700 West Avenue South, Zip 54601–4783; tel. 608/785–0940 **A**1 2 3 5 10 **F**1 3 4 5 6 8 9 11 13 14 15 16 17 18 19 20 21 22 23 25 26 27 28 29 30 31 32 34 35 36 40 43 44 45 50 52 53 54 55 56 57 58 59 61 64 65 66 68 69 70 71 72 74 75 76 77 78 79 80 81 82 84 85 86 87 88 89 90 93 94 97 98 99 100 101 102 103 104 105 107 108 109 110 111 112 114 115 117 118 119 120 121 123 124 127 129 130 131 132 134 135 143 144 145 146 147 148 **S** Mayo Clinic, Rochester, MN
Primary Contact: Timothy J. Johnson, President and Chief Executive Officer
COO: Joseph J. Kruse, Executive Vice President
CFO: Tom Tiggelaar, Vice President Finance
CMO: David Rushlow, Vice President Medical Affairs
CIO: Neal Sanger, Vice President Information Services
CNO: Diane Holmay, R.N., Vice President and Chief Nursing Officer
Web address: www.franciscankemp.org
Control: Church–operated, Nongovernment, not–for profit **Service:** General Medical and Surgical

Staffed Beds: 81 **Admissions:** 6754 **Census:** 69 **Outpatient Visits:** 95364 **Births:** 931 **Total Expense ($000):** 298349 **Payroll Expense ($000):** 158906 **Personnel:** 1963

LADYSMITH—Rusk County

★ **RUSK COUNTY MEMORIAL HOSPITAL (521328)**, 900 College Avenue West, Zip 54848–2116; tel. 715/532–5561 **A**10 18 **F**3 11 15 28 29 30 34 40 43 44 45 50 51 53 56 57 59 64 68 70 77 81 85 87 89 90 93 97 107 110 111 115 117 119 127 132 133 144 146 147 148 **P**6
Primary Contact: Charisse S. Oland, FACHE, Chief Executive Officer
CFO: David Kuehn, Chief Financial Officer
CMO: Ganesh Pawar, M.D., Chief of Staff
CHR: Rita Telitz, Chief Administrative Officer
CNO: Debra Frenn, FACHE, Chief Patient Care Officer
Web address: www.ruskhospital.org
Control: County–Government, nonfederal **Service:** General Medical and Surgical

Staffed Beds: 25 **Admissions:** 528 **Census:** 7 **Outpatient Visits:** 33814 **Births:** 0 **Total Expense ($000):** 21478 **Payroll Expense ($000):** 8964 **Personnel:** 140

LAKE GENEVA—Walworth County

MERCY WALWORTH HOSPITAL AND MEDICAL CENTER (521357), N2950 State Road 67, Zip 53147–2655; tel. 262/245–0535 **A**10 18 **F**3 5 9 11 13 15 18 26 29 31 34 40 44 45 50 54 55 57 59 64 65 70 74 75 76 77 78 79 81 82 85 86 89 92 93 94 96 97 100 101 103 104 107 108 110 111 114 118 119 129 130 131 132 135 144 146 147 148 **P**6 **S** Mercy Health System, Janesville, WI
Primary Contact: Jennifer Hallatt, Chief Operating Officer
CNO: Caryn Lynn Oleston, MSN, Chief Nursing Officer
Web address: www.mercyhealthsystem.org
Control: Other not–for–profit (including NFP Corporation) **Service:** General Medical and Surgical

Staffed Beds: 15 **Admissions:** 903 **Census:** 10 **Outpatient Visits:** 143142 **Births:** 209 **Total Expense ($000):** 72567 **Payroll Expense ($000):** 16750 **Personnel:** 270

LANCASTER—Grant County

✠ **GRANT REGIONAL HEALTH CENTER (521322)**, 507 South Monroe Street, Zip 53813–2054; tel. 608/723–2143 **A**1 10 18 **F**3 8 11 13 15 28 29 34 35 36 40 43 44 53 56 57 59 64 65 68 69 75 76 77 79 80 81 82 84 85 86 87 89 90 93 97 107 110 115 119 127 129 130 131 132 133 135 144 146 148 **P**6 **S** HealthTech Management Services, Brentwood, TN
Primary Contact: Nicole Clapp, R.N., MSN, FACHE, President and Chief Executive Officer
CFO: Dawn Bandy, Chief Financial Officer
CMO: Jessica Varnam, Chief of Staff
CIO: Ken Kaiser, Coordinator Information Systems
CHR: Stacy L. Martin, Director Human Resources
CNO: Jennifer Rutkowski, R.N., Vice President Professional Services
Web address: www.grantregional.com
Control: Other not–for–profit (including NFP Corporation) **Service:** General Medical and Surgical

Staffed Beds: 5 **Admissions:** 662 **Census:** 5 **Outpatient Visits:** 27345 **Births:** 179 **Total Expense ($000):** 24883 **Payroll Expense ($000):** 12168 **Personnel:** 159

MADISON—Dane County

☐ **MENDOTA MENTAL HEALTH INSTITUTE (524008)**, 301 Troy Drive, Zip 53704–1599; tel. 608/301–1000 **A**1 3 5 10 **F**6 29 30 38 44 56 68 75 82 86 87 98 100 101 103 104 105 130 143
Primary Contact: Greg Van Rybroek, Chief Executive Officer
CFO: Stacie Schiereck, Director Management Services
CMO: Molli Martha Rolli, M.D., Medical Director
CNO: Jane Walters, Director of Nursing
Web address: www.dhfs.state.wi.us
Control: State–Government, nonfederal **Service:** Psychiatric

Staffed Beds: 274 **Admissions:** 542 **Census:** 267 **Outpatient Visits:** 0 **Births:** 0 **Total Expense ($000):** 64919 **Payroll Expense ($000):** 41401 **Personnel:** 742

WI

Many Facility Codes have changed. Please refer to the AHA Guide Code Chart.
© 2016 AHA Guide

MERITER UNITYPOINT HEALTH (520089), 202 South Park Street, Zip 53715–1507; tel. 608/417–6000 **A**1 3 5 10 **F**3 4 5 9 11 12 13 15 17 18 20 22 24 26 28 29 30 31 32 34 35 36 37 40 41 43 45 46 48 49 50 53 56 57 58 59 64 65 66 68 70 71 72 74 75 76 78 79 80 81 84 85 86 87 90 92 93 96 97 98 99 100 101 102 103 104 105 106 107 108 111 115 117 118 119 126 130 132 135 145 146 147 148 **P**6 **S** UnityPoint Health, West Des Moines, IA
Primary Contact: Arthur Nizza, Chief Executive Officer
CFO: Beth Erdman, Chief Financial Officer
CMO: Geoff Priest, M.D., Chief Medical Officer
CIO: Denise Gomez, Assistant Vice President Information Systems
CHR: James Arnett, Vice President Human Resources
CNO: Pat Grunwald, MSN, Chief Nursing Officer
Web address: www.meriter.com
Control: Other not–for–profit (including NFP Corporation) **Service:** General Medical and Surgical

Staffed Beds: 304 **Admissions:** 15373 **Census:** 185 **Outpatient Visits:** 210933 **Births:** 4004 **Total Expense ($000):** 433539 **Payroll Expense ($000):** 183503 **Personnel:** 2371

SELECT SPECIALTY HOSPITAL–MADISON (522008), 801 Braxton Place, 2nd Floor, Zip 53715–1415; tel. 608/260–2700 **A**1 10 **F**1 3 29 30 35 60 65 68 75 85 86 119 130 148 **P**8 **S** Select Medical Corporation, Mechanicsburg, PA
Primary Contact: Raymond F. Carnevale, Chief Executive Officer
CHR: Mallary Stramowski, Chief Human Resources Officer
CNO: Dana McKinney, Chief Nursing Officer
Web address: www.madison.selectspecialtyhospitals.com
Control: Corporation, Investor–owned, for–profit **Service:** Long–Term Acute Care hospital

Staffed Beds: 58 **Admissions:** 480 **Census:** 42 **Outpatient Visits:** 0 **Births:** 0 **Total Expense ($000):** 28012 **Payroll Expense ($000):** 11023 **Personnel:** 175

ST. MARY'S HOSPITAL (520083), 700 South Park Street, Zip 53715–1830; tel. 608/251–6100 **A**1 3 10 **F**2 9 11 13 15 17 20 22 24 28 29 34 40 53 56 64 70 72 75 76 78 80 81 82 86 89 90 98 100 101 102 103 107 108 118 119 130 141 **S** SSM Health, Saint Louis, MO
Primary Contact: Jon Rozenfeld, President
COO: Kristin McManmon, Chief Operating Officer
CFO: Steve Caldwell, Vice President Finance and Chief Financial Officer
CHR: Linda Taplin Statz, System Vice President Human Resources
CNO: Ginger Malone, MSN, RN–B, Chief Nursing Officer
Web address: www.stmarysmadison.com
Control: Church–operated, Nongovernment, not–for profit **Service:** General Medical and Surgical

Staffed Beds: 362 **Admissions:** 19692 **Census:** 246 **Outpatient Visits:** 118220 **Births:** 3229 **Total Expense ($000):** 370234 **Payroll Expense ($000):** 131278 **Personnel:** 1754

UNIVERSITY OF WISCONSIN HOSPITALS AND CLINICS AUTHORITY (520098), 600 Highland Avenue, Zip 53792–0002; tel. 608/263–6400, (Includes UNIVERSITY OF WISCONSIN CHILDREN'S HOSPITAL ; AMERICAN FAMILY CHILDREN'S HOSPITAL, 1675 Highland Avenue, Zip 53705; tel. 608/890–5437; Jeffrey S. Poltawsky, Senior Vice President) **A**1 2 3 5 8 10 13 **F**3 5 6 8 9 12 15 16 17 18 19 20 21 22 23 24 25 26 27 28 29 30 31 32 33 34 35 36 37 40 41 43 44 45 46 47 48 49 50 51 52 53 54 55 56 57 58 59 60 61 62 64 68 70 72 74 77 78 79 80 81 82 83 84 85 86 87 88 89 90 92 93 94 95 97 98 100 102 103 107 108 110 111 112 114 115 116 117 118 119 120 121 123 124 126 129 130 131 132 134 135 136 137 138 139 140 141 142 145 146 147 148 **P**3
Primary Contact: Alan Kaplan, M.D., Chief Executive Officer
COO: Ron Sliwinski, Chief of Hospital Division
CFO: Robert Flannery, Chief Financial Officer
CMO: Peter Newcomer, M.D., Chief Medical Officer
CIO: Jocelyn DeWitt, Ph.D., Vice President and Chief Information Officer
CHR: Elizabeth T. Bolt, Chief Human Resources Officer
CNO: Beth Houlahan, MSN, Senior Vice President and Chief Nursing Officer
Web address: www.uwhealth.org
Control: Other not–for–profit (including NFP Corporation) **Service:** General Medical and Surgical

Staffed Beds: 566 **Admissions:** 30794 **Census:** 436 **Outpatient Visits:** 850846 **Births:** 0 **Total Expense ($000):** 1409277 **Payroll Expense ($000):** 490510 **Personnel:** 8877

WILLIAM S. MIDDLETON MEMORIAL VETERANS HOSPITAL, 2500 Overlook Terrace, Zip 53705–2286; tel. 608/256–1901, (Nonreporting) **A**1 3 5 **S** Department of Veterans Affairs, Washington, DC
Primary Contact: John J. Rohrer, Acting Director
COO: John J. Rohrer, Associate Director
CFO: Evarista Mikell, Assistant Finance Officer
CMO: Alan J. Bridges, M.D., Chief of Staff
CIO: Randall Margenau, Chief Information Officer
CHR: Stuart Souders, Chief, Human Resources
CNO: Rebecca Kordahl, R.N., Associate Director, Patient Care Services
Web address: www.madison.va.gov
Control: Veterans Affairs, Government, federal **Service:** General Medical and Surgical

Staffed Beds: 87

MANITOWOC—Manitowoc County

HOLY FAMILY MEMORIAL (520107), 2300 Western Avenue, Zip 54220–3712, Mailing Address: P.O. Box 1450, Zip 54221–1450; tel. 920/320–2011 **A**1 2 10 **F**3 4 5 8 11 13 15 17 20 22 26 28 29 30 31 34 36 40 43 45 46 47 48 49 50 51 53 54 56 57 58 59 62 63 64 65 68 70 75 76 77 78 79 80 81 82 85 86 89 93 97 104 107 108 110 111 115 118 119 121 130 132 135 144 146 148 **P**6 **S** Franciscan Sisters of Christian Charity Sponsored Ministries, Inc., Manitowoc, WI
Primary Contact: Mark P. Herzog, President and Chief Executive Officer
COO: Jane Curran–Meuli, Chief Operating Officer
CFO: Patricia Huettl, Vice President Finance and Chief Financial Officer
CMO: Steve Driggers, M.D., Chief Medical Officer
CIO: Theron Pappas, Director Management Information Systems
CHR: Laura M. Fielding, Administrative Director Organizational Development
CNO: Bonny Range, MSN, Chief Nursing Officer
Web address: www.hfmhealth.org
Control: Church–operated, Nongovernment, not–for profit **Service:** General Medical and Surgical

Staffed Beds: 67 **Admissions:** 2670 **Census:** 25 **Outpatient Visits:** 230656 **Births:** 226 **Total Expense ($000):** 124981 **Payroll Expense ($000):** 63023 **Personnel:** 674

MARINETTE—Marinette County

BAY AREA MEDICAL CENTER (520113), 3100 Shore Drive, Zip 54143–4242; tel. 715/735–6621 **A**1 10 20 **F**3 7 11 13 15 17 18 20 22 28 29 30 31 34 40 43 44 45 48 50 51 54 57 59 68 70 74 75 76 77 78 79 80 81 82 85 86 87 89 93 96 107 108 110 111 115 119 121 130 131 143 146 147 148 **P**8
Primary Contact: Edward A. Harding, FACHE, President and Chief Executive Officer
COO: Bernie VanCourt, Chief Operating Officer
CFO: Matt Huff, Chief Financial Officer
CMO: Richard Stein, M.D., Chief Medical Officer
CIO: Pete Eisenzoph, Director Information Technology
CHR: Ken Joyner, Vice President of Employee Services
CNO: Bernie VanCourt, Interim Chief Nursing Officer
Web address: www.bamc.org
Control: Other not–for–profit (including NFP Corporation) **Service:** General Medical and Surgical

Staffed Beds: 53 **Admissions:** 3031 **Census:** 31 **Outpatient Visits:** 40697 **Births:** 281 **Total Expense ($000):** 100765 **Payroll Expense ($000):** 42538 **Personnel:** 506

MARSHFIELD—Wood County

△ **MINISTRY SAINT JOSEPH'S HOSPITAL (520037)**, 611 St. Joseph Avenue, Zip 54449–1898; tel. 715/387–1713, (Includes SAINT JOSEPH'S CHILDEN'S HOSPITAL, 611 Saint Joseph Avenue, Zip 54449–1832; tel. 715/387–1713) **A**1 2 3 5 7 10 20 **F**3 5 6 7 9 11 12 13 16 17 18 19 20 22 24 26 27 28 29 30 31 34 35 36 38 40 41 43 44 49 50 56 57 59 61 64 68 69 70 72 74 75 76 77 78 79 80 81 82 83 84 85 86 87 88 89 90 93 96 98 100 101 102 103 108 111 112 116 117 118 119 120 121 122 123 124 126 130 132 135 136 144 146 147 148 **S** Ascension Health, Saint Louis, MO
Primary Contact: Brian Kief, Regional Vice President Ministry Health Care and President Ministry Saint Joseph's Hospital
CFO: William J. Hinner, Vice President Financial Analysis and Planning Ministry Health Care
CMO: Peter Stamas, M.D., Vice President Medical Affairs
CIO: Will Weider, Chief Information Officer
CHR: Cheryl F. Zima, Vice President Human Resources Ministry Health Care
CNO: Robin Kretschman, MSN, Vice President Patient Care Services
Web address: www.stjosephs–marshfield.org
Control: Church–operated, Nongovernment, not–for profit **Service:** General Medical and Surgical

Staffed Beds: 275 **Admissions:** 14934 **Census:** 222 **Outpatient Visits:** 55730 **Births:** 1009 **Total Expense ($000):** 311789 **Payroll Expense ($000):** 106292 **Personnel:** 1204

WI

Hospital, Medicare Provider Number, Address, Telephone, Approval, Facility, and Physician Codes, Health Care System

★ American Hospital Association (AHA) membership
□ The Joint Commission accreditation
○ Healthcare Facilities Accreditation Program
◇ DNV Healthcare Inc. accreditation
⇑ Center for Improvement in Healthcare Quality Accreditation
△ Commission on Accreditation of Rehabilitation Facilities (CARF) accreditation

NORWOOD HEALTH CENTER (524019), 1600 North Chestnut Avenue, Zip 54449–1499; tel. 715/384–2188, (Total facility includes 24 beds in nursing home–type unit) **A**10 **F**3 4 30 34 69 75 98 99 100 101 102 103 106 128 130 143 146 148 **P**6
Primary Contact: Jordan Bruce, Administrator
CFO: Jo Timmerman, Manager Accounting
CHR: Larry Shear, Administrative Assistant
Web address: www.co.wood.wi.us/norwood/index.htm
Control: County–Government, nonfederal **Service:** Psychiatric

Staffed Beds: 40 Admissions: 562 Census: 27 Outpatient Visits: 0 Births:
0 **Total Expense ($000):** 3382 **Payroll Expense ($000):** 1482 **Personnel:**
39

MAUSTON—Juneau County

☐ **MILE BLUFF MEDICAL CENTER (520109)**, 1050 Division Street, Zip 53948–1997; tel. 608/847–6161, (Total facility includes 106 beds in nursing home–type unit) **A**1 10 20 **F**3 10 11 13 15 18 28 29 30 31 34 35 36 40 43 44 45 46 50 56 57 59 60 62 63 64 65 66 68 69 71 75 76 77 78 79 80 81 82 85 86 87 89 92 93 94 96 97 107 108 110 111 112 114 115 117 118 119 125 127 128 129 130 131 132 135 143 144 145 146 148 **P**2
Primary Contact: James M. O'Keefe, President and Chief Executive Officer
Web address: www.milebluff.com
Control: Other not–for–profit (including NFP Corporation) **Service:** General Medical and Surgical

Staffed Beds: 114 Admissions: 1437 Census: 114 Outpatient Visits:
176098 **Births:** 175 **Total Expense ($000):** 71166 **Payroll Expense ($000):**
37728 **Personnel:** 492

MEDFORD—Taylor County

✠ **ASPIRUS MEDFORD HOSPITAL (521324)**, 135 South Gibson Street, Zip 54451–1696; tel. 715/748–8100, (Includes MEMORIAL NURSING HOME), (Total facility includes 109 beds in nursing home–type unit) **A**1 10 18 **F**1 3 8 10 11 13 15 18 28 29 31 32 34 35 36 40 41 43 50 53 55 57 58 59 60 64 65 68 75 76 77 78 81 82 85 86 87 89 90 93 97 107 110 111 115 116 118 119 125 127 128 129 130 131 132 133 135 144 146 147 148 **S** Aspirus, Inc., Wausau, WI
Primary Contact: Gregory A. Olson, President and Chief Executive Officer
CFO: Greg Shaw, Vice President of Finance
CMO: Troy Sennholz, M.D., Chief of Staff
CIO: Helen Volger, Director of Information Services
CHR: Angela C. Hupf, Vice President Human Resources and Community Relations
CNO: Jodi Johnson, Vice President of Nursing
Web address: www.aspirus.org
Control: Other not–for–profit (including NFP Corporation) **Service:** General Medical and Surgical

Staffed Beds: 124 Admissions: 937 Census: 86 Outpatient Visits: 74876
Births: 225 **Total Expense ($000):** 53750 **Payroll Expense ($000):** 24216
Personnel: 347

MENOMONEE FALLS—Waukesha County

✠ △ **COMMUNITY MEMORIAL HOSPITAL (520103)**, W180 N8085 Town Hall Road, Zip 53051–3518, Mailing Address: P.O. Box 408, Zip 53052–0408; tel. 262/251–1000 **A**1 2 3 7 10 **F**3 4 5 11 13 15 17 18 20 26 28 29 30 31 34 35 36 38 40 43 44 45 46 47 49 50 51 56 57 59 60 64 65 68 70 72 74 75 76 77 78 79 80 81 82 84 85 86 87 89 90 93 98 100 101 102 103 104 107 108 110 111 114 115 116 117 118 119 120 121 123 126 129 130 131 132 135 145 146 147 148
Primary Contact: Dennis Pollard, President of Community Memorial Hospital
COO: Allen Ericson, Chief Operating Officer, Community Hospital Division and President, St. Joseph's Hospital
CFO: Scott Hawig, Senior Vice President of Finance, Chief Financial Officer and Treasurer
CMO: David Goldberg, M.D., Vice President Medical Affairs and Chief Medical Officer
CIO: Will Showalter, Senior Vice President Information Systems, Chief Information Officer
CHR: Keith Allen, Senior Vice President and Chief Human Resources Officer
CNO: Teri Lux, Vice President Patient Care Services and Chief Nursing Officer
Web address: www.communitymemorial.com
Control: Other not–for–profit (including NFP Corporation) **Service:** General Medical and Surgical

Staffed Beds: 198 Admissions: 8462 Census: 102 Outpatient Visits: 84160
Births: 998 **Total Expense ($000):** 179585 **Payroll Expense ($000):** 62641
Personnel: 959

MENOMONIE—Dunn County

☐ **MAYO CLINIC HEALTH SYSTEM – RED CEDAR IN MENOMONIE (521340)**, 2321 Stout Road, Zip 54751–2397; tel. 715/235–5531 **A**1 10 18 **F**3 8 11 13 15 17 18 28 29 30 31 32 34 35 36 40 43 44 45 53 54 55 57 59 60 63 64 65 70 75 76 77 78 79 80 81 82 84 85 86 87 89 90 93 97 99 100 101 102 103 104 107 108 110 111 115 119 127 129 130 131 132 133 135 144 146 147 148 **P**6 **S** Mayo Clinic, Rochester, MN
Primary Contact: Steven Lindberg, Chief Administrative Officer
CFO: Jeanie Lubinsky, Chief Financial Officer
CMO: Mark Deyo Svendsen, M.D., Medical Director
CIO: Frank Wrogg, Director Information Technology
CHR: Leann Wurtzel, Director Human Resources
Web address: www.rcmc–mhs.org
Control: Other not–for–profit (including NFP Corporation) **Service:** General Medical and Surgical

Staffed Beds: 23 Admissions: 1331 Census: 13 Outpatient Visits: 106013
Births: 321 **Total Expense ($000):** 78060 **Payroll Expense ($000):** 37182
Personnel: 420

RED CEDAR MEDICAL CENTER–MAYO HEALTH SYSTEM See Mayo Clinic Health System – Red Cedar in Menomonie

MEQUON—Ozaukee County

COLUMBIA CENTER (520195), 13125 North Port Washington Road, Zip 53097–2416; tel. 262/243–7408 **A**10 **F**13 34 64 76 81 86 87 104
Primary Contact: Candy J. Casey, R.N., MS, President and Chief Executive Officer
CMO: Daniel Hagerman, M.D., President Medical Staff
Web address: www.columbiacenter.org
Control: Other not–for–profit (including NFP Corporation) **Service:** General Medical and Surgical

Staffed Beds: 6 Admissions: 521 Census: 4 Outpatient Visits: 284 Births:
519 **Total Expense ($000):** 6453 **Payroll Expense ($000):** 3042
Personnel: 39

✠ **COLUMBIA ST. MARY'S OZAUKEE HOSPITAL (520027)**, 13111 North Port Washington Road, Zip 53097–2416; tel. 262/243–7300 **A**1 2 10 **F**3 4 5 8 9 15 17 18 20 22 24 26 28 29 30 31 34 35 36 38 40 43 44 45 47 48 49 50 51 53 54 56 57 58 59 64 65 66 68 70 71 74 75 77 78 79 80 81 83 84 85 86 89 90 92 93 98 100 102 103 107 108 110 111 114 115 116 118 119 120 121 123 124 126 130 132 134 135 144 146 147 148 **P**6 **S** Ascension Health, Saint Louis, MO
Primary Contact: Travis Andersen, President and Chief Executive Officer
CFO: Rhonda Anderson, Executive Vice President Finance and Chief Financial Officer
CMO: David Shapiro, M.D., Vice President Medical Affairs and Chief Medical Officer
CIO: Mary Paul, Chief Information Officer
CHR: Cheryl Hill, Vice President Human Resources
Web address: www.columbia–stmarys.org
Control: Church–operated, Nongovernment, not–for profit **Service:** General Medical and Surgical

Staffed Beds: 112 Admissions: 5507 Census: 66 Outpatient Visits: 293620
Births: 0 **Total Expense ($000):** 148561 **Payroll Expense ($000):** 59606
Personnel: 748

MERRILL—Lincoln County

GOOD SAMARITAN HEALTH CENTER OF MERRILL See Ministry Good Samaritan Health Center

✠ **MINISTRY GOOD SAMARITAN HEALTH CENTER (521339)**, 601 South Center Avenue, Zip 54452–3404; tel. 715/536–5511 **A**1 10 18 **F**3 15 18 28 29 30 31 34 35 40 43 44 45 50 56 57 64 68 75 78 79 80 81 82 85 86 87 93 107 108 110 111 115 118 119 130 132 133 135 144 146 147 **S** Ascension Health, Saint Louis, MO
Primary Contact: Mary T. Krueger, President
CFO: David Jirovec, Director Finance
CHR: Nancy Kwiesielewicz, Human Resources Manager
CNO: Kristine McGarigle, R.N., Vice President Patient Care
Web address: www.ministryhealth.org
Control: Church–operated, Nongovernment, not–for profit **Service:** General Medical and Surgical

Staffed Beds: 10 Admissions: 544 Census: 4 Outpatient Visits: 19288
Births: 0 **Total Expense ($000):** 21135 **Payroll Expense ($000):** 11014
Personnel: 88

WI

Many Facility Codes have changed. Please refer to the AHA Guide Code Chart.

MILWAUKEE—Milwaukee County

★ △ **AURORA SINAI MEDICAL CENTER (520064)**, 945 North 12th Street, Zip 53233–1337, Mailing Address: P.O. Box 342, Zip 53201–0342; tel. 414/219–2000 **A**2 3 5 7 8 **F**1 3 5 6 11 12 13 15 17 18 20 22 26 28 29 30 31 32 34 35 36 37 38 40 44 45 46 49 50 51 54 55 56 57 59 60 64 65 68 70 72 74 75 76 77 78 79 80 81 82 84 85 86 87 89 90 91 92 93 94 96 102 103 107 108 110 111 114 118 119 123 126 129 130 131 132 135 144 146 147 148 **P**6 **S** Aurora Health Care, Milwaukee, WI
Primary Contact: Carolynn Glocka, R.N., President
CHR: Heidi Grow, Director Human Resources
CNO: Ania Horner, R.N., Vice President and Chief Nurse Executive
Web address: www.aurorahealthcare.org
Control: Other not–for–profit (including NFP Corporation) **Service:** General Medical and Surgical

Staffed Beds: 197 **Admissions:** 7987 **Census:** 105 **Outpatient Visits:** 268175 **Births:** 2104 **Total Expense ($000):** 183007 **Payroll Expense ($000):** 62550 **Personnel:** 997

✠ △ **AURORA ST. LUKE'S MEDICAL CENTER (520138)**, 2900 West Oklahoma Avenue, Zip 53215–4330, Mailing Address: P.O. Box 2901, Zip 53201–2901; tel. 414/649–6000, (Includes AURORA ST. LUKE'S SOUTH SHORE, 5900 South Lake Drive, Cudahy, Zip 53110–8903; tel. 414/769–9000) **A**1 2 3 5 7 8 10 **F**1 2 3 4 5 6 11 12 15 17 18 19 20 22 24 26 28 29 30 31 34 35 36 37 38 40 43 44 45 46 47 49 50 51 54 56 57 58 59 60 64 65 66 68 69 70 74 75 78 79 80 81 82 84 85 86 87 89 90 91 92 93 94 96 98 100 101 102 103 104 105 107 108 110 111 114 115 116 117 118 119 120 121 123 124 126 129 130 132 135 136 137 138 139 140 142 143 144 145 146 148 **P**6 **S** Aurora Health Care, Milwaukee, WI
Primary Contact: Marie Golanowski, R.N., MS, President
CFO: Nan Nelson, Senior Vice President Finance
CMO: Jeffrey A. Smith, M.D., Senior Vice President and Chief Medical Officer
CIO: Philip Loftus, Ph.D., Vice President and Chief Information Officer
CHR: Thomas C. Ter Horst, Vice President Human Resources
CNO: Faye Zwieg, Vice President and Chief Nursing Officer
Web address: www.aurorahealthcare.org
Control: Other not–for–profit (including NFP Corporation) **Service:** General Medical and Surgical

Staffed Beds: 732 **Admissions:** 34915 **Census:** 567 **Outpatient Visits:** 538474 **Births:** 0 **Total Expense ($000):** 1047631 **Payroll Expense ($000):** 290135 **Personnel:** 4596

✠ **CHILDREN'S HOSPITAL OF WISCONSIN (523300)**, 9000 West Wisconsin Avenue, Zip 53226–4810, Mailing Address: P.O. Box 1997, Zip 53201–1997; tel. 414/266–2000 **A**1 3 5 10 **F**12 20 22 24 28 29 34 36 38 40 43 51 60 61 64 72 75 77 78 81 82 86 87 88 89 93 99 100 104 107 108 111 119 130 131 136 137 138 140 141 **P**2 **S** Children's Hospital and Health System, Milwaukee, WI
Primary Contact: Peggy N. Troy, President and Chief Executive Officer
CFO: Marc Cadieux, Corporate Vice President and Chief Financial Officer
CMO: Michael Gutzeit, M.D., Chief Medical Officer
CIO: Michael B. Nauman, Chief Information Officer
CHR: Thomas Shanahan, Vice President, Human Resources
CNO: Nancy K. Korom, Chief Nursing Officer and Vice President
Web address: www.chw.org
Control: Other not–for–profit (including NFP Corporation) **Service:** Children's general

Staffed Beds: 297 **Admissions:** 10754 **Census:** 226 **Outpatient Visits:** 363792 **Births:** 0 **Total Expense ($000):** 557717 **Payroll Expense ($000):** 162423 **Personnel:** 2358

✠ △ **CLEMENT J. ZABLOCKI VETERANS AFFAIRS MEDICAL CENTER**, 5000 West National Avenue, Zip 53295–0001; tel. 414/384–2000, (Nonreporting) **A**1 2 3 5 7 **S** Department of Veterans Affairs, Washington, DC
Primary Contact: Daniel Zomchek, Ph.D., Executive Director
COO: James McClain, Deputy Director
CFO: John Lasota, Assistant Finance Officer
CMO: Michael Erdmann, M.D., Chief of Staff
CIO: Bryan Vail, Chief Information Officer
CHR: Kay Schwieger, Chief Human Resources Officer
CNO: Mary E. Brunn, R.N., Acting Associate Director Nursing
Web address: www.milwaukee.va.gov/
Control: Veterans Affairs, Government, federal **Service:** General Medical and Surgical

Staffed Beds: 637

✠ **COLUMBIA ST. MARY'S HOSPITAL MILWAUKEE (520051)**, 2301 North Lake Drive, Zip 53211–4508; tel. 414/291–1000, (Includes COLUMBIA ST. MARY'S COLUMBIA HOSPITAL, 2025 East Newport Avenue, Zip 53211–2990; tel. 414/961–3300; COLUMBIA ST. MARY'S MILWAUKEE HOSPITAL, 2323 North Lake Drive, Zip 53211–9682, Mailing Address: P.O. Box 503, Zip 53201–0503; tel. 414/291–1000), (Nonreporting) **A**1 2 3 5 10 **S** Ascension Health, Saint Louis, MO
Primary Contact: Travis Andersen, President and Chief Executive Officer
CFO: Rhonda Anderson, Executive Vice President Finance and Chief Financial Officer
CMO: David Shapiro, M.D., Vice President Medical Affairs and Chief Medical Officer
CIO: Mary Paul, Chief Information Officer
CHR: Cheryl Hill, Vice President Human Resources
Web address: www.columbia-stmarys.org
Control: Other not–for–profit (including NFP Corporation) **Service:** General Medical and Surgical

Staffed Beds: 266

✠ △ **FROEDTERT MEMORIAL LUTHERAN HOSPITAL (520177)**, 9200 West Wisconsin Avenue, Zip 53226–3596, Mailing Address: P.O. Box 26099, Zip 53226–0099; tel. 414/805–3000 **A**1 2 3 5 7 8 10 **F**3 6 12 13 15 17 18 20 22 24 26 29 30 31 34 35 37 38 40 43 44 45 46 47 48 49 50 51 52 54 55 56 57 58 59 60 61 64 68 70 74 75 76 77 78 79 80 81 84 85 86 87 90 91 92 93 94 95 96 97 98 100 107 108 110 111 113 114 115 116 117 118 119 120 121 123 124 126 129 130 131 132 134 135 136 137 138 139 140 141 142 145 146 147 148
Primary Contact: Catherine Buck, President
CFO: Scott Hawig, Senior Vice President Finance, Chief Financial Officer and Treasurer
CMO: Lee Biblo, M.D., Chief Medical Officer
CIO: Will Showalter, Senior Vice President and Chief Information Officer
CHR: Keith Allen, Senior Vice President and Chief Human Resources Officer
CNO: Kathleen Bechtel, MSN, Vice President Patient Care Services and Chief Nursing Officer
Web address: www.froedtert.com
Control: Other not–for–profit (including NFP Corporation) **Service:** General Medical and Surgical

Staffed Beds: 516 **Admissions:** 26749 **Census:** 395 **Outpatient Visits:** 698146 **Births:** 2272 **Total Expense ($000):** 1194856 **Payroll Expense ($000):** 286307 **Personnel:** 4703

★ **MILWAUKEE COUNTY BEHAVIORAL HEALTH DIVISION (524001)**, 9455 Watertown Plank Road, Zip 53226–3559; tel. 414/257–6995, (Total facility includes 1 beds in nursing home–type unit) **A**3 5 10 **F**66 87 98 99 100 102 103 104 105 128 130 146 **P**6
Primary Contact: Alicia Modjeska, Interim Administrator
COO: Steve Delgado, Operations Coordinator
CFO: Randy Oleszak, Director Fiscal Services
CMO: John Schneider, M.D., Medical Director
CIO: Chris Lindberg, Chief Information Officer
CHR: Ara Garcia, Manager Human Resources
CNO: Nancy Ann Marigomen, R.N., Director of Nursing
Web address: www.milwaukeecounty.org
Control: County–Government, nonfederal **Service:** Psychiatric

Staffed Beds: 59 **Admissions:** 1880 **Census:** 58 **Outpatient Visits:** 11213 **Births:** 0 **Total Expense ($000):** 163264 **Payroll Expense ($000):** 31645 **Personnel:** 477

✠ △ **SACRED HEART REHABILITATION INSTITUTE (523025)**, 2323 North Lake Drive, Zip 53211–4508; tel. 414/298–6750 **A**1 7 10 **F**9 29 34 54 64 75 77 86 90 93 100 102 103 130 131 **P**6 **S** Ascension Health, Saint Louis, MO
Primary Contact: Bill Heart, Chief Operating Officer
COO: Bill Heart, Chief Operating Officer
CFO: Rhonda Anderson, Executive Vice President Finance and Chief Financial Officer
CMO: David Shapiro, M.D., Vice President Medical Affairs and Chief Medical Officer
CIO: Mary Paul, Vice President and Chief Information Officer
CHR: Cheryl Hill, Vice President Human Resources
Web address: www.columbia-stmarys.org/SHRI
Control: Church–operated, Nongovernment, not–for profit **Service:** Rehabilitation

Staffed Beds: 31 **Admissions:** 312 **Census:** 14 **Outpatient Visits:** 10950 **Births:** 0 **Total Expense ($000):** 11416 **Payroll Expense ($000):** 5727 **Personnel:** 77

WI

Hospital, Medicare Provider Number, Address, Telephone, Approval, Facility, and Physician Codes, Health Care System

★ American Hospital Association (AHA) membership ◯ Healthcare Facilities Accreditation Program ⇑ Center for Improvement in Healthcare Quality Accreditation
□ The Joint Commission accreditation ◇ DNV Healthcare Inc. accreditation △ Commission on Accreditation of Rehabilitation Facilities (CARF) accreditation

✠ **SELECT SPECIALTY HOSPITAL–MILWAUKEE (522006)**, 8901 West Lincoln Avenue, 2nd Floor, Zip 53227–2409; Mailing Address: West Allis, tel. 414/328–7700 **A**1 10 **F**1 3 29 60 78 85 100 130 148 **S** Select Medical Corporation, Mechanicsburg, PA
Primary Contact: Mary Kay Diderrich, R.N., Chief Executive Officer
CMO: Matt Mathai, M.D., Medical Director
CHR: Chris Froh, Senior Coordinator Human Resources
CNO: Jane Cerra, Market Nurse Executive and Chief Nursing Officer
Web address: www.selectspecialtyhospitals.com/company/locations/milwaukee.aspx
Control: Corporation, Investor–owned, for–profit **Service:** Long–Term Acute Care hospital

Staffed Beds: 34 **Admissions:** 196 **Census:** 32 **Outpatient Visits:** 0 **Births:** 0 **Total Expense ($000):** 18573 **Payroll Expense ($000):** 6361 **Personnel:** 109

✠ **WHEATON FRANCISCAN HEALTHCARE – ST. FRANCIS (520078)**, 3237 South 16th Street, Zip 53215–4592; tel. 414/647–5000 **A**1 2 10 **F**9 13 15 20 22 24 28 29 34 38 40 54 56 64 72 75 76 77 78 80 81 82 86 87 93 98 100 101 102 103 104 107 108 111 118 119 130 131 144 147 **S** Ascension Health, Saint Louis, MO
Primary Contact: Coreen Dicus–Johnson, President
CFO: Aaron Bridgeland, Director Finance
CMO: Michelle Graham, M.D., Vice President Medical Affairs
CIO: Gregory Smith, Senior Vice President and Chief Information Officer
CHR: Robert Bauer, Vice President Human Resources
Web address: www.mywheaton.org/stfrancis
Control: Church–operated, Nongovernment, not–for profit **Service:** General Medical and Surgical

Staffed Beds: 177 **Admissions:** 8303 **Census:** 115 **Outpatient Visits:** 165753 **Births:** 934 **Total Expense ($000):** 176975 **Payroll Expense ($000):** 67556 **Personnel:** 795

✠ **WHEATON FRANCISCAN HEALTHCARE – ST. JOSEPH'S (520136)**, 5000 West Chambers Street, Zip 53210–1650; tel. 414/447–2000 **A**1 2 3 5 10 **F**3 6 8 11 13 15 17 18 20 22 24 26 28 29 30 31 33 34 35 37 40 41 43 45 46 48 49 50 53 54 56 58 59 64 65 68 70 72 74 75 76 77 79 80 81 82 83 84 85 87 89 90 91 92 93 94 95 96 97 107 108 109 110 111 112 113 114 115 117 118 119 129 130 131 133 143 144 145 146 147 148 **P**6 **S** Ascension Health, Saint Louis, MO
Primary Contact: Debra K. Standridge, President
CFO: Michael Petitt, Director of Finance
CMO: Rita Hanson, M.D., Vice President Medical Affairs
CIO: Andrew Donovan, Regional Director Information Services
CHR: Christopher Morris, Vice President Human Resources
CNO: Sharon Baughman, R.N., Senior Vice President Patient Services and Chief Nursing Officer
Web address: www.mywheaton.org/stjoseph
Control: Church–operated, Nongovernment, not–for profit **Service:** General Medical and Surgical

Staffed Beds: 205 **Admissions:** 8521 **Census:** 126 **Outpatient Visits:** 307647 **Births:** 2366 **Total Expense ($000):** 244192 **Payroll Expense ($000):** 90600 **Personnel:** 1158

MONROE—Green County

☐ **MONROE CLINIC (520028)**, 515 22nd Avenue, Zip 53566–1598; tel. 608/324–2000 **A**1 3 10 13 **F**3 5 6 8 9 13 15 17 18 20 22 26 28 29 30 31 32 34 35 37 38 40 43 44 45 46 49 50 55 56 57 59 62 63 65 68 70 74 75 76 77 79 80 81 82 84 85 86 90 93 97 99 100 101 102 103 104 107 108 110 111 112 115 117 119 126 129 130 131 132 135 144 145 146 147 148 **P**6
Primary Contact: Michael B. Sanders, President and Chief Executive Officer
CFO: Jim Nemeth, Chief Financial Officer
CMO: Mark Thompson, M.D., Chief Medical Officer
CIO: Carrie Blum, Chief Information Officer
CHR: Jane Monahan, Vice President Ministry, Spiritual Care and Human Resources
CNO: Paula Elmer, R.N., Vice President and Chief Nursing Officer
Web address: www.monroeclinic.org
Control: Other not–for–profit (including NFP Corporation) **Service:** General Medical and Surgical

Staffed Beds: 58 **Admissions:** 2592 **Census:** 23 **Outpatient Visits:** 268640 **Births:** 497 **Total Expense ($000):** 163764 **Payroll Expense ($000):** 81091 **Personnel:** 998

NEENAH—Winnebago County

☐ **CHILDREN'S HOSPITAL OF WISCONSIN–FOX VALLEY (523302)**, 130 Second Street, Zip 54956–2883; tel. 920/969–7900 **A**1 10 **F**29 34 38 72 75 77 86 89 93 100 130 **P**6 **S** Children's Hospital and Health System, Milwaukee, WI
Primary Contact: Peggy N. Troy, President and Chief Executive Officer
COO: Debra Franckowiak, Executive Director
CFO: Marc Cadieux, Corporate Vice President and Chief Financial Ofcr
CMO: Paul Myers, M.D., Neonatologist and Chief Medical Officer
CIO: Michael B. Nauman, Chief Information Officer and Corporate Vice President
CHR: Thomas Shanahan, Vice President, Human Resources
CNO: Nancy K. Korom, Chief Nursing Officer and Vice President
Web address: www.chw.org
Control: Other not–for–profit (including NFP Corporation) **Service:** Children's general

Staffed Beds: 42 **Admissions:** 1991 **Census:** 18 **Outpatient Visits:** 10641 **Births:** 0 **Total Expense ($000):** 23809 **Payroll Expense ($000):** 8994 **Personnel:** 113

☐ **THEDA CLARK MEDICAL CENTER (520045)**, 130 Second Street, Zip 54956–2883, Mailing Address: P.O. Box 2021, Zip 54957–2021; tel. 920/729–3100 **A**1 2 3 10 **F**4 5 7 9 11 13 15 17 20 22 28 29 34 36 40 43 51 53 55 56 60 64 69 70 75 76 78 80 82 86 87 88 90 93 98 99 101 102 103 104 105 107 108 111 118 119 130 144 147 **S** ThedaCare, Inc., Appleton, WI
Primary Contact: Brian Burmeister, Senior Vice President, ThedaCare Hospitals
CFO: Tim Olson, Senior Vice President Finance
CMO: Gregory L. Long, M.D., Chief Medical Officer
CIO: Keith Livingston, Senior Vice President and Chief Information Officer
CHR: Maureen Pistone, Senior Vice President Human Resources
Web address: www.thedacare.org
Control: Other not–for–profit (including NFP Corporation) **Service:** General Medical and Surgical

Staffed Beds: 151 **Admissions:** 7663 **Census:** 90 **Outpatient Visits:** 89802 **Births:** 1349 **Total Expense ($000):** 162977 **Payroll Expense ($000):** 64262 **Personnel:** 999

NEILLSVILLE—Clark County

★ **MEMORIAL MEDICAL CENTER – NEILLSVILLE (521323)**, 216 Sunset Place, Zip 54456–1799; tel. 715/743–3101, (Includes NEILLSVILLE MEMORIAL HOME), (Total facility includes 16 beds in nursing home–type unit) **A**10 18 **F**3 6 10 11 15 28 30 34 40 41 43 45 50 54 55 56 59 64 66 75 77 79 80 81 85 86 87 89 93 96 97 107 108 110 111 115 119 127 130 131 132 133 144 146 147 **P**6
Primary Contact: Ryan T. Neville, FACHE, President and Chief Executive Officer
CFO: Roger Sneath, Chief Financial Officer
CMO: Timothy Meyer, M.D., Chief of Staff
CIO: Derrick Longdo, Director Information Systems
CHR: Tamie Zarak, Director Human Resources
Web address: www.memorialmedcenter.org
Control: Other not–for–profit (including NFP Corporation) **Service:** General Medical and Surgical

Staffed Beds: 32 **Admissions:** 300 **Census:** 16 **Outpatient Visits:** 22717 **Births:** 0 **Total Expense ($000):** 24474 **Payroll Expense ($000):** 12735 **Personnel:** 191

NEW LONDON—Outagamie County

☐ **THEDACARE MEDICAL CENTER–NEW LONDON (521326)**, 1405 Mill Street, Zip 54961–0307, Mailing Address: P.O. Box 307, Zip 54961–0307; tel. 920/531–2000 **A**1 10 18 **F**3 7 8 11 13 15 28 29 34 35 40 43 44 45 47 56 59 64 65 68 75 76 79 80 81 82 83 85 86 87 89 90 91 93 107 108 110 111 112 115 119 127 131 132 133 135 141 146 148 **S** ThedaCare, Inc., Appleton, WI
Primary Contact: William Schmidt, President and Chief Executive Officer
CFO: Betty Gehring, Finance Director, Operations
CMO: Paul Hoell, M.D., President Medical Staff
CNO: Peggy School, Director of Nursing
Web address: www.thedacare.org
Control: Other not–for–profit (including NFP Corporation) **Service:** General Medical and Surgical

Staffed Beds: 25 **Admissions:** 759 **Census:** 10 **Outpatient Visits:** 30612 **Births:** 88 **Total Expense ($000):** 22808 **Payroll Expense ($000):** 11656 **Personnel:** 138

WI

NEW RICHMOND—St. Croix County

★ **WESTFIELDS HOSPITAL (521345)**, 535 Hospital Road, Zip 54017–1449; tel. 715/243–2600 **A**10 18 **F**1 3 13 15 28 29 30 31 32 34 35 38 40 43 44 45 47 50 56 57 59 64 68 70 74 75 76 77 78 79 80 81 82 84 86 87 89 90 93 97 107 109 110 111 115 117 119 129 130 131 132 133 145 146 148 **P**8 **S** HealthPartners, Bloomington, MN
Primary Contact: Steven Massey, President and Chief Executive Officer
CFO: Jason J. Luhrs, Vice President Fiscal Services
CMO: David O. DeGear, M.D., Vice President Medical Affairs
CIO: Patrice P. Wolff, Director Information Services
CHR: Chad P. Engstrom, Director Human Resources
Web address: www.westfieldshospital.com
Control: Other not–for–profit (including NFP Corporation) **Service:** General Medical and Surgical

> **Staffed Beds:** 25 **Admissions:** 782 **Census:** 6 **Outpatient Visits:** 80699 **Births:** 129 **Total Expense ($000):** 47328 **Payroll Expense ($000):** 16696 **Personnel:** 263

OCONOMOWOC—Waukesha County

✠ **OCONOMOWOC MEMORIAL HOSPITAL (520062)**, 791 Summit Avenue, Zip 53066–3896; tel. 262/569–9400 **A**1 2 10 **F**3 11 13 15 18 20 22 28 29 30 31 35 37 40 45 46 47 48 49 64 74 75 76 78 79 80 81 82 84 85 87 89 92 93 107 108 110 111 114 115 118 119 120 121 126 130 132 135 146 147 148 **S** ProHealth Care, Inc., Waukesha, WI
Primary Contact: Susan A. Edwards, Chief Executive Officer
COO: Mary Jo O'Malley, R.N., Vice President Diagnostics and Support Services
CMO: Brian Lipman, M.D., Medical Director and Medical Staff Services
CIO: Christine Bessler, Vice President Information Services
CHR: Edward Malindzak, Chief Human Resources Officer
CNO: Catherine Rapp, R.N., Vice President Nursing
Web address: www.prohealthcare.org/locations/locations–v2–detail/?id=1123
Control: Other not–for–profit (including NFP Corporation) **Service:** General Medical and Surgical

> **Staffed Beds:** 58 **Admissions:** 3016 **Census:** 24 **Outpatient Visits:** 72248 **Births:** 408 **Total Expense ($000):** 90175 **Payroll Expense ($000):** 21163 **Personnel:** 298

✠ **ROGERS MEMORIAL HOSPITAL (524018)**, 34700 Valley Road, Zip 53066–4599; tel. 262/646–4411, (Includes ROGERS MEMORIAL HOSPITAL–BROWN DEER, 4600 West Schroeder Drive, Brown Deer, Zip 53223; tel. 414/865–2500; Jim Kubicek, Vice President, Operations; ROGERS MEMORIAL HOSPITAL–WEST ALLIS, 11101 West Lincoln Avenue, West Allis, Zip 53227; tel. 414/327–3000; T. Orvin Fillman, Dr.PH, Vice President, Operations) **A**1 3 10 **F**5 29 34 38 56 75 86 87 98 99 100 101 102 103 104 105 130
Primary Contact: Paul A. Mueller, Chief Executive Officer
COO: Paul A. Mueller, Chief Operating Officer
CFO: Gerald A. Noll, Chief Financial Officer
CMO: Peter M. Lake, M.D., Chief Medical Officer
CIO: Wayne Mattson, Management Information Systems Specialist
CHR: Renee A. Patterson, Vice President Employment and Training Services
CNO: Teresa L. Schultz, R.N., Vice President of Patient Care
Web address: www.rogershospital.org
Control: Other not–for–profit (including NFP Corporation) **Service:** Psychiatric

> **Staffed Beds:** 208 **Admissions:** 15423 **Census:** 119 **Outpatient Visits:** 113767 **Births:** 0 **Total Expense ($000):** 96454 **Payroll Expense ($000):** 58568 **Personnel:** 2067

OCONTO—Oconto County

◇ **BELLIN HEALTH OCONTO HOSPITAL (521356)**, 820 Arbutus Avenue, Zip 54153–2004, Mailing Address: P.O. Box 357, Zip 54153–0357; tel. 920/835–1100 **A**10 18 21 **F**3 15 18 29 31 32 34 35 40 42 43 44 45 46 47 51 59 62 64 65 68 71 78 79 80 81 85 92 97 99 100 101 104 107 110 111 115 119 127 129 130 132 133 135 144 146 147 **P**8
Primary Contact: Laura Cormier, Director
Web address: www.bellin.org/facilities_amenities/oconto_hospital_medical_center/
Control: Other not–for–profit (including NFP Corporation) **Service:** General Medical and Surgical

> **Staffed Beds:** 10 **Admissions:** 141 **Census:** 1 **Outpatient Visits:** 15838 **Births:** 0 **Total Expense ($000):** 14052 **Payroll Expense ($000):** 4890 **Personnel:** 67

OCONTO FALLS—Oconto County

★ **HSHS ST. CLARE MEMORIAL HOSPITAL (521310)**, 855 South Main Street, Zip 54154–1296; tel. 920/846–3444 **A**10 18 **F**3 11 15 28 29 30 34 35 40 43 44 50 56 57 59 64 65 68 75 77 79 80 81 85 86 87 89 90 96 97 107 108 110 111 114 119 127 129 130 132 133 144 146 147 148 **P**2 5 **S** Hospital Sisters Health System, Springfield, IL
Primary Contact: Therese Handl, Chief Executive Officer
COO: Daniel DeGroot, Chief Operating Officer
CFO: Greg Simia, Chief Financial Officer
CMO: Ken Johnson, Chief Physician Executive
CIO: Shane Miller, Chief Information Officer
CHR: Christine Jensema, Chief People Officer
CNO: Kay Baranczyk, R.N., Chief Nursing Officer
Web address: www.cmhospital.org/index.html
Control: Other not–for–profit (including NFP Corporation) **Service:** General Medical and Surgical

> **Staffed Beds:** 9 **Admissions:** 664 **Census:** 7 **Outpatient Visits:** 24040 **Births:** 0 **Total Expense ($000):** 36394 **Payroll Expense ($000):** 14567 **Personnel:** 107

OSCEOLA—Polk County

OSCEOLA MEDICAL CENTER (521318), 2600 65th Avenue, Zip 54020–4370, Mailing Address: P.O. Box 218, Zip 54020–0218; tel. 715/294–2111 **A**10 18 **F**3 8 11 13 15 18 28 29 30 31 34 40 41 42 43 45 50 53 56 57 58 59 64 65 68 70 74 75 76 77 78 79 81 86 87 89 93 107 110 111 115 119 129 133 135 144 **P**6
Primary Contact: Tom G. Geskermann, Chief Executive Officer
CMO: Rene Milner, Chief Medical Officer
CIO: Shawn Kammerud, Manager Information Services
CHR: Margie Evenson, Manager Human Resources
Web address: www.osceolamedicalcenter.com
Control: Other not–for–profit (including NFP Corporation) **Service:** General Medical and Surgical

> **Staffed Beds:** 18 **Admissions:** 499 **Census:** 4 **Outpatient Visits:** 16227 **Births:** 77 **Total Expense ($000):** 31616 **Payroll Expense ($000):** 11067 **Personnel:** 187

OSHKOSH—Winnebago County

✠ **AURORA MEDICAL CENTER OF OSHKOSH (520198)**, 855 North Westhaven Drive, Zip 54904–7668; tel. 920/456–6000 **A**1 2 10 **F**3 8 11 12 13 15 17 18 20 22 26 29 30 34 37 40 43 47 49 53 54 56 60 64 68 70 71 74 75 76 78 79 80 81 82 85 86 87 89 92 93 94 107 108 109 110 111 113 114 115 117 118 119 120 121 122 123 129 130 131 145 146 147 148 **P**6 **S** Aurora Health Care, Milwaukee, WI
Primary Contact: Jeffrey Bard, President
CFO: Sandra Ewald, Vice President Finance
CMO: Bruce L. Van Cleave, M.D., Senior Vice President and Chief Medical Officer
CIO: Philip Loftus, Ph.D., Vice President and Chief Information Officer
CHR: Linda Mingus, Director Human Resources
CNO: Mary Beth Kingston, R.N., Executive Vice President and Chief Nursing Officer
Web address: www.aurorahealthcare.com
Control: Other not–for–profit (including NFP Corporation) **Service:** General Medical and Surgical

> **Staffed Beds:** 61 **Admissions:** 3072 **Census:** 25 **Outpatient Visits:** 128295 **Births:** 607 **Total Expense ($000):** 95947 **Payroll Expense ($000):** 26799 **Personnel:** 457

✠ △ **MERCY MEDICAL CENTER (520048)**, 500 South Oakwood Road, Zip 54904–7944; tel. 920/223–2000 **A**1 2 7 10 **F**4 5 11 13 15 16 17 20 22 28 29 34 38 40 43 51 53 56 64 70 75 76 78 80 81 82 86 87 88 89 90 93 98 103 104 107 108 111 119 130 131 144 147 **S** Ascension Health, Saint Louis, MO
Primary Contact: Jeremy Normington–Slay, FACHE, Chief Executive Officer
CFO: Jeff Badger, Chief Financial Officer
CMO: Mark W. Kehrberg, M.D., Senior Vice President and Chief Medical Officer
CIO: Will Weider, Chief Information Officer
CHR: Vince Gallucci, Senior Vice President Human Resources
Web address: www.affinityhealth.org
Control: Church–operated, Nongovernment, not–for profit **Service:** General Medical and Surgical

> **Staffed Beds:** 120 **Admissions:** 4966 **Census:** 51 **Outpatient Visits:** 140000 **Births:** 615 **Total Expense ($000):** 97201 **Payroll Expense ($000):** 40389 **Personnel:** 427

WI

Hospital, Medicare Provider Number, Address, Telephone, Approval, Facility, and Physician Codes, Health Care System

★ American Hospital Association (AHA) membership   ◯ Healthcare Facilities Accreditation Program   ⇑ Center for Improvement in Healthcare Quality Accreditation
☐ The Joint Commission accreditation   ◇ DNV Healthcare Inc. accreditation   △ Commission on Accreditation of Rehabilitation Facilities (CARF) accreditation

OSSEO—Trempealeau County

☐ **MAYO CLINIC HEALTH SYSTEM – OAKRIDGE IN OSSEO (521302)**, 13025 Eighth Street, Zip 54758–7634, Mailing Address: P.O. Box 70, Zip 54758–0070; tel. 715/597–3121, (Total facility includes 35 beds in nursing home–type unit) **A**1 10 18 **F**3 15 18 28 29 30 32 34 35 40 43 44 45 53 54 57 59 63 64 65 75 77 80 84 85 86 87 90 93 97 107 110 115 128 130 132 133 135 143 144 146 148 **P**6 **S** Mayo Clinic, Rochester, MN
Primary Contact: Dean Eide, Vice President
Web address: www.mayoclinichealthsystem.org/locations/osseo
Control: Other not–for–profit (including NFP Corporation) **Service:** General Medical and Surgical

Staffed Beds: 39 **Admissions:** 333 **Census:** 37 **Outpatient Visits:** 25792 **Births:** 0 **Total Expense ($000):** 21676 **Payroll Expense ($000):** 10990 **Personnel:** 163

PARK FALLS—Price County

★ **FLAMBEAU HOSPITAL (521325)**, 98 Sherry Avenue, Zip 54552–1467, Mailing Address: P.O. Box 310, Zip 54552–0310; tel. 715/762–2484 **A**10 18 **F**11 15 28 29 34 40 53 56 62 63 64 69 75 77 80 81 82 86 87 89 90 93 107 108 119 130 131
Primary Contact: James R. Braun, Chief Administrative Officer and Chief Financial Officer
CFO: James R. Braun, Chief Administrative Officer and Chief Financial Officer
CMO: Yusuf Kasirye, M.D., Chief of Staff
CHR: Elizabeth Harrop, Director, Human Resources
CNO: Elizabeth Schreiber, R.N., Director Patient Care Services
Web address: www.flambeauhospital.org
Control: Other not–for–profit (including NFP Corporation) **Service:** General Medical and Surgical

Staffed Beds: 25 **Admissions:** 603 **Census:** 5 **Outpatient Visits:** 27963 **Births:** 0 **Total Expense ($000):** 19912 **Payroll Expense ($000):** 8528 **Personnel:** 168

PEWAUKEE—Waukesha County

☒ **LIFECARE HOSPITALS OF WISCONSIN (522007)**, 2400 Golf Road, Zip 53072–5590; tel. 262/524–2600 **A**1 10 **F**1 3 29 34 77 86 90 96 107 130 148 **P**5 **S** LifeCare Management Services, Plano, TX
Primary Contact: Gayla Campbell, Interim Chief Executive Officer
CMO: John Daniels, M.D., Medical Director
CHR: Stephanie Matter, Manager Human Resources
CNO: Angela Osowski, Chief Nursing Officer
Web address: www.lifecare–hospitals.com
Control: Corporation, Investor–owned, for–profit **Service:** Long–Term Acute Care hospital

Staffed Beds: 27 **Admissions:** 378 **Census:** 27 **Outpatient Visits:** 0 **Births:** 0 **Total Expense ($000):** 20578 **Payroll Expense ($000):** 9136 **Personnel:** 117

PLATTEVILLE—Grant County

☒ **SOUTHWEST HEALTH (521354)**, 1400 Eastside Road, Zip 53818–9800; tel. 608/348–2331, (Includes SOUTHWEST HEALTH CENTER NURSING HOME, 808 South Washington Street, Cuba City, Zip 53807; tel. 608/744–2161), (Total facility includes 84 beds in nursing home–type unit) **A**1 10 18 **F**2 3 6 8 13 15 28 29 34 40 43 45 46 47 48 49 50 56 57 58 59 64 65 74 75 76 77 79 80 81 82 83 84 85 86 87 93 96 97 98 100 101 102 103 104 105 106 107 110 111 112 115 119 127 128 130 132 133 143 144 146 148
Primary Contact: Dan D. Rohrbach, President and Chief Executive Officer
CFO: Matthew Streeter, Chief Financial Officer
CMO: Andrew Klann, D.O., Chief of Staff
CIO: Todd Lull, Director Information Technology
CHR: Holly Beehn, Director Human Resources
CNO: Suzi Okey, Director of Nursing
Web address: www.southwesthealth.org
Control: Other not–for–profit (including NFP Corporation) **Service:** General Medical and Surgical

Staffed Beds: 119 **Admissions:** 847 **Census:** 87 **Outpatient Visits:** 47542 **Births:** 160 **Total Expense ($000):** 32730 **Payroll Expense ($000):** 17475 **Personnel:** 270

PLEASANT PRAIRIE—Kenosha County

★ **UNITED HOSPITAL SYSTEM, ST. CATHERINE'S MEDICAL CENTER CAMPUS**, 9555 76th Street, Zip 53158–1984; tel. 262/656–2011, (Nonreporting) **S** Ascension Health, Saint Louis, MO
Primary Contact: Richard O. Schmidt, Jr., President and Chief Executive Officer
Web address: www.uhsi.org
Control: Other not–for–profit (including NFP Corporation) **Service:** General Medical and Surgical

Staffed Beds: 202

PORTAGE—Columbia County

☐ **DIVINE SAVIOR HEALTHCARE (520041)**, 2817 New Pinery Road, Zip 53901–9240, Mailing Address: P.O. Box 387, Zip 53901–0387; tel. 608/742–4131, (Total facility includes 123 beds in nursing home–type unit) **A**1 10 **F**4 7 11 12 13 15 28 34 36 40 43 54 55 60 62 64 69 70 75 76 77 78 80 81 82 86 87 90 93 107 108 111 118 119 128 130 131 144 147 **P**6
Primary Contact: Michael Decker, President and Chief Executive Officer
CFO: Marlin Pete Nelson, Vice President Fiscal Services
CMO: Elizabeth Strabel, M.D., Chief Medical Staff
CHR: Carol J. Bank, Vice President Human Resources
Web address: www.dshealthcare.com
Control: Church–operated, Nongovernment, not–for profit **Service:** General Medical and Surgical

Staffed Beds: 133 **Admissions:** 1955 **Census:** 112 **Outpatient Visits:** 158875 **Births:** 209 **Total Expense ($000):** 70588 **Payroll Expense ($000):** 38347 **Personnel:** 613

PRAIRIE DU CHIEN—Crawford County

☒ **CROSSING RIVERS HEALTH MEDICAL CENTER (521330)**, 37868 U.S. Highway 18, Zip 53821–8416; tel. 608/357–2000 **A**1 10 18 **F**1 10 11 13 15 17 28 29 34 36 40 43 53 56 62 63 64 70 75 76 80 81 82 86 87 93 107 108 111 119 130 131 144 147
Primary Contact: William P. Sexton, Chief Executive Officer
CFO: Dave Breitbach, Chief Financial Officer
CMO: Steven Bush, Chief Medical Officer
CIO: John Daane, Information Systems Officer
CHR: Samantha Donahue, Director Human Resources
Web address: www.crossingrivers.org
Control: Other not–for–profit (including NFP Corporation) **Service:** General Medical and Surgical

Staffed Beds: 17 **Admissions:** 945 **Census:** 9 **Outpatient Visits:** 10759 **Births:** 113 **Total Expense ($000):** 46238 **Payroll Expense ($000):** 19177 **Personnel:** 285

PRAIRIE DU SAC—Sauk County

○ **SAUK PRAIRIE HEALTHCARE (520095)**, 260 26th Street, Zip 53578–1599; tel. 608/643–3311 **A**3 10 11 **F**3 11 13 15 29 36 40 43 47 48 53 56 69 75 76 79 80 81 85 86 90 93 97 107 108 110 111 115 118 119 127 129 130 131 132 133 135 144 146 147 **P**7
Primary Contact: Larry Schroeder, Chief Executive Officer
CFO: James Dregney, Vice President Finance and Operations, Chief Financial Officer
CMO: John McAuliffe, M.D., Medical Director
CHR: Robbi E. Bos, Vice President Human Resources
CNO: Denise Marie Cole–Ouzounian, Vice President Patient Services
Web address: www.saukprairiehealthcare.org/
Control: Other not–for–profit (including NFP Corporation) **Service:** General Medical and Surgical

Staffed Beds: 36 **Admissions:** 185 **Census:** 11 **Outpatient Visits:** 111043 **Births:** 316 **Total Expense ($000):** 82906 **Payroll Expense ($000):** 36622 **Personnel:** 456

RACINE—Racine County

☒ △ **WHEATON FRANCISCAN HEALTHCARE – ALL SAINTS (520096)**, 3801 Spring Street, Zip 53405–1690; tel. 262/687–4011, (Total facility includes 50 beds in nursing home–type unit) **A**1 2 7 10 **F**3 4 5 6 13 15 17 18 20 22 24 26 28 29 30 31 33 34 35 38 40 44 45 46 48 49 50 51 53 55 56 57 58 59 64 65 68 70 71 72 74 75 76 77 78 79 80 81 82 85 86 87 89 90 91 92 93 96 97 98 99 100 101 102 103 104 105 107 108 110 111 112 115 116 118 119 120 121 123 124 126 128 129 130 131 132 134 135 146 147 148 **P**6 **S** Ascension Health, Saint Louis, MO
Primary Contact: Susan Boland, R.N., MSN, President and Chief Executive Officer
CFO: Jeanne Gramza, Director Finance
CMO: Jerry Hardacre, M.D., Chief of Staff
CIO: Joanne Bisterfeldt, Chief Information Officer
CHR: Mary Jo Wodicka, Vice President Human Resources
CNO: Mary Elizabeth Ouimet, MSN, Senior Vice President and Chief Nursing Officer
Web address: www.allsaintshealth.com
Control: Church–operated, Nongovernment, not–for profit **Service:** General Medical and Surgical

Staffed Beds: 365 **Admissions:** 14356 **Census:** 225 **Outpatient Visits:** 592906 **Births:** 1699 **Total Expense ($000):** 314080 **Payroll Expense ($000):** 113819 **Personnel:** 2083

WI

Many Facility Codes have changed. Please refer to the AHA Guide Code Chart.   © 2016 AHA Guide

REEDSBURG—Sauk County

⊠ **REEDSBURG AREA MEDICAL CENTER (521351)**, 2000 North Dewey Street, Zip 53959–1097; tel. 608/524–6487 **A**1 10 18 **F**11 13 15 17 28 29 34 40 43 53 54 64 70 75 76 77 78 80 81 82 86 87 88 89 93 107 111 130 131 144 147 **P**2
Primary Contact: Robert Van Meeteren, President and Chief Executive Officer
COO: Dale Turner, Chief Operating Officer
CFO: Barry Borchert, Vice President Finance
Web address: www.ramchealth.com
Control: Other not–for–profit (including NFP Corporation) **Service:** General Medical and Surgical

Staffed Beds: 25 **Admissions:** 1443 **Census:** 13 **Outpatient Visits:** 81846
Births: 268 **Total Expense ($000):** 58624 **Payroll Expense ($000):** 24802
Personnel: 447

RHINELANDER—Oneida County

⊠ **MINISTRY SAINT MARY'S HOSPITALS (520019)**, 2251 North Shore Drive, Zip 54501–6710; tel. 715/361–2000, (Includes ST. MARY'S HOSPITAL, 1044 Kabel Avenue, Zip 54501; tel. 715/369–6600) **A**1 10 20 **F**3 4 5 13 15 18 28 29 30 31 34 35 40 44 45 49 50 54 57 59 64 65 68 74 75 76 77 78 79 80 81 82 84 85 86 87 89 91 92 93 94 96 98 99 100 101 103 104 107 108 110 111 115 116 117 119 120 121 123 130 131 132 144 146 148 **S** Ascension Health, Saint Louis, MO
Primary Contact: Sandra L. Anderson, President and Chief Executive Officer
COO: Laurie Oungst, Vice President and Chief Operating Officer
CFO: Jamon Lamers, Director Finance
CMO: Dean Pollnow, M.D., President Medical Staff
CIO: Howard Dobizl, Director Information Services for the Northern Region
CHR: Michelle Cornelius, Director Human Resources for the Northern Region
CNO: Ann Zenk, Vice President Patient Care Services
Web address: www.ministryhealth.org
Control: Church–operated, Nongovernment, not–for profit **Service:** General Medical and Surgical

Staffed Beds: 60 **Admissions:** 3052 **Census:** 29 **Outpatient Visits:** 109460
Births: 311 **Total Expense ($000):** 121808 **Payroll Expense ($000):** 62449
Personnel: 488

RICE LAKE—Barron County

⊠ **LAKEVIEW MEDICAL CENTER (520011)**, 1700 West Stout Street, Zip 54868–5000; tel. 715/234–1515 **A**1 10 20 **F**3 7 8 11 13 15 18 22 26 28 29 31 32 34 35 40 43 45 51 53 56 57 59 60 62 63 64 65 68 70 75 76 77 78 79 80 81 82 84 85 86 89 93 107 111 115 119 124 129 130 132 135 146 147 **P**5
Primary Contact: Edward H. Wolf, President and Chief Executive Officer
COO: Cindy Arts–Strenke, R.N., Chief Operating Officer and Chief Nursing Officer
CFO: Jacqueline Klein, Chief Financial Officer
CMO: John L. Olson, M.D., Medical Director
CIO: Brad Gerrits, Director Information Systems
CHR: Kathy Mitchell, Director Human Resources
Web address: www.lakeviewmedical.com
Control: Other not–for–profit (including NFP Corporation) **Service:** General Medical and Surgical

Staffed Beds: 40 **Admissions:** 2367 **Census:** 18 **Outpatient Visits:** 110736
Births: 468 **Total Expense ($000):** 67161 **Payroll Expense ($000):** 22275
Personnel: 404

RICHLAND CENTER—Richland County

⊠ **RICHLAND HOSPITAL (521341)**, 333 East Second Street, Zip 53581–1914; tel. 608/647–6321 **A**1 10 18 **F**2 3 8 12 13 15 18 28 31 34 35 40 43 45 46 50 56 57 58 59 64 65 66 68 70 76 78 79 80 81 85 86 89 92 93 97 107 110 114 119 127 129 130 131 132 133 135 143 144 146 148
Primary Contact: Bruce E. Roesler, FACHE, Chief Executive Officer
CFO: Karen Traynor, Chief Financial Officer
CMO: David May, Chief of Staff
CIO: Jerry Cooper, Manager Data Processing
CHR: Rhonda Sutton, Director Human Resources
CNO: Cindy Hanold, Chief Nursing Officer
Web address: www.richlandhospital.com
Control: Other not–for–profit (including NFP Corporation) **Service:** General Medical and Surgical

Staffed Beds: 25 **Admissions:** 1156 **Census:** 10 **Outpatient Visits:** 37307
Births: 186 **Total Expense ($000):** 35779 **Payroll Expense ($000):** 16004
Personnel: 248

RIPON—Fond Du Lac County

☐ **RIPON MEDICAL CENTER (521321)**, 845 Parkside Street, Zip 54971–8505, Mailing Address: P.O. Box 390, Zip 54971–0390; tel. 920/748–3101 **A**1 10 18 **F**3 11 13 15 17 18 28 29 30 31 32 34 35 40 43 44 45 50 51 53 57 59 68 69 70 75 76 77 79 80 81 82 85 86 87 88 89 93 96 97 107 108 109 110 111 114 118 119 130 131 132 133 134 135 143 144 146 147 148 **P**6
Primary Contact: Katherine Vergos, Chief Operating Officer
COO: Katherine Vergos, Chief Operating Officer
CFO: Bonnie Schmitz, Chief Financial Officer
CIO: Nancy Birschbach, Vice President and Chief Information Officer
CHR: Sue Edminster, Vice President Human Resources
Web address: www.agnesian.com
Control: Church–operated, Nongovernment, not–for profit **Service:** General Medical and Surgical

Staffed Beds: 18 **Admissions:** 507 **Census:** 5 **Outpatient Visits:** 29472
Births: 36 **Total Expense ($000):** 24366 **Payroll Expense ($000):** 10398
Personnel: 120

RIVER FALLS—St. Croix County

⊠ **RIVER FALLS AREA HOSPITAL (521349)**, 1629 East Division Street, Zip 54022–1571; tel. 715/425–6155 **A**1 2 10 18 **F**3 13 15 28 29 30 31 34 35 40 43 45 50 53 64 65 68 76 78 79 80 81 82 84 86 87 89 90 93 107 114 117 129 130 131 133 146 148 **S** Allina Health, Minneapolis, MN
Primary Contact: David R. Miller, President
COO: William Frommelt, Director Operations and Finance
CFO: William Frommelt, Director Operations and Finance
CHR: Kristen Novak, Manager Human Resources
Web address: www.allina.com
Control: Other not–for–profit (including NFP Corporation) **Service:** General Medical and Surgical

Staffed Beds: 10 **Admissions:** 868 **Census:** 8 **Outpatient Visits:** 22701
Births: 168 **Total Expense ($000):** 34406 **Payroll Expense ($000):** 12990
Personnel: 146

SHAWANO—Shawano County

⊠ **THEDACARE MEDICAL CENTER–SHAWANO (521346)**, 100 County Road B., Zip 54166–2127; tel. 715/526–2111 **A**1 10 18 **F**11 13 15 28 29 34 40 53 64 75 76 77 78 80 81 82 86 87 90 102 107 108 111 119 130 131 147 **S** ThedaCare, Inc., Appleton, WI
Primary Contact: Dorothy Erdmann, Chief Executive Officer
CFO: Kerry Lee Blanke, Chief Financial Officer
CMO: Mindy Frimodig, D.O., President Medical Staff ThedaCare Physicians Shawano
CIO: Jennifer Quinn, Quality and Safety Coordinator
CNO: Patricia A. Angelucci, MS, Director Patient Care Services
Web address: www.shawanomed.org
Control: Other not–for–profit (including NFP Corporation) **Service:** General Medical and Surgical

Staffed Beds: 22 **Admissions:** 1560 **Census:** 13 **Outpatient Visits:** 48850
Births: 266 **Total Expense ($000):** 41366 **Payroll Expense ($000):** 17277
Personnel: 229

SHEBOYGAN—Sheboygan County

⊠ **AURORA SHEBOYGAN MEMORIAL MEDICAL CENTER (520035)**, 2629 North Seventh Street, Zip 53083–4998; tel. 920/451–5000 **A**1 2 10 **F**3 4 8 13 17 18 20 22 26 28 29 30 31 32 34 35 36 40 41 43 44 45 49 50 53 54 56 57 59 60 64 65 68 70 72 74 75 76 78 79 80 81 82 85 86 87 89 90 93 94 96 98 99 100 102 103 104 105 107 108 111 112 114 115 118 119 120 121 123 129 130 131 132 135 146 147 148 **P**6 **S** Aurora Health Care, Milwaukee, WI
Primary Contact: David Graebner, President
CFO: Pamela Ott, Vice President Finance
CMO: Andrea Gavin, M.D., Chief Medical officer
CIO: Steve Serketich, Manager Information Services
CHR: Stacie A. Schneider, Director Human Resources
CNO: Lori Knitt, Chief Nursing Officer
Web address: www.aurorahealthcare.org
Control: Other not–for–profit (including NFP Corporation) **Service:** General Medical and Surgical

Staffed Beds: 136 **Admissions:** 5380 **Census:** 51 **Outpatient Visits:** 87679
Births: 872 **Total Expense ($000):** 123332 **Payroll Expense ($000):** 35566
Personnel: 603

WI

Hospital, Medicare Provider Number, Address, Telephone, Approval, Facility, and Physician Codes, Health Care System

★ American Hospital Association (AHA) membership   ○ Healthcare Facilities Accreditation Program   ⇑ Center for Improvement in Healthcare Quality Accreditation
☐ The Joint Commission accreditation   ◇ DNV Healthcare Inc. accreditation   △ Commission on Accreditation of Rehabilitation Facilities (CARF) accreditation

⊞ **ST. NICHOLAS HOSPITAL (520044)**, 3100 Superior Avenue, Zip 53081–1948; tel. 920/459–8300 **A**1 2 10 **F**3 8 11 13 15 17 18 20 22 26 28 29 30 31 34 35 36 38 40 43 44 45 47 49 50 53 57 59 60 62 63 64 65 68 70 74 75 76 79 80 81 84 85 86 87 89 90 92 93 107 108 110 111 115 116 117 118 119 120 121 123 129 130 132 146 148 **P**2 5 **S** Hospital Sisters Health System, Springfield, IL
Primary Contact: Andrew Bagnall, President and Chief Executive Officer
CFO: Greg Simia, Chief Financial Officer
CMO: Ken Johnson, Chief Physician Executive
CIO: Shane Miller, Chief Information Officer
CHR: Christine Jensema, Chief People Officer
CNO: Mary Martin, MSN, Chief Nursing Officer
Web address: www.stnicholashospital.org
Control: Church–operated, Nongovernment, not–for profit **Service:** General Medical and Surgical

Staffed Beds: 46 Admissions: 2622 Census: 25 Outpatient Visits: 71885
Births: 322 Total Expense ($000): 71538 Payroll Expense ($000): 21682
Personnel: 298

SHELL LAKE—Washburn County

☐ **INDIANHEAD MEDICAL CENTER (521342)**, 113 Fourth Avenue, Zip 54871–4457, Mailing Address: P.O. Box 300, Zip 54871–0300; tel. 715/468–7833 **A**1 10 18 **F**3 15 17 18 28 31 34 35 40 43 45 47 48 50 56 57 59 62 64 65 66 70 76 80 81 83 84 85 86 89 93 96 97 107 114 119 127 130 133 143 144 148 **P**5
Primary Contact: Paul Naglosky, Administrator
CFO: Michael Elliott, Controller
CMO: Allan Haesemeyer, M.D., Chief of Staff
CHR: Gwen Nielsen, Manager Human Resources
Web address: www.indianheadmedicalcenter.com
Control: Corporation, Investor–owned, for–profit **Service:** General Medical and Surgical

Staffed Beds: 16 Admissions: 371 Census: 4 Outpatient Visits: 9784
Births: 4 Total Expense ($000): 6980 Payroll Expense ($000): 2890
Personnel: 69

SPARTA—Monroe County

MAYO CLINIC HEALTH SYSTEM – FRANCISCAN HEALTHCARE IN SPARTA (521305), 310 West Main Street, Zip 54656–2171; tel. 608/269–2132 **A**10 18 **F**5 6 11 14 15 28 29 30 34 35 40 43 53 56 57 59 64 65 66 68 75 77 80 81 85 86 87 89 90 93 97 107 108 119 127 130 132 133 143 144 146 **S** Mayo Clinic, Rochester, MN
Primary Contact: Kimberly Hawthorne, Administrator
COO: Joseph J. Kruse, Chief Administrative Officer
CFO: Tom Tiggelaar, Vice President Finance ad Chief Financial Officer
CMO: Tracy Warsing, M.D., Site Leader Chief of Staff
CHR: Mike J. Hesch, Regional Administrator Human Resources
CNO: Diane Holmay, R.N., Chief Nursing Officer
Web address: www.mayoclinichealthsystem.org
Control: Church–operated, Nongovernment, not–for profit **Service:** General Medical and Surgical

Staffed Beds: 11 Admissions: 386 Census: 9 Outpatient Visits: 23371
Births: 0 Total Expense ($000): 19677 Payroll Expense ($000): 11303
Personnel: 159

SPOONER—Washburn County

★ **SPOONER HEALTH (521332)**, 1280 Chandler Drive, Zip 54801–1299; tel. 715/635–2111 **A**10 18 **F**13 15 17 29 34 40 43 56 62 64 70 76 78 80 81 86 87 89 90 93 107 111 119 130 **S** HealthTech Management Services, Brentwood, TN
Primary Contact: Michael Schafer, Chief Executive Officer and Administrator
CFO: Rebecca Busch, Chief Financial Officer
CMO: Mark Van Etten, M.D., Chief of Staff
CHR: Cindy Rouzer, Director Human Resources
CNO: Clint Miller, Chief Nursing Officier
Web address: www.spoonerhealth.com
Control: Other not–for–profit (including NFP Corporation) **Service:** General Medical and Surgical

Staffed Beds: 25 Admissions: 435 Census: 5 Outpatient Visits: 21389
Births: 42 Total Expense ($000): 17465 Payroll Expense ($000): 7114
Personnel: 108

ST. CROIX FALLS—Polk County

★ **ST. CROIX REGIONAL MEDICAL CENTER (521337)**, 235 State Street, Zip 54024–4117; tel. 715/483–3261 **A**10 18 **F**6 11 13 15 28 29 34 36 40 43 51 55 56 64 70 75 76 77 78 80 81 82 86 87 93 99 100 101 104 107 108 111 116 118 119 130 131 144 147 **P**5 6
Primary Contact: Dave Dobosenski, Chief Executive Officer
CFO: Sally Bajak, Chief Financial Officer
CMO: Jeffrey Hall, DPM, Chief Medical Officer
CIO: Brent McCurdy, Director Management Information
CHR: Lee Ann Vitalis, Executive Director Human Resources
CNO: Laura J. Jensen, Vice President Patient Care Services
Web address: www.scrmc.org
Control: Other not–for–profit (including NFP Corporation) **Service:** General Medical and Surgical

Staffed Beds: 25 Admissions: 1561 Census: 13 Outpatient Visits: 183647
Births: 277 Total Expense ($000): 66119 Payroll Expense ($000): 25704
Personnel: 387

STANLEY—Chippewa County

★ **MINISTRY OUR LADY OF VICTORY HOSPITAL (521311)**, 1120 Pine Street, Zip 54768–1297; tel. 715/644–5571 **A**10 18 **F**3 15 29 30 34 35 40 41 43 45 50 56 59 65 77 80 81 84 85 86 87 89 90 93 94 96 97 107 109 110 114 127 130 131 133 144 146 148 **P**2 **S** Ascension Health, Saint Louis, MO
Primary Contact: Vanessa Freitag, President
CFO: Terri Lewandowski, Director Financial Services
Web address: www.ministryhealth.org
Control: Other not–for–profit (including NFP Corporation) **Service:** General Medical and Surgical

Staffed Beds: 5 Admissions: 246 Census: 4 Outpatient Visits: 29720
Births: 0 Total Expense ($000): 16215 Payroll Expense ($000): 7672
Personnel: 74

STEVENS POINT—Portage County

⊞ **MINISTRY SAINT MICHAEL'S HOSPITAL (520002)**, 900 Illinois Avenue, Zip 54481–3196; tel. 715/346–5000 **A**1 10 19 **F**3 5 12 13 15 17 28 29 30 32 34 35 40 43 44 45 47 48 50 51 56 57 59 64 65 68 70 72 74 75 76 77 79 80 81 84 85 86 87 88 89 90 93 94 98 99 100 101 102 103 104 105 106 107 108 110 111 115 118 119 120 121 129 130 131 132 135 144 146 147 148 **S** Ascension Health, Saint Louis, MO
Primary Contact: Jeffrey L. Martin, President
CFO: William J. Hinner, Vice President Financial Analysis and Planning
CMO: Ryan Andrews, M.D., Chief Medical Officer
CIO: Will Weider, Chief Information Officer
CHR: Celia Shaunessy, Vice President Human Resources
CNO: Tom Veeser, Chief Nursing Officer
Web address: www.ministryhealth.org/SMH/home.nws
Control: Church–operated, Nongovernment, not–for profit **Service:** General Medical and Surgical

Staffed Beds: 50 Admissions: 4635 Census: 39 Outpatient Visits: 413606
Births: 460 Total Expense ($000): 175620 Payroll Expense ($000): 92717
Personnel: 519

SAINT MICHAEL'S HOSPITAL See Ministry Saint Michael's Hospital

STOUGHTON—Dane County

☐ **STOUGHTON HOSPITAL ASSOCIATION (521343)**, 900 Ridge Street, Zip 53589–1864; tel. 608/873–6611 **A**1 10 18 **F**3 4 6 8 14 15 26 28 29 34 35 36 40 41 45 53 54 56 57 59 62 64 65 68 70 71 75 77 79 80 81 85 86 87 89 90 91 93 98 100 103 106 107 111 115 127 129 130 131 132 133 135 144 146 147
Primary Contact: Terrence Brenny, President and Chief Executive Officer
CFO: Karen Myers, Vice President Financial Services
CMO: Guirish Agni, M.D., Chief of Staff
CIO: Karen Myers, Vice President Financial Services
CHR: Christopher Schmitz, Associate Vice President, Director Human Resources
CNO: Teresa Feidt, Chief Nursing Officer and Vice President, Patient Services
Web address: www.stoughtonhospital.com
Control: Other not–for–profit (including NFP Corporation) **Service:** General Medical and Surgical

Staffed Beds: 32 Admissions: 1018 Census: 17 Outpatient Visits: 53018
Births: 0 Total Expense ($000): 36558 Payroll Expense ($000): 15033
Personnel: 247

STURGEON BAY—Door County

DOOR COUNTY MEMORIAL HOSPITAL See Ministry Door County Medical Center

WI

Many Facility Codes have changed. Please refer to the AHA Guide Code Chart. © 2016 AHA Guide

★ **MINISTRY DOOR COUNTY MEDICAL CENTER (521358)**, 323 South 18th Avenue, Zip 54235–1495; tel. 920/743–5566, (Total facility includes 30 beds in nursing home–type unit) **A**10 18 **F**2 3 11 13 15 17 28 29 30 31 32 34 35 36 40 43 55 56 57 59 61 64 65 66 68 70 75 76 77 78 79 80 81 82 84 85 86 87 89 90 93 107 108 110 111 115 118 119 127 128 129 130 132 133 135 144 145 147 148 **P**6 **S** Ascension Health, Saint Louis, MO
Primary Contact: Gerald M. Worrick, President and Chief Executive Officer
CFO: Brian Stephens, Chief Financial Officer
CMO: James Heise, Chief Medical Officer
CIO: Mary Lopas, Chief Information Officer
CHR: Kelli Bowling, Chief Culture Officer
CNO: Jody Boes, Vice President Patient Care Services
Web address: www.ministryhealth.org
Control: Church–operated, Nongovernment, not–for profit **Service:** General Medical and Surgical

Staffed Beds: 55 **Admissions:** 1843 **Census:** 36 **Outpatient Visits:** 74818 **Births:** 134 **Total Expense ($000):** 67680 **Payroll Expense ($000):** 35611 **Personnel:** 474

SUMMIT—Waukesha County

⌧ **AURORA MEDICAL CENTER SUMMIT (520206)**, 36500 Aurora Drive, Zip 53066–4899; tel. 262/434–1000 **A**1 2 10 **F**3 8 11 12 13 15 17 18 19 20 22 24 26 28 29 30 31 32 34 35 36 40 41 43 44 45 47 48 49 50 53 54 55 57 59 60 64 68 70 72 74 75 76 79 80 81 82 84 85 86 87 89 90 93 94 96 107 108 110 111 114 115 116 117 119 120 121 123 124 126 129 130 131 132 135 147 **P**6 **S** Aurora Health Care, Milwaukee, WI
Primary Contact: Michael Bergmann, President
Web address: www.aurorahealthcare.org
Control: Other not–for–profit (including NFP Corporation) **Service:** General Medical and Surgical

Staffed Beds: 99 **Admissions:** 3228 **Census:** 35 **Outpatient Visits:** 93991 **Births:** 398 **Total Expense ($000):** 107001 **Payroll Expense ($000):** 30741 **Personnel:** 475

SUPERIOR—Douglas County

⌧ **ESSENTIA HEALTH ST. MARY'S HOSPITAL OF SUPERIOR (521329)**, 3500 Tower Avenue, Zip 54880–5395; tel. 715/817–7000 **A**1 10 18 **F**3 11 15 28 29 30 40 41 42 56 59 64 65 75 77 78 80 81 82 86 87 90 93 96 97 107 110 114 119 130 133 135 142 146 148 **S** Essentia Health, Duluth, MN
Primary Contact: Terry Jacobson, Administrator and Chief Executive Officer
Web address: www.essentiahealth.org/ EssentiaHealthStMarysHospitalofSuperiorFoundation/overview.aspx
Control: Other not–for–profit (including NFP Corporation) **Service:** General Medical and Surgical

Staffed Beds: 25 **Admissions:** 513 **Census:** 9 **Outpatient Visits:** 50639 **Births:** 0 **Total Expense ($000):** 32311 **Payroll Expense ($000):** 19054 **Personnel:** 208

TOMAH—Monroe County

⌧ **TOMAH MEMORIAL HOSPITAL (521320)**, 321 Butts Avenue, Zip 54660–1412; tel. 608/372–2181 **A**1 10 18 **F**3 8 11 12 13 14 18 28 30 31 32 34 35 40 41 43 50 56 57 59 63 64 65 68 76 77 79 80 81 82 83 84 85 86 87 89 90 93 107 111 115 119 129 130 132 133 135 144 146 148 **P**5 6 **S** HealthTech Management Services, Brentwood, TN
Primary Contact: Philip J. Stuart, Administrator and Chief Executive Officer
CFO: Joseph Zeps, Vice President Finance
CIO: LaVonne Smith, Director Health Information Technology
CHR: Brenda Reinert, Director Human Resources
CNO: Tracy Myhre, R.N., Chief Nursing Officer
Web address: www.tomahhospital.org
Control: Other not–for–profit (including NFP Corporation) **Service:** General Medical and Surgical

Staffed Beds: 25 **Admissions:** 1032 **Census:** 9 **Outpatient Visits:** 36421 **Births:** 321 **Total Expense ($000):** 38585 **Payroll Expense ($000):** 17085 **Personnel:** 246

⌧ **TOMAH VETERANS AFFAIRS MEDICAL CENTER**, 500 East Veterans Street, Zip 54660–3105; tel. 608/372–3971, (Nonreporting) **A**1 **S** Department of Veterans Affairs, Washington, DC
Primary Contact: Victoria Brahm, R.N., MSN, Acting Director
CFO: Jane Mashak–Ekern, Fiscal Officer
CMO: David Houlihan, M.D., Chief of Staff
CIO: Edward Hensel, Chief Information Officer
CHR: David Dechant, Chief Human Resources Officer
Web address: www.tomah.va.gov
Control: Veterans Affairs, Government, federal **Service:** General Medical and Surgical

Staffed Beds: 71

TOMAHAWK—Lincoln County

★ **MINISTRY SACRED HEART HOSPITAL (521313)**, 401 West Mohawk Drive, Zip 54487–2274; tel. 715/453–7700 **A**10 18 **F**3 5 15 28 29 30 34 35 40 45 49 50 57 59 65 68 75 77 80 81 84 86 87 89 91 92 93 96 99 100 101 104 107 109 115 119 130 131 133 146 **S** Ascension Health, Saint Louis, MO
Primary Contact: Sandra L. Anderson, President and Chief Executive Officer
COO: Laurie Oungst, Vice President, Operations
CFO: Jamon Lamers, Director Finance
CMO: Russ Sudbury, M.D., President Medical Staff
CIO: Howard Dobizl, Director Information Technology Services
CHR: Michelle Cornelius, Director Human Resources
CNO: Ann Zenk, Vice President Patient Care
Web address: www.ministryhealth.org
Control: Church–operated, Nongovernment, not–for profit **Service:** General Medical and Surgical

Staffed Beds: 11 **Admissions:** 305 **Census:** 3 **Outpatient Visits:** 20879 **Births:** 0 **Total Expense ($000):** 12003 **Payroll Expense ($000):** 7863 **Personnel:** 99

TWO RIVERS—Manitowoc County

⌧ **AURORA MEDICAL CENTER – MANITOWOC COUNTY (520034)**, 5000 Memorial Drive, Zip 54241–3900; tel. 920/794–5000 **A**1 2 10 **F**3 8 11 13 28 29 30 31 32 34 35 36 37 40 43 44 45 47 48 49 50 56 57 59 64 69 74 75 76 78 79 80 81 82 84 85 86 87 89 93 94 107 108 110 111 114 119 121 123 129 130 131 132 143 146 147 148 **P**6 **S** Aurora Health Care, Milwaukee, WI
Primary Contact: Cathie A. Kocourek, President
COO: Carrie L. Penovich, Chief Clinical Services Officer
CFO: Sandra Ewald, Vice President Finance
CMO: Paul Mihalakakos, M.D., Chief of Staff
CIO: Preston Simons, Chief Information Officer
CHR: Elizabeth A. Kirby, Senior Director Human Resources
CNO: Betsy Benz, R.N., Chief Nursing Officer
Web address: www.aurorahealthcare.org
Control: Other not–for–profit (including NFP Corporation) **Service:** General Medical and Surgical

Staffed Beds: 62 **Admissions:** 2097 **Census:** 16 **Outpatient Visits:** 80293 **Births:** 386 **Total Expense ($000):** 55672 **Payroll Expense ($000):** 17414 **Personnel:** 319

VIROQUA—Vernon County

VERNON MEMORIAL HEALTHCARE (521348), 507 South Main Street, Zip 54665–2096; tel. 608/637–2101 **A**10 18 **F**3 5 13 15 18 26 28 29 31 34 35 36 40 43 45 53 56 57 59 62 63 65 68 75 76 77 79 80 81 82 86 87 89 93 97 104 107 110 115 127 129 130 131 132 133 135 144 146 148 **P**6
Primary Contact: Kyle Bakkum, Chief Executive Officer and Administrator
COO: Kristy Wiltrout, R.N., Chief Operating Officer
CFO: Mary Koenig, Chief Financial Officer
CIO: Scott Adkins, Manager Information Technology
CHR: Kay Starr, Manager Human Resources
Web address: www.vmh.org
Control: Other not–for–profit (including NFP Corporation) **Service:** General Medical and Surgical

Staffed Beds: 25 **Admissions:** 1276 **Census:** 9 **Outpatient Visits:** 125904 **Births:** 151 **Total Expense ($000):** 65059 **Payroll Expense ($000):** 27241 **Personnel:** 358

WATERFORD—Racine County

☐ △ **LAKEVIEW SPECIALTY HOSPITAL AND REHABILITATION CENTER (522005)**, 1701 Sharp Road, Zip 53185–5214; tel. 262/534–7297 **A**1 7 10 **F**1 12 29 30 38 53 62 64 75 82 85 86 87 90 91 92 93 94 97 99 100 101 104 106 127 130 143 148 **P**6
Primary Contact: Christopher Slover, Chief Executive Officer
Web address: www.lakeviewsystem.com
Control: Corporation, Investor–owned, for–profit **Service:** Long–Term Acute Care hospital

Staffed Beds: 39 **Admissions:** 248 **Census:** 26 **Outpatient Visits:** 8062 **Births:** 0 **Total Expense ($000):** 12780 **Payroll Expense ($000):** 5835 **Personnel:** 140

WI

Hospital, Medicare Provider Number, Address, Telephone, Approval, Facility, and Physician Codes, Health Care System

★ American Hospital Association (AHA) membership   ◯ Healthcare Facilities Accreditation Program   ⇧ Center for Improvement in Healthcare Quality Accreditation
☐ The Joint Commission accreditation   ◇ DNV Healthcare Inc. accreditation   △ Commission on Accreditation of Rehabilitation Facilities (CARF) accreditation

WATERTOWN—Dodge County

⊞ **WATERTOWN REGIONAL MEDICAL CENTER (520116)**, 125 Hospital Drive, Zip 53098–3303; tel. 920/261–4210 **A**1 10 **F**3 8 10 11 13 15 18 20 22 26 28 29 34 35 36 40 45 46 48 50 53 54 56 57 59 64 68 69 74 75 76 77 78 79 80 81 82 83 85 86 87 89 90 91 92 93 94 97 104 107 108 109 110 111 112 114 117 118 119 120 121 125 127 129 130 131 132 135 144 146 147 148 **P**2 8
Primary Contact: Richard Keddington, Chief Executive Officer
COO: John P. Kosanovich, President
CFO: John Graf, Senior Vice President
CIO: Jennifer Laughlin, Chief Information Officer
CHR: Duane Floyd, Vice President Human Resources and Professional Services
CNO: Mary Kay Diderrich, R.N., Vice President Patient Services
Web address: www.watertownregional.com/Main/Home.aspx
Control: Corporation, Investor–owned, for–profit **Service:** General Medical and Surgical

Staffed Beds: 55 **Admissions:** 1709 **Census:** 16 **Outpatient Visits:** 202936 **Births:** 250 **Total Expense ($000):** 101448 **Payroll Expense ($000):** 41406 **Personnel:** 584

WAUKESHA—Waukesha County

☐ **REHABILITATION HOSPITAL OF WISCONSIN (523027)**, 1625 Coldwater Creek Drive, Zip 53188–8028; tel. 262/521–8800 **A**1 10 **F**3 29 34 35 57 64 65 74 75 79 86 90 91 93 96 97 130 148 **S** Kindred Healthcare, Louisville, KY
Primary Contact: Linda Newberry–Ferguson, Chief Executive Officer
CMO: Tim McAvoy, M.D., Medical Director
CHR: Jenny Franke, Director Human Resources
CNO: Sharon Behrens, R.N., Chief Clinical Officer
Web address: www.rehabhospitalwi.com
Control: Partnership, Investor–owned, for–profit **Service:** Rehabilitation

Staffed Beds: 40 **Admissions:** 756 **Census:** 29 **Outpatient Visits:** 5441 **Births:** 0 **Total Expense ($000):** 12857 **Payroll Expense ($000):** 6547 **Personnel:** 117

WAUKESHA COUNTY MENTAL HEALTH CENTER (524026), 2501 Airport Road, Zip 53188; tel. 262/548–7950 **A**10 **F**4 98 130 132
Primary Contact: Jeff Lewis, Administrator
Web address: www.waukeshacounty.gov/
Control: County–Government, nonfederal **Service:** Psychiatric

Staffed Beds: 28 **Admissions:** 694 **Census:** 17 **Outpatient Visits:** 0 **Births:** 0 **Total Expense ($000):** 6531 **Payroll Expense ($000):** 3334 **Personnel:** 49

⊞ **WAUKESHA MEMORIAL HOSPITAL (520008)**, 725 American Avenue, Zip 53188–5099; tel. 262/928–1000 **A**1 2 3 5 10 **F**3 4 5 6 11 12 13 15 20 22 24 26 28 29 30 31 34 35 37 40 42 44 45 46 47 49 50 56 57 58 59 64 68 72 74 75 76 78 79 80 81 82 84 85 87 89 92 93 97 98 100 101 102 103 105 107 108 110 111 114 115 116 117 118 119 120 121 123 124 126 129 130 132 135 146 147 148 **S** ProHealth Care, Inc., Waukesha, WI
Primary Contact: Susan A. Edwards, Chief Executive Officer
CMO: James D. Gardner, M.D., Vice President and Chief Medical Officer
CIO: Rodney Dykehouse, Senior Vice President Information Services
CHR: Nadine T. Guirl, Senior Vice President Human Resources
Web address: www.prohealthcare.org/locations/locations–v2–detail/?id=1119
Control: Other not–for–profit (including NFP Corporation) **Service:** General Medical and Surgical

Staffed Beds: 287 **Admissions:** 13317 **Census:** 150 **Outpatient Visits:** 304255 **Births:** 1626 **Total Expense ($000):** 397551 **Payroll Expense ($000):** 104163 **Personnel:** 1824

WAUPACA—Waupaca County

☐ **THEDACARE MEDICAL CENTER–WAUPACA (521334)**, 800 Riverside Drive, Zip 54981–1999; tel. 715/258–1000 **A**1 10 18 **F**11 13 17 28 29 34 40 64 70 75 76 78 80 81 82 86 87 88 89 90 107 111 119 130 144 147 **S** ThedaCare, Inc., Appleton, WI
Primary Contact: Craig A. Kantos, Chief Executive Officer
CFO: Kerry Lee Blanke, Director Financial Services
CMO: James Williams, M.D., Chief of Staff
CHR: Kevin Gossens, Director Human Resources
Web address: www.riversidemedical.org
Control: Other not–for–profit (including NFP Corporation) **Service:** General Medical and Surgical

Staffed Beds: 25 **Admissions:** 1027 **Census:** 11 **Outpatient Visits:** 37826 **Births:** 164 **Total Expense ($000):** 28414 **Payroll Expense ($000):** 14679 **Personnel:** 190

WAUPUN—Dodge County

☐ **WAUPUN MEMORIAL HOSPITAL (521327)**, 620 West Brown Street, Zip 53963–1799; tel. 920/324–5581 **A**1 10 18 **F**3 11 13 15 18 28 29 30 31 34 35 40 43 44 45 50 51 57 59 60 64 66 68 69 70 75 76 77 78 79 81 82 85 86 87 93 96 97 107 108 109 110 114 118 119 130 131 132 133 134 135 143 144 146 147 148 **P**6
Primary Contact: DeAnn Thurmer, Chief Operating Officer
COO: DeAnn Thurmer, Chief Operating Officer
CFO: Bonnie Schmitz, Chief Financial Officer
CMO: Derek Colmenares, M.D., Chief Medical Officer
CIO: Nancy Birschbach, Vice President and Chief Information Officer
CHR: Sue Edminster, Vice President Human Resources
CNO: DeAnn Thurmer, Chief Nursing Officer
Web address: www.agnesian.com
Control: Church–operated, Nongovernment, not–for profit **Service:** General Medical and Surgical

Staffed Beds: 25 **Admissions:** 903 **Census:** 8 **Outpatient Visits:** 52979 **Births:** 132 **Total Expense ($000):** 33401 **Payroll Expense ($000):** 14028 **Personnel:** 169

WAUSAU—Marathon County

⊞ △ **ASPIRUS WAUSAU HOSPITAL (520030)**, 333 Pine Ridge Boulevard, Zip 54401–4187; tel. 715/847–2121 **A**1 2 3 5 7 10 **F**3 6 7 8 11 12 13 15 17 18 20 22 24 26 28 29 30 31 34 35 36 40 43 44 45 46 47 49 50 51 54 55 56 57 58 59 60 64 65 68 69 70 71 72 74 75 76 78 79 80 81 82 83 84 85 86 87 89 90 92 93 96 97 100 102 103 107 108 110 111 114 115 116 117 118 119 120 121 123 124 126 129 130 132 135 143 144 145 146 147 148 **P**8 **S** Aspirus, Inc., Wausau, WI
Primary Contact: Darrell Lentz, President
CFO: Sidney C. Sczygelski, Senior Vice President Finance and Chief Financial Officer
CMO: William Wessels, M.D., Chief Medical Officer
CNO: Jeannine Burnat Nosko, Vice President Patient Care
Web address: www.aspirus.org
Control: Other not–for–profit (including NFP Corporation) **Service:** General Medical and Surgical

Staffed Beds: 229 **Admissions:** 12556 **Census:** 145 **Outpatient Visits:** 111704 **Births:** 1302 **Total Expense ($000):** 378906 **Payroll Expense ($000):** 132289 **Personnel:** 2231

★ **NORTH CENTRAL HEALTH CARE (524017)**, 1100 Lake View Drive, Zip 54403–6785; tel. 715/848–4600, (Total facility includes 206 beds in nursing home–type unit) **A**10 **F**4 5 6 29 38 56 75 77 80 87 93 98 99 101 102 103 104 128 130
Primary Contact: Michael Loy, Interim Chief Executive Officer
CFO: Brenda Glodowski, Chief Financial Officer
CHR: Sue Matis, Director Human Resources
Web address: www.norcen.org
Control: County–Government, nonfederal **Service:** Psychiatric

Staffed Beds: 235 **Admissions:** 2042 **Census:** 220 **Outpatient Visits:** 124432 **Births:** 0 **Total Expense ($000):** 31901 **Payroll Expense ($000):** 15585 **Personnel:** 359

NORTH CENTRAL HEALTH CARE FACILITIES See North Central Health Care

WAUWATOSA—Milwaukee County

⊞ **AURORA PSYCHIATRIC HOSPITAL (524000)**, 1220 Dewey Avenue, Zip 53213–2598; tel. 414/454–6600 **A**1 3 5 10 **F**4 5 29 30 32 34 35 38 44 50 54 57 59 64 68 75 86 87 98 99 100 101 102 103 104 105 106 130 132 134 135 **P**6 **S** Aurora Health Care, Milwaukee, WI
Primary Contact: Peter Carlson, Administrator
CFO: Susan Dwyer, Vice President Finance
CMO: Anthony Meyer, M.D., Medical Director
CIO: Philip Loftus, Ph.D., Vice President and Chief Information Officer
CHR: Pamela Gamb, Manager Human Resources
CNO: Jamie Lewiston, R.N., Chief Nursing Officer
Web address: www.aurorahealthcare.org
Control: Other not–for–profit (including NFP Corporation) **Service:** Psychiatric

Staffed Beds: 81 **Admissions:** 3831 **Census:** 50 **Outpatient Visits:** 62488 **Births:** 0 **Total Expense ($000):** 28287 **Payroll Expense ($000):** 15280 **Personnel:** 282

WI

Many Facility Codes have changed. Please refer to the AHA Guide Code Chart. © 2016 AHA Guide

WEST ALLIS—Milwaukee County

⊞ **AURORA WEST ALLIS MEDICAL CENTER (520139)**, 8901 West Lincoln Avenue, Zip 53227–2409, Mailing Address: P.O. Box 27901, Zip 53227–0901; tel. 414/328–6000 **A**1 2 3 10 **F**3 11 12 13 15 29 30 31 32 34 35 37 38 40 43 44 45 46 49 50 51 52 54 55 56 57 59 64 65 68 70 72 74 75 76 78 79 80 81 82 84 85 86 87 91 93 94 95 96 97 107 108 110 111 114 115 116 117 118 119 120 121 123 126 130 132 133 134 135 146 147 148 **P**6
S Aurora Health Care, Milwaukee, WI
Primary Contact: Richard A. Kellar, President
COO: Gerard Colman, Chief Operating Officer
CFO: Chris Hemmer, Director Finance
CMO: Andrew McDonagh, M.D., Chief Medical Officer
CIO: Philip Loftus, Ph.D., Chief Information Officer
CHR: Shannon Christenson, Director Human Resources
CNO: Kathy Becker, Ph.D., Vice President and Chief Nursing Officer
Web address: www.aurorahealthcare.org
Control: Other not–for–profit (including NFP Corporation) **Service:** General Medical and Surgical

Staffed Beds: 218 **Admissions:** 13155 **Census:** 146 **Outpatient Visits:** 148045 **Births:** 3456 **Total Expense ($000):** 200768 **Payroll Expense ($000):** 63351 **Personnel:** 1060

WEST BEND—Washington County

⊞ **ST. JOSEPH'S HOSPITAL (520063)**, 3200 Pleasant Valley Road, Zip 53095–9274; tel. 262/334–5533 **A**1 2 3 5 10 **F**3 4 8 13 15 17 26 28 29 30 31 34 35 40 44 45 46 47 48 49 50 56 57 59 60 63 64 68 70 75 76 77 78 79 80 81 85 86 87 89 90 98 100 101 107 108 110 111 114 115 116 117 118 119 120 121 123 129 130 132 135 145 146 147 148
Primary Contact: Allen Ericson, Chief Operating Officer, Community Hospital Division and President, St. Joseph's Hospital
COO: Allen Ericson, Chief Operating Officer, Community Hospital Division and President, St. Joseph's Hospital
CFO: Scott Hawig, Senior Vice President of Finance, Chief Financial Officer and Treasurer
CMO: Patrick Gardner, M.D., Associate Vice President, Medical Affairs, St. Joseph's Hospital
CIO: Will Showalter, Senior Vice President, Chief Information Officer
CHR: Keith Allen, Senior Vice President Human Resources
CNO: Teri Lux, Vice President Patient Care Services, Community Hospital Division, Chief Nursing Officer
Web address: www.froedtert.com
Control: Other not–for–profit (including NFP Corporation) **Service:** General Medical and Surgical

Staffed Beds: 78 **Admissions:** 3893 **Census:** 45 **Outpatient Visits:** 83941 **Births:** 732 **Total Expense ($000):** 103572 **Payroll Expense ($000):** 32105 **Personnel:** 461

WESTON—Marathon County

⊞ **MINISTRY SAINT CLARE'S HOSPITAL (520202)**, 3400 Ministry Parkway, Zip 54476–5220; tel. 715/393–3000 **A**1 10 **F**3 11 13 17 18 20 22 24 26 29 30 31 34 35 37 40 43 44 45 46 47 48 49 50 51 57 59 64 68 70 72 74 75 76 78 79 80 81 82 84 85 86 87 89 126 130 132 135 146 148 **S** Ascension Health, Saint Louis, MO
Primary Contact: Brian Kief, Interim President
CFO: Charlotte Esselman, Director Finance
CMO: Ryan Andrews, M.D., Chief Medical Officer
CIO: Tammy Hawkey, Manager Information Technology Client Services
CHR: Nancy Kwiesielewicz, Human Resources Manager
CNO: Sally E. Zillman, Interim Vice President, Patient Care Services
Web address: www.ministryhealth.org
Control: Church–operated, Nongovernment, not–for profit **Service:** General Medical and Surgical

Staffed Beds: 83 **Admissions:** 5642 **Census:** 53 **Outpatient Visits:** 19767 **Births:** 677 **Total Expense ($000):** 94480 **Payroll Expense ($000):** 33439 **Personnel:** 311

WHITEHALL—Trempealeau County

★ **GUNDERSEN TRI–COUNTY HOSPITAL AND CLINICS (521316)**, 18601 Lincoln Street, Zip 54773–8605; tel. 715/538–4361, (Total facility includes 47 beds in nursing home–type unit) **A**10 18 **F**7 10 11 15 28 34 40 43 53 56 64 69 75 81 82 86 89 90 93 107 108 128 130 144
Primary Contact: Brian Theiler, President and Chief Executive Officer
CFO: Roxane K. Schliech, Chief Financial Officer
CMO: Kim B. Breidenbach, Medical Director
CIO: John Waldera, Director Information Technology
CHR: Jill Wesener Dieck, Director Human Resources
CNO: Kelsey N. Underwood, Director of Nursing
Web address: www.gundersenhealth.org/tri–county
Control: Other not–for–profit (including NFP Corporation) **Service:** General Medical and Surgical

Staffed Beds: 50 **Admissions:** 346 **Census:** 45 **Outpatient Visits:** 28109 **Births:** 0 **Total Expense ($000):** 15342 **Payroll Expense ($000):** 7153 **Personnel:** 148

WILD ROSE—Waushara County

THEDA CARE MEDICAL CENTER – WILD ROSE (521303), 601 Grove Avenue, Zip 54984–6903, Mailing Address: P.O. Box 243, Zip 54984–0243; tel. 920/622–3257 **A**10 18 **F**11 15 28 29 34 40 43 56 64 75 77 80 81 86 87 89 90 93 99 100 101 102 103 104 107 111 119 131 144 147 **S** ThedaCare, Inc., Appleton, WI
Primary Contact: Craig A. Kantos, Chief Executive Officer
CFO: Thomas P. Krystowiak, Vice President Finance
CMO: Michael Staudinger, M.D., Chief of Staff
Web address: www.wildrosehospital.org
Control: Other not–for–profit (including NFP Corporation) **Service:** General Medical and Surgical

Staffed Beds: 25 **Admissions:** 301 **Census:** 6 **Outpatient Visits:** 14887 **Births:** 0 **Total Expense ($000):** 12917 **Payroll Expense ($000):** 7502 **Personnel:** 117

WINNEBAGO—Winnebago County

☐ **WINNEBAGO MENTAL HEALTH INSTITUTE (524002)**, 1300 South Drive, Zip 54985, Mailing Address: Box 9, Zip 54985–0009; tel. 920/235–4910 **A**1 5 10 **F**3 4 5 29 30 57 59 75 82 87 98 99 103 130 132 135 143 146 **P**7
Primary Contact: Thomas Speech, Ph.D., Director
COO: Chris Craggs, Deputy Director
CFO: Lisa Spanbauer, Financial Program Supervisor
CMO: Randy Kerswill, M.D., Medical Director
CIO: Terrance J. Sweet, Director Information Technology
CHR: Mary Howard, Director Human Resources
CNO: Lori Monroe, Director of Nursing
Web address: www.dhfs.state.wi.us/mh_winnebago
Control: State–Government, nonfederal **Service:** Psychiatric

Staffed Beds: 179 **Admissions:** 3112 **Census:** 179 **Outpatient Visits:** 0 **Births:** 0 **Total Expense ($000):** 54856 **Payroll Expense ($000):** 35249 **Personnel:** 651

WISCONSIN RAPIDS—Wood County

⊞ **ASPIRUS RIVERVIEW HOSPITAL AND CLINICS, INC. (520033)**, 410 Dewey Street, Zip 54494–4715, Mailing Address: P.O. Box 8080, Zip 54495–8080; tel. 715/423–6060 **A**1 2 10 **F**3 4 13 15 17 28 30 31 32 34 35 40 43 45 50 56 57 59 64 65 68 69 70 74 75 76 77 78 79 80 81 84 85 86 88 89 90 93 97 98 107 108 110 111 115 117 118 119 120 121 124 129 130 131 132 135 146 148 **S** Aspirus, Inc., Wausau, WI
Primary Contact: Todd Burch, Chief Executive Officer
CFO: Nancy Roth–Mallek, Vice President of Finance
CMO: Thomas Voelker, M.D., Chief Medical Officer
CIO: Marjorie Tell, Vice President Information Technology
CHR: Jessica Fox, Director of Human Resources
CNO: Peggy Ose, FACHE, Chief Nursing Officer
Web address: www.aspirus.org
Control: Other not–for–profit (including NFP Corporation) **Service:** General Medical and Surgical

Staffed Beds: 69 **Admissions:** 2213 **Census:** 17 **Outpatient Visits:** 40770 **Births:** 383 **Total Expense ($000):** 125613 **Payroll Expense ($000):** 36089 **Personnel:** 467

WI

Hospital, Medicare Provider Number, Address, Telephone, Approval, Facility, and Physician Codes, Health Care System
★ American Hospital Association (AHA) membership ○ Healthcare Facilities Accreditation Program ⇑ Center for Improvement in Healthcare Quality Accreditation
☐ The Joint Commission accreditation ◇ DNV Healthcare Inc. accreditation △ Commission on Accreditation of Rehabilitation Facilities (CARF) accreditation

WOODRUFF—Oneida County

⊠ **HOWARD YOUNG MEDICAL CENTER (520091)**, 240 Maple Street,
Zip 54568–9190, Mailing Address: P.O. Box 470, Zip 54568–0470;
tel. 715/356–8000 **A**1 5 10 20 **F**3 8 11 13 15 18 28 29 30 35 40 43 45 47
48 49 50 57 59 64 68 75 76 77 80 81 82 84 85 86 87 88 89 93 96 107
110 111 115 119 126 129 130 133 146 148 **P**6 **S** Ascension Health, Saint
Louis, MO
Primary Contact: Sandra L. Anderson, President and Chief Executive Officer
COO: Laurie Oungst, Vice President, Operations
CFO: Jamon Lamers, Director Finance
CMO: John Crump, M.D., Medical Staff President
CIO: Howard Dobizl, Director Information Technology Services
CHR: Michelle Cornelius, Director Human Resources
CNO: Deborah Karow, R.N., Vice President Patient Care Services
Web address: www.ministryhealth.org
Control: Church–operated, Nongovernment, not–for profit **Service:** General
Medical and Surgical

Staffed Beds: 38 **Admissions:** 2428 **Census:** 24 **Outpatient Visits:** 38405
Births: 272 **Total Expense ($000):** 51172 **Payroll Expense ($000):** 23613
Personnel: 327

WI

WYOMING

AFTON—Lincoln County

★ **STAR VALLEY MEDICAL CENTER (531313)**, 901 Adams Street,
Zip 83110–9621, Mailing Address: P.O. Box 579, Zip 83110–0579;
tel. 307/885–5800, (Total facility includes 24 beds in nursing home–type unit)
A10 18 **F**3 7 8 11 12 13 15 28 29 30 31 32 34 35 40 41 43 45 50 54 56 57
59 65 67 70 73 75 77 78 79 81 83 84 85 87 93 94 97 107 108 110 111
114 119 129 130 131 132 133 135 146 147 148 **P**6
Primary Contact: Charlie A. Button, President and Chief Executive Officer
CFO: Chad Turner, Chief Financial Officer
CMO: Christian Morgan, M.D., Chief of Staff
CIO: Denise Wheeler, Chief Information Officer
CHR: Trevor Merritt, Director Human Resources
CNO: Dave Dunn, Director of Nursing
Web address: www.svmcwy.org
Control: Hospital district or authority, Government, nonfederal **Service:** General
Medical and Surgical

Staffed Beds: 44 **Admissions:** 773 **Census:** 28 **Outpatient Visits:** 35554
Births: 104 **Total Expense ($000):** 33388 **Payroll Expense ($000):** 15083
Personnel: 258

BASIN—Big Horn County

SOUTH BIG HORN COUNTY HOSPITAL (531301), 388 South U.S. Highway
20, Zip 82410–8902; tel. 307/568–3311, (Total facility includes 37 beds in
nursing home–type unit) **A**10 18 **F**32 34 35 40 56 57 59 64 82 93 97 107 110
119 127 128 130 133 **P**4
Primary Contact: Jackie Claudson, Administrator
Web address: www.midwayclinic.com
Control: Hospital district or authority, Government, nonfederal **Service:** General
Medical and Surgical

Staffed Beds: 43 **Admissions:** 470 **Census:** 29 **Outpatient Visits:** 5263
Births: 0 **Total Expense ($000):** 6544 **Payroll Expense ($000):** 3814
Personnel: 87

BUFFALO—Johnson County

★ **JOHNSON COUNTY HEALTHCARE CENTER (531308)**, 497 West Lott Street,
Zip 82834–1691; tel. 307/684–5521, (Total facility includes 48 beds in nursing
home–type unit) **A**10 18 **F**11 13 15 28 31 40 57 62 63 67 70 76 78 79 81 89
93 107 119 130 133
Primary Contact: Sandy Ward, Administrator
CFO: Sandy Ward, Administrator
CMO: Brian Darnell, D.O., Chief of Staff
CIO: Laurie Hansen, Director Administrative Services
CHR: Karen Ferguson, Director Human Resources
CNO: Mary Whaley, Director of Acute Care
Web address: www.jchealthcare.com
Control: Hospital district or authority, Government, nonfederal **Service:** General
Medical and Surgical

Staffed Beds: 63 **Admissions:** 443 **Census:** 51 **Outpatient Visits:** 18641
Births: 43 **Total Expense ($000):** 20132 **Payroll Expense ($000):** 10954
Personnel: 177

CASPER—Natrona County

☐ **ELKHORN VALLEY REHABILITATION HOSPITAL (533027)**, 5715 East 2nd
Street, Zip 82609–4322; tel. 307/265–0005, (Nonreporting) **A**1 10 **S** Ernest
Health, Inc., Albuquerque, NM
Primary Contact: Michael Phillips, Chief Executive Officer
Web address: www.evrh.ernesthealth.com/
Control: Corporation, Investor–owned, for–profit **Service:** Rehabilitation

Staffed Beds: 40

◇ **MOUNTAIN VIEW REGIONAL HOSPITAL (530033)**, 6550 East Second Street,
Zip 82609–4321, Mailing Address: P.O. Box 51888, Zip 82605–1888;
tel. 307/995–8100, (Nonreporting) **A**10 11 **S** National Surgical Healthcare,
Chicago, IL
Primary Contact: Thomas Kopitnik, Acting Chief Executive Officer
Web address: www.mountainviewregionalhospital.com
Control: Partnership, Investor–owned, for–profit **Service:** Surgical

Staffed Beds: 23

◇ **SUMMIT MEDICAL CENTER (530034)**, 6350 East 2nd Street,
Zip 82609–4264; tel. 307/232–6600, (Nonreporting) **A**21
Primary Contact: Dennis D. Jack, Chief Executive Officer
CFO: Calvin Carey, Chief Financial Officer
CMO: Joseph Vigneri, M.D., Chief Medical Officer
CNO: Vanessa Sorensen, Chief Nursing Officer
Web address: www.summitmedicalcasper.com/
Control: Corporation, Investor–owned, for–profit **Service:** General Medical and
Surgical

Staffed Beds: 16

☐ **WYOMING BEHAVIORAL INSTITUTE (534004)**, 2521 East 15th Street,
Zip 82609–4126; tel. 307/237–7444, (Nonreporting) **A**1 10 **S** Universal Health
Services, Inc., King of Prussia, PA
Primary Contact: Joseph Gallagher, Chief Executive Officer
CFO: Carmel Bickford, Chief Financial Officer
CMO: Steven Brown, M.D., Medical Director
CHR: Jon Barra, Director Human Resources
Web address: www.wbihelp.com
Control: Corporation, Investor–owned, for–profit **Service:** Psychiatric

Staffed Beds: 129

⊞ **WYOMING MEDICAL CENTER (530012)**, 1233 East Second Street,
Zip 82601–2988; tel. 307/577–7201 **A**1 3 10 **F**3 7 11 12 13 18 20 22 24 28
29 30 31 34 35 40 41 43 45 46 48 49 50 51 57 59 60 61 68 70 74 76 79
81 82 85 86 87 89 97 102 107 108 114 118 119 120 121 123 124 126 129
130 132 135 144 146 147 148 **P**6
Primary Contact: Vickie L. Diamond, R.N., MS, President and Chief Executive
Officer
COO: Chad Pew, Chief Operating Officer and Senior Vice President
CFO: Yvonne Wigington, Vice President, Chief Financial Officer
CMO: Carol M. Solie, M.D., Chief Medical Officer
CIO: Rob Pettigrew, Director Information Technology
CNO: Jan Nixon, MS, Senior Vice President Patient Care Services and Chief
Nursing Officer
Web address: www.https://wyomingmedicalcenter.org/
Control: Other not–for–profit (including NFP Corporation) **Service:** General
Medical and Surgical

Staffed Beds: 217 **Admissions:** 8668 **Census:** 90 **Outpatient Visits:** 83855
Births: 1181 **Total Expense ($000):** 199168 **Payroll Expense ($000):**
71040 **Personnel:** 1058

CHEYENNE—Laramie County

⊞ △ **CHEYENNE REGIONAL MEDICAL CENTER (530014)**, 214 East 23rd
Street, Zip 82001–3790; tel. 307/634–2273 **A**1 2 3 5 7 10 20 **F**3 5 11 12 13
15 18 20 22 24 26 28 29 30 31 34 35 37 38 40 43 44 45 46 47 48 49 50
51 57 59 60 62 63 64 65 66 68 69 70 71 73 74 75 76 77 78 79 81 82 83
84 85 86 87 89 90 93 94 96 97 98 99 100 101 102 103 104 107 108 110
111 114 117 118 119 120 121 123 124 126 128 129 130 131 132 135 143
144 146 147 148 **P**6
Primary Contact: Patrick Madigan, Interim Chief Executive Officer
COO: Robin Roling, FACHE, Chief Operating Officer
CFO: Neil W. Bertrand, Interim Chief Financial Officer
CMO: Jeffrey Chapman, M.D., Chief Medical Officer
CIO: Craig Luzinski, FACHE, Vice President Performance Optimization
CHR: Craig Luzinski, FACHE, Vice President Performance Optimization
CNO: Tracy Garcia, MS, Chief Nursing Officer
Web address: www.cheyenneregional.org/
Control: County–Government, nonfederal **Service:** General Medical and Surgical

Staffed Beds: 238 **Admissions:** 10437 **Census:** 138 **Outpatient Visits:**
161597 **Births:** 1235 **Total Expense ($000):** 268994 **Payroll Expense
($000):** 106899 **Personnel:** 1692

WY

⊡ **CHEYENNE VETERANS AFFAIRS MEDICAL CENTER**, 2360 East Pershing Boulevard, Zip 82001–5392; tel. 307/778–7550, (Total facility includes 42 beds in nursing home–type unit) **A**1 **F**3 5 8 18 29 30 31 34 35 38 39 40 44 45 51 54 56 59 61 62 63 64 65 68 70 71 74 75 77 78 79 81 82 84 85 86 87 91 92 93 94 97 100 101 102 103 104 107 108 109 111 115 119 128 129 130 132 135 143 144 146 147 148 **P**6 **S** Department of Veterans Affairs, Washington, DC
Primary Contact: Paul L. Roberts, Director
CFO: Melvin Cranford, Chief Fiscal Services
CMO: Roger Johnson, M.D., Chief of Staff
CIO: Liz McCulloch, Chief Information Resource Management Systems
CHR: Ron Lester, Chief Human Resources
Web address: www.cheyenne.va.gov/
Control: Veterans Affairs, Government, federal **Service:** General Medical and Surgical

> **Staffed Beds:** 61 **Admissions:** 1039 **Census:** 47 **Outpatient Visits:** 273281 **Births:** 0 **Personnel:** 620

CODY—Park County

★ **WEST PARK HOSPITAL (531312)**, 707 Sheridan Avenue, Zip 82414–3409; tel. 307/527–7501, (Total facility includes 87 beds in nursing home–type unit) **A**10 18 **F**3 4 5 6 7 11 13 15 18 24 26 28 29 30 31 34 35 36 38 40 43 45 46 50 56 57 59 62 63 64 65 68 70 75 76 78 79 81 84 85 86 87 93 97 99 100 102 103 104 105 107 108 110 111 114 119 120 124 128 130 131 132 133 135 143 144 145 146 147 148 **S** QHR, Brentwood, TN
Primary Contact: Douglas A. McMillan, Administrator and Chief Executive Officer
CFO: Patrick G. McConnell, Chief Financial Officer
CMO: Gary Hart, M.D., Chief Medical Officer
CHR: Dick Smith, Director Human Resources
Web address: www.westparkhospital.org
Control: Hospital district or authority, Government, nonfederal **Service:** General Medical and Surgical

> **Staffed Beds:** 112 **Admissions:** 1919 **Census:** 89 **Outpatient Visits:** 67708 **Births:** 287 **Total Expense ($000):** 79347 **Payroll Expense ($000):** 31223 **Personnel:** 533

DOUGLAS—Converse County

★ **MEMORIAL HOSPITAL OF CONVERSE COUNTY (531302)**, 111 South Fifth Street, Zip 82633–2434, Mailing Address: P.O. Box 1450, Zip 82633–1450; tel. 307/358–2122 **A**10 18 **F**3 7 8 13 15 28 29 32 34 35 40 43 45 46 50 57 59 64 65 70 74 75 76 79 81 82 85 86 87 94 107 110 111 115 119 126 127 128 129 130 131 133 135 144 146 147 148 **P**6
Primary Contact: Ryan K. Smith, Chief Executive Officer
COO: Karl Edward Hertz, Assistant Administrator
CFO: Curtis R. Dugger, Chief Financial Officer
CMO: James Morgan, M.D., Chief Medical Officer
CIO: Dave Patterson, Chief Information Officer
CHR: Linda York, Director Human Resource
CNO: Cristy Dicklich–Cobb, Chief Nursing Officer
Web address: www.conversehospital.com
Control: County–Government, nonfederal **Service:** General Medical and Surgical

> **Staffed Beds:** 25 **Admissions:** 806 **Census:** 6 **Outpatient Visits:** 38197 **Births:** 171 **Total Expense ($000):** 51515 **Payroll Expense ($000):** 27053 **Personnel:** 362

EVANSTON—Uinta County

⊡ **EVANSTON REGIONAL HOSPITAL (530032)**, 190 Arrowhead Drive, Zip 82930–9266; tel. 307/789–3636 **A**1 10 20 **F**3 11 13 15 29 34 35 40 43 45 48 60 65 70 74 75 76 77 79 81 82 85 86 87 89 93 107 108 111 114 119 128 129 133 134 146 **P**6 **S** Quorum Health, Brentwood, TN
Primary Contact: Jeremy Davis, Chief Executive Officer
CHR: Joshua Jones, Director Human Resources
CNO: Cheri Willard, R.N., Chief Nursing Officer
Web address: www.evanstonregionalhospital.com
Control: Corporation, Investor–owned, for–profit **Service:** General Medical and Surgical

> **Staffed Beds:** 42 **Admissions:** 722 **Census:** 4 **Outpatient Visits:** 27534 **Births:** 239 **Total Expense ($000):** 22918 **Payroll Expense ($000):** 10902 **Personnel:** 148

WYOMING STATE HOSPITAL (534001), 830 Highway 150 South, Zip 82931–5341, Mailing Address: P.O. Box 177, Zip 82931–0177; tel. 307/789–3464, (Nonreporting) **A**10
Primary Contact: Rich Dunkley, Administrator
CFO: Paul Mullenax, Business Manager
CIO: Steve Baldwin, Manager Information Technology
Web address: www.health.wyo.gov/statehospital/index.html
Control: State–Government, nonfederal **Service:** Psychiatric

> **Staffed Beds:** 183

GILLETTE—Campbell County

★ ◇ **CAMPBELL COUNTY HEALTH (530002)**, 501 South Burma Avenue, Zip 82716–3426, Mailing Address: P.O. Box 3011, Zip 82717–3011; tel. 307/682–8811, (Total facility includes 125 beds in nursing home–type unit) **A**10 20 21 **F**3 5 6 7 11 13 15 18 20 22 26 28 29 30 31 34 35 38 40 43 45 50 51 53 54 56 59 60 62 63 64 65 66 68 70 71 73 74 75 76 77 78 79 81 82 84 85 86 87 88 91 93 94 96 97 98 99 100 101 102 103 104 105 107 108 109 110 111 114 115 116 118 119 120 121 125 129 130 131 132 133 134 135 143 144 146 147 148 **P**6
Primary Contact: Andy Fitzgerald, Chief Executive Officer
CFO: Dalton Huber, Chief Financial Officer
CIO: Chris Harrison, Manager Information Systems
CHR: John A. Fitch, Vice President Human Resources
CNO: Deb L. Tonn, Vice President Patient Care
Web address: www.ccmh.net
Control: Hospital district or authority, Government, nonfederal **Service:** General Medical and Surgical

> **Staffed Beds:** 198 **Admissions:** 3273 **Census:** 132 **Outpatient Visits:** 265810 **Births:** 852 **Total Expense ($000):** 162287 **Payroll Expense ($000):** 82138 **Personnel:** 1066

JACKSON—Teton County

⊡ **ST. JOHN'S MEDICAL CENTER AND LIVING CENTER (530015)**, 625 East Broadway Street, Zip 83001–8642, Mailing Address: P.O. Box 428, Zip 83001–0428; tel. 307/733–3636, (Total facility includes 60 beds in nursing home–type unit) **A**1 5 10 20 **F**3 11 12 13 15 29 30 31 34 35 37 40 43 44 45 46 49 50 51 53 54 57 59 62 63 67 68 70 74 75 76 77 78 79 81 82 84 85 86 87 97 107 108 110 111 115 119 129 130 132 133 135 144 145 146 148
Primary Contact: Lou Hochheiser, M.D., Chief Executive Officer
COO: Gary Tauner, Chief Operating Officer
CFO: John Kren, Chief Financial Officer
CIO: Lance Spranger, Chief Information Officer
CNO: Lynn Kirman, R.N., Chief Nursing Officer
Web address: www.tetonhospital.org
Control: Hospital district or authority, Government, nonfederal **Service:** General Medical and Surgical

> **Staffed Beds:** 108 **Admissions:** 1987 **Census:** 63 **Outpatient Visits:** 73300 **Births:** 474 **Total Expense ($000):** 92665 **Payroll Expense ($000):** 37526 **Personnel:** 603

KEMMERER—Lincoln County

★ **SOUTH LINCOLN MEDICAL CENTER (531315)**, 711 Onyx Street, Zip 83101–3214; tel. 307/877–4401, (Nonreporting) **A**10 18
Primary Contact: Kenneth W. Archer, Chief Executive Officer
CFO: Curtis Nielson, Chief Financial Officer
CMO: G. Christopher Krell, M.D., Chief of Staff
CIO: Kristin Housley, Chief Information Officer
CNO: Kathi Parks, Director of Nursing
Web address: www.southlincolnmedical.com
Control: Hospital district or authority, Government, nonfederal **Service:** General Medical and Surgical

> **Staffed Beds:** 40

LARAMIE—Albany County

⊡ **IVINSON MEMORIAL HOSPITAL (530025)**, 255 North 30th Street, Zip 82072–5140; tel. 307/742–2141 **A**1 10 20 **F**7 11 13 15 29 30 31 35 38 40 60 70 73 75 76 77 78 79 81 89 97 98 99 107 111 128 129 130 133 146
Primary Contact: Doug Faus, FACHE, Chief Executive Officer
COO: Holly Zajic, Chief Operating Officer
CFO: James G. Bands, IV, Chief Financial Officer
CMO: John Byers, M.D., Chief of Staff
CIO: Brandon Lewis, Director of Information Technology
CHR: Becky Kosach, Director Human Resources
CNO: Sharon Gern, R.N., Chief Nursing Officer
Web address: www.ivinsonhospital.org
Control: Hospital district or authority, Government, nonfederal **Service:** General Medical and Surgical

> **Staffed Beds:** 99 **Admissions:** 2090 **Census:** 24 **Outpatient Visits:** 34637 **Births:** 428 **Total Expense ($000):** 71838 **Payroll Expense ($000):** 26175 **Personnel:** 396

WY

Many Facility Codes have changed. Please refer to the AHA Guide Code Chart. © 2016 AHA Guide

LOVELL—Big Horn County

★ **NORTH BIG HORN HOSPITAL DISTRICT (531309)**, 1115 Lane 12,
Zip 82431–9537; tel. 307/548–5200, (Total facility includes 85 beds in nursing
home–type unit) **A**10 18 **F**3 6 7 10 15 28 29 30 34 35 36 40 41 45 50 56 57
59 62 64 65 66 68 71 75 79 81 82 85 86 87 93 97 107 110 114 119 127
128 130 131 132 133 135 143 146 147 148 **P**3 8
Primary Contact: Rick Schroeder, Chief Executive Officer
CFO: Lori Smith, Chief Financial Officer
CMO: Richard Jay, D.O., Chief of Staff
CIO: Lisa Strom, Director Information Systems
CHR: Barbara Shumway, Director Human Resources
CNO: Tina Toner, Director of Nursing
Web address: www.nbhh.com
Control: Hospital district or authority, Government, nonfederal **Service:** General
Medical and Surgical

Staffed Beds: 100 **Admissions:** 363 **Census:** 76 **Outpatient Visits:** 22936 **Births:** 0 **Total Expense ($000):** 16046 **Payroll Expense ($000):** 9090 **Personnel:** 184		

LUSK—Niobrara County

★ **NIOBRARA HEALTH AND LIFE CENTER (531314)**, 921 Ballencee Avenue,
Zip 82225, Mailing Address: P.O. Box 780, Zip 82225–0780;
tel. 307/334–4000, (Nonreporting) **A**10 18
Primary Contact: Chris Smolik, Chief Executive Officer
Web address: www.niobrarahospital.com
Control: Hospital district or authority, Government, nonfederal **Service:** General
Medical and Surgical

Staffed Beds: 24

NEWCASTLE—Weston County

★ **WESTON COUNTY HEALTH SERVICES (531303)**, 1124 Washington
Boulevard, Zip 82701–2972; tel. 307/746–4491, (Total facility includes 54 beds
in nursing home–type unit) **A**10 18 **F**3 28 29 35 40 41 43 50 57 59 62 64 77
93 107 114 119 129 130 135 148 **S** Regional Health, Rapid City, SD
Primary Contact: Maureen K. Cadwell, Chief Executive Officer
CFO: Lynn Moller, Chief Financial Officer
CMO: Chuck Franklin, M.D., Chief Medical Staff
CIO: Terri Frye, Information Technology Officer
CHR: Julie A. Sindlinger, Director of Human Resources
Web address: www.wchs–wy.org
Control: Hospital district or authority, Government, nonfederal **Service:** General
Medical and Surgical

Staffed Beds: 75 **Admissions:** 194 **Census:** 52 **Outpatient Visits:** 9162 **Births:** 0 **Total Expense ($000):** 13622 **Payroll Expense ($000):** 6255 **Personnel:** 137

POWELL—Park County

★ **POWELL VALLEY HEALTHCARE (531310)**, 777 Avenue H, Zip 82435–2296;
tel. 307/754–2267, (Total facility includes 100 beds in nursing home–type unit)
A10 18 **F**3 7 10 11 13 15 17 18 28 29 34 35 36 40 43 45 50 56 57 59 64
65 67 68 70 73 75 76 79 81 82 84 85 87 89 97 107 110 111 115 119 125
130 131 132 133 135 144 146 147 148 **P**1 6 **S** HealthTech Management
Services, Brentwood, TN
Primary Contact: Terry Odom, Chief Executive Officer
CFO: Mike Long, Chief Financial Officer
CMO: Valerie Lengfelder, M.D., Chief of Staff
CIO: Joshua Baxter, Director, Information Systems
CHR: Cassie Tinsley, Director, Human Resources
CNO: Arleen Campeau, R.N., Vice President of Patient Care Services, Chief
Nursing Officer
Web address: www.pvhc.org
Control: Other not-for-profit (including NFP Corporation) **Service:** General
Medical and Surgical

Staffed Beds: 125 **Admissions:** 504 **Census:** 88 **Outpatient Visits:** 36225 **Births:** 182

RAWLINS—Carbon County

★ **MEMORIAL HOSPITAL OF CARBON COUNTY (531316)**, 2221 West Elm
Street, Zip 82301–5108, Mailing Address: P.O. Box 460, Zip 82301–0460;
tel. 307/324–2221 **A**10 18 **F**3 7 11 13 15 29 31 34 35 40 45 50 57 59 65
68 70 79 81 85 93 107 110 111 114 119 129 133 135 146 147 **S** QHR,
Brentwood, TN
Primary Contact: Dana Barnett, Chief Executive Officer
CFO: David Pike, Interim Chief Financial Officer
CMO: David Cesko, M.D., Chief of Staff
CIO: Toby Schaef, Director Information Technology
CNO: Amber Green, R.N., Chief Clinical Officer
Web address: www.imhcc.com
Control: County–Government, nonfederal **Service:** General Medical and Surgical

Staffed Beds: 25 **Admissions:** 660 **Census:** 6 **Outpatient Visits:** 27796 **Births:** 95 **Total Expense ($000):** 23053 **Payroll Expense ($000):** 10054 **Personnel:** 152

RIVERTON—Fremont County

⊞ **SAGEWEST HEALTH CARE AT RIVERTON (530008)**, 2100 West Sunset Drive,
Zip 82501–2274; tel. 307/856–4161, (Includes SAGEWEST HEALTH CARE AT
LANDER, 1320 Bishop Randall Drive, Lander, Zip 82520–3996;
tel. 307/332–4420; Stephen M. Erixon, Chief Executive Officer) **A**1 10 20 **F**3 11
12 13 15 28 29 34 35 38 39 40 43 50 57 59 70 74 75 76 77 79 81 82 85
87 90 93 97 98 103 106 107 108 110 111 114 115 119 129 130 131 132
145 146 147 148 **P**7 **S** LifePoint Health, Brentwood, TN
Primary Contact: Stephen M. Erixon, Chief Executive Officer
COO: Derrick Brumfield, Chief Operating Officer
CFO: Jennifer Hamilton, Chief Financial Officer
CMO: Cielette Karn, M.D., Chief of Staff
CIO: Linda Tice, Director Information Systems
CHR: Dawn Nelson, Director Human Resources
CNO: Karen A. Lund, R.N., Chief Nursing Officer
Web address: www.sagewesthealthcare.com
Control: Corporation, Investor–owned, for–profit **Service:** General Medical and
Surgical

Staffed Beds: 71 **Admissions:** 2988 **Census:** 36 **Outpatient Visits:** 63147 **Births:** 521 **Total Expense ($000):** 60638 **Payroll Expense ($000):** 19306 **Personnel:** 348

ROCK SPRINGS—Sweetwater County

⊞ **MEMORIAL HOSPITAL OF SWEETWATER COUNTY (530011)**, 1200 College
Drive, Zip 82901–5868, Mailing Address: P.O. Box 1359, Zip 82902–1359;
tel. 307/362–3711 **A**1 10 20 **F**3 5 8 11 13 15 28 29 30 31 34 35 40 43 48
57 59 60 64 70 75 76 77 78 79 81 82 87 93 96 97 99 100 101 102 103
104 105 107 110 111 114 115 116 118 119 120 121 122 123 129 130 131
132 135 146 147
Primary Contact: Gerard D. Klein, Chief Executive Officer
COO: Mandeep Gill, Chief Operating Officer
CFO: Irene Richardson, Chief Financial Officer
CMO: Sigsbee Duck, M.D., President, Medical Staff
CHR: Amber Fisk, Director Human Resources
CNO: Kallie Mikkelsen, Vice President Nursing
Web address: www.sweetwatermemorial.com/default.aspx
Control: County–Government, nonfederal **Service:** General Medical and Surgical

Staffed Beds: 58 **Admissions:** 2254 **Census:** 18 **Outpatient Visits:** 160033 **Births:** 537 **Total Expense ($000):** 78188 **Payroll Expense ($000):** 32774 **Personnel:** 459

SHERIDAN—Sheridan County

⊞ **SHERIDAN MEMORIAL HOSPITAL (530006)**, 1401 West Fifth Street,
Zip 82801–2799; tel. 307/672–1000, (Nonreporting) **A**1 10 20
Primary Contact: Michael McCafferty, Chief Executive Officer
CFO: Charlotte Marie Mather, R.N., Chief Nursing Officer
CMO: John Addlesperger, D.O., Chief Medical Officer
CIO: Nyle Morgan, Chief Information Officer
CHR: Len Gross, Chief Human Resources Officer
Web address: www.sheridanhospital.org
Control: County–Government, nonfederal **Service:** General Medical and Surgical

Staffed Beds: 88

Hospital, Medicare Provider Number, Address, Telephone, Approval, Facility, and Physician Codes, Health Care System

★ American Hospital Association (AHA) membership   ○ Healthcare Facilities Accreditation Program   ⇑ Center for Improvement in Healthcare Quality Accreditation
□ The Joint Commission accreditation   ◇ DNV Healthcare Inc. accreditation   △ Commission on Accreditation of Rehabilitation Facilities (CARF) accreditation

WY

⊞ **SHERIDAN VETERANS AFFAIRS MEDICAL CENTER**, 1898 Fort Road, Zip 82801–8320; tel. 307/672–3473, (Total facility includes 40 beds in nursing home–type unit) **A**1 **F**29 30 38 39 45 50 53 56 59 62 63 64 65 75 77 82 83 84 85 86 87 93 94 97 98 100 103 106 107 111 119 127 129 130 132 135 143 146 147 148 **S** Department of Veterans Affairs, Washington, DC
Primary Contact: Gerald K. Darnell, PsyD, Interim Director
COO: Chandra Lake, Associate Director
CFO: Donna Fuerstenberg, Fiscal Chief
CMO: Wendell Robison, M.D., Chief of Staff
CIO: Anthony Giljum, Chief Information Officer
CHR: James Hardin, Human Resources Officer
Web address: www.sheridan.va.gov/
Control: Veterans Affairs, Government, federal **Service:** Psychiatric

Staffed Beds: 185 Admissions: 1287 Census: 146 Outpatient Visits: 117890 Births: 0 Total Expense ($000): 103527 Payroll Expense ($000): 40534 Personnel: 620

SUNDANCE—Crook County

★ **CROOK COUNTY MEDICAL SERVICES DISTRICT (531311)**, 713 Oak Street, Zip 82729, Mailing Address: P.O. Box 517, Zip 82729–0517; tel. 307/283–3501 **A**10 18 **F**7 40 41 44 57 59 64 65 67 68 75 89 90 107 127 128 130 133 143 147 148 **S** Regional Health, Rapid City, SD
Primary Contact: Nathan Hough, Chief Executive Officer
CFO: Betty Meyers, Chief Financial Officer
CMO: Jeremi Villano, M.D., Chief of Staff
CHR: Patricia Feist, Manager Human Resources
Web address: www.ccmsd.org/
Control: Hospital district or authority, Government, nonfederal **Service:** General Medical and Surgical

Staffed Beds: 16 Admissions: 125 Census: 2

THERMOPOLIS—Hot Springs County

★ **HOT SPRINGS COUNTY MEMORIAL HOSPITAL (531304)**, 150 East Arapahoe Street, Zip 82443–2498; tel. 307/864–3121 **A**10 18 **F**3 11 13 15 28 29 31 34 35 40 41 43 45 57 59 64 68 70 75 76 81 85 89 107 108 110 111 115 119 127 129 130 133 135 145 146 148 **S** HealthTech Management Services, Brentwood, TN
Primary Contact: Margie Molitor, FACHE, R.N., Chief Executive Officer
CFO: Shelly Larson, Chief Financial Officer
CHR: Patti Jeunehomme, Director Human Resources
Web address: www.hscmh.org
Control: County–Government, nonfederal **Service:** General Medical and Surgical

Staffed Beds: 25 Admissions: 452 Census: 5 Outpatient Visits: 13928 Births: 65 Total Expense ($000): 16159 Payroll Expense ($000): 5477 Personnel: 89

TORRINGTON—Goshen County

★ **COMMUNITY HOSPITAL (531307)**, 2000 Campbell Drive, Zip 82240–1597; tel. 307/532–4181 **A**10 18 **F**3 11 13 15 28 29 30 31 34 35 36 40 43 45 57 59 61 64 68 75 77 78 79 81 85 86 87 93 107 110 114 119 129 131 133 145 146 147 148 **P**1 5 6 **S** Banner Health, Phoenix, AZ
Primary Contact: Shelby Nelson, Interim Chief Executive Officer
CMO: Bonnie Randolph, M.D., Chief of Staff
CIO: Rod Miller, Chief Information Technology
Web address: www.bannerhealth.com/Locations/Wyoming/Community+Hospital/
Control: Other not–for–profit (including NFP Corporation) **Service:** General Medical and Surgical

Staffed Beds: 20 Admissions: 618 Census: 6 Outpatient Visits: 18305 Births: 70 Total Expense ($000): 19426 Payroll Expense ($000): 7993 Personnel: 133

WHEATLAND—Platte County

⊞ **PLATTE COUNTY MEMORIAL HOSPITAL (531305)**, 201 14th Street, Zip 82201–3201, Mailing Address: P.O. Box 848, Zip 82201–0848; tel. 307/322–3636 **A**1 10 18 **F**3 7 11 13 15 29 34 35 40 43 45 59 61 64 70 75 76 78 79 81 82 85 86 87 107 110 114 119 129 133 145 147 **S** Banner Health, Phoenix, AZ
Primary Contact: Shelby Nelson, Chief Executive Officer
CFO: James Cussins, Chief Financial Officer
CMO: Willard Woods, M.D., Chief Medical Officer
CIO: Robin May, Director Information Systems
CHR: Sandy Dugger, Chief Human Resources Officer
Web address: www.bannerhealth.com/Locations/Wyoming/Platte+County+Memorial+Hospital
Control: Other not–for–profit (including NFP Corporation) **Service:** General Medical and Surgical

Staffed Beds: 25 Admissions: 482 Census: 4 Outpatient Visits: 14717 Births: 46 Total Expense ($000): 13490 Payroll Expense ($000): 7950 Personnel: 127

WORLAND—Washakie County

★ **WASHAKIE MEDICAL CENTER (531306)**, 400 South 15th Street, Zip 82401–3531, Mailing Address: P.O. Box 700, Zip 82401–0700; tel. 307/347–3221 **A**10 18 **F**3 11 13 15 28 29 31 40 43 45 53 59 68 70 75 76 85 86 87 93 97 102 107 108 110 111 115 119 127 133 146 148 **S** Banner Health, Phoenix, AZ
Primary Contact: Jay Stallings, Chief Executive Officer
CFO: Jennifer Montgomery, Chief Financial Officer
CMO: Ryan Clifford, M.D., Chief of Staff
CHR: Jerry Clipp, Manager Human Resources
Web address: www.washakiemedicalcenter.com
Control: Other not–for–profit (including NFP Corporation) **Service:** General Medical and Surgical

Staffed Beds: 22 Admissions: 554 Census: 4 Births: 68 Total Expense ($000): 18867 Payroll Expense ($000): 7640 Personnel: 102

Many Facility Codes have changed. Please refer to the AHA Guide Code Chart.

© 2016 AHA Guide

WY

AMERICAN SAMOA

PAGO PAGO— County

LYNDON B. JOHNSON TROPICAL MEDICAL CENTER (640001), Faga'alu Village, Zip 96799, Mailing Address: P.O. Box LBJ, Zip 96799; tel. 684/633–1222, (Nonreporting) **A**10
Primary Contact: Patricia Tindall, Chief Executive Officer
Web address: www.asmca.org
Control: State–Government, nonfederal **Service:** General Medical and Surgical

Staffed Beds: 125

GUAM

AGANA—Guam County

⌧ **U. S. NAVAL HOSPITAL GUAM**, Zip 96910; Mailing Address: FPO, tel. 671/344–9340, (Nonreporting) **A**1 **S** Bureau of Medicine and Surgery, Department of the Navy, Falls Church, VA
Primary Contact: Captain Jeannie Comlish, Command Officer
Web address: www.med.navy.mil/sites/usnhguam/Pages/default.aspx
Control: Navy, Government, federal **Service:** General Medical and Surgical

Staffed Beds: 55

DEDEDO— County

★ **GUAM REGIONAL MEDICAL CITY**, 133 Route 3, Zip 96932, Mailing Address: P.O. Box 3830, Hagatna, Zip 96932; tel. 671/645–5500, (Nonreporting)
Primary Contact: Gloria Long, Chief Operating Officer
Web address: www.grmc.gu/
Control: Corporation, Investor–owned, for–profit **Service:** General Medical and Surgical

Staffed Beds: 130

TAMUNING—Guam County

☐ **GUAM MEMORIAL HOSPITAL AUTHORITY (650001)**, 850 Governor Carlos G. Camacho Road, Zip 96913; tel. 671/647–2108, (Nonreporting) **A**1 10
Primary Contact: Joseph P. Verga, FACHE, Chief Executive Officer
CFO: Alan Ulrich, Chief Financial Officer
CMO: James J. Stadler, M.D., Associate Administrator Medical Services
CIO: Vince Quichocho, Manager Information Systems
CHR: Elizabeth Claros, Administrator Personnel Services
Web address: www.gmha.org
Control: Hospital district or authority, Government, nonfederal **Service:** General Medical and Surgical

Staffed Beds: 104

MARSHALL ISLANDS

KWAJALEIN ISLAND— County

KWAJALEIN HOSPITAL, U.S. Army Kwajalein Atoll, Zip 96960, Mailing Address: Box 1702, APO, UNIT, Zip 96555–5000; tel. 805/355–2225, (Nonreporting) **S** Department of the Army, Office of the Surgeon General, Falls Church, VA
Primary Contact: Elaine McMahon, Administrator
Control: Army, Government, federal **Service:** General Medical and Surgical

Staffed Beds: 14

NORTHERN MARIANA ISLANDS

SAIPAN— County

★ **COMMONWEALTH HEALTH CENTER (660001)**, Navy Hill Road, Zip 96950, Mailing Address: P.O. Box 500409, Zip 96950; tel. 670/234–8950, (Nonreporting) **A**10
Primary Contact: Esther L. Muna, Chief Executive Officer
CFO: Priscilla Maratita Iakopo, Chief Financial Officer
CMO: John M. Tudela, M.D., Director of Medical Affairs
CIO: Anthony Reyes, Information Technology Director
CHR: Clarinda Ngiraisui, Human Resource Manager
CNO: Leslie Camacho, R.N., Director of Nursing
Web address: www.chcc.gov.mp
Control: Corporation, Investor–owned, for–profit **Service:** General Medical and Surgical

Staffed Beds: 86

PUERTO RICO

AGUADILLA—Aguadilla County

⌧ **HOSPITAL BUEN SAMARITANO (400079)**, Carr #2 Km 141–1 Avenue Severiano Cuevas, Zip 00603, Mailing Address: P.O. Box 4055, Zip 00605–4055; tel. 787/658–0000, (Nonreporting) **A**1 5 10
Primary Contact: Marilyn Morales, Interim Executive Director
CFO: Edwin Orama Acevedo, Financial Supervisor
CMO: Arturo Cedeno Llorens, M.D., Medical Director
CHR: Jose Garcia Rivera, Director Human Resources
CNO: Eneida Alicea Perez, Interim Nursing Director
Web address: www.hbspr.org
Control: Other not–for–profit (including NFP Corporation) **Service:** General Medical and Surgical

Staffed Beds: 154

AIBONITO—Aibonito County

⌧ **CENTRO DE SALUD CONDUCTUAL MENONITA–CIMA (404009)**, Carretera Estatal 14 Interior, Zip 00705, Mailing Address: PO Box 871, Zip 00705; tel. 787/714–2462, (Nonreporting) **A**1 10
Primary Contact: Pedro Melendez, Chief Executive Officer
Control: Other not–for–profit (including NFP Corporation) **Service:** Psychiatric

Staffed Beds: 20

⌧ **MENNONITE GENERAL HOSPITAL (400018)**, Calle Jose C. Vasquez, Zip 00705, Mailing Address: P.O. Box 372800, Cayey, Zip 00737–2800; tel. 787/535–1001 **A**1 10 **F**8 13 15 29 30 31 34 35 40 41 42 43 46 47 57 59 62 63 64 65 66 68 70 75 78 79 81 82 107 111 114 115 119 124 130 143 144 145 146 147 148 **P**5
Primary Contact: Pedro Melendez, Chief Executive Officer
COO: Marta R Mercado Suro, Chief Operating Officer
CFO: Jose E. Solivan, Chief Financial Officer
CMO: Victor Hernandez Miranda, M.D., Chief of Staff
CIO: Daniza Morales, Manager Information System
CHR: Evelyn Padilla Ortiz, Director Human Resources
CNO: Gloria Mercado, Director of Nursing
Web address: www.hospitalmenonita.com
Control: Other not–for–profit (including NFP Corporation) **Service:** General Medical and Surgical

Staffed Beds: 143 Admissions: 8806 Census: 99 Outpatient Visits: 153861 Births: 596 Total Expense ($000): 73472 Payroll Expense ($000): 25525 Personnel: 830

Hospital, Medicare Provider Number, Address, Telephone, Approval, Facility, and Physician Codes, Health Care System

★ American Hospital Association (AHA) membership   ○ Healthcare Facilities Accreditation Program   ⇑ Center for Improvement in Healthcare Quality
☐ The Joint Commission accreditation   ◇ DNV Healthcare Inc. accreditation   △ Commission on Accreditation of Rehabilitation Facilities (CARF) accreditation

ARECIBO—Arecibo County

✠ **HOSPITAL DR. CAYETANO COLL Y TOSTE (400087)**, 129 San Luis Avenue, Zip 00612, Mailing Address: P.O. Box 659, Zip 00613; tel. 787/650–7272 **A**1 3 10 **F**3 8 14 15 17 20 29 30 34 40 41 45 57 60 65 70 72 74 75 76 79 81 91 100 102 107 108 110 111 114 118 119 130 141 148
Primary Contact: Homar Perez, Chief Executive Officer and Vice President Administration
COO: Jamie Rivera, Chief Financial Officer
CFO: Agustin Gonzalez, Director Finance
CMO: Antoine Pavia, M.D., Medical Director
CIO: David Valle, Chief Information Officer
CHR: Yesenia Natal, Coordinator Human Resources
CNO: Iris Toledo, Chief Nursing Officer
Web address: www.cayetano@xsn.net
Control: Corporation, Investor–owned, for–profit **Service:** General Medical and Surgical

Staffed Beds: 184 Admissions: 9051 Census: 135 Outpatient Visits: 35795 Births: 769

★ **HOSPITAL METROPOLITANO DR. SUSONI (400117)**, Calle Palma #55, Zip 00612, Mailing Address: P.O. Box 145200, Zip 00614; tel. 787/650–1030 **A**10 **F**3 15 29 40 41 45 46 49 51 64 70 74 75 77 79 81 87 89 107 110 111 114 119 130 136 147 148
Primary Contact: Luis Martinez, Executive Director
CFO: Francisco Silva, Financial Director
CMO: Ada S. Miranda, M.D., Medical Director
CIO: Mayra Montano, Director Information Systems
CHR: Janira Hernandez, Coordinator Human Resources
CNO: Damaris Rios, Executive Nursing Director
Web address: www.metropavia.com/DrSusoni.cfm
Control: Corporation, Investor–owned, for–profit **Service:** General Medical and Surgical

Staffed Beds: 138 Admissions: 7556 Census: 108 Outpatient Visits: 29609 Births: 0 Total Expense ($000): 41618 Payroll Expense ($000): 13073

ARROYO—Arroyo County

★ **LAFAYETTE HOSPITAL (400026)**, Central Lafayette, Zip 00714, Mailing Address: P.O. Box 207, Zip 00714; tel. 787/839–3232, (Nonreporting) **A**10
Primary Contact: Ruth M. Ortiz Vargas, Administrator
CMO: Jose L. Pimentel Fernandez, Medical Director
Control: Corporation, Investor–owned, for–profit **Service:** General Medical and Surgical

Staffed Beds: 38

BAYAMON—Bayamon County

★ **DOCTOR'S CENTER OF BAYAMON (400102)**, Extension Hermanas Davila, Zip 00960, Mailing Address: P.O. Box 2957, Zip 00960; tel. 787/622–5420, (Nonreporting) **A**10
Primary Contact: Carlos Blanco, M.D., Administrator
Control: Corporation, Investor–owned, for–profit **Service:** General Medical and Surgical

Staffed Beds: 91

✠ **HOSPITAL HERMANOS MELENDEZ (400032)**, Route 2, KM 11–7, Zip 00960, Mailing Address: P.O. Box 306, Zip 00960; tel. 787/620–8181, (Includes PUERTO RICO CHILDREN'S HOSPITAL, P.O. Box 1999, tel. 787/474–1378; Tania Conde, Administrator), (Nonreporting) **A**1 3 10
Primary Contact: Maria T. Machado, Administrator
CFO: Luz D. Medina, Controller
CMO: Norma Ortiz, M.D., Medical Director
CIO: Leticia Santana, Administrator Medical Records
Web address: www.hospitalhermanosmelendez.net
Control: Corporation, Investor–owned, for–profit **Service:** General Medical and Surgical

Staffed Beds: 211

✠ **HOSPITAL SAN PABLO (400109)**, Calle Santa Cruz 70, Zip 00961–7020, Mailing Address: P.O. Box 236, Zip 00960–0236; tel. 787/740–4747 **A**1 3 5 10 **F**3 8 13 15 17 18 19 20 21 22 23 24 26 29 30 31 34 40 41 45 46 47 49 51 57 59 64 68 70 72 73 74 75 76 77 78 79 81 86 87 88 89 92 93 107 108 110 111 114 115 118 119 126 130 145 146 147 148 **P**1 6
Primary Contact: Claudia V. Guzman, Chief Executive Officer and Managing Director
Web address: www.sanpablo.com
Control: Corporation, Investor–owned, for–profit **Service:** General Medical and Surgical

Staffed Beds: 431 Admissions: 16079 Census: 300 Outpatient Visits: 56376 Births: 1249 Total Expense ($000): 141204 Payroll Expense ($000): 54659 Personnel: 1589

✠ **HOSPITAL UNIVERSITARIO DR. RAMON RUIZ ARNAU (400105)**, Avenue Laurel, Santa Juanita, Zip 00956; tel. 787/787–5151, (Nonreporting) **A**1 3 5 10 **S** Puerto Rico Department of Health, San Juan, PR
Primary Contact: Prudencio A. Laureano, Chief Executive Officer
CFO: Elsie Morales, Chief Financial Officer
CMO: Hector Cintron Principe, M.D., Director
CIO: Irma Duprey, Administrator Medical Records
CHR: Aurea De Leon, Chief Human Resources Officer
Control: State–Government, nonfederal **Service:** General Medical and Surgical

Staffed Beds: 102

CABO ROJO—Cabo Rojo County

✠ **HOSPITAL PSIQUIATRICO METROPOLITANO (404007)**, 108 Munoz Rivera Street, Zip 00623–4060, Mailing Address: P.O. Box 910, Zip 00623–0910; tel. 787/851–2025, (Nonreporting) **A**1 10
Primary Contact: Leonardo Colon, Executive Director
Web address: www.metropavia.com/CaboRojo.cfm
Control: Other not–for–profit (including NFP Corporation) **Service:** General Medical and Surgical

Staffed Beds: 43

CAGUAS—Caguas County

✠ **HOSPITAL HIMA SAN PABLO CAGUAS (400120)**, Avenida Munoz Marin, Zip 00726, Mailing Address: P.O. Box 4980, Zip 00726; tel. 787/653–3434 **A**1 2 3 5 10 **F**3 8 13 15 16 20 22 26 29 30 31 40 41 42 43 54 57 58 68 70 72 74 75 76 78 80 81 88 89 92 93 107 108 111 114 115 116 117 118 119 124 126 130 136 141 142 145 146 147 **P**8
Primary Contact: Jose E. Carballo, Executive Director
CFO: Luis A. Arroyo, Chief Financial Officer
CMO: Ivan E. Del Toro, M.D., Medical Director
CIO: Giovanni Piereschi, Vice President Enterprise Information and Chief Information Officer
CHR: Elena Robinson, Chief Human Resources Officer
CNO: Elenia Berrios, Chief Nursing Officer
Control: Corporation, Investor–owned, for–profit **Service:** General Medical and Surgical

Staffed Beds: 415 Admissions: 17935 Census: 323 Outpatient Visits: 85225 Births: 1780

☐ **HOSPITAL MENONITA DE CAGUAS (400104)**, P.O. Box 6660, Zip 00726–6660; tel. 787/653–0550, (Nonreporting) **A**1 5 10
Primary Contact: Rogelio Diaz, Administrator
Control: Other not–for–profit (including NFP Corporation) **Service:** General Medical and Surgical

Staffed Beds: 25

CAROLINA—Carolina County

✠ **HOSPITAL DE LA UNIVERSIDAD DE PUERTO RICO/DR. FEDERICO TRILLA (400112)**, 65th Infanteria, KM 8 3, Zip 00984, Mailing Address: P.O. Box 6021, Zip 00984; tel. 787/757–1800, (Nonreporting) **A**1 3 5 10
Primary Contact: Diraida Maldonado, Chief Executive Officer
COO: Diraida Maldonado, Chief Executive Officer
CFO: Yolanda Quinonez, Chief Financial Officer
CMO: Marina Roman, M.D., Medical Director
CIO: Francisco Perez, Manager Management Information Systems
CHR: Betzaida Jimenez, Director Human Resources
Web address: www.hospitalupr.org
Control: Corporation, Investor–owned, for–profit **Service:** General Medical and Surgical

Staffed Beds: 250

CASTANER—Lares County

★ **CASTANER GENERAL HOSPITAL (400010)**, KM 64–2, Route 135, Zip 00631, Mailing Address: P.O. Box 1003, Zip 00631; tel. 787/829–5010, (Nonreporting) **A**3 5 10
Primary Contact: Domingo Monroig, Executive Director
COO: Agustin Ponce, Supervisor Maintenance
CFO: Guillermo Jimenez, Director Finance
CMO: Jose O. Rodriguez, M.D., Medical Director
CIO: Domingo Monroig, Executive Director
CHR: Nydimar Salcedo, Chief Human Resources Officer
CNO: Margarita Rentas, R.N., Nursing Director
Control: Other not–for–profit (including NFP Corporation) **Service:** General Medical and Surgical

Staffed Beds: 24

Other Associated Areas

CAYEY—Cayey County

☒ **HOSPITAL MENONITA DE CAYEY (400013)**, 4 H. Mendoza Street,
Zip 00736–3801, Mailing Address: P.O. Box 373130, Zip 00737–3130;
tel. 787/263–1001, (Nonreporting) **A**1 5 10
Primary Contact: Pedro Melendez, Chief Executive Director
COO: Leda Marta R Mercado, Chief Operating Officer
CFO: Jose E. Solivan, Chief Financial Officer
CMO: Luis J Rodriquez Saenz, M.D., Medical Director
CIO: Daniza Morales, Chief Information Officer
CHR: Evelyn Padilla Ortiz, Director Human Resources
Web address: www.hospitalmenonita.com
Control: Other not–for–profit (including NFP Corporation) **Service:** General
Medical and Surgical

Staffed Beds: 208

CIDRA—Cidra County

☒ **FIRST HOSPITAL PANAMERICANO (404004)**, State Road 787 KM 1 5,
Zip 00739, Mailing Address: P.O. Box 1400, Zip 00739; tel. 787/739–5555,
(Nonreporting) **A**1 3 5 10 **S** Universal Health Services, Inc., King of Prussia, PA
Primary Contact: Astro Munoz, Executive Director
COO: Tim McCarthy, President Puerto Rico Division
CFO: Arthur Fernandez, Chief Financial Officer
CMO: Arlene Martinez–Nieto, M.D., Chief Medical Officer
CIO: Tomas Rodriguez, Chief Information Technology Officer
CHR: Shirley Ayala, Director Human Resources
Web address: www.hospitalpanamericano.com
Control: Corporation, Investor–owned, for–profit **Service:** Psychiatric

Staffed Beds: 153

COTO LAUREL—Ponce County

★ **HOSPITAL SAN CRISTOBAL (400113)**, 506 Carr Road, Zip 00780;
tel. 787/848–2100, (Nonreporting) **A**3 5 10
Primary Contact: Pedro L. Benetti–Loyola, Administrator
COO: Pedro L. Benetti–Loyola, Senior Executive and Vice President
CFO: Marian Collazo, Director Finance
CMO: Ramon Rodriguez Rivas, M.D., Medical Director
CIO: Ramon Acevedo, Supervisor Information Systems
CHR: Candie Rodriguez, Director Human Resources
Web address: www.hospitalsancristobal.com
Control: Corporation, Investor–owned, for–profit **Service:** Other specialty

Staffed Beds: 103

FAJARDO—Fajardo County

★ **CARIBBEAN MEDICAL CENTER (400131)**, 151 Avenue Osvaldo Molina,
Zip 00738–4013, Mailing Address: Call Box 70006, Zip 00738–7006;
tel. 787/801–0081, (Nonreporting) **A**10
Primary Contact: Rafael Santos, Executive Director
CMO: Miguel Rodriguez, Medical Director
Control: Other not–for–profit (including NFP Corporation) **Service:** General
Medical and Surgical

Staffed Beds: 39

☒ **HOSPITAL SAN PABLO DEL ESTE (400125)**, Avenida General Valero, 404,
Zip 00738, Mailing Address: P.O. Box 1028, Zip 00738–1028;
tel. 787/863–0505, (Nonreporting) **A**1 10
Primary Contact: Aixa Irizarry, Executive Director
CFO: Luis A. Arroyo, Chief Financial Officer
CMO: Manuel Navas, M.D., Medical Director
CHR: Vilma Rodriguez, Director Human Resources
Web address: www.sanpablo.com
Control: Corporation, Investor–owned, for–profit **Service:** General Medical and
Surgical

Staffed Beds: 145

GUAYAMA—Guayama County

☒ **HOSPITAL EPISCOPAL SAN LUCAS GUAYAMA (400048)**, Avenue Pedro
Albizu Campos, Zip 00784, Mailing Address: PO Box 10011, Zip 00785–1006;
tel. 787/864–4300, (Nonreporting) **A**1 3 5 10
Primary Contact: Julio Colon, CPA, Chief Executive Officer
COO: Arnaldo Rodriguez Sanchez, M.D., Chief Operating Officer
CFO: Rosemary De La Cruz, Chief Financial Officer
CMO: Gerson Jimenez, M.D., Medical Director
CHR: Ivette Lacot, Director Human Resources
Web address: www.ssepr.com
Control: Church–operated, Nongovernment, not–for profit **Service:** General
Medical and Surgical

Staffed Beds: 115

★ **HOSPITAL SANTA ROSA (400009)**, Veterans Avenue, Zip 00784, Mailing
Address: P.O. Box 10008, Zip 00785; tel. 787/864–0101 **A**10 **F**15 18 20 40
45 46 70 81 89 107 111 119 130
Primary Contact: Fernando Alarcon, Executive Director
CFO: Edwin De Jesus, Comptroller
CMO: Ausberto Alejandro, M.D., President
CIO: Waleska Rolon, Manager
Control: Other not–for–profit (including NFP Corporation) **Service:** General
Medical and Surgical

| **Staffed Beds:** 66 **Admissions:** 2478 **Census:** 26 **Outpatient Visits:** 40100 |
| **Births:** 0 **Personnel:** 122 |

GUAYNABO—Guaynabo County

PROFESSIONAL HOSPITAL GUAYNABO (400122), Carretera 199 Km 1.2
Avenue, Zip 00969, Mailing Address: PO Box 1609, Zip 00970;
tel. 787/708–6560, (Nonreporting) **A**3 10
Primary Contact: Leonardo Valentin, Chief Executive Officer
Web address: www.professionalhospital.com
Control: Other not–for–profit (including NFP Corporation) **Service:** Psychiatric

Staffed Beds: 54

HATO REY—San Juan County, See San Juan

HUMACAO—Humacao County

HOSPITAL DR. DOMINGUEZ See Hospital Oriente

☒ **HOSPITAL HIMA DE HUMACAO (400005)**, 3 Font Martelo Street,
Zip 00791–3342, Mailing Address: P.O. Box 639, Zip 00792–0639;
tel. 787/656–2424, (Nonreporting) **A**1 10
Primary Contact: Jenni Melendez, Executive Director
COO: Carlos M. Pineiro, President
CFO: Luis A. Arroyo, Chief Financial Officer
CMO: Francisco R. Carballo, M.D., Medical Director
CIO: Giovanni Piereschi, Vice President Management Information Systems
CHR: Iris Abreu, Supervisor Human Resources
Control: Corporation, Investor–owned, for–profit **Service:** General Medical and
Surgical

Staffed Beds: 64

★ **HOSPITAL ORIENTE (400011)**, 300 Font Martelo Street, Zip 00791–3230,
Mailing Address: P.O. Box 699, Zip 00792–0699; tel. 787/852–0505,
(Nonreporting) **A**10
Primary Contact: Marlene Morales, Administrator
CFO: Ivonne Rivera, Director Finance
CMO: Carmelo Herrero, M.D., Medical Director
CHR: Ivonne Lopez, Director Human Resources
Control: Corporation, Investor–owned, for–profit **Service:** General Medical and
Surgical

Staffed Beds: 71

★ **RYDER MEMORIAL HOSPITAL (400007)**, 355 Font Martelo Street,
Zip 00791–3249, Mailing Address: P.O. Box 859, Zip 00792–0859;
tel. 787/852–0768, (Nonreporting) **A**10
Primary Contact: Jose R. Feliciano, Chief Executive Officer
CFO: Jose O. Ortiz, Chief Financial Officer
CMO: Raul Ramos Pereira, M.D., Medical Director
CIO: Joseph V. Cruz, Chief Information Officer
CHR: Maria Figueroa, Director Human Resources
CNO: Aurelis Burgus, Nursing Director
Web address: www.hryder@prtc.net
Control: Other not–for–profit (including NFP Corporation) **Service:** General
Medical and Surgical

Staffed Beds: 165

MANATI—Manati County

☒ **DOCTORS CENTER (400118)**, KM 47–7, Zip 00674, Mailing Address: P.O. Box
30532, Zip 00674; tel. 787/854–3322 **A**1 10 **F**3 15 20 26 34 40 41 45 46 51
57 60 64 70 76 79 81 82 87 89 107 108 110 111 114 117 119 130 145
146 148 **P**6
Primary Contact: Carlos Blanco, M.D., Administrator
Control: Corporation, Investor–owned, for–profit **Service:** General Medical and
Surgical

| **Staffed Beds:** 250 **Admissions:** 15249 **Census:** 236 **Outpatient Visits:** 8326 |
| **Births:** 1147 **Total Expense ($000):** 82391 **Payroll Expense ($000):** 22180 |

Hospital, Medicare Provider Number, Address, Telephone, Approval, Facility, and Physician Codes, Health Care System

★ American Hospital Association (AHA) membership   ○ Healthcare Facilities Accreditation Program   ⇑ Center for Improvement in Healthcare Quality Accreditation
□ The Joint Commission accreditation   ◇ DNV Healthcare Inc. accreditation   △ Commission on Accreditation of Rehabilitation Facilities (CARF) accreditation

★ **HEALTHSOUTH HOSPITAL OF MANATI (403026)**, Carretera 2, Kilometro 47 7, Zip 00674; tel. 787/621–3800, (Nonreporting) **A**10 **S** HEALTHSOUTH Corporation, Birmingham, AL
Primary Contact: Waleska Crespo–Rivera, Chief Executive Officer
CFO: Jesus M. Corazon, Controller
CMO: Jamie L. Marrero, M.D., Medical Director
CHR: Erika Landrau, Director Human Resources
CNO: Evelyn Diaz, R.N., Chief Nursing Officer
Web address: www.healthsouth.com
Control: Corporation, Investor–owned, for–profit **Service:** Rehabilitation

Staffed Beds: 40

⊞ **HOSPITAL MANATI MEDICAL CENTER (400114)**, Calle Hernandez, Carrion 668, Zip 00674, Mailing Address: P.O. Box 1142, Zip 00674–1142; tel. 787/621–3700, (Nonreporting) **A**1 3 5 10
Primary Contact: Jose S. Rosado, Executive Director
CFO: Noriselle Rivera–Pol, Vice President Finance
CMO: Luis R. Rosa–Toledo, M.D., Medical Director
CIO: Alberto Medina, Information Technology Senior Consultant
CHR: Nilda Paravisini, Director Human Resources
Web address: www.manatimedical.com
Control: Corporation, Investor–owned, for–profit **Service:** General Medical and Surgical

Staffed Beds: 235

MAYAGUEZ—Mayaguez County

⊞ **BELLA VISTA HOSPITAL (400014)**, State Road 349, Zip 00680, Mailing Address: P.O. Box 1750, Zip 00681; tel. 787/834–6000, (Nonreporting) **A**1 3 5 10
Primary Contact: Luis Rivera Maldonado, Chief Executive Officer
CFO: Enrique Rivera, Chief Financial Officer
CMO: Miguel Cruz, M.D., Medical Director
CHR: Benjamin Astacio, Director Human Resources
Web address: www.bvhpr.org
Control: Church–operated, Nongovernment, not–for profit **Service:** General Medical and Surgical

Staffed Beds: 157

⊞ **DR. RAMON E. BETANCES HOSPITAL–MAYAGUEZ MEDICAL CENTER BRANCH (400103)**, 410 Hostos Avenue, Zip 00680–1501, Mailing Address: P.O. Box 600, Zip 00681–0600; tel. 787/652–9200, (Nonreporting) **A**1 3 5 10
Primary Contact: Jaime Maestre, Chief Executive Officer
CMO: Milton D. Carrero, M.D., Medical Director
CHR: Betsmari Medina, Director Human Resources
Control: State–Government, nonfederal **Service:** General Medical and Surgical

Staffed Beds: 181

★ **HOSPITAL PEREA (400123)**, 15 Basora Street, Zip 00681, Mailing Address: P.O. Box 170, Zip 00681; tel. 787/834–0101, (Nonreporting) **A**3 10 **S** United Medical Corporation, Windermere, FL
Primary Contact: Jorge I. Martinez, Executive Director
CFO: Joannie Garcia, CPA, Director Finance
CMO: Humberto Olivencia, M.D., Medical Director
Web address: www.paviahealth.com/perea_hospital.htm
Control: Corporation, Investor–owned, for–profit **Service:** General Medical and Surgical

Staffed Beds: 103

HOSPITAL SAN ANTONIO (18487), Calle Drive Ramon Emeterio Betances N. #18, Zip 00680; tel. 787/834–0050, (Nonreporting) **A**3 5
Primary Contact: Francisco Martinez, Executive Director
Control: Other not–for–profit (including NFP Corporation) **Service:** General Medical and Surgical

Staffed Beds: 25

MOCA— County

CENTRO DE TRAUMA (400127), Calle Menlo Miranda, Zip 00676; tel. 787/777–3535, (Nonreporting)
Control: Other not–for–profit (including NFP Corporation) **Service:** General Medical and Surgical

Staffed Beds: 25

★ **HOSPITAL SAN CARLOS BORROMEO (400111)**, 550 Concepcion Vera Ayala, Zip 00676; tel. 787/877–8000 **A**10 **F**8 15 29 30 34 40 45 70 74 75 76 79 81 89 107 111 115 119 130 133 145 146 148 **P**8
Primary Contact: Rosaida M. Crespo, Executive Director
COO: Rosaida M. Crespo, Executive Director
CFO: Irma Cabrera, Finance Director
CMO: Erick Nieves, M.D., Medical Director
CIO: Juan Carlos Soto, Director Information Systems
CHR: Migdalia Ortiz, Director Human Resources
CNO: Luz M. Velez, Director–Administration of Nursing Services
Web address: www.hscbpr.org
Control: Other not–for–profit (including NFP Corporation) **Service:** General Medical and Surgical

Staffed Beds: 106 Admissions: 4692 Census: 61 Outpatient Visits: 43354 Births: 643 Total Expense ($000): 26089 Payroll Expense ($000): 8938 Personnel: 361

PONCE—Ponce County

⊞ **DR. PILA'S HOSPITAL (400003)**, Avenida Las Americas, Zip 00731, Mailing Address: P.O. Box 1910, Zip 00733–1910; tel. 787/848–5600 **A**1 3 5 10 **F**8 15 20 22 29 30 34 35 36 40 41 45 49 50 57 59 62 64 65 70 72 75 77 79 81 86 87 100 107 110 111 114 119 130 146 148
Primary Contact: Rafael Alvarado, Chief Executive Officer
Web address: www.drpila.com
Control: Corporation, Investor–owned, for–profit **Service:** General Medical and Surgical

Staffed Beds: 143 Admissions: 6619 Census: 94 Outpatient Visits: 69062 Births: 457

⊞ **HOSPITAL DE DAMAS (400022)**, Ponce by Pass, Zip 00731; tel. 787/840–8686, (Nonreporting) **A**1 3 5 10
Primary Contact: Maria Torres Bernal, Administrator
CFO: Julio Colon, Financial Director
CMO: Pedro Benitez, M.D., Medical Director
CIO: Bienvenido Ortiz, Coordinator Information Systems
CHR: Gilberto Cuevas, Director Human Resources
CNO: Sandra Dominicci, Nursing Director
Web address: www.hospitaldamas.com
Control: Other not–for–profit (including NFP Corporation) **Service:** General Medical and Surgical

Staffed Beds: 251

HOSPITAL DE PSIQUIATRIA FORENSE, Road 14, Zip 00731; tel. 787/844–0210, (Nonreporting)
Web address: www.bestmentalhealthfacilities.com/hospital–psiquiatria–forenseponce–in–ponce–pr–731/
Control: State–Government, nonfederal **Service:** Psychiatric

Staffed Beds: 25

★ **HOSPITAL ONCOLOGICO ANDRES GRILLASCA (400028)**, Centro Medico De Ponce, Zip 00733, Mailing Address: P.O. Box 331324, Zip 00733–1324; tel. 787/848–0800, (Nonreporting) **A**3 5
Primary Contact: Manuel J. Vazquez, Executive Administrator
CMO: Roberto Velasquez, M.D., Medical Director
CIO: Maria T. Teissonniere, Director Public Relations
CHR: Carlos T. Santiago, Director Human Resources
Control: Other not–for–profit (including NFP Corporation) **Service:** Cancer

Staffed Beds: 49

★ **INSPIRA PONCE (404008)**, Calle Guadalupe, #184, Piso2, Zip 00730; tel. 787/709–4130, (Nonreporting) **A**10
Primary Contact: Alberto M. Varela, M.D., President
Web address: www.inspirapr.com
Control: Corporation, Investor–owned, for–profit **Service:** Psychiatric

Staffed Beds: 30

⊞ **ST. LUKE'S EPISCOPAL HOSPITAL (400044)**, 917 Tito Castro Avenue, Zip 00731–4717, Mailing Address: P.O. Box 336810, Zip 00733–6810; tel. 787/844–2080, (Nonreporting) **A**1 3 5 10
Primary Contact: Julio Colon, Interim President and Chief Executive Officer
CFO: Julio Colon, Chief Financial Officer
CMO: Jenaro Scarano, M.D., Medical Director
CHR: Juan Salazar, Director Human Resources
Web address: www.sanlucaspr.com
Control: Church–operated, Nongovernment, not–for profit **Service:** General Medical and Surgical

Staffed Beds: 334

RIO PIEDRAS—San Juan County, See San Juan

SAN GERMAN—San German County

☒ **HOSPITAL DE LA CONCEPCION (400021)**, Carr 2, Km 173, Bo Cain Alto, Zip 00683–3920, Mailing Address: P.O. Box 285, Zip 00683–0285; tel. 787/892–1860 **A**1 3 5 10 **F**8 13 15 18 20 29 30 40 45 46 58 59 70 72 74 75 76 79 81 87 89 91 111 115 130 145 146
Primary Contact: Felicita Bonilla, Administrator
COO: Gustavo Almodovar, Executive Director
CFO: Lizmari Calderon, Director Finance
CMO: Ivan Acosta, M.D., Medical Director
CIO: Daniel Ferreira, Director Management Information Systems
CHR: Ada Bermudez, Director Human Resources
CNO: Amanda Caraballo, Nursing Director
Web address: www.hospitalconcepcion.org
Control: Church–operated, Nongovernment, not–for profit **Service:** General Medical and Surgical

> **Staffed Beds:** 167 **Admissions:** 7527 **Census:** 132 **Outpatient Visits:** 49528 **Births:** 744 **Total Expense ($000):** 71686 **Payroll Expense ($000):** 25426

★ **HOSPITAL METROPOLITANO SAN GERMAN (400126)**, Calle Javilla Al Costado Parque de Bombas, Zip 00683; tel. 787/892–5300 **A**10 **F**3 13 40 45 70 76 89 107 110 111 114 115 119 148
Primary Contact: Luis Berdiel, Chief Executive Officer
Control: Individual, Investor–owned, for–profit **Service:** General Medical and Surgical

> **Staffed Beds:** 76 **Admissions:** 3312 **Census:** 46 **Outpatient Visits:** 40448 **Births:** 509

SAN JUAN—San Juan County
(Mailing Addresses - Hato Rey, Rio Piedras)

☒ **ASHFORD PRESBYTERIAN COMMUNITY HOSPITAL (400001)**, 1451 Avenue Ashford, Zip 00907–1511, Mailing Address: P.O. Box 9020032, Zip 00902–0032; tel. 787/721–2160 **A**1 5 10 **F**3 8 11 13 15 18 30 40 41 45 46 49 51 53 59 65 70 72 75 79 81 82 87 91 93 97 107 110 111 114 119 130 131 146 147 148 **P**5
Primary Contact: Pedro J. Gonzalez, FACHE, Chief Executive Officer
COO: Obdulia Medina, Associate Director for Administrative Support, Clinical Management and Ambulatory Care
CFO: Mayra Torres, CPA, Chief Financial Officer
CMO: Francisco de Torres, M.D., Medical Director
CIO: Sigfredo Irizarry, Information Technology Director
CHR: Irma Carrillo, Director Human Resources
CNO: Itza Soto, MSN, Nursing Executive
Web address: www.presbypr.com
Control: Other not–for–profit (including NFP Corporation) **Service:** General Medical and Surgical

> **Staffed Beds:** 181 **Admissions:** 10067 **Census:** 137 **Outpatient Visits:** 52526 **Births:** 2951 **Total Expense ($000):** 75562 **Payroll Expense ($000):** 24746 **Personnel:** 761

☒ **AUXILIO MUTUO HOSPITAL (400016)**, Ponce De Leon Avenue, Zip 00918–1000, Mailing Address: P.O. Box 191227, Zip 00919–1227; tel. 787/758–2000, (Nonreporting) **A**1 3 5 10
Primary Contact: Jorge L. Matta Serrano, Administrator
COO: Carmen Martin, Associate Administrator
CFO: Maria L. Marti, Director Fiscal Services
CMO: Jose Isado, M.D., Medical Director
CIO: Edgardo Rodriguez, Director Management Information Systems
CHR: Maria Vega, Director Human Resources
Web address: www.auxiliomutuo.com
Control: Other not–for–profit (including NFP Corporation) **Service:** General Medical and Surgical

> **Staffed Beds:** 483

☒ **CARDIOVASCULAR CENTER OF PUERTO RICO AND THE CARIBBEAN (400124)**, Americo Miranda Centro Medico, Zip 00936, Mailing Address: P.O. Box 366528, Zip 00936–6528; tel. 787/754–8500 **A**1 3 5 10 **F**3 17 18 19 20 21 22 23 24 25 26 29 30 34 40 57 60 67 68 70 75 86 87 89 100 107 108 114 115 118 119 130 135 137 140 148 **S** Puerto Rico Department of Health, San Juan, PR
Primary Contact: Carlos Cabrera, Executive Director
COO: Wilfredo Rabelo Millan, Chief Operating Officer
CFO: Arthur J. Fernandez del Valle, Chief Financial Officer
CMO: Jose E. Novoa Loyola, M.D., Medical Director
CIO: Eugenio Torres Ayala, Director Information Systems
CHR: Myriam T. Rodriguez Schmidt, Director Human Resources
CNO: Pedro Laureano Cantre, Chief Nursing Officer
Web address: www.cardiovascular.gobierno.pr
Control: City–Government, nonfederal **Service:** Heart

> **Staffed Beds:** 154 **Admissions:** 4646 **Census:** 101 **Outpatient Visits:** 33183 **Births:** 0

★ **DOCTORS' CENTER HOSPITAL SAN JUAN (400006)**, 1395 San Rafael Street, Zip 00909–2518, Mailing Address: Box 11338, Santurce Station, Zip 00910–3428; tel. 787/999–7620 **A**10 **F**29 40 41 45 46 70 76 77 78 81 89 107 119 130 148
Primary Contact: Norma Marrero, Executive Administrator
COO: Norma Marrero, Executive Administrator
CFO: Alejandro Santiago, Director Finance
CMO: Ubaldo Santiago, M.D., Chairman
CIO: Luis Alicea, Chief Information Officer
CHR: Carmen Perez, Director Human Resources
CNO: Lesbia Lopez, Chief Nursing Officer
Web address: www.tuhospitalfamiliar.com
Control: Corporation, Investor–owned, for–profit **Service:** General Medical and Surgical

> **Staffed Beds:** 152 **Admissions:** 6284 **Census:** 102 **Outpatient Visits:** 25518 **Births:** 187 **Total Expense ($000):** 33502 **Payroll Expense ($000):** 9879 **Personnel:** 404

★ **HEALTHSOUTH REHABILITATION HOSPITAL OF SAN JUAN (403025)**, University Hospital, 3rd Floor, Zip 00923, Mailing Address: P.O. Box 70344, Zip 00923; tel. 787/274–5100 **A**3 5 10 **F**29 77 90 93 **P**1 **S** HEALTHSOUTH Corporation, Birmingham, AL
Primary Contact: Daniel Del Castillo, Chief Executive Officer
CFO: Jesus M. Corazon, Controller
CMO: Eduardo Ramos, M.D., Medical Director
CHR: Frances Fuentes, Coordinator Human Resources
CNO: Zamarys Rivera, R.N., Chief Nursing Officer
Web address: www.healthsouthsanjuan.com
Control: Corporation, Investor–owned, for–profit **Service:** Rehabilitation

> **Staffed Beds:** 32 **Admissions:** 913 **Census:** 31 **Outpatient Visits:** 5619 **Births:** 0 **Total Expense ($000):** 7411 **Payroll Expense ($000):** 3499 **Personnel:** 99

★ **HOSPITAL DE PSIQUIATRIA (404006)**, Dr. Ramon Fernandez Marina, P.O. Box 2100, Zip 00936; tel. 787/766–4646, (Nonreporting) **A**3 5
Primary Contact: Griselle Hernandez, Executive Director
CMO: Brunilda Vazquez, Medical Director
CHR: Idalia Garcia, Chief Human Resources Officer
Control: State–Government, nonfederal **Service:** Psychiatric

> **Staffed Beds:** 153

☒ **HOSPITAL DEL MAESTRO (400004)**, 550 Sergio Cuevas, Zip 00918–3741, Mailing Address: P.O. Box 364708, Zip 00936–4708; tel. 787/758–8383, (Nonreporting) **A**1 10
Primary Contact: Jorge Torres Otero, Executive Director
CFO: Marisol Vargas, Director Finance
CMO: Jose Montalvo, M.D., Medical Director
CIO: Laura Rodriguez, Director Medical Records
CHR: Orlando Santiago, Human Resources Officer
Control: Corporation, Investor–owned, for–profit **Service:** General Medical and Surgical

> **Staffed Beds:** 250

☒ **HOSPITAL METROPOLITAN (400106)**, 1785 Carr 21, Zip 00921–3399, Mailing Address: P.O. Box 11981, Zip 00922; tel. 787/782–9999, (Nonreporting) **A**1 10
Primary Contact: Domingo Nevarez, Chief Executive Officer
CFO: Maritza Rodriguez, Chief Financial Officer
CMO: Maria de los Angeles Correa, M.D., Medical Director
CIO: Manuel Santiago, Chief Information Officer
Control: Corporation, Investor–owned, for–profit **Service:** General Medical and Surgical

> **Staffed Beds:** 127

☒ **HOSPITAL PAVIA–HATO REY (400128)**, 435 Ponce De Leon Avenue, Zip 00917–3428; tel. 787/641–2323, (Nonreporting) **A**1 3 5 10 **S** United Medical Corporation, Windermere, FL
Primary Contact: Guillermo Pastrana, Executive Director
Web address: www.paviahealth.com
Control: Corporation, Investor–owned, for–profit **Service:** General Medical and Surgical

> **Staffed Beds:** 180

Hospital, Medicare Provider Number, Address, Telephone, Approval, Facility, and Physician Codes, Health Care System

★ American Hospital Association (AHA) membership
☒ The Joint Commission accreditation
○ Healthcare Facilities Accreditation Program
◇ DNV Healthcare Inc. accreditation
⇑ Center for Improvement in Healthcare Quality Accreditation
△ Commission on Accreditation of Rehabilitation Facilities (CARF) accreditation

✠ **HOSPITAL PAVIA–SANTURCE (400019)**, 1462 Asia Street, Zip 00909–2143, Mailing Address: Box 11137, Santurce Station, Zip 00910–1137; tel. 787/727–6060 **A**1 10 **F**3 7 8 13 15 17 18 20 22 24 26 29 30 34 35 38 40 45 46 47 48 49 56 57 58 59 60 64 65 68 70 73 74 75 76 78 79 81 82 86 87 92 94 100 107 108 109 110 111 112 114 115 119 130 **S** United Medical Corporation, Windermere, FL
Primary Contact: Jose Luis Rodriguez, Chief Executive Officer
CFO: Francisco Espina, Director Finance
Web address: www.paviahealth.com
Control: Corporation, Investor–owned, for–profit **Service:** General Medical and Surgical

Staffed Beds: 197 **Admissions:** 9122 **Census:** 163 **Outpatient Visits:** 51909 **Births:** 1152 **Total Expense ($000):** 87465 **Payroll Expense ($000):** 24158

HOSPITAL PSIQUIATRICO CORRECCIONAL, PMB 302 P.O. Box 70344, Zip 00936; tel. 939/225–2400, (Nonreporting)
Primary Contact: Felicita E. Alvarado, Administrator
Control: State–Government, nonfederal **Service:** General Medical and Surgical

Staffed Beds: 25

✠ **HOSPITAL SAN FRANCISCO (400098)**, 371 Avenida De Diego, Zip 00923–1711, Mailing Address: P.O. Box 29025, Zip 00929–0025; tel. 787/767–5100, (Nonreporting) **A**1 10 **S** United Medical Corporation, Windermere, FL
Primary Contact: Marcos Aguila, Chief Executive Officer
CFO: Lizzette Rodriguez, Director Finance
CMO: Hector L. Cotto, M.D., Medical Director
CIO: Deborah Nieves, Director Management Information Systems
CHR: Sugehi Santiago, Director
Web address: www.metropavia.com/SanFrancisco.cfm
Control: Corporation, Investor–owned, for–profit **Service:** General Medical and Surgical

Staffed Beds: 150

★ **HOSPITAL SAN GERARDO (400121)**, 138 Avenue Winston Churchill, Zip 00926–6013; tel. 787/761–8383, (Nonreporting) **A**10
Primary Contact: Zaida Berlingeri, Administrator
Control: Other not–for–profit (including NFP Corporation) **Service:** Chronic disease

Staffed Beds: 60

✠ **I. GONZALEZ MARTINEZ ONCOLOGIC HOSPITAL (400012)**, Puerto Rico Medical Center, Hato Rey, Zip 00935, Mailing Address: P.O. Box 191811, Zip 00919–1811; tel. 787/765–2382, (Nonreporting) **A**1 2 3 5 10
Primary Contact: Jorge De Jesus, Executive Director
COO: Felix Ortiz Baez, Administrator
CFO: Yolanda Quinones, Director Finance
CMO: Carlos Chevere, M.D., Medical Director
CHR: Luz Maria Hernandez, Director Human Resources
Control: Other not–for–profit (including NFP Corporation) **Service:** General Medical and Surgical

Staffed Beds: 57

★ **INDUSTRIAL HOSPITAL**, Puerto Rico Medical Center, Zip 00936, Mailing Address: P.O. Box 365028, Zip 00936; tel. 787/754–2525, (Nonreporting)
Primary Contact: Jane Vega, Executive Director
CFO: Robert Bernier Casanova, Chief Financial Officer
CMO: Carmen Carrasquillo, M.D., Medical Director
CHR: Sonia M. Lebron, Human Resources Specialist
Control: State–Government, nonfederal **Service:** General Medical and Surgical

Staffed Beds: 108

✠ **SAN JORGE CHILDREN'S HOSPITAL**, 252 San Jorge Street, Santurce, Zip 00912–3310; tel. 787/727–1000, (Nonreporting) **A**1 3 5 **S** United Medical Corporation, Windermere, FL
Primary Contact: Domingo Cruz, Senior Vice President Operations
CFO: Jose Marrero, Director Finance
CMO: Luis Clavell, M.D., Medical Director
CIO: Rogelio Caballero, Chief Information Systems
CHR: Odette Burgos, Supervisor Human Resources
CNO: Leticia Fuentes, Nursing Director
Web address: www.sanjorgechildrenshospital.com
Control: Corporation, Investor–owned, for–profit **Service:** Children's general

Staffed Beds: 125

✠ **SAN JUAN CAPESTRANO HOSPITAL (404005)**, Rural Route 2, Box 11, Zip 00926; tel. 787/625–2900, (Nonreporting) **A**1 10 **S** Acadia Healthcare Company, Inc., Franklin, TN
Primary Contact: Marta Rivera Plaza, Chief Executive Officer and Managing Director
CFO: Julia Cruz, Chief Financial Officer
CMO: Jose' Alonso, M.D., Medical Director
CIO: Ana Morandeira, Director Marketing
CHR: Luis Rivera, Director Human Resources
Web address: www.sjcapestrano.com
Control: Corporation, Investor–owned, for–profit **Service:** Psychiatric

Staffed Beds: 108

✠ **SAN JUAN CITY HOSPITAL (400015)**, Puerto Rico Medical Center, Zip 00928, Mailing Address: PMB 79, P.O. Box 70344, Zip 00936–8344; tel. 787/766–2222, (Nonreporting) **A**1 3 5 10
Primary Contact: Jesus Nieves, Executive Director
COO: Norma Marcano, Chief Operating Officer
CFO: Jaime Rodriguez, Chief Financial Officer
CMO: Raul Reyes, M.D., Medical Director
CIO: Gustavo Mesa, Chief Information Officer
CHR: Jose Garcia, Chief Human Resources Officer
Web address: www.massalud.com
Control: City–Government, nonfederal **Service:** General Medical and Surgical

Staffed Beds: 267

★ **UNIVERSITY HOSPITAL (400061)**, Nineyas 869 Rio Piedras, Zip 00922, Mailing Address: P.O. Box 2116, Zip 00922; tel. 787/754–0101 **A**3 5 10 **F**3 31 39 45 49 60 70 74 75 76 77 78 79 80 82 87 92 93 96 100 119 130 136 146 148 **S** Puerto Rico Department of Health, San Juan, PR
Primary Contact: Jorge Matta Gonzalez, Executive Director
CFO: Janet Baez, Director
CMO: Ricardo Moscoso, M.D., Medical Director
CIO: Josue Martinez, Coordinator Information Systems
CHR: Ramomita Navarro, Director Human Resources
Control: State–Government, nonfederal **Service:** General Medical and Surgical

Staffed Beds: 220 **Admissions:** 9317 **Census:** 175 **Births:** 1129 **Personnel:** 774

✠ **UNIVERSITY PEDIATRIC HOSPITAL (403301)**, Barrio Monacenno, Carretera 22, Rio Piedras, Zip 00935, Mailing Address: P.O. Box 191079, San Juan, Zip 00910–1070; tel. 787/777–3535, (Nonreporting) **A**1 3 5 10 **S** Puerto Rico Department of Health, San Juan, PR
Primary Contact: Humberto Monserrate, Executive Director
CMO: Myrna Quinones Feliciano, M.D., Medical Director
Web address: www.md.rcm.upr.edu/pediatrics/university_pediatric_hospital.php
Control: State–Government, nonfederal **Service:** Children's general

Staffed Beds: 145

✠ △ **VETERANS AFFAIRS CARIBBEAN HEALTHCARE SYSTEM**, 10 Casia Street, Zip 00921–3201; tel. 787/641–7582, (Nonreporting) **A**1 2 3 5 7 8 **S** Department of Veterans Affairs, Washington, DC
Primary Contact: DeWayne Hamlin, Director
CFO: Oscar Rodriguez, Chief Fiscal Officer
CMO: Antonio Sanchez, M.D., Chief of Staff
CIO: Manuel Negron, Chief Information Technology Service
CHR: Omar Ahmed, Acting Manager Human Resources
CNO: Kathleen Ruiz, M.D., Associate Director Patient Care Services
Web address: www.caribbean.va.gov/
Control: Veterans Affairs, Government, federal **Service:** General Medical and Surgical

Staffed Beds: 330

UTUADO—San Juan County

★ **METROPOLITANO DE LA MONTANA (400130)**, Calle Issac Gonzalez, Zip 00641, Mailing Address: P.O. Box 2600, Zip 00641; tel. 787/933–1100, (Nonreporting) **A**10
Primary Contact: Fernando Colon, Administrator
Web address: www.metropavia.com/DeLaMontana.cfm
Control: Corporation, Investor–owned, for–profit **Service:** General Medical and Surgical

Staffed Beds: 25

VEGA BAJA—Vega Alta County

★ **WILMA N. VAZQUEZ MEDICAL CENTER (400115)**, KM 39 1/2 Road 2, Call Box 7001, Zip 00694; tel. 787/858–1580, (Nonreporting) **A**10
Primary Contact: Ramon J. Vilar, Administrator
COO: Jose O. Pabon, Director Operations
CFO: Youdie Reynolds–Gossette, Controller
CMO: Jorge Feria, M.D., President Medical Staff
CIO: Miguel Aponte, Supervisor Management Information Systems
CHR: Aymette Garcia, Manager Human Resources
Control: Corporation, Investor–owned, for–profit **Service:** General Medical and Surgical

Staffed Beds: 150

Many Facility Codes have changed. Please refer to the AHA Guide Code Chart. © 2016 AHA Guide

YAUCO—Yauco County

✠ **HOSPITAL METROPOLITANO DR. TITO MATTEI (400110)**, Carretera 128 KM 1, Zip 00698, Mailing Address: P.O. Box 5643, Zip 00698; tel. 787/856–1000 **A**1 5 10 **F**2 3 8 13 15 18 26 29 34 37 38 40 41 44 45 46 49 60 62 67 68 74 75 76 79 81 92 93 98 102 103 105 107 108 110 111 114 115 119 127 144 145 148 **P**8
Primary Contact: Dinorah Hernandez, Executive Director
CFO: Elizabeth Gonzalez, Chief Financial Officer
CMO: Manuel Ramirez Soto, M.D., Medical Director
CIO: Edson Ortiz, Chief Information Officer
Web address: www.hmyauco.com
Control: Corporation, Investor–owned, for–profit **Service:** General Medical and Surgical

Staffed Beds: 114 **Admissions:** 5719 **Census:** 75 **Births:** 253

VIRGIN ISLANDS

CHRISTIANSTED—St. Croix County

☐ **GOVERNOR JUAN F. LUIS HOSPITAL (480002)**, 4007 Estate Diamond Ruby, Zip 00820–4421; tel. 340/778–6311, (Nonreporting) **A**1 10
Primary Contact: Darice S. Plaskett, R.N., FACHE, Interim Chief Executive Officer
CFO: Rosalie Javois, Chief Financial Officer
CMO: Robert Centeno, M.D., Chief Medical Officer
CIO: Reuben D. Molloy, Chief Information Officer
CHR: Joan Jean–Baptiste, Vice President Human Resources
Web address: www.jflusvi.org
Control: State–Government, nonfederal **Service:** General Medical and Surgical

Staffed Beds: 108

SAINT THOMAS—St. Thomas County

☐ **SCHNEIDER REGIONAL MEDICAL CENTER (480001)**, 9048 Sugar Estate, Charlotte Amalie, Zip 00802; tel. 340/776–8311 **A**1 10 **F**1 3 4 8 13 15 16 17 18 20 22 26 29 30 31 34 40 41 45 46 49 50 55 56 57 59 60 64 65 67 68 70 72 73 74 75 76 77 78 79 80 81 85 86 87 88 90 91 92 93 94 97 98 100 101 102 107 108 114 119 121 128 130 132 148 **P**5
Primary Contact: Bernard Wheatley, FACHE, Chief Executive Officer
CMO: Thelma Ruth Watson, M.D., Medical Director
CIO: J. C. Creque, Director Management Information Systems
CHR: Marlene J. Adams, Director Human Resources
Web address: www.rlshospital.org
Control: Hospital district or authority, Government, nonfederal **Service:** General Medical and Surgical

Staffed Beds: 86 **Admissions:** 3508 **Census:** 61 **Outpatient Visits:** 22377 **Births:** 659 **Total Expense ($000):** 94946 **Payroll Expense ($000):** 38498 **Personnel:** 519

Hospital, Medicare Provider Number, Address, Telephone, Approval, Facility, and Physician Codes, Health Care System

★ American Hospital Association (AHA) membership
☐ The Joint Commission accreditation
○ Healthcare Facilities Accreditation Program
◇ DNV Healthcare Inc. accreditation
⇑ Center for Improvement in Healthcare Quality Accreditation
△ Commission on Accreditation of Rehabilitation Facilities (CARF) accreditation

U.S. Government Hospitals
Outside the United States, by Area

GERMANY

Heidelberg: ★ Heidelberg Army Community Hospital, APO, CMR 242, AE 09042

Landstuhl: ★ Landstuhl Army Regional Medical Center, APO, CMR 402, AE 09180

Wuerzburg: ★ Wuerzburg Army Community Hospital, APO, USAMEDDAC Wuerzburg, Ut 26610, AE 09244

ITALY

Naples: ★ U. S. Naval Hospital, FPO, none, AE 09619

SPAIN

Rota: ★ U. S. Naval Hospital, Rota, FPO, PSC 819, Box 18, AE 09645–2500

JAPAN

Yokosuka: ★ U. S. Naval Hospital, Box 1487, UNIT 96350

SOUTH KOREA

Seoul: ★ Brian Allgood Army Community Hospital, 121st General Hospital, UNIT 96205

Yongsan: Medcom 18th Commander, Facilities Division Eamc L EM, UNIT 96205

TAIWAN

Taipei: ★ U. S. Naval Hospital Taipei, No 300 Shin–Pai Road, Sec 2

This section is an index of all hospitals in alphabetical order by hospital name, followed by the city, state, and page reference to the hospital's listing in Section A.

Index of Hospitals

B

BANNER FORT COLLINS MEDICAL CENTER, FORT COLLINS, CO, p. A105
BANNER GATEWAY MEDICAL CENTER, GILBERT, AZ, p. A32
BANNER GOLDFIELD MEDICAL CENTER, APACHE JUNCTION, AZ, p. A31
BANNER HEART HOSPITAL, MESA, AZ, p. A34
BANNER IRONWOOD MEDICAL CENTER, SAN TAN VALLEY, AZ, p. A38
BANNER LASSEN MEDICAL CENTER, SUSANVILLE, CA, p. A95
BANNER PAYSON MEDICAL CENTER, PAYSON, AZ, p. A35
BANNER THUNDERBIRD MEDICAL CENTER, GLENDALE, AZ, p. A33
BAPTIST CHILDREN'S HOSPITAL, MIAMI, FLORIDA (see BAPTIST HEALTH SOUTH FLORIDA, BAPTIST HOSPITAL OF MIAMI), p. A136
BAPTIST EASLEY HOSPITAL, EASLEY, SC, p. A565
BAPTIST EMERGENCY HOSPITAL – HAUSMAN, SAN ANTONIO, TEXAS (see BAPTIST EMERGENCY HOSPITAL – THOUSAND OAKS), p. A645
BAPTIST EMERGENCY HOSPITAL – OVERLOOK, SAN ANTONIO, TEXAS (see BAPTIST EMERGENCY HOSPITAL – THOUSAND OAKS), p. A645
BAPTIST EMERGENCY HOSPITAL – SCHERTZ, SCHERTZ, TEXAS (see BAPTIST EMERGENCY HOSPITAL – THOUSAND OAKS), p. A645
BAPTIST EMERGENCY HOSPITAL – THOUSAND OAKS, SAN ANTONIO, TX, p. A645
BAPTIST EMERGENCY HOSPITAL – WESTOVER HILLS, SAN ANTONIO, TEXAS (see BAPTIST EMERGENCY HOSPITAL – THOUSAND OAKS), p. A645
BAPTIST HEALTH CORBIN, CORBIN, KY, p. A258
BAPTIST HEALTH EXTENDED CARE HOSPITAL, LITTLE ROCK, AR, p. A48
BAPTIST HEALTH FLOYD, NEW ALBANY, IN, p. A219
BAPTIST HEALTH LA GRANGE, LA GRANGE, KY, p. A262
BAPTIST HEALTH LEXINGTON, LEXINGTON, KY, p. A262
BAPTIST HEALTH LOUISVILLE, LOUISVILLE, KY, p. A264
BAPTIST HEALTH MADISONVILLE, MADISONVILLE, KY, p. A265
BAPTIST HEALTH MEDICAL CENTER – NORTH LITTLE ROCK, NORTH LITTLE ROCK, AR, p. A51
BAPTIST HEALTH MEDICAL CENTER–ARKADELPHIA, ARKADELPHIA, AR, p. A43
BAPTIST HEALTH MEDICAL CENTER–HEBER SPRINGS, HEBER SPRINGS, AR, p. A47
BAPTIST HEALTH MEDICAL CENTER–HOT SPRING COUNTY, MALVERN, AR, p. A49
BAPTIST HEALTH MEDICAL CENTER–LITTLE ROCK, LITTLE ROCK, AR, p. A48
BAPTIST HEALTH MEDICAL CENTER–STUTTGART, STUTTGART, AR, p. A53
BAPTIST HEALTH PADUCAH, PADUCAH, KY, p. A267
BAPTIST HEALTH REHABILITATION INSTITUTE, LITTLE ROCK, AR, p. A49
BAPTIST HEALTH RICHMOND, RICHMOND, KY, p. A268
BAPTIST HEALTH SOUTH FLORIDA, BAPTIST HOSPITAL OF MIAMI, MIAMI, FL, p. A136
BAPTIST HEALTH SOUTH FLORIDA, DOCTORS HOSPITAL, CORAL GABLES, FL, p. A126
BAPTIST HEALTH SOUTH FLORIDA, HOMESTEAD HOSPITAL, HOMESTEAD, FL, p. A131
BAPTIST HEALTH SOUTH FLORIDA, MARINERS HOSPITAL, TAVERNIER, FL, p. A148
BAPTIST HEALTH SOUTH FLORIDA, SOUTH MIAMI HOSPITAL, MIAMI, FL, p. A136
BAPTIST HEALTH SOUTH FLORIDA, WEST KENDALL BAPTIST HOSPITAL, MIAMI, FL, p. A136
BAPTIST HOSPITAL, PENSACOLA, FL, p. A142
BAPTIST HOSPITALS OF SOUTHEAST TEXAS, BEAUMONT, TX, p. A601
BAPTIST HOSPITALS OF SOUTHEAST TEXAS FANNIN BEHAVIORAL HEALTH CENTER, BEAUMONT, TEXAS (see BAPTIST HOSPITALS OF SOUTHEAST TEXAS), p. A601
BAPTIST MEDICAL CENTER, SAN ANTONIO, TX, p. A645
BAPTIST MEDICAL CENTER ATTALA, KOSCIUSKO, MS, p. A360
BAPTIST MEDICAL CENTER BEACHES, JACKSONVILLE BEACH, FL, p. A132
BAPTIST MEDICAL CENTER EAST, MONTGOMERY, AL, p. A23
BAPTIST MEDICAL CENTER JACKSONVILLE, JACKSONVILLE, FL, p. A131
BAPTIST MEDICAL CENTER LEAKE, CARTHAGE, MS, p. A356
BAPTIST MEDICAL CENTER NASSAU, FERNANDINA BEACH, FL, p. A128
BAPTIST MEDICAL CENTER SOUTH, JACKSONVILLE, FLORIDA (see BAPTIST MEDICAL CENTER JACKSONVILLE), p. A131
BAPTIST MEDICAL CENTER SOUTH, MONTGOMERY, AL, p. A23
BAPTIST MEDICAL CENTER YAZOO, YAZOO CITY, MS, p. A366
BAPTIST MEMORIAL HOSPITAL – MEMPHIS, MEMPHIS, TN, p. A588
BAPTIST MEMORIAL HOSPITAL FOR WOMEN, MEMPHIS, TN, p. A588

BAPTIST MEMORIAL HOSPITAL–BOONEVILLE, BOONEVILLE, MS, p. A356
BAPTIST MEMORIAL HOSPITAL–COLLIERVILLE, COLLIERVILLE, TN, p. A581
BAPTIST MEMORIAL HOSPITAL–DESOTO, SOUTHAVEN, MS, p. A365
BAPTIST MEMORIAL HOSPITAL–GOLDEN TRIANGLE, COLUMBUS, MS, p. A357
BAPTIST MEMORIAL HOSPITAL–HUNTINGDON, HUNTINGDON, TN, p. A584
BAPTIST MEMORIAL HOSPITAL–NORTH MISSISSIPPI, OXFORD, MS, p. A363
BAPTIST MEMORIAL HOSPITAL–TIPTON, COVINGTON, TN, p. A582
BAPTIST MEMORIAL HOSPITAL–UNION CITY, UNION CITY, TN, p. A594
BAPTIST MEMORIAL HOSPITAL–UNION COUNTY, NEW ALBANY, MS, p. A363
BAPTIST MEMORIAL REHABILITATION HOSPITAL, GERMANTOWN, TN, p. A583
BAPTIST MEMORIAL RESTORATIVE CARE HOSPITAL, MEMPHIS, TN, p. A588
BARAGA COUNTY MEMORIAL HOSPITAL, L'ANSE, MI, p. A328
BARBARA BUSH CHILDREN'S HOSPITAL, PORTLAND, MAINE (see MAINE MEDICAL CENTER), p. A294
BARBOURVILLE ARH HOSPITAL, BARBOURVILLE, KY, p. A257
BARIX CLINICS OF PENNSYLVANIA, LANGHORNE, PA, p. A542
BARLOW RESPIRATORY HOSPITAL, LOS ANGELES, CA, p. A70
BARNABAS HEALTH BEHAVIORAL HEALTH CENTER, TOMS RIVER, NJ, p. A424
BARNES–JEWISH HOSPITAL, SAINT LOUIS, MO, p. A379
BARNES–JEWISH HOSPITAL PSYCHIATRIC SUPPORT CENTER, SAINT LOUIS, MISSOURI (see BARNES–JEWISH HOSPITAL), p. A379
BARNES–JEWISH ST. PETERS HOSPITAL, SAINT PETERS, MO, p. A382
BARNES–JEWISH WEST COUNTY HOSPITAL, SAINT LOUIS, MO, p. A379
BARNES–KASSON COUNTY HOSPITAL, SUSQUEHANNA, PA, p. A555
BARNESVILLE HOSPITAL, BARNESVILLE, OH, p. A484
BARRETT HOSPITAL & HEALTHCARE, DILLON, MT, p. A387
BARROW REGIONAL MEDICAL CENTER, WINDER, GA, p. A169
BARSTOW COMMUNITY HOSPITAL, BARSTOW, CA, p. A56
BARTLETT REGIONAL HOSPITAL, JUNEAU, AK, p. A29
BARTON COUNTY MEMORIAL HOSPITAL, LAMAR, MO, p. A375
BARTON MEMORIAL HOSPITAL, SOUTH LAKE TAHOE, CA, p. A95
BARTOW REGIONAL MEDICAL CENTER, BARTOW, FL, p. A123
BASCOM PALMER EYE INSTITUTE–ANNE BATES LEACH EYE HOSPITAL, MIAMI, FL, p. A136
BASIN HEALTHCARE CENTER, ODESSA, TX, p. A639
BASSETT ARMY COMMUNITY HOSPITAL, FORT WAINWRIGHT, AK, p. A29
BASSETT MEDICAL CENTER, COOPERSTOWN, NY, p. A437
BASTROP REHABILITATION HOSPITAL, MONROE, LA, p. A283
BATES COUNTY MEMORIAL HOSPITAL, BUTLER, MO, p. A368
BATH COMMUNITY HOSPITAL, HOT SPRINGS, VA, p. A672
BATH VETERANS AFFAIRS MEDICAL CENTER, BATH, NY, p. A434
BATON ROUGE BEHAVIORAL HOSPITAL, BATON ROUGE, LA, p. A272
BATON ROUGE GENERAL MEDICAL CENTER, BATON ROUGE, LA, p. A272
BATON ROUGE GENERAL MEDICAL CENTER–BLUEBONNET, BATON ROUGE, LOUISIANA (see BATON ROUGE GENERAL MEDICAL CENTER), p. A272
BATON ROUGE REHABILITATION HOSPITAL, BATON ROUGE, LA, p. A272
BATTLE CREEK VETERANS AFFAIRS MEDICAL CENTER, BATTLE CREEK, MI, p. A319
BATTLE MOUNTAIN GENERAL HOSPITAL, BATTLE MOUNTAIN, NV, p. A404
BAUM HARMON MERCY HOSPITAL, PRIMGHAR, IA, p. A236
BAXTER REGIONAL MEDICAL CENTER, MOUNTAIN HOME, AR, p. A50
BAY AREA HOSPITAL, COOS BAY, OR, p. A525
BAY AREA MEDICAL CENTER, MARINETTE, WI, p. A709
BAY AREA REGIONAL MEDICAL CENTER, WEBSTER, TX, p. A656
BAY MEDICAL CENTER SACRED HEART HEALTH SYSTEM, PANAMA CITY, FL, p. A141
BAY PINES VETERANS AFFAIRS HEALTHCARE SYSTEM, BAY PINES, FL, p. A123
BAYCARE ALLIANT HOSPITAL, DUNEDIN, FL, p. A127
BAYFRONT HEALTH BROOKSVILLE, BROOKSVILLE, FL, p. A125
BAYFRONT HEALTH DADE CITY, DADE CITY, FL, p. A126
BAYFRONT HEALTH PORT CHARLOTTE, PORT CHARLOTTE, FL, p. A143

BAYFRONT HEALTH PUNTA GORDA, PUNTA GORDA, FL, p. A143
BAYFRONT HEALTH SPRING HILL, SPRING HILL, FLORIDA (see BAYFRONT HEALTH BROOKSVILLE), p. A125
BAYFRONT HEALTH ST. PETERSBURG, SAINT PETERSBURG, FL, p. A144
BAYHEALTH MEDICAL CENTER, DOVER, DE, p. A119
BAYHEALTH MEDICAL CENTER AT KENT GENERAL, DOVER, DELAWARE (see BAYHEALTH MEDICAL CENTER), p. A119
BAYHEALTH MEDICAL CENTER, MILFORD MEMORIAL HOSPITAL, MILFORD, DELAWARE (see BAYHEALTH MEDICAL CENTER), p. A119
BAYLOR ALL SAINTS MEDICAL CENTER AT FORT WORTH, FORT WORTH, TX, p. A617
BAYLOR EMERGENCY MEDICAL CENTER AT AUBREY, AUBREY, TX, p. A598
BAYLOR EMERGENCY MEDICAL CENTER MURPHY, PLANO, TEXAS (see BAYLOR EMERGENCY MEDICAL CENTER AT AUBREY), p. A598
BAYLOR EMERGENCY MEDICAL CENTERS – BURLESON, BURLESON, TX, p. A604
BAYLOR EMERGENCY MEDICAL CENTERS – COLLEYVILLE, COLLEYVILLE, TEXAS (see BAYLOR EMERGENCY MEDICAL CENTER AT AUBREY), p. A598
BAYLOR EMERGENCY MEDICAL CENTERS – KELLER, KELLER, TEXAS (see BAYLOR EMERGENCY MEDICAL CENTER AT AUBREY), p. A598
BAYLOR EMERGENCY MEDICAL CENTERS – MANSFIELD, MANSFIELD, TEXAS (see BAYLOR EMERGENCY MEDICAL CENTERS – BURLESON), p. A604
BAYLOR EMERGENCY MEDICAL CENTERS – ROCKWALL, ROCKWALL, TX, p. A643
BAYLOR INSTITUTE FOR REHABILITATION, DALLAS, TX, p. A609
BAYLOR INSTITUTE FOR REHABILITATION AT FORT WORTH, FORT WORTH, TX, p. A617
BAYLOR INSTITUTE FOR REHABILITATION AT FRISCO, FRISCO, TX, p. A619
BAYLOR JACK AND JANE HAMILTON HEART AND VASCULAR HOSPITAL, DALLAS, TX, p. A609
BAYLOR MEDICAL CENTER AT FRISCO, FRISCO, TX, p. A619
BAYLOR MEDICAL CENTER AT GARLAND, GARLAND, TX, p. A620
BAYLOR MEDICAL CENTER AT IRVING, IRVING, TX, p. A628
BAYLOR MEDICAL CENTER AT MCKINNEY, MCKINNEY, TX, p. A636
BAYLOR MEDICAL CENTER AT TROPHY CLUB, TROPHY CLUB, TX, p. A653
BAYLOR MEDICAL CENTER AT UPTOWN, DALLAS, TX, p. A609
BAYLOR ORTHOPEDIC AND SPINE HOSPITAL AT ARLINGTON, ARLINGTON, TX, p. A597
BAYLOR REGIONAL MEDICAL CENTER AT GRAPEVINE, GRAPEVINE, TX, p. A621
BAYLOR REGIONAL MEDICAL CENTER AT PLANO, PLANO, TX, p. A641
BAYLOR SCOTT & WHITE EMERGENCY HOSPITAL– CEDAR PARK, CEDAR PARK, TX, p. A605
BAYLOR SCOTT & WHITE MEDICAL CENTER – CARROLLTON, CARROLLTON, TX, p. A605
BAYLOR SCOTT & WHITE MEDICAL CENTER – HILLCREST, WACO, TX, p. A655
BAYLOR SCOTT & WHITE MEDICAL CENTER – SUNNYVALE, SUNNYVALE, TX, p. A651
BAYLOR SCOTT & WHITE MEDICAL CENTER – WHITE ROCK, DALLAS, TX, p. A609
BAYLOR SCOTT & WHITE MEDICAL CENTER AT WAXAHACHIE, WAXAHACHIE, TX, p. A656
BAYLOR ST. LUKE'S MEDICAL CENTER, HOUSTON, TX, p. A623
BAYLOR ST. LUKE'S MEDICAL CENTER MCNAIR CAMPUS, HOUSTON, TX, p. A623
BAYLOR SURGICAL HOSPITAL AT FORT WORTH, FORT WORTH, TX, p. A617
BAYLOR SURGICAL HOSPITAL AT LAS COLINAS, IRVING, TX, p. A628
BAYLOR UNIVERSITY MEDICAL CENTER, DALLAS, TX, p. A609
BAYNE–JONES ARMY COMMUNITY HOSPITAL, FORT POLK, LA, p. A277
BAYONNE MEDICAL CENTER, BAYONNE, NJ, p. A414
BAYPOINTE BEHAVIORAL HEALTH, MOBILE, AL, p. A22
BAYSHORE COMMUNITY HOSPITAL, HOLMDEL, NJ, p. A418
BAYSHORE MEDICAL CENTER, PASADENA, TX, p. A640
BAYSTATE CHILDREN'S HOSPITAL, SPRINGFIELD, MASSACHUSETTS (see BAYSTATE MEDICAL CENTER), p. A314
BAYSTATE FRANKLIN MEDICAL CENTER, GREENFIELD, MA, p. A310
BAYSTATE MEDICAL CENTER, SPRINGFIELD, MA, p. A314
BAYSTATE NOBLE HOSPITAL, WESTFIELD, MA, p. A316
BAYSTATE WING HOSPITAL, PALMER, MA, p. A313
BAYVIEW BEHAVIORAL HEALTH CAMPUS, CHULA VISTA, CALIFORNIA (see PARADISE VALLEY HOSPITAL), p. A79

BRIGHAM AND WOMEN'S FAULKNER HOSPITAL, BOSTON, MA, p. A306
BRIGHAM AND WOMEN'S HOSPITAL, BOSTON, MA, p. A306
BRIGHAM CITY COMMUNITY HOSPITAL, BRIGHAM CITY, UT, p. A659
BRIGHTON CENTER FOR RECOVERY, BRIGHTON, MI, p. A319
BRISTOL BAY AREA HEALTH CORPORATION, DILLINGHAM, AK, p. A29
BRISTOL HOSPITAL, BRISTOL, CT, p. A113
BRISTOL–MYERS SQUIBB CHILDREN'S HOSPITAL, NEW BRUNSWICK, NEW JERSEY (see ROBERT WOOD JOHNSON UNIVERSITY HOSPITAL), p. A420
BRISTOW MEDICAL CENTER, BRISTOW, OK, p. A509
BROADDUS HOSPITAL, PHILIPPI, WV, p. A699
BROADLAWNS MEDICAL CENTER, DES MOINES, IA, p. A229
BROADWATER HEALTH CENTER, TOWNSEND, MT, p. A391
BRODSTONE MEMORIAL HOSPITAL, SUPERIOR, NE, p. A402
BRONSON BATTLE CREEK, BATTLE CREEK, MI, p. A319
BRONSON LAKEVIEW HOSPITAL, PAW PAW, MI, p. A331
BRONSON METHODIST HOSPITAL, KALAMAZOO, MI, p. A328
BRONSON VICKSBURG HOSPITAL, VICKSBURG, MICHIGAN (see BRONSON METHODIST HOSPITAL), p. A328
BRONX CHILDREN'S PSYCHIATRIC CENTER,, NEW YORK (see NEW YORK CITY CHILDREN'S CENTER), p. A446
BRONX PSYCHIATRIC CENTER,, NY, p. A443
BRONX–LEBANON HOSPITAL CENTER HEALTH CARE SYSTEM,, NY, p. A444
BRONX–LEBANON SPECIAL CARE CENTER,, NEW YORK (see BRONX–LEBANON HOSPITAL CENTER HEALTH CARE SYSTEM), p. A444
BROOK LANE HEALTH SERVICES, HAGERSTOWN, MD, p. A301
BROOKDALE HOSPITAL MEDICAL CENTER, NEW YORK, NY, p. A444
BROOKE ARMY MEDICAL CENTER, FORT SAM HOUSTON, TX, p. A617
BROOKE GLEN BEHAVIORAL HOSPITAL, FORT WASHINGTON, PA, p. A539
BROOKHAVEN HOSPITAL, TULSA, OK, p. A521
BROOKHAVEN MEMORIAL HOSPITAL MEDICAL CENTER, PATCHOGUE, NY, p. A452
BROOKINGS HEALTH SYSTEM, BROOKINGS, SD, p. A572
BROOKLYN CHILDREN'S PSYCHIATRIC CENTER,, NEW YORK (see NEW YORK CITY CHILDREN'S CENTER), p. A446
BROOKLYN HOSPITAL CENTER,, NY, p. A444
BROOKS COUNTY HOSPITAL, QUITMAN, GA, p. A164
BROOKS MEMORIAL HOSPITAL, DUNKIRK, NY, p. A438
BROOKS REHABILITATION HOSPITAL, JACKSONVILLE, FL, p. A131
BROOKWOOD BAPTIST MEDICAL CENTER, BIRMINGHAM, AL, p. A16
BROUGHTON HOSPITAL, MORGANTON, NC, p. A470
BROWARD HEALTH CORAL SPRINGS, CORAL SPRINGS, FL, p. A126
BROWARD HEALTH IMPERIAL POINT, FORT LAUDERDALE, FL, p. A128
BROWARD HEALTH MEDICAL CENTER, FORT LAUDERDALE, FL, p. A128
BROWARD HEALTH NORTH, DEERFIELD BEACH, FL, p. A127
BROWN COUNTY COMMUNITY TREATMENT CENTER, GREEN BAY, WI, p. A706
BROWN COUNTY HOSPITAL, AINSWORTH, NE, p. A393
BROWNFIELD REGIONAL MEDICAL CENTER, BROWNFIELD, TX, p. A603
BROWNWOOD REGIONAL MEDICAL CENTER, BROWNWOOD, TX, p. A604
BRUNSWICK PSYCH CENTER, AMITYVILLE, NY, p. A433
BRYAN HOSPITAL, BRYAN, OHIO (see COMMUNITY HOSPITALS AND WELLNESS CENTERS), p. A485
BRYAN MEDICAL CENTER, LINCOLN, NE, p. A397
BRYAN MEDICAL CENTER–EAST, LINCOLN, NEBRASKA (see BRYAN MEDICAL CENTER), p. A397
BRYAN MEDICAL CENTER–WEST, LINCOLN, NEBRASKA (see BRYAN MEDICAL CENTER), p. A397
BRYAN W. WHITFIELD MEMORIAL HOSPITAL, DEMOPOLIS, AL, p. A19
BRYCE HOSPITAL, TUSCALOOSA, AL, p. A26
BRYLIN HOSPITALS, BUFFALO, NY, p. A435
BRYN MAWR HOSPITAL, BRYN MAWR, PA, p. A534
BRYN MAWR REHABILITATION HOSPITAL, MALVERN, PA, p. A543
BRYNN MARR HOSPITAL, JACKSONVILLE, NC, p. A467
BSA HOSPITAL, LLC, AMARILLO, TX, p. A596
BUCHANAN COUNTY HEALTH CENTER, INDEPENDENCE, IA, p. A232
BUCHANAN GENERAL HOSPITAL, GRUNDY, VA, p. A671
BUCKS COUNTY CAMPUS, LANGHORNE, PENNSYLVANIA (see ARIA – JEFFERSON HEALTH), p. A547
BUCKTAIL MEDICAL CENTER, RENOVO, PA, p. A553
BUCYRUS COMMUNITY HOSPITAL, BUCYRUS, OH, p. A485

BUENA VISTA REGIONAL MEDICAL CENTER, STORM LAKE, IA, p. A238
BUFFALO HOSPITAL, BUFFALO, MN, p. A340
BUFFALO PSYCHIATRIC CENTER, BUFFALO, NY, p. A435
BULLOCK COUNTY HOSPITAL, UNION SPRINGS, AL, p. A26
BUNKIE GENERAL HOSPITAL, BUNKIE, LA, p. A274
BURGESS HEALTH CENTER, ONAWA, IA, p. A235
BURKE MEDICAL CENTER, WAYNESBORO, GA, p. A169
BURKE REHABILITATION HOSPITAL, WHITE PLAINS, NY, p. A459
BURLESON ST. JOSEPH HEALTH CENTER, CALDWELL, TX, p. A604
BURNETT MEDICAL CENTER, GRANTSBURG, WI, p. A706
BUTLER COUNTY HEALTH CARE CENTER, DAVID CITY, NE, p. A395
BUTLER HEALTH SYSTEM, BUTLER, PA, p. A534
BUTLER HOSPITAL, PROVIDENCE, RI, p. A560
BYRD REGIONAL HOSPITAL, LEESVILLE, LA, p. A282

C

C. S. MOTT CHILDREN'S HOSPITAL, ANN ARBOR, MICHIGAN (see UNIVERSITY OF MICHIGAN HOSPITALS AND HEALTH CENTERS), p. A318
CABELL HUNTINGTON HOSPITAL, HUNTINGTON, WV, p. A696
CABINET PEAKS MEDICAL CENTER, LIBBY, MT, p. A389
CACHE VALLEY HOSPITAL, NORTH LOGAN, UT, p. A661
CALAIS REGIONAL HOSPITAL, CALAIS, ME, p. A292
CALCASIEU OAKS GERIATRIC PSYCHIATRIC HOSPITAL, LAKE CHARLES, LA, p. A281
CALDWELL MEDICAL CENTER, PRINCETON, KY, p. A268
CALDWELL MEMORIAL HOSPITAL, COLUMBIA, LA, p. A275
CALDWELL MEMORIAL HOSPITAL, LENOIR, NC, p. A468
CALHOUN HEALTH SERVICES, CALHOUN CITY, MS, p. A356
CALHOUN–LIBERTY HOSPITAL, BLOUNTSTOWN, FL, p. A123
CALIFORNIA HOSPITAL MEDICAL CENTER, LOS ANGELES, CA, p. A70
CALIFORNIA MEDICAL FACILITY, VACAVILLE, CA, p. A97
CALIFORNIA MENS COLONY CORRECTIONAL TREATMENT CENTER, SAN LUIS OBISPO, CA, p. A92
CALIFORNIA PACIFIC MEDICAL CENTER, SAN FRANCISCO, CA, p. A90
CALIFORNIA PACIFIC MEDICAL CENTER–DAVIES CAMPUS, SAN FRANCISCO, CA, p. A90
CALLAWAY DISTRICT HOSPITAL, CALLAWAY, NE, p. A394
CALUMET MEDICAL CENTER, CHILTON, WI, p. A704
CALVARY HOSPITAL,, NY, p. A444
CALVERT MEMORIAL HOSPITAL, PRINCE FREDERICK, MD, p. A302
CAMBRIDGE HEALTH ALLIANCE, CAMBRIDGE, MA, p. A308
CAMBRIDGE HOSPITAL, CAMBRIDGE, MASSACHUSETTS (see CAMBRIDGE HEALTH ALLIANCE), p. A308
CAMBRIDGE MEDICAL CENTER, CAMBRIDGE, MN, p. A340
CAMC MEMORIAL HOSPITAL, CHARLESTON, WEST VIRGINIA (see CHARLESTON AREA MEDICAL CENTER), p. A695
CAMC TEAYS VALLEY HOSPITAL, HURRICANE, WEST VIRGINIA (see CHARLESTON AREA MEDICAL CENTER), p. A695
CAMC WOMEN AND CHILDREN'S HOSPITAL, CHARLESTON, WEST VIRGINIA (see CHARLESTON AREA MEDICAL CENTER), p. A695
CAMDEN CLARK MEDICAL CENTER, PARKERSBURG, WV, p. A698
CAMDEN GENERAL HOSPITAL, CAMDEN, TN, p. A579
CAMERON MEMORIAL COMMUNITY HOSPITAL, ANGOLA, IN, p. A206
CAMERON REGIONAL MEDICAL CENTER, CAMERON, MO, p. A368
CAMPBELL COUNTY HEALTH, GILLETTE, WY, p. A722
CAMPBELLTON GRACEVILLE HOSPITAL, GRACEVILLE, FL, p. A130
CANANDAIGUA VETERANS AFFAIRS MEDICAL CENTER, CANANDAIGUA, NY, p. A436
CANDLER COUNTY HOSPITAL, METTER, GA, p. A163
CANDLER HOSPITAL, SAVANNAH, GA, p. A165
CANNON MEMORIAL HOSPITAL, PICKENS, SC, p. A569
CANONSBURG HOSPITAL, CANONSBURG, PA, p. A534
CANTON–POTSDAM HOSPITAL, POTSDAM, NY, p. A453
CANYON RIDGE HOSPITAL, CHINO, CA, p. A58
CANYON VISTA MEDICAL CENTER, SIERRA VISTA, AZ, p. A39
CAPE COD & ISLAND COMMUNITY MENTAL HEALTH CENTER, POCASSET, MA, p. A314
CAPE COD HOSPITAL, HYANNIS, MA, p. A311
CAPE CORAL HOSPITAL, CAPE CORAL, FL, p. A125
CAPE FEAR HOSPITAL, WILMINGTON, NORTH CAROLINA (see NEW HANOVER REGIONAL MEDICAL CENTER), p. A475
CAPE FEAR VALLEY – BLADEN COUNTY HOSPITAL, ELIZABETHTOWN, NC, p. A465

CAPE FEAR VALLEY MEDICAL CENTER, FAYETTEVILLE, NC, p. A465
CAPE REGIONAL MEDICAL CENTER, CAPE MAY COURT HOUSE, NJ, p. A415
CAPITAL DISTRICT PSYCHIATRIC CENTER, ALBANY, NY, p. A433
CAPITAL HEALTH MEDICAL CENTER–HOPEWELL, PENNINGTON, NJ, p. A422
CAPITAL HEALTH REGIONAL MEDICAL CENTER, TRENTON, NJ, p. A424
CAPITAL HOSPICE, ARLINGTON, VA, p. A667
CAPITAL MEDICAL CENTER, OLYMPIA, WA, p. A687
CAPITAL REGION MEDICAL CENTER, JEFFERSON CITY, MO, p. A372
CAPITAL REGIONAL MEDICAL CENTER, TALLAHASSEE, FL, p. A146
CAPTAIN JAMES A. LOVELL FEDERAL HEALTH CARE CENTER, NORTH CHICAGO, IL, p. A198
CARDINAL HILL REHABILITATION HOSPITAL, LEXINGTON, KY, p. A263
CARDIOVASCULAR CENTER OF PUERTO RICO AND THE CARIBBEAN, SAN JUAN, PR, p. A729
CARDON CHILDREN'S MEDICAL CENTER, MESA, ARIZONA (see BANNER DESERT MEDICAL CENTER), p. A34
CARE ONE AT RARITAN BAY MEDICAL CENTER, PERTH AMBOY, NJ, p. A422
CARE REGIONAL MEDICAL CENTER, ARANSAS PASS, TX, p. A597
CARELINK OF JACKSON, JACKSON, MI, p. A327
CAREPARTNERS HEALTH SERVICES, ASHEVILLE, NC, p. A460
CAREPOINT HEALTH –CHRIST HOSPITAL, JERSEY CITY, NJ, p. A418
CARIBBEAN MEDICAL CENTER, FAJARDO, PR, p. A727
CARIBOU MEMORIAL HOSPITAL AND LIVING CENTER, SODA SPRINGS, ID, p. A178
CARILION CLINIC CHILDREN'S HOSPITAL, ROANOKE, VIRGINIA (see CARILION ROANOKE MEMORIAL HOSPITAL), p. A678
CARILION CLINIC SAINT ALBANS HOSPITAL, CHRISTIANSBURG, VIRGINIA (see CARILION NEW RIVER VALLEY MEDICAL CENTER), p. A669
CARILION FRANKLIN MEMORIAL HOSPITAL, ROCKY MOUNT, VA, p. A678
CARILION GILES COMMUNITY HOSPITAL, PEARISBURG, VA, p. A675
CARILION NEW RIVER VALLEY MEDICAL CENTER, CHRISTIANSBURG, VA, p. A669
CARILION ROANOKE COMMUNITY HOSPITAL, ROANOKE, VIRGINIA (see CARILION ROANOKE MEMORIAL HOSPITAL), p. A678
CARILION ROANOKE MEMORIAL HOSPITAL, ROANOKE, VA, p. A678
CARILION STONEWALL JACKSON HOSPITAL, LEXINGTON, VA, p. A672
CARILION TAZEWELL COMMUNITY HOSPITAL, TAZEWELL, VA, p. A679
CARL ALBERT COMMUNITY MENTAL HEALTH CENTER, MCALESTER, OK, p. A514
CARL R. DARNALL ARMY MEDICAL CENTER, FORT HOOD, TX, p. A617
CARL VINSON VETERANS AFFAIRS MEDICAL CENTER, DUBLIN, GA, p. A159
CARLE FOUNDATION HOSPITAL, URBANA, IL, p. A204
CARLE HOOPESTON REGIONAL HEALTH CENTER, HOOPESTON, IL, p. A193
CARLINVILLE AREA HOSPITAL, CARLINVILLE, IL, p. A182
CARLISLE REGIONAL MEDICAL CENTER, CARLISLE, PA, p. A535
CARLSBAD MEDICAL CENTER, CARLSBAD, NM, p. A428
CARNEGIE TRI–COUNTY MUNICIPAL HOSPITAL, CARNEGIE, OK, p. A509
CARNEY HOSPITAL, BOSTON, MA, p. A306
CARO CENTER, CARO, MI, p. A320
CARO COMMUNITY HOSPITAL, CARO, MI, p. A320
CAROLINA CENTER FOR BEHAVIORAL HEALTH, GREER, SC, p. A567
CAROLINA PINES REGIONAL MEDICAL CENTER, HARTSVILLE, SC, p. A567
CAROLINAEAST HEALTH SYSTEM, NEW BERN, NC, p. A470
CAROLINAS CONTINUECARE HOSPITAL AT KINGS MOUNTAIN, KINGS MOUNTAIN, NC, p. A468
CAROLINAS CONTINUECARE HOSPITAL AT PINEVILLE, CHARLOTTE, NC, p. A462
CAROLINAS CONTINUECARE HOSPITAL AT UNIVERSITY, CHARLOTTE, NC, p. A462
CAROLINAS HEALTHCARE SYSTEM ANSON, WADESBORO, NC, p. A475
CAROLINAS HEALTHCARE SYSTEM BLUE RIDGE, MORGANTON, NC, p. A470
CAROLINAS HEALTHCARE SYSTEM LINCOLN, LINCOLNTON, NC, p. A469

CAROLINAS HEALTHCARE SYSTEM NORTHEAST, CONCORD, NC, p. A463
CAROLINAS HEALTHCARE SYSTEM PINEVILLE, CHARLOTTE, NC, p. A462
CAROLINAS HEALTHCARE SYSTEM UNION, MONROE, NC, p. A469
CAROLINAS HOSPITAL SYSTEM, FLORENCE, SC, p. A565
CAROLINAS HOSPITAL SYSTEM MARION, MULLINS, SC, p. A568
CAROLINAS MEDICAL CENTER, CHARLOTTE, NC, p. A462
CAROLINAS MEDICAL CENTER–MERCY, CHARLOTTE, NORTH CAROLINA (see CAROLINAS MEDICAL CENTER), p. A462
CAROLINAS MEDICAL CENTER–UNIVERSITY, CHARLOTTE, NC, p. A462
CAROLINAS REHABILITATION, CHARLOTTE, NC, p. A462
CAROMONT REGIONAL MEDICAL CENTER, GASTONIA, NC, p. A465
CARONDELET HOLY CROSS HOSPITAL, NOGALES, AZ, p. A35
CARONDELET ST. JOSEPH'S HOSPITAL, TUCSON, AZ, p. A40
CARONDELET ST. MARY'S HOSPITAL, TUCSON, AZ, p. A40
CARRIE TINGLEY HOSPITAL, ALBUQUERQUE, NEW MEXICO (see UNIVERSITY OF NEW MEXICO HOSPITALS), p. A428
CARRIER CLINIC, BELLE MEAD, NJ, p. A414
CARROLL COUNTY MEMORIAL HOSPITAL, CARROLLTON, KY, p. A258
CARROLL COUNTY MEMORIAL HOSPITAL, CARROLLTON, MO, p. A369
CARROLL HOSPITAL, WESTMINSTER, MD, p. A304
CARROLLTON SPRINGS, CARROLLTON, TX, p. A605
CARRUS REHABILITATION HOSPITAL, SHERMAN, TX, p. A648
CARRUS SPECIALTY HOSPITAL, SHERMAN, TX, p. A648
CARSON TAHOE CONTINUING CARE HOSPITAL, CARSON CITY, NV, p. A404
CARSON TAHOE HEALTH, CARSON CITY, NV, p. A404
CARSON VALLEY MEDICAL CENTER, GARDNERVILLE, NV, p. A404
CARTERET HEALTH CARE, MOREHEAD CITY, NC, p. A470
CARTERSVILLE MEDICAL CENTER, CARTERSVILLE, GA, p. A156
CARTHAGE AREA HOSPITAL, CARTHAGE, NY, p. A437
CARY MEDICAL CENTER, CARIBOU, ME, p. A292
CASA COLINA HOSPITAL AND HEALTH SYSTEMS, POMONA, CA, p. A83
CASCADE BEHAVIORAL HOSPITAL, TUKWILA, WA, p. A692
CASCADE MEDICAL CENTER, CASCADE, ID, p. A175
CASCADE MEDICAL CENTER, LEAVENWORTH, WA, p. A686
CASCADE VALLEY HOSPITAL AND CLINICS, ARLINGTON, WA, p. A682
CASEY COUNTY HOSPITAL, LIBERTY, KY, p. A264
CASS COUNTY MEMORIAL HOSPITAL, ATLANTIC, IA, p. A225
CASS REGIONAL MEDICAL CENTER, HARRISONVILLE, MO, p. A372
CASSIA REGIONAL MEDICAL CENTER, BURLEY, ID, p. A175
CASTANER GENERAL HOSPITAL, CASTANER, PR, p. A726
CASTLE MANOR (see FALL RIVER HOSPITAL), p. A574
CASTLE MEDICAL CENTER, KAILUA, HI, p. A171
CASTLE ROCK ADVENTIST HOSPITAL, CASTLE ROCK, CO, p. A102
CASTLEVIEW HOSPITAL, PRICE, UT, p. A662
CATALINA ISLAND MEDICAL CENTER, AVALON, CA, p. A55
CATAWBA HOSPITAL, CATAWBA, VA, p. A668
CATAWBA VALLEY MEDICAL CENTER, HICKORY, NC, p. A467
CATHOLIC MEDICAL CENTER, MANCHESTER, NH, p. A412
CATSKILL REGIONAL MEDICAL CENTER, HARRIS, NY, p. A440
CAVALIER COUNTY MEMORIAL HOSPITAL AND CLINICS, LANGDON, ND, p. A480
CAYUGA MEDICAL CENTER AT ITHACA, ITHACA, NY, p. A440
CCC AT PINEVIEW HOSPITAL, LAKESIDE, AZ, p. A34
CEDAR CITY HOSPITAL, CEDAR CITY, UT, p. A659
CEDAR COUNTY MEMORIAL HOSPITAL, EL DORADO SPRINGS, MO, p. A370
CEDAR CREST HOSPITAL AND RESIDENTIAL TREATMENT CENTER, BELTON, TX, p. A602
CEDAR HILLS HOSPITAL, PORTLAND, OR, p. A529
CEDAR PARK REGIONAL MEDICAL CENTER, CEDAR PARK, TX, p. A605
CEDAR RIDGE HOSPITAL, OKLAHOMA CITY, OK, p. A516
CEDAR SPRINGS HOSPITAL, COLORADO SPRINGS, CO, p. A102
CEDARS–SINAI MEDICAL CENTER, LOS ANGELES, CA, p. A70
CENTEGRA HOSPITAL – MCHENRY, MCHENRY, IL, p. A196
CENTEGRA HOSPITAL – WOODSTOCK, WOODSTOCK, IL, p. A205
CENTEGRA HOSPITAL–HUNTLEY, HUNTLEY, ILLINOIS (see CENTEGRA HOSPITAL – MCHENRY), p. A196
CENTENNIAL HILLS HOSPITAL MEDICAL CENTER, LAS VEGAS, NV, p. A405
CENTENNIAL MEDICAL CENTER, FRISCO, TX, p. A619
CENTENNIAL PEAKS HOSPITAL, LOUISVILLE, CO, p. A109
CENTER FOR BEHAVIORAL MEDICINE, KANSAS CITY, MO, p. A373

CENTER FOR DISABILITIES AND DEVELOPMENT, IOWA CITY, IOWA (see UNIVERSITY OF IOWA HOSPITALS AND CLINICS), p. A232
CENTER FOR FORENSIC PSYCHIATRY, SALINE, MI, p. A334
CENTERPOINT MEDICAL CENTER, INDEPENDENCE, MO, p. A372
CENTERPOINTE HOSPITAL, SAINT CHARLES, MO, p. A379
CENTERSTONE HOSPITAL, BRADENTON, FL, p. A124
CENTINELA HOSPITAL MEDICAL CENTER, INGLEWOOD, CA, p. A66
CENTRA LYNCHBURG GENERAL HOSPITAL, LYNCHBURG, VA, p. A672
CENTRA SOUTHSIDE COMMUNITY HOSPITAL, FARMVILLE, VA, p. A670
CENTRA SPECIALTY HOSPITAL, LYNCHBURG, VA, p. A672
CENTRA VIRGINIA BAPTIST HOSPITAL, LYNCHBURG, VIRGINIA (see CENTRA LYNCHBURG GENERAL HOSPITAL), p. A672
CENTRACARE HEALTH–LONG PRAIRIE, LONG PRAIRIE, MN, p. A345
CENTRACARE HEALTH–MELROSE, MELROSE, MN, p. A346
CENTRACARE HEALTH–MONTICELLO, MONTICELLO, MN, p. A347
CENTRACARE HEALTH–PAYNESVILLE, PAYNESVILLE, MN, p. A348
CENTRACARE HEALTH–SAUK CENTRE, SAUK CENTRE, MN, p. A351
CENTRAL ALABAMA VETERANS HEALTH CARE SYSTEM, MONTGOMERY, AL, p. A23
CENTRAL ARKANSAS VETERANS HEALTHCARE SYSTEM, LITTLE ROCK, AR, p. A49
CENTRAL CAROLINA HOSPITAL, SANFORD, NC, p. A473
CENTRAL COMMUNITY HOSPITAL, ELKADER, IA, p. A230
CENTRAL FLORIDA BEHAVIORAL HOSPITAL, ORLANDO, FL, p. A140
CENTRAL FLORIDA REGIONAL HOSPITAL, SANFORD, FL, p. A145
CENTRAL HARTNETT HOSPITAL, LILLINGTON, NORTH CAROLINA (see HARNETT HEALTH SYSTEM), p. A464
CENTRAL IOWA HEALTHCARE, MARSHALLTOWN, IA, p. A234
CENTRAL LOUISIANA STATE HOSPITAL, PINEVILLE, LA, p. A286
CENTRAL LOUISIANA SURGICAL HOSPITAL, ALEXANDRIA, LA, p. A271
CENTRAL MAINE MEDICAL CENTER, LEWISTON, ME, p. A293
CENTRAL MONTANA MEDICAL CENTER, LEWISTOWN, MT, p. A389
CENTRAL NEW YORK PSYCHIATRIC CENTER, MARCY, NY, p. A442
CENTRAL PENINSULA HOSPITAL, SOLDOTNA, AK, p. A30
CENTRAL PRISON HOSPITAL, RALEIGH, NC, p. A471
CENTRAL REGIONAL HOSPITAL, BUTNER, NC, p. A461
CENTRAL STATE HOSPITAL, MILLEDGEVILLE, GA, p. A163
CENTRAL STATE HOSPITAL, LOUISVILLE, KY, p. A264
CENTRAL STATE HOSPITAL, PETERSBURG, VA, p. A676
CENTRAL TEXAS MEDICAL CENTER, SAN MARCOS, TX, p. A648
CENTRAL TEXAS REHABILITATION HOSPITAL, AUSTIN, TX, p. A599
CENTRAL TEXAS VETERANS AFFAIRS HEALTH CARE SYSTEM, OLIN E. TEAGUE VETERANS MEDICAL CENTER, TEMPLE, TEXAS (see CENTRAL TEXAS VETERANS HEALTH CARE SYSTEM), p. A651
CENTRAL TEXAS VETERANS HEALTH CARE SYSTEM, TEMPLE, TX, p. A651
CENTRAL TEXAS VETERANS HEALTH CARE SYSTEM, DORIS MILLER VETERANS MEDICAL CENTER, WACO, TEXAS (see CENTRAL TEXAS VETERANS HEALTH CARE SYSTEM), p. A651
CENTRAL VALLEY GENERAL HOSPITAL, HANFORD, CA, p. A65
CENTRAL VALLEY MEDICAL CENTER, NEPHI, UT, p. A661
CENTRAL VALLEY SPECIALTY HOSPITAL, MODESTO, CA, p. A77
CENTRAL VIRGINIA TRAINING CENTER, MADISON HEIGHTS, VA, p. A673
CENTRASTATE HEALTHCARE SYSTEM, FREEHOLD, NJ, p. A417
CENTRO DE SALUD CONDUCTUAL MENONITA–CIMA, AIBONITO, PR, p. A725
CENTRO DE TRAUMA, MOCA, PR, p. A728
CGH MEDICAL CENTER, STERLING, IL, p. A204
CHADRON COMMUNITY HOSPITAL AND HEALTH SERVICES, CHADRON, NE, p. A395
CHAMBERS COUNTY PUBLIC HOSPITAL DISTRICT NO. 1, ANAHUAC, TX, p. A596
CHAMBERS MEMORIAL HOSPITAL, DANVILLE, AR, p. A44
CHAMBERSBURG HOSPITAL, CHAMBERSBURG, PA, p. A535
CHAN SOON–SHIONG MEDICAL CENTER, WINDBER, PA, p. A558
CHANDLER REGIONAL MEDICAL CENTER, CHANDLER, AZ, p. A31
CHAPMAN GLOBAL MEDICAL CENTER, ORANGE, CA, p. A80
CHARLES A. CANNON MEMORIAL HOSPITAL, NEWLAND, NC, p. A471

CHARLES A. DEAN MEMORIAL HOSPITAL, GREENVILLE, ME, p. A293
CHARLES GEORGE VETERANS AFFAIRS MEDICAL CENTER, ASHEVILLE, NC, p. A460
CHARLESTON AREA MEDICAL CENTER, CHARLESTON, WV, p. A695
CHARLIE NORWOOD VETERANS AFFAIRS MEDICAL CENTER, AUGUSTA, GA, p. A153
CHARLTON MEMORIAL HOSPITAL, FALL RIVER, MASSACHUSETTS (see SOUTHCOAST HOSPITALS GROUP), p. A310
CHASE COUNTY COMMUNITY HOSPITAL, IMPERIAL, NE, p. A397
CHATHAM HOSPITAL, SILER CITY, NC, p. A473
CHATUGE REGIONAL HOSPITAL AND NURSING HOME, HIAWASSEE, GA, p. A160
CHEMICAL DEPENDENCY CENTER, IOWA CITY, IOWA (see UNIVERSITY OF IOWA HOSPITALS AND CLINICS), p. A232
CHEROKEE INDIAN HOSPITAL, CHEROKEE, NC, p. A463
CHEROKEE MEDICAL CENTER, CENTRE, AL, p. A18
CHEROKEE NATION W.W. HASTINGS INDIAN HOSPITAL, TAHLEQUAH, OK, p. A520
CHEROKEE REGIONAL MEDICAL CENTER, CHEROKEE, IA, p. A227
CHERRY COUNTY HOSPITAL, VALENTINE, NE, p. A402
CHERRY HOSPITAL, GOLDSBORO, NC, p. A466
CHESAPEAKE REGIONAL HEALTHCARE, CHESAPEAKE, VA, p. A668
CHESHIRE MEDICAL CENTER, KEENE, NH, p. A411
CHESTATEE REGIONAL HOSPITAL, DAHLONEGA, GA, p. A157
CHESTER MENTAL HEALTH CENTER, CHESTER, IL, p. A183
CHESTER REGIONAL MEDICAL CENTER, CHESTER, SC, p. A563
CHESTNUT HILL HOSPITAL, PHILADELPHIA, PA, p. A547
CHESTNUT RIDGE HOSPITAL, MORGANTOWN, WEST VIRGINIA (see WEST VIRGINIA UNIVERSITY HOSPITALS), p. A698
CHEYENNE COUNTY HOSPITAL, SAINT FRANCIS, KS, p. A253
CHEYENNE REGIONAL MEDICAL CENTER, CHEYENNE, WY, p. A721
CHEYENNE VETERANS AFFAIRS MEDICAL CENTER, CHEYENNE, WY, p. A722
CHG CORNERSTONE HOSPITAL CONROE, CONROE, TX, p. A607
CHG HOSPITAL TUCSON, LLC, TUCSON, AZ, p. A40
CHI HEALTH BERGAN MERCY, OMAHA, NE, p. A399
CHI HEALTH CREIGHTON UNIVERSITY MEDICAL CENTER, OMAHA, NEBRASKA (see CHI HEALTH BERGAN MERCY), p. A399
CHI HEALTH GOOD SAMARITAN, KEARNEY, NE, p. A397
CHI HEALTH IMMANUEL, OMAHA, NE, p. A400
CHI HEALTH LAKESIDE, OMAHA, NE, p. A400
CHI HEALTH MERCY CORNING, CORNING, IA, p. A228
CHI HEALTH MERCY COUNCIL BLUFFS, COUNCIL BLUFFS, IA, p. A228
CHI HEALTH MIDLANDS, PAPILLION, NE, p. A401
CHI HEALTH MISSOURI VALLEY, MISSOURI VALLEY, IA, p. A234
CHI HEALTH NEBRASKA HEART, LINCOLN, NE, p. A397
CHI HEALTH PLAINVIEW, PLAINVIEW, NE, p. A401
CHI HEALTH SAINT FRANCIS, GRAND ISLAND, NE, p. A396
CHI HEALTH SCHUYLER, SCHUYLER, NE, p. A402
CHI HEALTH ST ELIZABETH, LINCOLN, NE, p. A398
CHI HEALTH ST. MARY'S, NEBRASKA CITY, NE, p. A398
CHI LAKEWOOD HEALTH, BAUDETTE, MN, p. A339
CHI LISBON HEALTH, LISBON, ND, p. A480
CHI MEMORIAL, CHATTANOOGA, TN, p. A580
CHI MERCY HEALTH, VALLEY CITY, ND, p. A482
CHI OAKES HOSPITAL, OAKES, ND, p. A481
CHI ST ALEXIUS HEALTH CARRINGTON MEDICAL CENTER, CARRINGTON, ND, p. A477
CHI ST. ALEXIUS HEALTH, BISMARCK, ND, p. A477
CHI ST. ALEXIUS HEALTH DEVILS LAKE HOSPITAL, DEVILS LAKE, ND, p. A478
CHI ST. ANTHONY HOSPITAL, PENDLETON, OR, p. A528
CHI ST. FRANCIS HEALTH, BRECKENRIDGE, MN, p. A340
CHI ST. GABRIEL'S HEALTH, LITTLE FALLS, MN, p. A345
CHI ST. JOSEPH'S HEALTH, PARK RAPIDS, MN, p. A348
CHI ST. LUKE'S HEALTH – PATIENTS MEDICAL CENTER, PASADENA, TX, p. A640
CHI ST. LUKE'S HEALTH BRAZOSPORT, LAKE JACKSON, TX, p. A631
CHI ST. LUKE'S HEALTH MEMORIAL LIVINGSTON, LIVINGSTON, TX, p. A633
CHI ST. LUKE'S HEALTH MEMORIAL LUFKIN, LUFKIN, TX, p. A634
CHI ST. LUKE'S HEALTH MEMORIAL SAN AUGUSTINE, SAN AUGUSTINE, TX, p. A647
CHI ST. LUKE'S HEALTH MEMORIAL SPECIALTY HOSPITAL, LUFKIN, TX, p. A634
CHI ST. VINCENT HOT SPRINGS, HOT SPRINGS, AR, p. A47
CHI ST. VINCENT INFIRMARY MEDICAL CENTER, LITTLE ROCK, AR, p. A49

CHI ST. VINCENT MEDICAL CENTER–NORTH, SHERWOOD, AR, p. A52
CHI ST. VINCENT MORRILTON, MORRILTON, AR, p. A50
CHICAGO LAKESHORE HOSPITAL, CHICAGO, IL, p. A183
CHICAGO LYING–IN (CLI), CHICAGO, ILLINOIS (see UNIVERSITY OF CHICAGO MEDICAL CENTER), p. A187
CHICAGO–READ MENTAL HEALTH CENTER, CHICAGO, IL, p. A183
CHICKASAW NATION MEDICAL CENTER, ADA, OK, p. A508
CHICOT MEMORIAL MEDICAL CENTER, LAKE VILLAGE, AR, p. A48
CHILD AND ADOLESCENT BEHAVIORAL HEALTH SERVICES, WILLMAR, MN, p. A353
CHILDEN'S REGIONAL HOSPITAL AT COOPER, CAMDEN, NEW JERSEY (see COOPER UNIVERSITY HEALTH CARE), p. A415
CHILDREN AT PROVIDENCE ST. VINCENT, PORTLAND, OREGON (see PROVIDENCE ST. VINCENT MEDICAL CENTER), p. A529
CHILDREN'S HEALTH CENTER, PHOENIX, ARIZONA (see ST. JOSEPH'S HOSPITAL AND MEDICAL CENTER), p. A37
CHILDREN'S HEALTH SYSTEM OF TEXAS, DALLAS, TX, p. A609
CHILDREN'S HEALTHCARE OF ATLANTA, ATLANTA, GA, p. A152
CHILDREN'S HEALTHCARE OF ATLANTA AT EGLESTON, ATLANTA, GEORGIA (see CHILDREN'S HEALTHCARE OF ATLANTA), p. A152
CHILDREN'S HEALTHCARE OF ATLANTA AT HUGHES SPALDING, ATLANTA, GEORGIA (see CHILDREN'S HEALTHCARE OF ATLANTA), p. A152
CHILDREN'S HEALTHCARE OF ATLANTA AT SCOTTISH RITE, ATLANTA, GEORGIA (see CHILDREN'S HEALTHCARE OF ATLANTA), p. A152
CHILDREN'S HEALTHCARE OF MISSISSIPPI, JACKSON, MISSISSIPPI (see UNIVERSITY OF MISSISSIPPI MEDICAL CENTER), p. A360
CHILDREN'S HOSPITAL, NEW ORLEANS, LA, p. A284
CHILDREN'S HOSPITAL AND MEDICAL CENTER, OMAHA, NE, p. A400
CHILDREN'S HOSPITAL AT BRONSON, KALAMAZOO, MICHIGAN (see BRONSON METHODIST HOSPITAL), p. A328
CHILDREN'S HOSPITAL AT DARTMOUTH, LEBANON, NEW HAMPSHIRE (see DARTMOUTH–HITCHCOCK MEDICAL CENTER), p. A412
CHILDREN'S HOSPITAL AT MONMOUTH MEDICAL CENTER, LONG BRANCH, NEW JERSEY (see MONMOUTH MEDICAL CENTER, LONG BRANCH CAMPUS), p. A419
CHILDREN'S HOSPITAL AT PROVIDENCE, ANCHORAGE, ALASKA (see PROVIDENCE ALASKA MEDICAL CENTER), p. A28
CHILDREN'S HOSPITAL AT SAINT FRANCIS, TULSA, OKLAHOMA (see SAINT FRANCIS HOSPITAL), p. A522
CHILDREN'S HOSPITAL COLORADO, AURORA, CO, p. A101
CHILDREN'S HOSPITAL LOS ANGELES, LOS ANGELES, CA, p. A70
CHILDREN'S HOSPITAL OF COLORADO AT MEMORIAL, COLORADO SPRINGS, COLORADO (see CHILDREN'S HOSPITAL COLORADO), p. A101
CHILDREN'S HOSPITAL OF GEORGIA, AUGUSTA, GEORGIA (see AUGUSTA UNIVERSITY MEDICAL CENTER), p. A153
CHILDREN'S HOSPITAL OF ILLINOIS, PEORIA, ILLINOIS (see OSF SAINT FRANCIS MEDICAL CENTER), p. A200
CHILDREN'S HOSPITAL OF MONTEFIORE,, NEW YORK (see MONTEFIORE MEDICAL CENTER), p. A446
CHILDREN'S HOSPITAL OF NEVADA AT UMC, LAS VEGAS, NEVADA (see UNIVERSITY MEDICAL CENTER), p. A407
CHILDREN'S HOSPITAL OF NEW JERSEY, NEWARK, NEW JERSEY (see NEWARK BETH ISRAEL MEDICAL CENTER), p. A420
CHILDREN'S HOSPITAL OF OKLAHOMA, OKLAHOMA CITY, OKLAHOMA (see OU MEDICAL CENTER), p. A517
CHILDREN'S HOSPITAL OF ORANGE COUNTY, ORANGE, CA, p. A81
CHILDREN'S HOSPITAL OF PHILADELPHIA, PHILADELPHIA, PA, p. A547
CHILDREN'S HOSPITAL OF PITTSBURGH OF UPMC, PITTSBURGH, PA, p. A550
CHILDREN'S HOSPITAL OF RICHMOND AT VCU–BROOK ROAD CAMPUS, RICHMOND, VA, p. A677
CHILDREN'S HOSPITAL OF SAN ANTONIO, SAN ANTONIO, TEXAS (see CHRISTUS SANTA ROSA HEALTH SYSTEM), p. A645
CHILDREN'S HOSPITAL OF SHREVEPORT, SHREVEPORT, LOUISIANA (see UNIVERSITY HEALTH SHREVEPORT), p. A288
CHILDREN'S HOSPITAL OF SOUTH CAROLINA AT MUSC, CHARLESTON, SOUTH CAROLINA (see MUSC MEDICAL CENTER OF MEDICAL UNIVERSITY OF SOUTH CAROLINA), p. A563
CHILDREN'S HOSPITAL OF SOUTHWEST FLORIDA, FORT MYERS, FLORIDA (see LEE MEMORIAL HOSPITAL), p. A129
CHILDREN'S HOSPITAL OF THE KING'S DAUGHTERS, NORFOLK, VA, p. A675
CHILDREN'S HOSPITAL OF WISCONSIN, MILWAUKEE, WI, p. A711

CHILDREN'S HOSPITAL OF WISCONSIN–FOX VALLEY, NEENAH, WI, p. A712
CHILDREN'S HOSPITAL, NAVICENT HEALTH, MACON, GEORGIA (see MEDICAL CENTER, NAVICENT HEALTH), p. A162
CHILDREN'S HOSPITALS AND CLINICS OF MINNESOTA, MINNEAPOLIS, MN, p. A346
CHILDREN'S HOSPITALS AND CLINICS OF MINNESOTA, SAINT PAUL, MINNESOTA (see CHILDREN'S HOSPITALS AND CLINICS OF MINNESOTA), p. A346
CHILDREN'S INN AT NIH, BETHESDA, MARYLAND (see NATIONAL INSTITUTES OF HEALTH CLINICAL CENTER), p. A299
CHILDREN'S MEDICAL CENTER, DAYTON, OH, p. A492
CHILDREN'S MEDICAL CENTER, MINEOLA, NEW YORK (see WINTHROP–UNIVERSITY HOSPITAL), p. A442
CHILDREN'S MEDICAL CENTER PLANO, PLANO, TX, p. A641
CHILDREN'S MEMORIAL HERMANN HOSPITAL, HOUSTON, TEXAS (see MEMORIAL HERMANN – TEXAS MEDICAL CENTER), p. A625
CHILDREN'S MERCY HOSPITALS AND CLINICS, KANSAS CITY, MO, p. A373
CHILDREN'S MERCY SOUTH, OVERLAND PARK, KS, p. A251
CHILDREN'S NATIONAL HEALTH SYSTEM, WASHINGTON, DC, p. A121
CHILDREN'S OF ALABAMA, BIRMINGHAM, AL, p. A16
CHILDREN'S SPECIALIZED HOSPITAL, NEW BRUNSWICK, NEW JERSEY (see CHILDREN'S SPECIALIZED HOSPITAL–PSE&G), p. A420
CHILDREN'S SPECIALIZED HOSPITAL–PSE&G, NEW BRUNSWICK, NJ, p. A420
CHILDRENS CARE HOSPITAL AND SCHOOL, SIOUX FALLS, SD, p. A576
CHILDRESS REGIONAL MEDICAL CENTER, CHILDRESS, TX, p. A606
CHILLICOTHE HOSPITAL DISTRICT, CHILLICOTHE, TX, p. A606
CHILLICOTHE VETERANS AFFAIRS MEDICAL CENTER, CHILLICOTHE, OH, p. A487
CHILTON MEDICAL CENTER, POMPTON PLAINS, NJ, p. A422
CHINESE HOSPITAL, SAN FRANCISCO, CA, p. A90
CHINLE COMPREHENSIVE HEALTH CARE FACILITY, CHINLE, AZ, p. A31
CHINO VALLEY MEDICAL CENTER, CHINO, CA, p. A58
CHIPPENHAM HOSPITAL, RICHMOND, VA, p. A677
CHIPPENHAM MEDICAL CENTER, RICHMOND, VIRGINIA (see CHIPPENHAM HOSPITAL), p. A677
CHIPPEWA COUNTY–MONTEVIDEO HOSPITAL, MONTEVIDEO, MN, p. A347
CHIPPEWA VALLEY HOSPITAL AND OAKVIEW CARE CENTER, DURAND, WI, p. A704
CHOATE MENTAL HEALTH CENTER, ANNA, IL, p. A180
CHOC CHILDREN'S AT MISSION HOSPITAL, MISSION VIEJO, CA, p. A76
CHOCTAW GENERAL HOSPITAL, BUTLER, AL, p. A17
CHOCTAW HEALTH CENTER, PHILADELPHIA, MS, p. A363
CHOCTAW MEMORIAL HOSPITAL, HUGO, OK, p. A513
CHOCTAW NATION HEALTH CARE CENTER, TALIHINA, OK, p. A520
CHOCTAW REGIONAL MEDICAL CENTER, ACKERMAN, MS, p. A355
CHRIS EVERT CHILDRENS HOSPITAL, FORT LAUDERDALE, FLORIDA (see BROWARD HEALTH MEDICAL CENTER), p. A128
CHRIST HOSPITAL, CINCINNATI, OH, p. A487
CHRISTIAN HEALTH CARE CENTER, WYCKOFF, NJ, p. A426
CHRISTIAN HOSPITAL, SAINT LOUIS, MO, p. A380
CHRISTIANA CARE HEALTH SYSTEM, NEWARK, DE, p. A119
CHRISTUS CONTINUING CARE DBA DUBUIS HOSPITAL OF PARIS, PARIS, TX, p. A640
CHRISTUS COUSHATTA HEALTH CARE CENTER, COUSHATTA, LA, p. A275
CHRISTUS DUBUIS HOSPITAL OF ALEXANDRIA, ALEXANDRIA, LA, p. A271
CHRISTUS DUBUIS HOSPITAL OF BEAUMONT, BEAUMONT, TX, p. A601
CHRISTUS DUBUIS HOSPITAL OF FORT SMITH, FORT SMITH, AR, p. A46
CHRISTUS DUBUIS HOSPITAL OF HOT SPRINGS, HOT SPRINGS NATIONAL PARK, AR, p. A47
CHRISTUS DUBUIS HOSPITAL OF PORT ARTHUR, PORT ARTHUR, TX, p. A642
CHRISTUS HEALTH SHREVEPORT–BOSSIER, SHREVEPORT, LA, p. A287
CHRISTUS HIGHLAND MEDICAL CENTER, SHREVEPORT, LOUISIANA (see CHRISTUS HEALTH SHREVEPORT–BOSSIER), p. A287
CHRISTUS MOTHER FRANCES HOSPITAL – JACKSONVILLE, JACKSONVILLE, TX, p. A629
CHRISTUS MOTHER FRANCES HOSPITAL – SULPHUR SPRINGS, SULPHUR SPRINGS, TX, p. A651

CHRISTUS MOTHER FRANCES HOSPITAL – TYLER, TYLER, TX, p. A654
CHRISTUS MOTHER FRANCES HOSPITAL – WINNSBORO, WINNSBORO, TX, p. A658
CHRISTUS SANTA ROSA HEALTH SYSTEM, SAN ANTONIO, TX, p. A645
CHRISTUS SANTA ROSA HOSPITAL – ALAMO HEIGHTS, SAN ANTONIO, TEXAS (see CHRISTUS SANTA ROSA HEALTH SYSTEM), p. A645
CHRISTUS SANTA ROSA HOSPITAL – NEW BRAUNFELS, NEW BRAUNFELS, TEXAS (see CHRISTUS SANTA ROSA HEALTH SYSTEM), p. A645
CHRISTUS SANTA ROSA–MEDICAL CENTER, SAN ANTONIO, TEXAS (see CHRISTUS SANTA ROSA HEALTH SYSTEM), p. A645
CHRISTUS SOUTHEAST TEXAS HOSPITAL, BEAUMONT, TX, p. A601
CHRISTUS SOUTHEAST TEXAS HOSPITAL–ST. MARY, PORT ARTHUR, TEXAS (see CHRISTUS SOUTHEAST TEXAS HOSPITAL), p. A601
CHRISTUS SOUTHEAST TEXAS JASPER MEMORIAL, JASPER, TX, p. A629
CHRISTUS SOUTHEAST TEXAS ORTHOPEDIC SPECIALTY CENTER, BEAUMONT, TX, p. A601
CHRISTUS SPOHN HOSPITAL ALICE, ALICE, TX, p. A595
CHRISTUS SPOHN HOSPITAL BEEVILLE, BEEVILLE, TX, p. A602
CHRISTUS SPOHN HOSPITAL CORPUS CHRISTI MEMORIAL, CORPUS CHRISTI, TX, p. A607
CHRISTUS SPOHN HOSPITAL CORPUS CHRISTI SHORELINE, CORPUS CHRISTI, TEXAS (see CHRISTUS SPOHN HOSPITAL CORPUS CHRISTI MEMORIAL), p. A607
CHRISTUS SPOHN HOSPITAL CORPUS CHRISTUS SOUTH, CORPUS CHRISTI, TEXAS (see CHRISTUS SPOHN HOSPITAL CORPUS CHRISTI MEMORIAL), p. A607
CHRISTUS SPOHN HOSPITAL KLEBERG, KINGSVILLE, TX, p. A630
CHRISTUS ST. FRANCES CABRINI HOSPITAL, ALEXANDRIA, LA, p. A271
CHRISTUS ST. MICHAEL HEALTH SYSTEM, TEXARKANA, TX, p. A652
CHRISTUS ST. MICHAEL HOSPITAL–ATLANTA, ATLANTA, TEXAS (see CHRISTUS ST. MICHAEL HEALTH SYSTEM), p. A652
CHRISTUS ST. MICHAEL REHABILITATION HOSPITAL, TEXARKANA, TX, p. A652
CHRISTUS ST. PATRICK HOSPITAL OF LAKE CHARLES, LAKE CHARLES, LA, p. A281
CHRISTUS ST. VINCENT PHYSICIANS MEDICAL CENTER, SANTA FE, NEW MEXICO (see CHRISTUS ST. VINCENT REGIONAL MEDICAL CENTER), p. A431
CHRISTUS ST. VINCENT REGIONAL MEDICAL CENTER, SANTA FE, NM, p. A431
CHRISTUS TRINITY MOTHER FRANCES REHABILITATION HOSPITAL, TYLER, TX, p. A654
CIBOLA GENERAL HOSPITAL, GRANTS, NM, p. A429
CIMARRON MEMORIAL HOSPITAL, BOISE CITY, OK, p. A509
CINCINNATI CHILDREN'S HOSPITAL MEDICAL CENTER, CINCINNATI, OH, p. A487
CINCINNATI VETERANS AFFAIRS MEDICAL CENTER, CINCINNATI, OH, p. A487
CIRCLES OF CARE, MELBOURNE, FL, p. A135
CITIZENS BAPTIST MEDICAL CENTER, TALLADEGA, AL, p. A25
CITIZENS MEDICAL CENTER, COLBY, KS, p. A241
CITIZENS MEDICAL CENTER, COLUMBIA, LA, p. A275
CITIZENS MEDICAL CENTER, VICTORIA, TX, p. A655
CITIZENS MEMORIAL HOSPITAL, BOLIVAR, MO, p. A367
CITRUS MEMORIAL HEALTH SYSTEM, INVERNESS, FL, p. A131
CITRUS VALLEY MEDICAL CENTER–INTER COMMUNITY CAMPUS, COVINA, CA, p. A60
CITRUS VALLEY MEDICAL CENTER–INTER–COMMUNITY CAMPUS, COVINA, CALIFORNIA (see CITRUS VALLEY MEDICAL CENTER–INTER COMMUNITY CAMPUS), p. A60
CITRUS VALLEY MEDICAL CENTER–QUEEN OF THE VALLEY CAMPUS, WEST COVINA, CALIFORNIA (see CITRUS VALLEY MEDICAL CENTER–INTER COMMUNITY CAMPUS), p. A60
CITY OF HOPE'S HELFORD CLINICAL RESEARCH HOSPITAL, DUARTE, CA, p. A61
CLAIBORNE COUNTY MEDICAL CENTER, PORT GIBSON, MS, p. A364
CLAIBORNE MEDICAL CENTER, TAZEWELL, TN, p. A593
CLAIBORNE MEMORIAL MEDICAL CENTER, HOMER, LA, p. A278
CLARA BARTON HOSPITAL, HOISINGTON, KS, p. A245
CLARA MAASS MEDICAL CENTER, BELLEVILLE, NJ, p. A414
CLAREMORE INDIAN HOSPITAL, CLAREMORE, OK, p. A510
CLARINDA REGIONAL HEALTH CENTER, CLARINDA, IA, p. A227
CLARION HOSPITAL, CLARION, PA, p. A535
CLARION PSYCHIATRIC CENTER, CLARION, PA, p. A535
CLARITY CHILD GUIDANCE CENTER, SAN ANTONIO, TX, p. A645
CLARK FORK VALLEY HOSPITAL, PLAINS, MT, p. A390
CLARK MEMORIAL HOSPITAL, JEFFERSONVILLE, IN, p. A215

CLARK REGIONAL MEDICAL CENTER, WINCHESTER, KY, p. A270
CLARKE COUNTY HOSPITAL, OSCEOLA, IA, p. A236
CLARKS SUMMIT STATE HOSPITAL, CLARKS SUMMIT, PA, p. A535
CLAXTON–HEPBURN MEDICAL CENTER, OGDENSBURG, NY, p. A451
CLAY COUNTY HOSPITAL, ASHLAND, AL, p. A15
CLAY COUNTY HOSPITAL, FLORA, IL, p. A190
CLAY COUNTY MEDICAL CENTER, CLAY CENTER, KS, p. A241
CLAY COUNTY MEMORIAL HOSPITAL, HENRIETTA, TX, p. A623
CLEAR BROOK LODGE, SHICKSHINNY, PA, p. A555
CLEAR LAKE REGIONAL MEDICAL CENTER, WEBSTER, TX, p. A656
CLEARVIEW REGIONAL MEDICAL CENTER, MONROE, GA, p. A163
CLEARWATER VALLEY HOSPITAL AND CLINICS, OROFINO, ID, p. A177
CLEMENT J. ZABLOCKI VETERANS AFFAIRS MEDICAL CENTER, MILWAUKEE, WI, p. A711
CLEVELAND AREA HOSPITAL, CLEVELAND, OK, p. A510
CLEVELAND CLINIC, CLEVELAND, OH, p. A488
CLEVELAND CLINIC CHILDREN'S HOSPITAL, CLEVELAND, OHIO (see CLEVELAND CLINIC), p. A488
CLEVELAND CLINIC CHILDREN'S HOSPITAL FOR REHABILITATION, CLEVELAND, OH, p. A489
CLEVELAND CLINIC FAIRVIEW HOSPITAL, CLEVELAND, OH, p. A489
CLEVELAND CLINIC FLORIDA, WESTON, FL, p. A150
CLEVELAND CLINIC REHABILITATION HOSPITAL, AVON, OH, p. A484
CLEVELAND CLINIC, MEDINA HOSPITAL, MEDINA, OH, p. A499
CLEVELAND REGIONAL MEDICAL CENTER, SHELBY, NC, p. A473
CLIFTON SPRINGS HOSPITAL AND CLINIC, CLIFTON SPRINGS, NY, p. A437
CLIFTON T. PERKINS HOSPITAL CENTER, JESSUP, MD, p. A301
CLIFTON–FINE HOSPITAL, STAR LAKE, NY, p. A456
CLINCH MEMORIAL HOSPITAL, HOMERVILLE, GA, p. A161
CLINCH VALLEY MEDICAL CENTER, RICHLANDS, VA, p. A677
CLINTON HOSPITAL, CLINTON, MA, p. A309
CLINTON MEMORIAL HOSPITAL, WILMINGTON, OH, p. A506
CLOUD COUNTY HEALTH CENTER, CONCORDIA, KS, p. A242
CLOVIS COMMUNITY MEDICAL CENTER, CLOVIS, CA, p. A59
COAL COUNTY GENERAL HOSPITAL, COALGATE, OK, p. A510
COALINGA REGIONAL MEDICAL CENTER, COALINGA, CA, p. A59
COAST PLAZA HOSPITAL, NORWALK, CA, p. A79
COASTAL CAROLINA HOSPITAL, HARDEEVILLE, SC, p. A567
COASTAL HARBOR TREATMENT CENTER, SAVANNAH, GA, p. A165
COATESVILLE VETERANS AFFAIRS MEDICAL CENTER, COATESVILLE, PA, p. A536
COBALT REHABILITATION HOSPITAL, SURPRISE, AZ, p. A39
COBLESKILL REGIONAL HOSPITAL, COBLESKILL, NY, p. A437
COBRE VALLEY REGIONAL MEDICAL CENTER, GLOBE, AZ, p. A33
COCHRAN MEMORIAL HOSPITAL, MORTON, TX, p. A637
COFFEE REGIONAL MEDICAL CENTER, DOUGLAS, GA, p. A158
COFFEY COUNTY HOSPITAL, BURLINGTON, KS, p. A241
COFFEYVILLE REGIONAL MEDICAL CENTER, COFFEYVILLE, KS, p. A241
COGDELL MEMORIAL HOSPITAL, SNYDER, TX, p. A649
COLE MEMORIAL, COUDERSPORT, PA, p. A536
COLEMAN COUNTY MEDICAL CENTER, COLEMAN, TX, p. A606
COLER REHABILITATION AND NURSING CARE CENTER, NEW YORK, NEW YORK (see NYC HEALTH + HOSPITALS / CARTER), p. A448
COLISEUM CENTER FOR BEHAVIORAL HEALTH, MACON, GEORGIA (see COLISEUM MEDICAL CENTERS), p. A162
COLISEUM MEDICAL CENTERS, MACON, GA, p. A162
COLISEUM NORTHSIDE HOSPITAL, MACON, GA, p. A162
COLLEGE HOSPITAL CERRITOS, CERRITOS, CA, p. A58
COLLEGE HOSPITAL COSTA MESA, COSTA MESA, CA, p. A60
COLLEGE MEDICAL CENTER, LONG BEACH, CA, p. A69
COLLEGE STATION MEDICAL CENTER, COLLEGE STATION, TX, p. A606
COLLETON MEDICAL CENTER, WALTERBORO, SC, p. A570
COLLINGSWORTH GENERAL HOSPITAL, WELLINGTON, TX, p. A657
COLONEL FLORENCE A. BLANCHFIELD ARMY COMMUNITY HOSPITAL, FORT CAMPBELL, KY, p. A260
COLORADO ACUTE LONG TERM HOSPITAL, DENVER, CO, p. A103
COLORADO CANYONS HOSPITAL AND MEDICAL CENTER, FRUITA, CO, p. A106
COLORADO MENTAL HEALTH INSTITUTE AT FORT LOGAN, DENVER, CO, p. A103
COLORADO MENTAL HEALTH INSTITUTE AT PUEBLO, PUEBLO, CO, p. A109

COLORADO PLAINS MEDICAL CENTER, FORT MORGAN, CO, p. A105
COLORADO RIVER MEDICAL CENTER, NEEDLES, CA, p. A79
COLQUITT REGIONAL MEDICAL CENTER, MOULTRIE, GA, p. A163
COLUMBIA BASIN HOSPITAL, EPHRATA, WA, p. A684
COLUMBIA CENTER, MEQUON, WI, p. A710
COLUMBIA COUNTY HEALTH SYSTEM, DAYTON, WA, p. A684
COLUMBIA MEMORIAL HOSPITAL, HUDSON, NY, p. A440
COLUMBIA MEMORIAL HOSPITAL, ASTORIA, OR, p. A524
COLUMBIA ST. MARY'S COLUMBIA HOSPITAL, MILWAUKEE, WISCONSIN (see COLUMBIA ST. MARY'S HOSPITAL MILWAUKEE), p. A711
COLUMBIA ST. MARY'S HOSPITAL MILWAUKEE, MILWAUKEE, WI, p. A711
COLUMBIA ST. MARY'S MILWAUKEE HOSPITAL, MILWAUKEE, WISCONSIN (see COLUMBIA ST. MARY'S HOSPITAL MILWAUKEE), p. A711
COLUMBIA ST. MARY'S OZAUKEE HOSPITAL, MEQUON, WI, p. A710
COLUMBUS COMMUNITY HOSPITAL, COLUMBUS, NE, p. A395
COLUMBUS COMMUNITY HOSPITAL, COLUMBUS, TX, p. A607
COLUMBUS COMMUNITY HOSPITAL, INC., COLUMBUS, WI, p. A704
COLUMBUS HOSPITAL LTACH, NEWARK, NJ, p. A420
COLUMBUS REGIONAL HEALTHCARE SYSTEM, WHITEVILLE, NC, p. A475
COLUMBUS REGIONAL HOSPITAL, COLUMBUS, IN, p. A208
COLUMBUS SPECIALTY HOSPITAL, COLUMBUS, GA, p. A156
COMANCHE COUNTY HOSPITAL, COLDWATER, KS, p. A241
COMANCHE COUNTY MEDICAL CENTER, COMANCHE, TX, p. A607
COMANCHE COUNTY MEMORIAL HOSPITAL, LAWTON, OK, p. A513
COMER CHILDREN'S HOSPITAL, CHICAGO, ILLINOIS (see UNIVERSITY OF CHICAGO MEDICAL CENTER), p. A187
COMMONWEALTH CENTER FOR CHILDREN AND ADOLESCENTS, STAUNTON, VA, p. A679
COMMONWEALTH HEALTH CENTER, SAIPAN, MP, p. A725
COMMONWEALTH REGIONAL SPECIALTY HOSPITAL, BOWLING GREEN, KY, p. A257
COMMUNITY BEHAVIORAL HEALTH CENTER, FRESNO, CA, p. A63
COMMUNITY BEHAVIORAL HEALTH HOSPITAL – ALEXANDRIA, ALEXANDRIA, MN, p. A338
COMMUNITY BEHAVIORAL HEALTH HOSPITAL – ANNANDALE, ANNANDALE, MN, p. A338
COMMUNITY BEHAVIORAL HEALTH HOSPITAL – BAXTER, BAXTER, MN, p. A339
COMMUNITY BEHAVIORAL HEALTH HOSPITAL – BEMIDJI, BEMIDJI, MN, p. A339
COMMUNITY BEHAVIORAL HEALTH HOSPITAL – FERGUS FALLS, FERGUS FALLS, MN, p. A342
COMMUNITY BEHAVIORAL HEALTH HOSPITAL – ROCHESTER, ROCHESTER, MN, p. A349
COMMUNITY BEHAVIORAL HEALTH HOSPITAL – ST. PETER, SAINT PETER, MN, p. A351
COMMUNITY CARE HOSPITAL, NEW ORLEANS, LA, p. A284
COMMUNITY FIRST MEDICAL CENTER, CHICAGO, IL, p. A183
COMMUNITY GENERAL HEALTH CENTER, FORT FAIRFIELD, MAINE (see THE AROOSTOOK MEDICAL CENTER), p. A295
COMMUNITY HEALTH CENTER OF BRANCH COUNTY, COLDWATER, MI, p. A321
COMMUNITY HEALTHCARE SYSTEM, ONAGA, KS, p. A250
COMMUNITY HEART AND VASCULAR HOSPITAL, INDIANAPOLIS, INDIANA (see COMMUNITY HOSPITAL EAST), p. A213
COMMUNITY HOSPITAL, TALLASSEE, AL, p. A25
COMMUNITY HOSPITAL, GRAND JUNCTION, CO, p. A106
COMMUNITY HOSPITAL, MUNSTER, IN, p. A219
COMMUNITY HOSPITAL, MCCOOK, NE, p. A398
COMMUNITY HOSPITAL, OKLAHOMA CITY, OK, p. A516
COMMUNITY HOSPITAL, TORRINGTON, WY, p. A724
COMMUNITY HOSPITAL EAST, INDIANAPOLIS, IN, p. A213
COMMUNITY HOSPITAL LONG BEACH, LONG BEACH, CA, p. A69
COMMUNITY HOSPITAL NORTH, INDIANAPOLIS, IN, p. A213
COMMUNITY HOSPITAL OF ANACONDA, ANACONDA, MT, p. A385
COMMUNITY HOSPITAL OF ANDERSON & MADISON COUNTY, ANDERSON, IN, p. A206
COMMUNITY HOSPITAL OF BREMEN, BREMEN, IN, p. A207
COMMUNITY HOSPITAL OF HUNTINGTON PARK, HUNTINGTON PARK, CA, p. A66
COMMUNITY HOSPITAL OF SAN BERNARDINO, SAN BERNARDINO, CA, p. A88
COMMUNITY HOSPITAL OF THE MONTEREY PENINSULA, MONTEREY, CA, p. A77
COMMUNITY HOSPITAL SOUTH, INDIANAPOLIS, IN, p. A213
COMMUNITY HOSPITAL–FAIRFAX, FAIRFAX, MO, p. A371

COMMUNITY HOSPITALS AND WELLNESS CENTERS, BRYAN, OH, p. A485
COMMUNITY HOSPITALS AND WELLNESS CENTERS–MONTPELIER, MONTPELIER, OH, p. A499
COMMUNITY HOWARD REGIONAL HEALTH, KOKOMO, IN, p. A216
COMMUNITY HOWARD SPECIALTY HOSPITAL, KOKOMO, IN, p. A216
COMMUNITY MEDICAL CENTER, MISSOULA, MT, p. A389
COMMUNITY MEDICAL CENTER, TOMS RIVER, NJ, p. A424
COMMUNITY MEDICAL CENTER OF IZARD COUNTY, CALICO ROCK, AR, p. A44
COMMUNITY MEDICAL CENTER, INC., FALLS CITY, NE, p. A395
COMMUNITY MEMORIAL HEALTHCARE, MARYSVILLE, KS, p. A249
COMMUNITY MEMORIAL HOSPITAL, VENTURA, CA, p. A98
COMMUNITY MEMORIAL HOSPITAL, VENTURA, CALIFORNIA (see COMMUNITY MEMORIAL HOSPITAL), p. A98
COMMUNITY MEMORIAL HOSPITAL, STAUNTON, IL, p. A204
COMMUNITY MEMORIAL HOSPITAL, SUMNER, IA, p. A238
COMMUNITY MEMORIAL HOSPITAL, CLOQUET, MN, p. A340
COMMUNITY MEMORIAL HOSPITAL, SYRACUSE, NE, p. A402
COMMUNITY MEMORIAL HOSPITAL, HAMILTON, NY, p. A440
COMMUNITY MEMORIAL HOSPITAL, TURTLE LAKE, ND, p. A481
COMMUNITY MEMORIAL HOSPITAL, HICKSVILLE, OH, p. A496
COMMUNITY MEMORIAL HOSPITAL, BURKE, SD, p. A572
COMMUNITY MEMORIAL HOSPITAL, REDFIELD, SD, p. A576
COMMUNITY MEMORIAL HOSPITAL, MENOMONEE FALLS, WI, p. A710
COMMUNITY MENTAL HEALTH CENTER, LAWRENCEBURG, IN, p. A217
COMMUNITY REGIONAL MEDICAL CENTER, FRESNO, CA, p. A63
COMMUNITY WESTVIEW HOSPITAL, INDIANAPOLIS, INDIANA (see COMMUNITY HOSPITAL EAST), p. A213
COMPASS BEHAVIORAL CENTER OF ALEXANDRIA, ALEXANDRIA, LA, p. A271
COMPASS BEHAVIORAL CENTER OF CROWLEY, CROWLEY, LA, p. A276
COMPASS BEHAVIORAL CENTER OF HOUMA, HOUMA, LA, p. A278
COMPLEX CARE HOSPITAL AT RIDGELAKE, SARASOTA, FL, p. A145
COMPLEX CARE HOSPITAL AT TENAYA, LAS VEGAS, NV, p. A405
CONCHO COUNTY HOSPITAL, EDEN, TX, p. A614
CONCORD HOSPITAL, CONCORD, NH, p. A410
CONCOURSE DIVISION,, NEW YORK (see BRONX–LEBANON HOSPITAL CENTER HEALTH CARE SYSTEM), p. A444
CONE HEALTH, GREENSBORO, NORTH CAROLINA (see MOSES H. CONE MEMORIAL HOSPITAL), p. A466
CONEMAUGH MEMORIAL MEDICAL CENTER, JOHNSTOWN, PA, p. A541
CONEMAUGH MEYERSDALE MEDICAL CENTER, MEYERSDALE, PA, p. A545
CONEMAUGH MINERS MEDICAL CENTER, HASTINGS, PA, p. A540
CONFLUENCE HEALTH/CENTRAL WASHINGTON HOSPITAL, WENATCHEE, WA, p. A693
CONFLUENCE HEALTH/WENATCHEE VALLEY HOSPITAL, WENATCHEE, WA, p. A693
CONIFER PARK, GLENVILLE, NY, p. A439
CONNALLY MEMORIAL MEDICAL CENTER, FLORESVILLE, TX, p. A617
CONNECTICUT CHILDREN'S MEDICAL CENTER, HARTFORD, CT, p. A114
CONNECTICUT DEPARTMENT OF CORRECTION'S HOSPITAL, SOMERS, CT, p. A116
CONNECTICUT MENTAL HEALTH CENTER, NEW HAVEN, CT, p. A116
CONNECTICUT VALLEY HOSPITAL, MIDDLETOWN, CT, p. A115
CONNECTICUT VETERANS HOME AND HOSPITAL, ROCKY HILL, CT, p. A116
CONROE REGIONAL MEDICAL CENTER, CONROE, TX, p. A607
CONTINUECARE HOSPITAL AT BAPTIST HEALTH CORBIN, CORBIN, KY, p. A258
CONTINUECARE HOSPITAL AT BAPTIST HEALTH PADUCAH, PADUCAH, KY, p. A268
CONTINUECARE HOSPITAL AT HENDRICK MEDICAL CENTER, ABILENE, TX, p. A595
CONTINUECARE HOSPITAL AT MADISONVILLE, MADISONVILLE, KY, p. A266
CONTINUECARE HOSPITAL AT MEDICAL CENTER (ODESSA), ODESSA, TX, p. A639
CONTINUECARE HOSPITAL AT MIDLAND MEMORIAL, MIDLAND, TX, p. A637
CONTINUECARE HOSPITAL AT PALMETTO HEALTH BAPTIST, COLUMBIA, SC, p. A564
CONTINUING CARE HOSPITAL, LEXINGTON, KY, p. A263
CONTINUING CARE HOSPITAL AT ST. LUKE'S, CEDAR RAPIDS, IA, p. A226

D

DELTA MEDICAL CENTER, MEMPHIS, TN, p. A588
DELTA MEMORIAL HOSPITAL, DUMAS, AR, p. A45
DELTA REGIONAL MEDICAL CENTER, GREENVILLE, MS, p. A358
DENTON REGIONAL MEDICAL CENTER, DENTON, TX, p. A612
DENVER HEALTH, DENVER, CO, p. A103
DEPAUL CENTER, WACO, TEXAS (see PROVIDENCE HEALTHCARE NETWORK), p. A656
DEQUINCY MEMORIAL HOSPITAL, DEQUINCY, LA, p. A276
DES MOINES DIVISION, DES MOINES, IOWA (see VETERANS AFFAIRS CENTRAL IOWA HEALTH CARE SYSTEM), p. A230
DES PERES HOSPITAL, SAINT LOUIS, MO, p. A380
DESERT REGIONAL MEDICAL CENTER, PALM SPRINGS, CA, p. A81
DESERT SPRINGS HOSPITAL MEDICAL CENTER, LAS VEGAS, NV, p. A405
DESERT VALLEY HOSPITAL, VICTORVILLE, CA, p. A98
DESERT VIEW HOSPITAL, PAHRUMP, NV, p. A407
DESERT WILLOW TREATMENT CENTER, LAS VEGAS, NV, p. A405
DESOTO MEMORIAL HOSPITAL, ARCADIA, FL, p. A123
DETAR HEALTHCARE SYSTEM, VICTORIA, TX, p. A655
DETAR HOSPITAL NORTH, VICTORIA, TEXAS (see DETAR HEALTHCARE SYSTEM), p. A655
DEVEREUX CHILDREN'S BEHAVIORAL HEALTH CENTER, MALVERN, PA, p. A543
DEVEREUX GEORGIA TREATMENT NETWORK, KENNESAW, GA, p. A161
DEVEREUX HOSPITAL AND CHILDREN'S CENTER OF FLORIDA, MELBOURNE, FL, p. A135
DEVEREUX TEXAS TREATMENT NETWORK, LEAGUE CITY, TX, p. A632
DEWITT HOSPITAL, DEWITT, AR, p. A45
DIAMOND CHILDREN'S HOSPITAL, TUCSON, ARIZONA (see BANNER – UNIVERSITY MEDICAL CENTER TUCSON), p. A40
DICKENSON COMMUNITY HOSPITAL, CLINTWOOD, VA, p. A669
DICKINSON COUNTY HEALTHCARE SYSTEM, IRON MOUNTAIN, MI, p. A327
DIGNITY HEALTH ARIZONA GENERAL HOSPITAL, LAVEEN, AZ, p. A34
DILEY RIDGE MEDICAL CENTER, CANAL WINCHESTER, OH, p. A486
DIMMIT REGIONAL HOSPITAL, CARRIZO SPRINGS, TX, p. A605
DISTRICT ONE HOSPITAL, FARIBAULT, MN, p. A342
DIVINE PROVIDENCE HOSPITAL, WILLIAMSPORT, PA, p. A558
DIVINE SAVIOR HEALTHCARE, PORTAGE, WI, p. A714
DIVISION OF ADOLESCENT MEDICINE, CINCINNATI CENTER FOR DEVELOPMENTAL DISORDERS, AND CONVALESCENT HOSPITAL FOR CHILDREN, CHILDREN'S HOSPITAL, CINCINNATI, OHIO (see CINCINNATI CHILDREN'S HOSPITAL MEDICAL CENTER), p. A487
DIXIE REGIONAL MEDICAL CENTER, SAINT GEORGE, UT, p. A663
DIXIE REGIONAL MEDICAL CENTER, ST. GEORGE, UTAH (see DIXIE REGIONAL MEDICAL CENTER), p. A663
DMC – CHILDREN'S HOSPITAL OF MICHIGAN, DETROIT, MI, p. A321
DMC – DETROIT RECEIVING HOSPITAL, DETROIT, MI, p. A321
DMC – REHABILITATION INSTITUTE OF MICHIGAN, DETROIT, MI, p. A321
DMC – SINAI–GRACE HOSPITAL, DETROIT, MI, p. A321
DMC HARPER UNIVERSITY HOSPITAL, DETROIT, MI, p. A322
DMC HURON VALLEY–SINAI HOSPITAL, COMMERCE TOWNSHIP, MI, p. A321
DOCTOR'S CENTER OF BAYAMON, BAYAMON, PR, p. A726
DOCTOR'S HOSPITAL, LEAWOOD, KS, p. A247
DOCTOR'S HOSPITAL AT RENAISSANCE, EDINBURG, TX, p. A614
DOCTOR'S HOSPITAL OF DEER CREEK, LEESVILLE, LA, p. A282
DOCTOR'S MEMORIAL HOSPITAL, PERRY, FL, p. A142
DOCTORS CENTER, MANATI, PR, p. A727
DOCTORS COMMUNITY HOSPITAL, LANHAM, MD, p. A302
DOCTORS HOSPITAL, AUGUSTA, GA, p. A153
DOCTORS HOSPITAL OF JEFFERSON, METAIRIE, LOUISIANA (see EAST JEFFERSON GENERAL HOSPITAL), p. A283
DOCTORS HOSPITAL OF LAREDO, LAREDO, TX, p. A632
DOCTORS HOSPITAL OF MANTECA, MANTECA, CA, p. A76
DOCTORS HOSPITAL OF SARASOTA, SARASOTA, FL, p. A145
DOCTORS HOSPITAL PARKWAY, HOUSTON, TEXAS (see UNITED MEMORIAL MEDICAL CARE), p. A627
DOCTORS MEDICAL CENTER OF MODESTO, MODESTO, CA, p. A77
DOCTORS MEMORIAL HOSPITAL, BONIFAY, FL, p. A124
DOCTORS NEUROMEDICAL HOSPITAL, BREMEN, IN, p. A207
DOCTORS NEUROPSYCHIATRIC HOSPITAL AND RESEARCH INSTITUTE, BREMEN, IN, p. A207
DOCTORS' CENTER HOSPITAL SAN JUAN, SAN JUAN, PR, p. A726
DOCTORS' HOSPITAL OF MICHIGAN, PONTIAC, MI, p. A332
DODGE COUNTY HOSPITAL, EASTMAN, GA, p. A159

DOERNBECHER CHILDREN'S HOSPITAL, PORTLAND, OREGON (see OHSU HOSPITAL), p. A529
DOMINICAN HOSPITAL, SANTA CRUZ, CA, p. A93
DOMINION HOSPITAL, FALLS CHURCH, VA, p. A669
DONALSONVILLE HOSPITAL, DONALSONVILLE, GA, p. A158
DORMINY MEDICAL CENTER, FITZGERALD, GA, p. A159
DOROTHEA DIX PSYCHIATRIC CENTER, BANGOR, ME, p. A291
DOUGLAS COUNTY COMMUNITY MENTAL HEALTH CENTER, OMAHA, NE, p. A400
DOUGLAS COUNTY HOSPITAL, ALEXANDRIA, MN, p. A338
DOUGLAS COUNTY MEMORIAL HOSPITAL, ARMOUR, SD, p. A572
DOVER BEHAVIORAL HEALTH SYSTEM, DOVER, DE, p. A119
DOWN EAST COMMUNITY HOSPITAL, MACHIAS, ME, p. A294
DOYLESTOWN HOSPITAL, DOYLESTOWN, PA, p. A537
DR. DAN C. TRIGG MEMORIAL HOSPITAL, TUCUMCARI, NM, p. A432
DR. J. CORRIGAN MENTAL HEALTH CENTER, FALL RIVER, MA, p. A309
DR. JOHN WARNER HOSPITAL, CLINTON, IL, p. A187
DR. PILA'S HOSPITAL, PONCE, PR, p. A728
DR. RAMON E. BETANCES HOSPITAL–MAYAGUEZ MEDICAL CENTER BRANCH, MAYAGUEZ, PR, p. A728
DR. SOLOMON CARTER FULLER MENTAL HEALTH CENTER, BOSTON, MA, p. A306
DREW MEMORIAL HOSPITAL, MONTICELLO, AR, p. A50
DRISCOLL CHILDREN'S HOSPITAL, CORPUS CHRISTI, TX, p. A608
DRUMRIGHT REGIONAL HOSPITAL, DRUMRIGHT, OK, p. A510
DUANE L. WATERS HOSPITAL, JACKSON, MI, p. A327
DUBLIN SPRINGS, DUBLIN, OH, p. A494
DUKE CHILDREN'S HOSPITAL & HEALTH CENTER, DURHAM, NORTH CAROLINA (see DUKE UNIVERSITY HOSPITAL), p. A464
DUKE RALEIGH HOSPITAL, RALEIGH, NC, p. A471
DUKE REGIONAL HOSPITAL, DURHAM, NC, p. A464
DUKE UNIVERSITY HOSPITAL, DURHAM, NC, p. A464
DUKES MEMORIAL HOSPITAL, PERU, IN, p. A220
DUNCAN REGIONAL HOSPITAL, DUNCAN, OK, p. A510
DUNDY COUNTY HOSPITAL, BENKELMAN, NE, p. A394
DUPONT HOSPITAL, FORT WAYNE, IN, p. A210
DURHAM VETERANS AFFAIRS MEDICAL CENTER, DURHAM, NC, p. A464
DWIGHT DAVID EISENHOWER ARMY MEDICAL CENTER, FORT GORDON, GA, p. A160

E

EAGLEVILLE HOSPITAL, EAGLEVILLE, PA, p. A537
EARLE E. MORRIS ALCOHOL AND DRUG TREATMENT CENTER, COLUMBIA, SC, p. A564
EAST ADAMS RURAL HEALTHCARE, RITZVILLE, WA, p. A689
EAST ALABAMA MEDICAL CENTER, OPELIKA, AL, p. A24
EAST ALABAMA MEDICAL CENTER–LANIER, VALLEY, ALABAMA (see EAST ALABAMA MEDICAL CENTER), p. A24
EAST CAMPUS, NORFOLK, NEBRASKA (see FAITH REGIONAL HEALTH SERVICES), p. A399
EAST CARROLL PARISH HOSPITAL, LAKE PROVIDENCE, LA, p. A282
EAST CENTRAL REGIONAL HOSPITAL, AUGUSTA, GA, p. A153
EAST CENTRAL REGIONAL HOSPITAL, GRACEWOOD, GEORGIA (see EAST CENTRAL REGIONAL HOSPITAL), p. A153
EAST COOPER MEDICAL CENTER, MOUNT PLEASANT, SC, p. A568
EAST GEORGIA REGIONAL MEDICAL CENTER, STATESBORO, GA, p. A166
EAST HOUSTON REGIONAL MEDICAL CENTER, HOUSTON, TEXAS (see BAYSHORE MEDICAL CENTER), p. A640
EAST JEFFERSON GENERAL HOSPITAL, METAIRIE, LA, p. A283
EAST LIVERPOOL CITY HOSPITAL, EAST LIVERPOOL, OH, p. A494
EAST LOS ANGELES DOCTORS HOSPITAL, LOS ANGELES, CA, p. A71
EAST MISSISSIPPI STATE HOSPITAL, MERIDIAN, MS, p. A362
EAST MORGAN COUNTY HOSPITAL, BRUSH, CO, p. A102
EAST MOUNTAIN HOSPITAL, BELLE MEAD, NJ, p. A414
EAST OHIO REGIONAL HOSPITAL, MARTINS FERRY, OH, p. A498
EAST ORANGE DIVISION, EAST ORANGE, NEW JERSEY (see VETERANS AFFAIRS NEW JERSEY HEALTH CARE SYSTEM), p. A416
EAST ORANGE GENERAL HOSPITAL, EAST ORANGE, NJ, p. A416
EAST RIDGE HOSPITAL, EAST RIDGE, TENNESSEE (see PARKRIDGE MEDICAL CENTER), p. A580
EAST TENNESSEE CHILDREN'S HOSPITAL, KNOXVILLE, TN, p. A585
EAST TEXAS MEDICAL CENTER ATHENS, ATHENS, TX, p. A598

EAST TEXAS MEDICAL CENTER BEHAVIORAL HEALTH CENTER, TYLER, TEXAS (see EAST TEXAS MEDICAL CENTER TYLER), p. A654
EAST TEXAS MEDICAL CENTER CARTHAGE, CARTHAGE, TX, p. A605
EAST TEXAS MEDICAL CENTER FAIRFIELD, FAIRFIELD, TX, p. A617
EAST TEXAS MEDICAL CENTER HENDERSON, HENDERSON, TX, p. A623
EAST TEXAS MEDICAL CENTER JACKSONVILLE, JACKSONVILLE, TX, p. A629
EAST TEXAS MEDICAL CENTER PITTSBURG, PITTSBURG, TX, p. A641
EAST TEXAS MEDICAL CENTER REHABILITATION HOSPITAL, TYLER, TX, p. A654
EAST TEXAS MEDICAL CENTER SPECIALTY HOSPITAL, TYLER, TX, p. A654
EAST TEXAS MEDICAL CENTER TRINITY, TRINITY, TX, p. A653
EAST TEXAS MEDICAL CENTER TYLER, TYLER, TX, p. A654
EAST TEXAS MEDICAL CENTER–QUITMAN, QUITMAN, TX, p. A642
EASTAR HEALTH SYSTEM, MUSKOGEE, OK, p. A515
EASTAR HEALTH SYSTEM, EAST CAMPUS, MUSKOGEE, OKLAHOMA (see EASTAR HEALTH SYSTEM), p. A515
EASTERN IDAHO REGIONAL MEDICAL CENTER, IDAHO FALLS, ID, p. A176
EASTERN LONG ISLAND HOSPITAL, GREENPORT, NY, p. A440
EASTERN LOUISIANA MENTAL HEALTH SYSTEM, JACKSON, LA, p. A278
EASTERN MAINE MEDICAL CENTER, BANGOR, ME, p. A291
EASTERN NEW MEXICO MEDICAL CENTER, ROSWELL, NM, p. A431
EASTERN NIAGARA HOSPITAL, LOCKPORT, NY, p. A441
EASTERN NIAGARA HOSPITAL LOCKPORT, LOCKPORT, NEW YORK (see EASTERN NIAGARA HOSPITAL), p. A441
EASTERN NIAGARA HOSPITAL NEWFANE, NEWFANE, NEW YORK (see EASTERN NIAGARA HOSPITAL), p. A441
EASTERN OKLAHOMA MEDICAL CENTER, POTEAU, OK, p. A518
EASTERN PLUMAS HEALTH CARE, PORTOLA, CA, p. A83
EASTERN REGIONAL MEDICAL CENTER, PHILADELPHIA, PA, p. A547
EASTERN SHORE HOSPITAL CENTER, CAMBRIDGE, MD, p. A299
EASTERN STATE HOSPITAL, LEXINGTON, KY, p. A263
EASTERN STATE HOSPITAL, WILLIAMSBURG, VA, p. A680
EASTERN STATE HOSPITAL, MEDICAL LAKE, WA, p. A686
EASTLAND MEMORIAL HOSPITAL, EASTLAND, TX, p. A614
EASTON HOSPITAL, EASTON, PA, p. A537
EASTPOINTE HOSPITAL, DAPHNE, AL, p. A18
EASTSIDE MEDICAL CENTER, SNELLVILLE, GA, p. A166
EASTSIDE PSYCHIATRIC HOSPITAL, TALLAHASSEE, FL, p. A146
EATON RAPIDS MEDICAL CENTER, EATON RAPIDS, MI, p. A323
ED FRASER MEMORIAL HOSPITAL AND BAKER COMMUNITY HEALTH CENTER, MACCLENNY, FL, p. A135
EDEN MEDICAL CENTER, CASTRO VALLEY, CA, p. A58
EDGEFIELD COUNTY HOSPITAL, EDGEFIELD, SC, p. A565
EDGERTON HOSPITAL AND HEALTH SERVICES, EDGERTON, WI, p. A705
EDGEWOOD SURGICAL HOSPITAL, TRANSFER, PA, p. A555
EDINBURG CHILDREN'S HOSPITAL, EDINBURG, TEXAS (see SOUTH TEXAS HEALTH SYSTEM), p. A614
EDINBURG REGIONAL MEDICAL CENTER, EDINBURG, TEXAS (see SOUTH TEXAS HEALTH SYSTEM), p. A614
EDWARD HINES, JR. VETERANS AFFAIRS HOSPITAL, HINES, IL, p. A193
EDWARD HOSPITAL, NAPERVILLE, IL, p. A198
EDWARDS COUNTY HOSPITAL AND HEALTHCARE CENTER, KINSLEY, KS, p. A246
EDWIN SHAW REHAB, CUYAHOGA FALLS, OH, p. A492
EFFINGHAM HOSPITAL, SPRINGFIELD, GA, p. A166
EINSTEIN MEDICAL CENTER ELKINS PARK, ELKINS PARK, PENNSYLVANIA (see EINSTEIN MEDICAL CENTER PHILADELPHIA), p. A547
EINSTEIN MEDICAL CENTER MONTGOMERY, EAST NORRITON, PA, p. A537
EINSTEIN MEDICAL CENTER PHILADELPHIA, PHILADELPHIA, PA, p. A547
EISENHOWER MEDICAL CENTER, RANCHO MIRAGE, CA, p. A84
EL CAMINO HOSPITAL, MOUNTAIN VIEW, CA, p. A78
EL CAMINO HOSPITAL LOS GATOS, LOS GATOS, CALIFORNIA (see EL CAMINO HOSPITAL), p. A78
EL CAMPO MEMORIAL HOSPITAL, EL CAMPO, TX, p. A615
EL CENTRO REGIONAL MEDICAL CENTER, EL CENTRO, CA, p. A61
EL PASO BEHAVIORAL HEALTH SYSTEM, EL PASO, TX, p. A615
EL PASO CHILDREN'S HOSPITAL, EL PASO, TX, p. A615
EL PASO LTAC HOSPITAL, EL PASO, TX, p. A615
EL PASO PSYCHIATRIC CENTER, EL PASO, TX, p. A615
EL PASO SPECIALTY HOSPITAL, EL PASO, TX, p. A615
ELBERT MEMORIAL HOSPITAL, ELBERTON, GA, p. A159

ELEANOR SLATER HOSPITAL, CRANSTON, RI, p. A560
ELECTRA MEMORIAL HOSPITAL, ELECTRA, TX, p. A616
ELGIN MENTAL HEALTH CENTER, ELGIN, IL, p. A189
ELIZA COFFEE MEMORIAL HOSPITAL, FLORENCE, AL, p. A20
ELKHART GENERAL HOSPITAL, ELKHART, IN, p. A209
ELKHORN VALLEY REHABILITATION HOSPITAL, CASPER, WY, p. A721
ELKVIEW GENERAL HOSPITAL, HOBART, OK, p. A512
ELLENVILLE REGIONAL HOSPITAL, ELLENVILLE, NY, p. A438
ELLETT MEMORIAL HOSPITAL, APPLETON CITY, MO, p. A367
ELLINWOOD DISTRICT HOSPITAL, ELLINWOOD, KS, p. A242
ELLIOT HOSPITAL, MANCHESTER, NH, p. A412
ELLIS FISCHEL CANCER CENTER, COLUMBIA, MISSOURI (see UNIVERSITY OF MISSOURI HOSPITALS AND CLINICS), p. A370
ELLIS HOSPITAL, SCHENECTADY, NY, p. A455
ELLIS HOSPITAL HEALTH CENTER, SCHENECTADY, NEW YORK (see ELLIS HOSPITAL), p. A455
ELLSWORTH COUNTY MEDICAL CENTER, ELLSWORTH, KS, p. A242
ELLWOOD CITY HOSPITAL, ELLWOOD CITY, PA, p. A538
ELMHURST MEMORIAL HOSPITAL,, IL, p. A189
ELMIRA PSYCHIATRIC CENTER, ELMIRA, NY, p. A438
ELMORE COMMUNITY HOSPITAL, WETUMPKA, AL, p. A26
ELMWOOD HEALTHCARE CENTER AT THE SPRINGS, GREEN SPRINGS, OH, p. A495
ELY–BLOOMENSON COMMUNITY HOSPITAL, ELY, MN, p. A342
EMANUEL MEDICAL CENTER, TURLOCK, CA, p. A97
EMANUEL MEDICAL CENTER, SWAINSBORO, GA, p. A167
EMERALD COAST BEHAVIORAL HOSPITAL, PANAMA CITY, FL, p. A141
EMERSON HOSPITAL, CONCORD, MA, p. A309
EMERUS COMMUNITY HOSPITAL, TOMBALL, TX, p. A653
EMERUS HOSPITAL – SUGAR LAND, SUGAR LAND, TX, p. A650
EMMA PENDLETON BRADLEY HOSPITAL, EAST PROVIDENCE, RI, p. A560
EMORY JOHNS CREEK HOSPITAL, JOHNS CREEK, GA, p. A161
EMORY REHABILITATION HOSPITAL, ATLANTA, GA, p. A152
EMORY SAINT JOSEPH'S HOSPITAL OF ATLANTA, ATLANTA, GA, p. A152
EMORY UNIVERSITY HOSPITAL, ATLANTA, GA, p. A152
EMORY UNIVERSITY HOSPITAL MIDTOWN, ATLANTA, GA, p. A152
EMORY UNIVERSITY ORTHOPAEDIC AND SPINE HOSPITAL, TUCKER, GEORGIA (see EMORY UNIVERSITY HOSPITAL), p. A152
EMORY WESLEY WOODS GERIATRIC HOSPITAL, ATLANTA, GEORGIA (see EMORY UNIVERSITY HOSPITAL), p. A152
ENCINO HOSPITAL MEDICAL CENTER,, CA, p. A71
ENDLESS MOUNTAIN HEALTH SYSTEMS, MONTROSE, PA, p. A545
ENGLEWOOD COMMUNITY HOSPITAL, ENGLEWOOD, FL, p. A128
ENGLEWOOD HOSPITAL AND MEDICAL CENTER, ENGLEWOOD, NJ, p. A417
ENLOE MEDICAL CENTER, CHICO, CA, p. A58
ENLOE MEDICAL CENTER–COHASSET, CHICO, CALIFORNIA (see ENLOE MEDICAL CENTER), p. A58
ENNIS REGIONAL MEDICAL CENTER, ENNIS, TX, p. A616
EPHRAIM MCDOWELL FORT LOGAN HOSPITAL, STANFORD, KY, p. A269
EPHRAIM MCDOWELL REGIONAL MEDICAL CENTER, DANVILLE, KY, p. A259
ERIE COUNTY MEDICAL CENTER, BUFFALO, NY, p. A435
ERIE VETERANS AFFAIRS MEDICAL CENTER, ERIE, PA, p. A538
ERIK AND MARGARET JONSSON HOSPITAL, DALLAS, TEXAS (see BAYLOR UNIVERSITY MEDICAL CENTER), p. A609
ERLANGER BLEDSOE HOSPITAL, PIKEVILLE, TN, p. A592
ERLANGER EAST HOSPITAL, CHATTANOOGA, TENNESSEE (see ERLANGER MEDICAL CENTER), p. A580
ERLANGER MEDICAL CENTER, CHATTANOOGA, TN, p. A580
ERLANGER NORTH HOSPITAL, CHATTANOOGA, TENNESSEE (see ERLANGER MEDICAL CENTER), p. A580
ESKENAZI HEALTH, INDIANAPOLIS, IN, p. A213
ESSENTIA HEALTH ADA, ADA, MN, p. A338
ESSENTIA HEALTH DULUTH, DULUTH, MN, p. A341
ESSENTIA HEALTH FARGO, FARGO, ND, p. A478
ESSENTIA HEALTH FOSSTON, FOSSTON, MN, p. A343
ESSENTIA HEALTH NORTHERN PINES MEDICAL CENTER, AURORA, MN, p. A338
ESSENTIA HEALTH SANDSTONE, SANDSTONE, MN, p. A351
ESSENTIA HEALTH ST. JOSEPH'S MEDICAL CENTER, BRAINERD, MN, p. A340
ESSENTIA HEALTH ST. MARY'S – DETROIT LAKES, DETROIT LAKES, MN, p. A341
ESSENTIA HEALTH ST. MARY'S HOSPITAL OF SUPERIOR, SUPERIOR, WI, p. A717
ESSENTIA HEALTH ST. MARY'S MEDICAL CENTER, DULUTH, MN, p. A342
ESSENTIA HEALTH–DEER RIVER, DEER RIVER, MN, p. A341
ESSENTIA HEALTH–GRACEVILLE, GRACEVILLE, MN, p. A343

ESSENTIA HEALTH–VIRGINIA, VIRGINIA, MN, p. A352
ESSEX COUNTY HOSPITAL CENTER, CEDAR GROVE, NJ, p. A415
ESTES PARK MEDICAL CENTER, ESTES PARK, CO, p. A105
ETHICUS HOSPITAL – GRAPEVINE, GRAPEVINE, TX, p. A621
EUCLID HOSPITAL, EUCLID, OH, p. A494
EUNICE EXTENDED CARE HOSPITAL, EUNICE, LOUISIANA (see LOUISIANA EXTENDED CARE HOSPITAL OF LAFAYETTE), p. A280
EUREKA COMMUNITY HEALTH SERVICES AVERA, EUREKA, SD, p. A573
EUREKA SPRINGS HOSPITAL, EUREKA SPRINGS, AR, p. A45
EVANGELICAL COMMUNITY HOSPITAL, LEWISBURG, PA, p. A543
EVANS MEMORIAL HOSPITAL, CLAXTON, GA, p. A156
EVANS U. S. ARMY COMMUNITY HOSPITAL, FORT CARSON, CO, p. A105
EVANSTON REGIONAL HOSPITAL, EVANSTON, WY, p. A722
EVANSVILLE PSYCHIATRIC CHILDREN CENTER, EVANSVILLE, IN, p. A210
EVANSVILLE STATE HOSPITAL, EVANSVILLE, IN, p. A210
EVERETT TOWER, OKLAHOMA CITY, OKLAHOMA (see OU MEDICAL CENTER), p. A517
EVERGREEN MEDICAL CENTER, EVERGREEN, AL, p. A19
EVERGREENHEALTH, KIRKLAND, WA, p. A686
EVERGREENHEALTH MONROE, MONROE, WA, p. A686
EXCELA FRICK HOSPITAL, MOUNT PLEASANT, PA, p. A545
EXCELA HEALTH WESTMORELAND HOSPITAL, GREENSBURG, PA, p. A539
EXCELA LATROBE AREA HOSPITAL, LATROBE, PA, p. A542
EXCELSIOR SPRINGS HOSPITAL, EXCELSIOR SPRINGS, MO, p. A370
EXEMPLA WEST PINES, WHEAT RIDGE, COLORADO (see LUTHERAN MEDICAL CENTER), p. A111
EXETER HOSPITAL, EXETER, NH, p. A411
EYE AND EAR CLINIC OF CHARLESTON, CHARLESTON, WV, p. A695
EYE AND EAR HOSPITAL OF PITTSBURGH, PITTSBURGH, PENNSYLVANIA (see UPMC PRESBYTERIAN SHADYSIDE), p. A551

F

F. F. THOMPSON HOSPITAL, CANANDAIGUA, NY, p. A436
F. W. HUSTON MEDICAL CENTER, WINCHESTER, KS, p. A256
FAIR OAKS (see HSHS HOLY FAMILY HOSPITAL IN GREENVILLE), p. A192
FAIR OAKS PAVILION, DELRAY BEACH, FLORIDA (see DELRAY MEDICAL CENTER), p. A127
FAIRBANKS, INDIANAPOLIS, IN, p. A213
FAIRBANKS MEMORIAL HOSPITAL, FAIRBANKS, AK, p. A29
FAIRCHILD MEDICAL CENTER, YREKA, CA, p. A100
FAIRFAX BEHAVIORAL HEALTH, KIRKLAND, WA, p. A686
FAIRFAX BEHAVIORAL HEALTH EVERETT, EVERETT, WASHINGTON (see FAIRFAX BEHAVIORAL HEALTH), p. A686
FAIRFAX COMMUNITY HOSPITAL, FAIRFAX, OK, p. A512
FAIRFIELD MEDICAL CENTER, LANCASTER, OH, p. A496
FAIRFIELD MEMORIAL HOSPITAL, FAIRFIELD, IL, p. A190
FAIRFIELD MEMORIAL HOSPITAL, WINNSBORO, SC, p. A571
FAIRLAWN REHABILITATION HOSPITAL, WORCESTER, MA, p. A316
FAIRMONT HOSPITAL, SAN LEANDRO, CALIFORNIA (see HIGHLAND HOSPITAL), p. A80
FAIRMONT REGIONAL MEDICAL CENTER, FAIRMONT, WV, p. A696
FAIRMOUNT BEHAVIORAL HEALTH SYSTEM, PHILADELPHIA, PA, p. A547
FAIRVIEW DEVELOPMENTAL CENTER, COSTA MESA, CA, p. A60
FAIRVIEW HOSPITAL, GREAT BARRINGTON, MA, p. A310
FAIRVIEW LAKES HEALTH SERVICES, WYOMING, MN, p. A354
FAIRVIEW NORTHLAND MEDICAL CENTER, PRINCETON, MN, p. A349
FAIRVIEW PARK HOSPITAL, DUBLIN, GA, p. A159
FAIRVIEW REGIONAL MEDICAL CENTER, FAIRVIEW, OK, p. A512
FAIRVIEW RIDGES HOSPITAL, BURNSVILLE, MN, p. A340
FAIRVIEW RIVERSIDE HOSPITAL, MINNEAPOLIS, MINNESOTA (see UNIVERSITY OF MINNESOTA MEDICAL CENTER, FAIRVIEW), p. A347
FAIRVIEW SOUTHDALE HOSPITAL, EDINA, MN, p. A342
FAIRWAY MEDICAL SURGICAL HOSPITAL, COVINGTON, LA, p. A275
FAITH COMMUNITY HOSPITAL, JACKSBORO, TX, p. A629
FAITH REGIONAL HEALTH SERVICES, NORFOLK, NE, p. A399
FALL RIVER HOSPITAL, HOT SPRINGS, SD, p. A574
FALLON MEDICAL COMPLEX, BAKER, MT, p. A385
FALLS COMMUNITY HOSPITAL AND CLINIC, MARLIN, TX, p. A635

FALMOUTH HOSPITAL, FALMOUTH, MA, p. A310
FANNIN REGIONAL HOSPITAL, BLUE RIDGE, GA, p. A154
FANNY ALLEN CAMPUS, COLCHESTER, VERMONT (see THE UNIVERSITY OF VERMONT HEALTH NETWORK UNIVERSITY OF VERMONT MEDICAL CENTER), p. A665
FARGO VETERANS AFFAIRS HEALTH CARE SYSTEM, FARGO, ND, p. A478
FAULKTON AREA MEDICAL CENTER, FAULKTON, SD, p. A573
FAUQUIER HOSPITAL, WARRENTON, VA, p. A680
FAWCETT MEMORIAL HOSPITAL, PORT CHARLOTTE, FL, p. A143
FAXTON CAMPUS, UTICA, NEW YORK (see FAXTON ST. LUKE'S HEALTHCARE), p. A457
FAXTON ST. LUKE'S HEALTHCARE, UTICA, NY, p. A457
FAYETTE COUNTY HOSPITAL, VANDALIA, IL, p. A204
FAYETTE COUNTY MEMORIAL HOSPITAL, WASHINGTON COURT HOUSE, OH, p. A505
FAYETTE MEDICAL CENTER, FAYETTE, AL, p. A20
FAYETTE REGIONAL HEALTH SYSTEM, CONNERSVILLE, IN, p. A208
FAYETTEVILLE VETERANS AFFAIRS MEDICAL CENTER, FAYETTEVILLE, NC, p. A465
FEATHER RIVER HOSPITAL, PARADISE, CA, p. A82
FEDERAL CORRECTIONAL INSTITUTE HOSPITAL, LITTLETON, CO, p. A108
FEDERAL MEDICAL CENTER, LEXINGTON, KY, p. A263
FERRELL HOSPITAL, ELDORADO, IL, p. A189
FERRY COUNTY MEMORIAL HOSPITAL, REPUBLIC, WA, p. A688
FHN MEMORIAL HOSPITAL, FREEPORT, IL, p. A190
FIELD MEMORIAL COMMUNITY HOSPITAL, CENTREVILLE, MS, p. A356
FIELDSTONE CENTER, BATTLE CREEK, MICHIGAN (see BRONSON BATTLE CREEK), p. A319
FILLMORE COMMUNITY MEDICAL CENTER, FILLMORE, UT, p. A659
FILLMORE COUNTY HOSPITAL, GENEVA, NE, p. A396
FIRELANDS REGIONAL HEALTH SYSTEM, SANDUSKY, OH, p. A502
FIRELANDS REGIONAL MEDICAL CENTER – MAIN CAMPUS, SANDUSKY, OHIO (see FIRELANDS REGIONAL HEALTH SYSTEM), p. A502
FIRELANDS REGIONAL MEDICAL CENTER SOUTH CAMPUS, SANDUSKY, OHIO (see FIRELANDS REGIONAL HEALTH SYSTEM), p. A502
FIRST BAPTIST MEDICAL CENTER, DALLAS, TX, p. A610
FIRST CARE HEALTH CENTER, PARK RIVER, ND, p. A481
FIRST HOSPITAL PANAMERICANO, CIDRA, PR, p. A727
FIRST HOSPITAL WYOMING VALLEY, KINGSTON, PA, p. A541
FIRST SURGICAL HOSPITAL, BELLAIRE, TX, p. A602
FIRST TEXAS HOSPITAL, CARROLLTON, TX, p. A605
FIRSTHEALTH MONTGOMERY MEMORIAL HOSPITAL, TROY, NC, p. A474
FIRSTHEALTH MOORE REGIONAL HOSPITAL, PINEHURST, NC, p. A471
FIRSTHEALTH RICHMOND MEMORIAL HOSPITAL, ROCKINGHAM, NC, p. A472
FIRSTLIGHT HEALTH SYSTEM, MORA, MN, p. A347
FISHER COUNTY HOSPITAL DISTRICT, ROTAN, TX, p. A644
FISHER–TITUS MEDICAL CENTER, NORWALK, OH, p. A500
FISHERMEN'S HOSPITAL, MARATHON, FL, p. A135
FITZGIBBON HOSPITAL, MARSHALL, MO, p. A376
FIVE RIVERS MEDICAL CENTER, POCAHONTAS, AR, p. A51
FLAGET MEMORIAL HOSPITAL, BARDSTOWN, KY, p. A257
FLAGLER HOSPITAL, SAINT AUGUSTINE, FL, p. A144
FLAGSTAFF MEDICAL CENTER, FLAGSTAFF, AZ, p. A32
FLAMBEAU HOSPITAL, PARK FALLS, WI, p. A714
FLEMING COUNTY HOSPITAL, FLEMINGSBURG, KY, p. A259
FLINT RIVER COMMUNITY HOSPITAL, MONTEZUMA, GA, p. A163
FLORENCE HOSPITAL AT ANTHEM, FLORENCE, AZ, p. A32
FLORIDA HOSPITAL, ORLANDO, FL, p. A140
FLORIDA HOSPITAL AT CONNERTON LONG TERM ACUTE CARE, LAND O'LAKES, FL, p. A134
FLORIDA HOSPITAL CARROLLWOOD, TAMPA, FL, p. A147
FLORIDA HOSPITAL CELEBRATION HEALTH, CELEBRATION, FLORIDA (see FLORIDA HOSPITAL), p. A140
FLORIDA HOSPITAL DELAND, DELAND, FL, p. A127
FLORIDA HOSPITAL EAST ORLANDO, ORLANDO, FLORIDA (see FLORIDA HOSPITAL), p. A140
FLORIDA HOSPITAL FISH MEMORIAL, ORANGE CITY, FL, p. A140
FLORIDA HOSPITAL FOR CHILDREN–WALT DISNEY PAVILION, ORLANDO, FLORIDA (see FLORIDA HOSPITAL), p. A140
FLORIDA HOSPITAL HEARTLAND MEDICAL CENTER, SEBRING, FL, p. A145
FLORIDA HOSPITAL KISSIMMEE, KISSIMMEE, FLORIDA (see FLORIDA HOSPITAL), p. A140
FLORIDA HOSPITAL LAKE PLACID, LAKE PLACID, FLORIDA (see FLORIDA HOSPITAL HEARTLAND MEDICAL CENTER), p. A145
FLORIDA HOSPITAL MEMORIAL MEDICAL CENTER, DAYTONA BEACH, FL, p. A127

FLORIDA HOSPITAL NEW SMYRNA, NEW SMYRNA BEACH, FL, p. A139

FLORIDA HOSPITAL NORTH PINELLAS, TARPON SPRINGS, FL, p. A148

FLORIDA HOSPITAL TAMPA, TAMPA, FL, p. A147

FLORIDA HOSPITAL WATERMAN, TAVARES, FL, p. A148

FLORIDA HOSPITAL WAUCHULA, WAUCHULA, FL, p. A149

FLORIDA HOSPITAL WESLEY CHAPEL, WESLEY CHAPEL, FL, p. A149

FLORIDA HOSPITAL ZEPHYRHILLS, ZEPHYRHILLS, FL, p. A150

FLORIDA HOSPITAL–ALTAMONTE, ALTAMONTE SPRINGS, FLORIDA (see FLORIDA HOSPITAL), p. A140

FLORIDA HOSPITAL–APOPKA, APOPKA, FLORIDA (see FLORIDA HOSPITAL), p. A140

FLORIDA HOSPITAL–FLAGLER, PALM COAST, FL, p. A141

FLORIDA HOSPITAL–OCEANSIDE, ORMOND BEACH, FLORIDA (see FLORIDA HOSPITAL MEMORIAL MEDICAL CENTER), p. A127

FLORIDA MEDICAL CENTER – A CAMPUS OF NORTH SHORE, FORT LAUDERDALE, FLORIDA (see NORTH SHORE MEDICAL CENTER), p. A137

FLORIDA STATE HOSPITAL, CHATTAHOOCHEE, FL, p. A125

FLOWERS HOSPITAL, DOTHAN, AL, p. A19

FLOYD COUNTY MEDICAL CENTER, CHARLES CITY, IA, p. A227

FLOYD MEDICAL CENTER, ROME, GA, p. A165

FLOYD VALLEY HEALTHCARE, LE MARS, IA, p. A233

FLUSHING HOSPITAL MEDICAL CENTER,, NY, p. A444

FOND DU LAC COUNTY MENTAL HEALTH CENTER, FOND DU LAC, WI, p. A705

FOOTHILL PRESBYTERIAN HOSPITAL, GLENDORA, CA, p. A65

FOOTHILL REGIONAL MEDICAL CENTER, TUSTIN, CA, p. A97

FORBES HOSPITAL, MONROEVILLE, PA, p. A545

FOREST HEALTH MEDICAL CENTER, YPSILANTI, MI, p. A337

FOREST VIEW PSYCHIATRIC HOSPITAL, GRAND RAPIDS, MI, p. A324

FORKS COMMUNITY HOSPITAL, FORKS, WA, p. A685

FORREST CITY MEDICAL CENTER, FORREST CITY, AR, p. A46

FORREST GENERAL HOSPITAL, HATTIESBURG, MS, p. A359

FORT BELKNAP U. S. PUBLIC HEALTH SERVICE INDIAN HOSPITAL, HARLEM, MT, p. A388

FORT BELVOIR COMMUNITY HOSPITAL, FORT BELVOIR, VA, p. A670

FORT DUNCAN REGIONAL MEDICAL CENTER, EAGLE PASS, TX, p. A614

FORT HAMILTON HOSPITAL, HAMILTON, OH, p. A496

FORT HEALTHCARE, FORT ATKINSON, WI, p. A705

FORT LAUDERDALE HOSPITAL, FORT LAUDERDALE, FL, p. A128

FORT LOUDOUN MEDICAL CENTER, LENOIR CITY, TN, p. A587

FORT MADISON COMMUNITY HOSPITAL, FORT MADISON, IA, p. A231

FORT SANDERS REGIONAL MEDICAL CENTER, KNOXVILLE, TN, p. A586

FORT WALTON BEACH MEDICAL CENTER, FORT WALTON BEACH, FL, p. A129

FORT WASHINGTON MEDICAL CENTER, OXEN HILL, MD, p. A302

FOUNDATION SURGICAL HOSPITAL OF EL PASO, EL PASO, TX, p. A615

FOUNDATION SURGICAL HOSPITAL OF SAN ANTONIO, SAN ANTONIO, TX, p. A646

FOUNDATIONS BEHAVIORAL HEALTH, DOYLESTOWN, PA, p. A537

FOUNTAIN VALLEY REGIONAL HOSPITAL AND MEDICAL CENTER, FOUNTAIN VALLEY, CA, p. A62

FOUR COUNTY COUNSELING CENTER, LOGANSPORT, IN, p. A217

FOUR WINDS HOSPITAL, KATONAH, NY, p. A441

FOUR WINDS HOSPITAL, SARATOGA SPRINGS, NY, p. A455

FOX CHASE CANCER CENTER–AMERICAN ONCOLOGIC HOSPITAL, PHILADELPHIA, PA, p. A548

FRAMINGHAM UNION HOSPITAL, FRAMINGHAM, MASSACHUSETTS (see METROWEST MEDICAL CENTER), p. A310

FRANCES MAHON DEACONESS HOSPITAL, GLASGOW, MT, p. A387

FRANCISCAN HEALTH RENSSELEAR, RENSSELAER, IN, p. A221

FRANCISCAN HEALTHCARE – MUNSTER, MUNSTER, IN, p. A219

FRANCISCAN HOSPITAL FOR CHILDREN, BOSTON, MA, p. A306

FRANCISCAN ST. ANTHONY HEALTH – CROWN POINT, CROWN POINT, IN, p. A209

FRANCISCAN ST. ANTHONY HEALTH – MICHIGAN CITY, MICHIGAN CITY, IN, p. A218

FRANCISCAN ST. ELIZABETH HEALTH – CRAWFORDSVILLE, CRAWFORDSVILLE, IN, p. A208

FRANCISCAN ST. ELIZABETH HEALTH – LAFAYETTE CENTRAL, LAFAYETTE, INDIANA (see FRANCISCAN ST. ELIZABETH HEALTH – LAFAYETTE EAST), p. A216

FRANCISCAN ST. ELIZABETH HEALTH – LAFAYETTE EAST, LAFAYETTE, IN, p. A216

FRANCISCAN ST. FRANCIS HEALTH – INDIANAPOLIS, INDIANAPOLIS, IN, p. A214

FRANCISCAN ST. FRANCIS HEALTH – MOORESVILLE, MOORESVILLE, IN, p. A218

FRANCISCAN ST. FRANCIS HEALTH–CARMEL, CARMEL, IN, p. A208

FRANCISCAN ST. JAMES HOSPITAL AND HEALTH CENTERS, OLYMPIA FIELDS, IL, p. A199

FRANCISCAN ST. MARGARET HEALTH – DYER, DYER, INDIANA (see FRANCISCAN ST. MARGARET HEALTH – HAMMOND), p. A212

FRANCISCAN ST. MARGARET HEALTH – HAMMOND, HAMMOND, IN, p. A212

FRANK R. HOWARD MEMORIAL HOSPITAL, WILLITS, CA, p. A100

FRANKFORD CAMPUS, PHILADELPHIA, PENNSYLVANIA (see ARIA – JEFFERSON HEALTH), p. A547

FRANKFORT REGIONAL MEDICAL CENTER, FRANKFORT, KY, p. A260

FRANKLIN COUNTY MEDICAL CENTER, PRESTON, ID, p. A178

FRANKLIN COUNTY MEMORIAL HOSPITAL, MEADVILLE, MS, p. A361

FRANKLIN COUNTY MEMORIAL HOSPITAL, FRANKLIN, NE, p. A395

FRANKLIN FOUNDATION HOSPITAL, FRANKLIN, LA, p. A277

FRANKLIN GENERAL HOSPITAL, HAMPTON, IA, p. A231

FRANKLIN HOSPITAL DISTRICT, BENTON, IL, p. A181

FRANKLIN MEDICAL CENTER, WINNSBORO, LA, p. A289

FRANKLIN MEMORIAL HOSPITAL, FARMINGTON, ME, p. A293

FRANKLIN REGIONAL HOSPITAL, FRANKLIN, NH, p. A411

FRANKLIN WOODS COMMUNITY HOSPITAL, JOHNSON CITY, TN, p. A585

FRAZIER REHAB INSTITUTE, LOUISVILLE, KY, p. A264

FREDERICK MEMORIAL HOSPITAL, FREDERICK, MD, p. A301

FREDONIA REGIONAL HOSPITAL, FREDONIA, KS, p. A243

FREEDOM PAIN HOSPITAL, SCOTTSDALE, AZ, p. A38

FREEMAN HEALTH SYSTEM, JOPLIN, MO, p. A372

FREEMAN HOSPITAL EAST, JOPLIN, MISSOURI (see FREEMAN HEALTH SYSTEM), p. A372

FREEMAN NEOSHO HOSPITAL, NEOSHO, MO, p. A377

FREEMAN REGIONAL HEALTH SERVICES, FREEMAN, SD, p. A574

FREMONT HEALTH, FREMONT, NE, p. A396

FREMONT HOSPITAL, FREMONT, CA, p. A63

FREMONT MEDICAL CENTER, FREMONT, CA, p. A63

FREMONT MEDICAL CENTER, YUBA CITY, CALIFORNIA (see RIDEOUT MEMORIAL HOSPITAL), p. A76

FRENCH HOSPITAL MEDICAL CENTER, SAN LUIS OBISPO, CA, p. A92

FRESNO HEART AND SURGICAL HOSPITAL, FRESNO, CA, p. A63

FRESNO SURGICAL HOSPITAL, FRESNO, CA, p. A63

FRIEND COMMUNITY HEALTHCARE SYSTEM, FRIEND, NE, p. A396

FRIENDS HOSPITAL, PHILADELPHIA, PA, p. A548

FRIO REGIONAL HOSPITAL, PEARSALL, TX, p. A640

FRISBIE MEMORIAL HOSPITAL, ROCHESTER, NH, p. A413

FROEDTERT MEMORIAL LUTHERAN HOSPITAL, MILWAUKEE, WI, p. A711

FRYE REGIONAL MEDICAL CENTER, HICKORY, NC, p. A467

FRYE REGIONAL MEDICAL CENTER–SOUTH CAMPUS, HICKORY, NORTH CAROLINA (see FRYE REGIONAL MEDICAL CENTER), p. A467

FULTON COUNTY HEALTH CENTER, WAUSEON, OH, p. A505

FULTON COUNTY HOSPITAL, SALEM, AR, p. A52

FULTON COUNTY MEDICAL CENTER, MC CONNELLSBURG, PA, p. A544

FULTON DIVISION,, NEW YORK (see BRONX–LEBANON HOSPITAL CENTER HEALTH CARE SYSTEM), p. A444

FULTON MEDICAL CENTER, FULTON, MO, p. A371

FULTON STATE HOSPITAL, FULTON, MO, p. A371

G

G. WERBER BRYAN PSYCHIATRIC HOSPITAL, COLUMBIA, SC, p. A564

G.V. (SONNY) MONTGOMERY VETERANS AFFAIRS MEDICAL CENTER, JACKSON, MS, p. A359

GADSDEN REGIONAL MEDICAL CENTER, GADSDEN, AL, p. A20

GAINESVILLE VETERANS AFFAIRS MEDICAL CENTER, GAINESVILLE, FLORIDA (see NORTH FLORIDA/SOUTH GEORGIA VETERAN'S HEALTH SYSTEM), p. A129

GALESBURG COTTAGE HOSPITAL, GALESBURG, IL, p. A191

GALION COMMUNITY HOSPITAL, GALION, OH, p. A495

GALLUP INDIAN MEDICAL CENTER, GALLUP, NM, p. A429

GARDEN CITY HOSPITAL, GARDEN CITY, MI, p. A324

GARDEN GROVE HOSPITAL AND MEDICAL CENTER, GARDEN GROVE, CA, p. A64

GARDEN PARK MEDICAL CENTER, GULFPORT, MS, p. A358

GARDENS REGIONAL HOSPITAL AND MEDICAL CENTER, HAWAIIAN GARDENS, CA, p. A65

GARDENVIEW NURSING HOME (see MINNESOTA VALLEY HEALTH CENTER), p. A344

GARFIELD COUNTY HEALTH CENTER, JORDAN, MT, p. A388

GARFIELD COUNTY PUBLIC HOSPITAL DISTRICT, POMEROY, WA, p. A688

GARFIELD MEDICAL CENTER, MONTEREY PARK, CA, p. A78

GARFIELD MEMORIAL HOSPITAL AND CLINICS, PANGUITCH, UT, p. A662

GARFIELD PARK HOSPITAL, CHICAGO, IL, p. A184

GARRETT REGIONAL MEDICAL CENTER, OAKLAND, MD, p. A302

GARRISON MEMORIAL HOSPITAL, GARRISON, ND, p. A479

GATEWAY REGIONAL MEDICAL CENTER, GRANITE CITY, IL, p. A191

GATEWAY REHABILITATION HOSPITAL, FLORENCE, KY, p. A260

GATEWAYS HOSPITAL AND MENTAL HEALTH CENTER, LOS ANGELES, CA, p. A71

GAYLORD HOSPITAL, WALLINGFORD, CT, p. A117

GEARY COMMUNITY HOSPITAL, JUNCTION CITY, KS, p. A246

GEISINGER HEALTHSOUTH REHABILITATION HOSPITAL, DANVILLE, PA, p. A536

GEISINGER MEDICAL CENTER, DANVILLE, PA, p. A536

GEISINGER WYOMING VALLEY MEDICAL CENTER, WILKES BARRE, PA, p. A557

GEISINGER–BLOOMSBURG HOSPITAL, BLOOMSBURG, PA, p. A533

GEISINGER–COMMUNITY MEDICAL CENTER, SCRANTON, PA, p. A554

GEISINGER–LEWISTOWN HOSPITAL, LEWISTOWN, PA, p. A543

GEISINGER–SHAMOKIN AREA COMMUNITY HOSPITAL, COAL TOWNSHIP, PENNSYLVANIA (see GEISINGER MEDICAL CENTER), p. A536

GENERAL HOSPITAL, CHARLESTON, WEST VIRGINIA (see CHARLESTON AREA MEDICAL CENTER), p. A695

GENERAL HOSPITAL, LOS ANGELES, CALIFORNIA (see LAC+USC MEDICAL CENTER), p. A72

GENERAL HOSPITAL, EUREKA, CALIFORNIA (see ST. JOSEPH HOSPITAL), p. A61

GENERAL JOHN J. PERSHING MEMORIAL HOSPITAL, BROOKFIELD, MO, p. A368

GENERAL LEONARD WOOD ARMY COMMUNITY HOSPITAL, FORT LEONARD WOOD, MO, p. A371

GENESIS BEHAVIORAL HOSPITAL, BREAUX BRIDGE, LA, p. A274

GENESIS HEALTHCARE SYSTEM, ZANESVILLE, OH, p. A507

GENESIS MEDICAL CENTER, DEWITT, DE WITT, IA, p. A229

GENESIS MEDICAL CENTER, ILLINI CAMPUS, SILVIS, IL, p. A203

GENESIS MEDICAL CENTER–ALEDO, ALEDO, IL, p. A180

GENESIS MEDICAL CENTER–DAVENPORT, DAVENPORT, IA, p. A228

GENESIS MEDICAL CENTER–EAST CAMPUS, DAVENPORT, IOWA (see GENESIS MEDICAL CENTER–DAVENPORT), p. A228

GENESIS MEDICAL CENTER–WEST CAMPUS, DAVENPORT, IOWA (see GENESIS MEDICAL CENTER–DAVENPORT), p. A228

GENESYS REGIONAL MEDICAL CENTER, GRAND BLANC, MI, p. A324

GENEVA GENERAL HOSPITAL, GENEVA, NY, p. A439

GENOA MEDICAL FACILITIES, GENOA, NE, p. A396

GEORGE C GRAPE COMMUNITY HOSPITAL, HAMBURG, IA, p. A231

GEORGE E. WEEMS MEMORIAL HOSPITAL, APALACHICOLA, FL, p. A123

GEORGE REGIONAL HOSPITAL, LUCEDALE, MS, p. A361

GEORGE W. TRUETT MEMORIAL HOSPITAL, DALLAS, TEXAS (see BAYLOR UNIVERSITY MEDICAL CENTER), p. A609

GEORGE WASHINGTON UNIVERSITY HOSPITAL, WASHINGTON, DC, p. A121

GEORGETOWN BEHAVIORAL HEALTH INSTITUTE, GEORGETOWN, TX, p. A620

GEORGETOWN COMMUNITY HOSPITAL, GEORGETOWN, KY, p. A260

GEORGIA REGIONAL HOSPITAL AT ATLANTA, DECATUR, GA, p. A158

GEORGIA REGIONAL HOSPITAL AT SAVANNAH, SAVANNAH, GA, p. A166

GEORGIANA HOSPITAL, GEORGIANA, AL, p. A20

GERALD CHAMPION REGIONAL MEDICAL CENTER, ALAMOGORDO, NM, p. A427

GHS – LAURENS COUNTY MEMORIAL HOSPITAL, CLINTON, SOUTH CAROLINA (see GREENVILLE HEALTH SYSTEM – LAURENS COUNTY MEMORIAL HOSPITAL), p. A563

GHS CHILDREN'S HOSPITAL, GREENVILLE, SOUTH CAROLINA (see GHS GREENVILLE MEMORIAL HOSPITAL), p. A566

GHS GREENVILLE MEMORIAL HOSPITAL, GREENVILLE, SC, p. A566

GHS GREER MEMORIAL HOSPITAL, GREER, SC, p. A567

GHS HILLCREST MEMORIAL HOSPITAL, SIMPSONVILLE, SC, p. A569

H

HAMMOND–HENRY HOSPITAL, GENESEO, IL, p. A191

HAMPSHIRE MEMORIAL HOSPITAL, ROMNEY, WV, p. A700

HAMPSTEAD HOSPITAL, HAMPSTEAD, NH, p. A411

HAMPTON BEHAVIORAL HEALTH CENTER, WESTAMPTON, NJ, p. A425

HAMPTON REGIONAL MEDICAL CENTER, VARNVILLE, SC, p. A570

HAMPTON ROADS SPECIALTY HOSPITAL, NEWPORT NEWS, VA, p. A674

HAMPTON VETERANS AFFAIRS MEDICAL CENTER, HAMPTON, VA, p. A671

HANCOCK COUNTY HEALTH SYSTEM, BRITT, IA, p. A226

HANCOCK MEDICAL CENTER, BAY SAINT LOUIS, MS, p. A355

HANCOCK REGIONAL HOSPITAL, GREENFIELD, IN, p. A212

HANNIBAL REGIONAL HOSPITAL, HANNIBAL, MO, p. A371

HANOVER HOSPITAL, HANOVER, KS, p. A244

HANOVER HOSPITAL, HANOVER, PA, p. A539

HANSEN FAMILY HOSPITAL, IOWA FALLS, IA, p. A233

HANSFORD HOSPITAL, SPEARMAN, TX, p. A649

HARBOR BEACH COMMUNITY HOSPITAL, HARBOR BEACH, MI, p. A326

HARBOR HOSPITAL OF SOUTHEAST TEXAS, BEAUMONT, TX, p. A601

HARBOR OAKS HOSPITAL, NEW BALTIMORE, MI, p. A330

HARBOR–UCLA MEDICAL CENTER, TORRANCE, CA, p. A96

HARDEMAN COUNTY MEMORIAL HOSPITAL, QUANAH, TX, p. A642

HARDIN COUNTY GENERAL HOSPITAL, ROSICLARE, IL, p. A202

HARDIN MEDICAL CENTER, SAVANNAH, TN, p. A592

HARDIN MEMORIAL HOSPITAL, ELIZABETHTOWN, KY, p. A259

HARDTNER MEDICAL CENTER, OLLA, LA, p. A286

HARDY WILSON MEMORIAL HOSPITAL, HAZLEHURST, MS, p. A359

HARLAN ARH HOSPITAL, HARLAN, KY, p. A261

HARLAN COUNTY HEALTH SYSTEM, ALMA, NE, p. A393

HARLEM GENERAL CARE UNIT AND HARLEM PSYCHIATRIC UNIT (see NYC HEALTH + HOSPITALS / HARLEM), p. A448

HARLINGEN MEDICAL CENTER, HARLINGEN, TX, p. A622

HARMON MEDICAL AND REHABILITATION HOSPITAL, LAS VEGAS, NV, p. A405

HARMON MEMORIAL HOSPITAL, HOLLIS, OK, p. A513

HARNETT HEALTH SYSTEM, DUNN, NC, p. A464

HARNEY DISTRICT HOSPITAL, BURNS, OR, p. A524

HARPER COUNTY COMMUNITY HOSPITAL, BUFFALO, OK, p. A509

HARPER HOSPITAL DISTRICT FIVE, HARPER, KS, p. A244

HARRINGTON MEMORIAL HOSPITAL, SOUTHBRIDGE, MA, p. A314

HARRIS HEALTH SYSTEM, HOUSTON, TX, p. A624

HARRIS REGIONAL HOSPITAL, SYLVA, NC, p. A474

HARRISBURG MEDICAL CENTER, HARRISBURG, IL, p. A192

HARRISON COMMUNITY HOSPITAL, CADIZ, OH, p. A486

HARRISON COUNTY COMMUNITY HOSPITAL, BETHANY, MO, p. A367

HARRISON COUNTY HOSPITAL, CORYDON, IN, p. A208

HARRISON MEDICAL CENTER, BREMERTON, WA, p. A682

HARRISON MEMORIAL HOSPITAL, CYNTHIANA, KY, p. A259

HARRY S. TRUMAN MEMORIAL VETERANS HOSPITAL, COLUMBIA, MO, p. A370

HARSHA BEHAVIORAL CENTER, TERRE HAUTE, IN, p. A222

HARTFORD HOSPITAL, HARTFORD, CT, p. A114

HARTGROVE HOSPITAL, CHICAGO, IL, p. A184

HASBRO CHILDREN'S HOSPITAL, PROVIDENCE, RHODE ISLAND (see RHODE ISLAND HOSPITAL), p. A561

HASKELL COUNTY COMMUNITY HOSPITAL, STIGLER, OK, p. A520

HASKELL MEMORIAL HOSPITAL, HASKELL, TX, p. A622

HASSENFELD CHILDRENS HOSPITAL OF NEW YORK AT NYU LANGONE MEDICAL CENTER, NEW YORK, NEW YORK (see NYU LANGONE MEDICAL CENTER), p. A449

HAVASU REGIONAL MEDICAL CENTER, LAKE HAVASU CITY, AZ, p. A34

HAVEN BEHAVIORAL HOSPITAL OF EASTERN PENNSYLVANIA, READING, PA, p. A553

HAVEN BEHAVIORAL HOSPITAL OF FRISCO, FRISCO, TX, p. A619

HAVEN BEHAVIORAL SENIOR CARE OF ALBUQUERQUE, ALBUQUERQUE, NM, p. A427

HAVEN BEHAVIORAL SENIOR CARE OF DAYTON, DAYTON, OH, p. A492

HAVEN SENIOR HORIZONS, PHOENIX, AZ, p. A36

HAVENWYCK HOSPITAL, AUBURN HILLS, MI, p. A318

HAWAII STATE HOSPITAL, KANEOHE, HI, p. A172

HAWARDEN REGIONAL HEALTHCARE, HAWARDEN, IA, p. A232

HAWTHORN CENTER, NORTHVILLE, MI, p. A331

HAWTHORN CHILDREN PSYCHIATRIC HOSPITAL, SAINT LOUIS, MO, p. A380

HAXTUN HOSPITAL DISTRICT, HAXTUN, CO, p. A107

HAYES GREEN BEACH MEMORIAL HOSPITAL, CHARLOTTE, MI, p. A320

HAYS MEDICAL CENTER, HAYS, KS, p. A244

HAYWARD AREA MEMORIAL HOSPITAL AND NURSING HOME, HAYWARD, WI, p. A707

HAYWOOD REGIONAL MEDICAL CENTER, CLYDE, NC, p. A463

HAZARD ARH REGIONAL MEDICAL CENTER, HAZARD, KY, p. A261

HAZEL HAWKINS MEMORIAL HOSPITAL, HOLLISTER, CA, p. A66

HCMC DEPARTMENT OF PEDIATRICS, MINNEAPOLIS, MINNESOTA (see HENNEPIN COUNTY MEDICAL CENTER), p. A346

HEALDSBURG DISTRICT HOSPITAL, HEALDSBURG, CA, p. A66

HEALTH ALLIANCE HOSPITAL – BROADWAY CAMPUS, KINGSTON, NY, p. A441

HEALTH ALLIANCE HOSPITAL – MARY'S AVENUE CAMPUS, KINGSTON, NY, p. A441

HEALTH CENTRAL HOSPITAL, OCOEE, FL, p. A139

HEALTH FIRST CAPE CANAVERAL HOSPITAL, COCOA BEACH, FL, p. A126

HEALTH FIRST HOLMES REGIONAL MEDICAL CENTER, MELBOURNE, FL, p. A135

HEALTH FIRST PALM BAY HOSPITAL, PALM BAY, FL, p. A141

HEALTH FIRST VIERA HOSPITAL, MELBOURNE, FL, p. A135

HEALTHALLIANCE HOSPITALS, LEOMINSTER, MA, p. A311

HEALTHBRIDGE CHILDREN'S HOSPITAL, ORANGE, CA, p. A81

HEALTHBRIDGE CHILDREN'S HOSPITAL OF HOUSTON, HOUSTON, TX, p. A624

HEALTHMARK REGIONAL MEDICAL CENTER, DEFUNIAK SPRINGS, FL, p. A127

HEALTHPARK, OWENSBORO, KENTUCKY (see OWENSBORO HEALTH REGIONAL HOSPITAL), p. A267

HEALTHPARK MEDICAL CENTER, FORT MYERS, FLORIDA (see LEE MEMORIAL HOSPITAL), p. A129

HEALTHSOURCE SAGINAW, INC., SAGINAW, MI, p. A333

HEALTHSOUTH BAKERSFIELD REHABILITATION HOSPITAL, BAKERSFIELD, CA, p. A56

HEALTHSOUTH BRAINTREE REHABILITATION HOSPITAL, BRAINTREE, MA, p. A307

HEALTHSOUTH CANE CREEK REHABILITATION HOSPITAL, MARTIN, TN, p. A587

HEALTHSOUTH CHATTANOOGA REHABILITATION HOSPITAL, CHATTANOOGA, TN, p. A580

HEALTHSOUTH CHESAPEAKE REHABILITATION HOSPITAL, SALISBURY, MD, p. A303

HEALTHSOUTH CITY VIEW REHABILITATION HOSPITAL, FORT WORTH, TX, p. A618

HEALTHSOUTH DEACONESS REHABILITATION HOSPITAL, EVANSVILLE, IN, p. A210

HEALTHSOUTH DESERT CANYON REHABILITATION HOSPITAL, LAS VEGAS, NV, p. A405

HEALTHSOUTH EAST VALLEY REHABILITATION HOSPITAL, MESA, AZ, p. A34

HEALTHSOUTH EMERALD COAST REHABILITATION HOSPITAL, PANAMA CITY, FL, p. A141

HEALTHSOUTH HARMARVILLE REHABILITATION HOSPITAL, PITTSBURGH, PA, p. A550

HEALTHSOUTH HOSPITAL OF MANATI, MANATI, PR, p. A728

HEALTHSOUTH HUNTINGTON REHABILITATION HOSPITAL, HUNTINGTON, WV, p. A696

HEALTHSOUTH LAKESHORE REHABILITATION HOSPITAL, BIRMINGHAM, AL, p. A16

HEALTHSOUTH LAKEVIEW REHABILITATION HOSPITAL, ELIZABETHTOWN, KY, p. A259

HEALTHSOUTH MOUNTAINVIEW REGIONAL REHABILITATION HOSPITAL, MORGANTOWN, WV, p. A698

HEALTHSOUTH NEW ENGLAND REHABILITATION HOSPITAL, WOBURN, MA, p. A316

HEALTHSOUTH NITTANY VALLEY REHABILITATION HOSPITAL, PLEASANT GAP, PA, p. A552

HEALTHSOUTH NORTHERN KENTUCKY REHABILITATION HOSPITAL, EDGEWOOD, KY, p. A259

HEALTHSOUTH PLANO REHABILITATION HOSPITAL, PLANO, TX, p. A641

HEALTHSOUTH READING REHABILITATION HOSPITAL, READING, PA, p. A553

HEALTHSOUTH REHABILITATION HOSPITAL, DOTHAN, AL, p. A19

HEALTHSOUTH REHABILITATION HOSPITAL, FAYETTEVILLE, AR, p. A45

HEALTHSOUTH REHABILITATION HOSPITAL, LARGO, FL, p. A134

HEALTHSOUTH REHABILITATION HOSPITAL, CONCORD, NH, p. A410

HEALTHSOUTH REHABILITATION HOSPITAL, ALBUQUERQUE, NM, p. A427

HEALTHSOUTH REHABILITATION HOSPITAL, KINGSPORT, TN, p. A585

HEALTHSOUTH REHABILITATION HOSPITAL – ABILENE, ABILENE, TX, p. A595

HEALTHSOUTH REHABILITATION HOSPITAL – AUSTIN, AUSTIN, TX, p. A599

HEALTHSOUTH REHABILITATION HOSPITAL – DALLAS, DALLAS, TX, p. A610

HEALTHSOUTH REHABILITATION HOSPITAL – HENDERSON, HENDERSON, NV, p. A405

HEALTHSOUTH REHABILITATION HOSPITAL – MID–CITIES, BEDFORD, TX, p. A602

HEALTHSOUTH REHABILITATION HOSPITAL AT DRAKE, CINCINNATI, OH, p. A487

HEALTHSOUTH REHABILITATION HOSPITAL AT MARTIN HEALTH, STUART, FL, p. A146

HEALTHSOUTH REHABILITATION HOSPITAL MEMPHIS–NORTH, MEMPHIS, TN, p. A588

HEALTHSOUTH REHABILITATION HOSPITAL MIDLAND–ODESSA, MIDLAND, TX, p. A637

HEALTHSOUTH REHABILITATION HOSPITAL NORTH TEXAS, RICHARDSON, TX, p. A643

HEALTHSOUTH REHABILITATION HOSPITAL OF ALEXANDRIA, ALEXANDRIA, LA, p. A271

HEALTHSOUTH REHABILITATION HOSPITAL OF ALTAMONTE SPRINGS, ALTAMONTE SPRINGS, FL, p. A123

HEALTHSOUTH REHABILITATION HOSPITAL OF ALTOONA, ALTOONA, PA, p. A532

HEALTHSOUTH REHABILITATION HOSPITAL OF ARLINGTON, ARLINGTON, TX, p. A597

HEALTHSOUTH REHABILITATION HOSPITAL OF AUSTIN, AUSTIN, TX, p. A599

HEALTHSOUTH REHABILITATION HOSPITAL OF BEAUMONT, BEAUMONT, TX, p. A601

HEALTHSOUTH REHABILITATION HOSPITAL OF CHARLESTON, CHARLESTON, SC, p. A562

HEALTHSOUTH REHABILITATION HOSPITAL OF COLORADO SPRINGS, COLORADO SPRINGS, CO, p. A102

HEALTHSOUTH REHABILITATION HOSPITAL OF COLUMBIA, COLUMBIA, SC, p. A564

HEALTHSOUTH REHABILITATION HOSPITAL OF CYPRESS, HOUSTON, TX, p. A624

HEALTHSOUTH REHABILITATION HOSPITAL OF DAYTON, DAYTON, OH, p. A493

HEALTHSOUTH REHABILITATION HOSPITAL OF ERIE, ERIE, PA, p. A538

HEALTHSOUTH REHABILITATION HOSPITAL OF FLORENCE, FLORENCE, SC, p. A565

HEALTHSOUTH REHABILITATION HOSPITAL OF FORT SMITH, FORT SMITH, AR, p. A46

HEALTHSOUTH REHABILITATION HOSPITAL OF FORT WORTH, FORT WORTH, TX, p. A618

HEALTHSOUTH REHABILITATION HOSPITAL OF FRANKLIN, FRANKLIN, TN, p. A583

HEALTHSOUTH REHABILITATION HOSPITAL OF FREDERICKSBURG, FREDERICKSBURG, VA, p. A670

HEALTHSOUTH REHABILITATION HOSPITAL OF HUMBLE, LLC, HUMBLE, TX, p. A628

HEALTHSOUTH REHABILITATION HOSPITAL OF JONESBORO, JONESBORO, AR, p. A48

HEALTHSOUTH REHABILITATION HOSPITAL OF LITTLETON, LITTLETON, CO, p. A108

HEALTHSOUTH REHABILITATION HOSPITAL OF MECHANICSBURG, MECHANICSBURG, PA, p. A544

HEALTHSOUTH REHABILITATION HOSPITAL OF MEMPHIS, MEMPHIS, TN, p. A588

HEALTHSOUTH REHABILITATION HOSPITAL OF MIAMI, CUTLER BAY, FL, p. A126

HEALTHSOUTH REHABILITATION HOSPITAL OF MONTGOMERY, MONTGOMERY, AL, p. A23

HEALTHSOUTH REHABILITATION HOSPITAL OF NORTH ALABAMA, HUNTSVILLE, AL, p. A21

HEALTHSOUTH REHABILITATION HOSPITAL OF NORTHERN VIRGINIA, ALDIE, VA, p. A667

HEALTHSOUTH REHABILITATION HOSPITAL OF OCALA, OCALA, FL, p. A139

HEALTHSOUTH REHABILITATION HOSPITAL OF PETERSBURG, PETERSBURG, VA, p. A676

HEALTHSOUTH REHABILITATION HOSPITAL OF ROCK HILL, ROCK HILL, SC, p. A569

HEALTHSOUTH REHABILITATION HOSPITAL OF SAN JUAN, SAN JUAN, PR, p. A729

HEALTHSOUTH REHABILITATION HOSPITAL OF SARASOTA, SARASOTA, FL, p. A145

HEALTHSOUTH REHABILITATION HOSPITAL OF SEWICKLEY, SEWICKLEY, PA, p. A554

HEALTHSOUTH REHABILITATION HOSPITAL OF SOUTHERN ARIZONA, TUCSON, AZ, p. A40

HEALTHSOUTH REHABILITATION HOSPITAL OF SPRING HILL, BROOKSVILLE, FL, p. A125

HEALTHSOUTH REHABILITATION HOSPITAL OF TALLAHASSEE, TALLAHASSEE, FL, p. A146

HEALTHSOUTH REHABILITATION HOSPITAL OF TEXARKANA, TEXARKANA, TX, p. A652

HEALTHSOUTH REHABILITATION HOSPITAL OF TINTON FALLS, TINTON FALLS, NJ, p. A424

HEALTHSOUTH REHABILITATION HOSPITAL OF TOMS RIVER, TOMS RIVER, NJ, p. A424
HEALTHSOUTH REHABILITATION HOSPITAL OF UTAH, SANDY, UT, p. A664
HEALTHSOUTH REHABILITATION HOSPITAL OF VINELAND, VINELAND, NJ, p. A424
HEALTHSOUTH REHABILITATION HOSPITAL OF VIRGINIA, RICHMOND, VA, p. A677
HEALTHSOUTH REHABILITATION HOSPITAL OF WESTERN MASSACHUSETTS, LUDLOW, MA, p. A311
HEALTHSOUTH REHABILITATION HOSPITAL OF YORK, YORK, PA, p. A559
HEALTHSOUTH REHABILITATION HOSPITAL ROUND ROCK, ROUND ROCK, TX, p. A644
HEALTHSOUTH REHABILITATION HOSPITAL THE VINTAGE, HOUSTON, TX, p. A624
HEALTHSOUTH REHABILITATION HOSPITAL THE WOODLANDS, CONROE, TX, p. A607
HEALTHSOUTH REHABILITATION HOSPITAL VISION PARK, SHENANDOAH, TX, p. A648
HEALTHSOUTH REHABILITATION HOSPITAL–LAS VEGAS, LAS VEGAS, NV, p. A406
HEALTHSOUTH REHABILITATION HOSPITAL–WICHITA FALLS, WICHITA FALLS, TX, p. A657
HEALTHSOUTH REHABILITATION INSTITUTE OF SAN ANTONIO, SAN ANTONIO, TX, p. A646
HEALTHSOUTH REHABILITATION INSTITUTE OF TUCSON, TUCSON, AZ, p. A40
HEALTHSOUTH REHABILITATION OF GADSDEN, GADSDEN, AL, p. A20
HEALTHSOUTH SCOTTSDALE REHABILITATION HOSPITAL, SCOTTSDALE, AZ, p. A38
HEALTHSOUTH SEA PINES REHABILITATION HOSPITAL, MELBOURNE, FL, p. A136
HEALTHSOUTH SOUTHERN HILLS REHABILITATION HOSPITAL, PRINCETON, WV, p. A699
HEALTHSOUTH SUGAR LAND REHABILITATION HOSPITAL, SUGAR LAND, TX, p. A650
HEALTHSOUTH SUNRISE REHABILITATION HOSPITAL, SUNRISE, FL, p. A146
HEALTHSOUTH TREASURE COAST REHABILITATION HOSPITAL, VERO BEACH, FL, p. A149
HEALTHSOUTH TUSTIN REHABILITATION HOSPITAL, TUSTIN, CA, p. A97
HEALTHSOUTH VALLEY OF THE SUN REHABILITATION HOSPITAL, GLENDALE, AZ, p. A33
HEALTHSOUTH WALTON REHABILITATION HOSPITAL, AUGUSTA, GA, p. A153
HEALTHSOUTH WESTERN HILLS REGIONAL REHABILITATION HOSPITAL, PARKERSBURG, WV, p. A699
HEART HOSPITAL OF AUSTIN, AUSTIN, TEXAS (see ST. DAVID'S MEDICAL CENTER), p. A600
HEART HOSPITAL OF LAFAYETTE, LAFAYETTE, LA, p. A280
HEART HOSPITAL OF NEW MEXICO, ALBUQUERQUE, NEW MEXICO (see LOVELACE MEDICAL CENTER), p. A427
HEART OF AMERICA MEDICAL CENTER, RUGBY, ND, p. A481
HEART OF FLORIDA REGIONAL MEDICAL CENTER, DAVENPORT, FL, p. A126
HEART OF LANCASTER REGIONAL MEDICAL CENTER, LITITZ, PA, p. A543
HEART OF TEXAS MEMORIAL HOSPITAL, BRADY, TX, p. A603
HEART OF THE ROCKIES REGIONAL MEDICAL CENTER, SALIDA, CO, p. A110
HEARTLAND BEHAVIORAL HEALTH SERVICES, NEVADA, MO, p. A377
HEARTLAND BEHAVIORAL HEALTHCARE, MASSILLON, OH, p. A498
HEARTLAND REGIONAL MEDICAL CENTER, MARION, IL, p. A195
HEATHERHILL CARE COMMUNITIES, CHARDON, OH, p. A486
HEBER VALLEY MEDICAL CENTER, HEBER CITY, UT, p. A660
HEBREW REHABILITATION CENTER, BOSTON, MA, p. A307
HEDRICK MEDICAL CENTER, CHILLICOTHE, MO, p. A369
HEGG MEMORIAL HEALTH CENTER AVERA, ROCK VALLEY, IA, p. A237
HELEN DEVOS CHILDREN'S HOSPITAL, GRAND RAPIDS, MICHIGAN (see SPECTRUM HEALTH – BUTTERWORTH HOSPITAL), p. A325
HELEN HAYES HOSPITAL, WEST HAVERSTRAW, NY, p. A458
HELEN KELLER HOSPITAL, SHEFFIELD, AL, p. A25
HELEN M. SIMPSON REHABILITATION HOSPITAL, HARRISBURG, PA, p. A539
HELEN NEWBERRY JOY HOSPITAL, NEWBERRY, MI, p. A331
HELEN NEWBERRY JOY HOSPITAL ANNEX (see HELEN NEWBERRY JOY HOSPITAL), p. A331
HELENA REGIONAL MEDICAL CENTER, HELENA, AR, p. A47
HEMET VALLEY MEDICAL CENTER, HEMET, CA, p. A66
HEMPHILL COUNTY HOSPITAL, CANADIAN, TX, p. A605
HENDERSON COUNTY COMMUNITY HOSPITAL, LEXINGTON, TN, p. A587

HENDERSON HEALTH CARE SERVICES, HENDERSON, NE, p. A397
HENDRICK HEALTH SYSTEM, ABILENE, TX, p. A595
HENDRICKS COMMUNITY HOSPITAL ASSOCIATION, HENDRICKS, MN, p. A344
HENDRICKS REGIONAL HEALTH, DANVILLE, IN, p. A209
HENDRY REGIONAL MEDICAL CENTER, CLEWISTON, FL, p. A126
HENNEPIN COUNTY MEDICAL CENTER, MINNEAPOLIS, MN, p. A346
HENRICO DOCTORS' HOSPITAL, RICHMOND, VA, p. A677
HENRICO DOCTORS' HOSPITAL – FOREST, RICHMOND, VIRGINIA (see HENRICO DOCTORS' HOSPITAL), p. A677
HENRICO DOCTORS' HOSPITAL – PARHAM, RICHMOND, VIRGINIA (see HENRICO DOCTORS' HOSPITAL), p. A677
HENRICO DOCTORS' HOSPITAL – RETREAT CAMPUS, RICHMOND, VIRGINIA (see HENRICO DOCTORS' HOSPITAL), p. A677
HENRY COUNTY HEALTH CENTER, MOUNT PLEASANT, IA, p. A234
HENRY COUNTY HOSPITAL, NEW CASTLE, IN, p. A219
HENRY COUNTY HOSPITAL, NAPOLEON, OH, p. A500
HENRY COUNTY MEDICAL CENTER, PARIS, TN, p. A592
HENRY FORD ALLEGIANCE HEALTH, JACKSON, MI, p. A327
HENRY FORD HOSPITAL, DETROIT, MI, p. A322
HENRY FORD KINGSWOOD HOSPITAL, FERNDALE, MI, p. A323
HENRY FORD MACOMB HOSPITAL – MOUNT CLEMENS CAMPUS, MOUNT CLEMENS, MICHIGAN (see HENRY FORD MACOMB HOSPITALS), p. A320
HENRY FORD MACOMB HOSPITALS, CLINTON TOWNSHIP, MI, p. A320
HENRY FORD WEST BLOOMFIELD HOSPITAL, WEST BLOOMFIELD, MI, p. A336
HENRY FORD WYANDOTTE HOSPITAL, WYANDOTTE, MI, p. A337
HENRY J. CARTER SPECIALTY HOSPITAL & NURSING FACILITY, NEW YORK, NEW YORK (see NYC HEALTH + HOSPITALS / CARTER), p. A448
HENRY MAYO NEWHALL HOSPITAL, VALENCIA, CA, p. A98
HEREFORD REGIONAL MEDICAL CENTER, HEREFORD, TX, p. A623
HERINGTON MUNICIPAL HOSPITAL, HERINGTON, KS, p. A244
HERITAGE OAKS HOSPITAL, SACRAMENTO, CA, p. A86
HERITAGE PARK SURGICAL HOSPITAL, SHERMAN, TX, p. A649
HERITAGE VALLEY HEALTH SYSTEM, BEAVER, PA, p. A533
HERMANN AREA DISTRICT HOSPITAL, HERMANN, MO, p. A372
HERMANN DRIVE SURGICAL HOSPITAL, HOUSTON, TX, p. A624
HERRIN HOSPITAL, HERRIN, IL, p. A192
HEYWOOD HOSPITAL, GARDNER, MA, p. A310
HI–DESERT MEDICAL CENTER, YUCCA VALLEY, CA, p. A100
HIALEAH HOSPITAL, HIALEAH, FL, p. A130
HIAWATHA COMMUNITY HOSPITAL, HIAWATHA, KS, p. A244
HICKORY TRAIL HOSPITAL, DESOTO, TX, p. A613
HIGH POINT REGIONAL HEALTH SYSTEM, HIGH POINT, NC, p. A467
HIGHBRIDGE WOODYCREST CENTER,, NEW YORK (see BRONX–LEBANON HOSPITAL CENTER HEALTH CARE SYSTEM), p. A444
HIGHLAND COMMUNITY HOSPITAL, PICAYUNE, MS, p. A364
HIGHLAND DISTRICT HOSPITAL, HILLSBORO, OH, p. A496
HIGHLAND HOSPITAL, OAKLAND, CA, p. A80
HIGHLAND HOSPITAL, ROCHESTER, NY, p. A454
HIGHLAND HOSPITAL, CHARLESTON, WV, p. A695
HIGHLAND RIDGE HOSPITAL, MIDVALE, UT, p. A660
HIGHLAND–CLARKSBURG HOSPITAL, CLARKSBURG, WV, p. A695
HIGHLANDS BEHAVIORAL HEALTH SYSTEM, LITTLETON, CO, p. A108
HIGHLANDS HOSPITAL, CONNELLSVILLE, PA, p. A536
HIGHLANDS MEDICAL CENTER, SCOTTSBORO, AL, p. A25
HIGHLANDS REGIONAL MEDICAL CENTER, SEBRING, FL, p. A145
HIGHLANDS REGIONAL MEDICAL CENTER, PRESTONSBURG, KY, p. A268
HIGHLANDS REHABILITATION HOSPITAL, EL PASO, TX, p. A615
HIGHLANDS–CASHIERS HOSPITAL, HIGHLANDS, NC, p. A467
HIGHLINE MEDICAL CENTER, BURIEN, WA, p. A683
HIGHLINE SPECIALTY CENTER, 12844 MILITARY ROAD FORK, TUKWILA, ZIP 98168; MARK BENEDUM, ADMINISTRATOR (see HIGHLINE MEDICAL CENTER), p. A683
HIGHSMITH–RAINEY SPECIALTY HOSPITAL, FAYETTEVILLE, NC, p. A465
HILL COUNTRY MEMORIAL HOSPITAL, FREDERICKSBURG, TX, p. A619
HILL CREST BEHAVIORAL HEALTH SERVICES, BIRMINGHAM, AL, p. A16
HILL HOSPITAL OF SUMTER COUNTY, YORK, AL, p. A27
HILL REGIONAL HOSPITAL, HILLSBORO, TX, p. A623

HILLCREST BAPTIST MEDICAL CENTER – HERRING AVENUE CAMPUS, 3000 HERRING AVENUE, ZIP 76708 (see BAYLOR SCOTT & WHITE MEDICAL CENTER – HILLCREST), p. A655
HILLCREST HOSPITAL, PITTSFIELD, MASSACHUSETTS (see BERKSHIRE MEDICAL CENTER), p. A314
HILLCREST HOSPITAL, CLEVELAND, OH, p. A489
HILLCREST HOSPITAL – SOUTH, TULSA, OK, p. A521
HILLCREST HOSPITAL CLAREMORE, CLAREMORE, OK, p. A510
HILLCREST HOSPITAL CUSHING, CUSHING, OK, p. A510
HILLCREST HOSPITAL HENRYETTA, HENRYETTA, OK, p. A512
HILLCREST MEDICAL CENTER, TULSA, OK, p. A521
HILLS & DALES GENERAL HOSPITAL, CASS CITY, MI, p. A320
HILLSBORO AREA HOSPITAL, HILLSBORO, IL, p. A193
HILLSBORO COMMUNITY HOSPITAL, HILLSBORO, KS, p. A244
HILLSDALE HOSPITAL, HILLSDALE, MI, p. A326
HILLSIDE REHABILITATION HOSPITAL, WARREN, OH, p. A504
HILO MEDICAL CENTER, HILO, HI, p. A170
HILTON HEAD HOSPITAL, HILTON HEAD ISLAND, SC, p. A567
HIRAM W. DAVIS MEDICAL CENTER, PETERSBURG, VA, p. A676
HOAG HOSPITAL IRVINE, IRVINE, CALIFORNIA (see HOAG MEMORIAL HOSPITAL PRESBYTERIAN), p. A79
HOAG MEMORIAL HOSPITAL PRESBYTERIAN, NEWPORT BEACH, CA, p. A79
HOAG ORTHOPEDIC INSTITUTE, IRVINE, CA, p. A66
HOBOKEN UNIVERSITY MEDICAL CENTER, HOBOKEN, NJ, p. A418
HOCKING VALLEY COMMUNITY HOSPITAL, LOGAN, OH, p. A497
HODGEMAN COUNTY HEALTH CENTER, JETMORE, KS, p. A245
HOKE HOSPITAL, RAEFORD, NC, p. A471
HOLDENVILLE GENERAL HOSPITAL, HOLDENVILLE, OK, p. A513
HOLLAND HOSPITAL, HOLLAND, MI, p. A326
HOLLY HILL HOSPITAL, RALEIGH, NC, p. A472
HOLLYWOOD PRESBYTERIAN MEDICAL CENTER, LOS ANGELES, CA, p. A71
HOLTON COMMUNITY HOSPITAL, HOLTON, KS, p. A245
HOLTZ CHILDREN'S HOSPITAL, MIAMI, FLORIDA (see JACKSON HEALTH SYSTEM), p. A136
HOLY CROSS GERMANTOWN HOSPITAL, GERMANTOWN, MD, p. A301
HOLY CROSS HOSPITAL, FORT LAUDERDALE, FL, p. A128
HOLY CROSS HOSPITAL, CHICAGO, IL, p. A184
HOLY CROSS HOSPITAL, SILVER SPRING, MD, p. A303
HOLY CROSS HOSPITAL, TAOS, NM, p. A432
HOLY FAMILY HOPSITAL AT MERRIMACK VALLEY, HAVERHILL, MASSACHUSETTS (see HOLY FAMILY HOSPITAL), p. A312
HOLY FAMILY HOSPITAL, METHUEN, MA, p. A312
HOLY FAMILY MEMORIAL, MANITOWOC, WI, p. A709
HOLY NAME MEDICAL CENTER, TEANECK, NJ, p. A424
HOLY REDEEMER HOSPITAL, MEADOWBROOK, PA, p. A544
HOLY ROSARY HEALTHCARE, MILES CITY, MT, p. A389
HOLY SPIRIT – A GEISINGER AFFILIATE, CAMP HILL, PA, p. A534
HOLYOKE MEDICAL CENTER, HOLYOKE, MA, p. A310
HOLZER MEDICAL CENTER, GALLIPOLIS, OH, p. A495
HOLZER MEDICAL CENTER – JACKSON, JACKSON, OH, p. A496
HONORHEALTH DEER VALLEY MEDICAL CENTER, PHOENIX, AZ, p. A36
HONORHEALTH JOHN C. LINCOLN MEDICAL CENTER, PHOENIX, AZ, p. A36
HONORHEALTH REHABILITATION HOSPITAL, SCOTTSDALE, AZ, p. A38
HONORHEALTH SCOTTSDALE OSBORN MEDICAL CENTER, SCOTTSDALE, AZ, p. A38
HONORHEALTH SCOTTSDALE SHEA MEDICAL CENTER, SCOTTSDALE, AZ, p. A39
HONORHEALTH SCOTTSDALE THOMPSON PEAK MEDICAL CENTER, SCOTTSDALE, AZ, p. A39
HOOD MEMORIAL HOSPITAL, AMITE, LA, p. A271
HOOPS FAMILY CHILDREN'S HOSPITAL, HUNTINGTON, WEST VIRGINIA (see CABELL HUNTINGTON HOSPITAL), p. A696
HOPEBRIDGE HOSPITAL, HOUSTON, TX, p. A624
HOPEDALE MEDICAL COMPLEX, HOPEDALE, IL, p. A193
HOPI HEALTH CARE CENTER, KEAMS CANYON, AZ, p. A33
HORIZON SPECIALTY HOSPITAL, LAS VEGAS, NV, p. A406
HORN MEMORIAL HOSPITAL, IDA GROVE, IA, p. A232
HORSHAM CLINIC, AMBLER, PA, p. A532
HORTON COMMUNITY HOSPITAL, HORTON, KS, p. A245
HOSPITAL BUEN SAMARITANO, AGUADILLA, PR, p. A725
HOSPITAL DE DAMAS, PONCE, PR, p. A728
HOSPITAL DE LA CONCEPCION, SAN GERMAN, PR, p. A729
HOSPITAL DE LA UNIVERSIDAD DE PUERTO RICO/DR. FEDERICO TRILLA, CAROLINA, PR, p. A726
HOSPITAL DE PSIQUIATRIA, SAN JUAN, PR, p. A729
HOSPITAL DE PSIQUIATRIA FORENSE, PONCE, PR, p. A728
HOSPITAL DEL MAESTRO, SAN JUAN, PR, p. A729
HOSPITAL DISTRICT NO 1 OF RICE COUNTY, LYONS, KS, p. A248
HOSPITAL DR. CAYETANO COLL Y TOSTE, ARECIBO, PR, p. A726

HOSPITAL EPISCOPAL SAN LUCAS GUAYAMA, GUAYAMA, PR, p. A727
HOSPITAL FOR EXTENDED RECOVERY, NORFOLK, VA, p. A675
HOSPITAL FOR SPECIAL CARE, NEW BRITAIN, CT, p. A115
HOSPITAL FOR SPECIAL SURGERY, NEW YORK, NY, p. A444
HOSPITAL HERMANOS MELENDEZ, BAYAMON, PR, p. A726
HOSPITAL HIMA DE HUMACAO, HUMACAO, PR, p. A727
HOSPITAL HIMA SAN PABLO CAGUAS, CAGUAS, PR, p. A726
HOSPITAL MANATI MEDICAL CENTER, MANATI, PR, p. A728
HOSPITAL MENONITA DE CAGUAS, CAGUAS, PR, p. A726
HOSPITAL MENONITA DE CAYEY, CAYEY, PR, p. A727
HOSPITAL METROPOLITAN, SAN JUAN, PR, p. A729
HOSPITAL METROPOLITANO DR. SUSONI, ARECIBO, PR, p. A726
HOSPITAL METROPOLITANO DR. TITO MATTEI, YAUCO, PR, p. A731
HOSPITAL METROPOLITANO SAN GERMAN, SAN GERMAN, PR, p. A729
HOSPITAL OF THE UNIVERSITY OF PENNSYLVANIA, PHILADELPHIA, PA, p. A548
HOSPITAL ONCOLOGICO ANDRES GRILLASCA, PONCE, PR, p. A728
HOSPITAL ORIENTE, HUMACAO, PR, p. A727
HOSPITAL PAVIA–HATO REY, SAN JUAN, PR, p. A729
HOSPITAL PAVIA–SANTURCE, SAN JUAN, PR, p. A730
HOSPITAL PEREA, MAYAGUEZ, PR, p. A728
HOSPITAL PSIQUIATRICO CORRECCIONAL, SAN JUAN, PR, p. A730
HOSPITAL PSIQUIATRICO METROPOLITANO, CABO ROJO, PR, p. A726
HOSPITAL SAN ANTONIO, MAYAGUEZ, PR, p. A728
HOSPITAL SAN CARLOS BORROMEO, MOCA, PR, p. A728
HOSPITAL SAN CRISTOBAL, COTO LAUREL, PR, p. A727
HOSPITAL SAN FRANCISCO, SAN JUAN, PR, p. A730
HOSPITAL SAN GERARDO, SAN JUAN, PR, p. A730
HOSPITAL SAN PABLO, BAYAMON, PR, p. A726
HOSPITAL SAN PABLO DEL ESTE, FAJARDO, PR, p. A727
HOSPITAL SANTA ROSA, GUAYAMA, PR, p. A727
HOSPITAL UNIVERSITARIO DR. RAMON RUIZ ARNAU, BAYAMON, PR, p. A726
HOT SPRINGS COUNTY MEMORIAL HOSPITAL, THERMOPOLIS, WY, p. A724
HOULTON REGIONAL HOSPITAL, HOULTON, ME, p. A293
HOUSTON COUNTY COMMUNITY HOSPITAL, ERIN, TN, p. A582
HOUSTON COUNTY MEDICAL CENTER, CROCKETT, TX, p. A608
HOUSTON MEDICAL CENTER, WARNER ROBINS, GA, p. A168
HOUSTON METHODIST HOSPITAL, HOUSTON, TX, p. A624
HOUSTON METHODIST SAN JACINTO HOSPITAL, BAYTOWN, TX, p. A601
HOUSTON METHODIST SAN JACINTO HOSPITAL – ALEXANDER, BAYTOWN, TEXAS (see HOUSTON METHODIST SAN JACINTO HOSPITAL), p. A601
HOUSTON METHODIST ST. CATHERINE HOSPITAL, KATY, TX, p. A629
HOUSTON METHODIST ST. JOHN HOSPITAL, NASSAU BAY, TX, p. A638
HOUSTON METHODIST SUGAR LAND HOSPITAL, SUGAR LAND, TX, p. A650
HOUSTON METHODIST WEST HOSPITAL, HOUSTON, TX, p. A624
HOUSTON METHODIST WILLOWBROOK HOSPITAL, HOUSTON, TX, p. A625
HOUSTON NORTHWEST MEDICAL CENTER, HOUSTON, TX, p. A625
HOUSTON PHYSICIANS HOSPITAL, WEBSTER, TX, p. A656
HOWARD A. RUSK REHABILITATION CENTER, COLUMBIA, MO, p. A370
HOWARD COUNTY GENERAL HOSPITAL, COLUMBIA, MD, p. A300
HOWARD COUNTY MEDICAL CENTER, SAINT PAUL, NE, p. A402
HOWARD MEMORIAL HOSPITAL, NASHVILLE, AR, p. A50
HOWARD UNIVERSITY HOSPITAL, WASHINGTON, DC, p. A121
HOWARD YOUNG MEDICAL CENTER, WOODRUFF, WI, p. A720
HSHS HOLY FAMILY HOSPITAL IN GREENVILLE, GREENVILLE, IL, p. A192
HSHS ST. ANTHONY'S MEMORIAL HOSPITAL, EFFINGHAM, IL, p. A188
HSHS ST. CLARE MEMORIAL HOSPITAL, OCONTO FALLS, WI, p. A713
HSHS ST. ELIZABETH'S HOSPITAL, BELLEVILLE, IL, p. A181
HSHS ST. FRANCIS HOSPITAL, LITCHFIELD, IL, p. A195
HSHS ST. JOSEPH'S HOSPITAL, BREESE, IL, p. A182
HSHS ST. JOSEPH'S HOSPITAL, HIGHLAND, IL, p. A192
HSHS ST. JOSEPH'S HOSPITAL, CHIPPEWA FALLS, WI, p. A704
HSHS ST. MARY'S HOSPITAL, DECATUR, IL, p. A188
HSHS ST. VINCENT HOSPITAL, GREEN BAY, WI, p. A707
HUDSON HOSPITAL AND CLINIC, HUDSON, WI, p. A707
HUGGINS HOSPITAL, WOLFEBORO, NH, p. A413
HUGH CHATHAM MEMORIAL HOSPITAL, ELKIN, NC, p. A465
HUHUKAM MEMORIAL HOSPITAL, SACATON, AZ, p. A38

HUMBOLDT COUNTY MEMORIAL HOSPITAL, HUMBOLDT, IA, p. A232
HUMBOLDT COUNTY MENTAL HEALTH, EUREKA, CA, p. A61
HUMBOLDT GENERAL HOSPITAL, WINNEMUCCA, NV, p. A409
HUNT REGIONAL MEDICAL CENTER, GREENVILLE, TX, p. A621
HUNTER HOLMES MCGUIRE VETERANS AFFAIRS MEDICAL CENTER–RICHMOND, RICHMOND, VA, p. A678
HUNTERDON MEDICAL CENTER, FLEMINGTON, NJ, p. A417
HUNTINGTON BEACH HOSPITAL, HUNTINGTON BEACH, CA, p. A66
HUNTINGTON HOSPITAL, HUNTINGTON, NY, p. A440
HUNTINGTON MEMORIAL HOSPITAL, PASADENA, CA, p. A82
HUNTINGTON VETERANS AFFAIRS MEDICAL CENTER, HUNTINGTON, WV, p. A697
HUNTSVILLE HOSPITAL, HUNTSVILLE, AL, p. A21
HUNTSVILLE HOSPITAL FOR WOMEN AND CHILDREN, HUNTSVILLE, ALABAMA (see HUNTSVILLE HOSPITAL), p. A21
HUNTSVILLE MEMORIAL HOSPITAL, HUNTSVILLE, TX, p. A628
HURLEY CHILDREN'S HOSPITAL, FLINT, MICHIGAN (see HURLEY MEDICAL CENTER), p. A323
HURLEY MEDICAL CENTER, FLINT, MI, p. A323
HURON MEDICAL CENTER, BAD AXE, MI, p. A318
HURON REGIONAL MEDICAL CENTER, HURON, SD, p. A574
HUTCHINSON HEALTH, HUTCHINSON, MN, p. A344
HUTCHINSON REGIONAL MEDICAL CENTER, HUTCHINSON, KS, p. A245

I

I-70 COMMUNITY HOSPITAL, SWEET SPRINGS, MO, p. A383
I. GONZALEZ MARTINEZ ONCOLOGIC HOSPITAL,, PR, p. A730
IBERIA EXTENDED CARE HOSPITAL, NEW IBERIA, LOUISIANA (see LOUISIANA EXTENDED CARE HOSPITAL OF LAFAYETTE), p. A280
IBERIA MEDICAL CENTER, NEW IBERIA, LA, p. A284
IBERIA REHABILITATION HOSPITAL, NEW IBERIA, LA, p. A284
ICON HOSPITAL, HUMBLE, TX, p. A628
ILLINI COMMUNITY HOSPITAL, PITTSFIELD, IL, p. A201
ILLINOIS VALLEY COMMUNITY HOSPITAL, PERU, IL, p. A200
INCLINE VILLAGE COMMUNITY HOSPITAL, INCLINE VILLAGE, NV, p. A405
INDIAN HEALTH SERVICE – QUENTIN N. BURDICK MEMORIAL HEALTH CARE FACILITY, BELCOURT, ND, p. A477
INDIAN HEALTH SERVICE HOSPITAL, RAPID CITY, SD, p. A575
INDIAN PATH MEDICAL CENTER, KINGSPORT, TN, p. A585
INDIAN RIVER MEDICAL CENTER, VERO BEACH, FL, p. A149
INDIANA ORTHOPAEDIC HOSPITAL, INDIANAPOLIS, IN, p. A214
INDIANA REGIONAL MEDICAL CENTER, INDIANA, PA, p. A541
INDIANA UNIVERSITY HEALTH ARNETT HOSPITAL, LAFAYETTE, IN, p. A216
INDIANA UNIVERSITY HEALTH BALL MEMORIAL HOSPITAL, MUNCIE, IN, p. A219
INDIANA UNIVERSITY HEALTH BEDFORD HOSPITAL, BEDFORD, IN, p. A206
INDIANA UNIVERSITY HEALTH BLACKFORD HOSPITAL, HARTFORD CITY, IN, p. A213
INDIANA UNIVERSITY HEALTH BLOOMINGTON HOSPITAL, BLOOMINGTON, IN, p. A207
INDIANA UNIVERSITY HEALTH GOSHEN HOSPITAL, GOSHEN, IN, p. A212
INDIANA UNIVERSITY HEALTH METHODIST HOSPITAL, INDIANAPOLIS, INDIANA (see INDIANA UNIVERSITY HEALTH UNIVERSITY HOSPITAL), p. A214
INDIANA UNIVERSITY HEALTH NORTH HOSPITAL, CARMEL, IN, p. A208
INDIANA UNIVERSITY HEALTH PAOLI HOSPITAL, PAOLI, IN, p. A220
INDIANA UNIVERSITY HEALTH SAXONY HOSPITAL, FISHERS, INDIANA (see INDIANA UNIVERSITY HEALTH UNIVERSITY HOSPITAL), p. A214
INDIANA UNIVERSITY HEALTH TIPTON HOSPITAL, TIPTON, IN, p. A223
INDIANA UNIVERSITY HEALTH UNIVERSITY HOSPITAL, INDIANAPOLIS, IN, p. A214
INDIANA UNIVERSITY HEALTH WEST HOSPITAL, AVON, IN, p. A206
INDIANA UNIVERSITY HEALTH WHITE MEMORIAL HOSPITAL, MONTICELLO, IN, p. A218
INDIANA UNIVERSITY HOSPITAL, INDIANAPOLIS, INDIANA (see INDIANA UNIVERSITY HEALTH UNIVERSITY HOSPITAL), p. A214
INDIANHEAD MEDICAL CENTER, SHELL LAKE, WI, p. A716
INDUSTRIAL HOSPITAL, SAN JUAN, PR, p. A730
INFIRMARY LONG TERM ACUTE CARE HOSPITAL, MOBILE, AL, p. A22
INGALLS MEMORIAL HOSPITAL, HARVEY, IL, p. A192
INLAND HOSPITAL, WATERVILLE, ME, p. A295

INLAND VALLEY MEDICAL CENTER, WILDOMAR, CALIFORNIA (see SOUTHWEST HEALTHCARE SYSTEM), p. A78
INOVA ALEXANDRIA HOSPITAL, ALEXANDRIA, VA, p. A667
INOVA FAIR OAKS HOSPITAL, FAIRFAX, VA, p. A669
INOVA FAIRFAX HOSPITAL, FALLS CHURCH, VA, p. A670
INOVA FAIRFAX HOSPITAL FOR CHILDREN, FALLS CHURCH, VIRGINIA (see INOVA FAIRFAX HOSPITAL), p. A670
INOVA LOUDOUN HOSPITAL, LEESBURG, VA, p. A672
INOVA MOUNT VERNON HOSPITAL, ALEXANDRIA, VA, p. A667
INSPIRA MEDICAL CENTER–ELMER, ELMER, NJ, p. A416
INSPIRA MEDICAL CENTER–VINELAND, VINELAND, NJ, p. A425
INSPIRA MEDICAL CENTER–WOODBURY, WOODBURY, NJ, p. A425
INSPIRA PONCE, PONCE, PR, p. A728
INSTITUTE FOR ORTHOPAEDIC SURGERY, LIMA, OH, p. A496
INSTITUTE OF LIVING, HARTFORD, CONNECTICUT (see HARTFORD HOSPITAL), p. A114
INTEGRIS BAPTIST MEDICAL CENTER, OKLAHOMA CITY, OK, p. A516
INTEGRIS BASS BAPTIST HEALTH CENTER, ENID, OK, p. A511
INTEGRIS BASS PAVILION, ENID, OK, p. A511
INTEGRIS CANADIAN VALLEY HOSPITAL, YUKON, OK, p. A523
INTEGRIS GROVE HOSPITAL, GROVE, OK, p. A512
INTEGRIS HEALTH EDMOND, EDMOND, OK, p. A511
INTEGRIS MENTAL HEALTH SYSTEM–SPENCER, SPENCER, OKLAHOMA (see INTEGRIS BAPTIST MEDICAL CENTER), p. A516
INTEGRIS MIAMI HOSPITAL, MIAMI, OK, p. A514
INTEGRIS SOUTHWEST MEDICAL CENTER, OKLAHOMA CITY, OK, p. A516
INTEGRITY TRANSITIONAL HOSPITAL, DENTON, TX, p. A612
INTERFAITH MEDICAL CENTER,, NY, p. A444
INTERMOUNTAIN HOSPITAL, BOISE, ID, p. A174
INTERMOUNTAIN MEDICAL CENTER, MURRAY, UT, p. A661
INTRACARE NORTH HOSPITAL, HOUSTON, TX, p. A625
IOWA CITY VETERANS AFFAIRS HEALTH CARE SYSTEM, IOWA CITY, IA, p. A232
IOWA MEDICAL AND CLASSIFICATION CENTER, CORALVILLE, IA, p. A227
IOWA SPECIALTY HOSPITAL–BELMOND, BELMOND, IA, p. A225
IOWA SPECIALTY HOSPITAL–CLARION, CLARION, IA, p. A227
IRA DAVENPORT MEMORIAL HOSPITAL, BATH, NY, p. A434
IRAAN GENERAL HOSPITAL, IRAAN, TX, p. A628
IREDELL HEALTH SYSTEM, STATESVILLE, NC, p. A474
IRELAND ARMY COMMUNITY HOSPITAL, FORT KNOX, KY, p. A260
IRON COUNTY MEDICAL CENTER, PILOT KNOB, MO, p. A378
IROQUOIS MEMORIAL HOSPITAL AND RESIDENT HOME, WATSEKA, IL, p. A204
IRWIN ARMY COMMUNITY HOSPITAL, JUNCTION CITY, KS, p. A246
IRWIN COUNTY HOSPITAL, OCILLA, GA, p. A164
ISLAND HOSPITAL, ANACORTES, WA, p. A682
IVINSON MEMORIAL HOSPITAL, LARAMIE, WY, p. A722

J

J. ARTHUR DOSHER MEMORIAL HOSPITAL, SOUTHPORT, NC, p. A474
J. C. BLAIR MEMORIAL HOSPITAL, HUNTINGDON, PA, p. A540
J. D. MCCARTY CENTER FOR CHILDREN WITH DEVELOPMENTAL DISABILITIES, NORMAN, OK, p. A515
J. PAUL JONES HOSPITAL, CAMDEN, AL, p. A18
JACK C. MONTGOMERY VETERANS AFFAIRS MEDICAL CENTER, MUSKOGEE, OK, p. A515
JACK D WEILER HOSPITAL OF ALBERT EINSTEIN COLLEGE OF MEDICINE,, NEW YORK (see MONTEFIORE MEDICAL CENTER), p. A446
JACK HUGHSTON MEMORIAL HOSPITAL, PHENIX CITY, AL, p. A24
JACKSON BEHAVIORAL HEALTH HOSPITAL, MIAMI, FLORIDA (see JACKSON HEALTH SYSTEM), p. A136
JACKSON COUNTY HOSPITAL DISTRICT, EDNA, TX, p. A614
JACKSON COUNTY MEMORIAL HOSPITAL, ALTUS, OK, p. A508
JACKSON COUNTY REGIONAL HEALTH CENTER, MAQUOKETA, IA, p. A234
JACKSON GENERAL HOSPITAL, RIPLEY, WV, p. A699
JACKSON HEALTH SYSTEM, MIAMI, FL, p. A136
JACKSON HOSPITAL, MARIANNA, FL, p. A135
JACKSON HOSPITAL AND CLINIC, MONTGOMERY, AL, p. A23
JACKSON MEDICAL CENTER, JACKSON, AL, p. A22
JACKSON MEMORIAL HOSPITAL, MIAMI, FLORIDA (see JACKSON HEALTH SYSTEM), p. A136
JACKSON NORTH MEDICAL CENTER, NORTH MIAMI BEACH, FLORIDA (see JACKSON HEALTH SYSTEM), p. A136
JACKSON PARISH HOSPITAL, JONESBORO, LA, p. A279

JACKSON PARK HOSPITAL AND MEDICAL CENTER, CHICAGO, IL, p. A184
JACKSON PURCHASE MEDICAL CENTER, MAYFIELD, KY, p. A266
JACKSON SOUTH COMMUNITY HOSPITAL, MIAMI, FLORIDA (see JACKSON HEALTH SYSTEM), p. A136
JACKSON–MADISON COUNTY GENERAL HOSPITAL, JACKSON, TN, p. A584
JACOBSON MEMORIAL HOSPITAL CARE CENTER, ELGIN, ND, p. A478
JAMAICA HOSPITAL MEDICAL CENTER,, NY, p. A445
JAMES A. HALEY VETERANS' HOSPITAL–TAMPA, TAMPA, FL, p. A147
JAMES AND CONNIE MAYNARD CHILDREN'S HOSPITAL, GREENVILLE, NORTH CAROLINA (see VIDANT MEDICAL CENTER), p. A466
JAMES B. HAGGIN MEMORIAL HOSPITAL, HARRODSBURG, KY, p. A261
JAMES CANCER HOSPITAL AND SOLOVE RESEARCH INSTITUTE, COLUMBUS, OH, p. A490
JAMES E. VAN ZANDT VETERANS AFFAIRS MEDICAL CENTER, ALTOONA, PA, p. A532
JAMES H. QUILLEN VETERANS AFFAIRS MEDICAL CENTER, MOUNTAIN HOME, TN, p. A590
JAMES J. PETERS VETERANS AFFAIRS MEDICAL CENTER,, NY, p. A445
JAMESON HOSPITAL, NEW CASTLE, PA, p. A546
JAMESTOWN REGIONAL MEDICAL CENTER, JAMESTOWN, ND, p. A480
JANE PHILLIPS MEMORIAL MEDICAL CENTER, BARTLESVILLE, OK, p. A509
JANE PHILLIPS NOWATA HEALTH CENTER, NOWATA, OK, p. A515
JANE TODD CRAWFORD HOSPITAL, GREENSBURG, KY, p. A261
JASPER COUNTY NURSING HOME (see JASPER GENERAL HOSPITAL), p. A355
JASPER GENERAL HOSPITAL, BAY SPRINGS, MS, p. A355
JASPER MEMORIAL HOSPITAL, MONTICELLO, GA, p. A163
JAY COUNTY HOSPITAL, PORTLAND, IN, p. A220
JAY HOSPITAL, JAY, FL, p. A132
JEANES HOSPITAL, PHILADELPHIA, PA, p. A548
JEFF DAVIS HOSPITAL, HAZLEHURST, GA, p. A160
JEFFERSON COMMUNITY HEALTH CENTER, FAIRBURY, NE, p. A395
JEFFERSON COUNTY HEALTH CENTER, FAIRFIELD, IA, p. A230
JEFFERSON COUNTY HOSPITAL, FAYETTE, MS, p. A357
JEFFERSON COUNTY HOSPITAL, WAURIKA, OK, p. A523
JEFFERSON DAVIS COMMUNITY HOSPITAL, PRENTISS, MS, p. A364
JEFFERSON HEALTHCARE, PORT TOWNSEND, WA, p. A688
JEFFERSON HOSPITAL, LOUISVILLE, GA, p. A162
JEFFERSON HOSPITAL, JEFFERSON HILLS, PA, p. A541
JEFFERSON MEDICAL CENTER, RANSON, WV, p. A699
JEFFERSON REGIONAL MEDICAL CENTER, PINE BLUFF, AR, p. A51
JELLICO COMMUNITY HOSPITAL, JELLICO, TN, p. A585
JENNERSVILLE REGIONAL HOSPITAL, WEST GROVE, PA, p. A557
JENNIE M. MELHAM MEMORIAL MEDICAL CENTER, BROKEN BOW, NE, p. A394
JENNIE STUART MEDICAL CENTER, HOPKINSVILLE, KY, p. A262
JENNINGS AMERICAN LEGION HOSPITAL, JENNINGS, LA, p. A279
JENNINGS SENIOR CARE HOSPITAL, JENNINGS, LA, p. A279
JEROLD PHELPS COMMUNITY HOSPITAL, GARBERVILLE, CA, p. A64
JEROME GOLDEN CENTER FOR BEHAVIORAL HEALTH, INC., WEST PALM BEACH, FL, p. A149
JERSEY CITY MEDICAL CENTER, JERSEY CITY, NJ, p. A418
JERSEY COMMUNITY HOSPITAL, JERSEYVILLE, IL, p. A194
JERSEY SHORE HOSPITAL, JERSEY SHORE, PA, p. A541
JERSEY SHORE UNIVERSITY MEDICAL CENTER, NEPTUNE, NJ, p. A420
JESSE BROWN VETERANS AFFAIRS MEDICAL CENTER, CHICAGO, IL, p. A184
JEWELL COUNTY HOSPITAL, MANKATO, KS, p. A248
JEWISH HOME OF SAN FRANCISCO, SAN FRANCISCO, CA, p. A90
JEWISH HOSPITAL, LOUISVILLE, KY, p. A264
JEWISH HOSPITAL–SHELBYVILLE, SHELBYVILLE, KY, p. A269
JFK JOHNSON REHABILITATION INSTITUTE, EDISON, NJ, p. A416
JFK MEDICAL CENTER, ATLANTIS, FL, p. A123
JFK MEDICAL CENTER, EDISON, NJ, p. A416
JFK MEDICAL CENTER NORTH CAMPUS, WEST PALM BEACH, FL, p. A149
JIM TALIAFERRO COMMUNITY MENTAL HEALTH, LAWTON, OK, p. A513
JOE DIMAGGIO CHILDREN'S HOSPITAL,, FLORIDA (see MEMORIAL REGIONAL HOSPITAL), p. A130

JOHN C. FREMONT HEALTHCARE DISTRICT, MARIPOSA, CA, p. A76
JOHN C. STENNIS MEMORIAL HOSPITAL, DE KALB, MS, p. A357
JOHN D. ARCHBOLD MEMORIAL HOSPITAL, THOMASVILLE, GA, p. A167
JOHN D. DINGELL VETERANS AFFAIRS MEDICAL CENTER, DETROIT, MI, p. A322
JOHN F. KENNEDY MEMORIAL HOSPITAL, INDIO, CA, p. A66
JOHN GEORGE PSYCHIATRIC HOSPITAL, SAN LEANDRO, CALIFORNIA (see HIGHLAND HOSPITAL), p. A80
JOHN H. STROGER JR. HOSPITAL OF COOK COUNTY, CHICAGO, IL, p. A184
JOHN HEINZ INSTITUTE OF REHABILITATION MEDICINE, WILKES–BARRE, PA, p. A558
JOHN J. MADDEN MENTAL HEALTH CENTER, HINES, IL, p. A193
JOHN J. PERSHING VETERANS AFFAIRS MEDICAL CENTER, POPLAR BLUFF, MO, p. A378
JOHN MUIR BEHAVIORAL HEALTH CENTER, CONCORD, CA, p. A59
JOHN MUIR MEDICAL CENTER, CONCORD, CONCORD, CA, p. A59
JOHN MUIR MEDICAL CENTER, WALNUT CREEK, WALNUT CREEK, CA, p. A99
JOHN PETER SMITH HOSPITAL, FORT WORTH, TEXAS (see JPS HEALTH NETWORK), p. A618
JOHN RANDOLPH MEDICAL CENTER, HOPEWELL, VA, p. A672
JOHN T. MATHER MEMORIAL HOSPITAL, PORT JEFFERSON, NY, p. A453
JOHNS HOPKINS ALL CHILDREN'S HOSPITAL, SAINT PETERSBURG, FL, p. A144
JOHNS HOPKINS BAYVIEW MEDICAL CENTER, BALTIMORE, MD, p. A296
JOHNS HOPKINS CHILDREN'S CENTER, BALTIMORE, MARYLAND (see JOHNS HOPKINS HOSPITAL), p. A296
JOHNS HOPKINS HOSPITAL, BALTIMORE, MD, p. A296
JOHNSON CITY MEDICAL CENTER, JOHNSON CITY, TN, p. A585
JOHNSON COUNTY COMMUNITY HOSPITAL, MOUNTAIN CITY, TN, p. A590
JOHNSON COUNTY HEALTHCARE CENTER, BUFFALO, WY, p. A721
JOHNSON COUNTY HOSPITAL, TECUMSEH, NE, p. A402
JOHNSON MEMORIAL HEALTH SERVICES, DAWSON, MN, p. A341
JOHNSON MEMORIAL HOSPITAL, FRANKLIN, IN, p. A211
JOHNSON MEMORIAL MEDICAL CENTER, STAFFORD SPRINGS, CT, p. A117
JOHNSON REGIONAL MEDICAL CENTER, CLARKSVILLE, AR, p. A44
JOHNSTON HEALTH, SMITHFIELD, NC, p. A473
JOHNSTON MEMORIAL HOSPITAL, ABINGDON, VA, p. A667
JOHNSTON R. BOWMAN HEALTH CENTER, CHICAGO, ILLINOIS (see RUSH UNIVERSITY MEDICAL CENTER), p. A186
JOHNSTON–WILLIS HOSPITAL, RICHMOND, VIRGINIA (see CHIPPENHAM HOSPITAL), p. A677
JOINT TOWNSHIP DISTRICT MEMORIAL HOSPITAL, SAINT MARYS, OH, p. A502
JONATHAN M. WAINWRIGHT MEMORIAL VETERANS AFFAIRS MEDICAL CENTER, WALLA WALLA, WA, p. A692
JONES MEMORIAL HOSPITAL, WELLSVILLE, NY, p. A458
JORDAN VALLEY MEDICAL CENTER, WEST JORDAN, UT, p. A664
JORDAN VALLEY MEDICAL CENTER WEST VALLEY CAMPUS, WEST VALLEY CITY, UT, p. A664
JOYCE EISENBERG–KEEFER MEDICAL CENTER, RESEDA, CA, p. A85
JPS HEALTH NETWORK, FORT WORTH, TX, p. A618
JULIAN F. KEITH ALCOHOL AND DRUG ABUSE TREATMENT CENTER, BLACK MOUNTAIN, NC, p. A460
JULIETTE MANOR NURSING HOME, COMMUNITY CLINICS (see BERLIN MEMORIAL HOSPITAL), p. A703
JUPITER MEDICAL CENTER, JUPITER, FL, p. A132

K

K. HOVNANIAN CHILDREN'S HOSPITAL, NEPTUNE, NEW JERSEY (see JERSEY SHORE UNIVERSITY MEDICAL CENTER), p. A420
KAATERSKILL CARE, CATSKILL, NEW YORK (see COLUMBIA MEMORIAL HOSPITAL), p. A440
KADLEC REGIONAL MEDICAL CENTER, RICHLAND, WA, p. A689
KAHI MOHALA BEHAVIORAL HEALTH, EWA BEACH, HI, p. A170
KAHUKU MEDICAL CENTER, KAHUKU, HI, p. A171
KAISER FOUNDATION HOSPITAL, MARTINEZ, CALIFORNIA (see KAISER PERMANENTE WALNUT CREEK MEDICAL CENTER), p. A99

KAISER FOUNDATION HOSPITAL WESTSIDE MEDICAL CENTER, HILLSBORO, OR, p. A526
KAISER FOUNDATION MENTAL HEALTH CENTER, LOS ANGELES, CALIFORNIA (see KAISER PERMANENTE LOS ANGELES MEDICAL CENTER), p. A71
KAISER PERMANENTE ANTIOCH MEDICAL CENTER, ANTIOCH, CA, p. A54
KAISER PERMANENTE BALDWIN PARK MEDICAL CENTER, BALDWIN PARK, CA, p. A56
KAISER PERMANENTE DOWNEY MEDICAL CENTER, DOWNEY, CA, p. A60
KAISER PERMANENTE FONTANA MEDICAL CENTER, FONTANA, CA, p. A62
KAISER PERMANENTE FRESNO MEDICAL CENTER, FRESNO, CA, p. A63
KAISER PERMANENTE LOS ANGELES MEDICAL CENTER, LOS ANGELES, CA, p. A71
KAISER PERMANENTE MANTECA MEDICAL CENTER, MANTECA, CA, p. A76
KAISER PERMANENTE MEDICAL CENTER, HONOLULU, HI, p. A170
KAISER PERMANENTE MORENO VALLEY MEDICAL CENTER, MORENO VALLEY, CA, p. A78
KAISER PERMANENTE OAKLAND MEDICAL CENTER, OAKLAND, CA, p. A80
KAISER PERMANENTE ONTARIO MEDICAL CENTER, ONTARIO, CALIFORNIA (see KAISER PERMANENTE FONTANA MEDICAL CENTER), p. A62
KAISER PERMANENTE ORANGE COUNTY ANAHEIM MEDICAL CENTER, ANAHEIM, CA, p. A54
KAISER PERMANENTE PANORAMA CITY MEDICAL CENTER,, CA, p. A71
KAISER PERMANENTE REDWOOD CITY MEDICAL CENTER, REDWOOD CITY, CA, p. A85
KAISER PERMANENTE RICHMOND MEDICAL CENTER, RICHMOND, CALIFORNIA (see KAISER PERMANENTE OAKLAND MEDICAL CENTER), p. A80
KAISER PERMANENTE RIVERSIDE MEDICAL CENTER, RIVERSIDE, CA, p. A85
KAISER PERMANENTE ROSEVILLE MEDICAL CENTER, ROSEVILLE, CA, p. A86
KAISER PERMANENTE SACRAMENTO MEDICAL CENTER, SACRAMENTO, CA, p. A86
KAISER PERMANENTE SAN DIEGO MEDICAL CENTER, SAN DIEGO, CA, p. A88
KAISER PERMANENTE SAN FRANCISCO MEDICAL CENTER, SAN FRANCISCO, CA, p. A90
KAISER PERMANENTE SAN JOSE MEDICAL CENTER, SAN JOSE, CA, p. A91
KAISER PERMANENTE SAN LEANDRO MEDICAL CENTER, SAN LEANDRO, CA, p. A91
KAISER PERMANENTE SAN RAFAEL MEDICAL CENTER, SAN RAFAEL, CA, p. A92
KAISER PERMANENTE SANTA CLARA MEDICAL CENTER, SANTA CLARA, CA, p. A93
KAISER PERMANENTE SANTA ROSA MEDICAL CENTER, SANTA ROSA, CA, p. A94
KAISER PERMANENTE SOUTH BAY MEDICAL CENTER,, CA, p. A72
KAISER PERMANENTE SOUTH SACRAMENTO MEDICAL CENTER, SACRAMENTO, CA, p. A86
KAISER PERMANENTE SOUTH SAN FRANCISCO, SOUTH SAN FRANCISCO, CA, p. A95
KAISER PERMANENTE SUNNYSIDE MEDICAL CENTER, CLACKAMAS, OR, p. A524
KAISER PERMANENTE VACAVILLE MEDICAL CENTER, VACAVILLE, CA, p. A97
KAISER PERMANENTE VALLEJO MEDICAL CENTER, VALLEJO, CA, p. A98
KAISER PERMANENTE WALNUT CREEK MEDICAL CENTER, WALNUT CREEK, CA, p. A99
KAISER PERMANENTE WEST LOS ANGELES MEDICAL CENTER, LOS ANGELES, CA, p. A72
KAISER PERMANENTE WOODLAND HILLS MEDICAL CENTER,, CA, p. A72
KALAMAZOO PSYCHIATRIC HOSPITAL, KALAMAZOO, MI, p. A328
KALEIDA HEALTH, BUFFALO, NY, p. A436
KALISPELL REGIONAL HEALTHCARE, KALISPELL, MT, p. A389
KALKASKA MEMORIAL HEALTH CENTER, KALKASKA, MI, p. A328
KANE COMMUNITY HOSPITAL, KANE, PA, p. A541
KANE COUNTY HOSPITAL, KANAB, UT, p. A660
KANSAS CITY ORTHOPAEDIC INSTITUTE, LEAWOOD, KS, p. A247
KANSAS CITY VETERANS AFFAIRS MEDICAL CENTER, KANSAS CITY, MO, p. A373
KANSAS HEART HOSPITAL, WICHITA, KS, p. A255
KANSAS MEDICAL CENTER, ANDOVER, KS, p. A240
KANSAS NEUROLOGICAL INSTITUTE, TOPEKA, KS, p. A254

KANSAS REHABILITATION HOSPITAL, TOPEKA, KS, p. A254
KANSAS SPINE AND SPECIALTY HOSPITAL, WICHITA, KS, p. A255
KANSAS SURGERY AND RECOVERY CENTER, WICHITA, KS, p. A256
KAPIOLANI MEDICAL CENTER FOR WOMEN & CHILDREN, HONOLULU, HI, p. A170
KARL AND ESTHER HOBLITZELLE MEMORIAL HOSPITAL, DALLAS, TEXAS (see BAYLOR UNIVERSITY MEDICAL CENTER), p. A609
KARMANOS CANCER CENTER, DETROIT, MI, p. A322
KATHERINE SHAW BETHEA HOSPITAL, DIXON, IL, p. A188
KAU HOSPITAL, PAHALA, HI, p. A172
KAUAI VETERANS MEMORIAL HOSPITAL, WAIMEA, HI, p. A173
KAWEAH DELTA MEDICAL CENTER, VISALIA, CA, p. A99
KEARNEY COUNTY HEALTH SERVICES, MINDEN, NE, p. A398
KEARNEY REGIONAL MEDICAL CENTER, KEARNEY, NE, p. A397
KEARNY COUNTY HOSPITAL, LAKIN, KS, p. A247
KECK HOSPITAL OF USC, LOS ANGELES, CA, p. A72
KEDREN COMMUNITY MENTAL HEALTH CENTER, LOS ANGELES, CA, p. A72
KEEFE MEMORIAL HOSPITAL, CHEYENNE WELLS, CO, p. A102
KELL WEST REGIONAL HOSPITAL, WICHITA FALLS, TX, p. A657
KELLER ARMY COMMUNITY HOSPITAL, WEST POINT, NY, p. A459
KEMPSVILLE CENTER FOR BEHAVIORAL HEALTH, NORFOLK, VA, p. A675
KENDALL REGIONAL MEDICAL CENTER, MIAMI, FL, p. A136
KENMARE COMMUNITY HOSPITAL, KENMARE, ND, p. A480
KENMORE MERCY HOSPITAL, KENMORE, NY, p. A441
KENNEDY HEALTH SYSTEM, CHERRY HILL, NJ, p. A415
KENNEDY KRIEGER INSTITUTE, BALTIMORE, MD, p. A296
KENNEDY UNIVERSITY HOSPITAL – STRATFORD, STRATFORD, NEW JERSEY (see KENNEDY HEALTH SYSTEM), p. A415
KENNEDY UNIVERSITY HOSPITAL – WASHINGTON TOWNSHIP, TURNERSVILLE, NEW JERSEY (see KENNEDY HEALTH SYSTEM), p. A415
KENSINGTON HOSPITAL, PHILADELPHIA, PA, p. A548
KENT COUNTY MEMORIAL HOSPITAL, WARWICK, RI, p. A561
KENTFIELD REHABILITATION AND SPECIALTY HOSPITAL, KENTFIELD, CA, p. A67
KENTUCKIANA MEDICAL CENTER, CLARKSVILLE, IN, p. A208
KENTUCKY CHILDREN'S HOSPITAL, LEXINGTON, KENTUCKY (see UNIVERSITY OF KENTUCKY ALBERT B. CHANDLER HOSPITAL), p. A263
KENTUCKY RIVER MEDICAL CENTER, JACKSON, KY, p. A262
KEOKUK AREA HOSPITAL, KEOKUK, IA, p. A233
KEOKUK COUNTY HEALTH CENTER, SIGOURNEY, IA, p. A237
KERN MEDICAL CENTER, BAKERSFIELD, CA, p. A56
KERN VALLEY HEALTHCARE DISTRICT, LAKE ISABELLA, CA, p. A68
KERNERSVILLE MEDICAL CENTER, KERNERSVILLE, NORTH CAROLINA (see NOVANT HEALTH FORSYTH MEDICAL CENTER), p. A476
KERRVILLE DIVISION, KERRVILLE, TEXAS (see SOUTH TEXAS VETERANS HEALTH CARE SYSTEM), p. A647
KERRVILLE STATE HOSPITAL, KERRVILLE, TX, p. A630
KERSHAWHEALTH, CAMDEN, SC, p. A562
KESSLER INSTITUTE FOR REHABILITATION, WEST ORANGE, NJ, p. A425
KESSLER INSTITUTE FOR REHABILITATION, CHESTER, NEW JERSEY (see KESSLER INSTITUTE FOR REHABILITATION), p. A425
KESSLER INSTITUTE FOR REHABILITATION, SADDLE BROOK, NEW JERSEY (see KESSLER INSTITUTE FOR REHABILITATION), p. A425
KESSLER INSTITUTE FOR REHABILITATION, WEST ORANGE, NEW JERSEY (see KESSLER INSTITUTE FOR REHABILITATION), p. A425
KETTERING MEDICAL CENTER, KETTERING, OH, p. A496
KEYSTONE NEWPORT NEWS, NEWPORT NEWS, VA, p. A674
KIDSPEACE CHILDREN'S HOSPITAL, OREFIELD, PA, p. A546
KIMBALL HEALTH SERVICES, KIMBALL, NE, p. A397
KIMBALL–RIDGE CENTER, WATERLOO, IOWA (see COVENANT MEDICAL CENTER), p. A238
KIMBLE HOSPITAL, JUNCTION, TX, p. A629
KINDRED CHICAGO LAKESHORE, CHICAGO, ILLINOIS (see KINDRED CHICAGO–CENTRAL HOSPITAL), p. A184
KINDRED CHICAGO–CENTRAL HOSPITAL, CHICAGO, IL, p. A184
KINDRED HOSITAL THE HEIGHTS, HOUSTON, TEXAS (see TOMBALL REGIONAL MEDICAL CENTER), p. A653
KINDRED HOSPITAL ARIZONA–NORTHWEST PHOENIX, PEORIA, ARIZONA (see KINDRED HOSPITAL ARIZONA–PHOENIX), p. A36
KINDRED HOSPITAL BAY AREA–TAMPA, TAMPA, FL, p. A147
KINDRED HOSPITAL BAYTOWN, BAYTOWN, TEXAS (see KINDRED HOSPITAL CLEAR LAKE), p. A656
KINDRED HOSPITAL CENTRAL TAMPA, TAMPA, FL, p. A147
KINDRED HOSPITAL CHICAGO NORTH, CHICAGO, ILLINOIS (see KINDRED CHICAGO–CENTRAL HOSPITAL), p. A184

KINDRED HOSPITAL CHICAGO–NORTHLAKE, NORTHLAKE, IL, p. A198
KINDRED HOSPITAL CLEAR LAKE, WEBSTER, TX, p. A656
KINDRED HOSPITAL COLORADO SPRINGS, COLORADO SPRINGS, CO, p. A102
KINDRED HOSPITAL DALLAS CENTRAL, DALLAS, TX, p. A610
KINDRED HOSPITAL DALLAS–WALNUT HILL, DALLAS, TEXAS (see KINDRED HOSPITAL–DALLAS), p. A610
KINDRED HOSPITAL – DENVER SOUTH, DENVER, CO, p. A104
KINDRED HOSPITAL DETROIT, DETROIT, MI, p. A322
KINDRED HOSPITAL EL PASO, EL PASO, TX, p. A615
KINDRED HOSPITAL HOUSTON MEDICAL CENTER, HOUSTON, TX, p. A625
KINDRED HOSPITAL–INDIANAPOLIS NORTH, INDIANAPOLIS, IN, p. A214
KINDRED HOSPITAL INDIANAPOLIS SOUTH, GREENWOOD, IN, p. A212
KINDRED HOSPITAL KANSAS CITY, KANSAS CITY, MO, p. A373
KINDRED HOSPITAL LAS VEGAS, DESERT SPRINGS CAMPUS, LAS VEGAS, NEVADA (see KINDRED HOSPITAL LAS VEGAS–SAHARA), p. A406
KINDRED HOSPITAL LAS VEGAS–SAHARA, LAS VEGAS, NV, p. A406
KINDRED HOSPITAL LIMA, LIMA, OH, p. A496
KINDRED HOSPITAL LOUISVILLE AT JEWISH HOSPITAL, LOUISVILLE, KENTUCKY (see KINDRED HOSPITAL–LOUISVILLE), p. A264
KINDRED HOSPITAL MELBOURNE, MELBOURNE, FL, p. A136
KINDRED HOSPITAL NEW JERSEY – RAHWAY, RAHWAY, NEW JERSEY (see KINDRED HOSPITAL–NEW JERSEY MORRIS COUNTY), p. A416
KINDRED HOSPITAL NEW JERSEY – WAYNE, WAYNE, NEW JERSEY (see KINDRED HOSPITAL–NEW JERSEY MORRIS COUNTY), p. A416
KINDRED HOSPITAL NORTH FLORIDA, GREEN COVE SPRINGS, FL, p. A130
KINDRED HOSPITAL NORTHLAND, KANSAS CITY, MO, p. A373
KINDRED HOSPITAL NORTHWEST INDIANA, HAMMOND, IN, p. A212
KINDRED HOSPITAL OCALA, OCALA, FL, p. A139
KINDRED HOSPITAL OF CENTRAL OHIO, MANSFIELD, OH, p. A497
KINDRED HOSPITAL OF CLEVELAND, CLEVELAND, OHIO (see KINDRED HOSPITAL CLEVELAND–GATEWAY), p. A489
KINDRED HOSPITAL OF NORTHERN INDIANA, MISHAWAKA, IN, p. A218
KINDRED HOSPITAL PEORIA, PEORIA, IL, p. A200
KINDRED HOSPITAL PHILADELPHIA – HAVERTOWN, HAVERTOWN, PENNSYLVANIA (see KINDRED HOSPITAL–PHILADELPHIA), p. A548
KINDRED HOSPITAL RANCHO, RANCHO CUCAMONGA, CA, p. A84
KINDRED HOSPITAL RIVERSIDE, PERRIS, CA, p. A82
KINDRED HOSPITAL ROME, ROME, GA, p. A165
KINDRED HOSPITAL SAN ANTONIO CENTRAL, SAN ANTONIO, TX, p. A647
KINDRED HOSPITAL SAN GABRIEL VALLEY, WEST COVINA, CALIFORNIA (see KINDRED HOSPITAL–LA MIRADA), p. A67
KINDRED HOSPITAL SANTA ANA, SANTA ANA, CALIFORNIA (see KINDRED HOSPITAL–LA MIRADA), p. A67
KINDRED HOSPITAL SEATTLE–FIRST HILL, SEATTLE, WASHINGTON (see KINDRED HOSPITAL SEATTLE–NORTHGATE), p. A689
KINDRED HOSPITAL SEATTLE–NORTHGATE, SEATTLE, WA, p. A689
KINDRED HOSPITAL SOUTH BAY, GARDENA, CA, p. A64
KINDRED HOSPITAL SOUTH FLORIDA–CORAL GABLES, CORAL GABLES, FLORIDA (see KINDRED HOSPITAL SOUTH FLORIDA–FORT LAUDERDALE), p. A128
KINDRED HOSPITAL SOUTH FLORIDA–FORT LAUDERDALE, FORT LAUDERDALE, FL, p. A128
KINDRED HOSPITAL SOUTH FLORIDA–HOLLYWOOD,, FLORIDA (see KINDRED HOSPITAL SOUTH FLORIDA–FORT LAUDERDALE), p. A128
KINDRED HOSPITAL SOUTH PHILADELPHIA, PHILADELPHIA, PA, p. A548
KINDRED HOSPITAL SPRING, HOUSTON, TEXAS (see KINDRED HOSPITAL TOMBALL), p. A653
KINDRED HOSPITAL ST. LOUIS–ST. ANTHONY'S, SAINT LOUIS, MISSOURI (see KINDRED HOSPITAL–ST. LOUIS), p. A380
KINDRED HOSPITAL SUGAR LAND, SUGAR LAND, TX, p. A650
KINDRED HOSPITAL TARRANT COUNTY–ARLINGTON, ARLINGTON, TX, p. A597
KINDRED HOSPITAL TARRANT COUNTY–FORT WORTH SOUTHWEST, FORT WORTH, TEXAS (see KINDRED HOSPITAL–FORT WORTH), p. A618
KINDRED HOSPITAL THE PALM BEACHES, RIVIERA BEACH, FL, p. A143
KINDRED HOSPITAL TOMBALL, TOMBALL, TX, p. A653

KINDRED HOSPITAL– OKLAHOMA CITY, OKLAHOMA CITY, OK, p. A516
KINDRED HOSPITAL–ALBUQUERQUE, ALBUQUERQUE, NM, p. A427
KINDRED HOSPITAL–AURORA, AURORA, CO, p. A101
KINDRED HOSPITAL–BALDWIN PARK, BALDWIN PARK, CA, p. A56
KINDRED HOSPITAL–BAY AREA, PASADENA, TEXAS (see KINDRED HOSPITAL–HOUSTON NORTHWEST), p. A625
KINDRED HOSPITAL–BAY AREA ST. PETERSBURG, SAINT PETERSBURG, FLORIDA (see KINDRED HOSPITAL BAY AREA–TAMPA), p. A147
KINDRED HOSPITAL–BOSTON, BRIGHTON, MA, p. A308
KINDRED HOSPITAL–BREA, BREA, CA, p. A57
KINDRED HOSPITAL–CHATTANOOGA, CHATTANOOGA, TN, p. A580
KINDRED HOSPITAL–DALLAS, DALLAS, TX, p. A610
KINDRED HOSPITAL–DAYTON, DAYTON, OH, p. A493
KINDRED HOSPITAL–DENVER, DENVER, CO, p. A103
KINDRED HOSPITAL–FLAMINGO, LAS VEGAS, NEVADA (see KINDRED HOSPITAL LAS VEGAS–SAHARA), p. A406
KINDRED HOSPITAL–FORT WORTH, FORT WORTH, TX, p. A618
KINDRED HOSPITAL–GREENSBORO, GREENSBORO, NC, p. A466
KINDRED HOSPITAL–HOUSTON NORTHWEST, HOUSTON, TX, p. A625
KINDRED HOSPITAL–INDIANAPOLIS, INDIANAPOLIS, IN, p. A214
KINDRED HOSPITAL–LA MIRADA, LA MIRADA, CA, p. A67
KINDRED HOSPITAL–LOS ANGELES, LOS ANGELES, CA, p. A72
KINDRED HOSPITAL–LOUISVILLE, LOUISVILLE, KY, p. A264
KINDRED HOSPITAL–MANSFIELD, MANSFIELD, TX, p. A635
KINDRED HOSPITAL–NEW JERSEY MORRIS COUNTY, DOVER, NJ, p. A416
KINDRED HOSPITAL–OKLAHOMA CITY SOUTH, OKLAHOMA CITY, OKLAHOMA (see KINDRED HOSPITAL– OKLAHOMA CITY), p. A516
KINDRED HOSPITAL–ONTARIO, ONTARIO, CA, p. A80
KINDRED HOSPITAL–PHILADELPHIA, PHILADELPHIA, PA, p. A548
KINDRED HOSPITAL–SAN ANTONIO, SAN ANTONIO, TX, p. A646
KINDRED HOSPITAL–SAN DIEGO, SAN DIEGO, CA, p. A88
KINDRED HOSPITAL–SAN FRANCISCO BAY AREA, SAN LEANDRO, CA, p. A92
KINDRED HOSPITAL–ST. LOUIS, SAINT LOUIS, MO, p. A380
KINDRED HOSPITAL–ST. LOUIS AT MERCY, SAINT LOUIS, MO, p. A380
KINDRED HOSPITAL–SYCAMORE, SYCAMORE, IL, p. A204
KINDRED HOSPITAL–WESTMINSTER, WESTMINSTER, CA, p. A99
KINDRED HOSPITAL–WHITE ROCK, DALLAS, TX, p. A610
KINDRED REHABILITATION HOSPITAL ARLINGTON, ARLINGTON, TX, p. A597
KINDRED REHABILITATION HOSPITAL CLEAR LAKE, WEBSTER, TX, p. A656
KINDRED REHABILITATION HOSPITAL NORTHEAST HOUSTON, HUMBLE, TX, p. A628
KING'S DAUGHTERS MEDICAL CENTER, ASHLAND, KY, p. A257
KING'S DAUGHTERS MEDICAL CENTER, BROOKHAVEN, MS, p. A356
KING'S DAUGHTERS MEDICAL CENTER OHIO, PORTSMOUTH, OH, p. A501
KING'S DAUGHTERS' HEALTH, MADISON, IN, p. A217
KINGMAN COMMUNITY HOSPITAL, KINGMAN, KS, p. A246
KINGMAN REGIONAL MEDICAL CENTER, KINGMAN, AZ, p. A33
KINGS MOUNTAIN HOSPITAL, KINGS MOUNTAIN, NC, p. A468
KINGSBORO PSYCHIATRIC CENTER,, NY, p. A445
KINGSBROOK JEWISH MEDICAL CENTER,, NY, p. A445
KINGWOOD MEDICAL CENTER, KINGWOOD, TX, p. A631
KINGWOOD PINES HOSPITAL, KINGWOOD, TX, p. A631
KIOWA COUNTY MEMORIAL HOSPITAL, GREENSBURG, KS, p. A244
KIOWA DISTRICT HOSPITAL AND MANOR, KIOWA, KS, p. A247
KIRBY MEDICAL CENTER, MONTICELLO, IL, p. A197
KIRKBRIDE CENTER, PHILADELPHIA, PA, p. A548
KIT CARSON COUNTY HEALTH SERVICE DISTRICT, BURLINGTON, CO, p. A102
KITTITAS VALLEY HEALTHCARE, ELLENSBURG, WA, p. A684
KITTSON MEMORIAL HEALTHCARE CENTER, HALLOCK, MN, p. A344
KLICKITAT VALLEY HEALTH, GOLDENDALE, WA, p. A685
KNAPP MEDICAL CENTER, WESLACO, TX, p. A657
KNOX COMMUNITY HOSPITAL, MOUNT VERNON, OH, p. A499
KNOX COUNTY HOSPITAL, KNOX CITY, TX, p. A631
KNOXVILLE DIVISION, KNOXVILLE, IOWA (see VETERANS AFFAIRS CENTRAL IOWA HEALTH CARE SYSTEM), p. A230
KNOXVILLE HOSPITAL & CLINICS, KNOXVILLE, IA, p. A233
KOHALA HOSPITAL, KOHALA, HI, p. A172
KONA COMMUNITY HOSPITAL, KEALAKEKUA, HI, p. A172
KOOTENAI BEHAVIORAL HEALTH, COEUR D'ALENE, IDAHO (see KOOTENAI HEALTH), p. A175
KOOTENAI HEALTH, COEUR D'ALENE, ID, p. A175

M

MANCHESTER MEMORIAL HOSPITAL, MANCHESTER, KY, p. A266

MANCHESTER VETERANS AFFAIRS MEDICAL CENTER, MANCHESTER, NH, p. A412

MANHASSET AMBULATORY CARE PAVILION, MANHASSET, NEW YORK (see LONG ISLAND JEWISH MEDICAL CENTER), p. A445

MANHATTAN EYE, EAR AND THROAT HOSPITAL, NEW YORK, NEW YORK (see LENOX HILL HOSPITAL), p. A445

MANHATTAN PSYCHIATRIC CENTER–WARD'S ISLAND, NEW YORK, NY, p. A445

MANHATTAN SURGICAL,, KS, p. A248

MANIILAQ HEALTH CENTER, KOTZEBUE, AK, p. A30

MANN–GRANDSTAFF VETERANS AFFAIRS MEDICAL CENTER, SPOKANE, WA, p. A691

MANNING REGIONAL HEALTHCARE CENTER, MANNING, IA, p. A234

MANSFIELD HOSPITAL, MANSFIELD, OHIO (see OHIOHEALTH MEDCENTRAL MANSFIELD HOSPITAL), p. A497

MAPLE GROVE HOSPITAL, MAPLE GROVE, MN, p. A345

MARCUM AND WALLACE MEMORIAL HOSPITAL, IRVINE, KY, p. A262

MARCUS DALY MEMORIAL HOSPITAL, HAMILTON, MT, p. A388

MARENGO MEMORIAL HOSPITAL, MARENGO, IA, p. A234

MARGARET MARY HEALTH, BATESVILLE, IN, p. A206

MARGARET R. PARDEE MEMORIAL HOSPITAL, HENDERSONVILLE, NC, p. A467

MARGARETVILLE HOSPITAL, MARGARETVILLE, NY, p. A442

MARIA FARERI CHILDREN'S HOSPITAL, VALHALLA, NEW YORK (see WESTCHESTER MEDICAL CENTER), p. A458

MARIA PARHAM MEDICAL CENTER, HENDERSON, NC, p. A466

MARIAN CENTER, SALT LAKE CITY, UT, p. A663

MARIAN REGIONAL MEDICAL CENTER, SANTA MARIA, CA, p. A93

MARIANJOY REHABILITATION HOSPITAL, WHEATON, IL, p. A205

MARIAS MEDICAL CENTER, SHELBY, MT, p. A391

MARICOPA INTEGRATED HEALTH SYSTEM, PHOENIX, AZ, p. A36

MARIETTA MEMORIAL HOSPITAL, MARIETTA, OH, p. A498

MARIN GENERAL HOSPITAL, GREENBRAE, CA, p. A65

MARINA DEL REY HOSPITAL, MARINA DEL REY, CA, p. A76

MARION GENERAL HOSPITAL, MARION, IN, p. A218

MARION GENERAL HOSPITAL, COLUMBIA, MS, p. A357

MARION VETERANS AFFAIRS MEDICAL CENTER, MARION, IL, p. A195

MARK TWAIN MEDICAL CENTER, SAN ANDREAS, CA, p. A88

MARLETTE REGIONAL HOSPITAL, MARLETTE, MI, p. A329

MARLTON REHABILITATION HOSPITAL, MARLTON, NJ, p. A419

MARSHALL BROWNING HOSPITAL, DU QUOIN, IL, p. A188

MARSHALL COUNTY HEALTHCARE CENTER AVERA, BRITTON, SD, p. A572

MARSHALL COUNTY HOSPITAL, BENTON, KY, p. A257

MARSHALL I. PICKENS HOSPITAL, GREENVILLE, SOUTH CAROLINA (see GHS GREENVILLE MEMORIAL HOSPITAL), p. A566

MARSHALL MEDICAL CENTER, PLACERVILLE, CA, p. A83

MARSHALL MEDICAL CENTER, LEWISBURG, TN, p. A587

MARSHALL MEDICAL CENTER NORTH, GUNTERSVILLE, AL, p. A21

MARSHALL MEDICAL CENTER SOUTH, BOAZ, AL, p. A17

MARTHA JEFFERSON HOSPITAL, CHARLOTTESVILLE, VA, p. A668

MARTHA'S VINEYARD HOSPITAL, OAK BLUFFS, MA, p. A313

MARTIN ARMY COMMUNITY HOSPITAL, FORT BENNING, GA, p. A159

MARTIN COUNTY HOSPITAL DISTRICT, STANTON, TX, p. A650

MARTIN GENERAL HOSPITAL, WILLIAMSTON, NC, p. A475

MARTIN HEALTH SYSTEM, STUART, FL, p. A146

MARTIN LUTHER KING, JR. COMMUNITY HOSPITAL, LOS ANGELES, CA, p. A72

MARTIN MEMORIAL HOSPITAL SOUTH, STUART, FLORIDA (see MARTIN HEALTH SYSTEM), p. A146

MARTINSBURG VETERANS AFFAIRS MEDICAL CENTER, MARTINSBURG, WV, p. A698

MARY BLACK HEALTH SYSTEM – GAFFNEY, GAFFNEY, SC, p. A566

MARY BLACK HEALTH SYSTEM–SPARTANBURG, SPARTANBURG, SC, p. A569

MARY BRECKINRIDGE ARH HOSPITAL, HYDEN, KY, p. A262

MARY FREE BED REHABILITATION HOSPITAL, GRAND RAPIDS, MI, p. A325

MARY GREELEY MEDICAL CENTER, AMES, IA, p. A225

MARY IMMACULATE HOSPITAL, NEWPORT NEWS, VA, p. A674

MARY LANNING HEALTHCARE, HASTINGS, NE, p. A396

MARY RUTAN HOSPITAL, BELLEFONTAINE, OH, p. A485

MARY S HARPER GERIATRIC PSYCHIATRY CENTER, TUSCALOOSA, AL, p. A26

MARY WASHINGTON HOSPITAL, FREDERICKSBURG, VA, p. A670

MARYMOUNT HOSPITAL, GARFIELD HEIGHTS, OH, p. A495

MASON DISTRICT HOSPITAL, HAVANA, IL, p. A192

MASON GENERAL HOSPITAL, SHELTON, WA, p. A690

MASONICARE HEALTH CENTER, WALLINGFORD, CT, p. A117

MASSAC MEMORIAL HOSPITAL, METROPOLIS, IL, p. A196

MASSACHUSETTS EYE AND EAR INFIRMARY, BOSTON, MA, p. A307

MASSACHUSETTS GENERAL HOSPITAL, BOSTON, MA, p. A307

MASSACHUSETTS HOSPITAL SCHOOL, CANTON, MA, p. A309

MASSENA MEMORIAL HOSPITAL, MASSENA, NY, p. A442

MASSGENERAL FOR CHILDREN AT NEWTON–WELLESLEY HOSPITAL, NEWTON, MASSACHUSETTS (see NEWTON–WELLESLEY HOSPITAL), p. A313

MASSGENERAL FOR CHILDREN AT NORTH SHORE MEDICAL CENTER, SALEM, MASSACHUSETTS (see NORTH SHORE MEDICAL CENTER), p. A314

MASSGENERAL HOSPITAL FOR CHILDREN, BOSTON, MASSACHUSETTS (see MASSACHUSETTS GENERAL HOSPITAL), p. A307

MAT–SU REGIONAL MEDICAL CENTER, PALMER, AK, p. A30

MATAGORDA REGIONAL MEDICAL CENTER, BAY CITY, TX, p. A601

MATHENY MEDICAL AND EDUCATIONAL CENTER, PEAPACK, NJ, p. A421

MATTEL CHILDREN'S HOSPITAL, LOS ANGELES, CALIFORNIA (see RONALD REAGAN UCLA MEDICAL CENTER), p. A74

MAUI MEMORIAL MEDICAL CENTER, WAILUKU, HI, p. A173

MAURY REGIONAL HOSPITAL, COLUMBIA, TN, p. A581

MAYERS MEMORIAL HOSPITAL DISTRICT, FALL RIVER MILLS, CA, p. A62

MAYHILL HOSPITAL, DENTON, TX, p. A612

MAYO CLINIC HEALTH SYSTEM – CHIPPEWA VALLEY IN BLOOMER, BLOOMER, WI, p. A703

MAYO CLINIC HEALTH SYSTEM – FRANCISCAN HEALTHCARE IN LA CROSSE, LA CROSSE, WI, p. A708

MAYO CLINIC HEALTH SYSTEM – FRANCISCAN HEALTHCARE IN SPARTA, SPARTA, WI, p. A716

MAYO CLINIC HEALTH SYSTEM – NORTHLAND IN BARRON, BARRON, WI, p. A702

MAYO CLINIC HEALTH SYSTEM – OAKRIDGE IN OSSEO, OSSEO, WI, p. A714

MAYO CLINIC HEALTH SYSTEM – RED CEDAR IN MENOMONIE, MENOMONIE, WI, p. A710

MAYO CLINIC HEALTH SYSTEM IN ALBERT LEA, ALBERT LEA, MN, p. A338

MAYO CLINIC HEALTH SYSTEM IN CANNON FALLS, CANNON FALLS, MN, p. A340

MAYO CLINIC HEALTH SYSTEM IN EAU CLAIRE, EAU CLAIRE, WI, p. A704

MAYO CLINIC HEALTH SYSTEM IN FAIRMONT, FAIRMONT, MN, p. A342

MAYO CLINIC HEALTH SYSTEM IN LAKE CITY, LAKE CITY, MN, p. A344

MAYO CLINIC HEALTH SYSTEM IN MANKATO, MANKATO, MN, p. A345

MAYO CLINIC HEALTH SYSTEM IN NEW PRAGUE, NEW PRAGUE, MN, p. A347

MAYO CLINIC HEALTH SYSTEM IN RED WING, RED WING, MN, p. A349

MAYO CLINIC HEALTH SYSTEM IN SAINT JAMES, SAINT JAMES, MN, p. A350

MAYO CLINIC HEALTH SYSTEM IN SPRINGFIELD, SPRINGFIELD, MN, p. A351

MAYO CLINIC HEALTH SYSTEM IN WASECA, WASECA, MN, p. A353

MAYO CLINIC HEALTH SYSTEM IN WAYCROSS, WAYCROSS, GA, p. A169

MAYO CLINIC HEALTH SYSTEM–ALBERT LEA AND AUSTIN, AUSTIN, MN, p. A339

MAYO CLINIC HOSPITAL, PHOENIX, AZ, p. A36

MAYO CLINIC HOSPITAL – METHODIST CAMPUS, ROCHESTER, MINNESOTA (see MAYO CLINIC HOSPITAL – ROCHESTER), p. A349

MAYO CLINIC HOSPITAL – ROCHESTER, ROCHESTER, MN, p. A349

MAYO CLINIC HOSPITAL – SAINT MARYS CAMPUS, ROCHESTER, MINNESOTA (see MAYO CLINIC HOSPITAL – ROCHESTER), p. A349

MAYO CLINIC JACKSONVILLE, JACKSONVILLE, FL, p. A131

MAYO REGIONAL HOSPITAL, DOVER–FOXCROFT, ME, p. A293

MCALESTER REGIONAL HEALTH CENTER, MCALESTER, OK, p. A514

MCALLEN HEART HOSPITAL, MCALLEN, TEXAS (see SOUTH TEXAS HEALTH SYSTEM), p. A614

MCALLEN MEDICAL CENTER, MCALLEN, TEXAS (see SOUTH TEXAS HEALTH SYSTEM), p. A614

MCBRIDE CLINIC ORTHOPEDIC HOSPITAL, OKLAHOMA CITY, OK, p. A516

MCCAMEY COUNTY HOSPITAL DISTRICT, MCCAMEY, TX, p. A636

MCCONE COUNTY HEALTH CENTER, CIRCLE, MT, p. A386

MCCREADY HEALTH, CRISFIELD, MD, p. A300

MCCULLOUGH–HYDE MEMORIAL HOSPITAL/TRIHEALTH, OXFORD, OH, p. A501

MCCURTAIN MEMORIAL HOSPITAL, IDABEL, OK, p. A513

MCDONOUGH DISTRICT HOSPITAL, MACOMB, IL, p. A195

MCDOWELL ARH HOSPITAL, MCDOWELL, KY, p. A266

MCDOWELL HOSPITAL, MARION, NC, p. A469

MCGEHEE–DESHA COUNTY HOSPITAL, MCGEHEE, AR, p. A50

MCKAY–DEE HOSPITAL CENTER, OGDEN, UT, p. A661

MCKEE MEDICAL CENTER, LOVELAND, CO, p. A109

MCKENZIE COUNTY HEALTHCARE SYSTEM, WATFORD CITY, ND, p. A482

MCKENZIE HEALTH SYSTEM, SANDUSKY, MI, p. A334

MCKENZIE REGIONAL HOSPITAL, MCKENZIE, TN, p. A588

MCKENZIE–WILLAMETTE MEDICAL CENTER, SPRINGFIELD, OR, p. A531

MCLANE CHILDREN'S HOSPITAL SCOTT & WHITE, TEMPLE, TEXAS (see SCOTT & WHITE MEMORIAL HOSPITAL), p. A652

MCLANE CHILDREN'S HOSPITAL SCOTT & WHITE, TEMPLE, TEXAS (see SCOTT & WHITE MEMORIAL HOSPITAL), p. A652

MCLAREN BAY REGION, BAY CITY, MI, p. A319

MCLAREN BAY REGION–WEST CAMPUS, BAY CITY, MICHIGAN (see MCLAREN BAY REGION), p. A319

MCLAREN BAY SPECIAL CARE, BAY CITY, MI, p. A319

MCLAREN CENTRAL MICHIGAN, MOUNT PLEASANT, MI, p. A330

MCLAREN FLINT, FLINT, MI, p. A323

MCLAREN GREATER LANSING, LANSING, MI, p. A328

MCLAREN GREATER LANSING, LANSING, MICHIGAN (see MCLAREN GREATER LANSING), p. A328

MCLAREN LAPEER REGION, LAPEER, MI, p. A328

MCLAREN MACOMB, MOUNT CLEMENS, MI, p. A330

MCLAREN NORTHERN MICHIGAN, PETOSKEY, MI, p. A331

MCLAREN OAKLAND, PONTIAC, MI, p. A332

MCLAREN ORTHOPEDIC HOSPITAL, LANSING, MICHIGAN (see MCLAREN GREATER LANSING), p. A328

MCLAREN PORT HURON, PORT HURON, MI, p. A332

MCLEAN HOSPITAL, BELMONT, MA, p. A305

MCLEOD HEALTH CHERAW, CHERAW, SC, p. A563

MCLEOD HEALTH CLARENDON, MANNING, SC, p. A568

MCLEOD LORIS SEACOAST HOSPITAL, LORIS, SC, p. A568

MCLEOD MEDICAL CENTER DILLON, DILLON, SC, p. A565

MCLEOD MEDICAL CENTER–DARLINGTON, DARLINGTON, SC, p. A565

MCLEOD REGIONAL MEDICAL CENTER, FLORENCE, SC, p. A566

MCLEOD SEACOAST, LITTLE RIVER, SOUTH CAROLINA (see MCLEOD LORIS SEACOAST HOSPITAL), p. A568

MCPHERSON HOSPITAL, MCPHERSON, KS, p. A249

MCREYNOLDS HALL (see OTSEGO MEMORIAL HOSPITAL), p. A324

MEADE DISTRICT HOSPITAL, MEADE, KS, p. A249

MEADOW WOOD BEHAVIORAL HEALTH SYSTEM, NEW CASTLE, DE, p. A119

MEADOWBROOK REHABILITATION HOSPITAL, GARDNER, KS, p. A243

MEADOWLANDS HOSPITAL MEDICAL CENTER, SECAUCUS, NJ, p. A423

MEADOWS PSYCHIATRIC CENTER, CENTRE HALL, PA, p. A535

MEADOWS REGIONAL MEDICAL CENTER, VIDALIA, GA, p. A168

MEADOWVIEW REGIONAL MEDICAL CENTER, MAYSVILLE, KY, p. A266

MEADVILLE MEDICAL CENTER, MEADVILLE, PA, p. A544

MEASE COUNTRYSIDE HOSPITAL, SAFETY HARBOR, FL, p. A144

MEASE DUNEDIN HOSPITAL, DUNEDIN, FL, p. A128

MEDICAL ARTS HOSPITAL, LAMESA, TX, p. A632

MEDICAL CENTER ALLIANCE, FORT WORTH, TX, p. A618

MEDICAL CENTER ARLINGTON, ARLINGTON, TX, p. A597

MEDICAL CENTER AT BOWLING GREEN, BOWLING GREEN, KY, p. A258

MEDICAL CENTER AT FRANKLIN, FRANKLIN, KY, p. A260

MEDICAL CENTER AT SCOTTSVILLE, SCOTTSVILLE, KY, p. A269

MEDICAL CENTER BARBOUR, EUFAULA, AL, p. A19

MEDICAL CENTER ENTERPRISE, ENTERPRISE, AL, p. A19

MEDICAL CENTER FRISCO, FRISCO, TEXAS (see MEDICAL CENTER OF PLANO), p. A641

MEDICAL CENTER HEALTH SYSTEM, ODESSA, TX, p. A639

MEDICAL CENTER HOSPITAL CAMPUS, BURLINGTON, VERMONT (see THE UNIVERSITY OF VERMONT HEALTH NETWORK UNIVERSITY OF VERMONT MEDICAL CENTER), p. A665

MEDICAL CENTER OF AURORA, AURORA, CO, p. A101

MEDICAL CENTER OF AURORA, AURORA, COLORADO (see MEDICAL CENTER OF AURORA), p. A101

MEDICAL CENTER OF AURORA NORTH, AURORA, COLORADO (see MEDICAL CENTER OF AURORA), p. A101

MEDICAL CENTER OF LEWISVILLE, LEWISVILLE, TX, p. A632

MEDICAL CENTER OF MCKINNEY, MCKINNEY, TX, p. A636

MEDICAL CENTER OF PEACH COUNTY, NAVICENT HEALTH, BRYON, GA, p. A155

MEDICAL CENTER OF PLANO, PLANO, TX, p. A641

MEDICAL CENTER OF SOUTH ARKANSAS, EL DORADO, AR, p. A45
MEDICAL CENTER OF SOUTHEAST TEXAS, BEAUMONT, TX, p. A601
MEDICAL CENTER OF THE ROCKIES, LOVELAND, CO, p. A109
MEDICAL CENTER OF TRINITY, TRINITY, FL, p. A148
MEDICAL CENTER, NAVICENT HEALTH, MACON, GA, p. A162
MEDICAL CITY CHILDREN'S HOSPITAL, DALLAS, TEXAS (see MEDICAL CITY DALLAS HOSPITAL), p. A610
MEDICAL CITY DALLAS HOSPITAL, DALLAS, TX, p. A610
MEDICAL WEST, BESSEMER, AL, p. A16
MEDICINE LODGE MEMORIAL HOSPITAL, MEDICINE LODGE, KS, p. A249
MEDINA MEMORIAL HOSPITAL, MEDINA, NY, p. A442
MEDINA REGIONAL HOSPITAL, HONDO, TX, p. A623
MEDSTAR FRANKLIN SQUARE MEDICAL CENTER, BALTIMORE, MD, p. A297
MEDSTAR GEORGETOWN UNIVERSITY HOSPITAL, WASHINGTON, DC, p. A121
MEDSTAR GOOD SAMARITAN HOSPITAL, BALTIMORE, MD, p. A297
MEDSTAR HARBOR HOSPITAL, BALTIMORE, MD, p. A297
MEDSTAR MONTGOMERY MEDICAL CENTER, OLNEY, MD, p. A302
MEDSTAR NATIONAL REHABILITATION HOSPITAL, WASHINGTON, DC, p. A121
MEDSTAR SOUTHERN MARYLAND HOSPITAL CENTER, CLINTON, MD, p. A300
MEDSTAR ST. MARY'S HOSPITAL, LEONARDTOWN, MD, p. A302
MEDSTAR UNION MEMORIAL HOSPITAL, BALTIMORE, MD, p. A297
MEDSTAR WASHINGTON HOSPITAL CENTER, WASHINGTON, DC, p. A122
MEE MEMORIAL HOSPITAL, KING CITY, CA, p. A67
MEEKER MEMORIAL HOSPITAL, LITCHFIELD, MN, p. A345
MELISSA MEMORIAL HOSPITAL, HOLYOKE, CO, p. A107
MELROSE–WAKEFIELD HOSPITAL, MELROSE, MASSACHUSETTS (see HALLMARK HEALTH SYSTEM), p. A316
MEMORIAL BEHAVIORAL HEALTH, GULFPORT, MISSISSIPPI (see MEMORIAL HOSPITAL AT GULFPORT), p. A358
MEMORIAL CAMPUS, WORCESTER, MASSACHUSETTS (see UMASS MEMORIAL MEDICAL CENTER), p. A316
MEMORIAL CHILDREN'S HOSPITAL, SAVANNAH, GEORGIA (see MEMORIAL HEALTH), p. A166
MEMORIAL CHILDREN'S HOSPITAL, SOUTH BEND, INDIANA (see MEMORIAL HOSPITAL OF SOUTH BEND), p. A222
MEMORIAL COMMUNITY HEALTH, AURORA, NE, p. A393
MEMORIAL COMMUNITY HOSPITAL AND HEALTH SYSTEM, BLAIR, NE, p. A394
MEMORIAL HEALTH, SAVANNAH, GA, p. A166
MEMORIAL HEALTH, MARYSVILLE, OH, p. A498
MEMORIAL HEALTH CARE SYSTEMS, SEWARD, NE, p. A402
MEMORIAL HEALTH SYSTEM, ABILENE, KS, p. A240
MEMORIAL HEALTHCARE, OWOSSO, MI, p. A331
MEMORIAL HERMANN – TEXAS MEDICAL CENTER, HOUSTON, TX, p. A625
MEMORIAL HERMANN GREATER HEIGHTS HOSPITAL, HOUSTON, TX, p. A625
MEMORIAL HERMANN KATY HOSPITAL, KATY, TX, p. A629
MEMORIAL HERMANN MEMORIAL CITY MEDICAL CENTER, HOUSTON, TX, p. A625
MEMORIAL HERMANN NORTHEAST, HUMBLE, TX, p. A628
MEMORIAL HERMANN ORTHOPEDIC AND SPINE HOSPITAL, BELLAIRE, TX, p. A602
MEMORIAL HERMANN PEARLAND MEDICAL CENTER, PEARLAND, TEXAS (see MEMORIAL HERMANN GREATER HEIGHTS HOSPITAL), p. A625
MEMORIAL HERMANN REHABILITATION HOSPITAL – KATY, KATY, TX, p. A630
MEMORIAL HERMANN SOUTHEAST HOSPITAL, HOUSTON, TEXAS (see MEMORIAL HERMANN GREATER HEIGHTS HOSPITAL), p. A625
MEMORIAL HERMANN SOUTHWEST HOSPITAL, HOUSTON, TEXAS (see MEMORIAL HERMANN GREATER HEIGHTS HOSPITAL), p. A625
MEMORIAL HERMANN SUGAR LAND HOSPITAL, SUGAR LAND, TX, p. A650
MEMORIAL HERMANN SURGICAL HOSPITAL KINGWOOD, KINGWOOD, TX, p. A631
MEMORIAL HERMANN SURGICAL HOSPITAL‰(FIRST COLONY, SUGAR LAND, TX, p. A650
MEMORIAL HERMANN THE WOODLANDS HOSPITAL, THE WOODLANDS, TEXAS (see MEMORIAL HERMANN GREATER HEIGHTS HOSPITAL), p. A625
MEMORIAL HOSPITAL, COLORADO SPRINGS, CO, p. A102
MEMORIAL HOSPITAL, BELLEVILLE, IL, p. A181
MEMORIAL HOSPITAL, CARTHAGE, IL, p. A182
MEMORIAL HOSPITAL, CHESTER, IL, p. A183
MEMORIAL HOSPITAL, NORTH CONWAY, NH, p. A413
MEMORIAL HOSPITAL, STILWELL, OK, p. A520

MEMORIAL HOSPITAL, YORK, PA, p. A559
MEMORIAL HOSPITAL, GONZALES, TX, p. A621
MEMORIAL HOSPITAL, SEMINOLE, TX, p. A648
MEMORIAL HOSPITAL, MARTINSVILLE, VA, p. A673
MEMORIAL HOSPITAL AND HEALTH CARE CENTER, JASPER, IN, p. A215
MEMORIAL HOSPITAL AND MANOR, BAINBRIDGE, GA, p. A154
MEMORIAL HOSPITAL AT GULFPORT, GULFPORT, MS, p. A358
MEMORIAL HOSPITAL EAST, SHILOH, IL, p. A203
MEMORIAL HOSPITAL HIXSON, HIXSON, TENNESSEE (see CHI MEMORIAL), p. A580
MEMORIAL HOSPITAL JACKSONVILLE, JACKSONVILLE, FL, p. A131
MEMORIAL HOSPITAL LOS BANOS, LOS BANOS, CA, p. A75
MEMORIAL HOSPITAL MIRAMAR, MIRAMAR, FL, p. A138
MEMORIAL HOSPITAL OF CARBON COUNTY, RAWLINS, WY, p. A723
MEMORIAL HOSPITAL OF CARBONDALE, CARBONDALE, IL, p. A182
MEMORIAL HOSPITAL OF CONVERSE COUNTY, DOUGLAS, WY, p. A722
MEMORIAL HOSPITAL OF GARDENA, GARDENA, CA, p. A64
MEMORIAL HOSPITAL OF LAFAYETTE COUNTY, DARLINGTON, WI, p. A704
MEMORIAL HOSPITAL OF RHODE ISLAND, PAWTUCKET, RI, p. A560
MEMORIAL HOSPITAL OF SALEM COUNTY, SALEM, NJ, p. A423
MEMORIAL HOSPITAL OF SOUTH BEND, SOUTH BEND, IN, p. A222
MEMORIAL HOSPITAL OF SWEETWATER COUNTY, ROCK SPRINGS, WY, p. A723
MEMORIAL HOSPITAL OF TAMPA, TAMPA, FL, p. A147
MEMORIAL HOSPITAL OF TEXAS COUNTY, GUYMON, OK, p. A512
MEMORIAL HOSPITAL PEMBROKE, PEMBROKE PINES, FL, p. A142
MEMORIAL HOSPITAL WEST, PEMBROKE PINES, FL, p. A142
MEMORIAL MEDICAL CENTER, MODESTO, CA, p. A77
MEMORIAL MEDICAL CENTER, MODESTO, CALIFORNIA (see MEMORIAL MEDICAL CENTER), p. A77
MEMORIAL MEDICAL CENTER, SPRINGFIELD, IL, p. A203
MEMORIAL MEDICAL CENTER, LAS CRUCES, NM, p. A430
MEMORIAL MEDICAL CENTER, PORT LAVACA, TX, p. A642
MEMORIAL MEDICAL CENTER – ASHLAND, ASHLAND, WI, p. A702
MEMORIAL MEDICAL CENTER – LEE CAMPUS, JOHNSTOWN, PENNSYLVANIA (see CONEMAUGH MEMORIAL MEDICAL CENTER), p. A541
MEMORIAL MEDICAL CENTER – NEILLSVILLE, NEILLSVILLE, WI, p. A712
MEMORIAL NURSING HOME (see ASPIRUS MEDFORD HOSPITAL), p. A710
MEMORIAL REGIONAL HOSPITAL,, FL, p. A130
MEMORIAL REGIONAL HOSPITAL SOUTH,, FLORIDA (see MEMORIAL REGIONAL HOSPITAL), p. A130
MEMORIAL SLOAN–KETTERING CANCER CENTER, NEW YORK, NY, p. A446
MEMORIAL SPECIALTY HOSPITAL, LAKE CHARLES, LA, p. A281
MEMPHIS MENTAL HEALTH INSTITUTE, MEMPHIS, TN, p. A589
MEMPHIS VETERANS AFFAIRS MEDICAL CENTER, MEMPHIS, TN, p. A589
MENA REGIONAL HEALTH SYSTEM, MENA, AR, p. A50
MENDOCINO COAST DISTRICT HOSPITAL, FORT BRAGG, CA, p. A62
MENDOTA MENTAL HEALTH INSTITUTE, MADISON, WI, p. A708
MENIFEE VALLEY MEDICAL CENTER, SUN CITY, CA, p. A95
MENLO PARK SURGICAL HOSPITAL, MENLO PARK, CA, p. A76
MENNINGER CLINIC, HOUSTON, TX, p. A626
MENNONITE GENERAL HOSPITAL, AIBONITO, PR, p. A725
MENORAH MEDICAL CENTER, OVERLAND PARK, KS, p. A251
MENTAL HEALTH CENTER, ALBUQUERQUE, NEW MEXICO (see UNIVERSITY OF NEW MEXICO HOSPITALS), p. A428
MENTAL HEALTH INSTITUTE, CHEROKEE, IA, p. A227
MENTAL HEALTH INSTITUTE, INDEPENDENCE, IA, p. A232
MENTAL HEALTH SERVICES FOR CLARK AND MADISON COUNTIES, SPRINGFIELD, OH, p. A502
MERCER HEALTH, COLDWATER, OH, p. A490
MERCY ALLEN HOSPITAL, OBERLIN, OH, p. A500
MERCY CHILDREN'S HOSPITAL, TOLEDO, OHIO (see MERCY ST. VINCENT MEDICAL CENTER), p. A504
MERCY CHILDREN'S HOSPITAL SPRINGFIELD, SPRINGFIELD, MISSOURI (see MERCY HOSPITAL SPRINGFIELD), p. A382
MERCY CHILDREN'S HOSPITAL ST. LOUIS, SAINT LOUIS, MISSOURI (see MERCY HOSPITAL ST. LOUIS), p. A380
MERCY FITZGERALD HOSPITAL, DARBY, PENNSYLVANIA (see MERCY FITZGERALD HOSPITAL), p. A536
MERCY FITZGERALD HOSPITAL, DARBY, PA, p. A536
MERCY GENERAL HOSPITAL, SACRAMENTO, CA, p. A86
MERCY GILBERT MEDICAL CENTER, GILBERT, AZ, p. A32
MERCY HARVARD HOSPITAL, HARVARD, IL, p. A192

MERCY HEALTH – ST. CHARLES HOSPITAL, OREGON, OH, p. A500
MERCY HEALTH – ANDERSON HOSPITAL, CINCINNATI, OH, p. A488
MERCY HEALTH – CLERMONT HOSPITAL, BATAVIA, OH, p. A484
MERCY HEALTH – FAIRFIELD HOSPITAL, FAIRFIELD, OH, p. A494
MERCY HEALTH – ST. ELIZABETH BOARDMAN HOSPITAL, BOARDMAN, OH, p. A485
MERCY HEALTH – ST. ELIZABETH YOUNGSTOWN HOSPITAL, YOUNGSTOWN, OH, p. A506
MERCY HEALTH – ST. JOSEPH WARREN HOSPITAL, WARREN, OH, A504
MERCY HEALTH – WEST HOSPITAL, CINCINNATI, OH, p. A488
MERCY HEALTH – WILLARD HOSPITAL, WILLARD, OH, p. A506
MERCY HEALTH HACKLEY CAMPUS, MUSKEGON, MI, p. A330
MERCY HEALTH LOVE COUNTY, MARIETTA, OK, p. A514
MERCY HEALTH ROCKFORD, ROCKFORD, MICHIGAN (see MERCY HEALTH SAINT MARY'S), p. A325
MERCY HEALTH SAINT MARY'S, GRAND RAPIDS, MI, p. A325
MERCY HEALTH, GENERAL CAMPUS, MUSKEGON, MICHIGAN (see MERCY HEALTH HACKLEY CAMPUS), p. A330
MERCY HEALTH, LAKESHORE CAMPUS, SHELBY, MI, p. A334
MERCY HEALTH, MERCY CAMPUS, MUSKEGON, MICHIGAN (see MERCY HEALTH HACKLEY CAMPUS), p. A330
MERCY HOSPITAL, MOUNDRIDGE, KS, p. A249
MERCY HOSPITAL, COON RAPIDS, MN, p. A341
MERCY HOSPITAL, MOOSE LAKE, MN, p. A347
MERCY HOSPITAL, BUFFALO, NY, p. A436
MERCY HOSPITAL – A CAMPUS OF PLANTATION GENERAL HOSPITAL, MIAMI, FLORIDA (see PLANTATION GENERAL HOSPITAL), p. A143
MERCY HOSPITAL ADA, ADA, OK, p. A508
MERCY HOSPITAL AND MEDICAL CENTER, CHICAGO, IL, p. A185
MERCY HOSPITAL AND TRAUMA CENTER, JANESVILLE, WI, p. A707
MERCY HOSPITAL ARDMORE, ARDMORE, OK, p. A508
MERCY HOSPITAL AURORA, AURORA, MO, p. A367
MERCY HOSPITAL BERRYVILLE, BERRYVILLE, AR, p. A43
MERCY HOSPITAL BOONEVILLE, BOONEVILLE, AR, p. A44
MERCY HOSPITAL CARTHAGE, CARTHAGE, MO, p. A369
MERCY HOSPITAL CASSVILLE, CASSVILLE, MO, p. A369
MERCY HOSPITAL COLUMBUS, COLUMBUS, KS, p. A242
MERCY HOSPITAL EL RENO, EL RENO, OK, p. A511
MERCY HOSPITAL FORT SCOTT, FORT SCOTT, KS, p. A243
MERCY HOSPITAL FORT SMITH, FORT SMITH, AR, p. A46
MERCY HOSPITAL HEALDTON, HEALDTON, OK, p. A512
MERCY HOSPITAL JEFFERSON, CRYSTAL CITY, MO, p. A370
MERCY HOSPITAL JOPLIN, JOPLIN, MO, p. A373
MERCY HOSPITAL KINGFISHER, KINGFISHER, OK, p. A513
MERCY HOSPITAL LEBANON, LEBANON, MO, p. A375
MERCY HOSPITAL LINCOLN, TROY, MO, p. A383
MERCY HOSPITAL LOGAN COUNTY, GUTHRIE, OK, p. A512
MERCY HOSPITAL OF DEFIANCE, DEFIANCE, OH, p. A493
MERCY HOSPITAL OF FOLSOM, FOLSOM, CA, p. A62
MERCY HOSPITAL OF FRANCISCAN SISTERS, OELWEIN, IA, p. A235
MERCY HOSPITAL OF PORTLAND, PORTLAND, ME, p. A294
MERCY HOSPITAL OKLAHOMA CITY, OKLAHOMA CITY, OK, p. A516
MERCY HOSPITAL OZARK, OZARK, AR, p. A51
MERCY HOSPITAL PARIS, PARIS, AR, p. A51
MERCY HOSPITAL ROGERS, ROGERS, AR, p. A52
MERCY HOSPITAL SPRINGFIELD, SPRINGFIELD, MO, p. A382
MERCY HOSPITAL ST. LOUIS, SAINT LOUIS, MO, p. A380
MERCY HOSPITAL TISHOMINGO, TISHOMINGO, OK, p. A521
MERCY HOSPITAL WALDRON, WALDRON, AR, p. A53
MERCY HOSPITAL WASHINGTON, WASHINGTON, MO, p. A383
MERCY HOSPITAL WATONGA, WATONGA, OK, p. A523
MERCY HOSPITALS OF BAKERSFIELD, BAKERSFIELD, CA, p. A56
MERCY IOWA CITY, IOWA CITY, IA, p. A232
MERCY MEDICAL CENTER, BALTIMORE, MD, p. A297
MERCY MEDICAL CENTER, SPRINGFIELD, MA, p. A315
MERCY MEDICAL CENTER, ROCKVILLE CENTRE, NY, p. A454
MERCY MEDICAL CENTER, WILLISTON, ND, p. A482
MERCY MEDICAL CENTER, CANTON, OH, p. A486
MERCY MEDICAL CENTER, ROSEBURG, OR, p. A530
MERCY MEDICAL CENTER, OSHKOSH, WI, p. A713
MERCY MEDICAL CENTER – WEST LAKES, WEST DES MOINES, IA, p. A239
MERCY MEDICAL CENTER MERCED, MERCED, CA, p. A76
MERCY MEDICAL CENTER MERCED–DOMINICAN CAMPUS, MERCED, CALIFORNIA (see MERCY MEDICAL CENTER MERCED), p. A76
MERCY MEDICAL CENTER MOUNT SHASTA, MOUNT SHASTA, CA, p. A78
MERCY MEDICAL CENTER REDDING, REDDING, CA, p. A84

MERCY MEDICAL CENTER–CEDAR RAPIDS, CEDAR RAPIDS, IA, p. A226

MERCY MEDICAL CENTER–CENTERVILLE, CENTERVILLE, IA, p. A227

MERCY MEDICAL CENTER–CLINTON, CLINTON, IA, p. A227

MERCY MEDICAL CENTER–DES MOINES, DES MOINES, IA, p. A229

MERCY MEDICAL CENTER–DUBUQUE, DUBUQUE, IA, p. A230

MERCY MEDICAL CENTER–DYERSVILLE, DYERSVILLE, IA, p. A230

MERCY MEDICAL CENTER–NEW HAMPTON, NEW HAMPTON, IA, p. A235

MERCY MEDICAL CENTER–NORTH IOWA, MASON CITY, IA, p. A234

MERCY MEDICAL CENTER–SIOUX CITY, SIOUX CITY, IA, p. A237

MERCY MEDICAL CENTER–WEST LAKES, WEST DES MOINES, IOWA (see MERCY MEDICAL CENTER–DES MOINES), p. A229

MERCY MEMORIAL HOSPITAL, URBANA, OH, p. A504

MERCY ORTHOPEDIC HOSPITAL FORT SMITH, FORT SMITH, ARKANSAS (see MERCY HOSPITAL FORT SMITH), p. A46

MERCY ORTHOPEDIC HOSPITAL SPRINGFIELD, OZARK, MISSOURI (see MERCY HOSPITAL SPRINGFIELD), p. A382

MERCY PHILADELPHIA HOSPITAL, PHILADELPHIA, PENNSYLVANIA (see MERCY FITZGERALD HOSPITAL), p. A536

MERCY REGIONAL MEDICAL CENTER, DURANGO, CO, p. A104

MERCY REGIONAL MEDICAL CENTER, VILLE PLATTE, LA, p. A289

MERCY REGIONAL MEDICAL CENTER, LORAIN, OH, p. A497

MERCY REHABILITATION HOSPITAL, CHESTERFIELD, MO, p. A369

MERCY REHABILITATION HOSPITAL OKLAHOMA CITY, OKLAHOMA CITY, OK, p. A516

MERCY REHABILITION HOSPITAL SPRINGFIELD, SPRINGFIELD, MO, p. A382

MERCY SAN JUAN MEDICAL CENTER, CARMICHAEL, CA, p. A58

MERCY SERVICES FOR AGING, CLINTON, IOWA (see MERCY MEDICAL CENTER–CLINTON), p. A227

MERCY SOUTHWEST HOSPITAL, BAKERSFIELD, CALIFORNIA (see MERCY HOSPITALS OF BAKERSFIELD), p. A56

MERCY ST. ANNE HOSPITAL, TOLEDO, OH, p. A503

MERCY ST. FRANCIS HOSPITAL, MOUNTAIN VIEW, MO, p. A377

MERCY ST. VINCENT MEDICAL CENTER, TOLEDO, OH, p. A504

MERCY TIFFIN HOSPITAL, TIFFIN, OH, p. A503

MERCY WALWORTH HOSPITAL AND MEDICAL CENTER, LAKE GENEVA, WI, p. A708

MERCYHEALTH ROCKTON AVENUE HOSPITAL, ROCKFORD, IL, p. A202

MERIDIAN HEALTH SERVICES, MUNCIE, IN, p. A219

MERIT HEALTH BATESVILLE, BATESVILLE, MS, p. A355

MERIT HEALTH BILOXI, BILOXI, MS, p. A355

MERIT HEALTH CENTRAL, JACKSON, MS, p. A360

MERIT HEALTH GILMORE MEMORIAL, AMORY, MS, p. A355

MERIT HEALTH MADISON, CANTON, MS, p. A356

MERIT HEALTH NATCHEZ, NATCHEZ, MS, p. A363

MERIT HEALTH NORTHWEST MISSISSIPPI, CLARKSDALE, MS, p. A356

MERIT HEALTH RANKIN, BRANDON, MS, p. A356

MERIT HEALTH RIVER OAKS, FLOWOOD, MS, p. A357

MERIT HEALTH RIVER REGION, VICKSBURG, MS, p. A365

MERIT HEALTH WESLEY, HATTIESBURG, MS, p. A359

MERIT HEALTH WOMAN'S HOSPITAL, FLOWOOD, MS, p. A357

MERITER UNITYPOINT HEALTH, MADISON, WI, p. A709

MERITUS MEDICAL CENTER, HAGERSTOWN, MD, p. A301

MESA HILLS SPECIALTY HOSPITAL, EL PASO, TX, p. A616

MESA SPRINGS, FORT WORTH, TX, p. A618

MESA VIEW REGIONAL HOSPITAL, MESQUITE, NV, p. A407

MESCALERO PUBLIC HEALTH SERVICE INDIAN HOSPITAL, MESCALERO, NM, p. A430

MESILLA VALLEY HOSPITAL, LAS CRUCES, NM, p. A430

MESQUITE REHABILITATION INSTITUTE, MESQUITE, TX, p. A636

MESQUITE SPECIALTY HOSPITAL, MESQUITE, TX, p. A636

METHODIST AMBULATORY SURGERY HOSPITAL – NORTHWEST, SAN ANTONIO, TX, p. A646

METHODIST BEHAVIORAL HOSPITAL OF ARKANSAS, MAUMELLE, AR, p. A50

METHODIST CHARLTON MEDICAL CENTER, DALLAS, TX, p. A610

METHODIST CHILDREN'S HOSPITAL, SAN ANTONIO, TEXAS (see METHODIST HOSPITAL), p. A646

METHODIST DALLAS MEDICAL CENTER, DALLAS, TX, p. A610

METHODIST HEALTHCARE MEMPHIS HOSPITALS, MEMPHIS, TN, p. A589

METHODIST HEALTHCARE–NORTH HOSPITAL, MEMPHIS, TENNESSEE (see METHODIST HEALTHCARE MEMPHIS HOSPITALS), p. A589

METHODIST HEALTHCARE–SOUTH HOSPITAL, MEMPHIS, TENNESSEE (see METHODIST HEALTHCARE MEMPHIS HOSPITALS), p. A589

METHODIST HOSPITAL, HENDERSON, KY, p. A261

METHODIST HOSPITAL, SAN ANTONIO, TX, p. A646

METHODIST HOSPITAL, PHILADELPHIA, PENNSYLVANIA (see THOMAS JEFFERSON UNIVERSITY HOSPITALS), p. A550

METHODIST HOSPITAL FOR SURGERY, ADDISON, TX, p. A595

METHODIST HOSPITAL OF CHICAGO, CHICAGO, IL, p. A185

METHODIST HOSPITAL OF SACRAMENTO, SACRAMENTO, CA, p. A86

METHODIST HOSPITAL OF SOUTHERN CALIFORNIA, ARCADIA, CA, p. A55

METHODIST HOSPITAL UNION COUNTY, MORGANFIELD, KY, p. A267

METHODIST HOSPITALS, GARY, IN, p. A212

METHODIST JENNIE EDMUNDSON HOSPITAL, COUNCIL BLUFFS, IA, p. A228

METHODIST LE BONHEUR GERMANTOWN HOSPITAL, GERMANTOWN, TENNESSEE (see METHODIST HEALTHCARE MEMPHIS HOSPITALS), p. A589

METHODIST MANSFIELD MEDICAL CENTER, MANSFIELD, TX, p. A635

METHODIST MCKINNEY HOSPITAL, MCKINNEY, TX, p. A636

METHODIST MEDICAL CENTER OF OAK RIDGE, OAK RIDGE, TN, p. A592

METHODIST OLIVE BRANCH HOSPITAL, OLIVE BRANCH, MS, p. A363

METHODIST REHABILITATION CENTER, JACKSON, MS, p. A360

METHODIST REHABILITATION HOSPITAL, DALLAS, TX, p. A610

METHODIST RICHARDSON MEDICAL CENTER, RICHARDSON, TX, p. A643

METHODIST SOUTHLAKE HOSPITAL, SOUTHLAKE, TX, p. A649

METHODIST SPECIALTY AND TRANSPLANT HOSPITAL, SAN ANTONIO, TEXAS (see METHODIST HOSPITAL), p. A646

METHODIST STONE OAK HOSPITAL, SAN ANTONIO, TX, p. A646

METHODIST TEXSAN HOSPITAL, SAN ANTONIO, TEXAS (see METHODIST HOSPITAL), p. A646

METHODIST WOMEN'S HOSPITAL, ELKHORN, NEBRASKA (see NEBRASKA METHODIST HOSPITAL), p. A400

METRO HEALTH HOSPITAL, WYOMING, MI, p. A337

METROHEALTH MEDICAL CENTER, CLEVELAND, OH, p. A489

METROPLEX ADVENTIST HOSPITAL, KILLEEN, TX, p. A630

METROPOLITAN GENERAL CARE UNIT, METROPOLITAN DRUG DETOXIFICATION AND METROPOLITAN PSYCHIATRIC UNIT (see NYC HEALTH + HOSPITALS / METROPOLITAN), p. A448

METROPOLITAN METHODIST HOSPITAL, SAN ANTONIO, TEXAS (see METHODIST HOSPITAL), p. A646

METROPOLITAN ST. LOUIS PSYCHIATRIC CENTER, SAINT LOUIS, MO, p. A380

METROPOLITAN STATE HOSPITAL, NORWALK, CA, p. A79

METROPOLITANO DE LA MONTANA, UTUADO, PR, p. A730

METROSOUTH MEDICAL CENTER, BLUE ISLAND, IL, p. A182

METROWEST MEDICAL CENTER, FRAMINGHAM, MA, p. A310

MIAMI COUNTY MEDICAL CENTER, PAOLA, KS, p. A251

MIAMI HEART CAMPUS AT MOUNT SINAI MEDICAL CENTER, MIAMI BEACH, FLORIDA (see MOUNT SINAI MEDICAL CENTER), p. A138

MIAMI JEWISH HOME AND HOSPITAL FOR AGED, MIAMI, FL, p. A137

MIAMI VALLEY HOSPITAL, DAYTON, OH, p. A493

MIAMI VALLEY HOSPITAL SOUTH, CENTERVILLE, OHIO (see MIAMI VALLEY HOSPITAL), p. A493

MIAMI VETERANS AFFAIRS HEALTHCARE SYSTEM, MIAMI, FL, p. A137

MICHAEL E. DEBAKEY VETERANS AFFAIRS MEDICAL CENTER, HOUSTON, TX, p. A626

MICHIANA BEHAVIORAL HEALTH CENTER, PLYMOUTH, IN, p. A220

MID COAST HOSPITAL, BRUNSWICK, ME, p. A292

MID–AMERICA REHABILITATION HOSPITAL, SHAWNEE MISSION, KS, p. A253

MID–COLUMBIA MEDICAL CENTER, THE DALLES, OR, p. A531

MID–HUDSON FORENSIC PSYCHIATRIC CENTER, NEW HAMPTON, NY, p. A443

MID–JEFFERSON EXTENDED CARE HOSPITAL, NEDERLAND, TX, p. A638

MID–VALLEY HOSPITAL, OMAK, WA, p. A687

MIDDLE PARK MEDICAL CENTER–KREMMLING, KREMMLING, CO, p. A107

MIDDLE TENNESSEE MENTAL HEALTH INSTITUTE, NASHVILLE, TN, p. A590

MIDDLESBORO ARH HOSPITAL, MIDDLESBORO, KY, p. A266

MIDDLESEX HOSPITAL, MIDDLETOWN, CT, p. A115

MIDHUDSON REGIONAL HOSPITAL OF WESTCHESTER MEDICAL CENTER, POUGHKEEPSIE, NEW YORK (see WESTCHESTER MEDICAL CENTER), p. A458

MIDLAND MEMORIAL HOSPITAL, MIDLAND, TX, p. A637

MIDLAND MEMORIAL HOSPITAL, MIDLAND, TEXAS (see MIDLAND MEMORIAL HOSPITAL), p. A637

MIDMICHIGAN MEDICAL CENTER – ALPENA, ALPENA, MI, p. A318

MIDMICHIGAN MEDICAL CENTER–CLARE, CLARE, MI, p. A320

MIDMICHIGAN MEDICAL CENTER–GLADWIN, GLADWIN, MI, p. A324

MIDMICHIGAN MEDICAL CENTER–GRATIOT, ALMA, MI, p. A318

MIDMICHIGAN MEDICAL CENTER–MIDLAND, MIDLAND, MI, p. A330

MIDSTATE MEDICAL CENTER, MERIDEN, CT, p. A115

MIDTOWN MEDICAL CENTER, COLUMBUS, GA, p. A156

MIDTOWN MEDICAL CENTER WEST, COLUMBUS, GA, p. A156

MIDWEST CITY SPECIALTY HOSPITAL, MIDWEST CITY, OK, p. A514

MIDWEST MEDICAL CENTER, GALENA, IL, p. A190

MIDWEST ORTHOPEDIC SPECIALTY HOSPITAL, FRANKLIN, WI, p. A705

MIDWEST SURGICAL HOSPITAL, OMAHA, NE, p. A400

MIDWESTERN REGIONAL MEDICAL CENTER, ZION, IL, p. A205

MIKE O'CALLAGHAN FEDERAL HOSPITAL, NELLIS AFB, NV, p. A407

MILAN GENERAL HOSPITAL, MILAN, TN, p. A590

MILBANK AREA HOSPITAL AVERA, MILBANK, SD, p. A574

MILDRED MITCHELL–BATEMAN HOSPITAL, HUNTINGTON, WV, p. A697

MILE BLUFF MEDICAL CENTER, MAUSTON, WI, p. A710

MILFORD HOSPITAL, MILFORD, CT, p. A115

MILFORD REGIONAL MEDICAL CENTER, MILFORD, MA, p. A312

MILFORD VALLEY MEMORIAL HOSPITAL, MILFORD, UT, p. A660

MILLARD FILLMORE SUBURBAN HOSPITAL, WILLIAMSVILLE, NEW YORK (see KALEIDA HEALTH), p. A436

MILLCREEK COMMUNITY HOSPITAL, ERIE, PA, p. A538

MILLE LACS HEALTH SYSTEM, ONAMIA, MN, p. A348

MILLER CHILDREN'S & WOMEN'S HOSPITAL LONG BEACH, LONG BEACH, CA, p. A70

MILLER COUNTY HOSPITAL, COLQUITT, GA, p. A156

MILLINOCKET REGIONAL HOSPITAL, MILLINOCKET, ME, p. A294

MILLS HEALTH CENTER, SAN MATEO, CALIFORNIA (see MILLS–PENINSULA HEALTH SERVICES), p. A57

MILLS–PENINSULA HEALTH SERVICES, BURLINGAME, CA, p. A57

MILLS–PENINSULA MEDICAL CENTER, BURLINGAME, CALIFORNIA (see MILLS–PENINSULA HEALTH SERVICES), p. A57

MILLWOOD HOSPITAL, ARLINGTON, TX, p. A597

MILWAUKEE COUNTY BEHAVIORAL HEALTH DIVISION, MILWAUKEE, WI, p. A711

MIMBRES MEMORIAL HOSPITAL, DEMING, NM, p. A429

MINDEN MEDICAL CENTER, MINDEN, LA, p. A283

MINERAL COMMUNITY HOSPITAL, SUPERIOR, MT, p. A391

MINERS' COLFAX MEDICAL CENTER, RATON, NM, p. A430

MINERS' HOSPITAL OF NEW MEXICO, RATON, NEW MEXICO (see MINERS' COLFAX MEDICAL CENTER), p. A430

MINIDOKA MEMORIAL HOSPITAL, RUPERT, ID, p. A178

MINIMALLY INVASIVE SURGERY HOSPITAL, LENEXA, KS, p. A248

MINISTRY DOOR COUNTY MEDICAL CENTER, STURGEON BAY, WI, p. A717

MINISTRY EAGLE RIVER MEMORIAL HOSPITAL, EAGLE RIVER, WI, p. A704

MINISTRY GOOD SAMARITAN HEALTH CENTER, MERRILL, WI, p. A710

MINISTRY OUR LADY OF VICTORY HOSPITAL, STANLEY, WI, p. A716

MINISTRY SACRED HEART HOSPITAL, TOMAHAWK, WI, p. A717

MINISTRY SAINT CLARE'S HOSPITAL, WESTON, WI, p. A719

MINISTRY SAINT JOSEPH'S HOSPITAL, MARSHFIELD, WI, p. A709

MINISTRY SAINT MARY'S HOSPITALS, RHINELANDER, WI, p. A715

MINISTRY SAINT MICHAEL'S HOSPITAL, STEVENS POINT, WI, p. A716

MINNEAPOLIS VETERANS AFFAIRS HEALTH CARE SYSTEM, MINNEAPOLIS, MN, p. A346

MINNEOLA DISTRICT HOSPITAL, MINNEOLA, KS, p. A249

MINNESOTA VALLEY HEALTH CENTER, LE SUEUR, MN, p. A344

MINNIE HAMILTON HEALTHCARE CENTER, GRANTSVILLE, WV, p. A696

MIRACLE MILE MEDICAL CENTER, LOS ANGELES, CA, p. A73

MIRIAM HOSPITAL, PROVIDENCE, RI, p. A560

MISSION CHILDREN'S HOSPITAL, ASHEVILLE, NORTH CAROLINA (see MISSION HOSPITAL), p. A460

MISSION COMMUNITY HOSPITAL,, CA, p. A73

MISSION HOSPITAL, MISSION VIEJO, CA, p. A77

MISSION HOSPITAL, ASHEVILLE, NC, p. A460

MISSION HOSPITAL, ASHEVILLE, NORTH CAROLINA (see MISSION HOSPITAL), p. A460

MISSION HOSPITAL – ST. JOSEPH'S CAMPUS, ASHEVILLE, NORTH CAROLINA (see MISSION HOSPITAL), p. A460

MISSION HOSPITAL LAGUNA BEACH, LAGUNA BEACH, CALIFORNIA (see MISSION HOSPITAL), p. A77

MISSION REGIONAL MEDICAL CENTER, MISSION, TX, p. A637

MISSION TRAIL BAPTIST HOSPITAL, SAN ANTONIO, TEXAS (see BAPTIST MEDICAL CENTER), p. A645

MISSISSIPPI BAPTIST MEDICAL CENTER, JACKSON, MS, p. A360
MISSISSIPPI STATE HOSPITAL, WHITFIELD, MS, p. A366
MISSOURI BAPTIST MEDICAL CENTER, SAINT LOUIS, MO, p. A380
MISSOURI BAPTIST SULLIVAN HOSPITAL, SULLIVAN, MO, p. A383
MISSOURI DELTA MEDICAL CENTER, SIKESTON, MO, p. A382
MISSOURI RIVER MEDICAL CENTER, FORT BENTON, MT, p. A387
MITCHELL COUNTY HOSPITAL, CAMILLA, GA, p. A155
MITCHELL COUNTY HOSPITAL, COLORADO CITY, TX, p. A606
MITCHELL COUNTY HOSPITAL HEALTH SYSTEMS, BELOIT, KS, p. A241
MITCHELL COUNTY REGIONAL HEALTH CENTER, OSAGE, IA, p. A235
MIZELL MEMORIAL HOSPITAL, OPP, AL, p. A24
MMO REHABILITATION AND WELLNESS CENTER, PLAQUEMINE, LA, p. A286
MOAB REGIONAL HOSPITAL, MOAB, UT, p. A660
MOBERLY REGIONAL MEDICAL CENTER, MOBERLY, MO, p. A377
MOBILE INFIRMARY MEDICAL CENTER, MOBILE, AL, p. A22
MOBRIDGE REGIONAL HOSPITAL, MOBRIDGE, SD, p. A575
MOCCASIN BEND MENTAL HEALTH INSTITUTE, CHATTANOOGA, TN, p. A580
MODESTO MEDICAL CENTER, MODESTO, CALIFORNIA (see KAISER PERMANENTE MANTECA MEDICAL CENTER), p. A76
MODOC MEDICAL CENTER, ALTURAS, CA, p. A54
MOHAWK VALLEY PSYCHIATRIC CENTER, UTICA, NY, p. A457
MOLOKAI GENERAL HOSPITAL, KAUNAKAKAI, HI, p. A172
MONADNOCK COMMUNITY HOSPITAL, PETERBOROUGH, NH, p. A413
MONCKS CORNER MEDICAL CENTER, MONCKS CORNER, SOUTH CAROLINA (see TRIDENT MEDICAL CENTER), p. A563
MONCRIEF ARMY COMMUNITY HOSPITAL, FORT JACKSON, SC, p. A566
MONMOUTH MEDICAL CENTER, LONG BRANCH CAMPUS, LONG BRANCH, NJ, p. A419
MONMOUTH MEDICAL CENTER, SOUTHERN CAMPUS, LAKEWOOD, NJ, p. A418
MONONGAHELA VALLEY HOSPITAL, MONONGAHELA, PA, p. A545
MONONGALIA GENERAL HOSPITAL, MORGANTOWN, WV, p. A698
MONROE CARELL JR. CHILDREN'S HOSPITAL AT VANDERBILT, NASHVILLE, TENNESSEE (see VANDERBILT UNIVERSITY MEDICAL CENTER), p. A591
MONROE CLINIC, MONROE, WI, p. A712
MONROE COUNTY HOSPITAL, MONROEVILLE, AL, p. A23
MONROE COUNTY HOSPITAL, FORSYTH, GA, p. A159
MONROE COUNTY HOSPITAL AND CLINICS, ALBIA, IA, p. A225
MONROE COUNTY MEDICAL CENTER, TOMPKINSVILLE, KY, p. A270
MONROE HOSPITAL, BLOOMFIELD, IN, p. A207
MONROE SURGICAL HOSPITAL, MONROE, LA, p. A283
MONROVIA MEMORIAL HOSPITAL, MONROVIA, CA, p. A77
MONTANA STATE HOSPITAL, WARM SPRINGS, MT, p. A391
MONTCLAIR HOSPITAL MEDICAL CENTER, MONTCLAIR, CA, p. A77
MONTEFIORE MEDICAL CENTER,, NY, p. A446
MONTEFIORE MEDICAL CENTER – NORTH DIVISION,, NEW YORK (see MONTEFIORE MEDICAL CENTER), p. A446
MONTEFIORE MOUNT VERNON, MOUNT VERNON, NY, p. A443
MONTEFIORE NEW ROCHELLE, NEW ROCHELLE, NY, p. A443
MONTEREY PARK HOSPITAL, MONTEREY PARK, CA, p. A78
MONTEVISTA HOSPITAL, LAS VEGAS, NV, p. A406
MONTGOMERY COUNTY EMERGENCY SERVICE, NORRISTOWN, PA, p. A546
MONTGOMERY COUNTY MEMORIAL HOSPITAL, RED OAK, IA, p. A236
MONTGOMERY DIVISION, MONTGOMERY, ALABAMA (see CENTRAL ALABAMA VETERANS HEALTH CARE SYSTEM), p. A23
MONTGOMERY GENERAL HOSPITAL, MONTGOMERY, WV, p. A698
MONTPELIER HOSPITAL, MONTPELIER, OHIO (see COMMUNITY HOSPITALS AND WELLNESS CENTERS), p. A485
MONTROSE MEMORIAL HOSPITAL, MONTROSE, CO, p. A109
MOORE COUNTY HOSPITAL DISTRICT, DUMAS, TX, p. A614
MOREHEAD MEMORIAL HOSPITAL, EDEN, NC, p. A464
MOREHOUSE GENERAL HOSPITAL, BASTROP, LA, p. A272
MORGAN COUNTY ARH HOSPITAL, WEST LIBERTY, KY, p. A270
MORGAN MEMORIAL HOSPITAL, MADISON, GA, p. A162
MORGAN STANLEY CHILDREN'S HOSPITAL OF NEW YORK–PRESBYTERIAN, NEW YORK, NEW YORK (see NEW YORK–PRESBYTERIAN HOSPITAL), p. A447
MORRILL COUNTY COMMUNITY HOSPITAL, BRIDGEPORT, NE, p. A394
MORRIS COUNTY HOSPITAL, COUNCIL GROVE, KS, p. A242

MORRIS HOSPITAL & HEALTHCARE CENTERS, MORRIS, IL, p. A197
MORRISON COMMUNITY HOSPITAL, MORRISON, IL, p. A197
MORRISTOWN MEDICAL CENTER, MORRISTOWN, NJ, p. A419
MORRISTOWN–HAMBLEN HEALTHCARE SYSTEM, MORRISTOWN, TN, p. A590
MORROW COUNTY HOSPITAL, MOUNT GILEAD, OH, p. A499
MORTON COUNTY HEALTH SYSTEM, ELKHART, KS, p. A242
MORTON GENERAL HOSPITAL, MORTON, WA, p. A686
MORTON HOSPITAL AND MEDICAL CENTER, TAUNTON, MA, p. A315
MORTON PLANT HOSPITAL, CLEARWATER, FL, p. A125
MORTON PLANT NORTH BAY HOSPITAL, NEW PORT RICHEY, FL, p. A138
MOSAIC LIFE CARE AT ST. JOSEPH, SAINT JOSEPH, MO, p. A379
MOSES H. CONE MEMORIAL HOSPITAL, GREENSBORO, NC, p. A466
MOSES LUDINGTON HOSPITAL, TICONDEROGA, NY, p. A457
MOSES TAYLOR HOSPITAL, SCRANTON, PA, p. A554
MOTION PICTURE AND TELEVISION FUND HOSPITAL AND RESIDENTIAL SERVICES,, CA, p. A73
MOUNDVIEW MEMORIAL HOSPITAL & CLINICS, FRIENDSHIP, WI, p. A706
MOUNT AUBURN HOSPITAL, CAMBRIDGE, MA, p. A309
MOUNT CARMEL, COLUMBUS, OH, p. A490
MOUNT CARMEL EAST HOSPITAL, COLUMBUS, OHIO (see MOUNT CARMEL), p. A490
MOUNT CARMEL NEW ALBANY SURGICAL HOSPITAL, NEW ALBANY, OH, p. A500
MOUNT CARMEL ST. ANN'S, WESTERVILLE, OH, p. A505
MOUNT CARMEL WEST HOSPITAL, COLUMBUS, OHIO (see MOUNT CARMEL), p. A490
MOUNT DESERT ISLAND HOSPITAL, BAR HARBOR, ME, p. A291
MOUNT GRANT GENERAL HOSPITAL, HAWTHORNE, NV, p. A404
MOUNT NITTANY MEDICAL CENTER, STATE COLLEGE, PA, p. A555
MOUNT SINAI BETH ISRAEL, NEW YORK, NY, p. A446
MOUNT SINAI BETH ISRAEL BROOKLYN,, NEW YORK (see MOUNT SINAI BETH ISRAEL), p. A446
MOUNT SINAI HOSPITAL, CHICAGO, IL, p. A185
MOUNT SINAI HOSPITAL, NEW YORK, NY, p. A446
MOUNT SINAI MEDICAL CENTER, MIAMI BEACH, FL, p. A138
MOUNT SINAI QUEENS,, NEW YORK (see MOUNT SINAI HOSPITAL), p. A446
MOUNT SINAI REHABILITATION HOSPITAL, HARTFORD, CT, p. A114
MOUNT SINAI ROOSEVELT HOSPITAL, NEW YORK, NEW YORK (see MOUNT SINAI ST. LUKE'S – ROOSEVELT), p. A446
MOUNT SINAI ST. LUKE'S – ROOSEVELT, NEW YORK, NY, p. A446
MOUNT ST. MARY'S HOSPITAL AND HEALTH CENTER, LEWISTON, NY, p. A441
MOUNTAIN CREST HOSPITAL, FORT COLLINS, COLORADO (see POUDRE VALLEY HOSPITAL), p. A105
MOUNTAIN LAKES MEDICAL CENTER, CLAYTON, GA, p. A156
MOUNTAIN POINT MEDICAL CENTER, LEHII, UTAH (see JORDAN VALLEY MEDICAL CENTER), p. A664
MOUNTAIN RIVER BIRTHING AND SURGERY CENTER, BLACKFOOT, ID, p. A174
MOUNTAIN VALLEY REGIONAL REHABILITATION HOSPITAL, PRESCOTT VALLEY, AZ, p. A38
MOUNTAIN VIEW HOSPITAL, GADSDEN, AL, p. A20
MOUNTAIN VIEW HOSPITAL, IDAHO FALLS, ID, p. A176
MOUNTAIN VIEW HOSPITAL, PAYSON, UT, p. A662
MOUNTAIN VIEW REGIONAL HOSPITAL, CASPER, WY, p. A721
MOUNTAIN VIEW REGIONAL MEDICAL CENTER, NORTON, VA, p. A675
MOUNTAIN VISTA MEDICAL CENTER, MESA, AZ, p. A34
MOUNTAIN WEST MEDICAL CENTER, TOOELE, UT, p. A664
MOUNTAINVIEW HOSPITAL, LAS VEGAS, NV, p. A406
MOUNTAINVIEW MEDICAL CENTER, WHITE SULPHUR SPRINGS, MT, p. A391
MOUNTAINVIEW REGIONAL MEDICAL CENTER, LAS CRUCES, NM, p. A430
MOUNTRAIL COUNTY MEDICAL CENTER, STANLEY, ND, p. A481
MT. ASCUTNEY HOSPITAL AND HEALTH CENTER, WINDSOR, VT, p. A666
MT. GRAHAM REGIONAL MEDICAL CENTER, SAFFORD, AZ, p. A38
MT. SAN RAFAEL HOSPITAL, TRINIDAD, CO, p. A111
MT. WASHINGTON PEDIATRIC HOSPITAL, BALTIMORE, MD, p. A297
MUENSTER MEMORIAL HOSPITAL, MUENSTER, TX, p. A638
MULESHOE AREA MEDICAL CENTER, MULESHOE, TX, p. A638
MULTICARE AUBURN MEDICAL CENTER, AUBURN, WA, p. A682
MULTICARE GOOD SAMARITAN HOSPITAL, PUYALLUP, WA, p. A688

MULTICARE MARY BRIDGE CHILDREN'S HOSPITAL AND HEALTH CENTER, TACOMA, WA, p. A692
MULTICARE TACOMA GENERAL HOSPITAL, TACOMA, WA, p. A692
MUNCY VALLEY HOSPITAL, MUNCY, PA, p. A546
MUNISING MEMORIAL HOSPITAL, MUNISING, MI, p. A330
MUNROE REGIONAL MEDICAL CENTER, OCALA, FL, p. A139
MUNSON HEALTHCARE CADILLAC HOSPITAL, CADILLAC, MI, p. A319
MUNSON HEALTHCARE CHARLEVOIX HOSPITAL, CHARLEVOIX, MI, p. A320
MUNSON HEALTHCARE GRAYLING HOSPITAL, GRAYLING, MI, p. A325
MUNSON MEDICAL CENTER, TRAVERSE CITY, MI, p. A335
MURPHY MEDICAL CENTER, MURPHY, NC, p. A470
MURRAY COUNTY MEDICAL CENTER, SLAYTON, MN, p. A351
MURRAY MEDICAL CENTER, CHATSWORTH, GA, p. A156
MURRAY–CALLOWAY COUNTY HOSPITAL, MURRAY, KY, p. A267
MUSC MEDICAL CENTER OF MEDICAL UNIVERSITY OF SOUTH CAROLINA, CHARLESTON, SC, p. A563
MUSCOGEE CREEK NATION MEDICAL CENTER, OKMULGEE, OK, p. A518
MUSCOGEE CREEK NATION PHYSICAL REHABILITATION CENTER, OKMULGEE, OK, p. A518
MYRTUE MEDICAL CENTER, HARLAN, IA, p. A232

N

NACOGDOCHES MEDICAL CENTER, NACOGDOCHES, TX, p. A638
NACOGDOCHES MEMORIAL HOSPITAL, NACOGDOCHES, TX, p. A638
NANTICOKE MEMORIAL HOSPITAL, SEAFORD, DE, p. A119
NANTUCKET COTTAGE HOSPITAL, NANTUCKET, MA, p. A312
NAPA STATE HOSPITAL, NAPA, CA, p. A78
NASH HEALTH CARE SYSTEMS, ROCKY MOUNT, NC, p. A472
NASHOBA VALLEY MEDICAL CENTER, AYER, MA, p. A305
NASHVILLE CAMPUS, NASHVILLE, TENNESSEE (see TENNESSEE VALLEY HEALTHCARE SYSTEM), p. A591
NASHVILLE GENERAL HOSPITAL, NASHVILLE, TN, p. A590
NASON HOSPITAL, ROARING SPRING, PA, p. A553
NASSAU UNIVERSITY MEDICAL CENTER, EAST MEADOW, NY, p. A438
NATCHAUG HOSPITAL, MANSFIELD CENTER, CT, p. A114
NATCHEZ COMMUNITY HOSPITAL, NATCHEZ, MS, p. A363
NATCHITOCHES REGIONAL MEDICAL CENTER, NATCHITOCHES, LA, p. A284
NATHAN LITTAUER HOSPITAL AND NURSING HOME, GLOVERSVILLE, NY, p. A439
NATIONAL INSTITUTES OF HEALTH CLINICAL CENTER, BETHESDA, MD, p. A299
NATIONAL JEWISH HEALTH, DENVER, CO, p. A104
NATIONAL PARK MEDICAL CENTER, HOT SPRINGS, AR, p. A47
NATIONWIDE CHILDREN'S HOSPITAL, COLUMBUS, OH, p. A490
NATIVIDAD MEDICAL CENTER, SALINAS, CA, p. A87
NAVAL HOSPITAL BEAUFORT, BEAUFORT, SC, p. A562
NAVAL HOSPITAL BREMERTON, BREMERTON, WA, p. A682
NAVAL HOSPITAL CAMP LEJEUNE, CAMP LEJEUNE, NC, p. A461
NAVAL HOSPITAL CAMP PENDLETON, CAMP PENDLETON, CA, p. A58
NAVAL HOSPITAL JACKSONVILLE, JACKSONVILLE, FL, p. A132
NAVAL HOSPITAL LEMOORE, LEMOORE, CA, p. A68
NAVAL HOSPITAL OAK HARBOR, OAK HARBOR, WA, p. A687
NAVAL HOSPITAL PENSACOLA, PENSACOLA, FL, p. A142
NAVAL MEDICAL CENTER, PORTSMOUTH, VA, p. A676
NAVAL MEDICAL CENTER SAN DIEGO, SAN DIEGO, CA, p. A88
NAVARRO REGIONAL HOSPITAL, CORSICANA, TX, p. A608
NAVOS, SEATTLE, WA, p. A689
NAZARETH HOSPITAL, PHILADELPHIA, PA, p. A549
NCH DOWNTOWN NAPLES HOSPITAL, NAPLES, FL, p. A138
NCH NORTH NAPLES HOSPITAL, NAPLES, FLORIDA (see NCH DOWNTOWN NAPLES HOSPITAL), p. A138
NEA BAPTIST MEMORIAL HOSPITAL, JONESBORO, AR, p. A48
NEBRASKA MEDICINE – BELLEVUE, BELLEVUE, NE, p. A394
NEBRASKA MEDICINE – NEBRASKA MEDICAL CENTER, OMAHA, NE, p. A400
NEBRASKA METHODIST HOSPITAL, OMAHA, NE, p. A400
NEBRASKA ORTHOPAEDIC HOSPITAL, OMAHA, NE, p. A400
NEBRASKA PENAL AND CORRECTIONAL HOSPITAL, LINCOLN, NE, p. A398
NEBRASKA SPINE HOSPITAL, OMAHA, NE, p. A400
NEILLSVILLE MEMORIAL HOME (see MEMORIAL MEDICAL CENTER – NEILLSVILLE), p. A712
NELL J. REDFIELD MEMORIAL HOSPITAL, MALAD CITY, ID, p. A177
NELSON COUNTY HEALTH SYSTEM, MCVILLE, ND, p. A480

NORTHSHORE HIGHLAND PARK HOSPITAL, HIGHLAND PARK, ILLINOIS (see NORTHSHORE UNIVERSITY HEALTH SYSTEM), p. A190

NORTHSHORE SKOKIE HOSPITAL, SKOKIE, ILLINOIS (see NORTHSHORE UNIVERSITY HEALTH SYSTEM), p. A190

NORTHSHORE UNIVERSITY HEALTH SYSTEM, EVANSTON, IL, p. A190

NORTH HOSPITAL, SAINT PETERSBURG, FL, p. A144

NORTHSIDE HOSPITAL, ATLANTA, GA, p. A152

NORTHSIDE HOSPITAL–CHEROKEE, CANTON, GA, p. A155

NORTHSIDE HOSPITAL–FORSYTH, CUMMING, GA, p. A157

NORTHSIDE MEDICAL CENTER, COLUMBUS, GA, p. A156

NORTHSIDE MEDICAL CENTER, YOUNGSTOWN, OH, p. A506

NORTHSIDE MEDICAL CENTER, YOUNGSTOWN, OHIO (see NORTHSIDE MEDICAL CENTER), p. A506

NORTHWEST CENTER FOR BEHAVIORAL HEALTH, FORT SUPPLY, OK, p. A512

NORTHWEST CHILDREN'S HOSPITAL, AMARILLO, TEXAS (see NORTHWEST TEXAS HEALTHCARE SYSTEM), p. A596

NORTHWEST COMMUNITY HOSPITAL, ARLINGTON HEIGHTS, IL, p. A180

NORTHWEST FLORIDA COMMUNITY HOSPITAL, CHIPLEY, FL, p. A125

NORTHWEST HILLS SURGICAL HOSPITAL, AUSTIN, TX, p. A599

NORTHWEST HOSPITAL, RANDALLSTOWN, MD, p. A303

NORTHWEST MEDICAL CENTER, WINFIELD, AL, p. A26

NORTHWEST MEDICAL CENTER, TUCSON, AZ, p. A40

NORTHWEST MEDICAL CENTER, MARGATE, FL, p. A135

NORTHWEST MEDICAL CENTER, ALBANY, MO, p. A367

NORTHWEST MEDICAL CENTER – BENTONVILLE, BENTONVILLE, ARKANSAS (see NORTHWEST MEDICAL CENTER – SPRINGDALE), p. A52

NORTHWEST MEDICAL CENTER – SPRINGDALE, SPRINGDALE, AR, p. A52

NORTHWEST MISSOURI PSYCHIATRIC REHABILITATION CENTER, SAINT JOSEPH, MO, p. A379

NORTHWEST OHIO PSYCHIATRIC HOSPITAL, TOLEDO, OH, p. A504

NORTHWEST PAVILION, AMARILLO, TEXAS (see NORTHWEST TEXAS HEALTHCARE SYSTEM), p. A596

NORTHWEST SPECIALTY HOSPITAL, POST FALLS, ID, p. A178

NORTHWEST SURGICAL HOSPITAL, OKLAHOMA CITY, OK, p. A516

NORTHWEST TEXAS HEALTHCARE SYSTEM, AMARILLO, TX, p. A596

NORTHWEST TEXAS SURGERY CENTER, AMARILLO, TX, p. A596

NORTHWESTERN LAKE FOREST HOSPITAL, LAKE FOREST, IL, p. A194

NORTHWESTERN MEDICAL CENTER, SAINT ALBANS, VT, p. A666

NORTHWESTERN MEDICINE CENTRAL DUPAGE HOSPITAL, WINFIELD, IL, p. A205

NORTHWESTERN MEDICINE DELNOR HOSPITAL, GENEVA, IL, p. A191

NORTHWESTERN MEDICINE KISHWAUKEE HOSPITAL, DEKALB, IL, p. A188

NORTHWESTERN MEDICINE VALLEY WEST HOSPITAL, SANDWICH, IL, p. A202

NORTHWESTERN MEMORIAL HOSPITAL, CHICAGO, IL, p. A185

NORTHWOOD DEACONESS HEALTH CENTER, NORTHWOOD, ND, p. A481

NORTON AUDUBON HOSPITAL, LOUISVILLE, KY, p. A264

NORTON BROWNSBORO HOSPITAL, LOUISVILLE, KY, p. A265

NORTON COMMUNITY HOSPITAL, NORTON, VA, p. A675

NORTON COUNTY HOSPITAL, NORTON, KS, p. A250

NORTON HEALTHCARE PAVILION, LOUISVILLE, KENTUCKY (see NORTON HOSPITAL), p. A265

NORTON HOSPITAL, LOUISVILLE, KY, p. A265

NORTON SOUND REGIONAL HOSPITAL, NOME, AK, p. A30

NORTON WOMEN'S AND KOSAIR CHILDREN'S HOSPITAL, LOUISVILLE, KY, p. A265

NORWALK HOSPITAL, NORWALK, CT, p. A116

NORWEGIAN AMERICAN HOSPITAL, CHICAGO, IL, p. A185

NORWOOD HEALTH CENTER, MARSHFIELD, WI, p. A710

NORWOOD HOSPITAL, NORWOOD, MA, p. A313

NOVANT HEALTH BRUNSWICK MEDICAL CENTER, BOLIVIA, NC, p. A461

NOVANT HEALTH CHARLOTTE ORTHOPAEDIC HOSPITAL, CHARLOTTE, NC, p. A462

NOVANT HEALTH FORSYTH MEDICAL CENTER, WINSTON–SALEM, NC, p. A476

NOVANT HEALTH HUNTERSVILLE MEDICAL CENTER, HUNTERSVILLE, NC, p. A467

NOVANT HEALTH MATTHEWS MEDICAL CENTER, MATTHEWS, NC, p. A469

NOVANT HEALTH MEDICAL PARK HOSPITAL, WINSTON–SALEM, NC, p. A476

NOVANT HEALTH PRESBYTERIAN MEDICAL CENTER, CHARLOTTE, NC, p. A463

NOVANT HEALTH ROWAN MEDICAL CENTER, SALISBURY, NC, p. A473

NOVANT HEALTH THOMASVILLE MEDICAL CENTER, THOMASVILLE, NC, p. A474

NOVANT HEALTH UVA HEALTH SYSTEM CULPEPER MEDICAL CENTER, CULPEPER, VA, p. A669

NOVANT HEALTH UVA HEALTH SYSTEM HAYMARKET MEDICAL CENTER, HAYMARKET, VA, p. A671

NOVANT HEALTH UVA HEALTH SYSTEM PRINCE WILLIAM MEDICAL CENTER, MANASSAS, VA, p. A673

NOVATO COMMUNITY HOSPITAL, NOVATO, CA, p. A80

NOXUBEE GENERAL HOSPITAL, MACON, MS, p. A361

NYACK HOSPITAL, NYACK, NY, p. A451

NYC HEALTH + HOSPITALS / BELLEVUE, NEW YORK, NY, p. A447

NYC HEALTH + HOSPITALS / CARTER, NEW YORK, NY, p. A448

NYC HEALTH + HOSPITALS / CONEY ISLAND,, NY, p. A448

NYC HEALTH + HOSPITALS / ELMHURST,, NY, p. A448

NYC HEALTH + HOSPITALS / HARLEM, NEW YORK, NY, p. A448

NYC HEALTH + HOSPITALS / JACOBI,, NY, p. A448

NYC HEALTH + HOSPITALS / KINGS COUNTY,, NY, p. A448

NYC HEALTH + HOSPITALS / LINCOLN,, NY, p. A448

NYC HEALTH + HOSPITALS / METROPOLITAN, NEW YORK, NY, p. A448

NYC HEALTH + HOSPITALS / NORTH CENTRAL BRONX,, NY, p. A449

NYC HEALTH + HOSPITALS / QUEENS,, NY, p. A449

NYC HEALTH + HOSPITALS / WOODHULL,, NY, p. A449

NYU LANGONE MEDICAL CENTER, NEW YORK, NY, p. A449

NYU LANGONE MEDICAL CENTER'S HOSPITAL FOR JOINT DISEASES, NEW YORK, NEW YORK (see NYU LANGONE MEDICAL CENTER), p. A449

NYU LUTHERAN (NYU HOSPITALS CENTER),, NEW YORK (see NYU LANGONE MEDICAL CENTER), p. A449

O

O'BLENESS MEMORIAL HOSPITAL, ATHENS, OH, p. A484

O'CONNOR HOSPITAL, SAN JOSE, CA, p. A91

O'CONNOR HOSPITAL, DELHI, NY, p. A438

OAK HILL HOSPITAL, BROOKSVILLE, FL, p. A125

OAK VALLEY HOSPITAL DISTRICT, OAKDALE, CA, p. A80

OAKBEND MEDICAL CENTER, RICHMOND, TX, p. A643

OAKDALE COMMUNITY HOSPITAL, OAKDALE, LA, p. A286

OAKLAND MERCY HOSPITAL, OAKLAND, NE, p. A399

OAKLAND REGIONAL HOSPITAL, SOUTHFIELD, MI, p. A334

OAKLAWN HOSPITAL, MARSHALL, MI, p. A330

OAKLAWN PSYCHIATRIC CENTER, GOSHEN, IN, p. A212

OAKLEAF SURGICAL HOSPITAL, EAU CLAIRE, WI, p. A705

OAKWOOD CORRECTIONAL FACILITY, LIMA, OH, p. A497

OASIS BEHAVIORAL HEALTH – CHANDLER, CHANDLER, AZ, p. A31

OASIS HOSPITAL, PHOENIX, AZ, p. A36

OCALA REGIONAL MEDICAL CENTER, OCALA, FL, p. A139

OCEAN BEACH HOSPITAL, ILWACO, WA, p. A685

OCEAN MEDICAL CENTER, BRICK TOWNSHIP, NJ, p. A415

OCEAN SPRINGS HOSPITAL, OCEAN SPRINGS, MISSISSIPPI (see SINGING RIVER HEALTH SYSTEM), p. A363

OCEANS BEHAVIORAL HEALTH CENTER PERMIAN BASIN, MIDLAND, TX, p. A637

OCEANS BEHAVIORAL HOSPITAL ABILENE, ABILENE, TX, p. A595

OCEANS BEHAVIORAL HOSPITAL FORT WORTH, FORT WORTH, TX, p. A618

OCEANS BEHAVIORAL HOSPITAL KATY, KATY, TX, p. A630

OCEANS BEHAVIORAL HOSPITAL LONGVIEW, LONGVIEW, TX, p. A633

OCEANS BEHAVIORAL HOSPITAL LUFKIN, LUFKIN, TX, p. A635

OCEANS BEHAVIORAL HOSPITAL OF ALEXANDRIA, ALEXANDRIA, LA, p. A271

OCEANS BEHAVIORAL HOSPITAL OF BATON ROUGE, BATON ROUGE, LA, p. A272

OCEANS BEHAVIORAL HOSPITAL OF BROUSSARD, BROUSSARD, LA, p. A274

OCEANS BEHAVIORAL HOSPITAL OF DE RIDDER, DERIDDER, LA, p. A276

OCEANS BEHAVIORAL HOSPITAL OF GREATER NEW ORLEANS, KENNER, LA, p. A279

OCEANS BEHAVIORAL HOSPITAL OF KENTWOOD, KENTWOOD, LA, p. A279

OCEANS BEHAVIORAL HOSPITAL OF LAKE CHARLES, LAKE CHARLES, LA, p. A281

OCEANS BEHAVIORAL HOSPITAL OF OPELOUSAS, OPELOUSAS, LA, p. A286

OCEANS BEHAVIORAL HOSPITAL PLANO, PLANO, TX, p. A642

OCEANS BEHAVIORAL HOSPITAL SAN MARCOS, SAN MARCOS, TX, p. A648

OCH REGIONAL MEDICAL CENTER, STARKVILLE, MS, p. A365

OCHILTREE GENERAL HOSPITAL, PERRYTON, TX, p. A641

OCHSNER BAPTIST MEDICAL CENTER, NEW ORLEANS, LOUISIANA (see OCHSNER MEDICAL CENTER), p. A285

OCHSNER EXTENDED CARE HOSPITAL OF KENNER, KENNER, LA, p. A279

OCHSNER MEDICAL CENTER, NEW ORLEANS, LA, p. A285

OCHSNER MEDICAL CENTER – KENNER, KENNER, LA, p. A279

OCHSNER MEDICAL CENTER – NORTH SHORE, SLIDELL, LA, p. A288

OCHSNER MEDICAL CENTER – WEST BANK, GRETNA, LOUISIANA (see OCHSNER MEDICAL CENTER), p. A285

OCHSNER MEDICAL CENTER FOR CHILDREN, NEW ORLEANS, LOUISIANA (see OCHSNER MEDICAL CENTER), p. A285

OCHSNER MEDICAL CENTER–BATON ROUGE, BATON ROUGE, LA, p. A272

OCHSNER ST. ANNE GENERAL HOSPITAL, RACELAND, LA, p. A286

OCONEE MEMORIAL HOSPITAL, SENECA, SC, p. A569

OCONEE REGIONAL MEDICAL CENTER, MILLEDGEVILLE, GA, p. A163

OCONOMOWOC MEMORIAL HOSPITAL, OCONOMOWOC, WI, p. A713

ODESSA MEMORIAL HEALTHCARE CENTER, ODESSA, WA, p. A687

ODESSA REGIONAL MEDICAL CENTER, ODESSA, TX, p. A639

OGALLALA COMMUNITY HOSPITAL, OGALLALA, NE, p. A399

OGDEN REGIONAL MEDICAL CENTER, OGDEN, UT, p. A661

OHIO COUNTY HOSPITAL, HARTFORD, KY, p. A261

OHIO HOSPITAL FOR PSYCHIATRY, COLUMBUS, OH, p. A490

OHIO STATE UNIVERSITY HOSPITALS EAST, COLUMBUS, OHIO (see OHIO STATE UNIVERSITY WEXNER MEDICAL CENTER), p. A491

OHIO STATE UNIVERSITY WEXNER MEDICAL CENTER, COLUMBUS, OH, p. A491

OHIO VALLEY HOSPITAL, MCKEES ROCKS, PA, p. A544

OHIO VALLEY MEDICAL CENTER, WHEELING, WV, p. A701

OHIO VALLEY SURGICAL HOSPITAL, SPRINGFIELD, OH, p. A502

OHIOHEALTH DOCTORS HOSPITAL, COLUMBUS, OH, p. A491

OHIOHEALTH DUBLIN METHODIST HOSPITAL, DUBLIN, OH, p. A494

OHIOHEALTH GRADY MEMORIAL HOSPITAL, DELAWARE, OH, p. A493

OHIOHEALTH GRANT MEDICAL CENTER, COLUMBUS, OH, p. A491

OHIOHEALTH HARDIN MEMORIAL HOSPITAL, KENTON, OH, p. A496

OHIOHEALTH MARION GENERAL HOSPITAL, MARION, OH, p. A498

OHIOHEALTH MEDCENTRAL MANSFIELD HOSPITAL, MANSFIELD, OH, p. A497

OHIOHEALTH MEDCENTRAL SHELBY HOSPITAL, SHELBY, OH, p. A502

OHIOHEALTH REHABILITATION HOSPITAL, COLUMBUS, OH, p. A491

OHIOHEALTH RIVERSIDE METHODIST HOSPITAL, COLUMBUS, OH, p. A491

OHSU HOSPITAL, PORTLAND, OR, p. A529

OJAI VALLEY COMMUNITY HOSPITAL, OJAI, CA, p. A80

OKEENE MUNICIPAL HOSPITAL, OKEENE, OK, p. A515

OKLAHOMA CENTER FOR ORTHOPEDIC AND MULTI–SPECIALTY SURGERY, OKLAHOMA CITY, OK, p. A516

OKLAHOMA CITY VETERANS AFFAIRS MEDICAL CENTER, OKLAHOMA CITY, OK, p. A517

OKLAHOMA FORENSIC CENTER, VINITA, OK, p. A523

OKLAHOMA HEART HOSPITAL, OKLAHOMA CITY, OK, p. A517

OKLAHOMA HEART HOSPITAL SOUTH CAMPUS, OKLAHOMA CITY, OK, p. A517

OKLAHOMA SPINE HOSPITAL, OKLAHOMA CITY, OK, p. A517

OKLAHOMA STATE UNIVERSITY MEDICAL CENTER, TULSA, OK, p. A521

OKLAHOMA SURGICAL HOSPITAL, TULSA, OK, p. A521

OLATHE MEDICAL CENTER, OLATHE, KS, p. A250

OLD BRIDGE DIVISION, OLD BRIDGE, NEW JERSEY (see RARITAN BAY MEDICAL CENTER), p. A422

OLD VINEYARD BEHAVIORAL HEALTH SERVICES, WINSTON–SALEM, NC, p. A476

OLEAN GENERAL HOSPITAL, OLEAN, NY, p. A451

OLMSTED MEDICAL CENTER, ROCHESTER, MN, p. A349

OLYMPIA MEDICAL CENTER, LOS ANGELES, CA, p. A73

OLYMPIC MEDICAL CENTER, PORT ANGELES, WA, p. A688

OMEGA HOSPITAL, METAIRIE, LA, p. A283

ONECORE HEALTH, OKLAHOMA CITY, OK, p. A517

ONEIDA HEALTHCARE, ONEIDA, NY, p. A452

ONSLOW MEMORIAL HOSPITAL, JACKSONVILLE, NC, p. A468

OPELOUSAS GENERAL HEALTH SYSTEM, OPELOUSAS, LA, p. A286

OPELOUSAS GENERAL HEALTH SYSTEM–SOUTH CAMPUS, OPELOUSAS, LOUISIANA (see OPELOUSAS GENERAL HEALTH SYSTEM), p. A286
OPTIM MEDICAL CENTER – SCREVEN, SYLVANIA, GA, p. A167
OPTIM MEDICAL CENTER – TATTNALL, REIDSVILLE, GA, p. A164
OPTIONS BEHAVIORAL HEALTH SYSTEM, INDIANAPOLIS, IN, p. A214
ORANGE CITY AREA HEALTH SYSTEM, ORANGE CITY, IA, p. A235
ORANGE COAST MEMORIAL MEDICAL CENTER, FOUNTAIN VALLEY, CA, p. A63
ORANGE COUNTY GLOBAL MEDICAL CENTER, INC., SANTA ANA, CA, p. A92
ORANGE COUNTY IRVINE MEDICAL CENTER, IRVINE, CALIFORNIA (see KAISER PERMANENTE ORANGE COUNTY ANAHEIM MEDICAL CENTER), p. A54
ORANGE PARK MEDICAL CENTER, ORANGE PARK, FL, p. A140
ORANGE REGIONAL MEDICAL CENTER, MIDDLETOWN, NY, p. A442
ORCHARD HOSPITAL, GRIDLEY, CA, p. A65
OREGON STATE HOSPITAL, SALEM, OR, p. A530
OREM COMMUNITY HOSPITAL, OREM, UT, p. A661
ORLANDO REGIONAL MEDICAL CENTER, ORLANDO, FL, p. A140
ORO VALLEY HOSPITAL, ORO VALLEY, AZ, p. A35
OROVILLE HOSPITAL, OROVILLE, CA, p. A81
ORTHOCOLORADO HOSPITAL, LAKEWOOD, CO, p. A108
ORTHOPAEDIC HOSPITAL OF LUTHERAN HEALTH NETWORK, FORT WAYNE, IN, p. A210
ORTHOPAEDIC HOSPITAL OF WISCONSIN – GLENDALE, GLENDALE, WI, p. A706
ORTONVILLE AREA HEALTH SERVICES, ORTONVILLE, MN, p. A348
OSAGE BEACH CENTER FOR COGNITIVE DISORDERS, OSAGE BEACH, MO, p. A378
OSAWATOMIE STATE HOSPITAL, OSAWATOMIE, KS, p. A250
OSBORNE COUNTY MEMORIAL HOSPITAL, OSBORNE, KS, p. A250
OSCAR G. JOHNSON VETERANS AFFAIRS MEDICAL CENTER, IRON MOUNTAIN, MI, p. A327
OSCEOLA COMMUNITY HOSPITAL, SIBLEY, IA, p. A237
OSCEOLA MEDICAL CENTER, OSCEOLA, WI, p. A713
OSCEOLA REGIONAL MEDICAL CENTER, KISSIMMEE, FL, p. A133
OSF HOLY FAMILY MEDICAL CENTER, MONMOUTH, IL, p. A197
OSF SAINT ANTHONY MEDICAL CENTER, ROCKFORD, IL, p. A202
OSF SAINT ANTHONY'S HEALTH CENTER, ALTON, IL, p. A180
OSF SAINT CLARE'S HOSPITAL, ALTON, ILLINOIS (see OSF SAINT ANTHONY'S HEALTH CENTER), p. A180
OSF SAINT ELIZABETH MEDICAL CENTER, OTTAWA, IL, p. A199
OSF SAINT FRANCIS MEDICAL CENTER, PEORIA, IL, p. A200
OSF SAINT JAMES – JOHN W. ALBRECHT MEDICAL CENTER, PONTIAC, IL, p. A201
OSF SAINT LUKE MEDICAL CENTER, KEWANEE, IL, p. A194
OSF SAINT PAUL MEDICAL CENTER, MENDOTA, IL, p. A196
OSF ST. FRANCIS HOSPITAL AND MEDICAL GROUP, ESCANABA, MI, p. A323
OSF ST. JOSEPH MEDICAL CENTER, BLOOMINGTON, IL, p. A181
OSF ST. MARY MEDICAL CENTER, GALESBURG, IL, p. A191
OSMOND GENERAL HOSPITAL, OSMOND, NE, p. A401
OSS ORTHOPAEDIC HOSPITAL, YORK, PA, p. A559
OSSINING CORRECTIONAL FACILITIES HOSPITAL, OSSINING, NY, p. A452
OSWEGO COMMUNITY HOSPITAL, OSWEGO, KS, p. A251
OSWEGO HOSPITAL, OSWEGO, NY, p. A452
OTHELLO COMMUNITY HOSPITAL, OTHELLO, WA, p. A687
OTIS R. BOWEN CENTER FOR HUMAN SERVICES, WARSAW, IN, p. A223
OTSEGO MEMORIAL HOSPITAL, GAYLORD, MI, p. A324
OTTAWA COUNTY HEALTH CENTER, MINNEAPOLIS, KS, p. A249
OTTO KAISER MEMORIAL HOSPITAL, KENEDY, TX, p. A630
OTTUMWA REGIONAL HEALTH CENTER, OTTUMWA, IA, p. A236
OU MEDICAL CENTER, OKLAHOMA CITY, OK, p. A517
OU MEDICAL CENTER EDMOND, EDMOND, OKLAHOMA (see OU MEDICAL CENTER), p. A517
OUACHITA COUNTY MEDICAL CENTER, CAMDEN, AR, p. A44
OUR CHILDREN'S HOUSE, DALLAS, TX, p. A611
OUR COMMUNITY HOSPITAL, SCOTLAND NECK, NC, p. A473
OUR LADY OF BELLEFONTE HOSPITAL, ASHLAND, KY, p. A257
OUR LADY OF FATIMA HOSPITAL, NORTH PROVIDENCE, RHODE ISLAND (see ST. JOSEPH HEALTH SERVICES OF RHODE ISLAND), p. A560
OUR LADY OF LOURDES MEDICAL CENTER, CAMDEN, NJ, p. A415
OUR LADY OF LOURDES MEMORIAL HOSPITAL, INC., BINGHAMTON, NY, p. A435

OUR LADY OF LOURDES REGIONAL MEDICAL CENTER, LAFAYETTE, LA, p. A281
OUR LADY OF PEACE, LOUISVILLE, KY, p. A265
OUR LADY OF THE ANGELS HOSPITAL, BOGALUSA, LA, p. A274
OUR LADY OF THE LAKE CHILDREN'S HOSPITAL, BATON ROUGE, LOUISIANA (see OUR LADY OF THE LAKE REGIONAL MEDICAL CENTER), p. A273
OUR LADY OF THE LAKE REGIONAL MEDICAL CENTER, BATON ROUGE, LA, p. A273
OVERLAKE MEDICAL CENTER, BELLEVUE, WA, p. A682
OVERLAND PARK REGIONAL MEDICAL CENTER, OVERLAND PARK, KS, p. A251
OVERLOOK MEDICAL CENTER, SUMMIT, NJ, p. A423
OVERTON BROOKS VETERANS AFFAIRS MEDICAL CENTER, SHREVEPORT, LA, p. A287
OWATONNA HOSPITAL, OWATONNA, MN, p. A348
OWENSBORO HEALTH MUHLENBERG COMMUNITY HOSPITAL, GREENVILLE, KY, p. A261
OWENSBORO HEALTH REGIONAL HOSPITAL, OWENSBORO, KY, p. A267
OZARK HEALTH MEDICAL CENTER, CLINTON, AR, p. A44
OZARKS COMMUNITY HOSPITAL, GRAVETTE, AR, p. A47
OZARKS COMMUNITY HOSPITAL, SPRINGFIELD, MO, p. A382
OZARKS MEDICAL CENTER, WEST PLAINS, MO, p. A384

P

P & S SURGICAL HOSPITAL, MONROE, LA, p. A283
PACIFIC ALLIANCE MEDICAL CENTER, LOS ANGELES, CA, p. A73
PACIFIC GROVE HOSPITAL, RIVERSIDE, CA, p. A86
PACIFICA HOSPITAL OF THE VALLEY,, CA, p. A73
PAGE HOSPITAL, PAGE, AZ, p. A35
PAGE MEMORIAL HOSPITAL, LURAY, VA, p. A672
PAGOSA SPRINGS MEDICAL CENTER, PAGOSA SPRINGS, CO, p. A109
PALACIOS COMMUNITY MEDICAL CENTER, PALACIOS, TX, p. A639
PALESTINE REGIONAL MEDICAL CENTER, PALESTINE, TX, p. A640
PALESTINE REGIONAL MEDICAL CENTER–EAST, PALESTINE, TX, p. A640
PALI MOMI MEDICAL CENTER, AIEA, HI, p. A170
PALM BEACH CHILDREN'S HOSPITAL, WEST PALM BEACH, FLORIDA (see ST. MARY'S MEDICAL CENTER), p. A150
PALM BEACH GARDENS MEDICAL CENTER, PALM BEACH GARDENS, FL, p. A141
PALM SPRINGS GENERAL HOSPITAL, HIALEAH, FL, p. A130
PALMDALE REGIONAL MEDICAL CENTER, PALMDALE, CA, p. A81
PALMER LUTHERAN HEALTH CENTER, WEST UNION, IA, p. A239
PALMERTON HOSPITAL, PALMERTON, PA, p. A546
PALMETTO GENERAL HOSPITAL, HIALEAH, FL, p. A130
PALMETTO HEALTH BAPTIST, COLUMBIA, SC, p. A564
PALMETTO HEALTH BAPTIST PARKRIDGE, COLUMBIA, SC, p. A564
PALMETTO HEALTH CHILDREN'S HOSPITAL, COLUMBIA, SOUTH CAROLINA (see PALMETTO HEALTH RICHLAND), p. A564
PALMETTO HEALTH RICHLAND, COLUMBIA, SC, p. A564
PALMETTO HEALTH TUOMEY, SUMTER, SC, p. A570
PALMETTO LOWCOUNTRY BEHAVIORAL HEALTH, CHARLESTON, SC, p. A563
PALMS OF PASADENA HOSPITAL, SAINT PETERSBURG, FL, p. A144
PALMS WEST HOSPITAL, LOXAHATCHEE, FL, p. A134
PALO ALTO COUNTY HEALTH SYSTEM, EMMETSBURG, IA, p. A230
PALO ALTO DIVISION, PALO ALTO, CALIFORNIA (see VA PALO ALTO HEALTH CARE SYSTEM), p. A82
PALO PINTO GENERAL HOSPITAL, MINERAL WELLS, TX, p. A637
PALO VERDE BEHAVIORAL HEALTH, TUCSON, AZ, p. A41
PALO VERDE HOSPITAL, BLYTHE, CA, p. A57
PALOMAR MEDICAL CENTER, ESCONDIDO, CA, p. A61
PALOS COMMUNITY HOSPITAL, PALOS HEIGHTS, IL, p. A199
PAM SPECIALTY HOSPITAL OF COVINGTON, COVINGTON, LA, p. A275
PAM SPECIALTY HOSPITAL OF HAMMOND, HAMMOND, LA, p. A278
PAM SPECIALTY HOSPITAL OF LAFAYETTE, LAFAYETTE, LA, p. A281
PAMPA REGIONAL MEDICAL CENTER, PAMPA, TX, p. A640
PANA COMMUNITY HOSPITAL, PANA, IL, p. A199
PAOLI HOSPITAL, PAOLI, PA, p. A547
PARADISE VALLEY HOSPITAL, NATIONAL CITY, CA, p. A79
PARIS COMMUNITY HOSPITAL, PARIS, IL, p. A199

PARIS REGIONAL MEDICAL CENTER, PARIS, TX, p. A640
PARIS REGIONAL MEDICAL CENTER, PARIS, TEXAS (see PARIS REGIONAL MEDICAL CENTER), p. A640
PARIS REGIONAL MEDICAL CENTER–SOUTH CAMPUS, PARIS, TEXAS (see PARIS REGIONAL MEDICAL CENTER), p. A640
PARK CITY MEDICAL CENTER, PARK CITY, UT, p. A662
PARK NICOLLET METHODIST HOSPITAL, SAINT LOUIS PARK, MN, p. A350
PARK PLACE SURGICAL HOSPITAL, LAFAYETTE, LA, p. A281
PARK PLAZA HOSPITAL, HOUSTON, TX, p. A626
PARK RIDGE HEALTH, HENDERSONVILLE, NC, p. A467
PARK ROYAL HOSPITAL, FORT MYERS, FL, p. A129
PARKER ADVENTIST HOSPITAL, PARKER, CO, p. A109
PARKLAND HEALTH & HOSPITAL SYSTEM, DALLAS, TX, p. A611
PARKLAND HEALTH CENTER – LIBERTY STREET, FARMINGTON, MO, p. A371
PARKLAND HEALTH CENTER–BONNE TERRE, BONNE TERRE, MO, p. A367
PARKLAND MEDICAL CENTER, DERRY, NH, p. A410
PARKRIDGE EAST HOSPITAL, CHATTANOOGA, TENNESSEE (see PARKRIDGE MEDICAL CENTER), p. A580
PARKRIDGE MEDICAL CENTER, CHATTANOOGA, TN, p. A580
PARKRIDGE VALLEY CHILD AND ADOLESCENT CAMPUS, CHATTANOOGA, TENNESSEE (see PARKRIDGE MEDICAL CENTER), p. A580
PARKRIDGE WEST HOSPITAL, JASPER, TENNESSEE (see PARKRIDGE MEDICAL CENTER), p. A580
PARKSIDE PSYCHIATRIC HOSPITAL AND CLINIC, TULSA, OK, p. A521
PARKVIEW ORTHO HOSPITAL, FORT WAYNE, IN, p. A211
PARKVIEW COMMUNITY HOSPITAL MEDICAL CENTER, RIVERSIDE, CA, p. A86
PARKVIEW HOSPITAL, WHEELER, TX, p. A657
PARKVIEW HOSPITAL RANDALLIA, FORT WAYNE, INDIANA (see PARKVIEW REGIONAL MEDICAL CENTER), p. A211
PARKVIEW HUNTINGTON HOSPITAL, HUNTINGTON, IN, p. A213
PARKVIEW LAGRANGE HOSPITAL, LAGRANGE, IN, p. A216
PARKVIEW MEDICAL CENTER, PUEBLO, CO, p. A110
PARKVIEW NOBLE HOSPITAL, KENDALLVILLE, IN, p. A215
PARKVIEW REGIONAL HOSPITAL, MEXIA, TX, p. A637
PARKVIEW REGIONAL MEDICAL CENTER, FORT WAYNE, IN, p. A211
PARKVIEW WABASH COUNTY HOSPITAL, WABASH, IN, p. A223
PARKVIEW WHITLEY HOSPITAL, COLUMBIA CITY, IN, p. A208
PARKWAY SURGICAL & CARDIOVASCULAR HOSPITAL, FORT WORTH, TEXAS (see WISE REGIONAL HEALTH SYSTEM), p. A612
PARKWEST MEDICAL CENTER, KNOXVILLE, TN, p. A586
PARKWOOD BEHAVIORAL HEALTH SYSTEM, OLIVE BRANCH, MS, p. A363
PARMER MEDICAL CENTER, FRIONA, TX, p. A619
PARRISH MEDICAL CENTER, TITUSVILLE, FL, p. A148
PARSONS STATE HOSPITAL AND TRAINING CENTER, PARSONS, KS, p. A252
PASSAVANT AREA HOSPITAL, JACKSONVILLE, IL, p. A194
PATEWOOD MEMORIAL HOSPITAL, GREENVILLE, SC, p. A566
PATHWAY REHABILITATION HOSPITAL, BOSSIER CITY, LA, p. A274
PATHWAYS OF TENNESSEE, JACKSON, TN, p. A584
PATHWAYS TREATMENT CENTER, KALISPELL, MONTANA (see KALISPELL REGIONAL HEALTHCARE), p. A389
PATIENTS CHOICE MEDICAL CENTER OF SMITH COUNTY, RALEIGH, MS, p. A364
PATIENTS' HOSPITAL OF REDDING, REDDING, CA, p. A84
PATRICK B. HARRIS PSYCHIATRIC HOSPITAL, ANDERSON, SC, p. A562
PATTON STATE HOSPITAL, PATTON, CA, p. A82
PAUL B. HALL REGIONAL MEDICAL CENTER, PAINTSVILLE, KY, p. A268
PAUL OLIVER MEMORIAL HOSPITAL, FRANKFORT, MI, p. A324
PAULDING COUNTY HOSPITAL, PAULDING, OH, p. A501
PAULS VALLEY GENERAL HOSPITAL, PAULS VALLEY, OK, p. A518
PAWHUSKA HOSPITAL, PAWHUSKA, OK, p. A518
PAWNEE COUNTY MEMORIAL HOSPITAL AND RURAL HEALTH CLINIC, PAWNEE CITY, NE, p. A401
PAWNEE VALLEY COMMUNITY HOSPITAL, LARNED, KS, p. A247
PAYNE WHITNEY PSYCHIATRIC CLINIC, NEW YORK, NEW YORK (see NEW YORK–PRESBYTERIAN HOSPITAL), p. A447
PEACEHEALTH COTTAGE GROVE COMMUNITY MEDICAL CENTER, COTTAGE GROVE, OR, p. A525
PEACEHEALTH KETCHIKAN MEDICAL CENTER, KETCHIKAN, AK, p. A29
PEACEHEALTH PEACE HARBOR MEDICAL CENTER, FLORENCE, OR, p. A525
PEACEHEALTH PEACE ISLAND MEDICAL CENTER, FRIDAY HARBOR, WA, p. A685
PEACEHEALTH SACRED HEART MEDICAL CENTER AT RIVERBEND, SPRINGFIELD, OR, p. A531

PEACEHEALTH SACRED HEART MEDICAL CENTER UNIVERSITY DISTRICT, EUGENE, OR, p. A525

PEACEHEALTH SOUTHWEST MEDICAL CENTER, VANCOUVER, WA, p. A692

PEACEHEALTH ST. JOHN MEDICAL CENTER, LONGVIEW, WA, p. A686

PEACEHEALTH ST. JOSEPH MEDICAL CENTER, BELLINGHAM, WA, p. A682

PEACEHEALTH UNITED GENERAL MEDICAL CENTER, SEDRO–WOOLLEY, WA, p. A690

PEACHFORD BEHAVIORAL HEALTH SYSTEM, ATLANTA, GA, p. A152

PEAK BEHAVIORAL HEALTH SERVICES, SANTA TERESA, NM, p. A431

PEAK VIEW BEHAVIORAL HEALTH, COLORADO SPRINGS, CO, p. A102

PEARL RIVER COUNTY HOSPITAL, POPLARVILLE, MS, p. A364

PEARLAND MEDICAL CENTER, PEARLAND, TX, p. A640

PECONIC BAY MEDICAL CENTER, RIVERHEAD, NY, p. A454

PECOS COUNTY MEMORIAL HOSPITAL, FORT STOCKTON, TX, p. A617

PECOS VALLEY LODGE, ROSWELL, NEW MEXICO (see NEW MEXICO REHABILITATION CENTER), p. A431

PEKIN HOSPITAL, PEKIN, IL, p. A200

PELHAM MEDICAL CENTER, GREER, SC, p. A567

PELLA REGIONAL HEALTH CENTER, PELLA, IA, p. A236

PEMBINA COUNTY MEMORIAL HOSPITAL AND WEDGEWOOD MANOR, CAVALIER, ND, p. A478

PEMBROKE HOSPITAL, PEMBROKE, MA, p. A313

PEMISCOT MEMORIAL HEALTH SYSTEM, HAYTI, MO, p. A372

PEN BAY MEDICAL CENTER, ROCKPORT, ME, p. A295

PENDER COMMUNITY HOSPITAL, PENDER, NE, p. A401

PENDER MEMORIAL HOSPITAL, BURGAW, NC, p. A461

PENINSULA HOSPITAL, LOUISVILLE, TN, p. A587

PENINSULA REGIONAL MEDICAL CENTER, SALISBURY, MD, p. A303

PENN HIGHLANDS BROOKVILLE, BROOKVILLE, PA, p. A534

PENN HIGHLANDS CLEARFIELD, CLEARFIELD, PA, p. A535

PENN HIGHLANDS DUBOIS, DUBOIS, PA, p. A537

PENN HIGHLANDS ELK, SAINT MARYS, PA, p. A553

PENN MEDICINE CHESTER COUNTY HOSPITAL, WEST CHESTER, PA, p. A557

PENN PRESBYTERIAN MEDICAL CENTER, PHILADELPHIA, PA, p. A549

PENN STATE CHILDREN'S HOSPITAL, HERSHEY, PENNSYLVANIA (see PENN STATE MILTON S. HERSHEY MEDICAL CENTER), p. A540

PENN STATE HEALTH ST. JOSEPH, READING, PA, p. A553

PENN STATE HERSHEY REHABILITATION HOSPITAL, HUMMELSTOWN, PA, p. A540

PENN STATE MILTON S. HERSHEY MEDICAL CENTER, HERSHEY, PA, p. A540

PENNSYLVANIA HOSPITAL, PHILADELPHIA, PA, p. A549

PENNSYLVANIA PSYCHIATRIC INSTITUTE, HARRISBURG, PA, p. A539

PENOBSCOT VALLEY HOSPITAL, LINCOLN, ME, p. A294

PENROSE HOSPITAL, COLORADO SPRINGS, COLORADO (see PENROSE–ST. FRANCIS HEALTH SERVICES), p. A103

PENROSE–ST. FRANCIS HEALTH SERVICES, COLORADO SPRINGS, CO, p. A103

PERHAM HEALTH, PERHAM, MN, p. A348

PERKINS COUNTY HEALTH SERVICES, GRANT, NE, p. A396

PERMIAN REGIONAL MEDICAL CENTER, ANDREWS, TX, p. A597

PERRY COMMUNITY HOSPITAL, LINDEN, TN, p. A587

PERRY COUNTY GENERAL HOSPITAL, RICHTON, MS, p. A364

PERRY COUNTY MEMORIAL HOSPITAL, TELL CITY, IN, p. A222

PERRY COUNTY MEMORIAL HOSPITAL, PERRYVILLE, MO, p. A378

PERRY HOSPITAL, PERRY, GA, p. A164

PERRY MEMORIAL HOSPITAL, PRINCETON, IL, p. A201

PERRY MEMORIAL HOSPITAL, PERRY, OK, p. A518

PERSHING GENERAL HOSPITAL, LOVELOCK, NV, p. A407

PERSON MEMORIAL HOSPITAL, ROXBORO, NC, p. A472

PERTH AMBOY DIVISION, PERTH AMBOY, NEW JERSEY (see RARITAN BAY MEDICAL CENTER), p. A422

PETALUMA VALLEY HOSPITAL, PETALUMA, CA, p. A82

PETERSBURG MEDICAL CENTER, PETERSBURG, AK, p. A30

PETERSON HEALTHCARE AND REHABILITATION HOSPITAL, WHEELING, WV, p. A701

PETERSON REGIONAL MEDICAL CENTER, KERRVILLE, TX, p. A630

PEYTON MANNING CHILDREN'S HOSPITAL, INDIANAPOLIS, INDIANA (see ST. VINCENT INDIANAPOLIS HOSPITAL), p. A215

PEYTON MANNING CHILDREN'S HOSPITAL AT ST. VINCENT, INDIANAPOLIS, INDIANA (see ST. VINCENT INDIANAPOLIS HOSPITAL), p. A215

PHELPS COUNTY REGIONAL MEDICAL CENTER, ROLLA, MO, p. A379

PHELPS MEMORIAL HEALTH CENTER, HOLDREGE, NE, p. A397

PHELPS MEMORIAL HOSPITAL CENTER, SLEEPY HOLLOW, NY, p. A455

PHILADELPHIA VETERANS AFFAIRS MEDICAL CENTER, PHILADELPHIA, PA, p. A549

PHILHAVEN, MOUNT GRETNA, PA, p. A545

PHILIP HEALTH SERVICES, PHILIP, SD, p. A575

PHILLIPS COUNTY HOSPITAL, PHILLIPSBURG, KS, p. A252

PHILLIPS COUNTY HOSPITAL, MALTA, MT, p. A389

PHILLIPS EYE INSTITUTE, MINNEAPOLIS, MN, p. A346

PHOEBE NORTH, ALBANY, GEORGIA (see PHOEBE PUTNEY MEMORIAL HOSPITAL), p. A151

PHOEBE PUTNEY MEMORIAL HOSPITAL, ALBANY, GA, p. A151

PHOEBE SUMTER MEDICAL CENTER, AMERICUS, GA, p. A151

PHOEBE WORTH MEDICAL CENTER, SYLVESTER, GA, p. A167

PHOENIX BEHAVIORAL HOSPITAL, RAYNE, LA, p. A286

PHOENIX CHILDREN'S HOSPITAL, PHOENIX, AZ, p. A37

PHOENIX VETERANS AFFAIRS HEALTH CARE SYSTEM, PHOENIX, AZ, p. A37

PHOENIXVILLE HOSPITAL, PHOENIXVILLE, PA, p. A550

PHS SANTA FE INDIAN HOSPITAL, SANTA FE, NM, p. A431

PHYLLIS AND DAVID KOMANSKY CENTER FOR CHILDREN'S HEALTH, NEW YORK, NEW YORK (see NEW YORK–PRESBYTERIAN HOSPITAL), p. A447

PHYSICIANS BEHAVIORAL HOSPITAL, SHREVEPORT, LA, p. A287

PHYSICIANS CARE SURGICAL HOSPITAL, ROYERSFORD, PA, p. A553

PHYSICIANS MEDICAL CENTER, HOUMA, LA, p. A278

PHYSICIANS REGIONAL, NAPLES, FLORIDA (see PHYSICIANS REGIONAL – PINE RIDGE), p. A138

PHYSICIANS REGIONAL – PINE RIDGE, NAPLES, FL, p. A138

PHYSICIANS SURGICAL HOSPITAL – PANHANDLE CAMPUS, AMARILLO, TX, p. A596

PHYSICIANS SURGICAL HOSPITAL – QUAIL CREEK, AMARILLO, TX, p. A596

PHYSICIANS' HOSPITAL IN ANADARKO, ANADARKO, OK, p. A508

PHYSICIANS' MEDICAL CENTER, NEW ALBANY, IN, p. A219

PHYSICIANS' SPECIALTY HOSPITAL, FAYETTEVILLE, AR, p. A45

PICKENS COUNTY MEDICAL CENTER, CARROLLTON, AL, p. A18

PIEDMONT FAYETTE HOSPITAL, FAYETTEVILLE, GA, p. A159

PIEDMONT GERIATRIC HOSPITAL, BURKEVILLE, VA, p. A668

PIEDMONT HENRY HOSPITAL, STOCKBRIDGE, GA, p. A167

PIEDMONT HOSPITAL, ATLANTA, GA, p. A153

PIEDMONT MEDICAL CENTER, ROCK HILL, SC, p. A569

PIEDMONT MOUNTAINSIDE HOSPITAL, JASPER, GA, p. A161

PIEDMONT NEWNAN HOSPITAL, NEWNAN, GA, p. A164

PIEDMONT NEWTON HOSPITAL, COVINGTON, GA, p. A157

PIGGOTT COMMUNITY HOSPITAL, PIGGOTT, AR, p. A51

PIH HEALTH HOSPITAL – DOWNEY, DOWNEY, CA, p. A61

PIH HEALTH HOSPITAL–WHITTIER, WHITTIER, CA, p. A99

PIKE COUNTY MEMORIAL HOSPITAL, LOUISIANA, MO, p. A376

PIKES PEAK REGIONAL HOSPITAL, WOODLAND PARK, CO, p. A111

PIKEVILLE MEDICAL CENTER, PIKEVILLE, KY, p. A268

PILGRIM PSYCHIATRIC CENTER, BRENTWOOD, NY, p. A435

PINCKNEYVILLE COMMUNITY HOSPITAL, PINCKNEYVILLE, IL, p. A200

PINE CREEK MEDICAL CENTER, DALLAS, TX, p. A611

PINE REST CHRISTIAN MENTAL HEALTH SERVICES, GRAND RAPIDS, MI, p. A325

PINE VALLEY SPECIALTY HOSPITAL, HOUSTON, TX, p. A626

PINECREST REHABILITATION HOSPITAL, DELRAY BEACH, FLORIDA (see DELRAY MEDICAL CENTER), p. A127

PINEVILLE COMMUNITY HOSPITAL ASSOCIATION, PINEVILLE, KY, p. A268

PINNACLE HEALTH SYSTEM, HARRISBURG, PA, p. A540

PINNACLE HOSPITAL, CROWN POINT, IN, p. A209

PINNACLE POINTE HOSPITAL, LITTLE ROCK, AR, p. A49

PINNACLE SPECIALTY HOSPITAL, TULSA, OK, p. A522

PINNACLEHEALTH AT COMMUNITY GENERAL OSTEOPATHIC HOSPITAL, HARRISBURG, PENNSYLVANIA (see PINNACLE HEALTH SYSTEM), p. A540

PINNACLEHEALTH AT HARRISBURG HOSPITAL, HARRISBURG, PENNSYLVANIA (see PINNACLE HEALTH SYSTEM), p. A540

PINNACLEHEALTH WEST SHORE HOSPITAL, MECHANICSBURG, PENNSYLVANIA (see PINNACLE HEALTH SYSTEM), p. A540

PIONEER COMMUNITY HOSPITAL OF ABERDEEN, ABERDEEN, MS, p. A355

PIONEER COMMUNITY HOSPITAL OF EARLY, BLAKELY, GA, p. A154

PIONEER COMMUNITY HOSPITAL OF PATRICK, STUART, VA, p. A679

PIONEER COMMUNITY HOSPITAL OF STOKES, DANBURY, NC, p. A463

PIONEER MEDICAL CENTER, BIG TIMBER, MT, p. A385

PIONEER MEMORIAL HOSPITAL, HEPPNER, OR, p. A526

PIONEER MEMORIAL HOSPITAL AND HEALTH SERVICES, VIBORG, SD, p. A577

PIONEER SPECIALTY HOSPITAL, PONTIAC, MI, p. A332

PIONEERS MEDICAL CENTER, MEEKER, CO, p. A109

PIONEERS MEMORIAL HEALTHCARE DISTRICT, BRAWLEY, CA, p. A57

PIPESTONE COUNTY MEDICAL CENTER AVERA, PIPESTONE, MN, p. A348

PLACENTIA–LINDA HOSPITAL, PLACENTIA, CA, p. A83

PLAINS MEMORIAL HOSPITAL, DIMMITT, TX, p. A613

PLAINS REGIONAL MEDICAL CENTER, CLOVIS, NM, p. A428

PLAINVIEW HOSPITAL, PLAINVIEW, NY, p. A452

PLANO SPECIALTY HOSPITAL, PLANO, TX, p. A642

PLANO SURGICAL HOSPITAL, PLANO, TX, p. A642

PLANTATION GENERAL HOSPITAL, PLANTATION, FL, p. A143

PLATEAU MEDICAL CENTER, OAK HILL, WV, p. A698

PLATTE COUNTY MEMORIAL HOSPITAL, WHEATLAND, WY, p. A724

PLATTE HEALTH CENTER AVERA, PLATTE, SD, p. A575

PLATTE VALLEY MEDICAL CENTER, BRIGHTON, CO, p. A102

PLAZA MEDICAL CENTER OF FORT WORTH, FORT WORTH, TX, p. A618

PLAZA SPECIALTY HOSPITAL, HOUSTON, TX, p. A626

PLEASANT VALLEY HOSPITAL, POINT PLEASANT, WV, p. A699

PLUM CREEK SPECIALTY HOSPITAL, AMARILLO, TX, p. A596

PLUMAS DISTRICT HOSPITAL, QUINCY, CA, p. A84

PMH MEDICAL CENTER, PROSSER, WA, p. A688

POCAHONTAS COMMUNITY HOSPITAL, POCAHONTAS, IA, p. A236

POCAHONTAS MEMORIAL HOSPITAL, BUCKEYE, WV, p. A694

POCONO MEDICAL CENTER, EAST STROUDSBURG, PA, p. A537

POINCIANA MEDICAL CENTER, KISSIMMEE, FL, p. A133

POINTE COUPEE GENERAL HOSPITAL, NEW ROADS, LA, p. A285

POLK MEDICAL CENTER, CEDARTOWN, GA, p. A156

POMERADO HOSPITAL, POWAY, CA, p. A84

POMERENE HOSPITAL, MILLERSBURG, OH, p. A499

POMONA VALLEY HOSPITAL MEDICAL CENTER, POMONA, CA, p. A83

PONDERA MEDICAL CENTER, CONRAD, MT, p. A386

POPLAR BLUFF REGIONAL MEDICAL CENTER, POPLAR BLUFF, MO, p. A378

POPLAR BLUFF REGIONAL MEDICAL CENTER–SOUTH CAMPUS, POPLAR BLUFF, MISSOURI (see POPLAR BLUFF REGIONAL MEDICAL CENTER), p. A378

POPLAR COMMUNITY HOSPITAL, POPLAR, MT, p. A390

POPLAR SPRINGS HOSPITAL, PETERSBURG, VA, p. A676

PORT ST. LUCIE HOSPITAL, PORT ST. LUCIE, FL, p. A143

PORTER ADVENTIST HOSPITAL, DENVER, CO, p. A104

PORTER MEDICAL CENTER, MIDDLEBURY, VT, p. A665

PORTER REGIONAL HOSPITAL, VALPARAISO, IN, p. A223

PORTER–STARKE SERVICES, VALPARAISO, IN, p. A223

PORTERVILLE DEVELOPMENTAL CENTER, PORTERVILLE, CA, p. A83

PORTLAND VETERANS AFFAIRS MEDICAL CENTER, PORTLAND, OR, p. A529

PORTNEUF MEDICAL CENTER, POCATELLO, ID, p. A178

PORTSMOUTH REGIONAL HOSPITAL, PORTSMOUTH, NH, p. A413

POST ACUTE MEDICAL SPECIALTY HOSPITAL OF CORPUS CHRISTI – NORTH, CORPUS CHRISTI, TX, p. A608

POST ACUTE MEDICAL SPECIALTY HOSPITAL OF CORPUS CHRISTI – SOUTH, CORPUS CHRISTI, TX, p. A608

POST ACUTE MEDICAL SPECIALTY HOSPITAL OF MILWAUKEE, GREENFIELD, WI, p. A707

POST ACUTE MEDICAL SPECIALTY HOSPITAL OF TEXARKANA – NORTH, TEXARKANA, TX, p. A652

POST ACUTE MEDICAL SPECIALTY HOSPITAL OF TULSA, TULSA, OK, p. A522

POST ACUTE MEDICAL SPECIALTY HOSPITAL OF VICTORIA, VICTORIA, TX, p. A655

POST ACUTE/WARM SPRINGS REHABILITATION HOSPITAL OF ALLEN, ALLEN, TX, p. A595

POST ACUTE/WARM SPRINGS REHABILITATION HOSPITAL OF SAN ANTONIO, SAN ANTONIO, TX, p. A646

POST ACUTE/WARM SPRINGS SPECIALTY HOSPITAL OF LULING, LULING, TX, p. A635

POST ACUTE/WARM SPRINGS SPECIALTY HOSPITAL OF NEW BRAUNFELS, NEW BRAUNFELS, TX, p. A638

POST ACUTE/WARM SPRINGS SPECIALTY HOSPITAL OF SAN ANTONIO, SAN ANTONIO, TX, p. A647

POST ACUTE/WARM SPRINGS SPECIALTY HOSPITAL OF VICTORIA, VICTORIA, TX, p. A655

POTOMAC VALLEY HOSPITAL, KEYSER, WV, p. A697

POTTSTOWN MEMORIAL MEDICAL CENTER, POTTSTOWN, PA, p. A552

POUDRE VALLEY HOSPITAL, FORT COLLINS, CO, p. A105

POWELL CONVALESCENT CENTER, DES MOINES, IOWA (see UNITYPOINT HEALTH – IOWA METHODIST MEDICAL CENTER), p. A229

POWELL VALLEY HEALTHCARE, POWELL, WY, p. A723

POWER COUNTY HOSPITAL DISTRICT, AMERICAN FALLS, ID, p. A174

PRAGUE COMMUNITY HOSPITAL, PRAGUE, OK, p. A519
PRAIRIE COMMUNITY HOSPITAL, TERRY, MT, p. A391
PRAIRIE LAKES HEALTHCARE SYSTEM, WATERTOWN, SD, p. A577
PRAIRIE RIDGE HOSPITAL AND HEALTH SERVICES, ELBOW LAKE, MN, p. A342
PRAIRIE ST. JOHN'S, FARGO, ND, p. A478
PRAIRIE VIEW, NEWTON, KS, p. A250
PRATT REGIONAL MEDICAL CENTER, PRATT, KS, p. A252
PRATTVILLE BAPTIST HOSPITAL, PRATTVILLE, AL, p. A25
PREMIER SURGICAL INSTITUTE, GALENA, KS, p. A243
PRENTICE WOMEN'S HOSPITAL, CHICAGO, ILLINOIS (see NORTHWESTERN MEMORIAL HOSPITAL), p. A185
PRESBYTERIAN ESPANOLA HOSPITAL, ESPANOLA, NM, p. A429
PRESBYTERIAN HEMBY CHILDREN'S HOSPITAL, CHARLOTTE, NORTH CAROLINA (see NOVANT HEALTH PRESBYTERIAN MEDICAL CENTER), p. A463
PRESBYTERIAN HOSPITAL, ALBUQUERQUE, NM, p. A428
PRESBYTERIAN KASEMAN HOSPITAL, ALBUQUERQUE, NEW MEXICO (see PRESBYTERIAN HOSPITAL), p. A428
PRESBYTERIAN RUST MEDICAL CENTER, RIO RANCHO, NEW MEXICO (see PRESBYTERIAN HOSPITAL), p. A428
PRESBYTERIAN TOWER, OKLAHOMA CITY, OKLAHOMA (see OU MEDICAL CENTER), p. A517
PRESBYTERIAN–ST. LUKE'S MEDICAL CENTER, DENVER, CO, p. A104
PRESENCE COVENANT MEDICAL CENTER, URBANA, IL, p. A204
PRESENCE HOLY FAMILY MEDICAL CENTER, DES PLAINES, IL, p. A188
PRESENCE MERCY MEDICAL CENTER, AURORA, IL, p. A180
PRESENCE RESURRECTION MEDICAL CENTER, CHICAGO, IL, p. A185
PRESENCE SAINT FRANCIS HOSPITAL, EVANSTON, IL, p. A190
PRESENCE SAINT JOSEPH HOSPITAL, CHICAGO, IL, p. A185
PRESENCE SAINT JOSEPH HOSPITAL, ELGIN, IL, p. A189
PRESENCE SAINT JOSEPH MEDICAL CENTER, JOLIET, IL, p. A194
PRESENCE SAINTS MARY & ELIZABETH MEDICAL CENTER, CHICAGO, IL, p. A186
PRESENCE SAINTS MARY & ELIZABETH MEDICAL CENTER, CLAREMONT AVENUE, CHICAGO, ILLINOIS (see PRESENCE SAINTS MARY & ELIZABETH MEDICAL CENTER), p. A186
PRESENCE ST. MARY'S HOSPITAL, KANKAKEE, IL, p. A194
PRESENCE UNITED SAMARITANS MEDICAL CENTER, DANVILLE, IL, p. A187
PRESENTATION MEDICAL CENTER, ROLLA, ND, p. A481
PRESTON MEMORIAL HOSPITAL, KINGWOOD, WV, p. A697
PREVOST MEMORIAL HOSPITAL, DONALDSONVILLE, LA, p. A276
PRIMARY CHILDREN'S HOSPITAL, SALT LAKE CITY, UT, p. A663
PRINCE GEORGE'S HOSPITAL CENTER, CHEVERLY, MD, p. A299
PRINCETON BAPTIST MEDICAL CENTER, BIRMINGHAM, AL, p. A17
PRINCETON COMMUNITY HOSPITAL, PRINCETON, WV, p. A699
PROFESSIONAL HOSPITAL GUAYNABO, GUAYNABO, PR, p. A727
PROGRESS WEST HOSPITAL, O'FALLON, MO, p. A377
PROMEDICA BAY PARK HOSPITAL, OREGON, OH, p. A500
PROMEDICA BIXBY HOSPITAL, ADRIAN, MI, p. A318
PROMEDICA DEFIANCE REGIONAL HOSPITAL, DEFIANCE, OH, p. A493
PROMEDICA FLOWER HOSPITAL, SYLVANIA, OH, p. A503
PROMEDICA FOSTORIA COMMUNITY HOSPITAL, FOSTORIA, OH, p. A494
PROMEDICA HERRICK HOSPITAL, TECUMSEH, MI, p. A335
PROMEDICA MEMORIAL HOSPITAL, FREMONT, OH, p. A495
PROMEDICA MONROE REGIONAL HOSPITAL, MONROE, MI, p. A330
PROMEDICA ST. LUKE'S HOSPITAL, MAUMEE, OH, p. A498
PROMEDICA TOLEDO HOSPITAL, TOLEDO, OH, p. A504
PROMEDICA WILDWOOD ORTHOPAEDIC AND SPINE HOSPITAL, TOLEDO, OHIO (see PROMEDICA TOLEDO HOSPITAL), p. A504
PROMISE HOSPITAL BATON ROUGE – MAIN CAMPUS, BATON ROUGE, LA, p. A273
PROMISE HOSPITAL OF BATON ROUGE – MID–CITY CAMPUS, BATON ROUGE, LA, p. A273
PROMISE HOSPITAL OF BATON ROUGE – OCHSNER CAMPUS, BATON ROUGE, LA, p. A273
PROMISE HOSPITAL OF DALLAS, DALLAS, TX, p. A611
PROMISE HOSPITAL OF EAST LOS ANGELES, LOS ANGELES, CA, p. A73
PROMISE HOSPITAL OF EAST LOS ANGELES, SUBURBAN MEDICAL CENTER CAMPUS, PARAMOUNT, CALIFORNIA (see PROMISE HOSPITAL OF EAST LOS ANGELES), p. A73
PROMISE HOSPITAL OF FLORIDA AT THE VILLAGES, OXFORD, FL, p. A141
PROMISE HOSPITAL OF FORT MYERS, FORT MYERS, FL, p. A129

PROMISE HOSPITAL OF LOUISIANA – BOSSIER CITY CAMPUS, BOSSIER CITY, LOUISIANA (see PROMISE HOSPITAL OF LOUISIANA – SHREVEPORT CAMPUS), p. A287
PROMISE HOSPITAL OF LOUISIANA – SHREVEPORT CAMPUS, SHREVEPORT, LA, p. A287
PROMISE HOSPITAL OF MIAMI, MIAMI, FL, p. A137
PROMISE HOSPITAL OF MISS LOU, VIDALIA, LA, p. A289
PROMISE HOSPITAL OF OVERLAND PARK, OVERLAND PARK, KS, p. A251
PROMISE HOSPITAL OF PHOENIX, MESA, AZ, p. A34
PROMISE HOSPITAL OF SALT LAKE, SALT LAKE CITY, UT, p. A663
PROMISE HOSPITAL OF SAN DIEGO, SAN DIEGO, CA, p. A88
PROMISE HOSPITAL OF VICKSBURG, VICKSBURG, MS, p. A365
PROMISE HOSPITAL OF WICHITA FALLS, WICHITA FALLS, TX, p. A657
PROVIDENCE – PROVIDENCE PARK HOSPITAL, NOVI CAMPUS, NOVI, MICHIGAN (see PROVIDENCE – PROVIDENCE PARK HOSPITAL, SOUTHFIELD CAMPUS), p. A334
PROVIDENCE – PROVIDENCE PARK HOSPITAL, SOUTHFIELD CAMPUS, SOUTHFIELD, MI, p. A334
PROVIDENCE ALASKA MEDICAL CENTER, ANCHORAGE, AK, p. A28
PROVIDENCE CENTRALIA HOSPITAL, CENTRALIA, WA, p. A683
PROVIDENCE CHILDREN'S HOSPITAL, EL PASO, TEXAS (see THE HOSPITALS OF PROVIDENCE MEMORIAL CAMPUS), p. A616
PROVIDENCE EVERETT MEDICAL CENTER – COLBY CAMPUS, EVERETT, WASHINGTON (see PROVIDENCE REGIONAL MEDICAL CENTER EVERETT), p. A684
PROVIDENCE EVERETT MEDICAL CENTER – PACIFIC CAMPUS, EVERETT, WASHINGTON (see PROVIDENCE REGIONAL MEDICAL CENTER EVERETT), p. A684
PROVIDENCE HEALTHCARE NETWORK, WACO, TX, p. A656
PROVIDENCE HOLY CROSS MEDICAL CENTER,, CA, p. A73
PROVIDENCE HOLY FAMILY HOSPITAL, SPOKANE, WA, p. A691
PROVIDENCE HOOD RIVER MEMORIAL HOSPITAL, HOOD RIVER, OR, p. A526
PROVIDENCE HOSPITAL, MOBILE, AL, p. A22
PROVIDENCE HOSPITAL, WASHINGTON, DC, p. A122
PROVIDENCE HOSPITAL, COLUMBIA, SC, p. A564
PROVIDENCE HOSPITAL NORTHEAST, COLUMBIA, SOUTH CAROLINA (see PROVIDENCE HOSPITAL), p. A564
PROVIDENCE KODIAK ISLAND MEDICAL CENTER, KODIAK, AK, p. A29
PROVIDENCE LITTLE COMPANY OF MARY MEDICAL CENTER – TORRANCE, TORRANCE, CA, p. A96
PROVIDENCE LITTLE COMPANY OF MARY MEDICAL CENTER SAN PEDRO,, CA, p. A73
PROVIDENCE MEDFORD MEDICAL CENTER, MEDFORD, OR, p. A528
PROVIDENCE MEDICAL CENTER, KANSAS CITY, KS, p. A246
PROVIDENCE MEDICAL CENTER, WAYNE, NE, p. A403
PROVIDENCE MILWAUKIE HOSPITAL, MILWAUKIE, OR, p. A528
PROVIDENCE MOUNT CARMEL HOSPITAL, COLVILLE, WA, p. A684
PROVIDENCE NEWBERG MEDICAL CENTER, NEWBERG, OR, p. A528
PROVIDENCE PORTLAND MEDICAL CENTER, PORTLAND, OR, p. A529
PROVIDENCE REGIONAL MEDICAL CENTER EVERETT, EVERETT, WA, p. A684
PROVIDENCE SACRED HEART MEDICAL CENTER & CHILDREN'S HOSPITAL, SPOKANE, WA, p. A691
PROVIDENCE SAINT JOHN'S HEALTH CENTER, SANTA MONICA, CA, p. A93
PROVIDENCE SAINT JOSEPH MEDICAL CENTER, BURBANK, CA, p. A57
PROVIDENCE SEASIDE HOSPITAL, SEASIDE, OR, p. A530
PROVIDENCE SEWARD MEDICAL CENTER, SEWARD, AK, p. A30
PROVIDENCE ST. JOSEPH MEDICAL CENTER, POLSON, MT, p. A390
PROVIDENCE ST. JOSEPH'S HOSPITAL, CHEWELAH, WA, p. A683
PROVIDENCE ST. MARY MEDICAL CENTER, WALLA WALLA, WA, p. A693
PROVIDENCE ST. PETER HOSPITAL, OLYMPIA, WA, p. A687
PROVIDENCE ST. VINCENT MEDICAL CENTER, PORTLAND, OR, p. A529
PROVIDENCE TARZANA MEDICAL CENTER,, CA, p. A74
PROVIDENCE VALDEZ MEDICAL CENTER, VALDEZ, AK, p. A30
PROVIDENCE VETERANS AFFAIRS MEDICAL CENTER, PROVIDENCE, RI, p. A560
PROVIDENCE WILLAMETTE FALLS MEDICAL CENTER, OREGON CITY, OR, p. A528
PROVIDENT HOSPITAL OF COOK COUNTY, CHICAGO, IL, p. A186
PROVO CANYON BEHAVIORAL HOSPITAL, OREM, UT, p. A661
PROWERS MEDICAL CENTER, LAMAR, CO, p. A108

PSYCHIATRIC INSTITUTE OF WASHINGTON, WASHINGTON, DC, p. A122
PSYCHIATRIC MEDICINE CENTER, SALEM, OREGON (see SALEM HOSPITAL), p. A530
PUERTO RICO CHILDREN'S HOSPITAL, BAYAMON, PUERTO RICO (see HOSPITAL HERMANOS MELENDEZ), p. A726
PULASKI MEMORIAL HOSPITAL, WINAMAC, IN, p. A224
PULLMAN REGIONAL HOSPITAL, PULLMAN, WA, p. A688
PUNXSUTAWNEY AREA HOSPITAL, PUNXSUTAWNEY, PA, p. A552
PURCELL MUNICIPAL HOSPITAL, PURCELL, OK, p. A519
PUSHMATAHA HOSPITAL & HOME HEALTH, ANTLERS, OK, p. A508
PUTNAM COMMUNITY MEDICAL CENTER, PALATKA, FL, p. A141
PUTNAM COUNTY HOSPITAL, GREENCASTLE, IN, p. A212
PUTNAM COUNTY MEMORIAL HOSPITAL, UNIONVILLE, MO, p. A383
PUTNAM GENERAL HOSPITAL, EATONTON, GA, p. A159
PUTNAM HOSPITAL CENTER, CARMEL, NY, p. A437

Q

QUARTZ MOUNTAIN MEDICAL CENTER, MANGUM, OK, p. A514
QUEEN OF THE VALLEY MEDICAL CENTER, NAPA, CA, p. A79
QUEEN'S MEDICAL CENTER – WEST OAHU, EWA BEACH, HAWAII (see QUEEN'S MEDICAL CENTER), p. A171
QUENTIN MEASE HOSPITAL, HOUSTON, TEXAS (see HARRIS HEALTH SYSTEM), p. A624
QUILLEN REHABILITATION HOSPITAL, JOHNSON CITY, TN, p. A585
QUINCY VALLEY MEDICAL CENTER, QUINCY, WA, p. A688
QUITMAN COUNTY HOSPITAL, MARKS, MS, p. A361

R

RADY CHILDREN'S HOSPITAL – SAN DIEGO, SAN DIEGO, CA, p. A88
RAINBOW MENTAL HEALTH FACILITY, KANSAS CITY, KS, p. A246
RAINY LAKE MEDICAL CENTER, INTERNATIONAL FALLS, MN, p. A344
RALEIGH GENERAL HOSPITAL, BECKLEY, WV, p. A694
RALPH H. JOHNSON VETERANS AFFAIRS MEDICAL CENTER, CHARLESTON, SC, p. A563
RANCHO LOS AMIGOS NATIONAL REHABILITATION CENTER, DOWNEY, CA, p. A61
RANCHO SPRINGS MEDICAL CENTER, MURRIETA, CALIFORNIA (see SOUTHWEST HEALTHCARE SYSTEM), p. A78
RANDALL CHILDREN'S HOSPITAL, PORTLAND, OREGON (see LEGACY EMANUEL HOSPITAL AND HEALTH CENTER), p. A529
RANDOLPH HOSPITAL, ASHEBORO, NC, p. A460
RANGE REGIONAL HEALTH SERVICES, HIBBING, MN, p. A344
RANGELY DISTRICT HOSPITAL, RANGELY, CO, p. A110
RANKEN JORDAN PEDIATRIC BRIDGE HOSPITAL, MARYLAND HEIGHTS, MO, p. A376
RANKIN COUNTY HOSPITAL DISTRICT, RANKIN, TX, p. A643
RANSOM MEMORIAL HOSPITAL, OTTAWA, KS, p. A251
RAPID CITY REGIONAL HOSPITAL, RAPID CITY, SD, p. A575
RAPIDES REGIONAL MEDICAL CENTER, ALEXANDRIA, LA, p. A271
RAPPAHANNOCK GENERAL HOSPITAL, KILMARNOCK, VA, p. A672
RARITAN BAY MEDICAL CENTER, PERTH AMBOY, NJ, p. A422
RAULERSON HOSPITAL, OKEECHOBEE, FL, p. A140
RAWLINS COUNTY HEALTH CENTER, ATWOOD, KS, p. A240
RAY COUNTY MEMORIAL HOSPITAL, RICHMOND, MO, p. A378
RC HOSPITAL AND CLINICS, OLIVIA, MN, p. A348
READING HOSPITAL, WEST READING, PA, p. A557
REAGAN MEMORIAL HOSPITAL, BIG LAKE, TX, p. A602
REBOUND BEHAVIORAL HEALTH, LANCASTER, SC, p. A568
RECEPTION AND MEDICAL CENTER, LAKE BUTLER, FL, p. A133
RED BAY HOSPITAL, RED BAY, AL, p. A25
RED BUD REGIONAL HOSPITAL, RED BUD, IL, p. A201
RED LAKE INDIAN HEALTH SERVICE HOSPITAL, RED LAKE, MN, p. A349
RED RIVER BEHAVIORAL CENTER, BOSSIER CITY, LA, p. A274
RED RIVER HOSPITAL, LLC, WICHITA FALLS, TX, p. A657
RED ROCK BEHAVIORAL HOSPITAL, LAS VEGAS, NV, p. A406
REDINGTON–FAIRVIEW GENERAL HOSPITAL, SKOWHEGAN, ME, p. A295
REDLANDS COMMUNITY HOSPITAL, REDLANDS, CA, p. A85
REDMOND REGIONAL MEDICAL CENTER, ROME, GA, p. A165

REDWOOD AREA HOSPITAL, REDWOOD FALLS, MN, p. A349
REDWOOD MEMORIAL HOSPITAL, FORTUNA, CA, p. A62
REEDSBURG AREA MEDICAL CENTER, REEDSBURG, WI,
p. A715
REEVES COUNTY HOSPITAL, PECOS, TX, p. A641
REEVES MEMORIAL MEDICAL CENTER, BERNICE, LA, p. A273
REFUGIO COUNTY MEMORIAL HOSPITAL, REFUGIO, TX, p. A643
REGENCY HOSPITAL CLEVELAND EAST, WARRENSVILLE
HEIGHTS, OH, p. A505
REGENCY HOSPITAL OF CENTRAL GEORGIA, MACON, GA,
p. A162
REGENCY HOSPITAL OF CLEVELAND – WEST, MIDDLEBURG
HEIGHTS, OHIO (see REGENCY HOSPITAL CLEVELAND EAST),
p. A505
REGENCY HOSPITAL OF COLUMBUS, COLUMBUS, OH, p. A491
REGENCY HOSPITAL OF FLORENCE, FLORENCE, SC, p. A566
REGENCY HOSPITAL OF GREENVILLE, GREENVILLE, SC,
p. A566
REGENCY HOSPITAL OF HATTIESBURG, HATTIESBURG, MS,
p. A359
REGENCY HOSPITAL OF MERIDIAN, MERIDIAN, MS, p. A362
REGENCY HOSPITAL OF MINNEAPOLIS, GOLDEN VALLEY, MN,
p. A343
REGENCY HOSPITAL OF NORTHWEST ARKANSAS –
SPRINGDALE, SPRINGDALE, AR, p. A52
REGENCY HOSPITAL OF NORTHWEST INDIANA, EAST CHICAGO,
IN, p. A209
REGENCY HOSPITAL OF PORTER COUNTY, PORTAGE, INDIANA
(see REGENCY HOSPITAL OF NORTHWEST INDIANA), p. A209
REGENCY HOSPITAL OF SOUTH ATLANTA, EAST POINT, GA,
p. A159
REGENCY HOSPITAL OF TOLEDO, SYLVANIA, OH, p. A503
REGINA HOSPITAL, HASTINGS, MN, p. A344
REGIONAL GENERAL HOSPITAL, WILLISTON, FL, p. A150
REGIONAL HEALTH SERVICES OF HOWARD COUNTY, CRESCO,
IA, p. A228
REGIONAL HOSPITAL FOR RESPIRATORY AND COMPLEX CARE,
BURIEN, WA, p. A683
REGIONAL HOSPITAL OF SCRANTON, SCRANTON, PA, p. A554
REGIONAL MEDICAL CENTER, MANCHESTER, IA, p. A234
REGIONAL MEDICAL CENTER, ORANGEBURG, SC, p. A569
REGIONAL MEDICAL CENTER BAYONET POINT, HUDSON, FL,
p. A131
REGIONAL MEDICAL CENTER OF SAN JOSE, SAN JOSE, CA,
p. A91
REGIONAL MENTAL HEALTH CENTER, MERRILLVILLE, IN,
p. A218
REGIONAL ONE HEALTH, MEMPHIS, TN, p. A589
REGIONAL ONE HEALTH EXTENDED CARE HOSPITAL,
MEMPHIS, TN, p. A589
REGIONAL REHABILITATION CENTER, SALEM, OREGON (see
SALEM HOSPITAL), p. A530
REGIONAL REHABILITATION HOSPITAL, PHENIX CITY, AL, p. A24
REGIONAL WEST GARDEN COUNTY, OSHKOSH, NE, p. A401
REGIONAL WEST MEDICAL CENTER, SCOTTSBLUFF, NE,
p. A402
REGIONS HOSPITAL, SAINT PAUL, MN, p. A350
REHABILITATION HOSPITAL OF FORT WAYNE, FORT WAYNE, IN,
p. A211
REHABILITATION HOSPITAL OF INDIANA, INDIANAPOLIS, IN,
p. A214
REHABILITATION HOSPITAL OF JENNINGS, JENNINGS, LA,
p. A279
REHABILITATION HOSPITAL OF RHODE ISLAND, NORTH
SMITHFIELD, RI, p. A560
REHABILITATION HOSPITAL OF SAVANNAH, SAVANNAH, GA,
p. A166
REHABILITATION HOSPITAL OF SOUTHERN NEW MEXICO, LAS
CRUCES, NM, p. A430
REHABILITATION HOSPITAL OF SOUTHWEST VIRGINIA, BRISTOL,
VA, p. A668
REHABILITATION HOSPITAL OF THE PACIFIC, HONOLULU, HI,
p. A171
REHABILITATION HOSPITAL OF WISCONSIN, WAUKESHA, WI,
p. A718
REHABILITATION HOSPITAL, NAVICENT HEALTH, MACON, GA,
p. A162
REHABILITATION INSTITUTE AT THE MOUNT KEMBLE DIVISION,
GORYEB CHILDREN'S HOSPITAL, MORRISTOWN, NEW JERSEY
(see MORRISTOWN MEDICAL CENTER), p. A419
REHABILITATION INSTITUTE OF CHICAGO, CHICAGO, IL, p. A186
REHABILITATION INSTITUTE OF OREGON, PORTLAND, OREGON
(see LEGACY GOOD SAMARITAN HOSPITAL AND MEDICAL
CENTER), p. A529
REHOBOTH MCKINLEY CHRISTIAN HEALTH CARE SERVICES,
GALLUP, NM, p. A429
REID HEALTH, RICHMOND, IN, p. A221
REISCH MEMORIAL NURSING HOME (see THOMAS H. BOYD
MEMORIAL HOSPITAL), p. A182

RENOWN CHILDREN'S HOSPITAL, RENO, NEVADA (see RENOWN
REGIONAL MEDICAL CENTER), p. A408
RENOWN REGIONAL MEDICAL CENTER, RENO, NV, p. A408
RENOWN REHABILITATION HOSPITAL, RENO, NV, p. A408
RENOWN SOUTH MEADOWS MEDICAL CENTER, RENO, NV,
p. A408
REPUBLIC COUNTY HOSPITAL, BELLEVILLE, KS, p. A240
RESEARCH MEDICAL CENTER, KANSAS CITY, MO, p. A373
RESEARCH PSYCHIATRIC CENTER, KANSAS CITY, MISSOURI
(see RESEARCH MEDICAL CENTER), p. A373
RESOLUTE HEALTH, NEW BRAUNFELS, TX, p. A639
RESTON HOSPITAL CENTER, RESTON, VA, p. A676
REYNOLDS ARMY COMMUNITY HOSPITAL, FORT SILL, OK,
p. A512
REYNOLDS MEMORIAL HOSPITAL, GLEN DALE, WV, p. A696
RHEA MEDICAL CENTER, DAYTON, TN, p. A582
RHODE ISLAND HOSPITAL, PROVIDENCE, RI, p. A561
RICE MEDICAL CENTER, EAGLE LAKE, TX, p. A614
RICE MEMORIAL HOSPITAL, WILLMAR, MN, p. A353
RICELAND MEDICAL CENTER, WINNIE, TX, p. A658
RICHARD H. HUTCHINGS PSYCHIATRIC CENTER, SYRACUSE,
NY, p. A456
RICHARD H. YOUNG BEHAVIORAL HEALTH CENTER, KEARNEY,
NEBRASKA (see CHI HEALTH GOOD SAMARITAN), p. A397
RICHARD L. ROUDEBUSH VETERANS AFFAIRS MEDICAL
CENTER, INDIANAPOLIS, IN, p. A214
RICHARD P. STADTER PSYCHIATRIC CENTER, GRAND FORKS,
ND, p. A479
RICHARDSON MEDICAL CENTER, RAYVILLE, LA, p. A286
RICHLAND HOSPITAL, RICHLAND CENTER, WI, p. A715
RICHLAND MEMORIAL HOSPITAL, OLNEY, IL, p. A199
RICHLAND PARISH HOSPITAL, DELHI, LA, p. A276
RICHMOND STATE HOSPITAL, RICHMOND, IN, p. A221
RICHMOND UNIVERSITY MEDICAL CENTER,, NY, p. A449
RIDDLE HOSPITAL, MEDIA, PA, p. A545
RIDEOUT MEMORIAL HOSPITAL, MARYSVILLE, CA, p. A76
RIDGE BEHAVIORAL HEALTH SYSTEM, LEXINGTON, KY, p. A263
RIDGECREST REGIONAL HOSPITAL, RIDGECREST, CA, p. A85
RIDGEVIEW BEHAVIORAL HOSPITAL, MIDDLE POINT, OH,
p. A499
RIDGEVIEW INSTITUTE, SMYRNA, GA, p. A166
RIDGEVIEW MEDICAL CENTER, WACONIA, MN, p. A352
RIDGEVIEW PSYCHIATRIC HOSPITAL AND CENTER, OAK RIDGE,
TN, p. A592
RIDGEVIEW SIBLEY MEDICAL CENTER, ARLINGTON, MN,
p. A338
RILEY HOSPITAL FOR CHILDREN AT INDIANA UNIVERSITY
HEALTH, INDIANAPOLIS, INDIANA (see INDIANA UNIVERSITY
HEALTH UNIVERSITY HOSPITAL), p. A214
RINGGOLD COUNTY HOSPITAL, MOUNT AYR, IA, p. A234
RIO GRANDE HOSPITAL, DEL NORTE, CO, p. A103
RIO GRANDE REGIONAL HOSPITAL, MCALLEN, TX, p. A636
RIO GRANDE STATE CENTER, HARLINGEN, TEXAS (see RIO
GRANDE STATE CENTER/SOUTH TEXAS HEALTH CARE
SYSTEM), p. A622
RIO GRANDE STATE CENTER/SOUTH TEXAS HEALTH CARE
SYSTEM, HARLINGEN, TX, p. A622
RIPON MEDICAL CENTER, RIPON, WI, p. A715
RIVENDELL BEHAVIORAL HEALTH, BOWLING GREEN, KY,
p. A258
RIVENDELL BEHAVIORAL HEALTH SERVICES OF ARKANSAS,
BENTON, AR, p. A43
RIVER BEND HOSPITAL, WEST LAFAYETTE, IN, p. A223
RIVER CREST HOSPITAL, SAN ANGELO, TX, p. A644
RIVER FALLS AREA HOSPITAL, RIVER FALLS, WI, p. A715
RIVER HOSPITAL, ALEXANDRIA BAY, NY, p. A433
RIVER OAKS CHILD AND ADOLESCENT HOSPITAL, NEW
ORLEANS, LOUISIANA (see RIVER OAKS HOSPITAL), p. A285
RIVER OAKS HOSPITAL, NEW ORLEANS, LA, p. A285
RIVER PARK HOSPITAL, HUNTINGTON, WV, p. A697
RIVER POINT BEHAVIORAL HEALTH, JACKSONVILLE, FL,
p. A132
RIVER REGION WEST CAMPUS, VICKSBURG, MISSISSIPPI (see
MERIT HEALTH RIVER REGION), p. A365
RIVER VALLEY MEDICAL CENTER, DARDANELLE, AR, p. A45
RIVER'S EDGE HOSPITAL AND CLINIC, SAINT PETER, MN,
p. A351
RIVERCREST SPECIALTY HOSPITAL, MISHAWAKA, IN, p. A218
RIVEREDGE HOSPITAL, FOREST PARK, IL, p. A190
RIVERLAND MEDICAL CENTER, FERRIDAY, LA, p. A276
RIVERSIDE COMMUNITY HOSPITAL, RIVERSIDE, CA, p. A86
RIVERSIDE DOCTORS' HOSPITAL, WILLIAMSBURG, VA, p. A680
RIVERSIDE HOSPITAL OF LOUISIANA, ALEXANDRIA, LA, p. A271
RIVERSIDE MEDICAL CENTER, KANKAKEE, IL, p. A194
RIVERSIDE MEDICAL CENTER, FRANKLINTON, LA, p. A277
RIVERSIDE PSYCHIATRIC INSTITUTE, RIVERSIDE BEHAVIORAL
HEALTH CENTER, HAMPTON, VIRGINIA (see RIVERSIDE
REGIONAL MEDICAL CENTER), p. A674
RIVERSIDE REGIONAL MEDICAL CENTER, NEWPORT NEWS, VA,
p. A674

RIVERSIDE REHABILITATION INSTITUTE, NEWPORT NEWS, VA,
p. A674
RIVERSIDE SHORE MEMORIAL HOSPITAL, NASSAWADOX, VA,
p. A674
RIVERSIDE TAPPAHANNOCK HOSPITAL, TAPPAHANNOCK, VA,
p. A679
RIVERSIDE UNIVERSITY HEALTH SYSTEM–MEDICAL CENTER,
MORENO VALLEY, CA, p. A78
RIVERSIDE WALTER REED HOSPITAL, GLOUCESTER, VA,
p. A671
RIVERTON HOSPITAL, RIVERTON, UT, p. A662
RIVERVALLEY BEHAVIORAL HEALTH HOSPITAL, OWENSBORO,
KY, p. A267
RIVERVIEW BEHAVIORAL HEALTH, TEXARKANA, AR, p. A53
RIVERVIEW HEALTH, NOBLESVILLE, IN, p. A220
RIVERVIEW HEALTH, CROOKSTON, MN, p. A341
RIVERVIEW MEDICAL CENTER, RED BANK, NJ, p. A423
RIVERVIEW PSYCHIATRIC CENTER, AUGUSTA, ME, p. A291
RIVERVIEW REGIONAL MEDICAL CENTER, GADSDEN, AL, p. A20
RIVERVIEW REGIONAL MEDICAL CENTER, CARTHAGE, TN,
p. A579
RIVERWOOD HEALTHCARE CENTER, AITKIN, MN, p. A338
RIVERWOODS BEHAVIORAL HEALTH SYSTEM, RIVERDALE, GA,
p. A164
RMC JACKSONVILLE, JACKSONVILLE, AL, p. A22
RML SPECIALTY HOSPITAL, CHICAGO, IL, p. A186
RML SPECIALTY HOSPITAL, HINSDALE, IL, p. A193
ROANE GENERAL HOSPITAL, SPENCER, WV, p. A700
ROANE MEDICAL CENTER, HARRIMAN, TN, p. A583
ROANOKE MEMORIAL REHABILITATION CENTER, ROANOKE,
VIRGINIA (see CARILION ROANOKE MEMORIAL HOSPITAL),
p. A678
ROBERT E. BUSH NAVAL HOSPITAL, TWENTYNINE PALMS, CA,
p. A97
ROBERT J. DOLE VETERANS AFFAIRS MEDICAL CENTER,
WICHITA, KS, p. A256
ROBERT PACKER HOSPITAL, SAYRE, PA, p. A553
ROBERT WOOD JOHNSON UNIVERSITY HOSPITAL, NEW
BRUNSWICK, NJ, p. A420
ROBERT WOOD JOHNSON UNIVERSITY HOSPITAL AT
HAMILTON, HAMILTON, NJ, p. A417
ROBERT WOOD JOHNSON UNIVERSITY HOSPITAL RAHWAY,
RAHWAY, NJ, p. A422
ROBERT WOOD JOHNSON UNIVERSITY HOSPITAL SOMERSET,
SOMERVILLE, NJ, p. A423
ROBLEY REX VETERANS AFFAIRS MEDICAL CENTER,
LOUISVILLE, KY, p. A265
ROCHELLE COMMUNITY HOSPITAL, ROCHELLE, IL, p. A201
ROCHESTER GENERAL HOSPITAL, ROCHESTER, NY, p. A454
ROCHESTER PSYCHIATRIC CENTER, ROCHESTER, NY, p. A454
ROCK COUNTY HOSPITAL, BASSETT, NE, p. A393
ROCK PRAIRIE BEHAVIORAL HEALTH, COLLEGE STATION, TX,
p. A606
ROCK SPRINGS, LLC, GEORGETOWN, TX, p. A620
ROCKCASTLE REGIONAL HOSPITAL AND RESPIRATORY CARE
CENTER, MOUNT VERNON, KY, p. A267
ROCKDALE HOSPITAL, ROCKDALE, TX, p. A643
ROCKDALE MEDICAL CENTER, CONYERS, GA, p. A157
ROCKEFELLER UNIVERSITY HOSPITAL, NEW YORK, NY, p. A449
ROCKFORD CENTER, NEWARK, DE, p. A119
ROCKLAND CHILDREN'S PSYCHIATRIC CENTER, ORANGEBURG,
NY, p. A452
ROCKLAND PSYCHIATRIC CENTER, ORANGEBURG, NY, p. A452
ROCKVILLE GENERAL HOSPITAL, VERNON, CT, p. A117
ROCKY MOUNTAIN HOSPITAL FOR CHILDREN, DENVER,
COLORADO (see PRESBYTERIAN–ST. LUKE'S MEDICAL
CENTER), p. A104
ROGER C. PEACE REHABILITATION HOSPITAL, GREENVILLE,
SOUTH CAROLINA (see GHS GREENVILLE MEMORIAL
HOSPITAL), p. A566
ROGER HUNTINGTON NURSING CENTER (see GHS GREER
MEMORIAL HOSPITAL), p. A567
ROGER MILLS MEMORIAL HOSPITAL, CHEYENNE, OK, p. A509
ROGER WILLIAMS MEDICAL CENTER, PROVIDENCE, RI, p. A561
ROGERS MEMORIAL HOSPITAL, OCONOMOWOC, WI, p. A713
ROGERS MEMORIAL HOSPITAL–BROWN DEER, BROWN DEER,
WISCONSIN (see ROGERS MEMORIAL HOSPITAL), p. A713
ROGERS MEMORIAL HOSPITAL–WEST ALLIS, WEST ALLIS,
WISCONSIN (see ROGERS MEMORIAL HOSPITAL), p. A713
ROLLING HILLS HOSPITAL, ADA, OK, p. A508
ROLLING HILLS HOSPITAL, FRANKLIN, TN, p. A583
ROLLING PLAINS MEMORIAL HOSPITAL, SWEETWATER, TX,
p. A651
ROLLINS–BROOK COMMUNITY HOSPITAL, LAMPASAS, TX,
p. A632
ROME MEMORIAL HOSPITAL, ROME, NY, p. A455
RONALD MCDONALD CHILDREN'S HOSPITAL, MAYWOOD,
ILLINOIS (see LOYOLA UNIVERSITY MEDICAL CENTER),
p. A196

RONALD REAGAN UCLA MEDICAL CENTER, LOS ANGELES, CA, p. A74
ROOKS COUNTY HEALTH CENTER, PLAINVILLE, KS, p. A252
ROOSEVELT GENERAL HOSPITAL, PORTALES, NM, p. A430
ROOSEVELT MEDICAL CENTER, CULBERTSON, MT, p. A386
ROOSEVELT WARM SPRINGS REHABILITATION AND SPECIALTY HOSPITALS – LTAC, WARM SPRINGS, GA, p. A168
ROOSEVELT WARM SPRINGS REHABILITATION AND SPECIALTY HOSPITALS – REHAB, WARM SPRINGS, GA, p. A168
ROPER ST. FRANCIS, CHARLESTON, SC, p. A563
ROPER ST. FRANCIS MOUNT PLEASANT HOSPITAL, MOUNT PLEASANT, SC, p. A568
ROSE MEDICAL CENTER, DENVER, CO, p. A104
ROSEBUD HEALTH CARE CENTER, FORSYTH, MT, p. A387
ROSELAND COMMUNITY HOSPITAL, CHICAGO, IL, p. A186
ROSS SKILLED NURSING FACILITY (see EASTERN MAINE MEDICAL CENTER), p. A291
ROSWELL PARK CANCER INSTITUTE, BUFFALO, NY, p. A436
ROTARY REHABILITATION HOSPITAL, MOBILE, ALABAMA (see MOBILE INFIRMARY MEDICAL CENTER), p. A22
ROTHMAN SPECIALTY HOSPITAL, BENSALEM, PA, p. A533
ROUNDUP MEMORIAL HEALTHCARE, ROUNDUP, MT, p. A390
ROXBOROUGH MEMORIAL HOSPITAL, PHILADELPHIA, PA, p. A549
ROXBURY TREATMENT CENTER, SHIPPENSBURG, PA, p. A555
ROYAL OAKS HOSPITAL, WINDSOR, MO, p. A384
RUBY VALLEY HOSPITAL, SHERIDAN, MT, p. A391
RUMFORD HOSPITAL, RUMFORD, ME, p. A295
RUNNELLS CENTER FOR REHABILITATION AND HEALTHCARE, BERKELEY HEIGHTS, NJ, p. A414
RUSH CHILDREN'S HOSPITAL, CHICAGO, ILLINOIS (see RUSH UNIVERSITY MEDICAL CENTER), p. A186
RUSH COUNTY MEMORIAL HOSPITAL, LA CROSSE, KS, p. A247
RUSH FOUNDATION HOSPITAL, MERIDIAN, MS, p. A362
RUSH MEMORIAL HOSPITAL, RUSHVILLE, IN, p. A221
RUSH OAK PARK HOSPITAL, OAK PARK, IL, p. A199
RUSH UNIVERSITY MEDICAL CENTER, CHICAGO, IL, p. A186
RUSH–COPLEY MEDICAL CENTER, AURORA, IL, p. A181
RUSK COUNTY MEMORIAL HOSPITAL, LADYSMITH, WI, p. A708
RUSK INSTITUTE AT NYU–HJD, NEW YORK, NEW YORK (see NYU LANGONE MEDICAL CENTER), p. A449
RUSK STATE HOSPITAL, RUSK, TX, p. A644
RUSSELL COUNTY HOSPITAL, RUSSELL SPRINGS, KY, p. A269
RUSSELL COUNTY MEDICAL CENTER, LEBANON, VA, p. A672
RUSSELL MEDICAL CENTER, ALEXANDER CITY, AL, p. A15
RUSSELL REGIONAL HOSPITAL, RUSSELL, KS, p. A252
RUSSELLVILLE HOSPITAL, RUSSELLVILLE, AL, p. A25
RUTHERFORD REGIONAL HEALTH SYSTEM, RUTHERFORDTON, NC, p. A473
RUTLAND REGIONAL MEDICAL CENTER, RUTLAND, VT, p. A666
RYDER MEMORIAL HOSPITAL, HUMACAO, PR, p. A727

S

SABETHA COMMUNITY HOSPITAL, SABETHA, KS, p. A253
SABINE COUNTY HOSPITAL, HEMPHILL, TX, p. A623
SABINE MEDICAL CENTER, MANY, LA, p. A282
SACRED HEART CHILDREN'S HOSPITAL, SPOKANE, WASHINGTON (see PROVIDENCE SACRED HEART MEDICAL CENTER & CHILDREN'S HOSPITAL), p. A691
SACRED HEART HOSPITAL, ALLENTOWN, PA, p. A532
SACRED HEART HOSPITAL, EAU CLAIRE, WI, p. A705
SACRED HEART HOSPITAL ON THE EMERALD COAST, MIRAMAR BEACH, FL, p. A138
SACRED HEART HOSPITAL ON THE GULF, PORT ST. JOE, FL, p. A143
SACRED HEART HOSPITAL PENSACOLA, PENSACOLA, FL, p. A142
SACRED HEART REHABILITATION INSTITUTE, MILWAUKEE, WI, p. A711
SADDLEBACK MEMORIAL MEDICAL CENTER, LAGUNA HILLS, CA, p. A68
SAFE HAVEN HOSPITAL OF POCATELLO, POCATELLO, ID, p. A178
SAFE HAVEN HOSPITAL OF TREASURE VALLEY, BOISE, ID, p. A174
SAGAMORE CHILDREN'S PSYCHIATRIC CENTER, DIX HILLS, NY, p. A438
SAGE MEMORIAL HOSPITAL, GANADO, AZ, p. A32
SAGE REHABILITATION HOSPITAL, BATON ROUGE, LA, p. A273
SAGEWEST HEALTH CARE AT LANDER, LANDER, WYOMING (see SAGEWEST HEALTH CARE AT RIVERTON), p. A723
SAGEWEST HEALTH CARE AT RIVERTON, RIVERTON, WY, p. A723
SAINT AGNES HOSPITAL, BALTIMORE, MD, p. A297
SAINT AGNES MEDICAL CENTER, FRESNO, CA, p. A64

SAINT ALPHONSUS MEDICAL CENTER – BAKER CITY, BAKER CITY, OR, p. A524
SAINT ALPHONSUS MEDICAL CENTER – NAMPA, NAMPA, ID, p. A177
SAINT ALPHONSUS MEDICAL CENTER – ONTARIO, ONTARIO, OR, p. A528
SAINT ALPHONSUS REGIONAL MEDICAL CENTER, BOISE, ID, p. A174
SAINT ANNE'S HOSPITAL, FALL RIVER, MA, p. A310
SAINT ANTHONY HOSPITAL, CHICAGO, IL, p. A186
SAINT BARNABAS MEDICAL CENTER, LIVINGSTON, NJ, p. A418
SAINT CLARE'S HEALTH CENTER AT SUSSEX, SUSSEX, NEW JERSEY (see SAINT CLARE'S HEALTH SYSTEM), p. A416
SAINT CLARE'S HEALTH SYSTEM, DENVILLE, NJ, p. A416
SAINT CLARE'S HOSPITAL/BOONTON TOWNSHIP, BOONTON TOWNSHIP, NEW JERSEY (see SAINT CLARE'S HEALTH SYSTEM), p. A416
SAINT CLARE'S HOSPITAL/DENVILLE, DENVILLE, NEW JERSEY (see SAINT CLARE'S HEALTH SYSTEM), p. A416
SAINT CLARE'S HOSPITAL/DOVER, DOVER, NEW JERSEY (see SAINT CLARE'S HEALTH SYSTEM), p. A416
SAINT ELIZABETH'S MEDICAL CENTER, WABASHA, MN, p. A352
SAINT ELIZABETHS HOSPITAL, WASHINGTON, DC, p. A122
SAINT FRANCIS HEALTHCARE SYSTEM, CAPE GIRARDEAU, MO, p. A368
SAINT FRANCIS HEART HOSPITAL, TULSA, OKLAHOMA (see SAINT FRANCIS HOSPITAL), p. A522
SAINT FRANCIS HOSPITAL, TULSA, OK, p. A522
SAINT FRANCIS HOSPITAL, MEMPHIS, TN, p. A589
SAINT FRANCIS HOSPITAL, CHARLESTON, WV, p. A695
SAINT FRANCIS HOSPITAL AND MEDICAL CENTER, HARTFORD, CT, p. A114
SAINT FRANCIS HOSPITAL SOUTH, TULSA, OK, p. A522
SAINT FRANCIS HOSPITAL–BARTLETT, BARTLETT, TN, p. A579
SAINT FRANCIS MEMORIAL HOSPITAL, SAN FRANCISCO, CA, p. A90
SAINT JOHN HOSPITAL, LEAVENWORTH, KS, p. A247
SAINT JOSEPH LONDON, LONDON, KY, p. A264
SAINT JOSEPH – MARTIN, MARTIN, KY, p. A266
SAINT JOSEPH BEREA, BEREA, KY, p. A257
SAINT JOSEPH EAST, LEXINGTON, KY, p. A263
SAINT JOSEPH HOSPITAL, DENVER, CO, p. A104
SAINT JOSEPH HOSPITAL, LEXINGTON, KY, p. A263
SAINT JOSEPH MOUNT STERLING, MOUNT STERLING, KY, p. A267
SAINT JOSEPH REGIONAL MEDICAL CENTER, MISHAWAKA, IN, p. A218
SAINT JOSEPH REGIONAL MEDICAL CENTER–PLYMOUTH CAMPUS, PLYMOUTH, IN, p. A220
SAINT JOSEPH'S CHILDEN'S HOSPITAL, MARSHFIELD, WISCONSIN (see MINISTRY SAINT JOSEPH'S HOSPITAL), p. A709
SAINT JOSEPH'S MEDICAL CENTER, YONKERS, NY, p. A459
SAINT LOUISE REGIONAL HOSPITAL, GILROY, CA, p. A64
SAINT LUKE INSTITUTE, SILVER SPRING, MD, p. A303
SAINT LUKE'S CUSHING HOSPITAL, LEAVENWORTH, KS, p. A247
SAINT LUKE'S EAST HOSPITAL, LEE'S SUMMIT, MO, p. A375
SAINT LUKE'S HOSPITAL OF KANSAS CITY, KANSAS CITY, MO, p. A374
SAINT LUKE'S NORTH HOSPITAL – BARRY ROAD, KANSAS CITY, MO, p. A374
SAINT LUKE'S NORTH HOSPITAL–SMITHVILLE CAMPUS, SMITHVILLE, MISSOURI (see SAINT LUKE'S NORTH HOSPITAL – BARRY ROAD), p. A374
SAINT LUKE'S SOUTH HOSPITAL, OVERLAND PARK, KS, p. A251
SAINT MARGARET MERCY HEALTHCARE CENTERS–NORTH CAMPUS, HAMMOND, INDIANA (see FRANCISCAN ST. MARGARET HEALTH – HAMMOND), p. A212
SAINT MARY'S HOSPITAL, WATERBURY, CT, p. A117
SAINT MARY'S REGIONAL MEDICAL CENTER, RUSSELLVILLE, AR, p. A52
SAINT MARY'S REGIONAL MEDICAL CENTER, RENO, NV, p. A408
SAINT MICHAEL'S MEDICAL CENTER, NEWARK, NJ, p. A421
SAINT PETER'S UNIVERSITY HOSPITAL, NEW BRUNSWICK, NJ, p. A420
SAINT SIMONS BY–THE–SEA HOSPITAL, SAINT SIMONS ISLAND, GA, p. A165
SAINT THOMAS DEKALB HOSPITAL, SMITHVILLE, TN, p. A593
SAINT THOMAS HICKMAN HOSPITAL, CENTERVILLE, TN, p. A580
SAINT THOMAS HIGHLANDS HOSPITAL, SPARTA, TN, p. A593
SAINT THOMAS HOSPITAL FOR SPINAL SURGERY, NASHVILLE, TN, p. A590
SAINT THOMAS MIDTOWN HOSPITAL, NASHVILLE, TN, p. A591
SAINT THOMAS RIVER PARK HOSPITAL, MC MINNVILLE, TN, p. A588

SAINT THOMAS RUTHERFORD HOSPITAL, MURFREESBORO, TN, p. A590
SAINT THOMAS STONES RIVER HOSPITAL, WOODBURY, TN, p. A594
SAINT THOMAS WEST HOSPITAL, NASHVILLE, TN, p. A591
SAINT VINCENT HOSPITAL, WORCESTER, MA, p. A316
SAINT VINCENT HOSPITAL, ERIE, PA, p. A538
SAKAKAWEA MEDICAL CENTER, HAZEN, ND, p. A479
SALEM CAMPUS, SALEM, MASSACHUSETTS (see NORTH SHORE MEDICAL CENTER), p. A314
SALEM HEALTH WEST VALLEY, DALLAS, OR, p. A525
SALEM HOSPITAL, SALEM, OR, p. A530
SALEM MEMORIAL DISTRICT HOSPITAL, SALEM, MO, p. A382
SALEM REGIONAL MEDICAL CENTER, SALEM, OH, p. A502
SALEM TOWNSHIP HOSPITAL, SALEM, IL, p. A202
SALEM VETERANS AFFAIRS MEDICAL CENTER, SALEM, VA, p. A678
SALINA REGIONAL HEALTH CENTER, SALINA, KS, p. A253
SALINA REGIONAL HEALTH CENTER– PENN CAMPUS, SALINA, KANSAS (see SALINA REGIONAL HEALTH CENTER), p. A253
SALINA REGIONAL HEALTH CENTER–SANTA FE CAMPUS, SALINA, KANSAS (see SALINA REGIONAL HEALTH CENTER), p. A253
SALINA SURGICAL HOSPITAL, SALINA, KS, p. A253
SALINAS VALLEY MEMORIAL HEALTHCARE SYSTEM, SALINAS, CA, p. A87
SALINE MEMORIAL HOSPITAL, BENTON, AR, p. A43
SALT LAKE BEHAVIORAL HEALTH, SALT LAKE CITY, UT, p. A663
SALT LAKE REGIONAL MEDICAL CENTER, SALT LAKE CITY, UT, p. A663
SAM RAYBURN MEMORIAL VETERANS CENTER, BONHAM, TEXAS (see VETERANS AFFAIRS NORTH TEXAS HEALTH CARE SYSTEM), p. A612
SAMARITAN ALBANY GENERAL HOSPITAL, ALBANY, OR, p. A524
SAMARITAN BEHAVIORAL HEALTH CENTER–DESERT SAMARITAN MEDICAL CENTER, MESA, ARIZONA (see BANNER DESERT MEDICAL CENTER), p. A34
SAMARITAN HEALTHCARE, MOSES LAKE, WA, p. A686
SAMARITAN HOSPITAL, TROY, NY, p. A457
SAMARITAN LEBANON COMMUNITY HOSPITAL, LEBANON, OR, p. A527
SAMARITAN MEDICAL CENTER, WATERTOWN, NY, p. A458
SAMARITAN MEMORIAL HOSPITAL, MACON, MO, p. A376
SAMARITAN NORTH LINCOLN HOSPITAL, LINCOLN CITY, OR, p. A527
SAMARITAN PACIFIC COMMUNITIES HOSPITAL, NEWPORT, OR, p. A528
SAME DAY SURGERY CENTER, RAPID CITY, SD, p. A575
SAMPSON REGIONAL MEDICAL CENTER, CLINTON, NC, p. A463
SAMUEL MAHELONA MEMORIAL HOSPITAL, KAPAA, HI, p. A172
SAMUEL SIMMONDS MEMORIAL HOSPITAL, BARROW, AK, p. A28
SAN ANGELO COMMUNITY MEDICAL CENTER, SAN ANGELO, TX, p. A644
SAN ANTONIO DIVISION, SAN ANTONIO, TEXAS (see SOUTH TEXAS VETERANS HEALTH CARE SYSTEM), p. A647
SAN ANTONIO REGIONAL HOSPITAL, UPLAND, CA, p. A97
SAN ANTONIO STATE HOSPITAL, SAN ANTONIO, TX, p. A647
SAN BERNARDINO MOUNTAINS COMMUNITY HOSPITAL DISTRICT, LAKE ARROWHEAD, CA, p. A68
SAN CARLOS APACHE HEALTHCARE CORPORATION, PERIDOT, AZ, p. A35
SAN DIEGO COUNTY PSYCHIATRIC HOSPITAL, SAN DIEGO, CA, p. A89
SAN DIMAS COMMUNITY HOSPITAL, SAN DIMAS, CA, p. A89
SAN FRANCISCO VA MEDICAL CENTER, SAN FRANCISCO, CA, p. A90
SAN GORGONIO MEMORIAL HOSPITAL, BANNING, CA, p. A56
SAN JOAQUIN COMMUNITY HOSPITAL, BAKERSFIELD, CA, p. A56
SAN JOAQUIN GENERAL HOSPITAL, FRENCH CAMP, CA, p. A63
SAN JOAQUIN VALLEY REHABILITATION HOSPITAL, FRESNO, CA, p. A64
SAN JORGE CHILDREN'S HOSPITAL, SAN JUAN, PR, p. A730
SAN JOSE BEHAVORIAL HEALTH, SAN JOSE, CA, p. A91
SAN JUAN CAPESTRANO HOSPITAL, SAN JUAN, PR, p. A730
SAN JUAN CITY HOSPITAL, SAN JUAN, PR, p. A730
SAN JUAN HOSPITAL, MONTICELLO, UT, p. A660
SAN JUAN REGIONAL MEDICAL CENTER, FARMINGTON, NM, p. A429
SAN JUAN REGIONAL MEDICAL CENTER REHABILITATION HOSPITAL, FARMINGTON, NEW MEXICO (see SAN JUAN REGIONAL MEDICAL CENTER), p. A429
SAN LEANDRO HOSPITAL, SAN LEANDRO, CA, p. A92
SAN LUIS VALLEY HEALTH, ALAMOSA, CO, p. A101
SAN LUIS VALLEY HEALTH CONEJOS COUNTY HOSPITAL, LA JARA, CO, p. A107
SAN MATEO MEDICAL CENTER, SAN MATEO, CA, p. A92

© 2016 AHA Guide

SELECT SPECIALTY HOSPITAL–QUAD CITIES, DAVENPORT, IA, p. A228
SELECT SPECIALTY HOSPITAL–SAGINAW, SAGINAW, MI, p. A333
SELECT SPECIALTY HOSPITAL–SAVANNAH, SAVANNAH, GA, p. A166
SELECT SPECIALTY HOSPITAL–SCOTTSDALE, SCOTTSDALE, AZ, p. A39
SELECT SPECIALTY HOSPITAL–SIOUX FALLS, SIOUX FALLS, SD, p. A576
SELECT SPECIALTY HOSPITAL–SOUTH DALLAS, DALLAS, TX, p. A611
SELECT SPECIALTY HOSPITAL–SPRINGFIELD, SPRINGFIELD, MO, p. A383
SELECT SPECIALTY HOSPITAL–ST. LOUIS, SAINT CHARLES, MO, p. A379
SELECT SPECIALTY HOSPITAL–TALLAHASSEE, TALLAHASSEE, FL, p. A146
SELECT SPECIALTY HOSPITAL–TRI CITIES, BRISTOL, TN, p. A579
SELECT SPECIALTY HOSPITAL–TULSA MIDTOWN, TULSA, OK, p. A522
SELECT SPECIALTY HOSPITAL–WESTERN MISSOURI, KANSAS CITY, MO, p. A374
SELECT SPECIALTY HOSPITAL–WICHITA, WICHITA, KS, p. A256
SELECT SPECIALTY HOSPITAL–WILMINGTON, WILMINGTON, DE, p. A120
SELECT SPECIALTY HOSPITAL–WINSTON–SALEM, WINSTON–SALEM, NC, p. A476
SELECT SPECIALTY HOSPITAL–YORK, YORK, PENNSYLVANIA (see SELECT SPECIALTY HOSPITAL–CENTRAL PENNSYLVANIA), p. A534
SELECT SPECIALTY HOSPITAL–YOUNGSTOWN, YOUNGSTOWN, OH, p. A506
SELECT SPECIALTY HOSPITAL–YOUNGSTOWN, BOARDMAN CAMPUS, WARREN, OHIO (see SELECT SPECIALTY HOSPITAL–YOUNGSTOWN), p. A506
SELF REGIONAL HEALTHCARE, GREENWOOD, SC, p. A567
SENECA HEALTHCARE DISTRICT, CHESTER, CA, p. A58
SENIOR HAVEN CONVALESCENT NURSING CENTER (see SANFORD CANBY MEDICAL CENTER), p. A340
SENTARA ALBEMARLE MEDICAL CENTER, ELIZABETH CITY, NC, p. A464
SENTARA CAREPLEX HOSPITAL, HAMPTON, VA, p. A671
SENTARA HALIFAX REGIONAL HOSPITAL, SOUTH BOSTON, VA, p. A678
SENTARA LEIGH HOSPITAL, NORFOLK, VA, p. A675
SENTARA NORFOLK GENERAL HOSPITAL, NORFOLK, VA, p. A675
SENTARA NORTHERN VIRGINIA MEDICAL CENTER, WOODBRIDGE, VA, p. A680
SENTARA OBICI HOSPITAL, SUFFOLK, VA, p. A679
SENTARA PRINCESS ANNE HOSPITAL, VIRGINIA BEACH, VA, p. A680
SENTARA RMH MEDICAL CENTER, HARRISONBURG, VA, p. A671
SENTARA VIRGINIA BEACH GENERAL HOSPITAL, VIRGINIA BEACH, VA, p. A680
SENTARA WILLIAMSBURG REGIONAL MEDICAL CENTER, WILLIAMSBURG, VA, p. A680
SEQUOIA HOSPITAL, REDWOOD CITY, CA, p. A85
SEQUOYAH MEMORIAL HOSPITAL, SALLISAW, OK, p. A519
SERENITY SPRINGS SPECIALTY HOSPITAL, RUSTON, LA, p. A287
SETON EDGAR B. DAVIS HOSPITAL, LULING, TX, p. A635
SETON HEALTH SYSTEM–ST. MARY'S HOSPITAL, TROY, NEW YORK (see ST. MARY'S HOSPITAL), p. A457
SETON HIGHLAND LAKES, BURNET, TX, p. A604
SETON MEDICAL CENTER, DALY CITY, CA, p. A60
SETON MEDICAL CENTER AUSTIN, AUSTIN, TX, p. A599
SETON MEDICAL CENTER HARKER HEIGHTS, HARKER HEIGHTS, TX, p. A622
SETON MEDICAL CENTER HAYS, KYLE, TX, p. A631
SETON MEDICAL CENTER WILLIAMSON, ROUND ROCK, TX, p. A644
SETON NORTHWEST HOSPITAL, AUSTIN, TX, p. A599
SETON SHOAL CREEK HOSPITAL, AUSTIN, TX, p. A599
SETON SMITHVILLE REGIONAL HOSPITAL, SMITHVILLE, TX, p. A649
SETON SOUTHWEST HOSPITAL, AUSTIN, TX, p. A600
SEVEN HILLS HOSPITAL, HENDERSON, NV, p. A405
SEVEN RIVERS REGIONAL MEDICAL CENTER, CRYSTAL RIVER, FL, p. A126
SEVIER VALLEY MEDICAL CENTER, RICHFIELD, UT, p. A662
SEWICKLEY VALLEY HOSPITAL, (A DIVISION OF VALLEY MEDICAL FACILITIES), SEWICKLEY, PA, p. A554
SEYMOUR HOSPITAL, SEYMOUR, TX, p. A648
SHADOW MOUNTAIN BEHAVIORAL HEALTH SYSTEM, TULSA, OK, p. A522
SHAMROCK GENERAL HOSPITAL, SHAMROCK, TX, p. A648

SHANDS LAKE SHORE REGIONAL MEDICAL CENTER, LAKE CITY, FL, p. A133
SHANDS LIVE OAK REGIONAL MEDICAL CENTER, LIVE OAK, FL, p. A134
SHANDS STARKE REGIONAL MEDICAL CENTER, STARKE, FL, p. A146
SHANNON MEDICAL CENTER, SAN ANGELO, TX, p. A645
SHANNON MEDICAL CENTER– ST. JOHN'S CAMPUS, SAN ANGELO, TEXAS (see SHANNON MEDICAL CENTER), p. A645
SHARE MEDICAL CENTER, ALVA, OK, p. A508
SHARKEY–ISSAQUENA COMMUNITY HOSPITAL, ROLLING FORK, MS, p. A364
SHARON HOSPITAL, SHARON, CT, p. A116
SHARON REGIONAL HEALTH SYSTEM, SHARON, PA, p. A555
SHARP CHULA VISTA MEDICAL CENTER, CHULA VISTA, CA, p. A58
SHARP CORONADO HOSPITAL AND HEALTHCARE CENTER, CORONADO, CA, p. A59
SHARP GROSSMONT HOSPITAL, LA MESA, CA, p. A67
SHARP MCDONALD CENTER, SAN DIEGO, CALIFORNIA (see SHARP MESA VISTA HOSPITAL), p. A89
SHARP MEMORIAL HOSPITAL, SAN DIEGO, CA, p. A89
SHARP MESA VISTA HOSPITAL, SAN DIEGO, CA, p. A89
SHASTA REGIONAL MEDICAL CENTER, REDDING, CA, p. A84
SHAWNEE MISSION MEDICAL CENTER, SHAWNEE MISSION, KS, p. A254
SHELBY BAPTIST MEDICAL CENTER, ALABASTER, AL, p. A15
SHELBY MEMORIAL HOSPITAL, SHELBYVILLE, IL, p. A202
SHELTERING ARMS HOSPITAL SOUTH, MIDLOTHIAN, VA, p. A674
SHELTERING ARMS REHABILITATION HOSPITAL, MECHANICSVILLE, VA, p. A673
SHENANDOAH MEDICAL CENTER, SHENANDOAH, IA, p. A237
SHENANDOAH MEMORIAL HOSPITAL, WOODSTOCK, VA, p. A681
SHENANGO VALLEY CAMPUS, FARRELL, PENNSYLVANIA (see UPMC HORIZON), p. A539
SHEPHERD CENTER, ATLANTA, GA, p. A153
SHEPPARD PRATT HEALTH SYSTEM, BALTIMORE, MD, p. A297
SHERIDAN COMMUNITY HOSPITAL, SHERIDAN, MI, p. A334
SHERIDAN COUNTY HEALTH COMPLEX, HOXIE, KS, p. A245
SHERIDAN MEMORIAL HOSPITAL, PLENTYWOOD, MT, p. A390
SHERIDAN MEMORIAL HOSPITAL, SHERIDAN, WY, p. A723
SHERIDAN VETERANS AFFAIRS MEDICAL CENTER, SHERIDAN, WY, p. A724
SHERMAN OAKS HOSPITAL,, CA, p. A74
SHOALS HOSPITAL, MUSCLE SHOALS, AL, p. A24
SHODAIR CHILDREN'S HOSPITAL, HELENA, MT, p. A388
SHORE MEDICAL CENTER, SOMERS POINT, NJ, p. A423
SHORE REHABILITATION INSTITUTE, BRICK, NJ, p. A414
SHOSHONE MEDICAL CENTER, KELLOGG, ID, p. A176
SHRINERS HOSPITALS FOR CHILDREN–BOSTON, BOSTON, MA, p. A307
SHRINERS HOSPITALS FOR CHILDREN–CHICAGO, CHICAGO, IL, p. A186
SHRINERS HOSPITALS FOR CHILDREN–CINCINNATI BURNS HOSPITAL, CINCINNATI, OH, p. A488
SHRINERS HOSPITALS FOR CHILDREN–GALVESTON, GALVESTON, TX, p. A620
SHRINERS HOSPITALS FOR CHILDREN–GREENVILLE, GREENVILLE, SC, p. A566
SHRINERS HOSPITALS FOR CHILDREN–HONOLULU, HONOLULU, HI, p. A171
SHRINERS HOSPITALS FOR CHILDREN–HOUSTON, HOUSTON, TX, p. A626
SHRINERS HOSPITALS FOR CHILDREN–LEXINGTON, LEXINGTON, KY, p. A263
SHRINERS HOSPITALS FOR CHILDREN–LOS ANGELES, LOS ANGELES, CA, p. A74
SHRINERS HOSPITALS FOR CHILDREN–NORTHERN CALIFORNIA, SACRAMENTO, CA, p. A87
SHRINERS HOSPITALS FOR CHILDREN–PHILADELPHIA, PHILADELPHIA, PA, p. A549
SHRINERS HOSPITALS FOR CHILDREN–PORTLAND, PORTLAND, OR, p. A530
SHRINERS HOSPITALS FOR CHILDREN–SALT LAKE CITY, SALT LAKE CITY, UT, p. A663
SHRINERS HOSPITALS FOR CHILDREN–SHREVEPORT, SHREVEPORT, LA, p. A288
SHRINERS HOSPITALS FOR CHILDREN–SPOKANE, SPOKANE, WA, p. A691
SHRINERS HOSPITALS FOR CHILDREN–SPRINGFIELD, SPRINGFIELD, MA, p. A315
SHRINERS HOSPITALS FOR CHILDREN–ST. LOUIS, SAINT LOUIS, MO, p. A380
SHRINERS HOSPITALS FOR CHILDREN–TAMPA, TAMPA, FL, p. A147
SHRINERS HOSPITALS FOR CHILDREN–TWIN CITIES, MINNEAPOLIS, MN, p. A347
SIBLEY MEMORIAL HOSPITAL, WASHINGTON, DC, p. A122

SIDNEY HEALTH CENTER, SIDNEY, MT, p. A391
SIDNEY REGIONAL MEDICAL CENTER, SIDNEY, NE, p. A402
SIERRA NEVADA MEMORIAL HOSPITAL, GRASS VALLEY, CA, p. A65
SIERRA SURGERY HOSPITAL, CARSON CITY, NEVADA (see CARSON TAHOE HEALTH), p. A404
SIERRA TUCSON, TUCSON, AZ, p. A41
SIERRA VIEW MEDICAL CENTER, PORTERVILLE, CA, p. A83
SIERRA VISTA HOSPITAL, SACRAMENTO, CA, p. A87
SIERRA VISTA HOSPITAL, TRUTH OR CONSEQUENCES, NM, p. A432
SIERRA VISTA REGIONAL MEDICAL CENTER, SAN LUIS OBISPO, CA, p. A92
SIGNATURE HEALTHCARE BROCKTON HOSPITAL, BROCKTON, MA, p. A308
SIGNATURE PSYCHIATRIC HOSPITAL, KANSAS CITY, MO, p. A374
SILOAM SPRINGS REGIONAL HOSPITAL, SILOAM SPRINGS, AR, p. A52
SILVER CROSS HOSPITAL, NEW LENOX, IL, p. A198
SILVER HILL HOSPITAL, NEW CANAAN, CT, p. A115
SILVER LAKE MEDICAL CENTER, LOS ANGELES, CA, p. A74
SILVER LAKE MEDICAL CENTER–INGLESIDE HOSPITAL, ROSEMEAD, CALIFORNIA (see SILVER LAKE MEDICAL CENTER), p. A74
SIMI VALLEY HOSPITAL, SIMI VALLEY, CA, p. A94
SIMPSON GENERAL HOSPITAL, MENDENHALL, MS, p. A362
SINAI CHILDREN'S HOSPITAL, CHICAGO, ILLINOIS (see MOUNT SINAI HOSPITAL), p. A185
SINAI HOSPITAL OF BALTIMORE, BALTIMORE, MD, p. A298
SINGING RIVER HEALTH SYSTEM, PASCAGOULA, MS, p. A363
SINGING RIVER HOSPITAL, PASCAGOULA, MISSISSIPPI (see SINGING RIVER HEALTH SYSTEM), p. A363
SIOUX CENTER HEALTH, SIOUX CENTER, IA, p. A237
SIOUX FALLS SPECIALTY HOSPITAL, SIOUX FALLS, SD, p. A576
SIOUX FALLS VETERANS AFFAIRS HEALTH CARE SYSTEM, SIOUX FALLS, SD, p. A576
SIOUXLAND SURGERY CENTER, DAKOTA DUNES, SD, p. A573
SISKIN HOSPITAL FOR PHYSICAL REHABILITATION, CHATTANOOGA, TN, p. A580
SISTER EMMANUEL HOSPITAL, MIAMI, FL, p. A137
SISTER KENNY REHABILITATION INSTITUTE, MINNEAPOLIS, MINNESOTA (see ABBOTT NORTHWESTERN HOSPITAL), p. A346
SISTERS OF CHARITY HOSPITAL OF BUFFALO, BUFFALO, NY, p. A436
SISTERSVILLE GENERAL HOSPITAL, SISTERSVILLE, WV, p. A700
SITKA COMMUNITY HOSPITAL, SITKA, AK, p. A30
SKAGIT REGIONAL HEALTH, MOUNT VERNON, WA, p. A686
SKIFF MEDICAL CENTER, NEWTON, IA, p. A235
SKY LAKES MEDICAL CENTER, KLAMATH FALLS, OR, p. A527
SKY RIDGE MEDICAL CENTER, LONE TREE, CO, p. A108
SKYLINE HOSPITAL, WHITE SALMON, WA, p. A693
SKYRIDGE MEDICAL CENTER – WESTSIDE CAMPUS, CLEVELAND, TENNESSEE (see TENNOVA HEALTHCARE – CLEVELAND), p. A581
SLEEPY EYE MEDICAL CENTER, SLEEPY EYE, MN, p. A351
SLIDELL MEMORIAL HOSPITAL, SLIDELL, LA, p. A288
SMITH COUNTY MEMORIAL HOSPITAL, SMITH CENTER, KS, p. A254
SMITH NORTHVIEW HOSPITAL, VALDOSTA, GEORGIA (see SOUTH GEORGIA MEDICAL CENTER), p. A168
SMYTH COUNTY COMMUNITY HOSPITAL, MARION, VA, p. A673
SNOQUALMIE VALLEY HOSPITAL DISTRICT, SNOQUALMIE, WA, p. A690
SNOWDEN AT FREDERICKSBURG, FREDERICKSBURG, VA, p. A670
SOCORRO GENERAL HOSPITAL, SOCORRO, NM, p. A432
SOIN MEDICAL CENTER, BEAVERCREEK, OH, p. A484
SOLARA HOSPITAL – BROWNSVILLE CAMPUS, BROWNSVILLE, TEXAS (see SOLARA HOSPITAL HARLINGEN), p. A622
SOLARA HOSPITAL HARLINGEN, HARLINGEN, TX, p. A622
SOLARA HOSPITAL MCALLEN, MCALLEN, TX, p. A636
SOLDIERS AND SAILORS MEMORIAL HOSPITAL, WELLSBORO, PA, p. A557
SOLDIERS AND SAILORS MEMORIAL HOSPITAL OF YATES COUNTY, PENN YAN, NY, p. A452
SOMERSET HOSPITAL, SOMERSET, PA, p. A555
SOMERVILLE HOSPITAL, SOMERVILLE, MASSACHUSETTS (see CAMBRIDGE HEALTH ALLIANCE), p. A308
SONOMA DEVELOPMENTAL CENTER, ELDRIDGE, CA, p. A61
SONOMA VALLEY HOSPITAL, SONOMA, CA, p. A94
SONOMA WEST MEDICAL CENTER, SEBASTOPOL, CA, p. A94
SONORA BEHAVIORAL HEALTH HOSPITAL, TUCSON, AZ, p. A41
SONORA REGIONAL MEDICAL CENTER, SONORA, CA, p. A94
SOUTH BALDWIN REGIONAL MEDICAL CENTER, FOLEY, AL, p. A20
SOUTH BAY HOSPITAL, SUN CITY CENTER, FL, p. A146
SOUTH BEACH PSYCHIATRIC CENTER,, NY, p. A449

SOUTH BIG HORN COUNTY HOSPITAL, BASIN, WY, p. A721

SOUTH CAMERON MEMORIAL HOSPITAL, CAMERON, LA, p. A274

SOUTH CAMPUS, VISALIA, CALIFORNIA (see KAWEAH DELTA MEDICAL CENTER), p. A99

SOUTH CAMPUS, AURORA, COLORADO (see MEDICAL CENTER OF AURORA), p. A101

SOUTH CAROLINA DEPARTMENT OF CORRECTIONS HOSPITAL, COLUMBIA, SC, p. A564

SOUTH CENTRAL KANSAS MEDICAL CENTER, ARKANSAS CITY, KS, p. A240

SOUTH CENTRAL REGIONAL MEDICAL CENTER, LAUREL, MS, p. A360

SOUTH COAST GLOBAL MEDICAL CENTER, SANTA ANA, CA, p. A92

SOUTH COUNTY HOSPITAL, WAKEFIELD, RI, p. A561

SOUTH DAVIS COMMUNITY HOSPITAL, BOUNTIFUL, UT, p. A659

SOUTH FLORIDA BAPTIST HOSPITAL, PLANT CITY, FL, p. A142

SOUTH FLORIDA STATE HOSPITAL,, FL, p. A130

SOUTH GEORGIA MEDICAL CENTER, VALDOSTA, GA, p. A168

SOUTH GEORGIA MEDICAL CENTER BERRIEN CAMPUS, NASHVILLE, GA, p. A164

SOUTH GEORGIA MEDICAL CENTER LANIER CAMPUS, LAKELAND, GA, p. A161

SOUTH HAVEN HEALTH SYSTEM, SOUTH HAVEN, MI, p. A334

SOUTH LAKE HOSPITAL, CLERMONT, FL, p. A125

SOUTH LINCOLN MEDICAL CENTER, KEMMERER, WY, p. A722

SOUTH LYON MEDICAL CENTER, YERINGTON, NV, p. A409

SOUTH MISSISSIPPI COUNTY REGIONAL MEDICAL CENTER, OSCEOLA, AR, p. A51

SOUTH MISSISSIPPI STATE HOSPITAL, PURVIS, MS, p. A364

SOUTH NASSAU COMMUNITIES HOSPITAL, OCEANSIDE, NY, p. A451

SOUTH OAKS HOSPITAL, AMITYVILLE, NY, p. A433

SOUTH PENINSULA HOSPITAL, HOMER, AK, p. A29

SOUTH POINTE HOSPITAL, WARRENSVILLE HEIGHTS, OH, p. A505

SOUTH SHORE HOSPITAL, CHICAGO, IL, p. A186

SOUTH SHORE HOSPITAL, SOUTH WEYMOUTH, MA, p. A314

SOUTH SUNFLOWER COUNTY HOSPITAL, INDIANOLA, MS, p. A359

SOUTH TEXAS BEHAVIORAL HEALTH CENTER, EDINBURG, TEXAS (see SOUTH TEXAS HEALTH SYSTEM), p. A614

SOUTH TEXAS HEALTH CARE SYSTEM, HARLINGEN, TEXAS (see RIO GRANDE STATE CENTER/SOUTH TEXAS HEALTH CARE SYSTEM), p. A622

SOUTH TEXAS HEALTH SYSTEM, EDINBURG, TX, p. A614

SOUTH TEXAS REGIONAL MEDICAL CENTER, JOURDANTON, TX, p. A629

SOUTH TEXAS REHABILITATION HOSPITAL, BROWNSVILLE, TX, p. A603

SOUTH TEXAS SPINE AND SURGICAL HOSPITAL, SAN ANTONIO, TX, p. A647

SOUTH TEXAS SURGICAL HOSPITAL, CORPUS CHRISTI, TX, p. A608

SOUTH TEXAS VETERANS HEALTH CARE SYSTEM, SAN ANTONIO, TX, p. A647

SOUTHAMPTON HOSPITAL, SOUTHAMPTON, NY, p. A456

SOUTHAMPTON MEMORIAL HOSPITAL, FRANKLIN, VA, p. A670

SOUTHCOAST BEHAVIORAL HEALTH, DARTMOUTH, MA, p. A309

SOUTHCOAST HOSPITALS GROUP, FALL RIVER, MA, p. A310

SOUTHEAST ALABAMA MEDICAL CENTER, DOTHAN, AL, p. A19

SOUTHEAST COLORADO HOSPITAL DISTRICT, SPRINGFIELD, CO, p. A110

SOUTHEAST GEORGIA HEALTH SYSTEM BRUNSWICK CAMPUS, BRUNSWICK, GA, p. A155

SOUTHEAST GEORGIA HEALTH SYSTEM CAMDEN CAMPUS, SAINT MARYS, GA, p. A165

SOUTHEAST HEALTH CENTER OF RIPLEY COUNTY, DONIPHAN, MO, p. A370

SOUTHEAST HEALTH CENTER OF STODDARD COUNTY, DEXTER, MO, p. A370

SOUTHEAST HOSPITAL, CAPE GIRARDEAU, MO, p. A369

SOUTHEAST MICHIGAN SURGICAL HOSPITAL, WARREN, MI, p. A336

SOUTHEAST MISSOURI MENTAL HEALTH CENTER, FARMINGTON, MO, p. A371

SOUTHEAST REGIONAL MEDICAL CENTER, KENTWOOD, LA, p. A279

SOUTHEAST REHABILITATION HOSPITAL, LAKE VILLAGE, AR, p. A48

SOUTHEASTERN HEALTH, LUMBERTON, NC, p. A469

SOUTHEASTERN OHIO REGIONAL MEDICAL CENTER, CAMBRIDGE, OH, p. A486

SOUTHEASTERN REGIONAL MEDICAL CENTER, NEWNAN, GA, p. A164

SOUTHEASTERN REGIONAL REHABILITATION CENTER, BEHAVIORAL HEALTH CARE OF CAPE FEAR VALLEY HEALTH SYSTEM, FAYETTEVILLE, NORTH CAROLINA (see CAPE FEAR VALLEY MEDICAL CENTER), p. A465

CAPE FEAR VALLEY REHABILITATION CENTER, FAYETTEVILLE, NORTH CAROLINA (see CAPE FEAR VALLEY MEDICAL CENTER), p. A465

SOUTHERN ARIZONA VETERANS AFFAIRS HEALTH CARE SYSTEM, TUCSON, AZ, p. A41

SOUTHERN CALIFORNIA HOSPITAL AT CULVER CITY, CULVER CITY, CA, p. A60

SOUTHERN CALIFORNIA HOSPITAL AT HOLLYWOOD, LOS ANGELES, CA, p. A74

SOUTHERN CALIFORNIA HOSPITAL AT VAN NUYS,, CALIFORNIA (see SOUTHERN CALIFORNIA HOSPITAL AT HOLLYWOOD), p. A74

SOUTHERN COOS HOSPITAL AND HEALTH CENTER, BANDON, OR, p. A524

SOUTHERN CRESCENT HOSPITAL FOR SPECIALTY CARE, RIVERDALE, GA, p. A164

SOUTHERN HILLS HOSPITAL AND MEDICAL CENTER, LAS VEGAS, NV, p. A406

SOUTHERN INDIANA REHABILITATION HOSPITAL, NEW ALBANY, IN, p. A219

SOUTHERN INYO HEALTHCARE DISTRICT, LONE PINE, CA, p. A69

SOUTHERN KENTUCKY REHABILITATION HOSPITAL, BOWLING GREEN, KY, p. A258

SOUTHERN MAINE HEALTH CARE – BIDDEFORD MEDICAL CENTER, BIDDEFORD, ME, p. A292

SOUTHERN MAINE HEALTH CARE – BIDDEFORD MEDICAL CENTER, BIDDEFORD, MAINE (see SOUTHERN MAINE HEALTH CARE – BIDDEFORD MEDICAL CENTER), p. A292

SOUTHERN NEVADA ADULT MENTAL HEALTH SERVICES, LAS VEGAS, NV, p. A406

SOUTHERN NEW HAMPSHIRE MEDICAL CENTER, NASHUA, NH, p. A412

SOUTHERN OCEAN MEDICAL CENTER, MANAHAWKIN, NJ, p. A419

SOUTHERN OHIO MEDICAL CENTER, PORTSMOUTH, OH, p. A501

SOUTHERN REGIONAL MEDICAL CENTER, RIVERDALE, GA, p. A164

SOUTHERN SURGICAL HOSPITAL, SLIDELL, LA, p. A288

SOUTHERN TENNESSEE REGIONAL HEALTH SYSTEM–LAWRENCEBURG, LAWRENCEBURG, TN, p. A586

SOUTHERN TENNESSEE REGIONAL HEALTH SYSTEM–PULASKI, PULASKI, TN, p. A592

SOUTHERN TENNESSEE REGIONAL HEALTH SYSTEM–SEWANEE, SEWANEE, TENNESSEE (see SOUTHERN TENNESSEE REGIONAL HEALTH SYSTEM–WINCHESTER), p. A594

SOUTHERN TENNESSEE REGIONAL HEALTH SYSTEM–WINCHESTER, WINCHESTER, TN, p. A594

SOUTHERN VIRGINIA MENTAL HEALTH INSTITUTE, DANVILLE, VA, p. A669

SOUTHERN VIRGINIA REGIONAL MEDICAL CENTER, EMPORIA, VA, p. A669

SOUTHERN WINDS HOSPITAL, HIALEAH, FLORIDA (see WESTCHESTER GENERAL HOSPITAL), p. A137

SOUTHLAKE CAMPUS, MERRILLVILLE, INDIANA (see METHODIST HOSPITALS), p. A212

SOUTHPOINTE HOSPITAL, SAINT LOUIS, MISSOURI (see ST. ALEXIUS HOSPITAL – BROADWAY CAMPUS), p. A381

SOUTHSIDE HOSPITAL, BAY SHORE, NY, p. A434

SOUTHSIDE REGIONAL MEDICAL CENTER, PETERSBURG, VA, p. A676

SOUTHVIEW MEDICAL CENTER, DAYTON, OHIO (see GRANDVIEW MEDICAL CENTER), p. A492

SOUTHWEST CONNECTICUT MENTAL HEALTH SYSTEM, BRIDGEPORT, CT, p. A113

SOUTHWEST GENERAL HEALTH CENTER, MIDDLEBURG HEIGHTS, OH, p. A499

SOUTHWEST GENERAL HOSPITAL, SAN ANTONIO, TX, p. A647

SOUTHWEST GEORGIA REGIONAL MEDICAL CENTER, CUTHBERT, GA, p. A157

SOUTHWEST HEALTH, PLATTEVILLE, WI, p. A714

SOUTHWEST HEALTH CENTER NURSING HOME, CUBA CITY, WISCONSIN (see SOUTHWEST HEALTH), p. A714

SOUTHWEST HEALTHCARE SERVICES, BOWMAN, ND, p. A477

SOUTHWEST HEALTHCARE SYSTEM, MURRIETA, CA, p. A78

SOUTHWEST IDAHO ADVANCED CARE HOSPITAL, BOISE, ID, p. A174

SOUTHWEST MEDICAL CENTER, LIBERAL, KS, p. A248

SOUTHWEST MEMORIAL HOSPITAL, CORTEZ, CO, p. A103

SOUTHWEST MISSISSIPPI REGIONAL MEDICAL CENTER, MCCOMB, MS, p. A361

SOUTHWESTERN MEDICAL CENTER, LAWTON, OK, p. A513

SOUTHWESTERN REGIONAL MEDICAL CENTER, TULSA, OK, p. A522

SOUTHWESTERN VERMONT MEDICAL CENTER, BENNINGTON, VT, p. A665

SOUTHWESTERN VIRGINIA MENTAL HEALTH INSTITUTE, MARION, VA, p. A673

SOUTHWOOD PSYCHIATRIC HOSPITAL, PITTSBURGH, PA, p. A551

SPALDING REGIONAL HOSPITAL, GRIFFIN, GA, p. A160

SPALDING REHABILITATION HOSPITAL, AURORA, CO, p. A101

SPANISH PEAKS REGIONAL HEALTH CENTER, WALSENBURG, CO, p. A111

SPARKS MEDICAL CENTER – VAN BUREN, VAN BUREN, AR, p. A53

SPARKS REGIONAL MEDICAL CENTER, FORT SMITH, AR, p. A46

SPARROW CARSON HOSPITAL, CARSON CITY, MI, p. A320

SPARROW CHILDREN'S CENTER, LANSING, MICHIGAN (see SPARROW HOSPITAL), p. A328

SPARROW CLINTON HOSPITAL, SAINT JOHNS, MI, p. A333

SPARROW HOSPITAL, LANSING, MI, p. A328

SPARROW IONIA HOSPITAL, IONIA, MI, p. A326

SPARROW SPECIALTY HOSPITAL, LANSING, MI, p. A328

SPARTA COMMUNITY HOSPITAL, SPARTA, IL, p. A203

SPARTANBURG HOSPITAL FOR RESTORATIVE CARE, SPARTANBURG, SC, p. A570

SPARTANBURG MEDICAL CENTER, SPARTANBURG, SC, p. A570

SPAULDING HOSPITAL FOR CONTINUING MEDICAL CARE CAMBRIDGE, CAMBRIDGE, MA, p. A309

SPAULDING REHABILITATION HOSPITAL, CHARLESTOWN, MA, p. A309

SPAULDING REHABILITATION HOSPITAL CAPE COD, EAST SANDWICH, MA, p. A309

SPEARE MEMORIAL HOSPITAL, PLYMOUTH, NH, p. A413

SPEARFISH REGIONAL HOSPITAL, SPEARFISH, SD, p. A577

SPEARFISH REGIONAL SURGERY CENTER, SPEARFISH, SOUTH DAKOTA (see SPEARFISH REGIONAL HOSPITAL), p. A577

SPECIALISTS HOSPITAL – SHREVEPORT, SHREVEPORT, LA, p. A288

SPECIALTY HOSPITAL, MONROE, LA, p. A283

SPECIALTY HOSPITAL JACKSONVILLE, JACKSONVILLE, FL, p. A132

SPECIALTY HOSPITAL OF CENTRAL JERSEY, LAKEWOOD, NJ, p. A418

SPECIALTY HOSPITAL OF LORAIN, AMHERST, OH, p. A483

SPECIALTY HOSPITAL OF MERIDIAN, MERIDIAN, MS, p. A362

SPECIALTY HOSPITAL OF WINNFIELD, WINNFIELD, LA, p. A289

SPECIALTY REHABILITATION HOSPITAL OF COUSHATTA, COUSHATTA, LA, p. A275

SPECTRUM HEALTH, GRAND RAPIDS, MICHIGAN (see SPECTRUM HEALTH – BUTTERWORTH HOSPITAL), p. A325

SPECTRUM HEALTH – BLODGETT CAMPUS, GRAND RAPIDS, MICHIGAN (see SPECTRUM HEALTH – BUTTERWORTH HOSPITAL), p. A325

SPECTRUM HEALTH – BUTTERWORTH HOSPITAL, GRAND RAPIDS, MI, p. A325

SPECTRUM HEALTH BIG RAPIDS HOSPITAL, BIG RAPIDS, MI, p. A319

SPECTRUM HEALTH GERBER MEMORIAL, FREMONT, MI, p. A324

SPECTRUM HEALTH KELSEY HOSPITAL, LAKEVIEW, MICHIGAN (see SPECTRUM HEALTH UNITED HOSPITAL), p. A325

SPECTRUM HEALTH LUDINGTON HOSPITAL, LUDINGTON, MI, p. A329

SPECTRUM HEALTH PENNOCK, HASTINGS, MI, p. A326

SPECTRUM HEALTH REED CITY HOSPITAL, REED CITY, MI, p. A332

SPECTRUM HEALTH SPECIAL CARE HOSPITAL, GRAND RAPIDS, MI, p. A325

SPECTRUM HEALTH UNITED HOSPITAL, GREENVILLE, MI, p. A325

SPECTRUM HEALTH ZEELAND COMMUNITY HOSPITAL, ZEELAND, MI, p. A337

SPENCER HOSPITAL, SPENCER, IA, p. A238

SPINE HOSPITAL OF LOUISIANA (FORMALLY THE NEUROMEDICAL CENTER SURGICAL HOSPITAL), BATON ROUGE, LA, p. A273

SPOONER HEALTH, SPOONER, WI, p. A716

SPOTSYLVANIA REGIONAL MEDICAL CENTER, FREDERICKSBURG, VA, p. A670

SPRING GROVE HOSPITAL CENTER, BALTIMORE, MD, p. A298

SPRING HARBOR HOSPITAL, WESTBROOK, ME, p. A295

SPRING MOUNTAIN SAHARA, LAS VEGAS, NV, p. A406

SPRING MOUNTAIN TREATMENT CENTER, LAS VEGAS, NV, p. A406

SPRING VALLEY HOSPITAL MEDICAL CENTER, LAS VEGAS, NV, p. A406

SPRING VIEW HOSPITAL, LEBANON, KY, p. A262

SPRINGBROOK BEHAVIORAL HEALTH SYSTEM, TRAVELERS REST, SC, p. A570

SPRINGBROOK HOSPITAL, BROOKSVILLE, FL, p. A125

SPRINGFIELD HOSPITAL, SPRINGFIELD, PENNSYLVANIA (see CROZER–CHESTER MEDICAL CENTER), p. A556

SPRINGFIELD HOSPITAL, SPRINGFIELD, VT, p. A666

SPRINGFIELD HOSPITAL CENTER, SYKESVILLE, MD, p. A303

SPRINGFIELD REGIONAL MEDICAL CENTER, SPRINGFIELD, OH, p. A503

SPRINGHILL MEDICAL CENTER, SPRINGHILL, LA, p. A288
SPRINGHILL MEMORIAL HOSPITAL, MOBILE, AL, p. A22
SPRINGS MEMORIAL HOSPITAL, LANCASTER, SC, p. A568
SPRINGWOODS BEHAVIORAL HEALTH HOSPITAL, FAYETTEVILLE, AR, p. A45
SSM CARDINAL GLENNON CHILDREN'S MEDICAL CENTER, SAINT LOUIS, MO, p. A381
SSM DEPAUL HEALTH CENTER, BRIDGETON, MO, p. A368
SSM HEALTH SAINT LOUIS UNIVERSITY HOSPITAL, SAINT LOUIS, MO, p. A381
SSM HEALTH SAINT LOUIS UNIVERSITY HOSPITAL–SOUTH, SAINT LOUIS, MISSOURI (see SSM HEALTH SAINT LOUIS UNIVERSITY HOSPITAL), p. A381
SSM HEALTH ST. FRANCIS HOSPITAL – MARYVILLE, MARYVILLE, MO, p. A376
SSM HEALTH ST. JOSEPH HOSPITAL – LAKE SAINT LOUIS, LAKE SAINT LOUIS, MO, p. A375
SSM HEALTH ST. MARY'S HOSPITAL – AUDRAIN, MEXICO, MO, p. A376
SSM HEALTH ST. MARY'S HOSPITAL – JEFFERSON CITY, JEFFERSON CITY, MO, p. A372
SSM HEALTH ST. MARY'S HOSPITAL CENTRALIA, CENTRALIA, IL, p. A182
SSM SELECT REHABILITATION HOSPITAL, RICHMOND HEIGHTS, MO, p. A378
SSM SELECT REHABILITATION HOSPITAL, BRIDGETON, MISSOURI (see SSM SELECT REHABILITATION HOSPITAL), p. A378
SSM ST. CLARE HOSPITAL, FENTON, MO, p. A371
SSM ST. JOSEPH HEALTH CENTER, SAINT CHARLES, MO, p. A379
SSM ST. JOSEPH HEALTH CENTER – WENTZVILLE, WENTZVILLE, MISSOURI (see SSM ST. JOSEPH HEALTH CENTER), p. A379
SSM ST. MARY'S HEALTH CENTER, SAINT LOUIS, MO, p. A381
ST LUKE'S HOSPITAL – ALLENTOWN CAMPUS, ALLENTOWN, PENNSYLVANIA (see ST. LUKE'S UNIVERSITY HOSPITAL – BETHLEHEM CAMPUS), p. A533
ST. ALEXIUS HOSPITAL – BROADWAY CAMPUS, SAINT LOUIS, MO, p. A381
ST. ALEXIUS HOSPITAL – FOREST PARK CAMPUS, SAINT LOUIS, MISSOURI (see ST. ALEXIUS HOSPITAL – BROADWAY CAMPUS), p. A381
ST. ALOISIUS MEDICAL CENTER, HARVEY, ND, p. A479
ST. ANDREW'S HEALTH CENTER, BOTTINEAU, ND, p. A477
ST. ANTHONY COMMUNITY HOSPITAL, WARWICK, NY, p. A458
ST. ANTHONY HOSPITAL, LAKEWOOD, CO, p. A108
ST. ANTHONY HOSPITAL, OKLAHOMA CITY, OK, p. A517
ST. ANTHONY HOSPITAL, GIG HARBOR, WA, p. A685
ST. ANTHONY NORTH HEALTH CAMPUS, WESTMINSTER, CO, p. A111
ST. ANTHONY REGIONAL HOSPITAL, CARROLL, IA, p. A226
ST. ANTHONY SHAWNEE HOSPITAL, SHAWNEE, OK, p. A520
ST. ANTHONY SUMMIT MEDICAL CENTER, FRISCO, CO, p. A105
ST. ANTHONY'S HOSPITAL, SAINT PETERSBURG, FL, p. A144
ST. ANTHONY'S MEDICAL CENTER, SAINT LOUIS, MO, p. A381
ST. ANTHONY'S REHABILITATION HOSPITAL, LAUDERDALE LAKES, FL, p. A134
ST. BARNABAS HOSPITAL,, NY, p. A449
ST. BERNARD HOSPITAL AND HEALTH CARE CENTER, CHICAGO, IL, p. A187
ST. BERNARD PARISH HOSPITAL, CHALMETTE, LA, p. A274
ST. BERNARDINE MEDICAL CENTER, SAN BERNARDINO, CA, p. A88
ST. BERNARDS MEDICAL CENTER, JONESBORO, AR, p. A48
ST. CATHERINE HOSPITAL, EAST CHICAGO, IN, p. A209
ST. CATHERINE HOSPITAL, GARDEN CITY, KS, p. A243
ST. CATHERINE MEMORIAL HOSPITAL, NEW ORLEANS, LA, p. A285
ST. CATHERINE OF SIENA MEDICAL CENTER, SMITHTOWN, NY, p. A456
ST. CATHERINE'S REHABILITATION HOSPITAL, NORTH MIAMI, FL, p. A139
ST. CHARLES BEND, BEND, OR, p. A524
ST. CHARLES HOSPITAL, PORT JEFFERSON, NY, p. A453
ST. CHARLES MADRAS, MADRAS, OR, p. A527
ST. CHARLES PARISH HOSPITAL, LULING, LA, p. A282
ST. CHARLES PRINEVILLE, PRINEVILLE, OR, p. A530
ST. CHARLES REDMOND, REDMOND, OR, p. A530
ST. CHARLES SURGICAL HOSPITAL, NEW ORLEANS, LA, p. A285
ST. CHRISTOPHER'S HOSPITAL FOR CHILDREN, PHILADELPHIA, PA, p. A549
ST. CLAIR HOSPITAL, PITTSBURGH, PA, p. A551
ST. CLAIRE REGIONAL MEDICAL CENTER, MOREHEAD, KY, p. A267
ST. CLARE HOSPITAL, LAKEWOOD, WA, p. A686
ST. CLARE HOSPITAL, BARABOO, WI, p. A702
ST. CLOUD HOSPITAL, SAINT CLOUD, MN, p. A350

ST. CLOUD REGIONAL MEDICAL CENTER, SAINT CLOUD, FL, p. A144
ST. CLOUD VETERANS AFFAIRS HEALTH CARE SYSTEM, SAINT CLOUD, MN, p. A350
ST. CROIX REGIONAL MEDICAL CENTER, ST. CROIX FALLS, WI, p. A716
ST. DAVID'S GEORGETOWN HOSPITAL, GEORGETOWN, TEXAS (see ST. DAVID'S MEDICAL CENTER), p. A600
ST. DAVID'S MEDICAL CENTER, AUSTIN, TX, p. A600
ST. DAVID'S NORTH AUSTIN MEDICAL CENTER, AUSTIN, TX, p. A600
ST. DAVID'S REHABILITATION CENTER, AUSTIN, TEXAS (see ST. DAVID'S MEDICAL CENTER), p. A600
ST. DAVID'S ROUND ROCK MEDICAL CENTER, ROUND ROCK, TX, p. A644
ST. DAVID'S SOUTH AUSTIN MEDICAL CENTER, AUSTIN, TX, p. A600
ST. DOMINIC–JACKSON MEMORIAL HOSPITAL, JACKSON, MS, p. A360
ST. ELIAS SPECIALTY HOSPITAL, ANCHORAGE, AK, p. A28
ST. ELIZABETH COMMUNITY HOSPITAL, RED BLUFF, CA, p. A84
ST. ELIZABETH COVINGTON, COVINGTON, KENTUCKY (see ST. ELIZABETH EDGEWOOD), p. A259
ST. ELIZABETH EDGEWOOD, EDGEWOOD, KY, p. A259
ST. ELIZABETH FLORENCE, FLORENCE, KY, p. A260
ST. ELIZABETH FORT THOMAS, FORT THOMAS, KY, p. A260
ST. ELIZABETH GRANT, WILLIAMSTOWN, KY, p. A270
ST. ELIZABETH HOSPITAL, GONZALES, LA, p. A277
ST. ELIZABETH HOSPITAL, ENUMCLAW, WA, p. A684
ST. ELIZABETH HOSPITAL, APPLETON, WI, p. A702
ST. ELIZABETH MEDICAL CENTER, UTICA, NY, p. A457
ST. ELIZABETH'S MEDICAL CENTER, BRIGHTON, MA, p. A308
ST. FRANCIS CAMPUS, WICHITA, KANSAS (see VIA CHRISTI HOSPITAL ON ST. FRANCIS), p. A256
ST. FRANCIS EASTSIDE, GREENVILLE, SOUTH CAROLINA (see BON SECOURS ST. FRANCIS HEALTH SYSTEM), p. A566
ST. FRANCIS HEALTH, TOPEKA, KS, p. A254
ST. FRANCIS HOSPITAL, WILMINGTON, DE, p. A120
ST. FRANCIS HOSPITAL, COLUMBUS, GA, p. A157
ST. FRANCIS HOSPITAL, FEDERAL WAY, WA, p. A685
ST. FRANCIS HOSPITAL, THE HEART CENTER, ROSLYN, NY, p. A455
ST. FRANCIS MEDICAL CENTER, COLORADO SPRINGS, COLORADO (see PENROSE–ST. FRANCIS HEALTH SERVICES), p. A103
ST. FRANCIS MEDICAL CENTER, LYNWOOD, CA, p. A75
ST. FRANCIS MEDICAL CENTER, MONROE, LA, p. A283
ST. FRANCIS MEDICAL CENTER, TRENTON, NJ, p. A424
ST. FRANCIS MEDICAL PLAZA, GRAND ISLAND, NEBRASKA (see CHI HEALTH SAINT FRANCIS), p. A396
ST. FRANCIS MEMORIAL HOSPITAL, WEST POINT, NE, p. A403
ST. FRANCIS NORTH HOSPITAL, MONROE, LOUISIANA (see ST. FRANCIS MEDICAL CENTER), p. A283
ST. FRANCIS NURSING CENTER (see MARY IMMACULATE HOSPITAL), p. A674
ST. FRANCIS REGIONAL MEDICAL CENTER, SHAKOPEE, MN, p. A351
ST. HELENA HOSPITAL CENTER FOR BEHAVIORAL HEALTH, VALLEJO, CA, p. A98
ST. HELENA HOSPITAL CLEAR LAKE, CLEARLAKE, CA, p. A59
ST. HELENA HOSPITAL NAPA VALLEY, SAINT HELENA, CA, p. A87
ST. HELENA PARISH HOSPITAL, GREENSBURG, LA, p. A277
ST. JAMES BEHAVIORAL HEALTH HOSPITAL, GONZALES, LA, p. A277
ST. JAMES HEALTHCARE, BUTTE, MT, p. A386
ST. JAMES HOSPITAL AND HEALTH CENTERS – CHICAGO HEIGHTS CAMPUS, CHICAGO HEIGHTS, ILLINOIS (see FRANCISCAN ST. JAMES HOSPITAL AND HEALTH CENTERS), p. A199
ST. JAMES HOSPITALS AND HEALTH CENTERS – OLYMPIA FIELDS CAMPUS, OLYMPIA FIELDS, ILLINOIS (see FRANCISCAN ST. JAMES HOSPITAL AND HEALTH CENTERS), p. A199
ST. JAMES MERCY HOSPITAL, HORNELL, NY, p. A440
ST. JAMES PARISH HOSPITAL, LUTCHER, LA, p. A282
ST. JOHN BROKEN ARROW, BROKEN ARROW, OK, p. A509
ST. JOHN HOSPITAL AND MEDICAL CENTER, DETROIT, MI, p. A322
ST. JOHN MACOMB–OAKLAND HOSPITAL, WARREN, MI, p. A336
ST. JOHN MACOMB–OAKLAND HOSPITAL, MADISON HEIGHTS CAMPUS, MADISON HEIGHTS, MICHIGAN (see ST. JOHN MACOMB–OAKLAND HOSPITAL), p. A336
ST. JOHN MACOMB–OAKLAND HOSPITAL, WARREN CAMPUS, WARREN, MICHIGAN (see ST. JOHN MACOMB–OAKLAND HOSPITAL), p. A336
ST. JOHN MEDICAL CENTER, WESTLAKE, OH, p. A505
ST. JOHN MEDICAL CENTER, TULSA, OK, p. A522
ST. JOHN OWASSO, OWASSO, OK, p. A518

ST. JOHN RIVER DISTRICT HOSPITAL, EAST CHINA, MI, p. A323
ST. JOHN SAPULPA, SAPULPA, OK, p. A519
ST. JOHN VIANNEY HOSPITAL, DOWNINGTOWN, PA, p. A536
ST. JOHN'S RIVERSIDE HOSPITAL – PARK CARE PAVILION, YONKERS, NEW YORK (see ST. JOHN'S RIVERSIDE HOSPITAL), p. A459
ST. JOHN'S CHILDREN'S HOSPITAL, SPRINGFIELD, ILLINOIS (see ST. JOHN'S HOSPITAL), p. A203
ST. JOHN'S EPISCOPAL HOSPITAL–SOUTH SHORE,, NY, p. A450
ST. JOHN'S HOSPITAL, SPRINGFIELD, IL, p. A203
ST. JOHN'S HOSPITAL, MAPLEWOOD, MN, p. A346
ST. JOHN'S MEDICAL CENTER AND LIVING CENTER, JACKSON, WY, p. A722
ST. JOHN'S PLEASANT VALLEY HOSPITAL, CAMARILLO, CA, p. A57
ST. JOHN'S REGIONAL MEDICAL CENTER, OXNARD, CA, p. A81
ST. JOHN'S REHABILITATION CENTER, JOPLIN, MISSOURI (see MERCY HOSPITAL JOPLIN), p. A373
ST. JOHN'S RIVERSIDE HOSPITAL, YONKERS, NY, p. A459
ST. JOHN'S RIVERSIDE HOSPITAL – DOBBS FERRY PAVILION, DOBBS FERRY, NEW YORK (see ST. JOHN'S RIVERSIDE HOSPITAL), p. A459
ST. JOSEPH CAMPUS, WICHITA, KANSAS (see VIA CHRISTI HOSPITAL ON ST. FRANCIS), p. A256
ST. JOSEPH HEALTH SERVICES OF RHODE ISLAND, NORTH PROVIDENCE, RI, p. A560
ST. JOSEPH HEALTH SYSTEM, TAWAS CITY, MI, p. A335
ST. JOSEPH HOSPITAL, CHEEKTOWAGA, NEW YORK (see SISTERS OF CHARITY HOSPITAL OF BUFFALO), p. A436
ST. JOSEPH HOSPITAL, EUREKA, CA, p. A61
ST. JOSEPH HOSPITAL, ORANGE, CA, p. A81
ST. JOSEPH HOSPITAL, FORT WAYNE, IN, p. A211
ST. JOSEPH HOSPITAL, BANGOR, ME, p. A291
ST. JOSEPH HOSPITAL, NASHUA, NH, p. A412
ST. JOSEPH HOSPITAL, BETHPAGE, NY, p. A434
ST. JOSEPH HOSPITAL FOR SPECIALTY CARE, PROVIDENCE, RHODE ISLAND (see ST. JOSEPH HEALTH SERVICES OF RHODE ISLAND), p. A560
ST. JOSEPH MEDICAL CENTER, KANSAS CITY, MO, p. A374
ST. JOSEPH MEDICAL CENTER, HOUSTON, TX, p. A626
ST. JOSEPH MEDICAL CENTER, TACOMA, WA, p. A692
ST. JOSEPH MEDICAL CENTER–DOWNTOWN READING, READING, PENNSYLVANIA (see PENN STATE HEALTH ST. JOSEPH), p. A553
ST. JOSEPH MEMORIAL HOSPITAL, MURPHYSBORO, IL, p. A197
ST. JOSEPH MERCY ANN ARBOR, YPSILANTI, MI, p. A337
ST. JOSEPH MERCY CHELSEA, CHELSEA, MI, p. A320
ST. JOSEPH MERCY LIVINGSTON HOSPITAL, HOWELL, MI, p. A326
ST. JOSEPH MERCY OAKLAND, PONTIAC, MI, p. A332
ST. JOSEPH REGIONAL HEALTH CENTER, BRYAN, TX, p. A604
ST. JOSEPH REGIONAL MEDICAL CENTER, LEWISTON, ID, p. A177
ST. JOSEPH'S BEHAVIORAL HEALTH CENTER, STOCKTON, CA, p. A95
ST. JOSEPH'S CHILDREN'S HOSPITAL, PATERSON, NEW JERSEY (see ST. JOSEPH'S HEALTHCARE SYSTEM), p. A421
ST. JOSEPH'S CHILDREN'S HOSPITAL, TAMPA, FLORIDA (see ST. JOSEPH'S HOSPITAL), p. A147
ST. JOSEPH'S HEALTHCARE SYSTEM, PATERSON, NJ, p. A421
ST. JOSEPH'S HOSPITAL, TAMPA, FL, p. A147
ST. JOSEPH'S HOSPITAL, SAVANNAH, GA, p. A166
ST. JOSEPH'S HOSPITAL, SAINT PAUL, MN, p. A351
ST. JOSEPH'S HOSPITAL, ELMIRA, NY, p. A438
ST. JOSEPH'S HOSPITAL, WEST BEND, WI, p. A719
ST. JOSEPH'S HOSPITAL – NORTH, LUTZ, FLORIDA (see ST. JOSEPH'S HOSPITAL), p. A147
ST. JOSEPH'S HOSPITAL AND HEALTH CENTER, DICKINSON, ND, p. A478
ST. JOSEPH'S HOSPITAL AND MEDICAL CENTER, PHOENIX, AZ, p. A37
ST. JOSEPH'S HOSPITAL BEHAVIORAL HEALTH CENTER, TAMPA, FLORIDA (see ST. JOSEPH'S HOSPITAL), p. A147
ST. JOSEPH'S HOSPITAL HEALTH CENTER, SYRACUSE, NY, p. A456
ST. JOSEPH'S HOSPITAL OF BUCKHANNON, BUCKHANNON, WV, p. A694
ST. JOSEPH'S HOSPITAL–SOUTH, RIVERVIEW, FLORIDA (see ST. JOSEPH'S HOSPITAL), p. A147
ST. JOSEPH'S MEDICAL CENTER, STOCKTON, CA, p. A95
ST. JOSEPH'S MERCY HOSPITAL–WEST, CLINTON TOWNSHIP, MICHIGAN (see HENRY FORD MACOMB HOSPITALS), p. A320
ST. JOSEPH'S MERCY–NORTH, ROMEO, MICHIGAN (see HENRY FORD MACOMB HOSPITALS), p. A320
ST. JOSEPH'S WAYNE HOSPITAL, WAYNE, NEW JERSEY (see ST. JOSEPH'S HEALTHCARE SYSTEM), p. A421
ST. JOSEPH'S WESTGATE MEDICAL CENTER, GLENDALE, ARIZONA (see ST. JOSEPH'S HOSPITAL AND MEDICAL CENTER), p. A37

STURGIS REGIONAL HOSPITAL, STURGIS, SD, p. A577
SUBURBAN COMMUNITY HOSPITAL, NORRISTOWN, PA, p. A546
SUBURBAN HOSPITAL, BETHESDA, MD, p. A299
SULLIVAN COUNTY COMMUNITY HOSPITAL, SULLIVAN, IN, p. A222
SULLIVAN COUNTY MEMORIAL HOSPITAL, MILAN, MO, p. A376
SUMMA AKRON CITY HOSPITAL, AKRON, OHIO (see SUMMA HEALTH SYSTEM), p. A483
SUMMA HEALTH SYSTEM, AKRON, OH, p. A483
SUMMA HEALTH SYSTEM BARBERTON HOSPITAL, BARBERTON, OHIO (see SUMMA HEALTH SYSTEM), p. A483
SUMMA REHAB HOSPITAL, AKRON, OH, p. A483
SUMMA SAINT THOMAS HOSPITAL, AKRON, OHIO (see SUMMA HEALTH SYSTEM), p. A483
SUMMA WESTERN RESERVE HOSPITAL, CUYAHOGA FALLS, OH, p. A492
SUMMERLIN HOSPITAL MEDICAL CENTER, LAS VEGAS, NV, p. A407
SUMMERS COUNTY ARH HOSPITAL, HINTON, WV, p. A696
SUMMERSVILLE REGIONAL MEDICAL CENTER, SUMMERSVILLE, WV, p. A700
SUMMERVILLE MEDICAL CENTER, SUMMERVILLE, SOUTH CAROLINA (see TRIDENT MEDICAL CENTER), p. A563
SUMMIT BEHAVIORAL HEALTHCARE, CINCINNATI, OH, p. A488
SUMMIT HEALTHCARE REGIONAL MEDICAL CENTER, SHOW LOW, AZ, p. A39
SUMMIT MEDICAL CENTER, EDMOND, OK, p. A511
SUMMIT MEDICAL CENTER, CASPER, WY, p. A721
SUMMIT OAKS HOSPITAL, SUMMIT, NJ, p. A424
SUMMIT PACIFIC MEDICAL CENTER, ELMA, WA, p. A684
SUMMIT SURGICAL, HUTCHINSON, KS, p. A245
SUMMITRIDGE HOSPITAL, LAWRENCEVILLE, GA, p. A162
SUMNER COUNTY HOSPITAL DISTRICT ONE, CALDWELL, KS, p. A241
SUMNER REGIONAL MEDICAL CENTER, WELLINGTON, KS, p. A255
SUMNER REGIONAL MEDICAL CENTER, GALLATIN, TN, p. A583
SUNBURY COMMUNITY HOSPITAL AND OUTPATIENT CENTER, SUNBURY, PA, p. A555
SUNCOAST BEHAVIORAL HEALTH CENTER, BRADENTON, FL, p. A124
SUNDANCE HOSPITAL, ARLINGTON, TX, p. A597
SUNNYSIDE COMMUNITY HOSPITAL AND CLINICS, SUNNYSIDE, WA, p. A691
SUNNYVIEW REHABILITATION HOSPITAL, SCHENECTADY, NY, p. A455
SUNRISE CANYON HOSPITAL, LUBBOCK, TX, p. A634
SUNRISE CHILDREN'S HOSPITAL (see SUNRISE HOSPITAL AND MEDICAL CENTER), p. A407
SUNRISE HOSPITAL AND MEDICAL CENTER, LAS VEGAS, NV, p. A407
SUNY DOWNSTATE MEDICAL CENTER UNIVERSITY HOSPITAL,, NY, p. A450
SURGERY SPECIALTY HOSPITALS OF AMERICA, PASADENA, TX, p. A640
SURGICAL HOSPITAL AT SOUTHWOODS, YOUNGSTOWN, OH, p. A506
SURGICAL HOSPITAL OF OKLAHOMA, OKLAHOMA CITY, OK, p. A517
SURGICAL INSTITUTE OF READING, WYOMISSING, PA, p. A558
SURGICAL SPECIALTY CENTER AT COORDINATED HEALTH, ALLENTOWN, PA, p. A532
SURGICAL SPECIALTY CENTER OF BATON ROUGE, BATON ROUGE, LA, p. A273
SURPRISE VALLEY HEALTH CARE DISTRICT, CEDARVILLE, CA, p. A58
SUSAN B. ALLEN MEMORIAL HOSPITAL, EL DORADO, KS, p. A242
SUTTER AMADOR HOSPITAL, JACKSON, CA, p. A66
SUTTER AUBURN FAITH HOSPITAL, AUBURN, CA, p. A55
SUTTER CENTER FOR PSYCHIATRY, SACRAMENTO, CA, p. A87
SUTTER CHILDREN'S CENTER, SACRAMENTO, CALIFORNIA (see SUTTER MEDICAL CENTER, SACRAMENTO), p. A87
SUTTER COAST HOSPITAL, CRESCENT CITY, CA, p. A60
SUTTER DAVIS HOSPITAL, DAVIS, CA, p. A60
SUTTER DELTA MEDICAL CENTER, ANTIOCH, CA, p. A54
SUTTER GENERAL HOSPITAL, SACRAMENTO, CALIFORNIA (see SUTTER MEDICAL CENTER, SACRAMENTO), p. A87
SUTTER LAKESIDE HOSPITAL, LAKEPORT, CA, p. A68
SUTTER MATERNITY AND SURGERY CENTER OF SANTA CRUZ, SANTA CRUZ, CA, p. A93
SUTTER MEDICAL CENTER, SACRAMENTO, SACRAMENTO, CA, p. A87
SUTTER ROSEVILLE MEDICAL CENTER, ROSEVILLE, CA, p. A86
SUTTER SANTA ROSA REGIONAL HOSPITAL, SANTA ROSA, CA, p. A94
SUTTER SOLANO MEDICAL CENTER, VALLEJO, CA, p. A98
SUTTER SURGICAL HOSPITAL – NORTH VALLEY, YUBA CITY, CA, p. A100
SUTTER TRACY COMMUNITY HOSPITAL, TRACY, CA, p. A96

SWAIN COMMUNITY HOSPITAL, BRYSON CITY, NC, p. A461
SWEDISH COVENANT HOSPITAL, CHICAGO, IL, p. A187
SWEDISH MEDICAL CENTER, ENGLEWOOD, CO, p. A105
SWEDISH MEDICAL CENTER–BALLARD, SEATTLE, WASHINGTON (see SWEDISH MEDICAL CENTER–FIRST HILL), p. A690
SWEDISH MEDICAL CENTER–CHERRY HILL CAMPUS, SEATTLE, WA, p. A689
SWEDISH MEDICAL CENTER–FIRST HILL, SEATTLE, WA, p. A690
SWEDISH/EDMONDS, EDMONDS, WA, p. A684
SWEDISH/ISSAQUAH, ISSAQUAH, WA, p. A685
SWEDISHAMERICAN – A DIVISION OF UW HEALTH, ROCKFORD, IL, p. A202
SWEENY COMMUNITY HOSPITAL, SWEENY, TX, p. A651
SWEETWATER HOSPITAL, SWEETWATER, TN, p. A593
SWIFT COUNTY–BENSON HOSPITAL, BENSON, MN, p. A339
SWISHER MEMORIAL HOSPITAL DISTRICT, TULIA, TX, p. A654
SYCAMORE MEDICAL CENTER, MIAMISBURG, OH, p. A499
SYCAMORE SHOALS HOSPITAL, ELIZABETHTON, TN, p. A582
SYCAMORE SPRINGS HOSPITAL, LAFAYETTE, IN, p. A216
SYLVAN GROVE HOSPITAL, JACKSON, GA, p. A161
SYOSSET HOSPITAL, SYOSSET, NY, p. A456
SYRACUSE VETERANS AFFAIRS MEDICAL CENTER, SYRACUSE, NY, p. A457
SYRINGA HOSPITAL AND CLINICS, GRANGEVILLE, ID, p. A176

T

T. C. THOMPSON CHILDREN'S HOSPITAL, CHATTANOOGA, TENNESSEE (see ERLANGER MEDICAL CENTER), p. A580
T. J. SAMSON COMMUNITY HOSPITAL, GLASGOW, KY, p. A261
T.J. HEALTH COLUMBIA, COLUMBIA, KY, p. A258
TAHOE FOREST HOSPITAL DISTRICT, TRUCKEE, CA, p. A97
TAHOE PACIFIC HOSPITALS, SPARKS, NV, p. A408
TAHOE PACIFIC HOSPITALS – WEST, RENO, NEVADA (see TAHOE PACIFIC HOSPITALS), p. A408
TAKOMA REGIONAL HOSPITAL, GREENEVILLE, TN, p. A583
TALLAHASSEE MEMORIAL HEALTHCARE, TALLAHASSEE, FL, p. A146
TALLAHATCHIE GENERAL HOSPITAL, CHARLESTON, MS, p. A356
TAMPA COMMUNITY HOSPITAL, TAMPA, FL, p. A148
TAMPA GENERAL HOSPITAL, TAMPA, FL, p. A148
TAMPA GENERAL HOSPITAL CHILDREN'S MEDICAL CENTER, TAMPA, FLORIDA (see TAMPA GENERAL HOSPITAL), p. A148
TANNER HIGGINS GENERAL HOSPITAL, BREMEN, GA, p. A155
TANNER MEDICAL CENTER–CARROLLTON, CARROLLTON, GA, p. A155
TANNER MEDICAL CENTER–VILLA RICA, VILLA RICA, GA, p. A168
TAUNTON STATE HOSPITAL, TAUNTON, MA, p. A315
TAYLOR HARDIN SECURE MEDICAL FACILITY, TUSCALOOSA, AL, p. A26
TAYLOR HOSPITAL, RIDLEY PARK, PENNSYLVANIA (see CROZER–CHESTER MEDICAL CENTER), p. A556
TAYLOR REGIONAL HOSPITAL, HAWKINSVILLE, GA, p. A160
TAYLOR REGIONAL HOSPITAL, CAMPBELLSVILLE, KY, p. A258
TAYLORVILLE MEMORIAL HOSPITAL, TAYLORVILLE, IL, p. A204
TECHE REGIONAL MEDICAL CENTER, MORGAN CITY, LA, p. A284
TEHACHAPI VALLEY HEALTHCARE DISTRICT, TEHACHAPI, CA, p. A95
TELECARE HERITAGE PSYCHIATRIC HEALTH CENTER, OAKLAND, CA, p. A80
TEMECULA VALLEY HOSPITAL, TEMECULA, CA, p. A96
TEMPE ST. LUKE'S HOSPITAL, TEMPE, ARIZONA (see ST. LUKE'S MEDICAL CENTER), p. A37
TEMPLE UNIVERSITY HOSPITAL, PHILADELPHIA, PA, p. A550
TEMPLE UNIVERSITY HOSPITAL – EPISCOPAL DIVISION, PHILADELPHIA, PENNSYLVANIA (see TEMPLE UNIVERSITY HOSPITAL), p. A550
TEN BROECK TENNESSEE TREATMENT FACILITY, COOKEVILLE, TN, p. A581
TEN LAKES CENTER, DENNISON, OH, p. A493
TENNESSEE VALLEY HEALTHCARE SYSTEM, NASHVILLE, TN, p. A591
TENNOVA HEALTHCARE – CLEVELAND, CLEVELAND, TN, p. A581
TENNOVA HEALTHCARE DYERSBURG REGIONAL MEDICAL CENTER, DYERSBURG, TN, p. A582
TENNOVA HEALTHCARE REGIONAL HOSPITAL OF JACKSON, JACKSON, TN, p. A584
TENNOVA HEALTHCARE VOLUNTEER COMMUNITY HOSPITAL, MARTIN, TN, p. A588
TENNOVA HEALTHCARE–CLARKSVILLE, CLARKSVILLE, TN, p. A581
TENNOVA HEALTHCARE–HARTON, TULLAHOMA, TN, p. A594

TENNOVA HEALTHCARE–JAMESTOWN, JAMESTOWN, TN, p. A584
TENNOVA HEALTHCARE–JEFFERSON MEMORIAL HOSPITAL, JEFFERSON CITY, TN, p. A584
TENNOVA HEALTHCARE–LAFOLLETTE MEDICAL CENTER, LA FOLLETTE, TN, p. A586
TENNOVA HEALTHCARE–LEBANON, LEBANON, TN, p. A586
TENNOVA HEALTHCARE–LEBANON MCFARLAND CAMPUS, LEBANON, TENNESSEE (see TENNOVA HEALTHCARE–LEBANON), p. A586
TENNOVA HEALTHCARE–SHELBYVILLE, SHELBYVILLE, TN, p. A593
TENNOVA NEWPORT MEDICAL CENTER, NEWPORT, TN, p. A591
TENNOVA NORTH KNOXVILLE MEDICAL CENTER, POWELL, TENNESSEE (see TENNOVA PHYSICIANS REGIONAL MEDICAL CENTER), p. A586
TENNOVA PHYSICIANS REGIONAL MEDICAL CENTER, KNOXVILLE, TN, p. A586
TENNOVA TURKEY CREEK MEDICAL CENTER, KNOXVILLE, TENNESSEE (see TENNOVA PHYSICIANS REGIONAL MEDICAL CENTER), p. A586
TENNOVA TURKEY CREEK MEDICAL CENTER, KNOXVILLE, TENNESSEE (see TENNOVA PHYSICIANS REGIONAL MEDICAL CENTER), p. A586
TERENCE CARDINAL COOKE HEALTH CARE CENTER, NEW YORK, NY, p. A450
TERRE HAUTE REGIONAL HOSPITAL, TERRE HAUTE, IN, p. A222
TERREBONNE GENERAL MEDICAL CENTER, HOUMA, LA, p. A278
TERRELL STATE HOSPITAL, TERRELL, TX, p. A652
TETON VALLEY HEALTH CARE, DRIGGS, ID, p. A176
TEWKSBURY HOSPITAL, TEWKSBURY, MA, p. A315
TEXAS CENTER FOR INFECTIOUS DISEASE, SAN ANTONIO, TX, p. A647
TEXAS CHILDREN'S HOSPITAL, HOUSTON, TX, p. A626
TEXAS CHILDREN'S HOSPITAL WEST CAMPUS, HOUSTON, TEXAS (see TEXAS CHILDREN'S HOSPITAL), p. A626
TEXAS COUNTY MEMORIAL HOSPITAL, HOUSTON, MO, p. A372
TEXAS GENERAL HOSPITAL, GRAND PRAIRIE, TX, p. A621
TEXAS GENERAL HOSPITAL – VAN ZANDT REGIONAL MEDICAL CENTER, GRAND SALINE, TX, p. A621
TEXAS HEALTH ARLINGTON MEMORIAL HOSPITAL, ARLINGTON, TX, p. A598
TEXAS HEALTH CENTER FOR DIAGNOSTIC & SURGERY, PLANO, TX, p. A642
TEXAS HEALTH HARRIS METHODIST HOSPITAL ALLIANCE, FORT WORTH, TX, p. A618
TEXAS HEALTH HARRIS METHODIST HOSPITAL AZLE, AZLE, TX, p. A600
TEXAS HEALTH HARRIS METHODIST HOSPITAL CLEBURNE, CLEBURNE, TX, p. A606
TEXAS HEALTH HARRIS METHODIST HOSPITAL FORT WORTH, FORT WORTH, TX, p. A618
TEXAS HEALTH HARRIS METHODIST HOSPITAL HURST–EULESS–BEDFORD, BEDFORD, TX, p. A602
TEXAS HEALTH HARRIS METHODIST HOSPITAL SOUTHLAKE, SOUTHLAKE, TX, p. A649
TEXAS HEALTH HARRIS METHODIST HOSPITAL SOUTHWEST FORT WORTH, FORT WORTH, TX, p. A619
TEXAS HEALTH HARRIS METHODIST HOSPITAL STEPHENVILLE, STEPHENVILLE, TX, p. A650
TEXAS HEALTH HEART & VASCULAR HOSPITAL ARLINGTON, ARLINGTON, TX, p. A598
TEXAS HEALTH HUGULEY HOSPITAL FORT WORTH SOUTH, BURLESON, TX, p. A604
TEXAS HEALTH PRESBYTERIAN HOSPITAL ALLEN, ALLEN, TX, p. A595
TEXAS HEALTH PRESBYTERIAN HOSPITAL DALLAS, DALLAS, TX, p. A611
TEXAS HEALTH PRESBYTERIAN HOSPITAL DENTON, DENTON, TX, p. A613
TEXAS HEALTH PRESBYTERIAN HOSPITAL FLOWER MOUND, FLOWER MOUND, TX, p. A617
TEXAS HEALTH PRESBYTERIAN HOSPITAL KAUFMAN, KAUFMAN, TX, p. A630
TEXAS HEALTH PRESBYTERIAN HOSPITAL OF ROCKWALL, ROCKWALL, TX, p. A643
TEXAS HEALTH PRESBYTERIAN HOSPITAL PLANO, PLANO, TX, p. A642
TEXAS HEALTH SPECIALTY HOSPITAL, FORT WORTH, TX, p. A619
TEXAS HEALTH SPRINGWOOD, BEDFORD, TEXAS (see TEXAS HEALTH HARRIS METHODIST HOSPITAL HURST–EULESS–BEDFORD), p. A602
TEXAS INSTITUTE FOR SURGERY AT TEXAS HEALTH PRESBYTERIAN DALLAS, DALLAS, TX, p. A611
TEXAS NEUROREHAB CENTER, AUSTIN, TX, p. A600
TEXAS ORTHOPEDIC HOSPITAL, HOUSTON, TX, p. A627

V

VETERANS AFFAIRS HUDSON VALLEY HEALTH CARE SYSTEM, MONTROSE, NY, p. A443
VETERANS AFFAIRS HUDSON VALLEY HEALTH CARE SYSTEM–MONTROSE CAMPUS, MONTROSE, NEW YORK (see VETERANS AFFAIRS HUDSON VALLEY HEALTH CARE SYSTEM), p. A443
VETERANS AFFAIRS ILLIANA HEALTH CARE SYSTEM, DANVILLE, IL, p. A187
VETERANS AFFAIRS LOMA LINDA HEALTHCARE SYSTEM, LOMA LINDA, CA, p. A69
VETERANS AFFAIRS MARYLAND HEALTH CARE SYSTEM–BALTIMORE DIVISION, BALTIMORE, MD, p. A298
VETERANS AFFAIRS MARYLAND HEALTH CARE SYSTEM–PERRY POINT DIVISION, PERRY POINT, MARYLAND (see VETERANS AFFAIRS MARYLAND HEALTH CARE SYSTEM–BALTIMORE DIVISION), p. A298
VETERANS AFFAIRS MEDICAL CENTER, PITTSBURGH, PENNSYLVANIA (see VETERANS AFFAIRS PITTSBURGH HEALTHCARE SYSTEM), p. A552
VETERANS AFFAIRS MEDICAL CENTER, PITTSBURGH, PENNSYLVANIA (see VETERANS AFFAIRS PITTSBURGH HEALTHCARE SYSTEM), p. A552
VETERANS AFFAIRS MEDICAL CENTER HOT SPRINGS CAMPUS, HOT SPRINGS, SOUTH DAKOTA (see VETERANS AFFAIRS BLACK HILLS HEALTH CARE SYSTEM), p. A574
VETERANS AFFAIRS MEDICAL CENTER WEST ROXBURY DIVISION, WEST ROXBURY, MASSACHUSETTS (see VETERANS AFFAIRS BOSTON HEALTHCARE SYSTEM BROCKTON DIVISION), p. A308
VETERANS AFFAIRS MONTANA HEALTH CARE SYSTEM, FORT HARRISON, MT, p. A387
VETERANS AFFAIRS NEBRASKA–WESTERN IOWA HEALTH CARE SYSTEM, OMAHA, NE, p. A401
VETERANS AFFAIRS NEBRASKA–WESTERN IOWA HEALTH CARE SYSTEM – LINCOLN, LINCOLN, NE, p. A398
VETERANS AFFAIRS NEW JERSEY HEALTH CARE SYSTEM, EAST ORANGE, NJ, p. A416
VETERANS AFFAIRS NEW YORK HARBOR HEALTHCARE SYSTEM,, NY, p. A450
VETERANS AFFAIRS NEW YORK HARBOR HEALTHCARE SYSTEM – MANHATTAN CAMPUS, NEW YORK, NEW YORK (see VETERANS AFFAIRS NEW YORK HARBOR HEALTHCARE SYSTEM), p. A450
VETERANS AFFAIRS NORTH TEXAS HEALTH CARE SYSTEM, DALLAS, TX, p. A612
VETERANS AFFAIRS NORTHERN INDIANA HEALTH CARE SYSTEM, FORT WAYNE, IN, p. A211
VETERANS AFFAIRS NORTHERN INDIANA HEALTH CARE SYSTEM–MARION CAMPUS, MARION, INDIANA (see VETERANS AFFAIRS NORTHERN INDIANA HEALTH CARE SYSTEM), p. A211
VETERANS AFFAIRS PACIFIC ISLANDS HEALTH CARE SYSTEM, HONOLULU, HI, p. A171
VETERANS AFFAIRS PALO ALTO HEALTH CARE SYSTEM, LIVERMORE DIVISION, LIVERMORE, CALIFORNIA (see VA PALO ALTO HEALTH CARE SYSTEM), p. A82
VETERANS AFFAIRS PITTSBURGH HEALTHCARE SYSTEM, PITTSBURGH, PA, p. A552
VETERANS AFFAIRS PUGET SOUND HEALTH CARE SYSTEM, SEATTLE, WA, p. A690
VETERANS AFFAIRS PUGET SOUND HEALTH CARE SYSTEM–AMERICAN LAKE DIVISION, TACOMA, WASHINGTON (see VETERANS AFFAIRS PUGET SOUND HEALTH CARE SYSTEM), p. A690
VETERANS AFFAIRS ROSEBURG HEALTHCARE SYSTEM, ROSEBURG, OR, p. A530
VETERANS AFFAIRS SALT LAKE CITY HEALTH CARE SYSTEM, SALT LAKE CITY, UT, p. A664
VETERANS AFFAIRS SIERRA NEVADA HEALTH CARE SYSTEM, RENO, NV, p. A408
VETERANS AFFAIRS SOUTHERN NEVADA HEALTHCARE SYSTEM, NORTH LAS VEGAS, NV, p. A407
VETERANS AFFAIRS ST. LOUIS HEALTH CARE SYSTEM, SAINT LOUIS, MO, p. A381
VETERANS AFFAIRS WESTERN NEW YORK HEALTHCARE SYSTEM–BATAVIA DIVISION, BATAVIA, NY, p. A434
VETERANS AFFAIRS WESTERN NEW YORK HEALTHCARE SYSTEM–BUFFALO DIVISION, BUFFALO, NY, p. A436
VETERANS HEALTH CARE SYSTEM OF THE OZARKS, FAYETTEVILLE, AR, p. A46
VETERANS MEMORIAL HOSPITAL, WAUKON, IA, p. A239
VIA CHRISTI HOSPITAL MANHATTAN, INC.,, KS, p. A248
VIA CHRISTI HOSPITAL ON ST. FRANCIS, WICHITA, KS, p. A256
VIA CHRISTI HOSPITAL ON ST. TERESA, WICHITA, KS, p. A256
VIA CHRISTI HOSPITAL PITTSBURG, PITTSBURG, KS, p. A252
VIA CHRISTI REHABILITATION HOSPITAL, WICHITA, KS, p. A256
VIBRA HOSPITAL OF AMARILLO, AMARILLO, TX, p. A596
VIBRA HOSPITAL OF BOISE, MERIDIAN, ID, p. A177
VIBRA HOSPITAL OF CENTRAL DAKOTAS, MANDAN, ND, p. A480

VIBRA HOSPITAL OF CHARLESTON, MT. PLEASANT, SC, p. A568
VIBRA HOSPITAL OF DENVER, THORNTON, CO, p. A111
VIBRA HOSPITAL OF FARGO, FARGO, ND, p. A479
VIBRA HOSPITAL OF FORT WAYNE, FORT WAYNE, IN, p. A211
VIBRA HOSPITAL OF MAHONING VALLEY, BOARDMAN, OH, p. A485
VIBRA HOSPITAL OF MAHONING VALLEY–TRUMBULL CAMPUS, WARREN, OHIO (see VIBRA HOSPITAL OF MAHONING VALLEY), p. A485
VIBRA HOSPITAL OF NORTHERN CALIFORNIA, REDDING, CA, p. A84
VIBRA HOSPITAL OF NORTHWESTERN INDIANA, CROWN POINT, IN, p. A209
VIBRA HOSPITAL OF RICHMOND, RICHMOND, VA, p. A678
VIBRA HOSPITAL OF SACRAMENTO, FOLSOM, CA, p. A62
VIBRA HOSPITAL OF SAN DIEGO, SAN DIEGO, CA, p. A89
VIBRA HOSPITAL OF SOUTHEASTERN MASSACHUSETTS, NEW BEDFORD, MA, p. A312
VIBRA HOSPITAL OF SOUTHEASTERN MICHIGAN, LLC, LINCOLN PARK, MI, p. A329
VIBRA HOSPITAL OF SPRINGFIELD, SPRINGFIELD, IL, p. A203
VIBRA HOSPITAL OF WESTERN MASSACHUSETTS, SPRINGFIELD, MA, p. A315
VIBRA HOSPITAL OF WESTERN MASSACHUSETTS–CENTRAL CAMPUS, ROCHDALE, MASSACHUSETTS (see VIBRA HOSPITAL OF WESTERN MASSACHUSETTS), p. A315
VIBRA REHABILITATION HOSPITAL LAKE TRAVIS, LAKEWAY, TX, p. A631
VIBRA REHABILITATION HOSPITAL OF AMARILLO, AMARILLO, TX, p. A596
VIBRA SPECIALTY HOSPITAL AT DESOTO, DESOTO, TX, p. A613
VIBRA SPECIALTY HOSPITAL OF PORTLAND, PORTLAND, OR, p. A530
VICTOR VALLEY GLOBAL MEDICAL CENTER, VICTORVILLE, CA, p. A98
VIDANT BEAUFORT HOSPITAL, WASHINGTON, NC, p. A475
VIDANT BERTIE HOSPITAL, WINDSOR, NC, p. A475
VIDANT CHOWAN HOSPITAL, EDENTON, NC, p. A464
VIDANT DUPLIN HOSPITAL, KENANSVILLE, NC, p. A468
VIDANT EDGECOMBE HOSPITAL, TARBORO, NC, p. A474
VIDANT MEDICAL CENTER, GREENVILLE, NC, p. A466
VIDANT ROANOKE–CHOWAN HOSPITAL, AHOSKIE, NC, p. A460
VILLA FELICIANA MEDICAL COMPLEX, JACKSON, LA, p. A278
VIRGINIA BEACH PSYCHIATRIC CENTER, VIRGINIA BEACH, VA, p. A680
VIRGINIA GAY HOSPITAL, VINTON, IA, p. A238
VIRGINIA HOSPITAL CENTER – ARLINGTON, ARLINGTON, VA, p. A667
VIRGINIA MASON MEDICAL CENTER, SEATTLE, WA, p. A690
VIRTUA MARLTON, MARLTON, NJ, p. A419
VIRTUA MEMORIAL, MOUNT HOLLY, NJ, p. A420
VIRTUA VOORHEES, VOORHEES, NJ, p. A425
VISTA DEL MAR HOSPITAL, VENTURA, CA, p. A98
VISTA MEDICAL CENTER EAST, WAUKEGAN, IL, p. A205
VISTA MEDICAL CENTER WEST, WAUKEGAN, IL, p. A205
VOORHEES PEDIATRIC FACILITY, VOORHEES, NEW JERSEY (see VIRTUA VOORHEES), p. A425

W

W. G. (BILL) HEFFNER VETERANS AFFAIRS MEDICAL CENTER, SALISBURY, NC, p. A473
W. J. MANGOLD MEMORIAL HOSPITAL, LOCKNEY, TX, p. A633
WABASH GENERAL HOSPITAL, MOUNT CARMEL, IL, p. A197
WADLEY REGIONAL MEDICAL CENTER, TEXARKANA, TX, p. A652
WADLEY REGIONAL MEDICAL CENTER AT HOPE, HOPE, AR, p. A47
WAGNER COMMUNITY MEMORIAL HOSPITAL AVERA, WAGNER, SD, p. A577
WAGONER COMMUNITY HOSPITAL, WAGONER, OK, p. A523
WAHIAWA GENERAL HOSPITAL, WAHIAWA, HI, p. A172
WAKE FOREST BAPTIST HEALTH–DAVIE MEDICAL CENTER, MOCKSVILLE, NC, p. A469
WAKE FOREST BAPTIST HEALTH–LEXINGTON MEDICAL CENTER, LEXINGTON, NC, p. A469
WAKE FOREST BAPTIST MEDICAL CENTER, WINSTON–SALEM, NC, p. A476
WAKEMED CARY HOSPITAL, CARY, NC, p. A462
WAKEMED NORTH FAMILY HEALTH AND WOMEN'S HOSPITAL, RALEIGH, NORTH CAROLINA (see WAKEMED RALEIGH CAMPUS), p. A472
WAKEMED RALEIGH CAMPUS, RALEIGH, NC, p. A472
WALBRIDGE MEMORIAL CONVALESCENT WING (see PIONEERS MEDICAL CENTER), p. A109
WALDEN PSYCHIATRIC CARE, WALTHAM, MA, p. A315

WALDO COUNTY GENERAL HOSPITAL, BELFAST, ME, p. A292
WALKER BAPTIST MEDICAL CENTER, JASPER, AL, p. A22
WALLA WALLA GENERAL HOSPITAL, WALLA WALLA, WA, p. A693
WALLOWA MEMORIAL HOSPITAL, ENTERPRISE, OR, p. A525
WALNUT HILL MEDICAL CENTER, DALLAS, TX, p. A612
WALTER B. JONES ALCOHOL AND DRUG ABUSE TREATMENT CENTER, GREENVILLE, NC, p. A466
WALTER P. REUTHER PSYCHIATRIC HOSPITAL, WESTLAND, MI, p. A336
WALTER REED NATIONAL MILITARY MEDICAL CENTER, BETHESDA, MD, p. A299
WALTHALL COUNTY GENERAL HOSPITAL, TYLERTOWN, MS, p. A365
WAMEGO HEALTH CENTER, WAMEGO, KS, p. A255
WAR MEMORIAL HOSPITAL, SAULT SAINTE MARIE, MI, p. A334
WAR MEMORIAL HOSPITAL, BERKELEY SPRINGS, WV, p. A694
WARD MEMORIAL HOSPITAL, MONAHANS, TX, p. A637
WARM SPRINGS MEDICAL CENTER, WARM SPRINGS, GA, p. A168
WARM SPRINGS REHABILITATION HOSPITAL OF THOUSAND OAKS, SAN ANTONIO, TEXAS (see POST ACUTE/WARM SPRINGS REHABILITATION HOSPITAL OF SAN ANTONIO), p. A646
WARM SPRINGS REHABILITATION HOSPITAL OF WESTOVER HILLS, SAN ANTONIO, TEXAS (see POST ACUTE/WARM SPRINGS REHABILITATION HOSPITAL OF SAN ANTONIO), p. A646
WARRACK CAMPUS, SANTA ROSA, CALIFORNIA (see SUTTER SANTA ROSA REGIONAL HOSPITAL), p. A94
WARREN GENERAL HOSPITAL, WARREN, PA, p. A556
WARREN MEMORIAL HOSPITAL, FRONT ROYAL, VA, p. A671
WARREN STATE HOSPITAL, WARREN, PA, p. A556
WARWICK MANOR BEHAVIORAL HEALTH, EAST NEW MARKET, MD, p. A300
WASHAKIE MEDICAL CENTER, WORLAND, WY, p. A724
WASHINGTON ADVENTIST HOSPITAL, TAKOMA PARK, MD, p. A304
WASHINGTON COUNTY HOSPITAL, CHATOM, AL, p. A18
WASHINGTON COUNTY HOSPITAL, NASHVILLE, IL, p. A198
WASHINGTON COUNTY HOSPITAL, WASHINGTON, KS, p. A255
WASHINGTON COUNTY HOSPITAL, PLYMOUTH, NC, p. A471
WASHINGTON COUNTY HOSPITAL AND CLINICS, WASHINGTON, IA, p. A238
WASHINGTON COUNTY MEMORIAL HOSPITAL, POTOSI, MO, p. A378
WASHINGTON COUNTY REGIONAL MEDICAL CENTER, SANDERSVILLE, GA, p. A165
WASHINGTON DC VETERANS AFFAIRS MEDICAL CENTER, WASHINGTON, DC, p. A122
WASHINGTON HEALTH SYSTEM GREENE, WAYNESBURG, PA, p. A557
WASHINGTON HOSPITAL, WASHINGTON, PA, p. A556
WASHINGTON HOSPITAL HEALTHCARE SYSTEM, FREMONT, CA, p. A63
WASHINGTON REGIONAL MEDICAL CENTER, FAYETTEVILLE, AR, p. A46
WATAUGA MEDICAL CENTER, BOONE, NC, p. A461
WATERBURY HOSPITAL, WATERBURY, CT, p. A117
WATERTOWN REGIONAL MEDICAL CENTER, WATERTOWN, WI, p. A718
WATSONVILLE COMMUNITY HOSPITAL, WATSONVILLE, CA, p. A99
WAUKESHA COUNTY MENTAL HEALTH CENTER, WAUKESHA, WI, p. A718
WAUKESHA MEMORIAL HOSPITAL, WAUKESHA, WI, p. A718
WAUPUN MEMORIAL HOSPITAL, WAUPUN, WI, p. A718
WAVERLY HEALTH CENTER, WAVERLY, IA, p. A239
WAYNE COUNTY HOSPITAL, CORYDON, IA, p. A228
WAYNE COUNTY HOSPITAL, MONTICELLO, KY, p. A266
WAYNE GENERAL HOSPITAL, WAYNESBORO, MS, p. A366
WAYNE HOSPITAL, GREENVILLE, OH, p. A495
WAYNE MEDICAL CENTER, WAYNESBORO, TN, p. A594
WAYNE MEMORIAL HOSPITAL, JESUP, GA, p. A161
WAYNE MEMORIAL HOSPITAL, GOLDSBORO, NC, p. A466
WAYNE MEMORIAL HOSPITAL, HONESDALE, PA, p. A540
WAYNESBORO HOSPITAL, WAYNESBORO, PA, p. A556
WEATHERFORD REGIONAL HOSPITAL, WEATHERFORD, OK, p. A523
WEATHERFORD REGIONAL MEDICAL CENTER, WEATHERFORD, TX, p. A656
WEATHERFORD REHABILITATION HOSPITAL, WEATHERFORD, TX, p. A656
WEBSTER COUNTY COMMUNITY HOSPITAL, RED CLOUD, NE, p. A402
WEBSTER COUNTY MEMORIAL HOSPITAL, WEBSTER SPRINGS, WV, p. A700
WEDOWEE HOSPITAL, WEDOWEE, AL, p. A26
WEED ARMY COMMUNITY HOSPITAL, FORT IRWIN, CA, p. A62
WEEKS MEDICAL CENTER, LANCASTER, NH, p. A411

WEIMAR MEDICAL CENTER, WEIMAR, TX, p. A656
WEIRTON MEDICAL CENTER, WEIRTON, WV, p. A700
WEISBROD MEMORIAL COUNTY HOSPITAL, EADS, CO, p. A104
WEISER MEMORIAL HOSPITAL, WEISER, ID, p. A179
WEISMAN CHILDREN'S REHABILITATION HOSPITAL, MARLTON, NJ, p. A419
WEKIVA SPRINGS, JACKSONVILLE, FL, p. A132
WELCH COMMUNITY HOSPITAL, WELCH, WV, p. A701
WELLINGTON REGIONAL MEDICAL CENTER, WEST PALM BEACH, FL, p. A150
WELLMONT BRISTOL REGIONAL MEDICAL CENTER, BRISTOL, TN, p. A579
WELLMONT HANCOCK COUNTY HOSPITAL, SNEEDVILLE, TN, p. A593
WELLMONT HAWKINS COUNTY MEMORIAL HOSPITAL, ROGERSVILLE, TN, p. A592
WELLMONT HOLSTON VALLEY MEDICAL CENTER, KINGSPORT, TN, p. A585
WELLMONT LONESOME PINE HOSPITAL, BIG STONE GAP, VA, p. A667
WELLSPAN EPHRATA COMMUNITY HOSPITAL, EPHRATA, PA, p. A538
WELLSPAN GETTYSBURG HOSPITAL, GETTYSBURG, PA, p. A539
WELLSPAN GOOD SAMARITAN HOSPITAL, LEBANON, PA, p. A543
WELLSPAN SURGERY AND REHABILLITATION HOSPITAL, YORK, PENNSYLVANIA (see WELLSPAN YORK HOSPITAL), p. A559
WELLSPAN YORK HOSPITAL, YORK, PA, p. A559
WELLSPRING FOUNDATION, BETHLEHEM, CT, p. A113
WELLSTAR ATLANTA MEDICAL CENTER, ATLANTA, GA, p. A153
WELLSTAR COBB HOSPITAL, AUSTELL, GA, p. A154
WELLSTAR DOUGLAS HOSPITAL, DOUGLASVILLE, GA, p. A158
WELLSTAR KENNESTONE HOSPITAL, MARIETTA, GA, p. A163
WELLSTAR PAULDING HOSPITAL, HIRAM, GA, p. A161
WELLSTAR WINDY HILL HOSPITAL, MARIETTA, GA, p. A163
WELLSTONE REGIONAL HOSPITAL, JEFFERSONVILLE, IN, p. A215
WENTWORTH–DOUGLASS HOSPITAL, DOVER, NH, p. A410
WERNERSVILLE STATE HOSPITAL, WERNERSVILLE, PA, p. A557
WESLACO REGIONAL REHABILITATION HOSPITAL, WESLACO, TX, p. A657
WESLEY CHILDREN'S HOSPITAL, WICHITA, KANSAS (see WESLEY MEDICAL CENTER), p. A256
WESLEY LONG COMMUNITY HOSPITAL, GREENSBORO, NORTH CAROLINA (see MOSES H. CONE MEMORIAL HOSPITAL), p. A466
WESLEY MEDICAL CENTER, WICHITA, KS, p. A256
WESLEY REHABILITATION HOSPITAL, WICHITA, KS, p. A256
WESLEY WOODLAWN HOSPITAL & ER, WICHITA, KANSAS (see WESLEY MEDICAL CENTER), p. A256
WEST ANAHEIM MEDICAL CENTER, ANAHEIM, CA, p. A54
WEST BOCA MEDICAL CENTER, BOCA RATON, FL, p. A124
WEST BRANCH REGIONAL MEDICAL CENTER, WEST BRANCH, MI, p. A336
WEST CALCASIEU CAMERON HOSPITAL, SULPHUR, LA, p. A288
WEST CAMPUS, NORFOLK, NEBRASKA (see FAITH REGIONAL HEALTH SERVICES), p. A399
WEST CARROLL MEMORIAL HOSPITAL, OAK GROVE, LA, p. A286
WEST CENTRAL GEORGIA REGIONAL HOSPITAL, COLUMBUS, GA, p. A157
WEST CHESTER HOSPITAL, WEST CHESTER, OH, p. A505
WEST CHESTER HOSPITAL SURGICAL CENTER, WEST CHESTER, OHIO (see WEST CHESTER HOSPITAL), p. A505
WEST COVINA MEDICAL CENTER, WEST COVINA, CA, p. A99
WEST FELICIANA PARISH HOSPITAL, SAINT FRANCISVILLE, LA, p. A287
WEST FLORIDA COMMUNITY CARE CENTER, MILTON, FL, p. A138
WEST FLORIDA HOSPITAL, PENSACOLA, FL, p. A142
WEST FLORIDA REHABILITATION INSTITUTE, PENSACOLA, FLORIDA (see WEST FLORIDA HOSPITAL), p. A142
WEST GABLES REHABILITATION HOSPITAL, MIAMI, FL, p. A137
WEST GEORGIA HEALTH, LAGRANGE, GA, p. A161
WEST HAVEN DIVISION, WEST HAVEN, CONNECTICUT (see VETERANS AFFAIRS CONNECTICUT HEALTHCARE SYSTEM), p. A118
WEST HILLS HOSPITAL, RENO, NV, p. A408
WEST HILLS HOSPITAL AND MEDICAL CENTER,, CA, p. A75
WEST HOLT MEMORIAL HOSPITAL, ATKINSON, NE, p. A393
WEST HOUSTON MEDICAL CENTER, HOUSTON, TX, p. A627
WEST JEFFERSON MEDICAL CENTER, MARRERO, LA, p. A283
WEST MARION COMMUNITY HOSPITAL, OCALA, FLORIDA (see OCALA REGIONAL MEDICAL CENTER), p. A139
WEST OAKS HOSPITAL, HOUSTON, TX, p. A627
WEST PALM BEACH VETERANS AFFAIRS MEDICAL CENTER, WEST PALM BEACH, FL, p. A150
WEST PARK HOSPITAL, CODY, WY, p. A722
WEST PENN HOSPITAL, PITTSBURGH, PA, p. A552

WEST RIVER REGIONAL MEDICAL CENTER, HETTINGER, ND, p. A479
WEST SHORE MEDICAL CENTER, MANISTEE, MI, p. A329
WEST SPRINGS HOSPITAL, GRAND JUNCTION, CO, p. A106
WEST SUBURBAN MEDICAL CENTER, OAK PARK, IL, p. A199
WEST TEXAS VETERANS AFFAIRS HEALTH CARE SYSTEM, BIG SPRING, TX, p. A603
WEST VALLEY MEDICAL CENTER, CALDWELL, ID, p. A175
WEST VIRGINIA UNIVERSITY CHILDREN'S HOSPITAL, MORGANTOWN, WEST VIRGINIA (see WEST VIRGINIA UNIVERSITY HOSPITALS), p. A698
WEST VIRGINIA UNIVERSITY HOSPITALS, MORGANTOWN, WV, p. A698
WESTCHESTER GENERAL HOSPITAL, MIAMI, FL, p. A137
WESTCHESTER MEDICAL CENTER, VALHALLA, NY, p. A458
WESTEND HOSPITAL, JENNINGS, LA, p. A279
WESTERLY HOSPITAL, WESTERLY, RI, p. A561
WESTERN ARIZONA REGIONAL MEDICAL CENTER, BULLHEAD CITY, AZ, p. A31
WESTERN MARYLAND HOSPITAL CENTER, HAGERSTOWN, MD, p. A301
WESTERN MARYLAND REGIONAL MEDICAL CENTER, CUMBERLAND, MD, p. A300
WESTERN MASSACHUSETTS HOSPITAL, WESTFIELD, MA, p. A316
WESTERN MENTAL HEALTH INSTITUTE, BOLIVAR, TN, p. A579
WESTERN MISSOURI MEDICAL CENTER, WARRENSBURG, MO, p. A383
WESTERN NEW YORK CHILDREN'S PSYCHIATRIC CENTER, WEST SENECA, NY, p. A459
WESTERN PLAINS MEDICAL COMPLEX, DODGE CITY, KS, p. A242
WESTERN PSYCHIATRIC INSTITUTE AND CLINIC, PITTSBURGH, PENNSYLVANIA (see UPMC PRESBYTERIAN SHADYSIDE), p. A551
WESTERN REGIONAL MEDICAL CENTER, GOODYEAR, AZ, p. A33
WESTERN STATE HOSPITAL, HOPKINSVILLE, KY, p. A262
WESTERN STATE HOSPITAL, STAUNTON, VA, p. A679
WESTERN STATE HOSPITAL, TACOMA, WA, p. A692
WESTFIELD MEMORIAL HOSPITAL, WESTFIELD, NY, p. A459
WESTFIELDS HOSPITAL, NEW RICHMOND, WI, p. A713
WESTLAKE HOSPITAL, MELROSE PARK, IL, p. A196
WESTON COUNTY HEALTH SERVICES, NEWCASTLE, WY, p. A723
WESTPARK SPRINGS, RICHMOND, TX, p. A643
WESTSIDE REGIONAL MEDICAL CENTER, PLANTATION, FL, p. A143
WESTSIDE SURGICAL HOSPITAL, HOUSTON, TX, p. A627
WESTWOOD LODGE HOSPITAL, WESTWOOD, MA, p. A316
WETZEL COUNTY HOSPITAL, NEW MARTINSVILLE, WV, p. A698
WHEATLAND MEMORIAL HEALTHCARE, HARLOWTON, MT, p. A388
WHEATON FRANCISCAN HEALTHCARE – ALL SAINTS, RACINE, WI, p. A714
WHEATON FRANCISCAN HEALTHCARE – ELMBROOK MEMORIAL, BROOKFIELD, WI, p. A703
WHEATON FRANCISCAN HEALTHCARE – FRANKLIN, FRANKLIN, WI, p. A706
WHEATON FRANCISCAN HEALTHCARE – ST. FRANCIS, MILWAUKEE, WI, p. A712
WHEATON FRANCISCAN HEALTHCARE – ST. JOSEPH'S, MILWAUKEE, WI, p. A712
WHEELING HOSPITAL, WHEELING, WV, p. A701
WHIDBEYHEALTH, COUPEVILLE, WA, p. A684
WHIDDEN MEMORIAL HOSPITAL, EVERETT, MASSACHUSETTS (see CAMBRIDGE HEALTH ALLIANCE), p. A308
WHITE MEMORIAL MEDICAL CENTER, LOS ANGELES, CA, p. A75
WHITE MOUNTAIN REGIONAL MEDICAL CENTER, SPRINGERVILLE, AZ, p. A39
WHITE PLAINS HOSPITAL CENTER, WHITE PLAINS, NY, p. A459
WHITE RIVER JUNCTION VETERANS AFFAIRS MEDICAL CENTER, WHITE RIVER JUNCTION, VT, p. A666
WHITE RIVER MEDICAL CENTER, BATESVILLE, AR, p. A43
WHITESBURG ARH HOSPITAL, WHITESBURG, KY, p. A270
WHITFIELD MEDICAL SURGICAL HOSPITAL, WHITFIELD, MISSISSIPPI (see MISSISSIPPI STATE HOSPITAL), p. A366
WHITING FORENSIC DIVISION OF CONNECTICUT VALLEY HOSPITAL, MIDDLETOWN, CONNECTICUT (see CONNECTICUT VALLEY HOSPITAL), p. A115
WHITINSVILLE MEDICAL CENTER, WHITINSVILLE, MASSACHUSETTS (see MILFORD REGIONAL MEDICAL CENTER), p. A312
WHITMAN HOSPITAL AND MEDICAL CENTER, COLFAX, WA, p. A683
WHITTEN CENTER, CLINTON, SC, p. A563
WHITTIER HOSPITAL MEDICAL CENTER, WHITTIER, CA, p. A100
WHITTIER PAVILION, HAVERHILL, MA, p. A310
WHITTIER REHABILITATION HOSPITAL, BRADFORD, MA, p. A307

WHITTIER REHABILITATION HOSPITAL, WESTBOROUGH, MA, p. A316
WICHITA COUNTY HEALTH CENTER, LEOTI, KS, p. A248
WICKENBURG COMMUNITY HOSPITAL, WICKENBURG, AZ, p. A41
WILBARGER GENERAL HOSPITAL, VERNON, TX, p. A655
WILCOX MEMORIAL HOSPITAL, LIHUE, HI, p. A172
WILKES REGIONAL MEDICAL CENTER, NORTH WILKESBORO, NC, p. A471
WILKES–BARRE GENERAL HOSPITAL, WILKES–BARRE, PA, p. A558
WILKES–BARRE GENERAL HOSPITAL, WILKES–BARRE, PENNSYLVANIA (see WILKES–BARRE GENERAL HOSPITAL), p. A558
WILKES–BARRE VETERANS AFFAIRS MEDICAL CENTER, WILKES–BARRE, PA, p. A558
WILLAMETTE VALLEY MEDICAL CENTER, MCMINNVILLE, OR, p. A527
WILLAPA HARBOR HOSPITAL, SOUTH BEND, WA, p. A690
WILLIAM AND INEZ MABIE SKILLED NURSING FACILITY, HOLLISTER, CALIFORNIA (see HAZEL HAWKINS MEMORIAL HOSPITAL), p. A66
WILLIAM BEAUMONT ARMY MEDICAL CENTER, EL PASO, TX, p. A616
WILLIAM BEE RIRIE HOSPITAL, ELY, NV, p. A404
WILLIAM J. MCCORD ADOLESCENT TREATMENT FACILITY, ORANGEBURG, SC, p. A569
WILLIAM NEWTON HOSPITAL, WINFIELD, KS, p. A256
WILLIAM P. CLEMENTS, JR. UNIVERSITY HOSPITAL, DALLAS, TX, p. A612
WILLIAM R. SHARPE, JR. HOSPITAL, WESTON, WV, p. A701
WILLIAM S. HALL PSYCHIATRIC INSTITUTE, COLUMBIA, SC, p. A564
WILLIAM S. MIDDLETON MEMORIAL VETERANS HOSPITAL, MADISON, WI, p. A709
WILLIAMSON MEDICAL CENTER, FRANKLIN, TN, p. A583
WILLIAMSON MEMORIAL HOSPITAL, WILLIAMSON, WV, p. A701
WILLIAMSPORT REGIONAL MEDICAL CENTER, WILLIAMSPORT, PA, p. A558
WILLIE D. MILLER EYE CENTER, CHATTANOOGA, TENNESSEE (see ERLANGER MEDICAL CENTER), p. A580
WILLINGWAY HOSPITAL, STATESBORO, GA, p. A166
WILLIS–KNIGHTON MEDICAL CENTER, SHREVEPORT, LA, p. A288
WILLIS–KNIGHTON PIERREMONT HEALTH CENTER, SHREVEPORT, LOUISIANA (see WILLIS–KNIGHTON MEDICAL CENTER), p. A288
WILLIS–KNIGHTON SOUTH – THE CENTER FOR WOMEN'S HEALTH, SHREVEPORT, LOUISIANA (see WILLIS–KNIGHTON MEDICAL CENTER), p. A288
WILLOW CREEK WOMEN'S HOSPITAL, JOHNSON, ARKANSAS (see NORTHWEST MEDICAL CENTER – SPRINGDALE), p. A52
WILLOW CREST HOSPITAL, MIAMI, OK, p. A514
WILLOW ROCK CENTER, SAN LEANDRO, CA, p. A92
WILLOW SPRINGS CENTER, RENO, NV, p. A408
WILLS MEMORIAL HOSPITAL, WASHINGTON, GA, p. A168
WILMA N. VAZQUEZ MEDICAL CENTER, VEGA BAJA, PR, p. A730
WILMINGTON TREATMENT CENTER, WILMINGTON, NC, p. A475
WILMINGTON VETERANS AFFAIRS MEDICAL CENTER, WILMINGTON, DE, p. A120
WILSON MEDICAL CENTER, NEODESHA, KS, p. A249
WILSON MEDICAL CENTER, WILSON, NC, p. A475
WILSON MEMORIAL HOSPITAL, SIDNEY, OH, p. A502
WILSON MEMORIAL REGIONAL MEDICAL CENTER, JOHNSON CITY, NEW YORK (see UNITED HEALTH SERVICES HOSPITALS–BINGHAMTON), p. A435
WILSON N. JONES REGIONAL MEDICAL CENTER, SHERMAN, TX, p. A649
WINCHESTER HOSPITAL, WINCHESTER, MA, p. A316
WINCHESTER MEDICAL CENTER, WINCHESTER, VA, p. A680
WINDHAM HOSPITAL, WILLIMANTIC, CT, p. A118
WINDHAVEN PSYCHIATRIC HOSPITAL, PRESCOTT VALLEY, AZ, p. A38
WINDMOOR HEALTHCARE OF CLEARWATER, CLEARWATER, FL, p. A125
WINDOM AREA HOSPITAL, WINDOM, MN, p. A353
WINDSOR–LAURELWOOD CENTER FOR BEHAVIORAL MEDICINE, WILLOUGHBY, OH, p. A506
WINKLER COUNTY MEMORIAL HOSPITAL, KERMIT, TX, p. A630
WINN ARMY COMMUNITY HOSPITAL, HINESVILLE, GA, p. A160
WINN PARISH MEDICAL CENTER, WINNFIELD, LA, p. A289
WINNEBAGO MENTAL HEALTH INSTITUTE, WINNEBAGO, WI, p. A719
WINNER REGIONAL HEALTHCARE CENTER, WINNER, SD, p. A578
WINNESHIEK MEDICAL CENTER, DECORAH, IA, p. A229
WINNIE PALMER HOSPITAL FOR WOMEN AND BABIES, ORLANDO, FLORIDA (see ORLANDO REGIONAL MEDICAL CENTER), p. A140

Y

Z

This section is an index of the key health care professionals for the hospitals and/or health care systems listed in this publication. The index is in alphabetical order, by individual, followed by the title, institutional affiliation, city, state and page reference to the hospital and/or health care system listing in section A and/or B.

A

AAGARD, Kim, Chief Financial Officer, Tri–County Hospital, Wadena, MN, p. A353

AASE, Katie, Director of Nursing, Rock County Hospital, Bassett, NE, p. A393

AASVED, Craig E., Chief Executive Officer, Shodair Children's Hospital, Helena, MT, p. A388

ABAIR, Cynthia, Associate Director, VA San Diego Healthcare System, San Diego, CA, p. A89

ABANG, Toni, M.D. Medical Director, HEALTHSOUTH Lakeview Rehabilitation Hospital, Elizabethtown, KY, p. A259

ABBATE, Anthony, Director of Information Services, San Ramon Regional Medical Center, San Ramon, CA, p. A92

ABBATIELLO, Michael, Chief Financial Officer, Spring Harbor Hospital, Westbrook, ME, p. A295

ABBEY, Kurtis, Chief Nursing Officer, Ozarks Medical Center, West Plains, MO, p. A384

ABBOTT, Dana, Market Human Resources Director, Shands Live Oak Regional Medical Center, Live Oak, FL, p. A134

ABBOTT, Jody, Senior Vice President and Chief Operating Officer, North Kansas City Hospital, North Kansas City, MO, p. A377

ABBOTT, Joe, Director Information Systems, North Ottawa Community Hospital, Grand Haven, MI, p. A324

ABBOTT, Justin, M.D. Medical Director, Sevier Valley Medical Center, Richfield, UT, p. A662

ABBOTT, Michael, Chief Operating Officer, Lewis–Gale Medical Center, Salem, VA, p. A678

ABBOTT, Peggy L., President and Chief Executive Officer, Ouachita County Medical Center, Camden, AR, p. A44

ABDA, William, Chief Human Resources Officer, Clarks Summit State Hospital, Clarks Summit, PA, p. A535

ABDELNASER, Mohammad, Chief Nursing Officer, Centinela Hospital Medical Center, Inglewood, CA, p. A66

ABE, Ann, Administrator and Chief Operating Officer, Orange County Global Medical Center, Inc., Santa Ana, CA, p. A92

ABEL, Danielle, Vice President of Patient Care Services, CHI LakeWood Health, Baudette, MN, p. A339

ABEL, David, Chief Financial Officer, Hardy Wilson Memorial Hospital, Hazlehurst, MS, p. A359

ABEL, Jeffrey, M.D. Chief Medical Officer, Ogden Regional Medical Center, Ogden, UT, p. A661

ABEL, Kevin, Chief Executive Officer, Lake Chelan Community Hospital, Chelan, WA, p. A683

ABEL, Stacy L., Director Human Resources, Craig Hospital, Englewood, CO, p. A105

ABELLERA, Roland, Vice President and Chief Operating Officer, St. Bernard Hospital and Health Care Center, Chicago, IL, p. A187

ABELY, Susan Cerrone
  Vice President and Chief Information Officer, Roger Williams Medical Center, Providence, RI, p. A561
  Chief Information Officer, St. Joseph Health Services of Rhode Island, North Providence, RI, p. A560

ABERCROMBIE, David, Controller, Baptist Health South Florida, Homestead Hospital, Homestead, FL, p. A131

ABERCROMBIE, David E., Chief Executive Officer, Montgomery County Memorial Hospital, Red Oak, IA, p. A236

ABERCROMBIE, Zach, Administrator, Citizens Baptist Medical Center, Talladega, AL, p. A25

ABERLE, James, Vice President, Chief Operations Officer, Yakima Valley Memorial Hospital, Yakima, WA, p. A693

ABERNATHY, Clint, President and Chief Operating Officer, Texas Health Harris Methodist Hospital Alliance, Fort Worth, TX, p. A618

ABEYTA, Mary Anna, R.N. Chief Nursing Officer, Holy Cross Hospital, Taos, NM, p. A432

ABINSAY, Alvin, M.D. Chief Medical Staff, Carolinas Hospital System Marion, Mullins, SC, p. A568

ABLA, Mike, Director of Nursing, Griffin Memorial Hospital, Norman, OK, p. A515

ABNEY, Stuart, Controller, Jasper Memorial Hospital, Monticello, GA, p. A163

ABOUD, Al, CPA Chief Financial Officer, Hackensack University Medical Center Mountainside, Montclair, NJ, p. A419

ABRAHAM, Akram, M.D. Chief of Staff, Harmon Memorial Hospital, Hollis, OK, p. A513

ABRAHAM, Brian, Chief Executive Officer, Mesquite Rehabilitation Institute, Mesquite, TX, p. A636

ABRAHAM, JiJi, Chief Financial Officer, Kaiser Permanente Riverside Medical Center, Riverside, CA, p. A85

ABRAHAMSON–BATY, Sherri, Director Patient Care Services, Cambridge Medical Center, Cambridge, MN, p. A340

ABRAHAMY, Ran, M.D. Chief of Staff, University Hospital and Medical Center, Tamarac, FL, p. A146

ABRAMS, Danielle, Manager Human Resources, Marketing and Executive Assistant, St. Vincent Clay Hospital, Brazil, IN, p. A207

ABRAMS, David, Vice President Human Resources, North Memorial Medical Center, Robbinsdale, MN, p. A349

ABREU, Iris, Supervisor Human Resources, Hospital HIMA de Humacao, Humacao, PR, p. A727

ABREU, John, Vice President and Chief Financial Officer, Portneuf Medical Center, Pocatello, ID, p. A178

ABRINA, Sofia, Administrator and Chief Nursing Officer, Huntington Beach Hospital, Huntington Beach, CA, p. A66

ABROMOVICH, Sari, Chief Executive Officer, Harbor Oaks Hospital, New Baltimore, MI, p. A330

ABRUTZ Jr., Joseph F., Administrator, Cameron Regional Medical Center, Cameron, MO, p. A368

ABSALON, Jeffrey, M.D
  Chief Physician Officer, St. Charles Bend, Bend, OR, p. A524
  Chief Physician Officer, St. Charles Redmond, Redmond, OR, p. A530

ABUNDO, Manuel, M.D. Chief of Staff, Wahiawa General Hospital, Wahiawa, HI, p. A172

ABY, Sherry, Director Information Management, Carlisle Regional Medical Center, Carlisle, PA, p. A535

ACCASHIAN, Chris, Chief Executive Officer, Bon Secours St. Francis Medical Center, Midlothian, VA, p. A673

ACERRA–WILLIAMS, Karen, Acting Director, Bedford Veterans Affairs Medical Center, Edith Nourse Rogers Memorial Veterans Hospital, Bedford, MA, p. A305

ACETO, Anthony, Vice President Human Resources, Norwalk Hospital, Norwalk, CT, p. A116

ACEVEDO, Edwin Orama, Financial Supervisor, Hospital Buen Samaritano, Aguadilla, PR, p. A725

ACEVEDO, Jose, M.D., President and Chief Executive Officer, Finger Lakes Health, Geneva, NY, p. B55

ACEVEDO, Jose, M.D.,
  President and Chief Executive Officer, Geneva General Hospital, Geneva, NY, p. A439
  President and Chief Executive Officer, Soldiers and Sailors Memorial Hospital of Yates County, Penn Yan, NY, p. A452

ACEVEDO, Ramon, Supervisor Information Systems, Hospital San Cristobal, Coto Laurel, PR, p. A727

ACHARYA, Ganesh, Chief Executive Officer, Good Samaritan Hospital, Bakersfield, CA, p. A56

ACHEBE, James Bob, M.D. President Medical Staff, South Shore Hospital, Chicago, IL, p. A186

ACHTER, Dick, Chief Financial Officer, Barrett Hospital & HealthCare, Dillon, MT, p. A387

ACHURY, Dario, Director of Information Management, St. Anthony's Rehabilitation Hospital, Lauderdale Lakes, FL, p. A134

ACKER, David B., FACHE, President and CEO, Canton–Potsdam Hospital, Potsdam, NY, p. A453

ACKER, David B., FACHE, President and CEO, St. Lawrence Health System, Potsdam, NY, p. B128

ACKER, Peter W., President and Chief Executive Officer, Carolinas HealthCare System Lincoln, Lincolnton, NC, p. A469

ACKERMAN, F. Kenneth, Chair, Hospital Operations, Mayo Clinic Hospital – Rochester, Rochester, MN, p. A349

ACKERMAN, Sigurd H., M.D., President and Chief Executive Officer, Silver Hill Hospital, New Canaan, CT, p. A115

ACKERSON, David, Chief Information Officer, Seattle Cancer Care Alliance, Seattle, WA, p. A689

ACKERT, Sara, Associate Director, Sioux Falls Veterans Affairs Health Care System, Sioux Falls, SD, p. A576

ACKLAND, Jeanne, Director of Finance, Fillmore County Hospital, Geneva, NE, p. A396

ACKLEY, Michael
  Chief Financial Officer, Kentucky River Medical Center, Jackson, KY, p. A262
  Chief Financial Officer, Three Rivers Medical Center, Louisa, KY, p. A264

ACKLIN, Traci, M.D. Chief of Staff, Montgomery General Hospital, Montgomery, WV, p. A698

ACKMAN, Jeffrey D., M.D. Chief of Staff, Shriners Hospitals for Children–Chicago, Chicago, IL, p. A186

ACKMAN, Laura, Chief Operating Officer and Administrator, Essentia Health Northern Pines Medical Center, Aurora, MN, p. A338

ACOSTA, Ivan, M.D. Medical Director, Hospital De La Concepcion, San German, PR, p. A729

ACOSTA, Louis, M.D. Chief of Staff, Silver Lake Medical Center, Los Angeles, CA, p. A74

ACOSTA–CARLSON, Francisca, M.D. Chief of Staff, Lexington Regional Health Center, Lexington, NE, p. A397

ACREE, Charis L., Vice President and Chief Operating Officer, West Georgia Health, Lagrange, GA, p. A161

ADAIR, Dale K., M.D. Chief Medical Officer, Wernersville State Hospital, Wernersville, PA, p. A557

ADAIR, Julie, Interim Corporate Chief Human Resources Officer, Fresno Heart and Surgical Hospital, Fresno, CA, p. A63

ADAM, Sheryl, Chief Financial Officer, Hanover Hospital, Hanover, KS, p. A244

ADAMO, James D., M.D. Medical Director, Harbor Oaks Hospital, New Baltimore, MI, p. A330

ADAMO, Peter J.
  Chief Executive Officer, Roxborough Memorial Hospital, Philadelphia, PA, p. A549
  Chief Executive Officer, Suburban Community Hospital, Norristown, PA, p. A546

ADAMOLEKUN, Michelle
  Vice President Human Resource Market Lead Florida/Alabama Ministry Market, Sacred Heart Hospital Pensacola, Pensacola, FL, p. A142
  Chief Human Resource Officer, St. Vincent's Medical Center Riverside, Jacksonville, FL, p. A132

ADAMS, Alan L., President, Memorial Hospital, Stilwell, OK, p. A520

ADAMS, Amy B., Executive Director Human Resources, Saint Francis Hospital South, Tulsa, OK, p. A522

ADAMS, Bob, Director Information Services, Bay Area Hospital, Coos Bay, OR, p. A525

ADAMS, Brian
  President and Chief Executive Officer, Florida Hospital at Connerton Long Term Acute Care, Land O'Lakes, FL, p. A134
  President and CEO, Florida Hospital Tampa, Tampa, FL, p. A147

ADAMS, Carla, Chief Nursing Officer, Northern Nevada Medical Center, Sparks, NV, p. A408

ADAMS, Cathleen, Chief Nursing Officer, CarePartners Health Services, Asheville, NC, p. A460

ADAMS, Charlotte, Director of Human Resources, Carolina Pines Regional Medical Center, Hartsville, SC, p. A567

ADAMS, Chris, Vice President Patient Care Services, Good Samaritan Regional Health Center, Mount Vernon, IL, p. A197

ADAMS, Cynthia, Vice President Human Resources, TriStar StoneCrest Medical Center, Smyrna, TN, p. A593

ADAMS, Emmy
  Chief Financial Officer, Mayhill Hospital, Denton, TX, p. A612
  Chief Financial Officer, Provo Canyon Behavioral Hospital, Orem, UT, p. A661

ADAMS, Essie, Director of Nursing, Kedren Community Mental Health Center, Los Angeles, CA, p. A72

ADAMS, Fiona, Interim Director, Southern Crescent Hospital for Specialty Care, Riverdale, GA, p. A164

ADAMS, Gini, Director Employee and Public Relations, Yuma District Hospital, Yuma, CO, p. A112

ADAMS, J'Dee, Chief Operating Officer, North Canyon Medical Center, Gooding, ID, p. A176

ADAMS, Jason, Chief Operating Officer, CHRISTUS St. Vincent Regional Medical Center, Santa Fe, NM, p. A431

ADAMS, Jason, M.D. Medical Staff President, Forest Health Medical Center, Ypsilanti, MI, p. A337

ADAMS, Jennifer B., Chief Operating Officer and Chief Financial Officer, Lake City Medical Center, Lake City, FL, p. A133

ADAMS, Jo, Director Human Resources, Donalsonville Hospital, Donalsonville, GA, p. A158

ADAMS, Karen, Vice President Human Resources, Baxter Regional Medical Center, Mountain Home, AR, p. A50

ADAMS, Kimberly, Manager Human Resources, Carroll County Memorial Hospital, Carrollton, KY, p. A258

ADAMS, Lana, Chief Financial Officer, Lafayette General Medical Center, Lafayette, LA, p. A280

ADAMS, Laura L., Vice President, Finance, St. Vincent Anderson Regional Hospital, Anderson, IN, p. A206

ADAMS, Leslie, Chief Nursing Executive, Saint Joseph Berea, Berea, KY, p. A257

ADAMS, Mark A., President and Chief Executive Officer, Methodist Rehabilitation Center, Jackson, MS, p. A360

ADAMS, Mark B., Chief Executive Officer, Ogden Regional Medical Center, Ogden, UT, p. A661

ADAMS, Marlene J., Director Human Resources, Schneider Regional Medical Center, Saint Thomas, VI, p. A731

ADAMS, Marsha, Interim Director Human Resources, Texas Health Harris Methodist Hospital Cleburne, Cleburne, TX, p. A606

ADAMS, Martin D., CPA Vice President Finance and Chief Financial Officer, Paris Community Hospital, Paris, IL, p. A199

ADAMS, Mary Jane, R.N. Senior Vice President and Chief Nursing Officer, University of Louisville Hospital, Louisville, KY, p. A265

ADAMS, Michael, Chief Operating Officer, Freedom Pain Hospital, Scottsdale, AZ, p. A38

ADAMS, Mike, M.D. Chief Medical Officer, Gateway Regional Medical Center, Granite City, IL, p. A191

ADAMS, Nancy D., R.N. Senior Vice President Chief Operating Officer and Chief Nurse Executive, Western Maryland Regional Medical Center, Cumberland, MD, p. A300

ADAMS, Norma, Director Human Resources, Southern Regional Medical Center, Riverdale, GA, p. A164

ADAMS, Patsy, Vice President Human Resources, Redmond Regional Medical Center, Rome, GA, p. A165

ADAMS, Renee, Director Information Technology, Chan Soon–Shiong Medical Center, Windber, PA, p. A558

ADAMS, Robert H., Vice President Operations, Jersey Shore University Medical Center, Neptune, NJ, p. A420

ADAMS, Robin, Director Human Resources, Reeves Memorial Medical Center, Bernice, LA, p. A273

ADAMS, Scott K., FACHE, Chief Executive Officer, Pullman Regional Hospital, Pullman, WA, p. A688

ADAMS, Shannon, Chief Financial Officer, Avera Holy Family Hospital, Estherville, IA, p. A230

ADAMS, Sharon, Chief Operating Officer, Danbury Hospital, Danbury, CT, p. A113

ADAMS, Sharon, R.N. Senior Vice President Patient Care Services and Chief Quality Officer, Mercy Medical Center, Springfield, MA, p. A315

ADAMS, Shaun, Chief Financial Officer, Tennova Healthcare–Harton, Tullahoma, TN, p. A594

ADAMS, Shawn, Chief Financial Officer, CHRISTUS Southeast Texas Hospital, Beaumont, TX, p. A601

ADAMS, Shelah, Chief Executive Officer, Timberlawn Mental Health System, Dallas, TX, p. A611

ADAMS, Stanley, Chief Financial Officer, Summit Healthcare Regional Medical Center, Show Low, AZ, p. A39

ADAMS, Susan, Chief Nursing Officer and Chief Operating Officer, Specialty Hospital of Lorain, Amherst, OH, p. A483

ADAMS, T. Gard, M.D. Chief of Staff, Caro Community Hospital, Caro, MI, p. A320

ADAMS, Tony, President, Barix Clinics of Pennsylvania, Langhorne, PA, p. A542

ADAMSKI, Joseph, Chief Nursing Officer, HEALTHSOUTH Rehabilitation Hospital, Concord, NH, p. A410

ADAMSON, James, Chief Executive Officer, Mountain View Hospital, Idaho Falls, ID, p. A176

ADAMSON, Nancy, Chief Nursing Officer, Banner Del E. Webb Medical Center, Sun City West, AZ, p. A39

ADCOCK, Robert S., Chief Executive Officer, Kindred Hospital–St. Louis at Mercy, Saint Louis, MO, p. A380

ADCOCK, William, Chief Financial Officer, Union General Hospital, Farmerville, LA, p. A276

ADDINGTON, Tom, Chief Information Officer, Saint Michael's Medical Center, Newark, NJ, p. A421

ADDISON, Holland M., M.D. Medical Director, Select Specialty Hospital – Belhaven, Jackson, MS, p. A360

ADDISON, Lenora, Vice President Patient Care and Nursing, MedStar Harbor Hospital, Baltimore, MD, p. A297

ADDISON, Lewis C., Senior Vice President and Chief Financial Officer, Centra Lynchburg General Hospital, Lynchburg, VA, p. A672

ADDLESPERGER, John, D.O. Chief Medical Officer, Sheridan Memorial Hospital, Sheridan, WY, p. A723

ADDO–SAMUELS, Deborah, Chief Executive Officer, Inova Mount Vernon Hospital, Alexandria, VA, p. A667

ADEDOKUN, Ade, M.D. Medical Director, Baylor Institute for Rehabilitation at Fort Worth, Fort Worth, TX, p. A617

ADELMAN, Michael, M.D., Medical Center Director, Wilkes–Barre Veterans Affairs Medical Center, Wilkes–Barre, PA, p. A558

ADEMA, Carolyn, Vice President, Human Resources, St. Tammany Parish Hospital, Covington, LA, p. A275

ADEN, Susie, Director of IP Services, Pocahontas Community Hospital, Pocahontas, IA, p. A236

ADER, Michael H., M.D. Vice President Medical Affairs, Hanover Hospital, Hanover, PA, p. A539

ADERS, Deb, MS Interim Chief Nursing Officer, Yuma Regional Medical Center, Yuma, AZ, p. A42

ADESSO, Patrick, Director Information Technology and Systems, Specialty Hospital Jacksonville, Jacksonville, FL, p. A132

ADKINS, Gary W., President, Parkview Noble Hospital, Kendallville, IN, p. A215

ADKINS, Kedrick D., Chief Financial Officer, Mayo Clinic Hospital – Rochester, Rochester, MN, p. A349

ADKINS, Kevin, Director Human Resources, Green Oaks Hospital, Dallas, TX, p. A610

ADKINS, Paige, Chief Financial Officer, Greenbrier Valley Medical Center, Ronceverte, WV, p. A700

ADKINS, Raymond, Chief Information Officer, Peninsula Regional Medical Center, Salisbury, MD, p. A303

ADKINS, Scott, Manager Information Technology, Vernon Memorial Healthcare, Viroqua, WI, p. A717

ADKINS, Tyler, Chief Financial Officer, Vaughan Regional Medical Center, Selma, AL, p. A25

ADLER, Josh, M.D. Chief Medical Officer, UCSF Medical Center, San Francisco, CA, p. A91

ADLER, Kenneth, M.D. Medical Director, Arrowhead Behavioral Health Hospital, Maumee, OH, p. A498

ADLER, Maurita, Director Information Services, Gottlieb Memorial Hospital, Melrose Park, IL, p. A196

ADMA, Vishal, M.D. Medical Director, KVC Prairie Ridge Psychiatric Hospital, Kansas City, KS, p. A246

ADORNATO, Sara F., Executive Director, Barnes–Kasson County Hospital, Susquehanna, PA, p. A555

ADORNETTO–GARCIA, Debra, MSN Chief Nursing Officer, Banner Gateway Medical Center, Gilbert, AZ, p. A32

ADRIAANSE, Steven W., Vice President and Chief Human Resources Officer, Tallahassee Memorial HealthCare, Tallahassee, FL, p. A146

ADVEY, Linda, Manager Information Systems, Glenbeigh Hospital and Outpatient Centers, Rock Creek, OH, p. A502

AEMMER, Anthony, Director of Nursing, Wellstone Regional Hospital, Jeffersonville, IN, p. A215

AFABLE, Richard, M.P.H., Interim President & Chief Executive Officer, Mission Hospital, Mission Viejo, CA, p. A77

AFANEH, Bassam, M.D. Chief of Staff, Deckerville Community Hospital, Deckerville, MI, p. A321

AFENYA, Kenneth, M.D. Chief of Staff, Baptist Memorial Hospital–Tipton, Covington, TN, p. A582

AFLAK, Ziba, Chief Financial Officer, Kindred Hospital–San Francisco Bay Area, San Leandro, CA, p. A92

AFZAL, Muhammed, M.D. Chief of Staff, Sutter Medical Center, Sacramento, Sacramento, CA, p. A87

AGANA, Ben, M.D. Medical Director, HEALTHSOUTH Rehabilitation Hospital The Woodlands, Conroe, TX, p. A607

AGEE, Joan, Vice President Patient Care Services, St. Joseph Regional Medical Center, Lewiston, ID, p. A177

AGEE, Nancy Howell, President and Chief Executive Officer, Carilion Clinic, Roanoke, VA, p. B26

AGENBROAD, Connie, Chief Executive Officer, Othello Community Hospital, Othello, WA, p. A687

AGLOINGA, Roy, Chief Administrative Officer, Norton Sound Regional Hospital, Nome, AK, p. A30

AGNEW, Mary Christine, R.N. Vice President and Chief Nursing Officer, Reading Hospital, West Reading, PA, p. A557

AGNI, Guirish, M.D. Chief of Staff, Stoughton Hospital Association, Stoughton, WI, p. A716

AGOSTINI, Scott, Director, Magee Rehabilitation Hospital, Philadelphia, PA, p. A548

AGOSTO, Paula M., R.N. Senior Vice President and Chief Nursing Officer, Children's Hospital of Philadelphia, Philadelphia, PA, p. A547

AGRELA, Ramona, Associate Chancellor & Chief Human Resources Executive, UC Irvine Medical Center, Orange, CA, p. A81

AGRESTI, Katie, R.N. Director Patient Care Services, Millcreek Community Hospital, Erie, PA, p. A538

AGUAS, Hugo, Vice President Human Resources, Inova Alexandria Hospital, Alexandria, VA, p. A667

AGUIAR–OLSEN, Rinely, M.D. Medical Director, Yuma Rehabilitation Hospital, Yuma, AZ, p. A42

AGUILA, Marcos, Chief Executive Officer, Hospital San Francisco, San Juan, PR, p. A730

AGUILAR, Gretchen, Director Patient Care and Chief Nursing Officer, Three Rivers Hospital, Brewster, WA, p. A683

AGUILAR, Marisa, Chief Operating Officer, Valley Baptist Medical Center–Brownsville, Brownsville, TX, p. A604

AGUILERA, Louie, Director Information Technology, Foundation Surgical Hospital of El Paso, El Paso, TX, p. A615

AGUINAGA, Miguel, M.D. Medical Director, Advanced Care Hospital of White County, Searcy, AR, p. A52

AGUIRRE, Casey W., D.O. Chief of Staff, Rangely District Hospital, Rangely, CO, p. A110

AGUIRRE, Jose, M.D. Medical Director, Carson Tahoe Continuing Care Hospital, Carson City, NV, p. A404

AGUIRRE, Kim, Director Finance, Northern Cochise Community Hospital, Willcox, AZ, p. A41

AHAINE, Israel, Chief Nursing Officer, West Oaks Hospital, Houston, TX, p. A627

AHEARN, Patrick, Chief Operating Officer and Senior Vice President, Saint Barnabas Medical Center, Livingston, NJ, p. A418

AHL, Dennis, Director Information Technology, Jefferson Community Health Center, Fairbury, NE, p. A395

AHLERS, Tim, Chief Operating Officer, UnityPoint Health – Finley Hospital, Dubuque, IA, p. A230

AHMAD, Shariq, M.D. Chief of Staff, Baptist Hospitals of Southeast Texas, Beaumont, TX, p. A601

AHMAD, Yousuf, Divisional Senior Vice President and Chief Network Transformation Officer, Mercy Health – Fairfield Hospital, Fairfield, OH, p. A494

AHMED, Ashraf, M.D. Senior Vice President Physician and Hospital Services, Alliance Community Hospital, Alliance, OH, p. A483

AHMED, Bilal, M.D. Medical Director, Wyoming County Community Hospital, Warsaw, NY, p. A458

AHMED, Imtiaz, Chief of Staff, Mercy Hospital Ada, Ada, OK, p. A508

AHMED, Mohammed Shafeeq, M.D. Vice President of Medical Affairs and Chief Medical Officer, Howard County General Hospital, Columbia, MD, p. A300

AHMED, Omar, Acting Manager Human Resources, Veterans Affairs Caribbean Healthcare System, San Juan, PR, p. A730

AHMED, Sajid, Chief Information and Innovation Officer, Martin Luther King, Jr. Community Hospital, Los Angeles, CA, p. A72

AHMED, Shabeer A., M.D. Clinical Director, Community Behavioral Health Hospital – Annandale, Annandale, MN, p. A338

AHNER, Dawn, Chief Financial Officer, Renown Rehabilitation Hospital, Reno, NV, p. A408

AHRENS, C. Todd, President and Chief Executive Officer, Hannibal Regional Hospital, Hannibal, MO, p. A371

AIELLO, Joseph, M.D. Chief of Staff, Asheville Specialty Hospital, Asheville, NC, p. A460

AIELLO, Louis
　Senior Vice President and Chief Financial Officer, Faxton St. Luke's Healthcare, Utica, NY, p. A457
　Chief Financial Officer, St. Elizabeth Medical Center, Utica, NY, p. A457

AIKEN, David, Chief Human Resources Officer, Madigan Army Medical Center, Tacoma, WA, p. A691

AIKEN, Patsy, Coordinator Human Resource, Spearfish Regional Hospital, Spearfish, SD, p. A577

AIKEN, Richard, M.D. Medical Director, Lakeland Behavioral Health System, Springfield, MO, p. A382

AILOR, Lorie, Chief Executive Officer, Orthopaedic Hospital of Lutheran Health Network, Fort Wayne, IN, p. A210

AINTABLIAN, Susan, Chief Information Officer, LAC–Olive View–UCLA Medical Center,, CA, p. A72

AIONA, Michael, M.D. Chief of Staff, Shriners Hospitals for Children–Portland, Portland, OR, p. A530

AIRHART, Steven, Chief Executive Officer, Hartgrove Hospital, Chicago, IL, p. A184

AIROSUS, Diane, Chief Financial Officer, Pembroke Hospital, Pembroke, MA, p. A313

AISEN, Mindy, M.D. Chief Medical Officer, Rancho Los Amigos National Rehabilitation Center, Downey, CA, p. A61

AISENBREY, Lisa, Administrator Human Resources and Support Services, Sidney Health Center, Sidney, MT, p. A391

AJANAH, Muhammed, M.D. Clinical Director, Clifton T. Perkins Hospital Center, Jessup, MD, p. A301

AJMAL, Farooq, Vice President and Chief Information Officer, Nassau University Medical Center, East Meadow, NY, p. A438

AKBARIAN, M., M.D. Medical Director, Curahealth Boston North Shore, Peabody, MA, p. A313

AKENS, Rick, Director Human Resources and Labor Relations, Methodist Medical Center of Oak Ridge, Oak Ridge, TN, p. A592

AKERS, Earl, Supervisor Information Technology, Salina Surgical Hospital, Salina, KS, p. A253

AKERS, Sandra, Bureau Director, Public Health Hospitals, Massachusetts Department of Public Health, Boston, MA, p. B85

AKERSON, Jeffrey D., M.D. Chief Medical Officer, Nebraska Medicine – Bellevue, Bellevue, NE, p. A394

AKHRAS, Omar, M.D. Chief of Staff, Putnam General Hospital, Eatonton, GA, p. A159

AKIF, Joe, Chief Clinical Officer and Chief Nursing Officer, Warren General Hospital, Warren, PA, p. A556

AKIN, Pam, Interim Chief Nursing Officer, Wilbarger General Hospital, Vernon, TX, p. A655

AKIN, Terry, President and Chief Executive Officer, Cone Health, Greensboro, NC, p. B41

AKIN, Terry, President and Chief Operating Officer, Moses H. Cone Memorial Hospital, Greensboro, NC, p. A466

AKINS, Tina, Director Human Resources, Lost Rivers Medical Center, Arco, ID, p. A174

AKOPYAN, George, Director Human Resources, Centinela Hospital Medical Center, Inglewood, CA, p. A66

AL–HASHMI, Samer, M.D. Chief Medical Staff, Stevens County Hospital, Hugoton, KS, p. A245

ALAGAR, Ravi, M.D. Medical Director, Curahealth Pittsburgh, Oakdale, PA, p. A546

ALAM, Md
Chief Information Officer, NYC Health + Hospitals / Jacobi,, NY, p. A448
Chief Information Officer, NYC Health + Hospitals / Metropolitan, New York, NY, p. A448

ALAM, Muhammed M., Medical Director, Turning Point Hospital, Moultrie, GA, p. A164

ALAMEDDINE, Hala, Chief Nursing Executive, Kindred Hospital Sugar Land, Sugar Land, TX, p. A650

ALARCON, Fernando, Executive Director, Hospital Santa Rosa, Guayama, PR, p. A727

ALASZEWSKI, Lydia, Chief Nursing Officer, Select Specialty Hospital–Macomb County, Mount Clemens, MI, p. A330

ALBANO, Valerie, Director, Human Resources, Regional Hospital for Respiratory and Complex Care, Burien, WA, p. A683

ALBANY, Karen, Chief Information Officer, Naval Medical Center, Portsmouth, VA, p. A676

ALBARANO, Francis G.
Administrator, St. Vincent Mercy Hospital, Elwood, IN, p. A209
Administrator, St. Vincent Randolph Hospital, Winchester, IN, p. A224

ALBAUGH, Jolene, R.N. Chief Nursing Officer, AMITA Health Adventist Medical Center Bolingbrook, Bolingbrook, IL, p. A182

ALBAUM, Michael, M.D. Senior Vice President and Chief Medical Officer, Southern Maine Health Care – Biddeford Medical Center, Biddeford, ME, p. A292

ALBERS, Craig, Vice President Patient Care and Chief Nursing Officer, Mercy Health – St. Charles Hospital, Oregon, OH, p. A500

ALBERT, Debra, MSN Senior Vice President Patient Care and Chief Nursing Officer, University of Chicago Medical Center, Chicago, IL, p. A187

ALBERT, Todd, M.D. Surgeon–in–Chief and Medical Director, Hospital for Special Surgery, New York, NY, p. A444

ALBERTINI, Bernie, Chief Administrative Officer, East Ohio Regional Hospital, Martins Ferry, OH, p. A498

ALBERTS, Patrick J., Senior Vice President and Chief Operating Officer, Monongahela Valley Hospital, Monongahela, PA, p. A545

ALBERTSON, Robert, M.D. Chief Medical Officer, CareLink of Jackson, Jackson, MI, p. A327

ALBIN, James
Chief Information Officer, Baylor St. Luke's Medical Center, Houston, TX, p. A623
Chief Information Officer, Regional Medical Center, Orangeburg, SC, p. A569

ALBIN, Lonnie, Interim Chief Executive Officer, Highlands Medical Center, Scottsboro, AL, p. A25

ALBOSTA, Kevin, Vice President, Chief Financial Officer, Covenant Healthcare, Saginaw, MI, p. A333

ALBRECHT, David L., President, Owatonna Hospital, Owatonna, MN, p. A348

ALBRECHT, Sandra, Interim Chief Financial Officer, Wellstar Atlanta Medical Center, Atlanta, GA, p. A153

ALBRECHTSEN, Bradley C., Chief Executive Officer and Administrator, Marian Center, Salt Lake City, UT, p. A663

ALBRIGHT, Bill, Director Human Resources, Stewart Memorial Community Hospital, Lake City, IA, p. A233

ALBRIGHT, Leslie, Vice President Information Systems, Bethesda Hospital East, Boynton Beach, FL, p. A124

ALBRIGHT, Mark, Chief Information Officer, Bay Area Regional Medical Center, Webster, TX, p. A656

ALBRIGHT, Sara Z., Vice President Human Resources, Bassett Medical Center, Cooperstown, NY, p. A437

ALBRIGHT, Tammy, Chief Nursing Officer, Takoma Regional Hospital, Greeneville, TN, p. A583

ALBRIGHT, Tina, Director Human Resources, National Park Medical Center, Hot Springs, AR, p. A47

ALCOCER, Deborah, Chief Information Officer, South Texas Rehabilitation Hospital, Brownsville, TX, p. A603

ALDANA, Eladio, Manager Information Systems, College Hospital Costa Mesa, Costa Mesa, CA, p. A60

ALDER, Cal, Director Information Technology, Rock County Hospital, Bassett, NE, p. A393

ALDERFER, Jennifer, Chief Executive Officer, North Suburban Medical Center, Thornton, CO, p. A111

ALDIS, Karen, Director of Nursing, Harper Hospital District Five, Harper, KS, p. A244

ALDRED, Linda W., Senior Vice President, Texas Children's Hospital, Houston, TX, p. A626

ALDREDGE, Sarah, M.D. Chief Medical Officer, Essentia Health Sandstone, Sandstone, MN, p. A351

ALDRICH, Alan, Chief Financial Officer, Central Montana Medical Center, Lewistown, MT, p. A389

ALDRIDGE, Kenneth, M.D. Vice President Medical Affairs, DCH Regional Medical Center, Tuscaloosa, AL, p. A26

ALEEM, Asaf, M.D. Medical Director, Peachford Behavioral Health System, Atlanta, GA, p. A152

ALEJANDRO, Ausberto, M.D. President, Hospital Santa Rosa, Guayama, PR, p. A727

ALEMAN, Ralph A., President and Chief Executive Officer, Citrus Memorial Health System, Inverness, FL, p. A131

ALEXAITIS, Irene, R.N. Vice President of Nursing and Patient Services and Chief Nursing Officer, UF Health Shands Hospital, Gainesville, FL, p. A130

ALEXANDA, Lisa, M.D. Vice President Medical Affairs, Parrish Medical Center, Titusville, FL, p. A148

ALEXANDER, Alan B., FACHE, Vice President and Administrator, The Medical Center at Caverna, Horse Cave, KY, p. A262

ALEXANDER, Angie, Chief Executive Officer, Allegiance Behavioral Health Center of Plainview, Plainview, TX, p. A641

ALEXANDER, April, Director Human Resources, NYC Health + Hospitals / Metropolitan, New York, NY, p. A448

ALEXANDER, Bobby, R.N. Chief Nursing Officer, Pinnacle Pointe Hospital, Little Rock, AR, p. A49

ALEXANDER, Brenda, System Vice President, Human Resources, SSM Health St. Mary's Hospital Centralia, Centralia, IL, p. A182

ALEXANDER, Brian, Chief Administrative Officer, Novato Community Hospital, Novato, CA, p. A80

ALEXANDER, Craig, Fiscal Specialist, Thomas B. Finan Center, Cumberland, MD, p. A300

ALEXANDER, David, Senior Vice President and Chief Financial Officer, St. Joseph's Healthcare System, Paterson, NJ, p. A421

ALEXANDER, Debra, Chief Information Officer, Safe Haven Hospital of Treasure Valley, Boise, ID, p. A174

ALEXANDER, Drew, Chief Nursing Officer, Cedar County Memorial Hospital, El Dorado Springs, MO, p. A370

ALEXANDER, Fred, M.D. Medical Director, Kaiser Permanente West Los Angeles Medical Center, Los Angeles, CA, p. A72

ALEXANDER, Jack, M.D. Chief Medical Officer, Mayo Clinic Health System in Red Wing, Red Wing, MN, p. A349

ALEXANDER, James, Regional Assistant Vice President, Financial Services, Monmouth Medical Center, Southern Campus, Lakewood, NJ, p. A418

ALEXANDER, Jane, Director Facility Administrative Services, Sagamore Children's Psychiatric Center, Dix Hills, NY, p. A438

ALEXANDER, Jason P., FACHE, Chief Executive Officer, East Cooper Medical Center, Mount Pleasant, SC, p. A568

ALEXANDER, Jeffrey, Chief Executive Officer, Select Specialty Hospital–Western Missouri, Kansas City, MO, p. A374

ALEXANDER, Jerry, Chief Executive Officer, Regency Hospital of Northwest Arkansas – Springdale, Springdale, AR, p. A52

ALEXANDER, Josette, Director, Human Resources, OhioHealth Rehabilitation Hospital, Columbus, OH, p. A491

ALEXANDER, Michael D., MS, Administrator, Wedowee Hospital, Wedowee, AL, p. A26

ALEXANDER, Thomas, Chief Executive Officer, Vibra Specialty Hospital at DeSoto, Desoto, TX, p. A613

ALEXANDER, Wendy F., Director Human Resources, Louisiana Heart Hospital, Lacombe, LA, p. A280

ALEXANDER–HINES, Joyce, R.N. Associate Director, Patient Care Services, Fayetteville Veterans Affairs Medical Center, Fayetteville, NC, p. A465

ALEXIADES, Nik, Chief Financial Officer, Clara Maass Medical Center, Belleville, NJ, p. A414

ALFANO, Alan, Medical Director, UVA–HEALTHSOUTH Rehabilitation Hospital, Charlottesville, VA, p. A668

ALFANO, Anthony, Vice President Executive Director, Montefiore New Rochelle, New Rochelle, NY, p. A443

ALFONSO, Eduardo, M.D. Chairman Ophthalmology, Bascom Palmer Eye Institute–Anne Bates Leach Eye Hospital, Miami, FL, p. A136

ALFORD, Charles
Vice President Finance, Vidant Beaufort Hospital, Washington, NC, p. A475
Vice President Financial Services, Vidant Edgecombe Hospital, Tarboro, NC, p. A474

ALFORD, Karla, Chief Information Officer, Greater Regional Medical Center, Creston, IA, p. A228

ALFORD, Michelle, R.N. Director of Nursing, Washington County Hospital, Chatom, AL, p. A18

ALFRED, Lorrie, Director Human Resources, Southern Surgical Hospital, Slidell, LA, p. A288

ALGER, Steve, Senior Vice President and Chief Financial Officer, Lakes Regional Healthcare, Spirit Lake, IA, p. A238

ALHADEFF, Joseph, M.D., President and Chief Executive Officer, OSS Orthopaedic Hospital, York, PA, p. A559

ALI, Irfan, Director Information Services, Saint Agnes Medical Center, Fresno, CA, p. A64

ALI, Mirza Z., M.D. Chief of Staff, Wilkes–Barre Veterans Affairs Medical Center, Wilkes–Barre, PA, p. A558

ALI, Muhammad, M.D. Chief Medical Officer, Sanford Tracy Medical Center, Tracy, MN, p. A352

ALI, Solomon, M.D. Chief of Staff, Fairview Regional Medical Center, Fairview, OK, p. A512

ALI, Syed Asif, M.D. Chief of Staff, Syracuse Veterans Affairs Medical Center, Syracuse, NY, p. A457

ALI–KHAN, Mir, M.D. Medical Director, Canyon Ridge Hospital, Chino, CA, p. A58

ALI–KHAN, Mujtaba, D.O. Chief Medical Officer, Conroe Regional Medical Center, Conroe, TX, p. A607

ALICE, Patricia, Chief Executive Officer, Arizona Orthopedic Surgical Hospital, Chandler, AZ, p. A31

ALICEA, Luis, Chief Information Officer, Doctors' Center Hospital San Juan, San Juan, PR, p. A729

ALICEA PEREZ, Eneida, Interim Nursing Director, Hospital Buen Samaritano, Aguadilla, PR, p. A725

ALKHOULI, Hassan, M.D
Chief Medical Officer, Garden Grove Hospital and Medical Center, Garden Grove, CA, p. A64
Medical Director, Huntington Beach Hospital, Huntington Beach, CA, p. A66
Chief Medical Officer, West Anaheim Medical Center, Anaheim, CA, p. A54

ALLA, Vamseedhar, M.D. Director Medical Staff, Connecticut Veterans Home and Hospital, Rocky Hill, CT, p. A116

ALLAN, John, Chief of Staff, Davis Regional Medical Center, Statesville, NC, p. A474

ALLARD, Joan, Director Human Resources, Heart of Florida Regional Medical Center, Davenport, FL, p. A126

ALLARD, Marie, Finance Manager, Brighton Center for Recovery, Brighton, MI, p. A319

ALLATT, Richard, M.D. Medical Director, HEALTHSOUTH Nittany Valley Rehabilitation Hospital, Pleasant Gap, PA, p. A552

ALLBEE, Roger, Chief Executive Officer and Administrator, Grace Cottage Hospital, Townshend, VT, p. A666

ALLBRITTON, James, Chief Financial Officer, Morehouse General Hospital, Bastrop, LA, p. A272

ALLDREDGE, Kim, Director Human Resources, Lawrence County Memorial Hospital, Lawrenceville, IL, p. A195

ALLEE, Erin, R.N. Director of Nursing, Royal Oaks Hospital, Windsor, MO, p. A384

ALLEMAN, Scott, Senior Vice President Patient Care Services and Chief Nursing Officer, UW Medicine/Valley Medical Center, Renton, WA, p. A688

ALLEN, Audrey, Coordinator Benefits, Dallas County Medical Center, Fordyce, AR, p. A46

ALLEN, Brian, M.D. President Medical Staff, Georgetown Community Hospital, Georgetown, KY, p. A260

ALLEN, Candice, Director of Nursing, Rio Grande Hospital, Del Norte, CO, p. A103

ALLEN, Carolyn, Vice President and Chief Financial Officer, Camden Clark Medical Center, Parkersburg, WV, p. A698

ALLEN, David B., Chief Executive Officer, Richland Memorial Hospital, Olney, IL, p. A199

ALLEN, Dawn, R.N. Chief Clinical Officer, Redwood Area Hospital, Redwood Falls, MN, p. A349

ALLEN, Devon, M.D. Chief of Medical Staff, Samuel Simmonds Memorial Hospital, Barrow, AK, p. A28

ALLEN, Donald, Chief Operating Officer, Unity Medical & Surgical Hospital, Mishawaka, IN, p. A218

ALLEN, Doug, Information Technology and System Director, Emory Johns Creek Hospital, Johns Creek, GA, p. A161

ALLEN, Elms, M.D
Senior Vice President Medical Affairs, Novant Health Forsyth Medical Center, Winston–Salem, NC, p. A476
Senior Vice President Medical Affairs, Novant Health Medical Park Hospital, Winston–Salem, NC, p. A476

ALLEN, Jason, Director Patient Care Services, Brook Lane Health Services, Hagerstown, MD, p. A301

ALLEN, Jennifer, Vice President Human Resources, Plantation General Hospital, Plantation, FL, p. A143

ALLEN, John, Chief Information Officer, Holzer Medical Center, Gallipolis, OH, p. A495

ALLEN, John P., Chief Executive Officer, Titus Regional Medical Center, Mount Pleasant, TX, p. A638

ALLEN, Judy, Human Resource Specialist, Carl Albert Community Mental Health Center, McAlester, OK, p. A514

ALLEN, Kandice K., R.N., Chief Executive Officer, Share Medical Center, Alva, OK, p. A508

ALLEN, Karen A., R.N. Chief Nursing Officer, Butler Health System, Butler, PA, p. A534

ALLEN, Keith
Senior Vice President and Chief Human Resources Officer, Community Memorial Hospital, Menomonee Falls, WI, p. A710
Senior Vice President and Chief Human Resources Officer, Froedtert Memorial Lutheran Hospital, Milwaukee, WI, p. A711
Senior Vice President Human Resources, St. Joseph's Hospital, West Bend, WI, p. A719

ALLEN, Kent, Director Human Resources, West Branch Regional Medical Center, West Branch, MI, p. A336

ALLEN, Linda M., Vice President Human Resources, The Children's Institute of Pittsburgh, Pittsburgh, PA, p. A551

ALLEN, Lori, Chief Financial Officer and Interim Chief Executive Officer, Anthony Medical Center, Anthony, KS, p. A240

ALLEN, Lucretia, Director Human Resources, Sweetwater Hospital, Sweetwater, TN, p. A593

ALLEN, Mark, Chief Operating Officer, Marian Regional Medical Center, Santa Maria, CA, p. A93

ALLEN, Mary Beth, Vice President Human Resources, Emory University Hospital, atlanta, GA, p. A152

ALLEN, Mike
Director Information Services, Shawnee Mission Medical Center, Shawnee Mission, KS, p. A254
Director Information Technology, Shriners Hospitals for Children–Salt Lake City, Salt Lake City, UT, p. A663
Director Information Services, Shriners Hospitals for Children–Spokane, Spokane, WA, p. A667

ALLEN, Myrna, R.N. Chief Operating and Nursing Officer, Martin Luther King, Jr. Community Hospital, Los Angeles, CA, p. A72

ALLEN, Nancy, R.N. Director, Patient Services and Chief Nursing Executive, Advocate Eureka Hospital, Eureka, IL, p. A189

ALLEN, Nikki, Patient Care Executive, Sutter Amador Hospital, Jackson, CA, p. A66

ALLEN, Patty, St. John's Vice President Finance, St. John's Hospital, Springfield, IL, p. A203

ALLEN, R. Keith, Senior Vice President Human Resources, University of Maryland Medical Center, Baltimore, MD, p. A298

ALLEN, Richard
Chief Executive Officer, Palmdale Regional Medical Center, Palmdale, CA, p. A81
Chief Executive Officer, Warren General Hospital, Warren, PA, p. A556

ALLEN, Rob, Chief Executive Officer, Sitka Community Hospital, Sitka, AK, p. A30

ALLEN, Robert
Chief Financial Officer, Keck Hospital of USC, Los Angeles, CA, p. A72
Chief Financial Officer, USC Norris Comprehensive Cancer Center, Los Angeles, CA, p. A74
Chief Financial Officer, USC Verdugo Hills Hospital, Glendale, CA, p. A65

ALLEN, Robin, Chief Executive Officer, The Hospital at Westlake Medical Center, Austin, TX, p. A600

ALLEN, Scott J., Director Human Resources, Hudson Hospital and Clinic, Hudson, WI, p. A707

ALLEN, Steve, M.D., Chief Executive Officer, Nationwide Children's Hospital, Columbus, OH, p. A490

ALLEN, Timothy J., FACHE,
Chief Executive Officer, Leonard J. Chabert Medical Center, Houma, LA, p. A278
Chief Executive Officer, Ochsner St. Anne General Hospital, Raceland, LA, p. A286

ALLEN, Timothy M., Vice President Human Resources, United Hospital Center, Bridgeport, WV, p. A694

ALLEN, Tracey, Controller, Central Texas Rehabilitation Hospital, Austin, TX, p. A599

ALLEN, Vicki, Chief Financial Officer, Chicot Memorial Medical Center, Lake Village, AR, p. A48

ALLEN, Vicki, R.N. Vice President Patient Care Services and Chief Nursing Officer, Harnett Health System, Dunn, NC, p. A464

ALLEN, Wain, M.D. Medical Director, Park City Medical Center, Park City, UT, p. A662

ALLEN, Wayne, Chief Financial Officer, Mendocino Coast District Hospital, Fort Bragg, CA, p. A62

ALLEN, Zac, CPA Chief Financial Officer, Cherokee Medical Center, Centre, AL, p. A18

ALLEN–JOHNSON, Angela, Director Information Services, Ephraim McDowell Regional Medical Center, Danville, KY, p. A259

ALLENSWORTH, Ed, M.D. Medical Director, Craig General Hospital, Vinita, OK, p. A522

ALLEY, David, Chief Financial Officer, Starr Regional Medical Center, Athens, TN, p. A579

ALLEY, John L., Chief Executive Officer, Woodlawn Hospital, Rochester, IN, p. A221

ALLEY, Jon, D.O. President Medical Staff, Cameron Memorial Community Hospital, Angola, IN, p. A206

ALLEY, Steve B., M.D. Chief of Staff, Crosbyton Clinic Hospital, Crosbyton, TX, p. A608

ALLGEIER, Patricia, R.N. Chief Nursing Officer, Boys Town National Research Hospital, Omaha, NE, p. A399

ALLGOOD, Libby, Chief Financial Officer, Kittitas Valley Healthcare, Ellensburg, WA, p. A684

ALLICON, Keary T., Vice President Finance and Chief Financial Officer, Baystate Wing Hospital, Palmer, MA, p. A313

ALLIES, Karla, Director Human Resources, Rosebud Health Care Center, Forsyth, MT, p. A387

ALLINSON, Randy, R.N. Patient Care Services Director, Central Valley Medical Center, Nephi, UT, p. A661

ALLISON, David G., President and Chief Executive Officer, University Medical Center, Lubbock, TX, p. A634

ALLISON, Joel T., Chief Executive Officer, Baylor Scott & White Health, Dallas, TX, p. B21

ALLISON, Lorraine, Human Resource Partner, PeaceHealth Peace Island Medical Center, Friday Harbor, WA, p. A685

ALLISON, Shannon, Chief Financial Officer, Houston County Community Hospital, Erin, TN, p. A582

ALLISON, Steve, Director Human Resources, Logan County Hospital, Oakley, KS, p. A250

ALLMAN, Rex, M.D. President Medical Staff, Pulaski Memorial Hospital, Winamac, IN, p. A224

ALLORE, Gary, Chief Financial Officer, Mercy Health Hackley Campus, Muskegon, MI, p. A330

ALLOWAY, Cindy
President, CHI Health Lakeside, Omaha, NE, p. A400
President, CHI Health Midlands, Papillion, NE, p. A401

ALLPHIN, Allan, M.D. Chief of Staff, Mercy Hospital Springfield, Springfield, MO, p. A382

ALLPORT, Jeff, Vice President, Chief Information Officer, Valley Presbyterian Hospital,, CA, p. A75

ALLRED, Al W., Chief Financial Officer, Florida Hospital New Smyrna, New Smyrna Beach, FL, p. A139

ALLRED, B. Dee, M.D. President Medical Staff, Jordan Valley Medical Center, West Jordan, UT, p. A664

ALLRED, Lowell C., M.D. Chief of Staff, Columbia Basin Hospital, Ephrata, WA, p. A684

ALLRED, William, M.D. Vice President Medical Affairs, St. John Medical Center, Tulsa, OK, p. A522

ALLSOP, Brian, Director Human Resources, Central Valley Medical Center, Nephi, UT, p. A661

ALLSTOTT, Patti, Administrative Coordinator Human Resources and Grant Writer, Pioneer Memorial Hospital, Heppner, OR, p. A526

ALLSTROM, Sheree, Director Human Resources, Acuity Hospital of South Texas, San Antonio, TX, p. A645

ALLUMS, Allyson, Director Medical Records, North Caddo Medical Center, Vivian, LA, p. A289

ALMANZA, Alejandro Miguel, Vice President and Human Resources, Emory Johns Creek Hospital, Johns Creek, GA, p. A161

ALMAUHY, Deborah, R.N. Chief Nursing Officer, Emory Rehabilitation Hospital, Atlanta, GA, p. A152

ALMEIDA, Sergio, Director Information Systems, West Houston Medical Center, Houston, TX, p. A627

ALMEIDA–SUAREZ, Mario, M.D. Chief of Staff, Larkin Community Hospital, South Miami, FL, p. A145

ALMENDINGER, J. Todd, President and Chief Executive Officer, Magruder Memorial Hospital, Port Clinton, OH, p. A501

ALMETER, Connie, Director of Nursing, Wyoming County Community Hospital, Warsaw, NY, p. A458

ALMODOVAR, Gustavo, Executive Director, Hospital De La Concepcion, San German, PR, p. A729

ALMOHAMMED, Salah, Chief of Staff, East Texas Medical Center Carthage, Carthage, TX, p. A605

ALO, Kathleen, Chief Nursing Officer, Mammoth Hospital, Mammoth Lakes, CA, p. A75

ALONSO, Gwen, Chief Nursing Officer, Florida Hospital Zephyrhills, Zephyrhills, FL, p. A150

ALONSO, Jose', M.D. Medical Director, San Juan Capestrano Hospital, San Juan, PR, p. A730

ALONZO, Patti, Manager Human Resources, Pacifica Hospital of the Valley, CA, p. A73

ALPERT, Jeffrey, M.D. Medical Director, Wichita County Health Center, Leoti, KS, p. A248

ALPERT, Len, Director Human Resources, Larkin Behavioral Health Services,, FL, p. A130

ALRASHEDY, Farhad H., M.D. Chief Medical Officer, Ferry County Memorial Hospital, Republic, WA, p. A688

ALREDGE, William, Administrator, Genesis Behavioral Hospital, Breaux Bridge, LA, p. A274

ALSADON, Danielle, Clinic/Hospital Manager, Kenmare Community Hospital, Kenmare, ND, p. A480

ALSIP, Bryan, M.D. Executive Vice President, Chief Medical Officer, University Health System, San Antonio, TX, p. A647

ALSTAD, Nancy, Director Human Resources, Fort HealthCare, Fort Atkinson, WI, p. A705

ALT, Melinda
Chief Financial Officer, Audubon County Memorial Hospital, Audubon, IA, p. A225
Chief Financial Officer, Guthrie County Hospital, Guthrie Center, IA, p. A231

ALTARAS, June, R.N.,
Chief Executive Officer, Swedish Medical Center–Cherry Hill Campus, Seattle, WA, p. A689
Chief Executive Officer, Swedish Medical Center–First Hill, Seattle, WA, p. A690

ALTEBARMAKIAN, Varouj, M.D. Physician in Chief, Kaiser Permanente Fresno Medical Center, Fresno, CA, p. A63

ALTENBURGER, Andy
Chief Information Officer, Delta Regional Medical Center, Greenville, MS, p. A358
Chief Information Officer, Marietta Memorial Hospital, Marietta, OH, p. A498

ALTENDORF, Amanda, Chief Human Resources and Quality Management, Richard P. Stadter Psychiatric Center, Grand Forks, ND, p. A479

ALTHOEN, David, Director Financial Planning and Analysis, Forest Health Medical Center, Ypsilanti, MI, p. A337

ALTHOUSE, Douglas, Chief Medical Staff, Kearney County Health Services, Minden, NE, p. A398

ALTMAN, III, Alexander B., Chief Financial Officer, Union County General Hospital, Clayton, NM, p. A428

ALTMAN, Angie, Director Human Resources, Shands Lake Shore Regional Medical Center, Lake City, FL, p. A133

ALTMAN, Brett Allen, FACHE, President and Chief Executive Officer, Skiff Medical Center, Newton, IA, p. A235

ALTMAN, Deana, Interim Chief Nursing Officer, Harney District Hospital, Burns, OR, p. A524

ALTMAN, Harold, M.D. Chief Medical Officer, ACMH Hospital, Kittanning, PA, p. A541

ALTMILLER, Steve, President and Chief Executive Officer, Good Shepherd Health System, Longview, TX, p. B58

ALTMILLER, Steve, President and Chief Executive Officer, Good Shepherd Medical Center, Longview, TX, p. A633

ALTOM, Andy, Chief Executive Officer, Methodist Behavioral Hospital of Arkansas, Maumelle, AR, p. A50

ALTON, Aaron K., President and Chief Executive Officer, Sisters of Mary of the Presentation Health System, Fargo, ND, p. B125

ALTOSE, Murray, M.D. Chief of Staff, Louis Stokes Cleveland Veterans Affairs Medical Center, Cleveland, OH, p. A489

ALTSHULER, Keith, President and Chief Administrative Officer, Fort Sanders Regional Medical Center, Knoxville, TN, p. A586

ALUISE, Tony, Chief Executive Officer, Three Gables Surgery Center, Proctorville, OH, p. A501

ALVARADO, Felicita E., Administrator, Hospital Psiquiatrico Correccional, San Juan, PR, p. A730

ALVARADO, Rafael, Chief Executive Officer, Dr. Pila's Hospital, Ponce, PR, p. A728

ALVARADO, Ramona, Interim Manager Human Resources, Adventist Medical Center–Reedley, Reedley, CA, p. A85

ALVAREZ, Dena C., R.N. COO & Chief Compliance Officer, Brodstone Memorial Hospital, Superior, NE, p. A402

ALVAREZ, Janie, Accounting Director, Cornerstone Regional Hospital, Edinburg, TX, p. A614

ALVAREZ, Jose, M.D. Chief Medical Staff, Circles of Care, Melbourne, FL, p. A135

ALVAREZ, Maria Charlotte, M.D. Chief of Staff, Sheridan Community Hospital, Sheridan, MI, p. A334

ALVAREZ, Valerie, Executive Assistant, Adventist Medical Center–Reedley, Reedley, CA, p. A85

ALVERSON, Tammy S., M.D. Chief of Staff, Coshocton County Memorial Hospital, Coshocton, OH, p. A492

ALVES, Richard, Chief Financial Officer, Kaiser Permanente Fresno Medical Center, Fresno, CA, p. A63

ALVEY, Raymond, Chief Financial Officer, SSM Health Saint Louis University Hospital, Saint Louis, MO, p. A381

ALWIN–POPP, Sue, Chief Clinical Officer, Edgerton Hospital and Health Services, Edgerton, WI, p. A705

ALWINE, Steven, Chief Executive Officer, HEALTHSOUTH Rehabilitation Hospital of York, York, PA, p. A559

ALZEIN, Bashar, M.D. President Medical Staff, Illini Community Hospital, Pittsfield, IL, p. A201

AMADO, Mitchell, Senior Vice President Finance and Chief Financial Officer, Glens Falls Hospital, Glens Falls, NY, p. A439

AMANTEA, Paul, Director Finance, University Hospitals Geauga Medical Center, Chardon, OH, p. A486

AMAR Jr., Eugene, Administrator, Kohala Hospital, Kohala, HI, p. A172

AMATO, James, Interim Chief Operating Officer, University of Virginia Medical Center, Charlottesville, VA, p. A668

AMBACHER, Linda, Interim Chief Nursing Officer, Hackettstown Medical Center, Hackettstown, NJ, p. A417

AMBERSON, Rosemarie, Vice President Human Resources, Aventura Hospital and Medical Center, Aventura, FL, p. A123

AMBROSE, Sherie
Vice President Patient Care Services, Mercy Medical Center Mount Shasta, Mount Shasta, CA, p. A78
Chief Nurse Executive, Sequoia Hospital, Redwood City, CA, p. A85

AMBROSIANI, Michael, Chief Financial Officer, Knox Community Hospital, Mount Vernon, OH, p. A499

AMBROSINI, Joseph, Director Human Resources, Olympia Medical Center, Los Angeles, CA, p. A73

AMDUR, Deborah, Director, Phoenix Veterans Affairs Health Care System, Phoenix, AZ, p. A37

AMENT, Arlinda K., R.N. Interim Chief Nursing Officer, Beatrice Community Hospital and Health Center, Beatrice, NE, p. A394

AMENT, Rick, Chief Executive Officer, Kindred Hospital–Indianapolis North, Indianapolis, IN, p. A214

AMERSON, Jeff, Director Information System, West Florida Hospital, Pensacola, FL, p. A142

AMES, Becky, Chief Executive Officer, Medical Center of Southeast Texas, Beaumont, TX, p. A601

AMES, Laura, Chief Executive Officer, Arbour Hospital, Boston, MA, p. A305

AMES, Laura, FACHE, Chief Executive Officer, HEALTHSOUTH New England Rehabilitation Hospital, Woburn, MA, p. A316

AMIN, Yogesh, M.D. Medical Director, Select Specialty Hospital–Fort Wayne, Fort Wayne, IN, p. A211

AMIRNENI, Vamsee, M.D. Chief of Staff, Mercy Allen Hospital, Oberlin, OH, p. A500

AMMAZZALORSO, Michael, M.D. Chief Medical Officer, Winthrop–University Hospital, Mineola, NY, p. A442

AMMONS, Eric, President, Mercy Hospital Jefferson, Crystal City, MO, p. A370

AMODO, Mitch, Vice President and Chief Financial Officer, Orange Regional Medical Center, Middletown, NY, p. A442

AMONS, Gene, R.N. Administrator, Beacon Behavioral Hospital, Bunkie, LA, p. A274

AMOROSE, Carl, Vice President Finance, Norton Hospital, Louisville, KY, p. A265

AMOROSO, Mitze, Chief Information Officer, Terence Cardinal Cooke Health Care Center, New York, NY, p. A450

AMOS, John
Chief Executive Officer, Yavapai Regional Medical Center – East, Prescott Valley, AZ, p. A38
President and Chief Executive Officer, Yavapai Regional Medical Center, Prescott, AZ, p. A37

AMOS, Robert, Vice President and Chief Financial Officer, Winchester Medical Center, Winchester, VA, p. A680

AMROM, George, M.D. Vice President Medical Affairs, Hahnemann University Hospital, Philadelphia, PA, p. A548

AMSBERRY, Shelly, Director of Nursing, Jennie M. Melham Memorial Medical Center, Broken Bow, NE, p. A394

AMSTUTZ, Charles, Director of Information Technology, Cascade Medical Center, Leavenworth, WA, p. A686

AMYX, Maleigha, Chief Information Officer, Rockcastle Regional Hospital and Respiratory Care Center, Mount Vernon, KY, p. A267

ANASTASI, Frank, Chief Financial Officer, Pennsylvania Hospital, Philadelphia, PA, p. A549

ANAYA, Michael A., FACHE, Chief Executive Officer, Select Specialty Hospital–Houston Medical Center, Houston, TX, p. A626

ANAYA, Sandra J., R.N., Chief Executive Officer, Palo Verde Hospital, Blythe, CA, p. A57

ANCHONDO, Laura, Administrator Human Resources, Kindred Hospital El Paso, El Paso, TX, p. A615

ANDERS, Anna, Vice President and Chief Nursing Officer, Carson Tahoe Health, Carson City, NV, p. A404

ANDERS, Jr., James M., Administrator and Chief Operating Officer, Kennedy Krieger Institute, Baltimore, MD, p. A296

ANDERS, Mark, Administrator, Villa Feliciana Medical Complex, Jackson, LA, p. A278

ANDERS, Robert, Chief Financial Officer, Ouachita County Medical Center, Camden, AR, p. A44

ANDERSEN, Donia L., Director of Nursing, Centennial Peaks Hospital, Louisville, CO, p. A109

ANDERSEN, Janet, Chief Financial Officer, East Texas Medical Center–Quitman, Quitman, TX, p. A642

ANDERSEN, John, Manager Information Systems, Sunnyside Community Hospital and Clinics, Sunnyside, WA, p. A691

ANDERSEN, Sue
Chief Financial Officer, French Hospital Medical Center, San Luis Obispo, CA, p. A92
Vice President and Service Area and Chief Financial Officer, Marian Regional Medical Center, Santa Maria, CA, p. A93

ANDERSEN, Toni, R.N. Chief Nurse Executive, Kaiser Permanente Fontana Medical Center, Fontana, CA, p. A62

ANDERSEN, Tracy, Chief Information Officer, St. Mary's Regional Medical Center, Enid, OK, p. A511

ANDERSEN, Travis
President and Chief Executive Officer, Columbia St. Mary's Hospital Milwaukee, Milwaukee, WI, p. A711
President and Chief Executive Officer, Columbia St. Mary's Ozaukee Hospital, Mequon, WI, p. A710

ANDERSON, Wendy, Director Human Resources, Eastern Idaho Regional Medical Center, Idaho Falls, ID, p. A176

ANDERSON, A. Elizabeth, Administrator, University of South Alabama Medical Center, Mobile, AL, p. A23

ANDERSON, Allen, Director Human Resources, Madison Healthcare Services, Madison, MN, p. A345

ANDERSON, Allyson, Chief Administrative Officer, Legacy Meridian Park Medical Center, Tualatin, OR, p. A531

ANDERSON, Angela L., Director Human Resources, Newton Medical Center, Newton, KS, p. A250

ANDERSON, Angie, Director Information Technology, Crawford County Memorial Hospital, Denison, IA, p. A229

ANDERSON, Ashley, Manager Human Resources, Winona Health, Winona, MN, p. A353

ANDERSON, Barbara M., President and Chief Executive Officer, Franciscan St. Anthony Health – Crown Point, Crown Point, IN, p. A209

ANDERSON, Benjamin, Chief Executive Officer and Administrator, Kearny County Hospital, Lakin, KS, p. A247

ANDERSON, Brad, Chief Financial Officer, Community Memorial Hospital, Cloquet, MN, p. A340

ANDERSON, Brian
Chief Financial Officer, Capital Medical Center, Olympia, WA, p. A687
Chief Financial Officer, Simi Valley Hospital, Simi Valley, CA, p. A94

ANDERSON, Calandra, Vice President Patient Care and Chief Nursing Officer, McLaren Oakland, Pontiac, MI, p. A332

ANDERSON, Charles, M.D
Chief Medical Officer, Desert Regional Medical Center, Palm Springs, CA, p. A81
Market Chief Medical Officer, John F. Kennedy Memorial Hospital, Indio, CA, p. A66

ANDERSON, Cherri, Chief Nursing Officer, Banner Behavioral Health Hospital – Scottsdale, Scottsdale, AZ, p. A38

ANDERSON, Chris, Chief Executive Officer, Baptist Health Systems, Jackson, MS, p. B20

ANDERSON, Chris, President & Chief Executive Officer, Mississippi Baptist Medical Center, Jackson, MS, p. A360

ANDERSON, Christine, Chief Nursing Officer and Vice President of Patient Care Services, LincolnHealth, Damariscotta, ME, p. A292

ANDERSON, Conde Nevin, M.D. Chief of Staff, DeTar Healthcare System, Victoria, TX, p. A655

ANDERSON, Craig, Director Management Information Systems, River Bend Hospital, West Lafayette, IN, p. A223

ANDERSON, Dana, Administrator, Long–Term Acute Care Hospital, Mosaic Life Care at St. Joseph, Saint Joseph, MO, p. A379

ANDERSON, Darla, Chief Financial Officer, Ridgeview Sibley Medical Center, Arlington, MN, p. A338

ANDERSON, Dave, FACHE Vice President Administration, Carolinas Healthcare System Union, Monroe, NC, p. A469

ANDERSON, David, Chief Executive Officer, Jackson Purchase Medical Center, Mayfield, KY, p. A266

ANDERSON, Dawn, Chief Nursing Officer, Select Specialty Hospital–Sioux Falls, Sioux Falls, SD, p. A576

ANDERSON, Dennis, Administrator and Director of Nursing, Signature Psychiatric Hospital, Kansas City, MO, p. A374

ANDERSON, Dianne J., R.N., President and Chief Executive Officer, Lawrence General Hospital, Lawrence, MA, p. A311

ANDERSON, Donna K., R.N. Chief Nursing Officer, Cannon Memorial Hospital, Pickens, SC, p. A569

ANDERSON, Duke, President and Chief Executive Officer, Hillsdale Hospital, Hillsdale, MI, p. A326

ANDERSON, Edward, Interim Chief Executive Officer, Johnson Regional Medical Center, Clarksville, AR, p. A44

ANDERSON, Edwin, M.D. Chief of Staff and Chief Medical Officer, Bigfork Valley Hospital, Bigfork, MN, p. A339

ANDERSON, Gaynell, M.D. Medical Director, St. Anthony Shawnee Hospital, Shawnee, OK, p. A520

ANDERSON, Gina, Human Resources Officer, Riverview Regional Medical Center, Carthage, TN, p. A579

ANDERSON, Greg E., Chief Financial Officer, Emory Health System, Emory University Hospital, atlanta, GA, p. A152

ANDERSON, Heidi, Chief Nursing Officer, Morton General Hospital, Morton, WA, p. A686

ANDERSON, Holly, Supervisor Human Resources, Sanford Rock Rapids Medical Center, Rock Rapids, IA, p. A236

ANDERSON, Jason, Chief Financial Officer, Mackinac Straits Health System, Inc., Saint Ignace, MI, p. A333

ANDERSON, Jimmy, Director of Information Systems, Tennova Healthcare Regional Hospital of Jackson, Jackson, TN, p. A584

ANDERSON, Joann, President and Chief Executive Officer, Southeastern Health, Lumberton, NC, p. A469

ANDERSON, Jodie, Director Human Resources, Mitchell County Regional Health Center, Osage, IA, p. A235

ANDERSON, John D., FACHE, Administrator, Marshall Medical Center South, Boaz, AL, p. A17

ANDERSON, John G., FACHE,
President and Chief Executive Officer, Anderson Regional Health System, Meridian, MS, p. A362
President and Chief Executive Officer, Anderson Regional Health System South, Meridian, MS, p. A362

ANDERSON, Jonathan, Medical Director, Western State Hospital, Staunton, VA, p. A679

ANDERSON, Kenneth, M.D. Vice President and Chief Medical Officer, Baptist Health Louisville, Louisville, KY, p. A264

ANDERSON, Kimball S., FACHE, Chief Executive Officer, Timpanogos Regional Hospital, Orem, UT, p. A661

ANDERSON, Kristin, Director, Human Resources, California Hospital Medical Center, Los Angeles, CA, p. A70

ANDERSON, Libby, Chief Financial Officer, Satanta District Hospital and Long Term Care, Satanta, KS, p. A253

ANDERSON, Louis, Chief Financial Officer, McLeod Health Cheraw, Cheraw, SC, p. A563

ANDERSON, Lucia E., Senior Vice President Operations and Chief Nurse Executive, Lake Region Healthcare, Fergus Falls, MN, p. A342

ANDERSON, Lynne, Chief Executive Officer, Stephens County Hospital, Toccoa, GA, p. A168

ANDERSON, Mark, Chief Financial Officer, Lane Regional Medical Center, Zachary, LA, p. A290

ANDERSON, Mark T., Chief Financial Officer, Danville Regional Medical Center, Danville, VA, p. A669

ANDERSON, Michael, M.D
Senior Vice President Quality and Chief Medical Officer, Harrison Medical Center, Bremerton, WA, p. A682
Chief Medical Officer, University Hospitals Cleveland Medical Center, Cleveland, OH, p. A490

ANDERSON, Michael Bruce, Ph.D. Chief Operating Officer, Metropolitan St. Louis Psychiatric Center, Saint Louis, MO, p. A380

ANDERSON, Mickey, M.D. Vice President Medical Affairs, Flaget Memorial Hospital, Bardstown, KY, p. A257

ANDERSON, Patricia, Chief Nursing Officer, Riverview Regional Medical Center, Carthage, TN, p. A579

ANDERSON, Patrick
Chief Information Officer and Senior Vice President, Hoag Memorial Hospital Presbyterian, Newport Beach, CA, p. A79
Chief Information Officer, Memorial Medical Center, Modesto, CA, p. A77

ANDERSON, Paula, Administrative Director Human Resources, Endless Mountain Health Systems, Montrose, PA, p. A545

ANDERSON, Randy, Chief Executive Officer, Canyon Vista Medical Center, Sierra Vista, AZ, p. A39

ANDERSON, Rhonda
Executive Vice President Finance and Chief Financial Officer, Columbia St. Mary's Hospital Milwaukee, Milwaukee, WI, p. A711
Executive Vice President Finance and Chief Financial Officer, Columbia St. Mary's Ozaukee Hospital, Mequon, WI, p. A710
Executive Vice President Finance and Chief Financial Officer, Sacred Heart Rehabilitation Institute, Milwaukee, WI, p. A711

ANDERSON, Richard A., President and Chief Executive Officer, St. Luke's University Health Network, Bethlehem, PA, p. B128

ANDERSON, Rick, M.D. Senior Vice President and Chief Medical Officer, TMC HealthCare, Tucson, AZ, p. A41

ANDERSON, Robert C., Interim Chief Financial Officer, Alameda Hospital, Alameda, CA, p. A54

ANDERSON, Jr., Robert G., Executive Vice President and Chief Operating Officer, OSF Saint Francis Medical Center, Peoria, IL, p. A200

ANDERSON, Rohan, Chief Information Officer, Doctors Memorial Hospital, Bonifay, FL, p. A124

ANDERSON, Rosemary, Administrator, CCC at PineView Hospital, Lakeside, AZ, p. A34

ANDERSON, Sandra, Chief Financial Officer, De Soto Regional Health System, Mansfield, LA, p. A282

ANDERSON, Sandra L.
President and Chief Executive Officer, Howard Young Medical Center, Woodruff, WI, p. A720
President and Chief Executive Officer, Ministry Eagle River Memorial Hospital, Eagle River, WI, p. A704
President and Chief Executive Officer, Ministry Sacred Heart Hospital, Tomahawk, WI, p. A717
President and Chief Executive Officer, Ministry Saint Mary's Hospitals, Rhinelander, WI, p. A715
ANDERSON, Scott, Chief Medical Officer, Banner Del E. Webb Medical Center, Sun City West, AZ, p. A39
ANDERSON, Sharla, Chief Executive Officer, CHRISTUS Trinity Mother Frances Rehabilitation Hospital, Tyler, TX, p. A654
ANDERSON, Shawn, Chief Operating Officer, Cary Medical Center, Caribou, ME, p. A292
ANDERSON, Sims, Manager Facility Automation, Terrell State Hospital, Terrell, TX, p. A652
ANDERSON, Stephanie, Executive Vice President and Chief Operating Officer, Woman's Hospital, Baton Rouge, LA, p. A273
ANDERSON, Stephen, M.D
Chief Medical Officer, Saint Joseph Regional Medical Center, Mishawaka, IN, p. A218
Chief Medical Officer, Saint Joseph Regional Medical Center–Plymouth Campus, Plymouth, IN, p. A220
ANDERSON, Steven
Chief Executive Officer, Jordan Valley Medical Center, West Jordan, UT, p. A664
Chief Executive Officer, Jordan Valley Medical Center West Valley Campus, West Valley City, UT, p. A664
ANDERSON, Susan, Director Information Systems, Texas Health Presbyterian Hospital Plano, Plano, TX, p. A642
ANDERSON, Suzanne P., Nurse Administrator, Intermountain Medical Center, Murray, UT, p. A661
ANDERSON, Terry, R.N. Director of Nursing Services, Chippewa County–Montevideo Hospital, Montevideo, MN, p. A347
ANDERSON, Thomas, M.D. Vice President Medical Affairs, Chambersburg Hospital, Chambersburg, PA, p. A535
ANDERSON, Thomas, Vice President Medical Affairs, Lakeview Hospital, Stillwater, MN, p. A352
ANDERSON, Thomas, M.D
Chief of Staff, Portland Veterans Affairs Medical Center, Portland, OR, p. A529
Vice President Medical Affairs, Waynesboro Hospital, Waynesboro, PA, p. A556
ANDERSON, Tim, Controller, Van Matre HealthSouth Rehabilitation Hospital, Rockford, IL, p. A202
ANDERSON, Jr., Timothy Craig, Chief Nursing Officer, Wellmont Bristol Regional Medical Center, Bristol, TN, p. A579
ANDERSON, Traci, Chief Financial Officer, Memorial Hospital, Seminole, TX, p. A648
ANDERSON, Valerie, Chief Nursing Officer, Select Specialty Hospital–Tri Cities, Bristol, TN, p. A579
ANDERSON, William, M.D. Medical Director, Rosebud Health Care Center, Forsyth, MT, p. A387
ANDERT, Nancy, Director Human Resources, Murray County Medical Center, Slayton, MN, p. A351
ANDERT, Vicki, Chief Nursing Officer, Eureka Springs Hospital, Eureka Springs, AR, p. A45
ANDRADA, Sally, Chief Information Officer, Los Alamitos Medical Center, Los Alamitos, CA, p. A70
ANDRADE, Marise, Controller, Southern Inyo Healthcare District, Lone Pine, CA, p. A69
ANDRAE, Andrea
Chief Financial Officer, Blue Mountain Hospital, Lehighton, PA, p. A543
Chief Financial Officer, Palmerton Hospital, Palmerton, PA, p. A546
ANDRE, Katelyn, Human Resource Coordinator, Select Specialty Hospital–Macomb County, Mount Clemens, MI, p. A330
ANDREAS, Ginger, Coordinator Personnel and Credentialing, El Campo Memorial Hospital, El Campo, TX, p. A615
ANDREAS, Lori, Chief Operating Officer, Johnson Memorial Health Services, Dawson, MN, p. A341
ANDREASEN, Raymond, M.D. Chief Medical Officer–Inpatient, California Medical Facility, Vacaville, CA, p. A97
ANDRES, Chad, Chief Information Officer, Desert View Hospital, Pahrump, NV, p. A407
ANDRES, Elizabeth, Director Human Resources, Atascadero State Hospital, Atascadero, CA, p. A55
ANDRES, Leonidas, M.D. Chief of Staff, Riceland Medical Center, Winnie, TX, p. A658
ANDRESEN, Daniel, Chief information Officer, Mercy Medical Center Merced, Merced, CA, p. A76
ANDREWS, Callie
Chief Operating Officer, Eastside Medical Center, Snellville, GA, p. A166
Chief Operating Officer and Facility Compliance Officer, WellStar Cobb Hospital, Austell, GA, p. A154

ANDREWS, Carolle, Vice President, Interim Human Resources Officer, Unconn John Dempsey Hospital, Farmington, CT, p. A114
ANDREWS, David, Manager Information Systems, Chicot Memorial Medical Center, Lake Village, AR, p. A48
ANDREWS, Fred J., Director of Nursing and Ancillary Services, Baylor Institute for Rehabilitation at Fort Worth, Fort Worth, TX, p. A617
ANDREWS, Jim, Chief Financial Officer, North Okaloosa Medical Center, Crestview, FL, p. A126
ANDREWS, John, M.D. Chief of Staff, East Texas Medical Center Tyler, Tyler, TX, p. A654
ANDREWS, Lisa, Director Human Resources, Lancaster Rehabilitation Hospital, Lancaster, PA, p. A542
ANDREWS, Maria R., MS, Director, Charlie Norwood Veterans Affairs Medical Center, Augusta, GA, p. A153
ANDREWS, Michael, Coordinator Information Systems, Harlan County Health System, Alma, NE, p. A393
ANDREWS, Michele, Chief Clinical Officer, Integrity Transitional Hospital, Denton, TX, p. A612
ANDREWS, Mike, Associate Administrator and Chief Operating Officer, OCH Regional Medical Center, Starkville, MS, p. A365
ANDREWS, Paul
Chief Executive Officer, The Brook at Dupont, Louisville, KY, p. A265
Chief Executive Officer, The Brook Hospital – KMI, Louisville, KY, p. A265
ANDREWS, Rebecca, Chief Financial Officer, Vibra Hospital of Northern California, Redding, CA, p. A84
ANDREWS, Ryan, M.D
Chief Medical Officer, Ministry Saint Clare's Hospital, Weston, WI, p. A719
Chief Medical Officer, Ministry Saint Michael's Hospital, Stevens Point, WI, p. A716
ANDREWS, Steve, Chief Financial Officer, Three Rivers Health, Three Rivers, MI, p. A335
ANDREWS, Sue E., Chief Financial Officer, O'Connor Hospital, Delhi, NY, p. A438
ANDREWS, Susan E., Chief Executive Officer, Touro Infirmary, New Orleans, LA, p. A285
ANDREWS, Terri, Director Information Technology, Alamance Regional Medical Center, Burlington, NC, p. A461
ANDRITSCH, Scott, Chief Financial Officer, Sullivan County Community Hospital, Sullivan, IN, p. A222
ANDRO, Ronald J., President and Chief Executive Officer, West Penn Hospital, Pittsburgh, PA, p. A552
ANDRUS, Helen
Chief Financial Officer, Providence Mount Carmel Hospital, Colville, WA, p. A684
Chief Financial Officer, Providence St. Joseph's Hospital, Chewelah, WA, p. A683
Chief Financial Officer, St. Luke's Rehabilitation Institute, Spokane, WA, p. A691
ANDRUS, Jonathon, Chief Executive Officer, Fairchild Medical Center, Yreka, CA, p. A100
ANDRUS, Terry W., President, East Alabama Medical Center, Opelika, AL, p. A24
ANDURSKY, John, Chief Financial Officer, Highlands Hospital, Connellsville, PA, p. A536
ANFINSON, Julie, Director Human Resources, Mercy Medical Center–Sioux City, Sioux City, IA, p. A237
ANGALICH, Dave, Director Information Services, Weirton Medical Center, Weirton, WV, p. A700
ANGELL, Deborah, Chief Financial Officer, Syracuse Veterans Affairs Medical Center, Syracuse, NY, p. A457
ANGELL, Nancy, Associate Administrator Personnel, Sagamore Children's Psychiatric Center, Dix Hills, NY, p. A438
ANGELO, Gregory, Chief Fiscal Program, James J. Peters Veterans Affairs Medical Center,, NY, p. A445
ANGELO, Thomas, Chief Executive Officer, Centra Southside Community Hospital, Farmville, VA, p. A670
ANGELUCCI, Patricia A., MS Director Patient Care Services, ThedaCare Medical Center–Shawano, Shawano, WI, p. A715
ANGERAMI, Deborah, Chief Operating Officer, Health First Viera Hospital, Melbourne, FL, p. A135
ANGERMEIER, Elizabeth, Director of Nursing, Evansville Psychiatric Children Center, Evansville, IN, p. A210
ANGLE, Mary Ann, R.N. Chief Nursing Officer, TriStar Summit Medical Center, Hermitage, TN, p. A584
ANGLIN, Jason, Chief Executive Officer, Memorial Medical Center, Port Lavaca, TX, p. A642
ANGUS, Jolyn M., R.N. Chief Nursing Officer, Miami Valley Hospital, Dayton, OH, p. A493
ANKIN, Michael G., M.D. Vice President Medical Affairs & Chief Medical Officer, Northwestern Lake Forest Hospital, Lake Forest, IL, p. A194
ANMUTH, Craig, M.D. Medical Director, Bacharach Institute for Rehabilitation, Pomona, NJ, p. A422
ANNA, Anna, R.N. Chief Nursing Officer, Conemaugh Miners Medical Center, Hastings, PA, p. A540

ANNARINO, Phillip, Vice President Human Resources, Fisher–Titus Medical Center, Norwalk, OH, p. A500
ANNECHARICO, Mary Alice
System Vice President and Chief Information Officer, Henry Ford Hospital, Detroit, MI, p. A322
System Vice President and Chief Information Officer, Henry Ford West Bloomfield Hospital, West Bloomfield, MI, p. A336
System Vice President and Chief Information Officer, Henry Ford Wyandotte Hospital, Wyandotte, MI, p. A337
ANNESSER, Sue, Director Information Systems, Freeman Neosho Hospital, Neosho, MO, p. A377
ANNIS, Donald E., Chief Executive Officer, Crawford Memorial Hospital, Robinson, IL, p. A201
ANOLIK, Adam, Chief Financial Officer, Highland Hospital, Rochester, NY, p. A454
ANSALDO, Luanne, Chief Operating Officer, Aventura Hospital and Medical Center, Aventura, FL, p. A123
ANSELL, David A., M.D. Senior Vice President Clinical Affairs and Chief Medical Officer, Rush University Medical Center, Chicago, IL, p. A186
ANSELL, L. V., M.D. Medical Director, Memorial Hermann Orthopedic and Spine Hospital, Bellaire, TX, p. A602
ANSELMA, M., Chief Operating Officer, OSF Saint Anthony's Health Center, Alton, IL, p. A180
ANSHUTZ, Margie, Chief Development Officer, Hamilton Center, Terre Haute, IN, p. A222
ANSI, Azena, Manager Health Information Management, Horizon Specialty Hospital, Las Vegas, NV, p. A406
ANSLEY, Pamela, Director Finance, Sutter Center for Psychiatry, Sacramento, CA, p. A87
ANSTINE, Larry, Interim Chief Operating Officer, UC Irvine Medical Center, Orange, CA, p. A81
ANTCZAK, Kenneth, Vice President Human Resources, St. Mary Mercy Hospital, Livonia, MI, p. A329
ANTES, John, President, Missouri Baptist Medical Center, Saint Louis, MO, p. A380
ANTHONY, Anne G., FACHE, President and Chief Executive Officer, Willow Crest Hospital, Miami, OK, p. A514
ANTHONY, Jean, R.N., President and Chief Executive Officer, Hills & Dales General Hospital, Cass City, MI, p. A320
ANTHONY, Kim, Director Human Resources, Burke Medical Center, Waynesboro, GA, p. A169
ANTHONY, Mark, Executive Vice President and Chief Operating Officer, Borgess Medical Center, Kalamazoo, MI, p. A327
ANTHONY, Michelle, Chief Nursing Officer, HEALTHSOUTH Rehabilitation Hospital of Virginia, Richmond, VA, p. A677
ANTHONY, Paula
Vice President Information Services, East Texas Medical Center Pittsburg, Pittsburg, TX, p. A641
Vice President Information Services, East Texas Medical Center Rehabilitation Hospital, Tyler, TX, p. A654
Vice President Information Services, East Texas Medical Center Specialty Hospital, Tyler, TX, p. A654
Vice President Information Services, East Texas Medical Center Tyler, Tyler, TX, p. A654
ANTHONY, Sharon, Chief Executive Officer, Select Specialty Hospital–Phoenix, Phoenix, AZ, p. A37
ANTINELLI, Mark, Manager Human Resources, Syracuse Veterans Affairs Medical Center, Syracuse, NY, p. A457
ANTINORI, James, M.D. Chief of Staff, Mountain West Medical Center, Tooele, UT, p. A664
ANTOINE, Greg, M.D. Chief of Staff, Fayetteville Veterans Affairs Medical Center, Fayetteville, NC, p. A465
ANTON, Lourdes, Director Human Resources, Palm Springs General Hospital, Hialeah, FL, p. A130
ANTONACCI, Amy, MSN Vice President Nursing Services, Alliance Community Hospital, Alliance, OH, p. A483
ANTONECCHIA, Paul, M.D. Vice President Medical Affairs and Chief Medical Officer, St. John's Riverside Hospital, Yonkers, NY, p. A459
ANTONIADES, Michael A.
President and Chief Executive Officer, Robert Wood Johnson University Hospital, New Brunswick, NJ, p. A420
President and Chief Executive Officer, Robert Wood Johnson University Hospital Somerset, Somerville, NJ, p. A423
ANTONSON, Pete, Chief Executive Officer, Northwood Deaconess Health Center, Northwood, ND, p. A481
ANTONUCCI, Lawrence, M.D
Chief Operating Officer, Cape Coral Hospital, Cape Coral, FL, p. A125
Chief Operating Officer, Gulf Coast Medical Center, Fort Myers, FL, p. A129
Chief Operating Officer, Lee Memorial Hospital, Fort Myers, FL, p. A129
ANTRUM, Sheila, R.N. President, UCSF Medical Center, San Francisco, CA, p. A91
ANWAR, Muhammad, M.D. Chief Medical Officer, Encino Hospital Medical Center,, CA, p. A71

ANYASO, Vanessa, Chief Human Resources, Tomball Regional Medical Center, Tomball, TX, p. A653

ANZURES, Rosey, Acting Chief Financial Officer, Central Texas Veterans Health Care System, Temple, TX, p. A651

APIKI, Zessica L., Accountant, Molokai General Hospital, Kaunakakai, HI, p. A172

APLAND, Wendy
  Regional Vice President of Finance/Chief Financial Officer, PeaceHealth Sacred Heart Medical Center at RiverBend, Springfield, OR, p. A531
  Interim Chief Financial Officer, PeaceHealth Sacred Heart Medical Center University District, Eugene, OR, p. A525

APOLINAR, Adam
  Chief Clinical Officer, Cumberland Surgical Hospital, San Antonio, TX, p. A645
  Chief Nursing Officer, Uvalde Memorial Hospital, Uvalde, TX, p. A654

APOLIONA, Nicole, M.D. Medical Director, Kula Hospital, Kula, HI, p. A172

APONTE, Miguel, Supervisor Management Information Systems, Wilma N. Vazquez Medical Center, Vega Baja, PR, p. A730

APPEL, Sheril, Chief Executive Officer, HEALTHSOUTH Rehabilitation Hospital of Arlington, Arlington, TX, p. A597

APPENHEIMER, A. Timothy, M.D. Vice President and Chief Medical Officer, Katherine Shaw Bethea Hospital, Dixon, IL, p. A188

APPLEBAUM, Jon D., Chief Executive Officer, Twin County Regional Healthcare, Galax, VA, p. A671

APPLEGATE, MaryJane, Chief Clinical Officer, Knoxville Hospital & Clinics, Knoxville, IA, p. A233

APPLEGEET, Carol, MSN Vice President and Chief Nursing Officer, Fort Hamilton Hospital, Hamilton, OH, p. A496

APPLETON, Joe, M.D. Chief of Surgery, Milan General Hospital, Milan, TN, p. A590

APRILE, Patricia, Chief Operating Officer, Southern Maine Health Care – Biddeford Medical Center, Biddeford, ME, p. A292

AQUILINA, Anthony, D.O. Chief Medical Officer, Geisinger–Community Medical Center, Scranton, PA, p. A554

AQUILINA, Joanne, Vice President Finance and Chief Financial Officer, Bethesda Hospital East, Boynton Beach, FL, p. A124

ARABIT, Aleen, Chief Executive Officer, Kindred Hospital–Houston Northwest, Houston, TX, p. A625

ARAD, Lana
  Chief Financial Officer, Good Samaritan Hospital, San Jose, CA, p. A91
  Chief Financial Officer, MountainView Hospital, Las Vegas, NV, p. A406

ARAGON, Juliette, Finance Director, Turquoise Lodge Hospital, Albuquerque, NM, p. A428

ARAKELIAN, Armen
  Chief Information Officer, Fulton County Medical Center, Mc Connellsburg, PA, p. A544
  Chief Information Officer, J. C. Blair Memorial Hospital, Huntingdon, PA, p. A540

ARAMBULA, Frank, Chief Financial Officer, Arrowhead Regional Medical Center, Colton, CA, p. A59

ARANDA, Heather R., R.N. Chief Nursing Officer, F. W. Huston Medical Center, Winchester, KS, p. A256

ARANIO, Lani, Regional Director Human Resources, Samuel Mahelona Memorial Hospital, Kapaa, HI, p. A172

ARATOW, Michael, M.D. Chief Information Officer, San Mateo Medical Center, San Mateo, CA, p. A92

ARAUJO, Marianne D., R.N. Vice President Nursing and Chief Nurse Executive, Advocate Good Shepherd Hospital, Barrington, IL, p. A181

ARAUJO, Markeeta, Chief Nursing Officer, Desert View Hospital, Pahrump, NV, p. A407

ARBAUGH, Ronnie, Director Human Resources, Grant Memorial Hospital, Petersburg, WV, p. A699

ARBON, Don, Vice President Finance, Mid–Columbia Medical Center, The Dalles, OR, p. A531

ARBON, Terron, R.N. Chief Nursing Officer, Salt Lake Regional Medical Center, Salt Lake City, UT, p. A663

ARBONEAUX, Wayne M., Chief Executive Officer, Assumption Community Hospital, Napoleonville, LA, p. A284

ARBUCKLE, Barry S., Ph.D., President and Chief Executive Officer, MemorialCare, Fountain Valley, CA, p. B88

ARBUTHNOT, Rena, Director Human Resources, Shriners Hospitals for Children–Shreveport, Shreveport, LA, p. A288

ARCANGELI, Barbara J., Vice President Human Resources, Newport Hospital, Newport, RI, p. A560

ARCE, Daisy, President Medical Staff, Weslaco Regional Rehabilitation Hospital, Weslaco, TX, p. A657

ARCENEAUX, Larrie, Chief Clinical Officer, Promise Hospital Baton Rouge – Main Campus, Baton Rouge, LA, p. A273

ARCH, Chrissy, Chief Financial Officer, Cherokee Indian Hospital, Cherokee, NC, p. A463

ARCH, John K., FACHE, Director, Boys Town National Research Hospital, Omaha, NE, p. A399

ARCHAMBEAULT, Shirley, Chief Information Officer, Medical Center of Lewisville, Lewisville, TX, p. A632

ARCHER, David, Director Information Systems, TriStar Ashland City Medical Center, Ashland City, TN, p. A579

ARCHER, Doug, Administrator, Memorial Hospital Los Banos, Los Banos, CA, p. A75

ARCHER, Joe, Chief Information Officer, Victor Valley Global Medical Center, Victorville, CA, p. A98

ARCHER, Kenneth W., Chief Executive Officer, South Lincoln Medical Center, Kemmerer, WY, p. A722

ARCHER, Matt, Chief Executive Officer, Tahoe Pacific Hospitals, Sparks, NV, p. A408

ARCHER, Stuart, Chief Executive Officer, Oceans Behavioral Hospital Katy, Katy, TX, p. A630

ARCHER–DUSTE, Helen, Chief Operating Officer, Kaiser Permanente San Francisco Medical Center, San Francisco, CA, p. A90

ARCHEY, Eugene, Chief Information Technology, VA Greater Los Angeles Healthcare System, Los Angeles, CA, p. A74

ARCHIBOLD, Robert, Director, Human Resources, St. Anthony North Health Campus, Westminster, CO, p. A111

ARCHULETA, Michael, Chief Information Technology Officer, Mt. San Rafael Hospital, Trinidad, CO, p. A111

ARCIDI, Alfred J., M.D.
  Senior Vice President, Whittier Rehabilitation Hospital, Bradford, MA, p. A307
  Senior Vice President, Whittier Rehabilitation Hospital, Westborough, MA, p. A316

ARCIDI, Alfred L., M.D., President, Whittier Health Network, Haverhill, MA, p. B155

ARCIDI, Alfred L., M.D., Chief Executive Officer, Whittier Pavilion, Haverhill, MA, p. A310

ARCILLA, Jelden, R.N. Vice President and Chief Nursing Officer, HonorHealth John C. Lincoln Medical Center, Phoenix, AZ, p. A36

ARD, Sheila, Chief Nursing Officer, Huntsville Memorial Hospital, Huntsville, TX, p. A628

ARDABELL, Toni R., Chief Executive Officer, Bon Secours Virginia, Bon Secours St. Francis Medical Center, Midlothian, VA, p. A673

ARDEMAGNI, Jeff, Chief Financial Officer, Medical Center Arlington, Arlington, TX, p. A597

ARDESHNA, Harish, Chief Medical Officer, Bluffton Regional Medical Center, Bluffton, IN, p. A207

ARDION, Doug, M.D. Chief Medical Officer, NCH Downtown Naples Hospital, Naples, FL, p. A138

ARDOIN, Cody, Director Human Resources, Mercy Regional Medical Center, Ville Platte, LA, p. A289

AREAUX, Rene, Vice President and Chief Operating Officer, Springhill Memorial Hospital, Mobile, AL, p. A22

ARELLANO, Edgar Alejandro, Chief Information Technologist, Three Rivers Hospital, Brewster, WA, p. A683

ARENDS, Candace, R.N. Chief Nursing Officer, United Hospital District, Blue Earth, MN, p. A339

ARETINO, Sandi, Chief Executive Officer, Tsehootsooi Medical Center, Fort Defiance, AZ, p. A32

ARGO, Brian, Chief Financial Officer, Singing River Health System, Pascagoula, MS, p. A363

ARGUETA, David
  Chief Executive Officer, St. Luke's Lakeside Hospital, The Woodlands, TX, p. A653
  Chief Executive Officer, St. Luke's The Woodlands Hospital, The Woodlands, TX, p. A653

ARGYROS, Gregory J., M.D. Senior Vice President, Medical Affairs & Chief Medical Officer, MedStar Washington Hospital Center, Washington, DC, p. A122

ARIAS, Taffy J., Chief Executive Officer, Martin General Hospital, Williamston, NC, p. A475

ARISPE, Joe, Director Information Systems, Wise Regional Health System, Decatur, TX, p. A612

ARIZMENDEZ, Maria Elena, M.D. Medical Director, Vibra Rehabilitation Hospital Lake Travis, Lakeway, TX, p. A631

ARIZPE, Robert C., Superintendent, San Antonio State Hospital, San Antonio, TX, p. A647

ARLEDGE, Denton
  Vice President and Chief Information Officer, WakeMed Cary Hospital, Cary, NC, p. A462
  Vice President and Chief Information Officer, WakeMed Raleigh Campus, Raleigh, NC, p. A472

ARLIEN, Dana, M.D. Chief Medical Officer, Willow Springs Center, Reno, NV, p. A408

ARMADA, Anthony A., Senior Vice President, Chief Executive Officer of Swedish Health Services and Providence Health and Services, Swedish Health Services, Seattle, WA, p. B131

ARMATO, Carl S., President and Chief Executive Officer, Novant Health, Winston Salem, NC, p. B98

ARMBRUSTER, Kent A W, M.D. Vice President Medical Affairs, Little Company of Mary Hospital and Health Care Centers, Evergreen Park, IL, p. A190

ARMBRUSTER, Rebecca, M.D. Chief Medical Officer, Jeanes Hospital, Philadelphia, PA, p. A548

ARMFIELD, Ben, Chief Financial Officer, Fresno Heart and Surgical Hospital, Fresno, CA, p. A63

ARMISTEAD, Russell, Chief Executive Officer, UF Health Jacksonville, Jacksonville, FL, p. A132

ARMOUR, John, Chief Information Officer, Bayshore Medical Center, Pasadena, TX, p. A640

ARMSTRONG, Alan, M.D. Chief Medical Officer, Pine Rest Christian Mental Health Services, Grand Rapids, MI, p. A325

ARMSTRONG, Deborah, Chief Operating Officer, Piedmont Henry Hospital, Stockbridge, GA, p. A167

ARMSTRONG, Evelyn, Chief Nursing Officer, HEALTHSOUTH Rehabilitation Hospital of Erie, Erie, PA, p. A538

ARMSTRONG, Gary, Executive Vice President, Methodist Rehabilitation Center, Jackson, MS, p. A360

ARMSTRONG, James, Manager Information Technology, UHS Delaware Valley Hospital, Walton, NY, p. A458

ARMSTRONG, Jeffery, CPA Chief Financial Officer, Granville Health System, Oxford, NC, p. A471

ARMSTRONG, Jeremy, FACHE, Chief Executive Officer, Mitchell County Hospital Health Systems, Beloit, KS, p. A241

ARMSTRONG, Kim, Chief Financial Officer, Windom Area Hospital, Windom, MN, p. A353

ARMSTRONG, Lori, R.N. Chief Nursing Officer, Kaiser Permanente Santa Clara Medical Center, Santa Clara, CA, p. A93

ARMSTRONG, Mark, M.D. Medical Director, Baylor Medical Center at Uptown, Dallas, TX, p. A609

ARMSTRONG, Neil G., FACHE Vice President and Chief Operating Officer, Divine Providence Hospital, Williamsport, PA, p. A558

ARMSTRONG, Robert, Senior Vice President and Chief Operating Officer, Lima Memorial Health System, Lima, OH, p. A496

ARMSTRONG, Roger
  Interim Chief Financial Officer, Pioneers Memorial Healthcare District, Brawley, CA, p. A57
  Vice President Finance and Chief Financial Officer, UnityPoint Health – Proctor, Peoria, IL, p. A200

ARMSTRONG, William C.
  Senior Vice President and Chief Financial Officer, Mercy Medical Center, Rockville Centre, NY, p. A454
  Vice President and Chief Financial Officer, St. Francis Hospital, The Heart Center, Roslyn, NY, p. A455

ARMSTRONG–HUFF, Glenda, Assistant Superintendent, Texas Center for Infectious Disease, San Antonio, TX, p. A647

ARNAU, Barbara, R.N. Chief Nursing Officer, Chestatee Regional Hospital, Dahlonega, GA, p. A157

ARNDELL, Scott, Chief Financial Officer, Twin Lakes Regional Medical Center, Leitchfield, KY, p. A262

ARNER, Steven C.
  Chief Operating Officer, Carilion Franklin Memorial Hospital, Rocky Mount, VA, p. A678
  President, Carilion Roanoke Memorial Hospital, Roanoke, VA, p. A678
  President, Carilion Roanoke Memorial Hospital, Roanoke, VA, p. A678

ARNESON, Brenda, Administrative Assistant, St. Andrew's Health Center, Bottineau, ND, p. A477

ARNESON, Garrett, Chief Executive Officer, LifeCare Hospitals of Chester County, West Chester, PA, p. A557

ARNETT, Jacob, Chief Information Technology Officer, Lakeside Behavioral Health System, Memphis, TN, p. A589

ARNETT, James, Vice President Human Resources, Meriter UnityPoint Health, Madison, WI, p. A709

ARNETT, Randal M., President and Chief Executive Officer, Southern Ohio Medical Center, Portsmouth, OH, p. A501

ARNETT, Sallie, Vice President Information Systems, Licking Memorial Hospital, Newark, OH, p. A500

ARNETT, Stuart
  Regional Vice President Finance, Aurora Lakeland Medical Center, Elkhorn, WI, p. A705
  Vice President Finance and Chief Financial Officer, Aurora Memorial Hospital of Burlington, Burlington, WI, p. A703

ARNHART, Carol, Vice President Finance and Chief Financial Officer, Siskin Hospital for Physical Rehabilitation, Chattanooga, TN, p. A580

ARNOLD, Ann, M.D. Medical Director, Medical Center of Plano, Plano, TX, p. A641

ARNOLD, Bill, President and Chief Executive Officer, Monmouth Medical Center, Long Branch Campus, Long Branch, NJ, p. A419

ARNOLD, Dustin, D.O. Chief Medical Officer, UnityPoint Health – St. Luke's Hospital, Cedar Rapids, IA, p. A226

ARNOLD, Jeffrey, M.D. Chief Medical Officer, Santa Clara Valley Medical Center, San Jose, CA, p. A91

ARNOLD, Kimberly N., R.N. Chief Nursing Officer and Interim Chief Quality Officer, AllianceHealth Woodward, Woodward, OK, p. A523

AUGUSTINE, David, Chief Executive Officer, Trego County–Lemke Memorial Hospital, Wakeeney, KS, p. A255

AUGUSTUS, Richard, M.D. Chief Medical Officer, West Valley Medical Center, Caldwell, ID, p. A175

AUGUSTYNIAK, Becky, Director Human Resources, Northside Medical Center, Columbus, GA, p. A156

AUKES, Amy
Regional Manager of Human Resources, Avera Dells Area Hospital, Dell Rapids, SD, p. A573
Human Resources Analyst, Avera Flandreau Hospital, Flandreau, SD, p. A573

AULWES, Linda, Human Resources Coordinator, Guttenberg Municipal Hospital, Guttenberg, IA, p. A231

AUNAN, II, Milton E., CPA Senior Vice President and Chief Financial Officer, UnityPoint Health – St. Luke's Hospital, Cedar Rapids, IA, p. A226

AURILIO, Lisa, R.N. Vice President Patient Services and Chief Nursing Officer, Akron Children's Hospital, Akron, OH, p. A483

AUSMAN, Dan F., President and Chief Executive Officer, Methodist Hospital of Southern California, Arcadia, CA, p. A55

AUSTIN, Aaron
Market Vice President Human Resources, CHI St. Vincent Hot Springs, Hot Springs, AR, p. A47
Market Vice President Human Resources, CHI St. Vincent Infirmary Medical Center, Little Rock, AR, p. A49
Market Vice President Human Resources, CHI St. Vincent Morrilton, Morrilton, AR, p. A50

AUSTIN, Arthur, M.D. Vice President Medical Affairs, Gerald Champion Regional Medical Center, Alamogordo, NM, p. A427

AUSTIN, Bill, Senior Vice President of Finance, Riverside Rehabilitation Institute, Newport News, VA, p. A674

AUSTIN, Dan
Director Information Technology, Arkansas Methodist Medical Center, Paragould, AR, p. A51
Manager Data Processing, Ashley County Medical Center, Crossett, AR, p. A44

AUSTIN, Debbie W., MSN Vice President Patient Care Services, P & S Surgical Hospital, Monroe, LA, p. A283

AUSTIN, Deborah, Chief People Officer, Physicians' Specialty Hospital, Fayetteville, AR, p. A45

AUSTIN, Donnica, Vice President, Operations, Holy Cross Hospital, Chicago, IL, p. A184

AUSTIN, Geoff, Interim Executive Director, University of Washington Medical Center, Seattle, WA, p. A690

AUSTIN, Joe, Executive Vice President and Chief Operating Officer, Phoebe Putney Memorial Hospital, Albany, GA, p. A151

AUSTIN, Judy, Director Human Resources, Campbellton Graceville Hospital, Graceville, FL, p. A130

AUSTIN, Laura, Chief Financial Officer and Chief Operating Officer, Community Hospital of Anaconda, Anaconda, MT, p. A385

AUSTIN, Sherri, MSN Chief Nursing Officer, Wrangell Medical Center, Wrangell, AK, p. A30

AUSTIN, Jr., W. William, Senior Vice President Finance, Riverside Shore Memorial Hospital, Nassawadox, VA, p. A674

AUSTIN, Warren, M.D. Vice President Medical Affairs, Bon Secours Maryview Medical Center, Portsmouth, VA, p. A676

AUSTIN–MOORE, Gale, Director Area Technology, Kaiser Permanente Vallejo Medical Center, Vallejo, CA, p. A98

AUTELLI, Oscar, Chief Information Officer, LAC+USC Medical Center, Los Angeles, CA, p. A72

AUTREY, Pamela Spencer, R.N. Chief Nursing Officer, Medical West, Bessemer, AL, p. A16

AUTRY, Paula R., FACHE, Chief Executive Officer, DMC – Sinai–Grace Hospital, Detroit, MI, p. A321

AVANT, Andre, Facility Automation Manager, Texas Center for Infectious Disease, San Antonio, TX, p. A647

AVATO, Rich, Director, St. Mary's Medical Center, West Palm Beach, FL, p. A150

AVELINO, Joseph, Chief Executive Officer, College Medical Center, Long Beach, CA, p. A69

AVERETT, Elaine, Chief Financial Officer, Grove Hill Memorial Hospital, Grove Hill, AL, p. A21

AVERILL, Clark, Director Information Technology, St. Luke's Hospital, Duluth, MN, p. A342

AVERNA, Russell
Vice President Human Resources, Spaulding Rehabilitation Hospital, Charlestown, MA, p. A309
Vice President of Human Resources, Spaulding Rehabilitation Hospital Cape Cod, East Sandwich, MA, p. A309

AVERY, Danny, Chief Financial Officer and Chief Operating Officer, Quartz Mountain Medical Center, Mangum, OK, p. A514

AVERY, Donald R., FACHE, President and Chief Executive Officer, Fairview Park Hospital, Dublin, GA, p. A159

AVERY III, John B., Administrator, Perry Community Hospital, Linden, TN, p. A587

AVERY, Jonathan, Chief Administrative Officer, Legacy Good Samaritan Hospital and Medical Center, Portland, OR, p. A529

AVIADO, Gail, Chief Nursing Officer, Montclair Hospital Medical Center, Montclair, CA, p. A77

AVIGDOR, Lauren, Director Human Resources, Advanced Specialty Hospital of Toledo, Toledo, OH, p. A503

AVILA, Brandi, Chief Nursing Officer, Martin County Hospital District, Stanton, TX, p. A650

AVVISATO, Michael, Senior Vice President and Chief Financial Officer, Allied Services Rehabilitation Hospital, Scranton, PA, p. A554

AVVISATO, Mike, Vice President and Chief Financial Officer, John Heinz Institute of Rehabilitation Medicine, Wilkes–Barre, PA, p. A558

AWALD, Tamara, Chief Nursing Officer and Chief Operating Officer, Saint Joseph Regional Medical Center–Plymouth Campus, Plymouth, IN, p. A220

AWALT, Scott, Chief Financial Officer, Sanford Hillsboro Medical Center, Hillsboro, ND, p. A480

AWAN, Naveed, FACHE, Chief Executive Officer, St. Helena Parish Hospital, Greensburg, LA, p. A277

AWOLOWO, Yinusa, Business Officer, Kingsboro Psychiatric Center,, NY, p. A445

AWWAD, Emad, Director Care Delivery Sites Information Systems and Technology, Lakeview Hospital, Stillwater, MN, p. A352

AXTELL, Vicki, Director Human Resources, Livingston HealthCare, Livingston, MT, p. A389

AYALA, Jose L., M.D. Chief Medical Officer, Valley Baptist Medical Center–Brownsville, Brownsville, TX, p. A604

AYALA, Lisa, R.N. Director Human Resources, Specialty Hospital Jacksonville, Jacksonville, FL, p. A132

AYALA, Shirley, Director Human Resources, First Hospital Panamericano, Cidra, PR, p. A727

AYCOCK, Jean, President and Chief Executive Officer, Oconee Regional Health Systems, Milledgeville, GA, p. B100

AYCOCK, Mark, Chief Operating Officer, Spartanburg Medical Center, Spartanburg, SC, p. A570

AYERS, James G., Chief Financial Officer, Piedmont Geriatric Hospital, Burkeville, VA, p. A668

AYERS, Jessi, Chief Financial Officer, Person Memorial Hospital, Roxboro, NC, p. A472

AYERS, Matthew, Chief Administrative Officer, Norton Hospital, Louisville, KY, p. A265

AYKUL, Nikki, Manager Business Office, LifeCare Hospitals of Pittsburgh, Pittsburgh, PA, p. A550

AYRES, Daniel M., President and Chief Executive Officer, Summersville Regional Medical Center, Summersville, WV, p. A700

AYRES, Michael, Senior Vice President and Chief Financial Officer, Maricopa Integrated Health System, Phoenix, AZ, p. A36

AYRES, Robert, Director Information Systems, Firelands Regional Health System, Sandusky, OH, p. A502

AYRES, Shane, Chief Financial Officer, Sanford Wheaton Medical Center, Wheaton, MN, p. A353

AZAR, Jennifer, Director Human Resources, Turning Point Hospital, Moultrie, GA, p. A164

AZCONA, Alain, Director Business Development, Aurora Behavioral Healthcare San Diego, San Diego, CA, p. A88

AZEVEDO, Michael, M.D. Medical Director, San Joaquin Valley Rehabilitation Hospital, Fresno, CA, p. A64

AZIZ, Samir, M.D. Medical Director, Fairfax Behavioral Health, Kirkland, WA, p. A686

AZIZKHAN, Richard G., M.D., President and Chief Executive Officer, Children's Hospital and Medical Center, Omaha, NE, p. A400

AZURE, Vernon, Clinical Director, Indian Health Service – Quentin N. Burdick Memorial Health Care Facility, Belcourt, ND, p. A477

B

BAAS, Daniel, R.N. Chief Nursing Officer, Baylor Emergency Medical Center at Aubrey, Aubrey, TX, p. A598

BAAS, Dina, Director Financial Services, Orange City Area Health System, Orange City, IA, p. A235

BABAKANIAN, Ed, Chief Information Officer, UC San Diego Health, San Diego, CA, p. A89

BABB, A. Mitch, Vice President, Operations, Duke Regional Hospital, Durham, NC, p. A464

BABB, Cindy, Executive Director Human Resources and Organizational Effectiveness, St. Vincent Kokomo, Kokomo, IN, p. A216

BABB, Dan, Chief Financial Officer, DMC – Rehabilitation Institute of Michigan, Detroit, MI, p. A321

BABB, Donald J., Chief Executive Officer, Citizens Memorial Hospital, Bolivar, MO, p. A367

BABB, Kathy, Manager Human Resources, Clifton Springs Hospital and Clinic, Clifton Springs, NY, p. A437

BABCOCK, Daniel, Chief Executive Officer, Marlette Regional Hospital, Marlette, MI, p. A329

BABCOCK, Janet, Director of Nursing, Dorothea Dix Psychiatric Center, Bangor, ME, p. A291

BABCOCK, Kimberly, Administrative Director of Operations, Kalkaska Memorial Health Center, Kalkaska, MI, p. A328

BABCOCK, Paul, Chief Financial Officer, Coulee Medical Center, Grand Coulee, WA, p. A685

BABCOCK, Robert, M.D. Chief of Staff, Canandaigua Veterans Affairs Medical Center, Canandaigua, NY, p. A436

BABER, Jonathan, Director Information Technology, Central State Hospital, Petersburg, VA, p. A676

BABICH, Eli, Chief Nursing Officer, Select Specialty Hospital–Pittsburgh/UPMC, Pittsburgh, PA, p. A551

BABINEAU, Timothy J., M.D., President and Chief Executive Officer, Lifespan Corporation, Providence, RI, p. B84

BABUSCIO, Cathy, Director Human Resources, Mat–Su Regional Medical Center, Palmer, AK, p. A30

BACA, Modesto, Chief Information Officer, Amarillo Veterans Affairs Health Care System, Amarillo, TX, p. A596

BACH, Dawn M., MS Chief Clinical Officer, Buena Vista Regional Medical Center, Storm Lake, IA, p. A238

BACHA, Fadi, M.D. Chief Medical Officer, Select Specialty Hospital–Lexington, Lexington, KY, p. A263

BACHE–WIIG, Ben, M.D., President, Abbott Northwestern Hospital, Minneapolis, MN, p. A346

BACHELDOR, H. Lee, D.O. Chief Medical Officer, St. John River District Hospital, East China, MI, p. A323

BACHER, Beth, Chief Executive Officer, HEALTHSOUTH Valley of the Sun Rehabilitation Hospital, Glendale, AZ, p. A33

BACHMAN, John Page, Corporate Vice President, St. John Medical Center, Tulsa, OK, p. A522

BACHMAN, Judith Lynn
Chief Operating Officer, Fox Chase Cancer Center–American Oncologic Hospital, Philadelphia, PA, p. A548
Chief Operating Officer, Jeanes Hospital, Philadelphia, PA, p. A548

BACHMAN, Roberta, Director Human Resources, Riverview Behavioral Health, Texarkana, AR, p. A53

BACHMEIER, Susan T., MSN Chief Nursing Officer, Wake Forest Baptist Health–Davie Medical Center, Mocksville, NC, p. A469

BACK, Barbara, Manager Human Resources, Encino Hospital Medical Center,, CA, p. A71

BACKER, Jacqueline Ann, Vice President of Human Resources, Providence Medical Center, Wayne, NE, p. A403

BACON, Jeff, D.O. Chief Medical Officer, Sterling Regional MedCenter, Sterling, CO, p. A110

BACON, Ken J., President and Chief Executive Officer, Shawnee Mission Medical Center, Shawnee Mission, KS, p. A254

BADALIAN, B. Joseph, Chief Executive Officer, Fountain Valley Regional Hospital and Medical Center, Fountain Valley, CA, p. A62

BADEN, Robert M., Chief Financial Officer, Lompoc Valley Medical Center, Lompoc, CA, p. A69

BADEN, Jr., Thomas, Chief Information Officer, Community Behavioral Health Hospital – Rochester, Rochester, MN, p. A349

BADGER, Jeff
Chief Financial Officer, Calumet Medical Center, Chilton, WI, p. A704
Chief Financial Officer, Mercy Medical Center, Oshkosh, WI, p. A713
Chief Financial Officer, St. Elizabeth Hospital, Appleton, WI, p. A702

BADILLO, Linda, M.D. Chief of Medical Staff, Medical Center of Trinity, Trinity, FL, p. A148

BADINGER, Sandy, Chief Financial Officer, Slidell Memorial Hospital, Slidell, LA, p. A288

BADR, Safwan, M.D. Executive Vice President and Chief Medical Officer, DMC – Detroit Receiving Hospital, Detroit, MI, p. A321

BAECHLE, Christopher, Chief Executive Officer, St. Luke's Rehabilitation Hospital, Chesterfield, MO, p. A369

BAEHSER, Deborah, Vice President Patient Care Services, Cape Regional Medical Center, Cape May Court House, NJ, p. A415

BAENEN, Sharla, R.N., President, Bellin Psychiatric Center, Green Bay, WI, p. A706

BAER, Douglas M., Chief Executive Officer, Brooks Rehabilitation Hospital, Jacksonville, FL, p. A131

BAEZ, Janet, Director, University Hospital, San Juan, PR, p. A730

BAEZ, Juan, M.D. President Medical Staff, Robert Wood Johnson University Hospital Rahway, Rahway, NJ, p. A422

BAGBY, Tonia J., PsyD, FACHE Acting Director, Veterans Affairs Pacific Islands Health Care System, Honolulu, HI, p. A171

BAGGERLY, Karen, Chief Nursing Officer and Vice President, Covenant Medical Center, Lubbock, TX, p. A634

BAGGETT, Al, M.D. Interim Chief of Staff, Taylor Regional Hospital, Hawkinsville, GA, p. A160

BAGGETT, Margarita, MSN Interim Chief Operating Officer, UC San Diego Health, San Diego, CA, p. A89

BAGLEY, Brenda, Director Human Resources, TMC Bonham Hospital, Bonham, TX, p. A603

BAGLEY, Peter, M.D. Medical Director, Fairlawn Rehabilitation Hospital, Worcester, MA, p. A316

BAGNALL, Andrew, President and Chief Executive Officer, St. Nicholas Hospital, Sheboygan, WI, p. A716

BAGNELL, Kelly, M.D. Chief of Staff, Providence St. Joseph Medical Center, Polson, MT, p. A390

BAHL, Barry I., Director, St. Cloud Veterans Affairs Health Care System, Saint Cloud, MN, p. A350

BAHLS, Fredrick, M.D. Chief of Staff, Veterans Affairs Central Iowa Health Care System, Des Moines, IA, p. A230

BAHNLEIN, Carl, Executive Vice President and Chief Operating Officer, Virginia Hospital Center – Arlington, Arlington, VA, p. A667

BAIDA–FRAGOSO, Nicolas, M.D. Clinical Director, El Paso Psychiatric Center, El Paso, TX, p. A615

BAIER, Roger, Chief Executive Officer, Sanford Mayville Medical Center, Mayville, ND, p. A480

BAIG, Mirza, M.D., Medical Director, UH Rehabilitation Hospital, Beachwood, OH, p. A484

BAILEY, Ann, Assistant Director Administration, Central State Hospital, Petersburg, VA, p. A676

BAILEY, Becky, R.N. Director Nursing, Kansas Surgery and Recovery Center, Wichita, KS, p. A256

BAILEY, Becky, Director Human Resources, Lincoln Hospital, Davenport, WA, p. A684

BAILEY, Brenda, Assistant Administrator, Windsor–Laurelwood Center for Behavioral Medicine, Willoughby, OH, p. A506

BAILEY, Bruce P., President and Chief Executive Officer, Tidelands Health, Georgetown, SC, p. B135

BAILEY, Cheryl, R.N. Chief Nursing Officer Vice President Patient Care Services, Cullman Regional Medical Center, Cullman, AL, p. A18

BAILEY, Cori, Accountant, Tyler Holmes Memorial Hospital, Winona, MS, p. A366

BAILEY, Craig, MS, Administrator, Colorado Acute Long Term Hospital, Denver, CO, p. A103

BAILEY, Dan, Director Information Systems, Norton Sound Regional Hospital, Nome, AK, p. A30

BAILEY, David, FACHE, Chief Executive Officer, Community Hospital of Bremen, Bremen, IN, p. A207

BAILEY, David J., M.D., President and Chief Executive Officer, Nemours, Jacksonville, FL, p. B94

BAILEY, Dawn A., R.N. Vice President Nursing and Chief Nursing Officer, Euclid Hospital, Euclid, OH, p. A494

BAILEY, Dianne, Chief Information Officer, Pana Community Hospital, Pana, IL, p. A199

BAILEY, Heather, Chief Human Resources Officer, Jefferson Healthcare, Port Townsend, WA, p. A688

BAILEY, Jodi J., Human Resources Director, Odessa Memorial Healthcare Center, Odessa, WA, p. A687

BAILEY, John E., Chief Financial Officer, Moore County Hospital District, Dumas, TX, p. A614

BAILEY, Jonathan D., Chief Executive Officer and Administrator, Hansford Hospital, Spearman, TX, p. A649

BAILEY, Joy, Director Information Technology, Sutter Amador Hospital, Jackson, CA, p. A66

BAILEY, Kathy C., FACHE, President and Chief Executive Officer, Carolinas Healthcare System Blue Ridge, Morganton, NC, p. A470

BAILEY, Kelly, Chief Executive Officer and Administrator, Kindred Hospital–White Rock, Dallas, TX, p. A610

BAILEY, Larry, Chief Executive Officer, Indiana University Health Paoli Hospital, Paoli, IN, p. A220

BAILEY, Leisa, M.D. Chief of Staff, Doctors Memorial Hospital, Bonifay, FL, p. A124

BAILEY, Lori, R.N. Vice President and Chief Nursing Officer, Ottumwa Regional Health Center, Ottumwa, IA, p. A236

BAILEY, Marquita, Chief Nursing Officer, DeKalb Regional Medical Center, Fort Payne, AL, p. A20

BAILEY, Matthew D., FACHE Chief Operating Officer, Indiana University Health Bloomington Hospital, Bloomington, IN, p. A207

BAILEY, Mikeana, Director Human Resources, Brownwood Regional Medical Center, Brownwood, TX, p. A604

BAILEY, Owen, FACHE, Chief Operating Officer, University of South Alabama Hospitals, Mobile, AL, p. B149

BAILEY, Robert W., Chief Information Officer, Hawthorn Center, Northville, MI, p. A331

BAILEY, Ron, Chief Financial Officer, Franklin Foundation Hospital, Franklin, LA, p. A277

BAILEY, Russell, Chief Executive Officer, Texas Rehabilitation Hospital of Fort Worth, Fort Worth, TX, p. A619

BAILEY, Scott, Chief Financial Officer, EASTAR Health System, Muskogee, OK, p. A515

BAILEY, Travis A., Vice President Administration, St. Claire Regional Medical Center, Morehead, KY, p. A267

BAILEY–NEWELL, Susan, Vice President Human Resources, Baylor St. Luke's Medical Center, Houston, TX, p. A623

BAILEY–OETKER, Jessica, Director Quality and Medical Staff, Providence Willamette Falls Medical Center, Oregon City, OR, p. A528

BAIN, Joel, Director Information Services, TriStar Summit Medical Center, Hermitage, TN, p. A584

BAIN, Mark, Chief Human Resources, Veterans Affairs Connecticut Healthcare System, West Haven, CT, p. A118

BAIN, Pat, Chief Nursing Officer, Lower Bucks Hospital, Bristol, PA, p. A534

BAIO, Katie, Human Resource Director, AMITA Health Adventist Medical Center Bolingbrook, Bolingbrook, IL, p. A182

BAIOCCO, Jeffrey D., Chief Financial Officer, Eastern Idaho Regional Medical Center, Idaho Falls, ID, p. A176

BAIR, Ada, Chief Executive Officer, Memorial Hospital, Carthage, IL, p. A182

BAIR, Connie, Human Resources Assistant, Pike County Memorial Hospital, Louisiana, MO, p. A376

BAIRD, David
Director of Information Systems, Intermountain Medical Center, Murray, UT, p. A661
Chief Information Officer, LDS Hospital, Salt Lake City, UT, p. A663
Chief Information Officer, The Orthopedic Specialty Hospital, Murray, UT, p. A661

BAIRD, Donna, Vice President Corporate Services, Bay Medical Center Sacred Heart Health System, Panama City, FL, p. A141

BAIRD, Glen, M.D. Chief of Staff, Shriners Hospitals for Children–Spokane, Spokane, WA, p. A691

BAIRD, John D., Chief Executive Officer, MetroSouth Medical Center, Blue Island, IL, p. A182

BAISCH, Kim, R.N. Associate Vice President Patient Care Services, Highline Medical Center, Burien, WA, p. A683

BAISDEN, Monica, Director Human Resources, Memorial Hermann Northeast, Humble, TX, p. A628

BAJAK, Sally, Chief Financial Officer, St. Croix Regional Medical Center, St. Croix Falls, WI, p. A716

BAJARI, Pamela R., R.N., Interim Administrator, Community Behavioral Health Hospital – Annandale, Annandale, MN, p. A338

BAJARI, Pamela R., R.N. Nurse Executive MHSATS, Community Behavioral Health Hospital – Rochester, Rochester, MN, p. A349

BAKAR, Anne L.
President and Chief Executive Officer, Telecare Heritage Psychiatric Health Center, Oakland, CA, p. A80
President and Chief Executive Officer, Willow Rock Center, San Leandro, CA, p. A92

BAKER, Alison, M.D. Chief of Staff, Missouri Baptist Sullivan Hospital, Sullivan, MO, p. A383

BAKER, Bonnie, Vice President Finance and Chief Financial Officer, Butler Hospital, Providence, RI, p. A560

BAKER, Bonnie, M.D. Chief Medical Services, Veterans Health Care System of the Ozarks, Fayetteville, AR, p. A46

BAKER, Brenda, Chief Financial Officer, Riverview Health, Noblesville, IN, p. A220

BAKER, Damon, D.O. Chief Medical Officer, Oklahoma State University Medical Center, Tulsa, OK, p. A521

BAKER, Deborah
Chief Nursing Officer, Helen Newberry Joy Hospital, Newberry, MI, p. A331
Interim Vice President, Nursing and Patient Care Services, Johns Hopkins Hospital, Baltimore, MD, p. A296
Vice President, Patient Care Services, Mount Auburn Hospital, Cambridge, MA, p. A309

BAKER, Denis, Chief Information Officer, Sarasota Memorial Health Care System, Sarasota, FL, p. A145

BAKER, Dennis, Chief Executive Officer, Select Specialty Hospital–Longview, Longview, TX, p. A633

BAKER, Donald, CPA Chief Financial Officer, Hillcrest Medical Center, Tulsa, OK, p. A521

BAKER, Frank, Chief Information Officer, Mary Breckinridge ARH Hospital, Hyden, KY, p. A262

BAKER, Gary E., Senior Vice President and Chief Executive Officer, HonorHealth Scottsdale Shea Medical Center, Scottsdale, AZ, p. A39

BAKER, Harlan T., Department Leader Information Systems, McDonough District Hospital, Macomb, IL, p. A195

BAKER, J. Matthew, M.D. President Medical Staff, Bertrand Chaffee Hospital, Springville, NY, p. A456

BAKER, Joann, Administrator, Doctors Memorial Hospital, Bonifay, FL, p. A124

BAKER, Joel, D.O. Chief Medical Officer, Wayne County Hospital, Corydon, IA, p. A228

BAKER, Jon, Chief Financial Officer, TriStar Hendersonville Medical Center, Hendersonville, TN, p. A584

BAKER, Judy, Chief Financial Officer, Kindred Hospital–Mansfield, Mansfield, TX, p. A635

BAKER, Kristie, Chief Nursing Officer, Two Rivers Behavioral Health System, Kansas City, MO, p. A374

BAKER, Maia, MSN Chief Nurse Executive, Rio Grande State Center/South Texas Health Care System, Harlingen, TX, p. A622

BAKER, Mark A., Chief Executive Officer, Jack Hughston Memorial Hospital, Phenix City, AL, p. A24

BAKER, Melissa
Director, Human Resources, Providence Little Company of Mary Medical Center – Torrance, Torrance, CA, p. A96
Director, Human Resources, Providence Little Company of Mary Medical Center San Pedro,, CA, p. A73

BAKER, Michael, D.O. Chief of Staff, Daviess Community Hospital, Washington, IN, p. A223

BAKER, Michelle, Director Information Systems, Indiana University Health White Memorial Hospital, Monticello, IN, p. A218

BAKER, Nichelle A., Chair Human Resources, Mayo Clinic Hospital, Phoenix, AZ, p. A36

BAKER, Paige, MSN Chief Nursing Officer, Lee's Summit Medical Center, Lee's Summit, MO, p. A375

BAKER, Patrick, R.N. Vice President, Chief Nursing Officer, West Chester Hospital, West Chester, OH, p. A505

BAKER, Paula F., President and Chief Executive Officer, Freeman Health System, Joplin, MO, p. A372

BAKER, Paula F., President and Chief Executive Officer, Freeman Health System, Joplin, MO, p. B57

BAKER, Paula F., President and Chief Executive Officer, Freeman Neosho Hospital, Neosho, MO, p. A377

BAKER, Phillip, Vice President and Chief Financial Officer, Fawcett Memorial Hospital, Port Charlotte, FL, p. A143

BAKER, R. Hal, M.D. Vice President and Chief Information Officer, WellSpan York Hospital, York, PA, p. A559

BAKER, Reese, Director Information Systems, Crittenden County Hospital, Marion, KY, p. A266

BAKER, Reta K., President, Mercy Hospital Fort Scott, Fort Scott, KS, p. A243

BAKER, Rodger H., President and Chief Executive Officer, Fauquier Hospital, Warrenton, VA, p. A680

BAKER, Ronald L., Chief Executive Officer, Saint Luke's East Hospital, Lee's Summit, MO, p. A375

BAKER, Roni, Director of Nursing, Herington Municipal Hospital, Herington, KS, p. A244

BAKER, Sharon, Director Support Services, Fairbanks, Indianapolis, IN, p. A213

BAKER, Shawna, M.D. Chief of Staff, Community Hospital of Anaconda, Anaconda, MT, p. A385

BAKER, Steve, Vice President and Chief Technology and Information Officer, Columbus Regional Hospital, Columbus, IN, p. A208

BAKER, Vanya, Director, Wilkes Regional Medical Center, North Wilkesboro, NC, p. A471

BAKER, W. Douglas, Director, Julian F. Keith Alcohol and Drug Abuse Treatment Center, Black Mountain, NC, p. A460

BAKER Jr., Wendell H., President, Vidant Edgecombe Hospital, Tarboro, NC, p. A474

BAKER–WITT, Francine, R.N., Interim Chief Executive Officer, Effingham Hospital, Springfield, GA, p. A166

BAKHTIER, Hasan, M.D. Medical Director, Community Mental Health Center, Lawrenceburg, IN, p. A217

BAKICH, Sandy, Director Information Management, Delano Regional Medical Center, Delano, CA, p. A60

BAKKEN, Mary, Executive Vice President and Chief Operating Officer, Silver Cross Hospital, New Lenox, IL, p. A198

BAKKUM, Kyle, Chief Executive Officer and Administrator, Vernon Memorial Healthcare, Viroqua, WI, p. A717

BALASIA, Tim, Chief Financial Officer, Johnson Memorial Hospital, Franklin, IN, p. A211

BALASUBRAMONY, Suresh, M.D. Chief Medical Officer, Minnie Hamilton HealthCare Center, Grantsville, WV, p. A696

BALAZY, Thomas E., M.D. Medical Director, Craig Hospital, Englewood, CO, p. A105

BALCAVAGE, Thomas, Vice President Information Systems and Chief Information Officer Technology, Kennedy Health System, Cherry Hill, NJ, p. A415

BALCEZAK, Thomas, M.D. Senior Vice President Medical Affairs and Chief Medical Officer, Yale–New Haven Hospital, New Haven, CT, p. A116

BALDAUF, Robb, Coordinator Information Systems, Lodi Community Hospital, Lodi, OH, p. A497

BALDERRAMA, Jose, Vice President Human Resources, Valley Hospital, Ridgewood, NJ, p. A423

BALDOSARO, Thomas
Chief Financial Officer, Inspira Medical Center–Elmer, Elmer, NJ, p. A416
Chief Financial Officer, Inspira Medical Center–Vineland, Vineland, NJ, p. A425
BALDRIDGE, Dava, R.N. Chief Nursing Officer, Hillcrest Hospital – South, Tulsa, OK, p. A521
BALDWIN, Barbara, Chief Information Officer, Anne Arundel Medical Center, Annapolis, MD, p. A296
BALDWIN, Bruce A., Chief Executive Officer, Newberry County Memorial Hospital, Newberry, SC, p. A569
BALDWIN, Ellen, R.N. Chief Nursing Officer, Texas Health Center for Diagnostic & Surgery, Plano, TX, p. A642
BALDWIN, Erin, M.P.H. Chief Operating Officer, Mahaska Health Partnership, Oskaloosa, IA, p. A236
BALDWIN, Gilda, Chief Executive Officer, Westchester General Hospital, Miami, FL, p. A137
BALDWIN, Nathan, M.D. President Medical Staff, Baptist Memorial Hospital–Booneville, Booneville, MS, p. A356
BALDWIN, Steve
Vice President Finance, The Willough at Naples, Naples, FL, p. A138
Manager Information Technology, Wyoming State Hospital, Evanston, WY, p. A722
BALDWIN, William, Chief Information Officer, Ashe Memorial Hospital, Jefferson, NC, p. A468
BALES, Brian, Director Plant Operations, HEALTHSOUTH Southern Hills Rehabilitation Hospital, Princeton, WV, p. A699
BALES, Correen, Executive Director Human Resources, UNM Sandoval Regional Medical Center, Albuquerque, NM, p. A428
BALES, Glenn, Chief Financial Officer, Providence Saint Joseph Medical Center, Burbank, CA, p. A57
BALES–CHUBB, Denyse, President and Chief Executive Officer, Florida Hospital Wesley Chapel, Wesley Chapel, FL, p. A149
BALFOUR, Ann M., R.N., President, St. Joseph Health System, Tawas City, MI, p. A335
BALKO, Tom, Manager Information Systems, Redwood Area Hospital, Redwood Falls, MN, p. A349
BALL, Cassie, Chief Financial Officer, Hilton Head Hospital, Hilton Head Island, SC, p. A567
BALL, Charlie, Chief Operating Officer, Specialty Rehabilitation Hospital of Coushatta, Coushatta, LA, p. A275
BALL, James, Chief Operating Officer, Executive, St. Anthony's Rehabilitation Hospital, Lauderdale Lakes, FL, p. A134
BALL, Jim, Chief Operating Officer, St. Catherine's Rehabilitation Hospital, North Miami, FL, p. A139
BALL, III, Johnny Percy, Assistant Administrator Human Resources, South Georgia Medical Center, Valdosta, GA, p. A168
BALL, Rodney, Vice President Finance, Carolinas HealthCare System NorthEast, Concord, NC, p. A463
BALLA, Matt, Chief Executive Officer, St. Vincent Dunn Hospital, Bedford, IN, p. A206
BALLANCE, William, Chief of Medical Staff, Vidant Bertie Hospital, Windsor, NC, p. A475
BALLARD, Christine A.
Vice President Human Resources, Muncy Valley Hospital, Muncy, PA, p. A546
Vice President Human Resources, Soldiers and Sailors Memorial Hospital, Wellsboro, PA, p. A557
Vice President Human Resources, Williamsport Regional Medical Center, Williamsport, PA, p. A558
BALLARD, Jerry, Director Information Systems, Central Florida Regional Hospital, Sanford, FL, p. A145
BALLARD, John, Ph.D., Chief Executive Officer, Kentucky River Medical Center, Jackson, KY, p. A262
BALLARD, Lorraine L., Director Human Resources, St. Helena Parish Hospital, Greensburg, LA, p. A277
BALLARD, Marsha, Human Resources, CHRISTUS Mother Frances Hospital – Jacksonville, Jacksonville, TX, p. A629
BALLARD, Richard R., Chief Executive Officer and Administrator, University of Miami Hospital and Clinics, Miami, FL, p. A137
BALLARD, Terri, Chief Nursing Officer, HEALTHSOUTH Northern Kentucky Rehabilitation Hospital, Edgewood, KY, p. A259
BALLESTERO, Susan, Vice President and Chief Human Resources Officer, Saint Peter's University Hospital, New Brunswick, NJ, p. A420
BALLIETT, Matt, Chief Information Officer, Coal County General Hospital, Coalgate, OK, p. A510
BALLIN, Daniel, Administrator, Riverside Rehabilitation Institute, Newport News, VA, p. A674
BALLINGHOFF, James R., MSN Chief Nursing Officer and Associate Executive Director, Penn Presbyterian Medical Center, Philadelphia, PA, p. A549
BALLMAN, Patricia, Director, Westfield Memorial Hospital, Westfield, NY, p. A459
BALLOU, Michele, M.D. Chief Medical Staff, LewisGale Hospital Alleghany, Low Moor, VA, p. A672

BALOGA–ALTIERI, Bonnie, Ph.D. Vice President Patient Care Services and Chief Nursing Officer, Children's Specialized Hospital–PSE&G, New Brunswick, NJ, p. A420
BALSANO, Tony, Vice President Finance, Saint Francis Healthcare System, Cape Girardeau, MO, p. A368
BALT, David, D.O. Chief Medical Officer, Avera Queen of Peace Hospital, Mitchell, SD, p. A575
BALTIERRA, David A., M.D. President Medical Staff, Jefferson Medical Center, Ranson, WV, p. A699
BALUNTANSKI, Brian, Chief Financial Officer, McLaren Macomb, Mount Clemens, MI, p. A330
BALZANO, Eric, Chief of Staff, Weirton Medical Center, Weirton, WV, p. A700
BALZANO, Janice, President and Chief Executive Officer, St. Petersburg General Hospital, Saint Petersburg, FL, p. A144
BAMAN, Raj, D.O. President Medical Staff, Samaritan North Lincoln Hospital, Lincoln City, OR, p. A527
BAMBERGER, Josh, Administrator, Runnells Center for Rehabilitation and Healthcare, Berkeley Heights, NJ, p. A414
BAMBRICK, Catherine, Chief Operating Officer, Kittitas Valley Healthcare, Ellensburg, WA, p. A684
BAMMEL, Paul, Vice President, Mayo Clinic Health System – Northland in Barron, Barron, WI, p. A702
BANBURY, Brian, Director Site Information Systems, Advocate Christ Medical Center, Oak Lawn, IL, p. A198
BANCO, Leonard, M.D. Senior Vice President and Chief Medical Officer, Bristol Hospital, Bristol, CT, p. A113
BANDA, Venkat, M.D. President Medical Staff, Promise Hospital of Baton Rouge – Ochsner Campus, Baton Rouge, LA, p. A273
BANDFIELD–KEOUGH, Kathryn, Vice President Patient Care Services, Munson Healthcare Cadillac Hospital, Cadillac, MI, p. A319
BANDLA, H., M.D. Chief Clinical Affairs, Walter P. Reuther Psychiatric Hospital, Westland, MI, p. A336
BANDS, IV, James G., Chief Financial Officer, Ivinson Memorial Hospital, Laramie, WY, p. A722
BANDY, Dawn, Chief Financial Officer, Grant Regional Health Center, Lancaster, WI, p. A708
BANDY, Don, Director Information Technology, AllianceHealth Deaconess, Oklahoma City, OK, p. A516
BANDY, P. Ross, M.D. Chief Medical Officer and Chief of Staff, Levi Hospital, Hot Springs National Park, AR, p. A47
BANE, William, Chief Financial Officer, Inova Loudoun Hospital, Leesburg, VA, p. A672
BANFIELD, Anne, Chief, Medical Staff, Davis Medical Center, Elkins, WV, p. A695
BANG, W. J., M.D. Chief of Staff, Reeves County Hospital, Pecos, TX, p. A641
BANGA, Alok, M.D. Medical Director, Sierra Vista Hospital, Sacramento, CA, p. A87
BANIEWICZ, John, M.D. Chief Medical Officer, Lake Health, Concord Township, OH, p. A491
BANK, Carol J., Vice President Human Resources, Divine Savior Healthcare, Portage, WI, p. A714
BANKER, Julie G., R.N. Chief Nursing Officer, Lehigh Regional Medical Center, Lehigh Acres, FL, p. A134
BANKERS, Diane, Senior Vice President, Nursing Services, FirstLight Health System, Mora, MN, p. A347
BANKS, Chester, Director Human Resources, East Orange General Hospital, East Orange, NJ, p. A416
BANKS, Elizabeth, Chief Executive Officer, Summit Behavioral Healthcare, Cincinnati, OH, p. A488
BANKS, Matthew, Chief Operating Officer, Lake Norman Regional Medical Center, Mooresville, NC, p. A470
BANKS, Maureen, R.N., President, Spaulding Hospital for Continuing Medical Care Cambridge, Cambridge, MA, p. A309
BANKS, Maureen, FACHE Chief Operating Officer, Spaulding Rehabilitation Hospital, Charlestown, MA, p. A309
BANKS, Maureen, R.N., President, Spaulding Rehabilitation Hospital Cape Cod, East Sandwich, MA, p. A309
BANKS, Robbi, Vice President, Human Resources, Medical Center Health System, Odessa, TX, p. A639
BANKS, Shane, M.D. Chief of Staff, Ogallala Community Hospital, Ogallala, NE, p. A399
BANKS, Walter, Director Human Resources, Baptist Memorial Hospital–Desoto, Southaven, MS, p. A365
BANKTSON, Julie, Manager Human Resources, Paul Oliver Memorial Hospital, Frankfort, MI, p. A324
BANNER, Fred, Chief Information Officer, Shore Medical Center, Somers Point, NJ, p. A423
BANUEDOS, Jorge, Director Human Resources, Metropolitan State Hospital, Norwalk, CA, p. A79
BAPTISTE, Ernest, Executive Director, NYC Health + Hospitals / Kings County,, NY, p. A448
BAQUET, Shawn, Chief of Staff, Iberia Medical Center, New Iberia, LA, p. A284
BARANCZYK, Kay, R.N. Chief Nursing Officer, HSHS St. Clare Memorial Hospital, Oconto Falls, WI, p. A713

BARANSKI, David J., Vice President Human Resources, Phoebe Putney Memorial Hospital, Albany, GA, p. A151
BARANSKI, Kenneth, Chief Financial Officer, Hills & Dales General Hospital, Cass City, MI, p. A320
BARBA, James J., President and Chief Executive Officer, Albany Medical Center, Albany, NY, p. A433
BARBADIAN, John, Vice President Human Resources, Tulare Regional Medical Center, Tulare, CA, p. A97
BARBAREE, Jerry, Director Human Resources, Baptist Memorial Hospital – Memphis, Memphis, TN, p. A588
BARBARIN, LaSharndra, Chief Executive Officer, Medical Center of Lewisville, Lewisville, TX, p. A632
BARBAROTTA, Ann Marie, Executive Director, Creedmoor Psychiatric Center,, NY, p. A444
BARBEE, Daniel, Interim Chief Executive Officer, The University of Toledo Medical Center, Toledo, OH, p. A504
BARBEE, Ovell, Senior Vice President, Human Resources, Spectrum Health – Butterworth Hospital, Grand Rapids, MI, p. A325
BARBER, Chris B., FACHE, President and Chief Executive Officer, St. Bernards Medical Center, Jonesboro, AR, p. A48
BARBER, Eric A., President and Chief Executive Officer, Mary Lanning Healthcare, Hastings, NE, p. A396
BARBER, Karen, R.N., Chief Executive Officer, Yoakum Community Hospital, Yoakum, TX, p. A658
BARBER, Keith, CPA, Chief Executive Officer, Houston Methodist Willowbrook Hospital, Houston, TX, p. A625
BARBER, Michael, Chief Operating Officer, Penn Medicine Chester County Hospital, West Chester, PA, p. A557
BARBER, Richard, M.D. Chief Medical Officer, Wilkes Regional Medical Center, North Wilkesboro, NC, p. A471
BARBER, Roxann E., Regional Ambulatory Care and Ancillary Services Officer, Presence Mercy Medical Center, Aurora, IL, p. A180
BARBER, Scott, Chief Executive Officer, Decatur County General Hospital, Parsons, TN, p. A592
BARBER, Wendi, Vice President Finance and Chief Financial Officer, Park Ridge Health, Hendersonville, NC, p. A467
BARBINI, Gerald J., President and Chief Executive Officer, Allegan General Hospital, Allegan, MI, p. A318
BARBO, Steve, R.N., Administrator, Citizens Medical Center, Columbia, LA, p. A275
BARBOUR, Alexis, Director Finance, Dublin Springs, Dublin, OH, p. A494
BARBOUR, Michael B., Chief Nursing Officer, Emerald Coast Behavioral Hospital, Panama City, FL, p. A141
BARBUAT, James P., Chief Financial Officer, Gunnison Valley Hospital, Gunnison, CO, p. A106
BARCELLONA, Nicholas J., Chief Financial Officer, Children's Hospital of Pittsburgh of UPMC, Pittsburgh, PA, p. A550
BARCHI, Daniel, Senior Vice President, Technical Services and Chief Information Officer, Bridgeport Hospital, Bridgeport, CT, p. A113
BARCLAY, Bonnie, Chief Nursing Officer, LifeCare Hospitals of Chester County, West Chester, PA, p. A557
BARCLAY, Duane, D.O. Chief Medical Officer, DeKalb Medical at Hillandale, Lithonia, GA, p. A162
BARCLAY, Emily, Vice President Human Resources, Dana–Farber Cancer Institute, Boston, MA, p. A306
BARCLAY, Rick, Vice President Support Services, Mercy Hospital Rogers, Rogers, AR, p. A52
BARCUS, Krista, Human Resources Leader, SSM Health St. Francis Hospital – Maryville, Maryville, MO, p. A376
BARD, Jeffrey, President, Aurora Medical Center of Oshkosh, Oshkosh, WI, p. A713
BARDEN, Sean
Executive Vice President and Chief Financial Officer, Mary Washington Hospital, Fredericksburg, VA, p. A670
Executive Vice President and Chief Financial Officer, Stafford Hospital, Stafford, VA, p. A679
BARDIER, Catherine, Vice President, Human Resources, Elliot Hospital, Manchester, NH, p. A412
BARDWELL, Carol A., R.N. Chief Nurse Executive, Martha's Vineyard Hospital, Oak Bluffs, MA, p. A313
BARDWELL, Jean, Vice President and Chief Financial Officer, Ranken Jordan Pediatric Bridge Hospital, Maryland Heights, MO, p. A376
BARDWELL, Sheila, Director Information Systems, Baptist Memorial Hospital–Golden Triangle, Columbus, MS, p. A357
BAREFOOT, Denise, Director of Information Technology, Carolina Pines Regional Medical Center, Hartsville, SC, p. A567
BAREIS, Charles, M.D. Medical Director, MacNeal Hospital, Berwyn, IL, p. A181
BARELA, Barbara, Director Human Resources, Gila Regional Medical Center, Silver City, NM, p. A431
BARFIELD, Donna, Chief Nursing Officer, Tennova Healthcare Volunteer Community Hospital, Martin, TN, p. A588

BARGINERE, Cynthia, MSN Vice President Clinical Nursing and Chief Nursing Officer, Rush University Medical Center, Chicago, IL, p. A186

BARHAM, Ed, M.D. Chief of Staff, Merit Health Woman's Hospital, Flowood, MS, p. A357

BARIOLA, Christopher L., Chief Executive Officer, Baptist Memorial Rehabilitation Hospital, Germantown, TN, p. A583

BARKEMA, Annette, Chief Financial Officer, Portland Veterans Affairs Medical Center, Portland, OR, p. A529

BARKER, Alanna, Director Human Resources, MetroSouth Medical Center, Blue Island, IL, p. A182

BARKER, James, Chief Executive Officer, West Shore Medical Center, Manistee, MI, p. A329

BARKER, Karen, Vice President and Chief Information Officer, Sinai Hospital of Baltimore, Baltimore, MD, p. A298

BARKER, Kathryn L., Chief Human Resources Management, Veterans Health Care System of the Ozarks, Fayetteville, AR, p. A46

BARKER, Louise, R.N., Chief Executive Officer, Central Louisiana Surgical Hospital, Alexandria, LA, p. A271

BARKER, Richard, Administrator, Mercy Health Love County, Marietta, OK, p. A514

BARKER, Russell
 Community Chief Executive Officer, McDowell ARH Hospital, McDowell, KY, p. A266
 Information Officer, U. S. Public Health Service Indian Hospital–Whiteriver, Whiteriver, AZ, p. A41

BARKER, Jr., William A., Vice President Administration, Pleasant Valley Hospital, Point Pleasant, WV, p. A699

BARKHYMER, Mary C., R.N. Vice President Patient Care Services and Chief Nursing Officer, UPMC St. Margaret, Pittsburgh, PA, p. A552

BARKMAN, Joseph, Vice President Financial Services, Oaklawn Psychiatric Center, Goshen, IN, p. A212

BARKSDALE, Mary, Director Human Resources, Person Memorial Hospital, Roxboro, NC, p. A472

BARKSDALE, Vickie, Manager Human Resources, North Oak Regional Medical Center, Senatobia, MS, p. A365

BARLAGE, Seth, Associate Medical Center Director, John J. Pershing Veterans Affairs Medical Center, Poplar Bluff, MO, p. A378

BARLEY, Leonard, M.D. Chief Medical Officer, Windsor–Laurelwood Center for Behavioral Medicine, Willoughby, OH, p. A506

BARLEY, Tammy, Director, Human Resources, HEALTHSOUTH Rehabilitation Hospital of Jonesboro, Jonesboro, AR, p. A48

BARLOW, Alan, Chief Executive Officer, Fort Belknap U. S. Public Health Service Indian Hospital, Harlem, MT, p. A388

BARLOW, Mark, M.D. Chief Medical Officer and President Medical Staff, Cornerstone Hospital of Houston at Clearlake, Webster, TX, p. A656

BARLOW, Roddex, Chief Operating Officer, The Hospitals of Providence Memorial Campus, El Paso, TX, p. A616

BARMECHA, Jitendra, M.D. Senior Vice President and Chief Information Officer, St. Barnabas Hospital,, NY, p. A449

BARNARD, Jeanna, FACHE, Chief Executive Officer, Bayshore Medical Center, Pasadena, TX, p. A640

BARNARD, Kerri, Director Human Resources, Larned State Hospital, Larned, KS, p. A247

BARNARD, Lawrence, President and Chief Executive Officer, St. Rose Dominican Hospitals – San Martin Campus, Las Vegas, NV, p. A406

BARNARD, Ryan, Chief Executive Officer, Swisher Memorial Hospital District, Tulia, TX, p. A654

BARNCORD, Sharon, Human Resource Business Partner, Kaiser Permanente South San Francisco, South San Francisco, CA, p. A95

BARNELL, Phil, Chief Medical Officer, HSHS St. Mary's Hospital, Decatur, IL, p. A188

BARNES, Alan, Chief Financial Officer, North Star Behavioral Health System, Anchorage, AK, p. A28

BARNES, Becky, Chief Operating Officer, Rapides Regional Medical Center, Alexandria, LA, p. A271

BARNES, Bridget, Vice President and Chief Information Officer, OHSU Hospital, Portland, OR, p. A529

BARNES, Deborah, Vice President and Chief Information Officer, Children's Hospital of The King's Daughters, Norfolk, VA, p. A675

BARNES, Donald K., Chief Human Resources Officer, Duke Raleigh Hospital, Raleigh, NC, p. A471

BARNES, Douglas A., M.D. Chief of Staff, Shriners Hospitals for Children–Houston, Houston, TX, p. A626

BARNES, Gary, Senior Vice President, Chief Information Officer, Medical Center Health System, Odessa, TX, p. A639

BARNES, George, M.D. Medical Director, Lakeview Regional Medical Center, Covington, LA, p. A275

BARNES, Gloria V., MSN Assistant Vice President Patient Care Services, Southeastern Regional Medical Center, Newnan, GA, p. A164

BARNES, Jacqueline, Manager Health Information, Select Specialty Hospital–Jackson, Jackson, MS, p. A360

BARNES, Jeff, Director Information Technology, Girard Medical Center, Girard, KS, p. A243

BARNES, Joe, Chief Financial Officer, Grant Memorial Hospital, Petersburg, WV, p. A699

BARNES, John, Administrative Director Human Resources, Beverly Hospital, Montebello, CA, p. A77

BARNES, Karen, Interim Chief Nursing Officer, Logan Regional Medical Center, Logan, WV, p. A697

BARNES, Larry, Vice President Information Technology, Salina Regional Health Center, Salina, KS, p. A253

BARNES, Laura P., MSN Vice President Patient Care Services and Chief Nursing Officer, East Tennessee Children's Hospital, Knoxville, TN, p. A585

BARNES, Leslie, Chief Financial Officer, Parkview Medical Center, Pueblo, CO, p. A110

BARNES, Marla, Director of Nursing, Pushmataha Hospital & Home Health, Antlers, OK, p. A508

BARNES, Michael, Chief Information Officer, North Valley Hospital, Whitefish, MT, p. A391

BARNES, P. Marie, Director, Human Resources, North Mississippi Medical Center–Pontotoc, Pontotoc, MS, p. A364

BARNES, Sherry, Director Health Information and Quality Management, Rolling Hills Hospital, Ada, OK, p. A508

BARNES, William H., FACHE, Administrator and Chief Executive Officer, Sweeny Community Hospital, Sweeny, TX, p. A651

BARNETT, Barbara, M.D. Medical Director, Glen Cove Hospital, Glen Cove, NY, p. A439

BARNETT, Dana, Chief Executive Officer, Memorial Hospital of Carbon County, Rawlins, WY, p. A723

BARNETT, DeLynn K., Director Human Resources, Lake Chelan Community Hospital, Chelan, WA, p. A683

BARNETT, Frederick, M.D. Chief of Staff, Metroplex Adventist Hospital, Killeen, TX, p. A630

BARNETT, Julia, Chief Nursing Officer, Union General Hospital, Blairsville, GA, p. A154

BARNETT, Kelly, Human Resource Officer, Brownfield Regional Medical Center, Brownfield, TX, p. A603

BARNETT, Laura, Executive Director, Human Resources, Brigham and Women's Faulkner Hospital, Boston, MA, p. A306

BARNETT, Lori, R.N. Chief Nursing Officer, Troy Community Hospital, Troy, PA, p. A556

BARNETT, Pam, R.N. Director of Nursing, Highland District Hospital, Hillsboro, OH, p. A496

BARNETT, Shawn, Vice President and Chief Financial Officer, CHRISTUS Santa Rosa Health System, San Antonio, TX, p. A645

BARNETT, Steve, President and Chief Executive Officer, McKenzie Health System, Sandusky, MI, p. A334

BARNETTE, Brian, Chief Information Officer, Shepherd Center, Atlanta, GA, p. A153

BARNHARDT, Bonnie, Executive Director Human Resources, Minnesota Valley Health Center, Le Sueur, MN, p. A344

BARNHART, Ann, Chief Executive Officer, Heart of Florida Regional Medical Center, Davenport, FL, p. A126

BARNHART, Cody, Chief Executive Officer, St. Luke's Medical Center, Crosby, ND, p. A478

BARNHART, David, Director Information Systems, Wuesthoff Medical Center – Rockledge, Rockledge, FL, p. A143

BARNHART, J. T., Chief Executive Officer, Dallas Medical Center, Dallas, TX, p. A609

BARNHART, Jeff, Chief Executive Officer, Lynn County Hospital District, Tahoka, TX, p. A651

BARNHART, Linda, Vice President and Chief Nursing Officer, Bethesda Hospital, Saint Paul, MN, p. A350

BARNO, Jill, M.D. Chief Medical Officer, Berger Health System, Circleville, OH, p. A488

BARONE, Richard, M.D. Medical Director, Montefiore New Rochelle, New Rochelle, NY, p. A443

BARONOFF, Peter R.
 Chief Executive Officer, Promise Healthcare, Boca Raton, FL, p. B108
 President and Chief Executive Officer, Success Healthcare, Boca Raton, FL, p. B129

BARR, Andrew, Executive Officer, Tripler Army Medical Center, Honolulu, HI, p. A171

BARR, Ann
 Chief Information Officer – Bay Area, California Pacific Medical Center, San Francisco, CA, p. A90
 Chief Information Officer – Bay Area, St. Luke's Hospital, San Francisco, CA, p. A90
 Chief Information Officer, Sutter Health Bay Area, Sutter Maternity and Surgery Center of Santa Cruz, Santa Cruz, CA, p. A93

BARR, Brent, Chief Information Officer, Minnie Hamilton HealthCare Center, Grantsville, WV, p. A696

BARR, Bret A., Executive Vice President and Chief Financial Officer, Conway Medical Center, Conway, SC, p. A565

BARR, Catherine
 Chief Operating Officer, Bethesda Hospital, Saint Paul, MN, p. A350
 Chief Operating Officer, St. John's Hospital, Maplewood, MN, p. A346
 Chief Operating Officer, St. Joseph's Hospital, Saint Paul, MN, p. A351
 Chief Operating Officer, Woodwinds Health Campus, Woodbury, MN, p. A353

BARR, Francine, MS, Chief Executive Officer, Bon Secours St. Mary's Hospital, Richmond, VA, p. A677

BARR, Kristine, Vice President Communication Services, O'Bleness Memorial Hospital, Athens, OH, p. A484

BARR, Kyle J., Senior Vice President, Chief Team Resources Officer, Morton Plant North Bay Hospital, New Port Richey, FL, p. A138

BARR, Laurie C.
 Vice President Human Resources, Salem Health West Valley, Dallas, OR, p. A525
 Vice President Human Resources, Salem Hospital, Salem, OR, p. A530

BARR, Mary Beth, R.N., Chief Executive Officer, Grant Memorial Hospital, Petersburg, WV, p. A699

BARR, Vivian C., Director Human Resources, Tanner Medical Center–Carrollton, Carrollton, GA, p. A155

BARRA, Jon, Director Human Resources, Wyoming Behavioral Institute, Casper, WY, p. A721

BARRALL, Audrey, Director Human Resources, St. Helena Hospital Clear Lake, Clearlake, CA, p. A59

BARRAMEDA, Maricar, Chief Information Officer, NYC Health + Hospitals / Lincoln, NY, p. A448

BARRERA, Edward, Director Communications, Encino Hospital Medical Center,, CA, p. A71

BARRERA, Liflor, Manager Human Resources, Wahiawa General Hospital, Wahiawa, HI, p. A172

BARRERE, Davie Ann, Coordinator Information Technology, Dahl Memorial Healthcare Association, Ekalaka, MT, p. A387

BARRETT, Anne J., Associate Executive Director Human Resources, Southside Hospital, Bay Shore, NY, p. A434

BARRETT, Cindy, Administrative Assistant, Patton State Hospital, Patton, CA, p. A82

BARRETT Jr., James W., Chief Executive Officer, Richardson Medical Center, Rayville, LA, p. A286

BARRETT, Jason P., Chief Operating Officer, Flagler Hospital, Saint Augustine, FL, p. A144

BARRETT, John, Regional Director Human Resources, Franciscan St. Anthony Health – Michigan City, Michigan City, IN, p. A218

BARRETT III, John E., Chief Executive Officer, Bon Secours–DePaul Medical Center, Norfolk, VA, p. A674

BARRETT, Kerry Flynn, Vice President Human Resources, Northern Westchester Hospital, Mount Kisco, NY, p. A443

BARRETT, Linda, Vice President of Information Services, Community Hospital of Bremen, Bremen, IN, p. A207

BARRETT, Lynn, Chief Nursing Officer, Centerpoint Medical Center, Independence, MO, p. A372

BARRETT, Pam, Human Resources Director, Colorado River Medical Center, Needles, CA, p. A79

BARRETT, Pamella, Director of Nursing, Post Acute Medical Specialty Hospital of Victoria, Victoria, TX, p. A655

BARRETT, Peggy, R.N. Chief Information Officer, Central Texas Rehabilitation Hospital, Austin, TX, p. A599

BARRETT, T. Marc, M.D. Senior Vice President and Chief Medical Officer, Providence Healthcare Network, Waco, TX, p. A656

BARRICK, Lisa, Controller, HEALTHSOUTH Scottsdale Rehabilitation Hospital, Scottsdale, AZ, p. A38

BARRILLEAUX, Scott G., FACHE, Chief Executive Officer, Drew Memorial Hospital, Monticello, AR, p. A50

BARRIO, Gabe, M.D. Chief of Staff, WhidbeyHealth, Coupeville, WA, p. A684

BARRIOS, Theresa, Interim Administrator, Curahealth New Orleans, New Orleans, LA, p. A284

BARROCAS, Albert, M.D. Chief Medical Officer, Wellstar Atlanta Medical Center, Atlanta, GA, p. A153

BARROW, Robert, Chief Executive Officer, Doctors' Hospital of Michigan, Pontiac, MI, p. A332

BARROW II, William F., President and Chief Executive Officer, Our Lady of Lourdes Regional Medical Center, Lafayette, LA, p. A281

BARROWS, Cheryl, Vice President Human Resources, Sturdy Memorial Hospital, Attleboro, MA, p. A305

BARRY, Anne, Deputy Commissioner, Minnesota Department of Human Services, Saint Paul, MN, p. B91

BARRY, Rick, Director Information Systems, Baylor Medical Center at Frisco, Frisco, TX, p. A619

BARRY, Thomas, Chief Executive Officer, Pulaski Memorial Hospital, Winamac, IN, p. A224

BARSOM, Michael, M.D., Executive Director, Metropolitan State Hospital, Norwalk, CA, p. A79

BARSOUM, Wael, President, Cleveland Clinic Florida, Weston, FL, p. A150

BARSTAD, Stacy
Chief Executive Officer, Sanford Tracy Medical Center, Tracy, MN, p. A352
Chief Executive Officer, Sanford Westbrook Medical Center, Westbrook, MN, p. A353

BARTAL, Ely, M.D., Chief Executive Officer, Kansas Surgery and Recovery Center, Wichita, KS, p. A256

BARTELL, Michael, Chief Executive Officer, Regional Rehabilitation Hospital, Phenix City, AL, p. A24

BARTELS, Dara, Chief Financial Officer, Gundersen Health System, La Crosse, WI, p. A708

BARTELS, Jennifer, Director Human Resources, Pawnee County Memorial Hospital and Rural Health Clinic, Pawnee City, NE, p. A401

BARTH, Marci, Chief Nursing Officer, Fayette County Hospital, Vandalia, IL, p. A204

BARTHEL, Gayle, Coordinator Human Resources, Select Specialty Hospital–Flint, Flint, MI, p. A323

BARTHOLOMEW, Brenda, Chief Nursing Officer, Gunnison Valley Hospital, Gunnison, UT, p. A660

BARTHOLOMEW, K. A., M.D. Medical Director, Faulkton Area Medical Center, Faulkton, SD, p. A573

BARTHOLOMEW, Shelley, Director Human Resources, Decatur County General Hospital, Parsons, TN, p. A592

BARTILSON, Jim, Manager Information Systems, South Peninsula Hospital, Homer, AK, p. A29

BARTINGALE, Robert, Administrator, Mayo Clinic Health System in Fairmont, Fairmont, MN, p. A342

BARTLETT, Beth, MSN Vice President Nursing, CHI Health Saint Francis, Grand Island, NE, p. A396

BARTLETT, Freda, Director of Nursing, Crosbyton Clinic Hospital, Crosbyton, TX, p. A608

BARTLETT, Jonathan L., Chief Executive Officer, Lewis–Gale Medical Center, Salem, VA, p. A678

BARTLETT, Karolyn, Assistant Administrator, Mayo Clinic Health System – Northland in Barron, Barron, WI, p. A702

BARTLETT, Regina, Chief Executive Officer, TriStar Hendersonville Medical Center, Hendersonville, TN, p. A584

BARTLETT, Richard, M.D. Chief Medical Officer, Basin Healthcare Center, Odessa, TX, p. A639

BARTLETT, Ronald E., Chief Financial Officer, Boston Medical Center, Boston, MA, p. A306

BARTLETT III, Thomas G., Administrator, Laird Hospital, Union, MS, p. A365

BARTLETT, Wayne, Director Information Systems, Alvarado Hospital Medical Center, San Diego, CA, p. A88

BARTLEY, Tracy, Manager Information Technology, Bath Community Hospital, Hot Springs, VA, p. A672

BARTO Jr.,, John K., President and Chief Executive Officer, New Hanover Regional Medical Center, Wilmington, NC, p. B95

BARTOLOTTA, Carmen J., Chief Nursing Officer, Missouri Baptist Sullivan Hospital, Sullivan, MO, p. A383

BARTON, Cheryl, R.N., Chief Executive Officer, Southeast Health Center of Ripley County, Doniphan, MO, p. A370

BARTON, Rod, Administrator, Cassia Regional Medical Center, Burley, ID, p. A175

BARTON, Thomas, M.D. Medical Director, TOPS Surgical Specialty Hospital, Houston, TX, p. A627

BARTON, Vikki, R.N. Chief Nursing Officer, Collingsworth General Hospital, Wellington, TX, p. A657

BARTOS, John M., Chief Executive Officer, Marcus Daly Memorial Hospital, Hamilton, MT, p. A388

BARTS, Dennis, Chief Executive Officer, Avista Adventist Hospital, Louisville, CO, p. A109

BARWICK, Kim, Vice President Human Resources, Anthony Medical Center, Anthony, KS, p. A240

BARWIS, Kurt A., FACHE, President and Chief Executive Officer, Bristol Hospital, Bristol, CT, p. A113

BASA, Rhea, Director Human Resources, Morrill County Community Hospital, Bridgeport, NE, p. A394

BASA–REYES, Fiona, Chief Executive Officer, Kindred Hospital–Baldwin Park, Baldwin Park, CA, p. A56

BASCH, Jim, Interim Chief Executive Officer, Coquille Valley Hospital, Coquille, OR, p. A525

BASCOM, Steven, M.D. Chief Medical Officer, Guthrie County Hospital, Guthrie Center, IA, p. A231

BASELGA, Jose, M.D., Physician–in–Chief, Memorial Sloan–Kettering Cancer Center, New York, NY, p. A446

BASEY, Marjorie, Chief Financial Officer, Rehabilitation Hospital of Indiana, Indianapolis, IN, p. A214

BASH, Camille, Chief Financial Officer, Doctors Community Hospital, Lanham, MD, p. A302

BASHIR, Chowdry, M.D. Chief of Staff, Richard L. Roudebush Veterans Affairs Medical Center, Indianapolis, IN, p. A214

BASLER, Cyndi, Chief Operating Officer, Iron County Medical Center, Pilot Knob, MO, p. A378

BASQUE, Tonya, Chief Nursing Officer, East Texas Medical Center Fairfield, Fairfield, TX, p. A617

BASQUILL, Debra, Director Human Resources, Jennersville Regional Hospital, West Grove, PA, p. A557

BASRIA, Deborah, Human Resources Payroll Administrator, Kindred Hospital Bay Area–Tampa, Tampa, FL, p. A147

BASS, Andrew C., M.D. Medical Director, Shands Live Oak Regional Medical Center, Live Oak, FL, p. A134

BASS, Darren, President, Cox Monett, Monett, MO, p. A377

BASS, Gordon B., Chief Operating Officer, Ann & Robert H. Lurie Children's Hospital of Chicago, Chicago, IL, p. A183

BASS, Louis A., Chief Executive Officer, Northeast Alabama Regional Medical Center, Anniston, AL, p. A15

BASS, Sonya, MS Chief Nursing Officer, Colorado Plains Medical Center, Fort Morgan, CO, p. A105

BASSETT, Kimberly S., R.N., Interim President, Norwood Hospital, Norwood, MA, p. A313

BASSO, Amanda J., President, Clay County Hospital, Flora, IL, p. A190

BASSO, Marty
Chief Financial Officer, Sibley Memorial Hospital, Washington, DC, p. A122
Senior Vice President Finance, Suburban Hospital, Bethesda, MD, p. A299

BASTIANELLO, Carol, Director Human Resources, Aspirus Iron River Hospitals & Clinics, Iron River, MI, p. A327

BASTIEN IV, Samuel A., Ph.D., Chief Executive Officer, Four Winds Hospital, Saratoga Springs, NY, p. A455

BASTING, Gregory, M.D
Vice President Medical Affairs, Allied Services Rehabilitation Hospital, Scranton, PA, p. A554
Vice President Medical Affairs, John Heinz Institute of Rehabilitation Medicine, Wilkes–Barre, PA, p. A558

BATA, Katie
Vice President Human Resources, Advocate Illinois Masonic Medical Center, Chicago, IL, p. A183
Vice President Human Resources, Advocate Lutheran General Hospital, Park Ridge, IL, p. A200

BATAL, Lucille M., Administrator, Baldpate Hospital, Haverhill, MA, p. A310

BATCHELOR, Dale, M.D. Chief Medical Officer, Saint Thomas West Hospital, Nashville, TN, p. A591

BATCHELOR, Daniela, Director Human Resources, Springhill Memorial Hospital, Mobile, AL, p. A22

BATCHLOR, Elaine, M.P.H., Chief Executive Officer, Martin Luther King, Jr. Community Hospital, Los Angeles, CA, p. A72

BATEMAN, Bryan S., Chief Executive Officer, Lake Area Medical Center, Lake Charles, LA, p. A281

BATEMAN, Jana, R.N. Chief Nursing Officer, East Texas Medical Center Jacksonville, Jacksonville, TX, p. A629

BATEMAN, Kenneth, CPA, Chief Executive Officer, Southeast Hospital, Cape Girardeau, MO, p. A369

BATEMAN, Kenneth, CPA, Chief Executive Officer, SoutheastHEALTH, Cape Girardeau, MO, p. B125

BATEMAN, Mark T., Interim Chief Operating Officer, Saint Agnes Medical Center, Fresno, CA, p. A64

BATEMAN, Steven B., Chief Executive Officer, St. Mark's Hospital, Salt Lake City, UT, p. A663

BATES, Beth, Chief Nursing Officer, Shoshone Medical Center, Kellogg, ID, p. A176

BATES, Christine, Chief Nursing Officer, Shodair Children's Hospital, Helena, MT, p. A388

BATES, Don, Chief Executive Officer, Golden Plains Community Hospital, Borger, TX, p. A603

BATES, Earl, Director Information Technology, Western Mental Health Institute, Bolivar, TN, p. A579

BATES, Joe, M.D. Clinical Director, Rusk State Hospital, Rusk, TX, p. A644

BATES, Leslie, Manager Human Resources, Alta View Hospital, Sandy, UT, p. A664

BATES, Margaret, Chief of Staff, Good Samaritan Hospital, Los Angeles, CA, p. A71

BATES, Ondrea, Senior Vice President, Operations and Continuum of Care, Henry Ford Allegiance Health, Jackson, MI, p. A327

BATES, Richard, Vice President of Medical Affairs, MidMichigan Medical Center – Alpena, Alpena, MI, p. A318

BATES, Robert A., Executive Director Finance and Chief Financial Officer, St. Vincent Carmel Hospital, Carmel, IN, p. A208

BATES, Victoria A., Director Human Resources, Memorial Hospital of Salem County, Salem, NJ, p. A423

BATH, Harneet, M.D. Vice President, Chief Medicine Officer, OSF Saint Anthony Medical Center, Rockford, IL, p. A202

BATISTE, Michele, Director Human Resources, Preston Memorial Hospital, Kingwood, WV, p. A697

BATORY, Robert J., Vice President Human Resources, WellSpan York Hospital, York, PA, p. A559

BATRASH, Ahmad, Chief of Staff, Kansas City Veterans Affairs Medical Center, Kansas City, MO, p. A373

BATSHAW, Mark L., M.D. Physician–in–Chief, Executive Vice President and Chief Academic Officer, Children's National Health System, Washington, DC, p. A121

BATTEY, Patrick M., M.D., Chief Executive Officer, Piedmont Hospital, Atlanta, GA, p. A153

BATTISTA, Edward
Vice President Human Resources, California Pacific Medical Center, San Francisco, CA, p. A90
Vice President Human Resources, Good Samaritan Hospital, San Jose, CA, p. A91
Vice President Human Resources, St. Luke's Hospital, San Francisco, CA, p. A90

BATTLE, Joe, Director, James A. Haley Veterans' Hospital–Tampa, Tampa, FL, p. A147

BATTLES, Lindsay, Director Human Resources, HEALTHSOUTH Rehabilitation Hospital – Dallas, Dallas, TX, p. A610

BATTS, Kayla, Manager Human Resources, Baptist Health La Grange, La Grange, KY, p. A262

BATTY, Jill I., Chief Financial Officer, Cambridge Health Alliance, Cambridge, MA, p. A308

BATTY, Mark, Chief Executive Officer, Rochelle Community Hospital, Rochelle, IL, p. A201

BATULIS, Scott, President and Chief Executive Officer, Greater Hudson Valley Health System, Middletown, NY, p. B59

BATULIS, Scott, President and Chief Executive Officer, Orange Regional Medical Center, Middletown, NY, p. A442

BATY, Krista, R.N. Chief Nursing Officer, Cedar Park Regional Medical Center, Cedar Park, TX, p. A605

BATZEL, Linnane, M.D. Senior Vice President Quality and Medical Affairs and Chief Medical Officer, UPMC Altoona, Altoona, PA, p. A532

BAUER, Brian, Chief Executive Officer, Lutheran Hospital of Indiana, Fort Wayne, IN, p. A210

BAUER, John, Chief Operating Officer, PAM Specialty Hospital of Covington, Covington, LA, p. A275

BAUER, Jonathan, Director Information Systems, Somerset Hospital, Somerset, PA, p. A555

BAUER Jr., K. Robert, Interim Chief Executive Officer, Northside Medical Center, Youngstown, OH, p. A506

BAUER, Kyle, Chief Financial Officer, Cuyuna Regional Medical Center, Crosby, MN, p. A341

BAUER, Robert
Vice President Human Resources, Midwest Orthopedic Specialty Hospital, Franklin, WI, p. A705
Vice President Human Resources, Wheaton Franciscan Healthcare – Franklin, Franklin, WI, p. A706
Vice President Human Resources, Wheaton Franciscan Healthcare – St. Francis, Milwaukee, WI, p. A712

BAUER, Roberta, M.D. Acting Chair Medical Staff, Cleveland Clinic Children's Hospital for Rehabilitation, Cleveland, OH, p. A489

BAUER, Sandra A., Director Human Resources, Jefferson Community Health Center, Fairbury, NE, p. A395

BAUER, Shar, Executive Secretary, Wishek Community Hospital and Clinics, Wishek, ND, p. A482

BAUER, Tracy, Chief Executive Officer, Midwest Medical Center, Galena, IL, p. A190

BAUER, William, Vice President Finance and Chief Financial Officer, Lehigh Valley Hospital – Hazleton, Hazleton, PA, p. A540

BAUER, William, M.D. Medical Director, Montevista Hospital, Las Vegas, NV, p. A406

BAUGHMAN, Sharon, R.N
Vice President Patient Services and Chief Nursing Officer, Wheaton Franciscan Healthcare – Elmbrook Memorial, Brookfield, WI, p. A703
Senior Vice President Patient Services and Chief Nursing Officer, Wheaton Franciscan Healthcare – St. Joseph's, Milwaukee, WI, p. A712

BAUM, David, M.D. Senior Vice President Medical Services, F. F. Thompson Hospital, Canandaigua, NY, p. A436

BAUM, Judy, Chief Executive Officer, Mountain Valley Regional Rehabilitation Hospital, Prescott Valley, AZ, p. A38

BAUMAN, Chris, Director of Nursing, Ballard Rehabilitation Hospital, San Bernardino, CA, p. A88

BAUMAN, Jonathan, M.D. Chief Medical Officer, Four Winds Hospital, Katonah, NY, p. A441

BAUMBERGER, David, M.D. Chief Medical Officer, Decatur Memorial Hospital, Decatur, IL, p. A188

BAUMERT, Steven P., President and Chief Executive Officer, Methodist Jennie Edmundson Hospital, Council Bluffs, IA, p. A228

BAUMGARDNER, Brian, Chief Executive Officer, West Florida Hospital, Pensacola, FL, p. A142

BAUMGARDNER, Charles J., President and Chief Executive Officer, Psychiatric Institute of Washington, Washington, DC, p. A122

BAUMGARDNER, David, Director Information Management, Union Hospital, Dover, OH, p. A493

BAUMGARTNER, Jennifer, Chief Information Officer, Perkins County Health Services, Grant, NE, p. A396

BAUMGARTNER, Michael A., President, SSM Health St. Francis Hospital – Maryville, Maryville, MO, p. A376

BAUNCHALK, James M., Deputy Chief Clinical Services, Dwight David Eisenhower Army Medical Center, Fort Gordon, GA, p. A160

BAUR, Heidi, R.N. Chief Nursing Officer, St. Christopher's Hospital for Children, Philadelphia, PA, p. A549

BAUSCHKA, Martha F., R.N. Vice President and Chief Nursing Officer, Southwest General Health Center, Middleburg Heights, OH, p. A499

BAUTE, Corey
　Vice President Human Resources, Franciscan St. Francis Health – Indianapolis, Indianapolis, IN, p. A214
　Vice President of Human Resource, Franciscan St. Francis Health–Carmel, Carmel, IN, p. A208

BAVA, Michele, Director Human Resources, Doctors Medical Center of Modesto, Modesto, CA, p. A77

BAVERSO, Lou, Vice President Operations, Magee–Womens Hospital of UPMC, Pittsburgh, PA, p. A551

BAW, Joseph, Director Human Resources, Riveredge Hospital, Forest Park, IL, p. A190

BAWA, Balraj, M.D. Assistant Director Medical Services, Central Virginia Training Center, Madison Heights, VA, p. A673

BAXA, Erin, M.D. Chief Medical Officer, Osborne County Memorial Hospital, Osborne, KS, p. A250

BAXLEY III, Edmond Russell, President and Chief Executive Officer, Beaufort Memorial Hospital, Beaufort, SC, p. A562

BAXTER, Greg, M.D. Senior Vice President Medical Affairs and Chief Medical Officer, Elliot Hospital, Manchester, NH, p. A412

BAXTER, Joshua, Director, Information Systems, Powell Valley Healthcare, Powell, WY, p. A723

BAXTER, Michael T., Chief Executive Officer, Parkview Medical Center, Pueblo, CO, p. A110

BAXTER, Robert O., Regional CEO, Lima, St. Rita's Medical Center, Lima, OH, p. A497

BAYARDO, Fernando, M.D. Chief Medical Officer, Presbyterian Espanola Hospital, Espanola, NM, p. A429

BAYER, Brian, Information Technology Site Leader, Kalamazoo Psychiatric Hospital, Kalamazoo, MI, p. A328

BAYLESS, Victoria, President and Chief Executive Officer, Anne Arundel Medical Center, Annapolis, MD, p. A296

BAYOUMY, Sam, Chief Executive Officer, Cleveland Clinic Rehabilitation Hospital, Avon, OH, p. A484

BAYTOS, David G., Chief Executive Officer, Methodist Olive Branch Hospital, Olive Branch, MS, p. A363

BAYUS, Robin, Chief Financial Officer, Rancho Los Amigos National Rehabilitation Center, Downey, CA, p. A61

BAZELEY, Stephen, M.D. Vice President Medical Affairs, ProMedica St. Luke's Hospital, Maumee, OH, p. A498

BAZEMORE, Webster Carl, M.D. Interim Chief of Staff, Charles George Veterans Affairs Medical Center, Asheville, NC, p. A460

BEA, Javon, President and Chief Executive Officer, MercyHealth Rockton Avenue Hospital, Rockford, IL, p. A192

BEA, Javon R., Chief Executive Officer, Mercy Harvard Hospital, Harvard, IL, p. A192

BEA, Javon R., President and Chief Executive Officer, Mercy Health System, Janesville, WI, p. B90

BEA, Javon R., President and Chief Executive Officer, Mercy Hospital and Trauma Center, Janesville, WI, p. A707

BEACH, Karrie, Vice President Finance, Community Memorial Hospital, Syracuse, NE, p. A402

BEACH, Sarah, Director of Nursing, Jerold Phelps Community Hospital, Garberville, CA, p. A64

BEACHMAN, Michelle, Chief Financial Officer, Twin Rivers Regional Medical Center, Kennett, MO, p. A374

BEADLE, Walter, Chief Information Officer, Physicians' Specialty Hospital, Fayetteville, AR, p. A45

BEADMAN, Cindi, Director Medical Records, Harper Hospital District Five, Harper, KS, p. A244

BEAL, Christopher, M.D. Chief of Staff, Sparrow Clinton Hospital, Saint Johns, MI, p. A333

BEAL, Dwight, Chief Fiscal Services, Jack C. Montgomery Veterans Affairs Medical Center, Muskogee, OK, p. A515

BEAL, Walter Edwin, Chief Executive Officer, Central Regional Hospital, Butner, NC, p. A461

BEALES, Julie, M.D. Chief of Staff, Hunter Holmes McGuire Veterans Affairs Medical Center–Richmond, Richmond, VA, p. A678

BEAM, William, M.D. Chief of Staff, Cornerstone Hospital of Huntington, Huntington, WV, p. A696

BEAMAN Jr.., Charles D., Chief Executive Officer, Palmetto Health, Columbia, SC, p. B102

BEAMAN, Frank, Chief Executive Officer, Faith Community Hospital, Jacksboro, TX, p. A629

BEAN, Howard, M.D. Chief Medical Officer, Mary Black Health System–Spartanburg, Spartanburg, SC, p. A569

BEAN, Roberta, R.N. Associate Chief Nursing Officer, Banner Fort Collins Medical Center, Fort Collins, CO, p. A105

BEAN, Todd, Chief Medical Officer, Cass County Memorial Hospital, Atlantic, IA, p. A225

BEANE, Jeff, Director Human Resources, Roane General Hospital, Spencer, WV, p. A700

BEAR, John, Hospital Administrator Officer and Supervisor Human Resources, Lawton Indian Hospital, Lawton, OK, p. A513

BEARD, Angie, Chief Nursing Officer, Northcrest Medical Center, Springfield, TN, p. A593

BEARD, Bert, Chief Executive Officer, Maria Parham Medical Center, Henderson, NC, p. A466

BEARD, Bradley, Regional President, Fairview Southdale Hospital, Edina, MN, p. A342

BEARD, Edward L., R.N. Chief Operating Officer and Chief Nursing Officer, Catawba Valley Medical Center, Hickory, NC, p. A467

BEARD, Gerald C., Chief Operating Officer, Healthmark Regional Medical Center, DeFuniak Springs, FL, p. A127

BEARD, Joan, Chief Nursing Officer, Northwest Florida Community Hospital, Chipley, FL, p. A125

BEARD, Rhonda
　Director Human Resources, Palestine Regional Medical Center, Palestine, TX, p. A640
　Director Human Resources, Palestine Regional Medical Center–East, Palestine, TX, p. A640

BEARD, Robert, Chief Clinical Officer, Vibra Hospital of Northwestern Indiana, Crown Point, IN, p. A209

BEARD, Tim, Chief Executive Officer, Cimarron Memorial Hospital, Boise City, OK, p. A509

BEARDEN, Amy, R.N. Vice President Patient Care Services and Chief Nursing Officer, St. Luke's Magic Valley Medical Center, Twin Falls, ID, p. A179

BEASLEY, Carla, Director of Nursing, Mitchell County Hospital, Camilla, GA, p. A155

BEASLEY, Jared, R.N. Vice President Patient Care, Parkview LaGrange Hospital, LaGrange, IN, p. A216

BEASLEY, Lynn W., FACHE, Interim Chief Executive Officer, Fort Madison Community Hospital, Fort Madison, IA, p. A231

BEASLEY, Ruth, Director Human Resources, Vanderbilt Stallworth Rehabilitation Hospital, Nashville, TN, p. A591

BEASLEY, Tareka, Director Human Resources, RiverWoods Behavioral Health System, Riverdale, GA, p. A164

BEATTIE, Kathryn, M.D. Senior Vice President and Chief Medical Officer, UW Medicine/Valley Medical Center, Renton, WA, p. A688

BEATTIE, Mac, Computer Network Specialist, Deer's Head Hospital Center, Salisbury, MD, p. A303

BEATTY, Alan L., Vice President Human Resources, Shore Medical Center, Somers Point, NJ, p. A423

BEATTY, Ann, Director Human Resources, Cleveland Clinic Fairview Hospital, Cleveland, OH, p. A489

BEATTY, Jim, Chief Operating Officer, Overland Park Regional Medical Center, Overland Park, KS, p. A251

BEATTY, John, Vice President Human Resources, Barnes–Jewish Hospital, Saint Louis, MO, p. A379

BEATTY, Robert, Chief Operating Officer, Highland Ridge Hospital, Midvale, UT, p. A660

BEATTY, Talia, Director Human Resources, Sunbury Community Hospital and Outpatient Center, Sunbury, PA, p. A555

BEATY, Holly, Chief Financial Officer, South Central Kansas Medical Center, Arkansas City, KS, p. A240

BEAUBIEN, Troy, Director Information Services, Manatee Memorial Hospital, Bradenton, FL, p. A124

BEAUCHAMP, Bill, Chief Financial Officer, St. Luke's Sugar Land Hospital, Sugar Land, TX, p. A650

BEAUCHANE, Nichole, Director Information Technology, RiverView Health, Crookston, MN, p. A341

BEAUDOIN, Dale, Vice President Human Resources, Lewis–Gale Medical Center, Salem, VA, p. A678

BEAULAC, Gary, Chief Operating Officer, Henry Ford Macomb Hospitals, Clinton Township, MI, p. A320

BEAULIEU, Jennifer, Director of Nursing, Intermountain Hospital, Boise, ID, p. A174

BEAULIEU, Lynn, R.N. Chief Nursing Officer, HEALTHSOUTH Walton Rehabilitation Hospital, Augusta, GA, p. A153

BEAULIEU, Michael Gregory, M.D. Chief Medical Officer, Helen Newberry Joy Hospital, Newberry, MI, p. A331

BEAUPRE, Paul, M.D., Chief Executive Officer, Good Samaritan Hospital, San Jose, CA, p. A91

BEAUREGARD, Paige, Chief Executive Officer, Regency Hospital of Greenville, Greenville, SC, p. A566

BEAUVAIS, Richard E., Ph.D., Chief Executive Officer, Wellspring Foundation, Bethlehem, CT, p. A113

BEAVEN, Stacey, R.N. Chief Nursing Officer, Saint Thomas Rutherford Hospital, Murfreesboro, TN, p. A590

BEAVER, Patrick, Chief Nursing Officer, North Shore Medical Center, Miami, FL, p. A137

BEAVER, Randy, Chief Information Officer, Palo Alto County Health System, Emmetsburg, IA, p. A230

BEAVER, Rhonda, Chief Operating Officer, Creek Nation Community Hospital, Okemah, OK, p. A515

BEAZLEY, Gary, Coordinator Information Systems, Baylor Scott & White Medical Center at Waxahachie, Waxahachie, TX, p. A656

BEBOW, Gary, FACHE, Administrator and Chief Executive Officer, White River Health System, Batesville, AR, p. B155

BEBOW, Gary, FACHE, Administrator and Chief Executive Officer, White River Medical Center, Batesville, AR, p. A43

BECHAMPS, Gerald, M.D
　Vice President of Medical Affairs, Hampshire Memorial Hospital, Romney, WV, p. A700
　Vice President Medical Affairs, War Memorial Hospital, Berkeley Springs, WV, p. A694

BECHTEL, Kathleen, MSN Vice President Patient Care Services and Chief Nursing Officer, Froedtert Memorial Lutheran Hospital, Milwaukee, WI, p. A711

BECK, Allan, Chief Executive Officer, Baylor Orthopedic and Spine Hospital at Arlington, Arlington, TX, p. A597

BECK, Ann
　Vice President and Chief Financial Officer, Carson Tahoe Continuing Care Hospital, Carson City, NV, p. A404
　Vice President Finance, Carson Tahoe Health, Carson City, NV, p. A404

BECK, David, Chief Operating Officer, Lane Regional Medical Center, Zachary, LA, p. A290

BECK, Debbie, Manager Human Resource and Payroll, Ochiltree General Hospital, Perryton, TX, p. A641

BECK, Gary E., Administrator, Sevier Valley Medical Center, Richfield, UT, p. A662

BECK, Howard, M.D. Chief of Staff, Grace Medical Center, Lubbock, TX, p. A634

BECK, J. Christopher, D.O. President Medical Staff, Aspen Valley Hospital District, Aspen, CO, p. A101

BECK, Paul, Acting Chief Medical Officer, St. Joseph Hospital, Orange, CA, p. A81

BECK, Rebecca
　President, Wellmont Hancock County Hospital, Sneedville, TN, p. A593
　President, Wellmont Hawkins County Memorial Hospital, Rogersville, TN, p. A592

BECK, Steve, MS Director Human Resources, Kearney Regional Medical Center, Kearney, NE, p. A397

BECK,PHR,MHROD, Brian, Vice President Human Resources, Oak Valley Hospital District, Oakdale, CA, p. A80

BECKER, Bernard H., Vice President and Chief Human Resources Officer, Stormont Vail Health, Topeka, KS, p. A254

BECKER, Cindy, Vice President and Chief Operating Officer, Highland Hospital, Rochester, NY, p. A454

BECKER, Eric
　Chief Operating Officer, Research Medical Center, Kansas City, MO, p. A373
　Chief Executive Officer, Texas Orthopedic Hospital, Houston, TX, p. A627

BECKER, Frank
　Chief Financial Officer, Lourdes Counseling Center, Richland, WA, p. A689
　Chief Financial Officer, Lourdes Medical Center, Pasco, WA, p. A687

BECKER, Kathleen R., JD, President, SSM Health Saint Louis University Hospital, Saint Louis, MO, p. A381

BECKER, Kathy, Ph.D. Vice President and Chief Nursing Officer, Aurora West Allis Medical Center, West Allis, WI, p. A719

BECKER, Kelly, Administrative Coordinator Human Resources, Kindred Hospital–Indianapolis North, Indianapolis, IN, p. A214

BECKER, Preston, Chief Executive Officer, Carson Valley Medical Center, Gardnerville, NV, p. A404

BECKER, Ralph W., Vice President, Chief Financial Officer, Saint Mary's Hospital, Waterbury, CT, p. A117

BECKES, Hap, Director Information Systems, Sullivan County Community Hospital, Sullivan, IN, p. A222

BECKETT, C. Donovan, Chief Medical Officer, Williamson Memorial Hospital, Williamson, WV, p. A701

BECKHAM, Steve, Director Human Resources, Magee General Hospital, Magee, MS, p. A361

BECKMAN, Beth P., R.N. Chief Nursing Officer, Baylor Regional Medical Center at Grapevine, Grapevine, TX, p. A621

BECKMANN, Gregory, Chief Executive Officer, CHI Health Plainview, Plainview, NE, p. A401

BECKMANN, Lauren A., Chief Nursing Officer, Parkland Health Center – Liberty Street, Farmington, MO, p. A371

BECKNER, Jana, Director Human Resources, LewisGale Hospital Pulaski, Pulaski, VA, p. A676

BECKSVOORT, Jennifer F., Senior Human Resource Business Partner, Spectrum Health Zeeland Community Hospital, Zeeland, MI, p. A337

BECKWITH, Jami, Director Human Resources, Choctaw Nation Health Care Center, Talihina, OK, p. A520

BEDARD, Lori, Chief Executive Officer, HEALTHSOUTH Rehabilitation Hospital of Spring Hill, Brooksville, FL, p. A125

BEDDOE, Chris, Chief Executive Officer, Sabine Medical Center, Many, LA, p. A282

BEDELL, Mikael, M.D. Medical Director, Cascade Medical Center, Cascade, ID, p. A175

BEDFORD, Tim, Chief Executive Officer, Emerald Coast Behavioral Hospital, Panama City, FL, p. A141

BEDGER, Kathy, Chief Nursing Officer, Penn Highlands Clearfield, Clearfield, PA, p. A535

BEDI, Andrew, Chief Operating Officer, TriStar Greenview Regional Hospital, Bowling Green, KY, p. A258

BEDICK, Jennifer L., Deputy Commander Nursing, Tripler Army Medical Center, Honolulu, HI, p. A171

BEDINGFIELD, Lance, Director Information Services, Dixie Regional Medical Center, Saint George, UT, p. A663

BEDSOLE, Jessica, Director, Human Resources, WellStar Paulding Hospital, Hiram, GA, p. A161

BEDZYK, J. Paul, Deputy Director Administration, Elmira Psychiatric Center, Elmira, NY, p. A438

BEEBE, Chris T., Director Human Resources, Raleigh General Hospital, Beckley, WV, p. A694

BEEBY, Lori, Director Information Systems, Community Hospital, McCook, NE, p. A398

BEECHLER, Jane, Director Healthcare Information Systems, Wyoming County Community Hospital, Warsaw, NY, p. A458

BEECHY, Andrew, Manager Information Technology Systems, Lee's Summit Medical Center, Lee's Summit, MO, p. A375

BEED, Donna E., Chief Information Management Division, Tripler Army Medical Center, Honolulu, HI, p. A171

BEEDLE, Chester
Chief Financial Officer, Kern Valley Healthcare District, Lake Isabella, CA, p. A68
Interim Chief Financial Officer, Tehachapi Valley Healthcare District, Tehachapi, CA, p. A95

BEEDY, Scott, Chief Financial Officer, Hansford Hospital, Spearman, TX, p. A649

BEEG, Gregg, Chief Financial Officer, McLaren Central Michigan, Mount Pleasant, MI, p. A330

BEEG, Gregg R., FACHE Chief Financial Officer, Oaklawn Hospital, Marshall, MI, p. A330

BEEHLER, Darryl, D.O. Chief of Staff, CHI St. Joseph's Health, Park Rapids, MN, p. A348

BEEHLER, Robert J., Interim President and Chief Executive Officer, Walla Walla General Hospital, Walla Walla, WA, p. A693

BEEHN, Holly, Director Human Resources, Southwest Health, Platteville, WI, p. A714

BEELER, Janelle E., Human Resource Manager, Baraga County Memorial Hospital, L'Anse, MI, p. A328

BEER, Ronald R., FACHE, Vice President, Clinical Operations, Geisinger Wyoming Valley Medical Center, Wilkes Barre, PA, p. A557

BEESON, John C., M.D. Chief Medical Officer, CHRISTUS St. Vincent Regional Medical Center, Santa Fe, NM, p. A431

BEGALSKE, Kathy, Chief Nursing Officer, Palmer Lutheran Health Center, West Union, IA, p. A239

BEGAY, Trudy, Human Resources Specialist, Hopi Health Care Center, Kearns Canyon, AZ, p. A33

BEGAYE, Lorraine, Supervisory Human Resource Specialist, Chinle Comprehensive Health Care Facility, Chinle, AZ, p. A31

BEGGANE, Thomas, Manager Human Resources, LAC–Olive View–UCLA Medical Center,, CA, p. A72

BEGLEY, Robyn, R.N. Chief Nursing Officer, AtlantiCare Regional Medical Center, Atlantic City, NJ, p. A414

BEHAN, Lawrence, Vice President Administration and Finance, Chief Financial Officer, Walden Psychiatric Care, Waltham, MA, p. A315

BEHAR, Robert, M.D., Chief Executive Officer, North Cypress Medical Center, Cypress, TX, p. A609

BEHM, Anthony, D.O. Chief of Staff, Erie Veterans Affairs Medical Center, Erie, PA, p. A538

BEHNE, Carl P., Administrator and Chief Executive Officer, Greene County Medical Center, Jefferson, IA, p. A233

BEHNER, Bruce M., Chief Operating Officer, Knox Community Hospital, Mount Vernon, OH, p. A499

BEHNKEN, Nick, Supervisor Information Technology, Red Bud Regional Hospital, Red Bud, IL, p. A201

BEHR, Richard A., Deputy Commander for Health Services, Reynolds Army Community Hospital, Fort Sill, OK, p. A512

BEHRENDT, Darcy, R.N. Vice President, Patient Care Services, CHI Health Missouri Valley, Missouri Valley, IA, p. A234

BEHRENDTSEN, Ole, M.D. Medical Director, Santa Barbara County Psychiatric Health Facility, Santa Barbara, CA, p. A93

BEHRENS, Colleen, Director Information Technology, Community Memorial Healthcare, Marysville, KS, p. A249

BEHRENS, Karen, Director Technology Services, Perry Memorial Hospital, Princeton, IL, p. A201

BEHRENS, Sharon, R.N. Chief Clinical Officer, Rehabilitation Hospital of Wisconsin, Waukesha, WI, p. A718

BEIDELSCHIES, Sandra, MSN Vice President Patient Services, Wood County Hospital, Bowling Green, OH, p. A485

BEIERMAN, Jennifer, Director Human Resources, Boone County Health Center, Albion, NE, p. A393

BEIFUS, Donna, Chief Executive Officer, HEALTHSOUTH Rehabilitation Hospital of Southern Arizona, Tucson, AZ, p. A40

BEIGHLE, John, Flight Chief Medical Information Systems, Wright Patterson Medical Center, Wright–Patterson AFB, OH, p. A506

BEIKMAN, Sara, Director of Nursing, Clay County Medical Center, Clay Center, KS, p. A241

BEILER, Jeffrey, Associate Director, Philadelphia Veterans Affairs Medical Center, Philadelphia, PA, p. A549

BEINDIT, Dawn, Director Work Life Services, St. John River District Hospital, East China, MI, p. A323

BEISSEL, Debbie, Chief Executive Officer, Surgical Institute of Reading, Wyomissing, PA, p. A558

BEISWENGER, Joel, Chief Executive Officer, Tri–County Hospital, Wadena, MN, p. A353

BEITCHER, Bob, Chief Executive Officer, Motion Picture and Television Fund Hospital and Residential Services,, CA, p. A73

BEITER, Amy, M.D., President and Chief Executive Officer, Carondelet St. Mary's Hospital, Tucson, AZ, p. A40

BEITING, Mark, Vice President Human Resources, Alta Bates Summit Medical Center – Summit Campus, Oakland, CA, p. A80

BEITZEL, Mark, Director Information Systems, Advocate Lutheran General Hospital, Park Ridge, IL, p. A200

BEJNAR, Darla, M.D. Chief Medical Officer, Socorro General Hospital, Socorro, NM, p. A432

BELAIR, Norman, Senior Vice President and Chief Financial Officer, Southern Maine Health Care – Biddeford Medical Center, Biddeford, ME, p. A292

BELCHER, Debbie, Director Human Resource, Vibra Rehabilitation Hospital Lake Travis, Lakeway, TX, p. A631

BELCHER, Laura, Interim Administrator, The Medical Center Albany, Albany, KY, p. A257

BELDECOS, Athena, M.D. Medical Director, Vibra Hospital of Charleston, Mt. Pleasant, SC, p. A568

BELENY, Charles, D.O. Chief of Staff, Jonathan M. Wainwright Memorial Veterans Affairs Medical Center, Walla Walla, WA, p. A692

BELGARDE, Donna, Human Resources Specialist, Indian Health Service – Quentin N. Burdick Memorial Health Care Facility, Belcourt, ND, p. A477

BELHASEN, F. K., M.D. Medical Director, Paul B. Hall Regional Medical Center, Paintsville, KY, p. A268

BELJIN, Dawn, R.N. Chief Nursing Officer, Dallas Medical Center, Dallas, TX, p. A609

BELKOSKI, Dave, Chief Financial Officer, University Hospital McDuffie, Thomson, GA, p. A167

BELKOSKI, David, Senior Vice President and Chief Financial Officer, University Hospital, Augusta, GA, p. A154

BELL, Brian, Associate Administrator and Chief Operating Officer, National Park Medical Center, Hot Springs, AR, p. A47

BELL, Cindy, Director Finance, Willow Crest Hospital, Miami, OK, p. A514

BELL, Gordon, M.D. Chief of Staff, Frances Mahon Deaconess Hospital, Glasgow, MT, p. A387

BELL, Heath, Vice President, Chief Information Officer, Northwestern Medicine Valley West Hospital, Sandwich, IL, p. A202

BELL, Hollis, M.D. Medical Director, Mercy Rehabilitation Hospital Springfield, Springfield, MO, p. A382

BELL, Julie, Interim Chief Executive Officer and Chief Nursing Officer, Covenant Specialty Hospital, Lubbock, TX, p. A634

BELL, Kae, Chief Financial Officer, Brentwood Hospital, Shreveport, LA, p. A287

BELL, Lorraine, Vice President Operations Human Resources, Scott & White Memorial Hospital, Temple, TX, p. A652

BELL, Madeline, President and Chief Executive Officer, Children's Hospital of Philadelphia, Philadelphia, PA, p. A547

BELL, Michael, Chief Operating Officer, Sierra Vista Regional Medical Center, San Luis Obispo, CA, p. A92

BELL, Pam, Vice President Patient Care Services and Chief Nursing Officer, Presence Resurrection Medical Center, Chicago, IL, p. A185

BELL, Randall C., M.D. Medical Director, LifeCare Hospitals of San Antonio, San Antonio, TX, p. A646

BELL, Roderick, Chief Financial Officer, College Hospital Cerritos, Cerritos, CA, p. A58

BELL, Rodric, M.D. Medical Director, HEALTHSOUTH Tustin Rehabilitation Hospital, Tustin, CA, p. A97

BELL, Roseanna, Chief Nurse Executive, MultiCare Auburn Medical Center, Auburn, WA, p. A682

BELL, Jr., Sammie, Chief Financial Officer, Tallahatchie General Hospital, Charleston, MS, p. A356

BELL, Scot, Chief Medical Officer, Anderson Regional Health System, Meridian, MS, p. A362

BELL, Sonja, Coordinator Human Resources, Sedgwick County Health Center, Julesburg, CO, p. A107

BELL, Stuart, M.D. Vice President Medical Affairs, MedStar Union Memorial Hospital, Baltimore, MD, p. A297

BELL, Talana, Chief Financial Officer, Flowers Hospital, Dothan, AL, p. A19

BELL, Tammie
Director Human Resources, McKenzie Regional Hospital, McKenzie, TN, p. A588
Director Human Resources, Tennova Healthcare Volunteer Community Hospital, Martin, TN, p. A588

BELL, W. Scot, M.D. Chief Medical Officer, Rush Foundation Hospital, Meridian, MS, p. A362

BELLAMY, David, Chief Financial Officer, McLaren Northern Michigan, Petoskey, MI, p. A331

BELLAND, Patrick, President, Fairview Ridges Hospital, Burnsville, MN, p. A340

BELLEAU, Christopher, M.D. Medical Director, Sage Rehabilitation Hospital, Baton Rouge, LA, p. A273

BELLEAU, Donella, Director Human Resources, Graham County Hospital, Hill City, KS, p. A244

BELLUCCI, Alessandro, M.D., Executive Director, North Shore University Hospital, Manhasset, NY, p. A442

BELLUCY, Regina, Vice President Human Resources, Bethesda Hospital East, Boynton Beach, FL, p. A124

BELMONT, Chris, Chief Information Officer and Vice President, University of Texas M.D. Anderson Cancer Center, Houston, TX, p. A627

BELMONT, James, Associate Director, Northern Arizona Veterans Affairs Health Care System, Prescott, AZ, p. A37

BELT, Katrina, Chief Financial Officer, Baptist Medical Center East, Montgomery, AL, p. A23

BELTRAN, Grace, Director Human Resources, Foundation Surgical Hospital of El Paso, El Paso, TX, p. A615

BELTZ, John, Chief Financial Officer, Hendry Regional Medical Center, Clewiston, FL, p. A126

BELZER, Leslie, Director Human Resources, Howard County Medical Center, Saint Paul, NE, p. A402

BEMENT, Douglas J., Chief Financial Officer, Kosciusko Community Hospital, Warsaw, IN, p. A223

BEN, Sabrina, Director Human Resources, North Star Behavioral Health System, Anchorage, AK, p. A28

BENAVIDES, Christina, Director Employee Services, Otto Kaiser Memorial Hospital, Kenedy, TX, p. A630

BENCITO ACA–AC, Norie Lee Reyes, R.N. Director of Nursing, Loma Linda University Behavioral Medicine Center, Redlands, CA, p. A85

BENCOMO, Dionisio, Chief Executive Officer, Select Specialty Hospital–Miami, Miami, FL, p. A137

BENDER, Brad, M.D. Chief of Staff, North Florida/South Georgia Veteran's Health System, Gainesville, FL, p. A129

BENDER, Daniel, Chief Operating Officer, South Bay Hospital, Sun City Center, FL, p. A146

BENDER, David B., M.D. Chief Medical Staff, Grafton City Hospital, Grafton, WV, p. A696

BENDER, Janette, Chief Financial Officer, Arkansas Valley Regional Medical Center, La Junta, CO, p. A107

BENDER, Robert, Chief Financial Officer, Banner Casa Grande Medical Center, Casa Grande, AZ, p. A31

BENDER, Steve, Chief Financial Officer, Wuesthoff Medical Center – Melbourne, Melbourne, FL, p. A136

BENDINELLI, Emily, Director of Nurses, Ashley County Medical Center, Crossett, AR, p. A44

BENDYNA, Peter J., Director Human Resources, Wyoming County Community Hospital, Warsaw, NY, p. A458

BENEDICT, Brian, Director of Information Technology, Murray–Calloway County Hospital, Murray, KY, p. A267

BENEDICT, Eva, R.N., President and Chief Executive Officer, Jones Memorial Hospital, Wellsville, NY, p. A458

BENEDICT, Joy M., Director Human Resources, Baptist Health Richmond, Richmond, KY, p. A268

BENEFIELD, Marlene, Director Human Resources, Cherokee Medical Center, Centre, AL, p. A18

BENEPAL, Jaspreet, Chief Nursing Officer, Contra Costa Regional Medical Center, Martinez, CA, p. A76

BENETTI–LOYOLA, Pedro L., Administrator, Hospital San Cristobal, Coto Laurel, PR, p. A727

BENFIELD, Angie, Human Resources Generalist, Union Medical Center, Union, SC, p. A570

BENFIELD, Ronald K.
Chief Financial Officer, PeaceHealth Southwest Medical Center, Vancouver, WA, p. A692
Chief Financial Officer, PeaceHealth St. John Medical Center, Longview, WA, p. A686

BENGSTON, Jennifer, M.D. Chief Medical Officer, Valley County Health System, Ord, NE, p. A401

BENGTSON, Paul R., Chief Executive Officer, Northeastern Vermont Regional Hospital, Saint Johnsbury, VT, p. A666

BENGYAK, Daniel, Vice President, Human Resources, St. Luke's Cornwall Hospital, Newburgh, NY, p. A450

BENHAM, D'Linda, Director of Nursing, Fisher County Hospital District, Rotan, TX, p. A644

BENINK, Eric, M.D. Chief Medical Officer, Northwest Community Hospital, Arlington Heights, IL, p. A180

BENITEZ, Pedro, M.D. Medical Director, Hospital De Damas, Ponce, PR, p. A728

BENJAMIN, Christian, MC, Commander, Mike O'Callaghan Federal Hospital, Nellis AFB, NV, p. A407

BENJAMIN, Kathleen, R.N. Chief Nursing Officer, MacNeal Hospital, Berwyn, IL, p. A181

BENNER, Brenda, Director Human Resources, HEALTHSOUTH Rehabilitation Hospital of Sarasota, Sarasota, FL, p. A145

BENNETT, Anthony, M.D. Chief Clinical Affairs, Baptist Health Medical Center–Little Rock, Little Rock, AR, p. A48

BENNETT, Bart, Chief Financial Officer, Springbrook Behavioral Health System, Travelers Rest, SC, p. A570

BENNETT, Charlotte, Vice President Human Resources, West Virginia University Hospitals, Morgantown, WV, p. A698

BENNETT, Courtney, Human Resource Manager, Alleghany Memorial Hospital, Sparta, NC, p. A474

BENNETT, Dan, Director Operations, Waldo County General Hospital, Belfast, ME, p. A292

BENNETT, Darnell, Director Finance, Horizon Specialty Hospital, Las Vegas, NV, p. A406

BENNETT, E. Kyle, President and Chief Executive Officer, Memorial Hospital and Health Care Center, Jasper, IN, p. A215

BENNETT, Edwin, Controller, Turning Point Hospital, Moultrie, GA, p. A164

BENNETT, Fay, Vice President Employee Services, Guadalupe Regional Medical Center, Seguin, TX, p. A648

BENNETT, Gary, M.D. Chief of Medical Staff, Chapman Global Medical Center, Orange, CA, p. A80

BENNETT, Kay
Vice President Human Resources, Baptist Medical Center East, Montgomery, AL, p. A23
System Director Human Resources, Baptist Medical Center South, Montgomery, AL, p. A23

BENNETT, Kimberly, R.N., Interim Chief Executive Officer and Director of Nursing, CHRISTUS Dubuis Hospital of Alexandria, Alexandria, LA, p. A271

BENNETT, Laurie, Director Human Resources, Sarasota Memorial Health Care System, Sarasota, FL, p. A145

BENNETT, Lee W.
Interim Chief Financial Officer, Cordova Community Medical Center, Cordova, AK, p. A28
Chief Financial Officer, Sitka Community Hospital, Sitka, AK, p. A30

BENNETT, Leo, M.D. Deputy Commander Clinical Services, Bassett Army Community Hospital, Fort Wainwright, AK, p. A29

BENNETT, Lisa, Chief Financial Officer, Waverly Health Center, Waverly, IA, p. A239

BENNETT, Mary Ann, Chief Nursing Officer, Glendora Community Hospital, Glendora, CA, p. A65

BENNETT, Mary Ann, R.N. Chief Operating Officer and Chief Nursing Officer, Springbrook Behavioral Health System, Travelers Rest, SC, p. A570

BENNETT, Melissa, Chief Nursing Officer, Trumbull Memorial Hospital, Warren, OH, p. A505

BENNETT, Nathan, M.D. Chief Medical Officer, Mercy Hospital Waldron, Waldron, AR, p. A53

BENNETT, Patti, Chief Nursing Officer and Senior Vice President, Good Shepherd Medical Center, Longview, TX, p. A633

BENNETT, Randall, Assistant Administrator, Uintah Basin Medical Center, Roosevelt, UT, p. A662

BENNETT, Richard G., M.D., President, Johns Hopkins Bayview Medical Center, Baltimore, MD, p. A296

BENNETT, Richard I., Senior Vice President and Chief Financial Officer, Delaware County Memorial Hospital, Drexel Hill, PA, p. A537

BENNETT, Rick
Administrator, Baton Rouge Behavioral Hospital, Baton Rouge, LA, p. A272
Administrator, St. James Behavioral Health Hospital, Gonzales, LA, p. A277

BENNETT, Robert, M.D. Medical Director, Millwood Hospital, Arlington, TX, p. A597

BENNETT, Ron, Chief Financial Officer, Abilene Regional Medical Center, Abilene, TX, p. A595

BENNETT, Sharon, Manager Information Systems, Cobre Valley Regional Medical Center, Globe, AZ, p. A33

BENNETT, Sheila, R.N. Vice President & Chief Nursing Officer, Floyd Medical Center, Rome, GA, p. A165

BENNETT, Tony N., Chief Executive Officer, HEALTHSOUTH Emerald Coast Rehabilitation Hospital, Panama City, FL, p. A141

BENNETT, W. Bradley, President and Chief Executive Officer, Fundamental Long Term Care Holdings, LLC, Sparks Glencoe, MD, p. B57

BENNETT, Wayne, Chief Financial Officer, Franklin Memorial Hospital, Farmington, ME, p. A293

BENOIT, Paul, Associate Administrator, Central Louisiana State Hospital, Pineville, LA, p. A286

BENOIT, Rebecca, R.N. Chief Nursing Officer, Lafayette General Medical Center, Lafayette, LA, p. A280

BENSEMA, David, Chief Information Officer, Baptist Health La Grange, La Grange, KY, p. A262

BENSON, Cheryl, Chief Operating Officer, Wernersville State Hospital, Wernersville, PA, p. A557

BENSON, Chris, Chief Financial Officer, DeKalb Regional Medical Center, Fort Payne, AL, p. A20

BENSON, Eric, Vice President Human Resources & Wellness, Sarah Bush Lincoln Health Center, Mattoon, IL, p. A196

BENSON, Kathryn, Human Resources Partner, Avera St. Anthony's Hospital, O'Neill, NE, p. A399

BENSON, Kevin, Chief Financial Officer, Ortonville Area Health Services, Ortonville, MN, p. A348

BENTLEY, Scott, Chief Financial Officer, Woman's Hospital of Texas, Houston, TX, p. A628

BENTON, Dennis C., Senior Vice President and Area Manager, Kaiser Permanente Woodland Hills Medical Center,, CA, p. A72

BENTON, Edred, Chief Executive Officer and Chief Operating Officer, Cleveland Area Hospital, Cleveland, OK, p. A510

BENTON, Nancy, Assistant Director Patient Care Services, Mann–Grandstaff Veterans Affairs Medical Center, Spokane, WA, p. A691

BENTON, Tony, Chief Operating Officer, Johnson City Medical Center, Johnson City, TN, p. A585

BENTZ, Douglas E., Chief Executive Officer, Roane General Hospital, Spencer, WV, p. A700

BENVENUTTI, Cathy, Human Resource Director, Hancock Medical Center, Bay Saint Louis, MS, p. A355

BENWARE, Joel, Vice President Information Technology and Compliance, Northwestern Medical Center, Saint Albans, VT, p. A666

BENZ, Betsy, R.N. Chief Nursing Officer, Aurora Medical Center – Manitowoc County, Two Rivers, WI, p. A717

BENZ Jr., Edward J., M.D., President and Chief Executive Officer, Dana–Farber Cancer Institute, Boston, MA, p. A306

BENZ, Mark A., President and Chief Executive Officer, Carondelet St. Joseph's Hospital, Tucson, AZ, p. A40

BENZ, Robert, M.D. Chief Medical Officer, Lankenau Medical Center, Wynnewood, PA, p. A558

BENZEL, Cindy, Manager Human Resources, Sanford Vermillion Medical Center, Vermillion, SD, p. A577

BEPLER, Gerold, Ph.D., President and Chief Executive Officer, Karmanos Cancer Center, Detroit, MI, p. A322

BERARDI, Paula, Manager Human Resources, Bournewood Health Systems, Brookline, MA, p. A308

BERCHER, Richard, M.D. Chief Medical Officer, Paris Regional Medical Center, Paris, TX, p. A640

BERCI, Haya, Executive Director of Nursing, Joyce Eisenberg–Keefer Medical Center, Reseda, CA, p. A85

BERDAN, Barclay E., FACHE, Chief Executive Officer, Texas Health Resources, Arlington, TX, p. B134

BERDIEL, Luis, Chief Executive Officer, Hospital Metropolitano San German, San German, PR, p. A729

BERENS, Jeff, MS Chief Nursing Officer, Sanford Vermillion Medical Center, Vermillion, SD, p. A577

BERENTES, Amy, R.N. Vice President Patient Care Services, Mercy Medical Center–Clinton, Clinton, IA, p. A227

BERETTA, Dante, M.D. Chief of Staff, CentraCare Health–Melrose, Melrose, MN, p. A346

BERG, Gary L., D.O. Chief Medical Officer, St. John Macomb–Oakland Hospital, Warren, MI, p. A336

BERG, James, FACHE, President, Texas Health Presbyterian Hospital Dallas, Dallas, TX, p. A611

BERG, Jon, M.D. Chief of Staff, Northwood Deaconess Health Center, Northwood, ND, p. A481

BERG, Tony L., M.D. Chief of Staff, Winner Regional Healthcare Center, Winner, SD, p. A578

BERG, William, Chief Information Officer, Naval Hospital Pensacola, Pensacola, FL, p. A142

BERGE, Ron, Executive Vice President and Chief Operating Officer, National Jewish Health, Denver, CO, p. A104

BERGEAUX, Scott, M.D. Chief Medical Staff, Abrom Kaplan Memorial Hospital, Kaplan, LA, p. A279

BERGEMANN, John, Director Human Resources, Crouse Hospital, Syracuse, NY, p. A456

BERGEN, Jan L., President and Chief Executive Officer, Lancaster General Hospital, Lancaster, PA, p. A542

BERGENFELD, Joel M., Chief Hospital Executive Officer, Hemet Valley Medical Center, Hemet, CA, p. A66

BERGENFELD, Joel M., Chief Executive Officer, Physicians for Healthy Hospitals, Hemet, CA, p. B103

BERGER, George, Controller, HEALTHSOUTH Rehabilitation Hospital of Altoona, Altoona, PA, p. A532

BERGER, Kathy, R.N. Interim Director, Veterans Affairs Montana Health Care System, Fort Harrison, MT, p. A387

BERGERON, Johnny, Chief Information Officer, Bunkie General Hospital, Bunkie, LA, p. A274

BERGERON, Pierre, Director Information Services, Wellington Regional Medical Center, West Palm Beach, FL, p. A150

BERGERON, Timothy, Deputy Commander, Administration, Bassett Army Community Hospital, Fort Wainwright, AK, p. A29

BERGERSON, Melissa, R.N. Chief Nursing Officer, Black River Memorial Hospital, Black River Falls, WI, p. A703

BERGES, Iris, Chief Executive Officer, Larkin Behavioral Health Services,, FL, p. A130

BERGFORT, Joe, Chief Information Officer, UCSF Medical Center, San Francisco, CA, p. A91

BERGHERM, Bruce, Chief Executive Officer, Florida Hospital Heartland Medical Center, Sebring, FL, p. A145

BERGHOLM, Brenda, MSN Chief Nursing Officer, Caribou Memorial Hospital and Living Center, Soda Springs, ID, p. A178

BERGLING, Richard Q., Chief Executive Officer, Morton County Health System, Elkhart, KS, p. A242

BERGMAN, Angela, Director Health Information Management, Van Matre HealthSouth Rehabilitation Hospital, Rockford, IL, p. A202

BERGMAN, Chris, Chief Financial Officer, Children's Medical Center, Dayton, OH, p. A492

BERGMAN, Jim, Director Human Resources, Northeast Regional Medical Center, Kirksville, MO, p. A375

BERGMAN–EVANS, Brenda
Chief Nursing Officer, CHI Health Lakeside, Omaha, NE, p. A400
Interim Chief Nursing Officer, CHI Health Mercy Council Bluffs, Council Bluffs, IA, p. A228
Chief Nursing Officer, CHI Health Midlands, Papillion, NE, p. A401

BERGMANN, Michael, President, Aurora Medical Center Summit, Summit, WI, p. A717

BERGMANN, Peter U., President and Chief Executive Officer, Sisters of Charity Hospital of Buffalo, Buffalo, NY, p. A436

BERGQUIST, Susan, Human Resources Generalist, Kindred Hospital–La Mirada, La Mirada, CA, p. A67

BERGSENG, John H., D.O. Vice President Medical Affairs, Glencoe Regional Health Services, Glencoe, MN, p. A343

BERGSTEDT, Sharon, Director of Nursing, Alaska Psychiatric Institute, Anchorage, AK, p. A28

BERGSTROM, Jenny, Project Manager Information Technology, Cloud County Health Center, Concordia, KS, p. A242

BERKOWITZ, David J., Vice President and Chief Operating Officer, HackensackUMC Palisades, North Bergen, NJ, p. A421

BERKRAM, Treasure, Chief Financial Officer, Northern Rockies Medical Center, Cut Bank, MT, p. A386

BERLINGERI, Zaida, Administrator, Hospital San Gerardo, San Juan, PR, p. A730

BERLINGHOFF, Kathleen, Director Human Resources, Sharon Hospital, Sharon, CT, p. A116

BERLOT, Alvin, M.D. Medical Director, Bucktail Medical Center, Renovo, PA, p. A553

BERLOWITZ, Dan, M.D. Acting Chief of Staff, Bedford Veterans Affairs Medical Center, Edith Nourse Rogers Memorial Veterans Hospital, Bedford, MA, p. A305

BERLUCCHI, Scott A., FACHE, President and Chief Executive Officer, Auburn Community Hospital, Auburn, NY, p. A434

BERLYN, Maria, Assistant Vice President Nursing Services, John Heinz Institute of Rehabilitation Medicine, Wilkes-Barre, PA, p. A558

BERMAN, Alan S., M.D. Medical Director, Mountain Valley Regional Rehabilitation Hospital, Prescott Valley, AZ, p. A38

BERMAN, Manuel S., FACHE, President and Chief Executive Officer, Tuality Healthcare, Hillsboro, OR, p. A526

BERMAN, Ronald, M.D. Chief of Staff, Mad River Community Hospital, Arcata, CA, p. A55

BERMUDEZ, Ada, Director Human Resources, Hospital De La Concepcion, San German, PR, p. A729

BERMUDEZ, Armand, M.D. Medical Director, Select Specialty Hospital of Southeast Ohio, Newark, OH, p. A500

BERMUDEZ, Yuri, M.D. Chief of Staff, South Texas Health System, Edinburg, TX, p. A614

BERNAL, Hector, Chief Executive Officer, Post Acute Medical Specialty Hospital of Corpus Christi – North, Corpus Christi, TX, p. A608

BERNAL, Leroy, Chief Operating Officer, Cumberland Surgical Hospital, San Antonio, TX, p. A645

BERNAL, Maria Torres, Administrator, Hospital De Damas, Ponce, PR, p. A728

BERNAL, Omar, Controller, El Paso Children's Hospital, El Paso, TX, p. A615

BERNARD, David P., FACHE, Chief Executive Officer, Houston Methodist San Jacinto Hospital, Baytown, TX, p. A601

BERNARD, Donald P.
Chief Financial Officer, Kaiser Permanente Fontana Medical Center, Fontana, CA, p. A62
Chief Financial Officer, St. John's Pleasant Valley Hospital, Camarillo, CA, p. A57
Chief Financial Officer, St. John's Regional Medical Center, Oxnard, CA, p. A81

BERNARD, Doug, M.D. Chief Medical Officer, White River Medical Center, Batesville, AR, p. A43

BERNARD, Robert, M.D. Chief of Staff, Alexandria Veterans Affairs Health Care System, Pineville, LA, p. A286

BERNARD, Traci, R.N., President, Chief Executive Officer and Chief Operating Officer, Texas Health Harris Methodist Hospital Southlake, Southlake, TX, p. A649

BERNARDI, Barbara, R.N. Nurse Executive, Jameson Hospital, New Castle, PA, p. A546

BERNARDO, Maria, M.D. Chief of Staff, Bullock County Hospital, Union Springs, AL, p. A26

BERNATIS, Terry D., Director Human Resources, Community HealthCare System, Onaga, KS, p. A250

BERND, Jason, Vice President, Novant Health Charlotte Orthopaedic Hospital, Charlotte, NC, p. A462

BERNERT–YAP, Kellie, Director Human Resources, Vibra Specialty Hospital of Portland, Portland, OR, p. A530

BERNEY, Bernadette, Director Human Resources, Pullman Regional Hospital, Pullman, WA, p. A688

BERNHARDT–KADLEC, Peggy, Chief Human Resources Officer, SEARHC MT. Edgecumbe Hospital, Sitka, AK, p. A30

BERNICK, Michael, Executive Vice President and Chief Financial Officer, Clarity Child Guidance Center, San Antonio, TX, p. A645

BERNIER, Justin, R.N. Director of Nursing, Seaside Behavioral Center, New Orleans, LA, p. A285

BERNS, Erin, Director Human Resources, Veterans Memorial Hospital, Waukon, IA, p. A239

BERNSEN, Tina, Chief Nursing Officer, Othello Community Hospital, Othello, WA, p. A687

BERNSTEIN, Lee
Regional Executive Vice President of Hospital and Chief Operating Officer, SSM Health St. Joseph Hospital – Lake Saint Louis, Lake Saint Louis, MO, p. A375
Regional Executive Vice President and Chief Operating Officer, SSM St. Clare Hospital, Fenton, MO, p. A371
Regional Executive Vice President and Chief Operating Officer, SSM St. Joseph Health Center, Saint Charles, MO, p. A379

BERNSTEIN, Les, Chief Information Officer, Cookeville Regional Medical Center, Cookeville, TN, p. A581

BERNSTEIN, Michael, Chief Financial Officer, Tulare Regional Medical Center, Tulare, CA, p. A97

BERNSTEIN, Paul E., M.D. Area Medical Director, Kaiser Permanente San Diego Medical Center, San Diego, CA, p. A88

BERRIGAN, Mary, Chief Operating Officer, Medical Center of Aurora, Aurora, CO, p. A101

BERRIOS, Elenia, Chief Nursing Officer, Hospital HIMA San Pablo Caguas, Caguas, PR, p. A726

BERRY, Carlos E., M.D. Acting Chief of Staff, Tuscaloosa Veterans Affairs Medical Center, Tuscaloosa, AL, p. A26

BERRY, Cheryl Furdge, Chief Nursing Officer, Baptist Memorial Hospital–Tipton, Covington, TN, p. A582

BERRY, David T.
President, System Clinical Operations, Children's Health System of Texas, Dallas, TX, p. A609
President, Children's Health Clinical Operations, Children's Medical Center Plano, Plano, TX, p. A641
President, Children's Health Clinical Operations, Our Children's House, Dallas, TX, p. A611

BERRY, Deborah, Director of Operations, Greene County Hospital, Leakesville, MS, p. A361

BERRY, Dennis, Chief Executive Officer, Tennessee Health Management, Parsons, TN, p. B134

BERRY, Donna, Interim Director of Nursing Services, Cedar Crest Hospital and Residential Treatment Center, Belton, TX, p. A602

BERRY, Greg, Chief Financial Officer, Doctors Medical Center of Modesto, Modesto, CA, p. A77

BERRY, James, Executive Vice President and Administrator, Northeastern Health System, Tahlequah, OK, p. A520

BERRY, Julie, Chief Information Officer, Saint Anne's Hospital, Fall River, MA, p. A310

BERRY, Linda, Vice President Human Resources, Guthrie Towanda Memorial Hospital, Towanda, PA, p. A555

BERRY, Rebecca
Vice President Human Resources, St. Charles Bend, Bend, OR, p. A524
Senior Director Human Resources, St. Charles Prineville, Prineville, OR, p. A530
Vice President Human Resources, St. Charles Redmond, Redmond, OR, p. A530

BERRY, Robert F., Chief Executive Officer, Lane Frost Health and Rehabilitation Center, Hugo, OK, p. A513

BERRY–BARBOSA, Lisa, Vice President Human Resources, Beth Israel Deaconess Hospital Plymouth, Plymouth, MA, p. A314

BERRYMAN, John David, M.D. Chief of Staff, Beckley Veterans Affairs Medical Center, Beckley, WV, p. A694

BERRYMAN, William R., M.D. Chief of Staff, Grand Junction Veterans Health Care System, Grand Junction, CO, p. A106

BERSANTE, Syd, R.N.,
President, St. Clare Hospital, Lakewood, WA, p. A686
President, St. Elizabeth Hospital, Enumclaw, WA, p. A684

BERSHAD, Joshua M., M.D. Senior Vice President Medical Affairs and Chief Medical Officer, Robert Wood Johnson University Hospital, New Brunswick, NJ, p. A420

BERSINGER, David, M.D. Chief of Staff, McLeod Health Cheraw, Cheraw, SC, p. A563

BERT, Alisa, Chief Financial Officer, Aventura Hospital and Medical Center, Aventura, FL, p. A123

BERTHIL, Emmanuel, Chief Clinical Officer, Vibra Hospital of Southeastern Massachusetts, New Bedford, MA, p. A312

BERTKE, Bradley J., President and Chief Ooperating Officer, Mercy St. Anne Hospital, Toledo, OH, p. A503

BERTRAND, Joan L., Vice President Human Resources, Adcare Hospital of Worcester, Worcester, MA, p. A316

BERTRAND, Neil W., Interim Chief Financial Officer, Cheyenne Regional Medical Center, Cheyenne, WY, p. A721

BERTSCH, Darrold, Chief Executive Officer, Sakakawea Medical Center, Hazen, ND, p. A479

BERTSCH, John, M.D. Chief of Staff, Euclid Hospital, Euclid, OH, p. A494

BERUBE, Cathy, Chief Financial Officer, I–70 Community Hospital, Sweet Springs, MO, p. A383

BERWALD, Margaret, R.N. Senior Vice President Patient Services, Torrance Memorial Medical Center, Torrance, CA, p. A96

BERZ, Derek, Chief Operating Officer, Kaiser Permanente Los Angeles Medical Center, Los Angeles, CA, p. A71

BERZAU, Ulrike, FACHE Administrator, St. Luke's Rehabilitation Institute, Spokane, WA, p. A691

BESCOE, Bradley, Chief Financial Officer, Straith Hospital for Special Surgery, Southfield, MI, p. A334

BESHEL, Michael, R.N. Vice President Patient Care and Chief Nursing Officer, Nazareth Hospital, Philadelphia, PA, p. A549

BESIO, Adam, Chief Information Officer, Memorial Medical Center, Port Lavaca, TX, p. A642

BESPALEC, Jason, M.D. Chief of Staff, Fillmore County Hospital, Geneva, NE, p. A396

BESS, Amy, Chief Financial Officer, Mizell Memorial Hospital, Opp, AL, p. A24

BESS, Charles, M.D. Medical Director, Potomac Valley Hospital, Keyser, WV, p. A697

BESS, Timothy A., Chief Executive Officer, Lake Cumberland Regional Hospital, Somerset, KY, p. A269

BESSE, Kim
Senior Vice President and Chief Human Resource Officer, Children's Health System of Texas, Dallas, TX, p. A609
Senior Vice President and Chief Human Resource Officer, Children's Medical Center Plano, Plano, TX, p. A641

BESSEY, Kerry, Senior Vice President and Chief Human Resources Officer, Memorial Sloan–Kettering Cancer Center, New York, NY, p. A446

BESSLER, Christine, Vice President Information Services, Oconomowoc Memorial Hospital, Oconomowoc, WI, p. A713

BESSLER, September, Director, Human Resources, Brookings Health System, Brookings, SD, p. A572

BESSON, Kathleen, Executive Vice President and Chief Operating Officer, CaroMont Regional Medical Center, Gastonia, NC, p. A465

BESST, Kara, President and Chief Executive Officer, Gritman Medical Center, Moscow, ID, p. A177

BEST, Rosa, Chief Nursing Officer, Rolling Plains Memorial Hospital, Sweetwater, TX, p. A651

BESTEN, Robert, Chief Financial Officer, Mary Breckinridge ARH Hospital, Hyden, KY, p. A262

BESTGEN, Pat, Manager Human Resources, Cameron Regional Medical Center, Cameron, MO, p. A368

BESWICK, Elizabeth, Vice President Human Resources and Public Relations, Carteret Health Care, Morehead City, NC, p. A470

BETANCES, Luis, Administrator, Westend Hospital, Jennings, LA, p. A279

BETANCOURT, Erika, Coordinator Human Resources, Cornerstone Regional Hospital, Edinburg, TX, p. A614

BETHELL, Mark, Chief Executive Officer, Springwoods Behavioral Health Hospital, Fayetteville, AR, p. A45

BETTCHER, Sue, R.N. Vice President of Nursing Services, Community Hospital of Bremen, Bremen, IN, p. A207

BETTEM, Kelly, Vice President, Ambulatory Services, Ohio Valley Medical Center, Wheeling, WV, p. A701

BETTINELLI, Stephanie M., Vice President of Human Resources, Winchester Hospital, Winchester, MA, p. A316

BETTS, Brooks, Director Information Systems and Chief Information Officer, Pen Bay Medical Center, Rockport, ME, p. A295

BETTS, Crystal
Chief Financial Officer, Incline Village Community Hospital, Incline Village, NV, p. A405
Chief Financial Officer, Tahoe Forest Hospital District, Truckee, CA, p. A97

BETTS, Kristen A., Director Team Resources, St. Anthony's Hospital, Saint Petersburg, FL, p. A144

BETTS, Tracy, Chief Financial Officer, Hardeman County Memorial Hospital, Quanah, TX, p. A642

BETZ, Paul, FACHE Chief Operating Officer and Senior Vice President, Maury Regional Hospital, Columbia, TN, p. A581

BEUCLER, MSN, RN, RB–NE, FACHE, Lori A., R.N. Vice President and Chief Nursing Officer, Williamsport Regional Medical Center, Williamsport, PA, p. A558

BEUS, Lance, Administrator, CHRISTUS Southeast Texas Jasper Memorial, Jasper, TX, p. A629

BEUTIN, Brian, MS, Chief Executive Officer, Banner Behavioral Health Hospital – Scottsdale, Scottsdale, AZ, p. A38

BEUTKE, Kenneth, President, OSF Saint Elizabeth Medical Center, Ottawa, IL, p. A199

BEVARD, Julie, Director Human Resources, Perkins County Health Services, Grant, NE, p. A396

BEVEL, John, Manager Information Systems, Shriners Hospitals for Children–Northern California, Sacramento, CA, p. A87

BEVERLY, Douglas H., Chief Executive Officer, HEALTHSOUTH Rehabilitation Hospital of North Alabama, Huntsville, AL, p. A21

BEVERLY, Esther, Vice President Human Resources, Tri–City Medical Center, Oceanside, CA, p. A80

BEVERS, Donald, Chief Financial Officer, Memorial Hospital of Salem County, Salem, NJ, p. A423

BEYER, Jim, Director Human Resources, Norman Regional Health System, Norman, OK, p. A515

BEYER, Laurie, Senior Vice President and Chief Financial Officer, Union Hospital, Elkton, MD, p. A300

BEYER, Teri, Chief Information Officer, Quality, Rice Memorial Hospital, Willmar, MN, p. A353

BEZARD, Herve, M.D. Chief of Staff, Boulder City Hospital, Boulder City, NV, p. A404

BHAGAT, Sarah, Chief Operating Officer and Vice President of Organizational Effectiveness, Lakeland Regional Health, Lakeland, FL, p. A134

BHAMBI, Brijesh, M.D. Chief Medical Officer, Bakersfield Heart Hospital, Bakersfield, CA, p. A55

BHAMBRA, Jody, Chief Nursing Officer, Hartgrove Hospital, Chicago, IL, p. A184

BHANDARI, Raj, M.D. Physician–in–Chief, Kaiser Permanente San Jose Medical Center, San Jose, CA, p. A91

BHARUCHA, Bomi, Chief Financial Officer, Reeves County Hospital, Pecos, TX, p. A641

BHATEJA, Renu, M.D. President Medical Staff, Ridgeview Psychiatric Hospital and Center, Oak Ridge, TN, p. A592

BHATIA, Sanjay, Chief Medical Officer, Lower Bucks Hospital, Bristol, PA, p. A534

BHAYANI, Sam B., M.D. Chief Medical Officer, Barnes–Jewish West County Hospital, Saint Louis, MO, p. A379

BHOORASINGH, Merlene, Administrator, Kindred Hospital Ocala, Ocala, FL, p. A139

BHUCHAR, Subodh, M.D. Chief of Staff, Kindred Hospital Sugar Land, Sugar Land, TX, p. A650

BIAGIONI, Donna K., R.N. Director of Nursing, Maniilaq Health Center, Kotzebue, AK, p. A30

BIANCHI, Patty, Chief Executive Officer, Pershing General Hospital, Lovelock, NV, p. A407

BIAS, Richard R., Chief Operating Officer, Lahey Hospital & Medical Center, Burlington, Burlington, MA, p. A308

BIBAL, Antoinette, Director Human Resources, Kindred Hospital–Baldwin Park, Baldwin Park, CA, p. A56

BIBB, Jeff, Chief Operating Officer, Oklahoma Center for Orthopedic and Multi–Specialty Surgery, Oklahoma City, OK, p. A516

BIBB, Lisa, Director Human Resources, San Angelo Community Medical Center, San Angelo, TX, p. A644

BIBBY, John, Vice President Human Resources, Los Robles Hospital and Medical Center, Thousand Oaks, CA, p. A96

BIBEAU, Roland R., FACHE, President, Novant Health Matthews Medical Center, Matthews, NC, p. A469

BIBER, Carl, Chief Financial Officer, Columbus Regional Healthcare System, Whiteville, NC, p. A475

BIBLO, Lee, M.D. Chief Medical Officer, Froedtert Memorial Lutheran Hospital, Milwaukee, WI, p. A711

BIBY, Thom, Chief Financial Officer, Tulsa Spine and Specialty Hospital, Tulsa, OK, p. A522

BICHIMER, Michael, Acting Vice President of Finance, OhioHealth MedCentral Mansfield Hospital, Mansfield, OH, p. A497

BICKEL, George, Director, Information Systems, Merit Health Biloxi, Biloxi, MS, p. A355

BICKEL, Jim, Chief Executive Officer, Columbus Regional Hospital, Columbus, IN, p. A208

BICKFORD, Carmel, Chief Financial Officer, Wyoming Behavioral Institute, Casper, WY, p. A721

BICKFORD, David, Chief Information Officer, Melissa Memorial Hospital, Holyoke, CO, p. A107

BIDDLE, Kenneth, Controller, Kensington Hospital, Philadelphia, PA, p. A548

BIDES, Adrienne, Assistant Chief Financial Officer and Budget Analyst, Big Spring State Hospital, Big Spring, TX, p. A602

BIDLEMAN, Angie, Chief Nursing Officer, Jane Phillips Memorial Medical Center, Bartlesville, OK, p. A509

BIE, Gary E., CPA Chief Financial Officer, Stony Brook University Hospital, Stony Brook, NY, p. A456

BIEBER, Courtney, Director Information Systems, Mercy Regional Medical Center, Ville Platte, LA, p. A289

BIEBER, Eric, M.D., President and Chief Executive Officer, Rochester Regional Health, Rochester, NY, p. B115

BIEBER, Judi, Senior Vice President Human Resources, Beth Israel Deaconess Medical Center, Boston, MA, p. A306

BIEDIGER, Daniel F., Vice President Human Resources, FirstHealth Moore Regional Hospital, Pinehurst, NC, p. A471

BIEGERT, Dara, Vice President Human Resources, Medical Center of Lewisville, Lewisville, TX, p. A632

BIEGLER, Elizabeth Anne, R.N
  Chief Nursing Officer, OhioHealth Dublin Methodist Hospital, Dublin, OH, p. A494
  Chief Nursing Officer, OhioHealth Grady Memorial Hospital, Delaware, OH, p. A493

BIEHL, Albert, M.D. Vice President Medical Affairs, Bethesda Hospital East, Boynton Beach, FL, p. A124

BIEKER, Jeff, Director Human Resource, Trego County–Lemke Memorial Hospital, Wakeeney, KS, p. A255

BIEL, Christopher, Chief Information Officer, Goodland Regional Medical Center, Goodland, KS, p. A244

BIELECKI, Thomas A., Chief Financial Officer, Geisinger Wyoming Valley Medical Center, Wilkes Barre, PA, p. A557

BIEN, John, Vice President Finance, United Hospital, Saint Paul, MN, p. A351

BIENIEK, Sherrie, M.D
  Medical Director, Atlantic Shores Hospital, Fort Lauderdale, FL, p. A128
  Medical Director, Fort Lauderdale Hospital, Fort Lauderdale, FL, p. A128

BIER, Alan, M.D. Executive Vice President and Chief Medical Officer, Gwinnett Hospital System, Lawrenceville, GA, p. A162

BIERI, Bryan, Manager Finance, Kansas City Veterans Affairs Medical Center, Kansas City, MO, p. A373

BIERLE, Dennis, Chief Operating Officer, Nebraska Medicine – Nebraska Medical Center, Omaha, NE, p. A400

BIERMAN, Debra, Associate Executive Director Human Resources, North Shore University Hospital, Manhasset, NY, p. A442

BIERMAN, Joan, Vice President Finance, Cherokee Regional Medical Center, Cherokee, IA, p. A227

BIERMAN, Marcia, M.D. Chief of Staff, North Shore Medical Center, Miami, FL, p. A137

BIERMAN, Ronald L., Chief Executive Officer, Affinity Medical Center, Massillon, OH, p. A498

BIERSCHENK, Cindy, Director Financial Services, Optim Medical Center – Screven, Sylvania, GA, p. A167

BIERSCHENK, Kevin, Chief Executive Officer, Dodge County Hospital, Eastman, GA, p. A159

BIERUT, Barbara, Chief Financial Officer, HEALTHSOUTH Rehabilitation Hospital of Sarasota, Sarasota, FL, p. A145

BIFFLE, Sandra, Personnel Clerk, Quitman County Hospital, Marks, MS, p. A361

BIGELOW, Barbara, Administrator, Providence Kodiak Island Medical Center, Kodiak, AK, p. A29

BIGELOW, David C., PharmD, Chief Executive Officer, Samaritan Pacific Communities Hospital, Newport, OR, p. A528

BIGELOW, Timothy, Director Human Resources, Butler Hospital, Providence, RI, p. A560

BIGGAR, Carrie, Chief Financial Officer, Osceola Regional Medical Center, Kissimmee, FL, p. A133

BIGGERSTAFF, David, Chief Operating Officer, Children's Hospital Colorado, Aurora, CO, p. A101

BIGGINS RN, Lillie, R.N., President, Texas Health Harris Methodist Hospital Fort Worth, Fort Worth, TX, p. A618

BIGGS, Daniel, Director Human Resources, Valley View Hospital, Glenwood Springs, CO, p. A106

BIGGS, Jeremy, Chief Executive Officer, Methodist Medical Center of Oak Ridge, Oak Ridge, TN, p. A592

BIGGS, Kelly, M.D. Chief Medical Officer, Tyrone Hospital, Tyrone, PA, p. A556

BIGHAM, Laurie S., R.N. Chief Nursing Officer, Lovelace Medical Center, Albuquerque, NM, p. A427

BIGLER, Pamela, MSN Senior Vice President, Chief Nursing Officer, Carle Foundation Hospital, Urbana, IL, p. A204

BIGLEY, John, M.D. Medical Director, Kaiser Permanente Baldwin Park Medical Center, Baldwin Park, CA, p. A56

BIGNAULT, Jon, M.D. Chief of Staff, Athens–Limestone Hospital, Athens, AL, p. A16

BIGONEY, Rebecca
  Executive Vice President and Chief Medical Officer, Mary Washington Hospital, Fredericksburg, VA, p. A670
  Executive Vice President and Chief Medical Officer, Stafford Hospital, Stafford, VA, p. A679

BIGOS, Ardelle, R.N. Chief Nursing Officer and Vice President Patient Care Services, Maine Coast Memorial Hospital, Ellsworth, ME, p. A293

BIHUNIAK, Peter, Vice President Finance, Robert Wood Johnson University Hospital Rahway, Rahway, NJ, p. A422

BIITTNER, Sallie, Vice President Human Resources, St. Joseph's Hospital Health Center, Syracuse, NY, p. A456

BILBREY, Mickey, President and Chief Executive Officer, QHR, Brentwood, TN, p. B110

BILL, Charles E., Chief Executive Officer, Bartlett Regional Hospital, Juneau, AK, p. A29

BILLECI, Theresa, Executive Director, Porterville Developmental Center, Porterville, CA, p. A83

BILLIG, Samantha, Chief Executive Officer, HEALTHSOUTH Rehabilitation Hospital – Henderson, Henderson, NV, p. A405

BILLING, Michael D., Administrator, Mid–Valley Hospital, Omak, WA, p. A687

BILLINGS, Mary Ann, Director of Nursing, Potomac Valley Hospital, Keyser, WV, p. A697

BILLINGS, Robert E., Chief Financial Officer, Largo Medical Center, Largo, FL, p. A134

BILLINGSLEA, Anidra, Health Insurance Management, HEALTHSOUTH Rehabilitation Hospital of Montgomery, Montgomery, AL, p. A23

BILLINGSLEY, Margaret, R.N. Chief Nursing Officer, T. J. Samson Community Hospital, Glasgow, KY, p. A261

BILLINGTON, Carole, R.N. Vice President Operations, Chief Nursing Officer, Saint Anne's Hospital, Fall River, MA, p. A310

BILLMEYER, Joe, Director, Information Services, Mercy Medical Center–Dubuque, Dubuque, IA, p. A230

BILLS, James, Chief Executive Officer, Logan Memorial Hospital, Russellville, KY, p. A269

BILLY, Frank, Chief Financial Officer, Kindred Hospital Bay Area–Tampa, Tampa, FL, p. A147

BILUNKA, Dianne C., Director Human Resources, Clarion Psychiatric Center, Clarion, PA, p. A535

BINDER, Buzz, Vice President Finance, Saint Joseph Hospital, Denver, CO, p. A104

BINDERMAN, Judi, Chief Information Technology Officer and Chief Medical Informatics Officer, St. Francis Medical Center, Lynwood, CA, p. A75

BINDRA, Pavel, M.D. Chief Medical Officer and Chief Information Officer, Citrus Valley Medical Center–Inter Community Campus, Covina, CA, p. A60

BINGHAM, Julie, IT Supervisor, San Juan Hospital, Monticello, UT, p. A660

BINGHAM, Leslie, Senior Vice President and Chief Executive Officer, Valley Baptist Medical Center–Brownsville, Brownsville, TX, p. A604

BINGHAM, Paulette, Director Nursing Services, Ohio Valley Hospital, McKees Rocks, PA, p. A544

BINGHAM, Ronald T., Chief Operating Officer, Antelope Valley Hospital, Lancaster, CA, p. A68

BINGMAN, Ryan, Director Operations, Grundy County Memorial Hospital, Grundy Center, IA, p. A231

BINKLEY, Sharon, Director Human Resources, Fairfax Community Hospital, Fairfax, OK, p. A512

BINTZ, Marilu, M.D. Chief of Staff, Gundersen Boscobel Area Hospital and Clinics, Boscobel, WI, p. A703

BIRCH, Misty, Director Human Resources, Castleview Hospital, Price, UT, p. A662

BIRCHMEIER, Kevin, Director Human Resources, Covenant Healthcare, Saginaw, MI, p. A333

BIRD, Alan, Chief Executive Officer, Franklin County Medical Center, Preston, ID, p. A178

BIRD, Jace, M.D. Chief Medical Officer, Missouri River Medical Center, Fort Benton, MT, p. A387

BIRD, Jeffrey C., M.D. Chief Operating Officer and Chief Medical Officer, Indiana University Health Ball Memorial Hospital, Muncie, IN, p. A219

BIRD, Lindsay, Director Finance, South Pointe Hospital, Warrensville Heights, OH, p. A505

BIRD, Michele
  Chief Human Resources Officer, Hemet Valley Medical Center, Hemet, CA, p. A66
  Chief Human Resources Officer, Menifee Valley Medical Center, Sun City, CA, p. A95

BIRDSONG, Brady, Chief Information Officer, Saint Elizabeths Hospital, Washington, DC, p. A122

BIRDZELL, JoAnn, Chief Executive Officer and Administrator, St. Catherine Hospital, East Chicago, IN, p. A209

BIREN, David, Chief Financial Officer, Mayo Clinic Health System in Lake City, Lake City, MN, p. A344

BIRENBERG, Allan, Vice President Medical Affairs, MedStar Harbor Hospital, Baltimore, MD, p. A297

BIRKEL, Sue M., R.N. Director of Nursing, Butler County Health Care Center, David City, NE, p. A395

BIRKENSTOCK, Timothy L., Chief Financial Officer, Nicklaus Children's Hospital, Miami, FL, p. A137

BIRKHOFER, Colleen, Chief Nursing Officer, Trenton Psychiatric Hospital, Trenton, NJ, p. A424

BIRMINGHAM, Karen, Director Human Resources, West Springs Hospital, Grand Junction, CO, p. A106

BIRSCHBACH, Nancy
  Vice President and Chief Information Officer, Agnesian HealthCare, Fond Du Lac, WI, p. A705
  Vice President and Chief Information Officer, Ripon Medical Center, Ripon, WI, p. A715
  Vice President and Chief Information Officer, Waupun Memorial Hospital, Waupun, WI, p. A718

BISCONE, Mark A.
  Chief Executive Officer, Pen Bay Medical Center, Rockport, ME, p. A295
  Chief Executive Officer, Waldo County General Hospital, Belfast, ME, p. A292

BISDORF, Jonathan, Director Information Technology, Ohio Valley Surgical Hospital, Springfield, OH, p. A502

BISH, Carol, Human Resources Coordinator, North Greenville Hospital, Travelers Rest, SC, p. A570

BISHARA, Reemon, M.D. Medical Director, Coastal Harbor Treatment Center, Savannah, GA, p. A165

BISHOP, Abby, Chief Information Officer, McLaren Port Huron, Port Huron, MI, p. A332

BISHOP, Amy Leigh, Director Human Resources, Red Bay Hospital, Red Bay, AL, p. A25

BISHOP, Bill, Chief Information Officer, Colquitt Regional Medical Center, Moultrie, GA, p. A163

BISHOP, Bryan, Chief Financial Officer, Heartland Behavioral Health Services, Nevada, MO, p. A377

BISHOP, Elizabeth, Business Office Manager, Salina Surgical Hospital, Salina, KS, p. A253

BISHOP, Janice E., R.N. Chief Nursing Officer, Tewksbury Hospital, Tewksbury, MA, p. A315

BISHOP, John
  Chief Executive Officer, Community Hospital Long Beach, Long Beach, CA, p. A69
  Chief Executive Officer, Long Beach Memorial Medical Center, Long Beach, CA, p. A69
  Chief Executive Officer, Madison Valley Medical Center, Ennis, MT, p. A387
  Chief Executive Officer, Miller Children's & Women's Hospital Long Beach, Long Beach, CA, p. A70
  President, St. Charles Madras, Madras, OR, p. A527
  President, St. Charles Prineville, Prineville, OR, p. A530

BISHOP, Steve, Chief Financial Officer, UP Health System–Portage, Hancock, MI, p. A326

BISIGNANI, Thomas, Chief Financial Officer, Moses Taylor Hospital, Scranton, PA, p. A554

BISSEL, Jane, Interim Chief Executive Officer, Fayette County Memorial Hospital, Washington Court House, OH, p. A505

BISSENDEN, Chris, Director Human Resources, Ogden Regional Medical Center, Ogden, UT, p. A661

BISSONETTE, Christine, R.N. Service Line Director for Acute Services, Kalkaska Memorial Health Center, Kalkaska, MI, p. A328

BISSONNETTE, Andre, Chief Financial Officer, North Country Hospital and Health Center, Newport, VT, p. A666

BISTERFELDT, Joanne, Chief Information Officer, Wheaton Franciscan Healthcare – All Saints, Racine, WI, p. A714

BITAR, Adib, M.D. Medical Director, Aurora Charter Oak Hospital, Covina, CA, p. A60

BITAR, Ali, M.D. Vice President Medical Affairs, DMC – Rehabilitation Institute of Michigan, Detroit, MI, p. A321

BITAR, Raghid, Chief of Medical Staff, Chatham Hospital, Siler City, NC, p. A473

BITHER, Dean, Chief Financial Officer, Inland Hospital, Waterville, ME, p. A295

BITNER, Janet, Chief Operating Officer, Texas NeuroRehab Center, Austin, TX, p. A600

BITSILLY, Christina, Human Resource Specialist, U. S. Public Health Service Indian Hospital, Crownpoint, NM, p. A429

BITSOLI, Deborah, CPA, President, Morton Hospital and Medical Center, Taunton, MA, p. A315

BITTNER, Augustine, Chief Information Officer, Robley Rex Veterans Affairs Medical Center, Louisville, KY, p. A265

BITTNER, David, Chief Financial Officer, Mount Sinai Rehabilitation Hospital, Hartford, CT, p. A114

BITZ, Joan, Chief Nursing Officer, Meeker Memorial Hospital, Litchfield, MN, p. A345

BIUSO, Joseph, M.D. Vice President and Chief of Medical Affairs, Floyd Medical Center, Rome, GA, p. A165

BIXLER, David, Chief Executive Officer, Daviess Community Hospital, Washington, IN, p. A223

BIXLER, Jacquelyn, Vice President Human Resources, BryLin Hospitals, Buffalo, NY, p. A435

BJARNASON, Dana, R.N. Vice President and Chief Nursing Officer, OHSU Hospital, Portland, OR, p. A529

BJELICH, Steven C., President and Chief Executive Officer, Saint Francis Healthcare System, Cape Girardeau, MO, p. A368

BJELLA, Karmon T., Chief Executive Officer, MidMichigan Medical Center – Alpena, Alpena, MI, p. A318

BJERKE, Carolyn, Director Human Resources, Mercy Hospital Kingfisher, Kingfisher, OK, p. A513

BJERKE, Erik, Chief Executive Officer, Madison Healthcare Services, Madison, MN, p. A345

BJERKNES, Dan, Director Human Resources, Mercy Medical Center, Williston, ND, p. A482

BJORDAHL, Kevin, M.D. Chief Medical Officer, Milbank Area Hospital Avera, Milbank, SD, p. A574

BJORNBERG, Christopher R., Chief Executive Officer, Cascade Medical Center, Cascade, ID, p. A175

BJORNSTAD, Brad, M.D. Vice President and Chief Medical Officer, Florida Hospital Tampa, Tampa, FL, p. A147

BLACK, Amy, Risk Manager/PI Director, Brynn Marr Hospital, Jacksonville, NC, p. A467

BLACK, Amy, R.N. Chief Operating Officer, Martha Jefferson Hospital, Charlottesville, VA, p. A668

BLACK, Jr., Charles, Chief Financial Officer, Rockcastle Regional Hospital and Respiratory Care Center, Mount Vernon, KY, p. A267

BLACK, Gary E., President and Chief Executive Officer, UNC Lenoir Healthcare, Kinston, NC, p. A468

BLACK, Jason, Chie Nursing Officer, West Anaheim Medical Center, Anaheim, CA, p. A54

BLACK, Jessica, Chief Executive Officer, Brentwood Meadows, Newburgh, IN, p. A219

BLACK, Marcey, Chief Financial Officer, Northwest Florida Community Hospital, Chipley, FL, p. A125

BLACK, Marilynn
Chief Information Officer, Northern Arizona Healthcare, Flagstaff Medical Center, Flagstaff, AZ, p. A32
Chief Information Officer, Northern Arizona Healthcare, Verde Valley Medical Center, Cottonwood, AZ, p. A32

BLACK, Michael, Director Human Resources, East Georgia Regional Medical Center, Statesboro, GA, p. A166

BLACK, Paul S.
Controller, H. C. Watkins Memorial Hospital, Quitman, MS, p. A364
Chief Financial Officer, Scott Regional Hospital, Morton, MS, p. A362
Interim Administrator, Winston Medical Center, Louisville, MS, p. A361

BLACK, Robert O., Chief Executive Officer, Linton Hospital, Linton, ND, p. A480

BLACK, Terri, Network Manager, Lucas County Health Center, Chariton, IA, p. A227

BLACK, Tim, Director Human Resources, Timpanogos Regional Hospital, Orem, UT, p. A661

BLACKADAR, Sam, M.D. Medical Director, Cordova Community Medical Center, Cordova, AK, p. A28

BLACKBEAR, Annabelle, Human Resources Specialist, U. S. Public Health Service Indian Hospital, Pine Ridge, SD, p. A575

BLACKBURN, Christy, R.N. Chief Nursing Officer, Candler County Hospital, Metter, GA, p. A163

BLACKBURN, Lisa R., Director Human Resources, St. Margaret's Hospital, Spring Valley, IL, p. A203

BLACKBURN, Mary, Vice President Operations and Chief Practice Officer, Hugh Chatham Memorial Hospital, Elkin, NC, p. A465

BLACKBURN, Susan, Chief Operating Officer, Providence St. Mary Medical Center, Walla Walla, WA, p. A693

BLACKFORD, Nate, Chief Operating Officer, Northwest Medical Center, Albany, MO, p. A367

BLACKHAM, Cami, R.N. Nurse Administrator, Sevier Valley Medical Center, Richfield, UT, p. A662

BLACKHURST, Kristi, Interim Vice President Operations, Asante Rogue Regional Medical Center, Medford, OR, p. A528

BLACKMON, Jenean
Assistant Vice President and Chief Information Officer, McLeod Medical Center Dillon, Dillon, SC, p. A565
Associate Vice President and Chief Information Officer, McLeod Regional Medical Center, Florence, SC, p. A566

BLACKWELL, Jack, Chief Financial Officer, Highlands Regional Medical Center, Prestonsburg, KY, p. A268

BLACKWELL, James, President and Chief Executive Officer, Clara Barton Hospital, Hoisington, KS, p. A245

BLACKWELL, Lenore, Director Human Resources, Tennova Healthcare–Harton, Tullahoma, TN, p. A594

BLACKWELL, Timothy, Manager Human Resources, Rolling Hills Hospital, Ada, OK, p. A508

BLACKWOOD, Jim, Chief Executive Officer, Tallahatchie General Hospital, Charleston, MS, p. A356

BLACKWOOD, Mark, M.D. Chief of Staff, Bolivar Medical Center, Cleveland, MS, p. A356

BLAD, Nathan, Chief Executive Officer, RC Hospital and Clinics, Olivia, MN, p. A348

BLADEN, Anthony M., Vice President Human Resources, Calvert Memorial Hospital, Prince Frederick, MD, p. A302

BLAHA, Bill, Manager Information Technology, Tri–County Hospital, Wadena, MN, p. A353

BLAHNIK, David, Chief Operating Officer, Twin Valley Behavioral Healthcare, Columbus, OH, p. A491

BLAIN, Brenda K., FACHE Chief Nursing Officer and Chief Operating Officer, Baylor Medical Center at Irving, Irving, TX, p. A628

BLAIR, Brenda, Vice President Human Resources, Alice Peck Day Memorial Hospital, Lebanon, NH, p. A411

BLAIR, Diane, Human Resources and Admissions, CHI Health Plainview, Plainview, NE, p. A401

BLAIR, Heidi L., Vice President Administration, Centerstone Hospital, Bradenton, FL, p. A124

BLAIR, Jan, Director Human Resources, Clinton Memorial Hospital, Wilmington, OH, p. A506

BLAIR, Judy, Senior Vice President Clinical Services and Chief Nursing Officer, Glendale Adventist Medical Center, Los Angeles, CA, p. A71

BLAIR, Mark, M.D. Medical Director, Dublin Springs, Dublin, OH, p. A494

BLAIR, Mendy, Chief Nursing Officer, Baptist Health Richmond, Richmond, KY, p. A268

BLAIR, Jr., Raymond W., M.D. Chief of Staff, Ennis Regional Medical Center, Ennis, TX, p. A616

BLAIR, Robert D., Chief Executive Officer, Spine Hospital of Louisiana (formerly the NeuroMedical Center Surgical Hospital), Baton Rouge, LA, p. A273

BLAKE, Alan, M.D. President Medical Staff, Samaritan Lebanon Community Hospital, Lebanon, OR, p. A527

BLAKE, Daphne, R.N. Chief Nursing Officer, Guadalupe Regional Medical Center, Seguin, TX, p. A648

BLAKE, Diane, Chief Executive Officer, Cascade Medical Center, Leavenworth, WA, p. A686

BLAKE, Jean, Chief Nursing Officer, University Hospitals Cleveland Medical Center, Cleveland, OH, p. A490

BLAKE, Kelly, Chief Executive Officer, Select Specialty Hospital–Johnstown, Johnstown, PA, p. A541

BLAKE, Robert, Chief Human Resources Officer Southwest Market, Memorial Hermann Sugar Land Hospital, Sugar Land, TX, p. A650

BLAKE, Sheryl Lewis, FACHE, President, Spectrum Health Pennock, Hastings, MI, p. A326

BLAKE, Skylier, R.N. Director of Nursing, El Paso LTAC Hospital, El Paso, TX, p. A615

BLAKE, Steven, Corporate Chief Financial Officer, East Los Angeles Doctors Hospital, Los Angeles, CA, p. A71

BLAKELEY, Scott, Acting Administrator, Oceans Behavioral Hospital Fort Worth, Fort Worth, TX, p. A618

BLAKELY, Michelle, Associate Director, Jesse Brown Veterans Affairs Medical Center, Chicago, IL, p. A184

BLAKEMORE, Chris, Interim Chief Information Officer, Good Shepherd Medical Center, Longview, TX, p. A633

BLAKENEY, Dell, Vice President and Chief Information Officer, South Central Regional Medical Center, Laurel, MS, p. A360

BLAKEY GORMAN, Mary, Director Human Resources, Northwest Missouri Psychiatric Rehabilitation Center, Saint Joseph, MO, p. A379

BLALOCK, Anthony P., M.D. Chief Medical Officer, Our Lady of Lourdes Regional Medical Center, Lafayette, LA, p. A281

BLALOCK, Cam, Senior Vice President Corporate Services, Nash Health Care Systems, Rocky Mount, NC, p. A472

BLALOCK, Tracey, MSN Chief Nurse Executive, Medical Center, Navicent Health, Macon, GA, p. A162

BLANC, Linda, R.N. Administrative Director of Nursing, Jefferson Medical Center, Ranson, WV, p. A699

BLANCHARD, Timothy D., Chief Financial Officer, Kingman Regional Medical Center, Kingman, AZ, p. A33

BLANCHARD, Wayne D., Chief Executive Officer, Kindred Hospital–Louisville, Louisville, KY, p. A264

BLANCHARD, William R., Chief Executive Officer, DeTar Healthcare System, Victoria, TX, p. A655

BLANCHAT, Tim, Chief Information Officer, Catawba Valley Medical Center, Hickory, NC, p. A467

BLANCHETTE, Edward A., M.D., Director, Connecticut Department of Correction's Hospital, Somers, CT, p. A116

BLANCO, Andres, Director Management Information Systems, Westside Regional Medical Center, Plantation, FL, p. A143

BLANCO, Carlos, M.D.,
Administrator, Doctor's Center of Bayamon, Bayamon, PR, p. A726
Administrator, Doctors Center, Manati, PR, p. A727

BLAND, Casey, Director of Nursing, Rush Foundation Hospital, Meridian, MS, p. A362

BLAND, David, Chief Executive Officer, South Davis Community Hospital, Bountiful, UT, p. A659

BLAND, Douglas, Manager Information Services, Spring View Hospital, Lebanon, KY, p. A262

BLANDING, Carlene, Commander, Bayne–Jones Army Community Hospital, Fort Polk, LA, p. A277

BLANEY, Gerard, Vice President Finance and Interim Chief Financial Officer, Einstein Medical Center Philadelphia, Philadelphia, PA, p. A547

BLANK, Arthur J., President and Chief Executive Officer, Mount Desert Island Hospital, Bar Harbor, ME, p. A291

BLANK, Kim, Director Human Resources, Lake Region Healthcare, Fergus Falls, MN, p. A342

BLANKE, Kerry Lee
Chief Financial Officer, ThedaCare Medical Center–Shawano, Shawano, WI, p. A715
Director Financial Services, ThedaCare Medical Center–Waupaca, Waupaca, WI, p. A718

BLANKENSHIP, Diana, Director Human Resources, Welch Community Hospital, Welch, WV, p. A701

BLANKENSHIP, Jeff, CP
Vice President and Chief Financial Officer, Jackson–Madison County General Hospital, Jackson, TN, p. A584
Chief Financial Officer, Pathways of Tennessee, Jackson, TN, p. A584

BLANKENSHIP, Stacy, Chief Nursing Officer, Mercy Hospital Washington, Washington, MO, p. A383

BLANTON, Christina, Administrative Assistant and Human Resources Coordinator, Select Specialty Hospital–Knoxville, Knoxville, TN, p. A586

BLANTON, Forest
Senior VP and Chief Information Officer, Memorial Hospital Miramar, Miramar, FL, p. A138
Chief Information Officer, Memorial Hospital Pembroke, Pembroke Pines, FL, p. A142
Chief Information Officer, Memorial Hospital West, Pembroke Pines, FL, p. A142
Administrator Process Engineering, Memorial Regional Hospital,, FL, p. A130

BLANTON, James
Chief Financial Officer, East Texas Medical Center Rehabilitation Hospital, Tyler, TX, p. A654
Chief Financial Officer, East Texas Medical Center Specialty Hospital, Tyler, TX, p. A654

BLANTON, Kevin, D.O. Chief of Staff, Goodall–Witcher Hospital Authority, Clifton, TX, p. A606

BLANTON, Ron, Chief Fiscal Services, Boise Veterans Affairs Medical Center, Boise, ID, p. A174

BLAS, Phil, Chief Information Officer, John C. Fremont Healthcare District, Mariposa, CA, p. A76

BLASER, Karla, Director Human Resources, UnityPoint Health – Trinity Muscatine, Muscatine, IA, p. A235

BLASIUS, Rita, Assistant Administrator and Chief Financial Officer, Avera St. Benedict Health Center, Parkston, SD, p. A575

BLASKO, Edward, Chief of Staff, Carolinas HealthCare System Anson, Wadesboro, NC, p. A475

BLASY, Christopher, M.D. Chief of Staff, Carl Vinson Veterans Affairs Medical Center, Dublin, GA, p. A159

BLAUER, Michael, Administrator, St. Luke's Elmore, Mountain Home, ID, p. A177

BLAUWET, Judy, M.P.H. Senior Vice President Operations and Chief Nursing Officer, Avera McKennan Hospital and University Health Center, Sioux Falls, SD, p. A576

BLAYLOCK, Darrell, Chief Executive Officer, Tennova Healthcare Volunteer Community Hospital, Martin, TN, p. A588

BLAYLOCK, Kevin, Chief Executive Officer, Oklahoma Spine Hospital, Oklahoma City, OK, p. A517

BLAYLOCK, L. Dwayne, Chief Executive Officer, Merit Health River Oaks, Flowood, MS, p. A357

BLAZAKIS, Shelly, Director Human Resources Services, Scripps Memorial Hospital–La Jolla, La Jolla, CA, p. A67

BLAZEK, Dennis, Chief Information Officer, Clarke County Hospital, Osceola, IA, p. A236

BLAZIER, Patty, Chief Nursing Officer, Hamilton Memorial Hospital District, McLeansboro, IL, p. A196

BLEAK, Jason, Administrator and Chief Executive Officer, Grover C. Dils Medical Center, Caliente, NV, p. A404

BLECHA, Timothy, M.D. Medical Director, Brodstone Memorial Hospital, Superior, NE, p. A402

BLEDSOE, Dana, R.N., Chief Executive Officer, Nemours Children's Hospital, Orlando, FL, p. A140

BLEDSOE, Kristi, R.N., Administrator, St. Vincent Frankfort Hospital, Frankfort, IN, p. A211

BLEDSOE, Richard, Director Information Systems, Mary Black Health System – Gaffney, Gaffney, SC, p. A566

BLESI, Michael, Director Information Technology, Rainy Lake Medical Center, International Falls, MN, p. A344

BLESSING, Brian, Chief Financial Officer, Texas Health Harris Methodist Hospital Azle, Azle, TX, p. A600

BLEVINS, Bonnie, R.N. Chief Financial Officer, Faith Community Hospital, Jacksboro, TX, p. A629

BLEVINS, Denzil, Director Information Systems, Montgomery General Hospital, Montgomery, WV, p. A698

BLEVINS, Matthew H., Chief Operating Officer, Gateway Regional Medical Center, Granite City, IL, p. A191

BLEVINS, Pam, R.N
   Director, Clinical Informatics, Blue Ridge Regional Hospital, Spruce Pine, NC, p. A474
   Director Information Technology Member Hospitals Mission, McDowell Hospital, Marion, NC, p. A469

BLIGHTON, Gordon, Director Resource Management, Naval Hospital Camp Pendleton, Camp Pendleton, CA, p. A58

BLISS, Howard, Director of Information Systems, Helen Newberry Joy Hospital, Newberry, MI, p. A331

BLIVEN, Donna, Vice President Patient Care Services and Chief Nursing Officer, Jones Memorial Hospital, Wellsville, NY, p. A458

BLOB, Burchkhard, Manager Human Resources, Central Virginia Training Center, Madison Heights, VA, p. A673

BLOCHLINGER, Pamela, Acting Vice President Finance, Cloud County Health Center, Concordia, KS, p. A242

BLOCK, Annie, Director Human Resources, Poplar Community Hospital, Poplar, MT, p. A390

BLOCK, Deborah, Vice President Nursing and Chief Nursing Officer, Oconee Regional Medical Center, Milledgeville, GA, p. A163

BLOCK, Linn, R.N. Chief Nursing Officer, Manning Regional Healthcare Center, Manning, IA, p. A234

BLODGETT, Debbie, Director Fiscal Services, Ochiltree General Hospital, Perryton, TX, p. A641

BLOEMER, Brad, Vice President Finance and Chief Financial Officer, Arkansas Methodist Medical Center, Paragould, AR, p. A51

BLOEMKER, Jeff, Chief Executive Officer, I–70 Community Hospital, Sweet Springs, MO, p. A383

BLOM, David P., President and Chief Executive Officer, OhioHealth, Columbus, OH, p. B100

BLOMQUIST, David, Director Information Technology, McKenzie–Willamette Medical Center, Springfield, OR, p. A531

BLOMSTEDT, Jason, Chief of Staff, Community Hospital, McCook, NE, p. A398

BLOOD, Barbara
   Director Human Resources, Lourdes Counseling Center, Richland, WA, p. A689
   Executive Director Human Resources, Lourdes Medical Center, Pasco, WA, p. A687

BLOOM, Laura, Director Human Resources, Coffee Regional Medical Center, Douglas, GA, p. A158

BLOOM, Stephanie L., FACHE, President, Chilton Medical Center, Pompton Plains, NJ, p. A422

BLOOMQUIST, Aaron
   Chief Financial Officer, Maple Grove Hospital, Maple Grove, MN, p. A345
   Chief Financial Officer, North Memorial Medical Center, Robbinsdale, MN, p. A349

BLOUGH Jr., Daniel D., Chief Executive Officer, Punxsutawney Area Hospital, Punxsutawney, PA, p. A552

BLUE, Gaea, R.N., Administrator and Chief Executive Officer, Avera Weskota Memorial Hospital, Wessington Springs, SD, p. A577

BLUE, Jan L., Vice President Human Resources, Hoag Memorial Hospital Presbyterian, Newport Beach, CA, p. A79

BLUE, Lee Ann, MSN Chief Nursing Officer and Executive Vice President Patient Care Services, Eskenazi Health, Indianapolis, IN, p. A213

BLUE, Yvonne, Chief Operations Officer, Moore County Hospital District, Dumas, TX, p. A614

BLUHM, Tom, Director Information Systems, Island Hospital, Anacortes, WA, p. A682

BLUM, Carrie, Chief Information Officer, Monroe Clinic, Monroe, WI, p. A712

BLUM, Daniel, President, Phelps Memorial Hospital Center, Sleepy Hollow, NY, p. A455

BLUM, Donald A., M.D. Chief of Staff, Wetzel County Hospital, New Martinsville, WV, p. A698

BLUM, Walter B., M.D. Chief of Staff, McLeod Medical Center Dillon, Dillon, SC, p. A565

BLUNK, Jim, D.O. Chief Medical Officer, Sumner County Hospital District One, Caldwell, KS, p. A241

BLURTON, Cheri
   Director Human Resources, HIPAA Privacy Officer, Great River Medical Center, Blytheville, AR, p. A43
   Director Human Resources, South Mississippi County Regional Medical Center, Osceola, AR, p. A51

BLYE, Colleen M., Executive Vice President and Chief Financial Officer, Montefiore Medical Center,, NY, p. A446

BLYTHE, Thomas W., System Vice President Human Resources, Good Samaritan Regional Health Center, Mount Vernon, IL, p. A197

BOAL, Jeremy, M.D
   Executive Vice President and Chief Medical Officer, Mount Sinai Beth Israel, New York, NY, p. A446
   Executive Vice President and Chief Medical Officer, Mount Sinai St. Luke's – Roosevelt, New York, NY, p. A446
   Executive Vice President and Chief Medical Officer, New York Eye and Ear Infirmary of Mount Sinai, New York, NY, p. A447

BOARD, Patricia, Vice President Human Resources, Community Hospital of Bremen, Bremen, IN, p. A207

BOARDMAN, Debra K., FACHE, President and Chief Executive Officer, Range Regional Health Services, Hibbing, MN, p. A344

BOAS, Erik, Vice President Finance, University of Maryland Charles Regional Medical Center, La Plata, MD, p. A302

BOATMAN, Robert, Director Information Technology, Richmond State Hospital, Richmond, IN, p. A221

BOATRIGHT, Donna, MSN, Chief Executive Officer, Rolling Plains Memorial Hospital, Sweetwater, TX, p. A651

BOBBITT, James, Vice President Human Resources, Saint Agnes Hospital, Baltimore, MD, p. A297

BOBBS, Kathy, FACHE, President and Chief Executive Officer, Women's and Children's Hospital, Lafayette, LA, p. A281

BOBEK, Bruce, President Professional Staff, Columbia Memorial Hospital, Astoria, OR, p. A524

BOBO, Matt, Chief Information Officer, Meade District Hospital, Meade, KS, p. A249

BOBSEINE, Shannon, Manager Human Resources, TLC Health Network – Lake Shore Hospital, Irving, NY, p. A440

BOCCELLATO, Judy, R.N. Chief Nursing Officer, Specialty Hospital of Central Jersey, Lakewood, NJ, p. A418

BOCHATON, Philippe, Chief Executive Officer, Lakeway Regional Medical Center, Lakeway, TX, p. A631

BOCHICCHIO, Daniel, M.D., Interim Director, Beckley Veterans Affairs Medical Center, Beckley, WV, p. A694

BOCKELMAN, Paul, Director, Central Alabama Veterans Health Care System, Montgomery, AL, p. A23

BOCKENEK, William, M.D. Chief Medical Officer, Carolinas Rehabilitation, Charlotte, NC, p. A462

BOCKMANN, Rick, Chief Executive Officer, Frank R. Howard Memorial Hospital, Willits, CA, p. A100

BODENHAM, Steve, Senior Manager Clinical Engineering, Indiana University Health North Hospital, Carmel, IN, p. A208

BODENNER, Nancy, Director Human Resources, St. Joseph Health System, Tawas City, MI, p. A335

BODENSTEINER, Kim, Chief Financial Officer, Essentia Health Fosston, Fosston, MN, p. A343

BODIN, Donna L., Vice President, Woman's Hospital, Baton Rouge, LA, p. A273

BODINE, Maureen, Chief Clinical Officer, Kindred Hospital–San Diego, San Diego, CA, p. A88

BODKINS, Melissa, R.N. Chief Clinical Officer, Tri Valley Health System, Cambridge, NE, p. A394

BODLE, Vickie, Chief Financial Officer, Lake Chelan Community Hospital, Chelan, WA, p. A683

BODLOVIC, Kirk
   Vice President and Chief Financial Officer, Providence St. Joseph Medical Center, Polson, MT, p. A390
   Regional Chief Financial Officer, St. Patrick Hospital, Missoula, MT, p. A389

BODNAR, Darrell, Director Information, Weeks Medical Center, Lancaster, NH, p. A411

BODWELL, Amy, Vice President Finance, Methodist Richardson Medical Center, Richardson, TX, p. A643

BOECKMANN, Patricia, R.N. Chief Operating Officer and Chief Nursing Officer, Straub Clinic & Hospital, Honolulu, HI, p. A171

BOEHLER, Richard, M.D., President and Chief Executive Officer, St. Joseph Hospital, Nashua, NH, p. A412

BOEHM, Scott D., Executive Vice President Human Resources and Facilities, Sanford Bismarck, Bismarck, ND, p. A477

BOEHMER, Bernard, M.D. Medical Director, Cassia Regional Medical Center, Burley, ID, p. A175

BOEHNKE, Winnie, Director Human Resources, Timberlawn Mental Health System, Dallas, TX, p. A611

BOEMER, Sally Mason
   Senior Vice President Finance, Massachusetts General Hospital, Boston, MA, p. A307
   Chief Financial Officer, North Shore Medical Center, Salem, MA, p. A314

BOEMMEL, Michael, Vice President and Chief Financial Officer, MedStar National Rehabilitation Hospital, Washington, DC, p. A121

BOEN, Stefanie, Chief Nursing Officer, Skyline Hospital, White Salmon, WA, p. A693

BOER, Jeff, Director Information Technology, Pulaski Memorial Hospital, Winamac, IN, p. A224

BOERGER, Judy, MSN Chief Nursing Executive, Parkview Regional Medical Center, Fort Wayne, IN, p. A211

BOERGER, Kathy, Director Human Resources, Upper Valley Medical Center, Troy, OH, p. A504

BOERSCHEL, Viva, Director of Nursing, Floyd County Medical Center, Charles City, IA, p. A227

BOERSMA, Wendy, Vice President and Chief Nursing Officer, Henry Ford Allegiance Health, Jackson, MI, p. A327

BOES, Jody, Vice President Patient Care Services, Ministry Door County Medical Center, Sturgeon Bay, WI, p. A717

BOESE, Chris, Vice President and Chief Nursing Officer, Regions Hospital, Saint Paul, MN, p. A350

BOETTGER, Denise, Vice President Nursing and Chief Nursing Officer, OSF Saint Anthony's Health Center, Alton, IL, p. A180

BOGARD, Tim, Manager Information Technology, Highland District Hospital, Hillsboro, OH, p. A496

BOGARDUS, Tim, Chief Executive Officer, Oasis Hospital, Phoenix, AZ, p. A36

BOGEDAIN, Carol, FACHE, Director, Veterans Affairs Roseburg Healthcare System, Roseburg, OR, p. A530

BOGEN, Mark A., Senior Vice President and Chief Financial Officer, South Nassau Communities Hospital, Oceanside, NY, p. A451

BOGERS, Christina, Chief Clinical Officer, North Valley Hospital, Whitefish, MT, p. A391

BOGGAN Jr.,, Daniel, Interim Chief Executive Officer, Alameda Health System, San Leandro, CA, p. B8

BOGGESS, Carrie
   Human Resource Generalist, Carilion Giles Community Hospital, Pearisburg, VA, p. A675
   Human Resources Generalist, Carilion Tazewell Community Hospital, Tazewell, VA, p. A679

BOGGESS, Jack
   Chief Executive Officer, HEALTHSOUTH Rehabilitation Hospital – Austin, Austin, TX, p. A599
   Chief Executive Officer, HealthSouth Rehabilitation Hospital Round Rock, Round Rock, TX, p. A644

BOGGS, Danny L., President and Chief Executive Officer, University Hospitals Samaritan Medical Center, Ashland, OH, p. A484

BOGGS, Michael S., Chief Executive Officer, Regency Hospital of Central Georgia, Macon, GA, p. A162

BOGGUS, Bradley, Chief Financial Officer, Clinton Memorial Hospital, Wilmington, OH, p. A506

BOGLE, Bryan, Chief Executive Officer, Winn Parish Medical Center, Winnfield, LA, p. A289

BOGLE, William J., Director Information Systems, North Arkansas Regional Medical Center, Harrison, AR, p. A47

BOGOLIN, Loretta, MSN Chief Nursing Officer and Vice President Care Services, Vassar Brothers Medical Center, Poughkeepsie, NY, p. A453

BOHACH, Christopher, DPM Chief of Staff, Mercy Health – Willard Hospital, Willard, OH, p. A506

BOHALL, Karen, Director Human Resources, Woman's Christian Association Hospital, Jamestown, NY, p. A441

BOHATY, Richard, Director Information Technology, CHI Health St Elizabeth, Lincoln, NE, p. A398

BOHLMANN, Charles, Chief Executive Officer, Iroquois Memorial Hospital and Resident Home, Watseka, IL, p. A204

BOHN, Terry, Director, Human Resources, Orange County Global Medical Center, Inc., Santa Ana, CA, p. A92

BOHNEN, Christa N., Director Human Resources, Ellsworth County Medical Center, Ellsworth, KS, p. A242

BOHNENKAMP, Russ, Chief Financial Officer, Chadron Community Hospital and Health Services, Chadron, NE, p. A395

BOICE, Sheila, Director Human Resources, Barton County Memorial Hospital, Lamar, MO, p. A375

BOIK, Reyne, Director Human Resources, Cascade Medical Center, Leavenworth, WA, p. A686

BOIKE, Darlene, Chief Financial Officer, Chippewa County–Montevideo Hospital, Montevideo, MN, p. A347

BOILEAU, Michel, M.D. Chief Clinical Officer, St. Charles Prineville, Prineville, OR, p. A530

BOILY, Cindy, MS
Senior Vice President and Chief Nursing Officer, WakeMed Cary Hospital, Cary, NC, p. A462
Senior Vice President and Chief Nursing Officer, WakeMed Raleigh Campus, Raleigh, NC, p. A472
BOIS, Alain, R.N. Director of Nursing, Northern Maine Medical Center, Fort Kent, ME, p. A293
BOISVERT, Gerald J., Vice President and Chief Financial Officer, Connecticut Children's Medical Center, Hartford, CT, p. A114
BOJO, Rolland, R.N. Chief Nursing Officer, Administrator Patient Care and Services, Catskill Regional Medical Center, Harris, NY, p. A440
BOJO, Rolland, R.N., Administrator, Grover M. Hermann Hospital, Callicoon, NY, p. A436
BOKA, Darin, Chief Information Officer, McLaren Oakland, Pontiac, MI, p. A332
BOKON, Mark, Chief Information Officer, Northwest Medical Center – Springdale, Springdale, AR, p. A52
BOKOVITZ, Beverly, R.N. Chief Nursing Officer, St. Anthony's Medical Center, Saint Louis, MO, p. A381
BOLAND, E. Kay, R.N. Vice President and Chief Nursing Officer, United Health Services Hospitals–Binghamton, Binghamton, NY, p. A435
BOLAND, Susan, MSN, President and Chief Executive Officer, Wheaton Franciscan Healthcare – All Saints, Racine, WI, p. A714
BOLANDER, Patrick C.
Chief Financial Officer, East Cooper Medical Center, Mount Pleasant, SC, p. A568
Chief Financial Officer, Georgetown Community Hospital, Georgetown, KY, p. A260
BOLCAVAGE, Ted, Vice President Division Controller, Inpatient, OhioHealth Rehabilitation Hospital, Columbus, OH, p. A491
BOLDA, Craig, Chief Operating Officer, St. Catherine Hospital, East Chicago, IN, p. A209
BOLDING, Kay, R.N. Vice President Patient Care Services and Chief Nursing Officer, Jackson County Memorial Hospital, Altus, OK, p. A508
BOLDUC, Tiana, Chief Information Officer, Mercy Hospital Ozark, Ozark, AR, p. A51
BOLEN, David, Vice President and Chief Financial Officer, Passavant Area Hospital, Jacksonville, IL, p. A194
BOLEN, Shannon, Director Human Resources, Baptist Memorial Hospital–Booneville, Booneville, MS, p. A356
BOLES, Bonnie, M.D.,
Administrator, Tanner Higgins General Hospital, Bremen, GA, p. A155
Administrator, Tanner Medical Center–Villa Rica, Villa Rica, GA, p. A168
BOLES, Glen
Vice President and Chief Financial Officer, CHRISTUS St. Michael Health System, Texarkana, TX, p. A652
Vice President and Chief Financial Officer, CHRISTUS St. Michael Rehabilitation Hospital, Texarkana, TX, p. A652
BOLES, Lee, Assistant Administrator and Chief Financial Officer, Hunt Regional Medical Center, Greenville, TX, p. A621
BOLEWARE, Mike, Administrator, Franklin County Memorial Hospital, Meadville, MS, p. A361
BOLEY, Jason, M.D. Medical Director, Rock Prairie Behavioral Health, College Station, TX, p. A606
BOLEY, Sarah, Director Human Resources, Wetzel County Hospital, New Martinsville, WV, p. A698
BOLIN, Cris
Chief Executive Officer, Delta Memorial Hospital, Dumas, AR, p. A45
Chief Financial Officer, Grand River Hospital District, Rifle, CO, p. A110
BOLIN, Kari, Chief Nursing Officer, Putnam Community Medical Center, Palatka, FL, p. A141
BOLIN, Paul, Vice President Human Resources, The Acadia Hospital, Bangor, ME, p. A291
BOLINGER, John, M.D. Vice President Medical Affairs, Union Hospital, Terre Haute, IN, p. A222
BOLLARD, Robert, Chief Financial Officer, HEALTHSOUTH Rehabilitation Hospital – Henderson, Henderson, NV, p. A405
BOLLICH, Mary, Director of Nurses, AMG Specialty Hospital–Lafayette, Lafayette, LA, p. A280
BOLLIER, Sheila A., Chief Executive Officer, HEALTHSOUTH Rehabilitation Hospital of Cypress, Houston, TX, p. A624
BOLLINGER, Bill, Chief Information Officer, Carroll County Memorial Hospital, Carrollton, MO, p. A369
BOLLINGER, Bruce, M.D. Medical Director, Baylor Surgical Hospital at Fort Worth, Fort Worth, TX, p. A617
BOLLINGER, Candace, Director of Nursing, Mercy Hospital Booneville, Booneville, AR, p. A44
BOLLMANN, Brett, Administrator, Memorial Hospital, Chester, IL, p. A183
BOLLU, Prabhu, Director Information Technology, Wilson N. Jones Regional Medical Center, Sherman, TX, p. A649

BOLOGNANI, Laurie, Human Resources Officer, Speare Memorial Hospital, Plymouth, NH, p. A413
BOLOR, Erlinda, R.N. Chief Nursing Officer, San Joaquin General Hospital, French Camp, CA, p. A63
BOLT, Elizabeth T., Chief Human Resources Officer, University of Wisconsin Hospitals and Clinics Authority, Madison, WI, p. A709
BOLTER, Cindy, Chief Nursing and Operations Officer, John Muir Behavioral Health Center, Concord, CA, p. A59
BOLTON, Jeffrey W., Chief Administrative Officer, Mayo Clinic Hospital – Rochester, Rochester, MN, p. A349
BOMAR, Jacob, Director Information Technology, Hardin Medical Center, Savannah, TN, p. A592
BOMBA, Douglas, Chief Financial Officer, Cameron Memorial Community Hospital, Angola, IN, p. A206
BOMGAARS, Scott, M.D. Vice President Medical Affairs, Methodist Jennie Edmundson Hospital, Council Bluffs, IA, p. A228
BOMSTAD, Heather, MSN Vice President Patient Care Services and Chief Nursing Officer, OSF Saint Paul Medical Center, Mendota, IL, p. A196
BONACQUISTI, Gary, M.D. Chief Medical Officer, Texas Health Presbyterian Hospital of Rockwall, Rockwall, TX, p. A643
BONAR, Carrie, Chief Information Officer, Southern California Hospital at Culver City, Culver City, CA, p. A60
BONAR, Lynette, Chief Executive Officer, Tuba City Regional Health Care Corporation, Tuba City, AZ, p. A40
BONAR Jr., Robert, Chief Executive Officer, Children's Hospitals and Clinics of Minnesota, Minneapolis, MN, p. A346
BONCZEK, Mary Ellen, R.N. Chief Nursing Executive, New Hanover Regional Medical Center, Wilmington, NC, p. A475
BOND, Lee, Chief Operating Officer, Singing River Health System, Pascagoula, MS, p. A363
BOND, Rodney, Director Information Technology, Northern Hospital of Surry County, Mount Airy, NC, p. A470
BOND, Sharon, Director Human Resources, College Station Medical Center, College Station, TX, p. A606
BONDI, Blaise, Chief Financial Officer, Centennial Medical Center, Frisco, TX, p. A619
BONDS, Cyrilla, Administrator, United Medical Rehabilitation Hospital, Hammond, LA, p. A278
BONDURANT, Barry, Administrator and Chief Executive Officer, Baptist Memorial Hospital–Union City, Union City, TN, p. A594
BONDURANT, Charles, Chief Information Officer, Meadows Regional Medical Center, Vidalia, GA, p. A168
BONFILIO, Nicholas, M.D. Chief of Staff, Great Falls Clinic Medical Center, Great Falls, MT, p. A388
BONI, Shirley M., Administrative Officer, San Carlos Apache Healthcare Corporation, Peridot, AZ, p. A35
BONILLA, Felicita, Administrator, Hospital De La Concepcion, San German, PR, p. A729
BONILLA, Tony, Chief Executive Officer, Healthbridge Children's Hospital of Houston, Houston, TX, p. A624
BONIN, Stephanie, Administrator, Acadia Optima Hospital, Lafayette, LA, p. A280
BONNAR, David, Chief Information Officer, Kaiser Permanente Fresno Medical Center, Fresno, CA, p. A63
BONNER, Brad, Executive Director, Human Resources and General Counsel, Crawford County Memorial Hospital, Denison, IA, p. A229
BONNER, Gwen, Chief Operating Officer, Saint Francis Hospital–Bartlett, Bartlett, TN, p. A579
BONNER, Lenne
President, Clearwater Valley Hospital and Clinics, Orofino, ID, p. A177
President, St. Mary's Hospital, Cottonwood, ID, p. A176
BONNER, Robert
Chief Financial Officer, Glendora Community Hospital, Glendora, CA, p. A65
Chief Financial Officer, Montclair Hospital Medical Center, Montclair, CA, p. A77
Chief Financial Officer, San Dimas Community Hospital, San Dimas, CA, p. A89
BONO, Anthony, Chief Nursing Officer, Grove City Medical Center, Grove City, PA, p. A539
BONOMO, Carrie, M.D. Chief of Staff, Riverland Medical Center, Ferriday, LA, p. A276
BONTRAGER, Mandy, Director Nursing, Holton Community Hospital, Holton, KS, p. A245
BONZO, Kelly, Director, Baptist Health Richmond, Richmond, KY, p. A268
BOO, Thomas, M.D. Chief of Staff, Northern Inyo Hospital, Bishop, CA, p. A57
BOOHER, Terresa O., Vice President of Patient Care Services, Highlands Regional Medical Center, Prestonsburg, KY, p. A268
BOOKER, Angela, Director of Nursing Services, Teton Valley Health Care, Driggs, ID, p. A176
BOOM, Marc L., M.D., Chief Executive Officer, Houston Methodist, Houston, TX, p. B71

BOONE, David J., Senior Vice President, Finance, Catawba Valley Medical Center, Hickory, NC, p. A467
BOONE, Donna, MS Chief Nursing Officer, Weatherford Regional Medical Center, Weatherford, TX, p. A656
BOONE III, Elwood Bernard, FACHE, President, Sentara Virginia Beach General Hospital, Virginia Beach, VA, p. A680
BOONE, Margie, Registered Health Information Technician, Cumberland River Hospital, Celina, TN, p. A580
BOONE, Richard, Chief Financial Officer, Johnson City Medical Center, Johnson City, TN, p. A585
BOORAS, Laura, Vice President Human Resources, Coliseum Medical Centers, Macon, GA, p. A162
BOORE, Chad, President, OSF St. Joseph Medical Center, Bloomington, IL, p. A181
BOORNAZIAN, John, M.D. Chief Medical Officer, Huggins Hospital, Wolfeboro, NH, p. A413
BOOSALIS, Mary H., President, Premier Health, Dayton, OH, p. B105
BOOTH, Christy, Chief Human Resources Officer, Doctors Memorial Hospital, Bonifay, FL, p. A124
BOOTH, Daniel, Vice President Operations and Chief Human Resources Officer, Inland Hospital, Waterville, ME, p. A295
BOOTH, Patrick M., FACHE, Chief Executive Officer, Fremont Health, Fremont, NE, p. A396
BORCHERS, Jonathan, M.D. Chief Medical Officer, Washington County Memorial Hospital, Potosi, MO, p. A378
BORCHERT, Barry, Vice President Finance, Reedsburg Area Medical Center, Reedsburg, WI, p. A715
BORCHI, Daniel, Chief Information Officer, Carilion New River Valley Medical Center, Christiansburg, VA, p. A669
BORDELON, Rock, President and Chief Executive Officer, Allegiance Health Management, Shreveport, LA, p. B8
BORDEN, Eric, Chief Operating Officer and Chief Financial Officer, Jewell County Hospital, Mankato, KS, p. A248
BORDEN, Sandy, Chief Financial Officer, Brodstone Memorial Hospital, Superior, NE, p. A402
BORDENKIRCHER, Kimberly Hupp, Chief Executive Officer, Henry County Hospital, Napoleon, OH, p. A500
BORDERS, James, M.D. Chief Medical Officer, Baptist Health Lexington, Lexington, KY, p. A262
BORDO, David, M.D
Vice President and Chief Medical Officer, Community First Medical Center, Chicago, IL, p. A183
Chief Medical Officer, Presence Holy Family Medical Center, Des Plaines, IL, p. A188
Chief Medical Officer, Presence Resurrection Medical Center, Chicago, IL, p. A185
BOREL, Patricia, Chief Financial Officer, Central Community Hospital, Elkader, IA, p. A230
BOREN, Kevin
Chief Financial Officer, Essentia Health Duluth, Duluth, MN, p. A341
Chief Financial Officer, Essentia Health Northern Pines Medical Center, Aurora, MN, p. A338
BORENGASSER, Connie, Chief Executive Officer, Vantage Point of Northwest Arkansas, Fayetteville, AR, p. A46
BORENS, Dwan, Director of Nursing, St. John Broken Arrow, Broken Arrow, OK, p. A509
BORER, Tom, Vice President Operations, ProMedica Fostoria Community Hospital, Fostoria, OH, p. A494
BORG, David E., Chief of Medical Staff, Community Medical Center, Inc., Falls City, NE, p. A395
BORGERSON, Carol, Business Office Manager and Chief Financial Officer, Madison Healthcare Services, Madison, MN, p. A345
BORGSTROM, Marna P., President and Chief Executive Officer, Yale New Haven Health, New Haven, CT, p. B156
BORGSTROM, Marna P., Chief Executive Officer, Yale–New Haven Hospital, New Haven, CT, p. A116
BORING, Ron, Senior Vice President and Chief Operating Officer, McLeod Regional Medical Center, Florence, SC, p. A566
BORIS, Diane
Vice President and Chief Financial Officer, Schuylkill Medical Center – Schuylkill East Norwegian Street, Pottsville, PA, p. A552
Chief Financial Officer, Schuylkill Medical Center – Schuylkill South Jackson Street, Pottsville, PA, p. A552
BORIS, Jamie, M.D. President Medical Staff, Washington Health System Greene, Waynesburg, PA, p. A557
BORJA, Catherine, M.D. Chairman Executive Committee Medical Staff, Naval Hospital Oak Harbor, Oak Harbor, WA, p. A687
BORLAND, Winston, FACHE, President and Chief Executive Officer, Medical Center Arlington, Arlington, TX, p. A597
BORMANN, Debra, Chief Executive Officer, Post Acute/Warm Springs Rehabilitation Hospital of San Antonio, San Antonio, TX, p. A646
BORMANN, Jim, Director Human Resources, Passavant Area Hospital, Jacksonville, IL, p. A194

BORN, Michael, M.D. Chief Medical Officer and Chief Quality Officer, SwedishAmerican – A Division of UW Health, Rockford, IL, p. A202

BORNICK, Brian, Chief Information Officer, Minneapolis Veterans Affairs Health Care System, Minneapolis, MN, p. A346

BOROWSKI, Thomas
Chief Information Officer, Mayo Clinic Health System in Saint James, Saint James, MN, p. A350
Administrator, Mayo Clinic Health System in Waseca, Waseca, MN, p. A353

BORRENPOHL, James, Market Site Director, Community Hospital of San Bernardino, San Bernardino, CA, p. A88

BORTEL, Karol, Vice President Financial Services, Wood County Hospital, Bowling Green, OH, p. A485

BORTKE, Todd, Director Information Systems, CHI St. Alexius Health, Bismarck, ND, p. A477

BORTZ, Tammy, Director of Finance, Peterson Healthcare and Rehabilitation Hospital, Wheeling, WV, p. A701

BORZON, Eve, R.N. Chief Operating Officer, NYC Health + Hospitals / Woodhull, NY, p. A449

BOS, Robbi E., Vice President Human Resources, Sauk Prairie Healthcare, Prairie Du Sac, WI, p. A714

BOSCIA, Michael, Chief Financial Officer, Bartow Regional Medical Center, Bartow, FL, p. A123

BOSCO, John, Senior Vice President and Chief Information Officer, Long Island Jewish Medical Center,, NY, p. A445

BOSCO, Maureen, Executive Director, Central New York Psychiatric Center, Marcy, NY, p. A442

BOSER, Andrew, Chief Executive Officer, Cuba Memorial Hospital, Cuba, NY, p. A437

BOSHUT, Sami, Chief Information Officer, Jamaica Hospital Medical Center,, NY, p. A445

BOSLEY, Elizabeth, R.N. Vice President Patient Services, St. Mary's Medical Center, Huntington, WV, p. A697

BOSS, Craig, M.D. Chief Medical Officer, Munson Healthcare Charlevoix Hospital, Charlevoix, MI, p. A320

BOST, Cecelia, Chief Operating Officer, Alliance HealthCare System, Holly Springs, MS, p. A359

BOST, Marcus, Director Information Services and Chief Information Officer, Adena Greenfield Medical Center, Greenfield, OH, p. A495

BOSTER, Brian, M.D. Medical Director, Select Specialty Hospital–Cincinnati, Cincinnati, OH, p. A488

BOSTIC, Deborah, R.N. Chief Nursing Officer, Texas Health Presbyterian Hospital Denton, Denton, TX, p. A613

BOSTIC, William, Administrative Assistant Human Resources, Surprise Valley Health Care District, Cedarville, CA, p. A58

BOSTON, Katie, Senior Vice President Patient Care Services, Union Hospital, Elkton, MD, p. A300

BOSTON III, Ward, Chief Executive Officer, Memorial Hospital of Tampa, Tampa, FL, p. A147

BOSTROM, Brenda, Director of Nursing, Coteau des Prairies Hospital, Sisseton, SD, p. A576

BOSTROM, Gary, Chief Executive Officer and Chief Financial Officer, East Adams Rural Healthcare, Ritzville, WA, p. A689

BOSTROM, Stuart, M.D. Director Medical Affairs, Sutter Roseville Medical Center, Roseville, CA, p. A86

BOSTWICK, John, Interim Chief Financial Officer, Henderson County Community Hospital, Lexington, TN, p. A587

BOSTWICK, Monte J., Market Chief Executive Officer, CHI St. Luke's Health Memorial Lufkin, Lufkin, TX, p. A634

BOSTWICK, Shari, Director Human Resources, New London Hospital, New London, NH, p. A412

BOSWELL, Debbie, Chief Operating Officer and Chief Nursing Officer, Mercy Medical Center, Roseburg, OR, p. A530

BOSWELL, Diane, Director Human Resources and Marketing, Salem Township Hospital, Salem, IL, p. A202

BOSWELL, John, Chief Human Resources Officer, University of Virginia Medical Center, Charlottesville, VA, p. A668

BOSWINKEL, Jan, M.D. Vice President Medical Operations and Chief Safety Officer, Children's Hospital of Philadelphia, Philadelphia, PA, p. A547

BOSWORTH, Dawn, Director Human Resources, Arrowhead Behavioral Health Hospital, Maumee, OH, p. A498

BOTHE, Jr., Albert, M.D. Chief Medical Officer, Geisinger Medical Center, Danville, PA, p. A536

BOTHNER, Joan, M.D. Chief Medical Officer, Children's Hospital Colorado, Aurora, CO, p. A101

BOTHUN, Crystal, Chief Financial Officer, Johnson Memorial Health Services, Dawson, MN, p. A341

BOTINE, Gary, Vice President, Chief Financial Officer, Mary Greeley Medical Center, Ames, IA, p. A225

BOTKIN, Gregory T., M.D. Chief of Staff, Boundary Community Hospital, Bonners Ferry, ID, p. A175

BOTLER, Joel, M.D. Chief Medical Officer, Maine Medical Center, Portland, ME, p. A294

BOTNEY, Mitchell, M.D. Vice President Medical Affairs and Chief Medical Officer, Missouri Baptist Medical Center, Saint Louis, MO, p. A380

BOTTCHER, Sharon A., R.N. Vice President Patient Care Services, MedStar Union Memorial Hospital, Baltimore, MD, p. A297

BOTTENFIELD, Dana, Vice President Human Resources, St. Jude Children's Research Hospital, Memphis, TN, p. A589

BOTTGER, Barry, Chief Financial Officer, Republic County Hospital, Belleville, KS, p. A240

BOTTOM, Paige, Director Operations, Wilmington Treatment Center, Wilmington, NC, p. A475

BOUCK, Nancy, Director Human Resources, Huron Medical Center, Bad Axe, MI, p. A318

BOUCOT, Mark, FACHE, President and Chief Executive Officer, Garrett Regional Medical Center, Oakland, MD, p. A302

BOUDREAUX, Angela, Director Information Technology, St. Charles Parish Hospital, Luling, LA, p. A282

BOUDREAUX, Scott, Chief Executive Officer, Louisiana Heart Hospital, Lacombe, LA, p. A280

BOUFFARD, Rodney, Superintendent, Riverview Psychiatric Center, Augusta, ME, p. A291

BOUGHAL, Ginni, Director Health Information and Information Technology, PeaceHealth Peace Harbor Medical Center, Florence, OR, p. A525

BOUHAROUN, Khalil, Chief Information Officer, The HSC Pediatric Center, Washington, DC, p. A122

BOULA, Rodney, Chief Executive Officer, Calais Regional Hospital, Calais, ME, p. A292

BOULENGER, Albert, Chief Executive Officer, Baptist Health South Florida, Baptist Hospital of Miami, Miami, FL, p. A136

BOULLION, Leona, Chief Operating Officer, Women's and Children's Hospital, Lafayette, LA, p. A281

BOUQUET, Sheena
Vice President, Lafayette General Medical Center, Lafayette, LA, p. A280
Vice President, Lafayette General Surgical Hospital, Lafayette, LA, p. A280

BOUQUIO, George, Director Human Resources, South Beach Psychiatric Center,, NY, p. A449

BOUR, Eric, FACS, President, GHS Hillcrest Memorial Hospital, Simpsonville, SC, p. A569

BOURGEOIS, Jeff, President and Chief Executive Officer, San Juan Regional Medical Center, Farmington, NM, p. A429

BOURLAND, Don, Vice President Human Resources, PeaceHealth Peace Harbor Medical Center, Florence, OR, p. A525

BOURLAND, Renee, Human Resources Specialist, San Antonio State Hospital, San Antonio, TX, p. A647

BOURN, Jennifer, Director, Health Information Services and Medical Staff Services, CenterPointe Hospital, Saint Charles, MO, p. A370

BOURNE, Kara, R.N. Chief Nursing Officer and Chief Operating Officer, Foothill Regional Medical Center, Tustin, CA, p. A97

BOURNE, Kimberly L., Chief Executive Officer, Taylorville Memorial Hospital, Taylorville, IL, p. A204

BOURQUE, Teresa, Sr. Administrator for Nursing/Chief Nurse, Hurley Medical Center, Flint, MI, p. A323

BOUTROS, Akram, FACHE, President and Chief Executive Officer, MetroHealth Medical Center, Cleveland, OH, p. A489

BOUTROS, Nashaat, M.D. Clinical Director, Center for Behavioral Medicine, Kansas City, MO, p. A373

BOUYEA, Lawanda Janine, Director Human Resources, Natividad Medical Center, Salinas, CA, p. A87

BOVIO Jr., Ernest L., Chief Executive Officer, High Point Regional Health System, High Point, NC, p. A467

BOWCUTT, Marilyn A., R.N. President and Chief Operating Officer, University Hospital, Augusta, GA, p. A154

BOWEN, Christine, R.N. Chief Nursing Officer, DMC Harper University Hospital, Detroit, MI, p. A322

BOWEN, Jill Berry, President and Chief Executive Officer, Northwestern Medical Center, St. Albans, VT, p. A666

BOWEN, John, Assistant Vice President and Administrator, Baptist Health Medical Center–Arkadelphia, Arkadelphia, AR, p. A43

BOWEN, Julie, Executive Director of Information Technology, Gibson Area Hospital and Health Services, Gibson City, IL, p. A191

BOWEN, Mary Beth, R.N. Vice President Nursing and Chief Nursing Officer, United Memorial Medical Center, Batavia, NY, p. A434

BOWEN, Rodger W., M.P.H. Chief Financial Officer, Scenic Mountain Medical Center, Big Spring, TX, p. A602

BOWEN, Stephen, Administrator, Lavaca Medical Center, Hallettsville, TX, p. A622

BOWEN, Tim, President, Integris Grove Hospital, Grove, OK, p. A512

BOWER, David, M.D. Chief of Staff, Atlanta Veterans Affairs Medical Center, Decatur, GA, p. A158

BOWER, James, M.D. Chief Medical Officer, Research Medical Center, Kansas City, MO, p. A373

BOWER, Kay, Associate Director for Patient Care Services, Battle Creek Veterans Affairs Medical Center, Battle Creek, MI, p. A319

BOWERMAN, Stephen, Senior Vice President, Chief Financial Officer, Midland Memorial Hospital, Midland, TX, p. A637

BOWERS, Daniel, Chief Operating Officer, Riverside Community Hospital, Riverside, CA, p. A86

BOWERS, David N., M.D. Medical Director, Siskin Hospital for Physical Rehabilitation, Chattanooga, TN, p. A580

BOWERS, Melodee, Director Human Resources, Carle Hoopeston Regional Health Center, Hoopeston, IL, p. A193

BOWERS, Michael, Interim Director for Administration, Naval Hospital Oak Harbor, Oak Harbor, WA, p. A687

BOWERS, Michael E., President, SSM St. Joseph Health Center, Saint Charles, MO, p. A379

BOWERS, Sharon, R.N. Manager of Community, Public and Employee Relations, Sheridan Community Hospital, Sheridan, MI, p. A334

BOWERS, Shelby, Director Marketing and Public Relations, Peninsula Hospital, Louisville, TN, p. A587

BOWERS, Tracy, Director Human Resources, Novant Health UVA Health System Prince William Medical Center, Manassas, VA, p. A673

BOWERSOX, Bruce D., Chief Executive Officer, Nelson County Health System, Mcville, ND, p. A480

BOWERY, Leslie, Director of Standards and Compliance, Cumberland Hospital, New Kent, VA, p. A674

BOWES, Arthur, Senior Vice President Human Resources, North Shore Medical Center, Salem, MA, p. A314

BOWES, Matthew, M.D. Chief of Staff, Mackinac Straits Health System, Inc., Saint Ignace, MI, p. A333

BOWES, William, Chief Financial Officer, UAMS Medical Center, Little Rock, AR, p. A49

BOWLEG, Teresa, R.N. Chief Nursing Officer, Murphy Medical Center, Murphy, NC, p. A470

BOWLES, Patrica, R.N. Chief Nursing Officer, Franklin County Medical Center, Preston, ID, p. A178

BOWLES, Tara, Employee Relations Director, Rawlins County Health Center, Atwood, KS, p. A240

BOWLING, Donald, M.D. Chief Medical Staff, Southampton Memorial Hospital, Franklin, VA, p. A670

BOWLING, Judy, Director Human Resources, Southeast Health Center of Stoddard County, Dexter, MO, p. A370

BOWLING, Kay, Chief Executive Officer, Centra Specialty Hospital, Lynchburg, VA, p. A672

BOWLING, Kelli, Chief Culture Officer, Ministry Door County Medical Center, Sturgeon Bay, WI, p. A717

BOWLING, Nancy, Director Human Resources, Shoals Hospital, Muscle Shoals, AL, p. A24

BOWMAN, Barbara, Chief Human Resource Officer, Ann & Robert H. Lurie Children's Hospital of Chicago, Chicago, IL, p. A183

BOWMAN, Dyan, Director Human Resources, Newberry County Memorial Hospital, Newberry, SC, p. A569

BOWMAN, Joe, Chief Financial Officer, TriStar Ashland City Medical Center, Ashland City, TN, p. A579

BOWMAN, Joseph E., Chief Financial Officer, TriStar StoneCrest Medical Center, Smyrna, TN, p. A593

BOWMAN, Julie, Senior Vice President, Patient Care and Chief Nursing Officer, Phoenix Children's Hospital, Phoenix, AZ, p. A37

BOWMAN, Ken, Chief Executive Officer, Van Matre HealthSouth Rehabilitation Hospital, Rockford, IL, p. A202

BOWMAN, Mark, M.D. President Medical Staff, Tillamook Regional Medical Center, Tillamook, OR, p. A531

BOWMAN, Maureen, Vice President and Chief Nursing Officer, Beaumont Hospital – Royal Oak, Royal Oak, MI, p. A333

BOWMAN, Scott, Administrator, Sweetwater Hospital, Sweetwater, TN, p. A593

BOWMAN, William, M.D. Vice President Medical Affairs, Moses H. Cone Memorial Hospital, Greensboro, NC, p. A466

BOWMER, Carolyn,Lawrence Memorial Hospital, Lawrence, KS, p. A247

BOWSER, John, Vice President, Chief Financial Officer, OSF Saint Luke Medical Center, Kewanee, IL, p. A194

BOX, Darrel, Chief Executive Officer, Lafayette Regional Health Center, Lexington, MO, p. A375

BOX, Justin K.
Senior Vice President & Chief Information Officer, Mary Washington Hospital, Fredericksburg, VA, p. A670
Senior Vice President and Chief Information Officer, Stafford Hospital, Stafford, VA, p. A679

BOX, Tom, CPA Chief Financial Officer, HEALTHSOUTH Rehabilitation Hospital–Wichita Falls, Wichita Falls, TX, p. A657

BOXELL, Shelley, R.N., Chief Nursing Officer and Interim Chief Operating Officer, Rehabilitation Hospital of Fort Wayne, Fort Wayne, IN, p. A211

BOYCE, Charlotte, Chief Nursing Officer, HEALTHSOUTH Rehabilitation Hospital Memphis–North, Memphis, TN, p. A588

BOYD, Aaron, M.D. Chief Medical Officer, Norman Regional Health System, Norman, OK, p. A515

BOYD, Cathy, Chief Nursing Officer, Select Specialty Hospital–Pontiac, Pontiac, MI, p. A332

BOYD, Christopher L., Senior Vice President and Area Manager, Kaiser Permanente Santa Clara Medical Center, Santa Clara, CA, p. A93

BOYD, Dennis, Chief Financial Officer, St. Mark's Medical Center, La Grange, TX, p. A631

BOYD, Diana, Vice President Nursing, Union Hospital, Dover, OH, p. A493

BOYD, Ellen, Director Human Resources, Emanuel Medical Center, Swainsboro, GA, p. A167

BOYD, John W., PsyD,
  Chief Executive Officer, Sutter Center for Psychiatry, Sacramento, CA, p. A87
  Chief Executive Officer, Sutter Solano Medical Center, Vallejo, CA, p. A98

BOYD Jr., Kenneth, President and Chief Executive Officer, McDonough District Hospital, Macomb, IL, p. A195

BOYD, Kim, Chief Financial Officer, Buchanan General Hospital, Grundy, VA, p. A671

BOYD, Steven, R.N. Nurse Executive, Levi Hospital, Hot Springs National Park, AR, p. A47

BOYD, Travis, Manager, Information Technology, Mercy Hospital Lincoln, Troy, MO, p. A383

BOYER, Aurelia, Senior Vice President and Chief Information Officer, New York–Presbyterian Hospital, New York, NY, p. A447

BOYER, Charlene, Chief Nursing Officer, Kaiser Permanente Oakland Medical Center, Oakland, CA, p. A80

BOYER, Cheryl T.
  Vice President Human Resources, Levindale Hebrew Geriatric Center and Hospital, Baltimore, MD, p. A296
  Vice President Human Resources, Sinai Hospital of Baltimore, Baltimore, MD, p. A298

BOYER, Craig, Vice President Finance, Sanford Bemidji Medical Center, Bemidji, MN, p. A339

BOYER, Gregory E., Interim Administrator, Renown Rehabilitation Hospital, Reno, NV, p. A408

BOYER, Jeanne, R.N. Director of Nurses, Parkland Health Center–Bonne Terre, Bonne Terre, MO, p. A367

BOYER, Jim, Vice President Information Technology and Chief Information Officer, Rush Memorial Hospital, Rushville, IN, p. A221

BOYER, Roderick, M.D. Medical Director, Select Specialty Hospital–Downriver, Wyandotte, MI, p. A337

BOYER, Steve, M.D. Chief Medical Officer, Regional West Garden County, Oshkosh, NE, p. A401

BOYER, William, Chief Financial Officer, Community Memorial Hospital, Redfield, SD, p. A576

BOYKIN, George G., Chief Executive Officer, Rebound Behavioral Health, Lancaster, SC, p. A568

BOYLAN, Gene, Interim Chief Operating Officer, First Hospital Wyoming Valley, Kingston, PA, p. A541

BOYLE, Donna, Director, JFK Medical Center North Campus, West Palm Beach, FL, p. A149

BOYLE, James W., M.D. Chief Medical Officer, UPMC Passavant, Pittsburgh, PA, p. A551

BOYLE, Kathy, R.N. Chief Nursing Officer, Denver Health, Denver, CO, p. A103

BOYLE, Lisa, M.D. Vice President Medical Affairs and Medical Director, MedStar Georgetown University Hospital, Washington, DC, p. A121

BOYLE, Patrick R.
  Vice President Human Resources, Geneva General Hospital, Geneva, NY, p. A439
  Vice President Human Resources, Soldiers and Sailors Memorial Hospital of Yates County, Penn Yan, NY, p. A452

BOYLE, Thomas W., Chief Financial Officer, St. Lawrence Rehabilitation Center, Lawrenceville, NJ, p. A418

BOYLES, Clay
  Director Human Resources, Peachford Behavioral Health System, Atlanta, GA, p. A152
  Executive Director, Human Resources, Piedmont Newnan Hospital, Newnan, GA, p. A164

BOYLES, George, Senior Vice President of Finance and Chief Financial Officer, Mercer Health, Coldwater, OH, p. A490

BOYLES, Lee, President, CHI St. Gabriel's Health, Little Falls, MN, p. A345

BOYLES, Mary Gen, Chief Nursing Officer, HEALTHSOUTH Rehabilitation Hospital of Altoona, Altoona, PA, p. A532

BOYLES, Michael E., Chief Executive Officer and Administrator, Southeast Colorado Hospital District, Springfield, CO, p. A110

BOYNE, Barbara, Executive Director, Operations, Bethesda North Hospital, Cincinnati, OH, p. A487

BOYNTON, Jr., James P., Chief Financial Officer, Carolina Center for Behavioral Health, Greer, SC, p. A567

BOYNTON, Kimberly, President and Chief Executive Officer, Crouse Hospital, Syracuse, NY, p. A456

BOYNTON, Stephanie, Administrator, Erlanger Bledsoe Hospital, Pikeville, TN, p. A592

BOYSEN, Doug, Chief Legal Counsel and Vice President Human Resources, Good Samaritan Regional Medical Center, Corvallis, OR, p. A525

BOYSEN, James, M.D. Executive Medical Director, Texas NeuroRehab Center, Austin, TX, p. A600

BOZELL, Jerry, Vice President, Human Resources, Jay County Hospital, Portland, IN, p. A220

BOZZUTO, Elizabeth, R.N. Chief Nursing Officer and Vice President, Saint Mary's Hospital, Waterbury, CT, p. A117

BRAAM, Richard, Vice President Finance, MedStar St. Mary's Hospital, Leonardtown, MD, p. A302

BRAASCH, David A., President, Alton Memorial Hospital, Alton, IL, p. A180

BRABAND, Jon D., FACHE, President and Chief Executive Officer, Glencoe Regional Health Services, Glencoe, MN, p. A343

BRABY, Heath, Director Fiscal Services, Shriners Hospitals for Children–Salt Lake City, Salt Lake City, UT, p. A663

BRACCINO, Nick, Interim President, Littleton Regional Hospital, Littleton, NH, p. A412

BRACEY, Donny, Director Information Services, Marion General Hospital, Columbia, MS, p. A357

BRACK, Nancy R., Vice President Human Resources, Community Memorial Hospital, Syracuse, NE, p. A402

BRACKEEN, Steven W., R.N. Chief Nursing Officer, Merit Health Northwest Mississippi, Clarksdale, MS, p. A356

BRACKEN, Thomas H., M.D. Vice President Medical Affairs, Mille Lacs Health System, Onamia, MN, p. A348

BRACKETT, Lori, Director Human Resources, HEALTHSOUTH Bakersfield Rehabilitation Hospital, Bakersfield, CA, p. A56

BRACKLEY, Donna, R.N. Senior Vice President Patient Care Services, John Muir Medical Center, Concord, Concord, CA, p. A59

BRACKS, Adam, Chief Executive Officer, AllianceHealth Seminole, Seminole, OK, p. A519

BRACY, Dale, Chief Financial Officer, College Hospital Costa Mesa, Costa Mesa, CA, p. A60

BRADBURY, Monica, Chief Executive Officer, Clarks Summit State Hospital, Clarks Summit, PA, p. A535

BRADDOCK, Mary B., Director Human Resources, Palo Pinto General Hospital, Mineral Wells, TX, p. A637

BRADFORD, Beth, Director Human Resources, Floyd Medical Center, Rome, GA, p. A165

BRADFORD, Randy L., Chief Executive Officer, Eastern Shore Hospital Center, Cambridge, MD, p. A299

BRADFORD, Scot, Chief Information Officer, Baylor Medical Center at Trophy Club, Trophy Club, TX, p. A653

BRADFORD, Susan, Director Nursing, Kansas Heart Hospital, Wichita, KS, p. A255

BRADICK, Joe, Chief Financial Officer, Forks Community Hospital, Forks, WA, p. A685

BRADLEY, Berninia, Director, Human Resources, Corona Regional Medical Center, Corona, CA, p. A59

BRADLEY, Betsy, Coordinator Performance Improvement, Central State Hospital, Milledgeville, GA, p. A163

BRADLEY, Carol, MS
  Senior Vice President and Chief Nursing Officer, Legacy Meridian Park Medical Center, Tualatin, OR, p. A531
  Senior Vice President and Chief Nursing Officer, Legacy Salmon Creek Medical Center, Vancouver, WA, p. A692

BRADLEY, Connie, R.N
  Chief Nursing Officer, Health First Cape Canaveral Hospital, Cocoa Beach, FL, p. A126
  Senior Vice President and Chief Nursing Officer, Health First Palm Bay Hospital, Palm Bay, FL, p. A141
  Senior Vice President and Chief Nursing Officer, Health First Viera Hospital, Melbourne, FL, p. A135

BRADLEY, Deidre, Vice President Human Resources, Clark Regional Medical Center, Winchester, KY, p. A270

BRADLEY, Douglas, M.D. Chief Medical Officer, Belton Regional Medical Center, Belton, MO, p. A367

BRADLEY, Eric, Director Computer Information Services, Summit Behavioral Healthcare, Cincinnati, OH, p. A488

BRADLEY, Linda, Chief Executive Officer, Centinela Hospital Medical Center, Inglewood, CA, p. A66

BRADLEY, Louis, Chief Executive Officer, Mesquite Specialty Hospital, Mesquite, TX, p. A636

BRADLEY Jr., Louis P., Chief Executive Officer, Promise Hospital of Dallas, Dallas, TX, p. A611

BRADLEY, Melody, Chief Nursing Officer, Miracle Mile Medical Center, Los Angeles, CA, p. A73

BRADLEY, Michelle, Director Health Information Management, AMG Specialty Hospital–Wichita, Wichita, KS, p. A255

BRADLEY, Sara, Chief Financial Officer, Oklahoma State University Medical Center, Tulsa, OK, p. A521

BRADLEY, Scott, Interim Chief Executive Officer, Houston County Community Hospital, Erin, TN, p. A582

BRADLEY, Stacye, R.N. Chief Nursing Officer, Union County General Hospital, Clayton, NM, p. A428

BRADLEY, Terri, CPA Vice President Financial Services and Chief Financial Officer, Western Missouri Medical Center, Warrensburg, MO, p. A383

BRADLEY, William L., President and Chief Executive Officer, Washington Regional Medical Center, Fayetteville, AR, p. A46

BRADSHAW, Benjamin, M.D. President Medical Staff, Texas Health Presbyterian Hospital Kaufman, Kaufman, TX, p. A630

BRADSHAW, David
  Chief Information Officer, Memorial Hermann – Texas Medical Center, Houston, TX, p. A625
  Chief Information Officer, Memorial Hermann Greater Heights Hospital, Houston, TX, p. A625
  Chief Information, Planning and Marketing Officer, Memorial Hermann Memorial City Medical Center, Houston, TX, p. A625
  Chief Information Officer, Memorial Hermann Rehabilitation Hospital – Katy, Katy, TX, p. A630

BRADSHAW, Jeremy, Chief Executive Officer, Desert Springs Hospital Medical Center, Las Vegas, NV, p. A405

BRADSHAW, Pamela, Chief Nursing Officer, Shannon Medical Center, San Angelo, TX, p. A645

BRADSHAW, Rita, Director Human Resources, Chatuge Regional Hospital and Nursing Home, Hiawassee, GA, p. A160

BRADSHAW, Sarah, Vice President Nursing, Lawrence Memorial Hospital, Lawrence, KS, p. A247

BRADSHAW, Thomas A., Vice President Operations, Wayne Memorial Hospital, Goldsboro, NC, p. A466

BRADTMILLER, Theresa, Chief Nursing Officer, Adams Memorial Hospital, Decatur, IN, p. A209

BRADY, Dan, Chief Financial Officer, LDS Hospital, Salt Lake City, UT, p. A663

BRADY, James, Area Information Officer, Kaiser Permanente Orange County Anaheim Medical Center, Anaheim, CA, p. A54

BRADY, Jeff
  Director Information Systems, Hazard ARH Regional Medical Center, Hazard, KY, p. A261
  Director Information Systems, McDowell ARH Hospital, McDowell, KY, p. A266
  Director Information Systems, Morgan County ARH Hospital, West Liberty, KY, p. A270
  Chief Information Officer, Tug Valley ARH Regional Medical Center, South Williamson, KY, p. A269

BRADY, John, Vice President Physician Services and Organizational Planning, Marianjoy Rehabilitation Hospital, Wheaton, IL, p. A205

BRADY, Karen, Chief Operating Officer, Chief Nursing Officer and Chief Information Officer, Legacy Silverton Medical Center, Silverton, OR, p. A531

BRADY, Kit, Vice President Human Resources, Gillette Children's Specialty Healthcare, Saint Paul, MN, p. A350

BRADY, Linda, M.D., President and Chief Executive Officer, Kingsbrook Jewish Medical Center,, NY, p. A445

BRADY, Lisa, Senior Vice President and Chief Operating Officer, St. Joseph's Healthcare System, Paterson, NJ, p. A421

BRADY, Mike, Director Information Technology, UP Health System–Bell, Ishpeming, MI, p. A327

BRADY, Patrick R., Chief Executive Officer, Sutter Roseville Medical Center, Roseville, CA, p. A86

BRADY, Tim, Director Information Systems, Mt. Washington Pediatric Hospital, Baltimore, MD, p. A297

BRADY, Tonya, Director of Operations, Jewish Hospital–Shelbyville, Shelbyville, KY, p. A269

BRAEGGER, Bryan, Interim Chief Executive Officer, Yakima Regional Medical and Cardiac Center, Yakima, WA, p. A693

BRAGDON, Carol, Director Human Resources, Saint Thomas Rutherford Hospital, Murfreesboro, TN, p. A590

BRAGG, Craig, Chief Executive Officer, TrustPoint Rehabilitation Hospital of Lubbock, Lubbock, TX, p. A634

BRAGG, Deborah L., Senior Vice President, Finance, Decatur Memorial Hospital, Decatur, IL, p. A188

BRAGG, Lisa, Vice President Human Resources, Knox Community Hospital, Mount Vernon, OH, p. A499

BRAHM, Victoria, MSN, Acting Director, Tomah Veterans Affairs Medical Center, Tomah, WI, p. A717

BRAIN, David, Interim Vice President Finance, St. James Healthcare, Butte, MT, p. A386

BRAINERD, Mary K., President and Chief Executive Officer, HealthPartners, Bloomington, MN, p. B65

BRAINSTEIN, Paul, M.D. Interim Chief Medical Officer, Chesapeake Regional Healthcare, Chesapeake, VA, p. A668

BRAITHWAITE, Robert, President and Chief Executive Officer, Hoag Memorial Hospital Presbyterian, Newport Beach, CA, p. A79

BRETTNER, Eric, Vice President and Chief Financial Officer, St. Mary's Medical Center, San Francisco, CA, p. A90

BREUDER, Andrew, M.D. Chief of Staff, Manchester Veterans Affairs Medical Center, Manchester, NH, p. A412

BREUER, Jason, Chief Executive Officer, Stevens Community Medical Center, Morris, MN, p. A347

BREUER, Rick, Chief Executive Officer and Administrator, Community Memorial Hospital, Cloquet, MN, p. A340

BREUM, Linda G., R.N. Chief Nursing Officer, Florida Hospital New Smyrna, New Smyrna Beach, FL, p. A139

BREVING, Robert, M.D. Chief of Staff, National Park Medical Center, Hot Springs, AR, p. A47

BREWER, Becca, Chief Operations Officer, Falls Community Hospital and Clinic, Marlin, TX, p. A635

BREWER, David, Chief Financial Officer, ProMedica Memorial Hospital, Fremont, OH, p. A495

BREWER, Gary L., Chief Executive Officer, Valley View Hospital, Glenwood Springs, CO, p. A106

BREWER, Jennifer Lynn, Chief Executive Officer, HEALTHSOUTH Plano Rehabilitation Hospital, Plano, TX, p. A641

BREWER, Jim, M.P.H. Chief Financial Officer, Healthmark Regional Medical Center, DeFuniak Springs, FL, p. A127

BREWER, Kaye, Vice President Human Resources, Maury Regional Hospital, Columbia, TN, p. A581

BREWER, Kelley, MSN, President, Lakeside Women's Hospital, Oklahoma City, OK, p. A516

BREWER, Peter G., Administrator, Shriners Hospitals for Children–Spokane, Spokane, WA, p. A691

BREWER, Rebecca, FACHE, Chief Executive Officer, Lake Wales Medical Center, Lake Wales, FL, p. A133

BREWER, RN, Ruby, Senior Vice President, Chief Nursing and Quality Officer, East Jefferson General Hospital, Metairie, LA, p. A283

BREXLER, James L., President and Chief Executive Officer, Doylestown Hospital, Doylestown, PA, p. A537

BREYFOGLE, Cynthia, FACHE, Director, Charles George Veterans Affairs Medical Center, Asheville, NC, p. A460

BREZA, Lisa, R.N. Vice President and Chief Nursing Officer, Robert Wood Johnson University Hospital at Hamilton, Hamilton, NJ, p. A417

BREZNY, Angie, Director Human Resources, Prague Community Hospital, Prague, OK, p. A519

BRIAN, David
　Chief Information Officer, Shriners Hospitals for Children–Cincinnati Burns Hospital, Cincinnati, OH, p. A488
　Director Information Services, Shriners Hospitals for Children–Lexington, Lexington, KY, p. A263

BRICHER, Joan
　Senior Vice President Finance and Chief Financial Officer, Goleta Valley Cottage Hospital, Santa Barbara, CA, p. A93
　Senior Vice President Finance and Chief Financial Officer, Santa Barbara Cottage Hospital, Santa Barbara, CA, p. A93

BRICKER, Tim
　President and Chief Executive Officer, Chandler Regional Medical Center, Chandler, AZ, p. A31
　President and Chief Executive Officer, Mercy Gilbert Medical Center, Gilbert, AZ, p. A32

BRICKHOUSE, Jerimiah
　Chief Information Officer, St. Charles Bend, Bend, OR, p. A524
　Chief Information Officer, St. Charles Redmond, Redmond, OR, p. A530

BRICKNER, Derek, President Medical Staff, Jamestown Regional Medical Center, Jamestown, ND, p. A480

BRICKNER, Greg, Vice President and Director, Business Development, Wellstar Atlanta Medical Center, Atlanta, GA, p. A153

BRIDEAU, Donald, M.D. Chief Medical Officer, Inova Mount Vernon Hospital, Alexandria, VA, p. A667

BRIDEN, David, Chief Information Officer, Exeter Hospital, Exeter, NH, p. A411

BRIDGE, Lauren M., R.N. Chief Nursing Officer, Kaiser Permanente Sunnyside Medical Center, Clackamas, OR, p. A524

BRIDGELAND, Aaron
　Director Finance, Midwest Orthopedic Specialty Hospital, Franklin, WI, p. A705
　Director Finance, Wheaton Franciscan Healthcare – Franklin, Franklin, WI, p. A706
　Director Finance, Wheaton Franciscan Healthcare – St. Francis, Milwaukee, WI, p. A712

BRIDGES, Alan J., M.D. Chief of Staff, William S. Middleton Memorial Veterans Hospital, Madison, WI, p. A709

BRIDGES, Carol, M.D. Medical Director, Broadwater Health Center, Townsend, MT, p. A391

BRIDGES, James M., Executive Vice President and Chief Operating Officer, Palmetto Health Baptist, Columbia, SC, p. A564

BRIDGES, Jane Ann, Chief Financial Officer, Nacogdoches Memorial Hospital, Nacogdoches, TX, p. A638

BRIDGES, Mary, Director Human Resources, Ouachita County Medical Center, Camden, AR, p. A44

BRIDGES, Richard, M.D. Chief of Staff, Hood Memorial Hospital, Amite, LA, p. A271

BRIDGES, Stephanie, Chief Executive Officer, Kindred Hospital–St. Louis, Saint Louis, MO, p. A380

BRIDGES–KEE, Lorinnsa, Chief Human Resources Officer, Baylor Scott & White Medical Center – White Rock, Dallas, TX, p. A609

BRIDGEWATER, Melinda, Director, Information Services, Montana State Hospital, Warm Springs, MT, p. A391

BRIESEMEISTER, Eric, Chief Executive Officer, UnityPoint Health – Jones Regional Medical Center, Anamosa, IA, p. A225

BRIETE, Mark, M.D. Vice President Medical Affairs, Mercy Hospital Jefferson, Crystal City, MO, p. A370

BRIGGS, Deborah, Vice President Human Resources, Marketing, Volunteer Services and Community Relations, Ellenville Regional Hospital, Ellenville, NY, p. A438

BRIGGS, Gary, Vice President Human Resources, TriStar Southern Hills Medical Center, Nashville, TN, p. A591

BRIGGS, Michael, M.D. Chief Medical Officer, Essentia Health Fargo, Fargo, ND, p. A478

BRIGGS, Paul, Executive Vice President and Chief Operating Officer, Presbyterian Hospital, Albuquerque, NM, p. A428

BRIGGS, Sharlet
　Interim Executive Officer, San Gorgonio Memorial Hospital, Banning, CA, p. A56
　Chief Operating Officer, San Joaquin Community Hospital, Bakersfield, CA, p. A56

BRIGGS, Thomas, Chief Financial Officer, AllianceHealth Madill, Madill, OK, p. A514

BRIGGS, Vicki R., Interim Chief Operating Officer, St. Vincent's Medical Center, Bridgeport, CT, p. A113

BRIGHAM, Randy, Director Human Resources, Haxtun Hospital District, Haxtun, CO, p. A107

BRIGHT, Kim, M.D. Clinical Director, Springfield Hospital Center, Sykesville, MD, p. A303

BRILEY, Jay, President, Vidant Duplin Hospital, Kenansville, NC, p. A468

BRILL, Beth K., Senior Director Human Resources, Barnesville Hospital, Barnesville, OH, p. A484

BRILL, Elizabeth, M.D. Chief Operating Officer, OhioHealth Riverside Methodist Hospital, Columbus, OH, p. A491

BRILL, Karen, R.N. Chief Nursing Officer, Vice President Care, Gillette Children's Specialty Healthcare, Saint Paul, MN, p. A350

BRILLI, Richard, M.D. Chief Medical Officer, Nationwide Children's Hospital, Columbus, OH, p. A490

BRILLIANT, Patrick D., President and Chief Executive Officer, Riverside Community Hospital, Riverside, CA, p. A86

BRILLIANT, Steven, M.D. Chief of Staff, Veterans Affairs Sierra Nevada Health Care System, Reno, NV, p. A408

BRINDLE, Charles B., M.D. Chief Medical Staff, Iowa Specialty Hospital–Belmond, Belmond, IA, p. A225

BRINER, Junior, Chief Operating Officer, Lawrence Memorial Hospital, Walnut Ridge, AR, p. A53

BRINKERHOFF, Douglas, M.D. Clinical Director, San Carlos Apache Healthcare Corporation, Peridot, AZ, p. A35

BRINKHAUS, Theresa, Chief Financial Officer, St. Helena Parish Hospital, Greensburg, LA, p. A277

BRINKMAN, Dan, R.N., Chief Executive Officer, Hilo Medical Center, Hilo, HI, p. A170

BRINKMAN, Janet, Director Human Resources, Colorado Plains Medical Center, Fort Morgan, CO, p. A105

BRINSON, David, Director Information Technology, Parkview Wabash County Hospital, Wabash, IN, p. A223

BRINSON, Pam, Nurse Executive, South Mississippi State Hospital, Purvis, MS, p. A364

BRIONES, Melba, M.D. Medical Director, Evansville State Hospital, Evansville, IN, p. A210

BRISBOE, Mark
　VP and Chief Financial Officer, Sparrow Clinton Hospital, Saint Johns, MI, p. A333
　VP and Chief Financial Officer, Sparrow Ionia Hospital, Ionia, MI, p. A326

BRISCOE, Betsy, Chief Executive Officer, Memorial Hospital, Seminole, TX, p. A648

BRISCOE, Janell
　Chief Executive Officer, HEALTHSOUTH City View Rehabilitation Hospital, Fort Worth, TX, p. A618
　Chief Executive Officer, HEALTHSOUTH Rehabilitation Hospital of Fort Worth, Fort Worth, TX, p. A618

BRISCOE, Mary Beth, Chief Financial Officer, University of Alabama Hospital, Birmingham, AL, p. A17

BRISENDINE, Chad
　Vice President and Chief Information Officer, St. Luke's Hospital – Miners Campus, Coaldale, PA, p. A535
　Chief Information Officer, St. Luke's Hospital – Quakertown Campus, Quakertown, PA, p. A553
　Chief Information Officer, St. Luke's University Hospital – Bethlehem Campus, Bethlehem, PA, p. A533

BRISSE, Thomas M., President and Chief Executive Officer, McLaren Macomb, Mount Clemens, MI, p. A330

BRISTER, Kim, Director Human Resources, WellSpan Gettysburg Hospital, Gettysburg, PA, p. A539

BRISTER, Marilyn, M.D. Chief of Staff, Texas Health Harris Methodist Hospital Stephenville, Stephenville, TX, p. A650

BRISTO, Cathie, Director Human Resources, Wilbarger General Hospital, Vernon, TX, p. A655

BRISTOL, Michelle, Director of Nursing, Clifton–Fine Hospital, Star Lake, NY, p. A456

BRISTOLL, Holly L.
　President, ProMedica Bay Park Hospital, Oregon, OH, p. A500
　President, ProMedica Fostoria Community Hospital, Fostoria, OH, p. A494

BRISTOW, III, Clyde A., MSN Senior Director Nursing and Clinical Services, Chief Nursing Officer, Wake Forest Baptist Health–Lexington Medical Center, Lexington, NC, p. A469

BRITO, Manuela, Chief Financial Officer, NYC Health + Hospitals / Carter, New York, NY, p. A448

BRITT, Kevin, Chief Operating Officer, Reynolds Memorial Hospital, Glen Dale, WV, p. A696

BRITT, Key, Associate Director, Greenwood Leflore Hospital, Greenwood, MS, p. A358

BRITT, Linda, Director Information Systems, Baptist Memorial Hospital–North Mississippi, Oxford, MS, p. A363

BRITT, Suzanne, Director Human Resources, Samaritan Memorial Hospital, Macon, MO, p. A376

BRITT, Tommy, Vice President of Human Resources, West Georgia Health, Lagrange, GA, p. A161

BRITTAIN, Libby, Director Human Resources, Steele Memorial Medical Center, Salmon, ID, p. A178

BRITTON, David, Interim Chief Financial Officer, Medina Memorial Hospital, Medina, NY, p. A442

BRITTON, John, Vice President Information Services, Fisher–Titus Medical Center, Norwalk, OH, p. A500

BRITTON, Lynn, President and Chief Executive Officer, Mercy Health, Chesterfield, MO, p. B89

BRITTON, Natalie, Director Human Resources, Legacy Silverton Medical Center, Silverton, OR, p. A531

BRITTON, William N., Associate Administrator Finance, Alfred I. duPont Hospital for Children, Wilmington, DE, p. A120

BROADBENT, Sherri, D.O. Chief of Staff, Madison County Health Care System, Winterset, IA, p. A239

BROADWATER, Gary W., Chief Financial Officer, McCready Health, Crisfield, MD, p. A300

BROADWAY, Brenda, Chief Nursing Officer, CHI St. Luke's Health Memorial Specialty Hospital, Lufkin, TX, p. A634

BROADWAY, Chris, Manager Information Technology, Mayers Memorial Hospital District, Fall River Mills, CA, p. A62

BROBST, Mary, R.N. Senior Vice President Patient Care Services and Chief Nursing Officer, Mercy Medical Center–Cedar Rapids, Cedar Rapids, IA, p. A226

BROCK, B. J., Nursing Director, Tanner Higgins General Hospital, Bremen, GA, p. A155

BROCK, Berna, Vice President Human Resources, Adena Pike Medical Center, Waverly, OH, p. A505

BROCK, Jamie, Director Human Resources, Chan Soon–Shiong Medical Center, Windber, PA, p. A558

BROCK, Kyle, Vice President Human Resources, Glens Falls Hospital, Glens Falls, NY, p. A439

BROCK, Lisa M., Chief Human Resource Officer, Overlake Medical Center, Bellevue, WA, p. A682

BROCK, Melinda, Director Human Resources, AllianceHealth Woodward, Woodward, OK, p. A523

BROCK, Nancy, Chief Financial Officer, Houston Methodist St. Catherine Hospital, Katy, TX, p. A629

BROCK, Paul, Administrator, East Central Regional Hospital, Augusta, GA, p. A153

BROCK, Robert
　Chief Financial Officer and Vice President, Rollins–Brook Community Hospital, Lampasas, TX, p. A632
　Vice President Finance, Saint Joseph – Martin, Martin, KY, p. A266

BROCK, Shea C., Chief Financial Officer, Navarro Regional Hospital, Corsicana, TX, p. A608

BROCK, Steve, Chief Financial Officer, Lynn County Hospital District, Tahoka, TX, p. A651

BROCK, Theresa, Vice President Nursing, Good Shepherd Health Care System, Hermiston, OR, p. A526

BROCK, William, Chief Information Officer, Atlanta Veterans Affairs Medical Center, Decatur, GA, p. A158

BROCKERT, Nicholas, President, Saint Luke's Cushing Hospital, Leavenworth, KS, p. A247

BROCKETTE, Darby, Chief Executive Officer, Ernest Health, Inc., Albuquerque, NM, p. B54

BROCKHAUS, Jennifer, Chief Information Officer, Sidney Regional Medical Center, Sidney, NE, p. A402

BROCKHOUSE, Dena M., Director Human Resources, Mercy Iowa City, Iowa City, IA, p. A232

BROCKMEYER, Heather, Human Resource Administrative Officer, Nevada Regional Medical Center, Nevada, MO, p. A377

BROCKMEYER, JoEllyn, Director Human Resources, Indiana University Health White Memorial Hospital, Monticello, IN, p. A218

BROCKUS, Harry, Chief Executive Officer, Carle Hoopeston Regional Health Center, Hoopeston, IL, p. A193

BROCKWELL, Linda, Chief Nursing Officer, Wickenburg Community Hospital, Wickenburg, AZ, p. A41

BRODBECK, MSN, RN–, Kathleen, Chief Nursing Officer, St. James Mercy Hospital, Hornell, NY, p. A440

BRODBECK, Lisa, Chief Financial Officer, Medical Center of Lewisville, Lewisville, TX, p. A632

BRODEUR, Mark S., FACHE, Chief Executive Officer, Select Specialty Hospital–Springfield, Springfield, MO, p. A383

BRODHEAD, Richard Ross, Director Human Resources, St. Vincent Randolph Hospital, Winchester, IN, p. A224

BRODHEAD, Ross
 Executive Director, Human Resources, St. Vincent Anderson Regional Hospital, Anderson, IN, p. A206
 Manager Human Resources, St. Vincent Mercy Hospital, Elwood, IN, p. A209

BRODIAN, Craig R., Vice President Human Resources, Johns Hopkins Bayview Medical Center, Baltimore, MD, p. A296

BRODRICK, Theresa M., R.N
 Chief Nursing Officer, Alamance Regional Medical Center, Burlington, NC, p. A461
 Executive Vice President and Chief Nursing Officer, Moses H. Cone Memorial Hospital, Greensboro, NC, p. A466

BRODY, Anne Marie, Director Information Systems Customer Service, Providence Saint Joseph Medical Center, Burbank, CA, p. A57

BROEKHUIS, Arlyn
 Chief Information Officer, Sanford Medical Center Fargo, Fargo, ND, p. A479
 Vice President and Chief Information Officer, Sanford USD Medical Center, Sioux Falls, SD, p. A576

BROERMANN, Robert
 Senior Vice President and Chief Financial Officer, Sentara Leigh Hospital, Norfolk, VA, p. A675
 Senior Vice President and Chief Financial Officer, Sentara Norfolk General Hospital, Norfolk, VA, p. A675
 Senior Vice President and Chief Financial Officer, Sentara Princess Anne Hospital, Virginia Beach, VA, p. A680

BROGAN Jr., Gerard, M.D., Executive Director, Huntington Hospital, Huntington, NY, p. A440

BROGGER, Portlyn
 Chief Executive Officer, Post Acute Medical Specialty Hospital of Victoria, Victoria, TX, p. A655
 Chief Executive Officer, Post Acute/Warm Springs Specialty Hospital of Victoria, Victoria, TX, p. A655

BROHAWN, Bill, Chief of Staff, Trace Regional Hospital, Houston, MS, p. A359

BROKAW, Sara, Vice President Patient Care Services, Bellevue Hospital, Bellevue, OH, p. A485

BROKENSHIRE, Shelia Kay, Vice President of Nursing, Van Wert County Hospital, Van Wert, OH, p. A504

BROMAN, Craig J., FACHE, President, St. Cloud Hospital, Saint Cloud, MN, p. A350

BROMLEY, Trudy, Vice President Human Resources, JFK Medical Center, Atlantis, FL, p. A123

BRONER, Eloise, President and Chief Executive Officer, Good Samaritan Hospital, Dayton, OH, p. A492

BRONHARD, John, Chief Financial Officer, HealthAlliance Hospitals, Leominster, MA, p. A311

BROOCKS, Kelli C., Director Human Resources, Public Relations and Physician Recruitment, Beauregard Memorial Hospital, De Ridder, LA, p. A276

BROOKE, William R., M.D. President Medical Staff, Pickens County Medical Center, Carrollton, AL, p. A18

BROOKER, Brian, Chief Executive Officer, Cypress Creek Hospital, Houston, TX, p. A624

BROOKER, Doug A., Chief Financial Officer, Bryan W. Whitfield Memorial Hospital, Demopolis, AL, p. A19

BROOKER, Paula, Director Information Services, Pleasant Valley Hospital, Point Pleasant, WV, p. A699

BROOKER, Susan E., R.N. Chief Clinical Officer, Vibra Specialty Hospital of Portland, Portland, OR, p. A530

BROOKES, Jeffrey, M.D
 Chief Medical Officer, Parkview LaGrange Hospital, LaGrange, IN, p. A216
 Medical Director, Parkview Whitley Hospital, Columbia City, IN, p. A208

BROOKMAN, Mark
 Chief Information Officer, Medical Center at Bowling Green, Bowling Green, KY, p. A258
 Vice President and Chief Information Officer, Medical Center at Franklin, Franklin, KY, p. A260
 Chief Information Officer, Medical Center at Scottsville, Scottsville, KY, p. A269
 Chief Information Officer, The Medical Center Albany, Albany, KY, p. A257
 Vice President, Chief Information Officer, The Medical Center at Caverna, Horse Cave, KY, p. A262

BROOKS, Albert, M.D. Chief Medical Staff Services, Washington Hospital Healthcare System, Fremont, CA, p. A63

BROOKS, Anthony, Chief Information Officer, Miami Veterans Affairs Healthcare System, Miami, FL, p. A137

BROOKS, April, Chief Nursing Officer, HEALTHSOUTH Rehabilitation Hospital of Columbia, Columbia, SC, p. A564

BROOKS, Brian, Information Manager, DeWitt Hospital, DeWitt, AR, p. A45

BROOKS, Colin B., Chief Financial Officer, Southwest General Hospital, San Antonio, TX, p. A647

BROOKS, David
 President, St. Joseph Mercy Ann Arbor, Ypsilanti, MI, p. A337
 President, St. Joseph Mercy Livingston Hospital, Howell, MI, p. A326

BROOKS, Harris W., Chief Executive Officer, Palo Pinto General Hospital, Mineral Wells, TX, p. A637

BROOKS, Jeffrey, M.D. Chief Medical Officer, Parkview Huntington Hospital, Huntington, IN, p. A213

BROOKS, Jerome M., Chief Operating Officer, South Texas Health System, Edinburg, TX, p. A614

BROOKS, Joe, Chief Financial Officer, Keystone Newport News, Newport News, VA, p. A674

BROOKS, Lisa, Chief Financial Officer, Comanche County Hospital, Coldwater, KS, p. A241

BROOKS, Lori, Director Human Resources, Red Bud Regional Hospital, Red Bud, IL, p. A201

BROOKS, Nick, Director of Information Systems, Citrus Memorial Health System, Inverness, FL, p. A131

BROOKS, Patrice Gay, Chief Executive Officer, Cumberland Hospital, New Kent, VA, p. A674

BROOKS, Robert M., FACHE Executive Vice President, Chief Operating Officer, Erlanger Medical Center, Chattanooga, TN, p. A580

BROOKS, Steven Michael, Vice President Human Resources, Southeastern Ohio Regional Medical Center, Cambridge, OH, p. A486

BROOKS, Troy, Assistant Administrator Fiscal Services, Piedmont Newton Hospital, Covington, GA, p. A157

BROOKS–WILLIAMS, Denise, President and Chief Executive Officer, Henry Ford Wyandotte Hospital, Wyandotte, MI, p. A337

BROOKSHIRE–HEAVIN, Keri S., Chief Nurse Executive, Phelps County Regional Medical Center, Rolla, MO, p. A379

BROPHY, Beth, Interim VP for Human Resources, Hurley Medical Center, Flint, MI, p. A323

BROSIUS, William, Vice President and Chief Financial Officer, Baylor St. Luke's Medical Center, Houston, TX, p. A623

BROSKEY, Steven, Associate Director, Veterans Affairs Roseburg Healthcare System, Roseburg, OR, p. A530

BROSNAHAN, Jan, Chief Financial Officer, Winona Health, Winona, MN, p. A353

BROSNAN, Kimberly, Director Human Resources, Norwood Hospital, Norwood, MA, p. A313

BROSS, James B., President, St. Luke's Hospital, Columbus, NC, p. A463

BROST, Wade, Interim Executive Director, Anoka–Metropolitan Regional Treatment Center, Anoka, MN, p. A338

BROTEN, Kurt
 Chief Financial Officer, Palmdale Regional Medical Center, Palmdale, CA, p. A81
 Chief Financial Officer, Vista Del Mar Hospital, Ventura, CA, p. A98

BROTHMAN, Joe, Assistant Vice President, Information Systems, MedStar Washington Hospital Center, Washington, DC, p. A122

BROUGHMAN, Robin, R.N. Chief Nursing Officer, LewisGale Hospital Alleghany, Low Moor, VA, p. A672

BROUGHMAN, Wade, Executive Vice President and Chief Financial Officer, Riverside Regional Medical Center, Newport News, VA, p. A674

BROUSSARD, Clifford M., FACHE, Administrator, WK Bossier Health Center, Bossier City, LA, p. A274

BROUSSARD, Heidi, Chief Nursing Officer, Abbeville General Hospital, Abbeville, LA, p. A271

BROUSSARD, Terry J., Interim Chief Nursing Officer, Our Lady of Lourdes Regional Medical Center, Lafayette, LA, p. A281

BROUWER, Heath, Administrator, Douglas County Memorial Hospital, Armour, SD, p. A572

BROVOLD, Diana, Chief Nurse Executive, MultiCare Mary Bridge Children's Hospital and Health Center, Tacoma, WA, p. A692

BROWDER, Renate, R.N. Director of Nursing, Lake City Community Hospital, Lake City, SC, p. A567

BROWER, Laura E., R.N. Chief Nursing Officer, Augusta University Medical Center, Augusta, GA, p. A153

BROWN, Alisa, Administrative Assistant, DeWitt Hospital, DeWitt, AR, p. A45

BROWN, Angel, Director Human Resources, Morton Plant Hospital, Clearwater, FL, p. A125

BROWN, Ann R., M.D., Director, VA Greater Los Angeles Healthcare System, Los Angeles, CA, p. A74

BROWN, Austin, Interim Chief Executive Officer, Seven Rivers Regional Medical Center, Crystal River, FL, p. A126

BROWN, B. Blaine, Vice President and General Counsel, Prattville Baptist Hospital, Prattville, AL, p. A25

BROWN, Bartley, D.O. Chief of Staff, St. Joseph's Hospital of Buckhannon, Buckhannon, WV, p. A694

BROWN, Bryan
 Director Information Services and Technology, Corpus Christi Medical Center, Corpus Christi, TX, p. A607
 Executive Director, Mercy Hospital Fort Smith, Fort Smith, AR, p. A46

BROWN, Chad J., M.P.H., President, Wake Forest Baptist Health–Davie Medical Center, Mocksville, NC, p. A469

BROWN, Cheryl, Administrator, Henderson Health Care Services, Henderson, NE, p. A397

BROWN, Chistiane, Assistant Vice President, MedStar Montgomery Medical Center, Olney, MD, p. A302

BROWN, Christi, Director Human Resources, Our Lady of the Angels Hospital, Bogalusa, LA, p. A274

BROWN, Crystal, M.D. Medical Director, Medical Center of Peach County, Navicent Health, Bryon, GA, p. A155

BROWN, Cynthia, Director of Nursing, Hill Hospital of Sumter County, York, AL, p. A27

BROWN, Damon, Chief Executive Officer, AllianceHealth Midwest, Midwest City, OK, p. A514

BROWN, Darin, Vice President Finance, Henry County Hospital, New Castle, IN, p. A219

BROWN, David A., Director Human Resources and Corporate Compliance, Pleasant Valley Hospital, Point Pleasant, WV, p. A699

BROWN, Deana, Director Administrative Services, Franciscan Health Rensselear, Rensselaer, IN, p. A221

BROWN, Debbie T., R.N. Chief Nursing Officer, EvergreenHealth Monroe, Monroe, WA, p. A686

BROWN, Deborah, Chief Nursing Officer, Logan Memorial Hospital, Russellville, KY, p. A269

BROWN, Debra L., Area Financial Officer, Kaiser Permanente Manteca Medical Center, Manteca, CA, p. A76

BROWN, Denise, Vice President Human Resources, Presence Saint Joseph Hospital, Chicago, IL, p. A185

BROWN, Derek, Chief Information Officer, Jellico Community Hospital, Jellico, TN, p. A585

BROWN, Doris, Chief Executive Officer and Administrator, Carnegie Tri–County Municipal Hospital, Carnegie, OK, p. A509

BROWN, Ed, Chief Information Officer, Medical Center, Navicent Health, Macon, GA, p. A162

BROWN, Eric, M.D. Physician Executive, Palmetto Health Richland, Columbia, SC, p. A564

BROWN, Geoffrey
 Vice President Information Systems, Inova Fairfax Hospital, Falls Church, VA, p. A670
 Chief Information Officer, Piedmont Fayette Hospital, Fayetteville, GA, p. A159
 Chief Information Officer, Piedmont Mountainside Hospital, Jasper, GA, p. A161

BROWN, George J., M.D., President and Chief Executive Officer, Legacy Health, Portland, OR, p. B80

BROWN, Howard, Chief Financial Officer, North Shore Medical Center, Miami, FL, p. A137

BROWN, James H., Chief Financial Officer, Centerpoint Medical Center, Independence, MO, p. A372

BROWN, Janice, Chief Financial Officer, Coosa Valley Medical Center, Sylacauga, AL, p. A25

BROWN, Jason, M.D. Chief Medical Officer, Banner Goldfield Medical Center, Apache Junction, AZ, p. A31

BROWN, Jason, Director Information Systems, Sanford Sheldon Medical Center, Sheldon, IA, p. A237

BROWN, Jay
 Vice President and Chief Information Officer, University of Cincinnati Medical Center, Cincinnati, OH, p. A488
 Senior Vice President, Chief Information Officer, West Chester Hospital, West Chester, OH, p. A505

BROWN, Jayma, Director of Nursing, Oakland Mercy Hospital, Oakland, NE, p. A399

BROWN, Jeffrey L., Director Information Systems, Lawrence General Hospital, Lawrence, MA, p. A311

BROWN, Jeffrey P., M.D. Chief Medical Officer, Indiana University Health Arnett Hospital, Lafayette, IN, p. A216

BROWN, Jenny, Human Resources Director, Vidant Beaufort Hospital, Washington, NC, p. A475

BROWN, Jill, Chief Financial Officer, Miller County Hospital, Colquitt, GA, p. A156

BROWN, Jim, Director Information Technology, Lynn County Hospital District, Tahoka, TX, p. A651

BROWN, John D., Director Information Systems, Pacific Alliance Medical Center, Los Angeles, CA, p. A73

BROWN, Jon, Chief Information Officer, Mission Hospital, Asheville, NC, p. A460

BROWN, Joni, Director Human Resources, Rehabilitation Hospital of Indiana, Indianapolis, IN, p. A214

BROWN, Joseph, Vice President Operations, Baylor Regional Medical Center at Plano, Plano, TX, p. A641

BROWN, Judy, Executive Vice President and Chief Operating Officer, East Jefferson General Hospital, Metairie, LA, p. A283

BROWN, Karen
    Senior Director of Human Resources, BridgePoint Hospital Capitol Hill, Washington, DC, p. A121
    Manager Information Technology, Guthrie Towanda Memorial Hospital, Towanda, PA, p. A555

BROWN, Karen C., Vice President Chief Operating Officer, OSF Saint Anthony Medical Center, Rockford, IL, p. A202

BROWN, Katie, Coordinator Human Resources, Pocahontas Memorial Hospital, Buckeye, WV, p. A694

BROWN, Ken, Vice President and Chief Human Resource Officer, Pratt Regional Medical Center, Pratt, KS, p. A252

BROWN, Kendra, Job Requisition Coordinator, Rusk State Hospital, Rusk, TX, p. A644

BROWN, Kevin, President and Chief Executive Officer, Piedmont Healthcare, Atlanta, GA, p. B104

BROWN, Kris, Associate Director, Bay Pines Veterans Affairs Healthcare System, Bay Pines, FL, p. A123

BROWN, LaRay, President and Chief Executive Officer, Interfaith Medical Center,, NY, p. A444

BROWN, Lewis, Director Information Technology, BSA Hospital, LLC, Amarillo, TX, p. A596

BROWN, Lisa, Director of Nursing, Pearl River County Hospital, Poplarville, MS, p. A364

BROWN, Liz, Manager Human Resources, Gunnison Valley Hospital, Gunnison, UT, p. A660

BROWN, Lorenzo, Chief Executive Officer, Florida Hospital DeLand, DeLand, FL, p. A127

BROWN, Lori, Chief Nursing Officer, Baptist Memorial Hospital–Union City, Union City, TN, p. A594

BROWN, Lori J., R.N. Vice President and Chief Nursing Executive, Borgess Medical Center, Kalamazoo, MI, p. A327

BROWN, Margaret, Director Medical Records, Vantage Point of Northwest Arkansas, Fayetteville, AR, p. A46

BROWN, Markham, M.D. Chief Medical Staff, Mike O'Callaghan Federal Hospital, Nellis AFB, NV, p. A407

BROWN, Marlon, Human Resources, Essex County Hospital Center, Cedar Grove, NJ, p. A415

BROWN, Martin, Vice President Information Services and Chief Information Officer, Nathan Littauer Hospital and Nursing Home, Gloversville, NY, p. A439

BROWN, Mary Beth, Director Human Resources, Bertrand Chaffee Hospital, Springville, NY, p. A464

BROWN, Mary J., MSN Vice President and Chief Nursing Officer, Mercy Medical Center–Des Moines, Des Moines, IA, p. A229

BROWN, Mary W., Senior Vice President Operations, St. Joseph's Hospital Health Center, Syracuse, NY, p. A456

BROWN, Michael, D.O. Chief of Staff, TMC Bonham Hospital, Bonham, TX, p. A603

BROWN, Michael L.
    Regional President and Chief Executive Officer, Presence Mercy Medical Center, Aurora, IL, p. A180
    Regional President and Chief Executive Officer, Presence Saint Joseph Hospital, Elgin, IL, p. A189

BROWN, Mike, Chief Financial Officer, Carlinville Area Hospital, Carlinville, IL, p. A182

BROWN, Molly B., Chief Operating Officer, University of Mississippi Medical Center Grenada, Grenada, MS, p. A358

BROWN, Nancy, R.N. Vice President Patient Care Services and Chief Nursing Officer, Norman Regional Health System, Norman, OK, p. A515

BROWN, Natalie, Chief Human Resources Management Services, Memphis Veterans Affairs Medical Center, Memphis, TN, p. A589

BROWN, Pam, Human Resources Manager, Behavioral HealthCare Center at Columbia, Columbia, TN, p. A581

BROWN, Pat, R.N. Chief Nursing Officer, San Gorgonio Memorial Hospital, Banning, CA, p. A56

BROWN, Patsy, Site Coordinator Human Resources, Erlanger Bledsoe Hospital, Pikeville, TN, p. A592

BROWN, Patti, M.D. Medical Director, HEALTHSOUTH Reading Rehabilitation Hospital, Reading, PA, p. A553

BROWN, Penny D., Director of Human Resources, Broaddus Hospital, Philippi, WV, p. A699

BROWN, Philip, D.O. Vice President Medical Affairs, The University of Vermont Health Network Central Vermont Medical Center, Berlin, VT, p. A665

BROWN, Phyllis, Chief Executive Officer, Marshall Medical Center, Lewisburg, TN, p. A587

BROWN, Randal, M.D. Chief of Staff, Guadalupe County Hospital, Santa Rosa, NM, p. A431

BROWN, Regenia, Vice President Human Resources, Magnolia Regional Health Center, Corinth, MS, p. A357

BROWN, Rex H., President and Chief Executive Officer, Hillsboro Area Hospital, Hillsboro, IL, p. A193

BROWN, Rickie F., Chief Financial Officer, Monroe County Medical Center, Tompkinsville, KY, p. A270

BROWN, Rita, Director Human Resources, Richardson Medical Center, Rayville, LA, p. A286

BROWN, Robert, M.D. Chief Medical Officer, Park Plaza Hospital, Houston, TX, p. A626

BROWN, Robert, Chief Operating Officer, Parkview Community Hospital Medical Center, Riverside, CA, p. A86

BROWN, Roberta, Chief Nursing Officer, Community Memorial Hospital, Staunton, IL, p. A204

BROWN, Robin
    Chief Executive, Senior Vice President, Scripps Green Hospital, La Jolla, CA, p. A67
    Chief Information Officer and Compliance Officer, St. Joseph Medical Center, Houston, TX, p. A626

BROWN, Rodger, Vice President Human Resources, North Mississippi Medical Center – Tupelo, Tupelo, MS, p. A365

BROWN, Rodney, Chief Executive Officer, Landmark Hospital of Cape Girardeau, Cape Girardeau, MO, p. A368

BROWN, Scott, Chief Financial Officer, Valir Rehabilitation Hospital, Oklahoma City, OK, p. A518

BROWN, Shane, Vice President and Chief Human Resources Officer, CGH Medical Center, Sterling, IL, p. A204

BROWN, Shannon, Chief Executive Officer, Huntsville Memorial Hospital, Huntsville, TX, p. A628

BROWN, Sharon, Vice President Human Resources, Sierra View Medical Center, Porterville, CA, p. A83

BROWN, Sharon, R.N. Vice President Patient Care and Chief Nursing Officer, St. Mary Medical Center, Langhorne, PA, p. A542

BROWN, Sharon, Deputy Commander Nursing, Winn Army Community Hospital, Hinesville, GA, p. A160

BROWN, Sherry, Director Human Resources, Cleveland Area Hospital, Cleveland, OK, p. A510

BROWN, Stephen A., Chief Financial Officer, Grace Cottage Hospital, Townshend, VT, p. A666

BROWN, Steve, M.D. Chief Quality Officer, Saint Alphonsus Regional Medical Center, Boise, ID, p. A174

BROWN, Steve
    Director Information Systems, Spalding Regional Hospital, Griffin, GA, p. A160
    Chief Information Officer, Sylvan Grove Hospital, Jackson, GA, p. A161
    Health Services Director, U. S. Penitentiary Infirmary, Lewisburg, PA, p. A543

BROWN, Steven
    Vice President Finance, Anderson Regional Health System, Meridian, MS, p. A362
    Vice President Finance, Anderson Regional Health System South, Meridian, MS, p. A362
    Vice President Fiscal Affairs, Mary Rutan Hospital, Bellefontaine, OH, p. A485

BROWN, Steven, M.D. Medical Director, Wyoming Behavioral Institute, Casper, WY, p. A721

BROWN, Steven E., FACHE, President and Chief Executive Officer, Mount Nittany Medical Center, State College, PA, p. A555

BROWN, Susan
    Chief Nursing Officer, El Paso Behavioral Health System, El Paso, TX, p. A615
    Chief Human Resources Officer, North Fulton Regional Hospital, Roswell, GA, p. A165

BROWN, Susan E., R.N. Senior Vice President, Chief Nursing Officer, Carolinas Healthcare System Blue Ridge, Morganton, NC, p. A470

BROWN, Theodore, Chief Operating Officer, Community Howard Regional Health, Kokomo, IN, p. A216

BROWN, Todd A., M.D. Medical Director, Logan Regional Hospital, Logan, UT, p. A660

BROWN, Tom, M.D. President Medical Staff, Wayne Hospital, Greenville, OH, p. A495

BROWN, Traci, Human Resources Generalist, Medical Arts Hospital, Lamesa, TX, p. A632

BROWN, Vance, M.D., President and Chief Executive Officer, Bassett Healthcare Network, Cooperstown, NY, p. B21

BROWN, Vance, M.D., President and Chief Executive Officer, Bassett Medical Center, Cooperstown, NY, p. A437

BROWN, Wendy W., M.D. Chief of Staff, Jesse Brown Veterans Affairs Medical Center, Chicago, IL, p. A184

BROWN, William A., FACHE, President and CEO, Baptist Health Paducah, Paducah, KY, p. A267

BROWN, William V., Chief Executive Officer, Audubon Behavioral Healthcare, Longview, TX, p. B16

BROWN, Willie, Director Administration, Naval Hospital Beaufort, Beaufort, SC, p. A562

BROWN, Winfield S., FACHE,
    President and Chief Executive Officer, Athol Memorial Hospital, Athol, MA, p. A305
    President and Chief Executive Officer, Heywood Hospital, Gardner, MA, p. A310

BROWN–ROBERTS, Bonita, Director Information Systems, Advocate Trinity Hospital, Chicago, IL, p. A183

BROWN–TEZERA, Belina, MSN Associate Director Patient Care Services, John D. Dingell Veterans Affairs Medical Center, Detroit, MI, p. A322

BROWNE, J. Timothy, FACHE, Chief Executive Officer, Carolina Pines Regional Medical Center, Hartsville, SC, p. A567

BROWNE, John
    Senior Chief Financial Officer, Kindred Hospital Riverside, Perris, CA, p. A82
    Assistant Administrator Finance, Kindred Hospital–Brea, Brea, CA, p. A57

BROWNE, Mark, M.D
    Covenant Health, Senior Vice President and Chief Medical Officer, Methodist Medical Center of Oak Ridge, Oak Ridge, TN, p. A592
    Chief Medical Officer, Roane Medical Center, Harriman, TN, p. A583

BROWNER, Warren S., M.P.H.,
    Chief Executive Officer, California Pacific Medical Center, San Francisco, CA, p. A90
    Chief Executive Officer, St. Luke's Hospital, San Francisco, CA, p. A90

BROWNEWELL, Victoria, Chief Nursing Officer, Houston Methodist West Hospital, Houston, TX, p. A624

BROWNFIELD, Mona, M.D. Chief Medical Staff, Cooper County Memorial Hospital, Boonville, MO, p. A368

BROWNING, Douglas
    Chief Financial Officer, Porter Regional Hospital, Valparaiso, IN, p. A223
    Chief Financial Officer, Texas Health Center for Diagnostic & Surgery, Plano, TX, p. A642

BROWNING, Michael
    Chief Financial Officer, Madison Health, London, OH, p. A497
    Chief Financial Officer, ProMedica Flower Hospital, Sylvania, OH, p. A503

BROWNSTEIN, Gregory, Chief Executive Officer, Westwood Lodge Hospital, Westwood, MA, p. A316

BROWNSWORTH, Ray, Chief Executive Officer, Van Buren County Hospital, Keosauqua, IA, p. A233

BROYHILL, David, Chief Information Management, Brooke Army Medical Center, Fort Sam Houston, TX, p. A617

BROYLES, Susan, Director Human Resources and Safety, Unicoi County Memorial Hospital, Erwin, TN, p. A582

BRUBAKER, Kathy M., R.N. Vice President and Chief Nursing Officer, St. Joseph Mercy Chelsea, Chelsea, MI, p. A320

BRUBAKER, Margaret M., Senior Vice President Human Resources, Brookdale Hospital Medical Center, New York, NY, p. A444

BRUCE, Bill, FACHE, Chief Executive Officer, Crawford County Memorial Hospital, Denison, IA, p. A229

BRUCE, Caleigh, Vice President Human Resources, Ferrell Hospital, Eldorado, IL, p. A189

BRUCE, Jordan, Administrator, Norwood Health Center, Marshfield, WI, p. A710

BRUCE, Karen, Director of Nursing, Keystone Newport News, Newport News, VA, p. A674

BRUCE, Michael D., Chief Executive Officer, Lake Martin Community Hospital, Dadeville, AL, p. A18

BRUCE, Mike, Chief Financial Officer, Elmore Community Hospital, Wetumpka, AL, p. A26

BRUCE, Paul, Chief Nursing Officer, Vibra Rehabilitation Hospital Lake Travis, Lakeway, TX, p. A631

BRUCE, Scott, Vice President Operations, St. Mary's Healthcare, Amsterdam, NY, p. A434

BRUCKNER, Alison, Chief Operating Officer, Cass County Memorial Hospital, Atlantic, IA, p. A225

BRUDNICKI, Gary F., Senior Executive Vice President, Chief Operating Officer and Chief Financial Officer, Westchester Medical Center, Valhalla, NY, p. A458

BRUEGGEMANN, Marty, Chief Medical Officer, Yakima Valley Memorial Hospital, Yakima, WA, p. A693

BRUELS, Raymond, Manager Information Technology, Natchitoches Regional Medical Center, Natchitoches, LA, p. A284

BRUENS, Dennis, Vice President Operations, St. Thomas More Hospital, Canon City, CO, p. A102

BRUFF, Edward, President and Chief Executive Officer, Covenant Healthcare, Saginaw, MI, p. A333

BRUGGEMAN, Chris, Chief Operating Officer, RiverView Health, Crookston, MN, p. A341

BRUHL, Lisa G., Chief Operating Officer, Lallie Kemp Medical Center, Independence, LA, p. A278

BRUHL, Steven, Chief Medical Officer, Mercy Tiffin Hospital, Tiffin, OH, p. A503

BRUHN, Julie, R.N. Associate Director Patient Care and Nurse Executive, Fargo Veterans Affairs Health Care System, Fargo, ND, p. A478

BRUHN, Julie, Administrative Operations Support Analyst, North Oaks Health System, Hammond, LA, p. B96

BRUI, Thomas M., Director Resource Management, Naval Hospital Lemoore, Lemoore, CA, p. A68

BRUINS, Melanie, Chief Talent Officer, Beaver Dam Community Hospitals, Beaver Dam, WI, p. A703

BRUMFIELD, Derrick, Chief Operating Officer, SageWest Health Care at Riverton, Riverton, WY, p. A723

BRUMFIELD, Rita, R.N. Chief Nursing Officer, Ste. Genevieve County Memorial Hospital, Ste. Genevieve, MO, p. A383

BRUMMER, Amy, R.N. Chief Nursing Officer, Saint Luke's North Hospital – Barry Road, Kansas City, MO, p. A374

BRUMMETT, Vince, Director Administrative Services, Merit Health Batesville, Batesville, MS, p. A355

BRUNDISE, Cynthia, Vice President Human Resources, St. Anthony Hospital, Oklahoma City, OK, p. A517

BRUNELLE, Diane, MSN Director Patient Care Services and Chief Nursing Officer, Shriners Hospitals for Children–Springfield, Springfield, MA, p. A315

BRUNER, Deborah, Chief Executive Officer and Administrator, Minneola District Hospital, Minneola, KS, p. A249

BRUNING, Troy, Director Information Technology, Meeker Memorial Hospital, Litchfield, MN, p. A345

BRUNKE, Renea, Vice President Human Resources, Chandler Regional Medical Center, Chandler, AZ, p. A31

BRUNN, Mary E., R.N. Acting Associate Director Nursing, Clement J. Zablocki Veterans Affairs Medical Center, Milwaukee, WI, p. A711

BRUNO, Catherine, FACHE Chief Information Officer, Eastern Maine Medical Center, Bangor, ME, p. A291

BRUNO, John P., Vice President Human Resources, St. Joseph's Healthcare System, Paterson, NJ, p. A421

BRUNO, Yolanda, M.D. Medical Director, NYC Health + Hospitals / Carter, New York, NY, p. A448

BRUNS, Susan, Chief Nursing Officer, Phoebe Sumter Medical Center, Americus, GA, p. A151

BRUNSON, Pam, Director Human Resources, South Baldwin Regional Medical Center, Foley, AL, p. A20

BRUNT, C. Hal, M.D. Medical Director, Lakeside Behavioral Health System, Memphis, TN, p. A589

BRUNTON, Hope, Chief Manpower Branch, Irwin Army Community Hospital, Junction City, KS, p. A246

BRUNTZ, Troy, Vice President Finance and Chief Financial Officer, Community Hospital, McCook, NE, p. A398

BRUS, Sarah, Director Human Resources, Doctor's Memorial Hospital, Perry, FL, p. A142

BRUSCO, Louis, M.D. Chief Medical Officer, Morristown Medical Center, Morristown, NJ, p. A419

BRUSVEN, Jessica, Chief Executive Officer, Marias Medical Center, Shelby, MT, p. A391

BRUTON, Jeff, Director Human Resources, Fairview Park Hospital, Dublin, GA, p. A159

BRUUN, Edward, President and Chief Executive Officer, Sparrow Clinton Hospital, Saint Johns, MI, p. A333

BRVENIK, Richard A., FACHE, President, Carteret Health Care, Morehead City, NC, p. A470

BRYAN, Darlene, R.N. Chief Nursing Officer, Humboldt General Hospital, Winnemucca, NV, p. A409

BRYAN, Douglas, President, Medical Staff, Mercy Harvard Hospital, Harvard, IL, p. A192

BRYAN, Jason, Director Human Resources, Middle Park Medical Center–Kremmling, Kremmling, CO, p. A107

BRYAN, Jay, President and Chief Executive Officer, Mercy Health, Lakeshore Campus, Shelby, MI, p. A334

BRYAN, Kenneth E., FACHE President and Chief Executive Officer, Harnett Health System, Dunn, NC, p. A464

BRYAN, Linda, Vice President Human Resources, Fawcett Memorial Hospital, Port Charlotte, FL, p. A143

BRYAN, Lynda, Vice President Human Resources, Northwest Medical Center, Margate, FL, p. A135

BRYAN, Margaret, Administrator, Shriners Hospitals for Children–Northern California, Sacramento, CA, p. A87

BRYAN, Mark, Chief Executive Officer, Delray Medical Center, Delray Beach, FL, p. A127

BRYAN, Sarah, Manager Human Resources, The Heart Hospital at Deaconess Gateway, Newburgh, IN, p. A220

BRYAN–SMITH, Lissa, Chief Administrative Officer, Geisinger–Bloomsburg Hospital, Bloomsburg, PA, p. A533

BRYANT, Amy, Chief Financial Officer, Cornerstone Hospital of Southwest Louisiana, Sulphur, LA, p. A288

BRYANT, Dawn, Vice President Human Resources, North Kansas City Hospital, North Kansas City, MO, p. A377

BRYANT, Gary
Chief Financial Officer, Bayonne Medical Center, Bayonne, NJ, p. A414
Executive Vice President and Chief Financial Officer, CarePoint Health –Christ Hospital, Jersey City, NJ, p. A418

BRYANT, Gerald W., R.N. Chief Nursing Officer, Scott & White Memorial Hospital, Temple, TX, p. A652

BRYANT, Karen, Chief Support Services Officer, Prowers Medical Center, Lamar, CO, p. A108

BRYANT, Kay, Executive Director Human Resources, Saint Clare's Health System, Denville, NJ, p. A416

BRYANT, Lidia, Director Human Resources, Ottumwa Regional Health Center, Ottumwa, IA, p. A236

BRYANT, Lisa G., Director Human Resources, Cannon Memorial Hospital, Pickens, SC, p. A569

BRYANT, Marcia, R.N. Vice President, Clinical Operations, The Outer Banks Hospital, Nags Head, NC, p. A470

BRYANT, Maureen A., FACHE, President, Northwestern Medicine Delnor Hospital, Geneva, IL, p. A191

BRYANT, Pam, Director Human Resources, Helen Keller Hospital, Sheffield, AL, p. A25

BRYANT, Ronald, President, Baystate Noble Hospital, Westfield, MA, p. A316

BRYANT, Rusty, Director Information Technology, Drew Memorial Hospital, Monticello, AR, p. A50

BRYANT, Valerie, Chief Financial Officer, Deckerville Community Hospital, Deckerville, MI, p. A321

BRYANT, William, Chief Executive Officer, LifeCare Hospital of Dayton, Miamisburg, OH, p. A499

BRYANT–MOBLEY, Phyllis, M.D. Director Medical Services, William S. Hall Psychiatric Institute, Columbia, SC, p. A564

BRYCE, Keith, Vice President Finance and Chief Financial Officer, Mt. Graham Regional Medical Center, Safford, AZ, p. A38

BRYDON, Paul, Chief Financial Officer, Antelope Valley Hospital, Lancaster, CA, p. A68

BRYER, Alex, Director Information Management, Los Robles Hospital and Medical Center, Thousand Oaks, CA, p. A96

BRYNER, Jennifer, Director Nursing, Petersburg Medical Center, Petersburg, AK, p. A30

BRYSON, Kellie, Director Human Resources, The Hospital at Westlake Medical Center, Austin, TX, p. A600

BUCCI, Annette, Senior Administrator Human Resources, Burke Rehabilitation Hospital, White Plains, NY, p. A459

BUCCI, Barbara A., R.N. Vice President Patient Care and Chief Nursing Officer, Mount St. Mary's Hospital and Health Center, Lewiston, NY, p. A441

BUCCIARELLI, Brant, Chief Information Officer, Riverview Health, Noblesville, IN, p. A220

BUCCOLO, Martin A., Ph.D., Chief Executive Officer, Four Winds Hospital, Katonah, NY, p. A441

BUCH, Naishadh, Chief Operating Officer, Lompoc Valley Medical Center, Lompoc, CA, p. A69

BUCHANAN, Dennis, Vice President Human Resources, New York Methodist Hospital,, NY, p. A447

BUCHANAN, Donald E., Interim Chief Executive Officer, Haskell County Community Hospital, Stigler, OK, p. A520

BUCHANAN, Donna, Director Nursing, Stroud Regional Medical Center, Stroud, OK, p. A520

BUCHANAN, Herbert, President, Indiana University Health University Hospital, Indianapolis, IN, p. A214

BUCHANAN, Jean, Director Human Resources, Broughton Hospital, Morganton, NC, p. A470

BUCHANAN, Robert, Chief Information Officer, Anna Jaques Hospital, Newburyport, MA, p. A313

BUCHANAN, Toni, Chief Financial Officer, Unicoi County Memorial Hospital, Erwin, TN, p. A582

BUCHANAN, Tracy, Chief Executive Officer and President, CarePartners Health Services, Asheville, NC, p. A460

BUCHART, Phyllis, Chief Operating Officer, Marina Del Rey Hospital, Marina Del Rey, CA, p. A76

BUCHE, Karen, Chief Human Resource Officer, Douglas County Community Mental Health Center, Omaha, NE, p. A400

BUCHELE, Paula, Chief Human Resources, Bay Pines Veterans Affairs Healthcare System, Bay Pines, FL, p. A123

BUCHER, Ben, Chief Executive Officer, Towner County Medical Center, Cando, ND, p. A477

BUCHHEIT, Anne, Coordinator Mental Health Local Information Systems, Buffalo Psychiatric Center, Buffalo, NY, p. A435

BUCHHEIT, Joe, Chief Financial Officer, Our Lady of Bellefonte Hospital, Ashland, KY, p. A257

BUCHHOLZ, Kari, Director Health Information Management, Wishek Community Hospital and Clinics, Wishek, ND, p. A482

BUCHHOLZ, Thomas, M.D. Physician–in–Chief and Executive Vice President, University of Texas M.D. Anderson Cancer Center, Houston, TX, p. A627

BUCHNESS, Michael P., M.D. Director Medical, Deer's Head Hospital Center, Salisbury, MD, p. A303

BUCIENSKI, Jennifer C., Vice President Human Resources, Hayes Green Beach Memorial Hospital, Charlotte, MI, p. A320

BUCK, Catherine, President, Froedtert Memorial Lutheran Hospital, Milwaukee, WI, p. A711

BUCK, Linda K., Vice President Human Resources, UnityPoint Health – Proctor, Peoria, IL, p. A200

BUCK, Nathan, R.N. Nursing Manager, Mountain River Birthing and Surgery Center, Blackfoot, ID, p. A174

BUCK, Phylis, Controller, HEALTHSOUTH Rehabilitation Hospital of Texarkana, Texarkana, TX, p. A652

BUCK, Shelly, Chief Nursing Executive and Chief Operating Officer, Bon Secours Baltimore Health System, Baltimore, MD, p. A296

BUCK, Tavia, Chief Nursing Officer, Roper St. Francis Mount Pleasant Hospital, Mount Pleasant, SC, p. A568

BUCK, William
Chief of Staff, Horton Community Hospital, Horton, KS, p. A245
Interim Chief Executive Officer, North Mississippi Medical Center–Hamilton, Hamilton, AL, p. A21

BUCKELEW, Rick, Chief Executive Officer, Austin Lakes Hospital, Austin, TX, p. A598

BUCKHOY, Sandra, Chief Clinical Officer, Kindred Hospital Chicago–Northlake, Northlake, IL, p. A198

BUCKLEY, David, Acting Chief Information Management Services, Oklahoma City Veterans Affairs Medical Center, Oklahoma City, OK, p. A517

BUCKLEY, John, M.D. President Medical Staff, Vibra Hospital of Denver, Thornton, CO, p. A111

BUCKLEY, Kalvin, Director Information Systems, Woodland Heights Medical Center, Lufkin, TX, p. A635

BUCKLEY, Karen L., R.N. Chief Nursing Officer, Community Behavioral Health Center, Fresno, CA, p. A63

BUCKLEY, Martha, Chief Medical Informatics Officer, Fairfield Medical Center, Lancaster, OH, p. A496

BUCKLEY, Patrick, Vice President Human Resources, St. Elizabeth Medical Center, Utica, NY, p. A457

BUCKLEY, William, M.D. Chief of Staff, Elkhart General Hospital, Elkhart, IN, p. A209

BUCKMINSTER, Joe, Manager Information Technology, Community Medical Center, Inc., Falls City, NE, p. A395

BUCKNER Jr., James E., FACHE, Chief Executive Officer, Dimmit Regional Hospital, Carrizo Springs, TX, p. A605

BUCKNER, Marlys, Chief Nursing Officer, Barton County Memorial Hospital, Lamar, MO, p. A375

BUCKNER, Twila, R.N. Chief Nursing Officer, Cass Regional Medical Center, Harrisonville, MO, p. A372

BUCKWORTH, Albert Bennett, Human Resources Administrative Director, Primary Children's Hospital, Salt Lake City, UT, p. A663

BUDA, Jeff, Chief Information Officer, Floyd Medical Center, Rome, GA, p. A165

BUDD, Edward, President and Chief Executive Officer, Thorek Memorial Hospital, Chicago, IL, p. A187

BUDDE, Rex P., President and Chief Executive Officer, Southern Illinois Hospital Services, Carbondale, IL, p. B126

BUDZINSKY, Chris
Vice President, Nursing and Chief Nursing Officer, AMITA Health Elk Grove Village, Elk Grove Village, IL, p. A189
Vice President, Nursing and Chief Nursing Officer, AMITA Health GlenOaks, Glendale Heights, IL, p. A191
Vice President Nursing and Chief Nursing Officer Alexian Brothers Acute Care Ministries, AMITA Health Hoffman Estates, Hoffman Estates, IL, p. A193

BUE, Cheryl, Health Information Transcriptionist, Faulkton Area Medical Center, Faulkton, SD, p. A573

BUEHLER, Bonnie, Chief Information Officer, St. Mary Medical Center, Langhorne, PA, p. A542

BUELL, Jack, Director Information Services, Sutter Lakeside Hospital, Lakeport, CA, p. A68

BUENVENIDA, Brenda, Director, Hiram W. Davis Medical Center, Petersburg, VA, p. A676

BUER, Shane, Vice President, Human Resources, Mercy Medical Center–Clinton, Clinton, IA, p. A227

BUFFENBARGER, Andrew, Chief Compliance Officer, Kirby Medical Center, Monticello, IL, p. A197

BUFFINGTON, John, Chief Operating Officer, San Juan Regional Medical Center, Farmington, NM, p. A429

BUFFINGTON, Mike, Manager Information Technology, Kansas Medical Center, Andover, KS, p. A240

BUFKIN, Ben, Human Resource Director, Bolivar Medical Center, Cleveland, MS, p. A356

BUGALLO–MUROS, Mariana, Vice President Chief Human Resources Officer, H. Lee Moffitt Cancer Center and Research Institute, Tampa, FL, p. A147

BUGAYONG, Carol, Human Resources Director, HealthSouth Rehabilitation Hospital of Tallahassee, Tallahassee, FL, p. A146

BUGG, Robert, Acting Chief Executive Officer, Broward Health North, Deerfield Beach, FL, p. A127

BUGNA, Eric, M.D. Chief of Staff, Eastern Plumas Health Care, Portola, CA, p. A83

BUHLKE, Brian, M.D. Medical Director, Genoa Medical Facilities, Genoa, NE, p. A396

BUI, Steven, M.D. Chief of Staff, Orange County Global Medical Center, Inc., Santa Ana, CA, p. A92

BUIT, Timothy, Executive Vice President and Chief Financial Officer, Bellevue Hospital, Bellevue, OH, p. A485

BULAU, Chris, Manager Information Technology, Ridgeview Sibley Medical Center, Arlington, MN, p. A338

BULEN, Susan, M.D. Medical Director, HEALTHSOUTH Rehabilitation Hospital of Southern Arizona, Tucson, AZ, p. A40

BULFIN, Joey, R.N. Interim Chief Executive Officer, St. Mary's Medical Center, West Palm Beach, FL, p. A150

BULLARD, Brandon
Chief Financial Officer, AllianceHealth Midwest, Midwest City, OK, p. A514
Chief Financial Officer, Bailey Medical Center, Owasso, OK, p. A518
Chief Financial Officer, Hillcrest Hospital Claremore, Claremore, OK, p. A510

BULLARD, Elizabeth, Chief Executive Officer, Northern Colorado Rehabilitation Hospital, Johnstown, CO, p. A107

BULLARD, John, Director Information Technology, St. Mary's Medical Center, Grand Junction, CO, p. A106

BULLARD, Patrick, Chief Financial Officer, Fayetteville Veterans Affairs Medical Center, Fayetteville, NC, p. A465

BULLINGTON, Benjamin P., M.D. Chief of Staff, Pioneer Medical Center, Big Timber, MT, p. A385

BULLINGTON, Gina, Chief Nursing Officer, TriStar Horizon Medical Center, Dickson, TN, p. A582

BULLOCK, David, Director Information Services, Northwest Medical Center, Tucson, AZ, p. A40

BULLOCK, Lance, M.D. Medical Director, St. James Behavioral Health Hospital, Gonzales, LA, p. A277

BULLOCK, Scott, Director Information Systems, Barstow Community Hospital, Barstow, CA, p. A56

BULMAN, Laurie, Director Human Resources, Winneshiek Medical Center, Decorah, IA, p. A229

BULMASH, Jack, M.D. Chief of Staff, Edward Hines, Jr. Veterans Affairs Hospital, Hines, IL, p. A193

BUMAN, Karen, Chief Nursing Executive, Myrtue Medical Center, Harlan, IA, p. A232

BUMANN, Tim, D.O. Chief of Staff, Abilene Regional Medical Center, Abilene, TX, p. A595

BUMBAUGH, Christopher
Executive Human Resources, Meritus Medical Center, Hagerstown, MD, p. A301
Executive Director, Human Resources, Western Maryland Regional Medical Center, Cumberland, MD, p. A300

BUMGARDNER, Chuck
Director Information Systems, Southeast Georgia Health System Brunswick Campus, Brunswick, GA, p. A155
Director, Southeast Georgia Health System Camden Campus, Saint Marys, GA, p. A165

BUMGARNER, William J., President, Spencer Hospital, Spencer, IA, p. A238

BUMP, Cathy, R.N. Chief Nursing Officer, Methodist Ambulatory Surgery Hospital – Northwest, San Antonio, TX, p. A646

BUNCH, David V., President and Chief Administrative Officer, Cumberland Medical Center, Crossville, TN, p. A582

BUNCH, Elicia, Chief Executive Officer, Centennial Peaks Hospital, Louisville, CO, p. A109

BUNCH, Jimm, President and Chief Executive Officer, Park Ridge Health, Hendersonville, NC, p. A467

BUNCH, Kim, Director Information Technology, Marshall Medical Center North, Guntersville, AL, p. A21

BUNCH, Mark, Director Finance, Othello Community Hospital, Othello, WA, p. A687

BUNCH, Mike, Executive Vice President, Chief Operating Officer and Chief Financial Officer, KershawHealth, Camden, SC, p. A562

BUNCH, Terri, R.N. Chief Nursing Officer, CHRISTUS Mother Frances Hospital – Sulphur Springs, Sulphur Springs, TX, p. A651

BUND, Linda, Chief Information Officer and Director Education, James J. Peters Veterans Affairs Medical Center,, NY, p. A445

BUNDY, Michael N., Chief Operating Officer, Cape Cod Hospital, Hyannis, MA, p. A311

BUNGER, Mary, R.N. Director Nursing Services, Kearney County Health Services, Minden, NE, p. A398

BUNKER, Marla, Vice President Nursing and Chief Operating Officer, War Memorial Hospital, Sault Sainte Marie, MI, p. A334

BUNN, Barry, M.D. Chief of Staff, Vidant Edgecombe Hospital, Tarboro, NC, p. A474

BUNNER, Blake, Chief Executive Officer, HEALTHSOUTH Deaconess Rehabilitation Hospital, Evansville, IN, p. A210

BUNSELMEYER, Becky, Director Information Services, Memorial Hospital, Chester, IL, p. A183

BUNTEN, Sherry, Director Patient Care Services, Aspirus Langlade Hospital, Antigo, WI, p. A702

BUNTING, Katherine, Chief Executive Officer, Fairfield Memorial Hospital, Fairfield, IL, p. A190

BUNTYN, Diane, MSN Vice President Patient Care Services, Southeast Alabama Medical Center, Dothan, AL, p. A19

BUNYARD, Steve
President, OhioHealth Dublin Methodist Hospital, Dublin, OH, p. A494
President, OhioHealth Grady Memorial Hospital, Delaware, OH, p. A493

BUONGIORNO, Michael J.
Executive Vice President Finance and Chief Financial Officer, Bryn Mawr Hospital, Bryn Mawr, PA, p. A534
Vice President Finance, Lankenau Medical Center, Wynnewood, PA, p. A558

BUPP, Steven, M.D. Medical Director, Sonora Behavioral Health Hospital, Tucson, AZ, p. A41

BURASCO, Carmen, Director Human Resources, Siloam Springs Regional Hospital, Siloam Springs, AR, p. A52

BURBANK, Jimmy, Chief Information Officer, U. S. Public Health Service Indian Hospital, Crownpoint, NM, p. A429

BURCH, Debra, Chief Nursing Officer, Burke Medical Center, Waynesboro, GA, p. A169

BURCH, Lee, Director Management Information Systems, Bayfront Health Brooksville, Brooksville, FL, p. A125

BURCH, Todd, Chief Executive Officer, Aspirus Riverview Hospital and Clinics, Inc., Wisconsin Rapids, WI, p. A719

BURCHAM Sr., Michael G., FACHE, Chief Executive Officer, Thayer County Health Services, Hebron, NE, p. A396

BURCHELL, Pam, Director Human Resources, Lawnwood Regional Medical Center & Heart Institute, Fort Pierce, FL, p. A129

BURCHETT, Claudia L., R.N. Vice President of Patient Services, Southern Ohio Medical Center, Portsmouth, OH, p. A501

BURCHETT, Travis, Troop Commander Human Resources, Colonel Florence A. Blanchfield Army Community Hospital, Fort Campbell, KY, p. A260

BURCHILL, Kevin R., Chief Executive Officer, Southcoast Behavioral Health, Dartmouth, MA, p. A309

BURCZEUSKI, Jason
Controller, Arms Acres, Carmel, NY, p. A436
Controller, Conifer Park, Glenville, NY, p. A439

BURDEN, Jennifer, Human Resources Director, TriStar Centennial Medical Center, Nashville, TN, p. A591

BURDICK, Ginny
Senior Vice President and Chief Human Resources Officer, Clovis Community Medical Center, Clovis, CA, p. A59
Vice President Human Resources, Community Behavioral Health Center, Fresno, CA, p. A63
Vice President Human Resources, Community Regional Medical Center, Fresno, CA, p. A63

BURDICK, Hoyt J., M.D. Vice President Medical Affairs, Cabell Huntington Hospital, Huntington, WV, p. A696

BURDICK, Steven A., Chief Executive Officer, Providence St. Mary Medical Center, Walla Walla, WA, p. A693

BURGER, Janice, Chief Executive, Providence St. Vincent Medical Center, Portland, OR, p. A529

BURGESS, Angela, Chief Information Officer, Randolph Hospital, Asheboro, NC, p. A460

BURGESS, Daniel, Chief Information Officer, MaineGeneral Medical Center, Augusta, ME, p. A291

BURGESS, John, Director Information Services, Hocking Valley Community Hospital, Logan, OH, p. A497

BURGESS, Robert L., President and Chief Executive Officer, St. Elizabeth Hospital, Gonzales, LA, p. A277

BURGESS, Steven, Administrator Human Resources, Henrico Doctors' Hospital, Richmond, VA, p. A677

BURGHART, Steven, President, SSM Cardinal Glennon Children's Medical Center, Saint Louis, MO, p. A381

BURGOS, Odette, Supervisor Human Resources, San Jorge Children's Hospital, San Juan, PR, p. A730

BURGUILLOS, Richard, Chief Financial Officer, Care One at Raritan Bay Medical Center, Perth Amboy, NJ, p. A422

BURGUS, Aurelis, Nursing Director, Ryder Memorial Hospital, Humacao, PR, p. A727

BURICK, Adam, M.D
Chief Medical Officer, PAM Specialty Hospital of Covington, Covington, LA, p. A275
Chief Medical Officer, Post Acute Medical Specialty Hospital of Victoria, Victoria, TX, p. A655
Chief Medical Officer, Post Acute/Warm Springs Specialty Hospital of Victoria, Victoria, TX, p. A655

BURICK, Marsha, Chief Financial Officer, Central Florida Behavioral Hospital, Orlando, FL, p. A140

BURINGRUD, Duane, M.D. Chief Medical and Quality Officer, Palomar Medical Center, Escondido, CA, p. A61

BURISH, Brent, Chief Executive Officer, St. Cloud Regional Medical Center, Saint Cloud, FL, p. A144

BURK, Kaye, Administrator, Noland Hospital Dothan, Dothan, AL, p. A19

BURK, Thomas J., Chief Operating Officer, Danville State Hospital, Danville, PA, p. A536

BURKE, Brian, M.D. President Medical Staff, Fairview Hospital, Great Barrington, MA, p. A310

BURKE, Christopher, Chief Executive Officer, Cedar Springs Hospital, Colorado Springs, CO, p. A102

BURKE, David J., Director Finance and Chief Financial Officer, Nantucket Cottage Hospital, Nantucket, MA, p. A312

BURKE, Dennis E., President and Chief Executive Officer, Good Shepherd Health Care System, Hermiston, OR, p. A526

BURKE, Dorothy, Chief Financial Officer, Southeast Colorado Hospital District, Springfield, CO, p. A110

BURKE, Greg, M.D. Medical Director, Geisinger HEALTHSOUTH Rehabilitation Hospital, Danville, PA, p. A536

BURKE, Jack J., MS Chief Operating Officer and Chief Nursing Officer, Antelope Valley Hospital, Lancaster, CA, p. A68

BURKE, James, M.D
Senior Vice President and Chief Medical Officer, HonorHealth Scottsdale Osborn Medical Center, Scottsdale, AZ, p. A38
Senior Vice President and Chief Medical Officer, HonorHealth Scottsdale Shea Medical Center, Scottsdale, AZ, p. A39

BURKE, James B., Chief Operating Officer, Hahnemann University Hospital, Philadelphia, PA, p. A548

BURKE, James M.
Chief Financial Officer, Day Kimball Hospital, Putnam, CT, p. A116
Vice President Finance, Chief Nursing Executive Medical Surgical Hospitals, Kent County Memorial Hospital, Warwick, RI, p. A561
Senior Vice President Finance, Memorial Hospital of Rhode Island, Pawtucket, RI, p. A560

BURKE, Jeff, Chief Information Officer, Bon Secours–Richmond Community Hospital, Richmond, VA, p. A677

BURKE, John, Chief Financial Officer, Nyack Hospital, Nyack, NY, p. A451

BURKE, Julie, Director Human Resources, New England Sinai Hospital and Rehabilitation Center, Stoughton, MA, p. A315

BURKE, Marsha, Senior Vice President and Chief Financial Officer, WellStar Windy Hill Hospital, Marietta, GA, p. A163

BURKE, Michael, Senior Vice President and Corporate Chief Financial Officer, NYU Langone Medical Center, New York, NY, p. A449

BURKE, Paul, Administrator, Schleicher County Medical Center, Eldorado, TX, p. A616

BURKE, Rebecca, R.N. Senior Vice President and Chief Nursing Officer, Kent County Memorial Hospital, Warwick, RI, p. A561

BURKE, Rose, Associate Director Patient Care Services, Marion Veterans Affairs Medical Center, Marion, IL, p. A195

BURKE, Timothy, M.D. Medical Director, The Brook Hospital – KMI, Louisville, KY, p. A265

BURKEL, Greg, Chief Financial Officer, Regional Health Services of Howard County, Cresco, IA, p. A228

BURKEL, Gregory, Chief Financial Officer, Mitchell County Regional Health Center, Osage, IA, p. A235

BURKET, Mark, Chief Executive Officer, Platte Health Center Avera, Platte, SD, p. A575

BURKETT, Doug, Manager Information Technology, L. V. Stabler Memorial Hospital, Greenville, AL, p. A21

BURKETT, Eric, M.D. Vice President Medical Affairs, Monmouth Medical Center, Long Branch Campus, Long Branch, NJ, p. A419

BURKETT, Evan, Chief Human Resource Officer, Sanford USD Medical Center, Sioux Falls, SD, p. A576

BURKEY, Brent, M.D. Chief Medical Officer, Cleveland Clinic Fairview Hospital, Cleveland, OH, p. A489

BURKEY, Kathleen, R.N. Vice President, Patient Care Service and Chief Nursing Officer, Grand View Health, Sellersville, PA, p. A554

BURKHARDT, Minnie, Chief Executive Officer, AllianceHealth Madill, Madill, OK, p. A514

BURKHART, Brad, Assistant Administrator, Harlan ARH Hospital, Harlan, KY, p. A261

BURKHART, James R., FACHE, President and Chief Executive Officer, Tampa General Hospital, Tampa, FL, p. A148

BUSS, Georganna, Chief Executive Officer, Harper County Community Hospital, Buffalo, OK, p. A509

BUSS, Theresa L., Regional Vice President Human Resources, Windham Hospital, Willimantic, CT, p. A118

BUSSELL, Walter
Chief Financial Officer, Memorial Hospital West, Pembroke Pines, FL, p. A142
Chief Financial Officer, Memorial Regional Hospital,, FL, p. A130

BUSSIERE, Mark, Administrator Human Resources, New Hampshire Hospital, Concord, NH, p. A410

BUSSLER, David, Chief Information Officer, Sheridan Community Hospital, Sheridan, MI, p. A334

BUSTLE, John P., Medical Chief of Staff, Bates County Memorial Hospital, Butler, MO, p. A368

BUTCHER, Gina, Chief Financial Officer, Garden City Hospital, Garden City, MI, p. A324

BUTCHER, Kay, Director Health Information Management, Stonewall Jackson Memorial Hospital, Weston, WV, p. A701

BUTCHER, Scott, Chief Executive Officer, HealthSouth Rehabilitation Institute of San Antonio, San Antonio, TX, p. A646

BUTE, Phil, Manager Information Technology, Clay County Hospital, Flora, IL, p. A190

BUTERBAUGH, Roger W., Chief Human Resources Officer, Charlie Norwood Veterans Affairs Medical Center, Augusta, GA, p. A153

BUTERBAUGH, William, Director Support Services, Fulton County Medical Center, Mc Connellsburg, PA, p. A544

BUTIKOFER, Lon D., Ph.D., Chief Executive Officer, Regional Medical Center, Manchester, IA, p. A234

BUTKER, Jeff, Chief Information Officer, Memorial Hospital, Martinsville, VA, p. A673

BUTLER, Anita M., Chief Executive Officer, Spartanburg Hospital for Restorative Care, Spartanburg, SC, p. A570

BUTLER, Brad, Network Administrator, Barton County Memorial Hospital, Lamar, MO, p. A375

BUTLER, Carol A., R.N. VP Patient Care Services & Operations, St. Anthony North Health Campus, Westminster, CO, p. A111

BUTLER, Catherine, M.D. Chief Medical Staff, Hancock County Health System, Britt, IA, p. A226

BUTLER, Chris, Chief Information Officer, Monmouth Medical Center, Long Branch Campus, Long Branch, NJ, p. A419

BUTLER, Dana, M.D. Medical Director, Sunrise Canyon Hospital, Lubbock, TX, p. A634

BUTLER, David, President and Chief Executive Officer, Tillamook Regional Medical Center, Tillamook, OR, p. A531

BUTLER, David K., M.D. Chief Medical Officer, Dignity Health Arizona General Hospital, Laveen, AZ, p. A34

BUTLER, Debby
Director Human Resources, Wadley Regional Medical Center, Texarkana, TX, p. A652
Director Human Resources, Wadley Regional Medical Center at Hope, Hope, AR, p. A47

BUTLER, Everett A., Interim Chief Executive Officer, Pembina County Memorial Hospital and Wedgewood Manor, Cavalier, ND, p. A478

BUTLER, Linda H., M.D. Chief Medical Officer, UNC REX Healthcare, Raleigh, NC, p. A472

BUTLER, Margaret, Vice President Human Resources, Abbott Northwestern Hospital, Minneapolis, MN, p. A346

BUTLER, Randy, Chief Financial Officer, West Florida Hospital, Pensacola, FL, p. A142

BUTLER, Rosemary M., R.N. Chief Nurse Executive, Kaiser Permanente Riverside Medical Center, Riverside, CA, p. A85

BUTLER, Stuart, Director Information Technology, Sweeny Community Hospital, Sweeny, TX, p. A651

BUTT, Qasim, M.D. Chief Medical Officer, Acuity Hospital of South Texas, San Antonio, TX, p. A645

BUTT, Zaahra, Chief Executive Officer, Select Specialty Hospital–Grosse Pointe, Grosse Pointe, MI, p. A326

BUTTELL, Phil, Chief Operating Officer, Centerpoint Medical Center, Independence, MO, p. A372

BUTTER, Hazel, Manager Human Resources, Hammond–Henry Hospital, Geneseo, IL, p. A191

BUTTERFIELD, Cindy, Director, Fiscal and Administrative Services, Connecticut Valley Hospital, Middletown, CT, p. A115

BUTTERFIELD, Jon
Chief Operating Officer, Jordan Valley Medical Center, West Jordan, UT, p. A664
Administrator and Chief Operating Officer, Jordan Valley Medical Center West Valley Campus, West Valley City, UT, p. A664

BUTTERFIELD, Scott, Chief Executive Officer, Select Specialty Hospital – Lincoln, Lincoln, NE, p. A398

BUTTERMORE, Bruce
Director Human Resources, Parkview LaGrange Hospital, LaGrange, IN, p. A216
Manager Human Resources, Parkview Noble Hospital, Kendallville, IN, p. A215

BUTTON, Charlie A., President and Chief Executive Officer, Star Valley Medical Center, Afton, WY, p. A721

BUTTS, Kim, System Nurse Executive, Anchor Hospital, Atlanta, GA, p. A152

BUTTS, Paula Yvonne, Chief Nursing Officer, Wellstar Atlanta Medical Center, Atlanta, GA, p. A153

BUTTS, Ursula N., FACHE Vice President of Patient Care Services, VCU Community Memorial Hospital, South Hill, VA, p. A679

BUTZINE, Bart, Director Information Technology, Community Hospital, Grand Junction, CO, p. A106

BUTZLER, Hilary, Director Human Resources, Cumberland Memorial Hospital, Cumberland, WI, p. A704

BUUCK, Brian, Chief Executive Officer, Ridgeview Psychiatric Hospital and Center, Oak Ridge, TN, p. A592

BUXTON, Barton, Ed.D., President and Chief Executive Officer, McLaren Lapeer Region, Lapeer, MI, p. A328

BUYOK, Tammy K., Vice President Support Services, St. Peter's Hospital, Helena, MT, p. A388

BUZACHERO, Victor, Corporate Senior Vice President for Innovation, Human Resources and Performance Management, Scripps Green Hospital, La Jolla, CA, p. A67

BYARS, Stephanie, Chief Nursing Officer, Unity Medical Center, Manchester, TN, p. A587

BYDA, Jeff, Vice President Information Technology, Mercy Fitzgerald Hospital, Darby, PA, p. A536

BYERS, John, M.D
Chief of Staff, Ivinson Memorial Hospital, Laramie, WY, p. A722
Medical Director, Select Specialty Hospital–Tri Cities, Bristol, TN, p. A579

BYERS, Suzann, Director of Nursing, Southern Indiana Rehabilitation Hospital, New Albany, IN, p. A219

BYERS, William, Chief Technology Officer, Western Maryland Regional Medical Center, Cumberland, MD, p. A300

BYERWALTER, Mariann, Interim President and Chief Executive Officer, Stanford Health Care, Palo Alto, CA, p. A82

BYLER, Karen, Information Technology Generalist, Warren State Hospital, Warren, PA, p. A556

BYNUM, Chigger, Chief Financial Officer, John Randolph Medical Center, Hopewell, VA, p. A672

BYNUM, Justin
Chief Operating Officer, Norwegian American Hospital, Chicago, IL, p. A185
Chief Financial Officer, Saint Anthony Hospital, Chicago, IL, p. A186

BYRD, Catherine, Vice President Patient Services, Parkview Noble Hospital, Kendallville, IN, p. A215

BYRD, Greg, Vice President Medical Affairs, Shenandoah Memorial Hospital, Woodstock, VA, p. A681

BYRD, Lu, R.N. Vice President Hospital Operations and Chief Nursing Officer, Billings Clinic, Billings, MT, p. A385

BYRD, O. Wayne, M.D. Chief of Staff, H. C. Watkins Memorial Hospital, Quitman, MS, p. A364

BYRD, Rebecca, President Medical Staff, Grandview Medical Center, Birmingham, AL, p. A16

BYRD–PELAEZ, Brenda, Chief Human Resources Management Office, Martinsburg Veterans Affairs Medical Center, Martinsburg, WV, p. A698

BYRNE, Bobbie, M.D
Executive Vice President and Chief Information Officer, Edward Hospital, Naperville, IL, p. A198
Vice President Information Systems and Chief Information Officer, Elmhurst Memorial Hospital,, IL, p. A189

BYRNE, Frank J., Vice President Finance, Newport Hospital, Newport, RI, p. A560

BYRNES, Matthew C., M.D. Chief Medical Officer, St. Catherine Hospital, Garden City, KS, p. A243

BYROM, David, Chief Executive Officer, Coryell Memorial Hospital, Gatesville, TX, p. A620

C

CAAMANO, Tero, Director Information Technology, Saint Clare's Health System, Denville, NJ, p. A416

CABALLERO, Rogelio, Chief Information Systems, San Jorge Children's Hospital, San Juan, PR, p. A730

CABIBBO, Tiffany, Vice President of Nursing, Baptist Health Madisonville, Madisonville, KY, p. A265

CABIGAO, Edwin, Chief Nursing Officer, Jewish Home of San Francisco, San Francisco, CA, p. A90

CABRERA, Carlos, Executive Director, Cardiovascular Center of Puerto Rico and the Caribbean, San Juan, PR, p. A729

CABRERA, Irma, Finance Director, Hospital San Carlos Borromeo, Moca, PR, p. A728

CABRERA, Sheelah, Chief Information Officer, La Rabida Children's Hospital, Chicago, IL, p. A184

CABUNOC, Brenda, Chief Human Resources, VA Greater Los Angeles Healthcare System, Los Angeles, CA, p. A74

CACCIAMANI, John D., M.D., Chief Executive Officer, Chestnut Hill Hospital, Philadelphia, PA, p. A547

CADE, Paul, Administrator and Chief Executive Officer, Baptist Memorial Hospital–Golden Triangle, Columbus, MS, p. A357

CADIEUX, Marc
Corporate Vice President and Chief Financial Officer, Children's Hospital of Wisconsin, Milwaukee, WI, p. A711
Corporate Vice President and Chief Financial Ofcr, Children's Hospital of Wisconsin–Fox Valley, Neenah, WI, p. A712

CADIGAN, Elizabeth, R.N. Senior Vice President Patient Care Services and Chief Nursing Officer, Cambridge Health Alliance, Cambridge, MA, p. A308

CADOGAN, David, Chief Medical Officer, Alaska Regional Hospital, Anchorage, AK, p. A28

CADORETTE, Brenda E., Chief Nursing Officer, Berkshire Medical Center, Pittsfield, MA, p. A314

CADWELL, Carrie, M.D. Chief Clinical Officer, Four County Counseling Center, Logansport, IN, p. A217

CADWELL, Maureen K., Chief Executive Officer, Weston County Health Services, Newcastle, WY, p. A723

CADY, Kathy, Coordinator Human Resources, Accounts Payable and Payroll, Safe Haven Hospital of Treasure Valley, Boise, ID, p. A174

CADY, Thomas, Vice President Human Resources, Heywood Hospital, Gardner, MA, p. A310

CADY, Tina, Controller, The Women's Hospital, Newburgh, IN, p. A220

CAFASSO, Michael, Vice President Operations, St. Mary–Corwin Medical Center, Pueblo, CO, p. A110

CAGLE, Jennifer, Director of Nursing, North Mississippi Medical Center–Hamilton, Hamilton, AL, p. A21

CAGLE, Karen, Chief Nursing Officer, Select Specialty Hospital–Nashville, Nashville, TN, p. A591

CAGNA, Ralph A.
Director Information Technology Operations, Cleveland Clinic Health System South Market, Marymount Hospital, Garfield Heights, OH, p. A495
Director Information Technology, South Pointe Hospital, Warrensville Heights, OH, p. A505

CAHALAN, Jay P., Chief Executive Officer, Columbia Memorial Hospital, Hudson, NY, p. A440

CAHILL, Donna, Vice President Human Resources, HackensackUMC Palisades, North Bergen, NJ, p. A421

CAHILL, Joseph, Executive Vice President and Chief Operating Officer, South Shore Hospital, South Weymouth, MA, p. A314

CAHILL, Marty, Chief Executive Officer, Samaritan Lebanon Community Hospital, Lebanon, OR, p. A527

CAHILL, Patricia, R.N. Vice President, Patient Care Services and Chief Nursing Officer, Bronx–Lebanon Hospital Center Health Care System,, NY, p. A444

CAHO–MOONEY, Linda, Chief Financial Officer, Claiborne County Medical Center, Port Gibson, MS, p. A364

CAHOJ, Lindsey, Chief Nursing Officer, Select Specialty Hospital–Wichita, Wichita, KS, p. A256

CAIN, Amy, District Director Human Resources, Kindred Hospital South Philadelphia, Philadelphia, PA, p. A548

CAIN, Donna, Director Information Systems Department, Cypress Fairbanks Medical Center, Houston, TX, p. A624

CAIN, Mark, Chief Executive Officer, Tennova Healthcare–LaFollette Medical Center, La Follette, TN, p. A586

CAIN, Roxie, Chief Financial Officer, Big Horn County Memorial Hospital, Hardin, MT, p. A388

CAIN, William, Controller, Penn Highlands Clearfield, Clearfield, PA, p. A535

CAINE, Jamie, Director of Human Resources, Valley Hospital, Spokane Valley, WA, p. A691

CAIRNS, Craig, M.D. Vice President Medical Affairs, Licking Memorial Hospital, Newark, OH, p. A500

CALAIS, C. Matthew, Senior Vice President and Chief Information Officer, Legacy Good Samaritan Hospital and Medical Center, Portland, OR, p. A529

CALAIS, Daniel, Superintendent, Bridgewater State Hospital, Bridgewater, MA, p. A308

CALAMARI, Frank A., President and Chief Executive Officer, Calvary Hospital,, NY, p. A444

CALAMARI, Jacquelyn, MSN Vice President and Chief Nursing Officer, Middlesex Hospital, Middletown, CT, p. A115

CALANDRELLA, Paul, Chief Operating Officer, Mt. Ascutney Hospital and Health Center, Windsor, VT, p. A666

CALANDRIELLO, John, Vice President and Chief Financial Officer, HackensackUMC Palisades, North Bergen, NJ, p. A421

CALARCO, Marge, Chief Nursing Executive, University of Michigan Hospitals and Health Centers, Ann Arbor, MI, p. A318

CALAWAY, Shearmaine, Director Human Resources, East Mississippi State Hospital, Meridian, MS, p. A362

CALBONE, Angelo G., President and Chief Executive Officer, Saratoga Hospital, Saratoga Springs, NY, p. A455

CALBY, Elizabeth, Vice President Human Resources, Advocate Good Samaritan Hospital, Downers Grove, IL, p. A188

CALDARI, Patricia, Vice President, Richmond University Medical Center,, NY, p. A449

CALDAS, Robert, D.O. Chief Medical Officer, Southcoast Hospitals Group, Fall River, MA, p. A310

CALDEIRA, Amy, Director Information Technology and Systems, Fort Walton Beach Medical Center, Fort Walton Beach, FL, p. A129

CALDERA, Ken, Director Human Resources, Kessler Institute for Rehabilitation, West Orange, NJ, p. A425

CALDERON, Lizmari, Director Finance, Hospital De La Concepcion, San German, PR, p. A729

CALDERONE, John A., Ph.D., Chief Executive Officer, Olympia Medical Center, Los Angeles, CA, p. A73

CALDWELL, Carolyn P., Chief Executive Officer, Desert Regional Medical Center, Palm Springs, CA, p. A81

CALDWELL, Charles, M.D. Chief of Staff, Byrd Regional Hospital, Leesville, LA, p. A282

CALDWELL, Dari, FACHE, President and Chief Operating Officer, Novant Health Rowan Medical Center, Salisbury, NC, p. A473

CALDWELL, Eric, Director Finance, Northside Hospital–Forsyth, Cumming, GA, p. A157

CALDWELL, Marita, Chief Financial Officer, Twin County Regional Healthcare, Galax, VA, p. A671

CALDWELL, Matthew T., Chief Executive Officer, Tennova Healthcare–Lebanon, Lebanon, TN, p. A586

CALDWELL, Nesa, Chief Nursing Officer, Solara Hospital Harlingen, Harlingen, TX, p. A622

CALDWELL, Paul, Facility Coordinator Information Technology Customer Relations, Page Hospital, Page, AZ, p. A35

CALDWELL, Steve, Vice President Finance and Chief Financial Officer, St. Mary's Hospital, Madison, WI, p. A709

CALDWELL Jr., William E., Chief Executive Officer, Wilson Medical Center, Wilson, NC, p. A475

CALEY, Carl
    Chief Financial Officer, Spring Valley Hospital Medical Center, Las Vegas, NV, p. A406
    Chief Financial Officer, St. Cloud Regional Medical Center, Saint Cloud, FL, p. A144

CALHOUN, Cathy, Director Human Resources, River Point Behavioral Health, Jacksonville, FL, p. A132

CALHOUN, Joshua, M.D. Medical Director, Hawthorn Children Psychiatric Hospital, Saint Louis, MO, p. A380

CALHOUN, Kevin P., Chief Executive Officer, Munising Memorial Hospital, Munising, MI, p. A330

CALHOUN, Kirk A., M.D., President, University of Texas Health Northeast, Tyler, TX, p. A654

CALHOUN, Robert, Chief Executive Officer, Greenbrier Valley Medical Center, Ronceverte, WV, p. A700

CALHOUN, Timothy
    Vice President Finance, Chief Financial Officer, Lakeland Hospital, Watervliet, Watervliet, MI, p. A336
    Vice President Finance and Chief Financial Officer, Lakeland Medical Center, St. Joseph, Saint Joseph, MI, p. A334

CALHOUN, William
    President, Community Hospitals, Health First Cape Canaveral Hospital, Cocoa Beach, FL, p. A126
    President, Community Hospitals, Health First Palm Bay Hospital, Palm Bay, FL, p. A141
    President, Community Hospitals, Health First Viera Hospital, Melbourne, FL, p. A135

CALIA, Christopher, Vice President Human Resources, CHI St. Luke's Health Brazosport, Lake Jackson, TX, p. A631

CALIFORNIA, Randy, Chief Operating Officer, Warren General Hospital, Warren, PA, p. A556

CALIGIURI, Michael, Chief Executive Officer, James Cancer Hospital and Solove Research Institute, Columbus, OH, p. A490

CALIME, Erica, Director Human Resources, Baylor Scott & White Medical Center – Carrollton, Carrollton, TX, p. A605

CALIVA, Todd, Chief Executive Officer, West Houston Medical Center, Houston, TX, p. A627

CALKIN, Steven, D.O. Vice President Medical Affairs, McLaren Oakland, Pontiac, MI, p. A332

CALKINS, Paul, M.D. Chief Medical Officer, Indiana University Health North Hospital, Carmel, IN, p. A208

CALL, Carie, Computer Support, Cassia Regional Medical Center, Burley, ID, p. A175

CALL, Dave, M.D. Medical Director, Kindred Hospital Colorado Springs, Colorado Springs, CO, p. A102

CALL, Stacie, R.N. Vice President Patient Care and Chief Nursing Officer, East Liverpool City Hospital, East Liverpool, OH, p. A494

CALL, Stacie, Chief Nursing Officer, Mercy Health – St. Elizabeth Boardman Hospital, Boardman, OH, p. A485

CALLAGHAN, Barbara, Interim Chief Executive Officer, Atrium Medical Center of Corinth, Corinth, TX, p. A607

CALLAGHAN, Jack, M.D., Chief Executive Officer, Guidance Center, Flagstaff, AZ, p. A32

CALLAGHAN III, James, M.D., President and Chief Executive Officer, Franciscan St. Francis Health – Indianapolis, Indianapolis, IN, p. A214

CALLAGHAN, Peter, President and Chief Operating Officer, Columbus Hospital LTACH, Newark, NJ, p. A420

CALLAHAN, Ame, Acting Manager Resource Management Service, Northern Arizona Veterans Affairs Health Care System, Prescott, AZ, p. A37

CALLAHAN, Charles D., Ph.D. Executive Vice President and Chief Operating Officer, Memorial Medical Center, Springfield, IL, p. A203

CALLAHAN, Christopher M., Vice President Human Resources, Exeter Hospital, Exeter, NH, p. A411

CALLAHAN, Kelly, Public Information Officer, Elgin Mental Health Center, Elgin, IL, p. A189

CALLAHAN, Kevin J., President and Chief Executive Officer, Exeter Hospital, Exeter, NH, p. A411

CALLAHAN, Larry A., Senior Vice President Human Resources, Grady Memorial Hospital, Atlanta, GA, p. A152

CALLAHAN, Mark, Chief Operating Officer, Mary Lanning Healthcare, Hastings, NE, p. A396

CALLAHAN, Mary Beth, Chief Financial Officer, McLaren Lapeer Region, Lapeer, MI, p. A328

CALLAHAN, Neil, Chief Executive Officer, Brooke Glen Behavioral Hospital, Fort Washington, PA, p. A539

CALLAHAN Jr., Robert W., Director, Lebanon Veterans Affairs Medical Center, Lebanon, PA, p. A542

CALLAHAN, Shannon, Director Human Resources, Sitka Community Hospital, Sitka, AK, p. A30

CALLAHAN, Teresa, MSN, Chief Executive Officer, Iraan General Hospital, Iraan, TX, p. A628

CALLAHAN, William, Chief Information Management Division, Bayne–Jones Army Community Hospital, Fort Polk, LA, p. A277

CALLAN, Michael, Executive Vice President and Chief Financial Officer, KidsPeace Children's Hospital, Orefield, PA, p. A546

CALLANAN, Patrick, Vice President Patient Care Services, Mercy Hospital Fort Scott, Fort Scott, KS, p. A243

CALLAS, Robin B., R.N. Vice President Human Resources, Rutherford Regional Health System, Rutherfordton, NC, p. A473

CALLECOD, David L., President and Chief Executive Officer, Lafayette General Health, Lafayette, LA, p. B79

CALLENS, Don, M.D. Chief Medical Officer, Liberty Dayton Regional Medical Center, Liberty, TX, p. A632

CALLENS, Paul A., Ph.D., Director, North Mississippi State Hospital, Tupelo, MS, p. A365

CALLICOAT, William, Chief Financial Officer, Summit Pacific Medical Center, Elma, WA, p. A684

CALLISTE, Gregory, FACHE, Chief Executive Officer, NYC Health + Hospitals / Woodhull,, NY, p. A449

CALLISTER, T. Brian, M.D. Chief Medical Officer, Tahoe Pacific Hospitals, Sparks, NV, p. A408

CALLMAN, Mark, M.D. Chief Medical Officer, Fawcett Memorial Hospital, Port Charlotte, FL, p. A143

CALLOWAY, Jennifer, Human Resources Coordinator, Asheville Specialty Hospital, Asheville, NC, p. A460

CALLOWAY, Maria, R.N. Chief Nursing Officer, Central Florida Regional Hospital, Sanford, FL, p. A145

CALMAN, Kurt, Chief Information Officer, United Memorial Medical Center, Batavia, NY, p. A434

CALUBAQUIB, Evelyn, Chief Nursing Officer, Greater El Monte Community Hospital, South El Monte, CA, p. A95

CALVARUSO, Gaspare, President, Capital Region Medical Center, Jefferson City, MO, p. A372

CALVERT, Mandy, Director Information Systems, Southern Coos Hospital and Health Center, Bandon, OR, p. A524

CALVERT, Sarah, Chief Nursing Officer, McGehee–Desha County Hospital, McGehee, AR, p. A50

CALVIN, Harley, D.O. Chief Medical Officer, Rush County Memorial Hospital, La Crosse, KS, p. A247

CALVIN, Irene, Vice President Human Resources, South Oaks Hospital, Amityville, NY, p. A433

CALVIN, Jeff, Chief Financial Officer, Michiana Behavioral Health Center, Plymouth, IN, p. A220

CAMA, Joseph, M.D. President Medical Staff, Guthrie Towanda Memorial Hospital, Towanda, PA, p. A555

CAMACHO, Joe, Information Officer, Spanish Peaks Regional Health Center, Walsenburg, CO, p. A111

CAMACHO, Leslie, R.N. Director of Nursing, Commonwealth Health Center, Saipan, MP, p. A725

CAMARA, Robert, M.D. Chief Medical Officer, Lake Huron Medical Center, Port Huron, MI, p. A332

CAMARDELLO, Heidi, Vice President Patient Care Services and Chief Nursing Officer, Little Falls Hospital, Little Falls, NY, p. A441

CAMERON, Carl, Director Information Systems, Holyoke Medical Center, Holyoke, MA, p. A310

CAMERON, Don, Chief Operating Officer, Allegiance Behavioral Health Center of Plainview, Plainview, TX, p. A641

CAMERON, Kim, Manager Health Information Services, Patients' Hospital of Redding, Redding, CA, p. A84

CAMMACK, Geri, R.N. Director of Nursing, Lost Rivers Medical Center, Arco, ID, p. A174

CAMMENGA, Randall, M.D. Vice President Medical Affairs, Indiana University Health Goshen Hospital, Goshen, IN, p. A212

CAMP III, Claude E. Chip™, FACHE, Chief Executive Officer, Brownwood Regional Medical Center, Brownwood, TX, p. A604

CAMP, David, Director Human Resources, St. Mary's Regional Medical Center, Enid, OK, p. A511

CAMP, Julie A., R.N., Interim Chief Executive Officer, Methodist Southlake Hospital, Southlake, TX, p. A649

CAMP, Lea Ann, R.N. Chief Nursing Officer, Greene County General Hospital, Linton, IN, p. A217

CAMPA, Melissa, Controller, Kindred Hospital El Paso, El Paso, TX, p. A615

CAMPANA, Thomas, M.D. Chief of Staff, Spectrum Health Reed City Hospital, Reed City, MI, p. A332

CAMPANELLA, Alfred, Chief Information Officer, Virtua Voorhees, Voorhees, NJ, p. A425

CAMPAS, Janice, Chief Financial Officer, Wichita County Health Center, Leoti, KS, p. A248

CAMPBELL, Amy, Chief Financial Officer, Community Hospital North, Indianapolis, IN, p. A213

CAMPBELL, Andrew, Associate Executive Director, NYC Health + Hospitals / Coney Island,, NY, p. A448

CAMPBELL, April, Director Human Resources, Broadwater Health Center, Townsend, MT, p. A391

CAMPBELL, Bernard M., Administrator Human Resources, LewisGale Hospital Alleghany, Low Moor, VA, p. A672

CAMPBELL, Brian, Director Professional Services, U. S. Public Health Service Indian Hospital–Whiteriver, Whiteriver, AZ, p. A41

CAMPBELL, Carla, R.N. Chief Nurse Officer, Mercy Hospital and Medical Center, Chicago, IL, p. A185

CAMPBELL, Chad, Chief Executive Officer, McKenzie–Willamette Medical Center, Springfield, OR, p. A531

CAMPBELL, Christine, Controller, Vanderbilt Stallworth Rehabilitation Hospital, Nashville, TN, p. A591

CAMPBELL, Cinthia, Chief Nursing Officer, HEALTHSOUTH Chattanooga Rehabilitation Hospital, Chattanooga, TN, p. A580

CAMPBELL, David, Administrator, Perry Hospital, Perry, GA, p. A164

CAMPBELL, Dean, Vice President Information Services and Chief Information Officer, Good Samaritan Hospital, Los Angeles, CA, p. A71

CAMPBELL, Deborah, Administrator, Thomas H. Boyd Memorial Hospital, Carrollton, IL, p. A182

CAMPBELL, Emily, Senior Director Human Resources, The University of Vermont Health Network – Alice Hyde Medical Center, Malone, NY, p. A442

CAMPBELL, Eric, Chief Financial Officer, Oswego Hospital, Oswego, NY, p. A452

CAMPBELL, Gayla, Interim Chief Executive Officer, LifeCare Hospitals of Wisconsin, Pewaukee, WI, p. A714

CAMPBELL, Ivy, Director of Nursing, Community Medical Center, Inc., Falls City, NE, p. A395

CAMPBELL, John
    Chief Information Officer, Spaulding Hospital for Continuing Medical Care Cambridge, Cambridge, MA, p. A309
    Chief Information Officer, Spaulding Rehabilitation Hospital, Charlestown, MA, p. A309
    Chief Information Officer, Spaulding Rehabilitation Hospital Cape Cod, East Sandwich, MA, p. A309

CAMPBELL, Kathy, Interim Chief Nursing Officer, Wellmont Holston Valley Medical Center, Kingsport, TN, p. A585

CAMPBELL, Melissa, Controller, Mercy Rehabilitation Hospital Springfield, Springfield, MO, p. A382

CAMPBELL, Melvin, M.D. Medical Staff Chairman, Brown County Hospital, Ainsworth, NE, p. A393

CAMPBELL, Pamela, M.D. Medical Director, Lincoln Prairie Behavioral Health Center, Springfield, IL, p. A203

CAMPBELL, Rose, R.N., President, Penn Highlands Elk, Saint Marys, PA, p. A553

CAMPBELL, Sandra M., R.N. Chief Nursing Officer, Dodge County Hospital, Eastman, GA, p. A159

CAMPBELL, Shari, Chief Operating Officer, Kearny County Hospital, Lakin, KS, p. A247

CAMPBELL, Sharon J., Director, Human Resources, Park Ridge Health, Hendersonville, NC, p. A467

CAMPBELL, Sherry May, Director of Human Resources, Medical Records, Seaside Behavioral Center, New Orleans, LA, p. A285

CAMPBELL, Stephen J., Chief Operating Officer, Pioneers Memorial Healthcare District, Brawley, CA, p. A57

CAMPBELL, Susie, Chief Executive Officer, Community Memorial Hospital, Staunton, IL, p. A204

CAMPBELL, Suzanne, Director Patient Services, Spearfish Regional Hospital, Spearfish, SD, p. A577

CAMPBELL, Teresa, R.N. Chief Nursing Executive, Sutter Lakeside Hospital, Lakeport, CA, p. A68

CAMPBELL, Todd, Senior Vice President and Chief Operating Officer, St. Mary's Medical Center, Huntington, WV, p. A697

CAMPEAU, Arleen, R.N. Vice President of Patient Care Services, Chief Nursing Officer, Powell Valley Healthcare, Powell, WY, p. A723

CAMPO, Mary Beth, MS Director of Nursing, Eastern Niagara Hospital, Lockport, NY, p. A441

CAMPOS, Christina, Administrator, Guadalupe County Hospital, Santa Rosa, NM, p. A431

CAMPOS-DIAZ, Evelyn, Director Human Resources, MedStar St. Mary's Hospital, Leonardtown, MD, p. A302

CAMPOVERDE, Jacqueline, Business Manager, Essex County Hospital Center, Cedar Grove, NJ, p. A415

CAMPS, Lourdes, R.N. Chief Nursing Officer, Hialeah Hospital, Hialeah, FL, p. A130

CANADY, Carolyn, Chief Financial Officer, Sierra Nevada Memorial Hospital, Grass Valley, CA, p. A65

CANALE, Joseph, Business Manager, Trenton Psychiatric Hospital, Trenton, NJ, p. A424

CANALEJO, Donald, Director Human Resources, Lower Keys Medical Center, Key West, FL, p. A133

CANALES, Joe
Director Human Resources, Seton Edgar B. Davis Hospital, Luling, TX, p. A635
Vice President Human Resources, Seton Medical Center Austin, Austin, TX, p. A599
Director Human Resources, Seton Shoal Creek Hospital, Austin, TX, p. A599
Vice President Human Resources, University Medical Center at Brackenridge, Austin, TX, p. A600

CANAVAN, Patrick J., PsyD Chief Operating Officer, Howard University Hospital, Washington, DC, p. A121

CANCEL, Diana, Director Human Resources, Glendora Community Hospital, Glendora, CA, p. A65

CANCILLA, Deborah, Senior Vice President, Information Services and Chief Information Officer, Pinnacle Health System, Harrisburg, PA, p. A540

CANDIA, Gary R., FACHE, Chief Administrative Officer, Abington-Lansdale Hospital Jefferson Health, Lansdale, PA, p. A542

CANDILL, James W., M.D. President Medical Staff, Eye and Ear Clinic of Charleston, Charleston, WV, p. A695

CANDIO, Christine M., FACHE, President and Chief Executive Officer, St. Luke's Hospital, Chesterfield, MO, p. A369

CANDULLO, Carl, Chief Information Officer, Munroe Regional Medical Center, Ocala, FL, p. A139

CANEDO, Jim, Chief Financial Officer, College Medical Center, Long Beach, CA, p. A69

CANFIELD, Brian, Chief Operating Officer, FirstHealth Moore Regional Hospital, Pinehurst, NC, p. A471

CANIZARO, Tom, Vice President and Chief Financial Officer, South Central Regional Medical Center, Laurel, MS, p. A360

CANLAS, Emma, Chief Financial Officer, Valley View Medical Center, Fort Mohave, AZ, p. A32

CANNIFF, Christopher, Executive Director, Human Resources, Harrington Memorial Hospital, Southbridge, MA, p. A314

CANNING, John, Chief Financial Officer, Blythedale Children's Hospital, Valhalla, NY, p. A457

CANNINGTON, H. D., Interim Chief Financial Officer, Fishermen's Hospital, Marathon, FL, p. A135

CANNON, Brenda, R.N. Director of Nursing, Laughlin Memorial Hospital, Greeneville, TN, p. A583

CANNON, Gayle, Director Human Resources, Childress Regional Medical Center, Childress, TX, p. A606

CANNON, Linda, Chief Medical Records Services, San Diego County Psychiatric Hospital, San Diego, CA, p. A89

CANNON, Matthew, Chief Executive Officer, Select Specialty Hospital-Saginaw, Saginaw, MI, p. A333

CANNON, Robert W., President, Barnes-Jewish Hospital, Saint Louis, MO, p. A379

CANO, Daniel, M.D. Chief Medical Officer, Citizens Medical Center, Victoria, TX, p. A655

CANTLEY, J. Scott, President and Chief Executive Officer, Marietta Memorial Hospital, Marietta, OH, p. A498

CANTLEY, J. Scott, President and Chief Executive Officer, Memorial Health System, Marietta, OH, p. B88

CANTRE, Pedro Laureano, Chief Nursing Officer, Cardiovascular Center of Puerto Rico and the Caribbean, San Juan, PR, p. A729

CANTRELL, David, CPA Vice President and Chief Financial Officer, West Hills Hospital and Medical Center,, CA, p. A75

CANTRELL, Dedra
Chief Information Officer, Emory Saint Joseph's Hospital of Atlanta, Atlanta, GA, p. A152
Chief Information Officer, Emory University Hospital, atlanta, GA, p. A152
Chief Information Officer, Emory University Hospital Midtown, Atlanta, GA, p. A152

CANTRELL, Tara, Director Human Resources, Davis Hospital and Medical Center, Layton, UT, p. A660

CANTU, Andrew, Chief Financial Officer, Kern Medical Center, Bakersfield, CA, p. A56

CANTU, Janie, Director Human Resources, Crosbyton Clinic Hospital, Crosbyton, TX, p. A608

CAPANNARI, Margaret, Director Information Systems, Advocate Illinois Masonic Medical Center, Chicago, IL, p. A183

CAPECE Jr., Vincent G., President and Chief Executive Officer, Middlesex Hospital, Middletown, CT, p. A115

CAPERS, Travis, FACHE, President, SSM St. Mary's Health Center, Saint Louis, MO, p. A381

CAPILI, Anthony, M.D. Chief of Staff, Chambers County Public Hospital District No. 1, Anahuac, TX, p. A596

CAPIOLA, Richard, M.D. Chief Medical Officer, Baton Rouge Behavioral Hospital, Baton Rouge, LA, p. A272

CAPITELLI, Robert, M.D. Senior Vice President and Chief Medical Officer, St. Tammany Parish Hospital, Covington, LA, p. A275

CAPITULO, Kathleen, Ph.D. Chief Nurse Executive, James J. Peters Veterans Affairs Medical Center,, NY, p. A445

CAPLAN, Margaret B., Director, Veterans Affairs Hudson Valley Health Care System, Montrose, NY, p. A443

CAPLE, Jocelyn, M.D. Chief Medical Officer, Frisbie Memorial Hospital, Rochester, NH, p. A413

CAPLER, Glenda, Interim Director of Nursing, Gordon Memorial Hospital, Gordon, NE, p. A396

CAPLES, Greg, Chief Operating Officer, TriStar Summit Medical Center, Hermitage, TN, p. A584

CAPO, Ann Marie, R.N. Chief Nursing Officer, Unconn John Dempsey Hospital, Farmington, CT, p. A114

CAPONI, Vincent C., President and Chief Executive Officer, St. Vincent's Medical Center, Bridgeport, CT, p. A113

CAPOTE, Henry, Interim Chief Financial Officer, Coral Gables Hospital, Coral Gables, FL, p. A126

CAPPEL, Blaine, Director Information Systems, Memorial Health System, Abilene, KS, p. A240

CAPPLEMAN, Troy, M.D. Chief of Staff, Tippah County Hospital, Ripley, MS, p. A364

CAPPS, Anita, R.N. Chief Nursing Executive, Community Hospital South, Indianapolis, IN, p. A213

CAPPS, Kim, Chief Financial Officer, Hayes Green Beach Memorial Hospital, Charlotte, MI, p. A320

CAPPS, Melissa, Site Leader Information Technology, St. Luke's Magic Valley Medical Center, Twin Falls, ID, p. A179

CAPPS, Rick, Chief Financial Officer, Cumberland County Hospital, Burkesville, KY, p. A258

CAPSHAW, Marcia, Chief Operating Officer, West Central Georgia Regional Hospital, Columbus, GA, p. A157

CAPUANO, Terry Ann, R.N
Chief Operating Officer, Lehigh Valley Hospital, Allentown, PA, p. A532
Chief Operating Officer, Lehigh Valley Hospital-Muhlenberg, Bethlehem, PA, p. A533

CAPUANO, Tony, Chief Operating Officer, EASTAR Health System, Muskogee, OK, p. A515

CAPUTO, Louis, Chief Executive Officer, TriStar StoneCrest Medical Center, Smyrna, TN, p. A593

CAPUTO, Michael, Chief Information Officer, MUSC Medical Center of Medical University of South Carolina, Charleston, SC, p. A563

CARABALLO, Amanda, Nursing Director, Hospital De La Concepcion, San German, PR, p. A729

CARACCIOLO, Kevin, Chief Human Resources Officer, Palm Beach Gardens Medical Center, Palm Beach Gardens, FL, p. A141

CARACCIOLO, Mary Jo, Director Human Resources, Wellington Regional Medical Center, West Palm Beach, FL, p. A150

CARALIS, George, Interim Chief Executive Officer, El Paso Children's Hospital, El Paso, TX, p. A615

CARBALLO, Francisco R., M.D. Medical Director, Hospital HIMA de Humacao, Humacao, PR, p. A727

CARBALLO, Jose E., Executive Director, Hospital HIMA San Pablo Caguas, Caguas, PR, p. A726

CARBONE, Dominick, M.D. Chief of Staff, Hugh Chatham Memorial Hospital, Elkin, NC, p. A465

CARD, Dean
Chief Financial Officer, Kindred Hospital South Florida-Fort Lauderdale, Fort Lauderdale, FL, p. A128
Chief Financial Officer, Kindred Hospital the Palm Beaches, Riviera Beach, FL, p. A143

CARD, Edwin, President Medical Staff, McDonough District Hospital, Macomb, IL, p. A195

CARD, Mike, Chief Information Officer, Audubon County Memorial Hospital, Audubon, IA, p. A225

CARDA, Greg, Vice President Finance, Missouri Delta Medical Center, Sikeston, MO, p. A382

CARDALI, Paul, M.D. Chief of Staff, Lakeway Regional Hospital, Morristown, TN, p. A590

CARDELL, Melinda H.
Interim Vice President and Chief Information Officer, Roper St. Francis, Charleston, SC, p. A563
Interim Chief Information Officer, Roper St. Francis Mount Pleasant Hospital, Mount Pleasant, SC, p. A568

CARDEN, Lamar, M.D. Chief Medical Officer, Jack Hughston Memorial Hospital, Phenix City, AL, p. A24

CARDENAS, Carlos, M.D., Chief Administrative Officer, Doctor's Hospital at Renaissance, Edinburg, TX, p. A614

CARDENAS, Lydia, Director Human Resources, River Crest Hospital, San Angelo, TX, p. A644

CARDENAS, Mark, Director Plant Operations, Vibra Hospital of Northern California, Redding, CA, p. A84

CARDENAS, Mitzi
Chief Information Officer, Truman Medical Center-Hospital Hill, Kansas City, MO, p. A374
Chief Information Officer, Truman Medical Center-Lakewood, Kansas City, MO, p. A374

CARDIFF, Michael, Systems Supervisor, Abrom Kaplan Memorial Hospital, Kaplan, LA, p. A279

CARDINAL, Joyce, Chief Nursing Executive, Jefferson Healthcare, Port Townsend, WA, p. A688

CARDLE, Lori, Senior Vice President, Chief Financial Officer, Valley Presbyterian Hospital,, CA, p. A75

CARDWELL, Marian, Chief Financial Officer, Potomac Valley Hospital, Keyser, WV, p. A697

CAREY, Ann
Vice President and Chief Information Officer, St. Vincent's Medical Center Riverside, Jacksonville, FL, p. A132
Chief Information Officer, St. Vincent's Medical Center Southside, Jacksonville, FL, p. A132

CAREY, Calvin, Chief Financial Officer, Summit Medical Center, Casper, WY, p. A721

CAREY, Eric R., Vice President Information Systems and Chief Information Officer, Valley Hospital, Ridgewood, NJ, p. A423

CAREY, Jeannie, R.N. Director Patient Care, Perry Memorial Hospital, Perry, OK, p. A518

CAREY, Robin, Director of Nursing, Jasper Memorial Hospital, Monticello, GA, p. A163

CARGONARA, Douglas, Ph.D. Chief Information Officer, Pilgrim Psychiatric Center, Brentwood, NY, p. A435

CARIGSON, John, Chief Financial Officer, Covenant Specialty Hospital, Lubbock, TX, p. A634

CARIKER, Kelly, Chief Information Officer, North Valley Hospital, Tonasket, WA, p. A692

CARLE, Chris, Senior Vice President and Chief Operating Officer, St. Elizabeth Florence, Florence, KY, p. A260

CARLETON, David
Chief Information Officer, Heritage Valley Health System, Beaver, PA, p. A533
Chief Information Officer, Sewickley Valley Hospital, (A Division of Valley Medical Facilities), Sewickley, PA, p. A554

CARLETON, Drew, Chief Executive Officer, Sundance Hospital, Arlington, TX, p. A597

CARLINO, James, Vice President Human Resources, Deborah Heart and Lung Center, Browns Mills, NJ, p. A415

CARLINO, Tracy, R.N. Chief Nursing Officer, Virtua Marlton, Marlton, NJ, p. A419

CARLISLE, Charles, Director, East Mississippi State Hospital, Meridian, MS, p. A362

CARLISLE, Sandy, Manager Human Resources, Holzer Medical Center – Jackson, Jackson, OH, p. A496

CARLOCK, Carey, Chief Executive Officer, Riveredge Hospital, Forest Park, IL, p. A190

CARLOS, Ilona, M.D. President Medical Staff, Thorek Memorial Hospital, Chicago, IL, p. A187

CARLSON, Bev, Chief Financial Officer, Delta County Memorial Hospital, Delta, CO, p. A103

CARLSON, Brian J., FACHE,
Chief Executive Officer, Sanford Medical Center Thief River Falls, Thief River Falls, MN, p. A352
Chief Executive Officer, Sanford Thief River Falls Behavioral Health Center, Thief River Falls, MN, p. A352

CARLSON, Daniel, M.D. Chief Medical Officer, Wellmont Holston Valley Medical Center, Kingsport, TN, p. A585

CARLSON, Kellie, Director Human Resources, Coastal Harbor Treatment Center, Savannah, GA, p. A165

CARLSON, Kim
Director Human Resources, Essentia Health Northern Pines Medical Center, Aurora, MN, p. A338
Senior Vice President Human Resources, FirstLight Health System, Mora, MN, p. A347

CARLSON, Kurt, Chief Executive Officer, Otis R. Bowen Center for Human Services, Warsaw, IN, p. A223

CARLSON, Peter, Administrator, Aurora Psychiatric Hospital, Wauwatosa, WI, p. A718

CARLSON, Richard, Chief Financial Officer, Crawford Memorial Hospital, Robinson, IL, p. A201

CARLSON, Sandee, Director of Nursing, Essentia Health Duluth, Duluth, MN, p. A341

CARLSON, Sarah, Director Human Resources, Essentia Health St. Joseph's Medical Center, Brainerd, MN, p. A340

CARLSON, Scott, Director, Mary Greeley Medical Center, Ames, IA, p. A225

CARLSON, Wendie, Chief Human Resources Officer, Jackson–Madison County General Hospital, Jackson, TN, p. A584

CARLSON, Wendy, Director Human Resources, Pathways of Tennessee, Jackson, TN, p. A584

CARLTON, Terrie, R.N. Vice President & Chief Nursing Officer, Palmetto Health Tuomey, Sumter, SC, p. A570

CARLYLE, Dave, Director Human Resources, Wayne County Hospital, Corydon, IA, p. A228

CARMAN, Susan, Chief Information Officer, United Health Services Hospitals–Binghamton, Binghamton, NY, p. A435

CARMAN, Thomas H., President and Chief Executive Officer, Samaritan Medical Center, Watertown, NY, p. A458

CARMELLINI, Tracy, M.D. Chief of Staff, Jennersville Regional Hospital, West Grove, PA, p. A557

CARMEN, Lee, Associate Vice President Health Care Information Systems, University of Iowa Hospitals and Clinics, Iowa City, IA, p. A232

CARMICHAEL, Craig, Vice President, Operations, University of Maryland St. Joseph Medical Center, Towson, MD, p. A304

CARMICHAEL, Gavin H., FACHE, Interim Chief Executive Officer, Alaska Psychiatric Institute, Anchorage, AK, p. A28

CARMODY, James, Vice President Human Resources, Wilkes–Barre General Hospital, Wilkes–Barre, PA, p. A558

CARMONA, Mariaelena, Chief Executive Officer, Highlands Rehabilitation Hospital, El Paso, TX, p. A615

CARNAHAN, II, Robert H., R.N. Chief Nursing Officer, Banner Churchill Community Hospital, Fallon, NV, p. A404

CARNES, Ruth, Manager Human Resources, Jennings American Legion Hospital, Jennings, LA, p. A279

CARNEVALE, Raymond F., Chief Executive Officer, Select Specialty Hospital–Madison, Madison, WI, p. A709

CARNEY, Adrienne, R.N. Director Nursing and Surgical Services, Kearney Regional Medical Center, Kearney, NE, p. A397

CARNEY, Glenn, Chief Operating Officer, Central Florida Regional Hospital, Sanford, FL, p. A145

CARNEY, Judi, M.D. President Medical Staff, Baptist Memorial Hospital for Women, Memphis, TN, p. A588

CARNEY, Kevin, Senior Information Systems Analyst, Pine Creek Medical Center, Dallas, TX, p. A611

CARNEY, Michael J., Chief Executive Officer, Brentwood Behavioral HealthCare of Mississippi, Jackson, MS, p. A359

CARO, Vique, Chief Information Officer, Cincinnati Veterans Affairs Medical Center, Cincinnati, OH, p. A487

CAROLINA, Dorinda, Chief Human Resources Officer, Aria – Jefferson Health, Philadelphia, PA, p. A547

CARON, Jacqueline, Chief Human Resources, Birmingham Veterans Affairs Medical Center, Birmingham, AL, p. A16

CARON, Phillip A.
Chief Financial Officer, East Texas Medical Center Carthage, Carthage, TX, p. A605
Chief Financial Officer, East Texas Medical Center Henderson, Henderson, TX, p. A623

CARON Jr.,, William L., President, MaineHealth, Portland, ME, p. B84

CAROZZA, Sally, Director Human Resources, West Penn Hospital, Pittsburgh, PA, p. A552

CARPEL, Emmett, M.D. Medical Director and Chief of Staff, Phillips Eye Institute, Minneapolis, MN, p. A346

CARPENTER, Allan, Chief Information Officer, Garfield Medical Center, Monterey Park, CA, p. A78

CARPENTER, Carolyn, Chief Operating Officer, Duke University Hospital, Durham, NC, p. A464

CARPENTER, Curt, Manager Information Technology, Coquille Valley Hospital, Coquille, OR, p. A525

CARPENTER, Dan
Chief Financial Officer, UnityPoint Health – Allen Hospital, Waterloo, IA, p. A239
Chief Financial Officer, UnityPoint Health – Finley Hospital, Dubuque, IA, p. A230

CARPENTER, Deb, Director Information Technology, Lourdes Medical Center, Pasco, WA, p. A687

CARPENTER, Jackie, Office Manager, Rock County Hospital, Bassett, NE, p. A393

CARPENTER, Leah A., Administrator and Chief Executive Officer, Memorial Hospital Miramar, Miramar, FL, p. A138

CARPENTER, Posie, R.N. Chief Administrative Officer, UCLA Medical Center–Santa Monica, Santa Monica, CA, p. A94

CARPENTER, Stephanie, Director of Nursing Services, Columbia County Health System, Dayton, WA, p. A684

CARPENTER III,, William F., Chairman and Chief Executive Officer, LifePoint Health, Brentwood, TN, p. B82

CARPER, Joleen, Vice President Quality and Risk, Tri–State Memorial Hospital, Clarkston, WA, p. A683

CARR, Ann, R.N. Chief Nursing Officer, Craig General Hospital, Vinita, OK, p. A522

CARR, Charles E., Vice President and Administrator, Carilion Stonewall Jackson Hospital, Lexington, VA, p. A672

CARR, David, M.D. Physician Medical Director, The Rehabilitation Institute of St. Louis, Saint Louis, MO, p. A381

CARR, Deborah, Vice President Human Resources, Orange Regional Medical Center, Middletown, NY, p. A442

CARR, Diane, Chief Information Officer, NYC Health + Hospitals / North Central Bronx,, NY, p. A449

CARR, George, Chief Information Officer, Bryan Medical Center, Lincoln, NE, p. A397

CARR, Mark E., Chief Information Resource Management, Jack C. Montgomery Veterans Affairs Medical Center, Muskogee, OK, p. A515

CARR, Randall
Director Human Resources, Parkwest Medical Center, Knoxville, TN, p. A586
Director Human Resources, Roane Medical Center, Harriman, TN, p. A583

CARR, Sheila, Chief Executive Officer, Wekiva Springs, Jacksonville, FL, p. A132

CARR, Tim, Chief Financial Officer, Methodist Ambulatory Surgery Hospital – Northwest, San Antonio, TX, p. A646

CARRADINE, Damon, Director Information Technology, Highland Hospital, Charleston, WV, p. A695

CARRANZA, Diana, Interim Director, Veterans Affairs Illiana Health Care System, Danville, IL, p. A187

CARRASCO, Anthony, Director Information Systems, Gardens Regional Hospital and Medical Center, Hawaiian Gardens, CA, p. A65

CARRASCO, Carlos, Chief Operating Officer, Orlando Regional Medical Center, Orlando, FL, p. A140

CARRASCO, Michelle, Director Human Resources, Palo Verde Behavioral Health, Tucson, AZ, p. A41

CARRASCO, Victor, Chief Executive Officer, Kindred Hospital Rancho, Rancho Cucamonga, CA, p. A84

CARRASQUILLO, Carmen, M.D. Medical Director, Industrial Hospital, San Juan, PR, p. A730

CARREJO, Angela, Director Human Resources, Nor–Lea General Hospital, Lovington, NM, p. A430

CARRELLI, Bobbie, Director Human Resources, Summit Behavioral Healthcare, Cincinnati, OH, p. A488

CARREON, Aleana, Executive Director, Sonoma Developmental Center, Eldridge, CA, p. A61

CARRERA, Lavern H., Senior Vice President Human Resources, Northside Medical Center, Youngstown, OH, p. A506

CARRERO, Milton D., M.D. Medical Director, Dr. Ramon E. Betances Hospital–Mayaguez Medical Center Branch, Mayaguez, PR, p. A728

CARRICO, Tom, Vice President of Operations, Hardin Memorial Hospital, Elizabethtown, KY, p. A259

CARRIER, Amy Frey, President, WellStar Cobb Hospital, Austell, GA, p. A154

CARRIER, Jeffrey, R.N. Chief Clinical Officer, Freeman Health System, Joplin, MO, p. A372

CARRIER, Patrick Brian, President and Chief Executive Officer, CHRISTUS St. Vincent Regional Medical Center, Santa Fe, NM, p. A431

CARRIERE, Archie, Information Technology Technician, Northlake Behavioral Health System, Mandeville, LA, p. A282

CARRIGG, John, Executive Vice President and Chief Operating Officer, United Health Services Hospitals–Binghamton, Binghamton, NY, p. A435

CARRILLO, Irma, Director Human Resources, Ashford Presbyterian Community Hospital, San Juan, PR, p. A729

CARRILLO, Todd, Chief Information Officer, Yoakum County Hospital, Denver City, TX, p. A613

CARRILLO, Zulema, Superintendent, El Paso Psychiatric Center, El Paso, TX, p. A615

CARRINGER, Rick
Vice President Finance and Support Services, LeConte Medical Center, Sevierville, TN, p. A593
Vice President and Chief Financial Officer, Methodist Medical Center of Oak Ridge, Oak Ridge, TN, p. A592

CARRINGTON, Ebone', Interim Executive Director, NYC Health + Hospitals / Harlem, New York, NY, p. A448

CARRINGTON, Paul Henry, Chief Nursing Officer, Pawnee Valley Community Hospital, Larned, KS, p. A247

CARROCINO, Joanne, FACHE, President and Chief Executive Officer, Cape Regional Medical Center, Cape May Court House, NJ, p. A415

CARROLL, Allen P., Senior Vice President and Chief Executive Officer, Bon Secours St. Francis Hospital, Charleston, SC, p. A562

CARROLL, Candice R., Nurse Executive, Riverside Regional Medical Center, Newport News, VA, p. A674

CARROLL, Eric, Chief Executive Officer, Unicoi County Memorial Hospital, Erwin, TN, p. A582

CARROLL, Jack, Director Human Resources, Spaulding Hospital for Continuing Medical Care Cambridge, Cambridge, MA, p. A309

CARROLL, Jack A., Ph.D., President and Chief Executive Officer, Magee Rehabilitation Hospital, Philadelphia, PA, p. A548

CARROLL, Jacqueline, Director Human Resources, Los Alamos Medical Center, Los Alamos, NM, p. A430

CARROLL, Jaime, R.N. Vice President Nursing, Sentara Albemarle Medical Center, Elizabeth City, NC, p. A464

CARROLL, Jaime, Department Head, Walter Reed National Military Medical Center, Bethesda, MD, p. A299

CARROLL, James H., Chief Information Officer, St. John Medical Center, Westlake, OH, p. A505

CARROLL, John, M.D. Chief Medical Officer, St. James Mercy Hospital, Hornell, NY, p. A440

CARROLL, Jonathan, Chief Information Officer, Unconn John Dempsey Hospital, Farmington, CT, p. A114

CARROLL, Karen, MSN Vice President and Chief Nursing Officer, Beaufort Memorial Hospital, Beaufort, SC, p. A562

CARROLL, Kristen, M.D. Chief of Staff, Shriners Hospitals for Children–Salt Lake City, Salt Lake City, UT, p. A663

CARROLL, Michael W., Administrator, Richland Parish Hospital, Delhi, LA, p. A276

CARROLL, Peggy, Chief Information Officer, Palos Community Hospital, Palos Heights, IL, p. A199

CARROLL, Richard, M.D
Chief Medical officer, AMITA Health Adventist Medical Center Bolingbrook, Bolingbrook, IL, p. A182
Vice PResident and Chief Medical Officer, AMITA Health GlenOaks, Glendale Heights, IL, p. A191

CARROLL, Susan, Chief Executive Officer, Inova Alexandria Hospital, Alexandria, VA, p. A667

CARROLL, Terrence, Ph.D. Vice President, Information Services, Dartmouth–Hitchcock Medical Center, Lebanon, NH, p. A412

CARROLL, Terri L., Vice President Financial Services, Hillsboro Area Hospital, Hillsboro, IL, p. A193

CARROLL, Velma, Chief Information Officer, Augusta Health, Fishersville, VA, p. A670

CARROLL, William, M.D. Chief Medical Executive, Sutter Santa Rosa Regional Hospital, Santa Rosa, CA, p. A94

CARRON, Patrick E., FACHE, President and Chief Executive Officer, Perry County Memorial Hospital, Perryville, MO, p. A378

CARRUTH, Gregory, Head Information Management, Naval Hospital Oak Harbor, Oak Harbor, WA, p. A687

CARRUTH, Keith, Chief Executive Officer, AMG Specialty Hospital–Houma, Houma, LA, p. A278

CARSON, Carole, Director of Nursing Operations, Rehabilitation Hospital of Southern New Mexico, Las Cruces, NM, p. A430

CARSON, Debbie, Director Human Resources, Promise Hospital of Vicksburg, Vicksburg, MS, p. A365

CARSON, Joe, Director Human Resources, Glen Oaks Hospital, Greenville, TX, p. A621

CARSON, Kara Jo, Chief Financial Officer, Pinckneyville Community Hospital, Pinckneyville, IL, p. A200

CARSON, Mitchell C., President and Chief Executive Officer, Longmont United Hospital, Longmont, CO, p. A108

CARSTENS, Cynthia L., R.N., President and Chief Executive Officer, Stewart Memorial Community Hospital, Lake City, IA, p. A233

CARSTENSEN, Karla, Director Patient Care, Avera Dells Area Hospital, Dell Rapids, SD, p. A573

CARTAGENA, Maria, M.D. Chief Medical Officer, BryLin Hospitals, Buffalo, NY, p. A435

CARTER, Barbara, Chief Nursing Officer, Cimarron Memorial Hospital, Boise City, OK, p. A509

CARTER, Billie, Chief Operating Officer and Assistant Administrator, Stonewall Memorial Hospital, Aspermont, TX, p. A598

CARTER, Charla, Human Resource Officer, Uvalde Memorial Hospital, Uvalde, TX, p. A654

CARTER, Christen, Director Public Relations, Roosevelt Warm Springs Rehabilitation and Specialty Hospitals – Rehab, Warm Springs, GA, p. A168

CARTER, D. Montez, President, St. Mary's Good Samaritan Hospital, Greensboro, GA, p. A160
CARTER, Dennis, M.D. Chief of Staff, Eastern Oklahoma Medical Center, Poteau, OK, p. A518
CARTER, Donna, MSN Chief Nursing Officer, Minden Medical Center, Minden, LA, p. A283
CARTER, Douglas S., M.D. Vice President and Chief Medical Officer, Major Hospital, Shelbyville, IN, p. A222
CARTER, Frank, Chief Financial Officer, Cornerstone Hospital of Huntington, Huntington, WV, p. A696
CARTER, Gary L., M.D. Vice President and Chief Medical Officer, North Kansas City Hospital, North Kansas City, MO, p. A377
CARTER, Jr., James R., Chief Operating Officer, Methodist Healthcare Memphis Hospitals, Memphis, TN, p. A589
CARTER, Jessica Y., Chief Financial Officer, Crisp Regional Hospital, Cordele, GA, p. A157
CARTER, Jim, Chief Operating Officer, Grady General Hospital, Cairo, GA, p. A155
CARTER, Leonard M., Vice President Human Resources, FHN Memorial Hospital, Freeport, IL, p. A190
CARTER, Leslia, Administrator, North Mississippi Medical Center–Pontotoc, Pontotoc, MS, p. A364
CARTER, Malinda Yvonne, Vice President Human Resources, Saint Anthony Hospital, Chicago, IL, p. A186
CARTER, Marcia, Director Human Resources, Bluegrass Community Hospital, Versailles, KY, p. A270
CARTER, Michael, Administrator Information Technology, Northwest Ohio Psychiatric Hospital, Toledo, OH, p. A504
CARTER, Michael C., Interim Chief Executive Officer, St. Mary's Medical Center, San Francisco, CA, p. A90
CARTER, Michael J., Chief Executive Officer, Eastern Oklahoma Medical Center, Poteau, OK, p. A518
CARTER, Misty, Director Human Resources and Chief Operating Officer, Great Plains Regional Medical Center, Elk City, OK, p. A511
CARTER, Priscilla, Chief Financial Officer, Mesa Hills Specialty Hospital, El Paso, TX, p. A616
CARTER, Rebecca W., FACHE, Chief Executive Officer and Chief Nursing Officer, Blue Ridge Regional Hospital, Spruce Pine, NC, p. A474
CARTER, Richard, M.D. Chief Medical Officer, Hamilton County Hospital, Syracuse, KS, p. A254
CARTER, Richard, Chief Executive Officer, Hunt Regional Healthcare, Greenville, TX, p. B71
CARTER, Richard, District Chief Executive Officer, Hunt Regional Medical Center, Greenville, TX, p. A621
CARTER, Richard, M.D. Chief of Staff, Tennova Healthcare–Jefferson Memorial Hospital, Jefferson City, TN, p. A584
CARTER, Steve, Chief Information Officer, Monongalia General Hospital, Morgantown, WV, p. A698
CARTER, Tamelia, Office Manager, Knox County Hospital, Knox City, TX, p. A631
CARTER, Teresa, Vice President Patient Care Services, OneCore Health, Oklahoma City, OK, p. A517
CARTER, Theodora, Administrative Director Human Resources, Hackensack University Medical Center at Pascack Valley, Westwood, NJ, p. A425
CARTER, Vickie, Information Systems Director, Sumner Regional Medical Center, Gallatin, TN, p. A583
CARTWRIGHT, Bryan, Chief Information Technology Officer, Missouri River Medical Center, Fort Benton, MT, p. A387
CARTWRIGHT, David, Director Management Information Systems, Danville Regional Medical Center, Danville, VA, p. A669
CARTWRIGHT, David A., Vice President Finance and Support Services, Advocate Condell Medical Center, Libertyville, IL, p. A195
CARTWRIGHT, Debra
Chief Financial Officer, St. Francis Health, Topeka, KS, p. A254
Chief Financial Officer, St. Joseph Medical Center, Kansas City, MO, p. A374
CARTWRIGHT, Kay B., R.N. Vice President and Chief Nursing Officer, Reid Health, Richmond, IN, p. A221
CARUCCI, Dean, Chief Executive Officer, Portsmouth Regional Hospital, Portsmouth, NH, p. A413
CARUGATI, Diane, Chief Operating Officer, Friends Hospital, Philadelphia, PA, p. A548
CARUSO, Diane M., MSN Chief Nursing Officer, HEALTHSOUTH Scottsdale Rehabilitation Hospital, Scottsdale, AZ, p. A38
CARUSO, Don, M.D., Chief Executive Officer and President, Cheshire Medical Center, Keene, NH, p. A411
CARUSO, Michael J., President and Chief Executive Officer, East Ohio Regional Hospital, Martins Ferry, OH, p. A498
CARUSO, Michael J., President and Chief Executive Officer, Ohio Valley Health Services and Education Corporation, Wheeling, WV, p. B100
CARUSO, Michael J., President and Chief Executive Officer, Ohio Valley Medical Center, Wheeling, WV, p. A701

CARVER, Carol, MSN Vice President Patient Services, Clarity Child Guidance Center, San Antonio, TX, p. A645
CARVER, Christy, R.N., Chief Executive Officer, LifeCare Hospitals of Dallas, Dallas, TX, p. A610
CARVETH, Barbara, Chief Financial Officer, University of Colorado Hospital, Aurora, CO, p. A101
CARVOLTH, Richard, M.D. Chief Medical Officer, Santa Rosa Memorial Hospital, Santa Rosa, CA, p. A94
CARYER, Steve, Chief Financial Officer, Community Memorial Hospital, Hicksville, OH, p. A496
CARYNSKI, Paula A., R.N., President, OSF Saint Anthony Medical Center, Rockford, IL, p. A202
CASABONA, Nicholas, Chief Information Officer, Winthrop–University Hospital, Mineola, NY, p. A442
CASALS, Patricia, MSN Chief Nursing Officer, Tyler Memorial Hospital, Tunkhannock, PA, p. A556
CASANO, Jayleen, Ph.D. Chief Operations and Nursing Officer, Abrazo Central Campus, Phoenix, AZ, p. A35
CASANOVA, Robert Bernier, Chief Financial Officer, Industrial Hospital, San Juan, PR, p. A730
CASAREZ, Margaret, Chief Financial Officer, San Joaquin Valley Rehabilitation Hospital, Fresno, CA, p. A64
CASAREZ, Teresa, Director Human Resources, New Mexico Rehabilitation Center, Roswell, NM, p. A431
CASCIO, Richard C., Interim Chief Executive Officer, University Health System, Shreveport, LA, p. B146
CASDORPH, Michael, Chief Operating Officer, Highland–Clarksburg Hospital, Clarksburg, WV, p. A695
CASE, Cliff, Chief Financial Officer, Mineral Community Hospital, Superior, MT, p. A391
CASE, Ed, Executive Vice President and Chief Financial Officer, Rehabilitation Institute of Chicago, Chicago, IL, p. A186
CASE, Harvey, President, Vidant Beaufort Hospital, Washington, NC, p. A475
CASE, Linda, Administrator, Hillside Rehabilitation Hospital, Warren, OH, p. A504
CASE, Matthew, USN, Director For Administration, Naval Medical Center, Portsmouth, VA, p. A676
CASERTA, Kevin, M.D
Chief Medical Officer, Providence Centralia Hospital, Centralia, WA, p. A683
Chief Medical Officer, Providence St. Peter Hospital, Olympia, WA, p. A687
CASEY, Candy J., MS, President and Chief Executive Officer, Columbia Center, Mequon, WI, p. A710
CASEY, Dina, Human Resources Officer, Lane County Hospital, Dighton, KS, p. A242
CASEY, Joseph, Chief Financial Officer, Sturdy Memorial Hospital, Attleboro, MA, p. A305
CASEY, Kevin, M.D. Chief Clinical Officer, St. Rita's Medical Center, Lima, OH, p. A497
CASEY, Rick, D.O. Chief Medical Staff, Cedar County Memorial Hospital, El Dorado Springs, MO, p. A370
CASH, Jeff, Senior Vice President and Chief Information Officer, Mercy Medical Center–Cedar Rapids, Cedar Rapids, IA, p. A226
CASH, Jordan, President, INTEGRIS Miami Hospital, Miami, OK, p. A514
CASHWELL, David, Chief Executive Officer, HEALTHSOUTH Rehabilitation Hospital of Virginia, Richmond, VA, p. A677
CASIANO, Manuel, M.D. Senior Vice President Medical Affairs, Frederick Memorial Hospital, Frederick, MD, p. A301
CASILLAS, Rosalind C., Chief Nursing Officer, Lawrence Memorial Hospital, Walnut Ridge, AR, p. A53
CASMER, Benjamin, FACHE Chief Operating Officer, Bay Area Regional Medical Center, Webster, TX, p. A656
CASNER, Trina, President and Chief Executive Officer, Pana Community Hospital, Pana, IL, p. A199
CASOLA, Frances, Senior Vice President Operations, Saint Joseph's Medical Center, Yonkers, NY, p. A459
CASON, Cathy, Chief Financial Officer, Jeff Davis Hospital, Hazlehurst, GA, p. A160
CASON, Diane, Chief Information Officer, Controller and Director Human Resources, Lake Butler Hospital Hand Surgery Center, Lake Butler, FL, p. A133
CASON, Randall R., FACHE, Senior Administrator, Via Christi Hospital Pittsburg, Pittsburg, KS, p. A252
CASON, Will, Vice President Human Resources, St. Rita's Medical Center, Lima, OH, p. A497
CASPER, Rylee, R.N. Chief Nursing Officer, Newman Memorial Hospital, Shattuck, OK, p. A519
CASPERSON, William, M.D. Vice President Medical Affairs, Memorial Hospital, Belleville, IL, p. A181
CASS, Jinilinn, Director Medical Records, Lakeview Regional Medical Center, Covington, LA, p. A275
CASS, Julene J., R.N. Director of Nursing, Community Memorial Hospital, Redfield, SD, p. A576
CASS, Paul, D.O. Chief Medical & Clinical Integration Officer, Wentworth–Douglass Hospital, Dover, NH, p. A410

CASSADY, Perry, M.D. Medical Director, Physicians' Medical Center, New Albany, IN, p. A219
CASSAGNE, Nancy R., FACHE, Chief Executive Officer, West Jefferson Medical Center, Marrero, LA, p. A283
CASSEDY, Ryan, Chief Executive Officer, Vibra Hospital of Fort Wayne, Fort Wayne, IN, p. A211
CASSEL, Asenath, Chief Nursing Officer, Wellington Regional Medical Center, West Palm Beach, FL, p. A150
CASSEL, Kari
Senior Vice President and Chief Information Officer, UF Health Jacksonville, Jacksonville, FL, p. A132
Senior Vice President and Chief Information Officer, UF Health Shands Hospital, Gainesville, FL, p. A130
CASSELL, Sally, Manager Human Resources, Ozark Health Medical Center, Clinton, AR, p. A44
CASSELS, William H., Administrator, DCH Regional Medical Center, Tuscaloosa, AL, p. A26
CASSIDAY, Cheryl, R.N. Director of Nursing, Chadron Community Hospital and Health Services, Chadron, NE, p. A395
CASSIDY, Donna, Chief Nursing Executive, South Haven Health System, South Haven, MI, p. A334
CASSIDY, Doris B., Associate Director, Veterans Health Care System of the Ozarks, Fayetteville, AR, p. A46
CASSIDY, John W., M.D., President, Chief Executive Officer and Chief Medical Officer, Nexus Health Systems, Houston, TX, p. B96
CASSIDY, Joseph J., Vice President and Chief Human Resources Officer, Holy Redeemer Hospital, Meadowbrook, PA, p. A544
CASSLE, Susie, R.N. Vice President Nursing Services, Hendrick Health System, Abilene, TX, p. A595
CASTANEDA, Edmundo
President, Mercy General Hospital, Sacramento, CA, p. A86
President, Mercy Hospital of Folsom, Folsom, CA, p. A62
CASTANEDA, Marissa, Chief Operating Officer and Director Marketing, Doctor's Hospital at Renaissance, Edinburg, TX, p. A614
CASTANEDA, Trevor, Chief Executive Officer, Tennova Newport Medical Center, Newport, TN, p. A591
CASTEEL, Brian, Information Technology Technician, Hardin County General Hospital, Rosiclare, IL, p. A202
CASTEEL, Karen, Director Human Resources, Palms of Pasadena Hospital, Saint Petersburg, FL, p. A144
CASTEEL, Lisa, Assistant Administrator and Chief Financial Officer, Henry County Medical Center, Paris, TN, p. A592
CASTEEL, Rick
Vice President Management Information Systems and Chief Information Officer, University of Maryland Harford Memorial Hospital, Havre De Grace, MD, p. A301
Vice President Management Information Systems and Chief Information Officer, University of Maryland Upper Chesapeake Medical Center, Bel Air, MD, p. A298
CASTELLO, Fred, M.D. Chief Medical Officer, Augusta Health, Fishersville, VA, p. A670
CASTILLO, Carol, Medical Director, Sonoma Developmental Center, Eldridge, CA, p. A61
CASTILLO, Dan A., FACHE, Chief Executive Officer, LAC+USC Medical Center, Los Angeles, CA, p. A72
CASTILLO, Edgar, Chief Financial Officer, Larkin Community Hospital, South Miami, FL, p. A145
CASTILLO, Paul, Chief Financial Officer, University of Michigan Hospitals and Health Centers, Ann Arbor, MI, p. A318
CASTILLO, Ralph A., CPA, Chief Executive Officer, Morgan Memorial Hospital, Madison, GA, p. A162
CASTILLO, Randall, Vice President, Operations, Mercy Hospital of Folsom, Folsom, CA, p. A62
CASTILLO, Renee, Chief Nursing Officer, Plains Memorial Hospital, Dimmitt, TX, p. A613
CASTILLO, Rita S., R.N. Chief Quality Officer and Risk Management, South Texas Regional Medical Center, Jourdanton, TX, p. A629
CASTLE, Bill, Chief Financial Officer, Huron Medical Center, Bad Axe, MI, p. A318
CASTLE, Dorothy, Director Human Resources, North Mississippi Medical Center–Eupora, Eupora, MS, p. A357
CASTLE, Eric, Director Information Services, Lawnwood Regional Medical Center & Heart Institute, Fort Pierce, FL, p. A129
CASTLE, Samantha, Chief Executive Officer, University Behavioral Health of Denton, Denton, TX, p. A613
CASTLEBERRY, Ginger, Corporate Risk Manager, Quality and Patient Safety, Valir Rehabilitation Hospital, Oklahoma City, OK, p. A518
CASTLEMAN, Pam, MSN Chief Nursing Officer, Regional One Health, Memphis, TN, p. A589
CASTON, David, Chief Executive Officer, Reeves Memorial Medical Center, Bernice, LA, p. A273
CASTOR, Susan, Chief Nursing Officer, HEALTHSOUTH Rehabilitation Hospital of Toms River, Toms River, NJ, p. A424

CASTRO, Ana, Director Information Services and Clinical Information Services, Gerald Champion Regional Medical Center, Alamogordo, NM, p. A427
CASTRO, Craig
Chief Executive Officer, Clovis Community Medical Center, Clovis, CA, p. A59
Chief Information Officer, Community Regional Medical Center, Fresno, CA, p. A63
CASTRO, Jill, M.D. Medical Director, HEALTHSOUTH Rehabilitation Hospital of Littleton, Littleton, CO, p. A108
CASTRO, Pete, D.O. Chief of Staff, Heart of Texas Memorial Hospital, Brady, TX, p. A603
CASTRO, Richard, Chief Executive Officer, Whittier Hospital Medical Center, Whittier, CA, p. A100
CASTRODALE, Andrew, M.D. Chief Medical Officer, Coulee Medical Center, Grand Coulee, WA, p. A685
CASTROMAN, Nellie, Chief Executive Officer, Select Specialty Hospital–Orlando, Orlando, FL, p. A140
CASTRONUEVO, Joseph, Director Information Management, St. Lawrence Rehabilitation Center, Lawrenceville, NJ, p. A418
CASWELL, Lori, Director Information Technology, Good Samaritan Medical Center, Brockton, MA, p. A308
CASWELL, Penny, Director of Nursing, Bloomington Meadows Hospital, Bloomington, IN, p. A207
CATALA, Lucy, Vice President Finance, Baylor All Saints Medical Center at Fort Worth, Fort Worth, TX, p. A617
CATALDO, Linda, Human Resources Secretary, Prevost Memorial Hospital, Donaldsonville, LA, p. A276
CATALIOTTI, Palmira, Senior Vice President, Chief Financial Officer and Treasurer, Winthrop–University Hospital, Mineola, NY, p. A442
CATANIA, Joseph M., President and Chief Executive Officer, Catholic Health Services, Lauderdale Lakes, FL, p. B30
CATANIA, Joseph M., Chief Executive Officer, St. Anthony's Rehabilitation Hospital, Lauderdale Lakes, FL, p. A134
CATAUDELLA, Mary, Corporate Director Human Resources, Jersey City Medical Center, Jersey City, NJ, p. A418
CATE, Maurine, Chief Executive Officer, Deaconess Hospital, Spokane, WA, p. A691
CATENA, Cornelio R., President and Chief Executive Officer, Wilkes–Barre General Hospital, Wilkes–Barre, PA, p. A558
CATES, Brett, Director Information Services, Weatherford Regional Medical Center, Weatherford, TX, p. A656
CATES, Jessica, Fiscal Manager, Western State Hospital, Hopkinsville, KY, p. A262
CATES, Rodney, Senior Vice President Human Resources, Covenant Children's Hospital, Lubbock, TX, p. A633
CATHEY, Michele, Interim Chief Financial officer, Martin County Hospital District, Stanton, TX, p. A650
CATHEY, Walt, Chief Executive Officer, Covenant Medical Center, Lubbock, TX, p. A634
CATINO, Anne, R.N. Vice President and Chief Nursing Officer, Holy Redeemer Hospital, Meadowbrook, PA, p. A544
CATLIN, Rexford, Chief Executive Officer, Endless Mountain Health Systems, Montrose, PA, p. A545
CATTALANI, Mark, M.D. Clinical Director, Richard H. Hutchings Psychiatric Center, Syracuse, NY, p. A456
CATTELL, JoAnne, Chief Nursing Officer, St. Petersburg General Hospital, Saint Petersburg, FL, p. A144
CATTELL, Nancy E., Vice President Human Resources, Liberty Hospital, Liberty, MO, p. A375
CATTON, Carolyn, Interim Chief Patient Care Officer, Beaver Dam Community Hospitals, Beaver Dam, WI, p. A703
CATTON, Jane, R.N. Chief Operating Officer and Chief Nursing Officer, Northwestern Medical Center, Saint Albans, VT, p. A666
CAUDILL, Allan, M.D. Chief of Staff, South Haven Health System, South Haven, MI, p. A334
CAUDILL, David, Administrator, Grisell Memorial Hospital District One, Ransom, KS, p. A252
CAUGHELL, David, M.D. Chief of Staff, Jane Phillips Nowata Health Center, Nowata, OK, p. A515
CAUGHEY, Michelle, M.D. Physician In Chief, Kaiser Permanente South San Francisco, South San Francisco, CA, p. A95
CAUSEY, Cynthia, Associate Administrator Human and Mission Services, McLeod Medical Center Dillon, Dillon, SC, p. A565
CAUSEY, Jack M., Chief Executive Officer, Leesville Rehabilitation Hospital, Leesville, LA, p. A282
CAUSEY, Jennifer, Chief Executive Officer, Select Specialty Hospital–Nashville, Nashville, TN, p. A591
CAUWENBERG, Jude, M.D. Chief of Staff, Ashtabula County Medical Center, Ashtabula, OH, p. A484
CAVA, Anthony, Chief Operating Officer, Bayshore Community Hospital, Holmdel, NJ, p. A418
CAVANAUGH, Cheryl, Senior Director Human Resources, Valley Regional Hospital, Claremont, NH, p. A410
CAVANAUGH, Paul, Director Human Resources, Friends Hospital, Philadelphia, PA, p. A548
CAVE, Rogelio, M.D. Medical Director, Roseland Community Hospital, Chicago, IL, p. A186

CAVELL, Richard, M.D. Medical Director, University Health Conway, Monroe, LA, p. A284
CAVEN, Tom, M.D. Vice President Medical Affairs, University Medical Center at Brackenridge, Austin, TX, p. A600
CAVENEY, Timothy, President, South Shore Hospital, Chicago, IL, p. A186
CAVERNO, John
Chief Human Resources Officer, Excela Frick Hospital, Mount Pleasant, PA, p. A545
Chief Human Resources Officer, Excela Health Westmoreland Hospital, Greensburg, PA, p. A539
CAWLEY, Karen, Chief Executive Officer, Curahealth Phoenix, Phoenix, AZ, p. A36
CAWLEY, Patrick J., M.D., Chief Executive Officer, MUSC Health and Vice President for Health Affairs, University, MUSC Medical Center of Medical University of South Carolina, Charleston, SC, p. A563
CAWOOD, Marina, Administrative Assistant, Middlesboro ARH Hospital, Middlesboro, KY, p. A266
CAYER, Gerald, Executive Vice President and Chief Operating Officer, Franklin Memorial Hospital, Farmington, ME, p. A293
CAYTON, Mical, Area Information Officer, Kaiser Permanente Antioch Medical Center, Antioch, CA, p. A54
CAZARES, Erik, Chief Nursing Officer, The Hospitals of Providence Sierra Campus, El Paso, TX, p. A616
CAZAYOUX, John, Chief Financial Officer, Pointe Coupee General Hospital, New Roads, LA, p. A285
CAZES, Anna Leah, Chief Nursing Officer, Baton Rouge General Medical Center, Baton Rouge, LA, p. A272
CEBALLOS, Gloria Alicia, MSN Chief Nursing Officer, AllianceHealth Midwest, Midwest City, OK, p. A514
CECAVA, Eric, Chief Operating Officer, Adena Medical Center, Chillicothe, OH, p. A486
CECCONI, Thomas E., President and Chief Executive Officer, Mercy Medical Center, Canton, OH, p. A486
CECH, Bob, Regional Finance Officer, Presence Saints Mary & Elizabeth Medical Center, Chicago, IL, p. A186
CECIL, Bruce, Chief Financial Officer, Fresno Surgical Hospital, Fresno, CA, p. A63
CECIL, Janell, R.N. Senior Vice President and Chief Nursing Officer, University of Tennessee Medical Center, Knoxville, TN, p. A586
CECIL, Jason, Vice President, Information, Capital Region Medical Center, Jefferson City, MO, p. A372
CECIL, Jon C.
Chief Human Resource Officer, Cape Coral Hospital, Cape Coral, FL, p. A125
Chief Human Resource Officer, Gulf Coast Medical Center, Fort Myers, FL, p. A129
Chief Human Resource Officer, Lee Memorial Hospital, Fort Myers, FL, p. A129
CEDENO LLORENS, Arturo, M.D. Medical Director, Hospital Buen Samaritano, Aguadilla, PR, p. A725
CEDOTAL, Kiley P., FACHE,
Chief Executive Officer, Promise Hospital Baton Rouge – Main Campus, Baton Rouge, LA, p. A273
Chief Executive Officer, Promise Hospital of Baton Rouge – Mid–City Campus, Baton Rouge, LA, p. A273
Chief Executive Officer, Promise Hospital of Baton Rouge – Ochsner Campus, Baton Rouge, LA, p. A273
CEHELYK, Bohdan, M.D. Chief Medical Officer, East Mountain Hospital, Belle Mead, NJ, p. A414
CELANO, Julie, Vice President Human Resources, Brigham and Women's Hospital, Boston, MA, p. A306
CELLA, Ann S., R.N. Senior Vice President, Patient Care Services, St. Francis Hospital, The Heart Center, Roslyn, NY, p. A455
CELLA, Robert, M.D
Chief Medical Officer, Albany Memorial Hospital, Albany, NY, p. A433
Chief Medical Officer, St. Peter's Hospital, Albany, NY, p. A433
CELSOR, Reba, Chief Executive Officer, Tennova Healthcare Dyersburg Regional Medical Center, Dyersburg, TN, p. A582
CELUCH, Paul
Corporate Human Resources Director, Community Hospital of Huntington Park, Huntington Park, CA, p. A66
Chief Human Resource Officer, East Los Angeles Doctors Hospital, Los Angeles, CA, p. A71
CEMATE, David D., FACHE Senior Vice President and Chief Operating Officer, Mercy Medical Center, Canton, OH, p. A486
CEMENO, Michael J., Chief Information Officer, Waterbury Hospital, Waterbury, CT, p. A117
CENTENO, Robert, M.D. Chief Medical Officer, Governor Juan F. Luis Hospital, Christiansted, VI, p. A731
CEPEDA, Aaron, Director Nursing Operations, South Texas Rehabilitation Hospital, Brownsville, TX, p. A603
CEPERO, Jesus, Ph.D. Chief Operating Officer and Chief Nursing Officer, Meritus Medical Center, Hagerstown, MD, p. A301

CERALDI, Christopher, M.D. Chief of Staff, Abbeville Area Medical Center, Abbeville, SC, p. A562
CERCEO, Richard, Executive Vice President and Chief Operating Officer, Mercy Hospital and Medical Center, Chicago, IL, p. A185
CERIMELE, Joseph, D.O. Medical Director, Hillside Rehabilitation Hospital, Warren, OH, p. A504
CERIMELE, Leeann, Vice President Human Resources, UPMC Passavant, Pittsburgh, PA, p. A551
CERISE, Fred, M.D., Chief Executive Officer, Parkland Health & Hospital System, Dallas, TX, p. A611
CERNAVA, Joanne, Director Human Resources, Marlton Rehabilitation Hospital, Marlton, NJ, p. A419
CERNOCH, Desiree, Director of Nurses, El Campo Memorial Hospital, El Campo, TX, p. A615
CERRA, Jane, Market Nurse Executive and Chief Nursing Officer, Select Specialty Hospital–Milwaukee, Milwaukee, WI, p. A712
CERVANTES, Jason
Corporate Chief Information Officer, Community Hospital of Huntington Park, Huntington Park, CA, p. A66
Chief Information Officer, East Los Angeles Doctors Hospital, Los Angeles, CA, p. A71
CERVINO, Noel A., President and Chief Executive Officer, University of Maryland Charles Regional Medical Center, La Plata, MD, p. A302
CESAREZ, Margaret, Chief Financial Officer, Gateway Rehabilitation Hospital, Florence, KY, p. A260
CESCA, Ken, Vice President Human Resources, MidState Medical Center, Meriden, CT, p. A115
CESKO, David, M.D. Chief of Staff, Memorial Hospital of Carbon County, Rawlins, WY, p. A723
CHA BRIDIER, Vicky, Chief Operating Officer, College Station Medical Center, College Station, TX, p. A606
CHABALOWSKI, Edward, Chief Financial Officer, Geisinger–Community Medical Center, Scranton, PA, p. A554
CHABOT, Judy, Chief Nursing Officer, Los Alamitos Medical Center, Los Alamitos, CA, p. A70
CHACKO, Benson, Chief Operating Officer, The Hospitals of Providence Sierra Campus, El Paso, TX, p. A616
CHACON, Barbara, Chief Financial Officer, The CORE Institute Specialty Hospital, Phoenix, AZ, p. A37
CHACON, Chanda Cashen, Executive Vice President and Chief Operating Officer, Arkansas Children's Hospital, Little Rock, AR, p. A48
CHADEK, Richard, M.D. Clinical Director, Lawton Indian Hospital, Lawton, OK, p. A513
CHADHA, Beenu, Chief Financial Officer, San Ramon Regional Medical Center, San Ramon, CA, p. A92
CHADOCK, Brandon, Director of Operations, Sistersville General Hospital, Sistersville, WV, p. A700
CHADWICK, Maureen C., R.N. Chief Nursing Officer, Saint Vincent Hospital, Erie, PA, p. A538
CHADWICK, Sharon M., Director Human Resources, Abrazo Arrowhead Campus, Glendale, AZ, p. A33
CHAFFIN, Linda, Director Medical Review, Baptist Memorial Hospital–Booneville, Booneville, MS, p. A356
CHAHANOVICH, Jen, President and Chief Executive Officer, Wilcox Memorial Hospital, Lihue, HI, p. A172
CHAILDIN, Roberta, Manager Human Resources, Parrish Medical Center, Titusville, FL, p. A148
CHALFANT, Cathie, Director Human Resources, Harrison County Community Hospital, Bethany, MO, p. A367
CHALIAN, Christopher, M.D. Medical Director, Casa Colina Hospital and Health Systems, Pomona, CA, p. A83
CHALK, Jackie, Director Human Resources, HEALTHSOUTH Rehabilitation Hospital, Largo, FL, p. A134
CHALKE, Dennis, Senior Vice President, Chief Financial Officer and Treasurer, Baystate Medical Center, Springfield, MA, p. A314
CHALKE, Sharron, R.N. VP, Nursing, Central Maine Medical Center, Lewiston, ME, p. A293
CHALONER, Robert S., President and Chief Executive Officer, Southampton Hospital, Southampton, NY, p. A456
CHALPHANT, Steve, Director Information Management Service Line, Wm. Jennings Bryan Dorn Veterans Affairs Medical Center, Columbia, SC, p. A564
CHALTRY, Richard, M.D. Director Medical Staff, Aspirus Ontonagon Hospital, Ontonagon, MI, p. A331
CHALUPA, Rebecca, MSN Chief Nursing Officer, Houston Methodist San Jacinto Hospital, Baytown, TX, p. A601
CHAMBERLIN, Kim, Vice President Patient Services and Chief Nursing Officer, Mercy Medical Center–North Iowa, Mason City, IA, p. A234
CHAMBERS, Bradley
President and Chief Executive Officer, MedStar Good Samaritan Hospital, Baltimore, MD, p. A297
President, MedStar Union Memorial Hospital, Baltimore, MD, p. A297
CHAMBERS, Erin, M.D. Chief Medical Officer, Houston County Community Hospital, Erin, TN, p. A582

CHAMBERS, Gwen, Executive Director Human Resources, Methodist Hospital of Southern California, Arcadia, CA, p. A55

CHAMBERS, Matthew
Chief Information Officer, Scott & White Hospital at Round Rock, Round Rock, TX, p. A644
Chief Information Officer, Scott & White Memorial Hospital, Temple, TX, p. A652

CHAMBERS, Regina, Vice President Human Resource, Rome Memorial Hospital, Rome, NY, p. A455

CHAMBLEE, Jane, Manager Human Resources, North Mississippi Medical Center–Iuka, Iuka, MS, p. A359

CHAMBLESS, Lesley
Assistant Vice President Human Resources, Carolinas HealthCare System Lincoln, Lincolnton, NC, p. A469
Assistant Vice President Workforce Relations, Carolinas HealthCare System NorthEast, Concord, NC, p. A463

CHAMBLISS, James W., Chief of Staff, Magnolia Regional Medical Center, Magnolia, AR, p. A49

CHAMPAGNE, Charles, Chief Financial Officer, Northeast Rehabilitation Hospital, Salem, NH, p. A413

CHAMPAGNE, Laurie, Controller, Curahealth New Orleans, New Orleans, LA, p. A284

CHAMPAVANNARATH, Vilakon, Director Information Systems, Bartow Regional Medical Center, Bartow, FL, p. A123

CHAMPION, Joshua I., Director, Florida Hospital–Flagler, Palm Coast, FL, p. A141

CHAN, Eric, M.D., Chief Executive Officer, Surgery Specialty Hospitals of America, Pasadena, TX, p. A640

CHAN, Fred, Chief Financial Officer, Intracare North Hospital, Houston, TX, p. A625

CHAN, Joyce, Chief Human Resources Officer, CentraCare Health–Melrose, Melrose, MN, p. A346

CHAN, Thomas T., Chief Financial Officer, Meritus Medical Center, Hagerstown, MD, p. A301

CHANAA, Ziad, M.D. Chief of Staff, Boone Memorial Hospital, Madison, WV, p. A697

CHANAGA, Luis, Chief Financial Officer, Grandview Medical Center, Dayton, OH, p. A492

CHANCE, Tammara, D.O. Chief of Staff, Boone County Hospital, Boone, IA, p. A226

CHANCELLOR, Jayme, Chief Operating Officer, Northside Hospital, Saint Petersburg, FL, p. A144

CHAND, Parveen, Chief Operating Officer, Eskenazi Health, Indianapolis, IN, p. A213

CHANDLER, Aileen, Chief Nursing Officer, Ogallala Community Hospital, Ogallala, NE, p. A399

CHANDLER, Christopher, Chief Executive Officer, Pioneer Community Hospital of Aberdeen, Aberdeen, MS, p. A355

CHANDLER, Laurie, Financial Officer, Prairie Community Hospital, Terry, MT, p. A391

CHANDLER, Loren, President, Mount Sinai Hospital, Chicago, IL, p. A185

CHANDLER, Ryan
President and Chief Executive Officer, Midtown Medical Center, Columbus, GA, p. A156
Chief Executive Officer, Midtown Medical Center West, Columbus, GA, p. A156
Interim Chief Executive Officer, Northside Medical Center, Columbus, GA, p. A156

CHANDLER, Vincent, Director Information Services, Porterville Developmental Center, Porterville, CA, p. A83

CHANDRASENA, Anita, M.D. Vice President Medical Affairs, Sequoia Hospital, Redwood City, CA, p. A85

CHANDY, Joseph, Administrator, Methodist Hospital of Chicago, Chicago, IL, p. A185

CHANEZ, Adolfo, Vice President Finance and Chief Financial Officer, Saddleback Memorial Medical Center, Laguna Hills, CA, p. A68

CHANG, Alex, Chief Operating Officer, Englewood Community Hospital, Englewood, FL, p. A128

CHANG, Jason, M.D. Chief Medical Director, Rehabilitation Hospital of the Pacific, Honolulu, HI, p. A171

CHANG, Jason, Executive Vice President and Chief Operating Officer, The Queen's Medical Center, Honolulu, HI, p. A171

CHANG, Myrna, Chief Nursing Executive, Sutter Davis Hospital, Davis, CA, p. A60

CHANG, Sang–ick, M.D. Chief Medical Officer, Highland Hospital, Oakland, CA, p. A80

CHANNELL, Lesley
Vice President Human Resources, Dominion Hospital, Falls Church, VA, p. A669
Vice President Human Resources, Reston Hospital Center, Reston, VA, p. A676

CHAPDELAINE, Debora R., Manager Information Technology, Aurora Medical Center, Kenosha, WI, p. A708

CHAPLIN, Steven, M.D. Medical Director, Kahi Mohala Behavioral Health, Ewa Beach, HI, p. A170

CHAPMAN, Cully, Chief Financial Officer, Lutheran Hospital of Indiana, Fort Wayne, IN, p. A210

CHAPMAN, Jeffrey, M.D. Chief Medical Officer, Cheyenne Regional Medical Center, Cheyenne, WY, p. A721

CHAPMAN, Jon, Fiscal Officer, Western State Hospital, Staunton, VA, p. A679

CHAPMAN, Judy, Interim Director Information Systems, Lock Haven Hospital, Lock Haven, PA, p. A543

CHAPMAN, Karen, Director Human Resources, Chester Regional Medical Center, Chester, SC, p. A563

CHAPMAN, Kathy, Chief Clinical Officer and Vice President of Patient Services, Allegan General Hospital, Allegan, MI, p. A318

CHAPMAN, Patrick, Assistant Vice President Operations, JFK Medical Center North Campus, West Palm Beach, FL, p. A149

CHAPMAN, Patrick, Ed.D., Chief Executive Officer, Tippah County Hospital, Ripley, MS, p. A364

CHAPMAN, Rachel, Nurse Manager, Noland Hospital Birmingham, Birmingham, AL, p. A17

CHAPMAN, Rick, Chief Information Officer, Kindred Hospital North Florida, Green Cove Springs, FL, p. A130

CHAPMAN, Roland, Chief Information Officer, Northern Navajo Medical Center, Shiprock, NM, p. A431

CHAPMAN, Scott, Administrator, Manhattan Surgical,, KS, p. A248

CHAPMAN, Teresa, Vice President Human Resources, Marianjoy Rehabilitation Hospital, Wheaton, IL, p. A205

CHAPPELL, Brandee, Director of Nursing, LifeCare Hospitals of North Carolina, Rocky Mount, NC, p. A472

CHAPPELL, Robert, M.D. Chief Medical Officer and Chief Quality Officer, Huntsville Hospital, Huntsville, AL, p. A21

CHAPPELL, Teresa, Chief Information Officer, Johnston Health, Smithfield, NC, p. A473

CHAPPLE, Albert J., R.N. Chief Clinical Officer, Kindred Rehabilitation Hospital Northeast Houston, Humble, TX, p. A628

CHAPPLE, Scott, Chief Operating Officer, Oroville Hospital, Oroville, CA, p. A81

CHARARA, Kassem, Chief Medical Officer, Beaumont Hospital – Taylor, Taylor, MI, p. A335

CHARDAVOYNE, Alan
Chief Financial Officer, Moses Ludington Hospital, Ticonderoga, NY, p. A457
Chief Financial Officer, The University of Vermont Health Network Elizabethtown Community Hospital, Elizabethtown, NY, p. A438

CHAREST, Richard
President & Chief Executive Officer, Landmark Medical Center, Woonsocket, RI, p. A561
Chief Executive Officer, Rehabilitation Hospital of Rhode Island, North Smithfield, RI, p. A560

CHARETTE, Deborah, Director of Nursing, East Mountain Hospital, Belle Mead, NJ, p. A414

CHARLAT, Richard A., Chief of Staff, Iowa City Veterans Affairs Health Care System, Iowa City, IA, p. A232

CHARLES, Charlotte, Director Acute Patient Services, Madison Community Hospital, Madison, SD, p. A574

CHARLES, Sally, Coordinator Human Resources, Grace Medical Center, Lubbock, TX, p. A634

CHARLES, Shaun, Director Information Technology, West Springs Hospital, Grand Junction, CO, p. A106

CHARLES, Timothy L., President and Chief Executive Officer, Mercy Medical Center–Cedar Rapids, Cedar Rapids, IA, p. A226

CHARLTON, Beth, Vice President Patient Services and Chief Nursing Officer, Covenant Healthcare, Saginaw, MI, p. A333

CHARLTON, Jr., Francis, M.D. Chief Medical Staff, St. Mary's Medical Center, San Francisco, CA, p. A90

CHARMEL, Patrick, President and Chief Executive Officer, Griffin Hospital, Derby, CT, p. A114

CHARTIER, Bridgett, Director of Nursing, Beartooth Billings Clinic, Red Lodge, MT, p. A390

CHARTIER, Dianne, R.N., Resource Chief Executive Officer, Curahealth Tucson, Tucson, AZ, p. A40

CHARTIER, Terry
Director, Information Systems, Mercy Medical Center–New Hampton, New Hampton, IA, p. A235
Director, Information Systems, Mercy Medical Center–North Iowa, Mason City, IA, p. A234

CHASE, Brenda, Chief Operating Officer, Mercy Hospital Rogers, Rogers, AR, p. A52

CHASE, Jean
Regional Manager Information Services, Aurora Lakeland Medical Center, Elkhorn, WI, p. A705
Regional Manager Information Services, Aurora Memorial Hospital of Burlington, Burlington, WI, p. A703

CHASE, Kyle, Chief Financial Officer, Glacial Ridge Health System, Glenwood, MN, p. A343

CHASE, Pansy, Director Human Resources, Vidant Duplin Hospital, Kenansville, NC, p. A468

CHASE, Robert, M.D
Physician Advisor, West Suburban Medical Center, Oak Park, IL, p. A199
Chief Medical Officer, Westlake Hospital, Melrose Park, IL, p. A196

CHASE, Susan, Vice President, Carolinas Rehabilitation, Charlotte, NC, p. A462

CHASIN, Marc, M.D. Chief Information Officer, St. Luke's Regional Medical Center, Boise, ID, p. A175

CHASSE, Floyd, Vice President Human Resources, Erlanger Medical Center, Chattanooga, TN, p. A580

CHASTAIN, James G., FACHE, Director, Mississippi State Hospital, Whitfield, MS, p. A366

CHASTAIN, Katherine L., R.N. Chief Nursing Officer, Sacred Heart Hospital on the Gulf, Port St. Joe, FL, p. A143

CHASTAIN, Stephen L., M.D. Chief Medical Officer, HEALTHSOUTH Rehabilitation Hospital at Martin Health, Stuart, FL, p. A146

CHASTANG, Mark J., M.P.H., Chief Executive Officer, Saint Elizabeths Hospital, Washington, DC, p. A122

CHASTANT, Lee, Chief Executive Officer, West Feliciana Parish Hospital, Saint Francisville, LA, p. A287

CHATANI, Kumar
Senior Vice President and Chief Information Officer Mount Sinai Health System, Mount Sinai Beth Israel, New York, NY, p. A446
Senior Vice President and Chief Information Officer Mount Sinai Health System, Mount Sinai Hospital, New York, NY, p. A446
Chief Information Officer, Mount Sinai Health System, Mount Sinai St. Luke's – Roosevelt, New York, NY, p. A446
Chief Information Officer, Mount Sinai Health System, New York Eye and Ear Infirmary of Mount Sinai, New York, NY, p. A447

CHATELAIN, Alicia, Director Human Resource, Hood Memorial Hospital, Amite, LA, p. A271

CHATELAIN, Vincent, Director Business Development, River Oaks Hospital, New Orleans, LA, p. A285

CHATLEY, Alice M., R.N. Vice President Acute Care Services, SSM Health St. Mary's Hospital – Jefferson City, Jefferson City, MO, p. A372

CHATMAN, Hubert, Chief Civilian Personnel, Wright Patterson Medical Center, Wright–Patterson AFB, OH, p. A506

CHATMAN, Jim, Chief Financial Officer, Maria Parham Medical Center, Henderson, NC, p. A466

CHATMAN, Mary, Ph.D. Senior Vice President, Chief Operating Officer and Chief Nursing Officer, Memorial Health, Savannah, GA, p. A166

CHATTERJEE, Kanan, M.D. Chief of Staff, Lebanon Veterans Affairs Medical Center, Lebanon, PA, p. A542

CHATTERTON, Bryan, Chief Executive Officer, Kindred Hospital–Indianapolis, Indianapolis, IN, p. A214

CHAUDHARY, Shahid, M.D. Chief Medical Officer, Avera St. Luke's Hospital, Aberdeen, SD, p. A572

CHAUDHRY, Riaz, M.D. Chief Medical Officer, Mercy Health – St. Charles Hospital, Oregon, OH, p. A500

CHAUSSARD, David, Chief Executive Officer, Hillcrest Hospital Claremore, Claremore, OK, p. A510

CHAVEZ, Irene, Senior Vice President and Area Manager, Kaiser Permanente San Jose Medical Center, San Jose, CA, p. A91

CHAVEZ, Kevin, Chief Executive Officer, BridgePoint Hospital National Harbor, Washington, DC, p. A121

CHAVEZ, Shari, Chief Nursing Officer, Swedish Medical Center, Englewood, CO, p. A105

CHAVEZ, Steven
Vice President Finance and Operations, Kettering Medical Center, Kettering, OH, p. A496
Vice President Finance and Operations, Sycamore Medical Center, Miamisburg, OH, p. A499

CHAVEZ, Virgil, Director Information Technology, Tsehootsooi Medical Center, Fort Defiance, AZ, p. A32

CHAVIS, Anthony D., M.D. Vice President Enterprise Medical Officer, Community Hospital Foundation, Community Hospital of the Monterey Peninsula, Monterey, CA, p. A77

CHAWLA, Nikki, M.D. Medical Director, AllianceHealth Seminole, Seminole, OK, p. A519

CHAYER, Olivia, Director, Human Resources, York Hospital, York, ME, p. A295

CHECK, Arthur, M.D. Chief Medical Officer, Story County Medical Center, Nevada, IA, p. A235

CHECKETTS, Lannie
Interim Assistant Chief Financial Officer, Saint Alphonsus Medical Center – Nampa, Nampa, ID, p. A177
Vice President Finance and Operations, Saint Alphonsus Medical Center – Ontario, Ontario, OR, p. A528

CHEEK, Holly, Vice President and Chief Nursing Officer, Columbus Regional Hospital, Columbus, IN, p. A208

CHEEMA, Linde, Vice President Human Resources, Sequoia Hospital, Redwood City, CA, p. A85

CHEESEMAN, Karen, Executive Vice President, Mackinac Straits Health System, Inc., Saint Ignace, MI, p. A333

CHEEVER, Liz, Administrator, Miracle Mile Medical Center, Los Angeles, CA, p. A73

CHEKOURAS, Christopher A., President and Chief Executive Officer, St. Mary's Regional Medical Center, Lewiston, ME, p. A293

CHEKURU, Naidu, M.D. Chief Medical Officer, Covenant Specialty Hospital, Lubbock, TX, p. A634

CHELLAPPA, Sheila, M.D. Chief of Staff, Coatesville Veterans Affairs Medical Center, Coatesville, PA, p. A536

CHEN, Bonny, M.D. Vice President and Chief Medical Officer, AMITA Health Adventist Medical Center – Hinsdale, Hinsdale, IL, p. A193

CHEN, David, M.D. Chief Medical Officer, Bozeman Health Deaconess Hospital, Bozeman, MT, p. A386

CHEN, Helen, M.D. Chief Medical Officer, Hebrew Rehabilitation Center, Boston, MA, p. A307

CHEN, Linda, President and Market Leader, MultiCare Mary Bridge Children's Hospital and Health Center, Tacoma, WA, p. A692

CHEN, Stephen, M.D. Chief Medicare, Alhambra Hospital Medical Center, Alhambra, CA, p. A54

CHEN, Van, M.D. Medical Director, Ballard Rehabilitation Hospital, San Bernardino, CA, p. A88

CHENEY, David, Chief Executive Officer, Banner Boswell Medical Center, Sun City, AZ, p. A39

CHENG, Alice, President and Chief Executive Officer, Beverly Hospital, Montebello, CA, p. A77

CHENG, Rebecca
   Chief Financial Officer, California Hospital Medical Center, Los Angeles, CA, p. A70
   Chief Financial Officer, Glendale Memorial Hospital and Health Center, Glendale, CA, p. A64

CHENG, Ringo, Director Information Technology, Surgery Specialty Hospitals of America, Pasadena, TX, p. A640

CHENNAULT, Paula, Administrator, Behavioral HealthCare Center at Columbia, Columbia, TN, p. A581

CHENNAULT, Scott, M.D. Chief of Staff, Burleson St. Joseph Health Center, Caldwell, TX, p. A604

CHENOWETH, Don, Chief Information Officer, Prince George's Hospital Center, Cheverly, MD, p. A299

CHENOWETH, Judy, Chief Nursing Officer, Russell County Hospital, Russell Springs, KY, p. A269

CHEPAK, Lois, R.N. Chief Clinical Officer, Eagleville Hospital, Eagleville, PA, p. A537

CHERAMIE, Bennett, Vice President Information Technology, Baton Rouge General Medical Center, Baton Rouge, LA, p. A272

CHERAY, James, M.D. Chief Medical Officer, Menorah Medical Center, Overland Park, KS, p. A251

CHERMSIDE, Paula L., Chief Executive Officer, Aspirus Grand View, Ironwood, MI, p. A327

CHERNOW, David S., President and Chief Executive Officer, Select Medical Corporation, Mechanicsburg, PA, p. B119

CHERONE, Nancy, Executive Director and Administrator, Nazareth Hospital, Philadelphia, PA, p. A549

CHERRNAY LEVY, Jennifer, Director Human Resources, Texas Institute for Surgery at Texas Health Presbyterian Dallas, Dallas, TX, p. A611

CHERRY, Deano, Chief Information Officer, Kane Community Hospital, Kane, PA, p. A541

CHERRY, Jean, Executive Vice President, Commonwealth Regional Specialty Hospital, Bowling Green, KY, p. A257

CHERRY, Jonathan M., President and Chief Executive Officer, LifeStream Behavioral Center, Leesburg, FL, p. A134

CHERRY, Kris, Ph.D. Chief Nursing Officer, Saint Francis Hospital–Bartlett, Bartlett, TN, p. A579

CHERRY, Robert, M.D
   Chief Medical Officer, Loyola University Medical Center, Maywood, IL, p. A196
   Chief Medical and Quality Officer, Ronald Reagan UCLA Medical Center, Los Angeles, CA, p. A74

CHERRY, Troy, Chief Financial Officer, Schick Shadel Hospital, Seattle, WA, p. A689

CHESLEK, Ingrid, R.N. Chief Nursing Officer, Mary Free Bed Rehabilitation Hospital, Grand Rapids, MI, p. A325

CHESLEY, Jeanine, Chief Executive Officer, New England Rehabilitation Hospital of Portland, Portland, ME, p. A294

CHESLEY, Judy S., M.D. Chief of Staff, Sanford Luverne Medical Center, Luverne, MN, p. A345

CHESLEY, Randy, Director Information Technology, Copley Hospital, Morrisville, VT, p. A665

CHESLEY, Walter, Senior Vice President Human Resources, Hennepin County Medical Center, Minneapolis, MN, p. A346

CHESNOS, Richard C., Senior Vice President Finance and Chief Financial Officer, St. Clair Hospital, Pittsburgh, PA, p. A551

CHESSARE, John B., FACHE, President and Chief Executive Officer, Greater Baltimore Medical Center, Baltimore, MD, p. A296

CHESSIN, Neil A., Vice President, Jameson Hospital, New Castle, PA, p. A546

CHESSON, Andrew, Chief Medical Officer, Catawba Valley Medical Center, Hickory, NC, p. A467

CHESSUM, George
   Senior Vice President and Chief Information Officer, Community First Medical Center, Chicago, IL, p. A183
   Vice President Information Systems, Presence Saint Francis Hospital, Evanston, IL, p. A190
   Senior Vice President Information Systems and Chief Information Officer, Presence Saint Joseph Hospital, Chicago, IL, p. A185

CHESTER, Julie, Vice President Human Resources, University Hospitals Cleveland Medical Center, Cleveland, OH, p. A490

CHESTER, Linnes L., USAF Administrator, Mike O'Callaghan Federal Hospital, Nellis AFB, NV, p. A407

CHESTER, William, Manager Human Resources, Grand Junction Veterans Health Care System, Grand Junction, CO, p. A106

CHESTNUT–RAULS, Monica, Vice President Human Resources, Peconic Bay Medical Center, Riverhead, NY, p. A454

CHEUNG, Alan, M.D. Vice President Medical Affairs, Castle Medical Center, Kailua, HI, p. A171

CHEUNG, Marilou, Assistant Administrator Finance, Kaiser Permanente Woodland Hills Medical Center,, CA, p. A72

CHEUNG, Raymond, M.D. Chief of Staff, San Ramon Regional Medical Center, San Ramon, CA, p. A92

CHEVERE, Carlos, M.D. Medical Director, I. Gonzalez Martinez Oncologic Hospital,, PR, p. A730

CHEW, Brian, Human Resources Officer, Holy Cross Hospital, Taos, NM, p. A432

CHEW, Roy G., Ph.D., President, Kettering Medical Center, Kettering, OH, p. A496

CHEWNING III, Larry H., President and Chief Executive Officer, Nash Health Care Systems, Rocky Mount, NC, p. A472

CHEYNET, Sandee, Vice President Administrative Services, Bluefield Regional Medical Center, Bluefield, WV, p. A694

CHHABRA, Ankit, Director Finance, Cleveland Clinic Fairview Hospital, Cleveland, OH, p. A489

CHIACCHIARO, Peter, Vice President Human Resources, St. Joseph Hospital, Bethpage, NY, p. A434

CHIANESE, Charles, Vice President Chief Operating Office, Children's Specialized Hospital–PSE&G, New Brunswick, NJ, p. A420

CHIANTELLA, Christopher, M.D. Chief Medical Officer, Inova Loudoun Hospital, Leesburg, VA, p. A672

CHIARCHIARO, Martha, Vice President Human Resources, Clinton Hospital, Clinton, MA, p. A309

CHIAVETTA, Robert, Vice President Finance, United Memorial Medical Center, Batavia, NY, p. A434

CHICK, Melanie, Chief Executive Officer, Baylor Medical Center at Trophy Club, Trophy Club, TX, p. A653

CHICKEN, Kurt, Director Support Services, Palmer Lutheran Health Center, West Union, IA, p. A239

CHIDESTER, Annamarie, R.N. Vice President, Patient Care Services, St. Joseph's Hospital of Buckhannon, Buckhannon, WV, p. A694

CHIEFFO, Ron, Chief Information Officer, Colorado River Medical Center, Needles, CA, p. A79

CHIKOWSKI, Julie, Administrator, Memorial Hospital of Lafayette County, Darlington, WI, p. A704

CHILCOTT, Stephen, Associate Director Human Resources, University of California, Davis Medical Center, Sacramento, CA, p. A87

CHILD, Clint L., R.N. Chief Nursing Officer, Saint Alphonsus Medical Center – Nampa, Nampa, ID, p. A177

CHILDERS, Bethany, Director Human Resources, Fremont Health, Fremont, NE, p. A396

CHILDERS, Christy, Director Information Technology, P & S Surgical Hospital, Monroe, LA, p. A283

CHILDERS, James R., Vice President and Chief Financial Officer, Gibson General Hospital, Princeton, IN, p. A221

CHILDERS, Linda, Director Human Resources, Wallowa Memorial Hospital, Enterprise, OR, p. A525

CHILDERS, Susan M., CPA, Chief Executive Officer, Mee Memorial Hospital, King City, CA, p. A67

CHILDS, Joe, M.D. Vice President Medical Services, East Tennessee Children's Hospital, Knoxville, TN, p. A585

CHILDS, Michelle, Senior Administrative Director Human Resources, Salinas Valley Memorial Healthcare System, Salinas, CA, p. A87

CHILES, Kevin, Vice President Human Resources, Hutchinson Regional Medical Center, Hutchinson, KS, p. A245

CHILES, Morton, M.D. Chief Medical Officer, Novant Health UVA Health System Culpeper Medical Center, Culpeper, VA, p. A669

CHILESE, Melody, Chief Nurse Executive, Hawthorn Children Psychiatric Hospital, Saint Louis, MO, p. A380

CHILESKI, Andy, Chief Information Officer and Vice President Facilities, Berger Health System, Circleville, OH, p. A488

CHILL, Martha O'Regan
   Interim Chief Information Officer, Wellmont Bristol Regional Medical Center, Bristol, TN, p. A579
   Interim Chief Information Officer, Wellmont Hancock County Hospital, Sneedville, TN, p. A593

CHILSON, Terrance, Chief of Staff, Tyler Memorial Hospital, Tunkhannock, PA, p. A556

CHILTON, Bryan, Director Information Systems, Navarro Regional Hospital, Corsicana, TX, p. A608

CHILTON, Hal, Senior Vice President and Chief Operating Officer, St. Helena Hospital Napa Valley, Saint Helena, CA, p. A87

CHIN, Ellyn, Vice President Finance, Gottlieb Memorial Hospital, Melrose Park, IL, p. A196

CHINBURG, Paul, M.D. Medical Director, Lane County Hospital, Dighton, KS, p. A242

CHING, Angelica, Director Information Systems, Monterey Park Hospital, Monterey Park, CA, p. A78

CHING, Geraldine, Assistant General Minister, Sisters of Saint Francis, Syracuse, NY, p. B125

CHINN, Tammie
   Director Marketing and Public Relations, Plateau Medical Center, Oak Hill, WV, p. A698
   Chief Human Resource Officer, Williamson Memorial Hospital, Williamson, WV, p. A701

CHINN, Terri, Vice President Finance, St. Mary's Medical Center, Grand Junction, CO, p. A106

CHINNOCK, Rachel, Chief Human Resources Officer, Latimer County General Hospital, Wilburton, OK, p. A523

CHIOLO, Denise, Chief Human Resources Officer, Phoenixville Hospital, Phoenixville, PA, p. A550

CHIPMAN, Glen, Chief Financial Officer, HealthSource Saginaw, Inc., Saginaw, MI, p. A333

CHIPMAN, Kim, Chief Clinical Officer, Kindred Hospital–White Rock, Dallas, TX, p. A610

CHIRICHELLA, Joseph, President and Chief Executive Officer, Deborah Heart and Lung Center, Browns Mills, NJ, p. A415

CHISHOLM, Ken, Director Human Resources, Martha's Vineyard Hospital, Oak Bluffs, MA, p. A313

CHISHOLM, Moody, Regional Vice President, Intermountain Medical Center, Murray, UT, p. A661

CHISHOLM, Sarah, Administrator, Oceans Behavioral Hospital of Kentwood, Kentwood, LA, p. A279

CHISHOLM, Sharon, Entity Human Resource Officer, Texas Health Presbyterian Hospital Allen, Allen, TX, p. A595

CHISSELL, Herbert G., M.D. Chief Medical Officer, Torrance State Hospital, Torrance, PA, p. A555

CHITTENDEN, Michael D., President, St. Vincent Carmel Hospital, Carmel, IN, p. A208

CHIUMINETTA, Leigh, Interim Chief Information Officer, St. Mary's Healthcare, Amsterdam, NY, p. A434

CHIVERS, John, Senior Vice President Finance, Sierra View Medical Center, Porterville, CA, p. A83

CHMIELEWSKI, Linda A., R.N. Vice President Operations, St. Cloud Hospital, Saint Cloud, MN, p. A350

CHMURA, David, Chief Information Officer, Copper Queen Community Hospital, Bisbee, AZ, p. A31

CHOATE, Charlotte, Director Information Systems, Trinity Hospital of Augusta, Augusta, GA, p. A154

CHODKOWSKI, Paul J., Chief Executive Officer, St. Anthony Summit Medical Center, Frisco, CO, p. A105

CHOINIERE, Leon, Vice President, Chief Financial Officer, St. Mary Medical Center, Long Beach, CA, p. A70

CHOINKA, Keith A., Vice President Information Systems and Chief Information Officer, St. Joseph Hospital, Nashua, NH, p. A412

CHOKSHI, Sushil, M.D. Chief Medical Officer, Faith Community Hospital, Jacksboro, TX, p. A629

CHOLGER, Dave, Chief Financial Officer, Woodlawn Hospital, Rochester, IN, p. A221

CHONG, Johnnette, Chief Financial Officer, Los Angeles Community Hospital at Los Angeles, Los Angeles, CA, p. A72

CHOPIN, Candice, Vice President Human Resources, Women's and Children's Hospital, Lafayette, LA, p. A281

CHOPRA, Praveen, Executive Vice President and Chief Information and Transformative Innovative Environment Officer, Thomas Jefferson University Hospitals, Philadelphia, PA, p. A550

CHORD, Ginger, Coordinator Human Resources, Sturgis Regional Hospital, Sturgis, SD, p. A577

CHOREY, Raymond M., President and Chief Executive Officer, Southeastern Ohio Regional Medical Center, Cambridge, OH, p. A486

CHOU, Rebecca
   Directory Information Systems, Palestine Regional Medical Center, Palestine, TX, p. A640
   Director Information Systems, Palestine Regional Medical Center–East, Palestine, TX, p. A640

CHOUDHURY, Golam, Chief of Staff, Desert Springs Hospital Medical Center, Las Vegas, NV, p. A405

CHOUDHURY, Seleem, R.N. Chief Nursing Officer, Northeastern Vermont Regional Hospital, Saint Johnsbury, VT, p. A666

CHOY, Ann N., Manager Human Resources and Payroll, Kuakini Medical Center, Honolulu, HI, p. A170

CHOZINSKI, Joseph P., M.D. Deputy Commander Clinical Services, Brooke Army Medical Center, Fort Sam Houston, TX, p. A617

CHRENCIK, Robert A., President and Chief Executive Officer, University of Maryland Medical System, Baltimore, MD, p. B147

CHRISTENSEN, Carl, Senior Vice President and Chief Information Officer, Northwestern Memorial HealthCare, Northwestern Memorial Hospital, Chicago, IL, p. A185

CHRISTENSEN, Claudia, Director, Human Resources, Mills–Peninsula Health Services, Burlingame, CA, p. A57

CHRISTENSEN, Connie, Chief Financial Officer, Morrill County Community Hospital, Bridgeport, NE, p. A394

CHRISTENSEN, David, M.D. Senior Vice President and Chief Medical Officer, Valley Children's Healthcare, Madera, CA, p. A75

CHRISTENSEN, Earlene, Director Human Resources, Fayette County Memorial Hospital, Washington Court House, OH, p. A505

CHRISTENSEN, Elizabeth B., Director Human Resources, Mercy Hospital of Portland, Portland, ME, p. A294

CHRISTENSEN, G. N., M.D. Chief Medical Officer, William Bee Ririe Hospital, Ely, NV, p. A404

CHRISTENSEN, Gwen, Vice President Finance, Aurora BayCare Medical Center, Green Bay, WI, p. A706

CHRISTENSEN, Jay, FACHE, Administrator, Mahaska Health Partnership, Oskaloosa, IA, p. A236

CHRISTENSEN, Jeffrey, Chief Executive Officer, HEALTHSOUTH Rehabilitation Institute of Tucson, Tucson, AZ, p. A40

CHRISTENSEN, Kim, Interim Chief Nursing Executive, Sheridan Community Hospital, Sheridan, MI, p. A334

CHRISTENSEN, Marilyn, Director Information Technology, Milford Hospital, Milford, CT, p. A115

CHRISTENSEN, Mark, Director, Finance, Cassia Regional Medical Center, Burley, ID, p. A175

CHRISTENSEN, Marti, Director of Psychiatric Nursing, Douglas County Community Mental Health Center, Omaha, NE, p. A400

CHRISTENSEN, Scott, Chief Executive Officer, Delta Regional Medical Center, Greenville, MS, p. A358

CHRISTENSEN, Todd
Chief Financial Officer, Kittson Memorial Healthcare Center, Hallock, MN, p. A344
Executive Director Fiscal Services, Sanford Medical Center Thief River Falls, Thief River Falls, MN, p. A352
Executive Director Finance, Sanford Thief River Falls Behavioral Health Center, Thief River Falls, MN, p. A352

CHRISTENSEN, Troy, Chief Financial Officer, Madison Memorial Hospital, Rexburg, ID, p. A178

CHRISTENSEN, W. R., M.D. Chief of Staff, East Texas Medical Center Pittsburg, Pittsburg, TX, p. A641

CHRISTENSEN–MORES, Donna, JD Director Human Resources, Myrtue Medical Center, Harlan, IA, p. A232

CHRISTENSON, Paul, Chief Financial Officer, Pampa Regional Medical Center, Pampa, TX, p. A640

CHRISTENSON, Ron, Chief Financial Officer, Morris County Hospital, Council Grove, KS, p. A242

CHRISTENSON, Shannon, Director Human Resources, Aurora West Allis Medical Center, West Allis, WI, p. A719

CHRISTIAN, Bruce, President and Chief Executive Officer, AMITA Health GlenOaks, Glendale Heights, IL, p. A191

CHRISTIAN, Glenn, Administrator, Mayo Clinic Health System in Cannon Falls, Cannon Falls, MN, p. A340

CHRISTIAN, Greg, Executive Director, Kaiser Permanente Fontana Medical Center, Fontana, CA, p. A62

CHRISTIAN, Karolyne, Director Human Resources, Byrd Regional Hospital, Leesville, LA, p. A282

CHRISTIANO, Barbara, Vice President, Patient Care Services and Chief Nursing Officer, University Medical Center of Princeton at Plainsboro, Plainsboro, NJ, p. A422

CHRISTIANSEN, Anne, Chief Financial Officer, Pioneer Memorial Hospital and Health Services, Viborg, SD, p. A577

CHRISTIANSEN, Hilary, Chief Financial Officer, George C Grape Community Hospital, Hamburg, IA, p. A231

CHRISTIANSEN, Keith, Chief Nursing Officer, Select Specialty Hospital–Erie, Erie, PA, p. A538

CHRISTIANSEN, Patrick, Ph.D., Chief Executive Officer, Inova Fairfax Hospital, Falls Church, VA, p. A670

CHRISTIANSEN, Sara, Interim Director Human Resources, Ridgeview Sibley Medical Center, Arlington, MN, p. A338

CHRISTIANSON, Clinton J., FACHE, President, Mercy Medical Center–Centerville, Centerville, IA, p. A227

CHRISTIANSON, Delano, Administrator, CentraCare Health–Sauk Centre, Sauk Centre, MN, p. A351

CHRISTIE, Janet L., Senior Vice President Human Resources, UF Health Shands Hospital, Gainesville, FL, p. A130

CHRISTINE, Gerald, Chief Financial Officer, Lakewood Ranch Medical Center, Bradenton, FL, p. A124

CHRISTION, Lydia, Director Human Resources, HEALTHSOUTH Rehabilitation Hospital, Dothan, AL, p. A19

CHRISTISON, George, M.D. Medical Director, Patton State Hospital, Patton, CA, p. A82

CHRISTMAN, Lawrence, Chief Financial Officer and Chief Operating Officer, Riverview Health, Noblesville, IN, p. A220

CHRISTMAN, Thomas C., Director Plant Operations, Kindred Hospital–St. Louis, Saint Louis, MO, p. A380

CHRISTMANN, Linda, M.D. Chief of Staff, Manatee Memorial Hospital, Bradenton, FL, p. A124

CHRISTOPH, Rebecca, Director Nursing and Patient Care Services, Mid–Valley Hospital, Omak, WA, p. A687

CHRISTOPHEL, Randal, President and Chief Executive Officer, Indiana University Health Goshen Hospital, Goshen, IN, p. A212

CHRISTY, Rose, Executive Director of Medical Services, Hamilton Center, Terre Haute, IN, p. A222

CHROBAK, Jeffrey, Vice President Finance and Chief Financial Officer, Sharon Regional Health System, Sharon, PA, p. A555

CHU, Benjamin K., M.D., President and Chief Executive Officer, Memorial Hermann Health System, Houston, TX, p. B88

CHU, Betty, M.D. Chief Medical Officer and Vice President of Medical Affairs, Henry Ford West Bloomfield Hospital, West Bloomfield, MI, p. A336

CHU, Edward, Chief Financial Officer, Leahi Hospital, Honolulu, HI, p. A170

CHUA, Jesus, M.D. Chief of Staff, Franklin Foundation Hospital, Franklin, LA, p. A277

CHUE, Bevins, M.D. Medical Director, HEALTHSOUTH Desert Canyon Rehabilitation Hospital, Las Vegas, NV, p. A405

CHUGHTAI, Omar, Vice President and Chief Operating Officer, West Hills Hospital and Medical Center,, CA, p. A75

CHUKWUMA, Lilian, Chief Financial Officer, United Medical Center, Washington, DC, p. A122

CHUN, Ryan, Information Resources Management, San Francisco VA Medical Center, San Francisco, CA, p. A90

CHUNG, Maria, CPA Director Fiscal Services, Shriners Hospitals for Children–Boston, Boston, MA, p. A307

CHUNG, Michael
Chief Financial Officer, AHMC Anaheim Regional Medical Center, Anaheim, CA, p. A54
Chief Financial Officer, Greater El Monte Community Hospital, South El Monte, CA, p. A95

CHUNG, Raymond, M.D. Chief of Staff, Phoenix Veterans Affairs Health Care System, Phoenix, AZ, p. A37

CHUNG, William, M.D. Chief of Staff, Chinese Hospital, San Francisco, CA, p. A90

CHUNN, Ashley, Director of Nursing, Atmore Community Hospital, Atmore, AL, p. A16

CHUNN, Debbie, Director Medical Records, Bastrop Rehabilitation Hospital, Monroe, LA, p. A283

CHURCH, Kim
Manager Human Resources, G. Werber Bryan Psychiatric Hospital, Columbia, SC, p. A564
Manager Human Resources, William S. Hall Psychiatric Institute, Columbia, SC, p. A564

CHURCHILL, Brigitte, Director of Human Resources, Mayo Clinic Health System in Waycross, Waycross, GA, p. A169

CHURCHILL, Julie, Chief Financial Officer, Cumberland Surgical Hospital, San Antonio, TX, p. A645

CHURCHILL, Larry, Director Information Services, AllianceHealth Woodward, Woodward, OK, p. A523

CHURCHILL, Sandi, Vice President Business Development and Operations, Professional Services, Advocate Good Samaritan Hospital, Downers Grove, IL, p. A188

CHURCHILL, Timothy A.
Interim Chief Executive Officer, Franklin Memorial Hospital, Farmington, ME, p. A293
President, Stephens Memorial Hospital, Norway, ME, p. A294

CHURCHWELL, Kevin B., M.D. Chief Operating Officer and Executive Vice President Health Affairs, Boston Children's Hospital, Boston, MA, p. A306

CIAMPA, Amy, Chief Financial Officer, Park Royal Hospital, Fort Myers, FL, p. A129

CIAMPA, Steve, Vice President Finance, Porter Medical Center, Middlebury, VT, p. A665

CIANCIOLO, Kirk, D.O. Chief Medical Officer, Blake Medical Center, Bradenton, FL, p. A124

CIANCIOTTO CROYLE, Allison, Vice President of Human Resources, Mercy Medical Center, Rockville Centre, NY, p. A454

CIANFLONE, Laura, Director Human Resources, Kenmore Mercy Hospital, Kenmore, NY, p. A441

CIANFRANI, Michelle, Director Information Technology, Gilbert Hospital, Gilbert, AZ, p. A32

CIAREFELLA, Donna, Director Human Resources, Vibra Hospital of Western Massachusetts, Springfield, MA, p. A315

CICCARELLI, John, Director Information Technology, Parkview Community Hospital Medical Center, Riverside, CA, p. A86

CICCARELLI, Thomas, Chief Information Officer, East Orange General Hospital, East Orange, NJ, p. A416

CICCONE, Josie, Director, Human Resources, Garden City Hospital, Garden City, MI, p. A324

CICE, Donna, Vice President Human Resources, Huntington Hospital, Huntington, NY, p. A440

CICERI, David P., M.D. Chief Medical Officer, Scott and White Continuing Care Hospital, Temple, TX, p. A652

CICHELLI, Andrew, M.D. Chief of Staff, East Georgia Regional Medical Center, Statesboro, GA, p. A166

CICIRETTI, Mary Louise, Director Human Resources, Riddle Hospital, Media, PA, p. A545

CIENCEWICKI, Michael, M.D. Vice President Medical Affairs, Raritan Bay Medical Center, Perth Amboy, NJ, p. A422

CIHA, Clayton, President and Chief Executive Officer, Alexian Brothers Behavioral Health Hospital, Hoffman Estates, IL, p. A193

CIHAK, Scott A., Chief Executive Officer, Kendall Regional Medical Center, Miami, FL, p. A136

CIMALA, Derek W.
Interim Chief Executive Officer, Bluefield Regional Medical Center, Bluefield, WV, p. A694
Interim Chief Executive Officer, Plateau Medical Center, Oak Hill, WV, p. A698

CIMINO, Jr., Michael A., Chief Financial Officer, Banner Behavioral Health Hospital – Scottsdale, Scottsdale, AZ, p. A38

CIMMINO, Denise, MSN Assistant Vice President, Nursing and Patient Care Services, CarePoint Health –Christ Hospital, Jersey City, NJ, p. A418

CINICOLA, John, M.D
Chief Medical Officer, Heritage Valley Health System, Beaver, PA, p. A533
Chief Medical Officer, Sewickley Valley Hospital, (A Division of Valley Medical Facilities), Sewickley, PA, p. A554

CINTRON, Jacob, FACHE, President and Chief Executive Officer, University Medical Center of El Paso, El Paso, TX, p. A616

CIOFFI, Cheryl, R.N. Senior Vice President Patient Care Services and Chief Nursing Officer, Frederick Memorial Hospital, Frederick, MD, p. A301

CIOTA, Mark, M.D.,
Chief Executive Officer, Mayo Clinic Health System in Albert Lea, Albert Lea, MN, p. A338
Chief Executive Officer, Mayo Clinic Health System–Albert Lea and Austin, Austin, MN, p. A339

CIRALDO, Lou, Information Services Representative, University Hospitals Geauga Medical Center, Chardon, OH, p. A486

CIRBA, Michael, Chief Information Officer, Good Shepherd Specialty Hospital, Bethlehem, PA, p. A533

CIRO, Maria, Director Human Resources, Acuity Specialty Hospital of New Jersey, Atlantic City, NJ, p. A414

CIRONE, Laura, Manager Human Resources, Rochelle Community Hospital, Rochelle, IL, p. A201

CIRPILI, Avni, Senior Vice President, Chief Nursing Officer, Menninger Clinic, Houston, TX, p. A626

CITA, Bob, Chief Information Officer, SEARHC MT. Edgecumbe Hospital, Sitka, AK, p. A30

CITAK, Michael, M.D. Chief Medical Officer, Lake Cumberland Regional Hospital, Somerset, KY, p. A469

CIUFO, Donna, R.N. Vice President and Chief Nurse Executive, Southern Ocean Medical Center, Manahawkin, NJ, p. A419

CIVAN, Dino, Chief Information Officer, NYC Health + Hospitals / Kings County,, NY, p. A448

CIVIC, Dave, M.D. Associate Director Clinical Services, U. S. Public Health Service Phoenix Indian Medical Center, Phoenix, AZ, p. A37

CIVITELLO, Dean
Vice President Human Resources, Saint Joseph's Medical Center, Yonkers, NY, p. A459
Vice President, Human Resources, Public Relations and Development, The University of Vermont Health Network–Champlain Valley Physicians Hospital, Plattsburgh, NY, p. A453

CLAASSENS, Nicolise, Nurse Executive, West Central Georgia Regional Hospital, Columbus, GA, p. A157

CLABAUGH, John, Director Human Resources, Saint Luke's East Hospital, Lee's Summit, MO, p. A375

CLABUESCH, Paul, President and Chief Executive Officer, Harbor Beach Community Hospital, Harbor Beach, MI, p. A326

CLACK, Deborah, Chief Nursing Officer, Hunt Regional Medical Center, Greenville, TX, p. A621

CLACK, Lee, R.N. Chief Nursing Officer, Lake Wales Medical Center, Lake Wales, FL, p. A133

CLADOUHOS, Joseph, Chief Executive Officer, Syringa Hospital and Clinics, Grangeville, ID, p. A176

CLAIR OLIVER, Delores, Chief Clinical Officer and Chief Operating Officer, BridgePoint Hospital Capitol Hill, Washington, DC, p. A121

CLANCY, Karen, Manager Information Systems Operations, Bath Veterans Affairs Medical Center, Bath, NY, p. A434

CLANCY, Mikki, Chief Operating Officer, Miami Valley Hospital, Dayton, OH, p. A493

CLANCY, Patricia, M.D. Director Medical Services, Maniilaq Health Center, Kotzebue, AK, p. A30

CLAPP, Ann R., Director Human Resources, HEALTHSOUTH Rehabilitation Hospital of Texarkana, Texarkana, TX, p. A652

CLAPP, Denise
Interim Executive Director, Lourdes Counseling Center, Richland, WA, p. A689
Chief Nursing Officer, Lourdes Medical Center, Pasco, WA, p. A687

CLAPP, Nicole, FACHE, President and Chief Executive Officer, Grant Regional Health Center, Lancaster, WI, p. A708

CLAPP, Steve, President and Chief Executive Officer, Curae Health, Clinton, TN, p. B43

CLARK, Allan W., M.D. Medical Director, Southwood Psychiatric Hospital, Pittsburgh, PA, p. A551

CLARK, Anna, Interim Chief Executive Officer, Copper Basin Medical Center, Copperhill, TN, p. A582

CLARK, Ashley, Coordinator Human Resources, Noland Hospital Birmingham, Birmingham, AL, p. A17

CLARK, Ben, Vice President and Chief Information Officer, Centra Lynchburg General Hospital, Lynchburg, VA, p. A672

CLARK, Chris, M.D. Senior Vice President Medical Affairs and Chief Medical Officer, Saint Vincent Hospital, Erie, PA, p. A538

CLARK, Dale
President, Mountain View Regional Medical Center, Norton, VA, p. A675
President, Wellmont Lonesome Pine Hospital, Big Stone Gap, VA, p. A667

CLARK, Dave, FACHE, Interim Chief Executive Officer, Hardeman County Memorial Hospital, Quanah, TX, p. A642

CLARK, David D., FACHE, President, Methodist Dallas Medical Center, Dallas, TX, p. A610

CLARK, Debra, Chief Nursing Officer, Bayfront Health Port Charlotte, Port Charlotte, FL, p. A143

CLARK, Ed, M.D. Chief Medical Officer, Primary Children's Hospital, Salt Lake City, UT, p. A663

CLARK, Eileen, Vice President Information Services, Charleston Area Medical Center, Charleston, WV, p. A695

CLARK, Heather, Chief Executive Officer, Caldwell Memorial Hospital, Columbia, LA, p. A275

CLARK, Janice, Manager Human Resources, Garfield Park Hospital, Chicago, IL, p. A184

CLARK, Jason, Director Quality Improvement, Risk Management and Information System, Greenwood County Hospital, Eureka, KS, p. A243

CLARK, Jean, Administrator, Kindred Hospital Seattle–Northgate, Seattle, WA, p. A689

CLARK, Jeff, Director Information Systems, Graham Regional Medical Center, Graham, TX, p. A621

CLARK, Jeffrey A., Vice President Human Resources, Kadlec Regional Medical Center, Richland, WA, p. A689

CLARK, Jeffrey B., Director, Walter Reed National Military Medical Center, Bethesda, MD, p. A299

CLARK, Jennifer, M.D. Chief Quality Officer and Chief Medical Officer, Hillcrest Medical Center, Tulsa, OK, p. A521

CLARK, Jeremy L., Market Chief Executive Officer, Hilton Head Hospital, Hilton Head Island, SC, p. A567

CLARK, John, Chief Financial Officer, Childrens Care Hospital and School, Sioux Falls, SD, p. A576

CLARK, Karen, MS Vice President Operations, Advocate South Suburban Hospital, Hazel Crest, IL, p. A192

CLARK, Karen
Director Administrative Services, Sonoma Developmental Center, Eldridge, CA, p. A61
Vice President Patient Care Services, St. Mary's Regional Medical Center, Lewiston, ME, p. A293

CLARK, Kent, M.D. Chief Medical Affairs and Quality, Waldo County General Hospital, Belfast, ME, p. A292

CLARK, Lisa, Director Human Resources, Willamette Valley Medical Center, McMinnville, OR, p. A527

CLARK, Mark
Human Resources Liaison, U. S. Air Force Regional Hospital, Elmendorf AFB, AK, p. A29
Chief Information Officer, Yampa Valley Medical Center, Steamboat Springs, CO, p. A110

CLARK, Mark A.
Vice President Operations, Good Samaritan Regional Health Center, Mount Vernon, IL, p. A197
Vice President Operations, SSM Health St. Mary's Hospital Centralia, Centralia, IL, p. A182

CLARK, Megan, Coordinator Human Resources, Genesis Medical Center–Aledo, Aledo, IL, p. A180

CLARK, Michael
Fiscal Administrative Manager, Connecticut Veterans Home and Hospital, Rocky Hill, CT, p. A116
Executive Vice President and Chief Financial Officer, FHN Memorial Hospital, Freeport, IL, p. A190
Chief Executive Officer, Spotsylvania Regional Medical Center, Fredericksburg, VA, p. A670

CLARK, Michael A., Administrator, McKay–Dee Hospital Center, Ogden, UT, p. A661

CLARK, N. Travis
President, Page Memorial Hospital, Luray, VA, p. A672
President, Shenandoah Memorial Hospital, Woodstock, VA, p. A681

CLARK, Nancy, Vice President Human Resources, Regional Medical Center at San Jose, San Jose, CA, p. A91

CLARK, Patrick, Manager Information Technology, Sunnyview Rehabilitation Hospital, Schenectady, NY, p. A455

CLARK Jr., Ralph H., FACHE, Chief Executive Officer, Medical Center Barbour, Eufaula, AL, p. A19

CLARK, Randal, Vice President Finance, Sebasticook Valley Health, Pittsfield, ME, p. A294

CLARK, Renee, R.N. Vice President Nursing Services and Performance Improvement, Fort HealthCare, Fort Atkinson, WI, p. A705

CLARK, Renee, Senior Vice President and Chief Operating Officer, Southcoast Hospitals Group, Fall River, MA, p. A310

CLARK, Rhonda, Interim Chief Nursing Officer, Alta Vista Regional Hospital, Las Vegas, NM, p. A430

CLARK, Robert J., President and Chief Executive Officer, Bristol Bay Area Health Corporation, Dillingham, AK, p. A29

CLARK, Robin, Chief Nursing Officer, Select Specialty Hospital–Greensboro, Greensboro, NC, p. A466

CLARK, Rodney, Chief Operating Officer, North Sunflower Medical Center, Ruleville, MS, p. A364

CLARK, Ron, M.D. Vice President Clinical Activities and Chief Medical Officer, VCU Medical Center, Richmond, VA, p. A678

CLARK, Sharon, Director Human Resources, Hillsboro Area Hospital, Hillsboro, IL, p. A193

CLARK, Shawn, Director Information Systems, The Physicians Centre Hospital, Bryan, TX, p. A604

CLARK, Stella, MSN Chief Nursing Officer, HSHS St. Joseph's Hospital, Chippewa Falls, WI, p. A704

CLARK, Steven, Chief Financial Officer, Easton Hospital, Easton, PA, p. A537

CLARK, Teresa, Chief Executive Officer and Administrator, Wichita County Health Center, Leoti, KS, p. A248

CLARK, Teresa J., R.N. Chief Nursing Officer, Cook Children's Medical Center, Fort Worth, TX, p. A618

CLARK, Theo, Director Financial Services, Promise Hospital of Phoenix, Mesa, AZ, p. A34

CLARK, Thomas A., Regional President and Chief Executive Officer, Avera Queen of Peace Hospital, Mitchell, SD, p. A575

CLARK, Troy, Chief Executive Officer, HEALTHSOUTH Rehabilitation Hospital, Kingsport, TN, p. A585

CLARK, Victoria, Interim Chief Executive Officer, La Paz Regional Hospital, Parker, AZ, p. A35

CLARK, William, M.D. Chief Clinical Affairs, Caro Center, Caro, MI, p. A320

CLARK, William H., Chief Financial Officer, Caldwell Memorial Hospital, Columbia, LA, p. A275

CLARKE, James, M.D. Vice President Medical Affairs and Clinical Effectiveness, Ocean Medical Center, Brick Township, NJ, p. A415

CLAROS, Elizabeth, Administrator Personnel Services, Guam Memorial Hospital Authority, Tamuning, GU, p. A725

CLARY, Brandon, Chief Executive Officer, Elbert Memorial Hospital, Elberton, GA, p. A159

CLARY, Elizabeth P., R.N., Vice President Behavioral Health, Peninsula Hospital, Louisville, TN, p. A587

CLATANOFF, Kris, Director Human Resources, St. Joseph Medical Center, Houston, TX, p. A626

CLAUDSON, Jackie, Administrator, South Big Horn County Hospital, Basin, WY, p. A721

CLAUDY, Frank, M.D. Vice President Medical Staff Affairs, Genesis Medical Center–Davenport, Davenport, IA, p. A228

CLAUNCH, Jeremy, Chief Financial Officer, Power County Hospital District, American Falls, ID, p. A174

CLAUSEN, Patricia J., R.N. Chief Nurse Executive, Kaiser Permanente Downey Medical Center, Downey, CA, p. A60

CLAUSSEN, Denise, R.N. Chief Nursing Officer, Texas Health Presbyterian Hospital Kaufman, Kaufman, TX, p. A630

CLAUSSEN, Tammy, Chief Human Resource Officer, Tri Valley Health System, Cambridge, NE, p. A394

CLAVELL, Luis, M.D. Medical Director, San Jorge Children's Hospital, San Juan, PR, p. A730

CLAWSON, Tonya, Manager Human Resources, Mercy Medical Center–Centerville, Centerville, IA, p. A227

CLAXTON, Anthony, M.D. Clinical Director, Terrell State Hospital, Terrell, TX, p. A652

CLAXTON, Tracey
Chief Financial Officer, Chester Regional Medical Center, Chester, SC, p. A563
Chief Financial Officer, Jennersville Regional Hospital, West Grove, PA, p. A557

CLAY, David, Chief Executive Officer, Sandhills Regional Medical Center, Hamlet, NC, p. A466

CLAYMORE, Krystal, Chief Financial Officer, Great Plains Health, North Platte, NE, p. A399

CLAYTON, Donald, M.D., President, Indiana University Health Arnett Hospital, Lafayette, IN, p. A216

CLAYTON, Edward, Chief Executive Officer, Phelps County Regional Medical Center, Rolla, MO, p. A379

CLAYTON, Julie, R.N. Chief Nursing Officer and Vice President Patient Care Services, Overlake Medical Center, Bellevue, WA, p. A682

CLAYTON, Kent G., Chief Executive Officer, Los Alamitos Medical Center, Los Alamitos, CA, p. A70

CLAYTON, Melissa S., CPA Chief Financial Officer, Northlake Behavioral Health System, Mandeville, LA, p. A282

CLAYTON, Philip A., President and Chief Executive Officer, Conway Medical Center, Conway, SC, p. A565

CLEARY, Mary Elizabeth, Chief Financial Officer, MacNeal Hospital, Berwyn, IL, p. A181

CLEARY, Steven R., Chief Financial Officer, Overland Park Regional Medical Center, Overland Park, KS, p. A251

CLEAVER, Chuck, Vice President and Chief Financial Officer, Martin Health System, Stuart, FL, p. A146

CLECKLER, Jason, Chief Executive Officer, Delta County Memorial Hospital, Delta, CO, p. A103

CLEGG, Travis, Vice President, Operations, Castle Medical Center, Kailua, HI, p. A171

CLELAND, Dub, Chief Financial Officer, Oklahoma Surgical Hospital, Tulsa, OK, p. A521

CLELAND, Richard, FACHE Site Administrator, Ira Davenport Memorial Hospital, Bath, NY, p. A434

CLELAND, William H., M.D. Chief Medical Officer, University of Mississippi Medical Center, Jackson, MS, p. A360

CLEMEN, Linda, R.N. Vice President and Chief Nursing Officer, Katherine Shaw Bethea Hospital, Dixon, IL, p. A188

CLEMENT, Bernie, Chief Information Officer, Thibodaux Regional Medical Center, Thibodaux, LA, p. A289

CLEMENT, Bruce, Chief Operating Officer, Slidell Memorial Hospital, Slidell, LA, p. A288

CLEMENT, Charles, Chief Executive Officer, SEARHC MT. Edgecumbe Hospital, Sitka, AK, p. A30

CLEMENT, Clayton L., Interim Administrator, Community Howard Specialty Hospital, Kokomo, IN, p. A216

CLEMENT, Kevin J., Chief Executive Officer, Landmark Hospital of Joplin, Joplin, MO, p. A372

CLEMENT, Michelle, Executive Assistant/Human Resources Director, Roundup Memorial Healthcare, Roundup, MT, p. A390

CLEMENTS, James, Chief Executive Officer, Cullman Regional Medical Center, Cullman, AL, p. A18

CLEMENTS, John R., Chief Financial Officer, McCullough–Hyde Memorial Hospital/TriHealth, Oxford, OH, p. A501

CLEMMENSEN, Scott
Vice President Human Resources and Leadership Enhancement, Capital Health Medical Center–Hopewell, Pennington, NJ, p. A422
Vice President Human Resources and Leadership Enhancement, Capital Health Regional Medical Center, Trenton, NJ, p. A424

CLEMMER, Deb, Vice President Human Resources, Bothwell Regional Health Center, Sedalia, MO, p. A382

CLEMONS, Deneace, Chief Operating Officer, Twin Lakes Regional Medical Center, Leitchfield, KY, p. A262

CLERE, Trevor, Director Information Technology, Mercy Medical Center, Canton, OH, p. A486

CLEVELAND, Cynthia, Ph.D. Associate Director for Patient Care Services and Nurse Executive, Birmingham Veterans Affairs Medical Center, Birmingham, AL, p. A16

CLEVENGER, Erin R., Chief Nursing Officer and Director of Quality, Memorial Medical Center, Port Lavaca, TX, p. A642

CLEWS, Donna, Ph.D. Vice President Patient Care Services, Berkeley Medical Center, Martinsburg, WV, p. A697

CLICK, Glenn, Chief Financial Officer, Sequoyah Memorial Hospital, Sallisaw, OK, p. A519

CLICK, Mike, R.N., Administrator, Brownfield Regional Medical Center, Brownfield, TX, p. A603

CLIFFE, Peggy, Chief Executive Officer, Select Specialty Hospital–Wichita, Wichita, KS, p. A256

CLIFFORD, Michael J., Director Finance, Wayne Memorial Hospital, Honesdale, PA, p. A540

CLIFFORD, Ryan, M.D. Chief of Staff, Washakie Medical Center, Worland, WY, p. A724

CLIFTON, Mark, Interim Chief Financial Officer, CHI St. Luke's Health Memorial Livingston, Livingston, TX, p. A633

CLINE, Richard, D.O. Chief of Staff, Lincoln County Health System, Fayetteville, TN, p. A583

CLINE, Vickie, Director Human Resources, Northwest Medical Center, Albany, MO, p. A367

CLINGENPEEL, Jeremy, Administrator, Satanta District Hospital and Long Term Care, Satanta, KS, p. A253

CLINGER, Dallas, Administrator, Power County Hospital District, American Falls, ID, p. A174

CLINITE, Ed, D.O. Chief of Staff, Sonora Regional Medical Center, Sonora, CA, p. A94

CLINTON, Lee, FACHE, Chief Executive Officer, Titusville Area Hospital, Titusville, PA, p. A555

CLINTON, Lori, Chief Nursing Officer, Sparta Community Hospital, Sparta, IL, p. A203

CLIPP, Jerry, Manager Human Resources, Washakie Medical Center, Worland, WY, p. A724

CLISTER, Martha L., Director Human Resources, Canonsburg Hospital, Canonsburg, PA, p. A534

CLOHSEY, Maria, Director of Nursing, Shore Rehabilitation Institute, Brick, NJ, p. A414

CLONCH, Les, Chief Information Officer, Texas Scottish Rite Hospital for Children, Dallas, TX, p. A611

CLONTS, Jolene, Director Human Resources, Logan Regional Hospital, Logan, UT, p. A660

CLOSE, Debra, Chief Executive Officer, Dukes Memorial Hospital, Peru, IN, p. A220

CLOUD, Avery, Vice President and Chief Information Officer, New Hanover Regional Medical Center, Wilmington, NC, p. A475

CLOUD, Sylvia, Director Human Resources, Silver Lake Medical Center, Los Angeles, CA, p. A74

CLOUGH, Jeanette G., President and Chief Executive Officer, Mount Auburn Hospital, Cambridge, MA, p. A309

CLOUGH, Sheila, Chief Executive Officer, Asante Ashland Community Hospital, Ashland, OR, p. A524

CLOUGH-BERRY, Cherie, Vice President, Finance, Hampstead Hospital, Hampstead, NH, p. A411

CLOUSE, Joseph, Chief Administrative Officer, Newport Hospital and Health Services, Newport, WA, p. A687

CLOUSE DAY, Sherry, Vice President Finance, Mercy Hospital Berryville, Berryville, AR, p. A43

CLOUTIER, Jonathan, Manager, Information Services, Buffalo Hospital, Buffalo, MN, p. A340

CLOUTIER, Mary, Director Human Resources, Adventist Behavioral Health Rockville, Rockville, MD, p. A303

CLOUTIER, Michael, Director Information Services, Trios Health, Kennewick, WA, p. A685

CLOVER, Robert, Superintendent and Chief Executive Officer, Logansport State Hospital, Logansport, IN, p. A217

CLOWES, Jennifer, Chief Financial Officer, Broadwater Health Center, Townsend, MT, p. A391

CLOYD, Elizabeth, R.N. Chief Nurse Executive and Executive Vice President, Harris Health System, Houston, TX, p. A624

CLUCK, Robert N., M.D. Vice President and Medical Director, Texas Health Arlington Memorial Hospital, Arlington, TX, p. A598

CLUFF, Ben, Chief Executive Officer, Ashley Regional Medical Center, Vernal, UT, p. A664

CLUNN, Amy, M.D. Medical Director, HEALTHSOUTH Rehabilitation Hospital of Ocala, Ocala, FL, p. A139

CLUTE, Gerald B.
Chief Executive Officer, Hollywood Presbyterian Medical Center, Los Angeles, CA, p. A71
Chief Executive Officer, Southern California Hospital at Culver City, Culver City, CA, p. A60

CLUTTS, Kathaleen, Chief Human Resources Officer, Des Peres Hospital, Saint Louis, MO, p. A380

CLYNE, Andrea, R.N. Chief Nursing Officer, Palms of Pasadena Hospital, Saint Petersburg, FL, p. A144

CLYNE, Mary Ellen, R.N., President and Chief Executive Officer, Clara Maass Medical Center, Belleville, NJ, p. A414

CMIEL, Peggy, R.N. Chief Nursing Officer, Chinese Hospital, San Francisco, CA, p. A90

COALTER, Barbara, Director Human Resources, Weirton Medical Center, Weirton, WV, p. A700

COATES, Janet E., R.N., President and Chief Executive Officer, CHRISTUS Mother Frances Hospital – Winnsboro, Winnsboro, TX, p. A658

COATES, Jennifer, Coordinator Information Technology, Purcell Municipal Hospital, Purcell, OK, p. A519

COATS, Daniel J., Vice President Operations, Mercy Hospital Ada, Ada, OK, p. A508

COATS, John, M.D. Chief Medical Staff, Morehouse General Hospital, Bastrop, LA, p. A272

COATS, Kevin, Chief Operating Officer and Chief Financial Officer, Baylor Medical Center at Frisco, Frisco, TX, p. A619

COBARRUBIAS, Samuel, M.D. Chief of Staff, Clinch Memorial Hospital, Homerville, GA, p. A161

COBB, April, Chief Nursing Officer, HEALTHSOUTH Lakeshore Rehabilitation Hospital, Birmingham, AL, p. A16

COBB, Heidi, R.N. Chief Nursing Officer, Medical Arts Hospital, Lamesa, TX, p. A632

COBB, Janice M., R.N. Chief Nursing Officer, Tennessee Valley Healthcare System, Nashville, TN, p. A591

COBB, Jason E., FACHE, Chief Executive Officer, Rapides Regional Medical Center, Alexandria, LA, p. A271

COBB, Jeff, Information Technologist, Guthrie County Hospital, Guthrie Center, IA, p. A231

COBB, Lindsay, Director Human Resources, Liberty Healthcare Systems, Bastrop, LA, p. A272

COBBLE, Emlyn, Vice President and Chief Support Officer, Parkwest Medical Center, Knoxville, TN, p. A586

COBBS, Wendy, Director of Human Resources, Promise Hospital of Baton Rouge – Ochsner Campus, Baton Rouge, LA, p. A273

COBURN, Meredith
Vice President Information Services, Saint Francis Hospital, Tulsa, OK, p. A522
Vice President, Information Systems, Saint Francis Hospital South, Tulsa, OK, p. A522

COBURN, Paul, Chief Financial Officer, Liberty Healthcare Systems, Bastrop, LA, p. A272

COBURN, Thomas C., M.D. Chief Medical Officer, Middle Park Medical Center–Kremmling, Kremmling, CO, p. A107

COCCA, Lisa, Chief Executive Officer, Belmont Pines Hospital, Youngstown, OH, p. A506

COCCHI, Dean, Chief Financial Officer, Kindred Hospital Ocala, Ocala, FL, p. A139

COCH, William, M.D. Medical Director, Jones Memorial Hospital, Wellsville, NY, p. A458

COCHENNET, Bradley, Chief Executive Officer, Pagosa Springs Medical Center, Pagosa Springs, CO, p. A109

COCHRAN, Avril, R.N. Vice President Patient Care Services, North Country Hospital and Health Center, Newport, VT, p. A666

COCHRAN, Dan, Chief Operating Officer, Mountain River Birthing and Surgery Center, Blackfoot, ID, p. A174

COCHRAN, Daniel, Vice President and Chief Financial Officer, Adventist Healthcare Shady Grove Medical Center, Rockville, MD, p. A303

COCHRAN, Janice, R.N. Director Patient Care, CHRISTUS Continuing Care dba Dubuis Hospital of Paris, Paris, TX, p. A640

COCHRAN, Kenneth, FACHE, President and Chief Executive Officer, Opelousas General Health System, Opelousas, LA, p. A286

COCHRAN, Lena, Director of Finance, Highlands–Cashiers Hospital, Highlands, NC, p. A467

COCHRAN, Sherry, Manager Human Resources, Cascade Behavioral Health, Tukwila, WA, p. A692

COCHRAN, Jr., Willie, M.D. Chief of Staff, Southern Regional Medical Center, Riverdale, GA, p. A164

COCHRANE, Andrew S., Chief Executive Officer, Maple Grove Hospital, Maple Grove, MN, p. A345

COCHRANE, Robert K., Interim Vice President, Finance, Cheshire Medical Center, Keene, NH, p. A411

COCKING, Kathy, R.N. Director of Clinical Services, Carson Valley Medical Center, Gardnerville, NV, p. A404

COCKRELL, Christopher, Executive Director Human Resources, Providence Hospital, Mobile, AL, p. A22

COCKRELL, Dennis, Director Human Resources, Gritman Medical Center, Moscow, ID, p. A177

COCKRELL, Tim, Chief Executive Officer, Patients Choice Medical Center of Smith County, Raleigh, MS, p. A364

COCO, Jeffrey, M.D. Chief Medical Officer, Touro Infirmary, New Orleans, LA, p. A285

CODER, Charles, Chief Financial Officer, Southside Regional Medical Center, Petersburg, VA, p. A676

CODER, Denise, Chief Human Resource Officer, Cass County Memorial Hospital, Atlantic, IA, p. A225

CODY, James, Director, Syracuse Veterans Affairs Medical Center, Syracuse, NY, p. A457

CODY, Kyllan, FACHE, Chief Executive Officer, Cook Children's Northeast Hospital, Hurst, TX, p. A628

COE, Jason, M.D. Medical Director, Greenbrier Behavior Health Hospital, Covington, LA, p. A275

COE, Jason C., President, Hackettstown Medical Center, Hackettstown, NJ, p. A417

COE, Susan
Vice President Human Resources, University of Maryland Shore Medical Center at Chestertown, Chestertown, MD, p. A299
Regional Vice President Human Resources, University of Maryland Shore Medical Center at Dorchester, Cambridge, MD, p. A299
Regional Vice President Human Resources, University of Maryland Shore Medical Center at Easton, Easton, MD, p. A300

COELLO, Jennifer, Chief Operating Officer, Clinch Valley Medical Center, Richlands, VA, p. A677

COEN, Vickie, Chief Clinical Officer and Nurse Executive, Pana Community Hospital, Pana, IL, p. A199

COFFEE, Heidi Malez, Chief Nursing Officer, East Georgia Regional Medical Center, Statesboro, GA, p. A166

COFFEE, Paula, Director Human Resources, St. Mary's of Michigan, Saginaw, MI, p. A333

COFFEE, Robert, Chief Information Officer, Creek Nation Community Hospital, Okemah, OK, p. A515

COFFELL, Randy, Manager Human Resources, Mid–Valley Hospital, Omak, WA, p. A687

COFFEY, C. Edward, M.D., President, Chief Executive Officer and Chief of Staff, Menninger Clinic, Houston, TX, p. A626

COFFEY, Daniel B., President and Chief Executive Officer, The Acadia Hospital, Bangor, ME, p. A291

COFFEY, Douglas W., R.N. Chief Nursing Officer, St. Mary's Regional Medical Center, Enid, OK, p. A511

COFFEY, Glenna, R.N., Chief Operating Officer, Bridgewell Hospital of Cincinnati, Cincinnati, OH, p. A487

COFFEY, Joseph, Director Facility Administration, Rochester Psychiatric Center, Rochester, NY, p. A454

COFFEY, Judy, R.N.,
Senior Vice President and Area Manager, Kaiser Permanente San Rafael Medical Center, San Rafael, CA, p. A92
Senior Vice President and Area Manager, Kaiser Permanente Santa Rosa Medical Center, Santa Rosa, CA, p. A94

COFFEY, Kevin, Chief Executive Officer, Winner Regional Healthcare Center, Winner, SD, p. A578

COFFEY, M. Justin, Vice President and Chief Information Officer, Medical Director Center for Brain Stimulation, Menninger Clinic, Houston, TX, p. A626

COFFEY, Timothy O., Senior Vice President Operations, Lake Charles Memorial Hospital, Lake Charles, LA, p. A281

COFFING, Sylvia K., R.N. Chief Nursing and Compliance Officer, Unity Medical & Surgical Hospital, Mishawaka, IN, p. A218

COFFMAN, Brian, Director Information System, National Park Medical Center, Hot Springs, AR, p. A47

COFFMAN, Courtney, Chief Financial Officer, Lower Bucks Hospital, Bristol, PA, p. A534

COFFMAN, Joan M., FACHE, President and Chief Executive Officer, HSHS St. Joseph's Hospital, Chippewa Falls, WI, p. A704

COFFMAN BARNES, Julie, M.D. Chief Medical Officer, Redmond Regional Medical Center, Rome, GA, p. A165

COFINAS, Rebecca, Vice President and Chief Operating Executive Operations, Scripps Memorial Hospital–Encinitas, Encinitas, CA, p. A61

COGGINS, Lisa, Chief Nursing Officer, Morton Hospital and Medical Center, Taunton, MA, p. A315

COGGINS, Parkes, Chief Executive Officer, Carolinas Hospital System Marion, Mullins, SC, p. A568

COHEE, Jonathan, Chief Executive Officer, Kindred Chicago–Central Hospital, Chicago, IL, p. A184

COHEN, Ginger, Chief Nurse Executive, St. Luke's Rehabilitation Institute, Spokane, WA, p. A691

COHEN, Jason, M.D. Chief Medical Officer, North Valley Hospital, Whitefish, MT, p. A391

COHEN, Jeffrey, M.D., President, Allegheny General Hospital, Pittsburgh, PA, p. A550

COHEN, Kathleena, R.N. Director of Nursing, Hampton Behavioral Health Center, Westampton, NJ, p. A425

COHEN, Larry, Interim Chief Executive Officer, Ocean Beach Hospital, Ilwaco, WA, p. A685

COHEN, Mark, M.D. Chief Medical Officer, Piedmont Hospital, Atlanta, GA, p. A153

COHEN, Philip A., Chief Executive Officer, Monterey Park Hospital, Monterey Park, CA, p. A78

COHEN, Robert, M.D. Chief Medical Officer, Sonoma Valley Hospital, Sonoma, CA, p. A94

COHICK, Jim, Chief Executive Officer, Kindred Hospital–Sycamore, Sycamore, IL, p. A204

COHILL, Michael J., Interim Chief Executive Officer, Sutter Medical Center, Sacramento, Sacramento, CA, p. A87

COKER, Cindy, Vice President, Patient Care Services, Vidant Chowan Hospital, Edenton, NC, p. A464

COKER, Joe, M.D. Chief of Staff, Great Plains Regional Medical Center, Elk City, OK, p. A511

COLADONATO DNP, RN, NEA–BC, Angela R., MSN Chief Nursing Officer, Penn Medicine Chester County Hospital, West Chester, PA, p. A557

COLAMARIA, James, Director of Nursing, Four Winds Hospital, Saratoga Springs, NY, p. A455

COLANGELO, Nicholas, Ph.D., Chief Executive Officer, Clear Brook Lodge, Shickshinny, PA, p. A555

COLAS, Chuck, M.D. Medical Director, Surprise Valley Health Care District, Cedarville, CA, p. A58

COLBERG, Gary R., FACHE, President and Chief Executive Officer, Methodist Hospital, Henderson, KY, p. A261

COLBURN, Douglas, Chief Information Officer, Northside Medical Center, Columbus, GA, p. A156

COLBURN, Tim A., President and Chief Executive Officer, Berger Health System, Circleville, OH, p. A488

COLBY, Dennis, M.D. Chief of Staff, Iowa Specialty Hospital–Clarion, Clarion, IA, p. A227

COLBY, Scott, President, Upper Connecticut Valley Hospital, Colebrook, NH, p. A410

COLCHER, Marian W., President and Chief Executive Officer, Valley Forge Medical Center and Hospital, Norristown, PA, p. A546

COLE, Annette E., R.N. Vice President and Chief Nursing Officer, Sky Lakes Medical Center, Klamath Falls, OR, p. A527

COLE, Bernadette Green, R.N. Chief Nursing Officer, Munson Healthcare Charlevoix Hospital, Charlevoix, MI, p. A320

COLE, Beth, Director Information Services, Lewis–Gale Medical Center, Salem, VA, p. A678

COLE, Cal, Director Information Systems, Winter Haven Hospital, Winter Haven, FL, p. A150

COLE, Carlene, Manager Human Resources, Kittson Memorial Healthcare Center, Hallock, MN, p. A344

COLE, F. Sessions, M.D. Chief Medical Officer, St. Louis Children's Hospital, Saint Louis, MO, p. A381

COLE, Georgeanne, Chief Executive Officer, Rehabilitation Hospital of Southwest Virginia, Bristol, VA, p. A668

COLE Jr., Harry, Administrator, Georgiana Hospital, Georgiana, AL, p. A20

COLE, James B., Chief Executive Officer, Virginia Hospital Center – Arlington, Arlington, VA, p. A667

COLE, Jason
    Director Finance, Scott & White Hospital – Llano, Llano, TX, p. A633
    Senior Director Finance, Scott & White Hospital at Round Rock, Round Rock, TX, p. A644
    Senior Director, Management Information Systems, Suburban Hospital, Bethesda, MD, p. A299

COLE, Karen S., FACHE, Chief Executive Officer, Shenandoah Medical Center, Shenandoah, IA, p. A237

COLE, Kirk, Interim Commissioner, Texas Department of State Health Services, Austin, TX, p. B134

COLE, Lori, Director Information Technology, Wayne Memorial Hospital, Goldsboro, NC, p. A466

COLE, Missy, Director Human Resources, HEALTHSOUTH Rehabilitation Hospital, Fayetteville, AR, p. A45

COLE, Nancye, R.N. Chief Operating Officer, Lovelace Westside Hospital, Albuquerque, NM, p. A427

COLE, Richard C., Chief of Staff, Pioneer Community Hospital of Patrick, Stuart, VA, p. A679

COLE, Robert, Chief Operating Officer, Connecticut Mental Health Center, New Haven, CT, p. A116

COLE–OUZOUNIAN, Denise Marie, Vice President Patient Services, Sauk Prairie Healthcare, Prairie Du Sac, WI, p. A714

COLEMAN, Alisa, Chief Executive Officer, Ferrell Hospital, Eldorado, IL, p. A189

COLEMAN, Amy, Director Human Resources, Loretto Hospital, Chicago, IL, p. A184

COLEMAN, Curt, FACHE,
    Chief Executive Officer, Genesis Medical Center, DeWitt, De Witt, IA, p. A229
    Administrator, Jackson County Regional Health Center, Maquoketa, IA, p. A234

COLEMAN, D. Scott, Medical Director, Livingston HealthCare, Livingston, MT, p. A389

COLEMAN, Donna, Coordinator Human Resources, Jackson County Hospital District, Edna, TX, p. A614

COLEMAN, Jr., Jim L., Chief Operating Officer, Parkridge Medical Center, Chattanooga, TN, p. A580

COLEMAN, Judy, Chief Financial Officer, Indiana University Health Ball Memorial Hospital, Indiana University Health Blackford Hospital, Hartford City, IN, p. A213

COLEMAN, Karen, Director of Nursing, Grove Hill Memorial Hospital, Grove Hill, AL, p. A21

COLEMAN, Keith T., Chief Financial Officer, Mount Carmel, Columbus, OH, p. A490

COLEMAN, Kevin, M.D. Chief Medical Officer, Grand River Hospital District, Rifle, CO, p. A110

COLEMAN, Melissa, Director Human Resources, HEALTHSOUTH Rehabilitation Hospital of Sewickley, Sewickley, PA, p. A554

COLERICK, Steven, Chief Executive Officer, Buena Vista Regional Medical Center, Storm Lake, IA, p. A238

COLETTA, Antonio
    Vice President Human Resources, Advocate BroMenn Medical Center, Normal, IL, p. A198
    Vice President Human Resources, Advocate Eureka Hospital, Eureka, IL, p. A189

COLETTA, Diane, Director Human Resources, Royal Oaks Hospital, Windsor, MO, p. A384

COLETTI, Edmund, Chief Executive Officer, Helen Hayes Hospital, West Haverstraw, NY, p. A458

COLEY, Brenda
    Executive Director, Metroplex Adventist Hospital, Killeen, TX, p. A630
    Executive Director, Rollins–Brook Community Hospital, Lampasas, TX, p. A632

COLGAN, Teresa, VP of Nursing, Great River Medical Center, West Burlington, IA, p. A239

COLGLAZIER, Garrett, Director Health Information Management, Sabetha Community Hospital, Sabetha, KS, p. A253

COLINERI, Lori, MSN Senior Vice President Nursing and Chief Nursing Officer, Robert Wood Johnson University Hospital, New Brunswick, NJ, p. A420

COLLAZO, Marian, Director Finance, Hospital San Cristobal, Coto Laurel, PR, p. A727

COLLETT, John, Vice President and Chief Financial Officer, Cayuga Medical Center at Ithaca, Ithaca, NY, p. A440

COLLETT, Josh, Director Human Resources, Pineville Community Hospital Association, Pineville, KY, p. A268

COLLETTI, Teresa, Director Patient Services, South Florida Baptist Hospital, Plant City, FL, p. A142

COLLEY, Sarah, Senior Vice President Human Resources, Regional One Health, Memphis, TN, p. A589

COLLIER, Betty, Chief Human Resources Officer, Johnson Regional Medical Center, Clarksville, AR, p. A44

COLLIER, Brad, Director, Piedmont Newton Hospital, Covington, GA, p. A157

COLLIER, Jack, M.D. Chief of Staff, MountainView Hospital, Las Vegas, NV, p. A406

COLLIER, Russell J., FACHE, President and Chief Executive Officer, Good Shepherd Medical Center–Marshall, Marshall, TX, p. A636

COLLIER, Shari, Chief Financial Officer, Presbyterian–St. Luke's Medical Center, Denver, CO, p. A104

COLLIER, Tammy, R.N. Vice President Patient Services, Texas Health Huguley Hospital Fort Worth South, Burleson, TX, p. A604

COLLINI, M. Patrick, M.D. President Medical Staff, USMD Hospital at Arlington, Arlington, TX, p. A598

COLLINS, Alesha Danielle, MSN Chief Nursing Officer, Howard Memorial Hospital, Nashville, AR, p. A50

COLLINS, Annasue, Chief Nursing Officer, Ten Broeck Tennessee Treatment Facility, Cookeville, TN, p. A581

COLLINS, Bobby
    Director Human Resources, Mountain View Regional Medical Center, Norton, VA, p. A675
    Director Human Resources, Wellmont Lonesome Pine Hospital, Big Stone Gap, VA, p. A667

COLLINS, Chauncey, Chief Operating Officer and Chief Financial Officer, Austen Riggs Center, Stockbridge, MA, p. A315

COLLINS, Dennis, Chief Financial Officer, The Brook Hospital – KMI, Louisville, KY, p. A265

COLLINS, Edmund, Chief Information Officer, Martin Health System, Stuart, FL, p. A146

COLLINS, Frances, Director of Nursing, Andrew McFarland Mental Health Center, Springfield, IL, p. A203

COLLINS, Gary, M.D. Chief Medical Officer, Aurora BayCare Medical Center, Green Bay, WI, p. A706

COLLINS, Harold E., JD Chief Financial Officer, Franciscan Healthcare – Munster, Munster, IN, p. A219

COLLINS, James M., President and Chief Executive Officer, St. Clair Hospital, Pittsburgh, PA, p. A551

COLLINS, Jeff, Chief Medical Officer, Providence St. Joseph's Hospital, Chewelah, WA, p. A683

COLLINS, Jeffrey A., M.D., Senior Vice President and Area Manager, Kaiser Permanente Roseville Medical Center, Roseville, CA, p. A86

COLLINS, John
    Chief Financial Officer, Anaheim Global Medical Center, Anaheim, CA, p. A54
    Corporate Chief Financial Officer, Chapman Global Medical Center, Orange, CA, p. A80
    Chief Financial Officer, Orange County Global Medical Center, Inc., Santa Ana, CA, p. A92
    Chief Financial Officer, South Coast Global Medical Center, Santa Ana, CA, p. A92

COLLINS, John F., President and Chief Executive Officer, Winthrop–University Hospital, Mineola, NY, p. A442

COLLINS, John P., Medical Center Director, Veterans Affairs Central Western Massachusetts Healthcare System, Leeds, MA, p. A311

COLLINS, John R., Chief Financial Officer, Hemet Valley Medical Center, Hemet, CA, p. A66

COLLINS, Karen S., R.N., Chief Executive Officer, Lady of the Sea General Hospital, Cut Off, LA, p. A276

COLLINS, Kevin J., M.D. Medical Director, St. Vincent Rehabilitation Hospital, Sherwood, AR, p. A52

COLLINS, Kimberly, M.D. Chief of Staff, Saint Thomas DeKalb Hospital, Smithville, TN, p. A593

COLLINS, Leonora, Chief Nursing Officer, Nashville General Hospital, Nashville, TN, p. A590

COLLINS, Pam, Director Human Resources, Fairway Medical Surgical Hospital, Covington, LA, p. A275

COLLINS, Pamela, Vice President Chief Patient Services Officer, McCullough–Hyde Memorial Hospital/TriHealth, Oxford, OH, p. A501

COLLINS, Richard F., M.D. Executive Vice President and Chief Medical Officer, Jefferson Hospital, Jefferson Hills, PA, p. A541

COLLINS, Ricky M., M.D. Chief of Staff, Whitesburg ARH Hospital, Whitesburg, KY, p. A270

COLLINS, Sandra, Chief Clinical Officer, Kindred Hospital–Philadelphia, Philadelphia, PA, p. A548

COLLINS, Sharon
    Director Human Resources and Chief Operating Officer, Russell Regional Hospital, Russell, KS, p. A252
    Chief Information Officer, Salem Veterans Affairs Medical Center, Salem, VA, p. A678

COLLINS, Sherry, Chief Nursing Officer, South Bay Hospital, Sun City Center, FL, p. A146

COLLINS, Teresa L., Chief Nursing Officer, Overland Park Regional Medical Center, Overland Park, KS, p. A251

COLLINS, Terry, Interim Chief Executive Officer, Aspen Valley Hospital District, Aspen, CO, p. A101

COLLINS, Thomas M., President, Chairman and Chief Executive Officer, Green Oaks Hospital, Dallas, TX, p. A610

COLLIPP, Dan, M.D. Chief of Staff, Wayne Memorial Hospital, Jesup, GA, p. A161

COLLISON, June, President, Community Hospital of San Bernardino, San Bernardino, CA, p. A88

COLLOM, Bobbie, Nursing Director, North Runnels Hospital, Winters, TX, p. A658

COLLOTTA, Sharon
    Director Human Resources, Mease Countryside Hospital, Safety Harbor, FL, p. A144
    Director Human Resources, Mease Dunedin Hospital, Dunedin, FL, p. A128

COLMAN, Gerard, Chief Operating Officer, Aurora West Allis Medical Center, West Allis, WI, p. A719

COLMENARES, Derek, M.D
    Chief Medical Officer, Agnesian HealthCare, Fond Du Lac, WI, p. A705
    Chief Medical Officer, Waupun Memorial Hospital, Waupun, WI, p. A718

COLOMBO, Armando, Chief Executive Officer, Vanderbilt Stallworth Rehabilitation Hospital, Nashville, TN, p. A591

COLOMBO, Lisa, R.N., Chief Executive Officer, Clinton Hospital, Clinton, MA, p. A309

COLON, Fernando, Administrator, Metropolitano De La Montana, Utuado, PR, p. A730

COLON, Julio, Financial Director, Hospital De Damas, Ponce, PR, p. A728

COLON, Julio, CPA, Chief Executive Officer, Hospital Episcopal San Lucas Guayama, Guayama, PR, p. A727

COLON, Julio
    Interim President and Chief Executive Officer, St. Luke's Episcopal Hospital, Ponce, PR, p. A728
    Chief Financial Officer, St. Luke's Episcopal Hospital, Ponce, PR, p. A728

COLON, Leonardo, Executive Director, Hospital Psiquiatrico Metropolitano, Cabo Rojo, PR, p. A726

COLON, Omar, M.D. Medical Director, HEALTHSOUTH Plano Rehabilitation Hospital, Plano, TX, p. A641

COLONES, Robert L., President and Chief Executive Officer, McLeod Health, Florence, SC, p. B87

COLONES, Robert L., President and Chief Executive Officer, McLeod Regional Medical Center, Florence, SC, p. A566

COLORADO, Judy, R.N. Chief Nursing Officer, Monmouth Medical Center, Southern Campus, Lakewood, NJ, p. A418

COLPITTS, Robert, Chief Human Resource Service, Bedford Veterans Affairs Medical Center, Edith Nourse Rogers Memorial Veterans Hospital, Bedford, MA, p. A305

COLSDEN, Kristen, Director of Nursing, Osmond General Hospital, Osmond, NE, p. A401

COLSON, Donna, Controller, Texas Rehabilitation Hospital of Arlington, Arlington, TX, p. A598

COLSON, Wayne, Chief Financial Officer, Southwestern Medical Center, Lawton, OK, p. A513

COLTHARP, Missy, Director, Baptist Memorial Hospital–Union County, New Albany, MS, p. A363

COLTON, Jan, M.D. Acting Clinical Director, U. S. Public Health Service Indian Hospital, Pine Ridge, SD, p. A575

COLUCCI, Eugene, Vice President Finance, Greenwich Hospital, Greenwich, CT, p. A114

COLUCCIO, Medrice, R.N.,
    Southwest Region Chief Executive, Providence Centralia Hospital, Centralia, WA, p. A683
    Chief Executive Officer, Providence St. Peter Hospital, Olympia, WA, p. A687

COLVARD, Dusty, Manager Information Technology, Tehachapi Valley Healthcare District, Tehachapi, CA, p. A95

COLVERT, Richard, Chief Information Officer, Royal Oaks Hospital, Windsor, MO, p. A384

COLVIN, Garren
Chief Executive Officer, St. Elizabeth Edgewood, Edgewood, KY, p. A259
Chief Executive Officer, St. Elizabeth Florence, Florence, KY, p. A260
Chief Executive Officer, St. Elizabeth Fort Thomas, Fort Thomas, KY, p. A260
Chief Executive Officer, St. Elizabeth Grant, Williamstown, KY, p. A270

COLVIN, Garren, Chief Executive Officer, St. Elizabeth Healthcare, Edgewood, KY, p. B128

COLVIN, William, Human Resources Officer, Claiborne Memorial Medical Center, Homer, LA, p. A278

COLWELL, Dean, D.O. Vice President Medical Affairs, OhioHealth Doctors Hospital, Columbus, OH, p. A491

COLWELL, Melodie, Chief Financial Officer, Drew Memorial Hospital, Monticello, AR, p. A50

COLYER, Valeri J.
Director Human Resources, Dickenson Community Hospital, Clintwood, VA, p. A669
Director Human Resources, Norton Community Hospital, Norton, VA, p. A675

COMAIANNI, Sheri, Vice President Human Resources, Bakersfield Memorial Hospital, Bakersfield, CA, p. A55

COMBEST, Felton, M.D. Vice President Medical Affairs, Magnolia Regional Health Center, Corinth, MS, p. A357

COMBS, Mark
Interim Director System Information Technology, Berkeley Medical Center, Martinsburg, WV, p. A697
Chief Information Security Officer, Jefferson Medical Center, Ranson, WV, p. A699

COMBS, Meri, R.N. Vice President and Chief Nursing Officer, Madera Community Hospital, Madera, CA, p. A75

COMBS, Mike, Manager Information Technology, Holdenville General Hospital, Holdenville, OK, p. A513

COMBS, Will, Director Information Technology, Harrison Community Hospital, Cadiz, OH, p. A486

COMER, Fannessa, Chief Executive Officer, Northern Navajo Medical Center, Shiprock, NM, p. A431

COMER, Jennifer, M.D. Medical Director, Valle Vista Hospital, Greenwood, IN, p. A212

COMER, Randy, Chief Operating Officer, Athens–Limestone Hospital, Athens, AL, p. A16

COMER, Scott M., Vice President Human Resources, Marshall Medical Center, Placerville, CA, p. A83

COMERFORD, Jennifer, Manager Information Services, MidState Medical Center, Meriden, CT, p. A115

COMITTO, Judy, Vice President Information Services and Chief Information Officer, Trinitas Regional Medical Center, Elizabeth, NJ, p. A416

COMLISH, Jeannie, Command Officer, U. S. Naval Hospital Guam, Agana, GU, p. A725

COMP, Susan, R.N. Senior Vice President and Chief Nursing Officer, Pinnacle Health System, Harrisburg, PA, p. A540

COMPTON, Brenda, Manager Information Technology, Plumas District Hospital, Quincy, CA, p. A84

COMPTON, Mark, Chief Financial Officer, Laughlin Memorial Hospital, Greeneville, TN, p. A583

COMPTON, Randy, Information Technology and System Director, Logan Memorial Hospital, Russellville, KY, p. A269

COMPTON, Ty, Chief Nursing Officer, Horton Community Hospital, Horton, KS, p. A245

COMPTON–OGLE, Carri, Administrative Officer, Heartland Behavioral Health Services, Nevada, MO, p. A377

CONANT, Cathy, Chief Human Resources and Personnel, Eastern Plumas Health Care, Portola, CA, p. A83

CONANT, Merrill, M.D. Chief of Staff, Western Plains Medical Complex, Dodge City, KS, p. A242

CONANT, Sonya, Senior Director Human Resources, Alaska Native Medical Center, Anchorage, AK, p. A28

CONAWAY, E. Edwin, M.D. Vice President Medical Affairs and Chief Medical Officer, Southeastern Ohio Regional Medical Center, Cambridge, OH, p. A486

CONCANNON, Laura, M.D. Regional Chief Medical Officer, Presence Saints Mary & Elizabeth Medical Center, Chicago, IL, p. A186

CONCEPCION, Walter, Chief Executive Officer, West Gables Rehabilitation Hospital, Miami, FL, p. A137

CONCORDIA, Elizabeth B., President and Chief Executive Officer, University of Colorado Health, Fort Collins, CO, p. B147

CONDIT, Brian, M.D
Chief Medical Officer, Johnston Memorial Hospital, Abingdon, VA, p. A667
Vice President Chief Medical Officer, Virginia Operations Medical Staff Services, Russell County Medical Center, Lebanon, VA, p. A672

CONDIT, Edward, President and Chief Executive Officer, St. Mary's General Hospital, Passaic, NJ, p. A421

CONDOLUCI, David, M.D. Senior Vice President and Chief Medical Officer, Kennedy Health System, Cherry Hill, NJ, p. A415

CONDON, Joseph
Entity Human Resources Officer, Texas Health Harris Methodist Hospital Fort Worth, Fort Worth, TX, p. A618
Director Human Resources, Texas Health Specialty Hospital, Fort Worth, TX, p. A619

CONDRY, Donna, Director Human Resources, UnityPoint Health – Jones Regional Medical Center, Anamosa, IA, p. A225

CONE, Maryann, Chief Operating Officer, Sharp Grossmont Hospital, La Mesa, CA, p. A67

CONEJO, David, Chief Executive Officer, Rehoboth McKinley Christian Health Care Services, Gallup, NM, p. A429

CONFALONE, Daniel, Chief Financial Officer and Vice President Finance, St. Mary Medical Center, Langhorne, PA, p. A542

CONFER, James, Manager Information Systems, Clarion Hospital, Clarion, PA, p. A535

CONGDON, James B., M.D. Medical Director, Horsham Clinic, Ambler, PA, p. A532

CONGER, Sue, Chief Operating Officer, Eastside Psychiatric Hospital, Tallahassee, FL, p. A146

CONKLIN, Jr., Michael E., Chief Financial Officer, St. Joseph Health Services of Rhode Island, North Providence, RI, p. A560

CONKLIN, Robin, R.N. Chief Nursing Officer, Carondelet St. Joseph's Hospital, Tucson, AZ, p. A40

CONKLING, Victoria, Vice President Patient Care Services and Chief Nursing Officer, UHS Delaware Valley Hospital, Walton, NY, p. A458

CONLEY, Carol, Chief Nursing Officer, Landmark Medical Center, Woonsocket, RI, p. A561

CONLEY, Joanna J., FACHE, Chief Executive Officer, Poinciana Medical Center, Kissimmee, FL, p. A133

CONLEY, Karen A., R.N. Chief Nursing Officer and Senior Vice President Patient Care Services, Newton–Wellesley Hospital, Newton Lower Falls, MA, p. A313

CONLEY, Kenneth, Controller, Calhoun Health Services, Calhoun City, MS, p. A356

CONLEY, Melissa, Director Human Resources, Midwest Medical Center, Galena, IL, p. A190

CONLEY, Michelle E., R.N. Chief Nursing Officer, Aria – Jefferson Health, Philadelphia, PA, p. A547

CONLEY, Teressa, President and Chief Executive Officer, St. Rose Dominican Hospitals – Rose de Lima Campus, Henderson, NV, p. A405

CONLEY, Theresa, Manager Human Resources, Cherokee Regional Medical Center, Cherokee, IA, p. A227

CONLEY, Thomas C., Vice President, Human Resources and Organizational Development, Northwestern Medical Center, Saint Albans, VT, p. A666

CONLON, John, M.D. Chief Medical Officer, Saint Anne's Hospital, Fall River, MA, p. A310

CONNAWAY, Jessica, Director Human Resources, Crossroads Community Hospital, Mount Vernon, IL, p. A197

CONNEL, Lorene, Chief Human Resources Management Service, Veterans Affairs Eastern Colorado Health Care System, Denver, CO, p. A104

CONNELL, Faith, Director of Nursing, Turning Point Hospital, Moultrie, GA, p. A164

CONNELL, Pam, Manager Human Resources, Windsor–Laurelwood Center for Behavioral Medicine, Willoughby, OH, p. A506

CONNELLEY, Bertha Mary, Director Human Resources, Austen Riggs Center, Stockbridge, MA, p. A315

CONNELLY, Jac, Chief Financial Officer, Rose Medical Center, Denver, CO, p. A104

CONNELLY, Kathryn, Manager Information Technology, Connecticut Valley Hospital, Middletown, CT, p. A115

CONNELLY, Steven, M.D., President and Chief Medical Officer, Park Nicollet Methodist Hospital, Saint Louis Park, MN, p. A350

CONNER, Gary F., Chief Financial Officer, City of Hope's Helford Clinical Research Hospital, Duarte, CA, p. A61

CONNER, Jeff, M.D. Chief Medical Staff, Loma Linda University Medical Center–Murrieta, Murrieta, CA, p. A78

CONNER, Stacey, Director Personnel, Ed Fraser Memorial Hospital and Baker Community Health Center, MacClenny, FL, p. A135

CONNERS, Stephanie, Senior Executive Vice President Chief Operating Officer and Chief Nursing Officer, Cooper University Health Care, Camden, NJ, p. A415

CONNERTON, Kathryn, President and Chief Executive Officer, Our Lady of Lourdes Memorial Hospital, Inc., Binghamton, NY, p. A435

CONNOLLY, Christine, M.D. Chief of Staff, Keefe Memorial Hospital, Cheyenne Wells, CO, p. A102

CONNOLLY, John, M.D. Vice President Medical Affairs, Beth Israel Deaconess Hospital Plymouth, Plymouth, MA, p. A314

CONNOLLY, Seam, Commissioner, Connecticut Veterans Home and Hospital, Rocky Hill, CT, p. A116

CONNOLLY, Teresa, R.N. Chief Nursing Officer, Mayo Clinic Hospital, Phoenix, AZ, p. A36

CONNOLLY ROBBINS, Danielle, Chief Nursing Officer, Select Specialty Hospital–Knoxville, Knoxville, TN, p. A586

CONNOR, Brian, FACHE Chief Operating Officer, Hillcrest Medical Center, Tulsa, OK, p. A521

CONNOR, Della, Director Human Resource, Sandhills Regional Medical Center, Hamlet, NC, p. A466

CONNOR III, Paul J., President and Chief Executive Officer, Eastern Long Island Hospital, Greenport, NY, p. A440

CONNOR, Starr, Chief Nursing Officer, Fairfield Memorial Hospital, Winnsboro, SC, p. A571

CONNOR, William, Assistant Administrator and Director Human Resources, River Hospital, Alexandria Bay, NY, p. A433

CONNORS, Alfred, M.D. Executive Vice President and Chief Quality Officer and Interim Chief Medical Officer, MetroHealth Medical Center, Cleveland, OH, p. A489

CONNORS, Dennis, Executive Director, Lenox Hill Hospital, New York, NY, p. A445

CONNORS, Lawrence J.
Chief Operating Officer, HSHS St. Vincent Hospital, Green Bay, WI, p. A707
Chief Operating Officer, St. Mary's Hospital Medical Center, Green Bay, WI, p. A707

CONNORS, Michael
Senior Vice President and Chief Financial Officer, Cape Cod Hospital, Hyannis, MA, p. A311
Senior Vice President and Chief Financial Officer, Falmouth Hospital, Falmouth, MA, p. A310

CONNOVICH, Ron D.
Chief Financial Officer, Greene Memorial Hospital, Xenia, OH, p. A506
Chief Financial Officer and Chief Operating Officer, Soin Medical Center, Beavercreek, OH, p. A484

CONNY, Sophia, Deputy Administrative Officer, U. S. Public Health Service Indian Hospital, Pine Ridge, SD, p. A575

CONOCENTI, Paul, Chief Information Officer, City of Hope's Helford Clinical Research Hospital, Duarte, CA, p. A61

CONOVER, Jevne, Chief Executive Officer, Great Lakes Specialty Hospital–Grand Rapids, Grand Rapids, MI, p. A324

CONRAD, Daniel S., M.D., President, Phillips Eye Institute, Minneapolis, MN, p. A346

CONRAD, Elizabeth P., Senior Vice President and Chief Human Resource Officer, Lahey Hospital & Medical Center, Burlington, Burlington, MA, p. A308

CONRAD, Heidi, Vice President and Chief Financial Officer, Regions Hospital, Saint Paul, MN, p. A350

CONRATH, Mark, Chief Financial Officer, Drumright Regional Hospital, Drumright, OK, p. A510

CONROW–VERVERIS, Stacy, Director Human Resources, Mineral Community Hospital, Superior, MT, p. A391

CONROY, Carol, R.N. Chief Nursing Officer, Southwestern Vermont Medical Center, Bennington, VT, p. A665

CONROY, Dorothy, Director Human Resources, Oakleaf Surgical Hospital, Eau Claire, WI, p. A705

CONROY, Joanne, M.D., Chief Executive Officer, Lahey Hospital & Medical Center, Burlington, Burlington, MA, p. A308

CONROY, Mary Ann, Chief Executive Officer, Terre Haute Regional Hospital, Terre Haute, IN, p. A222

CONROY, Michael, Chief Financial Officer, Pine Creek Medical Center, Dallas, TX, p. A611

CONROY, Mike, Chief Financial Officer, Methodist McKinney Hospital, McKinney, TX, p. A636

CONSBRUCK, Todd, President and Chief Executive Officer, Avera St. Anthony's Hospital, O'Neill, NE, p. A399

CONSIDINE, William H., President, Akron Children's Hospital, Akron, OH, p. A483

CONSIGLIO, Gayle, Chief Information Officer, McLaren Lapeer Region, Lapeer, MI, p. A328

CONSIGNEY, Ginger, Vice President Human Resources, Lake Charles Memorial Hospital, Lake Charles, LA, p. A281

CONSOLVER, Roberta, Chief Information Officer, Healthbridge Children's Hospital, Orange, CA, p. A81

CONSTANT, Jean–Charles, Administrator, Dover Behavioral Health System, Dover, DE, p. A119

CONTE, John, Director Facility Services and Real Estate, Wayne Memorial Hospital, Honesdale, PA, p. A540

CONTI, John, Director Finance, Shriners Hospitals for Children–Greenville, Greenville, SC, p. A566

CONTRERAS, Marta, Chief Nursing Officer and Chief Operating Officer, Foundation Surgical Hospital of El Paso, El Paso, TX, p. A615

CONVERY, Luanne, Vice President Patient Care Services, Putnam Hospital Center, Carmel, NY, p. A437

CONWAY, Jimmy, M.D. President Medical Staff, Northwest Surgical Hospital, Oklahoma City, OK, p. A516

CONWAY, Kevin, Chief Information Officer, UPMC Mercy, Pittsburgh, PA, p. A551

CONWILL, Michael, Director Human Resources, Corpus Christi Medical Center, Corpus Christi, TX, p. A607

COOGAN, Ben, Chief Operating Officer, Medical Center Arlington, Arlington, TX, p. A597

COOK, Aaron, Director Information Services, Lake Area Medical Center, Lake Charles, LA, p. A281

COOK, Annette, Application Support Specialist, Arkansas Valley Regional Medical Center, La Junta, CO, p. A107

COOK, Brenda, Chief Nursing Officer, Monroe Hospital, Bloomfield, IN, p. A207

COOK, Brian, FACHE, President and Chief Executive Officer, North Florida Regional Medical Center, Gainesville, FL, p. A129

COOK, Brooke, Director of Nursing, Strategic Behavioral Health – Wilmington, Leland, NC, p. A468

COOK, Carla, Director of Nursing, Scotland County Hospital, Memphis, MO, p. A376

COOK, Darrin, Chief Executive Officer and Administrator, Horizon Specialty Hospital, Las Vegas, NV, p. A406

COOK, David, Manager Information Systems, CHRISTUS Dubuis Hospital of Hot Springs, Hot Springs National Park, AR, p. A47

COOK, David, M.D. Chief Medical Officer, Novant Health Huntersville Medical Center, Huntersville, NC, p. A467

COOK, David A., Vice President and Chief Financial Officer, University Hospitals Elyria Medical Center, Elyria, OH, p. A494

COOK, Elizabeth, Chief Information Officer, Mizell Memorial Hospital, Opp, AL, p. A24

COOK, G. Anthony, M.D. Medical Director, Hemphill County Hospital, Canadian, TX, p. A605

COOK, Greg, Chief Financial Officer, Castleview Hospital, Price, UT, p. A662

COOK, Heidi, Chief Nursing Officer, Dr. John Warner Hospital, Clinton, IL, p. A187

COOK, Jaime, Director Human Resources, Riverside Tappahannock Hospital, Tappahannock, VA, p. A679

COOK, Janie, Director Information Systems, Passavant Area Hospital, Jacksonville, IL, p. A194

COOK, Jeffrey A., Chief Executive Officer, Appleton Area Health Services, Appleton, MN, p. A338

COOK, John
Vice President and Chief Financial Officer, Mercy Hospital and Trauma Center, Janesville, WI, p. A707
Senior Vice President & Chief Financial Officer, MercyHealth Rockton Avenue Hospital, Rockford, IL, p. A202
Interim Chief Information Officer, University of California, Davis Medical Center, Sacramento, CA, p. A87

COOK, Katheryn, R.N. Nurse Executive, Cincinnati Veterans Affairs Medical Center, Cincinnati, OH, p. A487

COOK, Kathy, MSN, President, Mercy Health – St. Joseph Warren Hospital, Warren, OH, p. A504

COOK, Kevin S., Chief Executive Officer, University Hospitals and Health System, Jackson, MS, p. B146

COOK, Kevin S., Chief Executive Officer, University of Mississippi Medical Center, Jackson, MS, p. A360

COOK, Kim, Interim Clinical Applications Services Manager, Tri-City Medical Center, Oceanside, CA, p. A80

COOK, LaMont, Administrator, F. W. Huston Medical Center, Winchester, KS, p. A256

COOK, Linda, Vice President Human Resources, St. Joseph Hospital, Eureka, CA, p. A61

COOK, Lottie, Superintendent, Evansville Psychiatric Children Center, Evansville, IN, p. A210

COOK, Marcia, Director Information Technology, Bates County Memorial Hospital, Butler, MO, p. A368

COOK, Mary Ann, R.N. Director of Nursing, Red Lake Indian Health Service Hospital, Red Lake, MN, p. A349

COOK, Natalie
Administrative Director of Human Resources, Manchester Memorial Hospital, Manchester, CT, p. A114
Administrative Director, Human Resources, Rockville General Hospital, Vernon, CT, p. A117

COOK, Pamela W., Chief Financial Officer, Trace Regional Hospital, Houston, MS, p. A359

COOK, Patrick, Vice President Support Services, Morgan Memorial Hospital, Madison, GA, p. A162

COOK, Ruth
Administrator, East Texas Medical Center Fairfield, Fairfield, TX, p. A617
Administrator, East Texas Medical Center Trinity, Trinity, TX, p. A653

COOK, Shelia, Director Information Systems, Novant Health Charlotte Orthopaedic Hospital, Charlotte, NC, p. A462

COOK, Sheliah, Director Human Resources, Boone Memorial Hospital, Madison, WV, p. A697

COOK, Sherry P., R.N. Chief Nursing Executive, Merit Health River Oaks, Flowood, MS, p. A357

COOK, Stacey M., MS Vice President, Human Resources, University of Maryland Charles Regional Medical Center, La Plata, MD, p. A302

COOK, Thomas J., Chief Executive Officer, UVA–HEALTHSOUTH Rehabilitation Hospital, Charlottesville, VA, p. A668

COOK, Thomas M., Chief Financial Officer, Good Samaritan Hospital, Vincennes, IN, p. A223

COOK, Wayne, Chief Executive Officer, Plano Specialty Hospital, Plano, TX, p. A642

COOK, Wendy J., Senior Vice President and Chief Financial Officer, Athens Regional Medical Center, Athens, GA, p. A151

COOK, William
Associate Warden Business Service, California Mens Colony Correctional Treatment Center, San Luis Obispo, CA, p. A92
Director, Southern Virginia Mental Health Institute, Danville, VA, p. A669
President and Chief Executive Officer, University of Colorado Hospital, Aurora, CO, p. A101

COOKE, Barbara
Director Health Information Systems, Montefiore Mount Vernon, Mount Vernon, NY, p. A443
Director Health Information Systems, Montefiore New Rochelle, New Rochelle, NY, p. A443

COOKE, David, Chief Nursing Officer, Sutter Surgical Hospital – North Valley, Yuba City, CA, p. A100

COOKE, Ellen, Chief Operating Officer, Sanford Medical Center Fargo, Fargo, ND, p. A479

COOKE, Jordan, Director Human Resources, Shadow Mountain Behavioral Health System, Tulsa, OK, p. A522

COOKE, Nancy, Chief Financial Officer, Weatherford Regional Medical Center, Weatherford, TX, p. A656

COOKE, Rebecca L., Director Human Resources, Kearney County Health Services, Minden, NE, p. A398

COOKE, Timothy J., Medical Center Director and Chief Executive Officer, Martinsburg Veterans Affairs Medical Center, Martinsburg, WV, p. A698

COOKE, William, M.D. Chief of Staff, Gundersen St. Joseph's Hospital and Clinics, Hillsboro, WI, p. A707

COOLEY, W. Carl, M.D. Chief Medical Officer, Crotched Mountain Rehabilitation Center, Greenfield, NH, p. A411

COOMBS, James, Chief Executive Officer, Grand River Hospital District, Rifle, CO, p. A110

COOMBS, Teri, R.N. Director Nursing Services, Cascade Medical Center, Cascade, ID, p. A175

COONER, Suzanne, MSN, Chief Executive Officer, Decatur County Hospital, Leon, IA, p. A233

COONEY, Darlene, Director Nursing, Sumner Regional Medical Center, Wellington, KS, p. A255

COONEY, Lauri Ann, Director Nursing, Wheatland Memorial Healthcare, Harlowton, MT, p. A388

COONS, Jennifer, Acting Chief Executive Officer, Sequoyah Memorial Hospital, Sallisaw, OK, p. A519

COOPER, Alisa, Manager Financial Resources, Michael E. DeBakey Veterans Affairs Medical Center, Houston, TX, p. A626

COOPER, Alison, Chief Financial Officer, Ward Memorial Hospital, Monahans, TX, p. A637

COOPER, Allison, Administrator, Physicians Behavioral Hospital, Shreveport, LA, p. A287

COOPER, Casey, Chief Executive Officer, Cherokee Indian Hospital, Cherokee, NC, p. A463

COOPER, Chad D., Chief Executive Officer, Riverwood Healthcare Center, Aitkin, MN, p. A338

COOPER, Curtis, Manager Information Systems, Pioneers Medical Center, Meeker, CO, p. A109

COOPER, Dena, Chief Financial Officer, Campbellton Graceville Hospital, Graceville, FL, p. A130

COOPER, Donald, Director Information Systems, Tennova Healthcare–Harton, Tullahoma, TN, p. A594

COOPER, Douglas, M.D. Chief Medical Officer, Grundy County Memorial Hospital, Grundy Center, IA, p. A231

COOPER Jr.,, Edwin H., MS, President and Chief Executive Officer, AcuityHealthcare, LP, Charlotte, NC, p. B5

COOPER, Jerry, Manager Data Processing, Richland Hospital, Richland Center, WI, p. A715

COOPER, John C., Chief Executive Officer, Fremont Hospital, Fremont, CA, p. A63

COOPER, Jon, Chief Administrative Officer, Norton Audubon Hospital, Louisville, KY, p. A264

COOPER, Mike, Chief Executive Officer, George E. Weems Memorial Hospital, Apalachicola, FL, p. A123

COOPER, Pamela, Director Finance, Providence Seaside Hospital, Seaside, OR, p. A530

COOPER, Shawnee, Director Human Resources, Magnolia Regional Medical Center, Magnolia, AR, p. A49

COOPER, Sheri, Director Human Resources, Union General Hospital, Farmerville, LA, p. A276

COOPER, Tim, Chief Financial Officer, PMH Medical Center, Prosser, WA, p. A688

COOPER–LOHR, Willie, Chief Financial Officer, Barnesville Hospital, Barnesville, OH, p. A484

COOPERMAN, Todd, M.D. Medical Director, HEALTHSOUTH Rehabilitation Hospital of Tinton Falls, Tinton Falls, NJ, p. A424

COOPWOOD, Reginald W., M.D., President and Chief Executive Officer, Regional One Health, Memphis, TN, p. A589

COOTS, Aaron, Information Technology Director, Mason District Hospital, Havana, IL, p. A192

COOTS, Lawrence, M.D. Chief Medical Officer, Orange Park Medical Center, Orange Park, FL, p. A140

COPE, Brent A., Chief Executive Officer, Silver Lake Medical Center, Los Angeles, CA, p. A74

COPE, Dave, Director Information Systems, Marshall County Hospital, Benton, KY, p. A257

COPELAND, Carolyn, Business Administrator, Madison State Hospital, Madison, IN, p. A217

COPELAND, Darlinda, Chief Operating Officer, Florida Hospital Memorial Medical Center, Daytona Beach, FL, p. A127

COPELAND, Gail, Director Management Information Systems, CrossRidge Community Hospital, Wynne, AR, p. A53

COPELAND, Gearline, R.N. Chief Nursing Officer, Saint Thomas Highlands Hospital, Sparta, TN, p. A593

COPELAND, Kristie M., Interim Chief Nursing Officer, Claiborne Memorial Medical Center, Homer, LA, p. A278

COPELAND, Robert, Interim Chief Executive Officer, Covenant Hospital Plainview, Plainview, TX, p. A641

COPELAND, Willie Mae, Chief Financial Officer, Harmon Memorial Hospital, Hollis, OK, p. A513

COPELAND, Yolanda, R.N. Senior Vice President and Chief Nursing Officer, Saint Agnes Hospital, Baltimore, MD, p. A297

COPEN, Greg, Chief Information Officer, Haywood Regional Medical Center, Clyde, NC, p. A463

COPENHAVER, Kathy, Director Human Resources, Haven Behavioral Hospital of Eastern Pennsylvania, Reading, PA, p. A553

COPES, Tammy, Director Information Systems, St. Mary's of Michigan Standish Hospital, Standish, MI, p. A335

COPPEDGE, Mitch, M.D. Chief Medical Officer, Grady Memorial Hospital, Chickasha, OK, p. A510

COPPLE, Brad
President, Northwestern Medicine Kishwaukee Hospital, DeKalb, IL, p. A188
Vice President Operations, Northwestern Medicine Valley West Hospital, Sandwich, IL, p. A202

COPPLE, Robert C., FACHE, Senior Administrator, Via Christi Hospital Manhattan, Inc.,, KS, p. A248

COPPOCK, R. Alan, FACHE, President and CEO, ContinueCARE Hospital at Baptist Health Corbin, Corbin, KY, p. A258

CORAZON, Jesus M.
Controller, HEALTHSOUTH Hospital of Manati, Manati, PR, p. A728
Controller, HEALTHSOUTH Rehabilitation Hospital of San Juan, San Juan, PR, p. A729

CORBET, Mark, Interim Chief Financial Officer, LAC+USC Medical Center, Los Angeles, CA, p. A72

CORBETT, David, M.D. Chief of Staff, Northwest Medical Center, Winfield, AL, p. A26

CORBIN, Michelle, M.D. Chief of Staff, Deer Lodge Medical Center, Deer Lodge, MT, p. A387

CORCIMIGLIA, Michael, Chief Operating Officer, Wyoming County Community Hospital, Warsaw, NY, p. A458

CORCORAN, John Russell, Vice President Medical Affairs, South County Hospital, Wakefield, RI, p. A561

CORCORAN, Joseph C., Chief Medical Officer, Brandon Regional Hospital, Brandon, FL, p. A124

CORCORAN, Kevin, Chief Financial Officer, Westside Regional Medical Center, Plantation, FL, p. A143

CORCORAN, Nancy R., Senior Vice President Human Resources and Quality Service, Hackensack University Medical Center, Hackensack, NJ, p. A417

CORCORAN, Rose, R.N. Chief Nursing Executive, Sutter Coast Hospital, Crescent City, CA, p. A60

CORD, Jennifer, R.N
Chief Ambulatory, Ancillary, and Mission Officer, Presence Covenant Medical Center, Urbana, IL, p. A204
Vice President Operations, Presence United Samaritans Medical Center, Danville, IL, p. A187

CORDDRY, David, Chief Financial Officer, Ten Broeck Tennessee Treatment Facility, Cookeville, TN, p. A581

CORDEAU, Peter, Chief Executive Officer, Sharon Hospital, Sharon, CT, p. A116

CORDER, Earline, Chief Fiscal, Charlie Norwood Veterans Affairs Medical Center, Augusta, GA, p. A153

CORDER, Scott, Controller, HEALTHSOUTH Rehabilitation Hospital at Drake, Cincinnati, OH, p. A487

CORDES, Debra, Chief Nursing Officer, Rehabilitation Hospital of Indiana, Indianapolis, IN, p. A214

CORDIA, Jennifer, Vice President and Chief Nursing Executive, Christian Hospital, Saint Louis, MO, p. A380

CORDOVA, Mandelyn, R.N. Director of Nurses, Guadalupe County Hospital, Santa Rosa, NM, p. A431

CORDOVA, Martin, Director Information Services, Centinela Hospital Medical Center, Inglewood, CA, p. A66

CORDOVA, Sheila, Director Clinical Services and Chief Operating Officer, Aurora Charter Oak Hospital, Covina, CA, p. A60

CORDOVES, America, Controller, Jerome Golden Center for Behavioral Health, Inc., West Palm Beach, FL, p. A149

CORDUM, Shelly L., R.N. System Chief Nursing Officer, Sparks Medical Center – Van Buren, Van Buren, AR, p. A53

CORDY, Roy, M.D. President Medical Staff, Presentation Medical Center, Rolla, ND, p. A481

COREA, Rohan, Director Healthcare Information Technology, College Medical Center, Long Beach, CA, p. A69

COREY, Mark, Chief Financial Officer, Behavioral Center of Michigan, Warren, MI, p. A336

CORFITS, Joe
Senior Vice President, Chief Financial Officer, UnityPoint Health – Iowa Methodist Medical Center, Des Moines, IA, p. A229
Chief Financial Officer, UnityPoint Health–Iowa Lutheran Hospital, Des Moines, IA, p. A229

CORKERY, Thomas B., D.O. Chief Medical Officer, Canonsburg Hospital, Canonsburg, PA, p. A534

CORLEW, Scott, M.D. Chief Medical Officer, Saint Thomas Rutherford Hospital, Murfreesboro, TN, p. A590

CORLEY, Becky, Director Human Resources, Tyler Holmes Memorial Hospital, Winona, MS, p. A366

CORLEY, Janet, Accountant, Malvern Institute, Malvern, PA, p. A544

CORLEY, Juli, Chief Information Officer, Edgefield County Hospital, Edgefield, SC, p. A565

CORMIER, Laura, Director, Bellin Health Oconto Hospital, Oconto, WI, p. A713

CORMIER, Philip M., Chief Executive Officer, Beverly Hospital, Beverly, MA, p. A305

CORN, Rick, Chief Information Officer, Huntsville Hospital, Huntsville, AL, p. A21

CORNEJO, C. Susan
Senior Vice President Finance and Chief Financial Officer, Providence Hospital, Mobile, AL, p. A22
Chief Financial Officer, Sacred Heart Hospital Pensacola, Pensacola, FL, p. A142

CORNEJO, Juan, M.D. Chief of Staff, Perry County Memorial Hospital, Tell City, IN, p. A222

CORNELIUS, David, Director Information Systems, Parkridge Medical Center, Chattanooga, TN, p. A580

CORNELIUS, Margaret E., Vice President Human Resources, Wyckoff Heights Medical Center,, NY, p. A450

CORNELIUS, Michelle
Director Human Resources, Howard Young Medical Center, Woodruff, WI, p. A720
Director Human Resources for Northern Region, Ministry Eagle River Memorial Hospital, Eagle River, WI, p. A704
Director Human Resources, Ministry Sacred Heart Hospital, Tomahawk, WI, p. A717
Director Human Resources for the Northern Region, Ministry Saint Mary's Hospitals, Rhinelander, WI, p. A715

CORNELIUS, Senta, Director Human Resources, West Valley Medical Center, Caldwell, ID, p. A175

CORNELIUS, Teresa, R.N. Interim Chief Nursing Officer, HSHS St. Joseph's Hospital, Highland, IL, p. A192

CORNELL, John, Vice President Finance, Meadows Regional Medical Center, Vidalia, GA, p. A168

CORNES, Robert S., Commander, Ireland Army Community Hospital, Fort Knox, KY, p. A260

CORNET, Trina, JD Vice President Human Resources, Jamaica Hospital Medical Center,, NY, p. A445

CORNETT, Sheila, Manager Human Resources, Hazard ARH Regional Medical Center, Hazard, KY, p. A261

CORNETT, Suzanne, Director Human Resources, Southern Kentucky Rehabilitation Hospital, Bowling Green, KY, p. A258

CORNICELLI, Kari
Chief Financial Officer, Sharp Grossmont Hospital, La Mesa, CA, p. A67
Chief Financial Officer, Sharp Memorial Hospital, San Diego, CA, p. A89
Chief Financial Officer, Sharp Mesa Vista Hospital, San Diego, CA, p. A89

CORNWALL, Thomas, M.D. Medical Director, Holly Hill Hospital, Raleigh, NC, p. A472

CORNWELL, Cheryl, Chief Financial Officer, Great Falls Clinic Medical Center, Great Falls, MT, p. A388

CORNWELL, Cheryl J., Chief Financial Officer, Lake District Hospital, Lakeview, OR, p. A527

CORNWELL, Richard, Chief Executive Officer, Surprise Valley Health Care District, Cedarville, CA, p. A58

CORONEL, Jorge, Chief Information Officer, Regional Hospital of Scranton, Scranton, PA, p. A554

CORPORA, Don, Executive Vice President and Chief Human Resources Officer, Akron General Medical Center, Akron, OH, p. A483

CORRADO, Bob, Chief Information Officer, Canandaigua Veterans Affairs Medical Center, Canandaigua, NY, p. A436

CORRADO, Theresa, Director Finance, St. Luke's Hospital – Quakertown Campus, Quakertown, PA, p. A553

CORREA, Elizabeth, Director Information Management, Big Spring State Hospital, Big Spring, TX, p. A602

CORREA, Maria de los Angeles, M.D. Medical Director, Hospital Metropolitano, San Juan, PR, p. A729

CORREA, Omar, Chief Financial Officer, Texas NeuroRehab Center, Austin, TX, p. A600

CORREA, Sharon, Vice President and Chief Information Officer, Glendale Adventist Medical Center, Los Angeles, CA, p. A71

CORREIA, Antonio, Chief Financial Officer, Holyoke Medical Center, Holyoke, MA, p. A310

CORREIA, Kathryn G., President and Chief Executive Officer, HealthEast Care System, Saint Paul, MN, p. B65

CORRIDON, Fran, Vice President Human Resources and Shared Services, Hackensack University Medical Center Mountainside, Montclair, NJ, p. A419

CORRIGAN, Heidi, Manager Human Resources, Trinity Hospital, Weaverville, CA, p. A99

CORRIGAN, Jeffrey T., Vice President Human Resources, Brattleboro Retreat, Brattleboro, VT, p. A665

CORRIGAN, Paula, Vice President and Chief Financial Officer, OSF Saint James – John W. Albrecht Medical Center, Pontiac, IL, p. A201

CORRIGAN, Thomas L., Senior Vice President Finance, Managed Care and Chief Financial Officer, Christiana Care Health System, Newark, DE, p. A119

CORS, William K., M.D. Vice President and Chief Medical Quality Officer, Pocono Medical Center, East Stroudsburg, PA, p. A537

CORSO, David, Chief Operating Officer, Beaver Dam Community Hospitals, Beaver Dam, WI, p. A703

CORTI, Ronald J., President and Chief Executive Officer, St. John's Riverside Hospital, Yonkers, NY, p. A459

CORUM, Sharon, Chief Financial Officer, Kingwood Pines Hospital, Kingwood, TX, p. A631

CORWIN, Florence, Director for Administration, Pilgrim Psychiatric Center, Brentwood, NY, p. A435

CORWIN, James, Interim Chief Financial Officer, Howard University Hospital, Washington, DC, p. A121

CORWIN, Nancy, Chief Operating Officer, Summit Surgical, Hutchinson, KS, p. A245

CORWIN, R. William, M.D. Vice President and Chief Medical Officer, Miriam Hospital, Providence, RI, p. A560

CORWIN, Steven J., M.D., President and Chief Executive Officer, New York Presbyterian Regional Hospital Network, New York, NY, p. B95

CORWIN, Steven J., M.D., President and Chief Executive Officer, New York–Presbyterian Hospital, New York, NY, p. A447

CORZINE, Judy, Administrative Director and Chief Information Officer, Stormont Vail Health, Topeka, KS, p. A254

COSBY, Dwan, Manager Human Resources, McLaren Oakland, Pontiac, MI, p. A332

COSBY, Ernestine Y., Vice President Clinical Services and Chief Nursing Officer, Sheppard Pratt Health System, Baltimore, MD, p. A297

COSGRAVE, Michael, Director, Information System, Speare Memorial Hospital, Plymouth, NH, p. A413

COSGROVE, Delos, M.D., President and Chief Executive Officer, Cleveland Clinic, Cleveland, OH, p. A488

COSGROVE, Delos, M.D., President and Chief Executive Officer, Cleveland Clinic Health System, Cleveland, OH, p. B34

COSLETT, John, R.N. Chief Nursing Officer, Kansas Spine and Specialty Hospital, Wichita, KS, p. A255

COSTA, Christopher P., M.D. Chief of Staff, Gordon Memorial Hospital, Gordon, NE, p. A396

COSTA, Joe
Chief Financial Officer, Veterans Affairs Boston Healthcare System, Boston, MA, p. A307
Acting Chief Fiscal Officer, Veterans Affairs Boston Healthcare System Brockton Division, Brockton, MA, p. A308

COSTA, Mark E., Executive Director, Kaiser Permanente Orange County Anaheim Medical Center, Anaheim, CA, p. A54

COSTA, Michael G.
Vice President Human Resources, Burleson St. Joseph Health Center, Caldwell, TX, p. A604
Director Human Resources, Grimes St. Joseph Health Center, Navasota, TX, p. A638
Vice President Human Resources, St. Joseph Regional Health Center, Bryan, TX, p. A604

COSTAKIS, Angie, Chief Information Officer, Claiborne Memorial Medical Center, Homer, LA, p. A278

COSTANTINO, Vincent
Vice President Operations and Human Resources, Raritan Bay Medical Center, Perth Amboy, NJ, p. A422
Chief Administrative Officer, St. Francis Medical Center, Trenton, NJ, p. A424

COSTANZO, Kristin L., Direct–In–Market Lead Human Relations Partner, St. Vincent's Blount, Oneonta, AL, p. A24

COSTELLA, Jeane L., Vice President, New York–Presbyterian/Hudson Valley Hospital, Cortlandt Manor, NY, p. A437

COSTELLO, Benny, Administrator, Post Acute Medical Specialty Hospital of Texarkana – North, Texarkana, TX, p. A652

COSTELLO, Jeff
Chief Financial Officer, Elkhart General Hospital, Elkhart, IN, p. A209
Chief Financial Officer, Memorial Hospital of South Bend, South Bend, IN, p. A222

COSTELLO, Jodi
Chief Executive Officer, Select Specialty Hospital – Boardman, Boardman, OH, p. A485
Chief Executive Officer, Select Specialty Hospital–Youngstown, Youngstown, OH, p. A506

COSTELLO, Susan, Chief Nursing Officer, Lucile Salter Packard Children's Hospital Stanford, Palo Alto, CA, p. A82

COSTER, Margaret C., MSN, President and Chief Executive Officer, Fairmont Regional Medical Center, Fairmont, WV, p. A696

COSTIC, Andrew
Regional Chief Financial Officer, Abraham Lincoln Memorial Hospital, Lincoln, IL, p. A195
Regional Chief Financial Officer, Taylorville Memorial Hospital, Taylorville, IL, p. A204

COSTIE, Glenn A., FACHE,
Interim Director, Cincinnati Veterans Affairs Medical Center, Cincinnati, OH, p. A487
Director, Dayton Veterans Affairs Medical Center, Dayton, OH, p. A492

COSTNER, Marc, Chief Financial Officer, Chestnut Hill Hospital, Philadelphia, PA, p. A547

COTA, Scott, M.D. Director Medical Services, Naval Hospital Lemoore, Lemoore, CA, p. A68

COTE, Gerri, Chief Operating Officer, Brattleboro Retreat, Brattleboro, VT, p. A665

COTE, Mary, Director Human Resources, New England Rehabilitation Hospital of Portland, Portland, ME, p. A294

COTNOIR, Laurie, Director Nursing and Quality, Upper Connecticut Valley Hospital, Colebrook, NH, p. A410

COTT, Gary, M.D. Executive Vice President Medical and Clinical Services, National Jewish Health, Denver, CO, p. A104

COTTEN, Brandon, Chief Financial Officer, DeWitt Hospital, DeWitt, AR, p. A45

COTTER, Bonny, Chief Nursing Officer, Baraga County Memorial Hospital, L'Anse, MI, p. A328

COTTER, Brian, Chief Executive Officer, Anaheim Global Medical Center, Anaheim, CA, p. A54

COTTER, Carole
Senior Vice President and Chief Information Officer, Emma Pendleton Bradley Hospital, East Providence, RI, p. A560
Vice President and Chief Information Officer, Miriam Hospital, Providence, RI, p. A560
Senior Vice President and Chief Information Officer, Rhode Island Hospital, Providence, RI, p. A561

COTTERMAN, Rob, Chief Executive Officer, Middle Tennessee Mental Health Institute, Nashville, TN, p. A590

COTTINGHAM, Jerod, Director Information Systems, Carlinville Area Hospital, Carlinville, IL, p. A182

COTTLE, Jeremy, Ph.D., Chief Executive Officer, Provo Canyon Behavioral Hospital, Orem, UT, p. A661

COTTLE, Mike, Chief Information Officer, Newton Medical Center, Newton, KS, p. A250

COTTO, Hector L., M.D. Medical Director, Hospital San Francisco, San Juan, PR, p. A730

COTTON, C. Gerald, Interim Chief Operating Officer, Baptist Medical Center Leake, Carthage, MS, p. A356

COTTON, Michael, Chief Financial Officer, Gadsden Regional Medical Center, Gadsden, AL, p. A20

COTTRELL, Leslie, R.N. Nurse Lead, Iroquois Memorial Hospital and Resident Home, Watseka, IL, p. A204

COTTRILL, Brian, Chief Information Officer, United Hospital Center, Bridgeport, WV, p. A694

COUCH, Beulah, Director Human Resources, Mary Breckinridge ARH Hospital, Hyden, KY, p. A262

COUCH, Bill, Chief Financial Officer, Ashley County Medical Center, Crossett, AR, p. A44

COUCH, Chad, Chief Medical Officer, Wellmont Bristol Regional Medical Center, Bristol, TN, p. A579

COUCHMAN, Diane, Vice President Patient Care Services and Chief Nursing Executive, Calvert Memorial Hospital, Prince Frederick, MD, p. A302

COUGHLIN, Ann, Director Human Resources, Boundary Community Hospital, Bonners Ferry, ID, p. A175

COUGHLIN, Cynthia, MS Chief Nursing Officer, Cheshire Medical Center, Keene, NH, p. A411

COUGHLIN, Kevin E., Senior Vice President System Development, Beth Israel Deaconess Hospital Plymouth, Plymouth, MA, p. A314

COUGHLIN, Michael, Chief Executive Officer, Crotched Mountain Rehabilitation Center, Greenfield, NH, p. A411

COULON, Linda, Administrator, Sage Rehabilitation Hospital, Baton Rouge, LA, p. A273

COULTER, Barbara
Director Information Systems, Franciscan St. Francis Health – Indianapolis, Indianapolis, IN, p. A214
Director Information Systems, Franciscan St. Francis Health – Mooresville, Mooresville, IN, p. A218

COULTER, Duane C., Interim Chief Financial Officer, Schoolcraft Memorial Hospital, Manistique, MI, p. A329

COUNTRYMAN, Cory, Chief Executive Officer, Walnut Hill Medical Center, Dallas, TX, p. A612

COUNTS, Virginia, Manager Human Resources, Scott & White Hospital – Brenham, Brenham, TX, p. A603

COUNTY–TEEMER, Vickie, Coordinator Human Resources, Mitchell County Hospital, Camilla, GA, p. A155

COURIS, John D., President and Chief Executive Officer, Jupiter Medical Center, Jupiter, FL, p. A132

COURNYER, Tim, Administrator, Forks Community Hospital, Forks, WA, p. A685

COURREGE, Gary, Chief Information Officer, Jennings American Legion Hospital, Jennings, LA, p. A279

COURTNEY, Christine, R.N. Vice President and Chief Nursing Officer, Providence Healthcare Network, Waco, TX, p. A656

COURTOIS, Harold, Chief Executive Officer, Russell Regional Hospital, Russell, KS, p. A252

COURTOIS, Robert, Vice President Finance, Otsego Memorial Hospital, Gaylord, MI, p. A324

COURY, Tiffany, Chief Operating Officer, Northern Nevada Medical Center, Sparks, NV, p. A408

COUSAR, Myra, Director Human Resources, Baptist Memorial Hospital–Tipton, Covington, TN, p. A582

COUSINEAU, Cathy, Director Human Resources, Kaiser Permanente Woodland Hills Medical Center,, CA, p. A72

COUTURE, Maureen, Chief Nursing Officer and Vice President Nursing, Cardinal Hill Rehabilitation Hospital, Lexington, KY, p. A263

COUVILLON, Larry, M.D. Chief Medical Officer, Memorial Hospital at Gulfport, Gulfport, MS, p. A358

COVA, Charles J., Senior Vice President, Operations, Marian Regional Medical Center, Santa Maria, CA, p. A93

COVAULT, Julie, Vice President Finance, Wilson Memorial Hospital, Sidney, OH, p. A502

COVAULT, Myra, Associate Vice President of Human Resources, Hardin Memorial Hospital, Elizabethtown, KY, p. A259

COVELL, Nancy, Director Human Resources, Cameron Memorial Community Hospital, Angola, IN, p. A206

COVELLI, Margaret, R.N. Chief Nursing Officer, Spring Valley Hospital Medical Center, Las Vegas, NV, p. A406

COVER, Barry, M.D. Medical Director, Magruder Memorial Hospital, Port Clinton, OH, p. A501

COVERT, David G., Chief Executive Officer, Green Valley Hospital, Green Valley, AZ, p. A33

COVERT, Kathy, MSN Vice President Human Resources, Schneck Medical Center, Seymour, IN, p. A222

COVERT, Michael H., FACHE,
Chief Executive Officer, Baylor St. Luke's Medical Center, Houston, TX, p. A623
Chief Executive Officer, Baylor St. Luke's Medical Center McNair Campus, Houston, TX, p. A623

COVERT, Terri, Vice President Human Resources, Mission Hospital, Mission Viejo, CA, p. A77

COVEY, Staci, MS,
President, Guthrie Towanda Memorial Hospital, Towanda, PA, p. A555
President, Troy Community Hospital, Troy, PA, p. A556

COVINGTON, Casey, M.D. President Elect, Medical Staff, Jennie Stuart Medical Center, Hopkinsville, KY, p. A262

COVINGTON, Celia, MSN Director of Nursing, St. Mary's Good Samaritan Hospital, Greensboro, GA, p. A160

COVINGTON, Jerome, M.D. Chief Medical Officer, Lower Keys Medical Center, Key West, FL, p. A133

COVONE, Ann Marie, Senior Vice President and Chief Financial Officer, Terence Cardinal Cooke Health Care Center, New York, NY, p. A450

COWAN, J. W., Administrator, Choctaw General Hospital, Butler, AL, p. A17

COWAN, Leslie, R.N. Chief Nursing Officer, Henry County Hospital, New Castle, IN, p. A219

COWAN, Ronald M., Vice President Information Systems, Geisinger–Lewistown Hospital, Lewistown, PA, p. A543

COWART, Mark, Chief Information Officer, Carl Vinson Veterans Affairs Medical Center, Dublin, GA, p. A159

COWART, Timothy, Chief Executive Officer, The Centers, Ocala, FL, p. A139

COWLES, John, Chief Financial Officer, Silver Lake Medical Center, Los Angeles, CA, p. A74

COWLING, Phyllis A., CPA, President and Chief Executive Officer, United Regional Health Care System, Wichita Falls, TX, p. A658

COWPERTHWAIT, Cheri, R.N., Chief Executive Officer, Lourdes Specialty Hospital of Southern New Jersey, Willingboro, NJ, p. A425

COX, Amber, Director Human Resources, East Texas Medical Center Carthage, Carthage, TX, p. A605

COX, Brian, Director Information Systems, Baptist Health Floyd, New Albany, IN, p. A219

COX, Carla C., Chief Nursing Officer, Indiana University Health Ball Memorial Hospital, Muncie, IN, p. A219

COX, David W., Chief Financial Officer, Marin General Hospital, Greenbrae, CA, p. A65

COX, Debbie D., Administrative Director Human Resources, Central Texas Medical Center, San Marcos, TX, p. A648

COX, Denida A., Chief Nursing Officer, Shoals Hospital, Muscle Shoals, AL, p. A24

COX, Dianne E., Vice President of Human Resources, Kaweah Delta Medical Center, Visalia, CA, p. A99

COX, Dina, Director Human Resources, Kansas Rehabilitation Hospital, Topeka, KS, p. A254

COX, Dorothy, Manager Information Systems, Hackettstown Medical Center, Hackettstown, NJ, p. A417

COX, Gwen, Director Nursing Services, Klickitat Valley Health, Goldendale, WA, p. A685

COX, Jeffrey
Chief Information Officer, Glendora Community Hospital, Glendora, CA, p. A65
Director Information Technology, San Dimas Community Hospital, San Dimas, CA, p. A89

COX, Ken, Chief Financial Officer, Allen Parish Hospital, Kinder, LA, p. A280

COX, Kenneth, M.D. Chief Medical Officer, Lucile Salter Packard Children's Hospital Stanford, Palo Alto, CA, p. A82

COX, Kenneth, Interim Chief Financial Officer, McKenzie County Healthcare System, Watford City, ND, p. A482

COX, Leigh, Chief Information Officer, WellStar Windy Hill Hospital, Marietta, GA, p. A163

COX, Lisa D., R.N. Chief Nursing Officer, Cypress Fairbanks Medical Center, Houston, TX, p. A624

COX, Lynna B., Director Health Information Services, Anson General Hospital, Anson, TX, p. A597

COX, Matthew, Chief Financial Officer, St. Joseph's Hospital and Medical Center, Phoenix, AZ, p. A37

COX, Randy, Chief Information Officer, St. Vincent Indianapolis Hospital, Indianapolis, IN, p. A215

COX, Raymond L., M.D. Chief Medical Officer, Providence Hospital, Washington, DC, p. A122

COX, Sandra, Controller, Permian Regional Medical Center, Andrews, TX, p. A597

COX, Sharon K., FACHE, Chief Executive Officer, Rawlins County Health Center, Atwood, KS, p. A240

COX, Sheila, Director Human Resources, Cibola General Hospital, Grants, NM, p. A429

COX, Steven, M.D. Chief Medical Officer, University of Texas Health Northeast, Tyler, TX, p. A654

COX, Walter R., M.D. President Medical Staff, Monongahela Valley Hospital, Monongahela, PA, p. A545

COX–HENLEY, Michelle, R.N. Associate Director for Patient and Nursing Services, Charlie Norwood Veterans Affairs Medical Center, Augusta, GA, p. A153

COY, Nelson, Director Human Resources, Tahoe Pacific Hospitals, Sparks, NV, p. A408

COYE, Ed
Director Information Technology Mission Health System Hospitals, Angel Medical Center, Franklin, NC, p. A465
Director Information Technology, Transylvania Regional Hospital, Brevard, NC, p. A461

COYLE, Joseph P., President and Chief Executive Officer, Southern Ocean Medical Center, Manahawkin, NJ, p. A419

COYLE, Michael F., Chief Executive Officer, Coteau des Prairies Hospital, Sisseton, SD, p. A576

COYNE, Margarita Frances, MS Interim Chief Nursing Officer, Roswell Park Cancer Institute, Buffalo, NY, p. A436

COYNE, Rose, Interim CFO, Haywood Regional Medical Center, Clyde, NC, p. A463

COZART, Adrienne, Vice President Human Resources, University Medical Center, Lubbock, TX, p. A634

CRABB, Ian, M.D. Chief Medical Officer, Nebraska Orthopaedic Hospital, Omaha, NE, p. A400

CRABBE, Amy J.
Vice President People Services, Charles A. Cannon Memorial Hospital, Newland, NC, p. A471
Senior Vice President Human Resources, Watauga Medical Center, Boone, NC, p. A461

CRABDREE, Nathan, Chief Financial Officer, MountainView Regional Medical Center, Las Cruces, NM, p. A430

CRABTREE, Douglas, Chief Executive Officer, Eastern Idaho Regional Medical Center, Idaho Falls, ID, p. A176

CRABTREE, Gordon, Interim Chief Executive Officer, University of Utah Health Care – Hospital and Clinics, Salt Lake City, UT, p. A664

CRABTREE, John D., M.D. Chief of Staff, Tennova Healthcare–Harton, Tullahoma, TN, p. A594

CRABTREE, Robert, M.D
Chief of Staff and Medical Director, Physicians Surgical Hospital – Panhandle Campus, Amarillo, TX, p. A596
Chief of Staff and Medical Director, Physicians Surgical Hospital – Quail Creek, Amarillo, TX, p. A596

CRABTREE, Susan, Director Human Resources, Simi Valley Hospital, Simi Valley, CA, p. A94

CRACOLICI, Frank J., President and Chief Executive Officer, St. Vincent Medical Center, Los Angeles, CA, p. A74

CRACROFT, Davis, M.D. Senior Director Medical Affairs, Scripps Mercy Hospital, San Diego, CA, p. A89

CRAFT, Brian, Group Finance Officer, Texas Health Presbyterian Hospital Dallas, Dallas, TX, p. A611

CRAFT, Christina, Director Information Systems, Washington County Hospital, Plymouth, NC, p. A471

CRAFT, Kirby, Chief Information Officer, Magee General Hospital, Magee, MS, p. A361

CRAFTS, Nicholas, Chief Executive Officer, Houston Physicians Hospital, Webster, TX, p. A656

CRAGGS, Chris, Deputy Director, Winnebago Mental Health Institute, Winnebago, WI, p. A719

CRAIG, Alan, M.D. Physician Advisor, Princeton Baptist Medical Center, Birmingham, AL, p. A17

CRAIG, Celine H., Director Human Resources, King's Daughters Medical Center, Brookhaven, MS, p. A356

CRAIG, Cheniere, Director Human Resources, P & S Surgical Hospital, Monroe, LA, p. A283

CRAIG, Donnette, Director Human Resources, CHRISTUS Coushatta Health Care Center, Coushatta, LA, p. A275

CRAIG, Elizabeth J., MSN Chief Nursing Officer and Vice President Patient Services, Temple University Hospital, Philadelphia, PA, p. A550

CRAIG, Emmett
Director Human Resources, Harlingen Medical Center, Harlingen, TX, p. A622
Chief Human Resources Officer, Knapp Medical Center, Weslaco, TX, p. A657

CRAIG, Glenn L., Chief Operating Officer, Louisiana Heart Hospital, Lacombe, LA, p. A280

CRAIG, Jeff, Chief Human Resource Management, Veterans Affairs Maryland Health Care System–Baltimore Division, Baltimore, MD, p. A298

CRAIG, Julian R., Chief Medical Officer, United Medical Center, Washington, DC, p. A122

CRAIG, Mike
Vice President, Chief Financial Officer, Indiana University Health Bedford Hospital, Bedford, IN, p. A206
Chief Financial Officer, Indiana University Health Bloomington Hospital, Bloomington, IN, p. A207

CRAIG, Pamela, R.N. Chief Nursing Officer, Seton Medical Center Harker Heights, Harker Heights, TX, p. A622

CRAIG, Patrice, Manager Human Resources, Southern Arizona Veterans Affairs Health Care System, Tucson, AZ, p. A41

CRAIG, Paul A., JD, Interim Chief Executive Officer, Keck Medicine of USC, Los Angeles, CA, p. B76

CRAIG, Rebecca W., Vice President and Chief Financial Officer, Wayne Memorial Hospital, Goldsboro, NC, p. A466

CRAIG, Scott, Medical Director, HEALTHSOUTH Rehabilitation Hospital of Franklin, Franklin, TN, p. A583

CRAIG, Sherry, Director Human Resources, Trace Regional Hospital, Houston, MS, p. A359

CRAIG, Tracy, Director Human Resources, Novant Health Huntersville Medical Center, Huntersville, NC, p. A467

CRAIG, William J., CPA Chief Financial Officer, Howard Memorial Hospital, Nashville, AR, p. A50

CRAIGER, Lisa, Vice President, Chief Nursing Officer, Jay County Hospital, Portland, IN, p. A220

CRAIGIE, James N., M.D. Vice President Medical Affairs, McLeod Loris Seacoast Hospital, Loris, SC, p. A568

CRAIGIN, Jane, Chief Executive Officer, St. Vincent Williamsport Hospital, Williamsport, IN, p. A224

CRAIN, Doris
Vice President Information Services, Broward Health Medical Center, Fort Lauderdale, FL, p. A128
Vice President and Chief Information Officer, Broward Health North, Deerfield Beach, FL, p. A127

CRAIN, Greg, FACHE, Vice President and Administrator, Baptist Health Medical Center–Little Rock, Little Rock, AR, p. A48

CRAIN, Michelle B., MSN, Administrator and Chief Operating Officer, Heart Hospital of Lafayette, Lafayette, LA, p. A280

CRAMBES, Terry, Manager Finance, Warren State Hospital, Warren, PA, p. A556

CRAMER, Brian J., Chief Executive Officer, Orthopaedic Hospital of Wisconsin – Glendale, Glendale, WI, p. A706

CRAMER, James R.
Vice President and Chief Information Officer, HonorHealth Scottsdale Osborn Medical Center, Scottsdale, AZ, p. A38
Vice President and Chief Information Officer, HonorHealth Scottsdale Shea Medical Center, Scottsdale, AZ, p. A39

CRAMER, Lonnie, Chief Operating Officer, Penrose–St. Francis Health Services, Colorado Springs, CO, p. A103

CRANDALL, Kristin, Director Human Resources, Bon Secours St. Mary's Hospital, Richmond, VA, p. A677

CRANDELL, Kristy, M.D. Medical Staff President, Red Bay Hospital, Red Bay, AL, p. A25

CRANE, David, Chief Executive Officer, National Surgical Healthcare, Chicago, IL, p. B94

CRANFORD, Melvin, Chief Fiscal Services, Cheyenne Veterans Affairs Medical Center, Cheyenne, WY, p. A722

CRATON, Deborah W., M.D. Chief Medical Officer, St. Vincent Dunn Hospital, Bedford, IN, p. A206

CRAVEN, Brian, Senior Vice President Finance, Magnolia Regional Health Center, Corinth, MS, p. A357

CRAVEN, Darcy, Chief Executive Officer, Carolinas Hospital System, Florence, SC, p. A565

CRAVEN, Denise, Director Information Systems Relationship Management, Springfield Regional Medical Center, Springfield, OH, p. A503

CRAVENS, Marc, Chief Financial Officer, Pinnacle Specialty Hospital, Tulsa, OK, p. A522

CRAW, David, Coordinator Information Technology, Dundy County Hospital, Benkelman, NE, p. A394

CRAWFORD, Arnita, Director Human Resources, Woman's Hospital of Texas, Houston, TX, p. A628

CRAWFORD, Jeff
Chief Executive Officer, HEALTHSOUTH Rehabilitation Hospital The Vintage, Houston, TX, p. A624
Chief Executive Officer, HEALTHSOUTH Rehabilitation Hospital The Woodlands, Conroe, TX, p. A607
Chief Executive Officer, HEALTHSOUTH Rehabilitation Hospital Vision Park, Shenandoah, TX, p. A648

CRAWFORD, Jim, Chief Financial Officer, Lawrence Medical Center, Moulton, AL, p. A24

CRAWFORD, John W.
Chief Financial Officer, Muscogee Creek Nation Medical Center, Okmulgee, OK, p. A518
Chief Financial Officer, St. John Sapulpa, Sapulpa, OK, p. A519

CRAWFORD, Linda, R.N. Chief Nursing Officer, Cookeville Regional Medical Center, Cookeville, TN, p. A581

CRAWFORD, Lucinda, Vice President Financial Services, Vidant Duplin Hospital, Kenansville, NC, p. A468

CRAWFORD, Mark W.
Chief Executive Officer, Northwest Texas Healthcare System, Amarillo, TX, p. A596
Chief Executive Officer, Northwest Texas Surgery Center, Amarillo, TX, p. A596

CRAWFORD, Pam, R.N. Vice President of Nursing and Chief Nursing Officer, OhioHealth MedCentral Mansfield Hospital, Mansfield, OH, p. A497

CRAWFORD, Ryan, Director Talent, Southwestern Regional Medical Center, Tulsa, OK, p. A522

CRAWFORD, Susan, Manager Human Resources, Fayette County Hospital, Vandalia, IL, p. A204

CRAWFORD, Thomas, Chicago Market Chief Information Officer, Louis A. Weiss Memorial Hospital, Chicago, IL, p. A184

CRAWFORD, Tom
Vice President Human Resources, DeKalb Medical at Downtown Decatur, Decatur, GA, p. A158
Vice President Human Resources, DeKalb Medical at Hillandale, Lithonia, GA, p. A162
Chief Information Officer, Jupiter Medical Center, Jupiter, FL, p. A132

CRAWFORD, Traci, R.N., Commander, Moncrief Army Community Hospital, Fort Jackson, SC, p. A566

CRAWFORD, Wendy, Chief Human Resource Officer, HonorHealth Scottsdale Thompson Peak Medical Center, Scottsdale, AZ, p. A39

CRAWFORD, Wes, Chief Executive Officer, Greenbrier Behavior Health Hospital, Covington, LA, p. A275

CRAYTON, Cory
Director Information Systems, Barrow Regional Medical Center, Winder, GA, p. A169
Director of Information Systems, Clearview Regional Medical Center, Monroe, GA, p. A163

CRAYTON, Karen, Administrator, AMG Specialty Hospital–Denham Springs, Denham Springs, LA, p. A276

CREAL, Sharon, Vice President Financial Operations, Scripps Memorial Hospital–Encinitas, Encinitas, CA, p. A61

CREAMER, Ken, Chief Human Resource, Amarillo Veterans Affairs Health Care System, Amarillo, TX, p. A596

CREASMAN, Ginny L.
Director, Aleda E. Lutz Veterans Affairs Medical Center, Saginaw, MI, p. A333
Associate Director, Richard L. Roudebush Veterans Affairs Medical Center, Indianapolis, IN, p. A214

CREEL, Keith, Vice President Operations, Good Shepherd Medical Center–Marshall, Marshall, TX, p. A636

CREEL, Mary Ann, Chief Information Resource Management, Martinsburg Veterans Affairs Medical Center, Martinsburg, WV, p. A698

CREIGHTON, Peggy F., R.N. Director of Nursing Services, Methodist Hospital Union County, Morganfield, KY, p. A267

CRENSHAW, Neville, D.O. Chief of Staff, Keokuk Area Hospital, Keokuk, IA, p. A233

CRENSHAW, Rachel H., Chief Operating Officer, Jack Hughston Memorial Hospital, Phenix City, AL, p. A24

CRENSHAW, William, M.D. Chief of Staff, Lady of the Sea General Hospital, Cut Off, LA, p. A276

CREPEAU, Diana, Director Human Resources, HEALTHSOUTH Rehabilitation Hospital of Colorado Springs, Colorado Springs, CO, p. A102

CREPS, Barbara, Director Human Resources and Accounting, Okeene Municipal Hospital, Okeene, OK, p. A515

CREQUE, J. C., Director Management Information Systems, Schneider Regional Medical Center, Saint Thomas, VI, p. A731

CRESPO, Rosaida M., Executive Director, Hospital San Carlos Borromeo, Moca, PR, p. A728

CRESPO–RIVERA, Waleska, Chief Executive Officer, HEALTHSOUTH Hospital of Manati, Manati, PR, p. A728

CRESWELL, Linda, Director Human Resource, Cypress Fairbanks Medical Center, Houston, TX, p. A624

CREWS, Carol
Chief Financial Officer, Tanner Higgins General Hospital, Bremen, GA, p. A155
Senior Vice President and Chief Financial Officer, Tanner Medical Center–Villa Rica, Villa Rica, GA, p. A168

CREWS, Kimberly, Vice President Finance and Chief Financial Officer, High Point Regional Health System, High Point, NC, p. A467

CRIBBS, Sammie, Vice President Clinical Services and Chief Nursing Officer, North Arkansas Regional Medical Center, Harrison, AR, p. A47

CRIBBS, Susan, D.O. Chief of Staff, Tehachapi Valley Healthcare District, Tehachapi, CA, p. A95

CRIDER, Terry, Information Technology Site Manager, NEA Baptist Memorial Hospital, Jonesboro, AR, p. A48

CRIGER, Sara J., President, Mercy Hospital, Coon Rapids, MN, p. A341

CRILLY, Tom
Executive Vice President, Chief Financial Officer, Newark–Wayne Community Hospital, Newark, NY, p. A450
Executive Vice President and Chief Financial Officer, Unity Hospital, Rochester, NY, p. A454

CRIM, Marcia, MSN, Chief Executive Officer, USMD Hospital at Arlington, Arlington, TX, p. A598

CRINER, Mark, Director Information Technology, Memorial Health Care Systems, Seward, NE, p. A402

CRIPE, Kimberly C.
President and Chief Executive Officer, Children's Hospital of Orange County, Orange, CA, p. A81
President and Chief Executive Officer, CHOC Children's at Mission Hospital, Mission Viejo, CA, p. A76

CRIPPIN, David, Chief Medical Officer, Buena Vista Regional Medical Center, Storm Lake, IA, p. A238

CRIPPS, Eric, Chief Financial Officer and Chief Operating Officer, Jackson Parish Hospital, Jonesboro, LA, p. A279

CRISTY, Kirk, Chief Financial Officer, Sanford Bismarck, Bismarck, ND, p. A477

CRISWELL, Jodie, Vice President Fiscal Services, Hammond–Henry Hospital, Geneseo, IL, p. A191

CRITCHLEY, Dan, Chief Information Officer, Banner – University Medical Center Tucson, Tucson, AZ, p. A40

CRITTENDEN, Shana, Chief Operating Officer, North Shore Medical Center, Miami, FL, p. A137

CROCKER, Daniel, M.D. Chief Medical Officer, LifeCare Hospitals of North Carolina, Rocky Mount, NC, p. A472

CROCKER, Phillip, Accounting Specialist, Black River Medical Center, Poplar Bluff, MO, p. A378

CROCKETT, James Scott, M.D. Chief of Staff, Falls Community Hospital and Clinic, Marlin, TX, p. A635

CROCKETT, Mandy Lee
Director Human Resources, San Luis Valley Health, Alamosa, CO, p. A101
Director Human Resources, San Luis Valley Health Conejos County Hospital, La Jara, CO, p. A107

CROCKETT, Timothy D., Chief Financial Officer, Breckinridge Memorial Hospital, Hardinsburg, KY, p. A261

CROFFUT, Tom, Chief Financial Officer, CenterPointe Hospital, Saint Charles, MO, p. A379

CROFT, Kim, R.N. Executive Director Human Resources, Pomerene Hospital, Millersburg, OH, p. A499

CROFTON, Michael
Senior Vice President and Chief Financial Officer, Bethesda North Hospital, Cincinnati, OH, p. A487
Chief Financial Officer, Good Samaritan Hospital, Cincinnati, OH, p. A487
Chief Financial Officer, TriHealth Evendale Hospital, Cincinnati, OH, p. A488

CROKER, James, Director Information Systems, St. Bernardine Medical Center, San Bernardino, CA, p. A88

CROLEY, John S., Vice President Business Operations, Texas Institute for Surgery at Texas Health Presbyterian Dallas, Dallas, TX, p. A611

CRONER, Robert, Senior Vice President and Chief Human Resources Officer, Children's Hospital of Philadelphia, Philadelphia, PA, p. A547

CRONIN, Annamarie, Director Human Resources, HEALTHSOUTH New England Rehabilitation Hospital, Woburn, MA, p. A316

CRONIN, David J., Regional Vice President Human Resources, Good Samaritan Medical Center, Brockton, MA, p. A308

CROOKS, John, Chair Information Services, Mayo Clinic Jacksonville, Jacksonville, FL, p. A131

CROOM, Jon–Paul, President and Chief Executive Officer, Merit Health Central, Jackson, MS, p. A360

CROOM Jr., Kennedy L., Administrator and Chief Executive Officer, Rhea Medical Center, Dayton, TN, p. A582

CROPLEY, Stacey, M.D. Chief Nursing Officer, Moore County Hospital District, Dumas, TX, p. A614

CROPPER, Douglas P., President and Chief Executive Officer, Genesis Health System, Davenport, IA, p. B57

CROPPER, Ronnie, Chief Operating Officer, Warren State Hospital, Warren, PA, p. A556

CROSBY, Evalie M., CPA Vice President Finance and Chief Financial Officer, Alice Peck Day Memorial Hospital, Lebanon, NH, p. A411

CROSBY, Robert
Chief Financial Officer, Athol Memorial Hospital, Athol, MA, p. A305
Senior Vice President and Chief Financial Officer, Heywood Hospital, Gardner, MA, p. A310

CROSHAW, Diane, Vice President Human Resources, Bacharach Institute for Rehabilitation, Pomona, NJ, p. A422

CROSLAND, Telita, Commander, Colonel Florence A. Blanchfield Army Community Hospital, Fort Campbell, KY, p. A260

CROSS, Carol, CPA Chief Financial Officer, Northeast Regional Medical Center, Kirksville, MO, p. A375

CROSS, John D., Chief Executive Officer, Kindred Hospital Sugar Land, Sugar Land, TX, p. A650

CROSS, Lynda, R.N. Director of Nurses, Nemaha Valley Community Hospital, Seneca, KS, p. A253

CROSS, Patricia, Chief Executive Officer, Life Line Hospital, Steubenville, OH, p. A503

CROSS, Renee
Senior Vice President and Chief Financial Officer, Saint Francis Hospital, Charleston, WV, p. A695
Chief Financial Officer, Thomas Memorial Hospital, South Charleston, WV, p. A700

CROSSAN, Eric, Chief Executive Officer, HEALTHSOUTH Walton Rehabilitation Hospital, Augusta, GA, p. A153

CROSSER, Roxanna, President, OSF St. Mary Medical Center, Galesburg, IL, p. A191

CROSSEY, Robert, D.O. Chief Medical Officer, LifeCare Hospitals of Pittsburgh – Monroeville, Monroeville, PA, p. A545

CROSSLAND, Jeanne, Director of Nursing, Shamrock General Hospital, Shamrock, TX, p. A648

CROSSLEY, Kent, M.D. Chief of Staff, Minneapolis Veterans Affairs Health Care System, Minneapolis, MN, p. A346

CROSSLEY, Rachel, R.N. Chief Patient Care Services, Veterans Affairs Sierra Nevada Health Care System, Reno, NV, p. A408

CROSTON, J. Kevin, M.D., Chief Executive Officer, North Memorial Health Care, Robbinsdale, MN, p. B96

CROTEAU, Gary, Assistant Vice President and Chief Information Officer, South County Hospital, Wakefield, RI, p. A561

CROTTY, Jr., Glenn, M.D. Executive Vice President and Chief Operating Officer, Charleston Area Medical Center, Charleston, WV, p. A695

CROTTY, Renee, Coordinator Marketing and Public Relations, Capital Medical Center, Olympia, WA, p. A687

CROUCH, Amy, Chief Financial Officer, Community Health Center of Branch County, Coldwater, MI, p. A321

CROUCH, James, Vice President Technical Services, Northwest Medical Center, Albany, MO, p. A367

CROUCH, Matthew, Chief Executive Officer and Managing Director, Peachford Behavioral Health System, Atlanta, GA, p. A152

CROUT, Tom, MS Director Human Resources, Central Louisiana State Hospital, Pineville, LA, p. A286

CROW, Angie, Director Finance, Saint Thomas Hospital for Spinal Surgery, Nashville, TN, p. A590

CROW, Regina, R.N. Interim Chief Nursing Officer, Louisiana Heart Hospital, Lacombe, LA, p. A280

CROW, Regina W., R.N. Chief Nursing Officer, Bothwell Regional Health Center, Sedalia, MO, p. A382

CROWDER, Jerry W., President and Chief Executive Officer, Bradford Health Services, Birmingham, AL, p. B24

CROWDER, Lonna, Director of Nursing, Phillips County Hospital, Malta, MT, p. A389

CROWE, Arthur, Director Information Systems, Peconic Bay Medical Center, Riverhead, NY, p. A454

CROWE, Darren, Chief Executive Officer, Crow/Northern Cheyenne Hospital, Crow Agency, MT, p. A386

CROWE, William R., President, Conemaugh Miners Medical Center, Hastings, PA, p. A540

CROWELL, Eric T.
President and Chief Executive Officer, UnityPoint Health – Iowa Methodist Medical Center, Des Moines, IA, p. A229
President and Chief Executive Officer, UnityPoint Health–Iowa Lutheran Hospital, Des Moines, IA, p. A229

CROWELL, Lynn, Chief Executive Officer, Arkansas Valley Regional Medical Center, La Junta, CO, p. A107

CROWELL, Pamela, Associate Director and Chief Operating Officer, Ralph H. Johnson Veterans Affairs Medical Center, Charleston, SC, p. A563

CROWELL, Robin, Chief Nursing Officer and Chief Operating Officer, Saint Thomas Hickman Hospital, Centerville, TN, p. A580

CROWL, Steve, Director of Information Services, Davis Medical Center, Elkins, WV, p. A695

CROWLEY, Thomas, President and Chief Executive Officer, Saint Elizabeth's Medical Center, Wabasha, MN, p. A352

CRUCETTI, Carol, R.N. Chief Nursing Officer, St. Mary's Hospital, Troy, NY, p. A457

CRUDDAS, Brian, Chief Operating Officer, Bayfront Health Port Charlotte, Port Charlotte, FL, p. A143

CRUICKSHANK, Roland, President, St. Luke's Hospital – The Vintage Hospital, Houston, TX, p. A626

CRUIKSHANK, Jennifer, R.N. Chief Operating Officer, Riverside University Health System–Medical Center, Moreno Valley, CA, p. A78

CRUM, Aaron, M.D. Chief Medical Officer, Pikeville Medical Center, Pikeville, KY, p. A268

CRUM, Dennis L., Senior Vice President and Chief Financial Officer, Tift Regional Medical Center, Tifton, GA, p. A167

CRUM Jr., Herbert, Chief Executive Officer, Craig General Hospital, Vinita, OK, p. A522

CRUMB, Robert, Chief Executive Officer, Schoolcraft Memorial Hospital, Manistique, MI, p. A329

CRUMLEY, Vickie L., Vice President Human Resources, Mary Rutan Hospital, Bellefontaine, OH, p. A485

CRUMP, John, M.D. Medical Staff President, Howard Young Medical Center, Woodruff, WI, p. A720

CRUMP, Rick, Chief Financial Officer, Lakeland Behavioral Health System, Springfield, MO, p. A382

CRUMPTON, Patsy Sue, R.N. Chief Nursing Officer, National Park Medical Center, Hot Springs, AR, p. A47

CRUNK, Frances H., Vice President and Chief Financial Officer, Florida Hospital Waterman, Tavares, FL, p. A148

CRUSE, Ray, Chief Executive Officer, Lakeland Hospital, Watervliet, Watervliet, MI, p. A336

CRUSON, Jim, Chief Information Officer, Riverview Behavioral Health, Texarkana, AR, p. A53

CRUTCHFIELD, David, Vice President, Information Services & Chief Information Officer, Conway Medical Center, Conway, SC, p. A565

CRUTHIRDS, Richard, Director Information Systems, Peterson Regional Medical Center, Kerrville, TX, p. A630

CRUZ, Arlene, Director, Rush Oak Park Hospital, Oak Park, IL, p. A199

CRUZ, Dimitri, Vice President Information Technology, Englewood Hospital and Medical Center, Englewood, NJ, p. A417

CRUZ, Domingo, Senior Vice President Operations, San Jorge Children's Hospital, San Juan, PR, p. A730

CRUZ, Joseph V., Chief Information Officer, Ryder Memorial Hospital, Humacao, PR, p. A727

CRUZ, Julia, Chief Financial Officer, San Juan Capestrano Hospital, San Juan, PR, p. A730

CRUZ, Michael, Senior Vice President Operations, BSA Hospital, LLC, Amarillo, TX, p. A596

CRUZ, Michael A., M.D., President, OSF Saint Francis Medical Center, Peoria, IL, p. A200

CRUZ, Miguel, M.D. Medical Director, Bella Vista Hospital, Mayaguez, PR, p. A728

CRUZ, Miguel, Medical Staff Credentialing Coordinator, HEALTHSOUTH Rehabilitation Hospital of Miami, Cutler Bay, FL, p. A126

CRYER, Betty, R.N. Administrator/Chief Nursing Officer, Anderson Regional Health System South, Meridian, MS, p. A362

CRYER, Selena, Director Human Resources, Ennis Regional Medical Center, Ennis, TX, p. A616

CSEPKE, Cheryl, Controller, Kindred Rehabilitation Hospital Northeast Houston, Humble, TX, p. A628

CUDWORTH, Craig R., Chief Executive Officer, Franklin Foundation Hospital, Franklin, LA, p. A277

CUELLAR, Eddie, Vice President Information Systems, Methodist Hospital, San Antonio, TX, p. A646

CUELLAR, Jacob, M.D., Chief Executive Officer, Laurel Ridge Treatment Center, San Antonio, TX, p. A646

CUENCA, Derrick, Chief Executive Officer, Lake Granbury Medical Center, Granbury, TX, p. A621

CUERO, Liza, Coordinator Human Resources, Central Texas Rehabilitation Hospital, Austin, TX, p. A599

CUEVAS, Gilberto, Director Human Resources, Hospital De Damas, Ponce, PR, p. A728

CUEVAS, Jacki, Director Health Information Services, Regional Rehabilitation Hospital, Phenix City, AL, p. A24

CULBERSON, David K., Chief Executive Officer, San Joaquin General Hospital, French Camp, CA, p. A63

CULBERT, Devon, Controller, The Hospital at Westlake Medical Center, Austin, TX, p. A600

CULLEN, III, James T., Director Finance, Wyoming County Community Hospital, Warsaw, NY, p. A458

CULLEN, John, M.D. Chief of Staff and Medical Director Long Term Care, Providence Valdez Medical Center, Valdez, AK, p. A30

CULLEN, John, Assistant Superintendent, Thomas B. Finan Center, Cumberland, MD, p. A300

CULLEN, Mark J., Chief Executive Officer, Compass Health, Crowley, LA, p. B41

CULLEN, Michael, Senior Vice President and Chief Financial Officer, South Shore Hospital, South Weymouth, MA, p. A314

CULLEN, Neil, Director Human Resources, HEALTHSOUTH Rehabilitation Hospital of Southern Arizona, Tucson, AZ, p. A40

CULLEN, Paul T., M.D. Vice President Medical Affairs, Washington Hospital, Washington, PA, p. A556

CULLEN, Scott, Chief Executive Officer, Northwest Hills Surgical Hospital, Austin, TX, p. A599

CULLITON, Gerald F., Medical Center Director, Veterans Affairs Connecticut Healthcare System, West Haven, CT, p. A118

CULLUM, Beth
Chief Operating Officer, Curahealth Boston North Shore, Peabody, MA, p. A313
Interim Chief Executive Officer, Select Specialty Hospital–Tulsa Midtown, Tulsa, OK, p. A522

CULP, Judy, Chief Financial Officer, Hill Regional Hospital, Hillsboro, TX, p. A623

CULPEPPER, Michelle, Director Human Resources, Chicago Lakeshore Hospital, Chicago, IL, p. A183

CULVER, Douglas, Chief Financial Officer, Mercy Hospital Carthage, Carthage, MO, p. A369

CULVER, Shawna, Director Information Systems, Western Plains Medical Complex, Dodge City, KS, p. A242

CUMBEE, Lib, Director Information Systems, Providence Hospital, Columbia, SC, p. A564

CUMBIE, Dan L., Chief Nursing Officer, Flowers Hospital, Dothan, AL, p. A19

CUMBO, Adam, Chief Financial Officer, Dukes Memorial Hospital, Peru, IN, p. A220

CUMING, Ric, Chief Nurse Executive, Christiana Care Health System, Newark, DE, p. A119

CUMMINGS, Allana, Chief Information Officer, Children's Healthcare of Atlanta, Atlanta, GA, p. A152

CUMMINGS, Brooke, Chief Financial Officer, Our Lady of the Angels Hospital, Bogalusa, LA, p. A274

CUMMINGS, Bruce D., President and Chief Executive Officer, L+M Healthcare, New London, CT, p. B79

CUMMINGS, Bruce D.
President and Chief Executive Officer, Lawrence + Memorial Hospital, New London, CT, p. A116
President and Chief Executive Officer, Westerly Hospital, Westerly, RI, p. A561

CUMMINGS, Greg, Chief Financial Officer, Texas Spine & Joint Hospital, Tyler, TX, p. A654

CUMMINGS, Jerry, Chief Operating Officer, Putnam County Memorial Hospital, Unionville, MO, p. A383

CUMMINGS, Kelly, Chief Nursing Officer, Abington–Lansdale Hospital Jefferson Health, Lansdale, PA, p. A542

CUMMINGS, Steve, M.D. Chief of Medical Staff, Stillwater Medical Center, Stillwater, OK, p. A520

CUMMINGS, Steven, Chief Operating Officer and Chief Information Officer, Baystate Noble Hospital, Westfield, MA, p. A316

CUMMINS, Frank L., Vice President Human Resources, HonorHealth Deer Valley Medical Center, Phoenix, AZ, p. A36

CUMMINS, Thomas H., M.D
Chief Medical Officer, CHI St. Vincent Hot Springs, Hot Springs, AR, p. A47
Chief Medical Officer, CHI St. Vincent Infirmary Medical Center, Little Rock, AR, p. A49
Senior Vice President and Chief Medical Officer, CHI St. Vincent Medical Center–North, Sherwood, AR, p. A52
Chief Medical Officer, CHI St. Vincent Morrilton, Morrilton, AR, p. A50

CUNNIGHAM, James, D.O. Chief of Staff, Audubon County Memorial Hospital, Audubon, IA, p. A225

CUNNINGHAM, Becky, Controller, Salem Memorial District Hospital, Salem, MO, p. A382

CUNNINGHAM, Brian, Chief Executive Officer, Gila Regional Medical Center, Silver City, NM, p. A431

CUNNINGHAM, Carol, Administrative Assistant, Highland Ridge Hospital, Midvale, UT, p. A660

CUNNINGHAM, Connie, Chief Information Officer, Ellwood City Hospital, Ellwood City, PA, p. A538

CUNNINGHAM, Gail, Interim Chief Medical Officer, University of Maryland St. Joseph Medical Center, Towson, MD, p. A304

CUNNINGHAM, Gary, Chief Nursing Officer, Dixie Regional Medical Center, Saint George, UT, p. A663

CUNNINGHAM, James C., M.D. Chief Medical Officer, Cook Children's Medical Center, Fort Worth, TX, p. A618

CUNNINGHAM, Julie, Associate Administrator and Chief Human Resources Officer, Pioneers Memorial Healthcare District, Brawley, CA, p. A57

CUNNINGHAM, Keith W., M.D. Medical Director, HEALTHSOUTH Scottsdale Rehabilitation Hospital, Scottsdale, AZ, p. A38

CUNNINGHAM, M. Edward, Chief Executive Officer, Gateway Regional Medical Center, Granite City, IL, p. A191

CUNNINGHAM, Michelle P., Chief Executive Officer, Highlands Hospital, Connellsville, PA, p. A536

CUNNINGHAM, Regina, Ph.D. Chief Nurse Executive, Hospital of the University of Pennsylvania, Philadelphia, PA, p. A548

CUPPS, Cheryl, Director Finance, Griffin Memorial Hospital, Norman, OK, p. A515

CURD, R. Blake, M.D., Chief Executive Officer, Sioux Falls Specialty Hospital, Sioux Falls, SD, p. A576

CURLEE, Robbin, Controller, RMC Jacksonville, Jacksonville, AL, p. A22

CURLING, Susan, M.D. Chief Medical Officer, Memorial Hermann Northeast, Humble, TX, p. A628

CURNEL, Robin, MSN Chief Operating Officer and Chief Nursing Officer, Crittenden County Hospital, Marion, KY, p. A266

CURPHY, Rona, President and Chief Executive Officer, Banner Casa Grande Medical Center, Casa Grande, AZ, p. A31

CURRAN, Dezerae, Director Human Resources, Osawatomie State Hospital, Osawatomie, KS, p. A250

CURRAN, Maria, Vice President Human Resources, VCU Medical Center, Richmond, VA, p. A678

CURRAN–MEULI, Jane, Chief Operating Officer, Holy Family Memorial, Manitowoc, WI, p. A709

CURRANCE, Lana, MSN, Chief Executive Officer, Peak View Behavioral Health, Colorado Springs, CO, p. A102

CURRANS, Sheila, Chief Executive Officer, Harrison Memorial Hospital, Cynthiana, KY, p. A259

CURREN, Robert
Director Information Technology, Center for Behavioral Medicine, Kansas City, MO, p. A373
Western Region Chief Information Technology Officer, Northwest Missouri Psychiatric Rehabilitation Center, Saint Joseph, MO, p. A379

CURRIE, Michelle, Chief Financial Officer, Richard P. Stadter Psychiatric Center, Grand Forks, ND, p. A479

CURRIE, Scott D., Vice President and Chief Financial Officer, MidMichigan Medical Center–Midland, Midland, MI, p. A330

CURRIE, Stuart, Chief Medical Officer, Tuality Healthcare, Hillsboro, OR, p. A526

CURRIN, Randy, Chief Operating Officer, Bay Medical Center Sacred Heart Health System, Panama City, FL, p. A141

CURRY, Cheryl, Chief Financial Officer, Littleton Adventist Hospital, Littleton, CO, p. A108

CURRY, Christopher, Chief Operating Officer, Iroquois Memorial Hospital and Resident Home, Watseka, IL, p. A204

CURRY, Jeffrey T.
Executive Vice President and Chief Financial Officer, Excela Frick Hospital, Mount Pleasant, PA, p. A545
Executive Vice President and Chief Financial Officer, Excela Health Westmoreland Hospital, Greensburg, PA, p. A539

D

DALTON, Wayne, Chief Financial Officer, Lakeview Hospital, Bountiful, UT, p. A659

DALY, Cindy, R.N. Director of Nursing, Syringa Hospital and Clinics, Grangeville, ID, p. A176

DALY, Derek, Chief Executive Officer, Liberty Medical Center, Chester, MT, p. A386

DALY, Linda, Vice President Human Resources, Auburn Community Hospital, Auburn, NY, p. A434

DALY, Thomas M., CPA Chief Financial Officer, University Hospital, Newark, NJ, p. A421

DALY, William, Chief Executive Officer, Pennsylvania Psychiatric Institute, Harrisburg, PA, p. A539

DAMA, Sunil, M.D. Medical Director, Select Specialty Hospital – Cincinnati North, Cincinnati, OH, p. A488

DAMBOISE, Robin, Director Human Resources, Northern Maine Medical Center, Fort Kent, ME, p. A293

DAMICO, Donna, Director Human Resources, Carolinas Hospital System, Florence, SC, p. A565

DAMM, Julie, Chief Financial Officer, Hancock County Health System, Britt, IA, p. A226

DAMMEYER, Matt, Ph.D. Chief Operating Officer, Central Peninsula Hospital, Soldotna, AK, p. A30

DAMODARAN, A. N., M.D. President Medical Staff, Starke Hospital, Knox, IN, p. A215

DAMON, Chad, Contractor, St. Vincent Dunn Hospital, Bedford, IN, p. A206

DAMON, Kerry, Director Human Resources, Baystate Franklin Medical Center, Greenfield, MA, p. A310

DAMRON, Greg, Vice President Finance and Chief Financial Officer, Augusta University Medical Center, Augusta, GA, p. A153

DAMRON, Paul, Chief Financial Officer, Highlands Regional Medical Center, Sebring, FL, p. A145

DAMRON, Tony, Vice President Information Services, Pikeville Medical Center, Pikeville, KY, p. A268

DAMSCHRODER, Robin, Chief Operating Officer, St. Joseph Mercy Livingston Hospital, Howell, MI, p. A326

DANBDALA, Kayyan, M.D. Medical Director, Schick Shadel Hospital, Seattle, WA, p. A689

DANCER, Stephanie, Manager Human Resources, Pauls Valley General Hospital, Pauls Valley, OK, p. A518

DANCH, Stephen M., Chief Financial Officer, UPMC Hamot, Erie, PA, p. A538

DANCY, Peter, Director, Alexandria Veterans Affairs Health Care System, Pineville, LA, p. A286

DANDORPH, Michael J., President and Chief Operating Officer, Rush University Medical Center, Chicago, IL, p. A186

DANDRIDGE, Thomas C., President and Chief Executive Officer, Regional Medical Center, Orangeburg, SC, p. A569

DANE, Brenda, Director, Human Resources, Highlands Regional Medical Center, Sebring, FL, p. A145

DANE, Jeff, Executive Vice President and Chief Financial Officer, University Medical Center, Lubbock, TX, p. A634

DANELLO, Sherry, MS
   Vice President and Chief Nursing Officer, Candler Hospital, Savannah, GA, p. A165
   Vice President and Chief Nursing Officer, St. Joseph's Hospital, Savannah, GA, p. A166

DANG, Cynthia, Vice President Human Resources, North Hills Hospital, North Richland Hills, TX, p. A639

DANGERFIELD, Wesley, Community Chief Executive Officer, Summers County ARH Hospital, Hinton, WV, p. A696

DANIEL, Christopher W., Administrator, Sterling Surgical Hospital, Slidell, LA, p. A288

DANIEL, Dena, Director Information Systems, Jackson County Memorial Hospital, Altus, OK, p. A508

DANIEL, Karen
   Director Human Resources, Bibb Medical Center, Centreville, AL, p. A18
   Chief Executive Officer, Warm Springs Medical Center, Warm Springs, GA, p. A148

DANIEL, Lisa, Chief Executive Officer, Memphis Mental Health Institute, Memphis, TN, p. A589

DANIEL, Ron, Manager Information Systems, Matheny Medical and Educational Center, Peapack, NJ, p. A421

DANIEL, S., M.D. Chief Medical Officer, Spring Valley Hospital Medical Center, Las Vegas, NV, p. A406

DANIEL, Steven G., Senior Vice President and Chief Operating Officer, CHRISTUS Spohn Hospital Alice, Alice, TX, p. A595

DANIELS, Alex, Chief Nurse Executive, U. S. Public Health Service Indian Hospital, Crownpoint, NM, p. A429

DANIELS, Andrew, Chief Executive Officer, The Memorial Hospital at Craig, Craig, CO, p. A103

DANIELS, Andy
   Chief Operating Officer, Bucyrus Community Hospital, Bucyrus, OH, p. A485
   Vice President Non–Clinical Operations and Information Systems, Galion Community Hospital, Galion, OH, p. A495

DANIELS, Anita
   Director, Bronx Psychiatric Center,, NY, p. A443
   Executive Director, New York City Children's Center,, NY, p. A446

DANIELS, Betty, M.D. Chief of Staff, St. Bernardine Medical Center, San Bernardino, CA, p. A88

DANIELS, Craig M., Chief Financial Officer, Moab Regional Hospital, Moab, UT, p. A660

DANIELS, D. Jeffery, Chief Executive Officer, Bingham Memorial Hospital, Blackfoot, ID, p. A174

DANIELS, Don, M.D. Chief Medical Officer, Rollins–Brook Community Hospital, Lampasas, TX, p. A632

DANIELS, Don, Executive Vice President and Chief Operating Officer, SwedishAmerican – A Division of UW Health, Rockford, IL, p. A202

DANIELS, John, M.D. Medical Director, LifeCare Hospitals of Wisconsin, Pewaukee, WI, p. A714

DANIELS, Judy, Vice President Human Resources, Our Lady of Bellefonte Hospital, Ashland, KY, p. A257

DANIELS, Karen, MSN Chief Nursing Officer, Halifax Regional Medical Center, Roanoke Rapids, NC, p. A472

DANIELS, Kristin, Manager Human Resources, Sutter Center for Psychiatry, Sacramento, CA, p. A87

DANIELS, Mark, M.D. Vice President Physician Enterprise, Northwestern Medicine Delnor Hospital, Geneva, IL, p. A191

DANIELS, S. Janette, Director Human Resources, HEALTHSOUTH Rehabilitation Hospital of Fort Smith, Fort Smith, AR, p. A46

DANIELS, Sarah, Vice President, Information Technology, Mayo Clinic Health System in Mankato, Mankato, MN, p. A345

DANIELS, Todd, M.D. Medical Director, HEALTHSOUTH Rehabilitation Hospital of Arlington, Arlington, TX, p. A597

DANIELS, Troy P., Chief Human Resources Officer, Forrest General Hospital, Hattiesburg, MS, p. A359

DANIELSON, Carol, R.N. Senior Vice President and Chief Nursing Officer, Gwinnett Hospital System, Lawrenceville, GA, p. A162

DANIELYAN, Arman, M.D. Chief of Staff, John Muir Behavioral Health Center, Concord, CA, p. A59

DANKER, Doug, Administrator, Mercy Hospital El Reno, El Reno, OK, p. A511

DANKERT, Sheri
   Chief Financial Officer, Mayo Clinic Health System in Albert Lea, Albert Lea, MN, p. A338
   Vice President Finance, Mayo Clinic Health System–Albert Lea and Austin, Austin, MN, p. A339

DANKO, Douglas, President and Chief Executive Officer, Jameson Hospital, New Castle, PA, p. A546

DANN, Doreen, R.N. Chief Operating Officer, Victor Valley Global Medical Center, Victorville, CA, p. A98

DANOWSKI, Dale G., R.N. Senior Vice President, Chief Nursing Officer, St. Vincent's Medical Center, Bridgeport, CT, p. A113

DANSBY, Tommy, Chief Medical Officer, Liberty Healthcare Systems, Bastrop, LA, p. A272

DANUSER, James, Chief Information Officer, Veterans Affairs Central Iowa Health Care System, Des Moines, IA, p. A230

DAOUD, Joudat, M.D. Chief of Staff, Community Health Center of Branch County, Coldwater, MI, p. A321

DAQUIOAG, Francis, Controller, Kahuku Medical Center, Kahuku, HI, p. A171

DARBONNE, Tina, Chief Financial Officer, Central Louisiana State Hospital, Pineville, LA, p. A286

DARBY, Kristin, Chief Information Officer, Eastern Regional Medical Center, Philadelphia, PA, p. A547

DARBY, Sharon, R.N. Vice President, Clinical Operations, Children's Hospital of Richmond at VCU–Brook Road Campus, Richmond, VA, p. A677

DARCEY, Patricia, R.N. Vice President/Chief Nursing Officer, Southampton Hospital, Southampton, NY, p. A456

DARDANO, Anthony, M.D. Chief Medical Officer, Delray Medical Center, Delray Beach, FL, p. A127

DARDEAU, Sean T., FACHE, Chief Executive Officer, Mary Black Health System–Spartanburg, Spartanburg, SC, p. A569

DAREY, Roland, M.D. Medical Director, Wamego Health Center, Wamego, KS, p. A255

DARLING, Cory, Chief Operating Officer, TriStar Hendersonville Medical Center, Hendersonville, TN, p. A584

DARLING, Rudy, Chief Operating Officer, Baxter Regional Medical Center, Mountain Home, AR, p. A50

DARMELIO, Matthew P., Chief of Staff, Monongalia General Hospital, Morgantown, WV, p. A698

DARNAUER, Kristina, M.D. Chief of Staff, Hospital District No 1 of Rice County, Lyons, KS, p. A248

DARNELL, Brian, D.O. Chief of Staff, Johnson County Healthcare Center, Buffalo, WY, p. A721

DARNELL, Gerald K., PsyD, Interim Director, Sheridan Veterans Affairs Medical Center, Sheridan, WY, p. A724

DARNELL, Linda, Director Management Information Systems, King's Daughters' Health, Madison, IN, p. A217

DARRINGTON, Gilbert, Director Human Resources, Jackson Hospital and Clinic, Montgomery, AL, p. A23

DARVIN, Ken, M.D. Chief of Staff, Stroud Regional Medical Center, Stroud, OK, p. A520

DASARO, Lynda, Director Human Resources, Sutter Roseville Medical Center, Roseville, CA, p. A86

DASCANI, Jimmy, Chief Executive Officer, Landmark Hospital of Southwest Florida, Naples, FL, p. A138

DASCENZO, Douglas R., MSN Chief Nursing Officer, St. Joseph Mercy Oakland, Pontiac, MI, p. A332

DASCHER Jr., Norman E.
   Chief Executive Officer, Samaritan Hospital, Troy, NY, p. A457
   Chief Executive Officer, St. Mary's Hospital, Troy, NY, p. A457

DASHIELD, Luanne G., Personnel Administrator, Deer's Head Hospital Center, Salisbury, MD, p. A303

DASKALAKIS, Tom G., Chief Administrative Officer, West Chester Hospital, West Chester, OH, p. A505

DASS, Karla, Director Human Resources, Regional General Hospital, Williston, FL, p. A150

DASSENKO, Dennis, Chief Information Officer, Essentia Health Duluth, Duluth, MN, p. A341

DAUBERT, Stephanie
   Chief Financial Officer, Nebraska Medicine – Bellevue, Bellevue, NE, p. A394
   Chief Financial Officer, Nebraska Medicine – Nebraska Medical Center, Omaha, NE, p. A400

DAUBY, Randall W., CPA, Chief Executive Officer, Pinckneyville Community Hospital, Pinckneyville, IL, p. A200

DAUGHDRILL, Diane, Director Human Resources, Jefferson Davis Community Hospital, Prentiss, MS, p. A364

DAUGHERTY, Alan
   Chief Executive Officer, Ennis Regional Medical Center, Ennis, TX, p. A616
   Chief Executive Officer, Parkview Regional Hospital, Mexia, TX, p. A637

DAUGHERTY, Beth Ann, R.N. Vice·President Care Services and Chief Nursing Executive, Sparrow Clinton Hospital, Saint Johns, MI, p. A333

DAUGHERTY, Don, Director Information Systems, Fleming County Hospital, Flemingsburg, KY, p. A259

DAUGHERTY, Marney, Worklife Services Consultant, Brighton Center for Recovery, Brighton, MI, p. A319

DAUGHERTY, Stephen J., Chief Executive Officer, Coliseum Northside Hospital, Macon, GA, p. A162

DAUM, Karen, R.N. Vice President and Chief Nursing Officer, Passavant Area Hospital, Jacksonville, IL, p. A194

DAUTERIVE, F. Ralph, M.D. Vice President Medical Affairs, Ochsner Medical Center–Baton Rouge, Baton Rouge, LA, p. A272

DAVACHI, Khosrow, Chief Medical Officer, BridgePoint Hospital National Harbor, Washington, DC, p. A121

DAVE, Bhaskar J., M.D., Superintendent, Mental Health Institute, Independence, IA, p. A232

DAVE', Rajesh J., M.D. Executive Vice President and Chief Medical Officer, United Health Services Hospitals–Binghamton, Binghamton, NY, p. A435

DAVENPORT, David, Director Human Resources, Washington County Hospital, Nashville, IL, p. A198

DAVENPORT, Douglas
   Chief Financial Officer, Bethesda Hospital, Saint Paul, MN, p. A350
   Senior Vice President and Chief Financial Officer, St. John's Hospital, Maplewood, MN, p. A346
   Senior Vice President and Chief Financial Officer, St. Joseph's Hospital, Saint Paul, MN, p. A351
   Senior Vice President and Chief Financial Officer, Woodwinds Health Campus, Woodbury, MN, p. A353

DAVENPORT, Ginger, Director Human Resources, Promise Hospital of Dallas, Dallas, TX, p. A611

DAVENPORT, Paula, Chief Nursing Officer, Princeton Baptist Medical Center, Birmingham, AL, p. A17

DAVENPORT, Polly J., R.N.,
   President, CHI St. Vincent Infirmary Medical Center, Little Rock, AR, p. A49
   Senior Vice President, Chief Operating Officer, President CHI St. Vincent Infirmary Medical Center a, CHI St. Vincent Medical Center–North, Sherwood, AR, p. A52

DAVENPORT, Sally M., MS, Interim Chief Executive Officer, Ephraim McDowell Fort Logan Hospital, Stanford, KY, p. A269

DAVENPORT, Sally M., MS, Chief Executive Officer, Ephraim McDowell Health, Danville, KY, p. B53

DAVENPORT, Sally M., MS, Chief Executive Officer, Ephraim McDowell Regional Medical Center, Danville, KY, p. A259

DAVES, Ronnie, Chief Executive Officer, North Okaloosa Medical Center, Crestview, FL, p. A126

DAVID, Biff, R.N., Administrator, St. Landry Extended Care Hospital, Opelousas, LA, p. A286

DAVID, Lim, Vice President Finance and Chief Financial Officer, Penn State Health St. Joseph, Reading, PA, p. A553

DAVID, Michelle, Chief Executive Officer, Valley Hospital Phoenix, Phoenix, AZ, p. A37

DAVID, R. Neal, Administrator and Chief of Staff, Madigan Army Medical Center, Tacoma, WA, p. A691

DAVID, Robert G., President, St. John Medical Center, Westlake, OH, p. A505

DAVIDOFF, Ravin, M.D. Chief Medical Officer, Boston Medical Center, Boston, MA, p. A306

DAVIDOW, Daniel N., M.D. Medical Director, Cumberland Hospital, New Kent, VA, p. A674

DAVIDSON, Brian, M.D., Interim President, St. Mary's Medical Center, Grand Junction, CO, p. A106

DAVIDSON, Camille, Director Human Resources, Stanton County Hospital, Johnson, KS, p. A246

DAVIDSON, Craig Val
    Chief Executive Officer and Administrator, Beaver Valley Hospital, Beaver, UT, p. A659
    Chief Executive Officer, Milford Valley Memorial Hospital, Milford, UT, p. A660

DAVIDSON, Diane, Senior Vice President Human Resources, Essentia Health Duluth, Duluth, MN, p. A341

DAVIDSON, Dianne, Chief Operating Officer, Union General Hospital, Farmerville, LA, p. A276

DAVIDSON, Elizabeth, R.N. Vice President, Patient Care Services, OSF Saint James – John W. Albrecht Medical Center, Pontiac, IL, p. A201

DAVIDSON, Gary, Senior Vice President and Chief Information Officer, Lancaster General Hospital, Lancaster, PA, p. A542

DAVIDSON, Gary, M.D. Medical Director, Select Specialty Hospital–Johnstown, Johnstown, PA, p. A541

DAVIDSON, Gordon L., Chief Financial Officer, Bozeman Health Deaconess Hospital, Bozeman, MT, p. A386

DAVIDSON, Gregg Agustin, FACHE, President and Chief Executive Officer, Skagit Regional Health, Mount Vernon, WA, p. B125

DAVIDSON, James
    Director of Information Services, Ferry County Memorial Hospital, Republic, WA, p. A688
    Chief Executive Officer, Saint Mary's Regional Medical Center, Russellville, AR, p. A52

DAVIDSON, James N., Troop Commander, Tripler Army Medical Center, Honolulu, HI, p. A171

DAVIDSON, John, Vice President Human Resources, Sharon Regional Health System, Sharon, PA, p. A555

DAVIDSON, Mac, Chief Executive Officer, Hermann Drive Surgical Hospital, Houston, TX, p. A624

DAVIDSON, Nancy, Senior Vice President and Chief Financial Officer, Jackson County Memorial Hospital, Altus, OK, p. A508

DAVIDSON, Rocky, Chief Financial Officer, Larkin Behavioral Health Services,, FL, p. A130

DAVIDSON, Rowena, Manager Business Office, AMG Specialty Hospital–Edmond, Edmond, OK, p. A511

DAVIDSON, Sammi, Administrative Director, Sanford Bagley Medical Center, Bagley, MN, p. A339

DAVIDSON, Stephen, Director Human Resources, Lafayette Regional Health Center, Lexington, MO, p. A375

DAVIDSON, Stuart, President Medical Staff, Mount Desert Island Hospital, Bar Harbor, ME, p. A291

DAVIDSON, Tim, M.D. Chief Executive Physician Services, Providence St. Mary Medical Center, Walla Walla, WA, p. A693

DAVIDSON, Tori, R.N. Chief Nursing Officer, Tsehootsooi Medical Center, Fort Defiance, AZ, p. A32

DAVIES, Janie, Chief Financial Officer, New Mexico Rehabilitation Center, Roswell, NM, p. A431

DAVILA, Susa, Chief Executive Officer, Desert View Hospital, Pahrump, NV, p. A407

DAVILA, Susan, Chief Executive Officer, Renown South Meadows Medical Center, Reno, NV, p. A408

DAVIN, Joni, Director Information and Business Management Service Line, Veterans Affairs Eastern Kansas Health Care System, Topeka, KS, p. A254

DAVINI, John, Vice President, St. Rose Hospital, Hayward, CA, p. A66

DAVIS, Adam
    Director Information Technology, CHG Hospital Tucson, LLC, Tucson, AZ, p. A40
    Chief Information Officer, Cornerstone Hospital–West Monroe, West Monroe, LA, p. A289

DAVIS, Amelia, Director of Nursing, CrossRidge Community Hospital, Wynne, AR, p. A53

DAVIS, Andrea, Chief Executive Officer, HEALTHSOUTH Desert Canyon Rehabilitation Hospital, Las Vegas, NV, p. A405

DAVIS, Andy, Chief Operating Officer, St. Vincent's Birmingham, Birmingham, AL, p. A17

DAVIS, Anne, Director Human Resources, Mason District Hospital, Havana, IL, p. A192

DAVIS, Astrid, R.N. Chief Nursing Officer, WellSpan York Hospital, York, PA, p. A559

DAVIS, Autherine, Director Human Resources, D. W. McMillan Memorial Hospital, Brewton, AL, p. A17

DAVIS, Barry L., FACHE, President and Chief Executive Officer, Arkansas Methodist Medical Center, Paragould, AR, p. A51

DAVIS, Betty, Director Administrative Services, Porterville Developmental Center, Porterville, CA, p. A83

DAVIS, Brenda, R.N. Vice President Patient Services, Indiana University Health Bedford Hospital, Bedford, IN, p. A206

DAVIS, Brent
    Human Resources Team Leader, Arkansas Heart Hospital, Little Rock, AR, p. A48
    Chief Financial Officer, Avista Adventist Hospital, Louisville, CO, p. A109
    Chief Financial Officer, Central Valley Medical Center, Nephi, UT, p. A661

DAVIS, C.J., Chief Executive Officer/ Executive Director, Four County Counseling Center, Logansport, IN, p. A217

DAVIS, Cathy J.
    Director Human Resources, ProMedica Bixby Hospital, Adrian, MI, p. A318
    Director Human Resources, ProMedica Herrick Hospital, Tecumseh, MI, p. A335

DAVIS, Charissa, Chief Nursing Officer and Director of Nursing, Oasis Behavioral Health – Chandler, Chandler, AZ, p. A31

DAVIS, Charlotte C., Director Human Resources, Lincoln Trail Behavioral Health System, Radcliff, KY, p. A268

DAVIS, Cheryl, M.D. Chief Medical Officer, Scotland Health Care System, Laurinburg, NC, p. A468

DAVIS, Daniel E., Chief Financial Officer, Kingwood Medical Center, Kingwood, TX, p. A631

DAVIS, Darcy, Chief Financial Officer, Lakeside Medical Center, Belle Glade, FL, p. A123

DAVIS, David
    Senior Vice President Finance, Kindred Hospital–New Jersey Morris County, Dover, NJ, p. A416
    Chief Operating Officer, Western Maryland Hospital Center, Hagerstown, MD, p. A301

DAVIS, Deborah W., Chief Operating Officer, VCU Medical Center, Richmond, VA, p. A678

DAVIS, Debra K., Director of Operations, Winner Regional Healthcare Center, Winner, SD, p. A578

DAVIS, Deland, Chief Financial Officer, Indian Health Service – Quentin N. Burdick Memorial Health Care Facility, Belcourt, ND, p. A477

DAVIS, Dell, Director Information Systems, United Memorial Medical Care, Houston, TX, p. A627

DAVIS, Dustin, Chief Executive Officer, Virginia Beach Psychiatric Center, Virginia Beach, VA, p. A680

DAVIS, Elaine, Chief Nursing Officer and Vice President Patient Services, Northeast Alabama Regional Medical Center, Anniston, AL, p. A15

DAVIS, Ellen, Service Unit Director, U. S. Public Health Service Indian Health Center, Pine Ridge, SD, p. A575

DAVIS, Evan, Director Technology and Environmental Services, Barbourville ARH Hospital, Barbourville, KY, p. A257

DAVIS, Gannon, Director Human Resources, Medical West, Bessemer, AL, p. A16

DAVIS, Gary
    Vice President Information Systems, Baptist Medical Center, San Antonio, TX, p. A645
    Director Information Systems, Great River Medical Center, West Burlington, IA, p. A239

DAVIS, Heather, M.D. Chief of Staff, Pender Memorial Hospital, Burgaw, NC, p. A461

DAVIS, Hervey E., Chief Executive Officer, Franklin Hospital District, Benton, IL, p. A181

DAVIS, Jack, Vice President Human Resources, Faxton St. Luke's Healthcare, Utica, NY, p. A457

DAVIS, James R., President and Chief Executive Officer, University Health Care System, Augusta, GA, p. B146

DAVIS, James R., Chief Executive Officer, University Hospital, Augusta, GA, p. A154

DAVIS, Janet, R.N. Senior Vice President and Chief Nursing Officer, Tampa General Hospital, Tampa, FL, p. A148

DAVIS, Janice, Interim Director Human Resources, Gifford Medical Center, Randolph, VT, p. A666

DAVIS, Jeff
    Chief Financial Officer, Harrison County Hospital, Corydon, IN, p. A208
    Senior Vice President Human Resources, Massachusetts General Hospital, Boston, MA, p. A307

DAVIS, Jeffrey, D.O. Chief Medical Officer, St. Mary's Medical Center, West Palm Beach, FL, p. A150

DAVIS, Jeremy, Chief Executive Officer, Evanston Regional Hospital, Evanston, WY, p. A722

DAVIS, John, Chief Human Resources Officer, Bristol Bay Area Health Corporation, Dillingham, AK, p. A29

DAVIS, John William
    Chief Executive Officer, Ochsner Medical Center – North Shore, Slidell, LA, p. A288
    Chief Executive Officer, Slidell Memorial Hospital, Slidell, LA, p. A288

DAVIS, Johnnie, Director Human Resources, Medicine Lodge Memorial Hospital, Medicine Lodge, KS, p. A249

DAVIS, Jon, Chief Financial Officer, Community Hospital–Fairfax, Fairfax, MO, p. A371

DAVIS, Jonathan S., FACHE, President, Martha Jefferson Hospital, Charlottesville, VA, p. A668

DAVIS, Justin
    Chief Executive Officer, Moses Taylor Hospital, Scranton, PA, p. A554
    Chief Executive Officer, Regional Hospital of Scranton, Scranton, PA, p. A554

DAVIS, Karen, Chief Nursing Officer and Vice President, Nursing, Howard County General Hospital, Columbia, MD, p. A300

DAVIS, Kassi, Director Patient Care Services, Willow Crest Hospital, Miami, OK, p. A514

DAVIS, Kenneth, Assistant Vice President Information Systems, Kennedy Krieger Institute, Baltimore, MD, p. A296

DAVIS, Kenneth L., M.D., President and Chief Executive, Mount Sinai Health System, New York, NY, p. B92

DAVIS, LaKeitha, Director Human Resources, Medical Center of South Arkansas, El Dorado, AR, p. A45

DAVIS, Lance, Associate Director, Miami Veterans Affairs Healthcare System, Miami, FL, p. A137

DAVIS, Leslie C., President, Magee–Womens Hospital of UPMC, Pittsburgh, PA, p. A551

DAVIS, Lisa, Vice President Finance, Saint Thomas West Hospital, Nashville, TN, p. A591

DAVIS, Lora, FACHE, Chief Executive Officer, Select Specialty Hospital–Tallahassee, Tallahassee, FL, p. A146

DAVIS, Lorraine, Vice President Human Resources, Horn Memorial Hospital, Ida Grove, IA, p. A232

DAVIS, Lyle E., Administrator, Cozad Community Hospital, Cozad, NE, p. A395

DAVIS, Malene S., R.N., President and Chief Executive Officer, Capital Hospice, Arlington, VA, p. A667

DAVIS, Mara, Interim Director, Veterans Affairs New Jersey Health Care System, East Orange, NJ, p. A416

DAVIS, Mark, Director Information Systems, Lake Taylor Transitional Care Hospital, Norfolk, VA, p. A675

DAVIS, Mark, M.D. Chief of Staff, Newberry County Memorial Hospital, Newberry, SC, p. A569

DAVIS, Mark, Chief Executive Officer, Pemiscot Memorial Health System, Hayti, MO, p. A372

DAVIS, Marla, Interim Chief Nursing Officer, PMH Medical Center, Prosser, WA, p. A688

DAVIS, Matt, Chief Executive Officer, Conroe Regional Medical Center, Conroe, TX, p. A607

DAVIS, Melissa, Chief Operating Officer, Andalusia Health, Andalusia, AL, p. A15

DAVIS, Myrna, Manager Human Resources, Palo Verde Hospital, Blythe, CA, p. A57

DAVIS, Natalie, R.N. Interim Chief Nursing Officer, McLeod Health Clarendon, Manning, SC, p. A568

DAVIS, Pam, Chief Nursing Officer, Galesburg Cottage Hospital, Galesburg, IL, p. A191

DAVIS, Pamela M., System President and Chief Executive Officer, Edward–Elmhurst Healthcare, Naperville, IL, p. B53

DAVIS, Patricia, Chief Nursing Officer, South Central Kansas Medical Center, Arkansas City, KS, p. A240

DAVIS, Paula M., Chief Human Resources Officer, Sonoma Valley Hospital, Sonoma, CA, p. A94

DAVIS, Rachel, Director, Sharp Coronado Hospital and Healthcare Center, Coronado, CA, p. A59

DAVIS, Randy
    Vice President and Chief Information Officer, CGH Medical Center, Sterling, IL, p. A204
    Chief Executive Officer, Northcrest Medical Center, Springfield, TN, p. A593

DAVIS, Ray
    Administrative Director, The Hospitals of Providence Memorial Campus, El Paso, TX, p. A616
    Administrative Director Information Systems, The Hospitals of Providence Sierra Campus, El Paso, TX, p. A616

DAVIS, Regana, Vice President Human Resources, Tri–State Memorial Hospital, Clarkston, WA, p. A683

DAVIS, Richard
    Chief Executive Officer, Central Peninsula Hospital, Soldotna, AK, p. A30
    Chief Financial Officer, George Washington University Hospital, Washington, DC, p. A121
    Chief Financial Officer, Saint Barnabas Medical Center, Livingston, NJ, p. A418

DAVIS, Richard O., Ph.D., President, Sibley Memorial Hospital, Washington, DC, p. A122

DAVIS, Rick, Chief Operating Officer and Support Services, Coshocton County Memorial Hospital, Coshocton, OH, p. A492

DAVIS, Robert, Chief Nursing Officer, Florida Hospital–Flagler, Palm Coast, FL, p. A141

DAVIS, Roger K., Director Human Resources, Bourbon Community Hospital, Paris, KY, p. A268

DAVIS, Ronald Anthony, Chief Financial Officer – UCLA Hospital System, Stewart & Lynda Resnick Neuropsychiatric Hospital at UCLA, Los Angeles, CA, p. A74

DAVIS, Roy, M.D. Chief Medical Officer, Providence Alaska Medical Center, Anchorage, AK, p. A28

DAVIS, Scott
  Manager Information Technology, Arkansas Surgical Hospital, North Little Rock, AR, p. A50
  Chief Executive Officer, Methodist Ambulatory Surgery Hospital – Northwest, San Antonio, TX, p. A646

DAVIS, Shawn, Chief Information Officer, Tuba City Regional Health Care Corporation, Tuba City, AZ, p. A40

DAVIS, Sondra, Vice President Human Resources & System Development, Harnett Health System, Dunn, NC, p. A464

DAVIS, Stephanie, Controller, HEALTHSOUTH Rehabilitation Hospital of Colorado Springs, Colorado Springs, CO, p. A102

DAVIS, Stephen, Chief Financial Officer, Illinois Valley Community Hospital, Peru, IL, p. A200

DAVIS, Steve, M.D. Chief Medical Officer, Campbellton Graceville Hospital, Graceville, FL, p. A130

DAVIS, Steve, Chief Financial Officer, Shands Lake Shore Regional Medical Center, Lake City, FL, p. A133

DAVIS, Steven T., Chief Executive Officer, Lock Haven Hospital, Lock Haven, PA, p. A543

DAVIS, Takeisha C., M.P.H., President and Chief Executive Officer, New Orleans East Hospital, New Orleans, LA, p. A285

DAVIS, Tammy, Director Human Resources, Union County Hospital, Anna, IL, p. A180

DAVIS, Terry, Manager Information Systems, Atchison Hospital, Atchison, KS, p. A240

DAVIS, Teshia, Chief Clinical Officer, Carolinas ContinueCARE Hospital at Pineville, Charlotte, NC, p. A462

DAVIS, Toby, Chief Nursing Officer, Good Samaritan Hospital, Bakersfield, CA, p. A56

DAVIS, Todd, M.D. Vice President Medical Affairs, Patient Safety Officer, CaroMont Regional Medical Center, Gastonia, NC, p. A465

DAVIS, Tommy, M.D. Chief of Staff, Oakdale Community Hospital, Oakdale, LA, p. A286

DAVIS, Tracye B., Acting Director, VA Long Beach Healthcare System, Long Beach, CA, p. A70

DAVIS, Trish, Chief Nursing Officer, Santa Rosa Medical Center, Milton, FL, p. A138

DAVIS, Verlene, Director Human Resources, Blue Mountain Hospital, John Day, OR, p. A527

DAVIS, Wayne, Manager Human Resources, Jesse Brown Veterans Affairs Medical Center, Chicago, IL, p. A184

DAVIS, MSN, Dan, R.N. Nurse Administrator, Park City Medical Center, Park City, UT, p. A662

DAVIS, RN, BSN, MBA, NEA–BC, Cindy, Chief Nursing Officer, PeaceHealth Southwest Medical Center, Vancouver, WA, p. A692

DAVIS–HAGENS, Patricia, R.N., Central Market Leader and President, The Jewish Hospital – Mercy Health, Cincinnati, OH, p. A488

DAVIS–HILL, Lori
  Chief Human Resource Officer, Banner Baywood Medical Center, Mesa, AZ, p. A34
  Chief Human Resource Officer, Banner Heart Hospital, Mesa, AZ, p. A34

DAVIS–SAMPSON, Sherri, Director Human Resources, Houston Methodist San Jacinto Hospital, Baytown, TX, p. A601

DAVISON, Trish, R.N. Chief Nursing Officer, Regional West Garden County, Oshkosh, NE, p. A401

DAVISSON, Deborah, MSN Chief Nursing Officer and Vice President, Patient Care Services, Holy Cross Hospital, Chicago, IL, p. A184

DAVY, Larry, Chief Executive Officer, Wallowa Memorial Hospital, Enterprise, OR, p. A525

DAWE, Jacqueline, R.N
  Chief Nursing Officer, Franklin Regional Hospital, Franklin, NH, p. A411
  Chief Nursing Officer, Lakes Region General Hospital, Laconia, NH, p. A411

DAWES, Christopher G., President and Chief Executive Officer, Lucile Salter Packard Children's Hospital Stanford, Palo Alto, CA, p. A82

DAWES, John M., FACHE, Chief Executive Officer, Moberly Regional Medical Center, Moberly, MO, p. A377

DAWSON, Al, Director of Nursing, Sistersville General Hospital, Sistersville, WV, p. A700

DAWSON, Anthony L., FACHE, Director, Veterans Affairs Gulf Coast Veterans Health Care System, Biloxi, MS, p. A355

DAWSON, John, Chief Executive Officer, Baptist Medical Center Attala, Kosciusko, MS, p. A360

DAWSON, Kane, Chief Executive Officer, First Baptist Medical Center, Dallas, TX, p. A610

DAWSON, Kathy, R.N. Chief Nursing Officer, Saddleback Memorial Medical Center, Laguna Hills, CA, p. A68

DAWSON, Nancy, M.D. Medical Director, Mayo Clinic Jacksonville, Jacksonville, FL, p. A131

DAWSON, Theresa, MSN Chief Nursing Officer, Oaklawn Hospital, Marshall, MI, p. A330

DAWSON, Trang, Chief Information Officer, Baylor Emergency Medical Center at Aubrey, Aubrey, TX, p. A598

DAWSON, Troy, M.D. President Medical Staff, Antelope Memorial Hospital, Neligh, NE, p. A399

DAX, Jennifer, Director Human Resources, Gundersen Boscobel Area Hospital and Clinics, Boscobel, WI, p. A703

DAY, Gordy, M.D. Medical Director, Schleicher County Medical Center, Eldorado, TX, p. A616

DAY, John M.
  Chief Operating Officer, Doctors NeuroMedical Hospital, Bremen, IN, p. A207
  Chief Executive Officer, Unity Medical & Surgical Hospital, Mishawaka, IN, p. A218

DAY, Mark, Chief Financial Officer, Twin Cities Hospital, Niceville, FL, p. A139

DAY, Regina
  Executive Director Finance, Mountain View Regional Medical Center, Norton, VA, p. A675
  Director of Finance, Wellmont Hancock County Hospital, Sneedville, TN, p. A593
  Executive Vice President of Finance, Wellmont Lonesome Pine Hospital, Big Stone Gap, VA, p. A667

DAY, Scott, Vice President Human Resources, Lutheran Medical Center, Wheat Ridge, CO, p. A111

DAY, Sherry Clouse, CP
  Vice President Finance and Regional Chief Financial Officer, Mercy Hospital Aurora, Aurora, MO, p. A367
  Chief Financial Officer, Mercy Hospital Cassville, Cassville, MO, p. A369
  Chief Financial Officer, Mercy St. Francis Hospital, Mountain View, MO, p. A377

DAY, Therese, Chief Financial Officer, UMass Memorial Medical Center, Worcester, MA, p. A316

DAY, Victoria, Chief Financial Officer and Vice President of Ancillary Services, Sharp Coronado Hospital and Healthcare Center, Coronado, CA, p. A59

DE BOND, Virginia, Chief Financial Officer, Woodlands Specialty Hospital, The Woodlands, TX, p. A653

DE FARIA, Ludmila, M.D. Chief Medical Officer, Eastside Psychiatric Hospital, Tallahassee, FL, p. A146

DE JESUS, Alexander, M.D. Medical Director, HEALTHSOUTH Rehabilitation Hospital of Sarasota, Sarasota, FL, p. A145

DE JESUS, Edwin, Comptroller, Hospital Santa Rosa, Guayama, PR, p. A727

DE JESUS, Hector M., Chief Operating Officer, Florida Hospital DeLand, DeLand, FL, p. A127

DE JESUS, Jorge, Executive Director, I. Gonzalez Martinez Oncologic Hospital, PR, p. A730

DE LA CRUZ, Rosemary, Chief Financial Officer, Hospital Episcopal San Lucas Guayama, Guayama, PR, p. A727

DE LA GARZA, Josiah, Chief Operating Officer, Baylor Scott & White Medical Center – Sunnyvale, Sunnyvale, TX, p. A651

DE LA PAZ, Christine, Director Human Resources, Aurora Charter Oak Hospital, Covina, CA, p. A60

DE LA PAZ, Eva, Chief Financial Officer, Post Acute Medical Specialty Hospital of Corpus Christi – South, Corpus Christi, TX, p. A608

DE LA TORRE, Ralph, M.D., Chairman and Chief Executive Officer, Steward Health Care System, LLC, Boston, MA, p. B129

DE LEON, Aurea, Chief Human Resources Officer, Hospital Universitario Dr. Ramon Ruiz Arnau, Bayamon, PR, p. A726

DE LEON, Darcy, Executive Director, Human Resources, Frank R. Howard Memorial Hospital, Willits, CA, p. A100

DE LEON, Dennis, M.D. Associate Chief Medical Officer and Vice President Medical Affairs, Highline Medical Center, Burien, WA, p. A683

DE LOS REYES, Jay
  Chief Operating Officer, HEALTHSOUTH Sunrise Rehabilitation Hospital, Sunrise, FL, p. A146
  Chief Operating Officer, Trumbull Memorial Hospital, Warren, OH, p. A505

DE LOS SANTOS, Conrad, President Medical Staff, Medical West, Bessemer, AL, p. A16

DE LOS SANTOS, Ruben, M.D. Chief Medical Officer, Fort Duncan Regional Medical Center, Eagle Pass, TX, p. A614

DE ONIS, Luis, Interim Chief Human Resources Officer, Stony Brook University Hospital, Stony Brook, NY, p. A456

DE PALO, Vera, M.D. Chief Medical Officer, Signature Healthcare Brockton Hospital, Brockton, MA, p. A308

DE PIANO, Linda, Ph.D., Chief Executive Officer, Jerome Golden Center for Behavioral Health, Inc., West Palm Beach, FL, p. A149

DE PREZ, Bernadette, Chief Operating Officer, Tennova Healthcare – Cleveland, Cleveland, TN, p. A581

DE TORRES, Francisco, M.D. Medical Director, Ashford Presbyterian Community Hospital, San Juan, PR, p. A729

DEAK, Terry, Chief Financial Officer, Lodi Memorial Hospital, Lodi, CA, p. A68

DEAKYNE, John R., Chief Financial Officer, Saint Mary's Regional Medical Center, Reno, NV, p. A408

DEAL, Jennifer, Chief Financial Officer, Johnson County Hospital, Tecumseh, NE, p. A402

DEAL, Larry, R.N., Chief Executive Officer, Vibra Hospital of Springfield, Springfield, IL, p. A203

DEAL, Lisa, Budget Analyst, U. S. Public Health Service Indian Hospital, Eagle Butte, SD, p. A573

DEAL, Roy, Chief Medical Officer, Emerald Coast Behavioral Hospital, Panama City, FL, p. A141

DEAN, Brian, FACHE, Chief Executive Officer, Memorial Hermann – Texas Medical Center, Houston, TX, p. A625

DEAN, Donna, Chief Financial Officer, Rainbow Mental Health Facility, Kansas City, KS, p. A246

DEAN, Douglas B., Chief Human Resources Officer, Children's of Alabama, Birmingham, AL, p. A16

DEAN, Joel, Director Information Services, Piedmont Medical Center, Rock Hill, SC, p. A569

DEAN, Laura, Director Human Resources, Wilson Medical Center, Neodesha, KS, p. A249

DEAN, Lloyd H., President and Chief Executive Officer, Dignity Health, San Francisco, CA, p. B49

DEAN, Morre, Chief Executive Officer, Porter Adventist Hospital, Denver, CO, p. A104

DEAN, Ronnie, Chief Executive Officer, Troy Regional Medical Center, Troy, AL, p. A26

DEAN, Sam, Chief Operating Officer, Merit Health Central, Jackson, MS, p. A360

DEAN, Thomas, M.D. Chief of Staff, Avera Weskota Memorial Hospital, Wessington Springs, SD, p. A577

DEANE, Leslie, Chief Executive Officer, Select Specialty Hospital–Winston–Salem, Winston–Salem, NC, p. A476

DEANS, Ken, Chief Information Officer, Chesapeake Regional Healthcare, Chesapeake, VA, p. A668

DEARDORFF, John A., Chief Executive Officer, Reston Hospital Center, Reston, VA, p. A676

DEARY, Shirley, Director Human Resources, Glenbeigh Hospital and Outpatient Centers, Rock Creek, OH, p. A502

DEATER, Gary A., Vice President Administration, Human Resources and Risk Management, Witham Health Services, Lebanon, IN, p. A217

DEATON, David, Chief Executive Officer, Ozark Health Medical Center, Clinton, AR, p. A44

DEATON, Eric, Executive Vice President, Chief Operating Officer and Corporate Operating, Wellmont Hancock County Hospital, Sneedville, TN, p. A593

DEATON, Mike, Chief Financial Officer, Ozark Health Medical Center, Clinton, AR, p. A44

DEATON, Susan Renodin, Human Resources Director, Logan Memorial Hospital, Russellville, KY, p. A269

DEATON, Tim, Chief Executive Officer, AMG Specialty Hospital – Covington, Covington, LA, p. A275

DEAVER, Lennie, M.D. Chief of Staff, Tri Valley Health System, Cambridge, NE, p. A394

DEBBAS, Elias, M.D. President Medical Staff, Fort Washington Medical Center, Oxen Hill, MD, p. A302

DEBEHNKE, Daniel J., M.D., Chief Executive Officer, Nebraska Medicine – Nebraska Medical Center, Omaha, NE, p. A400

DEBEVEC, Teresa, Chief Executive Officer, Cook Hospital and Convalescent Nursing Care Unit, Cook, MN, p. A341

DEBLANC, Hunt, M.D. Chief of Staff, Opelousas General Health System, Opelousas, LA, p. A286

DEBLASIS, John, Vice President, Belmont Community Hospital, Bellaire, OH, p. A484

DEBLIEUX, Dawna, Vice President Patient Care Services and Chief Nurse Executive, Natchitoches Regional Medical Center, Natchitoches, LA, p. A284

DEBLOIS, Georgean, M.D. Chairman Medical Staff, Chippenham Hospital, Richmond, VA, p. A677

DEBLOUW, Christina, Chief Executive Officer, Select Specialty Hospital–Flint, Flint, MI, p. A323

DEBOER, Cynthia D., Chief Financial Officer, Cedar Springs Hospital, Colorado Springs, CO, p. A102

DEBOER, K. C., President and Chief Executive Officer, Jamestown Regional Medical Center, Jamestown, ND, p. A480

DEBOLT, Larry W., Chief Financial Officer, Bluffton Regional Medical Center, Bluffton, IN, p. A207

DEBONA, Paul, Chief Executive Officer, Baylor Surgical Hospital at Fort Worth, Fort Worth, TX, p. A617

DEBOOY, Ann, R.N. Chief Nursing Officer, Memorial Medical Center, Las Cruces, NM, p. A430

DEBORD, Thomas, Chief Operating Officer, Overlake Medical Center, Bellevue, WA, p. A682

DECELIS, Lori, Director Human Resources, Hampton Behavioral Health Center, Westampton, NJ, p. A425

DECELL, Daniela, Chief Executive Officer, Las Colinas Medical Center, Irving, TX, p. A629

DECHABERT, Rebecca, Acting Director Personnel, New York State Psychiatric Institute, New York, NY, p. A447

DECHAIRO–MARINO, Ann, R.N. Chief Nursing Officer, Providence Holy Cross Medical Center,, CA, p. A73

DECHANT, David, Chief Human Resources Officer, Tomah Veterans Affairs Medical Center, Tomah, WI, p. A717

DECKARD, Rick, Chief Fiscal Service, Chillicothe Veterans Affairs Medical Center, Chillicothe, OH, p. A487

DECKARD, Steven D., Vice President Human Resources, Indiana University Health Bloomington Hospital, Bloomington, IN, p. A207

DECKER, Diann, Chief Human Resource Officer, Provo Canyon Behavioral Hospital, Orem, UT, p. A661

DECKER, Janet, Assistant Vice President, MedStar Union Memorial Hospital, Baltimore, MD, p. A297

DECKER, Jeanine, Manager Human Resources, Arizona State Hospital, Phoenix, AZ, p. A36

DECKER, Kathy, Interim Chief Nursing Officer, Northern Inyo Hospital, Bishop, CA, p. A57

DECKER, Kevin, Chief Executive Officer, Forrest City Medical Center, Forrest City, AR, p. A46

DECKER, Michael, President and Chief Executive Officer, Divine Savior Healthcare, Portage, WI, p. A714

DECKER, Wyatt, Chief Executive Officer, Mayo Clinic Hospital, Phoenix, AZ, p. A36

DECORTE, Raymond P., M.D. Chief Medical Officer, East Jefferson General Hospital, Metairie, LA, p. A283

DECREMER, Dean, Information Systems Manager, Dickinson County Healthcare System, Iron Mountain, MI, p. A327

DEDECKER, Troy, FACHE, Chief Executive Officer, Mid–America Rehabilitation Hospital, Shawnee Mission, KS, p. A253

DEDRICK, Jennifer, Chief Executive Officer, Glen Oaks Hospital, Greenville, TX, p. A621

DEE, Thomas A., Chief Executive Officer, Southwestern Vermont Medical Center, Bennington, VT, p. A665

DEERING, Linda, R.N., President, Advocate Sherman Hospital, Elgin, IL, p. A189

DEERING, Lisa, Administrator, Heatherhill Care Communities, Chardon, OH, p. A486

DEES, Edith, Vice President Information Services and Chief Information Officer, Holy Spirit – A Geisinger Affiliate, Camp Hill, PA, p. A534

DEFOE, Mike, Chief Financial Officer, Perry Memorial Hospital, Princeton, IL, p. A201

DEFOORE, Richard G., FACHE, Chief Executive Officer, Stamford Memorial Hospital, Stamford, TX, p. A650

DEFORD, Drexel, Chief Information Officer, Scripps Mercy Hospital, San Diego, CA, p. A89

DEFRANCESCO, Anthony, Associate Director, VA Long Beach Healthcare System, Long Beach, CA, p. A70

DEFURIO, Ken, President and Chief Executive Officer, Butler Health System, Butler, PA, p. A534

DEGEAR, David O., M.D. Vice President Medical Affairs, Westfields Hospital, New Richmond, WI, p. A713

DEGENNARO, Vincent, M.D. Chief of Staff, Miami Veterans Affairs Healthcare System, Miami, FL, p. A137

DEGINA, Anthony M., President and Chief Executive Officer, Largo Medical Center, Largo, FL, p. A134

DEGLANDON, Frances, Chief Financial Officer, Bunkie General Hospital, Bunkie, LA, p. A274

DEGNAN, William, Vice President Finance, Aria – Jefferson Health, Philadelphia, PA, p. A547

DEGRAVELLE, Eric, Director Human Resources, Thibodaux Regional Medical Center, Thibodaux, LA, p. A289

DEGROOT, Daniel, Chief Operating Officer, HSHS St. Clare Memorial Hospital, Oconto Falls, WI, p. A713

DEGROOT, Randy, President and Chief Executive Officer, Community Health Center of Branch County, Coldwater, MI, p. A321

DEHAVEN, Bryce, Chief Financial Officer, Medical Center of Aurora, Aurora, CO, p. A101

DEHERRERA, Barbara, Chief Nursing Officer, Garfield County Public Hospital District, Pomeroy, WA, p. A688

DEHNING, Cielo, M.D. Medical Director, Mid–America Rehabilitation Hospital, Shawnee Mission, KS, p. A253

DEIBEL, Justin, Senior Vice President and Chief Financial Officer, Mercy Medical Center, Baltimore, MD, p. A297

DEININGER, Robert, Chief Executive Officer, Florida Hospital Fish Memorial, Orange City, FL, p. A140

DEIS, Terrence G., FACHE, President, Saint Joseph London, London, KY, p. A264

DEITRICK, Diana, Director Information Services, Devereux Hospital and Children's Center of Florida, Melbourne, FL, p. A135

DEJACO, Lynn S., Chief Financial Officer, FirstHealth Moore Regional Hospital, Pinehurst, NC, p. A471

DEJESUS, David, Senior Vice President Human Resources, Southcoast Hospitals Group, Fall River, MA, p. A310

DEJONG, Tyler

    Director, Operational Finance, CHI Health Lakeside, Omaha, NE, p. A400

    Director of Operational Finance, CHI Health Midlands, Papillion, NE, p. A401

DEKASTLE, Reuben J., Chief Nursing Officer, Weiser Memorial Hospital, Weiser, ID, p. A179

DEKEYZER, Ron, Regional Director Information Systems, CHRISTUS St. Vincent Regional Medical Center, Santa Fe, NM, p. A431

DEKOK, Joni, Chief Nursing Officer, Sanford Sheldon Medical Center, Sheldon, IA, p. A237

DEKONING, Bernard L., M.D. Chief of Staff, Wm. Jennings Bryan Dorn Veterans Affairs Medical Center, Columbia, SC, p. A564

DEKREY, Dale, MS Associate Director Operations and Resources, Fargo Veterans Affairs Health Care System, Fargo, ND, p. A478

DEKREY, Daniel, M.D. Chief of Staff, Sanford Bemidji Medical Center, Bemidji, MN, p. A339

DEKRUSE, Jet L., Administrator, Humboldt County Mental Health, Eureka, CA, p. A61

DEL CASTILLO, Daniel, Chief Executive Officer, HEALTHSOUTH Rehabilitation Hospital of San Juan, San Juan, PR, p. A729

DEL GAUDIO, Frank J., Director and Chief Executive Officer, Essex County Hospital Center, Cedar Grove, NJ, p. A415

DEL GUIDICE, Mary Margaret, R.N. Chief Nursing Officer, Pennsylvania Hospital, Philadelphia, PA, p. A549

DEL RIO, R. Maximilien, M.D. Medical Director, Northern Virginia Mental Health Institute, Falls Church, VA, p. A670

DEL TORO, Gustavo, M.D. Chief Medical Officer, Wyckoff Heights Medical Center,, NY, p. A450

DEL TORO, Ivan E., M.D. Medical Director, Hospital HIMA San Pablo Caguas, Caguas, PR, p. A726

DELA TORRE, Victor, Command Legal Officer, Naval Hospital Lemoore, Lemoore, CA, p. A68

DELACROIX, Marc, Chief Information Officer, Signature Healthcare Brockton Hospital, Brockton, MA, p. A308

DELAGARDELLE, Pamela K., President and Chief Executive Officer, UnityPoint Health – Allen Hospital, Waterloo, IA, p. A239

DELAHANTY, Paula

    Regional Chief Nursing Officer, Pen Bay Medical Center, Rockport, ME, p. A295

    Regional Chief Nursing Officer, Waldo County General Hospital, Belfast, ME, p. A292

DELANEY, Bryan, Director Information Technology, Crossroads Community Hospital, Mount Vernon, IL, p. A197

DELANEY, Kristi, Director, Human Resources, Siskin Hospital for Physical Rehabilitation, Chattanooga, TN, p. A580

DELANEY, Patrick, Administrative Director, Operations, Robert Wood Johnson University Hospital Somerset, Somerville, NJ, p. A423

DELANO, John

    Vice President Chief Information Officer, Integris Baptist Medical Center, Oklahoma City, OK, p. A516

    Vice President and Chief Information Officer, Integris Southwest Medical Center, Oklahoma City, OK, p. A516

DELATTE, Sandra, Director Human Resources, Villa Feliciana Medical Complex, Jackson, LA, p. A278

DELAVAN, Karen, Interim Director Human Resources, Comanche County Medical Center, Comanche, TX, p. A607

DELEON, Arsenio V., M.D. Chief Medical Officer, Select Specialty Hospital-Macomb County, Mount Clemens, MI, p. A330

DELEON, Joseph, President, Texas Health Harris Methodist Hospital Southwest Fort Worth, Fort Worth, TX, p. A619

DELEON, Marcos

    Vice President Community Engagement, Truman Medical Center–Hospital Hill, Kansas City, MO, p. A374

    Vice President Community Engagement, Truman Medical Center–Lakewood, Kansas City, MO, p. A374

DELFS, Michael, Chief Executive Officer, Mercy Hospital, Moose Lake, MN, p. A347

DELGADO, Eric, Chief Financial Officer, Lakewood Regional Medical Center, Lakewood, CA, p. A68

DELGADO, Lupe, Coordinator Human Resources, Kindred Hospital Sugar Land, Sugar Land, TX, p. A650

DELGADO, Pete, President and Chief Executive Officer, Salinas Valley Memorial Healthcare System, Salinas, CA, p. A87

DELGADO, Steve, Operations Coordinator, Milwaukee County Behavioral Health Division, Milwaukee, WI, p. A711

DELGRECO, Trish, Director of Nursing, OhioHealth MedCentral Shelby Hospital, Shelby, OH, p. A502

DELIEN, Rudie, Director Human Resources, Devereux Georgia Treatment Network, Kennesaw, GA, p. A161

DELISE, Donna, Associate Director Patient Care Services, Oklahoma City Veterans Affairs Medical Center, Oklahoma City, OK, p. A517

DELLA FLORA, Thomas, Vice President and Chief Information Officer, Catholic Medical Center, Manchester, NH, p. A412

DELLA LANA, David, M.D. Chief of Staff, Fairchild Medical Center, Yreka, CA, p. A100

DELLASEGA, Dave, President and Chief Executive Officer, Great Plains Health Alliance, Inc., Wichita, KS, p. B58

DELLEA, Eugene A., President, Fairview Hospital, Great Barrington, MA, p. A310

DELLICK, Charles, Director Information Technology, Magruder Memorial Hospital, Port Clinton, OH, p. A501

DELLICKER, Sandra, Director of Human Resources, Saint Anne's Hospital, Fall River, MA, p. A310

DELLOCONO, John, Senior Vice President and Chief Financial Officer, CentraState Healthcare System, Freehold, NJ, p. A417

DELLSPERGER, Kevin, M.D. Chief Medical Officer, Augusta University Medical Center, Augusta, GA, p. A153

DELONE, Lori

    Senior Vice President Support Services and Chief Information Officer, Health First Cape Canaveral Hospital, Cocoa Beach, FL, p. A126

    Senior Vice President and Chief Information Officer, Health First Viera Hospital, Melbourne, FL, p. A135

DELONG, Patricia, Chief Nursing Officer, Essentia Health St. Joseph's Medical Center, Brainerd, MN, p. A340

DELORENZO, David, Senior Director Human Resources, Sisters of Charity Hospital of Buffalo, Buffalo, NY, p. A436

DELORME, Robert, Vice President Medical Affairs, Community Memorial Hospital, Hamilton, NY, p. A440

DELPHIN–RITTMON, Miriam, Ph.D., Commissioner, Connecticut Department of Mental Health and Addiction Services, Hartford, CT, p. B41

DELPLEACHE, Michael, Specialist Information Technology, Anchor Hospital, Atlanta, GA, p. A152

DELVEAUX, Joe, Manager Information Services, St. Francis Regional Medical Center, Shakopee, MN, p. A351

DEMARCO, Victor, Chief Financial Officer, Bronx–Lebanon Hospital Center Health Care System,, NY, p. A444

DEMAREST, Pamela, R.N. Chief Nursing Officer, UNM Sandoval Regional Medical Center, Albuquerque, NM, p. A428

DEMASIE, Dennis, Vice President Information Systems and Chief Information Officer, Rush–Copley Medical Center, Aurora, IL, p. A181

DEMATTEO, Kathleen, Chief Information Officer, Danbury Hospital, Danbury, CT, p. A113

DEMBLA, Preeti, Chief Medical Officer and Medical Director, Rehabilitation Hospital of Fort Wayne, Fort Wayne, IN, p. A211

DEMERICH, Lois B., Director Human Resources, Sentara Williamsburg Regional Medical Center, Williamsburg, VA, p. A680

DEMERS, Becky, R.N. Chief Operating Officer, Samaritan Healthcare, Moses Lake, WA, p. A686

DEMERS, Vickie, Chief Executive Officer, HEALTHSOUTH Lakeshore Rehabilitation Hospital, Birmingham, AL, p. A16

DEMETRIADES, James, Vice President, Operations, University Medical Center of Princeton at Plainsboro, Plainsboro, NJ, p. A422

DEMING, Mark, Administrator, Finance and Support, Beaumont Hospital – Taylor, Taylor, MI, p. A335

DEMING, Peggy, Executive Vice President and Chief Financial Officer, University Health System, San Antonio, TX, p. A647

DEMING, Terra, Director Human Resources, Otsego Memorial Hospital, Gaylord, MI, p. A324

DEMLAKIAN, Vahan, Director of Human Resources, Gateways Hospital and Mental Health Center, Los Angeles, CA, p. A71

DEMMEL, Ruth, M.D. Chief Medical Officer, Perkins County Health Services, Grant, NE, p. A396

DEMOE, Sara, Chief Financial Officer, North Canyon Medical Center, Gooding, ID, p. A176

DEMORLIS, John, M.D. Chief Medical Staff, Salem Memorial District Hospital, Salem, MO, p. A382

DEMORROW, Dawn P., Chief Human Resources Service, Wilkes–Barre Veterans Affairs Medical Center, Wilkes–Barre, PA, p. A558

DEMPSEY, Jeffrey, President and Chief Operating Officer, Mercy Health – St. Charles Hospital, Oregon, OH, p. A500

DEMPSEY, John J., Chief Executive Officer, Little Colorado Medical Center, Winslow, AZ, p. A41

DEMURO, Rob, M.D. Chief Medical Officer, The University of Vermont Health Network Elizabethtown Community Hospital, Elizabethtown, NY, p. A438

DENCKLAU, Larry, D.O. Chief of Staff, Lake Pointe Medical Center, Rowlett, TX, p. A644

DENEFF, Randall, Vice President Finance, Mary Free Bed Rehabilitation Hospital, Grand Rapids, MI, p. A325

DENEGRI, David, Chief Financial Officer, Parkwood Behavioral Health System, Olive Branch, MS, p. A363

DENEN, Bruce, Manager Data Processing, Fayette County Memorial Hospital, Washington Court House, OH, p. A505

DENG, Mei, Chief Financial Officer, MetroSouth Medical Center, Blue Island, IL, p. A182

DENHAM, Stephanie, Chief Financial Officer and Human Resources Officer, Phillips County Hospital, Malta, MT, p. A389

DENICOLA, Joseph, Chief Executive Officer and Managing Director, Arrowhead Behavioral Health Hospital, Maumee, OH, p. A498

DENIGRIS, Deborah, Chief Nursing Officer, Kingsboro Psychiatric Center,, NY, p. A445

DENIO, Arthur E., Vice President and Chief Financial Officer, NorthBay Medical Center, Fairfield, CA, p. A62

DENISIENKO, Mary, Vice President Human Resources, Palos Community Hospital, Palos Heights, IL, p. A199

DENISON, Rita, Director of Information Systems, Sturgis Hospital, Sturgis, MI, p. A335

DENKER, Jill, Executive Director Human Resources, Lexington Regional Health Center, Lexington, NE, p. A397

DENMARK, Donald, M.D
Chief Medical Officer, Carondelet St. Joseph's Hospital, Tucson, AZ, p. A40
Chief Medical Officer, Carondelet St. Mary's Hospital, Tucson, AZ, p. A40

DENNETT, Bryan, M.D. Chief of Staff, William Newton Hospital, Winfield, KS, p. A256

DENNIS, Jeanne, R.N. Chief Nursing Officer, Abraham Lincoln Memorial Hospital, Lincoln, IL, p. A195

DENNIS, Kera, Assistant Administrator, Finance, UW Medicine/Harborview Medical Center, Seattle, WA, p. A690

DENNIS, Michael, Director, William J. McCord Adolescent Treatment Facility, Orangeburg, SC, p. A569

DENNIS, Ronnie, Chief of Staff, Rolling Plains Memorial Hospital, Sweetwater, TX, p. A651

DENNISON, Cynthia, Assistant Chief Financial Officer 3, Mercy Tiffin Hospital, Tiffin, OH, p. A503

DENNO, Charles, Chief Financial Officer, Westwood Lodge Hospital, Westwood, MA, p. A316

DENNY, Donald, M.D. Senior Vice President, Medical Affairs, University Medical Center of Princeton at Plainsboro, Plainsboro, NJ, p. A422

DENO, Mark S., Chief Executive Officer, Spalding Rehabilitation Hospital, Aurora, CO, p. A101

DENSON, Anna, Human Resources Specialist, Choctaw Health Center, Philadelphia, MS, p. A363

DENSON, Paula Lajean, M.D. President, Tyler County Hospital, Woodville, TX, p. A658

DENT, Bruce, Human Resources Director, Heber Valley Medical Center, Heber City, UT, p. A660

DENT, Robert L., R.N. Senior Vice President, Chief Operating Officer and Chief Nursing Officer, Midland Memorial Hospital, Midland, TX, p. A637

DENTEN, Jane, MSN Vice President Nursing and Chief Nurse Executive, Advocate Lutheran General Hospital, Park Ridge, IL, p. A200

DENTON, Brian, Administrator, Mercy Hospital Kingfisher, Kingfisher, OK, p. A513

DENTON, Christopher, Chief Financial Officer, Henrico Doctors' Hospital, Richmond, VA, p. A677

DENTON, Genise, Manager Human Resources, John J. Pershing Veterans Affairs Medical Center, Poplar Bluff, MO, p. A378

DENTON, Joe, Executive Vice President and Chief Financial Officer, Mobile Infirmary Medical Center, Mobile, AL, p. A22

DENTON, Roy, M.D. Chief Medical Officer, Conway Regional Rehabilitation Hospital, Conway, AR, p. A44

DENTON, Tony, JD Senior Vice President and Chief Operating Officer, University of Michigan Hospitals and Health Centers, Ann Arbor, MI, p. A318

DENTONI, Terry, Chief Nursing Officer, Zuckerberg San Francisco General Hospital and Trauma Center, San Francisco, CA, p. A91

DENUCCI, Alex, Chief Financial Officer, Franciscan Hospital for Children, Boston, MA, p. A306

DEPASQUALE, Joseph, M.D. Interim Chief Medical Officer, Saint Michael's Medical Center, Newark, NJ, p. A421

DEPAULIS, Hugh, Interim Vice President and Chief Financial Officer, Mercy Medical Center–Sioux City, Sioux City, IA, p. A237

DEPINHO, Ronald A., M.D., President, University of Texas M.D. Anderson Cancer Center, Houston, TX, p. A627

DEPKO, Mike, Director Information Technology, Brown County Hospital, Ainsworth, NE, p. A393

DEPLONTY, Sandy, Senior Director Clinical Services, War Memorial Hospital, Sault Sainte Marie, MI, p. A334

DEPOOTER, Stephen, Chief Information Officer, Norwegian American Hospital, Chicago, IL, p. A185

DEPPERMAN, Kristi, Chief Financial Officer, Memphis Veterans Affairs Medical Center, Memphis, TN, p. A589

DEPRATO, Jeremy, Director Information Technology, Spine Hospital of Louisiana (formally the NeuroMedical Center Surgical Hospital), Baton Rouge, LA, p. A273

DERAMUS, Brenda, Manager Human Resources, Sutter Lakeside Hospital, Lakeport, CA, p. A68

DERBY, Richard P., Vice President Finance, Barton Memorial Hospital, South Lake Tahoe, CA, p. A95

DERFLINGER, Terri, Administrator, Mercy Hospital of Franciscan Sisters, Oelwein, IA, p. A235

DERMAN, Nancy, Director Human Resources, Southwest Connecticut Mental Health System, Bridgeport, CT, p. A113

DEROCHE, Glynis R., Chief Executive Officer, Acadia Vermilion Hospital, Lafayette, LA, p. A280

DEROCHE, Richard, Manager Information Technology, Deaconess Hospital, Spokane, WA, p. A691

DERONCEREY, Josiane, Director Human Resources, CarePoint Health –Christ Hospital, Jersey City, NJ, p. A418

DEROSA, Christina, Ph.D., Interim Chief Executive Officer and Chief Nursing Officer, Highlands–Cashiers Hospital, Highlands, NC, p. A467

DEROUEN, Jason, Director Management Information Systems, Grace Medical Center, Lubbock, TX, p. A634

DERRICO, Patricia, FACHE Chief Nursing Officer, Coliseum Northside Hospital, Macon, GA, p. A162

DERSCH, Stephen, M.D. President Medical Staff, Regency Hospital of Florence, Florence, SC, p. A566

DERUS, Charles, M.D. Vice President Medical Management, Advocate Good Samaritan Hospital, Downers Grove, IL, p. A188

DERUYTER, David N., M.D. President Medical Staff, Select Specialty Hospital Midtown Atlanta, Atlanta, GA, p. A152

DERYNCK, Dodie, Chief Nursing Officer, Avera Marshall Regional Medical Center, Marshall, MN, p. A346

DESAI, Ankur, Interim Chief Medical officer, Rome Memorial Hospital, Rome, NY, p. A455

DESAI, Maulik, M.D. Chief of Staff, Methodist Hospital Union County, Morganfield, KY, p. A267

DESAI, Nimesh, M.D. Medical Director, Massena Memorial Hospital, Massena, NY, p. A442

DESAI, Shailesh, M.D. Chief of Staff, Baum Harmon Mercy Hospital, Primghar, IA, p. A236

DESALVO, Susan, Manager Human Resources, Bath Veterans Affairs Medical Center, Bath, NY, p. A434

DESANTIS, John, Chief Financial Officer, Glenwood Regional Medical Center, West Monroe, LA, p. A289

DESANTIS, Vincent, Vice President Finance, Phelps Memorial Hospital Center, Sleepy Hollow, NY, p. A455

DESART, Amy, Vice President, Chief Financial Officer, Missouri Baptist Medical Center, Saint Louis, MO, p. A380

DESCHAMBEAU, Wayne G., President and Chief Executive Officer, Wayne Hospital, Greenville, OH, p. A495

DESCHENE, Normand E., FACHE, Chief Executive Officer, Lowell General Hospital, Lowell, MA, p. A311

DESCHRYVER, Joseph, Chief Executive Officer, Sierra Vista Regional Medical Center, San Luis Obispo, CA, p. A92

DESEI, Nitin, M.D. Medical Director, Regional Rehabilitation Hospital, Phenix City, AL, p. A24

DESHONG, Andre, Administrator, Behavioral Hospital of Longview, Longview, TX, p. A633

DESHPANDE, Jay, M.D. Senior Vice President and Chief Medical Officer, Arkansas Children's Hospital, Little Rock, AR, p. A48

DESIMINI, Esther, Administrator, Riverside Tappahannock Hospital, Tappahannock, VA, p. A679

DESIMONE, Maureen, Chief Operating Officer, Blythedale Children's Hospital, Valhalla, NY, p. A457

DESIMONE, Shane, M.D. Chief of Staff, Jane Todd Crawford Hospital, Greensburg, KY, p. A261

DESJARDINS, JoAnna B., Director Human Resources, Mena Regional Health System, Mena, AR, p. A50

DESJEUNES, Carol, Vice President and Chief Operating Officer, Psychiatric Institute of Washington, Washington, DC, p. A122

DESKINS, Juanita, Chief Operating Officer, Pikeville Medical Center, Pikeville, KY, p. A268

DESMARTEAU, Lisa Jo, Chief Financial Officer, Miami Jewish Home and Hospital for Aged, Miami, FL, p. A137

DESMOND, Debbie, Director Human Resources, Martha Jefferson Hospital, Charlottesville, VA, p. A668

DESMOND, Heather, Chief Financial Officer, Bibb Medical Center, Centreville, AL, p. A18

DESMOND, Jeffrey, M.D. Chief Medical Officer, University of Michigan Hospitals and Health Centers, Ann Arbor, MI, p. A318

DESMOND, P. Craig, Chief Executive Officer, Southwest General Hospital, San Antonio, TX, p. A647

DESOTELLE, Robert C., President and Chief Executive Officer, Asheville Specialty Hospital, Asheville, NC, p. A460

DESOTO, James, M.D
Vice President Medical Affairs, Mercy Medical Center Redding, Redding, CA, p. A84
Vice President Medical Affairs, St. Elizabeth Community Hospital, Red Bluff, CA, p. A84

DESOUZA, Jacqueline, Chief Executive Officer, Research Medical Center, Kansas City, MO, p. A373

DESPRES, Paul J., Chief Executive Officer, Eleanor Slater Hospital, Cranston, RI, p. A560

DESROCHES, Jeff, Manager Information Systems, AHMC Anaheim Regional Medical Center, Anaheim, CA, p. A54

DESTEFANO, Geraldine, R.N. Chief Nursing Officer, JFK Medical Center North Campus, West Palm Beach, FL, p. A149

DETANO, Teresa R., M.P.H., Chief Executive Officer, Select Specialty Hospital–Northern Kentucky, Fort Thomas, KY, p. A260

DETTERMAN, B. Lynn
President and Chief Executive Officer, Mercy Health – Willard Hospital, Willard, OH, p. A506
President and Chief Executive Officer, Mercy Hospital of Defiance, Defiance, OH, p. A493
President and Chief Executive Officer, Mercy Tiffin Hospital, Tiffin, OH, p. A503

DETTMER, Brantley, Hospital Administrator and Chief Operating Officer, Kaiser Foundation Hospital Westside Medical Center, Hillsboro, OR, p. A526

DETWILER, Courtney, R.N., Administrator, Hampton Roads Specialty Hospital, Newport News, VA, p. A674

DETWILER, Eric, Director Information Technology, Barnes–Kasson County Hospital, Susquehanna, PA, p. A555

DEUEL, Teresa L., Chief Executive Officer, Hodgeman County Health Center, Jetmore, KS, p. A245

DEURMIER, Carol, Chief Executive Officer, St. Michael's Hospital Avera, Tyndall, SD, p. A577

DEUTSCH, Stephen, Vice President Operations and Support, Spencer Hospital, Spencer, IA, p. A238

DEVANATHAN, Raja, M.D. Chief Medical Officer, Vibra Hospital of Northwestern Indiana, Crown Point, IN, p. A209

DEVANEY, Catherine, Chief Executive Officer, HEALTHSOUTH Rehabilitation Hospital, Concord, NH, p. A410

DEVANSKY, Gary W., Director, Coatesville Veterans Affairs Medical Center, Coatesville, PA, p. A536

DEVARAJ, Kiran S., Chief Medical Officer and Chief Clinical Officer, Highland Hospital, Charleston, WV, p. A695

DEVARAJAN, Vadakkipalayam N., Chief Medical Staff, St. Charles Parish Hospital, Luling, LA, p. A282

DEVAULT, Jennifer, Vice President Associate Services, F. F. Thompson Hospital, Canandaigua, NY, p. A436

DEVAULT, Rosanne, Chief Financial Officer, McKenzie–Willamette Medical Center, Springfield, OR, p. A531

DEVAULT, Roseann M., Chief Financial Officer, Tennova Healthcare–Jefferson Memorial Hospital, Jefferson City, TN, p. A584

DEVAUX, Sheri, Information Technology Manager, Connecticut Veterans Home and Hospital, Rocky Hill, CT, p. A116

DEVENUTO, Joseph, Vice President and Chief Information Officer, Norton Women's and Kosair Children's Hospital, Louisville, KY, p. A265

DEVERA, Rozelle, Director of Information Systems, Gateways Hospital and Mental Health Center, Los Angeles, CA, p. A71

DEVILLE, Linda F., Chief Executive Officer, Bunkie General Hospital, Bunkie, LA, p. A274

DEVIN, Brian V., Chief Executive Officer, Massachusetts Hospital School, Canton, MA, p. A309

DEVIN, Joseph, Chief Financial Officer, Boone County Hospital, Boone, IA, p. A226

DEVINE, Joseph W., FACHE, President and Chief Executive Officer, Kennedy Health System, Cherry Hill, NJ, p. A415

DEVITA, James, M.D. Chief Medical Officer, Tewksbury Hospital, Tewksbury, MA, p. A315

DEVITO, Joseph M., Vice President Finance and Chief Operating Officer, Geisinger–Bloomsburg Hospital, Bloomsburg, PA, p. A533

DEVLIN, James, Director Information Systems, St. Cloud Regional Medical Center, Saint Cloud, FL, p. A144

DEVOCELLE, Frank H., President and Chief Executive Officer, Olathe Medical Center, Olathe, KS, p. A250

DEVORE, Kathy, Administrator, ContinueCARE Hospital at Madisonville, Madisonville, KY, p. A266

DEVORE, Paul A., M.D. Medical Director, Gladys Spellman Specialty Hospital and Nursing Center, Cheverly, MD, p. A299

DEVORSETZ, Marc, Chief Executive Officer, Heritage Park Surgical Hospital, Sherman, TX, p. A649

DEW, Douglas, M.D. President Medical Staff, Flagler Hospital, Saint Augustine, FL, p. A144

DEWAN, Vijay, M.D. Clinical Director, Lincoln Regional Center, Lincoln, NE, p. A398

DEWANE, Patti, Vice President Finance and Treasurer, SwedishAmerican – A Division of UW Health, Rockford, IL, p. A202

DEWAR, William, M.D. Chief of Staff, Wayne Memorial Hospital, Honesdale, PA, p. A540

DEWBERRY, Robbie, Chief Executive Officer, Mitchell County Hospital, Colorado City, TX, p. A606

DEWERFF, Mike, President and Chief Executive Officer, UnityPoint Health – Trinity Regional Medical Center, Fort Dodge, IA, p. A230

DEWISPELARE, Cheryl M., Chief Human Resources Officer, Veterans Affairs Nebraska–Western Iowa Health Care System, Omaha, NE, p. A401

DEWITT, Alan Neil, Chief Medical Officer, Summit Healthcare Regional Medical Center, Show Low, AZ, p. A39

DEWITT, Drew, FACHE, Acting Associate Director, Edward Hines, Jr. Veterans Affairs Hospital, Hines, IL, p. A193

DEWITT, Jocelyn, Ph.D. Vice President and Chief Information Officer, University of Wisconsin Hospitals and Clinics Authority, Madison, WI, p. A709

DEWORTH, Gerald M., Associate Director, Carl Vinson Veterans Affairs Medical Center, Dublin, GA, p. A159

DEXTER, Heather, Chief Executive Officer, Emory Saint Joseph's Hospital of Atlanta, Atlanta, GA, p. A152

DEXTER, Sue, Administrative Department Leader Human Resources, McDonough District Hospital, Macomb, IL, p. A195

DEYARMIN, James A., Controller, Children's Hospital of Richmond at VCU–Brook Road Campus, Richmond, VA, p. A677

DEYO–ALLERS, Margaret, Vice President, Chief Nursing Officer, St. Luke's Cornwall Hospital, Newburgh, NY, p. A450

DEYOUNG, Keith, M.D. Chief Medical Staff, Wallowa Memorial Hospital, Enterprise, OR, p. A525

DHAWAN, Ajay, M.D. Chief of Staff, Veterans Affairs Northern Indiana Health Care System, Fort Wayne, IN, p. A211

DHILLON, Avtar, M.D. Medical Director, Keystone Newport News, Newport News, VA, p. A674

DHILLON, Lynette, Administrator, Oceans Behavioral Hospital of De Ridder, Deridder, LA, p. A276

DHINGRA, Ashok, M.D. Executive Medical Director, HEALTHSOUTH Deaconess Rehabilitation Hospital, Evansville, IN, p. A210

DHULIPALA, Vasudeva, M.D. Medical Director, HEALTHSOUTH Rehabilitation Hospital of Alexandria, Alexandria, LA, p. A271

DI BACCO, David J., Chief Operating Officer, Eastern Niagara Hospital, Lockport, NY, p. A441

DI BERNARDO, Deborah, Chief Information Officer, Saint Joseph's Medical Center, Yonkers, NY, p. A459

DIAL, Jody S., Chief Financial Officer, Timpanogos Regional Hospital, Orem, UT, p. A661

DIAL, Ray D., Director of Nursing, Nebraska Medicine – Bellevue, Bellevue, NE, p. A394

DIALTO, Margaret, Regional Chief Human Resource Officer, Staten Island University Hospital,, NY, p. A450

DIAMOND, Anne, JD, Chief Executive Officer, Unconn John Dempsey Hospital, Farmington, CT, p. A114

DIAMOND, Lester K., President, St. Dominic–Jackson Memorial Hospital, Jackson, MS, p. A360

DIAMOND, Timothy, Chief Information Officer, Methodist Hospitals, Gary, IN, p. A212

DIAMOND, Vickie L., MS, President and Chief Executive Officer, Wyoming Medical Center, Casper, WY, p. A721

DIANDA–MARTIN, Barb, Chief Nursing Officer, Mercy St. Anne Hospital, Toledo, OH, p. A503

DIANGELO, John A., President and Chief Executive Officer, Inspira Health Network, Mullica Hill, NJ, p. B73

DIANGELO, John A.
President and Chief Executive Officer, Inspira Medical Center–Elmer, Elmer, NJ, p. A416
President and Chief Executive Officer, Inspira Medical Center–Vineland, Vineland, NJ, p. A425
President and Chief Executive Officer, Inspira Medical Center–Woodbury, Woodbury, NJ, p. A425

DIASIO, Anthony J., Chief Financial Officer, Fox Chase Cancer Center–American Oncologic Hospital, Philadelphia, PA, p. A548

DIAZ, Al, M.D., Chief Executive Officer, Kindred Hospital Rome, Rome, GA, p. A165

DIAZ, Evelyn, R.N. Chief Nursing Officer, HEALTHSOUTH Hospital of Manati, Manati, PR, p. A728

DIAZ, Felipe, M.D. Chief of Staff, Bath Veterans Affairs Medical Center, Bath, NY, p. A434

DIAZ, Georgina, Chief Operating Officer, Palmetto General Hospital, Hialeah, FL, p. A130

DIAZ, Janine, Human Resources Manager, Emory Rehabilitation Hospital, Atlanta, GA, p. A152

DIAZ, Jesse, Chief Information Officer, Phoebe Putney Memorial Hospital, Albany, GA, p. A151

DIAZ, Jimmy, Director Information Technology, Odessa Regional Medical Center, Odessa, TX, p. A639

DIAZ, Jose, Director Information Systems, St. Mary's Medical Center of Evansville, Evansville, IN, p. A210

DIAZ, Joseph, M.D. Chief Medical Officer, Memorial Hospital of Rhode Island, Pawtucket, RI, p. A560

DIAZ, Rogelio, Administrator, Hospital Menonita De Caguas, Caguas, PR, p. A726

DIAZ, Ron, Manager Operations, Albany Stratton Veterans Affairs Medical Center, Albany, NY, p. A433

DIAZ, Steve, M.D. Chief Medical Officer, MaineGeneral Medical Center, Augusta, ME, p. A291

DIBBLE, Lynn, Vice President Patient Care Services, Guthrie Towanda Memorial Hospital, Towanda, PA, p. A555

DICESARE, Gayle, President and Chief Executive Officer, RiverValley Behavioral Health Hospital, Owensboro, KY, p. A267

DICESARE, Jan, Vice President Financial Operations, St. Vincent's East, Birmingham, AL, p. A17

DICICCO, Marilyn, Director Human Resources, Chestnut Hill Hospital, Philadelphia, PA, p. A547

DICK, Andy, Director Information Services, Saline Memorial Hospital, Benton, AR, p. A43

DICK, David, Chief Executive Officer, Huron Regional Medical Center, Huron, SD, p. A574

DICK, Frances, Chief Executive Officer, Oceans Behavioral Hospital Lufkin, Lufkin, TX, p. A635

DICK, Lynette, Director of Support Services, Ellsworth County Medical Center, Ellsworth, KS, p. A242

DICK, Mollie, Coordinator Human Resources, Wayne County Hospital, Monticello, KY, p. A266

DICK, Myra, Manager Business Office, AMG Specialty Hospital–Wichita, Wichita, KS, p. A255

DICKENS, Betty, Director Human Resources, Sierra Tucson, Tucson, AZ, p. A41

DICKENS, Robert, Chief Executive Officer, Select Specialty Hospital–South Dallas, Dallas, TX, p. A611

DICKENS, Shelby, Director, Patient Care Services, Fort Madison Community Hospital, Fort Madison, IA, p. A231

DICKERSON, Gene, M.D. Vice President Medical Affairs, Palmetto Health Tuomey, Sumter, SC, p. A570

DICKERSON, Kathy, Chief Financial Officer, HEALTHSOUTH Rehabilitation Hospital of Arlington, Arlington, TX, p. A597

DICKERSON, Melody Ford, Chief Nursing Officer, Memorial Hermann Greater Heights Hospital, Houston, TX, p. A625

DICKERSON, Taylor, Chief Information Officer, Lake City Medical Center, Lake City, FL, p. A133

DICKERSON, Toby, Chief Information Resources Management Services, Durham Veterans Affairs Medical Center, Durham, NC, p. A464

DICKEY, Ashley, Director Human Resources, Benson Hospital, Benson, AZ, p. A31

DICKEY, John M., Chief Administrative Officer, Mayo Clinic Health System in Eau Claire, Eau Claire, WI, p. A704

DICKEY, Mark, Director Business Development, Valir Rehabilitation Hospital, Oklahoma City, OK, p. A518

DICKEY, Sarah J., Director Human Resources, Marshall Browning Hospital, Du Quoin, IL, p. A188

DICKINSON, Ashley, Chief Operating Officer, Porter Regional Hospital, Valparaiso, IN, p. A223

DICKINSON, Cathy C., Vice President Human Resources, Baptist Health Medical Center – North Little Rock, North Little Rock, AR, p. A51

DICKINSON, Galen, Chief Financial Officer, Cary Medical Center, Caribou, ME, p. A292

DICKINSON, Lani, Interim Chief Nursing Officer, San Ramon Regional Medical Center, San Ramon, CA, p. A92

DICKLICH–COBB, Cristy, Chief Nursing Officer, Memorial Hospital of Converse County, Douglas, WY, p. A722

DICKMAN, Kathy, Director Information Technology, McCullough–Hyde Memorial Hospital/TriHealth, Oxford, OH, p. A501

DICKREITER, Adrian, Vice President Technology, Nix Health Care System, San Antonio, TX, p. A646

DICKS, Mandy, Director of Nursing, Lake Butler Hospital Hand Surgery Center, Lake Butler, FL, p. A133

DICKSON, Anita, Director Human Resources, Five Rivers Medical Center, Pocahontas, AR, p. A51

DICKSON, Eric, M.D., President and Chief Executive Officer, UMass Memorial Health Care, Inc., Worcester, MA, p. B139

DICKSON, James J., Administrator and Chief Executive Officer, Copper Queen Community Hospital, Bisbee, AZ, p. A31

DICKSON, Scott, Director Information Technology, Reeves Memorial Medical Center, Bernice, LA, p. A273

DICKSON, Thomas C.
Chief Executive Officer, Banner – University Medical Center South, Tucson, AZ, p. A40
Chief Executive Officer, Banner – University Medical Center Tucson, Tucson, AZ, p. A40

DICKSON, William, Executive Director, Capital District Psychiatric Center, Albany, NY, p. A433

DICUS–JOHNSON, Coreen
President, Midwest Orthopedic Specialty Hospital, Franklin, WI, p. A705
President, Wheaton Franciscan Healthcare – Franklin, Franklin, WI, p. A706
President, Wheaton Franciscan Healthcare – St. Francis, Milwaukee, WI, p. A712

DIDDLE, Derrick, Chief Information Officer, Colorado Canyons Hospital and Medical Center, Fruita, CO, p. A106

DIDENKO, Dima, Chief Financial Officer, Florida Hospital Tampa, Tampa, FL, p. A147

DIDERRICH, Mary Kay, R.N., Chief Executive Officer, Select Specialty Hospital–Milwaukee, Milwaukee, WI, p. A712

DIDERRICH, Mary Kay, R.N. Vice President Patient Services, Watertown Regional Medical Center, Watertown, WI, p. A718

DIEBLING, Tara, Chief Executive Officer, The Rehabilitation Institute of St. Louis, Saint Louis, MO, p. A381

DIEDERICH, John A., Senior Vice President Operations and Chief Operating Officer, Rush–Copley Medical Center, Aurora, IL, p. A181

DIEFFENBACH, Todd, Chief Financial Officer, Tyrone Hospital, Tyrone, PA, p. A556

DIERKENS, Janelle, Chief Administration Officer, New York State Psychiatric Institute, New York, NY, p. A447

DIERKER, Anne, Vice President Hospital Services, Pekin Hospital, Pekin, IL, p. A200

DIERS, Suzanne, R.N. Director Patient Care Services, Shriners Hospitals for Children–Portland, Portland, OR, p. A530

DIESTEL, Peter, Senior Vice President and Chief Operating Officer, Valley Hospital, Ridgewood, NJ, p. A423

DIETER, Brian, President and Chief Executive Officer, Mary Greeley Medical Center, Ames, IA, p. A225

DIETERICH, Kevin, Director Information Services, Inland Hospital, Waterville, ME, p. A295

DIETLIN, Steve, Chief Executive Officer, Tri–City Medical Center, Oceanside, CA, p. A80

DIETRICH, Brenda, Chief Human Resources Officer, Banner Boswell Medical Center, Sun City, AZ, p. A39

DIETRICK, Brian, Director Information Systems, Wilson Medical Center, Wilson, NC, p. A475

DIETSCH, Barry, Chief Financial Officer, Virginia Gay Hospital, Vinton, IA, p. A238

DIETSCHE, Jim, Chief Financial Officer, Bellin Memorial Hospital, Green Bay, WI, p. A706

DIETZ, Brian E., FACHE, Interim President and Chief Executive officer, St. Francis Hospital, Wilmington, DE, p. A120

DIETZ, Mark, Chief Medical Officer, CentraCare Health–Monticello, Monticello, MN, p. A347

DIETZ, Michael, Administrator, U. S. Air Force Hospital, Hampton, VA, p. A671

DIFRANCO, Vincent B., Chief Executive Officer, Plains Regional Medical Center, Clovis, NM, p. A428

DIGUILIO, Jason, Controller, UH Avon Rehabilitation Hospital, Avon, OH, p. A484

DIIESO, Nicholas T., R.N. Chief Operating Officer, Mount Auburn Hospital, Cambridge, MA, p. A309

DIIORIO, Emil, M.D., Chief Executive Officer, Surgical Specialty Center at Coordinated Health, Allentown, PA, p. A532

DIKE, Charles, M.D. Chief of Staff, Sanford Worthington Medical Center, Worthington, MN, p. A354

DILALLO, Kevin, Chief Executive Officer, Manatee Memorial Hospital, Bradenton, FL, p. A124

DILISI, Jeffrey P., Vice President and Chief Medical Officer, Virginia Hospital Center – Arlington, Arlington, VA, p. A667

DILL, Stephen, M.D. Chief of Staff, LeConte Medical Center, Sevierville, TN, p. A593

DILLARD, Evan S., FACHE, President and Chief Executive Officer, Forrest General Hospital, Hattiesburg, MS, p. A359

DILLEHUNT, David B.
Chief Information Officer, FirstHealth Montgomery Memorial Hospital, Troy, NC, p. A474
Chief Information Officer, FirstHealth Moore Regional Hospital, Pinehurst, NC, p. A471

DILLION, Tim, Vice President of Human Resources, Devereux Hospital and Children's Center of Florida, Melbourne, FL, p. A135

DILLON, Jim, Chief Financial Officer, Rangely District Hospital, Rangely, CO, p. A110

DILLON, Lorie, Chief Executive Officer, Geisinger HEALTHSOUTH Rehabilitation Hospital, Danville, PA, p. A536

DILLON, Mary E., MS Vice President Patient Care Services, Sisters of Charity Hospital of Buffalo, Buffalo, NY, p. A436

DILORENZO, Randolph, M.D. Medical Director, Syosset Hospital, Syosset, NY, p. A456

DILORETO, David, M.D. Executive Vice President and Chief Medical Officer, Presence Saint Francis Hospital, Evanston, IL, p. A190

DIMAMBRO, Christina, Chief Financial Officer, Havasu Regional Medical Center, Lake Havasu City, AZ, p. A34

DIMARCO, Lisa, R.N. Vice President Patient Care Service and Chief Nursing Officer, Little Company of Mary Hospital and Health Care Centers, Evergreen Park, IL, p. A190

DIMARE, John, M.D. Medical Director, Foothill Presbyterian Hospital, Glendora, CA, p. A65

DIMICHELE, Maria, Administrative Assistant, Kensington Hospital, Philadelphia, PA, p. A548

DIMITROVA, Gergana, M.D. Medical Director, Carolina Center for Behavioral Health, Greer, SC, p. A567

DIMM, Adam, Vice President Operations and Chief Operating Officer, J. C. Blair Memorial Hospital, Huntingdon, PA, p. A540

DIMMICK, Scott, Senior Vice President and Chief Human Resources Officer, Lakeland Regional Health, Lakeland, FL, p. A134

DIMMIG, Thomas, M.D. Medical Director, North Carolina Specialty Hospital, Durham, NC, p. A464

DIMOND, Margaret, Ph.D., President and Chief Executive Officer, Crittenton Hospital Medical Center, Rochester, MI, p. A332

DINGER, Bradley, Financial Representative, UPMC Northwest, Seneca, PA, p. A554

DINGILIAN, John, M.D. Chief Medical Officer, Simi Valley Hospital, Simi Valley, CA, p. A94

DINGLE, Steve, M.D. Chief Medical Officer, Arizona State Hospital, Phoenix, AZ, p. A36

DINGLEDINE, Jon, Senior Director Human Resources and Support Services, Mercer Health, Coldwater, OH, p. A490

DINGLER, Chance, M.D. Chief Medical Officer, Nocona General Hospital, Nocona, TX, p. A639

DINHAM, Vilma L., R.N. Chief Nursing Officer, Encino Hospital Medical Center,, CA, p. A71

DINKHA, Duncan, M.D. Chief of Staff, Morrison Community Hospital, Morrison, IL, p. A197

DINKINS, Vicki, Director Human Resources, South Georgia Medical Center Lanier Campus, Lakeland, GA, p. A161

DINON, Nancy, Vice President Human Resources, Health Central Hospital, Ocoee, FL, p. A139

DINSLAGE, Dennis, Vice President Finance and Chief Financial Officer, St. Francis Memorial Hospital, West Point, NE, p. A403

DINSMORE, Brad, Interim Chief Executive Officer, HEALTHSOUTH Rehabilitation Hospital of Austin, Austin, TX, p. A599

DION, Jeffrey P.
Vice President Finance and Chief Financial Officer, Newton–Wellesley Hospital, Newton Lower Falls, MA, p. A313
Vice President Finance, St. Elizabeth's Medical Center, Brighton, MA, p. A308

DIONISOPOULOS, Peter, Chief Medical Officer, CHI Health Nebraska Heart, Lincoln, NE, p. A397

DIPALMA, Maureen, Chief Financial Officer, Tewksbury Hospital, Tewksbury, MA, p. A315

DIPAOLO, Joseph, FACHE, President, Newton Medical Center, Newton, NJ, p. A421

DIPIERO, Annette, Human Resource Director, HEALTHSOUTH Rehabilitation Hospital at Martin Health, Stuart, FL, p. A146

DIPIETRO, Sandra P., Chief Financial Officer, St. Tammany Parish Hospital, Covington, LA, p. A275

DIPILLA, Victor, Vice President and Chief Business Development Officer, Christ Hospital, Cincinnati, OH, p. A487

DISANZO, Frank, Vice President and Chief Information Officer and Chief Strategy Officer, Saint Peter's University Hospital, New Brunswick, NJ, p. A420

DISESA, Verdi, M.D., President and Chief Executive Officer, Temple University Hospital, Philadelphia, PA, p. A550

DISLER, Jordi K., President, Parkview LaGrange Hospital, LaGrange, IN, p. A216

DISPOTO, I, Martha, R.N. Chief Nurse Executive, Anaheim Medical Center, Kaiser Permanente Orange County Anaheim Medical Center, Anaheim, CA, p. A54

DISSEN, James H., Chief Executive Officer, Highland–Clarksburg Hospital, Clarksburg, WV, p. A695

DISWOOD, Lavenia, R.N. Chief Nurse Executive, Northern Navajo Medical Center, Shiprock, NM, p. A431

DITMANSON, Paul, M.D. Clinical Director, Red Lake Indian Health Service Hospital, Red Lake, MN, p. A349

DITORO, Michael, Chief Operating Officer, Westlake Hospital, Melrose Park, IL, p. A196

DITTBENNER, Beth, Regional Director, Human Resources, Mayo Clinic Health System in Mankato, Mankato, MN, p. A345

DITTMANN, Jerry, Vice President Human Resources, Mount Nittany Medical Center, State College, PA, p. A555

DITTO, Debbie, CPA Controller, Lincoln Trail Behavioral Health System, Radcliff, KY, p. A268

DITURO, Beth, Divisional Chief Information Officer, Lenox Hill Hospital, New York, NY, p. A445

DITZLER, Andru, Chief Information Officer, Lebanon Veterans Affairs Medical Center, Lebanon, PA, p. A542

DIVELLO, Douglas F., President and Chief Executive Officer, The University of Vermont Health Network – Alice Hyde Medical Center, Malone, NY, p. A442

DIVERSI, Sarah, Chief Financial Officer, Our Community Hospital, Scotland Neck, NC, p. A473

DIVINS, Brooke, Manager Human Resources, Clarion Hospital, Clarion, PA, p. A535

DIVITO, Frank, Manager Information Systems, Jameson Hospital, New Castle, PA, p. A546

DIX, Roger J., Vice President Finance, Hannibal Regional Hospital, Hannibal, MO, p. A371

DIX, Theresa, R.N. Chief Nursing Officer, Wythe County Community Hospital, Wytheville, VA, p. A681

DIXON, Christy, Chief Human Resources Officer, HealthSouth Rehabilitation Hospital of Humble, LLC, Humble, TX, p. A628

DIXON, Debbie, Director Human Resources, Pampa Regional Medical Center, Pampa, TX, p. A640

DIXON, Del, Chief Information Officer, South Shore Hospital, South Weymouth, MA, p. A314

DIXON, Florine, Chief Operating Officer, Memorial Hospital, Carthage, IL, p. A182

DIXON, Gregg, CPA Chief Financial Officer, CarePartners Health Services, Asheville, NC, p. A460

DIXON, John, Chief Medical Officer, Mobile Infirmary Medical Center, Mobile, AL, p. A22

DIXON, Michael, Director Human Resources, Self Regional Healthcare, Greenwood, SC, p. A567

DIXON, Michael L., Director, Human Resources, Beaumont Hospital – Royal Oak, Royal Oak, MI, p. A333

DIXON, Sally J., Chief Executive Officer, Memorial Hospital, York, PA, p. A559

DIXON, Shannon, Manager Business Office, Weisbrod Memorial County Hospital, Eads, CO, p. A104

DIXON, Todd, R.N
Chief Operating Officer, Coliseum Medical Centers, Macon, GA, p. A162
Chief Operating Officer, Coliseum Northside Hospital, Macon, GA, p. A162

DIZNEY, Donald R., Chairman and Chief Executive Officer, United Medical Corporation, Windermere, FL, p. B140

DJOGAN, Djogan, Chief Financial Officer, Muscogee Creek Nation Physical Rehabilitation Center, Okmulgee, OK, p. A518

DOAN, Angela, Chief Financial Officer, Scott Memorial Hospital, Scottsburg, IN, p. A221

DOANE, Peter, M.D
Chief Medical Officer, Franklin Regional Hospital, Franklin, NH, p. A411
Chief Medical Officer, Lakes Region General Hospital, Laconia, NH, p. A411

DOBALIAN, Derek, M.D. Chief of Staff, Gardens Regional Hospital and Medical Center, Hawaiian Gardens, CA, p. A65

DOBBING, Eileen, R.N. Senior Vice President for Patient Care Services, Memorial Hospital of Rhode Island, Pawtucket, RI, p. A560

DOBBINS, Jim, Vice President Human Resources, UNC Lenoir Healthcare, Kinston, NC, p. A468

DOBBS, Jacee, Chief Information Officer, Citizens Medical Center, Colby, KS, p. A241

DOBBS, Stephanie, Chief Nursing Officer, Sanford Clear Lake Medical Center, Clear Lake, SD, p. A573

DOBIE, Linda, R.N. Vice President, Legal Affairs, Torrance Memorial Medical Center, Torrance, CA, p. A96

DOBIN, Jennifer, Executive Vice President Human Resources, Bayonne Medical Center, Bayonne, NJ, p. A414

DOBIZL, Howard
Director Information Technology Services, Howard Young Medical Center, Woodruff, WI, p. A720
Director Information Technology Services, Ministry Eagle River Memorial Hospital, Eagle River, WI, p. A704
Director Information Technology Services, Ministry Sacred Heart Hospital, Tomahawk, WI, p. A717
Director Information Services for the Northern Region, Ministry Saint Mary's Hospitals, Rhinelander, WI, p. A715

DOBOSENSKI, Dave, Chief Executive Officer, St. Croix Regional Medical Center, St. Croix Falls, WI, p. A716

DOBOSH, Jr., Joseph J., Vice President and Chief Financial Officer, Children's Specialized Hospital–PSE&G, New Brunswick, NJ, p. A420

DOBRAWA, Stanley
Area Technology Director, Kaiser Permanente San Rafael Medical Center, San Rafael, CA, p. A92
Area Technology Director, Kaiser Permanente Santa Rosa Medical Center, Santa Rosa, CA, p. A94

DOBRINSKI, Sandra, Director of Nursing, Comanche County Hospital, Coldwater, KS, p. A241

DOBROVICH, Michael, M.D. Chief Medical Officer, St. John Medical Center, Westlake, OH, p. A505

DOBSON, Glenda, Chief Executive Officer, Cypress Pointe Surgical Hospital, Hammond, LA, p. A277

DOBSON, Glenn E., Vice President, Finance and Chief Financial Officer, Aspirus Iron River Hospitals & Clinics, Iron River, MI, p. A327

DOBSON, Trey, M.D. Chief Medical Officer, Southwestern Vermont Medical Center, Bennington, VT, p. A665

DOCIMO, Anne, M.D. Executive Vice President and Chief Medical Officer, Jefferson Health, Thomas Jefferson University Hospitals, Philadelphia, PA, p. A550

DOCIMO, Steven G., M.D. Chief Medical Officer, Children's Hospital of Pittsburgh of UPMC, Pittsburgh, PA, p. A550

DODD, Jeff, M.D. Chief of Staff, Tahoe Forest Hospital District, Truckee, CA, p. A97

DODD, John, Vice President Human Resources, Central Peninsula Hospital, Soldotna, AK, p. A30

DODD, Kathy M., Director of Nursing, Southern Virginia Mental Health Institute, Danville, VA, p. A669

DODD, Pam, Chief Operating Officer, Harper County Community Hospital, Buffalo, OK, p. A509

DODDS, George, M.D. Medical Director, Gouverneur Hospital, Gouverneur, NY, p. A439

DODDS, Rick A.
President, Greene Memorial Hospital, Xenia, OH, p. A506
President, Soin Medical Center, Beavercreek, OH, p. A484

DODDS, Sheryl, Chief Clinical Officer, Florida Hospital, Orlando, FL, p. A140

DODERER, Marcella, FACHE, President and Chief Executive Officer, Arkansas Children's Hospital, Little Rock, AR, p. A48

DODGE, Cyndi, Director Human Resources, Vibra Hospital of Springfield, Springfield, IL, p. A203

DODGE, Terry, M.D. Chief of Staff, Chester Regional Medical Center, Chester, SC, p. A563

DODSON, Louise, R.N. Chief Operating Officer and Chief Nursing Officer, Wagoner Community Hospital, Wagoner, OK, p. A523

DODSON, Thomas, Executive Director, Buffalo Psychiatric Center, Buffalo, NY, p. A435

DODSWORTH, Richard, Chief Human Resource Officer, MacNeal Hospital, Berwyn, IL, p. A181

DOEHRING, Christopher, M.D
Vice President Medical Affairs, Franciscan St. Francis Health – Indianapolis, Indianapolis, IN, p. A214
Vice President of Medical Affairs, Franciscan St. Francis Health–Carmel, Carmel, IN, p. A208

DOELING, Mariann, R.N., President, CHI St Alexius Health Carrington Medical Center, Carrington, ND, p. A477

DOELLING, James, Chief Nurse Executive, VA Greater Los Angeles Healthcare System, Los Angeles, CA, p. A74

DOERFLER, Mary P., Chief Human Resources Officer, Central Texas Veterans Health Care System, Temple, TX, p. A651

DOERGE, Jean, R.N. Nurse Executive, Swedish/Edmonds, Edmonds, WA, p. A684

DOERGE, Jean B., MS Chief Nursing Executive, UnityPoint Health – Trinity Bettendorf, Bettendorf, IA, p. A225

DOERING, Dean, Chief Executive Officer, Central Prison Hospital, Raleigh, NC, p. A471

DOERR, Brian, Chief Information Officer, ContinueCARE Hospital at Baptist Health Corbin, Corbin, KY, p. A258

DOGGETT, Geri, Director Business, East Mississippi State Hospital, Meridian, MS, p. A362

DOGGETT, Sherri L., Vice President Patient Services, Mercy Medical Center–Centerville, Centerville, IA, p. A227

DOHERTY, Allison, Chief Financial Officer, Spine Hospital of Louisiana (formally the NeuroMedical Center Surgical Hospital), Baton Rouge, LA, p. A273

DOHERTY, Bryan, Management Information Technology Services I, Sagamore Children's Psychiatric Center, Dix Hills, NY, p. A438

DOHERTY, Donna, R.N. Vice President of Nursing and Chief Nursing Officer, Beth Israel Deaconess Hospital Plymouth, Plymouth, MA, p. A314

DOHERTY, Donnie, Director Information Systems, Fairfield Memorial Hospital, Winnsboro, SC, p. A571

DOHERTY, John, Vice President Finance, University of Minnesota Medical Center, Fairview, Minneapolis, MN, p. A347

DOHERTY, Randy, CPA, Chief Executive Officer, HEALTHSOUTH Braintree Rehabilitation Hospital, Braintree, MA, p. A307

DOHERTY, Ray, Director Information Technology, Clinton Memorial Hospital, Wilmington, OH, p. A506

DOHERTY, William J., M.D. Executive Vice President and Chief Operating Officer, Hallmark Health System, Melrose, MA, p. A312

DOHMANN, Eileen L., R.N
Senior Vice President and Chief Nursing Officer, Mary Washington Hospital, Fredericksburg, VA, p. A670
Senior Vice President and Chief Nursing Officer, Stafford Hospital, Stafford, VA, p. A679

DOI, Kathy, Executive Director Human Resources, AHMC Anaheim Regional Medical Center, Anaheim, CA, p. A54

DOIDGE, John C., Vice President Finance, Glencoe Regional Health Services, Glencoe, MN, p. A343

DOKKEN, Susan, Chief Human Resources, St. Joseph Regional Medical Center, Lewiston, ID, p. A177

DOKSUM, Kathryn, Director Finance, Samaritan North Lincoln Hospital, Lincoln City, OR, p. A527

DOLAN, John, Chief Financial Officer, Cimarron Memorial Hospital, Boise City, OK, p. A509

DOLAN, Mary, Regional Director Information Services and HIPAA Security Official, Shriners Hospitals for Children–Boston, Boston, MA, p. A307

DOLAN, Patricia R., R.N. Vice President/ Chief Nursing Officer, Florida Hospital Waterman, Tavares, FL, p. A148

DOLAN, Shari, Chief Financial Officer, Liberty Medical Center, Chester, MT, p. A386

DOLAN, Steve, Chief Information Officer, EastPointe Hospital, Daphne, AL, p. A18

DOLBEE, Hilary, Chief Financial Officer, Central Iowa Healthcare, Marshalltown, IA, p. A234

DOLE, Patricia, Vice President Patient Care Services, TLC Health Network – Lake Shore Hospital, Irving, NY, p. A440

DOLEN, Cassie, Vice President Finance and Chief Financial Officer, Hutchinson Regional Medical Center, Hutchinson, KS, p. A245

DOLLINS, Gary, Director Management Information Systems, Poplar Bluff Regional Medical Center, Poplar Bluff, MO, p. A378

DOLOHANTY–JOHNSON, Bridget, MSN Vice President Patient Care Services, Parkview Whitley Hospital, Columbia City, IN, p. A208

DOLORESCO, Laureen, R.N. Associate Director for Patient Care and Nursing Services, James A. Haley Veterans' Hospital–Tampa, Tampa, FL, p. A147

DOMALESKI, Vareen O'Keefe, MS Vice Patient Care Services and Chief Nursing Officer, Emma Pendleton Bradley Hospital, East Providence, RI, p. A560

DOMANICO, Lee, Chief Executive Officer, Marin General Hospital, Greenbrae, CA, p. A65

DOMANN, Debbie, Director of Operations, Fillmore County Hospital, Geneva, NE, p. A396

DOMANSKY, John, Vice President Operations, Rutherford Regional Health System, Rutherfordton, NC, p. A473

DOMAYER, Cory, Chief Financial Officer, Florida Hospital–Flagler, Palm Coast, FL, p. A141

DOMBROUSKI, Joyce, R.N. Regional Chief Nursing Officer, St. Patrick Hospital, Missoula, MT, p. A389

DOMEIER, Sandy, Director Patient Care Services, Ridgeview Sibley Medical Center, Arlington, MN, p. A338

DOMIAN, Catherine, R.N. Chief Nursing Officer, South Texas Health System, Edinburg, TX, p. A614

DOMINGO, Connie, M.D. Medical Director, Weisman Children's Rehabilitation Hospital, Marlton, NJ, p. A419

DOMINGO, Ramon, M.D. Chief of Staff, McCamey County Hospital District, McCamey, TX, p. A636

DOMINGUE, Buffy, Chief Executive Officer, Lafayette Surgical Specialty Hospital, Lafayette, LA, p. A280

DOMINGUEZ, Brenda, Director Human Resources, Cypress Creek Hospital, Houston, TX, p. A624

DOMINGUEZ, Ed, President Medical Staff, Vibra Specialty Hospital at DeSoto, Desoto, TX, p. A613

DOMINGUEZ, Jerry A., CPA Chief Financial Officer, East Texas Medical Center Trinity, Trinity, TX, p. A653

DOMINGUEZ, Marie, Commander, Martin Army Community Hospital, Fort Benning, GA, p. A159

DOMINICCI, Sandra, Nursing Director, Hospital De Damas, Ponce, PR, p. A728

DOMINO, Laura, R.N. Vice President Patient Care Services, Hammond–Henry Hospital, Geneseo, IL, p. A191

DOMINSKI, Paul, Vice President Human Resources, Park Nicollet Methodist Hospital, Saint Louis Park, MN, p. A350

DOMMER, Matthew, M.D. Chief Medical Officer, Bronson LakeView Hospital, Paw Paw, MI, p. A331

DOMON, Steven, M.D. Medical Director, Arkansas State Hospital, Little Rock, AR, p. A48

DONAGHY, Deirdre, M.D. Vice President Medical Affairs, St. Mary Medical Center, Langhorne, PA, p. A542

DONAHEY, Kenneth C., Chief Operating Officer, West Florida Hospital, Pensacola, FL, p. A142

DONAHUE, Edward, M.D. Chief Medical Officer, St. Joseph's Hospital and Medical Center, Phoenix, AZ, p. A37

DONAHUE, Kristine Marie, Administrator, Clinical Operations, Beaumont Hospital – Taylor, Taylor, MI, p. A335

DONAHUE, Michael, M.D. Medical Director, Select Specialty Hospital–Pittsburgh/UPMC, Pittsburgh, PA, p. A551

DONAHUE, Patrick, Vice President and Administrator, Methodist Hospital Union County, Morganfield, KY, p. A267

DONAHUE, Ruth, R.N. Chief Nursing Officer, Harrison County Hospital, Corydon, IN, p. A208

DONAHUE, Samantha, Director Human Resources, Crossing Rivers Health Medical Center, Prairie Du Chien, WI, p. A714

DONALD, Steve, M.D. Chief of Staff, Washington County Hospital, Chatom, AL, p. A18

DONALDSON, Brooke G., Assistant Administrator Human Resources, Jackson Hospital, Marianna, FL, p. A135

DONALDSON, Jill, Vice President Operations, MedStar Harbor Hospital, Baltimore, MD, p. A297

DONALDSON, Les, M.D. Chief of Staff, Roosevelt General Hospital, Portales, NM, p. A430

DONALDSON, Lori, Chief Financial Officer, UC San Diego Health, San Diego, CA, p. A89

DONALDSON, Nesha, Chief Financial Officer, Cullman Regional Medical Center, Cullman, AL, p. A18

DONALDSON, Tammy, Director of Nursing, Highlands Hospital, Connellsville, PA, p. A536

DONATELLE, Lawrence, M.D. Vice President Medical Affairs, St. Elizabeth Hospital, Appleton, WI, p. A702

DONATO, Cyndy, Vice President, Human Resources, Missouri Baptist Medical Center, Saint Louis, MO, p. A380

DONAWAY, Duane, Director Information Technology, Hendrick Health System, Abilene, TX, p. A595

DONELAN, Matthias B., M.D. Chief of Staff, Shriners Hospitals for Children–Boston, Boston, MA, p. A307

DONENWIRTH, Karl, Vice President Information Services, Northcoast Behavioral Healthcare, Northfield, OH, p. A500

DONGILLI Jr., Paul, FACHE,
President and Chief Executive Officer, Madonna Rehabilitation Hospital, Lincoln, NE, p. A398
President and Chief Executive Officer, Madonna Rehabilitation Hospital, Lincoln, NE, p. A398
President and Chief Executive Officer, Madonna Rehabilitation Specialty Hospital, Bellevue, NE, p. A394

DONHAM, Guyle, M.D. Chief of Staff, Comanche County Medical Center, Comanche, TX, p. A607

DONICA, Joanna, Director Human Resource, HEALTHSOUTH Rehabilitation Hospital of Beaumont, Beaumont, TX, p. A601

DONLEY, Linda, Vice President Operations, Ira Davenport Memorial Hospital, Bath, NY, p. A434

DONLIN, Bruce, Director Information Services, Mount Desert Island Hospital, Bar Harbor, ME, p. A291

DONLIN, John
Regional Director Human Resources – Boston, Erie, and Springfield, Shriners Hospitals for Children–Boston, Boston, MA, p. A307
Director Human Resources, Shriners Hospitals for Children–Springfield, Springfield, MA, p. A315

DONLIN, Michael T., FACHE, Administrator, Floyd Valley Healthcare, Le Mars, IA, p. A233

DONNELLY, Gloria, Director Human Resources, Euclid Hospital, Euclid, OH, p. A494

DONNELLY, James E., Chief Nursing Officer and Vice President Patient Care Services, UPMC Hamot, Erie, PA, p. A538

DONNELLY, Lane, M.D. Chief Medical Officer, Nemours Children's Hospital, Orlando, FL, p. A140

DONNELLY, Sheryl, Human Resources Specialist, State Hospital South, Blackfoot, ID, p. A174

DONNER, Larry, Administrator, University Health Conway, Monroe, LA, p. A284

DONOGHUE, Alicia, Director Human Resources, EastPointe Hospital, Daphne, AL, p. A18

DONOHUE, Carolyn Viall, MSN Vice President Nursing, Roper St. Francis, Charleston, SC, p. A563

DONOHUE, Mary Ann T., Ph.D. Chief Patient Care Services Officer, Stony Brook University Hospital, Stony Brook, NY, p. A456

DONOHUE–RYAN, MaryAnn, Vice President Patient Care Services, Englewood Hospital and Medical Center, Englewood, NJ, p. A417

DONOVAN, Andrew
Director Information Technology, Wheaton Franciscan Healthcare – Elmbrook Memorial, Brookfield, WI, p. A703
Regional Director Information Services, Wheaton Franciscan Healthcare – St. Joseph's, Milwaukee, WI, p. A712

DONOVAN, James W., President and Chief Executive Officer, LincolnHealth, Damariscotta, ME, p. A292

DONOVAN, Jenny, Director Human Resources, Wright Memorial Hospital, Trenton, MO, p. A383

DONOVAN, Kevin
Chief Executive Officer, Franklin Regional Hospital, Franklin, NH, p. A411
Chief Executive Officer, Lakes Region General Hospital, Laconia, NH, p. A411

DONOVAN, Kevin, President and Chief Executive Officer, LRGHealthcare, Laconia, NH, p. B84

DONOVAN, Mary, Controller, HEALTHSOUTH Rehabilitation Institute of Tucson, Tucson, AZ, p. A40

DONOVAN, Mike, Chief Financial Officer, Lemuel Shattuck Hospital, Jamaica Plain, MA, p. A311

DONOVAN, Patrick, M.D. Director Medical Staff, HEALTHSOUTH Rehabilitation Hospital of Fort Worth, Fort Worth, TX, p. A618

DONSON, Elliott, Chief Information Specialist, Lincoln Hospital, Davenport, WA, p. A684

DONZE, Richard D., D.O. Senior Vice President Medical Affairs, Penn Medicine Chester County Hospital, West Chester, PA, p. A557

DOODY, Kris A., R.N., Chief Executive Officer, Cary Medical Center, Caribou, ME, p. A292

DOOKEERAM, David, Chief Operating Officer, Porter Adventist Hospital, Denver, CO, p. A104

DOOLEY, Kim H., R.N. Director of Nursing, Lafayette General Surgical Hospital, Lafayette, LA, p. A280

DOOLEY, Lisa, Health Information Officer, Middlesboro ARH Hospital, Middlesboro, KY, p. A266

DOOLEY, Mark J., Chief Executive Officer, Wilson Memorial Hospital, Sidney, OH, p. A502

DOOLING, Edward, Vice President, Human Resources, Masonicare Health Center, Wallingford, CT, p. A117

DOOLITTLE, Jon D., President and Chief Executive Officer, Northwest Medical Center, Albany, MO, p. A367

DOORENBOS, Pamela, Medical Director, Medical Affairs, Maple Grove Hospital, Maple Grove, MN, p. A345

DORAK, John, Chief Information Officer, Nicholas H. Noyes Memorial Hospital, Dansville, NY, p. A438

DORAN, Judy, R.N. Vice President of Hospital Services and Chief Nurse Executive, Stanly Regional Medical Center, Albemarle, NC, p. A460

DORAN, T., M.D. Chief of Staff, Perry Memorial Hospital, Princeton, IL, p. A201

DORF, Jeffrey, M.D. Medical Director, Kindred Hospital–Albuquerque, Albuquerque, NM, p. A427

DORIA, Thomas, Vice President and Patient Services West, St. Anthony's Hospital, Saint Petersburg, FL, p. A144

DORIA, Tom
Vice President Patient Services – West, Morton Plant Hospital, Clearwater, FL, p. A125
Vice President and Patient Services – West, Morton Plant North Bay Hospital, New Port Richey, FL, p. A138

DORION, Heath, Physican Administrator, Mercy Health – St. Elizabeth Boardman Hospital, Boardman, OH, p. A485

DORITY, Paula, Director Human Resources, Martin County Hospital District, Stanton, TX, p. A650

DORMAN, Christopher, Senior Vice President/Chief Operating Officer, Tift Regional Medical Center, Tifton, GA, p. A167

DORMAN, Doug, Vice President Human Resources, GHS Greenville Memorial Hospital, Greenville, SC, p. A566

DORMAN, Julie, Human Resources Director, Parkwood Behavioral Health System, Olive Branch, MS, p. A363

DORMAN, Stephen, M.D. Chief Medical Officer, New Mexico Rehabilitation Center, Roswell, NM, p. A431

DORNOFF, Edward G., Associate Director, Battle Creek Veterans Affairs Medical Center, Battle Creek, MI, p. A319

DOROGY, Sharon, Chief Information Officer, The Children's Institute of Pittsburgh, Pittsburgh, PA, p. A551

DOROTHY, Jonnie, Senior Director Human Resources, Massena Memorial Hospital, Massena, NY, p. A442

DOROTIK, Brooke, M.D. Chief of Medical Staff, El Campo Memorial Hospital, El Campo, TX, p. A615

DORR, Amy
Vice President Human Resources, McLaren Greater Lansing, Lansing, MI, p. A328
Vice President Human Resources, McLaren Lapeer Region, Lapeer, MI, p. A328

DORRIS, Ronald E., Chief Executive Officer, Carrus Hospitals, Sherman, TX, p. B27

DORRIS, Steve, Chief Financial Officer, Poplar Bluff Regional Medical Center, Poplar Bluff, MO, p. A378

DORSCH, Anthony, Chief Financial Officer, Providence Alaska Medical Center, Anchorage, AK, p. A28

DORSEY, John T., M.D. Vice President Physician Services and Chief Medical Officer, MercyHealth Rockton Avenue Hospital, Rockford, IL, p. A202

DORSEY, William, M.D., Board Chairman and Chief Executive Officer, Jackson Park Hospital and Medical Center, Chicago, IL, p. A184

DORST, Jake, Chief Information Officer, Tahoe Forest Hospital District, Truckee, CA, p. A97

DORTON, Patty, Director of Nursing, Buchanan General Hospital, Grundy, VA, p. A671

DOSCHER, Suzanne C., Chief Executive Officer, Fairfield Memorial Hospital, Winnsboro, SC, p. A571

DOSHI, Nikunj, D.O. Chief Medical Officer, Banner Gateway Medical Center, Gilbert, AZ, p. A32

DOSS, Delilah, Director, Human Resources, MountainView Regional Medical Center, Las Cruces, NM, p. A430

DOSS, Mounir F.
Executive Vice President and Chief Financial Officer, Flushing Hospital Medical Center,, NY, p. A444
Executive Vice President and Chief Financial Officer, Jamaica Hospital Medical Center,, NY, p. A445

DOSSETT, Phyllis, Director of Clinical Services, Wellmont Hancock County Hospital, Sneedville, TN, p. A593

DUANE, Paul K.
Chief Financial Officer and Office of Health Reform, Palmetto Health Baptist, Columbia, SC, p. A564
Chief Financial Officer and Office of Health Reform, Palmetto Health Richland, Columbia, SC, p. A564

DUARTE, Ray, Director, Information Technology and Services, Monmouth Medical Center, Southern Campus, Lakewood, NJ, p. A418

DUBE, Cynthia, M.D. Medical Director, Mayo Clinic Health System–Albert Lea and Austin, Austin, MN, p. A339

DUBE, Sheri, Chief Operating Officer, St. David's North Austin Medical Center, Austin, TX, p. A600

DUBICKI, Robert, Executive Vice President and Chief Operating Officer, Kingsbrook Jewish Medical Center,, NY, p. A445

DUBROCA, Darryl S., Chief Executive Officer and Managing Director, Spring Mountain Sahara, Las Vegas, NV, p. A406

DUBROW, Melissa, Chief Operating Officer, Waynesboro Hospital, Waynesboro, PA, p. A556

DUBRUYNE, Sharon, Director Human Resources, College Hospital Costa Mesa, Costa Mesa, CA, p. A60

DUCEY, Ann, Chief Information Officer, Boys Town National Research Hospital, Omaha, NE, p. A399

DUCHARME, Adele, MSN, Chief Executive Officer, Saint Luke's Cushing Hospital, Leavenworth, KS, p. A247

DUCHARME, Maria, R.N. Senior Vice President Patient Care Services and Chief Nursing Officer, Miriam Hospital, Providence, RI, p. A560

DUCHAUSSEE, Michel, Chief Financial Officer, Atlantic Shores Hospital, Fort Lauderdale, FL, p. A128

DUCHEMIN, MaDena, Assistant Administrator Human Resources, John Randolph Medical Center, Hopewell, VA, p. A672

DUCHENE, Pam, R.N. Vice President Patient Care Services, St. Joseph Hospital, Nashua, NH, p. A412

DUCHESNEAU, Angy, Senior Director Human Resources, Lakeview Hospital, Stillwater, MN, p. A352

DUCHICELA, Jorge, M.D. Chief of Staff, Columbus Community Hospital, Columbus, TX, p. A607

DUCK, Sigsbee, M.D. President, Medical Staff, Memorial Hospital of Sweetwater County, Rock Springs, WY, p. A723

DUCKER, Thomas, M.D. Chief of Staff, Peterson Regional Medical Center, Kerrville, TX, p. A630

DUCKERT, Jon, Chief Executive Officer, Baylor Medical Center at Uptown, Dallas, TX, p. A609

DUCKWORTH, Allison G., R.N. Chief Operating Officer and Chief Nursing Officer, FirstHealth Richmond Memorial Hospital, Rockingham, NC, p. A472

DUCKWORTH, Bob, Director Information Systems, Medical West, Bessemer, AL, p. A16

DUDLEY, III, Edward L., Executive Vice President and Chief Financial Officer, Catholic Medical Center, Manchester, NH, p. A412

DUDLEY, Heather, Director Administrative Services, Brookhaven Hospital, Tulsa, OK, p. A521

DUDLEY, W. Steve, CPA Chief Financial Officer, Ed Fraser Memorial Hospital and Baker Community Health Center, MacClenny, FL, p. A135

DUERR, Joe, Chief Executive Officer, Anson General Hospital, Anson, TX, p. A597

DUET, Kendrick, Chief Operating Officer, Leonard J. Chabert Medical Center, Houma, LA, p. A278

DUFF, Jim, Chief Financial Officer, Colorado Mental Health Institute at Pueblo, Pueblo, CO, p. A109

DUFF, Mary Claire, CPA Chief Financial Officer, Ridgeview Psychiatric Hospital and Center, Oak Ridge, TN, p. A592

DUFFEE, Patrick, Director Medical Information Systems, Delta Medical Center, Memphis, TN, p. A588

DUFFEY, Pam, MSN Chief Nursing Officer, Texas Health Specialty Hospital, Fort Worth, TX, p. A619

DUFFIELD, Douglas, President and Chief Executive Officer, San Joaquin Community Hospital, Bakersfield, CA, p. A56

DUFFIN, Kelly L., Operations Officer, Intermountain Medical Center, Murray, UT, p. A661

DUFFORD, Shawn, M.D. Vice President Medical Affairs and Chief Medical Officer, Saint Joseph Hospital, Denver, CO, p. A104

DUFFY, Beth, Chief Operating Officer, Einstein Medical Center Montgomery, East Norriton, PA, p. A537

DUFFY, Daniel, D.O. Chief Medical Director, HealthSource Saginaw, Inc., Saginaw, MI, p. A333

DUFFY, Delilah, Interim Chief Nurse Officer, Central Montana Medical Center, Lewistown, MT, p. A389

DUFFY, Kenneth, M.D. Medical Director, Seiling Municipal Hospital, Seiling, OK, p. A519

DUFFY, Marie Theresa, Chief Operating Officer, CarePoint Health –Christ Hospital, Jersey City, NJ, p. A418

DUFFY, Pamela
Vice President Operations and Chief Nursing Officer, Northwestern Medicine Kishwaukee Hospital, DeKalb, IL, p. A188
Vice President Operations and Chief Nursing Officer, Northwestern Medicine Valley West Hospital, Sandwich, IL, p. A202

DUFT, Ryan, R.N. Chief Nursing Officer, Fredonia Regional Hospital, Fredonia, KS, p. A243

DUGAN, Elizabeth, Ph.D. Chief Nursing Officer, Inova Loudoun Hospital, Leesburg, VA, p. A672

DUGAN, Gary, M.D. Vice President Medical Affairs, Penn Highlands DuBois, DuBois, PA, p. A537

DUGAR, Edward, R.N. Chief Executive Officer, Hood Memorial Hospital, Amite, LA, p. A271

DUGGAL, Harpreet, M.D. Medical Director, Department of Health and Human Services, Humboldt County Mental Health, Eureka, CA, p. A61

DUGGAN, Allison A.N., FACS Chief Operating Officer, Oswego Hospital, Oswego, NY, p. A452

DUGGAN, Daniel, Chief Operating Officer, Bon Secours St. Francis Health System, Greenville, SC, p. A566

DUGGAN, Eileen, M.D. Medical Director, Crittenton Children's Center, Kansas City, MO, p. A373

DUGGAN, James E., Director Human Resources, Western Massachusetts Hospital, Westfield, MA, p. A316

DUGGAN, Margaret M., M.D. Chief Medical Officer, Brigham and Women's Faulkner Hospital, Boston, MA, p. A306

DUGGAN, Tonya, Director Human Resources, Northern Louisiana Medical Center, Ruston, LA, p. A287

DUGGAR, Susan, R.N. Vice President Nursing, Spartanburg Medical Center, Spartanburg, SC, p. A570

DUGGER, Curtis R., Chief Financial Officer, Memorial Hospital of Converse County, Douglas, WY, p. A722

DUGGER, Sandy, Chief Human Resources Officer, Platte County Memorial Hospital, Wheatland, WY, p. A724

DUHAIME, Robert A., R.N. Senior Vice President Clinical Operations and Chief Nursing Officer, Catholic Medical Center, Manchester, NH, p. A412

DUHANEY, Aphreikah, Chief Nursing Officer, Havasu Regional Medical Center, Lake Havasu City, AZ, p. A34

DUHE, Louis, Senior Director Information Technology, George Washington University Hospital, Washington, DC, p. A121

DUHE, Suzette, Chief Financial Officer, Louisiana Heart Hospital, Lacombe, LA, p. A280

DUHON, Thomas, Director Human Resources, Heart Hospital of Lafayette, Lafayette, LA, p. A280

DUKE, Kelly, Chief Executive Officer, Mimbres Memorial Hospital, Deming, NM, p. A429

DUKE, II, Lee M., M.D. Senior Vice President and Chief Physician Executive, Lancaster General Hospital, Lancaster, PA, p. A542

DUKE, Mary, Interim Chief Executive Officer, Lake City Community Hospital, Lake City, SC, p. A567

DUKES, Brenda, Director Human Resources, Sonoma Developmental Center, Eldridge, CA, p. A61

DUKOFF, Ruth, M.D. Medical Director, North Star Behavioral Health System, Anchorage, AK, p. A28

DULANEY, Paul, M.D. Chief of Staff, Troy Regional Medical Center, Troy, AL, p. A26

DULL, David, M.D. Chief Medical Officer, Penrose–St. Francis Health Services, Colorado Springs, CO, p. A103

DULL, Kevin B.
Senior Vice President Human Potential, MultiCare Auburn Medical Center, Auburn, WA, p. A682
Senior Vice President Human Potential, MultiCare Good Samaritan Hospital, Puyallup, WA, p. A688
Senior Vice PresidentHuman Potential, MultiCare Mary Bridge Children's Hospital and Health Center, Tacoma, WA, p. A692
Senior Vice President, Human Potential, MultiCare Tacoma General Hospital, Tacoma, WA, p. A692

DULNY, David
Chief Financial Officer, Providence Medical Center, Kansas City, KS, p. A246
Chief Financial Officer, Saint John Hospital, Leavenworth, KS, p. A247

DUMAL, Jennifer, R.N. Chief Operating Officer of Clinical and Chief Nursing Officer, Memorial Hospital at Gulfport, Gulfport, MS, p. A358

DUMKE, Steve, FACHE Executive Vice President and Chief Operating Officer, Christian Health Care Center, Wyckoff, NJ, p. A426

DUMONSEAU, Kent
Vice President Finance and Information Services, Hayward Area Memorial Hospital and Nursing Home, Hayward, WI, p. A707
Vice President Finance and Information Services, Memorial Medical Center – Ashland, Ashland, WI, p. A702

DUMONT, Amy, R.N. Chief Clinical Officer and Vice President Patient Care Services, Frisbie Memorial Hospital, Rochester, NH, p. A413

DUMONT, Frank, Assistant Vice President Human Resources and Corporate Compliance, Eastern Long Island Hospital, Greenport, NY, p. A440

DUMONT, Rene, Vice President Strategic Growth, St. Mary's Regional Medical Center, Lewiston, ME, p. A293

DUNAVAN, Chad, R.N. Vice President, Chief Nursing Officer, Medical Center Health System, Odessa, TX, p. A639

DUNCAN, Allison, Chief Financial Officer, Arrowhead Behavioral Health Hospital, Maumee, OH, p. A498

DUNCAN, Barbara, Chief Financial Officer, Habersham Medical Center, Demorest, GA, p. A158

DUNCAN, Charles, M.D. Medical Director, Kindred Hospital–San Antonio, San Antonio, TX, p. A646

DUNCAN, Cindy
Manager Human Resources, Plains Regional Medical Center, Clovis, NM, p. A428
Director Human Resources, Roosevelt General Hospital, Portales, NM, p. A430

DUNCAN, Cynthia, Chief Executive Officer, Roger Mills Memorial Hospital, Cheyenne, OK, p. A509

DUNCAN, Darryl L., President and Chief Executive Officer, Monongalia General Hospital, Morgantown, WV, p. A698

DUNCAN, Darryl L., President and Chief Executive Officer, Monongalia Health System, Morgantown, WV, p. B92

DUNCAN, Jeremy, Director Information Systems, Lawrence Medical Center, Moulton, AL, p. A24

DUNCAN, Jimmy, Vice President Human Resources, WellStar Kennestone Hospital, Marietta, GA, p. A163

DUNCAN, Leeann, Director Patient Care Services, Harbor Oaks Hospital, New Baltimore, MI, p. A330

DUNCAN, Linda, Director Human Resources, Lee's Summit Medical Center, Lee's Summit, MO, p. A375

DUNCAN, Lyman, Chief Financial Officer, San Juan Hospital, Monticello, UT, p. A660

DUNCAN, Michael J., President and Chief Executive Officer, Penn Medicine Chester County Hospital, West Chester, PA, p. A557

DUNCAN, Nathan, Chief Executive Officer, Lakeland Behavioral Health System, Springfield, MO, p. A382

DUNCAN, Thomas M., Executive Vice President and Chief Financial Officer, Miami Valley Hospital, Dayton, OH, p. A493

DUNCAN, Traci A., Vice President, Chief Nursing Officer, NorthBay Medical Center, Fairfield, CA, p. A62

DUNFEE, Michael H., Director, Hampton Veterans Affairs Medical Center, Hampton, VA, p. A671

DUNFORD, Bill, Manager, Northside Hospital–Cherokee, Canton, GA, p. A155

DUNGAN, Janice L., Senior Vice President Clinical Services, Lake Regional Health System, Osage Beach, MO, p. A378

DUNHAM, Cathy, Vice President Human Resources, McPherson Hospital, McPherson, KS, p. A249

DUNHAM, Shelly, Chief Executive Officer, Okeene Municipal Hospital, Okeene, OK, p. A515

DUNIGAN, Linda, Chief Executive Officer, Claiborne County Medical Center, Port Gibson, MS, p. A364

DUNIO, Gina, Chief Human Resources, James E. Van Zandt Veterans Affairs Medical Center, Altoona, PA, p. A532

DUNKER, Karla, Director Finance, Sedgwick County Health Center, Julesburg, CO, p. A107

DUNKIEL, Barbara, Director Human Resources, HEALTHSOUTH Sunrise Rehabilitation Hospital, Sunrise, FL, p. A146

DUNKIN, Jackie J., Director Human Resources, Platte Valley Medical Center, Brighton, CO, p. A102

DUNKIN, Jennifer, Chief Nursing Officer, Moberly Regional Medical Center, Moberly, MO, p. A377

DUNKLE, David, Vice President Medical Affairs, Johnson Memorial Hospital, Franklin, IN, p. A211

DUNKLEY, Rich, Administrator, Wyoming State Hospital, Evanston, WY, p. A722

DUNLAP, Mary Lou, Correctional Health Services Administrator, California Medical Facility, Vacaville, CA, p. A97

DUNLAY, Sherry, Chief Nursing Officer, SSM Health St. Mary's Hospital Centralia, Centralia, IL, p. A182

DUNLEAVY, Christopher, Senior Vice President Finance and Chief Financial Officer, Brigham and Women's Hospital, Boston, MA, p. A306

DUNLEY, Pamela L., MS Vice President Chief Nursing Officer and Chief Operating Officer, Elmhurst Memorial Hospital,, IL, p. A189

DUNLOP, Jr., James H., CP
Executive Vice President and Chief Financial Officer, Kenmore Mercy Hospital, Kenmore, NY, p. A441
Senior Vice President Finance and Chief Financial Officer, Mercy Hospital, Buffalo, NY, p. A436
Chief Financial Officer, Sisters of Charity Hospital of Buffalo, Buffalo, NY, p. A436

DUNMYER, Daniel C., Chief Executive Officer, Carolinas ContinueCARE Hospital at Pineville, Charlotte, NC, p. A462

DUNN, Daniel N., Vice President Operations, Wentworth–Douglass Hospital, Dover, NH, p. A410

DUNN, Dave, Director of Nursing, Star Valley Medical Center, Afton, WY, p. A721

DUNN, E. D., Vice President Human Resources, Virtua Memorial, Mount Holly, NJ, p. A420

DUNN, Edna, Chief Nursing Officer, Western Plains Medical Complex, Dodge City, KS, p. A242

DUNN, Hope, Chief Nursing Officer, HEALTHSOUTH East Valley Rehabilitation Hospital, Mesa, AZ, p. A34

DUNN, Jack, M.D. Chief of Staff, La Paz Regional Hospital, Parker, AZ, p. A35

DUNN, Janice, Chief Financial Officer, Saint Joseph Regional Medical Center–Plymouth Campus, Plymouth, IN, p. A220

DUNN, Leonard, M.D. Chief Medical Officer, BayCare Alliant Hospital, Dunedin, FL, p. A127

DUNN, Marcy
Vice President Information Services and Chief Information Officer, Good Samaritan Hospital Medical Center, West Islip, NY, p. A458
Vice President Information Services and Chief Information Officer, Mercy Medical Center, Rockville Centre, NY, p. A454
Vice President Information Services and Chief Information Officer, St. Francis Hospital, The Heart Center, Roslyn, NY, p. A455

DUNN, Margie, Director Human Resources, Middle Tennessee Mental Health Institute, Nashville, TN, p. A590

DUNN, Nicholas, Director Information Systems, Mena Regional Health System, Mena, AR, p. A50

DUNN, Patrick A., R.N. Chief Nursing Officer, Lea Regional Medical Center, Hobbs, NM, p. A429

DUNN, Rosemary, R.N. Chief Nursing Officer, Hahnemann University Hospital, Philadelphia, PA, p. A548

DUNN, Sheila, Assistant Administrator Human Resources, Dale Medical Center, Ozark, AL, p. A24

DUNN, Tandra, Director of Nursing, San Luis Valley Health Conejos County Hospital, La Jara, CO, p. A107

DUNN, Terry, Director Information Technology, Battle Mountain General Hospital, Battle Mountain, NV, p. A404

DUNNAM, Lorie, Superintendent, Big Spring State Hospital, Big Spring, TX, p. A602

DUNNE, Elizabeth, President and Chief Executive Officer, PeaceHealth, Vancouver, WA, p. B103

DUNNING, David K., Commanding Officer, Tripler Army Medical Center, Honolulu, HI, p. A171

DUNPHY–ALEXANDER, Shannon, Director, Mercy Harvard Hospital, Harvard, IL, p. A192

DUNWOODY, Robert, Chief Financial Officer, Lawnwood Regional Medical Center & Heart Institute, Fort Pierce, FL, p. A129

DUPLAN, Don, M.D. Chief of Staff, The Medical Center of Southeast Texas, Port Arthur, TX, p. A642

DUPPER, Harold, Chief Financial Officer, Platte Valley Medical Center, Brighton, CO, p. A102

DUPPER, Larry L., Chief Financial Officer, Valley View Hospital, Glenwood Springs, CO, p. A106

DUPPSTADT, Edwin, M.D. Chief Medical Officer, Medical Center Arlington, Arlington, TX, p. A597

DUPRE, Charlotte W., Interim Chief Executive Officer, Southern Regional Medical Center, Riverdale, GA, p. A164

DUPRE, Ritchie, Chief Executive Officer, St. Charles Parish Hospital, Luling, LA, p. A282

DUPREE, Lucy G., Director Human Resources, Columbia Memorial Hospital, Astoria, OR, p. A524

DUPREY, Irma, Administrator Medical Records, Hospital Universitario Dr. Ramon Ruiz Arnau, Bayamon, PR, p. A726

DUPUIS, Pamela M., R.N. Senior Vice President Patient Care Services, Montefiore New Rochelle, New Rochelle, NY, p. A443

DUQUETTE, Cathy E., Ph.D. Vice President Nursing and Chief Nursing Officer, Newport Hospital, Newport, RI, p. A560

DUQUETTE, Connie, Director Human Resources, Sharp Memorial Hospital, San Diego, CA, p. A89

DUQUETTE, William M., Chief Executive Officer, Baptist Health South Florida, Homestead Hospital, Homestead, FL, p. A131

DURAN, Aurelio, Chief of Staff, Orlando Regional Medical Center, Orlando, FL, p. A140

DURAN, Jody, Manager Information Systems, Livingston HealthCare, Livingston, MT, p. A389

DURAND, Crista F., President, Newport Hospital, Newport, RI, p. A560

DURAND, Mark, Assistant Administrator Operations, CHRISTUS Southeast Texas Jasper Memorial, Jasper, TX, p. A629

DURBAK, Ivan, Chief Information Officer, Bronx–Lebanon Hospital Center Health Care System,, NY, p. A444

DURBIN, Melissa, R.N. Chief Nursing Officer, Boca Raton Regional Hospital, Boca Raton, FL, p. A124

DURDEN, Rhonda, Chief Financial Officer, Emanuel Medical Center, Swainsboro, GA, p. A167

DURGIN, Manal, Network Medical Director, Devereux Hospital and Children's Center of Florida, Melbourne, FL, p. A135

DURHAM, Karla, Director of Information Systems, Baptist Health Madisonville, Madisonville, KY, p. A265

DURHAM, Laurie Lea, Chief Executive Officer, Prairie Community Hospital, Terry, MT, p. A391

DURHAM, Linda, Director Human Resources, Henderson County Community Hospital, Lexington, TN, p. A587

DURHAM, Thomas, Chief Nursing Officer, Ferry County Memorial Hospital, Republic, WA, p. A688

DURIS, Deb, Director of Nursing, Northwest Ohio Psychiatric Hospital, Toledo, OH, p. A504

DURNEY, Gerry, Chief Operating Officer, Good Samaritan Regional Medical Center, Suffern, NY, p. A456

DURNIOK, Brian
Vice President Human Resources, UPMC Hamot, Erie, PA, p. A538
Vice President Operations, UPMC Northwest, Seneca, PA, p. A554

DURON, Kety, Vice President Human Resources, Stanford Health Care, Palo Alto, CA, p. A82

DUROVICH, Christopher J., President and Chief Executive Officer, Children's Health System of Texas, Dallas, TX, p. A609

DURR, Amber, Human Resources Executive, Community Hospital–Fairfax, Fairfax, MO, p. A371

DURR, Durinda, Vice President Clinical Services and Chief Nursing Officer, Rome Memorial Hospital, Rome, NY, p. A455

DURST, Geoff, Vice President Finance, Avera St. Luke's Hospital, Aberdeen, SD, p. A572

DURST, Sue, R.N. Vice President Plant Operations, McLaren Macomb, Mount Clemens, MI, p. A330

DURSTELER, Courtney, Chief Human Resources Officer, Franklin County Medical Center, Preston, ID, p. A178

DURYEE, Edward E., Director Information Systems, Saint Francis Healthcare System, Cape Girardeau, MO, p. A368

DUSANG, Nina, Vice President Finance and Chief Financial Officer, DCH Regional Medical Center, Tuscaloosa, AL, p. A26

DUSENBERY, Jack, President and Chief Executive Officer, Covenant Medical Center, Waterloo, IA, p. A238

DUTCHER, Phillip C., Chief Operating Officer, NCH Downtown Naples Hospital, Naples, FL, p. A138

DUTHE, Robert J., Director Information Systems and Chief Information Officer, Cortland Regional Medical Center, Cortland, NY, p. A437

DUTLA, Nimal, M.D. Chief Medical Staff, Holzer Medical Center – Jackson, Jackson, OH, p. A496

DUTMERS, David, Manager Technology Information System, Spectrum Health United Hospital, Greenville, MI, p. A325

DUTTON, Angela, Chief Human Resources Management Service, Robley Rex Veterans Affairs Medical Center, Louisville, KY, p. A265

DUTTON, Rebecca, Director Human Resources, Larue D. Carter Memorial Hospital, Indianapolis, IN, p. A214

DUTTON, Teresa, R.N. Chief Nursing Officer, Heritage Park Surgical Hospital, Sherman, TX, p. A649

DUVAL, John, Chief Executive Officer, VCU Medical Center, Richmond, VA, p. A678

DUVAL, Rob, Chief Human Resources Officer, Emma Pendleton Bradley Hospital, East Providence, RI, p. A560

DUVALL, Richard, Chief Executive Officer, Carthage Area Hospital, Carthage, NY, p. A437

DUVALL, Wendy, Chief Executive Officer, Barton County Memorial Hospital, Lamar, MO, p. A375

DUVVURI, Vikas, M.D. Medical Director, Fremont Hospital, Fremont, CA, p. A63

DWIGHT, John
Regional Vice President and Chief Information Officer, Cascade Valley Hospital and Clinics, Arlington, WA, p. A682
Regional Vice President and Chief Information Officer, Skagit Regional Health, Mount Vernon, WA, p. A686

DWORKIN, Darren, Senior Vice President Enterpirse Information Systems and Chief Information Officer, Cedars–Sinai Medical Center, Los Angeles, CA, p. A70

DWORKIN, Jack H., M.D. Vice President Medical Affairs and Chief Medical Officer, CentraState Healthcare System, Freehold, NJ, p. A417

DWORKIN, Paul, M.D. Physician–in–Chief, Connecticut Children's Medical Center, Hartford, CT, p. A114

DWYER, Amy L., R.N. Chief Nursing Officer, Sacred Heart Hospital, Eau Claire, WI, p. A705

DWYER, Cathy, Senior Administrator Information Systems, Burke Rehabilitation Hospital, White Plains, NY, p. A459

DWYER, Glenda E., Interim President, The Aroostook Medical Center, Presque Isle, ME, p. A295

DWYER, James P., D.O
Executive Vice President and Chief Medical Officer, Virtua Memorial, Mount Holly, NJ, p. A420
Executive Vice President and Chief Medical Officer, Virtua Voorhees, Voorhees, NJ, p. A425

DWYER, Karla, R.N. Chief Nursing Officer, HEALTHSOUTH Rehabilitation Hospital–Wichita Falls, Wichita Falls, TX, p. A657

DWYER, Susan, Vice President Finance, Aurora Psychiatric Hospital, Wauwatosa, WI, p. A718

DWYER, William, Vice President Chief Human Resources Officer, Children's Specialized Hospital–PSE&G, New Brunswick, NJ, p. A420

DYCHE, Ginny, Director Community Relations, Aspen Valley Hospital District, Aspen, CO, p. A101

DYCUS, Steve, Director Marketing and Public Relations, Williamson Medical Center, Franklin, TN, p. A583

DYE, Blake A., President, St. Vincent Heart Center, Indianapolis, IN, p. A214

DYE, Chris, Director Information Systems, Saint Joseph – Martin, Martin, KY, p. A266

DYE, Dana, R.N., Vice President, Administrator and Chief Executive Officer, Baptist Memorial Hospital – Memphis, Memphis, TN, p. A588

DYE, Emily, Vice President Human Resources, TriStar Summit Medical Center, Hermitage, TN, p. A584

DYE, Kathy, Interim Administrator, Adena Greenfield Medical Center, Greenfield, OH, p. A495

DYE, Leslie, Chief Executive Officer, PHS Santa Fe Indian Hospital, Santa Fe, NM, p. A431

DYER, Kathleen, Vice President and Chief Information Officer, Adventist Behavioral Health Rockville, Rockville, MD, p. A303

DYKEHOUSE, Rod, Chief Information Officer, Penn State Milton S. Hershey Medical Center, Hershey, PA, p. A540

DYKEHOUSE, Rodney, Senior Vice President Information Services, Waukesha Memorial Hospital, Waukesha, WI, p. A718

DYKES, Bradford W., President and Chief Executive Officer, Indiana University Health Bedford Hospital, Bedford, IN, p. A206

DYKES, Nichole, Chief Financial Officer, HEALTHSOUTH Rehabilitation Hospital North Texas, Richardson, TX, p. A643

DYKSTERHOUSE, Trevor J., President, Forest Health Medical Center, Ypsilanti, MI, p. A337

DYKSTRA, Janet H., Chief Executive Officer, Osceola Community Hospital, Sibley, IA, p. A237

DYKSTRA, Lisa, Senior Vice President and Chief Information Officer, Ann & Robert H. Lurie Children's Hospital of Chicago, Chicago, IL, p. A183

DYLE, Amanda, Chief Financial Officer, Walker Baptist Medical Center, Jasper, AL, p. A22

DYRKACZ, Anna, Chief Financial Officer, Vibra Hospital of Western Massachusetts, Springfield, MA, p. A315

DYSART–CREDEUR, Amy, Administrator, Oceans Behavioral Hospital of Broussard, Broussard, LA, p. A274

DZIEDZICKI, Ron, R.N. Chief Operating Officer, University Hospitals Cleveland Medical Center, Cleveland, OH, p. A490

E

EADIE, Reginald J., M.D.,
Chief Executive Officer, DMC – Detroit Receiving Hospital, Detroit, MI, p. A321
Chief Executive Officer, DMC Harper University Hospital, Detroit, MI, p. A322

EADS, Barry, Chief Nursing Officer, HEALTHSOUTH Rehabilitation of Gadsden, Gadsden, AL, p. A20

EADY, Bruce, Chief Executive Officer, Mercy Rehabilitation Hospital Springfield, Springfield, MO, p. A382

EAGAR, Troy, Director Human Resources, Mountain Valley Regional Rehabilitation Hospital, Prescott Valley, AZ, p. A38

EAGEN, Mary K., R.N. Executive Vice President, Chief Nursing Officer, Parkland Health & Hospital System, Dallas, TX, p. A611

EAGER, David, Senior Vice President and Chief Financial Officer, Children's Health System of Texas, Dallas, TX, p. A609

EAGERTON, Gregory S., Ph.D. Nurse Executive, Durham Veterans Affairs Medical Center, Durham, NC, p. A464

EAKER, Blake, Interim Director Information Services, Uvalde Memorial Hospital, Uvalde, TX, p. A654

EAKS, C. Alan, Chief Executive Officer and Managing Director, Spring Mountain Treatment Center, Las Vegas, NV, p. A406

EARL, Anna, M.D. Chief of Staff, Liberty Medical Center, Chester, MT, p. A386

EARL, Mindy, Health Information Manager, Power County Hospital District, American Falls, ID, p. A174

EARLE, Audra, FACHE, Chief Executive Officer, Watsonville Community Hospital, Watsonville, CA, p. A99

EARLEY, Robert, President and Chief Executive Officer, JPS Health Network, Fort Worth, TX, p. A618

EARLEY, Tom, Chief Financial Officer, AllianceHealth Woodward, Woodward, OK, p. A523

EARLS, Sandra, Chief Financial Officer, Coalinga Regional Medical Center, Coalinga, CA, p. A59

EARLY, Elfie, Manager Data Services, Georgia Regional Hospital at Atlanta, Decatur, GA, p. A158

EARLY, Gerald L., M.D. Chief Medical Officer, Pullman Regional Hospital, Pullman, WA, p. A688

EARNSHAW, Dallas, Superintendent, Utah State Hospital, Provo, UT, p. A662

EASLEY, Evan, M.D. Chief Medical Officer, Carson Valley Medical Center, Gardnerville, NV, p. A404

EASLEY, Mike, Vice President and Chief Operating Officer, Sabine County Hospital, Hemphill, TX, p. A623

EAST, Becky, Senior Vice President, Chief Financial Officer, Bronson LakeView Hospital, Paw Paw, MI, p. A331

EASTBURG, Mark C., Ph.D., President and Chief Executive Officer, Pine Rest Christian Mental Health Services, Grand Rapids, MI, p. A325

EASTER, Susan, Chief Nursing Officer, Palacios Community Medical Center, Palacios, TX, p. A639

EASTERLING, Jamie, Executive Director, Operations, Good Samaritan Hospital, Cincinnati, OH, p. A487

EASTERWOOD, Diane J., Human Resources Business Partner, Kaiser Permanente San Francisco Medical Center, San Francisco, CA, p. A90

EASTHOPE, Kerry, Area Finance Officer, Kaiser Permanente Antioch Medical Center, Antioch, CA, p. A54

EASTMAN, David, Site Director, Ukiah Valley Medical Center, Ukiah, CA, p. A97

EASTON, Laura J., R.N., President and Chief Executive Officer, Caldwell Memorial Hospital, Lenoir, NC, p. A468

EATHERLY, Theresa, Chief Financial Officer, United Memorial Medical Care, Houston, TX, p. A627

EATON, Jim, Chief Financial Officer, Wise Regional Health System, Decatur, TX, p. A612

EATON, Philip, Interim Chief Executive Officer, Mountain West Medical Center, Tooele, UT, p. A664

EAVENSON, Steve, Vice President Finance, Mercy Health Saint Mary's, Grand Rapids, MI, p. A325

EAVES, Dan, Chief Executive Officer, Marshall Browning Hospital, Du Quoin, IL, p. A188

EBANGIT, Ruth, M.D. Chief of Staff and Medical Officer, Throckmorton County Memorial Hospital, Throckmorton, TX, p. A653

EBBETT, Patricia, Chief Human Resources Officer, Catawba Hospital, Catawba, VA, p. A668

EBERHARDT, Lisa, Chief Nursing Officer, Clark Fork Valley Hospital, Plains, MT, p. A390

EBERSOLE, Nathan, Controller, Calhoun–Liberty Hospital, Blountstown, FL, p. A123

EBERT Jr., Larry W., Chief Executive Officer, Northridge Medical Center, Commerce, GA, p. A157

EBERT, Michael, M.D. Chief of Staff, Veterans Affairs Connecticut Healthcare System, West Haven, CT, p. A118

EBERT–LOOMIS, Cynthia, R.N. Chief Nursing Officer, Summit Healthcare Regional Medical Center, Show Low, AZ, p. A39

EBERTH, Denise A., Chief Human Resources Officer, Allegan General Hospital, Allegan, MI, p. A318

EBLIN, Steven E., Chief Executive Officer / President, Randolph Hospital, Asheboro, NC, p. A460

EBNER, Joseph, M.D. Chief Medical Officer, Speare Memorial Hospital, Plymouth, NH, p. A413

EBRI, Patrick D., Ph.D
Vice President, Human Resources, Southeast Georgia Health System Brunswick Campus, Brunswick, GA, p. A155
Vice President Human Resources, Southeast Georgia Health System Camden Campus, Saint Marys, GA, p. A165

EBRIGHT, Brian, Chief Financial Officer, Salt Lake Regional Medical Center, Salt Lake City, UT, p. A663

ECKELS, Dan, Chief Financial Officer, Washington Regional Medical Center, Fayetteville, AR, p. A46

ECKENFELS, Susan, Chief Financial Officer, Ste. Genevieve County Memorial Hospital, Ste. Genevieve, MO, p. A383

ECKERSLEY, Jay, Interim Chief Executive Officer, Mercy Hospital of Portland, Portland, ME, p. A294

ECKERT, Mark, Vice President Finance, Ochsner Medical Center – Kenner, Kenner, LA, p. A279

ECKERT, Mary L., President and Chief Executive Officer, Millcreek Community Hospital, Erie, PA, p. A538

ECKERT, Susan E., R.N. Senior Vice President and Chief Nursing Officer, MedStar Washington Hospital Center, Washington, DC, p. A122

ECKES, Chad, Vice President Information Services and Chief Information Officer, Wake Forest Baptist Medical Center, Winston–Salem, NC, p. A476

ECKFORD, Marjorie, Chief Nursing Officer, Menlo Park Surgical Hospital, Menlo Park, CA, p. A76

ECKLAND, Christopher, M.D. Chief Medical Officer, Miami County Medical Center, Paola, KS, p. A251

ECKSTEIN, William, Chief Financial Officer, Columbus Specialty Hospital, Columbus, GA, p. A156

EDALATI, David, M.D. Medical Director, Meadowbrook Rehabilitation Hospital, Gardner, KS, p. A243

EDDEY, Gary E., M.D. Medical Director, Matheny Medical and Educational Center, Peapack, NJ, p. A421

EDDINGTON, Tonya, Coordinator Human Resources, Select Specialty Hospital–Springfield, Springfield, MO, p. A383

EDDLEMAN, Patricia, Fiscal Officer, Heartland Behavioral Healthcare, Massillon, OH, p. A498

EDDY, Lee Anne, Senior Vice President and Chief Nursing Officer, Arkansas Children's Hospital, Little Rock, AR, p. A48

EDELMAN, Marc D., Vice President Operations, Bristol Hospital, Bristol, CT, p. A113

EDEN, Tina M., Director of Nursing, Virginia Gay Hospital, Vinton, IA, p. A238

EDENFIELD, Janet, Director Financial Services, Georgia Regional Hospital at Savannah, Savannah, GA, p. A166

EDGAR, Joseph H., Senior Vice President Operations, WellSpan Gettysburg Hospital, Gettysburg, PA, p. A539

EDGAR, Nancy, Vice President Human Resources, Methodist Hospital, San Antonio, TX, p. A646

EDGAR, Steven, President and Chief Executive Officer, Denton Regional Medical Center, Denton, TX, p. A612

EDGEWORTH, Mitch, Chief Executive Officer, Vanderbilt University Medical Center, Nashville, TN, p. A591

EDIN, Scott D., Vice President, Finance and Chief Financial Officer, Northfield Hospital, Northfield, MN, p. A348

EDLER, Susie, R.N. Chief Nursing Officer, Dallas Behavioral Healthcare Hospital, Desoto, TX, p. A613

EDMINSTER, Sue
Vice President Human Resources, Agnesian HealthCare, Fond Du Lac, WI, p. A705
Vice President Human Resources, Ripon Medical Center, Ripon, WI, p. A715
Vice President Human Resources, Waupun Memorial Hospital, Waupun, WI, p. A718

EDMONDS, Kelly, Chief Financial Officer, Western Maryland Hospital Center, Hagerstown, MD, p. A301

EDMONDSON, Bobby, Controller, Regional Rehabilitation Hospital, Phenix City, AL, p. A24

EDMONDSON, James H., Chief Executive Officer, Southern Tennessee Regional Health System–Pulaski, Pulaski, TN, p. A592

EDMONSON, Cole, R.N. Vice President and Chief Nursing Officer, Texas Health Presbyterian Hospital Dallas, Dallas, TX, p. A611

EDMUNDS, Liza, Director Human Resources, Tennova Healthcare–Clarksville, Clarksville, TN, p. A581

EDMUNDSON, Reed
Chief Executive Officer, Bellville St. Joseph Health Center, Bellville, TX, p. A602
Administrator, Grimes St. Joseph Health Center, Navasota, TX, p. A638
Administrator, Madison St. Joseph Health Center, Madisonville, TX, p. A635

EDNEY, Daniel, M.D. Chief of Staff, Promise Hospital of Vicksburg, Vicksburg, MS, p. A365

EDRINGTON, Katherine, R.N. Administrator, Mercy Health – Anderson Hospital, Cincinnati, OH, p. A488

EDWARD, Adolphe, Chief Executive Officer, El Centro Regional Medical Center, El Centro, CA, p. A61

EDWARDS, Angela Imelda, R.N. Chief Nurse Executive, NYC Health + Hospitals / Woodhull,, NY, p. A449

EDWARDS, Annette, Chief Financial Officer, Odessa Memorial Healthcare Center, Odessa, WA, p. A687

EDWARDS, Becky, Manager Human Resources, Irwin County Hospital, Ocilla, GA, p. A164

EDWARDS Jr., Bob S., FACHE, Chief Executive Officer, Mendocino Coast District Hospital, Fort Bragg, CA, p. A62

EDWARDS, Bruce
Vice President Human Resources, Heritage Valley Health System, Beaver, PA, p. A533
Vice President Human Resources, Sewickley Valley Hospital, (A Division of Valley Medical Facilities), Sewickley, PA, p. A554

EDWARDS, Chris, M.D. Chief Medical Officer, Maury Regional Hospital, Columbia, TN, p. A581

EDWARDS, Dana, Chief Financial Officer, HEALTHSOUTH Sea Pines Rehabilitation Hospital, Melbourne, FL, p. A136

EDWARDS, Dennis, M.D. Vice President Medical Affairs, CHI Health Good Samaritan, Kearney, NE, p. A397

EDWARDS, Gregg
Vice President Human Resources, Asante Ashland Community Hospital, Ashland, OR, p. A524
Chief People Officer, Asante Rogue Regional Medical Center, Medford, OR, p. A528
Chief People Officer, Asante Three Rivers Medical Center, Grants Pass, OR, p. A526

EDWARDS, James D., Chief Executive Officer, Howard University Hospital, Washington, DC, p. A121

EDWARDS, Jeff, Manager Information Services, Mendocino Coast District Hospital, Fort Bragg, CA, p. A62

EDWARDS, John R., Administrator and Chief Executive Officer, Pacific Alliance Medical Center, Los Angeles, CA, p. A73

EDWARDS, Kathleen, Manager Information Systems Operation, HEALTHSOUTH Rehabilitation Hospital of Altoona, Altoona, PA, p. A532

EDWARDS, Kristy, M.D. Chief Medical Officer, Lillian M. Hudspeth Memorial Hospital, Sonora, TX, p. A649

EDWARDS, Marti, MS
Chief Nursing Officer, RML Specialty Hospital, Chicago, IL, p. A186
Chief Nursing Officer, RML Specialty Hospital, Hinsdale, IL, p. A193

EDWARDS, Matt, Vice President Nursing Services and Chief Nursing Officer, Anderson Regional Health System, Meridian, MS, p. A362

EDWARDS, Michael R., Administrator, Scott Regional Hospital, Morton, MS, p. A362

EDWARDS, Michelle, Executive Vice President Information Technology, Palmetto Health Baptist, Columbia, SC, p. A564

EDWARDS, Nicki E., Ph.D. Interim Chief Nursing Officer, Sierra Vista Regional Medical Center, San Luis Obispo, CA, p. A92

EDWARDS, Rebecca
Chief Nursing Officer, Greenwood Leflore Hospital, Greenwood, MS, p. A358
Director Human Resources, Martin General Hospital, Williamston, NC, p. A475
Chief Human Resources Officer, Penn Highlands Brookville, Brookville, PA, p. A534

EDWARDS, Rick, Vice President and Chief Financial Officer, Hancock Regional Hospital, Greenfield, IN, p. A212

EDWARDS, Samuel, M.D. Chief of Staff, Florida Hospital DeLand, DeLand, FL, p. A127

EDWARDS, Steven D., President and Chief Executive Officer, Cox Medical Centers, Springfield, MO, p. A382

EDWARDS, Steven D., President and Chief Executive Officer, CoxHealth, Springfield, MO, p. B43

EDWARDS, Susan, Vice President Human Resources, Novant Health UVA Health System Culpeper Medical Center, Culpeper, VA, p. A669

EDWARDS, Susan A., Chief Executive Officer, Oconomowoc Memorial Hospital, Oconomowoc, WI, p. A713

EDWARDS, Susan A., President and Chief Executive Officer, ProHealth Care, Inc., Waukesha, WI, p. B107

EDWARDS, Susan A., Chief Executive Officer, Waukesha Memorial Hospital, Waukesha, WI, p. A718

EDWARDS, Teresa L., President and Administrator, Sentara Leigh Hospital, Norfolk, VA, p. A675

EDWARDS, Terry, Controller, Kings Mountain Hospital, Kings Mountain, NC, p. A468

EDWARDS, Todd, Director Information Management Systems, CHI St. Luke's Health Brazosport, Lake Jackson, TX, p. A631

EDWARDS, William, Information Technology Generalist, Wernersville State Hospital, Wernersville, PA, p. A557

EESLEY, Michael S., Chief Executive Officer, Centegra Health System, Crystal Lake, IL, p. B31

EESLEY, Michael S.
Chief Executive Officer, Centegra Hospital – McHenry, McHenry, IL, p. A196
Chief Executive Officer, Centegra Hospital – Woodstock, Woodstock, IL, p. A205

EGAN, Kim, Executive Director Human Resources, Regions Hospital, Saint Paul, MN, p. A350

EGAN, Timothy, President and Chief Executive Officer, Roseland Community Hospital, Chicago, IL, p. A186

EGEN, Carol, R.N. Chief Nursing Officer, Rutland Regional Medical Center, Rutland, VT, p. A666

EGERTON, W. Eugene, M.D. Chief Medical Officer, University of Maryland Medical Center Midtown Campus, Baltimore, MD, p. A298

EGGEN, Caity, Chief Human Resource Officer, Cuyuna Regional Medical Center, Crosby, MN, p. A341

EGGERS, Judy, Manager Human Resources, Alliance HealthCare System, Holly Springs, MS, p. A359

EGGLESTON, Kirk W., Commanding Officer, Winn Army Community Hospital, Hinesville, GA, p. A160

EGGLESTON, Lara
Finance Manager, University Hospitals Conneaut Medical Center, Conneaut, OH, p. A492
Finance Manager, University Hospitals Geneva Medical Center, Geneva, OH, p. A495

EGGLESTON, Ryan, Chief Financial Officer, Desert View Hospital, Pahrump, NV, p. A407

EGYUD, Amber, Vice President Chief Nursing Officer, Forbes Hospital, Monroeville, PA, p. A545

EHASZ, James, Chief Financial Officer, Copper Queen Community Hospital, Bisbee, AZ, p. A31

EHLER, Phyllis, Director Human Resources, Avera St. Benedict Health Center, Parkston, SD, p. A575

EHLERS, Jeffrey, Chief Financial Officer, Memorial Health, Marysville, OH, p. A498

EHLINGER, Forrest, System Chief Financial Officer, Benefis Health System, Great Falls, MT, p. A388

EHLKE, Ranae, Administrative Secretary and Coordinator Risk Management and Human Resources, Kenmare Community Hospital, Kenmare, ND, p. A480

EHLY, Ronda S., R.N. Chief Nursing Officer, Mary Lanning Healthcare, Hastings, NE, p. A396

EHN, Jerry, Chief Operating Officer, Northfield Hospital, Northfield, MN, p. A348

EHN, Nicole, M.D. Chief of Staff, Van Diest Medical Center, Webster City, IA, p. A239

EHRAT, Michael, Chief Executive Officer, Memorial Hospital, Martinsville, VA, p. A673

EHRENBERGER, David, M.D. Chief Medical Officer, Avista Adventist Hospital, Louisville, CO, p. A109

EHRICH, Laurie, Chief Communications Officer, Wayne County Hospital, Corydon, IA, p. A228

EHRLICH, Frank, M.D
Chief Medical Officer, Health Alliance Hospital – Broadway Campus, Kingston, NY, p. A441
Chief Medical Officer, Health Alliance Hospital – Mary's Avenue Campus, Kingston, NY, p. A441

EHRLICH, Susan P., M.D., Chief Executive Officer, Zuckerberg San Francisco General Hospital and Trauma Center, San Francisco, CA, p. A91

EHTISHAM, Saad, R.N
Vice President and Chief Operating Officer, Leesburg Regional Medical Center, Leesburg, FL, p. A134
Vice President and Chief Operating Officer, The Villages Regional Hospital, The Villages, FL, p. A148

EICHENAUER, Donald T., Chief Executive Officer, Wyoming County Community Hospital, Warsaw, NY, p. A458

EICHENBERGER, Daniel J., M.D., President and Chief Executive Officer, Baptist Health Floyd, New Albany, IN, p. A219

EICHNER, John, Vice President Finance, TLC Health Network – Lake Shore Hospital, Irving, NY, p. A440

EIDAM, JoEllen, FACHE, Chief Executive Officer, Adams Memorial Hospital, Decatur, IN, p. A209

EIDE, Dean, Vice President, Mayo Clinic Health System – Oakridge in Osseo, Osseo, WI, p. A714

EIDE, Tom, Chief Financial Officer, Prairie St. John's, Fargo, ND, p. A478

EIFFERT, Sarah, Director Human Resources, Mercy Rehabilitation Hospital Springfield, Springfield, MO, p. A382

EIG, Blair, M.D. Senior Vice President Medical Affairs, Holy Cross Hospital, Silver Spring, MD, p. A303

EIKE, Gail, Chief Financial Officer, Sanford Jackson Medical Center, Jackson, MN, p. A344

EILBRACHT, Hans, Chief Information Officer, Hamilton Center, Terre Haute, IN, p. A222

EIMERS, Katy, Human Resources Officer, Syringa Hospital and Clinics, Grangeville, ID, p. A176

EINSWEILER, Desiree, Chief Executive Officer, Palo Alto County Health System, Emmetsburg, IA, p. A230

EIPE, Joseph, M.D. Chief Medical Officer, Pacifica Hospital of the Valley,, CA, p. A73

EISCHEID, Randy, Director Information Systems, St. Anthony Regional Hospital, Carroll, IA, p. A226

EISCHENS, Shelby, Chief Medical Officer, Brookings Health System, Brookings, SD, p. A572

EISELE, Karla, M.D. Clinical Director, State Hospital North, Orofino, ID, p. A177

EISEMANN, Bradley, Administrator, Beacon Children's Hospital, Luverne, AL, p. A22

EISEN, Robert A., Vice President Human Resources, Northern California Region, Queen of the Valley Medical Center, Napa, CA, p. A79

EISENMAN, Edward, Chief Executive Officer, Sunnyview Rehabilitation Hospital, Schenectady, NY, p. A455

EISENMANN, Claudia, Chief Executive Officer, Wilbarger General Hospital, Vernon, TX, p. A655

EISENTRAGER, Steve, President, Ohio Valley Surgical Hospital, Springfield, OH, p. A502

EISENZOPH, Pete, Director Information Technology, Bay Area Medical Center, Marinette, WI, p. A709

EISMAN, Michael, M.D. Medical Director, Schuyler Hospital, Montour Falls, NY, p. A443

EISNER, Nina W., Chief Executive Officer and Managing Director, Ridge Behavioral Health System, Lexington, KY, p. A263

EITZEN, Tamara, Chief Nursing Officer, Fairview Regional Medical Center, Fairview, OK, p. A512

EIXENBERGER, Timothy D., Chief Nursing Officer, Southcoast Hospitals Group, Fall River, MA, p. A310

EKEH, Cyril, Interim Medical Center Director, Central Arkansas Veterans Healthcare System, Little Rock, AR, p. A49

EKENGREN, Francie H., M.D. Chief Medical Officer, Wesley Medical Center, Wichita, KS, p. A256

EKEREN, Douglas R., Regional President and Chief Executive Officer, Avera Sacred Heart Hospital, Yankton, SD, p. A578

EKPO, Felix, Manager, Information Systems, Arrowhead Regional Medical Center, Colton, CA, p. A59

EL KHALILI, Nizar, M.D. Medical Director, Sycamore Springs Hospital, Lafayette, IN, p. A216

EL-DALATI, Sam, M.D. Chief Medical Officer, Mercy Regional Medical Center, Lorain, OH, p. A497

EL-MELIGI, Christi J., R.N., Chief Executive Officer, Sage Memorial Hospital, Ganado, AZ, p. A32

EL-SOLH, Ali, M.D. Interim Chief of Staff, Veterans Affairs Western New York Healthcare System–Buffalo Division, Buffalo, NY, p. A436

ELAM, Lora, R.N. Chief Nursing Officer, Wayne County Hospital, Monticello, KY, p. A266

ELAM, Moses D., M.D. Physician–in–Chief, Kaiser Permanente Manteca Medical Center, Manteca, CA, p. A76

ELARBEE, Vernon, Director of Human Resources, Florida Hospital North Pinellas, Tarpon Springs, FL, p. A148

ELBERT, Darlene M., R.N. Assistant Administrator and Chief Nursing Officer, Kossuth Regional Health Center, Algona, IA, p. A225

ELDER, Becky, Vice President Clinical Services, Perry County Memorial Hospital, Tell City, IN, p. A222

ELDER, Deborah, Director Human Resources, Scenic Mountain Medical Center, Big Spring, TX, p. A602

ELDIDY, Rene, M.D. Chief of Staff, CentraCare Health–Long Prairie, Long Prairie, MN, p. A345

ELDRED, Jamie, Controller, Klickitat Valley Health, Goldendale, WA, p. A685

ELDRIDGE, Janet, Director Human Resources and Personnel, Brooks County Hospital, Quitman, GA, p. A164

ELDRIDGE, Jim, Area Financial Officer, Kaiser Permanente Sacramento Medical Center, Sacramento, CA, p. A86

ELDRIDGE, Laurie, Chief Financial Officer, Marshall Medical Center, Placerville, CA, p. A83

ELDRIDGE, Lisa, Human Resources Officer, Thomas H. Boyd Memorial Hospital, Carrollton, IL, p. A182

ELEGANT, Bruce M., FACHE, President and Chief Executive Officer, Rush Oak Park Hospital, Oak Park, IL, p. A199

ELFERT, Mike, Director Information Services, Lourdes Medical Center of Burlington County, Willingboro, NJ, p. A425

ELGARICO, David, Chief Operating Officer, Touro Infirmary, New Orleans, LA, p. A285

ELI, Bev, Chief Nursing Officer, Cox Monett, Monett, MO, p. A377

ELIAS, Jose, Director Information Technology, Fort Duncan Regional Medical Center, Eagle Pass, TX, p. A614

ELICH, Elizabeth
Vice President Human Resources, Frye Regional Medical Center, Hickory, NC, p. A467
Vice President Human Resources, Piedmont Medical Center, Rock Hill, SC, p. A569

ELIE, Charlene, Vice President Patient Care Services, Clinton Hospital, Clinton, MA, p. A309

ELIOT, Jason L., Vice President Human Resources, Integris Baptist Medical Center, Oklahoma City, OK, p. A516

ELKINGTON, Bruce, Regional Chief Information Officer, St. Clare Hospital, Lakewood, WA, p. A686

ELKINGTON, Mark, M.D. Chief Medical Officer, Willow Crest Hospital, Miami, OK, p. A514

ELKINS, Carl, Director Information Technology, Rollins–Brook Community Hospital, Lampasas, TX, p. A632

ELKINS, James N., FACHE, Director, Texas Center for Infectious Disease, San Antonio, TX, p. A647

ELKINS, Wendy, Director Operations, Dundy County Hospital, Benkelman, NE, p. A394

ELLEDGE, David
Controller, Select Specialty Hospital–Knoxville, Knoxville, TN, p. A586
Controller, Select Specialty Hospital–North Knoxville, Powell, TN, p. A592

ELLEN, Jonathan D., M.D. Medical Director, HEALTHSOUTH Rehabilitation Hospital of Memphis, Memphis, TN, p. A588

ELLEN, Jonathan M., M.D., President, Johns Hopkins All Children's Hospital, Saint Petersburg, FL, p. A144

ELLENBURG, Cynthia, Director Health Information Services, Baptist Easley Hospital, Easley, SC, p. A565

ELLER, Bill, Director Information Technology, El Campo Memorial Hospital, El Campo, TX, p. A615

ELLER, Steven M.
Vice President Human Resources, Elkhart General Hospital, Elkhart, IN, p. A209
Chief Human Resources Officer, Beacon Health System, Memorial Hospital of South Bend, South Bend, IN, p. A222

ELLERSON, Thomas, Chief Information Officer, Our Lady of Lourdes Memorial Hospital, Inc., Binghamton, NY, p. A435

ELLEY, Michael, Chief Information Officer, Owensboro Health Regional Hospital, Owensboro, KY, p. A267

ELLINGTON, Christopher, Executive Vice President and Chief Financial Officer, University of North Carolina Hospitals, Chapel Hill, NC, p. A462

ELLIOTT, Amy, M.D. Director Medical Affairs, District One Hospital, Faribault, MN, p. A342

ELLIOTT, Barb, Interim President and Chief Executive Officer, Fairbanks, Indianapolis, IN, p. A213

ELLIOTT Jr., Charles W., Chief Executive Officer, Johnston Health, Smithfield, NC, p. A473

ELLIOTT, Jennifer, Chief Nursing Officer, Saint Thomas West Hospital, Nashville, TN, p. A591

ELLIOTT, Jim
Director Human Resources, Bryce Hospital, Tuscaloosa, AL, p. A26
Director Human Resources, Mary S Harper Geriatric Psychiatry Center, Tuscaloosa, AL, p. A26

ELLIOTT, Laura, Director Human Resources, Northeastern Nevada Regional Hospital, Elko, NV, p. A404

ELLIOTT, Lee Ann, R.N. Director of Nursing, Select Rehabilitation Hospital of Denton, Denton, TX, p. A613

ELLIOTT, Marye, Chief Nursing Officer, Eliza Coffee Memorial Hospital, Florence, AL, p. A20

ELLIOTT, Michael, M.D. Chief Medical Officer and Senior Vice President of Medical Affairs, Avera McKennan Hospital and University Health Center, Sioux Falls, SD, p. A576

ELLIOTT, Michael, Controller, Indianhead Medical Center, Shell Lake, WI, p. A716

ELLIOTT, Peyton, Vice President Operations, Houston Methodist West Hospital, Houston, TX, p. A624

ELLIOTT, R. James, Vice President Human Resources, The Charlotte Hungerford Hospital, Torrington, CT, p. A117

ELLIOTT, Rhonda M., Director Information Technology and Meaningful Use, Person Memorial Hospital, Roxboro, NC, p. A472

ELLIOTT, Robin, Personnel Officer, Community Memorial Hospital, Sumner, IA, p. A238

ELLIOTT, Shane, Associate Director Administration, Veterans Affairs Loma Linda Healthcare System, Loma Linda, CA, p. A69

ELLIOTT MSN, Randi, Chief Nursing Officer, Baylor Medical Center at Frisco, Frisco, TX, p. A619

ELLIS, Amanda, Chief Financial Officer, Barbourville ARH Hospital, Barbourville, KY, p. A257

ELLIS, Angela, R.N. Chief Nursing Officer, Terre Haute Regional Hospital, Terre Haute, IN, p. A222

ELLIS, Bob, Director of Nursing, D. W. McMillan Memorial Hospital, Brewton, AL, p. A17

ELLIS, Deb, Director Human Resources, Perry Memorial Hospital, Perry, OK, p. A518

ELLIS, Elmer G., FACHE, President and Chief Executive Officer, East Texas Medical Center Regional Healthcare System, Tyler, TX, p. B52

ELLIS, Kristin, Controller, Munson Healthcare Cadillac Hospital, Cadillac, MI, p. A319

ELLIS, Lisa, Chief Operating Officer, AllianceHealth Midwest, Midwest City, OK, p. A514

ELLIS, Mark, Director Information Technology, Lakeview Hospital, Bountiful, UT, p. A659

ELLIS, Michael J., FACHE, Chief Executive Officer, Hill Regional Hospital, Hillsboro, TX, p. A623

ELLIS, Michelle, Director Human Resources, Whitman Hospital and Medical Center, Colfax, WA, p. A683

ELLIS, Mike, Chief Financial Officer, Wickenburg Community Hospital, Wickenburg, AZ, p. A41

ELLIS, Rich, Chief Operating Officer, Frye Regional Medical Center, Hickory, NC, p. A467

ELLIS, Scott, D.O. Chief Medical Officer, The Memorial Hospital at Craig, Craig, CO, p. A103

ELLIS, Susan Renee', R.N. Vice President of Human Resources, Highlands Regional Medical Center, Prestonsburg, KY, p. A268

ELLIS, Thomas J., Vice President Human Resources, Mt. Washington Pediatric Hospital, Baltimore, MD, p. A297

ELLIS, Wendel, D.O. Chief Medical Staff, Greeley County Health Services, Tribune, KS, p. A255

ELLISH, Patti M., FACHE, President and Chief Executive Officer, St. Tammany Parish Hospital, Covington, LA, p. A275

ELLISON, Darcy, R.N. Senior Vice President, Chief Nursing Officer and Inpatient Flow, St. Mary's Medical Center of Evansville, Evansville, IN, p. A210

ELLISON, Keith, Chief Nursing Officer, Big Bend Regional Medical Center, Alpine, TX, p. A596

ELLISON, Laura, Chief Financial Officer, Bon Secours Baltimore Health System, Baltimore, MD, p. A296

ELLISON, Mike, Information Systems Lead, Summersville Regional Medical Center, Summersville, WV, p. A700

ELLISON, Patricia, Chief Financial Officer, Streamwood Behavioral Health Center, Streamwood, IL, p. A204

ELLISON, Tracey, Vice President Human Resources, Carroll Hospital, Westminster, MD, p. A304

ELLSWORTH, Anthon, Director Information Technology, Mt. Graham Regional Medical Center, Safford, AZ, p. A38

ELLWANGER, Dina, R.N. Chief Nursing Officer, Saint Alphonsus Medical Center – Ontario, Ontario, OR, p. A528

ELLZEY, Bob S., FACHE, President, Texas Health Harris Methodist Hospital Azle, Azle, TX, p. A600

ELMER, Paula, R.N. Vice President and Chief Nursing Officer, Monroe Clinic, Monroe, WI, p. A712

ELMORE, Kevin, Chief Information Officer, Covenant Hospital–Levelland, Levelland, TX, p. A632

ELMORE, Nadine, Chief Executive Officer, Dahl Memorial Healthcare Association, Ekalaka, MT, p. A387

ELMORE, Trent, Director Human Resources, Springs Memorial Hospital, Lancaster, SC, p. A568

ELROD, Emily, R.N. Director of Nursing, Saint Thomas Stones River Hospital, Woodbury, TN, p. A594

ELROD, James K., FACHE, President and Chief Executive Officer, Willis–Knighton Health System, Shreveport, LA, p. B155

ELROD, James K., FACHE, Chief Executive Officer, Willis–Knighton Medical Center, Shreveport, LA, p. A288

ELROD, Sonya, Interim Chief Nursing Officer, Elbert Memorial Hospital, Elberton, GA, p. A159

ELSBERRY, Kevin
Senior Vice President Human Resources, Mercy Medical Center – West Lakes, West Des Moines, IA, p. A239
Senior Vice President Human Resources, Mercy Medical Center–Des Moines, Des Moines, IA, p. A229

ELSBREE, Heidi, Vice President People and Culture, MercyHealth Rockton Avenue Hospital, Rockford, IL, p. A202

ELSE, Ryan, M.D. Vice President Medical Affairs, Mercy Hospital, Coon Rapids, MN, p. A341

ELSWICK, Beth, Administrative Assistant, Summers County ARH Hospital, Hinton, WV, p. A696

ELWELL, Richard, Senior Vice President and Chief Financial Officer, Elliot Hospital, Manchester, NH, p. A412

ELWELL, Russell, M.D. Medical Director, Westfield Memorial Hospital, Westfield, NY, p. A459

ELY, Thomas L., D.O. Chief Medical Officer, Tennova Healthcare–Clarksville, Clarksville, TN, p. A581

EMAMGHORAISHI, Anna, Human Resources, Midwest City Specialty Hospital, Midwest City, OK, p. A514

EMANUEL, Kate, Director Human Resources, Clarke County Hospital, Osceola, IA, p. A236

EMBREE, Steve, Chief Financial Officer, UP Health System–Marquette, Marquette, MI, p. A329

EMBREY, Jeffrey, M.D. Vice President Medical Affairs, Baylor Medical Center at Irving, Irving, TX, p. A628

EMBURY, Stuart, M.D. Chief Medical Officer, Phelps Memorial Health Center, Holdrege, NE, p. A397

EMDUR, Larry, D.O
Chief Medical Officer, Alvarado Hospital Medical Center, San Diego, CA, p. A88
Chief of Staff, Promise Hospital of San Diego, San Diego, CA, p. A88

EMEOTT, Sandra, R.N. Chief Nursing Officer, Northwest Medical Center, Margate, FL, p. A135

EMERICK, Ron, M.D. Chief of Staff, Doctor's Memorial Hospital, Perry, FL, p. A142

EMERSON, Leah, Director of Nursing, St. Luke Community Healthcare, Ronan, MT, p. A390

EMERSON, Sherri, Chief Nursing Officer and Chief Operating Officer, Texas Health Heart & Vascular Hospital Arlington, Arlington, TX, p. A598

EMERY, Andrew, Chief Executive Officer, Bayfront Health Punta Gorda, Punta Gorda, FL, p. A143

EMGE, Joann, Chief Executive Officer, Sparta Community Hospital, Sparta, IL, p. A203

EMIG, Laura, Director Marketing Operations, HEALTHSOUTH Rehabilitation Hospital of York, York, PA, p. A559

EMMINGER, Dianne, Vice President Information Services, ACMH Hospital, Kittanning, PA, p. A541

EMMONS, Michelle, Associate Executive Director, NYC Health + Hospitals / Kings County,, NY, p. A448

EMON, Dee, R.N
Vice President and Chief Information Officer, Wake Forest Baptist Health–Davie Medical Center, Mocksville, NC, p. A469
Chief Information Officer, Wake Forest Baptist Health–Lexington Medical Center, Lexington, NC, p. A469

EMPEY, Dennis
Chief Financial Officer, Kenmare Community Hospital, Kenmare, ND, p. A480
Chief Financial Officer, Trinity Health, Minot, ND, p. A481

ENCAPERA, Kimberly, M.D. Medical Director, Rehabilitation Hospital of Southern New Mexico, Las Cruces, NM, p. A430

ENCE, Michael, Computer Specialist, Sanpete Valley Hospital, Mount Pleasant, UT, p. A660

ENCKE, Faye, Director Information Management, HEALTHSOUTH Rehabilitation Hospital of Virginia, Richmond, VA, p. A677

ENDEN, Jay, M.D. Medical Director, Southside Hospital, Bay Shore, NY, p. A434

ENDERS Jr., Robert A.
President, Chatham Hospital, Siler City, NC, p. A473
Interim President and Chief Executive Officer, Wayne Memorial Hospital, Goldsboro, NC, p. A466

ENDOM, Beth W., R.N. Vice President and Chief Nursing Officer, South Central Regional Medical Center, Laurel, MS, p. A360

ENDRES, Jack A., FACHE Chief Financial Officer, East Texas Medical Center Jacksonville, Jacksonville, TX, p. A629

ENG, Bland, Chief Executive Officer, Brandon Regional Hospital, Brandon, FL, p. A124

ENG, Jeffrey, M.D. Medical Director, HEALTHSOUTH Rehabilitation Hospital of Montgomery, Montgomery, AL, p. A23

ENGBRECHT, Chad, Chief Financial Officer, Alvarado Parkway Institute Behavioral Health System, La Mesa, CA, p. A67

ENGEL, David, Chief Executive Officer, Phillips County Hospital, Phillipsburg, KS, p. A252

ENGEL, Dawn M., Chief Nursing Officer, Geary Community Hospital, Junction City, KS, p. A246

ENGELKE, Brian, Chief Financial Officer, Community Memorial Hospital, Staunton, IL, p. A204

ENGESSER, Edward, Chief Financial Officer and Chief Information Officer, Barlow Respiratory Hospital, Los Angeles, CA, p. A70

ENGFEHR, Tricia A., Chief Human Resources, Selby General Hospital, Marietta, OH, p. A498

ENGLAND, Dave, Director Human Resources, Lakeland Behavioral Health System, Springfield, MO, p. A382

ENGLAND, Donna, Director Medical Records, HEALTHSOUTH Rehabilitation Hospital of Fort Smith, Fort Smith, AR, p. A46

ENGLAND, Leslie, Chief of Staff, Merit Health Natchez, Natchez, MS, p. A363

ENGLAND, Mary Ann, Chief Nurse Executive, Wilcox Memorial Hospital, Lihue, HI, p. A172

ENGLAND, Richard N., Chief Financial Officer, Palo Verde Behavioral Health, Tucson, AZ, p. A41

ENGLAND, Stacy, Community Chief Nursing Officer, Middlesboro ARH Hospital, Middlesboro, KY, p. A266

ENGLAND, Teresa, R.N. Nurse Executive, Salem Veterans Affairs Medical Center, Salem, VA, p. A678

ENGLE, Dan, Chief Information Officer, Thayer County Health Services, Hebron, NE, p. A396

ENGLE, Dana E., Chief Executive Officer, Madison Health, London, OH, p. A497

ENGLE, Lisa, Director Information Technology, Texoma Medical Center, Denison, TX, p. A612

ENGLE, Sharon, Director Clinical Services, Noland Hospital Birmingham, Birmingham, AL, p. A17

ENGLE, Steve, Chief Operations Officer, Mad River Community Hospital, Arcata, CA, p. A55

ENGLEHART, Jay, M.D. Medical Director, Southeast Missouri Mental Health Center, Farmington, MO, p. A371

ENGLEHART, Michael, President and Chief Executive Officer, Presence Health, Chicago, IL, p. B105

ENGLERT, William, Chief Executive Officer, Allegheny Valley Hospital, Natrona Heights, PA, p. A546

ENGLERTH, LaDonna, Administrator, East Carroll Parish Hospital, Lake Providence, LA, p. A282

ENGLISH, Anne L., Director Human Resources, UHS Chenango Memorial Hospital, Norwich, NY, p. A451

ENGLISH, Dennis, M.D. Vice President Medical Affairs, Magee–Womens Hospital of UPMC, Pittsburgh, PA, p. A551

ENGLISH, Jeff
Vice President Human Resources, St. Mary's Health Care System, Athens, GA, p. A151
Interim Chief Executive Officer, St. Mary's Sacred Heart Hospital, Lavonia, GA, p. A162

ENGLISH, Julene, Director Human Resources, Kentfield Rehabilitation and Specialty Hospital, Kentfield, CA, p. A67

ENGLISH, Kathy L., R.N. Executive Vice President and Chief Operating Officer, Children's Hospital and Medical Center, Omaha, NE, p. A400

ENGLISH, Laurie, Senior Vice President and Chief Human Resource Officer, Excela Latrobe Area Hospital, Latrobe, PA, p. A542

ENGSTROM, Chad P., Director Human Resources, Westfields Hospital, New Richmond, WI, p. A713

ENGSTROM, Frederick, M.D. Chief Medical Officer, Brattleboro Retreat, Brattleboro, VT, p. A665

ENICKS, Charles, Chief Information Officer, Augusta University Medical Center, Augusta, GA, p. A153

ENJADY, Rainey, Administrative Officer, Mescalero Public Health Service Indian Hospital, Mescalero, NM, p. A430

ENNEN, Philip L.
Vice President and Chief Executive Officer, Community Hospitals and Wellness Centers, Bryan, OH, p. A485
President and Chief Executive Officer, Community Hospitals and Wellness Centers–Montpelier, Montpelier, OH, p. A499

ENNIS, Debra, R.N. Vice President and Chief Nursing Officer, Texas Health Harris Methodist Hospital Southlake, Southlake, TX, p. A649

ENNIS, Virgil, Chief Information Officer, Helen Hayes Hospital, West Haverstraw, NY, p. A458

ENOCHS, Darren, Director Human Resources, Promise Hospital of Overland Park, Overland Park, KS, p. A251

ENOKA, Christina, Director Human Resources and Risk Management, Kahi Mohala Behavioral Health, Ewa Beach, HI, p. A170

ENRICO–SIMON, Agnes, M.D. President Medical Staff, Pleasant Valley Hospital, Point Pleasant, WV, p. A699

ENRIQUEZ, Kelly, Chief Executive Officer, Sebastian River Medical Center, Sebastian, FL, p. A145

ENRIQUEZ, Marty, MS Vice President and Chief Nursing Officer, TMC HealthCare, Tucson, AZ, p. A41

ENRIQUEZ, Michael, Chief Operating Officer, OSS Orthopaedic Hospital, York, PA, p. A559

ENSEY, Jeremy, Chief Executive Officer, St. Luke Hospital and Living Center, Marion, KS, p. A248

ENSLEY, Terrasina, Director Human Resources, Fannin Regional Hospital, Blue Ridge, GA, p. A154

ENSMINGER, Jennifer, Chief Operating Officer, College Medical Center, Long Beach, CA, p. A69

ENSRUDE, Layne, Chief Financial Officer, First Care Health Center, Park River, ND, p. A481

ENTIN, Ari, Chief Information Officer, Natividad Medical Center, Salinas, CA, p. A87

ENTLER, Paul, D.O. Medical Director, Sparrow Specialty Hospital, Lansing, MI, p. A328

ENTWISTLE, David, President and Chief Executive Officer, Stanford Health Care, Palo Alto, CA, p. B129

ENTZMINGER, Julie, Manager Human Resources, CHI Oakes Hospital, Oakes, ND, p. A481

EOLOFF, Eric J., President, Mercy Hospital Washington, Washington, MO, p. A383

EPPERSON, Edward L., Chief Executive Officer, Carson Tahoe Health, Carson City, NV, p. A404

EPPERSON, Elysia, Director Human Resources, East Texas Medical Center Jacksonville, Jacksonville, TX, p. A629

EPPERSON, James, Interim Chief Nursing Officer, Grandview Medical Center, Birmingham, AL, p. A16

EPPERSON, Jeff, Chief Financial Officer, Millwood Hospital, Arlington, TX, p. A597

EPPLER, Todd, FACHE, Chief Executive Officer, De Soto Regional Health System, Mansfield, LA, p. A282

EPPLEY, Doug, Director of Nursing, Bridgewell Hospital of Cincinnati, Cincinnati, OH, p. A487

EPPS, Donna
Vice President and Chief Human Resources Officer, Lawrence + Memorial Hospital, New London, CT, p. A116
Vice President, Chief Human Resource Officer, Westerly Hospital, Westerly, RI, p. A561

EPPS, Jerry, M.D. Senior Vice President and Chief Medical Officer, University of Tennessee Medical Center, Knoxville, TN, p. A586

EPSTEIN, Michael, M.D. Senior Vice President Medical Affairs, Johns Hopkins All Children's Hospital, Saint Petersburg, FL, p. A144

ERDMAN, Beth, Chief Financial Officer, Meriter UnityPoint Health, Madison, WI, p. A709

ERDMAN, Donja, Chief Financial Officer, Marcus Daly Memorial Hospital, Hamilton, MT, p. A388

ERDMAN, John, M.D. Chief of Staff, Cornerstone Medical Center, Fort Oglethorpe, GA, p. A160

ERDMANN, Dorothy, Chief Executive Officer, ThedaCare Medical Center–Shawano, Shawano, WI, p. A715

ERDMANN, Michael, M.D. Chief of Staff, Clement J. Zablocki Veterans Affairs Medical Center, Milwaukee, WI, p. A711

ERDOS, Joseph, M.D. Chief Information Officer, Veterans Affairs Connecticut Healthcare System, West Haven, CT, p. A118

EREMAN, Melissa, R.N. Chief Nursing Officer, Coleman County Medical Center, Coleman, TX, p. A606

ERGLE, Jeanine, Chief Financial Officer, Bay Pines Veterans Affairs Healthcare System, Bay Pines, FL, p. A123

ERICKSON, Ashley M., Chief Executive Officer, Sanford Aberdeen Medical Center, Aberdeen, SD, p. A572

ERICKSON, Bonnie, Chief Executive Officer, Rainy Lake Medical Center, International Falls, MN, p. A344

ERICKSON, Brent J., Administrator, Wright Patterson Medical Center, Wright–Patterson AFB, OH, p. A506

ERICKSON, Doug, Chief Financial Officer, Prague Community Hospital, Prague, OK, p. A519

ERICKSON, Jake, Chief Operating Officer, Bingham Memorial Hospital, Blackfoot, ID, p. A174

ERICKSON, Karyn, Director Human Resources, Delta Medical Center, Memphis, TN, p. A588

ERICKSON, Kerrie, Vice President of Finance, Stevens Community Medical Center, Morris, MN, p. A347

ERICKSON, Nancy
  Administrator Information Systems, Kossuth Regional Health Center, Algona, IA, p. A225
  Human Resource Director, Southern Inyo Healthcare District, Lone Pine, CA, p. A69

ERICKSON, Robert J., Chief Executive Officer, St. Joseph Medical Center, Kansas City, MO, p. A374

ERICKSON, Vonnie, Human Resource Manager, Chippewa County–Montevideo Hospital, Montevideo, MN, p. A347

ERICSON, Allen
  Chief Operating Officer, Community Hospital Division and President, St. Joseph's Hospital, Community Memorial Hospital, Menomonee Falls, WI, p. A710
  Chief Operating Officer, Community Hospital Division and President, St. Joseph's Hospital, St. Joseph's Hospital, West Bend, WI, p. A719
  Chief Operating Officer, Community Hospital Division and President, St. Joseph's Hospital, St. Joseph's Hospital, West Bend, WI, p. A719

ERICSON, Bob, Chief Financial Officer, Hemphill County Hospital, Canadian, TX, p. A605

ERICSON, Kim
  Vice President Finance, Fairview Lakes Health Services, Wyoming, MN, p. A354
  Vice President Finance, Fairview Northland Medical Center, Princeton, MN, p. A349

ERIXON, Stephen M., Chief Executive Officer, SageWest Health Care at Riverton, Riverton, WY, p. A723

ERKEN, Carole L., Human Resources Leader, Kaiser Permanente Panorama City Medical Center,, CA, p. A71

ERLBACHER, David, M.D. Chief of Staff, Myrtue Medical Center, Harlan, IA, p. A232

ERLING, Brian, Group Chief Medical Officer, St. Anthony Hospital, Lakewood, CO, p. A108

ERMANN, William, President and Chief Executive Officer, Southwest Medical Center, Liberal, KS, p. A248

ERTEL, David, Chief Financial Officer, Einstein Medical Center Montgomery, East Norriton, PA, p. A537

ERUKHIMOU, Jeffrey, M.D. Medical Director, Curahealth Heritage Valley, Beaver, PA, p. A533

ERVIN, Fulton
  Senior Vice President and Chief Financial Officer, McLeod Medical Center Dillon, Dillon, SC, p. A565
  Chief Financial Officer, McLeod Regional Medical Center, Florence, SC, p. A566

ERVIN, Joan, Administrator, McLeod Medical Center Dillon, Dillon, SC, p. A565

ERVIN, Paul D., Chief Financial Officer, Valley Behavioral Health System, Barling, AR, p. A43

ERVIN, Richard, Chief Financial Officer, Tomball Regional Medical Center, Tomball, TX, p. A653

ERVING–MENGEL, Tammi, R.N. Vice President, Chief Nursing Officer, High Point Regional Health System, High Point, NC, p. A467

ERWAY, Robert, Director for Administration, Bronx Psychiatric Center,, NY, p. A443

ERWIN, Connie, Manager, Samaritan Lebanon Community Hospital, Lebanon, OR, p. A527

ESCARDA, Ron, Chief Executive Officer, Fairfax Behavioral Health, Kirkland, WA, p. A686

ESCHENBRENNER, Wade, Chief Financial Officer, Lexington Regional Health Center, Lexington, NE, p. A397

ESHLEMAN, James, D.O. President Medical Staff, Stephens Memorial Hospital, Norway, ME, p. A294

ESLAVA, Lee, Chief Medical Officer, South Baldwin Regional Medical Center, Foley, AL, p. A20

ESLINGER, Jennifer, President, Mobile Infirmary Medical Center, Mobile, AL, p. A22

ESPARZA, Becky, Human Resources, Crane Memorial Hospital, Crane, TX, p. A608

ESPARZA, Caroline, Sr. VP, COO & CNO, Simi Valley Hospital, Simi Valley, CA, p. A94

ESPELAND, Darryl, D.O
  Medical Director, Dahl Memorial Healthcare Association, Ekalaka, MT, p. A387
  Chief Medical Staff, Fallon Medical Complex, Baker, MT, p. A385

ESPINA, Francisco, Director Finance, Hospital Pavia–Santurce, San Juan, PR, p. A730

ESPINOZA, John, Chief Human Resources Officer, University Medical Center, Las Vegas, NV, p. A407

ESPINOZA, Judy, Chief Human Resources Officer, Via Christi Hospital on St. Francis, Wichita, KS, p. A256

ESPIRITU, DoreeAnn V., M.D., Interim Chair, Behavioral Health Services, Henry Ford Kingswood Hospital, Ferndale, MI, p. A323

ESPITIA, Judy, Chief Executive Officer, North Runnels Hospital, Winters, TX, p. A658

ESPOSITO, Mary H., Assistant Executive Director, Devereux Georgia Treatment Network, Kennesaw, GA, p. A161

ESPOSITO, Pamela, Director Administration, Buffalo Psychiatric Center, Buffalo, NY, p. A435

ESPY, Christine, Division Director, Mid–Columbia Medical Center, The Dalles, OR, p. A531

ESROCK, Brett A., President and Chief Executive Officer, Providence Healthcare Network, Waco, TX, p. A656

ESSELMAN, Charlotte, Director Finance, Ministry Saint Clare's Hospital, Weston, WI, p. A719

ESSENPREIS, Helen, MSN Chief Nursing Officer, HSHS St. Joseph's Hospital, Breese, IL, p. A182

ESSEX, Jeshahnton, Vice President of Administration, Riddle Hospital, Media, PA, p. A545

ESSMYER, Dale, M.D. Chief of Staff, Sullivan County Memorial Hospital, Milan, MO, p. A376

ESTAY, Mike, Chief Financial Officer, Hood Memorial Hospital, Amite, LA, p. A271

ESTES, Barbara, M.D. Chief of Staff, Calvert Memorial Hospital, Prince Frederick, MD, p. A302

ESTES, Benton D., Materials Management, Baptist Medical Center Yazoo, Yazoo City, MS, p. A366

ESTES, Melinda, M.D., President and Chief Executive Officer, Saint Luke's Health System, Kansas City, MO, p. B117

ESTES, Michael, Director Human Resources, University of Mississippi Medical Center, Jackson, MS, p. A360

ESTES, Stephen A., Chief Executive Officer, Rockcastle Regional Hospital and Respiratory Care Center, Mount Vernon, KY, p. A267

ESTEVEZ, Aurora, M.D. Chief Medical Officer, Texas Health Presbyterian Hospital Dallas, Dallas, TX, p. A611

ESTEVEZ, Mercy, Chief Executive Officer, Strategic Behavioral Health – Charlotte, Charlotte, NC, p. A463

ESTRADA, Luis, Director Multifacility Information Systems, North Shore Medical Center, Miami, FL, p. A137

ESTRADA, Marina, Director Human Resources, El Paso Children's Hospital, El Paso, TX, p. A615

ESTRELLA, Mario B., Chief Nursing Officer, Nacogdoches Medical Center, Nacogdoches, TX, p. A638

ETCHASON, Barbara, HR Manager, West Gables Rehabilitation Hospital, Miami, FL, p. A137

ETHERIDGE, Darold, Vice President and Chief Financial Officer, WellStar Cobb Hospital, Austell, GA, p. A154

ETHERINGTON, Betty, Chief Financial Officer, Humboldt County Memorial Hospital, Humboldt, IA, p. A232

ETHERINGTON, Rosalie, Superintendent and Chief Executive Officer, North Dakota State Hospital, Jamestown, ND, p. A480

ETHRIDGE, Sandy, Interim Chief Operating Officer, Baptist Medical Center, San Antonio, TX, p. A645

ETIENNE, Gracia, M.D. President Medical Staff, OSS Orthopaedic Hospital, York, PA, p. A559

ETTER, Carl J., Chief Executive and Senior Vice President, Scripps Memorial Hospital–Encinitas, Encinitas, CA, p. A61

ETTESTAD, Donita, R.N. Chief Nursing Officer, Rainy Lake Medical Center, International Falls, MN, p. A344

EUBANKS, Bill, Senior Vice President and Chief Information Officer, University Medical Center, Lubbock, TX, p. A634

EUBANKS, Susan, Chief Nursing Officer, Page Hospital, Page, AZ, p. A35

EULER, Barbara, Director Human Resources, Tennova Healthcare Regional Hospital of Jackson, Jackson, TN, p. A584

EULIARTE, Mary Ann, R.N
  Chief Operating Officer, Memorial Hermann Rehabilitation Hospital – Katy, Katy, TX, p. A630
  Chief Operating Officer and Chief Nursing Officer, TIRR Memorial Hermann, Houston, TX, p. A627

EURE, Thomas, Vice President Administration, Carolinas Healthcare System Blue Ridge, Morganton, NC, p. A470

EUSEBIO, Barbara, R.N. Vice President, Chief Nurse Executive, St. Mary's Medical Center, San Francisco, CA, p. A90

EUSTACE, Scott, Director Health Information Technology, Trenton Psychiatric Hospital, Trenton, NJ, p. A424

EVANCHO, Timothy R., Chief Financial Officer, Southeastern Ohio Regional Medical Center, Cambridge, OH, p. A486

EVANDER, Justin N., Administrator and Chief Operating Officer, Kaiser Permanente Sunnyside Medical Center, Clackamas, OR, p. A524

EVANOFF, John, M.D. Vice President Medical Affairs, ProMedica Flower Hospital, Sylvania, OH, p. A503

EVANS, Ann, Chief Nursing Officer, HEALTHSOUTH Huntington Rehabilitation Hospital, Huntington, WV, p. A696

EVANS, Arthur D., Chief Executive Officer and Administrator, Bryan W. Whitfield Memorial Hospital, Demopolis, AL, p. A19

EVANS, Brian, M.D. Chief of Medicine, Sierra Nevada Memorial Hospital, Grass Valley, CA, p. A65

EVANS, Brian G., FACHE, Chief Executive Officer, Clarke County Hospital, Osceola, IA, p. A236

EVANS, Chris, Vice President Operations, CHI Health Bergan Mercy, Omaha, NE, p. A399

EVANS, Cindy, R.N. Chief Nursing Officer, Legacy Good Samaritan Hospital and Medical Center, Portland, OR, p. A529

EVANS, Dave, Vice President Finance and Chief Financial Officer, Community Hospital of San Bernardino, San Bernardino, CA, p. A88

EVANS, Dawn, Manager Information Technology, SSM Health St. Mary's Hospital – Audrain, Mexico, MO, p. A376

EVANS, Dwight, M.D. Chief of Staff, Veterans Affairs Loma Linda Healthcare System, Loma Linda, CA, p. A69

EVANS, Eric, Chief Operating Officer, Woman's Hospital of Texas, Houston, TX, p. A628

EVANS, George, Vice President and Chief Information Officer, Candler Hospital, Savannah, GA, p. A165

EVANS, Heath, Assistant Chief Executive Officer, North Okaloosa Medical Center, Crestview, FL, p. A126

EVANS, Janice, Chief Financial Officer, John J. Madden Mental Health Center, Hines, IL, p. A193

EVANS, Jeff W., Vice President Information and Technology, Hannibal Regional Hospital, Hannibal, MO, p. A371

EVANS, Jeremy, Vice President Operations, Kootenai Health, Coeur D'Alene, ID, p. A175

EVANS, Kelley
  Chief Administrative Officer, Beartooth Billings Clinic, Red Lodge, MT, p. A390
  Chief Administrative Officer, Stillwater Community Hospital, Columbus, MT, p. A386

EVANS, Kirstie, Chief Financial Officer, Covington County Hospital, Collins, MS, p. A357

EVANS, Lola, Director of Nursing, Oakland Regional Hospital, Southfield, MI, p. A334

EVANS, Lorrie, Director Human Resources, Laurel Oaks Behavioral Health Center, Dothan, AL, p. A19

EVANS, Manuel J., Senior Vice President Finance and Chief Financial Officer, Holy Spirit – A Geisinger Affiliate, Camp Hill, PA, p. A534

EVANS, Melinda S.
  Vice President Finance, Saint Joseph East, Lexington, KY, p. A263
  Vice President Finance, Saint Joseph Hospital, Lexington, KY, p. A263

EVANS, Mendy, Vice President of Finance, Flaget Memorial Hospital, Bardstown, KY, p. A257

EVANS, Michael C., Chief Executive Officer and Deputy Director of Finance and Administration, Santa Barbara County Psychiatric Health Facility, Santa Barbara, CA, p. A93

EVANS, Michael K., Chief Executive Officer, Park Royal Hospital, Fort Myers, FL, p. A129

EVANS, Nina, R.N. Vice President and Chief Nursing Officer, St. Mary's Health Care System, Athens, GA, p. A151

EVANS, Paulette, MSN, President and Chief Executive Officer, HSHS St. Joseph's Hospital, Breese, IL, p. A182

EVANS, Robert B., Administrator and Chief Executive Officer, East Texas Medical Center Tyler, Tyler, TX, p. A654

EVANS, Rod, Chief Information Officer, Community HealthCare System, Onaga, KS, p. A250

EVANS, S. Lagina, R.N. Assistant Chief Nursing Officer, Optim Medical Center – Screven, Sylvania, GA, p. A167

EVANS, Sam, Chief Human Resources Management, G.V. (Sonny) Montgomery Veterans Affairs Medical Center, Jackson, MS, p. A359

EVANS, Scott, PharmD, Senior Vice President and Chief Executive Officer, Sharp Grossmont Hospital, La Mesa, CA, p. A67

EVANS, Stanley, M.D. Chief of Staff, Denton Regional Medical Center, Denton, TX, p. A612

EVANS, Susan
  Chief Nursing Officer, HEALTHSOUTH Nittany Valley Rehabilitation Hospital, Pleasant Gap, PA, p. A552
  Chief Nursing Officer, Old Vineyard Behavioral Health Services, Winston-Salem, NC, p. A476

EVANS, Tim, Assistant Financial Director, Devereux Children's Behavioral Health Center, Malvern, PA, p. A543

EVANS, Timothy, Vice President and Chief Financial Officer, Self Regional Healthcare, Greenwood, SC, p. A567

EVANS-HARRISON, Martina, R.N. Chief Nurse Executive, Methodist Hospital of Sacramento, Sacramento, CA, p. A86

EVE, John, Vice President Human Resources and Education, Wilson Memorial Hospital, Sidney, OH, p. A502

EVELIUS, Karen, Director Human Resources, MedStar Harbor Hospital, Baltimore, MD, p. A297

EVELYN, David M., M.D. Vice President Medical Affairs, Cayuga Medical Center at Ithaca, Ithaca, NY, p. A440

EVENS, James, Executive Director Human Resources, Cole Memorial, Coudersport, PA, p. A536

EVENS, Richard R., Chief Executive Officer, HEALTHSOUTH Northern Kentucky Rehabilitation Hospital, Edgewood, KY, p. A259

EVENS, Tamara, Director Human Resources, Moses Ludington Hospital, Ticonderoga, NY, p. A457

EVENSON, Margie, Manager Human Resources, Osceola Medical Center, Osceola, WI, p. A713

EVERDING, Dawn, Chief Financial Officer, Community Memorial Hospital, Sumner, IA, p. A238

EVERETT, John, Chief Financial Officer, Cogdell Memorial Hospital, Snyder, TX, p. A649

EVERETT, Leianne, Chief Executive Officer, Morton General Hospital, Morton, WA, p. A686

EVERETT, Michael, Chief Executive Officer, Scott Memorial Hospital, Scottsburg, IN, p. A221

EVERETT, Neil, Vice President Human Resources, UH Portage Medical Center, Ravenna, OH, p. A501

EVERHART, Martin S., Senior Vice President Human Resources, Robert Wood Johnson University Hospital, New Brunswick, NJ, p. A420

EVERLY, Nanette, Manager Human Resources and Administrative Assistant, Jefferson County Health Center, Fairfield, IA, p. A230

EVERS, Andrea, Director Information Technology, Haxtun Hospital District, Haxtun, CO, p. A107

EVERS, Anthony, Chief Financial Officer, Katherine Shaw Bethea Hospital, Dixon, IL, p. A188

EVERSOLE, Matt, Regional Vice President Information Services, Mercy Health – Anderson Hospital, Cincinnati, OH, p. A488

EVERT, Barbara, M.D
Vice President Medical Affairs, OhioHealth Dublin Methodist Hospital, Dublin, OH, p. A494
Vice President Medical Affairs, OhioHealth Grady Memorial Hospital, Delaware, OH, p. A493

EVINS, Starling C., M.D. Chief of Staff, Williamson Medical Center, Franklin, TN, p. A583

EVISCHI, Deland
Regional Chief Financial Officer, Southern Illinois, Good Samaritan Regional Health Center, Mount Vernon, IL, p. A197
Chief Financial Officer, SSM Health St. Mary's Hospital Centralia, Centralia, IL, p. A182

EVOLGA, Nancy K., Executive Director Human Resources, Florida Hospital New Smyrna, New Smyrna Beach, FL, p. A139

EWALD, Luanne T., Interim Chief Executive Officer, DMC – Children's Hospital of Michigan, Detroit, MI, p. A321

EWALD, Ronald, Chief Financial Officer, Inova Fairfax Hospital, Falls Church, VA, p. A670

EWALD, Sandra
Vice President Finance, Aurora Medical Center – Manitowoc County, Two Rivers, WI, p. A717
Vice President Finance, Aurora Medical Center of Oshkosh, Oshkosh, WI, p. A713

EWELL, Dorene L., Director Human Resources and Education, Harrisburg Medical Center, Harrisburg, IL, p. A192

EWELL, Sandy, Chief Nursing Officer, Timpanogos Regional Hospital, Orem, UT, p. A661

EWING, Brenda, Chief Nursing Officer, Sandhills Regional Medical Center, Hamlet, NC, p. A466

EWING, Chandler, Chief Executive Officer, Select Specialty Hospital–Jackson, Jackson, MS, p. A360

EWING, Thomas
Director Information Technology, Sentara CarePlex Hospital, Hampton, VA, p. A671
Director Information Technology, Sentara Northern Virginia Medical Center, Woodbridge, VA, p. A680

EXLINE, Michael
Chief Financial Officer, Carrus Rehabilitation Hospital, Sherman, TX, p. A648
Chief Financial Officer, Carrus Specialty Hospital, Sherman, TX, p. A648

EYE, Jeffrey L., R.N. Vice President Patient Care Services, Murray–Calloway County Hospital, Murray, KY, p. A267

EYLER, Sandra, M
Chief Nursing Officer, Sheltering Arms Hospital South, Midlothian, VA, p. A674
Chief Nursing Officer, Sheltering Arms Rehabilitation Hospital, Mechanicsville, VA, p. A673

EZZIE, Michael, Director of Medical Education and Interim Vice President of Medical Affairs, OhioHealth Grant Medical Center, Columbus, OH, p. A491

F

FAAS, Michael D., President and Chief Executive Officer, Metro Health Hospital, Wyoming, MI, p. A337

FABER, Chris, Human Resources Analyst, Stanford Health Care – ValleyCare, Pleasanton, CA, p. A83

FABER, Tammy, Director Human Resources, Hegg Memorial Health Center Avera, Rock Valley, IA, p. A237

FABIAN, Alan J., Chief Executive Officer, LewisGale Hospital Montgomery, Blacksburg, VA, p. A668

FABIAN, Roxanne, Director of Nursing–Acute Care, LifeCare Medical Center, Roseau, MN, p. A350

FABIANO, Tom, Director Human Resources, Mount Auburn Hospital, Cambridge, MA, p. A309

FABIN, Peggy, Director Human Resources, Phillips County Hospital, Phillipsburg, KS, p. A252

FABRICK, Peter, Vice President Clinical Operations, Mountain View Hospital, Idaho Falls, ID, p. A176

FABRY, Joseph, D.O. Chief of Staff, Sutter Maternity and Surgery Center of Santa Cruz, Santa Cruz, CA, p. A93

FACKRELL, Sherlyn, Finance Controller, Grover C. Dils Medical Center, Caliente, NV, p. A404

FACTEAU, Patrick M., Chief Financial Officer, Massena Memorial Hospital, Massena, NY, p. A442

FACTOR, David, M.D. Chief of Staff, Ashe Memorial Hospital, Jefferson, NC, p. A468

FADALE, Sean, President and Chief Executive Officer, Community Memorial Hospital, Hamilton, NY, p. A440

FADLER, Jeannie, R.N. Vice President Patient Care Services, Saint Francis Healthcare System, Cape Girardeau, MO, p. A368

FAGAN, Erin, Manager Human Resources, George Washington University Hospital, Washington, DC, p. A121

FAGAN, Mary, MSN Chief Nursing Officer, Rady Children's Hospital – San Diego, San Diego, CA, p. A88

FAGAN, Michael
Chief Financial Officer, Huntington Hospital, Huntington, NY, p. A440
Senior Vice President Finance, New York Methodist Hospital,, NY, p. A447

FAGBONGBE, Eniola, M.D. Chief Medical Staff, Grove Hill Memorial Hospital, Grove Hill, AL, p. A21

FAGERBERG, Lesley, Vice President Fiscal Services, Heart of the Rockies Regional Medical Center, Salida, CO, p. A110

FAGERSTROM, Joel, Executive Vice President and Chief Operating Officer, St. Luke's Hospital – Miners Campus, Coaldale, PA, p. A535

FAGG, Cindy, Fiscal Officer, Battle Mountain General Hospital, Battle Mountain, NV, p. A404

FAHEY, Dana, Manager Management Information Systems, Santa Barbara County Psychiatric Health Facility, Santa Barbara, CA, p. A93

FAHEY, Linda L., R.N. Chief Nurse Executive, Decatur Memorial Hospital, Decatur, IL, p. A188

FAHEY, Patrick, M.D
Chief Medical Director, RML Specialty Hospital, Chicago, IL, p. A186
Chief Medical Officer, RML Specialty Hospital, Hinsdale, IL, p. A193

FAHEY, Stephen P., Executive Director, Sierra Tucson, Tucson, AZ, p. A41

FAHEY, Walter, Chief Information Officer, Maimonides Medical Center,, NY, p. A445

FAILE, J. Gene, Chief Executive Officer and President, Wilkes Regional Medical Center, North Wilkesboro, NC, p. A471

FAILLA, Richard
Chief Executive Officer, Montevista Hospital, Las Vegas, NV, p. A406
Chief Executive Officer, Red Rock Behavioral Hospital, Las Vegas, NV, p. A406

FAIN, Marilyn, R.N. Chief Operating Officer, Banner Fort Collins Medical Center, Fort Collins, CO, p. A105

FAIN, Nona, Ph.D. Director of Nursing, Belmont Behavioral Hospital, Philadelphia, PA, p. A547

FAIR, Kenya, Chief Executive Officer, ICON Hospital, Humble, TX, p. A628

FAIRBANKS, Bruce, Vice President and Chief Financial Officer, Southeast Hospital, Cape Girardeau, MO, p. A369

FAIRCHILD, David, M.D. Chief Medical Officer, Tufts Medical Center, Boston, MA, p. A307

FAIRCHILDS, Constance, R.N. Vice President Patient Care Services, Emanuel Medical Center, Turlock, CA, p. A97

FAIRCLOTH, Gerald, FACHE, Chief Executive Officer, Twin Rivers Regional Medical Center, Kennett, MO, p. A374

FAIRCLOTH, Karen, Chief Financial Officer, Memorial Hospital and Manor, Bainbridge, GA, p. A154

FAIRFAX, Tom, Director Information Systems, Bothwell Regional Health Center, Sedalia, MO, p. A382

FAIRFAX, Walter, M.D. Chief Medical Officer, Kootenai Health, Coeur D'Alene, ID, p. A175

FAIRLEY, Dawn Ann, M.D. Chief of Staff, Putnam County Memorial Hospital, Unionville, MO, p. A383

FAIRLEY, Susan, Chief Nursing Officer, Barton Memorial Hospital, South Lake Tahoe, CA, p. A95

FAISAL, Mohammad, President Medical Staff, Shands Lake Shore Regional Medical Center, Lake City, FL, p. A133

FAKINOS, Maureen, Interim Chief Executive Officer, Southwest Idaho Advanced Care Hospital, Boise, ID, p. A174

FALCON, Hugo, M.D. Director Medical Services, Piedmont Geriatric Hospital, Burkeville, VA, p. A668

FALCONE, Lynn, Chief Executive Officer, Cuero Community Hospital, Cuero, TX, p. A608

FALIVENA, Richard, D.O. Vice President and Chief Medical Officer, Saratoga Hospital, Saratoga Springs, NY, p. A455

FALK, Chelsie, Chief Nursing Officer, Sanford Wheaton Medical Center, Wheaton, MN, p. A353

FALKENBERRY, Jody, Director Information Systems, Monroe County Hospital, Monroeville, AL, p. A23

FALL, J. Mark, Chief Executive Officer, CareLink of Jackson, Jackson, MI, p. A327

FALLEN, Barbara, FACHE, Director, Veterans Affairs Loma Linda Healthcare System, Loma Linda, CA, p. A69

FALLIS, Susan, Chief Nursing Officer, Buffalo Psychiatric Center, Buffalo, NY, p. A435

FALLON, Angela, Acting Chief Executive Officer, U. S. Public Health Service Indian Hospital–Sells, Sells, AZ, p. A39

FALLON, Jeanne M.
Senior Vice President and Chief Information Officer, Cape Cod Hospital, Hyannis, MA, p. A311
Chief Information Officer, Falmouth Hospital, Falmouth, MA, p. A310

FALLON, L. J., JD Executive Vice President, Chief Legal and Human Resources Officer, Carle Foundation Hospital, Urbana, IL, p. A204

FALSETTI, Domonic F., M.D. Chief of Staff and Medical Director, Mount St. Mary's Hospital and Health Center, Lewiston, NY, p. A441

FALTERMAN, Jr., James B., M.D. Medical Director, University Hospital and Clinics, Lafayette, LA, p. A281

FAMMARTINO, Gary, Administrator, St. Vincent Fishers Hospital, Fishers, IN, p. A210

FANALE, Linda, Chief Financial Officer, Conemaugh Miners Medical Center, Hastings, PA, p. A540

FANCHER, Diana, Chief Nursing Officer, University Medical Center of El Paso, El Paso, TX, p. A616

FANNIN, Allyson, Human Resources Officer, LaSalle General Hospital, Jena, LA, p. A278

FANNIN, Pam, Coordinator Human Resources, LifeCare Hospital of Dayton, Miamisburg, OH, p. A499

FANNING, Melinda, Chief Financial Officer and Controller, HEALTHSOUTH Southern Hills Rehabilitation Hospital, Princeton, WV, p. A699

FANNING, Teresa E., Director of Patient Care, Avera Hand County Memorial Hospital, Miller, SD, p. A574

FANNON, Susan, Chief Nursing Officer, Indian Path Medical Center, Kingsport, TN, p. A585

FANSELAU, Michael G.
Human Resource Leader, Kaiser Permanente San Rafael Medical Center, San Rafael, CA, p. A92
Human Resource Leader, Kaiser Permanente Santa Rosa Medical Center, Santa Rosa, CA, p. A94

FANSLER, Janet, R.N. Executive Vice President and Chief Nurse Executive, Lakeland Regional Health, Lakeland, FL, p. A134

FANTANO, Gene, Chief Financial Officer, Aurora Behavioral Healthcare San Diego, San Diego, CA, p. A88

FARAH, Tony, M.D. President Medical Staff, Allegheny General Hospital, Pittsburgh, PA, p. A550

FARBER, Bobbi, M.D. Chief Medical Officer, St. Francis Hospital, Columbus, GA, p. A157

FARBER, Nancy D., Chief Executive Officer, Washington Hospital Healthcare System, Fremont, CA, p. A63

FARBER, Niceta, Chief Executive Officer, Sheridan County Health Complex, Hoxie, KS, p. A245

FARELL, Clay, Chief Operation Officer, Los Alamitos Medical Center, Los Alamitos, CA, p. A70

FARGASON, Crayton A., M.D. Medical Director, Children's of Alabama, Birmingham, AL, p. A16

FELEGE, Lester, Controller, HEALTHSOUTH New England Rehabilitation Hospital, Woburn, MA, p. A316

FELICETTI, Jacqueline, Chief Human Resource Officer, Penn Medicine Chester County Hospital, West Chester, PA, p. A557

FELICI, Brian K., Chief Executive Officer, Wetzel County Hospital, New Martinsville, WV, p. A698

FELICIANO, Jose R., Chief Executive Officer, Ryder Memorial Hospital, Humacao, PR, p. A727

FELICIANO, Myrna Quinones, M.D. Medical Director, University Pediatric Hospital,, PR, p. A730

FELICIANO, Pablo, Manager Human Resources, Veterans Affairs Central Western Massachusetts Healthcare System, Leeds, MA, p. A311

FELIZ, Miriam, M.D. Medical Director, St. Catherine's Rehabilitation Hospital, North Miami, FL, p. A139

FELKNER, Joseph G.
Senior Vice President Finance and Chief Financial Officer, Health First Cape Canaveral Hospital, Cocoa Beach, FL, p. A126
Executive Vice President, Finance and Chief Financial Officer, Health First Holmes Regional Medical Center, Melbourne, FL, p. A135
Executive Vice President and Chief Financial Officer, Health First Palm Bay Hospital, Palm Bay, FL, p. A141
Executive Vice President and Chief Financial Officer, Health First Viera Hospital, Melbourne, FL, p. A135

FELL, David, M.D. Chief Medical Officer, Tulsa Spine and Specialty Hospital, Tulsa, OK, p. A522

FELLER, Julie, Executive Director Human Resources, Grays Harbor Community Hospital, Aberdeen, WA, p. A682

FELLOWS, James, M.D. Chief of Staff, Methodist Hospital, Henderson, KY, p. A261

FELLOWS, Rhonda, R.N. Chief Nursing Officer, Van Buren County Hospital, Keosauqua, IA, p. A233

FELLOWS, Steven A.
Executive Vice President and Chief Operating Officer, Goleta Valley Cottage Hospital, Santa Barbara, CA, p. A93
Executive Vice President and Chief Operating Officer, Santa Barbara Cottage Hospital, Santa Barbara, CA, p. A93
Executive Vice President and Chief Operating Officer, Santa Ynez Valley Cottage Hospital, Solvang, CA, p. A94

FELMLEE, Charles, Assistant Director Fiscal Services, Central Virginia Training Center, Madison Heights, VA, p. A673

FELPS, Kathy A., R.N., Chief Executive Officer, Regency Hospital of South Atlanta, East Point, GA, p. A159

FELTMAN, Steven, CPA Chief Financial Officer, Essentia Health–Virginia, Virginia, MN, p. A352

FELTON, David
Regional Chief Information Officer, LincolnHealth, Damariscotta, ME, p. A292
Manager Information Systems, Waldo County General Hospital, Belfast, ME, p. A292

FELTS, Dave, Chief Information Systems, Logan Regional Hospital, Logan, UT, p. A660

FENDER, Tamra, Chief Nursing Officer, Marias Medical Center, Shelby, MT, p. A391

FENDT, Phil, Chief Financial Officer, Memorial Community Health, Aurora, NE, p. A393

FENER, Michael
Executive Director, Plainview Hospital, Plainview, NY, p. A452
Executive Director, Syosset Hospital, Syosset, NY, p. A456

FENN, Mark, Director Human Resources, Pulaski Memorial Hospital, Winamac, IN, p. A224

FENNELL, Charles, Vice President Information Management, St. Joseph's Hospital Health Center, Syracuse, NY, p. A456

FENNELL, Colin, M.D. Chief Medical Officer, RiverView Health, Crookston, MN, p. A341

FENNELL, David, M.D. Acting Medical Director, Atascadero State Hospital, Atascadero, CA, p. A55

FENSKE, Bill, Chief Financial Officer, Rice Memorial Hospital, Willmar, MN, p. A353

FENSKE, Candace, Chief Executive Officer, Madelia Community Hospital, Madelia, MN, p. A345

FENSKE, Mary, Human Resource Business Partner, Spectrum Health United Hospital, Greenville, MI, p. A325

FENTER, Kim, Chief Financial Officer, Wilbarger General Hospital, Vernon, TX, p. A655

FENWICK, Sandra L., M.P.H., President and Chief Executive Officer, Boston Children's Hospital, Boston, MA, p. A306

FEOLA, Ferd, Chief Information Officer, Pocono Medical Center, East Stroudsburg, PA, p. A537

FERBER, Robert, M.D. Chief Clinical Innovation Officer, Nanticoke Memorial Hospital, Seaford, DE, p. A119

FERCH, Wayne
President and Chief Executive Officer, Adventist Medical Center – Hanford, Hanford, CA, p. A65
President and Chief Executive Officer, Adventist Medical Center–Reedley, Reedley, CA, p. A85
President and Chief Executive Officer, Central Valley General Hospital, Hanford, CA, p. A65

FERDOUS, Riza, Health Services Director, Ossining Correctional Facilities Hospital, Ossining, NY, p. A452

FERGUS, Gigi, Interim Chief Executive Officer, La Porte Hospital, La Porte, IN, p. A216

FERGUS, Janie
Director and Chief Information Officer, Saint Joseph East, Lexington, KY, p. A263
Director and Chief Information Officer, Saint Joseph Hospital, Lexington, KY, p. A263

FERGUS, Linda, Manager Information Technology, Allegheny Valley Hospital, Natrona Heights, PA, p. A546

FERGUSON, Allison, Director Human Resources, Avoyelles Hospital, Marksville, LA, p. A282

FERGUSON, Cathy, R.N. Vice President and Chief Nursing Officer, Hamilton Medical Center, Dalton, GA, p. A158

FERGUSON, Cheryl L., Associate Administrator, Sanford Canby Medical Center, Canby, MN, p. A340

FERGUSON, Clifford, Director Information Technology and Systems, Bayshore Medical Center, Pasadena, TX, p. A640

FERGUSON, Daniel, Chief of Staff, Grove City Medical Center, Grove City, PA, p. A539

FERGUSON, Deborah
Director, Human Resources, Sentara Albemarle Medical Center, Elizabeth City, NC, p. A464
Human Resources Consultant, Sentara Obici Hospital, Suffolk, VA, p. A679

FERGUSON, Denise, Chief Nursing Officer, Baptist Memorial Hospital–Collierville, Collierville, TN, p. A581

FERGUSON, G. Thomas, Senior Vice President and Chief Human Resources Officer, New York–Presbyterian Hospital, New York, NY, p. A447

FERGUSON, Gordon B., President and Chief Executive Officer, Saint Thomas Rutherford Hospital, Murfreesboro, TN, p. A590

FERGUSON, Karen, Director Human Resources, Johnson County Healthcare Center, Buffalo, WY, p. A721

FERGUSON, Louis D.
Chief Financial Officer, Palestine Regional Medical Center, Palestine, TX, p. A640
Chief Financial Officer, Palestine Regional Medical Center–East, Palestine, TX, p. A640

FERGUSON, Michael, Chief Financial Officer, Harbor Oaks Hospital, New Baltimore, MI, p. A330

FERGUSON, Nina L., Director Human Resources, Little Colorado Medical Center, Winslow, AZ, p. A41

FERGUSON, Randy, Chief Information Officer, Ridgecrest Regional Hospital, Ridgecrest, CA, p. A85

FERGUSON, Rick, Chief Executive Officer, Oklahoma Surgical Hospital, Tulsa, OK, p. A521

FERGUSON, Tonya, Director Human Resources, HEALTHSOUTH Rehabilitation Hospital of Virginia, Richmond, VA, p. A677

FERGUSON, Zeta, Chief Human Resources, Atlanta Veterans Affairs Medical Center, Decatur, GA, p. A158

FERIA, Jorge, M.D. President Medical Staff, Wilma N. Vazquez Medical Center, Vega Baja, PR, p. A730

FERNALD, Catherine Shull, MSN Chief Operating Officer – Bayonne Medical Center, Bayonne Medical Center, Bayonne, NJ, p. A414

FERNANDES, Roxanne, R.N. Chief Nursing Officer, Children's Hospitals and Clinics of Minnesota, Minneapolis, MN, p. A346

FERNANDEZ, Alexander, Chief Financial Officer, Broward Health Medical Center, Fort Lauderdale, FL, p. A128

FERNANDEZ, Arthur, Chief Financial Officer, First Hospital Panamericano, Cidra, PR, p. A727

FERNANDEZ, Aurelio, Chief Executive Officer, Memorial Healthcare System,, FL, p. B88

FERNANDEZ, Benigno J., M.D. Executive Medical Director, Laurel Ridge Treatment Center, San Antonio, TX, p. A646

FERNANDEZ, Darlene, Chief Financial Officer, UNM Sandoval Regional Medical Center, Albuquerque, NM, p. A428

FERNANDEZ, Jean, Chief Information Officer, Beth Israel Deaconess Hospital–Milton, Milton, MA, p. A312

FERNANDEZ, John, Chief Operating Officer, United Hospital Center, Bridgeport, WV, p. A694

FERNANDEZ, John R., President and Chief Executive Officer, Massachusetts Eye and Ear Infirmary, Boston, MA, p. A307

FERNANDEZ, Jose L. Pimentel, Medical Director, Lafayette Hospital, Arroyo, PR, p. A726

FERNANDEZ, Mark, M.D. Chief of Staff and President Medical Staff, Illinois Valley Community Hospital, Peru, IL, p. A200

FERNANDEZ, Ruben D., R.N. Vice President and Chief Nursing Officer, HackensackUMC Palisades, North Bergen, NJ, p. A421

FERNANDEZ, Tracey, Chief Financial Officer, St. Mary Medical Center, Apple Valley, CA, p. A55

FERNANDEZ DEL VALLE, Arthur J., Chief Financial Officer, Cardiovascular Center of Puerto Rico and the Caribbean, San Juan, PR, p. A729

FERNANDEZ–BRAVO, Grisel, R.N. Chief Nursing Officer, Memorial Hospital West, Pembroke Pines, FL, p. A142

FERNIANY, William, Ph.D., Chief Executive Officer, UAB Health System, Birmingham, AL, p. B139

FERNYAK, Susan, M.D. Interim Chief Medical Officer & Chief Quality Officer, San Mateo Medical Center, San Mateo, CA, p. A92

FERRACANE, Tony, Vice President Human Resources, St. Mary Medical Center, Hobart, IN, p. A213

FERRANCE, Randy, M.D. President Medical Staff, Riverside Tappahannock Hospital, Tappahannock, VA, p. A679

FERRANTI, Jeffrey, M.D. Chief Information Officer, Duke University Hospital, Durham, NC, p. A464

FERRARO, Claudio J., Senior Administrator, Via Christi Hospital on St. Teresa, Wichita, KS, p. A256

FERRAROTTI, Gianna, Director Human Resources North Region, OhioHealth Marion General Hospital, Marion, OH, p. A498

FERREIRA, Daniel, Director Management Information Systems, Hospital De La Concepcion, San German, PR, p. A729

FERRELL, Angie
Director Human Resources, Mercy Health – Anderson Hospital, Cincinnati, OH, p. A488
Director Human Resources, Mercy Health – Clermont Hospital, Batavia, OH, p. A484

FERRELL, Eileen Brennan, MS Vice President and Chief Nursing Officer, MedStar Georgetown University Hospital, Washington, DC, p. A121

FERRELL, Jennifer, Chief Nursing Officer, HEALTHSOUTH Rehabilitation Hospital of Memphis, Memphis, TN, p. A588

FERRELL, Marc C., President and Chief Executive Officer, BridgePoint Healthcare, Portsmouth, NH, p. B24

FERRELL, Ronald, Chief Information Officer, New Mexico Veterans Affairs Health Care System – Raymond G. Murphy Medical Center, Albuquerque, NM, p. A428

FERRELLI, John, Chief Executive Officer, Seton Medical Center, Daly City, CA, p. A60

FERREN, Alison, Vice President Information Technology and Chief Information Officer, Abington–Lansdale Hospital Jefferson Health, Lansdale, PA, p. A542

FERRERO, Marcia L., MS Chief Nursing Officer, Heritage Valley Health System, Beaver, PA, p. A533

FERRETTI, Andrea, Interim Chief Nursing Officer, Vice President and Associate Chief Nursing Officer Network of Care, Children's Hospital Colorado, Aurora, CO, p. A101

FERRIS, David, Chief Nursing Officer and Vice President Patient Care Services, Claxton–Hepburn Medical Center, Ogdensburg, NY, p. A451

FERRIS, Joseph, Chief Financial Officer, Veterans Affairs Black Hills Health Care System, Fort Meade, SD, p. A574

FERRIS, Mark, M.D. Medical Director, Kindred Hospital–White Rock, Dallas, TX, p. A610

FERRIS, Michael, M.D. Chief Medical Officer, CHI Health St Elizabeth, Lincoln, NE, p. A398

FERRONI, Karen, M.D. Medical Director, Holyoke Medical Center, Holyoke, MA, p. A310

FERRY, Jane, M.D. Vice President Medical Affairs, Grand View Health, Sellersville, PA, p. A554

FERRY, Thomas, Business Administrator, Oakwood Correctional Facility, Lima, OH, p. A497

FERTIG, Ashley
Chief Nursing Officer, University Hospitals Conneaut Medical Center, Conneaut, OH, p. A492
Chief Nursing Officer, University Hospitals Geneva Medical Center, Geneva, OH, p. A495

FESSER, James, Chief Nursing Officer, Palo Pinto General Hospital, Mineral Wells, TX, p. A637

FETTER, Lee F.
Interim President, Barnes–Jewish St. Peters Hospital, Saint Peters, MO, p. A382
Interim President, Progress West Hospital, O'Fallon, MO, p. A377

FETTER, Trevor, President and Chief Executive Officer, TENET Healthcare Corporation, Dallas, TX, p. B132

FETTEROLF, Kim, R.N. Chief Clinical Officer, Lourdes Specialty Hospital of Southern New Jersey, Willingboro, NJ, p. A425

FETTERS, Valerie, Chief Financial Officer, Hillsdale Hospital, Hillsdale, MI, p. A326

FEUCHT, Jason, Chief Financial Officer, Kossuth Regional Health Center, Algona, IA, p. A225

FEUER, Tammy, Chief Executive Officer, HEALTHSOUTH Rehabilitation Hospital of Vineland, Vineland, NJ, p. A424

FEUNNING, Charles, M.D. President Medical Staff, Summa Western Reserve Hospital, Cuyahoga Falls, OH, p. A492

FIBIYI, Abayomi, Chief Human Resources Officer, North Vista Hospital, North Las Vegas, NV, p. A407

FICCHI, Adrienne, Vice President Information Management, Philadelphia Veterans Affairs Medical Center, Philadelphia, PA, p. A549

FICICCHY, Teri, R.N. Chief Nursing Officer, Bon Secours St. Francis Health System, Greenville, SC, p. A566

FIDLER, Soniya, MS Chief Human Resources and Compliance Officer, Yampa Valley Medical Center, Steamboat Springs, CO, p. A110

FIDUCIA, Karen A., FACHE, President, Hospital Division, USMD Health System, Irving, TX, p. B150

FIELD, Clifford, M.D. Medical Director, Kau Hospital, Pahala, HI, p. A172

FIELD, Edward, Administrator, Loma Linda University Behavioral Medicine Center, Redlands, CA, p. A85

FIELD, Kori, Director of Nursing, Brodstone Memorial Hospital, Superior, NE, p. A402

FIELD, Laurie, Director Human Resources, Eaton Rapids Medical Center, Eaton Rapids, MI, p. A323

FIELDER, Barb, Vice President Finance, St. Joseph Mercy Chelsea, Chelsea, MI, p. A320

FIELDER, Jaf, Vice President and Administrator, Willis–Knighton Medical Center, Shreveport, LA, p. A288

FIELDING, Colene, Manager Business Office, Baylor Medical Center at Uptown, Dallas, TX, p. A609

FIELDING, Laura M., Administrative Director Organizational Development, Holy Family Memorial, Manitowoc, WI, p. A709

FIELDS, Donald R., Community Chief Executive Officer, Harlan ARH Hospital, Harlan, KY, p. A261

FIELDS, Greg, Director Information Technology, Elbert Memorial Hospital, Elberton, GA, p. A159

FIELDS, Laurie, Director Human Resources, ContinueCARE Hospital at Hendrick Medical Center, Abilene, TX, p. A595

FIERER, Jonathan, M.D. Chief of Staff, Martinsburg Veterans Affairs Medical Center, Martinsburg, WV, p. A698

FIERRO, Barbara, Director, Human Resources, St. Francis Hospital, The Heart Center, Roslyn, NY, p. A455

FIETEK, Denise, Information Technology, Rio Grande Hospital, Del Norte, CO, p. A103

FIFIELD, Michael, Vice President Human Resources, Oneida Healthcare, Oneida, NY, p. A452

FIGUEROA, Maria, Director Human Resources, Ryder Memorial Hospital, Humacao, PR, p. A727

FIGUEROA, Roseann, Director Human Resources, Doctors Hospital of Laredo, Laredo, TX, p. A632

FIKE, Ruthita J., Chief Executive Officer, Loma Linda University Behavioral Medicine Center, Redlands, CA, p. A85

FILADORA, II, Victor A., M.D. Chief Clinical Services, Roswell Park Cancer Institute, Buffalo, NY, p. A436

FILER, Christine, Director Human Resources, HEALTHSOUTH Rehabilitation Hospital of Altoona, Altoona, PA, p. A532

FILES, Ashley S., Director Human Resources and Public Relations and Marketing, Winn Parish Medical Center, Winnfield, LA, p. A289

FILES, Carol, Chief Financial Officer, Advanced Diagnostics Hospital, Houston, TX, p. A623

FILIPINI, Alfred, Manager Human Resources, Ancora Psychiatric Hospital, Hammonton, NJ, p. A417

FILIPOWICZ, Thomas, M.D. Medical Director, St. Luke's Hospital – Quakertown Campus, Quakertown, PA, p. A553

FILLER, Richard, Chief Financial Officer, Berger Health System, Circleville, OH, p. A488

FILLER, Scott, Chief Executive Officer, HEALTHSOUTH Rehabilitation Hospital of Altoona, Altoona, PA, p. A532

FILLINGIM, Jed, Acting Chief Operating Officer and Associate Director, G.V. (Sonny) Montgomery Veterans Affairs Medical Center, Jackson, MS, p. A359

FILLIPO, Brian, M.D. Chief Medical Officer, Robert Packer Hospital, Sayre, PA, p. A553

FILOSA, Frank, Fiscal Manager, Washington DC Veterans Affairs Medical Center, Washington, DC, p. A122

FILPI, Jeanette, Chief Executive Officer, Pioneer Community Hospital of Patrick, Stuart, VA, p. A679

FILSON, Debbie, Chief Financial Officer, Ashland Health Center, Ashland, KS, p. A240

FINAN Jr.,, John J., FACHE, President and Chief Executive Officer, Franciscan Missionaries of Our Lady Health System, Inc., Baton Rouge, LA, p. B56

FINAN, Timothy J., FACHE,
President and Chief Executive Officer, Bradford Regional Medical Center, Bradford, PA, p. A534
President and Chief Executive Officer, Olean General Hospital, Olean, NY, p. A451

FINAN, Timothy J., FACHE, President and Chief Executive Officer, Upper Allegheny Health System, Olean, NY, p. B149

FINCH, John
Vice President Information Services, Health Alliance Hospital – Broadway Campus, Kingston, NY, p. A441
Chief Information and Community Officer, Health Alliance Hospital – Mary's Avenue Campus, Kingston, NY, p. A441

FINCH, Kenneth A., President and Chief Executive Officer, Texas Health Huguley Hospital Fort Worth South, Burleson, TX, p. A604

FINCH, Kim, Chief Nursing Officer, Kosciusko Community Hospital, Warsaw, IN, p. A223

FINCH, Robert D., Vice President Human Resources, Athens Regional Medical Center, Athens, GA, p. A151

FINCH, Roy
Chief Operating Officer, Longview Regional Medical Center, Longview, TX, p. A633
Chief Executive Officer, Northern Louisiana Medical Center, Ruston, LA, p. A287

FINCH, Teresa, Chief Financial Officer, Trident Medical Center, Charleston, SC, p. A563

FINCHER, Jodi, Vice President Patient Care Services, Saint John Hospital, Leavenworth, KS, p. A247

FINDLAY, Andrew L., Deputy Commander Clinical Services, Tripler Army Medical Center, Honolulu, HI, p. A171

FINDLEY, Amber, Senior Director Nursing Services and NRC Administrator, Pleasant Valley Hospital, Point Pleasant, WV, p. A699

FINDLEY, John T, M.D. Chief Medical Officer, Beatrice Community Hospital and Health Center, Beatrice, NE, p. A394

FINE, Allan, Chief Operating Officer, New York Eye and Ear Infirmary of Mount Sinai, New York, NY, p. A447

FINE, James, M.D. Chief Information Officer, UW Medicine/Harborview Medical Center, Seattle, WA, p. A690

FINE, Mathew N., M.D. Chief Medical Officer, Oroville Hospital, Oroville, CA, p. A81

FINE, Peter S., FACHE, President and Chief Executive Officer, Banner Health, Phoenix, AZ, p. B18

FINELLI, Frederick, M.D. Vice President Medical Affairs, MedStar Montgomery Medical Center, Olney, MD, p. A302

FINELLI, Peter, Chief Financial Officer, Banner Payson Medical Center, Payson, AZ, p. A35

FINESTEIN, Brian, Chief Executive Officer, Saint Clare's Health System, Denville, NJ, p. A416

FINETTI, Yoany, R.N. Chief Nursing Officer, Barnes–Jewish West County Hospital, Saint Louis, MO, p. A379

FINK, Renee, CPA Chief Financial Officer, Dundy County Hospital, Benkelman, NE, p. A394

FINK, Tom, Vice President Regional Finance Officer, Range Regional Health Services, Hibbing, MN, p. A344

FINK, Walter, Chief Medical Officer, MultiCare Good Samaritan Hospital, Puyallup, WA, p. A688

FINKEL, Naomi, Nurse Executive, Montgomery County Emergency Service, Norristown, PA, p. A546

FINKENBINER, Joy, Vice President, Operations, Genesys Regional Medical Center, Grand Blanc, MI, p. A324

FINLAYSON, Susan D., MSN Senior Vice President of MMC Operations, Mercy Medical Center, Baltimore, MD, p. A297

FINLEY, Alan, Chief Operating Officer, Conway Regional Medical Center, Conway, AR, p. A44

FINLEY, Cindy, Chief Nursing Officer, Iron County Medical Center, Pilot Knob, MO, p. A378

FINLEY, Delvecchio, Chief Executive Officer, Highland Hospital, Oakland, CA, p. A80

FINLEY, Jane, Senior Vice President & Area Manager, Kaiser Permanente San Diego Medical Center, San Diego, CA, p. A88

FINLEY, Kevan, Chief Executive Officer, Oklahoma Forensic Center, Vinita, OK, p. A523

FINLEY, Kevin, D.O. Chief of Staff, Knox County Hospital, Knox City, TX, p. A631

FINLEY, Mike, M.D. Chief Medical Officer, CHRISTUS St. Michael Health System, Texarkana, TX, p. A652

FINLEY, Tommy, Chief Information Officer, Rutherford Regional Health System, Rutherfordton, NC, p. A473

FINLEY, Waynea
Senior Vice President Human Resources, PAM Specialty Hospital of Covington, Covington, LA, p. A275
Manager Human Resources, Post Acute Medical Specialty Hospital of Victoria, Victoria, TX, p. A655
System Director Human Resources, Post Acute/Warm Springs Rehabilitation Hospital of San Antonio, San Antonio, TX, p. A646
Corporate Director Human Resources, Post Acute/Warm Springs Specialty Hospital of Victoria, Victoria, TX, p. A655

FINLEY–HAZLE, Gabrielle, Chief Executive Officer, St. Mary's Medical Center, West Palm Beach, FL, p. A150

FINN, Barry C., President and Chief Executive Officer, Rush–Copley Medical Center, Aurora, IL, p. A181

FINN, Patti, Chief Executive Officer, Fulton County Health Center, Wauseon, OH, p. A505

FINNEGAN, Jay, Chief Executive Officer, St. Lucie Medical Center, Port St. Lucie, FL, p. A143

FINNEY, David, R.N. Vice President Nursing, UHS Chenango Memorial Hospital, Norwich, NY, p. A451

FINSTAD, Gary A., M.D. Chief of Staff, Kern Valley Healthcare District, Lake Isabella, CA, p. A68

FIORE–LOPEZ, Nicolette, R.N. Chief Nursing Officer, St. Charles Hospital, Port Jefferson, NY, p. A453

FIORENZO, V. James, President, UPMC Hamot, Erie, PA, p. A538

FIORET, Phil, M.D. Vice President Medical Affairs, King's Daughters Medical Center, Ashland, KY, p. A257

FIRES, Wiley M., Administrator, Shamrock General Hospital, Shamrock, TX, p. A648

FIRMAN, Julie, R.N
Vice President and Chief Nursing Officer, Memorial Hospital of Carbondale, Carbondale, IL, p. A182
Chief Nursing Officer, St. Joseph Memorial Hospital, Murphysboro, IL, p. A197

FIRMINGER, Barbara, Chief Administrative Officer, Verde Valley Medical Center, Cottonwood, AZ, p. A32

FIRTCH, William, M.D. Physician In Chief, Kaiser Permanente Redwood City Medical Center, Redwood City, CA, p. A85

FISCHBACH, John, Vice President of Finance, Chief Financial Officer, Lima Memorial Health System, Lima, OH, p. A496

FISCHELS, Diane, Senior Vice President and Chief Operating Officer, Mercy Medical Center–North Iowa, Mason City, IA, p. A234

FISCHER, Angie, Chief Financial Officer, Loring Hospital, Sac City, IA, p. A237

FISCHER, Jason
Chief Information Officer, PIH Health Hospital – Downey, Downey, CA, p. A61
Chief Information Officer, PIH Health Hospital–Whittier, Whittier, CA, p. A99

FISCHER, JC, Director Human Resources, Mercy Regional Medical Center, Lorain, OH, p. A497

FISCHER, Linda, Director Information Services, Huntington Hospital, Huntington, NY, p. A440

FISCHER, Lisa, Director Human Resources, Brown County Hospital, Ainsworth, NE, p. A393

FISCHER, Patricia, R.N., President and Chief Executive Officer, HSHS St. Francis Hospital, Litchfield, IL, p. A195

FISCHER, Robert, M.D. Medical Director, Methodist Hospital for Surgery, Addison, TX, p. A595

FISCHER, Sandra, Director Human Resources, W. G. (Bill) Heffner Veterans Affairs Medical Center, Salisbury, NC, p. A473

FISCHER, Steve, Chief Financial Officer, T. J. Samson Community Hospital, Glasgow, KY, p. A261

FISCHER, Steven P., Chief Financial Officer, Beth Israel Deaconess Medical Center, Boston, MA, p. A306

FISCHER, Tamara, Chief Nursing Officer, Okeene Municipal Hospital, Okeene, OK, p. A515

FISER, David, Vice President and Chief Information Officer, Akron General Medical Center, Akron, OH, p. A483

FISH, Carolyn, Director Human Resources, Mission Community Hospital, CA, p. A73

FISH, Elizabeth
Senior Director Site Executive and Information Technology, University of Maryland Shore Medical Center at Chestertown, Chestertown, MD, p. A299
Chief Information Officer, University of Maryland Shore Medical Center at Dorchester, Cambridge, MD, p. A299
Chief Information Officer, University of Maryland Shore Medical Center at Easton, Easton, MD, p. A300

FISHBAUGHER, David, Chief Medical Information, Mercy Iowa City, Iowa City, IA, p. A232

FISHEL, Stephanie, Vice President Patient Care Services and Chief Nursing Officer, Nathan Littauer Hospital and Nursing Home, Gloversville, NY, p. A439

FISHER, Alan, Chief Executive Officer, Doctors NeuroMedical Hospital, Bremen, IN, p. A207

FISHER, Charles, Chief Executive Officer, U. S. Public Health Service Indian Hospital, Eagle Butte, SD, p. A573

FISHER, David, Director Information Systems, Heart of Lancaster Regional Medical Center, Lititz, PA, p. A543

FISHER, David, M.D. Senior Vice President and Chief Medical Officer, Seattle Children's Hospital, Seattle, WA, p. A689

FISHER, David, Vice President Human Resources, Signature Healthcare Brockton Hospital, Brockton, MA, p. A308

FISHER, Diane, R.N. VP, Patient Care Services, Otsego Memorial Hospital, Gaylord, MI, p. A324

FISHER, J. Matthew, Chief Financial Officer, Russell Medical Center, Alexander City, AL, p. A15

FISHER, Jacob, Chief Executive Officer, Tampa Community Hospital, Tampa, FL, p. A148

FISHER, Jan E., Executive Vice President, Chief Operating Officer and Chief Administrative Officer, Williamsport Regional Medical Center, Williamsport, PA, p. A558

FISHER, Jennifer A., Manager Human Resources, Henry County Hospital, Napoleon, OH, p. A500

FISHER, John, M.D. Chief Medical Officer, Martin Luther King, Jr. Community Hospital, Los Angeles, CA, p. A72

FISHER, Kenneth, Associate Vice President Finance and Chief Financial Officer, University of Iowa Hospitals and Clinics, Iowa City, IA, p. A232

FISHER, Kerry, M.D. Medical Director, LDS Hospital, Salt Lake City, UT, p. A663

FISHER, Lynn, M.D. Chief of Staff, Rooks County Health Center, Plainville, KS, p. A252

FISHER, Mahana, M.D. Medical Director, Blue Mountain Hospital, Blanding, UT, p. A659

FISHER, Mathew, M.D. Medical Director, Springbrook Behavioral Health System, Travelers Rest, SC, p. A570

FISHER, Matt, Vice President Finance, St. Dominic–Jackson Memorial Hospital, Jackson, MS, p. A360

FISHER, Michael, President and Chief Executive Officer, Cincinnati Children's Hospital Medical Center, Cincinnati, OH, p. A487

FISHER, Michael W., Director, Portland Veterans Affairs Medical Center, Portland, OR, p. A529

FISHER, Richard, President and Chief Executive Officer, Fox Chase Cancer Center–American Oncologic Hospital, Philadelphia, PA, p. A548

FISHER, Robert E., Interim Chief Financial Officer, Susan B. Allen Memorial Hospital, El Dorado, KS, p. A242

FISHER, Ryan
Director of Human Resources, Blanchard Valley Hospital, Findlay, OH, p. A494
Director Human Resources, Bluffton Hospital, Bluffton, OH, p. A485

FISHER, Sharon, M.D. Chief of Staff, Bartlett Regional Hospital, Juneau, AK, p. A29

FISHER, Sharon, R.N. Chief Nursing Officer, Tyrone Hospital, Tyrone, PA, p. A556

FISHER, Teresa, R.N. Chief Nursing Officer, Fort Loudoun Medical Center, Lenoir City, TN, p. A587

FISHER, Teresa, Chief Nursing Officer, Lakewood Health System, Staples, MN, p. A352

FISHER, Thomas, Senior Vice President and Chief Financial Officer, University of Tennessee Medical Center, Knoxville, TN, p. A586

FISHER, Vicky, Ph.D. Chief Nurse Executive, Catawba Hospital, Catawba, VA, p. A668

FISHER–FORD, Karen, Director of Health Information Management, West Central Georgia Regional Hospital, Columbus, GA, p. A157

FISHKIN, Edward, M.D. Medical Director, NYC Health + Hospitals / Woodhull, NY, p. A449

FISK, Amber, Director Human Resources, Memorial Hospital of Sweetwater County, Rock Springs, WY, p. A723

FISK, Anita, Director Human Resources, Three Rivers Hospital, Brewster, WA, p. A683

FISK, Kathryn M., Chief Human Resources Officer, El Camino Hospital, Mountain View, CA, p. A78

FISK, Kellee J., Chief People Officer, Altru Health System, Grand Forks, ND, p. A479

FISLER, Eileen, Chief Financial Officer, Pacifica Hospital of the Valley,, CA, p. A73

FITCH, Andrew, Chief Financial Officer, St. Elias Specialty Hospital, Anchorage, AK, p. A28

FITCH, James A., Director Human Resources, Houston Methodist St. Catherine Hospital, Katy, TX, p. A629

FITCH, John A., Vice President Human Resources, Campbell County Health, Gillette, WY, p. A722

FITE, David, Director Information Technology, Towner County Medical Center, Cando, ND, p. A477

FITE, Theresa, R.N. Chief Financial Officer, Fleming County Hospital, Flemingsburg, KY, p. A259

FITTON, Lenora, D.O. Chief of Staff, Fayette County Memorial Hospital, Washington Court House, OH, p. A505

FITTS, Barry
Chief Information Officer, Hillside Rehabilitation Hospital, Warren, OH, p. A504
Chief Information Officer, Trumbull Memorial Hospital, Warren, OH, p. A505

FITZ Jr., Thomas E., Interim President and Chief Executive Officer, St. Joseph Regional Medical Center, Lewiston, ID, p. A177

FITZGERALD, Amy, Human Resources Manager, Copley Hospital, Morrisville, VT, p. A665

FITZGERALD, Andy, Chief Executive Officer, Campbell County Health, Gillette, WY, p. A722

FITZGERALD, George, Regional Director Information Systems, LifeCare Hospitals of Pittsburgh, Pittsburgh, PA, p. A550

FITZGERALD, John L., Chief Executive Officer, Inova Fair Oaks Hospital, Fairfax, VA, p. A669

FITZGERALD, Mike
Chief Financial Officer, Harrison Medical Center, Bremerton, WA, p. A682
Chief Financial Officer, St. Clare Hospital, Lakewood, WA, p. A686
Chief Financial Officer, St. Francis Hospital, Federal Way, WA, p. A685
Chief Financial Officer, St. Joseph Medical Center, Tacoma, WA, p. A692

FITZGERALD, Patty, Staff Services, Munson Healthcare Charlevoix Hospital, Charlevoix, MI, p. A320

FITZGERALD, Philip, Chief Operating Officer, John F. Kennedy Memorial Hospital, Indio, CA, p. A66

FITZMAURICE, Dennis, Interim Chief Executive Officer, Community First Medical Center, Chicago, IL, p. A183

FITZMAURICE, Sandy, MS Interim Chief Nursing Officer, Whitman Hospital and Medical Center, Colfax, WA, p. A683

FITZPATRICK, Anna, Director Human Resources, St. Anthony Regional Hospital, Carroll, IA, p. A226

FITZPATRICK, Daniel, Director Human Resources, Whitesburg ARH Hospital, Whitesburg, KY, p. A270

FITZPATRICK, James, M.D. Vice President Medical Affairs, Kenmore Mercy Hospital, Kenmore, NY, p. A441

FITZPATRICK, James G., FACHE, Chief Executive Officer, Mercy Medical Center–Sioux City, Sioux City, IA, p. A237

FITZPATRICK, Leigh, Director Human Resources, Arkansas Valley Regional Medical Center, La Junta, CO, p. A107

FITZPATRICK, Leigh Ann, Superintendent, Kerrville State Hospital, Kerrville, TX, p. A630

FITZSIMMONS, Shaun, Director Information Technology Services, Community Medical Center, Toms River, NJ, p. A424

FITZSIMONS, Patricia Sue, R.N. Senior Vice President Patient Services, Yale–New Haven Hospital, New Haven, CT, p. A116

FIX, Judith A., R.N. Senior Vice President and Chief Nursing Officer, Long Beach Memorial Medical Center, Long Beach, CA, p. A69

FLAHERTY, Daniel, M.D. Chief Medical Staff, Prairie Lakes Healthcare System, Watertown, SD, p. A577

FLAHERTY, John
Controller, Fairlawn Rehabilitation Hospital, Worcester, MA, p. A316
Chief Financial Officer, HEALTHSOUTH Rehabilitation Hospital of Western Massachusetts, Ludlow, MA, p. A311

FLAHERTY, Linda, R.N. Senior Vice President, Patient Care Services, McLean Hospital, Belmont, MA, p. A305

FLAHERTY, Patrick, Director Management Information, Naval Hospital Bremerton, Bremerton, WA, p. A682

FLAHERTY, Tom, Assistant Administrator, Los Angeles County Central Jail Hospital, Los Angeles, CA, p. A72

FLAKE, Robert, Chief Executive Officer, Middle Park Medical Center–Kremmling, Kremmling, CO, p. A107

FLAMING, Patrick, R.N. Director Inpatient Operations, Prairie View, Newton, KS, p. A250

FLAMM, Cindy, Manager Quality, Choate Mental Health Center, Anna, IL, p. A180

FLANAGAN, Carl J.
Chief Financial Officer, Blue Mountain Hospital, John Day, OR, p. A527
Chief Financial Officer, La Paz Regional Hospital, Parker, AZ, p. A35

FLANAGAN, Michael J., Senior Vice President and Chief Operating Officer, St. Clair Hospital, Pittsburgh, PA, p. A551

FLANAGAN, Thomas, M.D. Medical Director, Aurora Behavioral Healthcare San Diego, San Diego, CA, p. A88

FLANAGAN, Tom, Chief Operating Officer, Memorial Hermann – Texas Medical Center, Houston, TX, p. A625

FLANARY, Tresha, R.N. Chief Clinical Services Officer, Wamego Health Center, Wamego, KS, p. A255

FLANDERS, David, Chief Operating Officer, Candler County Hospital, Metter, GA, p. A163

FLANIGAN, Erin, Vice President Human Resources, Wentworth–Douglass Hospital, Dover, NH, p. A410

FLANIGAN, Kevin, M.D., Chief Executive Officer, Northern Inyo Hospital, Bishop, CA, p. A57

FLANNERY, Donna M., Chief Executive Officer, Mercy Rehabilitation Hospital, Chesterfield, MO, p. A369

FLANNERY, Lindsay, R.N. Vice President Patient Care Services, Avera Sacred Heart Hospital, Yankton, SD, p. A578

FLANNERY, Maureen, Vice President Clinic Operations, Straub Clinic & Hospital, Honolulu, HI, p. A171

FLANNERY, Robert, Chief Financial Officer, University of Wisconsin Hospitals and Clinics Authority, Madison, WI, p. A709

FLANZ, Bruce J.
President and Chief Executive Officer, Flushing Hospital Medical Center,, NY, p. A444
President and Chief Executive Officer, Jamaica Hospital Medical Center,, NY, p. A445

FLANZ, Bruce J., President and Chief Executive Officer, MediSys Health Network,, NY, p. B87

FLASCHENRIEM, Julie, Chief Information Officer, Park Nicollet Methodist Hospital, Saint Louis Park, MN, p. A350

FLASHER, Sara, Chief Nurse Executive, Warren State Hospital, Warren, PA, p. A556

FLATT, G. Wayne, D.O. Chief Medical Director, Pushmataha Hospital & Home Health, Antlers, OK, p. A508

FLATTERY, William
Vice President and Administrator Western Division, Carilion Giles Community Hospital, Pearisburg, VA, p. A675
Vice President and Administrator Western Division, Carilion New River Valley Medical Center, Christiansburg, VA, p. A669

FLAVIO, Chuck, Chief Executive Officer, Saint Simons by–the–Sea Hospital, Saint Simons Island, GA, p. A165

FLECHSIG, Randolph K., Administrator, Sheridan Community Hospital, Sheridan, MI, p. A334

FLECK, Julie, Chief Operating Officer, Parkview Ortho Hospital, Fort Wayne, IN, p. A211

FLEEGEL, Monica, Director Human Resources, Mayo Clinic Health System in Albert Lea, Albert Lea, MN, p. A338

FLEENOR, Dennis, R.N., Administrator, Muleshoe Area Medical Center, Muleshoe, TX, p. A638

FLEISCHMANN, Craig, Vice President Finance, University of Maryland Medical Center Midtown Campus, Baltimore, MD, p. A298

FLEISCHMANN, Katherine, Director of Nursing, Harlan County Health System, Alma, NE, p. A393

FLEISCHMANN, Tim, Chief Financial Officer, Tuality Healthcare, Hillsboro, OR, p. A526

FLEISHMAN, Samuel A., M.D. Chief Medical Officer, Cape Fear Valley Medical Center, Fayetteville, NC, p. A465

FLEITES, Fernando, Senior Vice President Human Resources, Bon Secours St. Francis Health System, Greenville, SC, p. A566

FLEMER, Andrew, Chief Operating Officer, South Georgia Medical Center, Valdosta, GA, p. A168

FLEMING, Jared, Director, Information Services, Lourdes Counseling Center, Richland, WA, p. A689

FLEMING, Joshua, Vice President Chief Clinical Officer, Leesburg Regional Medical Center, Leesburg, FL, p. A134

FLEMING, Michael, Chief People Officer, Banner – University Medical Center Phoenix, Phoenix, AZ, p. A36

FLEMING, Michelle M., Chief Nursing Officer, Essentia Health–Virginia, Virginia, MN, p. A352

FLEMING, Shane
Chief Financial Officer, Capital Health Medical Center–Hopewell, Pennington, NJ, p. A422
Chief Financial Officer, Capital Health Regional Medical Center, Trenton, NJ, p. A424

FLEMING, Valarie, MSN Chief Nursing Executive, California Hospital Medical Center, Los Angeles, CA, p. A70

FLEMING, Wanda C., Chief Executive Officer, Jefferson County Hospital, Fayette, MS, p. A357

FLEMING, William P., Chief Operating Officer, Norwood Hospital, Norwood, MA, p. A313

FLEMMING, Libby, Controller and Chief Information Officer, South Georgia Medical Center Lanier Campus, Lakeland, GA, p. A161

FLEMMING, Michael, Administrator, Cornerstone Behavioral Health Hospital of Union County, Berkeley Heights, NJ, p. A414

FLESNER, Lynn, Director of Nursing, Glacial Ridge Health System, Glenwood, MN, p. A343

FLETCHALL, Terry L., President and Chief Executive Officer, Santiam Hospital, Stayton, OR, p. A531

FLETCHER, Audrey, Chief Operating Officer, Madison Memorial Hospital, Rexburg, ID, p. A178

FLETCHER, Bill, Director Information Technology, Cooper County Memorial Hospital, Boonville, MO, p. A368

FLETCHER, Chris, Director of Human Resources, Fishermen's Hospital, Marathon, FL, p. A135

FLETCHER, Jennifer, Chief of Staff, Decatur County Memorial Hospital, Greensburg, IN, p. A212

FLETCHER, John, Chief Executive Officer, Patrick B. Harris Psychiatric Hospital, Anderson, SC, p. A562

FLETCHER, John R., President, Lehigh Valley Hospital – Hazleton, Hazleton, PA, p. A540

FLETCHER, Josie, Interim Chief Nursing Officer, Iberia Medical Center, New Iberia, LA, p. A284

FLETCHER, Kathy, R.N. Interim Chief Nursing Officer, Val Verde Regional Medical Center, Del Rio, TX, p. A612

FLETCHER, Kevin, Director Information Systems, Medical Center of McKinney, McKinney, TX, p. A636

FLETCHER, Michael, M.D. Vice President and Chief Medical Officer, Hancock Regional Hospital, Greenfield, IN, p. A212

FLETCHER, Stephanie L., CPA Chief Financial Officer, Union General Hospital, Blairsville, GA, p. A154

FLETCHER–JANZEN, David, Chief Executive Officer, Sycamore Springs Hospital, Lafayette, IN, p. A216

FLETT, Will, Vice President Finance and Chief Financial Officer, Avera Queen of Peace Hospital, Mitchell, SD, p. A575

FLICKEMA, James, Vice President Market Development, Otsego Memorial Hospital, Gaylord, MI, p. A324

FLICKINGER, Kenneth E., Chief Financial Officer, Penn Medicine Chester County Hospital, West Chester, PA, p. A557

FLINCHBAUGH, Robert, D.O. Chief Medical Officer, Winneshiek Medical Center, Decorah, IA, p. A229

FLINN, Charles, Vice President, Chief Operating Officer, Saint Mary's Hospital, Waterbury, CT, p. A117

FLINN, James, FACHE, Chief Executive Officer, St. Luke's Medical Center, Phoenix, AZ, p. A37

FLINT, Jennifer, Chief Financial Officer, Laird Hospital, Union, MS, p. A365

FLINT, Ruth, Chief Nursing Officer, St. Joseph Medical Center, Tacoma, WA, p. A692

FLIPPO, Mary Elizabeth, R.N. Vice President and Chief Nursing Officer, Martin Health System, Stuart, FL, p. A146

FLIS, James D., Chief Financial Officer, Livengrin Foundation, Bensalem, PA, p. A533

FLODEN, Scott, Chief Executive Officer, Promise Hospital of Phoenix, Mesa, AZ, p. A34

FLOOD, James, Director Information Systems, Claxton–Hepburn Medical Center, Ogdensburg, NY, p. A451

FLOOD, Rebecca L., R.N. Senior Vice President Nursing, New York Methodist Hospital,, NY, p. A447

FLOREN, Joshua, President, Texas Health Presbyterian Hospital Plano, Plano, TX, p. A642

FLORENTINE, Erich
  Chief People Officer, Inspira Medical Center–Elmer, Elmer, NJ, p. A416
  Chief People Officer, Inspira Medical Center–Vineland, Vineland, NJ, p. A425

FLORENTINE, Stephen J., Administrator, Bastrop Rehabilitation Hospital, Monroe, LA, p. A283

FLORES, Andrea, Director, Information Systems, Providence Little Company of Mary Medical Center – Torrance, Torrance, CA, p. A96

FLORES, Debbie, Chief Executive Officer, Banner Del E. Webb Medical Center, Sun City West, AZ, p. A39

FLORES, Debra A., MS, President and Administrator, Sentara CarePlex Hospital, Hampton, VA, p. A671

FLORES, Jacob, Chief Information Officer, Frio Regional Hospital, Pearsall, TX, p. A640

FLORES, Jeanne, Consultant to the President, Cedars–Sinai Medical Center, Los Angeles, CA, p. A70

FLORES, Jerome, Chief Financial Officer, Sunrise Canyon Hospital, Lubbock, TX, p. A634

FLORES, Linda, R.N. Vice President Nursing Services, Parkview Medical Center, Pueblo, CO, p. A110

FLORIT, Mary, Interim Chief Nursing Officer, Central Carolina Hospital, Sanford, NC, p. A473

FLORKOWSKI, Doug, Chief Executive Officer, Lawrence County Memorial Hospital, Lawrenceville, IL, p. A195

FLOURA, Kamal, M.D. Medical Director, Eastern State Hospital, Medical Lake, WA, p. A686

FLOWE, Kenneth, M.D. Chief Medical Officer, Rice Memorial Hospital, Willmar, MN, p. A353

FLOWERS, Deborah, Director Human Resources, Monroe County Hospital, Forsyth, GA, p. A159

FLOWERS, Frank M., M.D. Area Medical Director, Kaiser Permanente Riverside Medical Center, Riverside, CA, p. A85

FLOWERS, Michael, Director Information Management, Calhoun–Liberty Hospital, Blountstown, FL, p. A123

FLOWERS, Scott, Vice President Professional Services, Thibodaux Regional Medical Center, Thibodaux, LA, p. A289

FLOWERS, Taylor, Director Human Resources, Onslow Memorial Hospital, Jacksonville, NC, p. A468

FLOYD, Dorothy, Ph.D., Superintendent, Terrell State Hospital, Terrell, TX, p. A652

FLOYD, Duane, Vice President Human Resources and Professional Services, Watertown Regional Medical Center, Watertown, WI, p. A718

FLOYD, Jacqueline, Chief Nursing Officer, HEALTHSOUTH Rehabilitation Hospital of Fort Smith, Fort Smith, AR, p. A46

FLOYD, Kiley, Chief Executive Officer, Nemaha Valley Community Hospital, Seneca, KS, p. A253

FLOYD, Miranda, R.N. Chief Nursing Officer, Northwest Medical Center, Albany, MO, p. A367

FLOYD, Richard B., President, Advocate Lutheran General Hospital, Park Ridge, IL, p. A200

FLOYD, Robert, D.O. Chief Medical Staff, Davis County Hospital, Bloomfield, IA, p. A226

FLOYD, Terri, Chief Financial Officer, Bates County Memorial Hospital, Butler, MO, p. A368

FLOYD, William Brian, President, Vidant Medical Center, Greenville, NC, p. A466

FLUGUM, Aaron, Chief Executive Officer, Mercy Medical Center–New Hampton, New Hampton, IA, p. A235

FLUKE, Cinda, R.N. Chief Nursing Officer, Saint Joseph Mount Sterling, Mount Sterling, KY, p. A267

FLUTY, Lisa, Director Information Services, Baptist Health Lexington, Lexington, KY, p. A262

FLYGARE, Matthew, Director Human Resources, Mountain West Medical Center, Tooele, UT, p. A664

FLYNN, Brian, Chief Human Resources Officer, Veterans Affairs Northern Indiana Health Care System, Fort Wayne, IN, p. A211

FLYNN, Chanda, R.N. Chief Nursing Officer, Mary Black Health System–Spartanburg, Spartanburg, SC, p. A569

FLYNN, Cheryl, Senior Vice President Chief Human Resources Officer, Methodist Charlton Medical Center, Dallas, TX, p. A610

FLYNN, James, Chief Executive Officer, Heartland Regional Medical Center, Marion, IL, p. A195

FLYNN, Jerry, M.D. Chief of Staff, Southeast Colorado Hospital District, Springfield, CO, p. A110

FLYNN, Julianne, M.D. Chief of Staff, South Texas Veterans Health Care System, San Antonio, TX, p. A647

FLYNN, Kristin, Chief Human Resources Officer, Sierra Vista Regional Medical Center, San Luis Obispo, CA, p. A92

FLYNN, Loretta M., Consultant, Human Resources, Gulf Coast Medical Center, Wharton, TX, p. A657

FLYNN, Matthew J., Senior Vice President and Chief Financial Officer, Northwestern Lake Forest Hospital, Lake Forest, IL, p. A194

FLYNN, Patricia, Interim Chief Medical Officer, St. Jude Children's Research Hospital, Memphis, TN, p. A589

FLYNN, Patrick, Chief Financial Officer, Warm Springs Medical Center, Warm Springs, GA, p. A168

FLYNN, Timothy C., M.D. Chief of Staff, UF Health Shands Hospital, Gainesville, FL, p. A130

FOARD, Mesa, Director Information technology, William S. Hall Psychiatric Institute, Columbia, SC, p. A564

FOELSCH, Paul, Vice President and Chief Information Technology Officer, North Kansas City Hospital, North Kansas City, MO, p. A377

FOELSKE, Loren
  Vice President Finance, Northwestern Medicine Kishwaukee Hospital, DeKalb, IL, p. A188
  Vice President Finance, Northwestern Medicine Valley West Hospital, Sandwich, IL, p. A202

FOGARTY, John M., President and Chief Executive Officer, Beth Israel Deaconess Hospital–Needham Campus, Needham, MA, p. A312

FOGARTY, Kathleen R., MS, Director, Kansas City Veterans Affairs Medical Center, Kansas City, MO, p. A373

FOGELSON, Julia, R.N. Chief Operating Officer and Chief Nursing Executive, French Hospital Medical Center, San Luis Obispo, CA, p. A92

FOGG, Robert W., Director Finance, Lake Taylor Transitional Care Hospital, Norfolk, VA, p. A675

FOGLE, Dennis, Vice President of Human Resources, Rush Memorial Hospital, Rushville, IN, p. A221

FOJTASEK, Georgia R., R.N., President and Chief Executive Officer, Henry Ford Allegiance Health, Jackson, MI, p. A327

FOLEY, Chris, Chief of Medicine, Children's Hospital of The King's Daughters, Norfolk, VA, p. A675

FOLEY, Crystal, Director Human Resources, Rockdale Hospital, Rockdale, TX, p. A643

FOLEY, James T., CPA Vice President and Chief Financial Officer, Shore Medical Center, Somers Point, NJ, p. A423

FOLEY, Jay, Chief Operating Officer, Southwestern Regional Medical Center, Tulsa, OK, p. A522

FOLEY, John, Chief Information Officer, Allegheny General Hospital, Pittsburgh, PA, p. A550

FOLEY, Michael, M.D. Chief Medical Officer, North Okaloosa Medical Center, Crestview, FL, p. A126

FOLEY, Regina, R.N. Vice President Nursing and Operations, Ocean Medical Center, Brick Township, NJ, p. A415

FOLK, Jeffrey R., M.D. Vice President Medical Affairs and Chief Medical Officer, Piedmont Newnan Hospital, Newnan, GA, p. A164

FOLKENBERG, Todd, Chief Executive Officer, Castle Rock Adventist Hospital, Castle Rock, CO, p. A102

FOLKS, David G., M.D. Chief Medical Officer, New Hampshire Hospital, Concord, NH, p. A410

FOLL, Gary R., Chief Financial Officer, Atchison Hospital, Atchison, KS, p. A240

FOLLETT, Traci, Director Clinical Infomatics, Sierra View Medical Center, Porterville, CA, p. A83

FOLLOWELL, Rob, Chief Executive Officer, Southern Tennessee Regional Health System–Winchester, Winchester, TN, p. A594

FOLSKE, Lance, Chief Executive Officer, Carrollton Springs, Carrollton, TX, p. A605

FOLSOM, Lori S., Assistant Vice President Human Resources, Tift Regional Medical Center, Tifton, GA, p. A167

FOLTZ, JoAnn M., R.N., Chief Executive Officer, Sanford Wheaton Medical Center, Wheaton, MN, p. A353

FONDA, Joan, Chief Nursing Officer, Twin Cities Community Hospital, Templeton, CA, p. A96

FONDESSY, Terrence, M.D. Vice President Medical Affairs, ProMedica Fostoria Community Hospital, Fostoria, OH, p. A494

FONG, Joseph, Administrator, Providence Seward Medical Center, Seward, AK, p. A30

FONKEN, Paul, M.D. Chief of Staff, Estes Park Medical Center, Estes Park, CO, p. A105

FONTAINE, Melissa, Chief Operating Officer, UAMS Medical Center, Little Rock, AR, p. A49

FONTAINE, Tim, Chief Operating Officer, Pioneer Community Hospital of Stokes, Danbury, NC, p. A463

FONTAINE–WESTHART, Mark, Associate Director, Bedford Veterans Affairs Medical Center, Edith Nourse Rogers Memorial Veterans Hospital, Bedford, MA, p. A305

FONTENAULT, Richard, Director Information Systems, Green Oaks Hospital, Dallas, TX, p. A610

FONTENELLE, Mary, Executive Nurse Director, Eastern Louisiana Mental Health System, Jackson, LA, p. A278

FONTENOT, Micheal, Chief Financial Officer, Mercy Regional Medical Center, Ville Platte, LA, p. A289

FONTENOT, Teri G., FACHE, President and Chief Executive Officer, Woman's Hospital, Baton Rouge, LA, p. A273

FONTENOT, Theresa, Executive Director, Oceans Behavioral Hospital of Opelousas, Opelousas, LA, p. A286

FONZIE, Juril, Director Human Resources, Helena Regional Medical Center, Helena, AR, p. A47

FOOKES, Sherman, Chief Executive Officer, Savoy Medical Center, Mamou, LA, p. A282

FOOTE, Donald E., Fiscal Officer, Wilkes–Barre Veterans Affairs Medical Center, Wilkes–Barre, PA, p. A558

FOOTE, John, Chief Information Officer, Manchester Veterans Affairs Medical Center, Manchester, NH, p. A412

FOOTE, Mark, Chief Financial Officer, Madera Community Hospital, Madera, CA, p. A75

FORAND, Angela, Director, William S. Hall Psychiatric Institute, Columbia, SC, p. A564

FORBES, Brenda, Controller, HEALTHSOUTH Rehabilitation Hospital of Fort Smith, Fort Smith, AR, p. A46

FORBES, Dan, Vice President Human Resources, OHSU Hospital, Portland, OR, p. A529

FORBES, Geri, Chief Executive Officer, WhidbeyHealth, Coupeville, WA, p. A684

FORBES, Jonathan, Director Human Resources, Ashtabula County Medical Center, Ashtabula, OH, p. A484

FORBES, Ronald O., M.D. Medical Director, Central State Hospital, Petersburg, VA, p. A676

FORBES, Vidette J., R.N. Chief Nursing Officer and Chief Operating Officer, HEALTHSOUTH Rehabilitation Hospital – Austin, Austin, TX, p. A599

FORBORT, Gordy, Chief Financial Officer, FirstLight Health System, Mora, MN, p. A347

FORD, Alisa, Vice President Human Resources, The University of Kansas Hospital, Kansas City, KS, p. A246

FORD, Angelique, Administrator Human Resources, Spring Valley Hospital Medical Center, Las Vegas, NV, p. A406

FORD, Cindy, R.N. Chief Nursing Officer, Harrisburg Medical Center, Harrisburg, IL, p. A192

FORD, Cora, Vice President Human Resources, Our Lady of the Lake Regional Medical Center, Baton Rouge, LA, p. A273

FORD, James, Director Human Resources, Sparks Medical Center – Van Buren, Van Buren, AR, p. A53

FORD, Karen, Chief Nursing Officer, Sabine Medical Center, Many, LA, p. A282

FORD, LeeAnn, Director Human Resources and Imaging, The Physicians Centre Hospital, Bryan, TX, p. A604

FORD, Marcia F., Chief Operating Officer, Hawthorn Children Psychiatric Hospital, Saint Louis, MO, p. A380

FORD, Michael, Vice President Patient Services, Wood County Hospital, Bowling Green, OH, p. A485

FORD, Mike, Vice President Human Resources, Baptist Health Floyd, New Albany, IN, p. A219

FORD, Timothy R., President and Chief Executive Officer, Springfield Hospital, Springfield, VT, p. A666

FORDE, Steve, Chief Financial Officer, Nelson County Health System, Mcville, ND, p. A480

FORDE, Terry, President and Chief Executive Officer, Adventist HealthCare, Gaithersburg, MD, p. B7

FORDHAM, Karen, President, DMC Huron Valley–Sinai Hospital, Commerce Township, MI, p. A321

FORDYCE, Brian, Director Information Technology, Roosevelt Medical Center, Culbertson, MT, p. A386

FORDYCE, Carol, Director Patient Care Services, Sullivan County Memorial Hospital, Milan, MO, p. A376

FORDYCE, Michael L., President and Chief Executive Officer, Craig Hospital, Englewood, CO, p. A105

FOREMAN, Christopher, Director Human Resources, Santa Rosa Medical Center, Milton, FL, p. A138

FOREMAN, Kim, M.D. Chief of Staff, Texas Spine & Joint Hospital, Tyler, TX, p. A654

FOREMAN, Lee Ann
Vice President Human Resources, Mississippi Baptist Medical Center, Jackson, MS, p. A360
Vice President Human Resources, Select Specialty Hospital – Belhaven, Jackson, MS, p. A360

FOREMAN, Nena, Chief Nursing Officer, Palo Verde Hospital, Blythe, CA, p. A57

FORESE, Joseph, Chief Executive Officer, Mountain Lakes Medical Center, Clayton, GA, p. A156

FORESE, Laura, M.D. Executive Vice President and Chief Medical Officer, New York–Presbyterian Hospital, New York, NY, p. A447

FOREST, Karen, Health Care Manager, State Penitentiary Hospital, Walla Walla, WA, p. A693

FORET, Chris, M.D. Chief of Staff, Riverside Medical Center, Franklinton, LA, p. A277

FORET, Robert, Chief Financial Officer, Yoakum Community Hospital, Yoakum, TX, p. A658

FORGE, Brenda J., Vice President, Human Resources, Regional West Medical Center, Scottsbluff, NE, p. A402

FORGEY, Roger, Interim Chief Executive Officer, Mayo Clinic Health System in Waycross, Waycross, GA, p. A169

FORGEY, Warren, FACHE, President and Chief Executive Officer, Schneck Medical Center, Seymour, IN, p. A222

FORKEL, Todd
President and Chief Executive Officer, Avera St. Luke's Hospital, Aberdeen, SD, p. A572
Interim Chief Executive Officer, Avera St. Mary's Hospital, Pierre, SD, p. A575

FORKNER, Christine, Executive Vice President and Chief Financial Officer, National Jewish Health, Denver, CO, p. A104

FORMELLA, Nancy A., R.N. Chief Operating Officer, Beth Israel Deaconess Medical Center, Boston, MA, p. A306

FORNIER–JOHNSON, Michelle, Group Vice President Human Resources, St. Anthony Hospital, Lakewood, CO, p. A108

FORREST, Brian K.
Director Human Resources, Arnot Ogden Medical Center, Elmira, NY, p. A438
Director Human Resources, Ira Davenport Memorial Hospital, Bath, NY, p. A434
Vice President Human Resources, St. Joseph's Hospital, Elmira, NY, p. A438

FORREST, Mary Helen, R.N. Chief Nursing Officer, UAMS Medical Center, Little Rock, AR, p. A49

FORREST, Molly, President and Chief Executive Officer, Joyce Eisenberg–Keefer Medical Center, Reseda, CA, p. A85

FORRESTER, John M., Director Information Services, Hamilton Medical Center, Dalton, GA, p. A158

FORRESTT, Brian, Vice President Human Resources, Cayuga Medical Center at Ithaca, Ithaca, NY, p. A440

FORRY, Bryan, Chief Financial Officer, Houston Northwest Medical Center, Houston, TX, p. A625

FORSCH, Randall T., M.D. Chief Medical Officer, St. Joseph Mercy Chelsea, Chelsea, MI, p. A320

FORSYTH, Beth, Chief Operating Officer, Good Samaritan Medical Center, Lafayette, CO, p. A108

FORSYTH, Larry, Director Information Services, OU Medical Center, Oklahoma City, OK, p. A517

FORT, Claudio D., President and Chief Executive Officer, North Country Hospital and Health Center, Newport, VT, p. A666

FORT, Glenn, Chief Medical Officer, Landmark Medical Center, Woonsocket, RI, p. A561

FORTENBERRY, Denise, Chief Nursing Officer and Chief Compliance Officer, Cypress Pointe Surgical Hospital, Hammond, LA, p. A277

FORTENBERRY, Doris, Coordinator Human Resources, Delta Memorial Hospital, Dumas, AR, p. A45

FORTENBERRY, Rob, Chief Information Officer, Mann–Grandstaff Veterans Affairs Medical Center, Spokane, WA, p. A691

FORTIER, Jeanne M., R.N. Chief Nursing Officer and Interim Chief Operating Officer, Grace Cottage Hospital, Townshend, VT, p. A666

FORTIN, Amanda, Manager Finance, Decatur Health Systems, Oberlin, KS, p. A250

FORTIN, Laura, R.N. Chief Operating Officer, St. Joseph Medical Center, Houston, TX, p. A626

FORTNEY, John, M.D. Senior System Medical Advisor, Adena Medical Center, Chillicothe, OH, p. A486

FORTUNATO–HABIB, Mary, Chief Nursing Officer, HealthAlliance Hospitals, Leominster, MA, p. A311

FOSBERG, Renee, Chief Information Officer, Emerson Hospital, Concord, MA, p. A309

FOSINA, Michael, FACHE, President, New York–Presbyterian/Lawrence Hospital, Bronxville, NY, p. A435

FOSNESS, Nick, Chief Executive Officer, Marshall County Healthcare Center Avera, Britton, SD, p. A572

FOSNOCHT, Kevin, M.D. Chief Medical Officer and Associate Executive Director, Penn Presbyterian Medical Center, Philadelphia, PA, p. A549

FOSS, David, Chief Information Officer, New London Hospital, New London, NH, p. A412

FOSS, R. Coleman, Chief Executive Officer, Tennova Healthcare – Cleveland, Cleveland, TN, p. A581

FOSSUM, John, Chief Executive Officer, Ely–Bloomenson Community Hospital, Ely, MN, p. A342

FOSTER, Barbara A., Regional Human Resources Director, Select Specialty Hospital–Wilmington, Wilmington, DE, p. A120

FOSTER, Becky
Manager Human Resources, Sanford Tracy Medical Center, Tracy, MN, p. A352
Manager Human Resources, Sanford Westbrook Medical Center, Westbrook, MN, p. A353

FOSTER, Beverly, Chief Executive Officer, Kindred Hospital Chicago–Northlake, Northlake, IL, p. A198

FOSTER, Bob, Chief Information Officer, South Georgia Medical Center, Valdosta, GA, p. A168

FOSTER, Brian, Chief Information Officer, Vail Valley Medical Center, Vail, CO, p. A111

FOSTER, Carolyn
Chief Financial Officer, PeaceHealth Peace Island Medical Center, Friday Harbor, WA, p. A685
Interim Executive Director and Chief Financial Officer, PeaceHealth St. Joseph Medical Center, Bellingham, WA, p. A682

FOSTER, Charles, Regional Director Human Resources, CHRISTUS Southeast Texas Hospital, Beaumont, TX, p. A601

FOSTER, Chris, Director Health Information Management, Deer Lodge Medical Center, Deer Lodge, MT, p. A387

FOSTER, Gary, R.N. Associate Administrator, Banner Estrella Medical Center, Phoenix, AZ, p. A36

FOSTER, Gary, Vice President and Chief Financial Officer, Saratoga Hospital, Saratoga Springs, NY, p. A455

FOSTER, Kennetha, Chief Nursing Officer, Mission Regional Medical Center, Mission, TX, p. A637

FOSTER, Michael, Director Information Systems, East Cooper Medical Center, Mount Pleasant, SC, p. A568

FOSTER, Mickey, President, Moses H. Cone Memorial Hospital, Greensboro, NC, p. A466

FOSTER, Mike, Manager Information Systems, Moab Regional Hospital, Moab, UT, p. A660

FOSTER, Mitzi, Director Information Services, Southern Tennessee Regional Health System–Pulaski, Pulaski, TN, p. A592

FOSTER, Rebecca, MSN Chief Nursing Officer, Cumberland Medical Center, Crossville, TN, p. A582

FOSTER, Robert, Director Human Resources, L. V. Stabler Memorial Hospital, Greenville, AL, p. A21

FOSTER, Stephanie, MSN Chief Nursing Officer, Longview Regional Medical Center, Longview, TX, p. A633

FOSTER, Steven
Chief Executive Officer, Barstow Community Hospital, Barstow, CA, p. A56
Chief Executive Officer, CHI St. Luke's Health – Patients Medical Center, Pasadena, TX, p. A640

FOSTER, Terri, Hospital Finance Officer, Baylor Regional Medical Center at Grapevine, Grapevine, TX, p. A621

FOSTER, Timothy, Acting Chief Medical Officer, Newton–Wellesley Hospital, Newton Lower Falls, MA, p. A313

FOSTER, Wanda, R.N. Vice President Nursing, McDonough District Hospital, Macomb, IL, p. A195

FOTIADIS, George, M.D. Chief of Staff, Clarke County Hospital, Osceola, IA, p. A236

FOTTER, Robert, Chief Financial Officer, Pennsylvania Psychiatric Institute, Harrisburg, PA, p. A539

FOTTER, Robert L., Chief Information Officer, Littleton Regional Hospital, Littleton, NH, p. A412

FOUGHT, Scott, Vice President Finance, ProMedica Bay Park Hospital, Oregon, OH, p. A500

FOULKE, Elvia, Executive Vice President and Chief Operating Officer, Foothill Presbyterian Hospital, Glendora, CA, p. A65

FOUNTAIN, Aaron, Chief Information Officer, Brandon Regional Hospital, Brandon, FL, p. A124

FOUNTAIN, Wesley D., Chief Financial Officer, St. David's South Austin Medical Center, Austin, TX, p. A600

FOUREZ, Yvonne, Chief Financial Officer, Washington County Memorial Hospital, Potosi, MO, p. A378

FOURNIER, Joseph, Chief Human Resources Officer, University of Michigan Hospitals and Health Centers, Ann Arbor, MI, p. A318

FOURRE, Mark, Senior Vice President and Chief Medical Officer, LincolnHealth, Damariscotta, ME, p. A292

FOUSE, Carla, Chief Nursing Officer, St. Vincent Randolph Hospital, Winchester, IN, p. A224

FOUSE, Sarah, Associate Director of Patient Services, Captain James A. Lovell Federal Health Care Center, North Chicago, IL, p. A198

FOUST, Lisa
Senior Vice President Human Resources, John Muir Behavioral Health Center, Concord, CA, p. A59
Senior Vice President Human Resources, John Muir Medical Center, Concord, Concord, CA, p. A59
Senior Vice President, Human Resources, John Muir Medical Center, Walnut Creek, Walnut Creek, CA, p. A99

FOUTS, Phillip, Chief Financial Officer, Fannin Regional Hospital, Blue Ridge, GA, p. A154

FOUTZ, Patricia, Director Human Resources, Bath Community Hospital, Hot Springs, VA, p. A672

FOWLER, Andrew, Vice President Information Services, Atlantic General Hospital, Berlin, MD, p. A298

FOWLER, Andy, Senior Vice President Information Systems, Methodist Healthcare Memphis Hospitals, Memphis, TN, p. A589

FOWLER, Barry, Director Human and System Resources, Clark Fork Valley Hospital, Plains, MT, p. A390

FOWLER, Karen, MSN Chief Nursing Officer, The Hospitals of Providence Memorial Campus, El Paso, TX, p. A616

FOWLER, Kate, Chief Financial Officer, West Valley Medical Center, Caldwell, ID, p. A175

FOWLER, Kevin, Director Finance, Putnam County Hospital, Greencastle, IN, p. A212

FOWLER, Kevin N., President and Chief Executive Officer, Cabell Huntington Hospital, Huntington, WV, p. A696

FOWLER, Maureen, Director Human Resources, Conifer Park, Glenville, NY, p. A439

FOWLER, Ruth, Senior Vice President and Chief Financial Officer, Children's Healthcare of Atlanta, Atlanta, GA, p. A152

FOWLER, Steven, M.D. President Medical Staff, Genesis Medical Center, DeWitt, De Witt, IA, p. A229

FOX, Alan, Chief Financial Officer, Saint Francis Memorial Hospital, San Francisco, CA, p. A90

FOX, Carol J., M.D. Senior Vice President and Chief Medical Officer, Excela Latrobe Area Hospital, Latrobe, PA, p. A542

FOX, David, President, Advocate Good Samaritan Hospital, Downers Grove, IL, p. A188

FOX, Debra, Chief Nursing Officer, University Medical Center, Las Vegas, NV, p. A407

FOX, E. Kay, Director of Nursing, Black River Medical Center, Poplar Bluff, MO, p. A378

FOX, Jay, Chief Executive Officer, Scott & White Hospital at Round Rock, Round Rock, TX, p. A644

FOX, Jessica, Director of Human Resources, Aspirus Riverview Hospital and Clinics, Inc., Wisconsin Rapids, WI, p. A719

FOX, John, M.D. Medical Director, Vibra Hospital of San Diego, San Diego, CA, p. A89

FOX, John A., M.D. Chief of Staff, Shriners Hospitals for Children–Shreveport, Shreveport, LA, p. A288

FOX, John T., President and Chief Executive Officer, Beaumont Health, Southfield, MI, p. B22

FOX, Leana, MSN Interim Chief Nurse Executive, Bon Secours Maryview Medical Center, Portsmouth, VA, p. A676

FOX, Randy, Director Performance Improvement and Risk Management, Lakeland Behavioral Health System, Springfield, MO, p. A382

FOX, Starla, Director of Nursing, Bristol Bay Area Health Corporation, Dillingham, AK, p. A5

FOX, Susan, President and Chief Executive Officer, White Plains Hospital Center, White Plains, NY, p. A459

FOX, William, Chief Executive Officer, AMG Specialty Hospital – Las Vegas, Las Vegas, NV, p. A405

FOXX, Randy, Chief Financial Officer, Boone Memorial Hospital, Madison, WV, p. A697

FOY, Gregory S., Human Resources System Leader, Scheurer Hospital, Pigeon, MI, p. A331

FRACHISEUR, Kenny, Chief Information Officer, Ouachita County Medical Center, Camden, AR, p. A44

FRACICA, Phil, M.D. Vice President and Chief Medical Officer, Mercy Gilbert Medical Center, Gilbert, AZ, p. A32

FRACK, RN, Darla, R.N. Vice President, Patient Services, St. Luke's Hospital – Anderson Campus, Easton, PA, p. A537

FRAHER, Francis D., Vice President and Chief Financial Officer, Northwestern Memorial Hospital, Northwestern Memorial Hospital, Chicago, IL, p. A185

FRAIOLA, Anthony, Associate Administrator Administrative and Support Services, Hawaii State Hospital, Kaneohe, HI, p. A172

FRAKER, Steve, Chief Financial Officer, Banner Churchill Community Hospital, Fallon, NV, p. A404

FRALEY, Danny, Chief Clinical Officer, Acuity Hospital of South Texas, San Antonio, TX, p. A645

FRALEY, Janice, IT Entity Director – Information Services Division, Chatham Hospital, Siler City, NC, p. A473

FRALICKER, Tammy, MS Chief Nursing Officer, Crawford Memorial Hospital, Robinson, IL, p. A201

FRAME, Angela, Chief Financial Officer, Jackson General Hospital, Ripley, WV, p. A699

FRAME, Ken, Chief Nursing Officer, Ashtabula County Medical Center, Ashtabula, OH, p. A484

FRANCE, Cheryl, M.D. Chief Medical Officer, William R. Sharpe, Jr. Hospital, Weston, WV, p. A701

FRANCE, James, M.D. Chief of Staff, Conway Regional Medical Center, Conway, AR, p. A44

FRANCETICH, Kane, Chief Information Officer, Gritman Medical Center, Moscow, ID, p. A177

FRANCIK, Tamara, Human Resources Generalist, Thayer County Health Services, Hebron, NE, p. A396

FRANCIOLI, Carl H., Vice President Finance, Johns Hopkins Bayview Medical Center, Baltimore, MD, p. A296

FRANCIS, Anna, Chief Information Officer, Fairlawn Rehabilitation Hospital, Worcester, MA, p. A316

FRANCIS, Carolyn, R.N. Director of Nursing, LaSalle General Hospital, Jena, LA, p. A278

FRANCIS, Christy, Chief Executive Officer, Hemphill County Hospital, Canadian, TX, p. A605

FRANCIS, Duane, President and Chief Executive Officer, Mid–Columbia Medical Center, The Dalles, OR, p. A531

FRANCIS, Jeffrey, Vice President Finance and Chief Financial Officer, Methodist Jennie Edmundson Hospital, Council Bluffs, IA, p. A228

FRANCIS, Lana B., Chief Executive Officer, LaSalle General Hospital, Jena, LA, p. A278

FRANCIS, Mark J., President, Chief Executive Officer and Hospital Administrator, Colorado Canyons Hospital and Medical Center, Fruita, CO, p. A106

FRANCIS, Perry, Supervisory Information Technology Specialist, Chinle Comprehensive Health Care Facility, Chinle, AZ, p. A31

FRANCIS, Rebekah, J
    Chief Financial Officer, Aurora Behavioral Health System East, Tempe, AZ, p. A40
    Chief Financial Officer, Aurora Behavioral Health System West, Glendale, AZ, p. A33

FRANCISCO, Gerard E., M.D. Chief Medical Officer, TIRR Memorial Hermann, Houston, TX, p. A627

FRANCKOWIAK, Debra, Executive Director, Children's Hospital of Wisconsin–Fox Valley, Neenah, WI, p. A712

FRANCO, Glenda, Director, Human Resources, Vibra Hospital of Sacramento, Folsom, CA, p. A62

FRANCO, Luis, M.D. Medical Director, United Medical Rehabilitation Hospital, Hammond, LA, p. A278

FRANCO, Richard
    Chief Financial Officer, Abrazo West Campus, Goodyear, AZ, p. A33
    Chief Financial Officer, Community First Medical Center, Chicago, IL, p. A183

FRANCO, Roger, Director Human Resources, St. John's Episcopal Hospital–South Shore,, NY, p. A450

FRANCOIS, Brennan, Chief Executive Officer, Alliance Health Center, Meridian, MS, p. A362

FRANCOIS, Fritz, M.D. Chief Medical Officer, NYU Langone Medical Center, New York, NY, p. A449

FRANDSEN, Jeff, Chief Executive Officer, HEALTHSOUTH Rehabilitation Hospital of Utah, Sandy, UT, p. A664

FRANK, Barbara, Human Resource Specialist, Caro Center, Caro, MI, p. A320

FRANK, Daniel, Chief Financial Officer, Longmont United Hospital, Longmont, CO, p. A108

FRANK, Debra, Chief Financial Officer, Ness County Hospital District No 2, Ness City, KS, p. A250

FRANK, Jim, CPA, Chief Executive Officer, Providence Medical Center, Wayne, NE, p. A403

FRANK, Kevin, Administrator, Louisiana Extended Care Hospital of Lafayette, Lafayette, LA, p. A280

FRANK, Kim, Chief Human Resources Officer, Virginia Gay Hospital, Vinton, IA, p. A238

FRANK, Mitchell, Chief Financial Officer, Tennova Healthcare–Shelbyville, Shelbyville, TN, p. A593

FRANK, Patricia, Chief Nursing Officer, Henry County Hospital, Napoleon, OH, p. A500

FRANK, Robert A.
    Senior Vice President of Operations, University of Maryland Shore Medical Center at Chestertown, Chestertown, MD, p. A299
    Senior Vice President Operations, University of Maryland Shore Medical Center at Dorchester, Cambridge, MD, p. A299
    Senior Vice President of Operations, University of Maryland Shore Medical Center at Easton, Easton, MD, p. A300

FRANK, Stanley, Chief Executive Officer, Ohio Hospital for Psychiatry, Columbus, OH, p. A490

FRANK, Thomas, Chief Operating Officer, North Country Hospital and Health Center, Newport, VT, p. A666

FRANK–LIGHTFOOT, Loraine, R.N. Vice President, Patient Care Services and Chief Nursing Officer, Munson Medical Center, Traverse City, MI, p. A335

FRANKE, Jenny, Director Human Resources, Rehabilitation Hospital of Wisconsin, Waukesha, WI, p. A718

FRANKE, John, Chief Financial Officer, Baptist Health Lexington, Lexington, KY, p. A262

FRANKE, Paul, M.D. Chief Medical Officer, Alaska Native Medical Center, Anchorage, AK, p. A28

FRANKEL, Harris, M.D. Interim Chief Medical Officer, Nebraska Medicine – Nebraska Medical Center, Omaha, NE, p. A400

FRANKEL, Michele, Associate Executive Director Finance, Glen Cove Hospital, Glen Cove, NY, p. A439

FRANKEN, Stephanie, Vice President Operational Finance, St. Joseph's Hospital and Health Center, Dickinson, ND, p. A478

FRANKENSTEIN, Richard, M.D. Vice President and Chief Medical Officer, Henry Mayo Newhall Hospital, Valencia, CA, p. A98

FRANKL, Angie, Director Human Resources, Adair County Memorial Hospital, Greenfield, IA, p. A231

FRANKLIN, Chuck, M.D. Chief Medical Staff, Weston County Health Services, Newcastle, WY, p. A723

FRANKLIN, Clay, Chief Executive Officer, Plaza Medical Center of Fort Worth, Fort Worth, TX, p. A618

FRANKLIN, Ed, Chief Human Resources Officer, Page Hospital, Page, AZ, p. A35

FRANKLIN, James P., Administrator, Calhoun Health Services, Calhoun City, MS, p. A356

FRANKLIN, Jennifer, R.N. Chief Clinical Officer, Yoakum Community Hospital, Yoakum, TX, p. A658

FRANKLIN, Mary, R.N. Chief Nursing Officer, Merit Health Biloxi, Biloxi, MS, p. A355

FRANKLIN, Matthew, Director Human Resources, Warren General Hospital, Warren, PA, p. A556

FRANKLIN, Michael A., FACHE, President and Chief Executive Officer, Atlantic General Hospital, Berlin, MD, p. A298

FRANKLIN, Tammy, Manager Personnel and Marketing, Covenant Hospital–Levelland, Levelland, TX, p. A632

FRANKO, Stephen
    Vice President Finance and Chief Financial Officer, Mount St. Mary's Hospital and Health Center, Lewiston, NY, p. A441
    Vice President Finance and Chief Financial Officer, Regional Hospital of Scranton, Scranton, PA, p. A554
    Senior Vice President and Chief Financial Officer, St. Vincent's Medical Center, Bridgeport, CT, p. A113

FRANKOVITCH, John C., President and Chief Executive Officer, Weirton Medical Center, Weirton, WV, p. A700

FRANKS, RN, Cathy, Chief Operating Officer, Community Medical Center of Izard County, Calico Rock, AR, p. A44

FRANKS, Charles, Chief Human Resources, Louis Stokes Cleveland Veterans Affairs Medical Center, Cleveland, OH, p. A489

FRANKS, Dennis, Vice President Operations, Doctors' Hospital of Michigan, Pontiac, MI, p. A332

FRANKS, Dennis, FACHE, Chief Executive Officer, Neosho Memorial Regional Medical Center, Chanute, KS, p. A241

FRANSEN, Mitchell, Chief Financial Officer, Mesa View Regional Hospital, Mesquite, NV, p. A407

FRANSON, John K., M.D. Chief Medical Staff, Caribou Memorial Hospital and Living Center, Soda Springs, ID, p. A178

FRANTZ, Steven, Chief Financial Officer, Saint Francis Hospital, Memphis, TN, p. A589

FRANTZ, Vincent, M.D. Chief of Staff, Plumas District Hospital, Quincy, CA, p. A84

FRANZ, Eric, Vice President, Finance and Chief Financial Officer, Graham Hospital Association, Canton, IL, p. A182

FRANZ, Staci, Director Human Resources, St. Luke's Rehabilitation Institute, Spokane, WA, p. A691

FRANZ, Thomas, M.D. Medical Director, HEALTHSOUTH Harmarville Rehabilitation Hospital, Pittsburgh, PA, p. A550

FRANZEL, Carrie, Chief Nursing Officer, Huron Medical Center, Bad Axe, MI, p. A318

FRANZELLA, Susan, Human Resource Business Partner, Kaiser Permanente San Jose Medical Center, San Jose, CA, p. A91

FRARDO, Virgil, M.D. Medical Director, HEALTHSOUTH Rehabilitation Hospital–Wichita Falls, Wichita Falls, TX, p. A657

FRASCA, Edith, Controller and Chief Financial Officer, The Pavilion, Champaign, IL, p. A183

FRASER, Cathryn, Chief Human Resources Officer, Mayo Clinic Hospital – Rochester, Rochester, MN, p. A349

FRASER, James, Administrator Finance, Via Christi Hospital Manhattan, Inc.,, KS, p. A248

FRASER, John M., FACHE, President and Chief Executive Officer, Nebraska Methodist Health System, Inc., Omaha, NE, p. B94

FRASIER, Nora, R.N. Chief Nursing Officer, Methodist Mansfield Medical Center, Mansfield, TX, p. A635

FRATZKE, Mark, R.N., Senior Vice President and Area Manager, Kaiser Permanente Oakland Medical Center, Oakland, CA, p. A80

FRAUENHOFER, Chris, Chief Financial Officer, Maine Coast Memorial Hospital, Ellsworth, ME, p. A293

FRAYSER, P. P., Chief Executive Officer, Palo Verde Behavioral Health, Tucson, AZ, p. A41

FRAZEE, Kim, R.N. Vice President Physician and Business Development, Southern Ocean Medical Center, Manahawkin, NJ, p. A419

FRAZIER, Amy, Supervisor Management Information Systems, Wetzel County Hospital, New Martinsville, WV, p. A698

FRAZIER, Brandon, Chief Financial Officer, River Oaks Hospital, New Orleans, LA, p. A285

FRAZIER, Crystal, Director of Financial Operations, Stonewall Jackson Memorial Hospital, Weston, WV, p. A701

FRAZIER III, James P., Chief Executive Officer, Teche Regional Medical Center, Morgan City, LA, p. A284

FRAZIER, Joel L., M.D. Medical Director, OneCore Health, Oklahoma City, OK, p. A517

FRAZIER, Kimberly, R.N. Chief Nursing Officer, East Los Angeles Doctors Hospital, Los Angeles, CA, p. A71

FRAZIER, Shane, Chief Executive Officer, Pinnacle Pointe Hospital, Little Rock, AR, p. A49

FREAS, Mary Ann, Senior Vice President and Chief Financial Officer, Southwest General Health Center, Middleburg Heights, OH, p. A499

FRED, Mark, R.N. Chief Operating Officer, Kirby Medical Center, Monticello, IL, p. A197

FREDERICK, Brenda, Director Human Resources, Laurel Ridge Treatment Center, San Antonio, TX, p. A646

FREDERICK, Dessa, Manager Human Resources, St. James Behavioral Health Hospital, Gonzales, LA, p. A277

FREDERICK, Gretchen A., R.N. Director Patient Care Services, Buffalo Hospital, Buffalo, MN, p. A340

FREDERICK, John, Chief Financial Officer, West Central Georgia Regional Hospital, Columbus, GA, p. A157

FREDERICK, Ryannon, Chief Nursing Officer, Mayo Clinic Jacksonville, Jacksonville, FL, p. A131

FREDERICKS, Raymond F., President and Chief Executive Officer, JFK Health, Edison, NJ, p. B74

FREDERICKS, Raymond F., President and CEO, JFK Medical Center, Edison, NJ, p. A416

FREDERICKSON, Kathy, Information Systems Site Lead, Sutter Delta Medical Center, Antioch, CA, p. A54

FREDETTE, Beth, Chief Information Officer, Children's Medical Center, Dayton, OH, p. A492

FREDRICH, Nancy, R.N. Chief Clinical Officer, Cooper County Memorial Hospital, Boonville, MO, p. A368

FREDRICK, Joyce, Associate Director, Veterans Affairs Central Western Massachusetts Healthcare System, Leeds, MA, p. A311

FREDRICK, Rick, Director Information Technology, Cottage Hospital, Woodsville, NH, p. A413

FREDRICKSON, Kelley, Director Information Services, Plaza Medical Center of Fort Worth, Fort Worth, TX, p. A618

FREDRICKSON, Mark A., M.D. Medical Director, HEALTHSOUTH Rehabilitation Hospital Midland–Odessa, Midland, TX, p. A637

FREEBERN, Joseph, Executive Director, Mid–Hudson Forensic Psychiatric Center, New Hampton, NY, p. A443

FREEBORN, Fawn, Human Resources Generalist, Schoolcraft Memorial Hospital, Manistique, MI, p. A329

FREEBURG, Rick, Chief Executive Officer, Baptist Health South Florida, Mariners Hospital, Tavernier, FL, p. A148

FREEBURN, Mark, Chief Executive Officer, HEALTHSOUTH Rehabilitation Hospital of Mechanicsburg, Mechanicsburg, PA, p. A544

FREED, Glenn, D.O. Medical Director, St. Luke's Hospital – Miners Campus, Coaldale, PA, p. A535

FREED, Nancy, Chief Financial Officer, Seiling Municipal Hospital, Seiling, OK, p. A519

FREED, Stuart, M.D
    Chief Medical Officer, Confluence Health/Central Washington Hospital, Wenatchee, WA, p. A693
    Medical Director, Confluence Health/Wenatchee Valley Hospital, Wenatchee, WA, p. A693

FREED–SIGURDSSON, Anna, M.D. Medical Director, HEALTHSOUTH Rehabilitation Hospital – Dallas, Dallas, TX, p. A610

FREEDMAN, Barry R., President and Chief Executive Officer, Einstein Healthcare Network, Philadelphia, PA, p. B53

FREEDMAN, Barry R., President and Chief Executive Officer, Einstein Medical Center Philadelphia, Philadelphia, PA, p. A547

FREEDMAN, Kenneth, M.D. Chief Medical Officer, Lemuel Shattuck Hospital, Jamaica Plain, MA, p. A311

FREEDMAN, Rick, Commanding Officer, Naval Hospital Camp Lejeune, Camp Lejeune, NC, p. A461

FREEHILL, Sarah, Chief Nursing Officer, Arbuckle Memorial Hospital, Sulphur, OK, p. A520

FREEHOF, Leonard, Chief Executive Officer and Managing Director, Spring Valley Hospital Medical Center, Las Vegas, NV, p. A406

FREELAND, R. Alan, M.D. Chief Clinical Officer, Twin Valley Behavioral Healthcare, Columbus, OH, p. A491

FREEMAN, Brian, Vice President of Operations, Stanly Regional Medical Center, Albemarle, NC, p. A460

FREEMAN, Diane, R.N. Assistant Vice President and Chief Nursing Officer, St. Luke's Lakeside Hospital, The Woodlands, TX, p. A653

FREEMAN, Donald, President and Chief Executive Officer, Preferred Management Corporation, Shawnee, OK, p. B105

FREEMAN, Elizabeth Joyce, FACHE, Director, VA Palo Alto Health Care System, Palo Alto, CA, p. A82

FREEMAN, Jerry, Chief, Human Resources Management Services, Durham Veterans Affairs Medical Center, Durham, NC, p. A464

FREEMAN, Kimberlee, R.N. Vice President Patient Care Services and Chief Nursing Officer, Wayne Hospital, Greenville, OH, p. A495

FREEMAN, Louella, MSN Chief Nursing Officer, PeaceHealth Sacred Heart Medical Center at RiverBend, Springfield, OR, p. A531

FREEMAN, Marianne, Vice President Human Resources, Rockdale Medical Center, Conyers, GA, p. A157

FREEMAN, Michael
Director Human Resources, Alta Vista Regional Hospital, Las Vegas, NM, p. A430
Director Human Resources, Huhukam Memorial Hospital, Sacaton, AZ, p. A38

FREEMAN, Mike, Director Information Technology, Sentara Williamsburg Regional Medical Center, Williamsburg, VA, p. A680

FREEMAN, Peggy, Chief Physicians Services Officer, Dickinson County Healthcare System, Iron Mountain, MI, p. A327

FREEMAN, Richard
President and Chief Executive Officer, Robert Wood Johnson University Hospital at Hamilton, Hamilton, NJ, p. A417
Chief Medical Officer, St. Vincent Indianapolis Hospital, Indianapolis, IN, p. A215

FREEMAN, Robert, Director Human Resources, Sparks Regional Medical Center, Fort Smith, AR, p. A46

FREESE–DECKER, Christina, FACHE, President, Spectrum Health Hospital Group, Spectrum Health – Butterworth Hospital, Grand Rapids, MI, p. A325

FREID–SCHEPPKE, Denise, Chief Accounting Officer, Oakleaf Surgical Hospital, Eau Claire, WI, p. A705

FREIER, Toby, President, New Ulm Medical Center, New Ulm, MN, p. A347

FREIJ, Walid, M.D. Chief of Staff, Vaughan Regional Medical Center, Selma, AL, p. A25

FREILICH, Josh, Vice President and Chief Nurse Executive, Mercy Hospital of Folsom, Folsom, CA, p. A62

FREIMARK, Jeffrey P., Chief Executive Officer, Miami Jewish Home and Hospital for Aged, Miami, FL, p. A137

FREIN, Ethel, Chief Executive Officer, Bennett County Hospital and Nursing Home, Martin, SD, p. A574

FREITAG, Donald, M.D. Chief Medical Officer, Lynn County Hospital District, Tahoka, TX, p. A651

FREITAG, Vanessa, President, Ministry Our Lady of Victory Hospital, Stanley, WI, p. A716

FRELING, Eric, M.D. Director Medical Staff Affairs, Memorial Hospital West, Pembroke Pines, FL, p. A142

FRENCH, Dean, M.D., Chief Executive Officer, Community Medical Center, Missoula, MT, p. A389

FRENCH, Dean O., M.D. Chief of Staff, Faith Regional Health Services, Norfolk, NE, p. A399

FRENCH, Holly, Chief Financial Officer, Newman Regional Health, Emporia, KS, p. A242

FRENCH, Tracy
Chief Financial Officer, Banner Goldfield Medical Center, Apache Junction, AZ, p. A31
Chief Financial Officer, Banner Ironwood Medical Center, San Tan Valley, AZ, p. A38

FRENCH, William Chad, Chief Executive Officer, Davis Regional Medical Center, Statesville, NC, p. A474

FRENGLE, Kelley
Director, Human Resources, PeaceHealth Southwest Medical Center, Vancouver, WA, p. A692
Director, Human Resources, PeaceHealth St. John Medical Center, Longview, WA, p. A686

FRENN, Debra, FACHE Chief Patient Care Officer, Rusk County Memorial Hospital, Ladysmith, WI, p. A708

FRERER, Mary
Chief Human Resources Officer, Freeman Health System, Joplin, MO, p. A372
Chief Human Resources Officer, Freeman Neosho Hospital, Neosho, MO, p. A377

FRERICHS, Craig, Chief Information Technology Service, Grand Junction Veterans Health Care System, Grand Junction, CO, p. A106

FRESHOUR, David, Chief Executive Officer, Comanche County Medical Center, Comanche, TX, p. A607

FRESQUEZ, Juan, Chief Operating Officer, Houston Northwest Medical Center, Houston, TX, p. A625

FREUDENBERG, Liz, Chief Financial Officer, HEALTHSOUTH Rehabilitation Hospital of Littleton, Littleton, CO, p. A108

FREUDENBERGER, Joe, Chief Executive Officer, OakBend Medical Center, Richmond, TX, p. A643

FREY, Jack, Acting Business Manager, Greystone Park Psychiatric Hospital, Morris Plains, NJ, p. A419

FREY, Jeff, Business Administrator, Andrew McFarland Mental Health Center, Springfield, IL, p. A203

FREY, Paul, Director Information Technology Applications, Indiana Orthopaedic Hospital, Indianapolis, IN, p. A214

FREY, Rachel, Director Human Resources, Athens–Limestone Hospital, Athens, AL, p. A16

FREYER, Mary, Chief Operating Officer, Little Company of Mary Hospital and Health Care Centers, Evergreen Park, IL, p. A190

FREYER, Sharon, R.N. Chief Nursing Officer, Baptist Health Paducah, Paducah, KY, p. A267

FREYMULLER, Robert S., Chief Executive Officer, Summerlin Hospital Medical Center, Las Vegas, NV, p. A407

FREYTAG, Peter, Senior Vice President Finance and Chief Financial Officer, Bristol Hospital, Bristol, CT, p. A113

FRIANT, Jeff, Vice President Finance, Elmhurst Memorial Hospital,, IL, p. A189

FRIARTE, Pedro, Director of Physician Services, Coral Gables Hospital, Coral Gables, FL, p. A126

FRIBERG, Deborah G., Senior Vice President and Area Manager, Kaiser Permanente Manteca Medical Center, Manteca, CA, p. A76

FRICK, Mark P., Senior Vice President Human Resources, Somerset Hospital, Somerset, PA, p. A555

FRICK, Mary Jo, Director Finance, St. Catherine's Rehabilitation Hospital, North Miami, FL, p. A139

FRICKE, Rhett D., Chief Executive Officer, Ballinger Memorial Hospital, Ballinger, TX, p. A601

FRIDAY, Jason, M.D. Medical Director, Aurora Behavioral Health System East, Tempe, AZ, p. A40

FRIDAY, Lisa, Director Human Resources, Lake Area Medical Center, Lake Charles, LA, p. A281

FRIDKIN, Marjorie, M.D. Chief Medical Officer, Garrett Regional Medical Center, Oakland, MD, p. A302

FRIED, Guy, M.D. Chief Medical Officer, Magee Rehabilitation Hospital, Philadelphia, PA, p. A548

FRIED, Jeffrey M., FACHE, President and Chief Executive Officer, Beebe Healthcare, Lewes, DE, p. A119

FRIED, Tera, Manager Human Resources, West River Regional Medical Center, Hettinger, ND, p. A479

FRIEDELL, Benjamin, Vice President Medical Affairs, Aurelia Osborn Fox Memorial Hospital, Oneonta, NY, p. A452

FRIEDEN, Robert
Vice President Information Systems, Genesis Medical Center, Illini Campus, Silvis, IL, p. A203
Vice President Information Systems, Genesis Medical Center–Aledo, Aledo, IL, p. A180
Vice President Information Systems, Genesis Medical Center–Davenport, Davenport, IA, p. A228

FRIEDENBACH, Daryl, Director Fiscal Services, Floyd Valley Healthcare, Le Mars, IA, p. A233

FRIEDLINE, Jennifer, R.N. Director of Nursing, Mercy Rehabilitation Hospital Springfield, Springfield, MO, p. A382

FRIEDLY, Jennifer, Chief Operating Officer and Vice President, UnityPoint Health – Allen Hospital, Waterloo, IA, p. A239

FRIEDMAN, Jonathan, Public Affairs Officer, Captain James A. Lovell Federal Health Care Center, North Chicago, IL, p. A198

FRIEDMAN, Lloyd, M.D. Vice President Medical Affairs and Chief Operating Officer, Milford Hospital, Milford, CT, p. A115

FRIEDMAN, Ross, Chief Operating Officer, Greystone Park Psychiatric Hospital, Morris Plains, NJ, p. A419

FRIEDRICH III, Daniel J., Chief Executive Officer, Blake Medical Center, Bradenton, FL, p. A124

FRIEL, Donald F., Executive Vice President, Holy Redeemer Hospital, Meadowbrook, PA, p. A544

FRIELING, Jeff
Vice President Information Systems, Camden General Hospital, Camden, TN, p. A579
Vice President and Chief Information Officer, Jackson–Madison County General Hospital, Jackson, TN, p. A584
Chief Information Officer, Pathways of Tennessee, Jackson, TN, p. A584

FRIEND, Lori, Human Resources Director, AllianceHealth Seminole, Seminole, OK, p. A519

FRIER, Nancy, Chief Financial Officer, Eastern Oklahoma Medical Center, Poteau, OK, p. A518

FRIERSON, Cathy, Chief Human Resource Officer, Danbury Hospital, Danbury, CT, p. A113

FRIES, Richard W., Vice President Finance, Allegheny General Hospital, Pittsburgh, PA, p. A550

FRIESEN, Dale L., Chief Financial Officer, CareLink of Jackson, Jackson, MI, p. A327

FRIESEN, Lynette, Manager Human Resources, Henderson Health Care Services, Henderson, NE, p. A397

FRIESEN, Nancy, Chief Financial Officer, CentraCare Health–Monticello, Monticello, MN, p. A347

FRIGEN, Karen, Director Human Resources, Shriners Hospitals for Children–Twin Cities, Minneapolis, MN, p. A347

FRIGO, Dave
Vice President Financial Planning and Treasury, Akron General Medical Center, Akron, OH, p. A483
Chief Financial Officer, Edwin Shaw Rehab, Cuyahoga Falls, OH, p. A492
Director Finance and Controller, Lodi Community Hospital, Lodi, OH, p. A497

FRIGON, Shelby, Chief Financial Officer, Saint Luke's South Hospital, Overland Park, KS, p. A251

FRIGY, Alan, M.D. President Medical Staff, Pana Community Hospital, Pana, IL, p. A199

FRIMODIG, Mindy, D.O. President Medical Staff ThedaCare Physicians Shawano, ThedaCare Medical Center–Shawano, Shawano, WI, p. A715

FRISBEE, Kent, Director Human Resources, Saint Thomas Highlands Hospital, Sparta, TN, p. A593

FRISINA, Marcy, Chief Nursing Officer, Fawcett Memorial Hospital, Port Charlotte, FL, p. A143

FRITSCH, William, M.D. Medical Director, Landmark Hospital of Cape Girardeau, Cape Girardeau, MO, p. A368

FRITTON, Amy, Controller, Sierra Tucson, Tucson, AZ, p. A41

FRITTS, Doris, R.N., Executive Director, Same Day Surgery Center, Rapid City, SD, p. A575

FRITTS, Robert G., Chief Financial Officer and Senior Vice President, Carolinas Healthcare System Blue Ridge, Morganton, NC, p. A470

FROCHTZWAJG, Stanley, M.D. Chief Medical Officer, Community Memorial Hospital, Ventura, CA, p. A98

FROEHLICH, Shelley, R.N. Director Nursing Services, Newport Hospital and Health Services, Newport, WA, p. A687

FROEMKE, Janet, Human Resources Officer, CHI Lisbon Health, Lisbon, ND, p. A480

FROESE, Stacy, Regional Director Human Resources, Integris Bass Pavilion, Enid, OK, p. A511

FROH, Chris, Senior Coordinator Human Resources, Select Specialty Hospital–Milwaukee, Milwaukee, WI, p. A712

FROHNHOFER, Erin J.
Vice President Human Resources, Ohio Valley Hospital, McKees Rocks, PA, p. A544
Director Human Resources, Southwood Psychiatric Hospital, Pittsburgh, PA, p. A551

FROIO, Ann M., Interim Chief Executive Officer, Arizona State Hospital, Phoenix, AZ, p. A36

FROISLAND, Jeffrey R., Chief Financial Officer, Mayo Clinic Hospital, Phoenix, AZ, p. A36

FROMHOLD, John A., FACHE, Chief Executive Officer, Hackensack University Medical Center Mountainside, Montclair, NJ, p. A419

FROMM, Robert, M.D. Chief Medical Officer, Maricopa Integrated Health System, Phoenix, AZ, p. A36

FROMME, Pete, Chief Financial Officer, Fayette County Hospital, Vandalia, IL, p. A204

FROMMELT, William, Director Operations and Finance, River Falls Area Hospital, River Falls, WI, p. A715

FRONZA, Sarah, Interim President and Chief Executive Officer, Legacy Silverton Medical Center, Silverton, OR, p. A531

FROSCH, Kevin, Chief Financial Officer, Medina Regional Hospital, Hondo, TX, p. A623

FROST, Eric, Associate Vice President Human Resources, Upstate University Hospital, Syracuse, NY, p. A457

FROST, Joan, R.N. Chief Operating Officer, Mercy Hospital Washington, Washington, MO, p. A383

FROST, Mark I., M.D
Senior Vice President Medical Affairs, Laureate Psychiatric Clinic and Hospital, Tulsa, OK, p. A521
Senior Vice President Medical Affairs, Saint Francis Health System, Saint Francis Hospital, Tulsa, OK, p. A522
Senior Vice President Medical Affairs, Saint Francis Hospital South, Tulsa, OK, p. A522

FROST, Sarah
Administrator and Chief Operating Officer, Banner – University Medical Center South, Tucson, AZ, p. A40
Chief Operating Officer and Administrator, University of Arizona Medical Center – South Campus, Banner – University Medical Center Tucson, Tucson, AZ, p. A40

FRUGE, Janie, FACHE, Chief Executive Officer, West Calcasieu Cameron Hospital, Sulphur, LA, p. A288

FRUM, Judy, R.N. Chief Nursing Officer, Memorial Hospital Pembroke, Pembroke Pines, FL, p. A142

FRUM, R. David
President, Bridgton Hospital, Bridgton, ME, p. A292
President, Rumford Hospital, Rumford, ME, p. A295

FRY, Kenneth, Chief Financial Officer, Saint Alphonsus Regional Medical Center, Boise, ID, p. A174

FRY, Terry, R.N. Chief Nursing Officer, Upper Valley Medical Center, Troy, OH, p. A504

FRYE, Charles, Director Human Resources, Estes Park Medical Center, Estes Park, CO, p. A105

FRYE, Kelly D., Director Human Resources, Montgomery General Hospital, Montgomery, WV, p. A698

FRYE, Terri, Information Technology Officer, Weston County Health Services, Newcastle, WY, p. A723

FRYER, Ramona D., Chief Financial Officer, WK Bossier Health Center, Bossier City, LA, p. A274

FRYFOGLE, Anthoney, Chief Information Officer, George Regional Hospital, Lucedale, MS, p. A361

FUCCI, Thomas, FACHE, Chief Executive Officer, Select Specialty Hospital–Erie, Erie, PA, p. A538

FUCHS, Gwen, R.N. Director Perioperative Services and Interim Chief Nursing Officer, Great Plains Regional Medical Center, Elk City, OK, p. A511

FUCHS, Mary Ann, R.N. Vice President Patient Care and System Chief Nurse Executive, Duke University Hospital, Durham, NC, p. A464

FUEHRER, Susan, Director, Louis Stokes Cleveland Veterans Affairs Medical Center, Cleveland, OH, p. A489

FUENTES, Frances, Coordinator Human Resources, HEALTHSOUTH Rehabilitation Hospital of San Juan, San Juan, PR, p. A729

FUENTES, Leticia, Nursing Director, San Jorge Children's Hospital, San Juan, PR, p. A730

FUENTES Jr., Miguel A., President and Chief Executive Officer, Bronx–Lebanon Hospital Center Health Care System,, NY, p. A444

FUERSTENBERG, Donna, Fiscal Chief, Sheridan Veterans Affairs Medical Center, Sheridan, WY, p. A724

FUGATTE, Cheryl, MSN Vice President and Chief Nursing Officer, Jewish Hospital, Louisville, KY, p. A264

FUGITT, Jacki L., Director Employee Relations, OSF Saint Francis Medical Center, Peoria, IL, p. A200

FUGLEBERG, Jason, R.N. Vice President Patient Services and Chief Nursing Officer, Millinocket Regional Hospital, Millinocket, ME, p. A294

FUGLER, Shawna, R.N. Chief Nursing Officer, Memorial Hermann Surgical Hospital Kingwood, Kingwood, TX, p. A631

FUHRMAN, Bradley, M.D. Physician in Chief, El Paso Children's Hospital, El Paso, TX, p. A615

FUHRMAN, Dennis, Vice President Finance, Essentia Health Fargo, Fargo, ND, p. A478

FUHRMAN, L. Wesley, President and Chief Executive Officer, Warwick Manor Behavioral Health, East New Market, MD, p. A300

FUHRO, Mary, Chief Nursing Officer, Newark Beth Israel Medical Center, Newark, NJ, p. A420

FUHS, Veronica, Chief Executive Officer, Monroe County Hospital and Clinics, Albia, IA, p. A225

FUJINAKA, Jason, Manager Information System, Wahiawa General Hospital, Wahiawa, HI, p. A172

FULCHER, Cathe, Superintendent, Evansville State Hospital, Evansville, IN, p. A210

FULCHER, Kimberly, Chief Human Resources Officer, Halifax Health Medical Center of Daytona Beach, Daytona Beach, FL, p. A127

FULCHER, Martha, MSN Chief Nursing Officer, OCH Regional Medical Center, Starkville, MS, p. A365

FULKERSON, Judy, Director Human Resources, TriStar Greenview Regional Hospital, Bowling Green, KY, p. A258

FULKERSON, Richard, Director Fiscal Services, Shriners Hospitals for Children–Springfield, Springfield, MA, p. A315

FULKS, Chris, Vice President Finance, Lake Huron Medical Center, Port Huron, MI, p. A332

FULKS, Gerald N., President, West Georgia Health, Lagrange, GA, p. A161

FULLBRIGHT, Gary D., Comptroller, Citizens Memorial Hospital, Bolivar, MO, p. A367

FULLEN–ROBERTS, Shannon, Chief Nursing Officer, Russell County Medical Center, Lebanon, VA, p. A672

FULLER, Cara
Vice President Human Resources, UnityPoint Health – Trinity Bettendorf, Bettendorf, IA, p. A225
Vice President Human Resources, UnityPoint Health – Trinity Rock Island, Rock Island, IL, p. A201

FULLER, Cheryl, Director Information Resources, Kansas Neurological Institute, Topeka, KS, p. A254

FULLER, Dale, Vice President and Chief Information Officer, UPMC Altoona, Altoona, PA, p. A532

FULLER, David, FACHE, Chief Executive Officer, Gadsden Regional Medical Center, Gadsden, AL, p. A20

FULLER, David, Director Human Resources, Porter Medical Center, Middlebury, VT, p. A665

FULLER, Debbie, Director Health Information Systems and Chief Information Officer, Doctors Medical Center of Modesto, Modesto, CA, p. A77

FULLER, Jami, Manager Information Technology, Catalina Island Medical Center, Avalon, CA, p. A55

FULLER, Jane, Vice President Human Resources, North Florida Regional Medical Center, Gainesville, FL, p. A129

FULLER, Jeremy, Director Information Systems, Conroe Regional Medical Center, Conroe, TX, p. A607

FULLER, Jill, R.N., President and Chief Executive Officer, Prairie Lakes Healthcare System, Watertown, SD, p. A577

FULLER, Marion, Chief of Staff, West Shore Medical Center, Manistee, MI, p. A329

FULLMER, John, Chief Financial Officer, Bingham Memorial Hospital, Blackfoot, ID, p. A174

FULLUM, Jane, Vice President Patient Care Services, East Alabama Medical Center, Opelika, AL, p. A24

FULTON, Diane, MSN Chief Nursing Officer, Rapides Regional Medical Center, Alexandria, LA, p. A271

FULTON, Lorna, Director Human Resources, Vibra Hospital of Denver, Thornton, CO, p. A111

FULTON, Lynn, President, OSF Saint Luke Medical Center, Kewanee, IL, p. A194

FUNDERBURG, Michelle, Director Human Resources, Stephens Memorial Hospital, Breckenridge, TX, p. A603

FUNDERBURK, Mark, Executive Vice President and Administrator, University Medical Center, Lubbock, TX, p. A634

FUNG, Adrian, Director Information Systems, Tennova Healthcare–Lebanon, Lebanon, TN, p. A586

FUNK, Luann, Administrative Assistant and Manager Human Resources, Pana Community Hospital, Pana, IL, p. A199

FUNKHOUSER, Krisy L., Manager Human Resources, Willapa Harbor Hospital, South Bend, WA, p. A690

FUNKHOUSER, Lana, Vice President Human Resources, Indiana University Health West Hospital, Avon, IN, p. A206

FUQUA, David, Director Human Resources Management, University Health Shreveport, Shreveport, LA, p. A288

FUQUA, David G., Chief Executive Officer, Marshall County Hospital, Benton, KY, p. A257

FUQUA, Leon, Chief Operating Officer, Wise Regional Health System, Decatur, TX, p. A612

FURER, Darnell F., M
Vice President of Patient Care Services, Schuylkill Medical Center – Schuylkill East Norwegian Street, Pottsville, PA, p. A552
Vice President Patient Care Services and Chief Nursing Officer, Schuylkill Medical Center – Schuylkill South Jackson Street, Pottsville, PA, p. A552

FURGURSON, Carol, Chief Operating Officer, Saint Louise Regional Hospital, Gilroy, CA, p. A64

FURLONG, Marian M., FACHE, Chief Executive Officer, Hudson Hospital and Clinic, Hudson, WI, p. A707

FURLOW, Pete, Director Information Technology Services, Northeast Alabama Regional Medical Center, Anniston, AL, p. A15

FURNAS, David, Chief Information Officer, Gila Regional Medical Center, Silver City, NM, p. A431

FURNEY, June, R.N. Director of Nursing, Brooks County Hospital, Quitman, GA, p. A164

FURNISS, Scott, Senior Vice President and Chief Financial Officer, Saint Agnes Hospital, Baltimore, MD, p. A297

FURR, Robert, Director Information Services, Cannon Memorial Hospital, Pickens, SC, p. A569

FUSCHILLO, Ronald
Chief Information Officer, Renown Rehabilitation Hospital, Reno, NV, p. A408
Chief Information Officer, Renown South Meadows Medical Center, Reno, NV, p. A408

FUSCO, Kevin, Corporate Chief Operating Officer, Broward Health North, Deerfield Beach, FL, p. A127

FUSELIER, Gerald, Chief Operating Officer, Savoy Medical Center, Mamou, LA, p. A282

FUSELIER, Michael, FACHE Chief Financial Officer, Central Louisiana Surgical Hospital, Alexandria, LA, p. A271

FUSILERO, Jane, Vice President Chief Nursing Officer, H. Lee Moffitt Cancer Center and Research Institute, Tampa, FL, p. A147

FUTCH, Margaret A., Chief Executive Officer, HEALTHSOUTH Rehabilitation Hospital, Dothan, AL, p. A19

FUTRAL, Cindy, Director Human Resources, Elmore Community Hospital, Wetumpka, AL, p. A26

FUTRELL, Cynthia, MSN Chief Nursing Officer, Marion General Hospital, Marion, IN, p. A218

FYBEL, Gary G., FACHE, Chief Executive, Senior Vice President, Scripps Memorial Hospital–La Jolla, La Jolla, CA, p. A67

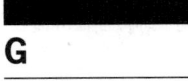

G

GAAL, James G., M.D. Chief of Medical Staff, Jackson General Hospital, Ripley, WV, p. A699

GAASCH, Andrew
Chief Financial Officer, Parker Adventist Hospital, Parker, CO, p. A109
Chief Financial Officer, Porter Adventist Hospital, Denver, CO, p. A104

GABALDON, Karen, Chief Management Information Systems, West Palm Beach Veterans Affairs Medical Center, West Palm Beach, FL, p. A150

GABEL, Christopher, Chief Operating Officer, Larkin Behavioral Health Services,, FL, p. A130

GABEL, Kelly, Chief of Staff, Citizens Medical Center, Colby, KS, p. A241

GABEL, Marcia, Chief Financial Officer, Lane County Hospital, Dighton, KS, p. A242

GABLE, Beth, Administrative Assistant, Jasper General Hospital, Bay Springs, MS, p. A355

GABLENZ, Gordon, Vice President Finance, Ridgeview Medical Center, Waconia, MN, p. A352

GABORIAULT, Randall, Chief Information Officer, Christiana Care Health System, Newark, DE, p. A119

GABRIEL, Joel, M.D. Medical Director, Memorial Health Care Systems, Seward, NE, p. A402

GABRIEL, Scott F., President, Parkview Whitley Hospital, Columbia City, IN, p. A208

GABRIEL, Shirley, Vice President and Chief Information Officer, University Hospital, Augusta, GA, p. A154

GABRIELE, Joan, Deputy Executive Director, NYC Health + Hospitals / Queens,, NY, p. A449

GABRIELLI, MSN, RN–, Melissa, Director of Nursing, River Crest Hospital, San Angelo, TX, p. A644

GABRYEL, Timothy, M.D. Vice President Medical Affairs and Medical Director, Mercy Hospital, Buffalo, NY, p. A436

GABUAT, Jesse, Interim Chief Nursing Officer, Aventura Hospital and Medical Center, Aventura, FL, p. A123

GADALLAH, Yousri, M.D. Chief Medical Officer, Pershing General Hospital, Lovelock, NV, p. A407

GADDAM, Sumalatha, Senior Vice President and Chief Information Officer, Kent County Memorial Hospital, Warwick, RI, p. A561

GADDAM, Summa, Chief Information Officer, Butler Hospital, Providence, RI, p. A560

GADDIS, Cathryn H., Director Human Resources, RiverValley Behavioral Health Hospital, Owensboro, KY, p. A267

GADDY, Pam, Director, Patient Care Services and Chief Nursing Officer, FirstHealth Montgomery Memorial Hospital, Troy, NC, p. A474

GADDY, Jr., Roger A., Chief Medical Officer, Fairfield Memorial Hospital, Winnsboro, SC, p. A571

GADE, Swami P., M.D. Medical Director, Tioga Medical Center, Tioga, ND, p. A481

GADEN, Paul, Chief Executive Officer, Providence Portland Medical Center, Portland, OR, p. A529

GADOMSKI, Veronica, R.N. Chief Nursing Officer, HEALTHSOUTH Rehabilitation Hospital, Albuquerque, NM, p. A427

GAEDE, John, Director Information Systems, El Centro Regional Medical Center, El Centro, CA, p. A61

GAFFOLI, Jill, Director Human Resources, Physicians Regional – Pine Ridge, Naples, FL, p. A138

GAFFORD, Deborah, Chief Financial Officer, Menorah Medical Center, Overland Park, KS, p. A251

GAFFORD, Grady Paul, Chief Financial Officer, Brownfield Regional Medical Center, Brownfield, TX, p. A603

GAGE, Bobby, Director Information Technology, Wabash General Hospital, Mount Carmel, IL, p. A197

GAGE, Eileen, R.N
Vice President Nursing, Geneva General Hospital, Geneva, NY, p. A439
Vice President Nursing, Soldiers and Sailors Memorial Hospital of Yates County, Penn Yan, NY, p. A452

GAGE, Kevin, Chief Financial Officer, Stamford Hospital, Stamford, CT, p. A117

GAGE, Mark, D.O. Medical Director, Brookhaven Hospital, Tulsa, OK, p. A521

GAGE, Susan, Financial Manager, Veterans Affairs Western New York Healthcare System–Buffalo Division, Buffalo, NY, p. A436

GAGER, Brian
Vice President Operations, Acute Care Hospitals, St. John's Hospital, Maplewood, MN, p. A346
Vice President, Acute Care Operations, St. Joseph's Hospital, Saint Paul, MN, p. A351
Vice President of Operations, Acute Care Hospitals, Woodwinds Health Campus, Woodbury, MN, p. A353

GAGLIARDI, Teresa, R.N. Chief Nursing Officer, Trinity Hospital Twin City, Dennison, OH, p. A493

GAGLIO, Tony, CPA Senior Vice President and Chief Financial Officer, Menninger Clinic, Houston, TX, p. A626

GAGNE, Cheryl, Vice President and Chief Nursing Officer, Southern New Hampshire Medical Center, Nashua, NH, p. A412

GAGNON, Andy, Manager Information Technology, Via Christi Hospital Manhattan, Inc.,, KS, p. A248

GAGNON, Lynne, Chief Nursing Officer, Valley Regional Hospital, Claremont, NH, p. A410

GAINER, Rolf B., M.D., Chief Executive Officer and Administrator, Brookhaven Hospital, Tulsa, OK, p. A521

GAINEY, Shari W.
Human Resource Director, Tanner Higgins General Hospital, Bremen, GA, p. A155
Chief Human Resource Officer, Tanner Medical Center–Villa Rica, Villa Rica, GA, p. A168

GAJ, Steve, Facility Chief Information Officer, Louis Stokes Cleveland Veterans Affairs Medical Center, Cleveland, OH, p. A489

GAJEWSKI, Christie, Director Human Resources, Pinckneyville Community Hospital, Pinckneyville, IL, p. A200

GALANDA, Chris, Chief Information Officer, Wilkes–Barre General Hospital, Wilkes–Barre, PA, p. A558

GALANG, Michael, M.D
Chief Information Officer, Mercy Hospital, Buffalo, NY, p. A436
Chief Information Officer, Sisters of Charity Hospital of Buffalo, Buffalo, NY, p. A436

GALARNEAU, Ciprian, Director Information Systems, Tri Valley Health System, Cambridge, NE, p. A394

GALARNEAU, Gerard, M.D., Chief Executive Officer and Chief Medical Officer, Catskill Regional Medical Center, Harris, NY, p. A440

GALATI, John P., Chief Executive Officer, TLC Health Network – Lake Shore Hospital, Irving, NY, p. A440

GALBRAITH, Kathleen B., FACHE, President, Duke Regional Hospital, Durham, NC, p. A464

GALDIERI, Lou, R.N.,
President, Mease Countryside Hospital, Safety Harbor, FL, p. A144
President, Mease Dunedin Hospital, Dunedin, FL, p. A128

GALE, Gabrielle, Chief Financial Officer, Lighthouse Care Center of Conway, Conway, SC, p. A565

GALE, Michael, Chief Financial Officer, Bournewood Health Systems, Brookline, MA, p. A308

GALEY, John P., M.D. Chief Medical Officer, Schoolcraft Memorial Hospital, Manistique, MI, p. A329

GALIPEAU, Michelle, Director Human Resources, St. Vincent's Birmingham, Birmingham, AL, p. A17

GALKOWSKI, James, Associate Director for Operations, Fayetteville Veterans Affairs Medical Center, Fayetteville, NC, p. A465

GALLAGHER, Chris, M.D. Chief Medical Officer, CHRISTUS Mother Frances Hospital – Sulphur Springs, Sulphur Springs, TX, p. A651

GALLAGHER, Deborah, Manager Human Resources, Ojai Valley Community Hospital, Ojai, CA, p. A80

GALLAGHER, Doug, Director Human Resources, Carolinas ContinueCARE Hospital at Pineville, Charlotte, NC, p. A462

GALLAGHER, J. P., Chief Operating Officer, NorthShore University Health System, Evanston, IL, p. A190

GALLAGHER, James, Chief Executive Officer, Oasis Behavioral Health – Chandler, Chandler, AZ, p. A31

GALLAGHER, Jeannie
jeanie.gallagher@bannerhealth.com, McKee Medical Center, Loveland, CO, p. A109
Chief Human Resource Officer, North Colorado Medical Center, Greeley, CO, p. A106

GALLAGHER, John, Chief Executive Officer, Sunnyside Community Hospital and Clinics, Sunnyside, WA, p. A691

GALLAGHER, Joseph, Chief Executive Officer, Wyoming Behavioral Institute, Casper, WY, p. A721

GALLAGHER, Karen, Vice President Human Resources and Learning, Brooks Rehabilitation Hospital, Jacksonville, FL, p. A131

GALLAGHER, Pamela, Chief Financial Officer, Providence Hospital, Columbia, SC, p. A564

GALLAGHER, Regen, M.D. Chief Medical Officer, Cary Medical Center, Caribou, ME, p. A292

GALLAGHER, Sherry, Director Nursing, Department of Health and Human Services, Humboldt County Mental Health, Eureka, CA, p. A61

GALLAGHER, Thomas E., Chief Financial Officer, Seton Edgar B. Davis Hospital, Luling, TX, p. A635

GALLAHOM, Gerty, Director Human Resources, Maniilaq Health Center, Kotzebue, AK, p. A30

GALLARDO, Kathleen, Chief Nursing Officer, Select Specialty Hospital–Flint, Flint, MI, p. A323

GALLARDO, Ysidro, Associate Administrator Human Resources, Hazel Hawkins Memorial Hospital, Hollister, CA, p. A66

GALLATI, Todd, FACHE, President and Chief Executive Officer, Trident Medical Center, Charleston, SC, p. A563

GALLAY, Emily, Vice President and Chief Information Officer, Lakeland Medical Center, St. Joseph, Saint Joseph, MI, p. A334

GALLEGOS, Colleen, Director Human Resources, Guadalupe County Hospital, Santa Rosa, NM, p. A431

GALLEGOS, Enrique, Chief Executive Officer, Laredo Medical Center, Laredo, TX, p. A632

GALLEGOS, Ken, Director Support Services and Information Technology, Medina Regional Hospital, Hondo, TX, p. A623

GALLI, Jodi B., R.N. Chief Nursing Officer, Kaiser Permanente Redwood City Medical Center, Redwood City, CA, p. A85

GALLIARDT, Scott, R.N., Chief Executive Officer, Cornerstone Hospital of Austin, Austin, TX, p. A599

GALLIART, Mark, Chief Executive Officer, McBride Clinic Orthopedic Hospital, Oklahoma City, OK, p. A516

GALLIK, Becky, Information Systems Manager, FirstLight Health System, Mora, MN, p. A347

GALLIN, John I., M.D., Director, National Institutes of Health Clinical Center, Bethesda, MD, p. A299

GALLO, Ronald, Director Human Resources, Blythedale Children's Hospital, Valhalla, NY, p. A457

GALLOGLY–SIMON, Catherine A., R.N. Chief Nursing Officer, Wyckoff Heights Medical Center,, NY, p. A450

GALLUCCI, Vince
Senior Vice President Human Resources, Mercy Medical Center, Oshkosh, WI, p. A713
Senior Vice President Human Resources, St. Elizabeth Hospital, Appleton, WI, p. A702

GALONSKY Jr., Ronald J.
Chief Executive Officer, Chapman Global Medical Center, Orange, CA, p. A80
Chief Executive Officer, South Coast Global Medical Center, Santa Ana, CA, p. A92

GALT, Nick
Chief Financial Officer, Las Colinas Medical Center, Irving, TX, p. A629
Chief Financial Officer, North Hills Hospital, North Richland Hills, TX, p. A639

GALUSHA, Fred, Chief Information Officer, St. Luke's Rehabilitation Institute, Spokane, WA, p. A691

GALVIN, Gary, Chief of the Medical Staff, Columbus Community Hospital, Inc., Columbus, WI, p. A704

GALYON, Darlene, Director Human Resources, Choctaw Memorial Hospital, Hugo, OK, p. A513

GAMACHE, Cynde, R.N. Vice President and Chief Nursing Officer, Baptist Hospital, Pensacola, FL, p. A142

GAMB, Pamela, Manager Human Resources, Aurora Psychiatric Hospital, Wauwatosa, WI, p. A718

GAMBLA, Kurt, D.O. Chief Medical Officer, Beaufort Memorial Hospital, Beaufort, SC, p. A562

GAMBLE, Brian, Chief Financial Officer, Karmanos Cancer Center, Detroit, MI, p. A322

GAMBLE, Kathleen, Fiscal Officer, Patton State Hospital, Patton, CA, p. A82

GAMBLE, Robert, M.D. Chief of Staff, Terrebonne General Medical Center, Houma, LA, p. A278

GAMBOA, Eileen, Director Human Resources, OakBend Medical Center, Richmond, TX, p. A643

GAMET, Nicki, R.N
Vice President and Chief Nursing Officer, Mercy Hospital Aurora, Aurora, MO, p. A367
Chief Nursing Officer, Mercy Hospital Cassville, Cassville, MO, p. A369

GAMEZ, Kriss
Director Human Resources, Baylor Regional Medical Center at Plano, Plano, TX, p. A641
Director Human Resources, The Heart Hospital Baylor Plano, Plano, TX, p. A642

GAMINO, Randall, Director Perot Site, St. Joseph's Medical Center, Stockton, CA, p. A95

GAMMAGE, Gloria, Chief Nursing Officer, Howard University Hospital, Washington, DC, p. A121

GAMMIERE, Thomas A., Chief Executive, Senior Vice President, Scripps Mercy Hospital, San Diego, CA, p. A89

GANDHI, Tejas, Ph.D. Chief Operating Officer, Baystate Medical Center, Springfield, MA, p. A314

GANDY, Galina, Vice President Information Technology, Columbia Memorial Hospital, Astoria, OR, p. A524

GANDY, Patrick W., CPA, Executive Vice President and Chief Executive Officer, Lafayette General Medical Center, Lafayette, LA, p. A280

GANGULY, Devabrata, M.D. Medical Director, CHRISTUS Continuing Care dba Dubuis Hospital of Paris, Paris, TX, p. A640

GANGULY, Indranil, Vice President and Chief Information Officer, JFK Medical Center, Edison, NJ, p. A416

GANLEY, Evan, Manager Human Resources, LifeCare Hospitals of Chester County, West Chester, PA, p. A557

GANN, Lisa, R.N. Chief Nursing Officer, TriStar Hendersonville Medical Center, Hendersonville, TN, p. A584

GANN, Michele, Vice President Patient Services, Mercy Hospital Berryville, Berryville, AR, p. A43

GANNON, Ronnie, Director Information Services, TriStar Southern Hills Medical Center, Nashville, TN, p. A591

GANS, Bruce M., M.D. Executive Vice President and Chief Medical Officer, Kessler Institute for Rehabilitation, West Orange, NJ, p. A425

GANSEMER, Sheila, R.N
Vice President Patient Care Services and Chief Nursing Officer, Midwest Orthopedic Specialty Hospital, Franklin, WI, p. A705
Vice President Patient Care Services and Chief Nursing Officer, Wheaton Franciscan Healthcare – Franklin, Franklin, WI, p. A706

GANSKE, Jary, Chief Financial Officer, Methodist Mansfield Medical Center, Mansfield, TX, p. A635

GANTNER, John, Executive Vice President Finance and Partner Company Operations, Jersey Shore University Medical Center, Neptune, NJ, p. A420

GANTZER, Ann M., Ph.D. Vice President Patient Services and Chief Nursing Officer, SwedishAmerican – A Division of UW Health, Rockford, IL, p. A202

GAPSTUR, Roxanna L., Ph.D. Chief Nursing Officer, Park Nicollet Methodist Hospital, Saint Louis Park, MN, p. A350

GARAY, Kenneth, M.D. Chief Medical Officer, Jersey City Medical Center, Jersey City, NJ, p. A418

GARBANZOS, Del, Director Human Resources, Delano Regional Medical Center, Delano, CA, p. A60

GARBARINO, James, Chief Financial Officer, Clay County Medical Center, Clay Center, KS, p. A241

GARBER, Mary, Vice President Finance, Mercy Hospital Ada, Ada, OK, p. A508

GARCIA, Andrew T., Acting Associate Director, Central Texas Veterans Health Care System, Temple, TX, p. A651

GARCIA, Ara, Manager Human Resources, Milwaukee County Behavioral Health Division, Milwaukee, WI, p. A711

GARCIA, Aymette, Manager Human Resources, Wilma N. Vazquez Medical Center, Vega Baja, PR, p. A730

GARCIA, Danette, Director Human Resources, HEALTHSOUTH Valley of the Sun Rehabilitation Hospital, Glendale, AZ, p. A33

GARCIA, Estevan, M.D. Chief Medical Officer, Brookdale Hospital Medical Center, New York, NY, p. A444

GARCIA, Evangeline, M.D. Clinical Director, Eastern Shore Hospital Center, Cambridge, MD, p. A299

GARCIA, Georgina R., R.N., Executive Director, Kaiser Permanente West Los Angeles Medical Center, Los Angeles, CA, p. A72

GARCIA, Gerard, Chief Human Resource Officer, University Hospital, Newark, NJ, p. A421

GARCIA, Idalia, Chief Human Resources Officer, Hospital de Psiquiatria, San Juan, PR, p. A729

GARCIA, Iris, Director, Information Services, Jerome Golden Center for Behavioral Health, Inc., West Palm Beach, FL, p. A149

GARCIA, Irma, Job Coordinator, Rio Grande State Center/South Texas Health Care System, Harlingen, TX, p. A622

GARCIA, Jacob, Chief Information Officer, Little Colorado Medical Center, Winslow, AZ, p. A41

GARCIA, Jannina, Director of Human Resources, Florida Hospital Fish Memorial, Orange City, FL, p. A140

GARCIA, Joanne, Chief Operating Officer, Kindred Chicago–Central Hospital, Chicago, IL, p. A184

GARCIA, Joannie, CPA Director Finance, Hospital Perea, Mayaguez, PR, p. A728

GARCIA, Jose, M.D. Chief Medical Staff, Dundy County Hospital, Benkelman, NE, p. A394

GARCIA, Jose, Chief Human Resources Officer, San Juan City Hospital, San Juan, PR, p. A730

GARCIA, Kathleen, Controller, St. John's Episcopal Hospital–South Shore,, NY, p. A450

GARCIA, Jr., Luis Mario, Director Human Resources, Houston Methodist Sugar Land Hospital, Sugar Land, TX, p. A650

GARCIA, Margaret, Manager Human Resources, Baylor Medical Center at Frisco, Frisco, TX, p. A619

GARCIA, Michael A., Vice President and Chief Information Officer, Jackson Health System, Miami, FL, p. A136

GARCIA, Orlando, M.D. Chief Medical Officer, Hialeah Hospital, Hialeah, FL, p. A130

GARCIA, Paul, Chief of Staff, Vidant Beaufort Hospital, Washington, NC, p. A475

GARCIA, Robert W., M.D. Chief Medical Officer, Iraan General Hospital, Iraan, TX, p. A628

GARCIA, Roland
Senior Vice President and Chief Information Officer, Baptist Medical Center Beaches, Jacksonville Beach, FL, p. A132
Senior Vice President and Chief Information Officer, Baptist Medical Center Jacksonville, Jacksonville, FL, p. A131

GARCIA, Sharon, Human Resources Representative, Medina Regional Hospital, Hondo, TX, p. A623

GARCIA, Shawn, Manager Human Resources, Memorial Hospital Los Banos, Los Banos, CA, p. A75

GARCIA, Sylvia, Chief Accounting Officer, South Texas Spine and Surgical Hospital, San Antonio, TX, p. A647

GARCIA, Tracy, MS Chief Nursing Officer, Cheyenne Regional Medical Center, Cheyenne, WY, p. A721

GARD, Emily, Chief Clinical Officer, Kindred Hospital–San Francisco Bay Area, San Leandro, CA, p. A92

GARDINER, Greg, Chief Clinical Officer, Ashley Regional Medical Center, Vernal, UT, p. A664

GARDINER, Karen, Human Resources Director, Bayfront Health Port Charlotte, Port Charlotte, FL, p. A143

GARDNER, Carla, Director of Nursing, Munson Healthcare Grayling Hospital, Grayling, MI, p. A325

GARDNER, Debra C., MSN, Administrator, Ten Lakes Center, Dennison, OH, p. A493

GARDNER, Greg, Senior Vice President and Chief Financial Officer, Indian River Medical Center, Vero Beach, FL, p. A149

GARDNER, Jacque, Administrative Assistant, Clinic Manager, Co–Chief Financial Officer and Chief Human Resources, McCone County Health Center, Circle, MT, p. A386

GARDNER, James D., M.D. Vice President and Chief Medical Officer, Waukesha Memorial Hospital, Waukesha, WI, p. A718

GARDNER, Joel, D.O. Chief Medical Officer, Brigham City Community Hospital, Brigham City, UT, p. A659

GARDNER, Kristin Day, Chief Nursing Officer, Berger Health System, Circleville, OH, p. A488

GARDNER, Michelle, M.D. Clinical Director, Dorothea Dix Psychiatric Center, Bangor, ME, p. A291

GARDNER, Nancy, Chief Nursing Officer, I–70 Community Hospital, Sweet Springs, MO, p. A383

GARDNER, Patrick, M.D. Associate Vice President, Medical Affairs, St. Joseph's Hospital, St. Joseph's Hospital, West Bend, WI, p. A719

GARDNER, Robb, Chief Executive Officer, Henry County Health Center, Mount Pleasant, IA, p. A234

GARDNER, Sharon, Manager Information Systems, SSM Health St. Joseph Hospital – Lake Saint Louis, Lake Saint Louis, MO, p. A375

GARDNER, William, Chief Clinical Officer, Bartlett Regional Hospital, Juneau, AK, p. A29

GARDNER, Zoe, Manager Human Resources, Sharp Chula Vista Medical Center, Chula Vista, CA, p. A58

GARES, Donna, MSN, Chief Executive Officer, Select Specialty Hospital–Wilmington, Wilmington, DE, p. A120

GARG, Rajesh K., JD, President and Chief Executive Officer, Cancer Treatment Centers of America, Schaumburg, IL, p. B25

GARISON, Jerri, R.N., President, Baylor Regional Medical Center at Plano, Plano, TX, p. A641

GARKO, Michael, Chief Financial Officer, St. Vincent Medical Center, Los Angeles, CA, p. A74

GARLETS, Mary, Director Human Resources, Mayo Clinic Health System in Cannon Falls, Cannon Falls, MN, p. A340

GARMAN, Denise M., Director Human Resources, WellSpan Good Samaritan Hospital, Lebanon, PA, p. A543

GARMAN, Mary E., MS Chief Operating Officer, Good Samaritan Hospital, Dayton, OH, p. A492

GARMAN, Michael, Chief Financial Officer, Avera St. Anthony's Hospital, O'Neill, NE, p. A399

GARMAN, Patrick H., Commander, Evans U. S. Army Community Hospital, Fort Carson, CO, p. A105

GARNAS, David, Chief Executive Officer, Sedgwick County Health Center, Julesburg, CO, p. A107

GARNER, Douglas, Vice President, Thomas Hospital, Fairhope, AL, p. A20

GARNER, Ethnee, R.N. Vice President Patient Care Services, Memorial Hospital, North Conway, NH, p. A413

GARNETT, Mark, M.D. Chief of Staff, Hansford Hospital, Spearman, TX, p. A649

GAROFOLA, Aaron, Chief Executive Officer, Bluffton Regional Medical Center, Bluffton, IN, p. A207

GARONE, Marlene, M.D. Vice President Medical Affairs and Medical Director, Woman's Christian Association Hospital, Jamestown, NY, p. A441

GARRAMONE, Kathy
Chief Financial Officer, NYC Health + Hospitals / Jacobi,, NY, p. A448
Chief Financial Officer, NYC Health + Hospitals / North Central Bronx,, NY, p. A449

GARRARD, Michael Eric, FACHE, Chief Executive Officer, Emory Rehabilitation Hospital, Atlanta, GA, p. A152

GARRED, Sr., John, M.D. Chief Medical Officer, Burgess Health Center, Onawa, IA, p. A235

GARREN–OSTER, Cynthia, Human Resource Manager, South Coast Global Medical Center, Santa Ana, CA, p. A92

GARRETT, Alan H., President and Chief Executive Officer, St. Mary Medical Center, Apple Valley, CA, p. A55

GARRETT, Courtney, CPA Senior Vice President, Chief Financial Officer, Children's Hospital, New Orleans, LA, p. A284

GARRETT, Dana M., R.N. Nursing Services Administrator, Taylor Regional Hospital, Campbellsville, KY, p. A258

GARRETT, David B.
Chief Information Officer, Novant Health Forsyth Medical Center, Winston–Salem, NC, p. A476
Chief Information Officer, Novant Health Matthews Medical Center, Matthews, NC, p. A469
Senior Vice President Information Technology, Novant Health Presbyterian Medical Center, Charlotte, NC, p. A463

GARRETT, Josh, Chief of Staff, Habersham Medical Center, Demorest, GA, p. A158

GARRETT, Kevin C., M.D
Chief Medical Officer, Bethesda Hospital, Saint Paul, MN, p. A350
Chief Medical Officer, St. John's Hospital, Maplewood, MN, p. A346
Chief Medical Officer, St. Joseph's Hospital, Saint Paul, MN, p. A351
Chief Medical Officer, Woodwinds Health Campus, Woodbury, MN, p. A353

GARRETT, Mark, Chief Information Officer, Shriners Hospitals for Children–Los Angeles, Los Angeles, CA, p. A74

GARRETT, Matthew, Director Information Systems, Flowers Hospital, Dothan, AL, p. A19

GARRETT, Nancy, Chief Analytics and Information Technology Officer, Hennepin County Medical Center, Minneapolis, MN, p. A346

GARRETT, Robert C., FACHE, Co–Chief Executive Officer, Hackensack Meridian Health, Edison, NJ, p. B59

GARRETT, Scott, Director of IS, Ottumwa Regional Health Center, Ottumwa, IA, p. A236

GARRETT, Walter J., Chief Executive Officer, Welch Community Hospital, Welch, WV, p. A701

GARRICK, Renee, M.D. Executive Medical Director, Westchester Medical Center, Valhalla, NY, p. A458

GARRIDO, Mary, Vice President and Regional Chief Information Officer, Valley Baptist Medical Center–Brownsville, Brownsville, TX, p. A604

GARRIOTT, Edie, Director Human Resources, Community Hospital South, Indianapolis, IN, p. A213

GARRISON, Eric L., Chief Information Officer, Laughlin Memorial Hospital, Greeneville, TN, p. A583

GARRISON, Tina, Vice President Operations, SSM DePaul Health Center, Bridgeton, MO, p. A368

GARRISON, Wes, St. Luke's Sugar Land Hospital, Sugar Land, TX, p. A650

GARRITY, Elizabeth, Director Human Resources, Meadowlands Hospital Medical Center, Secaucus, NJ, p. A423

GARRITY, Nerissa, Chief Financial Officer, Kula Hospital, Kula, HI, p. A172

GARROW, Dina, Chief Nursing Officer and Chief Operating Officer, Kindred Hospital–Baldwin Park, Baldwin Park, CA, p. A56

GARSA, Arebi, Interim Chief Financial Officer, North Valley Hospital, Whitefish, MT, p. A391

GARTLAND, Bryce D., M.D., Chief Executive Officer, Emory University Hospital, atlanta, GA, p. A152

GARTMAN, Kathy Degenstein, Chief Nursing Officer, Medical Center of South Arkansas, El Dorado, AR, p. A45

GARTNER, Katie, Director Health Information Management, CHI Health Good Samaritan, Kearney, NE, p. A397

GARTON, Debra, R.N. Chief Nursing Officer, OSS Orthopaedic Hospital, York, PA, p. A559

GARVEY, Heather, Chief Financial Officer, Raulerson Hospital, Okeechobee, FL, p. A140

GARVEY, James
Administrator, Essentia Health Duluth, Duluth, MN, p. A341
Executive Vice President, Operations and Administrator, Essentia Health St. Mary's Medical Center, Duluth, MN, p. A342

GARVEY, Rita, Chief Nursing Officer, Lawrence County Memorial Hospital, Lawrenceville, IL, p. A195

GARVEY, Sheila, Vice President Human Resources, Flushing Hospital Medical Center,, NY, p. A444

GARVEY, Thomas J., Senior Vice President Operations and Chief Financial Officer, Swedish Covenant Hospital, Chicago, IL, p. A187

GARVIN, Jan, Vice President Human Resources, Bryan Medical Center, Lincoln, NE, p. A397

GARY, Al, COO, Simpson General Hospital, Mendenhall, MS, p. A362

GARZA, Art, Chief Executive Officer, Valley Regional Medical Center, Brownsville, TX, p. A604

GARZA, Ismelda, Director Information Systems, Comanche County Medical Center, Comanche, TX, p. A607

GARZA, Jennifer, Chief Executive Officer, South Texas Health System, Edinburg, TX, p. A614

GARZA, Laura, Director Human Resources, Pine Valley Specialty Hospital, Houston, TX, p. A626

GARZA, Leo, Chief Executive Officer, South Texas Rehabilitation Hospital, Brownsville, TX, p. A603

GARZA, Oscar, M.D. Chief Medical Staff, Frio Regional Hospital, Pearsall, TX, p. A640

GARZA, Ruben, Interim Chief Executive Officer, Riverview Regional Medical Center, Gadsden, AL, p. A20

GARZA, Teri, Director Health Information Services, Knapp Medical Center, Weslaco, TX, p. A657

GARZA, Tom, Director Fiscal and Support, Rio Grande State Center/South Texas Health Care System, Harlingen, TX, p. A622

GASBARRE, Christopher, D.O. Community Medical Director, Spearfish Regional Hospital, Spearfish, SD, p. A577

GASH, Deborah
Vice President and Chief Information Officer, Crittenton Children's Center, Kansas City, MO, p. A373
Chief Information Officer, Saint Luke's Hospital of Kansas City, Kansas City, MO, p. A374
Chief Information Officer, Saint Luke's South Hospital, Overland Park, KS, p. A251

GASKILL–HAMES, Michelle, R.N., Senior Vice President & Area Manager, Kaiser Permanente Redwood City Medical Center, Redwood City, CA, p. A85

GASKINS, Michael, Director Information Technology, Lincoln Community Hospital and Nursing Home, Hugo, CO, p. A107

GASKINS, Michael W., Interim President and Chief Executive Officer, Hanover Hospital, Hanover, PA, p. A539

GASPARD, H. J., Chief Executive Officer, HEALTHSOUTH Rehabilitation Hospital of Beaumont, Beaumont, TX, p. A601

GASQUE, James, M.D. Chief Hospital Services, U. S. Air Force Medical Center Keesler, Keesler AFB, MS, p. A360

GASSEN, Bill, Chief Human Resource Officer, Sanford Medical Center Fargo, Fargo, ND, p. A479

GASTON, Jan, Administrator, Jasper Memorial Hospital, Monticello, GA, p. A163

GASTON, Kathy, Chief Nursing Officer, Baptist Medical Center East, Montgomery, AL, p. A23

GASTON, Tammy, Chief Information Officer, Smith County Memorial Hospital, Smith Center, KS, p. A254

GATES, Rose, Director Human Resources, Hayward Area Memorial Hospital and Nursing Home, Hayward, WI, p. A707

GATES, Tracy, Vice President Operations and Chief Operating Officer, Cortland Regional Medical Center, Cortland, NY, p. A437

GATHERS, Mary
Manager Information Systems, American Fork Hospital, American Fork, UT, p. A659
Director Information Systems, McKay–Dee Hospital Center, Ogden, UT, p. A661
Director Information Systems, Utah Valley Regional Medical Center, Provo, UT, p. A662

GATHRIGHT, Travis, Chief Information and Corporate Compliance Officer, Magee Rehabilitation Hospital, Philadelphia, PA, p. A548

GATO, Carlos A.
Director of Human Resources, Atlantic Shores Hospital, Fort Lauderdale, FL, p. A128
Director of Human Resources, Fort Lauderdale Hospital, Fort Lauderdale, FL, p. A128

GATRELL, Kristi, Chief Executive Officer, Big Horn County Memorial Hospital, Hardin, MT, p. A388

GATTMAN, Gregory B., Acute Care Executive, Palmetto Health Baptist, Columbia, SC, p. A564

GATTO, Tony, Director Management Information Systems, Flushing Hospital Medical Center,, NY, p. A444

GAU, Kimberley A., FACHE, Chief Executive Officer, Guttenberg Municipal Hospital, Guttenberg, IA, p. A231

GAUBERT, Steve C., Chief Financial Officer, Thibodaux Regional Medical Center, Thibodaux, LA, p. A289

GAUER, Natalie, Administrator, Milbank Area Hospital Avera, Milbank, SD, p. A574

GAUGHAN, Thomas, M.D. Chief Medical Officer, Kingman Regional Medical Center, Kingman, AZ, p. A33

GAUL, Mike, Director Information Technology, Golden Valley Memorial Healthcare, Clinton, MO, p. A369

GAULKE, Becky, Chief Nursing Officer, Ely–Bloomenson Community Hospital, Ely, MN, p. A342

GAULT, Cindy L., Chief Financial Officer, Union Medical Center, Union, SC, p. A570

GAURON, Patricia, Director Human Resources, Holy Family Hospital, Methuen, MA, p. A312

GAUTHIER, Bonnie B., President and Chief Executive Officer, The Hospital at Hebrew Health Care, West Hartford, CT, p. A118

GAUTHIER, Paul, Chief Information Resources Management, Veterans Affairs Montana Health Care System, Fort Harrison, MT, p. A387

GAUTNEY, Steven, Chief Executive Officer, Crisp Regional Hospital, Cordele, GA, p. A157

GAVALCHIK, Stephen M., FACHE, Community Chief Executive Officer, Morgan County ARH Hospital, West Liberty, KY, p. A270

GAVENS, Mark R., Executive Vice President Health System Hospital Operations and Chief Operating Officer of Cedars–Sinai Medical Center, Cedars–Sinai Medical Center, Los Angeles, CA, p. A70

GAVIN, Andrea, M.D. Chief Medical officer, Aurora Sheboygan Memorial Medical Center, Sheboygan, WI, p. A715

GAVIN, Donald, Chief Financial Officer, Southern Tennessee Regional Health System–Pulaski, Pulaski, TN, p. A592

GAVIN, Patrick J., President, Crozer–Chester Medical Center, Upland, PA, p. A556

GAVIN, Patrick J., President and Chief Executive Officer, Crozer–Keystone Health System, Springfield, PA, p. B43

GAVIN, Tammy, Chief Clinical Officer, White River Medical Center, Batesville, AR, p. A43

GAVIN, Todd, Chief Medical Officer, Madelia Community Hospital, Madelia, MN, p. A345

GAVINO, Rey, M.D. Chief of Staff, RMC Jacksonville, Jacksonville, AL, p. A22

GAVIS, Patricia, Chief Financial Officer, Ellenville Regional Hospital, Ellenville, NY, p. A438

GAVORA, George, Director Program Evaluation, Kingsboro Psychiatric Center,, NY, p. A445

GAVULIC, Melany, President & Chief Executive Officer, Hurley Medical Center, Flint, MI, p. A323

GAWALUCK, David
Vice President and Chief Information Officer, Excela Frick Hospital, Mount Pleasant, PA, p. A545
Vice President and Chief Information Officer, Excela Health Westmoreland Hospital, Greensburg, PA, p. A539
Vice President and Chief Information Officer, Excela Latrobe Area Hospital, Latrobe, PA, p. A542

GAWITH, Marlene, Director of Nursing, Ottawa County Health Center, Minneapolis, KS, p. A249

GAWLER, William, Chief Information Officer, Chillicothe Veterans Affairs Medical Center, Chillicothe, OH, p. A487

GAWNE, Bernard B., M.D. Vice President and Chief Medical Officer, Christ Hospital, Cincinnati, OH, p. A487

GAY, Christophe, M.D. Chief of Staff, Bellville St. Joseph Health Center, Bellville, TX, p. A602

GAY, Don, Director Human Resources, West Hills Hospital, Reno, NV, p. A408

GAY, Kristi
Chief Financial Officer, CHI St. Luke's Health Memorial Lufkin, Lufkin, TX, p. A634
Chief Financial Officer, CHI St. Luke's Health Memorial San Augustine, San Augustine, TX, p. A647

GAY, Michael, Chief Operating Officer, Habersham Medical Center, Demorest, GA, p. A158

GAY, Perry, President and Chief Executive Officer, Logansport Memorial Hospital, Logansport, IN, p. A217

GAY, Vickie, Chief Executive Officer, Montgomery General Hospital, Montgomery, WV, p. A698

GAYLER, Lisa, Director Human Resources, Kindred Hospital Colorado Springs, Colorado Springs, CO, p. A102

GAYLOR, Rosanne, M.D., Acting Executive Director, South Beach Psychiatric Center,, NY, p. A449

GAYNE, William, Chief Financial Officer, MedStar Washington Hospital Center, Washington, DC, p. A122

GAYNOR, Sheila, Director Human Resources, Perry County Memorial Hospital, Tell City, IN, p. A222

GAYTKO, Caren, Chief Nursing Officer, Regency Hospital of Minneapolis, Golden Valley, MN, p. A343

GAZAWAY, William, Information Technology Security Officer, AllianceHealth Ponca City, Ponca City, OK, p. A518

GAZECKI, Cindy, Senior Vice President, Hospital Operations, Seattle Children's Hospital, Seattle, WA, p. A689

GEARHARD, Cynthia, Chief Nursing Officer, St. Luke's Regional Medical Center, Boise, ID, p. A175

GEARHART, Danielle, Chief Executive Officer, Cooper County Memorial Hospital, Boonville, MO, p. A368

GEARY, David S., Chief Financial Officer, Cache Valley Hospital, North Logan, UT, p. A661

GEARY, Herb J.
Vice President Patient Care Services and Chief Nursing Officer, Santa Barbara Cottage Hospital, Santa Barbara, CA, p. A93
Chief Nursing Officer, Santa Ynez Valley Cottage Hospital, Solvang, CA, p. A94

GEBHARD, Scott, Executive VP and Chief Operating Officer, JFK Medical Center, Edison, NJ, p. A416

GEBHART, Cheryl
Director Human Resources Providence Health Plan and Providence Medical Group, Providence Newberg Medical Center, Newberg, OR, p. A528
Chief Human Resources Officer, Tuality Healthcare, Hillsboro, OR, p. A526

GEBHART Jr., Jim, FACHE, President, Mercy Hospital Oklahoma City, Oklahoma City, OK, p. A516

GEBHART, Ronald J., M.D. Chief of Staff, Veterans Affairs Salt Lake City Health Care System, Salt Lake City, UT, p. A664

GEDDINGS, Toni, Director Human Resources, Cullman Regional Medical Center, Cullman, AL, p. A18

GEDIES, Lucille, Chief Financial Officer, Mildred Mitchell–Bateman Hospital, Huntington, WV, p. A697

GEE, Kyle
Chief Financial Officer, Beartooth Billings Clinic, Red Lodge, MT, p. A390
Chief Financial Officer, Pioneer Medical Center, Big Timber, MT, p. A385
Regional Vice President Financial Operations, Roundup Memorial Healthcare, Roundup, MT, p. A390

GEE, Roland D., Interim Chief Executive Officer, Adams County Regional Medical Center, Seaman, OH, p. A502

GEE, Thomas H., Administrator, Henry County Medical Center, Paris, TN, p. A592

GEER, Nicholas, Chief Financial Officer, Dallas Medical Center, Dallas, TX, p. A609

GEERTS, Jodi, Chief Nursing Officer, Henry County Health Center, Mount Pleasant, IA, p. A234

GEESEY, Wanda, Director Human Resources, Pennsylvania Psychiatric Institute, Harrisburg, PA, p. A539

GEHLAUF, Dee Ann, Senior Vice President Business and Organization Development, Marietta Memorial Hospital, Marietta, OH, p. A498

GEHLHAUSEN, Sherri, Assistant Chief Financial Officer, Logansport Memorial Hospital, Logansport, IN, p. A217

GEHRIG, Ryan, President, Mercy Hospital Fort Smith, Fort Smith, AR, p. A46

GEHRING, Betty, Finance Director, Operations, ThedaCare Medical Center–New London, New London, WI, p. A712

GEHRING, Jay, Director Information Systems, Kingman Community Hospital, Kingman, KS, p. A246

GEHRING, Mikaela, Chief Operating Officer, Marengo Memorial Hospital, Marengo, IA, p. A234

GEHRING, Samuel, M.D. Chief of Staff, Fleming County Hospital, Flemingsburg, KY, p. A259

GEHRING, Terri, Vice President Operations, McPherson Hospital, McPherson, KS, p. A249

GEIER, Joyce, Director Nursing, Girard Medical Center, Girard, KS, p. A243

GEIER, Kathy, Director of Nursing, Chase County Community Hospital, Imperial, NE, p. A397

GEIGER, Deb, Executive Director of Acute Care, Harbor Beach Community Hospital, Harbor Beach, MI, p. A326

GEIGER, Judy, R.N. Chief Nursing Officer, Primary Children's Hospital, Salt Lake City, UT, p. A663

GEIGER, Ralph, M.D. Chief of Staff, Sebastian River Medical Center, Sebastian, FL, p. A145

GEIGLE, Joseph, Director Human Resources, Fort Hamilton Hospital, Hamilton, OH, p. A496

GEIL, Kristie A., VP, Chief Nursing Officer, CGH Medical Center, Sterling, IL, p. A204

GEISLER, Linda W., R.N. Vice President Patient Services, CentraState Healthcare System, Freehold, NJ, p. A417

GEIST, Jim, Chief Executive Officer, Capital Medical Center, Olympia, WA, p. A687

GEIST, Tammy, Chief Financial Officer, Novant Health Charlotte Orthopaedic Hospital, Charlotte, NC, p. A462

GEITZ, Cheri, Director Human Resources, Hansen Family Hospital, Iowa Falls, IA, p. A233

GEITZ, James, M.D. Chief of Staff, Newman Regional Health, Emporia, KS, p. A242

GEIVER, Betsy, Chief Human Resources Officer, Sioux Falls Veterans Affairs Health Care System, Sioux Falls, SD, p. A576

GELDERS, Albert, M.D. Chief of Staff, Oak Valley Hospital District, Oakdale, CA, p. A80

GELDHOF, Jay
Director Information Systems, Greater El Monte Community Hospital, South El Monte, CA, p. A95
Director Information Systems, Whittier Hospital Medical Center, Whittier, CA, p. A100

GELFAND, Andrew, M.D. Medical Director, Our Children's House, Dallas, TX, p. A611

GELL, Michael, Director Human Resources, Boys Town National Research Hospital, Omaha, NE, p. A399

GELLER, Harold S., Chief Executive Officer, CHI St. Anthony Hospital, Pendleton, OR, p. A528

GELLER, Mark, M.D., President and Chief Executive Officer, Nyack Hospital, Nyack, NY, p. A451

GELLER, Robert D., M.D. Vice President Medical Affairs, FHN Memorial Hospital, Freeport, IL, p. A190

GELLER, Warren, President and Chief Executive Officer, Englewood Hospital and Medical Center, Englewood, NJ, p. A417

GEMBOL, Leslie, MSN Chief Nursing Officer, Scott & White Hospital at Round Rock, Round Rock, TX, p. A644

GEMME, Donna T., R.N. Chief Nursing Officer Vice President Patient Care Services, MetroWest Medical Center, Framingham, MA, p. A310

GENDER, Aloma, MSN, Administrator and Chief Nursing Officer, CHRISTUS St. Michael Rehabilitation Hospital, Texarkana, TX, p. A652

GENESIO, Sabina, Finance Officer for Institutes, Colorado Mental Health Institute at Fort Logan, Denver, CO, p. A103

GENEVRO, Thomas A., Vice President Human Resources, Butler Health System, Butler, PA, p. A534

GENGLER, Laraine, Chief Financial Officer, Lindsborg Community Hospital, Lindsborg, KS, p. A248

GENNA, Nick, Administrator, Treasure Valley Hospital, Boise, ID, p. A175

GENNARO, John, FACHE, Director, Erie Veterans Affairs Medical Center, Erie, PA, p. A538

GENOVESE, Vincent P., M.D. President Medical Staff, Owensboro Health Muhlenberg Community Hospital, Greenville, KY, p. A261

GENSERT, Kurt, R.N. Vice President Operations, Platte Valley Medical Center, Brighton, CO, p. A102

GENTILE, John, M.D
Vice President Medical Affairs, Alta Bates Summit Medical Center, Berkeley, CA, p. A56
Vice President Medical Affairs, Alta Bates Summit Medical Center – Summit Campus, Oakland, CA, p. A80

GENTILE, Serge, Director Human Resources, Belmont Community Hospital, Bellaire, OH, p. A484

GENTNER, Rocky, Chief Financial Officer, Newport Bay Hospital, Newport Beach, CA, p. A79

GENTRY, Cheryl G.
Chief Executive Officer, Regency Hospital of Northwest Indiana, East Chicago, IN, p. A209
Interim Chief Executive Officer, Select Specialty Hospital Cleveland–Gateway, Cleveland, OH, p. A489

GENTRY, Jeanine, Chief Executive Officer, Steele Memorial Medical Center, Salmon, ID, p. A178

GENTRY, Jennifer, R.N. Chief Nursing Officer, CHRISTUS Spohn Hospital Corpus Christi Memorial, Corpus Christi, TX, p. A607

GENTRY, Kristen, Chief Operating Officer, Venice Regional Bayfront Health, Venice, FL, p. A149

GENTRY, Lee, FACHE, Vice President and Administrator, Baptist Health Rehabilitation Institute, Little Rock, AR, p. A49

GENTRY, Margie, Controller, T. J. Samson Community Hospital, Glasgow, KY, p. A261

GEOGHEGAN, Jeffrey, Chief Financial Officer, Unconn John Dempsey Hospital, Farmington, CT, p. A114

GEORGE, Alan E., Chief Executive Officer, Rockdale Medical Center, Conyers, GA, p. A157

GEORGE, Brad, Director Information Systems, Parkland Medical Center, Derry, NH, p. A410

GEORGE, Dana, Chief Human Resources Officer, Abrazo Central Campus, Phoenix, AZ, p. A35

GEORGE, Daniel M., Executive Vice President, Operations, Covenant Healthcare, Saginaw, MI, p. A333

GEORGE, Denise, R.N., President, Northern Dutchess Hospital, Rhinebeck, NY, p. A453

GEORGE, Gary, Senior Vice President Human Resources, Mercy St. Vincent Medical Center, Toledo, OH, p. A504

GEORGE, P. A., M.D. Chief of Staff, Madison Medical Center, Fredericktown, MO, p. A371

GEORGE, Patsy, R.N. Vice President and Chief Nursing Officer, Ohio Valley Medical Center, Wheeling, WV, p. A701

GEORGE, Saju, Chief Executive Officer, Garden City Hospital, Garden City, MI, p. A324

GEORGE, Shayne, Chief Executive Officer, Regional Medical Center Bayonet Point, Hudson, FL, p. A131

GEORGE, Susan, R.N. Associate Director Patient Care Services, Martinsburg Veterans Affairs Medical Center, Martinsburg, WV, p. A698

GEORGE, Tracy L., Chief Financial Officer, St. James Parish Hospital, Lutcher, LA, p. A282

GEORGE, William, M.D. Chief of Staff, Beartooth Billings Clinic, Red Lodge, MT, p. A390

GEORGES, Angelo, M.D. President Medical and Dental Staff, Wheeling Hospital, Wheeling, WV, p. A701

GEPFORD, John, Director Information Systems, EvergreenHealth Monroe, Monroe, WA, p. A686

GERACI, Jeff, Administrator, Quitman County Hospital, Marks, MS, p. A361

GERBER, Allen, M.D. Chief of Staff, Baptist Health Medical Center–Hot Spring County, Malvern, AR, p. A49

GERBER, Andrew, Ph.D., Medical Director and Chief Executive Officer, Austen Riggs Center, Stockbridge, MA, p. A315

GERBER, Greg, M.D. Chief Medical Officer, Aurora Lakeland Medical Center, Elkhorn, WI, p. A705

GERDES, Isaac, Chief Executive Officer, Sanford Webster Medical Center, Webster, SD, p. A577

GERDTS, Elizabeth, Chief Nursing Officer, NYC Health + Hospitals / North Central Bronx,, NY, p. A449

GERE, Zsaber, Chief Human Resource Officer, Banner Behavioral Health Hospital – Scottsdale, Scottsdale, AZ, p. A38

GERETY, Meghan, M.D. Chief of Staff, New Mexico Veterans Affairs Health Care System – Raymond G. Murphy Medical Center, Albuquerque, NM, p. A428

GERHART, Paul, Chief Financial Officer, Sanford Canton–Inwood Medical Center, Canton, SD, p. A572

GERIG, Stacey L., Chief Executive Officer, Odessa Regional Medical Center, Odessa, TX, p. A639

GERING, Paul, M.D. Vice President Medical Affairs, Saint Alphonsus Medical Center – Ontario, Ontario, OR, p. A528

GERKE, Daniel, Chief Nursing Officer, Wright Patterson Medical Center, Wright–Patterson AFB, OH, p. A506

GERKE, Sarah, Manager Human Resources, Dr. John Warner Hospital, Clinton, IL, p. A187

GERLACH, Carl, Chief Financial Officer, Curry General Hospital, Gold Beach, OR, p. A526

GERLACH, Matthew S.

  Chief Operating Officer, Children's Hospital of Orange County, Orange, CA, p. A81

  Chief Operating Officer, CHOC Children's at Mission Hospital, Mission Viejo, CA, p. A76

GERMANY, Alan

  Chief Executive Officer and Chief Restructuring Officer, Southern Inyo Healthcare District, Lone Pine, CA, p. A69

  Interim Chief Executive Officer, Tulare Regional Medical Center, Tulare, CA, p. A97

GERMUSKA, Natalie, MSN, Market Chief Executive Officer, Kindred Hospital–San Diego, San Diego, CA, p. A88

GERN, Sharon, R.N. Chief Nursing Officer, Ivinson Memorial Hospital, Laramie, WY, p. A722

GERNDT, Angie, Human Resources Manager, Central Community Hospital, Elkader, IA, p. A230

GERNHART, Diana, Senior Vice President and Hospital Chief Financial Officer, OHSU Hospital, Portland, OR, p. A529

GERRIOR, Marilyn, R.N. Chief Nursing Executive, Saint Louise Regional Hospital, Gilroy, CA, p. A64

GERRITS, Brad, Director Information Systems, Lakeview Medical Center, Rice Lake, WI, p. A715

GERSON, Elaine, Chief Clinical Officer and General Counsel, Aspen Valley Hospital District, Aspen, CO, p. A101

GERSTENBERGER, Linda

  Vice President Human Resources, St. Rose Dominican Hospitals – San Martin Campus, Las Vegas, NV, p. A406

  Vice President Human Resources, St. Rose Dominican Hospitals – Siena Campus, Henderson, NV, p. A405

GERSTNER, Nancy, Manager Human Resources, Robert J. Dole Veterans Affairs Medical Center, Wichita, KS, p. A256

GERVELER, Patrick M., Vice President Finance and Chief Financial Officer, Blessing Hospital, Quincy, IL, p. A201

GESKERMANN, Tom G., Chief Executive Officer, Osceola Medical Center, Osceola, WI, p. A713

GESME, Barbara L., MSN Vice President Patient Care Services & Chief Nurse Executive, Bon Secours St. Francis Medical Center, Midlothian, VA, p. A673

GESSEL, Thomas, FACHE, President and Chief Executive Officer, Mercy Regional Medical Center, Durango, CO, p. A104

GESSLING, Heather, M.D. Chief Medical Officer, Moberly Regional Medical Center, Moberly, MO, p. A377

GESSNER, Christopher A., President, Children's Hospital of Pittsburgh of UPMC, Pittsburgh, PA, p. A550

GETMAN, Sylvia, President and Chief Executive Officer, Adirondack Medical Center, Saranac Lake, NY, p. A455

GETSAY, Timothy, Chief Information Officer, Vice President of Performance & Information Mgmt, Gillette Children's Specialty Healthcare, Saint Paul, MN, p. A350

GETTINGER, Thomas

  Executive Vice President and Chief Operating Officer, Mary Washington Hospital, Fredericksburg, VA, p. A670

  Executive Vice President and Chief Operating Officer, Stafford Hospital, Stafford, VA, p. A679

GETTINGS, Scott, M.D

  Senior Vice President and Chief Medical Officer, Health First Palm Bay Hospital, Palm Bay, FL, p. A141

  Senior Vice President and Chief Medical Officer, Health First Viera Hospital, Melbourne, FL, p. A135

GETTYS, Sky, Chief Financial Officer, Fairfield Medical Center, Lancaster, OH, p. A496

GETWOOD, Charles, Assistant Chief Executive Officer, Calcasieu Oaks Geriatric Psychiatric Hospital, Lake Charles, LA, p. A281

GETZ, Liz, Chief Information Officer, Aultman Hospital, Canton, OH, p. A486

GEUDER, Denise, Vice President Patient Care Service and Chief Nursing Officer, Southwestern Regional Medical Center, Tulsa, OK, p. A522

GEURTS, Chuck, Manager Management Information Services, Aurora BayCare Medical Center, Green Bay, WI, p. A706

GEWECKE, Tyler, Information Technology Technician, Fillmore County Hospital, Geneva, NE, p. A396

GFELLER, Michael, Director Information Systems, Medical Center of Plano, Plano, TX, p. A641

GHAEMMAGHAMI, Chris A., M.D. Chief Medical Officer, University of Virginia Medical Center, Charlottesville, VA, p. A668

GHAFFARI, Bahram, President, Delano Regional Medical Center, Delano, CA, p. A60

GHALI, Sara, Chief Financial Officer, Green Valley Hospital, Green Valley, AZ, p. A33

GHERINGHELLI, Thomas, Senior Vice President, Chief Financial Officer, New England Baptist Hospital, Boston, MA, p. A307

GHERKE, Sheila, Director Human Resources, Minnie Hamilton HealthCare Center, Grantsville, WV, p. A696

GHIDOTTI, Craig J., Vice President Human Resources, Lake Health, Concord Township, OH, p. A491

GHION, christopher, Vice President and Chief Information Officer, Adventist Healthcare Shady Grove Medical Center, Rockville, MD, p. A303

GHOSH, Avijit, M.D., Chief Executive Officer, University of Illinois Hospital & Health Sciences System, Chicago, IL, p. A187

GHOSH, Tarun, Chief Information Officer, Rideout Memorial Hospital, Marysville, CA, p. A76

GHULUM, Evelyn, Chief Financial Officer, Jellico Community Hospital, Jellico, TN, p. A585

GIAGUINTO, Shelly, Chief Financial Officer, Highland–Clarksburg Hospital, Clarksburg, WV, p. A695

GIAMPA, Patricia L., Chief Nursing Officer, SEARHC MT. Edgecumbe Hospital, Sitka, AK, p. A30

GIANCOLA, Louis R., President and Chief Executive Officer, South County Hospital, Wakefield, RI, p. A561

GIANELLI, Arthur A., M.P.H., President, Mount Sinai St. Luke's – Roosevelt, New York, NY, p. A446

GIANG, Vernon, M.D

  Chief Medical Executive, California Pacific Medical Center, San Francisco, CA, p. A90

  Chief Medical Executive, St. Luke's Hospital, San Francisco, CA, p. A90

GIANGARDELLA, Mike, Vice President Finance and Administration, Salem Regional Medical Center, Salem, OH, p. A502

GIANNONE, John, M.D. Chief Medical Officer, UHS Delaware Valley Hospital, Walton, NY, p. A458

GIANNOSA, Amy, Director Human Resources, Havenwyck Hospital, Auburn Hills, MI, p. A318

GIANNUZZI, Donna, R.N

  Chief Patient Care Officer, Gulf Coast Medical Center, Fort Myers, FL, p. A129

  Chief Nursing Officer, Lee Memorial Hospital, Fort Myers, FL, p. A129

GIANSANTE, Joseph, Vice President Human Resources, Ellis Hospital, Schenectady, NY, p. A455

GIARDINA, Deborah, Director Human Resources and Medical Staff Services, Rehabilitation Hospital of Fort Wayne, Fort Wayne, IN, p. A211

GIBB, Matthew, M.D. Executive Vice President and System Chief Medical Officer, Carle Foundation Hospital, Urbana, IL, p. A204

GIBB, Randall K., M.D. Chief Medical Officer, Billings Clinic, Billings, MT, p. A385

GIBBENS, Lori, Controller, HEALTHSOUTH Rehabilitation Hospital of Erie, Erie, PA, p. A538

GIBBERMAN, Val, M.D. Acting Chief of Staff, Hampton Veterans Affairs Medical Center, Hampton, VA, p. A671

GIBBES, Gregg, Chief Executive Officer, Covington County Hospital, Collins, MS, p. A357

GIBBONS, Barbara, Vice President Patient Care Services, St. Joseph Hospital, Bethpage, NY, p. A434

GIBBONS, David

  Executive Vice President and Chief Operating Officer, UPMC Hamot, Erie, PA, p. A538

  President, UPMC Northwest, Seneca, PA, p. A554

GIBBONS, H. Ray, FACHE, Chief Executive Officer, Saint Alphonsus Medical Center – Baker City, Baker City, OR, p. A524

GIBBONS, Jason, Chief Financial Officer, Minidoka Memorial Hospital, Rupert, ID, p. A178

GIBBS, Christopher Michael, Director Information Management Systems, Taylor Regional Hospital, Campbellsville, KY, p. A258

GIBBS, Jeffrey S., M.D. Regional Vice President Medical Affairs, Skagit Regional Health, Mount Vernon, WA, p. A686

GIBBS, Kenneth, President and Chief Executive Officer, Maimonides Medical Center,, NY, p. A445

GIBBS, Lisa, Vice President, Finance, Atrium Medical Center, Middletown, OH, p. A499

GIBBS, Tim, Director of Information Technology, Information Security Officer, Children's Hospital of Richmond at VCU–Brook Road Campus, Richmond, VA, p. A677

GIBBS, Vickie, Director Nursing, Phillips County Hospital, Phillipsburg, KS, p. A252

GIBBS–MCELVY, Shelana, M.D. Medical Director, HEALTHSOUTH Rehabilitation Hospital of Sewickley, Sewickley, PA, p. A554

GIBNEY, Thomas, Senior Vice President and Chief Financial Officer, St. Luke's Cornwall Hospital, Newburgh, NY, p. A450

GIBSON, Amy, Chief Executive Officer, Jackson Medical Center, Jackson, AL, p. A22

GIBSON, Armetria, Human Resources Generalist, Select Specialty Hospital Midtown Atlanta, Atlanta, GA, p. A152

GIBSON, Belinda D., R.N. Senior Vice President Patient Services, BSA Hospital, LLC, Amarillo, TX, p. A596

GIBSON, Connie, R.N. Director Human Resources, Mary Black Health System – Gaffney, Gaffney, SC, p. A566

GIBSON, Elizabeth, Director Human Resources, Mid–America Rehabilitation Hospital, Shawnee Mission, KS, p. A253

GIBSON, J. Francis, Administrator and Chief Executive Officer, Orem Community Hospital, Orem, UT, p. A661

GIBSON, Jack, Administrator, Noland Hospital Tuscaloosa, Tuscaloosa, AL, p. A26

GIBSON, Joel, Vice President Human Resources, Henry Ford Macomb Hospitals, Clinton Township, MI, p. A320

GIBSON, Mary Helen, Director Human Resources, Floyd Valley Healthcare, Le Mars, IA, p. A233

GIBSON, Megan, Nurse Manager, River Bend Hospital, West Lafayette, IN, p. A223

GIBSON, Robert L., Director Employee Relations, OSF Saint Elizabeth Medical Center, Ottawa, IL, p. A199

GIBSON, Todd, Chief Financial Officer, Denton Regional Medical Center, Denton, TX, p. A612

GIBSON, Valerie, Chief Operating Officer, DMC Harper University Hospital, Detroit, MI, p. A322

GIBSON, William R., Chief Executive Officer, Lincoln Regional Center, Lincoln, NE, p. A398

GICCA, Ron, Chief Executive Officer, Wuesthoff Medical Center – Melbourne, Melbourne, FL, p. A136

GICZI, Mary Beth, Director Human Resources, HEALTHSOUTH Scottsdale Rehabilitation Hospital, Scottsdale, AZ, p. A38

GIDDINGS, Carleen, Information Technology System Leader, Scheurer Hospital, Pigeon, MI, p. A331

GIDDINGS, Claudia, R.N. Chief Nursing Officer, Our Community Hospital, Scotland Neck, NC, p. A473

GIDEON, Daniel L., FACHE, President, Methodist Hospital for Surgery, Addison, TX, p. A595

GIEGER, Julie

  Chief Financial Officer, Lackey Memorial Hospital, Forest, MS, p. A358

  Chief Financial Officer, Pioneer Community Hospital of Aberdeen, Aberdeen, MS, p. A355

  Chief Financial Officer, Pioneer Community Hospital of Patrick, Stuart, VA, p. A679

  Chief Financial Officer, Pioneer Community Hospital of Stokes, Danbury, NC, p. A463

GIER, Jennifer, Director Human Resources, Brynn Marr Hospital, Jacksonville, NC, p. A467

GIERTUGA, Garry, Site Manager Human Resources, Adventist La Grange Memorial Hospital, La Grange, IL, p. A194

GIESE, Kristine A., Chief Operating Officer, Providence Medical Center, Wayne, NE, p. A403

GIESING, Belva, Chief Nursing Officer, Crittenton Children's Center, Kansas City, MO, p. A373

GIETTER, Marci, Interim Executive Director, Shore Rehabilitation Institute, Brick, NJ, p. A414

GIFFORD, Ellen, Director Human Resources, AllianceHealth Deaconess, Oklahoma City, OK, p. A516

GIGLIOTTI, Vicki, Chief Clinical Officer, Moab Regional Hospital, Moab, UT, p. A660

GIJANTO, Charles, President and Chief Executive Officer, Oswego Hospital, Oswego, NY, p. A452

GIL, Julio, Manager Information Services, Hazel Hawkins Memorial Hospital, Hollister, CA, p. A66

GILBERT, Andrea F., FACHE, President, Bryn Mawr Hospital, Bryn Mawr, PA, p. A534

GILBERT, Cameron R., Ph.D., President and Chief Executive Officer, NeuroPsychiatric Hospitals, Mishawaka, IN, p. B94

GILBERT, Carla, Director Finance, Cedar County Memorial Hospital, El Dorado Springs, MO, p. A370

GILBERT, Christy

  Interim Chief Executive Officer, Doctors NeuroPsychiatric Hospital and Research Institute, Bremen, IN, p. A207

  Chief Executive Officer, RiverCrest Specialty Hospital, Mishawaka, IN, p. A218

GILBERT, Jack, Vice President Finance and Support Services, Advocate Illinois Masonic Medical Center, Chicago, IL, p. A183

GILBERT, James B., Chief Financial Officer, Palms of Pasadena Hospital, Saint Petersburg, FL, p. A144

GILBERT, Kevin, R.N. Vice President, Confluence Health/Wenatchee Valley Hospital, Wenatchee, WA, p. A693

GILBERT, Kim, R.N. Chief Nursing Officer, Electra Memorial Hospital, Electra, TX, p. A616

GILBERT, Thomas, Director Information Technology Services, Lake Cumberland Regional Hospital, Somerset, KY, p. A269

GILBERT, Thomas D., FACHE,
Chief Executive Officer, Wadley Regional Medical Center, Texarkana, TX, p. A652
Chief Executive Officer, Wadley Regional Medical Center at Hope, Hope, AR, p. A47

GILBERT, Valarie, R.N. Chief Nursing Officer, Texas Health Harris Methodist Hospital Azle, Azle, TX, p. A600

GILBERT, William L., Hospital Director, Arrowhead Regional Medical Center, Colton, CA, p. A59

GILBERTSON, Gerry, FACHE, Administrator, CentraCare Health–Melrose, Melrose, MN, p. A346

GILCHRIST, Doug, Chief Operating Officer, Summit Healthcare Regional Medical Center, Show Low, AZ, p. A39

GILDON, Lisa
Group Financial Officer, Texas Health Presbyterian Hospital Allen, Allen, TX, p. A595
Vice President and Chief Financial Officer, Texas Health Presbyterian Hospital Plano, Plano, TX, p. A642

GILENE, Joseph, President, Jewish Hospital, Louisville, KY, p. A264

GILES, Charles, M.D. President Medical Staff, T.J. Health Columbia, Columbia, KY, p. A258

GILES, Jared, Chief Operating Officer, Southwest Healthcare System, Murrieta, CA, p. A78

GILES, Kent, Interim Chief Executive Officer, Livingston Hospital and Healthcare Services, Salem, KY, p. A269

GILES, Lori, Interim Chief Nursing Officer, Athens Regional Medical Center, Athens, GA, p. A151

GILES, Steve, Chief Information Officer, Hollywood Presbyterian Medical Center, Los Angeles, CA, p. A71

GILES, William, Chief Executive Officer, Gordon Memorial Hospital, Gordon, NE, p. A396

GILFILLAN, Richard J., M.D., President and Chief Executive Officer, Trinity Health, Livonia, MI, p. B136

GILG, Ronald, Assistant Vice President Talent, Eastern Regional Medical Center, Philadelphia, PA, p. A547

GILGEN, Steve, Chief Financial Officer, Murphy Medical Center, Murphy, NC, p. A470

GILJUM, Anthony, Chief Information Officer, Sheridan Veterans Affairs Medical Center, Sheridan, WY, p. A724

GILKEY, Edward, M.D. Vice President Medical Affairs, St. Luke's Hospital – Warren Campus, Phillipsburg, NJ, p. A422

GILL, Alexander, Chief Executive Officer, Kindred Hospital Kansas City, Kansas City, MO, p. A373

GILL, Mandeep, Chief Operating Officer, Memorial Hospital of Sweetwater County, Rock Springs, WY, p. A723

GILL, Margaret, President and Chief Executive Officer, Memorial Health, Savannah, GA, p. A166

GILL, Mark, Vice President Finance and Chief Financial Officer, Cape Regional Medical Center, Cape May Court House, NJ, p. A415

GILLAM, Sally A., R.N. Chief Nursing Officer, St. David's South Austin Medical Center, Austin, TX, p. A600

GILLARD, Austin M., Chief Executive Officer, Clay County Medical Center, Clay Center, KS, p. A241

GILLEN, Mark T., Director of Operations, Owatonna Hospital, Owatonna, MN, p. A348

GILLES, Ken
Chief Information Officer, Essentia Health Fargo, Fargo, ND, p. A478
Associate Chief Information Officer, Essentia Health St. Mary's – Detroit Lakes, Detroit Lakes, MN, p. A341

GILLESPIE, Anne, R.N. Associate Director Patient Care and Nursing Services, Veterans Affairs Loma Linda Healthcare System, Loma Linda, CA, p. A69

GILLESPIE, Bob, Chief Operating Officer, Connally Memorial Medical Center, Floresville, TX, p. A617

GILLESPIE, Curt, Chief Executive Officer, Mental Health Services for Clark and Madison Counties, Springfield, OH, p. A502

GILLESPIE, Karen, Director Human Resources, Anderson County Hospital, Garnett, KS, p. A243

GILLESPIE, Lisa, M.D. Chief Medical Officer, Rockdale Medical Center, Conyers, GA, p. A157

GILLESPIE, Richard, Chief Executive Officer, Jefferson County Hospital, Waurika, OK, p. A523

GILLESPIE, Thomas, Chief Information Officer, Fulton State Hospital, Fulton, MO, p. A371

GILLESPIE, Tim, Manager Information Systems, Richland Memorial Hospital, Olney, IL, p. A199

GILLESPIE, Tina
Chief Operating Officer, Harrison County Community Hospital, Bethany, MO, p. A367
Vice President and Chief Financial Officer, Northwest Medical Center, Albany, MO, p. A367

GILLETTE, Karen, Associate Director Patient Care Services, Memphis Veterans Affairs Medical Center, Memphis, TN, p. A589

GILLETTE, Kathryn, President and Chief Executive Officer, Bayfront Health St. Petersburg, Saint Petersburg, FL, p. A144

GILLETTE, Nicole, R.N. Chief Nursing Officer, West Branch Regional Medical Center, West Branch, MI, p. A336

GILLETTE, Robert, Chief Information Officer, St. Elizabeth Medical Center, Utica, NY, p. A457

GILLETTE, Tom, Senior Vice President and Chief Information Officer, Mount Sinai Medical Center, Miami Beach, FL, p. A138

GILLIAM, David, M.D. Medical Director, Bloomington Meadows Hospital, Bloomington, IN, p. A207

GILLIAM, Eric
Chief Executive Officer, Saint Joseph Berea, Berea, KY, p. A257
President, Saint Joseph East, Lexington, KY, p. A263

GILLIAM, Leslie, Director Health Information Management, Dominion Hospital, Falls Church, VA, p. A669

GILLIAN, Tom, Chief Operating Officer, River Bend Hospital, West Lafayette, IN, p. A223

GILLIAND, Michael, M.D. Chief of Staff, CHI St. Luke's Health Brazosport, Lake Jackson, TX, p. A631

GILLIANO, Patti, Chief Nursing Officer, Lake Pointe Medical Center, Rowlett, TX, p. A644

GILLILAND, Sharon, Chief of Staff, Baraga County Memorial Hospital, L'Anse, MI, p. A328

GILLILAND, Terry, M.D
Chief Medical Officer, Sentara Leigh Hospital, Norfolk, VA, p. A675
Senior Vice President and Chief Medical Officer, Sentara Princess Anne Hospital, Virginia Beach, VA, p. A680

GILLIS, Anne, Chief Financial Officer, Holy Cross Hospital, Silver Spring, MD, p. A303

GILLIS, Melissa, Chief Executive Officer, Helen M. Simpson Rehabilitation Hospital, Harrisburg, PA, p. A539

GILLMAN, Kreg, Chief Executive Officer, Salt Lake Behavioral Health, Salt Lake City, UT, p. A663

GILLY, Mike, Chief Information Officer, Our Lady of the Angels Hospital, Bogalusa, LA, p. A274

GILMAN, Howard, M.D. Medical Executive, Christian Health Care Center, Wyckoff, NJ, p. A426

GILMAN, Kim
Chief Executive Officer, Phoebe Worth Medical Center, Sylvester, GA, p. A167
Chief Nursing Officer, Phoebe Worth Medical Center, Sylvester, GA, p. A167
Chief Executive Officer and Chief Nursing Officer, Southwest Georgia Regional Medical Center, Cuthbert, GA, p. A157
Chief Executive Officer and Chief Nursing Officer, Southwest Georgia Regional Medical Center, Cuthbert, GA, p. A157

GILMORE, Hugh V., M.D. Vice President Medical Affairs, Seton Medical Center Williamson, Round Rock, TX, p. A644

GILMORE, Linda, Chief Nursing Officer/Chief Administrative Officer, Littleton Regional Hospital, Littleton, NH, p. A412

GILMORE, Phillip K., FACHE, Chief Executive Officer, Ashley County Medical Center, Crossett, AR, p. A44

GILPIN, Michael W., Vice President Human Resources, Sampson Regional Medical Center, Clinton, NC, p. A463

GILSON, Sheila, R.N. Chief Operating Officer, Kaiser Permanente Redwood City Medical Center, Redwood City, CA, p. A85

GILTNER, Michelle, Interim Chief Nursing Officer, UH Regional Hospitals, Cleveland, OH, p. A490

GIN, Nancy, M.D. Area Associate Medical Director, Kaiser Permanente Orange County Anaheim Medical Center, Anaheim, CA, p. A54

GINGERICH, Jim, Administrator, Prairie Ridge Hospital and Health Services, Elbow Lake, MN, p. A342

GINGRAS, Sean, CPA Chief Financial Officer, Centerstone Hospital, Bradenton, FL, p. A124

GINGRICH, Joye, Director Patient Care Services and Chief Nursing Officer, J. C. Blair Memorial Hospital, Huntingdon, PA, p. A540

GINGRICH, Mary, Director Health Care Services, Kansas Neurological Institute, Topeka, KS, p. A254

GINN, Bobby, Chief Operating Officer, Crestwood Medical Center, Huntsville, AL, p. A21

GINN, Doug, Executive Vice President Operations, Peak Behavioral Health Services, Santa Teresa, NM, p. A431

GINNATY, Rayn, Vice President Nursing, Benefis Health System, Great Falls, MT, p. A388

GINSBERG, Ronald L., M.D. Vice President Medical Affairs, Northwest Hospital, Randallstown, MD, p. A303

GINSBURG, J. Lawrence, M.D. Vice President Medical Affairs, Evangelical Community Hospital, Lewisburg, PA, p. A543

GINTER, Gary, System Vice President and Chief Information Officer, Miami Valley Hospital, Dayton, OH, p. A493

GINTOLI, Eric, Administrator, Seaside Health System, Baton Rouge, LA, p. A273

GINTZIG, Donald R., President and Chief Executive Officer, WakeMed Cary Hospital, Cary, NC, p. A462

GINTZIG, Donald R., President and Chief Executive Officer, WakeMed Health & Hospitals, Raleigh, NC, p. B153

GINTZIG, Donald R., President and Chief Executive Officer, WakeMed Raleigh Campus, Raleigh, NC, p. A472

GIOIA, Anthony, Chief Financial Officer, Indiana Orthopaedic Hospital, Indianapolis, IN, p. A214

GIORDANO, Paul, Vice President Human Resources, South Nassau Communities Hospital, Oceanside, NY, p. A451

GIORDANO, Peter, Senior Director Human Resources, Harrison Community Hospital, Cadiz, OH, p. A486

GIORDANO, Roger, M.D. Medical Director, HEALTHSOUTH Rehabilitation Hospital of Virginia, Richmond, VA, p. A677

GIORDANO, Susan, R.N. Chief Nursing Officer, Hackensack University Medical Center at Pascack Valley, Westwood, NJ, p. A425

GIPP, Jana, Chief Executive Officer, Standing Rock Service Unit, Fort Yates Hospital, Indian Health Service, DHHS, Fort Yates, ND, p. A479

GIPSON, Linda Stephens, MSN Chief Nursing Officer, WhidbeyHealth, Coupeville, WA, p. A684

GIRALT, Juana, Chief Financial Officer, River Crest Hospital, San Angelo, TX, p. A644

GIRARD, Thomas R.
Vice President Human Resources, LincolnHealth, Damariscotta, ME, p. A292
Vice President Human Resources, Pen Bay Medical Center, Rockport, ME, p. A295

GIRARDIER, Cheryl, Director Information Technology, Millcreek Community Hospital, Erie, PA, p. A538

GIRARDY, James, M.D. Vice President, Chief Surgical Officer, OSF Saint Anthony Medical Center, Rockford, IL, p. A202

GIRTEN, David M., Corporate Director Financial Services, St. Vincent Seton Specialty Hospital, Indianapolis, IN, p. A215

GIRTY, Tara, Director Human Resources, Kiowa District Hospital and Manor, Kiowa, KS, p. A247

GISH, Kevin, Administrator and Vice President, Essentia Health Fosston, Fosston, MN, p. A343

GISLER, Greg, Chief Financial Officer, McBride Clinic Orthopedic Hospital, Oklahoma City, OK, p. A516

GISLESON, Joni, Director Finance, Palmer Lutheran Health Center, West Union, IA, p. A239

GISSEL, Betty, Vice President Human Resources, University of Tennessee Medical Center, Knoxville, TN, p. A586

GITMAN, Michael, M.D. Medical Director, North Shore University Hospital, Manhasset, NY, p. A442

GITTELMAN, Michael B.
Administrator, Bascom Palmer Eye Institute–Anne Bates Leach Eye Hospital, Miami, FL, p. A136
Interim Chief Executive Officer, University of Miami Hospital, Miami, FL, p. A137

GITTLER, Michelle, M.D. Medical Director, Schwab Rehabilitation Hospital, Chicago, IL, p. A186

GITZINGER, Matthew, Director of Operations, Vidant Duplin Hospital, Kenansville, NC, p. A468

GIUDICE, William A., Vice President and Chief Financial Officer, Tallahassee Memorial HealthCare, Tallahassee, FL, p. A146

GIULIANELLI, Victor, FACHE, President and Chief Executive Officer, St. Mary's Healthcare, Amsterdam, NY, p. A434

GIVENS, Linda S., MSN Chief Nursing Officer, Walla Walla General Hospital, Walla Walla, WA, p. A693

GIVENS, Michael K., FACHE Administrator, St. Bernards Medical Center, Jonesboro, AR, p. A48

GIVENS, Stephen K., Assistant Vice President and Administrator, Russell County Medical Center, Lebanon, VA, p. A672

GIZDIC, John H., President and Chief Executive Officer, New Hanover Regional Medical Center, Wilmington, NC, p. A475

GIZINSKI, Judy, Chief Operating Officer, Health First Palm Bay Hospital, Palm Bay, FL, p. A141

GIZZI, Jason, Controller, HEALTHSOUTH MountainView Regional Rehabilitation Hospital, Morgantown, WV, p. A698

GJOLBERG, Skip, FACHE, Administrator, St. Joseph's Hospital of Buckhannon, Buckhannon, WV, p. A694

GLADE, James G., Director Human Resources, Penn Highlands Clearfield, Clearfield, PA, p. A535

GLADEN, Tracy, Chief Financial Officer, Twin Valley Behavioral Healthcare, Columbus, OH, p. A491

GLADFELTER, Sharon, Health Information Officer, Brook Lane Health Services, Hagerstown, MD, p. A301

GLADSTONE, Art, R.N.,
President and Chief Executive Officer, Pali Momi Medical Center, Aiea, HI, p. A170
Chief Executive Officer, Straub Clinic & Hospital, Honolulu, HI, p. A171

GLANVILLE, Tristan, Chief Financial Officer, Adirondack Medical Center, Saranac Lake, NY, p. A455

GLANZER, Elgin, Chief Financial Officer, Memorial Health System, Abilene, KS, p. A240

GLASBERG, Michael, Senior Vice President, Chief Operating Officer, Dameron Hospital, Stockton, CA, p. A95

GLASER, Elaine, Chief Executive Officer, Valley Hospital Medical Center, Las Vegas, NV, p. A407

GLASER, Ruth, President, Pender Memorial Hospital, Burgaw, NC, p. A461

GLASNAPP, Sherry L., Director, Douglas County Community Mental Health Center, Omaha, NE, p. A400

GLASS, Debbie, Interim Chief Operating Officer, Providence Seaside Hospital, Seaside, OR, p. A530

GLASS, Ian, M.D. Chief Medical Officer, Tomball Regional Medical Center, Tomball, TX, p. A653

GLASS, Ina Louise, Administrator, Ephraim McDowell Fort Logan Hospital, Stanford, KY, p. A269

GLASS, Steven, Chief Financial Officer, Cleveland Clinic, Cleveland, OH, p. A488

GLASS, Wendy, Director Human Resources, Colleton Medical Center, Walterboro, SC, p. A570

GLASSBURN, David, Vice President Finance and Chief Financial Officer, Harlingen Medical Center, Harlingen, TX, p. A622

GLASSCOCK, Gary M., President and Chief Executive Officer, Noland Health Services, Inc., Birmingham, AL, p. B96

GLASSCOCK, Sheryl, Chief Nursing Officer, Lake Cumberland Regional Hospital, Somerset, KY, p. A269

GLASSMAN, Kimberly S., Ph.D. Chief Nursing Officer, NYU Langone Medical Center, New York, NY, p. A449

GLAUBKE, Nancy, Chief Executive Officer, Valley County Health System, Ord, NE, p. A401

GLAVES, Ann, Vice President Human Resources, St. Francis Regional Medical Center, Shakopee, MN, p. A351

GLAVIN, Jolene, R.N. Director Nursing, Salina Surgical Hospital, Salina, KS, p. A253

GLAZIER, Stephen, Chief Operating Officer, University of Texas Harris County Psychiatric Center, Houston, TX, p. A627

GLEASON, Jeffrey J., M.D. Chief Medical Officer, Cookeville Regional Medical Center, Cookeville, TN, p. A581

GLEASON, Ronald M., Chief Executive Officer, Mineral Community Hospital, Superior, MT, p. A391

GLEASON, Vallerie L., Chief Executive Officer, Newton Medical Center, Newton, KS, p. A250

GLEN, Diane M., Assistant Administrator, Barnes–Jewish West County Hospital, Saint Louis, MO, p. A379

GLEN, Susan, Chief Executive Officer, Select Specialty Hospital – Cincinnati North, Cincinnati, OH, p. A488

GLENN, Gary
Director Information Technology, Carrus Rehabilitation Hospital, Sherman, TX, p. A648
Director Information Technology, Carrus Specialty Hospital, Sherman, TX, p. A648

GLENN, Jeannette, Vice President Human Resources, Education and Training, McLeod Regional Medical Center, Florence, SC, p. A566

GLENN, Maggie, Director Human Resources, North Carolina Specialty Hospital, Durham, NC, p. A464

GLENN, Michael, M.D. Chief Medical Officer, Virginia Mason Medical Center, Seattle, WA, p. A690

GLENN, Mike, Chief Executive Officer, Jefferson Healthcare, Port Townsend, WA, p. A688

GLENN, Wil A., Director Communications, Larry B. Zieverink, Sr. Alcoholism Treatment Center, Raleigh, NC, p. A472

GLENNING, Robert, Executive Vice President Finance and Chief Financial Officer, Hackensack University Medical Center, Hackensack, NJ, p. A417

GLESSNER, Theresa, Vice President, Chief Nursing Officer, Newark–Wayne Community Hospital, Newark, NY, p. A450

GLICK, Jennifer, Manager Clinical Informatics, Oaklawn Psychiatric Center, Goshen, IN, p. A212

GLIDDEN, Elizabeth, Chief Nursing Officer, New England Rehabilitation Hospital of Portland, Portland, ME, p. A294

GLIDDEN, Nancy
Chief Financial Officer, Calais Regional Hospital, Calais, ME, p. A292
Chief Financial Officer and Vice President Finance, Mayo Regional Hospital, Dover–Foxcroft, ME, p. A293

GLIHA, Frank, Vice President of Patient Care, Mary Rutan Hospital, Bellefontaine, OH, p. A485

GLIHA, Jennie, Vice President Human Resources and Clinical Services, Aurelia Osborn Fox Memorial Hospital, Oneonta, NY, p. A452

GLIMP, Richard, M.D
Chief Medical Officer, Providence Little Company of Mary Medical Center – Torrance, Torrance, CA, p. A96
Chief Medical Officer, Providence Little Company of Mary Medical Center San Pedro,, CA, p. A73

GLOCKA, Carolynn, R.N., President, Aurora Sinai Medical Center, Milwaukee, WI, p. A711

GLODOWSKI, Brenda, Chief Financial Officer, North Central Health Care, Wausau, WI, p. A718

GLOFF, Vicki, Chief Financial Officer, Goodall–Witcher Hospital Authority, Clifton, TX, p. A606

GLOGGNER, Peter, Chief Human Resources Officer, Jupiter Medical Center, Jupiter, FL, p. A132

GLONER, James, Senior Vice President, North Philadelphia Health System, Philadelphia, PA, p. A549

GLORIA–BARRAZA, Patricia, Coordinator Human Resources, Mayhill Hospital, Denton, TX, p. A612

GLOSS, John, FACHE, Administrator, Shriners Hospitals for Children–St. Louis, Saint Louis, MO, p. A380

GLOTZBACK, Lee, Director Human Resources, Citrus Memorial Health System, Inverness, FL, p. A131

GLOVER, Cynthia, R.N. Vice President and Chief Nursing Officer, Reston Hospital Center, Reston, VA, p. A676

GLOVER, Doug, Controller, William S. Hall Psychiatric Institute, Columbia, SC, p. A564

GLOVER, Leslie, Director Operations, Mary Black Health System – Gaffney, Gaffney, SC, p. A566

GLOWA, Meghan, Director Human Resources, Sunnyview Rehabilitation Hospital, Schenectady, NY, p. A455

GLUBKA, Theresa, R.N., Chief Executive Officer, Eden Medical Center, Castro Valley, CA, p. A58

GLUCHOWSKI, Jeanne, Executive Director, Conifer Park, Glenville, NY, p. A439

GLUCK, Michael, M.D. Medical Director, LifeCare Hospitals of Mechanicsburg, Mechanicsburg, PA, p. A544

GLUECK, Dane, M.D. Chief of Staff, Progress West Hospital, O'Fallon, MO, p. A377

GLYER, David
Vice President Finance, Community Memorial Hospital, Ventura, CA, p. A98
Vice President Finance, Ojai Valley Community Hospital, Ojai, CA, p. A80

GLYNN, Cindy, Director Human Resources, Regional Rehabilitation Hospital, Phenix City, AL, p. A24

GLYNN, John
Executive Vice President, Chief Information Officer, Newark–Wayne Community Hospital, Newark, NY, p. A450
Chief Information Officer, Rochester General Hospital, Rochester, NY, p. A454
Senior Vice President and Chief Information Officer, Unity Hospital, Rochester, NY, p. A454

GLYNN, Margaret, M.D. Chief Medical Officer, North Mississippi Medical Center–luka, luka, MS, p. A359

GLYNN, Shari, Vice President Finance and Chief Financial Officer, Eaton Rapids Medical Center, Eaton Rapids, MI, p. A323

GNAGEY, Keith, Chief Executive Officer, Teton Valley Health Care, Driggs, ID, p. A176

GNAM, Gwen, R.N. Chief Nursing Officer, Henry Ford Hospital, Detroit, MI, p. A322

GNANN, Andrew, Vice President Operations, St. Vincent's East, Birmingham, AL, p. A17

GNEGY, David, M.D. Vice President of Medical Affairs, Camden Clark Medical Center, Parkersburg, WV, p. A698

GOACHER, Brad, Vice President Administration, Alton Memorial Hospital, Alton, IL, p. A180

GOAD, Pat, Director Human Resources, Hillcrest Hospital Claremore, Claremore, OK, p. A510

GOBEL, Bret, Chief Financial Officer, Sierra Vista Hospital, Truth or Consequences, NM, p. A432

GOBELL, James, Chief Financial Officer, UnityPoint Health – St. Luke's, Sioux City, IA, p. A238

GOBER, Kirby, Chief Executive Officer, Throckmorton County Memorial Hospital, Throckmorton, TX, p. A653

GOBLE, Jonathan R., FACHE, President and Chief Executive Officer, Indiana University Health North Hospital, Carmel, IN, p. A208

GOBLE, Mandy C., President and Chief Executive Officer, Mary Rutan Hospital, Bellefontaine, OH, p. A485

GOCHENOUR, Julia, Manager Information Systems, West River Regional Medical Center, Hettinger, ND, p. A479

GODAMUNNE, Karim, M.D. Chief Medical Officer, North Fulton Regional Hospital, Roswell, GA, p. A165

GODBEE, Mitchell, Chief of Staff, Capital Region Medical Center, Jefferson City, MO, p. A372

GODDARD, Mark, M.D. Medical Director, HEALTHSOUTH Rehabilitation Hospital at Drake, Cincinnati, OH, p. A487

GODFREY, John, M.D. Vice President and Chief Executive Officer, Hardin Memorial Hospital, Elizabethtown, KY, p. A259

GODFREY, Katrina, Director Human Resources, Mercy Hospital Ada, Ada, OK, p. A508

GODFREY, Kristine, Director Human Resources, Tennova Healthcare – Cleveland, Cleveland, TN, p. A581

GODINEZ, Roxanna M., Chief Executive Officer, Cornerstone Regional Hospital, Edinburg, TX, p. A614

GODLEY, James R., Vice President of Human Resources, Mayo Regional Hospital, Dover–Foxcroft, ME, p. A293

GODLEY, Maria, R.N., Chief Executive Officer, Northern Idaho Advanced Care Hospital, Post Falls, ID, p. A178

GODLEY, Patrick, Chief Financial Officer, Contra Costa Regional Medical Center, Martinez, CA, p. A76

GODWIN, Jr., Herman A., M.D. Senior Vice President and Medical Director, Watauga Medical Center, Boone, NC, p. A461

GODWIN, Jr., James C., Vice President, Human Resources, Bon Secours St. Francis Medical Center, Midlothian, VA, p. A673

GODWIN, Kristi, Interim Human Resource Director, Fairfield Memorial Hospital, Winnsboro, SC, p. A571

GOEB–BURKETT, Michele, R.N. Chief Nursing Officer, Florida Hospital Memorial Medical Center, Daytona Beach, FL, p. A127

GOEBEL, Bret, Finance Officer, Guadalupe County Hospital, Santa Rosa, NM, p. A431

GOEBEL, Cecilia B., R.N. Vice President and Chief Nursing Officer, Susan B. Allen Memorial Hospital, El Dorado, KS, p. A242

GOEBEL, Dennis, Chief Executive Officer, Murray County Medical Center, Slayton, MN, p. A351

GOEBEL, Donna, M.D. Chief Nursing Officer, Mitchell County Hospital, Colorado City, TX, p. A606

GOEBEL, Michael, FACHE,
Vice President and Chief Executive Officer, Adventist La Grange Memorial Hospital, La Grange, IL, p. A194
Vice President and Chief Executive Officer, AMITA Health Adventist Medical Center – Hinsdale, Hinsdale, IL, p. A193

GOEHRING, Jennifer, R.N. Assistant Chief Nursing Officer, Via Christi Hospital Manhattan, Inc.,, KS, p. A248

GOEHRING, Lawanda, MSN Chief Nursing Officer, Good Shepherd Penn Partners Specialty Hospital at Rittenhouse, Philadelphia, PA, p. A548

GOEL, Amitabh, M.D. Chief Medical Officer, University Hospitals Geneva Medical Center, Geneva, OH, p. A495

GOEL, Vineet, Chief Medical Officer, Carolinas HealthCare System Lincoln, Lincolnton, NC, p. A469

GOELZ, Gary, R.N. Chief Nursing Officer, Shands Lake Shore Regional Medical Center, Lake City, FL, p. A133

GOELZER, Mark L., M.D. Director Medical Affairs, Mercy Hospital and Trauma Center, Janesville, WI, p. A707

GOERINGER, Dawn Marie, Chief Clinical Care Officer, O'Connor Hospital, San Jose, CA, p. A91

GOESER, Stephen L., FACHE, President and Chief Executive Officer, Nebraska Methodist Hospital, Omaha, NE, p. A400

GOETTSCH, Barry, FACHE, Chief Executive Officer, Marengo Memorial Hospital, Marengo, IA, p. A234

GOETZ, Kathy L., Administrator, Mercy Medical Center – West Lakes, West Des Moines, IA, p. A239

GOFF, Gary E., M.D. Medical Director, Promise Hospital of Dallas, Dallas, TX, p. A611

GOFF, Vivian, R.N., Chief Executive Officer, Landmark Hospital of Athens, Athens, GA, p. A151

GOGGIN, Daniel
Senior Vice President and Chief Financial Officer, Burleson St. Joseph Health Center, Caldwell, TX, p. A604
Senior Vice President and Chief Financial Officer, Grimes St. Joseph Health Center, Navasota, TX, p. A638

GOGGIN, Kathy, Director Administrative Services, Devereux Georgia Treatment Network, Kennesaw, GA, p. A161

GOINS, Rick, Chief Operating Officer, Massac Memorial Hospital, Metropolis, IL, p. A196

GOLAN, Marc
Chief Financial Officer, Franciscan St. Anthony Health – Crown Point, Crown Point, IN, p. A209
Regional Chief Financial Officer, Franciscan St. Anthony Health – Michigan City, Michigan City, IN, p. A218
Chief Financial Officer, Franciscan St. Margaret Health – Hammond, Hammond, IN, p. A212

GOLANOWSKI, Marie, MS, President, Aurora St. Luke's Medical Center, Milwaukee, WI, p. A711

GOLD, Barbara, M.D. Chief Medical Officer, University of Minnesota Medical Center, Fairview, Minneapolis, MN, p. A347

GOLD, Joseph, M.D. Chief Medical Officer, McLean Hospital, Belmont, MA, p. A305

GOLD, Larry, Vice President, Information Services, Southern Virginia Regional Medical Center, Emporia, VA, p. A669

GOLDAMMER, Kyle, Chief Financial Officer, Sioux Falls Specialty Hospital, Sioux Falls, SD, p. A576

GOLDBERG, Andrew S., Associate Executive Director, Syosset Hospital, Syosset, NY, p. A456

GOLDBERG, David, Interim President and Chief Executive Officer, Canonsburg Hospital, Canonsburg, PA, p. A534

GOLDBERG, David, M.D. Vice President Medical Affairs and Chief Medical Officer, Community Memorial Hospital, Menomonee Falls, WI, p. A710

GOLDBERG, Frederick, M.D. Vice President Medical Affairs and Chief Medical Officer, Nathan Littauer Hospital and Nursing Home, Gloversville, NY, p. A439

GOLDBERG, Gary, M.D. Chief Medical Officer, North Hawaii Community Hospital, Kamuela, HI, p. A172

GOLDBERG, Jonathan, Senior Vice President and Chief Information Officer, Arkansas Children's Hospital, Little Rock, AR, p. A48

GOLDBERG, Larry M., President and Chief Executive Officer, Loyola University Medical Center, Maywood, IL, p. A196

GOLDBERG, Michael, Executive Director, Long Island Jewish Medical Center,, NY, p. A445

GOLDBERG, Paul R., Chief Financial Officer, Jersey City Medical Center, Jersey City, NJ, p. A418

GOLDBERG, Stephanie J., MSN Senior Vice President and Chief Nursing Officer, Hospital for Special Surgery, New York, NY, p. A444

GOLDBERGER, Joseph, M.D
Chief Medical Officer, Yavapai Regional Medical Center – East, Prescott Valley, AZ, p. A38
Chief Medical Officer, Yavapai Regional Medical Center, Prescott, AZ, p. A37

GOLDEN, Joy, Chief Executive Officer, Lakeside Behavioral Health System, Memphis, TN, p. A589

GOLDEN, Virginia L.
Chief Executive Officer, Albany Memorial Hospital, Albany, NY, p. A433
Chief Executive Officer, St. Peter's Hospital, Albany, NY, p. A433

GOLDENBERG, Dianne, Chief Executive Officer, Aventura Hospital and Medical Center, Aventura, FL, p. A123

GOLDENSTEIN, Rachel, R.N. Chief Nursing Officer, Buchanan County Health Center, Independence, IA, p. A232

GOLDFARB, I. William, Chief Medical Officer, West Penn Hospital, Pittsburgh, PA, p. A552

GOLDFARB, Timothy, Interim Chief Executive Officer, OHSU Hospital, Portland, OR, p. A529

GOLDFRACH, Andrew, Chief Executive Officer, UH Avon Rehabilitation Hospital, Avon, OH, p. A484

GOLDHAGEN, Michele, M.D. Chief of Staff, Russell Medical Center, Alexander City, AL, p. A15

GOLDIS, Glenn, Chief Medical Officer, Kern Medical Center, Bakersfield, CA, p. A56

GOLDMAN, David, M.D. Vice President Medical Affairs and Education, Prince George's Hospital Center, Cheverly, MD, p. A299

GOLDMAN, Eric, Chief Executive Officer, Palms West Hospital, Loxahatchee, FL, p. A134

GOLDMAN, Kris, Director Human Resources, Shriners Hospitals for Children–Salt Lake City, Salt Lake City, UT, p. A663

GOLDSCHMIDT, Pascal J., M.D., Chief Executive Officer, University of Miami Health System, Miami, FL, p. B148

GOLDSMITH, Cheri L.
Director Financial Services, Parkland Health Center – Liberty Street, Farmington, MO, p. A371
Director Financial Services, Parkland Health Center–Bonne Terre, Bonne Terre, MO, p. A367

GOLDSMITH, Dana L., M.D. Vice President Medical Affairs, Pen Bay Medical Center, Rockport, ME, p. A295

GOLDSMITH, Debra, Chief Executive Officer, CHI Health Mercy Corning, Corning, IA, p. A228

GOLDSTEIN, Allan, M.D. Medical Director and Chief of Staff, Select Specialty Hospital–Birmingham, Birmingham, AL, p. A17

GOLDSTEIN, Brian, M.D. Executive Vice President and Chief Operating Officer, University of North Carolina Hospitals, Chapel Hill, NC, p. A462

GOLDSTEIN, David, M.D. Chief Medical Officer, Contra Costa Regional Medical Center, Martinez, CA, p. A76

GOLDSTEIN, Gary W., M.D., President and Chief Executive Officer, Kennedy Krieger Institute, Baltimore, MD, p. A296

GOLDSTEIN, Gerald, M.D. Senior Vice President and Chief Medical Officer, Western Maryland Regional Medical Center, Cumberland, MD, p. A300

GOLDSTEIN, Lawrence, M.D. Chief Medical Officer, Vibra Hospital of Mahoning Valley, Boardman, OH, p. A485

GOLDSTEIN, Lisa, Executive Vice President and Chief Operating Officer, Hospital for Special Surgery, New York, NY, p. A444

GOLDSTEIN, Mark L., President and Chief Executive Officer, Anna Jaques Hospital, Newburyport, MA, p. A313

GOLDSTEIN, Sandy, R.N. Chief Nursing Officer, Banner Lassen Medical Center, Susanville, CA, p. A95

GOLDSTEIN, Steven I.
President and Chief Executive Officer, Highland Hospital, Rochester, NY, p. A454
President and Chief Executive Officer, Strong Memorial Hospital of the University of Rochester, Rochester, NY, p. A454

GOLDSTEIN, Steven I., General Director and Chief Executive Officer, University of Rochester Medical Center, Rochester, NY, p. B148

GOLDSZER, Robert, M.D. Senior Vice President and Chief Medical Officer, Mount Sinai Medical Center, Miami Beach, FL, p. A138

GOLIGHTLY, Beverly, Director Information Technology, St. Vincent's East, Birmingham, AL, p. A17

GOLKE, Rynae, Director Human Resources, Jacobson Memorial Hospital Care Center, Elgin, ND, p. A478

GOLL, Cheri, MSN Chief Nursing Executive, Advocate Sherman Hospital, Elgin, IL, p. A189

GOLLAHER, Jeffrey, Chief Executive Officer, Hendricks Community Hospital Association, Hendricks, MN, p. A344

GOLLINGER, Mary A., MS Director of Nursing, Schwab Rehabilitation Hospital, Chicago, IL, p. A186

GOLOLOBOV, Alexey, Chief Financial Officer, Columbus Hospital LTACH, Newark, NJ, p. A420

GOLOVAN, Ronald, M.D. Vice President Medical Operations, Lutheran Hospital, Cleveland, OH, p. A489

GOMAN, Valerie, M.D. President Medical Staff, Baylor Scott & White Medical Center at Waxahachie, Waxahachie, TX, p. A656

GOMBAR, Greg A.
Chief Financial Officer, Carolinas Medical Center, Charlotte, NC, p. A462
Chief Financial Officer, Carolinas Medical Center–University, Charlotte, NC, p. A462

GOMBERG, Sandra, Chief Operating Officer, Aria – Jefferson Health, Philadelphia, PA, p. A547

GOMES, Carol, FACHE Chief Operating Officer, Stony Brook University Hospital, Stony Brook, NY, p. A456

GOMEZ, Carmen, Director Human Resources, North Shore Medical Center, Miami, FL, p. A137

GOMEZ, Denise, Assistant Vice President Information Systems, Meriter UnityPoint Health, Madison, WI, p. A709

GOMEZ, Dianna, Chief Financial Officer, UVA–HEALTHSOUTH Rehabilitation Hospital, Charlottesville, VA, p. A668

GOMEZ, Dolores S., R.N. Chief Operating Officer, Mills–Peninsula Health Services, Burlingame, CA, p. A57

GOMEZ, Gloria, M.D. Medical Director, East Mississippi State Hospital, Meridian, MS, p. A362

GOMEZ, Jay Michael, Chief Financial Officer, Memorial Hermann Surgical Hospital Kingwood, Kingwood, TX, p. A631

GOMEZ, Jesse, Vice President Human Resources, University of Texas Health Northeast, Tyler, TX, p. A654

GOMEZ, Mike, Site Manager Medical Information Systems, Our Lady of Bellefonte Hospital, Ashland, KY, p. A257

GOMEZ, Omar, M.D. Chief of Staff, Cornerstone Regional Hospital, Edinburg, TX, p. A614

GOMEZ, Richard, Assistant Vice President Information Technology Division, Hillcrest Medical Center, Tulsa, OK, p. A521

GOMEZ, Robin, MSN, Administrator, Alvarado Hospital Medical Center, San Diego, CA, p. A88

GOMEZ, Sherry, Chief Nursing Officer, Spanish Peaks Regional Health Center, Walsenburg, CO, p. A111

GOMEZ–LUNA, Sandra, Medical Director, Southwest Connecticut Mental Health System, Bridgeport, CT, p. A113

GOMPF, Shelly, Director Human Resources, Douglas County Hospital, Alexandria, MN, p. A338

GONCZ, Gray, Vice President of Medical Affairs, Trinity Health System, Steubenville, OH, p. A503

GONDER, Christie, Chief Nursing Officer, Salinas Valley Memorial Healthcare System, Salinas, CA, p. A87

GONG, Christopher, M.D. Chief Staff, Huron Medical Center, Bad Axe, MI, p. A318

GONGAWARE, Robert, Senior Vice President Finance, Indiana Regional Medical Center, Indiana, PA, p. A541

GONYEA, Sonja, Director Human Resources, United Memorial Medical Center, Batavia, NY, p. A434

GONZALES, Amy, Director of Human Resources, McKenzie County Healthcare System, Watford City, ND, p. A482

GONZALES, Angela, Manager Human Resources, San Mateo Medical Center, San Mateo, CA, p. A92

GONZALES, Ed
Vice President Human Resources, Marian Regional Medical Center, Santa Maria, CA, p. A93
Vice President Human Resources, St. John's Pleasant Valley Hospital, Camarillo, CA, p. A57
Vice President Human Resources, St. John's Regional Medical Center, Oxnard, CA, p. A81

GONZALES, Jan, Director Human Resources, North Valley Hospital, Tonasket, WA, p. A692

GONZALES, Mary Ann, M.D. Medical Director, Central Texas Rehabilitation Hospital, Austin, TX, p. A599

GONZALES, Mike, Chief Financial Officer, Vibra Hospital of San Diego, San Diego, CA, p. A89

GONZALES, Mindy, Chief Human Resources Officer, Othello Community Hospital, Othello, WA, p. A687

GONZALES, Paula, Administrator, Emerus Community Hospital, Tomball, TX, p. A653

GONZALES, Rachel Ann, Chief Executive Officer, Madison Memorial Hospital, Rexburg, ID, p. A178

GONZALEZ, Agustin, Director Finance, Hospital Dr. Cayetano Coll Y Toste, Arecibo, PR, p. A726

GONZALEZ, Alan, Chief Operating Officer, Fort Duncan Regional Medical Center, Eagle Pass, TX, p. A614

GONZALEZ, Aurelio, Chief Financial Officer, University Hospital and Medical Center, Tamarac, FL, p. A146

GONZALEZ, David, Chief Clinical Officer, Advanced Diagnostics Hospital, Houston, TX, p. A623

GONZALEZ, David, M.D. Medical Director, Brook Lane Health Services, Hagerstown, MD, p. A301

GONZALEZ, Dinah L., Chief Financial Officer, Knapp Medical Center, Weslaco, TX, p. A657

GONZALEZ, Elizabeth, Chief Financial Officer, Hospital Metropolitano Dr. Tito Mattei, Yauco, PR, p. A731

GONZALEZ, Erin, Director Chief Human Resources, Abrazo Maryvale Campus, Phoenix, AZ, p. A35

GONZALEZ, Hugo, M.D. Chief Medical Officer, Sister Emmanuel Hospital, Miami, FL, p. A137

GONZALEZ, Jacqueline, Senior Vice President and Chief Nursing Officer, Nicklaus Children's Hospital, Miami, FL, p. A137

GONZALEZ, Jaime, Administrator, St. Catherine's Rehabilitation Hospital, North Miami, FL, p. A139

GONZALEZ, Jerry, Interim Chief Nursing Officer, Las Palmas Medical Center, El Paso, TX, p. A615

GONZALEZ, Joni, Controller, Kindred Hospital Dallas Central, Dallas, TX, p. A610

GONZALEZ, Jorge F., M.D
Chief Medical Officer, Florida Hospital Heartland Medical Center, Sebring, FL, p. A145
Vice President and Chief Nursing Officer, Florida Hospital Wauchula, Wauchula, FL, p. A149

GONZALEZ, Jorge Matta, Executive Director, University Hospital, San Juan, PR, p. A730

GONZALEZ, Laura, Interim Chief Nurse Executive, South Shore Hospital, Chicago, IL, p. A186

GONZALEZ, Pedro J., FACHE, Chief Executive Officer, Ashford Presbyterian Community Hospital, San Juan, PR, p. A729

GONZALEZ, Rainier, Chairman and Chief Executive Officer, Pacer Health Corporation, Miami Lakes, FL, p. B101

GONZALEZ, Richard, Chief Executive Officer, The Medical Center of Southeast Texas, Port Arthur, TX, p. A642

GONZALEZ, Roberto, Executive Director Human Resources, Hoboken University Medical Center, Hoboken, NJ, p. A418

GONZALEZ, Susan, Director of Clinical Services, Stanislaus Surgical Hospital, Modesto, CA, p. A77

GONZALEZ, Victoria, Chief Financial Officer, The Hospitals of Providence Sierra Campus, El Paso, TX, p. A616

GONZALEZ–FAJARDO, Ana, Human Resources Director, Palmetto General Hospital, Hialeah, FL, p. A130

GOOD, Jo, Director of Nursing, Palmetto Lowcountry Behavioral Health, Charleston, SC, p. A563

GOOD, Vance A., M.D. Chief Medical Staff, Troy Community Hospital, Troy, PA, p. A556

GOODALL, David, M.D. Chief Medical Staff, Essentia Health–Deer River, Deer River, MN, p. A341

GOODBALIAN, Terry
Vice President Finance and Chief Financial Officer, Henry Ford Macomb Hospitals, Clinton Township, MI, p. A320
Regional Chief Financial Officer, Henry Ford West Bloomfield Hospital, West Bloomfield, MI, p. A336
Vice President, Finance and Chief Financial Officer, Henry Ford Wyandotte Hospital, Wyandotte, MI, p. A337

GOODE, Jennifer, Director Human Resources, Russell County Hospital, Russell Springs, KY, p. A269

GOODE, Lori, Director Human Resources, Baptist Memorial Hospital–Union County, New Albany, MS, p. A363

GOODE, Shayne, Administrator, Post Acute/Warm Springs Specialty Hospital of New Braunfels, New Braunfels, TX, p. A638

GOODE, Vicky, Director Human Resources, LifeCare Hospitals of North Carolina, Rocky Mount, NC, p. A472

GOODIN, Antonia M., Interim Chief Executive Officer, Claiborne Memorial Medical Center, Homer, LA, p. A278

GOODIN, Scott, Interim Chief Financial Officer, Chinese Hospital, San Francisco, CA, p. A90

GOODING, Lari, Chief Executive Officer, Allendale County Hospital, Fairfax, SC, p. A565

GOODISON, Sharon A., R.N. Chief Nursing Officer, Jackson Hospital and Clinic, Montgomery, AL, p. A23

GOODLETT, Lisa, Senior Vice President and Chief Financial Officer, Laurel Regional Hospital, Laurel, MD, p. A302

GOODMAN, Brenda, Chief Nursing Officer, Medical Center of Peach County, Navicent Health, Bryon, GA, p. A155

GOODMAN, Charlene, Director Human Resources, Rush County Memorial Hospital, La Crosse, KS, p. A247

GOODMAN, David M., Ph.D. Chief Information Officer, Veterans Affairs Boston Healthcare System, Boston, MA, p. A307

GOODMAN, Doug, Vice President Human Resources, Brandon Regional Hospital, Brandon, FL, p. A124

GOODMAN, Larry J., M.D., Chief Executive Officer, Rush University Medical Center, Chicago, IL, p. A186

GOODMAN, Larry J., M.D., Chief Executive Officer, Rush University Medical Center, Chicago, IL, p. B116

GOODMAN, Louis, Senior Vice President Human Resources, Monongahela Valley Hospital, Monongahela, PA, p. A545

GOODMAN, Mary Jo, Chief Operating Officer, Park Plaza Hospital, Houston, TX, p. A626

GOODMAN, Steven, Chief Operating Officer, Willow Crest Hospital, Miami, OK, p. A514

GOODMAN, William H., Vice President Medical Affairs, Chief Medical Officer, Catholic Medical Center, Manchester, NH, p. A412

GOODNOW, John H., Chief Executive Officer, Benefis Health System, Great Falls, MT, p. A388

GOODNOW, John H., Chief Executive Officer, Benefis Health System, Great Falls, MT, p. B22

GOODPASTER, Amber, Chief Financial Officer, Clark Regional Medical Center, Winchester, KY, p. A270

GOODRICH, C. Harlan, Vice President and Chief Information Officer, MidMichigan Medical Center–Midland, Midland, MI, p. A330

GOODRICH, Craig, Chief Financial Officer, Virginia Mason Medical Center, Seattle, WA, p. A690

GOODRICH, Zane, Vice President Finance, East Tennessee Children's Hospital, Knoxville, TN, p. A585

GOODROW, Darrin
Chief Information Officer, Moses Ludington Hospital, Ticonderoga, NY, p. A457
Chief Information Officer, The University of Vermont Health Network – Alice Hyde Medical Center, Malone, NY, p. A442
Chief Information Officer, The University of Vermont Health Network Elizabethtown Community Hospital, Elizabethtown, NY, p. A438

GOODSON, David, Chief Executive Officer, Select Specialty Hospital–Pensacola, Pensacola, FL, p. A142

GOODSON, Jacob, Director Information Technology, North Oaks Medical Center, Hammond, LA, p. A277

GOODSPEED, Darwin, Director, Sioux Falls Veterans Affairs Health Care System, Sioux Falls, SD, p. A576

GOODSTEIN, Ruth, Controller, HEALTHSOUTH Sunrise Rehabilitation Hospital, Sunrise, FL, p. A146

GOODWIN, Jeremy, M.D. President, Medical Staff, Monroe County Hospital, Forsyth, GA, p. A159

GOODWIN, Jeronica, Senior Director Human Resources, Howard University Hospital, Washington, DC, p. A121

GOODWIN, Keith D., President and Chief Executive Officer, East Tennessee Children's Hospital, Knoxville, TN, p. A585

GOODWIN, Linda, Group Chief Nursing Officer, St. Anthony Hospital, Lakewood, CO, p. A108

GOODWIN, W. Jarrad, M.D. Director, University of Miami Hospital and Clinics, Miami, FL, p. A137

GOOLSBY, Elizabeth, Director, Fayetteville Veterans Affairs Medical Center, Fayetteville, NC, p. A465

GOPINATH, Anil, FACHE Regional Chief Medical Officer, Presence Mercy Medical Center, Aurora, IL, p. A180

GORANSON, Ken, Chief Financial Officer, Benson Hospital, Benson, AZ, p. A31

GORBY, Cherie, Chief Operations Officer, Memorial Hospital, Colorado Springs, CO, p. A102

GORBY, Karen S., FACHE, President and Chief Nursing Officer, Angel Medical Center, Franklin, NC, p. A465

GORCZYCA, Julie A., R.N. Chief Nursing Officer, Genesys Regional Medical Center, Grand Blanc, MI, p. A324

GORDIAN, Michael, Chief Financial Officer, Western Plains Medical Complex, Dodge City, KS, p. A242

GORDON, Cynthia, R.N., Chief Executive Officer, Shasta Regional Medical Center, Redding, CA, p. A84

GORDON, Dan, Chief Financial Officer, Feather River Hospital, Paradise, CA, p. A82

GORDON, Jackie, Chief Clinical Officer, Kindred Hospital Dallas Central, Dallas, TX, p. A610

GORDON, Jacqueline, R.N. Chief Nursing Officer, CHI St. Luke's Health Memorial Livingston, Livingston, TX, p. A633

GORDON, John Mark, Administrator, Chatuge Regional Hospital and Nursing Home, Hiawassee, GA, p. A160

GORDON, Kevin, M.D. Chief of Staff, AllianceHealth Durant, Durant, OK, p. A511

GORDON, Mandy, Human Resource Coordinator, Phoebe Worth Medical Center, Sylvester, GA, p. A167

GORDON, Mark, Chief Nursing Officer, Kern Valley Healthcare District, Lake Isabella, CA, p. A68

GORDON, Mark M.
Chief Executive Officer, Bon Secours Memorial Regional Medical Center, Mechanicsville, VA, p. A673
Chief Executive Officer, Bon Secours–Richmond Community Hospital, Richmond, VA, p. A677
Chief Executive Officer, Rappahannock General Hospital, Kilmarnock, VA, p. A672

GORDON, Nancy Gail, R.N. Chief Nursing Officer and Vice President of Nursing, Baptist Health South Florida, Homestead Hospital, Homestead, FL, p. A131

GORDON, Robert, Manager Information Systems, Halifax Regional Medical Center, Roanoke Rapids, NC, p. A472

GORDON, Steve, Director Human Resources, Lake City Medical Center, Lake City, FL, p. A133

GORDON, Steven R., President and Chief Executive Officer, Brattleboro Memorial Hospital, Brattleboro, VT, p. A665

GORDON, Susan, R.N. Chief Nursing Officer, Memorial Hospital, York, PA, p. A559

GORDON, Thomas, Chief Information Officer, Virtua Marlton, Marlton, NJ, p. A419

GORDON, Wayne
Chief Financial Officer, Memorial Hermann Rehabilitation Hospital – Katy, Katy, TX, p. A630
Chief Financial Officer, TIRR Memorial Hermann, Houston, TX, p. A627

GORDY, Joseph S., President and Chief Executive Officer, Flagler Hospital, Saint Augustine, FL, p. A144

GORE, Carol, MSN Chief Nursing Officer, Saint Mary's Regional Medical Center, Russellville, AR, p. A52

GORE, Gary R., Chief Executive Officer, Marshall Health System, Guntersville, AL, p. B85

GORE, Tim, Chief Financial Officer, Rivendell Behavioral Health, Bowling Green, KY, p. A258

GOREAU, Judy, R.N. Director of Nursing, Eastside Psychiatric Hospital, Tallahassee, FL, p. A146

GOREY, Peter, Administrative Coordinator, Rockland Children's Psychiatric Center, Orangeburg, NY, p. A452

GORLEWSKI, Todd, Senior Vice President and Chief Financial Officer, St. Barnabas Hospital,, NY, p. A449

GORMAN, Brandon, Controller, Bradley County Medical Center, Warren, AR, p. A53

GORMAN, Jodie, Director Human Resources, Salem Memorial District Hospital, Salem, MO, p. A382

GORMAN, Kathleen, MSN Executive Vice President Patient Care Services and Chief Operating Officer, Children's National Health System, Washington, DC, p. A121

GORMAN, Matt, Administrator, Polk Medical Center, Cedartown, GA, p. A156

GORMLEY, Ann H., Senior Vice President Human Resources, Pinnacle Health System, Harrisburg, PA, p. A540

GORMLEY, Maureen E., R.N. Chief Operating Officer, National Institutes of Health Clinical Center, Bethesda, MD, p. A299

GORMSEN, David, D.O. Vice President and Chief Medical Officer, Mercy Medical Center, Canton, OH, p. A486

GORN, Angela, Vice President, Norton Sound Regional Hospital, Nome, AK, p. A30

GORS, Ann, Chief Executive Officer, Kentfield Rehabilitation and Specialty Hospital, Kentfield, CA, p. A67

GORSKI, William R., M.D., President and Chief Executive Officer, SwedishAmerican – A Division of UW Health, Rockford, IL, p. A202

GOSCH, Shawn, Chief Financial Officer, Burgess Health Center, Onawa, IA, p. A235

GOSEY, J., M.D. Medical Director, Southern Surgical Hospital, Slidell, LA, p. A288

GOSHE, Nick, Chief Executive Officer, Rangely District Hospital, Rangely, CO, p. A110

GOSHIA, Rob, Chief Financial Officer, Paulding County Hospital, Paulding, OH, p. A501

GOSLEE, Belle, Chief Nursing Officer, HEALTHSOUTH Chesapeake Rehabilitation Hospital, Salisbury, MD, p. A303

GOSNEY, Brett, Chief Executive Officer, Animas Surgical Hospital, Durango, CO, p. A104

GOSS, J. Richard, M.D. Medical Director, UW Medicine/Harborview Medical Center, Seattle, WA, p. A690

GOSS, Norma, R.N. Chief Operating Officer and Chief Nursing Officer, Flaget Memorial Hospital, Bardstown, KY, p. A257

GOSS, Roger, Director, Information Services, North Sunflower Medical Center, Ruleville, MS, p. A364

GOSSELIN, Gail
Director Human Resources, Landmark Medical Center, Woonsocket, RI, p. A561
Director Human Resources, Rehabilitation Hospital of Rhode Island, North Smithfield, RI, p. A560

GOSSENS, Kevin, Director Human Resources, ThedaCare Medical Center–Waupaca, Waupaca, WI, p. A718

GOSSETT, Lisa, MSN Chief Nursing Officer, OhioHealth Riverside Methodist Hospital, Columbus, OH, p. A491

GOTSOULIAS, Kostas, Interim Chief Executive Officer, Aspire Hospital, Conroe, TX, p. A607

GOTTI, Sreekant, Director Information Systems, Desert Valley Hospital, Victorville, CA, p. A98

GOTTLIEB, Harold, M.D. Chief Medical Officer, Memorial Hermann Memorial City Medical Center, Houston, TX, p. A625

GOTTLIEB, Jonathan, M.D. Senior Vice President and Chief Medical Officer, University of Maryland Medical Center, Baltimore, MD, p. A298

GOTTSCHALK, Amy, M.D. Chief Medical Officer, Verde Valley Medical Center; Vice President Quality, Northern Arizona Healthcare, Verde Valley Medical Center, Cottonwood, AZ, p. A32

GOTTSCHALL, Dan, Senior Vice President and Chief Clinical Officer, St. Vincent's Medical Center, Bridgeport, CT, p. A113

GOUGEON, Michele L., Executive Vice President and Chief Operating Officer, McLean Hospital, Belmont, MA, p. A305

GOUGH, Galal S., M.D. Chief of Staff, Coast Plaza Hospital, Norwalk, CA, p. A79

GOUGH, MSN, RN–, Michelle, Chief Nursing Officer, Southwest Mississippi Regional Medical Center, McComb, MS, p. A361

GOULD, Dana L., Chief Operation Officer, Broaddus Hospital, Philippi, WV, p. A699

GOULD, Jacquelyn M., MS Vice President Patient Care Services and Chief Nursing Officer, WellSpan Good Samaritan Hospital, Lebanon, PA, p. A543

GOULD, Tamara, R.N. Vice President Clinical Services and Chief Nursing Officer, Wabash General Hospital, Mount Carmel, IL, p. A197

GOULD, William R., Vice President Human Resources, Saint Joseph Hospital, Denver, CO, p. A104

GOULET, James P., Vice President Operations, Columbus Community Hospital, Columbus, NE, p. A395

GOULSON, Dan, M.D. Chief Medical Officer, Our Lady of Bellefonte Hospital, Ashland, KY, p. A257

GOURLEY, Paul, M.D. Chief Hospital Services, U. S. Air Force Hospital, Hampton, VA, p. A671

GOVE, Cynthia A., Chief Operating Officer, Hampstead Hospital, Hampstead, NH, p. A411

GOVERO, Elizabeth, R.N., Interim President and Chief Executive Officer, HSHS St. Joseph's Hospital, Highland, IL, p. A192

GOVINDAIAH, Rajesh G., M.D. Chief Medical Officer, Memorial Medical Center, Springfield, IL, p. A203

GOVORCHIN, Pete, Senior Vice President Operations, Midwestern Regional Medical Center, Zion, IL, p. A205

GOWDER, Mike, Chief Executive Officer, Union General Hospital, Inc., Blairsville, GA, p. B140

GOWEN, Tina, System Controller, Westfield Memorial Hospital, Westfield, NY, p. A459

GOWER, Gary, Chief Information Officer, Appling Healthcare System, Baxley, GA, p. A154

GOYAL, Alok, M.D. Medical Director, Post Acute Medical Specialty Hospital of Milwaukee, Greenfield, WI, p. A707

GOYAL, Deepak, M.D. Chief of Staff, Jacobson Memorial Hospital Care Center, Elgin, ND, p. A478

GOYKOVICH, Stephen, D.O. Chief Medical Officer, Jersey Shore Hospital, Jersey Shore, PA, p. A541

GOYTIA–LEOS, Dina, M.D. Chief of Staff, Nix Health Care System, San Antonio, TX, p. A646

GOZA, Brian, Chief Information Officer, Hemphill County Hospital, Canadian, TX, p. A605

GOZIAH, Vicky, Software Administrator, Select Specialty Hospital – Northeast Atlanta, Atlanta, GA, p. A153

GRABER, Donald, M.D. Medical Director, Richmond State Hospital, Richmond, IN, p. A221

GRABUS, Christina, R.N. Chief Nursing Officer, Novant Health Thomasville Medical Center, Thomasville, NC, p. A474

GRACE, Jeffery, M.D. Clinical Director, Buffalo Psychiatric Center, Buffalo, NY, p. A435

GRACE, Michael A., President, UPMC Mercy, Pittsburgh, PA, p. A551

GRACE, Richard, Chief Administrative Officer, Mayo Clinic Health System in Saint James, Saint James, MN, p. A350

GRACE, Walter, Chief Executive Officer and Administrator, Baptist Memorial Hospital–Union County, New Albany, MS, p. A363

GRACIE, Michael, Chief Information Officer, Veterans Health Care System of the Ozarks, Fayetteville, AR, p. A46

GRADDY, Steve W.
Chief Financial Officer, Freeman Health System, Joplin, MO, p. A372
Chief Financial Officer, Freeman Neosho Hospital, Neosho, MO, p. A372

GRADY, John M., Associate Director, Veterans Affairs Hudson Valley Health Care System, Montrose, NY, p. A443

GRADY, Kevin, M.D. Chief Medical Officer, St. John Hospital and Medical Center, Detroit, MI, p. A322

GRADY, Raymond, FACHE, President and Chief Executive Officer, Methodist Hospitals, Gary, IN, p. A212

GRAEBER, Tod
Administrator, Community Memorial Hospital, Turtle Lake, ND, p. A481
Administrator, Garrison Memorial Hospital, Garrison, ND, p. A479

GRAEBNER, David, President, Aurora Sheboygan Memorial Medical Center, Sheboygan, WI, p. A715

GRAEBNER, Nancy Kay, President and Chief Executive Officer, St. Joseph Mercy Chelsea, Chelsea, MI, p. A320

GRAF, John, Senior Vice President, Watertown Regional Medical Center, Watertown, WI, p. A718

GRAFTON, Jennifer, Chief Financial Officer, Shands Live Oak Regional Medical Center, Live Oak, FL, p. A134

GRAGG, Connie, Director Human Resources, Saint Mary's Regional Medical Center, Russellville, AR, p. A52

GRAGNOLATI, Brian A., FACHE, President and Chief Executive Officer, Atlantic Health System, Morristown, NJ, p. B16

GRAH, John A., FACHE, Chief Executive Officer, Lakewood Regional Medical Center, Lakewood, CA, p. A68

GRAHAM, Bill, President, Sequoia Hospital, Redwood City, CA, p. A85

GRAHAM, Bonnie S., Director, San Francisco VA Medical Center, San Francisco, CA, p. A90

GRAHAM, Brenda, Chief Nursing Officer, Barbourville ARH Hospital, Barbourville, KY, p. A257

GRAHAM, Brooke, Human Resources Manager, Franklin Woods Community Hospital, Johnson City, TN, p. A585

GRAHAM, Christopher W., Chief Financial Officer, Community Memorial Hospital, Hamilton, NY, p. A440

GRAHAM, Connie, Public Information Officer, Mercy Health Love County, Marietta, OK, p. A514

GRAHAM, David B., M.D. Senior Vice President and Chief Information Officer, Memorial Medical Center, Springfield, IL, p. A203

GRAHAM, Gail L., Director, Veterans Affairs Central Iowa Health Care System, Des Moines, IA, p. A230

GRAHAM, Jay, Interim Chief Financial Officer, Brandywine Hospital, Coatesville, PA, p. A535

GRAHAM, Jeff
    Market Leader and President, Mercy Health – Anderson Hospital, Cincinnati, OH, p. A488
    Market Leader and President, Mercy Health – Clermont Hospital, Batavia, OH, p. A484

GRAHAM, John, M.D. Vice President Medical Affairs, Day Kimball Hospital, Putnam, CT, p. A116

GRAHAM, Jon, Chief Financial Officer, Vidant Roanoke–Chowan Hospital, Ahoskie, NC, p. A460

GRAHAM, Kathryn, Director Communications and Community Relations, Novato Community Hospital, Novato, CA, p. A80

GRAHAM, Kimberley, R.N. Chief Nursing Officer and Chief Operating Officer, Broward Health Coral Springs, Coral Springs, FL, p. A126

GRAHAM, Larry M., FACHE, President and Chief Executive Officer, Lake Charles Memorial Hospital, Lake Charles, LA, p. A281

GRAHAM, Michelle, M.D
    Vice President Medical Affairs, Wheaton Franciscan Healthcare – Franklin, Franklin, WI, p. A706
    Vice President Medical Affairs, Wheaton Franciscan Healthcare – St. Francis, Milwaukee, WI, p. A712

GRAHAM, Scott, Chief Executive Officer, Three Rivers Hospital, Brewster, WA, p. A683

GRAHAM, Shauna, Director of Professional Services Human Resources, Marketing Foundation, Litzenberg Memorial County Hospital, Central City, NE, p. A394

GRAHAM, Sheri
    Director Human Resources and Administrative Services, Parkland Health Center – Liberty Street, Farmington, MO, p. A371
    Director Human Resources and Administrative Services, Parkland Health Center–Bonne Terre, Bonne Terre, MO, p. A367

GRAHAM, Sonja, Chief Executive Officer, North Oak Regional Medical Center, Senatobia, MS, p. A365

GRAHAM, Susan, R.N. Nurse Executive, HealthSource Saginaw, Inc., Saginaw, MI, p. A333

GRAHAM, Yolanda, M.D. Medical Director, Devereux Georgia Treatment Network, Kennesaw, GA, p. A161

GRAMER, Johanna, Director Human Resources, Mimbres Memorial Hospital, Deming, NM, p. A429

GRAMZA, Jeanne, Director Finance, Wheaton Franciscan Healthcare – All Saints, Racine, WI, p. A714

GRANADO–VILLAR, Deise, M.D. Chief Medical Officer and Senior Vice President Medical Affairs, Nicklaus Children's Hospital, Miami, FL, p. A137

GRANATH, Brad, M.D. Chief of Staff, Humboldt General Hospital, Winnemucca, NV, p. A409

GRANATO, Jerome, M.D
    Senior Vice President and Chief Medical Officer, Excela Frick Hospital, Mount Pleasant, PA, p. A545
    Senior Vice President and Chief Medical Officer, Excela Health Westmoreland Hospital, Greensburg, PA, p. A539

GRAND, Lawrence N., MS Chief Operating Officer, Hunterdon Medical Center, Flemington, NJ, p. A417

GRANDIOSI, Joe, Director Information Technology, Southern Hills Hospital and Medical Center, Las Vegas, NV, p. A406

GRANER, Terry J., R.N. Vice President Patient Care, Abbott Northwestern Hospital, Minneapolis, MN, p. A346

GRANGER, Keith, President and Chief Executive Officer, Grandview Medical Center, Birmingham, AL, p. A16

GRANT, Chad M., President and Chief Executive Officer, McLaren Oakland, Pontiac, MI, p. A332

GRANT, Cheryl, Director Information Systems, Coastal Carolina Hospital, Hardeeville, SC, p. A567

GRANT, Debra, R.N. Chief Nursing Officer, Texas Health Harris Methodist Hospital Hurst–Euless–Bedford, Bedford, TX, p. A602

GRANT, Gail, Director Human Resources, CHI St. Francis Health, Breckenridge, MN, p. A340

GRANT, Howard R., M.D., President and Chief Executive Officer, Lahey Health, Burlington, MA, p. B79

GRANT, Mikki, Chief Information Officer, Fort Belknap U. S. Public Health Service Indian Hospital, Harlem, MT, p. A388

GRANT, Pauline, FACHE, Interim President and Chief Executive Officer, Broward Health, Fort Lauderdale, FL, p. B24

GRANT, Samuel, Chief Financial Officer, Stephens Memorial Hospital, Breckenridge, TX, p. A603

GRANT, Tonya, Director Human Resources, T.J. Health Columbia, Columbia, KY, p. A258

GRANT, Will, Chief Financial Officer, Cannon Memorial Hospital, Pickens, SC, p. A569

GRANTHAM, Charlie, Manager Information Systems, Carolinas Hospital System Marion, Mullins, SC, p. A568

GRANTHAM, James, Administrator and Chief Executive Officer, Baptist Memorial Hospital–Booneville, Booneville, MS, p. A356

GRANVILLE, Brian, Director Information Technology, Buena Vista Regional Medical Center, Storm Lake, IA, p. A238

GRANVILLE, Sabrina M., Senior Vice President and Chief Human Resources Officer, Lowell General Hospital, Lowell, MA, p. A311

GRANZOW, Steven L., Chief Executive Officer, Lincoln County Hospital, Lincoln, KS, p. A248

GRASER, David, Vice President and Chief Information Officer, Hillcrest Hospital – South, Tulsa, OK, p. A521

GRASS, Gerald, Chief Nursing Officer, Pioneer Community Hospital of Patrick, Stuart, VA, p. A679

GRASS, Linda J., Chief Executive Officer, Lower Bucks Hospital, Bristol, PA, p. A534

GRASSER, Tierney Lynn, Senior Vice President and Chief Financial Officer, Olathe Medical Center, Olathe, KS, p. A250

GRATCH, Amie, Director Financial Services, LifeCare Hospitals of Dallas, Dallas, TX, p. A610

GRATRIX, Katie E., Administrative Assistant III, Alaska Psychiatric Institute, Anchorage, AK, p. A28

GRATZ, Silvia, D.O. Chief Medical Officer, Fairmount Behavioral Health System, Philadelphia, PA, p. A547

GRAU, Leah, Director Human Resources, Tulane Medical Center, New Orleans, LA, p. A285

GRAUMANN, Julie, Director, AllianceHealth Clinton, Clinton, OK, p. A510

GRAVES, Amanda, Chief Information Systems, Washington DC Veterans Affairs Medical Center, Washington, DC, p. A122

GRAVES, Bruce, M.D. Chief of Staff, Hale Ho'ola Hamakua, Honokaa, HI, p. A170

GRAVES, Buddy, Chief Information Officer, Southern Surgical Hospital, Slidell, LA, p. A288

GRAVES, Deanna, Chief Executive Officer, Texas Specialty Hospital at Lubbock, Lubbock, TX, p. A634

GRAVES, Elsie, Chief Nursing Officer, Central Texas Medical Center, San Marcos, TX, p. A648

GRAVES, Jared, Chief Financial Officer, Byrd Regional Hospital, Leesville, LA, p. A282

GRAVES, Jennifer, MS, Chief Executive, Swedish/Edmonds, Edmonds, WA, p. A684

GRAVES, Jimmy, Interim Chief Executive Officer, Jefferson Davis Community Hospital, Prentiss, MS, p. A364

GRAVES, John A., Chief Executive Officer, Lillian M. Hudspeth Memorial Hospital, Sonora, TX, p. A649

GRAY, Albert, Chief Executive Officer, The Children's Center Rehabilitation Hospital, Bethany, OK, p. A509

GRAY, Anthony, Chief Financial Officer, LAC–Olive View–UCLA Medical Center,, CA, p. A72

GRAY, Bob, Chief Financial Officer, Aspire Hospital, Conroe, TX, p. A607

GRAY, Brett, Director Human Resource, Sanpete Valley Hospital, Mount Pleasant, UT, p. A660

GRAY, Carrie, Director of Nursing, Riverview Behavioral Health, Texarkana, AR, p. A53

GRAY, Christie, Chief Nursing Officer, Good Samaritan Hospital, Dayton, OH, p. A492

GRAY, Clarence, Chief Financial Officer, TriStar Horizon Medical Center, Dickson, TN, p. A582

GRAY, David L., FACHE, President, Baptist Health Louisville, Louisville, KY, p. A264

GRAY, Eric, Chief Financial Officer, HEALTHSOUTH Rehabilitation Hospital of Memphis, Memphis, TN, p. A588

GRAY, Gary, D.O., Chief Executive Officer, Natividad Medical Center, Salinas, CA, p. A87

GRAY, Janis
    Interim Chief Information Officer, Dupont Hospital, Fort Wayne, IN, p. A210
    Chief Information Officer, Rehabilitation Hospital of Fort Wayne, Fort Wayne, IN, p. A211

GRAY, Jason, M.D. Chief Medical Officer, Mercy Medical Center, Roseburg, OR, p. A530

GRAY, Jeremy, Chief Operating Officer, Chippenham Hospital, Richmond, VA, p. A677

GRAY, Jerry, Interim Chief Executive Officer, HEALTHSOUTH East Valley Rehabilitation Hospital, Mesa, AZ, p. A34

GRAY, Judy
    Vice President Human Resources, Albany Memorial Hospital, Albany, NY, p. A433
    Vice President Human Resources, St. Peter's Hospital, Albany, NY, p. A433

GRAY, Karen D., Director Human Resources, Vibra Hospital of Southeastern Michigan, LLC, Lincoln Park, MI, p. A329

GRAY, Kris David, Chief Medical Officer, Florida Hospital Memorial Medical Center, Daytona Beach, FL, p. A127

GRAY, Larry, President, Baptist Health Corbin, Corbin, KY, p. A258

GRAY, Marty, R.N. Director of Nursing, Wyandot Memorial Hospital, Upper Sandusky, OH, p. A504

GRAY, Mary, Director Human Resources, Lehigh Regional Medical Center, Lehigh Acres, FL, p. A134

GRAY, Michelle, Nurse Executive, Atrium Medical Center of Corinth, Corinth, TX, p. A607

GRAY, Mike, Corporate Vice President Human Resources, East Texas Medical Center Tyler, Tyler, TX, p. A654

GRAY, Patricia, Director Health Information Management, Cumberland Hall Hospital, Hopkinsville, KY, p. A261

GRAY, Roshanda, Assistant Administrator, Memorial Medical Center, Port Lavaca, TX, p. A642

GRAY, Sarah, Vice President Information Services, East Alabama Medical Center, Opelika, AL, p. A24

GRAY, Stephen, Chief Administrative Officer, Sutter Maternity and Surgery Center of Santa Cruz, Santa Cruz, CA, p. A93

GRAY, Tami, Chief Financial Officer, Irwin County Hospital, Ocilla, GA, p. A164

GRAY, Teresa, Chief Nursing Officer and Assistant Vice President, INTEGRIS Canadian Valley Hospital, Yukon, OK, p. A523

GRAY, Terry, Vice President Human Resources, Emanuel Medical Center, Turlock, CA, p. A97

GRAY, Thomas, M.D. Medical Director, Montana State Hospital, Warm Springs, MT, p. A391

GRAY, Tracy
    Chief Information Officer, Grady General Hospital, Cairo, GA, p. A155
    Senior Vice President Information Services, John D. Archbold Memorial Hospital, Thomasville, GA, p. A167
    Chief Information Officer, Mitchell County Hospital, Camilla, GA, p. A155

GRAYBEAL, Phillip, CP
    Chief Financial Officer, Page Memorial Hospital, Luray, VA, p. A672
    Vice President, Finance, Shenandoah Memorial Hospital, Woodstock, VA, p. A681
    Chief Financial Officer, Warren Memorial Hospital, Front Royal, VA, p. A671

GRAYBILL, Matthew P., Chief Operating Officer, Children's Medical Center, Dayton, OH, p. A492

GRAYSON, Barbara, Vice President Human Resources, Mercy Hospital Washington, Washington, MO, p. A383

GREAR, Esther, Director Hospital Social Work and Assistant Hospital Administrator, Windhaven Psychiatric Hospital, Prescott Valley, AZ, p. A38

GREASON, Linda, Vice President Human Resources, Milford Regional Medical Center, Milford, MA, p. A312

GREBOSKY, Jamie, M.D. Vice President of Medical Affairs, Asante Rogue Regional Medical Center, Medford, OR, p. A528

GRECCO, Jamie, Chief Human Resource Executive, NYC Health + Hospitals / Jacobi,, NY, p. A448

GRECO, Andrew, Chief Financial Officer, Calvary Hospital,, NY, p. A444

GRECO, Anthony C., Compliance Officer, Essex County Hospital Center, Cedar Grove, NJ, p. A415

GRECO, Margaret, Chief Human Resources, Keller Army Community Hospital, West Point, NY, p. A459

GREELEY, Donna, Director Human Resources, Spalding Rehabilitation Hospital, Aurora, CO, p. A101

GREEN, Amber, R.N. Chief Clinical Officer, Memorial Hospital of Carbon County, Rawlins, WY, p. A723

GREEN, Arnold, Senior Vice President and Chief Operating Officer, McLeod Loris Seacoast Hospital, Loris, SC, p. A568

GREEN, Barbara, Director Human Resources, O'Connor Hospital, Delhi, NY, p. A438

GREEN, Christi, R.N. Vice President, Human Resources, Frisbie Memorial Hospital, Rochester, NH, p. A413

GREEN, Christopher, Chief Financial Officer, Carolinas Hospital System Marion, Mullins, SC, p. A568

GREEN, Dante, Assistant Vice President Operations, New Orleans East Hospital, New Orleans, LA, p. A285

GREEN, Darryl, Director Administration, Naval Hospital Jacksonville, Jacksonville, FL, p. A132

GREEN, David, Chief Human Resources, West Palm Beach Veterans Affairs Medical Center, West Palm Beach, FL, p. A150

GREEN, David F., M.D. Chief Medical Officer, Concord Hospital, Concord, NH, p. A410

GREEN, Debra Jane, R.N. Director of Nursing, Turquoise Lodge Hospital, Albuquerque, NM, p. A428

GREEN, Dona, Chief Operating Officer, NYC Health + Hospitals / Queens,, NY, p. A449

GREEN, Elizabeth, Chief Human Resources Officer, Cooper University Health Care, Camden, NJ, p. A415

GREEN, Garry Kim, FACHE, Administrator, Shriners Hospitals for Children–Shreveport, Shreveport, LA, p. A288

GREEN, Gayle, Director of Nursing, Hale Ho'ola Hamakua, Honokaa, HI, p. A170

GREEN, Gene E., M.D., Chief Executive Officer, South Shore Hospital, South Weymouth, MA, p. A314

GREEN, Jack W., Administrator, Antelope Memorial Hospital, Neligh, NE, p. A399

GREEN, Jodie L., Chief Nursing Officer, Kindred Hospital Colorado Springs, Colorado Springs, CO, p. A102

GREEN, John
Vice President Professional Services and Facility Planning, Iredell Health System, Statesville, NC, p. A474
Vice President Finance, St. Peter's Hospital, Helena, MT, p. A388

GREEN, Julie, Vice President Human Resources, Cheshire Medical Center, Keene, NH, p. A411

GREEN, Karen, Chief Information Officer, Brooks Rehabilitation Hospital, Jacksonville, FL, p. A131

GREEN, Kaye, FACHE, Director, W. G. (Bill) Heffner Veterans Affairs Medical Center, Salisbury, NC, p. A473

GREEN, Ladonna, Director Human Resources, Glen Rose Medical Center, Glen Rose, TX, p. A620

GREEN Jr., Larry D., Chief Executive Officer, Windhaven Psychiatric Hospital, Prescott Valley, AZ, p. A38

GREEN, Marsha, Chief Executive Officer, Essentia Health–Deer River, Deer River, MN, p. A341

GREEN, Patrick, Interim Chief Executive Officer, St. Anthony Hospital, Lakewood, CO, p. A108

GREEN, Paul, Chief Clinical Officer, Kindred Hospital–Aurora, Aurora, CO, p. A101

GREEN, Ricky, Senior Human Resources Business Partner, Spectrum Health Big Rapids Hospital, Big Rapids, MI, p. A319

GREEN, Rose Marie, Director Human Resources, Humboldt General Hospital, Winnemucca, NV, p. A409

GREEN, Steve, Comptroller, Jasper General Hospital, Bay Springs, MS, p. A355

GREEN, Susan, Senior Vice President Finance, Chief Financial Officer, Lowell General Hospital, Lowell, MA, p. A311

GREEN, Tracy V., Chief Financial Officer, NYC Health + Hospitals / Metropolitan, New York, NY, p. A448

GREEN, Vincent, Medical Director, Greenville Health System – Laurens County Memorial Hospital, Clinton, SC, p. A563

GREENBERG, Mark, M.D
Chief Medical Officer, Cape Coral Hospital, Cape Coral, FL, p. A125
Medical Director, Gulf Coast Medical Center, Fort Myers, FL, p. A129

GREENBERG, Raymond, M.D., Executive Vice Chancellor, University of Texas System, Austin, TX, p. B149

GREENBLATT, James, M.D. Medical Officer, Vice President Medical Clinical Services, Walden Psychiatric Care, Waltham, MA, p. A315

GREENE, Arthur, M.D. Vice President Medical Affairs, Sentara CarePlex Hospital, Hampton, VA, p. A671

GREENE, Beth, Chief Operating Officer, Cherokee Indian Hospital, Cherokee, NC, p. A463

GREENE, Bradley, Chief Financial Officer, WellStar Douglas Hospital, Douglasville, GA, p. A158

GREENE, Cora, Chief Nursing Officer, Novant Health Rowan Medical Center, Salisbury, NC, p. A473

GREENE, Dustin, Chief Executive Officer, TriStar Horizon Medical Center, Dickson, TN, p. A582

GREENE, Erin, Coordinator Human Resources, Kindred Hospital–San Francisco Bay Area, San Leandro, CA, p. A92

GREENE, Hugh, President and Chief Executive Officer, Baptist Health, Jacksonville, FL, p. B19

GREENE, Kathleen, Director Human Resources, Promise Hospital of San Diego, San Diego, CA, p. A88

GREENE, Melodi, R.N. Chief Nursing Officer, Community Howard Regional Health, Kokomo, IN, p. A216

GREENE, Palmer, R.N. Chief Nursing Officer, Sierra Vista Hospital, Truth or Consequences, NM, p. A432

GREENE, Robert, Director Information Technology, Promise Hospital of Miss Lou, Vidalia, LA, p. A289

GREENE, Scott, Chief Information Officer, Tennova Healthcare–Clarksville, Clarksville, TN, p. A581

GREENE, Todd, Chief Executive Officer, Arizona Spine and Joint Hospital, Mesa, AZ, p. A34

GREENE, Tracie, Director Human Resources, Brigham City Community Hospital, Brigham City, UT, p. A659

GREENER, Angela, Chief Administrative Officer, West Jefferson Medical Center, Marrero, LA, p. A283

GREENFIELD, Tadd, Executive Vice President and Chief Operating Officer, Regional West Medical Center, Scottsbluff, NE, p. A402

GREENLEE, Kathryn M., R.N
Vice President, Clinical Services/CNO, ProMedica Bixby Hospital, Adrian, MI, p. A318
Vice President, Clinical Services/CNO, ProMedica Herrick Hospital, Tecumseh, MI, p. A335

GREENMAN, Jennifer, Vice President Chief Information Officer, H. Lee Moffitt Cancer Center and Research Institute, Tampa, FL, p. A147

GREENMAN, Sharon, Director Human Resources, Melissa Memorial Hospital, Holyoke, CO, p. A107

GREENWOOD, Les, President, Medical Staff, Davis Hospital and Medical Center, Layton, UT, p. A660

GREENWOOD, Sherri, Chief Nursing Officer, St. John's Hospital, Springfield, IL, p. A203

GREENWOOD, Susan, R.N. Vice President and Chief Nursing Officer, St. Bernards Medical Center, Jonesboro, AR, p. A48

GREER, Nancy, R.N. Vice President Nursing, Asante Three Rivers Medical Center, Grants Pass, OR, p. A526

GREER, Troy, Chief Executive Officer, Lovelace Medical Center, Albuquerque, NM, p. A427

GREGERSON, Scott, President and Chief Executive Officer, Stanford Health Care – ValleyCare, Pleasanton, CA, p. A83

GREGG, Richard, M.D. Medical Director, LifeCare Hospital of Dayton, Miamisburg, OH, p. A499

GREGG, Shawna, Director Human Resources, Porterville Developmental Center, Porterville, CA, p. A83

GREGG, Sherry, Chief Information Technology Officer, Beckley Veterans Affairs Medical Center, Beckley, WV, p. A694

GREGG, Thomas, Vice President Human Resources, St. Peter's Hospital, Helena, MT, p. A388

GREGG, Tom, Vice President Human Resources, CHI St. Alexius Health, Bismarck, ND, p. A477

GREGG, Travis, Director Support Services, Kearney Regional Medical Center, Kearney, NE, p. A397

GREGGAIN, Don, M.D. Physician Network Director, Tri–State Memorial Hospital, Clarkston, WA, p. A683

GREGONIS, Michael, Comptroller, Naval Hospital Jacksonville, Jacksonville, FL, p. A132

GREGOR, Brian, Manager Information Technology Operations, Glendale Memorial Hospital and Health Center, Glendale, CA, p. A64

GREGORIAN, Myra, Vice President and Chief Human Resources Officer, Children's Hospital Los Angeles, Los Angeles, CA, p. A70

GREGORICH, Miki, Director Human Resources, Pioneer Medical Center, Big Timber, MT, p. A385

GREGORY, Adina, Chief Operating Officer, Great Bend Regional Hospital, Great Bend, KS, p. A244

GREGORY, Audrey, MSN, Chief Executive Officer, Saint Francis Hospital, Memphis, TN, p. A589

GREGORY, Ben, Director, Walter B. Jones Alcohol and Drug Abuse Treatment Center, Greenville, NC, p. A466

GREGORY, Jan, Chief of Human Resources, Crittenden County Hospital, Marion, KY, p. A266

GREGORY, Jay, M.D. Chief Medical Officer, EASTAR Health System, Muskogee, OK, p. A515

GREGORY, Jim, Controller, Methodist Hospital of Chicago, Chicago, IL, p. A185

GREGORY, Phyllis, Registered Health Information Administrator, Southern Inyo Healthcare District, Lone Pine, CA, p. A69

GREGORY, Sean, Chief Executive Officer, Health First Holmes Regional Medical Center, Melbourne, FL, p. A135

GREGORY, Shawn, Chief Financial Officer, St. Petersburg General Hospital, Saint Petersburg, FL, p. A144

GREGORY, Trip, Senior Vice President Human Resources, Palmetto Health Baptist, Columbia, SC, p. A564

GREGOS, Ruth, Director Finance, Shriners Hospitals for Children–Tampa, Tampa, FL, p. A147

GREGSON, Mark, Interim Chief Executive Officer, Estes Park Medical Center, Estes Park, CO, p. A105

GREIMAN, Alan W., Chief Executive Officer and President, Royal Oaks Hospital, Windsor, MO, p. A384

GREINER, Walter, Chief Financial Officer, AtlantiCare Regional Medical Center, Atlantic City, NJ, p. A414

GREINER, William, M.D. Chief of Staff, F. W. Huston Medical Center, Winchester, KS, p. A256

GRENALDO, Paul, Executive Vice President and Chief Operating Officer, Doctors Community Hospital, Lanham, MD, p. A302

GRENDON, M. Todd, M.D. President Medical Staff, Presence Saint Joseph Hospital, Chicago, IL, p. A185

GRENIER, Raymond, Chief Financial Officer, Memorial Medical Center, Las Cruces, NM, p. A430

GRENNAN, Jr., M. Joseph, M.D. Senior Vice President and Chief Medical Officer, Reading Hospital, West Reading, PA, p. A557

GRESKOVICH, William, Chief Information Officer, Saint Agnes Hospital, Baltimore, MD, p. A297

GRESSLE, Charles, Chief Executive Officer, Medical Center of Plano, Plano, TX, p. A641

GREW, Kate, MSN Vice President/Chief Nurse Executive, Carolinas HealthCare System NorthEast, Concord, NC, p. A463

GREW, Terry, Chief Business Office, Hampton Veterans Affairs Medical Center, Hampton, VA, p. A671

GREY, Mitzi, Chief Operating Officer, Bath Community Hospital, Hot Springs, VA, p. A672

GRIBBIN, John, FACHE, President and Chief Executive Officer, CentraState Healthcare System, Freehold, NJ, p. A417

GRICE, William N., Executive Director, Kaiser Permanente Los Angeles Medical Center, Los Angeles, CA, p. A71

GRICUS, Peggy, R.N. Vice President, Patient Care Services and Chief Nursing Officer, Silver Cross Hospital, New Lenox, IL, p. A198

GRIDLEY, Mark, FACHE Executive Vice President and Chief Operating Officer, FHN Memorial Hospital, Freeport, IL, p. A190

GRIEB, Paula, R.N
Vice President Patient Care Service and Chief Nursing Officer, ProMedica Bay Park Hospital, Oregon, OH, p. A500
Chief Nursing Officer, ProMedica Fostoria Community Hospital, Fostoria, OH, p. A494

GRIEP, John, M.D. Chief Medical Director, St. Catherine Hospital, East Chicago, IN, p. A209

GRIESHEIM, Glen, Chief Executive Officer, Select Specialty Hospital–Des Moines, Des Moines, IA, p. A229

GRIEST, Mary, Vice President Finance and Chief Financial Officer, University Hospitals Samaritan Medical Center, Ashland, OH, p. A484

GRIFFEE, James, M.D. Chief Medical Officer, Slidell Memorial Hospital, Slidell, LA, p. A288

GRIFFES, Carol, Administrator, Duane L. Waters Hospital, Jackson, MI, p. A327

GRIFFIE, Lametria, Interim Chief Nursing Officer, HEALTHSOUTH Rehabilitation Hospital of Texarkana, Texarkana, TX, p. A652

GRIFFIN, Amy, Vice President Patient Care Services, John D. Archbold Memorial Hospital, Thomasville, GA, p. A167

GRIFFIN, Betty, Interim Chief Nursing Officer, Chester Regional Medical Center, Chester, SC, p. A563

GRIFFIN, Brad, Chief Executive Officer, Colleton Medical Center, Walterboro, SC, p. A570

GRIFFIN, Breanne, R.N. Executive Director, Nursing, Mercy Hospital Lincoln, Troy, MO, p. A383

GRIFFIN, Brian, Director Information Services, Springhill Medical Center, Springhill, LA, p. A288

GRIFFIN, Charles, Director of Nursing, Clay County Hospital, Ashland, AL, p. A15

GRIFFIN, Christopher B., Chief Executive Officer, D. W. McMillan Memorial Hospital, Brewton, AL, p. A17

GRIFFIN, Cindy
Chief Nursing Officer, Liberty Dayton Regional Medical Center, Liberty, TX, p. A632
Director Human Resources, Medical Center Barbour, Eufaula, AL, p. A19

GRIFFIN, Dean, Chief Executive Officer, Lawrence Medical Center, Moulton, AL, p. A24

GRIFFIN, Donald, CPA Chief Financial Officer, New London Hospital, New London, NH, p. A412

GRIFFIN, Douglas, M.D. Vice President Medical Officer, Sanford Medical Center Fargo, Fargo, ND, p. A479

GRIFFIN, Holly, R.N. Chief Nursing Officer, Lady of the Sea General Hospital, Cut Off, LA, p. A276

GRIFFIN, James, Manager Information Systems, Martin General Hospital, Williamston, NC, p. A475

GRIFFIN, Jared, Controller, Kindred Rehabilitation Hospital Arlington, Arlington, TX, p. A597

GRIFFIN, Jeannine, M.D. Chief of Staff, Memorial Medical Center, Port Lavaca, TX, p. A642

GRIFFIN, Jeff, Assistant Vice President Finance, Carolinas HealthCare System Anson, Wadesboro, NC, p. A475

GRIFFIN, Joe, Controller, HealthSouth Rehabilitation Hospital Round Rock, Round Rock, TX, p. A644

GRIFFIN, Leah, Chief Executive Officer, Big Sandy Medical Center, Big Sandy, MT, p. A385

GRIFFIN, Margaret Elizabeth, Chief Executive Officer, HonorHealth John C. Lincoln Medical Center, Phoenix, AZ, p. A36

GRIFFIN, Matthew, M.D. Vice President Medical Affairs, DMC – Sinai–Grace Hospital, Detroit, MI, p. A321

GRIFFIN, Paulette
Vice President Human Resources, DMC – Detroit Receiving Hospital, Detroit, MI, p. A321
Director Human Resources, DMC – Sinai–Grace Hospital, Detroit, MI, p. A321

GRIFFIN, Philip, Director of Operations, Rochester Psychiatric Center, Rochester, NY, p. A454

GRIFFIN–JONES, Christie, R.N. Chief Nursing Officer, HealthSouth Rehabilitation Hospital of Humble, LLC, Humble, TX, p. A628

GRIFFIN–MAHON, Selena, Assistant Vice President Human Resources, Bronx–Lebanon Hospital Center Health Care System, NY, p. A444

GRIFFIS, Daniel, M.D. Chief Medical Officer, Syringa Hospital and Clinics, Grangeville, ID, p. A176

GRIFFITH, Barbara, M.D. Chief Medical Officer, Duke Regional Hospital, Durham, NC, p. A464

GRIFFITH, Barbara, Vice President Human Resources, St. Anthony's Rehabilitation Hospital, Lauderdale Lakes, FL, p. A134

GRIFFITH, David, M.D. Medical Director, Texas Center for Infectious Disease, San Antonio, TX, p. A647

GRIFFITH, H. Wes, Chief Financial Officer, Tennova Healthcare – Cleveland, Cleveland, TN, p. A581

GRIFFITH, James D.
Chief Operating Officer, Tanner Higgins General Hospital, Bremen, GA, p. A155
Chief Operating Officer, Tanner Medical Center–Carrollton, Carrollton, GA, p. A155
Chief Operating Officer, Tanner Medical Center–Carrollton, Carrollton, GA, p. A155

GRIFFITH, Jeanne, Chief Nursing Officer, Coryell Memorial Hospital, Gatesville, TX, p. A620

GRIFFITH, John H., Ph.D., President & Chief Executive Officer, Kedren Community Mental Health Center, Los Angeles, CA, p. A72

GRIFFITH, Joshua, Manager Human Resources, Presbyterian Espanola Hospital, Espanola, NM, p. A429

GRIFFITH, Patti, R.N. Chief Nursing Officer, Methodist Hospital for Surgery, Addison, TX, p. A595

GRIFFITH, Susan M., Chief Operations Officer, Eastern State Hospital, Lexington, KY, p. A263

GRIFFITHS, Elaine, R.N. Chief Nursing Officer, Chesapeake Regional Healthcare, Chesapeake, VA, p. A668

GRIFFITHS, Mark, Director Management Information Systems, Incline Village Community Hospital, Incline Village, NV, p. A405

GRIGG, Dan, Chief Executive Officer, Harney District Hospital, Burns, OR, p. A524

GRIGG, William E., Senior Vice President and Chief Financial Officer, Methodist Hospital of Southern California, Arcadia, CA, p. A55

GRIGGS, Stacie, MIS Analyst, North Mississippi Medical Center–West Point, West Point, MS, p. A366

GRIGSBY, Jan, Vice President and Chief Financial Officer, Springhill Memorial Hospital, Mobile, AL, p. A22

GRIGSON, John A., Vice President and Chief Financial Officer, Covenant Medical Center, Lubbock, TX, p. A634

GRILL, Laura D., R.N. Executive Vice President and Administrator, East Alabama Medical Center, Opelika, AL, p. A24

GRILLO, Jorge C., Chief Information Officer, Canton–Potsdam Hospital, Potsdam, NY, p. A453

GRIMALDI, Richard, President Medical Staff, Highlands Hospital, Connellsville, PA, p. A536

GRIMER, Ginny, Director Human Resources, George E. Weems Memorial Hospital, Apalachicola, FL, p. A123

GRIMES, Pam, Director Human Resources, AMG Specialty Hospital–Edmond, Edmond, OK, p. A511

GRIMES, Paula, R.N. Chief Nursing Officer, NEA Baptist Memorial Hospital, Jonesboro, AR, p. A48

GRIMES, Teresa, Chief Executive Officer, Washington County Hospital, Chatom, AL, p. A18

GRIMES, Walter, Director Information Technology, Good Shepherd Medical Center–Marshall, Marshall, TX, p. A636

GRIMLEY, Karen A., Chief Nursing Executive, Ronald Reagan UCLA Medical Center, Los Angeles, CA, p. A74

GRIMM, Tamara, R.N. Chief Clinical Officer and Chief Nursing Officer, Cornerstone Hospital of Bossier City, Bossier City, LA, p. A274

GRIMM, William, Chief Information Officer, Henry County Hospital, Napoleon, OH, p. A500

GRIMMER, Michael, Chief Operating Officer, Athol Memorial Hospital, Athol, MA, p. A305

GRIMMETT, Teresa, Chief Executive Officer, Wayne Medical Center, Waynesboro, TN, p. A594

GRIMSHAW, Bruce P., FACHE, Chief Executive Officer, Southern California Hospital at Hollywood, Los Angeles, CA, p. A74

GRIMSHAW, Matthew, President, Mercy Medical Center, Williston, ND, p. A482

GRIMSLEY, Denise, R.N., Vice President and Administrator, Florida Hospital Wauchula, Wauchula, FL, p. A149

GRINER, Alisa R., Director, Human Resources, Memorial Health, Savannah, GA, p. A166

GRINNELL, Steven, Chief Executive Officer, Lourdes Hospital, Paducah, KY, p. A268

GRINNEY, Jay F., President and Chief Executive Officer, HEALTHSOUTH Corporation, Birmingham, AL, p. B65

GRIPPI, Michael, M.D. Chief Medical Officer, Good Shepherd Penn Partners Specialty Hospital at Rittenhouse, Philadelphia, PA, p. A548

GRISH, John, Chief Financial Officer, Johnson Memorial Medical Center, Stafford Springs, CT, p. A117

GRISHOW, Cathy, Director Human Resources, Ellett Memorial Hospital, Appleton City, MO, p. A367

GRISIER, Douglas, D.O. Medical Director, HEALTHSOUTH Rehabilitation Hospital of Erie, Erie, PA, p. A538

GRISNAK, Karen, R.N. Chief Operating Officer and Assistant Administrator Quality Services, Kaiser Permanente Vallejo Medical Center, Vallejo, CA, p. A98

GRISNER, Margaret, Chief Executive Officer, Kiowa District Hospital and Manor, Kiowa, KS, p. A247

GRISPINO, Frank, Vice President Operations, SSM Health St. Francis Hospital – Maryville, Maryville, MO, p. A376

GRISSLER, Brian G., President and Chief Executive Officer, Stamford Hospital, Stamford, CT, p. A117

GRISSOM, Robyn, Director Employee Relations, OSF Saint Anthony's Health Center, Alton, IL, p. A180

GRISSOM, Tina, Chief Information Technology Officer, Arkansas State Hospital, Little Rock, AR, p. A48

GROCE, Vicky, Chief Nursing Officer, Lincoln County Health System, Fayetteville, TN, p. A583

GROCHALA, Eugene
Vice President Information Systems, Capital Health Medical Center–Hopewell, Pennington, NJ, p. A422
Vice President Information Systems, Capital Health Regional Medical Center, Trenton, NJ, p. A424

GROCHOLSKI, James F., FACHE, Chief Executive Officer, Wesley Rehabilitation Hospital, Wichita, KS, p. A256

GROENEWEG, Jennifer, R.N. Director of Nursing, Spectrum Health Special Care Hospital, Grand Rapids, MI, p. A325

GROENIG, Matt, Vice President Finance, St. Luke's McCall, McCall, ID, p. A177

GROEPER, William E., Vice President Finance, Beloit Health System, Beloit, WI, p. A703

GROEPPER, Ronald
Senior Vice President and Area Manager, Kaiser Permanente San Francisco Medical Center, San Francisco, CA, p. A90
Senior Vice President and Area Manager, Kaiser Permanente South San Francisco, South San Francisco, CA, p. A95

GROESBECK, John
Area Finance Officer, Kaiser Permanente San Rafael Medical Center, San Rafael, CA, p. A92
Area Finance Officer, Kaiser Permanente Santa Rosa Medical Center, Santa Rosa, CA, p. A94

GROGAN, Ed, Vice President Information Services and Chief Information Officer, Calvert Memorial Hospital, Prince Frederick, MD, p. A302

GROGAN, Richard
Interim Chief Executive Officer, Palestine Regional Medical Center, Palestine, TX, p. A640
Interim Chief Executive Officer, Palestine Regional Medical Center–East, Palestine, TX, p. A640

GRONBACH, Sue, Director Human Resources, Providence – Providence Park Hospital, Southfield Campus, Southfield, MI, p. A334

GRONERT, Thomas, Chief Information Officer, University of Maryland St. Joseph Medical Center, Towson, MD, p. A304

GRONEWOLD, Russell, Chief Financial Officer, Bryan Medical Center, Lincoln, NE, p. A397

GRONOW, Thomas, Chief Operating Officer, University of Colorado Hospital, Aurora, CO, p. A101

GROOM, Scott C., Vice President Information Services and Chief Information Officer, Bassett Medical Center, Cooperstown, NY, p. A437

GROOMS, Kim, Administrator, King's Daughters Medical Center Ohio, Portsmouth, OH, p. A501

GROOMS, Jr., Richard Walter, Chief Human Resources Officer, AnMed Health Medical Center, Anderson, SC, p. A562

GROS, Albert, M.D. Chief Medical Officer, St. David's South Austin Medical Center, Austin, TX, p. A600

GROS, Mark, Director Human Resources, United Medical Rehabilitation Hospital, Hammond, LA, p. A278

GROSE, Jana, Chief Information Officer, Massena Memorial Hospital, Massena, NY, p. A442

GROSECLOSE, Cathy, Vice President Patient Care Services, Grady Memorial Hospital, Chickasha, OK, p. A510

GROSKREUTZ, Kevin
Division Chief Information Officer, Ancillary Systems, HSHS St. Joseph's Hospital, Chippewa Falls, WI, p. A704
Chief Information Officer, Sacred Heart Hospital, Eau Claire, WI, p. A705

GROSS, Barry L., M.D. Executive Vice President and Chief Medical Officer, Riverside Regional Medical Center, Newport News, VA, p. A674

GROSS, Cathy, Director Health Information Management Systems, Wrangell Medical Center, Wrangell, AK, p. A30

GROSS, Cindy, Director of Finance, Barnes–Jewish St. Peters Hospital, Saint Peters, MO, p. A382

GROSS, Denton, Director Information Services, Larue D. Carter Memorial Hospital, Indianapolis, IN, p. A214

GROSS, Kevin J., FACHE, President and Chief Executive Officer, Hillcrest Medical Center, Tulsa, OK, p. A521

GROSS, Kristin, Director Information Technology Center, Avera McKennan Hospital and University Health Center, Sioux Falls, SD, p. A576

GROSS, Len, Chief Human Resources Officer, Sheridan Memorial Hospital, Sheridan, WY, p. A723

GROSS, Mark
Senior Business Director Finance, Mercy Health, Lakeshore Campus, Shelby, MI, p. A334
Executive Vice President and Chief Financial Officer, South Haven Health System, South Haven, MI, p. A334

GROSS, Paul, Human Services and Finance Officer, Larry B. Zieverink, Sr. Alcoholism Treatment Center, Raleigh, NC, p. A472

GROSS, Peter A., M.D. Senior Vice President and Chief Medical Officer, Hackensack University Medical Center, Hackensack, NJ, p. A417

GROSS, Randy, Chief Operating Officer, Kendall Regional Medical Center, Miami, FL, p. A136

GROSS, Tina, MSN Chief Nursing Officer, Sparrow Specialty Hospital, Lansing, MI, p. A328

GROSSMAN, Drew, Chief Executive Officer, Broward Health Coral Springs, Coral Springs, FL, p. A126

GROSSMAN, Hannah, M.D. Chief Medical Officer, Los Robles Hospital and Medical Center, Thousand Oaks, CA, p. A96

GROSSMAN, Joseph
Chief Financial Officer, McDowell ARH Hospital, McDowell, KY, p. A266
Vice President Fiscal Affairs, Whitesburg ARH Hospital, Whitesburg, KY, p. A270

GROSSMAN, Martin, Chief of Staff, Aventura Hospital and Medical Center, Aventura, FL, p. A123

GROSSMAN, Robert I., M.D., Chief Executive Officer, NYU Langone Medical Center, New York, NY, p. A449

GROSSO, Michael, M.D. Senior Vice President Medical Affairs, Huntington Hospital, Huntington, NY, p. A440

GROTELUSCHEN, Ronald J., Chief Financial Officer, Coastal Carolina Hospital, Hardeeville, SC, p. A567

GROTH, McGarrett, Chief of Staff, Atchison Hospital, Atchison, KS, p. A240

GROVE, Julia, Chief Nursing Officer, Jackson Purchase Medical Center, Mayfield, KY, p. A266

GROVE, Lyle, Human Resources Director, North Dakota State Hospital, Jamestown, ND, p. A480

GROVER, Amy, Director, Appalachian Behavioral Healthcare, Athens, OH, p. A484

GROVER, James, Manager Data Processing, Atascadero State Hospital, Atascadero, CA, p. A55

GROVES, Ned, Executive Vice President and Administrator, Memorial Sloan–Kettering Cancer Center, New York, NY, p. A446

GROVES, Tandy, Coordinator Human Resources, Bailey Medical Center, Owasso, OK, p. A518

GROW, Heidi, Director Human Resources, Aurora Sinai Medical Center, Milwaukee, WI, p. A711

GROW, Julie E., Chief Financial Officer, Hocking Valley Community Hospital, Logan, OH, p. A497

GROWSE, Michael, M.D. Clinical Director, Federal Medical Center, Lexington, KY, p. A263

GRUBB, Michael
Chief Financial Officer, BridgePoint Hospital Capitol Hill, Washington, DC, p. A121
Chief Financial Officer, BridgePoint Hospital National Harbor, Washington, DC, p. A121

GRUBB, Nora, Chief Financial Officer, Big Sandy Medical Center, Big Sandy, MT, p. A385

GRUBBS, Stephen, Chief Executive Officer, Bay Medical Center Sacred Heart Health System, Panama City, FL, p. A141

GRUBER, Kreg, Chief Operating Officer, Memorial Hospital of South Bend, South Bend, IN, p. A222

GRUBER, Norman F., President and Chief Executive Officer, Salem Health, Salem, OR, p. B117

GRUBER, Scott, M.D. Chief of Staff, John D. Dingell Veterans Affairs Medical Center, Detroit, MI, p. A322

GRUEBER, Cynthia M., Senior Vice President and Chief Operating Officer, OHSU Hospital, Portland, OR, p. A529

GRUEN, Jeremy, Director Information Systems, Pike County Memorial Hospital, Louisiana, MO, p. A376

GRUHONJIC, Osman
  Chief Financial Officer, Lehigh Regional Medical Center, Lehigh Acres, FL, p. A134
  Chief Financial Officer, Venice Regional Bayfront Health, Venice, FL, p. A149

GRUN, Joseph, Chief Information Officer, New York State Psychiatric Institute, New York, NY, p. A447

GRUNDSTROM, Jason, Chief Executive Officer, Kindred Hospital Northland, Kansas City, MO, p. A373

GRUNER, Dean, M.D., President and Chief Executive Officer, ThedaCare, Inc., Appleton, WI, p. B135

GRUNHOVD, April, Chief Nursing Officer, RiverView Health, Crookston, MN, p. A341

GRUNWALD, Pat, MSN Chief Nursing Officer, Meriter UnityPoint Health, Madison, WI, p. A709

GRUVER, Laquita, Fiscal Officer, Grand Junction Veterans Health Care System, Grand Junction, CO, p. A106

GRUZENSKY, Denton, Director Human Resources, Feather River Hospital, Paradise, CA, p. A82

GRZYBOWSKI, John, M.D. Medical Director, Mayo Clinic Health System in Albert Lea, Albert Lea, MN, p. A338

GUACCIO, Anthony, President and Chief Executive Officer, Swedish Covenant Hospital, Chicago, IL, p. A187

GUADAGNOLI, Donald, M.D. Chief Medical Officer, Cape Cod Hospital, Hyannis, MA, p. A311

GUAJARDO, Carlos, Chief Financial Officer, South Texas Health System, Edinburg, TX, p. A614

GUAJARDO, Michael, Director Finance, CHRISTUS Spohn Hospital Alice, Alice, TX, p. A595

GUARINO, Celia, R.N. Vice President and Chief Nursing Officer, Holy Cross Hospital, Silver Spring, MD, p. A303

GUARINO, Rick, M.D. Vice President Medical Affairs, Wilson Medical Center, Wilson, NC, p. A475

GUARNESCHELLI, Philip, Senior Vice President and Chief Operating Officer, Pinnacle Health System, Harrisburg, PA, p. A540

GUARNI, Andrew, Chief Financial Officer, Hoag Memorial Hospital Presbyterian, Newport Beach, CA, p. A79

GUARNIERI, Candace
  Chief Financial Officer, Phoebe Worth Medical Center, Sylvester, GA, p. A167
  Chief Financial Officer, Southwest Georgia Regional Medical Center, Cuthbert, GA, p. A157

GUARRACINO, Joseph, Senior Vice President and Chief Financial Officer, White Plains Hospital Center, White Plains, NY, p. A459

GUARRERA, Frank, Executive Vice President and Chief Financial Officer, Motion Picture and Television Fund Hospital and Residential Services,, CA, p. A73

GUBERMAN, Wayne, Director Finance, Matheny Medical and Educational Center, Peapack, NJ, p. A421

GUDAHL, Shanna, Manager Human Resources, United Hospital District, Blue Earth, MN, p. A339

GUEHLSTORF, Daniel, M.D. Chief of Staff, Midwest Orthopedic Specialty Hospital, Franklin, WI, p. A705

GUELKER, Rhonda, Senior Director Finance, Rolling Plains Memorial Hospital, Sweetwater, TX, p. A651

GUERCI, Alan D., M.D., President and Chief Executive Officer, Catholic Health Services of Long Island, Rockville Centre, NY, p. B30

GUERIN, Stephanie, Chief Nursing Officer, HealthSouth Rehabilitation Hospital Round Rock, Round Rock, TX, p. A644

GUERRANT, Eric, M.D. President Medical Staff, Ephraim McDowell Regional Medical Center, Danville, KY, p. A259

GUERRERO, Bonnie, Director Human Resources, Valley View Medical Center, Fort Mohave, AZ, p. A32

GUERRERO, Marisa, Director Human Resources, Laredo Specialty Hospital, Laredo, TX, p. A632

GUERRIERO, Marianne, Nurse Executive, Christian Health Care Center, Wyckoff, NJ, p. A426

GUEST, William, M.D. Senior Vice President and Chief Medical Officer, Tift Regional Medical Center, Tifton, GA, p. A167

GUEVARA Jr., Al, FACHE, President, CHI St. Luke's Health Brazosport, Lake Jackson, TX, p. A631

GUEVIN, Scott, Chief Executive Officer, Penn State Hershey Rehabilitation Hospital, Hummelstown, PA, p. A540

GUFFEY, Dale, Chief Financial Officer, Lower Keys Medical Center, Key West, FL, p. A133

GUFFEY, Jay, Senior Vice President and Chief Operating Officer, Mercy Hospital Springfield, Springfield, MO, p. A382

GUGEL, Paul, Manager Information Technology, Marlette Regional Hospital, Marlette, MI, p. A329

GUGLIELMO, Elaine, Vice President Human Resources and Organizational Development, Stamford Hospital, Stamford, CT, p. A117

GUIDERA, Kenneth, M.D. Chief of Staff, Shriners Hospitals for Children–Twin Cities, Minneapolis, MN, p. A347

GUIDO–ALLEN, Debra, Vice President and Chief Nursing Officer, Beaumont Hospital – Troy, Troy, MI, p. A336

GUIDRY, Charles W., Chief Operating Officer, Abbeville General Hospital, Abbeville, LA, p. A271

GUIDRY, Linda, Human Resources Generalist, Abrom Kaplan Memorial Hospital, Kaplan, LA, p. A279

GUIDRY, Lloyd, Chief Operating Officer, Lady of the Sea General Hospital, Cut Off, LA, p. A276

GUIDRY, Selina, Chief Nursing Officer, Lafayette Surgical Specialty Hospital, Lafayette, LA, p. A280

GUIDRY, Trisha, Administrator, Baton Rouge Rehabilitation Hospital, Baton Rouge, LA, p. A272

GUIGNIER, Liz, Vice President Human Resources, Eisenhower Medical Center, Rancho Mirage, CA, p. A84

GUILD, Anthony
  Chief Executive Officer, Abilene Behavioral Health, Abilene, TX, p. A595
  Chief Executive Officer, Rolling Hills Hospital, Ada, OK, p. A508

GUILFOIL, Thomas, Director Human Resources, Baystate Wing Hospital, Palmer, MA, p. A313

GUILLORY, Larry, Chief Human Resources Officer, Baylor Emergency Medical Center at Aubrey, Aubrey, TX, p. A598

GUILLORY, Nicholas D., MSN, Interim Administrator, Oceans Behavioral Hospital of Alexandria, Alexandria, LA, p. A271

GUIMARAES, Antonio, M.D. Clinical Director, U. S. Public Health Service Indian Hospital, Cass Lake, MN, p. A340

GUIN Jr., Jamie W., Interim Administrator and Chief Executive Officer, Greeley County Health Services, Tribune, KS, p. A255

GUINA, Michelle, Manager Human Resources, Sutter Surgical Hospital – North Valley, Yuba City, CA, p. A100

GUINANE, Gerard, Vice President Human Resources, SwedishAmerican – A Division of UW Health, Rockford, IL, p. A202

GUINN, Judy, Chief Human Resources Officer, Graham Regional Medical Center, Graham, TX, p. A621

GUIRL, Nadine T., Senior Vice President Human Resources, Waukesha Memorial Hospital, Waukesha, WI, p. A718

GULARTE, Steven, Chief Executive Officer, Chambers County Public Hospital District No. 1, Anahuac, TX, p. A596

GULIHUR, Judith, Director Human Resources, McCamey County Hospital District, McCamey, TX, p. A636

GULL, Joann Bernadette, Chief Nursing Officer, NYC Health + Hospitals / Elmhurst,, NY, p. A448

GULLINGSRUD, Timothy M., Chief Executive Officer, Hayward Area Memorial Hospital and Nursing Home, Hayward, WI, p. A707

GULRICH, Erica, Chief Executive Officer, Northwest Medical Center, Margate, FL, p. A135

GUM, Gary, R.N. Chief Nursing Officer, Kindred Hospital–Albuquerque, Albuquerque, NM, p. A427

GUMATO, Sixta, M.D. Chief Medical Officer, Crane Memorial Hospital, Crane, TX, p. A608

GUMBINER, Carl H., M.D. Senior Vice President Medical Affairs and Chief Medical Officer, Children's Hospital and Medical Center, Omaha, NE, p. A400

GUMBS, Milton A., M.D. Vice President and Medical Director, Bronx–Lebanon Hospital Center Health Care System,, NY, p. A444

GUMMADI, Subhaker, M.D
  Chief Medical Staff, Promise Hospital Baton Rouge – Main Campus, Baton Rouge, LA, p. A273
  President Medical Staff, Promise Hospital of Baton Rouge – Mid–City Campus, Baton Rouge, LA, p. A273

GUMP, Linda A., Chief Clinical Services Officer, Aurora Medical Center, Kenosha, WI, p. A708

GUNABALAN, Raya, Chief Executive Officer, Behavioral Center of Michigan, Warren, MI, p. A336

GUNDERSEN, Robert A., Market Chief Executive Officer, Curahealth Stoughton, Stoughton, MA, p. A315

GUNDLAPALLI, Madhu, M.D. Clinical Director, Utah State Hospital, Provo, UT, p. A662

GUNDT, Kristin, Chief Nursing Officer, Community Hospital, Grand Junction, CO, p. A106

GUNKEL, Jeff, Chief Information Officer, Jamestown Regional Medical Center, Jamestown, ND, p. A480

GUNN, Deborah, Chief Information Officer, W. G. (Bill) Heffner Veterans Affairs Medical Center, Salisbury, NC, p. A473

GUNN, Terry, FACHE, Chief Executive Officer, KershawHealth, Camden, SC, p. A562

GUNNELL, Nancy
  Chief Human Resource Officer, West Suburban Medical Center, Oak Park, IL, p. A199
  Chief Human Resource Officer, Westlake Hospital, Melrose Park, IL, p. A196

GUNNERSEN, Nils, Administrator, Bertrand Chaffee Hospital, Springville, NY, p. A456

GUNTHER, DNP, Anne, R.N. Chief Nursing Officer, Aultman Hospital, Canton, OH, p. A486

GUNTLOW, Ann Marie, Chief Nursing Officer, Ellenville Regional Hospital, Ellenville, NY, p. A438

GUNUKULA, Srinivas, M.D. Chief of Staff, Dallas Regional Medical Center, Mesquite, TX, p. A636

GUOYAVATIN, Kora
  Chief Financial Officer, Garden Grove Hospital and Medical Center, Garden Grove, CA, p. A64
  Chief Financial Officer, West Anaheim Medical Center, Anaheim, CA, p. A54

GUPTA, Anil, M.D. Chief of Staff, Kindred Hospital–Baldwin Park, Baldwin Park, CA, p. A56

GUPTA, Arun, M.D. Vice President Medical Affairs, South Pointe Hospital, Warrensville Heights, OH, p. A505

GUPTA, Ashok K., M.D. Chief of Staff, Eaton Rapids Medical Center, Eaton Rapids, MI, p. A323

GUPTA, John, Executive Vice President and Chief Operating Officer, Brooklyn Hospital Center,, NY, p. A444

GUPTA, Saurabh, Chief Medical Officer, Rockford Center, Newark, DE, p. A119

GUPTA, Vijay D., M.D. President and Chief Executive Officer, Franciscan Healthcare – Munster, Munster, IN, p. A219

GURR, Lory, Chief Human Resources Division, Evans U. S. Army Community Hospital, Fort Carson, CO, p. A105

GURRAD, Trece, Vice President Patient Care Services, Columbia Memorial Hospital, Astoria, OR, p. A524

GURULE, Eric, Chief Information Officer, Turquoise Lodge Hospital, Albuquerque, NM, p. A428

GURUNG, Anju, M.D. Chief Medical Officer, Mahnomen Health Center, Mahnomen, MN, p. A345

GUSHEE, Dean, M.D. Medical Director, Mason General Hospital, Shelton, WA, p. A690

GUSHO, Michael, Chief Financial Officer, St. Joseph Mercy Oakland, Pontiac, MI, p. A332

GUSTAFSON, Brian, Chief Financial Officer, Veterans Affairs Montana Health Care System, Fort Harrison, MT, p. A387

GUSTAFSON, Connie, Director of Nursing, Jacobson Memorial Hospital Care Center, Elgin, ND, p. A478

GUSTAFSON, Michael, M.D., President, Brigham and Women's Faulkner Hospital, Boston, MA, p. A306

GUSTAFSON, Sarah S., Vice President of Finance, Grand Itasca Clinic and Hospital, Grand Rapids, MN, p. A343

GUSTER, Cherie M., R.N. Senior Vice President and Chief Nursing Officer, Akron General Medical Center, Akron, OH, p. A483

GUSTILO, Maria, M.D
  Medical Director, Osawatomie State Hospital, Osawatomie, KS, p. A250
  Medical Director, Rainbow Mental Health Facility, Kansas City, KS, p. A246

GUSTIN, Michael, Information Technology, John J. Pershing Veterans Affairs Medical Center, Poplar Bluff, MO, p. A378

GUTHMILLER, Martin W., Chief Executive Officer, Orange City Area Health System, Orange City, IA, p. A235

GUTHRIE, Pamela A., Chief Human Resources Officer, AllianceHealth Pryor, Pryor, OK, p. A519

GUTIERREZ, Albert, FACHE, President and Chief Executive Officer, Saint Joseph Regional Medical Center, Mishawaka, IN, p. A218

GUTIERREZ, Lori, Chief Financial Officer, Rochelle Community Hospital, Rochelle, IL, p. A201

GUTIERREZ, Michelle, Executive Director Human Resources, Orange Coast Memorial Medical Center, Fountain Valley, CA, p. A63

GUTIERREZ, Noe, Chief Financial Officer, Lake Granbury Medical Center, Granbury, TX, p. A621

GUTIERREZ, Santiago, M.D. Chief Medical Officer, Doctors Hospital of Laredo, Laredo, TX, p. A632

GUTIERREZ, Vickie, Director of Patient Care, Dr. Dan C. Trigg Memorial Hospital, Tucumcari, NM, p. A432

GUTIERREZ, Victor A., M.D. Medical Director, Allegiance Behavioral Health Center of Plainview, Plainview, TX, p. A641

GUTJAHR, Susan, Reimbursement Specialist, Sparta Community Hospital, Sparta, IL, p. A203

GUTMAN, Luisa, Senior Vice President and Chief Operating Officer, Holy Cross Hospital, Fort Lauderdale, FL, p. A128

GUTNICK, Michael, Executive Vice President and Chief Financial Officer, Memorial Sloan–Kettering Cancer Center, New York, NY, p. A446

GUTOW, Andrew, M.D. Medical Director, Menlo Park Surgical Hospital, Menlo Park, CA, p. A76

GUTOWSKI, Jennifer S., FACHE, Acting Director, Southern Arizona Veterans Affairs Health Care System, Tucson, AZ, p. A41

GUTSCH, Michael, Chief Executive Officer, Cumberland Memorial Hospital, Cumberland, WI, p. A704

GUTSCHENRITTER, John, Chief Financial Officer, Wilson Medical Center, Neodesha, KS, p. A249

GUTTENBERG, Ellen, Chief Operating Officer, Frances Mahon Deaconess Hospital, Glasgow, MT, p. A387

GUTTIN, Enrique, M.D. Chief of Staff, Wilmington Veterans Affairs Medical Center, Wilmington, DE, p. A120

GUTTMACHER, Laurence, M.D. Clinical Director, Rochester Psychiatric Center, Rochester, NY, p. A454

GUTZEIT, Michael, M.D. Chief Medical Officer, Children's Hospital of Wisconsin, Milwaukee, WI, p. A711

GUY, Glenda, Director, Health Information Management, Ten Broeck Tennessee Treatment Facility, Cookeville, TN, p. A581

GUYETTE, William, M.D. President Medical Staff, Livingston Hospital and Healthcare Services, Salem, KY, p. A269

GUZ, Andrew, Chief Executive Officer, Jennersville Regional Hospital, West Grove, PA, p. A557

GUZAK, Jason, Chief Financial Officer, Rock Springs, LLC, Georgetown, TX, p. A620

GUZMAN, Claudia V., Chief Executive Officer and Managing Director, Hospital San Pablo, Bayamon, PR, p. A726

GUZMAN, Lisa, Human Resource Vice President, Redlands Community Hospital, Redlands, CA, p. A85

GWATKIN, Betty Ann, Vice President Human Resources, Northeastern Vermont Regional Hospital, Saint Johnsbury, VT, p. A666

GWYN, Brian
President and Chief Executive Officer, Cleveland Regional Medical Center, Shelby, NC, p. A473
President Chief Operating Officer, Cleveland Regional Medical Center, Shelby, NC, p. A473
President and Chief Executive Officer, Kings Mountain Hospital, Kings Mountain, NC, p. A468

GYNTHER, Tracy, R.N. Vice President and Chief Nursing Officer, West Georgia Health, Lagrange, GA, p. A161

GYROS, Guy, Chief Financial Officer, Huntsville Memorial Hospital, Huntsville, TX, p. A628

H

HAACK, Wanda, MSN Chief Nursing Officer, Genesis Medical Center, DeWitt, De Witt, IA, p. A229

HAAG, Adam, Manager Information Technology, Coffey County Hospital, Burlington, KS, p. A241

HAAGENSON, Deb, R.N. Vice President of Patient Care, CHI St. Joseph's Health, Park Rapids, MN, p. A348

HAAK, Karen S., R.N. Chief Nursing Officer, Good Samaritan Hospital, Vincennes, IN, p. A223

HAAR, Clare A., Chief Executive Officer, Eastern Niagara Hospital, Lockport, NY, p. A441

HAAS, Christine, Chief Information Officer, Jersey Shore Hospital, Jersey Shore, PA, p. A541

HAAS, Robert, M.D. Chief Medical Officer, Liberty Hospital, Liberty, MO, p. A375

HAAS, Scott A., M.D. Chief Medical Officer, Eastern State Hospital, Lexington, KY, p. A263

HAAS, Steven J.
Chief Financial Officer, Health Alliance Hospital – Broadway Campus, Kingston, NY, p. A441
Chief Financial Officer, Health Alliance Hospital – Mary's Avenue Campus, Kingston, NY, p. A441

HAAS, Susan, Director Human Resources, Aurora Behavioral Healthcare San Diego, San Diego, CA, p. A88

HAASE, Patricia, Director Information Technology and Communications, Marian Regional Medical Center, Santa Maria, CA, p. A93

HAASE, Ronald
Chief Human Resources Officer, Northern Arizona Healthcare, Flagstaff Medical Center, Flagstaff, AZ, p. A32
Chief Human Resources Officer, Northern Arizona Healthcare, Verde Valley Medical Center, Cottonwood, AZ, p. A32

HAASKEN, Timothy W., Chief Financial Officer, LewisGale Hospital Montgomery, Blacksburg, VA, p. A668

HABIB, Noel, M.D. Chief Medical Officer, Huhukam Memorial Hospital, Sacaton, AZ, p. A38

HABIS, Saba, M.D. Chief Medical Officer, Freeman Health System, Joplin, MO, p. A372

HABOWSKI, Michael J., President and Chief Executive Officer, Ashtabula County Medical Center, Ashtabula, OH, p. A484

HACHEY, Michael
Senior Vice President and Chief Financial Officer, Emerson Hospital, Concord, MA, p. A309
Senior Vice President and Chief Financial Officer, Mercy Hospital of Portland, Portland, ME, p. A294

HACKBARTH, John, CPA Senior Vice President Finance and Chief Financial Officer, Owensboro Health Regional Hospital, Owensboro, KY, p. A267

HACKER, Leanne, Chief Financial Officer, Eastern New Mexico Medical Center, Roswell, NM, p. A431

HACKER, Mary Dee, R.N. Vice President, Patient Care Services and Chief Nursing Officer, Children's Hospital Los Angeles, Los Angeles, CA, p. A70

HACKER, Phillip
Chief Financial Officer, Stone County Medical Center, Mountain View, AR, p. A50
Chief Financial Officer, White River Medical Center, Batesville, AR, p. A43

HACKETT, Leslie, Chief Nursing Officer, Covenant Hospital Plainview, Plainview, TX, p. A641

HACKSTEDDE, Anita, M.D., President and Chief Executive Officer, Salem Regional Medical Center, Salem, OH, p. A502

HADAWAY, Krystal, DIrector Human Resources, HealthSource Saginaw, Inc., Saginaw, MI, p. A333

HADDADIN, Maen, M.D. President Medical Staff, CHI Health Mercy Corning, Corning, IA, p. A228

HADDICAN, James, Chief Financial Officer, Vice President Finance, Gillette Children's Specialty Healthcare, Saint Paul, MN, p. A350

HADDIX, Parker, Chief Executive Officer, William R. Sharpe, Jr. Hospital, Weston, WV, p. A701

HADDOX, Melissa, Controller, HEALTHSOUTH Rehabilitation Hospital of Cypress, Houston, TX, p. A624

HADLEY, David R., Managing Director and Chief Financial Officer, Integris Baptist Medical Center, Oklahoma City, OK, p. A516

HADLEY, Gerard, Vice President Finance for Brigham & Women's Faulkner Hospital and Vice President Finance and Controller, Brigham and Women's Faulkner Hospital, Boston, MA, p. A306

HADLEY, H. Roger, M.D. Vice President, Medical Affairs, Loma Linda University Medical Center, Loma Linda, CA, p. A69

HADLEY, Steven N., Chief Financial Officer, Kansas Medical Center, Andover, KS, p. A240

HADLEY, Susan, R.N. Chief Nursing Officer, Dickinson County Healthcare System, Iron Mountain, MI, p. A327

HADZEGA, Angela, Chief Financial Officer, Kane Community Hospital, Kane, PA, p. A541

HAEFELE, John, M.D. Chief Medical Officer, Community Memorial Healthcare, Marysville, KS, p. A249

HAEHN, Debra, Chief Financial Officer, Clay County Memorial Hospital, Henrietta, TX, p. A623

HAENELT, Michael, Chief Information Management, Weed Army Community Hospital, Fort Irwin, CA, p. A62

HAESEMEYER, Allan, M.D. Chief of Staff, Indianhead Medical Center, Shell Lake, WI, p. A716

HAESEMEYER, Christa, Chief Nursing Officer, Lincoln County Hospital, Lincoln, KS, p. A248

HAFEMAN, Paula, R.N.
Chief Nurse Executive, HSHS St. Vincent Hospital, Green Bay, WI, p. A707
Chief Nursing Officer, St. Mary's Hospital Medical Center, Green Bay, WI, p. A707

HAFFEY, Robert, R.N., President, Delaware County Memorial Hospital, Drexel Hill, PA, p. A537

HAFFORD, Juliet, Director Human Resources, Beaumont Hospital – Trenton, Trenton, MI, p. A335

HAFIZ, Irfan
Vice President Medical Affairs, Centegra Hospital – McHenry, McHenry, IL, p. A196
Vice President Medical Affairs, Centegra Hospital – Woodstock, Woodstock, IL, p. A205

HAGAN, Donald E., Chief Financial Officer, DeTar Healthcare System, Victoria, TX, p. A655

HAGAN, Eric, R.N., Executive Vice President and Administrator, Medical Center at Scottsville, Scottsville, KY, p. A269

HAGAN, Frank, Senior Vice President Finance, Saint Joseph's Medical Center, Yonkers, NY, p. A459

HAGEL, Bonnie, Chief Financial Officer, Logan County Hospital, Oakley, KS, p. A250

HAGELBERG, Robbi, Vice President Nursing Services and Chief Nursing Officer, Lakeview Hospital, Stillwater, MN, p. A352

HAGELTHORN, Diane, Human Resources Generalist, Modoc Medical Center, Alturas, CA, p. A54

HAGEN, Bruce P., President, OhioHealth Marion General Hospital, Marion, OH, p. A498

HAGEN, Lynne D., Human Resources Officer, Avera McKennan Hospital and University Health Center, Sioux Falls, SD, p. A576

HAGEN, Mary, R.N. VP and Chief Nursing Officer, UnityPoint Health – Allen Hospital, Waterloo, IA, p. A239

HAGEN, Paulette, Human Resources and Administrative Services Director, CentraCare Health–Paynesville, Paynesville, MN, p. A348

HAGENS, Gary, Chief Operating Officer and Chief Medical Officer, Springfield Regional Medical Center, Springfield, OH, p. A503

HAGENS, Paul, Vice President Human Resources, Doctors Community Hospital, Lanham, MD, p. A302

HAGER, Rhonda M., Director Human Resources, Stonewall Jackson Memorial Hospital, Weston, WV, p. A701

HAGERMAN, Daniel, M.D. President Medical Staff, Columbia Center, Mequon, WI, p. A710

HAGERSTROM, Paige A., System Director of Talent Management, St. Joseph Hospital, Bangor, ME, p. A291

HAGERTY, Cindy, Assistant Chief Nurse Officer and Administrator of Operations, Via Christi Rehabilitation Hospital, Wichita, KS, p. A256

HAGGARD, Tommy, Chief Executive Officer, Bluegrass Community Hospital, Versailles, KY, p. A270

HAGGART, Sandra, Chief Nursing Officer, St. Vincent Clay Hospital, Brazil, IN, p. A207

HAGHIGHAT, Dennis, M.D. Vice President Medical Affairs, St. Mary Medical Center, Apple Valley, CA, p. A55

HAGLER, Dan, M.D. Vice President and Chief Medical Officer, Carolinas HealthCare System NorthEast, Concord, NC, p. A463

HAGLUND, Nicole, Vice President of Nursing Services, Providence Medical Center, Wayne, NE, p. A403

HAGOOD, Teena, Chief Nursing Officer, Kimble Hospital, Junction, TX, p. A629

HAGUE, Samuel, M.D. Chief of Staff, AllianceHealth Blackwell, Blackwell, OK, p. A509

HAGY, Kelly, Director Human Resources, Cumberland Hall Hospital, Hopkinsville, KY, p. A261

HAGY, Michelle, Chief Financial Officer, Pikeville Medical Center, Pikeville, KY, p. A268

HAHEY, Joanne A.
Vice President Finance and Chief Financial Officer, University of Maryland Shore Medical Center at Chestertown, Chestertown, MD, p. A299
Senior Vice President and Chief Financial Officer, University of Maryland Shore Medical Center at Dorchester, Cambridge, MD, p. A299
Senior Vice President and Chief Financial Officer, University of Maryland Shore Medical Center at Easton, Easton, MD, p. A300

HAHN, Donna S., R.N. Vice President Acute Care and Chief Nurse Executive, Sentara RMH Medical Center, Harrisonburg, VA, p. A671

HAHN, Jen, Finance Manager, UH Portage Medical Center, Ravenna, OH, p. A501

HAHN, Joseph, M.D. Chief of Staff, Cleveland Clinic, Cleveland, OH, p. A488

HAHN, Kurt, M.D. Acting Clinical Director, Elmira Psychiatric Center, Elmira, NY, p. A438

HAHN, Lori, Vice President Nursing Services, Mercy Medical Center, Williston, ND, p. A482

HAHS, Seth, Chief of Staff, Salem Township Hospital, Salem, IL, p. A202

HAIGH, Sara, Associate Director, Durham Veterans Affairs Medical Center, Durham, NC, p. A464

HAIGLER, Tonda V., Chief Operating Officer, Merit Health Biloxi, Biloxi, MS, p. A355

HAIL, Brian, Chief Executive Officer, Cherokee Nation W.W. Hastings Indian Hospital, Tahlequah, OK, p. A520

HAIN, Jim, Chief Operating Officer, Lexington Regional Health Center, Lexington, NE, p. A397

HAINES, Beverly J., R.N., President, Patewood Memorial Hospital, Greenville, SC, p. A566

HAINES, Christopher, D.O. Vice President Chief Medical Officer, Children's Specialized Hospital–PSE&G, New Brunswick, NJ, p. A420

HAIR, Kelly, Director Information Technology, Abbeville General Hospital, Abbeville, LA, p. A271

HAISLIP, Heidi, M.D. Chief of Staff, AllianceHealth Madill, Madill, OK, p. A514

HAIZLIP, Jr., Thomas M., M.D. Chief of Staff, Charles A. Cannon Memorial Hospital, Newland, NC, p. A471

HAJEK, Julie, Director Human Resources, St. David's Medical Center, Austin, TX, p. A600

HAKENSON, Diana, Director of Patient Care Services, Newport Bay Hospital, Newport Beach, CA, p. A79

HALAKAN, Catherine, Senior Vice President, Albany Medical Center, Albany, NY, p. A433

HALAMA, George, Vice President Finance, McPherson Hospital, McPherson, KS, p. A249

HALAMKA, John, M.D. Chief Information Officer, Beth Israel Deaconess Medical Center, Boston, MA, p. A306

HALDEMAN, Larry, M.D. Executive Vice President and Chief Medical Officer, WellStar Windy Hill Hospital, Marietta, GA, p. A163

HALDEMAN, Richard, President and Chief Executive Officer, Southwestern Regional Medical Center, Tulsa, OK, p. A522

HALDER, Ranjay, M.D. Chief Medical Director, Centerstone Hospital, Bradenton, FL, p. A124

HALE, Becky, Director Human Resources, Hill Regional Hospital, Hillsboro, TX, p. A623

HALE, Byron, Chief Financial Officer, East Texas Medical Center Tyler, Tyler, TX, p. A654

HALE, Danny, Director Human Resources, Southwestern Medical Center, Lawton, OK, p. A513

HALE, Donna, Director of Nursing, Baptist Memorial Rehabilitation Hospital, Germantown, TN, p. A583

HALE, Kirsten
Coordinator Health Information Services, University Hospitals Conneaut Medical Center, Conneaut, OH, p. A492
Coordinator Health Informations Systems and Coding, University Hospitals Geneva Medical Center, Geneva, OH, p. A495

HALE, Margie, MSN, Chief Executive Officer, Baraga County Memorial Hospital, L'Anse, MI, p. A328

HALE, Renae, Chief Nursing Officer, Lincoln Prairie Behavioral Health Center, Springfield, IL, p. A203

HALE, Ron, Superintendent, Colorado Mental Health Institute at Pueblo, Pueblo, CO, p. A109

HALE, Steven D., Chief Executive Officer, Weiser Memorial Hospital, Weiser, ID, p. A179

HALE, Tonia, Chief Nursing Officer, Tennova Newport Medical Center, Newport, TN, p. A591

HALEN, Catherine, Vice President Human Resources, Beebe Healthcare, Lewes, DE, p. A119

HALES, Brent, Chief Financial Officer, Uintah Basin Medical Center, Roosevelt, UT, p. A662

HALES, Joe, Director Information Systems, Primary Children's Hospital, Salt Lake City, UT, p. A663

HALEY, Bob J., Chief Executive Officer, Pekin Hospital, Pekin, IL, p. A200

HALEY, James, M.D. Senior Vice President and Chief Medical Officer, Unity Hospital, Rochester, NY, p. A454

HALEY, Michael E., President, Indiana University Health Ball Memorial Hospital, Muncie, IN, p. A219

HALEY, Thomas
Information Technology Systems Site Director, CHI Health Lakeside, Omaha, NE, p. A400
Information Technology Services Site Director, CHI Health Mercy Council Bluffs, Council Bluffs, IA, p. A228
Information Technology Systems Site Director, CHI Health Midlands, Papillion, NE, p. A401

HALFEN, John, M.D. Medical Director, Lakewood Health System, Staples, MN, p. A352

HALFHILL, Patrick, Chief Financial Officer, Madison County Memorial Hospital, Madison, FL, p. A135

HALFORD, Dianne, Chief Financial Officer, Saint Clare's Health System, Denville, NJ, p. A416

HALIMI, Hamid, M.D. Medical Director, Select Specialty Hospital–Ann Arbor, Ypsilanti, MI, p. A337

HALL, Becky, R.N. Director Nursing, Rumford Hospital, Rumford, ME, p. A295

HALL, Carla, Director of Nursing, Highland Hospital, Charleston, WV, p. A695

HALL, Catherine, Manager Human Resources, Jefferson Hospital, Louisville, GA, p. A162

HALL, Dan, R.N. Director of Nursing, St. John Owasso, Owasso, OK, p. A518

HALL, Dana, Director of Nursing, Quitman County Hospital, Marks, MS, p. A361

HALL, David
Chief Information Officer, Pineville Community Hospital Association, Pineville, KY, p. A268
Senior Vice President and Chief Operating Officer, University of Tennessee Medical Center, Knoxville, TN, p. A586

HALL, Gary, Vice President of Information Technology, Estes Park Medical Center, Estes Park, CO, p. A105

HALL, George, M.D
Vice President Medical Affairs, St. Elizabeth Florence, Florence, KY, p. A260
Vice President Medical Affairs, St. Elizabeth Fort Thomas, Fort Thomas, KY, p. A260

HALL, Jeanne, Director Information Systems, Shriners Hospitals for Children–St. Louis, Saint Louis, MO, p. A380

HALL, Jeffrey, DPM Chief Medical Officer, St. Croix Regional Medical Center, St. Croix Falls, WI, p. A716

HALL, Jeremy, Assistant Administrator and Chief Financial Officer, Middlesboro ARH Hospital, Middlesboro, KY, p. A266

HALL, Jim, Acting Chief Information Officer, Central Arkansas Veterans Healthcare System, Little Rock, AR, p. A49

HALL, Kathy J., Administrator, St. Mary's Warrick Hospital, Boonville, IN, p. A207

HALL, Kenneth C., R.N. Chief Nursing Officer, Saint Joseph Regional Medical Center, Mishawaka, IN, p. A218

HALL, Kent, M.D. Vice President and Chief Medical Officer, The University of Vermont Health Network–Champlain Valley Physicians Hospital, Plattsburgh, NY, p. A453

HALL, Leslie, R.N. Senior Vice President–Chief Nursing Officer, Nash Health Care Systems, Rocky Mount, NC, p. A472

HALL, Linda, Administrator and Chief Executive Officer, Chillicothe Hospital District, Chillicothe, TX, p. A606

HALL, Margaret, M.D. Chief Medical Officer, Lakeside Women's Hospital, Oklahoma City, OK, p. A516

HALL, Mary A., Chief Medical Staff, McDowell ARH Hospital, McDowell, KY, p. A266

HALL, Melissa
Chief Nursing Officer, Coffey County Hospital, Burlington, KS, p. A241
Human Resources, Munising Memorial Hospital, Munising, MI, p. A330

HALL, Morrison, Chief Financial Officer, Pender Memorial Hospital, Burgaw, NC, p. A461

HALL, Richard, Chief Executive Officer, Samuel Simmonds Memorial Hospital, Barrow, AK, p. A28

HALL, Roger L.
President, Sacred Heart Hospital on the Emerald Coast, Miramar Beach, FL, p. A138
President, Sacred Heart Hospital on the Gulf, Port St. Joe, FL, p. A143

HALL, Sally, Manager Human Resources, South Texas Spine and Surgical Hospital, San Antonio, TX, p. A647

HALL, Stephanie, M.D
Chief Medical Officer, Keck Hospital of USC, Los Angeles, CA, p. A72
Medical Director, USC Norris Comprehensive Cancer Center, Los Angeles, CA, p. A74
Chief Medical Officer, USC Verdugo Hills Hospital, Glendale, CA, p. A65

HALL, Steve, Chief Financial Officer, Pekin Hospital, Pekin, IL, p. A200

HALL, Terry E., Chief of Staff, Harrison County Community Hospital, Bethany, MO, p. A367

HALL, Trudy, M.D. Vice President Medical Affairs, Laurel Regional Hospital, Laurel, MD, p. A302

HALL, Veronica, R.N. Chief Operating Officer, Henry Ford Hospital, Detroit, MI, p. A322

HALL, Wyatt, M.D. Chief Medical Officer, Longmont United Hospital, Longmont, CO, p. A108

HALLADAY, Mark, Director Information Services, F. F. Thompson Hospital, Canandaigua, NY, p. A436

HALLAGIN, Virginia, Chief Executive Officer, Keefe Memorial Hospital, Cheyenne Wells, CO, p. A102

HALLAL, Joseph, M.D. Chief Medical Officer, Inova Fairfax Hospital, Falls Church, VA, p. A670

HALLATT, Jennifer
Chief Operating Officer, Mercy Harvard Hospital, Harvard, IL, p. A192
Chief Operating Officer, Mercy Walworth Hospital and Medical Center, Lake Geneva, WI, p. A708

HALLER, III, William, M.D. Chief of Staff, Gadsden Regional Medical Center, Gadsden, AL, p. A20

HALLEY, Andrea, Director Human Resources, Hopedale Medical Complex, Hopedale, IL, p. A193

HALLEY, Lisa B., Vice President Human Resources, Holzer Medical Center, Gallipolis, OH, p. A495

HALLICK, Susan M., R.N. Executive Vice President and Chief Nursing Officer, Geisinger Medical Center, Danville, PA, p. A536

HALLIDAY, Lisa, Director Accounting Services, Taylor Regional Hospital, Hawkinsville, GA, p. A160

HALLISEY, Thomas, Chief Information Officer, United Medical Center, Washington, DC, p. A122

HALLIWILL, Donald B.
Chief Financial Officer, Carilion Franklin Memorial Hospital, Rocky Mount, VA, p. A678
Executive Vice President and Chief Financial Officer, Carilion Roanoke Memorial Hospital, Roanoke, VA, p. A678

HALLMARK, Todd, Chief Executive Officer, Choctaw Nation Health Care Center, Talihina, OK, p. A520

HALLOCK, Mirya, Administrator, Webster County Community Hospital, Red Cloud, NE, p. A402

HALPIN, Jean
President, OhioHealth MedCentral Mansfield Hospital, Mansfield, OH, p. A497
President, OhioHealth MedCentral Shelby Hospital, Shelby, OH, p. A502

HALPIN, Kim, Director Human Resources, Arms Acres, Carmel, NY, p. A436

HALSAN, Carole, R.N., Chief Executive Officer, Willapa Harbor Hospital, South Bend, WA, p. A690

HALSELL, David, Senior Vice President and Chief Financial Officer, Lake Regional Health System, Osage Beach, MO, p. A378

HALSTEAD, Lisa, Chief Nursing Officer, INTEGRIS Miami Hospital, Miami, OK, p. A514

HALTER, Bev, Director Human Resources and Payroll, Liberty Medical Center, Chester, MT, p. A386

HALTER, Kevin, Chief Executive Officer, Our Lady of Bellefonte Hospital, Ashland, KY, p. A257

HALTER, Michael P., Chief Executive Officer, Hahnemann University Hospital, Philadelphia, PA, p. A548

HALTOM, Shannon, Vice President, Patient Care Services, CHI St. Luke's Health Brazosport, Lake Jackson, TX, p. A631

HALVORSEN, Anita, FACHE Reginoal Strategy & Growth Officer, Presence Mercy Medical Center, Aurora, IL, p. A180

HALVORSEN, Lisa, Chief Nurse Executive, Providence Milwaukie Hospital, Milwaukie, OR, p. A528

HALVORSON, Marla, Director Human Resources, St. Luke's Hospital, Duluth, MN, p. A342

HAMAM, Hisham, M.D. Chief of Staff, Northern Cochise Community Hospital, Willcox, AZ, p. A41

HAMB, Aaron, M.D. Chief Medical Officer, Provident Hospital of Cook County, Chicago, IL, p. A186

HAMBLIN, James, Chief Financial Officer, White Mountain Regional Medical Center, Springerville, AZ, p. A39

HAMBRIDGE, Mark, Director Information Systems, Livingston Regional Hospital, Livingston, TN, p. A587

HAMBY, Kelley, Vice President Patient Care, Baptist Health Medical Center – North Little Rock, North Little Rock, AR, p. A51

HAMEL, Cathleen, Chief Nurse Executive, St. Rose Dominican Hospitals – Siena Campus, Henderson, NV, p. A405

HAMEL, Loren, M.D., President and Chief Executive Officer, Lakeland Health, Saint Joseph, MI, p. B79

HAMEL, Loren, M.D., President and Chief Executive Officer, Lakeland Medical Center, St. Joseph, Saint Joseph, MI, p. A334

HAMEL, Susan, Chief Nursing Officer, St. Luke's Hospital, Duluth, MN, p. A342

HAMILL, Dave H., President and Chief Executive Officer, Hampton Regional Medical Center, Varnville, SC, p. A570

HAMILTON, Adriana H., Chief Human Resources Officer, Hunter Holmes McGuire Veterans Affairs Medical Center–Richmond, Richmond, VA, p. A678

HAMILTON, Aggie, Chief Human Resources, Veterans Affairs Montana Health Care System, Fort Harrison, MT, p. A387

HAMILTON, Brandy, Chief Executive Officer, Suncoast Behavioral Health Center, Bradenton, FL, p. A124

HAMILTON, Catherine, Chief Nursing Officer, Hedrick Medical Center, Chillicothe, MO, p. A369

HAMILTON, Chanda, Chief Information Officer, Clifton T. Perkins Hospital Center, Jessup, MD, p. A301

HAMILTON, Crystal, R.N., Chief Executive Officer, Abrazo Maryvale Campus, Phoenix, AZ, p. A35

HAMILTON, Dan, Chief Operating Officer, Nor–Lea General Hospital, Lovington, NM, p. A430

HAMILTON, Geoff, Interim Chief Financial Officer, Morton General Hospital, Morton, WA, p. A686

HAMILTON, Jennifer
COO – Mary Bridge, MultiCare Mary Bridge Children's Hospital and Health Center, Tacoma, WA, p. A692
Chief Financial Officer, SageWest Health Care at Riverton, Riverton, WY, p. A723

HAMILTON, Kay A., MS, Chief Administrative Officer, Geisinger–Lewistown Hospital, Lewistown, PA, p. A543

HAMILTON, Marci, Chief Nursing Officer, Orthopaedic Hospital of Lutheran Health Network, Fort Wayne, IN, p. A210

HAMILTON, Marilyn, Director Human Resources, Promise Hospital Baton Rouge – Main Campus, Baton Rouge, LA, p. A273

HAMILTON, Nancy, Chief Human and Learning Resources, Veterans Affairs New Jersey Health Care System, East Orange, NJ, p. A416

HAMILTON, Patricia, R.N. Director of Nursing, Mildred Mitchell–Bateman Hospital, Huntington, WV, p. A697

HAMILTON, Peggy, Chief Financial Officer, Chambers County Public Hospital District No. 1, Anahuac, TX, p. A596

HAMILTON, Phil, R.N., Chief Executive Officer, General John J. Pershing Memorial Hospital, Brookfield, MO, p. A368

HAMILTON, Randal S., Chief Executive Officer, Select Specialty Hospital–Panama City, Panama City, FL, p. A142

HAMILTON, Scott
Vice President and Chief Financial Officer, Parkwest Medical Center, Knoxville, TN, p. A586
Chief Financial Officer, Peninsula Hospital, Louisville, TN, p. A587

HAMILTON, Sharon, Chief Nursing Officer, HEALTHSOUTH Emerald Coast Rehabilitation Hospital, Panama City, FL, p. A141

HAMILTON, Terry, President, St. John Macomb–Oakland Hospital, Warren, MI, p. A336

HAMILTON, Thomas, D.O. Chief Medical Officer, St. Francis Health, Topeka, KS, p. A254

HAMILTON, Toby, Chief Executive Officer, Emerus, The Woodlands, TX, p. B53

HAMILTON, Tom, M.D. Chief of Staff, Decatur County General Hospital, Parsons, TN, p. A592

HAMILTON–BEYER, Maggie, Chief Financial Officer, Knoxville Hospital & Clinics, Knoxville, IA, p. A233

HAMLIN, DeWayne, Director, Veterans Affairs Caribbean Healthcare System, San Juan, PR, p. A730

HAMLIN, Faye, Manager Human Resources, Julian F. Keith Alcohol and Drug Abuse Treatment Center, Black Mountain, NC, p. A460

HAMLIN, Scott J., Chief Financial Officer, Cincinnati Children's Hospital Medical Center, Cincinnati, OH, p. A487

HAMM, David, President and Chief Executive Officer, Good Samaritan Medical Center, Lafayette, CO, p. A108

HAMM, Jay, FACHE, Chief Acute Care Executive, Palmetto Health Richland, Columbia, SC, p. A564

HAMM, Sonja, Vice President Human and Foundation Resources, Lakes Regional Healthcare, Spirit Lake, IA, p. A238

HAMMAKER, Barry, M.D. Chief Medical Officer and Chief Clinical Officer, Vail Valley Medical Center, Vail, CO, p. A111

HAMMEL, Leah, Acting Administrator, Chester Mental Health Center, Chester, IL, p. A183

HAMMER, Michael, Chief Executive Officer, Sanford Worthington Medical Center, Worthington, MN, p. A354

HAMMER, Rebecca J., Chief Financial Officer, Davis Medical Center, Elkins, WV, p. A695

HAMMERAN, Kevin R., Chief Executive Officer and Administrator, Baptist Memorial Hospital for Women, Memphis, TN, p. A588

HAMMES, Chris, FACHE, Interim President, Integris Southwest Medical Center, Oklahoma City, OK, p. A516

HAMMES, Paul, Chief Executive Officer, Hugh Chatham Memorial Hospital, Elkin, NC, p. A465

HAMMETT, Doran, Chief Financial Officer, Petersburg Medical Center, Petersburg, AK, p. A30

HAMMETT, George, Director Human Resources, Carolina Center for Behavioral Health, Greer, SC, p. A567

HAMMETT, Richard A., Chief Executive Officer, Swedish Medical Center, Englewood, CO, p. A105

HAMMETT, Troy
Chief Financial Officer, CHI Memorial, Chattanooga, TN, p. A580
Vice President and Chief Financial Officer, OhioHealth Doctors Hospital, Columbus, OH, p. A491

HAMMOCK, Preston W., President and Chief Executive Officer, Alamance Regional Medical Center, Burlington, NC, p. A461

HAMMON, Selene Q., Chief Executive Officer, Dallas Behavioral Healthcare Hospital, Desoto, TX, p. A613

HAMMOND, Flora, M.D. Chief Medical Affairs, Rehabilitation Hospital of Indiana, Indianapolis, IN, p. A214

HAMMOND, Michael
Chief Financial Officer, Lourdes Medical Center of Burlington County, Willingboro, NJ, p. A425
Chief Financial Officer, Our Lady of Lourdes Medical Center, Camden, NJ, p. A415

HAMMOND, Patti, Chief Operating Officer, Adirondack Medical Center, Saranac Lake, NY, p. A455

HAMMOND, Reed, Chief Operating Officer, Conroe Regional Medical Center, Conroe, TX, p. A607

HAMMONDS, Janie, Human Resources Officer, Columbus Community Hospital, Columbus, TX, p. A607

HAMMONDS, Laura, Assistant Administrator, Jasper Memorial Hospital, Monticello, GA, p. A163

HAMNER, Candy, Vice President and Chief Nursing Officer, Levindale Hebrew Geriatric Center and Hospital, Baltimore, MD, p. A296

HAMON, Beta, Chief Medical Officer, Sanford Rock Rapids Medical Center, Rock Rapids, IA, p. A236

HAMON, Eric, Chief Financial Officer, Driscoll Children's Hospital, Corpus Christi, TX, p. A608

HAMP, Matthew, Chief Operating Officer, Sisters of Charity Hospital of Buffalo, Buffalo, NY, p. A436

HAMPF, Carl, M.D. Chief Medical Officer, Saint Thomas Hospital for Spinal Surgery, Nashville, TN, p. A590

HAMPSHIRE, Misty, Chief Financial Officer, Ozarks Community Hospital, Springfield, MO, p. A382

HAMPTON, Angie, Director Human Resources, Porter Regional Hospital, Valparaiso, IN, p. A223

HAMPTON, Connie, Nurse Executive, Carl Vinson Veterans Affairs Medical Center, Dublin, GA, p. A159

HAMPTON, David, M.D. Chief Medical Staff, Pampa Regional Medical Center, Pampa, TX, p. A640

HAMPTON, Jeff, Director Information Systems, Lehigh Regional Medical Center, Lehigh Acres, FL, p. A134

HAMPTON, Mary Ann, R.N. Chief Nursing Officer, Des Peres Hospital, Saint Louis, MO, p. A380

HAMRICK, Jan, Chief Financial Officer, Dodge County Hospital, Eastman, GA, p. A159

HAMSTRA, Nancy, Chief Operating Officer, University Hospital, Newark, NJ, p. A421

HAMULA, Michelle, Director of Nursing and Quality, Chan Soon–Shiong Medical Center, Windber, PA, p. A558

HAN, Kevin, Vice President and Chief Financial Officer, Stormont Vail Health, Topeka, KS, p. A254

HANCOCK, Brian, M.D., Director, Richard L. Roudebush Veterans Affairs Medical Center, Indianapolis, IN, p. A214

HANCOCK, J. Brian, M.D. Chief of Staff, Fargo Veterans Affairs Health Care System, Fargo, ND, p. A478

HANCOCK, Katherine, R.N. Executive Chief Nursing Officer, Cleveland Clinic, Cleveland, OH, p. A488

HANCOCK, Kerry, Director Human Resources, Bacon County Hospital and Health System, Alma, GA, p. A151

HANCOCK, Lori, Chief Business Officer, West Palm Beach Veterans Affairs Medical Center, West Palm Beach, FL, p. A150

HANCOCK, Melinda, Chief Financial Officer, VCU Medical Center, Richmond, VA, p. A678

HANCOCK, Myrna, Director Financial Services, Choctaw Health Center, Philadelphia, MS, p. A363

HANCOCK, Paul, M.D. Chief Medical Officer, Swedish Medical Center, Englewood, CO, p. A105

HANCOCK, Sharon, Chief Human Resources Officer, McCullough–Hyde Memorial Hospital/TriHealth, Oxford, OH, p. A501

HANCOCK, Stacey J., Vice President, Human Resources, Wellstar Atlanta Medical Center, Atlanta, GA, p. A153

HANCOCK, Todd, Senior Vice President and Chief Operating Officer, CHRISTUS Mother Frances Hospital – Tyler, Tyler, TX, p. A654

HANDEL, Daniel, M.D. Chief Medical Officer, MUSC Medical Center of Medical University of South Carolina, Charleston, SC, p. A563

HANDL, Therese, Chief Executive Officer, HSHS St. Clare Memorial Hospital, Oconto Falls, WI, p. A713

HANDLER, Michael, M.D. Vice President Medical Affairs and Chief Medical Officer, SSM Health St. Joseph Hospital – Lake Saint Louis, Lake Saint Louis, MO, p. A375

HANDLEY, Charles
Chief Financial Officer, Plaza Specialty Hospital, Houston, TX, p. A626
Chief Financial Officer, The Hospitals of Providence Memorial Campus, El Paso, TX, p. A616

HANDLEY, Jack, M.D. Chief Medical Officer, EvergreenHealth Monroe, Monroe, WA, p. A686

HANDLEY, Rhonda, Chief Financial Officer, Columbia Basin Hospital, Ephrata, WA, p. A684

HANDOL, Nelson, M.D. Medical Director, Laurel Oaks Behavioral Health Center, Dothan, AL, p. A19

HANDWERK, Ashley, Director, Human Resources, MedStar Union Memorial Hospital, Baltimore, MD, p. A297

HANDY, Steven P., CPA, Chief Executive Officer, Uniontown Hospital, Uniontown, PA, p. A556

HANEFELD, Darlene, Chief Human Resources Officer, Banner Churchill Community Hospital, Fallon, NV, p. A404

HANENBURG, Thomas S., Senior Vice President and Area Manager, Kaiser Permanente San Leandro Medical Center, San Leandro, CA, p. A91

HANEY, Judy, Chief Nursing Officer, Twin Rivers Regional Medical Center, Kennett, MO, p. A374

HANEY, Kathryn, Controller, HEALTHSOUTH Valley of the Sun Rehabilitation Hospital, Glendale, AZ, p. A33

HANEY, Mark, President, WellStar Paulding Hospital, Hiram, GA, p. A161

HANGER, Clint, Chief Executive Officer, Palmetto Lowcountry Behavioral Health, Charleston, SC, p. A563

HANGER, Kelvin, Chief Executive Officer, TriHealth Evendale Hospital, Cincinnati, OH, p. A488

HANIGAN, Hank, R.N., Chief Executive Officer, Whitman Hospital and Medical Center, Colfax, WA, p. A683

HANISCH, Denise, M.D. Chief of Staff, Avera St. Mary's Hospital, Pierre, SD, p. A575

HANKINS, Brad, Chief Operating Quality Officer, Lake Chelan Community Hospital, Chelan, WA, p. A683

HANKS, Claire H., R.N. Vice President and Chief Nursing Officer, Glendale Memorial Hospital and Health Center, Glendale, CA, p. A64

HANKS, John, Director Information Systems, East Tennessee Children's Hospital, Knoxville, TN, p. A585

HANKS, Susan, Chief Information Officer, Riverton Hospital, Riverton, UT, p. A662

HANKS, Tammy, Director Human Resources, Minidoka Memorial Hospital, Rupert, ID, p. A178

HANLEY, Bob, Chief Human Resources Officer, University of Chicago Medical Center, Chicago, IL, p. A187

HANLEY, Darlene S., FACHE, President and Chief Executive Officer, St. Lawrence Rehabilitation Center, Lawrenceville, NJ, p. A418

HANLEY, Matthew, Chief Financial Officer, OSF Saint Anthony's Health Center, Alton, IL, p. A180

HANLON, Jerad, Chief Operating Officer, Southside Regional Medical Center, Petersburg, VA, p. A676

HANNA, Casey, M.D. Chief of Staff, Wagoner Community Hospital, Wagoner, OK, p. A523

HANNA, Mitchell J.
Chief Executive Officer, Sutter Auburn Faith Hospital, Auburn, CA, p. A55
Chief Executive Officer, Sutter Coast Hospital, Crescent City, CA, p. A60

HANNA, Philip S., Chief Executive Officer, DeWitt Hospital, DeWitt, AR, p. A45

HANNA, Robb, Executive Director Information Technology, Lexington Regional Health Center, Lexington, NE, p. A397

HANNAH, Jill, Director Human Resources, James Cancer Hospital and Solove Research Institute, Columbus, OH, p. A490

HANNAH, Steven, Chief Executive Officer, Montrose Memorial Hospital, Montrose, CO, p. A109

HANNAN, Barbara E., R.N., Chief Executive Officer, Select Specialty Hospital–Northeast New Jersey, Rochelle Park, NJ, p. A423

HANNERS, Brandy, Chief Financial Officer, Memorial Hospital, Martinsville, VA, p. A673

HANNERS, Rodney B.
Chief Executive Officer, Keck Hospital of USC, Los Angeles, CA, p. A72
Chief Executive Officer, USC Norris Comprehensive Cancer Center, Los Angeles, CA, p. A74

HANNON, Barbara A., R.N. Interim Chief Nursing Officer and Chief Clinical Officer, Curry General Hospital, Gold Beach, OR, p. A526

HANNON, Edward J., Chief Executive Officer, Bates County Memorial Hospital, Butler, MO, p. A368

HANNON, Jennifer, Director Human Resources, Madison County Health Care System, Winterset, IA, p. A239

HANNON, Kay, Director Information Systems, Des Peres Hospital, Saint Louis, MO, p. A380

HANNON, Patricia, Chief Nursing Officer, Vaughan Regional Medical Center, Selma, AL, p. A25

HANNON, Trish, R.N., President and Chief Executive Officer, New England Baptist Hospital, Boston, MA, p. A307

HANOLD, Cindy, Chief Nursing Officer, Richland Hospital, Richland Center, WI, p. A715

HANS, Christopher, Chief Financial Officer, Riverside University Health System–Medical Center, Moreno Valley, CA, p. A78

HANSCOM, Kristine, Chief Financial Officer, Tufts Medical Center, Boston, MA, p. A307

HANSEL, Jimmie W., Ph.D., Chief Executive Officer, Edwards County Hospital and Healthcare Center, Kinsley, KS, p. A246

HANSEN, Becky, Chief Executive Officer, Southwest Healthcare Services, Bowman, ND, p. A477

HANSEN, Carolyn, Chief Nursing Officer, Bingham Memorial Hospital, Blackfoot, ID, p. A174

HANSEN, Chris, Senior Vice President Ambulatory Services and Chief Information Officer, The University of Kansas Hospital, Kansas City, KS, p. A246

HANSEN, Gayle B., R.N
Chief Operating Officer, Mayo Clinic Health System in Fairmont, Fairmont, MN, p. A342
Chief Integration Officer, Mayo Clinic Health System in Saint James, Saint James, MN, p. A350

HANSEN, Jay, Director Information Services, Oconee Memorial Hospital, Seneca, SC, p. A569

HANSEN, Karen, Vice President and Chief Operating Officer, Memorial Medical Center – Ashland, Ashland, WI, p. A702

HANSEN, Kristy, CPA Chief Financial Officer, Myrtue Medical Center, Harlan, IA, p. A232

HANSEN, Kyle, Corporate Director Information Systems, Riverside Medical Center, Kankakee, IL, p. A194

HANSEN, Kyle A., Chief Executive Officer, Logan Regional Hospital, Logan, UT, p. A660

HANSEN, Laurie
Associate Administrator, Emory Johns Creek Hospital, Johns Creek, GA, p. A161
Director Administrative Services, Johnson County Healthcare Center, Buffalo, WY, p. A721

HANSEN, Linda, Director Human Resources, Bakersfield Heart Hospital, Bakersfield, CA, p. A55

HANSEN, Maggie, R.N. Chief Nursing Officer, Memorial Regional Hospital,, FL, p. A130

HANSEN, Marcia A., R.N. Vice President Operations and Chief Nursing Officer, WellSpan Ephrata Community Hospital, Ephrata, PA, p. A538

HANSEN, Michael T., FACHE, President and Chief Executive Officer, Columbus Community Hospital, Columbus, NE, p. A395

HANSEN, Misty
Chief Financial Officer, Banner – University Medical Center South, Tucson, AZ, p. A40
Chief Financial Officer, Banner – University Medical Center Tucson, Tucson, AZ, p. A40

HANSEN, Paul, Administrator, Maniilaq Health Center, Kotzebue, AK, p. A30

HANSEN, Steven, Director Information Technology, Healdsburg District Hospital, Healdsburg, CA, p. A66

HANSEN, Tim, Interim Chief Human Resource Officer, Denver Health, Denver, CO, p. A103

HANSERT, Benjamin K., Administrator, North Baldwin Infirmary, Bay Minette, AL, p. A16

HANSON, Brent, Chief Executive Officer, Pine Valley Specialty Hospital, Houston, TX, p. A626

HANSON, Denise, Information Technology Specialist, St. Cloud Veterans Affairs Health Care System, Saint Cloud, MN, p. A350

HANSON, Emily, M.D. President, Medical Staff, St. Joseph Memorial Hospital, Murphysboro, IL, p. A197

HANSON, Gregory S., M.D., Chief Executive Officer, Clark Fork Valley Hospital, Plains, MT, p. A390

HANSON, Jane E., R.N
 Chief Operating Officer, Chandler Regional Medical Center, Chandler, AZ, p. A31
 Chief Operating Officer, Mercy Gilbert Medical Center, Gilbert, AZ, p. A32

HANSON, Jennifer, R.N., President and Chief Administrative Officer, LeConte Medical Center, Sevierville, TN, p. A593

HANSON, Jesica, Vice President and Chief Financial Officer, Bakersfield Memorial Hospital, Bakersfield, CA, p. A55

HANSON, Jim, Director Information Systems, Avera Queen of Peace Hospital, Mitchell, SD, p. A575

HANSON, Lesley, Director Human Resources, Lake District Hospital, Lakeview, OR, p. A527

HANSON, Mary Ann, Director Personnel, Mental Health Institute, Cherokee, IA, p. A227

HANSON, Paul, Chief Financial Officer, Bay Area Regional Medical Center, Webster, TX, p. A656

HANSON, Paul A., FACHE, President, Sanford USD Medical Center, Sioux Falls, SD, p. A576

HANSON, Rhonda, Director Human Resources, Huron Regional Medical Center, Huron, SD, p. A574

HANSON, Rita, M.D
 Vice President Medical Affairs, Wheaton Franciscan Healthcare – Elmbrook Memorial, Brookfield, WI, p. A703
 Vice President Medical Affairs, Wheaton Franciscan Healthcare – St. Joseph's, Milwaukee, WI, p. A712

HANSON, Samantha, Chief Human Resources Officer, Children's Hospitals and Clinics of Minnesota, Minneapolis, MN, p. A346

HANSON, Stephen C., Chief Executive Officer, Baptist Health, Louisville, KY, p. B19

HANSON, Tamra, Human Resource Manager, Dorothea Dix Psychiatric Center, Bangor, ME, p. A291

HANYAK, Diana C., Chief Executive Officer, HEALTHSOUTH Tustin Rehabilitation Hospital, Tustin, CA, p. A97

HANZLIK, Debra Dawn, R.N. Director of Nursing, Niobrara Valley Hospital, Lynch, NE, p. A398

HAPNEY, Sherry, Chief Financial Officer, HEALTHSOUTH Rehabilitation Hospital of Fort Worth, Fort Worth, TX, p. A618

HAPPEL, Terry J., M.D. Vice President and Chief Medical Officer, Chandler Regional Medical Center, Chandler, AZ, p. A31

HAQQANI, Rahim, M.D. Medical Director, Dallas Behavioral Healthcare Hospital, Desoto, TX, p. A613

HAQUE, Haroon, M.D. Medical Director, CHG Hospital Tucson, LLC, Tucson, AZ, p. A40

HARA, Karen, Personnel Management Specialist, Hawaii State Hospital, Kaneohe, HI, p. A172

HARALDSON, Richard, Chief Executive Officer, Sidney Health Center, Sidney, MT, p. A391

HARALSON, Gregory
 Chief Executive Officer, Memorial Hermann Sugar Land Hospital, Sugar Land, TX, p. A650
 Chief Operating Officer, Plaza Medical Center of Fort Worth, Fort Worth, TX, p. A618

HARALSON, Robert, Chief Financial Officer, Williamson Memorial Hospital, Williamson, WV, p. A701

HARARI, Jack L., M.D. Chief Medical Officer, West Boca Medical Center, Boca Raton, FL, p. A124

HARBAUGH, Charles, Director Human Resources, Mountain Lakes Medical Center, Clayton, GA, p. A156

HARBAUGH, Ken, Vice President and Chief Financial Officer, OSF Saint Francis Medical Center, Peoria, IL, p. A200

HARBERT, Jim, Chief Technology Officer, Anthony Medical Center, Anthony, KS, p. A240

HARBERTS, Jerry, Information Technologist, Madison Healthcare Services, Madison, MN, p. A345

HARBESON, Mary, R.N., Chief Executive Officer, Kindred Hospital Clear Lake, Webster, TX, p. A656

HARBIN, Cathy
 Chief Nursing Officer, Roosevelt Warm Springs Rehabilitation and Specialty Hospitals – LTAC, Warm Springs, GA, p. A168
 Chief Nursing Officer, Roosevelt Warm Springs Rehabilitation and Specialty Hospitals – Rehab, Warm Springs, GA, p. A168

HARBIN, Jason, Director of Nursing, Ward Memorial Hospital, Monahans, TX, p. A637

HARBISON, Linda, Chief Nursing Officer, Red Bud Regional Hospital, Red Bud, IL, p. A201

HARBOR, Mike, Chief Financial Officer, Nevada Regional Medical Center, Nevada, MO, p. A377

HARCHENKO, Vern, M.D. Chief of Staff, Garrison Memorial Hospital, Garrison, ND, p. A479

HARCLERODE, Timothy, Chief Executive Officer, Nason Hospital, Roaring Spring, PA, p. A553

HARCOURT, Jenifer, Chief Operating Officer, RiverWoods Behavioral Health System, Riverdale, GA, p. A164

HARCUP, Craig, M.D. Hospital Medical Director, Complex Care Hospital at Ridgelake, Sarasota, FL, p. A145

HARDACRE, Jerry, M.D. Chief of Staff, Wheaton Franciscan Healthcare – All Saints, Racine, WI, p. A714

HARDAN, Terry, Director Human Resources, Longview Regional Medical Center, Longview, TX, p. A633

HARDCASTLE, Brad, Chief Financial Officer, South Baldwin Regional Medical Center, Foley, AL, p. A20

HARDCASTLE, Kathy, Director Human Resources, Texas Health Presbyterian Hospital Denton, Denton, TX, p. A613

HARDEE, Gary R., M.D. Medical Director, Plains Memorial Hospital, Dimmitt, TX, p. A613

HARDEMAN, Diane, Director Personnel, Stephens County Hospital, Toccoa, GA, p. A168

HARDEN, Diane P.
 Chief Financial Officer, Leesburg Regional Medical Center, Leesburg, FL, p. A134
 Senior Vice President and Chief Financial Officer, The Villages Regional Hospital, The Villages, FL, p. A148

HARDESTY, Keith, Chief Financial Officer, Springfield Hospital Center, Sykesville, MD, p. A303

HARDIE, Rebecca K., Chief Nursing Officer, Baylor Scott & White Medical Center – Hillcrest, Waco, TX, p. A655

HARDIN, Cecil, CPA Chief Financial Officer, Catawba Hospital, Catawba, VA, p. A668

HARDIN, Ellen L., Chief Human Resources Officer, Mendocino Coast District Hospital, Fort Bragg, CA, p. A62

HARDIN, James, Human Resources Officer, Sheridan Veterans Affairs Medical Center, Sheridan, WY, p. A724

HARDIN, Leslie, Chief Executive Officer and Chief Financial Officer, Seymour Hospital, Seymour, TX, p. A648

HARDIN, Marci, Manager Information Technology, Nevada Regional Medical Center, Nevada, MO, p. A377

HARDIN, Mark, M.D. Medical Director, Ed Fraser Memorial Hospital and Baker Community Health Center, MacClenny, FL, p. A135

HARDIN, Nicholas, FACHE, Chief Executive Officer, HEALTHSOUTH Sugar Land Rehabilitation Hospital, Sugar Land, TX, p. A650

HARDING, Barry, Interim Chief Executive Officer and Chief Financial Officer, Sumner Regional Medical Center, Wellington, KS, p. A255

HARDING, Cathy, Chief Clinical Officer, Vibra Hospital of Springfield, Springfield, IL, p. A203

HARDING, Christina, Vice President Finance, Mount Desert Island Hospital, Bar Harbor, ME, p. A291

HARDING, Denise, Director Human Resources, Plumas District Hospital, Quincy, CA, p. A84

HARDING, Edward A., FACHE, President and Chief Executive Officer, Bay Area Medical Center, Marinette, WI, p. A709

HARDING, Geoff, Chief Clinical Officer, Promise Hospital of Salt Lake, Salt Lake City, UT, p. A663

HARDING, Gwen, Site Manager Information Systems, Bon Secours Memorial Regional Medical Center, Mechanicsville, VA, p. A673

HARDING, Helen, Chief Nursing Officer, Fairfield Medical Center, Lancaster, OH, p. A496

HARDING, John P., Chief Operating Officer, Children's Hospital of The King's Daughters, Norfolk, VA, p. A675

HARDING, John R., Chief Executive Officer, Lincoln County Health System, Fayetteville, TN, p. A583

HARDING, Rick, Administrator, Oceans Behavioral Hospital Plano, Plano, TX, p. A642

HARDMAN, Danny, FACHE Chief Nursing Officer, Hillcrest Medical Center, Tulsa, OK, p. A521

HARDOBY, Greg, Director Personnel, Runnells Center for Rehabilitation and Healthcare, Berkeley Heights, NJ, p. A414

HARDWICK, Garry, R.N. Chief Operating Officer, Newport Bay Hospital, Newport Beach, CA, p. A79

HARDY, Bob, Chief Operating Officer, Opelousas General Health System, Opelousas, LA, p. A286

HARDY, James, D.O. Chief of Staff, Dayton Veterans Affairs Medical Center, Dayton, OH, p. A492

HARDY, Janice, Chief Human Resource Management Service, Central Alabama Veterans Health Care System, Montgomery, AL, p. A23

HARDY, Kevin, Chief Financial Officer, HEALTHSOUTH Treasure Coast Rehabilitation Hospital, Vero Beach, FL, p. A149

HARDY, LaBon, Chief Information Officer, Ralph H. Johnson Veterans Affairs Medical Center, Charleston, SC, p. A563

HARDY, Melanie, D.O. Chief of Staff, Marias Medical Center, Shelby, MT, p. A391

HARDY, Valonia, Chief Healthy Living Officer, Tsehootsooi Medical Center, Fort Defiance, AZ, p. A32

HARGENS, Scott, Interim Administrator and Chief Executive Officer, Avera Flandreau Hospital, Flandreau, SD, p. A573

HARGENS, Scott James, Interim Administrator & Chief Executive Officer, Avera Dells Area Hospital, Dell Rapids, SD, p. A573

HARGER, Anita
 Chief Human Resource Officer, Kingman Regional Medical Center, Kingman, AZ, p. A33
 Director Human Resources, Mercy Gilbert Medical Center, Gilbert, AZ, p. A32

HARGETT, Stephen, Administrator Finance and Support Services, MUSC Medical Center of Medical University of South Carolina, Charleston, SC, p. A563

HARGETT, Stephen A., Senior Vice President and Chief Financial Officer, Marina Del Rey Hospital, Marina Del Rey, CA, p. A76

HARGIS, Bryan J., FACHE,
 Chief Executive Officer, Florence Hospital at Anthem, Florence, AZ, p. A32
 Chief Executive Officer, Gilbert Hospital, Gilbert, AZ, p. A32

HARGIS, Chris, Manager Finance, Alta View Hospital, Sandy, UT, p. A664

HARGRAVE, Dallas, Human Resources Director, Bartlett Regional Hospital, Juneau, AK, p. A29

HARGRAVE, David, Chief Information Officer, Ward Memorial Hospital, Monahans, TX, p. A637

HARGRAVE–THOMAS, Anne, Chief Executive Officer, Oakleaf Surgical Hospital, Eau Claire, WI, p. A705

HARGRODER, Ty, M.D. Chief of Staff, Acadia–St. Landry Hospital, Church Point, LA, p. A274

HARGROVE, Ben, Human Resources Director, LifeStream Behavioral Center, Leesburg, FL, p. A134

HARGROVE, Jeno, R.N. Director of Nursing, Columbus Community Hospital, Columbus, TX, p. A607

HARGROVE, Tressa B., Director Human Resources, Jackson Purchase Medical Center, Mayfield, KY, p. A266

HARIHARAN, Parma, M.D. Chief of Staff, Mercy Health – Clermont Hospital, Batavia, OH, p. A484

HARKER, Jodie, Director Human Resources, Van Diest Medical Center, Webster City, IA, p. A239

HARKEY, FACHE, Shirley S., R.N. Vice President, Patient Services, Wayne Memorial Hospital, Goldsboro, NC, p. A466

HARKINS, Shelly, M.D. Chief Medical Officer, HSHS St. Elizabeth's Hospital, Belleville, IL, p. A181

HARKLEROAD, Rod, R.N., Chief Executive Officer, Haywood Regional Medical Center, Clyde, NC, p. A463

HARKNESS, Charles, D.O. Vice President Medical Affairs, Southeast Alabama Medical Center, Dothan, AL, p. A19

HARLAN, Kevin W., President, Joint Township District Memorial Hospital, Saint Marys, OH, p. A502

HARLAN, Thomas P., Chief Executive Officer, ContinueCARE Hospital at Hendrick Medical Center, Abilene, TX, p. A595

HARLE, Connie, Chief Nursing Officer, Range Regional Health Services, Hibbing, MN, p. A344

HARLESS, Andrea, Director Information Services, Wythe County Community Hospital, Wytheville, VA, p. A681

HARLESS, Cheryl, Chief Nursing Officer, Doctors Medical Center of Modesto, Modesto, CA, p. A77

HARLIN, Tim, M.D. Chief Operations Officer, Denver Health, Denver, CO, p. A103

HARLOW, Donald, Director of Information Services, MountainView Regional Medical Center, Las Cruces, NM, p. A430

HARLOW, Tammy
 Director of Nursing, Grady General Hospital, Cairo, GA, p. A155
 Chief Nurse Executive, Riverview Regional Medical Center, Gadsden, AL, p. A20

HARLOW, Thomas R., FACHE, President, WellSpan Good Samaritan Hospital, Lebanon, PA, p. A543

HARLOWE, Michael, President and Chief Executive Officer, Indiana University Health Tipton Hospital, Tipton, IN, p. A223

HARMAN, Kenneth, Chief Executive Officer, Pioneers Medical Center, Meeker, CO, p. A109

HARMAN, Kimberly, Regional Manager Human Resources, Western State Hospital, Staunton, VA, p. A679

HARMON, Amy, Chief Financial Officer, Elkview General Hospital, Hobart, OK, p. A512

HARMON, Clifford K., Chief Executive Officer, Harrison Community Hospital, Cadiz, OH, p. A486

HARMON, Connie, Director of Nursing, Lakeland Hospital, Watervliet, Watervliet, MI, p. A336

HARMON, David, D.O. Vice President Medical Services, RiverValley Behavioral Health Hospital, Owensboro, KY, p. A267

HARMON, James
  Information Technology, Cypress Creek Hospital, Houston, TX, p. A624
  Network Administrator, West Oaks Hospital, Houston, TX, p. A627
HARMON, Jennifer, Director of Human Resources, St. Cloud Regional Medical Center, Saint Cloud, FL, p. A144
HARMON, Thomas, M.D. Vice President Medical Affairs, OhioHealth Riverside Methodist Hospital, Columbus, OH, p. A491
HARMS, Arlene, Chief Executive Officer, Rio Grande Hospital, Del Norte, CO, p. A103
HARMS, George
  Chief Financial Officer, Hays Medical Center, Hays, KS, p. A244
  Chief Financial Officer, Pawnee Valley Community Hospital, Larned, KS, p. A247
HARNED, Barbara, R.N. Chief Nursing Officer, Monroe County Hospital, Monroeville, AL, p. A23
HARNESS, Phil, Chief Executive Officer, Doctor's Hospital, Leawood, KS, p. A247
HARNEY, Geraldine, Chief Financial Officer, U. S. Public Health Service Phoenix Indian Medical Center, Phoenix, AZ, p. A37
HARNING, Richard, Vice President Finance and Chief Financial Officer, Allegan General Hospital, Allegan, MI, p. A318
HARPE, Michael, Vice President Human Resources, Community Hospital of Anderson & Madison County, Anderson, IN, p. A206
HARPER, Cindy, Manager Patient Data, Westfield Memorial Hospital, Westfield, NY, p. A459
HARPER, Corwin N.
  Senior Vice President and Area Manager, Kaiser Permanente Manteca Medical Center, Manteca, CA, p. A76
  Senior Vice President and Area Manager, Kaiser Permanente Vallejo Medical Center, Vallejo, CA, p. A98
HARPER, David
  Director, Site Information Systems, Advocate Eureka Hospital, Eureka, IL, p. A189
  Chief Information Officer, Wills Memorial Hospital, Washington, GA, p. A168
HARPER, Eric, Chief Information Officer, Southeastern Health, Lumberton, NC, p. A469
HARPER, James F., Senior Vice President and Chief Human Resources Officer, Tidelands Georgetown Memorial Hospital, Georgetown, SC, p. A566
HARPER, Kirk, R.N. Vice President, Nursing, Kadlec Regional Medical Center, Richland, WA, p. A689
HARPER, R. Andrew, M.D. Medical Director, University of Texas Harris County Psychiatric Center, Houston, TX, p. A627
HARPER, William F., M.D. Chief of Staff, Birmingham Veterans Affairs Medical Center, Birmingham, AL, p. A16
HARPER SPHR, Wally G., Vice President Human Resources, Gaylord Hospital, Wallingford, CT, p. A117
HARPER–O'CONNOR, Paul
  Interim Regional Administrator, Kula Hospital, Kula, HI, p. A172
  Interim Administrator, Lanai Community Hospital, Lanai City, HI, p. A172
HARR, Donald, Controller, Ray County Memorial Hospital, Richmond, MO, p. A378
HARREL, Mark, Chief Executive Officer, Phelps Memorial Health Center, Holdrege, NE, p. A397
HARRELL, Aaron, Director, Grove Hill Memorial Hospital, Grove Hill, AL, p. A21
HARRELL, Joy, R.N. Chief Nursing Officer, Mimbres Memorial Hospital, Deming, NM, p. A429
HARRELL, Michael, R.N.
  Chief Executive Officer, Promise Hospital of Miss Lou, Vidalia, LA, p. A289
  Chief Executive Officer, Promise Hospital of Vicksburg, Vicksburg, MS, p. A365
HARRELL, Paula, Chief Nursing Officer, Regional One Health Extended Care Hospital, Memphis, TN, p. A589
HARRELL, Steven W., FACHE Chief Operating Officer, Florida Hospital New Smyrna, New Smyrna Beach, FL, p. A139
HARRELL, Thomas, M.D., Commander, U. S. Air Force Medical Center Keesler, Keesler AFB, MS, p. A360
HARRELSON, Rick, M.D. President Medical Staff, Medical Center Enterprise, Enterprise, AL, p. A19
HARRIER, Margie, MSN Medical Center Chief Operations Officer, Kaiser Permanente Orange County Anaheim Medical Center, Anaheim, CA, p. A54
HARRIGAN, Robert, President, Summa Hospitals, Summa Health System, Akron, OH, p. A483
HARRIGER, Richard, Director of Emergency Services, Kimball Health Services, Kimball, NE, p. A397
HARRILSON, Annette, Chief Clinical Officer, Select Specialty Hospital Midtown Atlanta, Atlanta, GA, p. A152
HARRINGTON, Hal, Vice President Human Resources, Merit Health River Region, Vicksburg, MS, p. A365

HARRINGTON, Jason, FACHE, President and Chief Executive Officer, Lakes Regional Healthcare, Spirit Lake, IA, p. A238
HARRINGTON, Jeff, Chief Financial Officer, Children's Hospital Colorado, Aurora, CO, p. A101
HARRINGTON Jr., John L., FACHE, Chief Executive Officer, HonorHealth Deer Valley Medical Center, Phoenix, AZ, p. A36
HARRINGTON, Kathleen, Vice President Human Resources, Beth Israel Deaconess Hospital–Milton, Milton, MA, p. A312
HARRIS, Alicia, Director Fiscal Services, Mississippi State Hospital, Whitfield, MS, p. A366
HARRIS, Allen, M.D. Clinical Director, South Mississippi State Hospital, Purvis, MS, p. A364
HARRIS, Andrew E., President and Chief Executive Officer, Blue Mountain Health System, Lehighton, PA, p. B23
HARRIS, Andrew E.
  Chief Executive Officer, Blue Mountain Hospital, Lehighton, PA, p. A543
  Chief Executive Officer, Palmerton Hospital, Palmerton, PA, p. A546
HARRIS, Betty J., Director Human Resources, Southern California Hospital at Culver City, Culver City, CA, p. A60
HARRIS, Burt, Acting Chief Executive Officer, Canyon Ridge Hospital, Chino, CA, p. A58
HARRIS, C. Martin, M.D
  Chief Information Officer, Cleveland Clinic, Cleveland, OH, p. A488
  Chief Information Officer, Cleveland Clinic Children's Hospital for Rehabilitation, Cleveland, OH, p. A489
  Chief Information Officer, Cleveland Clinic Fairview Hospital, Cleveland, OH, p. A489
  Chief Information Officer, Lutheran Hospital, Cleveland, OH, p. A489
HARRIS, David, Director Information Systems, De Queen Medical Center, De Queen, AR, p. A45
HARRIS, Denise H., R.N. Chief Nursing Officer, Baptist Health South Florida, West Kendall Baptist Hospital, Miami, FL, p. A136
HARRIS, Donna, Chief Executive Officer, HEALTHSOUTH Rehabilitation Hospital of Jonesboro, Jonesboro, AR, p. A48
HARRIS, Dory, Director Human Resource, Teton Valley Health Care, Driggs, ID, p. A176
HARRIS, Ethan, Manager Information Systems, Mid–Valley Hospital, Omak, WA, p. A687
HARRIS, Howard, Vice President Human Resources, Regional Medical Center, Orangeburg, SC, p. A569
HARRIS, Jan, R.N. Director of Nursing, Stonewall Memorial Hospital, Aspermont, TX, p. A598
HARRIS, Janice M., Director Human Resources, University Medical Center of El Paso, El Paso, TX, p. A616
HARRIS, Jen, Director Health Information Management, Chase County Community Hospital, Imperial, NE, p. A397
HARRIS, Jerald, Chief Information Officer, Cornerstone Hospital of Houston at Clearlake, Webster, TX, p. A656
HARRIS, Jim
  Vice President Human Resources, Fairmont Regional Medical Center, Fairmont, WV, p. A696
  Director Information Technology, Grafton City Hospital, Grafton, WV, p. A696
HARRIS, Jo ell, Director of Nursing, Forest View Psychiatric Hospital, Grand Rapids, MI, p. A324
HARRIS, Joanne, Director Human Resources, Mount Desert Island Hospital, Bar Harbor, ME, p. A291
HARRIS, John, Chief Executive Officer, Memorial Medical Center, Las Cruces, NM, p. A430
HARRIS, John B., Vice President Finance and Chief Financial Officer, Community Hospital of Anderson & Madison County, Anderson, IN, p. A206
HARRIS, Julie, Chief Financial Officer, Riceland Medical Center, Winnie, TX, p. A658
HARRIS, Karen, R.N. Chief Nursing and Operations Officer, Henry Ford West Bloomfield Hospital, West Bloomfield, MI, p. A336
HARRIS, Kathy, Vice President, Mercy Hospital and Trauma Center, Janesville, WI, p. A707
HARRIS, Kelli, Chief Financial Officer, Crouse Hospital, Syracuse, NY, p. A456
HARRIS, Kevin, Director Information Systems, Titus Regional Medical Center, Mount Pleasant, TX, p. A638
HARRIS, Kristin, Interim Chief Executive Officer, Oceans Behavioral Health Center Permian Basin, Midland, TX, p. A637
HARRIS, Laurie, Chief Accountant, Kerrville State Hospital, Kerrville, TX, p. A630
HARRIS, Lee, Assistant Administrator Support Services, Memorial Health and Manor, Bainbridge, GA, p. A154
HARRIS, Lisa, M.D. Senior Vice President Medical Affairs, Our Lady of Lourdes Memorial Hospital, Inc., Binghamton, NY, p. A435
HARRIS, Lisa E., M.D., Chief Executive Officer, Eskenazi Health, Indianapolis, IN, p. A213

HARRIS, Madeline, R.N. Vice President and Chief Nursing Officer, The Queen's Medical Center, Honolulu, HI, p. A171
HARRIS, Marianna, Administrator, Osborne County Memorial Hospital, Osborne, KS, p. A250
HARRIS, Mark D., Deputy Commander Clinical Services, Fort Belvoir Community Hospital, Fort Belvoir, VA, p. A670
HARRIS, Merilyn, Administrator, Kau Hospital, Pahala, HI, p. A172
HARRIS, Michael, M.D. Chief Medical Officer, Englewood Hospital and Medical Center, Englewood, NJ, p. A417
HARRIS, Mike, Chief Operating Officer, AMG Specialty Hospital–Tulsa, Tulsa, OK, p. A521
HARRIS, Miriam, Director Finance, Oklahoma Forensic Center, Vinita, OK, p. A523
HARRIS, R. Brian, M.D. Chief of Staff, Reeves Memorial Medical Center, Bernice, LA, p. A273
HARRIS, Robert M., M.D. President Medical and Dental Staff, Bergen Regional Medical Center, Paramus, NJ, p. A421
HARRIS, Sandra L., R.N. Senior Vice President and Chief Operating Officer, Texas Health Arlington Memorial Hospital, Arlington, TX, p. A598
HARRIS, Shelley, MSN Chief Nursing Officer, HSHS St. Elizabeth's Hospital, Belleville, IL, p. A181
HARRIS, Shelly, Chief Executive Officer, Indian Health Service – Quentin N. Burdick Memorial Health Care Facility, Belcourt, ND, p. A477
HARRIS, Shirley, M.D. President Medical Staff, SSM Health St. Francis Hospital – Maryville, Maryville, MO, p. A376
HARRIS, Spencer, Senior Director Finance, Kadlec Regional Medical Center, Richland, WA, p. A689
HARRIS, Stuart, M.D. Chief of Staff, Trigg County Hospital, Cadiz, KY, p. A258
HARRIS, Sue, Vice President and Chief Nursing Officer, Methodist Medical Center of Oak Ridge, Oak Ridge, TN, p. A592
HARRIS, Susan, R.N. Chief Operating Officer, Medical Center, Navicent Health, Macon, GA, p. A162
HARRIS, Susan, Director Fiscal Services, Shriners Hospitals for Children–Cincinnati Burns Hospital, Cincinnati, OH, p. A488
HARRIS, Sylvia, Fiscal Director, Moccasin Bend Mental Health Institute, Chattanooga, TN, p. A580
HARRIS, Terri, R.N. Chief Nursing Officer, East Cooper Medical Center, Mount Pleasant, SC, p. A568
HARRIS, Timothy, M.D. Chief Quality Officer, Texas Health Presbyterian Hospital Denton, Denton, TX, p. A613
HARRIS, Vena, Director Human Resources, Minneola District Hospital, Minneola, KS, p. A249
HARRIS, William R., Chief Information Officer, Lawton Indian Hospital, Lawton, OK, p. A513
HARRISON, Alicia, Data Management Officer, Excelsior Springs Hospital, Excelsior Springs, MO, p. A370
HARRISON, Allen, Chief Executive Officer, St. David's North Austin Medical Center, Austin, TX, p. A600
HARRISON, Andre'
  Regional Human Resource Officer, Presence Saint Joseph Medical Center, Joliet, IL, p. A194
  Regional Chief Human Resources Officer, Presence St. Mary's Hospital, Kankakee, IL, p. A194
HARRISON, Charles, Chief Executive Officer, San Bernardino Mountains Community Hospital District, Lake Arrowhead, CA, p. A68
HARRISON, Chris, Manager Information Systems, Campbell County Health, Gillette, WY, p. A722
HARRISON, Dean M., President and Chief Executive Officer, Northwestern Memorial Healthcare, Chicago, IL, p. B97
HARRISON, Dean M., Chief Executive Officer, Northwestern Memorial Hospital, Chicago, IL, p. A185
HARRISON, Denise, Associate Director, Veterans Affairs Nebraska–Western Iowa Health Care System, Omaha, NE, p. A401
HARRISON, Dyan, Manager Health Information, Ochiltree General Hospital, Perryton, TX, p. A641
HARRISON, Jo L., Vice President of Patient Care Services, Southwest Medical Center, Liberal, KS, p. A248
HARRISON, Marva, R.N. Vice President and Chief Nursing Officer, Integris Southwest Medical Center, Oklahoma City, OK, p. A516
HARRISON, Randy, Chief Financial Officer, Raleigh General Hospital, Beckley, WV, p. A694
HARROD, Tracy, Director of Nursing, Greenwood County Hospital, Eureka, KS, p. A243
HARRON, Rick, Chief Financial Officer, Dominican Hospital, Santa Cruz, CA, p. A93
HARROP, Elizabeth, Director, Human Resources, Flambeau Hospital, Park Falls, WI, p. A714
HARROP, Phil, Executive Director Operations, Saint Alphonsus Medical Center – Nampa, Nampa, ID, p. A177
HARSHAWAT, Paras, M.D. Medical Director, Harsha Behavioral Center, Terre Haute, IN, p. A222

HARSHBARGER, Catherine S., R.N., Chief Executive Officer, Banner Lassen Medical Center, Susanville, CA, p. A95

HARSY, Brice, Chief Financial Officer, Marshall Browning Hospital, Du Quoin, IL, p. A188

HART, Amy, Chief Operating Officer, Cuyuna Regional Medical Center, Crosby, MN, p. A341

HART, Chet, Vice President Operations, Sentara CarePlex Hospital, Hampton, VA, p. A671

HART, Deborah, Chief Financial Officer, North Suburban Medical Center, Thornton, CO, p. A111

HART, Denise, Director Human Resources, Sullivan County Community Hospital, Sullivan, IN, p. A222

HART, Donna, Chief Information Officer, Provident Hospital of Cook County, Chicago, IL, p. A186

HART, Elizabeth, R.N. Chief Nursing Officer, Providence Saint Joseph Medical Center, Burbank, CA, p. A57

HART, Gary, M.D. Chief Medical Officer, West Park Hospital, Cody, WY, p. A722

HART, James, M.D. Medical Director, Rolling Hills Hospital, Franklin, TN, p. A583

HART, John, Chief Executive Officer, Fredonia Regional Hospital, Fredonia, KS, p. A243

HART, Joline, Vice President Human Resources, Franklin Memorial Hospital, Farmington, ME, p. A293

HART, Joseph, Director Finance and Support Services, Putnam Hospital Center, Carmel, NY, p. A437

HART, Ken, Vice President Operations, Saint Alphonsus Medical Center – Ontario, Ontario, OR, p. A528

HART, Lisa, Chief Executive Officer, Elkview General Hospital, Hobart, OK, p. A512

HART, Monique, Chief Financial Officer, Baptist Memorial Hospital–Tipton, Covington, TN, p. A582

HART, Pat, Director Human Resources, Three Rivers Medical Center, Louisa, KY, p. A264

HART, Richard, Chief Financial Officer, Stanislaus Surgical Hospital, Modesto, CA, p. A77

HART, Richard H., M.D., President and Chief Executive Officer, Loma Linda University Adventist Health Sciences Center, Loma Linda, CA, p. B84

HART, Scott, Controller, HEALTHSOUTH Lakeview Rehabilitation Hospital, Elizabethtown, KY, p. A259

HART–FLYNN, Wilma, MS
Vice President Patient Care Services and Chief Nursing Officer, Illinois Valley Community Hospital, Peru, IL, p. A200
Chief Nursing Officer, Morristown–Hamblen Healthcare System, Morristown, TN, p. A590

HARTBERG, David, Chief Executive Officer, Gundersen Boscobel Area Hospital and Clinics, Boscobel, WI, p. A703

HARTE, Brian J., M.D., President, Hillcrest Hospital, Cleveland, OH, p. A489

HARTGRAVES, Steve L., President and Chief Executive Officer, Jackson County Memorial Hospital, Altus, OK, p. A508

HARTKE, Michael, Executive Vice President, Chief Operating Officer, Northwest Community Hospital, Arlington Heights, IL, p. A180

HARTLE, Christopher L.
President, Seton Medical Center Hays, Kyle, TX, p. A631
President, Seton Medical Center Williamson, Round Rock, TX, p. A644

HARTLEY, Barbara, Chief Medical Officer, Benson Hospital, Benson, AZ, p. A31

HARTLEY, Diane L., Director of Patient Care Services, Beaumont Hospital – Wayne, Wayne, MI, p. A336

HARTLEY, Melinda D., R.N. Vice President Patient Care Services, Perry Hospital, Perry, GA, p. A164

HARTLEY, Michael, MS Chief Nursing Officer, Holly Hill Hospital, Raleigh, NC, p. A472

HARTLEY, Michael Ward, Director Human Resources, AllianceHealth Midwest, Midwest City, OK, p. A514

HARTLEY, Shauna, Administrator, Turquoise Lodge Hospital, Albuquerque, NM, p. A428

HARTLEY, Shawn, Chief Financial Officer, Crossroads Community Hospital, Mount Vernon, IL, p. A197

HARTLEY, Wannah, Controller, Winkler County Memorial Hospital, Kermit, TX, p. A630

HARTMAN, Daphane, Director Information Systems, College Station Medical Center, College Station, TX, p. A606

HARTMAN, Dennis, Chief Financial Officer, Excelsior Springs Hospital, Excelsior Springs, MO, p. A370

HARTMAN, Don, Director Human Resources, Sutter Davis Hospital, Davis, CA, p. A60

HARTMAN, Kathleen, Chief Nursing Officer, MetroSouth Medical Center, Blue Island, IL, p. A182

HARTMAN, Sally, Senior Vice President, Riverside Regional Medical Center, Newport News, VA, p. A674

HARTMAN, Susan, Chief Executive Officer, HEALTHSOUTH Nittany Valley Rehabilitation Hospital, Pleasant Gap, PA, p. A552

HARTMANN, Doreen, Chief Financial Officer, St. Joseph's Behavioral Health Center, Stockton, CA, p. A95

HARTMANN, Margot, Ph.D., President and Chief Executive Officer, Nantucket Cottage Hospital, Nantucket, MA, p. A312

HARTMANN, Peter M., M.D. Vice President Medical Affairs, WellSpan York Hospital, York, PA, p. A559

HARTMANN, Rob, Assistant Director Human Resources Management, University Health Conway, Monroe, LA, p. A284

HARTNETT, Tammy, Employee Relations Manager, UnityPoint Health – St. Luke's, Sioux City, IA, p. A238

HARTSELL, Scott, Chief Operating Officer, Bayfront Health Brooksville, Brooksville, FL, p. A125

HARTTER, Jr., Lynn E., Director Human Resources, Nemaha Valley Community Hospital, Seneca, KS, p. A253

HARTUNG, Andy, Director Information Systems, Self Regional Healthcare, Greenwood, SC, p. A567

HARTWELL, Tim, Chief Human Resources, Marion Veterans Affairs Medical Center, Marion, IL, p. A195

HARTWICK, Bryan
Vice President Human Resources, Alton Memorial Hospital, Alton, IL, p. A180
Vice President Human Resources, Christian Hospital, Saint Louis, MO, p. A380

HARTWIG, Michael, M.D. Chief of Staff, Perry Memorial Hospital, Perry, OK, p. A518

HARTZOG, Rick, Chief Information Officer, Merit Health Madison, Canton, MS, p. A356

HARVERY, Paul, President and Chief Executive Officer, CHRISTUS Mother Frances Hospital – Sulphur Springs, Sulphur Springs, TX, p. A651

HARVEY, Alice, Director of Nursing, Heatherhill Care Communities, Chardon, OH, p. A486

HARVEY, Anne, MSN Chief Nursing Officer, El Paso Specialty Hospital, El Paso, TX, p. A615

HARVEY, John, M.D., President and Chief Executive Officer, Oklahoma Heart Hospital, Oklahoma City, OK, p. A517

HARVEY, John, M.D. President and Chief Executive Officer, Oklahoma Heart Hospital, Oklahoma City, OK, p. A517

HARVEY, John, M.D., President and Chief Executive Officer, Oklahoma Heart Hospital South Campus, Oklahoma City, OK, p. A517

HARVEY, Kathy, D.O. Chief Medical Officer, Logan Regional Medical Center, Logan, WV, p. A697

HARVEY, Kevin, Chief Financial Officer, McKenzie Regional Hospital, McKenzie, TN, p. A588

HARVEY, Laurie, Controller, El Campo Memorial Hospital, El Campo, TX, p. A615

HARVEY, Linda, Chief Financial Officer, West Feliciana Parish Hospital, Saint Francisville, LA, p. A287

HARVEY, Michael, FACHE, President and Chief Executive Officer, Community Memorial Hospital, Syracuse, NE, p. A402

HARVILL, Brian
Vice President Financial Services, Vidant Bertie Hospital, Windsor, NC, p. A475
Vice President Financial Services, Vidant Chowan Hospital, Edenton, NC, p. A464

HARVIN, Schley, Information Technology Technician, Hood Memorial Hospital, Amite, LA, p. A271

HASBROUCK, Matthew Steven, Chief Operating Officer, Fairview Park Hospital, Dublin, GA, p. A159

HASELTON, David, Chief Medical Officer, Riverton Hospital, Riverton, UT, p. A662

HASHMI, Faraz, Chief Executive Officer, Texas General Hospital – Van Zandt Regional Medical Center, Grand Saline, TX, p. A621

HASHMI, Mubashir, Chief Information Officer, Pacifica Hospital of the Valley,, CA, p. A73

HASHMI, Suleman, President and Chief Executive Officer, Texas General Hospital, Grand Prairie, TX, p. A621

HASKELL, Jeffrey, M.D. Chief Medical Staff, Lost Rivers Medical Center, Arco, ID, p. A174

HASKINS, Betty, Interim Administrator, Camden General Hospital, Camden, TN, p. A579

HASKINS, Don, Administrative Director Human Resources, Southwest Mississippi Regional Medical Center, McComb, MS, p. A361

HASLER, Marge, R.N. Vice President Patient Care Services and Chief Nursing Officer, Beaumont Hospital – Farmington Hills, Farmington Hills, MI, p. A323

HASLETT, Tom, Interim Chief Information Officer, MacNeal Hospital, Berwyn, IL, p. A181

HASNI, Kamran, M.D. Chief of Medical Staff, Barbourville ARH Hospital, Barbourville, KY, p. A257

HASS, Roxanne, Director of Nursing, Madison St. Joseph Health Center, Madisonville, TX, p. A635

HASSAN, Tariq, M.D. Associate Director of Patient Care, Captain James A. Lovell Federal Health Care Center, North Chicago, IL, p. A198

HASSANI, Dahlia, Vice President of Medical Affairs, Baylor All Saints Medical Center at Fort Worth, Fort Worth, TX, p. A617

HASSELBRACK, Jeni, Director Human Resources, Gordon Hospital, Calhoun, GA, p. A155

HASSLER, Robert, M.D. Director Medical Affairs, Novant Health Brunswick Medical Center, Bolivia, NC, p. A461

HAST, Anne S., R.N., Chief Executive Officer, Advanced Surgical Hospital, Washington, PA, p. A556

HASTIN, Kathy, Administrative Assistant Human Resources, River Valley Medical Center, Dardanelle, AR, p. A45

HASTINGS, Clare, R.N. Chief Nurse Officer, National Institutes of Health Clinical Center, Bethesda, MD, p. A299

HASTINGS, Sarah M., Executive Director, Ridgeview Medical Center, Waconia, MN, p. A352

HASTINGS–SMITH, Julie, Chief Financial Officer, Abrazo Maryvale Campus, Phoenix, AZ, p. A35

HATALA, Alexander J., FACHE, President and Chief Executive Officer, Our Lady of Lourdes Medical Center, Camden, NJ, p. A415

HATCH, Tammy, Manager, Sebasticook Valley Health, Pittsfield, ME, p. A294

HATCHER, Amy, Chief Financial Officer, Children's Hospital and Medical Center, Omaha, NE, p. A400

HATCHER, Cole E., Chief Executive Officer, Weatherford Rehabilitation Hospital, Weatherford, TX, p. A656

HATCHER, Julie, Vice President Human Resources, O'Connor Hospital, San Jose, CA, p. A91

HATCHES, Ann
Director, Human Resources, Holy Cross Hospital, Chicago, IL, p. A184
Interim Director Human Resources, Mount Sinai Hospital, Chicago, IL, p. A185

HATFIELD, Chad, Chief Executive Officer, Barrow Regional Medical Center, Winder, GA, p. A169

HATFIELD, Jonathan, Supervisor Information Technology, Klickitat Valley Health, Goldendale, WA, p. A685

HATFIELD, Samantha L., M.D. Chief Medical Officer, Lawrence Memorial Hospital, Walnut Ridge, AR, p. A53

HATFIELD, Timothy A., Community Chief Executive Officer, Tug Valley ARH Regional Medical Center, South Williamson, KY, p. A269

HATHAWAY, William, M.D. Chief Medical Officer, Mission Hospital, Asheville, NC, p. A460

HATHCOCK, Claudette
Administrative Director Human Resources, University of Mississippi Medical Center Grenada, Grenada, MS, p. A358
Human Resources Director, University of Mississippi Medical Center Holmes County, Lexington, MS, p. A361

HATIRAS, Spiros, FACHE, President and Chief Executive Officer, Holyoke Medical Center, Holyoke, MA, p. A310

HATLESTAD, Jill, Vice President Human Resources and Marketing, Glencoe Regional Health Services, Glencoe, MN, p. A343

HATTERER–HOAG, Dawn, Director Human Resources, Psychiatric Institute of Washington, Washington, DC, p. A122

HATTON, Tad
Vice President Chief Operating Officer, Seton Medical Center Austin, Austin, TX, p. A599
Chief Operating Officer, St. David's Round Rock Medical Center, Round Rock, TX, p. A644

HAUBL, Eileen, Senior Vice President and Chief Financial Officer, Mission Hospital, Mission Viejo, CA, p. A77

HAUG, Darin L., D.O., President and Chief Executive Officer, Fitzgibbon Hospital, Marshall, MO, p. A376

HAUGE, Meri, R.N. Associate Director of Patient Care Services and Nurse Executive, St. Cloud Veterans Affairs Health Care System, Saint Cloud, MN, p. A350

HAUGH, William, Administrator, Georgetown Community Hospital, Georgetown, KY, p. A260

HAUGHEY, Tracie, Chief Executive Officer and Chief Financial Officer, Wills Memorial Hospital, Washington, GA, p. A168

HAULER, Jennifer, D.O. Chief Medical Officer, Upper Valley Medical Center, Troy, OH, p. A504

HAUN, Richard, Chief Financial Officer, Wuesthoff Medical Center – Rockledge, Rockledge, FL, p. A143

HAUPERT, John M., FACHE, Chief Executive Officer, Grady Memorial Hospital, Atlanta, GA, p. A152

HAUPT, Carolyn, Chief Financial Officer, PeaceHealth United General Medical Center, Sedro–Woolley, WA, p. A690

HAURO, Phyllis, Chief Executive Officer, Louisiana Continuing Care Hospital, Marrero, LA, p. A283

HAUSAUER, Patricia K., Director Finance, Baptist Medical Center Nassau, Fernandina Beach, FL, p. A128

HAUSE, Eileen, Chief Executive Officer, Kensington Hospital, Philadelphia, PA, p. A548

HAUSER, Mark J., M.D. Chief Medical Officer, Baptist Health South Florida, Baptist Hospital of Miami, Miami, FL, p. A136

HAUSER, Megan, Director Human Resources, Shriners Hospitals for Children–Philadelphia, Philadelphia, PA, p. A549

HAUSHALTER, Richard L., Senior Vice President Operations and Chief Operating Officer, Sentara RMH Medical Center, Harrisonburg, VA, p. A671

HAUSMANN, Jena, President and Chief Executive Officer, Children's Hospital Colorado, Aurora, CO, p. A101

HAUSMANN, Sherry, Senior Administrator, Via Christi Hospital on St. Francis, Wichita, KS, p. A256

HAUSWIRTH, Michael
Chief Operating Officer, Aspirus Keweenaw Hospital, Laurium, MI, p. A329
Chief Operating Officer, Aspirus Keweenaw Hospital, Laurium, MI, p. A329
Chief Operating Officer, Aspirus Ontonagon Hospital, Ontonagon, MI, p. A331
Chief Operating Officer, Aspirus Ontonagon Hospital, Ontonagon, MI, p. A331

HAUSWIRTH, Renay, Chief Financial Officer, Palo Alto County Health System, Emmetsburg, IA, p. A230

HAVARD, Greg, Chief Executive Officer, George Regional Hospital, Lucedale, MS, p. A361

HAVEN, Adrian C., Site Manager, Gallup Indian Medical Center, Gallup, NM, p. A429

HAVENS, Jennifer, Chief Executive Officer and Director of Nursing Operations, Grundy County Memorial Hospital, Grundy Center, IA, p. A231

HAVERSTOCK, Loren, Manager Human Resources, Harrison County Hospital, Corydon, IN, p. A208

HAVRILLA, David A., Chief Financial Officer, MedStar Montgomery Medical Center, Olney, MD, p. A302

HAWIG, Scott
Senior Vice President of Finance, Chief Financial Officer and Treasurer, Community Memorial Hospital, Menomonee Falls, WI, p. A710
Senior Vice President Finance, Chief Financial Officer and Treasurer, Froedtert Memorial Lutheran Hospital, Milwaukee, WI, p. A711
Senior Vice President of Finance, Chief Financial Officer and Treasurer, St. Joseph's Hospital, West Bend, WI, p. A719

HAWK, Kevin, Chief Executive Officer, Hillcrest Hospital Cushing, Cushing, OK, p. A510

HAWKEY, Tammy, Manager Information Technology Client Services, Ministry Saint Clare's Hospital, Weston, WI, p. A719

HAWKINS, Brian A., Director, Washington DC Veterans Affairs Medical Center, Washington, DC, p. A122

HAWKINS, Bryan, Controller, FirstHealth Montgomery Memorial Hospital, Troy, NC, p. A474

HAWKINS, Ellis, President, SSM St. Clare Hospital, Fenton, MO, p. A371

HAWKINS, Hillary, M.D. Medical Director, Sheltering Arms Rehabilitation Hospital, Mechanicsville, VA, p. A673

HAWKINS, Janine, R.N. Vice President Patient Care Services and Chief Nursing Officer, Dameron Hospital, Stockton, CA, p. A95

HAWKINS, Jason F.
President and Chief Executive Officer, Fulton County Medical Center, Mc Connellsburg, PA, p. A544
President and Chief Executive Officer, J. C. Blair Memorial Hospital, Huntingdon, PA, p. A540

HAWKINS, Kidada, Chief Executive Officer, Shoals Hospital, Muscle Shoals, AL, p. A24

HAWKINS, Sheri, Chief Nursing Officer, Shawnee Mission Medical Center, Shawnee Mission, KS, p. A254

HAWKINS, Tami, R.N. Vice President Patient Care and Chief Nursing Officer, Texas Health Presbyterian Hospital of Rockwall, Rockwall, TX, p. A643

HAWKINSON, Curtis R., Chief Executive Officer, Community Memorial Healthcare, Marysville, KS, p. A249

HAWLEY, Claudia, Director Human Resources, Mason General Hospital, Shelton, WA, p. A690

HAWLEY, Jason, Manager Information Services, Yuma District Hospital, Yuma, CO, p. A112

HAWLEY, Jerry, Interim Chief Executive Officer, Quincy Valley Medical Center, Quincy, WA, p. A688

HAWLEY, William, President and Chief Executive Officer, Fawcett Memorial Hospital, Port Charlotte, FL, p. A143

HAWLIK, Teresa, MSN Chief Nurse Executive, Nebraska Spine Hospital, Omaha, NE, p. A400

HAWTHORNE, Kimberly, Administrator, Mayo Clinic Health System – Franciscan Healthcare in Sparta, Sparta, WI, p. A716

HAWTOF, Jeffrey, M.D. Vice President Medical Operations and Informatics, Beebe Healthcare, Lewes, DE, p. A119

HAY, Morgan, Chief Financial Officer, Gerald Champion Regional Medical Center, Alamogordo, NM, p. A427

HAYDEN, James, M.D. Chief Medical Officer, J. C. Blair Memorial Hospital, Huntingdon, PA, p. A540

HAYDEN, Jamie, Chief Financial Officer, Eastland Memorial Hospital, Eastland, TX, p. A614

HAYDEN, John
Senior Vice President and Human Resources Officer, Bronson Battle Creek, Battle Creek, MI, p. A319
Senior Vice President and Chief Human Resources Officer, Bronson LakeView Hospital, Paw Paw, MI, p. A331
Vice President and Chief Human Resources Officer, Bronson Methodist Hospital, Kalamazoo, MI, p. A328

HAYDEN, Karen, Director Health Information Services, Performance Improvement and Risk Management, Valle Vista Hospital, Greenwood, IN, p. A212

HAYDEN–PUGH, Beverly P., R.N. Senior Vice President and Chief Nursing Officer, Valley Children's Healthcare, Madera, CA, p. A75

HAYEK, Anthony, D.O. Medical Director, Edwin Shaw Rehab, Cuyahoga Falls, OH, p. A492

HAYES, Audimarie, R.N. Chief Nursing Officer, North Texas Medical Center, Gainesville, TX, p. A620

HAYES, Brian T., Commander, David Grant USAF Medical Center, Travis AFB, CA, p. A96

HAYES, Cheryl, Vice President Patient Care Services, Kenmore Mercy Hospital, Kenmore, NY, p. A441

HAYES, David R., Chief Financial Officer, T.J. Health Columbia, Columbia, KY, p. A258

HAYES, Deborah Marie, R.N. Chief Hospital Officer and Chief Nursing Officer, Christ Hospital, Cincinnati, OH, p. A487

HAYES, Di, Chief Executive Officer, Hallmark Youthcare – Richmond, Richmond, VA, p. A677

HAYES, Donna, Controller, Decatur County General Hospital, Parsons, TN, p. A592

HAYES, Elaine, Controller, Sts. Mary & Elizabeth Hospital, Louisville, KY, p. A265

HAYES, Farrell, Chief Financial Officer, Cornerstone Medical Center, Fort Oglethorpe, GA, p. A160

HAYES, George E., FACHE, President and Chief Executive Officer, Memorial Hospital, Colorado Springs, CO, p. A102

HAYES, James L., Director Human Resources, Western State Hospital, Hopkinsville, KY, p. A262

HAYES, James M., Chief Executive Officer, UnityPoint Health – Trinity Muscatine, Muscatine, IA, p. A235

HAYES, Jo, Chief Nursing Officer, Horn Memorial Hospital, Ida Grove, IA, p. A232

HAYES, Judy M., R.N. Vice President Nursing and Chief Nursing Officer, Brigham and Women's Faulkner Hospital, Boston, MA, p. A306

HAYES, June, Chief Financial Officer, Harrisburg Medical Center, Harrisburg, IL, p. A192

HAYES, Kathe, Executive Director, Western New York Children's Psychiatric Center, West Seneca, NY, p. A459

HAYES, Kelly, Chief Financial Officer, Methodist Hospital for Surgery, Addison, TX, p. A595

HAYES, Kevin, M.D. Chief of Staff, Pioneer Community Hospital of Aberdeen, Aberdeen, MS, p. A355

HAYES, Lisa G., Chief Clinical Officer, AMG Specialty Hospital – Muncie, Muncie, IN, p. A218

HAYES, Paul, R.N., Executive Director, UW Medicine/Harborview Medical Center, Seattle, WA, p. A690

HAYES, Sharon, Chief Executive Officer, Palms of Pasadena Hospital, Saint Petersburg, FL, p. A144

HAYES, Stacy, R.N. Chief Nursing Officer, Arizona Spine and Joint Hospital, Mesa, AZ, p. A34

HAYES, Susan, Director Human Resources, Southeastern Health, Lumberton, NC, p. A469

HAYES, Tammy A., R.N. Chief Nurse Executive and Long Term Care Administrator, Northfield Hospital, Northfield, MN, p. A348

HAYES, Thomas P., Chief Executive Officer, Eastern Plumas Health Care, Portola, CA, p. A83

HAYES, Warren, Chief of Staff, Montgomery County Memorial Hospital, Red Oak, IA, p. A236

HAYES, William M., Chief Executive Officer, Northside Hospital–Cherokee, Canton, GA, p. A155

HAYGOOD, Rachel Joy, Director Information Technology, Tyler County Hospital, Woodville, TX, p. A658

HAYHURST, Leslie, Director Information Systems, Washington Health System Greene, Waynesburg, PA, p. A557

HAYMAN, Judy A., Ph.D., Acting Director, James E. Van Zandt Veterans Affairs Medical Center, Altoona, PA, p. A532

HAYMON, Beverly, Chief Financial Officer, Princeton Baptist Medical Center, Birmingham, AL, p. A17

HAYNES, Apryl, R.N., Vice President, Chief Operating Officer, Administrator, Seton Edgar B. Davis Hospital, Luling, TX, p. A635

HAYNES, Cassandra, Supervisor Human Resources and Employment, Phoebe Sumter Medical Center, Americus, GA, p. A151

HAYNES, Christopher, Chief Executive Officer, Kindred Hospital–Greensboro, Greensboro, NC, p. A466

HAYNES, Deatosha D., Interim Associates Director for Patient, Veterans Affairs Gulf Coast Veterans Health Care System, Biloxi, MS, p. A355

HAYNES, Elaine S., R.N. Vice President Patient Services and Chief Nursing Executive, Carolinas HealthCare System Lincoln, Lincolnton, NC, p. A469

HAYNES, Jamil, Regional Director Human Resources, INTEGRIS Miami Hospital, Miami, OK, p. A514

HAYNES, Jerry, President and Chief Executive Officer, Appalachian Regional Healthcare, Inc., Lexington, KY, p. B11

HAYNES, Jill, Financial Coach, Bath Veterans Affairs Medical Center, Bath, NY, p. A434

HAYNES, Jr., John H., M.D. Chief of Medical Staff, North Caddo Medical Center, Vivian, LA, p. A289

HAYNES, Ken, President and Chief Executive Officer, CHRISTUS Santa Rosa Health System, San Antonio, TX, p. A645

HAYNES, Laurie, Chief Financial Officer, Gulf Coast Medical Center, Panama City, FL, p. A141

HAYNES, Mark, M.D. Chief of Staff, Claiborne Memorial Medical Center, Homer, LA, p. A278

HAYNES, Robert Gerard, FACHE, Chief Executive Officer, Guadalupe Regional Medical Center, Seguin, TX, p. A648

HAYNES, William, Director Information Technology, Central Louisiana State Hospital, Pineville, LA, p. A286

HAYS, Cheryl M., FACHE, Administrator, Marshall Medical Center North, Guntersville, AL, p. A21

HAYS, Chuck, President and Chief Executive Officer, MaineGeneral Medical Center, Augusta, ME, p. A291

HAYS, Harry, Chief Executive Officer, Carroll County Memorial Hospital, Carrollton, KY, p. A258

HAYS, Larry, Director Information Technology, Southern Virginia Mental Health Institute, Danville, VA, p. A669

HAYS, Richard, M.D. Chief of Staff, Wellington Regional Medical Center, West Palm Beach, FL, p. A150

HAYS, Richard O., Chief Fiscal Service, Veterans Affairs Southern Nevada Healthcare System, North Las Vegas, NV, p. A407

HAYS, Timothy A., Vice President Human Resources, Johnston Health, Smithfield, NC, p. A473

HAYTAIAN, Mike, Head Director Information Resources Management, Naval Hospital Jacksonville, Jacksonville, FL, p. A132

HAYWARD, Ernest, M.D. Chief of Staff, Saddleback Memorial Medical Center, Laguna Hills, CA, p. A68

HAYWOOD, Nancy
Chief Financial Officer, Genesys Regional Medical Center, Grand Blanc, MI, p. A324
Chief Financial Officer, St. Mary's of Michigan, Saginaw, MI, p. A333

HAYWOOD, Stephanie, Director Human Resources, Southern Virginia Mental Health Institute, Danville, VA, p. A669

HAZELBAKER, Matthew, M.D. President Medical Staff, Memorial Health, Marysville, OH, p. A498

HAZZARD, Aaron, Interim Chief Executive Officer, Western Arizona Regional Medical Center, Bullhead City, AZ, p. A31

HEAD, David, M.D. Chief Medical Staff, Norton Sound Regional Hospital, Nome, AK, p. A30

HEAD, Susan, Director Nursing Services, U. S. Public Health Service Blackfeet Community Hospital, Saint Mary, MT, p. A390

HEADLAND, Mark
Chief Information Officer, Children's Hospital of Orange County, Orange, CA, p. A81
Chief Information Officer, CHOC Children's at Mission Hospital, Mission Viejo, CA, p. A76

HEADLEY, Kim, R.N. Chief Nursing Officer, HEALTHSOUTH Rehabilitation Hospital of Montgomery, Montgomery, AL, p. A23

HEALD, Robin R., Vice President Human Resources, Brattleboro Memorial Hospital, Brattleboro, VT, p. A665

HEALY, John, Manager Information Technology, Friends Hospital, Philadelphia, PA, p. A548

HEALY, Peter J., Chief Executive Officer, Beth Israel Deaconess Hospital–Milton, Milton, MA, p. A312

HEALY–COLLIER, Kathy, Chief Operating Officer, Brookwood Baptist Medical Center, Birmingham, AL, p. A16

HEARD, Alex, Chief Medical Officer, Falmouth Hospital, Falmouth, MA, p. A310

HEARD, Heather, Director Human Resources, Holdenville General Hospital, Holdenville, OK, p. A513

HEARD, John E., Chief Executive Officer, McGehee–Desha County Hospital, McGehee, AR, p. A50

HEARD, M. Denise, Director Business Services, North Mississippi Medical Center–Pontotoc, Pontotoc, MS, p. A364

HEARING, Ava, Chief Nursing Officer, Atrium Medical Center, Stafford, TX, p. A649

HEARNE, Diane, Director Human Resources, Arizona Spine and Joint Hospital, Mesa, AZ, p. A34

HEARNSBERGER, John, M.D. Chief of Staff, Howard Memorial Hospital, Nashville, AR, p. A50

HEART, Bill, Chief Operating Officer, Sacred Heart Rehabilitation Institute, Milwaukee, WI, p. A711

HEATER, Floyd, President and Chief Executive Officer, Warren Memorial Hospital, Front Royal, VA, p. A671

HEATH, Ed, FACHE, Chief Executive Officer, Owensboro Health Muhlenberg Community Hospital, Greenville, KY, p. A261

HEATH, Lisa, M.D. President Medical Staff, Saint Luke's South Hospital, Overland Park, KS, p. A251

HEATH, Merry, Chief Nursing Officer, Piedmont Fayette Hospital, Fayetteville, GA, p. A159

HEATH, Susan, R.N. Senior Vice President and Chief Nursing Officer, Seattle Children's Hospital, Seattle, WA, p. A689

HEATH, William, Chief Executive Officer, Regency Hospital of Hattiesburg, Hattiesburg, MS, p. A359

HEATHERLY, John, Assistant Administrator Support Services, Hunt Regional Medical Center, Greenville, TX, p. A621

HEATHERLY, Neil, Interim Chief Executive Officer, Tennova Physicians Regional Medical Center, Knoxville, TN, p. A586

HEATHERLY, Steve
Chief Executive Officer, Harris Regional Hospital, Sylva, NC, p. A474
Chief Executive Officer, Swain Community Hospital, Bryson City, NC, p. A461

HEATHERLY–LLOYD, Sara, Chief Operating Officer, Tennova Healthcare–LaFollette Medical Center, La Follette, TN, p. A586

HEATON, Crystal, Director of Finance, St. Mary's Warrick Hospital, Boonville, IN, p. A207

HEATON, John, M.D. Senior Vice President and Medical Director, Children's Hospital, New Orleans, LA, p. A284

HEBBERD, Hilda, R.N. Senior Director Clinical Services, Marlette Regional Hospital, Marlette, MI, p. A329

HEBEL, Barbara, Vice President Human Resources, Doylestown Hospital, Doylestown, PA, p. A537

HEBERT, Jr., Bernie, Chief Financial Officer, Doctors NeuroMedical Hospital, Bremen, IN, p. A207

HEBERT, Bryan, Director Information Systems, The Medical Center of Southeast Texas, Port Arthur, TX, p. A642

HEBERT, Gerard, Chief Financial Officer, Texoma Medical Center, Denison, TX, p. A612

HEBERT, Jeff, Interim Vice President Finance, Gifford Medical Center, Randolph, VT, p. A666

HEBERT, Katherine D., Chief Executive Officer, University Hospital and Clinics, Lafayette, LA, p. A281

HEBERT, Mark, M.D. President Medical Staff, Medical City Dallas Hospital, Dallas, TX, p. A610

HEBERT, Rachel, Chief Financial Officer, Heart Hospital of Lafayette, Lafayette, LA, p. A280

HEBERT, Raquel, Business Manager, Memorial Hermann Surgical HospitalG%(First Colony, Sugar Land, TX, p. A650

HEBERT, Timothy, Director Human Resources, Teche Regional Medical Center, Morgan City, LA, p. A284

HEBGEN, Lynn, Vice President Nursing, Upland Hills Health, Dodgeville, WI, p. A704

HECHLER, Tracy, Healthcare Director Information Services, Chippenham Hospital, Richmond, VA, p. A677

HECHT, David, M.D. Chief of Staff, James H. Quillen Veterans Affairs Medical Center, Mountain Home, TN, p. A590

HECKATHORNE, Daniel R., Chief Financial Officer, Memorial Hospital of Gardena, Gardena, CA, p. A64

HECKER, Julie, Vice President, Operations, UPMC Mercy, Pittsburgh, PA, p. A551

HECKER, Lisa, Director Human Resources, Hedrick Medical Center, Chillicothe, MO, p. A369

HECKERMAN, Ray, Chief Executive Officer and Managing Director, Coastal Harbor Treatment Center, Savannah, GA, p. A165

HECKERT Jr., Robert J., Chief Executive Officer, Gerald Champion Regional Medical Center, Alamogordo, NM, p. A427

HEDBERG, Beth, R.N. Director Nursing, Lindsborg Community Hospital, Lindsborg, KS, p. A248

HEDDE, Charles C., M.D. Chief Medical Officer, Good Samaritan Hospital, Vincennes, IN, p. A223

HEDDERMAN, Michael, Senior Vice President Finance and Chief Financial Officer, Marianjoy Rehabilitation Hospital, Wheaton, IL, p. A205

HEDGES, David, Chief Financial Officer, Southwestern Regional Medical Center, Tulsa, OK, p. A522

HEDLUND, Chris, Director Information Systems, Community Hospital–Fairfax, Fairfax, MO, p. A371

HEDRIX, Michael D., Administrator and President, Essentia Health Sandstone, Sandstone, MN, p. A351

HEEGAARD, William, M.D. Chief Medical Officer, Hennepin County Medical Center, Minneapolis, MN, p. A346

HEEMANN, John, Vice President and Chief Information Officer, Aspire Hospital, Conroe, TX, p. A607

HEETER, Eric, Superintendent, Larue D. Carter Memorial Hospital, Indianapolis, IN, p. A214

HEFFERNAN, Paul F., Vice President Human Resources, Women & Infants Hospital of Rhode Island, Providence, RI, p. A561

HEFFERNAN, Rebecca, Director Human Resources, MetroWest Medical Center, Framingham, MA, p. A310

HEFFERS, Margaret, Assistant Vice President Human Resources, Geisinger Wyoming Valley Medical Center, Wilkes Barre, PA, p. A557

HEFFLINGER, Larry, Director Information Systems, Fulton County Health Center, Wauseon, OH, p. A505

HEFLIN, Clyde, M.D. Chief Medical Officer, Curahealth Nashville, Nashville, TN, p. A590

HEFNER, Donna J., R.N., President and Chief Executive Officer, Sierra View Medical Center, Porterville, CA, p. A83

HEFNER, Kathy, Chief Nursing Officer, McDowell Hospital, Marion, NC, p. A469

HEGGEM, Mark, M.D. Chief Medical Officer, Riverwood Healthcare Center, Aitkin, MN, p. A338

HEGGEN, Karra, R.N. Vice President Nursing, Elkhart General Hospital, Elkhart, IN, p. A209

HEGGEN, Steve, Administrative Director Human Resources, St. Joseph Hospital, Fort Wayne, IN, p. A211

HEGGER, John, Director Information Systems, Union County Hospital, Anna, IL, p. A180

HEGSTROM, Michael T., M.D. Chief Medical Officer, Geisinger–Lewistown Hospital, Lewistown, PA, p. A543

HEGWOOD, Wayne, Chief Financial Officer, Acuity Hospital of South Texas, San Antonio, TX, p. A645

HEHEMANN, Bryan D., President and Chief Executive Officer, McCullough–Hyde Memorial Hospital/TriHealth, Oxford, OH, p. A501

HEICHERT, Susan
Senior Vice President and Chief Information Officer, Abbott Northwestern Hospital, Minneapolis, MN, p. A346
Chief Information Officer, Mercy Hospital, Coon Rapids, MN, p. A341
Senior Vice President, United Hospital, Saint Paul, MN, p. A351
Chief Information Officer, Unity Hospital, Fridley, MN, p. A343

HEIDER, John R., Vice President Finance, Augusta Health, Fishersville, VA, p. A670

HEIDT, Robert, Director Information Systems, Pembina County Memorial Hospital and Wedgewood Manor, Cavalier, ND, p. A478

HEIFNER, Bruce, Chief Financial Officer, Pella Regional Health Center, Pella, IA, p. A236

HEIFNER, Robert A., Chief Executive Officer, St. Luke's Sugar Land Hospital, Sugar Land, TX, p. A650

HEIKKINEN, Todd, Manager Sports Medicine and Rehabilitation Services, Orthopaedic Hospital of Wisconsin – Glendale, Glendale, WI, p. A706

HEILMAN, Brooke, Chief Financial Officer, Bowdle Hospital, Bowdle, SD, p. A572

HEIM, Chad, Management Information System Director, LifeStream Behavioral Center, Leesburg, FL, p. A134

HEIM, Nicole, Chief Information Officer, Milford Regional Medical Center, Milford, MA, p. A312

HEIM, Richard, President, Advocate South Suburban Hospital, Hazel Crest, IL, p. A192

HEIM, Tonya, R.N. Vice President Patient Services and Chief Nursing Officer, Memorial Hospital and Health Care Center, Jasper, IN, p. A215

HEIMALL, Michael S., Commander, William Beaumont Army Medical Center, El Paso, TX, p. A616

HEIMAN, Thomas, Vice President Information Services and Chief Information Officer, John T. Mather Memorial Hospital, Port Jefferson, NY, p. A453

HEIN, Jodi, R.N. Vice President Chief Nurse Executive, St. Mary Medical Center, Long Beach, CA, p. A70

HEINE, Ann, Chief Executive Officer, Surgical Specialty Center of Baton Rouge, Baton Rouge, LA, p. A273

HEINECK, Susan, M.D. President Professional Staff, Providence Seaside Hospital, Seaside, OR, p. A530

HEINEMANN, Don, Administrator and Chief Executive Officer, Blount Memorial Hospital, Maryville, TN, p. A588

HEINEMEIER, Robert, Interim Chief Financial Officer, Sonoma West Medical Center, Sebastopol, CA, p. A94

HEINISCH, Sheri, Compliance Officer, CHI Lisbon Health, Lisbon, ND, p. A480

HEINRICH, Bill, Chief Financial Officer, Florida Hospital Zephyrhills, Zephyrhills, FL, p. A150

HEINRICH, Kerry, JD,
Chief Executive Officer, Loma Linda University Children's Hospital, Loma Linda, CA, p. A69
Chief Executive Officer, Loma Linda University Medical Center, Loma Linda, CA, p. A69

HEINRICH, Michael G., Interim President and Chief Executive Officer, Mercy Iowa City, Iowa City, IA, p. A232

HEINRICHS, Alice, CPA Chief Financial Officer, Van Diest Medical Center, Webster City, IA, p. A239

HEINS, Patrick, Vice President Patient Care Services, Vidant Edgecombe Hospital, Tarboro, NC, p. A474

HEINSOHN, Carmel, M.D. Medical Director, Bournewood Health Systems, Brookline, MA, p. A308

HEINTZ, Shirley, R.N. Vice President Patient Care, Liberty Hospital, Liberty, MO, p. A375

HEINTZELMAN, Gayle, R.N. Site Administrator and Chief Nursing Officer, Mercy Health – Clermont Hospital, Batavia, OH, p. A484

HEINZ, Don, Interim Chief Executive Officer, Moundview Memorial Hospital & Clinics, Friendship, WI, p. A706

HEINZE, Kyle, Coordinator Information Technology, Riveredge Hospital, Forest Park, IL, p. A190

HEINZMAN, Jerry, Senior Vice President and Chief Financial Officer, Sampson Regional Medical Center, Clinton, NC, p. A463

HEINZMANN, Bill, Director Human Resources, Texoma Medical Center, Denison, TX, p. A612

HEISE, James, Chief Medical Officer, Ministry Door County Medical Center, Sturgeon Bay, WI, p. A717

HEISE, Rosemarie, Vice President Finance, Starke Hospital, Knox, IN, p. A215

HEISE, Teresa, Coordinator Management Information Systems, Pender Community Hospital, Pender, NE, p. A401

HEISEL, Diane, Acting Director, Center for Forensic Psychiatry, Saline, MI, p. A334

HEISER, Eric, Chief Information Resource Management, Sioux Falls Veterans Affairs Health Care System, Sioux Falls, SD, p. A576

HEISHMAN, Lisa, R.N. Vice President, Shenandoah Memorial Hospital, Woodstock, VA, p. A681

HEISMEYER, Joyce, Chief Operating Officer, Kansas Heart Hospital, Wichita, KS, p. A255

HEISSER, Randy, M.D. Medical Director, Kindred Hospital–Chattanooga, Chattanooga, TN, p. A580

HEIT, Ryan, Chief Financial Officer, Northern Nevada Medical Center, Sparks, NV, p. A408

HEITMAN, Susan, Chief Nursing Officer, Winneshiek Medical Center, Decorah, IA, p. A229

HEITMEYER, Paulette, Administrator and Chief Operating Officer, Marina Del Rey Hospital, Marina Del Rey, CA, p. A76

HEITZENRATER, James, Interim Chief Executive Officer, Calhoun–Liberty Hospital, Blountstown, FL, p. A123

HEITZMAN, Cynthia, R.N. Chief Nursing Officer, Seven Rivers Regional Medical Center, Crystal River, FL, p. A126

HELDRETH, Karen, Director Data Processing, Mercy Hospital El Reno, El Reno, OK, p. A511

HELDT, Katie, Chief Nursing Officer, Greene County Medical Center, Jefferson, IA, p. A233

HELFER, Cassandra, Chief Financial Officer, Ralph H. Johnson Veterans Affairs Medical Center, Charleston, SC, p. A563

HELFER, David, FACHE, President, Texas Institute for Surgery at Texas Health Presbyterian Dallas, Dallas, TX, p. A611

HELGERSON, Bryce R., Chief Administrative Officer, Legacy Salmon Creek Medical Center, Vancouver, WA, p. A692

HELGESEN, Roald, Chief Executive Officer, Alaska Native Medical Center, Anchorage, AK, p. A28

HELGESON, Heidi E., M.D. Chief Medical Officer, Rio Grande Hospital, Del Norte, CO, p. A103

HELGET, Peggy, R.N. Vice President Patient Services and Chief Nursing Officer, Methodist Jennie Edmundson Hospital, Council Bluffs, IA, p. A228

HELLA, Timothy, Chief Information Officer, Otsego Memorial Hospital, Gaylord, MI, p. A324

HELLAND, Don, M.D. Chief Medical Officer, Roosevelt Medical Center, Culbertson, MT, p. A386

HELLE, Dan, Human Resources Officer, Iowa City Veterans Affairs Health Care System, Iowa City, IA, p. A232

HELLELAND, Brian, Executive Vice President and Chief Operating Officer, St. Jude Medical Center, Fullerton, CA, p. A64

HELLER, Michael, Chief Financial Officer, Corry Memorial Hospital, Corry, PA, p. A536

HELLER, Tom, Vice President Operations and Human Resources, Camden Clark Medical Center, Parkersburg, WV, p. A698

HELLINGER, Jeffrey, Interim Chief Financial Officer, Lewis County General Hospital, Lowville, NY, p. A442

HELLYER, Nancy R., FACHE, Chief Executive Officer, CHRISTUS St. Frances Cabrini Hospital, Alexandria, LA, p. A271

HELM, Carrie, Chief Executive Officer, Arkansas Surgical Hospital, North Little Rock, AR, p. A50

HELM, Pamela E., Executive Director, Devereux Texas Treatment Network, League City, TX, p. A632

HELMS, Candace, Director Information Services, Good Samaritan Medical Center, West Palm Beach, FL, p. A149

HELMS, Ella Raye, Chief Executive Officer, Cogdell Memorial Hospital, Snyder, TX, p. A649

HELMS, James, Vice President Finance, Jones Memorial Hospital, Wellsville, NY, p. A458

HELMS, Joseph, Director Information Systems, DeKalb Regional Medical Center, Fort Payne, AL, p. A20

HELMS Jr.,, Robert N., Board Chair, President and Chief Executive Officer, Victory Healthcare, The Woodlands, TX, p. B152

HELPER, Mark A., Vice President, Chief Financial Officer, Munson Medical Center, Traverse City, MI, p. A335

HELSEL, David S., M.D., Chief Executive Officer, Spring Grove Hospital Center, Baltimore, MD, p. A298

HELSEL, Elizabeth, Chief Executive Officer, U. S. Public Health Service Indian Hospital, Parker, AZ, p. A35

HELSPER, Richard S., Chief Operating Officer, Genesis HealthCare System, Zanesville, OH, p. A507

HELSTROM, James, Chief Medical Officer, Fox Chase Cancer Center–American Oncologic Hospital, Philadelphia, PA, p. A548

HELTON, Deirdre, Director Human Resources, Lakeway Regional Hospital, Morristown, TN, p. A590

HELTON, Fay, Director Medical Records, Red River Hospital, LLC, Wichita Falls, TX, p. A657

HELTON, R.J., D.O. Chief of Staff, Coal County General Hospital, Coalgate, OK, p. A510

HELTON, Stephanie, Chief Financial Officer, Weatherford Regional Hospital, Weatherford, OK, p. A523

HELVEY, John, Chief Information Officer, Orchard Hospital, Gridley, CA, p. A65

HEMATILLAKE, M. Ganga, M.D. Chief of Staff, White River Junction Veterans Affairs Medical Center, White River Junction, VT, p. A666

HEMBREE, Greg, Senior Vice President and Chief Financial Officer, St. Francis Hospital, Columbus, GA, p. A157

HEMEON, Frank, Interim Chief Financial Officer, Catskill Regional Medical Center, Harris, NY, p. A440

HEMKER, Debbie, Senior Vice President and Area Manager, Kaiser Permanente Fresno Medical Center, Fresno, CA, p. A63

HEMKER, Robert, President and Chief Executive Officer, Palomar Health, Escondido, CA, p. B102

HEMMER, Chris, Director Finance, Aurora West Allis Medical Center, West Allis, WI, p. A719

HEMMING, Stuart, Chief Operating Officer, Portsmouth Regional Hospital, Portsmouth, NH, p. A413

HEMPEL, Stephen, M.D. President Medical Staff, Lakeland Medical Center, St. Joseph, Saint Joseph, MI, p. A334

HEMPHILL, Dana, Manager Human Resources, Shoshone Medical Center, Kellogg, ID, p. A176

HEMPHILL, Robyn, Interim Chief Executive Officer and Chief Nursing Officer, Monroe Surgical Hospital, Monroe, LA, p. A283

HEMPLER, Shannan, Director Human Resources, Norton County Hospital, Norton, KS, p. A250

HEMSATH, Randolph, M.D. Medical Director, Suncoast Behavioral Health Center, Bradenton, FL, p. A124

HENDEE, Daniel, Director, Philadelphia Veterans Affairs Medical Center, Philadelphia, PA, p. A549

HENDEL, Dawna, R.N. Chief Nursing Officer and Vice President Patient Care Services, Providence Saint John's Health Center, Santa Monica, CA, p. A93

HENDERSHOT, Richard
Chief Financial Officer, Casey County Hospital, Liberty, KY, p. A264
Chief Financial Officer, Jane Todd Crawford Hospital, Greensburg, KY, p. A261

HENDERSON, Claudia, Chief Human Resources, St. Elizabeth's Medical Center, Brighton, MA, p. A308

HENDERSON, David K., M.D. Deputy Director Clinical Care, National Institutes of Health Clinical Center, Bethesda, MD, p. A299

HENDERSON, David M., Director Human Resources, Summersville Regional Medical Center, Summersville, WV, p. A700

HENDERSON, Deborah, Acting Chief Financial Officer, Harry S. Truman Memorial Veterans Hospital, Columbia, MO, p. A370

HENDERSON, Donald G., FACHE, Chief Executive Officer, Central Florida Health, Leesburg, FL, p. B32

HENDERSON, Donald G., FACHE,
President and Chief Executive Officer, Leesburg Regional Medical Center, Leesburg, FL, p. A134
President and Chief Executive Officer, The Villages Regional Hospital, The Villages, FL, p. A148

HENDERSON, Gary, Chief Information Resources Management Services, Huntington Veterans Affairs Medical Center, Huntington, WV, p. A697

HENDERSON, Greg, Interim Administrator, Loma Linda University Medical Center–Murrieta, Murrieta, CA, p. A78

HENDERSON, Jace, Chief Financial Officer, Parkview Hospital, Wheeler, TX, p. A657

HENDERSON, Jessica, Employee Relations Specialist, Fitzgibbon Hospital, Marshall, MO, p. A376

HENDERSON, John
Chief Executive Officer, Childress Regional Medical Center, Childress, TX, p. A606
Chief Human Resources Management, James H. Quillen Veterans Affairs Medical Center, Mountain Home, TN, p. A590

HENDERSON, John, M.D. Chief Medical Officer, Unity Health White County Medical Center, Searcy, AR, p. A52

HENDERSON, Katherine, President, Seton Medical Center Austin, Austin, TX, p. A599

HENDERSON, Kathy, Director Human Resources, Willow Crest Hospital, Miami, OK, p. A514

HENDERSON, Larry, M.D. Medical Director, Greene County Hospital, Leakesville, MS, p. A361

HENDERSON, Lisa, Chief Operating Officer, Palacios Community Medical Center, Palacios, TX, p. A639

HENDERSON, Lori, Chief Nursing Officer, Vice President Clinical, Colorado Canyons Hospital and Medical Center, Fruita, CO, p. A106

HENDERSON, Lorrie, Ph.D., Chief Executive Officer, Huhukam Memorial Hospital, Sacaton, AZ, p. A38

HENDERSON, Melody, R.N. Chief Operating Officer and Chief Nursing Officer, Golden Plains Community Hospital, Borger, TX, p. A603

HENDERSON, Mike, Director Human Resources, Forest View Psychiatric Hospital, Grand Rapids, MI, p. A324

HENDERSON, Pamela S., Vice President Human Resources, Memorial Hospital of Carbondale, Carbondale, IL, p. A182

HENDERSON, Patricia, R.N. Vice President Nursing and Clinical Services, Glencoe Regional Health Services, Glencoe, MN, p. A343

HENDERSON, Paula
Vice President Human Resources, University of Maryland Medical Center Midtown Campus, Baltimore, MD, p. A298
Vice President Human Resources, University of Maryland Rehabilitation & Orthopaedic Institute, Baltimore, MD, p. A298

HENDERSON, Peggy, Director Health Information, Stringfellow Memorial Hospital, Anniston, AL, p. A15

HENDERSON, Rex, M.D. Chief of Staff, McDowell Hospital, Marion, NC, p. A469

HENDERSON, Sherry, Chief Financial Officer, Piedmont Henry Hospital, Stockbridge, GA, p. A167

HENDERSON, Sue, Human Resource Manager, Smyth County Community Hospital, Marion, VA, p. A673

HENDERSON, Travis, M.D. Chief of Staff, Mobridge Regional Hospital, Mobridge, SD, p. A575

HENDERSON, Volante, Director Human Resources, HEALTHSOUTH Walton Rehabilitation Hospital, Augusta, GA, p. A153

HENDLER, Robert S., M.D. Regional Chief Medical Officer, Centennial Medical Center, Frisco, TX, p. A619

HENDREN, Karen, Vice President of Finance and Operations, Mercy Hospital Ardmore, Ardmore, OK, p. A508

HENDRICK, Kirk, Director Information Systems, Northside Hospital, Saint Petersburg, FL, p. A144

HENDRICKS, Barbara A., Vice President, Human Resources, Nanticoke Memorial Hospital, Seaford, DE, p. A119

HENDRICKS, Marcia, FACHE,
Chief Executive Officer, Adair County Memorial Hospital, Greenfield, IA, p. A231
Chief Executive Officer, Madison County Health Care System, Winterset, IA, p. A239

HENDRICKSEN, Sherry, R.N. Chief Nursing Officer, ContinueCARE Hospital at Hendrick Medical Center, Abilene, TX, p. A595

HENDRICKSON, Leslie, Director Human Resources, Coteau des Prairies Hospital, Sisseton, SD, p. A576

HENDRICKSON, Roman, M.D. Medical Director, Ruby Valley Hospital, Sheridan, MT, p. A391

HENDRIX, Angie, Director of Nursing, Evergreen Medical Center, Evergreen, AL, p. A19

HENDRIX, Billie, R.N. Director of Nursing, W. J. Mangold Memorial Hospital, Lockney, TX, p. A633

HENDRIX, Jamie, Vice President Patient Care Services, Columbus Community Hospital, Inc., Columbus, WI, p. A704

HENDRIX, Jr., Michael A., Chief Financial Officer, St. Joseph Hospital, Bangor, ME, p. A291

HENDRIX, Ricky, M.D. Chief of Staff, Winn Parish Medical Center, Winnfield, LA, p. A289

HENDRIXSON, Mark, M.D. Chief Medical Officer, Tennova Healthcare–Jamestown, Jamestown, TN, p. A584

HENDRY, Christopher, M.D. Chief Medical Officer, Medical Center, Navicent Health, Macon, GA, p. A162

HENES, MSN, RN–, Jean M., R.N. Director of Nursing, Avera Creighton Hospital, Creighton, NE, p. A395

HENESSEE, Nolan, Vice President and Chief Information Officer, St. Joseph's Hospital, Savannah, GA, p. A166

HENINGER, Bev, Director of Nursing, Kenmare Community Hospital, Kenmare, ND, p. A480

HENKE, Georgia, Operational Account Manager, OSF Saint Anthony's Health Center, Alton, IL, p. A180

HENKE, Mark, Chief Financial Officer, Mena Regional Health System, Mena, AR, p. A50

HENKEL, Robert J., FACHE, President and Chief Executive Officer, Ascension Health, Saint Louis, MO, p. B12

HENKENIUS, Jim, Chief Financial Officer, Stewart Memorial Community Hospital, Lake City, IA, p. A233

HENLEY, Donald, Vice President Human Resources and Social Services, Grove City Medical Center, Grove City, PA, p. A539

HENLEY, Grace M., Assistant Administrator Human Resources, Highline Medical Center, Burien, WA, p. A683

HENNEBOLD, Julie, R.N. Interim Chief Nursing Officer, Winner Regional Healthcare Center, Winner, SD, p. A578

HENNEMAN, Diane, Chief Executive Officer, Havenwyck Hospital, Auburn Hills, MI, p. A318

HENNENBERG, Shayla, Director Human Resources, Essentia Health Ada, Ada, MN, p. A338

HENNESSEY, Ruth, Executive Vice President and Chief Administrative Officer, St. Francis Hospital, The Heart Center, Roslyn, NY, p. A455

HENNESSY, John, Chief Financial Officer, Bonner General Hospital, Sandpoint, ID, p. A178

HENNIGAN, Michael, M.D. Medical Director, HEALTHSOUTH Emerald Coast Rehabilitation Hospital, Panama City, FL, p. A141

HENNIKA, Billi Jo, Vice President Operations, McKenzie Health System, Sandusky, MI, p. A334

HENNING, Cindy, R.N. Chief Nursing Officer, Houston Northwest Medical Center, Houston, TX, p. A625

HENNING, William C., Administrator and Chief Executive Officer, Baptist Memorial Hospital–North Mississippi, Oxford, MS, p. A363

HENNIS, Michelle, Administrative Director Financial Services, Grace Hospital, Cleveland, OH, p. A489

HENRICH, Christy, Controller, Kindred Hospital of Northern Indiana, Mishawaka, IN, p. A218

HENRICI, Michael, Associate Administrator, Roxborough Memorial Hospital, Philadelphia, PA, p. A549

HENRICKS, William, Ph.D., Vice President and Chief Operating Officer, Seton Shoal Creek Hospital, Austin, TX, p. A599

HENRY, Aden, R.N. Vice President, Patient Care, La Rabida Children's Hospital, Chicago, IL, p. A184

HENRY, Andrea, Director of Nursing, Sweetwater Hospital, Sweetwater, TN, p. A593

HENRY, Anna, Chief Information Officer, Kimble Hospital, Junction, TX, p. A629

HENRY, Chris, Associate Administrator and Chief Financial Officer, Washington Hospital Healthcare System, Fremont, CA, p. A63

HENRY, Dane, Executive Vice President and Chief Operating Officer, DeKalb Medical at North Decatur, Decatur, GA, p. A158

HENRY, David, President and Chief Executive Officer, Northern Montana Hospital, Havre, MT, p. A388

HENRY, Donna, Vice President of Nursing Services, Four County Counseling Center, Logansport, IN, p. A217

HENRY, Heather, Manager Information Systems, Hammond–Henry Hospital, Geneseo, IL, p. A191

HENRY, James L., Director Human Resources, HEALTHSOUTH Sea Pines Rehabilitation Hospital, Melbourne, FL, p. A136

HENRY, Joy, R.N. Director Nurses, Faith Community Hospital, Jacksboro, TX, p. A629

HENRY, Joyce, Controller, HEALTHSOUTH Rehabilitation Hospital of York, York, PA, p. A559

HENRY, Peter, M.D. Chief Medical Officer, Essentia Health St. Joseph's Medical Center, Brainerd, MN, p. A340

HENRY, Roshonda, Chief Nursing Officer, HEALTHSOUTH Rehabilitation Hospital of Cypress, Houston, TX, p. A624

HENRY, Tim, Accountant, Chatuge Regional Hospital and Nursing Home, Hiawassee, GA, p. A160

HENRY, William
Director Human Resources, East Texas Medical Center Henderson, Henderson, TX, p. A623
Director Human Resources, East Texas Medical Center–Quitman, Quitman, TX, p. A642

HENRY JR., Jake, President and Chief Executive Officer, Saint Francis Health System, Tulsa, OK, p. B116

HENSEL, David, Director Financial Operations, OhioHealth Grady Memorial Hospital, Delaware, OH, p. A493

HENSEL, Edward, Chief Information Officer, Tomah Veterans Affairs Medical Center, Tomah, WI, p. A717

HENSLEIGH, David, Director Medical Staff, Clay County Hospital, Ashland, AL, p. A15

HENSLER, Paul J., Chief Executive Officer, Garfield Medical Center, Monterey Park, CA, p. A78

HENSLEY, Angela, Director of Nursing, Pathways of Tennessee, Jackson, TN, p. A584

HENSLEY, Anna
Chief Operating Officer, OhioHealth Dublin Methodist Hospital, Dublin, OH, p. A494
Chief Operating Officer, OhioHealth Grady Memorial Hospital, Delaware, OH, p. A493
HENSLEY, Barry, Director Information Systems, Logan Regional Medical Center, Logan, WV, p. A697
HENSLEY, Kristy, Director Human Resources, Indiana Orthopaedic Hospital, Indianapolis, IN, p. A214
HENSON, Lily, M.D. Chief Medical Officer, Piedmont Henry Hospital, Stockbridge, GA, p. A167
HENSON, Maureen, Vice President Human Resources, Rapid City Regional Hospital, Rapid City, SD, p. A575
HENSON, Pam, Executive Director, Pathways of Tennessee, Jackson, TN, p. A584
HENSON, Steve, Chief Executive Officer, Arkansas State Hospital, Little Rock, AR, p. A48
HENTHORN, Cheryl, Chief Executive Officer, Summa Rehab Hospital, Akron, OH, p. A483
HENTON, Thomas, Chief Executive Officer, Sumner County Hospital District One, Caldwell, KS, p. A241
HENTZEN PAGE, Ann, M.D., Chief Executive Officer, Summit Surgical, Hutchinson, KS, p. A245
HENZE, Mary Kay, Chief Nursing Officer, Hutchinson Health, Hutchinson, MN, p. A344
HENZE, Michael E., Chief Executive Officer, Lake Regional Health System, Osage Beach, MO, p. A378
HENZE, Rick, Chief Financial Officer, St. Mary's Healthcare, Amsterdam, NY, p. A434
HEPNER, Tim, M.D. Medical Director, St. John Owasso, Owasso, OK, p. A518
HERALD, Kathleen R., Vice President and Chief Information Officer, Lexington Medical Center, West Columbia, SC, p. A570
HERB, Beth, Administrator, State Correctional Institution at Camp Hill, Camp Hill, PA, p. A534
HERBECK, Marilyn, Coordinator Human Resources, Community Memorial Hospital, Staunton, IL, p. A204
HERBEK, Gary J., Chief Executive Officer, HEALTHSOUTH Rehabilitation Hospital of Fredericksburg, Fredericksburg, VA, p. A670
HERBER, Steven, M.D.,
President and Chief Executive Officer, St. Helena Hospital Center for Behavioral Health, Vallejo, CA, p. A98
President and Chief Executive Officer, St. Helena Hospital Napa Valley, Saint Helena, CA, p. A87
HERBERGER, Eva, Administrator Human Resources, USC Verdugo Hills Hospital, Glendale, CA, p. A65
HERBERT, Daniel, M.D. Medical Administrative Officer, Millinocket Regional Hospital, Millinocket, ME, p. A294
HERBERT, Janet, Vice President Operations and Chief Nursing Officer, Lake Huron Medical Center, Port Huron, MI, p. A332
HERBERT, Laurie, Vice President Operations, Three Rivers Health, Three Rivers, MI, p. A335
HERBOLD, Charlotte, Manager Business Officer, Garfield County Health Center, Jordan, MT, p. A388
HERBST, Gary, Senior Vice President and Chief Financial Officer, Kaweah Delta Medical Center, Visalia, CA, p. A99
HERDENER, Tony, Vice President Systems and Finance, Northeast Georgia Medical Center, Gainesville, GA, p. A160
HERDER, Debbie, Controller, Promise Hospital of Wichita Falls, Wichita Falls, TX, p. A657
HEREDIA, Paul, Chief Human Resources Officer, Citrus Valley Medical Center–Inter Community Campus, Covina, CA, p. A60
HEREFORD, James, Chief Operating Officer, Stanford Health Care, Palo Alto, CA, p. A82
HEREFORD, Michelle, Chief, UVA Transitional Care Hospital, Charlottesville, VA, p. A668
HERFINDAHL, Gary, M.D. Chief of Staff, Mercy Medical Center Mount Shasta, Mount Shasta, CA, p. A78
HERFORT, Oliver, M.D. Chief Medical Officer, Valley Regional Hospital, Claremont, NH, p. A410
HERGET, Jordan, Chief Operating Officer, Good Samaritan Hospital, San Jose, CA, p. A91
HERING, Kristine, R.N. Chief Nursing Officer, Speare Memorial Hospital, Plymouth, NH, p. A413
HERINGER, Mark, Interim Director Information Systems, St. Helena Hospital Napa Valley, Saint Helena, CA, p. A87
HERINK, Philip, Administrator, Schick Shadel Hospital, Seattle, WA, p. A689
HERMAN, David C., M.D., Chief Executive Officer, Essentia Health, Duluth, MN, p. B54
HERMAN, Jeff, Chief Executive Officer, Prairie St. John's, Fargo, ND, p. A478
HERMAN, John W.
President, Fairview Lakes Health Services, Wyoming, MN, p. A354
President, Fairview Northland Medical Center, Princeton, MN, p. A349

HERMAN, Michael
Chief Executive Officer, Riverview Regional Medical Center, Carthage, TN, p. A579
Chief Executive Officer, Trousdale Medical Center, Hartsville, TN, p. A584
HERMANN, Terri, R.N. Chief Nursing Officer, Franklin Hospital District, Benton, IL, p. A181
HERMES, Dina, Chief Financial Officer, Golden Plains Community Hospital, Borger, TX, p. A603
HERMOSA, Mercy, Director of Information System, Coral Gables Hospital, Coral Gables, FL, p. A126
HERNANDEZ, Ashley, Chief Information Technology Officer, Pender Memorial Hospital, Burgaw, NC, p. A461
HERNANDEZ, Bernadette, R.N. Chief Nursing Officer, Texas Specialty Hospital at Lubbock, Lubbock, TX, p. A634
HERNANDEZ, Debra T., Chief Nursing Officer, Seton Shoal Creek Hospital, Austin, TX, p. A599
HERNANDEZ, Dinorah, Executive Director, Hospital Metropolitano Dr. Tito Mattei, Yauco, PR, p. A731
HERNANDEZ Jr., George B., President and Chief Executive Officer, University Health System, San Antonio, TX, p. A647
HERNANDEZ, Griselda, Executive Director, Hospital de Psiquiatria, San Juan, PR, p. A729
HERNANDEZ, Jaime, Chief Executive Officer, Kempsville Center for Behavioral Health, Norfolk, VA, p. A675
HERNANDEZ, Janira, Coordinator Human Resources, Hospital Metropolitano Dr. Susoni, Arecibo, PR, p. A726
HERNANDEZ, Kim, Chief Human Resources Officer, AMG Specialty Hospital–Denham Springs, Denham Springs, LA, p. A276
HERNANDEZ, Kristen, Director Human Resources, HEALTHSOUTH Rehabilitation Hospital, Albuquerque, NM, p. A427
HERNANDEZ, Leonard, Chief Executive Officer, Coffey County Hospital, Burlington, KS, p. A241
HERNANDEZ, Luis, Chief Executive Officer, United Medical Center, Washington, DC, p. A122
HERNANDEZ, Luz Maria, Director Human Resources, I. Gonzalez Martinez Oncologic Hospital,, PR, p. A730
HERNANDEZ, Matt, Director of Information Technology and System, Kendall Regional Medical Center, Miami, FL, p. A136
HERNANDEZ, Reyna, Chief Financial Officer, HEALTHSOUTH Rehabilitation Hospital of Miami, Cutler Bay, FL, p. A126
HERNANDEZ, Sandi, Controller, Lafayette General Surgical Hospital, Lafayette, LA, p. A280
HERNANDEZ, Susan, R.N. Chief Nursing Officer, Rice Medical Center, Eagle Lake, TX, p. A614
HERNANDEZ, Susan, Chief Nurse Executive, University of Texas Southwestern Medical Center, Dallas, TX, p. A612
HERNANDEZ–KEEBLE, Sonia, Superintendent, Rio Grande State Center/South Texas Health Care System, Harlingen, TX, p. A622
HERNANDEZ–LICHTL, Javier, Chief Executive Officer, Baptist Health South Florida, West Kendall Baptist Hospital, Miami, FL, p. A126
HERNDON, Amy, Chief Finance Officer, Morristown–Hamblen Healthcare System, Morristown, TN, p. A590
HERNDON, David N., M.D. Chief of Staff, Shriners Hospitals for Children–Galveston, Galveston, TX, p. A620
HERNDON, Lori, R.N., President and Chief Executive Officer, AtlantiCare Regional Medical Center, Atlantic City, NJ, p. A414
HERNDON, Paula, R.N. Nurse Executive, Highland–Clarksburg Hospital, Clarksburg, WV, p. A695
HERNDON, Robert Scott
Vice President Chief Financial Officer, Seton Medical Center Austin, Austin, TX, p. A599
Chief Financial Officer, Seton Shoal Creek Hospital, Austin, TX, p. A599
Chief Financial Officer, University Medical Center at Brackenridge, Austin, TX, p. A600
HERNDON, Scott, Chief Financial Officer, Kendall Regional Medical Center, Miami, FL, p. A136
HEROLD, Mary, Director Human Resources, Share Medical Center, Alva, OK, p. A508
HERR, Brenda, Chief Nursing Officer, East Adams Rural Healthcare, Ritzville, WA, p. A689
HERR, Michael, Chief Operating Officer, Starr Regional Medical Center, Athens, TN, p. A579
HERRARA, Espie, Chief Financial Officer, Peak Behavioral Health Services, Santa Teresa, NM, p. A431
HERRERA, Jocelyn A.
Director Human Resources, Kaiser Permanente Orange County Anaheim Medical Center, Anaheim, CA, p. A54
Human Resources Director, Kaiser Permanente San Diego Medical Center, San Diego, CA, p. A88
HERRERA, Veronica, Director Human Resources, Las Encinas Hospital, Pasadena, CA, p. A82
HERRERA, Yamila, Director Human Resources, Hialeah Hospital, Hialeah, FL, p. A130

HERRERO, Carmelo, M.D. Medical Director, Hospital Oriente, Humacao, PR, p. A727
HERRICK, Stephen M., Ph.D., Director, Piedmont Geriatric Hospital, Burkeville, VA, p. A668
HERRIN, Curtis, Chief Financial Officer, Toppenish Community Hospital, Toppenish, WA, p. A692
HERRING, Donnette, Chief Information Officer, Vidant Medical Center, Greenville, NC, p. A466
HERRING, Randy, M.D. Chief of Staff, Coon Memorial Hospital, Dalhart, TX, p. A609
HERRING, Sherry, Chief Nursing Officer, UVA–HEALTHSOUTH Rehabilitation Hospital, Charlottesville, VA, p. A668
HERRINGTON, Bruce, M.D. Chief Medical Officer, South Georgia Medical Center Lanier Campus, Lakeland, GA, p. A161
HERRINGTON, Kristal, Senior Director, Human Resources, Twin County Regional Healthcare, Galax, VA, p. A671
HERRIOTT, Sue A., Executive Director Support Services, OSF St. Joseph Medical Center, Bloomington, IL, p. A181
HERRMAN, Edward, FACHE,
President, Integris Bass Baptist Health Center, Enid, OK, p. A511
President, Integris Bass Pavilion, Enid, OK, p. A511
HERRMANN, Deborah, M.D. Chief of Staff, I–70 Community Hospital, Sweet Springs, MO, p. A383
HERRMANN, Lee, Chief Healthcare Technology Officer, Santa Clara Valley Medical Center, San Jose, CA, p. A91
HERRMANN, Tim, R.N., Administrator, PeaceHealth Cottage Grove Community Medical Center, Cottage Grove, OR, p. A525
HERRON, Katherine, Director Human Resources, Richard H. Hutchings Psychiatric Center, Syracuse, NY, p. A456
HERRON, Mary Beth, Director of Human Resources, Illinois Valley Community Hospital, Peru, IL, p. A200
HERSEY, Robert, Chief Financial Officer, Northeastern Vermont Regional Hospital, Saint Johnsbury, VT, p. A666
HERSHBERGER, Scott, Acting Chief Information Management Services, Battle Creek Veterans Affairs Medical Center, Battle Creek, MI, p. A319
HERSHMAN, Sharon, R.N. Chief Nursing Officer, Providence Holy Family Hospital, Spokane, WA, p. A691
HERTEL, Cheryl, Coordinator Human Resources, Stamford Memorial Hospital, Stamford, TX, p. A650
HERTEL, Holly, Director Nursing, Larned State Hospital, Larned, KS, p. A247
HERTZ, Karl Edward, Assistant Administrator, Memorial Hospital of Converse County, Douglas, WY, p. A722
HERWIG, Brian J., Chief Executive Officer, Perry County Memorial Hospital, Tell City, IN, p. A222
HERZBERG, Deborah L., FACHE, Chief Executive Officer, Tri Valley Health System, Cambridge, NE, p. A394
HERZOG, Dean, Chief Financial Officer, Kona Community Hospital, Kealakekua, HI, p. A172
HERZOG, Mark P., President and Chief Executive Officer, Holy Family Memorial, Manitowoc, WI, p. A709
HERZOG, Paul F., Chief Operating Officer, University of New Mexico Hospitals, Albuquerque, NM, p. A428
HERZOG, Vernail, Chief Executive Officer, Allegiance Specialty Hospital of Greenville, Greenville, MS, p. A358
HESCH, Dennis, Executive Vice President Finance, System Chief Financial Officer, Carle Foundation Hospital, Urbana, IL, p. A204
HESCH, Mike J., Regional Administrator Human Resources, Mayo Clinic Health System – Franciscan Healthcare in Sparta, Sparta, WI, p. A716
HESS, David F., M.D., Chief Executive Officer, Reynolds Memorial Hospital, Glen Dale, WV, p. A696
HESS, Heidi, Chief Nursing Officer, Genesis Medical Center–Aledo, Aledo, IL, p. A180
HESS, Jim, Chief Operations Officer, Salt Lake Behavioral Health, Salt Lake City, UT, p. A663
HESS, Michael, M.D. Chief Medical Officer, Lakeview Hospital, Bountiful, UT, p. A659
HESS, Pamela
Chief Financial Officer, St. Joseph Hospital, Fort Wayne, IN, p. A211
Chief Financial Officer, St. Vincent's Medical Center Riverside, Jacksonville, FL, p. A132
Chief Financial Officer, St. Vincent's Medical Center Southside, Jacksonville, FL, p. A132
HESS, Phil, Chief Executive Officer, Philhaven, Mount Gretna, PA, p. A545
HESS, Steve
Vice President & Chief Information Officer, Medical Center of the Rockies, Loveland, CO, p. A109
Vice President Information Services and Chief Information Officer, University of Colorado Hospital, Aurora, CO, p. A101
HESS, Susan, Director Human Ressources, J. C. Blair Memorial Hospital, Huntingdon, PA, p. A540

HESSE, Fred, M.D. Medical Director, Arms Acres, Carmel, NY, p. A436

HESSE, Nancy, R.N. Senior Vice President Patient Care Services, Eastern Regional Medical Center, Philadelphia, PA, p. A547

HESSELRODE, Renee, Director Health Information Management, Landmark Hospital of Cape Girardeau, Cape Girardeau, MO, p. A368

HESSHEIMER, Susan, Director Human Resources, Johnson County Hospital, Tecumseh, NE, p. A402

HESSING, Jeffrey, M.D. Medical Director, Treasure Valley Hospital, Boise, ID, p. A175

HESSMAN, Mary Pat, Chief Fiscal, Northport Veterans Affairs Medical Center, Northport, NY, p. A451

HESTER, Amber, Chief Executive Officer, Curahealth Boston North Shore, Peabody, MA, p. A313

HESTER, Jr., Charles H., CPA Chief Financial Officer, Merit Health Northwest Mississippi, Clarksdale, MS, p. A356

HESTER, Josh, Chief Operating Officer, Troy Regional Medical Center, Troy, AL, p. A26

HESTER, Joyce, CPA Senior Vice President and Chief Financial Officer, CHRISTUS Mother Frances Hospital – Tyler, Tyler, TX, p. A654

HESTER, Kathy, Chief Nursing Officer, Orange Park Medical Center, Orange Park, FL, p. A140

HESTER, Michael, Chief Executive Officer, Liberty Regional Medical Center, Hinesville, GA, p. A160

HESTER, Steven, M.D. Vice President Medical Affairs, Norton Women's and Kosair Children's Hospital, Louisville, KY, p. A265

HESTON, Cathy, Chief Nursing Officer, Three Rivers Medical Center, Louisa, KY, p. A264

HETHERINGTON, Ray, Network Administrator, Wheatland Memorial Healthcare, Harlowton, MT, p. A388

HETLAGE, C. Kennon, FACHE, Administrator and Chief Executive Officer, Memorial Hospital West, Pembroke Pines, FL, p. A142

HETLETVED, Beth, Director of Nurses, Garrison Memorial Hospital, Garrison, ND, p. A479

HETRICK, Robert G., Vice President Finance and Chief Financial Officer, Morehead Memorial Hospital, Eden, NC, p. A464

HETT, Samantha, Manager Human Resources, Satanta District Hospital and Long Term Care, Satanta, KS, p. A253

HETTICH, E. Paul, Chief Financial Officer, BryLin Hospitals, Buffalo, NY, p. A435

HETTINGER, JoAnn, R.N. Director of Patient Care Services, Avera Weskota Memorial Hospital, Wessington Springs, SD, p. A577

HETTINGER, MaryLou, Director Quality Management, Devereux Children's Behavioral Health Center, Malvern, PA, p. A543

HETTINGER, Tiffany Erin, Associate Chief Nursing Officer, North Colorado Medical Center, Greeley, CO, p. A106

HETU, Maureen, Chief Information Officer, Our Lady of Lourdes Medical Center, Camden, NJ, p. A415

HETZ, Mark
Chief Information Officer, Asante Ashland Community Hospital, Ashland, OR, p. A524
Chief Information Officer, Asante Rogue Regional Medical Center, Medford, OR, p. A528
Chief Information Officer, Asante Three Rivers Medical Center, Grants Pass, OR, p. A526

HEURING, Ron, Director Information Systems, Perry County Memorial Hospital, Perryville, MO, p. A378

HEURTIN, John, Chief Financial Officer, Lee's Summit Medical Center, Lee's Summit, MO, p. A375

HEUSER, Keith E., President, CHI Mercy Health, Valley City, ND, p. A482

HEVER, Susan C., Director Human Resources, Brookhaven Memorial Hospital Medical Center, Patchogue, NY, p. A452

HEYDON, Larry, President and Chief Executive Officer, Johnson Memorial Hospital, Franklin, IN, p. A211

HEYN, Matthew M., Chief Executive Officer, Ransom Memorial Hospital, Ottawa, KS, p. A251

HEYWOOD, Matthew, Chief Executive Officer, Aspirus, Inc., Wausau, WI, p. B15

HIATT, Tim, Chief Information Officer, Brodstone Memorial Hospital, Superior, NE, p. A402

HIBBARD, Carrie, Human Resource Business Partner, Adventist Rehabilitation Hospital of Maryland, Rockville, MD, p. A303

HIBBS, Cathy, Chief Executive Officer, Carlsbad Medical Center, Carlsbad, NM, p. A428

HIBEN, Daniel, Chief Executive Officer, Oswego Community Hospital, Oswego, KS, p. A251

HIBSCHMAN, Kimberly, Chief Financial Officer, Riverview Behavioral Health, Texarkana, AR, p. A53

HICKEY, Beth, Vice President Finance, Advocate Lutheran General Hospital, Park Ridge, IL, p. A200

HICKEY, Christopher, Chief Financial Officer, Northwestern Medical Center, Saint Albans, VT, p. A666

HICKEY, Conner, Chief Operating Officer, Woodland Heights Medical Center, Lufkin, TX, p. A635

HICKEY, Marcia H., Senior Vice President Operations, The Hospital at Hebrew Health Care, West Hartford, CT, p. A118

HICKEY, Thomas P., Chief Executive Officer and Managing Director, Pembroke Hospital, Pembroke, MA, p. A313

HICKEY–BOYNTON, Meg, Director Human Resources and Marketing, Community Hospital of Anaconda, Anaconda, MT, p. A385

HICKLING, Andrea, Vice President Finance and Chief Financial Officer, Northern Hospital of Surry County, Mount Airy, NC, p. A470

HICKLING, Karen, Director Human Resources, Palmdale Regional Medical Center, Palmdale, CA, p. A81

HICKMAN, George, Executive Vice President and Chief Information Officer, Albany Medical Center, Albany, NY, p. A433

HICKMAN, Louise, R.N. Vice President of Patient Care Services, Jefferson Regional Medical Center, Pine Bluff, AR, p. A51

HICKMAN, Monica, Director Fiscal Services, Shriners Hospitals for Children–Spokane, Spokane, WA, p. A691

HICKMAN, Troy, Director Human Resources, Harper Hospital District Five, Harper, KS, p. A244

HICKS, Christia, Vice President Human Resources, Eskenazi Health, Indianapolis, IN, p. A213

HICKS, Crystal, R.N. Chief Nursing Officer, Harrison County Community Hospital, Bethany, MO, p. A367

HICKS, Dana, Director of Nursing, Community Medical Center of Izard County, Calico Rock, AR, p. A44

HICKS, Janelle, R.N. Vice President Patient Services, Hocking Valley Community Hospital, Logan, OH, p. A497

HICKS, Joan, Chief Information Officer, University of Alabama Hospital, Birmingham, AL, p. A17

HICKS, John R., President and Chief Executive Officer, Platte Valley Medical Center, Brighton, CO, p. A102

HICKS, Kevin J., President and CEO, Overland Park Regional Medical Center, Overland Park, KS, p. A251

HICKS, Michael L., Senior Vice President and Chief Operating Officer, Ingalls Memorial Hospital, Harvey, IL, p. A192

HICKS, Scott, Vice President, Clark Memorial Hospital, Jeffersonville, IN, p. A215

HICKS, Susan, Chief Executive Officer, Sky Ridge Medical Center, Lone Tree, CO, p. A108

HICKS, Terri, Chief Operating Officer and Chief Financial Officer, P & S Surgical Hospital, Monroe, LA, p. A283

HICKS, William, Interim Executive Director, NYC Health + Hospitals / Bellevue, New York, NY, p. A447

HICKSON, Stan, FACHE,
President and Chief Executive Officer, Johnston Memorial Hospital, Abingdon, VA, p. A667
President and Chief Executive Officer, Smyth County Community Hospital, Marion, VA, p. A673

HIDAY, Holly, Director Human Resources, Kalamazoo Psychiatric Hospital, Kalamazoo, MI, p. A328

HIEB, Dorothy, Director Human Resources, Sanford Chamberlain Medical Center, Chamberlain, SD, p. A572

HIEB, Laura, R.N. Chief Nursing Officer, Bellin Memorial Hospital, Green Bay, WI, p. A706

HIEBERT, Leslie, Chief Executive Officer, Klickitat Valley Health, Goldendale, WA, p. A685

HIGA, Russel, JD Regional Director Human Resources, Leahi Hospital, Honolulu, HI, p. A170

HIGDON, Ricky, Chief Executive Officer, AMG Specialty Hospital–Edmond, Edmond, OK, p. A511

HIGGINBOTHAM, G. Douglas, President and Chief Executive Officer, South Central Regional Medical Center, Laurel, MS, p. A360

HIGGINBOTHAM, Lee, Chief Executive Officer, Dominion Hospital, Falls Church, VA, p. A669

HIGGINBOTHAM, Michael, Chief Executive Officer, Cornerstone Hospital–Medical Center of Houston, Houston, TX, p. A624

HIGGINS, Alana
Regional Information Management Executive, CHRISTUS St. Michael Health System, Texarkana, TX, p. A652
Regional Information Management Executive, CHRISTUS St. Michael Rehabilitation Hospital, Texarkana, TX, p. A652

HIGGINS, JoAnn, Chief Nursing Officer and Assistant Administrator, Palo Alto County Health System, Emmetsburg, IA, p. A230

HIGGINS, John, Vice President and Chief Financial Officer, Good Samaritan Medical Center, Lafayette, CO, p. A108

HIGGINS, Kevin A., Chief Financial Officer, Olmsted Medical Center, Rochester, MN, p. A349

HIGGINS, Larisa, Administrator and Chief Operating Officer, Laredo Rehabilitation Hospital, Laredo, TX, p. A632

HIGGINS, Larry, Vice President Human Resources, King's Daughters Medical Center, Ashland, KY, p. A257

HIGGINS, Rodney, Chief Financial Officer, Deaconess Hospital, Spokane, WA, p. A691

HIGGINS, Thomas, M.D. Chief Medical Officer, Baystate Franklin Medical Center, Greenfield, MA, p. A310

HIGGINS, William, M.D. Vice President Medical Affairs, New York–Presbyterian/Hudson Valley Hospital, Cortlandt Manor, NY, p. A437

HIGGINS BOWERS, Shirley, Senior Vice President Human Resources, JFK Medical Center, Edison, NJ, p. A416

HIGGINSON, David, Executive Vice President and Chief Administrative Officer, Phoenix Children's Hospital, Phoenix, AZ, p. A37

HIGH, Kim, Chief Financial Officer, Baptist Memorial Hospital–Union County, New Albany, MS, p. A363

HIGHSMITH, Cameron, Chief Executive Officer, Washington County Hospital, Plymouth, NC, p. A471

HIGHTOWER, Bernita, Chief Human Resources, Martin Army Community Hospital, Fort Benning, GA, p. A159

HIGHTOWER, Skip
Chief Financial Officer, Brooks County Hospital, Quitman, GA, p. A164
Chief Financial Officer, Grady General Hospital, Cairo, GA, p. A155
Senior Vice President and Chief Financial Officer, John D. Archbold Memorial Hospital, Thomasville, GA, p. A167
Senior Vice President and Chief Financial Officer, Mitchell County Hospital, Camilla, GA, p. A155

HIJECK, Thomas W., R.N. Vice President Nursing Services and Chief Nursing Officer, Harrington Memorial Hospital, Southbridge, MA, p. A314

HILBERS, Cassie, R.N. Chief Nursing Officer, Gothenburg Memorial Hospital, Gothenburg, NE, p. A396

HILDEBRAND, Randall, M.D. Chief Medical Officer, Great Bend Regional Hospital, Great Bend, KS, p. A244

HILDEBRANDT, James, D.O. Vice President Medical Affairs, Sarah Bush Lincoln Health Center, Mattoon, IL, p. A196

HILDRETH, Beth, Vice President Human Resources, OhioHealth MedCentral Mansfield Hospital, Mansfield, OH, p. A497

HILDRETH, Joe, Director Information Technology, Three Rivers Hospital, Waverly, TN, p. A594

HILDWEIN, Robin, Chief Information Officer, Boca Raton Regional Hospital, Boca Raton, FL, p. A124

HILFIGER, Janie, President, Soldiers and Sailors Memorial Hospital, Wellsboro, PA, p. A557

HILL, Beth, Director Human Resources, Russell County Medical Center, Lebanon, VA, p. A672

HILL, Bettie, Chief Financial Officer, Poplar Springs Hospital, Petersburg, VA, p. A676

HILL, Cheryl
Vice President Human Resources, Columbia St. Mary's Hospital Milwaukee, Milwaukee, WI, p. A711
Vice President Human Resources, Columbia St. Mary's Ozaukee Hospital, Mequon, WI, p. A710
Vice President Human Resources, Sacred Heart Rehabilitation Institute, Milwaukee, WI, p. A711

HILL, Duane N., Chief Executive Officer, CHRISTUS Southeast Texas Orthopedic Specialty Center, Beaumont, TX, p. A601

HILL, Herbert, Director Human Resources, Klickitat Valley Health, Goldendale, WA, p. A685

HILL, Jack
Chief Operating Officer and Administrator, The Jewish Hospital – Mercy Health, Cincinnati, OH, p. A488
Vice President and Chief Operating Officer, Union Hospital Clinton, Clinton, IN, p. A208

HILL, James P., Senior Vice President Administrative Services, MedStar Washington Hospital Center, Washington, DC, p. A122

HILL, Janice, R.N., Administrator, Baptist Memorial Restorative Care Hospital, Memphis, TN, p. A588

HILL, Jason, M.D. Chief Medical Officer, Choctaw Nation Health Care Center, Talihina, OK, p. A520

HILL, Jean, Chief Nursing Officer and Chief Clinical Officer, St. Charles Parish Hospital, Luling, LA, p. A282

HILL, Jill, Director Information Technology, Utah State Hospital, Provo, UT, p. A662

HILL, Jr., Joe B., Vice President Human Resources, Trident Medical Center, Charleston, SC, p. A563

HILL, John, President and Chief Executive Officer, Bozeman Health, Bozeman, MT, p. B24

HILL, John, President and Chief Executive Officer, Bozeman Health Deaconess Hospital, Bozeman, MT, p. A386

HILL, Karen
Director Human Resources, Baylor Institute for Rehabilitation, Dallas, TX, p. A609
Departmental Personnel Officer, Zuckerberg San Francisco General Hospital and Trauma Center, San Francisco, CA, p. A91

HILL, Karen S., R.N. Chief Operating Officer and Chief Nursing Officer, Baptist Health Lexington, Lexington, KY, p. A262

HILL, Kerry
Chief Medical Officer, Vista Medical Center East, Waukegan, IL, p. A205
Chief Financial Officer, Vista Medical Center West, Waukegan, IL, p. A205
HILL, Leo, Chief Information Officer, Massachusetts Eye and Ear Infirmary, Boston, MA, p. A307
HILL, Nancy, R.N. Chief Nursing Officer, Johnson Regional Medical Center, Clarksville, AR, p. A44
HILL, Nancy L., R.N. Chief Operating Officer, North Hills Hospital, North Richland Hills, TX, p. A639
HILL, Ned, President and Chief Executive Officer, Northern Hospital of Surry County, Mount Airy, NC, p. A470
HILL, Patricia, Senior Director Nurse Executive, Sentara Northern Virginia Medical Center, Woodbridge, VA, p. A680
HILL, Robert, M.D
Vice President Medical Staff Affairs, Borgess Medical Center, Kalamazoo, MI, p. A327
Chief Medical Officer, Borgess-Lee Memorial Hospital, Dowagiac, MI, p. A322
HILL, Scott, Chief Executive Officer, Columbus Regional Healthcare System, Columbus, GA, p. B34
HILL, Stephen, Vice President and Chief Nursing Officer, Valley Baptist Medical Center-Harlingen, Harlingen, TX, p. A622
HILL, Stuart, Vice President and Treasurer, Unity Health White County Medical Center, Searcy, AR, p. A52
HILL, Terri L., Vice President and Administrator, Union Hospital Clinton, Clinton, IN, p. A208
HILL-DAVIS, Nancy L., Vice President Human Resources and Risk Management, Mercy Hospital and Medical Center, Chicago, IL, p. A185
HILLARD, Mary, R.N. Vice President Patient Care Services and Clinical Operations, Chief Nursing Executive, Advocate Condell Medical Center, Libertyville, IL, p. A195
HILLARY, Maureen, Chief Nursing Officer, Hayes Green Beach Memorial Hospital, Charlotte, MI, p. A320
HILLEGASS, Bonnie Essex, Chief Executive Officer, Harmon Medical and Rehabilitation Hospital, Las Vegas, NV, p. A405
HILLEMEIER, A. Craig, M.D., Chief Executive Officer, Penn State Hershey Health System, Hershey, PA, p. B103
HILLEMEIER, A. Craig, M.D., Chief Executive Officer, Penn State Milton S. Hershey Medical Center, Hershey, PA, p. A540
HILLESTAD, Tammy, Chief Nursing Officer, Brookings Health System, Brookings, SD, p. A572
HILLIARD, David J., D.O. Chief of Staff, Barnesville Hospital, Barnesville, OH, p. A484
HILLIS, David W., Chairman and Chief Executive Officer, Adcare Hospital of Worcester, Worcester, MA, p. A316
HILLMAN, Annette, Director Human Resources, Doctor's Hospital of Deer Creek, Leesville, LA, p. A282
HILLMAN, Brandon, Interim Administrator, Director of Hospital Services, CHRISTUS Coushatta Health Care Center, Coushatta, LA, p. A275
HILLS, Cindi, Director Human Resources, Riverwood Healthcare Center, Aitkin, MN, p. A338
HILLYER, Lisa L., Human Resources Manager, Box Butte General Hospital, Alliance, NE, p. A393
HILT, Monica, President and Chief Executive Officer, St. Elizabeth Hospital, Appleton, WI, p. A702
HILTON, Craig, Chief Executive Officer, Hampton Behavioral Health Center, Westampton, NJ, p. A425
HILTON, Daniel, M.D. Chief of Staff, Fountain Valley Regional Hospital and Medical Center, Fountain Valley, CA, p. A62
HILTON, Lois, Director Human Resources, DeSoto Memorial Hospital, Arcadia, FL, p. A123
HILTON, Richard G., Administrator and Chief Executive Officer, OCH Regional Medical Center, Starkville, MS, p. A365
HILTON-SIEBERT, Stephanie, MSN, President and Chief Executive Officer, Marion General Hospital, Marion, IN, p. A218
HILTUNEN, Theresa, Entity Information Officer, Penn Presbyterian Medical Center, Philadelphia, PA, p. A549
HILTZ, Paul C., FACHE,
President and Market Leader, Mercy Memorial Hospital, Urbana, OH, p. A504
Market President and Chief Executive Officer, Springfield Regional Medical Center, Springfield, OH, p. A503
HIMES, Judy N., Interim Chief Nursing Officer, Penn State Milton S. Hershey Medical Center, Hershey, PA, p. A540
HINCHEY, Paul P.
President and Chief Executive Officer, Candler Hospital, Savannah, GA, p. A165
President and Chief Executive Officer, St. Joseph's Hospital, Savannah, GA, p. A166
HINCKLEY, Fran X., Chief Information Officer, North Shore Medical Center, Salem, MA, p. A314
HINDMAN, Robbie, Vice President Patient Care Services and Chief Nursing Officer, Walker Baptist Medical Center, Jasper, AL, p. A22

HINDS, Bob, Executive Director, Bradford Health Services at Huntsville, Madison, AL, p. A22
HINDS, Nigel, Chief Financial Officer, Florida Hospital DeLand, DeLand, FL, p. A127
HINE, Kristy, Associate Vice President Finance, Geisinger-Lewistown Hospital, Lewistown, PA, p. A543
HINE, Rhonda, R.N. Interim Chief Nursing Executive, Mason District Hospital, Havana, IL, p. A192
HINEMAN, Elizabeth, M.D. Chief Medical Staff, Scott County Hospital, Scott City, KS, p. A253
HINER, Jill, Vice President and Chief Financial Officer, Summa Western Reserve Hospital, Cuyahoga Falls, OH, p. A492
HINER, Peggy, Director Human Resources, Wheatland Memorial Healthcare, Harlowton, MT, p. A388
HINES, Darlene,Fairfield Memorial Hospital, Winnsboro, SC, p. A571
HINES, Frederick W., President and Chief Executive Officer, Clarity Child Guidance Center, San Antonio, TX, p. A645
HINES, JeDonne, Chief Financial Officer, Intermountain Hospital, Boise, ID, p. A174
HINES, John, M.D. Chief of Staff, Arkansas Methodist Medical Center, Paragould, AR, p. A51
HINES, Linda, Vice President Information Technology and Information Systems, University of Maryland Rehabilitation & Orthopaedic Institute, Baltimore, MD, p. A298
HINES, Lisa, Director Nursing, Eastern Shore Hospital Center, Cambridge, MD, p. A299
HINES, Mary Beth, D.O. Chief Medical Officer, UP Health System-Portage, Hancock, MI, p. A326
HINES, Randall G., Ph.D., Chief Executive Officer, Anchor Hospital, Atlanta, GA, p. A152
HINESLEY, Jay, FACHE, Chief Executive Officer, Stringfellow Memorial Hospital, Anniston, AL, p. A15
HINKLE, Stacey, Director Information Technology, Banner Desert Medical Center, Mesa, AZ, p. A34
HINNER, William J.
Vice President Financial Analysis and Planning Ministry Health Care, Ministry Saint Joseph's Hospital, Marshfield, WI, p. A709
Vice President Financial Analysis and Planning, Ministry Saint Michael's Hospital, Stevens Point, WI, p. A716
HINOJOSA, Anna, MSN Interim Chief Nursing Officer, Knapp Medical Center, Weslaco, TX, p. A657
HINOJOZA, Rebecca, Chief Nursing Officer, Medina Regional Hospital, Hondo, TX, p. A623
HINRICHS, Becky Kay, Vice President Human Resources, Riverside Medical Center, Kankakee, IL, p. A194
HINRICHS, Sandy, Director Human Resources, Burnett Medical Center, Grantsburg, WI, p. A706
HINSHAW, Bruce, Director Human Resources, Artesia General Hospital, Artesia, NM, p. A428
HINTON, James H., President and Chief Executive Officer, Presbyterian Healthcare Services, Albuquerque, NM, p. B105
HINTON, Tommye, R.N. Chief Nursing Officer, Highland Hospital, Rochester, NY, p. A454
HINTZ, Lori, Coordinator Information Systems, Rochester Psychiatric Center, Rochester, NY, p. A454
HINTZE, Hart, Chief Nursing Officer, Banner Payson Medical Center, Payson, AZ, p. A35
HINTZE, Paul, M.D. Vice President Medical Affairs, Mercy Hospital St. Louis, Saint Louis, MO, p. A380
HIOTT, III, Jimmy O., Chief Financial Officer, Colleton Medical Center, Walterboro, SC, p. A570
HIPKISS, Tom, Vice President Finance, Forbes Hospital, Monroeville, PA, p. A545
HIRKALER, Kim, Director Human Resources, Bon Secours Community Hospital, Port Jervis, NY, p. A453
HIROMOTO, Brenda, Director of Nursing, Rehabilitation Hospital of the Pacific, Honolulu, HI, p. A171
HIROSE, Mivic, Executive Administrator, Laguna Honda Hospital and Rehabilitation Center, San Francisco, CA, p. A90
HIRSCH, Edward, M.D. Vice President Chief Medical and Quality Officer, Kaweah Delta Medical Center, Visalia, CA, p. A99
HIRSCH, Ted W., Senior Executive Director, Kalispell Regional Healthcare, Kalispell, MT, p. A389
HIRSCHBERG, Paula, R.N. Director of Nursing, Timberlawn Mental Health System, Dallas, TX, p. A611
HIRSHBERG, Mark I., Chief Operating Officer, Bothwell Regional Health Center, Sedalia, MO, p. A382
HIRST, Barb, R.N. Vice President Human Resources and Chief Nursing Officer, Salem Regional Medical Center, Salem, OH, p. A502
HISE, Landon, Chief Executive Officer, Cordell Memorial Hospital, Cordell, OK, p. A510
HISEY, Commie, D.O. Chief of Staff, Memorial Hospital, Gonzales, TX, p. A621
HITE DAVIS, Anissa J., Vice President Human Resources, St. Joseph's Hospital of Buckhannon, Buckhannon, WV, p. A694
HITT, Patricia A., Associate Director, Grand Junction Veterans Health Care System, Grand Junction, CO, p. A106

HIXENBAUGH, Cynthia, Director Human Resources, Pershing General Hospital, Lovelock, NV, p. A407
HIXSON, Kim, Vice President of Financial Officer and Chief Financial Officer, Providence Medical Center, Wayne, NE, p. A403
HJEMBO, Philip, Chief Financial Officer, St. Elizabeth Hospital, Enumclaw, WA, p. A684
HLAHOL, Jan, Manager Human Resources, Cleveland Clinic Children's Hospital for Rehabilitation, Cleveland, OH, p. A489
HLUCHY, Nicholas, Business Analyst, Support Services Manager, Baton Rouge Rehabilitation Hospital, Baton Rouge, LA, p. A267
HO, Sylvia, Director Health Information Systems, Grady Memorial Hospital, Chickasha, OK, p. A510
HO-SHING, Viodelda, Deputy Director Administration, Creedmoor Psychiatric Center,, NY, p. A444
HOAG, Abby, Director, Human Resources, UH Avon Rehabilitation Hospital, Avon, OH, p. A484
HOAGBIN, Joseph, M.D
Chief Medical Officer, CHI Health Immanuel, Omaha, NE, p. A400
Chief Quality Officer, CHI Health Mercy Council Bluffs, Council Bluffs, IA, p. A228
HOAR, Brad, Director Information and Technology, Cedar Park Regional Medical Center, Cedar Park, TX, p. A605
HOARD, Kaylee S., Chief Financial Officer, Cook Hospital and Convalescent Nursing Care Unit, Cook, MN, p. A341
HOBACK, Kim, Supervisor Information Systems, Athens-Limestone Hospital, Athens, AL, p. A16
HOBAN, Donna, M.D. Senior Vice President and Chief Medical Officer, Beaumont Hospital – Grosse Pointe, Grosse Pointe, MI, p. A326
HOBAN, Douglas M., Vice President and Chief Financial Officer, Mercy Hospital Lebanon, Lebanon, MO, p. A375
HOBAN, Robert E., Chief Executive Officer, St. John Hospital and Medical Center, Detroit, MI, p. A322
HOBART, Robert, Director Management Information Systems, Heartland Behavioral Healthcare, Massillon, OH, p. A498
HOBBS, Donna, Nurse Executive, U. S. Public Health Service Indian Hospital-Sells, Sells, AZ, p. A39
HOBBS, Ed, Director Information Services, DeKalb Health, Auburn, IN, p. A206
HOBBS, Emilie, Director Human Resources, Woodland Heights Medical Center, Lufkin, TX, p. A635
HOBBS, Keith, Chief Executive Officer, USC Verdugo Hills Hospital, Glendale, CA, p. A65
HOBBS, Mike, Chief Financial Officer, Clay County Hospital, Flora, IL, p. A190
HOBBS, Steve E.
Chief Financial Officer, Eliza Coffee Memorial Hospital, Florence, AL, p. A20
Chief Financial Officer, Shoals Hospital, Muscle Shoals, AL, p. A24
HOBBS, Tommy, Chief Executive Officer, Illinois Valley Community Hospital, Peru, IL, p. A200
HOBGOOD, Lisa, Chief Information Officer, The Heart Hospital at Deaconess Gateway, Newburgh, IN, p. A220
HOBGOOD, Marcus, Director Information Services, University Health Shreveport, Shreveport, LA, p. A288
HOBSON, Christopher Brian, Chief Operating Officer, Wellmont Bristol Regional Medical Center, Bristol, TN, p. A579
HOCATE, Crispin P., Professional and Support Services Officer, Texas Health Presbyterian Hospital Allen, Allen, TX, p. A595
HOCE, N. Kristopher, President, Morton Plant Hospital, Clearwater, FL, p. A125
HOCHHEISER, Lou, M.D., Chief Executive Officer, St. John's Medical Center and Living Center, Jackson, WY, p. A722
HOCHMAN, Rodney F., M.D., President and Chief Executive Officer, Providence St. Joseph Health, Renton, WA, p. B108
HOCHSTETLER, Amy, Chief Financial Officer, Orthopaedic Hospital of Lutheran Health Network, Fort Wayne, IN, p. A210
HOCK, Douglas G., Executive Vice President and Chief Operating Officer, Children's Hospital of Philadelphia, Philadelphia, PA, p. A547
HOCKENBERRY, Michael A., Senior Vice President and Chief Operating Officer, Hanover Hospital, Hanover, PA, p. A539
HOCKENBERRY, Tonda, Chief Nursing Officer, HEALTHSOUTH Western Hills Regional Rehabilitation Hospital, Parkersburg, WV, p. A699
HOCKENBURY, Debbie, Assistant Administrator and Chief Financial Officer, William Newton Hospital, Winfield, KS, p. A256
HOCKERSMITH, Lisa K., Vice P,resident Human Resources, Kern Medical Center, Bakersfield, CA, p. A56
HOCKERT, Steve, Chief Executive Officer, OneCore Health, Oklahoma City, OK, p. A517
HOCKING, Dale E., Chief Financial Officer, Jupiter Medical Center, Jupiter, FL, p. A132

HOCKING, Patrick
  Chief Financial Officer, Asante Ashland Community Hospital, Ashland, OR, p. A524
  Chief Financial Officer, Asante Rogue Regional Medical Center, Medford, OR, p. A528
  Chief Financial Officer, Asante Three Rivers Medical Center, Grants Pass, OR, p. A526
HOCUM, Timothy, Chief Financial Officer, Providence Kodiak Island Medical Center, Kodiak, AK, p. A29
HODGE, Ian, Chief Executive Officer, Yuma Rehabilitation Hospital, Yuma, AZ, p. A42
HODGE, Lisa, Manager, Human Resources, Rolling Hills Hospital, Franklin, TN, p. A583
HODGE, Montie, Vice President Information Technology and Chief Information Officer, Regional West Medical Center, Scottsbluff, NE, p. A402
HODGE, Pamela, R.N. Chief Nursing Officer and Coordinator Performance Improvement, Jellico Community Hospital, Jellico, TN, p. A585
HODGES, Alan, Chief Executive Officer, Hancock Medical Center, Bay Saint Louis, MS, p. A355
HODGES, Calvin, Director Human Resources, AllianceHealth Ponca City, Ponca City, OK, p. A518
HODGES, Craig, Director Information Services, Hancock Medical Center, Bay Saint Louis, MS, p. A355
HODGES, Dawn, Director Human Resources, Grand River Hospital District, Rifle, CO, p. A110
HODGES, Jay, Chief Financial Officer, TMC Bonham Hospital, Bonham, TX, p. A603
HODGES, Leisha, Human Resources Officer, Eastland Memorial Hospital, Eastland, TX, p. A614
HODGIN, Robin, R.N. Vice President Patient Services and Chief Nursing Officer, Northern Hospital of Surry County, Mount Airy, NC, p. A470
HODGSON, Judith Ann, Chief Nursing Officer, Cheyenne County Hospital, Saint Francis, KS, p. A253
HODNETT, Laura, Interim Chief Nursing Officer, Glen Rose Medical Center, Glen Rose, TX, p. A620
HODSON, Don, M.D. Chief Medical Officer, St. Luke Hospital and Living Center, Marion, KS, p. A248
HODZEDA, Angela, Chief Financial Officer, Jack Hughston Memorial Hospital, Phenix City, AL, p. A24
HOEFER, Robert William, FACHE Chief Operating Officer, SSM Health Saint Louis University Hospital, Saint Louis, MO, p. A381
HOEFLING, Tracy, Chief Financial Officer, The Heart Hospital at Deaconess Gateway, Newburgh, IN, p. A220
HOEFS, Dennis, Manager Information Technology, New Mexico Rehabilitation Center, Roswell, NM, p. A431
HOEHN, Charles, President, Medical Staff, Van Wert County Hospital, Van Wert, OH, p. A504
HOEHNS, Brent, M.D. Chief of Medical Staff, Knoxville Hospital & Clinics, Knoxville, IA, p. A233
HOEKEMA, Dale, M.D. Vice President Medical Affairs and Chief Medical Officer, Kadlec Regional Medical Center, Richland, WA, p. A689
HOELL, Paul, M.D. President Medical Staff, ThedaCare Medical Center–New London, New London, WI, p. A712
HOELSCHER, Steven C., Chief Operating Officer, Valley Regional Medical Center, Brownsville, TX, p. A604
HOERTZ, Joanne, Vice President of Nursing, Brooks Rehabilitation Hospital, Jacksonville, FL, p. A131
HOESCH, Marty, Director Information Systems, North Suburban Medical Center, Thornton, CO, p. A111
HOEY, Amy J., R.N. Executive Vice President and Chief Operating Officer, Lowell General Hospital, Lowell, MA, p. A311
HOFELICH, Kurt T., President, Sentara Norfolk General Hospital, Norfolk, VA, p. A675
HOFER, Maggie, Human Resources Representative, Hawarden Regional Healthcare, Hawarden, IA, p. A232
HOFER, Renee, Chief Financial Officer, St. Joseph's Hospital of Buckhannon, Buckhannon, WV, p. A694
HOFF, David L., Chief Executive Officer, Wayne Memorial Hospital, Honesdale, PA, p. A540
HOFF, Deanna, R.N. Director of Nursing, Bacon County Hospital and Health System, Alma, GA, p. A151
HOFF, Irv, Director Information Systems, Corona Regional Medical Center, Corona, CA, p. A59
HOFF, Linda, Senior Vice President and Chief Financial Officer, Legacy Mount Hood Medical Center, Gresham, OR, p. A526
HOFF, Margaret, Account Manager, Brown County Community Treatment Center, Green Bay, WI, p. A706
HOFFBERGER, Darren, D.O. Chief of Staff, Broward Health North, Deerfield Beach, FL, p. A127
HOFFER, Nolan, Senior Director, St. Luke's Rehabilitation Hospital, Boise, ID, p. A175
HOFFMAN, Barbara, M.D. Chief Medical Officer, St. Christopher's Hospital for Children, Philadelphia, PA, p. A549

HOFFMAN, Brad, Administrative Director Human Resources, Shawnee Mission Medical Center, Shawnee Mission, KS, p. A254
HOFFMAN, Brian, Director Human Resources, Lancaster Regional Medical Center, Lancaster, PA, p. A542
HOFFMAN, Brian, M.D. Chief Medical Services, Veterans Affairs Boston Healthcare System, Boston, MA, p. A307
HOFFMAN, Carole, Vice President, Parkridge Medical Center, Chattanooga, TN, p. A580
HOFFMAN, Chris, Chief Operating Officer, Highlands Regional Medical Center, Prestonsburg, KY, p. A268
HOFFMAN, Daniel, M.D. Administrative Medical Director, Good Samaritan Regional Health Center, Mount Vernon, IL, p. A197
HOFFMAN, Debbie, Vice President Patient Services, SSM Health St. Francis Hospital – Maryville, Maryville, MO, p. A376
HOFFMAN, Debra, Manager Human Resources, Kern Valley Healthcare District, Lake Isabella, CA, p. A68
HOFFMAN, Howard, M.D. Medical Director, Psychiatric Institute of Washington, Washington, DC, p. A122
HOFFMAN, Jeff, M.D. Chief Medical Officer, Atrium Medical Center, Middletown, OH, p. A499
HOFFMAN, Jerry, Chief Financial Officer, Platte Health Center Avera, Platte, SD, p. A575
HOFFMAN, III, Joseph E.
  Executive Vice President and Chief Financial Officer, University of Maryland Harford Memorial Hospital, Havre De Grace, MD, p. A301
  Executive Vice President and Chief Financial Officer, University of Maryland Upper Chesapeake Medical Center, Bel Air, MD, p. A298
HOFFMAN, Julie, Vice President Patient Care Services and Chief Nursing Officer, Mercy Gilbert Medical Center, Gilbert, AZ, p. A32
HOFFMAN, Marcus, Area Chief Financial Officer, Kaiser Permanente Orange County Anaheim Medical Center, Anaheim, CA, p. A54
HOFFMAN, Mary, Chief Administrative Officer and Chief Financial Officer, Mayo Clinic Health System in Waycross, Waycross, GA, p. A169
HOFFMAN, Pamela S., Director of Human Resources, Monroe Hospital, Bloomfield, IN, p. A207
HOFFMAN, Robert P., Vice President and Director Patient Care Services, Wilkes–Barre General Hospital, Wilkes–Barre, PA, p. A558
HOFFMAN, Todd, M.D. Medical Director, St. John Broken Arrow, Broken Arrow, OK, p. A509
HOFFMAN, Tom, Manager Information Systems, Wayne Memorial Hospital, Honesdale, PA, p. A540
HOFFMAN, Trudy, Executive Director, Northwest Center for Behavioral Health, Fort Supply, OK, p. A512
HOFFMAN, Val, Chief Financial Officer, Granite Falls Municipal Hospital and Manor, Granite Falls, MN, p. A343
HOFFMANN, Wanda, Director Human Resources, River Oaks Hospital, New Orleans, LA, p. A285
HOFFNER, Amy, Administrator, Kindred Rehabilitation Hospital Arlington, Arlington, TX, p. A597
HOFFPAUIR, Lisa, Chief Administrative Officer, Lakeway Regional Medical Center, Lakeway, TX, p. A631
HOFIUS, Chuck, Chief Executive Officer, Perham Health, Perham, MN, p. A348
HOFLER, Linda D., Ph.D. Senior Vice President, Nurse Executive, Vidant Medical Center, Greenville, NC, p. A466
HOFMAN, William, Manager Information Technology, Wilkes Regional Medical Center, North Wilkesboro, NC, p. A471
HOFMEISTER, Nancee, R.N. Chief Nursing Officer, EvergreenHealth, Kirkland, WA, p. A686
HOFSTETTER, Peter A., Chief Executive Officer, Willamette Valley Medical Center, McMinnville, OR, p. A527
HOGAN, Dan, Chief Financial Officer, DeSoto Memorial Hospital, Arcadia, FL, p. A123
HOGAN, Judith, Comptroller and Director Resources and Logistics, Naval Hospital Bremerton, Bremerton, WA, p. A682
HOGAN, Michael
  Chief Resource Management, General Leonard Wood Army Community Hospital, Fort Leonard Wood, MO, p. A371
  Chief Executive Officer, Port St. Lucie Hospital, Port St. Lucie, FL, p. A143
HOGAN, Richard, Chief Financial Officer, Pleasant Valley Hospital, Point Pleasant, WV, p. A699
HOGAN, Richard H., CPA Chief Financial Officer, Landmark Hospital of Cape Girardeau, Cape Girardeau, MO, p. A368
HOGAN, Ronald E.
  Chief Financial Officer, Our Lady of Lourdes Regional Medical Center, Lafayette, LA, p. A281
  Regional Chief Financial Officer, St. Francis Medical Center, Monroe, LA, p. A283
HOGAN, Sean, President, SSM DePaul Health Center, Bridgeton, MO, p. A368

HOGAN, Timothy J., FACHE,
  Regional President, Bayshore Community Hospital, Holmdel, NJ, p. A418
  Regional President, Riverview Medical Center, Red Bank, NJ, p. A423
HOGDSON, Judy, R.N. Chief Nursing Officer, Hospital District No 1 of Rice County, Lyons, KS, p. A248
HOGG, Donna, Supervisor Medical Records, Monroe County Hospital, Forsyth, GA, p. A159
HOGGARD, Amanda, President and Chief Operating Officer, Mission Hospital, Asheville, NC, p. A460
HOGUE, Vicky, R.N. Vice President Patient Services and Chief Nursing Officer, WellStar Paulding Hospital, Hiram, GA, p. A161
HOHENBERGER, Joseph, Chief Financial Officer, Ferrell Hospital, Eldorado, IL, p. A189
HOHENSHELL, Valerie, Director of Clinical Services, Memorial Hospital, Gonzales, TX, p. A621
HOLBERT, Brandon, Director, Information Services, Ocala Regional Medical Center, Ocala, FL, p. A139
HOLBROOK, Chip, M.D. Chief of Staff, Simpson General Hospital, Mendenhall, MS, p. A362
HOLBROOK, Curtis, M.D. Chief Medical Officer, Heritage Park Surgical Hospital, Sherman, TX, p. A649
HOLCOMB, Holly, R.N. Chief Operating Officer, Childress Regional Medical Center, Childress, TX, p. A606
HOLCOMB, Michelle, Human Resources, Webster County Memorial Hospital, Webster Springs, WV, p. A700
HOLCOMBE, Sheryl, Administrative Assistant, Brownfield Regional Medical Center, Brownfield, TX, p. A603
HOLDEMAN, Royce, Chief Financial Officer, Mercy Hospital, Moundridge, KS, p. A249
HOLDEN, Patricia, Chief Executive Officer, Mesa View Regional Hospital, Mesquite, NV, p. A407
HOLDEN, Peter J., President and Chief Executive Officer, Beth Israel Deaconess Hospital Plymouth, Plymouth, MA, p. A314
HOLDEN, Rhonda C., R.N. Chief Nursing Officer, Kittitas Valley Healthcare, Ellensburg, WA, p. A684
HOLDEN, Teal A., Chief Executive Officer, Memorial Hermann Surgical Hospital Kingwood, Kingwood, TX, p. A631
HOLDER, Hal
  Director Finance, SSM DePaul Health Center, Bridgeton, MO, p. A368
  Regional Chief Financial Officer, SSM Health St. Joseph Hospital – Lake Saint Louis, Lake Saint Louis, MO, p. A375
  Regional Chief Financial Officer–Hospital Operations, SSM St. Clare Hospital, Fenton, MO, p. A371
HOLDER, Kasey, M.D. Vice President Medical Affairs, St. Bernards Medical Center, Jonesboro, AR, p. A48
HOLDER, Michelle, Nurse Executive, Straith Hospital for Special Surgery, Southfield, MI, p. A334
HOLDER, Spencer, Chief Financial Officer, Riverland Medical Center, Ferriday, LA, p. A276
HOLDERMAN, Wanda, R.N., Chief Executive Officer, Fresno Heart and Surgical Hospital, Fresno, CA, p. A63
HOLEKAMP, Nicholas, M.D. Chief Medical Officer, Ranken Jordan Pediatric Bridge Hospital, Maryland Heights, MO, p. A376
HOLGUIN, Brenda, Manager Human Resources, El Paso Behavioral Health System, El Paso, TX, p. A615
HOLGUIN, Mindee, Manager Human Resources, Sierra Vista Hospital, Truth or Consequences, NM, p. A432
HOLIFIELD, Tracy, Director Information Systems, Merit Health Central, Jackson, MS, p. A360
HOLINER, Joel, M.D. Executive Medical Director, Green Oaks Hospital, Dallas, TX, p. A610
HOLLAND, Baxter C., M.D. Chief Medical Officer, Rutland Regional Medical Center, Rutland, VT, p. A666
HOLLAND, Brad D., Chief Executive Officer, Cedar Park Regional Medical Center, Cedar Park, TX, p. A605
HOLLAND, Charles, President and Chief Executive Officer, St. Bernard Hospital and Health Care Center, Chicago, IL, p. A187
HOLLAND, Cheyenne, Chief Financial Officer, The University of Vermont Health Network Central Vermont Medical Center, Berlin, VT, p. A665
HOLLAND, David
  Chief Information Officer, Herrin Hospital, Herrin, IL, p. A192
  Vice President Chief Innovation Officer, Memorial Hospital of Carbondale, Carbondale, IL, p. A182
  Vice President Information Services, St. Joseph Memorial Hospital, Murphysboro, IL, p. A197
HOLLAND, Gabrielle, Chief Financial Officer, Baylor Surgical Hospital at Las Colinas, Irving, TX, p. A628
HOLLAND, John F., Chief Executive Officer, LHP Hospital Group, Plano, TX, p. B81
HOLLAND, Kevin, Chief Executive Officer, Singing River Health System, Pascagoula, MS, p. A363
HOLLAND, Kwi, Vice President Information Services, Knox Community Hospital, Mount Vernon, OH, p. A499

HOLLAND, Michael, M.D., Chief Executive Officer, Rehabilitation Hospital of Jennings, Jennings, LA, p. A279

HOLLAND, Penny, Associate Director for Patient Care Services, Aleda E. Lutz Veterans Affairs Medical Center, Saginaw, MI, p. A333

HOLLAND, Shannon S., R.N. Chief Nursing Officer, Valley Hospital, Spokane Valley, WA, p. A691

HOLLAND, Sharron, Chief Financial Officer, Baptist Memorial Hospital–Huntingdon, Huntingdon, TN, p. A584

HOLLAND, Stephen, M.D. Vice President Chief Medical Officer and Medical Director, Gaylord Hospital, Wallingford, CT, p. A117

HOLLAND, Tiffany, Chief Nursing Officer, Bradley County Medical Center, Warren, AR, p. A53

HOLLAND, William, Chief Executive Officer, Drumright Regional Hospital, Drumright, OK, p. A510

HOLLEMAN, Ivan, Chief Financial Officer, Baxter Regional Medical Center, Mountain Home, AR, p. A50

HOLLEMAN, James, M.D. Chief of Staff, St. Luke's Hospital, Columbus, NC, p. A463

HOLLEMAN, Stephen B., Chief Financial Officer, Shepherd Center, Atlanta, GA, p. A153

HOLLIDAY, Jonathan, Manager Information Technology, Central Community Hospital, Elkader, IA, p. A230

HOLLIDAY, Michael T., Vice President Fiscal and Administrative Services, Van Wert County Hospital, Van Wert, OH, p. A504

HOLLIMAN, Emily L., Chief Executive Officer, Hackensack University Medical Center at Pascack Valley, Westwood, NJ, p. A425

HOLLINGER, Brad, Chairman and Chief Executive Officer, Vibra Healthcare, Mechanicsburg, PA, p. B151

HOLLINGER, Lori, Manager Human Resources, Fulton State Hospital, Fulton, MO, p. A371

HOLLINGSWORTH, Carl, Chief Financial Officer, Artesia General Hospital, Artesia, NM, p. A428

HOLLINGSWORTH, Christine, Chief Financial Officer, Phoenix Veterans Affairs Health Care System, Phoenix, AZ, p. A37

HOLLINGSWORTH, Nancy, MSN, President and Chief Executive Officer, Saint Agnes Medical Center, Fresno, CA, p. A64

HOLLINGSWORTH, Sherri
Chief Human Resources Officer, PIH Health Hospital – Downey, Downey, CA, p. A61
Chief Human Resources Officer, PIH Health Hospital–Whittier, Whittier, CA, p. A99

HOLLIS, Carla, President and Chief Executive Officer, Columbus Regional Healthcare System, Whiteville, NC, p. A475

HOLLIS, Clara, Administrator, Oceans Behavioral Hospital San Marcos, San Marcos, TX, p. A648

HOLLIS, Gary W., Comptroller, Arkansas State Hospital, Little Rock, AR, p. A48

HOLLIS, Tom, Chief Executive Officer, Ellett Memorial Hospital, Appleton City, MO, p. A367

HOLLISTER, Jerry, Chief Executive Officer, NorthEastern Center, Auburn, IN, p. A206

HOLLISTER, Richard, President of Medical Staff, Exeter Hospital, Exeter, NH, p. A411

HOLLON, Kim Norton, FACHE, President and Chief Executive Officer, Signature Healthcare Brockton Hospital, Brockton, MA, p. A308

HOLLOWAY, Kristina, Chief Human Resources Officer, Healdsburg District Hospital, Healdsburg, CA, p. A66

HOLLOWAY, Myra, Director Human Resources Management, Central State Hospital, Milledgeville, GA, p. A163

HOLLOWAY, Walter R., Chief Medical Officer, Ozarks Medical Center, West Plains, MO, p. A384

HOLLOWAY, Whitney, Chief Financial Officer, Berwick Hospital Center, Berwick, PA, p. A533

HOLM, Mary Ann, Office Clerk, Tioga Medical Center, Tioga, ND, p. A481

HOLM, Stan V., FACHE, Chief Executive Officer, Abrazo West Campus, Goodyear, AZ, p. A33

HOLMAN, Joel, Chief of Staff, Central Valley Medical Center, Nephi, UT, p. A661

HOLMAN, Steve M., Chief Executive Officer, Union Hospital, Terre Haute, IN, p. A222

HOLMAY, Diane, R.N
Vice President and Chief Nursing Officer, Mayo Clinic Health System – Franciscan Healthcare in La Crosse, La Crosse, WI, p. A708
Chief Nursing Officer, Mayo Clinic Health System – Franciscan Healthcare in Sparta, Sparta, WI, p. A716

HOLMBERG, Daniel, M.D. Director of Medical Affairs, New Ulm Medical Center, New Ulm, MN, p. A347

HOLMEN, Kenneth D., M.D., President and Chief Executive Officer, CentraCare Health, Saint Cloud, MN, p. B32

HOLMES, Dawne, Chief Financial Officer, Greenwood Leflore Hospital, Greenwood, MS, p. A358

HOLMES, Diana, Chief Nursing Officer, Central Regional Hospital, Butner, NC, p. A461

HOLMES, Ginnie, Chief Financial Officer, Electra Memorial Hospital, Electra, TX, p. A616

HOLMES, Heather, Director Health Information Systems, Merit Health Rankin, Brandon, MS, p. A356

HOLMES, Heidi, Chief Information Officer, Oklahoma State University Medical Center, Tulsa, OK, p. A521

HOLMES, James R., President and Chief Executive Officer, Redlands Community Hospital, Redlands, CA, p. A85

HOLMES, John, Business Manager, Ancora Psychiatric Hospital, Hammonton, NJ, p. A417

HOLMES, Phillip Walter, M.D. Chief of Staff, Prairie Ridge Hospital and Health Services, Elbow Lake, MN, p. A342

HOLMES, Terry R., M.D. Clinical Director, Moccasin Bend Mental Health Institute, Chattanooga, TN, p. A580

HOLMES, Troy, Director Finance, Advanced Specialty Hospital of Toledo, Toledo, OH, p. A503

HOLMSTROM, Talulah
Chief Medical Officer, Carolina Pines Regional Medical Center, Hartsville, SC, p. A567
Chief Medical Officer, KershawHealth, Camden, SC, p. A562

HOLOM, Randall G., Chief Executive Officer, Frances Mahon Deaconess Hospital, Glasgow, MT, p. A387

HOLSAPPLE, Kim, Human Resource Specialist, Chester Mental Health Center, Chester, IL, p. A183

HOLSCHBACH, Dennis, Chief Financial Officer and Director Human Resources, Ruby Valley Hospital, Sheridan, MT, p. A391

HOLSON, Debbie C., MSN, Chief Operating Officer, The HSC Pediatric Center, Washington, DC, p. A122

HOLSTEN, Robyn, Human Resources Director, Salt Lake Behavioral Health, Salt Lake City, UT, p. A663

HOLSTIEN, Bruce, President and Chief Executive Officer, Spartanburg Regional Healthcare System, Spartanburg, SC, p. B126

HOLT, Bebe, Vice President Chief Operating Officer, Novant Health UVA Health System Prince William Medical Center, Manassas, VA, p. A673

HOLT, Clayton, Chief Executive Officer, San Juan Hospital, Monticello, UT, p. A660

HOLT, David, Chief Operating Officer, Western State Hospital, Tacoma, WA, p. A692

HOLT, Kory
Division Controller Network Operations, Avera Dells Area Hospital, Dell Rapids, SD, p. A573
Assistant Vice President for Financial Integration, Avera Flandreau Hospital, Flandreau, SD, p. A573

HOLT, Peter, M.D. Director Medical Affairs, Saint Luke's Hospital of Kansas City, Kansas City, MO, p. A374

HOLT, Richard, R.N. Associate Director Patient Care Services, Veterans Affairs St. Louis Health Care System, Saint Louis, MO, p. A381

HOLT, Sherry, Director Human Resources, Unity Medical Center, Manchester, TN, p. A587

HOLT, Stephen R., M.D., Director, Captain James A. Lovell Federal Health Care Center, North Chicago, IL, p. A198

HOLT, Tabetha, Director of Human Resources, Riverside Walter Reed Hospital, Gloucester, VA, p. A671

HOLT, Thomas A., Chief Financial Officer, Conroe Regional Medical Center, Conroe, TX, p. A607

HOLT, Will, Director Information Technology, Harrison County Community Hospital, Bethany, MO, p. A367

HOLTER, Lee H., Chief Financial Officer, Columbia County Health System, Dayton, WA, p. A684

HOLTHAUS, Julie K., Director Human Resources, Sabetha Community Hospital, Sabetha, KS, p. A253

HOLTHAUS, Monica, Chief Financial Officer, Community HealthCare System, Onaga, KS, p. A250

HOLTZ, George, Director Human Resources, Sharp Grossmont Hospital, La Mesa, CA, p. A67

HOLTZ, Mark, Chief Operating Officer, Coordinated Health–Bethlehem, Bethlehem, PA, p. A533

HOLTZ, Noel, M.D. Chief Medical Officer, WellStar Douglas Hospital, Douglasville, GA, p. A158

HOLTZMAN, Michael, M.D. Medical Director, Kindred Hospital–St. Louis, Saint Louis, MO, p. A380

HOLUBEK, William, M.D. Chief Medical Officer, CarePoint Health –Christ Hospital, Jersey City, NJ, p. A418

HOLYFIELD, Linda S., MSN, President and Chief Executive Officer, P & S Surgical Hospital, Monroe, LA, p. A283

HOLYOAK, Mark, Chief Executive Officer, Castleview Hospital, Price, UT, p. A662

HOLZER, Traci, Chief Human Resources Officer, Doctors Hospital of Manteca, Manteca, CA, p. A76

HOMA, Jim, Chief Executive Officer, Heatherhill Care Communities, Chardon, OH, p. A486

HOMER, Kenneth, M.D. Chief Medical Officer, Holy Cross Hospital, Fort Lauderdale, FL, p. A128

HOMER, Margie, President, Southern Plains Medical Group, Oklahoma City, OK, p. B126

HOMYK, Linda, Chief Nursing Officer, Sewickley Valley Hospital, (A Division of Valley Medical Facilities), Sewickley, PA, p. A554

HONEA, Bert, M.D
Associate Chief Medical Officer Northern Colorado, Banner Fort Collins Medical Center, Fort Collins, CO, p. A105
Medical Director, McKee Medical Center, Loveland, CO, p. A109

HONEA, Bruce, Director Information Services, CHRISTUS Coushatta Health Care Center, Coushatta, LA, p. A275

HONEA, Michael, Chief Financial Officer, Glen Rose Medical Center, Glen Rose, TX, p. A620

HONERBRINK, Daniel, Vice President Finance and Chief Financial Officer, Fairmont Regional Medical Center, Fairmont, WV, p. A696

HONEYCUTT, Cynthia, Director Human Resources, Moccasin Bend Mental Health Institute, Chattanooga, TN, p. A580

HONEYCUTT, Robert C., Chief Executive Officer, Dignity Health Arizona General Hospital, Laveen, AZ, p. A34

HONSINGER, Melissa, Chief Operating Officer, St. Luke's Rehabilitation Hospital, Boise, ID, p. A175

HONTS, Gary, Chief Executive Officer, John F. Kennedy Memorial Hospital, Indio, CA, p. A66

HOOD, Cliff, Chief Operating Officer, Central Regional Hospital, Butner, NC, p. A461

HOOD, Kathy, Administrative Assistant Human Resources, Union General Hospital, Blairsville, GA, p. A154

HOOD, M. Michelle, FACHE, President and Chief Executive Officer, Eastern Maine Healthcare Systems, Brewer, ME, p. B52

HOOD, Ron, M.D. Chief of Staff, Sutter Amador Hospital, Jackson, CA, p. A66

HOOD, Sam, Director Human Resources, Heartland Regional Medical Center, Marion, IL, p. A195

HOOD, Tom, Chief Operating Officer, King's Daughters Medical Center, Brookhaven, MS, p. A356

HOOK, Diane, Chief Financial Officer, Wayne County Hospital, Corydon, IA, p. A228

HOOKER, Melvin, Chief Human Resources, New Mexico Veterans Affairs Health Care System – Raymond G. Murphy Medical Center, Albuquerque, NM, p. A428

HOOKER, Rita, Administrative Director Information Services, Bon Secours St. Francis Health System, Greenville, SC, p. A566

HOOLAHAN, Susan E., R.N. Vice President Patient Care Services and Chief Nursing Officer, UPMC Passavant, Pittsburgh, PA, p. A551

HOOP, Heather, Human Resources Generalist, Adams County Regional Medical Center, Seaman, OH, p. A502

HOOPER, Grady A., Chief Executive Officer, Hamilton General Hospital, Hamilton, TX, p. A622

HOOPER, Jason R., President and Chief Executive Officer, KVC Prairie Ridge Psychiatric Hospital, Kansas City, KS, p. A246

HOOPER, Joseph, President and Chief Executive Officer, Community Howard Regional Health, Kokomo, IN, p. A216

HOOPER, Robert A.
Director Human Resources, TriStar Skyline Madison Campus, Madison, TN, p. A587
Director Human Resources, TriStar Skyline Medical Center, Nashville, TN, p. A591

HOOVER, Alvin, FACHE, Chief Executive Officer, King's Daughters Medical Center, Brookhaven, MS, p. A356

HOOVER, Garrett W., FACHE, President, Guthrie Corning Hospital, Corning, NY, p. A437

HOOVER, Jeremy Steven, Chief Information Officer, Kiowa County Memorial Hospital, Greensburg, KS, p. A244

HOOVER, Leon, Director Information Systems, Hendry Regional Medical Center, Clewiston, FL, p. A126

HOPE, Lisa R., Director Human Resources, Owensboro Health Muhlenberg Community Hospital, Greenville, KY, p. A261

HOPE, Steve, Vice President Corporate Services, Methodist Rehabilitation Center, Jackson, MS, p. A360

HOPE, IV, William, Chief of Medical Staff, Vidant Chowan Hospital, Edenton, NC, p. A464

HOPKINS, Chris, Chief Executive Officer, Garfield County Health Center, Jordan, MT, p. A388

HOPKINS, Frances F., Chief Financial Officer, Sabine Medical Center, Many, LA, p. A282

HOPKINS, Jason, Director, Human Resources, Hamilton Medical Center, Dalton, GA, p. A158

HOPKINS, Jim, Chief Financial Officer, Cascade Medical Center, Leavenworth, WA, p. A686

HOPKINS, Joy, Vice President Patient Care Services, OSF St. Francis Hospital and Medical Group, Escanaba, MI, p. A323

HOPKINS, Kelli, Director Human Resources, Baptist Health Medical Center–Hot Spring County, Malvern, AR, p. A49

HOPKINS, Ken, Vice President Finance and Chief Financial Officer, Norman Regional Health System, Norman, OK, p. A515

HOPKINS, Kevin, Vice President of Operations, Cornerstone Medical Center, Fort Oglethorpe, GA, p. A160

HOPKINS, Ronald, D.O. Chief of Staff, Nor–Lea General Hospital, Lovington, NM, p. A430

HOPKINS, William, Director Finance, Carolinas Rehabilitation, Charlotte, NC, p. A462

HOPP, Eva, Chief Nurse Executive, Pinckneyville Community Hospital, Pinckneyville, IL, p. A200

HOPPEN, Claudine N., MSN Interim Chief Nursing Officer, DMC – Children's Hospital of Michigan, Detroit, MI, p. A321

HOPPS, Deborah, Chief Executive Officer, Vibra Rehabilitation Hospital Lake Travis, Lakeway, TX, p. A631

HOPSON, W. Briggs, M.D. Clinical Medical Director, Merit Health River Region, Vicksburg, MS, p. A365

HOPSTAD, Kyle, Chief Executive Officer, Broadwater Health Center, Townsend, MT, p. A391

HOPWOOD, James, Chief Financial Officer, Promise Hospital of Miss Lou, Vidalia, LA, p. A289

HOPWOOD, Jennifer, Vice President, Chief Nursing Officer, OSF Saint Francis Medical Center, Peoria, IL, p. A200

HORAN, Gary S., FACHE, President and Chief Executive Officer, Trinitas Regional Medical Center, Elizabeth, NJ, p. A416

HORAN, Sandra A., Executive Director, Margaretville Hospital, Margaretville, NY, p. A442

HORATH, Kevin, Vice President Human Resources, Decatur Memorial Hospital, Decatur, IL, p. A188

HORECKA, Richard, Chief Medical Officer, Swift County–Benson Hospital, Benson, MN, p. A339

HORINEK, ReChelle, Chief Financial Officer, Trego County–Lemke Memorial Hospital, Wakeeney, KS, p. A255

HORN, Jeff, Vice President, Information and Support Services, Jay County Hospital, Portland, IN, p. A220

HORN, Jon, M.D. Chief of Staff, Barrow Regional Medical Center, Winder, GA, p. A169

HORN, LeeAnn, Chief Nurse Executive, Providence Kodiak Island Medical Center, Kodiak, AK, p. A29

HORN, Sarah
    Chief Nursing Officer, Salem Health West Valley, Dallas, OR, p. A525
    Chief Nursing Officer, Salem Hospital, Salem, OR, p. A530

HORN, Syndi, Director Information Systems, Memorial Hospital, Carthage, IL, p. A182

HORNBURG, Tom, Director Information Systems, Mason General Hospital, Shelton, WA, p. A690

HORNE, Beth, System Administrator Information Technology, Preston Memorial Hospital, Kingwood, WV, p. A697

HORNE, Eilene, Manager Human Resources, Mountain View Hospital, Idaho Falls, ID, p. A176

HORNE, Harry, D.O. Chief of Staff, Cumberland River Hospital, Celina, TN, p. A580

HORNE, J. Mark, Senior Vice President, Ambulatory Services and Chief Operating Officer, Grand View Health, Sellersville, PA, p. A554

HORNE, Perry, Chief Nursing Officer, St. Cloud Regional Medical Center, Saint Cloud, FL, p. A144

HORNE, Theresa, MS Vice President Patient Care Services, St. Dominic–Jackson Memorial Hospital, Jackson, MS, p. A360

HORNER, Ania, R.N. Vice President and Chief Nurse Executive, Aurora Sinai Medical Center, Milwaukee, WI, p. A711

HORNER, Bryan, President and Chief Executive Officer, Shannon Medical Center, San Angelo, TX, p. A645

HORNER, Cheryl, Supervisor Data Processing, Community Memorial Hospital, Staunton, IL, p. A204

HORNER, Eva, Assistant Executive Director Operations, Devereux Hospital and Children's Center of Florida, Melbourne, FL, p. A135

HORNER, James, Chief Information Officer, Portland Veterans Affairs Medical Center, Portland, OR, p. A529

HORNER, John M., President and Chief Executive Officer, Major Hospital, Shelbyville, IN, p. A222

HORNICK, Gregory, MSN Chief Nursing Officer, Martin General Hospital, Williamston, NC, p. A475

HORNSBY, Donny, Director Fiscal Services, Memphis Mental Health Institute, Memphis, TN, p. A589

HORNUNG, Dona, Director Information and Technology Services, Doctors Hospital, Augusta, GA, p. A153

HORNUNG, Kurt, Director, Medical Center of Trinity, Trinity, FL, p. A148

HOROWITZ, Ira, M.D. Chief Medical Officer, Emory University Hospital, atlanta, GA, p. A152

HORRIGAN, Timothy, M.D. Chief Quality Officer, UnityPoint Health – Allen Hospital, Waterloo, IA, p. A239

HORSLEY, Steve, Vice President and Chief Information Officer, Moses H. Cone Memorial Hospital, Greensboro, NC, p. A466

HORSMAN, Sandra, Director, Veterans Affairs Black Hills Health Care System, Fort Meade, SD, p. A574

HORST, Brad
    Vice President, Human Resources, Bay Area Regional Medical Center, Webster, TX, p. A656
    Director Human Resources, Clear Lake Regional Medical Center, Webster, TX, p. A656

HORSTMAN, Jennifer M., R.N. Chief Nursing Officer and Chief Information Officer, Fairbanks, Indianapolis, IN, p. A213

HORTILLOSA, Maria, M.D. Chief of Staff, Middlesboro ARH Hospital, Middlesboro, KY, p. A266

HORTON, Alan, Administrator, Putnam General Hospital, Eatonton, GA, p. A159

HORTON, Eileen M., Senior Vice President, Administration, Capital Health Regional Medical Center, Trenton, NJ, p. A424

HORTON, Greg, Director Support Services, State Hospital South, Blackfoot, ID, p. A174

HORTON, Jerrilyn, R.N. Chief Nursing Officer, DeWitt Hospital, DeWitt, AR, p. A45

HORTON, Jim, Chief Executive Officer, Rankin County Hospital District, Rankin, TX, p. A643

HORTON, Kenny, Director Information Systems, Walker Baptist Medical Center, Jasper, AL, p. A22

HORTON, Kimberly, MSN, Chief Executive Officer, Vibra Hospital of Sacramento, Folsom, CA, p. A62

HORTON, Landon, Director of Nursing, Valley Behavioral Health System, Barling, AR, p. A43

HORTON, Marie, Director Associate Relations, Bartow Regional Medical Center, Bartow, FL, p. A123

HORTON, Sammy, Chief of Staff, Brownwood Regional Medical Center, Brownwood, TX, p. A604

HORTON, Warren, Information Technologist, Baptist Health Medical Center–Stuttgart, Stuttgart, AR, p. A53

HORVAT, Kami, Chief Financial Officer, West Covina Medical Center, West Covina, CA, p. A99

HORVATH, Alex
    Vice President Human Resources, Methodist Hospitals, Gary, IN, p. A212
    Vice President and Chief Human Resources Officer, TMC HealthCare, Tucson, AZ, p. A41

HORVATH, Holly, Director of Nursing, Jerome Golden Center for Behavioral Health, Inc., West Palm Beach, FL, p. A149

HOSKINS, Mary, Chief Executive Officer, Kindred Hospital Detroit, Detroit, MI, p. A322

HOSKINS, Pearly Graham, M.D. President Medical Staff, Cape Fear Valley – Bladen County Hospital, Elizabethtown, NC, p. A465

HOSKINS, Shirley
    Chief Operating Officer, Meadows Regional Medical Center, Vidalia, GA, p. A168
    Interim Chief Nursing Officer, St. Francis Hospital, Columbus, GA, p. A157

HOSLER, Stephan, Vice President Human Resources, Mercy Medical Center Redding, Redding, CA, p. A84

HOSS, Laurna, Human Resource Coordinator, Select Specialty Hospital–Omaha, Omaha, NE, p. A400

HOSTEENEZ, Vivie, Chief Financial Officer, San Carlos Apache Healthcare Corporation, Peridot, AZ, p. A35

HOSTETTER, Lynne, Vice President Human Resources, The HSC Pediatric Center, Washington, DC, p. A122

HOTA, Bala, Interim Chief Information Officer, John H. Stroger Jr. Hospital of Cook County, Chicago, IL, p. A184

HOTALING, Andrew, Chief Executive Officer, Forest View Psychiatric Hospital, Grand Rapids, MI, p. A324

HOTCHKISS, Jason, CPA Chief Financial Officer / Chief Operating Officer, Ottumwa Regional Health Center, Ottumwa, IA, p. A236

HOTCHKISS, Kaleigh, Controller, HEALTHSOUTH Rehabilitation Hospital of Southern Arizona, Tucson, AZ, p. A40

HOTES, Lawrence S., M.D. Chief Medical Officer, New England Sinai Hospital and Rehabilitation Center, Stoughton, MA, p. A315

HOTT, Judith, Chief Executive Officer, Thomas B. Finan Center, Cumberland, MD, p. A300

HOUCHIN, Kim, Chief Nursing Officer, Minnie Hamilton HealthCare Center, Grantsville, WV, p. A696

HOUGH, Nathan, Chief Executive Officer, Crook County Medical Services District, Sundance, WY, p. A724

HOUGHTON, Roxan, Director Human Resources, Promise Hospital of Miss Lou, Vidalia, LA, p. A289

HOULAHAN, Beth, MSN Senior Vice President and Chief Nursing Officer, University of Wisconsin Hospitals and Clinics Authority, Madison, WI, p. A709

HOULE, David, Executive Vice President and Chief Financial Officer, The Hospital at Hebrew Health Care, West Hartford, CT, p. A118

HOULIHAN, David, M.D. Chief of Staff, Tomah Veterans Affairs Medical Center, Tomah, WI, p. A717

HOUMANN, Lars D., President, Florida Hospital, Orlando, FL, p. A140

HOURANY, Joseph, Chief Medical Officer, Montclair Hospital Medical Center, Montclair, CA, p. A77

HOUSAND, Jill, Director Human Resources, Mesa Springs, Fort Worth, TX, p. A618

HOUSE, Alan, Chief Financial Officer, Margaret R. Pardee Memorial Hospital, Hendersonville, NC, p. A467

HOUSE, David
    Vice President, Baptist Health Extended Care Hospital, Little Rock, AR, p. A48
    Vice President and Chief Information Officer, Baptist Health Medical Center – North Little Rock, North Little Rock, AR, p. A51
    Vice President and Chief Information Officer, Baptist Health Medical Center–Arkadelphia, Arkadelphia, AR, p. A43
    Vice President and Chief Information Officer, Baptist Health Medical Center–Little Rock, Little Rock, AR, p. A48
    Vice President and Chief Information Officer, Baptist Health Rehabilitation Institute, Little Rock, AR, p. A49

HOUSE, Jennifer R., Chief Operations and Readiness, Reynolds Army Community Hospital, Fort Sill, OK, p. A512

HOUSE, John, M.D. Chief of Staff, Eureka Springs Hospital, Eureka Springs, AR, p. A45

HOUSEE, Robert, FACHE Chief Executive Officer, Pioneer Memorial Hospital, Heppner, OR, p. A526

HOUSER, David, M.D. Vice President Medical Affairs, Rapid City Regional Hospital, Rapid City, SD, p. A575

HOUSER, Kurt, Chief Operating Officer, University Medical Center, Las Vegas, NV, p. A407

HOUSER, Sara, Chief Nursing Officer, Ashe Memorial Hospital, Jefferson, NC, p. A468

HOUSER–HANFELDER, Sallie, FACHE, Director, Veterans Affairs Eastern Colorado Health Care System, Denver, CO, p. A104

HOUSH, Joe, District Director Human Resources, Kindred Hospital–Indianapolis, Indianapolis, IN, p. A214

HOUSLEY, Kristin, Chief Information Officer, South Lincoln Medical Center, Kemmerer, WY, p. A722

HOUSMAN, Bradley W., M.D. Chief Medical Officer, Baptist Health Paducah, Paducah, KY, p. A267

HOUSTON, Anthony, FACHE, President, CHI St. Vincent Hot Springs, Hot Springs, AR, p. A47

HOUSTON, Jerry, Director Information Systems, Jennie Stuart Medical Center, Hopkinsville, KY, p. A262

HOUSTON, Sally, M.D. Executive Vice President and Chief Medical Officer, Tampa General Hospital, Tampa, FL, p. A148

HOVAN, Keith A., R.N., President and Chief Executive Officer, Southcoast Hospitals Group, Fall River, MA, p. A310

HOVDENES, Jodi Lynn, Vice President of Patient Care, CHI St Alexius Health Carrington Medical Center, Carrington, ND, p. A477

HOVE, Barton A., President and Chief Executive Officer, Wellmont Health System, Kingsport, TN, p. B153

HOVENS, Michael R., M.D. Chief Medical Officer, Merit Health Batesville, Batesville, MS, p. A355

HOWARD, Catherine, Director Human Resources, Sentara Halifax Regional Hospital, South Boston, VA, p. A678

HOWARD, Cindy, Director Financial Services, Nell J. Redfield Memorial Hospital, Malad City, ID, p. A177

HOWARD, Dan, Director, Information Services, San Gorgonio Memorial Hospital, Banning, CA, p. A56

HOWARD, Daniel, Chief Financial Officer, Maine Veterans Affairs Medical Center, Augusta, ME, p. A291

HOWARD, Darcy, Chief Financial Officer, Citizens Medical Center, Colby, KS, p. A241

HOWARD, Eddie L.
    Vice President and Chief Operating Officer, East Texas Medical Center Rehabilitation Hospital, Tyler, TX, p. A654
    Chief Operating Officer, East Texas Medical Center Rehabilitation Hospital, Tyler, TX, p. A654
    Vice President and Chief Operating Officer, East Texas Medical Center Specialty Hospital, Tyler, TX, p. A654

HOWARD, Gary L., Senior Vice President and Chief Financial Officer, Hamilton Medical Center, Dalton, GA, p. A158

HOWARD, Greg M.
    Director Human Resource, Health Alliance Hospital – Broadway Campus, Kingston, NY, p. A441
    Vice President Human Resources, Health Alliance Hospital – Mary's Avenue Campus, Kingston, NY, p. A441

HOWARD, Gwenyth, Vice President Finance, St. Thomas More Hospital, Canon City, CO, p. A102

HOWARD, Jill, R.N. Chief Operating Officer, TriStar Skyline Madison Campus, Madison, TN, p. A587

HOWARD, Kari, Interim Director of Nursing, Pauls Valley General Hospital, Pauls Valley, OK, p. A518

HOWARD, Lisa M., Director, Veterans Affairs Sierra Nevada Health Care System, Reno, NV, p. A408

HOWARD, Loy M., President and Chief Executive Officer, Tanner Health System, Carrollton, GA, p. B131

HOWARD, Mary, Director Human Resources, Winnebago Mental Health Institute, Winnebago, WI, p. A719

HOWARD, Michele, Director of Nursing, Perry County Memorial Hospital, Tell City, IN, p. A222

HOWARD, Mike, Associate Administrator, Eliza Coffee Memorial Hospital, Florence, AL, p. A20

HOWARD, Opal R., Executive Director Human Resources, Florida Hospital Memorial Medical Center, Daytona Beach, FL, p. A127

HOWARD, Pamela B., R.N., Chief Executive Officer, Administrator and Risk Manager, Lake Butler Hospital Hand Surgery Center, Lake Butler, FL, p. A133

HOWARD, Ron, Chief Financial Officer, Holly Hill Hospital, Raleigh, NC, p. A472

HOWARD, Sabra, Manager Human Resources, Harlan ARH Hospital, Harlan, KY, p. A261

HOWARD, Shawn, Administrator, Latimer County General Hospital, Wilburton, OK, p. A523

HOWARD, Teresa, Manager Human Resources, Yoakum County Hospital, Denver City, TX, p. A613

HOWARD, Tim, Chief Human Resources Officer, Fountain Valley Regional Hospital and Medical Center, Fountain Valley, CA, p. A62

HOWARD, Tom, Chief Financial Officer, Texas Health Presbyterian Hospital Flower Mound, Flower Mound, TX, p. A617

HOWARD, Win, Chief Executive Officer, Asante Three Rivers Medical Center, Grants Pass, OR, p. A526

HOWARD–CROW, Dallis, Chief Human Resources Officer, Emory University Hospital Midtown, Atlanta, GA, p. A152

HOWAT, Greg, Vice President Human Resources, Eastern Maine Medical Center, Bangor, ME, p. A291

HOWDEN, William, Vice President Nursing, Good Samaritan Regional Medical Center, Corvallis, OR, p. A525

HOWE, Debbie, Chief Executive Officer, Weatherford Regional Hospital, Weatherford, OK, p. A523

HOWE, James L., Director Human Resources, Pinnacle Pointe Hospital, Little Rock, AR, p. A49

HOWE, Kenneth, Chief Medical Officer, Southern New Hampshire Medical Center, Nashua, NH, p. A412

HOWE, Mary Lenzini, Vice President Human Resources, Geisinger–Bloomsburg Hospital, Bloomsburg, PA, p. A533

HOWE, Vicki, Health Information Management, Ness County Hospital District No 2, Ness City, KS, p. A250

HOWELL, Amy M., Director Human Resources, St. Luke's Behavioral Health Center, Phoenix, AZ, p. A37

HOWELL, Bradley
    Chief Executive Officer, Roundup Memorial Healthcare, Roundup, MT, p. A390
    Interim Chief Executive Officer, Wheatland Memorial Healthcare, Harlowton, MT, p. A388

HOWELL, Carrie, Chief Financial Officer, Barstow Community Hospital, Barstow, CA, p. A56

HOWELL, Diana, Director Human Resources, Conroe Regional Medical Center, Conroe, TX, p. A607

HOWELL, Jerry, Administrator, Sabine County Hospital, Hemphill, TX, p. A623

HOWELL, Jill, Chief Nursing Officer, St. Luke's Jerome, Jerome, ID, p. A176

HOWELL, Kathy A., Vice President Human Resources, Lexington Medical Center, West Columbia, SC, p. A570

HOWELL, Kristie, System Information Technology Director, Southampton Memorial Hospital, Franklin, VA, p. A670

HOWELL, Nathan, President and Chief Executive Officer, Claxton–Hepburn Medical Center, Ogdensburg, NY, p. A451

HOWELL, Pat, Chief Nursing Officer, Community Memorial Hospital, Syracuse, NE, p. A402

HOWELL, R. Edward, Vice President and Chief Executive Officer, UVA Health System, Charlottesville, VA, p. B150

HOWELL, Ronene, Director Health Information Management, Bryce Hospital, Tuscaloosa, AL, p. A26

HOWELL, Sheri, Deputy Commander Nursing, Brooke Army Medical Center, Fort Sam Houston, TX, p. A617

HOWELLS, Stephen, Chief Financial Officer, Kane County Hospital, Kanab, UT, p. A660

HOWERTER, Mark, M.D. President Medical Staff, Columbus Community Hospital, Columbus, NE, p. A395

HOWERTON, Russell M., M.D. Chief Medical Officer, Wake Forest Baptist Medical Center, Winston–Salem, NC, p. A476

HOWERTON, Shawn, M.D., Chief Executive Officer and President, Medical Staff, Sampson Regional Medical Center, Clinton, NC, p. A463

HOWLAND, Sheryl, R.N. Executive Director, Patient Care Services, Community Hospital Long Beach, Long Beach, CA, p. A69

HOY, Jonathan B., Chief Financial Officer, Duke Regional Hospital, Durham, NC, p. A464

HOYER, Sara, Director Administrative Services, Kansas Neurological Institute, Topeka, KS, p. A254

HOYES, Garry W., Chief Executive Officer, Dublin Springs, Dublin, OH, p. A494

HOYOS, Kent, Chief Information Officer, Pomona Valley Hospital Medical Center, Pomona, CA, p. A83

HOYT, Nancy, R.N. Vice President Operations/Clinical and Chief Nursing Officer, Mercy Regional Medical Center, Durango, CO, p. A104

HRIT, Barbara, Controller, Beaumont Hospital – Farmington Hills, Farmington Hills, MI, p. A323

HRITZ, Diane, Chief Financial Officer, Advanced Surgical Hospital, Washington, PA, p. A556

HRON, Janine, Chief Executive Officer, Crittenton Children's Center, Kansas City, MO, p. A373

HRUBIAK, Dan, Associate Computer Program Analyst, Western New York Children's Psychiatric Center, West Seneca, NY, p. A459

HRUBY, Deidre, Director of Patient Care, Madelia Community Hospital, Madelia, MN, p. A345

HSIEH, Ketty, Senior Director Finance, UW Medicine/Northwest Hospital & Medical Center, Seattle, WA, p. A690

HSING, Shirley
    Senior Vice President and Chief Financial Officer, North Oaks Medical Center, Hammond, LA, p. A277
    Senior Vice President, Chief Financial Officer, North Oaks Health System, North Oaks Rehabilitation Hospital, Hammond, LA, p. A277

HSU, Wah Chung, Senior Vice President Finance, San Antonio Regional Hospital, Upland, CA, p. A97

HUANG, Joseph, M.D. Chief Medical and Quality Officer, Legacy Silverton Medical Center, Silverton, OR, p. A531

HUBBARD, Bill, Vice President, Operations, Carolinas HealthCare System NorthEast, Concord, NC, p. A463

HUBBARD, Blake W., FACHE, Chief Executive Officer, Foundation Surgical Hospital of San Antonio, San Antonio, TX, p. A646

HUBBARD, Brent
    Chief Operating Officer, Mercy Hospital Fort Smith, Fort Smith, AR, p. A46
    Chief Operating Officer, Mercy Hospital Ozark, Ozark, AR, p. A51
    Chief Operating Officer, Mercy Hospital Paris, Paris, AR, p. A51
    Chief Operating Officer, Mercy Hospital Waldron, Waldron, AR, p. A53

HUBBARD, Daniel, Chief Financial Officer, Sioux Falls Veterans Affairs Health Care System, Sioux Falls, SD, p. A576

HUBBARD, Gwen, Chief Nursing Officer, Sierra Vista Hospital, Sacramento, CA, p. A87

HUBBARD, Kathy
    Manager Human Resources, Nell J. Redfield Memorial Hospital, Malad City, ID, p. A177
    Controller, Ocean Beach Hospital, Ilwaco, WA, p. A685

HUBBARD, Lynn, R.N. Vice President and Chief Nursing Officer, Indian River Medical Center, Vero Beach, FL, p. A149

HUBBARD, Mark, Vice President Risk Management, Loma Linda University Behavioral Medicine Center, Redlands, CA, p. A85

HUBBARD, Norm, Executive Vice President, Seattle Cancer Care Alliance, Seattle, WA, p. A689

HUBBARD, Tyson, Director Human Resources, Stanislaus Surgical Hospital, Modesto, CA, p. A77

HUBBS III, Olas A., FACHE, President and Chief Executive Officer, Memorial Health, Marysville, OH, p. A498

HUBER, Dalton, Chief Financial Officer, Campbell County Health, Gillette, WY, p. A722

HUBER, Joseph M., Chief Financial Officer, Hospital of the University of Pennsylvania, Philadelphia, PA, p. A548

HUBER, Vicki Lynn, R.N. Chief Nursing Officer, Abrazo Scottsdale Campus, Phoenix, AZ, p. A35

HUBL, Bryan, M.D. Chief of Staff, Thayer County Health Services, Hebron, NE, p. A396

HUBLEY, Grover, M.D. President Medical Staff, Madison St. Joseph Health Center, Madisonville, TX, p. A635

HUBSCHMAN, Gary
    Administrative Director Finance, Sutter Auburn Faith Hospital, Auburn, CA, p. A55
    Administrative Director Finance, Sutter Roseville Medical Center, Roseville, CA, p. A86

HUCK, Karma, Chief Operating Officer, Scott County Hospital, Scott City, KS, p. A253

HUCKABEE, Mike, Network Administrator, Coryell Memorial Hospital, Gatesville, TX, p. A620

HUCKABY, Don, Chief Information Management Service, Veterans Affairs Eastern Colorado Health Care System, Denver, CO, p. A104

HUDA, Edith, Director Human Resources, Daniels Memorial Healthcare Center, Scobey, MT, p. A390

HUDAK, Corey, Director Human Resources, Memorial Hospital, York, PA, p. A559

HUDDLESTON, Tina, R.N. Chief Nursing Officer, Baylor Medical Center at Trophy Club, Trophy Club, TX, p. A653

HUDGENS, Roselyn, Director Human Resources, Ballinger Memorial Hospital, Ballinger, TX, p. A601

HUDGINS, Paul
    Associate Vice President Human Resources, Bascom Palmer Eye Institute–Anne Bates Leach Eye Hospital, Miami, FL, p. A136
    Associate Vice President Human Resources, University of Miami Hospital and Clinics, Miami, FL, p. A137

HUDNELL, Sharon, R.N. Chief Nursing Officer, WK Bossier Health Center, Bossier City, LA, p. A274

HUDSON, Beth, Chief Nursing Officer, Baylor Institute for Rehabilitation, Dallas, TX, p. A609

HUDSON, C. R., Senior Vice President and Chief Financial Officer, Henry Mayo Newhall Hospital, Valencia, CA, p. A98

HUDSON, Gary Mikeal, Administrator, East Texas Medical Center Carthage, Carthage, TX, p. A605

HUDSON, Janell, Chief Clinical Officer, Sanford Medical Center Thief River Falls, Thief River Falls, MN, p. A352

HUDSON, Kayce H., Executive Director Human Resources, Saddleback Memorial Medical Center, Laguna Hills, CA, p. A68

HUDSON, Kenneth J., Chief Financial Officer, Veterans Affairs Puget Sound Health Care System, Seattle, WA, p. A690

HUDSON, Kent, Chief Financial Officer, Kingman Community Hospital, Kingman, KS, p. A246

HUDSON, Larry C., Executive Vice President and Chief Financial Officer, Charleston Area Medical Center, Charleston, WV, p. A695

HUDSON, Lowell K., Chief Financial Officer, Glen Oaks Hospital, Greenville, TX, p. A621

HUDSON, Maggie, Chief Financial and Operations Officer, Santiam Hospital, Stayton, OR, p. A531

HUDSON, MeKinzie, Chief Financial Officer, Stafford County Hospital, Stafford, KS, p. A254

HUDSON, Mike, Administrator, Federal Correctional Institute Hospital, Littleton, CO, p. A108

HUDSON, Pamela, M.D., Chief Executive Officer, Crestwood Medical Center, Huntsville, AL, p. A21

HUDSON, Robbi, Chief Executive Officer, HEALTHSOUTH Rehabilitation Hospital–Wichita Falls, Wichita Falls, TX, p. A657

HUDSON–JINKS, Therese M., R.N. Chief Nursing Officer, Tufts Medical Center, Boston, MA, p. A307

HUEBNER, Thomas W., President, Rutland Regional Medical Center, Rutland, VT, p. A666

HUELSKAMP, Donald, Interim Chief Financial Officer, Harrison Community Hospital, Cadiz, OH, p. A486

HUENERGARDT, Sam D., Chief Executive Officer, Parker Adventist Hospital, Parker, CO, p. A109

HUERTA, Brad, Chief Executive Officer and Administrator, Lost Rivers Medical Center, Arco, ID, p. A174

HUERTA, Guillermo, M.D. Chief Medical Officer, Select Specialty Hospital–Omaha, Omaha, NE, p. A400

HUERTA, Jose
    Chief Executive Officer, El Paso LTAC Hospital, El Paso, TX, p. A615
    Chief Executive Officer, Mesa Hills Specialty Hospital, El Paso, TX, p. A616

HUERTER, Holly
    Vice President Human Resources, Methodist Jennie Edmundson Hospital, Council Bluffs, IA, p. A228
    Vice President Human Resources, Nebraska Methodist Hospital, Omaha, NE, p. A400

HUETTL, Patricia, Vice President Finance and Chief Financial Officer, Holy Family Memorial, Manitowoc, WI, p. A709

HUFF, Donnie, M.D. Chief Medical Officer, Livingston Regional Hospital, Livingston, TN, p. A587

HUFF, Jeff, Assistant Administrator Finance, Fayette Medical Center, Fayette, AL, p. A20

HUFF, Matt, Chief Financial Officer, Bay Area Medical Center, Marinette, WI, p. A709

HUFF, Michael H., Chief Executive Officer, Hamilton Hospital, Olney, TX, p. A639

HUFF, Shelly E., Manager Human Resources, Indiana University Health Tipton Hospital, Tipton, IN, p. A223

HUFFMAN, David, Vice President and Controller, Select Specialty Hospital–Wilmington, Wilmington, DE, p. A120

HUFFMAN, James, Chief Executive Officer and Administrator, Baptist Memorial Hospital–Desoto, Southaven, MS, p. A365

HUFFMAN, Joshua, M.D. Chief Medical Staff, Saint Joseph Berea, Berea, KY, p. A257

HUFFMAN, Sherry, Administrator Human Resources, Beaumont Hospital–Dearborn, Dearborn, MI, p. A321

HUFFMAN, Steve, Chief Information Officer, Elkhart General Hospital, Elkhart, IN, p. A209

HUFFNER, William, M.D
    Vice President Medical Affairs, Arnot Ogden Medical Center, Elmira, NY, p. A438
    Chief Medical Officer and Senior Vice President Medical Affairs, St. Joseph's Hospital, Elmira, NY, p. A438
    Chief Medical Officer, University of Maryland Shore Medical Center at Chestertown, Chestertown, MD, p. A299
    Vice President Medical Affairs, University of Maryland Shore Medical Center at Dorchester, Cambridge, MD, p. A299
    Chief Medical Officer, University of Maryland Shore Medical Center at Easton, Easton, MD, p. A300

HUFFSTUTLER, Brandon, Chief Information Officer, Electra Memorial Hospital, Electra, TX, p. A616

HUFNAGEL, Keith, Director Human Resources, Stillwater Medical Center, Stillwater, OK, p. A520

HUGGINS, Lois, Chief Human Resources Officer and Senior Vice President Human Resources, Rehabilitation Institute of Chicago, Chicago, IL, p. A186

HUGGINS, Michael C., Administrator Network System, Eastern Oklahoma Medical Center, Poteau, OK, p. A518

HUGHES, April, Chief Financial Officer, Peachford Behavioral Health System, Atlanta, GA, p. A152

HUGHES, Beth, Chief Executive Officer, St. Elizabeth's Medical Center, Brighton, MA, p. A308

HUGHES, Beverly, R.N. Vice President Nursing, Fayette County Memorial Hospital, Washington Court House, OH, p. A505

HUGHES, Bill, Chief Nursing Officer, Granville Health System, Oxford, NC, p. A471

HUGHES, Brandon, Director Human Resources, Hermann Area District Hospital, Hermann, MO, p. A372

HUGHES, Chad
  Information Officer, North Texas State Hospital, Vernon, TX, p. A655
  Chief Information Officer, North Texas State Hospital, Wichita Falls Campus, Wichita Falls, TX, p. A657

HUGHES, Constance, Director of Nursing, West Gables Rehabilitation Hospital, Miami, FL, p. A137

HUGHES, David S., Chief Financial Officer, Vidant Medical Center, Greenville, NC, p. A466

HUGHES, Dustan, M.D. Vice President Medical Affairs, Saint Alphonsus Medical Center – Nampa, Nampa, ID, p. A177

HUGHES, Elisabeth, Director Human Resources and Community Relations, Fairview Regional Medical Center, Fairview, OK, p. A512

HUGHES, James, Director Human Resources, Lake Cumberland Regional Hospital, Somerset, KY, p. A269

HUGHES, Jessica, Director Finance, Hawarden Regional Healthcare, Hawarden, IA, p. A232

HUGHES, John, FACHE, President and Chief Executive Officer, Central Iowa Healthcare, Marshalltown, IA, p. A234

HUGHES, Larry C., M.D. Chief Medical Staff, Limestone Medical Center, Groesbeck, TX, p. A622

HUGHES, Lee, R.N. Chief Nursing Officer, Flint River Community Hospital, Montezuma, GA, p. A163

HUGHES, Leigh Ann, Chief Financial Officer, Hardin Medical Center, Savannah, TN, p. A592

HUGHES, Lori, R.N. Chief Nursing Officer, Vice President Operations and Patient Care Services, Cottage Hospital, Woodsville, NH, p. A413

HUGHES, Mark A., M.D. Medical Director, River Park Hospital, Huntington, WV, p. A697

HUGHES, Sandra, Chief Financial Officer, Clinch Memorial Hospital, Homerville, GA, p. A161

HUGHES, Susan, Interim Director Human Resources, Winner Regional Healthcare Center, Winner, SD, p. A578

HUGHES, Terry, Director Information Systems, Nantucket Cottage Hospital, Nantucket, MA, p. A312

HUGHES, Thomas, President, St. Joseph Health Services of Rhode Island, North Providence, RI, p. A560

HUGHES, Veronica, Chief Nursing Officer, Mesilla Valley Hospital, Las Cruces, NM, p. A430

HUGHES–MICKEL, Leann, Chief Information Officer, Touro Infirmary, New Orleans, LA, p. A285

HUGHS, Mary, Chief Human Resources Officer, Our Lady of Lourdes Memorial Hospital, Inc., Binghamton, NY, p. A435

HUGHSON, John R., Vice President Operations, Scott & White Hospital – Brenham, Brenham, TX, p. A603

HULBERT, Kim, R.N. Chief Clinical Officer, Madison County Health Care System, Winterset, IA, p. A239

HULETT, Rachelle, Vice President Human Resources, McLaren Flint, Flint, MI, p. A323

HULETT, Wendi, Chief Nursing Officer, Artesia General Hospital, Artesia, NM, p. A428

HULL, Brad, Chief Financial Officer, Dale Medical Center, Ozark, AL, p. A24

HULL, Debbie, Chief Financial Officer, Fisher County Hospital District, Rotan, TX, p. A644

HULL, Kathy, President and Chief Executive Officer, Illini Community Hospital, Pittsfield, IL, p. A201

HULL, Ken, Director Human Resources, Inova Fairfax Hospital, Falls Church, VA, p. A670

HULSEY, Cathy, Manager of Human Resources, Cornerstone Medical Center, Fort Oglethorpe, GA, p. A160

HULSEY, Grant, Director Information Technology, Heritage Park Surgical Hospital, Sherman, TX, p. A649

HULSEY, Kelly, Chief Nursing Officer, Piedmont Hospital, Atlanta, GA, p. A153

HUMBLE, Kathryn G., Chief Human Resources Officer, Beatrice Community Hospital and Health Center, Beatrice, NE, p. A394

HUMBLE, Linnea, Director of Finance, Sutter Lakeside Hospital, Lakeport, CA, p. A68

HUME, Diana, Manager Human Resources, Methodist McKinney Hospital, McKinney, TX, p. A636

HUMES, Karen, Chief Information Officer, Titusville Area Hospital, Titusville, PA, p. A555

HUMES, Ronny, Chief Executive Officer, Magnolia Regional Health Center, Corinth, MS, p. A357

HUMME, Sarah, MSN Chief Operating Officer, Southwest General Hospital, San Antonio, TX, p. A647

HUMMEL, Angela, Vice President Human Resources, Evangelical Community Hospital, Lewisburg, PA, p. A543

HUMMELKE, Arlita, Manager Human Resources, Mercy Hospital Tishomingo, Tishomingo, OK, p. A521

HUMMER, Christopher R., President, Carolinas Healthcare System Pineville, Charlotte, NC, p. A462

HUMMER, Denise, R.N. Vice President Administrative Services, Community Memorial Hospital, Hamilton, NY, p. A440

HUMPHREY, Dale, Chief Executive Officer, Saint Thomas River Park Hospital, Mc Minnville, TN, p. A588

HUMPHREY, James, Vice President Talent Resources and Human Resources for South Side Operating Group, Penrose–St. Francis Health Services, Colorado Springs, CO, p. A103

HUMPHREY, Randy, Chief Financial Officer, Merit Health Wesley, Hattiesburg, MS, p. A359

HUMPHREYS, Corina, Chief Operating Officer, Weslaco Regional Rehabilitation Hospital, Weslaco, TX, p. A657

HUMPHREYS, Lynn, Director Human Resources, Henry County Health Center, Mount Pleasant, IA, p. A234

HUMPHRIES, Stefan, M.D. Medical Director, St. Luke's Rehabilitation Institute, Spokane, WA, p. A691

HUMPHRIES, Vickie Witcher
  Director Human Resources, Bon Secours Maryview Medical Center, Portsmouth, VA, p. A676
  Vice President Human Resources, Bon Secours–DePaul Medical Center, Norfolk, VA, p. A674
  Vice President Human Resources, Mary Immaculate Hospital, Newport News, VA, p. A674

HUNDAL, Ranjit, M.D. Chief Medical Executive, Mills–Peninsula Health Services, Burlingame, CA, p. A57

HUNDORFEAN, Cynthia, President and Chief Executive Officer, Allegheny Health Network, Pittsburgh, PA, p. B8

HUNGER, Bryan, Chief Executive Officer, Jefferson County Health Center, Fairfield, IA, p. A230

HUNGER, Dennis, Chief Executive Officer, Washington County Hospital and Clinics, Washington, IA, p. A238

HUNKINS, Theresa, R.N., Chief Executive Officer, Select Specialty Hospital–Durham, Durham, NC, p. A464

HUNSBERGER, Tom, Director Human Resources, Olmsted Medical Center, Rochester, MN, p. A349

HUNSICKER, Elizabeth, Chief Executive Officer, West Valley Medical Center, Caldwell, ID, p. A175

HUNT, Amy, Director Human Resources, Menorah Medical Center, Overland Park, KS, p. A251

HUNT, Cheri, R.N. Vice President Patient Care Services and Chief Nursing Officer, Children's Mercy Hospitals and Clinics, Kansas City, MO, p. A373

HUNT, Cheryl, Chief Clinical Officer, Kindred Hospital Kansas City, Kansas City, MO, p. A373

HUNT, D. Deann, Director Human Resources, Gibson General Hospital, Princeton, IN, p. A221

HUNT, Deloris, Corporate Vice President Human Resources, DMC Harper University Hospital, Detroit, MI, p. A322

HUNT, Don, M.D. Vice President Patient Centered Care and Chief Nursing Officer, University of Texas Health Northeast, Tyler, TX, p. A654

HUNT, John R., Chief Executive Officer, HEALTHSOUTH Rehabilitation Hospital of Western Massachusetts, Ludlow, MA, p. A311

HUNT, Julie, R.N. Chief Nursing Officer, Oro Valley Hospital, Oro Valley, AZ, p. A35

HUNT, Karen, Executive Director, Harsha Behavioral Center, Terre Haute, IN, p. A222

HUNT, Kathy, Chief Executive Officer, Elmwood Healthcare Center at the Springs, Green Springs, OH, p. A495

HUNT, Lynelle, Director of Nursing, Indian Health Service – Quentin N. Burdick Memorial Health Care Facility, Belcourt, ND, p. A477

HUNT, Mary Miles, Chief Executive Officer, Ballard Rehabilitation Hospital, San Bernardino, CA, p. A88

HUNT, Nick, Interim Director of Nursing, Mercy Hospital Waldron, Waldron, AR, p. A53

HUNT, Reta, Director of Nursing, Scott & White Hospital – Llano, Llano, TX, p. A633

HUNT, Richard, M.D. Chief Medical Officer, Kaiser Permanente Sunnyside Medical Center, Clackamas, OR, p. A524

HUNT, Ronald, Chief Executive Officer, Harbor Hospital of Southeast Texas, Beaumont, TX, p. A601

HUNT, W. Jeffrey, Chief Executive Officer, Brandywine Hospital, Coatesville, PA, p. A535

HUNT, Wade, Chief Operating Officer, PeaceHealth Southwest Medical Center, Vancouver, WA, p. A692

HUNT, William Robert, Chief Financial Officer, Reynolds Memorial Hospital, Glen Dale, WV, p. A696

HUNTER, Bridgette, Chief Operating Officer, Southwest Idaho Advanced Care Hospital, Boise, ID, p. A174

HUNTER, Byron, Vice President Human Resources, Cape Regional Medical Center, Cape May Court House, NJ, p. A415

HUNTER, Diana, Director of Nursing, Fort Belknap U. S. Public Health Service Indian Hospital, Harlem, MT, p. A388

HUNTER, Fred, R.N., Chief Executive Officer, Desert Valley Hospital, Victorville, CA, p. A98

HUNTER, Jerry, Vice President, Information Technology, Crotched Mountain Rehabilitation Center, Greenfield, NH, p. A411

HUNTER, Ken, R.N., Chief Executive Officer, Kimball Health Services, Kimball, NE, p. A397

HUNTER, Linda, Chief Nursing Officer, Spring View Hospital, Lebanon, KY, p. A262

HUNTER, Mary Ann, Director Nursing Services, Baptist Easley Hospital, Easley, SC, p. A565

HUNTER, Shelly
  Chief Financial Officer, Mercy Hospital Fort Scott, Fort Scott, KS, p. A243
  Chief Financial Officer, Mercy Hospital Joplin, Joplin, MO, p. A373

HUNTER, Stephanie, Chief Human Resources Officer, Veterans Affairs Ann Arbor Healthcare System, Ann Arbor, MI, p. A318

HUNTER, Terri Lynn, R.N. Nurse Administrator, American Fork Hospital, American Fork, UT, p. A659

HUNTER, Tracy, Chief Human Resources Officer, East Cooper Medical Center, Mount Pleasant, SC, p. A568

HUNTLEY, Adrienne
  Director Human Resources, HEALTHSOUTH Rehabilitation Hospital Memphis–North, Memphis, TN, p. A588
  Chief Human Resources Officer, Saint Francis Hospital–Bartlett, Bartlett, TN, p. A579

HUNTLEY, Devin, Vice President Operations, Community Medical Center, Missoula, MT, p. A389

HUNTON, David, M.D. Chief Medical Officer, Mercy Hospital Fort Smith, Fort Smith, AR, p. A46

HUNTSINGER, Kelli, Chief Operating Officer, Northern Inyo Hospital, Bishop, CA, p. A57

HUPF, Angela C., Vice President Human Resources and Community Relations, Aspirus Medford Hospital, Medford, WI, p. A710

HUPP, Diane, R.N. Chief Nursing Officer and Vice President, Patient Care Services, Children's Hospital of Pittsburgh of UPMC, Pittsburgh, PA, p. A550

HURD, Debra J., R.N
  Vice President Nursing Acute Care, St. John's Hospital, Maplewood, MN, p. A346
  Vice President Nursing, St. Joseph's Hospital, Saint Paul, MN, p. A351
  Vice President of Nursing, Acute Care Hospitals, Woodwinds Health Campus, Woodbury, MN, p. A353

HURD, Ross, Chief Information Officer, Lake Chelan Community Hospital, Chelan, WA, p. A683

HURFORD, Bill, Chief Medical Officer, University of Cincinnati Medical Center, Cincinnati, OH, p. A488

HURLBUT, Marty, M.D. Medical Director, HEALTHSOUTH Rehabilitation Hospital, Fayetteville, AR, p. A45

HURLEY, Al, Clinic Chief Operating Officer, Sanford Bismarck, Bismarck, ND, p. A477

HURLEY, Jeff, Vice President Human Resources, Flagler Hospital, Saint Augustine, FL, p. A144

HURLEY, Sandra, MS Chief Nursing Officer, Valley View Hospital, Glenwood Springs, CO, p. A106

HURLEY, William, M.D. Chief Medical Officer, Summit Pacific Medical Center, Elma, WA, p. A684

HUROWITZ, Marc P., D.O., President and Chief Executive Officer, Jeanes Hospital, Philadelphia, PA, p. A548

HURSH, John, Vice President Human Resources, Cox Medical Centers, Springfield, MO, p. A382

HURST, Paul, M.D. Chief Medical Officer, Banner Heart Hospital, Mesa, AZ, p. A34

HURST, Steve, Information Technology Specialist, Haskell County Community Hospital, Stigler, OK, p. A520

HURT, Carol Anne, Chief Nursing Officer, Tippah County Hospital, Ripley, MS, p. A364

HURT, Christie, M.D. Chief of Staff and Medical Director, Mercy Hospital Aurora, Aurora, MO, p. A367

HURT, Kelly, Chief Human Resources Officer Northern Colorado and Western Region, Banner Fort Collins Medical Center, Fort Collins, CO, p. A105

HURT, Todd, Administrator, State Hospital North, Orofino, ID, p. A177

HURT–DEITCH, Sally A., R.N., Market Chief Executive Officer, The Hospitals of Providence Memorial Campus, El Paso, TX, p. A616

HURTADO, Xochy, FACHE, Chief Executive Officer, Val Verde Regional Medical Center, Del Rio, TX, p. A612

IRISH–CLARDY, Katherine, M.D. Chief Medical Officer, Sparks Regional Medical Center, Fort Smith, AR, p. A46

IRIZARRI, David, Director Information Technology, Northwest Medical Center, Margate, FL, p. A135

IRIZARRY, Aixa, Executive Director, Hospital San Pablo Del Este, Fajardo, PR, p. A727

IRIZARRY, Lourdes, M.D. Chief of Staff, Albany Stratton Veterans Affairs Medical Center, Albany, NY, p. A433

IRIZARRY, Sigfredo, Information Technology Director, Ashford Presbyterian Community Hospital, San Juan, PR, p. A729

IRUEGAS, Javier, FACHE, Chief Executive Officer, Mission Regional Medical Center, Mission, TX, p. A637

IRVIN, Debbie, Director Health Information Management, BHC Alhambra Hospital, Rosemead, CA, p. A86

IRVIN, Donna, Director Human Resources, Baylor Medical Center at Trophy Club, Trophy Club, TX, p. A653

IRVIN, Mary, R.N. Senior Vice President and Chief Nursing Officer, Bethesda North Hospital, Cincinnati, OH, p. A487

IRVIN, Miriam, CNO, HEALTHSOUTH Rehabilitation Hospital, Fayetteville, AR, p. A45

IRVIN, Thomas M., Administrator Human Resources, Ranken Jordan Pediatric Bridge Hospital, Maryland Heights, MO, p. A376

IRVING, Edith E., R.N. Chief Nursing Officer, West Valley Medical Center, Caldwell, ID, p. A175

IRVING, MSN, RN–, Kelly Ann, Associate Director for Patient Care Services, Michael E. DeBakey Veterans Affairs Medical Center, Houston, TX, p. A626

IRVING, Mark, Manager Management Information Systems, OSF St. Francis Hospital and Medical Group, Escanaba, MI, p. A323

IRWIN, Robert G., Vice President Information Systems, Robert Wood Johnson University Hospital, New Brunswick, NJ, p. A420

IRWIN, Ruth, Associate Director Clinical Operations, Stewart & Lynda Resnick Neuropsychiatric Hospital at UCLA, Los Angeles, CA, p. A74

IRWIN, Vivian, Chief Financial Officer and Controller, HEALTHSOUTH Rehabilitation Hospital Midland–Odessa, Midland, TX, p. A637

ISAAC, Lisa, Chief Nursing Officer, Choctaw Nation Health Care Center, Talihina, OK, p. A520

ISAAC, Regina, Director of Nursing, Choctaw Health Center, Philadelphia, MS, p. A363

ISAACKS, David, Director, Harry S. Truman Memorial Veterans Hospital, Columbia, MO, p. A370

ISAACKS, Scott R., FACHE, Director and Chief Executive Officer, Ralph H. Johnson Veterans Affairs Medical Center, Charleston, SC, p. A563

ISAACS, Cynthia, Chief Executive Officer, Cornerstone Hospital of Huntington, Huntington, WV, p. A696

ISAACS, Diane, Director of Nursing, Ouachita County Medical Center, Camden, AR, p. A44

ISAACS, Michael R.
Vice President Human Resources, Vista Medical Center East, Waukegan, IL, p. A205
Vice President Human Resources, Vista Medical Center West, Waukegan, IL, p. A205

ISADO, Jose, M.D. Medical Director, Auxilio Mutuo Hospital, San Juan, PR, p. A729

ISBELL, Samantha, R.N. Chief Nursing Officer, Hamilton Hospital, Olney, TX, p. A639

ISBELL, Sherri, Chief Information Officer, Virginia Gay Hospital, Vinton, IA, p. A238

ISEKE, Richard, M.D. Vice President Medical Affairs, Winchester Hospital, Winchester, MA, p. A316

ISEMANN, William R., President and Chief Executive Officer, KidsPeace Children's Hospital, Orefield, PA, p. A546

ISENMANN, Debra, Human Resources Generalist, Cox Monett, Monett, MO, p. A377

ISHIZUKA, Paul, Chief Financial Officer and Chief Operating Officer, Samaritan Healthcare, Moses Lake, WA, p. A686

ISHKANIAN, Gary, M.D. Vice President Medical Affairs, Montefiore Mount Vernon, Mount Vernon, NY, p. A443

ISKANDAR, Said, M.D. Chief Medical Officer, Sentara Halifax Regional Hospital, South Boston, VA, p. A678

ISLAM, Asad, M.D. Chief Medical Officer, Mayhill Hospital, Denton, TX, p. A612

ISLEY, L. Lee, Ph.D., Chief Executive Officer, Granville Health System, Oxford, NC, p. A471

ISMAIL, Asad, M.D. Medical Director, Wellstone Regional Hospital, Jeffersonville, IN, p. A215

ISMAIL, Hummayun, M.D. Medical Director, Select Specialty Hospital–Wilmington, Wilmington, DE, p. A120

ISOM, Julie, Director Human Resources, Lakeview Hospital, Bountiful, UT, p. A659

ISON, Tamara
Senior Vice President and President, Spalding Regional Hospital, Griffin, GA, p. A160
Chief Operating Officer, Spalding Regional Hospital, Griffin, GA, p. A160
Senior Vice President and President, Sylvan Grove Hospital, Jackson, GA, p. A161
Chief Financial Officer, Sylvan Grove Hospital, Jackson, GA, p. A161

ISON, William G., Human Resources Manager, Select Specialty Hospital–Tri Cities, Bristol, TN, p. A579

ISRAEL, Corry, Director Human Resources, Western Plains Medical Complex, Dodge City, KS, p. A242

ISRAEL, Michael D., President and Chief Executive Officer, Westchester Medical Center, Valhalla, NY, p. A458

ISRAEL, Michael D., President and Chief Executive Officer, WMCHealth, Valhalla, NY, p. B155

ISSAI, Alice H.
Business Strategy and Finance Leader, Kaiser Permanente West Los Angeles Medical Center, Los Angeles, CA, p. A72
Chief Operating Officer, Keck Hospital of USC, Los Angeles, CA, p. A72

ITAGAKI, Brian, M.D. Chief of Staff, St. Vincent Medical Center, Los Angeles, CA, p. A74

ITO, Derek, Director Human Resources, Shriners Hospitals for Children–Honolulu, Honolulu, HI, p. A171

IVES, Matthew, Administrator and Chief Financial Officer, Keokuk County Health Center, Sigourney, IA, p. A237

IVES ERICKSON, Jeanette R., MS Senior Vice President Patient Care and Chief Nurse, Massachusetts General Hospital, Boston, MA, p. A307

IVEY, Bobbie, Chief Human Resource Officer, Drew Memorial Hospital, Monticello, AR, p. A50

IVEY, Kim, Director of Human Resources, Cumberland Hospital, New Kent, VA, p. A674

IVEY, Mark J., M.D. Medical Director, Great Lakes Specialty Hospital–Grand Rapids, Grand Rapids, MI, p. A324

IVIE, Brian K.
President, Mercy San Juan Medical Center, Carmichael, CA, p. A58
President and Chief Executive Officer, Methodist Hospital of Sacramento, Sacramento, CA, p. A86

IVIE, Jack, President, Glendale Memorial Hospital and Health Center, Glendale, CA, p. A64

IVORY, Brenda, Chief Executive Officer, Harlingen Medical Center, Harlingen, TX, p. A622

IVY, Michael, M.D. Senior Vice President for Medical Affairs and Chief Medical Officer, Bridgeport Hospital, Bridgeport, CT, p. A113

IWEIMRIN, Salvatore, R.N., Chief Executive Officer, Select Specialty Hospital–Battle Creek, Battle Creek, MI, p. A319

IYER, Raju, Chief Financial Officer, Regional Medical Center of San Jose, San Jose, CA, p. A91

IZAKOVIC, Martin, M.D. Vice President Medical Staff Affairs and Chief Medical Officer, Mercy Iowa City, Iowa City, IA, p. A232

IZZI, Denine, Senior Director Information Technology, Robert Wood Johnson University Hospital Rahway, Rahway, NJ, p. A422

IZZO, Carolyn, President and Chief Executive Officer, Ellwood City Hospital, Ellwood City, PA, p. A538

J

JABBARPOUR, Yad, M.D. Chief of Staff, Catawba Hospital, Catawba, VA, p. A668

JABLONSKI, Kevin, Chief Nursing Officer, CHRISTUS Mother Frances Hospital – Winnsboro, Winnsboro, TX, p. A658

JABLONSKI, Kevin M., Chief Nursing Officer, East Texas Medical Center Athens, Athens, TX, p. A598

JABLONSKI, Mark, Vice President Mission Integration, St. Jude Medical Center, Fullerton, CA, p. A64

JABOUR, Leon John
Regional Chief Information Officer, WellSpan Ephrata Community Hospital, Ephrata, PA, p. A538
Regional Chief Information Officer, WellSpan Good Samaritan Hospital, Lebanon, PA, p. A543

JACK, Claudia L., Director Associate Relations, Bayfront Health Brooksville, Brooksville, FL, p. A125

JACK, Dennis D., Chief Executive Officer, Summit Medical Center, Casper, WY, p. A721

JACKES, Frederick D., Assistant Administrator and Director Human Resources, Valley Forge Medical Center and Hospital, Norristown, PA, p. A546

JACKLIN, Bonnie, R.N. Chief Nursing Officer, McKay–Dee Hospital Center, Ogden, UT, p. A661

JACKMAN, Andrew, Director Information Technology, Corry Memorial Hospital, Corry, PA, p. A536

JACKSON, Alex
Chief Executive, Providence Holy Family Hospital, Spokane, WA, p. A691
Chief Executive, Providence Sacred Heart Medical Center & Children's Hospital, Spokane, WA, p. A691

JACKSON, Anthony, Chief Executive Officer, Roper St. Francis Mount Pleasant Hospital, Mount Pleasant, SC, p. A568

JACKSON, Barbara, Ed.D., Acting Facility Director, Taylor Hardin Secure Medical Facility, Tuscaloosa, AL, p. A26

JACKSON, Bryan G., Vice President and Chief Financial Officer, Jefferson Regional Medical Center, Pine Bluff, AR, p. A51

JACKSON, Carolyn, Chief Operating Officer, Hospital of the University of Pennsylvania, Philadelphia, PA, p. A548

JACKSON, Cindy, Director Human Resources, Phelps Memorial Health Center, Holdrege, NE, p. A397

JACKSON, Collette, R.N. Director of Clinical Services, St. Theresa Specialty Hospital, Kenner, LA, p. A279

JACKSON, Darryl, D.O. Chief of Staff, Prague Community Hospital, Prague, OK, p. A519

JACKSON, David, Chief Financial Officer, Baptist Medical Center Leake, Carthage, MS, p. A356

JACKSON, Evan, Vice President Information Technology, Middlesex Hospital, Middletown, CT, p. A115

JACKSON, III, Frank D., Facility Chief Information Officer, Veterans Affairs Illiana Health Care System, Danville, IL, p. A187

JACKSON, Gary, D.O. Medical Director, Lincoln County Medical Center, Ruidoso, NM, p. A431

JACKSON, Holly, Chief Operating Officer, Gulf Coast Medical Center, Panama City, FL, p. A141

JACKSON, James, M.D. Chief of Staff, Cornerstone Hospital of Bossier City, Bossier City, LA, p. A274

JACKSON, James E. T., M.P.H., Chief Administrative Officer, San Leandro Hospital, San Leandro, CA, p. A92

JACKSON Jr., James H., Executive Director, Greenwood Leflore Hospital, Greenwood, MS, p. A358

JACKSON, James V., Budget Director, Saint Elizabeths Hospital, Washington, DC, p. A122

JACKSON, Jeffrey, M.D. Medical Director, Houston Methodist Sugar Land Hospital, Sugar Land, TX, p. A650

JACKSON, Jennifer, MSN, Chief Administrative Officer, Chief Nursing Officer and Vice President, University of Cincinnati Medical Center, Cincinnati, OH, p. A488

JACKSON, Joanne, Administrator Human Resources, Community Relations and Quality Improvement, Amery Hospital and Clinic, Amery, WI, p. A702

JACKSON, John J., President, FirstHealth Richmond Memorial Hospital, Rockingham, NC, p. A472

JACKSON, Judy, Director Health Information Management and Privacy Officer, Shodair Children's Hospital, Helena, MT, p. A388

JACKSON, Kevin
Interim Chief Executive Officer, Harnett Health System, Dunn, NC, p. A464
On Site Administrator, Highsmith–Rainey Specialty Hospital, Fayetteville, NC, p. A465

JACKSON, Les, Manager Information Systems, Lower Keys Medical Center, Key West, FL, p. A133

JACKSON, Lynn, Administrator, Northside Hospital–Forsyth, Cumming, GA, p. A157

JACKSON, Margaret G., R.N. Vice President Patient Care Services and Chief Nursing Officer, SUNY Downstate Medical Center University Hospital, , NY, p. A450

JACKSON, Meg, Director Information Technology, Beauregard Memorial Hospital, De Ridder, LA, p. A276

JACKSON, Melinda R., Director Human Resources, Bates County Memorial Hospital, Butler, MO, p. A368

JACKSON, Michelle, Chief Financial Officer, BHC Alhambra Hospital, Rosemead, CA, p. A86

JACKSON, Patsy, Director of Nursing, Jay Hospital, Jay, FL, p. A132

JACKSON, Robert, Chief Financial Officer, Alliance Health Center, Meridian, MS, p. A362

JACKSON Jr., Robert, Chief Executive Officer, Grove City Medical Center, Grove City, PA, p. A539

JACKSON, Stephanie, M.D. Vice President and Chief Medical Officer, HonorHealth Scottsdale Thompson Peak Medical Center, Scottsdale, AZ, p. A39

JACKSON, Suzanne B., FACHE, Chief Executive Officer, John Randolph Medical Center, Hopewell, VA, p. A672

JACKSON, Thomas W., Chief Executive Officer, Tomball Regional Medical Center, Tomball, TX, p. A653

JACKSON, Tom, Chief Financial Officer, Parkridge Medical Center, Chattanooga, TN, p. A580

JACKSON, Vance, FACHE, President and Chief Executive Officer, Davis Health System, Elkins, WV, p. B43

JACKSON, Vance, FACHE, Chief Executive Officer, Davis Medical Center, Elkins, WV, p. A695

JACKSON, William, Director Medical Records, Millwood Hospital, Arlington, TX, p. A597

JACKSON, William L., Chief Medical Officer, Inova Alexandria Hospital, Alexandria, VA, p. A667

JACKSON, Jr., William L., M.D. Executive Vice President, Chief Medical Officer, Erlanger Medical Center, Chattanooga, TN, p. A580

JACO, Mary, Administrator, Shriners Hospitals for Children–Galveston, Galveston, TX, p. A620

JACOB, Cheryl, Chief Operating Officer, Saddleback Memorial Medical Center, Laguna Hills, CA, p. A68

JACOBI, Diane, Chief of Staff, SSM Health St. Mary's Hospital – Audrain, Mexico, MO, p. A376

JACOBI, Elizabeth
    Human Resources Director, LAC+USC Medical Center, Los Angeles, CA, p. A72
    Associate Director Human Resources, Rancho Los Amigos National Rehabilitation Center, Downey, CA, p. A61

JACOBI, Robert, Chief Financial Officer, Bob Wilson Memorial Grant County Hospital, Ulysses, KS, p. A255

JACOBS, Anastasia, Chief Human Resources Officer, Robert Wood Johnson University Hospital Somerset, Somerville, NJ, p. A423

JACOBS, Andrea, Chief Operating Officer, South Pointe Hospital, Warrensville Heights, OH, p. A505

JACOBS, Barbara S., MSN Vice President, Nursing and Chief Nursing Officer, Anne Arundel Medical Center, Annapolis, MD, p. A296

JACOBS, Brian, M.D. Vice President Chief Information Officer and Chief Medical Information Officer, Children's National Health System, Washington, DC, p. A121

JACOBS, Donna K., FACHE, President, SSM Health St. Mary's Hospital – Audrain, Mexico, MO, p. A376

JACOBS, Greg, Manager, McLaren Bay Special Care, Bay City, MI, p. A319

JACOBS, Ian, Chief, Human Resource Management Service, Louis A. Johnson Veterans Affairs Medical Center, Clarksburg, WV, p. A695

JACOBS, Jenny
    Director Human Resources, OSF Holy Family Medical Center, Monmouth, IL, p. A197
    Director Human Resources, OSF St. Mary Medical Center, Galesburg, IL, p. A191

JACOBS, Joey, Chairman and Chief Executive Officer, Acadia Healthcare Company, Inc., Franklin, TN, p. B4

JACOBS, Julie
    Director Human Resources, Oklahoma Forensic Center, Vinita, OK, p. A523
    Chief Financial Officer, Warren General Hospital, Warren, PA, p. A556

JACOBS, Lori, Chief Financial Officer, Edgefield County Hospital, Edgefield, SC, p. A565

JACOBS, Mark, Director Information Services, Pomerene Hospital, Millersburg, OH, p. A499

JACOBS, Michael
    Vice President Human Resources, Gladys Spellman Specialty Hospital and Nursing Center, Cheverly, MD, p. A299
    Vice President Human Resources, Prince George's Hospital Center, Cheverly, MD, p. A299

JACOBS, Richard, Vice President Finance and Chief Financial Officer, Canton–Potsdam Hospital, Potsdam, NY, p. A453

JACOBS, Robert
    Regional Director Information Management, CHRISTUS Southeast Texas Hospital, Beaumont, TX, p. A601
    Regional Information Management Executive, CHRISTUS Southeast Texas Jasper Memorial, Jasper, TX, p. A629

JACOBS, Trace, Director Information Technology, Santiam Hospital, Stayton, OR, p. A531

JACOBS, Yolanda, Coordinator Human Resources, Cornerstone Hospital of Houston at Clearlake, Webster, TX, p. A656

JACOBSEN, Barry, CPA, Chief Executive Officer, Myrtue Medical Center, Harlan, IA, p. A232

JACOBSEN, William D., Vice President and Administrator, Carilion Franklin Memorial Hospital, Rocky Mount, VA, p. A678

JACOBSON, Becky, Vice President Finance, St. Vincent Heart Center, Indianapolis, IN, p. A214

JACOBSON, Carlton, Vice President of Finance, St. Helena Hospital Clear Lake, Clearlake, CA, p. A59

JACOBSON, Gary, M.D. Chief Medical Officer, Pembroke Hospital, Pembroke, MA, p. A313

JACOBSON, Janet, Director Human Resources, Lakewood Health System, Staples, MN, p. A352

JACOBSON, Jenny, Manager Human Resources, Sanford Hillsboro Medical Center, Hillsboro, ND, p. A480

JACOBSON, John, Chief Financial Officer, Martin General Hospital, Williamston, NC, p. A475

JACOBSON, John L., Chief Executive Officer, Atchison Hospital, Atchison, KS, p. A240

JACOBSON, Lisa, Director of Nursing, Community Hospital of Huntington Park, Huntington Park, CA, p. A66

JACOBSON, Mark, D.O. Vice President Medical Affairs, WellSpan Ephrata Community Hospital, Ephrata, PA, p. A538

JACOBSON, Mary Jo, Chief Executive Officer, San Joaquin Valley Rehabilitation Hospital, Fresno, CA, p. A64

JACOBSON, Peter, President, Essentia Health St. Mary's – Detroit Lakes, Detroit Lakes, MN, p. A341

JACOBSON, Randolph
    Chief Financial Officer, Carrier Clinic, Belle Mead, NJ, p. A414
    Chief Financial Officer, East Mountain Hospital, Belle Mead, NJ, p. A414

JACOBSON, Renae A., Human Resources Officer, Ralph H. Johnson Veterans Affairs Medical Center, Charleston, SC, p. A563

JACOBSON, Rodney D., Administrator, Bear Lake Memorial Hospital, Montpelier, ID, p. A177

JACOBSON, Sam, Director Management Information Systems, Community Memorial Hospital, Cloquet, MN, p. A340

JACOBSON, Shirley
    Chief Financial Officer, Community Behavioral Health Hospital – Alexandria, Alexandria, MN, p. A338
    Chief Financial Officer, Community Behavioral Health Hospital – Rochester, Rochester, MN, p. A349
    Chief Financial Officer, Community Behavioral Health Hospital – St. Peter, Saint Peter, MN, p. A351

JACOBSON, Terry, Administrator and Chief Executive Officer, Essentia Health St. Mary's Hospital of Superior, Superior, WI, p. A717

JACOBSON, Wendy, President and Chief Executive Officer, Medina Memorial Hospital, Medina, NY, p. A442

JACOBY, Jamie, Chief Financial Officer, Connally Memorial Medical Center, Floresville, TX, p. A617

JACQUAY, Dena M., Chief Human Resource Officer, Parkview Huntington Hospital, Huntington, IN, p. A213

JACQUES, Shane
    Regional Chief Financial Officer, Aspirus Grand View, Ironwood, MI, p. A327
    Regional Chief Financial Officer – U.P., Aspirus Keweenaw Hospital, Laurium, MI, p. A329

JACQUES, Teresa, Interim Chief Financial Officer, Adventist Medical Center–Reedley, Reedley, CA, p. A85

JADCZAK, Audrey, R.N
    Vice President/Chief Nursing Officer, Lourdes Medical Center of Burlington County, Willingboro, NJ, p. A425
    Vice President Chief Nursing Officer, Our Lady of Lourdes Medical Center, Camden, NJ, p. A415

JADEJA, Neerav, Administrator, Paradise Valley Hospital, National City, CA, p. A79

JADLOWSKI, Susan, R.N., Chief Executive Officer, Memorial Hermann Greater Heights Hospital, Houston, TX, p. A625

JADWIN, Anne, Chief Nursing Officer, Fox Chase Cancer Center–American Oncologic Hospital, Philadelphia, PA, p. A548

JAFFE, Darcy, R.N. Chief Nursing Officer, UW Medicine/Harborview Medical Center, Seattle, WA, p. A690

JAFFE, Richard, M.D. Medical Director, Belmont Behavioral Hospital, Philadelphia, PA, p. A547

JAGER, Jonathon R., Chief Information Officer, St. Francis Hospital, Columbus, GA, p. A157

JAGER, Linda, Director Finance, Avera Weskota Memorial Hospital, Wessington Springs, SD, p. A617

JAGGI, Michael, D.O. Vice President and Chief Medical Officer, Hurley Medical Center, Flint, MI, p. A323

JAGOE, Patricia, Assistant Vice President Patient Care, Johnson Memorial Medical Center, Stafford Springs, CT, p. A117

JAHAN, Mohammad S., M.D. Clinical Director, Middle Tennessee Mental Health Institute, Nashville, TN, p. A590

JAHN, Andrew, President and Chief Executive Officer, Sonora Regional Medical Center, Sonora, CA, p. A94

JAHN, Barbara A., Chief Operating Officer, Saint Joseph Hospital, Denver, CO, p. A104

JAHN, David B., President and Chief Executive Officer, War Memorial Hospital, Sault Sainte Marie, MI, p. A334

JAHN, Gregory L., R.N., Chief Executive Officer, St. Luke's Behavioral Health Center, Phoenix, AZ, p. A37

JAHN, Kim C., Chief Plant Operations and Chief Information Officer, Manning Regional Healthcare Center, Manning, IA, p. A234

JAHNIG, Jay A., Chief Executive Officer, Faulkton Area Medical Center, Faulkton, SD, p. A573

JAHRE, Jeffrey, M.D. Vice President Medical and Academic Affairs, St. Luke's University Hospital – Bethlehem Campus, Bethlehem, PA, p. A533

JAIN, Ashok, M.D. Senior Vice President and Chief Medical Officer, Beaumont Hospital – Wayne, Wayne, MI, p. A336

JAKOUBECK, Denise, Director Human Resources, Hancock County Health System, Britt, IA, p. A226

JAKUBOWSKI, Michael, M.D. Chief Medical Officer, Mary Free Bed Rehabilitation Hospital, Grand Rapids, MI, p. A325

JALBERT, Susan L., R.N. Vice President Patient Care Services and Chief Nursing Officer, Northwest Hospital, Randallstown, MD, p. A303

JALOMO, Angie, Chief Nursing Officer, Lynn County Hospital District, Tahoka, TX, p. A651

JAMALEDDINE, Ghassan, M.D. Medical Director, NYC Health + Hospitals / Kings County, NY, p. A448

JAMES, Annette, R.N. Chief Nursing Officer, Creek Nation Community Hospital, Okemah, OK, p. A515

JAMES, Bruce, Chief Executive Officer, Union Hospital, Dover, OH, p. A493

JAMES, Craig, President, Alleghany Memorial Hospital, Sparta, NC, p. A474

JAMES, Donald, D.O. Chief Medical Officer, Phelps County Regional Medical Center, Rolla, MO, p. A379

JAMES, Douglas, Chief Nursing Officer, Caldwell Medical Center, Princeton, KY, p. A268

JAMES, Gregory L., D.O. Chief Medical Officer, St. Vincent's Birmingham, Birmingham, AL, p. A17

JAMES, Jaime, Entity Finance Officer, Texas Health Harris Methodist Hospital Hurst–Euless–Bedford, Bedford, TX, p. A602

JAMES, Janet, Director Human Resources, Trigg County Hospital, Cadiz, KY, p. A258

JAMES, Jobie, Chief Financial Officer, West Calcasieu Cameron Hospital, Sulphur, LA, p. A288

JAMES, Karen, Regional Director, Human Resources, The William W. Backus Hospital, Norwich, CT, p. A116

JAMES, Kenneth, Chief Executive Officer, Tennova Healthcare–Harton, Tullahoma, TN, p. A594

JAMES, Laura, Director Human Resources, St. Francis Medical Center, Trenton, NJ, p. A424

JAMES, Michael
    Chief Operations Officer, Jackson Hospital and Clinic, Montgomery, AL, p. A23
    Information Technology Technical Support Specialist 1, Villa Feliciana Medical Complex, Jackson, LA, p. A278

JAMES, Michelle
    Regional Chief Nursing Officer, Providence Centralia Hospital, Centralia, WA, p. A683
    Chief Nursing Officer, Providence St. Peter Hospital, Olympia, WA, p. A687

JAMES, Robert L., Director Human Resources, Beaumont Hospital – Wayne, Wayne, MI, p. A336

JAMES, Shelia, Director of Nursing, Riverland Medical Center, Ferriday, LA, p. A276

JAMES, Sherrie, R.N. Director of Nursing, The BridgeWay, North Little Rock, AR, p. A51

JAMES, Taya, Director, Mercy Hospital Berryville, Berryville, AR, p. A43

JAMES, Teri, Chief Financial Officer, Lafayette Regional Health Center, Lexington, MO, p. A375

JAMES, Thomas L., M.D. Chief Medical Officer, Trumbull Memorial Hospital, Warren, OH, p. A505

JAMES, William B., FACHE, President, Wake Forest Baptist Health–Lexington Medical Center, Lexington, NC, p. A469

JAMESON, David, M.D. Chief of Staff, Annie Jeffrey Memorial County Health Center, Osceola, NE, p. A401

JAMIESON, Donna F., Ph.D. Chief Nursing Officer, Aurora Medical Center, Kenosha, WI, p. A708

JAMIESON, Pamela, Vice President Patient Care Services and Chief Nursing Officer, University of Maryland St. Joseph Medical Center, Towson, MD, p. A304

JAMIN, David, Chief Financial Officer, St. Mary's Regional Medical Center, Enid, OK, p. A511

JANAK, Joy, Interim Chief Executive Officer, Gulf Coast Medical Center, Wharton, TX, p. A657

JANATKA, Lucille A.
    President and Chief Executive Officer, MidState Medical Center, Meriden, CT, p. A115
    President and Chief Executive Officer, Hartford HealthCare Central Region, The Hospital of Central Connecticut, New Britain, CT, p. A115

JANDIAL, Rajnish, M.D. Chief Medical Officer, San Dimas Community Hospital, San Dimas, CA, p. A89

JANEK, James D., Chief Executive Officer, Rice Medical Center, Eagle Lake, TX, p. A614

JANERELLA, Wendy, Controller, Bucktail Medical Center, Renovo, PA, p. A553

JANICAK, Dan, Chief Financial Officer, University of Mississippi Medical Center, Jackson, MS, p. A360

JANIS, Terry, Assistant Vice President, Park Plaza Hospital, Houston, TX, p. A626

JANKE, Paul, FACHE, President and Chief Executive Officer, Bay Area Hospital, Coos Bay, OR, p. A525

JANKOWSKI, Stan, Vice President and Chief Information Officer, Hospital for Special Care, New Britain, CT, p. A115

JANLOO, Arman, M.D. Chief Medical Staff, Fairfax Community Hospital, Fairfax, OK, p. A512

JANOSO, John R., Chief Executive Officer, Fairfield Medical Center, Lancaster, OH, p. A496

JANOWSKI, Kenneth, M.D. Chief Medical Officer, Hackettstown Medical Center, Hackettstown, NJ, p. A417

JANOYAN, Jano, M.D. Medical Director, Select Specialty Hospital–Knoxville, Knoxville, TN, p. A586

JANSEN, David, Vice President Human Resources, Karmanos Cancer Center, Detroit, MI, p. A322

JANSEN, John, Management Information Specialist, Hawaii State Hospital, Kaneohe, HI, p. A172

JANSSEN, Kathy, Director Medical Records, Mountrail County Medical Center, Stanley, ND, p. A481

JANSSEN, Paul, President and Chief Executive Officer, Henry County Hospital, New Castle, IN, p. A219

JANTZEN, Daniel, Senior Vice President and Chief Operating Officer, Dartmouth–Hitchcock Medical Center, Lebanon, NH, p. A412

JANTZEN, Tammi, Chief Operating Officer, Okeene Municipal Hospital, Okeene, OK, p. A515

JANUS, Tammy, Senior Vice President Human Resources, Mercy Medical Center, Baltimore, MD, p. A297

JANZEN, Wes, Chief Information Officer, Wamego Health Center, Wamego, KS, p. A255

JAQUEZ, Jason, Director Human Resources, Greater El Monte Community Hospital, South El Monte, CA, p. A95

JARAMILLO, Charles, Chief Operating Officer, New Mexico Behavioral Health Institute at Las Vegas, Las Vegas, NM, p. A430

JARBOE, Joe, Director Human Resources, Kosciusko Community Hospital, Warsaw, IN, p. A223

JARBOE, Lori, Chief Executive Officer, HEALTHSOUTH Lakeview Rehabilitation Hospital, Elizabethtown, KY, p. A259

JARM, Timothy L., President and Chief Executive Officer, Alliant Management Services, Louisville, KY, p. B9

JARMER, Ryan, Chief Information Officer, Naval Medical Center San Diego, San Diego, CA, p. A88

JAROPILLO, Erwin, Director Information Systems, Lake Wales Medical Center, Lake Wales, FL, p. A133

JARREAU, Jeff
Senior Vice President Human Resources, North Oaks Medical Center, Hammond, LA, p. A277
Senior Vice President, Human Resources, North Oaks Health System, North Oaks Rehabilitation Hospital, Hammond, LA, p. A277

JARREAU, Valerie Sparks, R.N. Chief Nursing Officer, Pointe Coupee General Hospital, New Roads, LA, p. A285

JARRELL, Lindsey, Vice President Information Services, St. Joseph's Hospital, Tampa, FL, p. A147

JARRETT, Adam D., M.D. Executive Vice President and Chief Medical Officer, Holy Name Medical Center, Teaneck, NJ, p. A424

JARRY, Jacques, Administrator, Bullock County Hospital, Union Springs, AL, p. A26

JARRY, Patricia, Manager Human Resources, Crenshaw Community Hospital, Luverne, AL, p. A22

JARVIS, Dinah, Director of Nursing, Pineville Community Hospital Association, Pineville, KY, p. A268

JARVIS, Keith, Director Information Systems, Longview Regional Medical Center, Longview, TX, p. A633

JARVIS, Tammy, Vice President Clinical Services and Chief Nursing Officer, Texas Institute for Surgery at Texas Health Presbyterian Dallas, Dallas, TX, p. A611

JASNOFF, Jeff, Senior Vice President Human Resources, Kindred Hospital–New Jersey Morris County, Dover, NJ, p. A416

JASPER, Harry, Chief Financial Officer, Jerold Phelps Community Hospital, Garberville, CA, p. A64

JASPER, Jerry
Chief Executive Officer, Vibra Hospital of Amarillo, Amarillo, TX, p. A596
Chief Executive Officer, Vibra Rehabilitation Hospital of Amarillo, Amarillo, TX, p. A596

JATCZAK, Tracy E., CPA Chief Financial Officer, Box Butte General Hospital, Alliance, NE, p. A393

JAUERSACK, Dawn, Vice President and Chief Financial Officer, Boca Raton Regional Hospital, Boca Raton, FL, p. A124

JAURON, Jason, Director Human Resources, Orange City Area Health System, Orange City, IA, p. A235

JAVOIS, Laurent D.
Regional Executive Officer, Hawthorn Children Psychiatric Hospital, Saint Louis, MO, p. A380
Regional Executive Officer, Metropolitan St. Louis Psychiatric Center, Saint Louis, MO, p. A380
Chief Executive Officer, St. Louis Psychiatric Rehabilitation Center, Saint Louis, MO, p. A381

JAVOIS, Rosalie, Chief Financial Officer, Governor Juan F. Luis Hospital, Christiansted, VI, p. A731

JAY, Richard, D.O. Chief of Staff, North Big Horn Hospital District, Lovell, WY, p. A723

JEAN–BAPTISTE, Joan, Vice President Human Resources, Governor Juan F. Luis Hospital, Christiansted, VI, p. A731

JEAN–LOUIS, Marie S., R.N. Chief Nursing Officer, Creedmoor Psychiatric Center,, NY, p. A444

JEAN–MARIE, Jonathan, Administrator and Chief Executive Officer, Kindred Hospital Riverside, Perris, CA, p. A82

JEANSONNE, Corey, Chief Nursing Officer, Bunkie General Hospital, Bunkie, LA, p. A274

JEDLICKA, Colleen, R.N. Chief Nursing Officer, Comanche County Medical Center, Comanche, TX, p. A607

JEFFERSON, Glenn, Chief Medical Officer, Garfield County Public Hospital District, Pomeroy, WA, p. A688

JEFFERSON, Kelly, Vice President, Operations, OSF St. Francis Hospital and Medical Group, Escanaba, MI, p. A323

JEFFRAS, Charles, Executive Director Human Resources, St. Vincent Carmel Hospital, Carmel, IN, p. A208

JEFFRESS, Chuck, Vice President Fiscal Services, CHI St. Luke's Health Brazosport, Lake Jackson, TX, p. A631

JEFFREY, Roberta, Chief Executive Officer, Holdenville General Hospital, Holdenville, OK, p. A513

JEFFRIES, John, Director Finance, HSHS St. Joseph's Hospital, Breese, IL, p. A182

JEHAN, Sayed, M.D. Interim Medical Director, Larned State Hospital, Larned, KS, p. A247

JELALIAN, Christine, M.D. Medical Director, St. Luke's Cornwall Hospital, Newburgh, NY, p. A450

JELDEN, Dennis, M.D. Chief of Staff, Melissa Memorial Hospital, Holyoke, CO, p. A107

JELKS, Kim, Fiscal Officer, Villa Feliciana Medical Complex, Jackson, LA, p. A278

JELLE, Laura, President, St. Clare Hospital, Baraboo, WI, p. A702

JEMJEMIAN, Norair, Chief Operating Officer, Los Robles Hospital and Medical Center, Thousand Oaks, CA, p. A96

JENE, Suzanne L., Interim Executive Director, Tennessee Valley Healthcare System, Nashville, TN, p. A591

JENKINS, Bonnie, Chief Financial Officer, Methodist Hospital of Sacramento, Sacramento, CA, p. A86

JENKINS, Brian, Director Human Resources, Arbour–Fuller Hospital, Attleboro, MA, p. A305

JENKINS, Debbie, Chief Human Resources Management Service, Veterans Affairs Sierra Nevada Health Care System, Reno, NV, p. A408

JENKINS, Denise, Chief Clinical Officer, Kindred Hospital–Brea, Brea, CA, p. A57

JENKINS, Jason, Senior Director of Nursing, Novant Health UVA Health System Haymarket Medical Center, Haymarket, VA, p. A671

JENKINS, Jimmy, M.D. Chief Medical Officer, Geary Community Hospital, Junction City, KS, p. A246

JENKINS, Keith, Director, Human Resources, Grandview Medical Center, Dayton, OH, p. A492

JENKINS, Linda, R.N. Vice President Patient Care Services, St. Jude Medical Center, Fullerton, CA, p. A64

JENKINS, Maynard, Regional Vice President Human Resources, Sutter Maternity and Surgery Center of Santa Cruz, Santa Cruz, CA, p. A93

JENKINS, Michelle, M.D. President Medical Staff, Herrin Hospital, Herrin, IL, p. A192

JENKINS, Rebecca, Director Human Resources Management, Harrison Memorial Hospital, Cynthiana, KY, p. A259

JENKINS, Roger T., Chief Executive Officer, Ethicus Hospital – Grapevine, Grapevine, TX, p. A621

JENKINS, Ruth, Chief Financial Officer, Ridgeview Institute, Smyrna, GA, p. A166

JENKINS, Scott, Administrator, Cheyenne County Hospital, Saint Francis, KS, p. A253

JENKS, Lyn, Chief Executive Officer, Munson Healthcare Charlevoix Hospital, Charlevoix, MI, p. A320

JENNER, Jody J., President and Chief Executive Officer, Broadlawns Medical Center, Des Moines, IA, p. A229

JENNETTE, Brian, Chief Financial Officer, Northside Hospital–Cherokee, Canton, GA, p. A155

JENNINGS, Jason, Chief Executive Officer, Scott & White Hospital – College Station, College Station, TX, p. A606

JENNINGS, Keith, Chief Information Officer, Massachusetts General Hospital, Boston, MA, p. A307

JENNINGS, Marilyn, Director Human Resources, Arise Austin Medical Center, Austin, TX, p. A598

JENNINGS, Mark, Chief Information Officer, Saint Anthony Hospital, Chicago, IL, p. A186

JENNINGS, Peter, M.D. Interim Chief Medical Officer, Sacred Heart Hospital Pensacola, Pensacola, FL, p. A142

JENNINGS, Shayla, Human Resources Director, Montgomery County Memorial Hospital, Red Oak, IA, p. A236

JENNINGS, William M., President and Chief Executive Officer, Bridgeport Hospital, Bridgeport, CT, p. A113

JENSEMA, Christine
Chief People Officer, HSHS St. Clare Memorial Hospital, Oconto Falls, WI, p. A713
Chief People Officer, HSHS St. Vincent Hospital, Green Bay, WI, p. A707
Chief People Officer, St. Mary's Hospital Medical Center, Green Bay, WI, p. A707
Chief People Officer, St. Nicholas Hospital, Sheboygan, WI, p. A716

JENSEN, Amy, Director Human Resources, Community Health Center of Branch County, Coldwater, MI, p. A321

JENSEN, Annelise, Chief Nursing Officer, Methodist Olive Branch Hospital, Olive Branch, MS, p. A363

JENSEN, Beth, Director Clinic Operations, Mobridge Regional Hospital, Mobridge, SD, p. A575

JENSEN, Camille, R.N. Chief Nursing Officer, McLaren Greater Lansing, Lansing, MI, p. A328

JENSEN, Christopher, Chief Financial Officer, Three Rivers Behavioral Health, West Columbia, SC, p. A570

JENSEN, Dave, Director Human Resources, Performance Improvement and Risk Management, Mountain View Hospital, Gadsden, AL, p. A20

JENSEN, Eric P., Chief Executive Officer, EvergreenHealth Monroe, Monroe, WA, p. A686

JENSEN, Janette, Manager Human Resources, Avera Holy Family Hospital, Estherville, IA, p. A230

JENSEN, Jeff, D.O
Vice President, Medical Affairs, Morton Plant Hospital, Clearwater, FL, p. A125
Vice President, Medical Affairs, Morton Plant North Bay Hospital, New Port Richey, FL, p. A138

JENSEN, Laura J., Vice President Patient Care Services, St. Croix Regional Medical Center, St. Croix Falls, WI, p. A716

JENSEN, Leanna, Vice President Finance and Chief Financial Officer, Cobleskill Regional Hospital, Cobleskill, NY, p. A437

JENSEN, Mary, Controller, Mountain View Hospital, Gadsden, AL, p. A20

JENSEN, Michael E., Chief Executive Officer, Davis Hospital and Medical Center, Layton, UT, p. A660

JENSEN, Neal, Chief Executive Officer, Cobre Valley Regional Medical Center, Globe, AZ, p. A33

JENSEN, Pamela, FACHE, President, ProMedica Memorial Hospital, Fremont, OH, p. A495

JENSEN, Paul, M.D. Chief of Staff, Regional Health Services of Howard County, Cresco, IA, p. A228

JENSEN, Renee K., Chief Executive Officer, Summit Pacific Medical Center, Elma, WA, p. A684

JENSEN, Ron, D.O. Chief Medical Officer and Vice President, Baylor Regional Medical Center at Grapevine, Grapevine, TX, p. A621

JENSEN, Ryan, Chief Executive Officer, Memorial Hospital of Salem County, Salem, NJ, p. A423

JENSEN, Sherry, Chief Financial Officer, Halifax Regional Medical Center, Roanoke Rapids, NC, p. A472

JENSEN, Tom, Chief Executive Officer, Grays Harbor Community Hospital, Aberdeen, WA, p. A682

JENSEN, Troy, Director Human Resources, HEALTHSOUTH Rehabilitation Hospital of Utah, Sandy, UT, p. A664

JENSEN, Twyla, Director Human Resources, Pioneers Medical Center, Meeker, CO, p. A109

JENTZ, Amy, M.D. Chief of Staff, Sparrow Ionia Hospital, Ionia, MI, p. A326

JEPPESEN, Kelly, Chief Medical Officer, San Juan Hospital, Monticello, UT, p. A660

JEPSEN, Christinia, R.N., Administrator, Parkland Health Center–Bonne Terre, Bonne Terre, MO, p. A367

JEPSON, Brian, President, OhioHealth Riverside Methodist Hospital, Columbus, OH, p. A491

JEPSON, Jeanne, Director Human Resources, Hackettstown Medical Center, Hackettstown, NJ, p. A417

JEPSON, Mark, Vice President, Silver Cross Hospital, New Lenox, IL, p. A198

JERGER, Greg, Chief Financial Officer, Memorial Health Care Systems, Seward, NE, p. A402

JERINA, Anthony T., Chief Nursing Officer, Hereford Regional Medical Center, Hereford, TX, p. A623

JERNIGAN, Donald L., Ph.D., President and Chief Executive Officer, Adventist Health System Sunbelt Health Care Corporation, Altamonte Springs, FL, p. B6

JERNIGAN, Pam, Chief Financial Officer, Unity Medical Center, Manchester, TN, p. A587

JESCH, Doug, Director Human Resources, Starke Hospital, Knox, IN, p. A215

JESIOLOWSKI, Craig A., FACHE, President, Saint Anne's Hospital, Fall River, MA, p. A310

JESSUP, Daniel, Chief Financial Officer, Legacy Silverton Medical Center, Silverton, OR, p. A531

JESTER, Denise, Chief Financial Officer, Nanticoke Memorial Hospital, Seaford, DE, p. A119

JESTILA–PELTOLA, Gail, Chief Financial Officer, Baraga County Memorial Hospital, L'Anse, MI, p. A328

JESURASA, Jebashini, Vice President, Chief Information Technology Officer, Wyckoff Heights Medical Center,, NY, p. A450

JETER, John
Assistant Administrator and Chief Financial Officer, Johnston Memorial Hospital, Abingdon, VA, p. A667
Chief Financial Officer, Russell County Medical Center, Lebanon, VA, p. A672
Assistant Vice President and Chief Financial Officer, Smyth County Community Hospital, Marion, VA, p. A673

JETER, John H., M.D., President and Chief Executive Officer, Hays Medical Center, Hays, KS, p. A244

JETT, Chris, Administrator, University of South Alabama Children's and Women's Hospital, Mobile, AL, p. A23

JETT, Heather, Director Patient Care Services, Peninsula Hospital, Louisville, TN, p. A587

JETTERGREN, Tess, Director Clinical Informatics, Essentia Health St. Mary's Medical Center, Duluth, MN, p. A342

JETTON, Dana, Chief Information Officer, AMG Specialty Hospital–Tulsa, Tulsa, OK, p. A521

JEUNEHOMME, Patti, Director Human Resources, Hot Springs County Memorial Hospital, Thermopolis, WY, p. A724

JEWELL, Keith, President, St. Mary's Medical Center of Evansville, Evansville, IN, p. A210

JEWETT, Lori, R.N. Vice President of Nursing and Chief Operating Officer, Falmouth Hospital, Falmouth, MA, p. A310

JEWETT, Sherri R., Chief Executive Officer, Valle Vista Hospital, Greenwood, IN, p. A212

JEYAKUMAR, Panch, M.D. Chief of Staff, Olympia Medical Center, Los Angeles, CA, p. A73

JEZIORSKE, John J., Director Human Resources, Abilene Regional Medical Center, Abilene, TX, p. A595

JEZSU, Peggy, Chief Nursing Officer, Alvarado Hospital Medical Center, San Diego, CA, p. A88

JIMENEZ, Betzaida, Director Human Resources, Hospital de la Universidad de Puerto Rico/Dr. Federico Trilla, Carolina, PR, p. A726

JIMENEZ, Cristina, Chief Operating Officer, Coral Gables Hospital, Coral Gables, FL, p. A126

JIMENEZ, Edward, Chief Executive Officer, UF Health Shands, Gainesville, FL, p. B139

JIMENEZ, Edward, Chief Executive Officer, UF Health Shands Hospital, Gainesville, FL, p. A130

JIMENEZ, Gerson, M.D. Medical Director, Hospital Episcopal San Lucas Guayama, Guayama, PR, p. A727

JIMENEZ, Guillermo, Director Finance, Castaner General Hospital, Castaner, PR, p. A726

JIMENEZ, Ronald, M.D., Chief Executive Officer, Florida Hospital–Flagler, Palm Coast, FL, p. A141

JIMESON, Jean–Marie, Manager Human Resources, Kansas Spine and Specialty Hospital, Wichita, KS, p. A255

JIMMERSON, Kevin, Business Manager, Mental Health Institute, Independence, IA, p. A232

JIN, Marvin, M.D. Medical Director, Parkside Psychiatric Hospital and Clinic, Tulsa, OK, p. A521

JIRON, Feliciano, Chief Executive Officer, Valley View Medical Center, Fort Mohave, AZ, p. A32

JIROVEC, David, Director Finance, Ministry Good Samaritan Health Center, Merrill, WI, p. A710

JITH, Gayathri S., M.P.H. Senior Vice President Strategy and Operations, Valley Presbyterian Hospital,, CA, p. A75

JOBBITT, Patty, Chief Operating Officer, DMC – Rehabilitation Institute of Michigan, Detroit, MI, p. A321

JOBE, Kenneth Lynn, Director Human Resources, Tyler County Hospital, Woodville, TX, p. A658

JOCHIM, Steven, Administrator, Cape Cod & Island Community Mental Health Center, Pocasset, MA, p. A314

JODER, Christina, Director Nursing Operations, Northern Colorado Rehabilitation Hospital, Johnstown, CO, p. A107

JODWAY, Timothy, Chief Financial Administrator, Beaumont Hospital–Dearborn, Dearborn, MI, p. A321

JOEL, Linda, Vice President Operations, Spectrum Health Special Care Hospital, Grand Rapids, MI, p. A325

JOHANNSEN, Lee, M.D. Chief Medical Officer, Central Texas Medical Center, San Marcos, TX, p. A648

JOHANTGES, Dawn, Chief Executive Officer, Kindred Hospital Colorado Springs, Colorado Springs, CO, p. A102

JOHE, David, M.D. President Medical Staff, Penn Highlands Elk, Saint Marys, PA, p. A553

JOHN, Aleyamma, R.N. Director of Nursing, Kensington Hospital, Philadelphia, PA, p. A548

JOHN, Julian, Chief Financial Officer, NYC Health + Hospitals / Kings County,, NY, p. A448

JOHN, M. Joseph, M.D. Chief of Staff, Berwick Hospital Center, Berwick, PA, p. A533

JOHNS, Dale, FACHE, Chief Executive Officer, Salt Lake Regional Medical Center, Salt Lake City, UT, p. A663

JOHNS, Dawn, Director Human Resources, Colquitt Regional Medical Center, Moultrie, GA, p. A163

JOHNS, Jeffery, M.D. Medical Director, Vanderbilt Stallworth Rehabilitation Hospital, Nashville, TN, p. A591

JOHNS, Paul, Chief Operating Officer, South Lake Hospital, Clermont, FL, p. A125

JOHNS, Thomas Bradford, M.D. Medical Director, Ridgeview Institute, Smyrna, GA, p. A166

JOHNS, Timothy, M.D. Chief Medical Officer, Gilbert Hospital, Gilbert, AZ, p. A32

JOHNSEN, Timothy J., MS, President, Integris Baptist Medical Center, Oklahoma City, OK, p. A516

JOHNSON, Aaron, Vice President Patient Care Services and Chief Nursing Officer, CHI St. Alexius Health Devils Lake Hospital, Devils Lake, ND, p. A478

JOHNSON, Alan, Chief Information Officer, Doctors Community Hospital, Lanham, MD, p. A302

JOHNSON, Allen
Chief Financial Officer, Truman Medical Center–Hospital Hill, Kansas City, MO, p. A374
Chief Financial Officer, Truman Medical Center–Lakewood, Kansas City, MO, p. A374

JOHNSON, Arlan D., Chief Executive Officer, Howard County Medical Center, Saint Paul, NE, p. A402

JOHNSON, Ashley L., Chief Operations Officer, Canyon Vista Medical Center, Sierra Vista, AZ, p. A39

JOHNSON, Barbara A.
Vice President Human Resources, Good Samaritan Hospital, Dayton, OH, p. A492
Vice President Human Resources, Miami Valley Hospital, Dayton, OH, p. A493

JOHNSON, Becky, Director Human Resources, Oakdale Community Hospital, Oakdale, LA, p. A286

JOHNSON, Belinda, R.N. Chief Nursing Officer/Chief Clinical Officer, Russellville Hospital, Russellville, AL, p. A25

JOHNSON, Betty, Associate Administrator, University Health Shreveport, Shreveport, LA, p. A288

JOHNSON, Billy, Chief Executive Officer, Coal County General Hospital, Coalgate, OK, p. A510

JOHNSON, Blake, M.D. Chief of Staff, Salt Lake Regional Medical Center, Salt Lake City, UT, p. A663

JOHNSON, Bonnie, R.N. Vice President of Patient Services, Perham Health, Perham, MN, p. A348

JOHNSON, Brandi, Site Manager Technology Information Systems, Spectrum Health Reed City Hospital, Reed City, MI, p. A332

JOHNSON, Brenda
Director Human Resources, Baptist Memorial Hospital–Collierville, Collierville, TN, p. A581
Director Human Resources, North Mississippi Medical Center–West Point, West Point, MS, p. A366

JOHNSON, Bret
Chief Financial Officer, Bon Secours St. Francis Hospital, Charleston, SC, p. A562
Chief Financial Officer, Roper St. Francis, Charleston, SC, p. A563
Chief Financial Officer, Roper St. Francis Mount Pleasant Hospital, Mount Pleasant, SC, p. A568

JOHNSON, Brett, Chief Executive Officer, Regency Hospital of Toledo, Sylvania, OH, p. A503

JOHNSON, Bryan L., Administrator, Alta View Hospital, Sandy, UT, p. A664

JOHNSON, III, C. Thomas, Vice President Finance and Chief Financial Officer, Southeastern Health, Lumberton, NC, p. A469

JOHNSON, Candace, Ph.D., President and Chief Executive Officer, Roswell Park Cancer Institute, Buffalo, NY, p. A436

JOHNSON, Casey R., Chief Financial Officer, Riverwood Healthcare Center, Aitkin, MN, p. A338

JOHNSON, Charles, M.D. Chief of Staff, Renown Regional Medical Center, Reno, NV, p. A408

JOHNSON, Cheryl, Regional Chief Information Officer, St. Joseph Medical Center, Kansas City, MO, p. A374

JOHNSON, Chris, R.N. Chief Nursing Officer, Davis Hospital and Medical Center, Layton, UT, p. A660

JOHNSON, Chris, M.D. Chief of Staff, Mercy Hospital Rogers, Rogers, AR, p. A52

JOHNSON, Christina, M.D. Vice President and Chief Clinical and Quality Officer, Lutheran Medical Center, Wheat Ridge, CO, p. A111

JOHNSON, Connie, Chief Financial Officer, Southwest Idaho Advanced Care Hospital, Boise, ID, p. A174

JOHNSON, Craig, D.O. Medical Director, St. Vincent Clay Hospital, Brazil, IN, p. A207

JOHNSON, Craig, Interim Chief Executive Officer, Vibra Hospital of Richmond, Richmond, VA, p. A678

JOHNSON, Craig A., Chief Executive Officer, Boundary Community Hospital, Bonners Ferry, ID, p. A175

JOHNSON, Cynthia J., R.N. Chief Nursing Officer, Los Robles Hospital and Medical Center, Thousand Oaks, CA, p. A96

JOHNSON, Danielle, Chief Operating Officer, Florida Hospital Fish Memorial, Orange City, FL, p. A140

JOHNSON, Darren, M.D. Chief of Staff, Tennova Healthcare Dyersburg Regional Medical Center, Dyersburg, TN, p. A582

JOHNSON, David
Chief Executive Officer, Navos, Seattle, WA, p. A689
Manager Information Services, Providence Kodiak Island Medical Center, Kodiak, AK, p. A29

JOHNSON, Deborah Carey, R.N., President and Chief Executive Officer, Eastern Maine Medical Center, Bangor, ME, p. A291

JOHNSON, Deeann, Director Human Resources, Saint Thomas River Park Hospital, Mc Minnville, TN, p. A588

JOHNSON, Denise, M.D. Medical Director, Meadville Medical Center, Meadville, PA, p. A544

JOHNSON, Dennis B., President and Chief Executive Officer, Hardin Memorial Hospital, Elizabethtown, KY, p. A259

JOHNSON, Derek, Chief Executive Officer, Laurel Oaks Behavioral Health Center, Dothan, AL, p. A19

JOHNSON, Sr., Derek, Chief Operating Officer, Franklin Hospital District, Benton, IL, p. A181

JOHNSON, Dian I., MSN Chief Nurse Executive, Staten Island University Hospital,, NY, p. A450

JOHNSON, Diana G., Acting Chief Human Resources Officer, Novato Community Hospital, Novato, CA, p. A80

JOHNSON, Diane, R.N. Vice President Patient Care Services and Chief Nursing Officer, Sinai Hospital of Baltimore, Baltimore, MD, p. A298

JOHNSON, Douglas E.
Interim Vice President Operations and Chief Financial Officer, Hudson Hospital and Clinic, Hudson, WI, p. A707
Chief Financial Officer, Lakeview Hospital, Stillwater, MN, p. A352

JOHNSON, Douglas V., Chief Executive Officer, Stanislaus Surgical Hospital, Modesto, CA, p. A77

JOHNSON, Doyle K., Administrator, Mercy Hospital, Moundridge, KS, p. A249

JOHNSON, Drew, Chief Financial Officer, Holdenville General Hospital, Holdenville, OK, p. A513

JOHNSON, Earle
Area Information Officer, Kaiser Permanente Panorama City Medical Center,, CA, p. A71
Area Information Officer, Kaiser Permanente Woodland Hills Medical Center,, CA, p. A72

JOHNSON, Eddie, Chief Information Technology Officer, Kansas City Veterans Affairs Medical Center, Kansas City, MO, p. A373

JOHNSON, Eric, Manager, United Medical Center, Washington, DC, p. A122

JOHNSON, Eunice, M.D. Chief Medical Staff, Kentucky River Medical Center, Jackson, KY, p. A262

JOHNSON, Gigi, Chief Nursing Officer, Kindred Hospital–Chattanooga, Chattanooga, TN, p. A580

JOHNSON, Greg
Vice President of Operations, Davis Medical Center, Elkins, WV, p. A695
IT Coordinator, North Shore Health, Grand Marais, MN, p. A343

JOHNSON, Greg K., Chief Operating Officer, Colquitt Regional Medical Center, Moultrie, GA, p. A163

JOHNSON, Gregory, D.D.S., Chief Executive Officer, Fairbanks Memorial Hospital, Fairbanks, AK, p. A29

JOHNSON, Heather, Director of Finance, Operations and Business Development, Buffalo Hospital, Buffalo, MN, p. A340

JOHNSON, Helen, R.N. Vice President Patient Services, Spectrum Health Ludington Hospital, Ludington, MI, p. A329

JOHNSON, J. David, M.D. Chief of Staff, East Texas Medical Center Specialty Hospital, Tyler, TX, p. A654

JOHNSON, Jack, R.N. Director of Nursing, Sanford Rock Rapids Medical Center, Rock Rapids, IA, p. A236

JOHNSON, James, Chief Financial officer, Franklin Hospital District, Benton, IL, p. A181

JOHNSON, Jamie, R.N. Vice President Nursing, Community Hospital of Anaconda, Anaconda, MT, p. A385

JOHNSON, Jamie, Director Human Resources, Miners' Colfax Medical Center, Raton, NM, p. A430

JOHNSON, Jani L., MSN, Chief Executive Officer, Saint Luke's Hospital of Kansas City, Kansas City, MO, p. A374

JOHNSON, Jason, Controller, F. W. Huston Medical Center, Winchester, KS, p. A256

JOHNSON, Jay, Chief Financial Officer, AllianceHealth Clinton, Clinton, OK, p. A510

JOHNSON, Jay R., FACHE, President and Chief Executive Officer, Duncan Regional Hospital, Duncan, OK, p. A510

JOHNSON, Jayne, Director Human Resources, Great Plains Health, North Platte, NE, p. A399

JOHNSON, Jeff, Director Information Systems, Saint Thomas River Park Hospital, Mc Minnville, TN, p. A588

JOHNSON, Jeffrey, Vice President, Memorial Hospital, Colorado Springs, CO, p. A102

JOHNSON, Jimmy, Chief Financial Officer, Blue Mountain Hospital, Blanding, UT, p. A659

JOHNSON, Jodi, Vice President of Nursing, Aspirus Medford Hospital, Medford, WI, p. A710

JOHNSON, Joe, FACHE, Chief Executive Officer, Florida Hospital Carrollwood, Tampa, FL, p. A147

JOHNSON, Joel, M.D. Chief Medical Staff, First Care Health Center, Park River, ND, p. A481

JOHNSON, John, M.D
Chief of Staff, Greenbrier Valley Medical Center, Ronceverte, WV, p. A700
Clinical Director, U. S. Public Health Service Indian Hospital, Crownpoint, NM, p. A429

JOHNSON, Juantina, Chief of Staff, Choctaw Health Center, Philadelphia, MS, p. A363

JOHNSON, Judith, Controller, HEALTHSOUTH Rehabilitation Hospital, Largo, FL, p. A134

JOHNSON, Juli, R.N., President, Parkview Huntington Hospital, Huntington, IN, p. A213

JOHNSON, Kathi, Chief Financial Officer, Eskenazi Health, Indianapolis, IN, p. A213

JOHNSON, Kathie A., Ph.D., Chief Executive Officer, Novant Health Thomasville Medical Center, Thomasville, NC, p. A474

JOHNSON, Kathryn
Chief Nursing Officer, Casa Colina Hospital and Health Systems, Pomona, CA, p. A83
Manager Human Resources, Marketing and Public Relations, St. Vincent Jennings Hospital, North Vernon, IN, p. A220

JOHNSON, Kawanda, Director of Nursing, Specialty Hospital of Meridian, Meridian, MS, p. A362

JOHNSON, Kayla, R.N. Vice President Patient Care Services and Chief Nursing Officer, St. Francis Medical Center, Monroe, LA, p. A283

JOHNSON, Kelly, R.N. Chief Nursing Officer, St. John Sapulpa, Sapulpa, OK, p. A519

JOHNSON, Ken
Chief Physician Executive, HSHS St. Clare Memorial Hospital, Oconto Falls, WI, p. A713
Chief Physician Executive, HSHS St. Vincent Hospital, Green Bay, WI, p. A707
President and Chief Executive Officer, Hutchinson Regional Medical Center, Hutchinson, KS, p. A245
Chief Physician Executive, St. Mary's Hospital Medical Center, Green Bay, WI, p. A707
Chief Physician Executive, St. Nicholas Hospital, Sheboygan, WI, p. A716

JOHNSON, Kendall, Chief Financial Officer, Baton Rouge General Medical Center, Baton Rouge, LA, p. A272

JOHNSON, Kenneth, Vice President, Sts. Mary & Elizabeth Hospital, Louisville, KY, p. A265

JOHNSON, Kevin, Chief Executive Officer, Mountain View Hospital, Payson, UT, p. A662

JOHNSON, Kirby, Chief Executive Officer, Davis County Hospital, Bloomfield, IA, p. A226

JOHNSON, Kristen, Chief Nursing Officer, Southwest Healthcare System, Murrieta, CA, p. A78

JOHNSON, Kurt E., President and Chief Executive Officer, Ingalls Memorial Hospital, Harvey, IL, p. A192

JOHNSON, Kyle
Vice President Finance, East Liverpool City Hospital, East Liverpool, OH, p. A494
Chief Information Officer, The Aroostook Medical Center, Presque Isle, ME, p. A295

JOHNSON, Laurie, Director – Human Resources, Via Christi Hospital Pittsburg, Pittsburg, KS, p. A252

JOHNSON, Linda, R.N. Vice President, Patient Services Risk Management and Chief Nursing Officer, Heart of the Rockies Regional Medical Center, Salida, CO, p. A110

JOHNSON, Lois, Administrator Fiscal Services, Ridgecrest Regional Hospital, Ridgecrest, CA, p. A85

JOHNSON, Lowell W., LFACHE, Chief Executive Officer, Presence Saint Joseph Medical Center, Joliet, IL, p. A194

JOHNSON, Margaret M., President, St. Vincent Northwest Region, St. Vincent Kokomo, Kokomo, IN, p. A216

JOHNSON, Marianne, Chief Nursing Officer, Trace Regional Hospital, Houston, MS, p. A359

JOHNSON, Marie
Chief Nursing Officer, Carrus Rehabilitation Hospital, Sherman, TX, p. A648
Chief Nursing Officer, Carrus Specialty Hospital, Sherman, TX, p. A648

JOHNSON, Marisa, M.D. Vice President Medical Affairs, CHRISTUS Health Shreveport–Bossier, Shreveport, LA, p. A287

JOHNSON, Mark, M.D. Chief Medical Officer, Mercy Hospital Oklahoma City, Oklahoma City, OK, p. A516

JOHNSON, Mark
Chief Financial Officer, Norwood Hospital, Norwood, MA, p. A313
Chief Information Officer, West Holt Memorial Hospital, Atkinson, NE, p. A393

JOHNSON, Matthew, Chief Executive Officer and President, Cherokee Regional Medical Center, Cherokee, IA, p. A227

JOHNSON, Melissa, Chief Financial Officer, Baptist Medical Center South, Montgomery, AL, p. A23

JOHNSON, Michael, Chief Executive Officer, Clearview Regional Medical Center, Monroe, GA, p. A163

JOHNSON, Michael, M.D. Medical Director, Salina Surgical Hospital, Salina, KS, p. A253

JOHNSON, Michael A., M.D. Chief of Staff, Bucyrus Community Hospital, Bucyrus, OH, p. A485

JOHNSON, Michael G., CPA Chief Financial Officer, Abrom Kaplan Memorial Hospital, Kaplan, LA, p. A279

JOHNSON, Michael T., FACHE, President and Chief Executive Officer, Regional Medical Center of San Jose, San Jose, CA, p. A91

JOHNSON, Mike
Vice President, Chief Information Officer, CaroMont Regional Medical Center, Gastonia, NC, p. A465
Chief Financial Officer, Lancaster Regional Medical Center, Lancaster, PA, p. A542

JOHNSON, Monte, Vice President, Medical Affairs, St. Francis Regional Medical Center, Shakopee, MN, p. A351

JOHNSON, Nancy, Chief Nursing Officer, Select Specialty Hospital–North Knoxville, Powell, TN, p. A592

JOHNSON, Nanette, Chief Nursing Officer, Orthopaedic Hospital of Wisconsin – Glendale, Glendale, WI, p. A706

JOHNSON, Nate, Chief Information Officer, Highlands Regional Medical Center, Sebring, FL, p. A145

JOHNSON, Neil, Chief Operating Officer, EvergreenHealth, Kirkland, WA, p. A686

JOHNSON, Nikki, Interim Chief Executive Officer, Cooperstown Medical Center, Cooperstown, ND, p. A478

JOHNSON, Pam, R.N. Chief Nursing Officer, McCurtain Memorial Hospital, Idabel, OK, p. A513

JOHNSON, Pamela
Treasurer and Chief Financial Officer, Geneva General Hospital, Geneva, NY, p. A439
Treasurer and Chief Financial Officer, Soldiers and Sailors Memorial Hospital of Yates County, Penn Yan, NY, p. A452

JOHNSON, Pamela O., MS Chief Nursing Officer, Mayo Clinic Hospital – Rochester, Rochester, MN, p. A349

JOHNSON, Patricia, R.N. Senior Vice President, Woman's Hospital, Baton Rouge, LA, p. A273

JOHNSON, Patrick, Director Human Resources, Pondera Medical Center, Conrad, MT, p. A386

JOHNSON, Paul F., President, GHS Greenville Memorial Hospital, Greenville, SC, p. A566

JOHNSON, Penny
Chief Financial Officer, Metroplex Adventist Hospital, Killeen, TX, p. A630
Chief Financial Officer, Texas Health Huguley Hospital Fort Worth South, Burleson, TX, p. A604

JOHNSON, Peri, Human Resources Director, West Central Georgia Regional Hospital, Columbus, GA, p. A157

JOHNSON, Peter A., Interim Chief Information Officer, Monadnock Community Hospital, Peterborough, NH, p. A413

JOHNSON, Phillip, Vice President, Chief Human Resources Officer, St. Luke's Regional Medical Center, Boise, ID, p. A175

JOHNSON, R. Milton, President and Chief Executive Officer, HCA, Nashville, TN, p. B60

JOHNSON, Ralph
Chief Information Officer, Franklin Memorial Hospital, Farmington, ME, p. A293
Chief Information Officer, Southern Maine Health Care – Biddeford Medical Center, Biddeford, ME, p. A292

JOHNSON, Ric, Associate Administrator, Mountain View Hospital, Payson, UT, p. A662

JOHNSON, Richard, M.D. Chief of Medical Staff, CHI St. Alexius Health Devils Lake Hospital, Devils Lake, ND, p. A478

JOHNSON, Richard F., Senior Vice President and Chief Information Officer, Indiana University Health University Hospital, Indianapolis, IN, p. A214

JOHNSON, Rick, Chief Executive Officer, HEALTHSOUTH Cane Creek Rehabilitation Hospital, Martin, TN, p. A587

JOHNSON, Robb, Director Operations, Hamilton Center, Terre Haute, IN, p. A222

JOHNSON, Roger, M.D. Chief of Staff, Cheyenne Veterans Affairs Medical Center, Cheyenne, WY, p. A722

JOHNSON, Ronald J., Director, Mann–Grandstaff Veterans Affairs Medical Center, Spokane, WA, p. A691

JOHNSON, Ronald W., FACHE, President and Chief Executive Officer, Shore Medical Center, Somers Point, NJ, p. A423

JOHNSON, Russell W., President and Chief Executive Officer, Lawrence Memorial Hospital, Lawrence, KS, p. A247

JOHNSON, Ryan K., Vice President Finance, Spectrum Health United Hospital, Greenville, MI, p. A325

JOHNSON, Sam, M.D. Chief Medical Officer, Northeast Georgia Medical Center, Gainesville, GA, p. A160

JOHNSON, Samuel, Chief Executive Officer, Wiregrass Medical Center, Geneva, AL, p. A20

JOHNSON, Scott H., Vice President Finance and Chief Financial Officer, St. Luke's Hospital, Chesterfield, MO, p. A369

JOHNSON, Sean, Chief Executive Officer, Baptist Medical Center Yazoo, Yazoo City, MS, p. A366

JOHNSON, Sharon, Director Health Information Management, Western State Hospital, Staunton, VA, p. A679

JOHNSON, Sheryl, Chief Information Officer, SwedishAmerican – A Division of UW Health, Rockford, IL, p. A202

JOHNSON, Shrea, Director Human Resources, Alliance Health Center, Meridian, MS, p. A362

JOHNSON, Steven, Interim Chief Executive Officer, Oconee Regional Medical Center, Milledgeville, GA, p. A163

JOHNSON, Steven P., Ph.D., President and Chief Executive Officer, Health First, Inc., Rockledge, FL, p. B65

JOHNSON, Steven P., FACHE, President and Chief Executive Officer, Susquehanna Health System, Williamsport, PA, p. B130

JOHNSON, Sy
Executive Vice President, Chief Operating Officer, Renown Regional Medical Center, Reno, NV, p. A408
Executive Vice President, Chief Operating Officer, Renown South Meadows Medical Center, Reno, NV, p. A408

JOHNSON, Talicia, Director Human Resources, Brentwood Hospital, Shreveport, LA, p. A287

JOHNSON, Tamatha, Director Human Resources, Stringfellow Memorial Hospital, Anniston, AL, p. A15

JOHNSON, Tammy Dawn, Director Human Resources, Wilson N. Jones Regional Medical Center, Sherman, TX, p. A649

JOHNSON, Thomas, Director Information Systems, Penn Highlands Brookville, Brookville, PA, p. A534

JOHNSON, Timothy, President and Chief Executive Officer, Eaton Rapids Medical Center, Eaton Rapids, MI, p. A323

JOHNSON, Timothy J., President and Chief Executive Officer, Mayo Clinic Health System – Franciscan Healthcare in La Crosse, La Crosse, WI, p. A708

JOHNSON, Todd, Chief Financial Officer, Longview Regional Medical Center, Longview, TX, p. A633

JOHNSON, Tom, Chief Human Resource Officer, Minneapolis Veterans Affairs Health Care System, Minneapolis, MN, p. A346

JOHNSON, Tracie, Director Information Services, Missouri Baptist Medical Center, Saint Louis, MO, p. A380

JOHNSON, RN, Trudy, R.N. Chief Nursing Officer, Santa Clara Valley Medical Center, San Jose, CA, p. A91

JOHNSON, Vern, Director Information Technology, Sullivan County Memorial Hospital, Milan, MO, p. A376

JOHNSON, Vernon, Administrator, Dale Medical Center, Ozark, AL, p. A24

JOHNSON, Victoria, R.N. Nursing Director of Surgical and Medical Services, The HealthCenter, Kalispell, MT, p. A389

JOHNSON, Wade C., FACHE, Chief Executive Officer, Valor Health, Emmett, ID, p. A176

JOHNSON, William, Director Information Systems, Shoals Hospital, Muscle Shoals, AL, p. A24

JOHNSON, William F., Chief Medical Officer, Tennova Healthcare – Cleveland, Cleveland, TN, p. A581

JOHNSON–HATCHER, Dawn, Chief Financial Officer, Lake Area Medical Center, Lake Charles, LA, p. A281

JOHNSON–MEKOTA, Judith, Director, Iowa City Veterans Affairs Health Care System, Iowa City, IA, p. A232

JOHNSON–THREAT, Yvette, Vice President Medical Affairs, MedStar Southern Maryland Hospital Center, Clinton, MD, p. A300

JOHNSRUD, Carolyn, Manager Human Resources, Missouri River Medical Center, Fort Benton, MT, p. A387

JOHNSRUD, Jill, Director of Nursing, Essentia Health–Graceville, Graceville, MN, p. A343

JOHNSTON, Christopher, Interim Chief Administrative Officer, PeaceHealth United General Medical Center, Sedro–Woolley, WA, p. A690

JOHNSTON, Diann, R.N. Vice President of Patient Care Services, Monmouth Medical Center, Long Branch Campus, Long Branch, NJ, p. A419

JOHNSTON, Don, Chief Information Officer, San Joaquin General Hospital, French Camp, CA, p. A63

JOHNSTON, Jeffrey A., President, Mercy Hospital St. Louis, Saint Louis, MO, p. A380

JOHNSTON, John, Chief Medical Officer, Specialty Hospital of Meridian, Meridian, MS, p. A362

JOHNSTON, Lori, Chief Information Officer, ProMedica Flower Hospital, Sylvania, OH, p. A503

JOHNSTON, Michael V., M.D. Chief Medical Officer and Senior Vice President Medical Programs, Kennedy Krieger Institute, Baltimore, MD, p. A296

JOHNSTON, Mike, Director Facilities Operations, Union General Hospital, Blairsville, GA, p. A154

JOHNSTON, Monte, Manager Human Resources, Coquille Valley Hospital, Coquille, OR, p. A525

JOHNSTON, Patricia, Vice President Information Services, Texas Health Harris Methodist Hospital Azle, Azle, TX, p. A600

JOHNSTON, Phyllis M., Vice President, Catawba Valley Medical Center, Hickory, NC, p. A467

JOHNSTON, Scott, Chief of Staff, Onslow Memorial Hospital, Jacksonville, NC, p. A468

JOHNSTON, Susan, Vice President Human Resources, East Alabama Medical Center, Opelika, AL, p. A24

JOHNSTON, Susanne, Manager Human Resources, Lincoln County Medical Center, Ruidoso, NM, p. A431

JOHNSTON, Word, Medical Director, Covington County Hospital, Collins, MS, p. A357

JOHNSTONE, Jennifer, Chief Clinical Officer, Kindred Hospital Rome, Rome, GA, p. A165

JOHRENDT, JT, Information Technology Network Specialist, Edgerton Hospital and Health Services, Edgerton, WI, p. A705

JOICE, Jason, M.D. Chief Medical Staff, AllianceHealth Pryor, Pryor, OK, p. A519

JOLLEY, Colby, D.O. Acting Chief of Staff, Haxtun Hospital District, Haxtun, CO, p. A107

JOLLEY, Sherry, Chief Clinical Officer, Lawrence Medical Center, Moulton, AL, p. A24

JOLLY, Gaye, FACHE, President/Chief Administrative Officer, Roane Medical Center, Harriman, TN, p. A583

JONAS, Stanley W., Chief Executive Officer, Alliance Community Hospital, Alliance, OH, p. A483

JONASON, Anna, Ph.D. Chief Nursing Officer, Colleton Medical Center, Walterboro, SC, p. A570

JONES, Adrienne, Director Human Resources, Creedmoor Psychiatric Center,, NY, p. A444

JONES, Alesia, Chief Human Resources Officer, University of Alabama Hospital, Birmingham, AL, p. A17

JONES, Allan, Controller, HEALTHSOUTH Rehabilitation Hospital of Jonesboro, Jonesboro, AR, p. A48

JONES, Amelia, Chief Operating Officer and Acting Chief Executive Officer, Oakland Regional Hospital, Southfield, MI, p. A334

JONES, Austin, CP
  Chief Financial Officer, Physicians Surgical Hospital – Panhandle Campus, Amarillo, TX, p. A596
  Chief Financial Officer, Physicians Surgical Hospital – Quail Creek, Amarillo, TX, p. A596

JONES, B. Konard, President, Hospital Division, NorthBay Medical Center, Fairfield, CA, p. A62

JONES, Beth, Chief Operating Officer, Reeves Memorial Medical Center, Bernice, LA, p. A273

JONES, Bill, Chief Executive Officer, Jackson County Hospital District, Edna, TX, p. A614

JONES, Brain, Director of Information Technology, Valley Hospital, Spokane Valley, WA, p. A691

JONES, Carol, Controller and Manager Business Office, Coryell Memorial Hospital, Gatesville, TX, p. A620

JONES, Carol S., MSN Interim Chief Nursing Officer, Morristown Medical Center, Morristown, NJ, p. A419

JONES, Carolyn, R.N. Chief Nursing Officer, Box Butte General Hospital, Alliance, NE, p. A393

JONES, Catherine, Chief Nursing Officer, Ancora Psychiatric Hospital, Hammonton, NJ, p. A417

JONES, Charlene, Chief Nursing Officer, Peterson Healthcare and Rehabilitation Hospital, Wheeling, WV, p. A701

JONES, Cheryl L., Vice President Human Resources and Organizational Development, BSA Hospital, LLC, Amarillo, TX, p. A596

JONES, Chris, Chief Executive Officer, Vibra Hospital of Northern California, Redding, CA, p. A84

JONES, Connie, Director Human Resources, Community Behavioral Health Hospital – Rochester, Rochester, MN, p. A349

JONES, Dale, Administrator, Noland Hospital Montgomery, Montgomery, AL, p. A23

JONES, Dana, R.N. Chief Nursing Officer, Springhill Medical Center, Springhill, LA, p. A288

JONES Jr., Danny L., FACHE, Chief Executive Officer, Abrazo Central Campus, Phoenix, AZ, p. A35

JONES, David, Chief Financial Officer, Alexian Brothers Behavioral Health Hospital, Hoffman Estates, IL, p. A193

JONES, David, M.D. Chief Medical Officer, Beauregard Memorial Hospital, De Ridder, LA, p. A276

JONES, David
  Chief Nursing Officer, HEALTHSOUTH Rehabilitation Hospital of Arlington, Arlington, TX, p. A597
  Service Chief, Riverside Shore Memorial Hospital, Nassawadox, VA, p. A674

JONES, David C., Administrator, North Caddo Medical Center, Vivian, LA, p. A289

JONES, Deborah
  Interim Chief Nursing Officer, Norwegian American Hospital, Chicago, IL, p. A185
  Controller, SCA Houston Hospital for Specialized Surgery, Houston, TX, p. A626

JONES, Derrick, Chief Executive Officer, Lovelace Rehabilitation Hospital, Albuquerque, NM, p. A427

JONES, Donald J., FACHE, Administrator, Fayette Medical Center, Fayette, AL, p. A20

JONES, Douglas A., Chief Operating Officer, Forrest General Hospital, Hattiesburg, MS, p. A359

JONES, Elaine, M.D. President Medical Staff, Roger Williams Medical Center, Providence, RI, p. A561

JONES, Evan, Executive Vice President and Chief Financial Officer, Lakeland Regional Health, Lakeland, FL, p. A134

JONES, Evelyn, R.N. Vice President Nursing Services, St. Bernard Hospital and Health Care Center, Chicago, IL, p. A187

JONES, Glen M., FACHE, Administrator, Red Bay Hospital, Red Bay, AL, p. A25

JONES, Greg, Chief Financial Officer, Wayne Memorial Hospital, Jesup, GA, p. A161

JONES, Holly A., Administrative Director Nursing Services, Illini Community Hospital, Pittsfield, IL, p. A201

JONES, Jacqueline V., Chief Civilian Personnel Branch, Reynolds Army Community Hospital, Fort Sill, OK, p. A512

JONES, Jason L., R.N. Chief Nursing Officer, Fannin Regional Hospital, Blue Ridge, GA, p. A154

JONES, Jeff, Director Human Resources, Greene Memorial Hospital, Xenia, OH, p. A506

JONES, Jeffrey
  Chief Financial Officer, Moses H. Cone Memorial Hospital, Greensboro, NC, p. A466
  Chief of Staff, Whitman Hospital and Medical Center, Colfax, WA, p. A683

JONES, Jeremy A., Administrator, Mercy Hospital Healdton, Healdton, OK, p. A512

JONES, John H., Chief of Staff, South Sunflower County Hospital, Indianola, MS, p. A359

JONES, Joshua, Director Human Resources, Evanston Regional Hospital, Evanston, WY, p. A722

JONES, Joyce, Director Human Resources, HEALTHSOUTH Rehabilitation Hospital, Kingsport, TN, p. A585

JONES, Judy, Chief Clinical Officer, Arkansas Surgical Hospital, North Little Rock, AR, p. A50

JONES, Julie L., Chief Nursing Officer, Community Hospital–Fairfax, Fairfax, MO, p. A371

JONES, Karen, Administrative Director Human Resources, Marion General Hospital, Marion, IN, p. A218

JONES, Karin, Chief Nursing Officer, HEALTHSOUTH Rehabilitation Hospital of Alexandria, Alexandria, LA, p. A271

JONES, Karol, Chief Nursing Officer, Huntsville Hospital, Huntsville, AL, p. A21

JONES, Kathy, Director Human Resources, Jackson Medical Center, Jackson, AL, p. A22

JONES, Ken M., Chief Operating Officer, UCSF Medical Center, San Francisco, CA, p. A91

JONES, Kenneth, Chief Executive Officer, St. Joseph Hospital, Fort Wayne, IN, p. A211

JONES, Kimberly, Coordinator Human Resources, Spine Hospital of Louisiana (formally the NeuroMedical Center Surgical Hospital), Baton Rouge, LA, p. A273

JONES, Kyle, Controller, Marshall Medical Center, Lewisburg, TN, p. A587

JONES, Lance, Chief Executive Officer, Coliseum Medical Centers, Macon, GA, p. A162

JONES, Liston, M.D. Medical Director, Springhill Memorial Hospital, Mobile, AL, p. A22

JONES, Lorrie Rickman, Ph.D., Director, Division of Mental Health, Department of Human Services, Springfield, IL, p. B51

JONES, Louis, Director Management Information Systems, Heart of Florida Regional Medical Center, Davenport, FL, p. A126

JONES, M. Steven
  President, UH Portage Medical Center, Ravenna, OH, p. A501
  President, University Hospitals Conneaut Medical Center, Conneaut, OH, p. A492
  President, University Hospitals Geauga Medical Center, Chardon, OH, p. A486
  President, University Hospitals Geauga Medical Center, Chardon, OH, p. A486
  President, University Hospitals Geneva Medical Center, Geneva, OH, p. A495

JONES, Mark, Chief Financial Officer, Hill Country Memorial Hospital, Fredericksburg, TX, p. A619

JONES, Mark A., President, Orlando Regional Medical Center, Orlando, FL, p. A140

JONES, Marsha, R.N. Director Nursing, Baptist Medical Center Yazoo, Yazoo City, MS, p. A366

JONES, Marshall
  Senior Vice President Human Resources, Maricopa Integrated Health System, Phoenix, AZ, p. A36
  Vice President Human Resources, Yuma Regional Medical Center, Yuma, AZ, p. A42

JONES, Mary Jane, R.N. Vice President Nursing Operations, Northridge Hospital Medical Center,, CA, p. A73

JONES, Matthew, Senior Director Support Services and Facilities, The University of Vermont Health Network – Alice Hyde Medical Center, Malone, NY, p. A442

JONES, Maud, Manager Medical Records, TOPS Surgical Specialty Hospital, Houston, TX, p. A627

JONES, MaxAnne, Director Human Resources, Rock Prairie Behavioral Health, College Station, TX, p. A606

JONES, Melinda, R.N. Chief Nursing Officer, Morehouse General Hospital, Bastrop, LA, p. A272

JONES, Mike, Executive Director, Marshall Medical Center, Placerville, CA, p. A83

JONES, Mitchell, Director Information Technology, Little River Memorial Hospital, Ashdown, AR, p. A43

JONES, Pam, MSN Associate Hospital Director and Chief Nursing Officer, Vanderbilt University Medical Center, Nashville, TN, p. A591

JONES, Pamela K., Executive Director of Finance, Baptist Health Corbin, Corbin, KY, p. A258

JONES, Pat, Director Information Systems, Merit Health River Oaks, Flowood, MS, p. A357

JONES, Patrice I., R.N. Vice President and Chief Nursing Officer, UF Health Jacksonville, Jacksonville, FL, p. A132

JONES, Percy E., M.D. Chief of Staff, Kindred Hospital–Greensboro, Greensboro, NC, p. A466

JONES, Philip L., Chief Financial Officer, Curahealth Nashville, Nashville, TN, p. A590

JONES, Phyllis, Chief Human Resources, Wm. Jennings Bryan Dorn Veterans Affairs Medical Center, Columbia, SC, p. A564

JONES, Rachel, Chief Financial Officer, Watsonville Community Hospital, Watsonville, CA, p. A99

JONES, Ransom, Information Technology Director, Covington County Hospital, Collins, MS, p. A357

JONES, Reginald
  Interim President and Chief Executive Officer, Fort Washington Medical Center, Oxen Hill, MD, p. A302
  Business Manager, Georgia Regional Hospital at Atlanta, Decatur, GA, p. A158

JONES, Rex, Chief Executive Officer, Bradley County Medical Center, Warren, AR, p. A53

JONES, Richard, M.D. Medical Director, HEALTHSOUTH Rehabilitation Hospital North Texas, Richardson, TX, p. A643

JONES, Richard W., Chief Financial Officer, Reading Hospital, West Reading, PA, p. A557

JONES, Rita A., Chief Executive Officer, Dundy County Hospital, Benkelman, NE, p. A394

JONES, Rob, Director of Nursing and Operations, Physicians' Medical Center, New Albany, IN, p. A219

JONES, Robert, Director Management Information Systems, St. Joseph Mercy Oakland, Pontiac, MI, p. A332

JONES, Roger, M.D. Interim Chief of Staff, Tennessee Valley Healthcare System, Nashville, TN, p. A591

JONES, Ruth, Chief Clinical Officer, Regency Hospital of Northwest Arkansas – Springdale, Springdale, AR, p. A52

JONES, Ruth Ann, Ed.D
  Senior Vice President, Chief Nursing Officer, University of Maryland Shore Medical Center at Chestertown, Chestertown, MD, p. A299
  Senior Vice President, Chief Nursing Officer, University of Maryland Shore Medical Center at Easton, Easton, MD, p. A300

JONES, Sarah, Chief Nurse Executive, Metropolitan St. Louis Psychiatric Center, Saint Louis, MO, p. A380

JONES, Scott, President and Chief Executive Officer, Midwestern Regional Medical Center, Zion, IL, p. A205

JONES, Sean, Director Human Resources, Merit Health Central, Jackson, MS, p. A360

JONES, Shannon, M.D. Medical Director and Attending Psychiatrist, Evansville Psychiatric Children Center, Evansville, IN, p. A210

JONES, Sharon, Chief Financial Officer, Evergreen Medical Center, Evergreen, AL, p. A19

JONES, Sherry J., Chief Financial Officer, Crestwood Medical Center, Huntsville, AL, p. A21

JONES, Staci, R.N. Chief Nursing Officer, Methodist McKinney Hospital, McKinney, TX, p. A636

JONES, Stacy, Chief Nursing Officer, HEALTHSOUTH MountainView Regional Rehabilitation Hospital, Morgantown, WV, p. A698

JONES, Stephen K., M.D. Vice President Medical Staff Affairs, St. Rose Dominican Hospitals – Rose de Lima Campus, Henderson, NV, p. A405

JONES Jr., Stephen K., FACHE, Chief Executive Officer, Clear Lake Regional Medical Center, Webster, TX, p. A656

JONES, Steven K., M.D. Medical Director, Advocate Eureka Hospital, Eureka, IL, p. A189

JONES, Tammie R., R.N. Chief Nursing Officer, St. Mary Medical Center, Hobart, IN, p. A213

JONES, Theresa, Manager Human Resources, St. Luke Community Healthcare, Ronan, MT, p. A390

JONES, Tim, Chief Executive Officer, Heart of Texas Memorial Hospital, Brady, TX, p. A603

JONES, Timothy P., Chief Operating Officer, Concord Hospital, Concord, NH, p. A410

JONES, Todd, President, Baptist Health Richmond, Richmond, KY, p. A268

JONES, Tom, Chief Information Officer, Fitzgibbon Hospital, Marshall, MO, p. A376

JONES, Tracey, Director Human Resources, Jackson Park Hospital and Medical Center, Chicago, IL, p. A184

JONES, Traci
Chief Financial Officer, University of South Alabama Children's and Women's Hospital, Mobile, AL, p. A23
Chief Financial Officer, University of South Alabama Medical Center, Mobile, AL, p. A23

JONES, Trennis, Senior Vice President and Chief Administrative Officer, Seton Northwest Hospital, Austin, TX, p. A599

JONES, Vernita, Site Manager, PHS Santa Fe Indian Hospital, Santa Fe, NM, p. A431

JONES, Wendy, Interim Chief Financial Officer, Blue Hill Memorial Hospital, Blue Hill, ME, p. A292

JONES, II, William, M.D. Chief Medical Officer, Baylor Scott & White Medical Center – White Rock, Dallas, TX, p. A609

JONES, Yameeka, Chief Executive Officer, Vibra Hospital of San Diego, San Diego, CA, p. A89

JONES, Yvette A., Health Information Management Director, Putnam Community Medical Center, Palatka, FL, p. A141

JONES MONNETT, Anna, MS Associate Director Patient Care Services, Dayton Veterans Affairs Medical Center, Dayton, OH, p. A492

JONES–BROWNING, Debbie, Vice President Operations and Physician Services and Chief Operating Officer, Rush Memorial Hospital, Rushville, IN, p. A221

JONES–FAIRBANKS, Trish, R.N. Chief Operating Officer, Linden Oaks Hospital, Naperville, IL, p. A198

JONGSMA, Michael, R.N. Chief Nursing Officer, Providence Little Company of Mary Medical Center – Torrance, Torrance, CA, p. A96

JONTZ, Doug, Senior Vice President Human Resources, Mercy Medical Center–Cedar Rapids, Cedar Rapids, IA, p. A226

JORDAN, Amy, Chief Nursing Officer/Vice President of Nursing, Gordon Hospital, Calhoun, GA, p. A155

JORDAN, Andrew, M.D. Chief of Staff, Tennova Healthcare–Lebanon, Lebanon, TN, p. A586

JORDAN, Bobby, Chief Executive Officer, Jackson Parish Hospital, Jonesboro, LA, p. A279

JORDAN, Gary W., FACHE, Chief Executive Officer, Wright Memorial Hospital, Trenton, MO, p. A383

JORDAN, Jill, Chief Executive Officer, Healthsouth Rehabilitation Hospital of Altamonte Springs, Altamonte Springs, FL, p. A123

JORDAN, Ken, Chief Financial Officer, Fountain Valley Regional Hospital and Medical Center, Fountain Valley, CA, p. A62

JORDAN, Lori, Executive Director, Griffin Memorial Hospital, Norman, OK, p. A515

JORDAN, Marie Kim, R.N
Senior Vice President and Chief Nursing Officer, Lehigh Valley Hospital, Allentown, PA, p. A532
Senior Vice President, Chief Nursing Officer, Lehigh Valley Hospital–Muhlenberg, Bethlehem, PA, p. A533

JORDAN, Michelle J., Administrator, Lewis and Clark Specialty Hospital, Yankton, SD, p. A578

JORDAN, Quincy, M.D. Chief of Staff, Flint River Community Hospital, Montezuma, GA, p. A163

JORDAN, Rhonda R., Chief Human Resources Officer, Virtua Marlton, Marlton, NJ, p. A419

JORDAN, Terry, M.D. Chief of Staff, Alliance Health Center, Meridian, MS, p. A362

JORDAN, Traci S., MS Chief Nursing Officer, University Health Conway, Monroe, LA, p. A284

JORDEN BEST, Rosemary, Director Human Resources, Tyrone Hospital, Tyrone, PA, p. A556

JORDEN–ELLIS, Danielle, Director, Bon Secours Baltimore Health System, Baltimore, MD, p. A296

JORE, Bernie, Chief Nursing Officer, St. Mary's of Michigan, Saginaw, MI, p. A333

JOSEHART, Carl E.
Chief Executive Officer, Memorial Hermann Rehabilitation Hospital – Katy, Katy, TX, p. A630
Chief Executive Officer, TIRR Memorial Hermann, Houston, TX, p. A627

JOSEPH, Elliot T., President and Chief Executive Officer, Hartford HealthCare, Hartford, CT, p. B59

JOSEPH, James, M.D. President Medical Staff, Geisinger–Bloomsburg Hospital, Bloomsburg, PA, p. A533

JOSEPH, Jason, Vice President, Information Services, Spectrum Health – Butterworth Hospital, Grand Rapids, MI, p. A325

JOSEPH–TAYLOR, Terri, Chief Human Resource Manager, Ochsner Medical Center – North Shore, Slidell, LA, p. A288

JOSEPHSON, Louis, Ph.D., President and Chief Executive Officer, Brattleboro Retreat, Brattleboro, VT, p. A665

JOSHI, Maulik, Executive Vice President, Integrated Care Delivery and Chief Operating Officer, Anne Arundel Medical Center, Annapolis, MD, p. A296

JOSHI, Nirmal, M.D. Senior Vice President Medical Affairs and Chief Medical Officer, Pinnacle Health System, Harrisburg, PA, p. A540

JOSLIN, Charlie, M.D. Chief of Staff, Ellinwood District Hospital, Ellinwood, KS, p. A242

JOSLIN, Tim A., President and Chief Executive Officer, Community Medical Centers, Fresno, CA, p. B40

JOSLYN, E. Allen, M.D. Chief Medical Officer, Bedford Memorial Hospital, Bedford, VA, p. A667

JOSLYN, J. Scott, Senior Vice President and Chief Information Officer, Saddleback Memorial Medical Center, Laguna Hills, CA, p. A68

JOUD, Mohammad A., M.D. Chief of Staff, Bayfront Health Brooksville, Brooksville, FL, p. A125

JOUDEH, Jalal, M.D
Chief of Staff, DeQuincy Memorial Hospital, DeQuincy, LA, p. A276
Chief Medical Officer, Specialty Rehabilitation Hospital of Coushatta, Coushatta, LA, p. A275

JOURDEN, Marti, FACHE Chief Quality Officer, St. Anthony Hospital, Oklahoma City, OK, p. A517

JOY, Michelle L., Chief Operating Officer, Carson Tahoe Health, Carson City, NV, p. A404

JOY, Mike, Administrator, Finance, Via Christi Hospital Pittsburg, Pittsburg, KS, p. A252

JOY, Jr., Roland Eugene, Vice President and Chief Nursing Officer, The Aroostook Medical Center, Presque Isle, ME, p. A295

JOY, Susan, Chief Nursing Officer, Hillside Rehabilitation Hospital, Warren, OH, p. A504

JOYAL, Shirley, Director Information Systems, Regional Medical Center of San Jose, San Jose, CA, p. A91

JOYCE, Allyson, Vice President Human Resources, Caro Community Hospital, Caro, MI, p. A320

JOYCE, Jodi S., R.N. Associate Vice Chancellor, Quality & Patient Safety, University of Illinois Hospital & Health Sciences System, Chicago, IL, p. A187

JOYCE, Maria, Chief Financial Officer, National Institutes of Health Clinical Center, Bethesda, MD, p. A299

JOYNER, Jeff, President, Aurelia Osborn Fox Memorial Hospital, Oneonta, NY, p. A452

JOYNER, Ken, Vice President of Employee Services, Bay Area Medical Center, Marinette, WI, p. A709

JOYNER, Thomas, Chief Financial Officer, Lakeside Behavioral Health System, Memphis, TN, p. A589

JUAREZ, Edward, M.D. Chief Medical Officer, Kindred Hospital El Paso, El Paso, TX, p. A615

JUAREZ, Elizabeth, M.D. Chief Medical Officer, Harlingen Medical Center, Harlingen, TX, p. A622

JUAREZ, Rose, Chief Civilian Personnel Branch, Brooke Army Medical Center, Fort Sam Houston, TX, p. A617

JUBAS, John, Vice President Finance, The Children's Institute of Pittsburgh, Pittsburgh, PA, p. A551

JUCHNOWICZ, Jean E., Director Human Resources, Merit Health Natchez, Natchez, MS, p. A363

JUDD, Martin H., Regional President and Chief Executive Officer, Presence Saints Mary & Elizabeth Medical Center, Chicago, IL, p. A186

JUDD, Russell V., Chief Executive Officer, Kern Medical Center, Bakersfield, CA, p. A56

JUDLIN, Karen Ann, Director Human Resources, St. Charles Parish Hospital, Luling, LA, p. A282

JUDYCKI–CREPEAULT, Christine, Chief Financial Officer, Adcare Hospital of Worcester, Worcester, MA, p. A316

JUENGER, Jacqueline, R.N. Chief Nursing Officer, HEALTHSOUTH Rehabilitation Hospital of Sarasota, Sarasota, FL, p. A145

JUHASZ, Robert S., D.O., President, South Pointe Hospital, Warrensville Heights, OH, p. A505

JUHL, Gregory, M.D. Medical Director, Norton Brownsboro Hospital, Louisville, KY, p. A265

JUHL, Stephanie, Administrator, Community Behavioral Health Hospital – Rochester, Rochester, MN, p. A349

JUHL, Valerie, Director of Health, Madelia Community Hospital, Madelia, MN, p. A345

JULE, Janet, Chief Nurse Executive, Kaiser Permanente Antioch Medical Center, Antioch, CA, p. A54

JULIAN, Bell, Associate Executive Director and Chief Financial Officer, James Cancer Hospital and Solove Research Institute, Columbus, OH, p. A490

JULIAN, Steve, M.D., President, Sentara Obici Hospital, Suffolk, VA, p. A679

JULIANA, Rich, Director Human Resources, Silver Hill Hospital, New Canaan, CT, p. A115

JUMP, Beth, Chief Information Officer, Logansport Memorial Hospital, Logansport, IN, p. A217

JUMPING EAGLE, Sara, Clinical Director, Standing Rock Service Unit, Fort Yates Hospital, Indian Health Service, DHHS, Fort Yates, ND, p. A479

JUNEAU, Cindy K., Chief Nursing Officer, Manger Quality and Risk, Avoyelles Hospital, Marksville, LA, p. A282

JUNEAU, James B., Chief Financial Officer, Opelousas General Health System, Opelousas, LA, p. A286

JUNEAU, Tina Louise, Director Human Resources, Bunkie General Hospital, Bunkie, LA, p. A274

JUNG, Darra, Director of Nursing, Union General Hospital, Farmerville, LA, p. A276

JUNG, Linnet, Chief Nursing Officer, North Suburban Medical Center, Thornton, CO, p. A111

JUNGE, Tamara, Chief Executive Officer, Northwest Ohio Psychiatric Hospital, Toledo, OH, p. A504

JUNGELS, Trisha, R.N. Chief Nursing Officer and Vice President Clinical Services, Jamestown Regional Medical Center, Jamestown, ND, p. A480

JUNGWIRTH, Scott, Chief Human Resources Officer, Providence Alaska Medical Center, Anchorage, AK, p. A28

JUNIS, Jennifer, R.N., President, OSF Saint Paul Medical Center, Mendota, IL, p. A196

JUNKINS, Curt M., Chief Operating Officer, Cedar Park Regional Medical Center, Cedar Park, TX, p. A605

JUNO, Russell, M.D. Chief of Staff, St. Mark's Medical Center, La Grange, TX, p. A631

JURCZYK, John A., FACHE, Interim President, Good Samaritan Medical Center, Brockton, MA, p. A308

JUREK, Chuck, Interim Administrator and Chief Operating Officer, Specialty Hospital of Winnfield, Winnfield, LA, p. A289

JURGENS, Chad, Chief Executive Officer, Jefferson Community Health Center, Fairbury, NE, p. A395

JURIS, Susan V., President, University Hospitals Ahuja Medical Center, Beachwood, OH, p. A484

JURKUS, Patti
Chief Executive Officer, Bedford Memorial Hospital, Bedford, VA, p. A667
Director Human Resources, Carilion New River Valley Medical Center, Christiansburg, VA, p. A669

JURY, Tina M., MSN Executive Vice President Hospital Operations and Chief Nursing Officer, AnMed Health Medical Center, Anderson, SC, p. A562

JUST, Lisa
President, Aurora Lakeland Medical Center, Elkhorn, WI, p. A705
President, Aurora Memorial Hospital of Burlington, Burlington, WI, p. A703

JUST, Paula
Vice President Human Resources, Health First Cape Canaveral Hospital, Cocoa Beach, FL, p. A126
Chief Human Resources Officer, Health First Holmes Regional Medical Center, Melbourne, FL, p. A135
Chief Human Resources Officer, Health First Palm Bay Hospital, Palm Bay, FL, p. A141
Chief Human Resources Officer, Health First Viera Hospital, Melbourne, FL, p. A135

JUSTESEN, Scott, M.D. Chief of Staff, Castleview Hospital, Price, UT, p. A662

JUSTICE, Jay, Chief Human Resource Officer, Adena Medical Center, Chillicothe, OH, p. A486

JUSTICE, Kim, Vice President Planning and Operations, Atlantic General Hospital, Berlin, MD, p. A298

JUSTIN–TANNER, Karen, R.N. Chief Nursing Officer, Fairbanks Memorial Hospital, Fairbanks, AK, p. A29

JUSTINE, Patrick, Chief Financial Officer, United Hospital District, Blue Earth, MN, p. A339

JUSTUS, Jason, Vice President Finance and Chief Financial Officer, Pomerene Hospital, Millersburg, OH, p. A499

JUTILA, Kathy, M.D. Chief of Staff, Wheatland Memorial Healthcare, Harlowton, MT, p. A388

JYRKAS, Wade A., Director Computer Information Systems, Lake Region Healthcare, Fergus Falls, MN, p. A342

K

KA'AKIMAKA, Holly, Director Human Resources, Hilo Medical Center, Hilo, HI, p. A170

KARN, Deborah, Chief Executive Officer, Kindred Hospital South Philadelphia, Philadelphia, PA, p. A548

KARNER, Diana M., R.N
Chief Nursing Officer, California Pacific Medical Center, San Francisco, CA, p. A90
Chief Nursing Executive, St. Luke's Hospital, San Francisco, CA, p. A90

KARNS, Kris, FACHE, Chief Executive Officer, Acuity Hospital of South Texas, San Antonio, TX, p. A645

KAROW, Deborah, R.N
Vice President Patient Care Services, Howard Young Medical Center, Woodruff, WI, p. A720
Vice President Patient Care Services, Ministry Eagle River Memorial Hospital, Eagle River, WI, p. A704

KARP, Bob, M.D. Chief Medical Officer, United Hospital District, Blue Earth, MN, p. A339

KARPF, Michael, M.D., Executive Vice President of Health Affairs, University of Kentucky Albert B. Chandler Hospital, Lexington, KY, p. A263

KARSOS, Felicia, R.N., President and Chief Executive Officer, Meadowlands Hospital Medical Center, Secaucus, NJ, p. A423

KARSTEN, Margo, Ph.D
Interim Chief Executive Officer, Banner Fort Collins Medical Center, Fort Collins, CO, p. A105
Interim Chief Executive Officer, McKee Medical Center, Loveland, CO, p. A109
Interim Chief Executive Officer, North Colorado Medical Center, Greeley, CO, p. A106

KARSTEN, Paul H., Vice President Finance and Chief Financial Officer, Pine Rest Christian Mental Health Services, Grand Rapids, MI, p. A325

KASABIAN, Carolyn, Chief Financial Officer, St. Mary's Regional Medical Center, Lewiston, ME, p. A293

KASIRYE, Yusuf, M.D. Chief of Staff, Flambeau Hospital, Park Falls, WI, p. A714

KASITZ, Todd, Vice President Finance, Newton Medical Center, Newton, KS, p. A250

KASMAN, Glenn
President and Market Leader, MultiCare Auburn Medical Center, Auburn, WA, p. A682
President and Market Leader, MultiCare Good Samaritan Hospital, Puyallup, WA, p. A688

KASNIC, Tracey A.
Senior Vice President Inpatient and Chief Nursing Officer, Confluence Health/Central Washington Hospital, Wenatchee, WA, p. A693
Chief Nursing Officer, Confluence Health/Wenatchee Valley Hospital, Wenatchee, WA, p. A693

KASPER, Katie, Chief Clinical Officer, UH Avon Rehabilitation Hospital, Avon, OH, p. A484

KASPER, Yobi, Chief Information Officer, Advanced Diagnostics Hospital, Houston, TX, p. A623

KASPERSKI, Joyce, Director Nursing, St. John River District Hospital, East China, MI, p. A323

KASS, Andrew J A, M.D. Assistant Superintendent, Albert J. Solnit Psychiatric Center – South Campus, Middletown, CT, p. A115

KASSAB, Jerry, President and Chief Executive Officer, Aspire Health Partners, Orlando, FL, p. A140

KASSAHN, Kristine, Chief Executive Officer, Fresno Surgical Hospital, Fresno, CA, p. A63

KASSER, Michael
Chief Financial Officer, Herrin Hospital, Herrin, IL, p. A192
Vice President Chief Financial Officer and Treasurer, Memorial Hospital of Carbondale, Carbondale, IL, p. A182

KASSIS, Charles, President, Mercy Medical Center Merced, Merced, CA, p. A76

KASSIS, Maher, M.D. Chief Medical Staff, Marcum and Wallace Memorial Hospital, Irvine, KY, p. A262

KASTANIS, John N., FACHE, President and Chief Executive Officer, University Hospital, Newark, NJ, p. A421

KATES, Josh, Information Technology Analyst, Andrew McFarland Mental Health Center, Springfield, IL, p. A203

KATES, Kenneth P., Chief Executive Officer, University of Iowa Hospitals and Clinics, Iowa City, IA, p. A232

KATHRINS, Richard J., Ph.D., President and Chief Executive Officer, Bacharach Institute for Rehabilitation, Pomona, NJ, p. A422

KATIGBAK, Michael, Chief Financial Officer, Sage Memorial Hospital, Ganado, AZ, p. A32

KATNENI, Jitendra P., M.D. Medical Director, Select Specialty Hospital–Flint, Flint, MI, p. A323

KATO, Laura
Vice President of Human Resources, San Antonio Regional Hospital, Upland, CA, p. A97
Vice President Human Resources, St. Francis Medical Center, Lynwood, CA, p. A75

KATSCHKE, Jr., R. William, M.D. Medical Director, Grover C. Dils Medical Center, Caliente, NV, p. A404

KATSIANIS, John, Senior Vice President and Chief Financial Officer, DeKalb Medical at North Decatur, Decatur, GA, p. A158

KATZ, Bonnie B., Vice President, Business Development and Support Operations, Sheppard Pratt Health System, Baltimore, MD, p. A297

KATZ, Jeffrey, M.D. Chief Medical Officer, Memorial Hermann – Texas Medical Center, Houston, TX, p. A625

KATZ, Michelle, Director Human Resources, HEALTHSOUTH Nittany Valley Rehabilitation Hospital, Pleasant Gap, PA, p. A552

KATZ, Mitchell H., M.D., Director, Los Angeles County–Department of Health Services, Los Angeles, CA, p. B84

KATZ, Richard, M.D. Vice President Medical Affairs, Mt. Washington Pediatric Hospital, Baltimore, MD, p. A297

KATZ, Robert, M.D. Vice President Clinical Affairs, University of New Mexico Hospitals, Albuquerque, NM, p. A428

KATZ, Yair
Chief Financial Officer, Community Hospital Long Beach, Long Beach, CA, p. A69
Chief Financial Officer, Long Beach Memorial Medical Center, Long Beach, CA, p. A69
Chief Financial Officer, Miller Children's & Women's Hospital Long Beach, Long Beach, CA, p. A70

KAUFFMAN, Angie, MSN, Chief Executive Officer, Westside Surgical Hospital, Houston, TX, p. A627

KAUFMAN, Cheryl
Director Health Information Management, Bayfront Health Dade City, Dade City, FL, p. A126
Information Technology Technician, Coteau des Prairies Hospital, Sisseton, SD, p. A576

KAUFMAN, Dan, Director Information Services, Paulding County Hospital, Paulding, OH, p. A501

KAUFMAN, Irvin A., M.D. Chief Medical Officer, Rady Children's Hospital – San Diego, San Diego, CA, p. A88

KAUFMAN, Robert
Director Financial Services, Central State Hospital, Petersburg, VA, p. A676
Fiscal Officer, Hiram W. Davis Medical Center, Petersburg, VA, p. A676

KAUFMAN, Ronald L., M.D. Chief Medical Officer, Lakewood Regional Medical Center, Lakewood, CA, p. A68

KAUPA, Michael, Executive Vice President and Chief Operating Officer, Park Nicollet Methodist Hospital, Saint Louis Park, MN, p. A350

KAUPAS, Bill, Chief Executive Officer, Post Acute/Warm Springs Rehabilitation Hospital of Allen, Allen, TX, p. A595

KAUTZ, Terri, Manager Human Resources, Weiser Memorial Hospital, Weiser, ID, p. A179

KAUZLARICH, Sidney A., M.D. Medical Director, Douglas County Community Mental Health Center, Omaha, NE, p. A400

KAVALIER, MaryJo, Administrator, Sartori Memorial Hospital, Cedar Falls, IA, p. A226

KAVANAGH, Darina, R.N. Chief Nursing Officer, Good Samaritan Hospital, San Jose, CA, p. A91

KAVANAGH, Sean, Director Information Technology, Pondera Medical Center, Conrad, MT, p. A386

KAVANAUGH, Paul B., President and Chief Executive Officer, Community Care Hospital, New Orleans, LA, p. A284

KAVANAUGH, Samantha, Chief Financial Officer, Riverview Psychiatric Center, Augusta, ME, p. A291

KAVTARADZE, David, M.D. Chief of Staff, Crisp Regional Hospital, Cordele, GA, p. A157

KAY, Kirk, Chief Financial Officer, Veterans Affairs Nebraska–Western Iowa Health Care System, Omaha, NE, p. A401

KAY, Nellie, Chief Executive Officer, Woodlands Specialty Hospital, The Woodlands, TX, p. A653

KAY, Robert W., Senior Vice President and Chief Financial Officer, Memorial Medical Center, Springfield, IL, p. A203

KAY–GARCIA, Lisa, Chief Information Officer, Kearny County Hospital, Lakin, KS, p. A247

KAYE, Jessie, Chief Executive Officer, Prairie View, Newton, KS, p. A250

KAYGA, Alicia R., R.N. Chief Nursing Officer, Brownwood Regional Medical Center, Brownwood, TX, p. A604

KAYSER, Sonya J., Human Resources Officer, Avera Marshall Regional Medical Center, Marshall, MN, p. A346

KAZA, Sunil, M.D
President Medical Staff, TriStar Skyline Madison Campus, Madison, TN, p. A587
President Medical Staff, TriStar Skyline Medical Center, Nashville, TN, p. A591

KAZMIERCZAK, Sara Marie, R.N. Director of Nursing, North Valley Health Center, Warren, MN, p. A353

KAZMIERCZAK, Stanley, Controller, Presence Saint Joseph Hospital, Chicago, IL, p. A185

KEANE, Dennis M., Vice President Finance and Chief Financial Officer, St. John's Riverside Hospital, Yonkers, NY, p. A459

KEANE, Fran, Vice President Human Resources, CentraState Healthcare System, Freehold, NJ, p. A417

KEANE, Merry Ann, Chief Administrative Officer, PeaceHealth Peace Island Medical Center, Friday Harbor, WA, p. A685

KEANE, Valerie E., FACHE Vice President Operations, Sentara Northern Virginia Medical Center, Woodbridge, VA, p. A680

KEARNEY, Karen
Vice President Inpatient Rehabilitation Services, Allied Services Rehabilitation Hospital, Scranton, PA, p. A554
Vice President Inpatient Rehabilitation Services, John Heinz Institute of Rehabilitation Medicine, Wilkes–Barre, PA, p. A558

KEARNEY, Lynn, Vice President, Nursing, Robert Wood Johnson University Hospital Somerset, Somerville, NJ, p. A423

KEARNEY, M. Clark, Vice President Human Resources, Saint Mary's Hospital, Waterbury, CT, p. A117

KEARNS, Debbie
Chief Executive Officer, Community Hospital, Oklahoma City, OK, p. A516
Chief Executive Officer, Northwest Surgical Hospital, Oklahoma City, OK, p. A516

KEARNS, Donald, M.D., President and Chief Executive Officer, Rady Children's Hospital – San Diego, San Diego, CA, p. A88

KEARNS, Peggy W., FACHE, Executive Director, Veterans Affairs Southern Nevada Healthcare System, North Las Vegas, NV, p. A407

KEATING, Michael, President and Chief Executive Officer, Christ Hospital, Cincinnati, OH, p. A487

KEATING, Todd, Chief Financial Officer, The University of Vermont Health Network University of Vermont Medical Center, Burlington, VT, p. A665

KEATON, Tony, Director Information Systems, Roane General Hospital, Spencer, WV, p. A700

KEATON, William A., Chief Executive Officer, Baylor Medical Center at Frisco, Frisco, TX, p. A619

KECK, Paul, M.D., President and Chief Executive Officer, Lindner Center of HOPE, Mason, OH, p. A498

KEDDINGTON, Richard, Chief Executive Officer, Watertown Regional Medical Center, Watertown, WI, p. A718

KEE, Agnes, Financial Manager, Gallup Indian Medical Center, Gallup, NM, p. A429

KEE, Robert, Chief Information Officer, NYC Health + Hospitals / Coney Island, NY, p. A448

KEEF, Shaun, Chief Financial Officer, Central Peninsula Hospital, Soldotna, AK, p. A30

KEEFE, Dennis D., President and Chief Executive Officer, Care New England Health System, Providence, RI, p. B26

KEEFE, Eileen, Chief Nursing Officer, Parkland Medical Center, Derry, NH, p. A410

KEEFER, Russ, Chief Human Resources Officer, Trios Health, Kennewick, WA, p. A685

KEEGAN, Julie, Vice President Finance, Craig Hospital, Englewood, CO, p. A105

KEEGAN, Justin, Director Support Services, Avera Gregory Hospital, Gregory, SD, p. A574

KEEL, Barry L., Administration, North Mississippi Medical Center–West Point, West Point, MS, p. A366

KEEL, Deborah C., Chief Executive Officer, North Fulton Regional Hospital, Roswell, GA, p. A165

KEEL, Patricia, Senior Vice President and Chief Financial Officer, St. Jude Children's Research Hospital, Memphis, TN, p. A589

KEELAN, John E., Administrator and Chief Executive Officer, Brodstone Memorial Hospital, Superior, NE, p. A402

KEELE, Denyce, Administrative Assistant and Human Resources Coordinator, Black River Medical Center, Poplar Bluff, MO, p. A378

KEELE, Paula
Manager Information Systems, Presence Covenant Medical Center, Urbana, IL, p. A204
Manager Information Systems, Presence United Samaritans Medical Center, Danville, IL, p. A187

KEELER, Dave, Chief Financial Officer, Pipestone County Medical Center Avera, Pipestone, MN, p. A348

KEELER, Jason, Executive Vice President and Chief Operating Officer, University of Chicago Medical Center, Chicago, IL, p. A187

KEELER, Jean M., President and Chief Executive Officer, Grand View Health, Sellersville, PA, p. A554

KEELER, Karl
Chief Executive Officer, Saint Alphonsus Medical Center – Nampa, Nampa, ID, p. A177
Chief Executive Officer, Saint Alphonsus Medical Center – Ontario, Ontario, OR, p. A528

KEELEY, Brian E., President and Chief Executive Officer, Baptist Health South Florida, Coral Gables, FL, p. B20

KEELEY, Katherine, M.D. Chief of Staff, Sunrise Hospital and Medical Center, Las Vegas, NV, p. A407

KEELING, Kathy, Director of Nursing, Rehabilitation Hospital of Rhode Island, North Smithfield, RI, p. A560

KEELING, Kevin, Chief Financial Officer, St. Lucie Medical Center, Port St. Lucie, FL, p. A143

KEELING, Lynda, Director of Nursing, Chambers Memorial Hospital, Danville, AR, p. A44

KEELING, Terri, Vice President Information Systems, UPMC McKeesport, McKeesport, PA, p. A544

KEEN, Kris, Chief Information Officer, Cameron Memorial Community Hospital, Angola, IN, p. A206

KEEN, Michael, Senior Vice President and Chief Financial Officer, Grand View Health, Sellersville, PA, p. A554

KEEN, Scott R., Chief Executive Officer, HonorHealth Rehabilitation Hospital, Scottsdale, AZ, p. A38

KEENAN, Bob, Chief Medical Officer, H. Lee Moffitt Cancer Center and Research Institute, Tampa, FL, p. A147

KEENAN, Nancy C., R.N. Senior Vice President and Chief Nursing Officer, Houston Methodist Willowbrook Hospital, Houston, TX, p. A625

KEENAN, Richard, Senior Vice President Finance and Chief Financial Officer, Valley Hospital, Ridgewood, NJ, p. A423

KEENER, Vicki, Administrative Assistant and Director Human Resources, Little River Memorial Hospital, Ashdown, AR, p. A43

KEENUM, Patricia, Health Information Management Systems Officer, Merit Health Northwest Mississippi, Clarksdale, MS, p. A356

KEEPSEAGLE, Joelle, Director of Nursing, Standing Rock Service Unit, Fort Yates Hospital, Indian Health Service, DHHS, Fort Yates, ND, p. A479

KEEVER, Jerry, Administrator, Sharkey–Issaquena Community Hospital, Rolling Fork, MS, p. A364

KEFALAS, George, Chief Medical Officer, Aultman Specialty Hospital, Canton, OH, p. A486

KEGLEY, Carl J., System Director Information Technology, Fairbanks Memorial Hospital, Fairbanks, AK, p. A29

KEGLEY, Glen, Chief Operating Officer, Hutchinson Health, Hutchinson, MN, p. A344

KEGLEY, Shawn, Director Information Services, Research Medical Center, Kansas City, MO, p. A373

KEHIAYAN, Nancy, Acting Director, Colorado Mental Health Institute at Fort Logan, Denver, CO, p. A103

KEHRBERG, Mark W., M.D
Chief Medical Officer, Calumet Medical Center, Chilton, WI, p. A704
Senior Vice President and Chief Medical Officer, Mercy Medical Center, Oshkosh, WI, p. A713

KEHUS, Frank, Interim Director, Marion Veterans Affairs Medical Center, Marion, IL, p. A195

KEIL, James, M.D. Chief Medical Officer, Niobrara Valley Hospital, Lynch, NE, p. A398

KEILER, Susan, Chief Operating Officer, St. Mary's Regional Medical Center, Lewiston, ME, p. A293

KEIM, Thomas, Chief Executive Officer, Ste. Genevieve County Memorial Hospital, Ste. Genevieve, MO, p. A383

KEIRNS, Melody, Manager Human Resources, F. W. Huston Medical Center, Winchester, KS, p. A256

KEISER, Trish, Comptroller, Avera Gregory Hospital, Gregory, SD, p. A574

KEISTER, Catharine L., Chief Nursing Officer, Sunbury Community Hospital and Outpatient Center, Sunbury, PA, p. A555

KEITEL, SPHR, Kal, Executive Director Human Resources, Baptist Health Paducah, Paducah, KY, p. A267

KEITH, Bridgette, Director Human Resources, HEALTHSOUTH Northern Kentucky Rehabilitation Hospital, Edgewood, KY, p. A259

KEITH, Darlene, Chief Information Systems, Alleghany Memorial Hospital, Sparta, NC, p. A474

KEITH, David N., FACHE, President and Chief Executive Officer, McAlester Regional Health Center, McAlester, OK, p. A514

KEITH, Jeannie, Director Patient Care Services and Nurse Executive, Shriners Hospitals for Children–Houston, Houston, TX, p. A626

KEITH, Leesa–Lee, R.N. Chief Nursing Officer, Baystate Franklin Medical Center, Greenfield, MA, p. A310

KEITH, Lorraine
Chief Nursing Officer, St. Vincent's Medical Center Riverside, Jacksonville, FL, p. A132
Chief Nursing Officer, St. Vincent's Medical Center Southside, Jacksonville, FL, p. A132

KELBAUGH, Brian, Chief Financial Officer, Summersville Regional Medical Center, Summersville, WV, p. A700

KELBLY, Kevin, Senior Vice President Finance and Corporate Fiscal Affairs, Carroll Hospital, Westminster, MD, p. A304

KELL, Douglas B., Chief Financial Officer, Freedom Pain Hospital, Scottsdale, AZ, p. A38

KELLAR, Brian, Chief Executive Officer, Page Hospital, Page, AZ, p. A35

KELLAR, Mark, R.N. Interim Chief Nursing Officer, Our Lady of the Angels Hospital, Bogalusa, LA, p. A274

KELLAR, Richard A., President, Aurora West Allis Medical Center, West Allis, WI, p. A719

KELLEHER, Cynthia, M.P.H., President and Chief Executive Officer, University of Maryland Rehabilitation & Orthopaedic Institute, Baltimore, MD, p. A298

KELLEHER, John, Vice President Information Technology and Chief Information Officer, Glens Falls Hospital, Glens Falls, NY, p. A439

KELLEHER, Mary, Vice President Human Resources, Holyoke Medical Center, Holyoke, MA, p. A310

KELLEHER, Mary Lou, R.N. Vice President, Nursing, Franciscan Hospital for Children, Boston, MA, p. A306

KELLEHER, Michael, Chief Medical Officer, Ann & Robert H. Lurie Children's Hospital of Chicago, Chicago, IL, p. A183

KELLENBARGER, Lance, Site Director Information Systems, St. Catherine Hospital, Garden City, KS, p. A243

KELLER, Allen, Director Human Resources, Sumner Regional Medical Center, Wellington, KS, p. A255

KELLER, Anita M., R.N. Chief Nursing Officer, Johnson Memorial Hospital, Franklin, IN, p. A211

KELLER, Ann, Supervisor Health Information Management, HEALTHSOUTH Walton Rehabilitation Hospital, Augusta, GA, p. A153

KELLER, Christine, Chief Administrative Officer, Bluffton Hospital, Bluffton, OH, p. A485

KELLER, Diane R., Chief Executive Officer, Memorial Community Health, Aurora, NE, p. A393

KELLER, Gretchen, Director Health Information, Neosho Memorial Regional Medical Center, Chanute, KS, p. A241

KELLER, Jack M., Chief Executive Officer, Saint Thomas Hickman Hospital, Centerville, TN, p. A580

KELLER, James
Chief Medical Officer, Advocate Trinity Hospital, Chicago, IL, p. A183
Chief Information Officer, Borgess–Lee Memorial Hospital, Dowagiac, MI, p. A322
Director Human Resources, NEA Baptist Memorial Hospital, Jonesboro, AR, p. A48

KELLER, Jane, R.N., Chief Executive Officer, Indiana Orthopaedic Hospital, Indianapolis, IN, p. A214

KELLER, Jill, R.N. Vice President for Nursing Services, Quality and Risk Management, Waynesboro Hospital, Waynesboro, PA, p. A556

KELLER, Jim, Site Director Information Services, Mercy Health Saint Mary's, Grand Rapids, MI, p. A325

KELLER, Justin, Chief Information Officer, Murray County Medical Center, Slayton, MN, p. A351

KELLER, Marsha, Director Human Resources, Kane Community Hospital, Kane, PA, p. A541

KELLER, Maryalice, Vice President Brand and Talent Management, Unity Hospital, Rochester, NY, p. A454

KELLER, Patricia, MSN Nurse Administrator, Mayo Clinic Health System – Northland in Barron, Barron, WI, p. A702

KELLER, Ruey, Acting Chief Information Officer, VA San Diego Healthcare System, San Diego, CA, p. A89

KELLER, Stewart, M.D. Medical Director, Mesa Springs, Fort Worth, TX, p. A618

KELLER, Thomas, President and Chief Executive Officer, Ozarks Medical Center, West Plains, MO, p. A384

KELLER, Wendy, Director Health Information Management, Atrium Medical Center of Corinth, Corinth, TX, p. A607

KELLERMAN, Laurie, MSN Chief Clinical Officer, Marshall Browning Hospital, Du Quoin, IL, p. A188

KELLERMAN, Scott, Chief Financial Officer, Ely–Bloomenson Community Hospital, Ely, MN, p. A342

KELLEY, Brent, Director Information Technology, Nor–Lea General Hospital, Lovington, NM, p. A430

KELLEY, Jalinda, Secretary of Interior Services, Chickasaw Nation Medical Center, Ada, OK, p. A508

KELLEY, Janice, Chief Financial Officer, Marshall County Hospital, Benton, KY, p. A257

KELLEY, Lewis, Interim Chief Executive Officer, Union General Hospital, Blairsville, GA, p. A154

KELLEY, Mary, Director Human Resources, The Outer Banks Hospital, Nags Head, NC, p. A470

KELLEY, Meera, M.D. Senior Vice President and Chief Medical Officer, Nash Health Care Systems, Rocky Mount, NC, p. A472

KELLEY, Neal, Vice President and Chief Operating Officer, Seton Medical Center Hays, Kyle, TX, p. A631

KELLEY, Sarah Jo, Director Human Resources, Ste. Genevieve County Memorial Hospital, Ste. Genevieve, MO, p. A383

KELLEY, Sharon, Chief Financial Officer, Clifton Springs Hospital and Clinic, Clifton Springs, NY, p. A437

KELLEY, Steven L., President and Chief Executive Officer, Ellenville Regional Hospital, Ellenville, NY, p. A438

KELLEY, Sue, Chief Financial Officer, Cordell Memorial Hospital, Cordell, OK, p. A510

KELLEY, Susan, R.N. Chief Nursing Officer, Abrazo Maryvale Campus, Phoenix, AZ, p. A35

KELLEY, Vicky, Chief Financial Officer, DeQuincy Memorial Hospital, DeQuincy, LA, p. A276

KELLEY, Warren, Chief Information Officer, Reynolds Memorial Hospital, Glen Dale, WV, p. A696

KELLEY, William, Medical Staff President, Stonewall Jackson Memorial Hospital, Weston, WV, p. A701

KELLIHER, Brandon, Chief Information Officer, Great Plains Health, North Platte, NE, p. A399

KELLOGG, Brewster, D.O. Chief Medical Officer, Rawlins County Health Center, Atwood, KS, p. A240

KELLOGG, Jason, M.D. Chief of Staff, Newport Bay Hospital, Newport Beach, CA, p. A79

KELLOGG, Susan, Administrator Patient Care Services, Carthage Area Hospital, Carthage, NY, p. A437

KELLS, Anne, Interim Chief Financial Officer, Appleton Area Health Services, Appleton, MN, p. A338

KELLUM, Craig, Director Management Information Systems, Cape Fear Valley – Bladen County Hospital, Elizabethtown, NC, p. A465

KELLY, Brian
Vice President Finance, Advocate South Suburban Hospital, Hazel Crest, IL, p. A192
Acting Chief Fiscal Service, San Francisco VA Medical Center, San Francisco, CA, p. A90

KELLY, Brian, M.D. Vice President Medical Affairs and Medical Director, Sturdy Memorial Hospital, Attleboro, MA, p. A305

KELLY, Brian E., M.D. President Medical Staff, Saint Elizabeth's Medical Center, Wabasha, MN, p. A352

KELLY, Charlene, Chief Nursing Officer, Kane County Hospital, Kanab, UT, p. A660

KELLY, Charles, D.O. Vice President Medical Affairs and Chief Medical Officer, Henry Ford Macomb Hospitals, Clinton Township, MI, p. A320

KELLY, Colan, Chief Financial Officer, Pineville Community Hospital Association, Pineville, KY, p. A268

KELLY, Dan, R.N. Chief Nursing Officer, Memorial Hermann Memorial City Medical Center, Houston, TX, p. A625

KELLY, Daniel J., President, CHI Health St. Mary's, Nebraska City, NE, p. A398

KELLY, Daniel R., Chief Executive Officer, McKenzie County Healthcare System, Watford City, ND, p. A482

KELLY, Derek J., M.D. Vice President Transformation and Chief Medical Information Officer, Swedish Covenant Hospital, Chicago, IL, p. A187

KELLY, Diane, Chief Operating Officer, Berkshire Medical Center, Pittsfield, MA, p. A314

KELLY, Edward, Chief Executive Officer and President, Milford Regional Medical Center, Milford, MA, p. A312

KELLY, Jr., James J., Senior Vice President and Chief Financial Officer, UF Health Shands Hospital, Gainesville, FL, p. A130

KELLY, Jim, Chief Operating Officer, Nantucket Cottage Hospital, Nantucket, MA, p. A312

KELLY, John, R.N. Chief Nursing Officer and Chief Operating Officer, UMass Memorial–Marlborough Hospital, Marlborough, MA, p. A312

KELLY, John J., M.D. Chief of Staff, Abington Hospital, Abington, PA, p. A532

KELLY, Kecia, R.N. Chief Nurse Executive, Kaiser Permanente Medical Center, Honolulu, HI, p. A170

KELLY, Laurence E., President and Chief Executive Officer, Nathan Littauer Hospital and Nursing Home, Gloversville, NY, p. A439

KELLY, Leo, M.D. Vice President Medical Management, Advocate Lutheran General Hospital, Park Ridge, IL, p. A200

KELLY, Mark
Administrator, Regional One Health Extended Care Hospital, Memphis, TN, p. A589
Vice President Finance, St. Francis Medical Center, Trenton, NJ, p. A424

KELLY, Maura, Vice President Fiscal Services, Pen Bay Medical Center, Rockport, ME, p. A295

KELLY, Melissa, Administrator, Pender Community Hospital, Pender, NE, p. A401

KELLY, Michael
Vice President, Christian Hospital, Saint Louis, MO, p. A380
Vice President Operations, Missouri Baptist Medical Center, Saint Louis, MO, p. A380

KELLY, Patrick J., FACHE, Director, Minneapolis Veterans Affairs Health Care System, Minneapolis, MN, p. A346

KELLY, Peter, President, Putnam Hospital Center, Carmel, NY, p. A437

KELLY, Raymond, R.N. Chief Nursing Officer, Texas Health Presbyterian Hospital Plano, Plano, TX, p. A642

KELLY, Roy, Facility Director, Hawthorn Center, Northville, MI, p. A331

KELLY, Scott A., Chief Executive Officer, Asante Rogue Regional Medical Center, Medford, OR, p. A528

KELLY, Shannon, Director Human Resources, Morton General Hospital, Morton, WA, p. A686

KELLY, Stephen, M.D. Chief Medical Officer, SSM St. Mary's Health Center, Saint Louis, MO, p. A381

KELLY, Steve, Interim Chief Executive Officer, Austin Oaks Hospital, Austin, TX, p. A598

KELLY, Teresa M., MSN Chief Nursing Officer, Chestnut Hill Hospital, Philadelphia, PA, p. A547

KELLY, Vicky, Chief Financial Officer, De Queen Medical Center, De Queen, AR, p. A45

KELLY, Virginia, Chief Financial Officer, Eastside Psychiatric Hospital, Tallahassee, FL, p. A146

KELMAN, Gregory, M.D. Area Medical Director, Kaiser Permanente Woodland Hills Medical Center, CA, p. A72

KEM, Mark, Vice President Finance and Chief Financial Officer, Chandler Regional Medical Center, Chandler, AZ, p. A31

KEMKA, Joseph, Chief Financial Officer, St. Bernard Parish Hospital, Chalmette, LA, p. A274

KEMKER, S. E., M.D. President Medical Staff, St. Vincent Salem Hospital, Salem, IN, p. A221

KEMM, Russ, M.D. Chief Medical Officer, Nevada Regional Medical Center, Nevada, MO, p. A377

KEMMERER, Jan, Director of Nursing, Mitchell County Hospital Health Systems, Beloit, KS, p. A241

KEMP, Thomas, Chief Information Officer, New York–Presbyterian/Queens,, NY, p. A447

KEMPF, Gary L., R.N., Administrator, Houston Methodist St. Catherine Hospital, Katy, TX, p. A629

KEMPIAK, Matthew, Director Human Resources and Administrative Services, Memorial Hospital of Gardena, Gardena, CA, p. A64

KEMPINSKI, Paul D., Chief Operating Officer, Alfred I. duPont Hospital for Children, Wilmington, DE, p. A120

KEMPTON, Matthew, Chief Executive Officer and Administrator, Stephens Memorial Hospital, Breckenridge, TX, p. A603

KENAGY, John Jay, Ph.D
Senior Vice President and Chief Information Officer, Legacy Meridian Park Medical Center, Tualatin, OR, p. A531
Senior Vice President and Chief Information Officer, Legacy Mount Hood Medical Center, Gresham, OR, p. A526

KENAGY, Rob, M.D. Senior Vice President and Chief Medical Officer, Stormont Vail Health, Topeka, KS, p. A254

KENDALL, Abigail, Chief Nursing Officer, Lake Granbury Medical Center, Granbury, TX, p. A621

KENDALL, Anthony
Vice President Human Resources, Baptist Health Extended Care Hospital, Little Rock, AR, p. A48
Vice President Human Resources, Baptist Health Medical Center–Arkadelphia, Arkadelphia, AR, p. A43
Vice President Human Resources, Baptist Health Medical Center–Little Rock, Little Rock, AR, p. A48
Vice President Human Resources, Baptist Health Rehabilitation Institute, Little Rock, AR, p. A49

KENDALL, Clint, R.N. Chief Nursing Officer, Clinch Valley Medical Center, Richlands, VA, p. A677

KENDALL, Dorothy, Medical Director, William J. McCord Adolescent Treatment Facility, Orangeburg, SC, p. A569

KENDLE, Melinda
Manager Business Office, Evansville Psychiatric Children Center, Evansville, IN, p. A210
Director Fiscal Management, Evansville State Hospital, Evansville, IN, p. A210

KENDLER, Lisa
Chief Financial Officer, Memorial Hermann Memorial City Medical Center, Houston, TX, p. A625
Chief Financial Officer, Memorial Hermann Sugar Land Hospital, Sugar Land, TX, p. A650

KENDRICK, Donovan, M.D. Chief Medical Officer, Baptist Medical Center South, Montgomery, AL, p. A23

KENDRICK, Gary G., Interim Chief Executive Officer, Morehouse General Hospital, Bastrop, LA, p. A272

KENDRICK, Ray, Chief Human Resources Officer, Memorial Hospital Miramar, Miramar, FL, p. A138

KENDRICK, Robert L., Chief Nursing Officer, Madison Memorial Hospital, Rexburg, ID, p. A178

KENNEDY, Anita J., Vice President Operations, Methodist Hospital of Sacramento, Sacramento, CA, p. A86

KENNEDY, Brad
Chief Executive Officer, HEALTHSOUTH Rehabilitation Hospital at Drake, Cincinnati, OH, p. A487
Chief Executive Officer, HealthSouth Rehabilitation Hospital of Dayton, Dayton, OH, p. A493

KENNEDY, Carol, Chief Clinical Officer, Barrett Hospital & HealthCare, Dillon, MT, p. A387

KENNEDY, Connie, Director Human Resources, Marlette Regional Hospital, Marlette, MI, p. A329

KENNEDY, Darla, Chief Information Officer, Foothill Regional Medical Center, Tustin, CA, p. A97

KENNEDY, Diana, Director Human Resources, Meadowview Regional Medical Center, Maysville, KY, p. A266

KENNEDY, Elizabeth M., Administrator, J. Paul Jones Hospital, Camden, AL, p. A18

KENNEDY, Jack L., R.N. Vice President and Chief Nursing Officer, Pratt Regional Medical Center, Pratt, KS, p. A252

KENNEDY, Jill M., R.N. Vice President, Ambulatory Patient Care Services, Bon Secours Memorial Regional Medical Center, Mechanicsville, VA, p. A673

KENNEDY, John, M.D. Vice President Medical Affairs, Mercy Health – Fairfield Hospital, Fairfield, OH, p. A494

KENNEDY, Kay, Chief Nurse Executive, WellStar Cobb Hospital, Austell, GA, p. A154

KENNEDY, Kimberly, Manager Human Resources, OSF Saint Paul Medical Center, Mendota, IL, p. A196

KENNEDY, Larkin, Chief Executive Officer, Rush Foundation Hospital, Meridian, MS, p. A362

KENNEDY, Mary, R.N. Chief Nursing Officer, Cleveland Clinic, Medina Hospital, Medina, OH, p. A499

KENNEDY, Pam, Director Human Resources, CHRISTUS St. Michael Rehabilitation Hospital, Texarkana, TX, p. A652

KENNEDY, Peggy S., R.N. Vice President and Chief Nurse Executive, Fremont Health, Fremont, NE, p. A396

KENNEDY, R. Scott, M.D. Chief Medical Officer and Hospital Chief Operating Officer, Olympic Medical Center, Port Angeles, WA, p. A688

KENNEDY, Ryan
Chief Financial Officer, Holy Name Medical Center, Teaneck, NJ, p. A424
Chief Operating Officer, Kingman Regional Medical Center, Kingman, AZ, p. A33

KENNEDY, Susan, Manager Human Resources, Novant Health Matthews Medical Center, Matthews, NC, p. A469

KENNEDY, Tiffany, Chief Nursing Officer, Breckinridge Memorial Hospital, Hardinsburg, KY, p. A261

KENNEDY, Timea, Director Human Resources, St. Mary–Corwin Medical Center, Pueblo, CO, p. A110

KENNEDY, Todd S., President and Chief Executive Officer, Providence Hospital, Mobile, AL, p. A22

KENNEMER, Darline, Controller, Methodist Rehabilitation Hospital, Dallas, TX, p. A610

KENNETH, Ron, M.D. Chief Medical Officer, Abrazo West Campus, Goodyear, AZ, p. A33

KENNETT, Jerry, M.D. Chief Medical Officer, Boone Hospital Center, Columbia, MO, p. A370

KENNEY, Catherine, Chief Nursing Officer, Pampa Regional Medical Center, Pampa, TX, p. A640

KENNEY, Mary Ellen, Chief Human Services, Manchester Veterans Affairs Medical Center, Manchester, NH, p. A412

KENNEY, Ronda, Chief Operating Officer, Eastern State Hospital, Medical Lake, WA, p. A686

KENNINGTON, Lynn, Chief Financial Officer, Alaska Regional Hospital, Anchorage, AK, p. A28

KENNISON, Barbara, Director Clinical Services, Aurora Behavioral Healthcare San Diego, San Diego, CA, p. A88

KENNY, Carolyn, Executive Vice President Clinical Care, Children's Healthcare of Atlanta, Atlanta, GA, p. A152

KENNY, Virginia, Chief Nursing Officer, Hancock Medical Center, Bay Saint Louis, MS, p. A355

KENT, Alan, Chief Executive Officer, Meadows Regional Medical Center, Vidalia, GA, p. A168

KENT, Blair, Administrator, Riverton Hospital, Riverton, UT, p. A662

KENT, David, M.D. Chief Medical Officer, Safe Haven Hospital of Treasure Valley, Boise, ID, p. A174

KENT, David, Chief Operating Officer, Southeastern Regional Medical Center, Newnan, GA, p. A164

KENT, Robert, D.O., President and Chief Executive Officer, Summa Western Reserve Hospital, Cuyahoga Falls, OH, p. A492

KENTERA, Amy, Chief Information Officer, Conifer Park, Glenville, NY, p. A439

KENTON, Bart, Chief Financial Officer, Holton Community Hospital, Holton, KS, p. A245

KENWOOD, Linda S., R.N. Chief Nursing Officer and Chief Operating Officer, Shore Medical Center, Somers Point, NJ, p. A423

KEOWN, Janet, Vice President Human Resources, Behavioral Health Network, Natchaug Hospital, Mansfield Center, CT, p. A114

KEPLER, Andrea, Chief Executive Officer, Wernersville State Hospital, Wernersville, PA, p. A557

KEPLER, Terry W.
Administrator, CHRISTUS Dubuis Hospital of Beaumont, Beaumont, TX, p. A601
Administrator, CHRISTUS Dubuis Hospital of Port Arthur, Port Arthur, TX, p. A642

KEPLINGER, Ron, Chief Information Officer, Western Maryland Hospital Center, Hagerstown, MD, p. A301

KEPNER, Donald L., Chief Financial Officer, Ashtabula County Medical Center, Ashtabula, OH, p. A484

KEPPLE, Jeffrey, M.D., Chief Executive Officer, Plumas District Hospital, Quincy, CA, p. A84

KEPPLER, Edward L., M.D. Chief Medical Officer, Marion General Hospital, Marion, IN, p. A218

KEPPLER, Matthew, Market Chief Executive Officer, Kindred Hospital Indianapolis South, Greenwood, IN, p. A212

KEPSHIRE, Bob, MS, Administrator and Chief Nursing Officer, University Hospital McDuffie, Thomson, GA, p. A167

KERBS, Curtis, Regional Chief Information Officer, Memorial Hospital, North Conway, NH, p. A413

KERCHENSKI, Marlene, Chief Nurse, U. S. Air Force Hospital, Hampton, VA, p. A671

KERDEL, Francisco, M.D. President Medical Staff, University of Miami Hospital, Miami, FL, p. A137

KERI, Alison, Director Human Resources, Hiawatha Community Hospital, Hiawatha, KS, p. A244

KERIAN–MASTERS, RN, BSN, Carol, Chief Nursing Officer, Regional Health Services of Howard County, Cresco, IA, p. A228

KERLIN, Kerry, Chief Information Officer, Roswell Park Cancer Institute, Buffalo, NY, p. A436

KERMEN, John, D.O. Chief Medical Staff, Mendocino Coast District Hospital, Fort Bragg, CA, p. A62

KERN, Daniel, Chief Executive Officer, Strategic Behavioral Health – Wilmington, Leland, NC, p. A468

KERN, Douglas W., Chief Executive Officer, Northcoast Behavioral Healthcare, Northfield, OH, p. A500

KERN, Gordon, M.D. Medical Director, Oswego Community Hospital, Oswego, KS, p. A251

KERN, Howard P., Chief Executive Officer, Sentara Healthcare, Norfolk, VA, p. B123

KERN, Howard P.
President and Chief Operating Officer, Sentara Leigh Hospital, Norfolk, VA, p. A675
Chief Operating Officer, Sentara Princess Anne Hospital, Virginia Beach, VA, p. A680

KERNAN, Jacqueline D., Vice President, Chief Nursing Officer, OSF Saint Luke Medical Center, Kewanee, IL, p. A194

KERNELL, Shane, Chief Executive Officer, Graham Regional Medical Center, Graham, TX, p. A621

KERNIVAN, Lorna, Chief Operating Officer, Palms West Hospital, Loxahatchee, FL, p. A134

KERNS, Elizabeth, Senior Vice President and Chief Information Officer, Lakeland Regional Health, Lakeland, FL, p. A134

KEROACK, Mark A., M.P.H., President and Chief Executive Officer, Baystate Health, Inc., Springfield, MA, p. B22

KEROACK, Mark A., M.P.H., President and Chief Executive Officer, Baystate Medical Center, Springfield, MA, p. A314

KERR, Jeff, M.D. Chief Medical Officer, Baylor Medical Center at McKinney, McKinney, TX, p. A636

KERR, Karen, R.N., President, South Florida Baptist Hospital, Plant City, FL, p. A142

KERR, Mark, Chief Executive Officer, Presentation Medical Center, Rolla, ND, p. A481

KERR, Michael D., Chief Executive Officer, Promise Hospital of East Los Angeles, Los Angeles, CA, p. A73

KERRINS, David, Vice President Information Services and Chief Information Officer, Dameron Hospital, Stockton, CA, p. A95

KERRWOOD, Patrick, Chief Executive Officer, Siloam Springs Regional Hospital, Siloam Springs, AR, p. A52

KERSCHEN, Susan, MS Vice President and Chief Nursing Officer, Good Samaritan Medical Center, Lafayette, CO, p. A108

KERSEY, Jerry, Director Employee Relations, Eastern State Hospital, Lexington, KY, p. A263

KERSTETTER, Kathleen, R.N. Chief Clinical Officer, Acuity Specialty Hospital of New Jersey, Atlantic City, NJ, p. A414

KERSTING, Clay, M.D. Chief Medical Staff, Newport Hospital and Health Services, Newport, WA, p. A687

KERSWILL, Randy, M.D. Medical Director, Winnebago Mental Health Institute, Winnebago, WI, p. A719

KERTIS, Robert, Vice President Finance, Calvert Memorial Hospital, Prince Frederick, MD, p. A302

KERWIN, George, President, Bellin Memorial Hospital, Green Bay, WI, p. A706

KERWOOD, Christine, Chief Nursing Officer, East Ohio Regional Hospital, Martins Ferry, OH, p. A498

KERWOOD, Lori A., Director Human Resources, Cooley Dickinson Hospital, Northampton, MA, p. A313

KESSEL, Jennifer, Assistant Vice President, Operations and Human Resources, Aultman Orrville Hospital, Orrville, OH, p. A501

KESSLER, Alexander, M.D. Chief of Staff, Northside Hospital–Cherokee, Canton, GA, p. A155

KESSLER, David, M.D. Clinical Director, U. S. Public Health Service Indian Hospital, Zuni, NM, p. A432

KESSLER, Dawn
Senior Vice President Human Resources, St. John's Hospital, Maplewood, MN, p. A346
Senior Vice President Human Resources, St. Joseph's Hospital, Saint Paul, MN, p. A351
System Director Human Resources Operations, Woodwinds Health Campus, Woodbury, MN, p. A353
KESSLER, Jeffrey R., Vice President Information Services, Dana–Farber Cancer Institute, Boston, MA, p. A306
KESSLER, John E., President and Chief Executive Officer, Salem Township Hospital, Salem, IL, p. A202
KESSLER, Joseph, Executive Vice President and Chief Financial Officer, KALEIDA Health, Buffalo, NY, p. A436
KESSLER, Renee A., Chief Operating Officer, Saint Thomas Midtown Hospital, Nashville, TN, p. A591
KESSLER, Terrence, Interim President and Chief Executive Officer, Providence Hospital, Columbia, SC, p. A564
KESSLER, Terrence, President and Chief Executive Officer, Sisters of Charity Health System, Cleveland, OH, p. B125
KESSNER, Jennifer, Financial Director, Roosevelt Medical Center, Culbertson, MT, p. A386
KESTER, Bonnie J., R.N. Vice President Patient Care Services and Chief Nursing Officer, Nantucket Cottage Hospital, Nantucket, MA, p. A312
KESTERSON, Matt
Director Information Services, Wadley Regional Medical Center, Texarkana, TX, p. A652
Director Information Services, Wadley Regional Medical Center at Hope, Hope, AR, p. A47
KETCH, Lynn
Human Resources Recruiter Generalist, INTEGRIS Canadian Valley Hospital, Yukon, OK, p. A523
Director, Integris Southwest Medical Center, Oklahoma City, OK, p. A516
KETCHAM, Krista, Chief Financial Officer, Buena Vista Regional Medical Center, Storm Lake, IA, p. A238
KETCHAM, Michael
Chief Medical Officer, Mountain View Regional Medical Center, Norton, VA, p. A675
President, Medical Staff, Wellmont Lonesome Pine Hospital, Big Stone Gap, VA, p. A667
KETCHEM, Tami, Human Resource Director, UP Health System–Bell, Ishpeming, MI, p. A327
KETCHER, Greg, Administrator, Lawton Indian Hospital, Lawton, OK, p. A513
KETTELLE, John, M.D. Chief Medical Officer, Banner – University Medical Center South, Tucson, AZ, p. A40
KETTERHAGEN, James P., M.D. Senior Vice President and Chief Medical Officer, Jewish Hospital, Louisville, KY, p. A264
KETTERING, Lisa, Chief Medical Officer, Yampa Valley Medical Center, Steamboat Springs, CO, p. A110
KETTERLING, Kimberly A., R.N. Vice President of Nursing, CHI Oakes Hospital, Oakes, ND, p. A481
KETTERMAN, Patricia P., R.N., President and Chief Administrative Officer, Claiborne Medical Center, Tazewell, TN, p. A593
KETTLER, Paul, M.D. Vice President Medical Affairs, Unity Hospital, Fridley, MN, p. A343
KEUTER, Mary Beth, Director Patient Care, Continuing Care Hospital at St. Luke's, Cedar Rapids, IA, p. A226
KEY, Lora, Chief Executive Officer, Sabetha Community Hospital, Sabetha, KS, p. A253
KEYONNIE, Christine, Chief Financial Officer, Tuba City Regional Health Care Corporation, Tuba City, AZ, p. A40
KEYS, Janice C., FACHE Senior Vice President, Chief Nurse Executive, Erlanger Medical Center, Chattanooga, TN, p. A580
KHADE, Kashmira, Coordinator Non–Clinical Services, Behavioral Center of Michigan, Warren, MI, p. A336
KHALEGHI, Trisha, Senior Vice President and Chief Executive Officer, Sharp Mesa Vista Hospital, San Diego, CA, p. A89
KHALIQUE, Tania, Director Human Resources, Vibra Hospital of San Diego, San Diego, CA, p. A89
KHAN, Atique, M.D. Medical Director, University Behavioral Health of Denton, Denton, TX, p. A613
KHAN, Dan, M.D. Chief Medical Officer, Yoakum County Hospital, Denver City, TX, p. A613
KHAN, Faraz, Chief Financial Officer, Doctors Hospital of Laredo, Laredo, TX, p. A632
KHAN, Humayun, M.D. Chief Medical Officer, Sacred Heart Hospital, Eau Claire, WI, p. A705
KHAN, Parvez, Chief of Staff, Beaumont Hospital–Dearborn, Dearborn, MI, p. A321
KHAN, Sarfraz, Medical Director, Meridian Health Services, Muncie, IN, p. A219
KHAN, Shahbaz, M.D. Medical Director, Two Rivers Behavioral Health System, Kansas City, MO, p. A374
KHAN, Waheed, M.D. President Medical Staff, Summers County ARH Hospital, Hinton, WV, p. A696

KHANCHANDANI, Ashok, Chief Financial Officer, Oroville Hospital, Oroville, CA, p. A81
KHANNA, Rajive
Chief Executive Officer, Grace Hospital, Cleveland, OH, p. A489
Chief Executive Officer, Grace Hospital, Cleveland, OH, p. A489
Chief Executive Officer, Specialty Hospital of Lorain, Amherst, OH, p. A483
KHARONOV, Arthur, Vice President Nursing, Columbus Hospital LTACH, Newark, NJ, p. A420
KHATAMI, Manoochehr, M.D. Medical Director, Hickory Trail Hospital, Desoto, TX, p. A613
KHDOUR, Adel, M.D. Chief Medical Officer, Indiana University Health White Memorial Hospital, Monticello, IN, p. A218
KHEMKA, Hemant, Chief Operating Officer, Surgery Specialty Hospitals of America, Pasadena, TX, p. A640
KHERA, Surendra, M.D. Vice President Medical Affairs, Chief Medical Officer, Chief Quality Officer, Saint Francis Hospital and Medical Center, Hartford, CT, p. A114
KHIAMI, Ahmad, Chief of Staff, Beckley ARH Hospital, Beckley, WV, p. A696
KHIM FUGATE, Guay, Chief Operations Officer, Kindred Hospital Riverside, Perris, CA, p. A82
KHOERL, Thomas, Vice President Finance, Spectrum Health Big Rapids Hospital, Big Rapids, MI, p. A319
KHOO, Alex, Interim Area Finance Officer, Kaiser Permanente San Francisco Medical Center, San Francisco, CA, p. A90
KHOW, Vida J., Chief Executive Officer, Gallup Indian Medical Center, Gallup, NM, p. A429
KIBAR, Nizar, M.D. Chief Medical Staff, Kiowa County Memorial Hospital, Greensburg, KS, p. A244
KIBBY, Rosalinda, Superintendent and Administrator, Columbia Basin Hospital, Ephrata, WA, p. A684
KIBORT, Phillip M., M.D. Vice President Medical Affairs and Chief Medical Officer, Children's Hospitals and Clinics of Minnesota, Minneapolis, MN, p. A346
KIDA, Sue, President, Kessler Institute for Rehabilitation, West Orange, NJ, p. A425
KIDD, David, Manager Human Resources, Sentara CarePlex Hospital, Hampton, VA, p. A671
KIDD, Larry R., R.N. Vice President and Chief Nursing Officer, Henry Mayo Newhall Hospital, Valencia, CA, p. A98
KIDD, Monica, MSN, Administrator, Parkview Hospital, Wheeler, TX, p. A657
KIDD, Sue, Chief Financial Officer, Horton Community Hospital, Horton, KS, p. A245
KIDD, Thomas J., Assistant Administrator and Chief Financial Officer, Macon County General Hospital, Lafayette, TN, p. A586
KIDDER, David M., D.O. Chief Medical Officer, Garfield County Health Center, Jordan, MT, p. A388
KIDDER, Suzanne F., Human Resources Officer, Opelousas General Health System, Opelousas, LA, p. A286
KIDDER–TUCK, Allison, Administrator, Compass Behavioral Center of Crowley, Crowley, LA, p. A276
KIEBZAK, Stanley F., R.N. Chief Nursing Officer, HEALTHSOUTH Rehabilitation Hospital The Vintage, Houston, TX, p. A624
KIEDROWSKI, Brian, M.D. Chief Medical Director, Miami Jewish Home and Hospital for Aged, Miami, FL, p. A137
KIEF, Brian
Interim President, Ministry Saint Clare's Hospital, Weston, WI, p. A719
Regional Vice President Ministry Health Care and President Ministry Saint Joseph's Hospital, Ministry Saint Joseph's Hospital, Marshfield, WI, p. A709
KIEFER, Michael L.
Director, Amarillo Veterans Affairs Health Care System, Amarillo, TX, p. A596
Director, West Texas Veterans Affairs Health Care System, Big Spring, TX, p. A603
KIEFER, William
Chief Operating Officer, Rehoboth McKinley Christian Health Care Services, Gallup, NM, p. A429
Chief Nursing Officer, TMC Bonham Hospital, Bonham, TX, p. A603
KIEFFER, Kelley
Chief Nursing Officer, Banner Baywood Medical Center, Mesa, AZ, p. A34
Chief Nursing Officer, Banner Heart Hospital, Mesa, AZ, p. A34
KIEHLE, Jessica, R.N. Chief Nursing Officer, Abilene Regional Medical Center, Abilene, TX, p. A595
KIELY, Sharon, M.D. Senior Vice President Medical Affairs and Chief Medical Officer, Stamford Hospital, Stamford, CT, p. A117
KIERNAN, Richard, Vice President Human Resources, Monmouth Medical Center, Long Branch Campus, Long Branch, NJ, p. A419

KIGER, Tom, Director Information Systems, Trinity Health System, Steubenville, OH, p. A503
KIGHT, Sheila, Director Human Resources, TriStar Horizon Medical Center, Dickson, TN, p. A582
KILARSKI, David J., FACHE, Chief Executive Officer, FirstHealth Moore Regional Hospital, Pinehurst, NC, p. A471
KILARSKI, David J., FACHE, Chief Executive Officer, FirstHealth of the Carolinas, Pinehurst, NC, p. B55
KILBORN, Mark, Director Information Systems, Springhill Memorial Hospital, Mobile, AL, p. A22
KILDAY, Kevin
Chief Financial Officer, Anna Jaques Hospital, Newburyport, MA, p. A313
Vice President Finance, Holy Family Hospital, Methuen, MA, p. A312
KILE, Steven, Vice President Human Resources, Indiana University Health North Hospital, Carmel, IN, p. A208
KILE, Steven E., Director Human Resources, Springfield Regional Medical Center, Springfield, OH, p. A503
KILEY, Dennis, Interim Chief Executive Officer, Takoma Regional Hospital, Greeneville, TN, p. A583
KILGORE, Julie, Vice President, Human Resources, Broadlawns Medical Center, Des Moines, IA, p. A229
KILLINGSWORTH, Meri, Chief Operating Officer, Hereford Regional Medical Center, Hereford, TX, p. A623
KILLORAN, Carrie
Interim President, Aurora Medical Center Grafton, Grafton, WI, p. A706
Interim President, Aurora Medical Center in Washington County, Hartford, WI, p. A707
KILO, Charles M., M.D. Vice President and Chief Medical Officer, OHSU Hospital, Portland, OR, p. A529
KILPATRICK, Von, Chief Nursing Officer, St. Vincent General Hospital District, Leadville, CO, p. A108
KIM, Donald, M.D. Chief Medical Officer, Memorial Regional Hospital,, FL, p. A130
KIM, Dong, M.D. Chief of Staff, Parkview Community Hospital Medical Center, Riverside, CA, p. A86
KIM, Eric, Chief Information Officer, Las Encinas Hospital, Pasadena, CA, p. A82
KIM, Hyon Su, M.D. Medical Director, Northlake Behavioral Health System, Mandeville, LA, p. A282
KIM, John, Chief Financial Officer, Anchor Hospital, Atlanta, GA, p. A152
KIM, Soon K., M.D., President and Chief Executive Officer, Signature Healthcare Services, Corona, CA, p. B124
KIMBALL, Kevin, Director Information Technology, Brooks Memorial Hospital, Dunkirk, NY, p. A438
KIMBLE, Becky, R.N. Chief Nursing Officer, HEALTHSOUTH Rehabilitation Hospital of Jonesboro, Jonesboro, AR, p. A48
KIMBLE, D. Gay, Director Human Resources, Susan B. Allen Memorial Hospital, El Dorado, KS, p. A242
KIMBLE, Robert J., Chief Financial Officer, William R. Sharpe, Jr. Hospital, Weston, WV, p. A701
KIMBREW, Missey, Director Human Resources, Grafton City Hospital, Grafton, WV, p. A696
KIMBRO, George, Vice President Finance, Angel Medical Center, Franklin, NC, p. A465
KIMBROUGH, Pam, M.D. Vice President Medical Affairs, Mercy Hospital Ardmore, Ardmore, OK, p. A508
KIMMEL, Arnold, Chief Executive Officer, Franciscan St. James Hospital and Health Centers, Olympia Fields, IL, p. A199
KIMMEL, Kyle, Chief Financial Officer, Bacon County Hospital and Health System, Alma, GA, p. A151
KIMMEL, Stephen, Chief Financial Officer, Cook Children's Medical Center, Fort Worth, TX, p. A618
KIMMES, Robert P., Chief Executive Officer, Skyline Hospital, White Salmon, WA, p. A693
KIMMET, Jackie, Chief Human Resource Officer, River's Edge Hospital and Clinic, Saint Peter, MN, p. A351
KIMMY, Sharon, Coordinator Human Resources, Corry Memorial Hospital, Corry, PA, p. A536
KIMPLE, Robin, Director Information Services, WellSpan Gettysburg Hospital, Gettysburg, PA, p. A539
KIMZEY, Mike, Chief Executive Officer and Administrator, Oklahoma Center for Orthopedic and Multi–Specialty Surgery, Oklahoma City, OK, p. A516
KINCAID, Kevin, Chief Executive Officer, Knoxville Hospital & Clinics, Knoxville, IA, p. A233
KINDER, Barbara, R.N. Chief Clinical Officer, Clark Regional Medical Center, Winchester, KY, p. A270
KINDERED, Deanne, Vice President Finance, Baylor Regional Medical Center at Plano, Plano, TX, p. A641
KINDRED, Bill, Chief Executive Officer, Russell County Hospital, Russell Springs, KY, p. A269
KINDRED, Bryan N., FACHE, President and Chief Executive Officer, DCH Health System, Tuscaloosa, AL, p. B44
KINDSCHI, Mark, Director Human Resources, Edgerton Hospital and Health Services, Edgerton, WI, p. A705

KING, Abner, Chief Operating Officer, Steele Memorial Medical Center, Salmon, ID, p. A178

KING, Beth, Chief Financial Officer, Jersey Community Hospital, Jerseyville, IL, p. A194

KING, Brent R., Chief Medical Officer and Chief Physician, Alfred I. duPont Hospital for Children, Wilmington, DE, p. A120

KING, Bruce, President and Chief Executive Officer, New London Hospital, New London, NH, p. A412

KING, Chris, Director Information Services, OhioHealth Marion General Hospital, Marion, OH, p. A498

KING, Christopher, Director Operations and Administrative Services, Matheny Medical and Educational Center, Peapack, NJ, p. A421

KING, Don
Chief Executive Officer, Saint Thomas Midtown Hospital, Nashville, TN, p. A591
Chief Executive Officer, Saint Thomas West Hospital, Nashville, TN, p. A591

KING, Donna, R.N. Vice President Clinical Operations and Chief Nursing Executive, Advocate Illinois Masonic Medical Center, Chicago, IL, p. A183

KING, Doug, M.D. Director Clinical Services, Western Mental Health Institute, Bolivar, TN, p. A579

KING, Elizabeth, Director, White Plains Hospital Center, White Plains, NY, p. A459

KING, Glenn, R.N
Vice President, Chief Nursing Officer, MidMichigan Medical Center–Clare, Clare, MI, p. A320
Vice President and Chief Nursing Officer, MidMichigan Medical Center–Gladwin, Gladwin, MI, p. A324

KING, Grace, Regional Director Human Resources, Broward Health North, Deerfield Beach, FL, p. A127

KING, Heath
Chief Financial Officer, Coliseum Medical Centers, Macon, GA, p. A162
Chief Financial Officer, Coliseum Northside Hospital, Macon, GA, p. A162

KING, Janine, M.D. Chief of Staff, East Los Angeles Doctors Hospital, Los Angeles, CA, p. A71

KING, Jay, Vice President Human Resources, Mercy Hospitals of Bakersfield, Bakersfield, CA, p. A56

KING, Jim, Executive Vice President and Chief Operating Officer, Jackson County Memorial Hospital, Altus, OK, p. A508

KING, Jo Nell, Director of Nursing, Northlake Behavioral Health System, Mandeville, LA, p. A282

KING, Joanie, Chief Financial Officer, Carteret Health Care, Morehead City, NC, p. A470

KING, JoAnne, Chief Operating Officer, Florida Hospital–Flagler, Palm Coast, FL, p. A141

KING, Kim, Director Human Resources and Public Relations, Baptist Memorial Hospital–Huntingdon, Huntingdon, TN, p. A584

KING, Lenetra S., Chief Operating Officer, Menorah Medical Center, Overland Park, KS, p. A251

KING, Louie
Chief Executive Officer, Benefis Teton Medical Center, Choteau, MT, p. A386
President, Harry Bold Nursing Home Administrator, Missouri River Medical Center, Fort Benton, MT, p. A387

KING, Paul, M.D. Medical Director, Parkwood Behavioral Health System, Olive Branch, MS, p. A363

KING, Ray, M.D. Senior Vice President and Chief Medical Officer, Henry Ford Allegiance Health, Jackson, MI, p. A327

KING, Rich, Vice President Information Technology, West Virginia University Hospitals, Morgantown, WV, p. A698

KING, Sam, Chief Financial Officer, Renown Regional Medical Center, Reno, NV, p. A408

KING, Sammy, Controller, HEALTHSOUTH Rehabilitation Hospital of Ocala, Ocala, FL, p. A139

KING, Sandra, Chief Nursing Officer, Sagamore Children's Psychiatric Center, Dix Hills, NY, p. A438

KING, Scott, M.D. Chief Medical Officer, Shenandoah Medical Center, Shenandoah, IA, p. A237

KING, Tamara, R.N. Chief Nurse Executive, Shepherd Center, Atlanta, GA, p. A153

KING, Val, Chief Information Officer, Val Verde Regional Medical Center, Del Rio, TX, p. A612

KINGHAM, Darrell L., CPA, Interim Chief Executive Officer and Chief Financial Officer, Beauregard Memorial Hospital, De Ridder, LA, p. A276

KINGRY, Jennifer, Chief Financial Officer, St. Vincent's Blount, Oneonta, AL, p. A24

KINGSLEY, Christi, Vice President Human Resources, West Calcasieu Cameron Hospital, Sulphur, LA, p. A288

KINGSTON, Eileen M., R.N. Nurse Executive, Associate Director Patient Care, Veterans Affairs Nebraska–Western Iowa Health Care System, Omaha, NE, p. A401

KINGSTON, Mary E., R.N.,
Chief Executive Officer, South Bay Community, Providence Little Company of Mary Medical Center – Torrance, Torrance, CA, p. A96
Chief Executive Officer, Providence Little Company of Mary Medical Center San Pedro,, CA, p. A73

KINGSTON, Mary Beth, R.N. Executive Vice President and Chief Nursing Officer, Aurora Medical Center of Oshkosh, Oshkosh, WI, p. A713

KINGSTON, Peggy, Chief Executive Officer, Select Specialty Hospital–Pontiac, Pontiac, MI, p. A332

KINI, M. Narendra, M.D., President and Chief Executive Officer, Nicklaus Children's Hospital, Miami, FL, p. A137

KINKAID, Steve
Director Information Systems, Blue Mountain Hospital, Lehighton, PA, p. A543
Director Information Systems, Palmerton Hospital, Palmerton, PA, p. A546

KINLEN, Thomas, Superintendent, Larned State Hospital, Larned, KS, p. A247

KINMAN, Amanda, Director of Finance, Saint Joseph Mount Sterling, Mount Sterling, KY, p. A267

KINMAN, Brett, Chief Operating Officer, Tomball Regional Medical Center, Tomball, TX, p. A653

KINNEER, James W., Vice President Organizational Development, Indiana Regional Medical Center, Indiana, PA, p. A541

KINNEMAN, Mary, R.N. Chief Nursing Officer, Vice President Patient Care Services, Norwood Hospital, Norwood, MA, p. A313

KINNEY, Janet, Chief Operating Officer, Northwest Florida Community Hospital, Chipley, FL, p. A125

KINSALA, Edeli, Chief Executive Officer, Sonora Behavioral Health Hospital, Tucson, AZ, p. A41

KINSEL, Mike, Controller, Federal Medical Center, Lexington, KY, p. A263

KINSELLA, Daniel F.
Vice President and Chief Information Officer, Northwestern Medicine Central DuPage Hospital, Winfield, IL, p. A205
Executive Vice President Information Technology, Northwestern Medicine Delnor Hospital, Geneva, IL, p. A191

KINSEY, Daniel, M.D. Medical Director, Oaklawn Psychiatric Center, Goshen, IN, p. A212

KINSEY, Wayne, Chief Executive Officer, Promise Hospital of Salt Lake, Salt Lake City, UT, p. A663

KINSLOW, Kathleen, Ed.D., Chief Executive Officer, Aria – Jefferson Health, Philadelphia, PA, p. A547

KINTZ, Ronald J.
Vice President and Treasurer, Arnot Ogden Medical Center, Elmira, NY, p. A438
Chief Financial Officer, Ira Davenport Memorial Hospital, Bath, NY, p. A434
Senior Vice President Finance and Chief Financial Officer, St. Joseph's Hospital, Elmira, NY, p. A438

KINYON, Craig C., President, Reid Health, Richmond, IN, p. A221

KINYON, David, Vice President of Operations and Outpatient Services, Asante Three Rivers Medical Center, Grants Pass, OR, p. A526

KINZIC, Elizabeth, M.D. Chief of Staff, Share Medical Center, Alva, OK, p. A508

KINZIE, Wesley, M.D. Chief of Staff, Stanislaus Surgical Hospital, Modesto, CA, p. A77

KIO, Kenneth, Manager Human Resources, Albany Stratton Veterans Affairs Medical Center, Albany, NY, p. A433

KIPP, Christine, Interim Vice President, Patient Care Services, Southeast Georgia Health System Brunswick Campus, Brunswick, GA, p. A155

KIPP, Kris M., Executive Director, Patient Services and Chief Nursing Officer, James Cancer Hospital and Solove Research Institute, Columbus, OH, p. A490

KIRACOFE, Darin, Director Information Resource Management, Broughton Hospital, Morganton, NC, p. A470

KIRALY, Denise G., Director, Human Resources and Organization Development, Lima Memorial Health System, Lima, OH, p. A496

KIRBOW, Keith, R.N. Vice President and Chief Nursing Officer, Good Shepherd Medical Center–Marshall, Marshall, TX, p. A636

KIRBY, Adrienne, President and Chief Executive Officer, Cooper University Health Care, Camden, NJ, p. A415

KIRBY, Brendan, M.D. Medical Director, Riverview Psychiatric Center, Augusta, ME, p. A291

KIRBY, Elizabeth A.
Senior Director, Human Resource Business Partner, Aurora BayCare Medical Center, Green Bay, WI, p. A706
Senior Director Human Resources, Aurora Medical Center – Manitowoc County, Two Rivers, WI, p. A717

KIRBY II, James M., President and Chief Executive Officer, Margaret R. Pardee Memorial Hospital, Hendersonville, NC, p. A467

KIRBY, Juliana Kay, R.N. Chief Nursing Officer, Tehachapi Valley Healthcare District, Tehachapi, CA, p. A95

KIRBY, Len, Chief Executive Officer, Garfield Park Hospital, Chicago, IL, p. A184

KIRBY, Penny V., MSN Chief Nursing Officer, McKenzie Regional Hospital, McKenzie, TN, p. A588

KIRBY, Ruby, Administrator, Bolivar General Hospital, Bolivar, TN, p. A579

KIRBY, Sarah, FACHE, Chief Executive Officer, Palmetto Health Baptist Parkridge, Columbia, SC, p. A564

KIRBY, Tracy
Assistant Vice President Business Relationship Management, CHI St. Vincent Hot Springs, Hot Springs, AR, p. A47
Assistant Vice President Business Relationship Management, CHI St. Vincent Infirmary Medical Center, Little Rock, AR, p. A49
Assistant Vice President Business Relationship Management, CHI St. Vincent Morrilton, Morrilton, AR, p. A50

KIRCH, Cyndi
Vice President Human Resources, Mercy General Hospital, Sacramento, CA, p. A86
Vice President Human Resources, Methodist Hospital of Sacramento, Sacramento, CA, p. A86

KIRCHER, Mark, Associate Vice President Finance, Norton Women's and Kosair Children's Hospital, Louisville, KY, p. A265

KIRCHNER, Doris, Chief Executive Officer, Vail Valley Medical Center, Vail, CO, p. A111

KIRCHNER, Kent, M.D. Chief of Staff, G.V. (Sonny) Montgomery Veterans Affairs Medical Center, Jackson, MS, p. A359

KIRCHNER, Susan M., Director Human Resources, Four Winds Hospital, Saratoga Springs, NY, p. A455

KIRISITS, Christopher, Chief Nursing Officer, Rochester Psychiatric Center, Rochester, NY, p. A454

KIRITANI, Tracy, Vice President and Chief Financial Officer, Clovis Community Medical Center, Clovis, CA, p. A59

KIRK, Darlene, Manager Finance, U. S. Public Health Service Indian Hospital, Crownpoint, NM, p. A429

KIRK Jr., H. Lee, FACHE, Administrator, Shriners Hospitals for Children–Springfield, Springfield, MA, p. A315

KIRK, J. Douglas, M.D. Chief Medical Officer, University of California, Davis Medical Center, Sacramento, CA, p. A87

KIRK, Jean, Chief Financial Officer, Bennett County Hospital and Nursing Home, Martin, SD, p. A574

KIRK, Paul, Vice President, Woman's Hospital, Baton Rouge, LA, p. A273

KIRK, Peggy, Senior Vice President Clinical Operations, Rehabilitation Institute of Chicago, Chicago, IL, p. A186

KIRK, Roger L., President and Chief Executive Officer, Bethesda Hospital East, Boynton Beach, FL, p. A124

KIRK, Vanessa, Director of Nursing, Kiowa County Memorial Hospital, Greensburg, KS, p. A244

KIRK, Warren J., Chief Executive Officer, Doctors Medical Center of Modesto, Modesto, CA, p. A77

KIRKBRIDE, James B., President and Chief Executive Officer, Susan B. Allen Memorial Hospital, El Dorado, KS, p. A242

KIRKER, Lynda I., Chief Financial Officer, Flagler Hospital, Saint Augustine, FL, p. A144

KIRKER NEA–BC, Donna, R.N. Vice President Patient Services and Chief Nursing Officer, Glens Falls Hospital, Glens Falls, NY, p. A439

KIRKHAM, Brett, Chief Operating Officer, AllianceHealth Deaconess, Oklahoma City, OK, p. A516

KIRKHAM, Paul, Chief Executive Officer, Keystone Newport News, Newport News, VA, p. A674

KIRKLAND–ROSE, Tina, Coordinator Human Resources, Select Specialty Hospital–Lexington, Lexington, KY, p. A263

KIRKPATRICK, Kyle
Chief Executive Officer, Baylor Emergency Medical Center at Aubrey, Aubrey, TX, p. A598
Chief Executive Officer, Baylor Emergency Medical Centers – Burleson, Burleson, TX, p. A604
Chief Executive Officer, Baylor Emergency Medical Centers – Rockwall, Rockwall, TX, p. A643

KIRKS, Linda, Chief Financial Officer, Baptist Medical Center, San Antonio, TX, p. A645

KIRMAN, Eleen, M.D. Chief Medical Officer, PeaceHealth St. John Medical Center, Longview, WA, p. A686

KIRMAN, Lynn, R.N. Chief Nursing Officer, St. John's Medical Center and Living Center, Jackson, WY, p. A722

KIROLLOS, Alan, M.D. President Medical Staff, UNC Lenoir Healthcare, Kinston, NC, p. A468

KIRSHNER, Arthur N., Chief Information Management, Winn Army Community Hospital, Hinesville, GA, p. A160

KIRSTEIN, Susan N., R.N. Chief Nursing Officer, Broadlawns Medical Center, Des Moines, IA, p. A229

KIRTON, Carl, Ph.D. Chief Nursing Officer, University Hospital, Newark, NJ, p. A421

KISACKY, Christina A., Vice President, Operations, UHS Chenango Memorial Hospital, Norwich, NY, p. A451

KISER, Greg, Chief Executive Officer, Three Rivers Medical Center, Louisa, KY, p. A264

KISER II, James R., Chief Executive Officer, Providence St. Joseph Medical Center, Polson, MT, p. A390

KISER, Pamela, R.N. Chief Nursing Executive and Vice President of Nursing, St. John Medical Center, Tulsa, OK, p. A522

KISER, Terry L.
Vice President and Chief Financial Officer, Tidelands Georgetown Memorial Hospital, Georgetown, SC, p. A566
Chief Financial Officer, Tidelands Waccamaw Community Hospital, Murrells Inlet, SC, p. A568

KISHNER, Janice, Chief Nursing Officer, St. Bernard Parish Hospital, Chalmette, LA, p. A274

KISKADDON, Robert, M.D. Chief Medical Officer, Margaret R. Pardee Memorial Hospital, Hendersonville, NC, p. A467

KISNER, Angela, Director Human Resources and Coordinator Medical Staff, Landmark Hospital of Cape Girardeau, Cape Girardeau, MO, p. A368

KISS, Meredith, Administrator, Elgin Mental Health Center, Elgin, IL, p. A189

KISSNER, Michael, Chief Executive Officer, HEALTHSOUTH Treasure Coast Rehabilitation Hospital, Vero Beach, FL, p. A149

KISTLER, Beckie, Director of Finance, Our Lady of Peace, Louisville, KY, p. A265

KISTLER, Mike, Chief Executive Officer, Shadow Mountain Behavioral Health System, Tulsa, OK, p. A522

KITTNER, Bonnie, R.N. Chief Nursing Officer, Mendocino Coast District Hospital, Fort Bragg, CA, p. A62

KITZKE, Kristopher, Chief Executive Officer, Select Specialty Hospital–Gainesville, Gainesville, FL, p. A129

KJERGAARD, Holly, Chief Nursing Officer, Audubon County Memorial Hospital, Audubon, IA, p. A225

KLANN, Andrew, D.O. Chief of Staff, Southwest Health, Platteville, WI, p. A714

KLASEK, Chance, CPA Chief Financial Officer, Jefferson Community Health Center, Fairbury, NE, p. A395

KLASKO, Stephen K., M.D., Chief Executive Officer, Jefferson Health, Radnor, PA, p. B74

KLASSEN, Brad, Information Technology Coordinator, Sanford Worthington Medical Center, Worthington, MN, p. A354

KLASSEN, Karen, Controller, HEALTHSOUTH Chattanooga Rehabilitation Hospital, Chattanooga, TN, p. A580

KLAUKA, Floyd, Chief Financial Officer, Brook Lane Health Services, Hagerstown, MD, p. A301

KLAUSTERMEIER, Lisa, R.N. Chief Nursing Officer, Anderson Hospital, Maryville, IL, p. A195

KLAWITER, Thomas, Chief Executive Officer, South Texas Spine and Surgical Hospital, San Antonio, TX, p. A647

KLAWITTER, Kyle, Vice President Human Resources, Summa Health System, Akron, OH, p. A483

KLEAS, Tara, Director Human Resources, HEALTHSOUTH Rehabilitation Hospital of Fort Worth, Fort Worth, TX, p. A618

KLEBE, Doug, Vice President Operational Finance, Mercy Medical Center, Roseburg, OR, p. A530

KLECKNER, Megan, Vice President and Administrator, Riverside Walter Reed Hospital, Gloucester, VA, p. A671

KLEEN, Kathy, Chief Nursing Officer, Tri–County Hospital, Wadena, MN, p. A353

KLEFFMAN, Angela, Director of Ancillary Services, Bigfork Valley Hospital, Bigfork, MN, p. A339

KLEHN, Paul, Chief Information Technology Officer, Liberty Hospital, Liberty, MO, p. A375

KLEIN, Aron
Vice President Finance, Advocate BroMenn Medical Center, Normal, IL, p. A198
Vice President of Finance, Advocate Eureka Hospital, Eureka, IL, p. A189

KLEIN, Barbara, R.N. Director of Nursing, Arms Acres, Carmel, NY, p. A436

KLEIN, Bernard, M.D., Chief Executive, Providence Holy Cross Medical Center,, CA, p. A73

KLEIN, Cindy, Chief Executive Officer, Lamb Healthcare Center, Littlefield, TX, p. A633

KLEIN, Cindy C., Vice President Human Resources, PeaceHealth St. Joseph Medical Center, Bellingham, WA, p. A682

KLEIN, David, Ph.D. Vice President Operations, Behavioral Health Network, Natchaug Hospital, Mansfield Center, CT, p. A114

KLEIN, David G., M.D., President, Saint Francis Memorial Hospital, San Francisco, CA, p. A90

KLEIN, Diany, Vice President Human Resources, Community Memorial Hospital, Ventura, CA, p. A98

KLEIN, Edward A., Chief Financial Officer, Johnston Health, Smithfield, NC, p. A473

KLEIN, Gerard D., Chief Executive Officer, Memorial Hospital of Sweetwater County, Rock Springs, WY, p. A723

KLEIN, Greg, Senior Director Finance, Novant Health Matthews Medical Center, Matthews, NC, p. A469

KLEIN, Jacqueline, Chief Financial Officer, Lakeview Medical Center, Rice Lake, WI, p. A715

KLEIN, Jillyn, Chief Operating Officer, Howard County Medical Center, Saint Paul, NE, p. A402

KLEIN, Julie, Chief Operating Officer, McKee Medical Center, Loveland, CO, p. A109

KLEIN, Kenneth, M.D. Vice President Medical Affairs, Beloit Health System, Beloit, WI, p. A703

KLEIN, Kyle, Assistant Chief Financial Officer, Mercy Health – West Hospital, Cincinnati, OH, p. A488

KLEIN, Perry, Chief Engineering, Mann–Grandstaff Veterans Affairs Medical Center, Spokane, WA, p. A691

KLEIN, Terrence, Vice President and Chief Operating Officer, Franciscan St. Elizabeth Health – Crawfordsville, Crawfordsville, IN, p. A208

KLEINBECK, Seth M., M.D. Chief of Staff, Baptist Health Medical Center–Stuttgart, Stuttgart, AR, p. A53

KLEINE, Doug, IT Director, St. Mary Medical Center, Apple Valley, CA, p. A55

KLEINHANZL, Thomas A., President and Chief Executive Officer, Frederick Memorial Hospital, Frederick, MD, p. A301

KLEINSASSER, Dustin, Information Technology and BioMed, Fall River Hospital, Hot Springs, SD, p. A574

KLEINSTEUBER, Kathy, Chief Executive Officer, Rehabilitation Hospital of Savannah, Savannah, GA, p. A166

KLENKE, Lisa R., R.N., Chief Executive Officer, Mercer Health, Coldwater, OH, p. A490

KLENNER, Susan, Chief Nursing Officer and Vice President of Hospital Operations, Olmsted Medical Center, Rochester, MN, p. A349

KLEPIN, Michael R., Administrator, Hunt Regional Medical Center, Greenville, TX, p. A621

KLESS, Adam, Chief Nursing Officer, Highlands Regional Medical Center, Sebring, FL, p. A145

KLESSENS, Thomas
Chief Financial Officer, Landmark Medical Center, Woonsocket, RI, p. A561
Chief Financial Officer, Rehabilitation Hospital of Rhode Island, North Smithfield, RI, p. A560

KLEVEN, Brian, Chief Financial Officer, St. Rose Dominican Hospitals – Siena Campus, Henderson, NV, p. A405

KLICKSTEIN, Judith S., Chief Information Officer, Cambridge Health Alliance, Cambridge, MA, p. A308

KLIEBERT, Lynn, Chief Financial Officer, Teche Regional Medical Center, Morgan City, LA, p. A284

KLIEWER, Chad, Information Technology Specialist, Mercy Hospital Kingfisher, Kingfisher, OK, p. A513

KLIMEK, David
Chief Human Resources Officer, Miami County Medical Center, Paola, KS, p. A251
Vice President Human Resources, Olathe Medical Center, Olathe, KS, p. A250

KLIMP, Mary J., FACHE, Administrator, Mayo Clinic Health System in New Prague, New Prague, MN, p. A347

KLINE, Brian S., Vice President and Chief Financial Officer, Penn Highlands DuBois, DuBois, PA, p. A537

KLINE, Donald E., President and Chief Executive Officer, Mercy Health – St. Elizabeth Youngstown Hospital, Youngstown, OH, p. A506

KLINE, Jack, M.D. Chief of Staff, Mercy Medical Center–New Hampton, New Hampton, IA, p. A235

KLINE, Julie, Senior Vice President Patient Services, Sonora Regional Medical Center, Sonora, CA, p. A94

KLINE, Mark W., M.D. Physician in Chief, Texas Children's Hospital, Houston, TX, p. A626

KLINE, Melissa, Chief Nursing Officer, MetroHealth Medical Center, Cleveland, OH, p. A489

KLINGA, Maria, Director Management Information Systems, Silver Hill Hospital, New Canaan, CT, p. A115

KLINGEMAN, Jennifer, Director of Nursing, Chester Mental Health Center, Chester, IL, p. A183

KLINGENBERG, Pat, Director Human Resources, Towner County Medical Center, Cando, ND, p. A477

KLINGLER, Stacie, R.N. Vice President of Patient Services, Franciscan Health Rensselaer, Rensselaer, IN, p. A221

KLINGSEIS, Robert, Director Information Systems, Desert Regional Medical Center, Palm Springs, CA, p. A81

KLINK, Sheryl, Chief Financial Officer, Piedmont Hospital, Atlanta, GA, p. A153

KLINKER, Suzanne M., Director, Bay Pines Veterans Affairs Healthcare System, Bay Pines, FL, p. A123

KLINKNER, Donna M., Chief Financial Officer, Madelia Community Hospital, Madelia, MN, p. A345

KLOCK, Kathy, R.N. Senior Vice President Clinical Operations and Human Resources, Gundersen Health System, La Crosse, WI, p. A708

KLOCKMAN, Dena, Chief Financial Officer, Ogallala Community Hospital, Ogallala, NE, p. A399

KLOCKO, Daniel, Vice President Human Resources, Kootenai Health, Coeur D'Alene, ID, p. A175

KLOECKNER, Vicki, Director Human Resources, HSHS Holy Family Hospital in Greenville, Greenville, IL, p. A192

KLOEWER, Ron, Chief Information Officer, Montgomery County Memorial Hospital, Red Oak, IA, p. A236

KLOPFER, Anthony Rudy, FACHE, Director, Veterans Affairs Eastern Kansas Health Care System, Topeka, KS, p. A254

KLOPP, Amanda, Director, Innovation and Clinical Integration, Penn State Health St. Joseph, Reading, PA, p. A553

KLOPPE, William, Chief Financail Officer, Geary Community Hospital, Junction City, KS, p. A246

KLOSTERMAN, Mark D., FACHE, President and Chief Executive Officer, Faith Regional Health Services, Norfolk, NE, p. A399

KLOSTERMAN, Mark D., FACHE, President and Chief Executive Officer, Faith Regional Health Services, Norfolk, NE, p. B55

KLOSTERMEIER, Janice, Vice President, Chief Financial Officer, Hollywood Presbyterian Medical Center, Los Angeles, CA, p. A71

KLUGE, Thomas S.
President, Hampshire Memorial Hospital, Romney, WV, p. A700
President, War Memorial Hospital, Berkeley Springs, WV, p. A694

KLUGHERZ, Greg, Vice President Corporate Services and Chief Financial Officer, St. Cloud Hospital, Saint Cloud, MN, p. A350

KLUNE, Peter
Chief Executive Officer, Kauai Veterans Memorial Hospital, Waimea, HI, p. A173
Chief Executive Officer, Samuel Mahelona Memorial Hospital, Kapaa, HI, p. A172

KMETZ, Thomas D., Division President, Kosair Children's Hospital, Louisville, KY, p. A264

KNACKSTEDT, Cameron, D.O. Chief Medical Staff, Harlan County Health System, Alma, NE, p. A393

KNACKSTEDT, Nathan, D.O. Chief of Staff, Clara Barton Hospital, Hoisington, KS, p. A245

KNAK, Roger, Administrator, Fairview Regional Medical Center, Fairview, OK, p. A512

KNAPHEIDE, Debbie, MSN, Site Administrator, Chief Nursing Officer and Chief Operating Officer, Carondelet Holy Cross Hospital, Nogales, AZ, p. A35

KNAPP, Brian A., Vice President Operations, Fairview Ridges Hospital, Burnsville, MN, p. A340

KNE, Tanya, M.D. Chief Medical Officer, Banner Desert Medical Center, Mesa, AZ, p. A34

KNECHT, Brian J., Chief Operating Officer, Regional Medical Center of San Jose, San Jose, CA, p. A91

KNECHT, John, Chief Medical Staff, Linton Hospital, Linton, ND, p. A480

KNEDLER, Marie E., FACHE,
President, CHI Health Bergan Mercy, Omaha, NE, p. A399
President, CHI Health Mercy Council Bluffs, Council Bluffs, IA, p. A228

KNEELAND, Misty, Chief Medical Staff, Medical Center of South Arkansas, El Dorado, AR, p. A45

KNEEPPEL, Dennis, R.N. Chief Nurse Executive and Chief Operating Officer, Kaiser Permanente San Rafael Medical Center, San Rafael, CA, p. A92

KNEISEL, Kristin, Interim Director, Information Services, Alice Peck Day Memorial Hospital, Lebanon, NH, p. A411

KNEPP, Gary, D.O. Chief Medical Officer and Chief Quality Officer, UnityPoint Health – Peoria, Peoria, IL, p. A200

KNIEVEL, Lon, Chief Executive Officer, Osmond General Hospital, Osmond, NE, p. A401

KNIFFIN, Fred, M.D., Interim President and Chief Executive Officer, Porter Medical Center, Middlebury, VT, p. A665

KNIGHT, Beth, Chief Nursing Officer, Nacogdoches Memorial Hospital, Nacogdoches, TX, p. A638

KNIGHT, Bethany, M.D. Chief of Staff, Community Medical Center of Izard County, Calico Rock, AR, p. A44

KNIGHT, C. Diane, M.D., Director and Chief Executive Officer, Memphis Veterans Affairs Medical Center, Memphis, TN, p. A589

KNIGHT, Calvin K., President and Chief Executive Officer, John Muir Health, Walnut Creek, CA, p. B74

KNIGHT, Christopher D., Vice President Finance and Chief Financial Officer, Reid Health, Richmond, IN, p. A221

KNIGHT, Deana, Chief Executive Officer, Select Specialty Hospital–Greensboro, Greensboro, NC, p. A466

KNIGHT, Don, Assistant Administrator and Risk Manager, Teche Regional Medical Center, Morgan City, LA, p. A284

KNIGHT, Jennifer, Manager Human Resources, Waynesboro Hospital, Waynesboro, PA, p. A556

KNIGHT, Kimber, Chief Financial Officer, Braxton County Memorial Hospital, Gassaway, WV, p. A696

KNIGHT, Laura, Chief Nursing Officer, Merit Health Central, Jackson, MS, p. A360

KNIGHT, Mark T., Executive Vice President and Chief Financial Officer, Jackson Health System, Miami, FL, p. A136

KNIGHT, Michael, M.D. Medical Director, Hampstead Hospital, Hampstead, NH, p. A411

KNIGHT, Ricardo, Interim Medical Director, Van Matre HealthSouth Rehabilitation Hospital, Rockford, IL, p. A202

KNIGHT, Sue, CPA Chief Operating Officer, St. Elizabeth Hospital, Gonzales, LA, p. A277

KNIGHT, Terry, Public Information Officer and Administrative Assistant, California Mens Colony Correctional Treatment Center, San Luis Obispo, CA, p. A92

KNIGHT, Warren, Chief Financial Officer, Baton Rouge Behavioral Hospital, Baton Rouge, LA, p. A272

KNIGHT, Wayne
Director Finance, St. Vincent Clay Hospital, Brazil, IN, p. A207
Chief Financial Officer, St. Vincent Frankfort Hospital, Frankfort, IN, p. A211

KNIGHTEN, Mary Lynne, R.N. Chief Nursing Officer and Vice President Patient Care Services, St. Francis Medical Center, Lynwood, CA, p. A75

KNIPP, Cindi, Director Human Resources, Rooks County Health Center, Plainville, KS, p. A252

KNITT, Lori, Chief Nursing Officer, Aurora Sheboygan Memorial Medical Center, Sheboygan, WI, p. A715

KNITTEL, Monty E., Chief Executive Officer, Feather River Hospital, Paradise, CA, p. A82

KNIZLEY, Andrew, Chief Executive Officer, Memorial Hermann Orthopedic and Spine Hospital, Bellaire, TX, p. A602

KNOBLOCH, Stanley
Director Fiscal Services, Sanford Luverne Medical Center, Luverne, MN, p. A345
Director Fiscal Services, Sanford Rock Rapids Medical Center, Rock Rapids, IA, p. A236

KNOCKE, Michael, Chief Information Officer, Kansas Spine and Specialty Hospital, Wichita, KS, p. A255

KNODE, Scott, Chief Financial Officer, Veterans Memorial Hospital, Waukon, IA, p. A239

KNOEPFFLER, Susan, R.N. Vice President Nursing, Huntington Hospital, Huntington, NY, p. A440

KNOEPFLER, David, M.D. Chief Medical Officer, Overlake Medical Center, Bellevue, WA, p. A682

KNOEPPEL, Cindy, Chief Nursing Officer, Newton Medical Center, Newton, KS, p. A250

KNOERL, Thomas, Vice President Finance, Spectrum Health Reed City Hospital, Reed City, MI, p. A332

KNOKE, Debra R., Chief Executive Officer, Sequoyah Memorial Hospital, Sallisaw, OK, p. A519

KNOLL, Charlotte, R.N. Chief Nursing Executive, CHRISTUS Health Shreveport–Bossier, Shreveport, LA, p. A287

KNORR, Kelly, Chief Financial Officer, First Hospital Wyoming Valley, Kingston, PA, p. A541

KNOSKE, Thomas, Chief Executive Officer, Regency Hospital Cleveland East, Warrensville Heights, OH, p. A505

KNOUP, Amy, Director Human Resources, Palo Alto County Health System, Emmetsburg, IA, p. A230

KNOUS, Gail, Interim Administrator, Basin Healthcare Center, Odessa, TX, p. A639

KNOWLES, B. K., D.O. Chief of Staff, General John J. Pershing Memorial Hospital, Brookfield, MO, p. A368

KNOWLES, Christy, Chief Human Resources Officer, Coosa Valley Medical Center, Sylacauga, AL, p. A25

KNOWLES, John, Director Human Resources, Clinch Valley Medical Center, Richlands, VA, p. A677

KNOWLES, Robert, M.D. Chief of Staff, Saint Thomas Highlands Hospital, Sparta, TN, p. A593

KNOWLES–SMITH, Peter, M.D. Medical Director, Bennett County Hospital and Nursing Home, Martin, SD, p. A574

KNOWLTON, Robert, Vice President and Chief Financial Officer, Baylor Medical Center at Garland, Garland, TX, p. A620

KNOX, Jody, Chief Operating Officer, Kindred Hospital Rancho, Rancho Cucamonga, CA, p. A84

KNOX, John, Senior Vice President and Chief Information Officer, Carolinas Medical Center–University, Charlotte, NC, p. A462

KNOX, Jud, President, York Hospital, York, ME, p. A295

KNOX, Roland, Chief Executive Officer, Northern Cochise Community Hospital, Willcox, AZ, p. A41

KNOX, Stacey A., Administrator, Rock County Hospital, Bassett, NE, p. A393

KNUDSEN, Mark, Director Fiscal Services, Shriners Hospitals for Children–Portland, Portland, OR, p. A530

KNUDSEN, Mary, Chief Nursing Officer, Northeast Regional Medical Center, Kirksville, MO, p. A375

KNUDSEN, Matthew, Director, Information Systems, Sheppard Pratt Health System, Baltimore, MD, p. A297

KNUDSON, Jenny, Chief Financial Officer, Hiawatha Community Hospital, Hiawatha, KS, p. A244

KNUTH, Kerry, Chief Operating Officer, Mercy Hospital of Defiance, Defiance, OH, p. A493

KNUTSON, Holly, Manager Information Technology, Kittson Memorial Healthcare Center, Hallock, MN, p. A344

KNUTSON, John P., M.D. Chief Medical Staff, Delta County Memorial Hospital, Delta, CO, p. A103

KNUTSON, Larry, Director Finance, CentraCare Health–Long Prairie, Long Prairie, MN, p. A345

KO, Tommy, M.D. Chief Medical Officer, St. Joseph Medical Center, Kansas City, MO, p. A374

KOBEL, Angela, Chief Information Officer, Southwest Memorial Hospital, Cortez, CO, p. A103

KOCH, Carol, Manager Human Resources, Callaway District Hospital, Callaway, NE, p. A394

KOCH, Douglas E., Market President, Aurora Medical Center, Kenosha, WI, p. A708

KOCH, Eric, Chief Nursing Officer, Northern Montana Hospital, Havre, MT, p. A388

KOCH, Holly, Chief Financial Officer, Girard Medical Center, Girard, KS, p. A243

KOCH, Jamie, R.N. Director of Nursing, Thayer County Health Services, Hebron, NE, p. A396

KOCH, Joseph G., Chief Executive Officer, Bourbon Community Hospital, Paris, KY, p. A268

KOCHEVAR, Vanessa, Chief Financial Officer, St. Mary–Corwin Medical Center, Pueblo, CO, p. A110

KOCHIE, Daniel A., CP
Chief Financial Officer, Samaritan Hospital, Troy, NY, p. A457
Chief Financial Officer, St. Mary's Hospital, Troy, NY, p. A457

KOCHIS, Mary Ellen, MSN Administrator Nursing Operations, Beaumont Hospital–Dearborn, Dearborn, MI, p. A321

KOCIOLA, Matthew, Senior Vice President and Chief Financial Officer, Somerset Hospital, Somerset, PA, p. A555

KOCOUREK, Cathie A., President, Aurora Medical Center – Manitowoc County, Two Rivers, WI, p. A717

KOCSIS, Dana, Vice President Nursing and Operations, Lodi Community Hospital, Lodi, OH, p. A497

KOCSIS, Violet, Chief Human Resources Officer, Hunterdon Medical Center, Flemington, NJ, p. A417

KOCZENT, Kurt, Executive Vice President and Chief Operating Officer, F. F. Thompson Hospital, Canandaigua, NY, p. A436

KOEBKE, Troy L.
Director Human Resources Management, Bellin Memorial Hospital, Green Bay, WI, p. A706
Director Human Resources, Bellin Psychiatric Center, Green Bay, WI, p. A706

KOEBNICK, Dale, Director Management Information Systems and Patient Access, Metroplex Adventist Hospital, Killeen, TX, p. A630

KOEHLER, Amy, Director Human Resources, Shelby Memorial Hospital, Shelbyville, IL, p. A202

KOEHLER, Maggie, Senior Vice President and Chief Financial Officer, Wilkes–Barre General Hospital, Wilkes–Barre, PA, p. A558

KOEHLER, Mike, Interim Chief Information Officer, Athens Regional Medical Center, Athens, GA, p. A151

KOELE, Craig, Chief Executive Officer, Cornerstone Hospital of Oklahoma–Muskogee, Muskogee, OK, p. A514

KOENIG, Jr., Donald E.
Executive Vice President and Regional Chief Operating Officer, President, St. Elizabeth Youngstown Hospital, Mercy Health – St. Elizabeth Youngstown Hospital, Youngstown, OH, p. A506
Chief Operating Officer, Mercy Health – St. Joseph Warren Hospital, Warren, OH, p. A504

KOENIG, Harris F., President and Chief Executive Officer, San Antonio Regional Hospital, Upland, CA, p. A97

KOENIG, Mary, Chief Financial Officer, Vernon Memorial Healthcare, Viroqua, WI, p. A717

KOEPKE, Eldon, Chief Financial Officer, Mitchell County Hospital Health Systems, Beloit, KS, p. A241

KOEPKE, Jennifer, R.N. Vice President of Patient Care Services and Chief Nursing Officer, Western Missouri Medical Center, Warrensburg, MO, p. A383

KOEPPEL–OLSEN, Carol, Vice President, Patient Care Services, Winter Haven Hospital, Winter Haven, FL, p. A150

KOERNER, Jill, Manager Employee Relations, Weisman Children's Rehabilitation Hospital, Marlton, NJ, p. A419

KOESSL, Brenda, R.N. Director of Nursing Services, Frances Mahon Deaconess Hospital, Glasgow, MT, p. A387

KOESTER, Jean, Manager Human Resources, Limestone Medical Center, Groesbeck, TX, p. A622

KOESTERER, Susan, Regional Director Finance, Alton Memorial Hospital, Alton, IL, p. A180

KOETTING, Edward, Chief Financial Officer, Bedford Veterans Affairs Medical Center, Edith Nourse Rogers Memorial Veterans Hospital, Bedford, MA, p. A305

KOHANKE, Crystal H., Group Vice President, Human Resources, CHRISTUS Santa Rosa Health System, San Antonio, TX, p. A645

KOHL, Randy T., M.D., Deputy Director, Health Services, Nebraska Penal and Correctional Hospital, Lincoln, NE, p. A398

KOHLBRENNER, Janis, R.N. Vice President Clinical Services and Chief Nursing Officer, Oneida Healthcare, Oneida, NY, p. A452

KOHLENBERG, Chris, Chief Financial Officer, Jennings American Legion Hospital, Jennings, LA, p. A279

KOHLENBERG, Darnell, R.N. Director of Nursing, Abrom Kaplan Memorial Hospital, Kaplan, LA, p. A279

KOHLER, Douglas, M.D. Vice President Medical Operations, Marymount Hospital, Garfield Heights, OH, p. A495

KOHLER, Mike, Chief Executive Officer, Emerus Hospital – Sugar Land, Sugar Land, TX, p. A650

KOHLER, Tracy, Chief Executive Officer, Kindred Hospital Tomball, Tomball, TX, p. A653

KOHR, Kathy, Chief Financial Officer, West Branch Regional Medical Center, West Branch, MI, p. A336

KOHRER, Tammy, Director of Nursing–Acute, Wahiawa General Hospital, Wahiawa, HI, p. A172

KOINZAN, Leigh Jean, Director Finance, Boys Town National Research Hospital, Omaha, NE, p. A399

KOKJOHN, Bradley J., Chief Financial Officer, Fort Madison Community Hospital, Fort Madison, IA, p. A231

KOLACZ, Nicole, Vice President Patient Services, Pomerene Hospital, Millersburg, OH, p. A499

KOLB, Andy, Chief Executive Officer, Stonewall Memorial Hospital, Aspermont, TX, p. A598

KOLB, Edward, M.D. Medical Director, Boys Town National Research Hospital, Omaha, NE, p. A399

KOLB, Pat, Manager Information Technology, McLeod Health Clarendon, Manning, SC, p. A568

KOLHEDE, Deborah, Vice President and Chief Operating Officer, St. Mary's Medical Center, San Francisco, CA, p. A90

KOLIN, Melissa, Chief Nursing Officer and Vice President Patient Care Services, Community Hospital of San Bernardino, San Bernardino, CA, p. A88

KOLKA, James, D.O. Chief Medical Officer, Norwegian American Hospital, Chicago, IL, p. A185

KOLLMEYER, Sherry, Vice President Human Resources, Youth Villages Inner Harbour Campus, Douglasville, GA, p. A158

KOLMAN, Bret G., FACHE, Chief Executive Officer, Lakeview Regional Medical Center, Covington, LA, p. A275

KOLODZIEJCYK, Wanda S., Director Human Resources, Cuero Community Hospital, Cuero, TX, p. A608

KOLODZIEJCZYK, Clayton, Chief Financial Officer, Meadowview Regional Medical Center, Maysville, KY, p. A266

KOLOJEJECHICK, Doreen, Chief Nursing Officer, Berwick Hospital Center, Berwick, PA, p. A533

KOLOSKY, John A., Executive Vice President and Chief Operating Officer, H. Lee Moffitt Cancer Center and Research Institute, Tampa, FL, p. A147

KOLSETH, Shelley V., Chief Financial Officer, Memorial Hospital of Tampa, Tampa, FL, p. A147

KOMAN, Stuart, Ph.D., President and Chief Executive Officer, Walden Psychiatric Care, Waltham, MA, p. A315

KOMANDURI, Ramanujam, M.D. Chief of Staff, Veterans Affairs Southern Nevada Healthcare System, North Las Vegas, NV, p. A407

KOMAR, Ellen M., R.N. Vice President Patient Care Services and Chief Nursing Officer, Stamford Hospital, Stamford, CT, p. A117

KOME, Hunter, Campus President, Oconee Memorial Hospital, Seneca, SC, p. A569

KOMENDA, John, Chief Financial Officer, Hendricks Regional Health, Danville, IN, p. A209

KOMINS, Jeff, M.D. Chief Medical Officer, Mercy Fitzgerald Hospital, Darby, PA, p. A536

KOMORNIK, Jeffrey, Director Human Resources, Milford Hospital, Milford, CT, p. A115

KONARSKI, Debbie, Interim Chief Financial Officer, Pottstown Memorial Medical Center, Pottstown, PA, p. A552

KONDASH, Dennis, D.O
Vice President Medical Affairs, Blue Mountain Hospital, Lehighton, PA, p. A543
Vice President Medical Affairs, Palmerton Hospital, Palmerton, PA, p. A546

KONDO, Reid, Interim Administrator, Leahi Hospital, Honolulu, HI, p. A170

KONECNE, Robin, Manager Human Resources, Kit Carson County Health Service District, Burlington, CO, p. A102

KONG, Mei, Chief Operating Officer, NYC Health + Hospitals / Coney Island,, NY, p. A448

KONGARA, Rama, Chief Financial Officer, St. James Behavioral Health Hospital, Gonzales, LA, p. A277

KONIECZEK, Raymond, Chief Human Resources Officer, John F. Kennedy Memorial Hospital, Indio, CA, p. A66

KONKEL, Robert, Manager Finance, James A. Haley Veterans' Hospital–Tampa, Tampa, FL, p. A147

KONOPKO, Stan, Chief Financial Officer, St. James Mercy Hospital, Hornell, NY, p. A440

KONSAVAGE, Christian, M.D. Chief of Staff, Cumberland County Hospital, Burkesville, KY, p. A258

KOOIMAN, Thomas, Chief Executive Officer, Granite Falls Municipal Hospital and Manor, Granite Falls, MN, p. A343

KOOKEN, Kyron, Administrator, Kindred Hospital Dallas Central, Dallas, TX, p. A610

KOON, Rion, Chief Information Management Division, William Beaumont Army Medical Center, El Paso, TX, p. A616

KOONTZ, David, Chief Executive Officer, St. Francis Hospital, Columbus, GA, p. A157

KOOP, Steven, M.D. Chief Medical Officer, Medical Director, Gillette Children's Specialty Healthcare, Saint Paul, MN, p. A350

KOOVAKADA, Philip, Chief Operating Officer, Nacogdoches Medical Center, Nacogdoches, TX, p. A638

KOOY, Donald C., President and Chief Executive Officer, McLaren Flint, Flint, MI, p. A323

KOPEL, Samuel, M.D. Medical Director, Maimonides Medical Center,, NY, p. A445

KOPFLE, Sue, Chief Human Resources Officer, University of Missouri Hospitals and Clinics, Columbia, MO, p. A370

KOPINSKI, Donna, Chief Financial Officer, Crittenton Hospital Medical Center, Rochester, MI, p. A332

KOPITNIK, Thomas, Acting Chief Executive Officer, Mountain View Regional Hospital, Casper, WY, p. A721

KOPPELMAN, Benjamin
  Interim President, CHI LakeWood Health, Baudette, MN, p. A339
  President, CHI St. Joseph's Health, Park Rapids, MN, p. A348

KOPPENHAVER, Colleen, Interim Chief Financial Officer, Presence Resurrection Medical Center, Chicago, IL, p. A185

KOPPERUD, Gordon, Director Operations, Sanford Westbrook Medical Center, Westbrook, MN, p. A353

KORBEL, Tamara, Director Management Information Systems, Ridgeview Medical Center, Waconia, MN, p. A352

KORDAHL, Rebecca, R.N. Associate Director, Patient Care Services, William S. Middleton Memorial Veterans Hospital, Madison, WI, p. A709

KORDUCKI, Stanley R., President, Wood County Hospital, Bowling Green, OH, p. A485

KORDUPEL, Maureen
  Director Information Technology Relationship Manager, Mercy Health – St. Elizabeth Boardman Hospital, Boardman, OH, p. A485
  Director Relationship Manager, Mercy Health – St. Elizabeth Youngstown Hospital, Youngstown, OH, p. A506

KORF, Rick, Chief Financial Officer, Yuma District Hospital, Yuma, CO, p. A112

KORICH, Frank, Senior Vice President, Operations, Geneva General Hospital, Geneva, NY, p. A439

KORKMAS, Ross, Chief Operating Officer, Medical Center of South Arkansas, El Dorado, AR, p. A45

KORN, Larry, Manager Finance, Southern Arizona Veterans Affairs Health Care System, Tucson, AZ, p. A41

KORN, Roy, M.D. Medical Director, Cobleskill Regional Hospital, Cobleskill, NY, p. A437

KORNBLATT, Lynne R.
  Chief Human Resources Officer, Einstein Medical Center Montgomery, East Norriton, PA, p. A537
  Chief Human Resources Officer, Einstein Medical Center Philadelphia, Philadelphia, PA, p. A547

KORNFIELD, Lee, M.D. Medical Director, St. Luke's Rehabilitation Hospital, Boise, ID, p. A175

KOROLY, Marla, M.D. Chief Medical Officer and Senior Vice President Medical Affairs, Northern Westchester Hospital, Mount Kisco, NY, p. A443

KOROM, Nancy K.
  Chief Nursing Officer and Vice President, Children's Hospital of Wisconsin, Milwaukee, WI, p. A711
  Chief Nursing Officer and Vice President, Children's Hospital of Wisconsin–Fox Valley, Neenah, WI, p. A712

KOROUSH, Anthony, Chief Executive Officer, Benewah Community Hospital, Saint Maries, ID, p. A178

KORPELA, Donita, R.N. Director of Patient Care Services, Mercy Hospital, Moose Lake, MN, p. A347

KORTE, Fred, Chief Financial Officer, McLaren Flint, Flint, MI, p. A323

KORTEMEYER, Jay, Chief Executive Officer, Brynn Marr Hospital, Jacksonville, NC, p. A467

KORTH, Mark D., President, Mercy Medical Center Redding, Redding, CA, p. A84

KORTH, Paul, Chief Executive Officer, Cookeville Regional Medical Center, Cookeville, TN, p. A581

KORTH–WHITE, Kirsten, Vice President Physician Network and Ambulatory Service, Munson Healthcare Grayling Hospital, Grayling, MI, p. A325

KOSACH, Becky, Director Human Resources, Ivinson Memorial Hospital, Laramie, WY, p. A722

KOSANOVICH, John, M.D. Executive Vice President Physician Enterprise and Chief Executive Officer, Covenant Medical Group, Covenant Healthcare, Saginaw, MI, p. A333

KOSANOVICH, John P., President, Watertown Regional Medical Center, Watertown, WI, p. A718

KOSCIELSKI, Matthew F., M.D. Medical Director, Kindred Hospital of Northern Indiana, Mishawaka, IN, p. A218

KOSE, William H., M.D
  Chief Quality Officer, Blanchard Valley Hospital, Findlay, OH, p. A494
  Vice President Quality and Medical Affairs, Bluffton Hospital, Bluffton, OH, p. A485

KOSEK, Kevin, Associate Director Operations, Iowa City Veterans Affairs Health Care System, Iowa City, IA, p. A232

KOSIER, Douglas D., Chief Operating Officer, Mason District Hospital, Havana, IL, p. A192

KOSLOW, Howard B., President and Chief Executive Officer, Promise Hospital of Miss Lou, Vidalia, LA, p. A289

KOSMAN, Beth, Director Health Information Management, Ringgold County Hospital, Mount Ayr, IA, p. A234

KOSNOSKY, David, M.D. Chief Medical Officer, University Hospitals Geauga Medical Center, Chardon, OH, p. A486

KOSTER, Tracy, Director Human Resources, Carlinville Area Hospital, Carlinville, IL, p. A182

KOSTERS, Gregory J., D.O. Chief Medical Officer, Osceola Community Hospital, Sibley, IA, p. A237

KOSTOK, Barbara, Manager Human Resources, Punxsutawney Area Hospital, Punxsutawney, PA, p. A552

KOSTURKO, MaryEllen, R.N. Senior Vice President Patient Care Operations and Chief Nursing Officer, Bridgeport Hospital, Bridgeport, CT, p. A113

KOSYLA, Gail, Chief Financial Officer, Hunterdon Medical Center, Flemington, NJ, p. A417

KOSZTYO, Carol, R.N. Vice President, Patient Care Services, Carrier Clinic, Belle Mead, NJ, p. A414

KOTIL, Drew, Director Information Technology, Crete Area Medical Center, Crete, NE, p. A395

KOTIN, Kathy, Chief Financial Officer, Banner – University Medical Center Phoenix, Phoenix, AZ, p. A36

KOTRBA, Mitchell, Chief Financial Officer, North Valley Health Center, Warren, MN, p. A353

KOTSONIS, Robert, Chief Operating Officer, Northeast Rehabilitation Hospital, Salem, NH, p. A413

KOTTENBROOK, Susan, Chief Executive Officer, Red River Behavioral Center, Bossier City, LA, p. A274

KOTTMANN, Bill, President and Chief Executive Officer, Edward Hospital, Naperville, IL, p. A198

KOTZEN, Michael S., Vice President and Chief Operating Officer, Virtua Voorhees, Voorhees, NJ, p. A425

KOULOVATOS, James E., Chief Executive Officer, Pecos County Memorial Hospital, Fort Stockton, TX, p. A617

KOUNS, Jaccel, MS, Vice President and Executive Director, Montefiore Mount Vernon, Mount Vernon, NY, p. A443

KOUNTZ, David, M.D. Senior Vice President Medical Affairs, Jersey Shore University Medical Center, Neptune, NJ, p. A420

KOUSKOLEKAS, Anthony, FACHE, President, Pelham Medical Center, Greer, SC, p. A567

KOUTOUZOS, Connie L., MSN, Chief Executive Officer, Aspirus Iron River Hospitals & Clinics, Iron River, MI, p. A327

KOVAC, John, Facility Chief Information Officer, Veterans Affairs Pittsburgh Healthcare System, Pittsburgh, PA, p. A552

KOVACH, Andrew L., Vice President Human Resources and Chief Administrative Officer, Newton Medical Center, Newton, NJ, p. A421

KOVACS, Tina, Chief Financial Officer, Saint Francis Hospital–Bartlett, Bartlett, TN, p. A579

KOVAL, Matthew, M.D. Vice President Medical Affairs, KidsPeace Children's Hospital, Orefield, PA, p. A546

KOVALSKI, Jerry, Director Information Systems, Madera Community Hospital, Madera, CA, p. A75

KOVICH, Lynn, Assistant Commissioner, Division of Mental Health and Addiction Services, Department of Human Services, State of New Jersey, Trenton, NJ, p. B51

KOWALSKI, Brad, Director Information Technology, Marcus Daly Memorial Hospital, Hamilton, MT, p. A388

KOWALSKI, David, Chief Executive Officer, Kindred Hospital–La Mirada, La Mirada, CA, p. A67

KOWALSKI, Patrick A., Chief Financial Officer, Mercy Health – Anderson Hospital, Cincinnati, OH, p. A488

KOWNACKI, Dawn, Director Human Resources, Brooke Glen Behavioral Hospital, Fort Washington, PA, p. A539

KOWNACKI, Hamila
  Chief Operating Officer, California Pacific Medical Center, San Francisco, CA, p. A90
  Chief Operating Officer, St. Luke's Hospital, San Francisco, CA, p. A90

KOZAI, Gerald T., PharmD, President and Chief Executive Officer, St. Francis Medical Center, Lynwood, CA, p. A75

KOZEL, Kenneth D., FACHE,
  President and Chief Executive Officer, University of Maryland Shore Medical Center at Chestertown, Chestertown, MD, p. A299
  President and Chief Executive Officer, University of Maryland Shore Medical Center at Dorchester, Cambridge, MD, p. A299
  President and Chief Executive Officer, University of Maryland Shore Medical Center at Easton, Easton, MD, p. A300

KOZEL, Mary Ann, Chief Fiscal, Wilmington Veterans Affairs Medical Center, Wilmington, DE, p. A120

KOZIKUSKI, Courtney, Chief Financial Officer, Perry Memorial Hospital, Perry, OK, p. A518

KOZIN, Scott, M.D. Chief of Staff, Shriners Hospitals for Children–Philadelphia, Philadelphia, PA, p. A549

KOZOROSKY, Laurie, Chief Executive Officer, Select Specialty Hospital–Laurel Highlands, Latrobe, PA, p. A542

KRABBENHOFT, Kelby K., President and Chief Executive Officer, Sanford Health, Sioux Falls, SD, p. B118

KRABILL, Emma, Chief Executive Officer, Scenic Mountain Medical Center, Big Spring, TX, p. A602

KRABLIN, Brett, M.D. Chief of Staff, Mercy Hospital Kingfisher, Kingfisher, OK, p. A513

KRAFT, Chris, Director Information Systems, York General Hospital, York, NE, p. A403

KRAHNERT, John F., M.D. Chief Medical Officer, FirstHealth Moore Regional Hospital, Pinehurst, NC, p. A471

KRAJEWSKI, David, Senior Vice President and Chief Financial Officer, Sinai Hospital of Baltimore, Baltimore, MD, p. A298

KRAJEWSKI, Denise, Chief Nursing Officer, Lakeway Regional Medical Center, Lakeway, TX, p. A631

KRAMER, Blake, Chief Executive Officer, Franklin Medical Center, Winnsboro, LA, p. A289

KRAMER, Chad, Chief Operating Officer, Berwick Hospital Center, Berwick, PA, p. A533

KRAMER, Danette, Chief Financial Officer, Regional Medical Center, Manchester, IA, p. A234

KRAMER, Janie, Chief Operating Officer, Sharp Memorial Hospital, San Diego, CA, p. A89

KRAMER, Karen, R.N. Vice President and System Chief Nursing Officer, Cox Medical Centers, Springfield, MO, p. A382

KRAMER, Kathryn, M.D. President Medical Staff, Pekin Hospital, Pekin, IL, p. A200

KRAMER, Kevin, Chief Executive Officer, Modoc Medical Center, Alturas, CA, p. A54

KRAMER, Lynette, M.D. Chief Medical Officer, Boone County Health Center, Albion, NE, p. A393

KRAMER, Michael, Chief Executive Officer, Mercy Health – West Hospital, Cincinnati, OH, p. A488

KRAMER, Richard, Chief Executive Officer, Northlake Behavioral Health System, Mandeville, LA, p. A282

KRAMER, Susan, Director of Human Resources, Levi Hospital, Hot Springs National Park, AR, p. A47

KRAML, Louis D., FACHE, Chief Executive Officer, Mountain River Birthing and Surgery Center, Blackfoot, ID, p. A174

KRAMPITS, Carrie, Director Human Resources, McKenzie Health System, Sandusky, MI, p. A334

KRANZ, Karl, M.D. Chief of Staff, Cascade Medical Center, Leavenworth, WA, p. A686

KRASON, Jane E., R.N., Chief Executive Officer, Appalachian Behavioral Healthcare, Athens, OH, p. A484

KRASS, Todd, Chief Executive Officer, Belton Regional Medical Center, Belton, MO, p. A367

KRAUKLIS, Gene
  Regional Vice President Human Resources, Aurora Lakeland Medical Center, Elkhorn, WI, p. A705
  Regional Vice President Human Resources, Aurora Memorial Hospital of Burlington, Burlington, WI, p. A703

KRAUS, Jason, Director Human Resources, Magruder Memorial Hospital, Port Clinton, OH, p. A501

KRAUS, John, M.D. Chief Medical Officer, Bryn Mawr Rehabilitation Hospital, Malvern, PA, p. A543

KRAUSE, Donna, Chief Information Officer, Harry S. Truman Memorial Veterans Hospital, Columbia, MO, p. A370

KRAUSE, Jill A., Director, Kalamazoo Psychiatric Hospital, Kalamazoo, MI, p. A328

KRAUSE, Kim, Director Human Resources, Baylor Jack and Jane Hamilton Heart and Vascular Hospital, Dallas, TX, p. A609

KRAUSE, Steven, Manager Information Technology, Franciscan Healthcare – Munster, Munster, IN, p. A219

KRAUSE, Wade, M.D. Chief Medical Officer, Connally Memorial Medical Center, Floresville, TX, p. A617

KRAUSS, James D., President, Sentara RMH Medical Center, Harrisonburg, VA, p. A671

KRAUTSCHEID, Steven P., Ancillary Services Administrator, Tuality Healthcare, Hillsboro, OR, p. A526

KRAVETZ, Michael, M.D. Medical Director, HEALTHSOUTH Valley of the Sun Rehabilitation Hospital, Glendale, AZ, p. A33

KRAVETZ, Todd, Chief of Staff, Wickenburg Community Hospital, Wickenburg, AZ, p. A41

KREATSOULAS, Nicholas
Senior Vice President and Chief Medical Officer and Chief Quality Officer, Mercy Health – St. Elizabeth Youngstown Hospital, Youngstown, OH, p. A506
Vice President Medical Affairs, Mercy Health – St. Joseph Warren Hospital, Warren, OH, p. A504

KREBS, Anne, Chief Financial Officer, Butler Health System, Butler, PA, p. A534

KREBS, Cindy, District Director Human Resources, Matagorda Regional Medical Center, Bay City, TX, p. A601

KREBS, George, M.D. Chief Medical Officer, Broughton Hospital, Morganton, NC, p. A470

KREBS, Mary Jane, FACHE, President, Spring Harbor Hospital, Westbrook, ME, p. A295

KREBSBACH, Mayla, Chief Executive Officer, Vista Del Mar Hospital, Ventura, CA, p. A98

KREELEY, Chris, Director Nursing, Marlton Rehabilitation Hospital, Marlton, NJ, p. A419

KREHBIEL, Rod, M.D. Chief of Staff, Klickitat Valley Health, Goldendale, WA, p. A685

KREIDER, David, Controller, WellSpan Ephrata Community Hospital, Ephrata, PA, p. A538

KREIDER, Robert Q., President and Chief Executive Officer, Devereux, Villanova, PA, p. B49

KREIDLER, Marlene, Executive Director Human Resources, San Joaquin Community Hospital, Bakersfield, CA, p. A56

KREITINGER, Tate J.
Interim Chief Executive Officer, North Valley Hospital, Whitefish, MT, p. A391
Chief Executive Officer, The HealthCenter, Kalispell, MT, p. A389

KREITZER, Teri, Director Human Resources, Saint Francis Healthcare System, Cape Girardeau, MO, p. A368

KREJCI, Kathy Blair, Chief Nursing Officer, Marshall Medical Center, Placerville, CA, p. A83

KRELL, G. Christopher, M.D. Chief of Staff, South Lincoln Medical Center, Kemmerer, WY, p. A722

KRELSTEIN, Michael, M.D. Medical Director, San Diego County Psychiatric Hospital, San Diego, CA, p. A89

KREMER, Ruth, Director Information Services, CentraCare Health–Monticello, Monticello, MN, p. A347

KREN, John, Chief Financial Officer, St. John's Medical Center and Living Center, Jackson, WY, p. A722

KRENOS, Lori L., R.N. Chief Nursing Officer, Bay Area Hospital, Coos Bay, OR, p. A525

KREPPS, John, Senior Vice President Finance, Silver Cross Hospital, New Lenox, IL, p. A198

KRETSCHMAN, Robin, MSN Vice President Patient Care Services, Ministry Saint Joseph's Hospital, Marshfield, WI, p. A709

KRETSCHMER, Suzanne, Chief Executive Officer, CHG Cornerstone Hospital Conroe, Conroe, TX, p. A607

KRETZ, Blake, President, Texas Health Arlington Memorial Hospital, Arlington, TX, p. A598

KRETZINGER, Curt, Chief Operating Officer, Mosaic Life Care at St. Joseph, Saint Joseph, MO, p. A379

KRETZSCHMER, Kendra, Patient Care System Leader, Scheurer Hospital, Pigeon, MI, p. A331

KREUTNER, Ron, Chief Financial Officer, San Joaquin General Hospital, French Camp, CA, p. A63

KREUTZER, Kevin, Chief Financial Officer, Russell Regional Hospital, Russell, KS, p. A252

KREUZ, Betsy, Chief Financial Officer, UPMC Altoona, Altoona, PA, p. A532

KREUZER, Jay E., FACHE, Chief Executive Officer, Kona Community Hospital, Kealakekua, HI, p. A172

KREVANS, Sarah, President and Chief Executive Officer, Sutter Health, Sacramento, CA, p. B130

KREYE, David, Chief Executive Officer, First Surgical Hospital, Bellaire, TX, p. A602

KRHOVSKY, David, M.D. Vice President, Medical Affairs, Spectrum Health – Butterworth Hospital, Grand Rapids, MI, p. A325

KRIEGER, Cathy, Human Resources Director, Greene County Medical Center, Jefferson, IA, p. A233

KRIEGER, Mark, Vice President and Chief Financial Officer, Barnes–Jewish Hospital, Saint Louis, MO, p. A379

KRIEGER, Robert M., Chief Executive Officer, Osceola Regional Medical Center, Kissimmee, FL, p. A133

KRIEGER, Tim, Director Information Systems, Harnett Health System, Dunn, NC, p. A464

KRIER, Jennifer, Vice President Human Resources, Wesley Medical Center, Wichita, KS, p. A256

KRILICH, Chad, M.D. Chief Med Officer–AMC/CMC, MultiCare Auburn Medical Center, Auburn, WA, p. A682

KRINKE, Susan, Chief Executive Officer, Kindred Hospital Lima, Lima, OH, p. A496

KRIPAKARAN, Kasturi, M.D. Medical Director, Andrew McFarland Mental Health Center, Springfield, IL, p. A203

KRIPINSKI, Laura, Chief Nursing Officer, Forks Community Hospital, Forks, WA, p. A685

KRISHNAN, Radha, M.D. Chief Medical Officer, Antelope Valley Hospital, Lancaster, CA, p. A68

KRISHNAN, Suresh, Vice President and Chief Information Officer, Loretto Hospital, Chicago, IL, p. A184

KRISHNASWAMY, Jaikumar, Chief Executive Officer, Baylor Scott & White Medical Center – White Rock, Dallas, TX, p. A609

KRISTEL, John, President and Chief Executive Officer, Good Shepherd Rehabilitation Hospital, Allentown, PA, p. A532

KRISTEL, John, President and Chief Executive Officer, Good Shepherd Rehabilitation Network, Allentown, PA, p. B58

KRITZ, Howard
Director Human Resources, NYC Health + Hospitals / Bellevue, New York, NY, p. A447
Senior Associate Executive Director, NYC Health + Hospitals / Carter, New York, NY, p. A448

KRITZER, Tammy, Vice President Clinic Operations, Mayo Clinic Health System–Albert Lea and Austin, Austin, MN, p. A339

KRIVENKO, Chuck, M.D. Chief Medical Officer, Clinical and Quality Services, Lee Memorial Hospital, Fort Myers, FL, p. A129

KRMPOTIC, Debra J., R.N., Chief Executive Officer, Banner Thunderbird Medical Center, Glendale, AZ, p. A33

KRODEL, Scott, Vice President Information Systems, Johnson Memorial Hospital, Franklin, IN, p. A211

KROESE, Brandi, Director Operations, West Springs Hospital, Grand Junction, CO, p. A106

KROESE, Robert D., FACHE, Chief Executive Officer, Pella Regional Health Center, Pella, IA, p. A236

KROHN, Karl, M.D. President Medical Staff, CHI St. Luke's Health Memorial Specialty Hospital, Lufkin, TX, p. A634

KROLICKI, Karen, Director, Human Resources, Beaumont Hospital – Taylor, Taylor, MI, p. A335

KROLL, Ronald, Chief Financial Officer, Mercy General Hospital, Sacramento, CA, p. A86

KROMER, Harold, Director, Site Information Systems, Advocate Condell Medical Center, Libertyville, IL, p. A195

KRONENBERG, Seth, M.D. Chief Medical Officer, Crouse Hospital, Syracuse, NY, p. A456

KROSOFF, Mary June, Chief Human Resources Officer, Highlands Hospital, Connellsville, PA, p. A536

KROUSE, Donald, M.D. Chief of Staff, Trinity Hospital, Weaverville, CA, p. A99

KROUSE, Michael
Chief Information Officer, OhioHealth Doctors Hospital, Columbus, OH, p. A491
Senior Vice President Chief Information Officer, OhioHealth Dublin Methodist Hospital, Dublin, OH, p. A494
Chief Information Officer Information Services, OhioHealth Grady Memorial Hospital, Delaware, OH, p. A493
Chief Information Officer, OhioHealth Grant Medical Center, Columbus, OH, p. A491
Chief Information Officer, OhioHealth Riverside Methodist Hospital, Columbus, OH, p. A491

KROUSE, Stephen W., Chief Human Resource Officer, St. Christopher's Hospital for Children, Philadelphia, PA, p. A549

KRUCKNER, Douglas, M.D. Medical Director, Stamford Memorial Hospital, Stamford, TX, p. A650

KRUEGER, Albert, M.D. Chief of Staff, Pioneers Medical Center, Meeker, CO, p. A109

KRUEGER, Christine, M.D. Chief of Staff, Munising Memorial Hospital, Munising, MI, p. A330

KRUEGER, David, Associate Director, Bath Veterans Affairs Medical Center, Bath, NY, p. A434

KRUEGER, Ellen, Director Human Resources, Chadron Community Hospital and Health Services, Chadron, NE, p. A395

KRUEGER, Eric, Chief Financial Officer, Mercy Hospital and Medical Center, Chicago, IL, p. A185

KRUEGER Jr., Harold L., Chief Executive Officer, Chadron Community Hospital and Health Services, Chadron, NE, p. A395

KRUEGER, James G., Ph.D., Chief Executive Officer, Rockefeller University Hospital, New York, NY, p. A449

KRUEGER, Justin, Chief Operating Officer, Mercy Health – Fairfield Hospital, Fairfield, OH, p. A494

KRUEGER, Mary T., President, Ministry Good Samaritan Health Center, Merrill, WI, p. A710

KRUEGER, Pete, Director Human Resources, Borgess–Lee Memorial Hospital, Dowagiac, MI, p. A322

KRUG, Robert J., M.D., Chief Executive Officer, Mount Sinai Rehabilitation Hospital, Hartford, CT, p. A114

KRUGEL, Gary M., Chief Financial Officer, Norwegian American Hospital, Chicago, IL, p. A185

KRUGER, Cory, Interim Chief Executive Officer, Nebraska Spine Hospital, Omaha, NE, p. A400

KRUGER, Dale K., Chief Executive Officer, Mahnomen Health Center, Mahnomen, MN, p. A345

KRUGER, George, CPA Chief Financial Officer, Comanche County Memorial Hospital, Lawton, OK, p. A513

KRUMMEL, Dere, Director Information Systems, Ochsner Medical Center – Kenner, Kenner, LA, p. A279

KRUMREY, Arthur J., Chief Information Officer, Loyola University Medical Center, Maywood, IL, p. A196

KRUMWIED, Robert D., President and Chief Executive Officer, Regional Mental Health Center, Merrillville, IN, p. A218

KRUPALA, Judith, R.N. Chief Nursing Officer, Cuero Community Hospital, Cuero, TX, p. A608

KRUSE, Joseph J.
Executive Vice President, Mayo Clinic Health System – Franciscan Healthcare in La Crosse, La Crosse, WI, p. A708
Chief Administrative Officer, Mayo Clinic Health System – Franciscan Healthcare in Sparta, Sparta, WI, p. A716

KRUSE, Marcia, R.N. Director Nursing, Logan County Hospital, Oakley, KS, p. A250

KRUSE, Victoria, Manager Human Resources, Franklin General Hospital, Hampton, IA, p. A231

KRUSIE, Kathleen R., FACHE, President, Community Hospital North, Indianapolis, IN, p. A213

KRUYER–COLLINS, Emyle
Director Human Resources, Doctors NeuroMedical Hospital, Bremen, IN, p. A207
Chief Human Resources Officer, Unity Medical & Surgical Hospital, Mishawaka, IN, p. A218

KRUZEL, Janet, Business Office Manager, CentraCare Health–Melrose, Melrose, MN, p. A346

KRUZICK, Michael, Acting Chief Financial Officer, Norwalk Hospital, Norwalk, CT, p. A116

KRUZNER, Melinda, Chief Financial Officer, Lexington Medical Center, West Columbia, SC, p. A570

KRYSTOWIAK, Thomas P.
Chief Financial Officer, Berlin Memorial Hospital, Berlin, WI, p. A703
Vice President Finance, Theda Care Medical Center – Wild Rose, Wild Rose, WI, p. A719

KRYZANIAK, Larry, Chief Financial Officer, Hennepin County Medical Center, Minneapolis, MN, p. A346

KRZASTEK, Sue, Vice President Human Resources, Augusta Health, Fishersville, VA, p. A670

KRZYMOWSKI, David, M.D. Chief of Staff, Sanpete Valley Hospital, Mount Pleasant, UT, p. A660

KUANGPARICHAT, Manoch, M.D. President Medical Staff, Excelsior Springs Hospital, Excelsior Springs, MO, p. A370

KUBACKI, Clayton, Controller, Kindred Hospital Detroit, Detroit, MI, p. A322

KUBALA, Joseph
Chief Financial Officer, St. Vincent Jennings Hospital, North Vernon, IN, p. A220
Director Financial and Support Services, St. Vincent Salem Hospital, Salem, IN, p. A221

KUBALL, Lana, Director Administrative Services, Lucas County Health Center, Chariton, IA, p. A227

KUBE, Don, M.D. Chief of Staff, Dickinson County Healthcare System, Iron Mountain, MI, p. A327

KUBIAK, Phillip J., President, Hampstead Hospital, Hampstead, NH, p. A411

KUBIAK, Richard, M.D. Vice President Medical Affairs, Peconic Bay Medical Center, Riverhead, NY, p. A454

KUBOTA, Andrea, R.N. Director Patient Care Services and Nurse Executive, Shriners Hospitals for Children–Honolulu, Honolulu, HI, p. A171

KUBOUSHEK, David, Chief, Fiscal Service, Durham Veterans Affairs Medical Center, Durham, NC, p. A464

KUCERA, Doug, Chief Financial Officer, Crete Area Medical Center, Crete, NE, p. A395

KUCERA, Kim, Chief Operating Officer, Mille Lacs Health System, Onamia, MN, p. A348

KUCICH, Vincent, FACH
Chief Medical Officer, Presence Covenant Medical Center, Urbana, IL, p. A204
Chief Medical Officer, Presence United Samaritans Medical Center, Danville, IL, p. A187

KUCKEWICH, Mike, Director Information Systems, Terre Haute Regional Hospital, Terre Haute, IN, p. A222

KUCZORA, Paul, Chief Executive Officer, Grant–Blackford Mental Health Center, Marion, IN, p. A217

KUDER, Merlin, Chief Information Officer, Hamilton County Hospital, Syracuse, KS, p. A254

KUDLA, Angela, R.N., Chief Nursing Officer, Select Specialty Hospital–Downriver, Wyandotte, MI, p. A337

KUEHLER, Sheila, R.N. Director of Nursing, Knox County Hospital, Knox City, TX, p. A631

KUEHN, David, Chief Financial Officer, Rusk County Memorial Hospital, Ladysmith, WI, p. A708

KUEHNEMUND, Bonnie, Comptroller, Heart of America Medical Center, Rugby, ND, p. A481

KUESTERSTEFFEN, Vicki, Chief Executive Officer, J. D. McCarty Center for Children With Developmental Disabilities, Norman, OK, p. A515

KUGHN, Yvonne, Chief Executive Officer, Southeast Michigan Surgical Hospital, Warren, MI, p. A336

KUHAR, Peggy A., R.N. Chief Nursing Officer, University Hospitals Geauga Medical Center, Chardon, OH, p. A486

KUHL, Nicholas, M.D. Chief of Staff, Spectrum Health Gerber Memorial, Fremont, MI, p. A324

KUHLMAN, Ian, Manager Information Technology, Shelby Memorial Hospital, Shelbyville, IL, p. A202

KUHN, Anita, Controller, Texas County Memorial Hospital, Houston, MO, p. A372

KUHN, Brenda, Ph.D
    Chief Nursing Officer, Greene Memorial Hospital, Xenia, OH, p. A506
    Chief Nursing Officer, Kettering Medical Center, Kettering, OH, p. A496
    Chief Nursing Officer, Sycamore Medical Center, Miamisburg, OH, p. A499

KUHN, Keith, Chief Executive Officer, Haven Behavioral Senior Care of Dayton, Dayton, OH, p. A492

KUHN, Margueritte, M.D. Vice President Medical Affairs, MidMichigan Medical Center–Midland, Midland, MI, p. A330

KUHN, Steve, Chief Financial Officer, River Park Hospital, Huntington, WV, p. A697

KUHNS, Jay, Vice President Human Resources, Johns Hopkins All Children's Hospital, Saint Petersburg, FL, p. A144

KUKELHAN, Alison, Manager Human Resources, Adams Memorial Hospital, Decatur, IN, p. A209

KULHANEK, Linda, Chief Financial Officer, Memorial Hermann Katy Hospital, Katy, TX, p. A629

KULICK, Daniel, M.D. Chief of Staff, Marlette Regional Hospital, Marlette, MI, p. A329

KULIK, Alec G., Administrator, Cleveland Clinic Children's Hospital for Rehabilitation, Cleveland, OH, p. A489

KULISZ, Michael, D.O
    Chief Medical Officer, Northwestern Medicine Kishwaukee Hospital, DeKalb, IL, p. A188
    Chief Medical Officer, Northwestern Medicine Valley West Hospital, Sandwich, IL, p. A202

KULLMAN, Betsy, R.N. Executive Vice President and Chief Nursing Officer, Medical Center at Bowling Green, Bowling Green, KY, p. A258

KULMA, Mariarose, R.N. Vice President Patient Services, East Texas Medical Center Tyler, Tyler, TX, p. A654

KUMAR, Daryn J., Chief Executive Officer, Memorial Medical Center, Modesto, CA, p. A77

KUMAR, Nanda, M.D. Chief of Staff, Vibra Hospital of Northern California, Redding, CA, p. A84

KUMMER, Margaret, Chief Human Resource Officer, Citizens Medical Center, Colby, KS, p. A241

KUNERT, Alicia, MS, Executive Director, Conway Regional Rehabilitation Hospital, Conway, AR, p. A44

KUNES, Courtney, Director Human Resources, Lock Haven Hospital, Lock Haven, PA, p. A543

KUNKEL, Stephanie, Vice President of Human Resources, Tampa Community Hospital, Tampa, FL, p. A148

KUNNAPPILLY, Chester, M.D., Interim Chief Executive Officer, San Mateo Medical Center, San Mateo, CA, p. A92

KUNSTLING, Ted, M.D. Chief Medical Officer, Duke Raleigh Hospital, Raleigh, NC, p. A471

KUNTZ, Alicia, Nurse Manager, LifeCare Hospitals of Mechanicsburg, Mechanicsburg, PA, p. A544

KUNZ, Donna
    Director Human Resources, Saint Luke's Cushing Hospital, Leavenworth, KS, p. A247
    Director Human Resources, Saint Luke's North Hospital – Barry Road, Kansas City, MO, p. A374
    Manager Human Resources, Saint Luke's South Hospital, Overland Park, KS, p. A251

KUNZ, Kara, Administrative Director Finance, Weiser Memorial Hospital, Weiser, ID, p. A179

KUNZA, Mary Kay, Manager Human Resources, Mercy Hospital Lincoln, Troy, MO, p. A383

KUPER, Kandi, Chief Nursing Officer, Kit Carson County Health Service District, Burlington, CO, p. A102

KUPFERSTEIN, Ron, Chief Executive Officer, Monrovia Memorial Hospital, Monrovia, CA, p. A77

KUPLEN, Carol, MSN, President and Chief Executive Officer, St. Luke's University Hospital – Bethlehem Campus, Bethlehem, PA, p. A533

KURAITIS, Kestutis V., M.D. Chief of Staff, Pioneers Memorial Healthcare District, Brawley, CA, p. A57

KURCAB, Jeff, Chief Financial Officer, LewisGale Hospital Pulaski, Pulaski, VA, p. A676

KURESKA, Kirk, Chief Executive Officer, RiverWoods Behavioral Health System, Riverdale, GA, p. A164

KURIAN, Santha, M.D. Chief of Staff, James E. Van Zandt Veterans Affairs Medical Center, Altoona, PA, p. A532

KURLE, Janet, Chief Financial Officer, Community Memorial Hospital, Turtle Lake, ND, p. A481

KUROKI, Helen, Senior Vice President and Chief Medical Officer, CHI Memorial, Chattanooga, TN, p. A580

KURRA, Shankar, M.D. Senior Vice President Medical Affairs, Fisher-Titus Medical Center, Norwalk, OH, p. A500

KURTZ, Kris, Controller, Metro Health Hospital, Wyoming, MI, p. A337

KURTZ, Maria
    Director Human Resources, Lutheran Hospital of Indiana, Fort Wayne, IN, p. A210
    Director Human Resources, Orthopaedic Hospital of Lutheran Health Network, Fort Wayne, IN, p. A210

KURTZ, Jr., Thomas F., Chief Operating Officer, Georgia Regional Hospital at Savannah, Savannah, GA, p. A166

KURTZ, Thomas M., President and Chief Executive Officer, Chan Soon-Shiong Medical Center, Windber, PA, p. A558

KURTZ, Tom, Vice President Information Services and Chief Information Officer, Memorial Healthcare, Owosso, MI, p. A331

KURZ, Kenneth R., M.D. Chief of Staff, MidState Medical Center, Meriden, CT, p. A115

KURZ, Sharon H., Ph.D., Chief Executive Officer, St. Elias Specialty Hospital, Anchorage, AK, p. A28

KUSHNER, Michael S., Senior Vice President and Chief Talent Officer, Nicklaus Children's Hospital, Miami, FL, p. A137

KUSLER, Julie, Manager Information Services, Avera St. Luke's Hospital, Aberdeen, SD, p. A572

KUSNIERZ, William J., Vice President and Chief Financial Officer, Springfield Regional Medical Center, Springfield, OH, p. A503

KUTCH, John M., President, Trinity Health, Minot, ND, p. A481

KUTCHER, Gregory, M.D., President and Chief Executive Officer, Mayo Clinic Health System in Mankato, Mankato, MN, p. A345

KUTILEK, Richard J., Chief Operating Officer, Calvary Hospital,, NY, p. A444

KUTNER, Jean, M.D. Chief Medical Officer, University of Colorado Hospital, Aurora, CO, p. A101

KUVSHINOFF, II, Boris, M.D. Chief Medical Officer, Roswell Park Cancer Institute, Buffalo, NY, p. A436

KUYKENDALL, Jana, Chief Executive Officer, Post Acute/Warm Springs Specialty Hospital of Luling, Luling, TX, p. A635

KUZAS, Betsy, Executive Vice President and Chief Operating Officer, Phoenix Children's Hospital, Phoenix, AZ, p. A37

KUZEE, Ann, Executive Director Human Resources, Riverview Health, Noblesville, IN, p. A220

KWIATEK, Susan, R.N., Executive Director, Glen Cove Hospital, Glen Cove, NY, p. A439

KWIESIELEWICZ, Nancy
    Human Resources Manager, Ministry Good Samaritan Health Center, Merrill, WI, p. A710
    Human Resources Manager, Ministry Saint Clare's Hospital, Weston, WI, p. A719

KYHNELL, Koreen H., Vice President Human Resources, Indiana University Health Arnett Hospital, Lafayette, IN, p. A216

KYLE, James, M.D. Chief Medical Officer, Tuba City Regional Health Care Corporation, Tuba City, AZ, p. A40

KYLER, Yvonne
    Director Human Resources, Texas Health Arlington Memorial Hospital, Arlington, TX, p. A598
    Director Human Resources, Texas Health Heart & Vascular Hospital Arlington, Arlington, TX, p. A598

KYRIACOU, George M., President and Chief Executive Officer, Gaylord Hospital, Wallingford, CT, p. A117

KYWI, Alberto
    Chief Information Officer, Goleta Valley Cottage Hospital, Santa Barbara, CA, p. A93
    Chief Information Officer, Santa Barbara Cottage Hospital, Santa Barbara, CA, p. A93

KYZAR, Debbie, Chief Financial Officer, Central Carolina Hospital, Sanford, NC, p. A473

L

L'ITALIEN, Mark, Director Information Services, Salem Regional Medical Center, Salem, OH, p. A502

LA CAVA, Joseph, Chief Nursing Officer and Director Of Anesthesia, DeSoto Memorial Hospital, Arcadia, FL, p. A123

LA CROIX, Kent, Supervisor Information Technology, Schoolcraft Memorial Hospital, Manistique, MI, p. A329

LA PORTE, Todd
    Chief Financial Officer, HonorHealth John C. Lincoln Medical Center, Phoenix, AZ, p. A36
    Senior Vice President and Chief Financial Officer, HonorHealth Scottsdale Osborn Medical Center, Scottsdale, AZ, p. A38
    Senior Vice President and Chief Financial Officer, HonorHealth Scottsdale Shea Medical Center, Scottsdale, AZ, p. A39

LABADIE, Wendy, Chief Human Resource Officer, Banner Estrella Medical Center, Phoenix, AZ, p. A36

LABAGNARA, James, M.D. Vice President Medical Affairs, St. Joseph's Healthcare System, Paterson, NJ, p. A421

LABAND, Andrew, Chief Information Officer, McLean Hospital, Belmont, MA, p. A305

LABARGE, Robert J., President and Chief Executive Officer, Sturgis Hospital, Sturgis, MI, p. A335

LABELLE, Douglas, M.D. Chief Medical Officer, UP Health System–Bell, Ishpeming, MI, p. A327

LABELLE, James, M.D
    Chief Medical Officer, Scripps Green Hospital, La Jolla, CA, p. A67
    Chief Medical Officer, Scripps Memorial Hospital–La Jolla, La Jolla, CA, p. A67

LABER, Susan, R.N. Chief Nursing Officer, Tampa Community Hospital, Tampa, FL, p. A148

LABIAGA, Kimberly, Human Resources Leader, Kaiser Permanente Fontana Medical Center, Fontana, CA, p. A62

LABONTE, Karen Y., Chief Nursing Officer, Northwest Medical Center – Springdale, Springdale, AR, p. A52

LABONTE, Robin, Leader Financial Care, York Hospital, York, ME, p. A295

LABORANTI, Sarah M., Interim Director Human Resources, Tennova Physicians Regional Medical Center, Knoxville, TN, p. A586

LABRIOLA, Terri, Human Resources Officer, Sierra Nevada Memorial Hospital, Grass Valley, CA, p. A65

LABRUM, Chad, Chief Financial Officer, Ashley Regional Medical Center, Vernal, UT, p. A664

LACAZE, Todd, Chief Financial Officer, Tulane Medical Center, New Orleans, LA, p. A285

LACEFIELD, Gayla, Director Human Resources, Howard Memorial Hospital, Nashville, AR, p. A50

LACEY, Carmen, R.N., President, Charles A. Cannon Memorial Hospital, Newland, NC, p. A471

LACEY, Paul, M.D. Chief Medical Staff, North Valley Hospital, Tonasket, WA, p. A692

LACHANCE, Eric, Chief Financial Officer, Munroe Regional Medical Center, Ocala, FL, p. A139

LACHAPELLE, Diana, Controller, HEALTHSOUTH Rehabilitation Hospital, Concord, NH, p. A410

LACHER, Paula A., MSN Chief Nursing Officer, West Penn Hospital, Pittsburgh, PA, p. A552

LACHINA, Ignazio, M.D. Medical Director, HEALTHSOUTH Rehabilitation Hospital of Cypress, Houston, TX, p. A624

LACHNEY, Cheryl, Director of Nursing, Compass Behavioral Center of Alexandria, Alexandria, LA, p. A271

LACHOWSKY, John, M.D. Chief Medical Officer, Mercy Hospital Ozark, Ozark, AR, p. A51

LACHTERMAN, Bruce, M.D. Chief of Medical Staff, St. Luke's Lakeside Hospital, The Woodlands, TX, p. A653

LACKEY, Lori, Chief Financial Officer, Sabetha Community Hospital, Sabetha, KS, p. A253

LACKNEY, Christopher J., Director Human Resources, Grace Cottage Hospital, Townshend, VT, p. A666

LACOT, Ivette, Director Human Resources, Hospital Episcopal San Lucas Guayama, Guayama, PR, p. A727

LACY, Albert, Associate Director of Information Technology, Tampa Community Hospital, Tampa, FL, p. A148

LACY, Angela, Director of Nursing, Bolivar General Hospital, Bolivar, TN, p. A579

LACY, Dwight A., Chief Executive Officer, Millwood Hospital, Arlington, TX, p. A597

LACY, Edward L., FACHE, Vice President and Administrator, Baptist Health Medical Center–Heber Springs, Heber Springs, AR, p. A47

LACY, Tyson, Chief Executive Officer and Superintendent, Lincoln Hospital, Davenport, WA, p. A684

LADAROLA, Sandra, Chief Nursing Officer, Waterbury Hospital, Waterbury, CT, p. A117

LADD, Bill, Director Information Services, Western Missouri Medical Center, Warrensburg, MO, p. A383

LADWIG, Michael, M.D. Chief of Staff, Marion Veterans Affairs Medical Center, Marion, IL, p. A195

LAEL, Marielle, R.N. Chief Nursing Officer, Select Specialty Hospital–Fort Wayne, Fort Wayne, IN, p. A211

LAFERNEY, Jimmy, M.D. Vice President Medical Staff Affairs, Baylor Medical Center at Frisco, Frisco, TX, p. A619

LAFFEY, Leah, R.N., Chief Executive Officer, HEALTHSOUTH Rehabilitation Hospital of Sewickley, Sewickley, PA, p. A554

LAFLAMME, Christine, R.N. Chief Nursing Officer, Seton Smithville Regional Hospital, Smithville, TX, p. A649

LAFLEUR, Cindy, Senior Administrator, Via Christi Rehabilitation Hospital, Wichita, KS, p. A256

LAFLEUR, Phillip, M.D. Medical Director, Westend Hospital, Jennings, LA, p. A279

LAFLEUR, Robert R., Administrator, Memorial Specialty Hospital, Lake Charles, LA, p. A281

LAFRANCOIS, Gregory, President and Chief Executive Officer, St. Aloisius Medical Center, Harvey, ND, p. A479

LAFRANCOIS, Mary, Vice President Human Resources, CHRISTUS Spohn Hospital Corpus Christi Memorial, Corpus Christi, TX, p. A607

LAGASSE, David A., Senior Vice President Fiscal Affairs, McLean Hospital, Belmont, MA, p. A305

LAGNESE, John, M.D. Vice President Medical Affairs, UPMC St. Margaret, Pittsburgh, PA, p. A552

LAGROU, Robert, D.O. Medical Director, Henry Ford Kingswood Hospital, Ferndale, MI, p. A323

LAGUNA, Michelle, Chief Nursing Officer, CHG Hospital Tucson, LLC, Tucson, AZ, p. A40

LAHASKY, Douglas
Chief Financial Officer, Avoyelles Hospital, Marksville, LA, p. A282
Chief Financial Officer, Winn Parish Medical Center, Winnfield, LA, p. A289

LAHAYE, Daniel, Manager, Savoy Medical Center, Mamou, LA, p. A282

LAHOOD, Amy, R.N. Director of Nursing, Acadia Vermilion Hospital, Lafayette, LA, p. A280

LAHOUT, Brenda, Chief Nurse Executive, Danville State Hospital, Danville, PA, p. A536

LAHTI, Molly, Director Human Resources, Parkland Medical Center, Derry, NH, p. A410

LAI, Daniel, Controller, HEALTHSOUTH Rehabilitation Hospital–Las Vegas, Las Vegas, NV, p. A406

LAI, Iris, Chief Executive Officer, Alhambra Hospital Medical Center, Alhambra, CA, p. A54

LAIBINIS, Walter, M.D. Chief Medical Officer, Soldiers and Sailors Memorial Hospital, Wellsboro, PA, p. A557

LAIGN, Michael B., President and Chief Executive Officer, Holy Redeemer Hospital, Meadowbrook, PA, p. A544

LAIL, Steve, Vice President Operations and Chief Operating Officer, Down East Community Hospital, Machias, ME, p. A294

LAIOSA, Sarah, M.D. Chief Medical Staff, Harney District Hospital, Burns, OR, p. A524

LAIRD, Alan, M.D. Chief Medical Officer, Orange City Area Health System, Orange City, IA, p. A235

LAIRD, Charles, Chief Executive Officer, Menorah Medical Center, Overland Park, KS, p. A251

LAIRD, Jeff, Controller, Stephens County Hospital, Toccoa, GA, p. A168

LAIRD, Shaw, Chief Information Officer, Chester Regional Medical Center, Chester, SC, p. A563

LAISTER, Judy K., Director, Human Resources, Methodist Mansfield Medical Center, Mansfield, TX, p. A635

LAKE, Chandra, Associate Director, Sheridan Veterans Affairs Medical Center, Sheridan, WY, p. A724

LAKE, Nathan, Vice President Human Resources, Prairie Lakes Healthcare System, Watertown, SD, p. A577

LAKE, Peter M., M.D. Chief Medical Officer, Rogers Memorial Hospital, Oconomowoc, WI, p. A713

LAKE, Rob, Interim Chief Executive Officer, Cedar Ridge Hospital, Oklahoma City, OK, p. A516

LAKE, Ryan, Director Medical Imaging and Information Technology, Glencoe Regional Health Services, Glencoe, MN, p. A343

LAKEY, Travis, Chief Financial Officer, Mayers Memorial Hospital District, Fall River Mills, CA, p. A62

LAKINS, Tom, Director Information Systems, Tennova Physicians Regional Medical Center, Knoxville, TN, p. A586

LAKSHMANAN, Rekha, M.D. Medical Director, Kindred Hospital–St. Louis at Mercy, Saint Louis, MO, p. A380

LALIBERTE, John, Chief Information Officer, St. Vincent's Blount, Oneonta, AL, p. A24

LALLY, James M., D.O., President and Chief Medical Officer, Chino Valley Medical Center, Chino, CA, p. A58

LALLY, Jr., Robert P., Vice President Finance, MedStar Franklin Square Medical Center, Baltimore, MD, p. A297

LAM, Shiva, M.D. Executive Medical Director, Austin Lakes Hospital, Austin, TX, p. A598

LAM, Thomas, Chief Medical Officer, Garfield Medical Center, Monterey Park, CA, p. A78

LAMADELEINE, Joseph, Chief Financial Officer, Veterans Affairs Connecticut Healthcare System, West Haven, CT, p. A118

LAMANTEER, Mike, M.D. Senior Vice President Medical Affairs, BSA Hospital, LLC, Amarillo, TX, p. A596

LAMARCHE, Heather, Manager Human Resources, AMG Specialty Hospital–Lafayette, Lafayette, LA, p. A280

LAMARCHE, Marie, Executive Director, Human Resources, Organizational Development, Employee Health, Harrison Medical Center, Bremerton, WA, p. A682

LAMARCHE, Maximo, M.D. Chief Medical Officer, AMG Specialty Hospital–Lafayette, Lafayette, LA, p. A280

LAMB, Andrew, M.D. Chief of Staff, Alamance Regional Medical Center, Burlington, NC, p. A461

LAMB, Cindy, Director Human Resources, Marias Medical Center, Shelby, MT, p. A391

LAMB, Deanna, Director Human Resources, Central Carolina Hospital, Sanford, NC, p. A473

LAMB, Hope, Manager Human Resources, Kimble Hospital, Junction, TX, p. A629

LAMB, Mollee, Manager Human Resources, LDS Hospital, Salt Lake City, UT, p. A663

LAMB, Thomas, Director Information Systems, Monongahela Valley Hospital, Monongahela, PA, p. A545

LAMB–PAGONE, Jerilynn, Nurse Executive, Connecticut Valley Hospital, Middletown, CT, p. A115

LAMBERT, Amand, Director Human Resources, Allen Parish Hospital, Kinder, LA, p. A280

LAMBERT, Barbara, Director Healthcare Compliance, Eastern State Hospital, Williamsburg, VA, p. A680

LAMBERT, Cheryl, Chief Financial Officer, Acuity Specialty Hospital of New Jersey, Atlantic City, NJ, p. A414

LAMBERT, Karen A., President, Advocate Good Shepherd Hospital, Barrington, IL, p. A181

LAMBERT, Lynn, Chief Financial Officer, Harnett Health System, Dunn, NC, p. A464

LAMBERT, Paul, M.D. Chief of Staff, Boise Veterans Affairs Medical Center, Boise, ID, p. A174

LAMBERT, Robert K., FACHE, President and Chief Executive Officer, Arnot Health, Elmira, NY, p. B12

LAMBERT, Suzanne, R.N. Regional Chief Nursing Officer and Support Services, Presence Saints Mary & Elizabeth Medical Center, Chicago, IL, p. A186

LAMBETH, Laura, Chief Executive Officer, Ashe Memorial Hospital, Jefferson, NC, p. A468

LAMBKE, Michael, M.D. Medical Director, Redington–Fairview General Hospital, Skowhegan, ME, p. A295

LAMBRECHT, Craig, M.D., President, Sanford Bismarck, Bismarck, ND, p. A477

LAMEBULL, Charlotte, Administrative Officer, Fort Belknap U. S. Public Health Service Indian Hospital, Harlem, MT, p. A388

LAMEN, Drake M., President, Chief Executive Officer and Chief Medical Officer, UHS Chenango Memorial Hospital, Norwich, NY, p. A451

LAMERS, Jamon
Director Finance, Howard Young Medical Center, Woodruff, WI, p. A720
Director Finance, Ministry Eagle River Memorial Hospital, Eagle River, WI, p. A704
Director Finance, Ministry Sacred Heart Hospital, Tomahawk, WI, p. A717
Director Finance, Ministry Saint Mary's Hospitals, Rhinelander, WI, p. A715

LAMEY, Mark, Commander, U. S. Air Force Regional Hospital, Elmendorf AFB, AK, p. A29

LAMEY, Rebecca, Vice President Human Resources, MaineGeneral Medical Center, Augusta, ME, p. A291

LAMLE, Sandra, Chief Financial Officer, Okeene Municipal Hospital, Okeene, OK, p. A515

LAMMERS, Sandra, Coordinator Human Resources and Finance, CHI Health Mercy Corning, Corning, IA, p. A228

LAMONT, Jennifer
Chief Financial Officer, West Suburban Medical Center, Oak Park, IL, p. A199
Chief Financial Officer, Westlake Hospital, Melrose Park, IL, p. A196

LAMONTE, David, Interim President, CHRISTUS Spohn Hospital Alice, Alice, TX, p. A595

LAMORELLA, Vincent M., Chief Financial Officer, Clarion Hospital, Clarion, PA, p. A535

LAMOUREUX, John P., Commander, Dwight David Eisenhower Army Medical Center, Fort Gordon, GA, p. A160

LAMOUREUX, Laurie, Director of Finance, Cooley Dickinson Hospital, Northampton, MA, p. A313

LAMPE, Michael, M.D. Chief of Staff, Kossuth Regional Health Center, Algona, IA, p. A225

LAMPE, Tammy K., Director Human Resources, Edwards County Hospital and Healthcare Center, Kinsley, KS, p. A246

LAMPLEY, Danny, Chief Operating Officer, Harrisburg Medical Center, Harrisburg, IL, p. A192

LAMPLEY, Joseph, D.O. Chief of Staff, Fisher County Hospital District, Rotan, TX, p. A644

LAMPTON, Lucius, M.D. Medical Director, Beacham Memorial Hospital, Magnolia, MS, p. A361

LANCASTER, Brian, Executive Director Information Management, Nebraska Medicine – Bellevue, Bellevue, NE, p. A394

LANCASTER, Penny, Controller, Cascade Medical Center, Cascade, ID, p. A175

LANCASTER, Tim, FACHE, President and Chief Executive Officer, Hendrick Health System, Abilene, TX, p. A595

LAND, Steve, Senior Administrator, Wamego Health Center, Wamego, KS, p. A255

LAND, Susann, M.D. Chief Medical Officer, Texas Health Harris Methodist Hospital Hurst–Euless–Bedford, Bedford, TX, p. A602

LANDENBERGER, Jason, Director of Nursing, Community Memorial Hospital, Turtle Lake, ND, p. A481

LANDERS, Alice, Administrative Director Operations, Texas Health Harris Methodist Hospital Hurst–Euless–Bedford, Bedford, TX, p. A602

LANDERS, Kimberly A., MS Vice President Patient Care Services, Morris Hospital & Healthcare Centers, Morris, IL, p. A197

LANDERS, Lalah, R.N. Director of Nursing, Saunders Medical Center, Wahoo, NE, p. A403

LANDERS, Wilson, Chief of Staff, Golden Plains Community Hospital, Borger, TX, p. A603

LANDINI, Kristin
Vice President Human Resources, Advocate South Suburban Hospital, Hazel Crest, IL, p. A192
Senior Vice President Human Resources, Advocate Trinity Hospital, Chicago, IL, p. A183

LANDIS, Catherine, R.N., Chief Executive Officer, HEALTHSOUTH Rehabilitation Hospital of Columbia, Columbia, SC, p. A564

LANDIS, Janie, Chief Financial Officer, Russell County Hospital, Russell Springs, KY, p. A269

LANDMAN, Adam, M.D. Chief Information Officer, Brigham and Women's Hospital, Boston, MA, p. A306

LANDMAN, Paul, Director Human Resources, Ellwood City Hospital, Ellwood City, PA, p. A538

LANDOLL, Therese, Interim Chief Financial Officer, Community Memorial Healthcare, Marysville, KS, p. A249

LANDRAU, Erika, Director Human Resources, HEALTHSOUTH Hospital of Manati, Manati, PR, p. A728

LANDRENEAU, John Derrick, Director of Marketing, Baton Rouge Rehabilitation Hospital, Baton Rouge, LA, p. A272

LANDRETH, Kathy, Interim Chief Executive Officer, Bath Community Hospital, Hot Springs, VA, p. A672

LANDRETH, Sandy, Director Human Resources, Seiling Municipal Hospital, Seiling, OK, p. A519

LANDRETH, Shannan, Information Systems, Livingston Hospital and Healthcare Services, Salem, KY, p. A269

LANDRUM, David, Chief Police Services, Atascadero State Hospital, Atascadero, CA, p. A55

LANDRY, Adam, Coordinator Computer Systems, Northern Maine Medical Center, Fort Kent, ME, p. A293

LANDRY, Candy, Chief Human Resource Officer, Eastside Psychiatric Hospital, Tallahassee, FL, p. A146

LANDRY, Donna F., Chief Operating Officer, Our Lady of Lourdes Regional Medical Center, Lafayette, LA, p. A281

LANDRY, Lisa G., Human Resources Director, Redington–Fairview General Hospital, Skowhegan, ME, p. A295

LANDRY, Nobie, Chief Financial Officer, Prevost Memorial Hospital, Donaldsonville, LA, p. A276

LANDRY, Ray A., Chief Executive Officer, Abbeville General Hospital, Abbeville, LA, p. A271

LANDRY NUNEZ, Lexis, Chief Executive Officer, St. Catherine Memorial Hospital, New Orleans, LA, p. A285

LANDSMAN, Joseph, President and Chief Executive Officer, University of Tennessee Medical Center, Knoxville, TN, p. A586

LANDSTROM, Gay L., Ph.D. Chief Nursing Officer, Dartmouth–Hitchcock Medical Center, Lebanon, NH, p. A412

LANDSTROM, Gay L., R.N., Interim Chief Executive Officer, Mt. Ascutney Hospital and Health Center, Windsor, VT, p. A666

LANDSTROM, John
Vice President Human Resources and Operations, RML Specialty Hospital, Chicago, IL, p. A186
Director Human Resources, RML Specialty Hospital, Hinsdale, IL, p. A193

LANE, Charles A., Chief Medical Officer, Anderson Hospital, Maryville, IL, p. A195

LANE, Diron
Director Information Systems, LewisGale Hospital Montgomery, Blacksburg, VA, p. A668
Director Information Systems, LewisGale Hospital Pulaski, Pulaski, VA, p. A676

LANE, Kevin, D.O. Chief of Staff, Hardeman County Memorial Hospital, Quanah, TX, p. A642

LANE, Kevin, Vice President Information Systems, Silver Cross Hospital, New Lenox, IL, p. A198

LANE, Kim, Chief Fiscal Service, Overton Brooks Veterans Affairs Medical Center, Shreveport, LA, p. A287

LANE, Mike, Chief Operating Officer, Twin Cities Community Hospital, Templeton, CA, p. A96

LANE, Richard, Chief Financial Officer, Mid–America Rehabilitation Hospital, Shawnee Mission, KS, p. A253

LANE, Sonia, Interim Chief Nursing Officer, UC Irvine Medical Center, Orange, CA, p. A81

LANEAUX, Eleanor, Director Information Systems, Placentia–Linda Hospital, Placentia, CA, p. A83

LANER, Jr., Richard, Manager Information Systems, Miners' Colfax Medical Center, Raton, NM, p. A430

LANEY, Samuel Mark, M.D., Chief Executive Officer, Mosaic Life Care at St. Joseph, Saint Joseph, MO, p. A379

LANG, Cyndi, Director Information Services, French Hospital Medical Center, San Luis Obispo, CA, p. A92

LANG, Gordon, M.D. Chief of Staff, Trego County–Lemke Memorial Hospital, Wakeeney, KS, p. A255

LANG, Jeff, President, UP Health System–Portage, Hancock, MI, p. A326

LANG, John Christopher, Chief Executive Officer, Cass Regional Medical Center, Harrisonville, MO, p. A372

LANG, Joseph, M.D. Chief of Staff, Carolinas ContinueCARE Hospital at Pineville, Charlotte, NC, p. A462

LANG, Linda, Chief Human Resources Officer, Marin General Hospital, Greenbrae, CA, p. A65

LANG, Nicholas P., M.D. Chief Medical Officer, UAMS Medical Center, Little Rock, AR, p. A49

LANG, Richard, Ed.D. Vice President and Chief Information Officer, Doylestown Hospital, Doylestown, PA, p. A537

LANG, Richard T., Chief Financial Officer, Gouverneur Hospital, Gouverneur, NY, p. A439

LANGAN, Lynn, Chief Nursing Officer, Quillen Rehabilitation Hospital, Johnson City, TN, p. A585

LANGBEHN, Jennifer, Medical Director, Mayo Clinic Health System in Saint James, Saint James, MN, p. A350

LANGBERG, Michael L., M.D. Senior Vice President Medical Affairs and Chief Medical Officer, Cedars–Sinai Medical Center, Los Angeles, CA, p. A70

LANGDON, Ashlee, Controller, Yalobusha General Hospital, Water Valley, MS, p. A366

LANGE, Connie, R.N. Vice President Quality, Inpatient and Community Services, Lakes Regional Healthcare, Spirit Lake, IA, p. A238

LANGENBERG, Shannon, Director Human Resources, Jackson County Regional Health Center, Maquoketa, IA, p. A234

LANGFORD, Terrie, Director Human Resources, Heritage Park Surgical Hospital, Sherman, TX, p. A649

LANGHOFF, Erik, Ph.D., Director, James J. Peters Veterans Affairs Medical Center,, NY, p. A445

LANGLITZ, Sara, Controller, Kindred Hospital Houston Medical Center, Houston, TX, p. A625

LANGLOIS, John, Interim Administrator, Walker Baptist Medical Center, Jasper, AL, p. A22

LANGMEAD, Paula A., Chief Executive Officer, Springfield Hospital Center, Sykesville, MD, p. A303

LANGSTON, David L.
Corporate Vice President Human Resources, East Texas Medical Center Rehabilitation Hospital, Tyler, TX, p. A654
Corporate Vice President Human Resources, East Texas Medical Center Specialty Hospital, Tyler, TX, p. A654

LANGSTON, Kimberly K., R.N., Chief Executive Officer, Scott and White Continuing Care Hospital, Temple, TX, p. A652

LANGSTON, Roxann, Chief Nursing Officer, East Texas Medical Center Trinity, Trinity, TX, p. A653

LANHAM, Gary, Chief Medical Officer, Parkridge Medical Center, Chattanooga, TN, p. A580

LANIER, Donna, R.N. Chief Nursing Officer, Delta Medical Center, Memphis, TN, p. A588

LANIER, Mary, Vice President, Post Acute Services and Site Administrator, California Pacific Medical Center–Davies Campus, San Francisco, CA, p. A90

LANIER, Regina, R.N. Senior Vice President and Chief Nursing Officer, Onslow Memorial Hospital, Jacksonville, NC, p. A468

LANKFORD, Deanna, Business Office Manager, Plano Specialty Hospital, Plano, TX, p. A642

LANKOWICZ, Andrew, FACHE, President, CHI St. Alexius Health Devils Lake Hospital, Devils Lake, ND, p. A478

LANNOYE, Craig, Vice President Operations, Wilson Memorial Hospital, Sidney, OH, p. A502

LANOUE, Cheryl, Chief Financial Officer, Ottawa County Health Center, Minneapolis, KS, p. A249

LANS, Sue, Comptroller, Harlan County Health System, Alma, NE, p. A393

LANSDOWNE, Lynn M., Vice President Human Resources, Pocono Medical Center, East Stroudsburg, PA, p. A537

LANTOS, Phyllis R., Executive Vice President, Corporate Chief Financial Officer and Treasurer, New York–Presbyterian Hospital, New York, NY, p. A447

LANTZY, William, Chief Financial Officer, DMC Huron Valley–Sinai Hospital, Commerce Township, MI, p. A321

LANZA, Nicholas, Controller, St. Mary's General Hospital, Passaic, NJ, p. A421

LANZA, Raymond, D.O. Medical Director, Runnells Center for Rehabilitation and Healthcare, Berkeley Heights, NJ, p. A414

LAPERLE, Linda M., Vice President Administrative Services, Androscoggin Valley Hospital, Berlin, NH, p. A410

LAPHAM, Lisa, President and Chief Executive Officer, HealthSource Saginaw, Inc., Saginaw, MI, p. A333

LAPLANT, Dawn, Manager Health Information Management, Brown County Community Treatment Center, Green Bay, WI, p. A706

LAPOSTA, Mary Jo, Ph.D. Senior Vice President Patient Care and Organizational Excellence, Saratoga Hospital, Saratoga Springs, NY, p. A455

LARA, Anne, Chief Information Officer, Union Hospital, Elkton, MD, p. A300

LARA, Sergio, M.D. Chief Medical Officer, Covenant Hospital Plainview, Plainview, TX, p. A641

LARAMIE, Robert, Chief Information Officer, Beverly Hospital, Beverly, MA, p. A305

LARAMIE, Wayne, Vice President Nursing, SSM St. Clare Hospital, Fenton, MO, p. A371

LARCAS, John, M.D. Acting Medical Director, Choate Mental Health Center, Anna, IL, p. A180

LAREAU, Daniel, Executive Director Operations and Information, St. Vincent Carmel Hospital, Carmel, IN, p. A208

LAREAU, Kim, Vice President and Chief Information Officer, Regions Hospital, Saint Paul, MN, p. A350

LARET, Mark R., Chief Executive Officer, UCSF Medical Center, San Francisco, CA, p. A91

LARIMER, Cynthia, M.D. Chief of Staff, Lake Butler Hospital Hand Surgery Center, Lake Butler, FL, p. A133

LARIMORE, Rhonda
Vice President, Human Resources, Children's Hospital of Pittsburgh of UPMC, Pittsburgh, PA, p. A550
Vice President Human Resources, Magee–Womens Hospital of UPMC, Pittsburgh, PA, p. A551

LARISCY, Robin Barton, M.D. Medical Director, Mary S Harper Geriatric Psychiatry Center, Tuscaloosa, AL, p. A26

LARIVEE, Theresa M., Chief Executive Officer, Pennsylvania Hospital, Philadelphia, PA, p. A549

LARIVIERE, Beckye, Controller, HEALTHSOUTH Rehabilitation Hospital of Charleston, Charleston, SC, p. A562

LARKIN, Kevin
Regional Chief Financial Officer, Presence Mercy Medical Center, Aurora, IL, p. A180
Regional Chief Financial Officer, Presence Saint Joseph Hospital, Elgin, IL, p. A189

LARKIN, Kim, Chief Information Officer, Washington County Hospital, Nashville, IL, p. A198

LARKINS, Gloria, Vice President Finance, DMC – Detroit Receiving Hospital, Detroit, MI, p. A321

LARMER, Jennifer, R.N. Chief Clinical Officer, Lincoln Hospital, Davenport, WA, p. A684

LARNER, Cheryl, Chief Financial Officer, Sentara CarePlex Hospital, Hampton, VA, p. A671

LAROSA, Vincent
Director of Information Systems, Landmark Medical Center, Woonsocket, RI, p. A561
Director of Information Technology Services, Rehabilitation Hospital of Rhode Island, North Smithfield, RI, p. A560

LAROWE, Mary E., FACHE, President and Chief Executive Officer, Brooks Memorial Hospital, Dunkirk, NY, p. A438

LARRISON Jr., Robert G., President, Carolinas Rehabilitation, Charlotte, NC, p. A462

LARSEN, Bill, Vice President Human Resources, Driscoll Children's Hospital, Corpus Christi, TX, p. A608

LARSEN, Catherine M., Director Marketing, Sutter Tracy Community Hospital, Tracy, CA, p. A96

LARSEN, Donald, M.D. Chief Medical Officer, Providence Saint John's Health Center, Santa Monica, CA, p. A93

LARSEN, Kevin, Associate Vice President, Business and Ancillary Services, Unconn John Dempsey Hospital, Farmington, CT, p. A114

LARSEN, Michael, Director Information Systems, Baylor Medical Center at Garland, Garland, TX, p. A620

LARSEN, Ryan C., FACHE, Chief Executive Officer, Community Medical Center, Inc., Falls City, NE, p. A395

LARSON, Alan, Chief Executive Officer, Danville Regional Medical Center, Danville, VA, p. A669

LARSON, Bill, Vice President Finance and Chief Financial Officer, Torrance Memorial Medical Center, Torrance, CA, p. A96

LARSON, Derek, Information Technology Network, Lakes Regional Healthcare, Spirit Lake, IA, p. A238

LARSON, Eric, Director Human Resources, HEALTHSOUTH Harmarville Rehabilitation Hospital, Pittsburgh, PA, p. A550

LARSON, Erick, Vice President and Chief Information Officer, Mid–Columbia Medical Center, The Dalles, OR, p. A531

LARSON, Gordon, Administrator, Pineville Community Hospital Association, Pineville, KY, p. A268

LARSON, Jennifer, M.D. Chief of Staff, Blue Ridge Regional Hospital, Spruce Pine, NC, p. A474

LARSON, Jon, M.D. Medical Director, HEALTHSOUTH Rehabilitation Institute of Tucson, Tucson, AZ, p. A40

LARSON, Karen, Chief Executive Officer, Fairview Developmental Center, Costa Mesa, CA, p. A60

LARSON, Karla, Director Human Resources, Stevens Community Medical Center, Morris, MN, p. A347

LARSON, Kay, R.N. Chief Nursing Officer, Essentia Health St. Mary's – Detroit Lakes, Detroit Lakes, MN, p. A341

LARSON, Michael, Vice President Chief Information Officer, MidMichigan Medical Center–Clare, Clare, MI, p. A320

LARSON, Mike, Chief Operating Officer, Essentia Health St. Joseph's Medical Center, Brainerd, MN, p. A340

LARSON, Pamela, Division Director Financial Services, Hutchinson Health, Hutchinson, MN, p. A344

LARSON, Rodney, M.D. Medical Director, Fall River Hospital, Hot Springs, SD, p. A574

LARSON, Ronald, Chief Financial Officer, VA San Diego Healthcare System, San Diego, CA, p. A89

LARSON, Sandra, MSN, Chief Executive Officer, Kindred Hospital–Philadelphia, Philadelphia, PA, p. A548

LARSON, Scott, M.D. Vice President Medical Affairs and Chief Medical Officer, Bronson Methodist Hospital, Kalamazoo, MI, p. A328

LARSON, Scott C., Chief Executive Officer, Sanford Canton–Inwood Medical Center, Canton, SD, p. A572

LARSON, Shelly, Chief Financial Officer, Hot Springs County Memorial Hospital, Thermopolis, WY, p. A724

LARSON, Steve, M.D. Director Information Systems, Mercy Medical Center–Sioux City, Sioux City, IA, p. A237

LARSON, Tammy, Chief Financial Officer, Towner County Medical Center, Cando, ND, p. A477

LARSON, Tracy, MS Vice President Patient Care Services and Chief Nursing Officer, Mercy Medical Center–Sioux City, Sioux City, IA, p. A237

LARSON, Walt, Vice President Finance, Tillamook Regional Medical Center, Tillamook, OR, p. A531

LARSON, Wendy, Chief Clinical Officer, Promise Hospital of Phoenix, Mesa, AZ, p. A34

LASALA, Frank, M.D. President Medical Staff, OSF Holy Family Medical Center, Monmouth, IL, p. A197

LASCANO, Terrance, Administrative Officer, U. S. Public Health Service Indian Hospital, Cass Lake, MN, p. A340

LASECKI, Matt, Interim Vice President Human Resources, Providence Hospital, Washington, DC, p. A122

LASH, Lashaunda, Manager Human Resources, Pioneer Community Hospital of Stokes, Danbury, NC, p. A463

LASHBROOK, Amy, Chief Financial Officer, Community Hospital of Bremen, Bremen, IN, p. A207

LASHER, Karen, Chief Nursing Officer, Vanderbilt Stallworth Rehabilitation Hospital, Nashville, TN, p. A591

LASHKARI, Haady, Chief Administrative Officer, Ojai Valley Community Hospital, Ojai, CA, p. A80

LASKER, Rose, Director Information Services, Bluefield Regional Medical Center, Bluefield, WV, p. A694

LASKOWSKI, Rose, R.N., Director, Caro Center, Caro, MI, p. A320

LASKY, Jr., John, Vice President, Chief Human Resources Officer, Temple University Hospital, Philadelphia, PA, p. A550

LASOTA, John, Assistant Finance Officer, Clement J. Zablocki Veterans Affairs Medical Center, Milwaukee, WI, p. A711

LASSITER, Rick, President and Chief Administrative Officer, Parkwest Medical Center, Knoxville, TN, p. A586

LASSITER, Susan S., FACHE, President and Chief Executive Officer, Vidant Roanoke–Chowan Hospital, Ahoskie, NC, p. A460

LASTER, Charles, Director Information Management, WK Bossier Health Center, Bossier City, LA, p. A274

LATER, Elizabeth B., R.N. Chief Nursing Officer, Ogden Regional Medical Center, Ogden, UT, p. A661

LATIBEAUDIERE, Jorge, Chief Financial Officer, Lea Regional Medical Center, Hobbs, NM, p. A429

LATIMER, Timothy, Chief Financial Officer, Great Bend Regional Hospital, Great Bend, KS, p. A244

LATIOLAIS, Ryan J., Director Information Systems, Our Lady of Lourdes Regional Medical Center, Lafayette, LA, p. A281

LATNEY, Cynthia, Chief Nursing Officer, Penrose–St. Francis Health Services, Colorado Springs, CO, p. A103

LATREILLE, William, M.D. Chief Medical Officer, The University of Vermont Health Network – Alice Hyde Medical Center, Malone, NY, p. A442

LATT, Laura, Vice President of Operations, North Memorial Medical Center, Robbinsdale, MN, p. A349

LATTERNER, Renee, Director Human Resources, Lake Wales Medical Center, Lake Wales, FL, p. A133

LATTIMORE, Justin, Chief Financial Officer, Iron County Medical Center, Pilot Knob, MO, p. A378

LATTIN, Gary, M.D. Vice President, Medical Affairs, Penn State Health St. Joseph, Reading, PA, p. A553

LATTO, Janet B., Chief Nursing Officer and Disaster Officer, Pacifica Hospital of the Valley,, CA, p. A73

LATUCHIE, Richard
Vice President Business Development, Rapid City Regional Hospital, Rapid City, SD, p. A575
Chief Information Officer, Spearfish Regional Hospital, Spearfish, SD, p. A577

LATULIPPE, Steve, President Medical Staff, East Liverpool City Hospital, East Liverpool, OH, p. A494

LAU, James, M.D. Area Medical Director, Kaiser Permanente Panorama City Medical Center,, CA, p. A71

LAUBENTHAL, Sherrie L., R.N. Chief Nursing Officer, Clarinda Regional Health Center, Clarinda, IA, p. A227

LAUDON, Larry A., Administrator, Community Behavioral Health Hospital – Bemidji, Bemidji, MN, p. A339

LAUE, Edward, M.D. Chief Medical Officer, Texas Health Huguley Hospital Fort Worth South, Burleson, TX, p. A604

LAUE, Jerry, Administrator, St. Vincent Clay Hospital, Brazil, IN, p. A207

LAUER, Bill, Chief Information Officer, Morris County Hospital, Council Grove, KS, p. A242

LAUF, Michael K., President and Chief Executive Officer, Cape Cod Healthcare, Inc., Hyannis, MA, p. B25

LAUF, Michael K.
President and Chief Executive Officer, Cape Cod Hospital, Hyannis, MA, p. A311
President and Chief Executive Officer, Falmouth Hospital, Falmouth, MA, p. A310

LAUFFER, Daniel, FACHE, President and Chief Executive Officer, Saint Francis Hospital, Charleston, WV, p. A695

LAUFFER, Daniel, FACHE, President and Chief Executive Officer, Thomas Health System, Inc., South Charleston, WV, p. B135

LAUFFER, Daniel, FACHE, President and Chief Executive Officer, Thomas Memorial Hospital, South Charleston, WV, p. A700

LAUFLE, Chuck, Director of Information Services, San Luis Valley Health, Alamosa, CO, p. A101

LAUGHLIN, Jennifer, Chief Information Officer, Watertown Regional Medical Center, Watertown, WI, p. A718

LAUGHLIN, Nancy, R.N. Chief Nursing Officer, Nebraska Orthopaedic Hospital, Omaha, NE, p. A400

LAUGHLIN, Warren, Vice President Human Resources, Longmont United Hospital, Longmont, CO, p. A108

LAUKAITIS, Fran, R.N., President, Methodist Charlton Medical Center, Dallas, TX, p. A610

LAUNIUS, Billie, Director Business Finance, Dallas County Medical Center, Fordyce, AR, p. A46

LAUREANO, Prudencio A., Chief Executive Officer, Hospital Universitario Dr. Ramon Ruiz Arnau, Bayamon, PR, p. A726

LAURENT, Merrill, M.D. Medical Director, AMG Specialty Hospital – Covington, Covington, LA, p. A275

LAURENTS, W. Robert, CPA Chief Financial Officer, Madison Parish Hospital, Tallulah, LA, p. A289

LAURETO, Rose Ann
Corporate Vice President Information Resources, ProMedica Bay Park Hospital, Oregon, OH, p. A500
Chief Information Officer, ProMedica Fostoria Community Hospital, Fostoria, OH, p. A494
Chief Information Officer, ProMedica Toledo Hospital, Toledo, OH, p. A504

LAURIN, George M., Interim Director Human Resources, Crisp Regional Hospital, Cordele, GA, p. A157

LAUTER, Keith A.
Vice President Finance, Franciscan St. Elizabeth Health – Crawfordsville, Crawfordsville, IN, p. A208
Regional Chief Financial Officer, Franciscan St. Francis Health – Indianapolis, Indianapolis, IN, p. A214
Chief Financial Officer, Franciscan St. Francis Health–Carmel, Carmel, IN, p. A208

LAUTEREN, Mark
Chief Information Officer, University of South Alabama Children's and Women's Hospital, Mobile, AL, p. A23
Chief Information Officer, University of South Alabama Medical Center, Mobile, AL, p. A23

LAUTNER, Marty, Vice President Finance and Chief Financial Officer, Cardinal Hill Rehabilitation Hospital, Lexington, KY, p. A263

LAUVE, Lisa R., R.N. Regional Chief Nursing Executive and Chief Operating Officer, CHRISTUS St. Frances Cabrini Hospital, Alexandria, LA, p. A271

LAUVER, David, M.D. Chief Division Hospital Based Care, Central Maine Medical Center, Lewiston, ME, p. A293

LAUZAU, Paul, Controller, Beaumont Hospital – Trenton, Trenton, MI, p. A335

LAVALLEY, Marlinda L., Chief Executive Officer, Gouverneur Hospital, Gouverneur, NY, p. A439

LAVELLE, John P., M.D. Chief Medical Officer, Parkview Hospital, Wheeler, TX, p. A657

LAVELY, Patricia A., FACHE Senior Vice President and Chief Information Officer, Gwinnett Hospital System, Lawrenceville, GA, p. A162

LAVER, Joseph H., M.D. Chief Medical Officer, Stony Brook University Hospital, Stony Brook, NY, p. A456

LAVERDIERE, Dana, Director Human Resources, St. Anthony Summit Medical Center, Frisco, CO, p. A105

LAVERY FRASCA, Denise Anne, MSN Vice President Patient Care Services and Chief Nursing Officer, Jeanes Hospital, Philadelphia, PA, p. A548

LAVIGNETTE, Brooke, Director of Nursing, Sycamore Springs Hospital, Lafayette, IN, p. A216

LAVIOLETTE, Judy, M.D
Chief Medical Officer, Texas Health Harris Methodist Hospital Azle, Azle, TX, p. A600
Chief Medical Officer, Texas Health Harris Methodist Hospital Cleburne, Cleburne, TX, p. A606

LAVOIE, Brad, Chief Financial Officer, Coastal Harbor Treatment Center, Savannah, GA, p. A165

LAW, Charles, Ph.D. Chief Operating Officer, Catawba Hospital, Catawba, VA, p. A668

LAW, Johnny, Area Information Officer, Kaiser Permanente Oakland Medical Center, Oakland, CA, p. A80

LAWHORN, David, M.D. Chief Medical Office, Shoshone Medical Center, Kellogg, ID, p. A176

LAWHORN, Renee, Director Medical Records, East Texas Medical Center Carthage, Carthage, TX, p. A605

LAWHORNE, Thomas, Chief Financial Officer, Regional Medical Center Bayonet Point, Hudson, FL, p. A131

LAWING, William, Chief of Medical Staff, Northern Hospital of Surry County, Mount Airy, NC, p. A470

LAWLER, Anne, Director Human Resources, North Mississippi Medical Center–Hamilton, Hamilton, AL, p. A21

LAWLER, Kay, Business Office Manager, North Mississippi Medical Center–West Point, West Point, MS, p. A366

LAWLER, Patrick, Chief Executive Officer, Youth Villages Inner Harbour Campus, Douglasville, GA, p. A158

LAWLESS, JoBeth, Chief Nursing Officer, Nursing Services and Director Emergency Management Services, Lucas County Health Center, Chariton, IA, p. A227

LAWLESS, Rosalie, Director Human Resources, Fairlawn Rehabilitation Hospital, Worcester, MA, p. A316

LAWONN, Kenneth
Senior Vice President and Chief Information Officer, CHI Health Mercy Corning, Corning, IA, p. A228
Senior Vice President and Chief Information Officer, CHI Health Schuyler, Schuyler, NE, p. A402
Senior Vice President and Chief Information Officer, Sharp Grossmont Hospital, La Mesa, CA, p. A67
Senior Vice President and Chief Information Officer, Sharp Memorial Hospital, San Diego, CA, p. A89
Senior Vice President Information Systems, Sharp Mesa Vista Hospital, San Diego, CA, p. A89

LAWRASON, Jock, M.D. Chief Medical Officer, Nantucket Cottage Hospital, Nantucket, MA, p. A312

LAWRENCE, Bruce, President and Chief Executive Officer, INTEGRIS Health, Oklahoma City, OK, p. B73

LAWRENCE, Glenda, R.N. Chief Nursing Officer, Red River Hospital, LLC, Wichita Falls, TX, p. A657

LAWRENCE, Jeffrey T., Chief Operating Officer, Denton Regional Medical Center, Denton, TX, p. A612

LAWRENCE, Kelsey, Manager Information Technology, Union County General Hospital, Clayton, NM, p. A428

LAWRENCE, Mark, Director Information Systems, Saint Francis Hospital–Bartlett, Bartlett, TN, p. A579

LAWRENCE, Paige, Assistant Administrator, University of Mississippi Medical Center Holmes County, Lexington, MS, p. A361

LAWRENCE, Sandra A J
Executive Vice President and Chief Financial Officer, Children's Mercy Hospitals and Clinics, Kansas City, MO, p. A373
Executive Vice President and Chief Financial Officer, Children's Mercy South, Overland Park, KS, p. A251

LAWRENCE, Stephanie
Chief Financial Officer, Kentfield Rehabilitation and Specialty Hospital, Kentfield, CA, p. A67
Chief Financial Officer, Vibra Specialty Hospital of Portland, Portland, OR, p. A530

LAWRENCE, Tiffany, Vice President of Finance, Sanford Medical Center Fargo, Fargo, ND, p. A479

LAWRENCE, William P., President and Chief Executive Officer, McLaren Central Michigan, Mount Pleasant, MI, p. A330

LAWRENSON, Victoria
Chief Operating Officer, Bullock County Hospital, Union Springs, AL, p. A26
Chief Operating Officer, Crenshaw Community Hospital, Luverne, AL, p. A22

LAWSON, Alvin R., FACHE, Chief Executive Officer, HEALTHSOUTH Western Hills Regional Rehabilitation Hospital, Parkersburg, WV, p. A699

LAWSON, Beth, Chief Nursing Officer, Union Medical Center, Union, SC, p. A570

LAWSON, David C., Senior Vice President Human Resources, St. Clare Hospital, Lakewood, WA, p. A686

LAWSON, Doug, Chief Operating Officer, Baylor University Medical Center, Dallas, TX, p. A609

LAWSON, Jerry, M.D. Chief of Medical Staff, Russell County Hospital, Russell Springs, KY, p. A269

LAWSON, Judy, Director Information Services, Norton Community Hospital, Norton, VA, p. A675

LAWSON, Michael, President and Chief Operating Officer, OhioHealth Grant Medical Center, Columbus, OH, p. A491

LAWSON, Penny, Human Resource Director, Quillen Rehabilitation Hospital, Johnson City, TN, p. A585

LAWSON, Ralph E., Executive Vice President and Chief Financial Officer, Baptist Health South Florida, Baptist Hospital of Miami, Miami, FL, p. A136

LAWSON, Sandra K., Interim Director Fiscal Services, Shriners Hospitals for Children–St. Louis, Saint Louis, MO, p. A380

LAWTON, Geoff, Vice President Operations, Littleton Adventist Hospital, Littleton, CO, p. A108

LAY, Jr., A. K., M.D. Chief Medical Officer, Jasper General Hospital, Bay Springs, MS, p. A355

LAY, Barbara, Chief Executive Officer, Pocahontas Memorial Hospital, Buckeye, WV, p. A694

LAYFIELD, Michael G., Interim Chief Executive Officer, Lauderdale Community Hospital, Ripley, TN, p. A592

LAYNE, Kristine, R.N. Chief Nursing Officer, Riverwood Healthcare Center, Aitkin, MN, p. A338

LAYTON, Ann, M.D. Chief of Staff, North Metro Medical Center, Jacksonville, AR, p. A47

LAYTON, Lane, Information Technology Director, Jeff Davis Hospital, Hazlehurst, GA, p. A160

LAYUGAN, Melvin, Director Human Resources, Horizon Specialty Hospital, Las Vegas, NV, p. A406

LAZARUS, David, M.D. Medical Director Clinical Affairs, Newton Medical Center, Newton, NJ, p. A421

LAZATIN, Lou, Administrator, Shriners Hospitals for Children–Los Angeles, Los Angeles, CA, p. A74

LAZO, Nelson, Chief Executive Officer, Baptist Health South Florida, Doctors Hospital, Coral Gables, FL, p. A126

LAZROFF, Gary, Vice President Human Resources, St. John Medical Center, Westlake, OH, p. A505

LAZZARO, III, Frank A., Chief Human Resources Officer, Phelps County Regional Medical Center, Rolla, MO, p. A379

LE, Emily, Director Information Technology and Services, Woman's Hospital of Texas, Houston, TX, p. A628

LE, Jennifer, Chief Financial Officer, Southern Hills Hospital and Medical Center, Las Vegas, NV, p. A406

LEA, Hampton P. S., Acting Chief Executive Officer, Eastern Louisiana Mental Health System, Jackson, LA, p. A278

LEA, Randy, M.D. Vice President and Chief Medical Officer, Alice Peck Day Memorial Hospital, Lebanon, NH, p. A411

LEA, Rich, Vice President Operations, Euclid Hospital, Euclid, OH, p. A494

LEACH, Craig, President and Chief Executive Officer, Torrance Memorial Medical Center, Torrance, CA, p. A96

LEACH, Deonca, Director, Human Resources, Carolinas Rehabilitation, Charlotte, NC, p. A462

LEACH, Leslie, Administrator, CHI St. Luke's Health Memorial Specialty Hospital, Lufkin, TX, p. A634

LEACH, Mary Anne, Vice President and Chief Information Officer, Children's Hospital Colorado, Aurora, CO, p. A101

LEACH, Ryan, Chief Information Officer, St. John's Hospital, Springfield, IL, p. A203

LEACH, Todd, Vice President and Chief Information Officer, University of Texas Medical Branch, Galveston, TX, p. A620

LEADBETTER, Dan, Information Technology Systems Site Lead, CHI LakeWood Health, Baudette, MN, p. A339

LEADBETTER, Jr., Raymond J., Revenue Cycle Consultant, Appling Healthcare System, Baxley, GA, p. A154

LEAHY, Kevin D., President and Chief Executive Officer, Franciscan Alliance, Mishawaka, IN, p. B56

LEAHY, Mary, M.D., Chief Executive Officer, Good Samaritan Regional Medical Center, Suffern, NY, p. A456

LEAHY, Mary P., Vice President Human Resources, St. Joseph Hospital, Orange, CA, p. A81

LEAHY, Rosanne, Vice President Nursing Services, CarolinaEast Health System, New Bern, NC, p. A470

LEAKE, Neta F., Administrative Assistant Human Resources, West Feliciana Parish Hospital, Saint Francisville, LA, p. A287

LEAKE, Sandy, MSN Associate Director, Nursing and Patient Care Services, Atlanta Veterans Affairs Medical Center, Decatur, GA, p. A158

LEAKEY, Kim, R.N. Chief Nursing Officer, Lafayette Regional Health Center, Lexington, MO, p. A375

LEAL, Carlos, Director Information Technology, Valley Regional Medical Center, Brownsville, TX, p. A604

LEAL, III, Enrique A., M.D. Chief of Staff, Sweeny Community Hospital, Sweeny, TX, p. A651

LEAL, Jr., Joseph M., M.D. Chief of Staff, Glendive Medical Center, Glendive, MT, p. A387

LEAMING, Larry E., FACHE, Chief Executive Officer, Roosevelt General Hospital, Portales, NM, p. A430

LEAMON, Jim, Chief Financial Officer, JFK Medical Center, Atlantis, FL, p. A123

LEAR, Richard
Director Information Systems, St. David's Medical Center, Austin, TX, p. A600
Director Information Systems, St. David's South Austin Medical Center, Austin, TX, p. A600

LEARSON, Jerome, Manager Information Technology and Chief Security Officer, Palo Verde Hospital, Blythe, CA, p. A57

LEARY, Edward B.
Chief Executive Officer, Vibra Hospital of Southeastern Massachusetts, New Bedford, MA, p. A312
Interim Chief Executive Officer, Vibra Hospital of Western Massachusetts, Springfield, MA, p. A315

LEASE, Faye, Director of Nursing, Reeves County Hospital, Pecos, TX, p. A641

LEASE–HOMEYER, Cheryl, Lead Information Technology Business Partner, Mercy Hospital Carthage, Carthage, MO, p. A369

LEASURE, Sandie, Senior Vice President Human Resources, O'Bleness Memorial Hospital, Athens, OH, p. A484

LEATHERS, Cynthia, R.N
Chief Nursing Officer, Integris Bass Baptist Health Center, Enid, OK, p. A511
Chief Nursing Officer, Integris Bass Pavilion, Enid, OK, p. A511

LEAVITT, Jared, Chief Operating Officer, Kern Medical Center, Bakersfield, CA, p. A56

LEAZER, Ronald, Chief Financial Officer, Gateway Regional Medical Center, Granite City, IL, p. A191

LEBEAU, Michelle, Senior Vice President, Chief Operating Officer, Chief Nursing Officer, The University of Vermont Health Network–Champlain Valley Physicians Hospital, Plattsburgh, NY, p. A453

LEBER, Ian, M.D. Chief Medical Officer, Bayshore Community Hospital, Holmdel, NJ, p. A418

LEBLANC, Ed, M.D. Vice President Medical Affairs, Seton Northwest Hospital, Austin, TX, p. A599

LEBLANC, Fernis, Chief Operating Officer, Ochsner St. Anne General Hospital, Raceland, LA, p. A286

LEBLANC, Julie, Director of Nursing, Memorial Specialty Hospital, Lake Charles, LA, p. A281

LEBLANC, Karen, Director, Applications, Samaritan Hospital, Troy, NY, p. A457

LEBOWITZ, Howard, M.D. Chief Medical Officer, Specialty Hospital of Central Jersey, Lakewood, NJ, p. A418

LEBRON, Juan, M.D. Medical Director, HEALTHSOUTH Sea Pines Rehabilitation Hospital, Melbourne, FL, p. A136

LEBRON, Sonia M., Human Resources Specialist, Industrial Hospital, San Juan, PR, p. A730

LEBRUN, James, Chief Executive Officer, Perkins County Health Services, Grant, NE, p. A396

LECATES, William W., M.D. Medical Director, Bassett Medical Center, Cooperstown, NY, p. A437

LECHICH, Anthony, M.D. Chief Medical Officer, Terence Cardinal Cooke Health Care Center, New York, NY, p. A450

LECHNER, David, M.D. Chief Medical Officer and Vice President Innovation, Community Medical Center, Missoula, MT, p. A389

LECHUGA, Mario, Director Human Resources, Turquoise Lodge Hospital, Albuquerque, NM, p. A428

LECKELT, Mitchell D., Chief Executive Officer, UP Health System–Bell, Ishpeming, MI, p. A327

LECKER, Marijo, Vice President, Martha Jefferson Hospital, Charlottesville, VA, p. A668

LECKEY, Scott
Chief Financial Officer, Banner Desert Medical Center, Mesa, AZ, p. A34
Vice President Finance, Baptist Health Paducah, Paducah, KY, p. A267

LECROY, Patricia Ann, MSN Interim Chief Nursing Officer, Piedmont Medical Center, Rock Hill, SC, p. A569

LEDBETTER, Joy, Vice President, Chief Human Resources Officer, UnityPoint Health – Peoria, Peoria, IL, p. A200

LEDDEN, Edwin L., Assistant Administrator and Director Human Resources, Henry County Medical Center, Paris, TN, p. A592

LEDELL, Michelle
Director Human Resource, Fairview Ridges Hospital, Burnsville, MN, p. A340
Director Human Resources, Fairview Southdale Hospital, Edina, MN, p. A342

LEDERER, Jane, R.N. Vice President and Chief Nursing Officer, Kingsbrook Jewish Medical Center,, NY, p. A445

LEDERMAN, Joel, Director Information Systems, Community Health Center of Branch County, Coldwater, MI, p. A321

LEDERMAN, Mark, Chief Information Officer, Interfaith Medical Center,, NY, p. A444

LEDFORD, Keith, M.D. Chief of Staff, Scenic Mountain Medical Center, Big Spring, TX, p. A602

LEDOUX, Roger C., Chief Executive Officer, Byrd Regional Hospital, Leesville, LA, p. A282

LEE, Brett D., Chief Executive Officer, Lake Pointe Medical Center, Rowlett, TX, p. A644

LEE, Byong, Chief Information Officer, Limestone Medical Center, Groesbeck, TX, p. A622

LEE, Charles, Director Clinical Operations, Brentwood Hospital, Shreveport, LA, p. A287

LEE, Cheryl, Director Human Resources, Eliza Coffee Memorial Hospital, Florence, AL, p. A20

LEE, Cheryl D., R.N. Vice President of Patient Care Services and Chief Nursing Officer, University of Maryland Rehabilitation & Orthopaedic Institute, Baltimore, MD, p. A298

LEE, Darren W.
President and Chief Executive Officer, St. John's Pleasant Valley Hospital, Camarillo, CA, p. A57
President and Chief Executive Officer, St. John's Regional Medical Center, Oxnard, CA, p. A81

LEE, David, Chief Executive Officer, Otto Kaiser Memorial Hospital, Kenedy, TX, p. A630

LEE, Dennis, Vice President and Chief Information Officer, Cabell Huntington Hospital, Huntington, WV, p. A696

LEE, Eric A., President and Chief Executive Officer, Jennie Stuart Medical Center, Hopkinsville, KY, p. A262

LEE, Evan W., M.D. Chief Medical Staff, Weiser Memorial Hospital, Weiser, ID, p. A179

LEE, James R., M.D. Chief of Staff, Hamilton General Hospital, Hamilton, TX, p. A622

LEE, James Y., Executive Vice President and Chief Operating Officer, New York–Presbyterian/Lawrence Hospital, Bronxville, NY, p. A435

LEE, Jeannie, Director Human Resources, Marshall County Hospital, Benton, KY, p. A257

LEE, Jenny, Human Resources Generalist, Essentia Health–Graceville, Graceville, MN, p. A343

LEE, John Paul, M.D. Chief of Staff, Lackey Memorial Hospital, Forest, MS, p. A358

LEE, John R., Chief Executive Officer, Mat–Su Regional Medical Center, Palmer, AK, p. A30

LEE, Joshua, Chief Information Officer, USC Norris Comprehensive Cancer Center, Los Angeles, CA, p. A74

LEE, Karen, MSN Chief Nursing Officer, Belton Regional Medical Center, Belton, MO, p. A367

LEE, Karen, Director Human Resources, Gallup Indian Medical Center, Gallup, NM, p. A429

LEE, Kayleen R., Chief Executive Officer, Sioux Center Health, Sioux Center, IA, p. A237

LEE, Kenneth, Division Chair, Human Resource Advisory, Mayo Clinic Health System in Eau Claire, Eau Claire, WI, p. A704

LEE, Kim, Chief Operating Officer, Faith Community Hospital, Jacksboro, TX, p. A629

LEE, Kwon, Chief Information Officer, Pennsylvania Hospital, Philadelphia, PA, p. A549

LEE, Lori L., Assistant Vice President Nursing, Nanticoke Memorial Hospital, Seaford, DE, p. A119

LEE, Mary C., Manager Human Resources, Jonathan M. Wainwright Memorial Veterans Affairs Medical Center, Walla Walla, WA, p. A692

LEE, Michael, President, Weeks Medical Center, Lancaster, NH, p. A411

LEE, Michael D., Chief Human Resources Officer, Adirondack Medical Center, Saranac Lake, NY, p. A455

LEE, Mihi, Chief Financial Officer, Coast Plaza Hospital, Norwalk, CA, p. A79

LEE, Mike, R.N. Chief Nursing Officer, Matagorda Regional Medical Center, Bay City, TX, p. A601

LEE, Nancy, Chief Nursing Officer, Placentia–Linda Hospital, Placentia, CA, p. A83

LEE, Nancy, R.N. Vice President Patient Care Services and Chief Nursing Officer, Stanford Health Care, Palo Alto, CA, p. A82

LEE, Nathan W., Chief Executive Officer, Mary Breckinridge ARH Hospital, Hyden, KY, p. A262

LEE, Randall, Vice President and Chief Operating Officer, Baptist Health South Florida, Baptist Hospital of Miami, Miami, FL, p. A136

LEE, Randy, M.D. Senior Vice President Medical Affairs, Community Hospital South, Indianapolis, IN, p. A213

LEE, Robbin, Chief Executive Officer, Wellington Regional Medical Center, West Palm Beach, FL, p. A150

LEE, Ryan, Chief Operating Officer, West Boca Medical Center, Boca Raton, FL, p. A124

LEE, S. Kwon, M.D. Chief of Staff, Vibra Hospital of Sacramento, Folsom, CA, p. A62

LEE, Sherry, Chief Nurse Executive, Fulton State Hospital, Fulton, MO, p. A371

LEE, Stacey, JD, Chief Executive Officer, Johnson Memorial Health Services, Dawson, MN, p. A341

LEE, Stephen, FACHE, President, Baptist Medical Center Nassau, Fernandina Beach, FL, p. A128

LEE, Terri
Chief Information Office, Tanner Higgins General Hospital, Bremen, GA, p. A155
Tanner Medical Center–Villa Rica, Villa Rica, GA, p. A168

LEE, Thomas G., Chief Financial Officer, Medicine Lodge Memorial Hospital, Medicine Lodge, KS, p. A249

LEE, Victor N., FACHE, President and Chief Executive Officer, Boone County Health Center, Albion, NE, p. A393

LEE, W. Bryan, Chief Operating Officer, Osceola Regional Medical Center, Kissimmee, FL, p. A133

LEE, Wendy, Chief Nursing Officer, Regional Rehabilitation Hospital, Phenix City, AL, p. A24

LEEGSTRA, Ruurd, Chief Financial Officer, Silver Hill Hospital, New Canaan, CT, p. A115

LEEK, Dustin, Vice President of Enterprise Technical Services, Health First Holmes Regional Medical Center, Melbourne, FL, p. A135

LEEKA, Andrew B., President and Chief Executive Officer, Good Samaritan Hospital, Los Angeles, CA, p. A71

LEEMING, Rosemary, M.D. Chief Medical Officer, UH Regional Hospitals, Cleveland, OH, p. A490

LEEPER, Doug, Chief Information Officer, Kaweah Delta Medical Center, Visalia, CA, p. A99

LEEPER, Kevin, Chief Executive Officer, Nevada Regional Medical Center, Nevada, MO, p. A377

LEESMAN, Keenan, Director Information Systems, Abraham Lincoln Memorial Hospital, Lincoln, IL, p. A195

LEFEVRE, Denise, Chief Information Officer, Oroville Hospital, Oroville, CA, p. A81

LEFF, Marc, Vice President Human Resources, St. John's Riverside Hospital, Yonkers, NY, p. A459

LEFFLER, Stephen, Chief Medical Officer, The University of Vermont Health Network University of Vermont Medical Center, Burlington, VT, p. A665

LEFKOW, Frances, Director Human Resources, La Rabida Children's Hospital, Chicago, IL, p. A184

LEFTON, Ray, Chief Financial Officer, Jeanes Hospital, Philadelphia, PA, p. A548

LEFTON, Ruth, Chief Operating Officer, Einstein Medical Center Philadelphia, Philadelphia, PA, p. A547

LEFTWICH, Hal W., FACHE, Chief Executive Officer, Fishermen's Hospital, Marathon, FL, p. A135

LEFTWITCH, Billy, Director, Information Technology, Wellstone Regional Hospital, Jeffersonville, IN, p. A215

LEGASPI, Johnson, Director Information Systems, Alhambra Hospital Medical Center, Alhambra, CA, p. A54

LEGAULT, Matthew, Chief Financial Officer, McLaren Oakland, Pontiac, MI, p. A332

LEGAY, Jeff, Interim Chief Financial Officer, UNC REX Healthcare, Raleigh, NC, p. A472

LEGEND, Rachel, MSH, LICSW Interim Chief Executive Officer, Arbour–Fuller Hospital, Attleboro, MA, p. A305

LEGER, Lynn, Director Information Systems, Ridgeview Institute, Smyrna, GA, p. A166

LEGERE, Tina, President, Central Maine Medical Center, Lewiston, ME, p. A293

LEGG, Alyce, Vice President Human Resources, University Hospitals Samaritan Medical Center, Ashland, OH, p. A484

LEGG, Debra Lynn, Associate Director Patient Care Services and Nurse Executive, Beckley Veterans Affairs Medical Center, Beckley, WV, p. A694

LEGGETT III, G. Raymond, President and Chief Executive Officer, CarolinaEast Health System, New Bern, NC, p. A470

LEGGETT, Sandra, Chief Operating Officer, Atchison Hospital, Atchison, KS, p. A240

LEGLEITER, Brenda, R.N., Chief Executive Officer, Rush County Memorial Hospital, La Crosse, KS, p. A247

LEGRAND III, Edwin C., Executive Director, Mississippi State Department of Mental Health, Jackson, MS, p. B92

LEGRAND, Kila, Chief Nursing Officer, Sanford Aberdeen Medical Center, Aberdeen, SD, p. A572

LEHMAN, Andy
Senior Vice President Technology and Analytics, Fort Hamilton Hospital, Hamilton, OH, p. A496
Senior Vice President Technology and Analytics, Grandview Medical Center, Dayton, OH, p. A492
Senior Vice President Technology & Analytics, Greene Memorial Hospital, Xenia, OH, p. A506
Senior Vice President Technology and Analytics, Kettering Medical Center, Kettering, OH, p. A496
Vice President Information Systems, Soin Medical Center, Beavercreek, OH, p. A484
Senior Vice President Technology and Analytics, Sycamore Medical Center, Miamisburg, OH, p. A499

LEHMAN, Brennan, Chief Information Officer, Mosaic Life Care at St. Joseph, Saint Joseph, MO, p. A379

LEHMAN, James, M.D
  Vice President Medical Affairs, Covenant Medical Center, Waterloo, IA, p. A238
  Vice President Medical Affairs, Mercy Hospital of Franciscan Sisters, Oelwein, IA, p. A235
  Vice President Medical Affairs, Sartori Memorial Hospital, Cedar Falls, IA, p. A226
LEHMAN, Ronda, PharmD Chief Operating Officer, SRPS, St. Rita's Medical Center, Lima, OH, p. A497
LEHMAN, Sandi, Chief Financial Officer, Humboldt General Hospital, Winnemucca, NV, p. A409
LEHN, Toby, Director of Nurses, Concho County Hospital, Eden, TX, p. A614
LEHNHOF–WATTS, Laurie
  Assistant Administrator Patient Services, East Texas Medical Center Rehabilitation Hospital, Tyler, TX, p. A654
  Assistant Administrator Risk Management Performance Improvement and Education, East Texas Medical Center Specialty Hospital, Tyler, TX, p. A654
LEIBMAN, Maurice, M.D. Chief Medical Officer, Memorial Hermann Greater Heights Hospital, Houston, TX, p. A625
LEICHMAN, Ann Marie, R.N. Vice President Patient Care Services and Chief Nursing Officer, Valley Hospital, Ridgewood, NJ, p. A423
LEIDY, R. Grant, Vice President Finance, Deborah Heart and Lung Center, Browns Mills, NJ, p. A415
LEIF, Sue, R.N. Director Human Resources, Annie Jeffrey Memorial County Health Center, Osceola, NE, p. A401
LEIGHTON, Heather, Director, Revenue Cycle and Privacy Officer, Upper Connecticut Valley Hospital, Colebrook, NH, p. A410
LEIGHTON, Richard, Financial Application Analyst, Unity Medical & Surgical Hospital, Mishawaka, IN, p. A218
LEINEN, Rick J., Chief Financial Officer, Montgomery County Memorial Hospital, Red Oak, IA, p. A236
LEININGER, Bethany, Manager Human Resource, Hillcrest Hospital Cushing, Cushing, OK, p. A510
LEISHER, Jr., George
  Chief Human Resources Officer, Antelope Valley Hospital, Lancaster, CA, p. A68
  Vice President Human Resources, Hollywood Presbyterian Medical Center, Los Angeles, CA, p. A71
LEISHER, Karla, Business Office Manager, Beaver County Memorial Hospital, Beaver, OK, p. A509
LEISING, Elizabeth, Chief Nursing Officer and Vice President, Outpatient Services, Margaret Mary Health, Batesville, IN, p. A206
LEIST, Vincent, President and Chief Executive Officer, North Arkansas Regional Medical Center, Harrison, AR, p. A47
LEITE, Dolores, Chief Human Resource Executive, NYC Health + Hospitals / North Central Bronx,, NY, p. A449
LEITNER, Mark, Administrator, East Texas Medical Center Henderson, Henderson, TX, p. A623
LEJEUNE, Lucille, Assistant Administrator and Chief Financial Officer, Acadia–St. Landry Hospital, Church Point, LA, p. A274
LEJSEK, Shari, Administrator, Patients' Hospital of Redding, Redding, CA, p. A84
LELAND, Joni, Director Human Resources, Memorial Hospital, Gonzales, TX, p. A621
LEM, Alan
  Vice President Finance, Fairview Ridges Hospital, Burnsville, MN, p. A340
  Vice President Finance, Fairview Southdale Hospital, Edina, MN, p. A342
LEMAIRE, Joseph M.
  Executive Vice President Finance and Partner Company Operations, Bayshore Community Hospital, Holmdel, NJ, p. A418
  Executive Vice President Finance, Riverview Medical Center, Red Bank, NJ, p. A423
  Executive Vice President, Southern Ocean Medical Center, Manahawkin, NJ, p. A419
LEMAISTRE, Collin, Chief Executive Officer, Baylor Scott & White Medical Center – Sunnyvale, Sunnyvale, TX, p. A651
LEMAISTRE, Court, FACHE Chief Operating Officer, Lafayette General Medical Center, Lafayette, LA, p. A280
LEMANSKI, Dennis R., D.O. Senior Vice President Medical Affairs and Medical Education/CMO, Henry Ford Wyandotte Hospital, Wyandotte, MI, p. A337
LEMASTERS, Debra J., Director Human Resources, Woodlawn Hospital, Rochester, IN, p. A221
LEMAY, Catherine, Vice President Finance, Millinocket Regional Hospital, Millinocket, ME, p. A294
LEMAY, Robert Raymond, R.N. Chief Nursing Officer, The Physicians Centre Hospital, Bryan, TX, p. A604
LEMBCKE, Brad, M.D. Vice President Medical Staff Affairs, Baylor University Medical Center, Dallas, TX, p. A609
LEMEL, Mark, Chief of Staff, Transylvania Regional Hospital, Brevard, NC, p. A461

LEMIEUX, Harry, Chief Information Officer, Harrington Memorial Hospital, Southbridge, MA, p. A314
LEMIEUX, Kandie, Administrative Assistant and Director Human Resources, Northern Rockies Medical Center, Cut Bank, MT, p. A386
LEMMER, Donn J., Chief Financial Officer and Chief Operating Officer, West Shore Medical Center, Manistee, MI, p. A329
LEMMERMAN, Deborah, Vice President, Human Resources, Hebrew Rehabilitation Center, Boston, MA, p. A307
LEMMONS, Joe, D.O. Chief of Staff, Lehigh Regional Medical Center, Lehigh Acres, FL, p. A134
LEMOINE, Kirk, Chief Executive Officer, Bienville Medical Center, Arcadia, LA, p. A272
LEMON, Brian J., President, Northwestern Medicine Central DuPage Hospital, Winfield, IL, p. A205
LEMON, Marc, Marketing Chief Excecutive Officer, Kindred Hospital–Aurora, Aurora, CO, p. A101
LEMON, Rita, Director Human Resources, Avera Queen of Peace Hospital, Mitchell, SD, p. A575
LEMON, Thomas R., Chief Executive Officer, Otsego Memorial Hospital, Gaylord, MI, p. A324
LEMONS, Elizabeth, Chief Operating Officer, Saint Thomas Rutherford Hospital, Murfreesboro, TN, p. A590
LEMONS, Kenneth, Commander, Reynolds Army Community Hospital, Fort Sill, OK, p. A512
LEMONTE, David, Vice President and Chief Operating Officer, CHRISTUS Spohn Hospital Kleberg, Kingsville, TX, p. A630
LENA, Ela C., Administrator and Vice President Operations, Bethesda Hospital East, Boynton Beach, FL, p. A124
LENAHAN, Kevin
  Director Corporate Accounting, Budgets, Grants and Reimbursements, Newton Medical Center, Newton, NJ, p. A421
  Vice President Finance and Chief Financial Officer, Overlook Medical Center, Summit, NJ, p. A423
LENAMOND, Kevin, Information Management Service Line Executive, Michael E. DeBakey Veterans Affairs Medical Center, Houston, TX, p. A626
LENARD, Gary, Director Human Resources, Hendricks Regional Health, Danville, IN, p. A209
LENDARIS, Nia, Regional Vice President Patient Care, St. Helena Hospital Napa Valley, Saint Helena, CA, p. A87
LENFANT, Rodney, Chief Financial Officer, OakBend Medical Center, Richmond, TX, p. A643
LENGFELDER, Valerie, M.D. Chief of Staff, Powell Valley Healthcare, Powell, WY, p. A723
LENKO, Paul, Unit Head, Information Technology, Mayo Clinic Hospital, Phoenix, AZ, p. A36
LENKOWSKI, Thomas, Chief Financial Officer, Speare Memorial Hospital, Plymouth, NH, p. A413
LENNARTZ, Randal P., CPA, President and Chief Executive Officer, Highland District Hospital, Hillsboro, OH, p. A496
LENNEN, Anthony B., President, Community Hospital South, Indianapolis, IN, p. A213
LENNON, Colin, Chief Financial Officer, Richard L. Roudebush Veterans Affairs Medical Center, Indianapolis, IN, p. A214
LENNON, Roslyn J., R.N. Chief Nursing Officer, West Suburban Medical Center, Oak Park, IL, p. A199
LENS, Amanda, Director, Human Resources, St. Mary Medical Center, Apple Valley, CA, p. A55
LENTENBRINK, Laura, Vice President, Human Resources, Borgess Medical Center, Kalamazoo, MI, p. A327
LENTZ, Darrell, President, Aspirus Wausau Hospital, Wausau, WI, p. A718
LENTZ, Matt, R.N. Director of Patient Services, Brown County Hospital, Ainsworth, NE, p. A393
LENZ, Jan, Chief Nursing Officer, Athens–Limestone Hospital, Athens, AL, p. A16
LENZO, Julie, Director Business Office, AMG Specialty Hospital–Albuquerque, Albuquerque, NM, p. A427
LEO, Elizabeth, Chief Human Resources Officer, Moses Taylor Hospital, Scranton, PA, p. A554
LEON, Daniel, Chief Financial Officer, Sherman Oaks Hospital,, CA, p. A74
LEON, Luis, Chief Operating Officer, Desert Valley Hospital, Victorville, CA, p. A98
LEONARD, Anne, R.N. Chief Nursing Officer, TriStar Greenview Regional Hospital, Bowling Green, KY, p. A258
LEONARD, Beckie, R.N. Chief Nursing Officer, Foundation Surgical Hospital of San Antonio, San Antonio, TX, p. A646
LEONARD, Bruce, M.D. Medical Director and Chief of Psychiatry, Colorado Mental Health Institute at Fort Logan, Denver, CO, p. A103
LEONARD, Chris, Chief Financial Officer, Rolling Hills Hospital, Franklin, TN, p. A583
LEONARD, Donavan, Chief Financial Officer, Baptist Memorial Hospital–Booneville, Booneville, MS, p. A356
LEONARD, Edward F., Executive Vice President and Chief Operating Officer, White Plains Hospital Center, White Plains, NY, p. A459

LEONARD, James C., M.D., President and Chief Executive Officer, Carle Foundation, Urbana, IL, p. B27
LEONARD, James C., M.D., President and Chief Executive Officer, Carle Foundation Hospital, Urbana, IL, p. A204
LEONARD, Mark, Vice President Finance, Beaumont Hospital – Troy, Troy, MI, p. A336
LEONARD, Mark T.
  Chief Executive Officer, Dickenson Community Hospital, Clintwood, VA, p. A669
  Chief Executive Officer, Norton Community Hospital, Norton, VA, p. A675
LEONARD, Robert, Director Information Services, Sierra Vista Regional Medical Center, San Luis Obispo, CA, p. A92
LEONARD, Wes, Chief Executive Officer, Whitten Center, Clinton, SC, p. A563
LEONARD, William H., President, Carolinas Medical Center–University, Charlotte, NC, p. A462
LEONDAR, Kimberly, Director Human Resources, Texas Health Harris Methodist Hospital Stephenville, Stephenville, TX, p. A650
LEONELIS, Lisa, Chief Information Officer, Veterans Affairs Salt Lake City Health Care System, Salt Lake City, UT, p. A664
LEOPARD, Erik, Manager Human Resource, Methodist Hospital for Surgery, Addison, TX, p. A595
LEOPARD, Jimmy, FACHE, Chief Executive Officer, Wagoner Community Hospital, Wagoner, OK, p. A523
LEPAK, Jason, M.D. Medical Director, St. John Sapulpa, Sapulpa, OK, p. A519
LEPE, Patti, Chief Financial Officer, Parkview Community Hospital Medical Center, Riverside, CA, p. A86
LEPP, Jerry, Chief Executive Officer, Ashley Medical Center, Ashley, ND, p. A477
LEPPER, Dale, Chief Information Officer, Antelope Valley Hospital, Lancaster, CA, p. A68
LEPPKE, Ben, Chief Information Officer, Satanta District Hospital and Long Term Care, Satanta, KS, p. A253
LEQUEUX, Veronica, Vice President Human Resources, Blake Medical Center, Bradenton, FL, p. A124
LERASH, Terrance, Interim President and Chief Executive Officer, Scheurer Hospital, Pigeon, MI, p. A331
LERCH, Gail, R.N
  Vice President, Kapiolani Medical Center for Women & Children, Honolulu, HI, p. A170
  Vice President Human Resources, Pali Momi Medical Center, Aiea, HI, p. A170
  Executive Vice President Human Resources, Straub Clinic & Hospital, Honolulu, HI, p. A171
LERCH, Shawn, Chief Executive Officer, Miners' Colfax Medical Center, Raton, NM, p. A430
LERNER, Jerome, M.D. Medical Director, Sierra Tucson, Tucson, AZ, p. A41
LEROY, Michael
  Senior Vice President and Chief Information Officer, DMC – Detroit Receiving Hospital, Detroit, MI, p. A321
  Senior Vice President and Chief Information Officer, DMC Harper University Hospital, Detroit, MI, p. A322
LESCH, Jason, Chief Financial Officer, Auburn Community Hospital, Auburn, NY, p. A434
LESCHER, Mary, Chief Clinical Officer, Doctor's Memorial Hospital, Perry, FL, p. A142
LESHER, Jennifer, Chief Financial Officer, Lock Haven Hospital, Lock Haven, PA, p. A543
LESIAK, Cindy, Vice President Patient Care Services and Director of Nursing, Boone County Health Center, Albion, NE, p. A393
LESINS, Ross, Chief Information Officer, Casa Colina Hospital and Health Systems, Pomona, CA, p. A83
LESKO, Joan, Director Technical Support and Services, KidsPeace Children's Hospital, Orefield, PA, p. A546
LESLIE, Andrea M., MSN Chief Nursing Officer, Spectrum Health United Hospital, Greenville, MI, p. A325
LESLIE, Bruce W., M.D. Chief of Staff, Grant Memorial Hospital, Petersburg, WV, p. A699
LESLIE, Desdemona, Finance Officer, U. S. Public Health Service Indian Hospital–Whiteriver, Whiteriver, AZ, p. A41
LESLIE, Donald P., M.D. Medical Director, Shepherd Center, Atlanta, GA, p. A153
LESLIE, Jeff, Director Information Technology, Berwick Hospital Center, Berwick, PA, p. A533
LESLIE, Kelly, Chief Financial Officer, Ferry County Memorial Hospital, Republic, WA, p. A688
LESLIE, Steve, Chief Financial Officer, Fairbanks Memorial Hospital, Fairbanks, AK, p. A29
LESNIAK, Jacklynn, R.N. Vice President Patient Care Services and Chief Nursing Officer, Midwestern Regional Medical Center, Zion, IL, p. A205
LESNICK, Kelly, Resource Manager Flight Commander, Wright Patterson Medical Center, Wright–Patterson AFB, OH, p. A506

LESNIEWSKI, Amy, Associate Director Patient Care Services, Alexandria Veterans Affairs Health Care System, Pineville, LA, p. A286

LESTER, Lisa, Chief Nursing Officer, HEALTHSOUTH Southern Hills Rehabilitation Hospital, Princeton, WV, p. A699

LESTER, Ron, Chief Human Resources, Cheyenne Veterans Affairs Medical Center, Cheyenne, WY, p. A722

LESTER, Wade K., Chief Nursing and Operations Officer, Mid–Jefferson Extended Care Hospital, Nederland, TX, p. A638

LESTER, William, M.D. Vice President Medical Affairs, Cardinal Hill Rehabilitation Hospital, Lexington, KY, p. A263

LETCHWORTH, Mike, Manager Information Systems, Cherry Hospital, Goldsboro, NC, p. A466

LETHI, Scott, R.N. Chief Nursing Officer, Fort Duncan Regional Medical Center, Eagle Pass, TX, p. A614

LETSON, Robert F., FACHE, Chief Executive Officer, South Peninsula Hospital, Homer, AK, p. A29

LETT, Bryan W., Chief Executive Officer, Haven Behavioral Hospital of Eastern Pennsylvania, Reading, PA, p. A553

LETT, Tammy, R.N. Chief Nursing Officer, HSHS Holy Family Hospital in Greenville, Greenville, IL, p. A192

LETTOW, Bonnie, Chief Financial Officer, Franklin General Hospital, Hampton, IA, p. A231

LEU, Christopher, President, Texas Health Harris Methodist Hospital Stephenville, Stephenville, TX, p. A650

LEUDECKE, Amelia, Director Human Resources, HealthSouth Rehabilitation Hospital Round Rock, Round Rock, TX, p. A644

LEUNG, Lawrence, M.D. Chief of Staff, VA Palo Alto Health Care System, Palo Alto, CA, p. A82

LEVANGER, Nathan, M.D. Chief of Staff, Teton Valley Health Care, Driggs, ID, p. A176

LEVECK, Dianna, Chief Human Resources Officer, Genesis HealthCare System, Zanesville, OH, p. A507

LEVEILLEE, Mary, Senior Vice President Patient Care Services and Chief Nursing Officer, Butler Hospital, Providence, RI, p. A560

LEVELING, Jim, Director Information Technology, Kansas City Orthopaedic Institute, Leawood, KS, p. A247

LEVER, Roger, M.D. President Medical Staff, The Outer Banks Hospital, Nags Head, NC, p. A470

LEVERICH, Karen, Chief Executive Officer, Promise Hospital of Overland Park, Overland Park, KS, p. A251

LEVERING, Theresa, Director Human Resources, Doctors Hospital of Sarasota, Sarasota, FL, p. A145

LEVESQUE, David, Director, Information Systems, New Hampshire Hospital, Concord, NH, p. A410

LEVI, John, Director Human Resources, St. Lawrence Rehabilitation Center, Lawrenceville, NJ, p. A418

LEVINE, Alan M., President and Chief Executive Officer, Mountain States Health Alliance, Johnson City, TN, p. B93

LEVINE, Alexandra, M.D. Chief Medical Officer, City of Hope's Helford Clinical Research Hospital, Duarte, CA, p. A61

LEVINE, Larry L., President and Chief Executive Officer, Blythedale Children's Hospital, Valhalla, NY, p. A457

LEVINE, Peter H., M.D. Executive Medical Director Behavioral Health Services, Adventist Behavioral Health Rockville, Rockville, MD, p. A303

LEVINE, Robert V., Executive Vice President and Chief Operating Officer, Flushing Hospital Medical Center,, NY, p. A444

LEVINSON, Adam, Associate Director, Information Services, University Behavioral Healthcare, Piscataway, NJ, p. A422

LEVISON, Julie, Director Human Resources, Providence Medford Medical Center, Medford, OR, p. A528

LEVITZ, Michele, Director Finance, St. Luke's Hospital – Miners Campus, Coaldale, PA, p. A535

LEVY, Becky
Chief Financial Officer, Paradise Valley Hospital, National City, CA, p. A79
Chief Operating Officer, Shasta Regional Medical Center, Redding, CA, p. A84

LEVY, Brian, M.D. Medical Director, AMG Specialty Hospital–Edmond, Edmond, OK, p. A511

LEVY, Scott S., M.D. Vice President and Chief Medical Officer, Doylestown Hospital, Doylestown, PA, p. A537

LEVY, Susan M., M.D. Vice President Medical Affairs, Levindale Hebrew Geriatric Center and Hospital, Baltimore, MD, p. A296

LEWANDOWSKI, James, Vice President Human Resources, Perry Memorial Hospital, Princeton, IL, p. A201

LEWANDOWSKI, Jim, Interim Director of Human Resources, Carson Tahoe Health, Carson City, NV, p. A404

LEWANDOWSKI, Terri, Director Financial Services, Ministry Our Lady of Victory Hospital, Stanley, WI, p. A716

LEWELLEN, Thomas, D.O. Chief of Staff, Delta Memorial Hospital, Dumas, AR, p. A45

LEWERKE, Jane, Manager Human Resources, Northern Arizona Veterans Affairs Health Care System, Prescott, AZ, p. A37

LEWGOOD, Tony, Administrator, Shriners Hospitals for Children–Lexington, Lexington, KY, p. A263

LEWIN, Jonathan S., M.D., President, Emory Healthcare, Atlanta, GA, p. B53

LEWIS, Alene, R.N. Chief Nursing Officer, Raleigh General Hospital, Beckley, WV, p. A694

LEWIS, Angel
Senior Vice President Administration, Cookeville Regional Medical Center, Cookeville, TN, p. A581
Senior Vice President, Cumberland River Hospital, Celina, TN, p. A580

LEWIS, Barbara, Chief Nursing Officer, AllianceHealth Seminole, Seminole, OK, p. A519

LEWIS, Brandon, Director of Information Technology, Ivinson Memorial Hospital, Laramie, WY, p. A722

LEWIS, Cameron, Chief Executive Officer, AllianceHealth Clinton, Clinton, OK, p. A510

LEWIS, III, Carlisle, Senior Vice President Legal and Human Resources, Sharp Mesa Vista Hospital, San Diego, CA, p. A89

LEWIS, Christine, Controller, Hermann Area District Hospital, Hermann, MO, p. A372

LEWIS, Colleen, Director Human Resources, Texas NeuroRehab Center, Austin, TX, p. A600

LEWIS, Craig, Chief Financial Officer, Sentara Albemarle Medical Center, Elizabeth City, NC, p. A464

LEWIS, Curtis, M.D. Chief of Staff, Grady Memorial Hospital, Atlanta, GA, p. A152

LEWIS, Dana, Director Clinical Services, Southern Kentucky Rehabilitation Hospital, Bowling Green, KY, p. A258

LEWIS, Daniel
Executive Vice President and Chief Operating Officer, MetroHealth Medical Center, Cleveland, OH, p. A489
Chief Medical Officer, Takoma Regional Hospital, Greeneville, TN, p. A583

LEWIS, Darlene, Vice President Human Resources, Canton–Potsdam Hospital, Potsdam, NY, p. A453

LEWIS, Dave, Director Information Services, SSM Health St. Francis Hospital – Maryville, Maryville, MO, p. A376

LEWIS, Dennis, M.D. Chief of Staff, Ashley Regional Medical Center, Vernal, UT, p. A664

LEWIS, Jr., Donald C., Vice President and Chief Financial Officer, Coffee Regional Medical Center, Douglas, GA, p. A158

LEWIS, Doug
Chief Financial Officer, St. Luke's Rehabilitation Hospital, Boise, ID, p. A175
Chief Financial Officer, Wheatland Memorial Healthcare, Harlowton, MT, p. A388

LEWIS, Douglas, Chief Financial Officer, Boulder City Hospital, Boulder City, NV, p. A404

LEWIS, Eric, Chief Executive Officer, Olympic Medical Center, Port Angeles, WA, p. A688

LEWIS, Gerry
Chief Information Officer, Seton Highland Lakes, Burnet, TX, p. A604
Chief Information Officer, Seton Medical Center Williamson, Round Rock, TX, p. A644
Chief Information Officer, Seton Northwest Hospital, Austin, TX, p. A599

LEWIS, Gordon, Chief Executive Officer, Burnett Medical Center, Grantsburg, WI, p. A706

LEWIS, Irvan "Wick", Vice President Human Resources, Mt. Graham Regional Medical Center, Safford, AZ, p. A38

LEWIS, J. Steve, Director Finance, Youth Villages Inner Harbour Campus, Douglasville, GA, p. A158

LEWIS, Jacob, Chief Financial Officer, Mark Twain Medical Center, San Andreas, CA, p. A88

LEWIS, Jeff, Administrator, Waukesha County Mental Health Center, Waukesha, WI, p. A718

LEWIS, John I., President and Chief Executive Officer, ACMH Hospital, Kittanning, PA, p. A541

LEWIS, Kent, Director Information Services, Southwestern Medical Center, Lawton, OK, p. A513

LEWIS, Lawrence E., Chief Executive Officer, Pioneers Memorial Healthcare District, Brawley, CA, p. A57

LEWIS, Luther J., FACHE, Chief Executive Officer, Five Rivers Medical Center, Pocahontas, AR, p. A51

LEWIS, Marcus, Chief Financial Officer, Cavalier County Memorial Hospital and Clinics, Langdon, ND, p. A480

LEWIS, Marie, Human Resources Liaison, Veterans Affairs St. Louis Health Care System, Saint Louis, MO, p. A381

LEWIS, Nannette M., Chief Executive Officer, Three Rivers Behavioral Health, West Columbia, SC, p. A570

LEWIS, Nicholas P., Chief Executive Officer, Hardin Medical Center, Savannah, TN, p. A592

LEWIS, Pam, Chief Compliance Officer, William R. Sharpe, Jr. Hospital, Weston, WV, p. A701

LEWIS, Paul, M.D. Chief Medical Officer, Vice President, Boulder Community Health, Boulder, CO, p. A101

LEWIS, Paul, Chief Executive Officer, Holy Rosary Healthcare, Miles City, MT, p. A389

LEWIS, Paula, Interim Chief Nursing Officer, Five Rivers Medical Center, Pocahontas, AR, p. A51

LEWIS, Rayburn, M.D., Chief Executive, Swedish/Issaquah, Issaquah, WA, p. A685

LEWIS, Robin, Chief Financial Officer, Kiowa District Hospital and Manor, Kiowa, KS, p. A247

LEWIS, Ron, President, Spectrum Health Zeeland Community Hospital, Zeeland, MI, p. A337

LEWIS, Rosalind, R.N. Chief Nursing Officer, Community HealthCare System, Onaga, KS, p. A250

LEWIS, Sharon, Director Information Systems, Forbes Hospital, Monroeville, PA, p. A545

LEWIS, Sheila, Administrator, Harmon Memorial Hospital, Hollis, OK, p. A513

LEWIS, Sherlyn, Manager Finance, The Orthopedic Specialty Hospital, Murray, UT, p. A661

LEWIS, Stephen, Chief Executive Officer, Chase County Community Hospital, Imperial, NE, p. A397

LEWIS, Thomas D., Acting Chief Executive Officer, Clifton T. Perkins Hospital Center, Jessup, MD, p. A301

LEWIS, Vicki, FACHE, President and Chief Executive Officer, Coffee Regional Medical Center, Douglas, GA, p. A158

LEWIS, Vickie, Chief Executive Officer, Central Florida Behavioral Hospital, Orlando, FL, p. A140

LEWIS, Winifred, R.N. Chief Nursing Officer, Roseland Community Hospital, Chicago, IL, p. A186

LEWISTON, Jamie, R.N. Chief Nursing Officer, Aurora Psychiatric Hospital, Wauwatosa, WI, p. A718

LEWKOWSKI, William, Executive Vice President Information Services and Chief Information Officer, Metro Health Hospital, Wyoming, MI, p. A337

LEYDEN, RN, Andrea, Chief Nursing Officer, Washington County Hospital and Clinics, Washington, IA, p. A238

LI, Ronald, Vice President Management Information Systems, Bergen Regional Medical Center, Paramus, NJ, p. A421

LI, Stephen, Vice President Management Information Systems, Jersey City Medical Center, Jersey City, NJ, p. A418

LI, Xiao H., M.D. Chief of Staff, Surgery Specialty Hospitals of America, Pasadena, TX, p. A640

LIAGRE, Ruthann, Vice President Human Resources, Memorial Healthcare, Owosso, MI, p. A331

LIANG, Bonnie, Divisional Finance Officer, Sutter Maternity and Surgery Center of Santa Cruz, Santa Cruz, CA, p. A93

LIBBY, Kenneth, Vice President Finance, VCU Community Memorial Hospital, South Hill, VA, p. A679

LIBCKE, Julia, R.N. VP Patient Care Services, DMC – Rehabilitation Institute of Michigan, Detroit, MI, p. A321

LIBERATORE, Kristi, Vice President and Chief Financial Officer, St. Joseph Hospital, Orange, CA, p. A81

LICHIUS, Sylvia Marie, R.N. Chief Nursing Officer, Morrill County Community Hospital, Bridgeport, NE, p. A394

LICHTENFELS, Suellen, Vice President and Chief Nursing Officer, Somerset Hospital, Somerset, PA, p. A555

LICHTENWALNER, Tom, Vice President Finance, St. Luke's University Hospital – Bethlehem Campus, Bethlehem, PA, p. A533

LICHTY, Scott, M.D. Physician, Sanford Sheldon Medical Center, Sheldon, IA, p. A237

LICINA, Leonard, Chief Executive Officer, Kahi Mohala Behavioral Health, Ewa Beach, HI, p. A170

LICKTEIQ, Teri, Director Human Resources, Pella Regional Health Center, Pella, IA, p. A236

LIDDELL, Sean, Manager Regional Service Information Technology, UnityPoint Health – Trinity Muscatine, Muscatine, IA, p. A235

LIDHOLM, Helen, Chief Executive Officer, Saint Mary's Regional Medical Center, Reno, NV, p. A408

LIEBER, Alan R., President, Overlook Medical Center, Summit, NJ, p. A423

LIEBERMAN, Jeffrey A., M.D., Executive Director, New York State Psychiatric Institute, New York, NY, p. A447

LIEBERMAN, Steven L., M.D. Chief of Staff, Veterans Affairs New Jersey Health Care System, East Orange, NJ, p. A416

LIEBERS, David, M.D. Chief Medical Officer and Vice President Medical Affairs, Ellis Hospital, Schenectady, NY, p. A455

LIECK, Amy, Chief Nursing Officer, Nix Community General Hospital, Dilley, TX, p. A613

LIEFER, Alan, M.D. President Medical Staff, Memorial Hospital, Chester, IL, p. A183

LIEPMAN, Michael, Chief Executive Officer, Cascade Valley Hospital and Clinics, Arlington, WA, p. A682

LIEPMAN, Michael T., Chief Executive Officer, Skagit Regional Health, Mount Vernon, WA, p. A686

LIESEN, Daniel, M.D
Chief Medical Officer, Vista Medical Center East, Waukegan, IL, p. A205
Chief Medical Officer, Vista Medical Center West, Waukegan, IL, p. A205

LIESMANN, George, M.D. Chief Medical Officer, Blessing Hospital, Quincy, IL, p. A201

LIETTE, Cindy, Vice President Patient Care Services, Mercer Health, Coldwater, OH, p. A490

LIGHT, Gary, Vice President and Chief Information Officer, Memorial Hospital and Health Care Center, Jasper, IN, p. A215

LIGHT, Laura, Director Human Resources, St. David's North Austin Medical Center, Austin, TX, p. A600

LIGHTBOURNE, Olieth, Chief Nursing Officer, Streamwood Behavioral Health Center, Streamwood, IL, p. A204

LIGHTCAP, Debora, Director Human Resources, Mercy Medical Center, Roseburg, OR, p. A530

LIGHTFOOT, William M., M.D. Vice President Medical Services, Providence Hospital, Mobile, AL, p. A22

LIGON, Kim, Director Information Services, DCH Regional Medical Center, Tuscaloosa, AL, p. A26

LIGON, Lynda, Chief Nursing Officer, Warm Springs Medical Center, Warm Springs, GA, p. A168

LIKES, Randle L., M.D. Chief Medical Officer, Timpanogos Regional Hospital, Orem, UT, p. A661

LILES, Bart, M.D. Chief of Staff, P & S Surgical Hospital, Monroe, LA, p. A283

LILES, Jerry, D.O.CHRISTUS Spohn Hospital Alice, Alice, TX, p. A595

LILES, Richard A., M.D. Medical Director, HEALTHSOUTH Rehabilitation Hospital, Largo, FL, p. A134

LILLEBOE, Linda, R.N. Director Operations, Carson Valley Medical Center, Gardnerville, NV, p. A404

LILLEY, Jeffrey, CPA, Chief Executive Officer, Princeton Community Hospital, Princeton, WV, p. A699

LILLY, Ryan S., Director, Maine Veterans Affairs Medical Center, Augusta, ME, p. A291

LILLY, Spencer, President, Carolinas Medical Center, Charlotte, NC, p. A462

LIM, Rosemarie, M.D. Chief Medical Officer, Paradise Valley Hospital, National City, CA, p. A79

LIMA, Robert, Director Information Systems, Massachusetts Hospital School, Canton, MA, p. A309

LIMAJ, Idriz, Chief Operating Officer and Executive Director, Levindale Hebrew Geriatric Center and Hospital, Baltimore, MD, p. A296

LIMBAGA, Aries, R.N. Chief Nursing Officer, Rancho Los Amigos National Rehabilitation Center, Downey, CA, p. A61

LIMBOCKER, Jeff, Chief Financial Officer, Our Lady of the Lake Regional Medical Center, Baton Rouge, LA, p. A273

LIMM, Whitney, M.D. Executive Vice President and Chief Physician Executive, The Queen's Medical Center, Honolulu, HI, p. A171

LIN, Dean Q., FACHE, President, Ocean Medical Center, Brick Township, NJ, p. A415

LIN, George, M.D. Physician Advisor, Hackensack University Medical Center at Pascack Valley, Westwood, NJ, p. A425

LIN, Isaac, Chief Executive Officer, Kindred Hospital South Bay, Gardena, CA, p. A64

LIN, James Y., D.O. Chief of Staff, Millcreek Community Hospital, Erie, PA, p. A538

LINAFELTER, Robb, Chief Executive Officer, Lincoln Surgical Hospital, Lincoln, NE, p. A398

LINARES, Manuel, Chief Executive Officer, North Shore Medical Center, Miami, FL, p. A137

LINBOOM, Elmer, M.D. Medical Staff President, Ministry Eagle River Memorial Hospital, Eagle River, WI, p. A704

LINCK, Cindy, Chief Nursing Officer, Cornerstone Hospital of Oklahoma–Shawnee, Shawnee, OK, p. A519

LINCKS, Brad, R.N. Chief Nursing Officer and Vice President, Our Lady of Peace, Louisville, KY, p. A265

LINCOLN, David R., FACHE, President and Chief Executive Officer, Covenant Health, Tewksbury, MA, p. B43

LINCOLN, Wendy, Chief Nursing Officer, Northside Hospital, Saint Petersburg, FL, p. A144

LIND, Mark, Chief Information Officer, Mammoth Hospital, Mammoth Lakes, CA, p. A75

LIND, Sharon, FACHE,
Chief Executive Officer, Banner Goldfield Medical Center, Apache Junction, AZ, p. A31
Chief Executive Officer, Banner Ironwood Medical Center, San Tan Valley, AZ, p. A38

LIND, Trent, Chief Executive Officer, Eastside Medical Center, Snellville, GA, p. A166

LINDBERG, Bob, Chief Operating Officer, Cumberland Memorial Hospital, Cumberland, WI, p. A704

LINDBERG, Chris, Chief Information Officer, Milwaukee County Behavioral Health Division, Milwaukee, WI, p. A711

LINDBERG, Michael, M.D. Chief Medical Officer, Monadnock Community Hospital, Peterborough, NH, p. A413

LINDBERG, Steven, Chief Administrative Officer, Mayo Clinic Health System – Red Cedar in Menomonie, Menomonie, WI, p. A710

LINDELL, Charles, Chief Executive Officer, St. Bernard Parish Hospital, Chalmette, LA, p. A274

LINDELL, Jonathan, Director Information Technology, Miracle Mile Medical Center, Los Angeles, CA, p. A73

LINDEMAN, Annette, Chief Clinical Officer, Curahealth Tucson, Tucson, AZ, p. A40

LINDEMAN, Barry K., Director Human Resources, Cardinal Hill Rehabilitation Hospital, Lexington, KY, p. A263

LINDEMAN, Gretchen, Director of Human Resources, Monterey Park Hospital, Monterey Park, CA, p. A78

LINDEMANN, Fran, Director Finance, Kell West Regional Hospital, Wichita Falls, TX, p. A657

LINDEMANN, Steve, Chief Financial Officer, Brookings Health System, Brookings, SD, p. A572

LINDEN, Kelly, Senior Vice President, Chief Operating Officer, St. Mary Medical Center, Apple Valley, CA, p. A55

LINDEN, Todd C., President and Chief Executive Officer, Grinnell Regional Medical Center, Grinnell, IA, p. A231

LINDLEY, Michael, Chief Executive Officer, Haven Behavioral Healthcare, Nashville, TN, p. B60

LINDQUIST, James, R.N. Chief Nursing Officer, JFK Medical Center, Edison, NJ, p. A416

LINDQUIST, Molly, Interim Chief Financial Officer, Chestatee Regional Hospital, Dahlonega, GA, p. A157

LINDQUIST, Peter, Vice President and Chief Nursing Officer, Providence Hospital, Mobile, AL, p. A22

LINDSAY–BELL, Davida, Area Human Resources Leader, Kaiser Permanente Antioch Medical Center, Antioch, CA, p. A54

LINDSAY–WOOD, Elizabeth, Interim Chief Information Officer, Overlook Medical Center, Summit, NJ, p. A423

LINDSEY, Craig, R.N. Vice President Clinical Services/Chief Nursing Officer, Park Ridge Health, Hendersonville, NC, p. A467

LINDSEY, Don, Vice President and Chief Information Officer, Tallahassee Memorial HealthCare, Tallahassee, FL, p. A146

LINDSEY, Hugh. M.D. Chief Medical Officer, Hayes Green Beach Memorial Hospital, Charlotte, MI, p. A320

LINDSEY, Jay, Chief Executive Officer, Plano Surgical Hospital, Plano, TX, p. A642

LINDSEY, Kim, Chief Human Resources Officer, Lourdes Hospital, Paducah, KY, p. A268

LINDSEY, Robbie, Chief Information Officer, Twin Lakes Regional Medical Center, Leitchfield, KY, p. A262

LINDSEY, Tony, M.D. Chief of Staff, University of North Carolina Hospitals, Chapel Hill, NC, p. A462

LINDSTROM, David, M.D. Vice President Medical Affairs, ProMedica Bay Park Hospital, Oregon, OH, p. A500

LINES, Brian, Chief Operating Officer, Ogden Regional Medical Center, Ogden, UT, p. A661

LING, Lori, Information Technician, Windom Area Hospital, Windom, MN, p. A353

LINGEN, Tom, M.D. Chief of Staff, Cumberland Memorial Hospital, Cumberland, WI, p. A704

LINGERFELT, Jeff, Chief Executive Officer, Hammond–Henry Hospital, Geneseo, IL, p. A191

LINGLE, Dan, Chief Nursing Officer, Banner Casa Grande Medical Center, Casa Grande, AZ, p. A31

LINGO, Jessica, Human Resource Generalist, Story County Medical Center, Nevada, IA, p. A235

LINHARES, James, Chief Executive Officer, BridgePoint Hospital Capitol Hill, Washington, DC, p. A121

LINK, Nate, M.D. Medical Director, NYC Health + Hospitals / Bellevue, New York, NY, p. A447

LINKENHOKER, Ellen, Chief Nursing Officer, LewisGale Hospital Montgomery, Blacksburg, VA, p. A668

LINN, Steven C., M.D
Chief Medical Officer, Inspira Medical Center–Elmer, Elmer, NJ, p. A416
Chief Medical Officer, Inspira Medical Center–Vineland, Vineland, NJ, p. A425

LINNA, Gina, Manager Human Resources, Aspirus Ontonagon Hospital, Ontonagon, MI, p. A331

LINNELL, Jon E., Interim Chief Executive Officer, North Valley Health Center, Warren, MN, p. A353

LINNINGTON, Darryl, Chief Financial Officer, McAlester Regional Health Center, McAlester, OK, p. A514

LINSCHEID, Carol, Vice President Human Resources, Enloe Medical Center, Chico, CA, p. A58

LINSCOTT, Jason, CPA Chief Financial Officer, Texas Health Presbyterian Hospital of Rockwall, Rockwall, TX, p. A643

LINSE, Margaret, Administrative Secretary and Director Human Resources, West Holt Memorial Hospital, Atkinson, NE, p. A393

LINSIN, Amy, Chief Human Resources Officer, Good Samaritan Medical Center, West Palm Beach, FL, p. A149

LINSTROM, Joseph, Vice President Operations, Suburban Hospital, Bethesda, MD, p. A299

LINTON, Dwight, Director Human Resources, DeTar Healthcare System, Victoria, TX, p. A655

LINTON, Randall L., M.D., President and Chief Executive Officer, Mayo Clinic Health System in Eau Claire, Eau Claire, WI, p. A704

LINTZ, Gordon, Chief Administrative Officer, Morristown–Hamblen Healthcare System, Morristown, TN, p. A590

LINVILLE, Kimberly, Chief Nursing Officer, Grant Memorial Hospital, Petersburg, WV, p. A699

LINZMAN, Rob, D.O. Chief of Staff, Jefferson County Hospital, Waurika, OK, p. A523

LIPARI, Cheryl, Manager Information Systems, Teche Regional Medical Center, Morgan City, LA, p. A284

LIPE, Curt, Vice President, Chief Financial Officer, OSF St. Mary Medical Center, Galesburg, IL, p. A191

LIPINSKI, Gary, M.D
Regional Chief Medical Officer, Presence Saint Joseph Medical Center, Joliet, IL, p. A194
Regional Chief Medical Officer, Presence St. Mary's Hospital, Kankakee, IL, p. A194

LIPMAN, Brian, M.D. Medical Director and Medical Staff Services, Oconomowoc Memorial Hospital, Oconomowoc, WI, p. A713

LIPMAN, Henry D.
Senior Vice President, Financial Strategy and External Relations, Franklin Regional Hospital, Franklin, NH, p. A411
Senior Vice President, Financial Strategy and External Relations, Lakes Region General Hospital, Laconia, NH, p. A411

LIPNER, Zach, Vice President Human Resources, Newark Beth Israel Medical Center, Newark, NJ, p. A420

LIPPERT, Brandt, Vice President Human Resources, Adena Greenfield Medical Center, Greenfield, OH, p. A495

LIPPINCOTT, Ken, M.D. Chief of Staff, North Mississippi State Hospital, Tupelo, MS, p. A365

LIPSCOMB, Teresa, Director Human Resources, Springbrook Behavioral Health System, Travelers Rest, SC, p. A570

LIPSCOMB, Tiffiny J., Manager Human Resources, Intermountain Medical Center, Murray, UT, p. A661

LIPSCOMB, Tracy, CPA Vice President Financial Services and Chief Financial Officer, Garrett Regional Medical Center, Oakland, MD, p. A302

LIPSKY, Richard, Chairman and Chief Executive Officer, Columbus Hospital LTACH, Newark, NJ, p. A420

LIPSTEIN, Steven H., President and Chief Executive Officer, BJC HealthCare, Saint Louis, MO, p. B23

LIPTAK, Valenda M., Chief Executive Officer, Western Massachusetts Hospital, Westfield, MA, p. A316

LIPTON, Pat
Director Team Resources, South Florida Baptist Hospital, Plant City, FL, p. A142
Director Team Resources, St. Joseph's Hospital, Tampa, FL, p. A147

LIRAKIS, Kathy, R.N. Chief Nursing Officer, Blue Hill Memorial Hospital, Blue Hill, ME, p. A292

LIRIO, Ruel R., M.D. Clinical Physician Advisor, Spectrum Health Zeeland Community Hospital, Zeeland, MI, p. A337

LISA, Mark P., FACHE, Chief Executive Officer, Twin Cities Community Hospital, Templeton, CA, p. A96

LISELL, Susan C., Vice President of Clinical Services, LifeCare Medical Center, Roseau, MN, p. A350

LISKA, Lee Ann, Chief Executive Officer, Augusta University Medical Center, Augusta, GA, p. A153

LISKE, Thomas, M.D. Chief Medical Officer, Kindred Hospital–Sycamore, Sycamore, IL, p. A204

LISKO, J. Stuart, Regional Director Operations, Critical Access Hospital Operations, Mercy Hospital Booneville, Booneville, AR, p. A44

LISKO, Stuart, Vice President, Chief Financial Officer and Compliance Officer, Levi Hospital, Hot Springs National Park, AR, p. A47

LISKOV, David, M.D. Medical Director, First Hospital Wyoming Valley, Kingston, PA, p. A541

LISONBEE, Rod, Chief Financial Officer, Utah Valley Regional Medical Center, Provo, UT, p. A662

LIST, Alan F., President and Chief Executive Officer, H. Lee Moffitt Cancer Center and Research Institute, Tampa, FL, p. A147

LISTER, Jack, Director Human Resources, Takoma Regional Hospital, Greeneville, TN, p. A583

LISTI, Daniel, Chief Operating Officer, Valley Baptist Medical Center–Harlingen, Harlingen, TX, p. A622

LISTON, John, Chief Operating Officer, McLaren Port Huron, Port Huron, MI, p. A332

LITAKER, Thomas
Regional Vice President and Chief Financial Officer, Cascade Valley Hospital and Clinics, Arlington, WA, p. A682
Regional Vice President and Chief Financial Officer, Skagit Regional Health, Mount Vernon, WA, p. A686

LITKA, Calvin, R.N. Director of Nursing, Horsham Clinic, Ambler, PA, p. A532

LITOVITZ, Gary, M.D. Medical Director, Dominion Hospital, Falls Church, VA, p. A669

LITSINGER, James
President and Chief Financial Officer, Sheltering Arms Hospital South, Midlothian, VA, p. A674
Vice President and Chief Financial Officer, Sheltering Arms Rehabilitation Hospital, Mechanicsville, VA, p. A673
LITTERER, Karen, MSN, Administrator and Chief Operating Officer, Seton Highland Lakes, Burnet, TX, p. A604
LITTERER, Karen, R.N. Administrator and Chief Operating Officer, Seton Highland Lakes, Burnet, TX, p. A604
LITTERER, Karen, MSN, Administrator and Chief Operating Officer, Seton Northwest Hospital, Austin, TX, p. A599
LITTERER, Karen, R.N. Administrator and Chief Operating Officer, Seton Northwest Hospital, Austin, TX, p. A599
LITTLE, Bridget, Deputy Commander Nursing, Bayne–Jones Army Community Hospital, Fort Polk, LA, p. A277
LITTLE, Christopher M., Vice President and Chief Financial Officer, Ellwood City Hospital, Ellwood City, PA, p. A538
LITTLE, Denise, Director Human Resources, St. Elizabeth Community Hospital, Red Bluff, CA, p. A84
LITTLE, Gary, M.D. Medical Director, George Washington University Hospital, Washington, DC, p. A121
LITTLE, James P., M.D. Medical Director, HEALTHSOUTH Rehabilitation Hospital, Kingsport, TN, p. A585
LITTLE, Jason, President and Chief Executive Officer, Baptist Memorial Health Care Corporation, Memphis, TN, p. B20
LITTLE, Lew, Interim Chief Executive Officer, LifeCare Management Services, Plano, TX, p. B81
LITTLE, Lou
Chief Executive Officer, HEALTHSOUTH MountainView Regional Rehabilitation Hospital, Morgantown, WV, p. A698
President and Chief Executive Officer, Sparrow Specialty Hospital, Lansing, MI, p. A328
LITTLE, Marlene, Senior Director, Little Falls Hospital, Little Falls, NY, p. A441
LITTLE, Monica, Coordinator Human Resources, Kindred Rehabilitation Hospital Clear Lake, Webster, TX, p. A656
LITTLE, Steven N., President and Chief Executive Officer, Agnesian HealthCare, Fond Du Lac, WI, p. A705
LITTLE, Suzanne, Human Resources Specialist, Columbia Basin Hospital, Ephrata, WA, p. A684
LITTLEDEER, Lenora, R.N. Director of Nursing, Lawton Indian Hospital, Lawton, OK, p. A513
LITTLEFIELD, Karen, Director Human Resources, Waldo County General Hospital, Belfast, ME, p. A292
LITTLEJOHN, Edward, Chief Operating Officer, Fountain Valley Regional Hospital and Medical Center, Fountain Valley, CA, p. A62
LITTLEPAGE, Dana, Interim Chief Nursing Officer, St. John's Pleasant Valley Hospital, Camarillo, CA, p. A57
LITTRELL, Angela P., CPA Chief Financial Officer and Chief Operating Officer, Fitzgibbon Hospital, Marshall, MO, p. A376
LITTRELL, Jeremy, Director Human Resources, Brodstone Memorial Hospital, Superior, NE, p. A402
LITTRELL, Mark, Chief Executive Officer, Lincoln Prairie Behavioral Health Center, Springfield, IL, p. A203
LIU, Marsha, Executive Vice President and Chief Financial Officer, Northwest Community Hospital, Arlington Heights, IL, p. A180
LIUZZA, Jed M., Chief Human Resources Officer, OU Medical Center, Oklahoma City, OK, p. A517
LIUZZO, Gary, Director Information Systems, Scotland Health Care System, Laurinburg, NC, p. A468
LIVELY, Corey, Chief Executive Officer, Great Plains Regional Medical Center, Elk City, OK, p. A511
LIVERMAN, Brett, Chief Financial Officer, Alleghany Memorial Hospital, Sparta, NC, p. A474
LIVERSAGE, Lavonne, Director, Fargo Veterans Affairs Health Care System, Fargo, ND, p. A478
LIVESAY, Jr., William, D.O. Medical Director, HEALTHSOUTH Rehabilitation Hospital of Charleston, Charleston, SC, p. A562
LIVIN, Lee
Chief Financial Officer, Yavapai Regional Medical Center – East, Prescott Valley, AZ, p. A38
Chief Financial Officer, Yavapai Regional Medical Center, Prescott, AZ, p. A37
LIVINGSTON, Carolyn, Director Human Resources, Salt Lake Regional Medical Center, Salt Lake City, UT, p. A663
LIVINGSTON, Charles
Administrator, Dakota Plains Surgical Center, Aberdeen, SD, p. A572
Chief Executive Officer, Midwest Surgical Hospital, Omaha, NE, p. A400
LIVINGSTON, Denise, Director Human Resources, St. Mary Medical Center, Long Beach, CA, p. A70
LIVINGSTON, Keith
Senior Vice President and Chief Information Officer, Appleton Medical Center, Appleton, WI, p. A702
Senior Vice President and Chief Information Officer, Theda Clark Medical Center, Neenah, WI, p. A712

LIVINGSTON, Richard, M.D. Medical Director, Valley Behavioral Health System, Barling, AR, p. A43
LIVINGSTON, Sam, Information Resource Consultant, G. Werber Bryan Psychiatric Hospital, Columbia, SC, p. A564
LIVSEY, Don, Vice President and Chief Information Officer, USCF Benioff Children's Hospital Oakland, Oakland, CA, p. A80
LIVVIX, Susan, R.N. Vice President Nursing Services, Paris Community Hospital, Paris, IL, p. A199
LIZZA, Beth, Chief Nursing Officer, Ohio Valley Surgical Hospital, Springfield, OH, p. A502
LJUNGQUIST, Diane, MS, Chief Executive Officer, Berwick Hospital Center, Berwick, PA, p. A533
LLANO, Manuel R.
Chief Executive Officer, Atlantic Shores Hospital, Fort Lauderdale, FL, p. A128
Chief Executive Officer, Fort Lauderdale Hospital, Fort Lauderdale, FL, p. A128
LLEWELLYN, Michael R., Chief Operating Officer, Laguna Honda Hospital and Rehabilitation Center, San Francisco, CA, p. A90
LLOYD II, Donald H., Chief Executive Officer, CHRISTUS St. Patrick Hospital of Lake Charles, Lake Charles, LA, p. A281
LLOYD, Richard, D.O. Chief of Staff, Harbor Beach Community Hospital, Harbor Beach, MI, p. A326
LLOYD, Russell E., Acting Director, Central Texas Veterans Health Care System, Temple, TX, p. A651
LO, Eric, M.D. Chief Medical Staff, Florida Hospital New Smyrna, New Smyrna Beach, FL, p. A139
LO, Wesley, Regional Chief Executive Officer, Maui Memorial Medical Center, Wailuku, HI, p. A173
LOBBAN, Victoria, Vice President Finance, New England Sinai Hospital and Rehabilitation Center, Stoughton, MA, p. A315
LOBECK, Charles C., Administrator, Shriners Hospitals for Children–Twin Cities, Minneapolis, MN, p. A347
LOCEY, Vicky, R.N. Chief Operating and Chief Nursing Officer, Kaiser Permanente Santa Rosa Medical Center, Santa Rosa, CA, p. A94
LOCHALA, Richard, Chief of Staff, Mena Regional Health System, Mena, AR, p. A50
LOCHRIDGE, Angela, Director Human Resources, Bradley County Medical Center, Warren, AR, p. A53
LOCK, Lesa, Chief Nursing Officer, Valley View Medical Center, Fort Mohave, AZ, p. A32
LOCKARD, Dennis, Vice President Fiscal Services and Chief Financial Officer, Wayne Hospital, Greenville, OH, p. A495
LOCKCUFF, Todd, Chief Financial Officer, Inova Alexandria Hospital, Alexandria, VA, p. A667
LOCKE, Cheryl, Vice President and Chief Human Resource Officer, Wake Forest Baptist Medical Center, Winston–Salem, NC, p. A476
LOCKE, Christopher, Chief Executive Officer, Saint Francis Hospital–Bartlett, Bartlett, TN, p. A579
LOCKE, Marianne, R.N. Associate Director Patient Care Services, Edward Hines, Jr. Veterans Affairs Hospital, Hines, IL, p. A193
LOCKE, Stuart, Chief Executive Officer, Southern Kentucky Rehabilitation Hospital, Bowling Green, KY, p. A258
LOCKERD, Marie Paul, M.D. Chief Medical Officer, Sanford Jackson Medical Center, Jackson, MN, p. A344
LOCKETT, Kevin, Interim Chief Financial Officer, Mayo Clinic Jacksonville, Jacksonville, FL, p. A131
LOCKHART, Jimmy Wayne, M.D. Medical Director, HEALTHSOUTH Treasure Coast Rehabilitation Hospital, Vero Beach, FL, p. A149
LOCKLAIR, Deborah, FACHE, Administrator, McLeod Health Clarendon, Manning, SC, p. A568
LOCKLEAR, Ann, Vice President, Human Resources, Scotland Health Care System, Laurinburg, NC, p. A468
LOCKWOOD, Melissa, Chief Executive Officer, Preston Memorial Hospital, Kingwood, WV, p. A697
LODGE, Dale M., Chief Executive Officer, Winchester Hospital, Winchester, MA, p. A316
LOE, Cindy, R.N. Director of Nursing, Essentia Health Northern Pines Medical Center, Aurora, MN, p. A338
LOEFFELHOLZ, Tim, Account Executive Information Technology, UnityPoint Health – Finley Hospital, Dubuque, IA, p. A230
LOELIGER, Eric, Vice President of Medical Affairs, Asante Three Rivers Medical Center, Grants Pass, OR, p. A526
LOEPP Jr., Robert A., FACHE, Chief Executive Officer, AMG Specialty Hospital–Wichita, Wichita, KS, p. A255
LOERA, Arnold, M.D. Clinical Director, Bristol Bay Area Health Corporation, Dillingham, AK, p. A29
LOERINC, Albert, M.D. Medical Director, Vibra Hospital of Southeastern Massachusetts, New Bedford, MA, p. A312
LOEWENSTEIN, Howard, Chief Information Resource Management Services, Jesse Brown Veterans Affairs Medical Center, Chicago, IL, p. A184
LOFFING, David, Chief Operating Officer, University of Illinois Hospital & Health Sciences System, Chicago, IL, p. A187
LOFGREN, Richard P., M.P.H., President and CEO, UC Health, Cincinnati, OH, p. B139

LOFTIS, Dennis
Senior Vice President and Chief Information Officer, Riverside Regional Medical Center, Newport News, VA, p. A674
Senior Vice President of Information Systems, Riverside Rehabilitation Institute, Newport News, VA, p. A674
LOFTIS, Michelle, Human Resources Officer, Ferry County Memorial Hospital, Republic, WA, p. A688
LOFTON, Jason, M.D. Medical Director, De Queen Medical Center, De Queen, AR, p. A45
LOFTON, Kevin E., FACHE, Chief Executive Officer, Catholic Health Initiatives, Englewood, CO, p. B28
LOFTON, Veronica, Acting Chief Executive Officer, Twin Valley Behavioral Healthcare, Columbus, OH, p. A491
LOFTUS, John, M.D. Chief of Staff, Kaiser Permanente Oakland Medical Center, Oakland, CA, p. A80
LOFTUS, Mary Virginia, Chief Nursing Officer, Specialists Hospital – Shreveport, Shreveport, LA, p. A288
LOFTUS, Philip, Ph.D
Vice President and Chief Information Officer, Aurora Medical Center of Oshkosh, Oshkosh, WI, p. A713
Vice President and Chief Information Officer, Aurora Psychiatric Hospital, Wauwatosa, WI, p. A718
Vice President and Chief Information Officer, Aurora St. Luke's Medical Center, Milwaukee, WI, p. A711
Chief Information Officer, Aurora West Allis Medical Center, West Allis, WI, p. A719
LOFURNO, Justin A., Director Human Resources, Providence Hospital, Columbia, SC, p. A564
LOGAN, Angela, Chief Nursing Officer, Lutheran Hospital of Indiana, Fort Wayne, IN, p. A210
LOGAN, Ann P., Ph.D., Chief Operating Officer, Hoboken University Medical Center, Hoboken, NJ, p. A418
LOGAN, Bradley, Chief Financial Officer, Franklin Woods Community Hospital, Johnson City, TN, p. A585
LOGAN, Denise, Director Human Resources, Specialty Rehabilitation Hospital of Coushatta, Coushatta, LA, p. A275
LOGAN, Michael, Chief Financial Officer, Norton Brownsboro Hospital, Louisville, KY, p. A265
LOGAN, Renee, Chief Financial Officer, Murray County Medical Center, Slayton, MN, p. A351
LOGAN–OWENS, Michelle, Acting Chief Executive Officer, Palmetto Health Tuomey, Sumter, SC, p. A570
LOGAR, Michael, Assistant Superintendent, Larue D. Carter Memorial Hospital, Indianapolis, IN, p. A214
LOGDSON, David, Chief Nursing Officer, Twin Lakes Regional Medical Center, Leitchfield, KY, p. A262
LOGOZZO, Vince, Director Information Technology, Aultman Orrville Hospital, Orrville, OH, p. A501
LOGSDON, Terri
Chief Financial Officer, Greenbrier Behavior Health Hospital, Covington, LA, p. A275
Chief Financial Officer, Hickory Trail Hospital, Desoto, TX, p. A613
LOH, Marcel C., FACHE, Chief Executive Officer, Providence Saint John's Health Center, Santa Monica, CA, p. A93
LOHMAN, Eric, M.D. Chief of Staff, Meadowview Regional Medical Center, Maysville, KY, p. A266
LOHMEIER, Justin, M.D. Chief of Staff, Baptist Memorial Hospital–Union County, New Albany, MS, p. A363
LOHN, Eric
Chief Financial Officer, Lake View Memorial Hospital, Two Harbors, MN, p. A352
Vice President and Chief Financial Officer, St. Luke's Hospital, Duluth, MN, p. A342
LOHR, Daniel E.
Regional Vice President Finance, The William W. Backus Hospital, Norwich, CT, p. A116
Regional Vice President Finance, Windham Hospital, Willimantic, CT, p. A118
LOHRMAN, Joseph W., Chief Executive Officer, Annie Jeffrey Memorial County Health Center, Osceola, NE, p. A401
LOHSTRETER, Thomas, M.D. Chief of Staff, Kittson Memorial Healthcare Center, Hallock, MN, p. A344
LOKKEN, Christine, Director of Finance, Bigfork Valley Hospital, Bigfork, MN, p. A339
LOLLIS, Sylvia, Director Human Resources, Osceola Regional Medical Center, Kissimmee, FL, p. A133
LOLLO, Trisha, President, Barnes–Jewish West County Hospital, Saint Louis, MO, p. A379
LOMAN, Sarah, Director Human Resources, Penobscot Valley Hospital, Lincoln, ME, p. A294
LOMBA, Maria R., Medical Director, New Braunfels Regional Rehabilitation Hospital, New Braunfels, TX, p. A638
LOMBARD, Lisa, Chief Medical Officer, OhioHealth Rehabilitation Hospital, Columbus, OH, p. A491
LOMBARD, Scott, Director of Care Management and Community Out Reach, Spectrum Health Reed City Hospital, Reed City, MI, p. A332

LOMBARDO, Alan, Associate Director, Hunter Holmes McGuire Veterans Affairs Medical Center–Richmond, Richmond, VA, p. A678

LOMEO, Jody, Chief Executive Officer, KALEIDA Health, Buffalo, NY, p. A436

LONERGAN, Araceli
Chief Executive Officer, Community Hospital of Huntington Park, Huntington Park, CA, p. A66
Chief Executive Officer, East Los Angeles Doctors Hospital, Los Angeles, CA, p. A71

LONEY, Chris, Director Personnel, Thomas B. Finan Center, Cumberland, MD, p. A300

LONG, Adrian, M.D. Executive Vice President and Chief Medical Officer, Saint Agnes Hospital, Baltimore, MD, p. A297

LONG, Angela S., Vice President Clinical Services and Chief Nursing Officer, Southeastern Ohio Regional Medical Center, Cambridge, OH, p. A486

LONG, Brian, FACHE, President and Chief Executive Officer, Memorial Healthcare, Owosso, MI, p. A331

LONG, Dennis, Director Human Resources, Western Missouri Medical Center, Warrensburg, MO, p. A383

LONG, Douglas, President and Chief Executive Officer, West Hills Hospital and Medical Center,, CA, p. A75

LONG, Erik
Controller, Baptist Health South Florida, Mariners Hospital, Tavernier, FL, p. A148
Controller, Baptist Health South Florida, South Miami Hospital, Miami, FL, p. A136

LONG, Floyd R., Chief Executive Officer, NYC Health + Hospitals / Carter, New York, NY, p. A448

LONG, Gloria, Chief Operating Officer, Guam Regional Medical City, Dededo, GU, p. A725

LONG, Gregory L., M.D
Chief Medical Officer, Appleton Medical Center, Appleton, WI, p. A702
Chief Medical Officer, Theda Clark Medical Center, Neenah, WI, p. A712

LONG, Jeremy, Manager Information Systems, St. Vincent Salem Hospital, Salem, IN, p. A221

LONG, Jessica, Chief Executive Officer, Cornerstone Medical Center, Fort Oglethorpe, GA, p. A160

LONG, Jonathan Ray, M.D. Chief of Staff, Weatherford Regional Hospital, Weatherford, OK, p. A523

LONG, Judy M., R.N. Chief Nursing Officer and Chief Operating Officer, Appling Healthcare System, Baxley, GA, p. A154

LONG, Karen, R.N. Vice President Nursing, Bayfront Health St. Petersburg, Saint Petersburg, FL, p. A144

LONG, Michelle
Human Resources Business Partner, Abraham Lincoln Memorial Hospital, Lincoln, IL, p. A195
Regional Human Resource Manager, Taylorville Memorial Hospital, Taylorville, IL, p. A204

LONG, Mike, Chief Financial Officer, Powell Valley Healthcare, Powell, WY, p. A723

LONG, Richard, M.D. Chief Medical Officer, UPMC Hamot, Erie, PA, p. A538

LONG, Stephanie, President and Chief Executive Officer, River Bend Hospital, West Lafayette, IN, p. A223

LONG, Steven V., FACHE, President and Chief Executive Officer, Hancock Regional Hospital, Greenfield, IN, p. A212

LONG, Terry, Chief Executive Officer, Cherokee Medical Center, Centre, AL, p. A18

LONG, Theresa, Chief Executive Officer, Danville State Hospital, Danville, PA, p. A536

LONGABAUGH, James, M.D. Chief Medical Staff, Sabetha Community Hospital, Sabetha, KS, p. A253

LONGACRE, Mark E., FACHE Chief Operating Officer, Nebraska Orthopaedic Hospital, Omaha, NE, p. A400

LONGBRAKE, Jeffery, President and Chief Executive Officer, Huron Medical Center, Bad Axe, MI, p. A318

LONGDO, Derrick, Director Information Systems, Memorial Medical Center – Neillsville, Neillsville, WI, p. A712

LONGEST, Bruce, M.D. President Medical Staff, Calhoun Health Services, Calhoun City, MS, p. A356

LONGEST, Sonya, M.D. Clinical Director, Walter B. Jones Alcohol and Drug Abuse Treatment Center, Greenville, NC, p. A466

LONGLEY, Frank, Business Partner Information Technology, Cleveland Clinic, Medina Hospital, Medina, OH, p. A499

LONGMORE, David, Chief Information Officer, Wilkes–Barre Veterans Affairs Medical Center, Wilkes–Barre, PA, p. A558

LONGMUIR, Bryan, Chief Resource Management, Madigan Army Medical Center, Tacoma, WA, p. A691

LONGMUIR, Marla, M.D. Chief Medical Officer, Mountrail County Medical Center, Stanley, ND, p. A481

LONGNECKER, Stacy, Chief of Staff, Ortonville Area Health Services, Ortonville, MN, p. A348

LONGO, Marybeth, Manager Human Resources, Trenton Psychiatric Hospital, Trenton, NJ, p. A424

LONGPRE, Donald J., Vice President Finance and Chief Financial Officer, North Ottawa Community Hospital, Grand Haven, MI, p. A324

LONGTIN, Brett, Chief Financial Officer, Lake Region Healthcare, Fergus Falls, MN, p. A342

LONIS, Robert, Interim Chief Financial Officer, Nashville General Hospital, Nashville, TN, p. A590

LOOMIS, Anna
Senior Vice President Chief Financial Officer, MultiCare Auburn Medical Center, Auburn, WA, p. A682
Senior Vice President Chief Financial Officer, MultiCare Good Samaritan Hospital, Puyallup, WA, p. A688
Senior Vice President Chief Financial Officer, MultiCare Mary Bridge Children's Hospital and Health Center, Tacoma, WA, p. A692
Senior Vice President,Chief Financial Officer, MultiCare Tacoma General Hospital, Tacoma, WA, p. A692

LOOMIS, Greg, President, Mercy Health Hackley Campus, Muskegon, MI, p. A330

LOOMIS, Randy, Chief Financial Officer, Dallas County Hospital, Perry, IA, p. A236

LOONEY, Zane, Chief Information Officer, St. Bernard Parish Hospital, Chalmette, LA, p. A274

LOOPER, Eric N.
Chief Executive Officer, Hill County Region, Scott & White Hospital – Llano, Llano, TX, p. A633
Chief Executive Officer, Scott & White Hospital – Marble Falls, Marble Falls, TX, p. A635

LOOSBROCK, Tammy
Senior Director, Sanford Luverne Medical Center, Luverne, MN, p. A345
Senior Director, Sanford Rock Rapids Medical Center, Rock Rapids, IA, p. A236

LOOSEMORE, Tim
Director, Franciscan St. Anthony Health – Crown Point, Crown Point, IN, p. A209
Regional Director Information Systems, Franciscan St. Anthony Health – Michigan City, Michigan City, IN, p. A218

LOPACHIN, Vicki, M.D. Chief Medical Officer, Mount Sinai Hospital, New York, NY, p. A446

LOPAS, Mary, Chief Information Officer, Ministry Door County Medical Center, Sturgeon Bay, WI, p. A717

LOPES, Michelle Anne, MSN Senior Vice President, Patient Care Services & Chief Nursing Officer, John Muir Medical Center, Walnut Creek, Walnut Creek, CA, p. A99

LOPEZ, Augustine, Chief Financial Officer, Salinas Valley Memorial Healthcare System, Salinas, CA, p. A87

LOPEZ, Cesar, R.N. Director of Nurses, Grimes St. Joseph Health Center, Navasota, TX, p. A638

LOPEZ, David S., FACHE Executive Vice President and Chief Operating Officer, Parkland Health & Hospital System, Dallas, TX, p. A631

LOPEZ, Enrique, M.D. Medical Director, Larry B. Zieverink, Sr. Alcoholism Treatment Center, Raleigh, NC, p. A472

LOPEZ, Ericca, Director Human Resources, Canyon Ridge Hospital, Chino, CA, p. A58

LOPEZ, Ivonne, Director Human Resources, Hospital Oriente, Humacao, PR, p. A727

LOPEZ, Leonard H., Chief Operating Officer, Hopi Health Care Center, Keams Canyon, AZ, p. A33

LOPEZ, Leonardo, President Medical Staff, OSF Saint Paul Medical Center, Mendota, IL, p. A196

LOPEZ, Lesbia, Chief Nursing Officer, Doctors' Center Hospital San Juan, San Juan, PR, p. A729

LOPEZ, Lisa M., Director Human Resources, San Joaquin General Hospital, French Camp, CA, p. A63

LOPEZ, Maria Rose, R.N. Chief of Nursing, Nix Health Care System, San Antonio, TX, p. A646

LOPEZ, Maritza, M.D. Chief of Staff, Sanford Canby Medical Center, Canby, MN, p. A340

LOPEZ, Rene, Chief Executive Officer, Knapp Medical Center, Weslaco, TX, p. A657

LOPEZ, Robert, Chief Medical Officer, Highland Community Hospital, Picayune, MS, p. A364

LOPEZ, Rosalio J., M.D. Senior Vice President and Chief Medical Officer, PIH Health Hospital–Whittier, Whittier, CA, p. A99

LOPEZ, Steve Kelley, Chief Executive Officer, Colorado River Medical Center, Needles, CA, p. A79

LOPEZ, Steven, M.D. Chief Medical Officer, Palmetto Lowcountry Behavioral Health, Charleston, SC, p. A563

LOPEZ, Susan Nordstrom, President, Advocate Illinois Masonic Medical Center, Chicago, IL, p. A183

LOPEZ, Valerie, CPA Chief Financial Officer, Uvalde Memorial Hospital, Uvalde, TX, p. A654

LOPREATO, Elayne, Chief Clinical Officer, Kindred Hospital the Palm Beaches, Riviera Beach, FL, p. A143

LORD, David, President, OSF St. Francis Hospital and Medical Group, Escanaba, MI, p. A323

LORD, Gregory D., M.D
Medical Director, Doctor's Hospital of Deer Creek, Leesville, LA, p. A282
Chief Medical Officer, Leesville Rehabilitation Hospital, Leesville, LA, p. A282

LORD, Jeff, Director of Nursing, Connecticut Veterans Home and Hospital, Rocky Hill, CT, p. A116

LORD, Robert L., JD, President and Chief Executive Officer, Martin Health System, Stuart, FL, p. A146

LORENTZ, Derick, Chief Financial Officer, Perkins County Health Services, Grant, NE, p. A396

LORENZ, Holly, R.N. Chief Nurse Executive, UPMC Presbyterian Shadyside, Pittsburgh, PA, p. A551

LORENZ, Paul E., Chief Executive Officer, Santa Clara Valley Medical Center, San Jose, CA, p. A91

LORENZEN, Shelli, Chief Human Resources Officer, Manning Regional Healthcare Center, Manning, IA, p. A234

LORENZO, Heather, M.D. Vice President and Chief Medical Officer, Meritus Medical Center, Hagerstown, MD, p. A301

LORIMER, IV, Lee, Regional Director Human Resources, McKay–Dee Hospital Center, Ogden, UT, p. A661

LORMAN, William J., Ph.D. Clinical Director, Livengrin Foundation, Bensalem, PA, p. A533

LORMAND, Jared, Vice President Information Technology, Opelousas General Health System, Opelousas, LA, p. A286

LORTON, Donald E., Executive Vice President, Bedford Memorial Hospital, Bedford, VA, p. A667

LORY, Marc H., Interim President and Chief Executive Officer, Schuylkill Health System, Pottsville, PA, p. B80

LOSITO, Glenna, R.N. Chief Nursing Officer, Cibola General Hospital, Grants, NM, p. A429

LOTHE, Eric L., FACHE Senior Vice President and Chief Operating Officer, UnityPoint Health–Iowa Lutheran Hospital, Des Moines, IA, p. A229

LOTHIAN, Nancy, Chief Operating Officer and Chief Information Officer, The University of Vermont Health Network Central Vermont Medical Center, Berlin, VT, p. A665

LOTT, Andrea, Vice President Information Services, Northeastern Vermont Regional Hospital, Saint Johnsbury, VT, p. A666

LOTT, Benjamin, Chief Executive Officer, Hardy Wilson Memorial Hospital, Hazlehurst, MS, p. A359

LOTT, Cynthia, Director Human Resources, Northern Virginia Mental Health Institute, Falls Church, VA, p. A670

LOTT, Laura, Administrative Director, Eastern Louisiana Mental Health System, Jackson, LA, p. A278

LOTT, Rodney, Director Management Information Systems and Facility Operations, Scott & White Hospital – Llano, Llano, TX, p. A633

LOTZE, Eberhard, M.D. Chief Medical Officer, Woman's Hospital of Texas, Houston, TX, p. A628

LOUBERT, Cheryl, M.D. Chief Medical Staff, MidMichigan Medical Center–Gladwin, Gladwin, MI, p. A324

LOUDEN CORBETT, Jeanette L., Chief Human Resources Officer, Highland Hospital, Oakland, CA, p. A80

LOUDERMILK, Kerry, Senior Vice President and Chief Financial Officer, Phoebe Putney Memorial Hospital, Albany, GA, p. A151

LOUGHERY, Vicki, R.N. Chief Nursing Officer, Monadnock Community Hospital, Peterborough, NH, p. A413

LOUGHRAN, Lisa, Chief Nursing Officer, Gunnison Valley Hospital, Gunnison, CO, p. A106

LOUGHRAN, Michael, Vice President Human Resources, Kennedy Krieger Institute, Baltimore, MD, p. A296

LOUGHREY, Barbara, Administrator, Northbrook Behavioral Health Hospital, Blackwood, NJ, p. A414

LOUIS, Alfred, M.D. Chief Medical Staff, Pine Valley Specialty Hospital, Houston, TX, p. A626

LOUK, Rodney, Vice President Information Systems, Washington Hospital, Washington, PA, p. A556

LOUKATOS, George, M.D. President Medical Staff Affairs, Merit Health Biloxi, Biloxi, MS, p. A355

LOVATO, Anthony, Director Information Technology, Coon Memorial Hospital, Dalhart, TX, p. A609

LOVDAHL, Brian A., Chief Financial Officer, Baldwin Area Medical Center, Baldwin, WI, p. A702

LOVE, Alex, Acting Manager Human Resources, Alexandria Veterans Affairs Health Care System, Pineville, LA, p. A286

LOVE, Bianca, Assistant Administrator Human Resources, Trinity Hospital Twin City, Dennison, OH, p. A493

LOVE, E. Clifford, Director Fiscal Services, Eastern State Hospital, Williamsburg, VA, p. A680

LOVE, Glenn Neil, M.D. Medical Director, Hilton Head Hospital, Hilton Head Island, SC, p. A567

LOVE, Jodi, R.N. Chief Nursing Officer, Helena Regional Medical Center, Helena, AR, p. A47

LOVE, Matthew
  Senior Vice President Finance, Mercy Health – St. Elizabeth Boardman Hospital, Boardman, OH, p. A485
  Senior Vice President Finance, Mercy Health – St. Elizabeth Youngstown Hospital, Youngstown, OH, p. A506
  Chief Financial Officer, Mercy Health – St. Joseph Warren Hospital, Warren, OH, p. A504
  Chief Executive Officer, Options Behavioral Health System, Indianapolis, IN, p. A214
LOVE, Tim, Director Information Services, Reid Health, Richmond, IN, p. A221
LOVE, Valerie, Manager Business Office, Heatherhill Care Communities, Chardon, OH, p. A486
LOVE–WATLER, Meylan, Chief Operating Officer, Lower Keys Medical Center, Key West, FL, p. A133
LOVEJOY, David, Chief Operations Officer, Riverview Psychiatric Center, Augusta, ME, p. A291
LOVEJOY, Leslie, R.N. Chief Nursing and Quality Officer, Sonoma Valley Hospital, Sonoma, CA, p. A94
LOVEJOY, Rob
  Chief Operating Officer, Sanford Medical Center Thief River Falls, Thief River Falls, MN, p. A352
  Chief Operating Officer, Sanford Thief River Falls Behavioral Health Center, Thief River Falls, MN, p. A352
LOVELACE, Alan, Vice President and Chief Financial Officer, Stillwater Medical Center, Stillwater, OK, p. A520
LOVELACE, Christina, Director Human Resources, Gunnison Valley Hospital, Gunnison, CO, p. A106
LOVELACE, Corey, Chief Operating Officer, Dupont Hospital, Fort Wayne, IN, p. A210
LOVELESS, Craig, Chief Executive Officer, Prowers Medical Center, Lamar, CO, p. A108
LOVELESS, Jane Doll, Vice President, Chief Information Officer, Grand View Health, Sellersville, PA, p. A554
LOVELESS, Kurt, Chief Executive Officer, The CORE Institute Specialty Hospital, Phoenix, AZ, p. A37
LOVELESS, Steve, President and Chief Executive Officer, St. Vincent Healthcare, Billings, MT, p. A385
LOVELL Jr., Charles D., FACHE, Chief Executive Officer, Barbourville ARH Hospital, Barbourville, KY, p. A257
LOVELL, Mark, Vice President and Chief Financial Officer, Palmetto Health Tuomey, Sumter, SC, p. A570
LOVELL, Stephanie, Vice President and General Counsel, Boston Medical Center, Boston, MA, p. A306
LOVELL, Terrence, Vice President Human Resources, Union Hospital, Elkton, MD, p. A300
LOVELLETTE, Teresa A., Manager Human Resources, Herrin Hospital, Herrin, IL, p. A192
LOVERA, Carlos, Director Information Systems, Montrose Memorial Hospital, Montrose, CO, p. A109
LOVERING, Keith, Information Technician, Miller County Hospital, Colquitt, GA, p. A156
LOVERING, Richard, Corporate Vice President Human Resources and Organizational Development, AtlantiCare Regional Medical Center, Atlantic City, NJ, p. A414
LOVERN, Ed, Chief Operating Officer, Piedmont Hospital, Atlanta, GA, p. A153
LOVERSO, Felice L., Ph.D., President and Chief Executive Officer, Casa Colina Hospital and Health Systems, Pomona, CA, p. A83
LOVING, David E., Chief Executive Officer, Des Peres Hospital, Saint Louis, MO, p. A380
LOVING, Tonya, Human Resources Director, UVA–HEALTHSOUTH Rehabilitation Hospital, Charlottesville, VA, p. A668
LOVING, William, M.D., Medical Director, Texas Star Recovery, Austin, TX, p. A600
LOVINGOOD, Toni, Chief Operating Officer, Murphy Medical Center, Murphy, NC, p. A470
LOVRICH, John
  Chief Financial Officer, Catalina Island Medical Center, Avalon, CA, p. A55
  Chief Financial Officer, Glenn Medical Center, Willows, CA, p. A100
LOVSHIN, Alex, Chief Operating Officer, Des Peres Hospital, Saint Louis, MO, p. A380
LOW, Kern, M.D. Chief Medical Officer, St. Thomas More Hospital, Canon City, CO, p. A102
LOW, Lewis, M.D
  Senior Vice President and Chief Medical Officer, Legacy Meridian Park Medical Center, Tualatin, OR, p. A531
  Chief Medical Officer, Legacy Mount Hood Medical Center, Gresham, OR, p. A526
  Senior Vice President and Chief Medical Officer, Legacy Salmon Creek Medical Center, Vancouver, WA, p. A692
LOWE, Bren, Chief Executive Officer, Livingston HealthCare, Livingston, MT, p. A389
LOWE, E. Rick, FACHE Operations Support Risk Management and Compliance, St. Francis Hospital, Columbus, GA, p. A157

LOWE, Greg, Chief Executive Officer, Lawnwood Regional Medical Center & Heart Institute, Fort Pierce, FL, p. A129
LOWE, Joe, Director Management Information Systems, Cumberland Medical Center, Crossville, TN, p. A582
LOWE, Lavah, Executive Vice President and Chief Operating Officer, Bayfront Health St. Petersburg, Saint Petersburg, FL, p. A144
LOWE, Lavah Boyers, Chief Nursing Officer, Avista Adventist Hospital, Louisville, CO, p. A109
LOWE, Phillip W., Chief Executive Officer, Monroe Hospital, Bloomfield, IN, p. A207
LOWE, Scott
  Director Human Resource, McAlester Regional Health Center, McAlester, OK, p. A514
  Interim Market Chief Executive Officer, Physicians Regional – Pine Ridge, Naples, FL, p. A138
LOWELL, David, M.D. Chief Medical Officer, Spaulding Rehabilitation Hospital Cape Cod, East Sandwich, MA, p. A309
LOWENTHAL, David, M.D. Clinical Director, New York State Psychiatric Institute, New York, NY, p. A447
LOWENTHAL, Steve B., M.D. Senior Vice President Medical Affairs and Chief Medical Officer, Rush–Copley Medical Center, Aurora, IL, p. A181
LOWERY, John, M.D. Deputy Commander Clinical Services, General Leonard Wood Army Community Hospital, Fort Leonard Wood, MO, p. A371
LOWMAN, LeeAnn, Director Human Resources, Lake Taylor Transitional Care Hospital, Norfolk, VA, p. A675
LOWREY, Linda, Human Resources Officer, Atmore Community Hospital, Atmore, AL, p. A16
LOWRY, Claudia Jean, R.N. Director of Nursing, Community Howard Specialty Hospital, Kokomo, IN, p. A216
LOY, Michael, Interim Chief Executive Officer, North Central Health Care, Wausau, WI, p. A718
LOYA, John R., Vice President Human Resources and Organizational Development, Columbus Regional Hospital, Columbus, IN, p. A208
LOYA, Theresa, R.N. Chief Nursing Officer, John C. Fremont Healthcare District, Mariposa, CA, p. A76
LOYA, Velma, Administrative Human Resource Coordinator, Rice Medical Center, Eagle Lake, TX, p. A614
LOYD, Chris, Director Human Resources, Methodist Richardson Medical Center, Richardson, TX, p. A643
LOYKE, Christopher, Chief Medical Officer, University Hospitals Parma Medical Center, Parma, OH, p. A501
LOYO–RODRIGUEZ, Raul J., Administrative Analyst III, San Diego County Psychiatric Hospital, San Diego, CA, p. A89
LOZADA, Leonardo J., M.D. Chief Physician Executive, Saint Luke's North Hospital – Barry Road, Kansas City, MO, p. A374
LOZANO, Angel, Chief Executive Officer, Lifecare Hospitals of South Texas–North McAllen, McAllen, TX, p. A636
LOZANO, Melanie, Chief Financial Officer, Concho County Hospital, Eden, TX, p. A614
LOZAR, Beverly, Chief Nursing Executive, St. Vincent Charity Medical Center, Cleveland, OH, p. A489
LOZIER, Tim, Director Human Resources, Vibra Specialty Hospital at DeSoto, Desoto, TX, p. A613
LUBARSKY, Neil, Senior Vice President, Finance and Chief Financial Officer, Thomas Jefferson University Hospitals, Philadelphia, PA, p. A550
LUBIN, Bertram, M.D., President and Chief Executive Officer, USCF Benioff Children's Hospital Oakland, Oakland, CA, p. A80
LUBINSKY, Jeanie, Chief Financial Officer, Mayo Clinic Health System – Red Cedar in Menomonie, Menomonie, WI, p. A710
LUBITSKY, John, Chief Executive Officer, Ancora Psychiatric Hospital, Hammonton, NJ, p. A417
LUBITZ, Robert, M.D. Vice President of Medical Affairs, WellStar Kennestone Hospital, Marietta, GA, p. A163
LUCAS, Jr., Benny Lee, Chief Nursing Executive, St. Joseph's Behavioral Health Center, Stockton, CA, p. A95
LUCAS, Bob, Vice President Operations, King's Daughters Medical Center, Ashland, KY, p. A257
LUCAS, Christine, Chief of Staff, Union County Hospital, Anna, IL, p. A180
LUCAS, Denise, R.N. Vice President Clinical Services and Chief Nursing Officer, Margaret R. Pardee Memorial Hospital, Hendersonville, NC, p. A467
LUCAS, Kasey, Administrator, Salem Memorial District Hospital, Salem, MO, p. A382
LUCAS, Kelly, Chief Information Officer, Sampson Regional Medical Center, Clinton, NC, p. A463
LUCAS, Marshall, M.D. Medical Director, Cypress Creek Hospital, Houston, TX, p. A624
LUCCHESI, Michael, M.D. Chief Medical Officer; Chair, Emergency Medicine, SUNY Downstate Medical Center University Hospital,, NY, p. A450

LUCE, Glenda, Chief Nursing Officer, Memorial Hospital of Gardena, Gardena, CA, p. A64
LUCE, Paul W., MSN, Vice President Operations, Miami County Medical Center, Paola, KS, p. A251
LUCERO, Brenda, Chief Clinical Officer, Cornerstone Hospital of Houston at Clearlake, Webster, TX, p. A656
LUCERO, Lupe, Manager Business Office, Presbyterian Espanola Hospital, Espanola, NM, p. A429
LUCEY, Jeffery, M.D. Clinical Director, Kingsboro Psychiatric Center,, NY, p. A445
LUCHSINGER, Catherine, R.N. Chief Nursing Officer, Halifax Health Medical Center of Daytona Beach, Daytona Beach, FL, p. A127
LUCIA, Sandra J., Director Health Information and Corporate Compliance Officer, Hampstead Hospital, Hampstead, NH, p. A411
LUCIANO, Lisa, D.O. Medical Director, Shore Rehabilitation Institute, Brick, NJ, p. A414
LUCIER, Robbyn, Director Human Resources, UP Health System–Portage, Hancock, MI, p. A326
LUCK, Richard, Ed.D., Facility Director, Woodrow Wilson Rehabilitation Center, Fishersville, VA, p. A670
LUCKE, Kim, Vice President Finance, Northern Montana Hospital, Havre, MT, p. A388
LUCKETT, Douglas R., President and Chief Executive Officer, CaroMont Regional Medical Center, Gastonia, NC, p. A465
LUCORE, Charles, M.D., President and Chief Executive Officer, St. John's Hospital, Springfield, IL, p. A203
LUDWIG, John A., R.N. Vice President Operations, Bridgton Hospital, Bridgton, ME, p. A292
LUDWIG, John A., R.N., BSN, MHA President and Chief Executive Officer, HSHS Holy Family Hospital in Greenville, Greenville, IL, p. A192
LUDWIG, Walter, Chief Operating Officer, Kenmore Mercy Hospital, Kenmore, NY, p. A441
LUDWIG–BEYMER, Patti, Ph.D. Vice President Chief Nursing Officer, Edward Hospital, Naperville, IL, p. A198
LUDWIGSEN, Kevin, Chief Information Officer, Southeastern Ohio Regional Medical Center, Cambridge, OH, p. A486
LUEBBERING, Tom, Vice President Finance, Capital Region Medical Center, Jefferson City, MO, p. A372
LUEBCKE, Diane, R.N. Director Nursing, Community Memorial Healthcare, Marysville, KS, p. A249
LUECHT, Jackie
  Director, Human Resources, Mercy Medical Center–New Hampton, New Hampton, IA, p. A235
  Chief Human Resources Officer, Mercy Medical Center–North Iowa, Mason City, IA, p. A234
LUEDDERS, Keith, Chief Operations Officer, Tri Valley Health System, Cambridge, NE, p. A394
LUEDERS, Kathy, R.N. Director of Nursing–Acute Care, Saint Elizabeth's Medical Center, Wabasha, MN, p. A352
LUEHRS, Bill, Chief Human Resources Officer, NorthShore University Health System, Evanston, IL, p. A190
LUEHRS, Paul R., Chief Operating Officer, Mercy San Juan Medical Center, Carmichael, CA, p. A58
LUFF, Brian, Chief Executive Officer, Quillen Rehabilitation Hospital, Johnson City, TN, p. A585
LUFKIN, Kirk, M.D. VPMA, McLaren Northern Michigan, Petoskey, MI, p. A331
LUFKIN, Scott, Director Information Technology, Grundy County Memorial Hospital, Grundy Center, IA, p. A231
LUGER, Gerald, M.D. President Medical Staff, Gottlieb Memorial Hospital, Melrose Park, IL, p. A196
LUGO, Cesar, Director Human Resources, Victor Valley Global Medical Center, Victorville, CA, p. A98
LUGO–ZENNER, Diana, R.N. Chief Nursing Officer, Citrus Valley Medical Center–Inter Community Campus, Covina, CA, p. A60
LUHRS, Jason J., Vice President Fiscal Services, Westfields Hospital, New Richmond, WI, p. A713
LUKE, Leslie Paul, Interim Chief Executive Officer, College Station Medical Center, College Station, TX, p. A606
LUKENS, Tammy, Director Information, Kosciusko Community Hospital, Warsaw, IN, p. A223
LUKER, Patricia A., President, OSF Holy Family Medical Center, Monmouth, IL, p. A197
LUKHARD, Kenneth W., President, Advocate Christ Medical Center, Oak Lawn, IL, p. A198
LUKISH, Kris, Human Resources Officer, Chippenham Hospital, Richmond, VA, p. A677
LULICH, Diane, Director Human Resources, Memorial Medical Center – Ashland, Ashland, WI, p. A702
LULL, Todd, Director Information Technology, Southwest Health, Platteville, WI, p. A714
LULOFF, Lynn, Chief Financial Officer, Winneshiek Medical Center, Decorah, IA, p. A229
LUMPKINS, Deborah, MSN Chief Nursing Officer, Maury Regional Hospital, Columbia, TN, p. A581
LUMPP, Karen, Senior Vice President and Chief Financial Officer, Trinitas Regional Medical Center, Elizabeth, NJ, p. A416

LUMSDEN, Chris A., Chief Executive Officer, Sentara Halifax Regional Hospital, South Boston, VA, p. A678

LUNA, Raul D., Chief Nurse Executive, El Paso Psychiatric Center, El Paso, TX, p. A615

LUNA, Tony, M.D. Chief of Staff, Minneola District Hospital, Minneola, KS, p. A249

LUND, Elizabeth, M.D. Chief of Staff, Tennova Healthcare Volunteer Community Hospital, Martin, TN, p. A588

LUND, Karen A., R.N. Chief Nursing Officer, SageWest Health Care at Riverton, Riverton, WY, p. A723

LUND, Maggie, Divisional Senior Vice President Human Resources, Mercy Health – Fairfield Hospital, Fairfield, OH, p. A494

LUND, Maggie A., System Vice President Human Resource Market and Labor, Mercy Health – St. Charles Hospital, Oregon, OH, p. A500

LUNDAL, David
    Senior Vice President Information Systems and Chief Information Officer, Presence Holy Family Medical Center, Des Plaines, IL, p. A188
    System Vice President, Information Systems and Chief Information Officer, Presence Saints Mary & Elizabeth Medical Center, Chicago, IL, p. A186

LUNDBERG, Lanetta, Vice President Culture and People, PeaceHealth Ketchikan Medical Center, Ketchikan, AK, p. A29

LUNDBERG, Ralph L., Director Human Resources, Yakima Regional Medical and Cardiac Center, Yakima, WA, p. A693

LUNDE, Susan, R.N. Director of Nursing, Fallon Medical Complex, Baker, MT, p. A385

LUNDQUIST, David W., President and Chief Executive Officer, Rome Memorial Hospital, Rome, NY, p. A455

LUNDY, Kelly, Chief Information Officer, PeaceHealth St. Joseph Medical Center, Bellingham, WA, p. A682

LUNDY, Marcel, Chief Information Officer, Putnam General Hospital, Eatonton, GA, p. A159

LUNDY, Noah, Director of Human Resources, Maine Coast Memorial Hospital, Ellsworth, ME, p. A293

LUNDY–PAINE, Robert, Director Information Systems, Alameda Hospital, Alameda, CA, p. A54

LUNGU, Jack, Administrator, Baypointe Behavioral Health, Mobile, AL, p. A22

LUNN, Stephen, Chief Executive Officer, Porter Regional Hospital, Valparaiso, IN, p. A223

LUNN, William, M.D., Chief Executive Officer, Tulane Medical Center, New Orleans, LA, p. A285

LUNNEBORG, Brandi, Chief Executive Officer, Phoebe Sumter Medical Center, Americus, GA, p. A151

LUNSFORD, Cindy, Executive Vice President and Chief Operating Officer, Peninsula Regional Medical Center, Salisbury, MD, p. A303

LUNSFORD, Kaye W., System Director Human Resources, St. Vincent's Medical Center Southside, Jacksonville, FL, p. A132

LUNT, Kimberly, Controller, HEALTHSOUTH Rehabilitation Hospital of Spring Hill, Brooksville, FL, p. A125

LUNTZ, Adam, Chief Financial Officer, Aultman Orrville Hospital, Orrville, OH, p. A501

LUOMA, Michael, M.D. Chief of Staff, Aspirus Keweenaw Hospital, Laurium, MI, p. A329

LUPINACCI, Michael, M.D. Medical Director, HEALTHSOUTH Rehabilitation Hospital of Mechanicsburg, Mechanicsburg, PA, p. A544

LUSKIN–HAWK, Roberta, M.D.,
    Chief Executive Officer, Presence Saint Francis Hospital, Evanston, IL, p. A190
    President and Chief Executive Officer, Presence Saint Joseph Hospital, Chicago, IL, p. A185

LUSSIER, Shirley G., Vice President Human Resources, Northeast Rehabilitation Hospital, Salem, NH, p. A413

LUSTERIO, Efren, Director of Nursing, Behavioral Center of Michigan, Warren, MI, p. A336

LUTES, Adrianne, Chief Executive Officer, Select Specialty Hospital Daytona Beach, Daytona Beach, FL, p. A127

LUTES, Michael
    President, Carolinas HealthCare System Anson, Wadesboro, NC, p. A475
    President, Carolinas Healthcare System Union, Monroe, NC, p. A469

LUTHER, Lori, CPA Chief Financial Officer, Indiana University Health Ball Memorial Hospital, Muncie, IN, p. A219

LUTHER, Tracie, Director of Labor Relations and Human Relations, Brooks Memorial Hospital, Dunkirk, NY, p. A438

LUTHER, Vera, M.D. Chief of Staff, Sabine County Hospital, Hemphill, TX, p. A623

LUTKENHAUS, Tiffany, Chief Nursing Officer, Muenster Memorial Hospital, Muenster, TX, p. A638

LUTTON, Lorraine, President, St. Joseph's Hospital, Tampa, FL, p. A147

LUTZ, Barbara, Vice President Human Resources, Heart of the Rockies Regional Medical Center, Salida, CO, p. A110

LUTZ, Denise, Chief Human Resources Officer, St. Joseph's Hospital and Health Center, Dickinson, ND, p. A478

LUTZ, Don, Director Information Technology, Easton Hospital, Easton, PA, p. A537

LUTZ, Kevin, DPM Chief Operating Officer, Grant, OhioHealth Grant Medical Center, Columbus, OH, p. A491

LUTZ, Terry, Chief Financial Officer, Scheurer Hospital, Pigeon, MI, p. A331

LUX, Teri
    Vice President Patient Care Services and Chief Nursing Officer, Community Memorial Hospital, Menomonee Falls, WI, p. A710
    Vice President Patient Care Services, Community Hospital Division, Chief Nursing Officer, St. Joseph's Hospital, West Bend, WI, p. A719

LUZINSKI, Craig, FACHE Vice President Performance Optimization, Cheyenne Regional Medical Center, Cheyenne, WY, p. A721

LYBARGER, Eric, Administrator, Pawnee Valley Community Hospital, Larned, KS, p. A247

LYDICK, Bryan, Chief Executive Officer, Redwood Area Hospital, Redwood Falls, MN, p. A349

LYLE, Janet, Chief Human Resources and Allied Health Services, Springfield Hospital, Springfield, VT, p. A666

LYMAN, Jeremy, Chief Executive Officer, Blue Mountain Hospital, Blanding, UT, p. A659

LYNCE, Danialle
    Business Partner Human Resources, University Hospitals Conneaut Medical Center, Conneaut, OH, p. A492
    Manager Human Resources, University Hospitals Geauga Medical Center, Chardon, OH, p. A486
    Business Partner Human Resources, University Hospitals Geneva Medical Center, Geneva, OH, p. A495

LYNCH, Becky, Manager Business Entity Management and Information Systems, OSF St. Mary Medical Center, Galesburg, IL, p. A191

LYNCH, Cecelia, R.N. Vice President Patient Care Services and Chief Nursing Officer, Lowell General Hospital, Lowell, MA, p. A311

LYNCH, Danile, Chief Operating Officer, Saint Luke Institute, Silver Spring, MD, p. A303

LYNCH, Elizabeth A., Vice President Human Resources, The Hospital of Central Connecticut, New Britain, CT, p. A115

LYNCH III, Ernest C., President and Chief Executive Officer, Medical Center of McKinney, McKinney, TX, p. A636

LYNCH, G. Michael, M.D. Chief Medical Officer, Inova Fair Oaks Hospital, Fairfax, VA, p. A669

LYNCH, Heather, M.D. Chief of Staff, Purcell Municipal Hospital, Purcell, OK, p. A519

LYNCH, James, Senior Vice President and Chief Medical Officer, Beaumont Hospital – Troy, Troy, MI, p. A336

LYNCH, John, M.D. Vice President and Chief Medical Officer, Barnes–Jewish Hospital, Saint Louis, MO, p. A379

LYNCH, John
    Vice President Chief Information Officer, Catskill Regional Medical Center, Harris, NY, p. A440
    Vice President and Chief Information Officer, Faxton St. Luke's Healthcare, Utica, NY, p. A457

LYNCH, Marc, D.O. Chief of Staff, Kindred Hospital–Ontario, Ontario, CA, p. A80

LYNCH, Megan, Manager Human Resources, Johnson Memorial Health Services, Dawson, MN, p. A341

LYNCH, Torie A., Manager Human Resources, Central Montana Medical Center, Lewistown, MT, p. A389

LYNCH, William, Executive Vice President and Chief Operating Officer, Jamaica Hospital Medical Center,, NY, p. A445

LYNCH–KILIC, Cathy, Vice President Human Resources, St. Mary's General Hospital, Passaic, NJ, p. A421

LYND, Samuel, Administrator and Chief Executive Officer, Baptist Memorial Hospital–Tipton, Covington, TN, p. A582

LYNE, Marjorie, Associate Director for Patient Care Services, Hunter Holmes McGuire Veterans Affairs Medical Center–Richmond, Richmond, VA, p. A678

LYNN, Christina, M.D. Medical Director, Three Rivers Behavioral Health, West Columbia, SC, p. A570

LYNN, Jason, Director Finance, St. Vincent's St. Clair, Pell City, AL, p. A24

LYNN, Samuel, Director Human Resources, Northwest Texas Healthcare System, Amarillo, TX, p. A596

LYNSKEY, Jeanne, Vice President and Chief Financial Officer, Milford Regional Medical Center, Milford, MA, p. A312

LYON, Beverly, R.N. Vice President Nursing, Milford Hospital, Milford, CT, p. A115

LYON, Tami, Director Human Resources, Community Memorial Hospital, Burke, SD, p. A572

LYONS, Althea C., Vice President Human Resources and Development, Beverly Hospital, Beverly, MA, p. A305

LYONS, Denise, Chief Nursing Officer, Cumberland Hall Hospital, Hopkinsville, KY, p. A261

LYONS, Jim, Chief Clinic Officer, Hutchinson Health, Hutchinson, MN, p. A344

LYONS, Lenny
    Administrator, Delta Community Medical Center, Delta, UT, p. A659
    Administrator, Fillmore Community Medical Center, Fillmore, UT, p. A659

LYONS, Michael
    Chief Executive Officer, Bay Area Regional Medical Center, Webster, TX, p. A656
    Regional Director Information Services, Shriners Hospitals for Children–Galveston, Galveston, TX, p. A620
    Regional Information Systems Director, Shriners Hospitals for Children–Shreveport, Shreveport, LA, p. A288

LYSAGHT, Marcia C., R.N. Associate Director Patient Care Services, Miami Veterans Affairs Healthcare System, Miami, FL, p. A137

LYSAGHT, William, Chief Financial Officer, Kindred Hospital Las Vegas–Sahara, Las Vegas, NV, p. A406

LYTHGOE, Derek
    Chief Financial Officer, Banner Baywood Medical Center, Mesa, AZ, p. A34
    Chief Financial Officer, Banner Heart Hospital, Mesa, AZ, p. A34

LYTLE, John, M.D. Chief of Staff, Jefferson Regional Medical Center, Pine Bluff, AR, p. A51

M

MAALIKI, Hikmat A., M.D. Chief of Staff, St. Luke Community Healthcare, Ronan, MT, p. A390

MAAS, Vernon, M.D. Vice President, Medical Affairs, St. Mary's Medical Center of Evansville, Evansville, IN, p. A210

MABRY, Jerry D., FACHE, Chief Executive Officer, National Park Medical Center, Hot Springs, AR, p. A47

MACAFEE, Francis M., Vice President Finance and Chief Financial Officer, Guthrie Corning Hospital, Corning, NY, p. A437

MACARONAS, Thomas, Chief Financial Officer, Labette Health, Parsons, KS, p. A252

MACATOL, Matthew, M.D. President Medical Staff, Marietta Memorial Hospital, Marietta, OH, p. A498

MACBRIDE, Samuel, M.D. Chief Medical Officer, Rehoboth McKinley Christian Health Care Services, Gallup, NM, p. A429

MACDONALD, Alan G., President and Chief Executive Officer, Hallmark Health System, Melrose, MA, p. A312

MACDONALD, Laurie, Vice President Finance, Penn Highlands Elk, Saint Marys, PA, p. A553

MACDONALD, Neil, Vice President Operations, MedStar Union Memorial Hospital, Baltimore, MD, p. A297

MACDOUGALL, David, Chief Financial Officer, United Health Services Hospitals–Binghamton, Binghamton, NY, p. A435

MACE, Rick, Chief Executive Officer, AMITA Health Adventist Medical Center Bolingbrook, Bolingbrook, IL, p. A182

MACE, Robert M., M.D., Chief Executive Officer, Webster County Memorial Hospital, Webster Springs, WV, p. A700

MACE, T. Paul, Chief Medical Officer, Garden Park Medical Center, Gulfport, MS, p. A358

MACFADYEN, James, M.D. Medical Director, St. John Vianney Hospital, Downingtown, PA, p. A536

MACGREGOR, Nancy, Chief Financial Officer, Salt Lake Behavioral Health, Salt Lake City, UT, p. A663

MACHADO, James, President, St. Vincent's Medical Center Clay County, Middleburg, FL, p. A138

MACHADO, Maria T., Administrator, Hospital Hermanos Melendez, Bayamon, PR, p. A726

MACHULSKY, RN, BSN,, Janet, Director of Nursing, St. Lawrence Rehabilitation Center, Lawrenceville, NJ, p. A418

MACIAS, Susan, Chief Human Resources Officer, Rehoboth McKinley Christian Health Care Services, Gallup, NM, p. A429

MACIEL, Maureen, M.D. Chief of Staff, Shriners Hospitals for Children–Tampa, Tampa, FL, p. A147

MACIOCE, Gary, President, Penn Highlands Clearfield, Clearfield, PA, p. A535

MACK, Charles, Vice President Finance and Chief Financial Officer, Merit Health Natchez, Natchez, MS, p. A363

MACK, Edward, M.D. Chief of Staff, Northport Veterans Affairs Medical Center, Northport, NY, p. A451

MACKENROTH, Robin D., Chief Operating Officer, Kaiser Permanente Riverside Medical Center, Riverside, CA, p. A85

MACKENZIE, Susan, Director, Providence Veterans Affairs Medical Center, Providence, RI, p. A560

MACKETT, Charles, M.D. Senior Vice President and Chief Medical Officer, Indian River Medical Center, Vero Beach, FL, p. A149

MACKINNON, Paul, R.N. Chief Operating Officer, HealthAlliance Hospitals, Leominster, MA, p. A311

MACKSOOD, Dan
Regional Senior Vice President and Chief Financial Officer, Good Samaritan Hospital Medical Center, West Islip, NY, p. A458
Regional Vice President and Chief Financial Officer, St. Catherine of Siena Medical Center, Smithtown, NY, p. A456
MACLAUCHLAN, Steven, Chief Executive Officer, Saint Vincent Hospital, Worcester, MA, p. A316
MACLAUGHLIN, Jeremy, Director Human Resources, Citizens Memorial Hospital, Bolivar, MO, p. A367
MACLEOD, Deborah, MS Vice President Nursing and Patient Care Services, Mid Coast Hospital, Brunswick, ME, p. A292
MACLEOD, Robert J., Chief Executive Officer, New Hampshire Hospital, Concord, NH, p. A410
MACNICOL, Daniel, Chief Executive Officer, HEALTHSOUTH Rehabilitation Hospital – Dallas, Dallas, TX, p. A610
MACPHEE, Alan, Chief Executive Officer, John C. Fremont Healthcare District, Mariposa, CA, p. A76
MACRI, Fredrick, Executive Vice President, Rhode Island Hospital, Providence, RI, p. A561
MACRI, William P., Chief Executive Officer, Curahealth Nashville, Nashville, TN, p. A590
MACUGA, Paul, Chief Human Resources Officer, The University of Vermont Health Network University of Vermont Medical Center, Burlington, VT, p. A665
MADAN, Sunil, M.D. Chief Medical Officer and Chief Population Health Officer, Doctors Community Hospital, Lanham, MD, p. A302
MADDEN, R. Craig, Director Employee Relations, Reynolds Memorial Hospital, Glen Dale, WV, p. A696
MADDOX, Dale, Chief Financial Officer, Medical Center of South Arkansas, El Dorado, AR, p. A45
MADDOX, Jamie, Chief Nursing Officer, CHRISTUS Mother Frances Hospital – Jacksonville, Jacksonville, TX, p. A629
MADER, Elaine, M.D. Chief of Staff, INTEGRIS Miami Hospital, Miami, OK, p. A514
MADER, Frank, Director Information Services, East Liverpool City Hospital, East Liverpool, OH, p. A494
MADER, Vikki, Director Health Information Services, Pratt Regional Medical Center, Pratt, KS, p. A252
MADIGAN, Catherine, Chief Nursing Officer, University of North Carolina Hospitals, Chapel Hill, NC, p. A462
MADIGAN, Patrick, Interim Chief Executive Officer, Cheyenne Regional Medical Center, Cheyenne, WY, p. A721
MADISON, Jeffrey, FACHE, Chief Executive Officer, Rockdale Hospital, Rockdale, TX, p. A643
MADKINS, Catrina, Controller and Chief Financial Officer, HEALTHSOUTH Plano Rehabilitation Hospital, Plano, TX, p. A641
MADRID, Melissa, R.N. Chief Nursing Officer, Harper County Community Hospital, Buffalo, OK, p. A509
MADSEN, Kristin, Chief Nursing Officer, Carson Tahoe Continuing Care Hospital, Carson City, NV, p. A404
MAEKAWA, Steve, Chief Financial Officer, Garfield Medical Center, Monterey Park, CA, p. A78
MAENIUS, Linda, Chief Financial Officer, Laurel Ridge Treatment Center, San Antonio, TX, p. A646
MAERTENS, Mary B., FACHE, President and Chief Executive Officer, Avera Marshall Regional Medical Center, Marshall, MN, p. A346
MAES, Jillian, Director Marketing and Public Relations, St. Thomas More Hospital, Canon City, CO, p. A102
MAES, Stephen, Director Information Systems, Franciscan St. James Hospital and Health Centers, Olympia Fields, IL, p. A199
MAESTAS, Sadie, Interim Chief Nursing Officer, Copper Queen Community Hospital, Bisbee, AZ, p. A31
MAESTRE, Jaime, Chief Executive Officer, Dr. Ramon E. Betances Hospital–Mayaguez Medical Center Branch, Mayaguez, PR, p. A728
MAGDANGAL, Connie, Executive Vice President and Chief Financial Officer, Bergen Regional Medical Center, Paramus, NJ, p. A421
MAGEE, Becky, Chief Information Officer, Washington Regional Medical Center, Fayetteville, AR, p. A46
MAGEE, James L., Executive Director, Piggott Community Hospital, Piggott, AR, p. A51
MAGEE, Michael J., Chief Financial Officer, Riverside Medical Center, Franklinton, LA, p. A277
MAGEE, Robert A.
Director Human Resources, Shriners Hospitals for Children–Galveston, Galveston, TX, p. A620
Director Human Resources, Shriners Hospitals for Children–Houston, Houston, TX, p. A626
MAGEE, William F., Chief Financial Officer, Alliance HealthCare System, Holly Springs, MS, p. A359
MAGES, Michael, Chief Executive Officer, Ashland Health Center, Ashland, KS, p. A240
MAGESKI, Denise, MSN Chief Nurse Executive, Northwestern Lake Forest Hospital, Lake Forest, IL, p. A194

MAGHAZEHE, Al, FACHE, President and Chief Executive Officer, Capital Health, Trenton, NJ, p. B26
MAGHAZEHE, Al, FACHE,
President and Chief Executive Officer, Capital Health Medical Center–Hopewell, Pennington, NJ, p. A422
President and Chief Executive Officer, Capital Health Regional Medical Center, Trenton, NJ, p. A424
MAGID, Philip, Director Fiscal Services, Shriners Hospitals for Children–Chicago, Chicago, IL, p. A186
MAGILL, Marc, Medical Center Director, Grand Junction Veterans Health Care System, Grand Junction, CO, p. A106
MAGNER, Johanna, Interim Chief Nursing Officer, Saint Michael's Medical Center, Newark, NJ, p. A421
MAGNER, Kile, Administrator, Ellinwood District Hospital, Ellinwood, KS, p. A242
MAGNESS, Grant, Assistant Chief Executive Officer, Brownwood Regional Medical Center, Brownwood, TX, p. A604
MAGNUSON, Johna, Director Nursing, Hillsboro Community Hospital, Hillsboro, KS, p. A244
MAGOON, Patrick M., President and Chief Executive Officer, Ann & Robert H. Lurie Children's Hospital of Chicago, Chicago, IL, p. A183
MAGRUDER, Joan, President, St. Louis Children's Hospital, Saint Louis, MO, p. A381
MAGU, Bharat, M.D. Chief Medical Officer, Yuma Regional Medical Center, Yuma, AZ, p. A42
MAGUIRE, David L., M.D. Vice President Medical Affairs, Baystate Wing Hospital, Palmer, MA, p. A313
MAGUIRE, Kimberly, R.N. Chief Nursing Officer, Mercy Health Hackley Campus, Muskegon, MI, p. A330
MAGUREAN, Vickie, Chief Financial Officer, Seven Rivers Regional Medical Center, Crystal River, FL, p. A126
MAGUTA, Sam, Coordinator Information Systems, Devereux Georgia Treatment Network, Kennesaw, GA, p. A161
MAHAJAN, Sumit, M.D. Chief Medical Staff, Hi–Desert Medical Center, Yucca Valley, CA, p. A100
MAHAN, Michelle K., Senior Vice President and Chief Financial Officer, Frederick Memorial Hospital, Frederick, MD, p. A301
MAHAN, Vic
Chief Information Officer, Chino Valley Medical Center, Chino, CA, p. A58
Director Information Systems, Garden Grove Hospital and Medical Center, Garden Grove, CA, p. A64
Director Information Technology, La Palma Intercommunity Hospital, La Palma, CA, p. A67
Director Information Technology, West Anaheim Medical Center, Anaheim, CA, p. A54
MAHAR, Priscilla, Chief Clinical Officer, Spectrum Health United Hospital, Greenville, MI, p. A325
MAHER, Donna, R.N. Chief Operating Officer, Morton Hospital and Medical Center, Taunton, MA, p. A315
MAHER, James M., Senior Vice President and Chief Financial Officer, Robert Wood Johnson University Hospital at Hamilton, Hamilton, NJ, p. A417
MAHER, Jennifer, Chief Executive Officer, Sutter Davis Hospital, Davis, CA, p. A60
MAHER, John P., Executive Vice President and Chief Financial Officer, Nassau University Medical Center, East Meadow, NY, p. A438
MAHER, Sean, Director Human Resources, Devereux Children's Behavioral Health Center, Malvern, PA, p. A543
MAHER, Thomas, Chief Executive Officer and Administrator, Boulder City Hospital, Boulder City, NV, p. A404
MAHERA, Tina, M.D. Chief Medical Officer, Garfield Park Hospital, Chicago, IL, p. A184
MAHEUX, Diane, Vice President Finance, Memorial Hospital, North Conway, NH, p. A413
MAHL, Morgan G., Director Human Resources, St. Luke's Hospital – Warren Campus, Phillipsburg, NJ, p. A422
MAHMOOD, Ahsan, M.D. Chief Medical Officer, Hamilton Center, Terre Haute, IN, p. A222
MAHMOOD, Khalid, M.D., President and Chairman, Crescent Medical Center Lancaster, Lancaster, TX, p. A632
MAHONE, William, President and Chief Executive Officer, Halifax Regional Medical Center, Roanoke Rapids, NC, p. A472
MAHONEY, Bryan, Chief Financial Officer, Columbia Memorial Hospital, Hudson, NY, p. A440
MAHONEY, James, Chief Information Officer, Memorial Hospital, York, PA, p. A559
MAHONEY, Nicole, Chief Financial Officer, Pioneer Memorial Hospital, Heppner, OR, p. A526
MAHONEY, Theresa, Director Human Resources, Fairmount Behavioral Health System, Philadelphia, PA, p. A547
MAHONEY, William K., President and Chief Executive Officer, Cox Medical Center Branson, Branson, MO, p. A368
MAHONY, Mary A., Commanding Officer, Naval Hospital Lemoore, Lemoore, CA, p. A68
MAHR–CHAN, Lydia, Director of Human Resources, Chinese Hospital, San Francisco, CA, p. A90

MAIDEN, Phillip, M.D. Medical Director, Belmont Pines Hospital, Youngstown, OH, p. A506
MAIER, Cindy, R.N. Director of Nursing, Ness County Hospital District No 2, Ness City, KS, p. A250
MAIER, Walter M., Chief of Staff, San Bernardino Mountains Community Hospital District, Lake Arrowhead, CA, p. A68
MAIETTA, Carol, Vice President Human Resources and Chief Learning Officer, St. Vincent's East, Birmingham, AL, p. A17
MAIJALA, Jussi, Vice President, Human Resources, Phelps Memorial Hospital Center, Sleepy Hollow, NY, p. A455
MAIN, Cleo, Finance Officer, U. S. Public Health Service Blackfeet Community Hospital, Saint Mary, MT, p. A390
MAINARDI, Carlo, M.D. Vice President Medical Affairs and Chief Medical Officer, Park Ridge Health, Hendersonville, NC, p. A467
MAINE, MSN, RN–, Cathy L., Chief Nursing Officer and Assistant Administrator, Smyth County Community Hospital, Marion, VA, p. A673
MAINES, Stephanie, Chief Nursing Officer, Crossroads Community Hospital, Mount Vernon, IL, p. A197
MAINIERI, Kathy, Human Resource Specialist, Sister Emmanuel Hospital, Miami, FL, p. A137
MAIZE, Makyla, Director Information Services, Washington County Hospital and Clinics, Washington, IA, p. A238
MAJAUSKAS, Joel, Chief Information Officer, Clifton Springs Hospital and Clinic, Clifton Springs, NY, p. A437
MAJCHRZAK, John, Chief Financial Officer, Touchette Regional Hospital, Centreville, IL, p. A183
MAJDALANI, Elias, Director Management Information Systems, Mildred Mitchell–Bateman Hospital, Huntington, WV, p. A697
MAJETICH, Stephen D., CPA Chief Financial Officer, Southwestern Vermont Medical Center, Bennington, VT, p. A665
MAJHAIL, Ruby, Chief Financial Officer, St. Luke's Behavioral Health Center, Phoenix, AZ, p. A37
MAJOR, Aprille, Director Human Resources, Foothill Regional Medical Center, Tustin, CA, p. A97
MAJOR, Kerry, R.N. Chief Nursing Officer, Cleveland Clinic Florida, Weston, FL, p. A150
MAJOR, Pattie, Chief Financial Officer, Paul B. Hall Regional Medical Center, Paintsville, KY, p. A268
MAJOR, Shelly, Chief Nursing Officer, Methodist Hospitals, Gary, IN, p. A212
MAJORS, Valerie, Director Information Services, Western State Hospital, Hopkinsville, KY, p. A262
MAJURE, Thomas K., Administrator, Our Community Hospital, Scotland Neck, NC, p. A473
MAKAROFF, Jason, Chief Operating Officer and Associate Vice President, Adventist Rehabilitation Hospital of Maryland, Rockville, MD, p. A303
MAKELA, Taylor, Director Information Technology, Baraga County Memorial Hospital, L'Anse, MI, p. A328
MAKEPEACE, Anne, Director Human Resources, New Ulm Medical Center, New Ulm, MN, p. A347
MAKI, Jacquelyn, Chief Nursing Officer, Oakleaf Surgical Hospital, Eau Claire, WI, p. A705
MAKI, Richard, R.N. Vice President Nursing and Chief Nursing Officer, Anna Jaques Hospital, Newburyport, MA, p. A313
MAKORO, Leslie, Director Information management Systems, Merit Health Natchez, Natchez, MS, p. A363
MAKOSKY, Michael
Chief Operating Officer, Bluefield Regional Medical Center, Bluefield, WV, p. A694
Chief Operating Officer, Plateau Medical Center, Oak Hill, WV, p. A698
MAKSOUD, Jane, R.N
Senior Vice President Human Resources and Labor Relations, Mount Sinai Health System, Mount Sinai Beth Israel, New York, NY, p. A446
Senior Vice President Human Resources and Labor Relations, Mount Sinai Hospital, New York, NY, p. A446
Senior Vice President Human Resources and Labor Relations, Mount Sinai Health System, Mount Sinai St. Luke's – Roosevelt, New York, NY, p. A446
Senior Vice President Human Resources and Labor Relations, Mount Sinai Health System, New York Eye and Ear Infirmary of Mount Sinai, New York, NY, p. A447
MAKSYMOW, Michael, Vice President Information Systems, Beebe Healthcare, Lewes, DE, p. A119
MAKUNDA, Beejadi, M.D. Chief Medical Officer, Heatherhill Care Communities, Chardon, OH, p. A486
MALAER, Gary, Chief Executive Officer, Wuesthoff Medical Center – Rockledge, Rockledge, FL, p. A143
MALAKAR, Crystal, Team Leader Inpatient Nursing, Bellin Psychiatric Center, Green Bay, WI, p. A706
MALAKOFF, Stacey, Executive Vice President and Chief Financial Officer, Hospital for Special Surgery, New York, NY, p. A444
MALAMED, Michael, M.D. Chief of Staff, Sherman Oaks Hospital,, CA, p. A74

MALAN, Glen, Vice President Information Technology and Chief Information Officer, Northwest Community Hospital, Arlington Heights, IL, p. A180

MALANEY, Scott C., President and Chief Executive Officer, Blanchard Valley Health System, Findlay, OH, p. B23

MALANEY, Scott C., President and Chief Executive Officer, Blanchard Valley Hospital, Findlay, OH, p. A494

MALANOWSKI, John S., Chief Human Resources Officer, Dartmouth–Hitchcock Medical Center, Lebanon, NH, p. A412

MALATEK, Jennifer, Chief Executive Officer, New Braunfels Regional Rehabilitation Hospital, New Braunfels, TX, p. A638

MALCOLM, Dru, Vice President and Chief Nursing Officer, Johnson City Medical Center, Johnson City, TN, p. A585

MALCOLMSON, James F., M.D. Chief of Staff, Sierra Vista Hospital, Truth or Consequences, NM, p. A432

MALDONADO, Diraida, Chief Executive Officer, Hospital de la Universidad de Puerto Rico/Dr. Federico Trilla, Carolina, PR, p. A726

MALDONADO, Luis Rivera, Chief Executive Officer, Bella Vista Hospital, Mayaguez, PR, p. A728

MALEK, Frank
  Chief Financial Officer, Nacogdoches Medical Center, Nacogdoches, TX, p. A638
  Chief Financial Officer, Northern Louisiana Medical Center, Ruston, LA, p. A287

MALENSEK, Frank, M.D. Chief Medical Officer, St. Vincent's East, Birmingham, AL, p. A17

MALEY, Shelley, Director Human Resources, St. Luke's Hospital – Quakertown Campus, Quakertown, PA, p. A553

MALIK, Amir, M.D. Cardiologist, Plaza Medical Center of Fort Worth, Fort Worth, TX, p. A618

MALIK, Azfar, M.D
  Chief Medical Officer, CenterPointe Hospital, Saint Charles, MO, p. A379
  Chief Medical Officer, Signature Psychiatric Hospital, Kansas City, MO, p. A374

MALIK, Chuck, Director Information Systems, Advocate Good Shepherd Hospital, Barrington, IL, p. A181

MALIK, Tariq F., CPA Chief Financial Officer, Signature Psychiatric Hospital, Kansas City, MO, p. A374

MALIN, Seth, M.D. President Medical and Dental Staff, Delaware County Memorial Hospital, Drexel Hill, PA, p. A537

MALINA, Joanne J., M.D. Chief of Staff, Veterans Affairs Hudson Valley Health Care System, Montrose, NY, p. A443

MALINAK, Matthew, Chief Executive Officer, Kindred Hospital–Fort Worth, Fort Worth, TX, p. A618

MALINDZAK, Edward, Chief Human Resources Officer, Oconomowoc Memorial Hospital, Oconomowoc, WI, p. A713

MALJOVEC, John, M.D. Medical Director, Warren General Hospital, Warren, PA, p. A556

MALLEK, Brent J.
  Chief Human Resources Officer, Conemaugh Memorial Medical Center, Johnstown, PA, p. A541
  Chief Human Resource Officer, Conemaugh Miners Medical Center, Hastings, PA, p. A540

MALLETT, Belinda, R.N. Vice President, Patient Care and Clinical Services, Soin Medical Center, Beavercreek, OH, p. A484

MALLETT, Teresa, Chief Financial Officer, Madison Community Hospital, Madison, SD, p. A574

MALLICOAT, Danny, Chief Executive Officer, Complex Care Hospital at Ridgelake, Sarasota, FL, p. A145

MALLIK, Subodh, M.D. Chief of Staff, Pecos County Memorial Hospital, Fort Stockton, TX, p. A617

MALLING, Timothy, M.D. Chief of Staff, CentraCare Health–Paynesville, Paynesville, MN, p. A348

MALLONEE, Teresa, Director Human Resources, Angel Medical Center, Franklin, NC, p. A465

MALLORY, Brenda, M.D. Medical Director, Penn State Hershey Rehabilitation Hospital, Hummelstown, PA, p. A540

MALLOY, Peter, Chief Information Officer, Cheshire Medical Center, Keene, NH, p. A411

MALM, Brad, Director Human Resources and Education, Lindsborg Community Hospital, Lindsborg, KS, p. A248

MALMSTROM, Ron, Information Research Specialist, Parsons State Hospital and Training Center, Parsons, KS, p. A252

MALONE, Donald, M.D., President, Lutheran Hospital, Cleveland, OH, p. A489

MALONE, MSN, RN–, Ginger, Chief Nursing Officer, St. Mary's Hospital, Madison, WI, p. A709

MALONE, Meredith, Chief Financial Officer, Tennova Healthcare Dyersburg Regional Medical Center, Dyersburg, TN, p. A582

MALONE, Michael, Vice President and Chief Human Resources Officer, Virginia Hospital Center – Arlington, Arlington, VA, p. A667

MALONE, Patty, M.D. Chief Medical Officer, Ocean Beach Hospital, Ilwaco, WA, p. A685

MALONE, Robert, Chief Executive Officer, U. S. Public Health Service Indian Hospital, Cass Lake, MN, p. A340

MALONE, Thomas, M.D., President and Chief Executive Officer, Summa Health, Akron, OH, p. B129

MALONE, Thomas, M.D., President and Chief Executive Officer, Summa Health System, Akron, OH, p. A483

MALONEY, Jay, M.D. Chief of Staff, Cabinet Peaks Medical Center, Libby, MT, p. A389

MALONEY, Patrick J.
  Chief Executive Officer, West Suburban Medical Center, Oak Park, IL, p. A199
  Chief Executive Officer, Westlake Hospital, Melrose Park, IL, p. A196

MALONEY, Paul V., Vice President Finance, Behavioral Health Network, Natchaug Hospital, Mansfield Center, CT, p. A114

MALOTT, Deanna, Director Human Resources, Henry County Hospital, New Castle, IN, p. A219

MALOTT, Gregg, Chief Financial Officer, Pulaski Memorial Hospital, Winamac, IN, p. A224

MALOTTE, Rebecca, Executive Director and Chief Nursing Officer, The Heart Hospital at Deaconess Gateway, Newburgh, IN, p. A220

MALSED, Brad, Area Chief Financial Officer, Kaiser Permanente Los Angeles Medical Center, Los Angeles, CA, p. A71

MALSEED, TJ, Vice President and Chief Information Officer, Children's Hospital Los Angeles, Los Angeles, CA, p. A70

MALTE, Robert H., Chief Executive Officer, EvergreenHealth, Kirkland, WA, p. A686

MALYSZEK, Richard, M.D. Chief of Staff, Pikes Peak Regional Hospital, Woodland Park, CO, p. A111

MAMANGAKIS, John P., Senior Vice President, Montefiore New Rochelle, New Rochelle, NY, p. A443

MAMBOURG, Rolland, M.D. Vice President Medical Affairs, Mercy Health Saint Mary's, Grand Rapids, MI, p. A325

MAMMONE, Tina, Ph.D. Chief Nursing Officer, University of Virginia Medical Center, Charlottesville, VA, p. A668

MANAKAS, Christopher, Chief Information Officer, Fort HealthCare, Fort Atkinson, WI, p. A705

MANAS, Julie, President and Chief Executive Officer, Sacred Heart Hospital, Eau Claire, WI, p. A705

MANCHUR, Fred M., Chief Executive Officer, Kettering Health Network, Dayton, OH, p. B76

MANDAL, Alan, Vice President Financial Operations, Scripps Memorial Hospital–La Jolla, La Jolla, CA, p. A67

MANDAL, Konoy, M.D. Medical Director, Centennial Peaks Hospital, Louisville, CO, p. A109

MANDANAS, Renato, M.D. Chief Medical Officer, Oswego Hospital, Oswego, NY, p. A452

MANDEL, David, M.D. Chief of Staff, East Texas Medical Center Trinity, Trinity, TX, p. A653

MANDERINO, Michelle, Chief Human Resources, North Florida/South Georgia Veteran's Health System, Gainesville, FL, p. A149

MANDHAN, Narain, M.D. Chief Medical Officer, Kirby Medical Center, Monticello, IL, p. A197

MANDI, Deepak, M.D. Chief of Staff, West Palm Beach Veterans Affairs Medical Center, West Palm Beach, FL, p. A150

MANDLER, Jeffrey M., Chief Executive Officer, Bayonne Medical Center, Bayonne, NJ, p. A414

MANDLER, Jeffrey M., Chief Executive Officer, CarePoint Health, Jersey City, NJ, p. B26

MANDRACCHIA, Vincent, DPM Chief Medical Officer, Broadlawns Medical Center, Des Moines, IA, p. A229

MANDSAGER, Richard, M.D., Executive Officer, Providence Alaska Medical Center, Anchorage, AK, p. A28

MANESTRINA, Robert, Vice President Human Resources, Inspira Medical Center–Woodbury, Woodbury, NJ, p. A425

MANFREDI, Susan, R.N. Vice President and Chief Nursing Officer, UW Medicine/Northwest Hospital & Medical Center, Seattle, WA, p. A690

MANGIN, Paul, Vice President Finance, Mercy Medical Center–Clinton, Clinton, IA, p. A227

MANGIONE, Ellen, M.D. Chief of Staff, Veterans Affairs Eastern Colorado Health Care System, Denver, CO, p. A104

MANGONA, John, Vice President, Chief Information Officer and Compliance Officer, Saratoga Hospital, Saratoga Springs, NY, p. A455

MANGRUM, Charlita, M.D. Chief of Staff, Sandhills Regional Medical Center, Hamlet, NC, p. A466

MANGUM, Cody, Director Operations, St. Luke's Elmore, Mountain Home, ID, p. A177

MANGUM, Rozanne, Administrative Assistant and Director Human Resources, Grover C. Dils Medical Center, Caliente, NV, p. A404

MANHEIMER, Dean, Senior Vice President Human Resources, Northwestern Memorial Healthcare, Northwestern Memorial Hospital, Chicago, IL, p. A185

MANIATIS, Theodore, M.D. Medical Director, Staten Island University Hospital,, NY, p. A450

MANKAD, Naishadh, M.D. Chief of Staff, Lea Regional Medical Center, Hobbs, NM, p. A429

MANKER, Marcia
  Chief Executive Officer, Orange Coast Memorial Medical Center, Fountain Valley, CA, p. A63
  Chief Executive Officer, Saddleback Memorial Medical Center, Laguna Hills, CA, p. A68

MANKINS, Mark L., M.D. Chief of Staff, Hamilton Hospital, Olney, TX, p. A639

MANKOSKI, Susan, Vice President Human Resources, SSM Health St. Mary's Hospital – Jefferson City, Jefferson City, MO, p. A372

MANLAGNIT, Maybelle, Senior Accounting Officer, Metropolitan State Hospital, Norwalk, CA, p. A79

MANLEY, Dennis, R.N. Chief Nursing Officer, Mercy Hospital Joplin, Joplin, MO, p. A373

MANLEY, John, Director Information Systems, Jackson General Hospital, Ripley, WV, p. A699

MANN, Brian, Chief Executive Officer, Select Specialty Hospital–Danville, Danville, PA, p. A536

MANN, Christopher, M.D. Medical Director, Cook Children's Northeast Hospital, Hurst, TX, p. A628

MANN, Corey, Director Human Resources, Memorial Health Care Systems, Seward, NE, p. A402

MANN, Julie D., Vice President and Chief Administrative Officer, Katherine Shaw Bethea Hospital, Dixon, IL, p. A188

MANN, Lindsay K., Chief Executive Officer, Kaweah Delta Medical Center, Visalia, CA, p. A99

MANN, Lori, R.N. Chief Nursing Officer, Howard A. Rusk Rehabilitation Center, Columbia, MO, p. A370

MANN, Rhonda, Chief Nursing Officer, Franklin Woods Community Hospital, Johnson City, TN, p. A585

MANN, Thomas, M.D. Chief Medical Officer, Dorminy Medical Center, Fitzgerald, GA, p. A159

MANNI, Joseph, Vice President Operations Chief Operating Officer, Deborah Heart and Lung Center, Browns Mills, NJ, p. A415

MANNICH, Andy, Regional Administrator, Georgia Regional Hospital at Savannah, Savannah, GA, p. A166

MANNING, Angela, Director Health Information Services, HEALTHSOUTH Sunrise Rehabilitation Hospital, Sunrise, FL, p. A146

MANNING, Austin Lane, Chief Operating Officer, Timpanogos Regional Hospital, Orem, UT, p. A661

MANNING, Claude, Chief Financial Officer, Palacios Community Medical Center, Palacios, TX, p. A639

MANNING, Donald, M.D. Clinical Director, Georgia Regional Hospital at Savannah, Savannah, GA, p. A166

MANNING, James, Administrator, Pathway Rehabilitation Hospital, Bossier City, LA, p. A274

MANNING, JoAnn, Chief Financial Officer, Emory Johns Creek Hospital, Johns Creek, GA, p. A161

MANNING, Kevin, R.N. Chief Nursing Officer, Kingwood Pines Hospital, Kingwood, TX, p. A631

MANNING, Kimberly, Chief Nursing Officer, Washington County Hospital, Plymouth, NC, p. A471

MANNING, Laura, Administrative Director, Guthrie Corning Hospital, Corning, NY, p. A437

MANNING, Lori, Administrator Human Resources, Western State Hospital, Tacoma, WA, p. A692

MANNING, Raymond, Director Information Technology, TLC Health Network – Lake Shore Hospital, Irving, NY, p. A440

MANNION, Stephen, Assistant Vice President Information Systems Customer Service, MedStar Franklin Square Medical Center, Baltimore, MD, p. A297

MANNIX, Mary N., FACHE, President and Chief Executive Officer, Augusta Health, Fishersville, VA, p. A670

MANNON, Jane, Interim Chief Human Resources Officer, Penn State Milton S. Hershey Medical Center, Hershey, PA, p. A540

MANNS, Bill, President, Mercy Health Saint Mary's, Grand Rapids, MI, p. A325

MANNY, Martin, Director, I.S., Providence St. Mary Medical Center, Walla Walla, WA, p. A693

MANOHARA, Anand, Chief Operating Officer, Good Samaritan Hospital, Bakersfield, CA, p. A56

MANSARD, Donna, Chief Executive Officer, Select Specialty Hospital–St. Louis, Saint Charles, MO, p. A379

MANSEAU, Jani, Vice President Operations and Chief Nursing Officer, Freedom Pain Hospital, Scottsdale, AZ, p. A38

MANSFIELD, Al, Chief Financial Officer, Saint Vincent Hospital, Erie, PA, p. A538

MANSFIELD, David, M.D. Chief of Staff, El Paso Specialty Hospital, El Paso, TX, p. A615

MANSFIELD, Deena, Director Human Resources, Ashley Regional Medical Center, Vernal, UT, p. A664

MANSFIELD, Jerry A., Ph.D. Executive Chief Nursing Officer & Chief Patient Experience Officer, MUSC Medical Center of Medical University of South Carolina, Charleston, SC, p. A563

MANSFIELD, Stephen L., FACHE, President and Chief Executive Officer, Methodist Health System, Dallas, TX, p. B91

MANSKE, Kristin, Chief Executive Officer, Greenwood Regional Rehabilitation Hospital, Greenwood, SC, p. A567

MANSKE, Lou Ann, Director Human Resources, Madonna Rehabilitation Hospital, Lincoln, NE, p. A398

MANSON, David, Manager Human Resources, Santa Clara Valley Medical Center, San Jose, CA, p. A91

MANSON, Kelly, Chief Financial Officer, Veterans Affairs Sierra Nevada Health Care System, Reno, NV, p. A408

MANSON III, William T., Chief Executive Officer, AnMed Health Medical Center, Anderson, SC, p. A562

MANSON III,, William T., Chief Executive Officer, AnMed Health, Anderson, SC, p. B10

MANSOOR, Ureej, M.D. Chief of Staff, Southeast Health Center of Ripley County, Doniphan, MO, p. A370

MANSTEDT, Chase, Chief Financial Officer, Saunders Medical Center, Wahoo, NE, p. A403

MANSUKHANI, Martin, Chief Financial Officer, Desert Valley Hospital, Victorville, CA, p. A98

MANSURE, John F., FACHE, President, GHS Greer Memorial Hospital, Greer, SC, p. A567

MANTERNACH, Paul, M.D. Senior Vice President Physician Integration, Mercy Medical Center–North Iowa, Mason City, IA, p. A234

MANTZ, David, Chief Executive Officer, Chicot Memorial Medical Center, Lake Village, AR, p. A48

MANUBENS, Claudio, M.D. Chief of Staff, Heart of Florida Regional Medical Center, Davenport, FL, p. A126

MANUEL, Shasta, Executive Director Finance, St. Anthony Hospital, Oklahoma City, OK, p. A517

MANUEL, Wendy, Vice President and Chief Financial Officer, Rehabilitation Hospital of the Pacific, Honolulu, HI, p. A171

MANZER, Andrew R., Chief Operating Officer, Bassett Medical Center, Cooperstown, NY, p. A437

MANZO, Arnold D., Vice President Human Resources, Saint Barnabas Medical Center, Livingston, NJ, p. A418

MANZO–LUNA, Hilda, Chief Nursing Officer, La Palma Intercommunity Hospital, La Palma, CA, p. A67

MANZOOR, Amir, M.D. Medical Director, Select Specialty Hospital–Panama City, Panama City, FL, p. A142

MAPARA, Anupam, M.D. Chief of Staff, Sutter Delta Medical Center, Antioch, CA, p. A54

MAPES, Kevin, Director Kansas Division System and Technology Service Center, St. Francis Health, Topeka, KS, p. A254

MAPLES, Michael, M.D. Vice President and Chief Medical Officer, Mississippi Baptist Medical Center, Jackson, MS, p. A360

MAPLES, Rickie, Interim Chief Financial Officer, Southeast Health Center of Ripley County, Doniphan, MO, p. A370

MAPPIN, F Gregory, M.D. Vice President Medical Affairs and Chief Medical Officer, Self Regional Healthcare, Greenwood, SC, p. A567

MARAAN, Sheila, Director of Nursing, Brynn Marr Hospital, Jacksonville, NC, p. A467

MARAS, Greg, Vice President Human Resources, Meadville Medical Center, Meadville, PA, p. A544

MARASA, Richard, M.D. President Medical Staff, Springfield Hospital, Springfield, VT, p. A666

MARBLE, Kevin, Director Information Technology, Oklahoma Forensic Center, Vinita, OK, p. A523

MARCANO, Norma, Chief Operating Officer, San Juan City Hospital, San Juan, PR, p. A730

MARCANTANO, Mark R., President and Chief Operating Officer, Women & Infants Hospital of Rhode Island, Providence, RI, p. A561

MARCANTEL, Bill, Chief Information Systems, Allen Parish Hospital, Kinder, LA, p. A280

MARCEAUX, Caroline, R.N. Chief Nursing Officer, Acadia General Hospital, Crowley, LA, p. A276

MARCELIN, Fitzgerald, M.D. Chief of Staff, Southern Virginia Regional Medical Center, Emporia, VA, p. A669

MARCH, Riley, Manager Information Technology, Southeast Health Center of Ripley County, Doniphan, MO, p. A370

MARCHAND, Gary G., President and Chief Executive Officer, Memorial Hospital at Gulfport, Gulfport, MS, p. A358

MARCHANT, Joseph, Administrator, Bibb Medical Center, Centreville, AL, p. A18

MARCHETTI, Mark E., President and Chief Executive Officer, Mt. Graham Regional Medical Center, Safford, AZ, p. A38

MARCHIK, Katie A.
Vice President, Consolidated Services, UnityPoint Health and Interim Chief Financial Officer, Trinity Regional Health Sy, UnityPoint Health – Trinity Muscatine, Muscatine, IA, p. A235
Interim Chief Financial Officer, UnityPoint Health – Trinity Rock Island, Rock Island, IL, p. A201

MARCO, Jr., James E., Interim Vice President, Human Resources, Oswego Hospital, Oswego, NY, p. A452

MARCOTTE, Melissa, Chief Financial Officer, Rainy Lake Medical Center, International Falls, MN, p. A344

MARCOVICI, Mia, M.D. Chief Medical Officer, Norristown State Hospital, Norristown, PA, p. A546

MARCOWITZ, David, M.D. Chief of Staff, Lucas County Health Center, Chariton, IA, p. A227

MARCRUM, Jennifer, Chief Financial Officer, Sumner County Hospital District One, Caldwell, KS, p. A241

MARCUCCI, John, M.D. Vice President Medical Affairs, Baylor Regional Medical Center at Plano, Plano, TX, p. A641

MARCUM, Amie, Human Resources Coordinator, ContinueCARE Hospital at Baptist Health Corbin, Corbin, KY, p. A258

MARCZEWSKI, Les, M.D. Chief Medical Officer, Loring Hospital, Sac City, IA, p. A237

MARDY, Paul, Chief Information Technology Officer, Tennessee Valley Healthcare System, Nashville, TN, p. A591

MAREK, Kyle, Manager Information Services, Carteret Health Care, Morehead City, NC, p. A470

MAREK, Rick, Vice President Medical Information Systems, Post Acute/Warm Springs Rehabilitation Hospital of San Antonio, San Antonio, TX, p. A646

MARGENAU, Randall, Chief Information Officer, William S. Middleton Memorial Veterans Hospital, Madison, WI, p. A709

MARGER, Brian, Chief Operating Officer, TriStar Ashland City Medical Center, Ashland City, TN, p. A579

MARGOLIS, Marilyn, MSN, Chief Executive Officer, Emory Johns Creek Hospital, Johns Creek, GA, p. A161

MARGOLIS, Ron, Chief Information Officer, University of New Mexico Health System, Albuquerque, NM, p. A428

MARGRAVES, Lisa, Chief Operating Officer, Director Clinical Services, Rock Springs, LLC, Georgetown, TX, p. A620

MARGULIS, Richard T., President and Chief Executive Officer, Brookhaven Memorial Hospital Medical Center, Patchogue, NY, p. A452

MARIANI, Julia, Vice President Business Operations, Northern Montana Hospital, Havre, MT, p. A388

MARIANI, Marilyn, R.N. Chief Nursing Officer, Lakeview Hospital, Bountiful, UT, p. A659

MARIANI, Meleah, Chief Nursing Officer, Spectrum Health Gerber Memorial, Fremont, MI, p. A324

MARICN, Tanya, Interim Vice President Human Resources, Mercy Hospital Springfield, Springfield, MO, p. A382

MARIETTA, John, M.D. Chief Medical Officer, St. David's Medical Center, Austin, TX, p. A600

MARIETTA, Megan, Chief Operating Officer, Kingwood Medical Center, Kingwood, TX, p. A631

MARIETTA, Richard, M.D. Medical Director, Clear Lake Regional Medical Center, Webster, TX, p. A656

MARIGOMEN, Nancy Ann, R.N. Director of Nursing, Milwaukee County Behavioral Health Division, Milwaukee, WI, p. A711

MARIN, Loyman, Chief Human Resources, Miami Veterans Affairs Healthcare System, Miami, FL, p. A137

MARINI, Frank, Vice President and Chief Information Officer, TMC HealthCare, Tucson, AZ, p. A41

MARINICH, Patsy, Chief Nursing Officer, Cumberland River Hospital, Celina, TN, p. A580

MARINO, A. Michael, M.D. Senior Vice President Medical Administration, Greenwich Hospital, Greenwich, CT, p. A114

MARINO, Christopher, M.D. Chief of Staff, Memphis Veterans Affairs Medical Center, Memphis, TN, p. A589

MARINO, Joseph, Chief Financial Officer, Suburban Community Hospital, Norristown, PA, p. A546

MARINO, Marchita H., Vice President Human Resources, Wuesthoff Medical Center – Rockledge, Rockledge, FL, p. A143

MARINOFF, Peter, President, Paul Oliver Memorial Hospital, Frankfort, MI, p. A324

MARION, Kristie, Chief Nurse Executive, Memorial Hospital Los Banos, Los Banos, CA, p. A75

MARIOTTI, Denise, Chief Human Resource Officer, Hospital of the University of Pennsylvania, Philadelphia, PA, p. A548

MARK, Joseph M., Interim Chief Executive Officer, Kaiser Permanente Vacaville Medical Center, Vacaville, CA, p. A97

MARKENSON, David, M.D. Chief Medical Officer, Sky Ridge Medical Center, Lone Tree, CO, p. A108

MARKER, Jason, M.D. Chief Medical Officer, Community Hospital of Bremen, Bremen, IN, p. A207

MARKER, John, Chief Nursing Officer, Women's and Children's Hospital, Lafayette, LA, p. A281

MARKESINO, Patricia A., FACHE Chief Nurse Executive and Chief Operating Officer, Providence Willamette Falls Medical Center, Oregon City, OR, p. A528

MARKETTI, Dean M., Vice President Finance, Morris Hospital & Healthcare Centers, Morris, IL, p. A197

MARKGRAF, Janelle K., Director Human Resources and Off Campus Services, Aspirus Langlade Hospital, Antigo, WI, p. A702

MARKHAM, Barbara, Chief Financial Officer, Glendive Medical Center, Glendive, MT, p. A387

MARKHAM, Kevin, Chief Financial Officer, EastPointe Hospital, Daphne, AL, p. A18

MARKHAM, Patricia A., Interim Chief Executive Officer, Cass County Memorial Hospital, Atlantic, IA, p. A225

MARKOS, Dennis R., Chief Executive Officer, Ed Fraser Memorial Hospital and Baker Community Health Center, MacClenny, FL, p. A135

MARKOWITZ, Bruce J., President and Chief Executive Officer, HackensackUMC Palisades, North Bergen, NJ, p. A421

MARKOWITZ, Stuart, M.D., President, Hartford Hospital, Hartford, CT, p. A114

MARKOWSKI, Stan, Chief Financial Officer, Palmetto Lowcountry Behavioral Health, Charleston, SC, p. A563

MARKS, Craig J., FACHE, Chief Executive Officer, PMH Medical Center, Prosser, WA, p. A688

MARKS, Jerry, Vice President Finance, Decatur County Memorial Hospital, Greensburg, IN, p. A212

MARKS, Kimberly W., Chief Executive Officer, Southampton Memorial Hospital, Franklin, VA, p. A670

MARKS, Marie, Chief Nursing Officer, Lake Norman Regional Medical Center, Mooresville, NC, p. A470

MARKS, Michael, M.D. Chief of Staff, Norwalk Hospital, Norwalk, CT, p. A116

MARKS, Stanley, M.D
Chief Medical Officer, Memorial Hospital Miramar, Miramar, FL, p. A138
Chief Medical Officer, Memorial Hospital Pembroke, Pembroke Pines, FL, p. A142

MARKSTROM, Susan, M.D. Chief of Staff, St. Cloud Veterans Affairs Health Care System, Saint Cloud, MN, p. A350

MARLATT, Pam, Business Systems Director, Essentia Health St. Joseph's Medical Center, Brainerd, MN, p. A340

MARLER, Ruth, Chief Nursing Officer and Chief Operating Officer, Johnston Health, Smithfield, NC, p. A473

MARLER, Steven R., Assistant Administrator, Parkland Health Center – Liberty Street, Farmington, MO, p. A371

MARLEY, Charles, D.O. Vice President Medical Affairs, WellSpan Gettysburg Hospital, Gettysburg, PA, p. A539

MARLEY, Kim, M.D. Chief Medical Officer, Chan Soon–Shiong Medical Center, Windber, PA, p. A558

MARLEY, Lee, VP/Information Services Chief Application Officer, Presbyterian Hospital, Albuquerque, NM, p. A428

MARLEY, Michael, Chief Information Officer, Veterans Affairs Central Western Massachusetts Healthcare System, Leeds, MA, p. A311

MARLIN, Chris, Director Human Resources, Orange Park Medical Center, Orange Park, FL, p. A140

MARLOW, Gary P., Chief Financial Officer, Beverly Hospital, Beverly, MA, p. A305

MARLOWE, Justin, Information Technology Director, Shands Live Oak Regional Medical Center, Live Oak, FL, p. A134

MARMANDE, Susanne, Administrator, Infirmary Long Term Acute Care Hospital, Mobile, AL, p. A22

MARNEY, Terri A., R.N. Director of Nursing, Plains Regional Medical Center, Clovis, NM, p. A428

MARON, Michael, President and Chief Executive Officer, Holy Name Medical Center, Teaneck, NJ, p. A424

MARONEY, Gerry, Chief Information Officer and Security Officer, Gaylord Hospital, Wallingford, CT, p. A117

MAROSTICA, Tony, Director Human Resources, Spanish Peaks Regional Health Center, Walsenburg, CO, p. A111

MAROTTA, Diane, Vice President Human Resources, John T. Mather Memorial Hospital, Port Jefferson, NY, p. A453

MAROUN, Christiane, M.D. Chief of Staff, Childrens Care Hospital and School, Sioux Falls, SD, p. A576

MARPLE, Richard, M.D. Chief Medical Officer, Baptist Medical Center, San Antonio, TX, p. A645

MARQUES, John
Vice President Chief Human Resources Officer, Banner – University Medical Center South, Tucson, AZ, p. A40
Vice President Human Resources, Banner – University Medical Center Tucson, Tucson, AZ, p. A40

MARQUES, Tony, Director Information Systems, Grace Cottage Hospital, Townshend, VT, p. A666

MARQUSEE, Joanne, President and Chief Executive Officer, Cooley Dickinson Hospital, Northampton, MA, p. A313

MARR, Debbie, Administrative Assistant and Director Human Resources, Fredonia Regional Hospital, Fredonia, KS, p. A243

MARRERO, Jamie L., M.D. Medical Director, HEALTHSOUTH Hospital of Manati, Manati, PR, p. A728

MARRERO, Jose, Director Finance, San Jorge Children's Hospital, San Juan, PR, p. A730

MARRERO, Norma, Executive Administrator, Doctors' Center Hospital San Juan, San Juan, PR, p. A729

MARRONI, Denise
Chief Financial Officer, Providence Centralia Hospital, Centralia, WA, p. A683
Chief Financial Officer, Providence St. Peter Hospital, Olympia, WA, p. A687

MARRUFO, Gabriel, Chief Financial Officer, Methodist Stone Oak Hospital, San Antonio, TX, p. A646

MARS, Tom L., R.N. Vice President Patient Care Services and Chief Nursing Officer, Camden Clark Medical Center, Parkersburg, WV, p. A698

MARSEE, DeWayne, Director Information Systems, Mercer Health, Coldwater, OH, p. A490

MARSH, J. Michael, President and Chief Executive Officer, Overlake Medical Center, Bellevue, WA, p. A682

MARSH, Leslie, Chief Executive Officer, Lexington Regional Health Center, Lexington, NE, p. A397

MARSH, Linda, Vice President Financial Services and Chief Financial Officer, Alhambra Hospital Medical Center, Alhambra, CA, p. A54

MARSH, Mark A., President, Health Central Hospital, Ocoee, FL, p. A139

MARSH, Mitch, Interim Executive Director, Terence Cardinal Cooke Health Care Center, New York, NY, p. A450

MARSH, Rob, Chief Executive Officer, Cedar Crest Hospital and Residential Treatment Center, Belton, TX, p. A602

MARSH, Toby, MSN Interim Chief Patient Care Services Officer, University of California, Davis Medical Center, Sacramento, CA, p. A87

MARSHAK, Glenn, M.D. Chief of Staff, Mission Community Hospital,, CA, p. A73

MARSHALL, David R., JD Chief Nursing and Patient Care Services Officer, University of Texas Medical Branch, Galveston, TX, p. A620

MARSHALL, Deborah K., Vice President Public Relations, Good Samaritan Regional Medical Center, Suffern, NY, p. A456

MARSHALL, Erika, Interim Chief Nursing Officer, Calais Regional Hospital, Calais, ME, p. A292

MARSHALL, Glen, Chief Executive Officer, Trios Health, Kennewick, WA, p. A685

MARSHALL, James I., President and Chief Executive Officer, Uintah Basin Medical Center, Roosevelt, UT, p. A662

MARSHALL, Jerry, Director Information Services, Information Technology Security Officer, United Regional Health Care System, Wichita Falls, TX, p. A658

MARSHALL, Jim, Chief Executive Officer, Pickens County Medical Center, Carrollton, AL, p. A18

MARSHALL, Julie, Chief Nursing Officer, The University of Vermont Health Network – Alice Hyde Medical Center, Malone, NY, p. A442

MARSHALL, Ken, M.D. Chief Medical Officer, Indiana University Health Bloomington Hospital, Bloomington, IN, p. A207

MARSHALL, Michael, Vice President Finance and Chief Financial Officer, Anderson Hospital, Maryville, IL, p. A195

MARSHALL, Patricia, Assistant Administrator Human Resources, Washington Health System Greene, Waynesburg, PA, p. A557

MARSHALL, Penny, Chief Nursing Officer, Bear River Valley Hospital, Tremonton, UT, p. A664

MARSHALL Jr., Robert L., FACHE, Chief Executive Officer, Bolivar Medical Center, Cleveland, MS, p. A356

MARSHALL, Thomas, Interim Chief Executive Officer, Lehigh Regional Medical Center, Lehigh Acres, FL, p. A134

MARSHBURN, Deborah, R.N. Chief Nursing Executive, Cape Fear Valley Medical Center, Fayetteville, NC, p. A465

MARSICO, Nick, Vice President and Chief Operating Officer, Magruder Memorial Hospital, Port Clinton, OH, p. A501

MARSO, Paul, Vice President Human Resources, Avera St. Mary's Hospital, Pierre, SD, p. A575

MARSTON, Shawn, Director Human Resources, Keystone Newport News, Newport News, VA, p. A674

MARTANIUK, Jean, Director Human Resources, Mt. Ascutney Hospital and Health Center, Windsor, VT, p. A666

MARTENS, Angela, Chief Financial Officer, Cumberland Memorial Hospital, Cumberland, WI, p. A704

MARTENS, Troy, Chief Operating Officer, UnityPoint Health – Trinity Regional Medical Center, Fort Dodge, IA, p. A230

MARTHONE, Frances, Chief Nursing Officer, Piedmont Henry Hospital, Stockbridge, GA, p. A167

MARTI, Maria L., Director Fiscal Services, Auxilio Mutuo Hospital, San Juan, PR, p. A729

MARTIN, Adam, Chief Operating Officer, Wythe County Community Hospital, Wytheville, VA, p. A681

MARTIN, Amanda, Manager Human Resources, Ohio Valley Surgical Hospital, Springfield, OH, p. A502

MARTIN, Angelia, M.D. Chief of Staff, Northwest Medical Center, Albany, MO, p. A367

MARTIN, Barbara, Chief Nursing Officer, Mercy St. Vincent Medical Center, Toledo, OH, p. A504

MARTIN, Barbara J., R.N.,
President and Chief Executive Officer, Vista Medical Center East, Waukegan, IL, p. A205
President and Chief Executive Officer, Vista Medical Center West, Waukegan, IL, p. A205

MARTIN, Brent
Administrator, LifeCare Hospitals of Shreveport, Shreveport, LA, p. A287
Administrator, LifeCare Specialty Hospital of North Louisiana, Ruston, LA, p. A287

MARTIN, Brian, Chief Executive Officer, Loring Hospital, Sac City, IA, p. A237

MARTIN, Bruce A., Vice President Human Resources, CarolinaEast Health System, New Bern, NC, p. A470

MARTIN, C. Gregory, M.D. Chief Medical Officer, Emerson Hospital, Concord, MA, p. A309

MARTIN, Carmen, Associate Administrator, Auxilio Mutuo Hospital, San Juan, PR, p. A729

MARTIN, Cary, Chief Executive Officer, Houston Healthcare System, Warner Robins, GA, p. B71

MARTIN, Cary, Chief Executive Officer, Houston Medical Center, Warner Robins, GA, p. A168

MARTIN, Cheryl
Chief Information Officer, Kingman Regional Medical Center, Kingman, AZ, p. A33
Chief Information Officer, Palmetto Health Tuomey, Sumter, SC, p. A570

MARTIN, Christine M., Vice President and Chief Financial Officer, Cleveland Regional Medical Center, Shelby, NC, p. A473

MARTIN, Connie
Vice President and Chief Support Officer, Methodist Medical Center of Oak Ridge, Oak Ridge, TN, p. A592
Chief Executive Officer and Administrator, Physicians Medical Center, Houma, LA, p. A278

MARTIN, Corey, M.D. Director Medical Affairs, Buffalo Hospital, Buffalo, MN, p. A340

MARTIN, Cyndie, Director, Coal County General Hospital, Coalgate, OK, p. A510

MARTIN, David, Assistant Administrator, Valley Hospital, Spokane Valley, WA, p. A691

MARTIN, David T., President, UPMC Passavant, Pittsburgh, PA, p. A551

MARTIN, David W., M.D. Vice President Chief Medical Officer, Seton Medical Center Austin, Austin, TX, p. A599

MARTIN, Deanna, Chief Executive Officer, HEALTHSOUTH Rehabilitation Hospital of Rock Hill, Rock Hill, SC, p. A569

MARTIN, Deborah
Regional Vice President Human Resources, Cascade Valley Hospital and Clinics, Arlington, WA, p. A682
Regional Vice President Human Resources, Skagit Regional Health, Mount Vernon, WA, p. A686

MARTIN, Debra, Chief Nursing Officer, Hamilton General Hospital, Hamilton, TX, p. A622

MARTIN, Garland, M.D. Chief of Staff, Appling Healthcare System, Baxley, GA, p. A154

MARTIN, Garry, Chief Fiscal, Veterans Affairs North Texas Health Care System, Dallas, TX, p. A612

MARTIN, Gregg
Manager Management Information Systems, Arnot Ogden Medical Center, Elmira, NY, p. A438
Chief Information Officer, Ira Davenport Memorial Hospital, Bath, NY, p. A434
Chief Information Officer, St. Joseph's Hospital, Elmira, NY, p. A438

MARTIN, Harvey C., M.D. Medical Director, Red River Hospital, LLC, Wichita Falls, TX, p. A657

MARTIN, Holly
Director Human Resource, Iowa Specialty Hospital–Belmond, Belmond, IA, p. A225
Human Resources Leader, Iowa Specialty Hospital–Clarion, Clarion, IA, p. A227

MARTIN, James, Chief Information Officer, River Park Hospital, Huntington, WV, p. A697

MARTIN, James C., M.D. Vice President and Chief Medical Officer, CHRISTUS Santa Rosa Health System, San Antonio, TX, p. A645

MARTIN, James D.
Chief Financial Officer, Hawthorn Children Psychiatric Hospital, Saint Louis, MO, p. A380
Chief Financial Officer, Metropolitan St. Louis Psychiatric Center, Saint Louis, MO, p. A380
Chief Financial Officer, St. Louis Psychiatric Rehabilitation Center, Saint Louis, MO, p. A381

MARTIN, Janice S., R.N. Chief Nursing Officer, Davis Regional Medical Center, Statesville, NC, p. A474

MARTIN, Jeanene R., M.P.H
Senior Vice President Human Resources and Chief People Officer, WakeMed Cary Hospital, Cary, NC, p. A462
Senior Vice President Human Resources, WakeMed Raleigh Campus, Raleigh, NC, p. A472

MARTIN, Jeffrey H., M.D. Chief of Staff, Murphy Medical Center, Murphy, NC, p. A470

MARTIN, Jeffrey L., President, Ministry Saint Michael's Hospital, Stevens Point, WI, p. A716

MARTIN, Jeremy, Chief Support Services Officer, St. James Parish Hospital, Lutcher, LA, p. A282

MARTIN, Jessica, Director Human Resources, Logan Regional Medical Center, Logan, WV, p. A697

MARTIN, Karen, R.N. Chief Nursing Officer, Marshall Medical Center, Lewisburg, TN, p. A587

MARTIN, Karen, Chief Nursing Officer, Springs Memorial Hospital, Lancaster, SC, p. A568

MARTIN, Keith, M.D. Vice President and Medical Director, CGH Medical Center, Sterling, IL, p. A204

MARTIN, Kelly, Chief Financial Officer, Fairchild Medical Center, Yreka, CA, p. A100

MARTIN, Kelly K., Human Resource Officer, Texas Health Presbyterian Hospital Plano, Plano, TX, p. A642

MARTIN, Kenneth A., M.D. Chief of Staff, Arkansas Surgical Hospital, North Little Rock, AR, p. A50

MARTIN, Kevin, R.N., Administrator, Shriners Hospitals for Children–Salt Lake City, Salt Lake City, UT, p. A663

MARTIN, Kevin P., M.D. Chief Medical Officer, Four Winds Hospital, Saratoga Springs, NY, p. A455

MARTIN, Konnie, Chief Executive Officer, San Luis Valley Health, Alamosa, CO, p. A101

MARTIN, Konnie, Chief Executive Officer, San Luis Valley Health, Alamosa, CO, p. B118

MARTIN, Kory Lann, M.D. Chief of Staff, Seymour Hospital, Seymour, TX, p. A648

MARTIN, Kristina, Chief Information Officer, Curry General Hospital, Gold Beach, OR, p. A526

MARTIN, Leslee, Manager Information Technology, HSHS St. Elizabeth's Hospital, Belleville, IL, p. A181

MARTIN, Marie T., Chief Nursing Officer Vice President Patient Care Services, Canton–Potsdam Hospital, Potsdam, NY, p. A453

MARTIN, Marlana, Director Human Resources, Benewah Community Hospital, Saint Maries, ID, p. A18

MARTIN, Mary, MSN Chief Nursing Officer, St. Nicholas Hospital, Sheboygan, WI, p. A716

MARTIN, Matthew, Director Resource Management, Naval Hospital Oak Harbor, Oak Harbor, WA, p. A687

MARTIN, Nick, Chief Information Officer, Minidoka Memorial Hospital, Rupert, ID, p. A178

MARTIN, Nikki, Chief Financial Officer, CHRISTUS Southeast Texas Jasper Memorial, Jasper, TX, p. A629

MARTIN, Patrick, Director Information Systems, Calvary Hospital,, NY, p. A444

MARTIN, Patrick, M.D. Medical Director, Wilmington Treatment Center, Wilmington, NC, p. A475

MARTIN, Patsy, Manager Human Resources, Select Rehabilitation Hospital of Denton, Denton, TX, p. A613

MARTIN, Paul, Chief Medical Officer, Grandview Medical Center, Dayton, OH, p. A492

MARTIN, Paul J., Director Human Resources, Kaiser Permanente Los Angeles Medical Center, Los Angeles, CA, p. A71

MARTIN, Ric, Information Specialist, Madison State Hospital, Madison, IN, p. A217

MARTIN, Richard A., MSN Senior Vice President and Chief Nursing Officer, Hoag Memorial Hospital Presbyterian, Newport Beach, CA, p. A79

MARTIN, Ronnie, Chief Executive Officer, San Luis Valley Health Conejos County Hospital, La Jara, CO, p. A107

MARTIN, Sabrina, Chief Executive Officer, Rehabilitation Hospital of Southern New Mexico, Las Cruces, NM, p. A430

MARTIN, Sharon E., M.D. President Medical Staff, Fulton County Medical Center, Mc Connellsburg, PA, p. A544

MARTIN, Sheila, Chief Nursing Officer, Clinton Memorial Hospital, Wilmington, OH, p. A506

MARTIN, Sherri, M.D. President Medical Staff, Shawnee Mission Medical Center, Shawnee Mission, KS, p. A254

MARTIN, Stacy L., Director Human Resources, Grant Regional Health Center, Lancaster, WI, p. A708

MARTIN, Susan, Vice President Finance, Middlesex Hospital, Middletown, CT, p. A115

MARTIN, Teresa, Chief Financial Officer, Two Rivers Behavioral Health System, Kansas City, MO, p. A374

MARTIN, Tom, Chief Strategy and Information Officer, EvergreenHealth, Kirkland, WA, p. A686

MARTIN, Tracie, M.D. Chief Medical Officer, Oakland Mercy Hospital, Oakland, NE, p. A399

MARTIN, Tracy, Chief Financial Officer, Logan Memorial Hospital, Russellville, KY, p. A269

MARTIN, Val, Director Financial Management Services Center, Veterans Affairs Salt Lake City Health Care System, Salt Lake City, UT, p. A664

MARTIN, W. Carl, Chief Operating Officer, Providence Hospital, Columbia, SC, p. A564

MARTIN, Wendy, Chief Financial Officer, Shands Starke Regional Medical Center, Starke, FL, p. A146

MARTIN–PRATT, Diane, Director Information Systems, Niagara Falls Memorial Medical Center, Niagara Falls, NY, p. A451

MARTINEAU, Loraine, Controller, Prairie Ridge Hospital and Health Services, Elbow Lake, MN, p. A342

MARTINEK, Jacquelyn, R.N. Chief Nursing Officer, Brookwood Baptist Medical Center, Birmingham, AL, p. A16

MARTINEZ, Albino, Director Budget and Finance, Miners' Colfax Medical Center, Raton, NM, p. A430

MARTINEZ, RN, BSN,, Angel, R.N. Director Patient Care Services, Shriners Hospitals for Children–Galveston, Galveston, TX, p. A620

MARTINEZ, Anthony, Director Information Technology, Lakeway Regional Medical Center, Lakeway, TX, p. A631

MARTINEZ, Darlene, Director Finance, New Mexico Behavioral Health Institute at Las Vegas, Las Vegas, NM, p. A430

MARTINEZ, Edward, Chief Information Officer, Nicklaus Children's Hospital, Miami, FL, p. A137

MARTINEZ, Eleanor, Chief Nursing Officer, Alhambra Hospital Medical Center, Alhambra, CA, p. A54

MARTINEZ, Enrique, M.D. Chief Medical Officer, The Hospitals of Providence Memorial Campus, El Paso, TX, p. A616

MARTINEZ, Fernando, Senior Vice President and Chief Information Officer, Parkland Health & Hospital System, Dallas, TX, p. A611

MARTINEZ, Francisco, Executive Director, Hospital San Antonio, Mayaguez, PR, p. A728

MARTINEZ, Frank
Senior Vice President Human Resources, East Jefferson General Hospital, Metairie, LA, p. A283
Vice President Human Resources, West Jefferson Medical Center, Marrero, LA, p. A283

MARTINEZ, Jason, Director Information Technology, West Valley Medical Center, Caldwell, ID, p. A175

MARTINEZ, Jeanine, Director Human Resources, Putnam General Hospital, Eatonton, GA, p. A159

MARTINEZ, Jorge I., Executive Director, Hospital Perea, Mayaguez, PR, p. A728

MARTINEZ, Jose, M.D. Chief Medical Officer, Northwest Medical Center, Margate, FL, p. A135

MARTINEZ, Josue, Coordinator Information Systems, University Hospital, San Juan, PR, p. A730

MARTINEZ, Katherine, Chief Nursing Officer, North Central Surgical Center, Dallas, TX, p. A611

MARTINEZ, Kathryn J., Chief Nursing Officer, FHN Memorial Hospital, Freeport, IL, p. A190

MARTINEZ, Leanne, Chief Executive Officer and Administrator, Fisher County Hospital District, Rotan, TX, p. A644

MARTINEZ, Lee, Chief Information Officer, Cooley Dickinson Hospital, Northampton, MA, p. A313

MARTINEZ, Louisa, Director of Nursing, Frio Regional Hospital, Pearsall, TX, p. A640

MARTINEZ, Luis, Executive Director, Hospital Metropolitano Dr. Susoni, Arecibo, PR, p. A726

MARTINEZ, Maria, Chief Nursing Officer, La Paz Regional Hospital, Parker, AZ, p. A35

MARTINEZ, Michelle, Chief Executive Officer, U. S. Public Health Service Indian Hospital–Whiteriver, Whiteriver, AZ, p. A41

MARTINEZ, Regina M., Director Human Resources, La Paz Regional Hospital, Parker, AZ, p. A35

MARTINEZ, Rosette, Acting Chief Executive Officer, Lemuel Shattuck Hospital, Jamaica Plain, MA, p. A311

MARTINEZ, Suzanne, Director Human Resources, Centennial Peaks Hospital, Louisville, CO, p. A109

MARTINEZ, Terri, Chief Financial Officer, Plains Memorial Hospital, Dimmitt, TX, p. A613

MARTINEZ, Tina, Director Human Resources, J. D. McCarty Center for Children With Developmental Disabilities, Norman, OK, p. A515

MARTINEZ, Virginia, Director Human Resources, Copper Queen Community Hospital, Bisbee, AZ, p. A31

MARTINEZ, Yolanda, Chief Fiscal Services, Edward Hines, Jr. Veterans Affairs Hospital, Hines, IL, p. A193

MARTINEZ, Yvette, Director Human Resources, Sutter Auburn Faith Hospital, Auburn, CA, p. A55

MARTINEZ–NIETO, Arlene, M.D. Chief Medical Officer, First Hospital Panamericano, Cidra, PR, p. A727

MARTING, Bill, Senior Vice President and Chief Financial Officer, The University of Kansas Hospital, Kansas City, KS, p. A246

MARTINSON, Erling, M.D. Medical Director, Nelson County Health System, Mcville, ND, p. A480

MARTINSON, Tiffany, Director Human Resources, Norton Sound Regional Hospital, Nome, AK, p. A30

MARTOCCIO, Debora, R.N. Chief Operating Officer, Florida Hospital at Connerton Long Term Acute Care, Land O'Lakes, FL, p. A134

MARTORANO, Ann, Chief Operating Officer, Halifax Health Medical Center of Daytona Beach, Daytona Beach, FL, p. A127

MARTUCCI, Kathleen, Chief Operating Officer, Helen Hayes Hospital, West Haverstraw, NY, p. A458

MARTZ, Dean
Chief Medical Officer, Providence Holy Family Hospital, Spokane, WA, p. A691
Chief Medical Officer, Providence Sacred Heart Medical Center & Children's Hospital, Spokane, WA, p. A691

MARTZ, Michael, Chief Information Officer, Ohio Valley Medical Center, Wheeling, WV, p. A701

MARVIN, Ryan, Support Services Director, Rawlins County Health Center, Atwood, KS, p. A240

MARX, Kenneth, Chief Executive Officer, Washington County Memorial Hospital, Potosi, MO, p. A378

MARX, Tomasine
Chief Financial Officer, St. John Hospital and Medical Center, Detroit, MI, p. A322
Chief Financial Officer, St. John Macomb–Oakland Hospital, Warren, MI, p. A336

MARX, Troy, Director Human Resources, Upland Hills Health, Dodgeville, WI, p. A704

MARZINZIK, John A., President and Chief Executive Officer, Frisbie Memorial Hospital, Rochester, NH, p. A413

MARZOLF, Steve, R.N. Chief Nursing Officer, Spectrum Health Pennock, Hastings, MI, p. A326

MASHAK–EKERN, Jane, Fiscal Officer, Tomah Veterans Affairs Medical Center, Tomah, WI, p. A717

MASI, George V., Chief Executive Officer, Harris Health System, Houston, TX, p. A624

MASIELLO, Matthew, M.D. Chief Medical Officer, The Children's Institute of Pittsburgh, Pittsburgh, PA, p. A551

MASKELL, Denise, Chief Information Officer, Springfield Hospital Center, Sykesville, MD, p. A303

MASLYN, Jay T., Chief Financial Officer, Nicholas H. Noyes Memorial Hospital, Dansville, NY, p. A438

MASON, Bill A., Chief Executive Officer, Meadow Wood Behavioral Health System, New Castle, DE, p. A119

MASON, Drew, Chief Operating Officer, Grandview Medical Center, Birmingham, AL, p. A16

MASON, Jill K., MS Chief Nursing Officer, Blessing Hospital, Quincy, IL, p. A201

MASON, Kathy, Chief Operating Officer, Atrium Medical Center of Corinth, Corinth, TX, p. A607

MASON, Kathy, R.N. Chief Nursing Officer, LifeCare Hospitals of Dallas, Dallas, TX, p. A610

MASON, Kay, Chief Financial Officer, Texas Health Heart & Vascular Hospital Arlington, Arlington, TX, p. A598

MASON, Keith, Chief Executive Officer, Bailey Medical Center, Owasso, OK, p. A518

MASON, Philip A., Chief Executive Officer, Bournewood Health Systems, Brookline, MA, p. A308

MASON, Phyllis, M.D. Chief Medical Officer, Natchitoches Regional Medical Center, Natchitoches, LA, p. A284

MASON, Rhonda, Vice President of Patient Care Services, Tri–State Memorial Hospital, Clarkston, WA, p. A683

MASON, Sally, Director Human Resources, Golden Plains Community Hospital, Borger, TX, p. A603

MASON, Sandra, MSN Director Nursing Services and Senior Nurse Executive, Robert E. Bush Naval Hospital, Twentynine Palms, CA, p. A97

MASON, Steve, Assistant Superintendent and Chief Operating Officer, Clifton T. Perkins Hospital Center, Jessup, MD, p. A301

MASON, William R., Chief Operating Officer, Brooke Glen Behavioral Hospital, Fort Washington, PA, p. A539

MASON–JONES, Taryn, Chief Nurse Executive, Norristown State Hospital, Norristown, PA, p. A546

MASON–WILLIAMS, Lois, Director of Human Resources, Northwest Ohio Psychiatric Hospital, Toledo, OH, p. A504

MASOOD, Shahid, M.D. Clinical Director, Mildred Mitchell–Bateman Hospital, Huntington, WV, p. A697

MASSA, Rhonda, Director of Nursing, Clarion Psychiatric Center, Clarion, PA, p. A535

MASSAAD, Aziz, M.D. Medical Staff President, Down East Community Hospital, Machias, ME, p. A294

MASSE, Roger A., FACHE, Chief Executive Officer, Ellsworth County Medical Center, Ellsworth, KS, p. A242

MASSELLA, Joan, Administrative Vice President and Chief Nursing Officer, St. Clair Hospital, Pittsburgh, PA, p. A551

MASSENGALE, David, Vice President and Chief Financial Officer, Methodist Hospital, Henderson, KY, p. A261

MASSENGILL, Leigh, Chief Executive Officer, Medical Center of Trinity, Trinity, FL, p. A148

MASSEY, Gina, Vice President Human Resources, Clarity Child Guidance Center, San Antonio, TX, p. A645

MASSEY, Rocco K., Community Chief Executive Officer, Beckley ARH Hospital, Beckley, WV, p. A694

MASSEY, Steven, President and Chief Executive Officer, Westfields Hospital, New Richmond, WI, p. A713

MASSEY, Terry, Chief Fiscal Services, Beckley Veterans Affairs Medical Center, Beckley, WV, p. A694

MASSIELLO, Martin, Executive Vice President and Chief Operating Officer, Eisenhower Medical Center, Rancho Mirage, CA, p. A84

MASSIET, Jill, R.N. Vice President Patient Care, Baptist Health Medical Center–Little Rock, Little Rock, AR, p. A48

MASSIMILLA, John P., FACHE Vice President Administration and Chief Operating Officer, Chambersburg Hospital, Chambersburg, PA, p. A535

MASSINGALE, David, Chief Financial Officer, Methodist Hospital Union County, Morganfield, KY, p. A267

MASSINI, Stephen M., Chief Financial Officer, Penn State Milton S. Hershey Medical Center, Hershey, PA, p. A540

MASSMAN, Patty, Director of Nursing, Granite Falls Municipal Hospital and Manor, Granite Falls, MN, p. A343

MAST, Delvin, R.N. Director of Nursing, Weatherford Regional Hospital, Weatherford, OK, p. A523

MAST, Duane, M.D. Medical Director, Hocking Valley Community Hospital, Logan, OH, p. A497

MAST, Joelle, Ph.D. Chief Medical Officer, Blythedale Children's Hospital, Valhalla, NY, p. A457

MAST, Nathan, Chief Executive Officer, Vibra Hospital of Mahoning Valley, Boardman, OH, p. A485

MASTERS, Emily, Director Human Resources and Marketing, Windom Area Hospital, Windom, MN, p. A353

MASTERS, Ken, Director Information Technology, Chambers Memorial Hospital, Danville, AR, p. A44

MASTERS, Kim, M.D. Medical Director, Saint Simons by–the–Sea Hospital, Saint Simons Island, GA, p. A165

MASTERS, Regina, R.N. Director of Nursing, Continuing Care Hospital, Lexington, KY, p. A263

MASTERSON, David J., President, Sentara Williamsburg Regional Medical Center, Williamsburg, VA, p. A680

MASTERSON, Paul, Chief Financial Officer, Genesis HealthCare System, Zanesville, OH, p. A507

MASTERSON, Sammie, Director Human Resources, Harney District Hospital, Burns, OR, p. A524

MASTERSON, William J., President and Chief Executive Officer, University Medical Center, New Orleans, LA, p. A285

MASTERTON, Melissa, Vice President, Novant Health Presbyterian Medical Center, Charlotte, NC, p. A463

MASTIN, Michelle, Chief Clinical Officer, Curahealth Boston North Shore, Peabody, MA, p. A313

MASTRO, Mary Lou, R.N., President and Chief Executive Officer, Elmhurst Memorial Hospital,, IL, p. A189

MASTROIANNI, Thomas, Administrative Director of Human Resources, Halifax Regional Medical Center, Roanoke Rapids, NC, p. A472

MASTROIANNI, Tom, Vice President Human Resources, New York–Presbyterian/Lawrence Hospital, Bronxville, NY, p. A435

MASTROMANNO, Christopher, Chief Operating Officer, NYC Health + Hospitals / Jacobi,, NY, p. A448

MASTROPIETRO, N. A., M.D. Medical Director, Lancaster Regional Medical Center, Lancaster, PA, p. A542

MATA, Maribel, Director Information Services, Doctors Hospital of Laredo, Laredo, TX, p. A632

MATA–GUERRERO, Rita, Director of Nursing, Weslaco Regional Rehabilitation Hospital, Weslaco, TX, p. A657

MATAMOROS, Mary L., R.N., Chief Executive Officer, Seaside Behavioral Center, New Orleans, LA, p. A285

MATEJICKA, Anthony, D.O. Vice President, Chief Medical Officer, Nyack Hospital, Nyack, NY, p. A451

MATEJKA, Cheryl
Chief Financial Officer, Mercy Hospital St. Louis, Saint Louis, MO, p. A380
Chief Financial Officer, Mercy Hospital Washington, Washington, MO, p. A383

MATENAER, Thomas M., Chief Financial Officer, Banner Gateway Medical Center, Gilbert, AZ, p. A32

MATENS, Brett, Chief Operating Officer, St. David's South Austin Medical Center, Austin, TX, p. A600

MATHAI, George, M.D. Chief of Staff, Three Rivers Hospital, Waverly, TN, p. A594

MATHAI, Matt, M.D. Medical Director, Select Specialty Hospital–Milwaukee, Milwaukee, WI, p. A712

MATHEIS, Tracey, Chief Operating Officer, Moberly Regional Medical Center, Moberly, MO, p. A377

MATHER, Charlotte Marie, R.N. Chief Nursing Officer, Sheridan Memorial Hospital, Sheridan, WY, p. A723

MATHER, Kelly, Chief Executive Officer, Sonoma Valley Hospital, Sonoma, CA, p. A94

MATHER, Martha S., Chief Operating Officer and Vice President, Our Lady of Peace, Louisville, KY, p. A265

MATHERS, Larry, M.D. Chief of Staff, Tennova Newport Medical Center, Newport, TN, p. A591

MATHES, Lisa L., Human Resources Director, Southwest Medical Center, Liberal, KS, p. A248

MATHEW, Finny, Chief Executive Officer, Crossroads Community Hospital, Mount Vernon, IL, p. A197

MATHEW, Mammen, M.D. Chief Rehabilitation Medicine, Woodrow Wilson Rehabilitation Center, Fishersville, VA, p. A670

MATHEW, Toby T., Medical Center Director, Overton Brooks Veterans Affairs Medical Center, Shreveport, LA, p. A287

MATHEWS, Arun, M.D. Chief Medical Officer (Acute), Medical Center Health System, Odessa, TX, p. A639

MATHEWS, Christine W., R.N. Vice President Nursing Services, Geisinger–Lewistown Hospital, Lewistown, PA, p. A543

MATHEWS, Daniel C., M.D. Medical Director, Cedar Crest Hospital and Residential Treatment Center, Belton, TX, p. A602

MATHEWS, Gary, M.D. Medical Doctor, Beaver County Memorial Hospital, Beaver, OK, p. A509

MATHEWS, Nimmy, Acting Director Quality Management, San Carlos Apache Healthcare Corporation, Peridot, AZ, p. A35

MATHEWS, Paul G., CPA, Administrator, Hardtner Medical Center, Olla, LA, p. A286

MATHEWSON, Patricia, Chief Nursing Officer, Tulare Regional Medical Center, Tulare, CA, p. A97

MATHIAS, Matt, Chief Operating Officer, LewisGale Hospital Montgomery, Blacksburg, VA, p. A668

MATHIEU, Angie, System Director Information Technology and Regional Chief Information Officer, The William W. Backus Hospital, Norwich, CT, p. A116

MATHIS, Ashley, Privacy Officer, Columbus Community Hospital, Columbus, TX, p. A607

MATHIS, Jane, Chief Financial Officer, Baylor Surgical Hospital at Fort Worth, Fort Worth, TX, p. A617

MATHIS, Patricia, Associate Director Patient Care Service, Richard L. Roudebush Veterans Affairs Medical Center, Indianapolis, IN, p. A214

MATHIS, Rebecca
    Chief Financial Officer, Adventist La Grange Memorial Hospital, La Grange, IL, p. A194
    Vice President and Chief Financial Officer, AMITA Health Adventist Medical Center – Hinsdale, Hinsdale, IL, p. A193
    Chief Financial Officer, AMITA Health Adventist Medical Center Bolingbrook, Bolingbrook, IL, p. A182

MATHIS, Robin, Director of Human Resources, Methodist Olive Branch Hospital, Olive Branch, MS, p. A363

MATHIS, Susan, R.N., Chief Executive Officer, CenterPointe Hospital, Saint Charles, MO, p. A379

MATHISEN, Arthur, FACHE, President and Chief Executive Officer, Copley Hospital, Morrisville, VT, p. A665

MATHUR, Ashish, M.D. Chief of Staff, Siloam Springs Regional Hospital, Siloam Springs, AR, p. A52

MATHURIN, Jr., Emile, M.D. Medical Director, HealthSouth Rehabilitation Hospital of Humble, LLC, Humble, TX, p. A628

MATHURIN, Venra, Vice President Human Resources, Interfaith Medical Center,, NY, p. A444

MATIS, Sue, Director Human Resources, North Central Health Care, Wausau, WI, p. A718

MATLACK, Victoria L.
    Director and Human Resources Business Partner, OhioHealth Dublin Methodist Hospital, Dublin, OH, p. A494
    Director and Human Resources Business Partner, OhioHealth Grady Memorial Hospital, Delaware, OH, p. A493

MATNEY, James L., President and Chief Executive Officer, Colquitt Regional Medical Center, Moultrie, GA, p. A163

MATNEY, Patty, Human Resources Consultant, Saint Thomas Hickman Hospital, Centerville, TN, p. A580

MATNEY, Tim, Chief Financial Officer, Logan Regional Medical Center, Logan, WV, p. A697

MATOS, Patricia, Chief Nursing Officer, Stewart & Lynda Resnick Neuropsychiatric Hospital at UCLA, Los Angeles, CA, p. A74

MATSINGER, John, D.O. Chief Medical Officer, Virtua Marlton, Marlton, NJ, p. A419

MATT, Robert Lawrence, Vice President and Chief Operating Officer, Hancock Regional Hospital, Greenfield, IN, p. A212

MATTER, Stephanie, Manager Human Resources, LifeCare Hospitals of Wisconsin, Pewaukee, WI, p. A714

MATTERN, Bonnie, Director Human Resources, CHI St. Alexius Health Devils Lake Hospital, Devils Lake, ND, p. A478

MATTERN, Joe, M.D. Chief Medical Officer, Jefferson Healthcare, Port Townsend, WA, p. A688

MATTERN, Karen, Director of Human Resources, Shriners Hospitals for Children–Spokane, Spokane, WA, p. A691

MATTES, Bryan, Associate Administrator, CrossRidge Community Hospital, Wynne, AR, p. A53

MATTES, James A., President and Chief Executive Officer, Grande Ronde Hospital, La Grande, OR, p. A527

MATTES, Mark David, R.N. Assistant Administrator/Patient Care Services, Golden Valley Memorial Healthcare, Clinton, MO, p. A369

MATTEUCCI, Dolly, Executive Director, Napa State Hospital, Napa, CA, p. A78

MATTHEI, Ruth, R.N. Chief Nursing Officer, Westlake Hospital, Melrose Park, IL, p. A196

MATTHEW, Mathew, M.D. Chief Medical Officer, Nazareth Hospital, Philadelphia, PA, p. A549

MATTHEWS, Adora, M.D. Medical Director, HEALTHSOUTH Rehabilitation Hospital of Florence, Florence, SC, p. A565

MATTHEWS, Bryan C., Director, Veterans Health Care System of the Ozarks, Fayetteville, AR, p. A46

MATTHEWS, Carol, Director Human Resources, Saline Memorial Hospital, Benton, AR, p. A43

MATTHEWS, Clinton, President and Chief Executive Officer, Reading Hospital, West Reading, PA, p. A557

MATTHEWS, Deborah, Senior Vice President, Tanner Medical Center–Villa Rica, Villa Rica, GA, p. A168

MATTHEWS, Gwen, MSN, Chief Executive Officer, Ukiah Valley Medical Center, Ukiah, CA, p. A97

MATTHEWS, Lori
    Vice President Information Technology System, Banner Baywood Medical Center, Mesa, AZ, p. A34
    Vice President, Information Technology System, Banner Heart Hospital, Mesa, AZ, p. A34

MATTHEWS, Melissa, Director Human Resources, Dahl Memorial Healthcare Association, Ekalaka, MT, p. A387

MATTHEWS, Michael, Vice President Human Resources, Holland Hospital, Holland, MI, p. A326

MATTHEWS, Oliver, M.D. Chief Medical Officer, Eliza Coffee Memorial Hospital, Florence, AL, p. A20

MATTHEWS, Paul, M.D. President of Medical Staff, Palo Alto County Health System, Emmetsburg, IA, p. A230

MATTHEWS, Ted, Chief Executive Officer, Eastland Memorial Hospital, Eastland, TX, p. A614

MATTHEY, Michael, Facility Chief Information Officer, Louis A. Johnson Veterans Affairs Medical Center, Clarksburg, WV, p. A695

MATTHIAS, Mark, M.D. Vice President of Medical Affairs, St. Cloud Hospital, Saint Cloud, MN, p. A350

MATTHIESSEN, Matthew, Chief Financial Officer, John C. Fremont Healthcare District, Mariposa, CA, p. A76

MATTICE, Gloria, R.N. Director Patient Care, George C Grape Community Hospital, Hamburg, IA, p. A231

MATTINGLY, Marty, Chief Human Resources Officer, St. Mary's Medical Center of Evansville, Evansville, IN, p. A210

MATTISON, Denise, Director Finance and Accounting Services, Mayo Clinic Health System in Eau Claire, Eau Claire, WI, p. A704

MATTISON, Kenneth R., Chief Executive Officer, Florida Hospital New Smyrna, New Smyrna Beach, FL, p. A139

MATTLY, Sheila, Chief Nursing Officer, Wayne County Hospital, Corydon, IA, p. A228

MATTNER, Matthew, Chief Operating Officer, Lutheran Hospital, Cleveland, OH, p. A489

MATTSON, Jodi, Director of Nursing, Cedar Springs Hospital, Colorado Springs, CO, p. A102

MATTSON, Wayne, Management Information Systems Specialist, Rogers Memorial Hospital, Oconomowoc, WI, p. A713

MATUS, Jose, M.D. Director Medical, Carrus Rehabilitation Hospital, Sherman, TX, p. A648

MATUSZKIEWICZ, Marcin, M.D. Chief of Staff and Medical Director, Jerold Phelps Community Hospital, Garberville, CA, p. A64

MATZENBACHER, Elaine, Chief Financial Officer, Washington County Hospital, Nashville, IL, p. A198

MATZIGKEIT, Linda, Senior Vice President Human Resources, Children's Healthcare of Atlanta, Atlanta, GA, p. A152

MAUCK, Jan, R.N. Chief Nursing Officer, Sarasota Memorial Health Care System, Sarasota, FL, p. A145

MAUCK, Lynn, R.N. Chief Operating Officer and Chief Nursing Officer, Fishermen's Hospital, Marathon, FL, p. A135

MAUL, Jim, Chief Information Officer and Director Information Services, Southampton Hospital, Southampton, NY, p. A456

MAURER, Gregory L., Chief Executive Officer, Sheridan Memorial Hospital, Plentywood, MT, p. A390

MAURER, Jackie, Fiscal Officer, Julian F. Keith Alcohol and Drug Abuse Treatment Center, Black Mountain, NC, p. A460

MAURER, Linda, Vice President Patient Care Services, Wilson Memorial Hospital, Sidney, OH, p. A502

MAURER, Marsha L., R.N. Chief Nursing Officer Patient Care Services, Beth Israel Deaconess Medical Center, Boston, MA, p. A306

MAURICE, Timothy, Chief Financial Officer, University of California, Davis Medical Center, Sacramento, CA, p. A87

MAURIELLO, Renee, Vice President, Chief Nursing Officer, Nyack Hospital, Nyack, NY, p. A451

MAURIN, Michael J., Chief Financial Officer, Southern Surgical Hospital, Slidell, LA, p. A288

MAUST, Richard, Chief Information Officer, RMC Jacksonville, Jacksonville, AL, p. A22

MAVROMATIS, Lou, Vice President Information Technology, MedStar Southern Maryland Hospital Center, Clinton, MD, p. A300

MAX, Cindy, Chief Nursing Officer, Shriners Hospitals for Children–Philadelphia, Philadelphia, PA, p. A549

MAXEY, Matt, R.N. Director of Nursing, Brookhaven Hospital, Tulsa, OK, p. A521

MAXFIELD, Matt T., FACHE, Chief Executive Officer, Seton Medical Center Harker Heights, Harker Heights, TX, p. A622

MAXIE, Bryan K.
    Administrator, Marion General Hospital, Columbia, MS, p. A357
    Administrator, Walthall County General Hospital, Tylertown, MS, p. A365

MAXSON, Diana, Director Human Resources, Trinity Hospital of Augusta, Augusta, GA, p. A154

MAXWELL, Dale, Executive Vice President and Chief Financial Officer, Presbyterian Hospital, Albuquerque, NM, p. A428

MAXWELL, Jody, Manager Business Office, Smith County Memorial Hospital, Smith Center, KS, p. A254

MAXWELL, John, Chief Executive Officer, Central Carolina Hospital, Sanford, NC, p. A473

MAXWELL, Phillip, Administrator, Compass Behavioral Center of Alexandria, Alexandria, LA, p. A271

MAXWELL, Ronnie, Director Information Systems, Glenwood Regional Medical Center, West Monroe, LA, p. A289

MAY, David, Chief of Staff, Richland Hospital, Richland Center, WI, p. A715

MAY, Frank, Chief Executive Officer, Yampa Valley Medical Center, Steamboat Springs, CO, p. A110

MAY, John, Chief Executive Officer, Sistersville General Hospital, Sistersville, WV, p. A700

MAY, Kevin B.
    System Director Finance, Charles A. Cannon Memorial Hospital, Newland, NC, p. A471
    Chief Financial Officer, Watauga Medical Center, Boone, NC, p. A461

MAY, Robin, Director Information Systems, Platte County Memorial Hospital, Wheatland, WY, p. A724

MAY, Ronald B., M.D. Vice President Medical Affairs, CarolinaEast Health System, New Bern, NC, p. A470

MAY, Scott, Area Director Technology, Kaiser Permanente Santa Clara Medical Center, Santa Clara, CA, p. A93

MAY, Sonja, Director Human Resources, Morton County Health System, Elkhart, KS, p. A242

MAY, Todd, M.D. Chief Medical Officer, Zuckerberg San Francisco General Hospital and Trauma Center, San Francisco, CA, p. A91

MAY, Troy, Chief Information Officer, University of Louisville Hospital, Louisville, KY, p. A265

MAY, Walter E., President and Chief Executive Officer, Pikeville Medical Center, Pikeville, KY, p. A268

MAY, William J., Administrator, Hawaii State Hospital, Kaneohe, HI, p. A172

MAYBEN, Casey, Chief Nursing Officer, East Texas Medical Center Pittsburg, Pittsburg, TX, p. A641

MAYER, David, Chief of Staff, Wayne County Hospital, Monticello, KY, p. A266

MAYER, Karen, R.N. Senior Vice President Patient Care Services, Rush Oak Park Hospital, Oak Park, IL, p. A199

MAYER, Peter, Director Information Systems, Bakersfield Heart Hospital, Bakersfield, CA, p. A55

MAYER, William, M.D. Vice President Medical Staff Services, St. Mary's Healthcare, Amsterdam, NY, p. A434

MAYEUX–HEBERT, Angela, Vice President Medical Affairs, Lafayette General Medical Center, Lafayette, LA, p. A280

MAYEWSKI, Raymond, M.D
    Chief Medical Officer, Highland Hospital, Rochester, NY, p. A454
    Chief Medical Officer, Strong Memorial Hospital of the University of Rochester, Rochester, NY, p. A454

MAYFIELD, Michael Bradley, M.D. Chief of Staff, Chicot Memorial Medical Center, Lake Village, AR, p. A48

MAYFIELD, William, M.D. Chief of Staff, TriStar StoneCrest Medical Center, Smyrna, TN, p. A593

MAYHLE, Douglas, M.D. Medical Director, Nicholas H. Noyes Memorial Hospital, Dansville, NY, p. A438

MAYLE, Connie, Vice President Administrative Services, UPMC Horizon, Greenville, PA, p. A539

MAYNARD, Bob, Chief Information Officer, Fairview Regional Medical Center, Fairview, OK, p. A512

MAYNARD, Rhonda, Chief Financial Officer, Tennova Physicians Regional Medical Center, Knoxville, TN, p. A586

MAYO, Andrew, Ph.D., Chief Executive Officer and Managing Director, North Star Behavioral Health System, Anchorage, AK, p. A28

MAYO, Cindy, FACHE, Chief Executive Officer, Providence Medford Medical Center, Medford, OR, p. A528

MAYO, Elena, Manager, Human Resources, San Dimas Community Hospital, San Dimas, CA, p. A89

MAYO, Hal, Chief Financial Officer, Liberty Dayton Regional Medical Center, Liberty, TX, p. A632

MAYO, Jim, M.D. Clinical Director, Cherry Hospital, Goldsboro, NC, p. A466

MAYO, Michael A., FACHE, President, Baptist Medical Center Jacksonville, Jacksonville, FL, p. A131

MAYO, Randy, Director Information Technology, William Newton Hospital, Winfield, KS, p. A256

MAYO, Robert, M.D
  Executive Vice President, Chief Medical Officer, Newark–Wayne Community Hospital, Newark, NY, p. A450
  Chief Medical Officer, Rochester General Hospital, Rochester, NY, p. A454
MAYO, Sarah, Vice President Financial Services, UNC Lenoir Healthcare, Kinston, NC, p. A468
MAYS, Christine, R.N
  Chief Operating Officer and Chief Nurse Executive, Saint Joseph East, Lexington, KY, p. A263
  Chief Operating Officer and Chief Nurse Executive, Saint Joseph Hospital, Lexington, KY, p. A263
MAYS, Dawn, Chief Nursing Officer, Scott Memorial Hospital, Scottsburg, IN, p. A221
MAYS, Raymond, M.D. Medical Director, River Crest Hospital, San Angelo, TX, p. A644
MAYS, Sherrie, MSN Vice President and Chief Nursing Officer, Baptist Health Corbin, Corbin, KY, p. A258
MAYSENT, Patty, Interim Chief Executive Officer, UC San Diego Health, San Diego, CA, p. A89
MAYSILLES, Nancy, R.N. Chief Nursing Officer, Medical Center of Trinity, Trinity, FL, p. A148
MAYSON, Mark J., M.D. Medical Director, Palmetto Health Baptist, Columbia, SC, p. A564
MAZANEC, Lori, Interim Chief Executive Officer, Box Butte General Hospital, Alliance, NE, p. A393
MAZOUR, Linda, M.D. President, Franklin County Memorial Hospital, Franklin, NE, p. A395
MAZUREK, Michele A., Interim Vice President Patient Care Services and Chief Nursing Officer, Mount Sinai Hospital, Chicago, IL, p. A185
MAZZA, Mary, Director Human Resources, HEALTHSOUTH Rehabilitation Hospital of Western Massachusetts, Ludlow, MA, p. A311
MAZZARELLA, Frank, M.D. Chief Medical Officer, Clara Maass Medical Center, Belleville, NJ, p. A414
MAZZARELLI, Anthony J., JD Senior Executive Vice President Chief Physician Executive, Cooper University Health Care, Camden, NJ, p. A415
MAZZO, Joe, Chief Operating Officer, Lakeview Hospital, Bountiful, UT, p. A659
MAZZO, Joseph, Chief Operating Officer, Saint Thomas River Park Hospital, Mc Minnville, TN, p. A588
MAZZOLA, Joe, D.O. Senior Vice President Medical Affairs and Chief Medical Officer, Carolinas Healthcare System Blue Ridge, Morganton, NC, p. A470
MAZZONI, Dean, President and Chief Executive Officer, Franciscan St. Anthony Health – Michigan City, Michigan City, IN, p. A218
MAZZUCA, Darryl, Director Management Information Systems, Little Company of Mary Hospital and Health Care Centers, Evergreen Park, IL, p. A190
MBENGA, Saul, Manager Information Technology, Alliance HealthCare System, Holly Springs, MS, p. A359
MC BRIDE, Brian, Chief Financial Officer, Rice Medical Center, Eagle Lake, TX, p. A614
MC KELLAR, Grey, Chief Operating Officer and Director of Performance Improvement and Risk, Kingwood Pines Hospital, Kingwood, TX, p. A631
MCADAMS, David, Chief Financial Officer, Lindner Center of HOPE, Mason, OH, p. A498
MCADOO, Jackie, Chief Financial Officer, Grady Memorial Hospital, Chickasha, OK, p. A510
MCAFEE, Thomas J., President, North Market, Northwestern Lake Forest Hospital, Lake Forest, IL, p. A194
MCALISTER, Stephanie, Controller, Tippah County Hospital, Ripley, MS, p. A364
MCALLISTER, Guy, Vice President and Chief Information Officer, Tift Regional Medical Center, Tifton, GA, p. A167
MCALLISTER, Ric, Chief Executive Officer, Windsor–Laurelwood Center for Behavioral Medicine, Willoughby, OH, p. A506
MCALLISTER, Yvonne, Senior Director Human Resources, Southern Maine Health Care – Biddeford Medical Center, Biddeford, ME, p. A292
MCALOON, Richard, Vice President Human Resources, Hartford Hospital, Hartford, CT, p. A114
MCANDREWS, Kevin
  Vice President Human Resources, Nexus Specialty Hospital, Shenandoah, TX, p. A648
  Vice President, Human Resources, Nexus Specialty Hospital The Woodlands, The Woodlands, TX, p. A652
MCARTHUR, Ronald L., Chief Executive Officer, Summit Healthcare Regional Medical Center, Show Low, AZ, p. A39
MCARTOR, Dana, R.N. Director of Nursing, Perkins County Health Services, Grant, NE, p. A396
MCAULIFFE, Gregory, M.D
  Chief Medical Officer, San Luis Valley Health, Alamosa, CO, p. A101
  Chief Medical Officer, San Luis Valley Health Conejos County Hospital, La Jara, CO, p. A107

MCAULIFFE, John, M.D. Medical Director, Sauk Prairie Healthcare, Prairie Du Sac, WI, p. A714
MCAVOY, Tim, M.D. Medical Director, Rehabilitation Hospital of Wisconsin, Waukesha, WI, p. A718
MCBEE, Gala, Administrator, Muscogee Creek Nation Physical Rehabilitation Center, Okmulgee, OK, p. A518
MCBREARTY, Michael, M.D. Vice President Medical Affairs, Thomas Hospital, Fairhope, AL, p. A20
MCBRIDE, Anne, Chief Executive Officer, Regional Hospital for Respiratory and Complex Care, Burien, WA, p. A683
MCBRIDE, Brandon, Operations Officer, Logan Regional Hospital, Logan, UT, p. A660
MCBRIDE, Dina, Chief Operating Officer and Director Human Resources, East Adams Rural Healthcare, Ritzville, WA, p. A689
MCBRIDE, Grace, Regional Chief Nursing Officer, Presence Mercy Medical Center, Aurora, IL, p. A180
MCBRIDE, Kate, Chief Operating Officer, Poplar Springs Hospital, Petersburg, VA, p. A676
MCBRIDE, Lamar, Chief Operating Officer, Northern Colorado Long Term Acute Hospital, Johnstown, CO, p. A107
MCBRIDE, III, Thomas Y., Executive Vice President and Chief Financial Officer, Gwinnett Hospital System, Lawrenceville, GA, p. A162
MCBROOM, Robert, M.D. Medical Director, Promise Hospital of Wichita Falls, Wichita Falls, TX, p. A657
MCBRYDE, Robin, Chief Information Officer, Alexandria Veterans Affairs Health Care System, Pineville, LA, p. A286
MCCAA, Karen, R.N. Vice President Patient Care Services and Chief Nursing Officer, Baptist Medical Center South, Montgomery, AL, p. A23
MCCABE, John B., M.D., Chief Executive Officer, Upstate University Hospital, Syracuse, NY, p. A457
MCCABE, John P., Executive Vice President, Shriners Hospitals for Children, Tampa, FL, p. B123
MCCABE, Mary, Chief Financial Officer, North Colorado Medical Center, Greeley, CO, p. A106
MCCABE, Patrick, Senior Vice President Finance and Chief Financial Officer, Bridgeport Hospital, Bridgeport, CT, p. A113
MCCABE Jr., Patrick G., FACHE, President and Chief Executive Officer, Levi Hospital, Hot Springs National Park, AR, p. A47
MCCABE, Rhonda, Chief Executive Officer, Physicians' Specialty Hospital, Fayetteville, AR, p. A45
MCCABE, Steve, Chief Executive Officer, Hill Crest Behavioral Health Services, Birmingham, AL, p. A16
MCCAFFERTY, Michael, Chief Executive Officer, Sheridan Memorial Hospital, Sheridan, WY, p. A723
MCCAFFREY, Roberta, Vice President and Chief Nursing Officer, Methodist Hospital of Southern California, Arcadia, CA, p. A55
MCCAHILL, Connie, R.N., President and Chief Executive Officer, Cameron Memorial Community Hospital, Angola, IN, p. A206
MCCAHILL, Mary, Chief Nursing Officer, Thorek Memorial Hospital, Chicago, IL, p. A187
MCCAIN, Carolyn, Director Human Resources, Northern Colorado Rehabilitation Hospital, Johnstown, CO, p. A107
MCCAIN, Rebecca J., Chief Executive Officer, Electra Memorial Hospital, Electra, TX, p. A616
MCCALL, Brad, JD,
  Chief Executive Officer, Physicians Surgical Hospital – Panhandle Campus, Amarillo, TX, p. A596
  Chief Executive Officer, Physicians Surgical Hospital – Quail Creek, Amarillo, TX, p. A596
MCCALL, Debbie, Director Human Resources, WK Bossier Health Center, Bossier City, LA, p. A274
MCCALL, Harlo, Chief Executive Officer, HEALTHSOUTH Rehabilitation Hospital of Texarkana, Texarkana, TX, p. A652
MCCALL, Lee, Chief Executive Officer, Neshoba County General Hospital, Philadelphia, MS, p. A363
MCCALL, Pam, Director Human Resources, Heatherhill Care Communities, Chardon, OH, p. A486
MCCALLISTER, Bob, Director Human Resources, Baptist Memorial Hospital–Golden Triangle, Columbus, MS, p. A357
MCCALLISTER, Darla, Chief Financial Officer, Lakeside Women's Hospital, Oklahoma City, OK, p. A516
MCCALLISTER, Dianne, M.D. Chief Medical Officer, Medical Center of Aurora, Aurora, CO, p. A101
MCCALLISTER, Sean, Administrator, St. Luke's McCall, McCall, ID, p. A177
MCCAMPBELL, Kellie, Coordinator Human Resources, Kindred Hospital–Chattanooga, Chattanooga, TN, p. A580
MCCAMPBELL, Marcia, M.D. Chief Medical Officer, Shasta Regional Medical Center, Redding, CA, p. A84
MCCANCE, Dan, D.O. Chief of Staff, Hillsdale Hospital, Hillsdale, MI, p. A326
MCCANDLESS, Barbara, Vice President Human Resources, St. Mary's Hospital, Troy, NY, p. A457
MCCANDLESS, David, Vice President Medical Affairs, UPMC Northwest, Seneca, PA, p. A554

MCCANN, Barbara, Director Human Resources, Sunrise Canyon Hospital, Lubbock, TX, p. A634
MCCANN, Kyle, Chief Operating Officer, St. Joseph's Hospital, Savannah, GA, p. A166
MCCANN, Lew, Director Management Information Systems, OSF Holy Family Medical Center, Monmouth, IL, p. A197
MCCARTAN, Mary E., Manager Human Resources, VA Long Beach Healthcare System, Long Beach, CA, p. A70
MCCARTER, Alyssa, Chief Financial Officer, W. J. Mangold Memorial Hospital, Lockney, TX, p. A633
MCCARTER, Scott, Chief Information Officer, Karmanos Cancer Center, Detroit, MI, p. A322
MCCARTHY, Barbara, Chief Executive Officer, Specialty Hospital Jacksonville, Jacksonville, FL, p. A132
MCCARTHY, Brian, Director Information Systems, Memorial Hospital of Salem County, Salem, NJ, p. A423
MCCARTHY, Cynthia L., MS Chief Nursing Officer, Texas Health Harris Methodist Hospital Stephenville, Stephenville, TX, p. A650
MCCARTHY, Linda M., R.N. VP/ Chief Nursing Officer, Citrus Memorial Health System, Inverness, FL, p. A131
MCCARTHY, Rick, Chief Information Officer, St. Vincent's Medical Center, Bridgeport, CT, p. A113
MCCARTHY, Tim, President Puerto Rico Division, First Hospital Panamericano, Cidra, PR, p. A727
MCCARTY, Daniel P., Chief Operating Officer, Orange City Area Health System, Orange City, IA, p. A235
MCCARTY, Jacob M., Chief Executive Officer, Kindred Hospital–San Francisco Bay Area, San Leandro, CA, p. A92
MCCARTY, Maryland, Director Information Systems, Wellstar Atlanta Medical Center, Atlanta, GA, p. A153
MCCARTY, Melany, R.N. Chief Clinical Officer, Vibra Hospital of Amarillo, Amarillo, TX, p. A596
MCCARTY, Tim, Chief Information Officer, OakBend Medical Center, Richmond, TX, p. A643
MCCARTY, Wendy, Director Human Resources, Hillsboro Community Hospital, Hillsboro, KS, p. A244
MCCASLIN, Anna, Chief Financial Officer, Nebraska Orthopaedic Hospital, Omaha, NE, p. A400
MCCASLIN, Jami, Director Human Resources, Providence Hood River Memorial Hospital, Hood River, OR, p. A526
MCCAUGHEY, James, Chief Strategy Officer, Lucile Salter Packard Children's Hospital Stanford, Palo Alto, CA, p. A82
MCCAULEY, Cynthia, Chief Financial Officer, Good Samaritan Medical Center, West Palm Beach, FL, p. A149
MCCAULEY, Dudley, Controller, Lincoln County Medical Center, Ruidoso, NM, p. A431
MCCAULEY, Jason, Administrator, Jane Phillips Nowata Health Center, Nowata, OK, p. A515
MCCAULEY, Sue E., Director Finance, Baum Harmon Mercy Hospital, Primghar, IA, p. A236
MCCAWLEY, Thomas J., Vice President, Beloit Health System, Beloit, WI, p. A703
MCCHESNEY, Lisa D., R.N. Senior Director Information Systems, UPMC Hamot, Erie, PA, p. A538
MCCLAIN, Barbara, Human Resources, Horton Community Hospital, Horton, KS, p. A245
MCCLAIN, James, Deputy Director, Clement J. Zablocki Veterans Affairs Medical Center, Milwaukee, WI, p. A711
MCCLAIN, Richard, M.D. Chief Medical Officer, Chickasaw Nation Medical Center, Ada, OK, p. A508
MCCLANAHAN, Gary, Chief Information Officer, Sequoyah Memorial Hospital, Sallisaw, OK, p. A519
MCCLARIGAN, Linda, R.N. Chief Nursing Officer, Adirondack Medical Center, Saranac Lake, NY, p. A455
MCCLASKEY, Cynthia, Ph.D., Director, Southwestern Virginia Mental Health Institute, Marion, VA, p. A673
MCCLEARY, Heather, Director Human Resources, Coulee Medical Center, Grand Coulee, WA, p. A685
MCCLEESE, Randy, Vice President Information Services and Chief Information Officer, St. Claire Regional Medical Center, Morehead, KY, p. A267
MCCLELLAN, Ashley, Chief Executive Officer, Woman's Hospital of Texas, Houston, TX, p. A628
MCCLELLAN, Kathryn, Chief Information Officer, Memorial Health, Savannah, GA, p. A166
MCCLELLAND, Michele
  Vice President Human Resources, Northwestern Medicine Kishwaukee Hospital, DeKalb, IL, p. A188
  Vice President Human Resources, Northwestern Medicine Valley West Hospital, Sandwich, IL, p. A202
MCCLELLAND, Patricia, Director Human Resources, South Texas Health System, Edinburg, TX, p. A614
MCCLENDON, Pat, MSN Chief Nursing Officer, Palmdale Regional Medical Center, Palmdale, CA, p. A81
MCCLINTIC, James, M.D. Vice President Medical Affairs, St. Anthony's Hospital, Saint Petersburg, FL, p. A144
MCCLINTICK, Cliff, Chief Information Officer, Lindner Center of HOPE, Mason, OH, p. A498

MCCLOSKEY, Louis, Chief Human Resources, Wilmington Veterans Affairs Medical Center, Wilmington, DE, p. A120

MCCLUNG, James W., Chief Executive Officer, HEALTHSOUTH Rehabilitation Hospital of Alexandria, Alexandria, LA, p. A271

MCCLUNG, Lyle, M.D. Chief of Staff, Carilion Stonewall Jackson Hospital, Lexington, VA, p. A672

MCCLURE, David K., President and Chief Executive Officer, Camden Clark Medical Center, Parkersburg, WV, p. A698

MCCLURE, Kenneth, M.D. Chief of Staff, Longview Regional Medical Center, Longview, TX, p. A633

MCCLURE, Thomas, M.D. Vice President Medical Affairs and Chief Medical Officer, Allegheny Valley Hospital, Natrona Heights, PA, p. A546

MCCLURG, Cathy, Director Human Resources, William Newton Hospital, Winfield, KS, p. A256

MCCLURG, Chris, Vice President Finance and Chief Financial Officer, St. Claire Regional Medical Center, Morehead, KY, p. A267

MCCLURKAN, Mac, Chief Information Officer, Oaklawn Hospital, Marshall, MI, p. A330

MCCLUSKEY, Diane, Chief Human Resources Officer, Placentia–Linda Hospital, Placentia, CA, p. A83

MCCLUSKEY, Scott Elton, Chief Financial Officer, Tyler County Hospital, Woodville, TX, p. A658

MCCLUSKEY, Tabb, M.D. Chief Medical Officer, Hendricks Community Hospital Association, Hendricks, MN, p. A344

MCCLUSKY, Derek, M.D. Chief of Staff, Northern Louisiana Medical Center, Ruston, LA, p. A287

MCCLYMONT, Troy, Chief Information Technology Officer, Sheridan Memorial Hospital, Plentywood, MT, p. A390

MCCOBB, David, Chief Information Officer, Foothill Presbyterian Hospital, Glendora, CA, p. A65

MCCOIC, Kristie, Clinic Operations Officer and Director Human Resources, Gundersen St. Joseph's Hospital and Clinics, Hillsboro, WI, p. A707

MCCOLLUM, Joann, Chief Nursing Officer, Bolivar Medical Center, Cleveland, MS, p. A356

MCCOLLUM, Kathleen, Senior Vice President, Clinical Integration and Chief Operating Officer, University of Maryland Baltimore Washington Medical Center, Glen Burnie, MD, p. A301

MCCOLLUM, Ken, Vice President, Human Resources, NorthBay Medical Center, Fairfield, CA, p. A62

MCCOLM, Denni, Chief Information Officer, Citizens Memorial Hospital, Bolivar, MO, p. A367

MCCOMB, Canise A., Director Human Resources, Graham Hospital Association, Canton, IL, p. A182

MCCONLOGUE, Lisa M., Ph.D., Chief Executive Officer and Managing Director, Fairmount Behavioral Health System, Philadelphia, PA, p. A547

MCCONNELL, George, Director, Earle E. Morris Alcohol and Drug Treatment Center, Columbia, SC, p. A564

MCCONNELL, John D., M.D., Chief Executive Officer, Wake Forest Baptist Health, Winston–Salem, NC, p. B153

MCCONNELL, John D., M.D., Chief Executive Officer, Wake Forest Baptist Medical Center, Winston–Salem, NC, p. A476

MCCONNELL, Linda M., R.N. Associate Medical Center Director Patient Care Services, James H. Quillen Veterans Affairs Medical Center, Mountain Home, TN, p. A590

MCCONNELL, Patrick G., Chief Financial Officer, West Park Hospital, Cody, WY, p. A722

MCCONNELL, Ron, Chief Operating Officer, UPMC Altoona, Altoona, PA, p. A532

MCCONNELL, William, Ph.D. Vice President Operations and Strategic Outreach, Mercy Regional Medical Center, Durango, CO, p. A104

MCCORD, Sam, Chief Nursing Officer, Willow Springs Center, Reno, NV, p. A408

MCCORMACK, J. David, Chief Executive Officer, Vaughan Regional Medical Center, Selma, AL, p. A25

MCCORMACK, Jane, R.N. Vice President, Chief Nursing Officer and Nursing and Patient Care Services, Unity Hospital, Rochester, NY, p. A454

MCCORMACK, Julie, Chief Operating Officer, Havasu Regional Medical Center, Lake Havasu City, AZ, p. A34

MCCORMICK, Brad, Chief Financial Officer, Natchitoches Regional Medical Center, Natchitoches, LA, p. A284

MCCORMICK, Daniel, M.D. Vice President Medical Staff Affairs, Franciscan St. Anthony Health – Crown Point, Crown Point, IN, p. A209

MCCORMICK, Dee Dawn, Director Personnel and Human Resources, Coon Memorial Hospital, Dalhart, TX, p. A609

MCCORMICK, Jason, Interim Chief Financial Officer, Melissa Memorial Hospital, Holyoke, CO, p. A107

MCCORMICK, Jayne, M.D. Chief Medical Officer CDS, Presbyterian Hospital, Albuquerque, NM, p. A428

MCCORMICK, John, President and Chief Executive Officer, Oak Valley Hospital District, Oakdale, CA, p. A80

MCCORMICK, Martha, Chief Executive Officer, Unity Medical Center, Manchester, TN, p. A587

MCCORMICK, Pam, Director Human Resources, Permian Regional Medical Center, Andrews, TX, p. A597

MCCOWN, Fran, Administrator, Haskell Memorial Hospital, Haskell, TX, p. A622

MCCOY, Adriene, MS Corporate Vice President, Baptist Health South Florida, Homestead Hospital, Homestead, FL, p. A131

MCCOY, Andrea C.S., M.D. Chief Medical Officer, Cape Regional Medical Center, Cape May Court House, NJ, p. A415

MCCOY, Craig, Chief Executive Officer, Bon Secours St. Francis Health System, Greenville, SC, p. A566

MCCOY, Doug, Chief Executive Officer, Kindred Hospital Las Vegas–Sahara, Las Vegas, NV, p. A406

MCCOY, Janice M., MS Chief Clinical Officer, Promise Hospital of Florida at The Villages, Oxford, FL, p. A141

MCCOY, Jessica, Director Human Resources, Cedar Springs Hospital, Colorado Springs, CO, p. A102

MCCOY, Mike, Chief Executive Officer, Chambers Memorial Hospital, Danville, AR, p. A44

MCCOY, Shawn W., Chief Administrative Officer, Deaconess Hospital, Evansville, IN, p. A210

MCCOY, Stephanie, President and Chief Executive Officer, Jackson General Hospital, Ripley, WV, p. A699

MCCRACKEN, Gail, M.D. Medical Director, Baptist Health Extended Care Hospital, Little Rock, AR, p. A48

MCCRANIE, Robbie, Director Human Resources, Plano Specialty Hospital, Plano, TX, p. A642

MCCRAW, Elizabeth, Vice President, Human Resources, CaroMont Regional Medical Center, Gastonia, NC, p. A465

MCCRAW, Nicki, Assistant Vice President Human Resources, UW Medicine/Harborview Medical Center, Seattle, WA, p. A690

MCCREA, Kim, Chief Human Resources Officer, Ortonville Area Health Services, Ortonville, MN, p. A348

MCCREA, Yvette, Chief Human Resources, Winn Army Community Hospital, Hinesville, GA, p. A160

MCCREARY, Michael, Chief of Services, Mercy Hospital Washington, Washington, MO, p. A383

MCCREARY, William, Vice President and Chief Information Officer, The University of Toledo Medical Center, Toledo, OH, p. A504

MCCRIMMON, Scott, Manager Information Technology, Northern Arizona Veterans Affairs Health Care System, Prescott, AZ, p. A37

MCCROSKEY, Mark, Vice President Operations, Northeastern Health System, Tahlequah, OK, p. A520

MCCUE, Jennifer, Director Patient Care, Summersville Regional Medical Center, Summersville, WV, p. A700

MCCUE, Raymond, M.D. Chief Medical Officer, Bon Secours–DePaul Medical Center, Norfolk, VA, p. A674

MCCUE, Robert N., Vice President Finance, Mid Coast Hospital, Brunswick, ME, p. A292

MCCUE, Steven
Chief Financial Officer, Clinton Hospital, Clinton, MA, p. A309
Chief Financial Officer, UMass Memorial–Marlborough Hospital, Marlborough, MA, p. A312

MCCULLEY, Becky, Chief Operations Officer, University of Texas Southwestern Medical Center, Dallas, TX, p. A612

MCCULLEY, Larry W., President and Chief Executive Officer, Touchette Regional Hospital, Centreville, IL, p. A183

MCCULLOCH, Greg, CPA Vice President of Finance and Chief Financial Officer, Sonora Regional Medical Center, Sonora, CA, p. A94

MCCULLOCH, Liz, Chief Information Resource Management Systems, Cheyenne Veterans Affairs Medical Center, Cheyenne, WY, p. A722

MCCULLOUGH, Barbara A., Vice President Human Resources, Washington Hospital, Washington, PA, p. A556

MCCULLOUGH, Bobby, Chief Operating Officer, Memorial Hospital Jacksonville, Jacksonville, FL, p. A131

MCCULLOUGH, Mary Kelly, Associate Director Patient Care Services, Lexington Veterans Affairs Medical Center, Lexington, KY, p. A263

MCCULLOUGH, Patrick, M.D. Chief Medical Services, Summit Behavioral Healthcare, Cincinnati, OH, p. A488

MCCULLOUGH, Wadra, Chief Nursing Officer, Spalding Regional Hospital, Griffin, GA, p. A160

MCCUNE, Anne, Chief Operating Officer, Lucile Salter Packard Children's Hospital Stanford, Palo Alto, CA, p. A82

MCCUNE, Becky, Director Human Resources, Community Relations and Education, Coffeyville Regional Medical Center, Coffeyville, KS, p. A241

MCCURDY, Brent, Director Management Information, St. Croix Regional Medical Center, St. Croix Falls, WI, p. A716

MCCURDY, Judy, R.N. Vice President and Chief Nursing Officer, St. Vincent Medical Center, Los Angeles, CA, p. A74

MCCURLEY, John, M.D. Chief Medical Officer, Bon Secours St. Francis Medical Center, Midlothian, VA, p. A673

MCCUTCHAN, Matt, Chief Financial Officer, Greater Regional Medical Center, Creston, IA, p. A228

MCCUTCHEON, Edna I.
Chief Executive Officer, Norristown State Hospital, Norristown, PA, p. A546
Chief Executive Officer, Torrance State Hospital, Torrance, PA, p. A555

MCCUTCHEON, Jr., Henry, Chief Financial Officer, Lake City Community Hospital, Lake City, SC, p. A567

MCDADE, E., R.N.Walter P. Reuther Psychiatric Hospital, Westland, MI, p. A336

MCDANALD, Matt, M.D. Chief Medical Officer, Baptist Health La Grange, La Grange, KY, p. A262

MCDANEL, Joyce
Vice President Human Resources and Education, UnityPoint Health – Iowa Methodist Medical Center, Des Moines, IA, p. A229
Vice President Human Resources and Education, UnityPoint Health–Iowa Lutheran Hospital, Des Moines, IA, p. A229

MCDANIEL, Amy, Administrator and Chief Executive Officer, Iowa Specialty Hospital–Belmond, Belmond, IA, p. A225

MCDANIEL, Burton, M.D. Medical Director, Roosevelt Warm Springs Rehabilitation and Specialty Hospitals – Rehab, Warm Springs, GA, p. A168

MCDANIEL, Graciela, Chief Financial Officer, Philadelphia Veterans Affairs Medical Center, Philadelphia, PA, p. A549

MCDANIEL, Kim, Director Human Resources, HEALTHSOUTH Rehabilitation Hospital of Montgomery, Montgomery, AL, p. A23

MCDANIEL, LaDonna, Financial Manager, Prattville Baptist Hospital, Prattville, AL, p. A25

MCDANIEL, Lisa A., Chief Human Resources Officer, Samaritan Healthcare, Moses Lake, WA, p. A686

MCDANIEL, Randy, Information Systems Director, Jackson Purchase Medical Center, Mayfield, KY, p. A266

MCDANIEL, Suzie Q., Chief Human Resource Officer, Bay Area Hospital, Coos Bay, OR, p. A525

MCDANIEL, Jr., W. Burton, M.D. Chief Medical Officer, Roosevelt Warm Springs Rehabilitation and Specialty Hospitals – LTAC, Warm Springs, GA, p. A168

MCDANNALD, E.R., Interim Chief Executive Officer, Taylor Regional Hospital, Hawkinsville, GA, p. A160

MCDAVID, Clarence, Vice President Human Resources, Rose Medical Center, Denver, CO, p. A104

MCDERMOTT, James, M.D. Chief of Staff, Sedan City Hospital, Sedan, KS, p. A253

MCDERMOTT, Mary, MS Senior Vice President Patient Care Services and Chief Nursing Officer, Phelps Memorial Hospital Center, Sleepy Hollow, NY, p. A455

MCDERMOTT, Michael P., M.D., President and Chief Executive Officer, Mary Washington Healthcare, Fredericksburg, VA, p. B85

MCDERMOTT, Michael P., M.D.,
President and Chief Executive Officer, Mary Washington Hospital, Fredericksburg, VA, p. A670
President and Chief Executive Officer, Stafford Hospital, Stafford, VA, p. A679

MCDERMOTT, Suzan, Director, Human Resources, Gouverneur Hospital, Gouverneur, NY, p. A439

MCDERMOTT–LORD, Sheila, Chief Executive Officer, Haven Behavioral Senior Care of Albuquerque, Albuquerque, NM, p. A427

MCDEVITT, Mike, Chief Information Officer, Children's of Alabama, Birmingham, AL, p. A16

MCDEVITT, Robert J., M.D. Chief of Staff, Wilson Memorial Hospital, Sidney, OH, p. A502

MCDIVITT, Robert P., FACHE, Director, Veterans Affairs Ann Arbor Healthcare System, Ann Arbor, MI, p. A318

MCDONAGH, Andrew, M.D. Chief Medical Officer, Aurora West Allis Medical Center, West Allis, WI, p. A719

MCDONALD, Amanda, MSN Chief Nurse Executive, Kerrville State Hospital, Kerrville, TX, p. A630

MCDONALD, Carl, Regional Director Human Resources, Broward Health Imperial Point, Fort Lauderdale, FL, p. A128

MCDONALD, Connie, Chief Financial Officer, Marion Veterans Affairs Medical Center, Marion, IL, p. A195

MCDONALD, Edward A., Chief Financial Officer, St. Helena Hospital Center for Behavioral Health, Vallejo, CA, p. A98

MCDONALD, Elizabeth, Director Human Resources, Wayne Memorial Hospital, Honesdale, PA, p. A540

MCDONALD, Frederick Joseph, Commanding Officer, Naval Hospital Oak Harbor, Oak Harbor, WA, p. A687

MCDONALD, Gary
Associate Administrator Human Resources, Stone County Medical Center, Mountain View, AR, p. A50
Chief Support Services Officer, White River Medical Center, Batesville, AR, p. A43

MCDONALD, Gregory, Vice President Finance and Chief Financial Officer, Roswell Park Cancer Institute, Buffalo, NY, p. A436

MCDONALD, Harold E., Deputy Executive Director and Senior Vice President Administration, Nassau University Medical Center, East Meadow, NY, p. A438

MCDONALD, Holly, Controller, Boundary Community Hospital, Bonners Ferry, ID, p. A175

MCDONALD, Jackie, Chief Nursing Officer, Allegiance Specialty Hospital of Kilgore, Kilgore, TX, p. A630

MCDONALD, Jeff, Information Technology Manager, Florida Hospital Wauchula, Wauchula, FL, p. A149

MCDONALD, John, M.D. Chief Medical Officer, North Hills Hospital, North Richland Hills, TX, p. A639

MCDONALD, John, Chief Operating Officer, Northwest Texas Healthcare System, Amarillo, TX, p. A596

MCDONALD, Joseph D., FACHE, President and Chief Executive Officer, Catholic Health System, Buffalo, NY, p. B31

MCDONALD, Larry, Director Human Resources, Miami Jewish Home and Hospital for Aged, Miami, FL, p. A137

MCDONALD, Mark, M.D., President and Chief Executive Officer, Institute for Orthopaedic Surgery, Lima, OH, p. A496

MCDONALD Jr., Michael S., Chief Executive Officer, Holly Hill Hospital, Raleigh, NC, p. A472

MCDONALD, Robert A., Secretary, Veterans Affairs, Department of Veterans Affairs, Washington, DC, p. B45

MCDONALD, Shari, Vice President Patient Care Services, Mercy Hospital, Buffalo, NY, p. A436

MCDONALD, Shelly, Chief Human Resources Officer, Ness County Hospital District No 2, Ness City, KS, p. A250

MCDONALD, Stanton B., M.D. Medical Director, Heber Valley Medical Center, Heber City, UT, p. A660

MCDONALD, Stuart, M.D. President Medical Staff, Kindred Hospital–Fort Worth, Fort Worth, TX, p. A618

MCDONALD, Susan, Vice President, Medical Affairs, Sentara RMH Medical Center, Harrisonburg, VA, p. A671

MCDONALD, Tedd, M.D. Chief Medical Officer, Banner Churchill Community Hospital, Fallon, NV, p. A404

MCDONALD–PINKETT, Shelly, Chief Medical Officer, Howard University Hospital, Washington, DC, p. A121

MCDONNELL, M. Therese, M.D. Interim Vice President Patient Safety, Quality and Medical Affairs, Sibley Memorial Hospital, Washington, DC, p. A122

MCDONNELL, Michael, M.D. Chief Medical Officer, Mercy Hospital and Medical Center, Chicago, IL, p. A185

MCDONNELL, Nancy, Manager Information Systems, Illinois Valley Community Hospital, Peru, IL, p. A200

MCDOUGLE, Mark, Executive Vice President and Chief Operating Officer, Maimonides Medical Center,, NY, p. A445

MCDOWELL, III, Arthur V., M.D. Vice President Clinical Affairs, Middlesex Hospital, Middletown, CT, p. A115

MCDOWELL, Jean, Chief Financial Officer, Kindred Hospital–Dallas, Dallas, TX, p. A610

MCDOWELL, Paul L.
Vice President Finance and Chief Financial Officer, King's Daughters Medical Center, Ashland, KY, p. A257
Deputy Chief Financial Officer, Mission Hospital, Asheville, NC, p. A460

MCDOWELL, Richard, M.D. Medical Director, Kona Community Hospital, Kealakekua, HI, p. A172

MCDOWELL, Richard, Chief Financial Officer, Ridge Behavioral Health System, Lexington, KY, p. A263

MCDOWELL, Wendy, R.N. Director of Nursing, Weisbrod Memorial County Hospital, Eads, CO, p. A104

MCDOWN, Missy, Director Information Systems, Via Christi Hospital Pittsburg, Pittsburg, KS, p. A252

MCDRURY, Martha M., R.N. Chief Operating Officer and Chief Nursing Officer, Holy Family Hospital, Methuen, MA, p. A312

MCEACHERN, John, Controller, Sebastian River Medical Center, Sebastian, FL, p. A145

MCEACHERN, Michael L., Chief Executive Officer, Promise Hospital of Wichita Falls, Wichita Falls, TX, p. A657

MCEACHIN, Brenda, Human Resources Director, Jeff Davis Hospital, Hazlehurst, GA, p. A160

MCELDOWNEY, Erin, Manager Human Resources, Haven Senior Horizons, Phoenix, AZ, p. A36

MCELLIGOTT, Daniel P., FACHE, President, CHI Health Saint Francis, Grand Island, NE, p. A396

MCELMURRAY, Dodie, Chief Operating Officer, Greenwood Leflore Hospital, Greenwood, MS, p. A358

MCELRATH, Matthew
Chief Human Resources Officer, Keck Hospital of USC, Los Angeles, CA, p. A72
Chief Human Resources Officer, USC Norris Comprehensive Cancer Center, Los Angeles, CA, p. A74

MCELROY, Sherry, Director Health Information Management, Osceola Community Hospital, Sibley, IA, p. A237

MCENTEE, Chris, Network Specialist, Van Buren County Hospital, Keosauqua, IA, p. A233

MCENTIRE, Ann, MSN Chief Nursing Officer, Citizens Baptist Medical Center, Talladega, AL, p. A25

MCEUEN, Jacqueline, Coordinator Human Resources, Bellville St. Joseph Health Center, Bellville, TX, p. A602

MCEWAN, Kevin, Vice President of Patient Care Service and Chief Nursing Officer, Down East Community Hospital, Machias, ME, p. A294

MCEWEN, Michelle, President and Chief Executive Officer, Speare Memorial Hospital, Plymouth, NH, p. A413

MCFADDEN, Janice, MSN Chief Nursing Officer, HEALTHSOUTH Rehabilitation Hospital – Dallas, Dallas, TX, p. A610

MCFADDEN, Mary T., MSN Chief Nurse Executive, Providence Portland Medical Center, Portland, OR, p. A529

MCFALL, Cathy, Human Resources Manager, Kiowa County Memorial Hospital, Greensburg, KS, p. A244

MCFALL, Michael, Chief Financial Officer, Kindred Rehabilitation Hospital Clear Lake, Webster, TX, p. A656

MCFALL, Vicky, Chief Executive Officer, Monroe County Medical Center, Tompkinsville, KY, p. A270

MCFALL–ROBERTS, Ebuni, Director Human Resources, Holly Hill Hospital, Raleigh, NC, p. A472

MCFARLAND, Nita, Director of Nursing, Kingman Community Hospital, Kingman, KS, p. A246

MCFARLAND, Rhonda
Director Human Resources, Carolinas HealthCare System Anson, Wadesboro, NC, p. A475
Director Human Resources, Carolinas Healthcare System Union, Monroe, NC, p. A469

MCFARLAND, Rodney, M.D. Medical Director, Freeman Neosho Hospital, Neosho, MO, p. A377

MCFARLAND, Tracee, Chief Financial Officer, Claiborne Medical Center, Tazewell, TN, p. A593

MCFARLANE, Kristy S., Director Human Resources, LifeCare Medical Center, Roseau, MN, p. A350

MCFARLANE, Michael
Director Human Resource, Hawthorn Children Psychiatric Hospital, Saint Louis, MO, p. A380
Director Human Resources, Metropolitan St. Louis Psychiatric Center, Saint Louis, MO, p. A380
Chief Human Resource Officer, St. Louis Psychiatric Rehabilitation Center, Saint Louis, MO, p. A381

MCFAUL, Joan, Senior Vice President and Chief Information Officer, Southcoast Hospitals Group, Fall River, MA, p. A310

MCFERRAN, Virginia, Chief Information Officer, UCLA Medical Center–Santa Monica, Santa Monica, CA, p. A94

MCGAHEY, Nikki, Information Officer, Jefferson County Hospital, Waurika, OK, p. A523

MCGANN, Robert, M.D. President Medical Staff, Jameson Hospital, New Castle, PA, p. A546

MCGARIGLE, Kristine, R.N. Vice President Patient Care, Ministry Good Samaritan Health Center, Merrill, WI, p. A710

MCGARVEY, Missy, Chief Information Officer, Twin Valley Behavioral Healthcare, Columbus, OH, p. A491

MCGEACHEY, Edward J., President and Chief Executive Officer, Southern Maine Health Care – Biddeford Medical Center, Biddeford, ME, p. A292

MCGEE, Angela, Vice President Nursing Services, Aultman Orrville Hospital, Orrville, OH, p. A501

MCGEE, Genemarie, R.N. Chief Nursing Officer, Sentara Leigh Hospital, Norfolk, VA, p. A675

MCGEE, Jessica
Chief Financial Officer, AMG Specialty Hospital–Denham Springs, Denham Springs, LA, p. A276
Chief Financial Officer, AMG Specialty Hospital–Lafayette, Lafayette, LA, p. A280

MCGEE, Kevin, Chief Executive Officer, River Point Behavioral Health, Jacksonville, FL, p. A132

MCGEE, Mark F., M.D. Chief Clinical Officer, Appalachian Behavioral Healthcare, Athens, OH, p. A484

MCGEE, Terry, Chief Operations Officer, Central State Hospital, Milledgeville, GA, p. A163

MCGEEHAN, Paul, M.D. Chief Medical Staff, Corry Memorial Hospital, Corry, PA, p. A536

MCGETTIGAN, Ryan, Chief Information Officer, Coatesville Veterans Affairs Medical Center, Coatesville, PA, p. A536

MCGHEE, Michael, M.D. Medical Director, Behavioral HealthCare Center at Clarksville, Clarksville, TN, p. A581

MCGIBBON, Monica, Chief Nursing Officer, Terence Cardinal Cooke Health Care Center, New York, NY, p. A450

MCGILL, Martha, Executive Vice President and Chief Operating Officer, Nicklaus Children's Hospital, Miami, FL, p. A137

MCGILL, Rusty, System Director Information Technology, Indiana University Health Arnett Hospital, Lafayette, IN, p. A216

MCGILL, Steve, Vice President Finance and Chief Financial Officer, Wabash General Hospital, Mount Carmel, IL, p. A197

MCGILL, Thomas, Chief Information Officer, Butler Health System, Butler, PA, p. A534

MCGILL, Timothy W., Chief Executive Officer, Livingston Regional Hospital, Livingston, TN, p. A587

MCGILVRAY, Greg, Chief Financial Officer, Medical Center Enterprise, Enterprise, AL, p. A19

MCGIMSEY, Erika, Controller, Jewish Hospital–Shelbyville, Shelbyville, KY, p. A269

MCGINLEY, Mary Ann, Ph.D. Senior Vice President, Patient Services and Chief Nursing Officer, Thomas Jefferson University Hospitals, Philadelphia, PA, p. A550

MCGINNIS, Christina, Director Information Technology, Menorah Medical Center, Overland Park, KS, p. A251

MCGINNIS, Jeff, M.D. President Medical Staff, Saint Joseph Mount Sterling, Mount Sterling, KY, p. A267

MCGINTY, Daniel B., President and Chief Executive Officer, Franciscan Sisters of Christian Charity Sponsored Ministries, Inc., Manitowoc, WI, p. B56

MCGIRL, John, Chief Human Resources Officer, NCH Downtown Naples Hospital, Naples, FL, p. A138

MCGLADE, James, Director Human Resources, United Hospital, Saint Paul, MN, p. A351

MCGLEW, Timothy, Chief Executive Officer, Kern Valley Healthcare District, Lake Isabella, CA, p. A68

MCGLON, Tracy, Director Human Resources, Gulf Coast Medical Center, Panama City, FL, p. A141

MCGLOTHLIN, Wylie, M.D. Chief Medical Officer, Henry County Hospital, New Castle, IN, p. A219

MCGLYNN, Mia, Director Management Information Systems, Plantation General Hospital, Plantation, FL, p. A143

MCGOLDRICK, Margaret M., President, Abington Hospital, Abington, PA, p. A532

MCGOVERN, Charles, Chief of Staff, Margaret Mary Health, Batesville, IN, p. A206

MCGOVERN, Julia, Vice President Human Resources, Chilton Medical Center, Pompton Plains, NJ, p. A422

MCGOVERN, Julie, Vice President Human Resources, Anne Arundel Medical Center, Annapolis, MD, p. A296

MCGOVERN, Pam, Director Technology, Huggins Hospital, Wolfeboro, NH, p. A413

MCGOVERN, Sandra, Chief Nursing Officer, UP Health System–Bell, Ishpeming, MI, p. A327

MCGOWAN, Donna, Administrator, Lane County Hospital, Dighton, KS, p. A242

MCGOWEN, Bernard A., M.D. Medical Director, Kindred Hospital Tarrant County–Arlington, Arlington, TX, p. A597

MCGOWIN, III, Norman F., M.D. Chief of Staff, L. V. Stabler Memorial Hospital, Greenville, AL, p. A21

MCGRAIL, David, Vice President Finance, Carney Hospital, Boston, MA, p. A306

MCGRAIL, Karen, District Director Human Resource, Kindred Hospital Detroit, Detroit, MI, p. A322

MCGRAIL, Robert, Chief Executive Officer, West Branch Regional Medical Center, West Branch, MI, p. A336

MCGRATH, Bradley, Administrator, New Mexico Rehabilitation Center, Roswell, NM, p. A431

MCGRATH, Denise B., Chief Executive Officer, HEALTHSOUTH Sea Pines Rehabilitation Hospital, Melbourne, FL, p. A136

MCGRATH, Kelly, Chief Medical Officer, Clearwater Valley Hospital and Clinics, Orofino, ID, p. A177

MCGRATH, Lynn, M.D. Vice President Medical Affairs, Deborah Heart and Lung Center, Browns Mills, NJ, p. A415

MCGRAW, Belinda
Director Human Resources, Boulder City Hospital, Boulder City, NV, p. A404
Director Human Resources, Complex Care Hospital at Tenaya, Las Vegas, NV, p. A405

MCGRAW, Karin L., FACHE, Director, Veterans Affairs Pittsburgh Healthcare System, Pittsburgh, PA, p. A552

MCGRAW, Kathleen, M.D. Chief Medical Officer, Brattleboro Memorial Hospital, Brattleboro, VT, p. A665

MCGRAW, Scott, M.D. Medical Director, Baylor Surgical Hospital at Las Colinas, Irving, TX, p. A628

MCGREAHAM, David S., M.D. Vice President Medical Affairs, Munson Medical Center, Traverse City, MI, p. A335

MCGREEVY, John, Chief Executive Officer, CHRISTUS Mother Frances Hospital – Tyler, Tyler, TX, p. A654

MCGREGOR, Catherine, Deputy Director Facility and Administrative Services, Capital District Psychiatric Center, Albany, NY, p. A433

MCGREGOR, Julie
Vice President and Chief People Officer, Jewish Hospital, Louisville, KY, p. A264
Director Human Resources, Sts. Mary & Elizabeth Hospital, Louisville, KY, p. A265

MCGREGOR, Robert, M.D. Chief Medical Officer, Akron Children's Hospital, Akron, OH, p. A483

MCGREW, David S., Chief Financial Officer, San Mateo Medical Center, San Mateo, CA, p. A92

MCGREW, Deborah A., Vice President and Chief Operating Officer, University of Texas Medical Branch, Galveston, TX, p. A620

MCGREW, Diane, Chief Nurse Executive, Montgomery County Memorial Hospital, Red Oak, IA, p. A236

MCGRIFF, Marchelle M., Chief Nursing Executive, Sutter Medical Center, Sacramento, Sacramento, CA, p. A87

MCGUCKEN, Holly, R.N. Chief Nursing Officer, Fort Walton Beach Medical Center, Fort Walton Beach, FL, p. A129

MCGUE, Lisa, Controller, HEALTHSOUTH Northern Kentucky Rehabilitation Hospital, Edgewood, KY, p. A259

MCGUE, Thomas E., M.D. Vice President Medical Affairs and Chief Medical Officer, Newport Hospital, Newport, RI, p. A560

MCGUFFIN, Patty, R.N. Chief Nursing Officer, Allen County Regional Hospital, Iola, KS, p. A245

MCGUIGAN, Kevin, M.D. Medical Director, St. Lawrence Rehabilitation Center, Lawrenceville, NJ, p. A418

MCGUILL, Gail, R.N. Chief Nursing Officer and Administrative Director of Patient Care Services, Shriners Hospitals for Children–Salt Lake City, Salt Lake City, UT, p. A663

MCGUINNESS, Luke, President and CEO, Health Quest Systems, Inc., LaGrangeville, NY, p. B65

MCGUINNESS, Patrick, Chief Information Management, Keller Army Community Hospital, West Point, NY, p. A459

MCGUIRE, Ann M., Regional Vice President Human Resources, Indiana University Health Ball Memorial Hospital, Muncie, IN, p. A219

MCGUIRE, Cynthia, FACHE, President and Chief Executive Officer, Monadnock Community Hospital, Peterborough, NH, p. A413

MCGUIRE, Matthew, President and Chief Executive Officer, Western Regional Medical Center, Goodyear, AZ, p. A33

MCGUIRE, Shane, Chief Executive Officer, Columbia County Health System, Dayton, WA, p. A684

MCGUIRK, Christina Marie, Chief Nursing Officer, Health Central Hospital, Ocoee, FL, p. A139

MCGUIRL, Mary, Director Information Systems, Oneida Healthcare, Oneida, NY, p. A452

MCGURK, Kevin, Controller, Bellin Psychiatric Center, Green Bay, WI, p. A706

MCHANEY, Tracy, Director Human Resources, Cedar Crest Hospital and Residential Treatment Center, Belton, TX, p. A602

MCHARDY, Bryson, M.D. President Medical Staff, Hannibal Regional Hospital, Hannibal, MO, p. A371

MCHUGH, Matthew, Director Information Services, Vaughan Regional Medical Center, Selma, AL, p. A25

MCHUGH, Michael J., M.D., Medical Director, Cleveland Clinic Children's Hospital for Rehabilitation, Cleveland, OH, p. A489

MCHUGH, William, M.D. Medical Director and Chief Medical Officer, Trinitas Regional Medical Center, Elizabeth, NJ, p. A416

MCILROY, Gail, Director Medical Records, Promise Hospital of Wichita Falls, Wichita Falls, TX, p. A657

MCILVAIN, Spencer, Director of Human Resources, Peterson Healthcare and Rehabilitation Hospital, Wheeling, WV, p. A701

MCILWAIN, T. Pinckney, M.D. Vice President and Chief Medical Officer, Charleston Area Medical Center, Charleston, WV, p. A695

MCINERNEY, Terry, Director of Nursing, Inpatient, Navos, Seattle, WA, p. A689

MCINTOSH, Craig, Chief Information Officer, Northwest Specialty Hospital, Post Falls, ID, p. A178

MCINTOSH, Ernasha, Interim Director of Nursing, Sage Memorial Hospital, Ganado, AZ, p. A32

MCINTOSH, Joe, Director Management Information Systems, Logansport State Hospital, Logansport, IN, p. A217

MCINTOSH, Tyler, Chief Financial Officer, Creek Nation Community Hospital, Okemah, OK, p. A515

MCINTYRE, Cindy, R.N. Administrative Director Clinical Services, Magee General Hospital, Magee, MS, p. A361

MCINTYRE, Daniel J., President and Chief Executive Officer, The Charlotte Hungerford Hospital, Torrington, CT, p. A117

MCINTYRE, Kathleen, Province Leader, American Province of Little Company of Mary Sisters, Evergreen Park, IL, p. B10

MCIWAIN, John, Director Human Resources, Wayne Memorial Hospital, Jesup, GA, p. A161

MCKAIN, Rick, Chief Executive Officer, Anderson County Hospital, Garnett, KS, p. A243

MCKALE, Brigitte, MSN Vice President and Chief Nurse Executive, Pali Momi Medical Center, Aiea, HI, p. A170

MCKAY, Amy, Chief Nursing Officer, Mid–America Rehabilitation Hospital, Shawnee Mission, KS, p. A253

MCKAY, Daniel E.
Chief Executive Officer, Sparks Medical Center – Van Buren, Van Buren, AR, p. A53
Chief Executive Officer, Sparks Regional Medical Center, Fort Smith, AR, p. A46

MCKAY, Danny H., Administrator, Noxubee General Hospital, Macon, MS, p. A361

MCKAY, Michael, Chief Information Officer, Wickenburg Community Hospital, Wickenburg, AZ, p. A41

MCKAY, Rebecca, Director Human Resources, Sweeny Community Hospital, Sweeny, TX, p. A651

MCKAY, Ronda, R.N. Vice President Patient Care Services, Chief Nursing Officer, Community Hospital, Munster, IN, p. A219

MCKEAN, Kathy, M.P.H. Vice President, Chief Nursing Executive, Riverview Medical Center, Red Bank, NJ, p. A423

MCKEE, Debra, R.N. Chief Clinical Officer and Chief Nursing Officer, Joint Township District Memorial Hospital, Saint Marys, OH, p. A502

MCKEE, Michele, Vice President and Chief Financial Officer, St. Louis Children's Hospital, Saint Louis, MO, p. A381

MCKEE, Robert J., Vice President Human Resources, Penn Highlands DuBois, DuBois, PA, p. A537

MCKEE, Jr., Willis P., M.D. Chief Medical Officer, Frankfort Regional Medical Center, Frankfort, KY, p. A260

MCKEEBY, Ben, Senior Vice President and Chief Information Officer, Grady Memorial Hospital, Atlanta, GA, p. A152

MCKEEBY, Jon W., Chief Information Officer, National Institutes of Health Clinical Center, Bethesda, MD, p. A299

MCKEEN, Marcia, Director Human Resources, Twin Valley Behavioral Healthcare, Columbus, OH, p. A491

MCKELDIN, Pat, Human Resource Business Partner, Kaiser Permanente Manteca Medical Center, Manteca, CA, p. A76

MCKENNA, Dennis, M.D. Interim Vice President Medical Affairs, Albany Medical Center, Albany, NY, p. A433

MCKENNA, Donald, President and Chief Executive Officer, St. Mary's Health Care System, Athens, GA, p. A151

MCKENNA, John F., Chief Executive Officer and Managing Director, Rockford Center, Newark, DE, p. A119

MCKENNA, Quinn, Chief Operating Officer, University of Utah Health Care – Hospital and Clinics, Salt Lake City, UT, p. A664

MCKENNERY, Kay, Interim Chief Executive Officer, Hickory Trail Hospital, Desoto, TX, p. A613

MCKENNEY, Jennifer, M.D. Chief Medical Officer, Fredonia Regional Hospital, Fredonia, KS, p. A243

MCKENZIE, Christine, Director Human Resources, Davis Regional Medical Center, Statesville, NC, p. A474

MCKENZIE, Jackie, Director Administrative Services, Beacham Memorial Hospital, Magnolia, MS, p. A361

MCKENZIE, Kimberly, MSN, Interim Chief Executive Officer, Harbor–UCLA Medical Center, Torrance, CA, p. A96

MCKENZIE, Nancy J., Chief Executive Officer, Greenwood County Hospital, Eureka, KS, p. A243

MCKENZIE, Sandra D., Executive Vice President and Chief Operating Officer, Hamilton Medical Center, Dalton, GA, p. A158

MCKENZIE, William G., President, Chief Executive Officer and Chairman, Gilliard Health Services, Montgomery, AL, p. B57

MCKEON, John, Vice President Human Resources, Kingsbrook Jewish Medical Center, NY, p. A445

MCKEON, Sean, Director, Information Technology, Franciscan Hospital for Children, Boston, MA, p. A306

MCKEOWN, Colleen
Senior Vice President and Area Manager, Kaiser Permanente Antioch Medical Center, Antioch, CA, p. A54
Senior Vice President and Area Manager, Kaiser Permanente Walnut Creek Medical Center, Walnut Creek, CA, p. A99

MCKERNAN, James E., Chief Operating Officer, Bronson Battle Creek, Battle Creek, MI, p. A319

MCKERNAN, Kathleen S., Director Information Systems, Pioneers Memorial Healthcare District, Brawley, CA, p. A57

MCKERNAN, Stephen W., Chief Executive Officer, University of New Mexico Hospitals, Albuquerque, NM, p. A428

MCKERNAN, Stephen W., Chief Executive Officer, University of New Mexico Hospitals, Albuquerque, NM, p. B148

MCKEVETT, Timothy M., President, Beloit Health System, Beloit, WI, p. A703

MCKIBBEN, Leeanna, R.N
Vice President Patient Services and Chief Nursing Officer, UPMC McKeesport, McKeesport, PA, p. A544
Vice President Patient Services and Chief Nursing Officer, UPMC Mercy, Pittsburgh, PA, p. A551

MCKIBBEN, Sean, President and Chief Operating Officer, Mount Carmel, Columbus, OH, p. A490

MCKIDDY, Paul, Director Information Technology, Monroe County Medical Center, Tompkinsville, KY, p. A270

MCKIE, Kathy, Director Human Resources, Montrose Memorial Hospital, Montrose, CO, p. A109

MCKILLIP, Ed, Director of Finance, Riddle Hospital, Media, PA, p. A545

MCKIMMY, Doyle L., FACHE, Chief Executive Officer, Jewell County Hospital, Mankato, KS, p. A248

MCKINLEY, Bryan, Chief Financial Officer, St. Mark's Hospital, Salt Lake City, UT, p. A663

MCKINLEY, Ernie, Chief Information Officer, University Medical Center, Las Vegas, NV, p. A407

MCKINLEY, Ivy
Regional Human Resources Officer, Community First Medical Center, Chicago, IL, p. A183
Director Human Resources, Presence Holy Family Medical Center, Des Plaines, IL, p. A188
Regional Lead Human Resources, Presence Resurrection Medical Center, Chicago, IL, p. A185

MCKINLEY, John, Director, Information Technology, Community Mental Health Center, Lawrenceburg, IN, p. A217

MCKINLEY, Mike, Information Security Officer, West Texas Veterans Affairs Health Care System, Big Spring, TX, p. A603

MCKINLEY, Ronald, Ph.D. Vice President Human Resources and Employee Services, University of Texas Medical Branch, Galveston, TX, p. A620

MCKINLEY, Jr., Rudolph, Vice President Operations and Chief Operating Officer, East Tennessee Children's Hospital, Knoxville, TN, p. A585

MCKINNEY, Brenda, Chief Executive Officer, Reeves County Hospital, Pecos, TX, p. A641

MCKINNEY, Bruce, Business Officer, Administrative Services, Central Prison Hospital, Raleigh, NC, p. A471

MCKINNEY, Dan, Administrator, Hermann Area District Hospital, Hermann, MO, p. A372

MCKINNEY, Dana, Chief Nursing Officer, Select Specialty Hospital–Madison, Madison, WI, p. A709

MCKINNEY, Daniel, Chief Operating Officer, Mary Black Health System–Spartanburg, Spartanburg, SC, p. A569

MCKINNEY, Gregory, M.D., Medical Director, Arkansas Department of Correction Hospital, Malvern, AR, p. A49

MCKINNEY, James, Warden, Iowa Medical and Classification Center, Coralville, IA, p. A227

MCKINNEY, Paul, Chief Executive Officer, Martin County Hospital District, Stanton, TX, p. A650

MCKINNON, Mark, M.D. Chief of Staff, North Runnels Hospital, Winters, TX, p. A658

MCKINNON, Ron, Chief Information Officer, Ellis Hospital, Schenectady, NY, p. A455

MCKINNON, Scott, President and Chief Executive Officer, Memorial Hospital, North Conway, NH, p. A413

MCKINNON, Shauna, Chief Executive Officer, Bayfront Health Dade City, Dade City, FL, p. A126

MCKINSTRY, Merissa, Chief Operating Officer, Dublin Springs, Dublin, OH, p. A494

MCKNIGHT, Craig L., Senior Vice President and Chief Financial Officer, Phoenix Children's Hospital, Phoenix, AZ, p. A37

MCKNIGHT, David, CPA Chief Financial Officer, Spotsylvania Regional Medical Center, Fredericksburg, VA, p. A670

MCKNIGHT, Richard B., Senior Vice President and Chief Information Officer, Novant Health Huntersville Medical Center, Huntersville, NC, p. A467

MCKNIGHT, Stephanie, Hospital Nursing Manager, Sanford Bagley Medical Center, Bagley, MN, p. A339

MCKNIGHT, Tim, M.D. Chief of Staff, Trinity Hospital Twin City, Dennison, OH, p. A493

MCKOY, Lori, Business Partner, Pender Memorial Hospital, Burgaw, NC, p. A461

MCKULA, Tim, Vice President Information Systems and Chief Information Officer, Rehabilitation Institute of Chicago, Chicago, IL, p. A186

MCKUNE, Jeff, Chief Health Informatics Officer, Phelps County Regional Medical Center, Rolla, MO, p. A379

MCLAIN, Allen, M.D. Chief of Staff, Grisell Memorial Hospital District One, Ransom, KS, p. A252

MCLAIN, Cindy, Chief Executive Officer, Select Specialty Hospital–Fort Smith, Fort Smith, AR, p. A46

MCLAIN, John R., Chief Executive Officer, Venice Regional Bayfront Health, Venice, FL, p. A149

MCLAIN, Kathy, Chief Financial Officer, Childress Regional Medical Center, Childress, TX, p. A606

MCLARIN, Benita, Chief Operating Officer, Santa Clara Valley Medical Center, San Jose, CA, p. A91

MCLARTY, Walter L.
Chief Human Resources Officer, Bethesda North Hospital, Cincinnati, OH, p. A487
Chief Human Resources Officer, Good Samaritan Hospital, Cincinnati, OH, p. A487

MCLAUGHLIN, Amy, CPA Chief Financial Officer, Manning Regional Healthcare Center, Manning, IA, p. A234

MCLAUGHLIN, Dan C., Chief Executive Officer, Menifee Valley Medical Center, Sun City, CA, p. A95

MCLAUGHLIN, Gary, Executive Vice President and Chief Financial Officer, Overlake Medical Center, Bellevue, WA, p. A682

MCLAUGHLIN, Kathryn, Chief Nursing Officer, Hemet Valley Medical Center, Hemet, CA, p. A66

MCLAUGHLIN, Leslie, Director of Business Development, Michiana Behavioral Health Center, Plymouth, IN, p. A220

MCLAUGHLIN, Maribeth, R.N. Vice President Patient Care Services, Magee–Womens Hospital of UPMC, Pittsburgh, PA, p. A551

MCLAUGHLIN, Pamela, Chief Financial Officer, HEALTHSOUTH Rehabilitation Hospital of Austin, Austin, TX, p. A599

MCLAUGHLIN, Rebecca, Chief Human Resource Officer, Banner Goldfield Medical Center, Apache Junction, AZ, p. A31

MCLAUGHLIN, Sherry, Director Human Resources, Forrest City Medical Center, Forrest City, AR, p. A46

MCLAURIN, Monty E., President and Chief Executive Officer, Indian Path Medical Center, Kingsport, TN, p. A585

MCLAWS, Douglas, D.O. Chief Medical Officer, Manning Regional Healthcare Center, Manning, IA, p. A234

MCLEAN, Anthony
President, Highline Medical Center, Burien, WA, p. A683
President, St. Francis Hospital, Federal Way, WA, p. A685
MCLEAN, Chris J., Chief Financial Officer, Methodist Healthcare Memphis Hospitals, Memphis, TN, p. A589
MCLEAN, Cindy J., R.N. Director of Nursing, Central Prison Hospital, Raleigh, NC, p. A471
MCLEAN, Georgia, Director Human Resources, Mount Sinai Medical Center, Miami Beach, FL, p. A138
MCLENDON, Carla
Director Human Resources, Appling Healthcare System, Baxley, GA, p. A154
Director Information Resource Management Services, Charles George Veterans Affairs Medical Center, Asheville, NC, p. A460
MCLENDON, Connie, Director Human Resources, Piedmont Mountainside Hospital, Jasper, GA, p. A161
MCLENDON, John
Senior Vice President and Chief Information Officer, AMITA Health Adventist Medical Center Bolingbrook, Bolingbrook, IL, p. A182
Vice President and Chief Information Officer, Johns Hopkins All Children's Hospital, Saint Petersburg, FL, p. A144
MCLENDON, Tom, Administrator, Evergreen Medical Center, Evergreen, AL, p. A19
MCLEOD, Les, Director of Nursing Services, Blue Mountain Hospital, John Day, OR, p. A527
MCLEOD, Margie, Director Information Technology, North Canyon Medical Center, Gooding, ID, p. A176
MCLEOD, Michael, M.D. Chief Medical Officer, Cuero Community Hospital, Cuero, TX, p. A608
MCLEOD, Sheldon, Chief Operating Officer, NYC Health + Hospitals / North Central Bronx,, NY, p. A449
MCLIN, Robert D., President and Chief Executive Officer, Good Samaritan Hospital, Vincennes, IN, p. A223
MCLOONE, J. Mark, FACHE, Chief Executive Officer, St. Christopher's Hospital for Children, Philadelphia, PA, p. A549
MCLOONE, Paul, M.D
Chief Medical Officer, UnityPoint Health – Trinity Bettendorf, Bettendorf, IA, p. A225
Chief Medical Officer, UnityPoint Health – Trinity Rock Island, Rock Island, IL, p. A201
MCMACKIN, Ann, President, Vassar Brothers Medical Center, Poughkeepsie, NY, p. A453
MCMAHAN, Mike, President, St. Francis Regional Medical Center, Shakopee, MN, p. A351
MCMAHAN, Steve, M.D. Chief Medical Officer, Glenwood Regional Medical Center, West Monroe, LA, p. A289
MCMAHON, Alisha, Director Human Resources, Mountrail County Medical Center, Stanley, ND, p. A481
MCMAHON, Andrew, Chief Fiscal Officer, Veterans Affairs Central Western Massachusetts Healthcare System, Leeds, MA, p. A311
MCMAHON, Chris, Chief Operating Officer, The Medical Center of Southeast Texas, Port Arthur, TX, p. A642
MCMAHON, Elaine, Administrator, Kwajalein Hospital, Kwajalein Island, MH, p. A725
MCMAHON, Eugene
Senior Vice President and Chief Medical Officer, Capital Health Medical Center–Hopewell, Pennington, NJ, p. A422
Senior Vice President and Chief Medical Officer, Capital Health Regional Medical Center, Trenton, NJ, p. A424
MCMAHON, Leigh, MS Senior Vice President Patient Care Services and Chief Nursing Officer, White Plains Hospital Center, White Plains, NY, p. A459
MCMAHON, Nancy, Vice President Human Resources, Miriam Hospital, Providence, RI, p. A560
MCMANMON, Kristin, Chief Operating Officer, St. Mary's Hospital, Madison, WI, p. A709
MCMANUS, Doug, Chief Medical Officer, Aurora Medical Center Grafton, Grafton, WI, p. A706
MCMANUS, Michael T., Chief Operating Officer, Memorial Hospital, Belleville, IL, p. A181
MCMANUS, Ronald, Senior Vice President Clinical Services and Business Entities, Peconic Bay Medical Center, Riverhead, NY, p. A454
MCMANUS, Tim, President and Chief Executive Officer, Chippenham Hospital, Richmond, VA, p. A677
MCMASTER, Sandra
Regional Chief Information Officer, Kauai Veterans Memorial Hospital, Waimea, HI, p. A173
Regional Chief Information Officer, Samuel Mahelona Memorial Hospital, Kapaa, HI, p. A172
MCMATH, Mark W., Chief Information Officer, Indiana University Health Bloomington Hospital, Bloomington, IN, p. A207
MCMEANS, TJ, Information Technology Technician, Black River Medical Center, Poplar Bluff, MO, p. A378
MCMENAMIN, Anneliese, Vice President Human Resources, Kennedy Health System, Cherry Hill, NJ, p. A415

MCMICHEN, Diane, Director Human Resources, DeKalb Regional Medical Center, Fort Payne, AL, p. A20
MCMILLAN, Deborah, Director Human Resources, Glenn Medical Center, Willows, CA, p. A100
MCMILLAN, Donn
Chief Information Officer, PeaceHealth Sacred Heart Medical Center University District, Eugene, OR, p. A525
Chief Information Officer, PeaceHealth Southwest Medical Center, Vancouver, WA, p. A692
MCMILLAN, Douglas A., Administrator and Chief Executive Officer, West Park Hospital, Cody, WY, p. A722
MCMILLAN, Jon R., Chief Financial Officer, Banner Lassen Medical Center, Susanville, CA, p. A95
MCMILLAN, Sheila, Chief Financial Officer, Park Nicollet Methodist Hospital, Saint Louis Park, MN, p. A350
MCMILLEN, Eric, Chief Executive Officer, Ochsner Medical Center–Baton Rouge, Baton Rouge, LA, p. A272
MCMILLION, Kelley, Chief Nursing Officer, Clay County Memorial Hospital, Henrietta, TX, p. A623
MCMINN, Ken, Director Information Technology, Scotland County Hospital, Memphis, MO, p. A376
MCMINN, Melvin, Director Human Resources, Wernersville State Hospital, Wernersville, PA, p. A557
MCMULLAN, Heidi, R.N. Chief Nursing Officer, Philhaven, Mount Gretna, PA, p. A545
MCMULLEN, Thomas A., Chief Financial Officer, Kindred Hospital–Philadelphia, Philadelphia, PA, p. A548
MCMULLIN, John, Chief Financial Officer, Rehoboth McKinley Christian Health Care Services, Gallup, NM, p. A429
MCMURRAY, Sharon, Director, Human Resources, Rock Springs, LLC, Georgetown, TX, p. A620
MCMURREN, Mary Anne, FACHE, Chief Administrative Officer, PeaceHealth Sacred Heart Medical Center University District, Eugene, OR, p. A525
MCMURREY, Jean Ann, R.N. Chief Nursing Officer, RMC Jacksonville, Jacksonville, AL, p. A22
MCMURRY, Timothy, Director, Wm. Jennings Bryan Dorn Veterans Affairs Medical Center, Columbia, SC, p. A564
MCNABB, Dana, Human Resources Manager, Field Memorial Community Hospital, Centreville, MS, p. A356
MCNABB, Teresita, R.N. Vice President Nursing Services, Terrebonne General Medical Center, Houma, LA, p. A278
MCNAIR, Lisa, CPA Senior Vice President and Chief Financial Officer, St. Joseph Regional Health Center, Bryan, TX, p. A604
MCNAIR, Rebekah, Director Human Resources, HEALTHSOUTH Chattanooga Rehabilitation Hospital, Chattanooga, TN, p. A580
MCNAIR, Scott, Chief Financial Officer, Neshoba County General Hospital, Philadelphia, MS, p. A363
MCNALLY, Joseph, M.D. Medical Director, Streamwood Behavioral Health Center, Streamwood, IL, p. A204
MCNALLY, Kathy, Chief Nursing Officer, HEALTHSOUTH Rehabilitation Hospital at Drake, Cincinnati, OH, p. A487
MCNALLY, Lou–Ann, Executive Director Human Resources and Staff Development, Claxton–Hepburn Medical Center, Ogdensburg, NY, p. A451
MCNALLY, Michael, Vice President Human Resources, United Health Services Hospitals–Binghamton, Binghamton, NY, p. A435
MCNAMARA, John, M.D. Senior Vice President, Chief Medical Officer, Torrance Memorial Medical Center, Torrance, CA, p. A96
MCNAMARA, Marilyn, M.D. Chief Medical Officer, Southwest General Health Center, Middleburg Heights, OH, p. A499
MCNAMARA, Mike, Chief Information Officer, Mee Memorial Hospital, King City, CA, p. A67
MCNAMARA, Steve, Chief Financial Officer, Orange Coast Memorial Medical Center, Fountain Valley, CA, p. A63
MCNAMARA, Thomas, D.O. Vice President Medical Affairs, WellStar Cobb Hospital, Austell, GA, p. A154
MCNAMARA, Timothy M.
Senior Vice President Human Resources, Bradford Regional Medical Center, Bradford, PA, p. A534
Senior Vice President Human Resources, Olean General Hospital, Olean, NY, p. A451
MCNAMEE, Hugar, D.O. Chief Medical Officer, Florida Hospital Zephyrhills, Zephyrhills, FL, p. A150
MCNATT, James, Chief Financial Officer, Baylor Scott & White Medical Center – Carrollton, Carrollton, TX, p. A605
MCNAUGHTON, Richard, Chief Information Management Service, Maine Veterans Affairs Medical Center, Augusta, ME, p. A291
MCNEA, Melvin, Chief Executive Officer, Great Plains Health, North Platte, NE, p. A399
MCNEAR, Michael, M.D. Chief Medical Officer, Jersey Community Hospital, Jerseyville, IL, p. A194
MCNEECE, Steve, Chief Executive Officer, Community Hospital of Anaconda, Anaconda, MT, p. A385
MCNEEL, Jacob, D.O. Chief of Staff, Plateau Medical Center, Oak Hill, WV, p. A698

MCNEEL, Wakelin, M.D. Medical Director, BHC Alhambra Hospital, Rosemead, CA, p. A86
MCNEIL, Ane, Vice President Human Resources, St. Joseph Mercy Oakland, Pontiac, MI, p. A332
MCNEIL, Greg R., Chief Executive Officer, Crittenden County Hospital, Marion, KY, p. A266
MCNEIL, John, President and Chief Executive Officer, Eastern Regional Medical Center, Philadelphia, PA, p. A547
MCNEIL, Karen
Chief Operating Officer, University Hospitals Conneaut Medical Center, Conneaut, OH, p. A492
Chief Operating Officer, University Hospitals Geneva Medical Center, Geneva, OH, p. A495
MCNEILL, Michael, Chief Financial Management, New Mexico Veterans Affairs Health Care System – Raymond G. Murphy Medical Center, Albuquerque, NM, p. A428
MCNEY, Jim, Senior Vice President Finance and Chief Financial Officer, North Kansas City Hospital, North Kansas City, MO, p. A377
MCNULTY III,, Joseph S., President and Chief Executive Officer, Pioneer Health Services, Magee, MS, p. B104
MCNULTY, Stephanie, Chief Operating Officer, St. Petersburg General Hospital, Saint Petersburg, FL, p. A144
MCNULTY, Timothy, Director Human Resources, Spring Harbor Hospital, Westbrook, ME, p. A295
MCNUTT, Elena, Chief Nursing Officer, Desert Springs Hospital Medical Center, Las Vegas, NV, p. A405
MCNUTT, Mike, Assistant Administrator, Covenant Hospital Plainview, Plainview, TX, p. A641
MCNUTT, Pamela
Vice President Information Systems, Methodist Charlton Medical Center, Dallas, TX, p. A610
Senior Vice President and Chief Information Officer, Methodist Dallas Medical Center, Dallas, TX, p. A610
Senior Vice President and Chief Information Officer, Methodist Mansfield Medical Center, Mansfield, TX, p. A635
Senior Vice President and Chief Information Officer, Methodist Richardson Medical Center, Richardson, TX, p. A643
MCPEAK, Sara, Chief Nursing Officer, Carlinville Area Hospital, Carlinville, IL, p. A182
MCPHERSON, Lon, M.D. Senior Vice President Medical Affairs and Chief Quality Officer, Munroe Regional Medical Center, Ocala, FL, p. A139
MCPHERSON, Rhonda, Vice President Human Resources, Fayette Regional Health System, Connersville, IN, p. A208
MCPHERSON, Stephen B., President and Chief Executive Officer, Masonicare Health Center, Wallingford, CT, p. A117
MCQUAID, David P., FACHE, Chief Executive Officer, Ohio State University Health System, Columbus, OH, p. B100
MCQUAID, David P., FACHE Chief Operating Officer, Ohio State University Wexner Medical Center, Columbus, OH, p. A491
MCQUAIDE, Ben, M.D. Chief of Staff, Clark Regional Medical Center, Winchester, KY, p. A270
MCQUAIDE, Teresa A., Chief Executive Officer, Trenton Psychiatric Hospital, Trenton, NJ, p. A424
MCQUILLEN, Paul, M.D. Chief Medical Officer, Jane Phillips Memorial Medical Center, Bartlesville, OK, p. A509
MCQUISTAN, Bob, Vice President Finance, York General Hospital, York, NE, p. A403
MCQUISTON, Mike, Administrative Director Human Resources, Wise Regional Health System, Decatur, TX, p. A612
MCRAE, Colin, Chief Executive Officer, Tennova Healthcare–Jefferson Memorial Hospital, Jefferson City, TN, p. A584
MCRIMMON, Dana, Chief Financial Officer, Mesilla Valley Hospital, Las Cruces, NM, p. A430
MCROBERTS, Kevin G., FACHE Senior Vice President of Operations, Lake Regional Health System, Osage Beach, MO, p. A378
MCROBERTS, Susan, R.N
Vice President and Chief Nursing Officer, Franciscan St. Francis Health – Indianapolis, Indianapolis, IN, p. A214
Chief Nursing Officer, Franciscan St. Francis Health–Carmel, Carmel, IN, p. A208
MCTAGGART, Jac, Chief Executive Officer, Sanford Hillsboro Medical Center, Hillsboro, ND, p. A480
MCTIGRIT, Chris, Manager Information Technology, Delta Memorial Hospital, Dumas, AR, p. A45
MCTIGUE, Mary, Vice President Patient Care Services and Chief Nursing Officer, Trinitas Regional Medical Center, Elizabeth, NJ, p. A416
MCTIGUE, Michael
Chief Information Officer, Clara Maass Medical Center, Belleville, NJ, p. A414
Chief Information Officer, Saint Barnabas Medical Center, Livingston, NJ, p. A418
MCVAY, Randy, Chief Executive Officer, Ocala Regional Medical Center, Ocala, FL, p. A139
MCVAY, Tara, Chief Nursing Officer, Logansport Memorial Hospital, Logansport, IN, p. A217

MCVEIGH, Kevin, Chief Human Resources Officer, Banner Desert Medical Center, Mesa, AZ, p. A34

MCVEY, Lynn, Chief Operating Officer, Meadowlands Hospital Medical Center, Secaucus, NJ, p. A423

MCVEY, Marian Lorraine, Chief Nursing Officer, North Greenville Hospital, Travelers Rest, SC, p. A570

MCVEY, Patrick, Chief Executive Officer, Select Specialty Hospital–Savannah, Savannah, GA, p. A166

MCVEY, Timothy J., Chief Financial Officer, Mission Regional Medical Center, Mission, TX, p. A637

MCWAY, Jacob, Senior Vice President and Chief Financial Officer, Cox Medical Centers, Springfield, MO, p. A382

MCWEY, Russ, M.D. Vice President and Chief Information Officer, Virginia Hospital Center – Arlington, Arlington, VA, p. A667

MCWHERTER, Joe, Chief Financial Officer, Baptist Memorial Hospital–Desoto, Southaven, MS, p. A365

MCWHORTER III, John B., President, Baylor University Medical Center, Dallas, TX, p. A609

MCWILLIAMS, Jill, Chief Nursing Officer, Sierra Nevada Memorial Hospital, Grass Valley, CA, p. A65

MEACHAM, Byanka, Director Human Resources, Montgomery County Emergency Service, Norristown, PA, p. A546

MEACHAM, Sherry, Coordinator Human Resources, Select Specialty Hospital–Winston–Salem, Winston–Salem, NC, p. A476

MEACHAM, Steve, Vice President Finance, King's Daughters' Health, Madison, IN, p. A217

MEACHEM, Michelle, Director Human Resources, The University of Vermont Health Network Elizabethtown Community Hospital, Elizabethtown, NY, p. A438

MEAD, Linda, Director Human Resources, Margaretville Hospital, Margaretville, NY, p. A442

MEAD, Richard, Senior Director Human Resources, Saint Francis Memorial Hospital, San Francisco, CA, p. A90

MEAD, Rick, Human Resources Leader, Kaiser Permanente Oakland Medical Center, Oakland, CA, p. A80

MEADE, Robert C., Chief Executive Officer, Doctors Hospital of Sarasota, Sarasota, FL, p. A145

MEADE, Stephanie, R.N. Chief Nursing Officer, Mercy Health – West Hospital, Cincinnati, OH, p. A488

MEADE, Teresa, R.N. Chief Nursing Officer, Boone Memorial Hospital, Madison, WV, p. A697

MEADOWS, Barbara, Chief Financial Manager, Captain James A. Lovell Federal Health Care Center, North Chicago, IL, p. A198

MEADOWS, Danny, M.D. Medical Director, Logansport State Hospital, Logansport, IN, p. A217

MEADOWS, Hal, M.D. Chief Medical Officer, Banner Lassen Medical Center, Susanville, CA, p. A95

MEADOWS, Mark, Chief Executive Officer, Lone Peak Hospital, Draper, UT, p. A659

MEADOWS, Nancy, Chief Financial Officer, Methodist Hospital, San Antonio, TX, p. A646

MEADOWS, Peri, Director Human Resources, Rhea Medical Center, Dayton, TN, p. A582

MEADOWS, Sheila M., Chief Human Resources Officer, Mission Hospital, Asheville, NC, p. A460

MEADOWS, Terri, Chief Nursing Executive, Merit Health Madison, Canton, MS, p. A356

MEADOWS, Theresa, Chief Information Officer, Cook Children's Medical Center, Fort Worth, TX, p. A618

MEANS, Dennis, M.D. Vice President Medical Affairs, Carilion New River Valley Medical Center, Christiansburg, VA, p. A669

MEARNS, Stephanie, Vice President Patient Care Services and Chief Nurse Executive, Seton Medical Center, Daly City, CA, p. A60

MEARNS, Stephanie, R.N. Vice President and Chief Nursing Officer, West Hills Hospital and Medical Center,, CA, p. A75

MEARS, Terry, Director Information Systems, Duke Regional Hospital, Durham, NC, p. A464

MECHAM, Cindy, Health Information Director, Mountain View Hospital, Payson, UT, p. A662

MEDAGLIA, Guy A., President and Chief Executive Officer, Saint Anthony Hospital, Chicago, IL, p. A186

MEDCIROS, Ron, Director Applied Information Technology, Worcester Recovery Center and Hospital, Worcester, MA, p. A317

MEDEIROS, Katherine A., President and Chief Executive Officer, Sierra Nevada Memorial Hospital, Grass Valley, CA, p. A65

MEDEROS, Ana J., Chief Executive Officer, Palmetto General Hospital, Hialeah, FL, p. A130

MEDINA, Alberto, Information Technology Senior Consultant, Hospital Manati Medical Center, Manati, PR, p. A728

MEDINA, Betsmari, Director Human Resources, Dr. Ramon E. Betances Hospital–Mayaguez Medical Center Branch, Mayaguez, PR, p. A728

MEDINA, Ed, M.D. Medical Director, Phillips County Hospital, Malta, MT, p. A389

MEDINA, Eleanor, M.D. Chief Medical Officer, Behavioral Center of Michigan, Warren, MI, p. A336

MEDINA, Luz D., Controller, Hospital Hermanos Melendez, Bayamon, PR, p. A726

MEDINA, Marco, Chief Information Officer, Stanton County Hospital, Johnson, KS, p. A246

MEDINA, Obdulia, Associate Director for Administrative Support, Clinical Management and Ambulatory Care, Ashford Presbyterian Community Hospital, San Juan, PR, p. A729

MEDINA, Patricia, Service Unit Director, U. S. Public Health Service Indian Hospital, Winnebago, NE, p. A403

MEDINA, Shelby, Chief Executive Officer, Windom Area Hospital, Windom, MN, p. A353

MEDLAND, Jacqueline, M
Regional Chief Nursing Officer, Presence Saint Joseph Medical Center, Joliet, IL, p. A194
Regional Chief Nursing Officer, Presence St. Mary's Hospital, Kankakee, IL, p. A194

MEDLEY, Adron, M.D. Chief Medical Staff, Northern Rockies Medical Center, Cut Bank, MT, p. A386

MEDLEY, Barry, Director Information Systems, Cook Medical Center–A Campus of Tift Regional Medical Center, Adel, GA, p. A151

MEDLEY, Dennis, Chief Executive Officer and Administrator, Physicians' Medical Center, New Albany, IN, p. A219

MEDLEY, Wathen, M.D. Chief Medical Officer, Owensboro Health Regional Hospital, Owensboro, KY, p. A267

MEDLIN, John, Chief Nursing Officer, North Carolina Specialty Hospital, Durham, NC, p. A464

MEDLIN, Marsha, Senior Vice President of Clinical and Operations, PAM Specialty Hospital of Covington, Covington, LA, p. A275

MEDLOCK, Darci, Manager Human Resources, St. Vincent Dunn Hospital, Bedford, IN, p. A206

MEDOVICH, Lisa, Chief Financial Officer, Peterson Regional Medical Center, Kerrville, TX, p. A630

MEE, Randall L., FACHE, Chief Executive Officer, Blue Mountain Hospital, John Day, OR, p. A527

MEE, Thomas, R.N., President and Chief Executive Officer, McLaren Greater Lansing, Lansing, MI, p. A328

MEEHAN, Neil S., D.O. Chief Medical Officer and Chief Medical Information Officer, Lawrence General Hospital, Lawrence, MA, p. A311

MEEK, Kevin Lee, R.N. Chief Nursing Officer, Dignity Health Arizona General Hospital, Laveen, AZ, p. A34

MEEKER, Brian, D.O. President Medical Staff, Virginia Gay Hospital, Vinton, IA, p. A238

MEEKER, Chris, M.D. Chief Medical Officer, Sanford Bismarck, Bismarck, ND, p. A477

MEEKER, Christina, Director Human Resources, Strategic Behavioral Health – Raleigh, Garner, NC, p. A465

MEEKER, Larry, Chief Executive Officer, Howard A. Rusk Rehabilitation Center, Columbia, MO, p. A370

MEEKER, Mark, D.O. Medical Staff President, OSF St. Mary Medical Center, Galesburg, IL, p. A191

MEEKINS, Lance, Chief Executive Officeer, Nocona General Hospital, Nocona, TX, p. A639

MEEKINS, Michelle, Manager Human Resources, Sentara Virginia Beach General Hospital, Virginia Beach, VA, p. A680

MEEKS, Deborah, Chief Nursing Officer, Harlingen Medical Center, Harlingen, TX, p. A622

MEENK, Susan
Vice President Service Area, Providence Centralia Hospital, Centralia, WA, p. A683
Vice President Human Resources, Providence St. Peter Hospital, Olympia, WA, p. A687

MEESE, Larry, Chief Executive Officer, Jackson Hospital, Marianna, FL, p. A135

MEESIG, Deborah, M.D. Chief of Staff, Chillicothe Veterans Affairs Medical Center, Chillicothe, OH, p. A487

MEGEHEE, Mark, Vice President and Chief Information Officer, Decatur Morgan Hospital, Decatur, AL, p. A18

MEGGERS, Marla, Chief Nursing Officer and Chief Operating Officer, Florence Hospital at Anthem, Florence, AZ, p. A32

MEGGERS, Marla, R.N. Chief Nursing Officer, Gilbert Hospital, Gilbert, AZ, p. A32

MEGLEMRE, Amy J., R.N. Senior Vice President and Chief Nursing Officer, Olathe Medical Center, Olathe, KS, p. A250

MEGLI, Cami, Controller, Morrison Community Hospital, Morrison, IL, p. A197

MEGLIOLA, Donna M., Assistant Vice President, Johnson Memorial Medical Center, Stafford Springs, CT, p. A117

MEGOW, Kimberly, M.D. Chief Medical Officer, South Georgia Medical Center, Valdosta, GA, p. A168

MEGUIAR, Ramon V., M.D. Chief Medical Officer, Memorial Health, Savannah, GA, p. A166

MEHAFFEY, SHRM–SCP, M. Beth, Senior Vice President Human Resources, Baptist Medical Center Jacksonville, Jacksonville, FL, p. A131

MEHARG, John, Director Health Information Technology, Norman Regional Health System, Norman, OK, p. A515

MEHINDRU, Vinay, M.D
Vice President/Chief Medical Officer, Florida Hospital Waterman, Tavares, FL, p. A148
Medical Director, Wuesthoff Medical Center – Rockledge, Rockledge, FL, p. A143

MEHR, Nicholle, Vice President Operations, McLaren Oakland, Pontiac, MI, p. A332

MEHTA, Kalpana, Chief Fiscal Services, Jesse Brown Veterans Affairs Medical Center, Chicago, IL, p. A184

MEHTA, Sonia, M.D., Chief Executive Officer and Chief Medical Officer, Loretto Hospital, Chicago, IL, p. A184

MEHTA, Umesh, M.D. Interim Chief Medical Officer, Carrier Clinic, Belle Mead, NJ, p. A414

MEIDINGER, Sue, Manager Business Office, Linton Hospital, Linton, ND, p. A480

MEIER, Suzanne S., System Director, Compensation and Human Resources Technology, Memorial Hermann Memorial City Medical Center, Houston, TX, p. A625

MEIERGERD, Jean, Chief Information Officer, St. Francis Memorial Hospital, West Point, NE, p. A403

MEIERS, Dawn, Coordinator Medical Staff and Personnel Services, Southeast Michigan Surgical Hospital, Warren, MI, p. A336

MEIGS, Jeffrey L., Chief Financial Officer, Louis A. Weiss Memorial Hospital, Chicago, IL, p. A184

MEIGS, Jr., John, M.D. Chief of Staff, Bibb Medical Center, Centreville, AL, p. A18

MEINDEL, Nympha, R.N. Chief Information Officer, North Shore University Hospital, Manhasset, NY, p. A442

MEINHART, Richard, Manager Information Systems, Daviess Community Hospital, Washington, IN, p. A223

MEINKE, Kenneth, Senior Vice President Administrative Services, Finance and Chief Financial Officer, Spartanburg Medical Center, Spartanburg, SC, p. A570

MEINKE, Victor E., Chief Financial Officer, Jewish Home of San Francisco, San Francisco, CA, p. A90

MEINKOTH, Jennifer, Chief Information Officer, Memorial Hospital, Belleville, IL, p. A181

MEISINGER, Alan, Chief Financial Officer, Herington Municipal Hospital, Herington, KS, p. A244

MEISNER, Anne, MSN, President and Chief Executive Officer, Southeastern Regional Medical Center, Newnan, GA, p. A164

MEITZ, Mary
Senior Vice President and Chief Financial Officer, Bronson Battle Creek, Battle Creek, MI, p. A319
Vice President Finance, Bronson Methodist Hospital, Kalamazoo, MI, p. A328

MEKHAEL, Hani, M.D. Chief Staff, Havenwyck Hospital, Auburn Hills, MI, p. A318

MEKO, Christian, Hospital Commander, General Leonard Wood Army Community Hospital, Fort Leonard Wood, MO, p. A371

MELAHN, William L., M.D. Vice President Medical Affairs and Chief Medical Officer, St. Claire Regional Medical Center, Morehead, KY, p. A267

MELAN, Kristen, Director Human Resources Administration, Good Shepherd Specialty Hospital, Bethlehem, PA, p. A533

MELANCON, Eric, Chief of Staff, Teche Regional Medical Center, Morgan City, LA, p. A284

MELAND, Jeff, M.D. Vice President, Chief Medical Officer, Northfield Hospital, Northfield, MN, p. A348

MELARAGNO, Robert, Vice President Finance, O'Bleness Memorial Hospital, Athens, OH, p. A484

MELBOURNE, John, M.D. Medical Director, Conifer Park, Glenville, NY, p. A439

MELBY, Gina, Chief Executive Officer, JFK Medical Center, Atlantis, FL, p. A123

MELBY, Larry, Chief Executive Officer, Select Specialty Hospital–Palm Beach, Lake Worth, FL, p. A133

MELBY, Rachel, Vice President, Chief Financial Officer, Crawford County Memorial Hospital, Denison, IA, p. A229

MELCHER, Nancy, Chief Nursing Officer, North Fulton Regional Hospital, Roswell, GA, p. A165

MELCHIODE, Joseph D., Chief Executive Officer, University Hospital and Medical Center, Tamarac, FL, p. A146

MELCHIOR, Eric L., Executive Vice President and Chief Financial Officer, Greater Baltimore Medical Center, Baltimore, MD, p. A296

MELEAR, Brian, R.N., Chief Executive Officer, Raulerson Hospital, Okeechobee, FL, p. A140

MELENDEZ, Alma, Controller, Dimmit Regional Hospital, Carrizo Springs, TX, p. A605

MELENDEZ, Jenni, Executive Director, Hospital HIMA de Humacao, Humacao, PR, p. A727

MELENDEZ, Jose, M.D. Chief Medical Officer, Memorial Hospital, Colorado Springs, CO, p. A102

MELENDEZ, Pedro
Chief Executive Officer, Centro De Salud Conductual Menonita–CIMA, Aibonito, PR, p. A725
Chief Executive Director, Hospital Menonita De Cayey, Cayey, PR, p. A727
Chief Executive Officer, Mennonite General Hospital, Aibonito, PR, p. A725

MELINE, Brenda, Manager Human Resources, Patients' Hospital of Redding, Redding, CA, p. A84

MELL, Kevin, Vice President Operations, MedStar Montgomery Medical Center, Olney, MD, p. A302

MELLETT, David, Chief Financial Officer, Harrison Memorial Hospital, Cynthiana, KY, p. A259

MELLGREN, Gustave, M.D. Chief of Staff, Glacial Ridge Health System, Glenwood, MN, p. A343

MELLO, Brett, Chief Information Officer, Cayuga Medical Center at Ithaca, Ithaca, NY, p. A440

MELLO, Paul, Manager Data Processing, Metropolitan State Hospital, Norwalk, CA, p. A79

MELLON, Stacy, Manager Human Resource, Hillsdale Hospital, Hillsdale, MI, p. A326

MELNIKOFF, Jean, Vice President Human Resources, Kaiser Permanente Medical Center, Honolulu, HI, p. A170

MELSON, Benjamin B., CPA Executive Vice President and Chief Financial Officer, Texas Children's Hospital, Houston, TX, p. A626

MELTON, Anne, Chief Nursing Officer, Sumner Regional Medical Center, Gallatin, TN, p. A583

MELTON, Chad, Chief Executive Officer, Wythe County Community Hospital, Wytheville, VA, p. A681

MELTON, Josh, Chief Information Officer, St. Bernards Medical Center, Jonesboro, AR, p. A48

MELTVEDT, Jr., Robert, M.D. Vice President Medical Affairs, Warren Memorial Hospital, Front Royal, VA, p. A671

MELTZER, David B., Chief Financial Officer, Texas Health Presbyterian Hospital Denton, Denton, TX, p. A613

MELTZER, Neil M., President and Chief Executive Officer, LifeBridge Health, Baltimore, MD, p. B81

MELVILLE, Carol, Director Human Resources, West Houston Medical Center, Houston, TX, p. A627

MELVIN, Daryl, Chief Executive Officer, Hopi Health Care Center, Kearns Canyon, AZ, p. A33

MELVIN, Susan, D.O. Chief Medical Officer, Long Beach Memorial Medical Center, Long Beach, CA, p. A69

MENDELOWITZ, Susan, FACHE, President, Administrator and Chief Operating Officer, Bergen Regional Medical Center, Paramus, NJ, p. A421

MENDEZ, Alex A., Executive Vice President of Operations and Chief Financial Officer, Mount Sinai Medical Center, Miami Beach, FL, p. A138

MENDEZ, Bryce H.P., Healthcare Policy Analyst, Bureau of Medicine and Surgery, Department of the Navy, Falls Church, VA, p. B25

MENDEZ, James, Chief Executive Officer, Kindred Hospital–Dallas, Dallas, TX, p. A610

MENDEZ, Kim K., Ed.D. Chief Nurse Officer, NYC Health + Hospitals / Bellevue, New York, NY, p. A447

MENDEZ, Lincoln S., Chief Executive Officer, Baptist Health South Florida, South Miami Hospital, Miami, FL, p. A136

MENDEZ, Nicholas Paul, Chief Executive Officer, PAM Specialty Hospital of Hammond, Hammond, LA, p. A278

MENDEZ, Samantha, Human Resources, Freedom Pain Hospital, Scottsdale, AZ, p. A38

MENDIOLA–BALDERAS, Rosie L., Director Information Systems, South Texas Health System, Edinburg, TX, p. A614

MENDITTO, Anthony, Ph.D. Interim Chief Operating Officer, Fulton State Hospital, Fulton, MO, p. A371

MENDIZABAL, Oscar, Chief Nursing Officer, Highlands Rehabilitation Hospital, El Paso, TX, p. A615

MENDOZA, Aniceta, R.N. Chief Nursing Officer, Valley Baptist Medical Center–Brownsville, Brownsville, TX, p. A604

MENDOZA, Carlos, Controller, Baptist Memorial Rehabilitation Hospital, Germantown, TN, p. A583

MENDOZA, Chris, Interim Chief Executive Officer, Toppenish Community Hospital, Toppenish, WA, p. A692

MENDOZA, Christopher, Chief Executive Officer, AllianceHealth Ponca City, Ponca City, OK, p. A518

MENDOZA, Dana, Chief Information Officer, Maui Memorial Medical Center, Wailuku, HI, p. A173

MENDOZA, Jackie, Chief Nursing Officer, CHI Health Nebraska Heart, Lincoln, NE, p. A397

MENDOZA, Joseph
Chief Financial Officer, Hillcrest Hospital Cushing, Cushing, OK, p. A510
Chief Financial Officer, Hillcrest Hospital Henryetta, Henryetta, OK, p. A512

MENDOZA, Joseph, M.D. Medical Director, Porterville Developmental Center, Porterville, CA, p. A83

MENDOZA, Yolanda, Director Human Resources, Rehabilitation Hospital of Southern New Mexico, Las Cruces, NM, p. A430

MENDYKA, Nick, Chief Financial Officer, University of Virginia Medical Center, Charlottesville, VA, p. A668

MENEFEE, Jason J., Chief Financial Officer, McCamey County Hospital District, McCamey, TX, p. A636

MENGLE, Scott, Vice President Human Resources, Penn State Health St. Joseph, Reading, PA, p. A553

MENNINGA, Cathy, R.N. Chief Nursing Officer, Ellett Memorial Hospital, Appleton City, MO, p. A367

MENNONNA, Guy, Senior Vice President Human Resources, Bergen Regional Medical Center, Paramus, NJ, p. A421

MENON, Rema, M.D. Clinical Director, Parsons State Hospital and Training Center, Parsons, KS, p. A252

MENSCH, Alan, M.D. Senior Vice President Medical Affairs, Plainview Hospital, Plainview, NY, p. A452

MENSEN, Amy, Chief Administrative Officer, Regional Medical Center, Manchester, IA, p. A234

MENTGEN, John, FACHE, President and Chief Executive Officer, Regional West Medical Center, Scottsbluff, NE, p. A402

MENTHCOAST, Lynn, Chief Fiscal Service, Tennessee Valley Healthcare System, Nashville, TN, p. A591

MENTINK, Terri, Chief Financial Officer, Oakland Mercy Hospital, Oakland, NE, p. A399

MENTZEL, Bridget, Director Human Resources, Mercy Health – West Hospital, Cincinnati, OH, p. A488

MENTZER, Larry, Chief Human Resources Officer, Veterans Affairs Roseburg Healthcare System, Roseburg, OR, p. A530

MENZIE, Sue, R.N. Director Patient Care, Sierra Tucson, Tucson, AZ, p. A41

MERCADO, Gloria, Director of Nursing, Mennonite General Hospital, Aibonito, PR, p. A725

MERCADO, Leda Marta R, Chief Operating Officer, Hospital Menonita De Cayey, Cayey, PR, p. A727

MERCER, David, Coordinator Information Systems, Baptist Memorial Hospital–Union City, Union City, TN, p. A594

MERCER, Shawna, Director Human Resources, Kansas Neurological Institute, Topeka, KS, p. A254

MERCER, William, M.D. Director, Peterson Healthcare and Rehabilitation Hospital, Wheeling, WV, p. A701

MERCHANT, Deven, M.D. Chief Medical Executive, Sutter Davis Hospital, Davis, CA, p. A60

MERCURI, Ralph, Vice President and Chief Financial Officer, Major Hospital, Shelbyville, IN, p. A222

MEREDITH, James, M.D. Chief of Staff, Forrest City Medical Center, Forrest City, AR, p. A46

MEREDITH, Katie, Chief Nursing Officer, Select Specialty Hospital–Lexington, Lexington, KY, p. A263

MEREDITH, Keith, Chief Operating Officer, Salem Regional Medical Center, Salem, OH, p. A502

MEREDITH, Linda, MSN Chief Operating Officer, Scott & White Hospital – Llano, Llano, TX, p. A633

MEREK, Gloria, Director of Nursing, Springfield Hospital Center, Sykesville, MD, p. A303

MERGEN, Lynn M., Chief Executive Officer, Hillcrest Hospital – South, Tulsa, OK, p. A521

MERIDA, Andy, Director Management Information Systems, Fayette Regional Health System, Connersville, IN, p. A208

MERILL, Doug, M.D. Chief Medical Officer, UC Irvine Medical Center, Orange, CA, p. A81

MERILLO, Myra, Supervisor Health Information Management, HEALTHSOUTH Rehabilitation Hospital of Spring Hill, Brooksville, FL, p. A125

MERINGOLO, Francis, Vice President Human Resources, UMass Memorial–Marlborough Hospital, Marlborough, MA, p. A312

MERIWETHER, Wayne, Chief Executive Officer, Twin Lakes Regional Medical Center, Leitchfield, KY, p. A262

MERK, Richard, Executive Vice President, Allegiance Behavioral Health Center of Plainview, Plainview, TX, p. A641

MERKEL, Rebecca, Privacy Officer, Franciscan St. Francis Health–Carmel, Carmel, IN, p. A208

MERKLE, John F., Medical Center Director, Tuscaloosa Veterans Affairs Medical Center, Tuscaloosa, AL, p. A26

MERKLER, Michael, Chief of Staff, McKenzie Health System, Sandusky, MI, p. A334

MERKLEY, Jason R., Chief Executive Officer, Brookings Health System, Brookings, SD, p. A572

MERKLIN, Paul, Vice President Finance and Chief Financial Officer, Manchester Memorial Hospital, Manchester, KY, p. A266

MERRENS, Edward J., M.D. Medical Director, Dartmouth–Hitchcock Medical Center, Lebanon, NH, p. A412

MERRIGAN, Mary C., Manager Public Relations, Sanford Vermillion Medical Center, Vermillion, SD, p. A577

MERRILL, Cheryl Bhima, MSN Senior Vice President Patient Care Services and Chief Nursing Officer, North Shore Medical Center, Salem, MA, p. A314

MERRILL, Chuck, M.D. Vice President Medical Affairs, Marian Regional Medical Center, Santa Maria, CA, p. A93

MERRILL, Mark H., President and Chief Executive Officer, Valley Health System, Winchester, VA, p. B150

MERRILL, Michael, M.D. Interim Vice President Medical Affairs, United Memorial Medical Center, Batavia, NY, p. A434

MERRILL, Rick W., System President and Chief Executive Officer, Cook Children's Medical Center, Fort Worth, TX, p. A618

MERRILL, Stacie, Chief Nursing Officer, Baylor Surgical Hospital at Fort Worth, Fort Worth, TX, p. A617

MERRILL, Stephanie, Chief Financial Officer, University Medical Center, Las Vegas, NV, p. A407

MERRITT, Becky A., Director Human Resources, Houston Methodist St. John Hospital, Nassau Bay, TX, p. A638

MERRITT, Belinda, M.D. Medical Director, HEALTHSOUTH Cane Creek Rehabilitation Hospital, Martin, TN, p. A587

MERRITT, Bradley, M.D. Medical Director, CHRISTUS Trinity Mother Frances Rehabilitation Hospital, Tyler, TX, p. A654

MERRITT, Janet, Chief Financial Officer, St. Vincent Williamsport Hospital, Williamsport, IN, p. A224

MERRITT, Tim E., Chief Executive Officer, SummitRidge Hospital, Lawrenceville, GA, p. A162

MERRITT, Trevor, Director Human Resources, Star Valley Medical Center, Afton, WY, p. A721

MERRY, Duane, Chief Information Officer, Little Falls Hospital, Little Falls, NY, p. A441

MERRYMAN, Angela, Chief Executive Officer, Select Specialty Hospital–McKeesport, McKeesport, PA, p. A544

MERRYMAN, Mary, Regional Director Information Management, CHRISTUS Health Shreveport–Bossier, Shreveport, LA, p. A287

MERRYMAN, Scott
Chief Financial Officer, CHRISTUS Coushatta Health Care Center, Coushatta, LA, p. A275
Chief Financial Officer, CHRISTUS Health Shreveport–Bossier, Shreveport, LA, p. A287
Chief Financial Officer, CHRISTUS St. Patrick Hospital of Lake Charles, Lake Charles, LA, p. A281

MERRYWELL, Paul, Chief Information Officer, Sycamore Shoals Hospital, Elizabethton, TN, p. A582

MERSON, John, M.D. Chief of Staff, John Muir Medical Center, Concord, Concord, CA, p. A59

MERSON, Wendy, Chief Executive Officer, Windmoor Healthcare of Clearwater, Clearwater, FL, p. A125

MERTZ, John, Chief Information Officer, South Nassau Communities Hospital, Oceanside, NY, p. A451

MESA, Gustavo, Chief Information Officer, San Juan City Hospital, San Juan, PR, p. A730

MESIC, John, M.D. Chief Medical Officer, Sutter Auburn Faith Hospital, Auburn, CA, p. A55

MESKAN, Paula, R.N. Chief Nursing Officer, River's Edge Hospital and Clinic, Saint Peter, MN, p. A351

MESORAS, Amber, Chief Human Resources Officer, Veterans Affairs Pittsburgh Healthcare System, Pittsburgh, PA, p. A552

MESSA–GILL, Nicole, Manager Human Resources, Northlake Behavioral Health System, Mandeville, LA, p. A282

MESSELT, Mary Jo
Senior Human Resources Manager, Mercy Hospital Logan County, Guthrie, OK, p. A512
Manager Human Resources, Mercy Hospital Watonga, Watonga, OK, p. A523

MESSER, Kelly, Director of Finance, Devereux Hospital and Children's Center of Florida, Melbourne, FL, p. A135

MESSERSMITH, Darrell, Director Information Systems, Platte Valley Medical Center, Brighton, CO, p. A102

MESSERSMITH, Scott E., Director Human Resources, Columbus Community Hospital, Columbus, NE, p. A395

MESSINA, Arlene, R.N. Director of Nursing, Riverside Doctors' Hospital, Williamsburg, VA, p. A680

MESSINA, Daniel J., FACHE, President and Chief Executive Officer, Richmond University Medical Center,, NY, p. A449

MESSMAN, Catherine, Chief Financial Officer, Mills–Peninsula Health Services, Burlingame, CA, p. A57

MESTAS, Lisa, Associate Administrator and System Chief Nursing Officer, University of South Alabama Medical Center, Mobile, AL, p. A23

MESTER, Sulynn, R.N. Chief Nursing Officer, Childress Regional Medical Center, Childress, TX, p. A606

MESZLER, Lori A., Chief Financial Officer, Helen Hayes Hospital, West Haverstraw, NY, p. A458

METCALF, Angie L., Vice President and Chief Human Resource Officer, Martin Health System, Stuart, FL, p. A146

METCALF, Chris, Director of Nursing, Utah State Hospital, Provo, UT, p. A662

METCALF, Emma, R.N., Director, Lexington Veterans Affairs Medical Center, Lexington, KY, p. A263

METCALF, Kathleen, Chief Information Officer, University Hospitals Samaritan Medical Center, Ashland, OH, p. A484

METCALF, Peter, M.D. President Medical Staff, Genesis Medical Center, Illini Campus, Silvis, IL, p. A203

METHE, Joan, Chief Information Officer, Mercy Medical Center, Springfield, MA, p. A315

METHVEN, Jeffrey M., Vice President Ambulatory Services and Chief Human Resources Officer, Saratoga Hospital, Saratoga Springs, NY, p. A455

METHVIN, Jeff, Manager Information Technology, St. Luke Hospital and Living Center, Marion, KS, p. A248

METIKO, Olushola, M.D. Medical Director, Central Prison Hospital, Raleigh, NC, p. A471

METINKO, Andrew, M.D. Chief Medical Officer, The HSC Pediatric Center, Washington, DC, p. A122

METIVIER, Roberta, Vice President Human Resources and Administrator, Western Main Nursing Home, Stephens Memorial Hospital, Norway, ME, p. A294

METRO, Michelle, Vice President Nursing, Cloud County Health Center, Concordia, KS, p. A242

METTEAUER, Kenneth, Chief Financial Officer, Redmond Regional Medical Center, Rome, GA, p. A165

METZ, Amy, Chief Executive Officer, Regency Hospital of Florence, Florence, SC, p. A566

METZ, Bruce, Ph.D. Senior Vice President and Chief Information Officer, Lahey Hospital & Medical Center, Burlington, Burlington, MA, p. A308

METZ, Carl
  Vice President, Ephraim McDowell Fort Logan Hospital, Stanford, KY, p. A269
  Vice President Human Resources, Ephraim McDowell Regional Medical Center, Danville, KY, p. A259

METZGER, Alysha, Director Human Resources, Hill Country Memorial Hospital, Fredericksburg, TX, p. A619

METZGER, Cynthia, Chief Nursing and Operations Officer, Little River Memorial Hospital, Ashdown, AR, p. A43

METZGER, John, Controller, NorthKey Community Care, Covington, KY, p. A259

METZGER, Terry, Vice President, Finance, St. Vincent Indianapolis Hospital, Indianapolis, IN, p. A215

MEUER, Lynn, Interim Chief Nursing Officer, Sibley Memorial Hospital, Washington, DC, p. A122

MEURER, Bryan, Director Information Systems, Mat–Su Regional Medical Center, Palmer, AK, p. A30

MEURER, Lynn, MSN Interim Chief Nursing Officer, WellStar Kennestone Hospital, Marietta, GA, p. A163

MEWHIRTER, Michael, President, Fort Hamilton Hospital, Hamilton, OH, p. A496

MEYER, Anthony, M.D. Medical Director, Aurora Psychiatric Hospital, Wauwatosa, WI, p. A718

MEYER, Cheryl, MSN Director of Nursing, Haven Behavioral Senior Care of Dayton, Dayton, OH, p. A492

MEYER, Cheryl, Director Human Resources, Palmer Lutheran Health Center, West Union, IA, p. A239

MEYER, Christopher T., D.O.,
  Chief Executive Officer and Chairman of the Board of Governors, Holzer Medical Center, Gallipolis, OH, p. A495
  Chief Executive Officer and Chairman of the Board of Governors, Holzer Medical Center – Jackson, Jackson, OH, p. A496

MEYER, Daniel T., President, Aurora BayCare Medical Center, Green Bay, WI, p. A706

MEYER, Francis, Vice President Information Systems Technology, KALEIDA Health, Buffalo, NY, p. A436

MEYER, Gordon, Director Human Resources, Oakland Regional Hospital, Southfield, MI, p. A334

MEYER, Joe S., Chief Financial Officer, Scott County Hospital, Scott City, KS, p. A253

MEYER, June, MSN Vice President Chief Nursing Officer, Laurel Regional Hospital, Laurel, MD, p. A302

MEYER, Karen, Vice President Finance and Chief Financial Officer, Rush Memorial Hospital, Rushville, IN, p. A221

MEYER, Kurt A.
  Chief Human Resource Officer, Saint Joseph Regional Medical Center, Mishawaka, IN, p. A218
  Chief Human Resources Officer, Saint Joseph Regional Medical Center–Plymouth Campus, Plymouth, IN, p. A220

MEYER, Mark, Chief Financial Officer, Grady Memorial Hospital, Atlanta, GA, p. A152

MEYER, Morgan, Chief Financial Officer, Howard County Medical Center, Saint Paul, NE, p. A402

MEYER, Nate, Director Finance, Douglas County Hospital, Alexandria, MN, p. A338

MEYER, Philip A., Vice President, Finance, Dearborn County Hospital, Lawrenceburg, IN, p. A217

MEYER, Renae, M.D. Chief Medical Officer, St. Francis Memorial Hospital, West Point, NE, p. A403

MEYER, Richard A., Chief Financial Officer, Mary Black Health System–Spartanburg, Spartanburg, SC, p. A569

MEYER, Robert L., President and Chief Executive Officer, Phoenix Children's Hospital, Phoenix, AZ, p. A37

MEYER, Roger, M.D. Chief of Staff, Friend Community Healthcare System, Friend, NE, p. A396

MEYER, Timothy, M.D. Chief of Staff, Memorial Medical Center – Neillsville, Neillsville, WI, p. A712

MEYER, Traci, Director Human Resources, Canyon Vista Medical Center, Sierra Vista, AZ, p. A39

MEYER, Wessel H., M.D., Acting Director, Veterans Affairs Central California Health Care System, Fresno, CA, p. A64

MEYERHOEFER, Todd, M.D. Vice President Medical Affairs, Union Hospital, Dover, OH, p. A493

MEYERS, Audrey, President and Chief Executive Officer, Valley Hospital, Ridgewood, NJ, p. A423

MEYERS, Betty, Chief Financial Officer, Crook County Medical Services District, Sundance, WY, p. A724

MEYERS, J. Cullen, Chief Executive Officer, PAM Specialty Hospital of Covington, Covington, LA, p. A275

MEYERS, Larry, Chief Information Officer, Wilson Memorial Hospital, Sidney, OH, p. A502

MEYERS, Mark S., M.D. Chief of Staff, Battle Mountain General Hospital, Battle Mountain, NV, p. A404

MEYERS, Russell, President and Chief Executive Officer, Midland Memorial Hospital, Midland, TX, p. A637

MEYERS, William, Chief Information Officer, St. Luke's Hospital, Chesterfield, MO, p. A369

MEZA, Eduardo, M.D. Medical Director, Prairie St. John's, Fargo, ND, p. A478

MEZA, Lourdes, Coordinator Human Resources, West Covina Medical Center, West Covina, CA, p. A99

MEZOFF, Adam, M.D. Vice President and Chief Medical Officer, Children's Medical Center, Dayton, OH, p. A492

MHERABI, Nader, Senior Vice President and Vice Dean, Chief Information Officer, NYU Langone Medical Center, New York, NY, p. A449

MIANO, Christena, Human Resources Director, Medical Center of Trinity, Trinity, FL, p. A148

MICCOLI, Vincent, Executive Director, Manhattan Psychiatric Center–Ward's Island, New York, NY, p. A445

MICHAEL, Amy J., Chief Operating Officer, Sullivan County Memorial Hospital, Milan, MO, p. A376

MICHAEL, Don, Vice President, Chief Financial Officer, Jay County Hospital, Portland, IN, p. A220

MICHAEL, Elizabeth, R.N. Vice President Patient Care Services and Chief Nursing Officer, Stillwater Medical Center, Stillwater, OK, p. A520

MICHAELS, Stephen T., M.D. Chief Operating Officer and Chief Medical Officer, MedStar St. Mary's Hospital, Leonardtown, MD, p. A302

MICHALEK, Debra, Chief Financial Officer, Fayette Regional Health System, Connersville, IN, p. A208

MICHALSKI, Carrie, President and Chief Executive Officer, RiverView Health, Crookston, MN, p. A341

MICHAUD, Thomas A., Chief Executive Officer, Foundation Surgical Hospital Affiliates, Oklahoma City, OK, p. B56

MICHEL, Diane, Senior Vice President, Chief Nursing Officer, Children's Hospital, New Orleans, LA, p. A284

MICHEL, George J., Chief Operating Officer, Larkin Community Hospital, South Miami, FL, p. A145

MICHEL, Randall, M.D. Chief of Staff, Lompoc Valley Medical Center, Lompoc, CA, p. A69

MICHEL–OGBORN, Deborah, Chief Information Resource Management, North Florida/South Georgia Veteran's Health System, Gainesville, FL, p. A129

MICHELE, Margorie, Chief Human Resources Officer, Penn Presbyterian Medical Center, Philadelphia, PA, p. A549

MICHELEN, Jeannith
  Associate Executive Director, NYC Health + Hospitals / Elmhurst,, NY, p. A448
  Senior Associate Executive Director, NYC Health + Hospitals / Lincoln,, NY, p. A448
  Senior Associate Executive Director, NYC Health + Hospitals / Queens,, NY, p. A449

MICHELETTI, Denise D., R.N., Director, Central Virginia Training Center, Madison Heights, VA, p. A673

MICHELETTI, Susan C., Chief Executive Officer, Emanuel Medical Center, Turlock, CA, p. A97

MICHELL, Pamela W., R.N. Vice President, Chief Nursing Officer, Munroe Regional Medical Center, Ocala, FL, p. A139

MICHELSON, Soad, M.D. Senior Medical Director, Clarity Child Guidance Center, San Antonio, TX, p. A645

MICHENER, Scott, M.D. Chief Medical Officer, Comanche County Memorial Hospital, Lawton, OK, p. A513

MICHL, Michelle, Director Human Resources, Mercy Medical Center Mount Shasta, Mount Shasta, CA, p. A78

MICKAL, Donald, M.D. Chief Medical Officer, Women's and Children's Hospital, Lafayette, LA, p. A281

MICKENS, Walt, FACHE, President and Chief Executive Officer, Queen of the Valley Medical Center, Napa, CA, p. A79

MICKIEWICZ, Nanette, M.D., President, Dominican Hospital, Santa Cruz, CA, p. A93

MIDDENDORF, Bruce, M.D. Chief Medical Officer, St. Mary's Health Care System, Athens, GA, p. A151

MIDDLEBROOKS, Mark, M.D. Medical Director, Noland Hospital Birmingham, Birmingham, AL, p. A17

MIDDLETON, Frank, M.D. Interim Chief Medical Officer, Phoebe Putney Memorial Hospital, Albany, GA, p. A151

MIDDLETON, Jackie, Vice President Human Resources, Methodist Dallas Medical Center, Dallas, TX, p. A610

MIDDLETON, James, MSN Chief Nursing Officer, Knox Community Hospital, Mount Vernon, OH, p. A499

MIDGETT, Steve, R.N. Chief Nursing Officer, HEALTHSOUTH Sugar Land Rehabilitation Hospital, Sugar Land, TX, p. A650

MIDKIFF, Rodney, Chief Executive Officer, Vibra Hospital of Northwestern Indiana, Crown Point, IN, p. A209

MIDKIFF, Stephen L., Chief Executive Officer, Lake Norman Regional Medical Center, Mooresville, NC, p. A470

MIDTLIEN, Tonia, Information Systems Support Specialist, Gundersen Boscobel Area Hospital and Clinics, Boscobel, WI, p. A703

MIEDLER, Michael, M.D. Chief Medical Officer, Continuing Care Hospital, Lexington, KY, p. A263

MIESNER, Gail, Chief Financial Officer, Memorial Hospital, Chester, IL, p. A183

MIGOYA, Carlos A., President and Chief Executive Officer, Jackson Health System, Miami, FL, p. A136

MIHALAKAKOS, Paul, M.D. Chief of Staff, Aurora Medical Center – Manitowoc County, Two Rivers, WI, p. A717

MIKELL, Evarista, Assistant Finance Officer, William S. Middleton Memorial Veterans Hospital, Madison, WI, p. A709

MIKELL, Jeffrey, M.D. Chief Medical Officer, Select Specialty Hospital – Northeast Atlanta, Atlanta, GA, p. A153

MIKHAIL, Ashraf, M.D. Medical Director, Brynn Marr Hospital, Jacksonville, NC, p. A467

MIKI, Nobuyuki, M.D. Vice President Medical Services and Chief Medical Officer, Kuakini Medical Center, Honolulu, HI, p. A170

MIKITARIAN Jr., George, FACHE, President and Chief Executive Officer, Parrish Medical Center, Titusville, FL, p. A148

MIKITKA, Joseph, Vice President Human Resources, Sacred Heart Hospital, Allentown, PA, p. A532

MIKKELSEN, Kallie, Vice President Nursing, Memorial Hospital of Sweetwater County, Rock Springs, WY, p. A723

MIKKELSON, Tom, M.D. Interim Chief Operating Officer, Touchette Regional Hospital, Centreville, IL, p. A183

MIKLAVIC, Kirk
  Director Human Resources, Bridgton Hospital, Bridgton, ME, p. A292
  Director, Human Resources, Central Maine Medical Center, Lewiston, ME, p. A293

MIKLOS, Maggie, Director Human Resources, Northside Hospital, Saint Petersburg, FL, p. A144

MIKOS, Kathleen A., R.N. Vice President and Chief Nursing Officer, Ingalls Memorial Hospital, Harvey, IL, p. A192

MIKULA, Joan, Interim Commissioner, Massachusetts Department of Mental Health, Boston, MA, p. B85

MIKULIC, Jeannie, Director Human Resources, Providence Portland Medical Center, Portland, OR, p. A529

MIKUTOWSKI, Melody, Chief Human Resources Management, Portland Veterans Affairs Medical Center, Portland, OR, p. A529

MILAM, Wendy, Chief Nursing Officer, HEALTHSOUTH Rehabilitation Hospital of Ocala, Ocala, FL, p. A139

MILAN, Isabel, R.N. Chief Nursing Officer, LAC+USC Medical Center, Los Angeles, CA, p. A72

MILAND, Shelly
  Group Finance Officer, Texas Health Harris Methodist Hospital Cleburne, Cleburne, TX, p. A606
  Group Financial Officer, Texas Health Harris Methodist Hospital Fort Worth, Fort Worth, TX, p. A618
  Chief Financial Officer, Texas Health Specialty Hospital, Fort Worth, TX, p. A619

MILANES, Carlos, Chief Executive Officer, Edgefield County Hospital, Edgefield, SC, p. A565

MILANO, Arthur D., Vice President Human Resources, Berkshire Medical Center, Pittsfield, MA, p. A314

MILATOVICH, Natasha, Association Vice President Human Resources, White Memorial Medical Center, Los Angeles, CA, p. A75

MILAZZO, John, Chief Financial Officer, Merit Health River Region, Vicksburg, MS, p. A365

MILBRANDT, David, M.D. Vice President Medical Affairs, Fairview Lakes Health Services, Wyoming, MN, p. A354

MILBRIDGE, Daniel, Administrator and Chief Operating Officer, Essentia Health–Virginia, Virginia, MN, p. A352

MILBURN, Sandra, Director Human Resources, HEALTHSOUTH Rehabilitation Hospital of Memphis, Memphis, TN, p. A588

MILBURN, Sharon, Chief Nursing Officer, Summers County ARH Hospital, Hinton, WV, p. A696

MILES, Ben, President, Parkview Regional Medical Center, Fort Wayne, IN, p. A211

MILES, Dana, Chief Nursing Officer and Chief Clinical Officer, Delta Memorial Hospital, Dumas, AR, p. A45

MILES, David K., President and Chief Executive Officer, The Children's Institute of Pittsburgh, Pittsburgh, PA, p. A551

MILES, John, Chief Financial Officer, Piedmont Newnan Hospital, Newnan, GA, p. A164

MILES, Karen, M.D. Medical Director, Strategic Behavioral Health – Raleigh, Garner, NC, p. A465

MILES, Kerry
Site Director, Providence Centralia Hospital, Centralia, WA, p. A683
Chief Information Officer, Providence St. Peter Hospital, Olympia, WA, p. A687

MILES, Lee Ann, Chief Financial Officer, Harrison County Community Hospital, Bethany, MO, p. A367

MILES, Paul V.
Chief Operating Officer, Morgan County ARH Hospital, West Liberty, KY, p. A270
Vice President Administration, Whitesburg ARH Hospital, Whitesburg, KY, p. A270

MILETO, Dottie, Chief Nursing Officer, Heart of Florida Regional Medical Center, Davenport, FL, p. A126

MILEY, Dennis C., Administrator, CentraCare Health–Paynesville, Paynesville, MN, p. A348

MILIAN, Tony, Chief Financial Officer, Palm Springs General Hospital, Hialeah, FL, p. A130

MILICEVIC, Heather, Director Human Resources, Summa Western Reserve Hospital, Cuyahoga Falls, OH, p. A492

MILIUS, Hank A., Chief Executive Officer, Meridian Health Services, Muncie, IN, p. A219

MILLAN, Wilfredo Rabelo, Chief Operating Officer, Cardiovascular Center of Puerto Rico and the Caribbean, San Juan, PR, p. A729

MILLARD, James M., President and Chief Executive Officer, Kenmore Mercy Hospital, Kenmore, NY, p. A441

MILLARD, Kathleen, Acting Director Nursing, Kalamazoo Psychiatric Hospital, Kalamazoo, MI, p. A328

MILLEN, Peter S., Chief Medical Officer MHSATS, Community Behavioral Health Hospital – Rochester, Rochester, MN, p. A349

MILLER, Alan B., Chairman and Chief Executive Officer, Universal Health Services, Inc., King of Prussia, PA, p. B142

MILLER, Alicia, Director Human Resources, Aspen Valley Hospital District, Aspen, CO, p. A101

MILLER, Andy, Chief Financial Officer, Memorial Hospital Jacksonville, Jacksonville, FL, p. A131

MILLER, Barbara, Manager Business Office, Regional General Hospital, Williston, FL, p. A150

MILLER, Ben, Chief Executive Officer, AMG Specialty Hospital–Lafayette, Lafayette, LA, p. A280

MILLER, Blaine K., Administrator, Republic County Hospital, Belleville, KS, p. A240

MILLER, Brent R., Manager Human Resources, Brown County Community Treatment Center, Green Bay, WI, p. A706

MILLER, Carol R., R.N. Chief Nursing Officer, Reynolds Memorial Hospital, Glen Dale, WV, p. A696

MILLER, Carrie, Director Human Resources, ProMedica Defiance Regional Hospital, Defiance, OH, p. A493

MILLER, Chad J., President and Chief Executive Officer, Morrow County Hospital, Mount Gilead, OH, p. A499

MILLER, Charles F., Chief Executive Officer, Tennova Healthcare Regional Hospital of Jackson, Jackson, TN, p. A584

MILLER, Chris K., Chief Financial Officer, Highland Hospital, Charleston, WV, p. A695

MILLER, Christine
General Counsel and Vice President Human Resources, Hanover Hospital, Hanover, PA, p. A539
Chief Human Resources Management Services, Maine Veterans Affairs Medical Center, Augusta, ME, p. A291

MILLER, Clint, Chief Nursing Officier, Spooner Health, Spooner, WI, p. A716

MILLER, Connie, Vice President Human Resources, Overland Park Regional Medical Center, Overland Park, KS, p. A251

MILLER, Daniel
Chief Executive Officer, Medical Center of Aurora, Aurora, CO, p. A101
Vice President Human Resources, University Hospitals Elyria Medical Center, Elyria, OH, p. A494
Human Resources Business Partner, University Hospitals Parma Medical Center, Parma, OH, p. A501

MILLER, David L., Chief Information Officer, UAMS Medical Center, Little Rock, AR, p. A49

MILLER, David R., President, River Falls Area Hospital, River Falls, WI, p. A715

MILLER, Debra, Administrator, Crosbyton Clinic Hospital, Crosbyton, TX, p. A608

MILLER, Derek, Senior Vice President and Chief Financial Officer, Southeast Alabama Medical Center, Dothan, AL, p. A19

MILLER, Diane, Administrator, Peterson Healthcare and Rehabilitation Hospital, Wheeling, WV, p. A701

MILLER, Dionne, Chief Operating Officer, Sutter Roseville Medical Center, Roseville, CA, p. A86

MILLER, Donald L., FACHE Vice President, Operations, St. Luke's Hospital, Chesterfield, MO, p. A369

MILLER, Douglas, M.D. Chief of Medical Staff, Clearview Regional Medical Center, Monroe, GA, p. A163

MILLER, Duane
Chief Financial Officer, Integris Bass Baptist Health Center, Enid, OK, p. A511
Chief Financial Officer, Integris Bass Pavilion, Enid, OK, p. A511

MILLER, Dyrek, M.D. Chief Medical Staff, Vidant Duplin Hospital, Kenansville, NC, p. A468

MILLER, Elaine G., Director of Nursing, Oaklawn Psychiatric Center, Goshen, IN, p. A212

MILLER, Elizabeth, CPA Chief Financial Officer, Stamford Memorial Hospital, Stamford, TX, p. A650

MILLER, Esteban, Chief Medical Officer, Black River Memorial Hospital, Black River Falls, WI, p. A703

MILLER, Gary L.
Senior Director Information Systems, Saint Joseph Regional Medical Center, Mishawaka, IN, p. A218
Regional Director Information Systems, Saint Joseph Regional Medical Center–Plymouth Campus, Plymouth, IN, p. A220

MILLER, Greg, Senior Vice President Operations, UF Health Jacksonville, Jacksonville, FL, p. A132

MILLER, Harvey, Director, G. Werber Bryan Psychiatric Hospital, Columbia, SC, p. A564

MILLER, Hope, Director of Medical Records, Peterson Healthcare and Rehabilitation Hospital, Wheeling, WV, p. A701

MILLER, J. D., M.D
Chief Medical Officer, Hazard ARH Regional Medical Center, Hazard, KY, p. A261
Vice President Medical Affairs, Morgan County ARH Hospital, West Liberty, KY, p. A270
Vice President Medical Affairs, Tug Valley ARH Regional Medical Center, South Williamson, KY, p. A269

MILLER, J. Todd, Vice President and Chief Operating Officer, Alice Peck Day Memorial Hospital, Lebanon, NH, p. A411

MILLER, James, Chief Financial Officer, Women's and Children's Hospital, Lafayette, LA, p. A281

MILLER, James L., Chief Financial Officer, Baptist Medical Center Yazoo, Yazoo City, MS, p. A366

MILLER, Jane E.
Director Human Resources, Avera Creighton Hospital, Creighton, NE, p. A395
Human Resources Officer, Avera Sacred Heart Hospital, Yankton, SD, p. A578

MILLER, Jason, M.P.H., Chief Executive Officer, The BridgeWay, North Little Rock, AR, p. A51

MILLER, Jason R., Chief Financial Officer, The Medical Center of Southeast Texas, Port Arthur, TX, p. A642

MILLER, Jay, Acting Director, Veterans Affairs Northern Indiana Health Care System, Fort Wayne, IN, p. A211

MILLER, Jeff, Chief Operating Officer, Citizens Memorial Hospital, Bolivar, MO, p. A367

MILLER, Jeff, M.D. Chief of Staff, Parkview Wabash County Hospital, Wabash, IN, p. A223

MILLER, Jennifer, Chief Executive Officer, Cross Creek Hospital, Austin, TX, p. A599

MILLER, Jeri, M.D. President Medical Staff, Fairview Park Hospital, Dublin, GA, p. A159

MILLER, Jon, Director Accounting and Information Services, Hancock Regional Hospital, Greenfield, IN, p. A212

MILLER, Joshua, Director Information Systems, Joint Township District Memorial Hospital, Saint Marys, OH, p. A502

MILLER, Joy, Chief Nursing Officer, Cornerstone Hospital of Little Rock, Little Rock, AR, p. A49

MILLER, Julie, Chief Operating Officer, Williamson Medical Center, Franklin, TN, p. A583

MILLER, Justin, M.D. Chief of Staff, Wabash General Hospital, Mount Carmel, IL, p. A197

MILLER, Karen, Chief Financial Officer, San Juan Regional Medical Center, Farmington, NM, p. A429

MILLER, Kay J., MSN Chief Nursing Officer, Memorial Hospital, Colorado Springs, CO, p. A102

MILLER, Ken
Chief Financial Officer, CHI St. Luke's Health Memorial Livingston, Livingston, TX, p. A633
Chief Financial Officer, CHI St. Luke's Health Memorial Specialty Hospital, Lufkin, TX, p. A634

MILLER, Kimberly J., FACHE, Chief Executive Officer, Beaver Dam Community Hospitals, Beaver Dam, WI, p. A703

MILLER, Kris, Senior Human Resources Business Partner, Spectrum Health Reed City Hospital, Reed City, MI, p. A332

MILLER, Laurie, Administrative Assistant, Sakakawea Medical Center, Hazen, ND, p. A479

MILLER, Leanne R., Director Human Resources, Community Hospital, McCook, NE, p. A398

MILLER, Linda, R.N. Senior Vice President Operations and Chief Nursing Officer, Our Lady of Lourdes Memorial Hospital, Inc., Binghamton, NY, p. A435

MILLER, Lisa, Director Human Resources, Hendry Regional Medical Center, Clewiston, FL, p. A126

MILLER, Lisa, R.N. Director of Nursing, North Sunflower Medical Center, Ruleville, MS, p. A364

MILLER, Maria, Controller, Beaumont Hospital – Grosse Pointe, Grosse Pointe, MI, p. A326

MILLER, Mark, Chief Financial Officer, Freeman Regional Health Services, Freeman, SD, p. A574

MILLER, Mark, FACHE, Chief Executive Officer, Lake City Medical Center, Lake City, FL, p. A133

MILLER, Mark, Director Information Systems, Perry County Memorial Hospital, Tell City, IN, p. A222

MILLER, Mark A., FACHE, Chief Executive Officer, Memorial Health System, Abilene, KS, p. A240

MILLER, Mary, Vice President Finance and Business Development, Mt. Washington Pediatric Hospital, Baltimore, MD, p. A297

MILLER, Mary Beth, M.D. Chief of Staff, Cheyenne County Hospital, Saint Francis, KS, p. A253

MILLER, Mathew, M.D. Vice President and Chief Medical Officer, St. Joseph Hospital, Eureka, CA, p. A61

MILLER, Matthew, M.D. Chief Medical Officer – WCHN, Danbury Hospital, Danbury, CT, p. A113

MILLER, Melissa, Director Human Resources, St. Elizabeth Hospital, Gonzales, LA, p. A277

MILLER, Michael J.
Director Human Resources, Barnes–Jewish St. Peters Hospital, Saint Peters, MO, p. A382
Director Human Resources, Progress West Hospital, O'Fallon, MO, p. A377

MILLER, Michele A., R.N. Vice President, Acute and Nursing Services, University Behavioral Healthcare, Piscataway, NJ, p. A422

MILLER, Nancy, R.N. Chief Nursing Officer, Van Matre HealthSouth Rehabilitation Hospital, Rockford, IL, p. A202

MILLER, Nicole, Director Human Resources, Riverside Shore Memorial Hospital, Nassawadox, VA, p. A674

MILLER, Patrick, Technology Coordinator, San Bernardino Mountains Community Hospital District, Lake Arrowhead, CA, p. A68

MILLER, Paul, Director of Operations, Sanford Chamberlain Medical Center, Chamberlain, SD, p. A572

MILLER, Peter, Chief Executive Officer, Vibra Hospital of Charleston, Mt. Pleasant, SC, p. A568

MILLER, Peter S., Chief Financial Officer, North Vista Hospital, North Las Vegas, NV, p. A407

MILLER, Phil, Chief Information Officer, Unity Health White County Medical Center, Searcy, AR, p. A52

MILLER, Redonda G., M.D., President, Johns Hopkins Hospital, Baltimore, MD, p. A296

MILLER, Richard, Administrator Finance, Banner Thunderbird Medical Center, Glendale, AZ, p. A33

MILLER, Richard B., Ph.D. Vice President Hospital Affairs and Chief Financial Officer, SUNY Downstate Medical Center University Hospital,, NY, p. A450

MILLER, Richard P., Chief Executive Officer, Virtua Health, Marlton, NJ, p. B153

MILLER, Rick
Director, Operations and Finance, District One Hospital, Faribault, MN, p. A342
President and Chief Operating Officer, Nationwide Children's Hospital, Columbus, OH, p. A490

MILLER, II, Robert R., Chief Operating Officer, NYC Health + Hospitals / Kings County,, NY, p. A448

MILLER, Rod, Chief Information Technology, Community Hospital, Torrington, WY, p. A724

MILLER, Sam, Chief Executive Officer, North Sunflower Medical Center, Ruleville, MS, p. A364

MILLER, Scott, Director Information Services, Forrest City Medical Center, Forrest City, AR, p. A46

MILLER, Shane
Chief Information Officer, HSHS St. Clare Memorial Hospital, Oconto Falls, WI, p. A713
Chief Information Officer, HSHS St. Vincent Hospital, Green Bay, WI, p. A707
Chief Information Officer, St. Mary's Hospital Medical Center, Green Bay, WI, p. A707
Chief Information Officer, St. Nicholas Hospital, Sheboygan, WI, p. A716

MILLER, Stacy, Entity Human Resources Officer, Texas Health Presbyterian Hospital Dallas, Dallas, TX, p. A611

MILLER, Steve, Director Information Systems, Baptist Medical Center South, Montgomery, AL, p. A23

MILLER, Steven
Chief Financial Officer, Florida Hospital North Pinellas, Tarpon Springs, FL, p. A148
Chief Financial Officer, Takoma Regional Hospital, Greeneville, TN, p. A583

MILLER, Susan, Financial Administrator, Faulkton Area Medical Center, Faulkton, SD, p. A573

MILLER, Suzanne, R.N. Senior Director Patient Care Services and Nursing, St. Luke's Wood River Medical Center, Ketchum, ID, p. A176

MILLER, Tamara, R.N., Administrator, Madison Community Hospital, Madison, SD, p. A574

MILLER, Ted, Chief Financial Officer, Baptist Health Floyd, New Albany, IN, p. A219

MILLER, Thomas, President and Chief Executive Officer, Quorum Health, Brentwood, TN, p. B112

MILLER, Thomas, M.D. Medical Director, University of Utah Health Care – Hospital and Clinics, Salt Lake City, UT, p. A664

MILLER, Valerie L., MSN Director of Nursing, Major Hospital, Shelbyville, IN, p. A222

MILLER, Wanda, R.N. Director of Clinical Services, Asheville Specialty Hospital, Asheville, NC, p. A460

MILLER, Weston, M.D. Chief Medical Officer, Abbeville General Hospital, Abbeville, LA, p. A271

MILLER, William, Coordinator Management Information Systems, Livengrin Foundation, Bensalem, PA, p. A533

MILLER-BALFOUR, Pam, Director Human Resources, Socorro General Hospital, Socorro, NM, p. A432

MILLER-COLLETTE, Melody M., Director Human Resources, North Okaloosa Medical Center, Crestview, FL, p. A126

MILLERMAIER, Ed, M.D. Chief Medical Officer, Bellin Memorial Hospital, Green Bay, WI, p. A706

MILLICAN, Sharon, Associate Director, Patient Care Services, South Texas Veterans Health Care System, San Antonio, TX, p. A647

MILLIGAN, Jan, Chief Nursing Officer, Cook Children's Northeast Hospital, Hurst, TX, p. A628

MILLIGAN, Jeffrey, Director, Veterans Affairs North Texas Health Care System, Dallas, TX, p. A612

MILLIGAN, John D., Vice President Finance and Chief Financial Officer, Oneida Healthcare, Oneida, NY, p. A452

MILLIRONS, Dennis C., FACHE, Interim President, Rapid City Regional Hospital, Rapid City, SD, p. A575

MILLIS, David, M.D. Clinical Director, Thomas B. Finan Center, Cumberland, MD, p. A300

MILLS, Bryan A., President and Chief Executive Officer, Community Health Network, Indianapolis, IN, p. B35

MILLS, Craig
  Chief Financial Officer, Heber Valley Medical Center, Heber City, UT, p. A660
  Vice President Human Resources, PeaceHealth Sacred Heart Medical Center University District, Eugene, OR, p. A525

MILLS, Dennis, Chief Human Resources Officer, San Ramon Regional Medical Center, San Ramon, CA, p. A92

MILLS, Gene, Director Information Technology, Scenic Mountain Medical Center, Big Spring, TX, p. A602

MILLS, Jerry, Chief Human Resources Management Services, San Francisco VA Medical Center, San Francisco, CA, p. A90

MILLS, Jim, Regional Director Information Technology, Sutter Medical Center, Sacramento, Sacramento, CA, p. A87

MILLS, John C., Senior Vice President Operations, Cleveland Clinic Fairview Hospital, Cleveland, OH, p. A489

MILLS, John E.H., President and Chief Executive Officer, United Medical Rehabilitation Hospital, Gretna, LA, p. A277

MILLS, John E.H., President & Chief Executive Officer, United Medical Rehabilitation Hospitals, Gretna, LA, p. B140

MILLS, Marianne, R.N. Chairperson, Stanton County Hospital, Johnson, KS, p. A246

MILLS, Scott, M.D. Vice President Medical Staff Administration and Chief Medical Officer, Mid Coast Hospital, Brunswick, ME, p. A292

MILLS, Sean
  Chief Financial Officer, Our Lady of Lourdes Memorial Hospital, Inc., Binghamton, NY, p. A435
  Chief Financial Officer, Samaritan Medical Center, Watertown, NY, p. A458

MILLS, Vicki L., Chief Financial Officer, Anderson County Hospital, Garnett, KS, p. A243

MILLS, William, M.D
  Senior Vice President Quality and Professional Affairs, Bradford Regional Medical Center, Bradford, PA, p. A534
  Senior Vice President Quality and Professional Affairs, Olean General Hospital, Olean, NY, p. A451

MILLS-MATHEWS, Marcy, Director Human Resources, Palms West Hospital, Loxahatchee, FL, p. A134

MILLSAPS, Janet
  Chief Human Resources Officer, Harris Regional Hospital, Sylva, NC, p. A474
  Vice President Human Resources, Haywood Regional Medical Center, Clyde, NC, p. A463

MILLSTEAD, Bart, Administrator, Memorial Hospital of Carbondale, Carbondale, IL, p. A182

MILNE, C. Dean, D.O. Medical Director, Complex Care Hospital at Tenaya, Las Vegas, NV, p. A405

MILNER, Rene, Chief Medical Officer, Osceola Medical Center, Osceola, WI, p. A713

MILO, Eleanor, Chief Nursing Officer, York Hospital, York, ME, p. A295

MILONE, Sheri, Chief Executive Officer and Administrator, Lovelace Women's Hospital, Albuquerque, NM, p. A427

MILOVICH, David, Vice President Human Resources, Saint Mary's Regional Medical Center, Reno, NV, p. A408

MILSTIEN, Kim S., Chief Executive Officer, Ventura County Medical Center, Ventura, CA, p. A98

MILTON, Kerry K., R.N. Chief Nursing Officer, St. Tammany Parish Hospital, Covington, LA, p. A275

MILTON, Paul A., Acting President and Chief Executive Officer, Ellis Hospital, Schenectady, NY, p. A455

MILTON, S. Byron, M.D. Medical Director, Emory Rehabilitation Hospital, Atlanta, GA, p. A152

MILUS, Lori, R.N. Director of Nursing, Aurora Behavioral Health System West, Glendale, AZ, p. A33

MILVET, Jr., Robert W., Chief Financial Officer, Preston Memorial Hospital, Kingwood, WV, p. A697

MIMOSO, Michael, FACHE, President and Chief Executive Officer, Community Medical Center, Toms River, NJ, p. A424

MIMS, Staci, Chief Nursing Officer, Dorminy Medical Center, Fitzgerald, GA, p. A159

MIMS, Tammy, Chief Executive Officer, Jeff Davis Hospital, Hazlehurst, GA, p. A160

MINARD, Keith, Chief Information Officer, Chinese Hospital, San Francisco, CA, p. A90

MINCEY, Wallace D., Interim Chief Executive Officer, Clinch Memorial Hospital, Homerville, GA, p. A161

MINCY, Lowney, Director Information Services, Southside Hospital, Bay Shore, NY, p. A434

MINDEN, Philip, Chief Executive Officer, Bartow Regional Medical Center, Bartow, FL, p. A123

MINEAR, Michael N.
  Senior Vice President and Chief Information Officer, Lehigh Valley Hospital, Allentown, PA, p. A532
  Senior Vice President and Chief Information Officer, Lehigh Valley Hospital–Muhlenberg, Bethlehem, PA, p. A533

MINEAU, Francine, Chief Nursing Officer, Baton Rouge Behavioral Hospital, Baton Rouge, LA, p. A272

MINER, Bill, M.D. Chief of Staff, Huron Regional Medical Center, Huron, SD, p. A574

MINER, Edwina A., R.N. Chief Nursing Officer, Ennis Regional Medical Center, Ennis, TX, p. A616

MINER, Greg, Administrator, Siouxland Surgery Center, Dakota Dunes, SD, p. A573

MINER, John, Chief Financial Officer, Kindred Hospital Central Tampa, Tampa, FL, p. A147

MINGLE, Regina, Senior Vice President and Chief Leadership Officer, Lancaster General Hospital, Lancaster, PA, p. A542

MINGS, William, M.D. Medical Director, Carl Albert Community Mental Health Center, McAlester, OK, p. A514

MINGUS, Linda, Director Human Resources, Aurora Medical Center of Oshkosh, Oshkosh, WI, p. A713

MINIER, Mary, Vice President Operations, Indiana University Health White Memorial Hospital, Monticello, IN, p. A218

MINIOR, Devin, M.D. Chief Medical Officer, Banner Casa Grande Medical Center, Casa Grande, AZ, p. A31

MINISSALE, Joseph, President, Methodist McKinney Hospital, McKinney, TX, p. A636

MINKIN, Robert
  President and Chief Executive Officer, O'Connor Hospital, San Jose, CA, p. A91
  Interim Chief Executive Officer, Saint Louise Regional Hospital, Gilroy, CA, p. A64

MINKS, Mike
  Chief Information Officer, Seton Edgar B. Davis Hospital, Luling, TX, p. A635
  Chief Information Officer VI, Seton Medical Center Austin, Austin, TX, p. A599
  Chief Information Officer, Seton Shoal Creek Hospital, Austin, TX, p. A599
  Vice President, University Medical Center at Brackenridge, Austin, TX, p. A600

MINNICK, Peggy N., Chief Executive Officer, BHC Alhambra Hospital, Rosemead, CA, p. A86

MINNIS, Rosanne, Business Officer, Rochester Psychiatric Center, Rochester, NY, p. A454

MINON, Maria, M.D
  Vice President Medical Affairs and Chief Medical Officer, Children's Hospital of Orange County, Orange, CA, p. A81
  Vice President Medical Affairs and Chief Medical Officer, CHOC Children's at Mission Hospital, Mission Viejo, CA, p. A76

MINOR, Amy, Chief Nursing Officer, Troy Regional Medical Center, Troy, AL, p. A26

MINOR, Athena, Chief Nursing Officer, Ohio County Hospital, Hartford, KY, p. A261

MINOR, Beverly, Chief Human Resources, Schleicher County Medical Center, Eldorado, TX, p. A616

MINOR, Blaine, M.D. Chief of Staff, Murray Medical Center, Chatsworth, GA, p. A156

MINSHEW, Tony L., Vice President, Patient Care Services, Conway Medical Center, Conway, SC, p. A565

MINSINGER, Linda, Vice President Hospital Division, Gifford Medical Center, Randolph, VT, p. A666

MINTON, Tamra, R.N. Vice President Patient Care Services and Chief Nursing Officer, UPMC East, Monroeville, PA, p. A545

MINTONYE, Traci, Chief Financial Officer, River Hospital, Alexandria Bay, NY, p. A433

MINTZ, Michael, M.D. Chief Medical Officer, South Texas Surgical Hospital, Corpus Christi, TX, p. A608

MIRABELLA, Ilene, Director Human Resources, Vibra Hospital of Southeastern Massachusetts, New Bedford, MA, p. A312

MIRANDA, Ada S., M.D. Medical Director, Hospital Metropolitano Dr. Susoni, Arecibo, PR, p. A726

MIRANDA, Ivette, Chief Executive Officer, HEALTHSOUTH Rehabilitation Hospital at Martin Health, Stuart, FL, p. A146

MIRANDA, Juliet, Chief Nursing Officer, Gardens Regional Hospital and Medical Center, Hawaiian Gardens, CA, p. A65

MIRANDA, Kim, Chief Financial Officer, St. Elizabeth Community Hospital, Red Bluff, CA, p. A84

MIRANDA, Kimberly
  Chief Financial Officer, Mercy Medical Center Mount Shasta, Mount Shasta, CA, p. A78
  Regional Vice President Finance and Chief Financial Officer, Mercy Medical Center Redding, Redding, CA, p. A84

MIRANDA, Michael, Chief of Staff, Mercy Hospital Booneville, Booneville, AR, p. A44

MIRANDA, Jr., Samuel, Chief Nursing Officer, Good Shepherd Specialty Hospital, Bethlehem, PA, p. A533

MIRANDA, Vicki, Vice President Human Resources, Dominican Hospital, Santa Cruz, CA, p. A93

MIRANDA, Victor Hernandez, M.D. Chief of Staff, Mennonite General Hospital, Aibonito, PR, p. A725

MIRZA, Irfan, Chief Financial Officer, Plantation General Hospital, Plantation, FL, p. A143

MIRZABEGIAN, Edward
  Chief Executive Officer, Garden Grove Hospital and Medical Center, Garden Grove, CA, p. A64
  Chief Executive Officer, Glendora Community Hospital, Glendora, CA, p. A65
  Chief Executive Officer, Huntington Beach Hospital, Huntington Beach, CA, p. A66
  Chief Executive Officer, Montclair Hospital Medical Center, Montclair, CA, p. A77

MISHKIND, Steven, M.D. Chief of Staff, DeSoto Memorial Hospital, Arcadia, FL, p. A123

MISHRA, Sanjeeb, M.D. Chief of Staff, University of Maryland Charles Regional Medical Center, La Plata, MD, p. A302

MISITANO, Anthony F., President and Chief Executive Officer, Post Acute Medical, LLC, Enola, PA, p. B104

MISITI, Joseph, M.D. President Medical Staff, Medina Memorial Hospital, Medina, NY, p. A442

MISKIMEN, Theresa, M.D. Vice President Medical Services, University Behavioral Healthcare, Piscataway, NJ, p. A422

MISKO, Michael, M.D. Chief Medical Officer, Citizens Memorial Hospital, Bolivar, MO, p. A367

MISLAN, Tim, MS Vice President and Chief Nurse Executive, Missouri Baptist Medical Center, Saint Louis, MO, p. A380

MISSERITTI, Colomba, Director Human Resources, Rochester Psychiatric Center, Rochester, NY, p. A454

MITCHAM, Debbie, Chief Financial Officer, Northside Hospital, Atlanta, GA, p. A152

MITCHEL, David M., Chief Executive Officer, Avoyelles Hospital, Marksville, LA, p. A282

MITCHELL, Adonna, Director Fiscal Services, North Mississippi Medical Center–Eupora, Eupora, MS, p. A357

MITCHELL, Andrew J., President and Chief Executive Officer, Peconic Bay Medical Center, Riverhead, NY, p. A454

MITCHELL, Barbara
  Director Human Resources, Oasis Behavioral Health – Chandler, Chandler, AZ, p. A31
  Senior Vice President Marketing and Human Resources, UW Medicine/Valley Medical Center, Renton, WA, p. A688

MITCHELL, Bridgett, Chief Clinical Officer, Advanced Specialty Hospital of Toledo, Toledo, OH, p. A503

MITCHELL, Camelia, M.D. Medical Director, Texas Rehabilitation Hospital of Arlington, Arlington, TX, p. A598

MITCHELL, Dave, Manager Information Services, Spectrum Health Gerber Memorial, Fremont, MI, p. A324

MITCHELL, David, Interim Chief Executive Officer, Baptist Emergency Hospital – Thousand Oaks, San Antonio, TX, p. A645

MITCHELL, Debbie, Director Human Resources, Woodrow Wilson Rehabilitation Center, Fishersville, VA, p. A670

MITCHELL, Elizabeth C., Chief Executive Officer and Chief Operating Officer, Specialty Hospital of Meridian, Meridian, MS, p. A362

MITCHELL, Errol
Chief Financial Officer, INTEGRIS Canadian Valley Hospital, Yukon, OK, p. A523
Vice President, Integris Southwest Medical Center, Oklahoma City, OK, p. A516

MITCHELL, Eulala, Director of Nursing, Pawnee County Memorial Hospital and Rural Health Clinic, Pawnee City, NE, p. A401

MITCHELL, Heath, Chief Operating Officer, Memorial Hospital, Seminole, TX, p. A648

MITCHELL, Jack C., FACHE, Chief Executive Officer, HEALTHSOUTH Rehabilitation Hospital, Fayetteville, AR, p. A45

MITCHELL, Jenifer, R.N. Director of Nursing Services, Mineral Community Hospital, Superior, MT, p. A391

MITCHELL, Jodie, Facility Financial Director, Sturgis Regional Hospital, Sturgis, SD, p. A577

MITCHELL, Joseph J., President, Trinity Hospital Twin City, Dennison, OH, p. A493

MITCHELL, Karen, Vice President Patient Care Services, Children's Hospital of The King's Daughters, Norfolk, VA, p. A675

MITCHELL, Kathy, R.N. Chief Nursing Officer, Doctors Hospital of Sarasota, Sarasota, FL, p. A145

MITCHELL, Kathy
Director Human Resources, Lakeview Medical Center, Rice Lake, WI, p. A715
Chief Nursing Officer, Owensboro Health Muhlenberg Community Hospital, Greenville, KY, p. A261

MITCHELL, Kenneth W., M.D. Medical Director, St. David's North Austin Medical Center, Austin, TX, p. A600

MITCHELL, Kent, Chief Financial Officer, Hamilton Memorial Hospital District, McLeansboro, IL, p. A196

MITCHELL, Leah, R.N. Interim Chief Information Officer, Salem Hospital, Salem, OR, p. A530

MITCHELL, Lori J., Chief Financial Officer, University of Washington Medical Center, Seattle, WA, p. A690

MITCHELL, Marsha, Director Human Resources, Fleming County Hospital, Flemingsburg, KY, p. A259

MITCHELL, Mary S., Chief Resource Management Services, Birmingham Veterans Affairs Medical Center, Birmingham, AL, p. A16

MITCHELL, Morris, Director Human Resources, Poplar Springs Hospital, Petersburg, VA, p. A676

MITCHELL, Naomi, Director Human Resources, Kentucky River Medical Center, Jackson, KY, p. A262

MITCHELL, Perry, M.D. Chief of Staff, Little Colorado Medical Center, Winslow, AZ, p. A41

MITCHELL, Rebekah, Chief Financial Officer, Madison County Health Care System, Winterset, IA, p. A239

MITCHELL, Richard R., Director Information Technology, Eagleville Hospital, Eagleville, PA, p. A537

MITCHELL, Sarah, Director Finance, Mary S Harper Geriatric Psychiatry Center, Tuscaloosa, AL, p. A26

MITCHELL, Scot, FACHE, Chief Executive Officer and Administrator, Cordova Community Medical Center, Cordova, AK, p. A14

MITCHELL, Steve, Chief Operating Officer, Memorial Medical Center, Modesto, CA, p. A77

MITCHELL, Susan
System Executive Vice President Human Resources, Edward Hospital, Naperville, IL, p. A198
Senior Vice President Human Resources, Elmhurst Memorial Hospital,, IL, p. A189
Vice President Patient Care Services, Vidant Roanoke–Chowan Hospital, Ahoskie, NC, p. A460

MITCHELL, Timothy, R.N. Chief Nursing Officer, Complex Care Hospital at Ridgelake, Sarasota, FL, p. A145

MITCHELL, Timothy, Chief Financial Officer, Fairfield Memorial Hospital, Winnsboro, SC, p. A571

MITCHELL, Vernadine, R.N. Chief Nursing Officer, De Soto Regional Health System, Mansfield, LA, p. A282

MITCHELL III, Walton F., Director, Catawba Hospital, Catawba, VA, p. A668

MITCHELL, William, Chief Executive Officer, Promise Hospital of San Diego, San Diego, CA, p. A88

MITCHELL SANCHEZ, Lexi, D.O. Chief of Staff, Clay County Memorial Hospital, Henrietta, TX, p. A623

MITCHUM, Linda, Director of Nursing, William J. McCord Adolescent Treatment Facility, Orangeburg, SC, p. A569

MITHUN, Robert, M.D. Physician in Chief, Kaiser Permanente San Francisco Medical Center, San Francisco, CA, p. A90

MITRICK, Joseph M., FACHE, President, Baptist Medical Center Beaches, Jacksonville Beach, FL, p. A132

MITRY, Norman F., President and Chief Executive Officer, Heritage Valley Health System, Beaver, PA, p. A533

MITRY, Norman F., President and Chief Executive Officer, Heritage Valley Health System, Beaver, PA, p. B70

MITRY, Norman F., President and Chief Executive Officer, Sewickley Valley Hospital, (A Division of Valley Medical Facilities), Sewickley, PA, p. A554

MITTAL, Vikrant, M.D. Chief Medical Officer, Danville State Hospital, Danville, PA, p. A536

MIYAMOTO, Faye, Assistant Vice President Human Resources, Rehabilitation Hospital of the Pacific, Honolulu, HI, p. A171

MIYASAWA, Patricia, CPA Director Fiscal Service, Shriners Hospitals for Children–Honolulu, Honolulu, HI, p. A171

MIYAUCHI, Kimberly, R.N. Chief Nursing Officer, Kingman Regional Medical Center, Kingman, AZ, p. A33

MIZE, William D., Chief Operating Officer, Trousdale Medical Center, Hartsville, TN, p. A584

MIZELL, Philip L., M.D. Medical Director, The BridgeWay, North Little Rock, AR, p. A51

MIZER, Alison, Chief Financial Officer, St. Anthony North Health Campus, Westminster, CO, p. A111

MIZIA, Robert, Director Information Systems and Chief Information Officer, Inspira Medical Center–Woodbury, Woodbury, NJ, p. A425

MIZONO, Gary, M.D. Physician–in–Chief, Kaiser Permanente San Rafael Medical Center, San Rafael, CA, p. A92

MLAWSKY, Karen, Senior Vice President and Chief Operations Officer, TMC HealthCare, Tucson, AZ, p. A41

MMEJE, Ikenna, Chief Executive Officer, Doctors Hospital of Manteca, Manteca, CA, p. A76

MOAD, Harold, Chief Operating Officer, Elkview General Hospital, Hobart, OK, p. A512

MOAK, Jennifer, Business Office Manager, Lawrence County Hospital, Monticello, MS, p. A362

MOAKLER, Thomas J., Chief Executive Officer, Houlton Regional Hospital, Houlton, ME, p. A293

MOALLEMIAN, Patrick, Chief Executive Officer, Chicago Lakeshore Hospital, Chicago, IL, p. A183

MOATS, Susan, R.N. Vice President of Patient Care Services and Chief Nursing Officer, The Heart Hospital Baylor Plano, Plano, TX, p. A642

MOAWAD, Gerald, Chief Medical Officer, BridgePoint Hospital Capitol Hill, Washington, DC, p. A121

MOBLEY, Cheryl, FACHE, President, Texas Health Specialty Hospital, Fort Worth, TX, p. A619

MOBLEY, Dana, Chief Information Officer, Our Community Hospital, Scotland Neck, NC, p. A473

MOCK, Presley, M.D. Chief of Staff, Texas Institute for Surgery at Texas Health Presbyterian Dallas, Dallas, TX, p. A611

MOCKLIN, Kevin, M.D. Director Medical Staff, Lake Charles Memorial Hospital, Lake Charles, LA, p. A281

MODISETT, Pamela, System Chief Financial Officer, Northwest Medical Center – Springdale, Springdale, AR, p. A52

MODJESKA, Alicia, Interim Administrator, Milwaukee County Behavioral Health Division, Milwaukee, WI, p. A711

MODLIN, Stacy, Chief Executive Officer, HEALTHSOUTH Sunrise Rehabilitation Hospital, Sunrise, FL, p. A146

MOE, Jonathan, Chief Executive Officer, Tyler Healthcare Center Avera, Tyler, MN, p. A352

MOEEN, Farida, M.D., Chief Executive Officer, United Memorial Medical Care, Houston, TX, p. A627

MOELLER, Deborah A., R.N. Chief Operating Officer, Lake Pointe Medical Center, Rowlett, TX, p. A644

MOEN, Belinda, R.N. Interim Director of Nursing, Mountrail County Medical Center, Stanley, ND, p. A481

MOEN, Larry, Chief Financial Officer, Coteau des Prairies Hospital, Sisseton, SD, p. A576

MOFFA, Salvatore, M.D. Vice President, Medical Affairs and Chief Medical Officer, Robert Wood Johnson University Hospital Somerset, Somerville, NJ, p. A423

MOFFAT, Jeanne, Manager Information Technology, Keefe Memorial Hospital, Cheyenne Wells, CO, p. A102

MOFFAT, Jennifer, Staff Accountant, Regional West Garden County, Oshkosh, NE, p. A401

MOFFATT, Dan, Chief Information Officer, Sanford Bemidji Medical Center, Bemidji, MN, p. A339

MOFFET, Chris, Director Information Services, Bob Wilson Memorial Grant County Hospital, Ulysses, KS, p. A255

MOFFITT, Brenda L., Chief Nursing Officer, Memorial Health System, Abilene, KS, p. A240

MOFFITT SOD, Rhonda, Chief Nursing Officer, First Hospital Wyoming Valley, Kingston, PA, p. A541

MOGERMAN, Shauna, Chief Executive Officer, Roxbury Treatment Center, Shippensburg, PA, p. A555

MOGG, Cassie, Chief Financial Officer, Covenant Hospital Plainview, Plainview, TX, p. A641

MOHAMED, Antonia, Acting Chief Information Officer, Birmingham Veterans Affairs Medical Center, Birmingham, AL, p. A16

MOHAMMED, Ehtaisham, M.D. Chief Medical Officer, Ridgeview Sibley Medical Center, Arlington, MN, p. A338

MOHAN, Amit, President and Chief Executive Officer, Barlow Respiratory Hospital, Los Angeles, CA, p. A70

MOHANDAS, Arjun, M.D. Chief of Staff, Seton Edgar B. Davis Hospital, Luling, TX, p. A635

MOHLER, Brittany, Director Human Resources, Essentia Health–Deer River, Deer River, MN, p. A341

MOHNK, Richard, Vice President Corporate Services, Bayhealth Medical Center, Dover, DE, p. A119

MOHNKERN, Pearl, Vice President and Director Human Resources, CHRISTUS St. Vincent Regional Medical Center, Santa Fe, NM, p. A431

MOHR, Amanda, Chief Nursing Officer, Greater Regional Medical Center, Creston, IA, p. A228

MOHR, Amy, Coordinator Human Resources, Forest Health Medical Center, Ypsilanti, MI, p. A337

MOHR, Angela, R.N. Vice President Nursing and Chief Operating Officer, St. Anthony Shawnee Hospital, Shawnee, OK, p. A520

MOHR, Catherine, R.N. Chief Nursing Officer, Robert Packer Hospital, Sayre, PA, p. A553

MOHR, Steve
Senior Vice President Finance and Chief Financial Officer, Loma Linda University Behavioral Medicine Center, Redlands, CA, p. A85
Senior Vice President Finance and Chief Financial Officer, Loma Linda University Medical Center, Loma Linda, CA, p. A69

MOISAN, Terrence, M.D., Chief Executive Officer, Palos Community Hospital, Palos Heights, IL, p. A199

MOK, Michelle, Chief Financial Officer, Redlands Community Hospital, Redlands, CA, p. A85

MOKDESSI, Margot, Interim Chief Financial Officer, Acadia Vermilion Hospital, Lafayette, LA, p. A280

MOKRY, Deborah, Chief Nurse Executive, St. Louis Psychiatric Rehabilitation Center, Saint Louis, MO, p. A381

MOL, Stacy E., CPA Director Finance, Spencer Hospital, Spencer, IA, p. A238

MOLACEK, Shane, Chief Information Officer, Valley County Health System, Ord, NE, p. A401

MOLBERT, Jamie, Chief Executive Officer, Rock Springs, LLC, Georgetown, TX, p. A620

MOLELUS, Elena, Manager Human Resources, Santa Barbara County Psychiatric Health Facility, Santa Barbara, CA, p. A93

MOLINA, Isabel, M.D. Chief Medical Officer, Lamb Healthcare Center, Littlefield, TX, p. A633

MOLINA, Luis F., Chief Executive Officer and Administrator, Community Hospital, Munster, IN, p. A219

MOLINA, Ricky, Director Marketing and Business Development, Rehabilitation Hospital of Southern New Mexico, Las Cruces, NM, p. A430

MOLINARO, Frank L., Chief Executive Officer, Abrazo Arrowhead Campus, Glendale, AZ, p. A33

MOLITOR, Margie, R.N., Chief Executive Officer, Hot Springs County Memorial Hospital, Thermopolis, WY, p. A724

MOLL, Ben, Assistant Chief Financial Officer, Nashoba Valley Medical Center, Ayer, MA, p. A305

MOLL, Eric, Chief Executive Officer, Mason General Hospital, Shelton, WA, p. A690

MOLL, Gudrun, R.N. Chief Nursing Officer, San Antonio Regional Hospital, Upland, CA, p. A97

MOLL, Jeffrey, M.D. Medical Director, Clarion Psychiatric Center, Clarion, PA, p. A535

MOLL, Michael A., M.D. Chief of Staff, Spanish Peaks Regional Health Center, Walsenburg, CO, p. A111

MOLLER, Dan, M.D. Chief Medical Officer, Willis–Knighton Medical Center, Shreveport, LA, p. A288

MOLLER, Lynn, Chief Financial Officer, Weston County Health Services, Newcastle, WY, p. A723

MOLLOHAN, Joan, Vice President Human Resources, Ochsner Medical Center, New Orleans, LA, p. A285

MOLLOY, Kevin
Senior Vice President and Chief Operating Officer, Mount Sinai Beth Israel, New York, NY, p. A446
Senior Vice President and Chief Operating Officer, Mount Sinai St. Luke's – Roosevelt, New York, NY, p. A446

MOLLOY, Laurel, Vice President Nursing and Rehab Services, UNC Lenoir Healthcare, Kinston, NC, p. A468

MOLLOY, Reuben D., Chief Information Officer, Governor Juan F. Luis Hospital, Christiansted, VI, p. A731

MOLMEN, David R., M.P.H., Chief Executive Officer, Altru Health System, Grand Forks, ND, p. A479

MOLNAR, Becky, Director of Finance, Cleveland Clinic, Medina Hospital, Medina, OH, p. A499

MOLONEY, Ellen, Interim President, Newton–Wellesley Hospital, Newton Lower Falls, MA, p. A313

MOLSBERGER, Shawn, Chief Operating Officer, Tennova Healthcare–Clarksville, Clarksville, TN, p. A581

MOLT, Brianna, Human Resources Director, Genoa Medical Facilities, Genoa, NE, p. A396

MOLYNEUX, Phyllis, Associate Administrator Human Resources and Education, Williamson Medical Center, Franklin, TN, p. A583

MOMEYER, Polly, Manager Human Resources, Millcreek Community Hospital, Erie, PA, p. A538

MONAHAN, Jane, Vice President Ministry, Spiritual Care and Human Resources, Monroe Clinic, Monroe, WI, p. A712

MONASTERIO, Eugene A., M.D. Medical Director, Children's Hospital of Richmond at VCU–Brook Road Campus, Richmond, VA, p. A677

MONCHER, Daniel J., Vice President and Chief Financial Officer, Firelands Regional Health System, Sandusky, OH, p. A502

MONCRIEF, William, ORH IT Client Executive, Oakland Regional Hospital, Southfield, MI, p. A334

MONCUS, Lisa, Human Resources Business Partner, Wake Forest Baptist Health–Davie Medical Center, Mocksville, NC, p. A469

MONCZEWSKI, Patricia, Chief Operating Officer, Mercy General Hospital, Sacramento, CA, p. A86

MONCZEWSKI, Patti, Interim Chief Executive Officer, Paris Regional Medical Center, Paris, TX, p. A640

MONCZEWSKI, Ted, Vice President Human Resources, St. Vincent Charity Medical Center, Cleveland, OH, p. A489

MONDA, Cam, D.O. Medical Director, Greenwood Regional Rehabilitation Hospital, Greenwood, SC, p. A567

MONETTE, Steven, Chief Financial Officer, Brattleboro Retreat, Brattleboro, VT, p. A665

MONGE, Candice, R.N. Chief Nurse Executive Officer, Marian Regional Medical Center, Santa Maria, CA, p. A93

MONGELL, Mitchell P., FACHE, Chief Executive Officer, Fort Walton Beach Medical Center, Fort Walton Beach, FL, p. A129

MONGER, Lloyd, Administrator, Tri Parish Rehabilitation Hospital, Leesville, LA, p. A282

MONGER, Shelton, Director Information Technology, Wayne Hospital, Greenville, OH, p. A495

MONIACI, Cathy, R.N., Administrator, Shriners Hospitals for Children–Houston, Houston, TX, p. A626

MONICAL, Robert, President and Chief Executive Officer, McPherson Hospital, McPherson, KS, p. A249

MONJE, Mary Anne, Chief Financial Officer and Chief Operating Officer, Whittier Hospital Medical Center, Whittier, CA, p. A100

MONJESKY, Kimberly, Chief Executive Officer, Pikes Peak Regional Hospital, Woodland Park, CO, p. A111

MONKRES, Paula, Administrative Assistant and Director Human Resources, Nocona General Hospital, Nocona, TX, p. A639

MONROE, Ame, Director Human Resources, Rolling Plains Memorial Hospital, Sweetwater, TX, p. A651

MONROE, Janet J., R.N., Chief Executive Officer, Greystone Park Psychiatric Hospital, Morris Plains, NJ, p. A419

MONROE, Jennifer, Chief Nursing Officer, Gulf Coast Medical Center, Wharton, TX, p. A657

MONROE, Lori, Director of Nursing, Winnebago Mental Health Institute, Winnebago, WI, p. A719

MONROE, Temple, Director Nursing Operations, Wilson Medical Center, Neodesha, KS, p. A249

MONROIG, Domingo, Executive Director, Castaner General Hospital, Castaner, PR, p. A726

MONROY–MILLER, Cherry, M.D. Acting Medical Director, Greystone Park Psychiatric Hospital, Morris Plains, NJ, p. A419

MONSANTO, Monte, Chief Information Systems, Russell County Hospital, Russell Springs, KY, p. A567

MONSERRATE, Humberto, Executive Director, University Pediatric Hospital,, PR, p. A730

MONSRUD, Michele, Director Human Resources, Clearview Regional Medical Center, Monroe, GA, p. A163

MONTAGNESE, Robert A., President and Chief Executive Officer, Licking Memorial Hospital, Newark, OH, p. A500

MONTALVO, Cary L., Chief Executive Officer, Solara Hospital Harlingen, Harlingen, TX, p. A622

MONTALVO, Eladio, Chief Executive Officer, Fort Duncan Regional Medical Center, Eagle Pass, TX, p. A614

MONTALVO, Jose, M.D. Medical Director, Hospital Del Maestro, San Juan, PR, p. A729

MONTANA, Jennifer, Manager Human Resources, Community Memorial Hospital, Hamilton, NY, p. A440

MONTANA–RHODES, Lou, Vice President of Patient Care Services, Vidant Beaufort Hospital, Washington, NC, p. A475

MONTANO, Mayra, Director Information Systems, Hospital Metropolitano Dr. Susoni, Arecibo, PR, p. A726

MONTANTE, Carl, Director Information Systems and Information Technology, Shriners Hospitals for Children–Portland, Portland, OR, p. A530

MONTANYE, Richard, Director Information Systems, Hunt Regional Medical Center, Greenville, TX, p. A621

MONTANYE–IRELAND, Cherelle, Chief Executive Officer, Hansen Family Hospital, Iowa Falls, IA, p. A233

MONTEL, Janet, Chief Financial Officer, Paris Regional Medical Center, Paris, TX, p. A640

MONTELONGO, Rick J., Chief Executive Officer, St. Mark's Medical Center, La Grange, TX, p. A631

MONTENEGRO, Diana, Director Human Resources, Baptist Health South Florida, South Miami Hospital, Miami, FL, p. A136

MONTER, Brian, R.N., President, UH Regional Hospitals, Cleveland, OH, p. A490

MONTGOMERY, Daniel, Chief Financial Officer, Specialists Hospital – Shreveport, Shreveport, LA, p. A288

MONTGOMERY, Jennifer, FACHE, President and Chief Executive Officer, McLaren Port Huron, Port Huron, MI, p. A332

MONTGOMERY, Jennifer, Chief Financial Officer, Washakie Medical Center, Worland, WY, p. A724

MONTGOMERY, Lee Anne, R.N., Administrator, Crenshaw Community Hospital, Luverne, AL, p. A22

MONTGOMERY, Margaret, Chief Nursing Officer, HEALTHSOUTH Reading Rehabilitation Hospital, Reading, PA, p. A553

MONTGOMERY, Mark, M.D. Chief Medical Officer, Texas Health Harris Methodist Hospital Southwest Fort Worth, Fort Worth, TX, p. A619

MONTGOMERY, Mary Jim, R.N. Chief Operating Officer, Crisp Regional Hospital, Cordele, GA, p. A157

MONTGOMERY, Peggy, Director Medical Records, Arrowhead Behavioral Health Hospital, Maumee, OH, p. A498

MONTGOMERY II, Raymond W., FACHE, President and Chief Executive Officer, Unity Health White County Medical Center, Searcy, AR, p. A52

MONTGOMERY, Robert, Chief Financial Officer, Shriners Hospitals for Children–Lexington, Lexington, KY, p. A263

MONTGOMERY, Susan, Chief Nursing Officer, Asante Ashland Community Hospital, Ashland, OR, p. A524

MONTGOMERY, Tina, Chief Financial Officer, Sidney Health Center, Sidney, MT, p. A391

MONTGOMERY, Vicki, Director and Chief Executive Officer, Central State Hospital, Petersburg, VA, p. A676

MONTMENY, Richard, Vice President Professional Services, On–Site Administrator, St. John's Pleasant Valley Hospital, Camarillo, CA, p. A57

MONTOIS, John D., Interim Chief Executive Officer, Highlands Regional Medical Center, Sebring, FL, p. A145

MONTOUR, Vina, Director Information Technology, U. S. Public Health Service Phoenix Indian Medical Center, Phoenix, AZ, p. A37

MONTOYA, Al, Interim Medical Center Director, White River Junction Veterans Affairs Medical Center, White River Junction, VT, p. A666

MONTOYA, Brooke, Director Human Resources, Lake Granbury Medical Center, Granbury, TX, p. A621

MONTOYA, Lionel J., Chief Financial Officer, Spanish Peaks Regional Health Center, Walsenburg, CO, p. A111

MONZINGO, Ashley, Human Resources, Accounts Payable and Payroll, TOPS Surgical Specialty Hospital, Houston, TX, p. A627

MONZON, Rogelio, Chief Financial Officer, Good Samaritan Hospital, Bakersfield, CA, p. A56

MOODY, Crystal R., Director Human Resources, Community Medical Center of Izard County, Calico Rock, AR, p. A44

MOODY, David, Vice President Human Resources, Salina Regional Health Center, Salina, KS, p. A253

MOODY, James, Chief Financial Officer, Donalsonville Hospital, Donalsonville, GA, p. A158

MOODY, Vicky, Director Human Resources, Houlton Regional Hospital, Houlton, ME, p. A293

MOOG, Darlene, Director Human Resources, HEALTHSOUTH Deaconess Rehabilitation Hospital, Evansville, IN, p. A210

MOON, Bob, Chief Financial Officer, CHRISTUS St. Vincent Regional Medical Center, Santa Fe, NM, p. A431

MOON, Jr., David, Director Information Systems, Lake City Community Hospital, Lake City, SC, p. A567

MOON, James, Chief Financial Officer, Pana Community Hospital, Pana, IL, p. A199

MOON, John, Associate Director, Veterans Affairs Eastern Kansas Health Care System, Topeka, KS, p. A254

MOONEY, Robert W., M.D. Medical Director, Willingway Hospital, Statesboro, GA, p. A166

MOONEY, Susan E., MS, President and Chief Executive Officer, Alice Peck Day Memorial Hospital, Lebanon, NH, p. A411

MOORE, Amy, Human Resources, Hamilton Hospital, Olney, TX, p. A639

MOORE III, Ben, President and Chief Executive Officer, River Hospital, Alexandria Bay, NY, p. A433

MOORE, Betty, Business Manager, North Mississippi Medical Center–Iuka, Iuka, MS, p. A359

MOORE, Bill, Chief Human Resources, El Centro Regional Medical Center, El Centro, CA, p. A61

MOORE, Bob, FACHE, Chief Executive Officer, Munroe Regional Medical Center, Ocala, FL, p. A139

MOORE, Brandon, FACHE, Administrator and Chief Executive Officer, Park Place Surgical Hospital, Lafayette, LA, p. A281

MOORE, Brett, CPA Assistant Administrator Finance, Sutter Amador Hospital, Jackson, CA, p. A66

MOORE, Brian, President and Chief Executive Officer, St. Mary–Corwin Medical Center, Pueblo, CO, p. A110

MOORE, C. Thomas, Chief Financial Officer, Delta Regional Medical Center, Greenville, MS, p. A358

MOORE, Carrie, Director Human Resources, Meadowbrook Rehabilitation Hospital, Gardner, KS, p. A243

MOORE, Cathy, Chief Nursing Officer, St. Luke's Hospital, Columbus, NC, p. A463

MOORE, Cecelia B., CPA Associate Vice Chancellor Finance, Vanderbilt University Medical Center, Nashville, TN, p. A591

MOORE, Christie, Director Human Resources, HEALTHSOUTH Rehabilitation Hospital – Mid–Cities, Bedford, TX, p. A602

MOORE, Courtney, CPA, Chief Executive Officer, Bleckley Memorial Hospital, Cochran, GA, p. A156

MOORE, Dana
Senior Vice President Information Services, St. Anthony Hospital, Lakewood, CO, p. A108
Senior Vice President Information Services, St. Anthony North Health Campus, Westminster, CO, p. A111

MOORE, Darrell W., Chief Executive Officer, Parkridge Medical Center, Chattanooga, TN, p. A580

MOORE, Deborah, Director Human Resources, Walter P. Reuther Psychiatric Hospital, Westland, MI, p. A336

MOORE, Debra, Chief Executive Officer, Parkside Psychiatric Hospital and Clinic, Tulsa, OK, p. A521

MOORE, Diane, Chief Financial Officer, Big Bend Regional Medical Center, Alpine, TX, p. A596

MOORE, Edward H., President and Chief Executive Officer, Harrington Memorial Hospital, Southbridge, MA, p. A314

MOORE, Elizabeth, Chief Operating Officer, Silver Hill Hospital, New Canaan, CT, p. A115

MOORE, Emily, Director Human Resources and Information Technology, Haskell Memorial Hospital, Haskell, TX, p. A622

MOORE, Ethel L., M.D. Director of Medical Affairs, Fort Belknap U. S. Public Health Service Indian Hospital, Harlem, MT, p. A388

MOORE, Harold, Chief Information Technology Officer, Spartanburg Medical Center, Spartanburg, SC, p. A570

MOORE, Harriet, R.N. Director of Nursing, Rock Springs, LLC, Georgetown, TX, p. A620

MOORE, James L., M.D. Senior Vice President and Chief Medical Officer, Athens Regional Medical Center, Athens, GA, p. A151

MOORE, Jane, Director, Fiscal Services, Quitman County Hospital, Marks, MS, p. A361

MOORE, Jason H., Vice President and Chief Operating Officer, Tallahassee Memorial HealthCare, Tallahassee, FL, p. A146

MOORE, Jeffrey Steve, Chief Financial Officer, Fort Walton Beach Medical Center, Fort Walton Beach, FL, p. A129

MOORE, Jody Dewen, District Director Human Resources, Kindred Hospital–San Diego, San Diego, CA, p. A88

MOORE, John, M.D. Medical Director, Granite County Medical Center, Philipsburg, MT, p. A390

MOORE, John, President, South Lake Hospital, Clermont, FL, p. A125

MOORE, John, M.D. Vice President Medical Affairs, SSM DePaul Health Center, Bridgeton, MO, p. A368

MOORE, John G., Vice President and Chief Financial Officer, Carolinas Healthcare System Union, Monroe, NC, p. A469

MOORE, Kandi, Administrator, Specialists Hospital – Shreveport, Shreveport, LA, p. A288

MOORE, Karen, Vice President Information Technology and Chief Information Officer, Southern Regional Medical Center, Riverdale, GA, p. A164

MOORE, Kathy D., Chief Executive Officer, St. Luke's Regional Medical Center, Boise, ID, p. A175

MOORE, Keri, Vice President Human Resources and Support Services, Presbyterian–St. Luke's Medical Center, Denver, CO, p. A104

MOORE, Kermit, R.N. Chief Operating Officer and Chief Nursing Officer, Nemaha County Hospital, Auburn, NE, p. A393

MOORE, Kim S., FACHE, President, CHI Health St Elizabeth, Lincoln, NE, p. A398

MOORE, Kyna, R.N. Director of Nursing, Bath Community Hospital, Hot Springs, VA, p. A672

MOORE, Leigh, Administrative Assistant Human Resources, H. C. Watkins Memorial Hospital, Quitman, MS, p. A364

MOORE, Linda, Manager Human Resources, Seymour Hospital, Seymour, TX, p. A648

MOORE, Margaret, Director Business Office, Sabine County Hospital, Hemphill, TX, p. A623

MOORE, Mark E., President and Chief Executive Officer, Indiana University Health Bloomington Hospital, Bloomington, IN, p. A207

MOORE, Matthew, Director of Financial Reporting, Effingham Hospital, Springfield, GA, p. A166

MOORE, Melinda, Director Human Resources, Deaconess Hospital, Spokane, WA, p. A691

MOORE, Michael, Director Information Systems, Troy Regional Medical Center, Troy, AL, p. A26

MOORE, Mike, President and Chief Operating Officer, Jane Phillips Memorial Medical Center, Bartlesville, OK, p. A509

MOORE, Neil J., President and Chief Executive Officer, Dimensions Healthcare System, Cheverly, MD, p. B50

MOORE, Nelda, Director Data Processing, Memorial Hospital and Manor, Bainbridge, GA, p. A154

MOORE, Nickie, Chief Financial Officer, North Sunflower Medical Center, Ruleville, MS, p. A364

MOORE, Norman, Director Information Services, Houston County Medical Center, Crockett, TX, p. A608

MOORE, Patricia J., Director Human Resource, Valley Behavioral Health System, Barling, AR, p. A43

MOORE, Paul, Chief Information Officer, Connecticut Mental Health Center, New Haven, CT, p. A116

MOORE, Paula, R.N. Chief Clinical Officer, Hugh Chatham Memorial Hospital, Elkin, NC, p. A465

MOORE, Randy, Chief Information Officer, Banner Lassen Medical Center, Susanville, CA, p. A95

MOORE, Rick
Chief Information Officer, Bethesda North Hospital, Cincinnati, OH, p. A487
Chief Information Officer, Good Samaritan Hospital, Cincinnati, OH, p. A487

MOORE, Robin A., Vice President Human Resources, Concord Hospital, Concord, NH, p. A410

MOORE, Ronald E., R.N. Vice President Professional Practice and Chief Nursing Officer, Charleston Area Medical Center, Charleston, WV, p. A695

MOORE, Sandee, Chief Operating Officer, Eastern Idaho Regional Medical Center, Idaho Falls, ID, p. A176

MOORE, Saunya, Chief Financial Officer, Parkside Psychiatric Hospital and Clinic, Tulsa, OK, p. A521

MOORE, Scott, Chief of Staff, Jay Hospital, Jay, FL, p. A132

MOORE, Shari, Chief Executive Officer, Methodist Rehabilitation Hospital, Dallas, TX, p. A610

MOORE, Steve, Chief Financial Officer, Southern Tennessee Regional Health System–Winchester, Winchester, TN, p. A594

MOORE, Sylvia, Vice President and Chief Operating Officer, Southeast Hospital, Cape Girardeau, MO, p. A369

MOORE, Tim
Chief Accounting Officer and Vice President Ancillary Services and Finance, Blessing Hospital, Quincy, IL, p. A201
Vice President Finance, Illini Community Hospital, Pittsfield, IL, p. A201

MOORE, Vernon, Senior Vice President Chief Business and Finance, University of Texas Health Northeast, Tyler, TX, p. A654

MOORE, Vonda, Chief Nursing Officer, Drew Memorial Hospital, Monticello, AR, p. A50

MOORE, Warren E., President and Chief Executive Officer, Children's Specialized Hospital–PSE&G, New Brunswick, NJ, p. A420

MOORE, William, Chief Information Officer, Parrish Medical Center, Titusville, FL, p. A148

MOORE–CONNELLY, Marci, M.D. Vice President Chief Medical Officer, Memorial Hospital of Carbondale, Carbondale, IL, p. A182

MOORE–HARDY, Cynthia, FACHE, President and Chief Executive Officer, Lake Health, Concord Township, OH, p. A491

MOOREHOUSE, Brett, FACHE Vice President and Chief Operating Officer, Ranken Jordan Pediatric Bridge Hospital, Maryland Heights, MO, p. A376

MOORER, Thad, Chief Information Officer, Eastside Psychiatric Hospital, Tallahassee, FL, p. A146

MOORHEAD, David, M.D. Chief Medical Officer, Florida Hospital, Orlando, FL, p. A140

MOORMAN, Gary L., D.O. Chief Medical Officer and Senior Vice President Medical Affairs, ProMedica Monroe Regional Hospital, Monroe, MI, p. A330

MORA, Debbie, Director, Southwest General Hospital, San Antonio, TX, p. A647

MORACA, Lynn, Director Human Resources, Lodi Community Hospital, Lodi, OH, p. A497

MORAHAN, John, Vice President Finance, St. Joseph Hospital, Bethpage, NY, p. A434

MORAHAN, John R., President and Chief Executive Officer, Penn State Health St. Joseph, Reading, PA, p. A553

MORALES, Anthony, M.D. Medical Director, Louisiana Heart Hospital, Lacombe, LA, p. A280

MORALES, Autumn, Chief Medical Staff Officer, Clarinda Regional Health Center, Clarinda, IA, p. A227

MORALES, Carmela, M.D. Chief of Staff, University Medical Center of El Paso, El Paso, TX, p. A616

MORALES, Daniza
Chief Information Officer, Hospital Menonita De Cayey, Cayey, PR, p. A727
Manager Information System, Mennonite General Hospital, Aibonito, PR, p. A725

MORALES, Elsie, Chief Financial Officer, Hospital Universitario Dr. Ramon Ruiz Arnau, Bayamon, PR, p. A726

MORALES, Joel, Chief Financial Officer, Fort Duncan Regional Medical Center, Eagle Pass, TX, p. A614

MORALES, John R., Chief Financial Officer, John H. Stroger Jr. Hospital of Cook County, Chicago, IL, p. A184

MORALES, Kathryn
Director of Finance, Hampshire Memorial Hospital, Romney, WV, p. A700
Director of Finance, War Memorial Hospital, Berkeley Springs, WV, p. A694

MORALES, Kristin, Chief Operating Officer, Harrington Memorial Hospital, Southbridge, MA, p. A314

MORALES, Marilyn, Interim Executive Director, Hospital Buen Samaritano, Aguadilla, PR, p. A725

MORALES, Marlene, Administrator, Hospital Oriente, Humacao, PR, p. A727

MORALES, Trish, Director Human Resources, Lakewood Ranch Medical Center, Bradenton, FL, p. A124

MORAN, Alina, Chief Executive Officer, NYC Health + Hospitals / Metropolitan, New York, NY, p. A448

MORAN, Barbara, R.N. Director Patient Care Services and Chief Nursing Officer, Grace Hospital, Cleveland, OH, p. A489

MORAN, Debbie, Executive Director, Carl Albert Community Mental Health Center, McAlester, OK, p. A514

MORAN, Michael Francis, Interim President and Chief Administrative Officer, Baystate Wing Hospital, Palmer, MA, p. A313

MORANDEIRA, Ana, Director Marketing, San Juan Capestrano Hospital, San Juan, PR, p. A730

MORASKO, Jerome, President and Chief Executive Officer, Avita Health System, Galion, OH, p. B18

MORASKO, Jerome
Chief Executive Officer, Bucyrus Community Hospital, Bucyrus, OH, p. A485
President and Chief Executive Officer, Galion Community Hospital, Galion, OH, p. A495

MORASKO, Robert A., Chief Executive Officer, Heart of the Rockies Regional Medical Center, Salida, CO, p. A110

MORAVICK, Donna, MSN, Executive Director, Southside Hospital, Bay Shore, NY, p. A434

MORDACH, John P., Senior Vice President and Chief Financial Officer, Rush University Medical Center, Chicago, IL, p. A186

MORDECAI, Steve, Director Human Resources, Griffin Hospital, Derby, CT, p. A114

MOREAU, Michelle, Chief Clinical Officer, AMG Specialty Hospital – Covington, Covington, LA, p. A275

MOREAU, Steven C., President and Chief Executive Officer, St. Joseph Hospital, Orange, CA, p. A81

MOREFIELD, Terri, Deputy Chief Human Resources Division, Bassett Army Community Hospital, Fort Wainwright, AK, p. A29

MOREIN, Sandy, Chief Nursing Officer, Mercy Regional Medical Center, Ville Platte, LA, p. A289

MORELAND, John, M.D. Chief Medical Officer, Marcus Daly Memorial Hospital, Hamilton, MT, p. A388

MORELAND, Tresha, M
Regional Vice President Human Resources, Dameron Hospital, Stockton, CA, p. A95
Vice President Human Resources, Rideout Memorial Hospital, Marysville, CA, p. A76

MORELL, Ixel, Chief Operating Officer, Sierra Vista Hospital, Sacramento, CA, p. A87

MORELLI, Gerald, Director Human Resources, Philadelphia Veterans Affairs Medical Center, Philadelphia, PA, p. A549

MORENO, Debbie, Chief Nursing Officer, Lodi Memorial Hospital, Lodi, CA, p. A68

MORENO, Jorge, Director Information Technology Operations, Canyon Vista Medical Center, Sierra Vista, AZ, p. A39

MORENO, Robin
Financial Officer, North Texas State Hospital, Vernon, TX, p. A655
Chief Financial Officer, North Texas State Hospital, Wichita Falls Campus, Wichita Falls, TX, p. A657

MORENO–COOK, Shannon, Chief Nursing Officer, St. Vincent Rehabilitation Hospital, Sherwood, AR, p. A52

MORETTE, Joseph M., Executive Vice President, Methodist Rehabilitation Center, Jackson, MS, p. A360

MORGAN, Bradley, Vice President of Operations, The Heart Hospital Baylor Denton, Denton, TX, p. A613

MORGAN, Charlene, Chief Nursing Officer, Henderson County Community Hospital, Lexington, TN, p. A587

MORGAN, Christian, M.D. Chief of Staff, Star Valley Medical Center, Afton, WY, p. A721

MORGAN, David, Vice President and Chief Financial Officer, Bristol Bay Area Health Corporation, Dillingham, AK, p. A29

MORGAN, Dennis P., Chief of Staff, Baptist Memorial Hospital–North Mississippi, Oxford, MS, p. A363

MORGAN, Derek
Vice President Human Resources, Kettering Medical Center, Kettering, OH, p. A496
Vice President Human Resources, Sycamore Medical Center, Miamisburg, OH, p. A499

MORGAN, Dirk, Vice President, Murray–Calloway County Hospital, Murray, KY, p. A267

MORGAN, Dwight, Information Technology System Director, Walla Walla General Hospital, Walla Walla, WA, p. A693

MORGAN, Eric, Interim Chief Executive Officer, Prattville Baptist Hospital, Prattville, AL, p. A25

MORGAN, James, M.D. Chief Medical Officer, Memorial Hospital of Converse County, Douglas, WY, p. A722

MORGAN, Janelle, Interim Director of Nursing, Howard County Medical Center, Saint Paul, NE, p. A402

MORGAN, Jeff, Director Information Systems, Northeastern Nevada Regional Hospital, Elko, NV, p. A404

MORGAN, Jeffrey H., Vice President Finance and Chief Financial Officer, Brooks Memorial Hospital, Dunkirk, NY, p. A438

MORGAN, Kelly C., President and Chief Executive Officer, Mercy Medical Center, Roseburg, OR, p. A530

MORGAN, Lisa, R.N. Vice President Patient Services, King's Daughters' Health, Madison, IN, p. A217

MORGAN, Lois, R.N. Vice President and Chief Nursing Officer, Methodist Hospital, Henderson, KY, p. A261

MORGAN, Lori, M.D. Chief Administrative Officer, Legacy Emanuel Hospital and Health Center, Portland, OR, p. A529

MORGAN, Mace, Director Information Systems, Minden Medical Center, Minden, LA, p. A283

MORGAN, Marguerite J., Administrator, Florida State Hospital, Chattahoochee, FL, p. A125

MORGAN, Mark E., Medical Center Director, Jack C. Montgomery Veterans Affairs Medical Center, Muskogee, OK, p. A515

MORGAN, Matthew, Associate Administrator, Hillcrest Hospital – South, Tulsa, OK, p. A521

MORGAN, Melody, Chief Financial Officer, Fairfield Memorial Hospital, Fairfield, IL, p. A190

MORGAN, Nyle, Chief Information Officer, Sheridan Memorial Hospital, Sheridan, WY, p. A723

MORGAN, Rose, MS Vice President Patient Care Services, Princeton Community Hospital, Princeton, WV, p. A699

MORGAN, Shawn, Finance Officer, Northern Navajo Medical Center, Shiprock, NM, p. A431

MORGAN, Susan
Chief Clinical Officer, AMG Specialty Hospital–Albuquerque, Albuquerque, NM, p. A427
Director of Nursing Services, Prairie Community Hospital, Terry, MT, p. A391

MORGAN, Teresa
Chief Financial Officer, McGehee–Desha County Hospital, McGehee, AR, p. A50
Assistant Vice President Human Resources, Shannon Medical Center, San Angelo, TX, p. A645

MORGAN, W. Hugh, M.D. Chief Medical Staff, Edgefield County Hospital, Edgefield, SC, p. A565

MORGAN–FINE, Richard, IT Director, Clarinda Regional Health Center, Clarinda, IA, p. A227

MORGESE, Vincent, M.D. Executive Vice President, Chief Operating Officer and Chief Medical Officer, Queen of the Valley Medical Center, Napa, CA, p. A79

MORIMOTO, Scott, Director Clinical Informatics, Rehabilitation Hospital of the Pacific, Honolulu, HI, p. A171

MORIN, Robert J., Vice President Finance and Chief Financial Officer, Sturgis Hospital, Sturgis, MI, p. A335

MORIN–SCRIBNER, Nicole, Director Human Resources, St. Mary's Regional Medical Center, Lewiston, ME, p. A293

MORISCO, Antonietta, M.D. Medical Director, Chairman Anesthesiology, Jamaica Hospital Medical Center,, NY, p. A445

MORISSETTE, Philip
Chief Financial Officer, Bridgton Hospital, Bridgton, ME, p. A292
Chief Financial Officer, Central Maine Medical Center, Lewiston, ME, p. A293

MORITZ, Mary, Administrator Human Resources, Humboldt County Memorial Hospital, Humboldt, IA, p. A232

MORK Jr., David L.
Chief Executive Officer, Roosevelt Warm Springs Rehabilitation and Specialty Hospitals – LTAC, Warm Springs, GA, p. A168
Chief Executive Officer, Roosevelt Warm Springs Rehabilitation and Specialty Hospitals – Rehab, Warm Springs, GA, p. A168

MORKEL, Derek, Chief Executive Officer, HealthTech Management Services, Brentwood, TN, p. B69

MORKRID, Shirley, Chief Nursing Officer, Liberty Medical Center, Chester, MT, p. A386

MORLEY, John, M.D., Acting Executive Director, NYC Health + Hospitals / Jacobi,, NY, p. A448

MORLEY, Michael, M.D. Chief of Staff, Arkansas Valley Regional Medical Center, La Junta, CO, p. A107

MORLOCK, Paul J., FACHE Vice President Human Resources and Occupational Health, Children's Hospital of The King's Daughters, Norfolk, VA, p. A675

MOSS, Shelby, Human Resource Officer, Sheridan County Health Complex, Hoxie, KS, p. A245

MOSS, Stuart, Chief Financial Officer, Marlton Rehabilitation Hospital, Marlton, NJ, p. A419

MOSSER, Kevin H., M.D., President and Chief Executive Officer, WellSpan Health, York, PA, p. B154

MOSSOFF, Alan, Director Finance, Northern Dutchess Hospital, Rhinebeck, NY, p. A453

MOST, Kevin, D.O. Vice President Medical Affairs, Northwestern Medicine Central DuPage Hospital, Winfield, IL, p. A205

MOSTOFI, Ann R., MSN Vice President Patient Care and Chief Nursing Officer, Eisenhower Medical Center, Rancho Mirage, CA, p. A84

MOTAKEF, Shahin, FACHE, Chief Executive Officer, Scott & White Memorial Hospital, Temple, TX, p. A652

MOTEJZIK, Thomas, Director Information Systems, Carlsbad Medical Center, Carlsbad, NM, p. A428

MOTONAGA, Gregg, M.D. Chief of Staff, Central Peninsula Hospital, Soldotna, AK, p. A30

MOTT, Daman, MSN Chief Nursing Officer, Doctors Hospital of Laredo, Laredo, TX, p. A632

MOTT, William, Chief Operating Officer, St. John Macomb–Oakland Hospital, Warren, MI, p. A336

MOTTE, Michael J., Chief Executive Officer, St. Alexius Hospital – Broadway Campus, Saint Louis, MO, p. A381

MOUGHAN, Jennifer L., Chief Human Resources Officer, Our Lady of Lourdes Medical Center, Camden, NJ, p. A415

MOUISSET, Rena B., Director Human Resources and Contract Compliance, St. Martin Hospital, Breaux Bridge, LA, p. A274

MOULTON, Susan, Director Health Information Management, Spring Harbor Hospital, Westbrook, ME, p. A295

MOUNIE, Mike, Director Finance, Sentara Obici Hospital, Suffolk, VA, p. A679

MOUNTAIN, J. Michael, Chief Financial Officer, RiverValley Behavioral Health Hospital, Owensboro, KY, p. A267

MOUSA, Ayman, Ph.D., Chief Executive Officer, Pacifica Hospital of the Valley,, CA, p. A73

MOUSA, Cindy, Director Human Resources, Touro Infirmary, New Orleans, LA, p. A285

MOUSTAKAKIS, John, Senior Vice President Information Systems and Chief Information Officer, Westchester Medical Center, Valhalla, NY, p. A458

MOVSESIAN, Gregory, M.D. Acting Chief of Staff, Aleda E. Lutz Veterans Affairs Medical Center, Saginaw, MI, p. A333

MOWAN, Chris
Chief Executive Officer, Medical City Dallas Hospital, Dallas, TX, p. A610
Chief Executive Officer, MountainView Hospital, Las Vegas, NV, p. A406

MOWDER, Kristan, Director Administration and Patient Care Services, Eastern State Hospital, Lexington, KY, p. A263

MOYA, Linda, Director Human Resources, Mesilla Valley Hospital, Las Cruces, NM, p. A430

MOYER, Dale, Vice President Information Systems, Evangelical Community Hospital, Lewisburg, PA, p. A543

MOYER, Debra, R.N
Chief Nursing Executive and Vice President Nursing Services, UnityPoint Health – Iowa Methodist Medical Center, Des Moines, IA, p. A229
Chief Nurse Executive, UnityPoint Health–Iowa Lutheran Hospital, Des Moines, IA, p. A229

MOYER, Douglas J., Chief Executive Officer, Southside Regional Medical Center, Petersburg, VA, p. A676

MOYER, Karen W., R.N. Senior Vice President and Chief Nursing Officer, Mount Sinai Medical Center, Miami Beach, FL, p. A138

MOYER, William E., President, St. Luke's Hospital – Miners Campus, Coaldale, PA, p. A535

MRAMOR, Joann, Director Human Resources, Seven Rivers Regional Medical Center, Crystal River, FL, p. A126

MUCARIA, Jaclyn, President and Chief Executive Officer, New York–Presbyterian/Queens,, NY, p. A447

MUCK, Erin, Vice President, Clinical Nursing, Crawford County Memorial Hospital, Denison, IA, p. A229

MUDEN, Todd, Section Head Information Management, Mayo Clinic Health System – Northland in Barron, Barron, WI, p. A702

MUDRY, Janel, Chief Operating Officer, Washington Health System Greene, Waynesburg, PA, p. A557

MUELLER, Arthur, Director Management Information Systems, Cuero Community Hospital, Cuero, TX, p. A608

MUELLER, Charles, M.D. Chief of Staff, Texas County Memorial Hospital, Houston, MO, p. A372

MUELLER, Jeff T., M.D. Chief Medical Officer, Medical Director, Mayo Clinic Hospital, Phoenix, AZ, p. A36

MUELLER, Karen, R.N. Chief Nursing Officer, Mount Desert Island Hospital, Bar Harbor, ME, p. A291

MUELLER, Michael E., Chief Financial Officer, Health Central Hospital, Ocoee, FL, p. A139

MUELLER, Paul, Chief Financial Officer, Sparta Community Hospital, Sparta, IL, p. A203

MUELLER, Paul A., Chief Executive Officer, Rogers Memorial Hospital, Oconomowoc, WI, p. A713

MUGAN, James, Senior Vice President for Clinical Services and Chief Operating Officer, Agnesian HealthCare, Fond Du Lac, WI, p. A705

MUHAMMAD, Mark, Manager Human Resources, Michael E. DeBakey Veterans Affairs Medical Center, Houston, TX, p. A626

MUHS, David, Chief Financial Officer, Henry County Health Center, Mount Pleasant, IA, p. A234

MUILENBURG, Jeff, Chief of Staff, Memorial Community Health, Aurora, NE, p. A393

MUIR, Brian, Chief of Staff, Minidoka Memorial Hospital, Rupert, ID, p. A178

MULDER, Dale R., Chief Executive Officer, Kindred Rehabilitation Hospital Clear Lake, Webster, TX, p. A656

MULDER, Doris, Vice President Nursing, Beloit Health System, Beloit, WI, p. A703

MULDER, Steven, M.D., President and Chief Executive Officer, Hutchinson Health, Hutchinson, MN, p. A344

MULDERIG, Marsha L., R.N. Chief Nursing Officer, Crisp Regional Hospital, Cordele, GA, p. A157

MULDOON, Patrick L., FACHE, President, UMass Memorial Medical Center, Worcester, MA, p. A316

MULDOON, Sean R., M.D. Senior Vice President and Chief Medical Officer–Kindred Healthcare, Hospital Division, Kindred Hospital Northland, Kansas City, MO, p. A373

MULIS, Becky, Director of Health Information Management Systems, Four County Counseling Center, Logansport, IN, p. A217

MULKEY, Peter, Chief Executive Officer, Clinch Valley Medical Center, Richlands, VA, p. A677

MULLEN, Thomas R., President and Chief Executive Officer, Mercy Medical Center, Baltimore, MD, p. A297

MULLENAX, Paul, Business Manager, Wyoming State Hospital, Evanston, WY, p. A722

MULLENDER, Monica, Director of Nursing, Osborne County Memorial Hospital, Osborne, KS, p. A250

MULLENS, Allen, M.D. Chief Medical Staff, Norton Community Hospital, Norton, VA, p. A675

MULLER, Donna L., Interim Chief Financial Officer, Hanover Hospital, Hanover, PA, p. A539

MULLER, Gary, Interim Chief Executive Officer, Elliot Hospital, Manchester, NH, p. A412

MULLER, Lynn, Chief Financial Officer, North Metro Medical Center, Jacksonville, AR, p. A47

MULLER, Oz, Director Human Resources, Porter Adventist Hospital, Denver, CO, p. A104

MULLER, Ralph W., President and Chief Executive Officer, University of Pennsylvania Health System, Philadelphia, PA, p. B148

MULLERY, Barbara M., Vice President Administration, Robert Wood Johnson University Hospital Rahway, Rahway, NJ, p. A422

MULLIGAN, Lisa, Commanding Officer, Naval Hospital Camp Pendleton, Camp Pendleton, CA, p. A58

MULLIGAN, Marie, R.N. Vice President Nursing, John T. Mather Memorial Hospital, Port Jefferson, NY, p. A453

MULLIN, Shelly, R.N., President and Market Leader, MultiCare Tacoma General Hospital, Tacoma, WA, p. A692

MULLINGS, Donna, Director of Nursing, Assumption Community Hospital, Napoleonville, LA, p. A284

MULLINS, Bandy, M.D. Chief of Staff, Summersville Regional Medical Center, Summersville, WV, p. A700

MULLINS, Brad, Director Information Technology, Gove County Medical Center, Quinter, KS, p. A252

MULLINS, Bryan, Chief Operating Officer, Johnston Memorial Hospital, Abingdon, VA, p. A667

MULLINS, Cindy, Director Information Technology, Saint Mary's Regional Medical Center, Reno, NV, p. A408

MULLINS, Dustin, Chief Resource Management, Bayne–Jones Army Community Hospital, Fort Polk, LA, p. A277

MULLINS, Erin, D.O. Chief Medical Staff, Dickenson Community Hospital, Clintwood, VA, p. A669

MULLINS, Kem, FACHE, President, WellStar Windy Hill Hospital, Marietta, GA, p. A163

MULLINS, Larry, Chief Executive Officer and Administrator, W. J. Mangold Memorial Hospital, Lockney, TX, p. A633

MULLINS, Larry A., FACHE, President and Chief Executive Officer, Samaritan Health Services, Corvallis, OR, p. B117

MULLINS, Michelle, Chief Information Officer, Oklahoma Heart Hospital, Oklahoma City, OK, p. A517

MULLIS, Jeffrey
Interim Chief Financial Officer, Bayfront Health Port Charlotte, Port Charlotte, FL, p. A143
Interim Chief Financial Officer, Clearview Regional Medical Center, Monroe, GA, p. A163

MULROONEY, JoAnn M., R.N. Chief Operating Officer, Trinity Health System, Steubenville, OH, p. A503

MULTACH, Mark, M.D. Chief Medical Officer, Mount Sinai Hospital, Chicago, IL, p. A185

MULTACK, Richard, D.O. Vice President Medical Management, Advocate South Suburban Hospital, Hazel Crest, IL, p. A192

MULVEHILL, Mitchell, Group Financial Officer, Texas Health Harris Methodist Hospital Southlake, Southlake, TX, p. A649

MULVEY, Lee, Human Resource Officer, Texas Health Harris Methodist Hospital Hurst–Euless–Bedford, Bedford, TX, p. A602

MUMOLIE, Gina, Senior Vice President and Chief Nurse Executive, Inspira Medical Center–Woodbury, Woodbury, NJ, p. A425

MUMPOWER, Rebecca, Director Marketing, Mesilla Valley Hospital, Las Cruces, NM, p. A430

MUNA, Esther L., Chief Executive Officer, Commonwealth Health Center, Saipan, MP, p. A725

MUNCHEL, Bryan, Senior Vice President and Chief Information Officer, PAM Specialty Hospital of Covington, Covington, LA, p. A275

MUNDY, Mark J., President and Chief Executive Officer, New York Methodist Hospital,, NY, p. A447

MUNDY, Stephens M., President and Chief Executive Officer, The University of Vermont Health Network–Champlain Valley Physicians Hospital, Plattsburgh, NY, p. A453

MUNFORD, Thedosia, Senior Vice President and Chief Nursing Officer, Providence Hospital, Washington, DC, p. A122

MUNGER, Richard, Administrator, Mount Grant General Hospital, Hawthorne, NV, p. A404

MUNGOVAN, Sandy, Chief Information Officer, Harbor–UCLA Medical Center, Torrance, CA, p. A96

MUNHOLLAND, Cleta
Administrator, Louisiana Extended Care Hospital West Monroe, West Monroe, LA, p. A289
Administrator, Specialty Hospital, Monroe, LA, p. A283

MUNIR, Amjad, M.D. Medical Director, HEALTHSOUTH Chattanooga Rehabilitation Hospital, Chattanooga, TN, p. A580

MUNOZ, Astro, Executive Director, First Hospital Panamericano, Cidra, PR, p. A727

MUNOZ, Thalia H., MS, Chief Executive Officer, Starr County Memorial Hospital, Rio Grande City, TX, p. A643

MUNSAYAC, Kirk,Jeff Davis Hospital, Hazlehurst, GA, p. A160

MUNSON, Bill, Vice President and Chief Financial Officer, Boulder Community Health, Boulder, CO, p. A101

MUNSON, Jennifer, Chief Financial Officer, Three Rivers Hospital, Brewster, WA, p. A683

MUNSON, Joan, Manager Information Systems, Fairchild Medical Center, Yreka, CA, p. A100

MUNSON, John, Vice President and Chief Financial Officer, St. Anthony Regional Hospital, Carroll, IA, p. A225

MUNSON, Kris, Director Human Resources, Arbour H. R. I. Hospital, Brookline, MA, p. A308

MUNTEFERING, Denise, Vice President Patient Care Services, Avera St. Benedict Health Center, Parkston, SD, p. A575

MUNTZ, Dana M., Chief Executive Officer, St. Vincent Salem Hospital, Salem, IN, p. A221

MUNTZ, Tim, President and Chief Executive Officer, St. Margaret's Hospital, Spring Valley, IL, p. A203

MUNYAN, Lori, Director, Human Resources, HEALTHSOUTH Rehabilitation Hospital of Toms River, Toms River, NJ, p. A424

MURANSKY, Ed, Owner, Surgical Hospital at Southwoods, Youngstown, OH, p. A506

MURCHISON, Sandra, Director Medical Records, Coosa Valley Medical Center, Sylacauga, AL, p. A25

MURDAUGH, Laura, Finance Director, William J. McCord Adolescent Treatment Facility, Orangeburg, SC, p. A569

MURDOCH, William, M.D. Medical Director, Loma Linda University Behavioral Medicine Center, Redlands, CA, p. A85

MURDOCK, Guy, Vice President Human Resources, Healthbridge Children's Hospital of Houston, Houston, TX, p. A624

MURDOCK, Holly, Human Resources Coordinator, Kindred Hospital Rome, Rome, GA, p. A165

MURDOCK, Mark, Associate Director, Dayton Veterans Affairs Medical Center, Dayton, OH, p. A492

MURDOCK–LANGAN, Patricia, M.D
Chief Medical Officer, CHI Health Lakeside, Omaha, NE, p. A400
Chief Medical Officer, CHI Health Midlands, Papillion, NE, p. A401

MURDY, James B., Chief Financial Officer, Belmont Community Hospital, Bellaire, OH, p. A484

MURFEE, Patrick, Chief Operating Officer, Hemphill County Hospital, Canadian, TX, p. A605

MURILLO, Jeremias, M.D. Chief Medical Officer, Newark Beth Israel Medical Center, Newark, NJ, p. A420

MURIN, William J., Chief Human Resources Officer, UC San Diego Health, San Diego, CA, p. A89

MURPHY, Brian, Senior Director Admissions and Referral Services, Hebrew Rehabilitation Center, Boston, MA, p. A307

MURPHY, Bruce, M.D., President and Chief Executive Officer, Arkansas Heart Hospital, Little Rock, AR, p. A48

MURPHY, Charles J., Associate Vice President Human Resources, Strong Memorial Hospital of the University of Rochester, Rochester, NY, p. A454

MURPHY, Christine, MS Chief Operating Officer, Liberty Healthcare Systems, Bastrop, LA, p. A272

MURPHY, Colleen, M.D. Chief of Staff, Clay County Hospital, Flora, IL, p. A190

MURPHY, David, Interim Chief Executive Officer, Fairview Health Services, Minneapolis, MN, p. B55

MURPHY, David, Interim Chief Executive Officer, University of Minnesota Medical Center, Fairview, Minneapolis, MN, p. A347

MURPHY, Dennis M., President, Indiana University Health, Indianapolis, IN, p. B72

MURPHY, Dennis M., Chief Operating Officer, Indiana University Health University Hospital, Indianapolis, IN, p. A214

MURPHY, Elizabeth A., R.N. Vice President for Patient Care Services, Mercy Health Saint Mary's, Grand Rapids, MI, p. A325

MURPHY, Evelyn, R.N. Chief Nursing Officer, St. Mary's Sacred Heart Hospital, Lavonia, GA, p. A162

MURPHY, J. Patrick, Chief Financial Officer, North Baldwin Infirmary, Bay Minette, AL, p. A16

MURPHY, James, Chief Executive Officer, South Texas Surgical Hospital, Corpus Christi, TX, p. A608

MURPHY, James M., Chief Medical Officer Regional Development and Outpatient Services, New London Hospital, New London, NH, p. A412

MURPHY, John B., M.D. Vice President Medical Affairs and Chief Medical Officer, Rhode Island Hospital, Providence, RI, p. A561

MURPHY, John M., M.D., President and Chief Executive Officer, Western Connecticut Health Network, Danbury Hospital, Danbury, CT, p. A113

MURPHY, John M., M.D., President and Chief Executive Officer, Western Connecticut Health Network, Danbury, CT, p. B155

MURPHY, Joseph, Chief Executive Officer, Las Encinas Hospital, Pasadena, CA, p. A82

MURPHY, Judy, Vice President Human Resources, Southwest General Health Center, Middleburg Heights, OH, p. A499

MURPHY, Julie
  Chief Financial Officer, Saint Luke's Cushing Hospital, Leavenworth, KS, p. A247
  Chief Financial Officer, Saint Luke's North Hospital – Barry Road, Kansas City, MO, p. A374

MURPHY, Kathy, Site Manager, Mescalero Public Health Service Indian Hospital, Mescalero, NM, p. A430

MURPHY, Kelly, Director Human Resources, Colorado Canyons Hospital and Medical Center, Fruita, CO, p. A106

MURPHY, Kevin, Director, Information Technology Services, Bayfront Health St. Petersburg, Saint Petersburg, FL, p. A144

MURPHY, Kyle, Director Information Technology, Mayhill Hospital, Denton, TX, p. A612

MURPHY, Linda, Chief Financial Officer, Osborne County Memorial Hospital, Osborne, KS, p. A250

MURPHY, Lionel
  Chief Executive Officer and Administrator, Bethesda Rehabilitation Hospital, Baton Rouge, LA, p. A272
  Chief Executive Officer, Southeast Regional Medical Center, Kentwood, LA, p. A279

MURPHY, Marie, Director Human Resources, Effingham Hospital, Springfield, GA, p. A166

MURPHY, Mary S., MS
  Regional Chief Nursing Officer, Adventist La Grange Memorial Hospital, La Grange, IL, p. A194
  Vice President and Chief Nursing Officer, AMITA Health Adventist Medical Center – Hinsdale, Hinsdale, IL, p. A193

MURPHY, Marybeth, Director Human Resources, Madison St. Joseph Health Center, Madisonville, TX, p. A635

MURPHY, Matthew, Chief Financial Officer, Marengo Memorial Hospital, Marengo, IA, p. A234

MURPHY, Maureen, M.D. Director of Medical Affairs, St. Clare Hospital, Baraboo, WI, p. A702

MURPHY, Michael, M.D. Chief Medical Officer, Sharp Grossmont Hospital, La Mesa, CA, p. A67

MURPHY, Michael, CPA, President & Chief Executive Officer, Sharp HealthCare, San Diego, CA, p. B123

MURPHY, Michael D., Chief Executive Officer, Abilene Regional Medical Center, Abilene, TX, p. A595

MURPHY, Michael J., FACHE, Director, Veterans Affairs Puget Sound Health Care System, Seattle, WA, p. A690

MURPHY, Nancy, Vice President, Human Resources, Franciscan Hospital for Children, Boston, MA, p. A306

MURPHY, Paul, Chief Information Officer, Lane Regional Medical Center, Zachary, LA, p. A290

MURPHY, Peter J., Senior Vice President and Chief Operating Officer, Franciscan St. Francis Health – Mooresville, Mooresville, IN, p. A218

MURPHY, Richard J., President and Chief Executive Officer, South Nassau Communities Hospital, Oceanside, NY, p. A451

MURPHY, Rita, Director Human Resources, Cobre Valley Regional Medical Center, Globe, AZ, p. A33

MURPHY, Sheryl, Chief Nursing Officer and Director of Clinical Services, PeaceHealth Peace Island Medical Center, Friday Harbor, WA, p. A685

MURPHY, Steve
  FM–East Region IS, Good Samaritan Regional Health Center, Mount Vernon, IL, p. A197
  Director Information Systems, SSM Health St. Mary's Hospital Centralia, Centralia, IL, p. A182

MURPHY, Steven, Executive Director, Devereux Hospital and Children's Center of Florida, Melbourne, FL, p. A135

MURPHY, Terry
  President and Chief Executive Officer, Bayhealth Medical Center, Dover, DE, p. A119
  Director Information Services, Phoenixville Hospital, Phoenixville, PA, p. A550

MURPHY, Theresa, Chief Nursing Officer, USC Verdugo Hills Hospital, Glendale, CA, p. A65

MURPHY, Timothy, R.N. Chief Nursing Officer, HEALTHSOUTH Desert Canyon Rehabilitation Hospital, Las Vegas, NV, p. A405

MURPHY, Timothy
  Vice President Human Resources, Mercy Hospital Fort Scott, Fort Scott, KS, p. A243
  Vice President Human Resources, Mercy Hospital Joplin, Joplin, MO, p. A373

MURPHY, Tom, Chief Executive Officer, Minidoka Memorial Hospital, Rupert, ID, p. A178

MURPHY–FROBISH, Erin, Vice President Human Resources, Morris Hospital & Healthcare Centers, Morris, IL, p. A197

MURPHY–MIJARES, Monique, Chief Information Officer, Valley View Medical Center, Fort Mohave, AZ, p. A32

MURRAY, Alexander, Interim Associate Director, Veterans Affairs Gulf Coast Veterans Health Care System, Biloxi, MS, p. A355

MURRAY, Brian, M.D. Medical Director, Erie County Medical Center, Buffalo, NY, p. A435

MURRAY, Brian, Chief Financial Officer, Gunnison Valley Hospital, Gunnison, UT, p. A660

MURRAY, Cindy, R.N. Chief Nursing Officer and Chief Operating Officer, Baylor Scott & White Medical Center at Waxahachie, Waxahachie, TX, p. A656

MURRAY, Denise R., Chief Executive Officer, Carolinas ContinueCARE Hospital at Kings Mountain, Kings Mountain, NC, p. A468

MURRAY, Diana, Director Information Systems, Grand River Hospital District, Rifle, CO, p. A110

MURRAY, Geno, President and Chief Executive Officer, Charles A. Dean Memorial Hospital, Greenville, ME, p. A293

MURRAY, Gerald
  President, UPMC Altoona, Altoona, PA, p. A532
  President, UPMC Bedford Memorial, Everett, PA, p. A538

MURRAY, J. Patrick, FACHE, President and Chief Executive Officer, Peterson Regional Medical Center, Kerrville, TX, p. A630

MURRAY, Julie, Chief Executive Officer, Litzenberg Memorial County Hospital, Central City, NE, p. A394

MURRAY, Kent, M.D. Chief of Staff, Robert J. Dole Veterans Affairs Medical Center, Wichita, KS, p. A256

MURRAY, Kevin, M.D. Director Medical Services, Lake Taylor Transitional Care Hospital, Norfolk, VA, p. A675

MURRAY, Kevin J., Senior Vice President, John T. Mather Memorial Hospital, Port Jefferson, NY, p. A453

MURRAY, Marisa, CPA Director Finance, HSHS St. Francis Hospital, Litchfield, IL, p. A195

MURRAY, Michael, Chief Financial Officer, CHRISTUS Continuing Care dba Dubuis Hospital of Paris, Paris, TX, p. A640

MURRAY, Sherri, Chief Financial Officer, Montgomery General Hospital, Montgomery, WV, p. A698

MURRAY, Susan, Director Information Services, Trident Medical Center, Charleston, SC, p. A563

MURRAY, Wesley E., Chief Executive Officer, Texas County Memorial Hospital, Houston, MO, p. A372

MURRELL, Joseph, Chief Executive Officer, Wayne County Hospital, Monticello, KY, p. A266

MURROW, Carol, Vice President Business Development, Cox Medical Center Branson, Branson, MO, p. A368

MURRY, Jim, Chief Information Officer, Stony Brook University Hospital, Stony Brook, NY, p. A456

MURT, Mary Lou, R.N. Senior Vice President Nursing, Monongahela Valley Hospital, Monongahela, PA, p. A545

MURTHY, Bangalore, M.D. Director Medical Staff, Jackson Park Hospital and Medical Center, Chicago, IL, p. A184

MURTHY, Krishna, M.D. Chief of Medical Staff, Gibson General Hospital, Princeton, IN, p. A221

MURZYN, Derek, Chief Executive Officer, Carolinas ContinueCARE Hospital at University, Charlotte, NC, p. A462

MUSACK, Scott, Chief Information Officer, Silver Lake Medical Center, Los Angeles, CA, p. A74

MUSGRAVE, Chelsea, Director of Human Resources, Clay County Hospital, Flora, IL, p. A190

MUSICH, Trisha E., R.N
  Chief Nursing Officer, Vista Medical Center East, Waukegan, IL, p. A205
  Chief Nursing Officer, Vista Medical Center West, Waukegan, IL, p. A205

MUSOIU, Robert, Director Human Resources, Fairfield Memorial Hospital, Fairfield, IL, p. A190

MUSSI, Natalie, President and Chief Executive Officer, Los Robles Hospital and Medical Center, Thousand Oaks, CA, p. A96

MUSSMAN, Rebekah, Chief Executive Officer, Crete Area Medical Center, Crete, NE, p. A395

MUSSO, Lewis C., Vice President Human Resources, Trinity Health System, Steubenville, OH, p. A503

MUSTACCHIA, Michele, Chief Human Resources Officer, Banner Gateway Medical Center, Gilbert, AZ, p. A32

MUSTARD, Ruth W., R.N. Associate Director Nursing and Patient Services, Wm. Jennings Bryan Dorn Veterans Affairs Medical Center, Columbia, SC, p. A564

MUSTIAN, J. Perry, President, Archbold Medical Center, Thomasville, GA, p. B11

MUSTIAN, J. Perry, President and Chief Executive Officer, John D. Archbold Memorial Hospital, Thomasville, GA, p. A167

MUSTIN, Deanna, R.N., Administrator, Bob Wilson Memorial Grant County Hospital, Ulysses, KS, p. A255

MUSUNURU, J.R., M.D., Executive Director, Fond Du Lac County Mental Health Center, Fond Du Lac, WI, p. A705

MUTTERER, Michael, Senior Vice President and Chief Nursing Officer, Riverside Medical Center, Kankakee, IL, p. A194

MUTZIGER, John, M.D. Chief Medical Officer, Laird Hospital, Union, MS, p. A365

MWANIKI, Mary, Chief Financial Officer, HEALTHSOUTH Rehabilitation Hospital – Mid–Cities, Bedford, TX, p. A602

MWEBE, David, M.D. Chief of Staff, Osmond General Hospital, Osmond, NE, p. A401

MYATT, Kevin A., Senior Vice President Human Resources, Yale–New Haven Hospital, New Haven, CT, p. A116

MYDLER, Todd, M.D. Vice President and Chief Medical Officer, Good Samaritan Medical Center, Lafayette, CO, p. A108

MYER, Amber, Director Medical Technology, Throckmorton County Memorial Hospital, Throckmorton, TX, p. A653

MYERS, Becky, Human Resources Specialist, Illini Community Hospital, Pittsfield, IL, p. A201

MYERS, Chrissy, R.N. Director of Nursing, Behavioral HealthCare Center at Clarksville, Clarksville, TN, p. A581

MYERS, Doug, Senior Vice President and Chief Financial Officer, USCF Benioff Children's Hospital Oakland, Oakland, CA, p. A80

MYERS, Douglas, Executive Vice President and Chief Financial Officer, Children's National Health System, Washington, DC, p. A121

MYERS, Ed, Administrator, Shriners Hospitals for Children–Philadelphia, Philadelphia, PA, p. A549

MYERS, Gabby, Human Resources Director, Advanced Diagnostics Hospital, Houston, TX, p. A623

MYERS, Gary, Chief Executive Officer, Mammoth Hospital, Mammoth Lakes, CA, p. A75

MYERS, Grace, MSN Vice President, Nurse Executive, Sentara Princess Anne Hospital, Virginia Beach, VA, p. A680

MYERS, Janet
  Administrator, South Georgia Medical Center Berrien Campus, Nashville, GA, p. A164
  Administrator, South Georgia Medical Center Lanier Campus, Lakeland, GA, p. A161

MYERS, Jeffrey D., President and Chief Executive Officer, Hamilton Medical Center, Dalton, GA, p. A158

MYERS, Jerry, M.D., Chief Executive Officer and Medical Director, Kell West Regional Hospital, Wichita Falls, TX, p. A657

MYERS, Jessica, Medical Director, Neshoba County General Hospital, Philadelphia, MS, p. A363

MYERS, Karen, Vice President Financial Services, Stoughton Hospital Association, Stoughton, WI, p. A716

MYERS, Kathy R., MS Chief Nursing Officer, Tennova Healthcare–LaFollette Medical Center, La Follette, TN, p. A586

MYERS, Keith G., Chairman and Chief Executive Officer, LHC Group, Lafayette, LA, p. B80

MYERS, Kevin
  Director Information Systems, Lake Granbury Medical Center, Granbury, TX, p. A621
  Director Information Technology, Wilson Medical Center, Neodesha, KS, p. A249

MYERS, Kimberly, Director Human Resources, Guthrie County Hospital, Guthrie Center, IA, p. A231

MYERS, Lisa, Director Human Resources, Heritage Oaks Hospital, Sacramento, CA, p. A86

MYERS, Loretta, MS Director, Patient Care, Floyd Valley Healthcare, Le Mars, IA, p. A233

MYERS, Lynn, Controller, Curahealth Tucson, Tucson, AZ, p. A40

MYERS, Mark, M.D. Chief Medical Officer, AMG Specialty Hospital–Tulsa, Tulsa, OK, p. A521

MYERS, Mary, R.N. Chief Nursing Officer, St. Vincent Indianapolis Hospital, Indianapolis, IN, p. A215

MYERS, Michael D., R.N., Chief Executive Officer, Veterans Memorial Hospital, Waukon, IA, p. A239

MYERS, Michelle F., Director Human Resources, Florida Hospital Wauchula, Wauchula, FL, p. A149

MYERS, Paul, M.D. Neonatologist and Chief Medical Officer, Children's Hospital of Wisconsin–Fox Valley, Neenah, WI, p. A712

MYERS, Philip, M.D. Vice President Medical Affairs, University Hospitals Samaritan Medical Center, Ashland, OH, p. A484

MYERS, Randy, Chief Information Officer, Information Technology, Mitchell County Hospital, Colorado City, TX, p. A606

MYERS, Robert T., Chief Operating Officer, Indiana University Health Goshen Hospital, Goshen, IN, p. A212

MYERS, Rosemary, Manager, Team Resources, Winter Haven Hospital, Winter Haven, FL, p. A150

MYERS, Russ, Chief Executive Officer, Yakima Valley Memorial Hospital, Yakima, WA, p. A693

MYERS, Shane P., Chief Operating Officer, Iberia Medical Center, New Iberia, LA, p. A284

MYERS, Sheri, Vice President Patient Care Services, McLaren Central Michigan, Mount Pleasant, MI, p. A330

MYERS, Tara, Director Human Resources, AnMed Health Rehabilitation Hospital, Anderson, SC, p. A562

MYERS, Theresa, Personnel Director, Fallon Medical Complex, Baker, MT, p. A385

MYERS, William, Chief Executive Officer, Montgomery County Emergency Service, Norristown, PA, p. A546

MYHRE, Tracy, R.N. Chief Nursing Officer, Tomah Memorial Hospital, Tomah, WI, p. A717

MYSTER, Jennifer, President, Buffalo Hospital, Buffalo, MN, p. A340

N

NABEL, Elizabeth, M.D., President, Brigham and Women's Hospital, Boston, MA, p. A306

NABORS, Teresa, Director of Nursing, Greenwood Regional Rehabilitation Hospital, Greenwood, SC, p. A567

NACEY, Marley, Director Finance, Sentara Virginia Beach General Hospital, Virginia Beach, VA, p. A680

NACHIMUTHU, Anbu, Chief Financial Officer, Atrium Medical Center of Corinth, Corinth, TX, p. A607

NACHTIGAL, Amy, Chief Financial Officer, Saint Luke's Hospital of Kansas City, Kansas City, MO, p. A374

NACHTRIEB, Han, Vice President Human Resources, Seattle Cancer Care Alliance, Seattle, WA, p. A689

NACION, Glenn, Vice President Human Resources, Trinitas Regional Medical Center, Elizabeth, NJ, p. A416

NADEAU, Barbara, Chief Human Resources Management Service, White River Junction Veterans Affairs Medical Center, White River Junction, VT, p. A666

NADEAU, Stephen, Senior Vice President Human Resources, Gwinnett Hospital System, Lawrenceville, GA, p. A162

NADER, Daniel, D.O. Chief of Staff, Southwestern Regional Medical Center, Tulsa, OK, p. A522

NADER, Keoni, Director Human Resources, Louis A. Weiss Memorial Hospital, Chicago, IL, p. A184

NADER, Mary, Director Information Technology, Spectrum Health Special Care Hospital, Grand Rapids, MI, p. A325

NADER, Rick Lee, Chief Financial Officer, Haxtun Hospital District, Haxtun, CO, p. A107

NADKARNI, Manasi, M.D. Vice President Medical Affairs, UnityPoint Health – Trinity Muscatine, Muscatine, IA, p. A235

NADLE, Patricia A., R.N. Chief Nursing Officer, St. Joseph Health Services of Rhode Island, North Providence, RI, p. A560

NADLER, Tammy R., Chief Financial Officer, Golden Valley Memorial Healthcare, Clinton, MO, p. A369

NADOLNY, Stephanie, Vice President of Hospital Operations, Spaulding Rehabilitation Hospital Cape Cod, East Sandwich, MA, p. A309

NAFZIGER, Laurie N., President and Chief Executive Officer, Oaklawn Psychiatric Center, Goshen, IN, p. A212

NAFZIGER, Steve, M.D. Vice President Medical Affairs, Parkview Medical Center, Pueblo, CO, p. A110

NAGARAJ, Alaka, M.D. Medical Director, Regency Hospital of Minneapolis, Golden Valley, MN, p. A343

NAGARAJ, Raghava, Chief Medical Officer, Wake Forest Baptist Health–Lexington Medical Center, Lexington, NC, p. A469

NAGATOSHI, Holly, R.N. Chief Nursing Officer, San Dimas Community Hospital, San Dimas, CA, p. A89

NAGEL, Donna, Director Human Resources, AMG Specialty Hospital–Tulsa, Tulsa, OK, p. A521

NAGEL, Melody, Chief Executive Officer, Select Specialty Hospital – Dallas Downtown, Dallas, TX, p. A611

NAGLER, Richard, M.D. Chief of Staff, Mayo Clinic Health System – Northland in Barron, Barron, WI, p. A702

NAGLOSKY, Paul, Administrator, Indianhead Medical Center, Shell Lake, WI, p. A716

NAGOWSKI, Michael, President and Chief Executive Officer, Cape Fear Valley Health System, Fayetteville, NC, p. B26

NAGOWSKI, Michael, Chief Executive Officer, Cape Fear Valley Medical Center, Fayetteville, NC, p. A465

NAGY, Jeff, Chief Financial Officer, River Bend Hospital, West Lafayette, IN, p. A223

NAGY, Kimberly, R.N. Executive Vice President, Patient Services and Chief Nursing Officer, Northwest Community Hospital, Arlington Heights, IL, p. A180

NAGY, Linda J., MSN Chief Nursing Officer, Brattleboro Retreat, Brattleboro, VT, p. A665

NAHAPETIAN, Arby, M.D. Vice President Medical Affairs and Quality, Glendale Adventist Medical Center, Los Angeles, CA, p. A71

NAHMENSEN, Robert, Chief Financial Officer and Chief Operations Officer, Stanton County Hospital, Johnson, KS, p. A246

NAIBERK, Donald T., Administrator, Butler County Health Care Center, David City, NE, p. A395

NAIL, Cheryl, R.N. Chief Nursing Officer, Baylor Scott & White Medical Center – White Rock, Dallas, TX, p. A609

NAIR, Chand, M.D. Medical Director, Brooke Glen Behavioral Hospital, Fort Washington, PA, p. A539

NAIR, Vijayachandran, M.D. Chief of Staff, John J. Pershing Veterans Affairs Medical Center, Poplar Bluff, MO, p. A378

NAJIEB, LaDonna, Service Area Director Human Resources, Providence Saint Joseph Medical Center, Burbank, CA, p. A57

NAJJAR, Maher, M.D. Medical Director, Kindred Hospital Chicago–Northlake, Northlake, IL, p. A198

NAJJAR, Milad, Information Technology, Freedom Pain Hospital, Scottsdale, AZ, p. A38

NAKAMOTO, Kenneth, M.D. Vice President Medical Affairs, Pomona Valley Hospital Medical Center, Pomona, CA, p. A83

NAKAMURA, Bridget, Director Information Systems, Simi Valley Hospital, Simi Valley, CA, p. A94

NAKASUJI, Jody, Chief Financial Officer, Harbor–UCLA Medical Center, Torrance, CA, p. A96

NALDI, Robert, Chief Financial Officer, Maimonides Medical Center,, NY, p. A445

NALEPPA, Margaret, Ph.D., President and Chief Executive Officer, Peninsula Regional Medical Center, Salisbury, MD, p. A303

NALL, Wes, Chief Financial Officer, Monroe County Hospital, Monroeville, AL, p. A23

NALLE, Tambara, Chief Financial Officer, Eastern State Hospital, Lexington, KY, p. A263

NALLEY, Leanna W., Director Human Resources, Texas Health Harris Methodist Hospital Southwest Fort Worth, Fort Worth, TX, p. A619

NAMBOODIRI, Hari, Chief Executive Officer, Solara Hospital McAllen, McAllen, TX, p. A636

NANANYAKKARA, Nalin, M.D. Chief of Staff, Corona Regional Medical Center, Corona, CA, p. A59

NANCE, Christi, R.N. Chief Nursing Officer, Northwest Specialty Hospital, Post Falls, ID, p. A178

NANCE, Sally S., Chief Executive Officer, Excelsior Springs Hospital, Excelsior Springs, MO, p. A370

NANIA, James A., System Vice President and Chief Financial Officer, Hallmark Health System, Melrose, MA, p. A312

NAPIER, Frank, Interim Chief Financial Officer, Cobre Valley Regional Medical Center, Globe, AZ, p. A33

NAPIER, Michelle, Director of Nursing, Central State Hospital, Louisville, KY, p. A264

NAPIER, Pamela, MSN Chief Nursing Officer, Mercy Health – Willard Hospital, Willard, OH, p. A506

NAPIER, Randy L.
President, Frazier Rehab Institute, Louisville, KY, p. A264
President, Southern Indiana Rehabilitation Hospital, New Albany, IN, p. A219

NAPIERKOWSKI, Daniel, M.D., President, Euclid Hospital, Euclid, OH, p. A494

NAPOLITANO, Mary Pat, Director Human Resources, Specialty Hospital of Central Jersey, Lakewood, NJ, p. A418

NAPP, Marc L., M.D. Vice President Medical Affairs, Lenox Hill Hospital, New York, NY, p. A445

NAPPER, Rick D., Market President, St. Joseph Regional Health Center, Bryan, TX, p. A604

NAPPS, Greg, Chief Executive Officer, Novant Health UVA Health System Culpeper Medical Center, Culpeper, VA, p. A669

NARAMORE, G. Harold, M.D. Chief Medical Officer and In house Legal Counsel, Blount Memorial Hospital, Maryville, TN, p. A588

NARANG, Steve, M.D., Chief Executive Officer, Banner – University Medical Center Phoenix, Phoenix, AZ, p. A36

NARANJO, Jason, Chief Executive Officer, Kindred Hospital–Mansfield, Mansfield, TX, p. A635

NARANJO, Maria, Director Human Resources, Memorial Hospital West, Pembroke Pines, FL, p. A142

NARBUTAS, Virgis
Chief Executive Officer, La Palma Intercommunity Hospital, La Palma, CA, p. A67
Chief Executive Officer, West Anaheim Medical Center, Anaheim, CA, p. A54

NAREMORE, Bruce, Senior Vice President and Chief Financial Officer, East Jefferson General Hospital, Metairie, LA, p. A283

NARROW, Ann, Director of Nursing, River Hospital, Alexandria Bay, NY, p. A433

NARY, Ed, Director Information Technology and Chief Compliance Officer, Wilbarger General Hospital, Vernon, TX, p. A655

NASET–PAYNE, Janet, MS Chief Nursing Officer, Van Diest Medical Center, Webster City, IA, p. A239

NASH, Donna, Director of Nursing, Monroe County Hospital, Forsyth, GA, p. A159

NASH, Ernest
Chief Financial Officer, South Texas Rehabilitation Hospital, Brownsville, TX, p. A603
Chief Financial Officer, Weslaco Regional Rehabilitation Hospital, Weslaco, TX, p. A657

NASH, Gayle, R.N. Chief Nursing Officer, MountainView Regional Medical Center, Las Cruces, NM, p. A430

NASH, Jacqueline, Controller, Beaumont Hospital – Wayne, Wayne, MI, p. A336

NASH, John D., FACHE, President and Chief Executive Officer, Franciscan Hospital for Children, Boston, MA, p. A306

NASH, Mary G., Ph.D. Chief Nursing Officer, Ohio State University Wexner Medical Center, Columbus, OH, p. A491

NASH, Rhonda, Director Health Information Management, Dallas Behavioral Healthcare Hospital, Desoto, TX, p. A613

NASH, Robert, M.D. Chief of Staff, Richland Memorial Hospital, Olney, IL, p. A199

NASH, Sandra, Chief Fiscal Service, James H. Quillen Veterans Affairs Medical Center, Mountain Home, TN, p. A590

NASH, Tim, M.D. Chief of Staff, Marshall Medical Center, Lewisburg, TN, p. A587

NASHID, Nadia, M.D. Chief of Staff, Windham Hospital, Willimantic, CT, p. A118

NASLUND, Kevin, Manager Information Technology, Cherokee Regional Medical Center, Cherokee, IA, p. A227

NASR, Anthony, M.D. Chief Medical Staff, Feather River Hospital, Paradise, CA, p. A82

NASRALLAH, Fadi, M.D. Vice President Medical Affairs, CHRISTUS Mother Frances Hospital – Tyler, Tyler, TX, p. A654

NASSIEF, Raymond, Senior Vice President, Hospital Operations and Support Services, John Muir Medical Center, Walnut Creek, Walnut Creek, CA, p. A99

NASSTROM, Jeff, D.O. Chief of Staff, Mitchell County Regional Health Center, Osage, IA, p. A235

NAST, Ed, M.D. Chief Medical Officer, Oak Hill Hospital, Brooksville, FL, p. A125

NATAL, Yesenia, Coordinator Human Resources, Hospital Dr. Cayetano Coll Y Toste, Arecibo, PR, p. A726

NATALONI, Tom, Senior Director Information Technology, Hahnemann University Hospital, Philadelphia, PA, p. A548

NATCHER, Charles, Chief Financial Officer, Kindred Hospital–Los Angeles, Los Angeles, CA, p. A72

NATELSON, Richard, M.D. Chief of Staff, Steele Memorial Medical Center, Salmon, ID, p. A178

NATEMAN, Barry, Manager Human Resources, French Hospital Medical Center, San Luis Obispo, CA, p. A92

NATH, Dilip, Sc.D. Associate Chief Information Officer, SUNY Downstate Medical Center University Hospital,, NY, p. A450

NATH, Pravene, Chief Information Officer, Stanford Health Care, Palo Alto, CA, p. A82

NATHAN, James R.
President and Chief Executive Officer, Cape Coral Hospital, Cape Coral, FL, p. A125
President and Chief Executive Officer, Gulf Coast Medical Center, Fort Myers, FL, p. A129

NATHAN, James R., President and Chief Executive Officer, Lee Memorial Health System, Fort Myers, FL, p. B80

NATHAN, James R., President and Chief Executive Officer, Lee Memorial Hospital, Fort Myers, FL, p. A129
NATHANSON, Andrea, Director Finance, Baystate Franklin Medical Center, Greenfield, MA, p. A310
NATHEM, Joanne, MSN Chief Clinical and Nursing Officer, Waverly Health Center, Waverly, IA, p. A239
NATOLI, Joseph B., Senior Vice President Business and Finance and Chief Financial Officer, University of Miami Hospital and Clinics, Miami, FL, p. A137
NATRAJAN, Sunil, M.D. Medical Director, Curahealth Tucson, Tucson, AZ, p. A40
NAU, James, Manager Computer and Applications Support, Delaware Psychiatric Center, New Castle, DE, p. A119
NAUMAN, Michael B.
  Chief Information Officer, Children's Hospital of Wisconsin, Milwaukee, WI, p. A711
  Chief Information Officer and Corporate Vice President, Children's Hospital of Wisconsin–Fox Valley, Neenah, WI, p. A712
NAVARRO, Israel, Chief Executive Officer, Integrity Transitional Hospital, Denton, TX, p. A612
NAVARRO, Ramomita, Director Human Resources, University Hospital, San Juan, PR, p. A730
NAVARRO, Tess, Chief Financial Officer, Laguna Honda Hospital and Rehabilitation Center, San Francisco, CA, p. A90
NAVAS, Manuel, M.D. Medical Director, Hospital San Pablo Del Este, Fajardo, PR, p. A727
NAWROCKI, Bernie
  Administrative Director Finance, ProMedica Bixby Hospital, Adrian, MI, p. A318
  Administrative Director Finance, ProMedica Herrick Hospital, Tecumseh, MI, p. A335
NAWROCKI, Edward
  President, St. Luke's Hospital – Anderson Campus, Easton, PA, p. A537
  President, St. Luke's Hospital – Quakertown Campus, Quakertown, PA, p. A553
NAYAK, Yeshavanth, M.D. Interim Chief Medical Officer, Community Medical Center, Toms River, NJ, p. A424
NAZ, Haroon, Chief Executive Officer, Pinnacle Hospital, Crown Point, IN, p. A209
NAZARIAN, Alexander, CPA Chief Financial Officer, Kirby Medical Center, Monticello, IL, p. A197
NAZARIO, Uriel, M.D. Chief of Medical Staff, Kindred Hospital North Florida, Green Cove Springs, FL, p. A130
NAZE, Jesse, Chief Financial Officer, Fall River Hospital, Hot Springs, SD, p. A574
NAZEER, Imran, M.D. Chief of Staff, Woodland Heights Medical Center, Lufkin, TX, p. A635
NAZEERI–SIMMONS, Iman, Chief Operating Officer, Zuckerberg San Francisco General Hospital and Trauma Center, San Francisco, CA, p. A91
NDOMEA, Feisal, Director Case Management, Kindred Hospital Sugar Land, Sugar Land, TX, p. A650
NDOW, Emmanuel, Chief Information Officer, Marion General Hospital, Marion, IN, p. A218
NEAL, Bob, Information Technology, Sparrow Ionia Hospital, Ionia, MI, p. A326
NEAL, David, MS Chief Nursing Officer, Providence Little Company of Mary Medical Center San Pedro,, CA, p. A73
NEAL, Greg, FACHE, President, Wellmont Bristol Regional Medical Center, Bristol, TN, p. A579
NEAL, Robert, Manager Information Technology Services, Newman Memorial Hospital, Shattuck, OK, p. A519
NEAL, Roger, Vice President Operations, Duncan Regional Hospital, Duncan, OK, p. A510
NEAL, Terri, Director Human Resources, Crittenton Children's Center, Kansas City, MO, p. A373
NEALE, Debra, R.N. Chief Nursing Officer, O'Connor Hospital, Delhi, NY, p. A438
NEALON, Matthew, Vice President, Chief Financial Officer, University of Cincinnati Medical Center, Cincinnati, OH, p. A488
NEAPOLITAN, David, Chief Financial Officer, Emanuel Medical Center, Turlock, CA, p. A97
NEAR, Holly, Chief Administrative Officer, Harsha Behavioral Center, Terre Haute, IN, p. A222
NEAT, Gary, Director Information Systems, Ephraim McDowell Fort Logan Hospital, Stanford, KY, p. A269
NECAS, Kevin, Chief Financial Officer, University of Missouri Hospitals and Clinics, Columbia, MO, p. A370
NEEB, Verette, R.N. Chief Nursing Officer, Baylor Medical Center at Uptown, Dallas, TX, p. A609
NEECE, Patrick, Chief Information Officer, Jefferson Regional Medical Center, Pine Bluff, AR, p. A51
NEEDHAM, Kim
  Assistant Chief Executive Officer, Vista Medical Center East, Waukegan, IL, p. A205
  Assistant Chief Executive Officer, Vista Medical Center West, Waukegan, IL, p. A205

NEEDHAM, Tammy, Chief Nursing Officer, Chatham Hospital, Siler City, NC, p. A473
NEEDLES, Kim, Manager Business Office, Patients' Hospital of Redding, Redding, CA, p. A84
NEELAGARU, Narasimhulu, M.D. Chief of Staff, Northridge Medical Center, Commerce, GA, p. A157
NEELY, Denise, R.N. Vice President and Chief Nursing Officer, Bronson Methodist Hospital, Kalamazoo, MI, p. A328
NEELY, Jill, Chief Financial Officer, Titusville Area Hospital, Titusville, PA, p. A555
NEELY, K. Dale, FACHE, Chief Executive Officer, HealthSouth Rehabilitation Hospital of Tallahassee, Tallahassee, FL, p. A146
NEELY, Kathy E., R.N
  Interim Vice President Patient Care Services, CHI St. Vincent Infirmary Medical Center, Little Rock, AR, p. A49
  Interim Vice President Patient Care Services, CHI St. Vincent Morrilton, Morrilton, AR, p. A50
NEELY, Randall, Chief Executive Officer, Simpson General Hospital, Mendenhall, MS, p. A362
NEENAN, Sharon, Interim Chief Nursing Officer, Grant, OhioHealth Grant Medical Center, Columbus, OH, p. A491
NEERGHEEN, Chabilal, M.D. Medical Director, Western Massachusetts Hospital, Westfield, MA, p. A316
NEESEN, Cindy, Director of Information Technology, Butler County Health Care Center, David City, NE, p. A395
NEET, Bradley D., FACHE, Chief Executive Officer, Southwest Healthcare System, Murrieta, CA, p. A78
NEFCY, Christine, M.D. Chief Medical Officer, McKay–Dee Hospital Center, Ogden, UT, p. A661
NEFF, Mark J., FACHE, President and Chief Executive Officer, St. Claire Regional Medical Center, Morehead, KY, p. A267
NEFF, Richard, M.D. Interim Chief Medical Officer, Flagstaff Medical Center, Flagstaff, AZ, p. A32
NEFF, William, M.D
  Chief Medical Officer, Medical Center of the Rockies, Loveland, CO, p. A109
  Chief Medical Officer, Poudre Valley Hospital, Fort Collins, CO, p. A105
NEGRON, Manuel, Chief Information Technology Service, Veterans Affairs Caribbean Healthcare System, San Juan, PR, p. A730
NEIKIRK, Richard, Chief Executive Officer, Cumberland County Hospital, Burkesville, KY, p. A258
NEIL, Eric, Interim Chief Information Officer, UW Medicine/Northwest Hospital & Medical Center, Seattle, WA, p. A690
NEIL, William, Vice President and Chief Information Officer, Indian River Medical Center, Vero Beach, FL, p. A149
NEILSON, Carol, CPA Controller, HEALTHSOUTH Sugar Land Rehabilitation Hospital, Sugar Land, TX, p. A650
NEILSON, Erinn, Chief Nursing Officer, Minidoka Memorial Hospital, Rupert, ID, p. A178
NEILSON, Karen, Administrator, Safe Haven Hospital of Pocatello, Pocatello, ID, p. A178
NEILSON, Richard, Director of Information Services, Timpanogos Regional Hospital, Orem, UT, p. A661
NEIMAN, Carla, Chief Financial Officer, Clark Fork Valley Hospital, Plains, MT, p. A390
NEITZEL, Monte, Chief Executive Officer, Greater Regional Medical Center, Creston, IA, p. A228
NELKIN MCCORMICK, Elizabeth, MSN Senior Vice President and Chief Nursing Officer, Memorial Sloan–Kettering Cancer Center, New York, NY, p. A446
NELL, Sergio, Director Information Systems, Watsonville Community Hospital, Watsonville, CA, p. A99
NELSON, Allison
  Chief Financial Officer, Sanford Canby Medical Center, Canby, MN, p. A340
  Chief Financial Officer, Sanford Clear Lake Medical Center, Clear Lake, SD, p. A573
NELSON, Barbara J., Ph.D. Chief Nursing Executive, Sutter Roseville Medical Center, Roseville, CA, p. A86
NELSON, Bill, Chief Executive Officer, Mille Lacs Health System, Onamia, MN, p. A348
NELSON, Carol, Director Human Resources, Montevista Hospital, Las Vegas, NV, p. A406
NELSON, Cory, Administrator, Genoa Medical Facilities, Genoa, NE, p. A396
NELSON, David, M.D. Medical Director, Barlow Respiratory Hospital, Los Angeles, CA, p. A70
NELSON, David, FACH
  Divisional Chief Financial Officer, HSHS St. Joseph's Hospital, Chippewa Falls, WI, p. A704
  Chief Financial Officer, Sacred Heart Hospital, Eau Claire, WI, p. A705
NELSON, David A., President, CHI St. Francis Health, Breckenridge, MN, p. A340
NELSON, Dawn, Director Human Resources, SageWest Health Care at Riverton, Riverton, WY, p. A723

NELSON, Deana, FACHE Executive Vice President and Chief Operating Officer, Tampa General Hospital, Tampa, FL, p. A148
NELSON, Diana, R.N. Associate Director for Patient Care Services/Nurse Executive, Jonathan M. Wainwright Memorial Veterans Affairs Medical Center, Walla Walla, WA, p. A692
NELSON, Elaine, R.N. Chief Nursing Officer, Texas Health Harris Methodist Hospital Fort Worth, Fort Worth, TX, p. A618
NELSON, Eric, Vice President, Ambulatory Services, Bethesda Hospital, Saint Paul, MN, p. A350
NELSON, Frederick, Administrator, Ochsner Extended Care Hospital of Kenner, Kenner, LA, p. A279
NELSON, Gina, Chief Financial Officer, Renown South Meadows Medical Center, Reno, NV, p. A408
NELSON, Jack, Vice President Finance and Chief Financial Officer, Ohio Valley Hospital, McKees Rocks, PA, p. A544
NELSON, Jackie, Director Human Resources, Hansford Hospital, Spearman, TX, p. A649
NELSON, James J., Senior Vice President Finance and Strategic Planning, Fort HealthCare, Fort Atkinson, WI, p. A705
NELSON, Jamie, Vice President and Chief Information Officer, Hospital for Special Surgery, New York, NY, p. A444
NELSON, Jeri, Chief Financial Officer, Eastern Plumas Health Care, Portola, CA, p. A83
NELSON, Joseph, M.D. President Medical Staff, Lewis–Gale Medical Center, Salem, VA, p. A678
NELSON, Julia, Vice President Human Resources, Northern Hospital of Surry County, Mount Airy, NC, p. A470
NELSON, Katey, Director Human Resources, Sevier Valley Medical Center, Richfield, UT, p. A662
NELSON, Kathleen, R.N. Chief Nursing Officer, Eastern Idaho Regional Medical Center, Idaho Falls, ID, p. A176
NELSON, Kathy
  Chief Financial Officer, Marshall Medical Center North, Guntersville, AL, p. A21
  Chief Financial Officer, Marshall Medical Center South, Boaz, AL, p. A17
NELSON, Kellie, Director Human Resources, Aurora Medical Center, Kenosha, WI, p. A708
NELSON, Kerri, Chief Financial Officer, Spectrum Health Ludington Hospital, Ludington, MI, p. A329
NELSON, Lucy, Director Finance, Vice President, Maniilaq Health Center, Kotzebue, AK, p. A30
NELSON, Lynn M., R.N. Chief Nursing Officer and Chief Operating Officer, St. John's Riverside Hospital, Yonkers, NY, p. A459
NELSON, Marlin Pete, Vice President Fiscal Services, Divine Savior Healthcare, Portage, WI, p. A714
NELSON, Martha
  Chief Financial Officer, Antelope Memorial Hospital, Neligh, NE, p. A399
  Chief Financial Officer, Niobrara Valley Hospital, Lynch, NE, p. A398
NELSON, Melissa, Assistant Administrator, Baptist Memorial Hospital for Women, Memphis, TN, p. A588
NELSON, Meredith, Chief Financial Officer, Willamette Valley Medical Center, McMinnville, OR, p. A527
NELSON, Michael
  Executive Vice President and Chief Financial Officer, Pomona Valley Hospital Medical Center, Pomona, CA, p. A83
  Chief Financial Officer, Select Specialty Hospital Midtown Atlanta, Atlanta, GA, p. A152
NELSON, Michael E., Chief Financial Officer, Riveredge Hospital, Forest Park, IL, p. A190
NELSON, Nan, Senior Vice President Finance, Aurora St. Luke's Medical Center, Milwaukee, WI, p. A711
NELSON, Nancy, Director Human Resources, Intermountain Hospital, Boise, ID, p. A174
NELSON, Nick, Director Support Services, Adams Memorial Hospital, Decatur, IN, p. A209
NELSON, Raymond, Acting Chief Information Resource Management, Fargo Veterans Affairs Health Care System, Fargo, ND, p. A478
NELSON, Rhonda, Chief Nursing Officer, Forrest City Medical Center, Forrest City, AR, p. A46
NELSON, Richard, Chief of Human Resources Management Services, Central Arkansas Veterans Healthcare System, Little Rock, AR, p. A49
NELSON, Robin, Chief Financial Officer, Gundersen St. Joseph's Hospital and Clinics, Hillsboro, WI, p. A707
NELSON, Rodney M., Chief Executive Officer, Mackinac Straits Health System, Inc., Saint Ignace, MI, p. A333
NELSON, Selena, Chief Financial Officer, Fallon Medical Complex, Baker, MT, p. A385
NELSON, Shelby
  Interim Chief Executive Officer, Community Hospital, Torrington, WY, p. A724
  Chief Executive Officer, Platte County Memorial Hospital, Wheatland, WY, p. A724

NELSON, Sherry, JD Chief Nursing Officer, Springfield Regional Medical Center, Springfield, OH, p. A503

NELSON, Siri, Chief Administrative Officer, Sutter Lakeside Hospital, Lakeport, CA, p. A68

NELSON, Stewart R., Chief Financial Officer, Sentara Halifax Regional Hospital, South Boston, VA, p. A678

NELSON, RN, Suzanne, R.N. Director of Nursing, Salt Lake Behavioral Health, Salt Lake City, UT, p. A663

NELSON, Tricia, Chief Financial Officer, RiverWoods Behavioral Health System, Riverdale, GA, p. A164

NELSON, Trudy, Chief Human Resource Officer, Niobrara Valley Hospital, Lynch, NE, p. A398

NELSON–JONES, Susan, Director Human Resources, Tehachapi Valley Healthcare District, Tehachapi, CA, p. A95

NEMAZIE, Siamack, M.D. Medical Director, Patient Safety Officer, Flushing Hospital Medical Center,, NY, p. A444

NEMECHEK, Victor, M.D. Chief of Staff and Chief Medical Officer, Sheridan County Health Complex, Hoxie, KS, p. A245

NEMETH, Jim
Senior Vice President of Patient Care Services and Chief Nursing Officer, Memorial Healthcare, Owosso, MI, p. A331
Chief Financial Officer, Monroe Clinic, Monroe, WI, p. A712

NEMI, Neil, Administrator Facility Information Center, Richard H. Hutchings Psychiatric Center, Syracuse, NY, p. A456

NEONAKIS, Stephanie W., Manager Human Resources, UH Regional Hospitals, Cleveland, OH, p. A490

NERMOE, Bryan, President, Sanford Bemidji Medical Center, Bemidji, MN, p. A339

NERO, Theresa R., R.N. Chief Nursing Officer, Kaiser Permanente San Jose Medical Center, San Jose, CA, p. A91

NESBITT, William, M.D. President Medical Staff, Texas Health Heart & Vascular Hospital Arlington, Arlington, TX, p. A598

NESMITH, Nikki, Interim Chief Operating Officer, Evans Memorial Hospital, Claxton, GA, p. A156

NESPOLI, John L., Chief Executive Officer, Sacred Heart Hospital, Allentown, PA, p. A532

NESS, David L., Vice President Operations, Grinnell Regional Medical Center, Grinnell, IA, p. A231

NESS, Edwin, President and Chief Executive Officer, Munson Healthcare, Traverse City, MI, p. B93

NESS, Jon, Chief Executive Officer, Kootenai Health, Coeur D'Alene, ID, p. A175

NESSEL, Mark
Executive Vice President and Chief Operating Officer, Lourdes Medical Center of Burlington County, Willingboro, NJ, p. A425
Chief Operating Officer, Our Lady of Lourdes Medical Center, Camden, NJ, p. A415

NESSELRODT, Derek, Director Information Systems, Grant Memorial Hospital, Petersburg, WV, p. A699

NESTER, Brian A., President and Chief Executive Officer, Lehigh Valley Health Network, Allentown, PA, p. B80

NESTER, Brian A.
President and Chief Executive Officer, Lehigh Valley Hospital, Allentown, PA, p. A532
President and Chief Executive Officer, Lehigh Valley Hospital–Muhlenberg, Bethlehem, PA, p. A533

NESTER, Darlene E.
Market Chief Human Resources Officer, Coastal Carolina Hospital, Hardeeville, SC, p. A567
Chief Human Resources Officer, Hilton Head Hospital, Hilton Head Island, SC, p. A567

NESTER, Michael
Administrator, H. C. Watkins Memorial Hospital, Quitman, MS, p. A364
Chief Executive Officer, Jasper General Hospital, Bay Springs, MS, p. A355

NESTER WOLFE, Cheryl R., President and Chief Executive Officer, Salem Hospital, Salem, OR, p. A530

NETH, Marvin, Chief Executive Officer, Callaway District Hospital, Callaway, NE, p. A394

NETTERVILLE, Chad, Administrator, Field Memorial Community Hospital, Centreville, MS, p. A356

NETTLES, Angela F., Director Human Resources, KershawHealth, Camden, SC, p. A562

NETTLES, Robert, Director Human Resources, MountainView Hospital, Las Vegas, NV, p. A406

NETZER, Craig, M.D. President Medical Staff, Wilcox Memorial Hospital, Lihue, HI, p. A172

NEUENDORF, Deborah, Vice President Administration, New York–Presbyterian/Hudson Valley Hospital, Cortlandt Manor, NY, p. A437

NEUENDORF, James, M.D. Medical Director, Saint Joseph's Medical Center, Yonkers, NY, p. A459

NEUENDORF, Michael, Chief Executive Officer, Merit Health Wesley, Hattiesburg, MS, p. A359

NEUGENT, Kevin, Chief Information Officer, Hayes Green Beach Memorial Hospital, Charlotte, MI, p. A320

NEUHAUS, Joan E.
Division Senior Vice President Chief Operating Officer, CHI Health Lakeside, Omaha, NE, p. A400
Division Senior Vice President, Chief Operating Officer, CHI Health Midlands, Papillion, NE, p. A401

NEUKIRCH, Jennifer, Chief Executive Officer, Avera Creighton Hospital, Creighton, NE, p. A395

NEUMAN, Joe, Chief Executive Officer, Concord Healthcare Group, Lakewood, NJ, p. B41

NEUMAN, Keith A.
Chief Information Officer, Lutheran Hospital of Indiana, Fort Wayne, IN, p. A210
Chief Information Officer, Orthopaedic Hospital of Lutheran Health Network, Fort Wayne, IN, p. A210

NEUMAN, Michael J., Vice President Finance, Kennedy Krieger Institute, Baltimore, MD, p. A296

NEUMANN, Charles W., President, University of Louisville Hospital, Louisville, KY, p. A265

NEUMANN, Jamie, Director Human Resources, Iroquois Memorial Hospital and Resident Home, Watseka, IL, p. A204

NEUMEISTER, Daniel P., Chief Operating Officer, SEARHC MT. Edgecumbe Hospital, Sitka, AK, p. A30

NEUNER, Kathy, R.N. Chief Nursing Officer, Clark Memorial Hospital, Jeffersonville, IN, p. A215

NEUVIRTH, Stephanie, Chief Human Resource and Diversity Officer, City of Hope's Helford Clinical Research Hospital, Duarte, CA, p. A61

NEVAREZ, Domingo, Chief Executive Officer, Hospital Metropolitano, San Juan, PR, p. A729

NEVILL, David S., Chief Executive Officer, HEALTHSOUTH Rehabilitation Hospital, Albuquerque, NM, p. A427

NEVILLE, Bette, R.N. Vice President and Chief Nursing Officer, Mercy Hospital of Portland, Portland, ME, p. A294

NEVILLE, Ryan T., FACHE, President and Chief Executive Officer, Memorial Medical Center – Neillsville, Neillsville, WI, p. A712

NEVIN, James, M.D. Vice President Medical Management, Advocate BroMenn Medical Center, Normal, IL, p. A198

NEVIN, Janice E., M.P.H., Chief Executive Officer, Christiana Care Health System, Newark, DE, p. A119

NEVIN, Janice E., M.P.H., Chief Executive Officer, Christiana Care Health System, Wilmington, DE, p. B32

NEVINS, Michael R.
Chief Financial Officer, St. John Broken Arrow, Broken Arrow, OK, p. A509
Chief Financial Officer, St. John Owasso, Owasso, OK, p. A518

NEVINS, Norm, Manager Human Resources, Kansas Medical Center, Andover, KS, p. A240

NEWBERRY–FERGUSON, Linda, Chief Executive Officer, Rehabilitation Hospital of Wisconsin, Waukesha, WI, p. A718

NEWBOLD, Philip A., Chief Executive Officer, Beacon Health System, South Bend, IN, p. B22

NEWBOLD, Philip A., Chief Executive Officer, Beacon Health System, Memorial Hospital of South Bend, South Bend, IN, p. A222

NEWBY, Doug, Chief Information Officer, Highlands Medical Center, Scottsboro, AL, p. A25

NEWBY, Glenda, Chief Executive Officer, Dallas Regional Medical Center, Mesquite, TX, p. A636

NEWBY, Nancy M., FACHE, President and Chief Executive Officer, Washington County Hospital, Nashville, IL, p. A198

NEWCOMB, James, M.D. Vice President Medical, Ochsner Medical Center – North Shore, Slidell, LA, p. A288

NEWCOMB, Michael, D.O
Senior Vice President and Chief Operating Officer, Legacy Meridian Park Medical Center, Tualatin, OR, p. A531
Senior Vice President and Chief Operating Officer, Legacy Mount Hood Medical Center, Gresham, OR, p. A526
Senior Vice President and Chief Operating Officer, Legacy Salmon Creek Medical Center, Vancouver, WA, p. A692

NEWCOMER, Jeremy, Director Information Services, Elmira Psychiatric Center, Elmira, NY, p. A438

NEWCOMER, Peter, M.D. Chief Medical Officer, University of Wisconsin Hospitals and Clinics Authority, Madison, WI, p. A709

NEWELL, Dan, Chief Financial Officer, Highlands Medical Center, Scottsboro, AL, p. A25

NEWELL, Janice
Chief Information Officer, Swedish Medical Center–Cherry Hill Campus, Seattle, WA, p. A689
Chief Information Officer, Swedish Medical Center–First Hill, Seattle, WA, p. A690

NEWELL, Rich, Chief Executive Officer, Pottstown Memorial Medical Center, Pottstown, PA, p. A552

NEWEY, Mark, D.O. Chief of Staff, Mercy Hospital Healdton, Healdton, OK, p. A512

NEWHILLER, Vicki, Chief Executive Officer, Great Falls Clinic Medical Center, Great Falls, MT, p. A388

NEWHOUSE, Paul R., President, Union Medical Center, Union, SC, p. A570

NEWLAND, Judy, R.N., Chief Nursing Officer, Incline Village Community Hospital, Incline Village, NV, p. A405

NEWLAND, Judy, R.N. Chief Operating Officer, Tahoe Forest Hospital District, Truckee, CA, p. A97

NEWMAN, Billy, Department Head, Naval Hospital Lemoore, Lemoore, CA, p. A68

NEWMAN, Carlotta, Director Human Resources, Barrow Regional Medical Center, Winder, GA, p. A169

NEWMAN, Cynthia, Manager Human Resources, Petersburg Medical Center, Petersburg, AK, p. A30

NEWMAN, Dan, Chief Executive Officer, Houston Methodist St. John Hospital, Nassau Bay, TX, p. A638

NEWMAN, Diane, FACHE, Administrator, Johnson County Hospital, Tecumseh, NE, p. A402

NEWMAN, Edith, Interim Administrator, John J. Madden Mental Health Center, Hines, IL, p. A193

NEWMAN, Karen, Ed.D. Vice President and Chief Nursing Officer, Baptist Health Louisville, Louisville, KY, p. A264

NEWMAN, Kurt, M.D., President and Chief Executive Officer, Children's National Health System, Washington, DC, p. A121

NEWMAN, Richard, Chief Human Resources Officer, Olympic Medical Center, Port Angeles, WA, p. A688

NEWMAN, Sonya, R.N. Chief Nursing Officer, Blount Memorial Hospital, Maryville, TN, p. A588

NEWMAN, Thomas M.
Chief Financial Officer, UPMC Passavant, Pittsburgh, PA, p. A551
Vice President Finance, UPMC St. Margaret, Pittsburgh, PA, p. A552

NEWMILLER, Vicki, Chief Operating Officer, Great Falls Clinic Medical Center, Great Falls, MT, p. A388

NEWPOWER, Nicole, Coordinator Human Resources, Kindred Hospital–Fort Worth, Fort Worth, TX, p. A618

NEWQUIST, Dennis, Director Information Systems, Abilene Regional Medical Center, Abilene, TX, p. A595

NEWSOM, Cynthia, Chief Executive Officer, Vibra Hospital of Boise, Meridian, ID, p. A177

NEWSOM, Paul, Chief Operating Officer, Kentuckiana Medical Center, Clarksville, IN, p. A208

NEWSOM, Terri, Vice President of Finance and Chief Financial Officer, GHS Greenville Memorial Hospital, Greenville, SC, p. A566

NEWSOME, Samuel C., M.D. Chief of Staff, Pioneer Community Hospital of Stokes, Danbury, NC, p. A463

NEWSWANGER, Jeff, M.D. Chief Medical Officer, Manchester Memorial Hospital, Manchester, KY, p. A266

NEWTON, Gail, R.N. Vice President Patient Care Services, St. Luke's Hospital – Warren Campus, Phillipsburg, NJ, p. A422

NEWTON, James R., Facility Director, Northern Virginia Mental Health Institute, Falls Church, VA, p. A670

NEWTON, Jennifer, R.N. Chief Nursing Officer, Neosho Memorial Regional Medical Center, Chanute, KS, p. A241

NEWTON, Keith, Chief Executive Officer, South Baldwin Regional Medical Center, Foley, AL, p. A20

NEWTON, Steven R., President, Baylor Regional Medical Center at Grapevine, Grapevine, TX, p. A621

NEWTON, Susan, Chief Financial Officer, Broward Health Imperial Point, Fort Lauderdale, FL, p. A128

NEWTON, Terri, Chief Nursing Officer, Lakewood Regional Medical Center, Lakewood, CA, p. A68

NEWTON, Wilma, Executive Vice President and Chief Financial Officer, St. Vincent's Birmingham, Birmingham, AL, p. A17

NEZBETH, Jacqueline, Human Resources Officer, Select Specialty Hospital of Southeast Ohio, Newark, OH, p. A500

NG, Anthony, M.D. Vice President and Chief Medical Officer, The Acadia Hospital, Bangor, ME, p. A291

NG, Thomas T., Chief Information Officer, Collingsworth General Hospital, Wellington, TX, p. A657

NG, Vincent
Director, Veterans Affairs Boston Healthcare System, Boston, MA, p. A307
Interim Director, Veterans Affairs Boston Healthcare System Brockton Division, Brockton, MA, p. A308

NGIRAISUI, Clarinda, Human Resource Manager, Commonwealth Health Center, Saipan, MP, p. A725

NGUYEN, Abby, R.N. Chief Nursing Officer, Genesis HealthCare System, Zanesville, OH, p. A507

NGUYEN, Anhtai H., M.D. Vice President Medical Affairs and Chief Medical Officer, Fauquier Hospital, Warrenton, VA, p. A680

NGUYEN, Bach, Director Information Systems, Northwest Texas Healthcare System, Amarillo, TX, p. A596

NGUYEN, Dat, M.D. Chief of Staff, Stanford Health Care – ValleyCare, Pleasanton, CA, p. A83

NGUYEN, Harry, Medical Director, The Woods at Parkside, Gahanna, OH, p. A495

NGUYEN, Nga, Manager Human Resources and Organizational Development, Glendale Memorial Hospital and Health Center, Glendale, CA, p. A64

NGUYEN, Son, M.D. President of Medical Staff, Integris Southwest Medical Center, Oklahoma City, OK, p. A516

NIBLOCK, Jenny, Chief Clinical Officer, Citizens Medical Center, Colby, KS, p. A241

NICAUD, Kent, Chief Operating Officer, Memorial Hospital at Gulfport, Gulfport, MS, p. A358

NICHELSON, Kathleen, Director Human Resources, Horsham Clinic, Ambler, PA, p. A532

NICHOLS, Amanda, M.D. Chief of Staff, Sistersville General Hospital, Sistersville, WV, p. A700

NICHOLS, Barbara, R.N., President and Chief Executive Officer, Corry Memorial Hospital, Corry, PA, p. A536

NICHOLS, Bryan, Chief Financial Officer, The Heart Hospital Baylor Plano, Plano, TX, p. A642

NICHOLS, Christopher, Chief Executive Officer, Horn Memorial Hospital, Ida Grove, IA, p. A232

NICHOLS, Cynthia, MSN, Chief Executive Officer, Lakeland Community Hospital, Haleyville, AL, p. A21

NICHOLS, Dia, Chief Executive Officer, Northside Hospital, Saint Petersburg, FL, p. A144

NICHOLS, Donna, R.N. Chief Nursing Officer, Goodall–Witcher Hospital Authority, Clifton, TX, p. A606

NICHOLS, Gretchen, R.N., Chief Administrative Officer, Legacy Mount Hood Medical Center, Gresham, OR, p. A526

NICHOLS, Kevin, Controller, Spectrum Health Gerber Memorial, Fremont, MI, p. A324

NICHOLS, Laura L., Director Human Resources, Hancock Regional Hospital, Greenfield, IN, p. A212

NICHOLS, Lisa, R.N.,
Interim Administrator, St. Vincent's Blount, Oneonta, AL, p. A24
Administrator, St. Vincent's St. Clair, Pell City, AL, p. A24

NICHOLS, Mark, FACHE, Chief Executive Officer, Starr Regional Medical Center, Athens, TN, p. A579

NICHOLS, Michael, Chief Information Officer, Masonicare Health Center, Wallingford, CT, p. A117

NICHOLS, Owen, PsyD, President and Chief Executive Officer, NorthKey Community Care, Covington, KY, p. A259

NICHOLS, Randy
Chief Financial Officer, Great River Medical Center, Blytheville, AR, p. A43
Chief Financial Officer, South Mississippi County Regional Medical Center, Osceola, AR, p. A51

NICHOLS, Robert R., M.D. Vice President Medical Affairs, Mercy Hospital Fort Scott, Fort Scott, KS, p. A243

NICHOLS, Robin, Chief Financial Officer, Coshocton County Memorial Hospital, Coshocton, OH, p. A492

NICHOLS, Suzanne, Director Human Resources, Muleshoe Area Medical Center, Muleshoe, TX, p. A638

NICHOLS, Terry, Chief Executive Officer, Iron County Medical Center, Pilot Knob, MO, p. A378

NICHOLSON, Britain, M.D. Chief Medical Officer, Massachusetts General Hospital, Boston, MA, p. A307

NICHOLSON, Charles, Vice President, Medical Affairs, Sentara Albemarle Medical Center, Elizabeth City, NC, p. A464

NICHOLSON, Chrissy, Vice President Human Resources, Delta Regional Medical Center, Greenville, MS, p. A358

NICHOLSON, Cindy, Director Human Resources, Shelby Baptist Medical Center, Alabaster, AL, p. A15

NICHOLSON, Debra, Manager Finance, Central Alabama Veterans Health Care System, Montgomery, AL, p. A23

NICHOLSON, Donna, Chief Nursing Officer, Gadsden Regional Medical Center, Gadsden, AL, p. A20

NICHOLSON, H. Stacy, M.D. Physician in Chief, Phoenix Children's Hospital, Phoenix, AZ, p. A37

NICHOLSON, Kristin, Coordinator Human Resources, Genesis Medical Center, DeWitt, De Witt, IA, p. A229

NICHOLSON, Molly, M
Chief Nurse Executive, Presence Covenant Medical Center, Urbana, IL, p. A204
Vice President of Patient Care/Chief Nurse Executive, Presence United Samaritans Medical Center, Danville, IL, p. A187

NICHOSON, Julia, M.D. Chief Medical Officer, Drew Memorial Hospital, Monticello, AR, p. A50

NICKEL, Kathleen, Director Communications, Mercy Medical Center, Roseburg, OR, p. A530

NICKELL, Jerry, Vice President Human Resource and Mission, Saint Alphonsus Medical Center – Baker City, Baker City, OR, p. A524

NICKELS, John, M.D. President Medical Staff, Grace Hospital, Cleveland, OH, p. A489

NICKENS, Wesley, M.D. Chief of Staff, Collingsworth General Hospital, Wellington, TX, p. A657

NICKISCH, Steve, Chief of Staff, Southeast Georgia Health System Camden Campus, Saint Marys, GA, p. A165

NICKRAND, Tami, Director Information Technology, Harbor Beach Community Hospital, Harbor Beach, MI, p. A326

NICKS, Bret, M.D. Chief Medical Officer and Chief of Staff, Wake Forest Baptist Health–Davie Medical Center, Mocksville, NC, p. A469

NICODEMUS, Lowell, Director Information Systems, Hendricks Regional Health, Danville, IN, p. A209

NICOLAY, Donald, M.D. Chief Medical Officer, Community Hospital, Grand Junction, CO, p. A106

NICOLL, C. Diana, M.D. Chief of Staff, San Francisco VA Medical Center, San Francisco, CA, p. A90

NICOLSON, Lynne T., M.D. Medical Director, Sunnyview Rehabilitation Hospital, Schenectady, NY, p. A455

NICOSIA, Chris, Chief Financial Officer, Corpus Christi Medical Center, Corpus Christi, TX, p. A607

NIECE, Pamela S., Director Human Resources, Orem Community Hospital, Orem, UT, p. A661

NIEDERPRUEM, Mark L., FACHE, Administrator, Shriners Hospitals for Children–Chicago, Chicago, IL, p. A186

NIELSEN, Colleen, Director Operations, Providence St. Joseph Medical Center, Polson, MT, p. A390

NIELSEN, Gregory A., FACHE, Chief Executive Officer, Clinton Memorial Hospital, Wilmington, OH, p. A506

NIELSEN, Gwen, Manager Human Resources, Indianhead Medical Center, Shell Lake, WI, p. A716

NIELSEN, Helen V.
Director Human Resources, Lovelace Medical Center, Albuquerque, NM, p. A427
Director Human Resources, Lovelace Rehabilitation Hospital, Albuquerque, NM, p. A427

NIELSEN, Kristine, Manager Human Resources, Memorial Community Hospital and Health System, Blair, NE, p. A394

NIELSEN, Randy, Director Information Technology, Morton General Hospital, Morton, WA, p. A686

NIELSEN, Wayne, Director Human Resources, Ocala Regional Medical Center, Ocala, FL, p. A139

NIELSON, Curtis, Chief Financial Officer, South Lincoln Medical Center, Kemmerer, WY, p. A722

NIELSON, Lars, M.D. Chief Medical Officer, Weeks Medical Center, Lancaster, NH, p. A411

NIELSON, Lori, Regional Finance Director, Park City Medical Center, Park City, UT, p. A662

NIELSON, P. Douglas, M.D. Chief of Staff, Kahuku Medical Center, Kahuku, HI, p. A171

NIELSON, Yvonne, Chief Nursing Officer, Director Quality Management and Regulatory Compliance, Mountain West Medical Center, Tooele, UT, p. A664

NIEMALA, Amanda, Director of Information Services, Bigfork Valley Hospital, Bigfork, MN, p. A339

NIEMANN, Larry, Chief Executive Officer, Select Specialty Hospital–Kansas City, Kansas City, KS, p. A246

NIEMANN, Lynne, Director Nurses and Patient Care, Community Memorial Hospital, Sumner, IA, p. A238

NIEMEIER, Mark, Director Human Resources, Twin Rivers Regional Medical Center, Kennett, MO, p. A374

NIEMUTH, Trisha, Director of Finance, LifeCare Hospitals of Mechanicsburg, Mechanicsburg, PA, p. A544

NIENHUIS, Jamie, Chief Nursing Officer, Cavalier County Memorial Hospital and Clinics, Langdon, ND, p. A480

NIERMAN, Peter, M.D. Chief Medical Officer, Chicago Lakeshore Hospital, Chicago, IL, p. A183

NIERMAN, Stephen A., President, Winter Haven Hospital, Winter Haven, FL, p. A150

NIERMANN, Michelle, Senior Vice President and Chief Operating Officer, UnityPoint Health – St. Luke's Hospital, Cedar Rapids, IA, p. A226

NIES, Lynn, Human Resources Officer, Erie Veterans Affairs Medical Center, Erie, PA, p. A538

NIESE, Mel, Chief Fiscal Service, VA Palo Alto Health Care System, Palo Alto, CA, p. A82

NIESSINK, Henry
Regional Director Information Technology Services, Mercy Medical Center Redding, Redding, CA, p. A84
Senior Manager Information Technology Systems, St. Elizabeth Community Hospital, Red Bluff, CA, p. A84

NIEVES, Deborah, Director Management Information Systems, Hospital San Francisco, San Juan, PR, p. A730

NIEVES, Erick, M.D. Medical Director, Hospital San Carlos Borromeo, Moca, PR, p. A728

NIEVES, Jesus, Executive Director, San Juan City Hospital, San Juan, PR, p. A730

NIGH, Andrew, M.D. Chief of Staff, Indiana University Health West Hospital, Avon, IN, p. A206

NIGHMAN, Mike, Facility Coordinator Information Systems, Shelby Baptist Medical Center, Alabaster, AL, p. A15

NIGHTENGALE, Randy, Chief Financial Officer, Pondera Medical Center, Conrad, MT, p. A386

NIGHTINGALE, Judi, R.N. Chief Nursing Officer, Riverside University Health System–Medical Center, Moreno Valley, CA, p. A78

NIGRIN, Daniel, M.D. Vice President Information Services and Chief Information Officer, Boston Children's Hospital, Boston, MA, p. A306

NIGRO, Lee, M.D. Chief Medical Officer, Blue Valley Hospital, Overland Park, KS, p. A251

NIHALANI, Sunil, M.D. Chief Medical Staff, Lake Wales Medical Center, Lake Wales, FL, p. A133

NIJOKA, Monica, Chief Nursing Office, Spine Hospital of Louisiana (formally the NeuroMedical Center Surgical Hospital), Baton Rouge, LA, p. A273

NIKOLIC, Srbo, Chief Financial Officer, Hartgrove Hospital, Chicago, IL, p. A184

NILES, Heather, Director Human Resources Operations, Mercy Harvard Hospital, Harvard, IL, p. A192

NILSSON, Keith, Chief Financial Officer, Cleveland Clinic Florida, Weston, FL, p. A150

NIMMO, Ben, M.D. Medical Director, Pinnacle Pointe Hospital, Little Rock, AR, p. A49

NIMMO, Brian, Director, Huntington Veterans Affairs Medical Center, Huntington, WV, p. A697

NIMS, Carrie, Director of Nursing, Post Acute/Warm Springs Specialty Hospital of San Antonio, San Antonio, TX, p. A647

NINNEMAN, David, Associate Director, Cincinnati Veterans Affairs Medical Center, Cincinnati, OH, p. A487

NIPPER, Nathan
Chief Operating Officer, Piedmont Fayette Hospital, Fayetteville, GA, p. A159
Vice President and Chief Operating Officer, Piedmont Newnan Hospital, Newnan, GA, p. A164

NIPPERT, Kathi, Acting Chief Human Resources Officer, Kansas City Veterans Affairs Medical Center, Kansas City, MO, p. A373

NISH, Paulette, Chief Nursing Officer, Jersey Shore Hospital, Jersey Shore, PA, p. A541

NISKANEN, Grant, M.D. Vice President Medical Affairs, Sky Lakes Medical Center, Klamath Falls, OR, p. A527

NISSEN, Beth, Director Human Resources, Troy Regional Medical Center, Troy, AL, p. A26

NIX, Bo, Chief Information Officer, Madison Valley Medical Center, Ennis, MT, p. A387

NIX, D. Mark, President and Chief Executive Officer, Infirmary Health System, Mobile, AL, p. B72

NIXDORF, David L., Director Support Services, Frances Mahon Deaconess Hospital, Glasgow, MT, p. A387

NIXON, Jan, MS Senior Vice President Patient Care Services and Chief Nursing Officer, Wyoming Medical Center, Casper, WY, p. A721

NIXON, Myra, Director Human Resources, HEALTHSOUTH Rehabilitation Hospital, Concord, NH, p. A410

NIZZA, Arthur, Chief Executive Officer, Meriter UnityPoint Health, Madison, WI, p. A709

NNAJI, Felix, Chief Medical Staff, Bolivar General Hospital, Bolivar, TN, p. A579

NOAK, Amy, Director Human Resources, St. David's Round Rock Medical Center, Round Rock, TX, p. A644

NOAKES, Timothy J., Chief Financial Officer, Memorial Hospital Los Banos, Los Banos, CA, p. A75

NOBLE, Angela, Director of Nursing, West Feliciana Parish Hospital, Saint Francisville, LA, p. A287

NOBLE, Damien, Director Information Technology and System, Colleton Medical Center, Walterboro, SC, p. A570

NOBLE, Dave, Director of Nursing, Livingston HealthCare, Livingston, MT, p. A389

NOBLE, James D., Chief Executive Officer, Horton Community Hospital, Horton, KS, p. A245

NOBLE, James S., Chief Financial Officer, Huntington Memorial Hospital, Pasadena, CA, p. A82

NOBLE, Kerry, Chief Executive Officer, Great Bend Regional Hospital, Great Bend, KS, p. A244

NOBLE, Kerry L., Chief Financial Officer, Pemiscot Memorial Health System, Hayti, MO, p. A372

NOBLE, Mallie S., Administrator, Mary Breckinridge ARH Hospital, Hyden, KY, p. A262

NOBLE, Paula, Chief Financial Officer and Treasurer, Ann & Robert H. Lurie Children's Hospital of Chicago, Chicago, IL, p. A183

NOBLE, Stacy, Administrator, Southeast Rehabilitation Hospital, Lake Village, AR, p. A48

NOBLES, Diane, Nurse Executive, East Mississippi State Hospital, Meridian, MS, p. A362

NOBLES, Sharon, Interim Chief Financial Officer, Baptist Hospital, Pensacola, FL, p. A142

NOBLIN, Jeff, FACHE, Chief Executive Officer, Southern Tennessee Regional Health System–Lawrenceburg, Lawrenceburg, TN, p. A586

NOBRIGA, Robert
Chief Financial Officer, North Hawaii Community Hospital, Kamuela, HI, p. A172
Executive Vice President and Chief Financial Officer, The Queen's Medical Center, Honolulu, HI, p. A171

NOCKOWITZ, Richard, M.D. Medical Director, Ohio Hospital for Psychiatry, Columbus, OH, p. A490

NOE, Sharon, Chief Executive Officer, Cobalt Rehabilitation Hospital, Surprise, AZ, p. A39

NOEL, Bill, Chief Operating Officer, Grand River Hospital District, Rifle, CO, p. A110

NOEL III, Philip J., Chief Executive Officer, Ottumwa Regional Health Center, Ottumwa, IA, p. A236

NOEL, Vicki, Vice President Human Resources, Southern Ohio Medical Center, Portsmouth, OH, p. A501

NOESS, Bobbi, Director of Nursing, Bowdle Hospital, Bowdle, SD, p. A572

NOFFSINGER, Sandy, Executive Assistant, Risk Manager and Director Marketing, Dundy County Hospital, Benkelman, NE, p. A394

NOGLER, Wendy, Director Human Resources, Lincoln County Health System, Fayetteville, TN, p. A583

NOKES, Gregory, Vice President Human Resources, Middlesex Hospital, Middletown, CT, p. A115

NOLAN, Douglas, M.D. Medical Director, Cherokee Nation W.W. Hastings Indian Hospital, Tahlequah, OK, p. A520

NOLAN, Heather, Director Information Services, Northern Louisiana Medical Center, Ruston, LA, p. A287

NOLAN, Jennifer
President, Our Lady of Peace, Louisville, KY, p. A265
President, Sts. Mary & Elizabeth Hospital, Louisville, KY, p. A265

NOLAN, Joe, Chief Operating Officer, Saint Clare's Health System, Denville, NJ, p. A416

NOLAN, Matthew, Chief Operating Officer, The University of Vermont Health Network Elizabethtown Community Hospital, Elizabethtown, NY, p. A438

NOLAN, Patrick B., Chief Operating Officer, Inspira Medical Center–Woodbury, Woodbury, NJ, p. A425

NOLAN, Rosemary, R.N. Chief Operating Officer, Temple University Hospital, Philadelphia, PA, p. A550

NOLAND, Pam, Director of Nursing, Northern Cochise Community Hospital, Willcox, AZ, p. A41

NOLD, Pam, Chief Nurse Executive, Northwest Missouri Psychiatric Rehabilitation Center, Saint Joseph, MO, p. A379

NOLEN, Benny, President, Saint Joseph Mount Sterling, Mount Sterling, KY, p. A267

NOLES, Coy, Chief Financial Officer Consultant, Hamilton Hospital, Olney, TX, p. A639

NOLL, Gerald, Vice President and Chief Financial Officer, Sheppard Pratt Health System, Baltimore, MD, p. A297

NOLL, Gerald A., Chief Financial Officer, Rogers Memorial Hospital, Oconomowoc, WI, p. A713

NOLL, Keith D., President, WellSpan York Hospital, York, PA, p. A559

NOLLETTE, Karen, Chief Financial Officer, West Holt Memorial Hospital, Atkinson, NE, p. A393

NOLLEY, Dexter, Chief Human Resources Officer, Duke Regional Hospital, Durham, NC, p. A464

NOLT, Lori, Director Information Technology, Philhaven, Mount Gretna, PA, p. A545

NOLTE, Darlene R., Chief Human Resource Officer, Craig General Hospital, Vinita, OK, p. A522

NOLTING, Evelyn, Chief Executive Officer and Managing Director, River Oaks Hospital, New Orleans, LA, p. A285

NONNEMAN, Lisa, Director Information Technology Services, Mary Lanning Healthcare, Hastings, NE, p. A396

NOONAN, Cindy, Chief Operating Officer, Stanford Health Care – ValleyCare, Pleasanton, CA, p. A83

NOONAN, Kathryn, Director Information Management, Lemuel Shattuck Hospital, Jamaica Plain, MA, p. A311

NOONE, Thomas, M.D. Chief Medical Officer, Bayfront Health Port Charlotte, Port Charlotte, FL, p. A143

NORBURY, Denise
Chief Executive Officer, Center for Behavioral Medicine, Kansas City, MO, p. A373
Regional Executive Officer, Northwest Missouri Psychiatric Rehabilitation Center, Saint Joseph, MO, p. A379

NORBY, Michael, Chief Financial Officer, Harris Health System, Houston, TX, p. A624

NORD, Gay, Chief Executive Officer, Methodist Hospital, San Antonio, TX, p. A646

NORD, Stanley K., Chief Financial Officer, West Houston Medical Center, Houston, TX, p. A627

NORDAHL, Richard E., Chief Executive Officer, Sanford Sheldon Medical Center, Sheldon, IA, p. A237

NORDBERG, Traci, Chief Human Resources Officer, Vanderbilt University Medical Center, Nashville, TN, p. A591

NORDBY, Shawn A., Chief Financial Officer, Mary Lanning Healthcare, Hastings, NE, p. A396

NORDING, Rodney, Vice President Organizational Support, Mayo Clinic Health System–Albert Lea and Austin, Austin, MN, p. A339

NORDLAND, Thomas, Chief Medical Officer, Fort HealthCare, Fort Atkinson, WI, p. A705

NORDLUND, Judy, R.N. Chief Nursing Officer, Trinity Hospital, Weaverville, CA, p. A99

NORDLUND, Sarah, Director of Nursing, Garfield County Health Center, Jordan, MT, p. A388

NORDSTROM, Janice, Director Human Resources, Landmark Hospital of Joplin, Joplin, MO, p. A372

NORDSTROM, Katie, Director Human Resources, Beartooth Billings Clinic, Red Lodge, MT, p. A390

NORDWICK, Thomas, Chief Executive Officer, Uvalde Memorial Hospital, Uvalde, TX, p. A654

NORDYKE, Melissa, Chief Financial Officer, Seton Smithville Regional Hospital, Smithville, TX, p. A649

NOREEN, James, M.D. Chief Medical Officer, Regina Hospital, Hastings, MN, p. A344

NOREEN, Ron, Director, Information Services, Southwest Mississippi Regional Medical Center, McComb, MS, p. A361

NORELDIN, Mohsen, M.D. President Medical Staff, Athol Memorial Hospital, Athol, MA, p. A305

NOREM, Ashley, Chief Information Systems, Starke Hospital, Knox, IN, p. A215

NOREN, Tom, M.D. Chief Medical Officer, UP Health System–Marquette, Marquette, MI, p. A329

NORGAARD, Margaret B.
Chief Executive Officer, Poplar Community Hospital, Poplar, MT, p. A390
Chief Executive Officer, Trinity Hospital, Wolf Point, MT, p. A392

NORICK, Laurence, M.D. Clinical Director, U. S. Public Health Service Indian Hospital, Parker, AZ, p. A35

NORIEGA, Donna, Chief Operating Officer, Arizona State Hospital, Phoenix, AZ, p. A36

NORMAN, Daniel, Regional Service Manager, UnityPoint Health – Allen Hospital, Waterloo, IA, p. A239

NORMAN, Debbie, Director Human Resources, Central Louisiana Surgical Hospital, Alexandria, LA, p. A271

NORMAN, Debbie, MSN Chief Nursing Officer, Elkview General Hospital, Hobart, OK, p. A512

NORMAN, Jimmy, Chief Financial Officer, Mountain Lakes Medical Center, Clayton, GA, p. A156

NORMAN, Laura, Chief Development and Information Officer, Windhaven Psychiatric Hospital, Prescott Valley, AZ, p. A38

NORMAN, Lori, Chief Financial Officer, HEALTHSOUTH Rehabilitation of Gadsden, Gadsden, AL, p. A20

NORMAN, Mark, Chief Executive Officer, Lackey Memorial Hospital, Forest, MS, p. A358

NORMAN, Mary, R.N. Chief Nursing Officer, Bear Valley Community Hospital, Big Bear Lake, CA, p. A57

NORMAN, Michael L., Executive Vice President and Chief Operating Officer, Landmark Hospital of Cape Girardeau, Cape Girardeau, MO, p. A368

NORMAN, Robin, Senior Vice President and Chief Financial Officer, Virginia Hospital Center – Arlington, Arlington, VA, p. A667

NORMAND, Lorrie, R.N., Interim Chief Executive Officer and Chief Nursing Officer, Texas Health Harris Methodist Hospital Cleburne, Cleburne, TX, p. A606

NORMINGTON–SLAY, Jeremy, FACHE, Chief Executive Officer, Mercy Medical Center, Oshkosh, WI, p. A713

NORQUEST, Cathy, Director Human Resources, York General Hospital, York, NE, p. A403

NORRIS, Charles, Chief Executive Officer, Memorial Hospital, Gonzales, TX, p. A621

NORRIS, Craig
Interim Chief Executive Officer, Saint Thomas DeKalb Hospital, Smithville, TN, p. A593
Interim Chief Executive Officer, Saint Thomas Highlands Hospital, Sparta, TN, p. A593
Interim Chief Executive Officer, Saint Thomas Stones River Hospital, Woodbury, TN, p. A594

NORRIS, David, Chief Medical Staff, Sweetwater Hospital, Sweetwater, TN, p. A593

NORRIS, Kathy, Director Human Resources, Bear Valley Community Hospital, Big Bear Lake, CA, p. A57

NORRIS, Lucy, Administrator Interim Chief Nursing Officer, MultiCare Good Samaritan Hospital, Puyallup, WA, p. A688

NORRIS, Ron, Chief Executive Officer, Select Specialty Hospital – Dallas Garland, Garland, TX, p. A620

NORTH, Ralene, Chief Nurse Executive, Massena Memorial Hospital, Massena, NY, p. A442

NORTHCUTT, Lynn, Chief Information Officer, Carolinas Hospital System, Florence, SC, p. A565

NORTHERN, Gail M., Director Human Resources, Blue Mountain Hospital, Blanding, UT, p. A659

NORTHUP, Carol, R.N. Chief Nursing Officer and Chief Operating Officer, J. Arthur Dosher Memorial Hospital, Southport, NC, p. A474

NORTHUP, Jeffrey, D.O. Chief Medical Officer, Knox Community Hospital, Mount Vernon, OH, p. A499

NORTON, Andrew J., M.D
Chief Medical Officer, Bryn Mawr Hospital, Bryn Mawr, PA, p. A534
Chief Medical Officer, Paoli Hospital, Paoli, PA, p. A547

NORTON, Debbie, Chief Financial Officer, Medical Center Barbour, Eufaula, AL, p. A19

NORTON, Jameson, Chief Executive Officer, North Tampa Behavioral Health, Wesley Chapel, FL, p. A149

NORTON, Julie, Chief Financial Officer, Avera McKennan Hospital and University Health Center, Sioux Falls, SD, p. A576

NORTON, Meg, Executive Vice President and Chief Administrative Officer, Rady Children's Hospital – San Diego, San Diego, CA, p. A88

NORTON, Robert G., President, North Shore Medical Center, Salem, MA, p. A314

NORTON, Sam, Interim Chief Information Officer, Indiana Regional Medical Center, Indiana, PA, p. A541

NORTON, Susan, Vice President Human Resources, Augusta University Medical Center, Augusta, GA, p. A153

NORVILLE, Amy, Vice President Support Services, St. Luke's Hospital, Columbus, NC, p. A463

NORWOOD, Lyle, M.D. Chief of Staff, Northside Medical Center, Columbus, GA, p. A156

NOSACKA, David
Chief Financial Officer, HSHS St. Elizabeth's Hospital, Belleville, IL, p. A181
Southern Illinois Division Chief Financial Officer, HSHS St. Joseph's Hospital, Highland, IL, p. A192

NOSACKA, Mark, Chief Executive Officer, Good Samaritan Medical Center, West Palm Beach, FL, p. A149

NOSBISCH, Don, Director Human Resources, Floyd County Medical Center, Charles City, IA, p. A227

NOSEWORTHY, Ed, Chief Executive Officer, Florida Hospital Memorial Medical Center, Daytona Beach, FL, p. A127

NOSEWORTHY, MD, John H., M.D., President and Chief Executive Officer, Mayo Clinic, Rochester, MN, p. B85

NOSKIN, Gary, Senior Vice President and Chief Medical Officer, Northwestern Memorial Hospital, Northwestern Memorial Hospital, Chicago, IL, p. A185

NOSKO, Jeannine Burnat, Vice President Patient Care, Aspirus Wausau Hospital, Wausau, WI, p. A718

NOSTRANT, Hunter, Chef Financial Officer, Helen Newberry Joy Hospital, Newberry, MI, p. A331

NOTEMAN, Laurali, Director Human Resources, Kane County Hospital, Kanab, UT, p. A660

NOTTEBART, Cathy, Interim Superintendent, Austin State Hospital, Austin, TX, p. A599

NOTTER, Pat, R.N. Chief Nursing Officer and Director Quality, Melissa Memorial Hospital, Holyoke, CO, p. A107

NOTTINGHAM, Cheryl, Chief Financial Officer, Atlantic General Hospital, Berlin, MD, p. A298

NOUNA, Nabil, M.D. Chief of Staff, Allegan General Hospital, Allegan, MI, p. A318

NOVAK, Charles, M.D. Chief Medical Officer, Intermountain Hospital, Boise, ID, p. A174

NOVAK, Christopher, Chief Operating Officer, Alexian Brothers Behavioral Health Hospital, Hoffman Estates, IL, p. A193

NOVAK, Georgene, Director Human Resources, Littleton Regional Hospital, Littleton, NH, p. A412

NOVAK, James
Interim Chief Executive Officer, LifeCare Hospitals of Pittsburgh, Pittsburgh, PA, p. A550
Interim Chief Executive Officer, LifeCare Hospitals of Pittsburgh – Monroeville, Monroeville, PA, p. A545

NOVAK, Kristen, Manager Human Resources, River Falls Area Hospital, River Falls, WI, p. A715

NOVAK, Michael, Vice President, Operations and Chief Information Officer, Saint Mary's Hospital, Waterbury, CT, p. A117

NOVAK, Sharon, CPA Vice President Finance, Adena Pike Medical Center, Waverly, OH, p. A505

NOVELLO, Regina, R.N. Chief Operating Officer, Healdsburg District Hospital, Healdsburg, CA, p. A66

NOVICK, Peggy, Vice President, Clinical Support and Outpatient Services, Milford Regional Medical Center, Milford, MA, p. A312

NOVOA LOYOLA, Jose E., M.D. Medical Director, Cardiovascular Center of Puerto Rico and the Caribbean, San Juan, PR, p. A729

NOVOSEL, Stacie, Vice President, Human Resources, South Bay Hospital, Sun City Center, FL, p. A146

NOVOTNY, Mark, M.D. Chief Medical Officer, Cooley Dickinson Hospital, Northampton, MA, p. A313

NOWACHEK, Debra S., Director Human Resources, Grinnell Regional Medical Center, Grinnell, IA, p. A231

NOWICKI, Becky, Director Human Resources, Michiana Behavioral Health Center, Plymouth, IN, p. A220

NOWICKI, Michelle, R.N. Chief Nurse Executive, Kaiser Permanente Baldwin Park Medical Center, Baldwin Park, CA, p. A56

NOWLIN, Angela, R.N. Senior VP, Operations, Magnolia Regional Health Center, Corinth, MS, p. A357

NOWLIN, Jeffrey D., President and Chief Operating Officer, St. John Medical Center, Tulsa, OK, p. A522

NOWLIN, Patricia, Director Accounting, Cooper County Memorial Hospital, Boonville, MO, p. A368

NOWLING, Tara, Director Human Resources, Monroe County Hospital, Monroeville, AL, p. A23

NOYES, Vikki, Executive Vice President and Chief Operating Officer, Confluence Health/Central Washington Hospital, Wenatchee, WA, p. A693

NUAKO, Kofi, M.D. President Medical Staff, Baptist Memorial Hospital–Union City, Union City, TN, p. A594

NUDD, Brandon M., Chief Operating Officer, Gordon Hospital, Calhoun, GA, p. A155

NUNEZ, Michael, Chief Financial Officer, University Medical Center of El Paso, El Paso, TX, p. A616

NUNEZ, Milton, Executive Director, NYC Health + Hospitals / Lincoln,, NY, p. A448

NUNEZ, Sheila, Director Human Resources, Eastern New Mexico Medical Center, Roswell, NM, p. A431

NUNLEY, Julie, R.N.,
  Chief Executive Officer, Banner Baywood Medical Center, Mesa, AZ, p. A34
  Chief Executive Officer, Banner Heart Hospital, Mesa, AZ, p. A34

NUNN, Brian, R.N. Chief Nursing Officer, Mary Black Health System – Gaffney, Gaffney, SC, p. A566

NUNN, Chalmers, M.D. Chief Medical Officer and Senior Vice President, Centra Lynchburg General Hospital, Lynchburg, VA, p. A672

NUNNELLY, Sarah, Chief Operating Officer, Princeton Baptist Medical Center, Birmingham, AL, p. A17

NURU, Betty, Director Human Resources, Millwood Hospital, Arlington, TX, p. A597

NURY, Alex, Chief Information Officer, Providence Tarzana Medical Center,, CA, p. A74

NUSBAUM, Neil, M.D. Chief of Staff, Veterans Affairs Central Western Massachusetts Healthcare System, Leeds, MA, p. A311

NUSS, Michelle, M.D. Chief Medical Officer, West Virginia University Hospitals, Morgantown, WV, p. A698

NUSS, Suzanne Langan, M.D. Chief Nursing Officer, Nebraska Medicine – Nebraska Medical Center, Omaha, NE, p. A400

NUSSBAUM, Joseph, M.D. Chief of Staff, California Hospital Medical Center, Los Angeles, CA, p. A70

NUSSBAUM, Mark, Vice President Operations, Marymount Hospital, Garfield Heights, OH, p. A495

NUTINSKY, Charles, Chief Medical Officer, Perry Hospital, Perry, GA, p. A164

NYAMU, Samuel, M.D. Chief Medical Officer, Sanford Aberdeen Medical Center, Aberdeen, SD, p. A542

NYBERG, Becky T., Chief Financial Officer, Bloomington Meadows Hospital, Bloomington, IN, p. A207

NYE, Jeff, Chief Financial Officer, Castle Medical Center, Kailua, HI, p. A171

NYIKES, Debra, Director Finance and Chief Financial Officer, Cleveland Clinic Children's Hospital for Rehabilitation, Cleveland, OH, p. A489

NYKAMP, Robert, Vice President and Chief Operating Officer, Pine Rest Christian Mental Health Services, Grand Rapids, MI, p. A325

NYLUND, Barbara, M.D. Chief of Staff, Novato Community Hospital, Novato, CA, p. A80

NYMOEN, Gary, Chief Financial Officer, Hialeah Hospital, Hialeah, FL, p. A130

NYP, Randall G., FACHE,
  Chief Executive Officer, Providence Medical Center, Kansas City, KS, p. A246
  President and Chief Executive Officer, Saint John Hospital, Leavenworth, KS, p. A247

NYSTROM, Dale, M.D. Chief Medical Officer, Physician, Hawarden Regional Healthcare, Hawarden, IA, p. A232

NZERUE, Chike, M.D. Chief Medical Officer, Nashville General Hospital, Nashville, TN, p. A590

O

O'BRIEN, Daniel R., Vice President and Chief Financial Officer, Community Hospital, Munster, IN, p. A219

O'BRIEN, David, M.D.,
  President, Redwood Memorial Hospital, Fortuna, CA, p. A62
  President, St. Joseph Hospital, Eureka, CA, p. A61

O'BRIEN, Eileen, Director Human Resources, Broward Health Coral Springs, Coral Springs, FL, p. A126

O'BRIEN, Elizabeth, Chief Financial Officer, Northern Nevada Adult Mental Health Services, Sparks, NV, p. A408

O'BRIEN, Jane E., M.D. Medical Director, Franciscan Hospital for Children, Boston, MA, p. A306

O'BRIEN, John, Chief Executive Officer, Manning Regional Healthcare Center, Manning, IA, p. A234

O'BRIEN, Karen, Director Human Resources, Gerald Champion Regional Medical Center, Alamogordo, NM, p. A427

O'BRIEN, Kelly, Chief Operating Officer, Riverview Medical Center, Red Bank, NJ, p. A423

O'BRIEN, Kevin, Chief Financial Officer, Share Medical Center, Alva, OK, p. A508

O'BRIEN, Laureen, Chief Information Officer, Providence Newberg Medical Center, Newberg, OR, p. A528

O'BRIEN, MaryAnn, Coordinator Human Resource, AMG Specialty Hospital – Covington, Covington, LA, p. A275

O'BRIEN, Renee, Director Human Resources, Greater Binghamton Health Center, Binghamton, NY, p. A435

O'BRIEN, Tim, Chief Operating Officer, North Suburban Medical Center, Thornton, CO, p. A111

O'BRIEN–EVANS, Yvonne M., MS Chief of Nursing, Pella Regional Health Center, Pella, IA, p. A236

O'BRIEN–PARADIS, Katie, M.D. Chief Medical Officer, CHI Oakes Hospital, Oakes, ND, p. A481

O'BRYANT, G. Mark, President and Chief Executive Officer, Tallahassee Memorial HealthCare, Tallahassee, FL, p. A146

O'CONNELL, Brian, Director Information Services, North Star Behavioral Health System, Anchorage, AK, p. A28

O'CONNELL, Kimberly, President, Roger Williams Medical Center, Providence, RI, p. A561

O'CONNELL, Melody M., Director Human Resources, St. Bernard Parish Hospital, Chalmette, LA, p. A274

O'CONNELL, Tim, Chief Financial Officer, Lincoln Hospital, Davenport, WA, p. A684

O'CONNOR, Betty, Chief Nursing Officer, Crouse Hospital, Syracuse, NY, p. A456

O'CONNOR, Colleen, Director Human Resources, Centerstone Hospital, Bradenton, FL, p. A124

O'CONNOR, Corey
  Vice President, Finance, Nexus Specialty Hospital, Shenandoah, TX, p. A648
  Vice President, Finance, Nexus Specialty Hospital The Woodlands, The Woodlands, TX, p. A652

O'CONNOR, David, Executive Vice President and Chief Financial Officer, CaroMont Regional Medical Center, Gastonia, NC, p. A465

O'CONNOR, Dennis, M.D. Medical Director, Ira Davenport Memorial Hospital, Bath, NY, p. A434

O'CONNOR, J. T., M.D. Medical Director, Mercy Health Love County, Marietta, OK, p. A514

O'CONNOR, James, Executive Vice President and Chief Administrative Officer, St. Charles Hospital, Port Jefferson, NY, p. A453

O'CONNOR, Kathy
  Vice President Finance, St. Joseph Mercy Ann Arbor, Ypsilanti, MI, p. A337
  Vice President Finance and Controller, St. Joseph Mercy Livingston Hospital, Howell, MI, p. A334

O'CONNOR, Kevin, D.O. President Medical Staff, Spectrum Health United Hospital, Greenville, MI, p. A325

O'CONNOR, Marcia, Chief Executive Officer, Choctaw Memorial Hospital, Hugo, OK, p. A513

O'CONNOR, Michael F., Senior Vice President Finance, WellSpan York Hospital, York, PA, p. A559

O'CONNOR, Michael P., M.D. Chief Medical Officer, Banner Baywood Medical Center, Mesa, AZ, p. A34

O'CONNOR, Nicholas, Vice President and Chief Information Officer, Plainview Hospital, Plainview, NY, p. A452

O'CONNOR, Patrick, Chief Operating Officer, Morris Hospital & Healthcare Centers, Morris, IL, p. A197

O'CONNOR, Thomas, President, United Hospital, Saint Paul, MN, p. A351

O'CONNOR, Tim, Area Finance Officer, Kaiser Permanente Santa Clara Medical Center, Santa Clara, CA, p. A93

O'CONNOR, Timothy P., Executive Vice President and Chief Financial Officer, Lahey Hospital & Medical Center, Burlington, Burlington, MA, p. A308

O'CONNOR–SNYDER, Judy, Chief Nursing Officer, Mercy Hospital Lebanon, Lebanon, MO, p. A375

O'DEA, Edward
  Executive Vice President and Chief Financial Officer, Lehigh Valley Hospital, Allentown, PA, p. A532
  Executive Vice President and Chief Financial Officer, Lehigh Valley Hospital–Muhlenberg, Bethlehem, PA, p. A533

O'DELL, Darrell, Director Information Services, Good Samaritan Hospital, San Jose, CA, p. A91

O'DELL, Michael, Chief Financial Officer, Sheridan County Health Complex, Hoxie, KS, p. A245

O'DONNELL, Jan, Chief Nursing Officer, South Texas Surgical Hospital, Corpus Christi, TX, p. A608

O'DONNELL, John, Director of Information Technology Services, Mary Black Health System–Spartanburg, Spartanburg, SC, p. A569

O'DONNELL, Michael F., CPA Chief Financial Officer, Peconic Bay Medical Center, Riverhead, NY, p. A454

O'DONNELL, Patrick W., CPA, President and Chief Executive Officer, Chambersburg Hospital, Chambersburg, PA, p. A535

O'DONNELL, Patrick W., CPA, President and Chief Executive Officer, Summit Health, Chambersburg, PA, p. B130

O'DONNELL, Randall L., Ph.D.,
  President and Chief Executive Officer, Children's Mercy Hospitals and Clinics, Kansas City, MO, p. A373
  President and Chief Executive Officer, Children's Mercy South, Overland Park, KS, p. A251

O'DONOGHUE, Brian, M.D. Chief Medical Officer, Breckinridge Memorial Hospital, Hardinsburg, KY, p. A261

O'FLANAGAN, Jayne
  Director Human Resources, Incline Village Community Hospital, Incline Village, NV, p. A405
  Chief Human Resources Officer, Tahoe Forest Hospital District, Truckee, CA, p. A97

O'GORMAN, Brenda, R.N. Interim Chief Nursing Officer, Select Specialty Hospital–Omaha, Omaha, NE, p. A400

O'GORMAN, Victoria, Administrator, Fremont Medical Center, Fremont, CA, p. A63

O'HARA, Denise, Vice President Human Resources, Wilson Medical Center, Wilson, NC, p. A475

O'HARA, Gene L., Interim Chief Executive Officer, Colorado Plains Medical Center, Fort Morgan, CO, p. A105

O'HARA, Kathleen, Vice President Human Resources, Erie County Medical Center, Buffalo, NY, p. A435

O'HARA, Michael
  Senior Executive Director Human Resources, Houston Medical Center, Warner Robins, GA, p. A168
  Senior Executive Director, Perry Hospital, Perry, GA, p. A164

O'HAVER, Tim, Chief Operating Officer, St. Joseph Medical Center, Tacoma, WA, p. A692

O'HAVER, Tim G., Chief Operating Officer, Summit Pacific Medical Center, Elma, WA, p. A684

O'KEEFE, James M., President and Chief Executive Officer, Mile Bluff Medical Center, Mauston, WI, p. A710

O'KEEFE, John
  Chief Nursing Officer, Day Kimball Hospital, Putnam, CT, p. A116
  Chief Executive Officer, Select Specialty Hospital–Gulfport, Gulfport, MS, p. A358

O'KEEFE, Kathy
  Executive Director, Pilgrim Psychiatric Center, Brentwood, NY, p. A435
  Interim Executive Director, Sagamore Children's Psychiatric Center, Dix Hills, NY, p. A438

O'KEEFE, Michael, Interim Chief Executive Officer, Community Memorial Hospital, Redfield, SD, p. A576

O'KEEFE, Sharon L., President, University of Chicago Medical Center, Chicago, IL, p. A187

O'KEEFE, Sharon L., President, University of Chicago Medicine, Chicago, IL, p. B147

O'KEEFE, Trish, R.N., President, Morristown Medical Center, Morristown, NJ, p. A419

O'KELLEY, J. Shannon, Chief Operating Officer, Ronald Reagan UCLA Medical Center, Los Angeles, CA, p. A74

O'LAIRE, Beth, Manager Human Resources, Calumet Medical Center, Chilton, WI, p. A704

O'LEARY, Bill, Chief Executive Officer, Pondera Medical Center, Conrad, MT, p. A386

O'LEARY, Daniel H., M.D. Chief Medical Officer, HealthAlliance Hospitals, Leominster, MA, p. A311

O'LEARY, Kevin J., Senior Vice President and Chief Financial Officer, Exeter Hospital, Exeter, NH, p. A411

O'LEARY, Megan A., Vice President Human Resources and Rehabilitation Services, McKenzie–Willamette Medical Center, Springfield, OR, p. A531

O'LEARY, Rand, FACHE, Chief Executive, Oregon Network, PeaceHealth Sacred Heart Medical Center at RiverBend, Springfield, OR, p. A531

O'LOUGHLIN, James F., President and Chief Executive Officer, Memorial Hospital Jacksonville, Jacksonville, FL, p. A131

O'MALLEY, Constance, President, Beaumont Hospital – Farmington Hills, Farmington Hills, MI, p. A323

O'MALLEY, Jon P., Chief Executive Officer, Select Specialty Hospital–Macomb County, Mount Clemens, MI, p. A330

O'MALLEY, Mary Jo, R.N. Vice President Diagnostics and Support Services, Oconomowoc Memorial Hospital, Oconomowoc, WI, p. A713

O'MALLEY, Trevor, Site Manager, Presence Saint Joseph Hospital, Elgin, IL, p. A189

O'NEAL, Charlotte, Vice President Human Resources, Research Medical Center, Kansas City, MO, p. A373

O'NEAL, Lewis Stephen, R.N. Chief Nursing Officer, Saint Joseph London, London, KY, p. A264

O'NEAL, Michael, Administrator and Chief Executive Officer, George C Grape Community Hospital, Hamburg, IA, p. A231

O'NEIL, Alan, Chief Executive Officer, Unity Medical Center, Grafton, ND, p. A479

O'NEIL, Jeremy, Administrator, Providence Valdez Medical Center, Valdez, AK, p. A30

O'NEIL, Terry, Chief Information Technology, Nazareth Hospital, Philadelphia, PA, p. A549

O'NEILL, Beth, Chief Nursing Officer, Morgan Memorial Hospital, Madison, GA, p. A162

O'NEILL, Jennifer A., R.N. Chief Nursing Officer, Vice President Patient Care Services, Saint Barnabas Medical Center, Livingston, NJ, p. A418

O'NEILL, Lynn, R.N. Chief Nursing Officer, Medical Center of Lewisville, Lewisville, TX, p. A632

O'NEILL, Melissa, Vice President Human Resources, Advocate Sherman Hospital, Elgin, IL, p. A189

O'NEILL, Michael, M.D. Chief Medical Officer, Eastside Medical Center, Snellville, GA, p. A166

O'NEILL, Stephan, Vice President Information Services, Hartford Hospital, Hartford, CT, p. A114

O'NEILL, Tana, R.N. Chief Nursing Officer, West Holt Memorial Hospital, Atkinson, NE, p. A393

O'REILLY, Frank, Director, Dr. J. Corrigan Mental Health Center, Fall River, MA, p. A309

O'ROURKE, Jane, Vice President, Patient Care Services and Chief Nursing Officer, Community Medical Center, Toms River, NJ, p. A424

O'ROURKE, Jane, R.N. Chief Nursing Officer, Vice President Operations, St. Peter's Hospital, Albany, NY, p. A433

O'ROURKE, Michael
Regional Human Resource Officer, Presence Mercy Medical Center, Aurora, IL, p. A180
Regional Human Resources Lead, Presence Saint Joseph Hospital, Elgin, IL, p. A189

O'SHEA, James, Chief Operating Officer, Baton Rouge Behavioral Hospital, Baton Rouge, LA, p. A272

O'SHEA, James E., Administrator, The Willough at Naples, Naples, FL, p. A138

O'STEEN, Neil, Director Information Technology, Bacon County Hospital and Health System, Alma, GA, p. A151

O'SULLIVAN, Barbara, M.D. Medical Director, Rockefeller University Hospital, New York, NY, p. A449

O'SULLIVAN, Paul, FACHE, Chief Executive Officer, Memorial Hermann Memorial City Medical Center, Houston, TX, p. A625

O. CONNOR, Joyce, Chief Operating Officer, Taunton State Hospital, Taunton, MA, p. A315

OAKES, Julie P., R.N. Manager Risk and Quality, Ocean Beach Hospital, Ilwaco, WA, p. A685

OAKES FERRUCCI, Susan, MS Vice President Patient Services and Chief Nursing Officer, Cobleskill Regional Hospital, Cobleskill, NY, p. A437

OAKLEY, Lisa, Chief Financial Officer, Harper County Community Hospital, Buffalo, OK, p. A509

OAKLEY, Sarah G., Vice President Nursing, North Kansas City Hospital, North Kansas City, MO, p. A377

OAKS, Dana C., Chief Executive Officer, JFK Medical Center North Campus, West Palm Beach, FL, p. A149

OAXACA, Norma, Director Human Resources, Peak Behavioral Health Services, Santa Teresa, NM, p. A431

OBER, Tammy L., Chief Executive Officer, Lancaster Rehabilitation Hospital, Lancaster, PA, p. A542

OBERHEU, Todd, Administrator, Lincoln County Medical Center, Ruidoso, NM, p. A431

OBERMIER, Jenny, VP, Director of Nursing, York General Hospital, York, NE, p. A403

OBERST, Larry, Vice President Finance, Spectrum Health Special Care Hospital, Grand Rapids, MI, p. A325

OBEY, Bianca A., Chief Financial Officer, Alexandria Veterans Affairs Health Care System, Pineville, LA, p. A286

OBORNY, Jane, Chief Financial Officer, Rush County Memorial Hospital, La Crosse, KS, p. A247

OCASIO, J. Manuel, Vice President Human Resources, Holy Cross Hospital, Silver Spring, MD, p. A303

OCHOA, Mark S., M.D. Deputy Commander, Clinical Services, Irwin Army Community Hospital, Junction City, KS, p. A246

OCHOA, Nikki, Interim Chief Financial Officer, St. Joseph's Medical Center, Stockton, CA, p. A95

OCHSENDORF, Derrick, Manager Information Technology and Systems, Johnson Memorial Health Services, Dawson, MN, p. A341

OCKER, Danielle, R.N., Director, Manchester Veterans Affairs Medical Center, Manchester, NH, p. A412

ODATO, David, Chief Administrative and Chief Human Resources Officer, UCSF Medical Center, San Francisco, CA, p. A91

ODDIS, Joseph M., Chief Executive Officer, Bon Secours Maryview Medical Center, Portsmouth, VA, p. A676

ODDO, Daniel, Chief Executive Officer, Pioneer Specialty Hospital, Pontiac, MI, p. A332

ODEGAARD, Daniel, FACHE, Chief Executive Officer, Perry Memorial Hospital, Perry, OK, p. A518

ODELL, Cheryl, R.N. Chief Nursing Officer, Sharp Mesa Vista Hospital, San Diego, CA, p. A89

ODELL, Michelle, Director of Public Affairs, Kaiser Permanente South Sacramento Medical Center, Sacramento, CA, p. A86

ODEN, Greg, Chief Medical Officer, Merit Health Central, Jackson, MS, p. A360

ODEN, Ryan, D.O. Chief of Staff, Arbuckle Memorial Hospital, Sulphur, OK, p. A520

ODETOYINBO, Adedapo, M.D. Chief Medical Office, Emory Johns Creek Hospital, Johns Creek, GA, p. A161

ODLE, Susan, Administrator, St. Joseph Memorial Hospital, Murphysboro, IL, p. A197

ODOM, David, Chief Information Officer, Rehoboth McKinley Christian Health Care Services, Gallup, NM, p. A429

ODOM, Jake, Chief Information Officer, Trinity Hospital, Weaverville, CA, p. A99

ODOM, Jennifer, Interim Director Human Resources, Flowers Hospital, Dothan, AL, p. A19

ODOM, Lee Ann, Division President, Beaumont Hospital – Taylor, Taylor, MI, p. A335

ODOM, Robbin, R.N. Chief Nursing Officer, Lake Area Medical Center, Lake Charles, LA, p. A281

ODOM, Terry, Chief Executive Officer, Powell Valley Healthcare, Powell, WY, p. A723

ODUWOLE, Adedapo, M.D. Medical Director, Lighthouse Care Center of Conway, Conway, SC, p. A565

OEHL, Varonica, Chief Financial Officer, Fort Lauderdale Hospital, Fort Lauderdale, FL, p. A128

OEHLKE, Tammy, Director Human Resources, St. Mark's Medical Center, La Grange, TX, p. A631

OEMKE, Brittany, Administrator, Hanover Hospital, Hanover, KS, p. A244

OESTREICH, Pearl, Director Human Resources, Scott & White Hospital – Llano, Llano, TX, p. A633

OETTING, Phyllis, Director Human Resources, Mitchell County Hospital Health Systems, Beloit, KS, p. A241

OETZEL, Gerald P., Chief Financial Officer, Temple University Hospital, Philadelphia, PA, p. A550

OFFUTT, Dan, Manager Finance, Knox County Hospital, Knox City, TX, p. A631

OFSTEDAL, Jeff, Manager Information Technology, Glacial Ridge Health System, Glenwood, MN, p. A343

OGASAWARA, Keith, M.D. Associate Medical Director and Professional Chief of Staff, Kaiser Permanente Medical Center, Honolulu, HI, p. A170

OGAWA, Quin
Chief Financial Officer, Kahi Mohala Behavioral Health, Ewa Beach, HI, p. A170
Vice President Finance and Chief Financial Officer, Kuakini Medical Center, Honolulu, HI, p. A170

OGBURN, J. Anthony, M.D. Chief Medical Officer, UNM Sandoval Regional Medical Center, Albuquerque, NM, p. A428

OGDEN, Judy, Director Information Technology, Franklin Medical Center, Winnsboro, LA, p. A289

OGDEN, Lesley, M.D., Chief Executive Officer, Samaritan North Lincoln Hospital, Lincoln City, OR, p. A527

OGDEN, Michael L., President and Chief Executive Officer, Little Falls Hospital, Little Falls, NY, p. A441

OGILVIE, Richard, Chief Information Officer, Southwestern Vermont Medical Center, Bennington, VT, p. A665

OGLESBY, Lorie A., Director of Human Resources, Baptist Health Madisonville, Madisonville, KY, p. A265

OGORZALEK, Ed, Chief Financial Officer, Rutland Regional Medical Center, Rutland, VT, p. A666

OGRINC, Mary L., R.N. Chief Nursing Officer, Senior Vice President Patient Services, Lake Health, Concord Township, OH, p. A491

OGROD, Eugene, M.D. Chief Medical Officer, Kingwood Medical Center, Kingwood, TX, p. A631

OH, Christina E., Chief Operating Officer, Piedmont Medical Center, Rock Hill, SC, p. A569

OHASHI, Curtis, Chief Executive Officer, Select Specialty Hospital–Cincinnati, Cincinnati, OH, p. A488

OHL, Connie, Acting Chief Human Resources, Veterans Affairs Illiana Health Care System, Danville, IL, p. A187

OHLER, Kevin, Director of Finance, Promise Hospital of San Diego, San Diego, CA, p. A88

OHM, Barbara, Administrator, The Orthopedic Specialty Hospital, Murray, UT, p. A661

OHMART, Dean, Chief Financial Officer, Coffeyville Regional Medical Center, Coffeyville, KS, p. A241

OHNOUTKA, Debra, Chief Executive Officer, St. Mary's Medical Center, Blue Springs, MO, p. A367

OHRT, James M., M.D. Director Medical Staff, Henderson Health Care Services, Henderson, NE, p. A397

OJEDA, Guadalupe, R.N. Chief Nursing Officer, West Covina Medical Center, West Covina, CA, p. A99

OJOMO, Karanita, M.D. Chief of Staff, LewisGale Hospital Pulaski, Pulaski, VA, p. A676

OKABE, David
Senior Vice President, Chief Financial Officer and Treasurer, Kapiolani Medical Center for Women & Children, Honolulu, HI, p. A170
Executive Vice President, Chief Financial Officer and Treasurer, Pali Momi Medical Center, Aiea, HI, p. A170
Executive Vice President, Chief Financial Officer and Treasurer, Straub Clinic & Hospital, Honolulu, HI, p. A171
Executive Vice President, Chief Financial Officer and Treasurer, Wilcox Memorial Hospital, Lihue, HI, p. A172

OKECHUKWU, Vitalis C., M.D. President Medical Staff, PAM Specialty Hospital of Lafayette, Lafayette, LA, p. A281

OKEN, Jeffrey, Vice President of Medical Affairs, Marianjoy Rehabilitation Hospital, Wheaton, IL, p. A205

OKERSON, Tara, Director Human Resources, Presentation Medical Center, Rolla, ND, p. A481

OKESON, Keith, President and Chief Executive Officer, LifeCare Medical Center, Roseau, MN, p. A350

OKEY, Suzi, Director of Nursing, Southwest Health, Platteville, WI, p. A714

OKONIEWSKI, Susan, M.D. Chief of Staff, CHI St. Gabriel's Health, Little Falls, MN, p. A345

OKSENDAHL, Elaine, Director Human Resources and Risk Management, Schick Shadel Hospital, Seattle, WA, p. A689

OKUHARA, Mary, Chief Human Resource Officer, Lakewood Regional Medical Center, Lakewood, CA, p. A68

OKUNO–JONES, Susan K., Vice President Patient Care Services and Chief Nursing Executive, Advocate Good Samaritan Hospital, Downers Grove, IL, p. A188

OLAND, Charisse S., FACHE, Chief Executive Officer, Rusk County Memorial Hospital, Ladysmith, WI, p. A708

OLANDER, Scott, Chief Financial Officer, EvergreenHealth Monroe, Monroe, WA, p. A686

OLASON, Roxanne, R.N. Vice President and Chief Nursing Officer, Skagit Regional Health, Mount Vernon, WA, p. A686

OLDEN, R. Don, Chief Executive Officer, Wahiawa General Hospital, Wahiawa, HI, p. A172

OLDER, Michael, M.D. President Medical Staff, Nashoba Valley Medical Center, Ayer, MA, p. A305

OLDHAM, Jennie, Director Human Resources, Goodall–Witcher Hospital Authority, Clifton, TX, p. A606

OLDHAM, Lawrence, Chief Financial Officer, Arise Austin Medical Center, Austin, TX, p. A598

OLDHAM, Marriner, M.D. Chief Medical Officer, U. S. Air Force Regional Hospital, Elmendorf AFB, AK, p. A29

OLDS, Debbie D., R.N. Director of Nursing, Willis–Knighton Medical Center, Shreveport, LA, p. A288

OLEJNICZAK, David R., Chief Operating Officer, St. John's Hospital, Springfield, IL, p. A203

OLEKSYK, Mike, M.D. Vice President and Chief Medical Officer, Baptist Hospital, Pensacola, FL, p. A142

OLESTON, Caryn Lynn, MS
Chief Nursing Officer, Mercy Harvard Hospital, Harvard, IL, p. A192
Chief Nursing Officer, Mercy Walworth Hospital and Medical Center, Lake Geneva, WI, p. A708

OLESZAK, Randy, Director Fiscal Services, Milwaukee County Behavioral Health Division, Milwaukee, WI, p. A711

OLEY, Edwin M., President and Chief Executive Officer, Mercy Regional Medical Center, Lorain, OH, p. A497

OLIGSCHLAEGER, David, Medical Staff President, Shelby Memorial Hospital, Shelbyville, IL, p. A202

OLINDE, Chad E., CPA, Administrator and Chief Executive Officer, Pointe Coupee General Hospital, New Roads, LA, p. A285

OLINGER, Richard P., Chief Financial Officer, Millcreek Community Hospital, Erie, PA, p. A538

OLINSKI, Janis, R.N. Vice President Clinical Services, Harrison Community Hospital, Cadiz, OH, p. A486

OLIPHANT, Gerald P., Executive Vice President and Chief Operating Officer, Good Samaritan Hospital, Cincinnati, OH, p. A487

OLIPHANT, Jenny, Executive Vice President and Chief Operating Officer, Bethesda North Hospital, Cincinnati, OH, p. A487

OLIPHANT, Phillip, Chief Information Officer, U. S. Air Force Regional Hospital, Elmendorf AFB, AK, p. A29

OLIVARES, Rafael, Controller, Starr County Memorial Hospital, Rio Grande City, TX, p. A643

OLIVAREZ, Lorenzo, Senior Vice President and Chief Financial Officer, BSA Hospital, LLC, Amarillo, TX, p. A596

OLIVAS, Ray, Chief Fiscal Service, West Texas Veterans Affairs Health Care System, Big Spring, TX, p. A603

OLIVE, Alan C., Chief Executive Officer, Northern Nevada Medical Center, Sparks, NV, p. A408

OLIVENCIA, Humberto, M.D. Medical Director, Hospital Perea, Mayaguez, PR, p. A728

OLIVER, Athan, Administrator and Chief Executive Officer, Iberia Rehabilitation Hospital, New Iberia, LA, p. A284

OLIVER III, Athan, R.N., MSN Chief Executive Officer, Iberia Medical Center, New Iberia, LA, p. A284

OLIVER, David, Director Information Systems, King's Daughters Medical Center, Ashland, KY, p. A257

OLIVER, Diane, R.N. Chief Nursing Officer, Parkwest Medical Center, Knoxville, TN, p. A586

OLIVER, Doug, Chief Financial Officer, Windhaven Psychiatric Hospital, Prescott Valley, AZ, p. A38

OLIVER, Kelley, R.N. Chief Nursing Officer, Physicians' Specialty Hospital, Fayetteville, AR, p. A45

OLIVER, Michelle
  Chief Nursing Officer, HSHS St. Mary's Hospital, Decatur, IL, p. A188
  Chief Nursing Executive, Shelby Memorial Hospital, Shelbyville, IL, p. A202

OLIVER, Rick, Information Technology, Hamilton Hospital, Olney, TX, p. A639

OLIVER, Rosalie
  Chief Financial Officer, Florida Hospital Heartland Medical Center, Sebring, FL, p. A145
  Senior Vice President and Chief Financial Officer, Florida Hospital Wauchula, Wauchula, FL, p. A149

OLIVER, Vincent, FACHE, Administrator, Island Hospital, Anacortes, WA, p. A682

OLIVERA, Sue, Vice President, Aultman Hospital, Canton, OH, p. A486

OLIVERAS, Freddy, Chief Information Officer, Martin County Hospital District, Stanton, TX, p. A650

OLIVERIO, John D., President and Chief Executive Officer, Wheaton Franciscan Healthcare, Wheaton, IL, p. B155

OLIVIER, Edward
  Chief Financial Officer, Charles A. Dean Memorial Hospital, Greenville, ME, p. A293
  Chief Financial Officer, Martha's Vineyard Hospital, Oak Bluffs, MA, p. A313

OLLI, Cindy, R.N. Chief Nursing Officer, Schoolcraft Memorial Hospital, Manistique, MI, p. A329

OLLIE, Edwin J., Executive Vice President and Chief Financial Officer, New Hanover Regional Medical Center, Wilmington, NC, p. A475

OLLIS, Linda Neu, FACHE Chief Operating Officer, Monongalia General Hospital, Morgantown, WV, p. A698

OLLSON, Joanne, Vice President Human Resources, Baystate Noble Hospital, Westfield, MA, p. A316

OLM-SHIPMAN, Bobby, Chief Executive Officer, Saint Luke's South Hospital, Overland Park, KS, p. A251

OLMSTEAD, David, Chief Human Resource Officer – Dallas Market, Lake Pointe Medical Center, Rowlett, TX, p. A644

OLMSTEAD, Linda, Director, Human Resources, UW Medicine/Northwest Hospital & Medical Center, Seattle, WA, p. A690

OLNEY, Garry M.
  Chief Operating Officer, Providence Little Company of Mary Medical Center – Torrance, Torrance, CA, p. A96
  Chief Operating Officer, Providence Little Company of Mary Medical Center San Pedro,, CA, p. A73

OLS, Timothy A., FACHE, President and Chief Executive Officer, Sarah Bush Lincoln Health Center, Mattoon, IL, p. A196

OLSCAMP, Karen E., President and Chief Executive Officer, University of Maryland Baltimore Washington Medical Center, Glen Burnie, MD, p. A301

OLSEN, Debbie, Human Resource Partner, Sparrow Ionia Hospital, Ionia, MI, p. A326

OLSEN, Justin, Chief Operating Officer, Children's Hospital, New Orleans, LA, p. A284

OLSEN, Karen M., R.N. Chief Nursing Officer, Mission Hospital, Asheville, NC, p. A460

OLSEN, Ryan, Vice President of Operations, St. Jude Medical Center, Fullerton, CA, p. A64

OLSEN, Sabrina, Chief Financial Officer, Duke University Hospital, Durham, NC, p. A464

OLSON, Brett J., M.D. Medical Chief of Staff, Lakes Regional Healthcare, Spirit Lake, IA, p. A238

OLSON, Cheryl, Interim Vice President, Pomerado Hospital, Poway, CA, p. A84

OLSON, Craig, Director Information Technology, Southwestern Regional Medical Center, Tulsa, OK, p. A522

OLSON, Dave, Director of Nursing, Montana State Hospital, Warm Springs, MT, p. A391

OLSON, Diana
  Chief Human Resources Officer, Mercy Health – Willard Hospital, Willard, OH, p. A506
  Director Human Resources, Mercy Tiffin Hospital, Tiffin, OH, p. A503

OLSON, Eric, Chief Financial Officer, Providence Portland Medical Center, Portland, OR, p. A529

OLSON, Erik, Chief Executive Officer, Renown Regional Medical Center, Reno, NV, p. A408

OLSON, Forrest, M.D. Chief Medical Officer, Enloe Medical Center, Chico, CA, p. A58

OLSON, Fred, Interim Chief Executive Officer, St. Peter's Hospital, Helena, MT, p. A388

OLSON, Gregory A., President and Chief Executive Officer, Aspirus Medford Hospital, Medford, WI, p. A710

OLSON, John L., M.D. Medical Director, Lakeview Medical Center, Rice Lake, WI, p. A715

OLSON, Kent, Administrator and Chief Executive Officer, Philip Health Services, Philip, SD, p. A575

OLSON, Kevin, Director Information Systems, St. Anthony Hospital, Oklahoma City, OK, p. A517

OLSON, Lacey, M.D. Chief Medical Staff, Sanford Chamberlain Medical Center, Chamberlain, SD, p. A572

OLSON, Lynn R., Director Human Resources, Hendricks Community Hospital Association, Hendricks, MN, p. A344

OLSON, Marcia
  Director Finance and Controller, Spearfish Regional Hospital, Spearfish, SD, p. A577
  Business Office Manager, Webster County Community Hospital, Red Cloud, NE, p. A402

OLSON, MariBeth, R.N. Vice President Patient Care Services, Mercy Hospital, Coon Rapids, MN, p. A341

OLSON, Mark, M.D. Chief of Staff, Lincoln Community Hospital and Nursing Home, Hugo, CO, p. A107

OLSON, Mark, Interim Chief Information Officer, Behavioral Health Network, Natchaug Hospital, Mansfield Center, CT, p. A114

OLSON, Michael R., Chief Executive Officer, Citizens Medical Center, Victoria, TX, p. A655

OLSON, Randall M., Chief Executive Officer, Lane Regional Medical Center, Zachary, LA, p. A290

OLSON, Tim
  Senior Vice President Finance, Appleton Medical Center, Appleton, WI, p. A702
  Senior Vice President Finance, Theda Clark Medical Center, Neenah, WI, p. A712

OLSON, Tracy L., Human Resource Officer, Avera St. Luke's Hospital, Aberdeen, SD, p. A572

OLSSON, Dave, Director of Marketing, Aspirus Keweenaw Hospital, Laurium, MI, p. A329

OLSZYK, Mark, M.D. Vice President Medical Affairs and Chief Medical Officer, Carroll Hospital, Westminster, MD, p. A304

OMAN, Michelle, D.O
  Chief Medical Officer, Essentia Health Northern Pines Medical Center, Aurora, MN, p. A338
  Chief Medical Officer, Essentia Health–Virginia, Virginia, MN, p. A352

OMAR, Sharif, Chief Executive Officer, Northwest Medical Center – Springdale, Springdale, AR, p. A52

OMEL, John, Regional Vice President, Human Resources, Santa Rosa Memorial Hospital, Santa Rosa, CA, p. A94

OMOLARA, Khar, M.D. Chief Medical Staff, Jefferson County Hospital, Fayette, MS, p. A357

OMOSAIYE, Bayode, FACHE, Chief Executive Officer, Shands Live Oak Regional Medical Center, Live Oak, FL, p. A134

OMRAN, Yasser, M.D. President Medical Staff, Pomerene Hospital, Millersburg, OH, p. A499

OMTA, Stephen R., Chief Operating Officer, PeaceHealth St. Joseph Medical Center, Bellingham, WA, p. A682

OMURA, David, Associate Director, Wm. Jennings Bryan Dorn Veterans Affairs Medical Center, Columbia, SC, p. A564

ONEAL, Karen, Chief Financial Officer, Burke Medical Center, Waynesboro, GA, p. A169

ONEILL, John Patrick, Administrator, Shriners Hospitals for Children–Boston, Boston, MA, p. A307

ONEILL, Steve, Chief Information Officer, NYC Health + Hospitals / Carter, New York, NY, p. A448

ONG, Hannah, Director, Medical Affairs, Saint Elizabeths Hospital, Washington, DC, p. A122

ONG, Richard B., Chief Information Officer, Saint Vincent Hospital, Erie, PA, p. A538

ONI, Buki, M.D. Chief Medical Officer, Kenmare Community Hospital, Kenmare, ND, p. A480

ONIFATHER, Jeff, Chief Financial Officer, Cornerstone of Medical Arts Center Hospital, Fresh Meadows, NY, p. A439

ONO, Craig, M.D. Chief of Staff, Shriners Hospitals for Children–Honolulu, Honolulu, HI, p. A171

ONOFRE, Bonnie, Chief Nursing Officer, South Lake Hospital, Clermont, FL, p. A125

OOSTRA, Randall D., FACHE, President and Chief Executive Officer, ProMedica Health System, Toledo, OH, p. B107

OPBROEK, Steve, Manager Information Technology, Skyline Hospital, White Salmon, WA, p. A693

OPHAUG, Courtney, FACHE, Chief Executive Officer, Banner Estrella Medical Center, Phoenix, AZ, p. A36

OPHEIKENS, Robyn, Assistant Administrator Human Resources, St. Mark's Hospital, Salt Lake City, UT, p. A663

OPPENHEIMER, Steven, Chief Executive Officer, Del Amo Hospital, Torrance, CA, p. A96

OPPONG, Bernard, D.O. Chief of Staff, Madison Health, London, OH, p. A497

OPRANDI, Allison, M.D. Chief Medical Officer, Aultman Hospital, Canton, OH, p. A486

OPRISKO, Judy P.
  Vice President, Allied Services Rehabilitation Hospital, Scranton, PA, p. A554
  Vice President Human Resources, John Heinz Institute of Rehabilitation Medicine, Wilkes–Barre, PA, p. A558

OPSTEDAHL, DeeAnna, R.N. Vice President Patient Care Services, St. Joseph's Hospital and Health Center, Dickinson, ND, p. A478

OPSUT, Jennifer, Interim Chief Operating Officer, West Valley Medical Center, Caldwell, ID, p. A175

ORAVEC, Jon, Vice President, Human Resources, Howard County General Hospital, Columbia, MD, p. A300

ORAZINE, Jay, Director Information Services, Baptist Health Paducah, Paducah, KY, p. A267

ORCUTT, David, Chief Executive Officer, Weatherford Regional Medical Center, Weatherford, TX, p. A656

ORDYNA, Daniel, Chief Executive Officer, Portneuf Medical Center, Pocatello, ID, p. A178

ORE, Ruta, Director Human Resources, Pottstown Memorial Medical Center, Pottstown, PA, p. A552

OREAR, Kathy, Director Human Resources, Newman Regional Health, Emporia, KS, p. A242

OREGEL, Omar, Controller, Kindred Hospital–Ontario, Ontario, CA, p. A80

OREKOYA, Layo, Director of Nursing, Clinical Services, Kindred Rehabilitation Hospital Arlington, Arlington, TX, p. A597

ORELLANA, Feliipe, Chief Medical Officer, Barnes–Jewish St. Peters Hospital, Saint Peters, MO, p. A382

OREMUS, Lisa, Interim Chief Human Resource Officer, Los Alamitos Medical Center, Los Alamitos, CA, p. A70

OREOL, Harry, Acting Chief Executive Officer, Patton State Hospital, Patton, CA, p. A82

ORFANIDIS, Deanna, Interim Chief Nursing Officer, Mt. Ascutney Hospital and Health Center, Windsor, VT, p. A666

ORIOL, Albert, Vice President Information Management and Chief Information Officer, Rady Children's Hospital – San Diego, San Diego, CA, p. A88

ORLANDI, Mary, Manager Human Resources, Carney Hospital, Boston, MA, p. A306

ORLANDO, Anthony T., Senior Vice President Finance, Englewood Hospital and Medical Center, Englewood, NJ, p. A417

ORLANDO, Charles, Interim Chief Executive Officer, Placentia–Linda Hospital, Placentia, CA, p. A83

ORLANDO, Kristin, Director Operations, Mid–Hudson Forensic Psychiatric Center, New Hampton, NY, p. A443

ORLANDO, Lorraine, Vice President Human Resources, New York–Presbyterian/Queens,, NY, p. A447

ORMAN Jr., Bernard A., Administrator, Samaritan Memorial Hospital, Macon, MO, p. A376

ORMOND, Evalyn, Chief Executive Officer, Union General Hospital, Farmerville, LA, p. A276

ORMOND, Jack, Chief Financial Officer, Cuba Memorial Hospital, Cuba, NY, p. A437

ORNELAS, Henry
  Chief Operating Officer, LAC+USC Medical Center, Los Angeles, CA, p. A72
  Chief Operating Officer, Salinas Valley Memorial Healthcare System, Salinas, CA, p. A87

OROZCO, Jorge, Chief Executive Officer, Rancho Los Amigos National Rehabilitation Center, Downey, CA, p. A61

ORR, Karen, Chief Nursing Officer, Providence Medical Center, Kansas City, KS, p. A246

ORR, Natassia, Chief Operating Officer, Broward Health Medical Center, Fort Lauderdale, FL, p. A128

ORR, Stephanie, Chief Nursing Officer, Steele Memorial Medical Center, Salmon, ID, p. A178

ORRICK, Charles H., Administrator, Donalsonville Hospital, Donalsonville, GA, p. A158

ORSINI, John
  Executive Vice President and Chief Financial Officer, Northwestern Medicine Central DuPage Hospital, Winfield, IL, p. A205
  Executive Vice President and Chief Financial Officer, Northwestern Medicine Delnor Hospital, Geneva, IL, p. A191

ORSINI, Thomas J., President and Chief Executive Officer, Lake Taylor Transitional Care Hospital, Norfolk, VA, p. A675

ORT, Linda, Chief Financial Officer, Piggott Community Hospital, Piggott, AR, p. A51

ORTEGA, Becky, Manager Human Resources, Avista Adventist Hospital, Louisville, CO, p. A109

ORTEGA, Cesar, M.D. Chief of Staff, United Memorial Medical Care, Houston, TX, p. A627

ORTEGA, Debbie, Chief Human Resource Officer and Vice President Administrative Services, Huntington Memorial Hospital, Pasadena, CA, p. A82

ORTEGA, Jose, Chief Operating Officer, Greater El Monte Community Hospital, South El Monte, CA, p. A95

ORTEGO, Ashley, Director Human Resources and Marketing, Springhill Medical Center, Springhill, LA, p. A288

ORTH, Charam, Director Human Resources, Frances Mahon Deaconess Hospital, Glasgow, MT, p. A387

ORTHAUS, Denis, Director Human Resources, Philhaven, Mount Gretna, PA, p. A545

ORTIZ, Anthony, Chief Financial Officer, Pecos County Memorial Hospital, Fort Stockton, TX, p. A617

ORTIZ, Bienvenido, Coordinator Information Systems, Hospital De Damas, Ponce, PR, p. A728

ORTIZ, Jr., Blas, Assistant Superintendent and Public Information Officer, Rio Grande State Center/South Texas Health Care System, Harlingen, TX, p. A622

ORTIZ, Carlos, Vice President Human Resources, New York Community Hospital,, NY, p. A446

ORTIZ, Edson, Chief Information Officer, Hospital Metropolitano Dr. Tito Mattei, Yauco, PR, p. A731

ORTIZ, Evelyn Padilla
  Director Human Resources, Hospital Menonita De Cayey, Cayey, PR, p. A727
  Director Human Resources, Mennonite General Hospital, Aibonito, PR, p. A725

ORTIZ, Francisco, M.D. Chief of Staff, Jackson County Hospital District, Edna, TX, p. A614

ORTIZ, Jose O., Chief Financial Officer, Ryder Memorial Hospital, Humacao, PR, p. A727

ORTIZ, Migdalia, Director Human Resources, Hospital San Carlos Borromeo, Moca, PR, p. A728

ORTIZ, Nancy, Director Human Resource and Marketing, Frio Regional Hospital, Pearsall, TX, p. A640

ORTIZ, Norma, M.D. Medical Director, Hospital Hermanos Melendez, Bayamon, PR, p. A726

ORTIZ BAEZ, Felix, Administrator, I. Gonzalez Martinez Oncologic Hospital,, PR, p. A730

ORTIZ VARGAS, Ruth M., Administrator, Lafayette Hospital, Arroyo, PR, p. A726

ORTO, Victoria K., R.N. Chief Nursing and Patient Care Services Officer, Duke Regional Hospital, Durham, NC, p. A464

ORTOLANI, Philip A., Vice President Operations, Mid Coast Hospital, Brunswick, ME, p. A292

ORTON, Wendy, Chief Nursing Officer, Alleghany Memorial Hospital, Sparta, NC, p. A474

OSANTOSKI, Tina, Director Human Resources, Harbor Beach Community Hospital, Harbor Beach, MI, p. A326

OSARIO, Cesar, Specialist Information Technology, Cedar Crest Hospital and Residential Treatment Center, Belton, TX, p. A602

OSBAHR, Leah, M.P.H., Chief Executive Officer, Helena Regional Medical Center, Helena, AR, p. A47

OSBERG, Art, M.D. Chief Medical Officer, Ocala Regional Medical Center, Ocala, FL, p. A139

OSBORN, Kim, Chief Financial Officer, Sequoia Hospital, Redwood City, CA, p. A85

OSBORN, Mary Ann, R.N. Senior Vice President and Chief Care Coordinator Officer, UnityPoint Health – St. Luke's Hospital, Cedar Rapids, IA, p. A226

OSBORN, Melodie
  Chief Nursing Officer, Renown Rehabilitation Hospital, Reno, NV, p. A408
  Chief Nursing Officer, Renown South Meadows Medical Center, Reno, NV, p. A408

OSBORN, Tom, D.O. Chief Medical Staff, Holdenville General Hospital, Holdenville, OK, p. A513

OSBORNE, Anna, Chief Human Resources Management Service, West Texas Veterans Affairs Health Care System, Big Spring, TX, p. A603

OSBORNE, Jay, M.D. Senior Vice President Medical Affairs, Northside Medical Center, Youngstown, OH, p. A506

OSBORNE, Phil, Director Information Technology, Bourbon Community Hospital, Paris, KY, p. A268

OSBURN, Jerry, Chief Executive Officer, Yoakum County Hospital, Denver City, TX, p. A613

OSBURNE, Theresa, Human Resources Strategic Partners, Providence Seaside Hospital, Seaside, OR, p. A530

OSCADAL, Martin
  Vice President Human Resources, St. Elizabeth Edgewood, Edgewood, KY, p. A259
  Senior Vice President Human Resources, St. Elizabeth Florence, Florence, KY, p. A260
  Senior Vice President Human Resources, St. Elizabeth Fort Thomas, Fort Thomas, KY, p. A260

OSE, Peggy, FACHE Chief Nursing Officer, Aspirus Riverview Hospital and Clinics, Inc., Wisconsin Rapids, WI, p. A719

OSEGARD, Jeff, Chief Information Officer, Cass County Memorial Hospital, Atlantic, IA, p. A225

OSEHOBO, Philip, M.D. Chief Medical Officer, Spalding Regional Hospital, Griffin, GA, p. A160

OSER, William F., M.D. Senior Vice President and Chief Medical Officer, JFK Medical Center, Edison, NJ, p. A416

OSINOWO, Thomas, M.D. Chief Clinical Officer, Northwest Ohio Psychiatric Hospital, Toledo, OH, p. A504

OSINSKI, Kathleen, Chief Human Resources Service, John D. Dingell Veterans Affairs Medical Center, Detroit, MI, p. A322

OSLIN, Dave, M.D. Chief of Staff, Philadelphia Veterans Affairs Medical Center, Philadelphia, PA, p. A549

OSOWSKI, Angela, Chief Nursing Officer, LifeCare Hospitals of Wisconsin, Pewaukee, WI, p. A714

OSSELLO, Susan, Chief Financial Officer, Granite County Medical Center, Philipsburg, MT, p. A390

OSTASZEWSKI, Patricia, MS, Chief Executive Officer, HEALTHSOUTH Rehabilitation Hospital of Toms River, Toms River, NJ, p. A424

OSTBERG, Melissa, Chief Financial Officer, Marias Medical Center, Shelby, MT, p. A391

OSTBLOOM, Jan, Human Resources Consultant, Our Lady of Peace, Louisville, KY, p. A265

OSTEEN, Tom J., Director Area Technology, Kaiser Permanente Manteca Medical Center, Manteca, CA, p. A76

OSTENDORF, Todd, Chief Financial Officer, Children's Hospitals and Clinics of Minnesota, Minneapolis, MN, p. A346

OSTENSON, Scott, Chief Financial Officer, Jacobson Memorial Hospital Care Center, Elgin, ND, p. A478

OSTER, Kurt, Human Resources Officer, Carl Vinson Veterans Affairs Medical Center, Dublin, GA, p. A159

OSTERBERG, Valerie, Chief Financial Officer, Sanford Vermillion Medical Center, Vermillion, SD, p. A577

OSTERHOUT, David, Assistant Superintendent and Chief Financial Officer, El Paso Psychiatric Center, El Paso, TX, p. A615

OSTERLY, Eric, Chief Financial Officer, Florida Hospital Fish Memorial, Orange City, FL, p. A140

OSTLIG, Jane, Chief Medical Officer, Sanford Mayville Medical Center, Mayville, ND, p. A480

OSTRANDER, Maria DC, R.N. Chief Nurse Executive, San Antonio State Hospital, San Antonio, TX, p. A647

OSTRANDER, Michael, Chief Financial Officer, Nathan Littauer Hospital and Nursing Home, Gloversville, NY, p. A439

OSTROW, Peter, M.D. President Medical Staff, Beth Israel Deaconess Hospital–Needham Campus, Needham, MA, p. A312

OSTROWSKY, Barry, President and Chief Executive Officer, RWJBarnabas Health, West Orange, NJ, p. B116

OSWALD, Kathy, Senior Vice President and Chief Human Resources Officer, Henry Ford Hospital, Detroit, MI, p. A322

OSWALD, Traci L., Vice President Human Resources, Galion Community Hospital, Galion, OH, p. A495

OTERO, Jorge Torres, Executive Director, Hospital Del Maestro, San Juan, PR, p. A729

OTHOLE, Jean, Chief Executive Officer, U. S. Public Health Service Indian Hospital, Zuni, NM, p. A432

OTOTIVO, Brenda, Executive Director, Jim Taliaferro Community Mental Health, Lawton, OK, p. A513

OTOTT, Kelly, R.N. Chief Nursing Officer, Washington County Hospital, Washington, KS, p. A255

OTREMBIAK, Robert J., Director of Learning, Southern IL Division, HSHS St. Joseph's Hospital, Breese, IL, p. A182

OTT, Darin, D.O. Chief of Staff, Kane County Hospital, Kanab, UT, p. A660

OTT, Laurie, Vice President Human Resources and President University Health Care Foundation, University Hospital, Augusta, GA, p. A154

OTT, Mark, M.D. Regional Chief Medical Director, Intermountain Medical Center, Murray, UT, p. A661

OTT, Pamela, Vice President Finance, Aurora Sheboygan Memorial Medical Center, Sheboygan, WI, p. A715

OTT, Ronald H.
  President, Excela Frick Hospital, Mount Pleasant, PA, p. A545
  President, Excela Health Westmoreland Hospital, Greensburg, PA, p. A539

OTTATI, David, Chief Executive Officer, Florida Hospital Waterman, Tavares, FL, p. A148

OTTE, Elaine, Chief Operating Officer, Clarinda Regional Health Center, Clarinda, IA, p. A227

OTTEN, Sharon A., Vice President Nursing, Advocate South Suburban Hospital, Hazel Crest, IL, p. A192

OTTENBACHER, John, Chief of Staff, Bowdle Hospital, Bowdle, SD, p. A572

OTTENS, Mark, Chief Nursing Officer, Baptist Memorial Hospital–North Mississippi, Oxford, MS, p. A363

OTTMAR, Kellie, Manager Information Services, East Adams Rural Healthcare, Ritzville, WA, p. A689

OTTO, Sara, Chief Compliance Officer, North Canyon Medical Center, Gooding, ID, p. A176

OTTO, Steve
  Chief Executive Officer, TriStar Skyline Madison Campus, Madison, TN, p. A587
  Chief Executive Officer, TriStar Skyline Medical Center, Nashville, TN, p. A591

OTTOLINO, Joseph, Chief Operating Officer, West Suburban Medical Center, Oak Park, IL, p. A199

OUBRE, Chris, Information Technology Director, Garden Park Medical Center, Gulfport, MS, p. A358

OUELETTE, Lisa, Director Human Resources, Beaumont Hospital – Troy, Troy, MI, p. A336

OUELLETTE, Demetra, Chief Operating Officer, Rehabilitation Hospital of Rhode Island, North Smithfield, RI, p. A560

OUIMET, Mary Elizabeth, MSN Senior Vice President and Chief Nursing Officer, Wheaton Franciscan Healthcare – All Saints, Racine, WI, p. A714

OUNGST, Laurie
  Vice President, Operations, Howard Young Medical Center, Woodruff, WI, p. A720
  Vice President, Operations, Ministry Eagle River Memorial Hospital, Eagle River, WI, p. A704
  Vice President, Operations, Ministry Sacred Heart Hospital, Tomahawk, WI, p. A717
  Vice President and Chief Operating Officer, Ministry Saint Mary's Hospitals, Rhinelander, WI, p. A715

OURS, Matt, Chief Executive Officer and Managing Director, Rivendell Behavioral Health, Bowling Green, KY, p. A258

OUSEY, Tracy, Director Human Resources, Washington County Hospital and Clinics, Washington, IA, p. A238

OUTHIER, Amy, Director Health Information Management, Weatherford Regional Hospital, Weatherford, OK, p. A523

OUTLAW, Debbie, R.N. Director Patient Care Services, Riverside Rehabilitation Institute, Newport News, VA, p. A674

OUZTS, Carey, Director of Nursing, Brentwood Hospital, Shreveport, LA, p. A287

OVANDO, Benjamin, Chief Operations Officer, Rancho Los Amigos National Rehabilitation Center, Downey, CA, p. A61

OVERBEY, William J., Chief Executive Officer, Kansas Rehabilitation Hospital, Topeka, KS, p. A254

OVERBY, Roger, Executive Director Information Systems, Greene County Medical Center, Jefferson, IA, p. A233

OVERCASH, Jenny, Director Human Resources, HEALTHSOUTH Huntington Rehabilitation Hospital, Huntington, WV, p. A696

OVERMAN, David S., President and Chief Operating Officer, Children's Hospitals and Clinics of Minnesota, Minneapolis, MN, p. A346

OVERSTREET, Alyson, Chief Financial Officer, Washington County Hospital, Chatom, AL, p. A18

OVERSTREET, Amy, Director Human Resources, Trousdale Medical Center, Hartsville, TN, p. A584

OVERTON, Deana, Director Human Resources, Mitchell County Hospital, Colorado City, TX, p. A606

OWEN, Christian, Chief Operating Officer, Horsham Clinic, Ambler, PA, p. A532

OWEN, Sabrina, Human Resources Officer, Veterans Affairs Central Iowa Health Care System, Des Moines, IA, p. A230

OWEN, Sandra, Interim Chief Executive Officer, Harper Hospital District Five, Harper, KS, p. A244

OWENS, Beverly, Controller, Rehabilitation Hospital, Navicent Health, Macon, GA, p. A162

OWENS, Brian, Chief Operating Officer, Lindner Center of HOPE, Mason, OH, p. A498

OWENS, Craig A., President, WellStar Douglas Hospital, Douglasville, GA, p. A158

OWENS, Daniel, Chief Executive Officer, Emory University Hospital Midtown, Atlanta, GA, p. A152

OWENS, Johnathan, Chief Executive Officer, Decatur Health Systems, Oberlin, KS, p. A250

OWENS, Jonathan, Chief Executive Officer, Coulee Medical Center, Grand Coulee, WA, p. A685

OWENS, Kevin, Chief Executive Officer, Quartz Mountain Medical Center, Mangum, OK, p. A514

OWENS, Mark, M.D. Vice President Medical Affairs, Mercy San Juan Medical Center, Carmichael, CA, p. A58

OWENS, Rick, Chief Financial Officer, D. W. McMillan Memorial Hospital, Brewton, AL, p. A17

OWENS, Stephanie, Manager Human Resources, McDowell ARH Hospital, McDowell, KY, p. A266

OWENSBY, Karen, R.N. Chief Clinical Officer, Florida Hospital North Pinellas, Tarpon Springs, FL, p. A148

OWENSBY, Terri, R.N. Chief Nursing Executive, Kaiser Permanente South Sacramento Medical Center, Sacramento, CA, p. A86

OWREY, Donald R., President, UPMC Horizon, Greenville, PA, p. A539

OWUSU, Frederick K., Chief Human Resources Officer, Desert Regional Medical Center, Palm Springs, CA, p. A81

OXENDALE, Sharon, Chief Operating Officer, MacNeal Hospital, Berwyn, IL, p. A181

OXFORD, Michelle, Chief Operating Officer, Acting Chief Executive Officer, Bakersfield Heart Hospital, Bakersfield, CA, p. A55

OXFORD, Tammy, Director Human Resources, Bob Wilson Memorial Grant County Hospital, Ulysses, KS, p. A255

OXLEY, Dawn, R.N. Associate Director Patient Care Services and Nurse Executive, Iowa City Veterans Affairs Health Care System, Iowa City, IA, p. A232

OXLEY, James, D.O. Vice President Medical Affairs, Orange Regional Medical Center, Middletown, NY, p. A442

OXLEY, Stephen, M.D. Chief Medical Officer, Central Regional Hospital, Butner, NC, p. A461

OXTON, Alice, Director Information Technology, Sentara Obici Hospital, Suffolk, VA, p. A679

OZBURN, Thomas H., Chief Executive Officer, TriStar Southern Hills Medical Center, Nashville, TN, p. A591

OZEL, A. Deniz, M.D. Chief Medical Director, Northeast Rehabilitation Hospital, Salem, NH, p. A413

OZMENT, Mary, Chief Nursing Officer, AllianceHealth Pryor, Pryor, OK, p. A519

OZUAH, Philip O., M.D. Executive Vice President and Chief Operating Officer, Montefiore Medical Center,, NY, p. A446

P

PAARLBERG, Ted, Chief Executive Officer, Kindred Hospital Peoria, Peoria, IL, p. A200

PAASCH, Michael
Regional Vice President and Chief Information Officer, SSM Cardinal Glennon Children's Medical Center, Saint Louis, MO, p. A381
Vice President, Regional Chief Information Officer, SSM St. Clare Hospital, Fenton, MO, p. A371
Regional Chief Information Officer, SSM St. Mary's Health Center, Saint Louis, MO, p. A381

PABLO, Gary M., M.D. Chief Medical Officer, Sacred Heart Hospital on the Emerald Coast, Miramar Beach, FL, p. A138

PABON, Jose O., Director Operations, Wilma N. Vazquez Medical Center, Vega Baja, PR, p. A730

PABON–RAMIREZ, Felix, Chief Information Officer, St. Charles Hospital, Port Jefferson, NY, p. A453

PACCA, Richard, Chief Medical Staff, Granville Health System, Oxford, NC, p. A471

PACCAPANICCIA, Dominic, Chief Operating Officer, Indiana Regional Medical Center, Indiana, PA, p. A541

PACE, Dewane, Chief Ancillary Operations, Valley View Hospital, Glenwood Springs, CO, p. A106

PACE, Kathleen, MSN Chief Nursing Officer, Englewood Community Hospital, Englewood, FL, p. A128

PACE, Kelly, Director Human Resource, Strategic Behavioral Health – Wilmington, Leland, NC, p. A468

PACEK, Thomas
Vice President Information Systems and Chief Information Officer, Inspira Medical Center–Elmer, Elmer, NJ, p. A416
Vice President Information Systems and Chief Information Officer, Inspira Medical Center–Vineland, Vineland, NJ, p. A425

PACEY, Amy, Vice President Human Resources, Good Samaritan Medical Center, Lafayette, CO, p. A108

PACHECO, Robert W., Vice President Finance, Women & Infants Hospital of Rhode Island, Providence, RI, p. A561

PACHUCKI, Jr., James J., Chief Financial Officer, Sunbury Community Hospital and Outpatient Center, Sunbury, PA, p. A555

PACINI, Jenna, Human Resources Specialist, Belmont Behavioral Hospital, Philadelphia, PA, p. A547

PACK, Kathy, Manager Human Resources, Copper Basin Medical Center, Copperhill, TN, p. A582

PACK, Natalie, Chief Financial Officer, St. David's North Austin Medical Center, Austin, TX, p. A600

PACK, William, Chief Financial Officer, Memorial Hermann – Texas Medical Center, Houston, TX, p. A625

PACK–HOOKFIN, Sherre, Administrator, Lallie Kemp Medical Center, Independence, LA, p. A278

PACKER, Eric, Chief Executive Officer, Cedar City Hospital, Cedar City, UT, p. A659

PACKER, Lee, Administrator, South Florida State Hospital,, FL, p. A130

PACKER, Steven J., M.D., President and Chief Executive Officer, Community Hospital of the Monterey Peninsula, Monterey, CA, p. A77

PACKNETT, Michael J., President and Chief Executive Officer, Parkview Health, Fort Wayne, IN, p. B102

PACURA, Lori, R.N., President, Holy Cross Hospital, Chicago, IL, p. A184

PACZKOWSKI, Rick, Chief Operating Officer, Timberlawn Mental Health System, Dallas, TX, p. A611

PADDEN, Ernest C., Chief Financial Officer, Bon Secours Maryview Medical Center, Portsmouth, VA, p. A676

PADEN, Tawnya, Director Human Resources, Weatherford Regional Hospital, Weatherford, OK, p. A523

PADGETT, Martin, President and Chief Executive Officer, Clark Memorial Hospital, Jeffersonville, IN, p. A215

PADGETT, Shirley, Director Human Resources, Cook Medical Center–A Campus of Tift Regional Medical Center, Adel, GA, p. A151

PADILLA, Gregory, Chief Executive Officer, Gardens Regional Hospital and Medical Center, Hawaiian Gardens, CA, p. A65

PADILLA, Julieta M., Chief Nursing Officer, Hollywood Presbyterian Medical Center, Los Angeles, CA, p. A71

PADILLA, Kathy, Director of Nursing, Marcus Daly Memorial Hospital, Hamilton, MT, p. A388

PADILLA, Rafael, R.N. Chief Nursing Officer, Florida Hospital at Connerton Long Term Acute Care, Land O'Lakes, FL, p. A134

PADULA, Judy, MSN Vice President Patient Care Services and Chief Nursing Officer, St. Joseph's Healthcare System, Paterson, NJ, p. A421

PAFFORD, Roger, M.D. Medical Director, Mineral Community Hospital, Superior, MT, p. A391

PAGANA, Charles C., M.D. Chief Medical Officer, Sunbury Community Hospital and Outpatient Center, Sunbury, PA, p. A555

PAGANELLI, Deborah, President, Texas Health Harris Methodist Hospital Hurst–Euless–Bedford, Bedford, TX, p. A602

PAGE, Alison, Chief Executive Officer, Baldwin Area Medical Center, Baldwin, WI, p. A702

PAGE, Bob, Chief Executive Officer, The University of Kansas Hospital, Kansas City, KS, p. A246

PAGE, Deborah, Chief Human Resources Officer, Duke University Hospital, Durham, NC, p. A464

PAGE, Keith Allen, President and Chief Executive Officer, Anderson Hospital, Maryville, IL, p. A195

PAGE, Nancy E., MS Interim Chief Nursing Officer, Upstate University Hospital, Syracuse, NY, p. A457

PAGE, Pattie, Director Marketing and Public Relations, Eastside Medical Center, Snellville, GA, p. A166

PAGE, III, Robert, Chief Information and Technology Officer, Memphis Veterans Affairs Medical Center, Memphis, TN, p. A589

PAGE, Sue, Director Human Resources, Monroe County Medical Center, Tompkinsville, KY, p. A270

PAGE, Susan M., President and Chief Executive Officer, Pratt Regional Medical Center, Pratt, KS, p. A252

PAGE, William E., CPA Chief Financial Officer, Franklin Medical Center, Winnsboro, LA, p. A289

PAGELER, Robert
Chief Information Officer, Confluence Health/Central Washington Hospital, Wenatchee, WA, p. A693
Chief Information Officer, Confluence Health/Wenatchee Valley Hospital, Wenatchee, WA, p. A693

PAGET, Cindy, Chief Human Resources Officer, Forks Community Hospital, Forks, WA, p. A685

PAGIDIPATI, Devaiah, M.D., Chief Executive Officer, Regional General Hospital, Williston, FL, p. A150

PAGLIUZZA, Greg, Chief Financial Officer, UnityPoint Health – Trinity Bettendorf, Bettendorf, IA, p. A225

PAGNINI, Janie, Administrator Accounting, Atascadero State Hospital, Atascadero, CA, p. A55

PAGUAGA, Ana, Director of Human Resources, Coral Gables Hospital, Coral Gables, FL, p. A126

PAHE, Gary, Manager Human Resources, Sage Memorial Hospital, Ganado, AZ, p. A32

PAHL, Jodi, Chief Nurse Executive, St. Rita's Medical Center, Lima, OH, p. A497

PAIER–MULLAN, Nicole, M.D. Medical Director, Upper Connecticut Valley Hospital, Colebrook, NH, p. A410

PAIGE, Peter G., Chief Medical Officer, Jackson Health System, Miami, FL, p. A136

PAINE, Lincoln, M.D. Medical Director, River Oaks Hospital, New Orleans, LA, p. A285

PAINE, Russ, Human Resources Officer, Murphy Medical Center, Murphy, NC, p. A470

PAINTER, Jeff, Manager Information Technology, Summit Pacific Medical Center, Elma, WA, p. A684

PAKKALA, Mark, Director Human Resources, Spectrum Health Special Care Hospital, Grand Rapids, MI, p. A325

PALADINO, James, Controller, New England Rehabilitation Hospital of Portland, Portland, ME, p. A294

PALAGI, Richard L., Chief Executive Officer, Northeastern Nevada Regional Hospital, Elko, NV, p. A404

PALANGE, Kathleen, R.N., Chief Administrative Officer, Menlo Park Surgical Hospital, Menlo Park, CA, p. A76

PALAZZOLO, Chris
President and Chief Executive Officer, Genesys Regional Medical Center, Grand Blanc, MI, p. A324
Health System President and Chief Executive Officer Mid–Michigan, St. Mary's of Michigan, Saginaw, MI, p. A333
President and Chief Executive Officer, St. Mary's of Michigan Standish Hospital, Standish, MI, p. A335

PALERMO, Robert, Vice President Finance, Ocean Medical Center, Brick Township, NJ, p. A415

PALETTA RN, MPA, NEA–BC, FACHE, Lisa A., R.N. Chief Nursing Officer, Utah Valley Regional Medical Center, Provo, UT, p. A662

PALETZ, Amanda, Director Marketing and Public Relations, LeConte Medical Center, Sevierville, TN, p. A593

PALICKA, Martha, Director Information Systems, Bartlett Regional Hospital, Juneau, AK, p. A29

PALIGO, Terry, Chief Financial Officer, Union County Hospital, Anna, IL, p. A180

PALKOWSKI, Chris, M.D. Physician in Chief, Kaiser Permanente Sacramento Medical Center, Sacramento, CA, p. A86

PALLIN, Angel, Senior Vice President of Operations, Mount Sinai Medical Center, Miami Beach, FL, p. A138

PALMER, Charles, Director Information Technology, Nanticoke Memorial Hospital, Seaford, DE, p. A119

PALMER, Debra L., MS Chief Human Resources Officer and Corporate Compliance Officer, Fairfield Medical Center, Lancaster, OH, p. A496

PALMER, Greg, Administrator Information Technology Network, Care Regional Medical Center, Aransas Pass, TX, p. A597

PALMER, Isaac, Chief Executive Officer, CHRISTUS Health Shreveport–Bossier, Shreveport, LA, p. A287

PALMER, Janel M., Director Human Resources, Greenwood County Hospital, Eureka, KS, p. A243

PALMER, Justin, Administrator, John C. Stennis Memorial Hospital, De Kalb, MS, p. A357

PALMER, Katie, Manager Human Resources, Sanford Aberdeen Medical Center, Aberdeen, SD, p. A572

PALMER, Keith, Assistant Administrator, Winkler County Memorial Hospital, Kermit, TX, p. A630

PALMER, Kelly, D.O. Medical Director, State Hospital South, Blackfoot, ID, p. A174

PALMER, Stephanie, Chief Nursing Officer, HEALTHSOUTH Valley of the Sun Rehabilitation Hospital, Glendale, AZ, p. A33

PALMER, Trisha, Director, St. James Healthcare, Butte, MT, p. A386

PALMIER, Michael L., Chief Human Resources Management, Overton Brooks Veterans Affairs Medical Center, Shreveport, LA, p. A287

PALO, Alan, Chief Financial Officer, Sarah D. Culbertson Memorial Hospital, Rushville, IL, p. A202

PALSROK, Jerri, Manager Business Office, Osceola Community Hospital, Sibley, IA, p. A237

PALUMBO, Michael, D.O. Vice President Medical Affairs and Chief Education, Inland Hospital, Waterville, ME, p. A295

PALUMBO, Michael, M.D. Executive Vice President and Medical Director, White Plains Hospital Center, White Plains, NY, p. A459

PALZER, Douglas C., Chief Executive Officer, Blue Valley Hospital, Overland Park, KS, p. A251

PAM, Brower, Chief Financial Officer, CHRISTUS Spohn Hospital Corpus Christi Memorial, Corpus Christi, TX, p. A607

PAMPERIEN, Linda, Chief Financial Officer, Texas County Memorial Hospital, Houston, MO, p. A372

PANDL, Therese B.
President and Chief Executive Officer, HSHS St. Vincent Hospital, Green Bay, WI, p. A707
President and Chief Executive Officer, St. Mary's Hospital Medical Center, Green Bay, WI, p. A707

PANDOLPH, Philip E., FACHE, Chief Executive Officer, Meadville Medical Center, Meadville, PA, p. A544

PANDOLPH, Philip E., FACHE, Chief Executive Officer, Meadville Medical Center, Meadville, PA, p. B87

PANDYA, Kamel, Director Information Services, San Antonio Regional Hospital, Upland, CA, p. A97

PANDYA, Sherrie, Administrator, Kane County Hospital, Kanab, UT, p. A660

PANICUCCI, Michele
Senior Vice President and Chief Financial Officer, Covenant Medical Center, Waterloo, IA, p. A238
Senior Vice President and Chief Financial Officer, Mercy Hospital of Franciscan Sisters, Oelwein, IA, p. A235
Senior Vice President and Chief Financial Officer, Sartori Memorial Hospital, Cedar Falls, IA, p. A226

PANKEY, Susan Kay, Chief Nursing Officer, Davis County Hospital, Bloomfield, IA, p. A226

PANKOW, Thomas, Chief Information Officer, Jackson Park Hospital and Medical Center, Chicago, IL, p. A184

PANKOWSKI, Charles, Manager Human Resources, Select Specialty Hospital–Columbus, Columbus, OH, p. A491

PANLASIGUI, Bonnie, Chief Administrative Officer, Alameda Hospital, Alameda, CA, p. A54

PANNELL, Ken, Chief Financial Officer, College Station Medical Center, College Station, TX, p. A606

PANNONE, Walter A., Chief Nursing Officer, Venice Regional Bayfront Health, Venice, FL, p. A149

PANNULLO, Ava, M.D. Vice President Medical Services and Physician in Chief, The Hospital at Hebrew Health Care, West Hartford, CT, p. A118

PANSA, Leonard F.
Senior Vice President Human Resources and Administrative Services, Mercy Medical Center, Springfield, MA, p. A315
Senior Vice President, Chief Human Resources Officer, Saint Francis Hospital and Medical Center, Hartford, CT, p. A114

PANTANO, Jane, R.N. Chief Nursing Officer, Pioneer Community Hospital of Stokes, Danbury, NC, p. A463

PANZA Jr., Louis J., President and Chief Executive Officer, Monongahela Valley Hospital, Monongahela, PA, p. A545

PAOLMELLI, Karen, Chief Operating Officer, Madera Community Hospital, Madera, CA, p. A75

PAOLUCCI, Benjamin, D.O. Chief of Staff, Southeast Michigan Surgical Hospital, Warren, MI, p. A336

PAPA, Alan
President, Akron General Medical Center, Akron, OH, p. A483
President and Chief Operating Officer, Edwin Shaw Rehab, Cuyahoga Falls, OH, p. A492
President and Chief Operating Officer, Lodi Community Hospital, Lodi, OH, p. A497

PAPA, AnnMarie, R.N. Vice President and Chief Nursing Officer, Einstein Medical Center Montgomery, East Norriton, PA, p. A537

PAPADAKOS, James, Chief Financial Officer, Signature Healthcare Brockton Hospital, Brockton, MA, p. A308

PAPALIA, John, Chief Executive Officer, HEALTHSOUTH Rehabilitation Hospital of Erie, Erie, PA, p. A538

PAPE, Becky A., R.N., Chief Executive Officer, Good Samaritan Regional Medical Center, Corvallis, OR, p. A525

PAPKA, Lauren, Chief Administrative Officer, St. Mary's Sacred Heart Hospital, Lavonia, GA, p. A162

PAPPAN, Clayton, Director Human Resources and Marketing, South Central Kansas Medical Center, Arkansas City, KS, p. A240

PAPPAS, Charles, M.D. Chief Operating Officer, Bascom Palmer Eye Institute–Anne Bates Leach Eye Hospital, Miami, FL, p. A136

PAPPAS, Kirk, M.D. Physician–in–Chief, Kaiser Permanente Santa Rosa Medical Center, Santa Rosa, CA, p. A94

PAPPAS, Michael, Chief Fiscal Service Officer, Louis Stokes Cleveland Veterans Affairs Medical Center, Cleveland, OH, p. A489

PAPPAS, Sharon H., Ph.D. Chief Nursing Officer, Porter Adventist Hospital, Denver, CO, p. A104

PAPPAS, Sheryl L., Chief Financial Officer, Sanford Webster Medical Center, Webster, SD, p. A577

PAPPAS, Theron, Director Management Information Systems, Holy Family Memorial, Manitowoc, WI, p. A709

PARADIS, Brian, Chief Operating Officer, Florida Hospital, Orlando, FL, p. A140

PARADIS, James, President, Paoli Hospital, Paoli, PA, p. A547

PARADIS, Jeanne, Director Information Services, The Acadia Hospital, Bangor, ME, p. A291

PARAUDA, Martina A., Director, Veterans Affairs New York Harbor Healthcare System,, NY, p. A450

PARAVATE, Chris, Chief Information Officer, Northeast Georgia Medical Center, Gainesville, GA, p. A160

PARAVISINI, Nilda, Director Human Resources, Hospital Manati Medical Center, Manati, PR, p. A728

PARCEL, Jim, Director Information Technology, Maury Regional Hospital, Columbia, TN, p. A581

PARCHER, Adam, Interim Executive Director, UW Medicine/Northwest Hospital & Medical Center, Seattle, WA, p. A690

PARCHMENT, Deborah, Executive Director, Kingsboro Psychiatric Center,, NY, p. A445

PARDUE, Helen, Interim Chief Nursing Officer, Johnson County Community Hospital, Mountain City, TN, p. A590

PAREEK, Yogesh, M.D. Clinical Director, Brown County Community Treatment Center, Green Bay, WI, p. A706

PARENT, Paula A., Chief Nursing Officer and Director of Human Resources, Cary Medical Center, Caribou, ME, p. A292

PARET, Jason, Chief Executive Officer, Catalina Island Medical Center, Avalon, CA, p. A55

PARETI, Donna, Business Unit Chief Financial Officer, Presence Holy Family Medical Center, Des Plaines, IL, p. A188

PARHAM, Eva, R.N. Chief Nurse Executive, Central State Hospital, Petersburg, VA, p. A676

PARHAM, Tracy
Health Care System Chief Information Officer, UNC REX Healthcare, Raleigh, NC, p. A472
University of North Carolina Hospitals, Chapel Hill, NC, p. A462

PARIGI, II, John S., Interim Chief Financial Officer, Healdsburg District Hospital, Healdsburg, CA, p. A66

PARIS, Cynthia K., R.N., President and Chief Executive Officer, Texas Health Presbyterian Hospital of Rockwall, Rockwall, TX, p. A643

PARIS, David, Chief Executive Officer, Perry County General Hospital, Richton, MS, p. A364

PARIS, John, M.D. Chief Medical Officer, Riverview Health, Noblesville, IN, p. A220

PARIS, Karen, Controller, Crittenden County Hospital, Marion, KY, p. A266

PARIS, Sherri, Chief Operating Officer, Providence Milwaukie Hospital, Milwaukie, OR, p. A528

PARIS, Trevor, M.D. Medical Director, Brooks Rehabilitation Hospital, Jacksonville, FL, p. A131

PARISI, James, Chief Executive Officer, Memorial Hermann Katy Hospital, Katy, TX, p. A629

PARISKY, Yuri, M.D. Chief of Staff, Mammoth Hospital, Mammoth Lakes, CA, p. A75

PARK, Bockhi
Chief Executive Officer, Encino Hospital Medical Center,, CA, p. A71
Chief Executive Officer, Sherman Oaks Hospital,, CA, p. A74

PARK, David B., Vice President, General Counsel, Methodist Hospital, Henderson, KY, p. A261

PARK, Denten, Chief Executive Officer, MountainView Regional Medical Center, Las Cruces, NM, p. A430

PARK, Gary L., President, University of North Carolina Hospitals, Chapel Hill, NC, p. A462

PARK, Jessica, Director Accounting, Penn Highlands Brookville, Brookville, PA, p. A534

PARK, Rustin, Director of Nursing, Seven Hills Hospital, Henderson, NV, p. A405

PARKER, Audrey, Budget Analyst, U. S. Public Health Service Indian Hospital, Winnebago, NE, p. A403

PARKER, Cindy, Chief Financial Officer and Director Human Resources, Throckmorton County Memorial Hospital, Throckmorton, TX, p. A653

PARKER, Cythia, Fiscal Director, Washington County Regional Medical Center, Sandersville, GA, p. A165

PARKER, Dan, M.D. Chief of Staff, Winona Health, Winona, MN, p. A353

PARKER, David, VP Information Technology, Magnolia Regional Health Center, Corinth, MS, p. A357

PARKER, Deanna, Director Human Relations, J. Arthur Dosher Memorial Hospital, Southport, NC, p. A474

PARKER, Donald J., President and Chief Executive Officer, Carrier Clinic, Belle Mead, NJ, p. A414

PARKER, Grace E., R.N. Chief Nursing Officer, University of Washington Medical Center, Seattle, WA, p. A690

PARKER, Janie, Chief Financial Officer, Hardin County General Hospital, Rosiclare, IL, p. A202

PARKER, Jon–Michael, R.N. Chief Nursing Officer, Lillian M. Hudspeth Memorial Hospital, Sonora, TX, p. A649

PARKER, Judy Goforth, Ph.D., Secretary of Health, Chickasaw Nation Medical Center, Ada, OK, p. A508

PARKER, Michael, M.D. Chief of Staff, Sharon Hospital, Sharon, CT, p. A116

PARKER, Richard, M.D., President, Marymount Hospital, Garfield Heights, OH, p. A495

PARKER, Robert, Chief Executive Officer, Meadowview Regional Medical Center, Maysville, KY, p. A266

PARKER, Sandra K., M.D. Chief Medical Officer, EastPointe Hospital, Daphne, AL, p. A18

PARKER, Theresa M., Regional Finance Director, Transylvania Regional Hospital, Brevard, NC, p. A461

PARKER, Thomas, Chief Executive Officer, Snoqualmie Valley Hospital District, Snoqualmie, WA, p. A690

PARKER, Tina, Director Human Resources, HEALTHSOUTH Rehabilitation Hospital Midland–Odessa, Midland, TX, p. A637

PARKER, Travis, Chief Human Resources, Southwest Memorial Hospital, Cortez, CO, p. A103

PARKER, Valerie, M.D. Clinical Director, U. S. Public Health Service Indian Hospital, Rosebud, SD, p. A576

PARKEY, Kasey, Coordinator Payroll and Benefits, Post Acute Medical Specialty Hospital of Corpus Christi – South, Corpus Christi, TX, p. A608

PARKHILL, Cherie, Chief Financial Officer, Crosbyton Clinic Hospital, Crosbyton, TX, p. A608

PARKHURST, James E., President and Chief Executive Officer, Newport Bay Hospital, Newport Beach, CA, p. A79

PARKINSON, Justin, M.D. President Medical Staff, Jordan Valley Medical Center West Valley Campus, West Valley City, UT, p. A664

PARKINSON, Michelle A., Director Human Resources, Prairie St. John's, Fargo, ND, p. A478

PARKS, Audrey, Senior Administrative Director Information Technology, Salinas Valley Memorial Healthcare System, Salinas, CA, p. A87

PARKS, Cary, Chief Information Resource Management, Hampton Veterans Affairs Medical Center, Hampton, VA, p. A671

PARKS, Dave, Chief Information Officer, Three Rivers Health, Three Rivers, MI, p. A335

PARKS, Ginger, Director Human Resources, Cape Fear Valley – Bladen County Hospital, Elizabethtown, NC, p. A465

PARKS, Jody, Administrator, Ottawa County Health Center, Minneapolis, KS, p. A249

PARKS, Kathi, Director of Nursing, South Lincoln Medical Center, Kemmerer, WY, p. A722

PARKS, Kyle, M.D. Chief of Staff, Evans Memorial Hospital, Claxton, GA, p. A156

PARKS, Michelle, Administrator, RiverValley Behavioral Health Hospital, Owensboro, KY, p. A267

PARKS, Richard H., FACHE, President and Chief Executive Officer, Covenant Health System, Lubbock, TX, p. B43

PARKS, Sherry, R.N. Chief Nursing Officer, Saint Alphonsus Regional Medical Center, Boise, ID, p. A174

PARKS, Vicki, Chief Financial Officer, Jackson Purchase Medical Center, Mayfield, KY, p. A266

PARLIKAR, Deven, President and Chief Executive Officer, San Carlos Apache Healthcare Corporation, Peridot, AZ, p. A35

PARMER, David N., Chief Executive Officer, Baptist Hospitals of Southeast Texas, Beaumont, TX, p. A601

PARMER, Michael, Chief Medical Officer, CarePartners Health Services, Asheville, NC, p. A460

PARNEL, George, Chief Financial Officer, Clifton T. Perkins Hospital Center, Jessup, MD, p. A301

PAROSKI, Margaret, M.D. Executive Vice President and Chief Medical Officer, KALEIDA Health, Buffalo, NY, p. A436

PARR, James
Chief Financial Officer, Salem Health West Valley, Dallas, OR, p. A525
Chief Financial Officer, Salem Hospital, Salem, OR, p. A530

PARR, Lynnette, Chief Financial Officer, Down East Community Hospital, Machias, ME, p. A294

PARRA, Kristin, Chief Nursing Officer, Yuma Rehabilitation Hospital, Yuma, AZ, p. A42

PARRA, Michelle, Director Human Resources, Kindred Hospital South Bay, Gardena, CA, p. A64

PARRINELLO, Kathleen M., Ph.D. Chief Operating Officer, Strong Memorial Hospital of the University of Rochester, Rochester, NY, p. A454

PARRISH, Becky, Director Human Resources, Southern Virginia Regional Medical Center, Emporia, VA, p. A669

PARRISH, Carl, Chief Fiscal Service, James E. Van Zandt Veterans Affairs Medical Center, Altoona, PA, p. A532

PARRISH, James G., FACHE, Chief Executive Officer, Humboldt General Hospital, Winnemucca, NV, p. A409

PARRISH, Pamela, Director Information Systems, Novant Health Brunswick Medical Center, Bolivia, NC, p. A461

PARRISH, Suann, Chief Financial Officer, Yoakum County Hospital, Denver City, TX, p. A613

PARRISH, Todd, M.D. Chief of Staff, East Texas Medical Center Jacksonville, Jacksonville, TX, p. A629

PARRY, Mary, Vice President Operations and Chief Operating Officer, Oneida Healthcare, Oneida, NY, p. A452

PARRY, Timothy, R.N. Chief Operating Officer, Highland District Hospital, Hillsboro, OH, p. A496

PARSLEY, George N., Chief Operating Officer, DeTar Healthcare System, Victoria, TX, p. A655

PARSON, Charlynne, Nurse Executive, Moccasin Bend Mental Health Institute, Chattanooga, TN, p. A580

PARSONS, Brad, FACHE, Administrator and Chief Executive Officer, NEA Baptist Memorial Hospital, Jonesboro, AR, p. A48

PARSONS, Debra, Chief Nursing Officer, Pikeville Medical Center, Pikeville, KY, p. A268

PARSONS, John, R.N. Chief Nursing Officer, TrustPoint Rehabilitation Hospital of Lubbock, Lubbock, TX, p. A634

PARSONS, Terri L., Administrator, Advanced Care Hospital of White County, Searcy, AR, p. A52

PARTEE, Paris I., Associate Administrator and Director Human Resources, John H. Stroger Jr. Hospital of Cook County, Chicago, IL, p. A184

PARTENZA, John, Vice President and Treasurer, Northern Westchester Hospital, Mount Kisco, NY, p. A443

PARTHEMORE, Warrenette, Director Human Resources, ProMedica Memorial Hospital, Fremont, OH, p. A495

PARTIN, James R., M.D. Chief Medical Director, Hill Country Memorial Hospital, Fredericksburg, TX, p. A619

PARTRIDGE, Susan, Director Human Resources, Nantucket Cottage Hospital, Nantucket, MA, p. A312

PARUCH, Randy J., Director, Information Systems, Holland Hospital, Holland, MI, p. A326

PASCASCIO, Dellone, Chief Nursing Officer, LAC–Olive View–UCLA Medical Center,, CA, p. A72

PASCASIO, Robert A., FACHE, Administrator and Chief Executive Officer, Ochiltree General Hospital, Perryton, TX, p. A641

PASCH, Deborah, Chief Nurse Executive, University of Missouri Hospitals and Clinics, Columbia, MO, p. A370

PASCO, Teri, Director Human Resources, East Liverpool City Hospital, East Liverpool, OH, p. A494

PASCOE, John, M.D. Executive Medical Director, Timberlawn Mental Health System, Dallas, TX, p. A611

PASCUAL, Bolivar, M.D. Medical Director, Essex County Hospital Center, Cedar Grove, NJ, p. A415

PASCUZZI, Robert, Chief Financial Officer, Mercy San Juan Medical Center, Carmichael, CA, p. A58

PASQUIN, Karen, Chief Nursing Officer, Southwest Memorial Hospital, Cortez, CO, p. A103

PASS, Christian
 Senior Vice President and Chief Financial Officer, John Muir Behavioral Health Center, Concord, CA, p. A59
 Interim Chief Financial Officer, John Muir Medical Center, Concord, Concord, CA, p. A59
 Senior Vice President & Chief Financial Officer, John Muir Medical Center, Walnut Creek, Walnut Creek, CA, p. A99

PASSANNANTE, Jr., Anthony, M.D. Vice President, Chief Medical Officer and Co–Chief Quality Officer, Saint Peter's University Hospital, New Brunswick, NJ, p. A420

PASSARELLI, Theresa, Human Resources Generalist, Warm Springs Medical Center, Warm Springs, GA, p. A168

PASSMANN, Frederic K., M.D. Chief of Staff, Stonewall Memorial Hospital, Aspermont, TX, p. A598

PASSMORE, Gary, Chief Information Officer, Endless Mountain Health Systems, Montrose, PA, p. A545

PASTERNAK, L. Reuven, M.P.H., Vice President for Health System and Chief Executive Officer, Stony Brook University Hospital, Stony Brook, NY, p. A456

PASTIAN, Andre, R.N. Chief Nursing Officer, Boulder City Hospital, Boulder City, NV, p. A404

PASTORE, Raymond, M.D. Chief Medical Officer, St. John's Episcopal Hospital–South Shore,, NY, p. A450

PASTRANA, Guillermo, Executive Director, Hospital Pavia–Hato Rey, San Juan, PR, p. A729

PASZTOR, Barbara J., R.N
 Vice President Patient Care Services and Chief Nursing Officer, Blanchard Valley Hospital, Findlay, OH, p. A494
 Vice President Nursing and Patient Care Services, Bluffton Hospital, Bluffton, OH, p. A485

PATCHELL, Lee, Lead Human Resources Business Partner, Presbyterian Hospital, Albuquerque, NM, p. A428

PATCHIN, J. Craig, Administrator, Shriners Hospitals for Children–Portland, Portland, OR, p. A530

PATE, David C., JD, President and Chief Executive Officer, St. Luke's Health System, Boise, ID, p. B128

PATE, John, M.D. Chief Medical Officer, Tri–County Hospital, Wadena, MN, p. A353

PATE, Lois, R.N. Chief Nursing Officer, Island Hospital, Anacortes, WA, p. A682

PATEL, Amita, M.D. Medical Director, Haven Behavioral Senior Care of Dayton, Dayton, OH, p. A492

PATEL, Ashok, M.D. Chief of Staff, Sanford Medical Center Thief River Falls, Thief River Falls, MN, p. A352

PATEL, Ben
 Chief Information Officer, Holy Cross Hospital, Chicago, IL, p. A184
 Chief Information Officer, Mount Sinai Hospital, Chicago, IL, p. A185

PATEL, Bimal
 President, Hartford HealthCare East Region, The William W. Backus Hospital, Norwich, CT, p. A116
 President, Hartford Healthcare East Region, Windham Hospital, Willimantic, CT, p. A118

PATEL, Binesh, Chief Medical Officer, DMC Huron Valley–Sinai Hospital, Commerce Township, MI, p. A321

PATEL, Deepak, M.D. Medical Director, Cumberland Hall Hospital, Hopkinsville, KY, p. A261

PATEL, Dilip, M.D. Chief of Staff, Greater El Monte Community Hospital, South El Monte, CA, p. A95

PATEL, Fatma, M.D. Vice President Medical Affairs, Niagara Falls Memorial Medical Center, Niagara Falls, NY, p. A451

PATEL, Govind, M.D. Medical Director, HEALTHSOUTH MountainView Regional Rehabilitation Hospital, Morgantown, WV, p. A698

PATEL, Hema, Director Medical Records, RiverWoods Behavioral Health System, Riverdale, GA, p. A164

PATEL, Hirat, M.D. Chief Operating Officer, Lakeview Regional Medical Center, Covington, LA, p. A275

PATEL, Malini, M.D. Medical Director, Elgin Mental Health Center, Elgin, IL, p. A189

PATEL, Natu M., M.D. Chief of Staff, Phoebe Worth Medical Center, Sylvester, GA, p. A167

PATEL, Nayan, Director Information Systems, The Heart Hospital Baylor Plano, Plano, TX, p. A642

PATEL, Nirav, M.D
 Chief of Staff, Los Alamitos Medical Center, Los Alamitos, CA, p. A70
 Interim Chief Medical Officer, SSM Health Saint Louis University Hospital, Saint Louis, MO, p. A381

PATEL, Paryus, M.D. Chief Medical Officer, Centinela Hospital Medical Center, Inglewood, CA, p. A66

PATEL, Prakash Chandra, M.D. Chief of Staff, Kindred Hospital–La Mirada, La Mirada, CA, p. A67

PATEL, Pravin, M.D. Acting President and Chief Executive Officer, Southern Virginia Mental Health Institute, Danville, VA, p. A669

PATEL, Pravinchandra, M.D. Chief Medical Officer, Barnes–Kasson County Hospital, Susquehanna, PA, p. A555

PATEL, Raj, M.D. Medical Director, LifeCare Hospitals of Chester County, West Chester, PA, p. A557

PATEL, Rajesh, M.D. Chief of Staff, Lock Haven Hospital, Lock Haven, PA, p. A543

PATEL, Rakesh, D.O. Medical Director, HEALTHSOUTH Rehabilitation Hospital of Altoona, Altoona, PA, p. A532

PATEL, Shalin, M.D. Chief Medical Officer, Memorial Hermann Rehabilitation Hospital – Katy, Katy, TX, p. A630

PATEL, Sharad, M.D. Medical Director, Florida Hospital at Connerton Long Term Acute Care, Land O'Lakes, FL, p. A134

PATEL, Shatish, M.D. Chief Medical Officer, Atrium Medical Center, Stafford, TX, p. A649

PATEL, Suresh, M.D. Chief Medical Officer, Cavalier County Memorial Hospital and Clinics, Langdon, ND, p. A480

PATEL, Viraj, M.D. Chief Medical Officer, Unity Medical & Surgical Hospital, Mishawaka, IN, p. A218

PATER, Tom
 Vice President Finance and Chief Financial Officer, RML Specialty Hospital, Chicago, IL, p. A186
 Chief Financial Officer, RML Specialty Hospital, Hinsdale, IL, p. A193

PATEY, Jeffrey A., M.D. Chief of Staff, Belmont Community Hospital, Bellaire, OH, p. A484

PATHAK, Ajay, President, OSF Saint Anthony's Health Center, Alton, IL, p. A180

PATHAK, Rajiv, Chief of Staff, Marshall Medical Center, Placerville, CA, p. A83

PATIL, Steve, Chief Financial Officer, W. G. (Bill) Heffner Veterans Affairs Medical Center, Salisbury, NC, p. A473

PATILLO, Laura, Manager Human Resources, Fresno Surgical Hospital, Fresno, CA, p. A63

PATINO, Beth, Chief Information Officer, DeKalb Medical at North Decatur, Decatur, GA, p. A158

PATINO, Michelle, Chief Executive Officer, Cumberland Surgical Hospital, San Antonio, TX, p. A645

PATONAI, Steven D., Interim Chief Executive Officer, Park Plaza Hospital, Houston, TX, p. A626

PATRICIO, Jr., Mars, Chief Financial Officer, Seven Hills Hospital, Henderson, NV, p. A405

PATRICK, Ann M., Vice President Human Resources, Northwest Community Hospital, Arlington Heights, IL, p. A180

PATRICK, Barbara, Director Human Resources, Chestatee Regional Hospital, Dahlonega, GA, p. A157

PATRICK, II, Calvin, Director Information Services, Florida Hospital New Smyrna, New Smyrna Beach, FL, p. A139

PATRICK, Chad, President and Chief Executive Officer, Orange Park Medical Center, Orange Park, FL, p. A140

PATRICK, Christian C., M.D. Chief Medical Officer, Baptist Memorial Hospital – Memphis, Memphis, TN, p. A588

PATRICK, Deborah A.
 Senior Vice President Human Resources, Lehigh Valley Hospital, Allentown, PA, p. A532
 Senior Vice President Human Resources, Lehigh Valley Hospital–Muhlenberg, Bethlehem, PA, p. A533

PATRICK, Devin, Manager Human Resources, Utah State Hospital, Provo, UT, p. A662

PATRICK, Lisa, Chief Operating Officer, Caldwell Memorial Hospital, Columbia, LA, p. A275

PATRICK, Ronald, Chief Financial Officer, Northwest Medical Center, Tucson, AZ, p. A40

PATRICK, Sandra, Chief Financial Officer, Three Rivers Hospital, Waverly, TN, p. A594

PATRICK, Sean, Director Information Systems, Gifford Medical Center, Randolph, VT, p. A666

PATRICK, Teresa, Human Resources Director, Ashe Memorial Hospital, Jefferson, NC, p. A468

PATRIZIO, Gino, Chief Executive Officer, Rideout Memorial Hospital, Marysville, CA, p. A76

PATTEN Jr., William D., Chief Executive Officer, Holy Cross Hospital, Taos, NM, p. A432

PATTERSON, Anthony, FACHE, Senior Vice President Inpatient Services, University of Alabama Hospital, Birmingham, AL, p. A17

PATTERSON, Barbara, Chief Financial Officer, Provident Hospital of Cook County, Chicago, IL, p. A186

PATTERSON, Benjamin, Chief Executive Officer, Fairway Medical Surgical Hospital, Covington, LA, p. A275

PATTERSON, Christina, Chief Financial Officer, Saint Thomas River Park Hospital, Mc Minnville, TN, p. A588

PATTERSON, Dave, Chief Information Officer, Memorial Hospital of Converse County, Douglas, WY, p. A722

PATTERSON, David, Director Human Resources, Parkside Psychiatric Hospital and Clinic, Tulsa, OK, p. A521

PATTERSON, Debbie, Director Health Information Management, Wesley Rehabilitation Hospital, Wichita, KS, p. A256

PATTERSON, Diane, Vice President, Chief Nursing Officer, Yakima Valley Memorial Hospital, Yakima, WA, p. A693

PATTERSON, Elmore, Chief Executive Officer, Greene County Health System, Eutaw, AL, p. A19

PATTERSON, Jan, Chief Nursing Officer, Avera St. Luke's Hospital, Aberdeen, SD, p. A572

PATTERSON, Jeff, Chief Executive Officer, Nacogdoches Medical Center, Nacogdoches, TX, p. A638

PATTERSON, Karen, Deputy Director Operations, Elmira Psychiatric Center, Elmira, NY, p. A438

PATTERSON, Larry R., Deputy Commander Administration, Bayne–Jones Army Community Hospital, Fort Polk, LA, p. A277

PATTERSON, Lisa, Director Human Resources, Pointe Coupee General Hospital, New Roads, LA, p. A285

PATTERSON, Marcia
 Chief Nursing Officer, Nor–Lea General Hospital, Lovington, NM, p. A430
 Chief Financial Officer, Valley Regional Medical Center, Brownsville, TX, p. A604

PATTERSON, Maria, Manager Health Information Management, Canyon Ridge Hospital, Chino, CA, p. A58

PATTERSON, Mark, M.D. Chief Medical Officer, Laughlin Memorial Hospital, Greeneville, TN, p. A583

PATTERSON, Michael C., Chief Executive Officer, Flint River Community Hospital, Montezuma, GA, p. A163

PATTERSON, Michael N., Chief Executive Officer, Havasu Regional Medical Center, Lake Havasu City, AZ, p. A34

PATTERSON, Mike, Director of Operations, Northside Hospital–Cherokee, Canton, GA, p. A155

PATTERSON, Renee A., Vice President Employment and Training Services, Rogers Memorial Hospital, Oconomowoc, WI, p. A713

PATTERSON, Robert, Vice President Human Resources and Rehabilitation Services, The University of Vermont Health Network Central Vermont Medical Center, Berlin, VT, p. A665

PATTERSON, Russ
 Site Manager Information Technology, St. Rose Dominican Hospitals – San Martin Campus, Las Vegas, NV, p. A406
 Director Information Technology, St. Rose Dominican Hospitals – Siena Campus, Henderson, NV, p. A405

PATTERSON, Sam, Chief Financial Officer, Bay Area Hospital, Coos Bay, OR, p. A525

PATTERSON, Steve, Chief Executive Officer, Kindred Hospital–Chattanooga, Chattanooga, TN, p. A580

PATTERSON, Stuart, M.D. Chief of Staff, Bartow Regional Medical Center, Bartow, FL, p. A123

PATTERSON, Tony, Chief Financial Officer, James B. Haggin Memorial Hospital, Harrodsburg, KY, p. A261

PATTERSON, DNP, Melanie, R.N. Vice President Patient Care Services and Chief Nursing Officer, Children's Hospital of Orange County, Orange, CA, p. A81

PATTI, Rosa, Chief Financial Officer, Cameron Regional Medical Center, Cameron, MO, p. A368

PATTON, Christina, Chief Financial Officer, Colorado Plains Medical Center, Fort Morgan, CO, p. A105

PATTON, Daniel, Director Information Systems, Henrico Doctors' Hospital, Richmond, VA, p. A677

PATTON, David J., President, UPMC St. Margaret, Pittsburgh, PA, p. A552

PATTON, Joy, Chief Information Services, Pampa Regional Medical Center, Pampa, TX, p. A640

PATTON, Kevin, Chief Executive Officer, Old Vineyard Behavioral Health Services, Winston–Salem, NC, p. A476

PATTON, Meghan
 Vice President Human Resources, Abington Hospital, Abington, PA, p. A532
 Vice President Human Resources, Abington–Lansdale Hospital Jefferson Health, Lansdale, PA, p. A542

PATTON, Melissa, MSN Director of Nursing, Dublin Springs, Dublin, OH, p. A494

PATTON, Sally K., R.N. Chief Nursing Officer, New London Hospital, New London, NH, p. A412

PATTON, William
Chief Executive Officer, Kindred Hospital– Oklahoma City, Oklahoma City, OK, p. A516
Chief Executive Officer, Kindred Hospital–San Antonio, San Antonio, TX, p. A646
PATZEK, Dorothy, Vice President Nursing, Blue Mountain Hospital, Lehighton, PA, p. A543
PAUL, Adam, Chief Financial Officer, Prairie Lakes Healthcare System, Watertown, SD, p. A577
PAUL, Darrick, Chief People Officer, MUSC Medical Center of Medical University of South Carolina, Charleston, SC, p. A563
PAUL, Donn, Chief Human Resources, Lackey Memorial Hospital, Forest, MS, p. A358
PAUL, Eric, Interim Chief Executive Officer, Mountain Vista Medical Center, Mesa, AZ, p. A34
PAUL, Joseph, Chief Financial Officer, Wellington Regional Medical Center, West Palm Beach, FL, p. A150
PAUL, Lise, Vice President Reimbursement and Network Planning, Hebrew Rehabilitation Center, Boston, MA, p. A307
PAUL, Mary
Chief Information Officer, Columbia St. Mary's Hospital Milwaukee, Milwaukee, WI, p. A711
Chief Information Officer, Columbia St. Mary's Ozaukee Hospital, Mequon, WI, p. A710
Vice President and Chief Information Officer, Sacred Heart Rehabilitation Institute, Milwaukee, WI, p. A711
PAUL, West, M.D
Senior Vice President, Chief Quality and Medical Staff Officer, WakeMed Cary Hospital, Cary, NC, p. A462
Senior Vice President and Chief Quality and Medical Staff Officer, WakeMed Raleigh Campus, Raleigh, NC, p. A472
PAULEY, Clarence, Senior Vice President and Chief Human Resources Officer, University of Cincinnati Medical Center, Cincinnati, OH, p. A488
PAULK, Tena, R.N. Program Director and Director Nursing, Bastrop Rehabilitation Hospital, Monroe, LA, p. A283
PAULOSKY, David, Chief Financial Officer, Phoenixville Hospital, Phoenixville, PA, p. A550
PAULS, Scott R., Director Information Technology– HealthNet Connect, Guttenberg Municipal Hospital, Guttenberg, IA, p. A231
PAULSEN, Susan, Director Human Resources, Northridge Hospital Medical Center,, CA, p. A73
PAULSON, Adam, Director Finance, CentraCare Health–Melrose, Melrose, MN, p. A346
PAULSON, Erik, Director of Finance, J. D. McCarty Center for Children With Developmental Disabilities, Norman, OK, p. A515
PAULSON, Gordon, Manager Human Resources, Glacial Ridge Health System, Glenwood, MN, p. A343
PAULSON, Mark E., Chief Executive Officer, Chippewa County–Montevideo Hospital, Montevideo, MN, p. A347
PAULSON, Sybil K., Administrator, North Oaks Rehabilitation Hospital, Hammond, LA, p. A277
PAULUS, Ronald A., M.D., President and Chief Executive Officer, Mission Health System, Asheville, NC, p. B91
PAULUS, Terri
Chief Nursing Officer, Banner Goldfield Medical Center, Apache Junction, AZ, p. A31
Chief Nursing Officer, Banner Ironwood Medical Center, San Tan Valley, AZ, p. A38
PAUTLER, J. Stephen, FACHE Chief Operating Officer, Peterson Regional Medical Center, Kerrville, TX, p. A630
PAVALONIS, Diane, Chief Nurse Executive, Western State Hospital, Staunton, VA, p. A679
PAVIA, Antoine, M.D. Medical Director, Hospital Dr. Cayetano Coll Y Toste, Arecibo, PR, p. A726
PAVIK, Sarah, Director Human Resources and Guest Services, Inova Loudoun Hospital, Leesburg, VA, p. A672
PAVILANIS, Charlotte J., R.N. Vice President of Clinical Services and Chief Nursing Officer, Sturgis Hospital, Sturgis, MI, p. A335
PAVLATOS, Thales, Medical Director, Ohio Valley Surgical Hospital, Springfield, OH, p. A502
PAWAR, Ganesh, M.D. Chief of Staff, Rusk County Memorial Hospital, Ladysmith, WI, p. A708
PAWLAK, Paul, President and Chief Executive Officer, Silver Cross Hospital, New Lenox, IL, p. A198
PAWLEK, Kenny, Chief Operating Officer, USC Verdugo Hills Hospital, Glendale, CA, p. A65
PAWLOWICZ, James E., Director Human Resources, Shriners Hospitals for Children–Chicago, Chicago, IL, p. A186
PAWLOWSKI, Phil, Chief Financial Officer, Glenbeigh Hospital and Outpatient Centers, Rock Creek, OH, p. A502
PAWOLA, Ken
Chief Operating Officer, RML Specialty Hospital, Chicago, IL, p. A186
Chief Operating Officer, RML Specialty Hospital, Hinsdale, IL, p. A193

PAXSON, Gary
Associate Administrator Information Systems, Stone County Medical Center, Mountain View, AR, p. A50
Chief Information Officer, White River Medical Center, Batesville, AR, p. A43
PAYNE, Angel, Clinical Director, Director of Nursing, Sonora Behavioral Health Hospital, Tucson, AZ, p. A41
PAYNE, Gary, Chief Executive Officer, Cardinal Hill Rehabilitation Hospital, Lexington, KY, p. A263
PAYNE, James, Director Information Systems, Southern Tennessee Regional Health System–Winchester, Winchester, TN, p. A594
PAYNE, Jason, Executive Vice President and Chief Operating Officer, Rush Foundation Hospital, Meridian, MS, p. A362
PAYNE, Judy H., Chief Executive Officer, Turning Point Hospital, Moultrie, GA, p. A164
PAYNE, Keela, Director Human Resources, Hamilton General Hospital, Hamilton, TX, p. A622
PAYNE, Kenneth G., Chief Financial Officer, Holzer Medical Center, Gallipolis, OH, p. A495
PAYNE, Michael, M.D. Chief of Staff, Dallas County Medical Center, Fordyce, AR, p. A46
PAYNE, Michael E., Administrator, Girard Medical Center, Girard, KS, p. A243
PAYNE, Rick, Director Information Systems, Santa Rosa Medical Center, Milton, FL, p. A138
PAYNE, Steven, Chief Financial Officer, Jordan Valley Medical Center West Valley Campus, West Valley City, UT, p. A664
PAYTON, Becky J., Vice President Human Resources, Mercy Hospital Oklahoma City, Oklahoma City, OK, p. A516
PAZDERNIK, Mary, Chief Financial Officer, Mahnomen Health Center, Mahnomen, MN, p. A345
PEA, Richard, Director Human Resources, Memorial Hospital and Health Care Center, Jasper, IN, p. A215
PEABODY, Kim, Chief Operating Officer, The Brook Hospital – KMI, Louisville, KY, p. A265
PEABODY, Paul, Vice President Information Technology and Chief Information Officer, Bronson LakeView Hospital, Paw Paw, MI, p. A331
PEACE III, Lother E., President and Chief Executive Officer, Russell Medical Center, Alexander City, AL, p. A15
PEACH, Larry, Chief Financial Officer, Jefferson County Health Center, Fairfield, IA, p. A230
PEACH, Susan M., R.N., Chief Executive Officer, Sumner Regional Medical Center, Gallatin, TN, p. A583
PEACOCK, Steve, Assistant Vice President, Plaza Specialty Hospital, Houston, TX, p. A626
PEAL, Chip, Chief Executive Officer, Frankfort Regional Medical Center, Frankfort, KY, p. A260
PEARCE, Charles T.
Chief Financial and Information Officer, Kalispell Regional Healthcare, Kalispell, MT, p. A389
Chief Financial and Information Officer, The HealthCenter, Kalispell, MT, p. A389
PEARCE, Darren
Administrator and Chief Executive Officer, Medical Center of Peach County, Navicent Health, Bryon, GA, p. A155
Chief Executive Officer, Monroe County Hospital, Forsyth, GA, p. A159
Executive Director, Rehabilitation Hospital, Navicent Health, Macon, GA, p. A162
PEARCE, Margaret, R.N. Chief Nursing Officer, University of Utah Health Care – Hospital and Clinics, Salt Lake City, UT, p. A664
PEARCH, William, Chief Information Officer, Yukon–Kuskokwim Delta Regional Hospital, Bethel, AK, p. A28
PEARCY, Joetta J., Director, Human Resources, Glendive Medical Center, Glendive, MT, p. A387
PEARCY, Steve, Director Human Resources, Community Hospital North, Indianapolis, IN, p. A213
PEARLMAN, Helen, Nurse Executive, Minneapolis Veterans Affairs Health Care System, Minneapolis, MN, p. A346
PEARSON, Bruce, Senior Vice President and Chief Operating Officer, HonorHealth Scottsdale Thompson Peak Medical Center, Scottsdale, AZ, p. A39
PEARSON, Christine, Vice President Finance and Chief Financial Officer, AnMed Health Medical Center, Anderson, SC, p. A562
PEARSON, Dawn, Director Human Resources, HEALTHSOUTH Rehabilitation Hospital of Vineland, Vineland, NJ, p. A424
PEARSON, Debra, Chief Financial Officer, Jonathan M. Wainwright Memorial Veterans Affairs Medical Center, Walla Walla, WA, p. A692
PEARSON, Gregory, Chief Executive Officer, Merit Health River Region, Vicksburg, MS, p. A365
PEARSON, Jeff
Chief Information Officer, CHRISTUS Mother Frances Hospital – Jacksonville, Jacksonville, TX, p. A629
Vice President and Chief Information Officer, CHRISTUS Mother Frances Hospital – Tyler, Tyler, TX, p. A654

PEARSON, Marshall, Director Management Information Systems, St. David's North Austin Medical Center, Austin, TX, p. A600
PEARSON, Matthew Paul
Chief Executive Officer, Select Specialty Hospital – Northeast Atlanta, Atlanta, GA, p. A153
Chief Executive Officer, Select Specialty Hospital–Atlanta, Atlanta, GA, p. A153
PEARSON, Susan, M.D. Chief Medical Officer, Mayo Clinic Health System in Mankato, Mankato, MN, p. A345
PEART, Carol, Chief Financial Officer, Chicago Lakeshore Hospital, Chicago, IL, p. A183
PEBURN, Eric, Chief Financial Officer, Halifax Health Medical Center of Daytona Beach, Daytona Beach, FL, p. A127
PECHOUS, Bryan, M.D. Vice President Medical Affairs, UnityPoint Health – Finley Hospital, Dubuque, IA, p. A230
PECK, Bob, Chief Financial Officer, Wesley Rehabilitation Hospital, Wichita, KS, p. A256
PECK, Charles A., M.D., Interim President and Chief Executive Officer, Athens Regional Medical Center, Athens, GA, p. A151
PECK, Darin, M.D. Chief of Staff, Charles A. Dean Memorial Hospital, Greenville, ME, p. A293
PECK, Michael D., Assistant Administrator, Caribou Memorial Hospital and Living Center, Soda Springs, ID, p. A178
PECK, Robert C., M.D. Chief Medical Officer, Mayo Clinic Health System in Eau Claire, Eau Claire, WI, p. A704
PEDANO, Andrea D., D.O. Chief Medical Officer, Suburban Community Hospital, Norristown, PA, p. A546
PEDERSEN, Darren, Coordinator Information Technology, Weisman Children's Rehabilitation Hospital, Marlton, NJ, p. A419
PEDERSEN, Paul E., M.D. Vice President and Chief Medical Officer, OSF St. Joseph Medical Center, Bloomington, IL, p. A181
PEDERSON, Bryan, Human Resources Manager, Tri–County Hospital, Wadena, MN, p. A353
PEDERSON, Karn, Manager Health Information Management, McKenzie County Healthcare System, Watford City, ND, p. A482
PEDERSON, Randall K., Chief Executive Officer, Tioga Medical Center, Tioga, ND, p. A481
PEDLEY, Joe, CPA Vice President and Chief Financial Officer, Lawrence Memorial Hospital, Lawrence, KS, p. A247
PEDLOW, Bernadette R., Senior Vice President Business and Chief Operating Officer, Albany Medical Center, Albany, NY, p. A433
PEDRETTI, Jennalee, Vice President Operations, Regional Health Services of Howard County, Cresco, IA, p. A228
PEDROZA, Fernando, Vice President Information Technology, Poudre Valley Hospital, Fort Collins, CO, p. A105
PEEBLES, Wanda V., Chief Nursing Officer, JPS Health Network, Fort Worth, TX, p. A618
PEEK, Doris, Chief Information Officer, Broward Health Imperial Point, Fort Lauderdale, FL, p. A128
PEEK, Scott, FACHE, President, Baylor Medical Center at McKinney, McKinney, TX, p. A636
PEELER, Cindy K., R.N. Chief Nursing Officer, Adair County Memorial Hospital, Greenfield, IA, p. A231
PEELGREN, Jim, Chief Information Officer, Tulare Regional Medical Center, Tulare, CA, p. A97
PEEPLES, John, Senior Vice President Human Resources, Laurel Regional Hospital, Laurel, MD, p. A302
PEER, Julie, President, Penn Highlands Brookville, Brookville, PA, p. A534
PEERY, Lori, Chief Human Resource Management Services, VA Palo Alto Health Care System, Palo Alto, CA, p. A82
PEET, Carole, MSN, President and Chief Executive Officer, St. Anthony North Health Campus, Westminster, CO, p. A111
PEET, Fred, Chief Information Officer, Yuma Regional Medical Center, Yuma, AZ, p. A42
PEGE, Diane, M.D. Vice President Medical Affairs, Sutter Lakeside Hospital, Lakeport, CA, p. A68
PEHRSON, Jared, M.D. Chief of Staff, Saunders Medical Center, Wahoo, NE, p. A403
PEIFFER, Paul, Chief Financial Officer and Vice President, Jackson Hospital and Clinic, Montgomery, AL, p. A23
PEIL, Michael, M.D. Chief Medical Director, Kindred Hospital Peoria, Peoria, IL, p. A200
PEIPERT, John, R.N. Chief Nursing Officer, HSHS St. Francis Hospital, Litchfield, IL, p. A195
PEKOFSKE, Robert, Vice President Finance, Advocate Christ Medical Center, Oak Lawn, IL, p. A198
PELACCIA, Joseph, President and Chief Executive Officer, Milford Hospital, Milford, CT, p. A115
PELFREY, Joy S., R.N. Vice President and Chief Nursing Officer, Cabell Huntington Hospital, Huntington, WV, p. A696
PELKOWSKI, Margaret, R.N. Vice President Patient Care Services, Calvary Hospital,, NY, p. A444
PELLE, Fred L., FACHE Chief Operating Officer, Wellmont Holston Valley Medical Center, Kingsport, TN, p. A585

PELLEGRIN, Kimberley, Director, Human Resources, Red River Hospital, LLC, Wichita Falls, TX, p. A657

PELLERIN, Yvonne, Chief Nursing Officer, St. Elizabeth Hospital, Gonzales, LA, p. A277

PELLICONE, John T., M.D. Chief Medical Officer, NYC Health + Hospitals / Metropolitan, New York, NY, p. A448

PELOT, Jeff, Interim Chief Information Officer, Denver Health, Denver, CO, p. A103

PELSMAN, Mara, Chief Executive Officer, Gateways Hospital and Mental Health Center, Los Angeles, CA, p. A71

PELTIER, Glenn, Chief Financial Officer, CHRISTUS Mother Frances Hospital – Winnsboro, Winnsboro, TX, p. A658

PELTIER, Robert, M.D
  Senior Vice President and Chief Medical Officer, North Oaks Medical Center, Hammond, LA, p. A277
  Senior Vice President, Chief Medical Officer, North Oaks Health System, North Oaks Rehabilitation Hospital, Hammond, LA, p. A277

PELTON, Deborah, R.N. Chief Nursing Officer, Texas Spine & Joint Hospital, Tyler, TX, p. A654

PELTON, Ed, Chief of Staff, Chadron Community Hospital and Health Services, Chadron, NE, p. A395

PELUSO, Joseph J., Chief Executive Officer, Tyrone Hospital, Tyrone, PA, p. A556

PEMBERTON, Edith, Chief Financial Officer, East Morgan County Hospital, Brush, CO, p. A102

PEMBERTON, Stacy, Chief Nursing Officer, Grand River Hospital District, Rifle, CO, p. A110

PEMELTON, Debbie, Director Human Resources, Weslaco Regional Rehabilitation Hospital, Weslaco, TX, p. A657

PENA, Carolina, Assistant Director Administrator, Larkin Community Hospital, South Miami, FL, p. A145

PENA, Jessica, Manager Finance, CHRISTUS Spohn Hospital Kleberg, Kingsville, TX, p. A630

PENA, Julie, Director Finance, Community Howard Specialty Hospital, Kokomo, IN, p. A216

PENA, Terry, Chief Operating Officer and Chief Nursing Officer, San Bernardino Mountains Community Hospital District, Lake Arrowhead, CA, p. A68

PENCE, Carla, President Medical Staff, Iredell Health System, Statesville, NC, p. A474

PENCO, Kris, Director Information Systems, Coffeyville Regional Medical Center, Coffeyville, KS, p. A241

PENDER, Carol, Assistant Vice President Human Resources, Walden Psychiatric Care, Waltham, MA, p. A315

PENDER, Debra, R.N. Vice President of Nursing, Mercy Hospital Ardmore, Ardmore, OK, p. A508

PENDERGAST, Jim, Administrator Human Resources, University of New Mexico Hospitals, Albuquerque, NM, p. A428

PENDERGRAFT, Tina, Chief Nursing Officer, Satanta District Hospital and Long Term Care, Satanta, KS, p. A253

PENDLETON, Gretchen, Director Human Resources, Suburban Community Hospital, Norristown, PA, p. A546

PENDLETON, Timothy, M.D. President Medical Staff, Penn Highlands Brookville, Brookville, PA, p. A534

PENICK, Lisa, R.N. Chief Nursing Officer, Carroll County Memorial Hospital, Carrollton, KY, p. A258

PENLAND, Jennifer
  Controller, Kindred Hospital Tarrant County–Arlington, Arlington, TX, p. A597
  Controller, Kindred Hospital–White Rock, Dallas, TX, p. A610

PENN, Shelia, Facility Director, Bryce Hospital, Tuscaloosa, AL, p. A26

PENN, Tripp, Chief Executive Officer, Upson Regional Medical Center, Thomaston, GA, p. A167

PENNACCHIO, Suzanne, Chief Nursing Officer, NYC Health + Hospitals / Jacobi,, NY, p. A448

PENNER, Jerome, Chief Executive Officer, Murray–Calloway County Hospital, Murray, KY, p. A267

PENNEY, Cindy L., R.N. Vice President Nursing, Mercy Iowa City, Iowa City, IA, p. A232

PENNEY, Jan, R.N. Vice President and Chief Nursing Officer, MidMichigan Medical Center–Midland, Midland, MI, p. A330

PENNINGTON, Brian Keith, President and Chief Executive Officer, Medical West, Bessemer, AL, p. A16

PENNINGTON, Kim, Chief Executive Officer, Select Specialty Hospital–Lexington, Lexington, KY, p. A263

PENNINGTON, Stephen G., Interim Chief Executive Officer, Lower Keys Medical Center, Key West, FL, p. A133

PENNINO, Jackie, Director Human Resources, Old Vineyard Behavioral Health Services, Winston–Salem, NC, p. A476

PENOVICH, Carrie L., Chief Clinical Services Officer, Aurora Medical Center – Manitowoc County, Two Rivers, WI, p. A717

PENQUE, Sue, R.N. Senior Vice President and Chief Nursing Officer, South Nassau Communities Hospital, Oceanside, NY, p. A451

PENROD, Kirt, Chief Financial Officer, Shadow Mountain Behavioral Health System, Tulsa, OK, p. A522

PENROSE, Lee, President and Chief Executive Officer, St. Jude Medical Center, Fullerton, CA, p. A64

PENTON, Lance, Director, Information Services, Memorial Hospital Jacksonville, Jacksonville, FL, p. A131

PENUEL, Jennifer, Director Human Resources, Madison Medical Center, Fredericktown, MO, p. A371

PEOPLES, Diane, Director Human Resources, Two Rivers Behavioral Health System, Kansas City, MO, p. A374

PEOPLES, Kathleen K., R.N. Vice President of Nursing, St. Vincent Kokomo, Kokomo, IN, p. A216

PEOPLES, Kyle, Director Technology Management Services, Springfield Hospital, Springfield, VT, p. A666

PEOPLES, Lynn, Interim Chief Nursing Officer, Person Memorial Hospital, Roxboro, NC, p. A472

PEOPLES, Phyllis L., President and Chief Executive Officer, Terrebonne General Medical Center, Houma, LA, p. A278

PEPE, Joseph, M.D., President and Chief Executive Officer, Catholic Medical Center, Manchester, NH, p. A412

PEPPEL, David, Director Operations, Richard H. Hutchings Psychiatric Center, Syracuse, NY, p. A456

PEPPLER, Lisa, Financial Manager, Parkview Whitley Hospital, Columbia City, IN, p. A208

PERAL, Sherry, Manager Information Systems, Oak Valley Hospital District, Oakdale, CA, p. A80

PERALTA, Pennie, R.N. VP, Nursing & Chief Nursing Officer, Bon Secours St. Francis Hospital, Charleston, SC, p. A562

PERCELLO, Thomas, Chief Financial Officer, Community Medical Center, Toms River, NJ, p. A424

PERCIVAL, Steve, Director Human Resources, Washington Regional Medical Center, Fayetteville, AR, p. A46

PEREACE, Vicki, Manager Human Resources, William Bee Ririe Hospital, Ely, NV, p. A404

PERECKO, Gary L., President, Riddle Hospital, Media, PA, p. A545

PEREIRA, Raul Ramos, M.D. Medical Director, Ryder Memorial Hospital, Humacao, PR, p. A727

PEREL, Michael
  Regional Chief Financial Officer, Kauai Veterans Memorial Hospital, Waimea, HI, p. A173
  Regional Chief Financial Officer, Samuel Mahelona Memorial Hospital, Kapaa, HI, p. A172

PEREZ, Brenda, R.N. Chief Clinical Officer, Kindred Hospital–White Rock, Dallas, TX, p. A610

PEREZ, Carmen, Director Human Resources, Doctors' Center Hospital San Juan, San Juan, PR, p. A729

PEREZ, David, Vice President and Chief Information Officer, Eisenhower Medical Center, Rancho Mirage, CA, p. A84

PEREZ, Edwin, M.D. Chief of Medical Staff, Marshall County Hospital, Benton, KY, p. A257

PEREZ, Francisco, Manager Management Information Systems, Hospital de la Universidad de Puerto Rico/Dr. Federico Trilla, Carolina, PR, p. A726

PEREZ, George, Chief Executive Officer, Campbellton Graceville Hospital, Graceville, FL, p. A130

PEREZ, Homar, Chief Executive Officer and Vice President Administration, Hospital Dr. Cayetano Coll Y Toste, Arecibo, PR, p. A726

PEREZ, Joe, Associate Director, South Texas Veterans Health Care System, San Antonio, TX, p. A647

PEREZ, Julie, Chief Financial Officer, St. David's Medical Center, Austin, TX, p. A600

PEREZ, Lisa, R.N. Director Nursing, Meadowbrook Rehabilitation Hospital, Gardner, KS, p. A243

PEREZ, Mercedes, Vice President Nursing, Larkin Community Hospital, South Miami, FL, p. A145

PEREZ, Miguel, Director Information Systems, Driscoll Children's Hospital, Corpus Christi, TX, p. A608

PEREZ, Nina, R.N. Chief Nursing Officer, North Okaloosa Medical Center, Crestview, FL, p. A126

PEREZ, Tony, M.D. President Medical Staff, Jewish Hospital–Shelbyville, Shelbyville, KY, p. A269

PERIMENIS, Vasilia, Vice President Human Resources, Novant Health Medical Park Hospital, Winston–Salem, NC, p. A476

PERJON, Cindy, Associate Director, Southwest Connecticut Mental Health System, Bridgeport, CT, p. A113

PERKERSON, Robyn, R.N., Administrator, LifeCare Hospitals of North Carolina, Rocky Mount, NC, p. A472

PERKES, Neil C., Operations Officer, Logan Regional Hospital, Logan, UT, p. A660

PERKET, William, Vice President Human Resources, North Country Hospital and Health Center, Newport, VT, p. A666

PERKINS, Brett, M.D. Chief Medical Staff, Madison County Memorial Hospital, Madison, FL, p. A135

PERKINS, Chris, Director Information Services, Clinch Valley Medical Center, Richlands, VA, p. A677

PERKINS, Dan
  Corporate Director Human Resources, Cornerstone Hospital–West Monroe, West Monroe, LA, p. A289
  Vice President of Human Resources, Solara Hospital Harlingen, Harlingen, TX, p. A622

PERKINS, Jeanne, Vice President Nursing and Interim Manager Human Resources, Bucyrus Community Hospital, Bucyrus, OH, p. A485

PERKINS, Kathryn, M.D
  Chief Medical Officer, Banner Boswell Medical Center, Sun City, AZ, p. A39
  Chief Medical Officer, Banner Thunderbird Medical Center, Glendale, AZ, p. A33

PERKINS, Mike, Vice President and Administrator, Baptist Health Extended Care Hospital, Little Rock, AR, p. A48

PERKINS, Richard, Chief Financial Officer, Baylor Scott & White Medical Center – Hillcrest, Waco, TX, p. A655

PERKINS, Tom, Chief Information Officer, Shannon Medical Center, San Angelo, TX, p. A645

PERKINS–PEPPERS, Andrea, Chief Information Officer, Forks Community Hospital, Forks, WA, p. A685

PERKO, Tina, Vice President Operations, Adena Pike Medical Center, Waverly, OH, p. A505

PERL, Lawrence, M.D. Chief Medical Officer, Columbia Memorial Hospital, Hudson, NY, p. A440

PERLA, Salvatore, President, Nashoba Valley Medical Center, Ayer, MA, p. A305

PERLICH, Gwynn, Vice President of Patient Services and Chief Nursing Officer, St. Vincent Carmel Hospital, Carmel, IN, p. A208

PERLSTEIN, David A., M.D., President and Chief Executive Officer, St. Barnabas Hospital,, NY, p. A449

PERMANN, Darcy, Interim Chief Executive Officer, Landmann–Jungman Memorial Hospital Avera, Scotland, SD, p. A576

PERMENTER, Ethan
  Chief Executive Officer, Behavioral Hospital of Bellaire, Houston, TX, p. A623
  Chief Executive Officer, Parkwood Behavioral Health System, Olive Branch, MS, p. A363

PERNICE, Paul, Vice President Finance, Beebe Healthcare, Lewes, DE, p. A119

PERRA, Scott H., FACHE,
  President and Chief Executive Officer, Faxton St. Luke's Healthcare, Utica, NY, p. A457
  Chief Executive Officer, St. Elizabeth Medical Center, Utica, NY, p. A457

PERRAS, Joseph, Chief Medical Officer, Mt. Ascutney Hospital and Health Center, Windsor, VT, p. A666

PERRATTO, Bonnie I., MSN Senior Vice President, Chief Nurse Executive, Bayhealth Medical Center, Dover, DE, p. A119

PERRIGOT, Keri, Manager Human Resources, Cassia Regional Medical Center, Burley, ID, p. A175

PERRIN, Mary R., President and Chief Executive Officer, Children's Hospital, New Orleans, LA, p. A284

PERRINE, Vicki, FACHE Chief Operating Officer, Claxton–Hepburn Medical Center, Ogdensburg, NY, p. A451

PERRITT, Daniel, Chief Financial Officer, Sunrise Hospital and Medical Center, Las Vegas, NV, p. A407

PERRON, Kirk, Administrator and Chief Administrative Officer, Jennings Senior Care Hospital, Jennings, LA, p. A279

PERROTTE, Kenneth, Director Operations, Rockland Children's Psychiatric Center, Orangeburg, NY, p. A452

PERROTTI, Paul R., CPA Chief Financial Officer, West Georgia Health, Lagrange, GA, p. A161

PERRY, Amy, President, Sinai Hospital of Baltimore, Baltimore, MD, p. A298

PERRY, Carol, R.N. Vice President and Chief Nursing Officer, Stormont Vail Health, Topeka, KS, p. A254

PERRY, Cheryl
  Director Human Resources, Paris Regional Medical Center, Paris, TX, p. A640
  Chief Financial Officer, Vibra Hospital of Southeastern Massachusetts, New Bedford, MA, p. A312

PERRY, Cynthia, M.D. Chief of Staff, Stephens Memorial Hospital, Breckenridge, TX, p. A603

PERRY, Darrin Keith, Chief Information Officer and Senior Vice President, St. Jude Children's Research Hospital, Memphis, TN, p. A589

PERRY, Doug, M.D. Chief of Staff, Baptist Medical Center Leake, Carthage, MS, p. A356

PERRY, Faye, Chief Nursing Officer, Tennova Healthcare–Clarksville, Clarksville, TN, p. A581

PERRY, Jan, R.N. Vice President Patient Care Services, Community Medical Center, Missoula, MT, p. A389

PERRY, Jeff
  Director Information Technology, St. John's Pleasant Valley Hospital, Camarillo, CA, p. A57
  Director Information Technology, St. John's Regional Medical Center, Oxnard, CA, p. A81
  Chief Operating Officer, UP Health System–Marquette, Marquette, MI, p. A329

PERRY, Karen, Chief Information Resource Management Services, James H. Quillen Veterans Affairs Medical Center, Mountain Home, TN, p. A590

PERRY, Kathleen, Senior Vice President and Chief Information Officer, Mercy Medical Center, Baltimore, MD, p. A297

PERRY, Matthew, Director Information Systems, Andalusia Health, Andalusia, AL, p. A15

PERRY, Matthew J., President and Chief Executive Officer, Genesis HealthCare System, Zanesville, OH, p. A507

PERRY, Michael, Chief Executive Officer, Michiana Behavioral Health Center, Plymouth, IN, p. A220

PERRY, Michael R., M.D., President and Chief Executive Officer, FHN Memorial Hospital, Freeport, IL, p. A190

PERRY, Nini, Chief Nursing Officer, Georgetown Behavioral Health Institute, Georgetown, TX, p. A620

PERRY, Phil, M.D. Regional Chief Medical Officer, Piedmont Medical Center, Rock Hill, SC, p. A569

PERRY, Rhonda S., Chief Financial Officer, Medical Center, Navicent Health, Macon, GA, p. A162

PERRY, Sally, Chief Executive Officer, Coastal Harbor Treatment Center, Savannah, GA, p. A165

PERRY, Shaun, Chief Information Officer, McGehee–Desha County Hospital, McGehee, AR, p. A50

PERRY, Solette, Regional Director Human Resources, Kauai Veterans Memorial Hospital, Waimea, HI, p. A173

PERRY, Stacey
Director of Nursing, Beaver County Memorial Hospital, Beaver, OK, p. A509
Chief Nursing Officer, Hamilton County Hospital, Syracuse, KS, p. A254

PERRY, Teresa J., Chief Financial Officer, UP Health System–Bell, Ishpeming, MI, p. A327

PERRY, Tim, Executive Director of Human Resources, Baptist Health Corbin, Corbin, KY, p. A258

PERRY, V. Mark, Chief Financial Officer, Adventist Medical Center–Portland, Portland, OR, p. A529

PERRYMAN, Daniel L., President and Chief Executive Officer, HSHS St. Mary's Hospital, Decatur, IL, p. A188

PERRYMAN, Mike, Chief Financial Officer, Baptist Memorial Hospital–Union City, Union City, TN, p. A594

PERSE, David F., M.D., President and Chief Executive Officer, St. Vincent Charity Medical Center, Cleveland, OH, p. A489

PERSILY, Cynthia A., R.N., President and Chief Executive Officer, Highland Hospital, Charleston, WV, p. A695

PERSINGER, Keith D., Senior Vice President Finance and Chief Financial Officer, University of Maryland Medical Center, Baltimore, MD, p. A298

PERSON, Lisa, MSN Vice President and Chief Nursing Officer, Mercy Hospital Springfield, Springfield, MO, p. A382

PERT, Robert M., Vice President Finance and Chief Financial Officer, United Regional Health Care System, Wichita Falls, TX, p. A658

PERUGINO, Tony, Director Finance, Vassar Brothers Medical Center, Poughkeepsie, NY, p. A453

PESCHEL, Colleen, Director Human Resources, Sutter Medical Center, Sacramento, Sacramento, CA, p. A87

PESKIN, Ted, M.D. Acute Care Medical Director, Hilo Medical Center, Hilo, HI, p. A170

PESTLE, Janet K., R.N. Vice President Nursing and Chief Nursing Officer, SSM Health St. Joseph Hospital – Lake Saint Louis, Lake Saint Louis, MO, p. A375

PETER, David, M.D
Senior Vice President Medical Affairs and Chief Medical Director, Akron General Medical Center, Akron, OH, p. A483
Senior Vice President Medical Affairs and Chief Medical Officer, Lodi Community Hospital, Lodi, OH, p. A497

PETER, Douglas G., M.D. Chief Medical Officer, Gallup Indian Medical Center, Gallup, NM, p. A429

PETER, Jan D., Vice President Fiscal Services and Chief Financial Officer, Good Shepherd Health Care System, Hermiston, OR, p. A526

PETER, John, M.D. Vice President Medical Affairs, SSM Cardinal Glennon Children's Medical Center, Saint Louis, MO, p. A381

PETERMAN, John, Vice President and Administrator, Riverside Shore Memorial Hospital, Nassawadox, VA, p. A674

PETERMAN, Tammy, R.N. Executive Vice President, Chief Operating Officer and Chief Nursing Officer, The University of Kansas Hospital, Kansas City, KS, p. A246

PETERMEIER, Jill, Senior Executive Human Resources, Central Iowa Healthcare, Marshalltown, IA, p. A234

PETERS, Amy, R.N. Interim Chief Operating Officer, Truman Medical Center–Lakewood, Kansas City, MO, p. A374

PETERS, Bruce
Vice President and Chief Operating Officer, Bakersfield Memorial Hospital, Bakersfield, CA, p. A55
Chief Executive Officer, Mercy Hospitals of Bakersfield, Bakersfield, CA, p. A56

PETERS, Candace, R.N. Director of Nursing, Webster County Community Hospital, Red Cloud, NE, p. A402

PETERS, Connie, R.N., President, CHI Health Schuyler, Schuyler, NE, p. A402

PETERS, Dave, Chief Human Resources Officer, Veterans Affairs Nebraska–Western Iowa Health Care System – Lincoln, Lincoln, NE, p. A398

PETERS, Gerald, Vice President Information Technologies and Chief Information Officer, Lake Health, Concord Township, OH, p. A491

PETERS, Holli, Director Health Information Management, Holton Community Hospital, Holton, KS, p. A245

PETERS, Jan, Vice President Human Resources, Saint Vincent Hospital, Worcester, MA, p. A316

PETERS, Joanna, Director Human Resources, Saunders Medical Center, Wahoo, NE, p. A403

PETERS, Mark J., M.D., President and Chief Executive Officer, East Jefferson General Hospital, Metairie, LA, p. A283

PETERS, Mary
Chief Nursing Officer, UnityPoint Health – Finley Hospital, Dubuque, IA, p. A230
Chief Information Officer, Womack Army Medical Center, Fort Bragg, NC, p. A465

PETERS, Pamela, Administrator, Child and Adolescent Behavioral Health Services, Willmar, MN, p. A353

PETERS, Patrick, Chief Executive Officer, Guthrie County Hospital, Guthrie Center, IA, p. A231

PETERS, Suzanne K., Vice President Human Resources, Munson Medical Center, Traverse City, MI, p. A335

PETERS, Violeta, R.N., Chief Executive Officer, Specialty Hospital of Central Jersey, Lakewood, NJ, p. A418

PETERS, Wayne, Administrator, Southern Virginia Mental Health Institute, Danville, VA, p. A669

PETERS–LEWIS, Angelleen, R.N. System Chief Nursing Officer, Women & Infants Hospital of Rhode Island, Providence, RI, p. A561

PETERSEN, Brenda, Human Resources, Sanford Wheaton Medical Center, Wheaton, MN, p. A353

PETERSEN, Debbie, R.N. Chief Operating Officer and Chief Nursing Officer, Spalding Rehabilitation Hospital, Aurora, CO, p. A101

PETERSEN, Julie, Interim Chief Executive Officer, Kittitas Valley Healthcare, Ellensburg, WA, p. A684

PETERSEN, Richard W., President and Chief Executive Officer, Maine Medical Center, Portland, ME, p. A294

PETERSEN, Susan, Human Resources, Lincoln Community Hospital and Nursing Home, Hugo, CO, p. A107

PETERSEN, Tina, Chief Nursing Officer, Hillcrest Hospital Cushing, Cushing, OK, p. A510

PETERSON, Alison, Vice President Medical Affairs, United Hospital, Saint Paul, MN, p. A351

PETERSON, Anne, Vice President Human Resources and Support Services, Licking Memorial Hospital, Newark, OH, p. A500

PETERSON, Bill, Director Human Resources, EASTAR Health System, Muskogee, OK, p. A515

PETERSON, Bonnie, Chief Executive Officer, Richard P. Stadter Psychiatric Center, Grand Forks, ND, p. A479

PETERSON, Brent A., Administrator, Cherry County Hospital, Valentine, NE, p. A402

PETERSON, Brett, Director of Information Services, Florida Hospital North Pinellas, Tarpon Springs, FL, p. A148

PETERSON, Bruce, Chief Information Officer, Rome Memorial Hospital, Rome, NY, p. A455

PETERSON, Carrie, Director of Nursing, Henderson Health Care Services, Henderson, NE, p. A397

PETERSON, Chad, Chief Information Officer, Northwood Deaconess Health Center, Northwood, ND, p. A481

PETERSON, Cheryl, Business Office Manager, Surgical Institute of Reading, Wyomissing, PA, p. A558

PETERSON, Christine, Chief Executive Officer, Post Acute Medical Specialty Hospital of Milwaukee, Greenfield, WI, p. A707

PETERSON, Cindy, Vice President and Chief Information Officer, Henry Mayo Newhall Hospital, Valencia, CA, p. A98

PETERSON, David
Senior Vice President, Chief Technology Officer, Erlanger Medical Center, Chattanooga, TN, p. A580
Chief Information Officer, Laurel Regional Hospital, Laurel, MD, p. A302

PETERSON, Denise, R.N. Vice President, Professional Nursing Practice & Quality, Chief Nursing Officer, Saint Francis Hospital and Medical Center, Hartford, CT, p. A114

PETERSON, Dennis, Chief Information Officer, George E. Weems Memorial Hospital, Apalachicola, FL, p. A123

PETERSON, Douglas R., President and Chief Executive Officer, Chippewa Valley Hospital and Oakview Care Center, Durand, WI, p. A704

PETERSON, Eric, Director, Ogden Regional Medical Center, Ogden, UT, p. A661

PETERSON, Erica, Chief Executive Officer, Sanford Chamberlain Medical Center, Chamberlain, SD, p. A572

PETERSON, Gary, M.D. Vice President Medical Affairs and Chief Medical Officer, St. Luke's Hospital, Duluth, MN, p. A342

PETERSON, James Kevin, Human Resources Leader, Kaiser Permanente South Sacramento Medical Center, Sacramento, CA, p. A86

PETERSON, Jeff, M.D. Chief of Staff, Essentia Health Ada, Ada, MN, p. A338

PETERSON, Jeffrey, M.D. Medical Director, Cooperstown Medical Center, Cooperstown, ND, p. A478

PETERSON, Jim, Chief Financial Officer, Steele Memorial Medical Center, Salmon, ID, p. A178

PETERSON, Josilyn, Chief Financial Officer, Ballinger Memorial Hospital, Ballinger, TX, p. A601

PETERSON, Judy, R.N. Chief Nursing Officer, East Texas Medical Center Carthage, Carthage, TX, p. A605

PETERSON, Julie, Chief Financial Officer, Sutter Delta Medical Center, Antioch, CA, p. A54

PETERSON, Kathy, Director Information Services, OSF Saint Anthony Medical Center, Rockford, IL, p. A202

PETERSON, Katie, R.N. Chief Nursing Officer, Pender Community Hospital, Pender, NE, p. A401

PETERSON, Larry, Chief Financial Officer, Allen County Regional Hospital, Iola, KS, p. A245

PETERSON, Linda, M.D. Vice President Medical Affairs, McLaren Greater Lansing, Lansing, MI, p. A328

PETERSON, Mackenzie, M.D. Chief of Staff, Anderson County Hospital, Garnett, KS, p. A243

PETERSON, Margaret R., R.N., President, California Hospital Medical Center, Los Angeles, CA, p. A70

PETERSON, Michael, FACHE, President, Androscoggin Valley Hospital, Berlin, NH, p. A410

PETERSON, Michael, M.D. Chief of Staff, Pineville Community Hospital Association, Pineville, KY, p. A268

PETERSON, Michael, FACHE Chief Operating Officer, Sebasticook Valley Health, Pittsfield, ME, p. A294

PETERSON, Natalie, Human Resources Director, Optim Medical Center – Screven, Sylvania, GA, p. A167

PETERSON, Polly, Information Technology Director, Winona Health, Winona, MN, p. A353

PETERSON, Randall, President and Chief Executive Officer, Stormont Vail Health, Topeka, KS, p. A254

PETERSON, Robert
Chief Financial Officer, Hackettstown Medical Center, Hackettstown, NJ, p. A417
Chief Executive Officer, Millinocket Regional Hospital, Millinocket, ME, p. A294

PETERSON, Ron, FACHE, President and Chief Executive Officer, Baxter Regional Medical Center, Mountain Home, AR, p. A50

PETERSON, Ron, Chief Information Officer, Pottstown Memorial Medical Center, Pottstown, PA, p. A552

PETERSON, Ronald R., President, Johns Hopkins Health System, Baltimore, MD, p. B75

PETERSON, Scott, M.D. President Medical Staff, Avera Flandreau Hospital, Flandreau, SD, p. A573

PETERSON, Scott
Chief Excutive Officer, HEALTHSOUTH Rehabilitation Hospital of Franklin, Franklin, TN, p. A583
Vice President of People and Organizational Development, Peninsula Regional Medical Center, Salisbury, MD, p. A303

PETERSON, Seth, Director Information Services, Coshocton County Memorial Hospital, Coshocton, OH, p. A492

PETERSON, Shelley, R.N. Vice President Patient Services and Chief Nursing Officer, St. Mary's Medical Center, Grand Junction, CO, p. A106

PETERSON, Stephen, Vice President, Operations and Chief Information Officer, Garrett Regional Medical Center, Oakland, MD, p. A302

PETERSON, Steve, M.D. Chief of Staff, CHI Health Plainview, Plainview, NE, p. A401

PETERSON, Thomas, M.D., President, Richard P. Stadter Psychiatric Center, Grand Forks, ND, p. A479

PETERSON, Tim, M.D. Chief of Staff, Meeker Memorial Hospital, Litchfield, MN, p. A345

PETERSON, Tracie, R.N. Chief Nursing Officer, Great Lakes Specialty Hospital–Grand Rapids, Grand Rapids, MI, p. A324

PETIK, Jason, Chief Executive Officer, Sidney Regional Medical Center, Sidney, NE, p. A402

PETITT, Dorie, Chief Nursing Officer, Post Acute Medical Specialty Hospital of Milwaukee, Greenfield, WI, p. A707

PETITT, Michael
Director of Finance, Wheaton Franciscan Healthcare – Elmbrook Memorial, Brookfield, WI, p. A703
Director of Finance, Wheaton Franciscan Healthcare – St. Joseph's, Milwaukee, WI, p. A712

PETRE, Patrick A., Chief Executive Officer, AHMC Anaheim Regional Medical Center, Anaheim, CA, p. A54

PETRIK, Jennifer, Interim Chief Nursing Officer, Deaconess Hospital, Spokane, WA, p. A691

PETRILLO, Mary Ann, R.N. Acting Associate Director Nursing and Patient Clinical Services, Bedford Veterans Affairs Medical Center, Edith Nourse Rogers Memorial Veterans Hospital, Bedford, MA, p. A305

PETRILLO, Nancy, Director Human Resources, Matheny Medical and Educational Center, Peapack, NJ, p. A421

PETRINA, Robert, Chief Financial Officer, Alta Bates Summit Medical Center, Berkeley, CA, p. A56

PETRINI, Lindsey, Chief Operating Officer, North Fulton Regional Hospital, Roswell, GA, p. A165

PETRITZ, Jennifer J., Director Human Resources, University of Washington Medical Center, Seattle, WA, p. A690

PETROVICH, Lawrence, M.D. Chief Medical Officer, York Hospital, York, ME, p. A295

PETROWER, Stacey, President, New York–Presbyterian/Hudson Valley Hospital, Cortlandt Manor, NY, p. A437

PETRY, Fernando, M.D. Vice President and Chief Medical Officer, Martin Health System, Stuart, FL, p. A146

PETRY, Gary, M.D. Chief of Staff, St. Vincent General Hospital District, Leadville, CO, p. A108

PETTEY, Robbie, Chief Financial Officer, National Park Medical Center, Hot Springs, AR, p. A47

PETTIGREW, Dennis, Chief Operating Officer, Saint Michael's Medical Center, Newark, NJ, p. A421

PETTIGREW, Rob, Director Information Technology, Wyoming Medical Center, Casper, WY, p. A721

PETTIJOHN, Trent, M.D. Chief Medical Officer, The Heart Hospital Baylor Plano, Plano, TX, p. A642

PETTINATO, Jim, Director Patient Care Services, Wayne Memorial Hospital, Honesdale, PA, p. A540

PETTIT, Amy, R.N. Vice President Nursing Services and Chief Nursing Officer, Schneck Medical Center, Seymour, IN, p. A222

PETTIT, Donny, Chief Financial Officer, Coon Memorial Hospital, Dalhart, TX, p. A609

PETTIT, Harlan, M.D. Chief of Medical Staff, Fishermen's Hospital, Marathon, FL, p. A135

PETTITE, Shirley F., Chief Human Resources Officer, Tennessee Valley Healthcare System, Nashville, TN, p. A591

PETTREY, Lisa J., R.N., Chief Executive Officer, Regency Hospital of Columbus, Columbus, OH, p. A491

PETTY, Jane, Director Human Resources, Southern Tennessee Regional Health System–Pulaski, Pulaski, TN, p. A592

PETTY, Russ, M.D. Chief of Staff, Towner County Medical Center, Cando, ND, p. A477

PETULA, Ronald J.
    Vice President Finance, Good Shepherd Penn Partners Specialty Hospital at Rittenhouse, Philadelphia, PA, p. A548
    Chief Financial Officer, Good Shepherd Rehabilitation Hospital, Allentown, PA, p. A532
    Chief Financial Officer, Good Shepherd Specialty Hospital, Bethlehem, PA, p. A533

PEW, Chad, Chief Operating Officer and Senior Vice President, Wyoming Medical Center, Casper, WY, p. A721

PFAFF, Joni, Chief Nursing Officer, Grisell Memorial Hospital District One, Ransom, KS, p. A252

PFAFF, Tony, Chief Executive Officer, Deer Lodge Medical Center, Deer Lodge, MT, p. A387

PFALTZGRAFF, George, Chief Medical Officer, Hansen Family Hospital, Iowa Falls, IA, p. A233

PFAU, Ben, Chief Facility and Information Officer, Bay Area Hospital, Coos Bay, OR, p. A525

PFAU, Beth, M.D. Chief Medical Officer, Larue D. Carter Memorial Hospital, Indianapolis, IN, p. A214

PFEFFER, Daniel William, Chief Nurse Executive, Weisman Children's Rehabilitation Hospital, Marlton, NJ, p. A419

PFEFFER, Michael, M.D
    Chief Information Officer, Ronald Reagan UCLA Medical Center, Los Angeles, CA, p. A74
    Chief Medical Informatics Officer, UCLA Health, Stewart & Lynda Resnick Neuropsychiatric Hospital at UCLA, Los Angeles, CA, p. A74

PFEFFER, Stacey, Senior Vice President Human Resources, Winthrop–University Hospital, Mineola, NY, p. A442

PFEIFER, Bradley D., Chief Executive Officer, West Holt Memorial Hospital, Atkinson, NE, p. A393

PFEIFER, Mark P., M.D. Senior Vice President and Chief Medical Officer, University of Louisville Hospital, Louisville, KY, p. A265

PFEIFFER, James A., FACHE, President and Chief Executive Officer, Self Regional Healthcare, Greenwood, SC, p. A567

PFEIFFER, Margaret, R.N. Vice President Patient Care Services, Good Samaritan Hospital, Los Angeles, CA, p. A71

PFISTER, Joann M., Director Human Resources, Providence Willamette Falls Medical Center, Oregon City, OR, p. A528

PFISTER, Pam, Chief Executive Officer, Morrison Community Hospital, Morrison, IL, p. A197

PFISTER, Scott, Director Finance, Providence St. Vincent Medical Center, Portland, OR, p. A529

PFITZER, Tony, Chief Executive Officer, Massac Memorial Hospital, Metropolis, IL, p. A196

PFRANK, Kym, Senior Vice President and Chief Operating Officer, Union Hospital, Terre Haute, IN, p. A222

PHAM, Bong, Chief Medical Officer, Kit Carson County Health Service District, Burlington, CO, p. A102

PHAM, K., M.D. Chief of Staff, Winkler County Memorial Hospital, Kermit, TX, p. A630

PHELAN, Cynthia, Vice President Human Resources, Lawrence General Hospital, Lawrence, MA, p. A311

PHELPS, Britton, Chief Executive Officer, Merit Health Madison, Canton, MS, p. A356

PHELPS, David E., President and Chief Executive Officer, Berkshire Health Systems, Inc., Pittsfield, MA, p. B23

PHELPS, David E., President and Chief Executive Officer, Berkshire Medical Center, Pittsfield, MA, p. A314

PHELPS, Gail, R.N. Chief Nursing Officer, Haxtun Hospital District, Haxtun, CO, p. A107

PHELPS, Joel, Chief Operating Officer, Salina Regional Health Center, Salina, KS, p. A253

PHELPS, Kathleen, Director Human Resources, Treasure Valley Hospital, Boise, ID, p. A175

PHELPS, Lisa, Senior Vice President, Human Resources, Phoenix Children's Hospital, Phoenix, AZ, p. A37

PHELPS, Rick, M.D. President and Chief Operating Officer, Elliot Hospital, Manchester, NH, p. A412

PHETTEPLACE, Danial, Director Information Technology, Gundersen St. Joseph's Hospital and Clinics, Hillsboro, WI, p. A707

PHILIP, Neena S., R.N. Assistant Vice President Nursing, Hoboken University Medical Center, Hoboken, NJ, p. A418

PHILIPCHUCK, Cynthia, R.N. Executive Director of Nursing, Gibson Area Hospital and Health Services, Gibson City, IL, p. A191

PHILIPP, Lawrence A., Interim Chief Executive Officer, Mark Twain Medical Center, San Andreas, CA, p. A88

PHILIPS III, Grady W., President, Winchester Medical Center, Winchester, VA, p. A680

PHILLIPS, Alan M., Controller, HEALTHSOUTH Nittany Valley Rehabilitation Hospital, Pleasant Gap, PA, p. A552

PHILLIPS, Barry, Executive Director Human Resources, Camden General Hospital, Camden, TN, p. A579

PHILLIPS, Bill, Vice President Information Services, University Health System, San Antonio, TX, p. A647

PHILLIPS, Bobby, Chief Nursing Officer, Medical Center Enterprise, Enterprise, AL, p. A19

PHILLIPS, Brent R., President and Chief Executive Officer, Regional Health, Rapid City, SD, p. B114

PHILLIPS, Courtney, Chief Executive Officer, South Sunflower County Hospital, Indianola, MS, p. A359

PHILLIPS, David D., Chief Executive Officer and Administrator, Barnesville Hospital, Barnesville, OH, p. A484

PHILLIPS, David L.
    Chief Executive Officer, St. John Broken Arrow, Broken Arrow, OK, p. A509
    President and Chief Executive Officer, St. John Owasso, Owasso, OK, p. A518
    Chief Executive Officer, St. John Sapulpa, Sapulpa, OK, p. A519

PHILLIPS, Donna, President, Bryn Mawr Rehabilitation Hospital, Malvern, PA, p. A543

PHILLIPS, Eddie, M.D
    Chief Medical Affairs, Baptist Health Medical Center – North Little Rock, North Little Rock, AR, p. A51
    Chief Medical Officer, Baptist Health Medical Center–Arkadelphia, Arkadelphia, AR, p. A43

PHILLIPS, Frank, M.D. Chief of Staff, Mary Black Health System – Gaffney, Gaffney, SC, p. A566

PHILLIPS, Glenn, Director Information Systems, Gadsden Regional Medical Center, Gadsden, AL, p. A20

PHILLIPS, Heath, Chief Executive Officer, Medical Center Enterprise, Enterprise, AL, p. A19

PHILLIPS, John
    Chief of Staff, Great River Medical Center, West Burlington, IA, p. A239
    Vice President Information Services, St. Joseph Regional Health Center, Bryan, TX, p. A604

PHILLIPS, John E., FACHE, President, Methodist Mansfield Medical Center, Mansfield, TX, p. A635

PHILLIPS, Kelly, M.D. Clinical Director and Chief Staff, Spring Grove Hospital Center, Baltimore, MD, p. A298

PHILLIPS, Kimberly A., Chief Financial Officer, The Children's Home of Pittsburgh, Pittsburgh, PA, p. A551

PHILLIPS, Lionel J., Vice President Financial Services, Fauquier Hospital, Warrenton, VA, p. A680

PHILLIPS, Lori, Vice President and Chief Nursing Officer, Gibson General Hospital, Princeton, IN, p. A221

PHILLIPS, Michael, Chief Executive Officer, Elkhorn Valley Rehabilitation Hospital, Casper, WY, p. A721

PHILLIPS, III, Monie, Director Clinical Informatics, Jackson Parish Hospital, Jonesboro, LA, p. A279

PHILLIPS, Paul, Chief Financial Officer, Taylor Regional Hospital, Campbellsville, KY, p. A258

PHILLIPS, Robert A., President, Shelby Baptist Medical Center, Alabaster, AL, p. A15

PHILLIPS, Sarah, Manager Human Resources, Morgan Memorial Hospital, Madison, GA, p. A162

PHILLIPS, Steve, Information Officer, Greene County General Hospital, Linton, IN, p. A217

PHILLIPS, Tammy, Director, Information Systems, Texas Health Presbyterian Hospital Dallas, Dallas, TX, p. A611

PHILLIPS, Todd, M.D. Chief Medical Officer, Monmouth Medical Center, Southern Campus, Lakewood, NJ, p. A418

PHILLIPS, Traci, Assistant Superintendent, Big Spring State Hospital, Big Spring, TX, p. A602

PHINNEY, Cody, Administrator, Northern Nevada Adult Mental Health Services, Sparks, NV, p. A408

PHIPPS, Jackie G., Director Human Resources, Johnston Memorial Hospital, Abingdon, VA, p. A667

PIANALTO, Eric, President, Mercy Hospital Rogers, Rogers, AR, p. A52

PIATKOWSKI, Shannon, Director Information Technology, Blake Medical Center, Bradenton, FL, p. A124

PIATT, Malcolm Keith, M.D., Interim Director, Northern Arizona Veterans Affairs Health Care System, Prescott, AZ, p. A37

PIAZZA, Tony, Director Human Resources, Titus Regional Medical Center, Mount Pleasant, TX, p. A638

PICAZA, Jose, M.D. Chief of Staff, Unicoi County Memorial Hospital, Erwin, TN, p. A582

PICCIONE, Jennifer, Chief Nursing and Clinical Services Officer, Madison Health, London, OH, p. A497

PICKARD, Bert, Chief Financial Officer, Merit Health Gilmore Memorial, Amory, MS, p. A355

PICKEL, Joseph, Director Resource Management, Walter Reed National Military Medical Center, Bethesda, MD, p. A299

PICKENS, Gayle, Chief Nursing Officer, Putnam County Memorial Hospital, Unionville, MO, p. A383

PICKENS, Ramona, Chief Operating Officer, East Cooper Medical Center, Mount Pleasant, SC, p. A568

PICKENS, Regina, Chief Financial Officer, Grafton City Hospital, Grafton, WV, p. A696

PICKERING, Sheridan, Chief Executive Officer, Muscogee Creek Nation Medical Center, Okmulgee, OK, p. A518

PICKETT, C. Judson, Chief of Staff, Trinity Hospital of Augusta, Augusta, GA, p. A154

PICKETT, Gregory D., M.D. Chief of Staff, Jackson County Memorial Hospital, Altus, OK, p. A508

PICKETT, Lisa C., M.D. Chief Medical Officer, Duke University Hospital, Durham, NC, p. A464

PICKLER, Nancy, Director of Human Resources, HEALTHSOUTH East Valley Rehabilitation Hospital, Mesa, AZ, p. A34

PICKUL, David, M.D. Chief Medical Officer, Circle Health, Lowell General Hospital, Lowell, MA, p. A311

PICOU, Timothy, Manager Information Technology, Lower Umpqua Hospital District, Reedsport, OR, p. A530

PIEDRAFITE, JoAnn, R.N. Chief Nursing Officer, Saint Vincent Hospital, Worcester, MA, p. A316

PIEH, Samuel, Chief Operating Officer, DMC Huron Valley–Sinai Hospital, Commerce Township, MI, p. A321

PIEPER, Blaine, Chief Executive Officer, Ohio County Hospital, Hartford, KY, p. A261

PIEPHOFF, James, Chief Medical Officer, OSF Saint Anthony's Health Center, Alton, IL, p. A180

PIERCE, Bonnie, MSN Associate Director for Patient Care Services, Jack C. Montgomery Veterans Affairs Medical Center, Muskogee, OK, p. A515

PIERCE, Christy, Director of Human Resources, Katherine Shaw Bethea Hospital, Dixon, IL, p. A188

PIERCE, Connie, Manager Human Resources, Coalinga Regional Medical Center, Coalinga, CA, p. A59

PIERCE, Felicia, R.N
    Chief Nursing Officer, Great River Medical Center, Blytheville, AR, p. A43
    Chief Nursing Officer, South Mississippi County Regional Medical Center, Osceola, AR, p. A51

PIERCE, Jeff M.
    Manager Human Resources, Marshall Medical Center, Lewisburg, TN, p. A587
    Manager Human Resources, Wayne Medical Center, Waynesboro, TN, p. A594

PIERCE, Jennifer
    Chief Clinical Officer, Kindred Hospital of Northern Indiana, Mishawaka, IN, p. A218
    Administrative Director of Finance, St. Anthony Shawnee Hospital, Shawnee, OK, p. A520

PIERCE, Kenneth, Chief Financial Officer, Brookhaven Hospital, Tulsa, OK, p. A521

PIERCE, Laura, Director Human Resources, Memorial Medical Center, Las Cruces, NM, p. A430

PIERCE, Margaret H., Executive Director, Kaiser Permanente Baldwin Park Medical Center, Baldwin Park, CA, p. A56

PIERCE, Michael L., Chief Executive Officer, Post Acute Medical Specialty Hospital of Corpus Christi – South, Corpus Christi, TX, p. A608

PIERCE, Pamela, Deputy Chief Executive Officer, Windhaven Psychiatric Hospital, Prescott Valley, AZ, p. A38

PIERCE, Pat, Director Information Systems, Lakewood Regional Medical Center, Lakewood, CA, p. A68

PIERDON, Steven, M.D. Executive Vice President and Chief Medical Officer, Geisinger Wyoming Valley Medical Center, Wilkes Barre, PA, p. A557

PIERESCHI, Giovanni
Vice President Management Information Systems, Hospital HIMA de Humacao, Humacao, PR, p. A727
Vice President Enterprise Information and Chief Information Officer, Hospital HIMA San Pablo Caguas, Caguas, PR, p. A726

PIERLUISI, Guillermo, Vice President of Medical Affairs, WellStar Paulding Hospital, Hiram, GA, p. A161

PIERRE, Andre, Chief Financial Officer, Forest View Psychiatric Hospital, Grand Rapids, MI, p. A324

PIERRE, Letonia, Coordinator Human Resources, Assumption Community Hospital, Napoleonville, LA, p. A284

PIERSON, Cindy, Clinical Services Manager, Highlands–Cashiers Hospital, Highlands, NC, p. A467

PIERSON, Jerome, Chief Medical Officer, Mercy Medical Center–Sioux City, Sioux City, IA, p. A237

PIERSON, Kyle, Chief Financial Officer, Minnie Hamilton HealthCare Center, Grantsville, WV, p. A696

PIERSON, Lois K., Chief Financial Officer, University of Texas Harris County Psychiatric Center, Houston, TX, p. A627

PIETSCH, Al, CPA Senior Vice President and Chief Financial Officer, University of Maryland Baltimore Washington Medical Center, Glen Burnie, MD, p. A301

PIETZ, Gerald
Vice President Finance, Mercy Hospital, Coon Rapids, MN, p. A341
Vice President Finance, Unity Hospital, Fridley, MN, p. A343

PIFER, Eric, M.D. Chief Medical Officer, El Camino Hospital, Mountain View, CA, p. A78

PIFKO, Duane, Interim Director Financial Services, Daniel Drake Center for Post Acute Care, Cincinnati, OH, p. A487

PIGG, Russell, Chief Executive Officer, Eliza Coffee Memorial Hospital, Florence, AL, p. A20

PIGOTT, John, M.D. Chief Medical Officer, Tulane Medical Center, New Orleans, LA, p. A285

PIKE, David, Interim Chief Financial Officer, Memorial Hospital of Carbon County, Rawlins, WY, p. A723

PIKE, Irving, M.D. Senior Vice President and Chief Medical Officer, John Muir Medical Center, Walnut Creek, Walnut Creek, CA, p. A99

PIKE, Pauline, Chief Operating Officer, Beverly Hospital, Beverly, MA, p. A305

PIKE, Randi, Director of Nursing, Pioneer Medical Center, Big Timber, MT, p. A385

PIKE, Ronald F., M.D. Medical Director, Adcare Hospital of Worcester, Worcester, MA, p. A316

PIKE, Tim, M.D. Chief Medical Officer, Portsmouth Regional Hospital, Portsmouth, NH, p. A413

PIKER, John F., M.D. Medical Director, Villa Feliciana Medical Complex, Jackson, LA, p. A278

PIKULA, Shirley, MSN Associate Director Patient Center Care, San Francisco VA Medical Center, San Francisco, CA, p. A90

PIL, Pieter, M.D. Chief Medical Staff, Martha's Vineyard Hospital, Oak Bluffs, MA, p. A313

PILANT, Jason B., Chief Operating Officer, Roane Medical Center, Harriman, TN, p. A583

PILCHER, Shane, Administrative Director Information Systems, Siskin Hospital for Physical Rehabilitation, Chattanooga, TN, p. A580

PILE, Larry, Director Human Resources, Deaconess Hospital, Evansville, IN, p. A210

PILEGGI, Anne, Administrator and Associate Vice President, CHRISTUS Mother Frances Hospital – Jacksonville, Jacksonville, TX, p. A629

PILEGGI, Tim
Interim Chief Financial Officer, Good Shepherd Medical Center, Longview, TX, p. A633
Interim Chief Financial Officer, Good Shepherd Medical Center–Marshall, Marshall, TX, p. A636

PILGRIM, Patti, Chief Financial Officer, Sutter Davis Hospital, Davis, CA, p. A60

PILLION, Scott, Chief Executive Officer, Helen Newberry Joy Hospital, Newberry, MI, p. A331

PILLSBURY, S. Gainer, M.D. Associate Chief Medical Officer, Community Hospital Long Beach, Long Beach, CA, p. A69

PILONG Jr., Alfred E., FACHE, President, Munson Medical Center and Chief Operating Officer, Munson HEalthcare, Munson Medical Center, Traverse City, MI, p. A335

PILOT, Dave, Chief Financial Officer, Essentia Health St. Joseph's Medical Center, Brainerd, MN, p. A340

PINA, Kate, Director Human Resources, Wickenburg Community Hospital, Wickenburg, AZ, p. A41

PINDERSKI, Christopher, M.D. Medical Director of Emergency Room, Black River Medical Center, Poplar Bluff, MO, p. A378

PINE, Richard M., President and Chief Executive Officer, Livengrin Foundation, Bensalem, PA, p. A533

PINEIRO, Carlos M., President, Hospital HIMA de Humacao, Humacao, PR, p. A727

PINER, Thomas J., Director for Resources Management, Naval Medical Center San Diego, San Diego, CA, p. A88

PINKELMAN, Janet, Director Human Resources, Faith Regional Health Services, Norfolk, NE, p. A399

PINKERTON, Jay, Chief of Staff, George Regional Hospital, Lucedale, MS, p. A361

PINKOSKY, Frank
Senior Vice President, Robert Packer Hospital, Sayre, PA, p. A553
Executive Vice President, Troy Community Hospital, Troy, PA, p. A556

PINO, Elena, Chief Operating Officer and Chief Nursing Officer, Mesa Hills Specialty Hospital, El Paso, TX, p. A616

PINO, Joseph, M.D. Chief Medical Officer, Regional Medical Center Bayonet Point, Hudson, FL, p. A131

PINON, Richard, Chief Medical Officer, Eastern New Mexico Medical Center, Roswell, NM, p. A431

PINSKY, Karen, M.D. Chief Medical Information Officer, Penn Medicine Chester County Hospital, West Chester, PA, p. A557

PINSON, Charles Wright, M.D., Deputy Vice Chancellor for Health Affairs and Chief Executive Officer of Vanderbilt Health System, Vanderbilt Health, Nashville, TN, p. B150

PINTO, Frank, Chief Information Officer, The Hospital of Central Connecticut, New Britain, CT, p. A115

PIPER, Kevin, Director Information Systems, Florida Hospital DeLand, DeLand, FL, p. A127

PIPER, Vicky, Vice President Human Resources, Loyola University Medical Center, Maywood, IL, p. A196

PIPGRASS, Michele, Chief Fiscal Service, Oklahoma City Veterans Affairs Medical Center, Oklahoma City, OK, p. A517

PIPKINS, David, Controller, HEALTHSOUTH Rehabilitation Hospital of Beaumont, Beaumont, TX, p. A601

PIPPIN, Kim, Chief Nursing Officer, Select Specialty Hospital–Augusta, Augusta, GA, p. A154

PIRKL, Rollie, Chief Financial Officer, Sierra Vista Regional Medical Center, San Luis Obispo, CA, p. A92

PIRO, Michael J., Chief Information Officer, St. John's Episcopal Hospital–South Shore,, NY, p. A450

PIRRI, SHRM–SCP, Christine, Vice President, Human Resources, Education and Volunteer Services, Cobleskill Regional Hospital, Cobleskill, NY, p. A437

PIRTLE, Kathleen, Director Human Resources, HEALTHSOUTH Rehabilitation Hospital–Wichita Falls, Wichita Falls, TX, p. A657

PIRTLE, Randy B., Chief Financial Officer, King's Daughters Medical Center, Brookhaven, MS, p. A356

PISANO, Thomas, M.D. Chief Professional Services, Connecticut Valley Hospital, Middletown, CT, p. A115

PISCIOTTA, Michael J., Chief Executive Officer, Southern Surgical Hospital, Slidell, LA, p. A288

PISPISA, D. Patricia, Executive Vice President Patient Care Services, Eastern Long Island Hospital, Greenport, NY, p. A440

PISTONE, Maureen
Senior Vice President Talent Development and Human Resources, Appleton Medical Center, Appleton, WI, p. A702
Senior Vice President Human Resources, Theda Clark Medical Center, Neenah, WI, p. A712

PISZCZATOSKI, Thomas J., Chief Human Resource Officer, St. Mary's Medical Center, West Palm Beach, FL, p. A150

PITCHER, Ellen, Chief Nursing Officer and Chief Operating Officer, El Paso Children's Hospital, El Paso, TX, p. A615

PITCHER, Kerry, Administrator, Hale Ho'ola Hamakua, Honokaa, HI, p. A170

PITCHFORD, Edward C., President and Chief Executive Officer, Cole Memorial, Coudersport, PA, p. A536

PITCOCK, Nancy, Vice President Nursing and Chief Nursing Officer, St. Vincent Anderson Regional Hospital, Anderson, IN, p. A206

PITMAN, David R., Vice President Finance, MedStar Harbor Hospital, Baltimore, MD, p. A297

PITTMAN, Cyndi, Chief Financial Officer, Baptist Memorial Hospital – Memphis, Memphis, TN, p. A588

PITTMAN, Jennifer, Chief Financial Officer, Shelby Baptist Medical Center, Alabaster, AL, p. A15

PITTMAN, Jeremy, Chief Financial Officer, Castle Rock Adventist Hospital, Castle Rock, CO, p. A102

PITTMAN, Keisha, Director Human Resources, HEALTHSOUTH Rehabilitation Hospital of Cypress, Houston, TX, p. A624

PITTMAN, Michael, Chief Nursing Officer, Memorial Hospital, Martinsville, VA, p. A673

PITTMAN, Scott M., Chief Operating Officer, Buchanan General Hospital, Grundy, VA, p. A671

PITTS, Celeste, Chief Financial Officer, Upper Connecticut Valley Hospital, Colebrook, NH, p. A410

PITTS, Lynn, Director Human Resources, Calhoun–Liberty Hospital, Blountstown, FL, p. A123

PITTS, Richard, D.O. Medical Director, Arrowhead Regional Medical Center, Colton, CA, p. A59

PITTS, Robert, Executive Director, Wilmington Treatment Center, Wilmington, NC, p. A475

PITTS, Sherry J., Chief Executive Officer, Merit Health Woman's Hospital, Flowood, MS, p. A357

PIVONKA, Mary, Director Quality Management, Rockland Children's Psychiatric Center, Orangeburg, NY, p. A452

PIZ, Tom, Director Human Resources, Fremont Hospital, Fremont, CA, p. A63

PIZARRO, Hugo A., Vice President Human Resources, Terence Cardinal Cooke Health Care Center, New York, NY, p. A450

PIZZANO, Michael, Chief Executive Officer, Kindred Hospital–New Jersey Morris County, Dover, NJ, p. A416

PIZZI, Chris, Chief Operating Officer and Chief Financial Officer, Providence Medford Medical Center, Medford, OR, p. A528

PIZZINO, Mary, Chief Information Officer, Effingham Hospital, Springfield, GA, p. A166

PLACE, Michael, M.D. Deputy Commander Clinical Services, Colonel Florence A. Blanchfield Army Community Hospital, Fort Campbell, KY, p. A260

PLAGGEMEYER, Rikki, Director Acute Care Nursing, Sturgis Regional Hospital, Sturgis, SD, p. A577

PLAISANCE, Stephen, Chief Financial Officer, Meeker Memorial Hospital, Litchfield, MN, p. A345

PLAMONDON, Richard, Vice President Finance and Chief Financial Officer, St. Joseph Hospital, Nashua, NH, p. A412

PLANO, Crystal, Controller, St. Vincent Dunn Hospital, Bedford, IN, p. A206

PLANT, Steven L., Chief Financial Officer, Cottage Hospital, Woodsville, NH, p. A413

PLANTE, Tim, R.N., President and Chief Executive Officer, Memorial Community Hospital and Health System, Blair, NE, p. A394

PLASKETT, Darice S., FACHE, Interim Chief Executive Officer, Governor Juan F. Luis Hospital, Christiansted, VI, p. A731

PLATE, James, M.D. Chief of Staff, Kimball Health Services, Kimball, NE, p. A397

PLATER, Queenie C., Vice President Human Resources for JHM Community Division, Sibley Memorial Hospital, Washington, DC, p. A122

PLATOU, Kenneth E. S., President, Mercy Medical Center Mount Shasta, Mount Shasta, CA, p. A78

PLATT, Anne, Chief Executive Officer, Sutter Amador Hospital, Jackson, CA, p. A66

PLATT, Dwayne, M.D. Chief Medical Officer, Conemaugh Meyersdale Medical Center, Meyersdale, PA, p. A545

PLATZ, Scott, Director Finance, UH Regional Hospitals, Cleveland, OH, p. A490

PLAUTH, William, M.D. Vice President Operations and Chief Medical Officer, Mercy Regional Medical Center, Durango, CO, p. A104

PLAVIAK, David J., Interim Chief Financial Officer, Novant Health UVA Health System Culpeper Medical Center, Culpeper, VA, p. A669

PLAVIN, Joshua, M.D. Medical Director Medicine Division, Gifford Medical Center, Randolph, VT, p. A666

PLAZA, Marta Rivera, Chief Executive Officer and Managing Director, San Juan Capestrano Hospital, San Juan, PR, p. A730

PLEDGER, Michelle, Coordinator Human Resources, Grady General Hospital, Cairo, GA, p. A155

PLEMEL, Jeff, Director Health Information, Chippewa County–Montevideo Hospital, Montevideo, MN, p. A347

PLEMMONS, Debra, Chief Nursing Officer, Middle Park Medical Center–Kremmling, Kremmling, CO, p. A107

PLESKOW, Eric D., President and Chief Executive Officer, BryLin Hospitals, Buffalo, NY, p. A435

PLESS, Katy, Director of Human Resources, CarePartners Health Services, Asheville, NC, p. A460

PLETZ, Richard Andrew, Chief Executive Officer, Plaza Specialty Hospital, Houston, TX, p. A626

PLISKO, Rick, Director information Systems, New York Methodist Hospital,, NY, p. A447

PLOPPER, Michael, M.D. Chief Medical Officer, Sharp Mesa Vista Hospital, San Diego, CA, p. A89

PLOSZEK, Michael, Vice President Physician Strategy and Clinical Operations, Advocate Good Shepherd Hospital, Barrington, IL, p. A181

PLOUCK, Tracy, Director, Ohio Department of Mental Health, Columbus, OH, p. B100

PLOUSHA–MOORE, Debra, Senior Vice President Human Resources, Carolinas Medical Center, Charlotte, NC, p. A462

PLUARD, Dennis, Vice President Finance and Operations, Sarah Bush Lincoln Health Center, Mattoon, IL, p. A196

PLUMLEE, Steve, Chief Executive Officer, Select Specialty Hospital–North Knoxville, Powell, TN, p. A592

PLUMMER, Doug, Chief Operating Officer, Sabine Medical Center, Many, LA, p. A282

PLUMMER, James S., Chief Executive Officer, Aurora Behavioral Healthcare San Diego, San Diego, CA, p. A88

PLUNKETT, Alicia, Chief Nurse Executive, Parkwood Behavioral Health System, Olive Branch, MS, p. A363

PLYMELL, Shane, Chief Operating Officer, Shannon Medical Center, San Angelo, TX, p. A645

POA, Ed, M.D. Chief Inpatient Services, Menninger Clinic, Houston, TX, p. A626

POBLETE, Ronald, M.D. President Medical and Dental Staff, St. Mary's General Hospital, Passaic, NJ, p. A421

POCCHIARI, Michael, Director Human Resources, Garden Park Medical Center, Gulfport, MS, p. A358

POCOCK, Donald, M.D
 Chief Medical Officer, Mease Countryside Hospital, Safety Harbor, FL, p. A144
 Chief Medical Officer, Mease Dunedin Hospital, Dunedin, FL, p. A128

PODE, Maureen, Co–Interim Executive Director, NYC Health + Hospitals / North Central Bronx,, NY, p. A449

PODESTA, Charles H., Chief Information Officer, UC Irvine Medical Center, Orange, CA, p. A81

PODGES, Christopher J., Chief Information Officer and Vice President Outpatient and Retail Services, Munson Medical Center, Traverse City, MI, p. A335

PODLEY, Sandra C., Administrator, Presbyterian Hospital, Albuquerque, NM, p. A428

PODOLSKY, Daniel, M.D., President, William P. Clements, Jr. University Hospital, Dallas, TX, p. A612

PODUSKA, Donna D., MS Chief Nursing Officer, Poudre Valley Hospital, Fort Collins, CO, p. A105

PODZIMEK, Marcia, Chief Human Resources Officer, Wagner Community Memorial Hospital Avera, Wagner, SD, p. A577

POE, Dale
 Vice President and Chief Financial Officer, Hospital Division, Wellmont Bristol Regional Medical Center, Bristol, TN, p. A579
 Vice President and Chief Financial Officer, Wellmont Hawkins County Memorial Hospital, Rogersville, TN, p. A592
 Vice President Finance and Operations, Wellmont Holston Valley Medical Center, Kingsport, TN, p. A585

POE, Terri Lyn, Interim Chief Nursing Officer, University of Alabama Hospital, Birmingham, AL, p. A17

POEHLER, Kathy, Vice President, Human Resources, University of Maryland Baltimore Washington Medical Center, Glen Burnie, MD, p. A301

POEST, Scott, Chief Information Officer, Lake Regional Health System, Osage Beach, MO, p. A378

POFAHL, Barnetta, Director Human Resources, Wagoner Community Hospital, Wagoner, OK, p. A523

POFF, Heather, Director Human Resources, Princeton Community Hospital, Princeton, WV, p. A699

POFFENBARGER, John, Director Fiscal Services, Northern Virginia Mental Health Institute, Falls Church, VA, p. A670

POGAS, George, CPA Senior Vice President and Chief Financial Officer, Witham Health Services, Lebanon, IN, p. A217

POGLIANO, Chris, M.D. Chief Medical Staff, Aspirus Grand View, Ironwood, MI, p. A327

POHJALA, Eric, Chief Financial Officer, Soldiers and Sailors Memorial Hospital, Wellsboro, PA, p. A557

POHJALA, Eric D.
 Executive Vice President and Chief Financial Officer, Muncy Valley Hospital, Muncy, PA, p. A546
 Executive Vice President and Chief Financial Officer, Williamsport Regional Medical Center, Williamsport, PA, p. A558

POHL, Ann–Marie J., R.N. Vice President and Chief Nursing Officer, Lima Memorial Health System, Lima, OH, p. A496

POHL, David F., M.D. Chief of Staff, Cornerstone Hospital of Austin, Austin, TX, p. A599

POHL, David L., M.D. Chief of Staff, Hillcrest Hospital – South, Tulsa, OK, p. A521

POIROT, Diane, Vice President Human Resources, Harris Health System, Houston, TX, p. A624

POISKER, Karen C., MSN Vice President Patient Care Services and Chief Nursing Officer, Peninsula Regional Medical Center, Salisbury, MD, p. A303

POISSON, Keith R., Executive Vice President and Chief Operating Officer, Greater Baltimore Medical Center, Baltimore, MD, p. A296

POLAND, David, Vice President Finance, Grove City Medical Center, Grove City, PA, p. A539

POLASHEK, Maurene, Chief Financial Officer, Oro Valley Hospital, Oro Valley, AZ, p. A35

POLHEBER, Richard, Chief Executive Officer, Benson Hospital, Benson, AZ, p. A31

POLHILL, James, M.D. Chief Medical Officer, Jefferson Hospital, Louisville, GA, p. A162

POLIKAITIS, Audrius, Chief Information Officer, University of Illinois Hospital & Health Sciences System, Chicago, IL, p. A187

POLING, Rodney, M.D. Medical Director, Behavioral HealthCare Center at Columbia, Columbia, TN, p. A581

POLING, Susan, Director Human Resources, King's Daughters' Health, Madison, IN, p. A217

POLITE, Elmer, Chief Financial Officer, East Georgia Regional Medical Center, Statesboro, GA, p. A166

POLITI, Victor, M.D., President and Chief Executive Officer, Nassau University Medical Center, East Meadow, NY, p. A438

POLITO, Janine, Chief Human Resources Officer, Banner Ironwood Medical Center, San Tan Valley, AZ, p. A38

POLIVKA, Maureen, Chief Nursing Officer, Hill Country Memorial Hospital, Fredericksburg, TX, p. A619

POLIZZI, Arturo, President, ProMedica Toledo Hospital, Toledo, OH, p. A504

POLK, Brent, M.D. Chair Department of Pediatrics and Vice President Academic Affairs, Children's Hospital Los Angeles, Los Angeles, CA, p. A70

POLK, Claire, Chief Financial Officer, Lake Norman Regional Medical Center, Mooresville, NC, p. A470

POLK, Monica, Interim Medical Director, Salt Lake Behavioral Health, Salt Lake City, UT, p. A663

POLKOW, Craig, Chief Executive Officer, DeKalb Health, Auburn, IN, p. A206

POLLACK, Neil, Senior Administrator, Terence Cardinal Cooke Health Care Center, New York, NY, p. A450

POLLACK, Richard, Vice President Information Services, VCU Medical Center, Richmond, VA, p. A678

POLLAK, Erich, M.D. Chief of Staff, West Covina Medical Center, West Covina, CA, p. A99

POLLARD, Amy, R.N., President and Chief Executive Officer, Nicholas H. Noyes Memorial Hospital, Dansville, NY, p. A438

POLLARD, Anthony, D.O. Chief Medical Officer, AMG Specialty Hospital – Las Vegas, Las Vegas, NV, p. A405

POLLARD, Dennis, President of Community Memorial Hospital, Community Memorial Hospital, Menomonee Falls, WI, p. A710

POLLMAN, Brian, Chief Medical Officer, Hutchinson Health, Hutchinson, MN, p. A344

POLLNOW, Dean, M.D. President Medical Staff, Ministry Saint Mary's Hospitals, Rhinelander, WI, p. A715

POLLOCK, Jeffrey, Chief Information Officer, Wentworth–Douglass Hospital, Dover, NH, p. A410

POLLOCK, Maureen King, Chief Executive Officer, Eagleville Hospital, Eagleville, PA, p. A537

POLO, Fabian, Chief Executive Officer, Baylor Institute for Rehabilitation, Dallas, TX, p. A609

POLO, James A., M.D. Chief Medical Officer, Western State Hospital, Tacoma, WA, p. A692

POLO, Therese, Medical Staff President, Carlinville Area Hospital, Carlinville, IL, p. A182

POLSELLI, Donna, Chief Operating Officer, Franciscan Hospital for Children, Boston, MA, p. A306

POLSTER, Peggy, Manager Personnel and Administrative Assistant, Falls Community Hospital and Clinic, Marlin, TX, p. A635

POLZIN, Greg
 Chief Financial Officer, Iowa Specialty Hospital–Belmond, Belmond, IA, p. A225
 Chief Financial Officer, Iowa Specialty Hospital–Clarion, Clarion, IA, p. A227

POMA, Frank W., President, St. John River District Hospital, East China, MI, p. A323

POMMETT, Jr., Francis A., Chief Operating Officer, Shands Lake Shore Regional Medical Center, Lake City, FL, p. A133

PONCE, Agustin, Supervisor Maintenance, Castaner General Hospital, Castaner, PR, p. A726

PONCE, Joseph A., Chief Information Management, Dwight David Eisenhower Army Medical Center, Fort Gordon, GA, p. A160

PONCE, Martha, Director Information Technologies and Telecommunications, Providence Saint John's Health Center, Santa Monica, CA, p. A93

POND, Dwight, TIS Boise, Saint Alphonsus Regional Medical Center, Boise, ID, p. A174

POND–BELL, Michele, R.N. Nurse Administrator, Cassia Regional Medical Center, Burley, ID, p. A175

PONDER, Beverly K., Executive Assistant and Human Resources Coordinator, Covington County Hospital, Collins, MS, p. A357

PONDER, David, Information Technology Officer, Claremore Indian Hospital, Claremore, OK, p. A510

PONETA, Jan, Director Information Services, Mercy Hospital Jefferson, Crystal City, MO, p. A370

PONOZZO, Nancy Lynn, MSN Chief Nursing Officer, Aspirus Iron River Hospitals & Clinics, Iron River, MI, p. A327

PONTICELLO, Nat, Vice President Human Resources, Valley Children's Healthcare, Madera, CA, p. A75

PONTIOUS, Becky, Human Resources/Accounting, Loring Hospital, Sac City, IA, p. A237

PONTIOUS, Michael, M.D. Chief of Staff, St. Mary's Regional Medical Center, Enid, OK, p. A511

POOCH, Fred, Supervisor Information Technology, Johnson County Hospital, Tecumseh, NE, p. A402

POOK, Lots, Chief Information Officer, National Jewish Health, Denver, CO, p. A104

POOLE, Karen, Chief Operating Officer, Boca Raton Regional Hospital, Boca Raton, FL, p. A124

POOLE, Rob, Director, Jane Phillips Memorial Medical Center, Bartlesville, OK, p. A509

POOLE–ADAMS, Veronica, R.N. Vice President, Chief Operating Officer and Chief Nursing Executive, Cleveland Regional Medical Center, Shelby, NC, p. A473

POORE, Justin, D.O. Chief Medical Staff, Cloud County Health Center, Concordia, KS, p. A242

POORE, Luke, Chief Executive Officer, Kearney County Health Services, Minden, NE, p. A398

POORE, Timothy T., Chief Executive Officer, HEALTHSOUTH Scottsdale Rehabilitation Hospital, Scottsdale, AZ, p. A38

POORTEN, Kevin
 President, Northwestern Medicine Kishwaukee Hospital, DeKalb, IL, p. A188
 President, Northwestern Medicine Valley West Hospital, Sandwich, IL, p. A202

POOS, Joshua, M.D. President Medical Staff, Community Memorial Hospital, Staunton, IL, p. A204

POPE, Alan R., M.D
 Vice President, Medical Affairs, Lourdes Medical Center of Burlington County, Willingboro, NJ, p. A425
 Chief Medical Officer, Our Lady of Lourdes Medical Center, Camden, NJ, p. A415

POPE, Alice H., Chief Financial Officer, HonorHealth Scottsdale Thompson Peak Medical Center, Scottsdale, AZ, p. A39

POPE, Brad W., Vice President Human Resources, CHI Memorial, Chattanooga, TN, p. A580

POPE, Eddie, Chief Information Officer, Lackey Memorial Hospital, Forest, MS, p. A358

POPE, James W., FACHE, President and Chief Executive Officer, Van Wert County Hospital, Van Wert, OH, p. A504

POPE, Jayne E., FACHE, Chief Executive Officer, Hill Country Memorial Hospital, Fredericksburg, TX, p. A619

POPE, Richard, Vice President Human Resources, Jackson County Memorial Hospital, Altus, OK, p. A508

POPE, Robert, Information Technology Director and Ministry Liaison, St. Vincent Anderson Regional Hospital, Anderson, IN, p. A206

POPHAN, Cameron, Chief Financial Officer, Spalding Regional Hospital, Griffin, GA, p. A160

POPKIN, Steven, Chief Executive Officer, Parkview Community Hospital Medical Center, Riverside, CA, p. A86

POPLI, Anand, Medical Director, Porter–Starke Services, Valparaiso, IN, p. A223

POPOVICH, John, M.D., President and Chief Executive Officer, Henry Ford Hospital, Detroit, MI, p. A322

POPOWYCZ, Alex, Senior Vice President / Chief Information Officer, Health First Palm Bay Hospital, Palm Bay, FL, p. A141

POPP, Adam, Director Information Systems, Avera St. Benedict Health Center, Parkston, SD, p. A575

POPP, Jason, Chief of Medical Staff, Rochelle Community Hospital, Rochelle, IL, p. A201

POPP, Susan, Controller, Kindred Hospital–Fort Worth, Fort Worth, TX, p. A618

POPPEN, Jeffrey, Chief Financial Officer, Sanford Aberdeen Medical Center, Aberdeen, SD, p. A572

POPPERT, Dale, M.D. Chief of Staff, Kaiser Permanente Antioch Medical Center, Antioch, CA, p. A54

POPPY, Bill, Chief Information Officer, Virginia Mason Medical Center, Seattle, WA, p. A690

POQUETTE, Gary R., FACHE, Chief Executive Officer, Penobscot Valley Hospital, Lincoln, ME, p. A294

PORADA, John, Chief Financial Officer, TriStar Southern Hills Medical Center, Nashville, TN, p. A591

PORCELLI, Cheri, MSN Chief Nursing Officer, Deer's Head Hospital Center, Salisbury, MD, p. A303

PORCO, Albert, Director Management Information Systems, HackensackUMC Palisades, North Bergen, NJ, p. A421

PORTCHY, Mindy, Manager Human Resources, Summit Pacific Medical Center, Elma, WA, p. A684

PORTER, Billy, Vice President Clinical Operations, CHRISTUS Health Shreveport–Bossier, Shreveport, LA, p. A287

PORTER, Bruce, Chief Financial Officer, Red River Hospital, LLC, Wichita Falls, TX, p. A657

PORTER, Cedric, M.D. President Medical Staff, Emanuel Medical Center, Swainsboro, GA, p. A167

PORTER, Daniel J., Senior Vice President and Chief Financial Officer, J. Arthur Dosher Memorial Hospital, Southport, NC, p. A474

PORTER, Dorothy L., Director of Compliance/Risk/Quality, Asheville Specialty Hospital, Asheville, NC, p. A460

PORTER, Glen, Vice President Human Resources, Essentia Health St. Mary's Medical Center, Duluth, MN, p. A342

PORTER, Greg, Chief Financial Officer, Rio Grande Hospital, Del Norte, CO, p. A103

PORTER, James, Chief Financial Officer, Brookdale Hospital Medical Center, New York, NY, p. A444

PORTER, James, M.D. Vice President Medical Affairs, Deaconess Hospital, Evansville, IN, p. A210

PORTER, James P., Chief Financial Officer, St. Bernard Hospital and Health Care Center, Chicago, IL, p. A187

PORTER, Jim, Chief Financial Officer, Southern Virginia Regional Medical Center, Emporia, VA, p. A669

PORTER, Jody, R.N. Senior Vice President Patient Care Services and Chief Nursing Officer, Greater Baltimore Medical Center, Baltimore, MD, p. A296

PORTER, John T., President and Chief Executive Officer, Avera Health, Sioux Falls, SD, p. B17

PORTER, Lance, Chief Executive Officer, Banner Payson Medical Center, Payson, AZ, p. A35

PORTER, Laura, Executive Director, Good Shepherd Penn Partners Specialty Hospital at Rittenhouse, Philadelphia, PA, p. A548

PORTER, Lisa, Director Human Resources, Leadership and Education, Veterans Affairs Salt Lake City Health Care System, Salt Lake City, UT, p. A664

PORTER, Patricia, Executive Director, South Oaks Hospital, Amityville, NY, p. A433

PORTER, Sharon, Chief Financial Officer, Massachusetts Hospital School, Canton, MA, p. A309

PORTER, Stephen D., President, Sentara Northern Virginia Medical Center, Woodbridge, VA, p. A680

PORTER, T. J., Director Human Resources, Bennett County Hospital and Nursing Home, Martin, SD, p. A574

PORTERFIELD, Liza, Chief Financial Officer, Regional Medical Center, Orangeburg, SC, p. A569

PORTMAN, Angela, Chief Executive Officer, Breckinridge Memorial Hospital, Hardinsburg, KY, p. A261

PORTNER, Barry, M.D. Chief of Staff, Prowers Medical Center, Lamar, CO, p. A108

PORWOLL, Amy, Vice President of Information Systems, St. Cloud Hospital, Saint Cloud, MN, p. A350

POSAR, Steven, M.D. Chief of Medicine, Doctors NeuroMedical Hospital, Bremen, IN, p. A207

POSCH, Tim B., Business Manager and Director Personnel, Parsons State Hospital and Training Center, Parsons, KS, p. A252

POSECAI, Scott J., Executive Vice President and Chief Financial Officer, Ochsner Medical Center, New Orleans, LA, p. A285

POSEY, Dawn, Chief Operating Officer, Promise Hospital of Vicksburg, Vicksburg, MS, p. A365

POSEY, Richard B., Director Human Resources, Baptist Easley Hospital, Easley, SC, p. A565

POSMOGA, Paul, Chief Financial Officer, Twin Cities Community Hospital, Templeton, CA, p. A96

POSPISIL, Matt E., Vice President, Clinical Operations, Nebraska Medicine – Bellevue, Bellevue, NE, p. A394

POST, Eleanor, R.N. Chief Nursing Officer, Rockdale Medical Center, Conyers, GA, p. A157

POST, John, M.D. Medical Director, Morrill County Community Hospital, Bridgeport, NE, p. A394

POST, Kevin, D.O. Chief Medical Officer, Hegg Memorial Health Center Avera, Rock Valley, IA, p. A237

POST, Kimberly
Senior Vice President and Chief Executive Officer, HonorHealth Scottsdale Osborn Medical Center, Scottsdale, AZ, p. A38
Senior Vice President and Chief Clinical Officer, HonorHealth Scottsdale Thompson Peak Medical Center, Scottsdale, AZ, p. A39

POST, Michael, Chief Executive Officer, Clarion Psychiatric Center, Clarion, PA, p. A535

POSTERNACK, Charles, M.D. Vice President, Boca Raton Regional Hospital, Boca Raton, FL, p. A124

POSTLER–SLATTERY, Diane, Ph.D., President and Chief Executive Officer, MidMichigan Health, Midland, MI, p. B91

POSTLETHWAIT, Betsy, President, Princeton Baptist Medical Center, Birmingham, AL, p. A17

POSTON, Anne, Director of Human Resources/Compliance, Lake City Community Hospital, Lake City, SC, p. A567

POSTULKA, Carol, Administrative Coordinator, Avera Gregory Hospital, Gregory, SD, p. A574

POTEATE, Kathy, Interim Director Human Resources, Hugh Chatham Memorial Hospital, Elkin, NC, p. A465

POTEETE, Robin
Manager Human Resources, Wellmont Hancock County Hospital, Sneedville, TN, p. A593
Manager Human Resources, Wellmont Hawkins County Memorial Hospital, Rogersville, TN, p. A592

POTITADKUL, Wendy, Chief Information Officer, Sunrise Canyon Hospital, Lubbock, TX, p. A634

POTTENGER, Jay, Administrator, Montana State Hospital, Warm Springs, MT, p. A391

POTTER, Carolyn
Vice President Human Resources, McLaren Bay Region, Bay City, MI, p. A319
Vice President Human Resources, McLaren Bay Special Care, Bay City, MI, p. A319
Vice President Human Resources, McLaren Central Michigan, Mount Pleasant, MI, p. A330

POTTER, Dianne P., Manager Human Resources, Parkview Whitley Hospital, Columbia City, IN, p. A208

POTTER, Val, Director Human Resources, St. Vincent Salem Hospital, Salem, IN, p. A221

POTTORFF, Kelly, Chief Executive Officer, Harrison County Community Hospital, Bethany, MO, p. A367

POTTS, Kevin, M.D. Medical Director, Kindred Hospital Detroit, Detroit, MI, p. A322

POTTS, Mary Ann, Director Personnel, Community Hospitals and Wellness Centers, Bryan, OH, p. A485

POUGNAUD, Teresa, Vice President Human Resources, McLeod Loris Seacoast Hospital, Loris, SC, p. A568

POULSON, Rhonda, Chief Nursing Officer and Vice President of Clinical Operations, CHI Memorial, Chattanooga, TN, p. A580

POUND, Steve, Vice President Human Resources, St. Joseph's Hospital, Savannah, GA, p. A166

POUND, Terry, Chief Financial Officer, Hospital District No 1 of Rice County, Lyons, KS, p. A248

POUND, Veronica, R.N., Administrator, Socorro General Hospital, Socorro, NM, p. A432

POVICH, Mark, D.O. Medical Director, OSF St. Francis Hospital and Medical Group, Escanaba, MI, p. A323

POWE, Lee, Director Management Information Systems, Hugh Chatham Memorial Hospital, Elkin, NC, p. A465

POWEL, Linda J., M.D. Medical Director, Odessa Memorial Healthcare Center, Odessa, WA, p. A687

POWELL, Adam, Program Manager, Marion Veterans Affairs Medical Center, Marion, IL, p. A195

POWELL, Candy, Administrator, Collingsworth General Hospital, Wellington, TX, p. A657

POWELL, Charles, Chief Financial Officer, Arkansas Surgical Hospital, North Little Rock, AR, p. A50

POWELL, D. Jerome, M.D
Chief Information Officer, Highland Hospital, Rochester, NY, p. A454
Chief Information Officer, Strong Memorial Hospital of the University of Rochester, Rochester, NY, p. A454

POWELL, Frank R., Chief Financial Officer, Piedmont Mountainside Hospital, Jasper, GA, p. A161

POWELL, Hannah, Chief Nursing Officer, Mercy Hospital Kingfisher, Kingfisher, OK, p. A513

POWELL, Holly, Chief Executive Officer, Select Specialty Hospital–Dallas, Carrollton, TX, p. A605

POWELL, Jackie, Director Human Resources, Pemiscot Memorial Health System, Hayti, MO, p. A372

POWELL, James R., Associate Administrator, Banner Gateway Medical Center, Gilbert, AZ, p. A32

POWELL, Jimmy, Manager Human Resources, Harry S. Truman Memorial Veterans Hospital, Columbia, MO, p. A370

POWELL, John, M.D. Chief Medical Officer, Caldwell Memorial Hospital, Lenoir, NC, p. A468

POWELL, Josh, Facility Controller, Cox Monett, Monett, MO, p. A377

POWELL, Kay, Director Human Resources, CHRISTUS Southeast Texas Jasper Memorial, Jasper, TX, p. A629

POWELL, Marissa, Human Resources Director, Sistersville General Hospital, Sistersville, WV, p. A700

POWELL, Michelle, Chief Executive Officer, Select Rehabilitation Hospital of Denton, Denton, TX, p. A613

POWELL, Mike, Chief Executive Officer, Fulton Medical Center, Fulton, MO, p. A371

POWELL, Parker, Chief Executive Officer, Glendive Medical Center, Glendive, MT, p. A387

POWELL, Tammy, M.P.H., President, St. Anthony Hospital, Oklahoma City, OK, p. A517

POWELL, Traci, Director Human Resources, HEALTHSOUTH Emerald Coast Rehabilitation Hospital, Panama City, FL, p. A141

POWELL, Troy, Chief Executive Officer, HEALTHSOUTH Rehabilitation Hospital of Charleston, Charleston, SC, p. A562

POWELL, Virginia, Director Finance, Wilmington Treatment Center, Wilmington, NC, p. A475

POWELL–STAFFORD, Valerie L., Chief Executive Officer, Englewood Community Hospital, Englewood, FL, p. A128

POWELSON, Jeffrey A., Chief Executive Officer, Broaddus Hospital, Philippi, WV, p. A699

POWER, Bob, Vice President Information Services, Good Samaritan Regional Medical Center, Corvallis, OR, p. A525

POWER, Robert
Vice President Information Services, Samaritan Lebanon Community Hospital, Lebanon, OR, p. A527
Chief Information Officer, Samaritan Pacific Communities Hospital, Newport, OR, p. A528
Associate Executive Director Finance, Southside Hospital, Bay Shore, NY, p. A434

POWERS, Barbara, R.N. Chief Nursing Officer, Austin Lakes Hospital, Austin, TX, p. A598

POWERS, Brent, M.D. Vice President/Chief Medical Officer, Lexington Medical Center, West Columbia, SC, p. A570

POWERS, Charles, M.D. Administrative Medical Director, WK Bossier Health Center, Bossier City, LA, p. A274

POWERS, Donald, Chairman, President and Chief Executive Officer, Community Healthcare System, Hammond, IN, p. B40

POWERS, Jamekia, Assistant Director Human Resources, Georgia Regional Hospital at Savannah, Savannah, GA, p. A166

POWERS, Judi, Chief Executive Officer, Advanced Care Hospital of Montana, Billings, MT, p. A385

POWERS, Kelli, Chief Financial Officer, Huntsville Hospital, Huntsville, AL, p. A21

POWERS, Mary, MS
Senior Vice President and Chief Nursing Officer, Manchester Memorial Hospital, Manchester, CT, p. A114
Senior Vice President and Chief Nursing Officer, Rockville General Hospital, Vernon, CT, p. A117

POWERS, Ryan J., Vice President Finance, Spectrum Health Zeeland Community Hospital, Zeeland, MI, p. A337

POWERS, Tim, Chief Executive Officer, North Canyon Medical Center, Gooding, ID, p. A176

POWRIE, Raymond, M.D. Senior Vice President Quality and Clinical Effectiveness, Women & Infants Hospital of Rhode Island, Providence, RI, p. A561

POYNTER, Carmen, Director Human Resources, Rockcastle Regional Hospital and Respiratory Care Center, Mount Vernon, KY, p. A267

PRABHU, Asha, M.D. Chief Medical Officer, Warren State Hospital, Warren, PA, p. A556

PRACHEIL, Michael, Chief Financial Officer, Gothenburg Memorial Hospital, Gothenburg, NE, p. A396

PRACHT, Matthew, Vice President Finance, Scotland Health Care System, Laurinburg, NC, p. A468

PRADA, Janina
Director Information Technology, El Paso Children's Hospital, El Paso, TX, p. A615
Director Information Services, University Medical Center of El Paso, El Paso, TX, p. A616

PRAFKA, David, Ed.D. Director of Human Resources, Vidant Edgecombe Hospital, Tarboro, NC, p. A474

PRAKASH, Amitabh, M.D. Chief Medical Officer, AHMC Anaheim Regional Medical Center, Anaheim, CA, p. A54

PRANTE, Melissa, Chief Financial Officer, Kimball Health Services, Kimball, NE, p. A397

PRASAD, Siripurapu, Chief of Staff, Harrison Community Hospital, Cadiz, OH, p. A486

PRATER, Judith, Director of Nursing, Pike County Memorial Hospital, Louisiana, MO, p. A376

PRATER, Marita, MS Vice President Patient Care Services, Sturdy Memorial Hospital, Attleboro, MA, p. A305

PRATER, Marsha A., Ph.D. Senior Vice President and Chief Nursing Officer, Memorial Medical Center, Springfield, IL, p. A203

PRATER, Robin, Director Human Resources, Howard A. Rusk Rehabilitation Center, Columbia, MO, p. A370

PRATHER, Jean, Director of Human Resources, Greene County General Hospital, Linton, IN, p. A217

PRATHER, Rachael, Chief Nursing Officer, Ferrell Hospital, Eldorado, IL, p. A189

PRATT, Audra, Chief Human Resource Officer, St. Vincent Indianapolis Hospital, Indianapolis, IN, p. A215

PRATT, Bailey
Interim Chief Financial Officer, Lincoln County Health System, Fayetteville, TN, p. A583
Chief Financial Officer, Saint Thomas Hickman Hospital, Centerville, TN, p. A580

PRATT, Dustin, M.D. Chief of Staff, Childress Regional Medical Center, Childress, TX, p. A606

PRATT, Lisa D.
Vice President, Human Resources, McLean Hospital, Belmont, MA, p. A305
Vice President Human Resources, Memorial Hospital of Rhode Island, Pawtucket, RI, p. A560

PRATT, Mary Ellen, FACHE, Chief Executive Officer, St. James Parish Hospital, Lutcher, LA, p. A282

PRATT, Ramona, Chief Operating Officer, PIH Health Hospital – Downey, Downey, CA, p. A61

PRATT, Timothy J., M.D. Vice President Medical Affairs and Chief Medical Officer, SSM St. Clare Hospital, Fenton, MO, p. A371

PRATT, Troy, Information Technology Site Director, Covenant Medical Center, Lubbock, TX, p. A634

PRAY, Jan, Coordinator Payroll and Benefits, Curahealth Boston North Shore, Peabody, MA, p. A313

PREAU, William, M.D. Medical Director, Fairway Medical Surgical Hospital, Covington, LA, p. A275

PREISINGER, Andrea, Director Human Resources, Menninger Clinic, Houston, TX, p. A626

PREMO, Mark, Senior Director HC Intelligence, Providence Portland Medical Center, Portland, OR, p. A529

PRENTISS, Kristin, Chief Financial Officer, Specialty Hospital of Central Jersey, Lakewood, NJ, p. A418

PRESCOTT, Tina, Vice President, Hospital Services, Jackson–Madison County General Hospital, Jackson, TN, p. A584

PRESNELL, Elizabeth, Assistant Vice President of Finance, St. Luke's Hospital, Columbus, NC, p. A463

PRESS, Robert, M.D. Senior Vice President, Vice Dean and Chief Hospital Operations, NYU Langone Medical Center, New York, NY, p. A449

PRESSER, Jonathan, Vice President Finance and Operations, Norton Audubon Hospital, Louisville, KY, p. A264

PRESSMAN, Eric, D.O. Chair Department of Medicine, Englewood Community Hospital, Englewood, FL, p. A128

PRESTEGAARD, Benjamin, Chief Medical Officer, UH Portage Medical Center, Ravenna, OH, p. A501

PRESTON, Tara
 Director Human Resources, Bingham Memorial Hospital, Blackfoot, ID, p. A174
 Director Human Resources, Mountain River Birthing and Surgery Center, Blackfoot, ID, p. A174

PRESTON, Troy, Director Human Resources, Schuyler Hospital, Montour Falls, NY, p. A443

PRESTRIDGE, Tim, Chief Operating Officer, Terre Haute Regional Hospital, Terre Haute, IN, p. A222

PRETE, Mark, M.D. Vice President Medical Affairs, The Charlotte Hungerford Hospital, Torrington, CT, p. A117

PRETTYMAN, Edgar E., PsyD, Chief Executive Officer, Texas NeuroRehab Center, Austin, TX, p. A600

PRETZLAFF, Robert, M.D
 Chief Medical Officer, St. Rose Dominican Hospitals – San Martin Campus, Las Vegas, NV, p. A406
 Chief Medical Officer, St. Rose Dominican Hospitals – Siena Campus, Henderson, NV, p. A405

PREWITT, Connie F., Chief Financial Officer, Billings Clinic, Billings, MT, p. A385

PREWITT, Margaret Elizabeth, Vice President Patient Services and Chief Nursing Officer, St. Catherine Hospital, Garden City, KS, p. A243

PRIBYL, Stephen J., FACHE, President, District One Hospital, Faribault, MN, p. A342

PRICE, Bernard J., Chief Human Resources Officer, Medical Center, Navicent Health, Macon, GA, p. A162

PRICE, Connie, M.D. Chief Medical Officer, Denver Health, Denver, CO, p. A103

PRICE, David, Chief Executive Officer, HonorHealth Scottsdale Thompson Peak Medical Center, Scottsdale, AZ, p. A39

PRICE, Ed, Chief Nurse Officer, Shelby Baptist Medical Center, Alabaster, AL, p. A15

PRICE, James, Assistant Administrator Finance and Operations, State Hospital South, Blackfoot, ID, p. A174

PRICE, John D., Chief Financial Officer, FirstHealth Richmond Memorial Hospital, Rockingham, NC, p. A472

PRICE, Julie, Chief Financial Officer, Rooks County Health Center, Plainville, KS, p. A252

PRICE, Kelley, R.N. Interim Chief Executive Officer, Battle Mountain General Hospital, Battle Mountain, NV, p. A404

PRICE, Kevin A.
 Vice President and Chief Operating Officer, Sparrow Clinton Hospital, Saint Johns, MI, p. A333
 Vice President and Chief Operating Officer, Sparrow Ionia Hospital, Ionia, MI, p. A326

PRICE, Kim, Chief Executive Officer, Franklin General Hospital, Hampton, IA, p. A231

PRICE, Larry, Chief Executive Officer, Limestone Medical Center, Groesbeck, TX, p. A622

PRICE, Lawrence, M.D., President and Chief Operating Officer, Butler Hospital, Providence, RI, p. A560

PRICE, Lori, President, Gottlieb Memorial Hospital, Melrose Park, IL, p. A196

PRICE, Lorraine B., Associate Director, Hampton Veterans Affairs Medical Center, Hampton, VA, p. A671

PRICE, Manuel, Director Information Systems, Brookwood Baptist Medical Center, Birmingham, AL, p. A16

PRICE, Meredith, Vice President Fiscal Services and Chief Financial Officer, St. Joseph's Hospital Health Center, Syracuse, NY, p. A456

PRICE, Norman M., FACHE, Chief Executive Officer and Administrator, Southwest Health Systems, Mccomb, MS, p. B126

PRICE, Norman M., FACHE, Chief Executive Officer, Southwest Mississippi Regional Medical Center, McComb, MS, p. A361

PRICE, Peggy Cain, Vice President and Chief Operating Officer, Lutheran Medical Center, Wheat Ridge, CO, p. A111

PRICE, Sam, Executive Vice President Finance/Chief Financial Officer, East Alabama Medical Center, Opelika, AL, p. A24

PRICE, Shari, Director Information Services, Baptist Health Louisville, Louisville, KY, p. A264

PRICE, Shelby, Chief Executive Officer, Louisiana State Hospitals, Baton Rouge, LA, p. B84

PRICE, Terry, Director Information Technology, Great Plains Regional Medical Center, Elk City, OK, p. A511

PRICE, Tonya, Chief Nursing Officer, Wilson N. Jones Regional Medical Center, Sherman, TX, p. A649

PRICE, Walter, Director Information Technology, Newport Hospital and Health Services, Newport, WA, p. A687

PRICKEL, Trisha, Director Information Systems, Margaret Mary Health, Batesville, IN, p. A206

PRIDDY, III, Ernest C., Chief Financial Officer, Old Vineyard Behavioral Health Services, Winston–Salem, NC, p. A476

PRIDDY, Steven L., M.D. Vice President Physician Affairs and Chief Medical Officer, St. Vincent Carmel Hospital, Carmel, IN, p. A208

PRIDEAUX, Heather, Chief Financial Officer, Rawlins County Health Center, Atwood, KS, p. A240

PRIDGEN, Kim, Chief Financial Officer, Northcrest Medical Center, Springfield, TN, p. A593

PRIES, Kathleen M., Director Human Resources, Nazareth Hospital, Philadelphia, PA, p. A549

PRIEST, David, Director Information Systems, Munson Healthcare Charlevoix Hospital, Charlevoix, MI, p. A320

PRIEST, Geoff, M.D. Chief Medical Officer, Meriter UnityPoint Health, Madison, WI, p. A709

PRIEST, Mike, M.D. Chief of Staff, Pawhuska Hospital, Pawhuska, OK, p. A518

PRIESTLEY, Betty, Manager Business Office, Pine Valley Specialty Hospital, Houston, TX, p. A626

PRIHODA, Matt, M.D. Chief of Staff, Washington County Hospital and Clinics, Washington, IA, p. A238

PRILUTSKY, Michael, Chief Operating Officer, Jersey City Medical Center, Jersey City, NJ, p. A418

PRINCE, Clay, M.D. Chief Medical Officer, Madison Memorial Hospital, Rexburg, ID, p. A178

PRINCE, Gayle, Director Human Resources, Washington County Regional Medical Center, Sandersville, GA, p. A165

PRINCE, Kem, Manager of Finance, Parkview Noble Hospital, Kendallville, IN, p. A215

PRINCE, Michael, Interim Chief Executive Officer, Lewis County General Hospital, Lowville, NY, p. A442

PRINCE, Sue, Director Information Systems, Northern Westchester Hospital, Mount Kisco, NY, p. A443

PRINCIPE, Hector Cintron, M.D. Director, Hospital Universitario Dr. Ramon Ruiz Arnau, Bayamon, PR, p. A726

PRINGLE, Robert W., M.D. Vice President Medical Affairs and Chief Medical Officer, Glens Falls Hospital, Glens Falls, NY, p. A439

PRINGLE–MILLER, Letitia, Administrative Director, Palmetto Health Tuomey, Sumter, SC, p. A570

PRINTY, Wayne, Chief Financial Officer and Senior Vice President Finance, LincolnHealth, Damariscotta, ME, p. A292

PRIORE, Jacqueline, Chief Nursing Officer, Samaritan Hospital, Troy, NY, p. A457

PRISELAC, Thomas M., President and Chief Executive Officer, Cedars–Sinai, West Hollywood, CA, p. B31

PRISELAC, Thomas M., President and Chief Executive Officer, Cedars–Sinai Medical Center, Los Angeles, CA, p. A70

PRISTER, James R.
 President and Chief Executive Officer, RML Specialty Hospital, Chicago, IL, p. A186
 President and Chief Executive Officer, RML Specialty Hospital, Hinsdale, IL, p. A193

PRITCHARD, Jason, Chief Financial Officer, Hackensack University Medical Center at Pascack Valley, Westwood, NJ, p. A425

PRITCHARD, Joann, Chief Financial Officer, Erie Veterans Affairs Medical Center, Erie, PA, p. A538

PRITCHETT, Greg, Chief Financial Officer, Cuero Community Hospital, Cuero, TX, p. A608

PRITCHETT, Lynette, Chief Executive Officer, Tennova Healthcare–Jamestown, Jamestown, TN, p. A584

PRITT, Wayne M., Commander, U. S. Air Force Hospital, Hampton, VA, p. A671

PRIVETT, David, Deputy Director, Western New York Children's Psychiatric Center, West Seneca, NY, p. A459

PROBASCO, Brent, Chief Financial Officer, Cass Regional Medical Center, Harrisonville, MO, p. A372

PROBST, Keith, M.D. Chief of Staff, Avera Holy Family Hospital, Estherville, IA, p. A230

PROBST, Nancy, R.N. Chief Nursing Officer, Bigfork Valley Hospital, Bigfork, MN, p. A339

PROBUS, Kimberly, Chief Nursing Officer, Opelousas General Health System, Opelousas, LA, p. A286

PROCHASKA, Jodi, Chief Financial Officer, Butler County Health Care Center, David City, NE, p. A395

PROCHILO, John F., Chief Executive Officer and Administrator, Northeast Rehabilitation Hospital, Salem, NH, p. A413

PROCHNOW, Bryan, Chief Financial Officer, Matagorda Regional Medical Center, Bay City, TX, p. A601

PROCTOR, Brandy, Director of Nursing, North Star Behavioral Health System, Anchorage, AK, p. A28

PROCTOR, Quinn, Director Human Resources, Claremore Indian Hospital, Claremore, OK, p. A510

PROCTOR, Sandra, R.N. Chief Nurse Executive, Memorial Medical Center, Modesto, CA, p. A77

PROCTOR, Scott, Chief Executive Officer, Safe Haven Hospital of Treasure Valley, Boise, ID, p. A174

PROCTOR, Stephen, Director of Human Resources/Risk, Russellville Hospital, Russellville, AL, p. A25

PROFOTA, Lori, R.N. Chief Nursing Officer, Copley Hospital, Morrisville, VT, p. A665

PROKOPCHAK, Greg, Senior Director Human Resources, Piedmont Hospital, Atlanta, GA, p. A153

PRONGER, Derk F., Chief Operating Officer, Munson Medical Center, Traverse City, MI, p. A335

PRONI, John, CPA Manager Finance and Operations, BayCare Alliant Hospital, Dunedin, FL, p. A127

PROPP, Elizabeth R., Vice President Finance and Chief Financial Officer, Dameron Hospital, Stockton, CA, p. A95

PROSKE, Donna, R.N., Executive Director, Staten Island University Hospital,, NY, p. A450

PROSKOCIL, Danielle, Director Human Resources, Valley County Health System, Ord, NE, p. A401

PROSPER, Charles
 Chief Executive Officer, Alta Bates Summit Medical Center, Berkeley, CA, p. A56
 Chief Executive Officer, Alta Bates Summit Medical Center – Summit Campus, Oakland, CA, p. A80

PROSSER, Alita, Chief Financial Officer, Scott & White Memorial Hospital, Temple, TX, p. A652

PROSSER, Edna, Chief Nursing Officer, Ozark Health Medical Center, Clinton, AR, p. A44

PROSSER, Joseph, M.D. Chief Medical Officer, Texas Health Harris Methodist Hospital Fort Worth, Fort Worth, TX, p. A618

PROSTKO, Michael, M.D. Chief of Staff, Rhea Medical Center, Dayton, TN, p. A582

PROUD, James, Vice President Human Resources and Marketing, Uniontown Hospital, Uniontown, PA, p. A556

PROUJANSKY, Roy, M.D., Chief Executive Officer, Alfred I. duPont Hospital for Children, Wilmington, DE, p. A120

PROVENZANO, Jeff
 Vice President and Chief Financial Officer, MidMichigan Medical Center–Clare, Clare, MI, p. A320
 Vice President and Chief Financial Officer, MidMichigan Medical Center–Gladwin, Gladwin, MI, p. A324
 Vice President and Chief Financial Officer, MidMichigan Medical Center–Gratiot, Alma, MI, p. A318

PROVINCE, Steven, Senior Vice President and Chief Operating Officer, Providence Healthcare Network, Waco, TX, p. A656

PRUESS, Mark, M.D. Chief Medical Staff, Sparta Community Hospital, Sparta, IL, p. A203

PRUETT–BAER, Karen, Senior Nurse Executive, Naval Hospital Oak Harbor, Oak Harbor, WA, p. A687

PRUITT, Jeffrey, M.D. Chief of Staff, Mercy Hospital of Defiance, Defiance, OH, p. A493

PRUITT, Michael W., Administrator and Chief Executive Officer, Coleman County Medical Center, Coleman, TX, p. A606

PRUKOP, Jeff, Director Professional Services, Jackson County Hospital District, Edna, TX, p. A614

PRUNCHUNAS, Edward M., Executive Vice President and Chief Financial Officer, Cedars–Sinai Medical Center, Los Angeles, CA, p. A70

PRUNOSKE, Mark, Chief Financial Officer and Senior Vice President Finance, F. F. Thompson Hospital, Canandaigua, NY, p. A436

PRUSATIS, Michael, Vice President Finance, DMC – Sinai–Grace Hospital, Detroit, MI, p. A321

PRYBYLO, Mary, President and Chief Executive Officer, St. Joseph Hospital, Bangor, ME, p. A291

PRYOR, David, President, Athens–Limestone Hospital, Athens, AL, p. A16

PRYOR, Jon, M.D., Chief Executive Officer, Hennepin County Medical Center, Minneapolis, MN, p. A346

PRYOR, Vincent, System Executive Vice President and Chief Financial Officer, Edward Hospital, Naperville, IL, p. A198

PRYOR, William B., Chief Human Resources Officer, Cape Fear Valley Medical Center, Fayetteville, NC, p. A465

PRZESTRZELSKI, David, Associate Director, Patient Care Services and Chief Nursing Executive, Charles George Veterans Affairs Medical Center, Asheville, NC, p. A460

PRZYBYLSKI, David, Controller, Sparrow Specialty Hospital, Lansing, MI, p. A328

PSAILA, Justin P., M.D. Vice President Medical Affairs, St. Luke's Hospital – Anderson Campus, Easton, PA, p. A537

PSCODNA, Susan, Director Human Resources, Mercy Hospital of Defiance, Defiance, OH, p. A493

PU, Steve, D.O. Chief Medical Officer, Poplar Bluff Regional Medical Center, Poplar Bluff, MO, p. A378

PUCKETT, Clay, Assistant Administrator and Chief Information Officer, Blount Memorial Hospital, Maryville, TN, p. A588

PUCKETT, Doug, President, Indiana University Health West Hospital, Avon, IN, p. A206

PUCKETT, Frank, M.D. Chief Medical Officer, Pocahontas Memorial Hospital, Buckeye, WV, p. A694

PUCKETT, Kristi, Director Human Resources, Grande Ronde Hospital, La Grande, OR, p. A527

PUCLIK, Becky, Division Chief People Officer, St. John's Hospital, Springfield, IL, p. A203

PUENTES, Francisco, Human Resource Officer, San Diego County Psychiatric Hospital, San Diego, CA, p. A89

PUFFENBERGER, James, Vice President and Chief Financial Officer, Mercy Hospital of Defiance, Defiance, OH, p. A493

PUFFENBERGER, Sheila, Manager Information Technology, Hillsdale Hospital, Hillsdale, MI, p. A326

PUGACH, Judy, Chief Nursing Officer, PIH Health Hospital – Downey, Downey, CA, p. A61

PUGH, Larry, Vice President and Chief Financial Officer, Beverly Hospital, Montebello, CA, p. A77

PUGH, Marcia, M.D. Chief Nursing Officer, Bryan W. Whitfield Memorial Hospital, Demopolis, AL, p. A19

PUGH, Melodee, Director Human Resources, Navarro Regional Hospital, Corsicana, TX, p. A608

PUGH, William H., Senior Vice President Corporate Finance and Chief Financial Officer, Pinnacle Health System, Harrisburg, PA, p. A540

PUGSLEY, Tim, Chief Information Officer, Nebraska Orthopaedic Hospital, Omaha, NE, p. A400

PUHL, Cathy A., Vice President Human Resources, Chambersburg Hospital, Chambersburg, PA, p. A535

PUHY, Dorothy E., Executive VP and Chief Operating Officer, Dana–Farber Cancer Institute, Boston, MA, p. A306

PUKALA, Shirley, R.N. Assistant Administrator Operations, St. Lawrence Rehabilitation Center, Lawrenceville, NJ, p. A418

PULASKI, Jason, Controller, HEALTHSOUTH Reading Rehabilitation Hospital, Reading, PA, p. A553

PULEO, Mark, Vice President and Chief Human Resources Officer, Henry Mayo Newhall Hospital, Valencia, CA, p. A98

PULIDO, Michael, Chief Administrative Officer, Mosaic Life Care at St. Joseph, Saint Joseph, MO, p. A379

PULLARKAT, Sajit, Chief Executive Officer and Managing Director, Centennial Hills Hospital Medical Center, Las Vegas, NV, p. A405

PULLEN, Connie, R.N. Chief Nursing Officer, Willamette Valley Medical Center, McMinnville, OR, p. A527

PULLIAM, Elizabeth, Chief Financial Officer, CHRISTUS Mother Frances Hospital – Jacksonville, Jacksonville, TX, p. A629

PULLIN, Dennis W., FACHE, President, MedStar Harbor Hospital, Baltimore, MD, p. A297

PULLMAN, Debbie, Director Finance, Avera Hand County Memorial Hospital, Miller, SD, p. A574

PULLMAN, Jayson, Chief Executive Officer, Hawarden Regional Healthcare, Hawarden, IA, p. A232

PULSIPHER, Gary W., President and Chief Executive Officer, Mercy Hospital Joplin, Joplin, MO, p. A373

PULVER, Dayna, Director of Nursing, Friend Community Healthcare System, Friend, NE, p. A396

PUMMEL, Keely, Director, Financial Operations, OhioHealth Dublin Methodist Hospital, Dublin, OH, p. A494

PUMPHREY, Robbin K., Chief Nursing Officer, Jackson Hospital, Marianna, FL, p. A135

PUNG, Margaret, R.N. Chief Nursing Officer, University of Texas Harris County Psychiatric Center, Houston, TX, p. A627

PUNJABI, Rishab, Chief Financial Officer, Kindred Hospital–La Mirada, La Mirada, CA, p. A67

PUNTEL, Jackie, Senior Director Human Resources, Cleveland Clinic Florida, Weston, FL, p. A150

PUORTO, Charlene, Chief Nursing Officer, Capital District Psychiatric Center, Albany, NY, p. A433

PURCELL, Deborah, Director of Information Technology, Caldwell Memorial Hospital, Lenoir, NC, p. A468

PURCELL, Terrance J.
Vice President Support Services and Ambulatory Care, Blue Mountain Hospital, Lehighton, PA, p. A543
Vice President Ambulatory Care and Support Services, Palmerton Hospital, Palmerton, PA, p. A546

PURCELL, Terry, Director Information Services, Lea Regional Medical Center, Hobbs, NM, p. A429

PURDY, Bruce, M.D. Chief of Staff, Muleshoe Area Medical Center, Muleshoe, TX, p. A638

PURINGTON, Denise, Vice President and Chief Information Officer, Elliot Hospital, Manchester, NH, p. A412

PURINTON, Sandy, Chief Nursing Officer, Trego County–Lemke Memorial Hospital, Wakeeney, KS, p. A255

PURKIS, Sharon, Administrator, Select Specialty Hospital–Muskegon, Muskegon, MI, p. A330

PUROHIT, Divyesh, M.D. Chief of Staff, Sullivan County Community Hospital, Sullivan, IN, p. A222

PUROHIT, Kumar, Chief Financial Officer, Rockford Center, Newark, DE, p. A119

PUROHIT, Shamb, Chief Financial Officer, Colquitt Regional Medical Center, Moultrie, GA, p. A163

PURRINGTON, Janice, Coordinator Medical Records, Avera Hand County Memorial Hospital, Miller, SD, p. A574

PURSLEY, Roger, Chief Executive Officer, Western Mental Health Institute, Bolivar, TN, p. A579

PURTLE, Mark, M.D
Vice President Medical Affairs, UnityPoint Health – Iowa Methodist Medical Center, Des Moines, IA, p. A229
Vice President Medical Affairs, UnityPoint Health–Iowa Lutheran Hospital, Des Moines, IA, p. A229

PURUSHOTHAM, Sanjay, Executive Director Information Systems, Bon Secours Baltimore Health System, Baltimore, MD, p. A296

PURVANCE, Clint, M.D., President and Chief Executive Officer, Barton Memorial Hospital, South Lake Tahoe, CA, p. A95

PURVES, Stephen A., FACHE, President and Chief Executive Officer, Maricopa Integrated Health System, Phoenix, AZ, p. A36

PURVIS, Jay, President and Chief Executive Officer, Wabash General Hospital, Mount Carmel, IL, p. A197

PURVIS, Kevin, Chief Information Officer, Community Howard Regional Health, Kokomo, IN, p. A216

PURVIS, Michael L., Chief Executive Officer, Cook Medical Center–A Campus of Tift Regional Medical Center, Adel, GA, p. A151

PURVIS, Mike, Chief Administrative Officer, Sutter Santa Rosa Regional Hospital, Santa Rosa, CA, p. A94

PUSHARD, Roland, Director of Nursing, Riverview Psychiatric Center, Augusta, ME, p. A291

PUSTINA, Karl, Vice President Finance, Upland Hills Health, Dodgeville, WI, p. A704

PUSZKARSKA, Lucyna M., M.D. Medical Director, Riveredge Hospital, Forest Park, IL, p. A190

PUTHOFF, Timothy, Chief Executive Officer, Houston Northwest Medical Center, Houston, TX, p. A625

PUTNAM, Mark, M.D. Medical Director, Haven Behavioral Hospital of Eastern Pennsylvania, Reading, PA, p. A553

PUTNAM, Maureen M., Director Human Resources, OSS Orthopaedic Hospital, York, PA, p. A559

PUTNAM, Stewart C., Executive Vice President and Chief Operating Officer, Unity Hospital, Rochester, NY, p. A454

PUTNAM, Timothy L., FACHE, President and Chief Executive Officer, Margaret Mary Health, Batesville, IN, p. A206

PUTZ, Kim, R.N. Director, Nursing Hospital, Minnesota Valley Health Center, Le Sueur, MN, p. A344

PUU, Linda, Hospital Administrator, Kaiser Permanente Medical Center, Honolulu, HI, p. A170

PUVOGEL, LuAnn, R.N., Chief Executive Officer, Salina Surgical Hospital, Salina, KS, p. A253

PUYAU, Susan, M.D. Medical Director, Woman's Hospital, Baton Rouge, LA, p. A273

PUZO, Thomas C., President and Chief Executive Officer, Cornerstone of Medical Arts Center Hospital, Fresh Meadows, NY, p. A439

PUZZUTO, David, M.D. Vice President Medical Affairs and Chief Medical Officer, Waterbury Hospital, Waterbury, CT, p. A117

PYE, Irma L.
Chief Human Resource Officer, Valley Baptist Medical Center–Brownsville, Brownsville, TX, p. A604
Senior Vice President and Chief Human Resource Officer, Valley Baptist Medical Center–Harlingen, Harlingen, TX, p. A622

PYGON, Bernard, M.D. Chief Medical Officer, University of Illinois Hospital & Health Sciences System, Chicago, IL, p. A187

PYLE, Diana, Director Human Resources and Executive Assistant to Chief Executive Officer, Cedar County Memorial Hospital, El Dorado Springs, MO, p. A370

PYLE, Julia, R.N. Chief Nursing Officer, Newman Regional Health, Emporia, KS, p. A242

PYLE, Rick, Director Information Systems, Harrisburg Medical Center, Harrisburg, IL, p. A192

PYLE FARRELL, Martha, Vice President Human Resources and General Counsel, Massachusetts Eye and Ear Infirmary, Boston, MA, p. A307

PYNE, Mel
Chief Executive Officer, Candler County Hospital, Metter, GA, p. A163
Chief Executive Officer, Dorminy Medical Center, Fitzgerald, GA, p. A159
Chief Executive Officer, Emanuel Medical Center, Swainsboro, GA, p. A167

PYRAH, Scott, Director Information Systems, St. Luke's Rehabilitation Hospital, Boise, ID, p. A175

Q

QUACH, Steve, M.D. Chief Medical Officer, Presbyterian–St. Luke's Medical Center, Denver, CO, p. A104

QUACKENBUSH, Kirk, M.D. Chief of Staff, Platte Valley Medical Center, Brighton, CO, p. A102

QUALIA, Leigh Ann, Director Human Resources, Val Verde Regional Medical Center, Del Rio, TX, p. A612

QUALLS, Brenda, Chief Financial Officer, Oconee Regional Medical Center, Milledgeville, GA, p. A163

QUALLS, Paul E., Chief Executive Officer, CHG Hospital Tucson, LLC, Tucson, AZ, p. A40

QUAM, David, M.D. Area Medical Director, Kaiser Permanente Fontana Medical Center, Fontana, CA, p. A62

QUAMMEN, Becky, Chief Information Officer, Howard University Hospital, Washington, DC, p. A121

QUARANTE, Dino, CPA Chief Financial Officer, Oasis Behavioral Health – Chandler, Chandler, AZ, p. A31

QUARLES, Christopher, M.D. Director Medical Services, Naval Hospital Jacksonville, Jacksonville, FL, p. A132

QUATE, Becky, Vice President Nursing and Patient Care Services, Iredell Health System, Statesville, NC, p. A474

QUATROCHE Jr., Thomas J., Chief Executive Officer, Erie County Medical Center, Buffalo, NY, p. A435

QUATTROCCHI, Robert, President and Chief Executive Officer, Northside Healthcare System, Atlanta, GA, p. B97

QUATTROCCHI, Robert, President and Chief Executive Officer, Northside Hospital, Atlanta, GA, p. A152

QUEBEDEAUX, Jay, Chief Executive Officer, Mena Regional Health System, Mena, AR, p. A50

QUEBODEAUX, Bryce, Chief Executive Officer, Abrom Kaplan Memorial Hospital, Kaplan, LA, p. A279

QUEEN, Sharon H., R.N. Chief Nursing Officer, Clearview Regional Medical Center, Monroe, GA, p. A163

QUENAN, James, M.D. Chief Medical Officer, Amery Hospital and Clinic, Amery, WI, p. A702

QUESNEL, Brenda, R.N. Vice President of Patient Care and Chief Nursing Officer, West Calcasieu Cameron Hospital, Sulphur, LA, p. A288

QUICCI, London, Chief Operating Officer, DMC – Sinai–Grace Hospital, Detroit, MI, p. A321

QUICHOCHO, Vince, Manager Information Systems, Guam Memorial Hospital Authority, Tamuning, GU, p. A725

QUIGLEY, Stephen J., Chief Executive Officer, Southwood Psychiatric Hospital, Pittsburgh, PA, p. A551

QUILLIN, Gayla, Administrator, Parmer Medical Center, Friona, TX, p. A619

QUIN, Robert, Vice President Finance and Chief Financial Officer, UnityPoint Health – Peoria, Peoria, IL, p. A200

QUINLAN, Christine, MS Chief Nursing Officer, Alexian Brothers Behavioral Health Hospital, Hoffman Estates, IL, p. A193

QUINLAN, Patrick J., M.D. Chief Executive Officer, Ochsner Medical Center, New Orleans, LA, p. A285

QUINLIVAN, John, Chief Executive Officer, Redmond Regional Medical Center, Rome, GA, p. A165

QUINLIVAN, Kathy, Director Management Information Systems, Avera Sacred Heart Hospital, Yankton, SD, p. A578

QUINN, Clifton, Chief Executive Officer, Regency Hospital of Meridian, Meridian, MS, p. A362

QUINN, Donna, Vice President Operations and Quality, Driscoll Children's Hospital, Corpus Christi, TX, p. A608

QUINN, Jennifer, Quality and Safety Coordinator, ThedaCare Medical Center–Shawano, Shawano, WI, p. A715

QUINN, Judith, Vice President Patient Care Services, Cape Cod Hospital, Hyannis, MA, p. A311

QUINN, Mary Anna, Executive Vice President, Chief Administrative Officer, St. Jude Children's Research Hospital, Memphis, TN, p. A589

QUINN, Paul, Information Systems Manager, Kern Valley Healthcare District, Lake Isabella, CA, p. A68

QUINONES, Kathleen
Interim Vice President Finance, Berkeley Medical Center, Martinsburg, WV, p. A697
Interim Vice President Finance, Jefferson Medical Center, Ranson, WV, p. A699

QUINONES, Yolanda, Director Finance, I. Gonzalez Martinez Oncologic Hospital,, PR, p. A730

QUINONEZ, Yolanda, Chief Financial Officer, Hospital de la Universidad de Puerto Rico/Dr. Federico Trilla, Carolina, PR, p. A726

QUINT–BOUZID, Marjorie, Chief Nursing Officer and Vice President Patient Care Services, Fort Washington Medical Center, Oxen Hill, MD, p. A302

QUINTANA, Francisco, Warden, Federal Medical Center, Lexington, KY, p. A263

QUINTANA, Jay, Vice President Operations, Cornerstone Hospital–West Monroe, West Monroe, LA, p. A289

QUINTO, Mike, Chief Information Officer, Watauga Medical Center, Boone, NC, p. A461

QUINTON, Byron, Chief Executive Officer, Clarion Hospital, Clarion, PA, p. A535

QUINTON, J. Ben, Administrator, William Newton Hospital, Winfield, KS, p. A256

QUINTYNE, Stephen, Chief Executive Officer, The Vines, Ocala, FL, p. A139

QUIRICONI, Stephan F.
Vice President Finance, Bon Secours Memorial Regional Medical Center, Mechanicsville, VA, p. A673
Vice President, Finance, Bon Secours St. Francis Medical Center, Midlothian, VA, p. A673
Chief Financial Officer, Bon Secours St. Mary's Hospital, Richmond, VA, p. A677

QUIRKE, David, Vice President Information Services, Frederick Memorial Hospital, Frederick, MD, p. A301

QUITO, Arturo L., M.D. Chief of Staff, Erlanger Bledsoe Hospital, Pikeville, TN, p. A592

QUO, Justin, Chief of Staff, CHI LakeWood Health, Baudette, MN, p. A339

R

RAAUM, Elizabeth, Manger Business Office, Roosevelt Medical Center, Culbertson, MT, p. A386

RAB, Shafiq, Chief Information Officer, Orange Regional Medical Center, Middletown, NY, p. A442

RABAGO, Janie, Chief Accountant, San Antonio State Hospital, San Antonio, TX, p. A647

RABE, Robbie G., Interim Vice President and Senior Director of Nursing, Seton Smithville Regional Hospital, Smithville, TX, p. A649

RABEL, Jonas, Vice President and Chief Nursing Officer, Integris Grove Hospital, Grove, OK, p. A512

RABIDEAU, Ray, M.D. Senior Vice President and Chief Medical Officer, Memorial Hospital, North Conway, NH, p. A413

RABIN, Barry, M.D. Medical Director, Linden Oaks Hospital, Naperville, IL, p. A198

RABINE, Traci, Vice President Clinic Operations, Prairie Lakes Healthcare System, Watertown, SD, p. A577

RABINOWITZ, Jordy, Senior Vice President Human Resources Operations, Westchester Medical Center, Valhalla, NY, p. A458

RABNER, Barry S., President and Chief Executive Officer, Princeton Healthcare System, University Medical Center of Princeton at Plainsboro, Plainsboro, NJ, p. A422

RABOIN, Kirk, Chief Administrative Officer, PeaceHealth St. John Medical Center, Longview, WA, p. A686

RABON, Catherine, M.D. Chief Medical Officer, McLeod Health Clarendon, Manning, SC, p. A568

RABORN, Janelle, Chief Operating Officer, Lovelace Women's Hospital, Albuquerque, NM, p. A427

RACHAL, Paul, M.D. Chief Medical Officer, Pointe Coupee General Hospital, New Roads, LA, p. A285

RACHUIG, Sue, Director Information Services, Tulane Medical Center, New Orleans, LA, p. A285

RACKLIFFE, David, Assistant Vice President Information Services, Bristol Hospital, Bristol, CT, p. A113

RACZEK, James, M.D. Sr. Vice President of Operations and Chief Medical Officer, Eastern Maine Medical Center, Bangor, ME, p. A291

RADANDT, Jeremiah, Chief Financial Officer, Primary Children's Hospital, Salt Lake City, UT, p. A663

RADCLIFF, Joey, Chief Financial Officer, Five Rivers Medical Center, Pocahontas, AR, p. A51

RADCLIFFE, Eric, M.D. Medical Director, United Hospital Center, Bridgeport, WV, p. A694

RADCLIFFE, Kerry, JD Chief Nursing Officer, Central Texas Rehabilitation Hospital, Austin, TX, p. A599

RADEMACHER, Frank
Senior Director Information Systems, St. Joseph Mercy Ann Arbor, Ypsilanti, MI, p. A337
Director, Information Systems, St. Joseph Mercy Livingston Hospital, Howell, MI, p. A326

RADER, Herbert, M.D. Advisor for Medical Affairs, New York Community Hospital,, NY, p. A446

RADFORD, Jeffrey, Chief Executive Officer, Select Specialty Hospital–Tri Cities, Bristol, TN, p. A579

RADKE, Erma, Director of Operations, Oakleaf Surgical Hospital, Eau Claire, WI, p. A705

RADKE, Sam, Interim Chief Executive Officer and Interim Chief Financial Officer, St. Vincent General Hospital District, Leadville, CO, p. A108

RADNER, Allen, M.D. Chief Medical Officer, Salinas Valley Memorial Healthcare System, Salinas, CA, p. A87

RADOTICH, Maureen, Director Human Resources, Providence Valdez Medical Center, Valdez, AK, p. A30

RADTKE, Lisa, Chief Administrative Officer, Winneshiek Medical Center, Decorah, IA, p. A229

RADU, Oana, Chief Executive Officer, Summit Oaks Hospital, Summit, NJ, p. A424

RADUNSKY, Daniel, M.D. Medical Staff President, Union County General Hospital, Clayton, NM, p. A428

RADZEVICH, Jason, Vice President Finance, Beth Israel Deaconess Hospital Plymouth, Plymouth, MA, p. A314

RAETHEL, Kathryn A., M.P.H., President and Chief Executive Officer, Castle Medical Center, Kailua, HI, p. A171

RAETZ, Elizabeth A., R.N. Vice President Nursing and Chief Nursing Officer, CHI Health St Elizabeth, Lincoln, NE, p. A398

RAFALA, Paula, Director, Human Resources, Memorial Medical Center, Modesto, CA, p. A77

RAFFERTY, Joseph, Interim Chief Executive Officer, Nix Health Care System, San Antonio, TX, p. A646

RAFFERTY, Joyce, Vice President Finance, The University of Vermont Health Network–Champlain Valley Physicians Hospital, Plattsburgh, NY, p. A453

RAFFERTY, Patrick W., Executive Vice President and Chief Operating Officer, Community Regional Medical Center, Fresno, CA, p. A63

RAFFETY, Leannette, Administrative Generalist, Stroud Regional Medical Center, Stroud, OK, p. A520

RAFFOUL, John, Chief Executive Officer, White Memorial Medical Center, Los Angeles, CA, p. A75

RAFUS, Matthew, Chief Information Officer, White River Junction Veterans Affairs Medical Center, White River Junction, VT, p. A666

RAGAIN, Michael, M.D
Chief Medical Officer, Texas Specialty Hospital at Lubbock, Lubbock, TX, p. A634
Chief Medical Officer and Senior Vice President, University Medical Center, Lubbock, TX, p. A634

RAGAN, Donna, R.N. Chief Nursing Officer, Shands Live Oak Regional Medical Center, Live Oak, FL, p. A134

RAGAR–THOMAS, Twila, Director Health Information Management and Quality Improvement, Timberlawn Mental Health System, Dallas, TX, p. A611

RAGAS, Rene, Chief Operating Officer, Our Lady of the Angels Hospital, Bogalusa, LA, p. A274

RAGER, Claudia, R.N. Vice President Patient Care Services, Conemaugh Memorial Medical Center, Johnstown, PA, p. A541

RAGGI, Bob, M.D. Chief Medical Officer, Providence Holy Cross Medical Center,, CA, p. A73

RAGGIO, James J., Chief Executive Officer, Lompoc Valley Medical Center, Lompoc, CA, p. A69

RAGGIO, Sharon, President and Chief Executive Officer, West Springs Hospital, Grand Junction, CO, p. A106

RAGLAND, Jane, President Medical Staff, CHRISTUS Mother Frances Hospital – Jacksonville, Jacksonville, TX, p. A629

RAGLE, Bertha, Director Personnel, CrossRidge Community Hospital, Wynne, AR, p. A53

RAGONA, Robert A., Senior Vice President Finance and Chief Financial Officer, Eastern Long Island Hospital, Greenport, NY, p. A440

RAGONESE–GREEN, Virginia, Chief Nursing Officer, HEALTHSOUTH Rehabilitation Hospital of Southern Arizona, Tucson, AZ, p. A40

RAGSDALE, Sarah, R.N. Chief Nursing Officer, Smith County Memorial Hospital, Smith Center, KS, p. A254

RAGUSA, Shannon Hawkins, Acting Administrator, MMO Rehabilitation and Wellness Center, Plaquemine, LA, p. A286

RAHDERT, Richard, M.D. Medical Director, River Bend Hospital, West Lafayette, IN, p. A223

RAHMAN, Randy
Chief Information Officer, Miami County Medical Center, Paola, KS, p. A251
Vice President and Chief Information Officer, Olathe Medical Center, Olathe, KS, p. A250

RAHMAN, Syed, M.D. Chief of Staff, Horizon Specialty Hospital, Las Vegas, NV, p. A406

RAHN, Douglas L., President and Chief Executive Officer, Passavant Area Hospital, Jacksonville, IL, p. A194

RAHN, Kevin, President Medical Staff, Orthopaedic Hospital of Lutheran Health Network, Fort Wayne, IN, p. A210

RAINA, Suresh, M.D. Vice President Medical Staff and Chief Medical Officer, HackensackUMC Palisades, North Bergen, NJ, p. A421

RAINBOLT, Mike, Chief Financial Officer, Rivendell Behavioral Health Services of Arkansas, Benton, AR, p. A43

RAINEY, Jackie, Chief Financial Officer, Little River Memorial Hospital, Ashdown, AR, p. A43

RAINEY, Mark J., Director Human Resources, Texas Health Presbyterian Hospital Kaufman, Kaufman, TX, p. A630

RAINS, Celeste, D.O. Chief of Staff, Logan County Hospital, Oakley, KS, p. A250

RAINS, Debbie, Coordinator Health Information Management, Erlanger Bledsoe Hospital, Pikeville, TN, p. A592

RAINS, Della, Chief Nursing Officer, ContinueCARE Hospital at Baptist Health Corbin, Corbin, KY, p. A258

RAINS, Gail, R.N. Director Patient Care Services, Shriners Hospitals for Children–Shreveport, Shreveport, LA, p. A288

RAINS, Jeff G., Chief Executive Officer, Baptist Medical Center East, Montgomery, AL, p. A23

RAINS, Jon–Michael
Chief Executive Officer, Carrus Rehabilitation Hospital, Sherman, TX, p. A648
Chief Executive Officer, Carrus Specialty Hospital, Sherman, TX, p. A648

RAINS, Paul, MSN, President, St. Joseph's Behavioral Health Center, Stockton, CA, p. A95

RAINS, Steve, Director Information Services, McKee Medical Center, Loveland, CO, p. A109

RAISNER, Gary, Chief Operating Officer, Norristown State Hospital, Norristown, PA, p. A546

RAJKUMAR, Anthony, Chief Executive Officer, NYC Health + Hospitals / Coney Island,, NY, p. A448

RAJPARA, Suresh, M.D. Chief Medical Officer, Jerome Golden Center for Behavioral Health, Inc., West Palm Beach, FL, p. A149

RAJU, Ramanathan, M.D., President, NYC Health + Hospitals, New York, NY, p. B98

RAK, Roger, Director Human Resources, South Shore Hospital, Chicago, IL, p. A186

RAK, Ronald C., JD, Chief Executive Officer, Saint Peter's University Hospital, New Brunswick, NJ, p. A420

RAKES, Lori, Chief Operating Officer, Cartersville Medical Center, Cartersville, GA, p. A156

RAKES–STEPHENS, Kim, M.D. Chief Medical Staff, Colleton Medical Center, Walterboro, SC, p. A570

RAKOV, Robert, M.D. Chief Medical Officer, Cogdell Memorial Hospital, Snyder, TX, p. A649

RALPH, Stephen A., President and Chief Executive Officer, Huntington Memorial Hospital, Pasadena, CA, p. A82

RALSTIN, Char, Director of Nursing, Haven Senior Horizons, Phoenix, AZ, p. A36

RAMA–BANAAG, Gemma, R.N. Chief Nursing Officer, Paradise Valley Hospital, National City, CA, p. A79

RAMAGE, Debra, Director Human Resources and Payroll, CHG Hospital Tucson, LLC, Tucson, AZ, p. A40

RAMAGE, Gary, M.D. Chief Medical Officer, McKenzie County Healthcare System, Watford City, ND, p. A482

RAMAN, Jayashree, Vice President and Chief Information Officer, Reading Hospital, West Reading, PA, p. A557

RAMAN, Reggie, M.D. Medical Director, Peninsula Hospital, Louisville, TN, p. A587

RAMAZANI, Regina, Chief Operating Officer, Garden Park Medical Center, Gulfport, MS, p. A358

RAMER, Gary, Manager Information Management, Jonathan M. Wainwright Memorial Veterans Affairs Medical Center, Walla Walla, WA, p. A692

RAMEY, Rita, Director Information Systems, Buchanan General Hospital, Grundy, VA, p. A671

RAMEY, Robert L., President, Baptist Health Madisonville, Madisonville, KY, p. A265

RAMEY, Steve, Chief Financial Officer, Southampton Memorial Hospital, Franklin, VA, p. A670

RAMIREZ, Albert, M.D. Medical Director, Kindred Rehabilitation Hospital Arlington, Arlington, TX, p. A597

RAMIREZ, Ana, Director of Nursing, Mesa Springs, Fort Worth, TX, p. A618

RAMIREZ, Arthur L., M.D
Medical Director, El Paso Behavioral Health System, El Paso, TX, p. A615
Medical Director, Mesilla Valley Hospital, Las Cruces, NM, p. A430

RAMIREZ, Corazon, M.D., Chief Executive Officer, Pine Creek Medical Center, Dallas, TX, p. A611

RAMIREZ, Eddy, Assistant Vice President Business Development, Ochsner Medical Center – Kenner, Kenner, LA, p. A279

RAMIREZ, Harvey, Chief Information Officer, Coleman County Medical Center, Coleman, TX, p. A606

RAMIREZ, Jaime, Chief Executive Officer, McCamey County Hospital District, McCamey, TX, p. A636

RAMIREZ, Karla, Chief Operating Officer, Laurel Ridge Treatment Center, San Antonio, TX, p. A646

RAMIREZ, Marcos A., Human Resources Business Partner, Baylor Scott & White Medical Center at Waxahachie, Waxahachie, TX, p. A656

RAMIREZ, Omar, Chief Executive Officer, Los Angeles Community Hospital at Los Angeles, Los Angeles, CA, p. A72

RAMIREZ, Ruben, M.D. Chief of Staff, Monterey Park Hospital, Monterey Park, CA, p. A78

RAMIREZ, Susan, Chief Nursing Officer, HEALTHSOUTH Rehabilitation Hospital–Las Vegas, Las Vegas, NV, p. A406

RAMIREZ, Willie, Manager Labor Relations, Laguna Honda Hospital and Rehabilitation Center, San Francisco, CA, p. A90

RAMLO, Ricki, Chief Operating Officer and Vice President Operations, Jamestown Regional Medical Center, Jamestown, ND, p. A480

RAMM, Crystal, Administrator, Grady General Hospital, Cairo, GA, p. A155

RAMOS, Eduardo, M.D. Medical Director, HEALTHSOUTH Rehabilitation Hospital of San Juan, San Juan, PR, p. A729

RAMOS, Eric, M.D. Division Chief Medical Officer, Southern Hills Hospital and Medical Center, Las Vegas, NV, p. A406

RAMOS, Holly, R.N. Chief Clinical Officer, Kindred Hospital–Ontario, Ontario, CA, p. A80

RAMOS, Jessie, Manager Human Resources, Skyline Hospital, White Salmon, WA, p. A693

RAMOS, Jet, Head Staff Administration, Naval Hospital Camp Pendleton, Camp Pendleton, CA, p. A58

RAMOS, Raymond, FACHE Chief Operating Officer, Doctors Hospital of Laredo, Laredo, TX, p. A632

RAMOS, Walter J., President and Chief Executive Officer, Carney Hospital, Boston, MA, p. A306

RAMPAT, Ananda, Chief Financial Officer, Northwest Medical Center, Margate, FL, p. A135

RAMPP, Randal D., M.D. Chief Medical Officer, Saint Thomas River Park Hospital, Mc Minnville, TN, p. A588

RAMSAMY, Dev, Chief Financial Officer, St. Rose Dominican Hospitals – San Martin Campus, Las Vegas, NV, p. A406

RAMSAY, Kathy, R.N. Director Communications and Development, Rooks County Health Center, Plainville, KS, p. A252

RAMSEY, David L., President and Chief Executive Officer, Charleston Area Medical Center, Charleston, WV, p. A695

RAMSEY, Kristin, R.N. Senior Vice President and Chief Nursing Executive, Northwestern Memorial Hospital, Northwestern Memorial Hospital, Chicago, IL, p. A185

RAMSEY, Lisa, Chief Financial Officer, Prairie View, Newton, KS, p. A250

RAMSEY, Paul G., M.D., Chief Executive Officer, UW Medicine, Seattle, WA, p. B150

RAMSEY, Rance, Chief Operating Officer, Martin County Hospital District, Stanton, TX, p. A650

RAMSEY, Rhonda, Controller, HEALTHSOUTH Deaconess Rehabilitation Hospital, Evansville, IN, p. A210

RAMSEY, Ross, M.D. Chief of Staff, Scheurer Hospital, Pigeon, MI, p. A331

RAMSEY, Roy M., Executive Director, Bradford Health Services at Warrior Lodge, Warrior, AL, p. A26

RAMSEY, Thomas, Chief Financial Officer, Hancock Medical Center, Bay Saint Louis, MS, p. A355

RAMTHUN, Jane, Chief Financial Officer, Story County Medical Center, Nevada, IA, p. A235

RANA, Chaula, M.D. Medical Director, HealthSouth Rehabilitation Institute of San Antonio, San Antonio, TX, p. A646

RANCK, Sonja, MSN Chief Operating Officer and Chief Nursing Officer, Skiff Medical Center, Newton, IA, p. A235

RANDALL, Bryan J.
Vice President Finance and Chief Financial Officer, Heritage Valley Health System, Beaver, PA, p. A533
Vice President Finance and Chief Financial Officer, Sewickley Valley Hospital, (A Division of Valley Medical Facilities), Sewickley, PA, p. A554

RANDALL, Cherry, Business Officer, Greater Binghamton Health Center, Binghamton, NY, p. A435

RANDALL, Kenneth W., Chief Executive Officer, Artesia General Hospital, Artesia, NM, p. A428

RANDLE, Emily, Vice President Operations, Orange Coast Memorial Medical Center, Fountain Valley, CA, p. A63

RANDOLPH, Arianne, Director Human Resources, Pikes Peak Regional Hospital, Woodland Park, CO, p. A111

RANDOLPH, Bonnie, M.D. Chief of Staff, Community Hospital, Torrington, WY, p. A724

RANDOLPH, Bruce, Chief Information Technology, Arizona State Hospital, Phoenix, AZ, p. A36

RANDOLPH, Geoffrey, M.D. Chief Medical Officer, Lutheran Hospital of Indiana, Fort Wayne, IN, p. A210

RANDOLPH, Joseph, M.D. Chairman Medical Executive Committee, Indiana Orthopaedic Hospital, Indianapolis, IN, p. A214

RANDOLPH, Karsten, Executive Vice President and Chief Financial Officer, Shawnee Mission Medical Center, Shawnee Mission, KS, p. A254

RANDOLPH, Jr., Leonard M., M.D. Senior Vice President and Chief Medical Officer, Mercy Health – Anderson Hospital, Cincinnati, OH, p. A488

RANDOLPH, Linda, Director Personnel Services, Washington County Hospital, Chatom, AL, p. A18

RANEY, Hollie, Director of Nursing, Dallas County Medical Center, Fordyce, AR, p. A46

RANG, Robert A., R.N., Chief Executive Officer, Wrangell Medical Center, Wrangell, AK, p. A30

RANGAVIZ, Rassoul, Chief Financial Officer, Copley Hospital, Morrisville, VT, p. A665

RANGE, Bonny, MSN Chief Nursing Officer, Holy Family Memorial, Manitowoc, WI, p. A709

RANGE, Penny, Chief Nursing Officer, Baylor Scott & White Medical Center – Sunnyvale, Sunnyvale, TX, p. A651

RANKIN, Beverley A., R.N. Vice President & Chief Nursing Officer, Alice Peck Day Memorial Hospital, Lebanon, NH, p. A411

RANKIN, Cynthia, Chief Nursing Officer, Lovelace Rehabilitation Hospital, Albuquerque, NM, p. A427

RANNEY, Timothy, M.D. Chief Medical Officer, Seton Medical Center, Daly City, CA, p. A60

RANSOM, Jim, Chief Executive Officer, HEALTHSOUTH Rehabilitation Hospital North Texas, Richardson, TX, p. A643

RANSOM, Natalie
Chief Nursing Officer, MountainView Hospital, Las Vegas, NV, p. A406
Chief Nursing Officer, North Florida Regional Medical Center, Gainesville, FL, p. A129

RANTZ III, August J., Founder and Chief Executive Officer, AMG Integrated Healthcare Management, Lafayette, LA, p. B10

RAO, Gutti, M.D
Medical Director, AMG Specialty Hospital–Greenwood, Greenwood, MS, p. A358
Chief of Staff, Greenwood Leflore Hospital, Greenwood, MS, p. A358

RAO, Kalapala, M.D. Medical Director, HEALTHSOUTH Western Hills Regional Rehabilitation Hospital, Parkersburg, WV, p. A699

RAPENSKE, Jennifer, Manager Financial Services, Mercy Medical Center–New Hampton, New Hampton, IA, p. A235

RAPP, Catherine, R.N. Vice President Nursing, Oconomowoc Memorial Hospital, Oconomowoc, WI, p. A713

RAPP, David, Chief Information Officer, Wheeling Hospital, Wheeling, WV, p. A701

RAPP, Ron, Controller, Cole Memorial, Coudersport, PA, p. A536

RAPPACH, Shannon, Chief Fiscal Services, Dayton Veterans Affairs Medical Center, Dayton, OH, p. A492

RAPPLEY, Marsha, M.D., Chief Executive Officer and Vice President for Health Sciences, VCU Health System, Richmond, VA, p. B150

RASCHKE, Judy, Director Human Resources, Pipestone County Medical Center Avera, Pipestone, MN, p. A348

RASHFORD, Jennifer, Manager Human Resources, LifeCare Hospitals of Mechanicsburg, Mechanicsburg, PA, p. A544

RASHID, Harun, Chief Information Officer, Magee–Womens Hospital of UPMC, Pittsburgh, PA, p. A551

RASK, Brenda, Vice President Operations, CHI St Alexius Health Carrington Medical Center, Carrington, ND, p. A477

RASKE, Jamie, Information Technology Lead, Avera St. Mary's Hospital, Pierre, SD, p. A575

RASMUSSEN, Cassie, M.D. Chief Medical Officer, Adair County Memorial Hospital, Greenfield, IA, p. A231

RASMUSSEN, Diane, Director Human Resources, Cambridge Medical Center, Cambridge, MN, p. A340

RASMUSSEN, Jeanell, R.N. Senior Vice President and Chief Nursing Officer, Harrison Medical Center, Bremerton, WA, p. A682

RASMUSSEN, John, Vice President for Information Technology, MedStar Georgetown University Hospital, Washington, DC, p. A121

RASMUSSEN, Kyle R., Chief Executive Officer, Meeker Memorial Hospital, Litchfield, MN, p. A345

RASMUSSEN, Rick, Chief Executive Officer, Northwest Specialty Hospital, Post Falls, ID, p. A178

RASMUSSEN, Scott, Director Human Resources, Lincoln Regional Center, Lincoln, NE, p. A398

RASMUSSON, Duane, Vice President Human Resources, St. Cloud Hospital, Saint Cloud, MN, p. A350

RASOOL, Chaudri, D.O. Chief of Staff, Palmer Lutheran Health Center, West Union, IA, p. A239

RASOR, Linda, R.N., Chief Executive Officer, Plains Memorial Hospital, Dimmitt, TX, p. A613

RASTER, Robert, M.D. Medical Director, Michiana Behavioral Health Center, Plymouth, IN, p. A220

RATAJ, Marianne, R.N. Chief Nursing Officer, Mercy Hospital Fort Smith, Fort Smith, AR, p. A46

RATCLIFF, David, M.D. Chief Medical Affairs, Washington Regional Medical Center, Fayetteville, AR, p. A46

RATCLIFF, Paul, Director Information Services, Baylor Scott & White Medical Center – Carrollton, Carrollton, TX, p. A605

RATCLIFFE, Alma, M.D. Executive Vice President Medical Staff and Business Development, Saint Clare's Health System, Denville, NJ, p. A416

RATH, Megan, Chief Financial Officer, Wishek Community Hospital and Clinics, Wishek, ND, p. A482

RATHBUN, Lori, Chief Executive Officer, Van Diest Medical Center, Webster City, IA, p. A239

RATHGABER, Scott W., M.D., Chief Executive Officer and Board Chair, Gundersen Health System, La Crosse, WI, p. A708

RATLIFF, Ada, Chief Information Officer, Claiborne County Medical Center, Port Gibson, MS, p. A364

RATLIFF, Bonnie, Chief Information Officer, Columbia Memorial Hospital, Hudson, NY, p. A440

RATLIFF, Kim, Director Health Information Management, Southwestern Virginia Mental Health Institute, Marion, VA, p. A673

RATLIFF, Maggie, Vice President Information Systems, Sarah Bush Lincoln Health Center, Mattoon, IL, p. A196

RATLIFF, Simon, Chief Operating Officer, Logan Regional Medical Center, Logan, WV, p. A697

RATLIFF, Steve, Director Information Technology, Guadalupe Regional Medical Center, Seguin, TX, p. A648

RATNASAMY, Suthanthira M., FACHE, Chief Executive Officer, Kindred Hospital Bay Area–Tampa, Tampa, FL, p. A147

RATNER, Jeffrey, M.D. Senior Vice President Medical Affairs, Mount Nittany Medical Center, State College, PA, p. A555

RATTLE, John, Chief Financial Officer, West Springs Hospital, Grand Junction, CO, p. A106

RATTRAY, Cindy Stewart, Director Human Resources, Jewish Hospital–Shelbyville, Shelbyville, KY, p. A269

RAU, Robin, Chief Executive Officer, Miller County Hospital, Colquitt, GA, p. A156

RAUB, Jessica, Director Health Information Management, Seven Hills Hospital, Henderson, NV, p. A405

RAUCH, Scott C., Vice President Human Resources, Reid Health, Richmond, IN, p. A221

RAUCH, Scott L., M.D., President, McLean Hospital, Belmont, MA, p. A305

RAUH, Bradley W., Vice President, Chief Operating Officer, Southwest General Health Center, Middleburg Heights, OH, p. A499

RAUH, Cindy, R.N. Vice President and Chief Nursing Officer, Duncan Regional Hospital, Duncan, OK, p. A510

RAUNER, Mary Ellen, R.N. Chief Nursing Officer, Suburban Community Hospital, Norristown, PA, p. A546

RAUPERS, Deb, MS
Vice President Patient Services and Chief Nursing Officer, Cayuga Medical Center at Ithaca, Ithaca, NY, p. A440
Chief Nursing Officer, Guthrie Corning Hospital, Corning, NY, p. A437

RAUSCHUBER, Mark, Associate Vice President, Chief Information Officer, University of Texas Southwestern Medical Center, Dallas, TX, p. A612

RAUTIO, Wendy, Chief Financial Officer, Munising Memorial Hospital, Munising, MI, p. A330

RAVELING, Lynn, Chief Financial Officer, Pocahontas Community Hospital, Pocahontas, IA, p. A236

RAWLINGS, Linda, Director Human Resources and Personnel, Three Rivers Hospital, Waverly, TN, p. A594

RAWLINGS, Michael, Interim Chief Operating Officer, NYC Health + Hospitals / Bellevue, New York, NY, p. A447

RAWLINGS, Patrick, Chief Human Resource Officer, Highland Hospital, Charleston, WV, p. A695

RAWLINGS, Sheri, Chief Information Officer, San Juan Regional Medical Center, Farmington, NM, p. A429

RAY, Beverly, Director Human Resources, Tennova Healthcare Dyersburg Regional Medical Center, Dyersburg, TN, p. A582

RAY, Brenda, Director Human Resources, Huntsville Memorial Hospital, Huntsville, TX, p. A628

RAY, Denise, President and Chief Executive Officer, Piedmont Mountainside Hospital, Jasper, GA, p. A161

RAY, Diane, R.N. Vice President and Chief Nursing Officer Patient Services, St. Luke's Hospital, Chesterfield, MO, p. A369

RAY, Donald, Vice President Operations, University of Maryland Medical Center Midtown Campus, Baltimore, MD, p. A298

RAY, Elaine, Administrator, Choate Mental Health Center, Anna, IL, p. A180

RAY, Evan, FACHE, President, St. Vincent's Birmingham, Birmingham, AL, p. A17

RAY, Jerilyn, Manager Human Resources, St. Elizabeth Hospital, Enumclaw, WA, p. A684

RAY, Joel, MSN Vice President and Chief Nursing Officer, UNC REX Healthcare, Raleigh, NC, p. A472

RAY, Kirk M., Chief Executive Officer, Kosciusko Community Hospital, Warsaw, IN, p. A223

RAY, Marge, Director Information Systems, Covenant Medical Center, Waterloo, IA, p. A238

RAY, Marilyn, MSN Chief Nursing Officer, Upson Regional Medical Center, Thomaston, GA, p. A167

RAY, Nancy L., R.N. Executive Vice President, Chief Nursing Executive, University Health System, San Antonio, TX, p. A647

RAY, Rachel, Chief Financial Officer, Unity Medical Center, Grafton, ND, p. A479

RAY, Roger A., M.D. Executive Vice President and Chief Medical Officer, Carolinas Medical Center, Charlotte, NC, p. A462

RAYBOURN, Gina, Director Health Information, Ellett Memorial Hospital, Appleton City, MO, p. A367

RAYLS, Kim, Director Human Resources, Twin Lakes Regional Medical Center, Leitchfield, KY, p. A262

RAYMER, Chris, R.N., Chief Executive Officer, Great River Medical Center, Blytheville, AR, p. A43

RAYMER, Chris, R.N. Chief Executive Officer and Chief Operating Officer, Great River Medical Center, Blytheville, AR, p. A43

RAYMER, Chris, R.N., Chief Executive Officer, Mississippi County Hospital System, Blytheville, AR, p. B92

RAYMER, Chris, R.N., Chief Executive Officer, South Mississippi County Regional Medical Center, Osceola, AR, p. A51

RAYMER, Chris, R.N. Chief Operating Officer and Chief Nursing Officer, South Mississippi County Regional Medical Center, Osceola, AR, p. A51

RAYMOND, Jane, Vice President and Chief Operating Officer, Reston Hospital Center, Reston, VA, p. A676

RAYMOND, Katherine, Chief Nursing Officer, St. Rose Dominican Hospitals – San Martin Campus, Las Vegas, NV, p. A406

RAYMOND, Mindy, Vice President Human Resources, Boca Raton Regional Hospital, Boca Raton, FL, p. A124

RAYMOND, Scott, Director Information Systems, Orange Coast Memorial Medical Center, Fountain Valley, CA, p. A63

RAYNER, Evan J., Chief Executive Officer, Madera Community Hospital, Madera, CA, p. A75

RAYNER, Thomas J., Senior Vice President and Chief Operating Officer, Kaweah Delta Medical Center, Visalia, CA, p. A99

RAYNES, Anthony, M.D. Psychiatrist in Chief, Arbour H. R. I. Hospital, Brookline, MA, p. A308

RAYNES, Scott
President, Baptist Hospital, Pensacola, FL, p. A142
President, Gulf Breeze Hospital, Gulf Breeze, FL, p. A130

RAYNOR, Robert, Human Resources Director, Park Royal Hospital, Fort Myers, FL, p. A129

RAYUDU, Subbu, M.D. Chief of Staff, Alliance HealthCare System, Holly Springs, MS, p. A359

RAZMIC, Tammy, Associate Administrator Finance and Chief Financial Officer, Inova Mount Vernon Hospital, Alexandria, VA, p. A667

RAZO, Virginia, Chief Executive Officer, Curry General Hospital, Gold Beach, OR, p. A526

REA, Jerry A., Ph.D.,
Superintendent, Osawatomie State Hospital, Osawatomie, KS, p. A250
Superintendent, Parsons State Hospital and Training Center, Parsons, KS, p. A252
Interim Superintendent, Rainbow Mental Health Facility, Kansas City, KS, p. A246

READ, Eddie, Interim Chief Financial Officer, Val Verde Regional Medical Center, Del Rio, TX, p. A612

READ, John, Chief Nursing Officer, Allegiance Specialty Hospital of Greenville, Greenville, MS, p. A358

READ, Paul, R.N. Vice President and Chief Nursing Officer, Springhill Memorial Hospital, Mobile, AL, p. A22

READ, Richard
Chief Financial Officer, Central Florida Regional Hospital, Sanford, FL, p. A145
Chief Financial Officer, Tennova Healthcare Regional Hospital of Jackson, Jackson, TN, p. A584

READER, G. Whitney, M.D. Chief Medical Officer, Kansas Medical Center, Andover, KS, p. A240

READING, Jared, M.D. Chief of Staff, Uvalde Memorial Hospital, Uvalde, TX, p. A654

REAGAN Jr., James H., Ph.D., Chief Executive Officer, Morris County Hospital, Council Grove, KS, p. A242

REAGAN, Kevin, M.D. Chief Medical Officer, CHI Health Bergan Mercy, Omaha, NE, p. A399

REALE, Kelli, Vice President Human Resources, UPMC McKeesport, McKeesport, PA, p. A544

REAM, Tom, Regional Chief Information Officer, Sutter Auburn Faith Hospital, Auburn, CA, p. A55

REAMER, Roger J., Chief Executive Officer, Memorial Health Care Systems, Seward, NE, p. A402

REAMES, Jim, Director Human Resources, Bayfront Health St. Petersburg, Saint Petersburg, FL, p. A144

REAMY, Tracy, Administrator, Bozeman Health Big Sky Medical Center, Big Sky, MT, p. A385

REANDEAU, Michael, Chief Information Officer, Mills–Peninsula Health Services, Burlingame, CA, p. A57

REANO, Paul, Chief Executive Officer, Pushmataha Hospital & Home Health, Antlers, OK, p. A508

REASER, Michelle, R.N. Chief Nursing Executive, Lancaster Regional Medical Center, Lancaster, PA, p. A542

REASONER, Vanessa, Chief Executive Officer, Grace Medical Center, Lubbock, TX, p. A634

REAVIS, Mack, M.D. President and Chief Medical Officer, Lakeland Regional Health, Lakeland, FL, p. A134

REBERRY, Darinda, R.N., President and Chief Executive Officer, Western Missouri Medical Center, Warrensburg, MO, p. A383

REBLOCK, Kimberly, M.D. Chief Operating Officer, The Children's Home of Pittsburgh, Pittsburgh, PA, p. A551

REBOCK, Michael, Chief Medical Officer, Beaumont Hospital – Farmington Hills, Farmington Hills, MI, p. A323

RECA, Sr., Thomas, Deputy Executive Director and Chief Financial Officer, Staten Island University Hospital,, NY, p. A450

RECH, Eunice A., MSN Chief Clinical Officer and Administrator of Quality Services, Tuality Healthcare, Hillsboro, OR, p. A526

RECHNER, Paula, M.D. Chief Medical Officer, War Memorial Hospital, Sault Sainte Marie, MI, p. A334

RECHSTEINER, Hans, M.D. Chief of Staff, Burnett Medical Center, Grantsburg, WI, p. A706

RECKDENWALD, Jeanine, Vice President Human Resources and Support Services, Bristol Hospital, Bristol, CT, p. A113

RECKERT, Sandy, Director Communications and Public Affairs, Johns Hopkins Bayview Medical Center, Baltimore, MD, p. A296

RECTOR, III, Fax, Director Information Technology, Sunbury Community Hospital and Outpatient Center, Sunbury, PA, p. A555

RECTOR, Jeanne, Chief Nursing Officer, Carroll County Memorial Hospital, Carrollton, MO, p. A369

RECUPERO, David, Chief Financial Officer, San Gorgonio Memorial Hospital, Banning, CA, p. A56

REDD, Dakota, R.N. Chief Clinical Officer, Kindred Hospital–St. Louis, Saint Louis, MO, p. A380

REDDING, Georgia, Director Human Resources, Forbes Hospital, Monroeville, PA, p. A545

REDDING, Lisa, Manager Human Resources, Morgan County ARH Hospital, West Liberty, KY, p. A270

REDDY, Challa, M.D. President Medical Staff, Mayo Regional Hospital, Dover–Foxcroft, ME, p. A293

REDDY, Lex, President and Chief Executive Officer, St. Rose Hospital, Hayward, CA, p. A66

REDDY, Prem, M.D., President and Chief Executive Officer, Prime Healthcare Services, Ontario, CA, p. B106

REDDY, Sunil, Chief Executive Officer, Care Regional Medical Center, Aransas Pass, TX, p. A597

REDFIELD, Gregg, Director Finance, CentraCare Health–Paynesville, Paynesville, MN, p. A348

REDHORSE–CHARLEY, Gloria, Director Human Resources, Northern Navajo Medical Center, Shiprock, NM, p. A431

REDING, Janeen K., Director Human Resources, CHI St. Anthony Hospital, Pendleton, OR, p. A528

REDINGTON, James, M.D. Chief of Staff, Bath Community Hospital, Hot Springs, VA, p. A672

REDMON, Gary, Chief Financial Officer, South Texas Regional Medical Center, Jourdanton, TX, p. A629

REDMOND, Michael, Senior Vice President and Chief Operating Officer, Crotched Mountain Rehabilitation Center, Greenfield, NH, p. A411

REDMOND, Paula, Controller, HEALTHSOUTH Tustin Rehabilitation Hospital, Tustin, CA, p. A97

REDRICK, Heather, Chief Nursing Officer, Emory Johns Creek Hospital, Johns Creek, GA, p. A161

REECE, Candice, Human Resources Director, Walla Walla General Hospital, Walla Walla, WA, p. A693

REECE, Morris A., EVP/COO, Laird Hospital, Union, MS, p. A365

REECER, Jeff, FACHE, Chief Executive Officer, Texas Health Presbyterian Hospital Denton, Denton, TX, p. A613

REED, Chris, Director of Nursing, Post Acute/Warm Springs Specialty Hospital of Victoria, Victoria, TX, p. A655

REED, Cindy, Director Community Relations, Austin State Hospital, Austin, TX, p. A599

REED, Fred, M.D. Chief of Staff, Lincoln Hospital, Davenport, WA, p. A684

REED, Gloria, Leader Human Resources, SSM DePaul Health Center, Bridgeton, MO, p. A368

REED, Helen, Director Health Information, North Mississippi Medical Center–Eupora, Eupora, MS, p. A357

REED, Jason, Chief Executive Officer, Beacham Memorial Hospital, Magnolia, MS, p. A361

REED, Jason, President and Chief Executive Officer, Oceans Healthcare, Lake Charles, LA, p. B99

REED, John E., M.D. Medical Director, Baptist Memorial Hospital–Golden Triangle, Columbus, MS, p. A357

REED, Karen, R.N
Chief Nursing Officer, St. Charles Bend, Bend, OR, p. A524
Chief Nursing Officer, St. Charles Redmond, Redmond, OR, p. A530

REED, Kathleen, Manager Human Resources, Missouri Baptist Sullivan Hospital, Sullivan, MO, p. A383

REED, Kirby, Director Information Systems, Franciscan Health Rensselear, Rensselaer, IN, p. A221

REED, Leslie, Chief Financial Officer, Wright Memorial Hospital, Trenton, MO, p. A383

REED, Linda
Vice President Information Systems and Chief Information Officer, Newton Medical Center, Newton, NJ, p. A421
Vice President and Chief Information Officer, St. Joseph's Healthcare System, Paterson, NJ, p. A421

REED, Margaret M., R.N. Chief Nursing Officer, Altru Health System, Grand Forks, ND, p. A479

REED, Pamela R., Chief Executive Officer, Kindred Hospital Melbourne, Melbourne, FL, p. A136

REED, Renee
Director Human Resources, Via Christi Hospital Manhattan, Inc.,, KS, p. A248
Director Human Resources, Wamego Health Center, Wamego, KS, p. A255

REED, Tim, Vice President and Chief Financial Officer, Yakima Valley Memorial Hospital, Yakima, WA, p. A693

REED, Tracy Collings, Vice President Patient Care Services, Chief Nursing Officer, Siskin Hospital for Physical Rehabilitation, Chattanooga, TN, p. A580

REED, Victoria L., FACHE, Chief Executive Officer, James B. Haggin Memorial Hospital, Harrodsburg, KY, p. A261

REEDER, Carol, R.N. Chief Nursing Officer, St. Joseph Hospital, Eureka, CA, p. A61

REEDER, Wendy, R.N. Chief Nursing Officer, Harrison Memorial Hospital, Cynthiana, KY, p. A259

REEDY, James Christopher, Chief Nursing Officer, Sutter Delta Medical Center, Antioch, CA, p. A54

REEDY, Janet, Manager Human Resources, St. Thomas More Hospital, Canon City, CO, p. A102

REEFER, John C., M.D. Director, Butler Health System, Butler, PA, p. A534

REEL, John, Chief Executive Officer, Texas Rehabilitation Hospital of Arlington, Arlington, TX, p. A598

REEL, Micah, Director of Bio–Med, Potomac Valley Hospital, Keyser, WV, p. A697

REEL, Stephanie L., Senior Vice President Information Services, Johns Hopkins Hospital, Baltimore, MD, p. A296

REES, Adam, President, Essentia Health St. Joseph's Medical Center, Brainerd, MN, p. A340

REES, Elizabeth, Chief Executive Officer, AMG Specialty Hospital–Tulsa, Tulsa, OK, p. A521

REES, Jeff, Director Information Systems, Bacharach Institute for Rehabilitation, Pomona, NJ, p. A422

REES, Matthew, Administrator, Jerold Phelps Community Hospital, Garberville, CA, p. A64

REESE, Bert
Chief Information Officer, Sentara Leigh Hospital, Norfolk, VA, p. A675
Chief Information Officer, Sentara Norfolk General Hospital, Norfolk, VA, p. A675
Chief Information Officer, Sentara Princess Anne Hospital, Virginia Beach, VA, p. A680

REESE, Jeff, Chief Financial Officer, Howard A. Rusk Rehabilitation Center, Columbia, MO, p. A370

REESE, Kathie, R.N., Regional Administrator and Chief Executive Officer, CHRISTUS Continuing Care dba Dubuis Hospital of Paris, Paris, TX, p. A640

REESE, Maryann, R.N. Chief Operating Officer, Saint Francis Healthcare System, Cape Girardeau, MO, p. A368

REESE, Mike, Chief Financial Officer, OU Medical Center, Oklahoma City, OK, p. A517

REESE, Todd, Director Human Resources, Castle Medical Center, Kailua, HI, p. A171

REESE, Willis L., Administrator, Falls Community Hospital and Clinic, Marlin, TX, p. A635

REETZ, Brenda, FACHE, Chief Executive Officer, Greene County General Hospital, Linton, IN, p. A217

REETZ, Renee, Director Human Resources, St. Mary's of Michigan Standish Hospital, Standish, MI, p. A335

REEVE, Jay A., Ph.D., President and Chief Executive Officer, Eastside Psychiatric Hospital, Tallahassee, FL, p. A146

REEVES, Amy D., Director Human Resources, Lakeway Regional Medical Center, Lakeway, TX, p. A631

REEVES, Cory, Chief Financial Officer, Gordon Hospital, Calhoun, GA, p. A155

REEVES, Danny, Chief Financial Officer, Penrose–St. Francis Health Services, Colorado Springs, CO, p. A103

REEVES, Katy, Vice President Human Resources, Fauquier Hospital, Warrenton, VA, p. A680

REEVES, Kaylene, Director, Tahoe Pacific Hospitals, Sparks, NV, p. A408

REEVES, Mike
Vice President, St. John Medical Center, Tulsa, OK, p. A522
Chief Information Officer, St. John Owasso, Owasso, OK, p. A518

REEVES, Pamela J., M.D., Director, John D. Dingell Veterans Affairs Medical Center, Detroit, MI, p. A322

REEVES, Steve, M.D. Chief Medical Staff, Greater Regional Medical Center, Creston, IA, p. A228

REEVES, Timothy, Administrator, Bucktail Medical Center, Renovo, PA, p. A553

REEVES, Valerie
Chief Financial Officer, Integris Grove Hospital, Grove, OK, p. A512
Chief Financial Officer, INTEGRIS Miami Hospital, Miami, OK, p. A514

REFFNER, Gina, Chief Financial Officer, Little Colorado Medical Center, Winslow, AZ, p. A41

REFNESS, Kristen, Chief Financial Officer, Linden Oaks Hospital, Naperville, IL, p. A198

REGAL, Wendy, Director Human Resources, Providence Tarzana Medical Center,, CA, p. A74

REGAN, Timothy, President and Chief Medical Officer, Lakeland Regional Health, Lakeland, FL, p. A134

REGEN, Debbie, R.N. Chief Nursing Officer, Hackensack University Medical Center Mountainside, Montclair, NJ, p. A419

REGIER, Donald, M.D. Chief Medical Officer, Sedgwick County Health Center, Julesburg, CO, p. A107

REGIER, Marion, Chief Executive Officer, Hillsboro Community Hospital, Hillsboro, KS, p. A244

REGIER, Steve, Chief Financial Officer, Kearney Regional Medical Center, Kearney, NE, p. A397

REGISTER, Kellie, Director of Nursing, Clinch Memorial Hospital, Homerville, GA, p. A161

REGISTER, Stephen, Chief Executive Officer, Greenleaf Center, Valdosta, GA, p. A168

REGULA, John
Chief Information Officer, Allied Services Rehabilitation Hospital, Scranton, PA, p. A554
Chief Information Officer, John Heinz Institute of Rehabilitation Medicine, Wilkes-Barre, PA, p. A558

REGULA, Terry, Chief Executive Officer, Aultman Specialty Hospital, Canton, OH, p. A486

REHBEIN, Beth, Chief Nursing and Quality Officer, Story County Medical Center, Nevada, IA, p. A235

REHM, Janice, Manager Human Resources, University of South Alabama Children's and Women's Hospital, Mobile, AL, p. A23

REHM, Micah, Chief Nursing Officer, Forrest General Hospital, Hattiesburg, MS, p. A359

REHMER, Patricia, President, Natchaug Hospital, Mansfield Center, CT, p. A114

REHN, Lindsay, Executive Director of Financial Operations, WellStar Paulding Hospital, Hiram, GA, p. A161

REHN, Ronald G.
Chief Executive Officer, Providence Mount Carmel Hospital, Colville, WA, p. A684
Chief Executive Officer, Providence St. Joseph's Hospital, Chewelah, WA, p. A683

REICH, David L., M.D., President and Chief Operating Officer, Mount Sinai Hospital, New York, NY, p. A446

REICH, Joel R., M.D
Senior Vice President Medical Affairs, Manchester Memorial Hospital, Manchester, CT, p. A114
Senior Vice President Medical Affairs, Rockville General Hospital, Vernon, CT, p. A117

REICHARD, Steve, Manager Information Systems, Brigham City Community Hospital, Brigham City, UT, p. A659

REICHERT, Don, Vice President Associate Chief Information Officer, MetroHealth Medical Center, Cleveland, OH, p. A489

REICHERT, James, Chief Medical Officer, Mercer Health, Coldwater, OH, p. A490

REICHFIELD, Michael L., President, OhioHealth Doctors Hospital, Columbus, OH, p. A491

REICHLE, Paula, Senior Vice President and Chief Operating Officer, Sparrow Hospital, Lansing, MI, p. A328

REICHMAN, Joseph, M.D. Vice President Medical Affairs and Clinical Effectiveness, Riverview Medical Center, Red Bank, NJ, p. A423

REID, Barbara S., Chief Executive Officer, Willingway Hospital, Statesboro, GA, p. A166

REID, Bernadette, Vice President, Information Technology and Chief Information Officer, Torrance Memorial Medical Center, Torrance, CA, p. A96

REID, Bev, Chief Financial Officer, St. Luke Hospital and Living Center, Marion, KS, p. A248

REID, Deressa, Interim Chief Executive Officer, Hoag Orthopedic Institute, Irvine, CA, p. A66

REID, Jamie, Information Systems Director, Methodist Hospital, Henderson, KY, p. A261

REID, Jim, Vice President and Chief Information Officer, Covenant Children's Hospital, Lubbock, TX, p. A633

REID, Kelly, Human Resources Director, South Mississippi State Hospital, Purvis, MS, p. A364

REID, Kenneth G., President and Chief Executive Officer, Carlinville Area Hospital, Carlinville, IL, p. A182

REID, Patricia, Director of Nursing, Marion General Hospital, Columbia, MS, p. A357

REID, Richard, Vice President Chief Finance Officer, Sparrow Carson Hospital, Carson City, MI, p. A320

REID, Stephanie, R.N. Vice President of Quality and Chief Nursing Officer, Carroll Hospital, Westminster, MD, p. A304

REIDER, Rochelle, Vice President Patient Care, Avera Queen of Peace Hospital, Mitchell, SD, p. A575

REIDER, Rodney D., President, Saint Alphonsus Regional Medical Center, Boise, ID, p. A174

REIDER, Stephen, R.N., Administrator, Springbrook Hospital, Brooksville, FL, p. A125

REIDER, Stephen, R.N. Director of Nursing, Assistant Vice President Patient Care Services, Walden Psychiatric Care, Waltham, MA, p. A315

REIDY, Margaret, M.D. Vice President Medical Affairs, UPMC Presbyterian Shadyside, Pittsburgh, PA, p. A551

REIFF, Troy T., Corporate Director Operations, St. Vincent Seton Specialty Hospital, Indianapolis, IN, p. A215

REILLY, Brian M., Chief Financial Officer, Robert Wood Johnson University Hospital, New Brunswick, NJ, p. A420

REILLY, Dennis A., President and Chief Executive Officer, Little Company of Mary Hospital and Health Care Centers, Evergreen Park, IL, p. A190

REILLY, Janelle, Chief Operating Officer, CHI Memorial, Chattanooga, TN, p. A580

REILLY, Jeff
Administrator, Bon Secours Community Hospital, Port Jervis, NY, p. A453
Chief Operating Officer, St. Anthony Community Hospital, Warwick, NY, p. A458

REILLY, John, M.D. Vice President Medical Affairs and Chief Medical Officer, Mercy Medical Center, Rockville Centre, NY, p. A454

REILLY, Richard, Deputy Executive Director, Syosset Hospital, Syosset, NY, p. A456

REILLY, Robert, Vice President and Chief Financial Officer, Anne Arundel Medical Center, Annapolis, MD, p. A296

REILLY, Theresa, MSN Senior Vice President Patient Services and Chief Nursing Officer, Abington Hospital, Abington, PA, p. A532

REILLY, Tiffany, Director Human Resources, Childrens Care Hospital and School, Sioux Falls, SD, p. A576

REIMER, Arlo, M.D. Chief of Staff, Kearny County Hospital, Lakin, KS, p. A247

REIMER, Randy, Chief Financial Officer, Adventist Behavioral Health Rockville, Rockville, MD, p. A303

REIMER, Ronda, R.N. Chief Nursing Officer and Assistant Administrator, Franklin General Hospital, Hampton, IA, p. A231

REIN, Mitchell S., M.D. Chief Medical Officer, North Shore Medical Center, Salem, MA, p. A314

REINART, Greg, Chief Executive Officer, Hereford Regional Medical Center, Hereford, TX, p. A623

REINBOTH, Thomas, Chief Financial Officer, Roxborough Memorial Hospital, Philadelphia, PA, p. A549

REINER, Mark, Chief Medical Office, Executive, St. Anthony's Rehabilitation Hospital, Lauderdale Lakes, FL, p. A134

REINER, Scott, President and Chief Executive Officer, Adventist Health, Roseville, CA, p. B5

REINERT, Brenda, Director Human Resources, Tomah Memorial Hospital, Tomah, WI, p. A717

REINERT, Chad, Chief Information Officer, Hamilton General Hospital, Hamilton, TX, p. A622

REINHARD, Diane, R.N. Vice President of Patient Care Services, Craig Hospital, Englewood, CO, p. A105

REINHARD, James S., M.D., Commissioner, Virginia Department of Mental Health, Richmond, VA, p. B152

REINHARD, Patrick, R.N. Chief Nursing Officer, Desert Valley Hospital, Victorville, CA, p. A98

REINHARD, Russ, Chief Executive, Providence Willamette Falls Medical Center, Oregon City, OR, p. A528

REINKE, Bradley, M.D. Vice President Medical Affairs and Chief Medical Officer, Dameron Hospital, Stockton, CA, p. A95

REINKE, N. Sue, Vice President Human Resources, Geisinger-Lewistown Hospital, Lewistown, PA, p. A543

REINKE, Peggy, R.N., Administrator, CHI Lisbon Health, Lisbon, ND, p. A480

REINKING, Cheryl, R.N. Chief Nursing Officer, El Camino Hospital, Mountain View, CA, p. A78

REINSVOLD, Suzie, Chief Operating Officer, Miller Children's & Women's Hospital Long Beach, Long Beach, CA, p. A70

REISELT, Doug
Vice President and Chief Information Officer, Baptist Memorial Hospital – Memphis, Memphis, TN, p. A588
Vice President and Chief Information Officer, Baptist Memorial Hospital-Collierville, Collierville, TN, p. A581

REISMAN, Ernestine O., Vice President Human Resources, Down East Community Hospital, Machias, ME, p. A294

REISMAN, Ronald, M.D. Chief Medical Director, St. Vincent Seton Specialty Hospital, Indianapolis, IN, p. A215

REISS, Deanna, Hospital Director of Nursing, Devereux Children's Behavioral Health Center, Malvern, PA, p. A543

REISZ, Carol, Chief Financial Officer, North Caddo Medical Center, Vivian, LA, p. A289

REITER, Margaret, Chief Nursing Officer, Capital Health Medical Center–Hopewell, Pennington, NJ, p. A422

REITZ, Brent, President, Adventist Rehabilitation Hospital of Maryland, Rockville, MD, p. A303

REITZ, Judy A., Sc.D. Executive Vice President and Chief Operating Officer, Johns Hopkins Hospital, Baltimore, MD, p. A296

REITZ, Robert, Ph.D., Chief Executive Officer, Fulton State Hospital, Fulton, MO, p. A371

REITZEL, David, Chief Information Officer, Brookdale Hospital Medical Center, New York, NY, p. A444

REKOWSKI, Christian, Information Technology Director, Optim Medical Center – Screven, Sylvania, GA, p. A167

RELPH, Daren, Chief Executive Officer, Wayne County Hospital, Corydon, IA, p. A228

REMALEY, Anne, Vice President Human Resources, ACMH Hospital, Kittanning, PA, p. A541

REMARK, Megan, Chief Executive Officer, Regions Hospital, Saint Paul, MN, p. A350

REMBOLD, Abbey
Human Resources Senior Generalist, Hampshire Memorial Hospital, Romney, WV, p. A700
Manager, Human Resource Business Partnerships, Shenandoah Memorial Hospital, Woodstock, VA, p. A681
Human Resources Senior Generalist, War Memorial Hospital, Berkeley Springs, WV, p. A694

REMIGIO, Odalys, Assistant Vice President, Finance, Baptist Health South Florida, West Kendall Baptist Hospital, Miami, FL, p. A136

REMILLARD, John R.
Interim Chief Executive Officer, Moses Ludington Hospital, Ticonderoga, NY, p. A457
Interim Chief Executive Officer, The University of Vermont Health Network Elizabethtown Community Hospital, Elizabethtown, NY, p. A438

REMINGTON, Amanda
Director Human Resources, Spalding Regional Hospital, Griffin, GA, p. A160
Director Human Resources, Sylvan Grove Hospital, Jackson, GA, p. A161

REMSPECHER, Mark, Director Human Resources, Southeast Missouri Mental Health Center, Farmington, MO, p. A371

RENDA, Nick, Chief Financial Officer, Merit Health Woman's Hospital, Flowood, MS, p. A357

RENDER-LEACH, Cynthia, Director Human Resources, Highland Community Hospital, Picayune, MS, p. A364

RENEAU, John D., Medical Director, HEALTHSOUTH Rehabilitation Hospital–Las Vegas, Las Vegas, NV, p. A406

RENFREE, Mark, Chief Financial Officer, La Rabida Children's Hospital, Chicago, IL, p. A184

RENIER, Hugh, M.D
Vice President Medical Affairs, Essentia Health Duluth, Duluth, MN, p. A341
Vice President Medical Affairs, Essentia Health St. Mary's Medical Center, Duluth, MN, p. A342

RENKIEWICZ, Ginger L., Chief Clinical Officer, Chief Nursing Executive, and Chief Quality Officer, UnityPoint Health – Trinity Rock Island, Rock Island, IL, p. A201

RENN, Amy Katherine, Interim Administrator, Patient Care and Nursing, Via Christi Hospital Pittsburg, Pittsburg, KS, p. A252

RENNEKER, James M., MSN Vice President and Chief Nursing Officer, Loretto Hospital, Chicago, IL, p. A184

RENNER, Dianne, Director Human Resources, Logansport State Hospital, Logansport, IN, p. A217

RENO, Kelly, R.N. Chief Nursing Officer, Menorah Medical Center, Overland Park, KS, p. A251

RENO, Mike, Chief Operating Officer, Hill Country Memorial Hospital, Fredericksburg, TX, p. A619

RENO, III, William, M.D. President Medical Staff, Merit Health Wesley, Hattiesburg, MS, p. A359

RENSHAW, Dee, Chief Executive Officer, Hillcrest Hospital Henryetta, Henryetta, OK, p. A512

RENTAS, Margarita, R.N. Nursing Director, Castaner General Hospital, Castaner, PR, p. A726

RENTFRO, Donald R., Chief Executive Officer, L. V. Stabler Memorial Hospital, Greenville, AL, p. A21

RENTSCH, Richard E., President, Stroud Regional Medical Center, Stroud, OK, p. A520

RENTZ, Norman G., President and Chief Executive Officer, Cannon Memorial Hospital, Pickens, SC, p. A569

RENZ, Evan, Chief Executive Officer, Brooke Army Medical Center, Fort Sam Houston, TX, p. A617

REOHR, Sara, Regional Controller, West Gables Rehabilitation Hospital, Miami, FL, p. A137

REPAC, Kimberly S., Senior Vice President and Chief Financial Officer, Western Maryland Regional Medical Center, Cumberland, MD, p. A300

REPASS, Lois, Quality Assurance Specialist and Coordinator Performance Improvement, Northern Nevada Adult Mental Health Services, Sparks, NV, p. A408

REPETTI III, Gregory George, FACHE, Chief Executive Officer, Valley Hospital, Spokane Valley, WA, p. A691

REPIQUE, R. John, R.N., Chief Executive Officer, Friends Hospital, Philadelphia, PA, p. A548

REPKO, Keith D., Director, Veterans Affairs St. Louis Health Care System, Saint Louis, MO, p. A381

REPPERT, Joseph A., Executive Vice President and Chief Financial Officer, North Mississippi Medical Center – Tupelo, Tupelo, MS, p. A365

REPPY, William
Interim President, Schuylkill Medical Center – Schuylkill East Norwegian Street, Pottsville, PA, p. A552
Interim President, Schuylkill Medical Center – Schuylkill South Jackson Street, Pottsville, PA, p. A552

RESENDEZ, James R., Chief Executive Officer, Doctors Hospital of Laredo, Laredo, TX, p. A632

RESETAR, Gayle L.
Chief Operating Officer, Tidelands Georgetown Memorial Hospital, Georgetown, SC, p. A566
Vice President and Chief Operating Officer, Tidelands Georgetown Memorial Hospital, Georgetown, SC, p. A566
Chief Operating Officer, Tidelands Waccamaw Community Hospital, Murrells Inlet, SC, p. A568

RESLER, Lori, R.N. Chief Nurse, Sullivan County Community Hospital, Sullivan, IN, p. A222

RESSLER, Dennis, Chief Financial Officer, St. Vincent Kokomo, Kokomo, IN, p. A216

RESTREPO, Macarena, Manager Business Office, Sister Emmanuel Hospital, Miami, FL, p. A137

RESTREPO, Nicolas, M.D. Vice President Medical Affairs, Winchester Medical Center, Winchester, VA, p. A680

RESTUCCIA, Michael, Chief Information Officer, Hospital of the University of Pennsylvania, Philadelphia, PA, p. A548

RESTUM, William H., Ph.D., Chief Executive Officer, DMC – Rehabilitation Institute of Michigan, Detroit, MI, p. A321

RETALIC, Tammy B., R.N. Chief Nursing Officer, Hebrew Rehabilitation Center, Boston, MA, p. A307

RETCHIN, Sheldon, M.D., Chief Executive Officer, Ohio State University Wexner Medical Center, Columbus, OH, p. A491

RETTGER, Linda, M.D. President Medical Staff, Kane Community Hospital, Kane, PA, p. A541

RETTIG, Linda, Director Financial Services, Washington County Hospital, Washington, KS, p. A255

REULAND, Charlie, Sc.D. Executive Vice President and Chief Operating Officer, Johns Hopkins Bayview Medical Center, Baltimore, MD, p. A296

REUST, Michele, Controller, Memorial Hospital of Texas County, Guymon, OK, p. A512

REUTTINGER, H. Rex, D.O. Chief Medical Officer, Administration, Garden City Hospital, Garden City, MI, p. A324

REVAL, Mary, R.N. Chief Nursing Officer, Gulf Coast Medical Center, Panama City, FL, p. A141

REVELS, Beverly, Director Human Resources, Sutter Amador Hospital, Jackson, CA, p. A66

REVELS, Tonya, Senior Strategic Business Partner, McDowell Hospital, Marion, NC, p. A469

REVERMAN, Larry, Director Information Systems, Clark Memorial Hospital, Jeffersonville, IN, p. A215

REVIEL, Jackie, R.N., Chief Executive Officer, Allen Parish Hospital, Kinder, LA, p. A280

REWERTS, Karen
System Vice President of Finance, SSM Cardinal Glennon Children's Medical Center, Saint Louis, MO, p. A381
System Vice President Finance, SSM St. Joseph Health Center, Saint Charles, MO, p. A379
System Vice President of Finance, SSM St. Mary's Health Center, Saint Louis, MO, p. A381

REXFORD, Linda, Director Human Resources, Weeks Medical Center, Lancaster, NH, p. A411

REXWINKLE, Lori, Chief Nursing Officer, Coffeyville Regional Medical Center, Coffeyville, KS, p. A241

REYES, Anthony, Information Technology Director, Commonwealth Health Center, Saipan, MP, p. A725

REYES, Glenda, Chief Financial Officer, Northwest Medical Center, Winfield, AL, p. A26

REYES, Raul, M.D. Medical Director, San Juan City Hospital, San Juan, PR, p. A730

REYES, Roxanne, Director of Nursing, Cornerstone Regional Hospital, Edinburg, TX, p. A614

REYKA, Michael, Chief Executive Officer, Western Maryland Hospital Center, Hagerstown, MD, p. A301

REYMAN, Reed, President, St. Joseph's Hospital and Health Center, Dickinson, ND, p. A478

REYNA, Krista, Chief Nursing Officer, McBride Clinic Orthopedic Hospital, Oklahoma City, OK, p. A516

REYNGOUDT, Mark, Chief Financial Officer, Carlisle Regional Medical Center, Carlisle, PA, p. A535

REYNOLDS, Angela D., Chief Financial Officer, Lewis–Gale Medical Center, Salem, VA, p. A678

REYNOLDS, Denise, Chief Nursing Officer, Memorial Hospital Miramar, Miramar, FL, p. A138

REYNOLDS, Doug, Area Finance Officer, Kaiser Permanente Redwood City Medical Center, Redwood City, CA, p. A85

REYNOLDS, Hope, Executive Director Human Resources and Support Services, Margaret R. Pardee Memorial Hospital, Hendersonville, NC, p. A467

REYNOLDS, Ian, Chief Medical Officer, Advanced Diagnostics Hospital, Houston, TX, p. A623

REYNOLDS, James B., M.D. Medical Director, Northwest Missouri Psychiatric Rehabilitation Center, Saint Joseph, MO, p. A379

REYNOLDS, Jay, M.D. Chief Medical Officer and Chief Clinical Officer, The Aroostook Medical Center, Presque Isle, ME, p. A295

REYNOLDS, Katelyn, Manager Human Resources, Greeley County Health Services, Tribune, KS, p. A255

REYNOLDS, Lennetta M., Administrative Supervisor, Community Behavioral Health Hospital – Annandale, Annandale, MN, p. A338

REYNOLDS, Mike
Chief Financial Officer, Delta Medical Center, Memphis, TN, p. A588
Chief Financial Officer, Newberry County Memorial Hospital, Newberry, SC, p. A569

REYNOLDS, Paul, M.D. Medical Director, Coleman County Medical Center, Coleman, TX, p. A606

REYNOLDS, Ray, Chief Executive Officer, Glen Rose Medical Center, Glen Rose, TX, p. A620

REYNOLDS, Robert, Director Information Systems, Mary Rutan Hospital, Bellefontaine, OH, p. A485

REYNOLDS, Ronald J., Vice President East Lycoming Operations and Chief Administrative Officer, Muncy Valley Hospital, Muncy, PA, p. A546

REYNOLDS, Scott, Vice President Finance, Mercy Hospital Springfield, Springfield, MO, p. A382

REYNOLDS, Teresa
Chief Operating Officer, Haywood Regional Medical Center, Clyde, NC, p. A463
Interim Chief Nursing Officer, Starr Regional Medical Center, Athens, TN, p. A579

REYNOLDS, Todd, Chief Information Officer, Memorial Medical Center – Ashland, Ashland, WI, p. A702

REYNOLDS, Vance V., CPA, Chief Executive Officer, Aiken Regional Medical Centers, Aiken, SC, p. A562

REYNOLDS–GOSSETTE, Youdie, Controller, Wilma N. Vazquez Medical Center, Vega Baja, PR, p. A730

REZAC, Julie A., R.N. Chief Operating Officer, Saunders Medical Center, Wahoo, NE, p. A403

RHEE, Carolyn F., Chief Executive Officer, LAC–Olive View–UCLA Medical Center,, CA, p. A72

RHEINHEIMER, Rick, Chief Clinical Officer, Kindred Hospital–Chattanooga, Chattanooga, TN, p. A580

RHINE, Kathleen, President and Chief Executive Officer, Presence St. Mary's Hospital, Kankakee, IL, p. A194

RHINEHART, Jennie R., Administrator and Chief Executive Officer, Community Hospital, Tallassee, AL, p. A25

RHOADES, Charles E., M.D., Chief Executive Officer, Kansas City Orthopaedic Institute, Leawood, KS, p. A247

RHOADES, Mark, Vice President and Chief Human Resources Officer, Duncan Regional Hospital, Duncan, OK, p. A510

RHOADES, Shelly, Chief Financial Officer, Clarion Psychiatric Center, Clarion, PA, p. A535

RHOADS, Jack, M.D. Medical Director, Landmark Hospital of Joplin, Joplin, MO, p. A372

RHOADS, Pam, Chief Financial Officer, Fairfax Behavioral Health, Kirkland, WA, p. A686

RHODES, Brigett, Director Human Resource, Lawrence Memorial Hospital, Walnut Ridge, AR, p. A53

RHODES, David, M.D. Senior Vice President Medical Affairs and Chief Medical Officer, Rapides Regional Medical Center, Alexandria, LA, p. A271

RHODES, Helen, R.N. Associate Director Operations, Veterans Affairs Northern Indiana Health Care System, Fort Wayne, IN, p. A211

RHODES, J. Gary, FACHE, Chief Executive Officer, Kane Community Hospital, Kane, PA, p. A541

RHODES, Jerome E., Chief Executive Officer, CRC Health Group, Inc., Cupertino, CA, p. B43

RHODES, Pamela, R.N. Vice President Patient Care Services and Chief Nursing Officer, Northern Dutchess Hospital, Rhinebeck, NY, p. A453

RHODES, Tracey, Coordinator Human Resources, Evergreen Medical Center, Evergreen, AL, p. A19

RHONE, Steve, R.N. Vice President Patient Care Services, Beebe Healthcare, Lewes, DE, p. A119

RHYMES, Raphael, Administrator, Liberty Healthcare Systems, Bastrop, LA, p. A272

RHYNALDS, Kayla, Interim Chief Financial Officer, Kearney County Health Services, Minden, NE, p. A398

RHYNE, Catherine A., M.P.H. Chief Nursing Officer, Gerald Champion Regional Medical Center, Alamogordo, NM, p. A427

RHYNE, Craig, M.D. Chief Medical Officer, Covenant Medical Center, Lubbock, TX, p. A634

RHYNE, Dennis, M.D. Acting Medical Director, Fairbanks, Indianapolis, IN, p. A213

RHYNE, Tim, Personnel Officer, Ventura County Medical Center, Ventura, CA, p. A98

RIAL, Joanne, Chief Financial Officer, Cumberland Hospital, New Kent, VA, p. A674

RIALS, Joe, Director Fiscal Services, North Mississippi State Hospital, Tupelo, MS, p. A365

RIALS, Loren, Chief Financial Officer, Carolinas Hospital System, Florence, SC, p. A565

RIANO, Omaira D., Chief Nursing Officer, HEALTHSOUTH Sunrise Rehabilitation Hospital, Sunrise, FL, p. A146

RIAZ, Mohammad, M.D. Chief of Staff, Raulerson Hospital, Okeechobee, FL, p. A140

RIBA, Chris, Director Human Resources, Baldwin Area Medical Center, Baldwin, WI, p. A702

RICARDO, Jennifer, Director of Human Resources, Westchester General Hospital, Miami, FL, p. A137

RICARTTI, Rebecca R., Interim Director Human Resources, Garfield Medical Center, Monterey Park, CA, p. A78

RICCI, Lynn, President and Chief Executive Officer, Hospital for Special Care, New Britain, CT, p. A115

RICCIARDI, Patrice, Director Human Resources, Columbus Hospital LTACH, Newark, NJ, p. A420

RICCIO, Dustin, M.D.
President, Clifton Springs Hospital and Clinic, Clifton Springs, NY, p. A437
President Eastern Region, Newark–Wayne Community Hospital, Newark, NY, p. A450

RICCIO, John A., M.D. Chief Medical Officer, Auburn Community Hospital, Auburn, NY, p. A434

RICCIONI, Mich
Chief Financial Officer, Petaluma Valley Hospital, Petaluma, CA, p. A82
Vice President and Chief Financial Officer, Northern California Region, Queen of the Valley Medical Center, Napa, CA, p. A79
Chief Financial Officer, Santa Rosa Memorial Hospital, Santa Rosa, CA, p. A94
Chief Financial Officer, St. Joseph Hospital, Eureka, CA, p. A61

RICCITELLI, Anthony, Chief Operating Officer, Worcester Recovery Center and Hospital, Worcester, MA, p. A317

RICCITELLI, Vincent, Vice President Finance, Hoboken University Medical Center, Hoboken, NJ, p. A418

RICE, Aimee, Human Resources Manager, Riverview Psychiatric Center, Augusta, ME, p. A291

RICE, Amy, Chief Financial Officer, Helena Regional Medical Center, Helena, AR, p. A47

RICE, Ann Madden, Chief Executive Officer, University of California, Davis Medical Center, Sacramento, CA, p. A87

RICE, Bernard, Chief Compliance Officer, Rangely District Hospital, Rangely, CO, p. A110

RICE, Carolyn, M.D. Director Medical Services, Naval Hospital Pensacola, Pensacola, FL, p. A142

RICE, Craig, Director Information, Schneck Medical Center, Seymour, IN, p. A222

RICE, Devin, Director Information Systems, Clifton–Fine Hospital, Star Lake, NY, p. A456

RICE, James W., Director, Oscar G. Johnson Veterans Affairs Medical Center, Iron Mountain, MI, p. A327

RICE, Mark, CPA Chief Financial Officer, Jersey Shore Hospital, Jersey Shore, PA, p. A541

RICE, Mark, Chief Executive Officer, Mid–Jefferson Extended Care Hospital, Nederland, TX, p. A638

RICE, Peter, M.D. Medical Director, PeaceHealth Ketchikan Medical Center, Ketchikan, AK, p. A29

RICE, Rebecca, FACHE, Chief Executive Officer, Upper Valley Medical Center, Troy, OH, p. A504

RICE, Tim, President and Chief Executive Officer, Lakewood Health System, Staples, MN, p. A352

RICH, Anna, Chief Financial Officer, Complex Care Hospital at Tenaya, Las Vegas, NV, p. A405

RICH, Bill, Chief Executive Officer, Tennova Healthcare–Shelbyville, Shelbyville, TN, p. A593

RICH, Judy F., President and Chief Executive Officer, TMC HealthCare, Tucson, AZ, p. A41

RICH, Kori, Chief Executive Officer, The Physicians Centre Hospital, Bryan, TX, p. A604

RICH, Mark, Director Information Services, Ashley Regional Medical Center, Vernal, UT, p. A664

RICH, Philip, M.D. Chief Medical Officer, West Hills Hospital, Reno, NV, p. A408

RICHARD, Benjamin, Regional Information Technology Director, Santa Rosa Memorial Hospital, Santa Rosa, CA, p. A94

RICHARD, Brandi, Chief Nursing Officer, Michiana Behavioral Health Center, Plymouth, IN, p. A220

RICHARD, Brent, Administrative Director Information Systems, Southern Ohio Medical Center, Portsmouth, OH, p. A501

RICHARD, Christina, Market Chief Executive Officer, Kindred Hospital Tarrant County–Arlington, Arlington, TX, p. A597

RICHARD, Marilyn, Director Human Resources, Daviess Community Hospital, Washington, IN, p. A223

RICHARD, Paul F., Executive Vice President, Sanford Medical Center Fargo, Fargo, ND, p. A479

RICHARD, Scott, Vice President Finance and Chief Financial Officer, St. Elizabeth Hospital, Gonzales, LA, p. A277

RICHARD, Thomas, Director Budget and Revenue Cycle, Redwood Area Hospital, Redwood Falls, MN, p. A349

RICHARD, Tim, IT Coordinator, Crawford Memorial Hospital, Robinson, IL, p. A201

RICHARDS, Craig A., Chief Executive Officer, Mildred Mitchell–Bateman Hospital, Huntington, WV, p. A697

RICHARDS, Frank
Chief Information Officer, Geisinger Medical Center, Danville, PA, p. A536
Chief Information Officer, Geisinger Wyoming Valley Medical Center, Wilkes Barre, PA, p. A557

RICHARDS, Jaena, Chief Financial Officer, Deer Lodge Medical Center, Deer Lodge, MT, p. A387

RICHARDS, Jon, Chief Financial Officer, Tennova Newport Medical Center, Newport, TN, p. A591

RICHARDS, Jonathan, Chief Financial Officer, David Grant USAF Medical Center, Travis AFB, CA, p. A96

RICHARDS, Judith, Director of Nursing, Adcare Hospital of Worcester, Worcester, MA, p. A316

RICHARDS, Kelly, MS
Senior Vice President and Chief Nursing Officer, Covenant Medical Center, Waterloo, IA, p. A238
Senior Vice President and Chief Nursing Officer, Mercy Hospital of Franciscan Sisters, Oelwein, IA, p. A235
Senior Vice President and Chief Nursing Officer, Sartori Memorial Hospital, Cedar Falls, IA, p. A226

RICHARDS, Mandy, R.N. Vice President Patient Care, United Hospital, Saint Paul, MN, p. A351

RICHARDS, Nate, Director Information Technology, Mitchell County Hospital Health Systems, Beloit, KS, p. A241

RICHARDS, Sheila K., Human Resources Director, Dallas Medical Center, Dallas, TX, p. A609

RICHARDS, Stanlee, Chief Nurse Executive, NYC Health + Hospitals / Carter, New York, NY, p. A448

RICHARDS, Suzanne, FACHE, Chief Executive Officer, KPC Healthcare, Inc., Santa Ana, CA, p. B78

RICHARDS, Suzanne, Chief Executive Officer, Orange County Global Medical Center, Inc., Santa Ana, CA, p. A92

RICHARDS, Suzanne, FACHE, Chief Executive Officer, Victor Valley Global Medical Center, Victorville, CA, p. A98

RICHARDS, Thom
Chief Information Technology, Adair County Memorial Hospital, Greenfield, IA, p. A231
Director Information Technology, Knoxville Hospital & Clinics, Knoxville, IA, p. A233

RICHARDSON, David, M.D. Chief of Staff, Delta Medical Center, Memphis, TN, p. A588

RICHARDSON, Denise, R.N. Senior Vice President and Chief Nursing Officer, St. Barnabas Hospital,, NY, p. A449

RICHARDSON, Dorothy, Director Human Resources, Van Matre HealthSouth Rehabilitation Hospital, Rockford, IL, p. A202

RICHARDSON, Dwayne, Chief Operating Officer, Placentia–Linda Hospital, Placentia, CA, p. A83

RICHARDSON, Greg H., Assistant Administrator Human Resources, Piedmont Newton Hospital, Covington, GA, p. A157

RICHARDSON, Irene, Chief Financial Officer, Memorial Hospital of Sweetwater County, Rock Springs, WY, p. A723

RICHARDSON, James, Chief Medical Officer, Holy Cross Hospital, Chicago, IL, p. A184

RICHARDSON, Judy, M.D. President Medical Staff, Mid–Columbia Medical Center, The Dalles, OR, p. A531

RICHARDSON, Karen K., Senior Vice President and Chief Financial Officer, Providence Healthcare Network, Waco, TX, p. A656

RICHARDSON, Keith, President and Chief Executive Officer, East Liverpool City Hospital, East Liverpool, OH, p. A494

RICHARDSON, Kevin, M.D. Chief of Staff, Southwest Mississippi Regional Medical Center, McComb, MS, p. A361

RICHARDSON, Kirk, R.N. Vice President, Chief Operating Officer, and Chief Nursing Officer, Bronson LakeView Hospital, Paw Paw, MI, p. A331

RICHARDSON, Kitty J., Administrator, Wilson N. Jones Regional Medical Center, Sherman, TX, p. A649

RICHARDSON, Kristy, Director of Nursing, De Queen Medical Center, De Queen, AR, p. A45

RICHARDSON, Mark D., President and Chief Executive Officer, Great River Medical Center, West Burlington, IA, p. A239

RICHARDSON Jr., Nathaniel, President, Decatur Morgan Hospital, Decatur, AL, p. A18

RICHARDSON, Jr., Paul McKinley, Vice President, Medical Affairs, Conway Medical Center, Conway, SC, p. A565

RICHARDSON, Robert, Information Technology Administrator, Porter Regional Hospital, Valparaiso, IN, p. A223

RICHARDSON, Rodney, Director of Information Technology, Baptist Health Corbin, Corbin, KY, p. A258

RICHARDSON, Sarah, Director Information Systems, Belton Regional Medical Center, Belton, MO, p. A367

RICHARDSON, Stanley, Coordinator Human Resources and Payroll Benefits, Kindred Hospital–San Antonio, San Antonio, TX, p. A646

RICHARDSON, Terika, M.P.H., President, Advocate Trinity Hospital, Chicago, IL, p. A183

RICHARDSON, Terrie, Coordinator Human Resources, Select Specialty Hospital–Augusta, Augusta, GA, p. A154

RICHARDSON, Timothy J., M.D. Chief of Staff, Maine Veterans Affairs Medical Center, Augusta, ME, p. A291

RICHARDSON, William T., President and Chief Executive Officer, Tift Regional Health System, Tifton, GA, p. B135

RICHARDSON, William T., President and Chief Executive Officer, Tift Regional Medical Center, Tifton, GA, p. A167

RICHARDVILLE, Craig D.
Senior Vice President and Chief Information Officer, Carolinas Medical Center, Charlotte, NC, p. A462
Chief Information Officer, Carolinas Rehabilitation, Charlotte, NC, p. A462
Chief Information Officer, Cleveland Regional Medical Center, Shelby, NC, p. A473

RICHARSON, Shauna, Interim Chief Executive Officer, Kit Carson County Health Service District, Burlington, CO, p. A102

RICHASON, Amie
Vice President Human Resources, Leesburg Regional Medical Center, Leesburg, FL, p. A134
Vice President Human Resources, The Villages Regional Hospital, The Villages, FL, p. A148

RICHBOURG, Gail A., Director Human Resources, McLeod Health Clarendon, Manning, SC, p. A568

RICHCREEK, Keith, Manager Technical Services, Lafayette Regional Health Center, Lexington, MO, p. A375

RICHENS, Ken, Chief Information Officer, Central Valley Medical Center, Nephi, UT, p. A661

RICHER, R. David, Chief Executive Officer, Fairlawn Rehabilitation Hospital, Worcester, MA, p. A316

RICHERT, Ed, M.D. Chief of Staff, Modoc Medical Center, Alturas, CA, p. A54

RICHERT, Tadd M.
Chief Financial Officer, CHI St. Vincent Hot Springs, Hot Springs, AR, p. A47
Chief Financial Officer, CHI St. Vincent Infirmary Medical Center, Little Rock, AR, p. A49
Senior Vice President and Chief Financial Officer, CHI St. Vincent Medical Center–North, Sherwood, AR, p. A52
Chief Financial Officer, CHI St. Vincent Morrilton, Morrilton, AR, p. A50

RICHETTI, Michael, Chief Financial Officer, Chilton Medical Center, Pompton Plains, NJ, p. A422

RICHHART, David, Vice President Fiscal Services, Community Medical Center, Missoula, MT, p. A389

RICHMAN, Craig, M.D. Medical Director, Meadows Psychiatric Center, Centre Hall, PA, p. A535

RICHMAN, Jonathan, M.D. Chief of Staff, Chase County Community Hospital, Imperial, NE, p. A397

RICHMAN, Timothy, President, Calumet Medical Center, Chilton, WI, p. A704

RICHMOND, Andy, Director Information Technology, Choctaw Memorial Hospital, Hugo, OK, p. A513

RICHMOND, Craig, Senior Vice President and Chief Financial Officer, MetroHealth Medical Center, Cleveland, OH, p. A489

RICHMOND, Ira, Associate Director Patient Care Services, Veterans Affairs Pittsburgh Healthcare System, Pittsburgh, PA, p. A552

RICHOUX, Jacquelyn, Chief Financial Officer, Lady of the Sea General Hospital, Cut Off, LA, p. A276

RICHTER, Daniel, M.D. Chief of Staff, CHI Health Missouri Valley, Missouri Valley, IA, p. A234

RICHTER, Thomas V., Chief Executive Officer, Pioneer Memorial Hospital and Health Services, Viborg, SD, p. A577

RICK, Bob, Vice President Information Technology, USMD Hospital at Arlington, Arlington, TX, p. A598

RICKARD, Sheryl, Chief Executive Officer, Bonner General Hospital, Sandpoint, ID, p. A178

RICKENS, Chris, R.N. Senior Vice President and Chief Nursing Officer, UPMC Altoona, Altoona, PA, p. A532

RICKS, Edward, Vice President and Chief Information Officer, Beaufort Memorial Hospital, Beaufort, SC, p. A562

RICKS, Loretha, Human Resources Supervisor, Southampton Memorial Hospital, Franklin, VA, p. A670

RICKS, Michael R.
Chief Operating Officer, Hoag Memorial Hospital Presbyterian, Newport Beach, CA, p. A79
Chief Operating Officer, St. Joseph's Medical Center, Stockton, CA, p. A95

RICO, Carrie, Chief Human Resource Officer, Keefe Memorial Hospital, Cheyenne Wells, CO, p. A102

RICO, Richard, Vice President and Chief Financial Officer, Sky Lakes Medical Center, Klamath Falls, OR, p. A527

RIDALL, Jackie, Director Human Resources, Berwick Hospital Center, Berwick, PA, p. A533

RIDDER, Terri, Director Human Resources, St. Francis Memorial Hospital, West Point, NE, p. A403

RIDDLE, Kent, Chief Executive Officer, Mary Free Bed Rehabilitation Hospital, Grand Rapids, MI, p. A325

RIDDLES, Lawrence, M.D. Executive Vice President Medical Affairs and Quality, St. Dominic–Jackson Memorial Hospital, Jackson, MS, p. A360

RIDGE, Carolyn, Chief Financial Officer, Lakeview Regional Medical Center, Covington, LA, p. A275

RIDGE, Frederick R., Chief of Staff, Greene County General Hospital, Linton, IN, p. A217

RIDGEWAY, Kerrie, R.N. Chief Nursing Officer, Pocahontas Memorial Hospital, Buckeye, WV, p. A694

RIDLEN, Deborah, CPA Vice President Fiscal Services and Chief Financial Officer, Schneck Medical Center, Seymour, IN, p. A222

RIDLEY, John, Executive Vice President & Chief Operating Officer, Decatur Memorial Hospital, Decatur, IL, p. A188

RIDLEY, Pam, Director Information Systems, Henry County Medical Center, Paris, TN, p. A592

RIDLEY, Zena, Director Human Resources, Harbor Oaks Hospital, New Baltimore, MI, p. A330

RIDNER, Sheila, R.N. Director of Nursing, Behavioral HealthCare Center at Columbia, Columbia, TN, p. A581

RIEBER, Dan, Chief Financial Officer, Memorial Hospital, Colorado Springs, CO, p. A102

RIEBER, Jim, Director Information Systems, Perham Health, Perham, MN, p. A348

RIECHERS, Thomas, M.D. Chief Medical Staff, Mercy Hospital Washington, Washington, MO, p. A383

RIECK, Amy, Human Resources Officer, Greater Regional Medical Center, Creston, IA, p. A228

RIEDEL, Sherry, Chief Financial Management Service, John D. Dingell Veterans Affairs Medical Center, Detroit, MI, p. A322

RIEDLINGER, Joann, Vice President Nursing and Manager Information Systems, Bucyrus Community Hospital, Bucyrus, OH, p. A485

RIEG, Kevin, M.D. President Medical Staff, Via Christi Rehabilitation Hospital, Wichita, KS, p. A256

RIEGE, Michael J., Administrator, Virginia Gay Hospital, Vinton, IA, p. A238

RIEGER, Bill, Chief Information Officer, Flagler Hospital, Saint Augustine, FL, p. A144

RIEGER, Tim, Chief Financial Officer, St. Rita's Medical Center, Lima, OH, p. A497

RIEGERT, Patricia, Director Fiscal Services, Danville State Hospital, Danville, PA, p. A536

RIEKE, Diane, Director Patient Care Services, Patients' Hospital of Redding, Redding, CA, p. A84

RIEKS, Katie, Chief Nursing Officer, Hansen Family Hospital, Iowa Falls, IA, p. A233

RIEMER, Stephanie J., President, Munson Healthcare Grayling Hospital, Grayling, MI, p. A325

RIER, Kirk, Chief Operating Officer, Iowa Specialty Hospital–Clarion, Clarion, IA, p. A227

RIES, Heather, MSN Chief Nursing Officer, Regional Medical Center, Manchester, IA, p. A234

RIESER, Michael, M.D. Medical Director, Ridge Behavioral Health System, Lexington, KY, p. A263

RIETSEMA, Wouter, M.D. Chief Quality and Information Officer, The University of Vermont Health Network–Champlain Valley Physicians Hospital, Plattsburgh, NY, p. A453

ROBBINS, Dan, Information Technology and Account Executive, St. Vincent Medical Center, Los Angeles, CA, p. A74

ROBBINS, Danielle A., Vice President Human Resources, St. Catherine of Siena Medical Center, Smithtown, NY, p. A456

ROBBINS, Jr., Donald, M.D. Chief Staff, Hills & Dales General Hospital, Cass City, MI, p. A320

ROBBINS, Jan, M.D. Chief of Staff, Tennova Healthcare–LaFollette Medical Center, La Follette, TN, p. A586

ROBBINS, Joe, M.D. Vice President Medical Affairs, Sentara Williamsburg Regional Medical Center, Williamsburg, VA, p. A680

ROBBINS, Shannon, Chief Operating Officer, Ohio Hospital for Psychiatry, Columbus, OH, p. A490

ROBEANO, Karen, R.N. Chief Nursing Officer and Vice President Patient Care Services, FirstHealth Moore Regional Hospital, Pinehurst, NC, p. A471

ROBERGE, Jeremy
Director Reimbursement, Androscoggin Valley Hospital, Berlin, NH, p. A410
President and Chief Executive Officer, Huggins Hospital, Wolfeboro, NH, p. A413
Chief Financial Officer, Huggins Hospital, Wolfeboro, NH, p. A413

ROBERSON, Ed, Director Information Systems, Houston Northwest Medical Center, Houston, TX, p. A625

ROBERSON, Joe, Chief Executive Officer, HEALTHSOUTH Rehabilitation Hospital – Abilene, Abilene, TX, p. A595

ROBERSON, Lynda, Senior Program Director, Rusk State Hospital, Rusk, TX, p. A644

ROBERSON, Meika, M.D. Chief Medical Officer, Hoboken University Medical Center, Hoboken, NJ, p. A418

ROBERSON, Scotty, Assistant Administrator and Chief Nursing Officer, University of South Alabama Children's and Women's Hospital, Mobile, AL, p. A23

ROBERT, Thomas W., Senior Vice President of Finance and Chief Financial Officer, Mercy Medical Center, Springfield, MA, p. A315

ROBERTS, Alden, M.D. Chief Medical Officer, PeaceHealth Southwest Medical Center, Vancouver, WA, p. A692

ROBERTS, Allyson, CPA Chief Financial Officer, Nor–Lea General Hospital, Lovington, NM, p. A430

ROBERTS, Andrew, Interim Chief Human Resources Officer, Veterans Affairs Gulf Coast Veterans Health Care System, Biloxi, MS, p. A355

ROBERTS, Barbara, Chief Financial Officer, Robley Rex Veterans Affairs Medical Center, Louisville, KY, p. A265

ROBERTS, Bert, Controller, Miracle Mile Medical Center, Los Angeles, CA, p. A73

ROBERTS, Brad, Network Administrator, Swisher Memorial Hospital District, Tulia, TX, p. A654

ROBERTS, Cassidi, R.N. Chief Nursing Officer, Medical Center of McKinney, McKinney, TX, p. A636

ROBERTS, Cathy, Vice President Mission Integration and Human Resources, Mercy Regional Medical Center, Durango, CO, p. A104

ROBERTS, Charles, M.D
Executive Vice President and Executive Medical Director, Children's Mercy Hospitals and Clinics, Kansas City, MO, p. A373
Medical Director, Children's Mercy South, Overland Park, KS, p. A251

ROBERTS, Cheryl, Chief Nursing Officer, McCamey County Hospital District, McCamey, TX, p. A636

ROBERTS, Curt L., Chief Executive Officer, Select Specialty Hospital–Augusta, Augusta, GA, p. A154

ROBERTS, Cyndi, Director Human Resources, Plaza Medical Center of Fort Worth, Fort Worth, TX, p. A618

ROBERTS, David, M.D Chief Medical Officer, Jackson–Madison County General Hospital, Jackson, TN, p. A584

ROBERTS, Deborah, R.N. Chief Nursing Officer, The CORE Institute Specialty Hospital, Phoenix, AZ, p. A37

ROBERTS, Debra, Director of Human Resources, St. Luke's Lakeside Hospital, The Woodlands, TX, p. A653

ROBERTS, Greg, Superintendent, Oregon State Hospital, Salem, OR, p. A530

ROBERTS, Jack, Director Information Systems, Twin County Regional Healthcare, Galax, VA, p. A671

ROBERTS, Jason
Director of Information Services, Barton Memorial Hospital, South Lake Tahoe, CA, p. A95
Director Information System, Carson Valley Medical Center, Gardnerville, NV, p. A404

ROBERTS, Jeff, Director Information Technology, Pinckneyville Community Hospital, Pinckneyville, IL, p. A200

ROBERTS, Joanne, M.D. Chief Medical Officer, Providence Regional Medical Center Everett, Everett, WA, p. A684

ROBERTS, Kathryn, Director Human Resources, Mercy Medical Center–Dubuque, Dubuque, IA, p. A230

ROBERTS, Kenneth D., President, John T. Mather Memorial Hospital, Port Jefferson, NY, p. A453

ROBERTS, Kevin A., FACHE, President and Chief Executive Officer, Glendale Adventist Medical Center, Los Angeles, CA, p. A71

ROBERTS, Krista, Chief Operating Officer, St. Mary's Regional Medical Center, Enid, OK, p. A511

ROBERTS, Laurel, R.N. Chief Nursing Officer, Rolling Hills Hospital, Franklin, TN, p. A583

ROBERTS, Lisa, Chief Operating Officer, Purcell Municipal Hospital, Purcell, OK, p. A519

ROBERTS, Matthew S., Chief Executive Officer, Glenwood Regional Medical Center, West Monroe, LA, p. A289

ROBERTS, Michael, Chief Information Officer, Highlands Regional Medical Center, Prestonsburg, KY, p. A268

ROBERTS, Michele, Hospital Recruiter, Kindred Hospital–Greensboro, Greensboro, NC, p. A466

ROBERTS, Nancy, Chief Operating Officer, Providence St. Vincent Medical Center, Portland, OR, p. A529

ROBERTS, Pamela W., Chief Executive Officer, Henderson County Community Hospital, Lexington, TN, p. A587

ROBERTS, Paul L., Director, Cheyenne Veterans Affairs Medical Center, Cheyenne, WY, p. A722

ROBERTS, Paula, Chief Nursing Officer, Cumberland Hospital, New Kent, VA, p. A674

ROBERTS, Phillip G., Vice President Finance and Chief Financial Officer, Columbus Community Hospital, Inc., Columbus, WI, p. A704

ROBERTS, Rob, Director Information Technology, Benson Hospital, Benson, AZ, p. A31

ROBERTS, Robert C.
Vice President, Baptist Health Extended Care Hospital, Little Rock, AR, p. A48
Senior Vice President Financial Services, Baptist Health Medical Center – North Little Rock, North Little Rock, AR, p. A51
Vice President and Chief Financial Officer, Baptist Health Medical Center–Arkadelphia, Arkadelphia, AR, p. A43
Senior Vice President Financial Services, Baptist Health Medical Center–Little Rock, Little Rock, AR, p. A48
Senior Vice President, Baptist Health Rehabilitation Institute, Little Rock, AR, p. A49

ROBERTS, Roslyn, Manager, Northside Hospital–Cherokee, Canton, GA, p. A155

ROBERTS, Stacie, Coordinator Human Resources, Our Children's House, Dallas, TX, p. A611

ROBERTS, Teresa, Chief Financial Officer, Ringgold County Hospital, Mount Ayr, IA, p. A234

ROBERTS, Todd, Manager Business Operations, Peninsula Hospital, Louisville, TN, p. A587

ROBERTSHAW, Hazel, R.N. Chief Nursing Officer, Vice President Patient Services, F. F. Thompson Hospital, Canandaigua, NY, p. A436

ROBERTSON, Carla, Chief Operating Officer and Chief Financial Officer, Saline Memorial Hospital, Benton, AR, p. A43

ROBERTSON, Casey, Chief Executive Officer, Longview Regional Medical Center, Longview, TX, p. A633

ROBERTSON, Darcy, Chief Financial Officer, Page Hospital, Page, AZ, p. A35

ROBERTSON, Elizabeth, Area Controller, HEALTHSOUTH Rehabilitation Hospital – Dallas, Dallas, TX, p. A610

ROBERTSON Jr., James A., Chief Executive Officer, Bothwell Regional Health Center, Sedalia, MO, p. A382

ROBERTSON, John L., Administrator, West Central Georgia Regional Hospital, Columbus, GA, p. A157

ROBERTSON, Larry, President, Texas Health Center for Diagnostic & Surgery, Plano, TX, p. A642

ROBERTSON, Laura, R.N., Chief Executive Officer, Banner Desert Medical Center, Mesa, AZ, p. A34

ROBERTSON, Michael, Chief Executive Officer, Piedmont Newnan Hospital, Newnan, GA, p. A164

ROBERTSON, Misty, R.N. Chief Nursing Officer, Bonner General Hospital, Sandpoint, ID, p. A178

ROBERTSON, Pamela, President and Chief Executive Officer, CHRISTUS Spohn Hospital Corpus Christi Memorial, Corpus Christi, TX, p. A607

ROBERTSON, Patricia Dianne, Chief Financial Officer, Mercy Hospital Watonga, Watonga, OK, p. A523

ROBERTSON, Steve
Vice President, Kapiolani Medical Center for Women & Children, Honolulu, HI, p. A170
Senior Vice President, Pali Momi Medical Center, Aiea, HI, p. A170
Executive Vice President and Chief Information Officer, Straub Clinic & Hospital, Honolulu, HI, p. A171
Executive Vice President Revenue Cycle Management and Chief Information Officer, Wilcox Memorial Hospital, Lihue, HI, p. A172

ROBERTSON, Tana, Chief Operating Officer, McCamey County Hospital District, McCamey, TX, p. A636

ROBERTSON, William G., President and Chief Executive Officer, MultiCare Health System, Tacoma, WA, p. B93

ROBERTSON–KECK, Karen, Vice President Human Resources, MedStar Franklin Square Medical Center, Baltimore, MD, p. A297

ROBESON, Gail, Vice President Patient Services, Huron Regional Medical Center, Huron, SD, p. A574

ROBICHAUX, Martha, Chief Human Resources Officer, John C. Fremont Healthcare District, Mariposa, CA, p. A76

ROBICHEAUX, James Warren, FACHE, Senior Administrator, East Texas Medical Center Pittsburg, Pittsburg, TX, p. A641

ROBINS, Scott, M.D. Chief Medical Officer, Covenant Children's Hospital, Lubbock, TX, p. A633

ROBINSON, Adam M., Director, Veterans Affairs Maryland Health Care System–Baltimore Division, Baltimore, MD, p. A298

ROBINSON, Alan, Chief Financial Officer, Logan Regional Hospital, Logan, UT, p. A660

ROBINSON, Anthony, Manager, Human Resources, Mercy Hospital of Folsom, Folsom, CA, p. A62

ROBINSON, Bradley, Chief Financial Officer, Evans U. S. Army Community Hospital, Fort Carson, CO, p. A105

ROBINSON, Cliff, M.D. Chief of Staff, Central Alabama Veterans Health Care System, Montgomery, AL, p. A23

ROBINSON, David, President Medical and Dental Staff, Community Hospital, Munster, IN, p. A219

ROBINSON, David, D.O. Medical Director, St. Joseph's Behavioral Health Center, Stockton, CA, p. A95

ROBINSON, Elena, Chief Human Resources Officer, Hospital HIMA San Pablo Caguas, Caguas, PR, p. A726

ROBINSON, Eric
Chief Executive Officer, Merit Health Natchez, Natchez, MS, p. A363
Chief Executive Officer, Natchez Community Hospital, Natchez, MS, p. A363

ROBINSON, Girard, M.D. Senior Vice President Medical and Clinical Affairs, Spring Harbor Hospital, Westbrook, ME, p. A295

ROBINSON, Glenn A., President, Baylor Scott & White Medical Center – Hillcrest, Waco, TX, p. A655

ROBINSON, Herbert, M.D. Vice President, Chief Medical Information Officer, North Oaks Health System, North Oaks Rehabilitation Hospital, Hammond, LA, p. A277

ROBINSON, James, Chief Financial Officer, George E. Weems Memorial Hospital, Apalachicola, FL, p. A123

ROBINSON, Jeanne, Director Human Resources, Inova Fair Oaks Hospital, Fairfax, VA, p. A669

ROBINSON, Jennifer, Administrator, Behavioral HealthCare Center at Clarksville, Clarksville, TN, p. A581

ROBINSON, Jennifer B., Vice President Human Resources, St. Petersburg General Hospital, Saint Petersburg, FL, p. A144

ROBINSON, Lance, Associate Director, Amarillo Veterans Affairs Health Care System, Amarillo, TX, p. A596

ROBINSON, Mark, FACHE, President and Chief Executive Officer, Capital Regional Medical Center, Tallahassee, FL, p. A146

ROBINSON, Mark, Associate Administrator and Chief Financial Officer, Hazel Hawkins Memorial Hospital, Hollister, CA, p. A66

ROBINSON, Mary, Chief Nursing Officer and Vice President Patient Care Services, Texas Health Harris Methodist Hospital Southwest Fort Worth, Fort Worth, TX, p. A619

ROBINSON, Patrick C., M.D., Interim Chief Executive Officer, DeQuincy Memorial Hospital, DeQuincy, LA, p. A276

ROBINSON, Paul H., M.D. Medical Director, American Fork Hospital, American Fork, UT, p. A659

ROBINSON, Phil, Chief Financial Officer, Saint Agnes Medical Center, Fresno, CA, p. A64

ROBINSON, Phillip D., President, Lankenau Medical Center, Wynnewood, PA, p. A558

ROBINSON, Ron, Business Partner, Lutheran Hospital, Cleveland, OH, p. A489

ROBINSON, Stephen, Chief Executive Officer, Ochsner Medical Center – Kenner, Kenner, LA, p. A279

ROBINSON, Susan Beth, Vice President Human Resources, St. Mary's Medical Center, Huntington, WV, p. A697

ROBINSON, Tim, Executive Vice President, Chief Financial and Administrative Officer and Treasurer, Nationwide Children's Hospital, Columbus, OH, p. A490

ROBINSON, Vance, Chief Information Officer, Iberia Medical Center, New Iberia, LA, p. A284

ROBINSON, William, Director Human Resources, HEALTHSOUTH Rehabilitation Hospital of Erie, Erie, PA, p. A538

ROBISON, Bruce, Vice President and Chief Information Officer, Cox Medical Centers, Springfield, MO, p. A382

ROBISON, Keith, Chief Information Officer, Woman's Christian Association Hospital, Jamestown, NY, p. A441

ROBISON, Neely, Director Human Resources, The BridgeWay, North Little Rock, AR, p. A51

ROBISON, Rob, Director Information Technology, Medical Center of South Arkansas, El Dorado, AR, p. A45

ROBISON, Ryan, Chief Nursing Officer, Sanpete Valley Hospital, Mount Pleasant, UT, p. A660

ROBISON, Wendell, M.D. Chief of Staff, Sheridan Veterans Affairs Medical Center, Sheridan, WY, p. A724

ROBL, Chris, Human Resources, Ellinwood District Hospital, Ellinwood, KS, p. A242

ROBLES, Burt, Vice President Information Services, Robert Packer Hospital, Sayre, PA, p. A553

ROBSON, Melissa, President, Novant Health UVA Health System Prince William Medical Center, Manassas, VA, p. A673

ROCA, Robert, M.D. Vice President Medical Affairs, Sheppard Pratt Health System, Baltimore, MD, p. A297

ROCHA, Israel, Chief Executive Officer, NYC Health + Hospitals / Elmhurst, NY, p. A448

ROCHA, Julie, Vice President Human Resources, Mercy Medical Center Merced, Merced, CA, p. A76

ROCHE, Richard, Administrator, Lakeside Medical Center, Belle Glade, FL, p. A123

ROCHELEAU, John, Vice President Business Support and Information Technology, Bellin Memorial Hospital, Green Bay, WI, p. A706

ROCHER, Leslie, Senior Vice President and Chief Medical Officer, Beaumont Hospital – Royal Oak, Royal Oak, MI, p. A333

ROCHESTER, Charmaine, Vice President Finance, Bon Secours–DePaul Medical Center, Norfolk, VA, p. A674

ROCHIER, Dennis, Chief Medical Officer, Renown South Meadows Medical Center, Reno, NV, p. A408

ROCK, Betty Ann, Vice President Nursing and Chief Nursing Officer, Uniontown Hospital, Uniontown, PA, p. A556

ROCK, Brian, Director of Information Systems, VCU Community Memorial Hospital, South Hill, VA, p. A679

ROCK, David, Executive Vice President and Chief Operating Officer, Wyckoff Heights Medical Center,, NY, p. A450

ROCKSMITH, Eugenio, M.D. Medical Director, HEALTHSOUTH Rehabilitation Hospital of Vineland, Vineland, NJ, p. A424

ROCKWALL, Kyle, Chief Executive Officer, Reagan Memorial Hospital, Big Lake, TX, p. A602

ROCKWELL, Jane, Director Support Services, North Metro Medical Center, Jacksonville, AR, p. A47

ROCKWELL, Karla, Director of Nursing, Doctors Memorial Hospital, Bonifay, FL, p. A124

ROCKWOOD, John D., President, MedStar National Rehabilitation Hospital, Washington, DC, p. A121

ROCKWOOD, Sylvia, Director Human Resources, Carlisle Regional Medical Center, Carlisle, PA, p. A535

RODDEN, Celeste, Chief Information Officer, Hillcrest Hospital Claremore, Claremore, OK, p. A510

RODDY, Thomas, Chief Executive Officer, HEALTHSOUTH Rehabilitation Hospital of Montgomery, Montgomery, AL, p. A23

RODEN, George
Vice President Human Resources, Mercy Hospital Aurora, Aurora, MO, p. A367
Vice President Human Resources, Mercy Hospital Cassville, Cassville, MO, p. A369

RODENBAUGH, Cathy, Director Human Resources, Holy Rosary Healthcare, Miles City, MT, p. A389

RODER, Darla, Chief Operating Officer, Cavalier County Memorial Hospital and Clinics, Langdon, ND, p. A480

RODERICK, Travis W., Chief Executive Officer, Premier Surgical Institute, Galena, KS, p. A243

RODERMAN, Nicki, Chief Nursing Officer, Denton Regional Medical Center, Denton, TX, p. A612

RODGE, Mark, Director Information Systems, Eaton Rapids Medical Center, Eaton Rapids, MI, p. A323

RODGERS, April, Vice President, Human Resources, Holy Name Medical Center, Teaneck, NJ, p. A424

RODGERS, Bruce C., Chief Administrative Officer, Salem Health West Valley, Dallas, OR, p. A525

RODGERS, Dondie, Interim Chief Nursing Officer, Memorial Hospital of Texas County, Guymon, OK, p. A512

RODGERS, Jamie, Interim Chief Executive Officer, Choctaw Regional Medical Center, Ackerman, MS, p. A355

RODGERS, Larry, Chief Executive Officer, Poplar Bluff Regional Medical Center, Poplar Bluff, MO, p. A378

RODGERS, Lee, M.D. Vice President Quality, United Regional Health Care System, Wichita Falls, TX, p. A658

RODIER, James Barton, M.D. Chief Quality Officer, Health Central Hospital, Ocoee, FL, p. A139

RODIS, John F., M.D., President, Saint Francis Hospital and Medical Center, Hartford, CT, p. A114

RODOWICZ, Darlene, Chief Financial Officer, Berkshire Medical Center, Pittsfield, MA, p. A314

RODRIGUES, Pablo, M.D. Medical Director, Vibra Hospital of Amarillo, Amarillo, TX, p. A596

RODRIGUEZ, Alex
Vice President and Chief Information Officer, St. Elizabeth Edgewood, Edgewood, KY, p. A259
Vice President and Chief Information Officer, St. Elizabeth Florence, Florence, KY, p. A260
Vice President and Chief Information Officer, St. Elizabeth Fort Thomas, Fort Thomas, KY, p. A260

RODRIGUEZ, Angie, Human Resource Manager, Carson Tahoe Continuing Care Hospital, Carson City, NV, p. A404

RODRIGUEZ, Ben A., Chief Executive Officer, Hialeah Hospital, Hialeah, FL, p. A130

RODRIGUEZ, Candie, Director Human Resources, Hospital San Cristobal, Coto Laurel, PR, p. A727

RODRIGUEZ, Edgardo, Director Management Information Systems, Auxilio Mutuo Hospital, San Juan, PR, p. A729

RODRIGUEZ, Heather, Chief Nursing Officer, Fresno Heart and Surgical Hospital, Fresno, CA, p. A63

RODRIGUEZ, Jaime, Chief Financial Officer, San Juan City Hospital, San Juan, PR, p. A730

RODRIGUEZ, Jose Luis, Chief Executive Officer, Hospital Pavia–Santurce, San Juan, PR, p. A730

RODRIGUEZ, Jose O., M.D. Medical Director, Castaner General Hospital, Castaner, PR, p. A726

RODRIGUEZ, Joseph R., Chief Executive Officer, Georgetown Behavioral Health Institute, Georgetown, TX, p. A620

RODRIGUEZ, Laura, Director Medical Records, Hospital Del Maestro, San Juan, PR, p. A729

RODRIGUEZ, Lea, R.N. Chief Nursing Officer, Vice President Patient Care Services, Clara Maass Medical Center, Belleville, NJ, p. A414

RODRIGUEZ, Leticia, Chief Executive Officer, Ward Memorial Hospital, Monahans, TX, p. A637

RODRIGUEZ, Lizzette, Director Finance, Hospital San Francisco, San Juan, PR, p. A730

RODRIGUEZ, Marco, Chief Financial Officer, Valley Baptist Medical Center–Harlingen, Harlingen, TX, p. A622

RODRIGUEZ, Mario, Chief Executive Officer, Laredo Specialty Hospital, Laredo, TX, p. A632

RODRIGUEZ, Maritza, Chief Financial Officer, Hospital Metropolitan, San Juan, PR, p. A729

RODRIGUEZ, Miguel, Medical Director, Caribbean Medical Center, Fajardo, PR, p. A727

RODRIGUEZ, Oscar, Chief Fiscal Officer, Veterans Affairs Caribbean Healthcare System, San Juan, PR, p. A730

RODRIGUEZ, Patricia M., Senior Vice President and Area Manager, Kaiser Permanente South Sacramento Medical Center, Sacramento, CA, p. A86

RODRIGUEZ, Ramon J., President and Chief Executive Officer, Wyckoff Heights Medical Center,, NY, p. A450

RODRIGUEZ, Rufus, M.D. Medical Director, Mayo Clinic Health System in Fairmont, Fairmont, MN, p. A342

RODRIGUEZ, Sara
Chief Financial Officer, Kindred Hospital Sugar Land, Sugar Land, TX, p. A650
Human Resources, Seton Smithville Regional Hospital, Smithville, TX, p. A649

RODRIGUEZ, Susanna, Director Human Resources, Westend Hospital, Jennings, LA, p. A279

RODRIGUEZ, Tammy, Vice President of Patient Care Services, Rollins–Brook Community Hospital, Lampasas, TX, p. A632

RODRIGUEZ, Tomas, Chief Information Technology Officer, First Hospital Panamericano, Cidra, PR, p. A727

RODRIGUEZ, Tony, Director Human Resources, South Texas Rehabilitation Hospital, Brownsville, TX, p. A603

RODRIGUEZ, Vilma, Director Human Resources, Hospital San Pablo Del Este, Fajardo, PR, p. A727

RODRIGUEZ, Wilfredo, M.D. Chief of Staff, Battle Creek Veterans Affairs Medical Center, Battle Creek, MI, p. A319

RODRIGUEZ SCHMIDT, Myriam T., Director Human Resources, Cardiovascular Center of Puerto Rico and the Caribbean, San Juan, PR, p. A729

RODRIQUEZ, Daisy, Director Human Resources, Fort Duncan Regional Medical Center, Eagle Pass, TX, p. A614

RODRIQUEZ, Monica, Director of Human Resources, Stewart & Lynda Resnick Neuropsychiatric Hospital at UCLA, Los Angeles, CA, p. A74

ROE, Daniel, M.D. Chief Operating Officer, Copper Queen Community Hospital, Bisbee, AZ, p. A31

ROE, Timothy J., M.D., President and Chief Executive Officer, Rehabilitation Hospital of the Pacific, Honolulu, HI, p. A171

ROEBACK, Jason, Chief Executive Officer, Sharon Regional Health System, Sharon, PA, p. A553

ROEBKEN, Curtis, M.D. Chief Medical Staff, Kentfield Rehabilitation and Specialty Hospital, Kentfield, CA, p. A67

ROEBUCK, Amanda, Director Patient Care Services, Genoa Medical Facilities, Genoa, NE, p. A396

ROEDER, Donna, Chief Financial Officer, Jackson County Regional Health Center, Maquoketa, IA, p. A234

ROEDER, Werner, M.D. Vice President Medical Affairs, New York–Presbyterian/Lawrence Hospital, Bronxville, NY, p. A435

ROEDERER, Chris, Senior Vice President Human Resources, Tampa General Hospital, Tampa, FL, p. A148

ROEHR, Richard, Chief Operating Officer, AMITA Health Adventist Medical Center Bolingbrook, Bolingbrook, IL, p. A182

ROEHRLE, Andreas, Director Finance, Sentara Williamsburg Regional Medical Center, Williamsburg, VA, p. A680

ROEMER, Dennis, Executive Vice President and Chief Financial Officer, Lancaster General Hospital, Lancaster, PA, p. A542

ROESER, William, President and Chief Executive Officer, Sparrow Ionia Hospital, Ionia, MI, p. A326

ROESLER, Bruce E., FACHE, Chief Executive Officer, Richland Hospital, Richland Center, WI, p. A715

ROETMAN, James D., President and Chief Executive Officer, Pocahontas Community Hospital, Pocahontas, IA, p. A236

ROEVER, Judy, MSN Chief Nursing Officer, Scenic Mountain Medical Center, Big Spring, TX, p. A602

ROFFELSEN, Michael S., Chief Executive Officer, Kindred Hospital South Florida–Fort Lauderdale, Fort Lauderdale, FL, p. A128

ROGALSKI, Robert, Chief Executive Officer, Excela Health, Greensburg, PA, p. B55

ROGALSKI, Ted, Administrator, Genesis Medical Center–Aledo, Aledo, IL, p. A180

ROGAN, Edie, Manager Human Resources, Eastern State Hospital, Williamsburg, VA, p. A680

ROGERS, Aaron, Chief Executive Officer, Trinity Hospital, Weaverville, CA, p. A99

ROGERS, B. Carter, Chief of Staff, Piedmont Newton Hospital, Covington, GA, p. A157

ROGERS, Carrie, Chief Nursing Officer, Southern Tennessee Regional Health System–Lawrenceburg, Lawrenceburg, TN, p. A586

ROGERS, Cathy M., Manager Human Resources, Greenville Health System – Laurens County Memorial Hospital, Clinton, SC, p. A563

ROGERS, David, Chief Executive Officer, Ortonville Area Health Services, Ortonville, MN, p. A348

ROGERS, Doris, Vice President Human Resources, Saint Luke's Hospital of Kansas City, Kansas City, MO, p. A374

ROGERS, Eric, Chief Information Officer, Hebrew Rehabilitation Center, Boston, MA, p. A307

ROGERS, Gregory H., President, MidMichigan Medical Center–Midland, Midland, MI, p. A330

ROGERS, James H., FACHE, Chief Executive Officer, Cornerstone Hospital of Little Rock, Little Rock, AR, p. A49

ROGERS, Jared, M.D.,
President and Chief Executive Officer, Presence Covenant Medical Center, Urbana, IL, p. A204
President and Chief Executive Officer, Presence United Samaritans Medical Center, Danville, IL, p. A187

ROGERS, Joseph J., Vice President and Chief Operating Officer, Redwood Memorial Hospital, Fortuna, CA, p. A62

ROGERS, Judith, Ph.D., President and Chief Executive Officer, Holy Cross Hospital, Silver Spring, MD, p. A303

ROGERS, Kathy, Vice President Marketing, San Luis Valley Health Conejos County Hospital, La Jara, CO, p. A107

ROGERS, Keith
Administrator, CHRISTUS Dubuis Hospital of Fort Smith, Fort Smith, AR, p. A46
Administrator, CHRISTUS Dubuis Hospital of Hot Springs, Hot Springs National Park, AR, p. A47

ROGERS, LaDonna, Director Human Resources, T. J. Samson Community Hospital, Glasgow, KY, p. A261

ROGERS, Lucy, Chief Information Resource Management Systems, Veterans Affairs North Texas Health Care System, Dallas, TX, p. A612

ROGERS, Mark G.
Interim Vice President Finance and Chief Financial Officer, Genesis Medical Center, Illini Campus, Silvis, IL, p. A203
Chief Financial Officer, Genesis Medical Center–Aledo, Aledo, IL, p. A180
Interim Vice President Finance and Chief Financial Officer, Genesis Medical Center–Davenport, Davenport, IA, p. A228

ROGERS, Matt, Chief Financial Officer, Philhaven, Mount Gretna, PA, p. A545

ROGERS, Michael, Vice President Fiscal Services, Brattleboro Memorial Hospital, Brattleboro, VT, p. A665

ROGERS, Patricia, Director of Nursing, Dahl Memorial Healthcare Association, Ekalaka, MT, p. A387

ROGERS, Randy, FACHE Chief Financial Officer, Rapides Regional Medical Center, Alexandria, LA, p. A271

ROGERS, Rhonda, Chief Financial Officer, Des Peres Hospital, Saint Louis, MO, p. A380

ROGERS, Rich, Vice President Information Services, GHS Greenville Memorial Hospital, Greenville, SC, p. A566

ROGERS, Richard K., FACHE Vice President Human Resources, Wayne Memorial Hospital, Goldsboro, NC, p. A466

ROGERS, II, Robert T., M.D. Medical Director, Canton–Potsdam Hospital, Potsdam, NY, p. A453

© 2016 AHA Guide

ROGERS, Selwyn O., M.D. Vice President and Chief Medical Officer, University of Texas Medical Branch, Galveston, TX, p. A620

ROGERS, Sherry L., MS Chief Nursing Officer, Redington–Fairview General Hospital, Skowhegan, ME, p. A295

ROGERS, Tammy, Director Human Resources, Mt. San Rafael Hospital, Trinidad, CO, p. A111

ROGERS, Valerie J., Director of Nursing, Cherokee Nation W.W. Hastings Indian Hospital, Tahlequah, OK, p. A520

ROGERS, W. Kent, Chief Executive Officer, Southwest Memorial Hospital, Cortez, CO, p. A103

ROGERS, William, Chief Medical Officer, Merit Health Gilmore Memorial, Amory, MS, p. A355

ROGNESS, Robin, Vice President and Chief Financial Officer, Mercy Hospital of Folsom, Folsom, CA, p. A62

ROGOLS, Kevin L., FACHE, Administrator, Kalkaska Memorial Health Center, Kalkaska, MI, p. A328

ROGOZ, Brian, Vice President Finance and Treasurer, The Hospital of Central Connecticut, New Britain, CT, p. A115

ROHAN, Colleen, Director Human Resources, Little Company of Mary Hospital and Health Care Centers, Evergreen Park, IL, p. A190

ROHAN, Heather J., Chief Executive Officer, TriStar Centennial Medical Center, Nashville, TN, p. A591

ROHAN, Patrick, Interim Chief Executive Officer, Plantation General Hospital, Plantation, FL, p. A143

ROHLEDER, Scott, Chief Information Officer, Hays Medical Center, Hays, KS, p. A244

ROHMAN, Cindy, R.N. Vice President/Chief Nursing Officer, Lexington Medical Center, West Columbia, SC, p. A570

ROHN, Stephen G., M.D. Vice President and Chief Medical Officer, Hamilton Medical Center, Dalton, GA, p. A158

ROHRBACH, Dan D., President and Chief Executive Officer, Southwest Health, Platteville, WI, p. A714

ROHRBACK, Allen, Chief Executive Officer, Madison Valley Medical Center, Ennis, MT, p. A387

ROHRER, Harry
  Chief Financial Officer, Bascom Palmer Eye Institute–Anne Bates Leach Eye Hospital, Miami, FL, p. A136
  Chief Financial Officer, University of Miami Hospital, Miami, FL, p. A137
  Chief Financial Officer, University of Miami Hospital and Clinics, Miami, FL, p. A137

ROHRER, John J., Acting Director, William S. Middleton Memorial Veterans Hospital, Madison, WI, p. A709

ROHRER, Mark, M.D. Chief Medical Officer, Kindred Hospital–Boston, Brighton, MA, p. A308

ROHRICH, George A., FACHE, Chief Executive Officer, River's Edge Hospital and Clinic, Saint Peter, MN, p. A351

ROIZ, JoAnn, Director Human Resources, HEALTHSOUTH Tustin Rehabilitation Hospital, Tustin, CA, p. A97

ROKOSZ, Gregory, D.O. Senior Vice President Medical and Academic Affairs, Saint Barnabas Medical Center, Livingston, NJ, p. A418

ROLAND, Brian, Chief Executive Officer, Muenster Memorial Hospital, Muenster, TX, p. A638

ROLDAN, Lanyce, Interim Chief Nursing Officer, Lancaster General Hospital, Lancaster, PA, p. A542

ROLEK, Jim, Chief Human Resources Officer, Vice President, Clara Maass Medical Center, Belleville, NJ, p. A414

ROLEY, Margaret, Chief Nursing Officer, South Baldwin Regional Medical Center, Foley, AL, p. A20

ROLFE, David, Chief Information Officer, Madonna Rehabilitation Hospital, Lincoln, NE, p. A398

ROLFF, Christi, Director Business Development, San Joaquin Valley Rehabilitation Hospital, Fresno, CA, p. A64

ROLING, Robin, FACHE Chief Operating Officer, Cheyenne Regional Medical Center, Cheyenne, WY, p. A721

ROLLI, Molli Martha, M.D. Medical Director, Mendota Mental Health Institute, Madison, WI, p. A708

ROLLING, Andy, Director of Finance, Regina Hospital, Hastings, MN, p. A344

ROLLINS, David, Chief Resource Management Division, Reynolds Army Community Hospital, Fort Sill, OK, p. A512

ROLLINS, David W., Chief Financial Officer, Mt. San Rafael Hospital, Trinidad, CO, p. A111

ROLLINS, James
  Chief Financial Officer, Arbour H. R. I. Hospital, Brookline, MA, p. A308
  Chief Financial Officer, Arbour–Fuller Hospital, Attleboro, MA, p. A305

ROLLINS, Larry, Supervisor Information Technology, McCamey County Hospital District, McCamey, TX, p. A636

ROLLINS, Skip, Chief Information Officer, Freeman Health System, Joplin, MO, p. A372

ROLON, Waleska, Manager, Hospital Santa Rosa, Guayama, PR, p. A727

ROMACK, Lenae, Manager Human Resources, Baylor Institute for Rehabilitation at Fort Worth, Fort Worth, TX, p. A617

ROMAN, Eloy, M.D. Chief of Staff, Palmetto General Hospital, Hialeah, FL, p. A130

ROMAN, Jody, Chief Human Resource Officer, Hillside Rehabilitation Hospital, Warren, OH, p. A504

ROMAN, Linda K., Administrator, Coast Plaza Hospital, Norwalk, CA, p. A79

ROMAN, Marina, M.D. Medical Director, Hospital de la Universidad de Puerto Rico/Dr. Federico Trilla, Carolina, PR, p. A726

ROMANELLO, Marcus, Chief Medical Officer, Fort Hamilton Hospital, Hamilton, OH, p. A496

ROMANIA, Matt, Director of Nursing, Soldiers and Sailors Memorial Hospital, Wellsboro, PA, p. A557

ROMANICK, Odile, Chief information Officer, Day Kimball Hospital, Putnam, CT, p. A116

ROMANIELLO, Guy, Director Fiscal Services, Belmont Behavioral Hospital, Philadelphia, PA, p. A547

ROMANO, C. James, M.D. Chief Medical Officer, St. Francis Medical Center, Trenton, NJ, p. A424

ROMANO, Jana, Manager Human Resources, Good Shepherd Penn Partners Specialty Hospital at Rittenhouse, Philadelphia, PA, p. A548

ROMANO, Sara, R.N. Vice President, Mountain View Hospital, Gadsden, AL, p. A20

ROMANOWSKI, Ellen, Chief Nursing Officer, HEALTHSOUTH Rehabilitation Hospital of Miami, Cutler Bay, FL, p. A126

ROMANS, Alan, Director Information Technology, Ashland Health Center, Ashland, KS, p. A240

ROMBERGER, Randall R., Administrator, Shriners Hospitals for Children–Greenville, Greenville, SC, p. A566

ROMEO, John, Chief Information Officer, Mercy Hospital and Medical Center, Chicago, IL, p. A185

ROMERO, Brenda, Administrator, Presbyterian Espanola Hospital, Espanola, NM, p. A429

ROMERO, Edward, Chief Financial Officer, Rehabilitation Hospital of Fort Wayne, Fort Wayne, IN, p. A211

ROMERO, Frank, M.D
  Chief Medical Officer, Cox Medical Centers, Springfield, MO, p. A382
  Vice President Medical Affairs and Chief Medical Officer, Cox Monett, Monett, MO, p. A377

ROMERO, Matt, Chief Financial Officer, Oak Hill Hospital, Brooksville, FL, p. A125

ROMITO, Edmund J., Chief Information Officer, Genesis HealthCare System, Zanesville, OH, p. A507

ROMOFF, Jeffrey A., President and Chief Executive Officer, UPMC, Pittsburgh, PA, p. B149

RONAN, Barry P., President and Chief Executive Officer, Western Maryland Regional Medical Center, Cumberland, MD, p. A300

RONAN, John, President and Chief Executive Officer, Blue Hill Memorial Hospital, Blue Hill, ME, p. A292

RONCA, Cyndi, Director Human Resources, Twin Cities Hospital, Niceville, FL, p. A139

RONDE, Christa, Assistant Chief Financial Officer, Palo Verde Hospital, Blythe, CA, p. A57

RONE, Tom, Chief Clinical Officer, Curahealth Nashville, Nashville, TN, p. A590

RONKE, Lisa, Director Finance, St. Michael's Hospital Avera, Tyndall, SD, p. A577

ROODMAN, Richard D., Chief Executive Officer, UW Medicine/Valley Medical Center, Renton, WA, p. A688

ROOF, Marie, Executive Vice President Information Systems, Vibra Specialty Hospital of Portland, Portland, OR, p. A530

ROOKER, Mark, Director Information Systems, Susan B. Allen Memorial Hospital, El Dorado, KS, p. A242

ROONEY, Al, Director Information Systems, St. Vincent Healthcare, Billings, MT, p. A385

ROONEY, David, Administrator Operations, Winneshiek Medical Center, Decorah, IA, p. A229

ROONEY, Jeffrey, Chief Financial Officer, University of Illinois Hospital & Health Sciences System, Chicago, IL, p. A187

ROONEY, Michael T., M.D. Chief of Staff, St. Joseph Regional Medical Center, Lewiston, ID, p. A177

ROONEY, Thomas, Chief Information Resource Management, Veterans Affairs Hudson Valley Health Care System, Montrose, NY, p. A443

ROOP, Terri, Director Patient Care Services, Dickenson Community Hospital, Clintwood, VA, p. A669

ROOS, Joel A., Commanding Officer, Naval Medical Center San Diego, San Diego, CA, p. A88

ROOSA, Carol, Vice President Information Services and Chief Information Officer, Athol Memorial Hospital, Athol, MA, p. A305

ROOT, Jim, Vice President Human Resources, Saint Elizabeth's Medical Center, Wabasha, MN, p. A352

ROOT, Rodney Mark, D.O. Vice President Medical Affairs, Bakersfield Memorial Hospital, Bakersfield, CA, p. A55

ROPER, Embra, Chief Medical Officer, Regional Hospital for Respiratory and Complex Care, Burien, WA, p. A683

ROPER, Sandra, Chief Human Resources, General Leonard Wood Army Community Hospital, Fort Leonard Wood, MO, p. A371

ROPER, William L., M.P.H., Chief Executive Officer, UNC Health Care, Chapel Hill, NC, p. B139

ROQUE, Lee Ann, Director of Human Resources, Mary Black Health System–Spartanburg, Spartanburg, SC, p. A569

RORRER, Michael, M.D. Chief of Staff, Carilion Tazewell Community Hospital, Tazewell, VA, p. A679

ROSA–TOLEDO, Luis R., M.D. Medical Director, Hospital Manati Medical Center, Manati, PR, p. A728

ROSAAEN, Nancy, Chief Executive Officer, McCone County Health Center, Circle, MT, p. A386

ROSADO, Jose S., Executive Director, Hospital Manati Medical Center, Manati, PR, p. A728

ROSALES, Alvina, R.N. Chief Nursing Officer, Tuba City Regional Health Care Corporation, Tuba City, AZ, p. A40

ROSATI, Rosemarie, Interim President and Chief Executive Officer, University Behavioral Healthcare, Piscataway, NJ, p. A422

ROSBOROUGH, Brian S., M.D. Chief Medical Officer, OSF Saint Elizabeth Medical Center, Ottawa, IL, p. A199

ROSCOE, Joan, Chief Information Officer, Winchester Medical Center, Winchester, VA, p. A680

ROSE, Cheryl, Human Resources Director, Fulton County Medical Center, Mc Connellsburg, PA, p. A544

ROSE, Hugh, Vice President Fiscal Management, Palos Community Hospital, Palos Heights, IL, p. A199

ROSE, J. Anthony, President and Chief Executive Officer, Catawba Valley Medical Center, Hickory, NC, p. A467

ROSE, Julia, R.N. Director of Nursing, Braxton County Memorial Hospital, Gassaway, WV, p. A696

ROSE, Kim, Chief Information Technology, Crouse Hospital, Syracuse, NY, p. A456

ROSE, Mary R., R.N. Chief Clinical Officer, Community Health Center of Branch County, Coldwater, MI, p. A321

ROSE, May, Director Human Resources, Memorial Hospital, Chester, IL, p. A183

ROSE, Michael S., President and Chief Executive Officer, Southern New Hampshire Medical Center, Nashua, NH, p. A412

ROSE, Regina P., R.N. Vice President Nursing Services, Mid–Columbia Medical Center, The Dalles, OR, p. A531

ROSE, Richard T., Associate Director, Manchester Veterans Affairs Medical Center, Manchester, NH, p. A412

ROSE, Robert, R.N. Senior Vice President and System Chief Nursing Officer, CHRISTUS Mother Frances Hospital – Tyler, Tyler, TX, p. A654

ROSE, Robin, R.N. Chief Operating Officer, Gibson Area Hospital and Health Services, Gibson City, IL, p. A191

ROSE, Silvia, Director Patient Care Services, Vidant Bertie Hospital, Windsor, NC, p. A475

ROSE, Steven P., Chief Financial Officer, Conway Regional Medical Center, Conway, AR, p. A44

ROSE, Steven A., R.N., President and Chief Executive Officer, Nanticoke Memorial Hospital, Seaford, DE, p. A119

ROSEMORE, Michael, M.D. Medical Director, HEALTHSOUTH Lakeshore Rehabilitation Hospital, Birmingham, AL, p. A16

ROSEN, Barry, M.D. Vice President Medical Management, Advocate Good Shepherd Hospital, Barrington, IL, p. A181

ROSEN, Jules, M.D. Chief Medical Officer, West Springs Hospital, Grand Junction, CO, p. A106

ROSEN, Linda, M.D., Chief Executive Officer, Hawaii Health Systems Corporation, Honolulu, HI, p. B60

ROSEN, Michael, M.D. Chief Medical Officer, Havasu Regional Medical Center, Lake Havasu City, AZ, p. A34

ROSEN, Raymond, FACHE Vice President Operations, WellSpan York Hospital, York, PA, p. A559

ROSENA, Robens, Director Information Systems, Delray Medical Center, Delray Beach, FL, p. A127

ROSENBALM, Jennifer, Manager Business Office, Veterans Affairs Nebraska–Western Iowa Health Care System, Omaha, NE, p. A401

ROSENBAUM, Victor, Chief Operating Officer, Alaska Regional Hospital, Anchorage, AK, p. A28

ROSENBERG, Andrew, M.D. Chief Information Officer, University of Michigan Hospitals and Health Centers, Ann Arbor, MI, p. A318

ROSENBERG, Julie, Administrator, Essentia Health–Graceville, Graceville, MN, p. A343

ROSENBERG, Steven, Chief Financial Officer, Danbury Hospital, Danbury, CT, p. A113

ROSENBERG, Stuart E., President and Chief Executive Officer, Johnson Memorial Medical Center, Stafford Springs, CT, p. A117

ROSENBERGER, Robert, Chief Financial Officer, Adena Medical Center, Chillicothe, OH, p. A486

ROSENBERGER–SLAMPACK, Janie, Market Chief Executive Officer, Curahealth Pittsburgh, Oakdale, PA, p. A546

ROWLANDS, Dewey R., Vice President and Chief Financial Officer, Rome Memorial Hospital, Rome, NY, p. A455

ROWLEY, Charla, Chief Financial Officer, Southwest Mississippi Regional Medical Center, McComb, MS, p. A361

ROWLEY, Mike, Chief Executive Officer, Springbrook Behavioral Health System, Travelers Rest, SC, p. A570

ROY, Joel, Manager Information Systems, The Brook Hospital – KMI, Louisville, KY, p. A265

ROY, Rock, Professional Services Director, Power County Hospital District, American Falls, ID, p. A174

ROY, Schindelheim, M.D. Chief of Staff, Mee Memorial Hospital, King City, CA, p. A67

ROYAL, Keli, Chief Human Resources Officer, Shenandoah Medical Center, Shenandoah, IA, p. A237

ROYAL, Shawanna, R.N. Director Nursing, Strategic Behavioral Health – Raleigh, Garner, NC, p. A465

ROYAL, Ty, Executive Director of Support Services and Human Resources, Gibson Area Hospital and Health Services, Gibson City, IL, p. A191

ROYSTER, Kirsten, Chief Executive Officer, Novant Health Medical Park Hospital, Winston–Salem, NC, p. A476

ROZELL, Becky, Chief Human Resources Officer, Madison Health, London, OH, p. A497

ROZENBOOM, Steve, Chief Financial Officer, Holy Cross Hospital, Taos, NM, p. A432

ROZENFELD, Jon, President, St. Mary's Hospital, Madison, WI, p. A709

ROZNOVSKY, Karen, Director Human Resources, Yoakum Community Hospital, Yoakum, TX, p. A658

RUBANO, Kathleen A., MSN Chief Nursing Officer, Corpus Christi Medical Center, Corpus Christi, TX, p. A607

RUBAR, Jackie, Administrative Assistant and Director Human Resources, Leesville Rehabilitation Hospital, Leesville, LA, p. A282

RUBE, David M., M.D. Clinical Director, New York City Children's Center,, NY, p. A446

RUBEN, Wanda, R.N. Chief Nursing Officer, Garden Grove Hospital and Medical Center, Garden Grove, CA, p. A64

RUBENS, Deborah, Director Human Resources, Shriners Hospitals for Children–Northern California, Sacramento, CA, p. A87

RUBERG, Greg, Administrator, Lake View Memorial Hospital, Two Harbors, MN, p. A352

RUBERTI, Charlene, Director Information Technology Development, Ancora Psychiatric Hospital, Hammonton, NJ, p. A417

RUBIN, Nancy, Vice President Human Resources, Motion Picture and Television Fund Hospital and Residential Services,, CA, p. A73

RUBIN, Randy
    Senior Vice President and Chief Financial Officer, Mercy Medical Center – West Lakes, West Des Moines, IA, p. A239
    Senior Vice President and Chief Financial Officer, Mercy Medical Center–Des Moines, Des Moines, IA, p. A229

RUBIN, Vincent, Chief Financial Officer, Southern California Hospital at Culver City, Culver City, CA, p. A60

RUBINATE, Donna, R.N. Chief Operating Officer, Good Samaritan Medical Center, Brockton, MA, p. A308

RUBINO, Mark, M.D., President, Forbes Hospital, Monroeville, PA, p. A545

RUBIO, Felipe, M.D. Medical Director, Kindred Hospital–Dayton, Dayton, OH, p. A493

RUCH, Jordan, Vice President and Chief Information Officer, Robert Wood Johnson University Hospital Somerset, Somerville, NJ, p. A423

RUCHTI, Robert D., Chief Executive Officer, Buchanan General Hospital, Grundy, VA, p. A671

RUCKER, Alisa, Vice President Finance and Chief Financial Officer, Washington Hospital, Washington, PA, p. A556

RUCKER, Jodi, Chief Nursing Officer, ProMedica Memorial Hospital, Fremont, OH, p. A495

RUCKER, Rick, Chief Operating Officer, Highland Hospital, Charleston, WV, p. A695

RUCKER, William H., Administrator, Riverland Medical Center, Ferriday, LA, p. A276

RUDBERG, Susan, M.D. Chief Medical Officer, Range Regional Health Services, Hibbing, MN, p. A344

RUDD, Adam, Chief Executive Officer, Southern Hills Hospital and Medical Center, Las Vegas, NV, p. A406

RUDD, Barry, Chief Information Officer, Mayo Clinic Health System in Waycross, Waycross, GA, p. A169

RUDD, John, President and Chief Executive Officer, Cayuga Health System, Ithaca, NY, p. B31

RUDD, John, President and Chief Executive Officer, Cayuga Medical Center at Ithaca, Ithaca, NY, p. A440

RUDDEN, Elizabeth, Vice President Human Resources, Connecticut Children's Medical Center, Hartford, CT, p. A114

RUDEK, Charles M., Chief Information Officer, UPMC St. Margaret, Pittsburgh, PA, p. A552

RUDIS, Lorrie, Vice President, Human Resources, Crotched Mountain Rehabilitation Center, Greenfield, NH, p. A411

RUDITZ, Bettiann S., MS Chief Nursing Officer, Broward Health North, Deerfield Beach, FL, p. A127

RUDQUIST, Debra, FACHE, President and Chief Executive Officer, Amery Hospital and Clinic, Amery, WI, p. A702

RUDZIK, Carrie, Chief Administrative Officer, Eastern State Hospital, Lexington, KY, p. A263

RUDZIK, Donna, Director Human Resources, CHRISTUS Mother Frances Hospital – Sulphur Springs, Sulphur Springs, TX, p. A651

RUE, Loring, M.D. Senior Vice President, Quality Patient Safety and Clinical Effectiveness, University of Alabama Hospital, Birmingham, AL, p. A17

RUECKERT, Sebastian, M.D
    Vice President and Chief Medical Officer, Alton Memorial Hospital, Alton, IL, p. A180
    Chief Medical Officer, Christian Hospital, Saint Louis, MO, p. A380

RUEDISUELI, Amy, Vice President of Finance, McKenzie Health System, Sandusky, MI, p. A334

RUELLO, Rocky, Vice President Human Resources, Mercy Hospital St. Louis, Saint Louis, MO, p. A380

RUFF, Robin, Chief Financial Officer, Pikes Peak Regional Hospital, Woodland Park, CO, p. A111

RUFF, Victoria, M.D. Medical Director, Select Specialty Hospital–Columbus, Columbus, OH, p. A491

RUFFIN, Marshall, Chief Information Officer, Inova Fair Oaks Hospital, Fairfax, VA, p. A669

RUFFOLO, Joseph A., President and Chief Executive Officer, Niagara Falls Memorial Medical Center, Niagara Falls, NY, p. A451

RUGE, Randy, Chief Executive Officer, Paulding County Hospital, Paulding, OH, p. A501

RUGGIERO, Taren, R.N. Vice President and Chief Nursing Officer, Holy Cross Hospital, Fort Lauderdale, FL, p. A128

RUGH, MariJo, Chief Information Officer, Valley View Hospital, Glenwood Springs, CO, p. A106

RUIZ, Javier, M.D
    Medical Director, Intracare North Hospital, Houston, TX, p. A625
    Medical Director, Kingwood Pines Hospital, Kingwood, TX, p. A631

RUIZ, Kathleen, M.D. Associate Director Patient Care Services, Veterans Affairs Caribbean Healthcare System, San Juan, PR, p. A730

RUIZ, Mary, Chief Executive Officer, Centerstone Hospital, Bradenton, FL, p. A124

RUIZ, Patricia, Chief Nursing Officer, NYC Health + Hospitals / Coney Island, NY, p. A448

RUIZ, Tony, Senior Vice President, Chief Operating Officer, Medical Center Health System, Odessa, TX, p. A639

RULAND, Jyl
    Chief Financial Officer, Clearwater Valley Hospital and Clinics, Orofino, ID, p. A177
    Chief Financial Officer, St. Mary's Hospital, Cottonwood, ID, p. A176

RULE, Carlton, M.D., Chief Executive Officer, O'Connor Hospital, Delhi, NY, p. A438

RULLI, Sheila, Director Human Resources, KidsPeace Children's Hospital, Orefield, PA, p. A546

RUMMEL, Jennifer
    Director Human Resources, East Texas Medical Center Athens, Athens, TX, p. A598
    Director Human Resources, East Texas Medical Center Fairfield, Fairfield, TX, p. A617

RUNNELS, Clay, Vice President Chief Medical Officer Washington County, Johnson City Medical Center, Johnson City, TN, p. A585

RUNYAN, Duane, Chief Executive Officer and Managing Director, Willow Springs Center, Reno, NV, p. A408

RUNYAN, Mark
    Director Information Systems, Jordan Valley Medical Center West Valley Campus, West Valley City, UT, p. A664
    Director Information Services, Salt Lake Regional Medical Center, Salt Lake City, UT, p. A663

RUNYON, Annette, Vice President and Administrator, Medical Center at Franklin, Franklin, KY, p. A260

RUPA, Maitra, M.D. Acting Medical Director, Chester Mental Health Center, Chester, IL, p. A183

RUPERT, Chris, Interim Chief Executive Officer, River Crest Hospital, San Angelo, TX, p. A644

RUPERT, Duke, Chief Operating Officer, Allegheny General Hospital, Pittsburgh, PA, p. A550

RUPERT, James M., Chief Fiscal Services, Battle Creek Veterans Affairs Medical Center, Battle Creek, MI, p. A319

RUPERT, Michael J., Chief Financial Officer, VA Long Beach Healthcare System, Long Beach, CA, p. A70

RUPP, Connie, MSN Executive Vice President and Chief Nursing Officer, Regional West Medical Center, Scottsbluff, NE, p. A402

RUPP, Robert, Chief Executive Officer, Medical Center of South Arkansas, El Dorado, AR, p. A45

RUPPERT, Jennifer, Chief Financial Officer, Iowa City Veterans Affairs Health Care System, Iowa City, IA, p. A232

RUPPERT SCHILLER, Kerri
    Senior Vice President and Chief Financial Officer, Children's Hospital of Orange County, Orange, CA, p. A81
    Senior Vice President and Chief Financial Officer, CHOC Children's at Mission Hospital, Mission Viejo, CA, p. A76

RUSCITTO, Kathryn H., President, St. Joseph's Hospital Health Center, Syracuse, NY, p. A456

RUSH, Andy, Senior Vice President and Chief Operating Officer, Somerset Hospital, Somerset, PA, p. A555

RUSH, Ann Marie, Chief Financial Officer, Penobscot Valley Hospital, Lincoln, ME, p. A294

RUSH, Christopher, Chief Financial Officer, Specialty Hospital of Meridian, Meridian, MS, p. A362

RUSH, Cindy, Director Human Resources, Clay County Medical Center, Clay Center, KS, p. A241

RUSH, Ed, President and Chief Executive Officer, Iredell Health System, Statesville, NC, p. A474

RUSH, Jeff, Chief Financial Officer, Rutherford Regional Health System, Rutherfordton, NC, p. A473

RUSH, Matthew, FACHE, President and Chief Executive Officer, Hayes Green Beach Memorial Hospital, Charlotte, MI, p. A320

RUSHIN, Denise, Director Human Resources, Poplar Bluff Regional Medical Center, Poplar Bluff, MO, p. A378

RUSHING, Heath, Chief Executive Officer, Memorial Hermann Northeast, Humble, TX, p. A628

RUSHING, Kelley J., Chief Executive Officer, Caldwell Medical Center, Princeton, KY, p. A268

RUSHING, R. Lynn, Chief Executive Officer, Brook Lane Health Services, Hagerstown, MD, p. A301

RUSHING, Randy, Chief Financial Officer, Massac Memorial Hospital, Metropolis, IL, p. A196

RUSHING, Richard, Chief of Staff, King's Daughters Medical Center, Brookhaven, MS, p. A356

RUSHLOW, David, Vice President Medical Affairs, Mayo Clinic Health System – Franciscan Healthcare in La Crosse, La Crosse, WI, p. A708

RUSINKO, Steve, Chief Financial Officer, Eastern Regional Medical Center, Philadelphia, PA, p. A547

RUSK, Scott, M.D. Vice President Medical Administration, Mercy Hospital of Portland, Portland, ME, p. A294

RUSNACZYK, John, Senior Vice President and Chief Financial Officer, St. Vincent Charity Medical Center, Cleveland, OH, p. A489

RUSNAK, Greg, Executive Vice President and Chief Operating Officer, GHS Greenville Memorial Hospital, Greenville, SC, p. A566

RUSS, Nicole L., Director Colleague Relations, Alliance Community Hospital, Alliance, OH, p. A483

RUSSEL, Kimberly A., FACHE, President and Chief Executive Officer, Bryan Health, Lincoln, NE, p. B25

RUSSELL, Bill, Senior Chief Information Officer, Mission Hospital, Mission Viejo, CA, p. A77

RUSSELL, Brant, R.N. Chief Operating Officer, St. John Hospital and Medical Center, Detroit, MI, p. A322

RUSSELL, Chris, Chief Information Officer, Faith Community Hospital, Jacksboro, TX, p. A629

RUSSELL, Dardanella, Chief Human Resources Management Service, Veterans Affairs Hudson Valley Health Care System, Montrose, NY, p. A443

RUSSELL, David, President and Chief Executive Officer, Adventist Medical Center–Portland, Portland, OR, p. A529

RUSSELL, Donald
    Senior Vice President and Chief Human Resources Officer, AMITA Health Elk Grove Village, Elk Grove Village, IL, p. A189
    Senior Vice President and Chief Human Resources Officer, AMITA Health GlenOaks, Glendale Heights, IL, p. A191
    Senior Vice President and Chief Human Resources Officer, AMITA Health Hoffman Estates, Hoffman Estates, IL, p. A193

RUSSELL, Erin, Controller, Kindred Hospital–San Antonio, San Antonio, TX, p. A646

RUSSELL, Freda, R.N., Chief Executive Officer and Chief Nursing Officer, Three Rivers Hospital, Waverly, TN, p. A594

RUSSELL, Georgette, Vice President of Talent & Organizational Effectiveness, Sparrow Carson Hospital, Carson City, MI, p. A320

RUSSELL, John D., President and Chief Executive Officer, Columbus Community Hospital, Inc., Columbus, WI, p. A704

RUSSELL, Jon
  Senior Vice President and Chief Information Officer, John Muir Medical Center, Concord, Concord, CA, p. A59
  Senior Vice President & Chief Information Officer, John Muir Medical Center, Walnut Creek, Walnut Creek, CA, p. A99
RUSSELL, Kathy, R.N. Chief Nursing Officer, Bluegrass Community Hospital, Versailles, KY, p. A270
RUSSELL, Kendrick, Chief Human Resources Officer, Abrazo Scottsdale Campus, Phoenix, AZ, p. A35
RUSSELL, Kim, M.D. Chief of Staff, Scott & White Hospital – Llano, Llano, TX, p. A633
RUSSELL, Laurie, Director Human Resources, Lea Regional Medical Center, Hobbs, NM, p. A35
RUSSELL, Linda, Vice President and Chief Nursing Officer, Self Regional Healthcare, Greenwood, SC, p. A567
RUSSELL, Michelle, Chief Executive Officer, Lafayette Regional Rehabilitation Hospital, Lafayette, IN, p. A216
RUSSELL, Nancy, Chief Financial Officer, Clifton–Fine Hospital, Star Lake, NY, p. A456
RUSSELL, Patti, Vice President Nursing, Masonicare Health Center, Wallingford, CT, p. A117
RUSSELL, Randall, Vice President and Chief Financial Officer, Memorial Hospital and Health Care Center, Jasper, IN, p. A215
RUSSELL, Robert, Chief Executive Officer, Select Specialty Hospital Midtown Atlanta, Atlanta, GA, p. A152
RUSSELL, Robert J., Associate Executive Director Operations, Penn Presbyterian Medical Center, Philadelphia, PA, p. A549
RUSSELL, Shelia, Director Human Resources, Tennova Healthcare–Jamestown, Jamestown, TN, p. A584
RUSSELL, Shelly, Chief Executive Officer, Mitchell County Regional Health Center, Osage, IA, p. A235
RUSSELL, Sherrie
  Vice President and Chief Information Officer, Alexian Brothers Behavioral Health Hospital, Hoffman Estates, IL, p. A193
  Senior Vice President & Chief Information Officer, AMITA Health Elk Grove Village, Elk Grove Village, IL, p. A189
  Senior Vice President and Chief Information Officer, AMITA Health GlenOaks, Glendale Heights, IL, p. A191
  Senior Vice President and Chief Information Officer, AMITA Health Hoffman Estates, Hoffman Estates, IL, p. A193
RUSSELL, Susan
  Chief Financial Officer, OCH Regional Medical Center, Starkville, MS, p. A365
  Chief Nursing Officer, Singing River Health System, Pascagoula, MS, p. A363
RUSSELL, William B., Chief Executive Officer, Three Rivers Health, Three Rivers, MI, p. A335
RUSSELL–JENKINS, Shane, M.D. Medical Director, Windhaven Psychiatric Hospital, Prescott Valley, AZ, p. A38
RUSSO, Arthur, M.D. Director Medical Affairs, Harrington Memorial Hospital, Southbridge, MA, p. A314
RUSSO, Cindy, MS, President and Chief Administrative Officer, Baystate Franklin Medical Center, Greenfield, MA, p. A310
RUSSO, Kimberly, Chief Executive Officer, George Washington University Hospital, Washington, DC, p. A121
RUSSO, Mike, Vice President Information Systems, Grimes St. Joseph Health Center, Navasota, TX, p. A638
RUSSO, Paul M., FACHE, Director, Miami Veterans Affairs Healthcare System, Miami, FL, p. A137
RUST, Jeff, Information Technology Systems Site Manager, Mercy Medical Center, Williston, ND, p. A482
RUTH, Daniel R., President and Chief Executive Officer, Jewish Home of San Francisco, San Francisco, CA, p. A90
RUTH, Joseph, Executive Vice President and Chief Operating Officer, Sparrow Hospital, Lansing, MI, p. A328
RUTHER, Randy, Vice President Finance and Chief Financial Officer, Little Company of Mary Hospital and Health Care Centers, Evergreen Park, IL, p. A190
RUTHERFORD, Dennis E., CP
  Chief Financial Officer, Florence Hospital at Anthem, Florence, AZ, p. A32
  Chief Financial Officer, Gilbert Hospital, Gilbert, AZ, p. A32
RUTHERFORD, Jeremiah, Chief Medical Officer, Cornerstone Hospital of Oklahoma–Muskogee, Muskogee, OK, p. A514
RUTHERFORD, Peter, M.D.,
  Chief Executive Officer, Confluence Health/Central Washington Hospital, Wenatchee, WA, p. A693
  Chief Executive Officer, Confluence Health/Wenatchee Valley Hospital, Wenatchee, WA, p. A693
RUTHERFORD, Ronald, Chief Information Officer, Beth Israel Deaconess Hospital Plymouth, Plymouth, MA, p. A314
RUTHERFORD, Theresa, FACHE, President and Chief Executive Officer, HSHS St. Anthony's Memorial Hospital, Effingham, IL, p. A188
RUTHS, Steve, M.D. Chief Medical Officer, Vista Del Mar Hospital, Ventura, CA, p. A98
RUTKOWSKI, Jennifer, R.N. Vice President Professional Services, Grant Regional Health Center, Lancaster, WI, p. A708

RUTKOWSKI, Jim, Chief Financial Officer, United Hospital Center, Bridgeport, WV, p. A694
RUTLEDGE, Debra K., R.N. Vice President Nursing Services, CHI Health Plainview, Plainview, NE, p. A401
RUTLEDGE, Rebel, Director Human Resources, Grady Memorial Hospital, Chickasha, OK, p. A510
RUWOLDT, Steven T., Chief Operating Officer, Memorial Medical Center, Las Cruces, NM, p. A430
RUYTER, Mary J., Chief Executive Officer, Sanford Jackson Medical Center, Jackson, MN, p. A344
RYALS, Billie, Director Human Resources, Sullivan County Memorial Hospital, Milan, MO, p. A376
RYAN, Chris, Chief Information Officer, Auburn Community Hospital, Auburn, NY, p. A434
RYAN, Christie, Chief Nursing Officer, HEALTHSOUTH Rehabilitation Hospital of Sewickley, Sewickley, PA, p. A554
RYAN, Christina M., R.N., Chief Executive Officer, The Women's Hospital, Newburgh, IN, p. A220
RYAN, Connie, Chief Nursing Officer, Select Specialty Hospital–Tulsa Midtown, Tulsa, OK, p. A522
RYAN, David P., Vice President Human Resources, Hallmark Health System, Melrose, MA, p. A312
RYAN, Debora, R.N. Vice President Patient Care, St. Francis Regional Medical Center, Shakopee, MN, p. A351
RYAN, Dennis, Senior Vice President and Chief Financial Officer, Children's Hospital of The King's Daughters, Norfolk, VA, p. A675
RYAN, Frank, Chief Financial Officer, Manchester Veterans Affairs Medical Center, Manchester, NH, p. A412
RYAN, Jacqueline, Director Human Resources, Mayo Clinic Health System in Lake City, Lake City, MN, p. A344
RYAN, John Jack, M.D. Chief Medical Officer, Oakland Regional Hospital, Southfield, MI, p. A334
RYAN, Kimberly, President, Wellstar Atlanta Medical Center, Atlanta, GA, p. A153
RYAN, Lisa M., Coordinator Human Resources, Hampstead Hospital, Hampstead, NH, p. A411
RYAN, Maria, Ph.D., Chief Executive Officer, Cottage Hospital, Woodsville, NH, p. A413
RYAN, Mike, Director of Information Services, Gunnison Valley Hospital, Gunnison, UT, p. A660
RYAN, Patrice
  Vice President Human Resources, Goleta Valley Cottage Hospital, Santa Barbara, CA, p. A93
  Vice President Human Resources, Santa Barbara Cottage Hospital, Santa Barbara, CA, p. A93
  Vice President Human Resources, Santa Ynez Valley Cottage Hospital, Solvang, CA, p. A94
RYAN, Patrick G., Chief Executive Officer, Promise Hospital of Fort Myers, Fort Myers, FL, p. A129
RYAN, Patrick J., Chief Human Resources Officer, Helen Hayes Hospital, West Haverstraw, NY, p. A458
RYAN, Rebecca, Interim Director Human Resources and Employee Health, Ukiah Valley Medical Center, Ukiah, CA, p. A97
RYAN, Robert, M.D. Chief Medical Officer, Guadalupe Regional Medical Center, Seguin, TX, p. A648
RYAN, Sharon, Regional Controller, Select Specialty Hospital–Macomb County, Mount Clemens, MI, p. A330
RYAN, Tim, Chief Financial Officer, Centennial Peaks Hospital, Louisville, CO, p. A109
RYAN, William, Vice President and Chief Financial Officer, UF Health Jacksonville, Jacksonville, FL, p. A132
RYBA, Janice L., JD, Chief Executive Officer, St. Mary Medical Center, Hobart, IN, p. A213
RYBA, Thomas L., Chief Executive Officer, Lighthouse Care Center of Conway, Conway, SC, p. A565
RYBA, Tomi S., President and Chief Executive Officer, El Camino Hospital, Mountain View, CA, p. A78
RYBICKI, Catherine, Vice President Physician Services and Chief Operating Officer, Spectrum Health Big Rapids Hospital, Big Rapids, MI, p. A319
RYBICKI, Cathy, Chief Operating Officer, Spectrum Health Reed City Hospital, Reed City, MI, p. A332
RYBOLT, Andrew, Vice President and Chief Financial Officer, Redwood Memorial Hospital, Fortuna, CA, p. A62
RYCKMAN, George, D.O. Chief of Staff, Paul Oliver Memorial Hospital, Frankfort, MI, p. A324
RYDER, Doug, President, Holy Cross Germantown Hospital, Germantown, MD, p. A301
RYDER, Jeff, Director Information Systems, Saint Joseph Mount Sterling, Mount Sterling, KY, p. A267
RYDER, John E.
  Chief Operating Officer, Borgess–Lee Memorial Hospital, Dowagiac, MI, p. A322
  Chief Operating Officer, Borgess–Lee Memorial Hospital, Dowagiac, MI, p. A322
  Administrator and Chief Operating Officer, Borgess–Pipp Hospital, Plainwell, MI, p. A331

RYDER, Ronald, D.O. President of the Medical Staff, Robert Wood Johnson University Hospital at Hamilton, Hamilton, NJ, p. A417
RYDER, Troy, Director of Nursing, Aspire Hospital, Conroe, TX, p. A607
RYDGREN, Barbara, Administrator, Glenn Medical Center, Willows, CA, p. A100
RYERSE, David, Chief Executive Officer, Daniels Memorial Healthcare Center, Scobey, MT, p. A390
RYKERT, Lauren P., Senior Vice President, Houston Methodist Hospital, Houston, TX, p. A624
RYLAND, Jennifer M., R.N. Chief Administrative Officer, Jackson Medical Center, Jackson, AL, p. A22
RYLE, Barry W., Chief Information Officer, Oswego Hospital, Oswego, NY, p. A452
RYLE, Deborah L., Administrator and Chief Executive Officer, St. David's Round Rock Medical Center, Round Rock, TX, p. A644
RYMER, Brandy, Coordinator Human Resources, Murray Medical Center, Chatsworth, GA, p. A156
RYON, Joel, M.D. Chief of Staff, Henry County Health Center, Mount Pleasant, IA, p. A234
RYS, Jan, Chief Executive Officer, Straith Hospital for Special Surgery, Southfield, MI, p. A334
RZENDZIAN, Michael, Chief Financial Officer, Baylor Emergency Medical Center at Aubrey, Aubrey, TX, p. A598
RZOMP, Kimberly
  Vice President and Chief Financial Officer, Chambersburg Hospital, Chambersburg, PA, p. A535
  Vice President Finance, Waynesboro Hospital, Waynesboro, PA, p. A556

S

SAAD, Michael, Vice President and Chief Information Officer, University of Tennessee Medical Center, Knoxville, TN, p. A586
SAADAT, Annette, Human Resources Business Partner, Saint Joseph Mount Sterling, Mount Sterling, KY, p. A267
SAALFELD, Thomas, Senior Vice President and Chief Operating Officer, St. Elizabeth Fort Thomas, Fort Thomas, KY, p. A260
SAARI, Heidi L., Director, Human Resources, Upper Connecticut Valley Hospital, Colebrook, NH, p. A410
SAAVEDRA, JayLynn, Chief Information Officer, U. S. Public Health Service Indian Hospital, Parker, AZ, p. A35
SABANDIT, Elizabeth, Director Human Resources, Alhambra Hospital Medical Center, Alhambra, CA, p. A54
SABELLA, Deborah, R.N., Chief Executive Officer, Landmark Hospital of Columbia, Columbia, MO, p. A370
SABHARRWAL, Parajeet, Chief Executive Officer, Minimally Invasive Surgery Hospital, Lenexa, KS, p. A248
SABIA, John, M.D. Vice President Medical Affairs, Northern Dutchess Hospital, Rhinebeck, NY, p. A453
SABIN, Margaret D., President and Chief Executive Officer, Penrose–St. Francis Health Services, Colorado Springs, CO, p. A103
SABLE, Kenneth N., M.D., President, Jersey Shore University Medical Center, Neptune, NJ, p. A420
SABOTTA, John, Director Information Systems, St. Margaret's Hospital, Spring Valley, IL, p. A203
SABUS, Matthew, Director Information Systems, Boone County Hospital, Boone, IA, p. A226
SACCOIO, Saria, M.D. Chief Medical Officer, Bon Secours St. Francis Health System, Greenville, SC, p. A566
SACHARSKI, Steve, Chief Financial Officer, Havenwyck Hospital, Auburn Hills, MI, p. A318
SACHDEV, Aruna, M.D. Medical Director, Massachusetts Hospital School, Canton, MA, p. A309
SACHDEVA, Sandeep, M.D. Vice President Medical Affairs, Swedish/Edmonds, Edmonds, WA, p. A684
SACHEDINA, Azeem, M.D. Chief of Staff, Broward Health Coral Springs, Coral Springs, FL, p. A126
SACHS, III, Henry T., M.D. Medical Director, Emma Pendleton Bradley Hospital, East Providence, RI, p. A560
SACHTJEN, Mistie, Chief Executive Officer, Community Memorial Hospital, Burke, SD, p. A572
SACHTLEBEN, Michael, President, MedStar Georgetown University Hospital, Washington, DC, p. A121
SACKETT, John, President SGMC and Executive Vice President and Chief Operating Officer, Adventist Healthcare Shady Grove Medical Center, Rockville, MD, p. A303
SACKETT, Walter, President, Sycamore Medical Center, Miamisburg, OH, p. A499
SACKMANN, Charles, M.D. Chief of Staff, East Adams Rural Healthcare, Ritzville, WA, p. A689

SACKRISON, Jeffrey
President, Vidant Bertie Hospital, Windsor, NC, p. A475
President, Vidant Chowan Hospital, Edenton, NC, p. A464
SADA, Judy, Chief Financial Officer, Memorial Hospital Miramar, Miramar, FL, p. A138
SADAU, Ernie W., Chief Executive Officer, CHRISTUS Health, Irving, TX, p. B33
SADLER, Donna, Director Human Resources, Arkansas State Hospital, Little Rock, AR, p. A48
SADLER, Joy, Director Human Resources, Bear River Valley Hospital, Tremonton, UT, p. A664
SADOFF, Jennifer, Chief Executive Officer, Moab Regional Hospital, Moab, UT, p. A660
SADR, Farrokh, M.D. Chief Medical Officer, Sacred Heart Hospital, Allentown, PA, p. A532
SADRO, Cheryl A., Executive Vice President Chief Business and Finance Officer, University of Texas Medical Branch, Galveston, TX, p. A620
SADVARY, Thomas J., FACHE, Chief Executive Officer, HonorHealth, Scottsdale, AZ, p. B70
SAENZ, Luis J Rodriquez, M.D. Medical Director, Hospital Menonita De Cayey, Cayey, PR, p. A727
SAENZ, Melanie, Regional Human Resources Officer, Presence Saints Mary & Elizabeth Medical Center, Chicago, IL, p. A186
SAFFA, Steve, Director Human Resources, St. Francis Health, Topeka, KS, p. A254
SAFLEY, Thomas, Chief Financial Officer, St. Joseph Regional Medical Center, Lewiston, ID, p. A177
SAFYER, Steven M., M.D., President and CEO, Montefiore Health System,, NY, p. B92
SAFYER, Steven M., M.D., President and Chief Executive Officer, Montefiore Medical Center,, NY, p. A446
SAGE, Kelly, Chief Nursing Officer, HSHS St. Anthony's Memorial Hospital, Effingham, IL, p. A188
SAGMIT, Rodney, Chief Information Management, VA Long Beach Healthcare System, Long Beach, CA, p. A70
SAHA, Sanjay K., Chief Operating Officer, Sibley Memorial Hospital, Washington, DC, p. A122
SAHLOLBEI, Hossain, M.D. Chief of Staff, Palo Verde Hospital, Blythe, CA, p. A57
SAHLSTROM, Christopher, M.D. Chief of Staff, Mat–Su Regional Medical Center, Palmer, AK, p. A30
SAHMAUNT, Sarabeth, Supervisory Accountant, Lawton Indian Hospital, Lawton, OK, p. A513
SAIA, Carrie L., Chief Executive Officer, Holton Community Hospital, Holton, KS, p. A245
SAINBERT, Wilmino, Chief Human Resources Management Service, Northport Veterans Affairs Medical Center, Northport, NY, p. A451
SAINTZ, Jeffrey, Vice President Human Resources, Titusville Area Hospital, Titusville, PA, p. A555
SAIYED, Ashfaq, M.D. Medical Director, Irwin County Hospital, Ocilla, GA, p. A164
SAIZ, Claudia, Chief Operating Officer, Advanced Care Hospital of Southern New Mexico, Las Cruces, NM, p. A429
SAJID, Muhammad W., M.D. Medical Director, Lincoln Trail Behavioral Health System, Radcliff, KY, p. A268
SAKALOSKY, Matt, Director Information Services and Chief Information Officer, Fremont Health, Fremont, NE, p. A396
SAKOVITS, Steven, Vice President Information Systems and Chief Information Officer, Stamford Hospital, Stamford, CT, p. A117
SALAKI, Jana, Regional Director Human Resources, WellSpan Ephrata Community Hospital, Ephrata, PA, p. A538
SALAMANCA, Mary, Director Human Resources, HEALTHSOUTH Rehabilitation Hospital of Spring Hill, Brooksville, FL, p. A125
SALAMONE, Joanna, Senior Vice President Clinical Services and Chief Nursing Officer, Southern Maine Health Care – Biddeford Medical Center, Biddeford, ME, p. A292
SALANDI, John, Chief Executive Officer, Landmark Hospital of Savannah, Savannah, GA, p. A166
SALANGER, Matthew J., President and Chief Executive Officer, United Health Services, Binghamton, NY, p. B140
SALANGER, Matthew J., President and Chief Executive Officer, United Health Services Hospitals–Binghamton, Binghamton, NY, p. A435
SALAS, Dawn, Controller, HEALTHSOUTH Rehabilitation Hospital at Martin Health, Stuart, FL, p. A146
SALAS, Victor, M.D. President Medical Staff, UnityPoint Health – Jones Regional Medical Center, Anamosa, IA, p. A225
SALAWAY, Tarek
Chief Operating Officer, Mission Hospital, Mission Viejo, CA, p. A77
Chief Operating Officer, USC Norris Comprehensive Cancer Center, Los Angeles, CA, p. A74
SALAZAR, Eloisa, Chief Financial Officer, South Texas Veterans Health Care System, San Antonio, TX, p. A647
SALAZAR, Juan, Director Human Resources, St. Luke's Episcopal Hospital, Ponce, PR, p. A728

SALAZAR, Leanne, Chief Nursing Officer, Oak Hill Hospital, Brooksville, FL, p. A125
SALAZAR, Linda C., Information Technology Leader, Kaiser Permanente Baldwin Park Medical Center, Baldwin Park, CA, p. A56
SALAZAR, Pamela, M.D. Chief of Staff, HEALTHSOUTH Walton Rehabilitation Hospital, Augusta, GA, p. A153
SALCEDO, Martha, Interim Director Human Resources, Whittier Hospital Medical Center, Whittier, CA, p. A100
SALCEDO, Nydimar, Chief Human Resources Officer, Castaner General Hospital, Castaner, PR, p. A726
SALDIVAR, Antoninette, Vice President, Human Resources, BridgePoint Hospital National Harbor, Washington, DC, p. A121
SALEEBY, Manhal, M.D. Chief of Staff, VCU Community Memorial Hospital, South Hill, VA, p. A679
SALEEM, David, Director Information Technology, Greystone Park Psychiatric Hospital, Morris Plains, NJ, p. A419
SALEM, Gary, M.D. Vice President Medical Affairs, McLaren Lapeer Region, Lapeer, MI, p. A328
SALEM, Michael, M.D., President and Chief Executive Officer, National Jewish Health, Denver, CO, p. A104
SALGADO, Joe, M.D. Chief of Staff, Artesia General Hospital, Artesia, NM, p. A428
SALIBA, K. Michael, M.D. Medical Director, Shadow Mountain Behavioral Health System, Tulsa, OK, p. A522
SALINAS, Amaro, Assistant Administrator and Human Resource Officer, Starr County Memorial Hospital, Rio Grande City, TX, p. A643
SALINAS, Daniel, M.D. Senior Vice President and Chief Medical Officer, Children's Healthcare of Atlanta, Atlanta, GA, p. A152
SALINAS, Noe
Vice President Information Technology, Nexus Specialty Hospital, Shenandoah, TX, p. A648
Vice President Information Technology, Nexus Specialty Hospital The Woodlands, The Woodlands, TX, p. A652
SALING, Christopher, Manager Human Resources, Park City Medical Center, Park City, UT, p. A662
SALISBURY, Dennis, M.D. Vice President for Medical Affairs, St. James Healthcare, Butte, MT, p. A386
SALISBURY, Renee A., Director Human Resources, OSF Saint Luke Medical Center, Kewanee, IL, p. A194
SALISBURY, Tracy
Regional Manager Human Resources, Central State Hospital, Petersburg, VA, p. A676
Director Human Resources, Hiram W. Davis Medical Center, Petersburg, VA, p. A676
SALLER, William, Chief Financial Officer, Rio Grande Regional Hospital, McAllen, TX, p. A636
SALLEY, Wanda, Vice President Human Resources, West Florida Hospital, Pensacola, FL, p. A142
SALLIS, Tom, Director Information Systems, Sparks Regional Medical Center, Fort Smith, AR, p. A46
SALLOUM, Fadi, M.D. Medical Director, Select Specialty Hospital–Pontiac, Pontiac, MI, p. A332
SALMAN, Wael, M.D. Vice President Medical Affairs, Memorial Healthcare, Owosso, MI, p. A331
SALMANULLAH, Muhammad, Chief Medical Director, HEALTHSOUTH Rehabilitation Hospital, Concord, NH, p. A410
SALNAS, Todd
President, Petaluma Valley Hospital, Petaluma, CA, p. A82
President, Santa Rosa Memorial Hospital, Santa Rosa, CA, p. A94
SALO, Saliba, President, Northridge Hospital Medical Center,, CA, p. A73
SALOM, Ira, M.D. Clinical Director, Northern Navajo Medical Center, Shiprock, NM, p. A431
SALOME, Jenny, Chief Financial Officer and Assistant Administrator, Northwest Hills Surgical Hospital, Austin, TX, p. A599
SALOMON, Kathryn, Director Human Resources, Kona Community Hospital, Kealakekua, HI, p. A172
SALTAFORMAGGIO, Cheri, Chief Executive Officer, St. Charles Surgical Hospital, New Orleans, LA, p. A285
SALTER, Cherry B., Director of Nursing, Hardtner Medical Center, Olla, LA, p. A286
SALTONSTALL, Christine, Chief Financial Officer, Kindred Hospital–Baldwin Park, Baldwin Park, CA, p. A56
SALVADOR, Ed, Chief Financial Officer, St. Jude Medical Center, Fullerton, CA, p. A64
SALVATI, Mario, Director Fiscal Services, Shriners Hospitals for Children–Philadelphia, Philadelphia, PA, p. A549
SALVI, Donna, Chief Nursing Officer, Watsonville Community Hospital, Watsonville, CA, p. A99
SALVINO, Sonia, Vice President Finance, University Hospitals Cleveland Medical Center, Cleveland, OH, p. A490
SALVITTI, Alfred P., Chief Financial Officer, Eagleville Hospital, Eagleville, PA, p. A537
SALVO, Stephen, Vice President Human Resources, Anna Jaques Hospital, Newburyport, MA, p. A313

SALVO, Thomas, Associate Executive Director Human Resources, Glen Cove Hospital, Glen Cove, NY, p. A439
SALY, David, Director, Information Services, Largo Medical Center, Largo, FL, p. A134
SALYER, Steven, Senior Vice President and Chief Operating Officer, Indian River Medical Center, Vero Beach, FL, p. A149
SALZMAN, Shona, Chief Operating Officer, William Newton Hospital, Winfield, KS, p. A256
SAMBASIVAN, Venkataraman, M.D. Chief Medical Officer, Lourdes Medical Center, Pasco, WA, p. A687
SAMET, Kenneth A., President and Chief Executive Officer, MedStar Health, Columbia, MD, p. B87
SAMILO, Nick
Vice President Finance and Chief Financial Officer, Frisbie Memorial Hospital, Rochester, NH, p. A413
Vice President Fiscal Services and Chief Financial Officer, Stanly Regional Medical Center, Albemarle, NC, p. A460
SAMMARCO, Michael, M.D. Chief Financial Officer, Erie County Medical Center, Buffalo, NY, p. A435
SAMMONS, Craig, Chief Financial Officer, Sky Ridge Medical Center, Lone Tree, CO, p. A108
SAMMS, Caswell, Network Chief Financial Officer, NYC Health + Hospitals / Lincoln,, NY, p. A448
SAMORA, Martha, FACHE, Chief Executive Officer, HEALTHSOUTH Bakersfield Rehabilitation Hospital, Bakersfield, CA, p. A56
SAMPAGA, Arthur, Assistant Director Nursing, Hilo Medical Center, Hilo, HI, p. A170
SAMPSON, Arthur J., FACHE, President, Miriam Hospital, Providence, RI, p. A560
SAMPSON, Bob
Vice President, Human Resources, EvergreenHealth, Kirkland, WA, p. A686
Vice President Human Resources, Redwood Memorial Hospital, Fortuna, CA, p. A62
SAMPSON, Jill, Director Human Resources, Lemuel Shattuck Hospital, Jamaica Plain, MA, p. A311
SAMS, Carla, R.N. Director of Nursing, Liberty Healthcare Systems, Bastrop, LA, p. A272
SAMSON, Ley, Director Management Information Systems, Clear Lake Regional Medical Center, Webster, TX, p. A656
SAMUDRALA, Siresha, M.D. Medical Director, Mercy Rehabilitation Hospital, Chesterfield, MO, p. A369
SAMUEL, Nicole, Chief Financial Officer, Sierra Vista Hospital, Sacramento, CA, p. A87
SAMUELS, Christopher, Chief of Staff, Skyline Hospital, White Salmon, WA, p. A693
SAMUELS, Steven, M.D. Medical Director, Kindred Hospital Indianapolis South, Greenwood, IN, p. A212
SAMUELSON, Melissa A., R.N. Chief Nurse Executive, Poplar Bluff Regional Medical Center, Poplar Bluff, MO, p. A378
SAMYN, Mike, Vice President, Finance and Chief Financial Officer, St. Mary Mercy Hospital, Livonia, MI, p. A329
SAMZ, Jeff, Chief Operating Officer, Huntsville Hospital, Huntsville, AL, p. A21
SAN FILIPPO, Bruce, M.D. Chief Medical Officer, Memorial Medical Center, Las Cruces, NM, p. A430
SANBORN, Michael, MS, President, Baylor Scott & White Medical Center – Carrollton, Carrollton, TX, p. A605
SANBORN, Randall, Director Information Systems, Garden City Hospital, Garden City, MI, p. A324
SANCHEZ, Annette, Chief Clinical Officer, Kindred Hospital North Florida, Green Cove Springs, FL, p. A130
SANCHEZ, Antonio, M.D. Chief of Staff, Veterans Affairs Caribbean Healthcare System, San Juan, PR, p. A730
SANCHEZ, Arnaldo Rodriguez, M.D. Chief Operating Officer, Hospital Episcopal San Lucas Guayama, Guayama, PR, p. A727
SANCHEZ, Emalie, Director Human Resources, Baylor Medical Center at Uptown, Dallas, TX, p. A609
SANCHEZ, Esperanza, Chief Clinical Officer, Kindred Hospital–La Mirada, La Mirada, CA, p. A67
SANCHEZ, Freddie, Director Information Systems, Fountain Valley Regional Hospital and Medical Center, Fountain Valley, CA, p. A62
SANCHEZ, John, Vice President Human Resources, White Plains Hospital Center, White Plains, NY, p. A459
SANCHEZ, Jose R., President and Chief Executive Officer, Norwegian American Hospital, Chicago, IL, p. A185
SANCHEZ, Nancy, Senior Vice President and Vice Dean Human Resources, NYU Langone Medical Center, New York, NY, p. A449
SANCHEZ, Rebecca, R.N. Director of Nursing, Texas Center for Infectious Disease, San Antonio, TX, p. A647

SANCHEZ–BICKLEY, Michelle
Vice President Human Resources, Renown Regional Medical Center, Reno, NV, p. A408
Vice President Human Resources, Renown Rehabilitation Hospital, Reno, NV, p. A408
Vice President Human Resources, Renown South Meadows Medical Center, Reno, NV, p. A408
SANCHEZ–RICO, Gloria, Chief Nursing Officer and Vice President, Huntington Memorial Hospital, Pasadena, CA, p. A82
SAND, Michelle, R.N. Vice President and Chief Nursing Officer, Cascade Valley Hospital and Clinics, Arlington, WA, p. A682
SANDAGER, Brian, Chief Information Officer, Lowell General Hospital, Lowell, MA, p. A311
SANDBERG, Karl, M.D. Chief Medical Officer, Chambers Memorial Hospital, Danville, AR, p. A44
SANDBERG, Sue, R.N. Chief Operating Officer, UNC REX Healthcare, Raleigh, NC, p. A472
SANDBERG, Todd, Chief Executive Officer and Administrator, Ridgeview Sibley Medical Center, Arlington, MN, p. A338
SANDBULTE, Nyla H., R.N. Director of Nursing, Sanford Luverne Medical Center, Luverne, MN, p. A345
SANDEFUR, Gwen L., Chief Operating Officer, Spectrum Health – Butterworth Hospital, Grand Rapids, MI, p. A325
SANDER, Cindy, Coordinator Human Resources, Kindred Hospital–St. Louis, Saint Louis, MO, p. A380
SANDERS, Amy, Chief Human Resources, Captain James A. Lovell Federal Health Care Center, North Chicago, IL, p. A198
SANDERS, Carolyn Lucey, Senior Vice President Patient Services and Chief Nursing Officer, University of Colorado Hospital, Aurora, CO, p. A101
SANDERS, David, Chief Financial Officer, Springhill Medical Center, Springhill, LA, p. A288
SANDERS, David S., Chief Executive Officer, Fannin Regional Hospital, Blue Ridge, GA, p. A154
SANDERS, Diane M., Chief Nursing Officer, Trios Health, Kennewick, WA, p. A685
SANDERS, Gale H., Director, Gadsden Regional Medical Center, Gadsden, AL, p. A20
SANDERS, Harv, Chief Financial Officer, Rhea Medical Center, Dayton, TN, p. A582
SANDERS, Jeff, Senior Vice President, Chief Operating Officer, Maine Medical Center, Portland, ME, p. A294
SANDERS, Jeffrey, M.D. Chief of Staff, Carson Tahoe Health, Carson City, NV, p. A404
SANDERS, Kelly B., Vice President Human Resources, Good Shepherd Health Care System, Hermiston, OR, p. A526
SANDERS, Kimberly, Chief Nursing Officer, Baptist Memorial Hospital–Huntingdon, Huntingdon, TN, p. A584
SANDERS, Kris, Chief Financial Officer, Methodist Olive Branch Hospital, Olive Branch, MS, p. A363
SANDERS, Kyle, Chief Financial Officer, NEA Baptist Memorial Hospital, Jonesboro, AR, p. A48
SANDERS, Michael, Chief Executive Officer, AMG Specialty Hospital–Feliciana, Clinton, LA, p. A275
SANDERS, Michael B., President and Chief Executive Officer, Monroe Clinic, Monroe, WI, p. A712
SANDERS, Michael R., MS Chief Operating Officer, Promise Hospital Baton Rouge – Main Campus, Baton Rouge, LA, p. A273
SANDERS, R. Bradley, D.O. Executive Medical Director, Alvarado Parkway Institute Behavioral Health System, La Mesa, CA, p. A67
SANDERS, Robert, M.D. Chief Medical Officer, Texoma Medical Center, Denison, TX, p. A612
SANDERS, Ryan, Director Information Services, Midtown Medical Center West, Columbus, GA, p. A156
SANDERS, Steve, Chief Financial Officer, Washington County Hospital and Clinics, Washington, IA, p. A238
SANDERS, Susie Sherrod, Budget Officer, Cherry Hospital, Goldsboro, NC, p. A466
SANDIFER, Ron, Chief Information Officer, Community Memorial Hospital, Ventura, CA, p. A98
SANDIN, James H., M.D. Assistant Administrator Medical Affairs, Hunt Regional Medical Center, Greenville, TX, p. A621
SANDLES, Christopher, Associate Director, Michael E. DeBakey Veterans Affairs Medical Center, Houston, TX, p. A626
SANDLIN, Keith, Chief Executive Officer, Cartersville Medical Center, Cartersville, GA, p. A156
SANDLIN, Michael, M.D. Chief of Staff, Muscogee Creek Nation Medical Center, Okmulgee, OK, p. A518
SANDMANN, Patty, Senior Director of Nursing, Burgess Health Center, Onawa, IA, p. A235
SANDS, Naomi, Administrative Assistant and Manager Human Resources, Swift County–Benson Hospital, Benson, MN, p. A339
SANDS, Sherry, R.N. Chief Nursing Officer, Southern Tennessee Regional Health System–Pulaski, Pulaski, TN, p. A592
SANDS, Tiffany, Manager Health Information, Arbuckle Memorial Hospital, Sulphur, OK, p. A520

SANDSTROM, C. Bruce, Vice President and Chief Financial Officer, The Aroostook Medical Center, Presque Isle, ME, p. A295
SANFORD, Lisa
VP Patient Care/CNO, Holy Rosary Healthcare, Miles City, MT, p. A389
Chief Nursing Officer, St. Luke's Elmore, Mountain Home, ID, p. A177
SANFORD, Ricca, Director Human Resources, Regional West Garden County, Oshkosh, NE, p. A401
SANFORD, Sharon K., Director Human Resources, Jersey Community Hospital, Jerseyville, IL, p. A194
SANFORD, Stacy, Chief Executive Officer, Oceans Behavioral Hospital Abilene, Abilene, TX, p. A595
SANGER, David, M.D. Chief Medical Officer, Pawnee Valley Community Hospital, Larned, KS, p. A247
SANGER, Ken, R.N. Chief Nursing Officer, Crittenton Hospital Medical Center, Rochester, MI, p. A332
SANGER, Neal, Vice President Information Services, Mayo Clinic Health System – Franciscan Healthcare in La Crosse, La Crosse, WI, p. A708
SANGHI, Harishankar, M.D. Clinical Director, St. Lawrence Psychiatric Center, Ogdensburg, NY, p. A451
SANKARAN, Jaya, M.D. Chief of Staff, St. Mary's of Michigan Standish Hospital, Standish, MI, p. A335
SANKE, Kristina, Chief Financial Officer, Orchard Hospital, Gridley, CA, p. A65
SANKOORIKAL, Joseph, M.D. Chief Medical Staff, Kansas Rehabilitation Hospital, Topeka, KS, p. A254
SANKS, Claude, Chief Medical Staff, Effingham Hospital, Springfield, GA, p. A166
SANSOM, Christine R., Chief Nursing Officer, McLaren Port Huron, Port Huron, MI, p. A332
SANSONE, John, Director Human Resources, Monadnock Community Hospital, Peterborough, NH, p. A413
SANTA ANA, Coleen F., President, Sentara Albemarle Medical Center, Elizabeth City, NC, p. A464
SANTAMARIA, Mark A., President, MidMichigan Medical Center–Gratiot, Alma, MI, p. A318
SANTANA, Leticia, Administrator Medical Records, Hospital Hermanos Melendez, Bayamon, PR, p. A726
SANTANGELO, Craig, Director Information Services, Medical Center Arlington, Arlington, TX, p. A597
SANTANGELO, Joe, M.D. Vice President of Medical Affairs, Munson Healthcare Cadillac Hospital, Cadillac, MI, p. A319
SANTANGELO, John, Director Information Technology, Cleveland Clinic Florida, Weston, FL, p. A150
SANTANGELO, Linda, Ph.D., Director, Desert Willow Treatment Center, Las Vegas, NV, p. A405
SANTARELLI, James, M.D. President Medical Staff, Aurora Medical Center, Kenosha, WI, p. A708
SANTIAGO, Alejandro, Director Finance, Doctors' Center Hospital San Juan, San Juan, PR, p. A729
SANTIAGO, Carlos T., Director Human Resources, Hospital Oncologico Andres Grillasca, Ponce, PR, p. A728
SANTIAGO, Julio, M.D. Chief of Staff, Genesis Medical Center–Aledo, Aledo, IL, p. A180
SANTIAGO, Manuel, Chief Information Officer, Hospital Metropolitan, San Juan, PR, p. A729
SANTIAGO, Orlando, Human Resources Officer, Hospital Del Maestro, San Juan, PR, p. A729
SANTIAGO, Sugehi, Director, Hospital San Francisco, San Juan, PR, p. A730
SANTIAGO, Ubaldo, M.D. Chairman, Doctors' Center Hospital San Juan, San Juan, PR, p. A729
SANTIESTEBAN, Nancy, Director Patient Care Services, Presbyterian Espanola Hospital, Espanola, NM, p. A429
SANTILLI, Robert J., Chief Executive Officer, Gunnison Valley Hospital, Gunnison, CO, p. A106
SANTINA, Ray, Director Information Systems, Psychiatric Institute of Washington, Washington, DC, p. A122
SANTISTEVAN, Vivian, Chief Human Resources, Tsehootsooi Medical Center, Fort Defiance, AZ, p. A32
SANTMAN, Kim D., Vice President Finance, St. Margaret's Hospital, Spring Valley, IL, p. A203
SANTORA, Judith, Human Resources Business Partner, Marymount Hospital, Garfield Heights, OH, p. A495
SANTOS, Daniel, Director Ancillary Services, Pacifica Hospital of the Valley,, CA, p. A73
SANTOS, David, President and Chief Executive Officer, St. Helena Hospital Clear Lake, Clearlake, CA, p. A59
SANTOS, Deborah, R.N. Chief Nursing Officer, HEALTHSOUTH Rehabilitation Hospital of Western Massachusetts, Ludlow, MA, p. A311
SANTOS, Gloria N., R.N
Chief Nursing Officer, Florida Hospital Heartland Medical Center, Sebring, FL, p. A145
Vice President and Chief Nursing Officer, Florida Hospital Wauchula, Wauchula, FL, p. A149

SANTOS, Ismael, Director Human Resources, Valle Vista Hospital, Greenwood, IN, p. A212
SANTOS, Lori
Vice President Finance, Albany Memorial Hospital, Albany, NY, p. A433
Chief Financial Officer, St. Peter's Hospital, Albany, NY, p. A433
SANTOS, Rafael, Executive Director, Caribbean Medical Center, Fajardo, PR, p. A727
SANTOS, Thomas, R.N. Chief Nursing Officer, Parkview Community Hospital Medical Center, Riverside, CA, p. A86
SANTOS–ROHEU, Jose, Chief Executive Officer, Peak Behavioral Health Services, Santa Teresa, NM, p. A431
SANTULLI, Patricia, Director Human Resources, Elmira Psychiatric Center, Elmira, NY, p. A438
SANVILLE, David, Chief Financial Officer, Mt. Ascutney Hospital and Health Center, Windsor, VT, p. A666
SANWARI, Murtaza, Chief Operating Officer, Kaiser Permanente Panorama City Medical Center,, CA, p. A71
SANZ, Sean M., Chief Executive Officer, Novant Health Forsyth Medical Center, Winston–Salem, NC, p. A476
SANZONE, Frank, Manager Information Technology, Brighton Center for Recovery, Brighton, MI, p. A319
SAPMAZ, Cagri, Information Technology Director, Bolivar Medical Center, Cleveland, MS, p. A356
SAPORITO, Angie, Administrator, Mercy Hospital Columbus, Columbus, KS, p. A242
SAPORITO, Joann L., R.N. Vice President Nursing Services, Oak Valley Hospital District, Oakdale, CA, p. A80
SAPP, Tracy, Director Human Resources, HEALTHSOUTH Rehabilitation Hospital of Ocala, Ocala, FL, p. A139
SAPPENFIELD, Debra, R.N. Chief Nursing Officer, Hemphill County Hospital, Canadian, TX, p. A605
SAPPINGTON–CRITTENDEN, Shana, Chief Operating Officer, Westside Regional Medical Center, Plantation, FL, p. A143
SAPRA, Sonney, Director Information Systems and Chief Information Officer, Tuality Healthcare, Hillsboro, OR, p. A526
SARBACHER, James, Chief Information Officer, State Hospital North, Orofino, ID, p. A177
SARDANA, Sadhana, M.D. Clinical Director, Rockland Children's Psychiatric Center, Orangeburg, NY, p. A452
SARDELLA, Jeff, Director Information Technology, Terrebonne General Medical Center, Houma, LA, p. A278
SARDONE, Frank J., President and Chief Executive Officer, Bronson Battle Creek, Battle Creek, MI, p. A319
SARDONE, Frank J., President and Chief Executive Officer, Bronson Healthcare Group, Kalamazoo, MI, p. B24
SARDONE, Frank J., President and Chief Executive Officer, Bronson Methodist Hospital, Kalamazoo, MI, p. A328
SARDUY, Innette Mary, M.P.H. Associate Director Patient Care Services and Nurse Executive, Louis Stokes Cleveland Veterans Affairs Medical Center, Cleveland, OH, p. A489
SARGEANT, Marty, Chief Operating Officer, City of Hope's Helford Clinical Research Hospital, Duarte, CA, p. A61
SARGENT, Kimberly, Vice President Patient Services, St. Luke's Hospital – Miners Campus, Coaldale, PA, p. A535
SARGENT, Kurt, CP
Vice President, Operational Finance, CHI St Alexius Health Carrington Medical Center, Carrington, ND, p. A477
Vice President Operational Finance, CHI St. Alexius Health Devils Lake Hospital, Devils Lake, ND, p. A478
SARGENT, Reed
Assistant Administrator Finance, Cedar City Hospital, Cedar City, UT, p. A659
Assistant Administrator Finance, Garfield Memorial Hospital and Clinics, Panguitch, UT, p. A662
SARGENT, Teresa, Vice President Human Resources, Saint Alphonsus Regional Medical Center, Boise, ID, p. A174
SARIDAKIS, Michael, M.D. Physician Adviser, Tennova Healthcare Regional Hospital of Jackson, Jackson, TN, p. A584
SARMENTO, Joann, Manager Human Resources, Fairchild Medical Center, Yreka, CA, p. A100
SARNECKI, Adrienne, R.N
Chief Nurse Executive, Spaulding Hospital for Continuing Medical Care Cambridge, Cambridge, MA, p. A309
Chief Nursing Officer, Spaulding Rehabilitation Hospital Cape Cod, East Sandwich, MA, p. A309
SAROFIN, Michelle, Superintendent, Albert J. Solnit Psychiatric Center – South Campus, Middletown, CT, p. A115
SARRAFIAN, Zareh, Chief Executive Officer, Riverside University Health System–Medical Center, Moreno Valley, CA, p. A78
SARROS, Steven, Vice President and Chief Information Officer, Baptist Hospital, Pensacola, FL, p. A142
SARROUI, B., M.D. Chief of Staff, Advanced Specialty Hospital of Toledo, Toledo, OH, p. A503
SARTAIN, Jarred, M.D. President Medical Staff, North Mississippi Medical Center–Hamilton, Hamilton, AL, p. A21
SARTAIN, Lisa M., Vice President, Human Resources, Bellevue Hospital, Bellevue, OH, p. A485

SCHAFSNITZ, Patricia, Director of Nursing Services, McKenzie Health System, Sandusky, MI, p. A334

SCHALES, Marion, Chief Financial Officer, Highland Hospital, Oakland, CA, p. A80

SCHALL, Dee, R.N. Chief Nursing Officer, Baptist Health Medical Center–Hot Spring County, Malvern, AR, p. A49

SCHALSKI, Paula
Director Human Resources, Atoka County Medical Center, Atoka, OK, p. A509
Director Human Resources, Pushmataha Hospital & Home Health, Antlers, OK, p. A508

SCHAMP, Cindy K., President, Baylor Medical Center at Irving, Irving, TX, p. A628

SCHANDL, Brian, Chief Information Officer, Marshall Browning Hospital, Du Quoin, IL, p. A188

SCHANWALD, Pamela R., Chief Executive Officer, The Children's Home of Pittsburgh, Pittsburgh, PA, p. A551

SCHAPP, Susan, Vice President Finance and Treasurer, The Charlotte Hungerford Hospital, Torrington, CT, p. A117

SCHARBER, Laurel, Administrative Assistant and Coordinator Human Resources, Kindred Hospital–Ontario, Ontario, CA, p. A80

SCHARDIN, Janice, MS, Administrator and Chief Executive Officer, Avera De Smet Memorial Hospital, De Smet, SD, p. A573

SCHARENBROCK, Chris, M.D. Chief Medical Staff, David Grant USAF Medical Center, Travis AFB, CA, p. A96

SCHARFF, Tom, Director Information Services, University Hospital and Medical Center, Tamarac, FL, p. A146

SCHARNBERG, Cathi Rae, R.N. Vice President Patient Services, Avera Holy Family Hospital, Estherville, IA, p. A230

SCHARNHORST, Alicia, Human Resources and Administrative Assistant, Garfield County Public Hospital District, Pomeroy, WA, p. A688

SCHARR, Vickie, Chief Financial Officer, Bakersfield Heart Hospital, Bakersfield, CA, p. A55

SCHATZLEIN, Michael, M.D..
President and Chief Executive Officer, St. Vincent's Medical Center Riverside, Jacksonville, FL, p. A132
President and Chief Executive Officer, St. Vincent's Medical Center Southside, Jacksonville, FL, p. A132

SCHAUF, Jeffrey, Director Information Systems, Wesley Medical Center, Wichita, KS, p. A256

SCHAUF, Kyle, M.D. President Medical Staff, Integris Grove Hospital, Grove, OK, p. A512

SCHAUF, Victoria, M.D. Chief of Staff, Ridgecrest Regional Hospital, Ridgecrest, CA, p. A85

SCHAUFELE, Julie, M.D. Medical Director, Elkview General Hospital, Hobart, OK, p. A512

SCHAWL, Bud, Chief Executive Officer, Kindred Hospital–Albuquerque, Albuquerque, NM, p. A427

SCHAY, Maria, Chief Information Officer, Veterans Affairs New York Harbor Healthcare System,, NY, p. A450

SCHEERER, Dan, M.D. Chief Medical Officer, Genesis HealthCare System, Zanesville, OH, p. A507

SCHEETZ, Allison, M.D. Medical Director, Rehabilitation Hospital, Navicent Health, Macon, GA, p. A162

SCHEFFLER, Tom, Chief Fiscal Officer, Veterans Affairs Maryland Health Care System–Baltimore Division, Baltimore, MD, p. A298

SCHEIB, Garry L., Chief Executive Officer, Hospital of the University of Pennsylvania, Philadelphia, PA, p. A548

SCHEINBERG, Paul, M.D. Chief of Staff, Emory Saint Joseph's Hospital of Atlanta, Atlanta, GA, p. A152

SCHEINBLUM, Richard, Chief Financial Officer, Monadnock Community Hospital, Peterborough, NH, p. A413

SCHELBAR, E. Joe, M.D. Medical Director, Select Specialty Hospital–Tulsa Midtown, Tulsa, OK, p. A522

SCHELL, James, M.D. Vice President Medical Affairs, Saint Francis Healthcare System, Cape Girardeau, MO, p. A368

SCHEMER, Tonia, Interim Chief Human Resources, St. Joseph Mercy Livingston Hospital, Howell, MI, p. A326

SCHENCK, Debbie, Administrator, Omega Hospital, Metairie, LA, p. A283

SCHENKER, Amy, Human Resources Director, Shriners Hospitals for Children–Tampa, Tampa, FL, p. A147

SCHEPMANN, Jane, Vice President and Chief Nursing Officer, Clara Barton Hospital, Hoisington, KS, p. A245

SCHEPPERS, Levi, Chief Executive Officer, Nebraska Orthopaedic Hospital, Omaha, NE, p. A400

SCHEPPERS, Lisa, Chief Medical Officer, Regional West Medical Center, Scottsbluff, NE, p. A402

SCHER, Kathleen, Ed.D. Chief Nursing Officer, Jamaica Hospital Medical Center,, NY, p. A445

SCHERLE, Patricia A., Chief Nursing Officer, Memorial Hospital of Salem County, Salem, NJ, p. A423

SCHERLER, Jay, Vice President Finance and Chief Information Officer, Providence Healthcare Network, Waco, TX, p. A656

SCHERNECK, Michael D., President and Chief Executive Officer, Southeast Georgia Health System, Brunswick, GA, p. B125

SCHERNECK, Michael D.
President and Chief Executive Officer, Southeast Georgia Health System Brunswick Campus, Brunswick, GA, p. A155
President and Chief Executive Officer and Chief Financial Officer, Southeast Georgia Health System Camden Campus, Saint Marys, GA, p. A165

SCHEVING, Travis, Chief Financial Officer, Holy Rosary Healthcare, Miles City, MT, p. A389

SCHEXNAYDER, Glenn, M.D. Chief of Staff, Prevost Memorial Hospital, Donaldsonville, LA, p. A276

SCHICK, Eric
Senior Vice President, Chief Administrative Officer and Chief Financial Officer, Laureate Psychiatric Clinic and Hospital, Tulsa, OK, p. A521
Senior Vice President and Chief Financial Officer, Saint Francis Health System, Saint Francis Hospital, Tulsa, OK, p. A522
Chief Financial Officer, Saint Francis Hospital South, Tulsa, OK, p. A522

SCHIEBER, Steven M., FACHE, Chief Executive Officer, Hedrick Medical Center, Chillicothe, MO, p. A369

SCHIEFELBEIN, Shelia, Coordinator Human Resources, Northwest Florida Community Hospital, Chipley, FL, p. A125

SCHIERECK, Stacie, Director Management Services, Mendota Mental Health Institute, Madison, WI, p. A708

SCHIESL, Troy, Director Information Services, Bellin Psychiatric Center, Green Bay, WI, p. A706

SCHIESLER, Hannah, Interim Assistant Director Human Resources, Baptist Hospitals of Southeast Texas, Beaumont, TX, p. A601

SCHIFFER, Christopher, Administrator, Community Behavioral Health Hospital – St. Peter, Saint Peter, MN, p. A351

SCHILLER, Ann Mattia, Vice President Human Resources, College Medical Center, Long Beach, CA, p. A69

SCHILLING, Helen, M.D. Medical Director, Kindred Rehabilitation Hospital Northeast Houston, Humble, TX, p. A628

SCHIMEROWSKI, Deb
Vice President Finance and Chief Financial Officer, Presence Covenant Medical Center, Urbana, IL, p. A204
Regional Finance Officer, Presence Saint Joseph Medical Center, Joliet, IL, p. A194
Regional Chief Financial Officer, Presence St. Mary's Hospital, Kankakee, IL, p. A194
Chief Financial Officer, Presence United Samaritans Medical Center, Danville, IL, p. A187

SCHIMMING, Christopher, M.D. Medical Director, Mayo Clinic Health System in Waseca, Waseca, MN, p. A353

SCHIMMING, Michael B.
Director Financial Services, Shriners Hospitals for Children–Galveston, Galveston, TX, p. A620
Director Fiscal Services, Shriners Hospitals for Children–Houston, Houston, TX, p. A626

SCHINDEL, Lester P., Chief Executive Officer, CharterCare Health Partners, Providence, RI, p. B32

SCHIPPER, Brad J., Chief Operating Officer, Sanford USD Medical Center, Sioux Falls, SD, p. A576

SCHIRALLI, Rocco, President/Chief Executive Officer, Porter–Starke Services, Valparaiso, IN, p. A223

SCHIROS, Judith
Chief Executive Officer, ContinueCARE Hospital at Medical Center (Odessa), Odessa, TX, p. A639
Chief Executive Officer, ContinueCARE Hospital at Midland Memorial, Midland, TX, p. A637

SCHLABACH, Michael, M.D. Chief Medical Officer, Scott & White Hospital – Brenham, Brenham, TX, p. A603

SCHLAGER, Robert, M.D. Chief Medical Officer, Sebasticook Valley Health, Pittsfield, ME, p. A294

SCHLANGEN, Greg, R.N. Chief Operating Officer, Carolina Center for Behavioral Health, Greer, SC, p. A567

SCHLATTER, Christina, Chief Financial Officer, Oswego Community Hospital, Oswego, KS, p. A251

SCHLECHTER, Sandy, Chief Executive Officer, Bowdle Hospital, Bowdle, SD, p. A572

SCHLEETER, Larry C., Chief Human Resources Officer, Memorial Health, Marysville, OH, p. A498

SCHLEGEL, Patricia, Executive Director Finance, Minnesota Valley Health Center, Le Sueur, MN, p. A344

SCHLEICHER, Larry, Manager Information Services, Dr. John Warner Hospital, Clinton, IL, p. A187

SCHLEIF, John V., Senior Vice President and Chief Operating Officer, Henry Mayo Newhall Hospital, Valencia, CA, p. A98

SCHLEMMER, Tom, Chief Financial Officer, St. Mary's Medical Center, West Palm Beach, FL, p. A150

SCHLENKER, Jim, Chief Operating Officer, Good Shepherd Health Care System, Hermiston, OR, p. A526

SCHLESINGER, J. Tuerk, Chief Executive Officer, AltaPointe Health Systems, Mobile, AL, p. B10

SCHLESKE, Brenda, Administrator, Community Behavioral Health Hospital – Fergus Falls, Fergus Falls, MN, p. A342

SCHLESSMAN, Alissa, Administrator, Beaver County Memorial Hospital, Beaver, OK, p. A509

SCHLEY, Kurt, Market Chief Executive Officer, CHI St. Alexius Health, Bismarck, ND, p. A477

SCHLICHTING, Nancy M., Chief Executive Officer, Henry Ford Health System, Detroit, MI, p. B70

SCHLICHTMANN, Phyllis J., Chief Executive Officer, Marlton Rehabilitation Hospital, Marlton, NJ, p. A419

SCHLIECH, Roxane K., Chief Financial Officer, Gundersen Tri–County Hospital and Clinics, Whitehall, WI, p. A719

SCHLOSS, William, Senior Vice President, Administrator, Laureate Psychiatric Clinic and Hospital, Tulsa, OK, p. A521

SCHLUNTZ, Ana, Coordinator Human Resources and Benefits, Harlan County Health System, Alma, NE, p. A393

SCHLUTER, Robin M., Chief Executive Officer, Regional Health Services of Howard County, Cresco, IA, p. A228

SCHMAEDECKE, Dena, Vice President Human Resources, North Suburban Medical Center, Thornton, CO, p. A111

SCHMEDEMANN, Isabel, R.N. Chief Nursing Officer and Chief Operating Officer, Fulton Medical Center, Fulton, MO, p. A371

SCHMELLING, Robin, Chief Information Officer, Hi–Desert Medical Center, Yucca Valley, CA, p. A100

SCHMID, Nancy, Chief Executive Officer, Healdsburg District Hospital, Healdsburg, CA, p. A66

SCHMID, Nancy A., R.N. Associate Director Patient Care Services, Coatesville Veterans Affairs Medical Center, Coatesville, PA, p. A536

SCHMIDT, Allen J., M.D. President, Medical Staff, Decatur Morgan Hospital, Decatur, AL, p. A18

SCHMIDT, Anne, Vice President of Patient Care Services and Chief Nursing Officer, South County Hospital, Wakefield, RI, p. A561

SCHMIDT, Barbara, Chief Executive Officer, Mesa Springs, Fort Worth, TX, p. A618

SCHMIDT, Bobbi, Chief Nursing Officer, Select Specialty Hospital–Cincinnati, Cincinnati, OH, p. A488

SCHMIDT, Constance, FACHE Vice President Patient Care Services and Chief Nursing Officer, St. Mary–Corwin Medical Center, Pueblo, CO, p. A110

SCHMIDT, David, R.N. Chief Nursing Officer, Jennersville Regional Hospital, West Grove, PA, p. A557

SCHMIDT, Holly, Chief Information Officer, Hill Country Memorial Hospital, Fredericksburg, TX, p. A619

SCHMIDT, Janie, Director of Nursing, Greeley County Health Services, Tribune, KS, p. A255

SCHMIDT, Joan E., Director Human Resources, Elmwood Healthcare Center at the Springs, Green Springs, OH, p. A495

SCHMIDT, Julie, Director Human Resources, Grand Itasca Clinic and Hospital, Grand Rapids, MN, p. A343

SCHMIDT, Kristin, R.N. Chief Nursing Officer, Desert Regional Medical Center, Palm Springs, CA, p. A81

SCHMIDT, Loretta, President, Saint Joseph Regional Medical Center–Plymouth Campus, Plymouth, IN, p. A220

SCHMIDT, Mark C., President, Lead–Deadwood Regional Hospital, Deadwood, SD, p. A573

SCHMIDT, Milan, Medical Director, North Shore Health, Grand Marais, MN, p. A343

SCHMIDT Jr., Richard O.
President and Chief Executive Officer, United Hospital System, St. Catherine's Medical Center Campus, Pleasant Prairie, WI, p. A714
President and Chief Executive Officer, United Hospital System–Kenosha Campus, Kenosha, WI, p. A708

SCHMIDT, Robert F., Director Human Resources, Hocking Valley Community Hospital, Logan, OH, p. A497

SCHMIDT, Rosanne, R.N. Chief Nursing Officer, CHI St. Alexius Health, Bismarck, ND, p. A477

SCHMIDT, Steve, Director Information Systems, Evans Memorial Hospital, Claxton, GA, p. A156

SCHMIDT, Timothy, MS, Chief Executive Officer, Bay Area Regional Medical Center, Webster, TX, p. A656

SCHMIDT, Veronica, President, Custer Regional Hospital, Custer, SD, p. A573

SCHMIDT, William, President and Chief Executive Officer, ThedaCare Medical Center–New London, New London, WI, p. A712

SCHMIDTBERGER, Sheryl
Chief Financial Officer, AllianceHealth Blackwell, Blackwell, OK, p. A509
Chief Financial Officer, AllianceHealth Ponca City, Ponca City, OK, p. A518

SCHMIEDT, Jason, Chief Financial Officer, Clinch Valley Medical Center, Richlands, VA, p. A677

SCHMIER, Joseph, Interim Director Human Resources, North Valley Hospital, Whitefish, MT, p. A391

SCHMIESING, Karee, Director of Nursing, Sleepy Eye Medical Center, Sleepy Eye, MN, p. A351

SCHMITS, Peggy, Director, Nursing Operations, New Braunfels Regional Rehabilitation Hospital, New Braunfels, TX, p. A638

SCHMITT, John, Senior Vice President and Chief Financial Officer, Kingsbrook Jewish Medical Center,, NY, p. A445

SCHMITT, Joseph
Chief Information Officer, St. Elizabeth's Medical Center, Brighton, MA, p. A308
Chief Financial Officer, VA Greater Los Angeles Healthcare System, Los Angeles, CA, p. A74

SCHMITT, III, Joseph, Senior Vice President Finance and Chief Financial Officer, Henry Ford Hospital, Detroit, MI, p. A322

SCHMITT, Karl, M.D. Chief of Staff, St. Elizabeth Edgewood, Edgewood, KY, p. A259

SCHMITT, Peggy, President and Chief Executive Officer, North Kansas City Hospital, North Kansas City, MO, p. A377

SCHMITT II, Robert C., Chief Executive Officer, Gibson Area Hospital and Health Services, Gibson City, IL, p. A191

SCHMITT, Thomas M., Chief Executive Officer, Kansas Spine and Specialty Hospital, Wichita, KS, p. A255

SCHMITZ, Bonnie
Vice President and Chief Financial Officer, Agnesian HealthCare, Fond Du Lac, WI, p. A705
Chief Financial Officer, Ripon Medical Center, Ripon, WI, p. A715
Chief Financial Officer, Waupun Memorial Hospital, Waupun, WI, p. A718

SCHMITZ, Christopher, Associate Vice President, Director Human Resources, Stoughton Hospital Association, Stoughton, WI, p. A716

SCHMITZ, Douglas, Director of Nursing, Long–Term Acute Care Hospital, Mosaic Life Care at St. Joseph, Saint Joseph, MO, p. A379

SCHMITZ, Jessica, Director of Nursing, Roosevelt Medical Center, Culbertson, MT, p. A386

SCHMITZ, Joseph, Chief Financial Officer, St. Cloud Veterans Affairs Health Care System, Saint Cloud, MN, p. A350

SCHMOTZER, Dave, Chief Financial Officer, Bryn Mawr Rehabilitation Hospital, Malvern, PA, p. A543

SCHMOYER, Leah, Human Resources Director, Buffalo Hospital, Buffalo, MN, p. A340

SCHMUS, Angie, Chief Information Technology, Aleda E. Lutz Veterans Affairs Medical Center, Saginaw, MI, p. A333

SCHNABEL, Annette, FACHE, President and Chief Executive Officer, Perry Memorial Hospital, Princeton, IL, p. A201

SCHNACK, Tim H.
Vice President Financial Services, CHI Health Bergan Mercy, Omaha, NE, p. A399
Chief Financial Officer, CHI Health Immanuel, Omaha, NE, p. A400
Chief Financial Officer, CHI Health Plainview, Plainview, NE, p. A401
Chief Financial Officer, CHI Health Schuyler, Schuyler, NE, p. A402
Vice President Operations Finance, CHI Health St. Mary's, Nebraska City, NE, p. A398

SCHNACKEL, Donald, Chief Financial Officer, Carthage Area Hospital, Carthage, NY, p. A437

SCHNEDLER, Lisa W., FACHE, President and Chief Executive Officer, Upland Hills Health, Dodgeville, WI, p. A704

SCHNEIDER, Barbara, R.N., Chief Executive Officer, Foothill Regional Medical Center, Tustin, CA, p. A97

SCHNEIDER, Barry S., Chief Executive Officer, Galesburg Cottage Hospital, Galesburg, IL, p. A191

SCHNEIDER, Brenda, Chief Financial Officer, Skyline Hospital, White Salmon, WA, p. A693

SCHNEIDER, Brian, Chief Financial Officer, Dupont Hospital, Fort Wayne, IN, p. A210

SCHNEIDER, Carol L., President and Chief Executive Officer, Mercy Hospital and Medical Center, Chicago, IL, p. A185

SCHNEIDER, David R., Executive Director, Aspirus Langlade Hospital, Antigo, WI, p. A702

SCHNEIDER, Doug, Director Information Systems, Raulerson Hospital, Okeechobee, FL, p. A140

SCHNEIDER, Frank, FACHE, Chief Executive Officer, Gateway Rehabilitation Hospital, Florence, KY, p. A260

SCHNEIDER, Gina, Director Human Resources, Northwest Specialty Hospital, Post Falls, ID, p. A178

SCHNEIDER, Jennifer S., Vice President of Finance, Saint Francis Hospital and Medical Center, Hartford, CT, p. A114

SCHNEIDER, Jessie, Director Human Resources, Community Memorial Healthcare, Marysville, KS, p. A249

SCHNEIDER, John, M.D. Medical Director, Milwaukee County Behavioral Health Division, Milwaukee, WI, p. A711

SCHNEIDER, John, Human Resources Director, Putnam Community Medical Center, Palatka, FL, p. A141

SCHNEIDER, Shanon, Chief Information Officer, Greeley County Health Services, Tribune, KS, p. A255

SCHNEIDER, Stacie A., Director Human Resources, Aurora Sheboygan Memorial Medical Center, Sheboygan, WI, p. A715

SCHNEIDER, Stephen, Manager Information Services, Alaska Psychiatric Institute, Anchorage, AK, p. A28

SCHNEIDER, Steve, Manager Behavioral Services and Director Operations, New Ulm Medical Center, New Ulm, MN, p. A347

SCHNEIDER, Steven E., M.D. Chief Medical Officer, Saint Mary's Hospital, Waterbury, CT, p. A117

SCHNEIDER, Thomas D., D.O. Chief of Staff, Jack C. Montgomery Veterans Affairs Medical Center, Muskogee, OK, p. A515

SCHNEIDER, Valerie, Director Human Resources, Gove County Medical Center, Quinter, KS, p. A252

SCHNELL, Dawn, Chief Nursing Officer, Sanford Jackson Medical Center, Jackson, MN, p. A344

SCHNIEDERS, Michael H., FACHE, President, CHI Health Good Samaritan, Kearney, NE, p. A397

SCHNIER, Martin, D.O. Chief of Staff, West Texas Veterans Affairs Health Care System, Big Spring, TX, p. A603

SCHNITTKER, Kira, Director of Nursing, St. Vincent's Blount, Oneonta, AL, p. A24

SCHNOOR, Jeff, Director Information Systems, Swedish Medical Center, Englewood, CO, p. A105

SCHOCK, Marilyn, Chief Operating Officer, Poudre Valley Hospital, Fort Collins, CO, p. A105

SCHOELLER, Betsy V., Director Human Resources and Education, Mary Greeley Medical Center, Ames, IA, p. A225

SCHOEN, Greg, M.D. Regional Medical Director, Fairview Northland Medical Center, Princeton, MN, p. A349

SCHOEN, Lynn, Chief Executive Officer, Kindred Hospital–Dayton, Dayton, OH, p. A493

SCHOENDALER, Hannah, Chief Nursing Officer, Sheridan County Health Complex, Hoxie, KS, p. A245

SCHOENECKER, Perry L., M.D. Chief of Staff, Shriners Hospitals for Children–St. Louis, Saint Louis, MO, p. A380

SCHOENER, Timothy E.
Chief Information Officer, Muncy Valley Hospital, Muncy, PA, p. A546
Senior Vice President and Chief Information Officer, Soldiers and Sailors Memorial Hospital, Wellsboro, PA, p. A557
Vice President and Chief Information Officer, Williamsport Regional Medical Center, Williamsport, PA, p. A558

SCHOENIG, Thomas
Chief Information Officer, Adventist La Grange Memorial Hospital, La Grange, IL, p. A194
Regional Chief Information Officer, Texas Health Huguley Hospital Fort Worth South, Burleson, TX, p. A604

SCHOENIG, Tom, Regional Director Information Services, Valley Hospital Medical Center, Las Vegas, NV, p. A407

SCHOEPLEIN, Kevin D., Chief Executive Officer, OSF Healthcare System, Peoria, IL, p. B101

SCHOETTLE, Steve, M.D. Chief Medical Staff, Ozark Health Medical Center, Clinton, AR, p. A44

SCHOFIELD, Joseph, Chief Operating Officer, Suburban Community Hospital, Norristown, PA, p. A546

SCHOFIELD, Sherry, Director Human Resources, Memorial Hospital, Martinsville, VA, p. A673

SCHOLEFIELD, Robert, M
Executive Vice President and Chief Operating Officer, Faxton St. Luke's Healthcare, Utica, NY, p. A457
Chief Operating Officer, St. Elizabeth Medical Center, Utica, NY, p. A457

SCHOLL, Shyanne, Interim Human Resources Director, Friend Community Healthcare System, Friend, NE, p. A396

SCHOLZ, Suzanne, Director Medical Records, Horsham Clinic, Ambler, PA, p. A532

SCHON, John, Administrator and Chief Executive Officer, Dickinson County Healthcare System, Iron Mountain, MI, p. A327

SCHONEBERY, Jeremy, Director Information Technology, Heart of America Medical Center, Rugby, ND, p. A481

SCHONLAU, Dan
Interim President, CHI Health Nebraska Heart, Lincoln, NE, p. A397
Chief Financial Officer and Vice President of Finance, CHI Health St Elizabeth, Lincoln, NE, p. A398

SCHONS, Jeri, R.N. Chief Nursing Officer, Sanford Tracy Medical Center, Tracy, MN, p. A352

SCHOOL, Peggy, Director of Nursing, ThedaCare Medical Center–New London, New London, WI, p. A712

SCHOOLER, Rick, Vice President and Chief Information Officer, Orlando Regional Medical Center, Orlando, FL, p. A140

SCHOOMAKER, Eric B., Surgeon General, Department of the Army, Office of the Surgeon General, Falls Church, VA, p. B44

SCHOPP, Mary Ellen, Senior Vice President Human Resources, Rush University Medical Center, Chicago, IL, p. A186

SCHOR, Mark, Chief Executive Officer, Belmont Behavioral Hospital, Philadelphia, PA, p. A547

SCHORER, Emily
Senior Vice President Human Resources, Cape Cod Hospital, Hyannis, MA, p. A311
Vice President, Human Resources, Falmouth Hospital, Falmouth, MA, p. A310

SCHORI, Melissa, M.D. Medical Director, NYC Health + Hospitals / Lincoln,, NY, p. A448

SCHOTT, Connie, Vice President, Human Resources, Ozarks Medical Center, West Plains, MO, p. A384

SCHOTT, Lynn, Director Information Technology, Mobridge Regional Hospital, Mobridge, SD, p. A575

SCHOTTEL, Roxanne, Chief Executive Officer, Washington County Hospital, Washington, KS, p. A255

SCHOULTIES, Daniel L., M.D. Vice President Medical Affairs, Good Samaritan Hospital, Dayton, OH, p. A492

SCHOWENGERDT, Daniel, M.D. Chief of Staff, Comanche County Hospital, Coldwater, KS, p. A241

SCHRADER, Guillermo, M.D. Acting Medical Director, Eastern State Hospital, Williamsburg, VA, p. A680

SCHRAEDER, David, Director Information Systems, Russell Regional Hospital, Russell, KS, p. A252

SCHRAGE, Larry E., FACHE, Chief Executive Officer, Haxtun Hospital District, Haxtun, CO, p. A107

SCHRAMM, Michael, Chief Executive Officer, Rice Memorial Hospital, Willmar, MN, p. A353

SCHRAMM, Steven R., Chief Financial Officer, Mountain View Hospital, Payson, UT, p. A662

SCHRANK, Kenton, M.D. President Medical Staff, Wilson N. Jones Regional Medical Center, Sherman, TX, p. A649

SCHREEG, Timothy M., President and Chief Executive Officer, Franciscan Health Rensselaer, Rensselaer, IN, p. A221

SCHREFFLER, Mary Jane, Director Human Resources, Meadows Psychiatric Center, Centre Hall, PA, p. A535

SCHREIBER, Anne, Manager Human Resources, Fairfax Behavioral Health, Kirkland, WA, p. A686

SCHREIBER, Elizabeth, R.N. Director Patient Care Services, Flambeau Hospital, Park Falls, WI, p. A714

SCHREIER, Garett E., R.N. Associate Director, Nursing and Patient Care Services, Ralph H. Johnson Veterans Affairs Medical Center, Charleston, SC, p. A563

SCHREIER, Susan, R.N. Vice President of Patient and Nursing Services and Chief Nursing Officer, MercyHealth Rockton Avenue Hospital, Rockford, IL, p. A202

SCHREINER, David L., FACHE, President and Chief Executive Officer, Katherine Shaw Bethea Hospital, Dixon, IL, p. A188

SCHREINER, Jim, Chief Information Officer, Graham Hospital Association, Canton, IL, p. A182

SCHRIER, Erick, Supervisor Information Technology, Van Diest Medical Center, Webster City, IA, p. A239

SCHROCK, Bonnie W., FACHE Chief Operating Officer, Baptist Health Paducah, Paducah, KY, p. A267

SCHRODER, Loren D., Chief Financial Officer, Phelps Memorial Health Center, Holdrege, NE, p. A397

SCHROEDER, Brian D., M.D. Senior Vice President and Chief Medical Officer, Sparrow Hospital, Lansing, MI, p. A328

SCHROEDER, Catherine, Deputy Chief Information Officer, Brigham and Women's Faulkner Hospital, Boston, MA, p. A306

SCHROEDER, Cygnet, D.O. Medical Director, HEALTHSOUTH Rehabilitation Hospital of Fort Smith, Fort Smith, AR, p. A46

SCHROEDER, Destiny, Information Systems Director, Rawlins County Health Center, Atwood, KS, p. A240

SCHROEDER, Heather, R.N. Chief Nurse Executive and Vice President of Nursing, Aurora BayCare Medical Center, Green Bay, WI, p. A706

SCHROEDER, Joanne, President and Chief Executive Officer, South Haven Health System, South Haven, MI, p. A334

SCHROEDER, Larry, Chief Executive Officer, Sauk Prairie Healthcare, Prairie Du Sac, WI, p. A714

SCHROEDER, Rick, Chief Executive Officer, North Big Horn Hospital District, Lovell, WY, p. A723

SCHROEDER, Russell, Chief Nursing Officer, SSM Health Saint Louis University Hospital, Saint Louis, MO, p. A381

SCHROEDER, Steve, M.D. Chief of Staff, Avera Hand County Memorial Hospital, Miller, SD, p. A574

SCHROEDL, Greg, M.D. Vice President, Medical and Chief Medical Officer, UW Medicine/Northwest Hospital & Medical Center, Seattle, WA, p. A690

SCHROEPPEL, Stacie
Director of Human Resources, Baptist Memorial Rehabilitation Hospital, Germantown, TN, p. A583
Director Human Resources, Lakeside Behavioral Health System, Memphis, TN, p. A589

SCHROYER, Amy, Vice President Administration and Senior Site Executive, Daniel Drake Center for Post Acute Care, Cincinnati, OH, p. A487

SCHROYER, Mike, R.N., President, St. Vincent Anderson Regional Hospital, Anderson, IN, p. A206

SCHRUMPF, Jason, President, Missouri Delta Medical Center, Sikeston, MO, p. A382

SCHUBACH, Michael, Director Human Resources, Carroll County Memorial Hospital, Carrollton, MO, p. A369

SCHUCKMAN, Tim, Chief Financial Officer, Jennie M. Melham Memorial Medical Center, Broken Bow, NE, p. A394

SCHUE, Janine
Executive Vice President, Chief Human Resources Officer, Newark–Wayne Community Hospital, Newark, NY, p. A450
Senior Vice President Human Resources, Rochester General Hospital, Rochester, NY, p. A454
SCHUE, Yvonne, R.N. Chief Nursing Officer, Brownfield Regional Medical Center, Brownfield, TX, p. A603
SCHUELER, Joe, Chief Financial Officer, Morrow County Hospital, Mount Gilead, OH, p. A499
SCHUERCH, Timothy, President and Chief Executive Officer, Maniilaq Health Center, Kotzebue, AK, p. A30
SCHUESSLER, Dwight, Chief Information Officer, Iowa City Veterans Affairs Health Care System, Iowa City, IA, p. A232
SCHUETT, Susan M., Chief Information Officer, Olmsted Medical Center, Rochester, MN, p. A474
SCHUH, Jason, M.D. Chief of Staff, Wise Regional Health System, Decatur, TX, p. A612
SCHUITEMAN, Jackson, Chief Financial Officer, Sioux Center Health, Sioux Center, IA, p. A237
SCHULER, Allison, R.N. Chief Nursing Officer, Baptist Medical Center Attala, Kosciusko, MS, p. A360
SCHULER, Kathy, R.N. Vice President of Patient Care Services, Winchester Hospital, Winchester, MA, p. A316
SCHULTE, Mark, FACHE, President, Sturgis Regional Hospital, Sturgis, SD, p. A577
SCHULTEIS, Chris, Vice President/Chief Financial Officer, Southampton Hospital, Southampton, NY, p. A456
SCHULTHEIS, Hal, Director Information Systems, TriStar Hendersonville Medical Center, Hendersonville, TN, p. A584
SCHULTZ, Bradley, Chief Financial Officer, Wesley Medical Center, Wichita, KS, p. A256
SCHULTZ, David W., FACHE,
President, Harrison Medical Center, Bremerton, WA, p. A682
President, St. Anthony Hospital, Gig Harbor, WA, p. A685
SCHULTZ, Diana, Chief Executive Officer, Mesilla Valley Hospital, Las Cruces, NM, p. A430
SCHULTZ, Jacky, MSN, Interim President, Suburban Hospital, Bethesda, MD, p. A299
SCHULTZ, Jim, Chief Executive Officer, Edgerton Hospital and Health Services, Edgerton, WI, p. A705
SCHULTZ, Kurt
Group Chief Financial Officer, CHG Hospital Tucson, LLC, Tucson, AZ, p. A40
Chief Financial Officer, Cornerstone Hospital–West Monroe, West Monroe, LA, p. A289
Chief Financial Officer, Solara Hospital Harlingen, Harlingen, TX, p. A622
SCHULTZ, Mary Kay, Director Human Resources, Sturgis Hospital, Sturgis, MI, p. A335
SCHULTZ, Merrilee, Chief Finance, Sanford USD Medical Center, Sioux Falls, SD, p. A576
SCHULTZ, Rachelle H., President and Chief Executive Officer, Winona Health, Winona, MN, p. A353
SCHULTZ, Sharon A., MSN Chief Nurse Executive and Vice President, Tri–City Medical Center, Oceanside, CA, p. A80
SCHULTZ, Teresa L., R.N. Vice President of Patient Care, Rogers Memorial Hospital, Oconomowoc, WI, p. A713
SCHULTZ, Vince, M.D. Chief Medical Officer, Munson Healthcare Grayling Hospital, Grayling, MI, p. A325
SCHULZ, Charles K., Chief Executive Officer, York General Hospital, York, NE, p. A403
SCHULZ, Ken, Chief Operating Officer, North Dakota State Hospital, Jamestown, ND, p. A480
SCHULZ, Larry A., Chief Executive Officer, Lake Region Healthcare, Fergus Falls, MN, p. A342
SCHULZ, Leah, Director of Nursing, North Dakota State Hospital, Jamestown, ND, p. A480
SCHULZ, Marcie, Director Patient Care, Sakakawea Medical Center, Hazen, ND, p. A479
SCHULZ, Patricia, Vice President, Human Resources, Children's Hospital and Medical Center, Omaha, NE, p. A400
SCHULZ, Susan G., Director Patient Care Services, Beaumont Hospital – Trenton, Trenton, MI, p. A335
SCHUMACHER, Ann, FACHE, President, CHI Health Immanuel, Omaha, NE, p. A400
SCHUMACHER, Debbie
Chief Human Resource Officer, Clearwater Valley Hospital and Clinics, Orofino, ID, p. A177
Chief Human Resource Officer, St. Mary's Hospital, Cottonwood, ID, p. A176
SCHUMACHER, Kevin, Director of Information Systems, LifeCare Medical Center, Roseau, MN, p. A350
SCHUMACHER, Larry P., MSN, Chief Executive Officer, CHI Memorial, Chattanooga, TN, p. A580
SCHUMACHER, Paul, Chief Operating Officer, McLeod Health Clarendon, Manning, SC, p. A568
SCHUMACHER, Rodney, Interim Chief Executive Officer, Eastern New Mexico Medical Center, Roswell, NM, p. A431
SCHUMANN, Vera, Director of Finance and Controller, North Shore Health, Grand Marais, MN, p. A343

SCHURKAMP, Christine, Senior Human Resources Business Partner, Spectrum Health Gerber Memorial, Fremont, MI, p. A324
SCHUSTER, Carol E., R.N. Chief Nursing Officer and Vice President Patient Care Services, Franciscan St. Anthony Health – Crown Point, Crown Point, IN, p. A209
SCHUSTER, Christine C., R.N., President and Chief Executive Officer, Emerson Hospital, Concord, MA, p. A309
SCHUSTER, Emmett C., President and Chief Executive Officer, Gibson General Hospital, Princeton, IN, p. A221
SCHUSTER, Janet, R.N. Chief Nursing Officer, Lutheran Hospital, Cleveland, OH, p. A489
SCHUSTER, Jolene, Chief Financial Officer, Grisell Memorial Hospital District One, Ransom, KS, p. A252
SCHUSTER, Lexie, Vice President Human Resources, Good Samaritan Hospital, Los Angeles, CA, p. A71
SCHWAB, Bob, M.D. Chief Medical Officer, Texas Health Presbyterian Hospital Allen, Allen, TX, p. A595
SCHWABENBAUER, Mary Ann, Director Information Technology, Penn Highlands Elk, Saint Marys, PA, p. A553
SCHWAEGEL, Glen
Vice President and Chief Financial Officer, Barnes–Jewish St. Peters Hospital, Saint Peters, MO, p. A382
Chief Financial Officer, Progress West Hospital, O'Fallon, MO, p. A377
SCHWAGER, Mary A., Director Human Resources, Antelope Memorial Hospital, Neligh, NE, p. A399
SCHWALL, Garry, Chief Operating Officer, Winthrop–University Hospital, Mineola, NY, p. A442
SCHWAN, Joni, Director Human Resources, Excelsior Springs Hospital, Excelsior Springs, MO, p. A370
SCHWAN, Karin, Chief Nursing Officer, Vice President Patient Care Services, University Hospitals Samaritan Medical Center, Ashland, OH, p. A484
SCHWANER, III, Charles, Chief Financial Officer, Doctors Hospital of Sarasota, Sarasota, FL, p. A145
SCHWANKE, Daniel, Interim President, ProMedica Monroe Regional Hospital, Monroe, MI, p. A330
SCHWARM, Tony, President, Missouri Baptist Sullivan Hospital, Sullivan, MO, p. A383
SCHWARTZ, Ave, Chief Information Officer, Austen Riggs Center, Stockbridge, MA, p. A315
SCHWARTZ, David, M.D
Chief Medical Officer, Saint Francis Hospital, Memphis, TN, p. A589
Chief Medical Officer, Saint Francis Hospital–Bartlett, Bartlett, TN, p. A579
SCHWARTZ, David M., D.O. Vice President, Medical Affairs, Sentara Northern Virginia Medical Center, Woodbridge, VA, p. A680
SCHWARTZ, Jonathon, M.D. Chief Medical Officer, Spaulding Hospital for Continuing Medical Care Cambridge, Cambridge, MA, p. A309
SCHWARTZ, Kenneth V., M.D. Medical Director, Griffin Hospital, Derby, CT, p. A114
SCHWARTZ, Kim, Assistant Administrator of Human Resources and Physician Services, Boone County Hospital, Boone, IA, p. A226
SCHWARTZ, Michael, M.D. Chief of Staff, College Hospital Costa Mesa, Costa Mesa, CA, p. A60
SCHWARTZ, Mitchell B., M.D. Chief Medical Officer, Anne Arundel Medical Center, Annapolis, MD, p. A296
SCHWARTZ, Peggy, Vice President Human Resources, Wayne Hospital, Greenville, OH, p. A495
SCHWARTZ, Peter
Director of Information Systems, Carrier Clinic, Belle Mead, NJ, p. A414
Director Information Systems, East Mountain Hospital, Belle Mead, NJ, p. A414
SCHWARTZ, Roberta, Ph.D., Executive Vice President, Houston Methodist Hospital, Houston, TX, p. A624
SCHWARTZ, Ronald, M.D. Medical Director, Masonicare Health Center, Wallingford, CT, p. A117
SCHWARTZ, Sharon, Director Medical Records, Scott & White Hospital – Brenham, Brenham, TX, p. A603
SCHWARZ, John, Vice President Administration, Lankenau Medical Center, Wynnewood, PA, p. A558
SCHWARZBACH, Jerry, M.D. Medical Director, East Texas Medical Center Rehabilitation Hospital, Tyler, TX, p. A654
SCHWARZKOPF, Ruth, R.N. Chief Nursing Officer, West Boca Medical Center, Boca Raton, FL, p. A124
SCHWEBLER, Michael W., President and Chief Executive Officer, Dearborn County Hospital, Lawrenceburg, IN, p. A217
SCHWECHHEIMER, Betsy L., Chief Operating Officer, Tewksbury Hospital, Tewksbury, MA, p. A315
SCHWEERS, Michele, Vice President and Chief Human Resources Officer, Monmouth Medical Center, Southern Campus, Lakewood, NJ, p. A418

SCHWEICKHARDT, Mary Jo, Vice President Human Resources, MedStar Georgetown University Hospital, Washington, DC, p. A121
SCHWEIGERT, Nicole, Director Human Resources, Texas Health Presbyterian Hospital Flower Mound, Flower Mound, TX, p. A617
SCHWEIGHART, Karen, MS, Administrator, Andrew McFarland Mental Health Center, Springfield, IL, p. A203
SCHWEIKART, Jay
Chief Financial Officer, Kindred Hospital Chicago–Northlake, Northlake, IL, p. A198
Chief Financial Officer, Kindred Hospital–Sycamore, Sycamore, IL, p. A204
SCHWEITZER, Michael, M.D. Chief Medical Officer, St. Vincent Healthcare, Billings, MT, p. A385
SCHWIEGER, Kay, Chief Human Resources Officer, Clement J. Zablocki Veterans Affairs Medical Center, Milwaukee, WI, p. A711
SCHWIND, David, Chief Financial Officer, Capital Hospice, Arlington, VA, p. A667
SCHWINGLER, Joyce, Chief Financial Officer, Eureka Community Health Services Avera, Eureka, SD, p. A573
SCHWOEBLE, Walt, Vice President Human Resources, Akron Children's Hospital, Akron, OH, p. A483
SCIARRA, Michael, M.D. Chief Medical Officer, Meadowlands Hospital Medical Center, Secaucus, NJ, p. A423
SCIARRO, Jason
President and Chief Operating Officer, Centegra Hospital – McHenry, McHenry, IL, p. A196
President and Chief Operating Officer, Centegra Hospital – Woodstock, Woodstock, IL, p. A205
SCIMECA, Paul, Senior Vice President Operations and Chief Operating Officer, Glens Falls Hospital, Glens Falls, NY, p. A439
SCIONTI, Jeff, Interim Chief Executive Officer, Parkland Medical Center, Derry, NH, p. A410
SCIORTINO, John E., Senior Vice President and Chief Operating Officer, New York–Presbyterian/Queens, NY, p. A447
SCIOSCIA, Angela, M.D. Chief Medical Officer, UC San Diego Health, San Diego, CA, p. A89
SCLAMA, Tony, M.D. Vice President Medical Affairs, MedStar Franklin Square Medical Center, Baltimore, MD, p. A297
SCOBIE, Robbin, Vice President Nursing, Aurelia Osborn Fox Memorial Hospital, Oneonta, NY, p. A452
SCOFIELD, Mark, M.D. Chief Medical Officer, Shelby Baptist Medical Center, Alabaster, AL, p. A15
SCOGGIN, Terry, Chief Financial Officer, Titus Regional Medical Center, Mount Pleasant, TX, p. A638
SCOGGINS, James, Director of Nursing, Arkansas State Hospital, Little Rock, AR, p. A48
SCOGGINS, Mib, Chief Executive Officer, McLeod Health Cheraw, Cheraw, SC, p. A563
SCOGNA, Stephen, President and Chief Executive Officer, Northwest Community Hospital, Arlington Heights, IL, p. A180
SCOPELLITI, Joseph A., M.D., President and Chief Executive Officer, Guthrie Clinic, Sayre, PA, p. B59
SCORZELLI, Gerard, Chief Financial Officer, Albany Stratton Veterans Affairs Medical Center, Albany, NY, p. A433
SCOTFORD, Lucrecia, Executive Vice President and Chief Operations Officer, Bristol Bay Area Health Corporation, Dillingham, AK, p. A29
SCOTT, Charles F., Chief Executive Officer, Piedmont Henry Hospital, Stockbridge, GA, p. A167
SCOTT, Colleen M., Vice President Finance, Waterbury Hospital, Waterbury, CT, p. A117
SCOTT, Craig, Interim Director Management Information Systems, University of Miami Hospital, Miami, FL, p. A137
SCOTT, Damien, Chief Information Officer, Emanuel Medical Center, Swainsboro, GA, p. A167
SCOTT, Daniel, Director of Information Systems, Good Samaritan Hospital, Vincennes, IN, p. A223
SCOTT, David W., President and Chief Executive Officer, Ohio Valley Hospital, McKees Rocks, PA, p. A544
SCOTT, Doug, Director Human Resources, RMC Jacksonville, Jacksonville, AL, p. A22
SCOTT, Ernie, Director Human Resources, Natchitoches Regional Medical Center, Natchitoches, LA, p. A284
SCOTT, Henry, Executive Director, Technical Services, Piedmont Newnan Hospital, Newnan, GA, p. A164
SCOTT, James, M.D
Vice President Medical Affairs, Candler Hospital, Savannah, GA, p. A165
Vice President Medical Affairs, St. Joseph's Hospital, Savannah, GA, p. A166
SCOTT, Jeffrey, Chief Information Officer, St. Vincent Kokomo, Kokomo, IN, p. A216
SCOTT, Jennifer, Director of Informatics, CarePartners Health Services, Asheville, NC, p. A460

SCOTT, Jo Ellen, R.N. Senior Vice President of Patient Care Services and Chief Nursing Officer, Indiana University Health Tipton Hospital, Tipton, IN, p. A223

SCOTT, Jon W., Chief Executive Officer, Meadowbrook Rehabilitation Hospital, Gardner, KS, p. A243

SCOTT, Joseph F., FACHE, President and Chief Executive Officer, Jersey City Medical Center, Jersey City, NJ, p. A418

SCOTT, Julie, Chief Nursing Officer, HEALTHSOUTH Rehabilitation Hospital of York, York, PA, p. A559

SCOTT, Karen M., Vice President Patient Care, Frank R. Howard Memorial Hospital, Willits, CA, p. A100

SCOTT, Lincoln, Vice President Human Resources, Southeast Hospital, Cape Girardeau, MO, p. A369

SCOTT, M Daryl, Assistant Vice President, Jefferson Regional Medical Center, Pine Bluff, AR, p. A51

SCOTT, Margie, M.D. Chief of Staff, Central Arkansas Veterans Healthcare System, Little Rock, AR, p. A49

SCOTT, Martha Lynn, Chief Patient Care Officer, Covington County Hospital, Collins, MS, p. A357

SCOTT, Monica, Chief Financial Officer, Great Plains Regional Medical Center, Elk City, OK, p. A511

SCOTT, Paul, M.D. Chief of Staff, Hudson Hospital and Clinic, Hudson, WI, p. A707

SCOTT, Rhonda A., Ph.D. Chief Nursing Officer and Executive Vice President, Grady Memorial Hospital, Atlanta, GA, p. A152

SCOTT, Robert F., Vice President and Chief Human Resources Officer, Memorial Medical Center, Springfield, IL, p. A203

SCOTT, Roger, D.O. Vice President Medical Affairs and Chief Medical Officer, Cortland Regional Medical Center, Cortland, NY, p. A437

SCOTT, Sharon, Health Information Director, Allegiance Specialty Hospital of Greenville, Greenville, MS, p. A358

SCOTT, Steve, Chief Operating Officer, Sheridan Community Hospital, Sheridan, MI, p. A334

SCOTT, Susan, Chief Nurse Executive, Ventura County Medical Center, Ventura, CA, p. A98

SCOTT, Thomas, Chief Operating Officer, Chilton Medical Center, Pompton Plains, NJ, p. A422

SCOTT, Thomas W., Senior Vice President and Chief Operating Officer, CentraState Healthcare System, Freehold, NJ, p. A417

SCOTT, Tina, Acting Health Director, Choctaw Health Center, Philadelphia, MS, p. A363

SCOTT, Todd, Chief Financial Officer, Vibra Hospital of Sacramento, Folsom, CA, p. A62

SCOTT, Veronica, Business Office Manager, Midwest City Specialty Hospital, Midwest City, OK, p. A514

SCOTT, William, Chief Financial Officer, Promise Hospital of Overland Park, Overland Park, KS, p. A251

SCOTT, William, M.D. Vice President Medical Affairs, Regional Medical Center of San Jose, San Jose, CA, p. A91

SCOTT, William P., M.D. Chief of Staff, River Valley Medical Center, Dardanelle, AR, p. A45

SCOTTO, Dan, Director Information Technology, Eastern Long Island Hospital, Greenport, NY, p. A440

SCOVILL, Terry, Chief Executive Officer, Intracare North Hospital, Houston, TX, p. A625

SCOWN, Kent, Director Operations and Information Services, Jerold Phelps Community Hospital, Garberville, CA, p. A64

SCREMIN, Karen, Vice President Finance, Lutheran Medical Center, Wheat Ridge, CO, p. A111

SCRIVO, Jr., Joseph A., Director Human Resources, Mercy Hospital, Buffalo, NY, p. A436

SCROGGIN, Christy, Chief Operating Officer, Conway Regional Rehabilitation Hospital, Conway, AR, p. A44

SCROGGS, Amy, Chief Nursing Officer, Delano Regional Medical Center, Delano, CA, p. A60

SCRUGGS, Sherry, Administrator, Milan General Hospital, Milan, TN, p. A590

SCUDDER, Angela, MSN Vice President Patient Care Services, Dearborn County Hospital, Lawrenceburg, IN, p. A217

SCUDERI, Denise, Vice President Patient Care Services, Mayo Regional Hospital, Dover-Foxcroft, ME, p. A293

SCULL, Stephen W., Vice President Ethics and Compliance officer, Rapides Regional Medical Center, Alexandria, LA, p. A271

SCULLY, Charles
   Chief Information Officer, HonorHealth Scottsdale Thompson Peak Medical Center, Scottsdale, AZ, p. A39
   Chief Information Officer, Renown Regional Medical Center, Reno, NV, p. A408

SCULLY, Kem, Chief Executive Officer, Purcell Municipal Hospital, Purcell, OK, p. A519

SCULLY, Trish
   Manager Employment Services, Massachusetts Hospital School, Canton, MA, p. A309
   Director Human Resources, Taunton State Hospital, Taunton, MA, p. A315

SCZYGELSKI, Sidney C., Senior Vice President Finance and Chief Financial Officer, Aspirus Wausau Hospital, Wausau, WI, p. A718

SEAGER, Jerry, Assistant Vice President and Chief Financial Officer, Inova Fair Oaks Hospital, Fairfax, VA, p. A669

SEAGO, Terri, Chief Financial Officer, Baptist Memorial Hospital–Collierville, Collierville, TN, p. A581

SEAGRAM, Patricia, Vice President Human Resources, Henry Ford Allegiance Health, Jackson, MI, p. A327

SEAGROVES, Matthew, Chief Financial Officer, Bayfront Health Brooksville, Brooksville, FL, p. A125

SEAL, John, Director Human Resources, Riverside Medical Center, Franklinton, LA, p. A277

SEAL, Ronald T., Chief Executive Officer, Texoma Medical Center, Denison, TX, p. A612

SEALE, Corey A., Chief Operating Officer, Kaiser Permanente Moreno Valley Medical Center, Moreno Valley, CA, p. A78

SEALE, Jonathan, Chief Information Officer, Erie Veterans Affairs Medical Center, Erie, PA, p. A538

SEALS, Molly
   System Vice President, Human Resources Program Delivery and Youngstown Market, Mercy Health – St. Elizabeth Boardman Hospital, Boardman, OH, p. A485
   System Vice President, HR Program Delivery, Mercy Health – St. Elizabeth Youngstown Hospital, Youngstown, OH, p. A506

SEALS, Robert, D.O. Medical Director, Sparrow Carson Hospital, Carson City, MI, p. A320

SEALS–BARNES, II, Sylvia, Director Human Resources, St. Helena Hospital Napa Valley, Saint Helena, CA, p. A87

SEAMON, Robert L., Chief Executive Officer, Clifton–Fine Hospital, Star Lake, NY, p. A456

SEARLE, Anne, Chief Information Officer, University Medical Center of Princeton at Plainsboro, Plainsboro, NJ, p. A422

SEARLS, Barbara, Chief Financial Officer, SEARHC MT. Edgecumbe Hospital, Sitka, AK, p. A30

SEARLS, Gary, Chief Financial Officer, Northside Hospital, Saint Petersburg, FL, p. A144

SEARS, Erin Clare, Associate Director of Operations, Providence Veterans Affairs Medical Center, Providence, RI, p. A560

SEARS, Marilyn, President and Chief Executive Officer, Shelby Memorial Hospital, Shelbyville, IL, p. A202

SEASE, Peggy, Vice President Human Resources, DCH Regional Medical Center, Tuscaloosa, AL, p. A26

SEATON, Tracy, Director of Nursing, Taylorville Memorial Hospital, Taylorville, IL, p. A204

SEAVER, Roger E., President and Chief Executive Officer, Henry Mayo Newhall Hospital, Valencia, CA, p. A98

SEBASTIAN, Peggy A., R.N., President and Chief Executive Officer, HSHS St. Elizabeth's Hospital, Belleville, IL, p. A181

SEBEK, Brenda Jean, R.N. Vice President Patient Care Services, CHI Health St. Mary's, Nebraska City, NE, p. A398

SECK, Nancy K., Chief Nursing Officer, Mesa View Regional Hospital, Mesquite, NV, p. A407

SECKINGER, Mark R., President, O'Bleness Memorial Hospital, Athens, OH, p. A484

SECOR, April, R.N. Chief Nursing Officer, Hillcrest Hospital Henryetta, Henryetta, OK, p. A512

SECOR, Diane K., Director Human Resources, Lawrence Medical Center, Moulton, AL, p. A24

SECREST, Jack, M.D. Chief Medical Officer, St. Mary's Hospital, Cottonwood, ID, p. A176

SECURRO, Matthew J., Vice President, Human Resources, Conway Medical Center, Conway, SC, p. A565

SEDA, Jolene R., Vice President People and Culture, Yakima Valley Memorial Hospital, Yakima, WA, p. A693

SEDGLEY, Don, President, Novant Health UVA Health System Haymarket Medical Center, Haymarket, VA, p. A671

SEDMINIK, Vince, Chief Executive Officer, Springhill Medical Center, Springhill, LA, p. A288

SEEDER, Rachael, Controller, Santiam Hospital, Stayton, OR, p. A531

SEEKINS, DeAnne, Director, Durham Veterans Affairs Medical Center, Durham, NC, p. A464

SEELEY, Kevin, Chief Information Officer, Mike O'Callaghan Federal Hospital, Nellis AFB, NV, p. A407

SEELEY, Pam, Chief Nursing Officer, Elmira Psychiatric Center, Elmira, NY, p. A438

SEELEY, Steven, Vice President, Chief Operating Officer, Chief Nursing Officer, Jupiter Medical Center, Jupiter, FL, p. A132

SEELY, Paula, Manager Human Resources, Kossuth Regional Health Center, Algona, IA, p. A225

SEEMS, Steven, Director of Information Technology, Phillips County Hospital, Phillipsburg, KS, p. A252

SEESE, Rebecca, Chief Operating Officer, U. S. Air Force Regional Hospital, Elmendorf AFB, AK, p. A29

SEEVER, Jennifer, Regional Chief Financial Officer, Sedan City Hospital, Sedan, KS, p. A253

SEGAL, Jonathan, Chief Financial Officer, New York State Psychiatric Institute, New York, NY, p. A447

SEGAL, Rebecca, Chief Operating Officer, Lake Cumberland Regional Hospital, Somerset, KY, p. A269

SEGAL, Stanton, M.D. Chief Medical Officer, Aria – Jefferson Health, Philadelphia, PA, p. A547

SEGAL, Tanya, Director, Easton Hospital, Easton, PA, p. A537

SEGAR–MILLER, Cindy, R.N., Chief Executive Officer, Williamson Memorial Hospital, Williamson, WV, p. A701

SEGER, LaDonna, Director Information Services, Saint Luke's North Hospital – Barry Road, Kansas City, MO, p. A374

SEGIN, Robert
   Executive Vice President & Chief Financial Officer, Virtua Marlton, Marlton, NJ, p. A419
   Chief Financial Officer, Virtua Memorial, Mount Holly, NJ, p. A420

SEGURA, Ezra, Chief Executive Officer, Utah Valley Specialty Hospital, Provo, UT, p. A662

SEGURA, Mario, Director of Nursing, Starr County Memorial Hospital, Rio Grande City, TX, p. A643

SEHRT, Lori
   Associate Chief Financial Officer Northern Colorado, Banner Fort Collins Medical Center, Fort Collins, CO, p. A105
   Chief Financial Officer, McKee Medical Center, Loveland, CO, p. A109

SEIBERT, Jenee, Director Finance, Fulton County Health Center, Wauseon, OH, p. A505

SEIBERT, Nancy, Director Human Resources, Franklin Hospital District, Benton, IL, p. A181

SEIBOLD, Spencer Garrett, M.D. Chief of Medical Staff, Power County Hospital District, American Falls, ID, p. A174

SEID, Lynette, Area Chief Financial Officer, Kaiser Permanente San Diego Medical Center, San Diego, CA, p. A88

SEIDL, Doris A., Vice President Human Resources, McLaren Port Huron, Port Huron, MI, p. A332

SEIDLER, Richard A., FACHE,
   President and Chief Executive Officer, UnityPoint Health – Trinity Bettendorf, Bettendorf, IA, p. A225
   President and Chief Executive Officer, UnityPoint Health – Trinity Rock Island, Rock Island, IL, p. A201

SEIDMAN, Robert
   Chief Operating Officer, Health Alliance Hospital – Broadway Campus, Kingston, NY, p. A441
   Chief Operating Officer, Health Alliance Hospital – Mary's Avenue Campus, Kingston, NY, p. A441

SEIFER, Jill, Vice President Human Resources, Oaklawn Psychiatric Center, Goshen, IN, p. A212

SEIM, Lori, R.N. Director Nursing Services, First Care Health Center, Park River, ND, p. A481

SEIRER, Jeff, Interim Chief Financial Officer, Via Christi Hospital on St. Francis, Wichita, KS, p. A256

SEITZ, Kimberly A., Area Human Resources Leader, Kaiser Permanente Redwood City Medical Center, Redwood City, CA, p. A85

SEITZ, Stewart R., Chief Executive Officer, Gladys Spellman Specialty Hospital and Nursing Center, Cheverly, MD, p. A299

SEITZ, Tawnya, Chief Financial Officer, Lincoln County Hospital, Lincoln, KS, p. A248

SELBY, Eric, R.N. Chief Nursing Officer, Chicot Memorial Medical Center, Lake Village, AR, p. A48

SELF, Chris, Chief Operating Officer, Manchester Memorial Hospital, Manchester, KY, p. A266

SELF, Joshua, Chief Executive Officer, Mary Black Health System – Gaffney, Gaffney, SC, p. A566

SELFRIDGE, Tara, Manager Human Resources, Purcell Municipal Hospital, Purcell, OK, p. A519

SELHORST, Sonya, R.N. Administrator and Chief Nursing Officer, Mercy Hospital of Defiance, Defiance, OH, p. A493

SELIG, Doug R., Vice President of Patient Services, Parkview Huntington Hospital, Huntington, IN, p. A213

SELIGA, Patricia, R.N. Chief Nursing Officer, Moses Taylor Hospital, Scranton, PA, p. A554

SELIGMAN, Joel, President and Chief Executive Officer, Northern Westchester Hospital, Mount Kisco, NY, p. A443

SELIGMAN, Morris H., M.D. Chief Medical Officer and Chief Medical Information Officer, Sycamore Shoals Hospital, Elizabethton, TN, p. A582

SELL, Paula, Director Human Resources, Allen County Regional Hospital, Iola, KS, p. A245

SELL, Teri, Payroll and Personnel Coordinator, Jennie M. Melham Memorial Medical Center, Broken Bow, NE, p. A394

SELLARDS, Michael G., Chief Executive Officer, Pallottine Health Services, Huntington, WV, p. B102

SELLARDS, Michael G., President and Chief Executive Officer, St. Mary's Medical Center, Huntington, WV, p. A697

SELLE, Ginger, Vice President Patient Care Services, St. Clare Hospital, Baraboo, WI, p. A702

SELLE, Justin, Chief Executive Officer, Pike County Memorial Hospital, Louisiana, MO, p. A376

SELLERS, Laura, Director Information Systems, Youth Villages Inner Harbour Campus, Douglasville, GA, p. A158

SELLERS, Mary, Chief Information Officer, Navos, Seattle, WA, p. A689

SELLERS, Robert R., Chief Executive Officer, Optim Medical Center – Screven, Sylvania, GA, p. A167

SELLHEIM, Kevin, Administrator, Sleepy Eye Medical Center, Sleepy Eye, MN, p. A351

SELLS, Alicia, Interim Chief Nursing Officer, Shenandoah Medical Center, Shenandoah, IA, p. A237

SELLS, Anita, Director Human Resources, Galesburg Cottage Hospital, Galesburg, IL, p. A191

SELLS, Matt, CPA Chief Financial Officer, Shenandoah Medical Center, Shenandoah, IA, p. A237

SELMAN, J. Peter, FACHE, Chief Executive Officer, Baptist Medical Center South, Montgomery, AL, p. A23

SELMON, Patricia, Director Public Relations and Chief Human Resources, Jefferson County Hospital, Fayette, MS, p. A357

SELNER, Ralph, Chief Executive Officer, Kindred Hospital Central Tampa, Tampa, FL, p. A147

SELPH, Wendy, Director Human Resources, Dodge County Hospital, Eastman, GA, p. A159

SELSOR, Doug, Director Finance, Select Rehabilitation Hospital of Denton, Denton, TX, p. A613

SELTZER, Paul, M.D. Chief of Staff, JFK Medical Center North Campus, West Palm Beach, FL, p. A149

SELVAM, A. Panneer, M.D. Chief of Staff, Northern Arizona Veterans Affairs Health Care System, Prescott, AZ, p. A37

SELVIDGE, Sandra, Chief Fiscal Service, Cincinnati Veterans Affairs Medical Center, Cincinnati, OH, p. A487

SELZ, Timothy P., Vice President, Orange Regional Medical Center, Middletown, NY, p. A442

SELZER, Stephen R., Interim Chief Executive Officer, Minden Medical Center, Minden, LA, p. A283

SEMAR, Dale, Controller, Pauls Valley General Hospital, Pauls Valley, OK, p. A518

SEMELSBERGER, Kimberly, CPA Chief Financial Officer, Nason Hospital, Roaring Spring, PA, p. A553

SEMERDJIAN, Nancy, R.N. Chief Nursing Officer, NorthShore University Health System, Evanston, IL, p. A190

SEMERE, Jana
  Chief Nursing Officer, Leonard J. Chabert Medical Center, Houma, LA, p. A278
  Chief Nursing Officer, Ochsner St. Anne General Hospital, Raceland, LA, p. A286

SEMEYN, Janice, D.O. Vice President, Medical Staff, Clarion Hospital, Clarion, PA, p. A535

SEMINARO, Anthony, Chief Financial Officer, Hillside Rehabilitation Hospital, Warren, OH, p. A504

SEMINGSON, John H., Chief Executive Officer, Ruby Valley Hospital, Sheridan, MT, p. A391

SEMRAU, Clint, Chief of Staff, Baldwin Area Medical Center, Baldwin, WI, p. A702

SENDAYDIEGO, Fe, Director Information Systems, Sonoma Valley Hospital, Sonoma, CA, p. A94

SENGER, Richard, Chief Financial Officer, Portsmouth Regional Hospital, Portsmouth, NH, p. A413

SENGER, Tricia, Chief Financial Officer, St. Luke's Elmore, Mountain Home, ID, p. A177

SENKER, Margaret, Chief Information Officer, Veterans Affairs Western New York Healthcare System–Buffalo Division, Buffalo, NY, p. A436

SENKER, Thomas J., FACHE, Chief Executive Officer, MedStar Montgomery Medical Center, Olney, MD, p. A302

SENNEFF, Robert G., FACHE, President and Chief Executive Officer, Graham Hospital Association, Canton, IL, p. A182

SENNETT, Paul, Chief Financial Officer, Centinela Hospital Medical Center, Inglewood, CA, p. A66

SENNHOLZ, Troy, M.D. Chief of Staff, Aspirus Medford Hospital, Medford, WI, p. A710

SENNISH, James, Vice President Human Resources, Firelands Regional Health System, Sandusky, OH, p. A502

SENSAT, Marsha, R.N. Chief Nursing Officer, Pikes Peak Regional Hospital, Woodland Park, CO, p. A111

SENSING, Phillip, Chief Financial Officer, South Bay Hospital, Sun City Center, FL, p. A146

SEPP Jr., Howard W., Vice President and Administrator, Southeast Georgia Health System Camden Campus, Saint Marys, GA, p. A165

SERAFIN, Deborah J., Vice President Human Resources, Mount St. Mary's Hospital and Health Center, Lewiston, NY, p. A441

SERAPHINE, Jeffrey G., FACHE, Division President, Duke LifePoint Healthcare, Brentwood, TN, p. B51

SERENO, Joseph, Chief Financial Officer, Lovelace Women's Hospital, Albuquerque, NM, p. A427

SERFLING, G. Aubrey, President and Chief Executive Officer, Eisenhower Medical Center, Rancho Mirage, CA, p. A84

SERKETICH, Steve, Manager Information Services, Aurora Sheboygan Memorial Medical Center, Sheboygan, WI, p. A715

SERLE, John, FACHE, President and Chief Executive Officer, Lourdes Medical Center, Pasco, WA, p. A687

SERNYAK, Michael, M.D., Director, Connecticut Mental Health Center, New Haven, CT, p. A116

SERRANO, Jorge L. Matta, Administrator, Auxilio Mutuo Hospital, San Juan, PR, p. A729

SERRANO, Lorenzo, Chief Executive Officer, Winkler County Memorial Hospital, Kermit, TX, p. A630

SERRATT, Jim, Chief Executive Officer, Westpark Springs, Richmond, TX, p. A643

SESSIONS, Jerry W., M.D. Chief Medical Staff, Springhill Medical Center, Springhill, LA, p. A288

SESSIONS, Tracey, Administrator, State Hospital South, Blackfoot, ID, p. A174

SESSLER, Connie, Director Human Resources, ProMedica St. Luke's Hospital, Maumee, OH, p. A498

SESTERHENN, Steven, Vice President, UnityPoint Health – Allen Hospital, Waterloo, IA, p. A239

SETCHEL, David P., President, St. Francis Health, Topeka, KS, p. A254

SETHI, Sanjiv, M.D. Medical Director, Fulton State Hospital, Fulton, MO, p. A371

SETHNEY, Julie, R.N. Vice President Patient Care, Fairview Ridges Hospital, Burnsville, MN, p. A340

SETTLE, Andrea, Director Human Resources, Taylor Regional Hospital, Campbellsville, KY, p. A258

SETTLES, Allicia, Chief Nursing Officer, East Texas Medical Center–Quitman, Quitman, TX, p. A642

SETTLES, April, Chief Financial Officer, Greene County General Hospital, Linton, IN, p. A217

SETTLES, Laura, Director Human Resources, Baylor Medical Center at Garland, Garland, TX, p. A620

SETZER, Jeffery, Administrator Information Systems, J. D. McCarty Center for Children With Developmental Disabilities, Norman, OK, p. A515

SETZKORN–MEYER, Marsha, Director Public Relations and Marketing, Hillsboro Community Hospital, Hillsboro, KS, p. A244

SEVCO, Mark
  President, UPMC East, Monroeville, PA, p. A545
  President, UPMC McKeesport, McKeesport, PA, p. A544

SEVERA, Jeff, D.O. Chief of Staff, Vidant Roanoke–Chowan Hospital, Ahoskie, NC, p. A460

SEVERANCE, Matthew J., FACHE, Chief Executive Officer, Roper St. Francis, Charleston, SC, p. A563

SEVILLIAN, Clarence, President and Chief Executive Officer, McLaren Bay Region, Bay City, MI, p. A319

SEWALLS, Travis, Chief Medical Officer, Baptist Health Madisonville, Madisonville, KY, p. A265

SEWATSKY, Mary, M.D. Chief Medical Officer, Moses Taylor Hospital, Scranton, PA, p. A554

SEWELL, Lance, Chief Financial Officer, South Lake Hospital, Clermont, FL, p. A125

SEWELL, Sue, Chief Nursing Officer, Wise Regional Health System, Decatur, TX, p. A612

SEWICK, Alayne, Vice President Human Resources, Medical Center of McKinney, McKinney, TX, p. A636

SEXTON, Charles, Manager Human Resources, Cumberland Medical Center, Crossville, TN, p. A582

SEXTON, Cindy, Chief Financial Officer, St. David's Round Rock Medical Center, Round Rock, TX, p. A644

SEXTON, Kevin, Director Information Systems, Raleigh General Hospital, Beckley, WV, p. A694

SEXTON, William P., Chief Executive Officer, Crossing Rivers Health Medical Center, Prairie Du Chien, WI, p. A714

SEYMOUR, Barbara, Vice President of Nursing, Health First Holmes Regional Medical Center, Melbourne, FL, p. A135

SEYMOUR, Claudette, Director Personnel, Memphis Mental Health Institute, Memphis, TN, p. A589

SEYMOUR, Jose, Chief Information Resource Management, James A. Haley Veterans' Hospital–Tampa, Tampa, FL, p. A147

SEYMOUR, Russell, Chief Information Management Division, Reynolds Army Community Hospital, Fort Sill, OK, p. A512

SEYMOUR, Ryan, Chief Executive Officer, Baylor Institute for Rehabilitation at Frisco, Frisco, TX, p. A619

SEYMOUR, Sally, Chief Operating Officer, Fawcett Memorial Hospital, Port Charlotte, FL, p. A143

SHACKELFORD, Gerald, Staff Support Specialist, Texas Center for Infectious Disease, San Antonio, TX, p. A647

SHACKELFORD, Paul, M.D. Chief Medical Officer, Vidant Medical Center, Greenville, NC, p. A466

SHACKLETON, Carol, M.D. Medical Director, Gothenburg Memorial Hospital, Gothenburg, NE, p. A396

SHADENSACK, Don, Vice President Clinical Services, OSF St. Mary Medical Center, Galesburg, IL, p. A191

SHADOWEN, Michael, M.D. Chief of Staff, T. J. Samson Community Hospital, Glasgow, KY, p. A261

SHADOWENS, Karen, Director Finance and Chief Financial Officer, West Chester Hospital, West Chester, OH, p. A505

SHAFER, Robert
  Vice President Finance, Mercy Medical Center–Dubuque, Dubuque, IA, p. A230
  Vice President Finance, Mercy Medical Center–Dyersville, Dyersville, IA, p. A230

SHAFER, Timothy, M.D. Medical Director, Grace Cottage Hospital, Townshend, VT, p. A666

SHAFFER, David, MSN Chief Nurse Executive, Meadville Medical Center, Meadville, PA, p. A544

SHAFICI, Khaled, M.D. President Medical Staff, Cornerstone Hospital–West Monroe, West Monroe, LA, p. A289

SHAFIU, Mohamed, M.D. Chief of Staff, Val Verde Regional Medical Center, Del Rio, TX, p. A612

SHAH, Beena, M.D. Chief of Staff and Chief Medical Officer, Anaheim Global Medical Center, Anaheim, CA, p. A54

SHAH, Jayendra H., M.D. Chief Medical Officer, Southern Arizona Veterans Affairs Health Care System, Tucson, AZ, p. A41

SHAH, Paresh, Director Information Systems, Reston Hospital Center, Reston, VA, p. A676

SHAH, Shalin, Chief Operating Officer, Regional Medical Center Bayonet Point, Hudson, FL, p. A131

SHAH, Syed, M.D. Chief of Staff, Pioneer Memorial Hospital and Health Services, Viborg, SD, p. A577

SHAH, Vital, M.D., Chief Executive Officer ad Chief Medical Officer, Central State Hospital, Louisville, KY, p. A264

SHAHAN, Mary Jo, Vice President and Chief Financial Officer, West Virginia University Hospitals, Morgantown, WV, p. A698

SHAHAN, Matthew, Chief Executive Officer, West River Regional Medical Center, Hettinger, ND, p. A479

SHAHEEN, Jim, President, Strategic Behavioral Health, LLC, Memphis, TN, p. B129

SHAHI, Niloo, Chief Operating Officer, LAC–Olive View–UCLA Medical Center,, CA, p. A72

SHAHRYAR, Syed, M.D. Medical Director, Promise Hospital of Phoenix, Mesa, AZ, p. A34

SHAHZADA, Kamran, M.D. Chief Medical Staff, South Central Kansas Medical Center, Arkansas City, KS, p. A240

SHAIFFER, Mandy, Chief Nursing Officer, Mt. San Rafael Hospital, Trinidad, CO, p. A111

SHAKER, Mark S., President and Chief Executive Officer, Miami Valley Hospital, Dayton, OH, p. A493

SHALLOCK, James R., Chief Financial Officer, Memorial Hermann Greater Heights Hospital, Houston, TX, p. A625

SHAMBURG, Steffen, M.D. Chief of Staff, Hiawatha Community Hospital, Hiawatha, KS, p. A244

SHANAHAN, Thomas
  Vice President, Human Resources, Children's Hospital of Wisconsin, Milwaukee, WI, p. A711
  Vice President, Human Resources, Children's Hospital of Wisconsin–Fox Valley, Neenah, WI, p. A712
  Chief Financial Officer and Senior Vice President, Raritan Bay Medical Center, Perth Amboy, NJ, p. A422

SHAND, Natalie, M.D. Vice President Integrative Medicine and Chief Medical Officer, Freedom Pain Hospital, Scottsdale, AZ, p. A38

SHANER, Patricia, Interim Chief Human Resources Officer, Ogallala Community Hospital, Ogallala, NE, p. A399

SHANLEY, Diane, Deputy Service Unit Director, U. S. Public Health Service Indian Hospital–Sells, Sells, AZ, p. A39

SHANLEY, Linda L., Vice President, Chief Information Officer, Saint Francis Hospital and Medical Center, Hartford, CT, p. A114

SHANNON, David A., President and Chief Executive Officer, Jersey Shore Hospital, Jersey Shore, PA, p. A541

SHANNON, Greg, Director Human Resources, Golden Valley Memorial Healthcare, Clinton, MO, p. A369

SHANNON, John Jay, M.D., Chief Executive Officer, Cook County Health and Hospitals System, Chicago, IL, p. B41

SHANNON, John Jay, M.D.,
  Chief Executive Officer, John H. Stroger Jr. Hospital of Cook County, Chicago, IL, p. A184
  Chief Executive Officer, Provident Hospital of Cook County, Chicago, IL, p. A186

SHANNON, Patrick, Chief Operating Officer, Baptist Hospitals of Southeast Texas, Beaumont, TX, p. A601

SHANNON, Richard, M.D. Chief of Staff, Montrose Memorial Hospital, Montrose, CO, p. A109

SHANNON, Scott, Director Finance, Socorro General Hospital, Socorro, NM, p. A432

SHAPE, Amy, Information Technology, North Dakota State Hospital, Jamestown, ND, p. A480

SHAPIRO, David, M.D
Vice President Medical Affairs and Chief Medical Officer, Columbia St. Mary's Hospital Milwaukee, Milwaukee, WI, p. A711
Vice President Medical Affairs and Chief Medical Officer, Columbia St. Mary's Ozaukee Hospital, Mequon, WI, p. A710
Vice President Medical Affairs and Chief Medical Officer, Sacred Heart Rehabilitation Institute, Milwaukee, WI, p. A711
SHAPIRO, Ira, M.D. Chief Medical Officer, St. Mary's Regional Medical Center, Lewiston, ME, p. A293
SHAPIRO, Louis A., President and Chief Executive Officer, Hospital for Special Surgery, New York, NY, p. A444
SHAPIRO, Marc, M.D. Chief Medical Officer, St. Helena Hospital Clear Lake, Clearlake, CA, p. A59
SHAPIRO, Steven D., M.D
Chief Medical Officer, Bon Secours St. Francis Hospital, Charleston, SC, p. A562
Vice President Medical Affairs, Roper St. Francis, Charleston, SC, p. A563
Chief Medical Officer, Roper St. Francis Mount Pleasant Hospital, Mount Pleasant, SC, p. A568
SHAPPLEY, Robert, Chief Operating Officer, Lakewood Regional Medical Center, Lakewood, CA, p. A68
SHARANGPANI, Rojesh, M.D. Chief of Staff, Capital Medical Center, Olympia, WA, p. A687
SHARBER–HOWELL, Sheryl, Administrator, Creek Nation Community Hospital, Okemah, OK, p. A515
SHARKEY, Linda, R.N. Vice President Patient Care Services and Chief Nurse Executive, Fauquier Hospital, Warrenton, VA, p. A680
SHARLOW, Joseph, M.D. Chief of Staff, Ste. Genevieve County Memorial Hospital, Ste. Genevieve, MO, p. A383
SHARMA, Adhi, M.D. Chief Medical Officer, South Nassau Communities Hospital, Oceanside, NY, p. A451
SHARMA, Aika, M.D. President Medical Staff, Alameda Hospital, Alameda, CA, p. A54
SHARMA, Chandra, M.D. Chief of Staff, Welch Community Hospital, Welch, WV, p. A701
SHARMA, Roger, Chief Financial Officer, Citrus Valley Medical Center–Inter Community Campus, Covina, CA, p. A60
SHARMA, Satish C., M.D. Chief of Staff, Providence Veterans Affairs Medical Center, Providence, RI, p. A560
SHARON, Joesph P., Associate Director, Wilkes–Barre Veterans Affairs Medical Center, Wilkes–Barre, PA, p. A558
SHARON, Sandy, Senior Vice President and Area Manager, Kaiser Permanente Sacramento Medical Center, Sacramento, CA, p. A86
SHARP, Alan
Chief Financial Officer, Saint Thomas DeKalb Hospital, Smithville, TN, p. A593
Chief Financial Officer, Saint Thomas Stones River Hospital, Woodbury, TN, p. A594
SHARP, Cheryl, Chief Financial Office, Miami County Medical Center, Paola, KS, p. A251
SHARP, Cindy, M.D. Chief Medical Officer, Madison Valley Medical Center, Ennis, MT, p. A387
SHARP, Gina, FACHE, President, Linden Oaks Hospital, Naperville, IL, p. A198
SHARP, John K., Chief Financial Officer, Seton Medical Center Harker Heights, Harker Heights, TX, p. A622
SHARP, Julie, Supervisor Human Resources, Chase County Community Hospital, Imperial, NE, p. A397
SHARP, Patrick, Chief Operating Officer, Range Regional Health Services, Hibbing, MN, p. A344
SHARP, Rebecca, Chief Financial Officer, Wagoner Community Hospital, Wagoner, OK, p. A523
SHARP, Rhian, Director Human Resources, Anchor Hospital, Atlanta, GA, p. A152
SHARP, Richard, M.D. Medical Director, CHRISTUS St. Michael Rehabilitation Hospital, Texarkana, TX, p. A652
SHARP, Tanya, Vice President of Fiscal Services and Chief Financial Officer, Boone County Health Center, Albion, NE, p. A393
SHARP, Tony, Supervisor Information System, Sweetwater Hospital, Sweetwater, TN, p. A593
SHARPE, RN, Deborah, R.N. Director of Nursing, West Springs Hospital, Grand Junction, CO, p. A106
SHARPTON, Debra, Director of Nursing, Devereux Georgia Treatment Network, Kennesaw, GA, p. A161
SHARTLE, William, Senior Vice President Human Resources, Holy Spirit – A Geisinger Affiliate, Camp Hill, PA, p. A534
SHARUM, Gary, Administrator, Mercy Hospital Tishomingo, Tishomingo, OK, p. A521
SHARUM, Melinda
Director of Human Resources, Mercy Hospital Ardmore, Ardmore, OK, p. A508
Director Human Resources, Mercy Hospital Healdton, Healdton, OK, p. A512

SHARY, Dave, Administrator Human Resources, Ridgecrest Regional Hospital, Ridgecrest, CA, p. A85
SHATRAW, Thomas, Director Human Resources, Samaritan Medical Center, Watertown, NY, p. A458
SHAUGHNESSY, John, Chief Financial Officer, McLeod Health Clarendon, Manning, SC, p. A568
SHAUGHNESSY, Mary
Vice President Finance, Spaulding Hospital for Continuing Medical Care Cambridge, Cambridge, MA, p. A309
Vice President Finance, Spaulding Rehabilitation Hospital, Charlestown, MA, p. A309
Vice President Finance, Spaulding Rehabilitation Hospital Cape Cod, East Sandwich, MA, p. A309
SHAULL, Ty, Chief Operating Officer, Wyandot Memorial Hospital, Upper Sandusky, OH, p. A504
SHAUNESSY, Celia, Vice President Human Resources, Ministry Saint Michael's Hospital, Stevens Point, WI, p. A716
SHAVER, Chris
Vice President Human Resources, Covenant Medical Center, Lubbock, TX, p. A634
Vice President Human Resources, Covenant Specialty Hospital, Lubbock, TX, p. A634
SHAVER, Jennifer
Director of Nursing, Gouverneur Hospital, Gouverneur, NY, p. A439
Director of Nursing, Lewis County General Hospital, Lowville, NY, p. A442
SHAVER, John, Chief Financial Officer, Baystate Noble Hospital, Westfield, MA, p. A316
SHAVER, Robert D., M.D. Vice President Medical Affairs, WellSpan Good Samaritan Hospital, Lebanon, PA, p. A543
SHAW, David
Vice President Information Systems, Eskenazi Health, Indianapolis, IN, p. A213
Vice President and Chief Operating Officer, Susan B. Allen Memorial Hospital, El Dorado, KS, p. A242
SHAW, David B., Chief Executive Officer and Administrator, Nor–Lea General Hospital, Lovington, NM, p. A430
SHAW, Douglas A., Chief Executive Officer, Mad River Community Hospital, Arcata, CA, p. A55
SHAW, Gary, President, Cambridge Medical Center, Cambridge, MN, p. A340
SHAW, Greg, Vice President of Finance, Aspirus Medford Hospital, Medford, WI, p. A710
SHAW, Howard, M.D. Chief Medical Officer, Great Plains Health, North Platte, NE, p. A399
SHAW, Jan, Director Personnel, River Bend Hospital, West Lafayette, IN, p. A223
SHAW, Jean, Chief Financial Officer, Valley Regional Hospital, Claremont, NH, p. A410
SHAW, John C., M.D. Medical Director, Southern Indiana Rehabilitation Hospital, New Albany, IN, p. A219
SHAW, Kathy, Chief Executive Officer, Haven Senior Horizons, Phoenix, AZ, p. A36
SHAW, Kendra, Chief Information Officer, Baldwin Area Medical Center, Baldwin, WI, p. A702
SHAW, Kimberly, Vice President Patient Care and Chief Nursing Executive, Mercy Medical Center Redding, Redding, CA, p. A84
SHAW, Mandy, M.D. Chief of Staff, Sidney Regional Medical Center, Sidney, NE, p. A402
SHAW, Michael R., Chief Executive Officer, Complex Care Hospital at Tenaya, Las Vegas, NV, p. A405
SHAW, Patrick D., Chief Executive Officer, Grafton City Hospital, Grafton, WV, p. A696
SHAW, Shane, M.D. Chief of Staff, CHI St. Luke's Health Memorial Livingston, Livingston, TX, p. A633
SHAW, Violet, R.N. Director of Nursing, Grafton City Hospital, Grafton, WV, p. A696
SHAWAN, Christy, Chief Executive Officer, Black River Medical Center, Poplar Bluff, MO, p. A378
SHAWGO, Darla, Director Human Resources, Sparta Community Hospital, Sparta, IL, p. A203
SHAWN, D.J., Director Human Resources, AllianceHealth Madill, Madill, OK, p. A514
SHEA, Drew, Chief Financial Officer, Baylor Scott & White Medical Center – White Rock, Dallas, TX, p. A609
SHEA, Kevin, M.D. Chief of Staff, Carolinas Hospital System, Florence, SC, p. A565
SHEA, Natalie, Chief Nursing Officer, Central Community Hospital, Elkader, IA, p. A230
SHEA, Peggy, Human Resources Lead, Mad River Community Hospital, Arcata, CA, p. A55
SHEAFF, Charles, M.D. President Medical Staff, Passavant Area Hospital, Jacksonville, IL, p. A194
SHEAR, Larry, Administrative Assistant, Norwood Health Center, Marshfield, WI, p. A710
SHEARER, Christopher, M.D. Chief Medical Officer, HonorHealth John C. Lincoln Medical Center, Phoenix, AZ, p. A36

SHEARER, Laura, R.N. Senior Vice President and Chief Nursing Officer, Phoebe Putney Memorial Hospital, Albany, GA, p. A151
SHEARER, Ron, M.D. Regional Medical Director, PeaceHealth Peace Harbor Medical Center, Florence, OR, p. A525
SHEARN, Daniel, R.N. Vice President Patient Services and Chief Nursing Officer, UPMC Northwest, Seneca, PA, p. A554
SHEARS, Ann Marie, Vice President Patient Care Services, Robert Wood Johnson University Hospital Rahway, Rahway, NJ, p. A422
SHECKLER, Robert L., Administrator, Avera Gettysburg Hospital, Gettysburg, SD, p. A574
SHEEHAN, Karen, Vice President and Chief Information Officer, Swedish Covenant Hospital, Chicago, IL, p. A187
SHEEHAN, T J, Chief Financial Officer, Lauderdale Community Hospital, Ripley, TN, p. A592
SHEEHAN, Terrence P., M.D. Medical Director, Adventist Rehabilitation Hospital of Maryland, Rockville, MD, p. A303
SHEEHAN, William, M.D. Medical Director, Hawaii State Hospital, Kaneohe, HI, p. A172
SHEEHY, Earl N., Administrator, Ray County Memorial Hospital, Richmond, MO, p. A378
SHEEHY, Joseph, Chief Executive Officer and Managing Director, The Pavilion, Champaign, IL, p. A183
SHEERIN, Cathy, R.N. Director Patient Care Services, Glen Cove Hospital, Glen Cove, NY, p. A439
SHEERIN, Rick
Vice President Fiscal Services, Floyd Medical Center, Rome, GA, p. A165
Chief Financial Officer, Polk Medical Center, Cedartown, GA, p. A156
SHEETS, Cindy, Vice President Information Systems and Chief Information Officer, OhioHealth MedCentral Mansfield Hospital, Mansfield, OH, p. A497
SHEETS, Jim, Chief Executive Officer and Administrator, LDS Hospital, Salt Lake City, UT, p. A663
SHEFFIELD, Aubrey, Administrative Assistant Human Resources and Public Relations, Grove Hill Memorial Hospital, Grove Hill, AL, p. A21
SHEFFIELD, Nichol, Chief Executive Officer, Pacific Grove Hospital, Riverside, CA, p. A86
SHEFIELD, Jennifer, M.D. Chief of Staff, West River Regional Medical Center, Hettinger, ND, p. A479
SHEFTE, David H., Chief Executive Officer, HEALTHSOUTH Rehabilitation Hospital of Littleton, Littleton, CO, p. A108
SHEGOLEV, Igor, Vice President Human Resources, Carondelet St. Joseph's Hospital, Tucson, AZ, p. A40
SHEHAN, Mary, R.N. Senior Vice President and Chief Nursing Officer, Swedish Covenant Hospital, Chicago, IL, p. A187
SHEHATA, Nady, M.D. Vice President Medical Affairs, Sisters of Charity Hospital of Buffalo, Buffalo, NY, p. A436
SHEHI, G. Michael, M.D., Chief Executive Officer, Mountain View Hospital, Gadsden, AL, p. A20
SHEHI, Jay, Chief Executive Officer, Rivendell Behavioral Health Services of Arkansas, Benton, AR, p. A43
SHEIKH, Arsalan, Chief of Medicine, Bon Secours Baltimore Health System, Baltimore, MD, p. A296
SHELAK, Matt, Chief Operating Officer, Lower Bucks Hospital, Bristol, PA, p. A534
SHELBURNE, John D., M.D. Chief of Staff, Durham Veterans Affairs Medical Center, Durham, NC, p. A464
SHELBY, Dennis R., Chief Executive Officer, Wilson Medical Center, Neodesha, KS, p. A249
SHELBY, Joyce, Manager Human Resources, Hardin County General Hospital, Rosiclare, IL, p. A202
SHELDEN, Diana, Chief Nursing Officer, Stone County Medical Center, Mountain View, AR, p. A50
SHELDON, Ed, Warden and Chief Executive Officer, Oakwood Correctional Facility, Lima, OH, p. A497
SHELDON, Lyle Ernest, FACHE,
President and Chief Executive Officer, University of Maryland Harford Memorial Hospital, Havre De Grace, MD, p. A301
President and Chief Executive Officer, University of Maryland Upper Chesapeake Medical Center, Bel Air, MD, p. A298
SHELDON, Lyle Ernest, FACHE, President and Chief Executive Officer, Upper Chesapeake Health System, Bel Air, MD, p. B150
SHELDON, Mo P., FACHE, Chief Executive Officer and Administrator, Odessa Memorial Healthcare Center, Odessa, WA, p. A687
SHELDON, Richard, M.D. Vice President Medical Affairs, San Gorgonio Memorial Hospital, Banning, CA, p. A56
SHELFORD, Dave, Assistant Superintendent, Richmond State Hospital, Richmond, IN, p. A221
SHELL, John, M.D. Chief Medical Officer, Coffey County Hospital, Burlington, KS, p. A241
SHELLENBERGER, David, Chief Operating Officer, St. John Vianney Hospital, Downingtown, PA, p. A536
SHELT, Elizabeth, Civilian Personnel Officer, Dwight David Eisenhower Army Medical Center, Fort Gordon, GA, p. A160

SHELTON, Amy, Chief Nursing Officer, St. Vincent's East, Birmingham, AL, p. A17

SHELTON, Carol, Director Human Resources, Lovelace Women's Hospital, Albuquerque, NM, p. A427

SHELTON, Darlene, Coordinator Team Resources, BayCare Alliant Hospital, Dunedin, FL, p. A127

SHELTON, Jared, Chief Executive Officer, Texas Health Presbyterian Hospital Allen, Allen, TX, p. A595

SHELTON, Jeffrey, Chief Executive Officer, Sterling Regional MedCenter, Sterling, CO, p. A110

SHELTON, John
President and Chief Executive Officer, DeKalb Medical at Downtown Decatur, Decatur, GA, p. A158
Executive Vice President and Chief Operating Officer, DeKalb Medical at Downtown Decatur, Decatur, GA, p. A158
President and Chief Executive Officer, DeKalb Medical at Hillandale, Lithonia, GA, p. A162
Chief Operating Officer, DeKalb Medical at Hillandale, Lithonia, GA, p. A162
President and Chief Executive Officer, DeKalb Medical at North Decatur, Decatur, GA, p. A158

SHELTON, John, President and Chief Executive Officer, DeKalb Regional Health System, Decatur, GA, p. B44

SHELTON, Kathy, Director Human Resources, East Texas Medical Center Pittsburg, Pittsburg, TX, p. A641

SHELTON, Richard, M.D. Chief Medical Officer, Baptist Health Richmond, Richmond, KY, p. A268

SHELTON, Tom, Coordinator of Nursing Services, Porterville Developmental Center, Porterville, CA, p. A83

SHELVOCK, Kathy, R.N. Assistant Administrator Patient Care Services, Fairchild Medical Center, Yreka, CA, p. A100

SHEN, Mark W., M.D., President and Chief Executive Officer, Dell Children's Medical Center of Central Texas, Austin, TX, p. A599

SHENDELL–FALIK, Nancy, R.N. Senior Vice President, Chief Operating Officer and Chief Nursing Officer, Baystate Medical Center, Springfield, MA, p. A314

SHENGLE, Lori, Director Information Technology, Morrill County Community Hospital, Bridgeport, NE, p. A394

SHEPARD, Bridget, Vice President Human Resources, Wabash General Hospital, Mount Carmel, IL, p. A197

SHEPARD, Karen, Senior Vice President and Chief Financial Officer, St. Charles Prineville, Prineville, OR, p. A530

SHEPARD, Megan, Director Clinical Services, Odessa Memorial Healthcare Center, Odessa, WA, p. A687

SHEPARD, Sheila, Controller, HealthSouth Rehabilitation Hospital of Humble, LLC, Humble, TX, p. A628

SHEPARDSON, Dean, Chief Financial Officer, Banner Estrella Medical Center, Phoenix, AZ, p. A36

SHEPARDSON, Heather S.
Chief Human Resource Officer, Carilion Franklin Memorial Hospital, Rocky Mount, VA, p. A678
Vice President Human Resources, Carilion Roanoke Memorial Hospital, Roanoke, VA, p. A678

SHEPHARD, Bryan, Chief Financial Officer, TriStar Summit Medical Center, Hermitage, TN, p. A584

SHEPHARD, Russ, Senior Systems Analyst, Tennova Healthcare Dyersburg Regional Medical Center, Dyersburg, TN, p. A582

SHEPHERD, Laura, Director Human Resources, Texas Health Huguley Hospital Fort Worth South, Burleson, TX, p. A604

SHEPHERD, RN, BSN, Linda M., Chief Nursing Officer, LewisGale Hospital Pulaski, Pulaski, VA, p. A676

SHEPHERD, Thomas, Executive Vice President and Chief Operating Officer, Gwinnett Hospital System, Lawrenceville, GA, p. A162

SHEPLER, Mary, R.N. Vice President and Chief Nursing Officer, Saint Joseph Hospital, Denver, CO, p. A104

SHEPPARD, Sandy, Vice President Patient Services, Wilkes Regional Medical Center, North Wilkesboro, NC, p. A471

SHEPPARD, Sharon, Manager Human Resources, Sycamore Shoals Hospital, Elizabethton, TN, p. A582

SHEPPARD, Varinya, R.N. Chief Nursing Officer, St. Elizabeth Medical Center, Utica, NY, p. A457

SHERBONDY, Beverly, Assistant Vice President, Human Resources, Jeanes Hospital, Philadelphia, PA, p. A548

SHERBONDY, Lori, Director Human Resources, Battle Mountain General Hospital, Battle Mountain, NV, p. A404

SHERER, Janet, Chief of Patient Care Services, Springfield Hospital, Springfield, VT, p. A666

SHERER, Susan, Chief Information Resource Management, Dayton Veterans Affairs Medical Center, Dayton, OH, p. A492

SHERIDAN, Cheryl, R.N. Senior Vice President Patient Care Services, Rochester General Hospital, Rochester, NY, p. A454

SHERIDAN, Elizabeth
Chief Operating Officer and Chief Nursing Executive, Inspira Medical Center–Elmer, Elmer, NJ, p. A416
Chief Operating Officer and Chief Nursing Executive, Inspira Medical Center–Vineland, Vineland, NJ, p. A425

SHERIDAN, Kolbe, Chief Operating Officer, Heartland Regional Medical Center, Marion, IL, p. A195

SHERIDAN, Phil, Chief Executive Officer, Beckett Springs, West Chester, OH, p. A505

SHERIDAN, Tristen, Chief Executive Officer and Administrator, Weisbrod Memorial County Hospital, Eads, CO, p. A104

SHERMAN, Angelina, R.N. Chief Nursing Officer, The Rehabilitation Institute of St. Louis, Saint Louis, MO, p. A381

SHERMAN, Frederick C., M.D. Chief Medical Officer, The Children's Home of Pittsburgh, Pittsburgh, PA, p. A551

SHERMAN, Sheila, Vice President Patient Care Services, Vail Valley Medical Center, Vail, CO, p. A111

SHERMAN, Stephanie, Chief Human Resources Officer, West Boca Medical Center, Boca Raton, FL, p. A124

SHERON, William E., Chief Executive Officer, Wooster Community Hospital, Wooster, OH, p. A506

SHERRILL, Angela
Chief Information Officer, Laird Hospital, Union, MS, p. A365
Corporate Director Information System, Rush Foundation Hospital, Meridian, MS, p. A362
Corporate Director Information System, Specialty Hospital of Meridian, Meridian, MS, p. A362

SHERROD, Michael, Chief Executive Officer, TriStar Greenview Regional Hospital, Bowling Green, KY, p. A258

SHERROD, Rhonda Kay, MSN, Administrator, Shands Lake Shore Regional Medical Center, Lake City, FL, p. A133

SHERRON, Tammy M., Vice President Finance, CarolinaEast Health System, New Bern, NC, p. A470

SHERRY, Mark A., Director Human Resources, Scott & White Hospital at Round Rock, Round Rock, TX, p. A644

SHERWIN, Charles H., Vice President of Business Development and Clinical Services, MidMichigan Medical Center – Alpena, Alpena, MI, p. A318

SHERWOOD, Matthew M., Chief Financial Officer, Unity Medical & Surgical Hospital, Mishawaka, IN, p. A218

SHETTLESWORTH, Amanda, Director Human Resources, Bloomington Meadows Hospital, Bloomington, IN, p. A207

SHEW, Angel, Director Area Technology, Kaiser Permanente South San Francisco, South San Francisco, CA, p. A95

SHEWBRIDGE, Richard K., M.D. Vice President Medical Operations, Cleveland Clinic, Medina Hospital, Medina, OH, p. A499

SHEYKA, Patricia, Chief Nursing Officer, Gila Regional Medical Center, Silver City, NM, p. A431

SHICKOLOVICH, William, Chief Information Officer, Tufts Medical Center, Boston, MA, p. A307

SHIELDS, Charlie
President and Chief Executive Officer, Truman Medical Center–Hospital Hill, Kansas City, MO, p. A374
President and Chief Executive Officer, Truman Medical Center–Lakewood, Kansas City, MO, p. A374

SHIELDS, Charlie, President and Chief Executive Officer, Truman Medical Centers, Kansas City, MO, p. B138

SHIELDS, Diane, Chief Human Resources Officer, MidMichigan Medical Center – Alpena, Alpena, MI, p. A318

SHIFF, Mary Treacy, Chief Financial Officer, Kindred Chicago–Central Hospital, Chicago, IL, p. A184

SHIFFERMILLER, William, M.D. Vice President Medical Affairs, Nebraska Methodist Hospital, Omaha, NE, p. A400

SHIHADY, Sharon, Director Human Resources, HEALTHSOUTH Cane Creek Rehabilitation Hospital, Martin, TN, p. A587

SHILKAITIS, Mary, Vice President Patient Care and Chief Nursing Officer, Rush–Copley Medical Center, Aurora, IL, p. A181

SHILLING, Angie, Chief Executive Officer, Baum Harmon Mercy Hospital, Primghar, IA, p. A236

SHILLING, Stacy, Controller, St. Vincent Rehabilitation Hospital, Sherwood, AR, p. A52

SHIM, Eunmee, R.N. Vice President Operations, Adventist Healthcare Shady Grove Medical Center, Rockville, MD, p. A303

SHIMAMOTO, Kevin, Vice President and Chief Informational Officer, Valley Children's Healthcare, Madera, CA, p. A75

SHINER, Cindy, Manager Human Resources, Lebanon Veterans Affairs Medical Center, Lebanon, PA, p. A542

SHINGLETON, Kathy J., Ed.D. Vice President, Human Resources, Virginia Mason Medical Center, Seattle, WA, p. A690

SHINICK, Mary K., Vice President Human Resources, Nyack Hospital, Nyack, NY, p. A451

SHININGER, Kimberly R., Manger, Human Resources, Parkview Wabash County Hospital, Wabash, IN, p. A223

SHIPIERSKI, Sally, Controller, Geisinger HEALTHSOUTH Rehabilitation Hospital, Danville, PA, p. A536

SHIPLEY, Carolyn, Chief Nursing Officer, Roane Medical Center, Harriman, TN, p. A583

SHIPLEY, Janice, M.D. Chief Medical Officer, Cibola General Hospital, Grants, NM, p. A429

SHIPLEY, Kurt, Chief Financial Officer, Jordan Valley Medical Center, West Jordan, UT, p. A664

SHIPLEY, Sheila, Human Resources Educator, Signature Psychiatric Hospital, Kansas City, MO, p. A374

SHIPP, Geraldine H., Director of Risk Management, Sampson Regional Medical Center, Clinton, NC, p. A463

SHIRAH, Anita, Director Human Resources, University of South Alabama Medical Center, Mobile, AL, p. A23

SHIRLEY, Christian, Director Human Resources, Geisinger HEALTHSOUTH Rehabilitation Hospital, Danville, PA, p. A536

SHIRLEY, Douglas E., Senior Executive Vice President and Chief Financial Officer, Cooper University Health Care, Camden, NJ, p. A415

SHIRLEY, Steve, Chief Information Officer, Parkview Medical Center, Pueblo, CO, p. A110

SHISLER, Catherine, Director Information Services, Baylor Medical Center at Irving, Irving, TX, p. A628

SHIVELY, Lori, Vice President of Finance, Munson Healthcare Grayling Hospital, Grayling, MI, p. A325

SHIVERY, Toni M.
Vice President Human Resources, University of Maryland Harford Memorial Hospital, Havre De Grace, MD, p. A301
Vice President Human Resources, University of Maryland Upper Chesapeake Medical Center, Bel Air, MD, p. A298

SHMERLING, James E., President, Connecticut Children's Medical Center, Hartford, CT, p. A114

SHOBE, Franklin, Administrator and Chief Executive Officer, Black Hills Surgery Center, Rapid City, SD, p. A575

SHOBE, Susan, Director Administration and Support Services, Alton Mental Health Center, Alton, IL, p. A180

SHOCK, Ernest, Chief Nursing Officer, Abbeville Area Medical Center, Abbeville, SC, p. A562

SHOCKEY, Kathryn L., Director Human Resources, Lead–Deadwood Regional Hospital, Deadwood, SD, p. A573

SHOCKLEY, Mary, Director Human Resources, Russell Medical Center, Alexander City, AL, p. A15

SHOCKNEY, Brian T., FACHE Chief Operating Officer, Indiana University Health Arnett Hospital, Lafayette, IN, p. A216

SHOEMAKER, Matt, D.O. Vice President and Chief Medical Officer, Southeast Hospital, Cape Girardeau, MO, p. A369

SHOENER, Carl, Chief Information Officer, Lehigh Valley Hospital – Hazleton, Hazleton, PA, p. A540

SHOFNER, Connie, Chief Nursing Officer, Carlsbad Medical Center, Carlsbad, NM, p. A428

SHOLLER, Peter, M.D. Medical Director, Spectrum Health Special Care Hospital, Grand Rapids, MI, p. A325

SHOLTIS, Bridget, Chief Financial Officer, McLaren Port Huron, Port Huron, MI, p. A332

SHOMAKER, Susan, Director Information Management Systems, J. Arthur Dosher Memorial Hospital, Southport, NC, p. A474

SHOOK, Susan, Interim Chief Executive officer, Murray Medical Center, Chatsworth, GA, p. A156

SHOR, Joel, M.D. Chief of Staff, Bluefield Regional Medical Center, Bluefield, WV, p. A694

SHORB, Gary S., President and Chief Executive Officer, Methodist Le Bonheur Healthcare, Memphis, TN, p. B91

SHORES, Larry, M.D. Executive Medical Director, Cedar Springs Hospital, Colorado Springs, CO, p. A102

SHORT, Kathy, D.O. Family Practice, Carroll County Memorial Hospital, Carrollton, KY, p. A258

SHORT, M. Andrew, Vice President Information Services, Samaritan Medical Center, Watertown, NY, p. A458

SHORT, Margaret W., Coordinator Information Technology, Webster County Memorial Hospital, Webster Springs, WV, p. A700

SHORT, Penny, R.N. Chief Operating Officer, Nanticoke Memorial Hospital, Seaford, DE, p. A119

SHORT, Peter H., M.D. Senior Vice President Medical Affairs, Beverly Hospital, Beverly, MA, p. A305

SHORT, Steve, Executive Vice President Finance and Administration and Chief Financial Officer, Tampa General Hospital, Tampa, FL, p. A148

SHORT, Ted, Chief Financial Officer, Fairview Park Hospital, Dublin, GA, p. A159

SHORT, W. L., M.D. Chief Medical Officer, Memorial Health System, Abilene, KS, p. A240

SHOUKAIR, Sami, M.D. Chief Medical Officer, La Palma Intercommunity Hospital, La Palma, CA, p. A67

SHOUP, Barbara, R.N. Chief Nursing Officer, Brighton Center for Recovery, Brighton, MI, p. A319

SHOUP, Emily, Director Nursing Services, Roundup Memorial Healthcare, Roundup, MT, p. A390

SHOUSE, Shellie, Chief Financial Officer, Bluegrass Community Hospital, Versailles, KY, p. A270

SHOVALD, Terri, Chief Executive Officer, First Texas Hospital, Carrollton, TX, p. A605

SHOWALTER, Will
Senior Vice President Information Systems, Chief Information Officer, Community Memorial Hospital, Menomonee Falls, WI, p. A710
Senior Vice President and Chief Information Officer, Froedtert Memorial Lutheran Hospital, Milwaukee, WI, p. A711
Senior Vice President, Chief Information Officer, St. Joseph's Hospital, West Bend, WI, p. A719
Senior Vice President Information Technology, Wellmont Holston Valley Medical Center, Kingsport, TN, p. A585
SHOWS, Carla
Human Resource and Payroll Clerk, George Regional Hospital, Lucedale, MS, p. A361
Payroll Clerk, Greene County Hospital, Leakesville, MS, p. A361
SHREEVE, Susan, Chief Financial Officer, Research Medical Center, Kansas City, MO, p. A373
SHRESTHA, Sanjeeb, M.D. Chief Medical Staff, Weatherford Regional Medical Center, Weatherford, TX, p. A656
SHREVE, Susan, Executive Director Information Technology, Boone Memorial Hospital, Madison, WV, p. A697
SHREVES, Melissa, Director Human Resources, Monongalia General Hospital, Morgantown, WV, p. A698
SHREWSBURY, Kim, Vice President and Chief Financial Officer, Decatur Morgan Hospital, Decatur, AL, p. A18
SHRIVASTAVA, Rakesh, M.D. Chief Medical Officer, Cornerstone Hospital of Oklahoma–Shawnee, Shawnee, OK, p. A519
SHRIVER, Debra, R.N. Chief Nurse Executive, UnityPoint Health – Trinity Regional Medical Center, Fort Dodge, IA, p. A230
SHRIVER, Kren K., M.D. Clinical Director, Capital District Psychiatric Center, Albany, NY, p. A433
SHROADES, David W., Vice President Technology Services, Alliance Community Hospital, Alliance, OH, p. A483
SHROCK, Lynda J., Vice President Human Resources, Logansport Memorial Hospital, Logansport, IN, p. A217
SHROFF, Divya, Chief Medical Officer, TriStar Ashland City Medical Center, Ashland City, TN, p. A579
SHROFF, Rajendra, M.D. Administrative Medical Director, SSM Health St. Mary's Hospital Centralia, Centralia, IL, p. A182
SHROYER, Linda K., Administrator, Potomac Valley Hospital, Keyser, WV, p. A697
SHUBIN, Allan, Chief Financial Officer, Pacific Alliance Medical Center, Los Angeles, CA, p. A73
SHUEY, Keith, M.D. Chief Medical Staff, Johnson County Hospital, Tecumseh, NE, p. A402
SHUFFLEBARGER, Tom, Chief Operating Officer, Children's of Alabama, Birmingham, AL, p. A16
SHUFORD, Little, Manager Medical Information, Kindred Hospital–Greensboro, Greensboro, NC, p. A466
SHUGARMAN, Mark D., Administrator, Shriners Hospitals for Children–Cincinnati Burns Hospital, Cincinnati, OH, p. A488
SHUGART, Susan C., Chief Operating Officer, Carolina Pines Regional Medical Center, Hartsville, SC, p. A567
SHUGHART, Deborah A.
Vice President and Chief Financial Officer, Fulton County Medical Center, Mc Connellsburg, PA, p. A544
Vice President and Chief Financial Officer, J. C. Blair Memorial Hospital, Huntingdon, PA, p. A540
SHUGRUE, Dianne, President and Chief Executive Officer, Glens Falls Hospital, Glens Falls, NY, p. A439
SHULER, Conrad K., M.D. Chief Medical Officer, Oconee Memorial Hospital, Seneca, SC, p. A569
SHULIK, David, Vice President and Chief Financial Officer, UPMC Horizon, Greenville, PA, p. A539
SHULL, Jennifer, R.N. Chief Nursing Officer, Florida Hospital Fish Memorial, Orange City, FL, p. A140
SHULTS, Randi L., Chief Executive Officer, North Carolina Specialty Hospital, Durham, NC, p. A464
SHUMAKER, Bradley, Chief Medical Officer, Kendall Regional Medical Center, Miami, FL, p. A136
SHUMAN, Betty, Director Human Resources, Wesley Rehabilitation Hospital, Wichita, KS, p. A256
SHUMAN, Daniel, D.O. Chief Medical Officer, Ashland Health Center, Ashland, KS, p. A240
SHUMATE, Karen J., R.N. Chief Operating Officer, Lawrence Memorial Hospital, Lawrence, KS, p. A247
SHUMATE, Kim, Human Resources Officer, Ohio State University Wexner Medical Center, Columbus, OH, p. A491
SHUMWAY, Barbara, Director Human Resources, North Big Horn Hospital District, Lovell, WY, p. A723
SHUPERT, Charlene
Director Staff Services, Carrus Rehabilitation Hospital, Sherman, TX, p. A648
Director Staff Services, Carrus Specialty Hospital, Sherman, TX, p. A648
SHUPP, Susan, Chief Human Resources Officer, Nemaha County Hospital, Auburn, NE, p. A393
SHUTE, Keith M., M.D. Senior Vice President Medical Affairs and Clinical Services, Androscoggin Valley Hospital, Berlin, NH, p. A410

SHUTE, Leonard J., Chief Financial Officer, Strong Memorial Hospital of the University of Rochester, Rochester, NY, p. A454
SHUTER, Mark H., President and Chief Executive Officer, Adena Health System, Chillicothe, OH, p. B5
SHUTER, Mark H., President and Chief Executive Officer, Adena Medical Center, Chillicothe, OH, p. A486
SHYSHKA, Susan, Associate Director, VA Greater Los Angeles Healthcare System, Los Angeles, CA, p. A74
SIAL, Ajay, Chief Financial Officer, UC Irvine Health, UC Irvine Medical Center, Orange, CA, p. A81
SIAL, Jay, Chief Financial Officer, Loyola University Medical Center, Maywood, IL, p. A196
SIBBITT, Stephen, M.D. Chief Medical Officer, Scott & White Memorial Hospital, Temple, TX, p. A652
SIBLEY, Beth, Director of Nursing, Sage Rehabilitation Hospital, Baton Rouge, LA, p. A273
SIBLEY, Cherie, R.N., Chief Executive Officer, Clark Regional Medical Center, Winchester, KY, p. A270
SIBLEY, Jeri, Director Revenue Cycle, Riverside Tappahannock Hospital, Tappahannock, VA, p. A679
SICA, Vincent A., President and Chief Executive Officer, DeSoto Memorial Hospital, Arcadia, FL, p. A123
SICHTS, Pam, Director Human Resources, Sycamore Springs Hospital, Lafayette, IN, p. A216
SICILIA, Bruce, M.D. Medical Director, HEALTHSOUTH Rehabilitation Hospital of York, York, PA, p. A559
SIDDIQI, Ather, M.D
Medical Director, Nexus Specialty Hospital, Shenandoah, TX, p. A648
Medical Director, Nexus Specialty Hospital The Woodlands, The Woodlands, TX, p. A652
SIDDIQI, Syed, M.D. President Medical Staff, Raleigh General Hospital, Beckley, WV, p. A694
SIDDIQUI, Hugh, Senior Applications Analyst, Linden Oaks Hospital, Naperville, IL, p. A198
SIDDIQUI, Joseph, Vice President Human Resources, The Aroostook Medical Center, Presque Isle, ME, p. A295
SIDES, Tim, Chief Financial Officer, Valle Vista Hospital, Greenwood, IN, p. A212
SIDMAN, Robert, M.D. Regional Vice President, Medical Affairs, The William W. Backus Hospital, Norwich, CT, p. A116
SIEBENALER, Christopher, Chief Executive Officer, Houston Methodist Sugar Land Hospital, Sugar Land, TX, p. A650
SIEBERT, Kristy, Manager Finance, John J. Pershing Veterans Affairs Medical Center, Poplar Bluff, MO, p. A378
SIEBERT, Matt, Assistant Administrator Ancillary Services, Hermann Area District Hospital, Hermann, MO, p. A372
SIEDLECKI, Cathy, Director Human Resources, Carthage Area Hospital, Carthage, NY, p. A437
SIEG, Greg, Director Information Technology, HealthSource Saginaw, Inc., Saginaw, MI, p. A333
SIEGEL, Fredric, M.D. Chief of Staff, Desert View Hospital, Pahrump, NV, p. A407
SIEGEL, Lesley, M.D. Medical Director, Albert J. Solnit Psychiatric Center – South Campus, Middletown, CT, p. A115
SIEGEL, Tiffany, Director of Nursing, Fulton County Health Center, Wauseon, OH, p. A505
SIEGELMAN, Gary M., M.D. Senior Vice President and Chief Medical Officer, Bayhealth Medical Center, Dover, DE, p. A119
SIEGFRIED, Carole A., MSN Campus Nurse Executive, Palmetto Health Richland, Columbia, SC, p. A564
SIEGLE, Lora, M.D. Chief Medical Officer, Morris County Hospital, Council Grove, KS, p. A242
SIEGLEN, Linda, M.D. Chief Medical Officer, Mission Hospital, Mission Viejo, CA, p. A77
SIEGMAN, Ira, M.D. Chief Medical Officer, Northside Hospital, Saint Petersburg, FL, p. A144
SIEGRIST, Steve, Director of Human Resources, Mesa View Regional Hospital, Mesquite, NV, p. A407
SIEK, Terry, MSN Chief Nursing Officer, Hays Medical Center, Hays, KS, p. A244
SIEMERS, Thomas R., Chief Executive Officer, J. Arthur Dosher Memorial Hospital, Southport, NC, p. A474
SIEWERT, Charles
Director Human Resources, Buffalo Psychiatric Center, Buffalo, NY, p. A435
Director Human Resources, Western New York Children's Psychiatric Center, West Seneca, NY, p. A459
SIFERS, Carl, Director Information Technology and System Services, Centerpoint Medical Center, Independence, MO, p. A372
SIFFRING, Connie K., Chief Executive Officer, Select Specialty Hospital–Quad Cities, Davenport, IA, p. A228
SIFRI, Christi, Chief Nursing Executive, Regional Hospital for Respiratory and Complex Care, Burien, WA, p. A683
SIGEL, Heather, Director of Clinical Services, War Memorial Hospital, Berkeley Springs, WV, p. A694

SIGLAR, Harold L., Interim Chief Executive Officer, Raleigh General Hospital, Beckley, WV, p. A694
SIGLER, Wes, Administrator, North Mississippi Medical Center–Eupora, Eupora, MS, p. A357
SIGNOR, Kristin, Director Finance, Sunnyview Rehabilitation Hospital, Schenectady, NY, p. A455
SIGREST, Marion, M.D. Chief of Staff, Baptist Medical Center Yazoo, Yazoo City, MS, p. A366
SIGSBURY, John R., President, SSM Health St. Mary's Hospital Centralia, Centralia, IL, p. A182
SILARD, Kathleen A., R.N. Executive Vice President Operations and Chief Operating Officer, Stamford Hospital, Stamford, CT, p. A117
SILAS, Maria, Manager Human Resources, SUNY Downstate Medical Center University Hospital,, NY, p. A450
SILBER, Steven, M.D. Senior Vice President Medical Affairs, New York Methodist Hospital,, NY, p. A447
SILLS, Doug, Chief Executive Officer, Santa Rosa Medical Center, Milton, FL, p. A138
SILLS, John T., Chief Information Officer, Health Central Hospital, Ocoee, FL, p. A139
SILSBEE, Dave, Chief Information Officer, Cary Medical Center, Caribou, ME, p. A292
SILVA, Carmen, R.N. Chief Operating Officer, Doctors Hospital of Manteca, Manteca, CA, p. A76
SILVA, Francisco, Financial Director, Hospital Metropolitano Dr. Susoni, Arecibo, PR, p. A726
SILVA, Shawn, Chief Executive Officer, Heritage Oaks Hospital, Sacramento, CA, p. A86
SILVA–STEELE, Jamie A., R.N., President and Chief Executive Officer, UNM Sandoval Regional Medical Center, Albuquerque, NM, p. A428
SILVER, Jonathan, Chief Financial Officer, Ballard Rehabilitation Hospital, San Bernardino, CA, p. A88
SILVER, Michael R., M.D. Vice President Medical Affairs, Rush Oak Park Hospital, Oak Park, IL, p. A199
SILVER, Timothy, M.D. Medical Director, Sheltering Arms Hospital South, Midlothian, VA, p. A674
SILVERMAN, Daniel C., M.D
Chief Medical Officer, Acute Care Troy, Samaritan Hospital, Troy, NY, p. A457
Vice President and Chief Medical Officer, Sinai Hospital of Baltimore, Baltimore, MD, p. A298
Chief Medical Officer, St. Mary's Hospital, Troy, NY, p. A457
SILVERSTEIN, Douglas M., President, NorthShore University Health System, Evanston, IL, p. A190
SILVERSTEIN, Joel, M.D. Chief Medical Officer, Copley Hospital, Morrisville, VT, p. A665
SILVERSTEIN, Kenneth L., Chief Clinical Officer, Christiana Care Health System, Newark, DE, p. A119
SILVERTHORNE, Samuel, Chief Information Officer, U. S. Air Force Medical Center Keesler, Keesler AFB, MS, p. A360
SILVESTRI, Scott, Chief Financial Officer, Hospital Financial Operations, Robert Packer Hospital, Sayre, PA, p. A553
SILVEUS, Patrick, M.D. Medical Director, Kosciusko Community Hospital, Warsaw, IN, p. A223
SILVEY, Christie, Director People Services, HSHS St. Joseph's Hospital, Highland, IL, p. A192
SILVIA, Charles B., M.D. Chief Medical Officer and Vice President Medical Affairs, Peninsula Regional Medical Center, Salisbury, MD, p. A303
SIM, Carol, President and Chief Executive Officer, Siskin Hospital for Physical Rehabilitation, Chattanooga, TN, p. A580
SIMCHUK, Cathy J., Chief Operating Officer, Providence Holy Family Hospital, Spokane, WA, p. A691
SIMIA, Greg
Chief Financial Officer, HSHS St. Clare Memorial Hospital, Oconto Falls, WI, p. A713
Chief Financial Officer, HSHS St. Vincent Hospital, Green Bay, WI, p. A707
Chief Financial Officer, St. Mary's Hospital Medical Center, Green Bay, WI, p. A707
Chief Financial Officer, St. Nicholas Hospital, Sheboygan, WI, p. A716
SIMKINS, Palma, Chief Human Resources Management Services, Battle Creek Veterans Affairs Medical Center, Battle Creek, MI, p. A319
SIMMONS, Angela L., Chief Executive Officer, HealthSouth Rehabilitation Hospital of Humble, LLC, Humble, TX, p. A628
SIMMONS, Barbara, R.N., Chief Executive Officer, Westside Regional Medical Center, Plantation, FL, p. A143
SIMMONS, Brad
Chief Operating Officer, Saint Luke's Hospital of Kansas City, Kansas City, MO, p. A374
Chief Operating Officer, University of California, Davis Medical Center, Sacramento, CA, p. A87
SIMMONS, Daniel F., Senior Vice President and Treasurer, Monongahela Valley Hospital, Monongahela, PA, p. A545
SIMMONS, Dorlynn, Chief Executive Officer, Mescalero Public Health Service Indian Hospital, Mescalero, NM, p. A430

SIMMONS, Dwayne, Interim Chief Information Officer, St. Luke's Cornwall Hospital, Newburgh, NY, p. A450

SIMMONS, Eileen
Chief Financial Officer, Magee–Womens Hospital of UPMC, Pittsburgh, PA, p. A551
Chief Financial Officer, UPMC Hospital Network, UPMC Mercy, Pittsburgh, PA, p. A551
Chief Financial Officer, UPMC Presbyterian Shadyside, Pittsburgh, PA, p. A551

SIMMONS, Jeanette, Chief Operating Officer, Center for Behavioral Medicine, Kansas City, MO, p. A373

SIMMONS, Leslie, R.N., President and Chief Executive Officer, Carroll Hospital, Westminster, MD, p. A304

SIMMONS, Linda V., President and Chief Executive Officer, Decatur County Memorial Hospital, Greensburg, IN, p. A212

SIMMONS, Nancy B., Executive Vice President and Chief Administrative Officer, Good Samaritan Hospital Medical Center, West Islip, NY, p. A458

SIMMONS, Preston M., FACHE, Chief Executive Officer, Providence Regional Medical Center Everett, Everett, WA, p. A684

SIMMONS, Randy, Chief Executive Officer, Prague Community Hospital, Prague, OK, p. A519

SIMMONS, Steven, Chief Human Resources Officer, Hahnemann University Hospital, Philadelphia, PA, p. A548

SIMMONS, Tim C., Chief Executive Officer, Hopebridge Hospital, Houston, TX, p. A624

SIMMS, Sr., Michael S., Vice President Human Resources, Northeast Alabama Regional Medical Center, Anniston, AL, p. A15

SIMMS, Miquel Noelani, R.N. Chief Nursing Officer, North Hawaii Community Hospital, Kamuela, HI, p. A172

SIMODEJKA, John E., Chief Executive Officer, Select Specialty Hospital–Central Pennsylvania, Camp Hill, PA, p. A534

SIMON, Anha, Director Human Resources, Riceland Medical Center, Winnie, TX, p. A658

SIMON, Ashley, Chief Financial Officer, Kansas Surgery and Recovery Center, Wichita, KS, p. A256

SIMON, Daniel I., M.D., President, University Hospitals Cleveland Medical Center, Cleveland, OH, p. A490

SIMON, Deborah R., R.N.,
President and Chief Executive Officer, UnityPoint Health – Peoria, Peoria, IL, p. A200
President and Chief Executive Officer, UnityPoint Health – Proctor, Peoria, IL, p. A200

SIMON, Joan M., R.N. Chief Nursing Officer, Kootenai Health, Coeur D'Alene, ID, p. A175

SIMON, Kareen, Vice President of Operations, Wheeling Hospital, Wheeling, WV, p. A701

SIMON, Kenneth B., M.D. Chief of Staff, Veterans Affairs Gulf Coast Veterans Health Care System, Biloxi, MS, p. A355

SIMON, Lisa M.
Senior Vice President Chief Financial Officer, East Ohio Regional Hospital, Martins Ferry, OH, p. A498
Senior Vice President and Chief Financial Officer, Ohio Valley Medical Center, Wheeling, WV, p. A701

SIMON, Lloyd, M.D. Medical Director, Eastern Long Island Hospital, Greenport, NY, p. A440

SIMON, Mark, System Chief Information Officer, Benefis Health System, Great Falls, MT, p. A388

SIMON, Richard, M.D. Chief of Staff, Unconn John Dempsey Hospital, Farmington, CT, p. A114

SIMON, Stuart, M.D. Medical Director, North Central Surgical Center, Dallas, TX, p. A611

SIMON, Teresa, Director Information Systems, Nacogdoches Medical Center, Nacogdoches, TX, p. A638

SIMON, Thresa, M.D. Medical Director, Poplar Springs Hospital, Petersburg, VA, p. A676

SIMONIN, Steven J., Chief Executive Officer, Iowa Specialty Hospital–Clarion, Clarion, IA, p. A227

SIMONIN, Steven J., Chief Executive Officer, Iowa Specialty Hospitals, Clarion, IA, p. B74

SIMONS, Janice, FACHE, Chief Executive Officer, Medina Regional Hospital, Hondo, TX, p. A623

SIMONS, Preston, Chief Information Officer, Aurora Medical Center – Manitowoc County, Two Rivers, WI, p. A717

SIMONSON, John F., M.D. President Medical Staff, Memorial Community Hospital and Health System, Blair, NE, p. A394

SIMONSON, Paul, Vice President, Trinity Health, Minot, ND, p. A481

SIMPATICO, Thomas, M.D., Facility Director and Network System Manager, Chicago–Read Mental Health Center, Chicago, IL, p. A183

SIMPSON, Brenda, R.N. Chief Nursing Officer, Largo Medical Center, Largo, FL, p. A134

SIMPSON, Brenda, Chief Nursing Officer, Northeast Georgia Medical Center, Gainesville, GA, p. A160

SIMPSON, Chris, Chief Executive Officer, Cornerstone Hospital–West Monroe, West Monroe, LA, p. A289

SIMPSON, Greg, Chief Nursing Officer, St. Joseph Medical Center, Kansas City, MO, p. A374

SIMPSON, Joan W., Manager Human Resources, Lauderdale Community Hospital, Ripley, TN, p. A592

SIMPSON, Keith J., Chief Operating Officer, Jennings American Legion Hospital, Jennings, LA, p. A279

SIMPSON, Laura, Director Human Resources, Sabine County Hospital, Hemphill, TX, p. A623

SIMPSON, Jr., Lee A., Chief Executive Officer, Post Acute Medical Specialty Hospital of Tulsa, Tulsa, OK, p. A522

SIMPSON, Mark, Director of Nursing, Welch Community Hospital, Welch, WV, p. A701

SIMPSON, Michelle, Chief Nursing Officer and Quality Leader, Lauderdale Community Hospital, Ripley, TN, p. A592

SIMPSON, Mikael
Chief Executive Officer, Nexus Specialty Hospital, Shenandoah, TX, p. A648
Chief Executive Officer, Nexus Specialty Hospital The Woodlands, The Woodlands, TX, p. A652

SIMPSON, Rae, R.N. Chief Nursing Officer, Western State Hospital, Tacoma, WA, p. A692

SIMPSON, Robert, Vice President Operations, Methodist Richardson Medical Center, Richardson, TX, p. A643

SIMPSON, Shannon, Director Information Services, St. Elizabeth Hospital, Gonzales, LA, p. A277

SIMPSON, Shawndra, Interim Chief Executive Officer, Sutter Surgical Hospital – North Valley, Yuba City, CA, p. A100

SIMPSON, Sheila, Vice President Human Resources, Palmetto Lowcountry Behavioral Health, Charleston, SC, p. A563

SIMPSON, Steve, Chief Executive Officer, Lakeway Regional Hospital, Morristown, TN, p. A590

SIMPSON, Tanya, Chief Nursing Officer, Regional Medical Center Bayonet Point, Hudson, FL, p. A131

SIMPSON–TUGGLE, Deloris, Vice President Human Resources and Organizational Development and Chief Human Resources Officer, Greater Baltimore Medical Center, Baltimore, MD, p. A296

SIMS, Anthony, M.D. Chief of Staff, DeKalb Regional Medical Center, Fort Payne, AL, p. A20

SIMS, Brian, Chief Executive Officer, Lucas County Health Center, Chariton, IA, p. A227

SIMS, Charles, M.D. Chief of Staff, St. Luke's The Woodlands Hospital, The Woodlands, TX, p. A653

SIMS, Gregory F., Chief Executive Officer, Hamilton Memorial Hospital District, McLeansboro, IL, p. A196

SIMS, Jason, M.D. Chief Medical Officer, Cleveland Area Hospital, Cleveland, OK, p. A510

SIMS, Jason, Facility Information Security Officer, North Hills Hospital, North Richland Hills, TX, p. A639

SIMS, Jeffrey, Chief Executive Officer, Heartland Behavioral Healthcare, Massillon, OH, p. A498

SIMS, Jyric, FACHE Chief Operating Officer, Tulane Medical Center, New Orleans, LA, p. A285

SIMS, Lynn, Director Information Technology, Davis County Hospital, Bloomfield, IA, p. A226

SIMS, Mark E., Chief Executive Officer, Grand Strand Regional Medical Center, Myrtle Beach, SC, p. A568

SINCICH, Robert, Vice President Human Resources, Trumbull Memorial Hospital, Warren, OH, p. A505

SINCLAIR, Brad, Chief Financial Officer, Merit Health River Oaks, Flowood, MS, p. A357

SINCLAIR, Elyria, Director Human Resources, Crestwood Medical Center, Huntsville, AL, p. A21

SINCLAIR, Kathy, Vice President Human Resources, Spartanburg Medical Center, Spartanburg, SC, p. A570

SINCLAIR, Laura, Director Human Resources, Kansas City Orthopaedic Institute, Leawood, KS, p. A247

SINCLAIR, Michael, Chief Executive Officer, Rooks County Health Center, Plainville, KS, p. A252

SINCLAIR, Noreen, Human Resources Administrator, Connecticut Veterans Home and Hospital, Rocky Hill, CT, p. A116

SINCLAIR–CHUNG, Opal, R.N. Chief Nursing Officer, Deputy Executive Director, NYC Health + Hospitals / Kings County,, NY, p. A448

SINCOCK, Gregory M., Information Technology Leader, Kaiser Permanente West Los Angeles Medical Center, Los Angeles, CA, p. A72

SINDELAR, David, Chief Executive Officer, St. Anthony's Medical Center, Saint Louis, MO, p. A381

SINDELAR, Michael, Vice President and Chief Financial Officer, Fremont Health, Fremont, NE, p. A396

SINDLINGER, Julie A., Director of Human Resources, Weston County Health Services, Newcastle, WY, p. A723

SINEK, James J., FACHE, President, Boone Hospital Center, Columbia, MO, p. A370

SINGER, Brent, Chief Financial Officer, St. Anthony's Medical Center, Saint Louis, MO, p. A381

SINGH, Amarjit, M.D., President and Chief Executive Officer, Brunswick Psych Center, Amityville, NY, p. A433

SINGH, Armandeep, Chief Medical Officer, Monroe Hospital, Bloomfield, IN, p. A207

SINGH, Brij, Medical Staff Director, Kindred Hospital Rome, Rome, GA, p. A165

SINGH, Deepraj, M.D. Medical Director, Montgomery County Emergency Service, Norristown, PA, p. A546

SINGH, Gagandeep, M.D. Chief Medical Officer Behavioral Health, Banner Behavioral Health Hospital – Scottsdale, Scottsdale, AZ, p. A38

SINGH, Gurmant, Chief Medical Officer, Good Samaritan Hospital, Bakersfield, CA, p. A56

SINGH, Himanshu, M.D. Associate Director, Veterans Affairs Ann Arbor Healthcare System, Ann Arbor, MI, p. A318

SINGH, Inderjit, M.D. Clinical Director, Pilgrim Psychiatric Center, Brentwood, NY, p. A435

SINGH, Vijayant, M.D. Chief Medical Officer, Bayonne Medical Center, Bayonne, NJ, p. A414

SINGLES, James L., Chief Financial Officer, Marlette Regional Hospital, Marlette, MI, p. A329

SINGLETARY–TWYMAN, Michelle, Chief Nursing Officer, Rockford Center, Newark, DE, p. A119

SINGLETON, Al, M.D. Chief Psychiatry and Chief Medical Staff, Colorado Mental Health Institute at Pueblo, Pueblo, CO, p. A109

SINGLETON, J. Knox, President and Chief Executive Officer, Inova Health System, Falls Church, VA, p. B73

SINGLETON, Roy, Director Computer Information Systems, Palmdale Regional Medical Center, Palmdale, CA, p. A81

SINHA, Sunil K., M.D. Chief Medical Officer, Bon Secours Memorial Regional Medical Center, Mechanicsville, VA, p. A673

SINIARD, Sandra, Vice President of Patient Care Services, Cornerstone Medical Center, Fort Oglethorpe, GA, p. A160

SINICKAS, Robert, Director Information Services, Marianjoy Rehabilitation Hospital, Wheaton, IL, p. A205

SINICROPE, Jr., Frank J., Vice President Financial Services, Princeton Community Hospital, Princeton, WV, p. A699

SINISI, Albert, Director Information Systems, Doctors' Hospital of Michigan, Pontiac, MI, p. A332

SINK, Kristi M., Interim President, University Hospitals Parma Medical Center, Parma, OH, p. A501

SINNOTT, James, M.D. Chief Medical Staff, Coquille Valley Hospital, Coquille, OR, p. A525

SINNOTT, Lisa M., Director Human Resources, Lourdes Specialty Hospital of Southern New Jersey, Willingboro, NJ, p. A425

SINOPOLI, Angelo, M.D. Vice President Clinical Integration and Chief Medical Officer, GHS Greenville Memorial Hospital, Greenville, SC, p. A566

SINOTTE, Brian, Chief Executive Officer, UP Health System–Marquette, Marquette, MI, p. A329

SIOSON, Stephanie
Director Human Resources, Garden Grove Hospital and Medical Center, Garden Grove, CA, p. A64
Director Human Resources, Huntington Beach Hospital, Huntington Beach, CA, p. A66
Director Human Resources, La Palma Intercommunity Hospital, La Palma, CA, p. A67
Director Human Resources, West Anaheim Medical Center, Anaheim, CA, p. A54

SIOUFI, Habib, M.D. Chief Medical Officer, UMass Memorial–Marlborough Hospital, Marlborough, MA, p. A312

SIPEK, John, Supervisor Client Services, Aurora Medical Center in Washington County, Hartford, WI, p. A707

SIREK, David, Chief Information Officer, Myrtue Medical Center, Harlan, IA, p. A232

SIRK, Donald, Director Information Systems, MedStar St. Mary's Hospital, Leonardtown, MD, p. A302

SIROIS, Peter, Chief Executive Officer, Northern Maine Medical Center, Fort Kent, ME, p. A293

SIROTTA, Ted, Chief Financial Officer, Vail Valley Medical Center, Vail, CO, p. A111

SISILLO, Sabato, M.D
Chief Medical Officer, Providence Medical Center, Kansas City, KS, p. A246
Chief Medical Officer, Saint John Hospital, Leavenworth, KS, p. A247

SISK, Bryan W., Associate Director Patient and Nursing Services, Central Texas Veterans Health Care System, Temple, TX, p. A651

SISK, Glenn C., President, Coosa Valley Medical Center, Sylacauga, AL, p. A25

SISK, Jack, Chief Financial Officer, Punxsutawney Area Hospital, Punxsutawney, PA, p. A552

SISK, Lori, R.N.,
Chief Executive Officer, Sanford Canby Medical Center, Canby, MN, p. A340
Chief Executive Officer, Sanford Clear Lake Medical Center, Clear Lake, SD, p. A573

SISK, Rodney, Chief Financial Officer, Trinity Hospital of Augusta, Augusta, GA, p. A154

SISK, Susan, Chief Financial Officer, CHI St. Alexius Health, Bismarck, ND, p. A477

SISLER, Debbie, Director Human Resources, Vidant Roanoke–Chowan Hospital, Ahoskie, NC, p. A460

SISON, Joseph, M.D. Medical Director, Heritage Oaks Hospital, Sacramento, CA, p. A86

SISSON, Travis, Chief Executive Officer, Merit Health Batesville, Batesville, MS, p. A355

SISSON, William G., President, Baptist Health Lexington, Lexington, KY, p. A262

SISTO, Steven A., Senior Vice President and Chief Operating Officer, Methodist Hospital of Southern California, Arcadia, CA, p. A55

SISTRUNK, Heather, R.N. Chief Operating Officer, Merit Health River Oaks, Flowood, MS, p. A357

SITLINGER, James, Chief Human Resources Management, Charles George Veterans Affairs Medical Center, Asheville, NC, p. A460

SITTIG, Kevin, M.D. Senior Associate Dean and Chief Medical Officer, University Health Shreveport, Shreveport, LA, p. A288

SIU, Max, Chief Information Officer, Hackensack University Medical Center Mountainside, Montclair, NJ, p. A419

SIVAK, Steven, M.D. Chief Medical Officer, Einstein Physicians Philadelphia, Einstein Medical Center Philadelphia, Philadelphia, PA, p. A547

SIVLEY, Susanna S., Chief Personnel Officer, Highlands Medical Center, Scottsboro, AL, p. A25

SIWEK, Steven M., M.D., President and Chief Executive Officer, Freedom Pain Hospital, Scottsdale, AZ, p. A38

SIX, Deborah, Coordinator Data Processing, Wayne Memorial Hospital, Jesup, GA, p. A161

SJOBERG, Rochelle, Director Human Resources, Ely–Bloomenson Community Hospital, Ely, MN, p. A342

SKABELUND, Hoyt, Chief Executive Officer, Banner Churchill Community Hospital, Fallon, NV, p. A404

SKAGGS, Lynda, Chief Nursing Officer, Fleming County Hospital, Flemingsburg, KY, p. A259

SKALA, Pat, Chief Information Officer, Laguna Honda Hospital and Rehabilitation Center, San Francisco, CA, p. A90

SKARKA, Kathy, MSN Executive Vice President Patient Care Services, Nassau University Medical Center, East Meadow, NY, p. A438

SKARULIS, Patricia, Senior Vice President and Chief Information Systems Officer, Memorial Sloan–Kettering Cancer Center, New York, NY, p. A446

SKARZYNSKI, Joseph, M.D. Medical Director, NYC Health + Hospitals / North Central Bronx,, NY, p. A449

SKEEN, Steven, R.N
 Chief Clinical Officer, Medical Center Barbour, Eufaula, AL, p. A19
 Chief Nursing Officer, Mizell Memorial Hospital, Opp, AL, p. A24

SKELDON, Timothy K., Senior Vice President and Chief Financial Officer, Parrish Medical Center, Titusville, FL, p. A148

SKELLY, Stephanie, President Medical Staff, Red Bud Regional Hospital, Red Bud, IL, p. A201

SKELTON, Jenny, System Integration Manager, The Women's Hospital, Newburgh, IN, p. A220

SKELTON, Katie, MSN Vice President Nursing and Chief Nursing Officer, St. Joseph Hospital, Orange, CA, p. A81

SKIBBA, Joshua, Chief Medical Officer, Ohio County Hospital, Hartford, KY, p. A261

SKIDMORE, Jocelyn, Director Finance, SSM Health St. Francis Hospital – Maryville, Maryville, MO, p. A376

SKIDMORE, Kim, Chief Executive Officer, Community Medical Center of Izard County, Calico Rock, AR, p. A44

SKIEM, Paul, Senior Vice President Human Resources, Presence Saint Francis Hospital, Evanston, IL, p. A190

SKILLINGS, Charles E., President and Chief Executive Officer, St. Anthony Shawnee Hospital, Shawnee, OK, p. A520

SKILLINGS, Lois N., MSN, President and Chief Executive Officer, Mid Coast Hospital, Brunswick, ME, p. A292

SKINNER, Christopher, Chief of Staff, Spectrum Health Big Rapids Hospital, Big Rapids, MI, p. A319

SKINNER, Gary, Director Information Technology, Rehabilitation Hospital of Indiana, Indianapolis, IN, p. A214

SKINNER, Gwendolyn, Executive Director, Devereux Georgia Treatment Network, Kennesaw, GA, p. A161

SKINNER, Kellcie, Controller, Newman Memorial Hospital, Shattuck, OK, p. A519

SKINNER, Kristina, Director Quality, Sanpete Valley Hospital, Mount Pleasant, UT, p. A660

SKINNER, Marjorie, Director Finance, Pershing General Hospital, Lovelock, NV, p. A407

SKINNER, Richard, Chief Information Technology Officer, University of Virginia Medical Center, Charlottesville, VA, p. A668

SKINNER, Sue, Vice President of Patient Care Services, Grand Itasca Clinic and Hospital, Grand Rapids, MN, p. A343

SKIPPER, Kymberli, Manager Human Resources, Prattville Baptist Hospital, Prattville, AL, p. A25

SKIPPER, Michelle, Director Human Resources, Kaiser Permanente Riverside Medical Center, Riverside, CA, p. A85

SKJOLDEN, Jessica, M.D. Chief of Staff, St. Andrew's Health Center, Bottineau, ND, p. A477

SKLAMBERG, Todd, President, Sunrise Hospital and Medical Center, Las Vegas, NV, p. A407

SKLAR, Joel, M.D. Chief Medical Officer, Marin General Hospital, Greenbrae, CA, p. A65

SKLIRIS, Demetre, Chief Medical Officer, Avera Dells Area Hospital, Dell Rapids, SD, p. A573

SKOCH, Michael, M.D. Chief Medical Officer, Mary Lanning Healthcare, Hastings, NE, p. A396

SKOGSBERGH, Jim H., President and Chief Executive Officer, Advocate Health Care, Downers Grove, IL, p. B7

SKORA, Lori, Chief Executive Officer, Kindred Hospital of Northern Indiana, Mishawaka, IN, p. A218

SKOW, Glenn, M.D. Chief of Staff, Fayette County Hospital, Vandalia, IL, p. A204

SKOWRON, Paul, Chief Executive Officer, Dr. John Warner Hospital, Clinton, IL, p. A187

SKRINDE, Tracie, Senior Human Resources Partner, PeaceHealth United General Medical Center, Sedro–Woolley, WA, p. A690

SKRIPPS, Michele M., R.N., Chief Executive Officer, AnMed Health Rehabilitation Hospital, Anderson, SC, p. A562

SKULA, Erika, President and Chief Executive Officer, Manchester Memorial Hospital, Manchester, KY, p. A266

SKUPIEN, Mary Beth, Director, Battle Creek Veterans Affairs Medical Center, Battle Creek, MI, p. A319

SKVARENINA, Michael, Assistant Vice President Information Systems, Holy Name Medical Center, Teaneck, NJ, p. A424

SKYLES, Jill, R.N
 Vice President Patient Care Services and Chief Nurse Executive, Barnes–Jewish St. Peters Hospital, Saint Peters, MO, p. A382
 Vice President Patient Care Services and Chief Nurse Executive, Progress West Hospital, O'Fallon, MO, p. A377

SLABA, Bryan, Chief Executive Officer, Wagner Community Memorial Hospital Avera, Wagner, SD, p. A577

SLABIK, Shauna, Chief Financial Officer, Sanford Mayville Medical Center, Mayville, ND, p. A480

SLACK, Randy, Chief Executive Officer, CHI St. Luke's Health Memorial Livingston, Livingston, TX, p. A633

SLADKY, Todd J., Chief Financial Officer, Great River Medical Center, West Burlington, IA, p. A239

SLAGLE, Julie A., R.N. Vice President Patient Care Services, Sidney Regional Medical Center, Sidney, NE, p. A402

SLATE, Sonny, Chief Operating Officer, Georgia Regional Hospital at Atlanta, Decatur, GA, p. A158

SLATER, Craig M., M.D. Chief Medical Officer, Carolinas Healthcare System Union, Monroe, NC, p. A469

SLATER, Mark, Director Information Systems, Lake Pointe Medical Center, Rowlett, TX, p. A644

SLATER–NESUOLD, Stephanie, Director of Nursing, Landmark Hospital of Joplin, Joplin, MO, p. A372

SLATON, Brenda, Superintendent, Rusk State Hospital, Rusk, TX, p. A644

SLATTERY, Greg, Vice President Information, Community Hospitals and Wellness Centers, Bryan, OH, p. A485

SLATTERY, Susan L., Director Human Resources, UnityPoint Health – St. Luke's Hospital, Cedar Rapids, IA, p. A226

SLATTMAN, Robin, Chief Nursing Officer, Memorial Health, Marysville, OH, p. A498

SLAVIN, Kevin J., FACHE, President and Chief Executive Officer, St. Joseph's Healthcare System, Paterson, NJ, p. A421

SLAVIN, Peter L., M.D., President, Massachusetts General Hospital, Boston, MA, p. A307

SLAWITSKY, Bruce, Vice President Human Resources, Hospital for Special Surgery, New York, NY, p. A444

SLAYDON, Cindy, Chief Nursing Executive, Sparks Regional Medical Center, Fort Smith, AR, p. A46

SLAYMAN, Aubree, Director Patient Services, Miami County Medical Center, Paola, KS, p. A251

SLAYTON, Val, M.D. Vice President Medical Affairs, Sts. Mary & Elizabeth Hospital, Louisville, KY, p. A265

SLEDGE, Cynthia Moore, M.D. Medical Director, Bryce Hospital, Tuscaloosa, AL, p. A26

SLEDGE, Tasha, Director Human Resources, Texas Health Harris Methodist Hospital Southlake, Southlake, TX, p. A649

SLEDGE, Tom, Chief Operating Officer, Northwest Medical Center – Springdale, Springdale, AR, p. A52

SLEEPER, Justin, Vice President Clinical Operations, Behavioral Health Network, Natchaug Hospital, Mansfield Center, CT, p. A114

SLEIME, Melanie, Director Human Resources, Memorial Hospital, North Conway, NH, p. A413

SLEITER, Michelle, Chief Executive Officer, Humboldt County Memorial Hospital, Humboldt, IA, p. A232

SLESSOR, Steve Robert, Chief Executive Officer, Buchanan County Health Center, Independence, IA, p. A232

SLICK, Lois, Director Human Resources, CHI LakeWood Health, Baudette, MN, p. A339

SLIDER, Carol, Chief Nursing Officer, Titus Regional Medical Center, Mount Pleasant, TX, p. A638

SLIETER Jr., Richard G., Administrator, Community Behavioral Health Hospital – Baxter, Baxter, MN, p. A339

SLIGER, Susan, Director Human Resources, War Memorial Hospital, Sault Sainte Marie, MI, p. A334

SLINGERLAND, Micki J., Chief Operating Officer, TriStar Centennial Medical Center, Nashville, TN, p. A591

SLITER, Elizabeth, M.D. Chairman Medical Staff, Decatur Health Systems, Oberlin, KS, p. A250

SLIWA, James, M.D. Chief Medical Officer, Rehabilitation Institute of Chicago, Chicago, IL, p. A186

SLIWINSKI, Jeff, Chief Financial Officer, Clear Lake Regional Medical Center, Webster, TX, p. A656

SLIWINSKI, Ron, Chief of Hospital Division, University of Wisconsin Hospitals and Clinics Authority, Madison, WI, p. A709

SLOAN, Gary, Chief Executive Officer, San Ramon Regional Medical Center, San Ramon, CA, p. A92

SLOAN, Patrick, Chief Financial Officer, Sandhills Regional Medical Center, Hamlet, NC, p. A466

SLOAN, Prudence, Coordinator Human Resources, Select Specialty Hospital–Pittsburgh/UPMC, Pittsburgh, PA, p. A551

SLOAN, Ronald A., FACHE, President, The Outer Banks Hospital, Nags Head, NC, p. A470

SLOAN, Steve, Chief Financial Officer, Lake Cumberland Regional Hospital, Somerset, KY, p. A269

SLOCUM, Brandon H., Senior Vice President and Chief Financial Officer, Medical West, Bessemer, AL, p. A16

SLOCUM, Gregg Y., Chief Financial Officer, Valley Forge Medical Center and Hospital, Norristown, PA, p. A546

SLONIM, Anthony D., Dr.PH, President and Chief Executive Officer, Renown Health, Reno, NV, p. B114

SLONIM, Sheryl A., Executive Vice President and Chief Nursing Officer, Holy Name Medical Center, Teaneck, NJ, p. A424

SLONINA, Marrianne, Director Human Resources, Georgetown Community Hospital, Georgetown, KY, p. A260

SLOPER, Carol, Manager Information Technology, Cheyenne County Hospital, Saint Francis, KS, p. A253

SLOTERBEEK, Meridell, Chief Executive Officer, Select Specialty Hospital–Scottsdale, Scottsdale, AZ, p. A39

SLOVER, Christopher, Chief Executive Officer, Lakeview Specialty Hospital and Rehabilitation Center, Waterford, WI, p. A717

SLUBOWSKI, Michael A., FACHE, Chief Executive Officer, SCL Health, Broomfield, CO, p. B119

SLUCK, Jeana, R.N. Executive Director Nursing Clinical Inpatient Departments, Allied Services Rehabilitation Hospital, Scranton, PA, p. A554

SLUKA, Joseph, Chief Executive Officer, St. Charles Bend, Bend, OR, p. A524

SLUKA, Joseph, President and Chief Executive Officer, St. Charles Health System, Inc., Bend, OR, p. B127

SLUKA, Joseph, Chief Executive Officer, St. Charles Redmond, Redmond, OR, p. A530

SLUSHER, Carlene, Director Finance, Seneca Healthcare District, Chester, CA, p. A58

SLUSHER, Michael, Community Chief Executive Officer, Middlesboro ARH Hospital, Middlesboro, KY, p. A266

SLUSHER, W. James (Jamie), M.D. Chief of Staff, Jackson Parish Hospital, Jonesboro, LA, p. A279

SLUTSKER, Vladimir, Medical Director, HEALTHSOUTH Rehabilitation of Gadsden, Gadsden, AL, p. A20

SLY–FRANKLIN, Michelle, Chief Executive Officer, Sullivan County Community Hospital, Sullivan, IN, p. A222

SMAJSTRLA, Julie, Director Nursing, Seymour Hospital, Seymour, TX, p. A648

SMALL, Becky, Chief Human Resources Officer, Kindred Hospital–Aurora, Aurora, CO, p. A101

SMALL, Brenda, Chief Clinical Officer, AMG Specialty Hospital–Greenwood, Greenwood, MS, p. A358

SMALL, David, M.D
 Chief Medical Officer, Greene Memorial Hospital, Xenia, OH, p. A506
 Chief Medical Officer, Soin Medical Center, Beavercreek, OH, p. A484

SMALL, Deborah C., R.N. Vice President Patient Care Services and Chief Nursing Officer, Cleveland Clinic Fairview Hospital, Cleveland, OH, p. A489

SMALL, Donna, R.N. Chief Nursing Officer, St. Mary's Medical Center, West Palm Beach, FL, p. A150

SMALL, Jonathan, Chief Operations Information and Technology, John D. Dingell Veterans Affairs Medical Center, Detroit, MI, p. A322

SMALL, Terry L., Assistant Chief Executive Officer, William R. Sharpe, Jr. Hospital, Weston, WV, p. A701

SMALL–PLENTY, Paula, Human Resources Officer, Big Horn County Memorial Hospital, Hardin, MT, p. A388

SMALLEY, Ben, Chief Executive Officer, Bear River Valley Hospital, Tremonton, UT, p. A664

SMALLWOOD, Ravae, IS Coordinator, CHI Health Missouri Valley, Missouri Valley, IA, p. A234

SMANIK, Robert E., FACHE, President and Chief Executive Officer, Day Kimball Hospital, Putnam, CT, p. A116

SMARR, Susan, M.D. Physician–in–Chief, Kaiser Permanente Santa Clara Medical Center, Santa Clara, CA, p. A93

SMART, Dan, Chief Information Management Officer, Permian Regional Medical Center, Andrews, TX, p. A597

SMART, George J., Vice President Finance and Information Technology, MidMichigan Medical Center – Alpena, Alpena, MI, p. A318

SMART, Joanne F., M.D. Director Medical Affairs, Indiana University Health Bedford Hospital, Bedford, IN, p. A206

SMART, Melissa, Communication ad Public Relations Specialist, Texas Health Presbyterian Hospital Denton, Denton, TX, p. A613

SMART, Paul, CPA Chief Financial Officer, Franklin County Medical Center, Preston, ID, p. A178

SMART, Robert M., Chief Executive Officer, HEALTHSOUTH Rehabilitation Hospital – Mid–Cities, Bedford, TX, p. A602

SMART, Stephanie, Chief Nursing Officer, United Hospital Center, Bridgeport, WV, p. A694

SMEDLEY, Jessie, Chief Executive Officer, Weslaco Regional Rehabilitation Hospital, Weslaco, TX, p. A657

SMEEKS, Frank C., M.D. Chief Medical Officer, Frye Regional Medical Center, Hickory, NC, p. A467

SMELTZER, Sharon, Chief Executive Officer, Mercy Rehabilitation Hospital Oklahoma City, Oklahoma City, OK, p. A516

SMENDIK, Douglas, M.D. Chief Medical Officer, Spectrum Health Pennock, Hastings, MI, p. A326

SMIDT, Jessica, R.N. Director of Nursing, Pipestone County Medical Center Avera, Pipestone, MN, p. A348

SMIGA, Lance, Chief Financial Officer, Jackson County Hospital District, Edna, TX, p. A614

SMILEY, Christy, Leader Human Resources, SSM Health St. Mary's Hospital – Audrain, Mexico, MO, p. A376

SMILEY, Jon D., Interim Chief Executive Officer, Garfield County Public Hospital District, Pomeroy, WA, p. A688

SMITH, Agnes A., MSN Chief Nursing Officer, Twin County Regional Healthcare, Galax, VA, p. A671

SMITH, Alan H.
 Chief Financial Officer, Huntington Beach Hospital, Huntington Beach, CA, p. A66
 Chief Financial Officer, La Palma Intercommunity Hospital, La Palma, CA, p. A67

SMITH, Andrew, M.D. Chief of Staff, Guttenberg Municipal Hospital, Guttenberg, IA, p. A231

SMITH, Andrew, Chief Information Management, Madigan Army Medical Center, Tacoma, WA, p. A691

SMITH, Barbara H., Senior Vice President & Chief Operating Officer, Robert Wood Johnson University Hospital at Hamilton, Hamilton, NJ, p. A417

SMITH, Bennie, Chief Information Officer, Lady of the Sea General Hospital, Cut Off, LA, p. A276

SMITH, Bernie, Chief Financial Officer, Troy Community Hospital, Troy, PA, p. A556

SMITH, Bethany
 Director of Finance, CHI Oakes Hospital, Oakes, ND, p. A481
 Controller, HEALTHSOUTH Cane Creek Rehabilitation Hospital, Martin, TN, p. A587

SMITH, Betsy, Chief Nursing Officer, Effingham Hospital, Springfield, GA, p. A166

SMITH, Beverly Bzdek, Chief Nursing Officer, Southside Regional Medical Center, Petersburg, VA, p. A676

SMITH, Bill, M.D. Chief of Staff, Cullman Regional Medical Center, Cullman, AL, p. A18

SMITH, Blythe, Administrative Assistant, Faulkton Area Medical Center, Faulkton, SD, p. A573

SMITH, Bobby, Vice President Physician Services and Quality, Illinois Valley Community Hospital, Peru, IL, p. A200

SMITH, Bradley, President and Chief Executive Officer, Rush Memorial Hospital, Rushville, IN, p. A221

SMITH, Brenda, Director Financial Services, Alliance Health Center, Meridian, MS, p. A362

SMITH, Brent, Chief Executive Officer, Comanche County Memorial Hospital, Lawton, OK, p. A513

SMITH, Brent, M.D. Chief Medical Officer and Vice President Clinical Integration, Edward Hospital, Naperville, IL, p. A198

SMITH, Brian
 Chief Financial Officer, Beth Israel Deaconess Hospital–Needham Campus, Needham, MA, p. A312
 Director of Operations, Wamego Health Center, Wamego, KS, p. A255

SMITH, Carl, Director Information Systems, King's Daughters Medical Center, Brookhaven, MS, p. A356

SMITH, Carol, Vice President Patient Care and Chief Nursing Officer, Tift Regional Medical Center, Tifton, GA, p. A167

SMITH, Cheryl, Manager Human Resources, New Braunfels Regional Rehabilitation Hospital, New Braunfels, TX, p. A638

SMITH, Chris, Chief Information Officer, Falls Community Hospital and Clinic, Marlin, TX, p. A635

SMITH, Connie, President and Chief Executive Officer, Commonwealth Health Corporation, Bowling Green, KY, p. B34

SMITH, Connie, Chief Executive Officer, Medical Center at Bowling Green, Bowling Green, KY, p. A258

SMITH, Dan
 Director Human Resources, Austin Lakes Hospital, Austin, TX, p. A598
 Director Human Resources, Memorial Hospital, Carthage, IL, p. A182

SMITH, Daniel
 Chief Executive Officer, Memorial Hermann Surgical Hospital‰(First Colony, Sugar Land, TX, p. A650
 Chief Financial Officer, TOPS Surgical Specialty Hospital, Houston, TX, p. A627

SMITH, Daniel B.
 Vice President Finance, Good Samaritan Regional Medical Center, Corvallis, OR, p. A525
 Vice President Finance, Samaritan Albany General Hospital, Albany, OR, p. A524
 Vice President Finance, Samaritan Lebanon Community Hospital, Lebanon, OR, p. A527
 Chief Financial Officer, Samaritan Pacific Communities Hospital, Newport, OR, p. A528

SMITH, Darrin, Vice President Human Resources, Parkview Medical Center, Pueblo, CO, p. A110

SMITH, Darwin K., Vice President Human Resources, Union Hospital, Dover, OH, p. A493

SMITH, David, President and Chief Executive Officer, Cornerstone Healthcare Group, Dallas, TX, p. B42

SMITH, David, President, Cornerstone Hospital of Southwest Louisiana, Sulphur, LA, p. A288

SMITH, Deborah S., R.N. Vice President, Chief Nursing Officer, OSF St. Joseph Medical Center, Bloomington, IL, p. A181

SMITH, Debra
 Chief Executive Officer, Gundersen St. Joseph's Hospital and Clinics, Hillsboro, WI, p. A707
 Chief Nursing Officer, HEALTHSOUTH Rehabilitation Hospital, Kingsport, TN, p. A585

SMITH, Denise
 Director Financial Services, Florida State Hospital, Chattahoochee, FL, p. A125
 Director Health Information, HEALTHSOUTH Chattanooga Rehabilitation Hospital, Chattanooga, TN, p. A580
 Director Human Resources, HSHS St. Mary's Hospital, Decatur, IL, p. A188

SMITH, Diana B., Chief Financial Officer, Promise Hospital of Dallas, Dallas, TX, p. A611

SMITH, Diane, Chief Nursing Officer, Baptist Health Extended Care Hospital, Little Rock, AR, p. A48

SMITH, Dianne, Director Personnel and Human Resources, Potomac Valley Hospital, Keyser, WV, p. A697

SMITH, Dick, Director Human Resources, West Park Hospital, Cody, WY, p. A722

SMITH, Donald, President Medical Staff, Bellevue Hospital, Bellevue, OH, p. A485

SMITH, Donna M., Chief Nursing Officer, Barstow Community Hospital, Barstow, CA, p. A56

SMITH, Donna P., R.N. Vice President Chief Operating Officer and Chief Nursing Officer, Clifton Springs Hospital and Clinic, Clifton Springs, NY, p. A437

SMITH, Donnie
 Chief Human Resources Officer, Laird Hospital, Union, MS, p. A365
 Director Human Resources, Rush Foundation Hospital, Meridian, MS, p. A362
 Director of Human Resources, Specialty Hospital of Meridian, Meridian, MS, p. A362

SMITH, Doug
 Chief Financial Officer, McKay–Dee Hospital Center, Ogden, UT, p. A661
 Chief Financial Officer, Rock Prairie Behavioral Health, College Station, TX, p. A606

SMITH, Edward H., President and Chief Executive Officer, St. Anthony Regional Hospital, Carroll, IA, p. A226

SMITH, Elizabeth A., Director of Nursing, John J. Pershing Veterans Affairs Medical Center, Poplar Bluff, MO, p. A378

SMITH, Eric, Chief Financial Officer, Bayfront Health St. Petersburg, Saint Petersburg, FL, p. A144

SMITH, Ericka, Chief Operating Officer, Monterey Park Hospital, Monterey Park, CA, p. A78

SMITH, Erin, Chief Operating Officer, East Georgia Regional Medical Center, Statesboro, GA, p. A166

SMITH, Eugene, Chief Information Officer, Maniilaq Health Center, Kotzebue, AK, p. A30

SMITH, Jr., Forrest "Bud" H., Chief Financial Officer, Fulton State Hospital, Fulton, MO, p. A371

SMITH, G. Todd, President, St. Elizabeth Community Hospital, Red Bluff, CA, p. A84

SMITH, Geoffrey, Chief Financial Officer, Lebanon Veterans Affairs Medical Center, Lebanon, PA, p. A542

SMITH, Gia, Chief Executive Officer, Central Valley Specialty Hospital, Modesto, CA, p. A77

SMITH, Greg, Chief Medical Officer, Lake Region Healthcare, Fergus Falls, MN, p. A342

SMITH, Greg, CPA Chief Financial Officer, Woman's Hospital, Baton Rouge, LA, p. A273

SMITH, Gregory
 Senior Vice President and Chief Information Officer, Midwest Orthopedic Specialty Hospital, Franklin, WI, p. A705
 Senior Vice President and Chief Information Officer, Wheaton Franciscan Healthcare – Franklin, Franklin, WI, p. A706
 Senior Vice President and Chief Information Officer, Wheaton Franciscan Healthcare – St. Francis, Milwaukee, WI, p. A712

SMITH, Gretchen, Vice President Nursing and Compliance and Risk, Rush Memorial Hospital, Rushville, IN, p. A221

SMITH, Harley, Chief Executive Officer, TMC Bonham Hospital, Bonham, TX, p. A603

SMITH, Heather
 President, Conemaugh Meyersdale Medical Center, Meyersdale, PA, p. A545
 Chief Operating Officer, Welch Community Hospital, Welch, WV, p. A701

SMITH, Holt, Chief Financial Officer, Springs Memorial Hospital, Lancaster, SC, p. A568

SMITH, Jack, Acting Chief Information Resources Management Service, Veterans Affairs Sierra Nevada Health Care System, Reno, NV, p. A408

SMITH, Jackie, R.N. Chief Nursing Officer, Holdenville General Hospital, Holdenville, OK, p. A513

SMITH, James E.
 Superintendent, North Texas State Hospital, Vernon, TX, p. A655
 Superintendent, North Texas State Hospital, Wichita Falls Campus, Wichita Falls, TX, p. A657

SMITH, James M., M.D. Medical Director, Bastrop Rehabilitation Hospital, Monroe, LA, p. A283

SMITH, Jameson, Chief Executive Officer, Saint Joseph Hospital, Denver, CO, p. A104

SMITH, Jamesy, D.O. Chief of Staff, Parkland Health Center – Liberty Street, Farmington, MO, p. A371

SMITH, Jamie, Supervisor Health Information Management Systems, HEALTHSOUTH Rehabilitation Hospital of Sewickley, Sewickley, PA, p. A554

SMITH, Janet, Chief Financial Officer, Troy Regional Medical Center, Troy, AL, p. A26

SMITH, Jason
 Chief Medical Officer, Beaver Dam Community Hospitals, Beaver Dam, WI, p. A703
 Chief Nursing Officer, Piedmont Newnan Hospital, Newnan, GA, p. A164

SMITH, Jay, Director Information Systems, Brownwood Regional Medical Center, Brownwood, TX, p. A604

SMITH, Jeanna, Administrative Assistant and Human Resources Officer, Polk Medical Center, Cedartown, GA, p. A156

SMITH, Jeff, Chief Information Officer, Holy Cross Hospital, Fort Lauderdale, FL, p. A128

SMITH, Jeffrey A., M.D. Senior Vice President and Chief Medical Officer, Aurora St. Luke's Medical Center, Milwaukee, WI, p. A711

SMITH, Jesse, Director of Nursing, Keefe Memorial Hospital, Cheyenne Wells, CO, p. A102

SMITH, Jill, Administrative Coordinator, J. Paul Jones Hospital, Camden, AL, p. A18

SMITH, Jim, Director Information Systems, Washington County Memorial Hospital, Potosi, MO, p. A378

SMITH, Jo Beth
 Vice President Human Resources, Decatur County Hospital, Leon, IA, p. A233
 Chief Operating Officer, Medical Arts Hospital, Lamesa, TX, p. A632

SMITH, Joanne C., M.D., President and Chief Executive Officer, Rehabilitation Institute of Chicago, Chicago, IL, p. A186

SMITH, Jodi, Administrative Assistant Human Resources, Eureka Springs Hospital, Eureka Springs, AR, p. A45

SMITH, Jon
 Chief Executive Officer, Caribou Memorial Hospital and Living Center, Soda Springs, ID, p. A178
 Chief Financial Officer, Lost Rivers Medical Center, Arco, ID, p. A174

SMITH, Jonathan, Assistant Administrator and Chief Financial Officer, Blount Memorial Hospital, Maryville, TN, p. A588

SMITH, Joseph S., Chief Executive Officer, Boone County Hospital, Boone, IA, p. A226

SMITH, Julia
Chief Financial Officer, Kindred Hospital Rome, Rome, GA, p. A165
Chief Financial Officer, Kindred Hospital–Chattanooga, Chattanooga, TN, p. A580
Chief Financial Officer, Vibra Hospital of Charleston, Mt. Pleasant, SC, p. A568

SMITH, Julie, Director Human Resources, HEALTHSOUTH Lakeshore Rehabilitation Hospital, Birmingham, AL, p. A16

SMITH, Julie, R.N. Director of Nursing, Jersey Community Hospital, Jerseyville, IL, p. A194

SMITH, Julie, Senior Human Resources Strategic Partner, Providence Milwaukie Hospital, Milwaukie, OR, p. A528

SMITH, Justus, Interim Chief Nursing Officer, Williamson Memorial Hospital, Williamson, WV, p. A701

SMITH, Karen S., Director Information Services, Chilton Medical Center, Pompton Plains, NJ, p. A422

SMITH, Karyl, Director Human Resources, Harbor–UCLA Medical Center, Torrance, CA, p. A96

SMITH, Kathy A., MSN Nurse Executive, Summit Behavioral Healthcare, Cincinnati, OH, p. A488

SMITH, Kelli, M.D. Chief of Staff, Magee General Hospital, Magee, MS, p. A361

SMITH, Kelly C., Senior Vice President and Division President, Beaumont Hospital–Dearborn, Dearborn, MI, p. A321

SMITH, Kenneth, M.D. Emergency Medicine Medical Director, Coalinga Regional Medical Center, Coalinga, CA, p. A59

SMITH, Kenneth P., Chief of Staff, John C. Fremont Healthcare District, Mariposa, CA, p. A76

SMITH, Kevin, D.O. Chief of Staff, Otsego Memorial Hospital, Gaylord, MI, p. A324

SMITH, Kevin E., Chief Operating Officer, Scott & White Hospital at Round Rock, Round Rock, TX, p. A644

SMITH, Kevin L., Area Finance Officer, Kaiser Permanente South Sacramento Medical Center, Sacramento, CA, p. A86

SMITH, Kevin M., Director Human Resources, Indian Path Medical Center, Kingsport, TN, p. A585

SMITH, Kim, Director Business Office, Doctor's Hospital of Deer Creek, Leesville, LA, p. A282

SMITH, Kris, Controller, Madison St. Joseph Health Center, Madisonville, TX, p. A635

SMITH, Kyle, Director Information Systems, Iredell Health System, Statesville, NC, p. A474

SMITH, Larry, Senior Vice President and Chief Financial Officer, UW Medicine/Valley Medical Center, Renton, WA, p. A688

SMITH, LaVonne, Director Health Information Technology, Tomah Memorial Hospital, Tomah, WI, p. A717

SMITH, Leighton, M.D. Chief Medical Officer, Florida Hospital Fish Memorial, Orange City, FL, p. A140

SMITH, Leora, Information System and Health Information Management Team Leader, Phelps Memorial Health Center, Holdrege, NE, p. A397

SMITH, Linda C., M.D. Medical Director, HEALTHSOUTH Rehabilitation Hospital of Beaumont, Beaumont, TX, p. A601

SMITH, Linda T., Director Human Resources, Clay County Hospital, Ashland, AL, p. A15

SMITH, Linda V., Vice President Human Resources, Central Florida Regional Hospital, Sanford, FL, p. A145

SMITH, Lori
Chief Financial Officer, North Big Horn Hospital District, Lovell, WY, p. A723
Vice President Human Resources, St. Bernards Medical Center, Jonesboro, AR, p. A48

SMITH, Lorie, Director Human Resources, Nason Hospital, Roaring Spring, PA, p. A553

SMITH, Lory Beth, Manager Human Resource, South Texas Surgical Hospital, Corpus Christi, TX, p. A608

SMITH, M. Scott, President, St. Anthony's Hospital, Saint Petersburg, FL, p. A144

SMITH, Marisa, Director, Tomball Regional Medical Center, Tomball, TX, p. A653

SMITH, Mark, M.D. Chief Medical Officer, Methodist Richardson Medical Center, Richardson, TX, p. A643

SMITH, Mark
Director Human Resources, Providence Holy Family Hospital, Spokane, WA, p. A691
Director Human Resources, Providence Sacred Heart Medical Center & Children's Hospital, Spokane, WA, p. A691

SMITH, Marsh, Manager Health Information, University Behavioral Health of Denton, Denton, TX, p. A613

SMITH, Marshall E., Chief Executive Officer, Regency Hospital of Minneapolis, Golden Valley, MN, p. A343

SMITH, Martha, Chief Executive Officer, Kapiolani Medical Center for Women & Children, Honolulu, HI, p. A170

SMITH, Martha, R.N. Chief Nursing Officer, New Orleans East Hospital, New Orleans, LA, p. A285

SMITH, Martha M., R.N. Chief Nursing Officer, Park Plaza Hospital, Houston, TX, p. A626

SMITH, Mary Clare, M.D., Director, Western State Hospital, Staunton, VA, p. A679

SMITH, Mary Jo, Chief Human Resources Officer, University of Illinois Hospital & Health Sciences System, Chicago, IL, p. A187

SMITH, Marybeth
Director Human Resources, Saint Francis Hospital, Charleston, WV, p. A695
Director Human Resources, Thomas Memorial Hospital, South Charleston, WV, p. A700

SMITH, Matthew, M.D. Vice President Medical Affairs and Chief Medical Officer, Baylor Scott & White Medical Center – Carrollton, Carrollton, TX, p. A605

SMITH, Megan, M.D. Chief Medical Staff, Community Memorial Hospital, Burke, SD, p. A572

SMITH, Melinda, Chief Information Systems, H. C. Watkins Memorial Hospital, Quitman, MS, p. A364

SMITH, Melissa, Controller, Select Specialty Hospital–Jackson, Jackson, MS, p. A360

SMITH, Melissa A., Deputy Director, Delaware Psychiatric Center, New Castle, DE, p. A119

SMITH, Michael, Director of Nursing, Cypress Creek Hospital, Houston, TX, p. A624

SMITH, Michael, M.D. Vice President Medical Affairs, St. Joseph Mercy Oakland, Pontiac, MI, p. A332

SMITH, Michael K., D.O. Vice President Medical Affairs, McLaren Macomb, Mount Clemens, MI, p. A330

SMITH, Michelle, Coordinator Human Resources, Baton Rouge Rehabilitation Hospital, Baton Rouge, LA, p. A272

SMITH, Michelle T., R.N. Vice President Nursing Chief Nursing Officer Chief Experience Officer, GHS Greenville Memorial Hospital, Greenville, SC, p. A566

SMITH, Mickey, Chief Executive Officer, Oak Hill Hospital, Brooksville, FL, p. A125

SMITH, Mike
Chief Information Officer, Cape Coral Hospital, Cape Coral, FL, p. A125
Chief Information Officer, Gulf Coast Medical Center, Fort Myers, FL, p. A129
Chief Information Officer, Lee Memorial Hospital, Fort Myers, FL, p. A129

SMITH, Millie, Interim Chief Financial Officer, Galesburg Cottage Hospital, Galesburg, IL, p. A191

SMITH, Missy, Coordinator Human Resources, Scotland County Hospital, Memphis, MO, p. A376

SMITH, Mona R., Chief Nursing Officer, Green Valley Hospital, Green Valley, AZ, p. A33

SMITH, Moneca, Chief Nursing Offcer, The University of Toledo Medical Center, Toledo, OH, p. A504

SMITH, Nadine, Director Human Resources, Reeves County Hospital, Pecos, TX, p. A641

SMITH, Natalie R., R.N. Vice President Patient Care Services and Chief Nursing Officer, Portneuf Medical Center, Pocatello, ID, p. A178

SMITH, Neil, D.O., President, Cleveland Clinic Fairview Hospital, Cleveland, OH, p. A489

SMITH, Nekisha, Director Health Information Systems, Riverland Medical Center, Ferriday, LA, p. A276

SMITH, Nicholas T., Chief Executive Officer, Palm Springs General Hospital, Hialeah, FL, p. A130

SMITH, Norine, Chief Executive Officer, Red Lake Indian Health Service Hospital, Red Lake, MN, p. A349

SMITH, Oliver, President and Chief Executive Officer, Paris Community Hospital, Paris, IL, p. A199

SMITH, Pam, Chief Nursing Officer, HEALTHSOUTH Rehabilitation Hospital North Texas, Richardson, TX, p. A643

SMITH, Patricia, Chief Nursing Officer, Oconee Memorial Hospital, Seneca, SC, p. A569

SMITH, Patrick, M.D. Chief Medical Officer, Abrazo Arrowhead Campus, Glendale, AZ, p. A33

SMITH, Patrick, Director Information Technology, Clay County Hospital, Ashland, AL, p. A15

SMITH, Peg, Vice President and Chief Nursing Officer, Chandler Regional Medical Center, Chandler, AZ, p. A31

SMITH, Phyllis, Vice President Human Resources, Northeastern Health System, Tahlequah, OK, p. A520

SMITH, Phyllis J., Associate Director, Birmingham Veterans Affairs Medical Center, Birmingham, AL, p. A16

SMITH, Randall, Executive Vice President, Jackson Park Hospital and Medical Center, Chicago, IL, p. A184

SMITH, Rebecca T., Chief Operating Officer and Vice President, Caldwell Memorial Hospital, Lenoir, NC, p. A468

SMITH, Rebekah, R.N., President and Chief Executive Officer, Lake Huron Medical Center, Port Huron, MI, p. A332

SMITH, Rhonda
Chief Nursing Officer, Benewah Community Hospital, Saint Maries, ID, p. A178
Director Human Resources, Shriners Hospitals for Children–Portland, Portland, OR, p. A530
Applications Support Manager, UH Portage Medical Center, Ravenna, OH, p. A501

SMITH, Rhonda E., R.N
Vice President Patient Care Services and Chief Nursing Officer, Union Hospital, Terre Haute, IN, p. A222
Chief Nursing Officer, Union Hospital Clinton, Clinton, IN, p. A208

SMITH, Rich
Vice President Human Resources, Kaiser Foundation Hospital Westside Medical Center, Hillsboro, OR, p. A526
Vice President Human Resources, Kaiser Permanente Sunnyside Medical Center, Clackamas, OR, p. A524

SMITH, Richard, Chief of Staff, Carroll County Memorial Hospital, Carrollton, MO, p. A369

SMITH, Richard C.
Senior Vice President and Chief Financial Officer, JFK Medical Center, Edison, NJ, p. A416
Senior Vice President Finance, Shore Rehabilitation Institute, Brick, NJ, p. A414

SMITH, Rick
Director Information Services, Cibola General Hospital, Grants, NM, p. A429
Chief Operating Officer, Health Central Hospital, Ocoee, FL, p. A139
Director Information Systems, Tennova Healthcare–Jamestown, Jamestown, TN, p. A584
Senior Vice President Human Resources and Chief Administrative Officer, Vail Valley Medical Center, Vail, CO, p. A111

SMITH, Robert M., M.D., Director, VA San Diego Healthcare System, San Diego, CA, p. A89

SMITH, Robert T., M.D
Chief Medical Officer, Kettering Medical Center, Kettering, OH, p. A496
Chief Medical Officer, Sycamore Medical Center, Miamisburg, OH, p. A499

SMITH, Robin C., Chief Nursing Officer, Indiana University Health White Memorial Hospital, Monticello, IN, p. A218

SMITH, Rodney, President and Chief Executive Officer, Harrisburg Medical Center, Harrisburg, IL, p. A192

SMITH, Roy, Chief Financial Officer, Onslow Memorial Hospital, Jacksonville, NC, p. A468

SMITH, Ruth, Chief Human Resource Officer, Banner Lassen Medical Center, Susanville, CA, p. A95

SMITH, Ryan J., Administrator, Mayo Clinic Health System in Saint James, Saint James, MN, p. A350

SMITH, Ryan K.
Senior Vice President Information Technology, Banner – University Medical Center South, Tucson, AZ, p. A40
Chief Executive Officer, Memorial Hospital of Converse County, Douglas, WY, p. A722

SMITH, Scott, M.D. Chief Medical Officer, Adams Memorial Hospital, Decatur, IN, p. A209

SMITH, Scott M., Chief Executive Officer, Mercy Regional Medical Center, Ville Platte, LA, p. A289

SMITH, Sherry, Manager Human Resources, Dallas County Hospital, Perry, IA, p. A236

SMITH, Shirley M., Chief Financial Officer, Andalusia Health, Andalusia, AL, p. A15

SMITH, Sid, Director Information Resources, Larned State Hospital, Larned, KS, p. A247

SMITH, Skip, Vice President Finance, Iredell Health System, Statesville, NC, p. A474

SMITH, Stacy, R.N., Chief Executive Officer, Valir Rehabilitation Hospital, Oklahoma City, OK, p. A518

SMITH, Stephen
President, Selby General Hospital, Marietta, OH, p. A498
Associate Administrator, Turning Point Hospital, Moultrie, GA, p. A164

SMITH, Steve
Assistant Vice President Finance, CHI St. Gabriel's Health, Little Falls, MN, p. A345
Chief Financial Officer, Kansas Heart Hospital, Wichita, KS, p. A255

SMITH, Steve, M.D. Chief of Staff, Providence Kodiak Island Medical Center, Kodiak, AK, p. A29

SMITH, Steven, Chief Information Officer, NorthShore University Health System, Evanston, IL, p. A190

SMITH, Steven L., Chief Executive Officer, Matagorda Regional Medical Center, Bay City, TX, p. A601

SMITH, Stormy, Chief Nursing Officer, Chillicothe Hospital District, Chillicothe, TX, p. A606

SMITH, Suzanne E., R.N. Chief Nursing Officer, San Juan Regional Medical Center, Farmington, NM, p. A429

SMITH, Taylor, Chief Financial Officer, Eureka Springs Hospital, Eureka Springs, AR, p. A45

SMITH, Teresa, Chief Financial Officer, Memorial Hospital, Carthage, IL, p. A182

SMITH, Terrance, M.D. Chairman Medical Staff, Sanford Clear Lake Medical Center, Clear Lake, SD, p. A573

SMITH, Thomas, M.D. Vice President Medical Affairs, Hutchinson Regional Medical Center, Hutchinson, KS, p. A245

SMITH III, Thomas C., FACHE, Director, Birmingham Veterans Affairs Medical Center, Birmingham, AL, p. A16

SMITH, Thomas G., Administrator and Chief Executive Officer, Audubon County Memorial Hospital, Audubon, IA, p. A225

SMITH, Tiffany, Director Human Resources, Wellstone Regional Hospital, Jeffersonville, IN, p. A215

SMITH, Tim

Director Information Systems, Iroquois Memorial Hospital and Resident Home, Watseka, IL, p. A204

Senior Vice President and Chief Executive Officer, Sharp Memorial Hospital, San Diego, CA, p. A89

SMITH, Todd A., Chief Executive Officer, Aurora Charter Oak Hospital, Covina, CA, p. A60

SMITH, Toni, Chief Nursing Officer, Kern Medical Center, Bakersfield, CA, p. A56

SMITH, Tonya, President, Munson Healthcare Cadillac Hospital, Cadillac, MI, p. A319

SMITH, Tracy, Director Human Resources, Mercy St. Francis Hospital, Mountain View, MO, p. A377

SMITH, Trevor, Chief Management Information Services, Gunnison Valley Hospital, Gunnison, CO, p. A106

SMITH, Tripp, Chief Executive Officer, HEALTHSOUTH Rehabilitation Hospital, Largo, FL, p. A134

SMITH, Trisha, Chief Financial Officer, Mimbres Memorial Hospital, Deming, NM, p. A429

SMITH, Tyson, M.D. Chief Medical Officer, Haywood Regional Medical Center, Clyde, NC, p. A463

SMITH, Vanessa, Chief Human Resources Officer, Community Medical Center, Toms River, NJ, p. A424

SMITH, Vicki, Director of Nursing, The Pavilion at Williamsburg Place, Williamsburg, VA, p. A680

SMITH, Vincent

Chief Information Officer, NYC Health + Hospitals / Elmhurst, NY, p. A448

Chief Information Officer, NYC Health + Hospitals / Queens,, NY, p. A449

SMITH, Wade, Chief Operating Officer, Drew Memorial Hospital, Monticello, AR, p. A50

SMITH, Wayne T., Chairman, President and Chief Executive Officer, Community Health Systems, Inc., Franklin, TN, p. B35

SMITH, Wendell, Chief Operating Officer, St. James Behavioral Health Hospital, Gonzales, LA, p. A277

SMITH-HILL, Janet

Senior Vice President Human Resources, Novant Health Forsyth Medical Center, Winston-Salem, NC, p. A476

Senior Vice President Human Resources, Novant Health Presbyterian Medical Center, Charlotte, NC, p. A463

SMITH-ZUBA, Lorraina, R.N. Chief Nursing Officer, Porter Medical Center, Middlebury, VT, p. A665

SMITHERS, John, Network Specialist, River Hospital, Alexandria Bay, NY, p. A433

SMITHHART, Paula, Director Human Resources, Coryell Memorial Hospital, Gatesville, TX, p. A620

SMITHSON, Pamela, Vice President Nursing, Davis Medical Center, Elkins, WV, p. A695

SMITHSON, Tracey, MSN Chief Nursing Officer, North Hills Hospital, North Richland Hills, TX, p. A639

SMOAK, Tim, Administrator, McLeod Medical Center–Darlington, Darlington, SC, p. A565

SMOCK, Tait, Manager Information Systems, Pella Regional Health Center, Pella, IA, p. A236

SMOKER, Bret, M.D. Clinical Director, PHS Santa Fe Indian Hospital, Santa Fe, NM, p. A431

SMOLIK, Chris, Chief Executive Officer, Niobrara Health and Life Center, Lusk, WY, p. A723

SMOOT, Steve, Administrator, Utah Valley Regional Medical Center, Provo, UT, p. A662

SMORRA, Colleen, Assistant Administrator, Hackensack University Medical Center at Pascack Valley, Westwood, NJ, p. A425

SMOTHERS, Kevin, M.D. Vice President Chief Medical Officer, Adventist Healthcare Shady Grove Medical Center, Rockville, MD, p. A303

SMOTHERS, Mark, M.D. Chief Medical Officer, University of Mississippi Medical Center Holmes County, Lexington, MS, p. A361

SMOTHERS, Stephen, Director Information Systems, Medical Center Enterprise, Enterprise, AL, p. A19

SMYTH, Thomas, President and Chief Executive Officer, University of Maryland St. Joseph Medical Center, Towson, MD, p. A304

SNAPP, Jeremy, Director Information Systems, Lindsborg Community Hospital, Lindsborg, KS, p. A248

SNAPP, III, William R.

Vice President and Chief Financial Officer, Ephraim McDowell Fort Logan Hospital, Stanford, KY, p. A269

Vice President Finance and Chief Financial Officer, Ephraim McDowell Regional Medical Center, Danville, KY, p. A259

SNAVELY, Gretchen, Director Human Resources, Holton Community Hospital, Holton, KS, p. A245

SNEAD, Raymond A., FACHE, Interim Chief Executive Officer, South Georgia Medical Center, Valdosta, GA, p. A168

SNEATH, Roger, Chief Financial Officer, Memorial Medical Center – Neillsville, Neillsville, WI, p. A712

SNEDEGAR, Michael, Chief Financial Officer, Bourbon Community Hospital, Paris, KY, p. A268

SNEED, Farron, FACHE, Chief Executive Officer, Lovelace Westside Hospital, Albuquerque, NM, p. A427

SNEERINGER, Rhonda, M.D. Chief Medical Officer, Barton Memorial Hospital, South Lake Tahoe, CA, p. A95

SNELGROVE, Steven C., President, Howard County General Hospital, Columbia, MD, p. A300

SNELL, Peggy, Chief Finance Officer, Cherry County Hospital, Valentine, NE, p. A402

SNENK, Don, Chief Financial Officer, Mercy Fitzgerald Hospital, Darby, PA, p. A536

SNIDE, Jeaniffr P., Chief Nursing Officer, Crete Area Medical Center, Crete, NE, p. A395

SNIDER, Charles, Vice President Human Resources, Oak Hill Hospital, Brooksville, FL, p. A125

SNIDER, Cheryl, Director Human Resources, St. Vincent General Hospital District, Leadville, CO, p. A108

SNIDER, Glenn R., M.D., Interim Director, Louis A. Johnson Veterans Affairs Medical Center, Clarksburg, WV, p. A695

SNIDER, Tim, Senior Vice President for Finance, Upper Valley Medical Center, Troy, OH, p. A504

SNIDER, Timothy, Manager Information Systems, Fannin Regional Hospital, Blue Ridge, GA, p. A154

SNIPES, Rob, Administrator, Optim Medical Center – Tattnall, Reidsville, GA, p. A164

SNODGRASS, Liz, Chief Financial Officer, Trigg County Hospital, Cadiz, KY, p. A258

SNOOK, Joel, Chief Financial Officer, Westchester General Hospital, Miami, FL, p. A137

SNOW, Dorothy, M.D. Chief of Staff, Veterans Affairs Maryland Health Care System–Baltimore Division, Baltimore, MD, p. A298

SNOW, Jason T., Director People Services, HSHS St. Elizabeth's Hospital, Belleville, IL, p. A181

SNOW, John, Vice President Ancillary and Support Services, Iredell Health System, Statesville, NC, p. A474

SNOW, Meldon L., Chief Executive Officer, Logan County Hospital, Oakley, KS, p. A250

SNOW, Ryan, Director Human Resources, Habersham Medical Center, Demorest, GA, p. A158

SNOWDON, Susan, Director Information Technology, Four Winds Hospital, Saratoga Springs, NY, p. A455

SNYDER, Alice, Vice President, Chief Nursing Officer, OSF St. Mary Medical Center, Galesburg, IL, p. A191

SNYDER, Bobby

Chief Executive Officer, Midwest City Specialty Hospital, Midwest City, OK, p. A514

Interim Chief Executive Officer, Plum Creek Specialty Hospital, Amarillo, TX, p. A596

SNYDER, Daniel B., FACHE, Acting Director, James H. Quillen Veterans Affairs Medical Center, Mountain Home, TN, p. A590

SNYDER, David, M.D. Chief of Staff, DeKalb Medical at Downtown Decatur, Decatur, GA, p. A158

SNYDER, Jeffrey, Chief Executive Officer, Pocono Medical Center, East Stroudsburg, PA, p. A537

SNYDER, John, Executive Vice President and System Chief Operating Officer, Carle Foundation Hospital, Urbana, IL, p. A204

SNYDER, Kristi, Vice President Human Resources, Charleston Area Medical Center, Charleston, WV, p. A695

SNYDER, Kristy, Director Human Resources, Fulton County Health Center, Wauseon, OH, p. A505

SNYDER, Kyle C., Chief Administrative Officer, Holy Spirit – A Geisinger Affiliate, Camp Hill, PA, p. A534

SNYDER, Leah, Director Health Information Services, Loring Hospital, Sac City, IA, p. A237

SNYDER, Mary E., Chief Operations Officer, Montrose Memorial Hospital, Montrose, CO, p. A109

SNYDER, Matthew, R.N. Director of Nursing, Johnson County Hospital, Tecumseh, NE, p. A402

SNYDER, Norman, M.D. Medical Director, Vantage Point of Northwest Arkansas, Fayetteville, AR, p. A46

SNYDER, Phyllis, Chief Nursing Officer, AHMC Anaheim Regional Medical Center, Anaheim, CA, p. A54

SNYDER, R. Brad, Chief Operating Officer, Torrance State Hospital, Torrance, PA, p. A555

SNYDER, Renae, Chief Financial Officer, Sakakawea Medical Center, Hazen, ND, p. A479

SNYDER, Ron, Chief Operating Officer, OhioHealth Hardin Memorial Hospital, Kenton, OH, p. A496

SNYDER, Steve, Chief Financial Officer, Ohio Hospital for Psychiatry, Columbus, OH, p. A490

SNYDER, Tony, Administrator and Chief Executive Officer, Pomerene Hospital, Millersburg, OH, p. A499

SNYDER, Vicky, Chief Operating Officer, Cleveland Clinic, Medina Hospital, Medina, OH, p. A499

SOARES, Jair C., M.D., Executive Director, University of Texas Harris County Psychiatric Center, Houston, TX, p. A627

SOBECK, Brenda, Director of Human Resources, Jones Memorial Hospital, Wellsville, NY, p. A458

SOBER, Joseph, President, Mercy Allen Hospital, Oberlin, OH, p. A500

SOBIECK, Bridget, Director of Nursing, North Shore Health, Grand Marais, MN, p. A343

SODERHOLM, Jon, President, Avera Heart Hospital of South Dakota, Sioux Falls, SD, p. A576

SODERLING, Marcia, R.N. Hospital Nurse Executive, Legacy Mount Hood Medical Center, Gresham, OR, p. A526

SOEKEN, Charles

Director Information Technology, Providence Medical Center, Kansas City, KS, p. A246

Director Information Technology, Saint John Hospital, Leavenworth, KS, p. A247

SOEKORO, Julie, Chief Financial Officer, Grandview Medical Center, Birmingham, AL, p. A16

SOGARD, Matt, Chief Executive Officer, Lee's Summit Medical Center, Lee's Summit, MO, p. A375

SOGLIN, David, Chief Medical Officer, La Rabida Children's Hospital, Chicago, IL, p. A184

SOHN, Steven, M.D. President Medical Staff, Dallas County Hospital, Perry, IA, p. A236

SOILEAU, D. Kirk, FACHE, Chief Executive Officer, Natchitoches Regional Medical Center, Natchitoches, LA, p. A284

SOIMAN, Erika, CPA Chief Financial Officer, NYC Health + Hospitals / Woodhull,, NY, p. A449

SOKOLA, Thomas P., Chief Administrative Officer, Geisinger Medical Center, Danville, PA, p. A536

SOLA', Ivan', President Medical Staff, Carlisle Regional Medical Center, Carlisle, PA, p. A535

SOLAIMAN, Shereen, Vice President Human Resources, OhioHealth Riverside Methodist Hospital, Columbus, OH, p. A491

SOLARE, Frank A., Chief Executive Officer, Kindred Hospital Northwest Indiana, Hammond, IN, p. A212

SOLAZZO, Mark J., Regional Chief Operating Officer, Syosset Hospital, Syosset, NY, p. A456

SOLBERG, Bradley V., FACHE, President, OSF Saint James – John W. Albrecht Medical Center, Pontiac, IL, p. A201

SOLBERG, Don, M.D. Chief Medical Officer, Kittitas Valley Healthcare, Ellensburg, WA, p. A684

SOLCHER, Barry, M.D. Chief of Staff, The Physicians Centre Hospital, Bryan, TX, p. A604

SOLDO, Stephen, M.D. Chief Medical Officer, Saint Agnes Medical Center, Fresno, CA, p. A64

SOLER, Eddie, Chief Financial Officer, Florida Hospital, Orlando, FL, p. A140

SOLES, Jason, Manager Information Systems, St. James Mercy Hospital, Hornell, NY, p. A440

SOLHEIM, John H., Chief Executive Officer, Cuyuna Regional Medical Center, Crosby, MN, p. A341

SOLIE, Carol M., M.D. Chief Medical Officer, Wyoming Medical Center, Casper, WY, p. A721

SOLIMAN, Russell

System Manager Client Services and Management Information Services, Presence Saint Joseph Medical Center, Joliet, IL, p. A194

Director Information Services, Presence St. Mary's Hospital, Kankakee, IL, p. A194

SOLIN, Andrea

Chief Financial Officer, Lovelace Rehabilitation Hospital, Albuquerque, NM, p. A427

Chief Financial Officer, Lovelace Westside Hospital, Albuquerque, NM, p. A427

SOLINSKI, Ruth, Senior Director Human Resources, UP Health System–Marquette, Marquette, MI, p. A329

SOLIS, Gloria, R.N. Chief Nursing Officer, Saint Luke's East Hospital, Lee's Summit, MO, p. A375

SOLIVAN, Jose E.

Chief Financial Officer, Hospital Menonita De Cayey, Cayey, PR, p. A727

Chief Financial Officer, Mennonite General Hospital, Aibonito, PR, p. A725

SOLIZ, Mindy
Director Human Resources, CHRISTUS Spohn Hospital Alice, Alice, TX, p. A595
Director Human Resource Strategy, CHRISTUS Spohn Hospital Kleberg, Kingsville, TX, p. A630
SOLLENBERGER, Donna K., Executive Vice President and Chief Executive Officer, University of Texas Medical Branch, Galveston, TX, p. A620
SOLOM, Mike, Director Information Technology, Signature Psychiatric Hospital, Kansas City, MO, p. A374
SOLOMITA, Joy B., R.N. Vice President and Chief Nursing Officer, Florida Hospital Tampa, Tampa, FL, p. A147
SOLOMON, John, M.D., Director, South Carolina Department of Corrections Hospital, Columbia, SC, p. A564
SOLOMON, Oliver, M.D. Chief Medical Officer, Glendora Community Hospital, Glendora, CA, p. A65
SOLOMON, Tina, Executive Director Finance, Winter Haven Hospital, Winter Haven, FL, p. A150
SOLOMON–OWENS, Felicia, Director Human Resources, Fayette Medical Center, Fayette, AL, p. A20
SOLORIO, Roberta, Vice President, Chief Human Resource Officer, Midland Memorial Hospital, Midland, TX, p. A637
SOLORZANO, Rosa, Interim Director Human Resources, Toppenish Community Hospital, Toppenish, WA, p. A692
SOLOW, Jodie Sartor, Director Human Resources, Chatham Hospital, Siler City, NC, p. A473
SOLTIS, Les, Director – Human Resources, St. Francis Hospital, Federal Way, WA, p. A685
SOLVERSON, Paul, Chief Information Officer, St. Luke's Lakeside Hospital, The Woodlands, TX, p. A653
SOMERS, Tyrel, M.D. Chief Medical Officer, Russell Regional Hospital, Russell, KS, p. A252
SOMERVILLE, Jacqueline G., R.N. Senior Vice President for Patient Care Services and Chief Nursing Officer, Brigham and Women's Hospital, Boston, MA, p. A306
SOMERVILLE, Susan, R.N., President, Mount Sinai Beth Israel, New York, NY, p. A446
SOMMERS, Belinda, Chief Information Officer, Lake Charles Memorial Hospital, Lake Charles, LA, p. A281
SOMMERS, Dorene M., Associate Director Patient Care Services, Erie Veterans Affairs Medical Center, Erie, PA, p. A538
SOMMERS, Thomas W., FACHE, Chief Executive Officer, Beatrice Community Hospital and Health Center, Beatrice, NE, p. A394
SONATORE, Carol, D.O. Medical Director, HEALTHSOUTH Rehabilitation Hospital of Toms River, Toms River, NJ, p. A424
SONDAG, Timothy, Senior Nursing Officer, Hopedale Medical Complex, Hopedale, IL, p. A193
SONDERMAN, Betty, Manager Human Resources, Ridgeview Institute, Smyrna, GA, p. A166
SONDERMAN, Thomas, M.D. Vice President and Chief Medical Officer, Columbus Regional Hospital, Columbus, IN, p. A208
SONEL, Ali, M.D. Chief of Staff, Veterans Affairs Pittsburgh Healthcare System, Pittsburgh, PA, p. A552
SONENREICH, Steven D., President and Chief Executive Officer, Mount Sinai Medical Center, Miami Beach, FL, p. A138
SONG, Daniel, Chief Financial Officer, Monterey Park Hospital, Monterey Park, CA, p. A78
SONGER, Lucille, Chief Nursing Officer, Athol Memorial Hospital, Athol, MA, p. A305
SONGY, David, President and Chief Executive Officer, Saint Luke Institute, Silver Spring, MD, p. A303
SONNENBERG, Martha, M.D. Chief of Staff, Southern California Hospital at Culver City, Culver City, CA, p. A60
SONNENBERG, Stephanie
Director Information Technology, ProMedica Bixby Hospital, Adrian, MI, p. A318
Director Information Technology, ProMedica Herrick Hospital, Tecumseh, MI, p. A335
SONNENBERG, William, M.D. President Medical Staff, Titusville Area Hospital, Titusville, PA, p. A555
SONNENSCHEIN, Silvia, M.D. Chief of Staff, Kohala Hospital, Kohala, HI, p. A172
SONTZ, Jennifer
Director Human Resources, Evansville Psychiatric Children Center, Evansville, IN, p. A210
Director Human Resources, Evansville State Hospital, Evansville, IN, p. A210
SOOHOO, Richard, Chief Financial Officer, Sutter Medical Center, Sacramento, Sacramento, CA, p. A87
SOPER, Brent, Chief Financial Officer, San Joaquin Community Hospital, Bakersfield, CA, p. A56
SOPIARZ, Ed, Chief Financial Officer, University Behavioral Health of Denton, Denton, TX, p. A613
SOPKO, Joseph A., M.D. Chief Medical Officer, St. Vincent Charity Medical Center, Cleveland, OH, p. A489
SOPT, Michael, M.D. Chief of Staff, Brooks County Hospital, Quitman, GA, p. A164

SORAN, Andrei, MSN, Chief Executive Officer, Verity Health System, Los Angeles, CA, p. B151
SORBELLO, Bud, Director Management Information Systems, New York–Presbyterian/Hudson Valley Hospital, Cortlandt Manor, NY, p. A437
SORENSEN, Bonny
Chief Financial Officer, Wadley Regional Medical Center, Texarkana, TX, p. A652
Chief Financial Officer, Wadley Regional Medical Center at Hope, Hope, AR, p. A47
SORENSEN, Damon
Chief Financial Officer, McLaren Bay Region, Bay City, MI, p. A319
Chief Financial Officer, McLaren Bay Special Care, Bay City, MI, p. A319
SORENSEN, Shannon, Chief Executive Officer, Brown County Hospital, Ainsworth, NE, p. A393
SORENSEN, Vanessa, Chief Nursing Officer, Summit Medical Center, Casper, WY, p. A721
SORENSEN–BAKER, Cindi, Chief Operating Officer, Riverwood Healthcare Center, Aitkin, MN, p. A338
SORENSON Jr.,, Charles W., M.D., President and Chief Executive Officer, Intermountain Healthcare, Inc., Salt Lake City, UT, p. B73
SORENSON, Chris
Chief Information Officer, Sheltering Arms Hospital South, Midlothian, VA, p. A674
Chief Information Officer, Sheltering Arms Rehabilitation Hospital, Mechanicsville, VA, p. A673
SORENSON, Dennis, Supervisor Information Technology, South Haven Health System, South Haven, MI, p. A334
SORENSON, Eric C., Chief Financial Officer, Veterans Affairs Loma Linda Healthcare System, Loma Linda, CA, p. A69
SORENSON, Euretta, R.N. Chief Nursing Officer, CentraCare Health–Monticello, Monticello, MN, p. A347
SORENSON, Sheri, Manager Business Office, Highland Ridge Hospital, Midvale, UT, p. A660
SORENSON, Tawnya, Director of Nursing, Kittson Memorial Healthcare Center, Hallock, MN, p. A344
SOREY, Sharon D., R.N., Administrator, Mercy Hospital Paris, Paris, AR, p. A51
SOROKO, Theresa, M.D. Chief Medical Officer, Hackensack University Medical Center Mountainside, Montclair, NJ, p. A419
SORRELL, Rachel, Chief Financial Officer, Tsehootsooi Medical Center, Fort Defiance, AZ, p. A32
SORRELL, Sr., Ralph W., Chief Financial Officer, Adena Greenfield Medical Center, Greenfield, OH, p. A495
SORRELLS, Dwane, Chief Information Officer, Choctaw Nation Health Care Center, Talihina, OK, p. A505
SOSA, Phillip, Chief Financial Officer, El Paso Behavioral Health System, El Paso, TX, p. A615
SOSA–GUERRERO, Sandra, Chief Executive Officer, Larkin Community Hospital, South Miami, FL, p. A145
SOSNOW, Peter L., Medical Director, O'Connor Hospital, Delhi, NY, p. A438
SOSTMAN, Dirk, M.D. Executive Vice President, Chief Medical Officer and Chief Academic Officer, Houston Methodist Hospital, Houston, TX, p. A624
SOTERAKIS, Jack, M.D. Executive Vice President Medical Affairs, St. Francis Hospital, The Heart Center, Roslyn, NY, p. A455
SOTO, Ciria, Director Human Resources, Sonora Behavioral Health Hospital, Tucson, AZ, p. A41
SOTO, Itza, MSN Nursing Executive, Ashford Presbyterian Community Hospital, San Juan, PR, p. A729
SOTO, Juan Carlos, Director Information Systems, Hospital San Carlos Borromeo, Moca, PR, p. A728
SOTO, Manuel Ramirez, M.D. Medical Director, Hospital Metropolitano Dr. Tito Mattei, Yauco, PR, p. A731
SOTOIZAGUIRRE, Felix, Chief Financial Officer, North Fulton Regional Hospital, Roswell, GA, p. A165
SOTOS, Steven, M.D. President Medical Staff, LifeCare Hospitals of Pittsburgh, Pittsburgh, PA, p. A550
SOTUS–NAWAR, Athena, M.D. Medical Director, Anchor Hospital, Atlanta, GA, p. A152
SOUDERS, Stuart, Chief, Human Resources, William S. Middleton Memorial Veterans Hospital, Madison, WI, p. A709
SOUKUP, Paul, Chief Financial Officer, St. Luke Community Healthcare, Ronan, MT, p. A390
SOULE, Joyce M., R.N. Chief Nursing Officer, Wesley Medical Center, Wichita, KS, p. A256
SOURBEER, Jay C., Commanding Officer, Robert E. Bush Naval Hospital, Twentynine Palms, CA, p. A97
SOUTHER, Geoffrey C., Chief Operating Officer, New Hampshire Hospital, Concord, NH, p. A410
SOUTHERN, Joel, MSN, Chief Executive Officer, Merit Health Northwest Mississippi, Clarksdale, MS, p. A356
SOUTHWICK, Bill, R.N. Chief Nursing Officer, Mountain Vista Medical Center, Mesa, AZ, p. A34

SOUTHWORTH, Scott, M.D. Medical Director, South Davis Community Hospital, Bountiful, UT, p. A659
SOUZA, Darlene, Vice President, St. Joseph Health Services of Rhode Island, North Providence, RI, p. A560
SOUZA, Greg, Vice President Human Resources, Lucile Salter Packard Children's Hospital Stanford, Palo Alto, CA, p. A82
SOUZA, Jim, Chief Medical Officer, St. Luke's Regional Medical Center, Boise, ID, p. A175
SOUZA, Liz, Coordinator Nursing Services, Atascadero State Hospital, Atascadero, CA, p. A55
SOVETSKHY, Ed, Director Information Services, Portsmouth Regional Hospital, Portsmouth, NH, p. A413
SOWDERS, Dale, President and Chief Executive Officer, Holland Hospital, Holland, MI, p. A326
SOWELL, Ronald G.
Executive Vice President, Commonwealth Regional Specialty Hospital, Bowling Green, KY, p. A257
Executive Vice President, Medical Center at Bowling Green, Bowling Green, KY, p. A258
Executive Vice President, Medical Center at Franklin, Franklin, KY, p. A260
Chief Financial Officer, Medical Center at Scottsville, Scottsville, KY, p. A269
Executive Vice President, Chief Financial Officer, The Medical Center Albany, Albany, KY, p. A257
Executive Vice President and Chief Financial Officer, The Medical Center at Caverna, Horse Cave, KY, p. A262
SOWELL, Vincent, Chief Nursing Officer, Otto Kaiser Memorial Hospital, Kenedy, TX, p. A630
SOWERS, Chuck, Vice President Finance and Chief Financial Officer, Mercy Gilbert Medical Center, Gilbert, AZ, p. A32
SOWERS, Kevin W., MSN, President, Duke University Hospital, Durham, NC, p. A464
SPACK, Paula, R.N. Vice President Nursing, Punxsutawney Area Hospital, Punxsutawney, PA, p. A552
SPACKMAN, Jared, Chief Operating Officer, Davis Hospital and Medical Center, Layton, UT, p. A660
SPACONE, Celia, M.D. Director Operations, Buffalo Psychiatric Center, Buffalo, NY, p. A435
SPADE, Ann M., Chief Nursing Executive, Carlisle Regional Medical Center, Carlisle, PA, p. A535
SPADONI, Robert S., Vice President of Hospital Operations, Rush Oak Park Hospital, Oak Park, IL, p. A199
SPAFFORD, Mark, Interim Chief Financial Officer, Estes Park Medical Center, Estes Park, CO, p. A105
SPAGNA, Lauren, Marketing Director, West Boca Medical Center, Boca Raton, FL, p. A124
SPAHLINGER, David, M.D., President, University of Michigan Hospitals and Health Centers, Ann Arbor, MI, p. A318
SPAHR, Kristen, Director of Marketing, DeSoto Memorial Hospital, Arcadia, FL, p. A123
SPAIN, Jeanine R., R.N. Vice President Hospital Operations and Chief Nursing Officer, UnityPoint Health – Peoria, Peoria, IL, p. A200
SPAIN, Steve, Chief Operating Officer, Larned State Hospital, Larned, KS, p. A247
SPANBAUER, Lisa, Financial Program Supervisor, Winnebago Mental Health Institute, Winnebago, WI, p. A719
SPANGHER, Guido, M.D. Clinical Director, Big Spring State Hospital, Big Spring, TX, p. A602
SPANGLER, Mark, M.D. Chief Medical Officer, Gibson Area Hospital and Health Services, Gibson City, IL, p. A191
SPANGLER, Michael, Health Information Management Services Supervisor, HealthSouth Rehabilitation Hospital of Tallahassee, Tallahassee, FL, p. A146
SPANGLER, Wendell J., M.D. Chief of Staff, Paulding County Hospital, Paulding, OH, p. A501
SPANN, Debbie, Director Human Resources, Morehouse General Hospital, Bastrop, LA, p. A272
SPANN, Lori, Director Human Resources, Iberia Medical Center, New Iberia, LA, p. A284
SPANO, Dennis, M.D. Medical Director, Mayo Clinic Health System in Lake City, Lake City, MN, p. A344
SPANO, Jason, Manager Information Technology, Prowers Medical Center, Lamar, CO, p. A108
SPARE, John, Accountant, Parsons State Hospital and Training Center, Parsons, KS, p. A252
SPARGER, Kathy, R.N. Chief Nursing Officer, Baptist Health South Florida, South Miami Hospital, Miami, FL, p. A136
SPARKMAN, Dena C., FACHE, Community Chief Executive Officer, Whitesburg ARH Hospital, Whitesburg, KY, p. A270
SPARKMAN, Jill, Director Human Resources, Odessa Regional Medical Center, Odessa, TX, p. A639
SPARKS, Dennis, Vice President Human Resources, Saint Michael's Medical Center, Newark, NJ, p. A421
SPARKS, Gary R.
Administrator, CrossRidge Community Hospital, Wynne, AR, p. A53
Interim President, Lawrence Memorial Hospital, Walnut Ridge, AR, p. A53

SPARKS, Holly H., Chief Clinical Officer, South Sunflower County Hospital, Indianola, MS, p. A359

SPARKS, Jason, Director, Human Resources, HEALTHSOUTH Rehabilitation Hospital at Drake, Cincinnati, OH, p. A487

SPARKS, Jennifer, Human Resources Generalist, Complex Care Hospital at Ridgelake, Sarasota, GA, p. A145

SPARKS, Lisa, R.N. Chief Nursing Officer and Vice President Patient Care Services, Indiana University Health West Hospital, Avon, IN, p. A206

SPARKS, Richard G., President and Chief Executive Officer, Appalachian Regional Healthcare System, Boone, NC, p. B10

SPARKS, Richard G., Chief Executive Officer, Watauga Medical Center, Boone, NC, p. A461

SPARKS, Wendy, Chief Operating Officer, North Colorado Medical Center, Greeley, CO, p. A106

SPARLING, Nicki, Manager Human Resources, Major Hospital, Shelbyville, IN, p. A222

SPARPANA, Eileen, Chief Financial Officer, Dickinson County Healthcare System, Iron Mountain, MI, p. A327

SPARROW, Francis D., M.D. Medical Director, Philhaven, Mount Gretna, PA, p. A545

SPARROW, Robert T., M.D. Vice President, Chief Medical Officer, OSF Saint Francis Medical Center, Peoria, IL, p. A200

SPARTZ, Dale A., Chief Human Resources Officer, University of Utah Health Care – Hospital and Clinics, Salt Lake City, UT, p. A664

SPARZO, John, M.D. Vice President Medical Affairs, Hendricks Regional Health, Danville, IN, p. A209

SPATH, Deborah, Interim Director, Albany Stratton Veterans Affairs Medical Center, Albany, NY, p. A433

SPEAK, Brent, Chief of Staff, Northeast Regional Medical Center, Kirksville, MO, p. A375

SPEARE, Mark, Senior Associate Director Patient Relations and Human Resources, UCLA Medical Center–Santa Monica, Santa Monica, CA, p. A94

SPEARMAN, John, President and Chief Operating Officer, Laurel Regional Hospital, Laurel, MD, p. A302

SPEARS, David, D.O. Chief of Staff, Selby General Hospital, Marietta, OH, p. A498

SPEARS, Kevin, Chief Executive Officer, HEALTHSOUTH Rehabilitation Hospital of Memphis, Memphis, TN, p. A588

SPEARS, LaLana, Supervisor Accounting, Claremore Indian Hospital, Claremore, OK, p. A510

SPEARS, Michael, Human Resource Leader, St. Anthony Shawnee Hospital, Shawnee, OK, p. A520

SPEAS, Ryan, Director Finance, Livingston HealthCare, Livingston, MT, p. A389

SPEASE, Dorothy, Manager Business Office, Douglas County Memorial Hospital, Armour, SD, p. A572

SPECK, Michelle, Senior Vice President Human Resources, USMD Hospital at Fort Worth, Fort Worth, TX, p. A619

SPECK, Michelle A.
Vice President Human Resources, UPMC Altoona, Altoona, PA, p. A532
Vice President Human Resources, UPMC Bedford Memorial, Everett, PA, p. A538

SPECKMAN, Kelly Ann, Chief Financial Officer, Kearny County Hospital, Lakin, KS, p. A247

SPEECH, Thomas, Ph.D., Director, Winnebago Mental Health Institute, Winnebago, WI, p. A719

SPEELMAN, Steven, Director Information Systems, Novant Health UVA Health System Culpeper Medical Center, Culpeper, VA, p. A669

SPEER, Kevin, Chief Executive Officer, Hendricks Regional Health, Danville, IN, p. A209

SPEER, Linda, M.D. Interim Chief Medical Officer, The University of Toledo Medical Center, Toledo, OH, p. A504

SPEER-SMITH, Carol, R.N. Chief Nursing Officer, Oroville Hospital, Oroville, CA, p. A81

SPEES, M. Shane, President and Chief Executive Officer, North Mississippi Health Services, Inc., Tupelo, MS, p. B96

SPEICHER, Larry, Chief Executive Officer, Kearney Regional Medical Center, Kearney, NE, p. A397

SPEIER, Ryan, Vice President Administration, KVC Prairie Ridge Psychiatric Hospital, Kansas City, KS, p. A246

SPEIGHT, Becky, Chief Financial Officer, Lake Pointe Medical Center, Rowlett, TX, p. A644

SPEIGHT, Marianne, Vice President Information System and Chief Information Officer, Cincinnati Children's Hospital Medical Center, Cincinnati, OH, p. A487

SPELL, Kenneth R., Vice President Operations, Baptist Health South Florida, Homestead Hospital, Homestead, FL, p. A131

SPELL, Nicole
Director Human Resources, Vidant Bertie Hospital, Windsor, NC, p. A475
Director Human Resources, Vidant Chowan Hospital, Edenton, NC, p. A464

SPELLBERG, Brad, M.D. Chief Medical Officer, LAC+USC Medical Center, Los Angeles, CA, p. A72

SPELLMAN, Warren K., Chief Executive Officer, Grady Memorial Hospital, Chickasha, OK, p. A510

SPELLMEIER, Rhonda, R.N. Director of Nursing, Sabetha Community Hospital, Sabetha, KS, p. A253

SPELLS-WILSON, Debbie, R.N. Chief Nursing Officer, Trinity Hospital of Augusta, Augusta, GA, p. A154

SPENCE, Andre, Chief Medical Staff, Sanford Bagley Medical Center, Bagley, MN, p. A339

SPENCE, Ben
Chief Financial Officer, Cape Coral Hospital, Cape Coral, FL, p. A125
Chief Financial Officer, Gulf Coast Medical Center, Fort Myers, FL, p. A129
Chief Financial Officer, Lee Memorial Hospital, Fort Myers, FL, p. A129

SPENCE, Karie, Director Human Resources, Miller County Hospital, Colquitt, GA, p. A156

SPENCE, Karla, Director of Nursing, St. Andrew's Health Center, Bottineau, ND, p. A477

SPENCE, Monte, Chief Operating Officer, Rehabilitation Hospital of Indiana, Indianapolis, IN, p. A214

SPENCE, Sheldon, Director of Revenue Cycle, IT, Memorial Hospital of Texas County, Guymon, OK, p. A512

SPENCE, Steven Walter, M.D. Chief Medical Officer, Jackson Hospital, Marianna, FL, p. A135

SPENCE, Terri
Chief Information Officer, Bon Secours Maryview Medical Center, Portsmouth, VA, p. A676
Vice President and Regional Chief Information Officer, Bon Secours St. Francis Medical Center, Midlothian, VA, p. A673
Chief Information Officer, Bon Secours St. Mary's Hospital, Richmond, VA, p. A677
Vice President Information Services, Mary Immaculate Hospital, Newport News, VA, p. A674

SPENCE, William, Director, Roseland Community Hospital, Chicago, IL, p. A186

SPENCER, Erich, Chief Human Resource Officer, Fairview Northland Medical Center, Princeton, MN, p. A349

SPENCER, Jim, Director Information System, McLeod Health Cheraw, Cheraw, SC, p. A563

SPENCER, Marianne, R.N. Vice President Operations and Chief Operating Officer, Edward Hospital, Naperville, IL, p. A198

SPENCER, Marie, Chief Nursing Officer and Senior Administrator, Burke Rehabilitation Hospital, White Plains, NY, p. A459

SPENCER, Mark, D.O. Chief of Staff, North Canyon Medical Center, Gooding, ID, p. A176

SPENCER, Mike, Chief Information Officer, Henry County Hospital, New Castle, IN, p. A219

SPENCER, Misti, Director Inpatient Services, Selby General Hospital, Marietta, OH, p. A498

SPENCER, Sarah, M.D. Chief of Staff, South Peninsula Hospital, Homer, AK, p. A29

SPENCER, Scott, Chief Financial Officer, South Shore Hospital, Chicago, IL, p. A186

SPENCER, Susan, Chief Financial Officer, Samaritan Memorial Hospital, Macon, MO, p. A376

SPENCER, Todd, M.D. Chief Medical Staff, Adventist Medical Center–Reedley, Reedley, CA, p. A85

SPENST, Brett, Chief Executive Officer, Littleton Adventist Hospital, Littleton, CO, p. A108

SPERBER-WEISS, Doreen, Ph.D. Chief Nursing Officer, Greystone Park Psychiatric Hospital, Morris Plains, NJ, p. A419

SPERLING, Deanna, President and Chief Executive Officer, Barnabas Health Behavioral Health Center, Toms River, NJ, p. A424

SPERLING, Louis J., Vice President Human Resources, Rhode Island Hospital, Providence, RI, p. A561

SPERLING, Walter, M.D. Medical Director, Ellenville Regional Hospital, Ellenville, NY, p. A438

SPERRING, Jeff, M.D., Chief Executive Officer, Seattle Children's Hospital, Seattle, WA, p. A689

SPICER, Charles, President and Chief Executive Officer, OU Medical Center, Oklahoma City, OK, p. A517

SPICER, Joan G., R.N. Chief Nursing Officer, San Mateo Medical Center, San Mateo, CA, p. A92

SPICER, Michael J., President and Chief Executive Officer, Saint Joseph's Medical Center, Yonkers, NY, p. A459

SPICER, Randy, Information Technology Supervisor, Central State Hospital, Louisville, KY, p. A264

SPICER, Sam, M.D. Vice President Medical Affairs, New Hanover Regional Medical Center, Wilmington, NC, p. A475

SPIDLE, Tara, Chief Financial Officer, Decatur County Hospital, Leon, IA, p. A233

SPIEGEL, Kevin M., President and Chief Executive Officer, Erlanger Health System, Chattanooga, TN, p. B53

SPIEGEL, Kevin M., Chief Executive Officer, Erlanger Medical Center, Chattanooga, TN, p. A580

SPIER, Deborah, Administrator, Oceans Behavioral Hospital of Greater New Orleans, Kenner, LA, p. A279

SPIER, Scott A., M.D. Senior Vice President Medical Affairs, Mercy Medical Center, Baltimore, MD, p. A297

SPIGEL, Michael, Executive Vice President & Chief Operating Officer, Brooks Rehabilitation Hospital, Jacksonville, FL, p. A131

SPIGNER, Jason
Vice President Human Resources, Advocate Condell Medical Center, Libertyville, IL, p. A195
Vice President Human Resources, Advocate Good Shepherd Hospital, Barrington, IL, p. A181

SPIKE, Jennifer, Director Human Resources, St. James Mercy Hospital, Hornell, NY, p. A440

SPILLERS, David S., Chief Executive Officer, Huntsville Hospital, Huntsville, AL, p. A21

SPILLERS, David S., Chief Executive Officer, Huntsville Hospital Health System, Huntsville, AL, p. B71

SPILSBURY, Lauren, R.N. Vice President for Patient Care Services, Redlands Community Hospital, Redlands, CA, p. A85

SPINA, Lori, Vice President Human Resources, Good Samaritan Hospital Medical Center, West Islip, NY, p. A458

SPINA, Patricia, R.N. Director of Nursing, Runnells Center for Rehabilitation and Healthcare, Berkeley Heights, NJ, p. A414

SPINALE, Joseph W., D.O. Senior Vice President and Chief Medical Officer, Kent County Memorial Hospital, Warwick, RI, p. A561

SPINGOS, Maria, Director of Nursing, Fort Lauderdale Hospital, Fort Lauderdale, FL, p. A128

SPINHARNEY, Sarah, Senior Vice President, Baptist Medical Center, San Antonio, TX, p. A645

SPISSO, Johnese, Chief Executive Officer, Ronald Reagan UCLA Medical Center, Los Angeles, CA, p. A74

SPITSER, Christy
Vice President Finance and Business Development, Saint Joseph London, London, KY, p. A264
Vice President Finance, Saint Joseph Berea, Berea, KY, p. A257

SPIVEY, Amy, Chief Medical Officer, McCullough–Hyde Memorial Hospital/TriHealth, Oxford, OH, p. A501

SPIVEY, Courtney, Chief Nursing Officer, Hardin County General Hospital, Rosiclare, IL, p. A202

SPIVEY, David A., President and Chief Executive Officer, St. Mary Mercy Hospital, Livonia, MI, p. A329

SPLITT, Richie, FACHE, Interim President and Chief Executive Officer, Norman Regional Health System, Norman, OK, p. A515

SPOELMA, Susan G., MSN Chief Nursing Officer, Healdsburg District Hospital, Healdsburg, CA, p. A66

SPOELMAN, Roger, Interim President and Chief Executive Officer, Mount Carmel St. Ann's, Westerville, OH, p. A505

SPONG, Bernadette, Chief Financial Officer, Orlando Regional Medical Center, Orlando, FL, p. A140

SPONSLER, Betsy A., Chief Financial Officer, Valley Hospital Medical Center, Las Vegas, NV, p. A407

SPOON, Barry, M.D. Chief of Staff, Mercy St. Francis Hospital, Mountain View, MO, p. A377

SPOONER, Jennifer, Controller, HealthSouth Rehabilitation Hospital of Tallahassee, Tallahassee, FL, p. A146

SPORE, Larry, Chief Financial Officer, Lawrence County Memorial Hospital, Lawrenceville, IL, p. A195

SPRACKLEN, Aaron, M.D. Professional Staff President, Grande Ronde Hospital, La Grande, OR, p. A527

SPRADA, Mark, R.N., Interim Chief Executive Officer, Broward Health Medical Center, Fort Lauderdale, FL, p. A128

SPRADLIN, John, Information Systems Director, Franklin Foundation Hospital, Franklin, LA, p. A277

SPRAGGINS, Tommy, Director Information Services, Russell Medical Center, Alexander City, AL, p. A15

SPRAGUE, F. Remington, M.D. Chief Medical Officer, Mercy Health Hackley Campus, Muskegon, MI, p. A330

SPRAGUE, Sharon, Superintendent, Dorothea Dix Psychiatric Center, Bangor, ME, p. A291

SPRAKER, Larissa, Vice President Business Development and Chief Strategy Officer, Mercy Gilbert Medical Center, Gilbert, AZ, p. A32

SPRANGER, Lance, Chief Information Officer, St. John's Medical Center and Living Center, Jackson, WY, p. A722

SPRATLIN, Larry, Chief Financial Officer, Saint Thomas Rutherford Hospital, Murfreesboro, TN, p. A590

SPREER-ALBERT, Frances, Chief Financial Officer and Executive Vice President, Albany Medical Center, Albany, NY, p. A433

SPRENGEL, Julie, Chief Executive Officer, Providence Saint Joseph Medical Center, Burbank, CA, p. A57

SPRIGGS, Larry, Controller, HealthSouth Rehabilitation Institute of San Antonio, San Antonio, TX, p. A646

SPRINGATE, Brian, Chief Executive Officer, Fleming County Hospital, Flemingsburg, KY, p. A259

SPRINGER, Amy, Medical Director, Webster County Community Hospital, Red Cloud, NE, p. A402

SPRINGER, Madge, Director Human Resources, Florida Hospital Waterman, Tavares, FL, p. A148

SPRINGER, Sharon, Chief Nursing Officer, Cameron Memorial Community Hospital, Angola, IN, p. A206

SPRINGER, Theresa, Chief Nursing Officer, OSF Holy Family Medical Center, Monmouth, IL, p. A197

SPRINGMANN, Tressa
Vice President and Chief Information Officer, Levindale Hebrew Geriatric Center and Hospital, Baltimore, MD, p. A296
Vice President and Chief Information Officer, Northwest Hospital, Randallstown, MD, p. A303

SPRINKEL, George, Chief Financial Officer, Tennova Healthcare–Clarksville, Clarksville, TN, p. A581

SPROTT, Kendell R., JD, Chief Executive Officer, Matheny Medical and Educational Center, Peapack, NJ, p. A421

SPROUT, Merry, R.N. Chief Nursing Officer, Antelope Memorial Hospital, Neligh, NE, p. A399

SPROWL, Chris, M.D. Vice President, PeaceHealth St. Joseph Medical Center, Bellingham, WA, p. A682

SPRUYT, Jim, Chief Executive Officer, Rolling Hills Hospital, Franklin, TN, p. A583

SPRYS, Michael, D.O. Chief of Staff, Medical Arts Hospital, Lamesa, TX, p. A632

SPUHLER, Richard, Chief Executive Officer, Brigham City Community Hospital, Brigham City, UT, p. A659

SPURGEON, Sharon A., Chief Executive Officer, Coalinga Regional Medical Center, Coalinga, CA, p. A59

SPURLOCK, James, D.O. Chief of Staff, Saint Thomas Stones River Hospital, Woodbury, TN, p. A594

SPYKERMAN, Connie, Chief Nursing Officer, Pelham Medical Center, Greer, SC, p. A567

SPYROW, Florence (Flo), Chief Administrative Officer, Flagstaff Medical Center, Flagstaff, AZ, p. A32

SQUIRES, Danny
Chief Financial Officer, Wake Forest Baptist Health–Davie Medical Center, Mocksville, NC, p. A469
Vice President and Chief Financial Officer, Wake Forest Baptist Health–Lexington Medical Center, Lexington, NC, p. A469

SQUIRES, Elizabeth, R.N. Chief Nursing Officer, HealthSouth Rehabilitation Hospital of Tallahassee, Tallahassee, FL, p. A146

SQUIRES, Paula C., Senior Vice President, Chief Human Resources Officer and Chief Human Resources Officer, Baystate Medical Center, Springfield, MA, p. A314

SQUIRES, Teresa, R.N. Chief Nursing Officer, Lake District Hospital, Lakeview, OR, p. A527

SREBINSKI, Ron, Chief Financial Officer, Caro Community Hospital, Caro, MI, p. A320

SRIBNICK, Wayne, M.D. Senior Vice President and Chief Medical Officer, Providence Hospital, Columbia, SC, p. A564

SRINIVASAN, Parthasarathy, M.D. President Medical Staff, Galesburg Cottage Hospital, Galesburg, IL, p. A191

SRIPADA, Subra
Executive Vice President, Chief Transportation Officer and Chief Information Officer, Beaumont Hospital – Farmington Hills, Farmington Hills, MI, p. A323
Executive Vice President, Chief Transportation Officer and Chief Information Officer, Beaumont Hospital – Grosse Pointe, Grosse Pointe, MI, p. A326
Executive Vice President, Chief Transportation Officer and Chief Information Officer, Beaumont Hospital – Royal Oak, Royal Oak, MI, p. A333
Exec. Vice President, Chief Transformation Officer and Chief Information Officer, Beaumont Hospital – Taylor, Taylor, MI, p. A335
Executive Vice President, Chief Transformation Officer and Chief Information Officer, Beaumont Hospital – Trenton, Trenton, MI, p. A335
Executive Vice President, Chief Transportation Officer and Chief Information Officer, Beaumont Hospital – Troy, Troy, MI, p. A336
Executive Vice President, Chief Transformation Officer and Chief Information Officer, Beaumont Hospital – Wayne, Wayne, MI, p. A336
Executive Vice President, Chief Transformation Officer and Chief Information Officer, Beaumont Hospital–Dearborn, Dearborn, MI, p. A321

SRIVASTAVA, Mohit, M.D. Chief of Staff, Bunkie General Hospital, Bunkie, LA, p. A274

ST PIERRE, Jay, Chief Financial Officer, North Florida Regional Medical Center, Gainesville, FL, p. A129

ST. CLAIR, Jeffery M., President and Chief Executive Officer, Springhill Memorial Hospital, Mobile, AL, p. A22

ST. GERMAIN, Jackie, Chief Executive Officer, Rock Prairie Behavioral Health, College Station, TX, p. A606

ST. LEGER, John, Chief Executive Officer, Select Specialty Hospital–Pittsburgh/UPMC, Pittsburgh, PA, p. A551

ST. LOUIS, Charles, Director of Patient Care Services, Kahi Mohala Behavioral Health, Ewa Beach, HI, p. A170

ST. PETER, Colette, Senior Manager Human Resources, Mercy Hospital Carthage, Carthage, MO, p. A369

ST. PIERRE, Fran, Chief Nursing Officer, Hood Memorial Hospital, Amite, LA, p. A271

STAATS, Jason, Chief Executive Officer, Cumberland Hall Hospital, Hopkinsville, KY, p. A261

STABRYLA, Della, Director of Nursing, Ellwood City Hospital, Ellwood City, PA, p. A538

STACEY, Brian, Chief Financial Officer, NYC Health + Hospitals / Queens,, NY, p. A449

STACEY, Susan, Chief Nursing Officer, Providence Sacred Heart Medical Center & Children's Hospital, Spokane, WA, p. A691

STACHOVSKY, Jeanne M., Director Human Resources, Slidell Memorial Hospital, Slidell, LA, p. A288

STACIE, Beverly, Director Human Resources, Clifton T. Perkins Hospital Center, Jessup, MD, p. A301

STACKHOUSE, Jenni, Chief Financial Officer, River Point Behavioral Health, Jacksonville, FL, p. A132

STACKHOUSE, Rebecca J., Interim Director, Salem Veterans Affairs Medical Center, Salem, VA, p. A678

STACKHOUSE, Sharon, Assistant Administrator and Director Risk Management, Peachford Behavioral Health System, Atlanta, GA, p. A152

STACY, Doug, Director Information Technology, UP Health System–Marquette, Marquette, MI, p. A329

STADHEIM, Barbara, Chief Nursing Officer, West River Regional Medical Center, Hettinger, ND, p. A479

STADLER, James J., M.D. Associate Administrator Medical Services, Guam Memorial Hospital Authority, Tamuning, GU, p. A725

STADLER, Thomas, M.D. Vice President Medical Affairs and Chief Medical Officer, Madonna Rehabilitation Hospital, Lincoln, NE, p. A398

STAFFORD, Walt, Chief Information Officer, Halifax Health Medical Center of Daytona Beach, Daytona Beach, FL, p. A127

STAFFORD, Walt, Director Information Technology, Chatuge Regional Hospital and Nursing Home, Hiawassee, GA, p. A160

STAGEMAN–TYRER, Dawn, R.N. Chief Nursing Officer, Mackinac Straits Health System, Inc., Saint Ignace, MI, p. A333

STAGG, Kevin, Executive Vice President Finance and Chief Financial Officer, Christian Health Care Center, Wyckoff, NJ, p. A426

STAGGS, Nathan, Chief Executive Officer, Pauls Valley General Hospital, Pauls Valley, OK, p. A518

STAHL, Anthony
Chief Executive Officer, Central Texas Medical Center, San Marcos, TX, p. A648
Vice President, Florida Hospital Heartland Medical Center, Sebring, FL, p. A145

STAHL, Daniel, D.O. Chief of Staff, Rush Memorial Hospital, Rushville, IN, p. A221

STAHL, Kathy, Chief Nursing Officer, Wheeling Hospital, Wheeling, WV, p. A701

STAHL, Pam, Regional Chief Human Resources Officer, Providence Holy Cross Medical Center,, CA, p. A73

STAHL, Sherri, R.N. Senior Vice President for Hospital Services, Chambersburg Hospital, Chambersburg, PA, p. A535

STAHL, Steven J., Director Human Resources, Columbia County Health System, Dayton, WA, p. A684

STAHL, William D., Chief Operating Officer, Rooks County Health Center, Plainville, KS, p. A252

STAHLKUPPE, Robert F., M.D. Chief of Staff, Chatuge Regional Hospital and Nursing Home, Hiawassee, GA, p. A160

STAIGER, Tom, M.D. Medical Director, University of Washington Medical Center, Seattle, WA, p. A690

STAIGL, Chris, Chief Nursing Officer, TriStar Southern Hills Medical Center, Nashville, TN, p. A591

STALCUP, Connie, Manager Information Systems, Murphy Medical Center, Murphy, NC, p. A470

STALCUP, Linda, Chief Executive Officer, Stevens County Hospital, Hugoton, KS, p. A245

STALKER, Neil, M.D. Chief of Staff, Dukes Memorial Hospital, Peru, IN, p. A220

STALL, Kristi, Chief Human Resources Officer, Mahnomen Health Center, Mahnomen, MN, p. A345

STALLINGS, Jay, Chief Executive Officer, Washakie Medical Center, Worland, WY, p. A724

STALLINGS, Jennifer, Chief Clinical Officer, Kindred Hospital Indianapolis South, Greenwood, IN, p. A212

STALLINGS, Terry, M.D. Chief Medical Officer, West Florida Hospital, Pensacola, FL, p. A142

STALLINGS–SICARD, Lori, R.N. Chief Nursing Officer, DMC Huron Valley–Sinai Hospital, Commerce Township, MI, p. A321

STALLWORTH, David, M.D. Chief of Staff, Monroe County Hospital, Monroeville, AL, p. A23

STALLWORTH, Monica, M.D. Chief of Staff, Western Maryland Hospital Center, Hagerstown, MD, p. A301

STALLWORTH, Terresa, M.D. Clinical Director, San Antonio State Hospital, San Antonio, TX, p. A647

STALNAKER, Avah, Chief Executive Officer, Stonewall Jackson Memorial Hospital, Weston, WV, p. A701

STALNAKER, Jeffrey, M.D. Vice President, Medical Affairs, Health First Cape Canaveral Hospital, Cocoa Beach, FL, p. A126

STALNAKER, Kevin P., CPA Assistant Chief Executive Officer, Stonewall Jackson Memorial Hospital, Weston, WV, p. A701

STAMAS, Peter, M.D. Vice President Medical Affairs, Ministry Saint Joseph's Hospital, Marshfield, WI, p. A709

STAMBAUGH, Lynn E., R.N., Chief Executive Officer, Sarah D. Culbertson Memorial Hospital, Rushville, IL, p. A202

STAMM, Pam, Chief Nursing Officer, Throckmorton County Memorial Hospital, Throckmorton, TX, p. A653

STAMOS, George D., M.D. Chief Medical Officer, Overland Park Regional Medical Center, Overland Park, KS, p. A251

STAMPOHAR, Jeffry, Chief Executive Officer, Hancock County Health System, Britt, IA, p. A226

STANDER, Paul, M.D. Chief Medical Officer, Banner – University Medical Center Phoenix, Phoenix, AZ, p. A36

STANDIFORD, Steven B., M.D. Chief of Staff, Eastern Regional Medical Center, Philadelphia, PA, p. A547

STANDLEE, Cynthia, R.N. Chief Nursing Officer, Estes Park Medical Center, Estes Park, CO, p. A105

STANDRIDGE, Debra K.
President, Wheaton Franciscan Healthcare – Elmbrook Memorial, Brookfield, WI, p. A703
President, Wheaton Franciscan Healthcare – St. Joseph's, Milwaukee, WI, p. A712

STANDRIDGE, Sonya, Chief Nursing Officer, Copper Basin Medical Center, Copperhill, TN, p. A582

STANEK, Janet, Senior Vice President and Chief Operating Officer, Stormont Vail Health, Topeka, KS, p. A254

STANFORD, Brian, Administrator, Burleson St. Joseph Health Center, Caldwell, TX, p. A604

STANFORD, Brion
Director Human Resources, Merit Health Biloxi, Biloxi, MS, p. A355
Director Human Resources, New Orleans East Hospital, New Orleans, LA, p. A285

STANFORD, Edward, M.D. Chief Medical officer, Doctors Medical Center of Modesto, Modesto, CA, p. A77

STANFORD, Tracy, Director Human Resources, Baylor All Saints Medical Center at Fort Worth, Fort Worth, TX, p. A617

STANGE, Della G., Director Human Resources, Southwest Healthcare System, Murrieta, CA, p. A78

STANGE KOLO, Tracey
Vice President, Human Resources, UPMC Mercy, Pittsburgh, PA, p. A551
Vice President Human Resources, UPMC St. Margaret, Pittsburgh, PA, p. A552

STANGL, Abbey, Chief Financial Officer, Cass County Memorial Hospital, Atlantic, IA, p. A225

STANHILL, Keith
Chief Human Resources Officer, Saint Francis Hospital, Memphis, TN, p. A589
Chief Human Resources Officer, Twin Cities Community Hospital, Templeton, CA, p. A96

STANIC, Steve M.
Vice President and Chief Information Officer, Mississippi Baptist Medical Center, Jackson, MS, p. A360
Vice President and Chief Information Officer, Select Specialty Hospital – Belhaven, Jackson, MS, p. A360

STANKO, Shelley, M.D. Chief Medical Officer, Saint Joseph London, London, KY, p. A264

STANLEY, Cassandra, Director Personnel, Eastern Shore Hospital Center, Cambridge, MD, p. A299

STANLEY, Donna K., R.N. Chief Nursing Officer, East Texas Medical Center Henderson, Henderson, TX, p. A623

STANLEY, Jennifer, M.D. Chief Medical Officer, St. Vincent Jennings Hospital, North Vernon, IN, p. A220

STANLEY, Laurie, Manager Human Resources, Cook Children's Northeast Hospital, Hurst, TX, p. A628

STANLEY, Mark, Director Fiscal Services, Middle Tennessee Mental Health Institute, Nashville, TN, p. A590

STANLEY, Robert, Chief Financial Officer, Texas Specialty Hospital at Lubbock, Lubbock, TX, p. A634

STANSBERY, Shawn, M.D. Chief of Staff, Wood County Hospital, Bowling Green, OH, p. A485

STANSBURY, Kevin M., Chief Executive Officer, Lincoln Community Hospital and Nursing Home, Hugo, CO, p. A107

STANSKI, Vickie, Financial Manager, Parkview LaGrange Hospital, LaGrange, IN, p. A216

STANTON, Lowell, Chief Financial Officer, Houston Methodist Sugar Land Hospital, Sugar Land, TX, p. A650

STANTON, Melanie, R.N
Chief Nursing Officer, Sycamore Shoals Hospital, Elizabethton, TN, p. A582
Chief Nursing Officer, Unicoi County Memorial Hospital, Erwin, TN, p. A582

STANTON, Mike, D.O. Medical Director, Baylor Medical Center at Trophy Club, Trophy Club, TX, p. A653

STANUSH, Chris, Director Information Management, San Antonio State Hospital, San Antonio, TX, p. A647

STAPLES, Janet, Vice President Human Resources, South Central Regional Medical Center, Laurel, MS, p. A360

STAPLETON, Carla J., Director Human Resources, Paul B. Hall Regional Medical Center, Paintsville, KY, p. A268

STAPLETON, Kathleen, Chief Financial Officer, Baptist Easley Hospital, Easley, SC, p. A565

STAPLETON, Michael, President and Chief Executive Officer, F. F. Thompson Hospital, Canandaigua, NY, p. A436

STAPLETON, Robert, Director Administration, Richard H. Hutchings Psychiatric Center, Syracuse, NY, p. A456

STARA, Jeanne, R.N. Chief Nursing Officer, AllianceHealth Ponca City, Ponca City, OK, p. A518

STARCHER, John M., President and Chief Executive Officer, Mercy Health, Cincinnati, OH, p. B89

STARESINIC, Barbara, Director Human Resources, Hi–Desert Medical Center, Yucca Valley, CA, p. A100

STARK, Charles A., FACHE, President and Chief Executive Officer, Brookwood Baptist Medical Center, Birmingham, AL, p. A16

STARK, David, Chief Financial Officer, Lancaster Rehabilitation Hospital, Lancaster, PA, p. A542

STARK, David A., FACHE Executive Vice President and Chief Operating Officer, UnityPoint Health – Iowa Methodist Medical Center, Des Moines, IA, p. A229

STARK, Donna
Director Human Resources, Baylor Medical Center at Irving, Irving, TX, p. A628
Director Human Resources, Baylor Regional Medical Center at Grapevine, Grapevine, TX, p. A621

STARK, Patricia Ann, R.N. CNO, Florida Hospital DeLand, DeLand, FL, p. A127

STARK, Sharon, R.N. Manager Clinical Information Systems, Methodist McKinney Hospital, McKinney, TX, p. A636

STARK, Steve, Chief Executive Officer, Orchard Hospital, Gridley, CA, p. A65

STARKEBAUM, Gordon, M.D. Chief of Staff, Veterans Affairs Puget Sound Health Care System, Seattle, WA, p. A690

STARKES, Henry, M.D. Medical Director, Orchard Hospital, Gridley, CA, p. A65

STARKEY, Thomas, M.D. Deputy Commander FDR Clinical Services, Bayne–Jones Army Community Hospital, Fort Polk, LA, p. A277

STARLING, James F., M.D. Chief Medical Officer, Danville Regional Medical Center, Danville, VA, p. A669

STARLING, Susan, President and Chief Executive Officer, Marcum and Wallace Memorial Hospital, Irvine, KY, p. A262

STARMANN–HARRISON, Mary, R.N., President and Chief Executive Officer, Hospital Sisters Health System, Springfield, IL, p. B70

STARNES, Gregory D., Chief Executive Officer, Fayette County Hospital, Vandalia, IL, p. A204

STARON, Willard, Chief Financial Officer, Crittenton Children's Center, Kansas City, MO, p. A373

STARR, Candie, Chief Operating Officer and Ethics and Compliance Officer, Methodist Stone Oak Hospital, San Antonio, TX, p. A646

STARR, Kay, Manager Human Resources, Vernon Memorial Healthcare, Viroqua, WI, p. A717

STASI, Joseph P., Chief Financial Officer, Saint Luke's East Hospital, Lee's Summit, MO, p. A375

STASIK, Randall
President, Spectrum Health Gerber Memorial, Fremont, MI, p. A324
Interim President, Spectrum Health Ludington Hospital, Ludington, MI, p. A329

STASKIN, David, Director Human Resources, HEALTHSOUTH Rehabilitation Hospital of Mechanicsburg, Mechanicsburg, PA, p. A544

STASNEY, Amy, Chief Executive Officer, Cornerstone Hospital of Houston at Clearlake, Webster, TX, p. A656

STASTNY, Eric, Vice President Human Resources, Emerson Hospital, Concord, MA, p. A309

STASTNY, Mark, Vice President and Chief Information Officer, Children's Hospital and Medical Center, Omaha, NE, p. A400

STATEN, Gary L., Chief Executive Officer, Trace Regional Hospital, Houston, MS, p. A359

STATES, Chuck, Director Information Systems, Punxsutawney Area Hospital, Punxsutawney, PA, p. A552

STATON, Donna, Chief Information Officer, Fauquier Hospital, Warrenton, VA, p. A680

STATON, John, Senior Vice President Operations, Olathe Medical Center, Olathe, KS, p. A250

STATON, Paul
Chief Financial Officer, Ronald Reagan UCLA Medical Center, Los Angeles, CA, p. A74
Chief Financial Officer, UCLA Medical Center–Santa Monica, Santa Monica, CA, p. A94

STATUTO, Richard, President and Chief Executive Officer, Bon Secours Health System, Inc., Marriottsville, MD, p. B23

STATZ, Chris, Chief Financial Officer, Lincoln Prairie Behavioral Health Center, Springfield, IL, p. A203

STATZ, Linda Taplin, System Vice President Human Resources, St. Mary's Hospital, Madison, WI, p. A709

STAUB, David, M.D. Chief of Staff, Coteau des Prairies Hospital, Sisseton, SD, p. A576

STAUB, Julie, Chief Human Resources Officer, Jackson Health System, Miami, FL, p. A136

STAUBACH, Virginia, R.N. Chief Nursing Officer and Senior Director of Nursing Services, Gaylord Hospital, Wallingford, CT, p. A117

STAUDINGER, Michael, M.D. Chief of Staff, Theda Care Medical Center – Wild Rose, Wild Rose, WI, p. A719

STAUFFER, Karla, Executive Director People Resources, Billings Clinic, Billings, MT, p. A385

STAUFFER, Keith, Regional Chief Information Officer, CHI St Alexius Health Carrington Medical Center, Carrington, ND, p. A477

STAUSS, Laura, Director of Human Resources, Huggins Hospital, Wolfeboro, NH, p. A413

STAWNIAK, Laura, R.N. Chief Nursing Executive, Memorial Community Hospital and Health System, Blair, NE, p. A394

STEAD, William, Associate Vice Chancellor Health Affairs, Director Informatics Center and Chief Strategy and Information Officer, Vanderbilt University Medical Center, Nashville, TN, p. A591

STEADHAM, Emily, Administrator, Grove Hill Memorial Hospital, Grove Hill, AL, p. A21

STEADHAM, Mark B., President and Chief Executive Officer, Morris Hospital & Healthcare Centers, Morris, IL, p. A197

STEARNS, Charles, Area Information Officer, Kaiser Foundation Hospital Westside Medical Center, Hillsboro, OR, p. A526

STEARNS, Zebediah, M.D. Chief of Staff, Mercy Regional Medical Center, Ville Platte, LA, p. A289

STECKEL, Cindy, Ph.D. Vice President Chief Nurse and Operations Executive, Scripps Memorial Hospital–La Jolla, La Jolla, CA, p. A67

STECKER, Tim, Chief Financial Officer, Kindred Hospital–Denver, Denver, CO, p. A103

STECKLER, Michael J., President and Chief Executive Officer, Jennie M. Melham Memorial Medical Center, Broken Bow, NE, p. A394

STEED, Robert A., Director Information Systems, Capital Regional Medical Center, Tallahassee, FL, p. A146

STEEL, Diana, Vice President Human Resources, West Hills Hospital and Medical Center, CA, p. A75

STEELE, Anthony, M.D. Chief Medical Officer, Witham Health Services, Lebanon, IN, p. A217

STEELE, Chrys, Director Information Systems, Springs Memorial Hospital, Lancaster, SC, p. A568

STEELE, David, Vice President Information Technology, Leesburg Regional Medical Center, Leesburg, FL, p. A134

STEELE, Erik N., D.O. Senior Vice President and Chief Medical Officer, Summa Health System, Akron, OH, p. A483

STEELE, Mark, M.D
Chief Medical Officer, Truman Medical Center–Hospital Hill, Kansas City, MO, p. A374
Chief Medical Officer, Truman Medical Center–Lakewood, Kansas City, MO, p. A374

STEELE, Michael, M.D. Chief of Staff, Perry County Memorial Hospital, Perryville, MO, p. A378

STEELE, Richele, Vice President, Marketing and Public Relations, Community Hospital Long Beach, Long Beach, CA, p. A69

STEELE, Sherri, Chief Nursing Officer, Providence Medford Medical Center, Medford, OR, p. A528

STEELE, Terry L., Vice President Finance and Chief Financial Officer, Holland Hospital, Holland, MI, p. A326

STEELE, Tina, Chief Executive Officer and Chief Financial Officer, Fairfax Community Hospital, Fairfax, OK, p. A512

STEELE, Wes, M.D. Chief of Staff, Fairmont Regional Medical Center, Fairmont, WV, p. A696

STEELMAN, Jeffrey, Director Information Systems, LewisGale Hospital Alleghany, Low Moor, VA, p. A672

STEELY, Karen, Administrator, Murray Medical Center, Chatsworth, GA, p. A156

STEEN, Jon, Director Human Resources, Davis Medical Center, Elkins, WV, p. A695

STEENPORT, John, Information Systems Manager, Aspirus Grand View, Ironwood, MI, p. A327

STEFFEN, Daniel, Vice President Operations, Unity Hospital, Fridley, MN, p. A343

STEFFEN, Elizabeth, Director Information Technology, Seneca Healthcare District, Chester, CA, p. A58

STEFFEN, Elly, Administrator, Continuing Care Hospital at St. Luke's, Cedar Rapids, IA, p. A226

STEFFEN, Lorri, Chief Executive Officer and Administrator, Osage Beach Center for Cognitive Disorders, Osage Beach, MO, p. A378

STEFFENS, Aaron, Chief Operating Officer, Mercy Hospital Oklahoma City, Oklahoma City, OK, p. A516

STEFFIN, Renee, Chief Nursing Officer, Cuyuna Regional Medical Center, Crosby, MN, p. A341

STEFL, William, Director Information Systems, Mercy Health Hackley Campus, Muskegon, MI, p. A330

STEFO, Andrew, Senior Vice President Finance and Chief Financial Officer, Ingalls Memorial Hospital, Harvey, IL, p. A192

STEGALL, Christopher A., Regional Chief Financial Officer and Chief Operating Officer, Promise Hospital of Vicksburg, Vicksburg, MS, p. A365

STEGER, Elizabeth, FACHE Chief Nursing Officer, Seton Medical Center Austin, Austin, TX, p. A599

STEGGE, Sherri, Director Human Resources, Kaiser Permanente Vallejo Medical Center, Vallejo, CA, p. A98

STEHMER, Marie F., Senior Director of Human Resources, PeaceHealth Sacred Heart Medical Center at RiverBend, Springfield, OR, p. A531

STEICHEN, Barry L.
Executive Vice President and Chief Operating Officer, Saint Francis Health System, Saint Francis Hospital, Tulsa, OK, p. A522
Executive Vice President and Chief Operating Officer, Saint Francis Hospital South, Tulsa, OK, p. A522

STEICHEN, Elizabeth, Human Resources, Lewis and Clark Specialty Hospital, Yankton, SD, p. A578

STEIDLE, Ernie, Chief Operating Officer, Woodrow Wilson Rehabilitation Center, Fishersville, VA, p. A670

STEIGER, Nancy, R.N., Chief Executive, PeaceHealth Southwest Medical Center, Vancouver, WA, p. A692

STEIGMAN, Don S., Chief Operating Officer, Jackson Health System, Miami, FL, p. A136

STEIGMEYER, Robert P., President and Chief Executive Officer, Concord Hospital, Concord, NH, p. A410

STEIMEL, Ronald
Executive Vice President and Chief Administrative Officer, Mercy Medical Center, Rockville Centre, NY, p. A454
Executive Vice President and Chief Administrative Officer, St. Joseph Hospital, Bethpage, NY, p. A434

STEIN, Cathy, Chief Inpatient Services, Sagamore Children's Psychiatric Center, Dix Hills, NY, p. A438

STEIN, Eric H., FACHE, President and Chief Executive Officer, Cobleskill Regional Hospital, Cobleskill, NY, p. A437

STEIN, Keith L., M.D
Chief Medical Officer, Baptist Medical Center Beaches, Jacksonville Beach, FL, p. A132
Senior Vice President Medical Affairs and Chief Medical Officer, Baptist Medical Center Jacksonville, Jacksonville, FL, p. A131

STEIN, Patrick, M.D. Clinical Director, Western New York Children's Psychiatric Center, West Seneca, NY, p. A459

STEIN, Paul, Chief Operating Officer, MaineGeneral Medical Center, Augusta, ME, p. A291

STEIN, Richard, M.D. Chief Medical Officer, Bay Area Medical Center, Marinette, WI, p. A709

STEIN, Robert, M.D. Vice President Medical Management, Advocate Christ Medical Center, Oak Lawn, IL, p. A198

STEIN, Robert, Chief Executive Officer, Kindred Hospital Houston Medical Center, Houston, TX, p. A625

STEIN, Sandra, Chief Human Resources Management, Veterans Affairs Central California Health Care System, Fresno, CA, p. A64

STEIN, Sheldon J., President and Chief Executive Officer, Mt. Washington Pediatric Hospital, Baltimore, MD, p. A297

STEINBERG, James P., M.D. Chief Medical Officer, Emory University Hospital Midtown, Atlanta, GA, p. A152

STEINBLOCK, Matthew, Director Information Systems, Community Memorial Hospital, Syracuse, NE, p. A402

STEINER, J. Scott, Chief Executive Officer, MacNeal Hospital, Berwyn, IL, p. A181

STEINER, Jeffrey T., Vice President Finance, Memorial Hospital at Gulfport, Gulfport, MS, p. A358

STEINER, Thomas K., Interim Chief Executive Officer, Burke Medical Center, Waynesboro, GA, p. A169

STEINES, Jeanne, D.O. Medical Director, Connecticut Mental Health Center, New Haven, CT, p. A116

STEINGALL, Patricia, MS Vice President, Patient Care Services, Hunterdon Medical Center, Flemington, NJ, p. A417

STEINHART, Curt, M.D. Chief Medical Officer, OU Medical Center, Oklahoma City, OK, p. A517

STEINKE, Paul, D.O., President and Chief Executive Officer, CGH Medical Center, Sterling, IL, p. A204

STEINKE, Paul, Chief Financial Officer, Providence Holy Cross Medical Center,, CA, p. A73

STEINKRUGER, Roger W., Chief Executive Officer, Community Hospital–Fairfax, Fairfax, MO, p. A371

STEINMANN, David R.
Administrator, Mercy Hospital Lebanon, Lebanon, MO, p. A375
Administrator, Mercy St. Francis Hospital, Mountain View, MO, p. A377

STEINMANN, Robin, Administrative Director Human Resources, Anderson Hospital, Maryville, IL, p. A195

STEINSICK, Bill, M.D. Chief Medical Staff, Asante Ashland Community Hospital, Ashland, OR, p. A524

STEITZ, David P., Chief Executive Officer, Carlisle Regional Medical Center, Carlisle, PA, p. A535

STELL, G. Max, M.D. Medical Director, Minden Medical Center, Minden, LA, p. A283

STELLER, Wayne, Vice President Chief Nursing Officer, The Acadia Hospital, Bangor, ME, p. A291

STELLING, Jonathan, M.D. Vice President Medical Affairs, CHI Health St. Mary's, Nebraska City, NE, p. A398

STELTENPOHL, Robert
Vice President and Chief Financial Officer, Frazier Rehab Institute, Louisville, KY, p. A264
Vice President, Southern Indiana Rehabilitation Hospital, New Albany, IN, p. A219

STELTER, Carolyn, M.D. Chief of Staff, Minnesota Valley Health Center, Le Sueur, MN, p. A344

STELZER, Jason, Director Human Resources, St. Clare Hospital, Baraboo, WI, p. A702

STELZER, Mark, M.D. President Medical Staff, Floyd Valley Healthcare, Le Mars, IA, p. A233

STENCEL, Lindsay, Chief Administrative Officer, Baptist Memorial Hospital–Collierville, Collierville, TN, p. A581

STENDEL–FREELS, Robin, Coordinator Human Resources, AMG Specialty Hospital–Albuquerque, Albuquerque, NM, p. A427

STENERSON, David, Vice President and Chief Financial Officer, OSF Saint Anthony Medical Center, Rockford, IL, p. A202

STENGER, John D., Acting Associate Director, Charlie Norwood Veterans Affairs Medical Center, Augusta, GA, p. A153

STENGER, Sandra, Acting Chief Human Resources, Cincinnati Veterans Affairs Medical Center, Cincinnati, OH, p. A487

STENNETT, Kevin T., M.D. Chief of Staff, W. J. Mangold Memorial Hospital, Lockney, TX, p. A633

STENSON, James, Chief Information Officer, Syracuse Veterans Affairs Medical Center, Syracuse, NY, p. A457

STENSRUD, Kirk A., Chief Executive Officer, Glacial Ridge Health System, Glenwood, MN, p. A343

STEPANSKY, David, M.D. Chief Medical Officer, Phoenixville Hospital, Phoenixville, PA, p. A550

STEPHANY, Mark
Executive Director, Elmira Psychiatric Center, Elmira, NY, p. A438
Executive Director, Greater Binghamton Health Center, Binghamton, NY, p. A435

STEPHENS, Brian, Chief Financial Officer, Ministry Door County Medical Center, Sturgeon Bay, WI, p. A717

STEPHENS, Carrie, Director Information Technology, Saunders Medical Center, Wahoo, NE, p. A403

STEPHENS, Debra, Director Personnel, Riverland Medical Center, Ferriday, LA, p. A276

STEPHENS, Eddy, Vice President Information Technology, Mobile Infirmary Medical Center, Mobile, AL, p. A22

STEPHENS, Ellen, Vice President Information Services, Mercy Hospital Oklahoma City, Oklahoma City, OK, p. A516

STEPHENS, Heather, Director of Information Health Technology, St. Clare Hospital, Baraboo, WI, p. A702

STEPHENS, Jeremy, Vice President and Chief Human Resources Officer, St. Joseph Mercy Chelsea, Chelsea, MI, p. A320

STEPHENS, Kathy, Vice President of Patient Care, Decatur County Memorial Hospital, Greensburg, IN, p. A212

STEPHENS, Larry
Chief Financial Officer, Collingsworth General Hospital, Wellington, TX, p. A657
Chief Financial Officer, Kimble Hospital, Junction, TX, p. A629
Chief Financial Officer, Sabine County Hospital, Hemphill, TX, p. A623
Chief Financial Officer, Schleicher County Medical Center, Eldorado, TX, p. A616

STEPHENS, Linda, R.N. Chief Nursing Officer, Memorial Hermann Northeast, Humble, TX, p. A628

STEPHENS, Mike, Chief Financial Officer, NCH Downtown Naples Hospital, Naples, FL, p. A138

STEPHENS, Peggy, M.D., Superintendent and Medical Director, Madison State Hospital, Madison, IN, p. A217

STEPHENS, Ronald, Commander, Womack Army Medical Center, Fort Bragg, NC, p. A465

STEPHENS, Royce
Director Finance, Intermountain Medical Center, Murray, UT, p. A661
Chief Financial Officer, Riverton Hospital, Riverton, UT, p. A662

STEPHENS, Ruth M., R.N., Administrator, Pawnee County Memorial Hospital and Rural Health Clinic, Pawnee City, NE, p. A401

STEPHENS, Terry A., Chief Executive Officer, River Park Hospital, Huntington, WV, p. A697

STEPHENS, PHR, Maria, Director Human Resources, Education and Occupational Health and Wellness, VCU Community Memorial Hospital, South Hill, VA, p. A679

STEPHENSON, Ben, M.D. Chief of Staff, Phillips County Hospital, Phillipsburg, KS, p. A252

STEPHENSON, Darlene, Chief Executive Officer, Mary Immaculate Hospital, Newport News, VA, p. A674

STEPHENSON, Melinda, Chief Executive Officer, Kingwood Medical Center, Kingwood, TX, p. A631

STEPHENSON, Ron, Chief Operating Officer, Brookhaven Memorial Hospital Medical Center, Patchogue, NY, p. A452

STEPP, Dana, Human Resources Officer, Marcum and Wallace Memorial Hospital, Irvine, KY, p. A262

STERBACH, Maureen, Vice President Human Resources, St. Joseph's Hospital and Medical Center, Phoenix, AZ, p. A37

STERLING, Terrie, R.N. Chief Operating Officer, Our Lady of the Lake Regional Medical Center, Baton Rouge, LA, p. A273

STERN, Barry, President and Chief Executive Officer, New York Community Hospital,, NY, p. A446

STERNBERG, Paul, M.D. Professor and Chairman, Vanderbilt University Medical Center, Nashville, TN, p. A591

STERUD, Brian, Chief Information Officer, Faith Regional Health Services, Norfolk, NE, p. A399

STESNEY–RIDENOUR, Chris, President, Beaumont Hospital – Trenton, Trenton, MI, p. A335

STETTHEIMER, Timothy, Vice President and Chief Information Officer, St. Vincent's Birmingham, Birmingham, AL, p. A17

STEUTER, Krista, Director Human Resources, Catalina Island Medical Center, Avalon, CA, p. A55

STEVEN, Eva, Chief Financial Officer, Roosevelt General Hospital, Portales, NM, p. A430

STEVENS, Ann Marie, R.N., Chief Executive Officer, Tyler Memorial Hospital, Tunkhannock, PA, p. A556

STEVENS, Belinda, Chief Executive Officer, Access Hospital Dayton, Dayton, OH, p. A492

STEVENS, Ben, Chief Financial Officer, Buchanan County Health Center, Independence, IA, p. A232

STEVENS, Bryan N., Chief Financial Officer, Field Memorial Community Hospital, Centreville, MS, p. A356

STEVENS, Chris E., Chief Information Officer, Billings Clinic, Billings, MT, p. A385

STEVENS, Dori, Chief Executive Officer, Sutter Delta Medical Center, Antioch, CA, p. A54

STEVENS, Emily, Chief Nursing Officer, Mat–Su Regional Medical Center, Palmer, AK, p. A30

STEVENS, Janis, Director Human Resources, Raulerson Hospital, Okeechobee, FL, p. A140

STEVENS, Jeffrey, Senior Vice President and Chief Human Resource Officer, Thomas Jefferson University Hospitals, Philadelphia, PA, p. A550

STEVENS, Kelly, Manager Human Resources, St. Joseph Memorial Hospital, Murphysboro, IL, p. A197

STEVENS, Lisa, Chief Clinical Officer and Chief Operating Officer, Vibra Hospital of Northern California, Redding, CA, p. A84

STEVENS, Lori A., MSN Interim Chief Nursing Officer, Verde Valley Medical Center, Cottonwood, AZ, p. A32

STEVENS, Maeanne, R.N. Chief Nursing Officer, OSF Saint Elizabeth Medical Center, Ottawa, IL, p. A199

STEVENS, Mark, M.D. Chief Medical Staff, Marion General Hospital, Columbia, MS, p. A357

STEVENS, Mark
Director Human Resources, St. Luke's Jerome, Jerome, ID, p. A176
Senior Director Human Resources, St. Luke's Magic Valley Medical Center, Twin Falls, ID, p. A179

STEVENS, Rick, President, Christian Hospital, Saint Louis, MO, p. A380

STEVENS, Robert, President and Chief Executive Officer, Ridgeview Medical Center, Waconia, MN, p. A352

STEVENS, Robert, President and Chief Executive Officer, Ridgeview Medical Center, Waconia, MN, p. B114

STEVENS, Rodney, R.N. East Central Region Director of Nursing Practice, Indiana University Health Blackford Hospital, Hartford City, IN, p. A213

STEVENS, Scot, Assistant Administrator, Salt Lake Regional Medical Center, Salt Lake City, UT, p. A663

STEVENS, Shelbourn, President, Novant Health Brunswick Medical Center, Bolivia, NC, p. A461

STEVENS, Susan
Information Technology Specialist, Fallon Medical Complex, Baker, MT, p. A385
Director Human Resources, The HealthCenter, Kalispell, MT, p. A389
Human Resources Strategic Business Partner, Transylvania Regional Hospital, Brevard, NC, p. A461

STEVENS, Tammy, Chief Executive Officer, Madison County Memorial Hospital, Madison, FL, p. A135

STEVENS, Tom, Director Personnel, Morehead Memorial Hospital, Eden, NC, p. A464

STEVENS, Velinda, President, Kalispell Regional Healthcare, Kalispell, MT, p. A389

STEVENS, Vicki, Human Resources Executive, Northfield Hospital, Northfield, MN, p. A348

STEVENSON, Angela, Chief Financial Officer, Carl Vinson Veterans Affairs Medical Center, Dublin, GA, p. A159

STEVENSON, Angelia, Manager Finance, Tuscaloosa Veterans Affairs Medical Center, Tuscaloosa, AL, p. A26

STEVENSON, Brett
Controller, Kindred Hospital Kansas City, Kansas City, MO, p. A373
Controller, Kindred Hospital Northland, Kansas City, MO, p. A373

STEVENSON, John, M.D. Senior Vice President and Chief Medical Officer, South Shore Hospital, South Weymouth, MA, p. A314

STEVENSON, Michael, Chief Executive Officer, Murphy Medical Center, Murphy, NC, p. A470

STEVERSON, Denise, Director Human Resources, Dorminy Medical Center, Fitzgerald, GA, p. A159

STEVES, Sonja
Senior Vice President Human Resources and Marketing, Legacy Emanuel Hospital and Health Center, Portland, OR, p. A529
Vice President Marketing, Legacy Good Samaritan Hospital and Medical Center, Portland, OR, p. A529
Vice President Human Resources and Marketing, Legacy Meridian Park Medical Center, Tualatin, OR, p. A531
Senior Vice President Human Resources, Legacy Mount Hood Medical Center, Gresham, OR, p. A526
Senior Vice President Human Resources, Legacy Salmon Creek Medical Center, Vancouver, WA, p. A692

STEWARD, Rachel, Director Human Resources, Hillcrest Hospital – South, Tulsa, OK, p. A521

STEWARD, Todd E., FACHE, Chief Executive Officer, St. David's South Austin Medical Center, Austin, TX, p. A600

STEWART, Anne, Vice President and Chief Nursing Officer, Beaumont Hospital – Grosse Pointe, Grosse Pointe, MI, p. A326

STEWART, Christine R., FACHE, Chief Executive Officer, Russellville Hospital, Russellville, AL, p. A25

STEWART, Clint
Chief Financial Officer, Blue Ridge Regional Hospital, Spruce Pine, NC, p. A474
Regional Director of Finance East, McDowell Hospital, Marion, NC, p. A469

STEWART, Craig, Chief Financial Officer, Gila Regional Medical Center, Silver City, NM, p. A431

STEWART, Daniel, M.D. Vice President Medical Affairs, Bronson Battle Creek, Battle Creek, MI, p. A319

STEWART, David K., Senior Vice President and Chief Financial Officer, Mercy Medical Center, Canton, OH, p. A486

STEWART, Douglas, PsyD, President, Unity Hospital, Rochester, NY, p. A454

STEWART, Greg, Chief Executive Officer, Wellstone Regional Hospital, Jeffersonville, IN, p. A215

STEWART, Hedda, Director Human Resources, Neshoba County General Hospital, Philadelphia, MS, p. A363

STEWART, Inez, Vice President, Boston Children's Hospital, Boston, MA, p. A306

STEWART, Jane, Director Information Services, JFK Medical Center, Atlantis, FL, p. A123

STEWART, Jessi, Director Human Resources, Rockford Center, Newark, DE, p. A119

STEWART, John, Director Finance, Burke Rehabilitation Hospital, White Plains, NY, p. A459

STEWART, Kelly, Director of Human Resources, Community Mental Health Center, Lawrenceburg, IN, p. A214

STEWART, Kendall, M.D. Chief Medical Officer, Southern Ohio Medical Center, Portsmouth, OH, p. A501

STEWART, Marc, M.D. Vice President and Medical Director, Seattle Cancer Care Alliance, Seattle, WA, p. A689

STEWART, Marty, Director Information Services, AnMed Health Medical Center, Anderson, SC, p. A562

STEWART, Michael K., Chief Executive Officer, Navarro Regional Hospital, Corsicana, TX, p. A608

STEWART, Michele, R.N. Chief Operating Officer, Mercy Hospital Joplin, Joplin, MO, p. A373

STEWART, Nancy, Chief Nursing Officer, Millwood Hospital, Arlington, TX, p. A597

STEWART, Pamela, Director of Nursing, Washington County Regional Medical Center, Sandersville, GA, p. A165

STEWART, Patty, Chief Financial Officer, Memorial Hospital, Gonzales, TX, p. A621

STEWART, Paul, M.D. Medical Director, Kindred Hospital Las Vegas–Sahara, Las Vegas, NV, p. A406

STEWART, Paul R., President and Chief Executive Officer, Sky Lakes Medical Center, Klamath Falls, OR, p. A527

STEWART, Roxane, Chief Financial Officer, Magnolia Regional Medical Center, Magnolia, AR, p. A49

STEWART, Russell L., D.O. Chief Medical Officer, Braxton County Memorial Hospital, Gassaway, WV, p. A696

STEWART, Scott, M.D. Vice President Medical Management, Good Samaritan Medical Center, Brockton, MA, p. A308

STEWART, Scott, Manager Information Services, Rochelle Community Hospital, Rochelle, IL, p. A201

STEWART, Stephen, M.D. Vice President Medical Affairs, SSM Health St. Mary's Hospital – Jefferson City, Jefferson City, MO, p. A372

STEWART, Steve, Administrator, Meade District Hospital, Meade, KS, p. A249

STEWART, Terri L., R.N. Chief Nursing Officer, Saint Francis Hospital, Memphis, TN, p. A589

STEWART, Tim, Chief Information Officer, Abbeville Area Medical Center, Abbeville, SC, p. A562

STEWART, SPHR, SHRM–SCP, Ronnelle, Chief Human Resources Officer, Brookwood Baptist Medical Center, Birmingham, AL, p. A16

STIDHAM, Cindy
Executive Director of Patient Care, Mountain View Regional Medical Center, Norton, VA, p. A675
Executive Director of Patient Care Services, Wellmont Lonesome Pine Hospital, Big Stone Gap, VA, p. A667

STIEKES, Robert, Chief Financial Officer, Tyler Memorial Hospital, Tunkhannock, PA, p. A556

STIFF, Patrick, Coordinator Information Technology, Madison County Memorial Hospital, Madison, FL, p. A135

STIFFARM, Kevin J., Chief Executive Officer, Indian Health Service Hospital, Rapid City, SD, p. A575

STIKELEATHER, Janie, Director Marketing and Community Relations, Davis Regional Medical Center, Statesville, NC, p. A474

STILES, Geoffrey, M.D. Chief Medical Officer, Sharp Memorial Hospital, San Diego, CA, p. A89

STILGENBAUER, Mike, Director Finance, Marymount Hospital, Garfield Heights, OH, p. A495

STILLER, Brian G.
Director Medical Center, Veterans Affairs Western New York Healthcare System–Batavia Division, Batavia, NY, p. A434
Director Medical Center, Veterans Affairs Western New York Healthcare System–Buffalo Division, Buffalo, NY, p. A436

STILLMAN, Michelle, Director of Care Management, Asheville Specialty Hospital, Asheville, NC, p. A460

STILSON, Dwain, Chief Financial Officer, Mosaic Life Care at St. Joseph, Saint Joseph, MO, p. A379

STILTNER, Wanda, Director Human Resources, Buchanan General Hospital, Grundy, VA, p. A671

STIMPSON, Dan, Chief Financial Officer, Banner Del E. Webb Medical Center, Sun City West, AZ, p. A39

STIMSON, Judi
Chief Financial Officer, Desert Regional Medical Center, Palm Springs, CA, p. A81
Chief Financial Officer, Palm Beach Gardens Medical Center, Palm Beach Gardens, FL, p. A141

STIMSON, Michael, Chief Nursing Officer, Manchester Memorial Hospital, Manchester, KY, p. A266

STINGLEY, Susan D., Chief Nursing Officer, Kearny County Hospital, Lakin, KS, p. A247

STINSON, Katy, Director Information Services, AllianceHealth Durant, Durant, OK, p. A511

STINSON, Martha, Director of Information Technology, Palms West Hospital, Loxahatchee, FL, p. A134

STIPE, Christopher R., FACHE, Chief Executive Officer, Clarinda Regional Health Center, Clarinda, IA, p. A227

STITH, Melanie
Vice President Human Resources, Roper St. Francis, Charleston, SC, p. A563
Vice President Human Resources, Roper St. Francis Mount Pleasant Hospital, Mount Pleasant, SC, p. A568

STITT, Bobby, R.N.,
Administrator, Mercy Hospital Watonga, Watonga, OK, p. A523
Chief Executive Officer, Seiling Municipal Hospital, Seiling, OK, p. A519

STITT, Patrick, Director of Information Systems, Fishermen's Hospital, Marathon, FL, p. A135

STOB, David, Chief Financial Officer, Kindred Hospital Seattle–Northgate, Seattle, WA, p. A689

STOBER, Karick, Chief Financial Officer, PAM Specialty Hospital of Covington, Covington, LA, p. A275

STOBO, John D., M.D., Executive Vice President and Chief Executive Officer, University of California Systemwide Administration, Oakland, CA, p. B147

STOCK, Constance, M.D. Chief Medical Officer, Sturgis Regional Hospital, Sturgis, SD, p. A577

STOCK, Greg K., Chief Executive Officer, Thibodaux Regional Medical Center, Thibodaux, LA, p. A289

STOCK, Lesa, R.N. Chief Clinical Officer, Citizens Memorial Hospital, Bolivar, MO, p. A367

STOCK, Neil, Director Technology and Facilities, Mercy Regional Medical Center, Durango, CO, p. A104

STOCKARD, Herbert, M.D. Chief Medical Officer, Mercy St. Anne Hospital, Toledo, OH, p. A503

STOCKER, Trena, Chief Nursing Executive, Marcum and Wallace Memorial Hospital, Irvine, KY, p. A262

STOCKHAUSEN, Christopher, Chief Financial Officer, UPMC McKeesport, McKeesport, PA, p. A544

STOCKS, Alton, M.D., Interim President and Chief Executive Officer, Chesapeake Regional Healthcare, Chesapeake, VA, p. A668

STOCKS, Gregory, M.D. Chief of Staff, Texas Orthopedic Hospital, Houston, TX, p. A627

STOCKSTILL, Mark, R.N., Administrator, Highland Community Hospital, Picayune, MS, p. A364

STOCKTON, David Bradley, Chief Operating Officer, Redmond Regional Medical Center, Rome, GA, p. A165

STOCKTON, Kevin, Chief Executive Officer, Northwest Medical Center, Tucson, AZ, p. A40

STOCKTON, Linda, Chief Financial Officer, Bayfront Health Dade City, Dade City, FL, p. A126

STOCKTON, Rick, Chief Executive Officer, Promise Hospital of Louisiana – Shreveport Campus, Shreveport, LA, p. A287

STODDARD, Mark R., President, Central Valley Medical Center, Nephi, UT, p. A661

STODDARD, Mark R., President and Chairman, Rural Health Group, Nephi, UT, p. B115

STOGSDILL, Vicki, R.N. Chief Nursing Officer, Owensboro Health Regional Hospital, Owensboro, KY, p. A267

STOJAKOVICH, Edward R.
Chief Financial Officer, Dominion Hospital, Falls Church, VA, p. A669
Chief Financial Officer, Reston Hospital Center, Reston, VA, p. A676

STOKER, Rick, Director Management Information Systems, TriStar Horizon Medical Center, Dickson, TN, p. A582

STOKER, Vicki, Chief Nursing Officer, University Behavioral Health of Denton, Denton, TX, p. A613

STOKES, Elia, Chief Financial Officer, Plaza Medical Center of Fort Worth, Fort Worth, TX, p. A618

STOKES, Eric, Vice President of Operations, Decatur County Memorial Hospital, Greensburg, IN, p. A212

STOKES, Laura
Director Human Resources, Roosevelt Warm Springs Rehabilitation and Specialty Hospitals – LTAC, Warm Springs, GA, p. A168
Director Human Resources, Roosevelt Warm Springs Rehabilitation and Specialty Hospitals – Rehab, Warm Springs, GA, p. A168

STOKES, Letha, Chief Executive Officer, Medical Arts Hospital, Lamesa, TX, p. A632

STOKES, Priscilla, MS Vice President Patient Care and Hospital Operations, UnityPoint Health – St. Luke's, Sioux City, IA, p. A238

STOKES, Randell G., Chief Executive Officer, LifeCare Hospitals of San Antonio, San Antonio, TX, p. A646

STOKES, Tina, Manager Human Resources, Regency Hospital of Florence, Florence, SC, p. A566

STOKOE, Shelby
Chief Financial Officer, Providence Holy Family Hospital, Spokane, WA, p. A691
Senior Director Finance, Providence Sacred Heart Medical Center & Children's Hospital, Spokane, WA, p. A691

STOLBA, Robert J., Chief Executive Officer, Mason District Hospital, Havana, IL, p. A192

STOLDT, Garrick J., Vice President and Chief Financial Officer, Saint Peter's University Hospital, New Brunswick, NJ, p. A420

STOLLER, Theo, Chief Executive Officer, Jacobson Memorial Hospital Care Center, Elgin, ND, p. A478

STOLTENBERG, John, M.D. Vice President Medical Affairs, Fairview Ridges Hospital, Burnsville, MN, p. A340

STOLTMAN, Erin, Administrator, Essentia Health Ada, Ada, MN, p. A338

STOLTZ, Kyla, Vice President Human Resources, Centerpoint Medical Center, Independence, MO, p. A372

STOLTZ, Lori, Chief Financial Officer, Benewah Community Hospital, Saint Maries, ID, p. A178

STOLYAR, Edward B., D.O. Director Management Information Systems, New York Community Hospital,, NY, p. A446

STOMBERG, LeAnn, Chief Financial Officer, Minneapolis Veterans Affairs Health Care System, Minneapolis, MN, p. A346

STONE, Bud, Director Information Systems, Eastern State Hospital, Lexington, KY, p. A263

STONE, Connie, R.N. Chief Nursing Officer, MedStar Montgomery Medical Center, Olney, MD, p. A302

STONE, Dan, Senior Community Chief Executive Officer, Hazard ARH Regional Medical Center, Hazard, KY, p. A261

STONE, Darlene, Vice President Human Resources, Baptist Hospital, Pensacola, FL, p. A142

STONE, Duncan, D.D.S. Chief Medical Staff, Mississippi State Hospital, Whitfield, MS, p. A366

STONE, Janice, Chief Operating Officer, Spectrum Health Gerber Memorial, Fremont, MI, p. A324

STONE, Jeanette, Vice President Operations, Baptist Health South Florida, South Miami Hospital, Miami, FL, p. A136

STONE, Jeff, Director Human Resources, Marshall Medical Center North, Guntersville, AL, p. A21

STONE, Jill, Manager Human Resources, Lynn County Hospital District, Tahoka, TX, p. A651

STONE, Joanna, Chief Nursing Officer, Livingston Hospital and Healthcare Services, Salem, KY, p. A269

STONE, Levi Ross, R.N. Chief Nursing Officer and Chief Operating Officer, Odessa Regional Medical Center, Odessa, TX, p. A639

STONE, Matt, Chief Executive Officer, Resolute Health, New Braunfels, TX, p. A639

STONE, Patricia, R.N. Senior Vice President Operations and Chief Nursing Officer, White Memorial Medical Center, Los Angeles, CA, p. A75

STONE, Richard, Manager, Technical Services, UHS Chenango Memorial Hospital, Norwich, NY, p. A451

STONE, Robert, President and Chief Executive Officer, City of Hope's Helford Clinical Research Hospital, Duarte, CA, p. A61

STONE, Ronald W., Regional Chief Human Resource Officer, Long Island Jewish Medical Center,, NY, p. A445

STONE, Susan, Director Human Resources, Claiborne Medical Center, Tazewell, TN, p. A593

STONE, Susan, Ph.D., Senior Vice President and Chief Executive Officer, Sharp Coronado Hospital and Healthcare Center, Coronado, CA, p. A59

STONE, Terry, Chief Financial Officer and Chief Information Officer, Willapa Harbor Hospital, South Bend, WA, p. A690

STONE, Thomas J., FACHE, Chief Executive Officer, Doctor's Memorial Hospital, Perry, FL, p. A142

STONE Jr., Timothy D., President and Chief Executive Officer, Decatur Memorial Hospital, Decatur, IL, p. A188

STONEHOCKER, Terali, Interim Chief Executive Officer, Ferry County Memorial Hospital, Republic, WA, p. A688

STONER, Donald, M.D. Chief Medical Officer, Halifax Health Medical Center of Daytona Beach, Daytona Beach, FL, p. A127

STONER, Steve, Chief Information Officer, Richard L. Roudebush Veterans Affairs Medical Center, Indianapolis, IN, p. A214

STONESTREET, Jana S., R.N. Chief Nursing Officer, Tulane Medical Center, New Orleans, LA, p. A285

STOOPS, Stephens, M.D. Chief Medical Officer, Osceola Regional Medical Center, Kissimmee, FL, p. A133

STOPPER, Jim, CPA Chief Financial Officer, Evangelical Community Hospital, Lewisburg, PA, p. A543

STOPPLER, Maria, Chief Executive Officer, Granite County Medical Center, Philipsburg, MT, p. A390

STORCK, Craig, Chief Operating Officer, Blue Valley Hospital, Overland Park, KS, p. A251

STORCK, William H., Chief Financial Officer, Monroe County Hospital, Forsyth, GA, p. A159

STORER, William, M.D. Medical Director, St. Vincent Heart Center, Indianapolis, IN, p. A214

STOREY, Kam, Director Human Resources, Sebastian River Medical Center, Sebastian, FL, p. A145

STOREY, Kevin L., Vice President and Administrator, Baptist Health Medical Center–Stuttgart, Stuttgart, AR, p. A53

STOREY, Paul, FACHE, President and Chief Executive Officer, Helen Keller Hospital, Sheffield, AL, p. A25

STORFJELL, Judith, Ph.D. Senior Vice President and Chief Nursing Officer, Loma Linda University Medical Center, Loma Linda, CA, p. A69

STORM, Dave, Director Business Support, HSHS St. Anthony's Memorial Hospital, Effingham, IL, p. A188

STORR, Katie, Director of Human Resources, Mississippi State Hospital, Whitfield, MS, p. A366

STORTO, David E., President, Spaulding Rehabilitation Hospital, Charlestown, MA, p. A309

STORY Sr., Otis L., President and Chief Executive Officer, East Orange General Hospital, East Orange, NJ, p. A416

STOTLER, Sherry, R.N. Chief Nursing Officer, Maricopa Integrated Health System, Phoenix, AZ, p. A36

STOTTLEMYRE, Georgan L., Chief Human Relations Officer, Northern Inyo Hospital, Bishop, CA, p. A57

STOTTS, Vicki, Coordinator Human Resources, Flint River Community Hospital, Montezuma, GA, p. A163

STOUGH, Robin
Chief Financial Officer, Belmont Pines Hospital, Youngstown, OH, p. A506
Chief Financial Officer, Windsor–Laurelwood Center for Behavioral Medicine, Willoughby, OH, p. A506

STOUT, Amanda, Chief Nursing Officer, Minneola District Hospital, Minneola, KS, p. A249

STOUT, Bess, Director Human Resources, Tennova Healthcare–LaFollette Medical Center, La Follette, TN, p. A586

STOUT, Deana
Vice President Financial Services, MedStar Good Samaritan Hospital, Baltimore, MD, p. A297
Vice President Finance, MedStar Union Memorial Hospital, Baltimore, MD, p. A297

STOUT, Kimberly Dawn, Chief Nursing Officer, McAlester Regional Health Center, McAlester, OK, p. A514

STOUT, Patsy, Director Personnel, Richland Parish Hospital, Delhi, LA, p. A276

STOUT–TORRES, Sherri, R.N. Chief Nursing Executive, Sutter Maternity and Surgery Center of Santa Cruz, Santa Cruz, CA, p. A93

STOVALL, Henry, President, Sacred Heart Hospital Pensacola, Pensacola, FL, p. A142

STOVALL, Richard G., Senior Vice President Fiscal Services and Chief Financial Officer, Southern Regional Medical Center, Riverdale, GA, p. A164

STOVER, Benny, Vice President Finance, Mercy Hospital Rogers, Rogers, AR, p. A52

STOVER, George M., Chief Executive Officer, Hospital District No 1 of Rice County, Lyons, KS, p. A248

STOVER, Nick, Director Information Systems, Plateau Medical Center, Oak Hill, WV, p. A698

STOVER, Patricia A., Administrator Nursing, Doylestown Hospital, Doylestown, PA, p. A537

STOVER, Raymond
President and Chief Executive Officer, MidMichigan Medical Center–Clare, Clare, MI, p. A320
President and Chief Executive Officer, MidMichigan Medical Center–Gladwin, Gladwin, MI, p. A324

STOVER, Rhett, Chief Executive Officer, Oklahoma State University Medical Center, Tulsa, OK, p. A521

STOVER, Ryan, Chief Executive Officer, Norton County Hospital, Norton, KS, p. A250

STOVER, Theresa, Chief Human Resource Officer, Edgefield County Hospital, Edgefield, SC, p. A565

STOVERINK, Mike, Chief Financial Officer, Richland Memorial Hospital, Olney, IL, p. A199

STOWE, Mary
Senior Vice President and Chief Nursing Officer, Children's Health System of Texas, Dallas, TX, p. A609
Senior Vice President and Chief Nursing Officer, Children's Medical Center Plano, Plano, TX, p. A641

STOWELL, Dana A., Chief Information Officer, McCurtain Memorial Hospital, Idabel, OK, p. A513

STOWMAN, Amber, Controller, CHI Lisbon Health, Lisbon, ND, p. A480

STOY, Gale, Manager Information Systems, Mid Coast Hospital, Brunswick, ME, p. A292

STOYANOFF, Pamela
Executive Vice President and Chief Operating Officer, Methodist Charlton Medical Center, Dallas, TX, p. A610
Executive Vice President and Chief Operating Officer, Methodist Dallas Medical Center, Dallas, TX, p. A610

STRABEL, Elizabeth, M.D. Chief Medical Staff, Divine Savior Healthcare, Portage, WI, p. A714

STRACHAN, Eileen, Coordinator Human Resources, Kindred Hospital–Sycamore, Sycamore, IL, p. A204

STRACHAN, Ronald
Chief Information Officer, McLaren Bay Region, Bay City, MI, p. A319
Chief Information Officer, McLaren Flint, Flint, MI, p. A323

STRACK, Kirk, Vice President and Chief Financial Officer, Clark Memorial Hospital, Jeffersonville, IN, p. A215

STRADER, Lynn, Chief Financial Officer, Chippenham Hospital, Richmond, VA, p. A677

STRADER, Yvonne M., Chief Nursing Officer, Providence St. Mary Medical Center, Walla Walla, WA, p. A693

STRADI, Silvia, Chief Nursing Officer, Palms West Hospital, Loxahatchee, FL, p. A134

STRAHAN, Greg, Interim Chief Executive Officer, Owensboro Health, Owensboro, KY, p. B101

STRAHAN, Greg, Interim Chief Executive Officer, Owensboro Health Regional Hospital, Owensboro, KY, p. A267

STRAIN, Donna, Director Human Resources, Ray County Memorial Hospital, Richmond, MO, p. A378

STRAIN, Lynn, R.N. Chief Nursing Officer, Slidell Memorial Hospital, Slidell, LA, p. A288

STRAMOWSKI, Mallary, Chief Human Resources Officer, Select Specialty Hospital–Madison, Madison, WI, p. A709

STRANATHAN, Sidney, D.O. Chief of Staff, Anthony Medical Center, Anthony, KS, p. A240

STRAND, Eric, Director Information Services, North Florida Regional Medical Center, Gainesville, FL, p. A129

STRAND, Joy A., Chief Executive Officer, McCready Health, Crisfield, MD, p. A300

STRANGE, Cheryl, Interim Chief Executive Officer, Western State Hospital, Tacoma, WA, p. A692

STRANGE, John, President and Chief Executive Officer, St. Luke's Hospital, Duluth, MN, p. A342

STRANGE, Roger, Chief Information Officer, St. Vincent Heart Center, Indianapolis, IN, p. A214

STRASH, Shawn G., Chief Executive Officer, Arise Austin Medical Center, Austin, TX, p. A598

STRASSER, Michael, Vice President and Chief Financial Officer, Mercy Medical Center Merced, Merced, CA, p. A76

STRASSNER III, Lawrence F., Ph.D. Senior Vice President Operations and Chief Nursing Officer, MedStar Franklin Square Medical Center, Baltimore, MD, p. A297

STRATTON, James
Regional Vice President Finance, SSM Health St. Mary's Hospital – Audrain, Audrain, Mexico, MO, p. A376
Vice President Finance, SSM Health St. Mary's Hospital – Jefferson City, Jefferson City, MO, p. A372

STRATTON, Joseph, FACHE, Chief Executive Officer, Geary Community Hospital, Junction City, KS, p. A246

STRATTON, Mary, Director Human Resources, River Park Hospital, Huntington, WV, p. A697

STRATTON, Tracie, Chief Nursing Officer, Los Alamos Medical Center, Los Alamos, NM, p. A430

STRAUGHAN, Janet, Manager Human Resources, Highlands Rehabilitation Hospital, El Paso, TX, p. A615

STRAUGHAN, John, Director Information Technology, Wallowa Memorial Hospital, Enterprise, OR, p. A525

STRAUMAN, Karen S., R.N. Chief Nurse Executive, Kaiser Permanente Fresno Medical Center, Fresno, CA, p. A63

STRAUMANIS, John P., M.D. Vice President Medical Affairs and Chief Medical Officer, University of Maryland Rehabilitation & Orthopaedic Institute, Baltimore, MD, p. A298

STRAUSBAUGH, Andrew, Chief Administrative Officer, Norton Brownsboro Hospital, Louisville, KY, p. A265

STRAUSS, Alan
Chief Financial Officer, Carondelet Holy Cross Hospital, Nogales, AZ, p. A35
Chief Financial Officer, Carondelet St. Joseph's Hospital, Tucson, AZ, p. A40

STRAUSS, Karen, Chief Human Resources Officer, ProMedica Flower Hospital, Sylvania, OH, p. A503

STRAWN, Jill, Chief Executive Officer, HEALTHSOUTH Rehabilitation Hospital of Florence, Florence, SC, p. A565

STRAWN, Keith A., Vice President Human Resources, New Hanover Regional Medical Center, Wilmington, NC, p. A475

STRAWSER, Debbie A., Director Human Resources, Lindner Center of HOPE, Mason, OH, p. A498

STRAYER, Lorna, President and Chief Executive Officer, Fisher–Titus Medical Center, Norwalk, OH, p. A500

STRAYHAM, Joan, R.N., Chief Executive Officer, Stone County Hospital, Wiggins, MS, p. A366

STRAYHORN, Shelly, R.N
Chief Nursing Officer, Wadley Regional Medical Center, Texarkana, TX, p. A652
Chief Nursing Officer, Wadley Regional Medical Center at Hope, Hope, AR, p. A47

STRBICH, Steve, D.O. Chief of Staff, Spectrum Health Ludington Hospital, Ludington, MI, p. A329

STREATER, Vivian, Co–Acting Chief Executive Officer, Broughton Hospital, Morganton, NC, p. A470

STRECKER, Robert, M.D. Chief of Staff, Colorado River Medical Center, Needles, CA, p. A79

STREDNEY, Thomas, Chief Human Resources Management Service, Aleda E. Lutz Veterans Affairs Medical Center, Saginaw, MI, p. A333

STREET, Gene, Chief Nursing Officer, Barrow Regional Medical Center, Winder, GA, p. A169

STREET, Rex, Senior Vice President and Chief Financial Officer, Alamance Regional Medical Center, Burlington, NC, p. A461

STREET, Scott, Chief Executive Officer, Nacogdoches Memorial Hospital, Nacogdoches, TX, p. A638

STREETER, Alan W., Chief Financial Officer, Beatrice Community Hospital and Health Center, Beatrice, NE, p. A394

STREETER, Matthew, Chief Financial Officer, Southwest Health, Platteville, WI, p. A714

STREETER, Maxine, Administrator, Reception and Medical Center, Lake Butler, FL, p. A133

STREETER, Robert, M.D. Vice President Medical Affairs, Mercy Medical Center Merced, Merced, CA, p. A76

STREICH, Rebecca, Manager Human Resources and Education Manager, Hutchinson Health, Hutchinson, MN, p. A344

STREIT, Loren, Director Human Resources, Geary Community Hospital, Junction City, KS, p. A246

STREJC, Irene T., M.P.H. Vice President, Nursing, Methodist Richardson Medical Center, Richardson, TX, p. A643

STRICKER, Sean, Chief Executive Officer, Kindred Hospital San Antonio Central, San Antonio, TX, p. A647

STRICKER, Steven, M.D. Physician in Chief, Kaiser Permanente Vallejo Medical Center, Vallejo, CA, p. A98

STRICKLAND, Barrie, Chief Financial Officer, UCSF Medical Center, San Francisco, CA, p. A91

STRICKLAND, Connie, Chief Executive Officer, Select Specialty Hospital–Oklahoma City, Oklahoma City, OK, p. A517

STRICKLAND, David, Area Information Officer, Kaiser Permanente Los Angeles Medical Center, Los Angeles, CA, p. A71

STRICKLAND, Lee, Regional Director Information Technology, Park Ridge Health, Hendersonville, NC, p. A467

STRICKLAND, Morris S., Chief Financial Officer, Helen Keller Hospital, Sheffield, AL, p. A25

STRICKLAND, Wallace, President and Chief Executive Officer, Rush Health Systems, Meridian, MS, p. B115

STRICKLING, Keith
Chief Financial Officer, Atmore Community Hospital, Atmore, AL, p. A16
Chief Accountant, Jay Hospital, Jay, FL, p. A132

STRIEBICH, Shannon
Chief Executive Officer, St. Joseph Mercy Oakland, Pontiac, MI, p. A332
Chief Operating Officer, St. Mary Mercy Hospital, Livonia, MI, p. A329

STRIKE, Helen J., R.N., President, Unity Hospital, Fridley, MN, p. A343

STRING, Sherrie
Senior Vice President Human Resources, Bayshore Community Hospital, Holmdel, NJ, p. A418
Senior Vice President Human Resources, Ocean Medical Center, Brick Township, NJ, p. A415
Senior Vice President Human Resources, Riverview Medical Center, Red Bank, NJ, p. A423

STRINGFELLOW, Grace, M.D. Chief of Staff, Veterans Affairs Nebraska–Western Iowa Health Care System, Omaha, NE, p. A401

STRIPLIN, Elizabeth, Chief Financial Officer, Rehabilitation Hospital of Southern New Mexico, Las Cruces, NM, p. A430

STRITTMATTER, Julie, Director Human Resources, Baylor University Medical Center, Dallas, TX, p. A609

STROBEL, Deb, R.N. Chief Nursing Officer, Russell Regional Hospital, Russell, KS, p. A252

STROBEL, Jane, Vice President and Chief Financial Officer, Mercy Regional Medical Center, Durango, CO, p. A104

STROBEL, Rand
Regional Chief Information Officer, Information Technology Services, Harrison Medical Center, Bremerton, WA, p. A682
Regional Chief Information Officer, St. Francis Hospital, Federal Way, WA, p. A685
Vice President Information Technology and Compliance, St. Joseph Medical Center, Tacoma, WA, p. A692

STRODE, Marc, Chief Executive Officer, Methodist Stone Oak Hospital, San Antonio, TX, p. A646

STROEMEL, Douglas M.
President, Mercy Hospital Aurora, Aurora, MO, p. A367
Administrator, Mercy Hospital Berryville, Berryville, AR, p. A43
President, Mercy Hospital Cassville, Cassville, MO, p. A369

STROH, Rhonda, Chief Human Resources Officer, Community Memorial Hospital, Redfield, SD, p. A576

STROHECKER, Sharon, R.N. Vice President Clinical Operations and Chief Nursing Officer, Penn State Health St. Joseph, Reading, PA, p. A553

STROHLA, Patti, Director of Clinical Information, Mt. Ascutney Hospital and Health Center, Windsor, VT, p. A666

STROM, Lisa, Director Information Systems, North Big Horn Hospital District, Lovell, WY, p. A723

STROMBERG, Audrey, Administrator, Roosevelt Medical Center, Culbertson, MT, p. A386

STROMSTAD, Darlene, FACHE, President and Chief Executive Officer, Waterbury Hospital, Waterbury, CT, p. A117

STRONG, David, Chief Financial Officer/Vice President Finance, Cox Medical Center Branson, Branson, MO, p. A368

STRONG, David W., President and Chief Executive Officer, Orlando Health, Orlando, FL, p. B101

STRONG, Patricia, Interim Chief Executive Officer, Cumberland River Hospital, Celina, TN, p. A580

STRONG, Tanya, Manager Information Technology, Harney District Hospital, Burns, OR, p. A524

STROSS, Daniel
Chief Information Officer, Genesys Regional Medical Center, Grand Blanc, MI, p. A324
Chief Information Officer, St. Joseph Health System, Tawas City, MI, p. A335
Chief Information Officer, St. Mary's of Michigan, Saginaw, MI, p. A333
STROTHER, James
Site Director Information Technology Systems, Mercy Medical Center – West Lakes, West Des Moines, IA, p. A239
Site Director Information Technology Systems, Mercy Medical Center–Des Moines, Des Moines, IA, p. A229
STROTHKAMP, Brad, Chief Information Systems, Lakeland Behavioral Health System, Springfield, MO, p. A382
STROUCKEN, Christian, Chief Operating Officer, Carney Hospital, Boston, MA, p. A306
STROUD, Justin, Chief Financial Officer, Merit Health Central, Jackson, MS, p. A360
STROUD, Teresa, Chief Financial Officer, Salem Township Hospital, Salem, IL, p. A202
STROUD, William, M.D. Physician Advisor, East Cooper Medical Center, Mount Pleasant, SC, p. A568
STROUP, Jeff, Chief Operating Officer, Oklahoma State University Medical Center, Tulsa, OK, p. A521
STROUSE, Thomas, M.D. Medical Director and Professor of of Clinic Psych, Stewart & Lynda Resnick Neuropsychiatric Hospital at UCLA, Los Angeles, CA, p. A74
STRUB, Lisa
Chief Operating Officer, Centennial Peaks Hospital, Louisville, CO, p. A109
Interim Chief Executive Officer, Highlands Behavioral Health System, Littleton, CO, p. A108
STRUTTON, Jill, Director Personnel Systems, University of Texas Harris County Psychiatric Center, Houston, TX, p. A627
STRUYK, Douglas A., President and Chief Executive Officer, Christian Health Care Center, Wyckoff, NJ, p. A426
STRZELECKI, Sarah, Ed.D. Chief Nursing Officer, Phoenixville Hospital, Phoenixville, PA, p. A550
STRZEMPKO, Stanley, M.D. Vice President Medical Affairs and Chief Medical Officer, Baystate Noble Hospital, Westfield, MA, p. A316
STUART, Conan, Director Information Services, East Georgia Regional Medical Center, Statesboro, GA, p. A166
STUART, Danna, M.D. Chief Medical Officer, Newman Memorial Hospital, Shattuck, OK, p. A519
STUART, Jimmy D., Administrator, Kimble Hospital, Junction, TX, p. A629
STUART, Leslie, Chief Financial Officer, Cypress Creek Hospital, Houston, TX, p. A624
STUART, Philip J., Administrator and Chief Executive Officer, Tomah Memorial Hospital, Tomah, WI, p. A717
STUART, Robin, Chief Executive Officer, Morrill County Community Hospital, Bridgeport, NE, p. A394
STUART, Wendy, Chief Nursing Officer, Kendall Regional Medical Center, Miami, FL, p. A136
STUBBS, Don, Vice President Human Resources, Candler Hospital, Savannah, GA, p. A165
STUBBS, Kay, Chief Nursing Officer, Northwest Medical Center, Tucson, AZ, p. A40
STUBITSCH, Brian, M.D. Chief Medical Officer, Edgerton Hospital and Health Services, Edgerton, WI, p. A705
STUCK, Julie, R.N., Chief Executive Officer, Hocking Valley Community Hospital, Logan, OH, p. A497
STUCKY, Nancy, Director Human Resources and Public Relations, Kingman Community Hospital, Kingman, KS, p. A246
STUCZYNSKI, Joseph, Assistant Administrator Finance and Support, Memorial Hospital Pembroke, Pembroke Pines, FL, p. A142
STUDEBAKER, Shelly, Director Management Information Systems, Clinch Memorial Hospital, Homerville, GA, p. A161
STUDER, Tim, President Medical Staff, Perham Health, Perham, MN, p. A348
STUDLEY, Jason A., FACHE, President and Chief Executive Officer, Trinity Hospital of Augusta, Augusta, GA, p. A154
STUENKEL, Kurt, FACHE, President and Chief Executive Officer, Floyd Medical Center, Rome, GA, p. A165
STUERSEL, Marie, Director Human Resources, Seneca Healthcare District, Chester, CA, p. A58
STUEVE, Angela, M.D. Chief Medical Officer, Nemaha Valley Community Hospital, Seneca, KS, p. A253
STUEVE, Jo W., Executive Vice President and Co–Chief Operating Officer, Children's Mercy Hospitals and Clinics, Kansas City, MO, p. A373
STUHLMILLER, Michael, Chief Financial Officer, Mann–Grandstaff Veterans Affairs Medical Center, Spokane, WA, p. A691
STULTS, Cynthia S., Executive Assistant and Human Resources Director, Rangely District Hospital, Rangely, CO, p. A110
STULTS, Kim, Director, Information Systems, Bellevue Hospital, Bellevue, OH, p. A485

STUMBO, Kathy, President, Saint Joseph – Martin, Martin, KY, p. A266
STUMME, Sarah, Director Human Resources, Owatonna Hospital, Owatonna, MN, p. A348
STUMP, Lisa, Interim Chief Information Officer, Yale–New Haven Hospital, New Haven, CT, p. A116
STUMP, Veronica, Director of Nursing, Carilion Giles Community Hospital, Pearisburg, VA, p. A675
STUMPO, Barbara J., R.N. Vice President Patient Care Services, Griffin Hospital, Derby, CT, p. A114
STUNKARD, Jill, R.N. Associate Chief Nurse Executive and Interim Chief Nursing Officer, Einstein Medical Center Philadelphia, Philadelphia, PA, p. A547
STURGEON, Jim, Area Director Human Resources, Kindred Hospital Las Vegas–Sahara, Las Vegas, NV, p. A406
STURGEON, Wade, Chief Operating Officer and Chief Financial Officer, Bear Valley Community Hospital, Big Bear Lake, CA, p. A57
STURGILL, Lori
Vice President Business Partnership, Mercy Hospital Fort Scott, Fort Scott, KS, p. A243
Vice President Business Partnership, Mercy Hospital Springfield, Springfield, MO, p. A382
STURGIS, Gayle, R.N. Nurse Administrator, Heber Valley Medical Center, Heber City, UT, p. A660
STURGIS, Jonathan, Chief Financial Officer, Houston Methodist San Jacinto Hospital, Baytown, TX, p. A601
STURGIS, Paul
Director Human Resources, DMC – Rehabilitation Institute of Michigan, Detroit, MI, p. A321
Vice President and Chief Human Resources Officer, Sparrow Hospital, Lansing, MI, p. A328
Chief Human Resource Officer, Sparrow Specialty Hospital, Lansing, MI, p. A328
STURLER, Kelly, Chief Nursing Officer, McKee Medical Center, Loveland, CO, p. A109
STURSA, Robin, Chief Information Officer, St. Vincent Charity Medical Center, Cleveland, OH, p. A489
STUWE, Shannon, Director of Nursing, Faulkton Area Medical Center, Faulkton, SD, p. A573
STYER, Brent
Chief Information Officer, Summers County ARH Hospital, Hinton, WV, p. A696
Director Information Technology, Whitesburg ARH Hospital, Whitesburg, KY, p. A270
STYLES, Kelly R., Vice President and Chief Information Officer, Connecticut Children's Medical Center, Hartford, CT, p. A114
STYRON, Stacie, Chief Nursing Officer, Lamb Healthcare Center, Littlefield, TX, p. A633
SUAREZ, Irma, Deputy Executive Director, NYC Health + Hospitals / Woodhull,, NY, p. A449
SUAREZ, Orlando, Director Information Technology, Larkin Community Hospital, South Miami, FL, p. A145
SUBIA, Corina, Director Human Resources, Ward Memorial Hospital, Monahans, TX, p. A637
SUBLER, Jeffrey R., Vice President Support Services, Wayne Hospital, Greenville, OH, p. A495
SUBLETTE, Elizabeth, Director Finance, Providence Willamette Falls Medical Center, Oregon City, OR, p. A528
SUBRAMANIAN, Aarti, Vice President and Chief Financial Officer, Psychiatric Institute of Washington, Washington, DC, p. A122
SUCATO, Daniel J., M.D. Chief of Staff, Texas Scottish Rite Hospital for Children, Dallas, TX, p. A611
SUCHER, Therese O., Senior Vice President Operations, Southern Regional Medical Center, Riverdale, GA, p. A164
SUDAK, Mariellena, MSN, Interim Vice President and Chief Nursing Officer, Palomar Medical Center, Escondido, CA, p. A61
SUDBURY, Russ, M.D. President Medical Staff, Ministry Sacred Heart Hospital, Tomahawk, WI, p. A717
SUDDUTH, Tony, Chief Financial Officer, Trios Health, Kennewick, WA, p. A685
SUDICKY, Mary, Chief Financial Officer, St. Mary Medical Center, Hobart, IN, p. A213
SUDOLCAN, Joseph, M.D. Medical Director, Reagan Memorial Hospital, Big Lake, TX, p. A602
SUEHS, JoAnne, Manager Human Resources, Chapman Global Medical Center, Orange, CA, p. A80
SUGAR, Bev, Associate Administrator and Director Human Resources, Inova Mount Vernon Hospital, Alexandria, VA, p. A667
SUGDEN, Elizabeth, M.D. Chief Medical Officer, St. Luke's Jerome, Jerome, ID, p. A176
SUGG, Amy, Director Human Resources, Scott Regional Hospital, Morton, MS, p. A362
SUGGS, Heather, Manager Human Resources, Jay Hospital, Jay, FL, p. A132
SUHR, Nancy, Manager Human Resources, Pender Community Hospital, Pender, NE, p. A401

SUITTER, Marie, Chief Financial Officer, The Acadia Hospital, Bangor, ME, p. A291
SUKENIK, Richard, CPA Vice President Finance and Chief Financial Officer, Chan Soon–Shiong Medical Center, Windber, PA, p. A558
SUKSI, Eugene, Interim Chief Executive Officer, Tehachapi Valley Healthcare District, Tehachapi, CA, p. A95
SULIK, Sandra, M.D. Vice President Medical Affairs, St. Joseph's Hospital Health Center, Syracuse, NY, p. A456
SULIT, Teresa, Director of Human Resources, Seven Hills Hospital, Henderson, NV, p. A405
SULLINS, Jacqueline C., R.N. Chief Nursing Officer, Merit Health Rankin, Brandon, MS, p. A356
SULLIVAN, Christopher, M.D. Chief Medical Officer, Centerpoint Medical Center, Independence, MO, p. A372
SULLIVAN, Daniel, D.O. Chief Medical Officer, Vice President Medical Administration, Elmhurst Memorial Hospital,, IL, p. A189
SULLIVAN, Danita S., R.N. Chief Nursing Officer, Touro Infirmary, New Orleans, LA, p. A285
SULLIVAN, David, Director Human Resources, OhioHealth Doctors Hospital, Columbus, OH, p. A491
SULLIVAN, Denis, Chief Human Resources Management, Veterans Affairs Black Hills Health Care System, Fort Meade, SD, p. A574
SULLIVAN, Donald, M.D. Medical Director, HEALTHSOUTH Rehabilitation Hospital Memphis–North, Memphis, TN, p. A588
SULLIVAN, Gregory, Manager Human Resources, Girard Medical Center, Girard, KS, p. A243
SULLIVAN, James, M.D. Chief Medical Officer, Butler Hospital, Providence, RI, p. A560
SULLIVAN, Jennie, Chief Executive Officer, Wray Community District Hospital, Wray, CO, p. A111
SULLIVAN, Jennifer
Chief Executive Officer, Curahealth Heritage Valley, Beaver, PA, p. A533
President and Chief Executive Officer, St. James Mercy Hospital, Hornell, NY, p. A440
SULLIVAN, John, President, MedStar Washington Hospital Center, Washington, DC, p. A122
SULLIVAN, Katherine, Director, Human Resources, Moab Regional Hospital, Moab, UT, p. A660
SULLIVAN, Keith, Director, Chillicothe Veterans Affairs Medical Center, Chillicothe, OH, p. A487
SULLIVAN, Lowery, M.D. Chief Medical Officer, Northwestern Medical Center, Saint Albans, VT, p. A666
SULLIVAN, Martha, Chief Information Officer, Harrison Memorial Hospital, Cynthiana, KY, p. A259
SULLIVAN, Mary Patricia, R.N. Chief Nursing Officer, Overlook Medical Center, Summit, NJ, p. A423
SULLIVAN, Maurita, Vice President, Mayo Clinic Health System – Northland in Barron, Barron, WI, p. A702
SULLIVAN, Michael, M.D
Chief Medical Officer, Northern Maine Medical Center, Fort Kent, ME, p. A293
Medical Director Emergency Services, PeaceHealth Peace Island Medical Center, Friday Harbor, WA, p. A685
SULLIVAN, Michael Dean, M.D. Chief of Staff, Mercy Hospital El Reno, El Reno, OK, p. A511
SULLIVAN, Patrick L., Chief Operating Officer, St. John's Episcopal Hospital–South Shore,, NY, p. A450
SULLIVAN, Peter, Chief Executive Officer, Riverside Medical Center, Franklinton, LA, p. A277
SULLIVAN, Staci, R.N. Chief Nursing Officer, Lane Regional Medical Center, Zachary, LA, p. A290
SULLIVAN, Steve, Chief Information Officer, Johnson Regional Medical Center, Clarksville, AR, p. A44
SULLIVAN, Theresa, Chief Executive Officer, Samaritan Healthcare, Moses Lake, WA, p. A686
SULLIVAN, Thomas, Vice President Fiscal Services, Harrington Memorial Hospital, Southbridge, MA, p. A314
SULLIVAN, William, Chief Financial Officer, Mount Auburn Hospital, Cambridge, MA, p. A309
SULLIVAN SMITH, Mary, R.N. Senior Vice President, Chief Operating Officer and Chief Nursing Officer, New England Baptist Hospital, Boston, MA, p. A307
SULLIVANT, Laura, Area Chief Information Officer, Kaiser Permanente San Diego Medical Center, San Diego, CA, p. A88
SULSER, Jamey, Director Human Resources, South Davis Community Hospital, Bountiful, UT, p. A659
SULU, Dorothy, Budget Analyst, Hopi Health Care Center, Keams Canyon, AZ, p. A33
SULZEN, Jessica, Director Human Resources, Belton Regional Medical Center, Belton, MO, p. A367
SUMMERLIN, Craig, Chief Human Resources Officer, Singing River Health System, Pascagoula, MS, p. A363
SUMMERLIN, Valerie, R.N. Chief Nursing Officer, Adventist Rehabilitation Hospital of Maryland, Rockville, MD, p. A303

SWEITZER, Gregory, Chief Medical Officer, Wright Patterson Medical Center, Wright–Patterson AFB, OH, p. A506

SWENSON, Daniel J., FACHE, Administrator and Chief Executive Officer, CentraCare Health–Long Prairie, Long Prairie, MN, p. A345

SWENSON, Jennifer, President and Chief Executive Officer, Simi Valley Hospital, Simi Valley, CA, p. A94

SWENSON, Nena, Financial Manager, Tahoe Pacific Hospitals, Sparks, NV, p. A408

SWENSON, Nina, Director Business Services, Newport Bay Hospital, Newport Beach, CA, p. A79

SWENSON, Paula C., R.N. Vice President and Chief Nursing Officer, St. Catherine Hospital, East Chicago, IN, p. A209

SWENSON, Warren, Chief Financial Officer, United Medical Rehabilitation Hospital, Hammond, LA, p. A278

SWICK, Michael D., President and Chief Executive Officer, Lima Memorial Health System, Lima, OH, p. A496

SWIDERSKI, Tom, Chief Financial Officer, Orthopaedic Hospital of Wisconsin – Glendale, Glendale, WI, p. A706

SWIFT, Brian M., Senior Administrator Plant Operations, Burke Rehabilitation Hospital, White Plains, NY, p. A459

SWIFT, Diane, Director Medical Records, I–70 Community Hospital, Sweet Springs, MO, p. A383

SWIFT, Kyle, Chief Executive Officer, Woodland Heights Medical Center, Lufkin, TX, p. A635

SWIFT, Nick, Chief Financial Officer, Maury Regional Hospital, Columbia, TN, p. A581

SWIGER, Jared, Director Information Systems, Ashtabula County Medical Center, Ashtabula, OH, p. A484

SWILLEY Jr., Bryanie W., Interim Chief Executive Officer, St. Joseph Medical Center, Houston, TX, p. A626

SWINDELL, Terry
Controller, Bolivar General Hospital, Bolivar, TN, p. A579
Chief Financial Officer, Camden General Hospital, Camden, TN, p. A579

SWINDLE, Patrick, Administrator, East Texas Medical Center–Quitman, Quitman, TX, p. A642

SWINGLE, Dale, Vice President Information Services, Troy Community Hospital, Troy, PA, p. A556

SWINT, Ken
Director Finance, ProMedica Defiance Regional Hospital, Defiance, OH, p. A493
Vice President Finance and Chief Financial Officer, ProMedica Fostoria Community Hospital, Fostoria, OH, p. A494

SWINT, Patricia
Director Information Management Systems, ProMedica Defiance Regional Hospital, Defiance, OH, p. A493
Director Information Technology, ProMedica St. Luke's Hospital, Maumee, OH, p. A498

SWISHER, Kay, Chief Nursing Officer, Greenville Health System – Laurens County Memorial Hospital, Clinton, SC, p. A563

SWISSHELM, Patricia, Acting Chief Fiscal Service, Lexington Veterans Affairs Medical Center, Lexington, KY, p. A263

SWITAJ, Timothy, Deputy Commander for Clinical Services, Reynolds Army Community Hospital, Fort Sill, OK, p. A512

SWOFFORD, William, M.D. Chief of Staff, Miller County Hospital, Colquitt, GA, p. A156

SWORDS, James, Director Human Resources, Lewis County General Hospital, Lowville, NY, p. A442

SY, Annette
Chief Nursing Officer, Keck Hospital of USC, Los Angeles, CA, p. A72
Chief Nursing Officer, USC Norris Comprehensive Cancer Center, Los Angeles, CA, p. A74

SYED, Imran, Manager Technology Information Services, Spectrum Health Zeeland Community Hospital, Zeeland, MI, p. A337

SYED, Mamoon
Vice President Human Resources, Children's Hospital of Orange County, Orange, CA, p. A81
Vice President Human Resources, CHOC Children's at Mission Hospital, Mission Viejo, CA, p. A76
Vice President Human Resources, Rady Children's Hospital – San Diego, San Diego, CA, p. A88

SYKES, Angel, Director Human Resources, Memorial Hospital and Manor, Bainbridge, GA, p. A154

SYKES, Christina, Director Human Resources, Labette Health, Parsons, KS, p. A252

SYKES, Lisa
IS/Communications Director, Carolinas HealthCare System Anson, Wadesboro, NC, p. A475
Manager, Information Services, Carolinas HealthCare System NorthEast, Concord, NC, p. A463
Director Information Services, Carolinas Healthcare System Union, Monroe, NC, p. A469

SYKES, Rebecca S.
Senior Vice President Resource Management, Chief Information Officer, Mercy Health – St. Charles Hospital, Oregon, OH, p. A500
Chief Information Officer, Mercy St. Anne Hospital, Toledo, OH, p. A503

SYLVESTER, Joy L., Director, Human Resources and Education, South Lake Hospital, Clermont, FL, p. A125

SYLVIA–HUTCHINSON, Doreen M., Vice President Operations and Chief Nurse Executive, Fairview Hospital, Great Barrington, MA, p. A310

SYNDERGAARD, Christy, Vice President Nursing, Cherokee Regional Medical Center, Cherokee, IA, p. A227

SYNNESTVEDT, Eric, Director Information Technology, Southside Regional Medical Center, Petersburg, VA, p. A676

SYPIEN, Troy
Director Information Technology and Systems, Medical City Dallas Hospital, Dallas, TX, p. A610
Director Information Technology and Systems, TriStar Skyline Madison Campus, Madison, TN, p. A587
Director Information Technology and Systems, TriStar Skyline Medical Center, Nashville, TN, p. A591

SYPITKOWSKI, Rita, Director of Patient Services, Coalinga Regional Medical Center, Coalinga, CA, p. A59

SZABO, Charleen R., FACHE, Director, West Palm Beach Veterans Affairs Medical Center, West Palm Beach, FL, p. A150

SZABO, Sandor, M.D. Chief of Staff, VA Long Beach Healthcare System, Long Beach, CA, p. A70

SZCZEPANSKI, Bernadette S.
Senior Vice President, Human Resources, Centegra Hospital – McHenry, McHenry, IL, p. A196
Senior Vice President Human Resources, Centegra Hospital – Woodstock, Woodstock, IL, p. A205

SZCZUROWSKI, Richard, Director Human Resources, Norristown State Hospital, Norristown, PA, p. A546

SZEKELY, Lauraine, R.N. Senior Vice President, Patient Care, Northern Westchester Hospital, Mount Kisco, NY, p. A443

SZEWCZYK, Edwin, Chief Financial Officer, Wetzel County Hospital, New Martinsville, WV, p. A698

SZKLANY, Chelsea, Hospital Administrator, Southern Nevada Adult Mental Health Services, Las Vegas, NV, p. A406

SZOSTEK, Joshua, Chief Financial Officer, Specialty Hospital Jacksonville, Jacksonville, FL, p. A132

SZUMEL, Richard C., M.D., Chief Executive Officer, Union Hospital, Elkton, MD, p. A300

SZURA, Kathleen, R.N. Chief Nursing Officer, HEALTHSOUTH Bakersfield Rehabilitation Hospital, Bakersfield, CA, p. A56

SZYMANSKI, Michael, Chief Financial Officer, Doctors Hospital of Manteca, Manteca, CA, p. A76

SZYSKA, Julie, Chief Operating Officer, Havenwyck Hospital, Auburn Hills, MI, p. A318

T

TAAFFE, Janette, Vice President, Human Resource, St. Luke's Hospital, Chesterfield, MO, p. A369

TABAK, Jeremy, M.D. President Medical Staff, Baptist Health South Florida, South Miami Hospital, Miami, FL, p. A136

TABB, Kevin, M.D., President and Chief Executive Officer, Beth Israel Deaconess Medical Center, Boston, MA, p. A306

TABIBI, Wasae S., M.D. President Medical Staff, Plaza Specialty Hospital, Houston, TX, p. A626

TABOADO, Ketty, Chief Financial Officer, Gladys Spellman Specialty Hospital and Nursing Center, Cheverly, MD, p. A299

TABOR, J. Britton, Executive Vice President, Chief Financial Officer, Erlanger Medical Center, Chattanooga, TN, p. A580

TABOR, Jeffrey, Director Human Resources, Jackson General Hospital, Ripley, WV, p. A699

TABOR, Randy, Director Fiscal Services, Shriners Hospitals for Children–Shreveport, Shreveport, LA, p. A288

TABORA, Knaya, Chief Operating Officer and Chief Nursing Officer, Colorado River Medical Center, Needles, CA, p. A79

TABUENCA, Arnold, M.D. Medical Director, Riverside University Health System–Medical Center, Moreno Valley, CA, p. A78

TACHIBANA, Charleen, R.N. Senior Vice President and Chief Nursing Officer, Virginia Mason Medical Center, Seattle, WA, p. A690

TACKITT, Sue, Chief Nursing Officer, Connally Memorial Medical Center, Floresville, TX, p. A617

TADURAN, Virgilio, M.D. Chief Medical Officer, Satanta District Hospital and Long Term Care, Satanta, KS, p. A253

TAFFE, Patrick, Vice President Information Services, North Memorial Medical Center, Robbinsdale, MN, p. A349

TAFOYA, Debbie, Vice President and Chief Information Officer, Huntington Memorial Hospital, Pasadena, CA, p. A82

TAFOYA, Debra, Director Human Resources, HEALTHSOUTH Rehabilitation Hospital–Las Vegas, Las Vegas, NV, p. A406

TAFT, Kenneth L., Executive Vice President and Chief Operating Officer, Bronson Methodist Hospital, Kalamazoo, MI, p. A328

TAFUR, Mario, M.D. Chief of Staff, St. Luke's Behavioral Health Center, Phoenix, AZ, p. A37

TAGGART, Travis, Director Information Technology, RiverValley Behavioral Health Hospital, Owensboro, KY, p. A267

TAGGE, Gordon, M.D. President Medical Staff, Three Rivers Hospital, Brewster, WA, p. A683

TAHAN, Pamela S., Chief Operating Officer, Wellington Regional Medical Center, West Palm Beach, FL, p. A150

TAHBO, Robin, Financial Management Officer, U. S. Public Health Service Indian Hospital, Parker, AZ, p. A35

TAILLEFER, Marguerite, M.D. Acting President Medical Staff, Sarah D. Culbertson Memorial Hospital, Rushville, IL, p. A202

TAKACS, Susan, Market Chief Operating Officer, Physicians Regional – Pine Ridge, Naples, FL, p. A138

TAKES, Kay, R.N.,
President, Mercy Medical Center–Dubuque, Dubuque, IA, p. A230
President, Mercy Medical Center–Dyersville, Dyersville, IA, p. A230

TAKEUCHI, Susi, Chief Human Resources and Organization Development Officer, Ronald Reagan UCLA Medical Center, Los Angeles, CA, p. A74

TALBERT, Adrienne, Interim Administrator, North Greenville Hospital, Travelers Rest, SC, p. A570

TALBERT, Bradley S., FACHE, Chief Executive Officer, Piedmont Medical Center, Rock Hill, SC, p. A569

TALBOT, Angela, Chief Manager Human Resources, Hamilton County Hospital, Syracuse, KS, p. A254

TALBOT, Jack, Director, Human Resources, West Chester Hospital, West Chester, OH, p. A505

TALBOT, Lisa, Director Human Resources, St. David's South Austin Medical Center, Austin, TX, p. A600

TALBOT, Tom, Chief Executive Officer, Community Mental Health Center, Lawrenceburg, IN, p. A217

TALBOTT, Ellen E., R.N. Vice President Patient Care Services, McLaren Bay Region, Bay City, MI, p. A319

TALBOTT, Sarah, Chief Nursing Officer, Sanford Chamberlain Medical Center, Chamberlain, SD, p. A572

TALENTO, Rick, Senior Vice President and Chief Financial Officer, Providence Hospital, Washington, DC, p. A122

TALLANT–BALL, Mary Jo, Director Health Information Systems, Dallas Medical Center, Dallas, TX, p. A609

TALLARICO, Dominica, President, Advocate Condell Medical Center, Libertyville, IL, p. A195

TALLEY, Cyndi, Director Information Systems, TriStar Greenview Regional Hospital, Bowling Green, KY, p. A258

TALLEY, Linda, MS Vice President and Chief Nursing Officer, Children's National Health System, Washington, DC, p. A121

TALLEY, Michael R., M.D. Chief of Staff, Okeene Municipal Hospital, Okeene, OK, p. A515

TALLEY, Rockey, M.D. Chief Medical Officer, AllianceHealth Midwest, Midwest City, OK, p. A514

TALLEY, Stephanie S.
Director Human Resources, Centennial Medical Center, Frisco, TX, p. A619
Market Chief Human Resource Officer, The Hospitals of Providence Memorial Campus, El Paso, TX, p. A616
Chief Human Resource Officer, The Hospitals of Providence Sierra Campus, El Paso, TX, p. A616

TALLON, Joe, Vice President Finance, Salina Regional Health Center, Salina, KS, p. A253

TALLON, Richard, Chief Financial Officer, Jefferson County Hospital, Waurika, OK, p. A523

TAM, David A., M.D. Chief Operating Officer, Providence Saint John's Health Center, Santa Monica, CA, p. A93

TAM, Paulina, Vice President of Operations, Tampa Community Hospital, Tampa, FL, p. A148

TAMANAHA, Nona
Vice President, Human Resources, North Hawaii Community Hospital, Kamuela, HI, p. A172
Vice President Human Resources, The Queen's Medical Center, Honolulu, HI, p. A171

TAMBURELLO, Leonardo, Divisional Chief Financial Officer, New York Community Hospital,, NY, p. A446

TAMMARO, Vincent, Chief Financial Officer, Yale–New Haven Hospital, New Haven, CT, p. A116

TAMMINEN, John, M.D. President Medical Staff, Carilion Giles Community Hospital, Pearisburg, VA, p. A675

TAN, Bradford, M.D. Chief Medical Officer, Midwestern Regional Medical Center, Zion, IL, p. A205

TANAKA, Steven, Chief Information Officer, Pomerado Hospital, Poway, CA, p. A84

TANCREDO, Beth, Director Operations, South Florida Baptist Hospital, Plant City, FL, p. A142

TANDE, Brett, Chief Financial Officer, Santa Ynez Valley Cottage Hospital, Solvang, CA, p. A94

TANDON, Satwant, M.D. Director of Clinical Services, Oklahoma Forensic Center, Vinita, OK, p. A523

TANDY, Gary R., Chief Financial Officer, General John J. Pershing Memorial Hospital, Brookfield, MO, p. A368

TANDY, William C., Chief Information Officer, Hanover Hospital, Hanover, PA, p. A539

TANEBAUM, Cynthia, Director Information Services, MedStar Harbor Hospital, Baltimore, MD, p. A297

TANEJA, K. Singh, Chief Operating Officer, Prince George's Hospital Center, Cheverly, MD, p. A299

TANEY, Amy, Chief Human Resource Officer, Highland Hospital, Rochester, NY, p. A454

TANG, Francis, Chief Information Officer, Rancho Los Amigos National Rehabilitation Center, Downey, CA, p. A61

TANG, Shirley, R.N. Chief Nursing Officer, Monterey Park Hospital, Monterey Park, CA, p. A78

TANGEMAN, Todd, Chief Operating Officer, Newton Medical Center, Newton, KS, p. A250

TANGUAY, Denis, Chief Information Officer, Central Maine Medical Center, Lewiston, ME, p. A293

TANJUAKIO, Robert, Chief Information Resources Management, Edward Hines, Jr. Veterans Affairs Hospital, Hines, IL, p. A193

TANKEL, Nancy, R.N. Chief Nurse Executive, Kaiser Permanente Woodland Hills Medical Center,, CA, p. A72

TANNENBAUM, Scott, M.D. Medical Director, HEALTHSOUTH Sunrise Rehabilitation Hospital, Sunrise, FL, p. A146

TANNER, Ashley, Director of Nursing, Wiregrass Medical Center, Geneva, AL, p. A20

TANNER, Douglas, Administrator, Atmore Community Hospital, Atmore, AL, p. A16

TANNER, Laureen K., FACHE, President and Chief Executive Officer, Ranken Jordan Pediatric Bridge Hospital, Maryland Heights, MO, p. A376

TANNOS, Paul, Chief Financial Officer, The Physicians Centre Hospital, Bryan, TX, p. A604

TANTHOREY, Geoff, Director Information Systems, Granville Health System, Oxford, NC, p. A471

TAPLETT, Dean, Controller, Quincy Valley Medical Center, Quincy, WA, p. A688

TAPLEY, Jahni, JD, Interim Chief Executive Officer, McCurtain Memorial Hospital, Idabel, OK, p. A513

TAPP, Gina
Director Human Resources, Samaritan North Lincoln Hospital, Lincoln City, OR, p. A527
Director Human Resources, Samaritan Pacific Communities Hospital, Newport, OR, p. A528

TAPPER, Shane, Director Management Information Systems, Fort Madison Community Hospital, Fort Madison, IA, p. A231

TARAMASCO, Chris, R.N. Chief Nursing Officer, Brandon Regional Hospital, Brandon, FL, p. A124

TARAR, Ahmad, M.D. Medical Director, Heartland Behavioral Health Services, Nevada, MO, p. A377

TARASOVICH, James
Chief Financial Officer, Mayo Clinic Health System in Saint James, Saint James, MN, p. A350
Chief Financial Officer, Mayo Clinic Health System in Springfield, Springfield, MN, p. A351

TARASOVITCH, James, Chief Financial Officer, Mayo Clinic Health System in Mankato, Mankato, MN, p. A345

TARBAY, Amy, Director Nursing Services, Naval Hospital Pensacola, Pensacola, FL, p. A142

TARBELL, Tim, Director Operations, Scott & White Hospital – Taylor, Taylor, TX, p. A651

TARBET, Joyce, M.D. Chief Medical Officer, Murray County Medical Center, Slayton, MN, p. A351

TAROLA, Robert, Executive Vice President and Chief Financial Officer, Southcoast Physicians Group, Fall River, MA, p. A310

TARRANT, Jeffrey S., FACHE, Chief Executive Officer, AllianceHealth Durant, Durant, OK, p. A511

TARRANT, Maureen, Chief Executive Officer, Presbyterian–St. Luke's Medical Center, Denver, CO, p. A104

TARTAGLIA, Judith C., President and Chief Executive Officer, The University of Vermont Health Network Central Vermont Medical Center, Berlin, VT, p. A665

TARULLI, Pamela, Senior Vice President Human Resources, Good Samaritan Regional Medical Center, Suffern, NY, p. A456

TARVER, Dennis, Director Information Technology, Elkview General Hospital, Hobart, OK, p. A512

TARVER, Jeanette, Director of Finance, Sonoma Valley Hospital, Sonoma, CA, p. A94

TARVER, Rebecca, Chief Nursing Officer, Bates County Memorial Hospital, Butler, MO, p. A368

TARVES, Paul E., R.N. Vice President Nursing Services, Evangelical Community Hospital, Lewisburg, PA, p. A543

TASSE, Joseph M., FACHE, Interim Chief Executive Officer, Trinity Health System, Steubenville, OH, p. A503

TASSEY, Karen, FACHE Chief Operating Officer, Columbia Memorial Hospital, Hudson, NY, p. A440

TASSIN, Bruce J., President, Saint Joseph Hospital, Lexington, KY, p. A263

TASSO, Tina, Manager Human Resources, The Orthopedic Specialty Hospital, Murray, UT, p. A661

TATE, Charlene, M.D. Chief Medical Staff and Clinical Services, Eleanor Slater Hospital, Cranston, RI, p. A560

TATE, Charles, Director Information Technology, Lallie Kemp Medical Center, Independence, LA, p. A278

TATE, James, M.D. Chief of Staff, Patients' Hospital of Redding, Redding, CA, p. A84

TATE, Jean, Vice President Human Resources, RiverView Health, Crookston, MN, p. A341

TATE, Joel W., FACHE, Chief Executive Officer, Clay County Hospital, Ashland, AL, p. A15

TATRO, Chad, Supervisor Information Systems, Northeast Regional Medical Center, Kirksville, MO, p. A375

TATUM, Monica, Chief Executive Officer and Administrator, Longleaf Hospital, Alexandria, LA, p. A271

TATUM, Stanley D., FACHE, Chief Executive Officer, St. Mary's Regional Medical Center, Enid, OK, p. A511

TAUL, Kelly, Business Manager, Meadowbrook Rehabilitation Hospital, Gardner, KS, p. A243

TAUNER, Gary, Chief Operating Officer, St. John's Medical Center and Living Center, Jackson, WY, p. A722

TAUNTON, David, M.D. Chief of Staff, Texas Health Harris Methodist Hospital Southlake, Southlake, TX, p. A649

TAUPIN, Michel, M.D. Chief Medical Officer, Abington–Lansdale Hospital Jefferson Health, Lansdale, PA, p. A542

TAUTZ, Linda, Interim Chief Executive Officer, Vibra Hospital of Denver, Thornton, CO, p. A111

TAVARY, James, Chief Executive Officer, Wickenburg Community Hospital, Wickenburg, AZ, p. A41

TAVELLA, Christopher
Acting Executive Director, Rockland Children's Psychiatric Center, Orangeburg, NY, p. A452
Executive Director, Rockland Psychiatric Center, Orangeburg, NY, p. A452

TAVENNER, Matt, Chief Executive Officer, Southern Virginia Regional Medical Center, Emporia, VA, p. A669

TAWNEY, Michael W., D.O. Vice President Medical Affairs, McLaren Port Huron, Port Huron, MI, p. A332

TAYLOR, Adam, Manager Information Technology, Northern Inyo Hospital, Bishop, CA, p. A57

TAYLOR, Alfred P., President and Chief Executive Officer, Stanly Regional Medical Center, Albemarle, NC, p. A460

TAYLOR, Alice, MSN, Chief Executive Officer, Broward Health Imperial Point, Fort Lauderdale, FL, p. A128

TAYLOR, Allison H., R.N. Chief Nursing Officer and Vice President Clinical Services, Sampson Regional Medical Center, Clinton, NC, p. A463

TAYLOR, Amy, Chief Financial Officer, Oklahoma Center for Orthopedic and Multi–Specialty Surgery, Oklahoma City, OK, p. A516

TAYLOR, Anthony, Manager Information Technology, Cherokee Indian Hospital, Cherokee, NC, p. A463

TAYLOR, Beth, Vice President, Human Resources, Newton–Wellesley Hospital, Newton Lower Falls, MA, p. A313

TAYLOR, Brenda, Director Information Systems, Texas Health Harris Methodist Hospital Cleburne, Cleburne, TX, p. A606

TAYLOR, Brett, Manager Information, Van Wert County Hospital, Van Wert, OH, p. A504

TAYLOR, Carol M., R.N., Regional Director Clinical Operations, Group Health Cooperative Central Hospital, Seattle, WA, p. A689

TAYLOR, Cecilia, Chief Financial Officer, Midwestern Regional Medical Center, Zion, IL, p. A205

TAYLOR, Cherie, Chief Executive Officer, Northern Rockies Medical Center, Cut Bank, MT, p. A386

TAYLOR, Cheryl, R.N. Director of Nursing, Henry Ford Kingswood Hospital, Ferndale, MI, p. A323

TAYLOR, Christina, Director Human Resources, The Brook Hospital – KMI, Louisville, KY, p. A265

TAYLOR, Dana Shantel, Director Organizational Development, Fairfield Memorial Hospital, Fairfield, IL, p. A190

TAYLOR, Debra, Chief Nursing Officer, Paris Regional Medical Center, Paris, TX, p. A640

TAYLOR, Dwayne, Chief Executive Officer, Sycamore Shoals Hospital, Elizabethton, TN, p. A582

TAYLOR, Ernest Lee, M.D. Vice President Medical Affairs, St. Mary's Medical Center, Huntington, WV, p. A697

TAYLOR, Eulon Ross, Clinical Director, North Texas State Hospital, Wichita Falls Campus, Wichita Falls, TX, p. A657

TAYLOR, Faye M., R.N. Director of Nursing, Stephens County Hospital, Toccoa, GA, p. A168

TAYLOR, Gregory W., M.D. Vice President and Chief Operating Officer, High Point Regional Health System, High Point, NC, p. A467

TAYLOR, Heather, Human Resources Manager, Tippah County Hospital, Ripley, MS, p. A364

TAYLOR, Heidi, Chief Financial Officer, Morton Hospital and Medical Center, Taunton, MA, p. A315

TAYLOR, Janey, Chief Information and Technology, Overton Brooks Veterans Affairs Medical Center, Shreveport, LA, p. A287

TAYLOR, Jay, M.D. Chief of Staff, Pondera Medical Center, Conrad, MT, p. A386

TAYLOR, Jeff, Vice President Finance, St. Luke's Regional Medical Center, Boise, ID, p. A175

TAYLOR, Jeremy, Director Information Services, Saint Francis Hospital, Charleston, WV, p. A695

TAYLOR, Jim, Chief Business Office, North Florida/South Georgia Veteran's Health System, Gainesville, FL, p. A129

TAYLOR, Joel
Chief Information Officer, Bayonne Medical Center, Bayonne, NJ, p. A414
Chief Information Officer, Hoboken University Medical Center, Hoboken, NJ, p. A418

TAYLOR, Joel C., Interim Chief Executive Officer, Coastal Carolina Hospital, Hardeeville, SC, p. A567

TAYLOR, Judd, Chief Financial Officer, Ogden Regional Medical Center, Ogden, UT, p. A661

TAYLOR, Julia, Area Director Human Resources, Vibra Hospital of Charleston, Mt. Pleasant, SC, p. A568

TAYLOR, Julie, FACHE, Chief Executive Officer, Alaska Regional Hospital, Anchorage, AK, p. A28

TAYLOR, Konnie, Chief Financial Officer, Carl Albert Community Mental Health Center, McAlester, OK, p. A514

TAYLOR, Kristie, Chief Financial Officer, Southern Tennessee Regional Health System–Lawrenceburg, Lawrenceburg, TN, p. A586

TAYLOR, Linda, Chief Human Resources Officer, Goodland Regional Medical Center, Goodland, KS, p. A244

TAYLOR, Lisa, Director of Nursing, Mountain View Hospital, Payson, UT, p. A662

TAYLOR, Lora, Director Human Resources and Compliance Officer, Keokuk Area Hospital, Keokuk, IA, p. A233

TAYLOR, Marc, IS Director, Mountain West Medical Center, Tooele, UT, p. A664

TAYLOR, Marcia, Chief Executive Officer, Select Specialty Hospital–Memphis, Memphis, TN, p. A589

TAYLOR, Meredith, Controller, South Sunflower County Hospital, Indianola, MS, p. A359

TAYLOR, Merle, Vice President Operations, UPMC St. Margaret, Pittsburgh, PA, p. A552

TAYLOR, Michael
Chief Information Officer, Bon Secours St. Francis Hospital, Charleston, SC, p. A562
Vice President Finance, Northridge Hospital Medical Center,, CA, p. A73
Vice President Financial Services and Chief Financial Officer, St. Rose Hospital, Hayward, CA, p. A66

TAYLOR, Michael V.
Senior Vice President Human Resources, Sentara Leigh Hospital, Norfolk, VA, p. A675
Vice President Human Resources, Sentara Princess Anne Hospital, Virginia Beach, VA, p. A680

TAYLOR, Mimi
Corporate Vice President Information Technology, Baptist Health South Florida, Baptist Hospital of Miami, Miami, FL, p. A136
Corporate Vice President Information Technology, Baptist Health South Florida, Homestead Hospital, Homestead, FL, p. A131
Vice President Information Technology, Baptist Health South Florida, Mariners Hospital, Tavernier, FL, p. A148
Vice President Information Technology, Baptist Health South Florida, South Miami Hospital, Miami, FL, p. A136

TAYLOR, Nathan, Director of Nursing, Heartland Behavioral Health Services, Nevada, MO, p. A377

TAYLOR, Patrick, M.D., President and Chief Executive Officer, Holy Cross Hospital, Fort Lauderdale, FL, p. A128

TAYLOR, Paul
Administrator, Ozarks Community Hospital, Gravette, AR, p. A47
Chief Executive Officer, Ozarks Community Hospital, Springfield, MO, p. A382

TAYLOR, Randy, Chief Information Technology Officer, Perry Memorial Hospital, Perry, OK, p. A518

TAYLOR, Renae, Chief Nursing Officer, Southeastern Health, Lumberton, NC, p. A469

TAYLOR, Richard, Chief Financial Officer, Western Mental Health Institute, Bolivar, TN, p. A579

TAYLOR, Robbie, Director Human Resources, North Sunflower Medical Center, Ruleville, MS, p. A364

TAYLOR, Robert, Director Information Services, St. Christopher's Hospital for Children, Philadelphia, PA, p. A549

TAYLOR, Ross, M.D. Clinical Director, Austin State Hospital, Austin, TX, p. A599

TAYLOR, Sarah, Chief Human Resources, National Jewish Health, Denver, CO, p. A104

TAYLOR, Scott J., President and Chief Executive Officer, St. Catherine Hospital, Garden City, KS, p. A243

TAYLOR, Scotty, Information Technology Director, East Mississippi State Hospital, Meridian, MS, p. A362

TAYLOR, Sharon, Human Resources Director, Allegiance Specialty Hospital of Greenville, Greenville, MS, p. A358

TAYLOR, Stacy, Chief Financial Officer, Nemaha County Hospital, Auburn, NE, p. A393

TAYLOR, Steve, Chief Information Officer, Anderson Regional Health System South, Meridian, MS, p. A362

TAYLOR, Steve, M.D. Chief Medical Officer, Sarasota Memorial Health Care System, Sarasota, FL, p. A145

TAYLOR, Steven L., Chief Executive Officer, Harrison County Hospital, Corydon, IN, p. A208

TAYLOR, Sue O., Vice President Nursing, Vidant Duplin Hospital, Kenansville, NC, p. A468

TAYLOR, Susan L., JD, Chief Executive Officer, College Hospital Costa Mesa, Costa Mesa, CA, p. A60

TAYLOR, Todd, Chief Executive Officer, Stafford County Hospital, Stafford, KS, p. A254

TAYLOR, Tyrone, Chief Financial Officer, Veterans Affairs New Jersey Health Care System, East Orange, NJ, p. A416

TAYLOR, Venus, Director Human Resources, BHC Alhambra Hospital, Rosemead, CA, p. A86

TEAFORD, Carrie, Vice President Finance, Saint Thomas Midtown Hospital, Nashville, TN, p. A591

TEAGUE, Dean, Chief Executive Officer, Calvert Memorial Hospital, Prince Frederick, MD, p. A302

TEAHL, Bradley, Director Human Resources, HEALTHSOUTH Rehabilitation Hospital of York, York, PA, p. A559

TEAL, Amy, Chief Executive Officer, HEALTHSOUTH Reading Rehabilitation Hospital, Reading, PA, p. A553

TEAL, Barbara, R.N. Associate Director Patient Care Services and Nurse Executive, Sioux Falls Veterans Affairs Health Care System, Sioux Falls, SD, p. A576

TEAL, Cydney, M.D. Vice President Medical Affairs, Union Hospital, Elkton, MD, p. A300

TEAS, Gregory, M.D. Chief Medical Officer, Alexian Brothers Behavioral Health Hospital, Hoffman Estates, IL, p. A193

TEASDALE, Peggy, Director Human Resources, Southeast Health Center of Ripley County, Doniphan, MO, p. A370

TEATER, Phyllis, Chief Information Officer, Ohio State University Wexner Medical Center, Columbus, OH, p. A491

TEATSORTH, Neil, Vice President Human Resources, Norwegian American Hospital, Chicago, IL, p. A185

TEBBE, James, M.D. Vice President Medical Affairs, Ochsner Medical Center – Kenner, Kenner, LA, p. A279

TEDDER, Cookie, Human Resources Manager, Texas Health Center for Diagnostic & Surgery, Plano, TX, p. A642

TEDESCHI, Anthony, M.P.H., Chief Executive Officer and Chief Medical Officer, Louis A. Weiss Memorial Hospital, Chicago, IL, p. A184

TEDESCO, Art, Interim Chief Financial Officer, Gaylord Hospital, Wallingford, CT, p. A117

TEFFETELLER, Scott L., President, Community Hospital East, Indianapolis, IN, p. A213

TEICHMEIER, Laura, Director Human Resources, Memorial Community Health, Aurora, NE, p. A393

TEISSONNIERE, Maria T., Director Public Relations, Hospital Oncologico Andres Grillasca, Ponce, PR, p. A728

TEITELBAUM, Karen, Chief Executive Officer, Schwab Rehabilitation Hospital, Chicago, IL, p. A186

TEITELBAUM, Karen, President and Chief Executive Officer, Sinai Health System, Chicago, IL, p. B124

TEJADA, Vanessa, Director Human Resources, HealthSouth Rehabilitation Institute of San Antonio, San Antonio, TX, p. A646

TEJEDA, Nicholas R., FACHE, Chief Executive Officer, The Hospitals of Providence East Campus, El Paso, TX, p. A616

TELHIARD, Nicole, Chief Nursing Officer, Our Lady of the Lake Regional Medical Center, Baton Rouge, LA, p. A273

TELITZ, Rita, Chief Administrative Officer, Rusk County Memorial Hospital, Ladysmith, WI, p. A708

TELL, Marjorie, Vice President Information Technology, Aspirus Riverview Hospital and Clinics, Inc., Wisconsin Rapids, WI, p. A719

TELLOR, Tammy, Acting Director Human Resources, Choate Mental Health Center, Anna, IL, p. A180

TELTHORSTER, M.ED, CCP, Marcia M., Vice President Human Resources, University Medical Center of Princeton at Plainsboro, Plainsboro, NJ, p. A422

TEMPELMEYER, Zak, M.D. Chief Medical Staff, Community Memorial Hospital, Syracuse, NE, p. A402

TEMPEST, Wendy, Director Human Resources, Vibra Hospital of Northern California, Redding, CA, p. A84

TEMPLE, Amber L., Director Human Resources, Morrison Community Hospital, Morrison, IL, p. A197

TEMPLE, Gina, Chief Nurse Executive, Sutter Auburn Faith Hospital, Auburn, CA, p. A55

TEMPLETON, Carrie E., FACHE, Chief Executive Officer, Lafayette General Surgical Hospital, Lafayette, LA, p. A280

TEMPLETON, Gary, M.D. Medical Director, Regency Hospital of Northwest Arkansas – Springdale, Springdale, AR, p. A52

TEMPLETON, Sheryl, Chief Financial Officer, Scotland County Hospital, Memphis, MO, p. A376

TEMPLETON, III, William, M.D. Medical Director, Clark Memorial Hospital, Jeffersonville, IN, p. A215

TEMPLIN, Nancy, Vice President Finance and Chief Financial Officer, Johns Hopkins All Children's Hospital, Saint Petersburg, FL, p. A144

TEN HAAF, Patricia, Ph.D., Director, John J. Pershing Veterans Affairs Medical Center, Poplar Bluff, MO, p. A378

TENEWITZ, Edward, M.D. Chief of Staff, Healthmark Regional Medical Center, DeFuniak Springs, FL, p. A127

TENGERES, Michael A., Corporate Vice President and Chief Financial Officer, Bassett Medical Center, Cooperstown, NY, p. A437

TENHOUSE, Steven D., FACHE, Chief Executive Officer, Kirby Medical Center, Monticello, IL, p. A197

TENNARO, Sonja, Ed.D. Senior Vice President Clinical Operations, New York Eye and Ear Infirmary of Mount Sinai, New York, NY, p. A447

TENNEY, Ralph

   Chief Information Officer, Crittenton Hospital Medical Center, Rochester, MI, p. A332

   Chief Information Officer, St. John Hospital and Medical Center, Detroit, MI, p. A322

   Chief Information Officer, St. John Macomb–Oakland Hospital, Warren, MI, p. A336

TENNISON, Gary, M.D. Chief of Staff, Crawford Memorial Hospital, Robinson, IL, p. A201

TENNYSON, Ruby, Director Administration, Naval Hospital Jacksonville, Jacksonville, FL, p. A132

TENREIRO, Edgardo J., Interim Chief Executive Officer and Chief Operating Officer, Baton Rouge General Medical Center, Baton Rouge, LA, p. A272

TEOLIS, Matthew

   Interim President and Chief Executive Officer, Vice President of Medical Affairs, Franciscan Healthcare – Munster, Munster, IN, p. A219

   Interim President and Chief Executive Officer, Vice President of Medical Affairs, Franciscan St. Margaret Health – Hammond, Hammond, IN, p. A212

TEPEDINO, Miguel, M.D. Chief Medicine, Lake City Medical Center, Lake City, FL, p. A133

TEPPER, Gil, M.D., Chief Executive Officer, Miracle Mile Medical Center, Los Angeles, CA, p. A73

TER HORST, Thomas C., Vice President Human Resources, Aurora St. Luke's Medical Center, Milwaukee, WI, p. A711

TERBUSH, Jennifer, Vice President, Patient Services, Hills & Dales General Hospital, Cass City, MI, p. A320

TERI, Anthony, Director Information Technology, Hackensack University Medical Center at Pascack Valley, Westwood, NJ, p. A425

TERPENING, Ken, Chief Nursing Officer, Mad River Community Hospital, Arcata, CA, p. A55

TERPSTRA, Kelli, R.N. Chief Nursing Officer, Our Children's House, Dallas, TX, p. A611

TERRELL, Greg, Senior Vice President and Chief Operating Officer, Norman Regional Health System, Norman, OK, p. A515

TERRELL, Jay, Manager Management Information Systems, Riverview Regional Medical Center, Gadsden, AL, p. A20

TERRELL, Michael T., Chief Financial Officer, Brandon Regional Hospital, Brandon, FL, p. A124

TERRESON, Gregg, Chief Financial Officer, Cascade Behavioral Hospital, Tukwila, WA, p. A692

TERRINONI, Gary G., President and Chief Executive Officer, Brooklyn Hospital Center,, NY, p. A444

TERRY, Sr., Darrell K., Senior Vice President Operations, Newark Beth Israel Medical Center, Newark, NJ, p. A420

TERRY, Michael, President and Chief Executive Officer, Salina Regional Health Center, Salina, KS, p. B117

TERRY, Micheal, President and Chief Executive Officer, Salina Regional Health Center, Salina, KS, p. A253

TERRY, Randi, Site Director Management Information Systems, Munson Healthcare Cadillac Hospital, Cadillac, MI, p. A319

TERRY, Richard, Vice President & Chief Information Officer, Sparrow Carson Hospital, Carson City, MI, p. A320

TERRY, Teresa, Director Human Resource, Payroll, Fisher County Hospital District, Rotan, TX, p. A644

TERRY–WILLIAMS, Teresa, Chief Nursing Officer, Pennsylvania Psychiatric Institute, Harrisburg, PA, p. A539

TERSHAKOVEC, George R., M.D. President Medical Staff, Baptist Health South Florida, Homestead Hospital, Homestead, FL, p. A131

TERTEL, Jenifer K., Director Human Resources, Medical City Dallas Hospital, Dallas, TX, p. A610

TERWILLIGER, Michael, Chief Financial Officer, Friends Hospital, Philadelphia, PA, p. A548

TERZANO, Valerie, MSN Senior Vice President Nursing, Winthrop–University Hospital, Mineola, NY, p. A442

TESKE, Mark, Chief Financial Officer, Hill Crest Behavioral Health Services, Birmingham, AL, p. A16

TESSARZIK, Connie, Business Manager, Albert J. Solnit Psychiatric Center – South Campus, Middletown, CT, p. A115

TESSMAN, Lisa, Manager Information Technology, Fayette County Hospital, Vandalia, IL, p. A204

TESTA, Nick, M.D. Chief Medical Officer, Providence Saint Joseph Medical Center, Burbank, CA, p. A57

TETTEH, Walter, Director Human Resources, DMC – Children's Hospital of Michigan, Detroit, MI, p. A321

TETZ, Warren, Senior Vice President and Chief Operating Officer, Glendale Adventist Medical Center, Los Angeles, CA, p. A71

TEUBNER, Sandra, Chief Financial Officer, St. Aloisius Medical Center, Harvey, ND, p. A479

TEUFEL, George, Vice President Finance, Advocate Good Shepherd Hospital, Barrington, IL, p. A181

TEVES, Alicia, Coordinator Human Resources, Molokai General Hospital, Kaunakakai, HI, p. A172

TEWKSBURY, Randy E., Senior Vice President Finance and Chief Financial Officer, Mount Nittany Medical Center, State College, PA, p. A555

THACKER, Adam, Chief Operating Officer, Good Samaritan Hospital, Vincennes, IN, p. A223

THACKER, Roland, Chief Financial Officer, Northside Medical Center, Columbus, GA, p. A156

THAKOR, Pratapji, M.D. Chief of Staff, South Mississippi County Regional Medical Center, Osceola, AR, p. A51

THALER, Klaus, FACS Chief Medical Officer, Houston Methodist San Jacinto Hospital, Baytown, TX, p. A601

THAMA, Todd, Chief Operating Officer, Fairfax Behavioral Health, Kirkland, WA, p. A686

THAMES, Robert P., President and Chief Executive Officer, Northern Arizona Healthcare, Flagstaff, AZ, p. B97

THAMES, Thomas B., M.D., President, Sentara Princess Anne Hospital, Virginia Beach, VA, p. A680

THARASRI, Luke, Interim Chief Executive Officer, Sonoma West Medical Center, Sebastopol, CA, p. A94

THARP, Beth S., R.N., President and Chief Executive Officer, Community Hospital of Anderson & Madison County, Anderson, IN, p. A206

THARP, Stephen, M.D. Medical Director, St. Vincent Frankfort Hospital, Frankfort, IN, p. A211

THAUNG, Htin, M.D. Chief Medical Officer, Ward Memorial Hospital, Monahans, TX, p. A637

THAYER, Charles, M.D. Chief Medical Officer, Morton Hospital and Medical Center, Taunton, MA, p. A315

THAYER, Gilbert M., M.D. Chief Medical Staff, Hardin Medical Center, Savannah, TN, p. A592

THAYER, Kendra, MSN Vice President, Clinical Services and Chief Nursing Officer, Garrett Regional Medical Center, Oakland, MD, p. A302

THEILER, Brian, President and Chief Executive Officer, Gundersen Tri–County Hospital and Clinics, Whitehall, WI, p. A719

THEIRING, James, Chief Executive Officer, Mission Community Hospital,, CA, p. A73

THEISEN, Janet

   Chief Information Officer, Sanford Tracy Medical Center, Tracy, MN, p. A352

   Chief Information Officer, Sanford Westbrook Medical Center, Westbrook, MN, p. A353

THELEN, Raymond Scott, Vice President and Chief Financial Officer, Masonicare Health Center, Wallingford, CT, p. A117

THEOBALD, Terry, Chief Information Officer, Ventura County Medical Center, Ventura, CA, p. A98

THEODOROU, Andreas, Chief Medical Officer, Banner – University Medical Center Tucson, Tucson, AZ, p. A40

THEOHARES, Nick, Executive Director, Operations, St. Vincent Anderson Regional Hospital, Anderson, IN, p. A206

THERIAC, Gary, Director Information Technology, Lawrence County Memorial Hospital, Lawrenceville, IL, p. A195

THERIOT, Lyle, Director Human Resources, Lakeview Regional Medical Center, Covington, LA, p. A275

THERIOT, Paul, Chief Executive Officer, East Georgia Regional Medical Center, Statesboro, GA, p. A166

THEROULT, Thomas N., Chief Executive Officer, Select Specialty Hospital–Omaha, Omaha, NE, p. A400

THERRIEN, Charles D., President and Chief Executive Officer, Maine Coast Memorial Hospital, Ellsworth, ME, p. A293

THERRIEN, Tinna, Chief Information Officer and Director Clinical Infomatics, Gothenburg Memorial Hospital, Gothenburg, NE, p. A396

THETFORD, Carol, Chief Nursing Officer, Baptist Memorial Hospital for Women, Memphis, TN, p. A588

THEUS, Thomas L., M.D. Chief of Medicine, Midtown Medical Center West, Columbus, GA, p. A156

THEUS, Will, M.D. Chief of Staff, Gordon Hospital, Calhoun, GA, p. A155

THIBERT, Kimberly, R.N. Vice President Patient Care Services and Chief Nursing Officer, Samaritan Medical Center, Watertown, NY, p. A458

THIBODEAU, Helene, R.N. Vice President Patient Care Services, Northeast Rehabilitation Hospital, Salem, NH, p. A413

THIBODEAU, Jan, Director Human Resources, HEALTHSOUTH Southern Hills Rehabilitation Hospital, Princeton, WV, p. A699

THIBODEAUX, Anita, Chief Nursing Officer, Beauregard Memorial Hospital, De Ridder, LA, p. A276

THIBODEAUX, Annette, Director Human Resources, Savoy Medical Center, Mamou, LA, p. A282

THIBODEAUX, Douglas, M.D. Chief Medical Officer, OakBend Medical Center, Richmond, TX, p. A643

THIEL, Stefanie
Senior Human Resources Business Partner, Saint Alphonsus Medical Center – Nampa, Nampa, ID, p. A177
Senior Human Resources Business Partner, Saint Alphonsus Medical Center – Ontario, Ontario, OR, p. A528

THIELEMIER, Kevin, Director Human Resources, Arkansas Methodist Medical Center, Paragould, AR, p. A51

THIELEN, Kurt, Associate Director, Minneapolis Veterans Affairs Health Care System, Minneapolis, MN, p. A346

THIELKE, Jayne, Chief Financial Officer, Swift County–Benson Hospital, Benson, MN, p. A339

THIEME, Ron, Ph.D. Chief Knowledge and Information Officer, Community Hospital North, Indianapolis, IN, p. A213

THIES, Dana, Director of Nursing, Meadows Psychiatric Center, Centre Hall, PA, p. A535

THIESCHAFER, Cheryl, Acting Director, St. Cloud Veterans Affairs Health Care System, Saint Cloud, MN, p. A350

THIESFELD RAUEN, Rebecca A., Director Human Resources, Maple Grove Hospital, Maple Grove, MN, p. A345

THILGES, Charles, Chief Financial Officer, Veterans Affairs Pittsburgh Healthcare System, Pittsburgh, PA, p. A552

THILGES, Michael, Chief Financial Officer, Clarke County Hospital, Osceola, IA, p. A236

THILL, Jennifer, Chief of Staff, Mid–Valley Hospital, Omak, WA, p. A687

THIMIS, Nicholas, Chief Information Officer, West Jefferson Medical Center, Marrero, LA, p. A283

THIRUMALAREDDY, Joseph, M.D. Chief of Staff, Wishek Community Hospital and Clinics, Wishek, ND, p. A482

THOELE, Theresa, Director Human Resources, Coffey County Hospital, Burlington, KS, p. A241

THOENDEL, Victor, M.D. Chief Medical Officer, Butler County Health Care Center, David City, NE, p. A395

THOMAN, Dawn, Vice President Human Resources, Cloud County Health Center, Concordia, KS, p. A242

THOMAN, Michele, R.N. Chief Nursing Officer, NCH Downtown Naples Hospital, Naples, FL, p. A138

THOMAS, Amy, Vice President Finance, Memorial Hospital, Belleville, IL, p. A181

THOMAS, Andrea, Chief Operating Officer, St. Cloud Regional Medical Center, Saint Cloud, FL, p. A144

THOMAS, Andrew, M.D. Chief Medical Officer, Ohio State University Wexner Medical Center, Columbus, OH, p. A491

THOMAS, Brian E., Administrator, Alton Mental Health Center, Alton, IL, p. A180

THOMAS, Brian N., Interim Chief Executive Officer, Jefferson Regional Medical Center, Pine Bluff, AR, p. A51

THOMAS, Brook, Chief Financial Officer, West Boca Medical Center, Boca Raton, FL, p. A124

THOMAS, IV, Calvin, Chief Operating Officer, St. Lucie Medical Center, Port St. Lucie, FL, p. A143

THOMAS, Chris, FACHE, President and Chief Executive Officer, Community Hospital, Grand Junction, CO, p. A106

THOMAS, Clay, Chief Operating Officer, Covenant Children's Hospital, Lubbock, TX, p. A633

THOMAS, Curt, Administrator, Ness County Hospital District No 2, Ness City, KS, p. A250

THOMAS, David, President Medical Staff, Riddle Hospital, Media, PA, p. A545

THOMAS, Deana, Vice President Finance and Chief Financial Officer, North Arkansas Regional Medical Center, Harrison, AR, p. A47

THOMAS, Debora, Chief Financial Officer, Florida Hospital Memorial Medical Center, Daytona Beach, FL, p. A127

THOMAS, Debra A., Vice President of Patient Care Services and Chief Nursing Officer, Penn Highlands Brookville, Brookville, PA, p. A534

THOMAS, Denise, Chief Financial Officer, Spring View Hospital, Lebanon, KY, p. A262

THOMAS, Dennis, Chief Nursing Officer, Hardeman County Memorial Hospital, Quanah, TX, p. A642

THOMAS, Gene, Vice President, Information Systems, Chief Information Officer, Memorial Hospital at Gulfport, Gulfport, MS, p. A358

THOMAS, George, M.D. Chief of Staff, Palo Pinto General Hospital, Mineral Wells, TX, p. A637

THOMAS, Gina, Chief Nursing Officer & Director of Patient Care Services, Richland Memorial Hospital, Olney, IL, p. A199

THOMAS, Jayne
Chief Nursing Officer, AllianceHealth Deaconess, Oklahoma City, OK, p. A516
Chief Nursing Officer, Southwestern Medical Center, Lawton, OK, p. A513

THOMAS, Jeff, Chief Financial Officer, Heartland Regional Medical Center, Marion, IL, p. A195

THOMAS, Jennifer, Chief Operating Officer and Director of Public Relations, Lake Butler Hospital Hand Surgery Center, Lake Butler, FL, p. A133

THOMAS, Jill, Director of Nursing, Western State Hospital, Hopkinsville, KY, p. A262

THOMAS, Joan, Chief Financial Officer, Novant Health Brunswick Medical Center, Bolivia, NC, p. A461

THOMAS, John, Chief Operating Officer, San Mateo Medical Center, San Mateo, CA, p. A92

THOMAS, John A., M.D. Chief Medical Staff, Culberson Hospital, Van Horn, TX, p. A655

THOMAS, Karen A.
Vice President and Chief Information Officer, Bryn Mawr Hospital, Bryn Mawr, PA, p. A534
Chief Information Officer, Bryn Mawr Rehabilitation Hospital, Malvern, PA, p. A543
Acting Vice President and Chief Information Officer, Lankenau Medical Center, Wynnewood, PA, p. A558
Vice President and Chief Information Officer, Paoli Hospital, Paoli, PA, p. A547

THOMAS, Keith, M.D. Chief of Staff, Blue Mountain Hospital, John Day, OR, p. A527

THOMAS, Kirk E., Vice President Operations, Geisinger–Lewistown Hospital, Lewistown, PA, p. A543

THOMAS, Maggie, Vice President Human Resources and Practice Management, South County Hospital, Wakefield, RI, p. A561

THOMAS, Michael, Associate Administrator, Wayne County Hospital, Corydon, IA, p. A228

THOMAS, Michael S., President and Chief Administrative Officer, John Muir Medical Center, Concord, Concord, CA, p. A59

THOMAS, Michelle, Vice President Human Resources, Berkeley Medical Center, Martinsburg, WV, p. A697

THOMAS, Nicky, Director Human Resources, Baptist Memorial Hospital–Union City, Union City, TN, p. A594

THOMAS, Patric, Corporate Vice President Information Services, Scripps Green Hospital, La Jolla, CA, p. A67

THOMAS, Patricia F., Chief Nursing Officer, Sentara Halifax Regional Hospital, South Boston, VA, p. A678

THOMAS, Paula, R.N. Vice President Patient Services, UPMC Bedford Memorial, Everett, PA, p. A538

THOMAS, Jr., Phillip, Director Human Resources, Jackson Parish Hospital, Jonesboro, LA, p. A279

THOMAS, Ron, M.D. Chief Medical Officer, Florida Hospital–Flagler, Palm Coast, FL, p. A141

THOMAS, Ronda, Chief Nursing Officer, Atoka County Medical Center, Atoka, OK, p. A509

THOMAS, Russell, M.D. Chief of Staff, Rice Medical Center, Eagle Lake, TX, p. A614

THOMAS, Ruth, Chief Operating Officer, Mercy Fitzgerald Hospital, Darby, PA, p. A536

THOMAS, Sarah, Director of Human Resources, HEALTHSOUTH Rehabilitation Hospital of Littleton, Littleton, CO, p. A108

THOMAS, Scott, Administrative Director Human Resources and Communications, Granville Health System, Oxford, NC, p. A471

THOMAS, Shawn M., Director Human Resources, Banner Payson Medical Center, Payson, AZ, p. A35

THOMAS, Sue, Manager Human Resources, Beckley ARH Hospital, Beckley, WV, p. A694

THOMAS, Suji, R.N., MSN Chief Executive Officer, HEALTHSOUTH Rehabilitation Hospital of Tinton Falls, Tinton Falls, NJ, p. A424

THOMAS, Sylvia, Chief Nursing Officer, Jack Hughston Memorial Hospital, Phenix City, AL, p. A24

THOMAS, Warner L., FACHE, President and Chief Executive Officer, Ochsner Health System, New Orleans, LA, p. B99

THOMAS, Jr., William, M.D. Medical Director Clinical and Internal Affairs, Molokai General Hospital, Kaunakakai, HI, p. A172

THOMAS–BOYD, Sharon, Chief Operating Officer, Oaklawn Hospital, Marshall, MI, p. A330

THOMAS–FOLDS, Lana, System Director Human Resources, Jack Hughston Memorial Hospital, Phenix City, AL, p. A24

THOMAS–WILLIAMS, Jovita, Associate Vice President Human Resources, The University of Toledo Medical Center, Toledo, OH, p. A504

THOMASON, Joe D., Chief Executive Officer, Centennial Medical Center, Frisco, TX, p. A619

THOMMAN, Connie, Director of Nursing, Covenant Hospital–Levelland, Levelland, TX, p. A632

THOMPSON, Alan, M.D. President Medical Staff, Warm Springs Medical Center, Warm Springs, GA, p. A168

THOMPSON, Amy, M.D., Chief Executive Officer, Covenant Children's Hospital, Lubbock, TX, p. A633

THOMPSON, Becki, President, CHI Oakes Hospital, Oakes, ND, p. A481

THOMPSON, Becky, Chief Financial Officer, CHI St. Francis Health, Breckenridge, MN, p. A340

THOMPSON, Belinda, Coordinator Human Resources, HEALTHSOUTH Chesapeake Rehabilitation Hospital, Salisbury, MD, p. A303

THOMPSON, Bobby, Director Information Technology, Stephens Memorial Hospital, Breckenridge, TX, p. A603

THOMPSON, Cathy, Manager Human Resources, Paris Community Hospital, Paris, IL, p. A199

THOMPSON, Chad
Chief Executive Officer, Friend Community Healthcare System, Friend, NE, p. A396
Chief Financial Officer, Lallie Kemp Medical Center, Independence, LA, p. A278
Chief Executive Officer, Regional West Garden County, Oshkosh, NE, p. A401

THOMPSON, Charles, M.D. Chief Medical Officer, Nacogdoches Medical Center, Nacogdoches, TX, p. A638

THOMPSON, Charolette, Chief Financial Officer, Reeves Memorial Medical Center, Bernice, LA, p. A273

THOMPSON, Cheryl
Facility Director Human Resources, Connecticut Valley Hospital, Middletown, CT, p. A115
Chief Nursing Officer, Garden Park Medical Center, Gulfport, MS, p. A358

THOMPSON, Chris
Chief Financial Officer, Delta Community Medical Center, Delta, UT, p. A659
Chief Financial Officer, Fillmore Community Medical Center, Fillmore, UT, p. A659
Chief Financial Officer, Sanpete Valley Hospital, Mount Pleasant, UT, p. A660
Chief Financial Officer, Sevier Valley Medical Center, Richfield, UT, p. A662

THOMPSON, Cindy, Chief Financial Officer, Northwest Surgical Hospital, Oklahoma City, OK, p. A516

THOMPSON, Craig, Chief Operating Officer, Golden Valley Memorial Healthcare, Clinton, MO, p. A369

THOMPSON, Craig B., M.D., President and Chief Executive Officer, Memorial Sloan–Kettering Cancer Center, New York, NY, p. A446

THOMPSON, Dale, Chief Financial Officer, McLaren Greater Lansing, Lansing, MI, p. A328

THOMPSON, David, M.D. Chief of Staff, Richardson Medical Center, Rayville, LA, p. A286

THOMPSON, David
Chief Financial Officer, St. Anthony Hospital, Lakewood, CO, p. A108
Chief Financial Officer, St. Anthony Summit Medical Center, Frisco, CO, p. A105

THOMPSON, David M., Chief Executive Officer, Sutter Tracy Community Hospital, Tracy, CA, p. A96

THOMPSON, Debbie, Chief Financial Officer, Sweetwater Hospital, Sweetwater, TN, p. A593

THOMPSON, Donna K., Chief Executive Officer, Allegiance Health Center of Ruston, Ruston, LA, p. A287

THOMPSON, Douglas, Chief Information Officer, Upson Regional Medical Center, Thomaston, GA, p. A167

THOMPSON, Dwight, Chief Financial Officer, Altru Health System, Grand Forks, ND, p. A479

THOMPSON, Ethan, Chief Executive Officer, St. Theresa Specialty Hospital, Kenner, LA, p. A279

THOMPSON, Greg
Chief Medical Officer, Gundersen Health System, La Crosse, WI, p. A708
Corporate Director, Human Resources, Orlando Regional Medical Center, Orlando, FL, p. A140

THOMPSON, Ivan, Vice President, Chief Human Resource Officer, University of Texas Southwestern Medical Center, Dallas, TX, p. A612

THOMPSON, James H., FACHE, Owner and Chief Executive Officer, Healthmark Regional Medical Center, DeFuniak Springs, FL, p. A127

THOMPSON, Jeffrey D., Chief Executive Officer, Baylor Institute for Rehabilitation at Fort Worth, Fort Worth, TX, p. A617

THOMPSON, John W., M.D. Chief of Staff, Eastern Louisiana Mental Health System, Jackson, LA, p. A278

THOMPSON, Julie
Chief Operating Officer and Chief Nursing Officer, Bluffton Regional Medical Center, Bluffton, IN, p. A207
Manager Personnel and Payroll, Mayers Memorial Hospital District, Fall River Mills, CA, p. A62

THOMPSON, Kim, Vice President and Chief Financial Officer, Ozarks Medical Center, West Plains, MO, p. A384

THOMPSON, II, Lennis, Vice President and Chief Financial Officer, Hardin Memorial Hospital, Elizabethtown, KY, p. A259

THOMPSON, Linda
Chief Operating Officer, Fairfax Community Hospital, Fairfax, OK, p. A512
Senior Vice President, Human Resources and Service Excellence, New England Baptist Hospital, Boston, MA, p. A307

THOMPSON, Lisa, MSN Director of Nursing, Hiawatha Community Hospital, Hiawatha, KS, p. A244

THOMPSON, Lori L., Manager Human Resources, Nebraska Orthopaedic Hospital, Omaha, NE, p. A400

THOMPSON, Marion A., FACHE, Chief Executive Officer, Allen County Regional Hospital, Iola, KS, p. A245

THOMPSON, Mark, Market Chief Financial Officer Northern Region and Chief Financial Officer, Mercy Health – St. Charles Hospital, Oregon, OH, p. A500

THOMPSON, Mark, M.D. Chief Medical Officer, Monroe Clinic, Monroe, WI, p. A712

THOMPSON, Mark, Vice President Financial Services, Rapid City Regional Hospital, Rapid City, SD, p. A575

THOMPSON, Mark W., M.D., Commanding Officer, Carl R. Darnall Army Medical Center, Fort Hood, TX, p. A617

THOMPSON, Matthew J., Chief Executive Officer, Sparrow Carson Hospital, Carson City, MI, p. A320

THOMPSON, Nate, Chief Executive Officer, Story County Medical Center, Nevada, IA, p. A235

THOMPSON, Ormand P., President, Thomas Hospital, Fairhope, AL, p. A20

THOMPSON, Pamela, Chief Operations Officer, Huhukam Memorial Hospital, Sacaton, AZ, p. A38

THOMPSON, Patti, Chief Operating Officer, San Luis Valley Health, Alamosa, CO, p. A101

THOMPSON, Randell, Chief Nursing Officer, Plateau Medical Center, Oak Hill, WV, p. A698

THOMPSON, Reanna, R.N. Chief Operating Officer and Chief Nursing Officer, PIH Health Hospital–Whittier, Whittier, CA, p. A99

THOMPSON, Ronnie, Chief Financial Officer, Belton Regional Medical Center, Belton, MO, p. A367

THOMPSON, Sarah, Director Health Information Management, Hardtner Medical Center, Olla, LA, p. A286

THOMPSON, Selva, R.N. Chief Nurse Executive, Gallup Indian Medical Center, Gallup, NM, p. A429

THOMPSON, Sheila, Director Human Resources, Hamilton Memorial Hospital District, McLeansboro, IL, p. A196

THOMPSON, Sherene, Director Human Resources, Houston Methodist Willowbrook Hospital, Houston, TX, p. A625

THOMPSON, Steve, Vice President, Finance, Beaumont Hospital – Royal Oak, Royal Oak, MI, p. A333

THOMPSON, Stuart, Vice President Human Resources, Memorial Hospital Jacksonville, Jacksonville, FL, p. A131

THOMPSON, Thomas R., Chief Executive Officer, Regina Hospital, Hastings, MN, p. A344

THOMPSON, Tim
Senior Vice President, Chief Information Officer, South Florida Baptist Hospital, Plant City, FL, p. A142
Senior Vice President and Chief Informatics Officer, St. Anthony's Hospital, Saint Petersburg, FL, p. A144

THOMPSON, Timothy
Senior Vice President and Chief Information Officer, Morton Plant Hospital, Clearwater, FL, p. A125
Senior Vice President and Chief Information Officer, Morton Plant North Bay Hospital, New Port Richey, FL, p. A138

THOMPSON, Sr., Timothy L., Senior Vice President and Chief Information Officer, Houston Methodist Hospital, Houston, TX, p. A624

THOMPSON, Tina H., Coordinator Human Resources, FirstHealth Montgomery Memorial Hospital, Troy, NC, p. A474

THOMPSON, Trinise, Director Human Resources, St. Luke's Medical Center, Phoenix, AZ, p. A37

THOMPSON, Vera, Director Human Resources, Kingsboro Psychiatric Center,, NY, p. A445

THOMPSON, Wayne, Executive Vice President and Chief Information Officer, Mount Nittany Medical Center, State College, PA, p. A555

THOMPSON, Wesley, M.D. President Medical Staff, Fairfield Memorial Hospital, Fairfield, IL, p. A190

THOMPSON, William, Chief Financial Officer, Mississippi Baptist Medical Center, Jackson, MS, p. A360

THOMPSON, William, M.D. Chief Medical Officer, Saint Thomas Midtown Hospital, Nashville, TN, p. A591

THOMPSON, William P., President and Chief Executive Officer, SSM Health, Saint Louis, MO, p. B127

THOMPSON–COOK, Timothy, Chief Operating Officer, Contra Costa Regional Medical Center, Martinez, CA, p. A76

THOMSEN, Sue, Chief Financial Officer, New Braunfels Regional Rehabilitation Hospital, New Braunfels, TX, p. A638

THOMSEN, Vicki
Director Human Resources, Aurora Behavioral Health System East, Tempe, AZ, p. A40
Director Human Resources, Aurora Behavioral Health System West, Glendale, AZ, p. A33

THOMSON, Doug, M.D. Chief Medical Officer, Commonwealth Regional Specialty Hospital, Bowling Green, KY, p. A257

THOMSON, Ken, M.D. Medical Director, Memorial Hermann Surgical Hospital‰(First Colony, Sugar Land, TX, p. A650

THOMSON, Nicole, Chief Financial Officer, Saint Louise Regional Hospital, Gilroy, CA, p. A64

THOMSON, Steven, M.D. Medical Director, Heartland Behavioral Healthcare, Massillon, OH, p. A498

THOMURE, Tiffany, M.D. Medical Director, Rock Springs, LLC, Georgetown, TX, p. A620

THORE, Joe, Chief Operating Officer, Ashe Memorial Hospital, Jefferson, NC, p. A468

THORELL, Nicole, R.N. Chief Nursing Officer, Lexington Regional Health Center, Lexington, NE, p. A397

THORESON, Scott D., FACHE, Administrator, Mayo Clinic Health System in Springfield, Springfield, MN, p. A351

THORMODSON, Cyndee, Vice President, Operational Finance, CHI Mercy Health, Valley City, ND, p. A482

THORN, III, Eugene A., Vice President Finance and Chief Financial Officer, Union Hospital, Dover, OH, p. A493

THORN, Margaret, Interim Director of Nursing, Red Bay Hospital, Red Bay, AL, p. A25

THORN, Mark, FACHE Executive Director, Finance, Mercy Hospital Lincoln, Troy, MO, p. A383

THORNBRUGH, Mitchell, Administrative Officer, Cherokee Nation W.W. Hastings Indian Hospital, Tahlequah, OK, p. A520

THORNE, Dana, Administrator Human Resources, Valley Hospital Medical Center, Las Vegas, NV, p. A407

THORNE Jr., William, Chief Executive Officer, Acoma–Canoncito–Laguna Hospital, Acoma, NM, p. A427

THORNELL, Louise, Interim Chief Nursing Officer, CHRISTUS St. Michael Health System, Texarkana, TX, p. A652

THORNELL, Timothy, FACHE, Chief Executive Officer, Lea Regional Medical Center, Hobbs, NM, p. A429

THORNSBERRY, Michael, M.D. Chief Medical Officer, Texas Health Specialty Hospital, Fort Worth, TX, p. A619

THORNTON, Carol, Director Human Resources, Cherry Hospital, Goldsboro, NC, p. A466

THORNTON, Cayetano, Chief Information Officer, Walter Reed National Military Medical Center, Bethesda, MD, p. A299

THORNTON, Daryl W., Chief Operating Officer, Kansas Medical Center, Andover, KS, p. A240

THORNTON, Jan, Chief Nursing Officer, Bay Medical Center Sacred Heart Health System, Panama City, FL, p. A141

THORNTON, Jillisa, Director of Nursing, Coastal Harbor Treatment Center, Savannah, GA, p. A165

THORNTON, Laird, Director Information Systems, Alta Vista Regional Hospital, Las Vegas, NM, p. A430

THORNTON, Matt, Chief Executive Officer, Liberty Dayton Regional Medical Center, Liberty, TX, p. A632

THORNTON Jr.,, Robert M., Chief Executive Officer, Sunlink Health Systems, Atlanta, GA, p. B130

THORPE, Linda, Chief Executive Officer, East Morgan County Hospital, Brush, CO, p. A102

THORPE, Wendy, Area Director Information Systems, St. Joseph Hospital, Eureka, CA, p. A61

THORSEN, Erik, Chief Executive Officer, Columbia Memorial Hospital, Astoria, OR, p. A524

THORWALD, Robert, Chief Information Officer, Washington Hospital Healthcare System, Fremont, CA, p. A63

THOTAKURA, Raj, M.D. Medical Director, Old Vineyard Behavioral Health Services, Winston–Salem, NC, p. A476

THRASHER, Amanda, Director Nursing, Ellsworth County Medical Center, Ellsworth, KS, p. A242

THRASHER, Kimberly, Controller, HEALTHSOUTH Lakeshore Rehabilitation Hospital, Birmingham, AL, p. A16

THRASHER, Sherri, Executive Human Resources Partner, Spectrum Health Pennock, Hastings, MI, p. A326

THREEWITS, Sheree, Director Human Resources, Manatee Memorial Hospital, Bradenton, FL, p. A124

THULI, Karen, Coordinator Information Systems, Upland Hills Health, Dodgeville, WI, p. A704

THUN, Todd, Director Human Resources, Montana State Hospital, Warm Springs, MT, p. A351

THUNELL, Adam, Chief Operating Officer and Vice President Operations, Community Memorial Hospital, Ventura, CA, p. A98

THURBER, Joe, Director Information Technology, Central Regional Hospital, Butner, NC, p. A461

THURMAN, Jason, Chief of Staff, TriStar Hendersonville Medical Center, Hendersonville, TN, p. A584

THURMER, DeAnn, Chief Operating Officer, Waupun Memorial Hospital, Waupun, WI, p. A718

THURSTON, Thomas, M.D. Medical Director, J. D. McCarty Center for Children With Developmental Disabilities, Norman, OK, p. A515

THYGESON, Cindy, M.D. Director Medical Affairs, Sutter Center for Psychiatry, Sacramento, CA, p. A87

THYNE, Shannon, Chief Medical Officer, LAC–Olive View–UCLA Medical Center,, CA, p. A72

TIBBITS, Dick, Vice President and Chief Operating Officer, Florida Hospital Tampa, Tampa, FL, p. A147

TIBBITS, Richard M., Vice President and Chief Operating Officer, Loma Linda University Medical Center–Murrieta, Murrieta, CA, p. A78

TIBBS, E. W., President and Chief Executive Officer, Centra Health, Inc., Lynchburg, VA, p. B32

TIBBS, E. W., President and Chief Executive Officer, Centra Lynchburg General Hospital, Lynchburg, VA, p. A672

TICE, Darlette, Chief Nursing Officer, Manatee Memorial Hospital, Bradenton, FL, p. A124

TICE, Evan, Director Information Technology and Systems, Sky Ridge Medical Center, Lone Tree, CO, p. A108

TICE, Heidi, Chief Financial Officer, Cheyenne County Hospital, Saint Francis, KS, p. A253

TICE, Kirk C., President and Chief Executive Officer, Robert Wood Johnson University Hospital Rahway, Rahway, NJ, p. A422

TICE, Linda, Director Information Systems, SageWest Health Care at Riverton, Riverton, WY, p. A723

TICHENOR, Florence, Director Information Technology, Copper Basin Medical Center, Copperhill, TN, p. A582

TICHENOR, John, Chief Financial Officer, Ohio County Hospital, Hartford, KY, p. A261

TIDWELL, Joseph, Administrator, Phoenix Behavioral Hospital, Rayne, LA, p. A286

TIDWELL, Tim, Human Resources Director, Wiregrass Medical Center, Geneva, AL, p. A20

TIDWELL, Wesley, Chief Operating Officer, Memorial Hermann Greater Heights Hospital, Houston, TX, p. A625

TIEDE, Brad, Director Information Systems, Memorial Community Health, Aurora, NE, p. A393

TIEDT, Douglas, M.D. Chief of Staff, Springs Memorial Hospital, Lancaster, SC, p. A568

TIEDT, Jerry, Director Information Systems, Waverly Health Center, Waverly, IA, p. A239

TIEFENTHALER, Brenda Marie, R.N. Vice President Patient Care and Informatics, Spencer Hospital, Spencer, IA, p. A238

TIERNAN, Kelley, Chief Financial Officer, Claxton–Hepburn Medical Center, Ogdensburg, NY, p. A451

TIERNEY, Gregory, M.D. President, BMG and BHS Chief Medical Officer, Benefis Health System, Great Falls, MT, p. A388

TIERNEY, Mark A., Chief Financial Officer, Manatee Memorial Hospital, Bradenton, FL, p. A124

TIFFANY, Carolyn, Deputy Commander Clinical Service, Carl R. Darnall Army Medical Center, Fort Hood, TX, p. A617

TIGGELAAR, Tom
Vice President Finance, Mayo Clinic Health System – Franciscan Healthcare in La Crosse, La Crosse, WI, p. A708
Vice President Finance ad Chief Financial Officer, Mayo Clinic Health System – Franciscan Healthcare in Sparta, Sparta, WI, p. A716

TILGHMAN, Bradley, Controller, HEALTHSOUTH Emerald Coast Rehabilitation Hospital, Panama City, FL, p. A141

TILLER, Debra, Director Personnel and Administrative Secretary, Healthmark Regional Medical Center, DeFuniak Springs, FL, p. A127

TILLER, Joni R., R.N. Chief Nursing Officer, Integris Baptist Medical Center, Oklahoma City, OK, p. A516

TILLIRSON, Mike, D.O. Executive Vice President and Chief Medical Officer, AnMed Health Medical Center, Anderson, SC, p. A562

TILLMAN, Jill, Assistant Chief Executive Officer, Brandywine Hospital, Coatesville, PA, p. A535

TILLMAN, Kanner, Chief Financial Officer, Encino Hospital Medical Center,, CA, p. A71

TILLMAN, Michael C., President and Chief Executive Officer, United Hospital Center, Bridgeport, WV, p. A694

TILLMAN, Pamela P., R.N., Chief Executive Officer, Pioneer Community Hospital of Stokes, Danbury, NC, p. A463

TILLMAN, Randy, M.D. Chief Medical Staff, Promise Hospital of Miss Lou, Vidalia, LA, p. A289

TILLMAN–TAYLOR, Susan, Manager Human Resources, Southern Ocean Medical Center, Manahawkin, NJ, p. A419

TILSON, Natalie, Controller, HEALTHSOUTH Rehabilitation Hospital, Kingsport, TN, p. A585

TIMANUS, Anthony, Chief Executive Officer, Avera Gregory Hospital, Gregory, SD, p. A574

TIMBERS, Christopher, Vice President and Chief Information Officer, NorthBay Medical Center, Fairfield, CA, p. A62

TIMBERS, Christopher T., Chief Information Officer, Sibley Memorial Hospital, Washington, DC, p. A122

TIMLIN, Marie, R.N. Chief Nursing Officer, Yampa Valley Medical Center, Steamboat Springs, CO, p. A110

TIMM, Karen, R.N. Vice President Patient Services, St. Anthony Regional Hospital, Carroll, IA, p. A226

TIMM, Mark
Executive Director Human Resources, Yavapai Regional Medical Center – East, Prescott Valley, AZ, p. A38
Executive Director Human Resources, Yavapai Regional Medical Center, Prescott, AZ, p. A37

TIMM, Matt, M.D. Medical Director, Pender Community Hospital, Pender, NE, p. A401

TIMMER, Kari, Chief Financial Officer, Hegg Memorial Health Center Avera, Rock Valley, IA, p. A237

TIMMERMAN, Jo, Manager Accounting, Norwood Health Center, Marshfield, WI, p. A710

TIMMONS, William, Chief Executive Officer, Los Ninos Hospital, Phoenix, AZ, p. A36

TIMPE, David A., Interim President and Chief Executive Officer, Childrens Care Hospital and School, Sioux Falls, SD, p. A576

TIMPE, Ron, Chief Financial Officer, Floyd County Medical Center, Charles City, IA, p. A227

TINCH, Roberta, Chief Operations Officer, Spotsylvania Regional Medical Center, Fredericksburg, VA, p. A670

TINCHER, Pat, Director Finance, Aspirus Langlade Hospital, Antigo, WI, p. A702

TINDALL, Patricia, Chief Executive Officer, Lyndon B. Johnson Tropical Medical Center, Pago Pago, AS, p. A725

TINDLE, Jeff A., Chief Executive Officer, Carroll County Memorial Hospital, Carrollton, MO, p. A369

TINDLE, Tim, Chief Information Officer, Harris Health System, Houston, TX, p. A624

TINGLE, Billy, Interim Chief Executive Officer, Oakdale Community Hospital, Oakdale, LA, p. A286

TINGSTAD, Jonathan, Vice President and Chief Financial Officer, Seattle Cancer Care Alliance, Seattle, WA, p. A689

TINKER, Allen, Administrator, Nix Community General Hospital, Dilley, TX, p. A613

TINKER, Peter, Chief Human Resources Officer, James J. Peters Veterans Affairs Medical Center,, NY, p. A445

TINNERELLO, Jeremy, R.N. Chief Operations Officer, Glenwood Regional Medical Center, West Monroe, LA, p. A289

TINNEY, Sean, FACHE Chief Operating Officer, Medical West, Bessemer, AL, p. A16

TINSA, Udom, M.D. Medical Director, Ashley Medical Center, Ashley, ND, p. A477

TINSLEY, Cassie, Director, Human Resources, Powell Valley Healthcare, Powell, WY, p. A723

TINSLEY III, Edward D., Chief Executive Officer, McLeod Loris Seacoast Hospital, Loris, SC, p. A568

TINSLEY, Nancy, President, Rochester General Hospital, Rochester, NY, p. A454

TIPPIN, Russell, Chief Executive Officer and Administrator, Permian Regional Medical Center, Andrews, TX, p. A597

TIPPS, Linda, Director Human Resources, Southern Tennessee Regional Health System–Winchester, Winchester, TN, p. A594

TIPTON, Gina, Director of Operations, Rehabilitation Hospital, Navicent Health, Macon, GA, p. A162

TIPTON, Maggie, Chief Information Officer, Unicoi County Memorial Hospital, Erwin, TN, p. A582

TIPTON, Peggy, Chief Operating Officer and Chief Nursing Officer, Oklahoma Heart Hospital, Oklahoma City, OK, p. A517

TIPTON, Teri, MSN Chief Nursing Officer and Vice President Patient Care Services, Nebraska Methodist Hospital, Omaha, NE, p. A400

TIRA, Cheryl, Director Information Systems, Columbus Community Hospital, Columbus, NE, p. A395

TIRADO, Norma, Vice President, Human Resources and Health Information Technology, Lakeland Hospital, Watervliet, Watervliet, MI, p. A336

TIRMAN, Kerry, Chief Executive Officer, Mercy St. Vincent Medical Center, Toledo, OH, p. A504

TISDALE, Willis E., Director Human Resources, Shriners Hospitals for Children–Greenville, Greenville, SC, p. A566

TISDALL, Renae, Chief Financial Officer, Mobridge Regional Hospital, Mobridge, SD, p. A575

TISSIER, Becky, Chief Fiscal Service, Veterans Affairs Illiana Health Care System, Danville, IL, p. A187

TITO, David, M.D. President Medical Staff, Riverside Community Hospital, Riverside, CA, p. A86

TITSWORTH, Sue, Director Human Resources, Coleman County Medical Center, Coleman, TX, p. A606

TITTLE, JoDee, Director Community and Human Resources, St. Charles Madras, Madras, OR, p. A527

TITUS, Monica, President and Chief Executive Officer, Acuity Specialty Hospital of New Jersey, Atlantic City, NJ, p. A414

TOBEY, Shelley R., R.N. Chief Operating Officer and Chief Nursing Officer, Texas Health Presbyterian Hospital Flower Mound, Flower Mound, TX, p. A617

TOBIN, Hugh, Chief Financial Officer, Davis Regional Medical Center, Statesville, NC, p. A474

TOBIN, Ryan, Chief Operating Officer, Rose Medical Center, Denver, CO, p. A104

TOBLER, Randy, M.D., Chief Executive Officer, Scotland County Hospital, Memphis, MO, p. A376

TOCCO–BRADLEY, Rosalie, Ph.D
Chief Medical Officer, St. Joseph Mercy Ann Arbor, Ypsilanti, MI, p. A337
Chief Medical Officer, St. Joseph Mercy Livingston Hospital, Howell, MI, p. A326

TODD, Bob, Director Information Systems, Mount Auburn Hospital, Cambridge, MA, p. A309

TODD, Fred O., Senior Vice President Finance, McLeod Loris Seacoast Hospital, Loris, SC, p. A568

TODD, Kimberly, Chief Nursing Officer, AllianceHealth Clinton, Clinton, OK, p. A510

TODD, Nate, Chief Financial Officer, Central Arkansas Veterans Healthcare System, Little Rock, AR, p. A49

TODD, Robbie, Director Information Technology, Horn Memorial Hospital, Ida Grove, IA, p. A232

TODD, Steve J., Chief Executive Officer, St. Luke Community Healthcare, Ronan, MT, p. A390

TODOROW, Thomas, Chief Financial Officer and Executive Vice President, Children's Hospital of Philadelphia, Philadelphia, PA, p. A547

TOEDT, Michael E., M.D. Director Clinical Services, Cherokee Indian Hospital, Cherokee, NC, p. A463

TOJINO, Allan, Director, Information Systems, Paradise Valley Hospital, National City, CA, p. A79

TOLBERT, Catherine L., FACHE Chief Nursing Officer, Mercy Health – St. Elizabeth Youngstown Hospital, Youngstown, OH, p. A506

TOLBERT, James, Director Information Systems, EASTAR Health System, Muskogee, OK, p. A515

TOLEDO, Iris, Chief Nursing Officer, Hospital Dr. Cayetano Coll Y Toste, Arecibo, PR, p. A726

TOLINE, Tyler, FACHE, Chief Executive Officer, Saunders Medical Center, Wahoo, NE, p. A403

TOLLEFSON, Sue, Coordinator Payroll Personnel, Granite Falls Municipal Hospital and Manor, Granite Falls, MN, p. A343

TOLLIVER, Amy, Administrator, Magee General Hospital, Magee, MS, p. A361

TOLSON, Rick
Chief Administrative Officer and Chief Human Resources Officer, Christ Hospital, Cincinnati, OH, p. A487
Divisional Chief People Officer, HSHS St. Joseph's Hospital, Chippewa Falls, WI, p. A704

TOMAS, George, Director Information Services, Griffin Hospital, Derby, CT, p. A114

TOMASESKI, Gina, Chief Executive Officer, Continuum Rehabilitation Hospital of North Texas, Flower Mound, TX, p. A617

TOMASO, Nancy, Vice President, Patient Care Services, Milford Regional Medical Center, Milford, MA, p. A312

TOMBERLIN, Terri, Human Resources Director, Curry General Hospital, Gold Beach, OR, p. A529

TOME, Julie, M.D. Vice President North Central Region Medical Affairs, OhioHealth Marion General Hospital, Marion, OH, p. A498

TOME, Michael, M.D. Medical Director, Kaiser Permanente Los Angeles Medical Center, Los Angeles, CA, p. A71

TOMLIN, Jeff, M.D. Chief Medical and Quality Officer, EvergreenHealth, Kirkland, WA, p. A686

TOMLIN, Kerry W., Associate Administrator, Clay County Hospital, Ashland, AL, p. A15

TOMLINSON, Charles M., M.D. Chief Medical Officer, Cleveland Regional Medical Center, Shelby, NC, p. A473

TOMLINSON, Daniel, Chair Human Resources, Mayo Clinic Jacksonville, Jacksonville, FL, p. A131

TOMLINSON, David
Executive Vice President Chief Financial Officer and Chief Information Officer, Centegra Hospital – McHenry, McHenry, IL, p. A196
Executive Vice President Chief Financial Officer and Chief Information Officer, Centegra Hospital – Woodstock, Woodstock, IL, p. A205

TOMLINSON, Sallie, Manager Human Resources, Arbuckle Memorial Hospital, Sulphur, OK, p. A520

TOMMASINO, Sylvia, Interim Administrator, Lower Umpqua Hospital District, Reedsport, OR, p. A530

TOMORY, Gerald, M.D
Regional Medical Director, Kauai Veterans Memorial Hospital, Waimea, HI, p. A173
Regional Medical Director, Samuel Mahelona Memorial Hospital, Kapaa, HI, p. A172

TOMPKINS, Charles, M.D. Chief of Staff, Crenshaw Community Hospital, Luverne, AL, p. A22

TOMPKINS, Kim, Director Information Services, DeTar Healthcare System, Victoria, TX, p. A655

TOMSU, Karen, MSN Chief Nursing Officer, Baptist Hospitals of Southeast Texas, Beaumont, TX, p. A601

TONER, Tina, Director of Nursing, North Big Horn Hospital District, Lovell, WY, p. A723

TONEY, Mark, President and Chief Executive Officer, Brookdale Hospital Medical Center, New York, NY, p. A444

TONEY, Patty, R.N. Chief Nurse Executive, CHRISTUS Santa Rosa Health System, San Antonio, TX, p. A645

TONG, Cheryl, Corporate Chief Financial Officer, Community Hospital of Huntington Park, Huntington Park, CA, p. A66

TONJES, Ken, Interim Chief Administrative Officer, PeaceHealth Ketchikan Medical Center, Ketchikan, AK, p. A29

TONKINSON, Robert
Chief Operating Officer and Chief Financial Officer, Mercy Allen Hospital, Oberlin, OH, p. A500
Chief Operating Officer and Chief Financial Officer, Mercy Regional Medical Center, Lorain, OH, p. A497

TONN, Deb L., Vice President Patient Care, Campbell County Health, Gillette, WY, p. A722

TONNU, Lannie, Senior Vice President and Chief Financial Officer, Children's Hospital Los Angeles, Los Angeles, CA, p. A70

TOOKE, Ryan, Chief Executive Officer, Rosebud Health Care Center, Forsyth, MT, p. A387

TOOLE, LaDon, Vice President Network Operations, Mitchell County Hospital, Camilla, GA, p. A155

TOOLE, Patricia, Vice President Human Resources, East Mountain Hospital, Belle Mead, NJ, p. A414

TOOLE, Trish, Vice President Administrative Services, Carrier Clinic, Belle Mead, NJ, p. A414

TOON, William, Chief Information Officer, Baptist Hospitals of Southeast Texas, Beaumont, TX, p. A601

TOPOLEWSKI, Ted, Chief Executive Officer, Madison Parish Hospital, Tallulah, LA, p. A289

TOPPEN, Jacki, Director of Nursing, Prairie St. John's, Fargo, ND, p. A478

TOPPER, David, Chief Executive Officer, Alta Healthcare System, Los Angeles, CA, p. B10

TORBETT, Russell B., Director Human Resources, Creek Nation Community Hospital, Okemah, OK, p. A515

TORCHIA, Joseph, M.D. Senior Vice President Medical Affairs and Chief Medical Officer, Holy Spirit – A Geisinger Affiliate, Camp Hill, PA, p. A534

TORCHIA, Jude, Chief Executive Officer, OrthoColorado Hospital, Lakewood, CO, p. A108

TORCHIA MSN, RN, NEA–BC, Lisa F., MSN Vice President and Chief Nursing Officer, Holy Spirit – A Geisinger Affiliate, Camp Hill, PA, p. A534

TORCHIANA, David, M.D., Chief Executive Officer, Partners HealthCare System, Inc., Boston, MA, p. B102

TORGE, Andrew, Director Human Resources, Shasta Regional Medical Center, Redding, CA, p. A84

TORMANEN, John, Director Mission and Human Resources, CHI St. Joseph's Health, Park Rapids, MN, p. A348

TOROSSIAN, Lynn M., President and Chief Executive Officer, Henry Ford West Bloomfield Hospital, West Bloomfield, MI, p. A336

TORREGROSSA, Tonia, Chief Nursing Officer, Texas Rehabilitation Hospital of Arlington, Arlington, TX, p. A598

TORRES, Anthony, Manager Information Technology, Blue Mountain Hospital, Blanding, UT, p. A659

TORRES, Harvey, Chief Financial Officer, Valley Baptist Medical Center–Brownsville, Brownsville, TX, p. A604

TORRES, Maribel, Executive Vice President Patient Care Services and Chief Nursing Officer, United Medical Center, Washington, DC, p. A122

TORRES, Mayra, CPA Chief Financial Officer, Ashford Presbyterian Community Hospital, San Juan, PR, p. A729

TORRES, Robert D., Interim Administrator, Houston County Medical Center, Crockett, TX, p. A608

TORRES, Victor, Information Technology Specialist Administrator, El Paso Behavioral Health System, El Paso, TX, p. A615

TORRES AYALA, Eugenio, Director Information Systems, Cardiovascular Center of Puerto Rico and the Caribbean, San Juan, PR, p. A729

TORSCH, Peter, Chief Financial Officer, St. Charles Parish Hospital, Luling, LA, p. A282

TORTELLA, Anthony, Chief Financial Officer, Fairmount Behavioral Health System, Philadelphia, PA, p. A547

TOSI, Stephen E., M.D. Chief Medical Officer, UMass Memorial Medical Center, Worcester, MA, p. A316

TOSTEBERG, Chris, Superintendent, Mental Health Institute, Cherokee, IA, p. A227

TOSTENSON, Brad, Chief Information Officer, Essentia Health–Graceville, Graceville, MN, p. A343

TOSTI, Debra, Chief Executive Officer, Tewksbury Hospital, Tewksbury, MA, p. A315

TOTAH, Sam, Chief Operating Officer, Kaiser Permanente San Diego Medical Center, San Diego, CA, p. A88

TOUCHSTONE, Pat, Chief Nursing Officer, Crane Memorial Hospital, Crane, TX, p. A608

TOUMBIS, C., M.D. Chief of Staff, Citrus Memorial Health System, Inverness, FL, p. A131

TOUPS, Sharon A., Senior Vice President and Chief Operating Officer, St. Tammany Parish Hospital, Covington, LA, p. A275

TOURIGNY, Barry
    Vice President Human Resources and Organizational Development, Cabell Huntington Hospital, Huntington, WV, p. A696
    Human Resources Director, Johnson City Medical Center, Johnson City, TN, p. A585

TOUSIGNANT, Grace, R.N
    Chief Nursing Officer, Aspirus Grand View, Ironwood, MI, p. A327
    Chief Nursing Officer, Aspirus Keweenaw Hospital, Laurium, MI, p. A329

TOUVELLE, Cynthia, R.N. Senior Director Care Management and Chief Nursing Officer, Barnesville Hospital, Barnesville, OH, p. A484

TOWERY, O. B., M.D. Chief of Staff, John Muir Behavioral Health Center, Concord, CA, p. A59

TOWLE, Sonya, Director Human Resources, Mercy Hospital, Moose Lake, MN, p. A347

TOWN, Alex, Vice President Finance, Tri–State Memorial Hospital, Clarkston, WA, p. A683

TOWNDROW, Geraldine, R.N. Senior Vice President Nursing, Lutheran Medical Center, Wheat Ridge, CO, p. A111

TOWNE, Jana, Nurse Executive, U. S. Public Health Service Indian Hospital–Whiteriver, Whiteriver, AZ, p. A41

TOWNER, Chad, Chief Executive Officer, Dupont Hospital, Fort Wayne, IN, p. A210

TOWNES, Tim, Director Information Systems, Grandview Medical Center, Birmingham, AL, p. A16

TOWNLEY, Nancy, R.N. Senior Vice President Operations, United Regional Health Care System, Wichita Falls, TX, p. A658

TOWNSEND, Alan, Interim Chief Financial Officer, JPS Health Network, Fort Worth, TX, p. A618

TOWNSEND, Dona E., Chief Nursing Officer, Navarro Regional Hospital, Corsicana, TX, p. A608

TOWNSEND, Gary, Chief Information Officer, Hurley Medical Center, Flint, MI, p. A323

TOWNSEND, Michael, Chief Information Officer, James Cancer Hospital and Solove Research Institute, Columbus, OH, p. A490

TOWNSEND, Roxane A., M.D., Chief Executive Officer, UAMS Medical Center, Little Rock, AR, p. A49

TOWNSEND, Sammuel, LAN Administrator, University of Mississippi Medical Center Holmes County, Lexington, MS, p. A361

TOWNSEND, Stanley, Chief Executive Officer, Stone County Medical Center, Mountain View, AR, p. A50

TOWNSEND, Tanya, Senior Vice President, Chief Information Officer (part of LCMC), Children's Hospital, New Orleans, LA, p. A284

TOWNSEND, Theodore E., FACHE, President and Chief Executive Officer, UnityPoint Health – St. Luke's Hospital, Cedar Rapids, IA, p. A226

TOWNSLEY, Malcolm, M.D. Chief of Staff, CHI St. Anthony Hospital, Pendleton, OR, p. A528

TOWRISS, Douglas, Vice President and Chief Medical Officer, Schneck Medical Center, Seymour, IN, p. A222

TOY, Linda, Director Information Systems, Havasu Regional Medical Center, Lake Havasu City, AZ, p. A34

TOY Jr., Stanley, M.D., Chief Executive Officer, Greater El Monte Community Hospital, South El Monte, CA, p. A95

TOYE, Lawrence J., Chief Financial Officer, Kindred Hospital–Boston, Brighton, MA, p. A308

TRAC, Vincent, Chief Executive Officer, Kindred Hospital–Ontario, Ontario, CA, p. A80

TRACEY, Karen, Chief Human Resources, Select Specialty Hospital–Greensboro, Greensboro, NC, p. A466

TRACY, Allen R., Senior Vice President and Chief Financial Officer, St. John Medical Center, Westlake, OH, p. A505

TRACY, Pat, Administrator, Ridgeview Behavioral Hospital, Middle Point, OH, p. A499

TRACY, Jr., Thomas, Chief Medical Officer, Penn State Milton S. Hershey Medical Center, Hershey, PA, p. A540

TRACY, Timothy J., Chief Executive Officer, Sanford Vermillion Medical Center, Vermillion, SD, p. A577

TRACZ, Robert B., CPA Senior Vice President and Chief Financial Officer, Lake Health, Concord Township, OH, p. A491

TRAFTON, Terry, Chief Executive Officer, Two Rivers Behavioral Health System, Kansas City, MO, p. A374

TRAHAN, Jennifer Lynch, Assistant Vice President Human Resources, Our Lady of Lourdes Regional Medical Center, Lafayette, LA, p. A281

TRAHAN, John, Director Information Systems, Women's and Children's Hospital, Lafayette, LA, p. A281

TRAHAN, Leslie, Chief Executive Officer, South Cameron Memorial Hospital, Cameron, LA, p. A274

TRAHERN, Sheri, FACHE, Chief Executive Officer, St. Thomas More Hospital, Canon City, CO, p. A102

TRAHEY, Thomas F., M.D. Vice President Medical Affairs, Novant Health Rowan Medical Center, Salisbury, NC, p. A473

TRAIL, Alan, Director Information Systems, Owensboro Health Muhlenberg Community Hospital, Greenville, KY, p. A261

TRAINER, Michael, Chief Financial Officer, Akron Children's Hospital, Akron, OH, p. A483

TRAINOR, Karyn, Director Human Resources, St. Patrick Hospital, Missoula, MT, p. A389

TRAINOR, Paul, Chief Financial Officer, Southern New Hampshire Medical Center, Nashua, NH, p. A412

TRAISTER, Lynne, Controller, HEALTHSOUTH Rehabilitation Hospital of Tinton Falls, Tinton Falls, NJ, p. A424

TRAMMELL, Patrick, Chief Executive Officer, DeKalb Regional Medical Center, Fort Payne, AL, p. A20

TRAMP, Francis G., President, Burgess Health Center, Onawa, IA, p. A235

TRAN, Ann, Chief Financial Officer, Pike County Memorial Hospital, Louisiana, MO, p. A376

TRAN, Kha H., M.D. Vice President Medical Affairs, Lima Memorial Health System, Lima, OH, p. A496

TRAN, Khiem, M.D. Acting Chief of Staff, Veterans Affairs Illiana Health Care System, Danville, IL, p. A187

TRAN, Lac, Senior Vice President Information Services, Rush University Medical Center, Chicago, IL, p. A186

TRAN, Richard, Director Information Technology, Galesburg Cottage Hospital, Galesburg, IL, p. A191

TRAN, Thanh, Chief Executive Officer, North Central Surgical Center, Dallas, TX, p. A611

TRANSIER, Rhonda, Financial Officer, Rusk State Hospital, Rusk, TX, p. A644

TRANTALIS, Carolyn, R.N
    Regional Vice President, Clinical Services and Operations, The William W. Backus Hospital, Norwich, CT, p. A116
    Chief Operating Officer, East Region, Windham Hospital, Willimantic, CT, p. A118

TRANTHAM, Susan, Director Human Resources, HEALTHSOUTH Rehabilitation Hospital of Florence, Florence, SC, p. A565

TRAPANI, Joseph, Chief Executive Officer, Poplar Springs Hospital, Petersburg, VA, p. A676

TRAPP, John, Vice President Medical Affairs, Bryan Medical Center, Lincoln, NE, p. A397

TRAPP, Nancy A., MSN Director of Nursing, Saint Thomas DeKalb Hospital, Smithville, TN, p. A593

TRAUTMAN, Bob, Chief Executive Officer, Saline Memorial Hospital, Benton, AR, p. A43

TRAVIS, Calee, R.N. Chief Nursing Officer, Centennial Medical Center, Frisco, TX, p. A619

TRAVIS, David A.
    Chief Financial Officer, East Texas Medical Center Athens, Athens, TX, p. A598
    Chief Financial Officer, East Texas Medical Center Fairfield, Fairfield, TX, p. A617

TRAVIS, Dee Dee, Director Community Relations, Calais Regional Hospital, Calais, ME, p. A292

TRAVIS, Thomas, Surgeon General, Department of the Air Force, Washington, DC, p. B44

TRAXLER, Martin J., Chief Executive Officer, Robley Rex Veterans Affairs Medical Center, Louisville, KY, p. A265

TRAYLOR, Desiree, Chief Information Officer, Chickasaw Nation Medical Center, Ada, OK, p. A508

TRAYLOR, Jerri Sue, Director Human Resources and Community and Employee Wellness, The Women's Hospital, Newburgh, IN, p. A220

TRAYNOR, Karen, Chief Financial Officer, Richland Hospital, Richland Center, WI, p. A715

TRCZINSKI, Judi, Vice President and Chief Human Resources Officer, Hospital for Special Care, New Britain, CT, p. A115

TREACY, Nancy, Director Finance, Cambridge Medical Center, Cambridge, MN, p. A340

TREACY–SHIFF, Mary, Vice President Finance, Advocate Good Samaritan Hospital, Downers Grove, IL, p. A188

TREADWAY, Michael G., Controller, CHRISTUS Trinity Mother Frances Rehabilitation Hospital, Tyler, TX, p. A654

TREADWELL, Karen, Director Human Resources, Lake Martin Community Hospital, Dadeville, AL, p. A18

TREASE, Kevin, Chief Information Officer, Antelope Memorial Hospital, Neligh, NE, p. A399

TREASURE, Jeffrey
    Chief Financial Officer, Northern Arizona Healthcare, Flagstaff Medical Center, Flagstaff, AZ, p. A32
    Chief Financial Officer, Northern Arizona Healthcare, Verde Valley Medical Center, Cottonwood, AZ, p. A32

TREASURE, Martin
    Director Human Resources, Schuylkill Medical Center – Schuylkill East Norwegian Street, Pottsville, PA, p. A552
    Director Human Resources, Schuylkill Medical Center – Schuylkill South Jackson Street, Pottsville, PA, p. A552

TREECE, Amy, M.D. Medical Director, North Greenville Hospital, Travelers Rest, SC, p. A570

TREGLOWN, Brad, Director Information Systems, Redmond Regional Medical Center, Rome, GA, p. A165

TREHAN, Rajeev, M.D. Chief of Staff, Veterans Affairs Eastern Kansas Health Care System, Topeka, KS, p. A254

TREITLER, Scot, Chief Financial Officer and Chief Operating Officer, Cypress Pointe Surgical Hospital, Hammond, LA, p. A277

TREMAINE, Lisa, Manager Human Resources, Carson Valley Medical Center, Gardnerville, NV, p. A404

TREMONTI, Carl
    Chief Financial Officer, Mease Countryside Hospital, Safety Harbor, FL, p. A144
    Chief Financial Officer, Mease Dunedin Hospital, Dunedin, FL, p. A128
    Chief Financial Officer, Morton Plant Hospital, Clearwater, FL, p. A125
    Chief Financial Officer, Morton Plant North Bay Hospital, New Port Richey, FL, p. A138
    Chief Financial Officer, South Florida Baptist Hospital, Plant City, FL, p. A142
    Chief Financial Officer, St. Anthony's Hospital, Saint Petersburg, FL, p. A144

TREMONTI, Yvette, Chief Financial Officer, H. Lee Moffitt Cancer Center and Research Institute, Tampa, FL, p. A147

TRENARY, Thomas J., President, Baylor Medical Center at Garland, Garland, TX, p. A620

TRENDE, Gary D., FACHE Associate Director, Tuscaloosa Veterans Affairs Medical Center, Tuscaloosa, AL, p. A26

TRENSCHEL, Robert, M.P.H. President and Chief Executive Officer, Yuma Regional Medical Center, Yuma, AZ, p. A42

TRENT, Cindy, Manager Personnel, Fall River Hospital, Hot Springs, SD, p. A574

TRETINA, Mike, Senior Vice President and Chief Financial Officer, Bayhealth Medical Center, Dover, DE, p. A119

TRETTER, Stan, M.D. Chief Medical Officer, Memorial Hospital and Health Care Center, Jasper, IN, p. A215

TREVATHAN, Dave, Director Information Systems, Rose Medical Center, Denver, CO, p. A104

TREVINO, Carlos, Chief Operating Officer, Mission Regional Medical Center, Mission, TX, p. A637

TREVINO, Chris, M.D. Chief Medical Officer, St. Elizabeth Hospital, Gonzales, LA, p. A277

TREVINO, Jorge, Chief Operations Officer, Baylor Scott & White Medical Center – White Rock, Dallas, TX, p. A609

TREVINO, Malissa, Director Human Resources, Pecos County Memorial Hospital, Fort Stockton, TX, p. A617

TREVINO, Paul, Chief Executive Officer, CHRISTUS Southeast Texas Hospital, Beaumont, TX, p. A601

TREVISANI, Michael F., M.D. Senior Vice President and Chief Medical Officer, Faxton St. Luke's Healthcare, Utica, NY, p. A457

TREXLER, Donald D., Chief Executive Officer, Acadia General Hospital, Crowley, LA, p. A276

TRIANA, Rudy, M.D. Chief of Staff, Jackson Purchase Medical Center, Mayfield, KY, p. A266

TRICKEY, Donna, R.N. Chief Nursing Officer, Fairview Park Hospital, Dublin, GA, p. A159

TRIEBES, David G., Chief Executive Officer, Samaritan Albany General Hospital, Albany, OR, p. A524

TRIGG, Terry, Director Human Resources, Merit Health Wesley, Hattiesburg, MS, p. A359

TRIGIANI, Charles, D.O. Medical Director, Hampton Behavioral Health Center, Westampton, NJ, p. A425

TRIMBLE, Charley O., Chief Executive Officer, Lubbock Heart & Surgical Hospital, Lubbock, TX, p. A634

TRIMBLE, Deborah, R.N., Chief Executive Officer, Paul B. Hall Regional Medical Center, Paintsville, KY, p. A268

TRIMBLE, Donald, CPA Chief Financial Officer, Vibra Specialty Hospital at DeSoto, Desoto, TX, p. A613

TRIMBLE, Melody, Chief Executive Officer, Johnson City Medical Center, Johnson City, TN, p. A585

TRIMM, Robert M., Chief Executive Officer, Washington County Regional Medical Center, Sandersville, GA, p. A165

TRIMMER, Mary R., Interim Chief Operating Officer, Mount Carmel, Columbus, OH, p. A490

TRIMMER, Matthew, Director Information Services, Holy Cross Hospital, Silver Spring, MD, p. A303

TRINCHETTO, Thomas, M.D. Chief Medical Officer, Doctors Hospital of Sarasota, Sarasota, FL, p. A145

TRINH, Khiet, M.D. Chief Medical Officer, Bon Secours St. Mary's Hospital, Richmond, VA, p. A677

TRIPLETT, Daniel, Acting Chief Operating Officer, Springfield Hospital Center, Sykesville, MD, p. A303

TRIPLETT, John, D.O. President Medical Staff, Saint Joseph – Martin, Martin, KY, p. A266

TRIPLETT, Robin, Chief Financial Officer, Southern Coos Hospital and Health Center, Bandon, OR, p. A524

TRIPP, Gina, Director Information Systems, TIRR Memorial Hermann, Houston, TX, p. A627

TRIPP, Kelly, Chief Executive Officer, Ten Broeck Tennessee Treatment Facility, Cookeville, TN, p. A581

TRIPPEL, Donald E., Chief Financial Officer, Hugh Chatham Memorial Hospital, Elkin, NC, p. A465

TRITTIN, Kim, Manager Human Resources, Mayo Clinic Health System in Red Wing, Red Wing, MN, p. A349

TRIVEDI, Harsh, M.D., President and Chief Executive Officer, Sheppard Pratt Health System, Baltimore, MD, p. A297

TRIVETTE, Chastity, Chief Executive Officer, Johnson County Community Hospital, Mountain City, TN, p. A590

TROCINO, Mark, Chief Information Officer, DeKalb Medical at Hillandale, Lithonia, GA, p. A162

TROEGER, Janice K., R.N. Chief Nursing Officer, Borgess–Lee Memorial Hospital, Dowagiac, MI, p. A322

TROGMAN, Richard, FACHE Chief Operating Officer, Kaiser Permanente Woodland Hills Medical Center,, CA, p. A72

TROLLOPE, Grant, Chief Financial Officer, Northeastern Nevada Regional Hospital, Elko, NV, p. A404

TROMBATORE, Beverly, R.N. Director Managed Information Systems, Matagorda Regional Medical Center, Bay City, TX, p. A601

TROMBLEE, Julie, R.N. Chief Nursing Officer, The University of Vermont Health Network Elizabethtown Community Hospital, Elizabethtown, NY, p. A438

TROMPETER, Dawn
Chief Financial Officer, OSF Saint Elizabeth Medical Center, Ottawa, IL, p. A199
Vice President Finance I–80 Region and Chief Financial Officer, OSF Saint Paul Medical Center, Mendota, IL, p. A196

TRONCONE, Michael T., Chief Human Resources Officer, Calvary Hospital, NY, p. A444

TROSCLAIR, Andree, Vice President Human Resources, Arkansas Children's Hospital, Little Rock, AR, p. A48

TROSIN, Jill A., R.N. Vice President Patient Care Services, Chief Nursing Officer, ProMedica St. Luke's Hospital, Maumee, OH, p. A498

TROTTER, Kristin, Chief Nursing Officer, Lovelace Regional Hospital – Roswell, Roswell, NM, p. A431

TROTTER, Wally, Director Human Resources, Mountain View Hospital, Payson, UT, p. A662

TROTTIER, Timothy R., Chief Executive Officer, Spring View Hospital, Lebanon, KY, p. A262

TROUBLEFIELD, David, Chief Communications Officer, Hemphill County Hospital, Canadian, TX, p. A605

TROUP, Bill, M.D. Chief of Staff, Stanton County Hospital, Johnson, KS, p. A246

TROUP, Matthew, Chief Executive Officer, Conway Regional Medical Center, Conway, AR, p. A44

TROUT, Gene, Chief Financial Officer, Weirton Medical Center, Weirton, WV, p. A700

TROUTMAN, Gary, CPA Chief Financial Officer, Baptist Hospitals of Southeast Texas, Beaumont, TX, p. A601

TROWHILL, Jan, Director Health Information Management Systems, HEALTHSOUTH Cane Creek Rehabilitation Hospital, Martin, TN, p. A587

TROXELL, Larry, Administrator, Stroud Regional Medical Center, Stroud, OK, p. A520

TROY, Patrick J., R.N. Associate Director Patient Care Services, Veterans Affairs New Jersey Health Care System, East Orange, NJ, p. A416

TROY, Peggy N., President and Chief Executive Officer, Children's Hospital and Health System, Milwaukee, WI, p. B32

TROY, Peggy N.
President and Chief Executive Officer, Children's Hospital of Wisconsin, Milwaukee, WI, p. A711
President and Chief Executive Officer, Children's Hospital of Wisconsin–Fox Valley, Neenah, WI, p. A712

TROYER, David, Chief Information Officer, Veterans Affairs Northern Indiana Health Care System, Fort Wayne, IN, p. A211

TROYER, Devin, M.D. Medical Director, HEALTHSOUTH Rehabilitation Hospital of Columbia, Columbia, SC, p. A564

TROYO–SAUVIAC, Glynda, Chief Executive Officer, Vibra Hospital of Central Dakotas, Mandan, ND, p. A480

TRUE, Terry, M.D. Chief of Staff, Shoals Hospital, Muscle Shoals, AL, p. A24

TRUEBLOOD, Susan
Regional Hospital Administrator, Central State Hospital, Milledgeville, GA, p. A163
Chief Executive Officer, Georgia Regional Hospital at Atlanta, Decatur, GA, p. A158

TRUESDALE, Jr., Fred A., Administrator, North Mississippi Medical Center–Iuka, Iuka, MS, p. A359

TRUESDELL, Shannon, Chief Operating Officer, Marshall Medical Center, Placerville, CA, p. A83

TRUITT, Louise
Vice President Human Resources, Capital Regional Medical Center, Tallahassee, FL, p. A146
Human Resource Director, Coliseum Northside Hospital, Macon, GA, p. A162

TRUJILLO, Jesse, Chief Information Officer, St. Mark's Hospital, Salt Lake City, UT, p. A663

TRUMAN, Julia
Vice President Human Resources, Fort Walton Beach Medical Center, Fort Walton Beach, FL, p. A129
Chief Operating Officer, MultiCare Tacoma General Hospital, Tacoma, WA, p. A692

TRUMAN, Lisa, Chief Nursing Officer, HEALTHSOUTH Sea Pines Rehabilitation Hospital, Melbourne, FL, p. A136

TRUMAN, Mark, Vice President of Operations, Baptist Health Floyd, New Albany, IN, p. A219

TRUMAN, Michael A., Chief Executive Officer, Riverview Behavioral Health, Texarkana, AR, p. A53

TRUMBULL, Kathryn E., R.N. Chief Nursing Officer and Vice President Patient Care Services, Samaritan Healthcare, Moses Lake, WA, p. A686

TRUPP, Gary, President Medical Staff, Good Shepherd Health Care System, Hermiston, OR, p. A526

TRUSSELL, Paul, Vice President Human Resources, Pioneer Community Hospital of Patrick, Stuart, VA, p. A679

TRYON, Ellen, R.N. Chief Nursing Officer, Adventist Medical Center–Portland, Portland, OR, p. A529

TSAI, James, M.D., President, New York Eye and Ear Infirmary of Mount Sinai, New York, NY, p. A447

TSALATE, Cynthia, Human Resource Specialist, U. S. Public Health Service Indian Hospital, Zuni, NM, p. A432

TSAMBIRAS, Petros, M.D. Chief of Staff, Bayfront Health Dade City, Dade City, FL, p. A126

TSAO, Sean, Director Information Technology, Blue Mountain Hospital, John Day, OR, p. A527

TSCHABRUN, Dawn M., R.N., Chief Executive Officer, Lovelace Regional Hospital – Roswell, Roswell, NM, p. A431

TSENG, Allen, Chief Operations Officer, Memorial Hermann Memorial City Medical Center, Houston, TX, p. A625

TSO, Ron, Chief Executive Officer, Chinle Comprehensive Health Care Facility, Chinle, AZ, p. A31

TSUNEISHI, Lani, Chief Nursing Officer, Hawaii State Hospital, Kaneohe, HI, p. A172

TUAZON, Nelson, R.N. Chief Nursing Officer, Baptist Medical Center, San Antonio, TX, p. A645

TUBBS, John, M.D
Chief of Staff, Rock County Hospital, Bassett, NE, p. A393
Chief of Staff, West Holt Memorial Hospital, Atkinson, NE, p. A393

TUBBS, Mary Beth, Chief Nursing Officer, Sunnyside Community Hospital and Clinics, Sunnyside, WA, p. A691

TUBERVILLE, Abby, Human Resource Manager, Fillmore County Hospital, Geneva, NE, p. A396

TUCK, Colleen, Chief Nursing Officer, Livingston Regional Hospital, Livingston, TN, p. A587

TUCK, Greg, Area Information Officer, Kaiser Permanente San Jose Medical Center, San Jose, CA, p. A91

TUCKER, Albert, Chief Financial Officer, Miami Veterans Affairs Healthcare System, Miami, FL, p. A137

TUCKER, Andy, Chief Financial Officer, South Mississippi State Hospital, Purvis, MS, p. A364

TUCKER, Cathy, Director Human Resources, Iraan General Hospital, Iraan, TX, p. A628

TUCKER, Gary C., President and Chief Executive Officer, Mount St. Mary's Hospital and Health Center, Lewiston, NY, p. A441

TUCKER, Ian, M.D. Vice President Medical Affairs, Johnson Memorial Medical Center, Stafford Springs, CT, p. A117

TUCKER, III, Jessie Lee, Ph.D. Senior Vice President and Chief Operating Officer, Robert Wood Johnson University Hospital, New Brunswick, NJ, p. A420

TUCKER, John
Chief Nursing Executive, Center for Behavioral Medicine, Kansas City, MO, p. A373
Chief Executive Officer, Mt. San Rafael Hospital, Trinidad, CO, p. A111

TUCKER, Joseph B., Senior Vice President and Chief Financial Officer, Fort Washington Medical Center, Oxen Hill, MD, p. A302

TUCKER, Joshua, Administrator, Mercy Hospital Logan County, Guthrie, OK, p. A512

TUCKER, Mona, Director Human Resources, Seton Medical Center Harker Heights, Harker Heights, TX, p. A622

TUCKER, Rebecca, Chief Financial Officer, Memorial Hermann Northeast, Humble, TX, p. A628

TUCKER, Ron, Business Office Manager, Kiowa County Memorial Hospital, Greensburg, KS, p. A244

TUCKER, Steven E., President, Conemaugh Memorial Medical Center, Johnstown, PA, p. A541

TUCKER, Theresa, Human Resources Officer, Sioux Center Health, Sioux Center, IA, p. A237

TUDELA, John M., M.D. Director of Medical Affairs, Commonwealth Health Center, Saipan, MP, p. A725

TUDOR, Nathan, Vice President and Chief Executive Officer, CHRISTUS Spohn Hospital Beeville, Beeville, TX, p. A602

TUELL, William J., MSN, Facility Director, Commonwealth Center for Children and Adolescents, Staunton, VA, p. A679

TUER, Patrick, Chief Executive Officer, Select Specialty Hospital–Columbus, Columbus, OH, p. A491

TUFT, Paul R., President, Southwest Healthcare System, Scottsdale, AZ, p. B126

TULISIAK, Thomas, M.D., President, Cleveland Clinic, Medina Hospital, Medina, OH, p. A499

TULLIS, Bea, Chief Financial Officer and Budget Officer, Broughton Hospital, Morganton, NC, p. A470

TULLMAN, Stephen M., Chief Executive Officer, Phoenixville Hospital, Phoenixville, PA, p. A550

TUMA, Bonnie, Human Resources Team Lead, National Institutes of Health Clinical Center, Bethesda, MD, p. A299

TUMA, Roman, Chief Medical Officer, Easton Hospital, Easton, PA, p. A537

TUMLIN, Richard, Chief Operating Officer, TriStar Southern Hills Medical Center, Nashville, TN, p. A591

TUMMONS, Coleen, Chief Executive Officer, Gove County Medical Center, Quinter, KS, p. A252

TUMMURU, Ramireddy K., M.D. Chief Medical Officer, Porter Regional Hospital, Valparaiso, IN, p. A223

TUNGATE, Rex A.
Chief Executive Officer, Casey County Hospital, Liberty, KY, p. A264
Chief Executive Officer, Jane Todd Crawford Hospital, Greensburg, KY, p. A261

TUNNELL, Richard, Chief Information Officer, University Hospital, Newark, NJ, p. A421

TUNSON, Lynn, Manager Medical Records, Complex Care Hospital at Tenaya, Las Vegas, NV, p. A405

TUPPER, David, Chief Executive Officer, Vibra Specialty Hospital of Portland, Portland, OR, p. A530

TUPPONCE, David, M.D., Chief Executive Officer, Abrazo Scottsdale Campus, Phoenix, AZ, p. A35

TURBAK, Shelly, R.N. Chief Nursing Officer, Prairie Lakes Healthcare System, Watertown, SD, p. A577

TUREK, Beth, Site Manager Information Systems, Advocate South Suburban Hospital, Hazel Crest, IL, p. A192

TUREK, Derrill Kent, R.N. Chief Nursing Officer, Blue Mountain Hospital, Blanding, UT, p. A659

TURK, Edward, Vice President Finance, Scripps Mercy Hospital, San Diego, CA, p. A89

TURKAL, Nick M.D., President and Chief Executive Officer, Aurora Health Care, Milwaukee, WI, p. B16

TURKAL–BARRETT, Kari, Flight Commander Resource Management Officer, Mike O'Callaghan Federal Hospital, Nellis AFB, NV, p. A407

TURKEL, Brooks, Chief Executive Officer, Lancaster Regional Medical Center, Lancaster, PA, p. A542

TURLEY, Mary Ann, D.O. Medical Director, HonorHealth Deer Valley Medical Center, Phoenix, AZ, p. A36

TURLEY, Matt, Interim Director Information Systems, Greenbrier Valley Medical Center, Ronceverte, WV, p. A700

TURLEY, Susan S., Chief Financial Officer, Doctor's Hospital at Renaissance, Edinburg, TX, p. A614

TURMAN, Anna, Chief Operating Officer, Chadron Community Hospital and Health Services, Chadron, NE, p. A395

TURMAN, Tracy Penn, Chief Executive Officer, HEALTHSOUTH Rehabilitation Hospital of Petersburg, Petersburg, VA, p. A676

TURNA, Tarlochan, M.D. Medical Director, Mayo Clinic Health System in Cannon Falls, Cannon Falls, MN, p. A340

TURNBULL, James, Chief Information Officer, University of Utah Health Care – Hospital and Clinics, Salt Lake City, UT, p. A664

TURNBULL, Rosie, Director Human Resources, St. Lawrence Psychiatric Center, Ogdensburg, NY, p. A451

TURNER, Barbara, Director of Nursing, Austen Riggs Center, Stockbridge, MA, p. A315

TURNER, Bill, Vice President Human Resources, Valir Rehabilitation Hospital, Oklahoma City, OK, p. A518

TURNER, Brenda C.
Chief Human Resources Officer, Palomar Medical Center, Escondido, CA, p. A61
Chief Human Resources Officer, Pomerado Hospital, Poway, CA, p. A84

TURNER, Carol, President and Chief Executive Officer, Atrium Medical Center, Middletown, OH, p. A499

TURNER, Chad, Chief Financial Officer, Star Valley Medical Center, Afton, WY, p. A721

TURNER, Cheryl, Administrator, Compass Behavioral Center of Houma, Houma, LA, p. A278

TURNER, Cindy R., Chief Executive Officer, Bacon County Hospital and Health System, Alma, GA, p. A151

TURNER, Dale, Chief Operating Officer, Reedsburg Area Medical Center, Reedsburg, WI, p. A715

TURNER, Dave, Chief Financial Officer, Royal Oaks Hospital, Windsor, MO, p. A384

TURNER, Glenda, Director Personnel, Oakwood Correctional Facility, Lima, OH, p. A497

TURNER, Howard D., Chief Executive Officer, Abbeville Area Medical Center, Abbeville, SC, p. A562

TURNER, Jeff, FACHE, Chief Executive Officer, Moore County Hospital District, Dumas, TX, p. A614

TURNER, Joel, Director of Nursing, George Regional Hospital, Lucedale, MS, p. A361

TURNER, Karissa, Vice President Operations, Wabash General Hospital, Mount Carmel, IL, p. A197

TURNER, Kathy, Director Human Resources, East Texas Medical Center Trinity, Trinity, TX, p. A653

TURNER, Kelly, Senior Vice President Finance and Chief Financial Officer, Glendale Adventist Medical Center, Los Angeles, CA, p. A71

TURNER, Kevin, M.D. Medical Director, Pathways of Tennessee, Jackson, TN, p. A584

TURNER, Laurie
Chief Nursing Officer, TriStar Skyline Madison Campus, Madison, TN, p. A587
Chief Nursing Officer, TriStar Skyline Medical Center, Nashville, TN, p. A591

TURNER, Mark
Director Information Systems, Beverly Hospital, Montebello, CA, p. A77
Manager Information Technology, Ojai Valley Community Hospital, Ojai, CA, p. A80

TURNER, Mark J.
President and Chief Executive Officer, Memorial Hospital, Belleville, IL, p. A181
President and Chief Executive Officer, Memorial Hospital East, Shiloh, IL, p. A203

TURNER, Marquita, Chief Nursing Officer, Atrium Medical Center, Middletown, OH, p. A499

TURNER, Maurita, Team Leader Health Information Systems Services, Madison St. Joseph Health Center, Madisonville, TX, p. A635

TURNER, Melissa, Senior Vice President Human Resources, Bridgeport Hospital, Bridgeport, CT, p. A113

TURNER, Michael, Director Human Resources, Moberly Regional Medical Center, Moberly, MO, p. A377

TURNER, Nancy, Director Communications, Sutter Roseville Medical Center, Roseville, CA, p. A86

TURNER, Peggy, Assistant Vice President and Director of Nursing, Unity Health White County Medical Center, Searcy, AR, p. A52

TURNER, Randy, Chief Human Resource Management Services, Boise Veterans Affairs Medical Center, Boise, ID, p. A174

TURNER, Robert A., Chief Executive Officer, AD Hospital East, Houston, TX, p. A623

TURNER, Robert L., Ph.D., Chief Executive Officer, Seven Hills Hospital, Henderson, NV, p. A405

TURNER, Sara, Director Human Resources, Alvarado Hospital Medical Center, San Diego, CA, p. A88

TURNER, Saundra G., Director Human Resources, Mercy Hospital Jefferson, Crystal City, MO, p. A370

TURNER, Scott, Co–Chief Operating Officer, University of Iowa Hospitals and Clinics, Iowa City, IA, p. A232

TURNER, Sherrilyn, Director Human Resources, Southeast Colorado Hospital District, Springfield, CO, p. A110

TURNER, Spencer, President, Texas Health Presbyterian Hospital Flower Mound, Flower Mound, TX, p. A617

TURNER, Steve, Director Information Technology, Salem Township Hospital, Salem, IL, p. A202

TURNER, Teri, Chief Nursing Officer, Haskell Memorial Hospital, Haskell, TX, p. A622

TURNEY, Brian, Chief Executive Officer, Kingman Regional Medical Center, Kingman, AZ, p. A33

TURNEY, David, Chief Information Officer, Cochran Memorial Hospital, Morton, TX, p. A637

TURNQUIST, Carrie, Director Human Resources, Buena Vista Regional Medical Center, Storm Lake, IA, p. A238

TURO, Albert, Vice President Human Resources, St. Mary's Healthcare, Amsterdam, NY, p. A434

TURPIN, Debra, R.N. Vice President Patient Care Services and Chief Nursing Officer, Alton Memorial Hospital, Alton, IL, p. A180

TURPIN, James
Human Resources, Breckinridge Memorial Hospital, Hardinsburg, KY, p. A261
Chief of Staff, Ephraim McDowell Fort Logan Hospital, Stanford, KY, p. A269

TURQUEZA, Sandra
Senior Human Resources Business Partner, Saint Joseph London, London, KY, p. A264
Human Resources Business Partner, Saint Joseph Berea, Berea, KY, p. A257

TURSKY, Martin, President and Chief Executive Officer, Firelands Regional Health System, Sandusky, OH, p. A502

TURSO, Janet, Controller, HEALTHSOUTH Rehabilitation Hospital of Toms River, Toms River, NJ, p. A424

TURTON, Jonathan, FACHE, President and Chief Executive Officer, Baptist Medical Center, San Antonio, TX, p. A645

TUSA, Edward A., Chief Financial Officer, Mayo Clinic Health System in Cannon Falls, Cannon Falls, MN, p. A340

TUSCANY, Joanne E.
Director Human Resources, St. John Hospital and Medical Center, Detroit, MI, p. A322
Director Worklife Services, St. John Macomb–Oakland Hospital, Warren, MI, p. A336

TUSTEN, Jay, Chief Executive Officer, Stanton County Hospital, Johnson, KS, p. A246

TUSZYNSKI, Thomas, M.D. Chief of Staff, Samaritan Healthcare, Moses Lake, WA, p. A686

TUTT, Michael, M.D. Chief Medical Officer, Tsehootsooi Medical Center, Fort Defiance, AZ, p. A32

TUTTLE, Casey, Director Information Technology, Sistersville General Hospital, Sistersville, WV, p. A700

TUTTLE, Chad, President, Spectrum Health Special Care Hospital, Grand Rapids, MI, p. A325

TUTTLE, Kathryn, R.N. Director of Nursing, Memorial Medical Center – Ashland, Ashland, WI, p. A702

TVEIT, Charles B., Chief Executive Officer, Lake District Hospital, Lakeview, OR, p. A527

TWARDY, Cindi, Manager Human Resources, Meeker Memorial Hospital, Litchfield, MN, p. A345

TWEED, Frances, Executive Director and Administrator, New Mexico Behavioral Health Institute at Las Vegas, Las Vegas, NM, p. A430

TWEEDEL, Patricia, Chief Nursing Officer, PAM Specialty Hospital of Lafayette, Lafayette, LA, p. A281

TWIDWELL, Lisa, Administrator, Madison Medical Center, Fredericktown, MO, p. A371

TWIGG, Nicole, Director Human Resources, Brook Lane Health Services, Hagerstown, MD, p. A301

TWILLA, Mark, Chief Executive Officer, Kindred Hospital the Palm Beaches, Riviera Beach, FL, p. A143

TYE, Angie, Director Human Resources, Waverly Health Center, Waverly, IA, p. A239

TYLER, Holley, R.N. Chief Nursing Officer, Woman's Hospital of Texas, Houston, TX, p. A628

TYLER, Kevin L., M.D. President Medical Staff, Penn Highlands Clearfield, Clearfield, PA, p. A535

TYLER, Philene, Chief Finance Officer, Chinle Comprehensive Health Care Facility, Chinle, AZ, p. A31

TYLER, Richard, Corporate Director Human Resources, Conway Regional Medical Center, Conway, AR, p. A44

TYLER, Rick, M.D
Vice President Medical Affairs, CHRISTUS Southeast Texas Hospital, Beaumont, TX, p. A601
Vice President Medical Affairs, CHRISTUS St. Patrick Hospital of Lake Charles, Lake Charles, LA, p. A281

TYLER, Rob, Chief Financial Officer, West Oaks Hospital, Houston, TX, p. A627

TYLER, Rosamond M., Administrator, Tyler Holmes Memorial Hospital, Winona, MS, p. A366

TYLER, Tanya, Vice President Human Resources, CHI St. Luke's Health Memorial Lufkin, Lufkin, TX, p. A634

TYLKOWSKI, Chester, M.D. Chief of Staff, Shriners Hospitals for Children–Lexington, Lexington, KY, p. A263

TYNER, Marilou Patalinjug, M.D. Medical Director, Highland–Clarksburg Hospital, Clarksburg, WV, p. A695

TYNER, W. Russell, President and Chief Executive Officer, Baptist Health, Montgomery, AL, p. B19

TYNES, Jr., L. Lee, M.D. Medical Director, Central Louisiana State Hospital, Pineville, LA, p. A286

TYO, Joanne, Chief Executive Officer, Carolinas ContinueCARE Hospital at Pineville, Charlotte, NC, p. A462

TYRA, Diana, Director Health Information, Kentucky River Medical Center, Jackson, KY, p. A262

TYRA, J. Allen, Chief Executive, Merit Health Gilmore Memorial, Amory, MS, p. A355

TYRER, Andrew, Chief Operating Officer, TriStar StoneCrest Medical Center, Smyrna, TN, p. A593

TYRRELL, RN, Wade Alan, Chief Nursing Officer, Sterling Regional MedCenter, Sterling, CO, p. A110

TYSLAND, Tanya, Chief Executive Officer, Palmer Lutheran Health Center, West Union, IA, p. A239

TYSON, Bernard J., Chairman and Chief Executive Officer, Kaiser Foundation Hospitals, Oakland, CA, p. B75

TYSON, Charlotte C., Chief Executive Officer, LewisGale Hospital Alleghany, Low Moor, VA, p. A672

TYSON, Rhoda, Chief Information Officer, Central Alabama Veterans Health Care System, Montgomery, AL, p. A23

U

UBER, Charlotte M., Chief Executive Officer, Warren State Hospital, Warren, PA, p. A556

UDALL, Ben, M.D. Chief of Staff, Kimble Hospital, Junction, TX, p. A629

UDOVICH, Christopher, M.D. Chief of Staff, Silver Cross Hospital, New Lenox, IL, p. A198

UFFER, Mark H., Chief Executive Officer, Corona Regional Medical Center, Corona, CA, p. A59

UGHOUWA, Ejiro, M.D. Chief of Staff, Allen Parish Hospital, Kinder, LA, p. A280

UGWUEKE, Michael O., President and Chief Executive Officer, Methodist Healthcare Memphis Hospitals, Memphis, TN, p. A589

UHARRIET, Bart, Director Information Services, Mississippi State Hospital, Whitfield, MS, p. A366

UHL, Jason, Chief Information Officer, Floyd Valley Healthcare, Le Mars, IA, p. A233

UHL, Michael, Chief Operating Officer, Atrium Medical Center, Middletown, OH, p. A499

UHLIK, Allen, M.D. Chief of Staff, Copper Basin Medical Center, Copperhill, TN, p. A582

UHLIR, Tricia, Chief Executive Officer, Fall River Hospital, Hot Springs, SD, p. A574

ULBRICHT, John E., Chief Executive Officer, South Texas Regional Medical Center, Jourdanton, TX, p. A629

ULERY, Brian
Senior Vice President and Chief Operating Officer, Saint Francis Hospital, Charleston, WV, p. A695
Chief Operating Officer, Thomas Memorial Hospital, South Charleston, WV, p. A700

ULETT, John, Vice President and Chief Information Officer, CentraState Healthcare System, Freehold, NJ, p. A417

ULFERTS, Wendy, R.N. Chief Nursing Officer, Rice Memorial Hospital, Willmar, MN, p. A353

ULI, James
Chief Financial Officer, Loma Linda University Medical Center–Murrieta, Murrieta, CA, p. A78
Chief Financial Officer, Providence Saint John's Health Center, Santa Monica, CA, p. A93

ULIBARRI, Laura, M.D. Chief of Staff, Catalina Island Medical Center, Avalon, CA, p. A55

ULICNY, Gary R., Ph.D., President and Chief Executive Officer, Shepherd Center, Atlanta, GA, p. A153

ULMER, Becky, R.N. Director of Nursing, Jasper General Hospital, Bay Springs, MS, p. A355

ULMER, Carlton, Chief Executive Officer, Gulf Coast Medical Center, Panama City, FL, p. A141

ULMER, Carol, Chief Executive Officer, Select Specialty Hospital–Sioux Falls, Sioux Falls, SD, p. A576

ULREICH, Shawn, R.N. Vice President Clinical Operations and Chief Nursing Executive, Spectrum Health – Butterworth Hospital, Grand Rapids, MI, p. A325

ULREY, Chris, Director Management Information Systems, St. Luke's Behavioral Health Center, Phoenix, AZ, p. A37

ULRICH, Alan
Chief Financial Officer, Bartlett Regional Hospital, Juneau, AK, p. A29
Chief Financial Officer, Guam Memorial Hospital Authority, Tamuning, GU, p. A725

ULRICH Jr., James P., President and Chief Executive Officer, Community Hospital, McCook, NE, p. A398

ULSETH, Randy, Chief Executive Officer, FirstLight Health System, Mora, MN, p. A347

ULVELING, Kyle, M.D. Chief of Staff, St. Anthony Regional Hospital, Carroll, IA, p. A226

UMHAU, John, M.D. Clinical Director, U. S. Public Health Service Indian Hospital–Whiteriver, Whiteriver, AZ, p. A41

UNDERDAHL, Steve, Chief Executive Officer, Northfield Hospital, Northfield, MN, p. A348

UNDERHILL, Robert, Director of Business Services, Central State Hospital, Louisville, KY, p. A264

UNDERHILL, Tom, M.D. Chief Medical Officer, Walla Walla General Hospital, Walla Walla, WA, p. A693

UNDERWOOD, Bill, Chief Executive Officer, Select Specialty Hospital–Fort Wayne, Fort Wayne, IN, p. A211

UNDERWOOD, Debbie, Manager Human Resources, Plains Memorial Hospital, Dimmitt, TX, p. A613

UNDERWOOD, Jerri C., R.N. Chief Nursing Officer, Parkridge Medical Center, Chattanooga, TN, p. A580

UNDERWOOD, Kelsey N., Director of Nursing, Gundersen Tri–County Hospital and Clinics, Whitehall, WI, p. A719

UNDERWOOD, Ken, Chief Executive Officer, Hazel Hawkins Memorial Hospital, Hollister, CA, p. A66

UNDERWOOD, Martha, Chief Human Resources Officer, Saint Thomas Midtown Hospital, Nashville, TN, p. A591

UNDERWOOD, Patricia A., Chief Financial Officer, Magee Rehabilitation Hospital, Philadelphia, PA, p. A548

UNDERWOOD, Robert, M.D. Chief Medical Officer, St. Mary–Corwin Medical Center, Pueblo, CO, p. A110

UNDERWOOD, Vickie, Director Human Resources, Wyandot Memorial Hospital, Upper Sandusky, OH, p. A504

UNDERWOOD, Virgil, Chief Executive Officer, Boone Memorial Hospital, Madison, WV, p. A697

UNDLIN, Cassie, Chief Operating Officer, Navos, Seattle, WA, p. A689

UNELL, Deonna, Chief Executive Officer, Baylor Surgical Hospital at Las Colinas, Irving, TX, p. A628

UNG, David
Director, Information Technology, California Hospital Medical Center, Los Angeles, CA, p. A70
Site Director, St. Mary Medical Center, Long Beach, CA, p. A70

UNGER, Henry D., M.D. Senior Vice President and Chief Medical Officer, Holy Redeemer Hospital, Meadowbrook, PA, p. A544

UNGER, Kevin L., Ph.D.,
President and Chief Executive Officer, Medical Center of the Rockies, Loveland, CO, p. A109
President and Chief Executive Officer, Poudre Valley Hospital, Fort Collins, CO, p. A105

UNITAN, Carol, M.D. Chief Medical Officer, Kaiser Foundation Hospital Westside Medical Center, Hillsboro, OR, p. A526

UNRUH, Greg, Chief Executive Officer, Citizens Medical Center, Colby, KS, p. A241

UNZEN, John, Chief Financial Officer, Mille Lacs Health System, Onamia, MN, p. A348

UPCHURCH, Jim, M.D. Chief Medical Officer, Crow/Northern Cheyenne Hospital, Crow Agency, MT, p. A386

UPCRAFT, Jeffrey, Director Information Services, Southwest Healthcare System, Murrieta, CA, p. A78

UPFIELD, Jaclyn, Chief Operating Officer, G. Werber Bryan Psychiatric Hospital, Columbia, SC, p. A564

UPSHAW, Joy, Chief Nursing Officer, Oklahoma State University Medical Center, Tulsa, OK, p. A521

UPTON, Carol, Regional Area Practice Manager, Merit Health Gilmore Memorial, Amory, MS, p. A355

UPTON, Daniel, Vice President and Chief Financial Officer, Doylestown Hospital, Doylestown, PA, p. A537

UPTON, Kerry L., Administrative Director Human Resources, Care Regional Medical Center, Aransas Pass, TX, p. A597

UPTON, Matthew
Chief Medical Officer and Chief Medical Information Officer, Saint Francis Hospital, Charleston, WV, p. A695
Chief Medical Information Officer, Thomas Memorial Hospital, South Charleston, WV, p. A700

URADNIK, Michael, Chief Executive Officer, Cascade Behavioral Hospital, Tukwila, WA, p. A692

URAIZEE, Rizwan A., Chief Financial Officer, Kedren Community Mental Health Center, Los Angeles, CA, p. A72

URBAN, Frank, Chief Financial Officer, Southwood Psychiatric Hospital, Pittsburgh, PA, p. A551

URBAN, Louise, R.N., President and Chief Executive Officer, Jefferson Hospital, Jefferson Hills, PA, p. A541

URBAN, Thomas S., Market Leader and President, Mercy Health – Fairfield Hospital, Fairfield, OH, p. A494

URBAN, Tom, Director Human Resources, Wills Memorial Hospital, Washington, GA, p. A168

URBANCSIK, Don
Director Finance, Euclid Hospital, Euclid, OH, p. A494
Director Finance, Lutheran Hospital, Cleveland, OH, p. A489

URBANIAK, Cindy, Chief Executive Officer, Kittson Memorial Healthcare Center, Hallock, MN, p. A344

URBANSKI, Pamela A., R.N. Chief Nursing Officer, Senior Vice President, Patient Care Services, ProMedica Monroe Regional Hospital, Monroe, MI, p. A330

URBINA, Ana, Chief Financial Officer, Atrium Medical Center, Stafford, TX, p. A649

URBISTONDO, Lisa, Chief Financial Officer, Medical Center of Peach County, Navicent Health, Bryon, GA, p. A155

URDANETA, Alfonso, M.D. President Medical Staff, Washington County Hospital, Nashville, IL, p. A198

URLAUB, Charles J., President and Chief Executive Officer, Mercy Hospital, Buffalo, NY, p. A436

URQUHART, Mary, R.N. Vice President Patient Care, Brattleboro Memorial Hospital, Brattleboro, VT, p. A665

URQUHART, Mary Beth, Vice President Patient Care Services and Director of Quality, New England Sinai Hospital and Rehabilitation Center, Stoughton, MA, p. A315

URSIN, Ronnie, R.N. Chief Nursing Officer, Northern Louisiana Medical Center, Ruston, LA, p. A287

USELMAN, Melissa, Chief Financial Officer, Gundersen Boscobel Area Hospital and Clinics, Boscobel, WI, p. A703

USHIJIMA, Arthur A., FACHE, President and Chief Executive Officer, Queen's Health Systems, Honolulu, HI, p. B112

USHIJIMA, Arthur A., FACHE, President, The Queen's Medical Center, Honolulu, HI, p. A171

UTECHT, Tom, M.D
Senior Vice President and Chief Quality Officer, Community Behavioral Health Center, Fresno, CA, p. A63
Chief Medical and Quality Officer, Community Regional Medical Center, Fresno, CA, p. A63
Corporate Chief Quality Officer, Fresno Heart and Surgical Hospital, Fresno, CA, p. A63

UTEMARK, Paul, Chief Executive Officer, Fillmore County Hospital, Geneva, NE, p. A396

UTLEY, Donna, Vice President Human Resources, Mercy San Juan Medical Center, Carmichael, CA, p. A58

UTLEY, Renee, Chief Financial Officer, Hamilton Center, Terre Haute, IN, p. A222

UTTENDORFSKY, Rob, Director Information Management, Lewis County General Hospital, Lowville, NY, p. A442

UTTER, Camille, R.N. Chief Nursing Officer, Scotland Health Care System, Laurinburg, NC, p. A468

UTTERBACK, Julie, Chief Financial Officer, Roane Medical Center, Harriman, TN, p. A583

UYEMURA, Monte, M.D. Chief of Staff, Wray Community District Hospital, Wray, CO, p. A111

V

VAAGENES, Carl P., Chief Executive Officer, Douglas County Hospital, Alexandria, MN, p. A338

VAALER, Mark, M.D
Chief Medical Officer, South Florida Baptist Hospital, Plant City, FL, p. A142
Vice President Medical Staff Affairs, St. Joseph's Hospital, Tampa, FL, p. A147

VACCARO, Michael, Chief Nursing Officer, Novant Health Presbyterian Medical Center, Charlotte, NC, p. A463

VACCARO, Stacey, Chief Operating Officer, The Children's Institute of Pittsburgh, Pittsburgh, PA, p. A551

VACHON, Scott, Director Information Technology, Littleton Regional Healthcare, Littleton, NH, p. A412

VADEN, Jim, Director Information Systems, Lauderdale Community Hospital, Ripley, TN, p. A592

VADYAK, Karen, Chief Nursing Officer, Easton Hospital, Easton, PA, p. A537

VAEZAZIZI, Reza, M.D. Chief of Staff, Southwest Healthcare System, Murrieta, CA, p. A78

VAGUE, Jeff, Regional Manager Information Systems, Mercy Hospitals of Bakersfield, Bakersfield, CA, p. A56

VAHLBERG, Susan, Director Employee and Community Relations, Valor Health, Emmett, ID, p. A176

VAIL, B. J., Director Information Systems, Morehouse General Hospital, Bastrop, LA, p. A272

VAIL, Bryan, Chief Information Officer, Clement J. Zablocki Veterans Affairs Medical Center, Milwaukee, WI, p. A711

VAIL, Lisa M., R.N. Chief Nursing Officer and Vice President of Patient Care Services, Bryan Medical Center, Lincoln, NE, p. A397

VAIL, Ronald, M.D. Chief of Staff, Lower Umpqua Hospital District, Reedsport, OR, p. A530

VAILLANCOURT, Alex, Chief Information Officer, Christ Hospital, Cincinnati, OH, p. A487

VAILLANCOURT, Stacy, Vice President Marketing, Communications, Advocacy and Human Resources, Saint Agnes Medical Center, Fresno, CA, p. A64

VAIOLETI, Stephany, Chief Executive Officer, Kahuku Medical Center, Kahuku, HI, p. A171

VAKHARIA, Bharat, M.D. President Medical Staff, Sturgis Hospital, Sturgis, MI, p. A335

VALBUENA, Richard, M.D. Medical Director, Latimer County General Hospital, Wilburton, OK, p. A523

VALDENEGRO, Maria, Chief Financial Officer, Meadow Wood Behavioral Health System, New Castle, DE, p. A119

VALDERAZ, Leonard, Administrator, Sunrise Canyon Hospital, Lubbock, TX, p. A634

VALDESPINO, Gustavo A., President and Chief Executive Officer, Valley Presbyterian Hospital,, CA, p. A75

VALENCERINA, Madeline, Chief Operating Officer, Kedren Community Mental Health Center, Los Angeles, CA, p. A72

VALENTE, Anthony, M.D. Vice President Medical Affairs, Lehigh Valley Hospital – Hazleton, Hazleton, PA, p. A540

VALENTE, T. J., M.D. Medical Director, LifeStream Behavioral Center, Leesburg, FL, p. A134

VALENTIN, Leonardo, Chief Executive Officer, Professional Hospital Guaynabo, Guaynabo, PR, p. A727

VALENTINE, Lisa R., Chief Operating Officer, Henrico Doctors' Hospital, Richmond, VA, p. A677

VALENTINE, Mark
President, The Heart Hospital Baylor Denton, Denton, TX, p. A613
President, The Heart Hospital Baylor Plano, Plano, TX, p. A642

VALENTINE, Robert A., President, CHI Health Missouri Valley, Missouri Valley, IA, p. A234

VALENTINI, Rudolph, M.D. Chief Medical Officer, DMC – Children's Hospital of Michigan, Detroit, MI, p. A321

VALENTO, Jessica, Director Information Systems, Range Regional Health Services, Hibbing, MN, p. A344

VALLE, Bernardo, Vice President Human Resources, USMD Hospital at Arlington, Arlington, TX, p. A598

VALLE, David, Chief Information Officer, Hospital Dr. Cayetano Coll Y Toste, Arecibo, PR, p. A726

VALLE, Karla, Area Chief Financial Officer, Kaiser Permanente Panorama City Medical Center,, CA, p. A71

VALLELY, Ian, Information Technology Site Leader, Sequoia Hospital, Redwood City, CA, p. A85

VALLES, John, Senior Vice President and Chief Financial Officer, Loretto Hospital, Chicago, IL, p. A184

VALLIDO, Gabe, Chief Information Officer, Naval Hospital Camp Pendleton, Camp Pendleton, CA, p. A58

VALLIERE, George, Chief Executive Officer, Claremore Indian Hospital, Claremore, OK, p. A510

VALLIERE, Mark, M.D. Senior Vice President Medical Affairs and Chief Medical Officer, Mercy Medical Center–Cedar Rapids, Cedar Rapids, IA, p. A226

VAN BOENING, Jon, President and Chief Executive Officer, Bakersfield Memorial Hospital, Bakersfield, CA, p. A55

VAN BUSKIRK, George F., M.D. Chief of Staff, Bay Pines Veterans Affairs Healthcare System, Bay Pines, FL, p. A123

VAN CAMP, Keith, Vice President Information Services, St. Dominic–Jackson Memorial Hospital, Jackson, MS, p. A360

VAN CLEAVE, Bruce L., M.D. Senior Vice President and Chief Medical Officer, Aurora Medical Center of Oshkosh, Oshkosh, WI, p. A713

VAN CLEAVE, Chad, Chief Financial Officer, Columbus Community Hospital, Columbus, NE, p. A395

VAN CLEAVE, Vanetta, Chief Financial Officer, Yukon–Kuskokwim Delta Regional Hospital, Bethel, AK, p. A28

VAN DECAR, Tama, M.D. Chief Medical Officer, Fort Walton Beach Medical Center, Fort Walton Beach, FL, p. A129

VAN DER VEER, Jon, D.O. Vice President Medical Affairs, Greene County Medical Center, Jefferson, IA, p. A233

VAN DRIEL, Allen, FACHE, Administrator, Smith County Memorial Hospital, Smith Center, KS, p. A254

VAN EECKHOUT, Barbara, M.D. Chief of Staff, Los Alamos Medical Center, Los Alamos, NM, p. A430

VAN EPERN, Keri, Manager Human Resources, Aspirus Grand View, Ironwood, MI, p. A327

VAN ESSENDELFT, Seth
Vice President and Chief Financial Officer, Lawrence + Memorial Hospital, New London, CT, p. A116
Vice President and Chief Financial Officer, Westerly Hospital, Westerly, RI, p. A561

VAN ETTEN, Mark, M.D. Chief of Staff, Spooner Health, Spooner, WI, p. A716

VAN GALDER, Jeanne, Chief Executive Officer, Chestatee Regional Hospital, Dahlonega, GA, p. A157

VAN GORDER, Chris D., FACHE, President and Chief Executive Officer, Scripps Health, San Diego, CA, p. B119

VAN GUNDY, Dan, Director of Information Technology Systems and Hardwire, Major Hospital, Shelbyville, IN, p. A222

VAN GUNDY, Milt, M.D. President Medical Staff, Central Iowa Healthcare, Marshalltown, IA, p. A234

VAN HOET, Jim, Chief Financial Officer, Coffey County Hospital, Burlington, KS, p. A241

VAN HOFF, Cynthia, Chief Financial Officer, Sutter Solano Medical Center, Vallejo, CA, p. A98

VAN HOUDEN, Charles, M.D. Chief Medical Officer, Neosho Memorial Regional Medical Center, Chanute, KS, p. A241

VAN HYNING, Jill, Director Human Resources, Richland Memorial Hospital, Olney, IL, p. A199

VAN KAMPEN, Cindy, Chief Nursing Officer, North Ottawa Community Hospital, Grand Haven, MI, p. A324

VAN LEEUWE, Matthew
Chief Operating Officer, Abilene Regional Medical Center, Abilene, TX, p. A595
Interim Chief Executive Officer, Big Bend Regional Medical Center, Alpine, TX, p. A596

VAN LUVEN, Audrey C., Senior Vice President and Chief Human Resources Officer, Christiana Care Health System, Newark, DE, p. A119

VAN MEETEREN, Robert, President and Chief Executive Officer, Reedsburg Area Medical Center, Reedsburg, WI, p. A715

VAN METER, David, Deputy Director, James A. Haley Veterans' Hospital–Tampa, Tampa, FL, p. A147

VAN METER, Rex, President, INTEGRIS Canadian Valley Hospital, Yukon, OK, p. A523

VAN NATTA, Timothy, M.D. Chief Medical Officer, Harbor–UCLA Medical Center, Torrance, CA, p. A96

VAN NORMAN, Steven, M.D. Medical Director, Dixie Regional Medical Center, Saint George, UT, p. A663

VAN RYBROEK, Greg, Chief Executive Officer, Mendota Mental Health Institute, Madison, WI, p. A708

VAN SCOYK, Mitch, Manager Information Systems, Delta County Memorial Hospital, Delta, CO, p. A103

VAN VICKLE, Robin, Chief Financial Officer, Bristow Medical Center, Bristow, OK, p. A509

VAN VOLKENBURG, Mark, Chief Executive Officer, HEALTHSOUTH Harmarville Rehabilitation Hospital, Pittsburgh, PA, p. A550

VAN VRANKEN, Arthur, M.D. Chief Medical Officer, Essentia Health–Graceville, Graceville, MN, p. A343

VAN VRANKEN, Ross, Executive Director, University of Utah Neuropsychiatric Institute, Salt Lake City, UT, p. A664

VAN WHY, Susan, Director Human Resources, St. Luke's Hospital – Miners Campus, Coaldale, PA, p. A535

VAN WINKLE, James, M.D. Chief of Staff, Unity Medical Center, Manchester, TN, p. A587

VAN WINKLE, Melanie, Chief Financial Officer, Mammoth Hospital, Mammoth Lakes, CA, p. A75

VAN ZANTEN, Lorinda, MSN, Chief Executive Officer, Providence Newberg Medical Center, Newberg, OR, p. A528

VANASKIE, William F., Executive Vice President and Chief Operating Officer, Maricopa Integrated Health System, Phoenix, AZ, p. A36

VANBOEKEL, Tony, Director Information Systems, Shasta Regional Medical Center, Redding, CA, p. A84

VANBREF, Margaret, M.D., President and Chief Executive Officer, Rhode Island Hospital, Providence, RI, p. A561

VANBUREN, Nikki, Chief Nursing Officer, Johnston Memorial Hospital, Abingdon, VA, p. A667

VANCE, Amy, Executive Vice President and Chief Operating Officer, Novant Health Matthews Medical Center, Matthews, NC, p. A469

VANCE, Derek, Chief Executive Officer, LewisGale Hospital Pulaski, Pulaski, VA, p. A676

VANCE, Ellen B.
Chief Human Resources Officer, Sheltering Arms Hospital South, Midlothian, VA, p. A674
Chief Human Resource Officer, Sheltering Arms Rehabilitation Hospital, Mechanicsville, VA, p. A673

VANCE, Mark, M.D. Chief Medical Officer, Quincy Valley Medical Center, Quincy, WA, p. A688

VANCE, Stacie, Chief Nursing Officer and Vice President Operations, Indiana Orthopaedic Hospital, Indianapolis, IN, p. A214

VANCE, Steven
Chief Financial Officer, Dixie Regional Medical Center, Saint George, UT, p. A663
Information Technology Director, Lake District Hospital, Lakeview, OR, p. A527

VANCONIA, R. Brent, President, SSM Health St. Mary's Hospital – Jefferson City, Jefferson City, MO, p. A372

VANCOURT, Bernie, Chief Operating Officer, Bay Area Medical Center, Marinette, WI, p. A709

VANDENBARK, Heather, Human Resources Specialist, State Hospital North, Orofino, ID, p. A177

VANDENBERG, Andra, Director Human Resources, Butler County Health Care System, David City, NE, p. A395

VANDENBOSCH, Dan, Chief Information Officer, Madison County Health Care System, Winterset, IA, p. A239

VANDENBOSCH, Darryl, President, St. Bernardine Medical Center, San Bernardino, CA, p. A88

VANDER, Allen, M.D. Chief Medical Staff, Thibodaux Regional Medical Center, Thibodaux, LA, p. A289

VANDER KOLK, Keith, President and Chief Executive Officer, Saint Agnes Hospital, Baltimore, MD, p. A297

VANDERBEEK, Sam, Chief Information Officer, W. J. Mangold Memorial Hospital, Lockney, TX, p. A633

VANDERHOOFT, J. Eric, M.D. President Medical Staff, St. Mark's Hospital, Salt Lake City, UT, p. A663

VANDERLINDEN, Mark A., Chief Financial Officer, Greene County Medical Center, Jefferson, IA, p. A233

VANDERMARK, Jay H., Chief Financial Officer, Veterans Affairs Northern Indiana Health Care System, Fort Wayne, IN, p. A211

VANDERMEER, Nick, Director Information Systems, Banner Payson Medical Center, Payson, AZ, p. A35

VANDERPOL, Antoinette, Chief of Staff, Avera St. Benedict Health Center, Parkston, SD, p. A575

VANDERPOOL, Lee, Vice President, Dominican Hospital, Santa Cruz, CA, p. A93

VANDERSLICE, Douglas M., Senior Vice President and Chief Financial Officer, Boston Children's Hospital, Boston, MA, p. A306

VANDERSTEEG, James, President and Chief Executive Officer, Covenant Health, Knoxville, TN, p. B42

VANDERSTEK, Eliott R., Chief Fiscal Service, Veterans Affairs Eastern Colorado Health Care System, Denver, CO, p. A104

VANDERSTOUW, Karl, Vice President Information Systems, UNC Lenoir Healthcare, Kinston, NC, p. A468

VANDERVLIET, William, M.D. Vice President Medical Affairs, Holland Hospital, Holland, MI, p. A326

VANDERWEGE, Larry, Administrator, Lindsborg Community Hospital, Lindsborg, KS, p. A248

VANDEVEER Jr., Alden M., FACHE, Chief Executive Officer, Palacios Community Medical Center, Palacios, TX, p. A639

VANDEWATER, David T., President and Chief Executive Officer, Ardent Health Services, Nashville, TN, p. B11

VANDEWEGE, Dana, Director Human Resources, Capital Medical Center, Olympia, WA, p. A687

VANDONKELAAR, Rodney
Chief Financial Officer, Carolina Pines Regional Medical Center, Hartsville, SC, p. A567
Chief Financial Officer, Saint Thomas Highlands Hospital, Sparta, TN, p. A593

VANDORT, Patti J., MSN Vice President Nursing/Chief Nursing Officer, Holland Hospital, Holland, MI, p. A326

VANDRIEL, Mary Kay
President, Spectrum Health Big Rapids Hospital, Big Rapids, MI, p. A319
President, Spectrum Health Reed City Hospital, Reed City, MI, p. A332

VANDRUFF, John, M.D. Chief of Staff, Banner Payson Medical Center, Payson, AZ, p. A35

VANEK, James, Chief Executive Officer, Columbus Community Hospital, Columbus, TX, p. A607

VANES, Wendell, Chief Financial Officer, Saint Mary's Regional Medical Center, Russellville, AR, p. A52

VANGENDEREN, Nathan, Executive Vice President and Chief Financial Officer, Mercy Medical Center–Cedar Rapids, Cedar Rapids, IA, p. A226

VANHAREN, James, M.D. Medical Director, Forest View Psychiatric Hospital, Grand Rapids, MI, p. A324

VANHOOSIER, Adria, Administrator, Riverside Doctors' Hospital, Williamsburg, VA, p. A680

VANHOUWELING, Mason, Chief Executive Officer, University Medical Center, Las Vegas, NV, p. A407

VANHOY, Michael, Director of Quality, UVA–HEALTHSOUTH Rehabilitation Hospital, Charlottesville, VA, p. A668

VANNATTER, Mistie, Chief Nursing Officer, Advanced Care Hospital of White County, Searcy, AR, p. A52

VANNETT, Vince, Director Human Resources, Jellico Community Hospital, Jellico, TN, p. A585

VANO, Ann, Vice President, Human Resources, Crittenton Hospital Medical Center, Rochester, MI, p. A332

VANOSDOL, Thomas J.
Chief Operating Officer, St. Vincent's Medical Center Riverside, Jacksonville, FL, p. A132
Chief Operating Officer, St. Vincent's Medical Center Southside, Jacksonville, FL, p. A132

VANSANT, Scott, M.D. Chief Medical Officer, Central State Hospital, Milledgeville, GA, p. A163

VANSTRIEN, Amy, Director Talent Operations, Midwestern Regional Medical Center, Zion, IL, p. A205

VANTONGEREN, Teri, Director Information Services, Spectrum Health Pennock, Hastings, MI, p. A326

VANWICHEN, Ward C., Chief Executive Officer, Phillips County Hospital, Malta, MT, p. A389

VANWYHE, Brenda, Senior Vice President Finance and Chief Financial Officer, Rush–Copley Medical Center, Aurora, IL, p. A181

VARA Jr.,, Raymond P., President and Chief Executive Officer, Hawaii Pacific Health, Honolulu, HI, p. B60

VARELA, Alberto M., M.D., President, INSPIRA Ponce, Ponce, PR, p. A728

VARELA, Nancy, Director Human Resources, Patton State Hospital, Patton, CA, p. A82

VARGA, Patrick, Chief Operating Officer, Mercy Medical Center Redding, Redding, CA, p. A84

VARGAS, Barbara, Interim Chief Nursing Officer, Fountain Valley Regional Hospital and Medical Center, Fountain Valley, CA, p. A62

VARGAS, Jose L., M.D. Medical Director, West Gables Rehabilitation Hospital, Miami, FL, p. A137

VARGAS, Margie, Chief Human Resources Officer, Memorial Regional Hospital,, FL, p. A130

VARGAS, Marisol, Director Finance, Hospital Del Maestro, San Juan, PR, p. A729

VARGAS, Nancy
Director Human Resources, Mark Twain Medical Center, San Andreas, CA, p. A88
Chief Human Resources, St. Joseph's Behavioral Health Center, Stockton, CA, p. A95
Vice President Human Resources, St. Joseph's Medical Center, Stockton, CA, p. A95

VARGAS–MAHAR, Monica, FACHE, Chief Executive Officer, The Hospitals of Providence Sierra Campus, El Paso, TX, p. A616

VARGHESE, Roy, M.D. Chief of Staff, Mary Breckinridge ARH Hospital, Hyden, KY, p. A262

VARGHESE, Shibu, Vice President Human Resources, University of Texas M.D. Anderson Cancer Center, Houston, TX, p. A627

VARIALE, Vincenzo, Chief Executive Officer, North Vista Hospital, North Las Vegas, NV, p. A407

VARIAN, Grant, M.D. Medical Director, Mary Rutan Hospital, Bellefontaine, OH, p. A485

VARK, Lawrence, M.D. Chief Medical Officer, Creek Nation Community Hospital, Okemah, OK, p. A515

VARLAND, Drew, Chief Nursing Officer and Chief Operating Officer, Pioneers Medical Center, Meeker, CO, p. A109

VARLEY, Kevin
Chief Financial Officer, Curahealth Heritage Valley, Beaver, PA, p. A533
Chief Financial Officer, Curahealth Pittsburgh, Oakdale, PA, p. A546
Chief Financial Officer, Kindred Hospital South Philadelphia, Philadelphia, PA, p. A548

VARNADO, Anjanette, M.D. Chief Medical Officer, St. Helena Parish Hospital, Greensburg, LA, p. A277

VARNADO, Darryl, Executive Vice President and Chief People Officer, Children's National Health System, Washington, DC, p. A121

VARNADO, Kim, R.N. Chief Nursing Officer, Highland Community Hospital, Picayune, MS, p. A364

VARNADOE, Milo, Director Information Systems, Warm Springs Medical Center, Warm Springs, GA, p. A168

VARNAM, Jessica, Chief of Staff, Grant Regional Health Center, Lancaster, WI, p. A708

VARNER, Terry, Administrator, Yalobusha General Hospital, Water Valley, MS, p. A366

VARNEY, Tim, R.N. Chief Nursing Officer, Select Specialty Hospital–Ann Arbor, Ypsilanti, MI, p. A337

VARNUM, Daniel, President and Chief Executive Officer, Mercy Medical Center–North Iowa, Mason City, IA, p. A234

VARTANIAN, Sarkis, Chief Nursing Officer, Whittier Hospital Medical Center, Whittier, CA, p. A100

VARTELAS, Helene M., MSN, Chief Executive Officer, Connecticut Valley Hospital, Middletown, CT, p. A115

VASCONCELLOS, Jacques, Director, Operations, Winter Haven Hospital, Winter Haven, FL, p. A150

VASEK, Barbara, Director Information Technology, Yoakum Community Hospital, Yoakum, TX, p. A658

VASHISHTA, Ashok, M.D. Vice President Medical Affairs, McLaren Central Michigan, Mount Pleasant, MI, p. A330

VASIL, Kathleen, Vice President Finance, St. Charles Hospital, Port Jefferson, NY, p. A453

VASQUEZ, Alberto, Administrator, Garfield Memorial Hospital and Clinics, Panguitch, UT, p. A662

VASQUEZ, Christann
Executive Vice President and Chief Operating Officer, University Health System, San Antonio, TX, p. A647
President, University Medical Center at Brackenridge, Austin, TX, p. A600

VASQUEZ, George
Chief Technology Officer, Clovis Community Medical Center, Clovis, CA, p. A59
Vice President Information Services, Community Behavioral Health Center, Fresno, CA, p. A63
Corporate Chief Information Officer, Fresno Heart and Surgical Hospital, Fresno, CA, p. A63

VASQUEZ, Jill, Manager Human Resources, Spectrum Health Ludington Hospital, Ludington, MI, p. A329

VASQUEZ, Kenneth, Associate Director, JFK Medical Center North Campus, West Palm Beach, FL, p. A149

VASQUEZ, Miguel, Chief Executive Officer, Sister Emmanuel Hospital, Miami, FL, p. A137

VASQUEZ, Nelson, Vice President Finance, Jackson Park Hospital and Medical Center, Chicago, IL, p. A184

VASS, Paula, Vice President Clinical Operations, Walden Psychiatric Care, Waltham, MA, p. A315

VASSALL, John, M.D
Chief Medical Officer, Swedish Medical Center–Cherry Hill Campus, Seattle, WA, p. A689
Chief Medical Officer, Swedish Medical Center–First Hill, Seattle, WA, p. A690

VASTOLA, David, Medical Director, SEARHC MT. Edgecumbe Hospital, Sitka, AK, p. A30

VASUNAGA, Amy, Chief Nurse Executive, Leahi Hospital, Honolulu, HI, p. A170

VATH, Richard, M.D. Vice President Medical Affairs, Our Lady of the Lake Regional Medical Center, Baton Rouge, LA, p. A273

VATSAVAI, Sundararama R., M.D. Medical Director, Baton Rouge Rehabilitation Hospital, Baton Rouge, LA, p. A272

VAUGHAN, Aaron, Coordinator Information Systems, Pocahontas Memorial Hospital, Buckeye, WV, p. A694

VAUGHAN, Alan, Director Information Technology, Share Medical Center, Alva, OK, p. A508

VAUGHAN, Amanda, Chief Financial Officer, St. Catherine Hospital, Garden City, KS, p. A243

VAUGHAN, Brandon, Chief Financial Officer and Vice President Finance, Jamestown Regional Medical Center, Jamestown, ND, p. A480

VAUGHAN, Page H., Chief Executive Officer, Chester Regional Medical Center, Chester, SC, p. A563

VAUGHAN, Peggy, M.D
Senior Vice President Medical Affairs, University of Maryland Harford Memorial Hospital, Havre De Grace, MD, p. A301
Senior Vice President Medical Affairs, University of Maryland Upper Chesapeake Medical Center, Bel Air, MD, p. A298

VAUGHAN, Rob, Chief Financial Officer, Carilion New River Valley Medical Center, Christiansburg, VA, p. A669

VAUGHAN, Steve, Chief Executive Officer, Pearl River County Hospital, Poplarville, MS, p. A364

VAUGHN, Barbara, R.N. Chief Nursing Officer, Baylor Scott & White Medical Center – Carrollton, Carrollton, TX, p. A605

VAUGHN, Debbie, R.N. Chief Nursing Officer, Glenwood Regional Medical Center, West Monroe, LA, p. A289

VAUGHN, Kerry, Chief Information Officer, St. Mary's Health Care System, Athens, GA, p. A151

VAUGHN, Kevin P., Chief Financial Officer, Kansas Spine and Specialty Hospital, Wichita, KS, p. A255

VAUGHN, Michael, Director of Nursing, Southeast Rehabilitation Hospital, Lake Village, AR, p. A48

VAUGHN, Sandy
Director Information Services, Baylor All Saints Medical Center at Fort Worth, Fort Worth, TX, p. A617
Director Information Systems, Baylor Regional Medical Center at Grapevine, Grapevine, TX, p. A621

VAUGHN, Sharma, Chief Nursing Officer, Rangely District Hospital, Rangely, CO, p. A110

VAUGHN, Ted W., Director Human Resources, UnityPoint Health – Trinity Regional Medical Center, Fort Dodge, IA, p. A230

VAUGHN, Vickie, Chief Nursing Officer, Tennova Healthcare–Shelbyville, Shelbyville, TN, p. A593

VAVARUTSOS, Tony, Director Information Systems, Thorek Memorial Hospital, Chicago, IL, p. A187

VAZIRI, H. Kevin, President, Woodland Healthcare, Woodland, CA, p. A100

VAZQUEZ, Brunilda, Medical Director, Hospital de Psiquiatria, San Juan, PR, p. A729

VAZQUEZ, Emilio, M.D. Chief Medical Officer, DeKalb Health, Auburn, IN, p. A206

VAZQUEZ, Francisco, Director, Robert J. Dole Veterans Affairs Medical Center, Wichita, KS, p. A256

VAZQUEZ, Manuel J., Executive Administrator, Hospital Oncologico Andres Grillasca, Ponce, PR, p. A728

VEACH, Jamie, Chief Operating Officer, Clay County Hospital, Flora, IL, p. A190

VEAL, Bonita Wells, Chief Nursing Officer, Anaheim Global Medical Center, Anaheim, CA, p. A54

VEDRAL–BARON, Jennifer, Commander, Fort Belvoir Community Hospital, Fort Belvoir, VA, p. A670

VEEHASSELT, Helen, Interim Chief Executive Officer, North Valley Hospital, Tonasket, WA, p. A692

VEERAMACHANENI, Harish, M.D. Chief of Staff, Wayne Medical Center, Waynesboro, TN, p. A594

VEESER, Tom, Chief Nursing Officer, Ministry Saint Michael's Hospital, Stevens Point, WI, p. A716

VEGA, James, Director Information Systems, Palm Beach Gardens Medical Center, Palm Beach Gardens, FL, p. A141

VEGA, Jane, Executive Director, Industrial Hospital, San Juan, PR, p. A730

VEGA, Maria, Director Human Resources, Auxilio Mutuo Hospital, San Juan, PR, p. A729

VEGA, Mary, R.N. Vice President Nursing, St. Margaret's Hospital, Spring Valley, IL, p. A203

VEILLETTE, Michael D.
Senior Vice President and Chief Financial Officer, Manchester Memorial Hospital, Manchester, CT, p. A114
Senior Vice President and Chief Financial Officer, Rockville General Hospital, Vernon, CT, p. A117

VEILLEUX, Jeffrey
Senior Vice President and Chief Financial Officer, Swedish Medical Center–Cherry Hill Campus, Seattle, WA, p. A689
Executive Vice President and Chief Financial Officer, Swedish Medical Center–First Hill, Seattle, WA, p. A690

VEILLON, Paul, CP
Chief Financial Officer, CHRISTUS Dubuis Hospital of Fort Smith, Fort Smith, AR, p. A46
Chief Financial Officer, CHRISTUS Dubuis Hospital of Hot Springs, Hot Springs National Park, AR, p. A47
Chief Financial Officer, Kindred Hospital–St. Louis at Mercy, Saint Louis, MO, p. A380

VEITZ, Larry W., President, Spearfish Regional Hospital, Spearfish, SD, p. A577

VELA, Javier, Director Information Technology, Baylor Medical Center at Uptown, Dallas, TX, p. A609

VELA, Manuel, President and Chief Executive Officer, Valley Baptist Medical Center–Harlingen, Harlingen, TX, p. A622

VELASCO, Paul, IT Manager, Kit Carson County Health Service District, Burlington, CO, p. A102

VELASQUEZ, Alfred T., Area Information Officer, Kaiser Permanente Riverside Medical Center, Riverside, CA, p. A85

VELASQUEZ, Carol Nunley, R.N. Chief Nursing Officer, Lake Chelan Community Hospital, Chelan, WA, p. A683

VELASQUEZ, Lin, Vice President Human Resources, Saint Louise Regional Hospital, Gilroy, CA, p. A64

VELASQUEZ, Roberto, M.D. Medical Director, Hospital Oncologico Andres Grillasca, Ponce, PR, p. A728

VELEZ, Luz M., Director–Administration of Nursing Services, Hospital San Carlos Borromeo, Moca, PR, p. A728

VELEZ, Pablo, Chief Executive Officer, Sharp Chula Vista Medical Center, Chula Vista, CA, p. A58

VELEZ, Raul
Director Information Systems, Eliza Coffee Memorial Hospital, Florence, AL, p. A20
Director Information Systems, Huntsville Memorial Hospital, Huntsville, TX, p. A628

VELUSWAMY, Ragupathy, M.D. Vice President Medical Affairs, Wilkes–Barre General Hospital, Wilkes-Barre, PA, p. A558

VENABLE, Mark, Interim Director Human Resources, Shriners Hospitals for Children–St. Louis, Saint Louis, MO, p. A380

VENABLE, Robert, M.D. Chief Medical Staff, Washington County Hospital, Plymouth, NC, p. A471

VENDETTI, Marilouise, M.D. Chief Medical Officer, AtlantiCare Regional Medical Center, Atlantic City, NJ, p. A414

VENEZIANO, Terri, Interim Chief Nursing Officer, Columbus Regional Healthcare System, Whiteville, NC, p. A475

VENGCO, Joel L., MS Vice President, Chief Information Officer, Baystate Medical Center, Springfield, MA, p. A314

VENHUIZEN, Pamela, Chief Human Resources Officer, Cooperstown Medical Center, Cooperstown, ND, p. A478

VENOIT, Jon–Paul, Chief Operating Officer, Masonicare Health Center, Wallingford, CT, p. A117

VENTURA, Sylvia A., R.N. Chief Nursing Officer, Olympia Medical Center, Los Angeles, CA, p. A73

VENUTO, Frank, Chief Human Capital Officer, Nebraska Medicine – Nebraska Medical Center, Omaha, NE, p. A400

VENZANT, Shamada, Manager Health Information, Specialty Hospital of Winnfield, Winnfield, LA, p. A289

VERA, Luis F., M.D. Medical Director, Kensington Hospital, Philadelphia, PA, p. A548

VERAGIWALA, Jignesh, Chief of Staff, Mercy Hospital Logan County, Guthrie, OK, p. A512

VERBEKE, Lori, Chief Financial Officer, Timberlawn Mental Health System, Dallas, TX, p. A611

VERBUS, John R., Senior Vice President and Chief Operating Officer, Frederick Memorial Hospital, Frederick, MD, p. A301

VERCHOTA, Robert P., Vice President Support Services, Regina Hospital, Hastings, MN, p. A344

VERDEJA, Juan–Carlos, M.D. President of Medical Staff, Baptist Health South Florida, West Kendall Baptist Hospital, Miami, FL, p. A136

VERDON, Chris, Director Finance, Phillips Eye Institute, Minneapolis, MN, p. A346

VERFURTH, Larry, D.O
Chief Medical Officer and Senior Vice President, Good Shepherd Medical Center, Longview, TX, p. A633
Executive Vice President and Chief Medical Officer, Good Shepherd Medical Center–Marshall, Marshall, TX, p. A636

VERGA, Joseph P., FACHE, Chief Executive Officer, Guam Memorial Hospital Authority, Tamuning, GU, p. A725

VERGARA, Aimee, Chief Executive Officer, Hospital for Extended Recovery, Norfolk, VA, p. A675

VERGONIO, Merlinda, Chief Information Management and Technology, U. S. Air Force Hospital, Hampton, VA, p. A671

VERGOS, Katherine, Chief Operating Officer, Ripon Medical Center, Ripon, WI, p. A715

VERHASSELT, Helen, Chief Financial Officer, North Valley Hospital, Tonasket, WA, p. A692

VERINDER, David, President and Chief Executive Officer, Sarasota Memorial Health Care System, Sarasota, FL, p. A145

VERMA, Virendar, M.D. Medical Director, HEALTHSOUTH Rehabilitation Hospital of Jonesboro, Jonesboro, AR, p. A48

VERMEER, Kevin, President and Chief Executive Officer, UnityPoint Health, West Des Moines, IA, p. B141

VERMILLION, Kerry, Senior Vice President Finance and Chief Financial Officer, Gulf Breeze Hospital, Gulf Breeze, FL, p. A130

VERMULEN, Peter, Director Information Technology, Schick Shadel Hospital, Seattle, WA, p. A689

VERRET, Dean, Vice President Financial Services, Terrebonne General Medical Center, Houma, LA, p. A278

VERRETTE, Paul, M.D. Chief Medical Officer, St. Bernard Parish Hospital, Chalmette, LA, p. A274

VERRETTE, Paula, M.D. Senior Vice President Quality and Physician Services and Chief Medical Officer, Huntington Memorial Hospital, Pasadena, CA, p. A82

VERRILL, Alan, M.D. President Medical Staff, Bridgton Hospital, Bridgton, ME, p. A292

VERSECKES, Mike, Financial Officer, Terrell State Hospital, Terrell, TX, p. A652

VERSTEEG, Linda, Director of Nursing, Hegg Memorial Health Center Avera, Rock Valley, IA, p. A237

VERTIN, Amy, M.D. Chief of Staff, Crete Area Medical Center, Crete, NE, p. A395

VESSEY, Joe, Chief Financial Officer, Grays Harbor Community Hospital, Aberdeen, WA, p. A682

VETTER, Rich, M.D. Associate Chief, Essentia Health St. Mary's – Detroit Lakes, Detroit Lakes, MN, p. A341

VIALL, John, M.D. Vice President Medical Affairs, Holzer Medical Center, Gallipolis, OH, p. A495

VIALL, Sandra E., MSN Chief Nursing Officer, Hendry Regional Medical Center, Clewiston, FL, p. A126

VIATOR, Dionne, CPA Chief Financial Officer, Iberia Medical Center, New Iberia, LA, p. A284

VIBETO, Brett, M.D. Chief of Staff, Mercy Medical Center, Williston, ND, p. A482

VIBHAKAR, Neel, M.D. Senior Vice President and Chief Medical Officer, University of Maryland Baltimore Washington Medical Center, Glen Burnie, MD, p. A301

VICE, Harmonee, Chief Executive Officer, University General Hospital, Houston, TX, p. A627

VICE, Jeff
Chief Operating Officer, St. Joseph Hospital, Fort Wayne, IN, p. A211
Chief Executive Officer, Starke Hospital, Knox, IN, p. A215

VICENS–RIVERA Jr., Enrique A., JD, Chief Executive Officer, HEALTHSOUTH Rehabilitation Hospital of Miami, Cutler Bay, FL, p. A126

VICENTE, Oscar, Chief Financial Officer, Palmetto General Hospital, Hialeah, FL, p. A130

VICENTI, Darren, M.D. Clinical Director, Hopi Health Care Center, Keams Canyon, AZ, p. A33

VICK, Dan J., M.D. Vice President of Medical Affairs and Chief Medical Officer, Oneida Healthcare, Oneida, NY, p. A452

VICKERS, Cynthia, R.N. Assistant Administrator for Nursing Services, Memorial Hospital and Manor, Bainbridge, GA, p. A154

VICKERS, Dave, Chief Financial Officer, Los Alamitos Medical Center, Los Alamitos, CA, p. A70

VICKERS, Kathy, Director Human Resources, Vantage Point of Northwest Arkansas, Fayetteville, AR, p. A46

VICKERY, Angie, Director of Nursing, Wills Memorial Hospital, Washington, GA, p. A168

VICKERY, Ian, Director Information Technology, D. W. McMillan Memorial Hospital, Brewton, AL, p. A17

VICKERY, Tim, Chief Information Officer, St. Mary's Sacred Heart Hospital, Lavonia, GA, p. A162

VICKROY, Joseph, M.D. Medical Director, HEALTHSOUTH Rehabilitation Hospital of Utah, Sandy, UT, p. A664

VICKS, Ray, Senior Vice President, Finance and Chief Financial Officer, The HSC Pediatric Center, Washington, DC, p. A122

VICTORIA, Mario, M.D. Vice President, Medical Affairs, Samaritan Medical Center, Watertown, NY, p. A458

VIDONI–CLARK, Clotilde, R.N. Chief Nurse Executive, Saint Elizabeths Hospital, Washington, DC, p. A122

VIDRINE, Charmaine R., CPA Chief Financial Officer, Acadia General Hospital, Crowley, LA, p. A276

VIEIRA, Jeanie, Chief Executive Officer, Providence Hood River Memorial Hospital, Hood River, OR, p. A526

VIEIRA, Terri, President and Chief Executive Officer, Sebasticook Valley Health, Pittsfield, ME, p. A294

VIELKIND, James, Chief Financial Officer, Little Falls Hospital, Little Falls, NY, p. A441

VIENNEAU, Marie E., FACHE, President and Chief Executive Officer, Mayo Regional Hospital, Dover–Foxcroft, ME, p. A293

VIERLING, Taryn, Chief Nursing Officer, Select Specialty Hospital of Southeast Ohio, Newark, OH, p. A500

VIG, Vibha, Chief of Staff, Merit Health Madison, Canton, MS, p. A356

VIGIL, Carlos, M.D. President Medical Staff, San Antonio Regional Hospital, Upland, CA, p. A97

VIGIL, Kevin, Director Information Systems, Los Alamos Medical Center, Los Alamos, NM, p. A430

VIGILANTE, Sarah, Manager Human Resources, Mammoth Hospital, Mammoth Lakes, CA, p. A75

VIGNERI, Joseph, M.D. Chief Medical Officer, Summit Medical Center, Casper, WY, p. A721

VILANOVA, Lynda, Director Patient Care Services, Shriners Hospitals for Children–Spokane, Spokane, WA, p. A691

VILAR, Ramon J., Administrator, Wilma N. Vazquez Medical Center, Vega Baja, PR, p. A730

VILHAUER, Beverly, Chief Executive Officer, Wishek Community Hospital and Clinics, Wishek, ND, p. A482

VILLA, Alex, Chief Executive Officer, Tennova Healthcare–Clarksville, Clarksville, TN, p. A581

VILLAFUERTE, Herbert, Chief Operating Officer/Chief Nursing Officer, Garfield Medical Center, Monterey Park, CA, p. A78

VILLANI, Travis A., FACHE, Chief Executive Officer and Administrator, Physicians' Hospital in Anadarko, Anadarko, OK, p. A508

VILLANO, Jeremi, M.D. Chief of Staff, Crook County Medical Services District, Sundance, WY, p. A724

VILLANUEVA, Andrew, M.D. Interim Chief Medical Officer, Lahey Hospital & Medical Center, Burlington, Burlington, MA, p. A308

VILLARREAL, Xavier, FACHE, Chief Executive Officer, North Hills Hospital, North Richland Hills, TX, p. A639

VILLARRUZ, Alex, Chief Executive Officer, Healthbridge Children's Hospital, Orange, CA, p. A81

VILLEGAS, Lorraine, Manager Human Resources, Paradise Valley Hospital, National City, CA, p. A79

VILUMS, Karlis, Chief Financial Officer, Broadlawns Medical Center, Des Moines, IA, p. A229

VINAS, Elmo, Director Human Resources, Franklin Foundation Hospital, Franklin, LA, p. A277

VINCENT, Adam, Chief Executive Officer, Mayhill Hospital, Denton, TX, p. A612

VINCENT, Ben, FACHE, Chief Executive Officer, Braxton County Memorial Hospital, Gassaway, WV, p. A696

VINCENT, Cynthia, Vice President Finance and Operations, St. Francis Regional Medical Center, Shakopee, MN, p. A351

VINCENT, David, Director Information Systems, Canonsburg Hospital, Canonsburg, PA, p. A534

VINCENT, Joan M., Vice President Patient Care Services and Chief Nurse Executive, Adventist Healthcare Shady Grove Medical Center, Rockville, MD, p. A303

VINCENT, Larry, Director Human Resources, Delta County Memorial Hospital, Delta, CO, p. A103

VINCENT, Laurence Marie, Chief Nursing Officer, University Hospital and Clinics, Lafayette, LA, p. A281

VINCENT, Mitch, Vice President Organizational Support, Range Regional Health Services, Hibbing, MN, p. A344

VINCENT, Paula, MSN, President and Chief Operating Officer, Novant Health Presbyterian Medical Center, Charlotte, NC, p. A463

VINCENT, Shawn, Interim Chief Operating Officer, Augusta University Medical Center, Augusta, GA, p. A153

VINCENZ, Felix T., Chief Operating Officer, St. Louis Psychiatric Rehabilitation Center, Saint Louis, MO, p. A381

VINCIFORA, Teresa, Chief Operating Officer, Benson Hospital, Benson, AZ, p. A31

VINYARD, Roy G., FACHE, President and Chief Executive Officer, Asante Health System, Medford, OR, p. B12

VIOLETTE, Brenda, M.D. Director Medical Staff, Firelands Regional Health System, Sandusky, OH, p. A502

VIOLI, Ronald L., Chief Executive Officer, Wheeling Hospital, Wheeling, WV, p. A701

VIRDEN, Larkin, Interim Chief Executive Officer, ContinueCARE Hospital at Palmetto Health Baptist, Columbia, SC, p. A564

VIRGEN, Tomas, R.N. Chief Operating Officer, El Centro Regional Medical Center, El Centro, CA, p. A61

VIRGIL, Cindy L., MSN Senior Vice President Patient Care Services, Indiana Regional Medical Center, Indiana, PA, p. A541

VIRJI, Ayaz, M.D. Chief of Staff, Johnson Memorial Health Services, Dawson, MN, p. A341

VIRKLER, Joe, Chief Information Officer, Carthage Area Hospital, Carthage, NY, p. A437

VISAGGIO, Stella, Chief Operating Officer, Hackettstown Medical Center, Hackettstown, NJ, p. A417

VISH, Nancy, R.N., President, Baylor Jack and Jane Hamilton Heart and Vascular Hospital, Dallas, TX, p. A609

VISSERS, Robert, M.D., Chief Executive Officer, Boulder Community Health, Boulder, CO, p. A101

VITAL, Dale, Chief Nursing Officer, Orange Coast Memorial Medical Center, Fountain Valley, CA, p. A63

VITALE–NOLEN, Roberta A., Administrator, Patient Care Services, New Hampshire Hospital, Concord, NH, p. A410

VITALI, Joe, Director Information Technology, Parkside Psychiatric Hospital and Clinic, Tulsa, OK, p. A521

VITALI, Vincent S.
Chief Information Officer, RML Specialty Hospital, Chicago, IL, p. A186
Chief Information Officer, RML Specialty Hospital, Hinsdale, IL, p. A193

VITALIS, Lee Ann, Executive Director Human Resources, St. Croix Regional Medical Center, St. Croix Falls, WI, p. A716

VITIELLO, Jon, Chief Financial Officer, Mercy Hospital Oklahoma City, Oklahoma City, OK, p. A516

VITOLAS, Victor, Acting Chief Information Technology Services, Central Texas Veterans Health Care System, Temple, TX, p. A651

VIVIANO, Paul S., President and Chief Executive Officer, Children's Hospital Los Angeles, Los Angeles, CA, p. A70

VIVIT, Romeo, Chief Surgeon, U. S. Public Health Service Indian Hospital, Rosebud, SD, p. A576

VLAHAVAS, Beth, R.N. Vice President Patient Care Services and Chief Nursing Officer, Mercy Medical Center, Rockville Centre, NY, p. A454

VLARS, Scott, Chief Information Technology Services, Wilmington Veterans Affairs Medical Center, Wilmington, DE, p. A120

VLODARCHYK, Coreen, R.N. Vice President, Patient Care Services and Chief Nursing Officer, Barnes–Jewish Hospital, Saint Louis, MO, p. A379

VLOSICH, Wade, Director, Oklahoma City Veterans Affairs Medical Center, Oklahoma City, OK, p. A517

VOCCA, Lori A., Vice President Human Resources, Providence Regional Medical Center Everett, Everett, WA, p. A684

VOECKS, Barbara, Chief Information Officer, Ortonville Area Health Services, Ortonville, MN, p. A348

VOELKEL, Jill, Chief Nursing Officer, Pinnacle Specialty Hospital, Tulsa, OK, p. A522

VOELKEL, Jonathon, Administrator, Culberson Hospital, Van Horn, TX, p. A655

VOELKER, Justin, Chief Financial Officer, Valley Hospital, Spokane Valley, WA, p. A691

VOELKER, Thomas, M.D. Chief Medical Officer, Aspirus Riverview Hospital and Clinics, Inc., Wisconsin Rapids, WI, p. A719

VOGE, Chris, Chief of Staff, French Hospital Medical Center, San Luis Obispo, CA, p. A92

VOGEL, Clay, Chief Executive Officer, Hamlin Memorial Hospital, Hamlin, TX, p. A622

VOGELSANG, Mark, Director Information Services, Providence Holy Family Hospital, Spokane, WA, p. A691

VOGENTIZ, William, M.D. Medical Director, AnMed Health Rehabilitation Hospital, Anderson, SC, p. A562

VOGT, Dennis, Director Information Technology, Madison Health, London, OH, p. A497

VOGT, Sam, Manager Human Resources, The Hospital at Hebrew Health Care, West Hartford, CT, p. A118

VOHS, Lester, Manager Information Systems, Cass Regional Medical Center, Harrisonville, MO, p. A372

VOIGT, Jordan, Administrator, Genesis Medical Center–Davenport, Davenport, IA, p. A228

VOINCHE, Chris G., Chief Executive Officer, Riverside Hospital of Louisiana, Alexandria, LA, p. A271

VOISELLE, Dana, Director Human Resources and Community Relations, Baptist Medical Center Beaches, Jacksonville Beach, FL, p. A132

VOKOUN, Cory, Chief Nursing Officer, Nevada Regional Medical Center, Nevada, MO, p. A377

VOLANTO, John, Vice President, Chief Operating Officer, Nyack Hospital, Nyack, NY, p. A451

VOLGER, Helen, Director of Information Services, Aspirus Medford Hospital, Medford, WI, p. A710

VOLINSKI, Douglas R., Vice President and Chief Financial Officer, Duncan Regional Hospital, Duncan, OK, p. A510

VOLK, Charles T., M.D. Regional Chief Medical Officer, CHRISTUS Spohn Hospital Corpus Christi Memorial, Corpus Christi, TX, p. A607

VOLKERDING, Elizabeth, Director Workforce Excellence, San Juan Regional Medical Center, Farmington, NM, p. A429

VOLKERT, Brent, Director Information Technology, Ferrell Hospital, Eldorado, IL, p. A189

VOLLER, Kristi, Director of Nursing, Mobridge Regional Hospital, Mobridge, SD, p. A575

VOLLMER, Cyndy, Director Human Resources, Southern Coos Hospital and Health Center, Bandon, OR, p. A524

VOLOCH, Bill, President and Chief Executive Officer, Wesley Medical Center, Wichita, KS, p. A256

VOLPE, Buddy, Director Human Resources, Peterson Regional Medical Center, Kerrville, TX, p. A630

VOLPE, Michele M., Chief Executive Officer, Penn Presbyterian Medical Center, Philadelphia, PA, p. A549

VOLSCH, Joyce, Vice President, Nursing Services, Miller Children's & Women's Hospital Long Beach, Long Beach, CA, p. A70

VON BEHREN, Rachel, Director Financial Services, UnityPoint Health – Jones Regional Medical Center, Anamosa, IA, p. A225

VONACHEN, April, Chief Financial Officer and Vice President Financial Services, Cumberland Medical Center, Crossville, TN, p. A582

VONK, Brandon, Nurse Administrator, LDS Hospital, Salt Lake City, UT, p. A663

VOORHEES, Michael, MS, Executive Director, East Mountain Hospital, Belle Mead, NJ, p. A414

VOSBURGH, Mary M., R.N
Vice President Nursing and Chief Nursing Officer, Arnot Ogden Medical Center, Elmira, NY, p. A438
Vice President Nursing and Chief Nursing Officer, St. Joseph's Hospital, Elmira, NY, p. A438

VOSHELL, Shane, Director Human Resources, Adventist Medical Center–Portland, Portland, OR, p. A529

VOSKAMP, Lynne, R.N. Vice President of Nursing, Capital Region Medical Center, Jefferson City, MO, p. A372

VOSS, Daryle, FACHE, President, Mercy Hospital Ardmore, Ardmore, OK, p. A508

VOSS, Kathy, Director Human Resources, CentraCare Health–Monticello, Monticello, MN, p. A347

VOSS, Robert, Chief Financial Officer, Laredo Specialty Hospital, Laredo, TX, p. A632

VOSS, Wayne M., Chief Executive Officer, Houston Methodist West Hospital, Houston, TX, p. A624

VOSSBERG, Brad, M.D. Chief Rehabilitation, Community Howard Specialty Hospital, Kokomo, IN, p. A216

VOSSLER, Jeffrey W., Chief Financial Officer, Joint Township District Memorial Hospital, Saint Marys, OH, p. A502

VOWELL, Christy, D.O. Chief of Staff, North Mississippi Medical Center–Eupora, Eupora, MS, p. A357

VOZOS, Frank J., FACS, President and Chief Executive Officer, Barnabas Health Behavioral Health Center, Monmouth Medical Center, Southern Campus, Lakewood, NJ, p. A418

VRANA, Daniel A.
Controller, HEALTHSOUTH Harmarville Rehabilitation Hospital, Pittsburgh, PA, p. A550
Area Controller, HEALTHSOUTH Rehabilitation Hospital of Sewickley, Sewickley, PA, p. A554

VRBA, Frank, Chief Information Officer, Annie Jeffrey Memorial County Health Center, Osceola, NE, p. A401

VRBAS, Laken, R.N. Director of Nursing, Dundy County Hospital, Benkelman, NE, p. A394

VREELAND, Matthew, M.D. Chief Medical Officer, FirstHealth Richmond Memorial Hospital, Rockingham, NC, p. A472

VRONKO, Jeremy, Manager, Information Services, Spectrum Health Ludington Hospital, Ludington, MI, p. A329

VROTSOS, Darlene, R.N. Senior Vice President and Chief Nursing Officer, Virginia Hospital Center – Arlington, Arlington, VA, p. A667

VU, Young, Chief Information Officer, Meadville Medical Center, Meadville, PA, p. A544

VUCHAK, Jerry
Vice President Information Systems, Barnes–Jewish Hospital, Saint Louis, MO, p. A379
Vice President Information Systems, Barnes–Jewish West County Hospital, Saint Louis, MO, p. A379

VUKICH, David, M.D. Senior Vice President, Chief Medical Officer and Chief Quality Officer, UF Health Jacksonville, Jacksonville, FL, p. A132

VUKSTA, Jeanne, Chief Financial Officer, Bacharach Institute for Rehabilitation, Pomona, NJ, p. A422

VUTRANO, Frank A., Chief Financial Officer, Wyckoff Heights Medical Center,, NY, p. A450

W

WABLE, Chad W., President and Chief Executive Officer, Saint Mary's Hospital, Waterbury, CT, p. A117

WACHOWIAK, Darrell, Associate Vice President Operations, ProMedica Bay Park Hospital, Oregon, OH, p. A500

WACHTEL, Andrew, Chief Executive Officer, AllianceHealth Blackwell, Blackwell, OK, p. A509

WACK, Mark, Senior Vice President and Chief Financial Officer, Touro Infirmary, New Orleans, LA, p. A285

WADA, Takashi, Interim Director, Santa Barbara County Psychiatric Health Facility, Santa Barbara, CA, p. A93

WADDELL, Kathy, Administrator, Wayne General Hospital, Waynesboro, MS, p. A366

WADDELL, Lesa, Director Human Resources, Marengo Memorial Hospital, Marengo, IA, p. A234

WADE, Bruce, Director Human Resources, Indiana University Health Bedford Hospital, Bedford, IN, p. A206

WADE, RN, BSN,, Cynthia, R.N. Executive Vice President and Chief Operating Officer, LincolnHealth, Damariscotta, ME, p. A292

WADE, Donald Lee, Chief Financial Officer, Goodland Regional Medical Center, Goodland, KS, p. A244

WADE, Donna, Senior Director Human Resources, Comanche County Memorial Hospital, Lawton, OK, p. A513

WADE, Glenn, Director Information Systems, Saint Thomas Highlands Hospital, Sparta, TN, p. A593

WADE, Hong, Chief Financial Officer, Sweeny Community Hospital, Sweeny, TX, p. A651

WADE, Jonathan O., Chief Executive Officer, Jersey Community Hospital, Jerseyville, IL, p. A194

WADE, Karen, Chief Information Officer, U. S. Public Health Service Indian Hospital–Sells, Sells, AZ, p. A39

WADE, Susan, Vice President, Hendrick Health System, Abilene, TX, p. A595

WADEWITZ, Martin, Chief Operations Officer/ Vice President, Operations, Angel Medical Center, Franklin, NC, p. A465

WADLE, Don, Vice President Clinical and Support Services, Portneuf Medical Center, Pocatello, ID, p. A178

WADMAN, Timothy, Chief Executive Officer, SSM Select Rehabilitation Hospital, Richmond Heights, MO, p. A378

WADSWORTH, Barbara A., MSN Chief Nursing Officer, Bryn Mawr Hospital, Bryn Mawr, PA, p. A534

WAFFORD, Marty, Executive Officer of Support and Programs, Chickasaw Nation Medical Center, Ada, OK, p. A508

WAGERS, Rick, Senior Executive Vice President and Chief Financial Officer, Regional One Health, Memphis, TN, p. A589

WAGGENER, Yvonne, Chief Financial Officer, San Bernardino Mountains Community Hospital District, Lake Arrowhead, CA, p. A68

WAGGONER, Jeff, M.D. Chief of Staff, Weisbrod Memorial County Hospital, Eads, CO, p. A104

WAGGONER, Michelle, Chief Executive Officer, Community Memorial Hospital, Hicksville, OH, p. A496

WAGLE, Roberta, Director Human Resources, Pinnacle Specialty Hospital, Tulsa, OK, p. A522

WAGMEISTER, Lee, M.D. President Medical Staff, The Heart Hospital at Deaconess Gateway, Newburgh, IN, p. A220

WAGNER, Dale, Chief Financial Officer, Kindred Hospital–Westminster, Westminster, CA, p. A99

WAGNER, David D., Chief Information Management Service, Veterans Affairs Gulf Coast Veterans Health Care System, Biloxi, MS, p. A355

WAGNER, David S., Chief Executive Officer, Pearland Medical Center, Pearland, TX, p. A640

WAGNER, Elaina, Director Human Resources, Sunnyside Community Hospital and Clinics, Sunnyside, WA, p. A691

WAGNER, Fred, Chief Financial Officer, OSF St. Francis Hospital and Medical Group, Escanaba, MI, p. A323

WAGNER, Gwendolyn Dianne, R.N. Chief Nursing Officer, Mission Community Hospital,, CA, p. A73

WAGNER, Janet, R.N., Chief Executive Officer, Mills–Peninsula Health Services, Burlingame, CA, p. A57

WAGNER, Linda, Chief Financial Officer, Sanford Worthington Medical Center, Worthington, MN, p. A354

WAGNER, Linda S., FACHE, Chief Executive Officer, Seneca Healthcare District, Chester, CA, p. A58

WAGNER, Lynne, R.N. Chief Nursing Officer, Rose Medical Center, Denver, CO, p. A104

WAGNER, Michael, M.D., President and Chief Executive Officer, Tufts Medical Center, Boston, MA, p. A307

WAGNER, Randall J., Chief Operating Officer, Mercy Health Saint Mary's, Grand Rapids, MI, p. A325

WAGNER, Russell R., Executive Vice President and Chief Financial Officer, Holy Redeemer Hospital, Meadowbrook, PA, p. A544

WAGNER, Sarah, Human Resources Officer, Memorial Hospital of Texas County, Guymon, OK, p. A512

WAGNER, Sherrie A., Manager Human Resources, The CORE Institute Specialty Hospital, Phoenix, AZ, p. A37

WAGNER, Sherry, Director Human Resources, Oklahoma Center for Orthopedic and Multi–Specialty Surgery, Oklahoma City, OK, p. A516

WAGNER, Suzie, Director Human Resources, HEALTHSOUTH Rehabilitation Hospital of Alexandria, Alexandria, LA, p. A271

WAGNER, Terry, R.N. Chief Operating Officer, Pocahontas Memorial Hospital, Buckeye, WV, p. A694

WAGNER, Terry, Chief Information Officer, Upstate University Hospital, Syracuse, NY, p. A457

WAGNER, Timothy, M.D. Chief Medical Staff, Yoakum Community Hospital, Yoakum, TX, p. A658

WAGNER, Tom, Interim Vice President Finance, Avera St. Mary's Hospital, Pierre, SD, p. A575

WAGNER, Vanessa, Chief Financial Officer, Lawrence Memorial Hospital, Walnut Ridge, AR, p. A53

WAGNON, LaNell, Director Medical Records, Comanche County Hospital, Coldwater, KS, p. A241

WAGNON, William, Chief Executive Officer, Henrico Doctors' Hospital, Richmond, VA, p. A677

WAGONER, Craig
  Chief Executive Officer, Community Behavioral Health Center, Fresno, CA, p. A63
  Chief Executive Officer, Community Regional Medical Center, Fresno, CA, p. A63

WAGONER, Dean, Director Human Resources, Good Samaritan Hospital, Vincennes, IN, p. A223

WAGONER, Renee, R.N. Director of Nursing, Gove County Medical Center, Quinter, KS, p. A252

WAHAB, Amir J., M.D. Medical Staff President, Abraham Lincoln Memorial Hospital, Lincoln, IL, p. A195

WAHL, Carol R., R.N. Vice President Patient Care Services, CHI Health Good Samaritan, Kearney, NE, p. A397

WAHL, Josephine Sclafani, R.N. VP, Patient Care Services & CNO, Henry Ford Wyandotte Hospital, Wyandotte, MI, p. A337

WAHL, Tony, Chief Executive Officer, Texas Spine & Joint Hospital, Tyler, TX, p. A654

WAHLERS, Brenda, M.D. Chief of Staff, Cole Memorial, Coudersport, PA, p. A536

WAHLMEIER, James E., Administrator and Chief Executive Officer, Kingman Community Hospital, Kingman, KS, p. A246

WAHLUND, Keith, Vice President Human Resources, Essentia Health Fargo, Fargo, ND, p. A478

WAIBEL, David, M.D. Medical Director, Clarks Summit State Hospital, Clarks Summit, PA, p. A535

WAIBEL, Jason, Interim Chief Executive Officer, HEALTHSOUTH Rehabilitation Hospital of Northern Virginia, Aldie, VA, p. A667

WAIDE, Mary Beth, R.N., Chief Executive Officer, Deer's Head Hospital Center, Salisbury, MD, p. A303

WAIN, Matthew, Chief Operating Officer, MUSC Medical Center of Medical University of South Carolina, Charleston, SC, p. A563

WAIND, Mark, Chief Information Officer, Altru Health System, Grand Forks, ND, p. A479

WAITE, Douglas, M.D. Chief Medical Officer, Saint Vincent Hospital, Worcester, MA, p. A316

WAITE, Douglas D.
  Senior Vice President and Chief Financial Officer, Seton Highland Lakes, Burnet, TX, p. A604
  Senior Vice President and Chief Financial Officer, Seton Medical Center Williamson, Round Rock, TX, p. A644
  Chief Financial Officer, Seton Northwest Hospital, Austin, TX, p. A599

WAITES, Alan, Chief Financial Officer, Gove County Medical Center, Quinter, KS, p. A252

WAITES, Cherri, Chief Executive Officer, Cloud County Health Center, Concordia, KS, p. A242

WAJDA, David, Chief Financial Officer, Nazareth Hospital, Philadelphia, PA, p. A549

WAKEFIELD, Brett
  Vice President Human Resources, Gottlieb Memorial Hospital, Melrose Park, IL, p. A196
  Director Human Resources, Thorek Memorial Hospital, Chicago, IL, p. A187

WAKEFIELD, Jeff, CPA Chief Financial Officer, Marion General Hospital, Marion, IN, p. A218

WAKEFIELD, Mamie
  Vice President Finance and Chief Financial Officer, Emma Pendleton Bradley Hospital, East Providence, RI, p. A560
  Chief Financial Officer, Miriam Hospital, Providence, RI, p. A560
  Senior Vice President and Chief Financial Officer, Rhode Island Hospital, Providence, RI, p. A561

WAKEMAN, Daniel L., President, ProMedica St. Luke's Hospital, Maumee, OH, p. A498

WAKIM, Tina, Vice President Information, Northside Hospital, Atlanta, GA, p. A152

WAKULCHIK, Grace, R.N. Chief Operating Officer, Akron Children's Hospital, Akron, OH, p. A483

WALAS, Steven, Chief Executive Officer, HEALTHSOUTH Chesapeake Rehabilitation Hospital, Salisbury, MD, p. A303

WALCEK, Peter, Vice President Finance, Wentworth–Douglass Hospital, Dover, NH, p. A410

WALCH, Tina, M.D. Medical Director, South Oaks Hospital, Amityville, NY, p. A433

WALCZYK–JOERS, Barbara, President and Chief Executive Officer, Gillette Children's Specialty Healthcare, Saint Paul, MN, p. A350

WALD, Barry, Chief Financial Officer, Wilkes Regional Medical Center, North Wilkesboro, NC, p. A471

WALDBART, Andy, Department Manager, Heart of the Rockies Regional Medical Center, Salida, CO, p. A110

WALDBILLIG, Karla, Director Human Resources, UnityPoint Health – Finley Hospital, Dubuque, IA, p. A230

WALDBILLIG, Kurt, Chief Executive Officer, Swift County–Benson Hospital, Benson, MN, p. A339

WALDEN, Anita, Vice President and Chief Nursing Officer, Decatur Morgan Hospital, Decatur, AL, p. A18

WALDERA, John, Director Information Technology, Gundersen Tri–County Hospital and Clinics, Whitehall, WI, p. A719

WALDO, Bruce
  Chief Executive Officer, Aurora Behavioral Health System East, Tempe, AZ, p. A40
  Chief Executive Officer, Aurora Behavioral Health System West, Glendale, AZ, p. A33

WALDO, Gail, Director Information Technology, Rockdale Medical Center, Conyers, GA, p. A157

WALDOW, Dee, Chief Financial Officer, Palo Pinto General Hospital, Mineral Wells, TX, p. A637

WALDRON, Michele, Senior Vice President and Chief Financial Officer, Valley Children's Healthcare, Madera, CA, p. A75

WALDRON, Ray, Director Information Technology, Gordon Memorial Hospital, Gordon, NE, p. A396

WALDRON, Sheila, Finance Manager, Providence Milwaukie Hospital, Milwaukie, OR, p. A528

WALDRON, Vincent John, M.D. President Medical Staff, Indiana University Health Paoli Hospital, Paoli, IN, p. A220

WALDROP, Catherine M., Administrator, Sterlington Rehabilitation Hospital, Bastrop, LA, p. A272

WALDROP, Cathy, Director, Hospital Nursing Services, North Mississippi Medical Center–Pontotoc, Pontotoc, MS, p. A364

WALDRUM, Michael, M.D., Chief Executive Officer, Vidant Health, Greenville, NC, p. B152

WALI, Jyotika, M.D. Chief of Staff, Kindred Hospital–Brea, Brea, CA, p. A57

WALIGURA, R. Curtis, D.O. Vice President Medical Affairs, Chief Medical Officer, UPMC McKeesport, McKeesport, PA, p. A544

WALKENHORST, Debbie G.
  Network Vice President, SSM Cardinal Glennon Children's Medical Center, Saint Louis, MO, p. A381
  System Vice President Talent Management, SSM St. Joseph Health Center, Saint Charles, MO, p. A379

WALKER, Alene, Director Human Resources, Quincy Valley Medical Center, Quincy, WA, p. A688

WALKER, Alexander J., Executive Vice President Operations and Strategic Development, Catholic Medical Center, Manchester, NH, p. A412

WALKER, Amy, Chief Nursing Officer, Delta Regional Medical Center, Greenville, MS, p. A358

WALKER, Angela, Manager Human Resources, Aspire Hospital, Conroe, TX, p. A607

WALKER, Angela, M.D. Medical Director, HEALTHSOUTH Rehabilitation Hospital, Albuquerque, NM, p. A427

WALKER, Annette
  Director, Atlanta Veterans Affairs Medical Center, Decatur, GA, p. A158
  Acting Medical Center Director, Jesse Brown Veterans Affairs Medical Center, Chicago, IL, p. A184
  Associate Director, John D. Dingell Veterans Affairs Medical Center, Detroit, MI, p. A322

WALKER, Beth, Chief Information Officer, Emanuel Medical Center, Turlock, CA, p. A97

WALKER, Beth, R.N., President, FirstHealth Montgomery Memorial Hospital, Troy, NC, p. A474

WALKER, C. O., M.D. Chief of Staff, Donalsonville Hospital, Donalsonville, GA, p. A158

WALKER, Candace, Chief Financial Officer, East Central Regional Hospital, Augusta, GA, p. A153

WALKER, Carol, Chief Financial Officer, Oklahoma Heart Hospital, Oklahoma City, OK, p. A517

WALKER, Cass
  Vice President Administrative & Support Services, Franklin Regional Hospital, Franklin, NH, p. A411
  Vice President Administrative & Support Services, Lakes Region General Hospital, Laconia, NH, p. A411

WALKER, Charity, Controller and Regional Business Officer Manager, Greenwood Regional Rehabilitation Hospital, Greenwood, SC, p. A567

WALKER, Charles, Director Information Technology, Kimball Health Services, Kimball, NE, p. A397

WALKER, Cheri, R.N. Chief Nursing Officer, King's Daughters Medical Center, Brookhaven, MS, p. A356

WALKER, Christopher, Chief Nursing Officer, Sharp Coronado Hospital and Healthcare Center, Coronado, CA, p. A59

WALKER, Codie, Chief Financial Officer, Salem Veterans Affairs Medical Center, Salem, VA, p. A678

WALKER, Dan, Chief Nursing Officer, Lincoln Community Hospital and Nursing Home, Hugo, CO, p. A107

WALKER, David M., M.D., Medical Center Director, G.V. (Sonny) Montgomery Veterans Affairs Medical Center, Jackson, MS, p. A359

WALKER, Donna, Chief Nurse Executive, Weeks Medical Center, Lancaster, NH, p. A411

WALKER, Durwin, M.D. Chief Medical Officer, AMG Specialty Hospital–Denham Springs, Denham Springs, LA, p. A276

WALKER, Gale N., President and Chief Executive Officer, Avera St. Benedict Health Center, Parkston, SD, p. A575

WALKER, Gregory J., Chief Executive Officer, Wentworth–Douglass Hospital, Dover, NH, p. A410

WALKER, Imani, M.D. Medical Director, Gateways Hospital and Mental Health Center, Los Angeles, CA, p. A71

WALKER, Jan
  Director Human Resources, Centra Lynchburg General Hospital, Lynchburg, VA, p. A672
  Director Human Resources, Glenwood Regional Medical Center, West Monroe, LA, p. A289

WALKER, Janice L., R.N
  Chief Operating Officer, Baylor All Saints Medical Center at Fort Worth, Fort Worth, TX, p. A617
  Chief Nursing Officer and Chief Operating Officer, Baylor Medical Center at Garland, Garland, TX, p. A620

WALKER, Jeff, Chief Operating Officer, James Cancer Hospital and Solove Research Institute, Columbus, OH, p. A490

WALKER, Jeremy Tyler, Vice President and Chief Financial Officer, Hendrick Health System, Abilene, TX, p. A595

WALKER, Kathy, Chief Financial Officer, Trinity Hospital, Weaverville, CA, p. A99

WALKER, Kimberly, Director of Human Resources, Northcrest Medical Center, Springfield, TN, p. A593

WALKER, Kristie, Director of Human Resources, Wythe County Community Hospital, Wytheville, VA, p. A681

WALKER, LeRoy, Vice President Human Resources, DeKalb Medical at North Decatur, Decatur, GA, p. A158

WALKER, Lynette, R.N. Vice President Human Resources, Baptist Health Lexington, Lexington, KY, p. A262

WALKER, Marilyn, R.N. Chief Nursing Officer, Houston County Medical Center, Crockett, TX, p. A608

WALKER, Mary, Manager Information Technology, HEALTHSOUTH Rehabilitation Hospital–Wichita Falls, Wichita Falls, TX, p. A657

WALKER, Matthew, Chief Executive Officer and Administrator, William Bee Ririe Hospital, Ely, NV, p. A404

WALKER, Melissa, CPA Chief Financial Officer, North Texas Medical Center, Gainesville, TX, p. A620

WALKER, Nicole, Human Resource Officer, Cavalier County Memorial Hospital and Clinics, Langdon, ND, p. A480

WALKER, Pandora, Director, Human Resources, Beaumont Hospital – Grosse Pointe, Grosse Pointe, MI, p. A326

WALKER, Randy
  Chief Nursing Officer, Hillcrest Hospital Claremore, Claremore, OK, p. A510
  Vice President, Methodist Dallas Medical Center, Dallas, TX, p. A610
  Director Nursing Services, State Hospital South, Blackfoot, ID, p. A174

WALKER, Renee, Director Human Resources, Bastrop Rehabilitation Hospital, Monroe, LA, p. A283

WALKER, Robert, M.D. Medical Director, HEALTHSOUTH Southern Hills Rehabilitation Hospital, Princeton, WV, p. A699

WALKER, Robert L., President and Chief Executive Officer, Texas Scottish Rite Hospital for Children, Dallas, TX, p. A611

WALKER, Robin, Chief Nursing Officer, Field Memorial Community Hospital, Centreville, MS, p. A356

WALKER, Scott, Chief Financial Officer, Southeastern Regional Medical Center, Newnan, GA, p. A164

WALKER, Tim, Manager Information Services, PeaceHealth Ketchikan Medical Center, Ketchikan, AK, p. A29

WALKER, Todd
  Campus President, Baptist Easley Hospital, Easley, SC, p. A565
  Director Operations, Greenville Health System – Laurens County Memorial Hospital, Clinton, SC, p. A563

WALKER, Traci, Chief Executive Officer, Atoka County Medical Center, Atoka, OK, p. A509

WALKER, Troy, Director Finance, St. Clare Hospital, Baraboo, WI, p. A702

WALKER, Tyree, Chief Human Resources Officer, Vidant Medical Center, Greenville, NC, p. A466

WALKER, Virginia, Vice President Nursing Services and Chief Nursing Officer, Kuakini Medical Center, Honolulu, HI, p. A170

WALKER Jr., William J., Chief Executive Officer, Memorial Hospital and Manor, Bainbridge, GA, p. A154

WALKUP, Jessica, Controller, HEALTHSOUTH Western Hills Regional Rehabilitation Hospital, Parkersburg, WV, p. A699

WALL, Daniel J., President and Chief Executive Officer, Emma Pendleton Bradley Hospital, East Providence, RI, p. A560

WALL, Doug, M.D. Vice President Medical Affairs, Novant Health UVA Health System Prince William Medical Center, Manassas, VA, p. A673

WALL, Kathryn S.
  Executive Vice President, Human Resources and Organizational Development, Mary Washington Hospital, Fredericksburg, VA, p. A670
  Executive Vice President Human Resources and Organizational Development, Stafford Hospital, Stafford, VA, p. A679

WALL, Lorraine, Chief Nursing Officer, Olympic Medical Center, Port Angeles, WA, p. A688

WALLACE, Arthur, Chief Financial Officer, Broward Health Coral Springs, Coral Springs, FL, p. A126

WALLACE, Brad, Director Information Services, Grays Harbor Community Hospital, Aberdeen, WA, p. A682

WALLACE, Carolyn, Director Human Resources, Connecticut Mental Health Center, New Haven, CT, p. A116

WALLACE, Cynthia, M.D. Medical Director, Vibra Specialty Hospital of Portland, Portland, OR, p. A530

WALLACE, David, Chief Executive Officer, AllianceHealth Woodward, Woodward, OK, p. A523

WALLACE, Dianne, County Information Manager, Douglas County Community Mental Health Center, Omaha, NE, p. A400

WALLACE, Donna Geiken, Chief Operating Officer and Chief Financial Officer, CHRISTUS Mother Frances Hospital – Sulphur Springs, Sulphur Springs, TX, p. A651

WALLACE, Glenn, Chief Executive Officer, Medical Center Alliance, Fort Worth, TX, p. A618

WALLACE, Jennifer, Chief Executive Officer, AMG Specialty Hospital–Greenwood, Greenwood, MS, p. A358

WALLACE, Kelly, Senior Vice President and Chief Financial Officer, Seattle Children's Hospital, Seattle, WA, p. A689

WALLACE, Kent, Chief Operating Officer, Kindred Healthcare, Louisville, KY, p. B76

WALLACE, Kristina, R.N. Chief Operating Officer, OU Medical Center, Oklahoma City, OK, p. A517

WALLACE, Lisa, R.N. Chief Nursing Officer, Redmond Regional Medical Center, Rome, GA, p. A165

WALLACE, Mark, Chief Financial Officer, Cumberland Hall Hospital, Hopkinsville, KY, p. A261

WALLACE, Mark A., FACHE, President and Chief Executive Officer, Texas Children's Hospital, Houston, TX, p. A626

WALLACE, Mark T., Director Human Resources, Lodi Memorial Hospital, Lodi, CA, p. A68

WALLACE, Martha, Administrator, California Mens Colony Correctional Treatment Center, San Luis Obispo, CA, p. A92

WALLACE, Melanie, Manager Human Resources, Sutter Tracy Community Hospital, Tracy, CA, p. A96

WALLACE, Michael S., President and Chief Executive Officer, Fort HealthCare, Fort Atkinson, WI, p. A705

WALLACE, Nancy
  Vice President Human Resources, CHI Health Bergan Mercy, Omaha, NE, p. A399
  Vice President Human Resources, CHI Health Immanuel, Omaha, NE, p. A400
  Division Senior Vice President, Chief Human Resource Officer, CHI Health Lakeside, Omaha, NE, p. A400
  Senior Vice President Human Resources, CHI Health Mercy Council Bluffs, Council Bluffs, IA, p. A228
  Division Senior Vice President, Chief Human Resource Officer, CHI Health Midlands, Papillion, NE, p. A401
  Vice President Human Resources, CHI Health, CHI Health Saint Francis, Grand Island, NE, p. A396
  Vice President Human Resources, CHI Health Schuyler, Schuyler, NE, p. A402
  Senior Vice President, Chief Human Resources Officer, CHI Health St Elizabeth, Lincoln, NE, p. A398

WALLACE, Patrick L., Administrator, East Texas Medical Center Athens, Athens, TX, p. A598

WALLACE, Penny, Chief Financial Officer, Guadalupe Regional Medical Center, Seguin, TX, p. A648

WALLACE, Richard V., Chief Financial Officer, Houston County Medical Center, Crockett, TX, p. A608

WALLACE, Tabatha, Director Human Resources, Bayfront Health Dade City, Dade City, FL, p. A126

WALLACE-MOORE, Patrice, Chief Executive Officer and Executive Director, Arms Acres, Carmel, NY, p. A436

WALLEN, Carla, Manager Human Resources, Cass Regional Medical Center, Harrisonville, MO, p. A372

WALLENTINE, Jeffrey, Chief of Staff, Mountain View Hospital, Payson, UT, p. A662

WALLER, Ernie, Director Information Technology, Ed Fraser Memorial Hospital and Baker Community Health Center, MacClenny, FL, p. A135

WALLER, Kenneth, Fiscal Administrator, Deer's Head Hospital Center, Salisbury, MD, p. A303

WALLER, Patricia A., R.N. Assistant Administrator Patient Care Services, Piedmont Newton Hospital, Covington, GA, p. A157

WALLER, Raymond A., Director, Brighton Center for Recovery, Brighton, MI, p. A319

WALLINE, Linda K., R.N. Vice President Nursing, Columbus Community Hospital, Columbus, NE, p. A395

WALLING, Vernon, M.D. Executive Medical Director, West Oaks Hospital, Houston, TX, p. A627

WALLINGA, Joel, Chief Financial Officer, Veterans Affairs Ann Arbor Healthcare System, Ann Arbor, MI, p. A318

WALLINGA, Melvin, M.D. Medical Director, St. Michael's Hospital Avera, Tyndall, SD, p. A577

WALLIS, Carla, Director Human Resources, North Ottawa Community Hospital, Grand Haven, MI, p. A324

WALLIS, Pam B., MSN Vice President Nursing Services, Magnolia Regional Health Center, Corinth, MS, p. A357

WALLMAN, Gerald H., Administrator, West Covina Medical Center, West Covina, CA, p. A99

WALLS, Craig, M.D. Chief Medical Officer, Natividad Medical Center, Salinas, CA, p. A87

WALLS, Martha Delaney, R.N. Chief Nursing Officer, Crestwood Medical Center, Huntsville, AL, p. A21

WALLS, Randy, Manager Information Services, Fairbanks, Indianapolis, IN, p. A213

WALLS, Ron, M.D. Executive Vice President and COO, Brigham and Women's Hospital, Boston, MA, p. A306

WALLSCHLAEGER, Erich, Chief Financial Officer, Cedar Park Regional Medical Center, Cedar Park, TX, p. A605

WALMSLEY III, George J., CPA, President and Chief Executive Officer, North Philadelphia Health System, Philadelphia, PA, p. A549

WALMUS, Adam C., FACHE, Director, Michael E. DeBakey Veterans Affairs Medical Center, Houston, TX, p. A626

WALRATH, Andrea, Chief Operating Officer, Forest Health Medical Center, Ypsilanti, MI, p. A337

WALRAVEN, Jeff, Chief Executive Officer, Lindsay Municipal Hospital, Lindsay, OK, p. A514

WALSER, Bill, Coordinator Technology, Cameron Regional Medical Center, Cameron, MO, p. A368

WALSH, Brad, M.D. Chief of Staff, Ashley County Medical Center, Crossett, AR, p. A44

WALSH, Catherine
  Interim Chief Nursing Officer, Mercy Allen Hospital, Oberlin, OH, p. A500
  Interim Nursing Executive, Mercy Regional Medical Center, Lorain, OH, p. A497

WALSH, Cynthia, Chief Nursing Officer, Grays Harbor Community Hospital, Aberdeen, WA, p. A682

WALSH, Dan, Chief Information Officer, Aria – Jefferson Health, Philadelphia, PA, p. A547

WALSH, Gerard W., Chief Executive Officer, St. John's Episcopal Hospital–South Shore,, NY, p. A450

WALSH, John
  Chief Executive Officer, Trumbull Memorial Hospital, Warren, OH, p. A505
  Chief Fiscal Services, Veterans Affairs Hudson Valley Health Care System, Montrose, NY, p. A443

WALSH, Kate, M.P.H., President and Chief Executive Officer, Boston Medical Center, Boston, MA, p. A306

WALSH, Ken, Chief Financial Officer, St. Luke's Medical Center, Phoenix, AZ, p. A37

WALSH, Kim, Chief Nursing Officer, Signature Healthcare Brockton Hospital, Brockton, MA, p. A308

WALSH, Len, Executive Vice President and Chief Operating Officer, St. Barnabas Hospital,, NY, p. A449

WALSH, Linda, R.N. Vice President Chief Nursing Executive, Bayshore Community Hospital, Holmdel, NJ, p. A418

WALSH, Marcia S., M.P.H. Chief Operating Officer, Community HealthCare System, Onaga, KS, p. A250

WALSH, Marilyn J., Vice President Human Resources, Kent County Memorial Hospital, Warwick, RI, p. A561

WALSH, Mary, R.N
  Vice President Patient Care Services and Chief Nursing Officer, Mount Sinai Beth Israel, New York, NY, p. A446
  Vice President Patient Care Services and Chief Nursing Officer, Mount Sinai St. Luke's – Roosevelt, New York, NY, p. A446

WALSH, Mary Beth, M.D., Chief Executive Officer, Burke Rehabilitation Hospital, White Plains, NY, p. A459

WALSH, Michael
  Senior Vice President Finance and Chief Financial Officer, Abington Hospital, Abington, PA, p. A532
  Senior Vice President Finance and Chief Financial Officer, Abington–Lansdale Hospital Jefferson Health, Lansdale, PA, p. A542

WALSH, Michele M., Chief Nursing Officer, St. Mary's Healthcare, Amsterdam, NY, p. A434

WALSH, William P., Senior Vice President Hospital Affairs and Managing Director, SUNY Downstate Medical Center University Hospital,, NY, p. A450

WALSTON, John, Chief Information Officer, Southern Arizona Veterans Affairs Health Care System, Tucson, AZ, p. A41

WALTER, Gayle, Director of Nursing, Thomas B. Finan Center, Cumberland, MD, p. A300

WALTER, Melissa, Director Human Resources, Clarinda Regional Health Center, Clarinda, IA, p. A227

WALTER, Stephen
Senior Vice President and Chief Financial Officer, Community Behavioral Health Center, Fresno, CA, p. A63
Senior Vice President and Chief Financial Officer, Community Regional Medical Center, Fresno, CA, p. A63
WALTERS, Anthony, Chief Executive Officer, Valley Behavioral Health System, Barling, AR, p. A43
WALTERS, Cindy, Chief Executive Officer, Acadia–St. Landry Hospital, Church Point, LA, p. A274
WALTERS, Jane, Director of Nursing, Mendota Mental Health Institute, Madison, WI, p. A708
WALTERS, Janice, Executive Director, Revenue Systems and Information Technology, Cole Memorial, Coudersport, PA, p. A536
WALTERS, Julie, Chief Nursing Officer, Hillsdale Hospital, Hillsdale, MI, p. A326
WALTERS, Kevin, Chief Financial Officer, St. Rose Dominican Hospitals – Rose de Lima Campus, Henderson, NV, p. A405
WALTERS, Leah, R.N. Director of Nursing, Mountain Valley Regional Rehabilitation Hospital, Prescott Valley, AZ, p. A38
WALTERS, Leslie, MSN Chief Nursing Officer, Clarion Hospital, Clarion, PA, p. A535
WALTERS, Patrick, Chief Executive Officer, Inova Loudoun Hospital, Leesburg, VA, p. A672
WALTERS, Todd, Director of UHC Information Technology Services, University Health Conway, Monroe, LA, p. A284
WALTHALL, Wayne, Vice President and Chief Financial Officer, St. John Medical Center, Tulsa, OK, p. A522
WALTHER, Diane, Controller, Henry County Hospital, Napoleon, OH, p. A500
WALTON, Amy E., M.D. Chief Medical Officer, Seton Shoal Creek Hospital, Austin, TX, p. A599
WALTON, Carlyle L. E., FACHE,
Chief Executive Officer, Metroplex Adventist Hospital, Killeen, TX, p. A630
Chief Executive Officer, Rollins–Brook Community Hospital, Lampasas, TX, p. A632
WALTON, Dawn, Chief Financial Officer, Children's of Alabama, Birmingham, AL, p. A16
WALTON, Gary, M.D. Chief Medical Officer, Hill Hospital of Sumter County, York, AL, p. A27
WALTON, Georgian, Director Human Resources, Elbert Memorial Hospital, Elberton, GA, p. A159
WALTON, Greg, Chief Information Officer, El Camino Hospital, Mountain View, CA, p. A78
WALTON, Robert M., Healthcare System Director, South Texas Veterans Health Care System, San Antonio, TX, p. A647
WALTZ, Brenda M., FACHE, Chief Executive Officer, Garden Park Medical Center, Gulfport, MS, p. A358
WALTZ, Dan, Vice President and Chief Information Officer, MidMichigan Medical Center–Gladwin, Gladwin, MI, p. A324
WALZ, Rachel A., Director Patient Care, CentraCare Health–Paynesville, Paynesville, MN, p. A348
WAMPLER, Beth A., R.N. Chief Nursing Officer, Fayette Regional Health System, Connersville, IN, p. A208
WAMPLER, Janice, Controller and Chief Information Technology Officer, Monroe Hospital, Bloomfield, IN, p. A207
WAMPLER, Tamara, Chief Nursing Executive, Claremore Indian Hospital, Claremore, OK, p. A510
WAMSLEY, Marie, Chief Financial Officer, Memorial Hospital of Lafayette County, Darlington, WI, p. A704
WANG, Ted, Chief Financial Officer, Providence Tarzana Medical Center,, CA, p. A74
WANG, William Norberto, M.D. Chief Operating Officer, NYC Health + Hospitals / Metropolitan, New York, NY, p. A448
WANG, MD, Shu–Ming, Vice President Medical Affairs, CHI Health Saint Francis, Grand Island, NE, p. A396
WANGER, David S., Chief Executive Officer, Newman Memorial Hospital, Shattuck, OK, p. A519
WANGSMO, Gary L., Chief Financial Officer, Mee Memorial Hospital, King City, CA, p. A67
WANGSNESS, Erik, President, Washington Adventist Hospital, Takoma Park, MD, p. A304
WANLY, Bahaa, Interim Chief Operating Officer, Salem Hospital, Salem, OR, p. A530
WANNER, David
Director Information Technology, Kenmare Community Hospital, Kenmare, ND, p. A480
Chief Information Officer, Trinity Health, Minot, ND, p. A481
WANNER, Joe, Chief Financial Officer, Wallowa Memorial Hospital, Enterprise, OR, p. A525
WANTLAND, Margaret, Chief Financial Officer, Kindred Hospital–Albuquerque, Albuquerque, NM, p. A427
WAPPELHORST, Andrea, Chief Nursing Officer, TOPS Surgical Specialty Hospital, Houston, TX, p. A627
WARBURTON, John B., Chief Executive Officer, Red River Hospital, LLC, Wichita Falls, TX, p. A657
WARD, Brook, Executive Vice President, Washington Hospital, Washington, PA, p. A556

WARD, Celia F., Controller and Chief Financial Officer, Doctors Memorial Hospital, Bonifay, FL, p. A124
WARD, Charlotte, Entity Financial Officer, Texas Health Harris Methodist Hospital Southwest Fort Worth, Fort Worth, TX, p. A619
WARD, Chris
Chief Nursing Officer, Comanche County Memorial Hospital, Lawton, OK, p. A513
Director Management Information Systems, Dorminy Medical Center, Fitzgerald, GA, p. A159
WARD, David M., Chief Financial Officer and Chief Acquisition Officer, Cabell Huntington Hospital, Huntington, WV, p. A696
WARD, Dillon, Management Information Systems Specialist, Tennova Healthcare–LaFollette Medical Center, La Follette, TN, p. A586
WARD, Elizabeth S., Chief Financial Officer, University of Texas Southwestern Medical Center, Dallas, TX, p. A612
WARD, Greg, Vice President Support and Ancillary Services, Copley Hospital, Morrisville, VT, p. A665
WARD, Jeffery, Director Human Resources, Cedar Park Regional Medical Center, Cedar Park, TX, p. A605
WARD, Julie, Vice President Finance, Northeastern Health System, Tahlequah, OK, p. A520
WARD, Julie, MSN Chief Nursing Officer, St. Joseph's Hospital and Medical Center, Phoenix, AZ, p. A37
WARD, Julie R., MSN Vice President Patient Care Services, Hutchinson Regional Medical Center, Hutchinson, KS, p. A245
WARD, Kevin, Chief Operating Officer, Jewish Home of San Francisco, San Francisco, CA, p. A90
WARD, Kevin J., Vice President and Chief Financial Officer, New York–Presbyterian/Queens, NY, p. A447
WARD, Lesli, Vice President Human Resources, UF Health Jacksonville, Jacksonville, FL, p. A132
WARD, Lisa, Director Management Information Systems, Columbus Regional Healthcare System, Whiteville, NC, p. A475
WARD, Louis James, Interim Chief Executive Officer, Mayers Memorial Hospital District, Fall River Mills, CA, p. A62
WARD, Louise, Vice President Financial and Support Services, Roane General Hospital, Spencer, WV, p. A700
WARD, Mark, M.D. Chief of Staff, Roundup Memorial Healthcare, Roundup, MT, p. A390
WARD, Michael
Director Information Services, Anderson Hospital, Maryville, IL, p. A195
Chief Executive Officer, HEALTHSOUTH Rehabilitation Hospital–Las Vegas, Las Vegas, NV, p. A406
WARD, Mike
Covenant Health, Senior Vice President and Chief Information Officer, Methodist Medical Center of Oak Ridge, Oak Ridge, TN, p. A592
Chief Information Officer, Morristown–Hamblen Healthcare System, Morristown, TN, p. A590
Senior Vice President Chief Information Officer, Roane Medical Center, Harriman, TN, p. A583
WARD, Rhonda, R.N. Chief Nursing Officer, Littleton Adventist Hospital, Littleton, CO, p. A108
WARD, Robert, Chief Executive Officer, Select Rehabilitation Hospital of San Antonio, San Antonio, TX, p. A647
WARD, Rory
Chief Financial Officer, Atoka County Medical Center, Atoka, OK, p. A509
Chief Financial Officer, Pushmataha Hospital & Home Health, Antlers, OK, p. A508
WARD, Sandy, Administrator, Johnson County Healthcare Center, Buffalo, WY, p. A721
WARD, Silva, Director Human Resources, Center for Behavioral Medicine, Kansas City, MO, p. A373
WARD, Stormy, Chief Nurse Executive, Big Spring State Hospital, Big Spring, TX, p. A602
WARD, Virginia, Human Resources Officer, Robert E. Bush Naval Hospital, Twentynine Palms, CA, p. A97
WARD, Wendy, Director Human Resources, Mercy Hospital El Reno, El Reno, OK, p. A511
WARDA, Paul, Chief Financial Officer, MedStar Georgetown University Hospital, Washington, DC, p. A121
WARDELL, Patrick R., Chief Executive Officer, Cambridge Health Alliance, Cambridge, MA, p. A308
WARDEN, Michael S., Senior Vice President Information Technology, Banner – University Medical Center Phoenix, Phoenix, AZ, p. A36
WARDROP, Daniel, M.D. Medical Director, Heart of the Rockies Regional Medical Center, Salida, CO, p. A110
WARE, Bobbie K., R.N. Vice President Patient Care and Chief Nursing Officer, Mississippi Baptist Medical Center, Jackson, MS, p. A360
WARE, Bobbie K., FACHE, Chief Executive Officer and Chief Nursing Officer, Select Specialty Hospital – Belhaven, Jackson, MS, p. A360

WARE, Dana, M.D. Chief of Staff, Seneca Healthcare District, Chester, CA, p. A58
WARE, John, Director of Human Resources, Venice Regional Bayfront Health, Venice, FL, p. A149
WARE, Judy
Director Human Resources, Johnson Memorial Hospital, Franklin, IN, p. A211
Chief Financial Officer, Putnam General Hospital, Eatonton, GA, p. A159
WARE, Karen, Director Human Resources, AllianceHealth Blackwell, Blackwell, OK, p. A509
WARE, Kathy, Director of Nursing, Daniels Memorial Healthcare Center, Scobey, MT, p. A390
WARE, Risa, Commander, Irwin Army Community Hospital, Junction City, KS, p. A246
WAREING, Colleen, Vice President Patient Care Services, Atlantic General Hospital, Berlin, MD, p. A298
WARFIELD, William, Chief Human Resources Management, Veterans Affairs Boston Healthcare System, Boston, MA, p. A307
WARING, Lance, Director Human Resources, Texas Health Harris Methodist Hospital Azle, Azle, TX, p. A600
WARLICK, Mark, Chief Information Officer, Memorial Hospital of South Bend, South Bend, IN, p. A222
WARLITNER, Todd, Vice President Business Operations, The Outer Banks Hospital, Nags Head, NC, p. A470
WARM, Ira, Senior Vice President Human Resources, Brooklyn Hospital Center,, NY, p. A444
WARMAN, Debbie, Vice President Human Resources, MetroHealth Medical Center, Cleveland, OH, p. A489
WARMAN Jr., Harold C., FACHE, President and Chief Executive Officer, Highlands Regional Medical Center, Prestonsburg, KY, p. A268
WARMBOLD, Steve, Director Information Management Service Line, Veterans Affairs St. Louis Health Care System, Saint Louis, MO, p. A381
WARMERDAM, David, Chief Financial Officer, Brynn Marr Hospital, Jacksonville, NC, p. A467
WARNER, Grady, Director of Information Technology, Burgess Health Center, Onawa, IA, p. A235
WARNER, John, M.D., Chief Executive Officer, University of Texas Southwestern Medical Center, Dallas, TX, p. A612
WARNER, Norma, Area Director Health Information Management, Kindred Hospital–Fort Worth, Fort Worth, TX, p. A618
WARNER, Petra, Interim Chief of Staff, Shriners Hospitals for Children–Cincinnati Burns Hospital, Cincinnati, OH, p. A488
WARNER–PACHECO, Paula, Chief Human Resources, Rio Grande Hospital, Del Norte, CO, p. A103
WARNING, Kendra, Chief Financial Officer, Davis County Hospital, Bloomfield, IA, p. A226
WARNOCK, Dawn, Director Medical Records, Taylor Regional Hospital, Hawkinsville, GA, p. A160
WARREN, Charlene, R.N. Chief Nursing Officer, Greenbrier Valley Medical Center, Ronceverte, WV, p. A700
WARREN, Danny, Chief Financial Officer, Lake Wales Medical Center, Lake Wales, FL, p. A133
WARREN, Denise Wilder, R.N
Executive Vice President and Chief Operating Officer, WakeMed Cary Hospital, Cary, NC, p. A462
Executive Vice President and Chief Operating Officer, WakeMed Raleigh Campus, Raleigh, NC, p. A472
WARREN, Gidgett, Director of Nursing, T.J. Health Columbia, Columbia, KY, p. A258
WARREN, Jana, Human Resources Business Partner, Piedmont Henry Hospital, Stockbridge, GA, p. A167
WARREN, Jennifer, Chief Financial Officer, Purcell Municipal Hospital, Purcell, OK, p. A519
WARREN, Karen, Fiscal Officer, Porterville Developmental Center, Porterville, CA, p. A83
WARREN, Linda, Director Human Resources, Cogdell Memorial Hospital, Snyder, TX, p. A649
WARREN, Michael D., President, Good Samaritan Regional Health Center, Mount Vernon, IL, p. A197
WARREN, Sarah, Coordinator Human Resources, Hickory Trail Hospital, Desoto, TX, p. A613
WARREN, Seth, President and Chief Executive Officer, Riverview Health, Noblesville, IN, p. A220
WARREN, Shanna, Director Human Resources, Medical Center of Plano, Plano, TX, p. A641
WARREN Jr., Wm. Michael, President and Chief Executive Officer, Children's of Alabama, Birmingham, AL, p. A16
WARRENER, Gerald, M.D. Chief Medical Officer, Parkview Noble Hospital, Kendallville, IN, p. A215
WARRINER, Ken, Market Chief Financial Officer, Physicians Regional – Pine Ridge, Naples, FL, p. A138
WARRINGTON, Sr., James E., M.D. Chief of Staff, Quitman County Hospital, Marks, MS, p. A361
WARSHAW, Leah, Coordinator Human Resources, Select Specialty Hospital–Ann Arbor, Ypsilanti, MI, p. A337

WARSING, Tracy, M.D. Site Leader Chief of Staff, Mayo Clinic Health System – Franciscan Healthcare in Sparta, Sparta, WI, p. A716

WARTENBERG, Daniel, M.P.H., Chief Executive Officer, Southwest Connecticut Mental Health System, Bridgeport, CT, p. A113

WAS, Gregory J., CPA, Chief Executive Officer, White Mountain Regional Medical Center, Springerville, AZ, p. A39

WASDEN, Mitchell L., Ed.D., Chief Executive Officer and Chief Operating Officer, University of Missouri Health Care, Columbia, MO, p. B148

WASDEN, Mitchell L., Ed.D., Chief Executive Officer and Chief Operating Officer, University of Missouri Hospitals and Clinics, Columbia, MO, p. A370

WASEF, Maha, M.D. Chief of Staff, Merit Health Northwest Mississippi, Clarksdale, MS, p. A356

WASEK, Arthur A., Director Human Resources, Merit Health Batesville, Batesville, MS, p. A355

WASHBURN, Geoffrey A., Vice President, Regional Medical Center Bayonet Point, Hudson, FL, p. A131

WASHBURN, Kimberly D., Director Human Resources, Snoqualmie Valley Hospital District, Snoqualmie, WA, p. A690

WASHBURN, Sheryl M., MSN Chief Nursing Officer, Gritman Medical Center, Moscow, ID, p. A177

WASHBURN, Tonya, M.D. Medical Director, Valir Rehabilitation Hospital, Oklahoma City, OK, p. A518

WASHECKA, James, Chief Financial Officer, Hillcrest Hospital – South, Tulsa, OK, p. A521

WASHINGTON, A. Eugene, M.D., President and Chief Executive Officer, Duke University Health System, Durham, NC, p. B51

WASHINGTON, Carol, MSN, Chief Executive Officer, Lafayette Physical Rehabilitation Hospital, Lafayette, LA, p. A280

WASHINGTON, Carolyn, Director of Human Resources, United Memorial Medical Care, Houston, TX, p. A627

WASHINGTON, Charletta, Chief Operations Officer, United Medical Center, Washington, DC, p. A122

WASHINGTON, Glen A., Chief Executive Officer, Pleasant Valley Hospital, Point Pleasant, WV, p. A699

WASHINGTON, Lorraine, Vice President Human Resources, St. Dominic–Jackson Memorial Hospital, Jackson, MS, p. A360

WASHINGTON, Stephanie
Human Resources Director, Baptist Medical Center Attala, Kosciusko, MS, p. A360
Director Community Relations and Human Resources, Baptist Medical Center Yazoo, Yazoo City, MS, p. A366

WASHINGTON, Vindell, M.D. Vice President Performance Excellence and Technology, Our Lady of the Lake Regional Medical Center, Baton Rouge, LA, p. A273

WASILICK, Tamara, Director Operations, KidsPeace Children's Hospital, Orefield, PA, p. A546

WATERBURY, Brad, Director Human Resources, Bonner General Hospital, Sandpoint, ID, p. A178

WATERS, Bill, M.D. Chief Medical Officer, Tanner Higgins General Hospital, Bremen, GA, p. A155

WATERS, Danny, Director, Information Services, Palms of Pasadena Hospital, Saint Petersburg, FL, p. A144

WATERS, Eric, Vice President Operations, Pen Bay Medical Center, Rockport, ME, p. A295

WATERS, Gina, Director Human Resources, Evans Memorial Hospital, Claxton, GA, p. A156

WATERS, Glenn D., FACHE, President, Morton Plant Mease Health Care, Clearwater, FL, p. B92

WATERS, Jerod, Chief Nursing Officer, Chickasaw Nation Medical Center, Ada, OK, p. A508

WATERS, Karen, Chief Nursing Officer, St. Mary's Warrick Hospital, Boonville, IN, p. A207

WATERS, Laura M., Vice President Human Resources, Garrett Regional Medical Center, Oakland, MD, p. A302

WATERS, Nancy, Interim Chief Information Officer, High Point Regional Health System, High Point, NC, p. A467

WATERS, Stephen F., M.D. Medical Director, Atlantic General Hospital, Berlin, MD, p. A298

WATERS, IV, William, M.D. Executive Vice President, Tanner Medical Center–Villa Rica, Villa Rica, GA, p. A168

WATERSTON, Judith C., MS, President and Chief Executive Officer, New England Sinai Hospital and Rehabilitation Center, Stoughton, MA, p. A315

WATHEN, Cheryl A., Interim Chief Financial Officer, Deaconess Hospital, Evansville, IN, p. A210

WATHEN, Jim A., Interim Chief Executive Officer, Southern Coos Hospital and Health Center, Bandon, OR, p. A524

WATHEN, Susan R., Vice President Human Resources, Hannibal Regional Hospital, Hannibal, MO, p. A371

WATKINS, Anne Marie, Chief Nurse Executive, Kaiser Permanente San Diego Medical Center, San Diego, CA, p. A88

WATKINS, Chris, Director of Information Technology, Craig Hospital, Englewood, CO, p. A105

WATKINS, Christi, R.N. Chief Operating Officer, Palestine Regional Medical Center, Palestine, TX, p. A640

WATKINS, James, M.D. President Medical Staff, Providence Willamette Falls Medical Center, Oregon City, OR, p. A528

WATKINS, Joycelyn, R.N. Chief Nursing Officer, Magnolia Regional Medical Center, Magnolia, AR, p. A49

WATKINS, Pamela, Chief Financial Officer, Atlanta Veterans Affairs Medical Center, Decatur, GA, p. A158

WATKINS, Paul, Chief Administrative Officer, UCLA Medical Center–Santa Monica, Santa Monica, CA, p. A94

WATKINS, Rolanda, Chief Human Resources Management Service, Dayton Veterans Affairs Medical Center, Dayton, OH, p. A492

WATKINS, Terri, R.N. Chief Nursing Officer, Castleview Hospital, Price, UT, p. A662

WATRY, Margaret, Director of Patient Care Services and Nurse Executive, Phillips Eye Institute, Minneapolis, MN, p. A346

WATSON, B. Keith, M.D. Chief Medical Staff, North Mississippi Medical Center–West Point, West Point, MS, p. A366

WATSON, Betty A., Chief Financial Officer, Syringa Hospital and Clinics, Grangeville, ID, p. A176

WATSON, Brent, M.D. Chief Medical Staff, Roane General Hospital, Spencer, WV, p. A700

WATSON, Cheryl, Chief Information Officer, Howard County Medical Center, Saint Paul, NE, p. A402

WATSON, Dalph, Director of Human Resources, Beaumont Hospital – Farmington Hills, Farmington Hills, MI, p. A323

WATSON, Dean, M.D. Chief Medical Officer, Tallahassee Memorial HealthCare, Tallahassee, FL, p. A146

WATSON, Deborah, Senior Vice President and Chief Operating Officer, Bayhealth Medical Center, Dover, DE, p. A119

WATSON, Deborah, R.N
Chief Nursing Officer, Providence Mount Carmel Hospital, Colville, WA, p. A684
Chief Nursing Officer, Providence St. Joseph's Hospital, Chewelah, WA, p. A683

WATSON, Dolores, Director Health Information Management, Arms Acres, Carmel, NY, p. A436

WATSON, H. Alan, FACHE, Chief Executive Officer, Maury Regional Health System, Columbia, TN, p. B85

WATSON, H. Alan, FACHE, Chief Executive Officer, Maury Regional Hospital, Columbia, TN, p. A581

WATSON, Heath
Controller, HEALTHSOUTH Rehabilitation Hospital, Dothan, AL, p. A19
Controller, HEALTHSOUTH Rehabilitation Hospital of Montgomery, Montgomery, AL, p. A23

WATSON, James, Chief Financial Officer, University of Chicago Medical Center, Chicago, IL, p. A187

WATSON, James B., President, Schuyler Hospital, Montour Falls, NY, p. A443

WATSON, Kathy, R.N., Administrator and Chief Nursing Officer, Saint Thomas Hospital for Spinal Surgery, Nashville, TN, p. A590

WATSON, Kerry
Interim President and Chief Operating Officer, Arnot Ogden Medical Center, Elmira, NY, p. A438
Interim President and Chief Operating Officer, St. Joseph's Hospital, Elmira, NY, p. A438

WATSON, Lisa, Chief Executive Officer, St. Vincent Rehabilitation Hospital, Sherwood, AR, p. A52

WATSON, Luke, M.D. Chief of Staff, College Medical Center, Long Beach, CA, p. A69

WATSON, MSN, RN–, Margie, Chief Nursing Officer, Sabine County Hospital, Hemphill, TX, p. A623

WATSON, Michael, M.D. Chief of Staff, Memorial Hospital, Seminole, TX, p. A648

WATSON, Nancy
Director Human Resources, Mercy Hospital, Coon Rapids, MN, p. A341
Vice President Human Resources, Unity Hospital, Fridley, MN, p. A343

WATSON, Jr., Nathan, M.D. Chief of Staff, Carrus Specialty Hospital, Sherman, TX, p. A648

WATSON, Rob, M.D. Chief Medical Officer, Scott & White Hospital at Round Rock, Round Rock, TX, p. A644

WATSON, Robert, JD, Administrator, Mercy Hospital Carthage, Carthage, MO, p. A369

WATSON, Shane, Chief Executive Officer, Red Bud Regional Hospital, Red Bud, IL, p. A201

WATSON, Susan, MSN Vice President, Bronson Battle Creek, Battle Creek, MI, p. A319

WATSON, Teresa C., Vice President Administration, Carolinas HealthCare System Lincoln, Lincolnton, NC, p. A469

WATSON, Thelma Ruth, M.D. Medical Director, Schneider Regional Medical Center, Saint Thomas, VI, p. A731

WATSON, Thomas, M.D. Chief of Staff, Mayers Memorial Hospital District, Fall River Mills, CA, p. A62

WATSON, Trey, Network Administrator, Sumner County Hospital District One, Caldwell, KS, p. A241

WATSON, Vicki, Manager Human Resources, Select Specialty Hospital–Jackson, Jackson, MS, p. A360

WATSON, Virgil, Chief Executive Officer, South Central Kansas Medical Center, Arkansas City, KS, p. A240

WATT, Andrew, M.D. Vice President, Chief Information Officer and Chief Medical Information Officer, Southern New Hampshire Medical Center, Nashua, NH, p. A412

WATT, Ella, Chief Financial Officer, University of New Mexico Hospitals, Albuquerque, NM, p. A428

WATTENBARGER, J. Michael, M.D. Chief of Staff, Shriners Hospitals for Children–Greenville, Greenville, SC, p. A566

WATTENBARGER, Mike, Chief Information Officer, LifeCare Hospitals of San Antonio, San Antonio, TX, p. A646

WATTERS, Greg, Chief Financial Officer, El Paso Specialty Hospital, El Paso, TX, p. A615

WATTOO, Dost, M.D. Chief of Staff, Valley Hospital Medical Center, Las Vegas, NV, p. A407

WATTS, Blake, Chief Operating Officer, Rockdale Medical Center, Conyers, GA, p. A157

WATTS, Dawn, Chief Executive Officer, HEALTHSOUTH Rehabilitation Hospital of Fort Smith, Fort Smith, AR, p. A46

WATTS, Gail, Director, St. Vincent Medical Center, Los Angeles, CA, p. A74

WATTS, Hugh, M.D. Chief of Staff, Shriners Hospitals for Children–Los Angeles, Los Angeles, CA, p. A74

WATTS, Lynda, R.N. Vice President Patient Care Services, University Hospital, Augusta, GA, p. A154

WATTS-JOHNSON, Christine M., Assistant Vice President, Madera Community Hospital, Madera, CA, p. A75

WAY, Dee, Director Human Resources, Jerold Phelps Community Hospital, Garberville, CA, p. A64

WAYNE, Ann, Interim Chief Executive Officer and Managing Director, Meadows Psychiatric Center, Centre Hall, PA, p. A535

WAYNE, Denise, Chief Executive Officer, Vibra Hospital of Southeastern Michigan, LLC, Lincoln Park, MI, p. A329

WAYNE, Jason, Network Administrator, Suburban Community Hospital, Norristown, PA, p. A546

WAYTULA, Elizabeth, Chief Executive Officer, Cornerstone Hospital of Oklahoma–Shawnee, Shawnee, OK, p. A519

WEADICK, James F., Administrator and Chief Executive Officer, Piedmont Newton Hospital, Covington, GA, p. A157

WEAKHEE, Michael, Chief Executive Officer, U. S. Public Health Service Phoenix Indian Medical Center, Phoenix, AZ, p. A37

WEATHERFORD, Dennis, Chief Executive Officer, Putnam County Hospital, Greencastle, IN, p. A212

WEATHERLY, Daniel R.
Interim Chief Executive Officer, Cape Fear Valley – Bladen County Hospital, Elizabethtown, NC, p. A465
Chief Operating Officer, Cape Fear Valley Medical Center, Fayetteville, NC, p. A465

WEATHERSBY, Mae C., R.N. Chief Clinical Officer, Vibra Specialty Hospital at DeSoto, Desoto, TX, p. A613

WEATHERWAX, Lisa, R.N. Chief Nursing Officer, Iowa Specialty Hospital–Belmond, Belmond, IA, p. A225

WEATHERWAX, Marlene, Vice President and Chief Financial Officer, Columbus Regional Hospital, Columbus, IN, p. A208

WEAVER, Angie L., Director Human Resources, Merit Health Gilmore Memorial, Amory, MS, p. A355

WEAVER, Chris S., M.D. Chief Medical Officer, Eskenazi Health, Indianapolis, IN, p. A213

WEAVER, Daryl W., Interim Chief Executive Officer, Baptist Medical Center Leake, Carthage, MS, p. A356

WEAVER, Douglas K., FACHE, President, AllianceHealth Pryor, Pryor, OK, p. A519

WEAVER, Harry, M.D. Chief of Staff, Covenant Hospital–Levelland, Levelland, TX, p. A632

WEAVER, Jason, Director Information Systems, Southern Tennessee Regional Health System–Lawrenceburg, Lawrenceburg, TN, p. A586

WEAVER, Jeff, Chief Financial Officer, Medical Arts Hospital, Lamesa, TX, p. A632

WEAVER, Joe, Chief Executive Officer, RMC Jacksonville, Jacksonville, AL, p. A22

WEAVER, Judy K., MS, Chief Executive Officer, Acuity Specialty Hospitals Ohio Valley, Steubenville, OH, p. A503

WEAVER, Kimberli, Chief Nursing Officer, L. V. Stabler Memorial Hospital, Greenville, AL, p. A21

WEAVER, Lisa, Nurse Executive, Lakeside Behavioral Health System, Memphis, TN, p. A589

WEAVER, Rudolph D., Vice President Human Resources, Southwestern Vermont Medical Center, Bennington, VT, p. A665

WEAVER, Rusty, Manager Information Technology, Pauls Valley General Hospital, Pauls Valley, OK, p. A518

WEAVER, William, Chief Executive Officer, Brentwood Hospital, Shreveport, LA, p. A287

WEBB, Amy, Chief Operating Officer, Cascade Medical Center, Leavenworth, WA, p. A686

WEBB Jr., Charles L., Chief Executive Officer, Lincoln Trail Behavioral Health System, Radcliff, KY, p. A268

WEBB, Darrallyn, R.N. Chief Nursing Officer, Conway Regional Rehabilitation Hospital, Conway, AR, p. A44

WEBB, David, Chief Financial Officer, Baptist Memorial Hospital–Golden Triangle, Columbus, MS, p. A357

WEBB, Dee, Vice President Human Resources, St. Bernardine Medical Center, San Bernardino, CA, p. A88

WEBB, Donald, Chief Executive Officer, Williamson Medical Center, Franklin, TN, p. A583

WEBB, Glenn T., M.D. Medical Director, Ten Broeck Tennessee Treatment Facility, Cookeville, TN, p. A581

WEBB, Jeffrey D., CPA Chief Financial Officer, Franciscan Health Rensselaer, Rensselaer, IN, p. A221

WEBB, Joseph, Chief Executive Officer, Nashville General Hospital, Nashville, TN, p. A590

WEBB, Karen, M.D. Chief Medical Officer, Des Peres Hospital, Saint Louis, MO, p. A380

WEBB, Kimberly, Chief Financial Officer, Kootenai Health, Coeur D'Alene, ID, p. A175

WEBB, Linda, R.N. Chief Nursing Executive, Pulaski Memorial Hospital, Winamac, IN, p. A224

WEBB, Lisa
Vice President for Operational Finance, CHI Health Good Samaritan, Kearney, NE, p. A397
Vice President Operational Finance, CHI Health Saint Francis, Grand Island, NE, p. A396

WEBB, Melanie R.
Director Human Resources, Houston Northwest Medical Center, Houston, TX, p. A625
Chief Human Resources Officer, Park Plaza Hospital, Houston, TX, p. A626

WEBB, Paula, Chief Financial Officer and Compliance Officer, Lake Butler Hospital Hand Surgery Center, Lake Butler, FL, p. A133

WEBB, Renick, M.D. Chief Medical Director, Central Louisiana Surgical Hospital, Alexandria, LA, p. A271

WEBB, Steven B., FACHE, Vice President and Administrator, Baptist Health Medical Center – North Little Rock, North Little Rock, AR, p. A51

WEBB, William, Assistant Superintendent, Eastern Shore Hospital Center, Cambridge, MD, p. A299

WEBBER, Cathy, Director of Health Information Management, Franklin County Memorial Hospital, Franklin, NE, p. A395

WEBBER, Chelsea, Director Human Resources, LifeCare Hospitals of Pittsburgh – Monroeville, Monroeville, PA, p. A545

WEBBER, Deborah G., Chief Operating Officer, AHMC Anaheim Regional Medical Center, Anaheim, CA, p. A54

WEBBER, Denise, President and Chief Executive Officer, Stillwater Medical Center, Stillwater, OK, p. A520

WEBBER, Joyce, Chief Financial Officer, Spalding Rehabilitation Hospital, Aurora, CO, p. A101

WEBER, Ann, M.D. Chief Medical Officer, North Florida Regional Medical Center, Gainesville, FL, p. A129

WEBER, Barbara, Chief Operating Officer, Advocate Lutheran General Hospital, Park Ridge, IL, p. A200

WEBER, Carmen, Administrator, Eureka Community Health Services Avera, Eureka, SD, p. A573

WEBER, Deborah, Chief Human Resource Officer, Northeast Georgia Medical Center, Gainesville, GA, p. A160

WEBER, Frank, Chief Executive Officer, Select Specialty Hospital–Charleston, Charleston, WV, p. A695

WEBER, Gordon, Chief Operating Officer, Clarks Summit State Hospital, Clarks Summit, PA, p. A535

WEBER, Lauren, Administrator, Oceans Behavioral Hospital Longview, Longview, TX, p. A633

WEBER, Mark, M.D. President Medical Staff, West Branch Regional Medical Center, West Branch, MI, p. A336

WEBER, Pete M., President and Chief Executive Officer, Gordon Hospital, Calhoun, GA, p. A155

WEBER, Rebecca
Senior Vice President and Chief Information Officer, Bayshore Community Hospital, Holmdel, NJ, p. A418
Senior Vice President and Chief Information Officer, Jersey Shore University Medical Center, Neptune, NJ, p. A420
Senior Vice President and Chief Information Officer, Ocean Medical Center, Brick Township, NJ, p. A415
Senior Vice President Information Technology, Riverview Medical Center, Red Bank, NJ, p. A423
Senior Vice President and Chief Information Officer, Southern Ocean Medical Center, Manahawkin, NJ, p. A419

WEBER, Stephen, M.D. Chief Medical Officer, University of Chicago Medical Center, Chicago, IL, p. A187

WEBER, Tiffany, Chief Financial Officer, Sterling Regional MedCenter, Sterling, CO, p. A110

WEBER, Trish, R.N. Vice President Operations and Chief Nursing Officer, Franciscan St. Anthony Health – Michigan City, Michigan City, IN, p. A218

WEBER, Wilson, Chief Operating Officer, ContinueCARE Hospital at Baptist Health Corbin, Corbin, KY, p. A258

WEBSTER, Cindy, Vice President Financial Services, Licking Memorial Hospital, Newark, OH, p. A500

WEBSTER, Gwen, M.D. President Medical Staff, Texas Health Presbyterian Hospital Plano, Plano, TX, p. A642

WEBSTER, Janice, Director Human Resources, West Oaks Hospital, Houston, TX, p. A627

WEBSTER, Kathleen, R.N. Vice President Patient Services, New York–Presbyterian/Hudson Valley Hospital, Cortlandt Manor, NY, p. A437

WEBSTER, Mark
President and Chief Executive Officer, Cortland Regional Medical Center, Cortland, NY, p. A437
Vice President Finance, New York–Presbyterian/Hudson Valley Hospital, Cortlandt Manor, NY, p. A437

WEBSTER, Nancy, Chief Administrative Officer, St. Luke's Rehabilitation Institute, Spokane, WA, p. A691

WEBSTER, Richard, R.N., President, Thomas Jefferson University Hospitals, Philadelphia, PA, p. A550

WEBSTER, William W., FACHE, President and Chief Executive Officer, Medical Center Health System, Odessa, TX, p. A639

WECKENBORG, Janet, Vice President Operations, Capital Region Medical Center, Jefferson City, MO, p. A372

WECKESSER, Kim, Director Human Resources, West Shore Medical Center, Manistee, MI, p. A329

WEDDLE, Chari, Chief Human Resource Management Service, Richard L. Roudebush Veterans Affairs Medical Center, Indianapolis, IN, p. A214

WEDGEWORTH, Joyce, Financial Clerk, Hill Hospital of Sumter County, York, AL, p. A27

WEDO, Aaron, Manager, Human Resources, Grundy County Memorial Hospital, Grundy Center, IA, p. A231

WEE, Donald, Chief Executive Officer, Tri–State Memorial Hospital, Clarkston, WA, p. A683

WEED, III, John, M.D. Medical Director, Rockdale Hospital, Rockdale, TX, p. A643

WEED, Warren
Director Human Resources, Merit Health River Oaks, Flowood, MS, p. A357
Director Associate Relations, Merit Health Woman's Hospital, Flowood, MS, p. A357

WEEKS, Doug, Executive Vice President Operations, Baptist Health Medical Center – North Little Rock, North Little Rock, AR, p. A51

WEEKS, Ed, Manager Information Services, Paris Community Hospital, Paris, IL, p. A199

WEELDREYER, Jim, Manager Information Technology, Pershing General Hospital, Lovelock, NV, p. A407

WEEMS, Reva S., Director Human Resources, Gateway Regional Medical Center, Granite City, IL, p. A191

WEEMS, Taylor, Vice President, Chief Information Officer, Midland Memorial Hospital, Midland, TX, p. A637

WEG, Jennifer, R.N. Chief Nursing Officer, Sanford Worthington Medical Center, Worthington, MN, p. A354

WEGHORST, George, M.D. Chief Medical Officer, Providence Newberg Medical Center, Newberg, OR, p. A528

WEGLARZ, Ron, Chief Executive Officer and Managing Director, Streamwood Behavioral Health Center, Streamwood, IL, p. A204

WEGLEITNER, Theodore, Chief Executive Officer, Lakeview Hospital, Stillwater, MN, p. A352

WEGNER, Michael, Senior Vice President and Chief Operating Officer, Mercy Medical Center–Des Moines, Des Moines, IA, p. A229

WEHBEH, Wehbeh, M.D. Chief Medical Officer, NYC Health + Hospitals / Coney Island,, NY, p. A448

WEHE, Brad, Chief Operating Officer, Altru Health System, Grand Forks, ND, p. A479

WEHLING, Ed, Chief Medical Staff, Decatur County Hospital, Leon, IA, p. A233

WEHLING, Robert D., Interim Chief Financial Officer, Saint Alphonsus Medical Center – Baker City, Baker City, OR, p. A524

WEHMEYER, Jeffrey, Director Information Technology, Hermann Area District Hospital, Hermann, MO, p. A372

WEHNER, Jill, Vice President Financial Services, Harbor Beach Community Hospital, Harbor Beach, MI, p. A326

WEHRMEISTER, Erica, Chief Operating Officer, St. Vincent Indianapolis Hospital, Indianapolis, IN, p. A215

WEIDEMANN, Donald, Administrator, Dr. Dan C. Trigg Memorial Hospital, Tucumcari, NM, p. A432

WEIDER, Will
Chief Information Officer, Calumet Medical Center, Chilton, WI, p. A704
Chief Information Officer, Mercy Medical Center, Oshkosh, WI, p. A713
Chief Information Officer, Ministry Saint Joseph's Hospital, Marshfield, WI, p. A709
Chief Information Officer, Ministry Saint Michael's Hospital, Stevens Point, WI, p. A716
Chief Information Officer, St. Elizabeth Hospital, Appleton, WI, p. A702

WEIDNER, Deborah, Medical Director, Natchaug Hospital, Mansfield Center, CT, p. A114

WEIDNER, Peter, Director Information Technology, St. John's Riverside Hospital, Yonkers, NY, p. A459

WEIER, Jeffrey Paul, Chief Executive Officer, Kindred Hospital of Central Ohio, Mansfield, OH, p. A497

WEIGEL, Cherry, Director Health Information Management, RC Hospital and Clinics, Olivia, MN, p. A348

WEIL, David S., Senior Vice President and Administrator, Saint Francis Hospital South, Tulsa, OK, p. A522

WEILAND, David, M.D. Chief Medical Officer, Largo Medical Center, Largo, FL, p. A134

WEIMER, Linn, Chief Information Officer, Adena Medical Center, Chillicothe, OH, p. A486

WEINBAUM, Frederic, M.D. Executive Vice President Operations and Chief Medical Officer, Southampton Hospital, Southampton, NY, p. A456

WEINER, Gary
Vice President Information Technology, Chief Information Officer, Community Hospital, Munster, IN, p. A219
Chief Information Officer, St. Catherine Hospital, East Chicago, IN, p. A209
Vice President Information Technology and Chief Information Officer, St. Mary Medical Center, Hobart, IN, p. A213

WEINER, Jerome, M.D. Senior Vice President Medical Affairs, Good Samaritan Hospital Medical Center, West Islip, NY, p. A458

WEINER, Ronald, Vice President Finance and Chief Financial Officer, Magruder Memorial Hospital, Port Clinton, OH, p. A501

WEINGART, Steve, Chief Financial Officer, Los Alamos Medical Center, Los Alamos, NM, p. A430

WEINGARTNER, Ronald, Vice President Administration, St. Charles Hospital, Port Jefferson, NY, p. A453

WEINHOLD, Robert, Chief Executive Officer, Foundations Behavioral Health, Doylestown, PA, p. A537

WEINKRANTZ, Alan, Chief Financial Officer, Finance, University Behavioral Healthcare, Piscataway, NJ, p. A422

WEINMANN, Jay, Chief Financial Officer, NYC Health + Hospitals / Bellevue, New York, NY, p. A447

WEINMANN, Shannon, Human Resources Manager, Community Medical Center, Inc., Falls City, NE, p. A395

WEINMEISTER, Kurt, Chief Executive Officer, San Dimas Community Hospital, San Dimas, CA, p. A89

WEINREIS, Brian, Vice President Operations and Finance, Abbott Northwestern Hospital, Minneapolis, MN, p. A346

WEINSTEIN, Barry S., Chief Financial Officer, Four Winds Hospital, Katonah, NY, p. A441

WEINSTEIN, Brian, M.D. Chief of Staff, Westside Regional Medical Center, Plantation, FL, p. A143

WEINSTEIN, Freddie, M.D. Chief Medical Officer, Dominican Hospital, Santa Cruz, CA, p. A93

WEINSTEIN, Gary B., Chief Executive Officer, Washington Health System, Washington, PA, p. B153

WEINSTEIN, Gary B., President and Chief Executive Officer, Washington Hospital, Washington, PA, p. A556

WEINSTEIN, James, MS, President and Chief Executive Officer, Dartmouth–Hitchcock Medical Center, Lebanon, NH, p. A412

WEINSTEIN, James, Chief Financial Officer, Lourdes Specialty Hospital of Southern New Jersey, Willingboro, NJ, p. A425

WEIR, Tim W., Chief Executive Officer, Olmsted Medical Center, Rochester, MN, p. A349

WEIS, Brian, M.D. Chief Medical Officer, Northwest Texas Healthcare System, Amarillo, TX, p. A596

WEIS, Charles
Executive Vice President and Chief Financial Officer, Holy Cross Hospital, Chicago, IL, p. A184
Chief Financial Officer, Mount Sinai Hospital, Chicago, IL, p. A185
Chief Financial Officer, Schwab Rehabilitation Hospital, Chicago, IL, p. A186

WEIS, Harry, Chief Executive Officer, Tahoe Forest Health System, Truckee, CA, p. B131

WEIS, Harry, Chief Executive Officer, Tahoe Forest Hospital District, Truckee, CA, p. A97

WEIS, Maurine, MSN Vice President Nursing and Chief Nursing Officer, ProMedica Flower Hospital, Sylvania, OH, p. A503

WEIS, Robert
Director Information Systems, Bingham Memorial Hospital, Blackfoot, ID, p. A174
Director Information Technology, Mountain River Birthing and Surgery Center, Blackfoot, ID, p. A174
WEIS, Wade, Chief Financial Officer and Senior Director Finance, Grande Ronde Hospital, La Grande, OR, p. A527
WEISENBERGER, Scott, Chief Executive Officer, Malvern Institute, Malvern, PA, p. A544
WEISENFREUND, Jochanan, M.D. Senior Vice President Academic and Medical Affairs, Interfaith Medical Center,, NY, p. A444
WEISER, Marcus, D.O. Chief of Staff, Community HealthCare System, Onaga, KS, p. A250
WEISFIELD, Phyllis, Chief Executive Officer and Managing Director, Horsham Clinic, Ambler, PA, p. A532
WEISHAPL, Natasha, Manager Business Office and Human Resources, Decatur Health Systems, Oberlin, KS, p. A250
WEISNER, Brad, Executive Vice President and Chief Operating Officer, Nash Health Care Systems, Rocky Mount, NC, p. A472
WEISS, Allen S., M.D., President and Chief Executive Officer, NCH Downtown Naples Hospital, Naples, FL, p. A138
WEISS, Anthony, M.D. Medical Director, Upstate University Hospital, Syracuse, NY, p. A457
WEISS, Barry J., Chairman of the Board, College Health Enterprises, Santa Fe Springs, CA, p. B34
WEISS, David
Vice President Information System, Alton Memorial Hospital, Alton, IL, p. A180
Commanding Officer, Naval Hospital Bremerton, Bremerton, WA, p. A682
WEISS, Gary, Chief Financial Officer, NorthShore University Health System, Evanston, IL, p. A190
WEISS, Patrice M., Chief Medical Officer, Carilion Franklin Memorial Hospital, Rocky Mount, VA, p. A678
WEISS, Phyllis, Director Human Resources, Alameda Hospital, Alameda, CA, p. A54
WEISS, Terri, Chief Financial Officer, HEALTHSOUTH Rehabilitation Hospital Vision Park, Shenandoah, TX, p. A648
WEISSENBERGER, Ralf, Director Information Systems, White Memorial Medical Center, Los Angeles, CA, p. A75
WEISSER, Lisa, Supervisor Finance, Wagner Community Memorial Hospital Avera, Wagner, SD, p. A577
WEISSLER, Jonathan, M.D. Chief Medical Officer, LifeCare Hospitals of Dallas, Dallas, TX, p. A610
WEISTREICH, Tracy, Ph.D. Associate Director Patient Care Services/Nurse Executive, Veterans Affairs Roseburg Healthcare System, Roseburg, OR, p. A530
WEISUL, Jonathan, M.D. Vice President Medical Affairs and Chief Medical Officer, CHRISTUS Coushatta Health Care Center, Coushatta, LA, p. A275
WELANDER, Jennifer, CP
Senior Vice President Finance and Chief Financial Officer, St. Charles Bend, Bend, OR, p. A524
Senior Vice President Finance and Chief Financial Officer, St. Charles Redmond, Redmond, OR, p. A530
WELCH, Abbey, Director Human Resources, Harmon Memorial Hospital, Hollis, OK, p. A513
WELCH, Andrew, Director, New Mexico Veterans Affairs Health Care System – Raymond G. Murphy Medical Center, Albuquerque, NM, p. A428
WELCH, Bryant, Chief Human Resources, Washington Hospital Healthcare System, Fremont, CA, p. A63
WELCH, David, M.D. Medical Director, Clifton–Fine Hospital, Star Lake, NY, p. A456
WELCH, David, Director Information Technology, Simpson General Hospital, Mendenhall, MS, p. A362
WELCH, Denise, Chief Financial Officer, Arbuckle Memorial Hospital, Sulphur, OK, p. A520
WELCH, Don, Chief Financial Officer, Walla Walla General Hospital, Walla Walla, WA, p. A693
WELCH, Donald E., Chief Operating Officer, Florida Hospital Zephyrhills, Zephyrhills, FL, p. A150
WELCH, Douglas, Chief Executive Officer, Doctors Hospital, Augusta, GA, p. A153
WELCH, Gary A., Assistant to the Chief Executive Officer and Administrative Director Support Systems, Bon Secours Memorial Regional Medical Center, Mechanicsville, VA, p. A673
WELCH, Jeffrey M., Chief Executive Officer, Palm Beach Gardens Medical Center, Palm Beach Gardens, FL, p. A141
WELCH, Melissa, Director Health Information Management, Oakdale Community Hospital, Oakdale, LA, p. A286
WELCH, Nicole, Chief Human Resources Officer, Fairbanks Memorial Hospital, Fairbanks, AK, p. A29
WELCH, Rosemary C., R.N. Vice President and Chief Nursing Officer, MedStar National Rehabilitation Hospital, Washington, DC, p. A121

WELCH, Shelly
Senior Vice President Patient Services and Chief Nursing Officer, North Oaks Medical Center, Hammond, LA, p. A277
Senior Vice President, Patient Services, Chief Nursing Officer, North Oaks Health System, North Oaks Rehabilitation Hospital, Hammond, LA, p. A277
WELCH, Sherri, R.N. Chief Nursing Officer, College Station Medical Center, College Station, TX, p. A606
WELCH, Thomas, M.D. Chief Medical Officer, Mercy St. Vincent Medical Center, Toledo, OH, p. A504
WELCH, Tony, Vice President Human Resources, Southeast Alabama Medical Center, Dothan, AL, p. A19
WELDAY, Doug, Senior Vice President Finance, Spectrum Health – Butterworth Hospital, Grand Rapids, MI, p. A325
WELDING, Theodore L., Chief Executive Officer, Promise Hospital of Miami, Miami, FL, p. A137
WELDON, Jim, Chief Information Officer, St. Anthony's Medical Center, Saint Louis, MO, p. A381
WELDY, Alan, Vice President Human Resources, Compliance and Legal Services, Indiana University Health Goshen Hospital, Goshen, IN, p. A212
WELKIE MBA, Katy, R.N., Chief Executive Officer, Primary Children's Hospital, Salt Lake City, UT, p. A663
WELLBROCK, Jenna, Chief Nursing Officer, Gateway Rehabilitation Hospital, Florence, KY, p. A260
WELLER, Deidre, CPA Controller, Spectrum Health Pennock, Hastings, MI, p. A326
WELLING, Lynn, M.D. Chief Medical Officer, Sharp Chula Vista Medical Center, Chula Vista, CA, p. A58
WELLING, Michele, M.D. Chief of Staff, Bluegrass Community Hospital, Versailles, KY, p. A270
WELLMAN, James, Senior Director Information Services, Comanche County Memorial Hospital, Lawton, OK, p. A513
WELLMAN, Sonia I., Chief Operating Officer, Oak Hill Hospital, Brooksville, FL, p. A125
WELLMANN, Jane, Chief Financial Officer, Scott & White Hospital – Brenham, Brenham, TX, p. A603
WELLS, A. Shane, Chief Financial Officer, Cornerstone Hospital of Houston at Clearlake, Webster, TX, p. A656
WELLS, Benjamin, Chief Financial Officer, Red Bud Regional Hospital, Red Bud, IL, p. A201
WELLS, Carol, R.N. Chief Nursing Officer, Central Louisiana Surgical Hospital, Alexandria, LA, p. A271
WELLS, Craig, Chief Information Officer, George C Grape Community Hospital, Hamburg, IA, p. A231
WELLS, Dale W., Chief Financial and Operating Officer, Alliance Community Hospital, Alliance, OH, p. A483
WELLS, James, R.N. Chief Nursing Officer, EASTAR Health System, Muskogee, OK, p. A515
WELLS, Jason, Chief Human Resources Management Service, Fargo Veterans Affairs Health Care System, Fargo, ND, p. A478
WELLS, Jonathan, Supervisor Information Technology, Kansas Surgery and Recovery Center, Wichita, KS, p. A256
WELLS, Mallory Gulley, CPA Chief Financial Officer, Richardson Medical Center, Rayville, LA, p. A286
WELLS, Mary Ellen, FACHE, Administrator, CentraCare Health–Monticello, Monticello, MN, p. A347
WELLS, Michelle, Director of Nursing, River Oaks Hospital, New Orleans, LA, p. A285
WELLS, Pamela, R.N. Chief Nursing Officer, Sharp Memorial Hospital, San Diego, CA, p. A89
WELLS, Robert, M.D. Chief Medical Officer, Providence Portland Medical Center, Portland, OR, p. A529
WELLS, Roxie, President, Hoke Hospital, Raeford, NC, p. A471
WELLS, Scott E., MSN Vice President Patient Care Services, CaroMont Regional Medical Center, Gastonia, NC, p. A465
WELLS, Troy R., Chief Executive Officer, Baptist Health, Little Rock, AR, p. B19
WELLS, Valerie, Manager Human Resources, HEALTHSOUTH Rehabilitation Hospital The Woodlands, Conroe, TX, p. A607
WELSER, Jeremy, Director Information Systems, Bonner General Hospital, Sandpoint, ID, p. A178
WELSH, Dennis, Chief Executive Officer, Down East Community Hospital, Machias, ME, p. A294
WELSH Jr., J. Luckey, Chief Executive Officer, Cherry Hospital, Goldsboro, NC, p. A466
WELSH, Joyce, R.N. Vice President of Clinical Services and Chief Nursing Officer, Emerson Hospital, Concord, MA, p. A309
WELSH, Terrence, Chief Medical Administrator, Fairfield Medical Center, Lancaster, OH, p. A496
WELTER, Matt, Chief Medical Officer, Cache Valley Hospital, North Logan, UT, p. A661
WELTON, George, Chief Executive Officer, Kindred Hospital – Denver South, Denver, CO, p. A104
WEMPE, John M., M.D. Chief of Staff, Sioux Falls Veterans Affairs Health Care System, Sioux Falls, SD, p. A576

WENDELL, David, Manager, Information Systems, St. Mary's Medical Center, Huntington, WV, p. A697
WENDELL, Sean, Chief Executive Officer, Beacon Behavioral Hospital, Lutcher, LA, p. A282
WENGER, Cheryl, Manager Health Information and Quality Assurance, Hiawatha Community Hospital, Hiawatha, KS, p. A244
WENGER, Jill, Director Human Resources, Atchison Hospital, Atchison, KS, p. A240
WENGER–KELLER, David, M.D. Chief of Staff, Fort Madison Community Hospital, Fort Madison, IA, p. A231
WENTWORTH, Cynthia, Chief Human Resource Officer, East Morgan County Hospital, Brush, CO, p. A102
WENTZ, Amber, Director of Clinical Information Systems & Clinical Informatics, Skiff Medical Center, Newton, IA, p. A235
WENTZ, Robert J., President and Chief Executive Officer, Oroville Hospital, Oroville, CA, p. A81
WENTZEL, Chris, M.D. Interim Medical Director, Guthrie Corning Hospital, Corning, NY, p. A437
WENZEL, Matthew, President and Chief Executive Officer, Saint Luke's North Hospital – Barry Road, Kansas City, MO, p. A374
WERFT, Ronald C., President and Chief Executive Officer, Cottage Health, Santa Barbara, CA, p. B42
WERFT, Ronald C.
President and Chief Executive Officer, Goleta Valley Cottage Hospital, Santa Barbara, CA, p. A93
President and Chief Executive Officer, Santa Barbara Cottage Hospital, Santa Barbara, CA, p. A93
President and Chief Executive Officer, Santa Ynez Valley Cottage Hospital, Solvang, CA, p. A94
WERKIN, Dave, Vice President Finance and Chief Financial Officer, Trinity Health System, Steubenville, OH, p. A503
WERKSTELL, Scott, Director Information System, T. J. Samson Community Hospital, Glasgow, KY, p. A261
WERMAGER, Teresa, Human Resources Business Partner, Skiff Medical Center, Newton, IA, p. A235
WERNER, Edward, Director Human Resources, HEALTHSOUTH Reading Rehabilitation Hospital, Reading, PA, p. A553
WERNER, John W., Chief Executive Officer, Oakland Mercy Hospital, Oakland, NE, p. A399
WERNER, Kurt, M.D. Chief of Staff, Veterans Affairs Montana Health Care System, Fort Harrison, MT, p. A387
WERNICK, Joel, President and Chief Executive Officer, Phoebe Putney Health System, Albany, GA, p. B103
WERNICK, Joel, President and Chief Executive Officer, Phoebe Putney Memorial Hospital, Albany, GA, p. A151
WERNKE, Chris, Chief Operating Officer, Dominican Hospital, Santa Cruz, CA, p. A93
WERRBACH, John P., President and Chief Executive Officer, AMITA Health Elk Grove Village, Elk Grove Village, IL, p. A189
WERTH–SWEENEY, Stacey, Facility Operating Officer, Lincoln Regional Center, Lincoln, NE, p. A398
WERTHMAN, Ronald J., Senior Vice President Finance, Chief Financial Officer and Treasurer, Johns Hopkins Hospital, Baltimore, MD, p. A296
WERTZ, Jackie, Director Human Resources, George C Grape Community Hospital, Hamburg, IA, p. A231
WERTZ, Randy S., Chief Executive Officer, Golden Valley Memorial Healthcare, Clinton, MO, p. A369
WESCOATT, Sampson, Manager Information Technology, Molokai General Hospital, Kaunakakai, HI, p. A172
WESCOTT, Lisle, President, SSM Health St. Joseph Hospital – Lake Saint Louis, Lake Saint Louis, MO, p. A375
WESENER DIECK, Jill, Director Human Resources, Gundersen Tri–County Hospital and Clinics, Whitehall, WI, p. A719
WESLEY, Deb, MSN Chief Nursing Officer, Children's of Alabama, Birmingham, AL, p. A16
WESLEY, Jim, Senior Vice President and Chief Information Officer, John Muir Behavioral Health Center, Concord, CA, p. A59
WESLEY, Mary Lou, R.N. Senior Vice President and Chief Nursing Officer, Sparrow Hospital, Lansing, MI, p. A328
WESSELS, Jana, Associate Vice President Human Resources, University of Iowa Hospitals and Clinics, Iowa City, IA, p. A232
WESSELS, William, M.D. Chief Medical Officer, Aspirus Wausau Hospital, Wausau, WI, p. A718
WEST, Aaron, M.D. Chief Medical Officer, Memorial Hospital Jacksonville, Jacksonville, FL, p. A131
WEST, Andrea, MS Vice President of Human Resources, Columbus Regional Healthcare System, Whiteville, NC, p. A475
WEST, Brenda
Assistant Vice President, Information Services, Einstein Medical Center Montgomery, East Norriton, PA, p. A537
Vice President, Information Services and Interim Chief Information Officer, Einstein Medical Center Philadelphia, Philadelphia, PA, p. A547

WEST, Brenda, R.N. Chief Nursing Officer, Summit Pacific Medical Center, Elma, WA, p. A684

WEST, Bridgette, Director Patient Access Services, Cobleskill Regional Hospital, Cobleskill, NY, p. A437

WEST, Charles, M.D. Chief Medical Officer, Randolph Hospital, Asheboro, NC, p. A460

WEST, Darren, M.D. Interim Chief Medical Officer, Banner Ironwood Medical Center, San Tan Valley, AZ, p. A38

WEST, David, Administrator, Deckerville Community Hospital, Deckerville, MI, p. A321

WEST, James R., President and Chief Executive Officer, PIH Health, Whittier, CA, p. B104

WEST, James R.
President and Chief Executive Officer, PIH Health Hospital – Downey, Downey, CA, p. A61
President and Chief Executive Officer, PIH Health Hospital–Whittier, Whittier, CA, p. A99

WEST, Jennifer, R.N. Chief Nursing Officer, South Texas Spine and Surgical Hospital, San Antonio, TX, p. A647

WEST, Judith M., Senior Vice President Human Resources and Chief Human Resources Officer, Maine Medical Center, Portland, ME, p. A294

WEST, Kenneth, Chief Operating Officer, Medical Center of Trinity, Trinity, FL, p. A148

WEST, Margaret M., MS, Chief Executive Officer, Magnolia Regional Medical Center, Magnolia, AR, p. A49

WEST, Melissa, Chief Financial Officer, Cedar Crest Hospital and Residential Treatment Center, Belton, TX, p. A602

WEST, Michael, Manager Systems Account, New England Sinai Hospital and Rehabilitation Center, Stoughton, MA, p. A315

WEST, Michael C., M.D. Chief of Staff, McCurtain Memorial Hospital, Idabel, OK, p. A513

WEST, Steve, M.D. Chief Medical Officer, Capital Regional Medical Center, Tallahassee, FL, p. A146

WEST, Steven J., Chief Executive Officer, Indiana University Health Blackford Hospital, Hartford City, IN, p. A213

WEST, Tamara, R.N. Vice President Patient Care, Nicholas H. Noyes Memorial Hospital, Dansville, NY, p. A438

WESTENFELDER, Grant, M.D. Chief Medical Officer, Midwest Medical Center, Galena, IL, p. A190

WESTER, K. Scott, FACHE, President and Chief Executive Officer, Our Lady of the Lake Regional Medical Center, Baton Rouge, LA, p. A273

WESTERCHIL, Beth, Chief Nursing Officer, Byrd Regional Hospital, Leesville, LA, p. A282

WESTERHEIDE, Karen, Chief Financial Officer, Veterans Affairs St. Louis Health Care System, Saint Louis, MO, p. A381

WESTERMAN, Mandy, Chief Executive Officer, West Oaks Hospital, Houston, TX, p. A627

WESTFALL, Gay, Senior Vice President Human Resources, Kaiser Permanente Sacramento Medical Center, Sacramento, CA, p. A86

WESTFALL, Roger, Director, Western State Hospital, Hopkinsville, KY, p. A262

WESTFIELD, Brian W., MSN, Director, Jonathan M. Wainwright Memorial Veterans Affairs Medical Center, Walla Walla, WA, p. A692

WESTIN, Robert, M.D. Chief Medical Officer, Cuyuna Regional Medical Center, Crosby, MN, p. A341

WESTMAN, Ken, Chief Executive Officer, Barrett Hospital & HealthCare, Dillon, MT, p. A387

WESTMORELAND, Penny
Chief Financial Officer, Lakeland Community Hospital, Haleyville, AL, p. A21
Chief Financial Officer, Red Bay Hospital, Red Bay, AL, p. A25
Chief Financial Officer, Russellville Hospital, Russellville, AL, p. A25

WESTON, Betty, Chief Human Resources Officer, U. S. Public Health Service Phoenix Indian Medical Center, Phoenix, AZ, p. A37

WESTON, Dana, Chief Executive Officer, Morehead Memorial Hospital, Eden, NC, p. A464

WESTON, Nancy R., R.N. Vice President Nursing Services, Memorial Hospital, Belleville, IL, p. A181

WESTON, Susan, CPA Chief Financial Officer, Mountrail County Medical Center, Stanley, ND, p. A481

WESTON, Terry, M.D. Vice President Physician Services, OhioHealth MedCentral Mansfield Hospital, Mansfield, OH, p. A497

WESTON–HALL, Patricia, Chief Executive Officer, Glenbeigh Hospital and Outpatient Centers, Rock Creek, OH, p. A502

WESTOVER, Teresa, Director Human Resources, North Texas Medical Center, Gainesville, TX, p. A620

WESTPHAL, Chris, Chief Information Technology Officer, Southeast Colorado Hospital District, Springfield, CO, p. A110

WESTPHAL, Laura R., Vice President Patient Care Services, Castle Medical Center, Kailua, HI, p. A171

WESTRUM, Jennifer, Administrator, Community Behavioral Health Hospital – Alexandria, Alexandria, MN, p. A338

WESTRY, Tanza, Chief Financial Officer, Hunter Holmes McGuire Veterans Affairs Medical Center–Richmond, Richmond, VA, p. A678

WESTWOOD, Denise P., Chief Nursing Officer, Weirton Medical Center, Weirton, WV, p. A700

WETHAL, Robert, R.N. Vice President and Chief Nursing Officer, Mercy Medical Center–Dubuque, Dubuque, IA, p. A230

WETHERELL, Russell J., President, Grandview Medical Center, Dayton, OH, p. A492

WETHINGTON, Bud
Chief Executive Officer, T. J. Samson Community Hospital, Glasgow, KY, p. A261
Chief Executive Officer, T.J. Health Columbia, Columbia, KY, p. A258

WETTON, Darlene, R.N., Chief Executive Officer, Temecula Valley Hospital, Temecula, CA, p. A96

WETZ, Staci, Chief Financial Officer, Shannon Medical Center, San Angelo, TX, p. A645

WETZEL, James L., M.D. Senior Vice President, Chief Medical Officer, Olathe Medical Center, Olathe, KS, p. A250

WETZEL, Lou, M.D. Chief of Staff, The University of Kansas Hospital, Kansas City, KS, p. A246

WEYMOUTH, Deborah K., FACHE, President and Chief Executive Officer, HealthAlliance Hospitals, Leominster, MA, p. A311

WEYMOUTH, Linda, Chief Financial Officer, Suncoast Behavioral Health Center, Bradenton, FL, p. A124

WHALEN, David, Chief Executive Officer, Twin Cities Hospital, Niceville, FL, p. A139

WHALEN, Eileen, R.N., President and Chief Operating Officer, The University of Vermont Health Network University of Vermont Medical Center, Burlington, VT, p. A665

WHALEN, Patti, Manager Human Resources, Wichita County Health Center, Leoti, KS, p. A248

WHALEN, Scott, FACHE,
President and Chief Executive Officer, Saint Vincent Hospital, Erie, PA, p. A538
President and Chief Executive Officer, Westfield Memorial Hospital, Westfield, NY, p. A459

WHALEN, Thomas, Vice President Finance, Good Samaritan Medical Center, Brockton, MA, p. A308

WHALEN, Thomas V., M.D
Chief Medical Officer, Lehigh Valley Hospital, Allentown, PA, p. A532
Executive Vice President and Chief Medical Officer, Lehigh Valley Hospital–Muhlenberg, Bethlehem, PA, p. A533

WHALEY, Joseph, Chief, Human Resources Management Service, Fayetteville Veterans Affairs Medical Center, Fayetteville, NC, p. A465

WHALEY, Mary, Director of Acute Care, Johnson County Healthcare Center, Buffalo, WY, p. A721

WHALEY, Shay, Administrator, Hale County Hospital, Greensboro, AL, p. A21

WHARTON, Danny, Chief Nursing Officer, Carolina Pines Regional Medical Center, Hartsville, SC, p. A567

WHARTON, Joe H., M.D. Chief of Staff, Bradley County Medical Center, Warren, AR, p. A53

WHEAT, Ken, Senior Vice President and Chief Financial Officer, Eisenhower Medical Center, Rancho Mirage, CA, p. A84

WHEAT, Terry, R.N. Director of Patient Care Services, Shriners Hospitals for Children–Chicago, Chicago, IL, p. A186

WHEATCRAFT, Cory, Information Technology and Purchasing Officer, Windsor–Laurelwood Center for Behavioral Medicine, Willoughby, OH, p. A506

WHEATLEY, Bernard, FACHE, Chief Executive Officer, Schneider Regional Medical Center, Saint Thomas, VI, p. A731

WHEATLEY, Jane, Chief Executive Officer, Taylor Regional Hospital, Campbellsville, KY, p. A258

WHEATLEY, Richard, Chief Information Officer, Cape Regional Medical Center, Cape May Court House, NJ, p. A415

WHEATLEY, Samuel N., Chief Medical Officer, Columbus Regional Healthcare System, Whiteville, NC, p. A475

WHEATLEY, Sonya, Human Resources Manager, Central State Hospital, Louisville, KY, p. A264

WHEATLEY, Stephen J., Director of Operations, Franciscan St. Francis Health–Carmel, Carmel, IN, p. A208

WHEATON, David, Director Human Resources, Blue Hill Memorial Hospital, Blue Hill, ME, p. A292

WHEATON, Tammy H., Interim Chief Nursing Officer, Union County Hospital, Anna, IL, p. A180

WHEELAN, Kevin, M.D. Medical Director, Baylor Jack and Jane Hamilton Heart and Vascular Hospital, Dallas, TX, p. A609

WHEELER, Brent, Vice President Ancillary and Support Services, McLaren Flint, Flint, MI, p. A323

WHEELER, Cambria, Communications and Marketing, St. Helena Hospital Clear Lake, Clearlake, CA, p. A59

WHEELER, Dane, Chief Financial Officer, Adams Memorial Hospital, Decatur, IN, p. A209

WHEELER, Dawne, Chief Executive Officer, Select Specialty Hospital–Canton, Canton, OH, p. A486

WHEELER, Denise, Chief Information Officer, Star Valley Medical Center, Afton, WY, p. A721

WHEELER, Frankie, Director, Human Resources, Saint Elizabeths Hospital, Washington, DC, p. A122

WHEELER, James A., Vice President Human Relations and Community Development, Androscoggin Valley Hospital, Berlin, NH, p. A410

WHEELER, Kevin, Information Technology Leader, Kaiser Permanente Walnut Creek Medical Center, Walnut Creek, CA, p. A99

WHEELER, Lynette, MS
Chief Nursing Officer, Truman Medical Center–Hospital Hill, Kansas City, MO, p. A374
Chief Nursing Officer, Truman Medical Center–Lakewood, Kansas City, MO, p. A374

WHEELER, Newman, Chief Financial Officer and Chief Operating Officer, Covenant Hospital–Levelland, Levelland, TX, p. A632

WHEELER, Pamela R., Director Human Resources, Scott County Hospital, Scott City, KS, p. A253

WHEELER, Penny Ann, M.D. President and Chief Medical Officer, Abbott Northwestern Hospital, Minneapolis, MN, p. A346

WHEELER, Penny Ann, M.D., Chief Executive Officer, Allina Health, Minneapolis, MN, p. B9

WHEELER, Philip, Director Finance, Mercy Health – Clermont Hospital, Batavia, OH, p. A484

WHEELER, Rebecca, Director Finance, Kaiser Permanente Baldwin Park Medical Center, Baldwin Park, CA, p. A56

WHEELER, Robert
Controller, HEALTHSOUTH Rehabilitation Hospital of Florence, Florence, SC, p. A565
Vice President Human Resources, South Shore Hospital, South Weymouth, MA, p. A314

WHEELER, Terry J., Chief Executive Officer, Cypress Fairbanks Medical Center, Houston, TX, p. A624

WHEELER, Tina, R.N. Director Nursing, William Newton Hospital, Winfield, KS, p. A256

WHEELER, William, M.D. Chief of Staff, Benewah Community Hospital, Saint Maries, ID, p. A178

WHEELER, Zachariah P., Senior Vice President Human Resources, John D. Archbold Memorial Hospital, Thomasville, GA, p. A167

WHEELER–MOORE, Juanita, Director Financial Services, Four Winds Hospital, Saratoga Springs, NY, p. A455

WHEELES, Locke, Information Technology Manager, Field Memorial Community Hospital, Centreville, MS, p. A356

WHEELUS, Matthew, Chief Operating Officer, Spring Valley Hospital Medical Center, Las Vegas, NV, p. A406

WHELAN, Laurie A., Senior Vice President Finance and Chief Financial Officer, Hospital for Special Care, New Britain, CT, p. A115

WHELAN, Thomas, Chief Executive Officer, Cibola General Hospital, Grants, NM, p. A429

WHERRY, Richard, M.D. Chief of Staff, Chestatee Regional Hospital, Dahlonega, GA, p. A157

WHERRY, Robin, Risk Manager and Director Quality Assurance and Health Information Management, HEALTHSOUTH MountainView Regional Rehabilitation Hospital, Morgantown, WV, p. A698

WHICHARD, Forrest, Chief Financial Officer, Ochsner Medical Center – North Shore, Slidell, LA, p. A288

WHICHARD, Nick, Chief Information Officer, St. Luke's Hospital, Columbus, NC, p. A463

WHIDDON, William, Chief Financial Officer, Woodland Heights Medical Center, Lufkin, TX, p. A635

WHILDEN, Sean
Chief Financial Officer, Houston Medical Center, Warner Robins, GA, p. A168
Chief Financial Officer, Perry Hospital, Perry, GA, p. A164

WHILEY, Karen, R.N. Vice President Patient Care Services, Fairview Northland Medical Center, Princeton, MN, p. A349

WHILLOCK, Mary C., R.N. Associate Nursing Officer and Chief Operating Officer, Florida Hospital Carrollwood, Tampa, FL, p. A147

WHIPKEY, Jared, Chief Financial Officer, Santa Rosa Medical Center, Milton, FL, p. A138

WHIPPLE, C. Cynthia, Director of Nursing, Muncy Valley Hospital, Muncy, PA, p. A546

WHIPPLE, James, Chief Executive Officer, Marshall Medical Center, Placerville, CA, p. A83

WHIPPLE, Jennifer, Director Nursing, Lane County Hospital, Dighton, KS, p. A242

WHIPPLE, Michael, Chief Financial Officer, Mercy St. Anne Hospital, Toledo, OH, p. A503

WHISENHUNT, Mickey, Interim Chief Nursing Officer, Regional Medical Center, Orangeburg, SC, p. A569

WHITACRE, James, Chief Executive Officer, AMG Specialty Hospital – Muncie, Muncie, IN, p. A218

WHITAKER, Brittany, Chief Financial Officer, Placentia–Linda Hospital, Placentia, CA, p. A83

WHITAKER, Catherine, MSN Vice President and Chief Nursing Officer, University of Maryland Baltimore Washington Medical Center, Glen Burnie, MD, p. A301

WHITAKER, Charles, Director Information Technology, Madison Parish Hospital, Tallulah, LA, p. A289

WHITAKER, Cynthia, Chief Nursing Officer, Henry County Medical Center, Paris, TN, p. A592

WHITAKER, Doris, Vice President and Manager, Mercy Hospital Booneville, Booneville, AR, p. A44

WHITAKER, E. Berton, FACHE, Interim Chief Executive Officer, Gifford Medical Center, Randolph, VT, p. A666

WHITAKER, James B., President, Circles of Care, Melbourne, FL, p. A135

WHITAKER, Jimmy, Director Information Systems, Central Carolina Hospital, Sanford, NC, p. A473

WHITAKER, Neil, M.D. Chief Medical Director, Orem Community Hospital, Orem, UT, p. A661

WHITAKER, Robert
  Chief Executive Officer, Hamilton County Hospital, Syracuse, KS, p. A254
  Vice President of Operations, Southwest Medical Center, Liberal, KS, p. A248

WHITE, Alexander, Vice President Medical Affairs, Carney Hospital, Boston, MA, p. A306

WHITE, Andrea, Chief Executive Officer, Select Specialty Hospital–Birmingham, Birmingham, AL, p. A17

WHITE, Beverly, MS, Facility Director, Mary S Harper Geriatric Psychiatry Center, Tuscaloosa, AL, p. A26

WHITE, Brian
  Director Strategic Planning, Vidant Bertie Hospital, Windsor, NC, p. A475
  Director Strategic Operations, Vidant Chowan Hospital, Edenton, NC, p. A464

WHITE, Brian M., President, Northwest Hospital, Randallstown, MD, p. A303

WHITE, Bruce, Administrator, Covenant Hospital–Levelland, Levelland, TX, p. A632

WHITE, Bruce D., Chief Executive Officer, Knox Community Hospital, Mount Vernon, OH, p. A499

WHITE, Catherine, Chief Financial Officer, Harney District Hospital, Burns, OR, p. A524

WHITE, Cindy, CPA Vice President of Operations, INTEGRIS Canadian Valley Hospital, Yukon, OK, p. A523

WHITE, Darrell, R.N., Administrator and Chief Nursing Officer, TriStar Ashland City Medical Center, Ashland City, TN, p. A579

WHITE, Darryl, M.D. Chief of Staff, East Texas Medical Center Fairfield, Fairfield, TX, p. A617

WHITE, Deborah, Coordinator Human Resource, Faith Community Hospital, Jacksboro, TX, p. A629

WHITE, Denise, MS
  Chief Nurse Executive, Carolinas HealthCare System Anson, Wadesboro, NC, p. A475
  Chief Nurse Executive, Carolinas Healthcare System Union, Monroe, NC, p. A469

WHITE, Diane, Chief Clinical Officer and Chief Nursing Officer, BridgePoint Hospital National Harbor, Washington, DC, p. A121

WHITE, Diane K., MSN Chief Clinical Officer, Kindred Hospital South Philadelphia, Philadelphia, PA, p. A548

WHITE, Donna, Director Human Resources, HEALTHSOUTH Rehabilitation Hospital of Charleston, Charleston, SC, p. A562

WHITE, Dudley R., Administrator and Chief Executive Officer, Concho County Hospital, Eden, TX, p. A614

WHITE, Gary B., M.D. Chief Medical Staff, Uintah Basin Medical Center, Roosevelt, UT, p. A662

WHITE, Harold, Vice Chancellor, University Health Shreveport, Shreveport, LA, p. A288

WHITE, J. B., Director Information Systems, Merit Health River Region, Vicksburg, MS, p. A365

WHITE, James P., M.D. Chief Medical Officer, Integris Baptist Medical Center, Oklahoma City, OK, p. A516

WHITE, Jason, M.D
  Chief Medical Officer, McLaren Bay Region, Bay City, MI, p. A319
  Vice President of Medical Affairs, McLaren Flint, Flint, MI, p. A323

WHITE, Jean, Vice President Finance, Avera Heart Hospital of South Dakota, Sioux Falls, SD, p. A576

WHITE, Jeffrey L., Senior Vice President and Chief Financial Officer, Beaufort Memorial Hospital, Beaufort, SC, p. A562

WHITE, Jennifer, Chief of Staff, Mayo Clinic Health System in Springfield, Springfield, MN, p. A351

WHITE, Jim, Chief Information Officer, Lompoc Valley Medical Center, Lompoc, CA, p. A69

WHITE, Joanne, Chief Information Officer, Wood County Hospital, Bowling Green, OH, p. A485

WHITE, Joel, Chief Operating Officer, Select Specialty Hospital–Omaha, Omaha, NE, p. A400

WHITE, John D., Chief Financial Officer, Wythe County Community Hospital, Wytheville, VA, p. A681

WHITE, John R., Administrator, Shriners Hospitals for Children–Honolulu, Honolulu, HI, p. A171

WHITE, Karen, Interim Vice President of Human Resources, Navos, Seattle, WA, p. A689

WHITE, Kay, Director Human Resources and Diversity, Carolinas Hospital System Marion, Mullins, SC, p. A568

WHITE, Kelli, Director, Human Resources, CenterPointe Hospital, Saint Charles, MO, p. A379

WHITE, Kelly Lynn, Vice President of Patient Care and Chief Nursing Officer, North Memorial Medical Center, Robbinsdale, MN, p. A349

WHITE, Kevin A., Administrator, Medicine Lodge Memorial Hospital, Medicine Lodge, KS, p. A249

WHITE, Knicole S., Director Human Resources, Kendall Regional Medical Center, Miami, FL, p. A136

WHITE, Linda E., President and Chief Executive Officer, Deaconess Health System, Evansville, IN, p. B44

WHITE, Lindy P., Chief Executive Officer, Franklin Woods Community Hospital, Johnson City, TN, p. A585

WHITE, Marsha L., Chief Nursing Executive, CHRISTUS St. Patrick Hospital of Lake Charles, Lake Charles, LA, p. A281

WHITE, Mary–Louise, M.D., Chief Executive Officer, Dr. Solomon Carter Fuller Mental Health Center, Boston, MA, p. A306

WHITE, Mike, Chief Financial Officer, Hansen Family Hospital, Iowa Falls, IA, p. A233

WHITE, Nathan, Chief Information Officer, Charles A. Cannon Memorial Hospital, Newland, NC, p. A471

WHITE, Pamela K., R.N. Chief Nursing Officer and Vice President, Mayo Clinic Health System in Eau Claire, Eau Claire, WI, p. A704

WHITE, Patricia, Vice President Human Resources, Seton Medical Center, Daly City, CA, p. A60

WHITE, Patty, MS, President, St. Joseph's Hospital and Medical Center, Phoenix, AZ, p. A37

WHITE, Randall, Chief Executive Officer, Fayette Regional Health System, Connersville, IN, p. A208

WHITE, Randy, Chief Nursing Officer, Baptist Memorial Hospital–Union County, New Albany, MS, p. A363

WHITE, Robert, Director Information Technology, Helena Regional Medical Center, Helena, AR, p. A47

WHITE, Sabrina, Coordinator Human Resources, Select Specialty Hospital–Charleston, Charleston, WV, p. A695

WHITE, Sam R., Chief Nursing Officer, Gateway Regional Medical Center, Granite City, IL, p. A191

WHITE, Shelia, Director Human Resources, Bon Secours–Richmond Community Hospital, Richmond, VA, p. A677

WHITE, Shirley, Director Human Resources, Ashley County Medical Center, Crossett, AR, p. A44

WHITE, Susan, R.N. Chief Nursing Officer, Bay Area Regional Medical Center, Webster, TX, p. A656

WHITE, Terri, Commissioner, Oklahoma Department of Mental Health and Substance Abuse Services, Oklahoma City, OK, p. B101

WHITE, Vicki, R.N. Chief Nurse Executive, Mills–Peninsula Health Services, Burlingame, CA, p. A57

WHITE, Vicki, Chief Nursing Officer, Santa Rosa Memorial Hospital, Santa Rosa, CA, p. A94

WHITE, Vickie, Director of Nursing, Keokuk Area Hospital, Keokuk, IA, p. A233

WHITE, Wendy
  Vice President Human Resources, CHRISTUS Health Shreveport–Bossier, Shreveport, LA, p. A287
  Regional Vice President Human Resources, CHRISTUS St. Frances Cabrini Hospital, Alexandria, LA, p. A271
  Assistant Administrator Human Resources, CHRISTUS St. Patrick Hospital of Lake Charles, Lake Charles, LA, p. A281

WHITE, Wesley D., Chief Financial Officer, Teton Valley Health Care, Driggs, ID, p. A176

WHITE, Willie, M.D. Director Medical Staff, J. Paul Jones Hospital, Camden, AL, p. A18

WHITE HOUSE, Judy, Vice President Human Resources, St. Mary's Medical Center, Grand Junction, CO, p. A106

WHITE–JACOBS, Mary Beth, R.N., President and Chief Executive Officer, Black River Memorial Hospital, Black River Falls, WI, p. A703

WHITE–TREVINO, Karen, Chief Nursing Officer, West Florida Hospital, Pensacola, FL, p. A142

WHITED, Steve, Chief Executive Officer, Minnie Hamilton HealthCare Center, Grantsville, WV, p. A696

WHITEHEAD, Alva W., M.D. Vice President Medical Services, McLeod Regional Medical Center, Florence, SC, p. A566

WHITEHEAD, Noemi, Administrative Director Human Resources, Sutter Delta Medical Center, Antioch, CA, p. A54

WHITEHORN, Jeffrey T., Chief Executive Officer, TriStar Summit Medical Center, Hermitage, TN, p. A584

WHITEHOUSE, Alan, Chief Information Officer, West Georgia Health, Lagrange, GA, p. A161

WHITEHURST, Rob, Chief, Office of Information and Technology, Veterans Affairs Ann Arbor Healthcare System, Ann Arbor, MI, p. A318

WHITESEL, Carol, MSN Vice President Patient Care Services and Chief Nursing Officer, Community Hospital of Anderson & Madison County, Anderson, IN, p. A206

WHITESIDE, Anne, Vice President Nursing, Winchester Medical Center, Winchester, VA, p. A680

WHITESIDE, John
  Interim Chief Executive Officer, Los Alamos Medical Center, Los Alamos, NM, p. A430
  Chief Operating Officer, Mercy Regional Medical Center, Ville Platte, LA, p. A289

WHITESIDE, Patrick, Manager Information Services, Spectrum Health Big Rapids Hospital, Big Rapids, MI, p. A319

WHITFIELD, Bruce, CPA, Chief Executive Officer and Chief Financial Officer, Cabinet Peaks Medical Center, Libby, MT, p. A389

WHITFIELD Jr., Charles H., President and Chief Executive Officer, Laughlin Memorial Hospital, Greeneville, TN, p. A583

WHITFIELD, Jay, Chief Financial Officer, Baylor University Medical Center, Dallas, TX, p. A609

WHITFIELD, Jo Ann, Business Officer, Walter B. Jones Alcohol and Drug Abuse Treatment Center, Greenville, NC, p. A466

WHITFIELD, Teresa L., MS Chief Nursing Officer, Seneca Healthcare District, Chester, CA, p. A58

WHITING, Barbara, Director Health Information Management, Promise Hospital of Vicksburg, Vicksburg, MS, p. A365

WHITING, Joseph K., FACHE, Interim Chief Executive Officer, Keokuk Area Hospital, Keokuk, IA, p. A233

WHITIS, Matt, Chief Medical Officer, Mahaska Health Partnership, Oskaloosa, IA, p. A236

WHITLATCH, Kristie, President, King's Daughters Medical Center, Ashland, KY, p. A257

WHITLEY, Darla, Manager Health Information Technology, Syringa Hospital and Clinics, Grangeville, ID, p. A176

WHITLEY, Kay, President and Chief Executive Officer, Spanish Peaks Regional Health Center, Walsenburg, CO, p. A111

WHITLEY, Myra, Vice President, Human Resources, Columbus Specialty Hospital, Columbus, GA, p. A156

WHITLEY, Pam, R.N. Chief Operating Officer and Chief Nursing Officer, Green Oaks Hospital, Dallas, TX, p. A610

WHITMER, Carl, President and Chief Executive Officer, IASIS Healthcare, Franklin, TN, p. B71

WHITMIRE, Janice, Interim President, Baylor All Saints Medical Center at Fort Worth, Fort Worth, TX, p. A617

WHITMORE, Ray B., Chief Financial Officer, McCurtain Memorial Hospital, Idabel, OK, p. A513

WHITMORE, Robin, Chief Nursing Officer, MidMichigan Medical Center–Gratiot, Alma, MI, p. A318

WHITMORE, Stewart, Chief Financial Officer, Putnam Community Medical Center, Palatka, FL, p. A141

WHITMORE, W. Patrick, Chief Financial Officer, Medical Center of Plano, Plano, TX, p. A641

WHITNEY, Donald, Director Human Resources, Kindred Hospital–Albuquerque, Albuquerque, NM, p. A427

WHITNUM, Rhonda, Director Health Improvement Management, Prague Community Hospital, Prague, OK, p. A519

WHITSON, Charles P., CPA Senior Vice President Finance, Lake Charles Memorial Hospital, Lake Charles, LA, p. A281

WHITT, Alicia, R.N. Chief Nursing Officer, Stephens Memorial Hospital, Breckenridge, TX, p. A603

WHITT, Charles Christopher, Chief Nursing Officer, River Park Hospital, Huntington, WV, p. A697

WHITT, Stevan, M.D. Chief Medical Officer, University of Missouri Hospitals and Clinics, Columbia, MO, p. A370

WHITTAKER, Kelly, Vice President Nursing, Caro Community Hospital, Caro, MI, p. A320

WHITTAKER, Shawn, Chief Nursing Officer, Miller County Hospital, Colquitt, GA, p. A156

WHITTAKER, Sheena, M.D. Chief Medical Officer, Maine Coast Memorial Hospital, Ellsworth, ME, p. A293

WHITTEMORE, Marjorie, Director Human Resources, Rio Grande Regional Hospital, McAllen, TX, p. A636

WHITTEMORE, Scott
  Chief Financial Officer and Chief of Ancillary Services, Springfield Hospital, Springfield, VT, p. A666
  Chief Financial Officer, University of Mississippi Medical Center Grenada, Grenada, MS, p. A358
  Chief Financial Officer, University of Mississippi Medical Center Holmes County, Lexington, MS, p. A361

WHITTEN, Jacquelyn, R.N. Chief Nurse Executive and Vice President Nursing, Advocate Trinity Hospital, Chicago, IL, p. A183

WHITTEN, Lynnette, Chief Financial Officer, Cochran Memorial Hospital, Morton, TX, p. A637

WHITTINGTON, Bruce, Vice President Human Resources, Pawnee Valley Community Hospital, Larned, KS, p. A247

WHITTINGTON, Dorothy, Chief Financial Officer, University Health Conway, Monroe, LA, p. A284

WHITTINGTON, Hilary, Chief Financial Officer, Jefferson Healthcare, Port Townsend, WA, p. A688

WHITTINGTON, Laurie A., Chief Operating Officer, Memorial Health, Marysville, OH, p. A498

WHITTINGTON, Shane, Chief Financial Officer, Caldwell Medical Center, Princeton, KY, p. A268

WHITTINGTON–GEPPERT, Kelley, Director Human Resources, Munson Healthcare Cadillac Hospital, Cadillac, MI, p. A319

WHITTON, Beth, Director Human Resources, Ocean Beach Hospital, Ilwaco, WA, p. A685

WHOLLEY, Diane, Director Fiscal Services, Bridgewater State Hospital, Bridgewater, MA, p. A308

WHORLEY, Chris, Chief Information Officer, Nashville General Hospital, Nashville, TN, p. A590

WHYBROW, Peter, M.D., Chief Executive Officer, Stewart & Lynda Resnick Neuropsychiatric Hospital at UCLA, Los Angeles, CA, p. A74

WIATREK, Joseph, Director Information Technology, Otto Kaiser Memorial Hospital, Kenedy, TX, p. A630

WIBBENMEYER, Christopher, Director Human Resources, Perry County Memorial Hospital, Perryville, MO, p. A378

WIBBENS, Cheryl, M.D. Vice President Medical Staff Affairs, Memorial Hospital of South Bend, South Bend, IN, p. A222

WIBBLESMAN, Christopher, M.D. Chief of Staff, Colorado Canyons Hospital and Medical Center, Fruita, CO, p. A106

WIBORG, Shelley, MS Director of Nursing, OSF Holy Family Medical Center, Monmouth, IL, p. A197

WICKE, III, Julius, Vice President Finance and Hospital Financial Officer, Baylor Jack and Jane Hamilton Heart and Vascular Hospital, Dallas, TX, p. A609

WICKE, Regina, Chief Financial Officer, Columbus Community Hospital, Columbus, TX, p. A607

WICKENS, Amy Lynn, Executive Director Human Resources, Decatur County Memorial Hospital, Greensburg, IN, p. A212

WICKER, Kenneth R., Chief Executive Officer, Bayfront Health Brooksville, Brooksville, FL, p. A125

WICKIZER, Jr., Boyd, M.D. Chief Medical Officer, Southside Regional Medical Center, Petersburg, VA, p. A676

WICKLANDER, Jeff, President, North Memorial Medical Center, Robbinsdale, MN, p. A349

WICKLINE, Melissa, Director Marketing, Greenbrier Valley Medical Center, Ronceverte, WV, p. A700

WICKLUND, Grant, President and Chief Executive Officer, Lutheran Medical Center, Wheat Ridge, CO, p. A111

WIDEMAN, Jeff, Director Information Systems, Merit Health Gilmore Memorial, Amory, MS, p. A355

WIDENER, Steve, Chief Executive Officer, Jefferson Hospital, Louisville, GA, p. A162

WIDENER, William, Chief Executive Officer, Goodland Regional Medical Center, Goodland, KS, p. A244

WIDGER, Judy, M.D. Chief of Staff, Healdsburg District Hospital, Healdsburg, CA, p. A66

WIDICK, Brent, Superintendent, Kansas Neurological Institute, Topeka, KS, p. A254

WIDNER, Eric W., Division President, Beaumont Hospital – Wayne, Wayne, MI, p. A336

WIDRA, Linda S., R.N., Interim Chief Executive Officer, Lakewood Ranch Medical Center, Bradenton, FL, p. A124

WIEBE, Robert, M.D. Chief Medical Officer, Mercy General Hospital, Sacramento, CA, p. A86

WIECHART, Michael, President and Chief Executive Officer, RCCH HealthCare Partners, Brentwood, TN, p. B113

WIECZOREK, Pawel, Director Information Technology, BryLin Hospitals, Buffalo, NY, p. A435

WIEMAN, Jason S., Commander, Weed Army Community Hospital, Fort Irwin, CA, p. A62

WIEMANN, Michael, M.D., President, Providence – Providence Park Hospital, Southfield Campus, Southfield, MI, p. A334

WIENS, Ron, Chief Financial Officer, Shodair Children's Hospital, Helena, MT, p. A388

WIENTJES, Keri, Director Human Resources, Mobridge Regional Hospital, Mobridge, SD, p. A575

WIERZBICKI, Barb, Manager Human Resources, Select Specialty Hospital–Downriver, Wyandotte, MI, p. A337

WIESNER, Jerry, Chief Executive Officer, Union County General Hospital, Clayton, NM, p. A428

WIEWORA, Ron, M.D. Chief Medical Officer, Lakeside Medical Center, Belle Glade, FL, p. A123

WIGGINS, Carla, Director Human Resources, Livingston Hospital and Healthcare Services, Salem, KY, p. A269

WIGGINS, John, Chief Financial Officer, Evans Memorial Hospital, Claxton, GA, p. A156

WIGGINS, Marjorie, Senior Vice President, Chief Nursing Officer, Maine Medical Center, Portland, ME, p. A294

WIGHTMAN, Lori, FACHE, Chief Executive Officer, Mercy Hospital Ada, Ada, OK, p. A508

WIGINGTON, Yvonne, Vice President, Chief Financial Officer, Wyoming Medical Center, Casper, WY, p. A721

WIGMAN, Cathryn, Director Human Resources, HEALTHSOUTH Braintree Rehabilitation Hospital, Braintree, MA, p. A307

WIGNALL, Terry A., Director Human Resources, St. Vincent Seton Specialty Hospital, Indianapolis, IN, p. A215

WIIK, Jennifer, Chief Nursing Officer, Ortonville Area Health Services, Ortonville, MN, p. A348

WIJAYA, Joanne, Chief Operating Officer, Hampton Behavioral Health Center, Westampton, NJ, p. A425

WIJEWARDANE, Chamath, Director Information Technology, OCH Regional Medical Center, Starkville, MS, p. A365

WILBANKS, John F., FACH
Chief Operating Officer, Baptist Medical Center Beaches, Jacksonville Beach, FL, p. A132
Chief Operating Officer, Baptist Medical Center Jacksonville, Jacksonville, FL, p. A131

WILBUR, Bruce, M.D. Chief Medical Officer, Good Samaritan Hospital, San Jose, CA, p. A91

WILBUR, Thomas W., Chief Executive Officer and Superintendent, Newport Hospital and Health Services, Newport, WA, p. A687

WILBURN, Sue, Vice President Human Resources and Organizational Development, East Tennessee Children's Hospital, Knoxville, TN, p. A585

WILCHER, Greta
Senior Vice President and Chief Financial Officer, Mercy Hospital Fort Smith, Fort Smith, AR, p. A46
Senior Vice President and Chief Financial Officer, Mercy Hospital Waldron, Waldron, AR, p. A53

WILCHER, Kelly, Chief Executive Officer, Carson Tahoe Continuing Care Hospital, Carson City, NV, p. A404

WILCOX, Bill, Chief Information Technology Officer, Bristol Bay Area Health Corporation, Dillingham, AK, p. A29

WILCOX, Billy, Group Controller, Cornerstone Hospital of Bossier City, Bossier City, LA, p. A274

WILCOX, Byron, Chief Financial Management Officer, Standing Rock Service Unit, Fort Yates Hospital, Indian Health Service, DHHS, Fort Yates, ND, p. A479

WILCOX, Jack, Chief Financial Officer, Ennis Regional Medical Center, Ennis, TX, p. A616

WILCOX, James, Chief Executive Officer, El Paso Specialty Hospital, El Paso, TX, p. A615

WILCOX, John, Chief Information Officer, Ozarks Medical Center, West Plains, MO, p. A384

WILCOX, Kyle M., Vice President Finance, Grinnell Regional Medical Center, Grinnell, IA, p. A231

WILCOX, William H., President and Chief Executive Officer, United Surgical Partners International, Addison, TX, p. B141

WILCZEK, Joseph, Chief Executive Officer, St. Elizabeth Hospital, Enumclaw, WA, p. A684

WILCZEK, Vincent Scot, Controller, Pratt Regional Medical Center, Pratt, KS, p. A252

WILD, James, M.D. Medical Director, TLC Health Network – Lake Shore Hospital, Irving, NY, p. A440

WILDE, Gary, President and Chief Executive Officer, Community Memorial Health System, Ventura, CA, p. B41

WILDE, Gary, President and Chief Executive Officer, Community Memorial Hospital, Ventura, CA, p. A98

WILDE, Kathy R., R.N. Chief Nursing Officer, Hennepin County Medical Center, Minneapolis, MN, p. A346

WILDER, Claudia, R.N. Chief Nursing Executive, Baylor University Medical Center, Dallas, TX, p. A609

WILDER, Janet, Director Human Resources, Barbourville ARH Hospital, Barbourville, KY, p. A257

WILDER, Rita, Chief Executive Officer, Select Specialty Hospital–Knoxville, Knoxville, TN, p. A586

WILDER, Susan
Director Financial Services, Roosevelt Warm Springs Rehabilitation and Specialty Hospitals – LTAC, Warm Springs, GA, p. A168
Director Financial Services, Roosevelt Warm Springs Rehabilitation and Specialty Hospitals – Rehab, Warm Springs, GA, p. A168

WILDHAGEN, Quentin, Systems Administrator, Community Medical Center of Izard County, Calico Rock, AR, p. A44

WILDI, Lorri, Interim Chief Executive Officer, Coshocton County Memorial Hospital, Coshocton, OH, p. A492

WILEY, Chuck, Manager Information Systems, Harrison County Hospital, Corydon, IN, p. A208

WILEY, Donald J., President and Chief Executive Officer, St. Joseph's Medical Center, Stockton, CA, p. A95

WILEY, George, Chief Financial Officer, Desert Springs Hospital Medical Center, Las Vegas, NV, p. A405

WILEY, Mark, Manager Information Systems Development, UPMC Bedford Memorial, Everett, PA, p. A538

WILFORD, Linda, CPA Senior Vice President and Chief Financial Officer, Holy Cross Hospital, Fort Lauderdale, FL, p. A128

WILHELM, Christine, Chief Operating Officer, Munson Healthcare Charlevoix Hospital, Charlevoix, MI, p. A320

WILHELM, Connie, Chief Financial Officer, Swisher Memorial Hospital District, Tulia, TX, p. A654

WILHELM, Paul, M.D. Chief of Staff, Kiowa District Hospital and Manor, Kiowa, KS, p. A247

WILHITE, James, Director Systems Information, North Mississippi State Hospital, Tupelo, MS, p. A365

WILHITE, Jerald, Administrator Human Resources, Heartland Behavioral Healthcare, Massillon, OH, p. A498

WILHOITE, David, CPA Senior Vice President Finance and Chief Financial Officer, Trousdale Medical Center, Hartsville, TN, p. A584

WILK, Leonard, President and Chief Executive Officer, AMITA Health Hoffman Estates, Hoffman Estates, IL, p. A193

WILK, Michael, Senior Vice President Financial Services and Chief Financial Officer, Pocono Medical Center, East Stroudsburg, PA, p. A537

WILKE, Kris, Manager Health Information, Granite Falls Municipal Hospital and Manor, Granite Falls, MN, p. A343

WILKEN, Thomas
Senior Vice President and Chief Human Resources Officer, CHRISTUS Mother Frances Hospital – Tyler, Tyler, TX, p. A654
Vice President Human Resources, Seton Medical Center Williamson, Round Rock, TX, p. A644

WILKENS, Gregory, M.D. Chief of Staff, Jellico Community Hospital, Jellico, TN, p. A585

WILKENS, Katy, Chief Nursing Officer and Vice President, Northern Arizona Healthcare, Flagstaff Medical Center, Flagstaff, AZ, p. A32

WILKER, Johnathan, Vice President Finance and Chief Financial Officer, Faith Regional Health Services, Norfolk, NE, p. A399

WILKERSON, Donald H., Chief Executive Officer, St. David's Medical Center, Austin, TX, p. A600

WILKERSON, Jacquelyn, R.N. Chief Nursing Officer, Conway Regional Medical Center, Conway, AR, p. A44

WILKERSON–UDDYBACK, Patricia, M.D. Chief Medical Officer, DMC Harper University Hospital, Detroit, MI, p. A322

WILKES, Chris, MS Director Human Resources, Blount Memorial Hospital, Maryville, TN, p. A588

WILKES, Margaret, Chief Fiscal Officer, Charles George Veterans Affairs Medical Center, Asheville, NC, p. A460

WILKIE, Chance, Information Technology Specialist, Indian Health Service – Quentin N. Burdick Memorial Health Care Facility, Belcourt, ND, p. A477

WILKIE, Paula, Chief Financial Officer, Presentation Medical Center, Rolla, ND, p. A481

WILKINS, Michael, Chief Operating Officer, Advocate Christ Medical Center, Oak Lawn, IL, p. A198

WILKINSON, Kyle, Chief Financial Officer, Morgan Memorial Hospital, Madison, GA, p. A162

WILKINSON, Mark, M.D. Chief Medical Officer, Indian Path Medical Center, Kingsport, TN, p. A585

WILKINSON, Paul G., Chief Operating Officer, Providence St. Peter Hospital, Olympia, WA, p. A687

WILKS, Angela, Finance Director, Missouri Baptist Sullivan Hospital, Sullivan, MO, p. A383

WILL, DeDe, Director Finance, Douglas County Community Mental Health Center, Omaha, NE, p. A400

WILL, Nicole, Human Resources Officer, Herington Municipal Hospital, Herington, KS, p. A244

WILLAMS, Brandon, Chief Financial Officer, Brookwood Baptist Medical Center, Birmingham, AL, p. A16

WILLAMS, Kyle, Director Information Technology, Kirby Medical Center, Monticello, IL, p. A197

WILLAMS, Mike, Chief Information Officer, FHN Memorial Hospital, Freeport, IL, p. A190

WILLARD, Cheri, R.N. Chief Nursing Officer, Evanston Regional Hospital, Evanston, WY, p. A722

WILLARD, Craig, Director Information Technology and Systems, Frankfort Regional Medical Center, Frankfort, KY, p. A260

WILLARD, Ruth, Chief Nursing Officer, TriStar StoneCrest Medical Center, Smyrna, TN, p. A593

WILLCOXON, Phil, Chief Executive Officer, Delta Medical Center, Memphis, TN, p. A588

WILLE, Lesley A., Executive Director, Kaiser Permanente South Bay Medical Center,, CA, p. A72

WILLEKE, Louis R., Administrator, Refugio County Memorial Hospital, Refugio, TX, p. A643

WILLEMSEN, Jane, President and Chief Administrative Officer, John Muir Medical Center, Walnut Creek, Walnut Creek, CA, p. A99

WILLERT, Todd, Chief Executive Officer, Community HealthCare System, Onaga, KS, p. A250

WILLET, Terry, Chief Financial Officer, Allen Parish Hospital, Kinder, LA, p. A280

WILLETT, Charles, Administrator and Chief Executive Officer, Fulton County Hospital, Salem, AR, p. A52

WILLETT, Richard, Chief Executive Officer, Redington–Fairview General Hospital, Skowhegan, ME, p. A295

WILLETT, Simon, Director Administrative Operations, South Texas Veterans Health Care System, San Antonio, TX, p. A647

WILLETT, Vita M.
Senior Vice President, Kaiser Permanente Moreno Valley Medical Center, Moreno Valley, CA, p. A78
Executive Director, Kaiser Permanente Riverside Medical Center, Riverside, CA, p. A85

WILLEY, Randy, Business Manager, Lincoln Regional Center, Lincoln, NE, p. A398

WILLHITE, Jean, Director Human Resources, Sutter Solano Medical Center, Vallejo, CA, p. A98

WILLIAMS, Adrian, Chief Executive Officer, Serenity Springs Specialty Hospital, Ruston, LA, p. A287

WILLIAMS, Alec, Chief Information Officer, Southwest General Health Center, Middleburg Heights, OH, p. A499

WILLIAMS, Amber, Vice President and Chief Financial Officer, Southwest Medical Center, Liberal, KS, p. A248

WILLIAMS, Amy W., M.D. Chief Medical Officer, Mayo Clinic Hospital – Rochester, Rochester, MN, p. A349

WILLIAMS, Andrew G., Chief Executive Officer, Frio Regional Hospital, Pearsall, TX, p. A640

WILLIAMS, Antoinette, Chief Nursing Officer, John H. Stroger Jr. Hospital of Cook County, Chicago, IL, p. A184

WILLIAMS, Arthur, M.D. Medical Director, HEALTHSOUTH Braintree Rehabilitation Hospital, Braintree, MA, p. A307

WILLIAMS, Avilla, MS, President, INTEGRIS Health Edmond, Edmond, OK, p. A511

WILLIAMS, Beverly, R.N. Chief Nursing Officer, Washington County Memorial Hospital, Potosi, MO, p. A378

WILLIAMS, Bob, President and Chief Executive Officer, BSA Hospital, LLC, Amarillo, TX, p. A596

WILLIAMS, Brian, M.D. Chief of Medical Staff, Florida Hospital North Pinellas, Tarpon Springs, FL, p. A148

WILLIAMS, Brian, Web Services and Information Technology Manager, St. Joseph's Hospital of Buckhannon, Buckhannon, WV, p. A694

WILLIAMS, Brian A., Chief Executive Officer, Labette Health, Parsons, KS, p. A252

WILLIAMS, Brit, M.D. President Medical Staff, Dr. John Warner Hospital, Clinton, IL, p. A187

WILLIAMS, Bryan, R.N. Vice President Patient Care Services, CHI St. Vincent Hot Springs, Hot Springs, AR, p. A47

WILLIAMS, Cara, Director Human Resources, Scripps Memorial Hospital–Encinitas, Encinitas, CA, p. A61

WILLIAMS, CarolAnn, Chief Financial Officer, Massachusetts Eye and Ear Infirmary, Boston, MA, p. A307

WILLIAMS, Catherine, M.D. Medical Director, Lewis County General Hospital, Lowville, NY, p. A442

WILLIAMS, Cecille, Assistant Administrator, Shamrock General Hospital, Shamrock, TX, p. A648

WILLIAMS, Chris J., FACHE Vice President Operations, Perry Memorial Hospital, Princeton, IL, p. A201

WILLIAMS, Dan, Vice President Finance and Support, Liberty Hospital, Liberty, MO, p. A375

WILLIAMS, Dana, Chief Financial Officer, Baptist Memorial Hospital–North Mississippi, Oxford, MS, p. A363

WILLIAMS, Dana D., Chief Executive Officer, Jennings American Legion Hospital, Jennings, LA, p. A279

WILLIAMS, Darek, Director Human Resources, Elgin Mental Health Center, Elgin, IL, p. A189

WILLIAMS, Darlene, R.N., Administrator, CHI St. Luke's Health Memorial San Augustine, San Augustine, TX, p. A647

WILLIAMS, David, Director Information Technology, Franklin Hospital District, Benton, IL, p. A181

WILLIAMS, David L., M.D. Chief Medical Officer, St. Vincent Kokomo, Kokomo, IN, p. A216

WILLIAMS, David R., Chief Executive Officer, Centerpoint Medical Center, Independence, MO, p. A372

WILLIAMS, Dionne, Director Human Resources, Vaughan Regional Medical Center, Selma, AL, p. A25

WILLIAMS, Frank L., Executive Vice President/ Medical Director, Kedren Community Mental Health Center, Los Angeles, CA, p. A72

WILLIAMS, Gary
Administrator, SCA Houston Hospital for Specialized Surgery, Houston, TX, p. A626
Executive Director, The Pavilion at Williamsburg Place, Williamsburg, VA, p. A680

WILLIAMS, Ginger, FACHE, President and Chief Executive Officer, Oaklawn Hospital, Marshall, MI, p. A330

WILLIAMS, Greg
Chief Financial Officer, PIH Health Hospital – Downey, Downey, CA, p. A61
Chief Financial Officer, PIH Health Hospital–Whittier, Whittier, CA, p. A99

WILLIAMS, Jackie, Director Human Resources, Merit Health Madison, Canton, MS, p. A356

WILLIAMS, James, M.D. Chief of Staff, ThedaCare Medical Center–Waupaca, Waupaca, WI, p. A718

WILLIAMS, Jason, Director Information Systems, Olympia Medical Center, Los Angeles, CA, p. A73

WILLIAMS, Jeanne, M.D. Chief of Staff, Clark Fork Valley Hospital, Plains, MT, p. A390

WILLIAMS, Jeremy, Chief Financial Officer, Banner Boswell Medical Center, Sun City, AZ, p. A39

WILLIAMS, Jim, Chief Financial Officer, Minden Medical Center, Minden, LA, p. A283

WILLIAMS, Joan, Administrative Assistant/Human Resources, Lamb Healthcare Center, Littlefield, TX, p. A633

WILLIAMS, John
Chief Information Officer, Bay Pines Veterans Affairs Healthcare System, Bay Pines, FL, p. A123
Administrator and Chief Executive Officer, Nell J. Redfield Memorial Hospital, Malad City, ID, p. A177
Chief Financial Officer, Upson Regional Medical Center, Thomaston, GA, p. A167

WILLIAMS, Jr., John D., Chief Financial Officer, Veterans Affairs Gulf Coast Veterans Health Care System, Biloxi, MS, p. A355

WILLIAMS, Joyce, Consultant Human Resources and Organizational Development, Memorial Hermann Rehabilitation Hospital – Katy, Katy, TX, p. A630

WILLIAMS, Julie
Chief Financial Officer, Muenster Memorial Hospital, Muenster, TX, p. A638
Chief Financial Officer, Smith County Memorial Hospital, Smith Center, KS, p. A254

WILLIAMS, Kathy, Chief Nursing Officer, Eastern New Mexico Medical Center, Roswell, NM, p. A431

WILLIAMS, KC, Director, MIS Operations, Lima Memorial Health System, Lima, OH, p. A496

WILLIAMS, Kenneth, Chief Information Officer, Fayetteville Veterans Affairs Medical Center, Fayetteville, NC, p. A465

WILLIAMS, Kim, R.N
Director of Nursing, Mercy Hospital Logan County, Guthrie, OK, p. A512
Chief Operating Officer, Providence Regional Medical Center Everett, Everett, WA, p. A684

WILLIAMS, L. Dale, M.D. Vice President and Chief Medical Director, High Point Regional Health System, High Point, NC, p. A467

WILLIAMS, Laci, Director Human Resources, Kearny County Hospital, Lakin, KS, p. A247

WILLIAMS, Lana R., Chief Nursing Officer, Arkansas Methodist Medical Center, Paragould, AR, p. A51

WILLIAMS, Lauren, M
Vice President of Professional Services and Chief Nursing Officer, Lawrence + Memorial Hospital, New London, CT, p. A116
Vice President Patient Care Services and Chief Nursing Officer, Westerly Hospital, Westerly, RI, p. A561

WILLIAMS, Linda, Director of Nursing, Villa Feliciana Medical Complex, Jackson, LA, p. A278

WILLIAMS, Lorie, R.N. Vice President Nursing, Samaritan Pacific Communities Hospital, Newport, OR, p. A528

WILLIAMS, Lynn
Vice President, Commonwealth Regional Specialty Hospital, Bowling Green, KY, p. A257
Vice President Human Resources, Medical Center at Bowling Green, Bowling Green, KY, p. A258
Vice President Human Resources, Medical Center at Scottsville, Scottsville, KY, p. A269
Vice President, Human Resources, The Medical Center Albany, Albany, KY, p. A257
Vice President, Human Resources, The Medical Center at Caverna, Horse Cave, KY, p. A262

WILLIAMS, Margaret, Chief Financial Officer, Baptist Memorial Hospital for Women, Memphis, TN, p. A588

WILLIAMS, Margo L., R.N. Chief Nursing Officer, Anderson County Hospital, Garnett, KS, p. A243

WILLIAMS, Mark
Chief Physician Executive, Brookwood Baptist Medical Center, Birmingham, AL, p. A16
Chief Financial Officer, Citrus Memorial Health System, Inverness, FL, p. A131

WILLIAMS, Mark, M.D. Vice President and Chief Medical Officer, Miami Valley Hospital, Dayton, OH, p. A493

WILLIAMS, Mary, Director Human Resources, Medina Memorial Hospital, Medina, NY, p. A442

WILLIAMS, Matthew, R.N. Chief Financial Officer, Olympia Medical Center, Los Angeles, CA, p. A73

WILLIAMS, Michael, Chief Information Officer, Lawrence Memorial Hospital, Lawrence, KS, p. A247

WILLIAMS, Michael D., President and Chief Executive Officer, Community Hospital Corporation, Plano, TX, p. B40

WILLIAMS, Michael F., Chief Financial Officer, Limestone Medical Center, Groesbeck, TX, p. A622

WILLIAMS, Michael L., FACHE Vice President Human Resources, Community Howard Regional Health, Kokomo, IN, p. A216

WILLIAMS, Michelle, Administrator, Sedan City Hospital, Sedan, KS, p. A253

WILLIAMS, Mickey, Manager Information Technology, Moccasin Bend Mental Health Institute, Chattanooga, TN, p. A580

WILLIAMS, Nancy Fincher, Administrator, Brooks County Hospital, Quitman, GA, p. A164

WILLIAMS, Nicole, Director of Human Resources Operations, DMC Huron Valley–Sinai Hospital, Commerce Township, MI, p. A321

WILLIAMS, Pam, Chief Executive Officer, Minnesota Valley Health Center, Le Sueur, MN, p. A344

WILLIAMS, Pamela G., Director Human Resources, Unity Health White County Medical Center, Searcy, AR, p. A52

WILLIAMS Sr., Perry E., Administrator and Chief Executive Officer, Alliance HealthCare System, Holly Springs, MS, p. A359

WILLIAMS, Qiana, Director, Human Resource Business Partner, Grant, OhioHealth Grant Medical Center, Columbus, OH, p. A491

WILLIAMS, R. D., Chief Executive Officer, Hendry Regional Medical Center, Clewiston, FL, p. A126

WILLIAMS, Randy, Director Management Information Systems, Maria Parham Medical Center, Henderson, NC, p. A466

WILLIAMS, Reginald, M.D. Medical Staff President, Curry General Hospital, Gold Beach, OR, p. A526

WILLIAMS, Rich, Director Human Resources, Upson Regional Medical Center, Thomaston, GA, p. A167

WILLIAMS, Richard, Chief Operating Officer, Southwest Mississippi Regional Medical Center, McComb, MS, p. A361

WILLIAMS, Robert, R.N., Chief Executive Officer, HEALTHSOUTH Southern Hills Rehabilitation Hospital, Princeton, WV, p. A699

WILLIAMS, Robert D., Chief Executive Officer, Sunbury Community Hospital and Outpatient Center, Sunbury, PA, p. A555

WILLIAMS, Robert J., M.D. Chief Medical Staff, Wills Memorial Hospital, Washington, GA, p. A168

WILLIAMS, Roberta A., Director of Nursing, U. S. Public Health Service Indian Hospital, Cass Lake, MN, p. A340

WILLIAMS, Roby D., Administrator, Hardin County General Hospital, Rosiclare, IL, p. A202

WILLIAMS, Roderick L., M.P.H., President, University Health Shreveport, Shreveport, LA, p. A288

WILLIAMS, Rodney W., M.D. Vice President Medical Affairs, Good Samaritan Regional Medical Center, Suffern, NY, p. A456

WILLIAMS, Ronald G., Administrator, Central Louisiana State Hospital, Pineville, LA, p. A286

WILLIAMS, Sandra
Chief Financial Officer, Cape Fear Valley – Bladen County Hospital, Elizabethtown, NC, p. A465
Chief Financial Officer, Cape Fear Valley Medical Center, Fayetteville, NC, p. A465

WILLIAMS, Scott, Chief Operating Officer, Cookeville Regional Medical Center, Cookeville, TN, p. A581

WILLIAMS, Sean J., President and Chief Executive Officer, Mercy Medical Center–Clinton, Clinton, IA, p. A227

WILLIAMS, Shane, Director Information Systems, Davis Hospital and Medical Center, Layton, UT, p. A660

WILLIAMS, Sharon, Vice President Finance and Information Technology, Avera Marshall Regional Medical Center, Marshall, MN, p. A346

WILLIAMS, Sheila, Vice President and Administrator, Baptist Health Medical Center–Hot Spring County, Malvern, AR, p. A49

WILLIAMS, Sheri, Chief Operating Officer, Guadalupe Regional Medical Center, Seguin, TX, p. A648

WILLIAMS, Stephanie
Coordinator Human Resources, Kindred Rehabilitation Hospital Northeast Houston, Humble, TX, p. A628
Market Director Human Resources, Lake Norman Regional Medical Center, Mooresville, NC, p. A470

WILLIAMS, Stephanie, R.N. Chief Nursing Officer, Washington Hospital Healthcare System, Fremont, CA, p. A63

WILLIAMS, Stephen, Chief Executive Officer, Norton Healthcare, Louisville, KY, p. B97

WILLIAMS, Sue Ann, Chief Executive Officer, Southeast Health Center of Stoddard County, Dexter, MO, p. A370

WILLIAMS, Susan, R.N. Chief Nursing Officer, Baptist Health Medical Center–Stuttgart, Stuttgart, AR, p. A53

WILLIAMS, Susan, M.D
Chief Medical Officer, Conemaugh Memorial Medical Center, Johnstown, PA, p. A541
Chief Medical Officer, Conemaugh Miners Medical Center, Hastings, PA, p. A540

WILLIAMS, Tammy J., R.N. Chief Nursing Officer and Senior Vice President, University Medical Center, Lubbock, TX, p. A634

WILLIAMS, Teresa, R.N.,
Regional Administrator, Mercy Hospital Booneville, Booneville, AR, p. A44
Administrator and Director of Nursing, Mercy Hospital Ozark, Ozark, AR, p. A51

WILLIAMS, Thaddeus, Controller, HEALTHSOUTH Rehabilitation Hospital Memphis–North, Memphis, TN, p. A588

WILLIAMS, Todd, M.D. President Medical Staff, Eastern Idaho Regional Medical Center, Idaho Falls, ID, p. A176

WILLIAMS, Todd
Interim Chief Financial Officer, Forrest City Medical Center, Forrest City, AR, p. A46
Chief Financial Officer, Siloam Springs Regional Hospital, Siloam Springs, AR, p. A52

WILLIAMS, Tom, Vice President Human Resources, Lake Regional Health System, Osage Beach, MO, p. A378

WILLIAMS, Tonja, R.N., President, Continuing Care Hospital, Lexington, KY, p. A263

WILLIAMS, Tricia, President and Chief Executive Officer, Florida Hospital North Pinellas, Tarpon Springs, FL, p. A148

WILLIAMS, Jr., Wendell H., M.D. Medical Director, Specialty Hospital Jacksonville, Jacksonville, FL, p. A132

WILLIAMSON, Alan, M.D. Chief Medical Officer, Eisenhower Medical Center, Rancho Mirage, CA, p. A84

WILLIAMSON, Barry, President Medical Staff, Southeastern Health, Lumberton, NC, p. A469

WILLIAMSON, John, Human Resources Site Manager, Baptist Health South Florida, Mariners Hospital, Tavernier, FL, p. A148

WILLIAMSON, Johnny, M.D. Chief Medical Officer, Hartgrove Hospital, Chicago, IL, p. A184

WILLIAMSON, Katherine, Director of Human Resources, Central Regional Hospital, Butner, NC, p. A461

WILLIAMSON, Marilyn, Chief Human Resources Officer, Rainbow Mental Health Facility, Kansas City, KS, p. A246

WILLIAMSON, Sharon, Chief Information Technology, Robert J. Dole Veterans Affairs Medical Center, Wichita, KS, p. A256

WILLIE, David, Chief Financial Officer, Yuma Regional Medical Center, Yuma, AZ, p. A42

WILLIFORD, Sandy, Chief Health Information Management and Revenue Administration, Charlie Norwood Veterans Affairs Medical Center, Augusta, GA, p. A153

WILLINGHAM, Alex, M.D. Medical Director, Post Acute/Warm Springs Rehabilitation Hospital of San Antonio, San Antonio, TX, p. A646

WILLINGHAM, John, Chief Executive Officer and Managing Director, Carolina Center for Behavioral Health, Greer, SC, p. A567

WILLIS, Barbara, Chief Nursing Officer and Chief Operating Officer, Stonewall Jackson Memorial Hospital, Weston, WV, p. A701

WILLIS, Bill, Director Information Technology, River Point Behavioral Health, Jacksonville, FL, p. A132

WILLIS, Brenda, Director of Nursing, Doctor's Hospital of Deer Creek, Leesville, LA, p. A282

WILLIS, Darrell, M.D. Chief of Staff, Dr. Dan C. Trigg Memorial Hospital, Tucumcari, NM, p. A432

WILLIS, Jayne, Vice President Nursing and Chief Nursing Officer, Orlando Regional Medical Center, Orlando, FL, p. A140

WILLIS, Jonathon, Director Information Services, Tennova Healthcare–Shelbyville, Shelbyville, TN, p. A593

WILLIS, Joshua, Chief Executive Officer, West Florida Community Care Center, Milton, FL, p. A138

WILLIS, Joy, Acting Chief Fiscal Service, G.V. (Sonny) Montgomery Veterans Affairs Medical Center, Jackson, MS, p. A359

WILLIS, Kathy, M.D. Medical Director, Lallie Kemp Medical Center, Independence, LA, p. A278

WILLIS, Raymond, IT Manager, Choctaw Health Center, Philadelphia, MS, p. A363

WILLIS, Robert, Director Human Resources, North Shore Health, Grand Marais, MN, p. A343

WILLIS, Sandra, Director of Human Resources, Citizens Baptist Medical Center, Talladega, AL, p. A25

WILLIS, Toni, M.D. Medical Director, HEALTHSOUTH Rehabilitation Hospital – Mid–Cities, Bedford, TX, p. A602

WILLIS, Wendy L., Vice President Human Resources, Children's Hospital, New Orleans, LA, p. A284

WILLIS, William L., Administrator, Oceans Behavioral Hospital of Lake Charles, Lake Charles, LA, p. A281

WILLMANN, Adam, President and Chief Executive Officer, Goodall–Witcher Hospital Authority, Clifton, TX, p. A606

WILLMON, Brian, M.D. Medical Director, Plains Regional Medical Center, Clovis, NM, p. A428

WILLMORE, Lois, Supervisor Health Information Management, Cedar County Memorial Hospital, El Dorado Springs, MO, p. A370

WILLMS, Frederick, M.D. Chief Medical Officer, Piedmont Fayette Hospital, Fayetteville, GA, p. A159

WILLOUGHBY, Kirsten, Director of Nursing, Big Horn County Memorial Hospital, Hardin, MT, p. A388

WILLS, Andrea, R.N. Chief Nursing Executive, Munising Memorial Hospital, Munising, MI, p. A330

WILLS, Andy, M.D. Medical Director, Colquitt Regional Medical Center, Moultrie, GA, p. A163

WILLS, Kim, Chief Operating Officer, Cook Medical Center–A Campus of Tift Regional Medical Center, Adel, GA, p. A151

WILLS, Laura S.
Administrator, Noland Hospital Birmingham, Birmingham, AL, p. A17
Administrator, Noland Hospital Shelby, Alabaster, AL, p. A15

WILLS, Michele, Registered Health Information Administrator, Caro Center, Caro, MI, p. A320

WILLS, Robert, M.D. Chief Medical Officer, Arise Austin Medical Center, Austin, TX, p. A598

WILLS, Shannon, Director Human Resources, Delray Medical Center, Delray Beach, FL, p. A127

WILLSHER, Jay, Chief Operating Officer, UnityPoint Health – Trinity Bettendorf, Bettendorf, IA, p. A225

WILLSIE, Brett, Vice President Human Resources, Sentara Northern Virginia Medical Center, Woodbridge, VA, p. A680

WILLWERTH, Deborah J., MSN, Chief Executive Officer, Heart of Lancaster Regional Medical Center, Lititz, PA, p. A543

WILLYARD, Deborah, R.N. Senior Director Clinical Services, Mercy Medical Center – West Lakes, West Des Moines, IA, p. A239

WILMOT, Joan, Chief Finance Officer, White River Junction Veterans Affairs Medical Center, White River Junction, VT, p. A666

WILMOTH, Donna, Vice President Patient Care Services and Chief Nursing Officer, Sentara Williamsburg Regional Medical Center, Williamsburg, VA, p. A680

WILMS, Mike, Director Information Systems, Regional Medical Center Bayonet Point, Hudson, FL, p. A131

WILSON, Alice, FACHE Vice President Administration, St. Luke's Hospital – Warren Campus, Phillipsburg, NJ, p. A422

WILSON, Amy, M.D. Medical Director, Baylor Institute for Rehabilitation, Dallas, TX, p. A609

WILSON, Amy, Chief Operating Officer and Chief Nursing Officer, Sacred Heart Hospital Pensacola, Pensacola, FL, p. A142

WILSON, Bill, Chief Financial Officer, North Carolina Specialty Hospital, Durham, NC, p. A464

WILSON, Bobbie, Director Human Resources, Crete Area Medical Center, Crete, NE, p. A395

WILSON, Carolyn, R.N
Chief Operating Officer, Beaumont Hospital – Farmington Hills, Farmington Hills, MI, p. A323
Chief Operating Officer, Beaumont Hospital – Grosse Pointe, Grosse Pointe, MI, p. A326
Chief Operating Officer, Beaumont Hospital – Royal Oak, Royal Oak, MI, p. A333
Chief Operating Officer, Beaumont Hospital – Taylor, Taylor, MI, p. A335
Chief Operating Officer, Beaumont Hospital – Trenton, Trenton, MI, p. A335
Chief Operating Officer, Beaumont Hospital – Troy, Troy, MI, p. A336
Chief Operating Officer, Beaumont Hospital – Wayne, Wayne, MI, p. A336

WILSON, Carolyn, Chief Operating Officer, Beaumont Hospital–Dearborn, Dearborn, MI, p. A321

WILSON, Charlene J., Vice President Human Resources, St. Francis Hospital, Wilmington, DE, p. A120

WILSON, Chase, Chief Financial Officer, Sycamore Shoals Hospital, Elizabethton, TN, p. A582

WILSON, Christopher, M.D. Inpatient Medical Director, South Texas Rehabilitation Hospital, Brownsville, TX, p. A603

WILSON, Christy, Chief Financial Officer, Merit Health Rankin, Brandon, MS, p. A356

WILSON, Colleen, Chief Nursing Officer, Southern Inyo Healthcare District, Lone Pine, CA, p. A69

WILSON, Craig, Chief Medical Officer, St. Vincent Fishers Hospital, Fishers, IN, p. A210

WILSON, David C., Chief Executive Officer, North Mississippi Medical Center – Tupelo, Tupelo, MS, p. A365

WILSON, David R., M.D. Chief of Staff, St. Vincent's Blount, Oneonta, AL, p. A24

WILSON, Deanna, VP Patient Care Services/Site Manager, Aspirus Ontonagon Hospital, Ontonagon, MI, p. A331

WILSON, Deb, Director Human Resources, Kalispell Regional Healthcare, Kalispell, MT, p. A389

WILSON, Deborah J., Senior Vice President and Chief Financial Officer, Lawrence General Hospital, Lawrence, MA, p. A311

WILSON, Debra, Vice President and Chief Nursing Officer, Saint Luke's Hospital of Kansas City, Kansas City, MO, p. A374

WILSON, Dottie D., Director Human Resources, Pickens County Medical Center, Carrollton, AL, p. A18

WILSON, Eleanor, R.N. Vice President and Chief Operating Officer, Doylestown Hospital, Doylestown, PA, p. A537

WILSON, Elizabeth, Administrator, The NeuroMedical Center Rehabilitation Hospital, Baton Rouge, LA, p. A273

WILSON, Elizabeth M., Coordinator Human Resources, Select Specialty Hospital – Cincinnati North, Cincinnati, OH, p. A488

WILSON, Fiore, Director Information Systems, Castleview Hospital, Price, UT, p. A662

WILSON, Hamlin J.
Senior Vice President Human Resources, Wellmont Bristol Regional Medical Center, Bristol, TN, p. A579
Senior Vice President Human Resources, Wellmont Holston Valley Medical Center, Kingsport, TN, p. A585

WILSON, Jason, Administrator and Chief Executive Officer, American Fork Hospital, American Fork, UT, p. A659

WILSON, Jim, Vice President Information Technology, Promise Hospital of San Diego, San Diego, CA, p. A88

WILSON, Jodi, President and Chief Operating Officer, Diley Ridge Medical Center, Canal Winchester, OH, p. A486

WILSON, John R., Vice President, Human Resources, Murray–Calloway County Hospital, Murray, KY, p. A267

WILSON, Kari, R.N. Vice President Patient Care Services and Chief Nursing Officer, SSM Health St. Mary's Hospital – Audrain, Mexico, MO, p. A376

WILSON, Kathey, Acting Chief Executive Officer, U. S. Public Health Service Indian Hospital, Rosebud, SD, p. A576

WILSON, Kim, Human Resources Coordinator, Cordova Community Medical Center, Cordova, AK, p. A28

WILSON, Kimberly P., Director Human Resources, University of Kentucky Albert B. Chandler Hospital, Lexington, KY, p. A263

WILSON, Lawrence, M.D. Vice President, Chief Medical Officer, Midland Memorial Hospital, Midland, TX, p. A637

WILSON, Lerae, Vice President Patient Services and Chief Nursing Officer, St. Claire Regional Medical Center, Morehead, KY, p. A267

WILSON, Loretta, Administrator, Hill Hospital of Sumter County, York, AL, p. A27

WILSON, Mallory, Administrative Assistant and Human Resources Coordinator, Select Specialty Hospital–North Knoxville, Powell, TN, p. A592

WILSON, Maurice, Director of Nursing, Novant Health Charlotte Orthopaedic Hospital, Charlotte, NC, p. A462

WILSON, Nadine, Manager, Human Resources, Jerome Golden Center for Behavioral Health, Inc., West Palm Beach, FL, p. A149

WILSON, Nancy, Senior Vice President and Chief Financial Officer, St. Francis Medical Center, Lynwood, CA, p. A75

WILSON, Nathan, R.N. Vice President and Chief Nursing Officer, Baptist Health La Grange, La Grange, KY, p. A262

WILSON, Nicole, Manager Human Resources, St. Theresa Specialty Hospital, Kenner, LA, p. A279

WILSON, Owetha, Chief Information Officer, Atoka County Medical Center, Atoka, OK, p. A509

WILSON, Patricia, Senior Vice President Human Resources, Englewood Hospital and Medical Center, Englewood, NJ, p. A417

WILSON, Regina, R.N. Director of Nursing, Share Medical Center, Alva, OK, p. A508

WILSON, Robert, D.O. Director Medical Services, Eagleville Hospital, Eagleville, PA, p. A537

WILSON, Robert E.
Vice President and Chief Information Officer, Crozer–Chester Medical Center, Upland, PA, p. A556
Vice President and Chief Information Officer, Delaware County Memorial Hospital, Drexel Hill, PA, p. A537

WILSON, Roy, M.D
Medical Director, Metropolitan St. Louis Psychiatric Center, Saint Louis, MO, p. A380
Medical Director, St. Louis Psychiatric Rehabilitation Center, Saint Louis, MO, p. A381

WILSON, Sara, Director Human Resources, Cheyenne County Hospital, Saint Francis, KS, p. A253

WILSON, Sherry, R.N. Chief Nursing Officer, Mayers Memorial Hospital District, Fall River Mills, CA, p. A62

WILSON, Stephan A., Chief Financial Officer, Montrose Memorial Hospital, Montrose, CO, p. A109

WILSON, Terrance E.
President and CEO, Franciscan St. Elizabeth Health – Crawfordsville, Crawfordsville, IN, p. A208
President and CEO, Franciscan St. Elizabeth Health – Lafayette East, Lafayette, IN, p. A216

WILSON, Tracy, Chief Executive Officer, Kindred Rehabilitation Hospital Northeast Houston, Humble, TX, p. A628

WILSON, Vicki, Human Resources Director, Dixie Regional Medical Center, Saint George, UT, p. A663

WILSON RN, MSN,CEN, Sondra Dianne, R.N. Assistant Administrator and Chief Nursing Officer, Tyler County Hospital, Woodville, TX, p. A658

WILSON–NEIL, Carla, FACHE Chief Operating Officer, Spectrum Health Pennock, Hastings, MI, p. A326

WILSON–STUBBS, Yolande, Regional Chief Operating Officer, Presence Holy Family Medical Center, Des Plaines, IL, p. A188

WILTERMOOD, Michael C., President and Chief Executive Officer, Enloe Medical Center, Chico, CA, p. A58

WILTROUT, Kristy, R.N. Chief Operating Officer, Vernon Memorial Healthcare, Viroqua, WI, p. A717

WILTROUT, Terry, President, Washington Health System Greene, Waynesburg, PA, p. A557

WIMMER, Keri, R.N. Patient Care Director, CentraCare Health–Melrose, Melrose, MN, p. A346

WIMSATT, Michael, Director Human Resources, Piedmont Geriatric Hospital, Burkeville, VA, p. A668

WINBERY, Ben, Chief Financial Officer, Vantage Point of Northwest Arkansas, Fayetteville, AR, p. A46

WINDAS, Allison Leigh, Director of Patient Care Services, Shriners Hospitals for Children–Greenville, Greenville, SC, p. A566

WINDHAM, Joel
  Vice President Human Resources, Anderson Regional Health System, Meridian, MS, p. A362
  Vice President Human Resources, Anderson Regional Health System South, Meridian, MS, p. A362

WINDHAM, Michael D., Chief Executive Officer, Northwest Medical Center, Winfield, AL, p. A26

WINDHAM, William, Chief Operating Officer, Medical Center of McKinney, McKinney, TX, p. A636

WINDLAND, J. Michael, M.D. Chief of Staff, Southern Tennessee Regional Health System–Pulaski, Pulaski, TN, p. A592

WINDLE, Jane, R.N. Director of Nurses, North Mississippi Medical Center–West Point, West Point, MS, p. A366

WINDOLOVICH, Winona, Associate Chief Information Officer, Zuckerberg San Francisco General Hospital and Trauma Center, San Francisco, CA, p. A91

WINDROW, Matthew, M.D. Chief of Staff, Medina Regional Hospital, Hondo, TX, p. A623

WINDSOR, Bonnie, Senior Vice President Human Resources, Johns Hopkins Hospital, Baltimore, MD, p. A296

WINEGARNER, Rodney, Chief Financial Officer, Mercy Hospitals of Bakersfield, Bakersfield, CA, p. A56

WINEKAUF, Glen, Chief Executive Officer, Select Specialty Hospital–Evansville, Evansville, IN, p. A210

WINFREE, Kersey, M.D. Chief Medical Officer, St. Anthony Hospital, Oklahoma City, OK, p. A517

WING, Lilly, Chief Nursing Officer, Three Rivers Behavioral Health, West Columbia, SC, p. A570

WING, Yakesun, Business Strategy and Finance Leader, Kaiser Permanente Walnut Creek Medical Center, Walnut Creek, CA, p. A99

WINGATE, Phyllis A., FACHE, President, Carolinas HealthCare System NorthEast, Concord, NC, p. A463

WINGET, Mary, Director Human Resources, Minden Medical Center, Minden, LA, p. A283

WINGFIELD, Gena, Senior Vice President and Chief Financial Officer, Arkansas Children's Hospital, Little Rock, AR, p. A48

WINIGER, Cecilia, Community Outreach and Communication Manager, Frank R. Howard Memorial Hospital, Willits, CA, p. A100

WINK, Jeri, Director Human Resources, Grandview Medical Center, Birmingham, AL, p. A16

WINKELMAN, Dan, President and Chief Executive Officer, Yukon–Kuskokwim Delta Regional Hospital, Bethel, AK, p. A28

WINKLE, Derek, Director Human Resources, LeConte Medical Center, Sevierville, TN, p. A593

WINKLER, Gordon W., Administrator and Chief Executive Officer, Ringgold County Hospital, Mount Ayr, IA, p. A234

WINN, Ann M., M.D. Chief Nursing Officer, Methodist Stone Oak Hospital, San Antonio, TX, p. A646

WINN, Holly, FACHE Chief Operating Officer, Black River Memorial Hospital, Black River Falls, WI, p. A703

WINNER, Douglas, Chief Financial Officer, Providence – Providence Park Hospital, Southfield Campus, Southfield, MI, p. A334

WINNETT, Steve, Chief Executive Officer, Advanced Diagnostics Hospital, Houston, TX, p. A623

WINNEY, Beverly, Chief Nursing Officer, Washington Regional Medical Center, Fayetteville, AR, p. A46

WINSETT, Gracia, Chief Financial Officer, Wellstone Regional Hospital, Jeffersonville, IN, p. A215

WINSLOW, Virgil, Chief Financial Officer, Texas Orthopedic Hospital, Houston, TX, p. A627

WINSTON, Bob, M.D. Medical Director, Acadia Vermilion Hospital, Lafayette, LA, p. A280

WINSTON, Patricia A., FACHE Vice President, Chief Administrative Officer and Chief Operating Officer, SUNY Downstate Medical Center University Hospital,, NY, p. A450

WINT, Jesse, Director of Nursing, Hardin Medical Center, Savannah, TN, p. A592

WINTER, Jon R., D.O. Chief of Staff, Camden General Hospital, Camden, TN, p. A579

WINTER, Melissa, R.N. Chief Operating Officer and Chief Nursing Officer, Baylor Medical Center at McKinney, McKinney, TX, p. A636

WINTER, Mike, CPA Controller, Wilson N. Jones Regional Medical Center, Sherman, TX, p. A649

WINTER–CLARK, Jan, Chief Executive Officer, Bristow Medical Center, Bristow, OK, p. A509

WINTERS, Gene, Chief Financial Officer, Northwest Texas Healthcare System, Amarillo, TX, p. A596

WINTERS, Heidi, Business Partner Human Resources, CHI Health Missouri Valley, Missouri Valley, IA, p. A234

WINTERS, Janice, Controller, Pickens County Medical Center, Carrollton, AL, p. A18

WINTERS, Mary, Interim Chief Nursing Officer, St. James Healthcare, Butte, MT, p. A386

WINTERS, Shane, Chief Information Officer, Jersey Community Hospital, Jerseyville, IL, p. A194

WINTHER, Mark, M.D. Medical Director, Little Falls Hospital, Little Falls, NY, p. A441

WINTHROP, Michael, President, Bellevue Hospital, Bellevue, OH, p. A485

WIRJO, Jonathan, M.D. Medical Director, Seven Hills Hospital, Henderson, NV, p. A405

WIRTHGEN, Doug
  Chief Information Officer, VA Palo Alto Health Care System, Palo Alto, CA, p. A82
  Facility Chief Information Officer, Veterans Affairs Loma Linda Healthcare System, Loma Linda, CA, p. A69

WIRTZ, David
  Supervisor Information Technology, Evansville Psychiatric Children Center, Evansville, IN, p. A210
  Senior LAN Administrator, Evansville State Hospital, Evansville, IN, p. A210

WISE, Dan, Manager Information Technology, Sarah D. Culberson Memorial Hospital, Rushville, IL, p. A202

WISE, Elizabeth, R.N. Chief Nursing Officer and Vice President, Patient Care Services, Saint Peter's University Hospital, New Brunswick, NJ, p. A420

WISE, Jennifer, Chief Nursing Officer, Franklin Foundation Hospital, Franklin, LA, p. A277

WISE, Jerry R., Chief Executive Officer, Habersham Medical Center, Demorest, GA, p. A158

WISE, Josh, Director Information Technology, Lawrence Memorial Hospital, Walnut Ridge, AR, p. A53

WISE, Kim, Director Human Resources, South Haven Health System, South Haven, MI, p. A334

WISE, Robert P., President and Chief Executive Officer, Hunterdon Medical Center, Flemington, NJ, p. A417

WISE, Teresa, R.N. Chief Nursing Officer, Mena Regional Health System, Mena, AR, p. A50

WISE, Toby, Chief Nursing Officer, Winn Parish Medical Center, Winnfield, LA, p. A289

WISEMANN, Jacob, Chief Financial Officer, Parkland Medical Center, Derry, NH, p. A410

WISEMORE, Donna S., R.N. Vice President and Chief Nursing Officer, DeKalb Health, Auburn, IN, p. A206

WISLER, Tam, Director Human Resources, Dublin Springs, Dublin, OH, p. A494

WISMER, Doug, Chief Financial Officer, Thayer County Health Services, Hebron, NE, p. A396

WISNER, Donna, Chief Financial Officer, Dr. John Warner Hospital, Clinton, IL, p. A187

WISNIESKI, Thomas, FACHE, Director, North Florida/South Georgia Veteran's Health System, Gainesville, FL, p. A129

WISNIEWSKI, Cass, Interim Chief Financial Officer, Hurley Medical Center, Flint, MI, p. A323

WISNOSKI, Joseph, Vice President Finance and Chief Financial Officer, John T. Mather Memorial Hospital, Port Jefferson, NY, p. A453

WISSMAN, Sheryl, M.D. Chief Medical Officer, Crittenton Hospital Medical Center, Rochester, MI, p. A332

WISWELL, Ashleigh, Director Human Resources, Moore County Hospital District, Dumas, TX, p. A614

WITCHER–BOATENG, Bernetta, Ph.D. Director Quality Improvement Services and Compliance, Southwest Connecticut Mental Health System, Bridgeport, CT, p. A113

WITENSKE, James, Chief Information Officer, Jefferson Hospital, Jefferson Hills, PA, p. A541

WITHAM, Val
  Director of Health Information, Avera Dells Area Hospital, Dell Rapids, SD, p. A573
  Director Health Information, Avera Flandreau Hospital, Flandreau, SD, p. A573

WITHERELL, Jodi, Vice President Patient Care and Quality, Brooks Memorial Hospital, Dunkirk, NY, p. A438

WITHERSPOON, Lynn, Vice President and Chief Information Officer, Ochsner Medical Center, New Orleans, LA, p. A285

WITHINGTON, Amber, R.N. Chief Nursing Officer, Rawlins County Health Center, Atwood, KS, p. A240

WITKOWICZ, Victor J., Senior Vice President and Chief Financial Officer, Madonna Rehabilitation Hospital, Lincoln, NE, p. A398

WITMER, Bruce, M.D. Medical Director, Fresno Surgical Hospital, Fresno, CA, p. A63

WITT, David, Chief Financial Officer, Meadows Psychiatric Center, Centre Hall, PA, p. A535

WITT, David A., Vice President Finances, Houston Methodist St. John Hospital, Nassau Bay, TX, p. A638

WITT, Jana, Chief Executive Officer, Cedar County Memorial Hospital, El Dorado Springs, MO, p. A370

WITT, Laura, Administrator Human Resources, Banner Thunderbird Medical Center, Glendale, AZ, p. A33

WITT, Lori, Site Finance Director, Marcum and Wallace Memorial Hospital, Irvine, KY, p. A262

WITT, Sarah, Director Human Resources, Richmond State Hospital, Richmond, IN, p. A221

WITT, Stephen, President and Chief Executive Officer, College Hospital Cerritos, Cerritos, CA, p. A58

WITT, Thomas J., M.D.,
  President and Chief Executive Officer, Mayo Clinic Health System in Cannon Falls, Cannon Falls, MN, p. A340
  President and Chief Executive Officer, Mayo Clinic Health System in Lake City, Lake City, MN, p. A344
  President and Chief Executive Officer, Mayo Clinic Health System in Red Wing, Red Wing, MN, p. A349

WITT, Ty, M.D. Chief Medical Officer, Lake Chelan Community Hospital, Chelan, WA, p. A683

WITTE, Kari, Director Patient Care, Windom Area Hospital, Windom, MN, p. A353

WITTE, Russell, Director Information Technology, Citizens Medical Center, Victoria, TX, p. A655

WITTENSTEIN, Robin D., Ed.D. Director and Chief Operating Officer, Penn State Milton S. Hershey Medical Center, Hershey, PA, p. A540

WITTERSTAETER, Ellen, FACHE, Chief Executive Officer, HEALTHSOUTH Rehabilitation Hospital of Ocala, Ocala, FL, p. A139

WITTHAUS, Patricia, Director Information Services, Valley Regional Hospital, Claremont, NH, p. A410

WITTMAN, Thomas, Chief Information Officer, Jewish Hospital, Louisville, KY, p. A264

WITTROCK, Edward A., Vice President Regional System, Mayo Clinic Health System – Chippewa Valley in Bloomer, Bloomer, WI, p. A703

WITTWER, Julie, Chief Financial Officer, South Texas Surgical Hospital, Corpus Christi, TX, p. A608

WLEKLINSKI, Maria, Chief Nursing Officer, Siloam Springs Regional Hospital, Siloam Springs, AR, p. A52

WODARZ, Christopher A., Chief, Resource Management Division, Tripler Army Medical Center, Honolulu, HI, p. A171

WODICKA, Mary Jo, Vice President Human Resources, Wheaton Franciscan Healthcare – All Saints, Racine, WI, p. A714

WOELKERS, Joe, Executive Vice President and Chief Staff, University of Texas Health Northeast, Tyler, TX, p. A654

WOELTJEN, Bill, Chief Financial Officer, Sarasota Memorial Health Care System, Sarasota, FL, p. A145

WOEN, Linda, Director Human Resources, Yuma Rehabilitation Hospital, Yuma, AZ, p. A42

WOERNER, Steve, President and Chief Executive Officer, Driscoll Children's Hospital, Corpus Christi, TX, p. A608

WOHLFARDT, Diana, Director Human Resources, Nashville General Hospital, Nashville, TN, p. A590

WOHLFORD, Steve, Chief Operating Officer, Johnson Memorial Hospital, Franklin, IN, p. A211

WOHLMAN, John, Manager Information Systems, Shoshone Medical Center, Kellogg, ID, p. A176

WOIRHAYE, Ted, R.N. Director of Nursing, Ruby Valley Hospital, Sheridan, MT, p. A391

WOISKE, Edward, M.D. Chief Medical Officer, Avera Marshall Regional Medical Center, Marshall, MN, p. A346

WOJNO, Kathy, R.N. Vice President Nursing Services and Chief Nursing Officer, Beverly Hospital, Montebello, CA, p. A77

WOJNO, Kathy, MSN, Interim Administrator, Memorial Hospital of Gardena, Gardena, CA, p. A64

WOJTALEWICZ, Jeanette, Chief Financial Officer, CHI Health Mercy Council Bluffs, Council Bluffs, IA, p. A228

WOLAK, Robert, Chief Information Resource Management Service, G.V. (Sonny) Montgomery Veterans Affairs Medical Center, Jackson, MS, p. A359

WOLCOTT, Daniel, President and Chief Executive Officer, Lodi Memorial Hospital, Lodi, CA, p. A68

WOLD, Lynn, President and Chief Executive Officer, UnityPoint Health – St. Luke's, Sioux City, IA, p. A238

WOLESKE, Chris, Chief Operating Officer, Bellin Psychiatric Center, Green Bay, WI, p. A706

WOLF, Brenda J., President and Chief Executive Officer, La Rabida Children's Hospital, Chicago, IL, p. A184

WOLF, Chris, Director Information Technology, Clay County Medical Center, Clay Center, KS, p. A241

WOLF, Edward H., President and Chief Executive Officer, Lakeview Medical Center, Rice Lake, WI, p. A715

WOLF, Gregory A., Director Information Systems, Shriners Hospitals for Children–Honolulu, Honolulu, HI, p. A171

WOLF, Heidi, R.N. Chief Nursing Officer, The Medical Center of Southeast Texas, Port Arthur, TX, p. A642

WOLF, Jack, Vice President Information Systems, Montefiore Medical Center,, NY, p. A446

WOLF, Manuela, R.N., Chief Executive Officer, Harlan County Health System, Alma, NE, p. A393

WOLF, Marc, Assistant Vice President Human Resources, St. Barnabas Hospital,, NY, p. A449

WOLF, R. Chris, Chief Executive Officer, Alta Vista Regional Hospital, Las Vegas, NM, p. A430

WOLF, Randall, Vice President Finance, Perry County Memorial Hospital, Perryville, MO, p. A378

WOLF, Robin, Chief Nursing Officer, Complex Care Hospital at Tenaya, Las Vegas, NV, p. A405

WOLF, Scott A., D.O., President and Chief Executive Officer, Mercy Medical Center, Springfield, MA, p. A315

WOLF, Sherry L., M.D. Chief of Medical Staff, Chillicothe Hospital District, Chillicothe, TX, p. A606

WOLF, Stephanne, Chief Nursing Officer, Morris County Hospital, Council Grove, KS, p. A242

WOLF, Tricia, Director Information Technology, OSS Orthopaedic Hospital, York, PA, p. A559

WOLFE, Anita, Chief Nurse Executive, MultiCare Tacoma General Hospital, Tacoma, WA, p. A692

WOLFE, Brian, Chief of Staff, Allen County Regional Hospital, Iola, KS, p. A245

WOLFE, Cathy Allyson, Chief Nursing Officer, Parkview Wabash County Hospital, Wabash, IN, p. A223

WOLFE, Darryl, Chief Financial Officer, Olympic Medical Center, Port Angeles, WA, p. A688

WOLFE, John, Chief Financial Officer, Saint Elizabeth's Medical Center, Wabasha, MN, p. A352

WOLFE, Lois, Director Human Resources, Geisinger–Community Medical Center, Scranton, PA, p. A554

WOLFE, Philip R., President and Chief Executive Officer, Gwinnett Hospital System, Lawrenceville, GA, p. A162

WOLFE, Phillip R., Chief Executive Officer, Kindred Hospital–Los Angeles, Los Angeles, CA, p. A72

WOLFE, Scott Anthony, Chief Financial Officer, Piedmont Fayette Hospital, Fayetteville, GA, p. A159

WOLFE, Scott R., CPA, President, St. Luke's Hospital – Warren Campus, Phillipsburg, NJ, p. A422

WOLFE, Stephen A., President and Chief Executive Officer, Indiana Regional Medical Center, Indiana, PA, p. A541

WOLFE, Teresa E., Manager Human Resources, Kansas Heart Hospital, Wichita, KS, p. A255

WOLFENBARGER, Carol C., MSN, President and Chief Executive Officer, McDowell Hospital, Marion, NC, p. A469

WOLFF, David, Director Information Technology, Newberry County Memorial Hospital, Newberry, SC, p. A569

WOLFF, Patrice P.
    Director Management Information Systems, Amery Hospital and Clinic, Amery, WI, p. A702
    Director Information Services, Westfields Hospital, New Richmond, WI, p. A713

WOLFF, Peter, M.D. President Medical Staff, Cascade Valley Hospital and Clinics, Arlington, WA, p. A682

WOLFGANG, Tony, Chief Financial Officer, Coatesville Veterans Affairs Medical Center, Coatesville, PA, p. A536

WOLFORD, Dennis A., FACHE, Chief Executive Officer, Macon County General Hospital, Lafayette, TN, p. A586

WOLKART, Kristin, R.N., President and Chief Executive Officer, St. Francis Medical Center, Monroe, LA, p. A283

WOLLEBEN, Robert G., Chief Executive Officer, Massena Memorial Hospital, Massena, NY, p. A442

WOLOSZYN, Daniel B., Chief Executive Officer, Rehabilitation Hospital of Indiana, Indianapolis, IN, p. A214

WOLTEMATH, Kelli, D.O. Chief Medical Staff, George C Grape Community Hospital, Hamburg, IA, p. A231

WOLTER, Nicholas, M.D., Chief Executive Officer, Billings Clinic, Billings, MT, p. A385

WOLTERMAN, Robert K., Chief Executive Officer, Ochsner Medical Center, New Orleans, LA, p. A285

WOLTHER, Eunice, Public Information Officer, Colorado Mental Health Institute at Pueblo, Pueblo, CO, p. A109

WOLTHUIZEN, Dianne, Director Human Resources, Sanford Sheldon Medical Center, Sheldon, IA, p. A237

WOLZ, John, M.D. Chief Medical Staff, Yuma District Hospital, Yuma, CO, p. A112

WOMACK, James, Administrator, Mitchell County Hospital, Camilla, GA, p. A155

WOMEODU, Robin, M.D. Chief Medical Officer, Methodist Healthcare Memphis Hospitals, Memphis, TN, p. A589

WONG, Anne Marie, M.D. Chief Medical Officer, Grays Harbor Community Hospital, Aberdeen, WA, p. A682

WONG, Art, Chief Financial Officer, Heritage Oaks Hospital, Sacramento, CA, p. A86

WONG, Bryan, M.D. Medical Director, Ventura County Medical Center, Ventura, CA, p. A98

WONG, Davies, M.D. Medical Director, Kindred Hospital–San Diego, San Diego, CA, p. A88

WONG, Dionne, Vice President and Chief Human Resources Officer, Broward Health Medical Center, Fort Lauderdale, FL, p. A128

WONG, Karen, Chief Human Resources Officer, Mee Memorial Hospital, King City, CA, p. A67

WONG, Phil, PsyD Chief Operating Officer, Gateways Hospital and Mental Health Center, Los Angeles, CA, p. A71

WONG, Wesley, M.D. Acting Vice President Medical and Academic Affairs, Community Hospital North, Indianapolis, IN, p. A213

WONSER, Matt, Director, Information Services, Providence Regional Medical Center Everett, Everett, WA, p. A684

WOOD, Aaron C., Chief Executive Officer and Administrator, Sanpete Valley Hospital, Mount Pleasant, UT, p. A660

WOOD, Brian, Director Human Resources, Southern Hills Hospital and Medical Center, Las Vegas, NV, p. A406

WOOD, Bud, Chief Human Resources Officer, Saint Thomas West Hospital, Nashville, TN, p. A591

WOOD, Cathy, Vice President, Human Resources, Memorial Hospital at Gulfport, Gulfport, MS, p. A358

WOOD, David P., FACHE, Director, Boise Veterans Affairs Medical Center, Boise, ID, p. A174

WOOD, Drew, Director Information Technology, Eureka Springs Hospital, Eureka Springs, AR, p. A45

WOOD, Erik, Chief Executive Officer, Pioneer Medical Center, Big Timber, MT, p. A385

WOOD, Gregory C., President and Chief Executive Officer, Scotland Health Care System, Laurinburg, NC, p. A468

WOOD, Jim
    Chief Administrative Officer, Confluence Health/Central Washington Hospital, Wenatchee, WA, p. A693
    Chief Human Resources Officer, Confluence Health/Wenatchee Valley Hospital, Wenatchee, WA, p. A693

WOOD, Joann, M.D. Chief Medical Officer, Baptist Memorial Hospital–Desoto, Southaven, MS, p. A365

WOOD, John, Regional Chief Executive Officer, Baylor Scott & White Emergency Hospital– Cedar Park, Cedar Park, TX, p. A605

WOOD, Joseph, Vice President and Chief Information Officer, Brookhaven Memorial Hospital Medical Center, Patchogue, NY, p. A452

WOOD, Joyce, Vice President Organizational Improvement and Chief Nursing Officer, Riverview Health, Noblesville, IN, p. A220

WOOD, Kevin, Interim Chief Clinical Officer, Promise Hospital of San Diego, San Diego, CA, p. A88

WOOD, Lawrence, M.D. Chief Medical Officer, Littleton Adventist Hospital, Littleton, CO, p. A108

WOOD, Lisa, Chief Financial Officer, Brown County Hospital, Ainsworth, NE, p. A393

WOOD, Jr., Phillip E., Chief Information Officer, Cape Fear Valley Medical Center, Fayetteville, NC, p. A465

WOOD, Richard, Chief Financial Officer, Seton Medical Center, Daly City, CA, p. A60

WOOD, Sandy, MSN Vice President Patient Services and Chief Nursing Officer, O'Bleness Memorial Hospital, Athens, OH, p. A484

WOOD, Thomas, M.D. Chief Medical Officer, Page Hospital, Page, AZ, p. A35

WOOD, Tina, Chief Financial Officer, DMC Harper University Hospital, Detroit, MI, p. A322

WOOD, Troy, Chief Executive Officer, Lakeview Hospital, Bountiful, UT, p. A659

WOOD, William, M.D. Vice President Medical Affairs, St. Joseph Hospital, Bangor, ME, p. A291

WOOD, William E., M.D. Chief of Staff, Sequoyah Memorial Hospital, Sallisaw, OK, p. A519

WOOD–ALLEN, Diane, MS Chief Nursing Officer, Concord Hospital, Concord, NH, p. A410

WOODALL, Jay, Chief Executive Officer, Corpus Christi Medical Center, Corpus Christi, TX, p. A607

WOODALL, Lois, Director Human Resources, Lighthouse Care Center of Conway, Conway, SC, p. A565

WOODARD, Andy, Chief Financial Officer, Forrest General Hospital, Hattiesburg, MS, p. A359

WOODARD, James, Chief Nursing Officer, St. Thomas More Hospital, Canon City, CO, p. A102

WOODARD, Victor, Manager Information Technology, Dodge County Hospital, Eastman, GA, p. A159

WOODBECK, Terry L., Administrator, Tulsa Spine and Specialty Hospital, Tulsa, OK, p. A522

WOODCOCK, Lisa, Director Human Resources, Gordon Memorial Hospital, Gordon, NE, p. A396

WOODDELL, Mike, Director Information Services, Fairmont Regional Medical Center, Fairmont, WV, p. A696

WOODHOUSE, Janice, Director of Nursing, Missouri River Medical Center, Fort Benton, MT, p. A387

WOODIN, Joseph L., Chief Executive Officer, Martha's Vineyard Hospital, Oak Bluffs, MA, p. A313

WOODLOCK, Kristin M., R.N., Acting Commissioner, New York State Office of Mental Health, Albany, NY, p. B95

WOODRICH, John T., President and Chief Operating Officer, Bryan Medical Center, Lincoln, NE, p. A397

WOODRING, Mark, Chief Executive Officer, Coffeyville Regional Medical Center, Coffeyville, KS, p. A241

WOODRUFF, Kathy, R.N. Chief Nursing Officer, Marshall Medical Center North, Guntersville, AL, p. A21

WOODRUFF, Stephen, M.D. Chief Medical Officer, NEA Baptist Memorial Hospital, Jonesboro, AR, p. A48

WOODS, Bob, Chief Information Officer, Stanford Health Care – ValleyCare, Pleasanton, CA, p. A83

WOODS, Brian
    Human Resources Director, Andalusia Health, Andalusia, AL, p. A15
    Director Human Resources, Tennova Healthcare–Shelbyville, Shelbyville, TN, p. A593

WOODS, Cheryl, Chief Nursing Officer, Ochsner Medical Center – North Shore, Slidell, LA, p. A288

WOODS, Dan, President, WellStar Kennestone Hospital, Marietta, GA, p. A163

WOODS, Jr., Duane L., Chief Financial Officer, Fisher–Titus Medical Center, Norwalk, OH, p. A500

WOODS, Eugene A., FACHE, President and Chief Executive Officer, Carolinas Healthcare System, Charlotte, NC, p. B27

WOODS, Fred, Chief Financial Officer, The BridgeWay, North Little Rock, AR, p. A51

WOODS, Jeffrey, Chief Executive Officer, TrustPoint Hospital, Murfreesboro, TN, p. A590

WOODS, Jennifer, R.N. Chief Nursing Officer, McLaren Northern Michigan, Petoskey, MI, p. A331

WOODS, Josh, Director Information Systems, Camden Clark Medical Center, Parkersburg, WV, p. A698

WOODS, Julia, R.N. Vice President and Chief Nursing Officer, Saint Luke's South Hospital, Overland Park, KS, p. A251

WOODS, Marlene, Director Human Resources, Day Kimball Hospital, Putnam, CT, p. A116

WOODS, Matthew, Vice President Finance, Winchester Hospital, Winchester, MA, p. A316

WOODS, Rashawn, Vice President Human Resources, Barlow Respiratory Hospital, Los Angeles, CA, p. A70

WOODS, Rebecca, Chief Information Officer, Porter Medical Center, Middlebury, VT, p. A665

WOODS, Regetta, Chief Nursing Officer and Chief Clinical Officer, Promise Hospital of Miss Lou, Vidalia, LA, p. A289

WOODS, Suzanne
    President and Chief Executive Officer, Flowers Hospital, Dothan, AL, p. A19
    Senior Vice President of Nursing, Memorial Hospital Jacksonville, Jacksonville, FL, p. A131

WOODS, Theresa L., MSN Chief Nursing Officer, Jennings American Legion Hospital, Jennings, LA, p. A279

WOODS, Trina, Administrator, Noland Hospital Anniston, Anniston, AL, p. A15

WOODS, Willard, M.D. Chief Medical Officer, Platte County Memorial Hospital, Wheatland, WY, p. A724

WOODSON, Leslie, R.N. Chief Nursing Officer, Shasta Regional Medical Center, Redding, CA, p. A84

WOODSON, Stephen, D.O. Chief of Staff, Haskell County Community Hospital, Stigler, OK, p. A520

WOODWARD, Ashley, Director Financial Services, Valley County Health System, Ord, NE, p. A401

WOODWARD, David E., Executive Director, Devereux Children's Behavioral Health Center, Malvern, PA, p. A543

WOODWARD, James L., President and Chief Executive Officer, St. Mary Medical Center, Langhorne, PA, p. A542

WOODWARD, Lisa J., R.N. Vice President, Patient Care Continuum and Chief Nursing Officer, Sarah Bush Lincoln Health Center, Mattoon, IL, p. A196

WOODWARD, Martin D., Director Acute Care Services, Larry B. Zieverink, Sr. Alcoholism Treatment Center, Raleigh, NC, p. A472

WOODWARD, Russell, M.D. Chief Medical Officer, Methodist Hospital, San Antonio, TX, p. A646

WOODYARD, Elizabeth, MSN, Chief Executive Officer, Petersburg Medical Center, Petersburg, AK, p. A30

WOODYARD, Nancy, Chief Financial Officer, Neosho Memorial Regional Medical Center, Chanute, KS, p. A241

WOOLRIDGE, Joseph, Chief Financial Officer, Brownwood Regional Medical Center, Brownwood, TX, p. A604

WOOLEY, Jacqueline, Vice President, Southern New Hampshire Medical Center, Nashua, NH, p. A412

WOOLLEY, Diane, Vice President Human Resources, Waterbury Hospital, Waterbury, CT, p. A117

WOOLLEY, Jacqueline, Vice President Human Resources, St. Joseph Hospital, Nashua, NH, p. A412

WOOLLEY, Sheila, R.N. Vice President, Patient Care Services, Wentworth–Douglass Hospital, Dover, NH, p. A410

WOOLRIDGE, Regina, Director Human Resources, Cumberland Surgical Hospital, San Antonio, TX, p. A645

WOOLSTENHULME, Daren, Chief Financial Officer, HEALTHSOUTH Rehabilitation Hospital of Utah, Sandy, UT, p. A664

WOOTEN, Scott
Senior Vice President and Chief Financial Officer, Baptist Medical Center Beaches, Jacksonville Beach, FL, p. A132
Senior Vice President and Chief Financial Officer, Baptist Medical Center Jacksonville, Jacksonville, FL, p. A131

WOOTTON, Aaron, Vice President Health Information Systems, Henry Ford Allegiance Health, Jackson, MI, p. A327

WORATSCHEK, Alan, System Director of Information Services, Desert Springs Hospital Medical Center, Las Vegas, NV, p. A405

WORD, Jenni, R.N. Chief Nursing Officer, Wallowa Memorial Hospital, Enterprise, OR, p. A525

WORDEKEMPER, Jerry, President and Chief Executive Officer, St. Francis Memorial Hospital, West Point, NE, p. A403

WORDEN, Beth, Director Nursing Services, McPherson Hospital, McPherson, KS, p. A249

WORDEN, Kieth Anne, Director Human Resources, Mildred Mitchell–Bateman Hospital, Huntington, WV, p. A697

WORKMAN, Jennifer, Director Human Resources, Jane Phillips Memorial Medical Center, Bartlesville, OK, p. A509

WORKMAN, Jessika M., Chief Nursing Officer, Wesley Rehabilitation Hospital, Wichita, KS, p. A256

WORKMAN, Mark, M.D. Chief Medical Officer, West Jefferson Medical Center, Marrero, LA, p. A283

WORLEY III, John C., Chief Executive Officer, Cache Valley Hospital, North Logan, UT, p. A661

WORLEY, Joseph, Human Resources Coordinator, Regency Hospital of Hattiesburg, Hattiesburg, MS, p. A359

WORLEY, Stella, Director of Finance, Keefe Memorial Hospital, Cheyenne Wells, CO, p. A102

WORMAN, Scott, Chief of Staff, Tri–City Medical Center, Oceanside, CA, p. A80

WORRELL, James W., Chief Financial Officer, Pioneers Medical Center, Meeker, CO, p. A109

WORRICK, Gerald M., President and Chief Executive Officer, Ministry Door County Medical Center, Sturgeon Bay, WI, p. A717

WORSOWICZ, Gregory, M.D. Medical Director, Howard A. Rusk Rehabilitation Center, Columbia, MO, p. A370

WORTHAM, Christopher, Chief Executive Officer, HEALTHSOUTH Rehabilitation Hospital Midland–Odessa, Midland, TX, p. A637

WORTHAM, Turner, Chief Financial Officer, Grand Strand Regional Medical Center, Myrtle Beach, SC, p. A568

WORTHY, David, M.D. Vice President and Chief Medical Officer, Baptist Health Corbin, Corbin, KY, p. A258

WORTMAN, Rand J., President and Chief Executive Officer, Kadlec Regional Medical Center, Richland, WA, p. A689

WOZNIKAITIS, Linda, Chief Financial Officer, Southwest Connecticut Mental Health System, Bridgeport, CT, p. A113

WRAALSTAD, Kimber L., FACHE, Administrator, North Shore Health, Grand Marais, MN, p. A343

WRAGGE, Jean, Chief Nursing Officer, Limestone Medical Center, Groesbeck, TX, p. A622

WRATCHFORD, R. Austin, Chief Operating Officer, Parkview Regional Hospital, Mexia, TX, p. A637

WRAY, Charlotte, MSN, President, University Hospitals Elyria Medical Center, Elyria, OH, p. A494

WRAY, Christine R.
President, MedStar Southern Maryland Hospital Center, Clinton, MD, p. A300
President, MedStar St. Mary's Hospital, Leonardtown, MD, p. A302

WRAY, Dean, Vice President Finance, Southern Ohio Medical Center, Portsmouth, OH, p. A501

WRAY, Jeremy, D.O. Medical Director, Sage Memorial Hospital, Ganado, AZ, p. A32

WRAY, Thomas, Director Information, Geisinger–Bloomsburg Hospital, Bloomsburg, PA, p. A533

WREN, Mark A., M.D. Medical Director, HEALTHSOUTH Rehabilitation Hospital of Texarkana, Texarkana, TX, p. A652

WREN, Timothy, Chief Financial Officer, Abbeville Area Medical Center, Abbeville, SC, p. A562

WRIGHT, Albert, PharmD, President and Chief Executive Officer, West Virginia University Health System, Morgantown, WV, p. B154

WRIGHT, Albert, PharmD, President and Chief Executive Officer, West Virginia University Hospitals, Morgantown, WV, p. A698

WRIGHT, Ann L., R.N. Assistant Central Delivery System CNO, Presbyterian Hospital, Albuquerque, NM, p. A428

WRIGHT, April, Human Resources Officer, Collingsworth General Hospital, Wellington, TX, p. A657

WRIGHT, Bennie B., M.D. Chief of Staff, North Sunflower Medical Center, Ruleville, MS, p. A364

WRIGHT, Betsy T., President and Chief Executive Officer, Woman's Christian Association Hospital, Jamestown, NY, p. A441

WRIGHT, Brady, Information Technology Network Administrator, Washington County Hospital, Chatom, AL, p. A18

WRIGHT, Calvin, Chief Information Officer, Hutchinson Regional Medical Center, Hutchinson, KS, p. A245

WRIGHT, Carlene, Chief Financial Officer, Vibra Hospital of Amarillo, Amarillo, TX, p. A596

WRIGHT, Carol, Chief Nursing Officer, AllianceHealth Madill, Madill, OK, p. A514

WRIGHT, Charles, Chief Financial Officer, Ashe Memorial Hospital, Jefferson, NC, p. A468

WRIGHT, Charles T., President and Chief Executive Officer, St. James Healthcare, Butte, MT, p. A386

WRIGHT, Connie, Vice President Human Resources, Texas Scottish Rite Hospital for Children, Dallas, TX, p. A611

WRIGHT, Creighton, M.D. Vice President Medical Administration, Mercy Health – West Hospital, Cincinnati, OH, p. A488

WRIGHT, Dan, Vice President Human Resources, Children's Mercy South, Overland Park, KS, p. A251

WRIGHT, Daniel, Director Information Technology, Saint Alphonsus Medical Center – Nampa, Nampa, ID, p. A177

WRIGHT, Debra J., R.N., Chief Executive Officer, Howard Memorial Hospital, Nashville, AR, p. A50

WRIGHT, Dustin, Chief Executive Officer, Community Memorial Hospital, Sumner, IA, p. A238

WRIGHT, Fran, Director of Nursing, Broadwater Health Center, Townsend, MT, p. A391

WRIGHT, James, M.D. Chief Financial Officer, Cypress Fairbanks Medical Center, Houston, TX, p. A606

WRIGHT, Jennifer, Vice President Regional Human Resources, CHRISTUS St. Michael Health System, Texarkana, TX, p. A652

WRIGHT, Jody, Interim Chief Nursing Officer, Mercy Medical Center–New Hampton, New Hampton, IA, p. A235

WRIGHT, Joe, Chief Financial Officer, Mitchell County Hospital, Colorado City, TX, p. A606

WRIGHT, Julie M., Director Human Resources, Ridgeview Psychiatric Hospital and Center, Oak Ridge, TN, p. A592

WRIGHT, Kenneth, Chief Financial Officer, Robert Wood Johnson University Hospital Somerset, Somerville, NJ, p. A423

WRIGHT, Krista, Director Human Resources, St. Vincent Frankfort Hospital, Frankfort, IN, p. A211

WRIGHT, Linda
Chief Financial Officer, HEALTHSOUTH Rehabilitation Hospital of Alexandria, Alexandria, LA, p. A271
Director Information, Ottawa County Health Center, Minneapolis, KS, p. A249

WRIGHT, Mark
Vice President, Aultman Hospital, Canton, OH, p. A486
Chief Financial Officer, Aultman Specialty Hospital, Canton, OH, p. A486

WRIGHT, Mark J., Vice President Finance, Aurelia Osborn Fox Memorial Hospital, Oneonta, NY, p. A452

WRIGHT, Mary, Vice President Nursing Services and Chief Nursing Officer, Cortland Regional Medical Center, Cortland, NY, p. A437

WRIGHT, Maura, Chief Nursing Officer, Southern Hills Hospital and Medical Center, Las Vegas, NV, p. A406

WRIGHT, Nancy, M.D. Chief Medical Staff, Alta Vista Regional Hospital, Las Vegas, NM, p. A430

WRIGHT, Peter J., FACHE, Chief Executive Officer, Valley Regional Hospital, Claremont, NH, p. A410

WRIGHT, II, Philoron A., FACHE Chief Operating Officer, Munroe Regional Medical Center, Ocala, FL, p. A139

WRIGHT, Robert
Senior Human Resource Advisor, East Ohio Regional Hospital, Martins Ferry, OH, p. A498
Senior Human Resource Advisor, Ohio Valley Medical Center, Wheeling, WV, p. A701

WRIGHT, Robert, M.D. Chief of Staff, Washington County Regional Medical Center, Sandersville, GA, p. A165

WRIGHT, Robert N., Chief Executive Officer, Newman Regional Health, Emporia, KS, p. A242

WRIGHT, Rory, M.D. President Medical Staff, Orthopaedic Hospital of Wisconsin – Glendale, Glendale, WI, p. A706

WRIGHT, Sandra Gayle, Chief Executive Officer, Tyler County Hospital, Woodville, TX, p. A658

WRIGHT, Sharon, R.N. Vice President and Chief Nursing Officer, Hardin Memorial Hospital, Elizabethtown, KY, p. A259

WRIGHT, Stephanie, Director Human Resources Management, VA San Diego Healthcare System, San Diego, CA, p. A89

WRIGHT, Stuart M., CPA Chief Financial Officer, Upstate University Hospital, Syracuse, NY, p. A457

WRIGHT, Terri, Vice President and Chief Nursing Officer, Warren Memorial Hospital, Front Royal, VA, p. A671

WRIGHT, Tom, Director Human Resources, Kindred Hospital Riverside, Perris, CA, p. A82

WRIGHT, Trevor, Chief Operating Officer, Loma Linda University Medical Center, Loma Linda, CA, p. A69

WRIGHT, Wes, Senior Vice President and Chief Information Officer, Seattle Children's Hospital, Seattle, WA, p. A689

WRIGHT–WHITAKER, Ruth, Director Information Services, Cornerstone Medical Center, Fort Oglethorpe, GA, p. A160

WRINN, Denise, Vice President Finance and Chief Financial Officer, Cortland Regional Medical Center, Cortland, NY, p. A437

WROBBEL, Patricia A., Senior Vice President and Chief Nurse Executive, Westchester Medical Center, Valhalla, NY, p. A458

WROBLEWSKI, Edmund, M.D
Vice President Medical Affairs and Chief Medical Officer, Goleta Valley Cottage Hospital, Santa Barbara, CA, p. A93
Vice President Medical Affairs and Chief Medical Officer, Santa Barbara Cottage Hospital, Santa Barbara, CA, p. A93
Vice President Medical Affairs and Chief Medical Officer, Santa Ynez Valley Cottage Hospital, Solvang, CA, p. A94

WROGG, Frank, Director Information Technology, Mayo Clinic Health System – Red Cedar in Menomonie, Menomonie, WI, p. A710

WU, Jonathan, M.D., President and Chairman, AHMC & Healthcare, Inc., Alhambra, CA, p. B8

WU, Jonathan, Vice President Human Resources, Valley Presbyterian Hospital, CA, p. A75

WU, Kenneth, M.D. Medical Director, Marlton Rehabilitation Hospital, Marlton, NJ, p. A419

WUCHTER, Greg, MSN, Administrator, Good Shepherd Specialty Hospital, Bethlehem, PA, p. A533

WUENSCHEL, Diedra, D.O. President Medical Staff, Coryell Memorial Hospital, Gatesville, TX, p. A620

WUKITSCH, Michael
Vice President Human Resources, Northwestern Medicine Central DuPage Hospital, Winfield, IL, p. A205
Vice President Human Resources, Northwestern Medicine Delnor Hospital, Geneva, IL, p. A191

WUNDERWALD, Wendie, R.N. Vice President Patient Care Services, Samaritan Lebanon Community Hospital, Lebanon, OR, p. A527

WURGLER, Brad D., Chief Financial Officer, Perham Health, Perham, MN, p. A348

WURSTER, Rosemary H., Vice President Patient Care Services, Riddle Hospital, Media, PA, p. A545

WURTZEL, Leann, Director Human Resources, Mayo Clinic Health System – Red Cedar in Menomonie, Menomonie, WI, p. A710

WYACO, Melissa, Chief Nurse Executive, Hopi Health Care Center, Keams Canyon, AZ, p. A33

WYATT, Basil, Chief Financial Officer, AMG Specialty Hospital–Tulsa, Tulsa, OK, p. A521

WYATT, Christopher B., Chief Executive Officer, Cavalier County Memorial Hospital and Clinics, Langdon, ND, p. A480

WYATT, Christy, R.N. Interim Chief Nursing Officer, Jackson Parish Hospital, Jonesboro, LA, p. A279

WYATT, Jana, Chief Executive Officer, Mizell Memorial Hospital, Opp, AL, p. A24

WYATT, Leslie G., Senior Vice President Children's Services and Executive Director, Children's Hospital of Richmond at VCU–Brook Road Campus, Richmond, VA, p. A677

WYBLE, Karen, R.N., Chief Executive Officer, St. Martin Hospital, Breaux Bridge, LA, p. A274

WYDICK, Sue, Director Human Resources, Ohio County Hospital, Hartford, KY, p. A261

WYDRA, Lana, Vice President Human Resources, Nathan Littauer Hospital and Nursing Home, Gloversville, NY, p. A439

WYER, Jolena, R.N. Chief Nursing Officer, Oklahoma Center for Orthopedic and Multi–Specialty Surgery, Oklahoma City, OK, p. A516

WYERS, Michael, Chief Financial Officer, Medical Center of Trinity, Trinity, FL, p. A148

WYLIE, Eugene, Chief Human Resources Officer, Veterans Affairs Loma Linda Healthcare System, Loma Linda, CA, p. A69

WYLIE, Patrick, Director Information Systems, Petaluma Valley Hospital, Petaluma, CA, p. A82

WYMAN, Alan, Chief Information Officer, Providence Hospital, Washington, DC, p. A122

WYMAN, David, President and Chief Executive Officer, Gracie Square Hospital, New York, NY, p. A444

WYMER, Melanie, Director Human Resources, Highland District Hospital, Hillsboro, OH, p. A496

WYNN, Katherine, Director Human Resource, Oklahoma Heart Hospital, Oklahoma City, OK, p. A517

WYNN, Paige
Chief Financial Officer, Dorminy Medical Center, Fitzgerald, GA, p. A159
Administrator, Irwin County Hospital, Ocilla, GA, p. A164

WYSE, Debbie, Controller, Quillen Rehabilitation Hospital, Johnson City, TN, p. A585

WYSOCKI, Greg, Chief Financial Officer, Austin Lakes Hospital, Austin, TX, p. A598

WYSONG–HARDER, Alyson, Chief Executive Officer, Heartland Behavioral Health Services, Nevada, MO, p. A377

Y

YABLONKA, Eric, Vice President and Chief Information Officer, University of Chicago Medical Center, Chicago, IL, p. A187

YABUT, Eduardo, M.D. Medical Director, North Dakota State Hospital, Jamestown, ND, p. A480

YAEGER, Eric, M.D
Chief Medical Officer, Kindred Hospital–Aurora, Aurora, CO, p. A101
Medical Director, Kindred Hospital–Denver, Denver, CO, p. A103

YAHNER, Michael, Chief Financial Officer, Torrance State Hospital, Torrance, PA, p. A555

YAKE, Laurie B., Vice President Finance, Aurora Medical Center, Kenosha, WI, p. A708

YAKLIN, Shelleye, President and Chief Executive Officer, North Ottawa Community Hospital, Grand Haven, MI, p. A324

YAKULIS, Paul, MS Senior Vice President Human Resources, Lankenau Medical Center, Wynnewood, PA, p. A558

YALLOWITZ, Joseph, M.D. Vice President Medical Affairs, Valley Hospital, Ridgewood, NJ, p. A423

YAMADA, Chrissy, CPA Chief Financial Officer, EvergreenHealth, Kirkland, WA, p. A686

YAMADA, Jeff, Vice President, Yakima Valley Memorial Hospital, Yakima, WA, p. A693

YAMAN, Tonguc, Deputy Chief Information Officer, NYC Health + Hospitals / Bellevue, New York, NY, p. A447

YANCY, Daniel, Chief Executive Officer, Riceland Medical Center, Winnie, TX, p. A658

YANES, John C., Chief Executive Officer, Andalusia Health, Andalusia, AL, p. A15

YANEZ, Maria J., Chief Financial Officer, Baptist Health South Florida, Doctors Hospital, Coral Gables, FL, p. A126

YANGA, Ismael David, M.D. Chief Medical Officer, Brighton Center for Recovery, Brighton, MI, p. A319

YANIK, Sahin, M.D
Vice President Medical Associate, St. John's Pleasant Valley Hospital, Camarillo, CA, p. A57
Vice President Medical Administration, St. John's Regional Medical Center, Oxnard, CA, p. A81

YANNI, Anthony, M.D. Vice President Medical Affairs, Regional Hospital of Scranton, Scranton, PA, p. A554

YANNI, Jason, Senior Financial Analyst, Novant Health Huntersville Medical Center, Huntersville, NC, p. A467

YAO, Eveline F., Commander, U. S. Air Force Regional Hospital, Eglin AFB, FL, p. A128

YAP, Elvy, Director of Finance, Rush Oak Park Hospital, Oak Park, IL, p. A199

YAP, Eric, Chief Executive Officer, OhioHealth Rehabilitation Hospital, Columbus, OH, p. A491

YARBOROUGH, Dianne, Director of Information Technology, Centennial Medical Center, Frisco, TX, p. A619

YARBROUGH, Michelle, Coordinator Human Resources, Allegiance Specialty Hospital of Kilgore, Kilgore, TX, p. A630

YARBROUGH, Ruth, Vice President, MercyHealth Rockton Avenue Hospital, Rockford, IL, p. A202

YARLING, John, M.D. Medical Director, Four County Counseling Center, Logansport, IN, p. A217

YARMEL, Jeffrey N., Chief Operating Officer, St. Mary Medical Center, Langhorne, PA, p. A542

YARN, Jayce, Director Information Technology, Marias Medical Center, Shelby, MT, p. A391

YAROCH, Julie, D.O.,
President, ProMedica Bixby Hospital, Adrian, MI, p. A318
President, ProMedica Herrick Hospital, Tecumseh, MI, p. A335

YARRAMSETTI, Sri
Chief Information Officer, Chapman Global Medical Center, Orange, CA, p. A80
Chief Information Officer, Orange County Global Medical Center, Inc., Santa Ana, CA, p. A92

YATES, Ann C., R.N. Director Patient Care and Clinical Services, St. Vincent Mercy Hospital, Elwood, IN, p. A209

YATES, Jackie, R.N. Nurse Executive, Mississippi State Hospital, Whitfield, MS, p. A366

YATES, Katie, Chief Financial Officer, South Sunflower County Hospital, Indianola, MS, p. A359

YATES, Ralph, D.O
Chief Medical Officer, Salem Health West Valley, Dallas, OR, p. A525
Chief Medical Officer, Salem Hospital, Salem, OR, p. A530

YATES, Randy, M.D. Chief Medical Officer, Straub Clinic & Hospital, Honolulu, HI, p. A171

YATSATTIE, Clyde, Administrative Officer, U. S. Public Health Service Indian Hospital, Zuni, NM, p. A432

YAWORSKY, Jason
Chief Information Officer, Bradford Regional Medical Center, Bradford, PA, p. A534
Senior Vice President Information Systems and Chief Information Officer, Olean General Hospital, Olean, NY, p. A451

YAZAWA, Albert, M.D. Regional Medical Director, Leahi Hospital, Honolulu, HI, p. A170

YBARRA, Farra, R.N. Chief Nursing Officer, Coal County General Hospital, Coalgate, OK, p. A510

YE, Ye, Chief of Staff, York General Hospital, York, NE, p. A403

YEAGER, Angela, Director Information Technology, Palacios Community Medical Center, Palacios, TX, p. A639

YEAGER, Dianne, Chief Executive Officer, Crane Memorial Hospital, Crane, TX, p. A608

YEAGER, Kevin, Vice President Fiscal Services, Holzer Medical Center – Jackson, Jackson, OH, p. A496

YEASTED, G. Alan, M.D. Senior Vice President and Chief Medical Officer, St. Clair Hospital, Pittsburgh, PA, p. A551

YEATES, Alan H., Vice President Fiscal Services, Wyandot Memorial Hospital, Upper Sandusky, OH, p. A504

YEATES, Diane, Chief Operating Officer, Terrebonne General Medical Center, Houma, LA, p. A278

YEATS, Melania, M.D. Chief Medical Officer, San Juan Regional Medical Center, Farmington, NM, p. A429

YECNY, Rick, Chief Executive Officer and Chief Mission Officer, PeaceHealth Peace Harbor Medical Center, Florence, OR, p. A525

YEDVAB, Lauren, Chief Operating Officer, New York Methodist Hospital,, NY, p. A447

YEE, Brenda, MSN, Chief Executive Officer, Chinese Hospital, San Francisco, CA, p. A90

YEE, Martin, M.D. Medical Director, HEALTHSOUTH East Valley Rehabilitation Hospital, Mesa, AZ, p. A34

YEH, Ada, Chief Operating Officer and Chief Nursing Officer, Chapman Global Medical Center, Orange, CA, p. A80

YEHL, Warren
Chief Operating Officer, Eastern New Mexico Medical Center, Roswell, NM, p. A431
Chief Operating Officer, MountainView Regional Medical Center, Las Cruces, NM, p. A430

YEHLEN, Lorraine, R.N. Vice President Patient Care Services, DCH Regional Medical Center, Tuscaloosa, AL, p. A26

YELKEN, Kari, R.N. Director of Nursing, Franklin County Memorial Hospital, Franklin, NE, p. A395

YELTON, Gene, Director Support Services, Keystone Newport News, Newport News, VA, p. A674

YETMAN, Robert, M.D. Medical Director, Healthbridge Children's Hospital of Houston, Houston, TX, p. A624

YETTER, Tad A., M.D. President Medical Staff, Mason District Hospital, Havana, IL, p. A192

YEUNG, Christopher A., M.D. Chief of Staff, The CORE Institute Specialty Hospital, Phoenix, AZ, p. A37

YHLEN, David, Chief Operating Officer, Inspira Medical Center–Elmer, Elmer, NJ, p. A416

YI, Brenda, Director Medical Resource Management and Chief Financial Officer, U. S. Air Force Medical Center Keesler, Keesler AFB, MS, p. A360

YIM, Janet, Director Information Services, St. Mary Mercy Hospital, Livonia, MI, p. A329

YIN, Khin, Medical Director, Rehabilitation Hospital of Rhode Island, North Smithfield, RI, p. A560

YINGLING, Barbara, R.N. Vice President Patient Care Services and Chief Nursing Officer, Mercy Medical Center, Canton, OH, p. A486

YINGLING, Regina, Supervisor, Sandhills Regional Medical Center, Hamlet, NC, p. A466

YITTA, Prasad, M.D. Medical Director, River Hospital, Alexandria Bay, NY, p. A433

YOCHELSON, Michael R., M.D. Vice President and Medical Director, MedStar National Rehabilitation Hospital, Washington, DC, p. A121

YOCHUM, Richard E., FACHE, President and Chief Executive Officer, Pomona Valley Hospital Medical Center, Pomona, CA, p. A83

YODER, Cathy, Chief Financial Officer, St. Joseph's Hospital, Tampa, FL, p. A147

YODER, Lamont M., FACHE, Chief Executive Officer, Banner Gateway Medical Center, Gilbert, AZ, p. A32

YODER, Leslie, Executive Director, Finance, Community Hospital South, Indianapolis, IN, p. A213

YOE, Adam, Chief Executive Officer, HEALTHSOUTH Rehabilitation Hospital Memphis–North, Memphis, TN, p. A588

YOGEL, Louis, M.D. Chief of Staff, Broward Health Medical Center, Fort Lauderdale, FL, p. A128

YON, Robin, Site Finance Director, Mercy Health – Fairfield Hospital, Fairfield, OH, p. A494

YOO, George, M.D. Chief Medical Officer, Karmanos Cancer Center, Detroit, MI, p. A322

YOON, Chris, M.D. Medical Director, HEALTHSOUTH Bakersfield Rehabilitation Hospital, Bakersfield, CA, p. A56

YORK, Christopher, FACHE, President, Baylor Scott & White Medical Center at Waxahachie, Waxahachie, TX, p. A656

YORK, Don, Vice President and Chief Human Resource Officer, Sky Lakes Medical Center, Klamath Falls, OR, p. A527

YORK, Jack
Chief Information Officer, Pioneer Community Hospital of Patrick, Stuart, VA, p. A679
Chief Information Officer, Pioneer Community Hospital of Stokes, Danbury, NC, p. A463

YORK, Linda, Director Human Resource, Memorial Hospital of Converse County, Douglas, WY, p. A722

YORK, Robert Scott, M.D. Chief of Staff, Avoyelles Hospital, Marksville, LA, p. A282

YORK, Russell W., Vice President and Chief Financial Officer, Select Specialty Hospital – Belhaven, Jackson, MS, p. A360

YOSHII, Brian, Vice President Information Technology and Chief Information Officer, The Queen's Medical Center, Honolulu, HI, p. A171

YOSKO, Kathleen C., President, Marianjoy Rehabilitation Hospital, Wheaton, IL, p. A205

YOST, Gregg W., Chief Human Resources Officer, Gardens Regional Hospital and Medical Center, Hawaiian Gardens, CA, p. A65

YOUNADAM, Sandro, M.D. Chief Medical Officer, Ottumwa Regional Health Center, Ottumwa, IA, p. A236

YOUNG, Aaron, Chief Information Officer, Summit Healthcare Regional Medical Center, Show Low, AZ, p. A39

YOUNG, Abby, Chief Nursing Officer, Iowa Specialty Hospital–Clarion, Clarion, IA, p. A227

YOUNG, Angela, Human Resources Officer, Chillicothe Veterans Affairs Medical Center, Chillicothe, OH, p. A487

YOUNG, Anita, Chief Operating Officer, Florida Hospital Waterman, Tavares, FL, p. A148

YOUNG, Anthony, Information Services Specialist, Chester Mental Health Center, Chester, IL, p. A183

YOUNG, Anthony R., Chief Executive Officer, EASTAR Health System, Muskogee, OK, p. A515

YOUNG, Barry, Director Human Resources, Western Mental Health Institute, Bolivar, TN, p. A579

YOUNG, Bev, Director Human Resources, Frankfort Regional Medical Center, Frankfort, KY, p. A260

YOUNG, Bryce A.
Chief Operating Officer, Hays Medical Center, Hays, KS, p. A244
Chief Operating Officer, Pawnee Valley Community Hospital, Larned, KS, p. A247

YOUNG, C. Ray, M.D. Chief Medical Officer, Bourbon Community Hospital, Paris, KY, p. A268

YOUNG, David, M.D. Area Information Officer, Kaiser Permanente Fontana Medical Center, Fontana, CA, p. A62

YOUNG, David, Senior Vice President Planning and Technology, Trousdale Medical Center, Hartsville, TN, p. A584

YOUNG, Eric, Director Information Technology and Systems, South Bay Hospital, Sun City Center, FL, p. A146

YOUNG, Eric, M.D. Chief of Staff, Veterans Affairs Ann Arbor Healthcare System, Ann Arbor, MI, p. A318

YOUNG, Eric L.
Vice President Finance and Chief Financial Officer, Marietta Memorial Hospital, Marietta, OH, p. A498
Chief Financial Officer, Selby General Hospital, Marietta, OH, p. A498

YOUNG, James, Senior Vice President Finance and Chief Financial Officer, Howard County General Hospital, Columbia, MD, p. A300

YOUNG, James, M.D. Chief of Staff, McGehee–Desha County Hospital, McGehee, AR, p. A50

YOUNG, Jeffrey, Chief Human Resource Officer, South Texas Veterans Health Care System, San Antonio, TX, p. A647

YOUNG, Jeffrey D., Chief Information Officer, Children's Hospitals and Clinics of Minnesota, Minneapolis, MN, p. A346

YOUNG, Jeremie, M.D. Chief of Staff, Regional General Hospital, Williston, FL, p. A150

YOUNG, Joanna, R.N. Chief Nursing Officer, North Vista Hospital, North Las Vegas, NV, p. A407

YOUNG, Joyce, Ph.D
Vice President, Patient Services and Chief Nursing Officer, St. Joseph Mercy Ann Arbor, Ypsilanti, MI, p. A337
Vice President, Patient Services and Chief Nursing Officer, St. Joseph Mercy Livingston Hospital, Howell, MI, p. A326

YOUNG, Kathlene A., FACHE, Chief Executive Officer, Borgess Medical Center, Kalamazoo, MI, p. A327

YOUNG, Kevin, FACHE, President, Adventist Behavioral Health Rockville, Rockville, MD, p. A303

YOUNG, Lisa, CP
Chief Financial Officer, Carolinas ContinueCARE Hospital at Kings Mountain, Kings Mountain, NC, p. A468
Chief Financial Officer, ContinueCARE Hospital at Baptist Health Corbin, Corbin, KY, p. A258
Chief Financial Officer, ContinueCARE Hospital at Hendrick Medical Center, Abilene, TX, p. A595

YOUNG, Martha, Director Human Resources, Cumberland County Hospital, Burkesville, KY, p. A258

YOUNG, Mary, Director Human Resources, Colorado Mental Health Institute at Pueblo, Pueblo, CO, p. A109

YOUNG, Mary C., Chief Executive Officer, Moccasin Bend Mental Health Institute, Chattanooga, TN, p. A580

YOUNG, Michael, Chief Financial Officer, Mad River Community Hospital, Arcata, CA, p. A55

YOUNG, Michael A., FACHE, President and Chief Executive Officer, Pinnacle Health System, Harrisburg, PA, p. A540

YOUNG, Pam, Director Human Resources, Davis County Hospital, Bloomfield, IA, p. A226

YOUNG, Patty, R.N. Chief Nursing Officer, Ashland Health Center, Ashland, KS, p. A240

YOUNG, Rhonda, Human Resource Director, HEALTHSOUTH Rehabilitation of Gadsden, Gadsden, AL, p. A20

YOUNG, Richard T., FACHE, Director, Walter P. Reuther Psychiatric Hospital, Westland, MI, p. A336

YOUNG, Rickie, Chief Nursing Officer, Stamford Memorial Hospital, Stamford, TX, p. A650

YOUNG, Roberta, Vice President Nursing, Sanford Medical Center Fargo, Fargo, ND, p. A479

YOUNG, Sabrina, Administrative Support Director, South Mississippi State Hospital, Purvis, MS, p. A364

YOUNG, Sheila, Vice President Human Resources, Mobile Infirmary Medical Center, Mobile, AL, p. A22

YOUNG, Stephanie, Associate Director, Aleda E. Lutz Veterans Affairs Medical Center, Saginaw, MI, p. A333

YOUNG, Stephen W., Chief Operating Officer, Doctors Hospital of Sarasota, Sarasota, FL, p. A145

YOUNG, Steven W., Director, Veterans Affairs Salt Lake City Health Care System, Salt Lake City, UT, p. A664

YOUNG, Terry, Chief Information Officer, Plains Memorial Hospital, Dimmitt, TX, p. A613

YOUNG, William, Chief Information Officer, Berkshire Medical Center, Pittsfield, MA, p. A314

YOUNG Jr., William A., President and Chief Executive Officer, Southwest General Health Center, Middleburg Heights, OH, p. A499

YOUNGBLOOD, Erin R., Chief Human Resources Officer, Behavioral Center of Michigan, Warren, MI, p. A336

YOUNGMAN, Darrell, D.O. Chief Medical Officer, Via Christi Hospital on St. Francis, Wichita, KS, p. A256

YOUNGS, Patsy, President, Texas Health Presbyterian Hospital Kaufman, Kaufman, TX, p. A630

YOURTEE, Edward, M.D. Chief Medical Officer, Parkland Medical Center, Derry, NH, p. A410

YOURZEK, Tari, Chief Nursing Officer, Boundary Community Hospital, Bonners Ferry, ID, p. A175

YOUSAITIS, Zoe, Director Human Resources, Eagleville Hospital, Eagleville, PA, p. A537

YOUSO, Michael, Chief Executive Officer, Grand Itasca Clinic and Hospital, Grand Rapids, MN, p. A343

YOUSUF, Faraaz, Chief Operating Officer, Sutter Medical Center, Sacramento, Sacramento, CA, p. A87

YU, Henry
Vice President Finance and Chief Financial Officer, California Pacific Medical Center, San Francisco, CA, p. A90
Vice President Finance and Chief Financial Officer, St. Luke's Hospital, San Francisco, CA, p. A90

YUHAS, Joel P., FACHE, President and Chief Executive Officer, St. Mary Medical Center, Long Beach, CA, p. A70

YUHAS, John, D.O. Medical Director, Elmwood Healthcare Center at the Springs, Green Springs, OH, p. A495

YUNGMANN, Michael, President, Morton Plant North Bay Hospital, New Port Richey, FL, p. A138

YUNUSOV, Ed
Chief Information Officer, Creedmoor Psychiatric Center,, NY, p. A444
Coordinator Facility Information Center, New York City Children's Center,, NY, p. A446

YUST, Randall C.
Chief Operating Officer and Chief Financial Officer, Indiana University Health North Hospital, Carmel, IN, p. A208
Chief Financial Officer NCR, Indiana University Health Tipton Hospital, Tipton, IN, p. A223

Z

ZAAS, David, M.D., Chief Executive Officer, Duke Raleigh Hospital, Raleigh, NC, p. A471

ZABAWSKI, Denise, Vice President Information Services and Chief Information Officer, Nationwide Children's Hospital, Columbus, OH, p. A490

ZABEL, Sarah, Vice President, Operations, Swedish/Edmonds, Edmonds, WA, p. A684

ZABIELSKI, Gerald C., M.D. Chief Medical Staff, Wright Memorial Hospital, Trenton, MO, p. A383

ZABROWSKI, John, Chief Financial Officer, St. Mary's Medical Center of Evansville, Evansville, IN, p. A210

ZACHARIASEN, Keith, Chief Financial Officer, Wamego Health Center, Wamego, KS, p. A255

ZACHARY, Kevin, Chief Executive Officer, Logan Regional Medical Center, Logan, WV, p. A697

ZACHRICH, Jane, Chief Nursing Officer, Community Memorial Hospital, Hicksville, OH, p. A496

ZADYLAK, Robert, M.D. Vice President Medical Management, Advocate Illinois Masonic Medical Center, Chicago, IL, p. A183

ZAFEREO, Carolyn, Chief Accounting Officer, Citizens Medical Center, Victoria, TX, p. A655

ZAFONTE, Ross, D.O. Chief, Physical Medicine and Rehabilitation and Vice President Medical Affairs, Research and Education, Spaulding Rehabilitation Hospital, Charlestown, MA, p. A309

ZAGERMAN, Robert, Chief Financial Officer, Brooke Glen Behavioral Hospital, Fort Washington, PA, p. A539

ZAHN, Chip, Chief Operating Officer, Las Colinas Medical Center, Irving, TX, p. A629

ZAID, Ahmad, Chief Executive Officer, Atrium Medical Center, Stafford, TX, p. A649

ZAIDI, Syed A., M.D. Chief of Staff, Lauderdale Community Hospital, Ripley, TN, p. A592

ZAJEC, Doris A., Director Human Resources, South Pointe Hospital, Warrensville Heights, OH, p. A505

ZAJIC, Holly, Chief Operating Officer, Ivinson Memorial Hospital, Laramie, WY, p. A722

ZAJICEK, Tammy, Director of Nursing, Jackson County Hospital District, Edna, TX, p. A614

ZAKAI, Aminadav, M.D. Medical Director, Arbour–Fuller Hospital, Attleboro, MA, p. A305

ZALDIVAR, Rogelio, M.D. Medical Director, Westchester General Hospital, Miami, FL, p. A137

ZALESKI, Theodore, M.D. Vice President Clinical Effectiveness, Southern Ocean Medical Center, Manahawkin, NJ, p. A419

ZALMAN, Tisha, Chief Executive Officer, El Campo Memorial Hospital, El Campo, TX, p. A615

ZALUD, Nicolette, Customer Site Manager, McLaren Central Michigan, Mount Pleasant, MI, p. A330

ZALUSKI, Heather, M.D. President Medical Staff, Shodair Children's Hospital, Helena, MT, p. A388

ZAMBRELLO, Sally, Chief Information Officer, Carondelet St. Joseph's Hospital, Tucson, AZ, p. A40

ZAMORA DE AGUERO, Hilde, Human Resources Site Director, Baptist Health South Florida, West Kendall Baptist Hospital, Miami, FL, p. A136

ZAMPINI, Maria, Chief Operating Officer, University Medical Center of El Paso, El Paso, TX, p. A616

ZANDER, Cynthia L., Vice President and Chief Operating Officer, CGH Medical Center, Sterling, IL, p. A204

ZANE, Kristi, Chief Human Resources Officer, Crawford Memorial Hospital, Robinson, IL, p. A201

ZANI, Carl, Chief Technology Director, Memorial Health, Marysville, OH, p. A498

ZANIS, Tina
Director Information Technology, Schuylkill Medical Center – Schuylkill East Norwegian Street, Pottsville, PA, p. A552
Director Information Systems, Schuylkill Medical Center – Schuylkill South Jackson Street, Pottsville, PA, p. A552

ZANNI, David M., Associate Administrator, Adena Pike Medical Center, Waverly, OH, p. A505

ZANT, Dan, M.D. Chief of Staff, Morgan Memorial Hospital, Madison, GA, p. A162

ZARAK, Tamie, Director Human Resources, Memorial Medical Center – Neillsville, Neillsville, WI, p. A712

ZASTOUPIL, Rockford, Administrator, Mountrail County Medical Center, Stanley, ND, p. A481

ZAUNER, Janiece, Chief Nursing Officer, Providence Seaside Hospital, Seaside, OR, p. A530

ZAUNER, Mike, Chief Executive Officer, Sierra Vista Hospital, Sacramento, CA, p. A87

ZAVATCHEN, Nancy, Director Information Technology, Cullman Regional Medical Center, Cullman, AL, p. A18

ZAVODNICK, Jacquelyn, M.D. Medical Director, Devereux Children's Behavioral Health Center, Malvern, PA, p. A543

ZAWACKI, Brenda, Chief Operating Manager, Providence Kodiak Island Medical Center, Kodiak, AK, p. A29

ZDEBLICK, Mike, Chief Operating Officer, El Camino Hospital, Mountain View, CA, p. A78

ZDRODOWSKI, Michael, Vice President of Operations and Ambulatory Services, Munson Healthcare Cadillac Hospital, Cadillac, MI, p. A319

ZECHMAN, David M., FACHE, President and Chief Executive Officer, McLaren Northern Michigan, Petoskey, MI, p. A331

ZEDNICEK, Allison, Chief Executive Officer, West Hills Hospital, Reno, NV, p. A408

ZEH, Jeffrey C., President, Indiana University Health White Memorial Hospital, Monticello, IN, p. A218

ZEHM, Laura, Vice President and Chief Financial Officer, Community Hospital of the Monterey Peninsula, Monterey, CA, p. A77

ZEHNER, Douglas A., Chief Financial Officer, Newark Beth Israel Medical Center, Newark, NJ, p. A420

ZEHR, John, M.D. Chief Medical Officer, Waverly Health Center, Waverly, IA, p. A239

ZEIGLER, Michele
Vice President and Chief Information Officer, Chambersburg Hospital, Chambersburg, PA, p. A535
Vice President Information Services, Waynesboro Hospital, Waynesboro, PA, p. A556

ZEISEL, Henry
Chief Financial Officer, Northern Region, AMITA Health Elk Grove Village, Elk Grove Village, IL, p. A189
Chief Financial Officer, Northern Region, AMITA Health GlenOaks, Glendale Heights, IL, p. A191
Chief Financial Officer, Northern Region, AMITA Health Hoffman Estates, Hoffman Estates, IL, p. A193

ZEITLER, Irvin, D.O. Vice President Medical Affairs, Shannon Medical Center, San Angelo, TX, p. A645

ZEITLER, Jenny, Network Administrator, North Okaloosa Medical Center, Crestview, FL, p. A126

ZELENKA, Anthony
President and Chief Operating Officer, Berkeley Medical Center, Martinsburg, WV, p. A697
Chief Executive Officer, Jefferson Medical Center, Ranson, WV, p. A699

ZELIN, Mira, D.O. Medical Director, HEALTHSOUTH Rehabilitation Hospital of Spring Hill, Brooksville, FL, p. A125

ZELL, John R., Chief Financial Officer, OSF St. Joseph Medical Center, Bloomington, IL, p. A181

ZELLA, William, Chief Executive Officer, Arbour H. R. I. Hospital, Brookline, MA, p. A308

ZELLER, Brad, Vice President Operations, Hayward Area Memorial Hospital and Nursing Home, Hayward, WI, p. A707

ZELLER, Paul, Vice President Human Resources, MedStar Southern Maryland Hospital Center, Clinton, MD, p. A300

ZELLER, Sonya M., R.N. Vice President, Chief Operating Officer and Chief Nursing Officer, Indiana University Health Paoli Hospital, Paoli, IN, p. A220

ZEMAN, Brian, Chief Human Resources, Salem Veterans Affairs Medical Center, Salem, VA, p. A678

ZENDER, Dale, President Hospital Services NW, PeaceHealth St. Joseph Medical Center, Bellingham, WA, p. A682

ZENGOTITA, Jamie, M.D. Chief Medical Staff, Mercy Hospital Cassville, Cassville, MO, p. A369

ZENK, Ann
Vice President Patient Care, Ministry Sacred Heart Hospital, Tomahawk, WI, p. A717
Vice President Patient Care Services, Ministry Saint Mary's Hospitals, Rhinelander, WI, p. A715

ZENNA, Rita, R.N. Vice President Patient Care Services, Deborah Heart and Lung Center, Browns Mills, NJ, p. A415

ZENONE, Michael J., Chief Financial Officer, Emerald Coast Behavioral Hospital, Panama City, FL, p. A141

ZENTY III,, Thomas F., President and Chief Executive Officer, University Hospitals, Cleveland, OH, p. B146

ZEOLI, Diane, Chief Executive Officer, Kindred Hospital–Brea, Brea, CA, p. A57

ZEPHIER, Michelle, Human Resource Specialist, U. S. Public Health Service Indian Hospital, Rosebud, SD, p. A576

ZEPS, Joseph, Vice President Finance, Tomah Memorial Hospital, Tomah, WI, p. A717

ZERINGUE, Rhonda, R.N. Chief Nursing Officer, St. James Parish Hospital, Lutcher, LA, p. A282

ZERRER, Lana, M.D. Chief of Staff, Harry S. Truman Memorial Veterans Hospital, Columbia, MO, p. A370

ZEVENBERGEN, Glenn, Chief Executive Officer, Hegg Memorial Health Center Avera, Rock Valley, IA, p. A237

Index of Health Care Professionals

ZEWE, Jeff S., R.N
Chief Operating Officer, Bradford Regional Medical Center, Bradford, PA, p. A534
Senior Vice President, Chief Operating Officer, Olean General Hospital, Olean, NY, p. A451

ZEYNELOGLU, Nejat, Vice President and Chief Quality Medical Officer, Brookhaven Memorial Hospital Medical Center, Patchogue, NY, p. A452

ZHANG, Jian Q., MSN Chief Operating Officer, Chinese Hospital, San Francisco, CA, p. A90

ZHIRKIN, Georgii, Chief Financial Officer, Community Mental Health Center, Lawrenceburg, IN, p. A217

ZICHAL, Frances J., Chief Executive Officer, Central Community Hospital, Elkader, IA, p. A230

ZIDANSEK, John A., Chief Executive Officer, Easton Hospital, Easton, PA, p. A537

ZIEGLER, John C., FACHE Vice President Human Resources, Memorial Hospital, Belleville, IL, p. A181

ZIEGLER, Peter, M.D. Acting Chief Medical Officer, U. S. Public Health Service Indian Hospital–Sells, Sells, AZ, p. A39

ZIELAZINSKI, Mark, Chief Information and Technology Integration Officer, Marin General Hospital, Greenbrae, CA, p. A65

ZIELINSKI, Sharon
Manager Health Information, HEALTHSOUTH Rehabilitation Hospital of Erie, Erie, PA, p. A538
Chief Information Resource Officer, Veterans Affairs Maryland Health Care System–Baltimore Division, Baltimore, MD, p. A298

ZIEMER, Patrick C., Chief Executive Officer, Alvarado Parkway Institute Behavioral Health System, La Mesa, CA, p. A67

ZIEMIANSKI, Karen, R.N. Senior Vice President Nursing, Erie County Medical Center, Buffalo, NY, p. A435

ZIENIEWICZ, Stephen P., FACHE, President and Chief Executive Officer, Saint Barnabas Medical Center, Livingston, NJ, p. A418

ZIEROLD, Bob, Senior Vice President Human Resources, Christian Health Care Center, Wyckoff, NJ, p. A426

ZIGLOR, Danyale
Assistant Vice President Human Resources, WellStar Cobb Hospital, Austell, GA, p. A154
Assistant Director Human Resources, WellStar Douglas Hospital, Douglasville, GA, p. A158

ZILE, Ron, M.D. Chief of Staff, Highland District Hospital, Hillsboro, OH, p. A496

ZILKOW, Jon, Chief Financial Officer, Southwest Healthcare System, Murrieta, CA, p. A78

ZILLER, Andrew, M.D. Chief Medical Officer, Rose Medical Center, Denver, CO, p. A104

ZILLMAN, Sally E., Interim Vice President, Patient Care Services, Ministry Saint Clare's Hospital, Weston, WI, p. A719

ZIMA, Cheryl F., Vice President Human Resources Ministry Health Care, Ministry Saint Joseph's Hospital, Marshfield, WI, p. A709

ZIMMEL, Robert, Senior Vice President Human Resources, St. Luke's University Hospital – Bethlehem Campus, Bethlehem, PA, p. A533

ZIMMER, Jan, R.N. Chief Nursing Officer, Tennova Healthcare Regional Hospital of Jackson, Jackson, TN, p. A584

ZIMMERLY, Kara, Manager Human Resources, ProMedica Bay Park Hospital, Oregon, OH, p. A500

ZIMMERMAN, Aimee, R.N. Chief Operations Officer, Logan County Hospital, Oakley, KS, p. A250

ZIMMERMAN, Anne, Senior Director Patient Care Services and Chief Nursing Officer, Mercy Tiffin Hospital, Tiffin, OH, p. A503

ZIMMERMAN, David, M.D. Chief of Staff, Swain Community Hospital, Bryson City, NC, p. A461

ZIMMERMAN, Don, Director Human Resources, Morris County Hospital, Council Grove, KS, p. A242

ZIMMERMAN, Michael
Human Resource Officer, Presence Covenant Medical Center, Urbana, IL, p. A204
Human Resource Officer, Presence United Samaritans Medical Center, Danville, IL, p. A187

ZIMMERMAN, Michael P., Chief Executive Officer, Sierra Vista Hospital, Truth or Consequences, NM, p. A432

ZIMMERMAN, Nancy, R.N., Administrator, Comanche County Hospital, Coldwater, KS, p. A241

ZIMMERMAN, Robert, Vice President Financial Services, Munson Healthcare Charlevoix Hospital, Charlevoix, MI, p. A320

ZIMMERMANN, Deb T., R.N. Chief Nursing Officer and Vice President Patient Care Services, VCU Medical Center, Richmond, VA, p. A678

ZIMMERMANN, Wayne, Chief Operating Officer, NYC Health + Hospitals / Elmhurst,, NY, p. A448

ZINK, Jayne, Director of Nursing, Ohio Hospital for Psychiatry, Columbus, OH, p. A490

ZINK, Summer, Chief Financial Officer, Ellinwood District Hospital, Ellinwood, KS, p. A242

ZINKER, Dena, MSN Vice President Patient Services, Colquitt Regional Medical Center, Moultrie, GA, p. A163

ZINKULA, Lisa, Chief Financial Officer, Grundy County Memorial Hospital, Grundy Center, IA, p. A231

ZINN, David, M.D. Vice President Medical Affairs, Northeast Alabama Regional Medical Center, Anniston, AL, p. A15

ZINN, Troy
Chief Executive Officer, Little River Cameron Hospital, Cameron, TX, p. A605
Chief Executive Officer, Memorial Hospital of Texas County, Guymon, OK, p. A512

ZINNER, Barbara, Chief Nursing Officer, Marymount Hospital, Garfield Heights, OH, p. A495

ZIOBRO, Ron, Interim Chief Executive Officer, First Hospital Wyoming Valley, Kingston, PA, p. A541

ZIOLKOWSKI, David, Chief Executive Officer, Person Memorial Hospital, Roxboro, NC, p. A472

ZIRBSER, Glenn, Senior Vice President Finance and Chief Financial Officer, Kennedy Health System, Cherry Hill, NJ, p. A415

ZIRGER, Marion, Chief Financial Officer, Minneola District Hospital, Minneola, KS, p. A249

ZIRKELBACH, Mark, Chief Information Officer, Loma Linda University Medical Center, Loma Linda, CA, p. A69

ZIRKELBACK, Mark, Chief Information Officer, Loma Linda University Behavioral Medicine Center, Redlands, CA, p. A85

ZIRKLE, William, Manager Information Systems, Sentara Halifax Regional Hospital, South Boston, VA, p. A678

ZISKIN, Robert, Chief Information Officer, Northport Veterans Affairs Medical Center, Northport, NY, p. A451

ZOCH, Jeremy, Executive Vice President and Chief Operating Officer, St. Joseph Hospital, Orange, CA, p. A81

ZOESCH, Jim, Information Technology Director, PMH Medical Center, Prosser, WA, p. A688

ZOGELMAN, Sharon, Director Human Resources, St. Luke Hospital and Living Center, Marion, KS, p. A248

ZOLKIWSKY, Walter R., M.D. Chief Medical Officer, Reston Hospital Center, Reston, VA, p. A676

ZOMCHEK, Daniel, Ph.D., Executive Director, Clement J. Zablocki Veterans Affairs Medical Center, Milwaukee, WI, p. A711

ZOOK, Danette, Chief Financial Officer, Mercy Medical Center–North Iowa, Mason City, IA, p. A234

ZOOK, Lori, Chief Financial Officer, River's Edge Hospital and Clinic, Saint Peter, MN, p. A351

ZORZA, Elizabeth, Assistant Administrator, OSF St. Francis Hospital and Medical Group, Escanaba, MI, p. A323

ZOUCHA, Larry, Chief Information Officer, Boone County Health Center, Albion, NE, p. A393

ZUANICH, Elizabeth
Chief Financial Officer, Providence Little Company of Mary Medical Center – Torrance, Torrance, CA, p. A96
Chief Financial Officer, Providence Little Company of Mary Medical Center San Pedro,, CA, p. A73

ZUBER, Steven, Vice President, Methodist Jennie Edmundson Hospital, Council Bluffs, IA, p. A228

ZUBRICKI, Thomas, Vice President Finance, Chief Financial Officer, Crotched Mountain Rehabilitation Center, Greenfield, NH, p. A411

ZUEL, Sally, Vice President Human Resources, Union Hospital, Terre Haute, IN, p. A222

ZUHD, Dajani, M.D. President Medical Staff, Punxsutawney Area Hospital, Punxsutawney, PA, p. A552

ZUINO, Matthew
Senior Vice President Hospital Services, Virtua Marlton, Marlton, NJ, p. A419
Senior Vice President Hospital Services, Virtua Memorial, Mount Holly, NJ, p. A420
Senior Vice President Hospital Services, Virtua Voorhees, Voorhees, NJ, p. A425

ZULIANI, Michael E., Chief Executive Officer, HEALTHSOUTH Huntington Rehabilitation Hospital, Huntington, WV, p. A696

ZULTANKY, Lynne, Director Corporate Communications and Media Relations, Bon Secours–DePaul Medical Center, Norfolk, VA, p. A674

ZUMPANO, Anthony, Chief Financial Officer, Penn Presbyterian Medical Center, Philadelphia, PA, p. A549

ZUMWALT, Philip, M.D. Chief of Staff, Iroquois Memorial Hospital and Resident Home, Watseka, IL, p. A204

ZUNNO, Gerard, R.N. Vice President Patient Care Services, Peconic Bay Medical Center, Riverhead, NY, p. A454

ZUTZ–WICZEK, Sandy, Chief Operating Officer, FirstLight Health System, Mora, MN, p. A347

ZVANUT, Michelle, Vice President Human Resources, Boone Hospital Center, Columbia, MO, p. A370

ZWANZIGER, Marcia, Vice President Finance, Huron Regional Medical Center, Huron, SD, p. A574

ZWEIFEL, Mary A.
President and Chief Executive Officer, Sheltering Arms Hospital South, Midlothian, VA, p. A674
President and Chief Executive Officer, Sheltering Arms Rehabilitation Hospital, Mechanicsville, VA, p. A673

ZWENG, Thomas, M.D
Senior Vice President Medical Affairs, Novant Health Matthews Medical Center, Matthews, NC, p. A469
Executive Vice President Medical Affairs, Novant Health Presbyterian Medical Center, Charlotte, NC, p. A463

ZWIEFEL, Laura, Chief Nursing Officer and Assistant Administration, Hancock County Health System, Britt, IA, p. A226

ZWIEG, Faye, Vice President and Chief Nursing Officer, Aurora St. Luke's Medical Center, Milwaukee, WI, p. A711

ZWINGER, Glenn, Manager Information Systems Services, Veterans Affairs Puget Sound Health Care System, Seattle, WA, p. A690

ZWIRCHITZ, Faith, Director Nursing and Professional Practice, Maple Grove Hospital, Maple Grove, MN, p. A345

ZYCH, Anita, Director of Nursing, Arrowhead Behavioral Health Hospital, Maumee, OH, p. A498

ZYLA, Jeffrey, Chief Financial Officer, Abrazo Scottsdale Campus, Phoenix, AZ, p. A35

AHA Membership Categories

The American Hospital Association is primarily an organization of hospitals and related institutions. Its object, according to its bylaws, is "to promote high–quality health care and health services for all the people through leadership in the development of public policy, leadership in the representation and advocacy of hospital and health care organization interests, and leadership in the provision of services to assist hospitals and health care organizations in meeting the health care needs of their communities."

Institutional Members

Hospitals or health services organizations or systems which provide a continuum of integrated, community health resources and which include at least one licensed hospital that is owned, leased, managed or religiously sponsored.

Institutional members include hospitals, health care systems, integrated delivery systems, and physician hospital organizations (PHOs) and health maintenance organizations (HMOs) wholly or partially owned by or owning a member hospital or system. An Institutional member hospital, health care system or integrated delivery system may, at its discretion and upon approval of a membership application by the Association chief executive officer, extend membership to the health care provider organizations, other than a hospital that it owns, leases, or fully controls.

Freestanding Health Care Provider Organizations

These are health provider organizations, other than registered hospitals, that provide patient care services, including, but not limited to, ambulatory, preventive, rehabilitative, specialty, post–acute and continuing care, as well as physician groups, health insurance services, and staff and group model health maintenance organizations without a hospital component. Freestanding Health Care Provider Organizations members are not owned or controlled by an Institutional member hospital, health care system or integrated delivery system member. They may, however, be part of an organization eligible for, but not holding, Institutional membership.

Other Organizations

This category includes organizations interested in the objectives of the American Hospital Association, but not eligible for Institutional or Freestanding Health Care Provider Organization Membership. Organizations eligible for Other membership shall include, but not be limited to, associations, societies, foundations, corporations, educational and academic institutions, companies, government agencies, international health providers, and organizations having an interest in and a desire to support the objectives of the Association.

Provisional Members

Hospitals that are in the planning or construction stage and that, on completion, will be eligible for institutional membership. Provisional membership may also be granted to applicant institutions that cannot, at present, meet the requirements of Institutional or Freestanding Health Care Provider Organization membership.

Government Institution Group Members

Groups of government hospitals operated by the same unit of government may obtain institutional membership under a group plan. Membership dues are based on a special schedule set forth in the bylaws of the AHA.

Other Institutional Members

Hospitals

U.S. hospitals and hospitals in areas associated with the U.S. that are Institutional members of the American Hospital Association are included in the list of hospitals in section A. Canadian Institutional members of the American Hospital Association are listed below.

Canada

ALBERTA

Lamont: LAMONT HEALTH CARE CENTRE, P.O. Bag 10, Zip T0B 2R0; tel. 780/895–2211; Harold James, Executive Director

MANITOBA

Winnipeg: RIVERVIEW HEALTH CENTRE, 1 Morley Avenue East, Zip R3L 2P4; tel. 204/452–3411; Norman R. Kasian, President and Chief Executive Officer

ONTARIO

Renfrew: RENFREW VICTORIA HOSPITAL, 499 Raglan Street North, Zip K7V 1P6; tel. 613/432–4851; Randy V. Penney, Executive Director

Thornhill: SHOULDICE HOSPITAL, 7750 Bayview Avenue, Zip L3T 4A3; tel. 905/889–1125; John Hughes, Chief Administrative Officer

Associated University Programs in Health Administration

IOWA

Iowa City: DEPARTMENT OF HEALTH MANAGEMENT AND POLICY, UNIVERSITY OF IOWA, 105 River Street, N232A CPHB, Zip 52246; tel. 319/384–3830; Keith Mueller, Ph.D., Professor and Head

MARYLAND

Bethesda: NAVY MEDICINE PROFESSIONAL DEVELOPMENT CENTER, Naval Medicine, Education and Training Command, Zip 20889–5611; tel. 301/295–1251; Commander DuWayne Griepentrog, Director Administration

MISSOURI

Columbia: UNIVERSITY OF MISSOURI, HEALTH MANAGEMENT AND INFORMATICS, CE707 Clinical Support and Education Building, DC 00600, One Hospital Drive, Zip 65212; tel. 573/882–6179; Eduardo Simoes, M.D., Chair

TEXAS

San Antonio: ARMY–BAYLOR UNIVERSITY PROGRAM IN HEALTH CARE ADMINISTRATION, 3151 Scott Road, Building 2841, Zip 78234–6135; tel. 210/221–6443; Lieutenant Colonel M. Nicholas Coppola, Program Director

Sheppard AFB: U. S. AIR FORCE SCHOOL OF HEALTH CARE SCIENCES, Building 1900, MST/114, Academic Library, Zip 76311; tel. 817/851–2511

PUERTO RICO

San Juan: SCHOOL OF PUBLIC HEALTH, P.O. Box 5067, Zip 00936; tel. 809/767–9626; Orlando Nieves, Dean

Hospital Schools
of Nursing

PENNSYLVANIA
New Castle: JAMESON HOSPITAL School of Nursing

Nonhospital Preacute and Postacute Care Facilities

CALIFORNIA

Winterhaven: U. S. PUBLIC HEALTH SERVICE INDIAN HOSPITAL, P.O. Box 1368, Zip 85366–1368; tel. 760/572–0217; Geniel Harrison, M.D., Clinic Director

DELAWARE

Newark: HEALTH CARE CENTER AT CHRISTIANA, 200 Hygeia Drive, Zip 19714

FLORIDA

Jacksonville: NEMOURS CHILDREN'S CLINIC, 807 Children's Way, Zip 32207; tel. 904/390–3600; William A. Cover, Administrator

GEORGIA

Calhoun: ALLIANT HEALTH PLANS, INC., 401 South Wall Street, Suite 201, Zip 30701; tel. 706/629–8848; Judy Pair, Chief Executive Officer
GEORGIA HEALTH PLUS, 401 South Wall Street, Suite 201, Zip 30701; tel. 706/629–1833
Rome: CENTREX, 420 East Second Avenue, Zip 30161; tel. 706/235–1006; Dee B. Russell, M.D., Chief Executive Officer
COMMUNITY HOSPICECARE, P.O. Box 233, Zip 30162–0233; tel. 706/232–0807; Kurt Stuenkel, FACHE, President and Chief Executive Officer
FLOYD HOME HEALTH AGENCY, P.O. Box 6248, Zip 30162–6248; tel. 706/802–4600; Kurt Stuenkel, FACHE, President and Chief Executive Officer
FLOYD MEDICAL OUTPATIENT SURGERY, P.O. Box 233, Zip 30162–0233; tel. 706/802–2070; Kurt Stuenkel, FACHE, President and Chief Executive Officer
FLOYD REHABILITATION CENTER, P.O. Box 233, Zip 30162–0233; tel. 706/802–2091; Kurt Stuenkel, FACHE, President and Chief Executive Officer

HAWAII

Honolulu: MALUHIA HOSPITAL, 1027 Hala Drive, Zip 96817; tel. 808/832–5874; Derek Akiyoshi, Chief Executive Officer

ILLINOIS

Oak Forest: OAK FOREST HEALTH CENTER OF COOK COUNTY, 15900 South Cicero Avenue, Zip 60452–4006; tel. 708/687–7200

MAINE

Damariscotta: COVE'S EDGE, 26 Schooner Street, Zip 04543; tel. 207/563–4645; Judy McGuire, Administrator
MILES MEDICAL GROUP, INC., 35 Miles Street, Zip 04543; tel. 207/563–1234; Stacey Miller–Friant, Director
Kennebunk: SOUTHERN MAINE HEALTH AND HOME SERVICES, P.O. Box 739, Zip 04043; tel. 207/985–4767; Elaine Brady, R.N., Executive Director

MARYLAND

Baltimore: ST. AGNES HEALTH SERVICES, 900 Caton Avenue, Zip 21229; tel. 410/368–2945; Peter Clay, Senior Vice President Managed Care
ST. AGNES HOME CARE AND HOSPICE, 3421 Benson Avenue, Suite G100, Zip 21227; tel. 410/368–2825; Robin Dowell, Director
Ellicott City: ST. AGNES NURSING AND REHABILITATION CENTER, 3000 North Ridge Road, Zip 21043; tel. 410/461–7577; Barbara A. Gustke, R.N., Administrator Extended Care Facility

MASSACHUSETTS

Boston: JOSLIN DIABETES CENTER, One Joslin Place, Zip 02215; tel. 617/732–2400; John L. Brooks, III., President and Chief Executive Officer
Springfield: BAY STATE VISITING NURSE ASSOCIATION AND HOSPICE, 50 Maple Street, Zip 01105; tel. 413/781–5070; Ruth Odgren, President

MICHIGAN

Big Rapids: MECOSTA HEALTH SERVICES, 650 Linden Street, Zip 49307; tel. 231/796–3200; Gail Bullard, R.N., Director
Sault Sainte Marie: SAULT SAINTE MARIE TRIBAL HEALTH AND HUMAN SERVICES CENTER, 2864 Ashmun Street, Zip 49783; tel. 906/495–5651; Russell Vizina, Division Director Health

MINNESOTA

Albany: CENTRACARE CLINIC – ALBANY, 300 Third Avenue, Zip 56307–9363; tel. 320/845–2157; Tressa Schmidt, Administrator

MISSOURI

Independence: SURGI–CARE CENTER OF INDEPENDENCE, 2311 Redwood Avenue, Zip 64057; tel. 816/373–7995

NEBRASKA

North Platte: GREAT PLAINS PHO, INC., P.O. Box 1167, Zip 69103; tel. 308/535–7496; Todd Hlavaty, M.D., Chairman

NEW JERSEY

Jersey City: ST. FRANCIS HOSPITAL, 25 McWilliams Place, Zip 07302–1698; tel. 201/418–1000
Millburn: ATLANTIC HOME CARE AND HOSPICE, 33 Bleeker Street, Zip 07041; tel. 973/379–8400; Susan Quinn, Administrator
Morristown: ALLIANCE IMAGING CENTER, 65 Maple Street, Zip 07960; tel. 973/267–5700; Barbara Picorale, Administrator
Succasunna: DIALYSIS CENTER OF NORTHWEST NEW JERSEY, 170 Righter Road, Zip 07876; tel. 973/584–1117; Carol Cahill, Administrator

NEW MEXICO

Albuquerque: ALBUQUERQUE IHS HEALTH CENTER, 801 Vassar Drive N.E., Zip 87106–2799; tel. 505/248–4000; Maria Rickert, Chief Executive Officer

NEW YORK

Tuckahoe: HOME NURSING ASSOCIATION OF WESTCHESTER, 69 Main Street, Zip 10707; tel. 919/961–2818; Mary Wehrberger, Director

NORTH CAROLINA

Jefferson: AMH SEGRAVES CARE CENTER, 200 Hospital Avenue, Zip 28640; tel. 336/246–7101
Wilson: WILMED NURSING CARE CENTER, 1705 Tarboro Street S.W., Zip 27893–3428; tel. 252/399–8998; Gene Fulcher, Administrator

OHIO

Cleveland: METROHEALTH CENTER FOR SKILLED NURSING CARE, 4229 Pearl Road, Zip 44109; tel. 216/957–3675; Yvette Bozman, Administrator

OKLAHOMA

Clinton: U. S. PUBLIC HEALTH SERVICE INDIAN HOSPITAL, Route 1, Box 3060, Zip 73601–9303; tel. 580/323–2884
Eufaula: EUFALA INDIAN HEALTH CENTER, 800 Forest Avenue, Zip 74432; tel. 918/689–2547; Shelly Crow, Health System Administrator
Okmulgee: OKMULGEE INDIAN HEALTH SYSTEM, 1313 East 20th, Zip 74447; tel. 918/758–1926; Jo Ann Skaggs, Administrator
Sapulpa: SAPULPA INDIAN HEALTH CENTER, 1125 East Clevelend, Zip 74066; tel. 918/224–9310

PENNSYLVANIA

Warminster: ABINGTON MEMORIAL HEALTH CENTER – WARMINSTER CAMPUS, 225 Newtown Road, Zip 18974–5221; tel. 215/441–6600; Katie Farrell, Chief Executive Officer

TEXAS

Dallas: SURGICARE OF TRAVIS CENTER, INC., 13355 Noel Road, Suite 650, Zip 75240–6694; tel. 713/520–1782
Houston: GRAMERCY OUTPATIENT SURGERY CENTER. LTD., 2727 Gramercy, Zip 77025; tel. 713/660–6900; Hamel Patel, Administrator
WEST HOUSTON SURGICARE, 970 Campbell Road, Zip 77024; tel. 713/461–3547
Webster: BAY AREA SURGICARE CENTER, 502 Medical Center Boulevard, Zip 77598; tel. 281/332–2433; Carol Simons, Administrator

WISCONSIN

Green Bay: UNITY HOSPICE, P.O. Box 28345, Zip 54324–8345; tel. 920/494–0225; Donald Seibel, Executive Director

Provisional Hospitals

This listing includes organizations that, as of September 16, 2015, were in the planning or construction stage and that, on completion, will be eligible for Institutional membership. Some hospitals are granted provisional membership for reasons related to other Association requirements. Hospitals classified as provisional members for reasons other than being under construction are indicated by a bullet (●).

TEXAS

El Paso: THE HOSPITALS OF PROVIDENCE TRANSMOUNTAIN CAMPUS, 2000 Transmountain Road, Zip 79911; tel. 915/500–6560; Nicholas R. Tejeda, FACHE, Chief Executive Officer

Associate Members

Ambulatory Centers and Home Care Agencies

United States

NEW HAMPSHIRE

DARTMOUTH COLLEGE HEALTH SERVICE, 7 Rope Ferry Road, Hanover, Zip 03755–1421; tel. 603/650–1400; John H. Turco, M.D., Director

NEW YORK

MIDTOWN SURGERY CENTER, 305 East 47th Street, New York, Zip 10017–2303; tel. 212/751–2100; Julia Ferguson, Director, Operations

PENNSYLVANIA

WILLS EYE HOSPITAL, 840 Walnut Street, Philadelphia, Zip 19107–5109; tel. 215/928–3000; Joseph P. Bilson, Executive Director

Blue Cross Plans

United States

ARIZONA

BLUE CROSS AND BLUE SHIELD OF ARIZONA, Box 13466, Phoenix, Zip 85002–3466; tel. 602/864–4541; Vishu Jhaveri, M.D., Senior Vice President and Chief Medical Officer

The members listed in bold are Associate Advantage members. © 2016 AHA Guide

Other Members

UNITED STATES

Accreditation Organizations:

THE JOINT COMMISSION, One Renaissance Boulevard, Oakbrook Terrace, Illinois Zip 60181; tel. 630/792–5000; Mark Chassin, President; www.jointcommission.org

Architecture:

DEVENNEY GROUP ARCHITECTS, 201 West Indian School Road, Phoenix, Arizona Zip 85013–3203; tel. 602/943–8950; Julie Barkenbush, Chief Executive Officer; www.devenneygroup.com

EARL SWENSSON ASSOCIATES, INC., 2100 West End Avenue, Suite 1200, Nashville, Tennessee Zip 37203; tel. 615/329–9445; Richard L. Miller, President; www.esarch.com

HDR ARCHITECTURE, INC., 33 West Monroe Street, Suite 1750, Chicago, Illinois Zip 60603–5662; tel. 312/470–9532; Ashley Tucker, Strategic Program Manager, Healthcare; www.hdrinc.com

MATTHEI AND COLIN ASSOCIATES, 332 South Michigan Avenue, Suite 614, Chicago, Illinois Zip 60604; tel. 312/939–4002; Ronald G. Kobold, Managing Partner

MESSER CONSTRUCTION COMPANY, 5158 Fishwick Drive, Cincinnati, Ohio Zip 45216; tel. 513/242–1541; Tiffany Witham, Director Marketing; www.messer.com

Bank:

BANK OF AMERICA, 101 South Tryon Street, Charlotte, North Carolina Zip 28255–0001; tel. 704/388–2255; Gayle Higaki, Senior Vice President; www.bankofamerica.com

HEALTHCARE ASSOCIATES CREDIT UNION, 1151 East Warrenville Road, Naperville, Illinois Zip 60563; tel. 630/276–5771; Jennifer Kleinhenz, Senior Vice President Strategic Initiatives; www.hacu.org

TD BANK, 2130 Centre Park West Drive, 2nd Floor, West Palm Beach, Florida Zip 33409–6411; tel. 561/352–2086; Colleen Mullaney, Senior Vice President; www.tdbank.com

Communication Systems Org:

AVAILITY, LLC, 740 East Campbell Road, Suite 1000, Richardson, Texas Zip 75081–1886; tel. 972/383–6326; Travis Froehlich, Director, Corporate Communications; www.availity.com

Consulting Firm:

AON HEWITT, 5600 West 83rd Street, 8200 Tower, Minneapolis, Minnesota Zip 55402–3721; tel. 952/807–0768; James Craig Nelson, Senior Vice President; www.stratford360.com

ARAMARK, 1101 Market Street, Philadelphia, Pennsylvania Zip 19107–2988; tel. 856/858–3822; Denise Spillane, Vice President Marketing and Communications

ARIAS INFORMATION SOLUTIONS LLC, 3233 North Arlington Heights Road, Suite 201, Arlington Heights, Illinois Zip 60004–1579; tel. 847/340–8307; Raymond C. Arias, Managing Partner; www.ariasis.com

AZEUS CONVENE BOARD PORTAL, 750 Third Avenue, Floor 9th, New York, New York Zip 10017–2703; tel. 800/795–2024; Michael Lim, Junior Associate; www.azeusconvene.com

BENEFIT RECOVERY ANALYSTS, INC., 403 West Fisher Avenue, Greensboro, North Carolina Zip 27401; tel. 336/273–0737; Judy Tisdale, Accounting Manager; www.benefitrecoveryanalysts.com

BMGI, 1200 17th Street, Suite 180, Denver, Colorado Zip 80202–5815; tel. 303/827–0010; Scott McAllister, Senior Performance Excellence Consultant; www.bmgi.com/default.aspx

BOSTON CONSULTING GROUP, Exchange Place, 31st Floor, Boston, Massachusetts Zip 02109; tel. 617/973–1200; Julia Eleuteri, Lead Researcher; www.bcg.com

BOXWOOD TECHNOLOGY, INC, 11350 McCormick Road, Suite 101, Hunt Valley, Maryland Zip 21031; tel. 888/491–8833; John Bell, Chairman; www.boxwoodtech.com

BURWOOD GROUP, INC., 125 South Wacker Drive, Suite 2950, Chicago, Illinois Zip 60602; tel. 312/327–4600; Mark Theoharous, President; www.burwood.com

CARE TECH SOLUTIONS, 901 Wilshire Drive, Suite 100, Troy, Michigan Zip 48084; tel. 248/823–0950; Jody Meehan, Vice President, Marketing, Communications, and Government Affairs; www.caretech.com/

CBRCC INC., 4475 Morris Park Drive, Suite B., Charlotte, North Carolina Zip 28227–8254; tel. 704/573–4535; Judy B. Courtemanche, President; www.courtemanche-assocs.com

CLEARWATER COMPLIANCE LLC, 106 Windward Point, Hendersonville, Tennessee Zip 37075–5108; tel. 615/800–7988; Kathy S. Ebbert, Chief Operating Officer; www.clearwatercompliance.com

CONIFER HEALTH SOLUTIONS, 2401 Internet Boulevard, Suite 201, Frisco, Texas Zip 75034–5977; tel. 972/335–6120; Vanessa Harris, Senior Market Research Specialist; www.coniferhealth.com

DRAEGER, 3135 Quarry Road, Telford, Pennsylvania Zip 18969–1042; tel. 215/660–2310; Susan Thornton, Senior Marketing Manager, Information Technology Solutions; www.draeger.com

ECLIPSYS, 76 Batterson Park Road, Farmington, Connecticut Zip 06032; tel. 860/246–3000; Marvin S. Goldwasser, Vice President Product Marketing, Patient Flow and Performance Management; www.eclipsys.com

EIDE BAILLY, LLP, 800 Nicollet Mall, Suite 1300, Minneapolis, Minnesota Zip 55402–7033; tel. 612/253–6582; Jen Dreis, Marketing Manager; www.eidebailly.com/healthcare

ELSEVIER, INC., 1600 John F. Kennedy Boulevard, Philadelphia, Pennsylvania Zip 19103–2808; tel. 215/239–3516; Peter Rush, Senior Director Customer Insight and Marketing Services; www.elsevier.com

ERNST & YOUNG, 150 Fourth Avenue North, Suite 1400, Nashville, Tennessee Zip 37219–2409; tel. 615/252–8254; Darryl McQuate, Manager; www.ey.com

ERNST & YOUNG, 5 Times Square, 14th Floor, New York, New York Zip 10036–6530; tel. 212/773–3000; Frank Bresz, Senior Manager; www.ey.com/global/content.nsf/us/home

EXECUTIVE HEALTH RESOURCES, INC., 15 Campus Boulevard, Suite 200, Newtown Square, Pennsylvania Zip 19073; tel. 610/446–6100; Michele Bowman, Vice President, Marketing and Communications; www.ehrdocs.com

GETWELLNETWORK, INC., 7920 Norfolk Avenue, 11th Floor, Bethesda, Maryland Zip 20814–2500; tel. 240/482–3200; Michael B. O'Neil, Jr., President and Chief Executive Officer; www.getwellnetwork.com

GOLDMAN, SACHS AND COMPANY, 200 West Street, New York, New York Zip 10282–2198; Cynthia Rivera, Public Sector and Infrastructure Banking

GPS HEALTHCARE CONSULTANTS, 12935 North Forty Drive, Suite 204, Saint Louis, Missouri Zip 63141; tel. 314/450–5880; Keith Petti, President and Chief Executive Officer; www.gpshealthcon.com

H. R. S. INTERNATIONAL, 25 East Washington, 6th Floor, Chicago, Illinois Zip 60602; tel. 312/236–7770; Carrie Parks, Marketing Specialist; www.hrsolutions.com

HEALTHCARE CHAPLAINCY NETWORK, INC., 65 Broadway, 12th Floor, New York, New York Zip 10010; tel. 212/644–1111; Father Eric J. Hall, President and Chief Executive Officer; www.healthcarechaplaincy.org

HEALTHCARE MANAGEMENT PARTNERS, LLC, 1515 Market Street, Suite 1200, Philadelphia, Pennsylvania Zip 19102–1932; tel. 215/854–4086; Scott K. Phillips, Managing Director; www.hcmpllc.com

HEALTHCARESOURCE, 100 Sylvan Road, Suite 100, Woburn, Massachusetts Zip 01801–1851; tel. 800/691–3737; Sean Parlin, Strategic Alliances Manager; www.healthcaresource.com

HEALTHEQUITY, INC., 15 West Scenic Pointe Drive, Suite 100, Draper, Utah Zip 84020–6120; tel. 801/727–1000; Stephen Neeleman, Founder and Vice Chairman; www.healthequity.com

HEALTHPORT, 925 North Point Parkway, Alpharetta, Georgia Zip 30005–5210; tel. 770/360–1700; Catherine Valyi, Vice President Marketing; www.healthport.com

IBM, 1 New Orchard Road, Armonk, New York Zip 10504–1722; tel. 781/575–2727; Charles Andrews, Chief Executive Officer; www.ibm.com

INTEGRATED HEALTHCARE STRATEGIES, 901 Marquette Avenue South, Suite 2100, Minneapolis, Minnesota Zip 55402–3713; tel. 612/339–0919; Julie McCauley, Senior Vice President, Corporate; www.ihstrategies.com

KAUFMAN HALL, 5202 Old Orchard Road, Suite N700, Skokie, Illinois Zip 60077; tel. 847/441–8780; Jason H. Sussman, Partner; www.kaufmanhall.com

KURT SALMON ASSOCIATES, 1355 Peachtree Street N.E., Suite 900, Atlanta, Georgia Zip 30309–0900; tel. 404/892–0321; Nancy Snell, Senior Research Analyst; www.kurtsalmon.com

LATHAM AND WATKINS, LLP, 633 West 5th Street, Suite 4000, Los Angeles, California Zip 90071; tel. 213/485–1234; Daniel K. Settelmayer, Partner; www.lw.com

LEXISNEXIS, 1000 Alderman Drive, Alpharetta, Georgia Zip 30005; tel. 404/577–1779; Sarah J. Stansberry, Senior Director, Marketing; www.lexisnexis.com

LIVEPROCESS, 271 Grove Avenue, Building D., Verona, New Jersey Zip 07044; tel. 973/571–2500; Nathaniel Weiss, Chief Executive Officer; www.liveprocess.com

LYRA HEALTH, 200 Park Road, Burlingame, California Zip 94010–4206; tel. 650/477–2991; David Ebersman, Chief Executive Officer; www.lyrahealth.com

MCDONALD HOPKINS, LLC, 600 Superior Avenue East, Suite 2100, Cleveland, Ohio Zip 44114–2690; tel. 216/348–5400; Richard S. Cooper, Member; www.mcdonaldhopkins.com

MCKESSON CORPORATION, 1 Post Street, 33rd Floor, San Francisco, California Zip 94104–5203; tel. 404/338–2985; Anastasia Agapoff, Assistant Manager, Library Operations

MEDASSETS, 100 North Pointe Center East, Suite 200, Alpharetta, Georgia Zip 30022–1506; tel. 314/579–1896; Ron DeCarlo, Senior Vice President; www.medassets.com

MEDITECH INFORMATION, tel. 781/821–3000; Howard Messing, President and Chief Executive Officer; www.meditech.com

NATIONAL CENTER FOR HEALTH STATISTICS, 3311 Toledo Road, Hyattsville, Maryland Zip 20782–2064; tel. 800/232–4636; Cynthia G. Link, Lead Administrative Officer; www.cdc.gov

NAVEX GLOBAL, 6000 Meadows Road, Suite 200, Lake Oswego, Oregon Zip 97035–3172; tel. 503/924–1640; Stephen J. Molen, Vice President Strategic Solutions; www.navexglobal.com

NORTH AMERICAN PARTNERS IN ANESTHESIA, 68 South Service Road, Suite 350, Melville, New York Zip 11747–2358; tel. 516/945–3000; Jill Aaronson, Marketing Coordinator; www.napaanesthesia.com

PACIFIC ADR CONSULTING, 316 Occidental Avenue South, Suite 500, Seattle, Washington Zip 98104–2874; tel. 206/624–3388; Gregg Bertram, President; www.pacificadrconsulting.com

PACKETMOTION, INC., 260 Santa Ana Court, Sunnyvale, California Zip 94085–4512; tel. 408/449–4300; Ravi Khatod, Senior Vice President, Sales and Business Development; www.packetmotion.com

PASCAL METRICS INC., 1025 Thomas Jefferson Street N.W., Suite 420E, Washington, District of Columbia Zip 20007–5241; tel. 202/333–9090; Drew Ladner, President and Chief Executive Officer; www.pascalmetrics.com

PEER CONSULTING, 2856 80Th Avenue S.E., Suite 200, Mercer Island, Washington Zip 98040–2984; tel. 206/236–1300; Rick Nunn, Senior Managing Partner; www.peerconsulting.net

PHYSICIAN WELLNESS SERVICES, 5000 West 36th Street, Suite 230, Minneapolis, Minnesota Zip 55416–2771; tel. 877/731–3949; Lori Brostrom, Vice President Marketing; www.physicianwellnessservices.com

PRACTICELINK, 415 2nd Avenue, Hinton, West Virginia Zip 25951–2427; tel. 314/323–9698; Eric Martin, Physician Job Placement Services

PREMIERE GLOBAL SERVICES, 3280 Peachtree Road N.W., Suite 1000, Atlanta, Georgia Zip 30305–2422; tel. 404/543–9449; Mark H. Horne, Vice President Marketing, Notifications and Reminders; www.premiereglobal.com

QUAMMEN HEALTH CARE CONSULTANTS, 522B Brandies Circle, Suite 4, Murfreesboro, Tennessee Zip 37128–4873; tel. 407/539–2015; Robecca Quammen, President; www.quammengroup.com

REIMBURSEMENT SERVICES GROUP, INC., 360 Park Avenue South, 17th Floor, New York, New York Zip 10010–1710; tel. 212/857–5269; Michele Manuel, Director of Sales and Marketing; www.reimburse-services.com

RYCAN, P.O. Box 306, Marshall, Minnesota Zip 56258–0306; tel. 800/201–3324; Marg Louwagie, Administrative Assistant; www.rycan.com

SAMUELI INSTITUTE, 1737 King Street, Suite 600, Alexandria, Virginia Zip 22314–2764; tel. 703/299–4800; Bonnie R. Sakallaris, Vice President Optimal Healing Environments; www.siib.org

SERVICE MANAGEMENT SYSTEMS, 7135 Charlotte Pike, Nashville, Tennessee Zip 37209–5015; tel. 615/399–1839; Gary Blanks, Division Manager; www.smsclean.com

SIEMENS HEALTHCARE, 51 Valley Stream Parkway, Malvern, Pennsylvania Zip 19355; tel. 610/448–4500; Amar Shah, Senior Manager, Corporate Communication; www.medical.siemens.com

SODEXO HEALTH CARE, 86 Hopmeadow Street, Simsbury, Connecticut Zip 06089; tel. 860/325–1220; Shirley Palmieri, Director Creative Services; www.sodexo.com

SPECIALTYCARE, 3100 West End Avenue, Suite 800, Nashville, Tennessee Zip 37203; tel. 615/345–5400; David Peterson, Senior Vice President Marketing; www.specialtycare.net

STAKEHOLDER ADVISORY SERVICES, LLC, 56 Grayson Drive, Belle Mead, New Jersey Zip 08502–4916; tel. 609/651–8959; Jeffrey Resnick, Managing Partner

STOCKAMP AND ASSOCIATES, INC., 6000 S.W. Meadows Road, Suite 300, Lake Oswego, Oregon Zip 97035; tel. 503/303–1200; Karen Andrews, Senior Marketing Manager; www.stockamp.com

STRATA DECISION TECHNOLOGY, tel. 312/726–1227; Dan Michelson, Chief Executive Officer; www.stratadecision.com

STROUDWATER ASSOCIATES, 50 Sewall Street, Suite 102, Portland, Maine Zip 04102–2646; tel. 207/221–8255; Marc Voyvodich, Chief Executive Officer

SULLIVAN COTTER & ASSOCIATES, INC, 200 West Madison Street, Suite 2450, Chicago, Illinois Zip 60606–3499; tel. 312/564–5883; Mary Kelley, Director of Marketing; www.sullivancotter.com

SULLIVAN, COTTER AND ASSOCIATES, INC., 1100 Peachtree Street, Suite 620, Atlanta, Georgia Zip 30309; tel. 678/551–7190; Maureen Cotter, Director Research and Information; www.sullivancotter.com

SURGICAL CARE AFFILIATES, 3000 Galleria Boulevard, Suite 500, Birmingham, Alabama Zip 35244; tel. 205/545–2759; Julie Dunn, Vice President; www.scasurgery.com

SYMPLR, 616 Cypress Creek Parkway, Suite 800, Houston, Texas Zip 77090–3029; tel. 281/863–9500; Rick Pleczko, Chief Executive Officer; www.vcsdatabase.com

SYSCOM SERVICES, INC, 1010 Wayne Avenue, Suite 320, Silver Spring, Maryland Zip 20910; tel. 301/768–0118; Lee Weinstein, President; www.syscomservices.com

TEAMHEALTH, 265 Brookview Centre Way, Suite 400, Knoxville, Tennessee Zip 37919; tel. 865/293–5486; Mike Snow, Chief Executive Officer; www.teamhealth.com

THE CHARTIS GROUP, 220 West Kinzie Street, 5th Floor, Chicago, Illinois Zip 60654–4912; tel. 877/667–4700; Katy Pinter, Principal; www.chartis.com

THE HSM GROUP, LTD, 8777 East Via de Ventura #188, Scottsdale, Arizona Zip 85258; tel. 480/947–8078; Sheryl Bronkesh, President; www.hsmgroup.com

THE STUDER GROUP, 8222 Douglas Avenue, Suite 780, Dallas, Texas Zip 75225–5923; tel. 972/860–0551; B. G. Porter, Chief Executive Officer and President; www.studergroup.com

TRUVEN HEALTH ANALYTICS, 6200 South Syracuse Way, Suite 300, Greenwood Village, Colorado Zip 80111–4740; tel. 303/486–6400; Julie Weigel, Assistant of Vice President Sales; www.truvenhealth.com

UGHS AUTIMIS BILLING INC, 7324 Southwest Freeway, Suite 700, Houston, Texas Zip 77074–2019; tel. 425/452–0630; Brandon Griffin, Chief Executive Officer; www.edifecs.com

VALUES COACH, INC., PO Box 490, Solon, Iowa Zip 52333–0490; tel. 319/624–3889; Joe Tye, Head Coach and Chief Executive Officer

VECNA TECHNOLOGIES, INC., 36 Cambridgepark Drive, Cambridge, Massachusetts Zip 02140; tel. 617/864–0636; Amanda Baldi, Director, Marketing and Communications; www.vecna.com

VERITY, INC, 5758 West Las Positas Boulevard, Suite 100, Pleasanton, California Zip 94588; tel. 925/598–3003; Michael Pliner, President; www.verity.com

VERRAS HEALTHCARE INTERNATIONAL, tel. 888/791–5556; Robert T. Langston, Partner

VGM GROUP INC., 1111 West San Marnan Drive, Waterloo, Iowa Zip 50701–9007; tel. 319/274–6643; Kelly Turner, Advocacy Director; www.vgm.com

VIIAD SYSTEMS LLC, 1170 Wheeler Way, Suite 200, Langhorne, Pennsylvania Zip 19047–3243; tel. 866/498–4423; Tricia Bradley, Director, Sales and Marketing Support; www.viiad.com

WASTE MANAGEMENT, 1001 Fannin St. Suite 4000, Houston, Texas Zip 77002–6711; tel. 713/265–1352; Bill Turpin, Director Strategic Development

WESTERN HEALTHCARE ALLIANCE, 715 Horizon Drive, Suite 401, Grand Junction, Colorado Zip 81506–8731; tel. 970/683–5223; Carolyn S. Bruce, Chief Executive Officer; www.wha1.org

XANITOS, INC., 3809 West Chester Pike, Suite 210, Newtown Square, Pennsylvania Zip 19073–2304; tel. 484/654–2300; Graeme A. Crothall, Chairman and Chief Executive Officer; www.xanitos.com

Educational Services:

NATIONAL RURAL HEALTH RESOURCE CENTER, 525 South Lake Avenue, Suite 320, Duluth, Minnesota Zip 55802; tel. 218/727–9390; Sally Buck, Chief Executive Officer; www.ruralcenter.org

RAYTHEON PROFESSIONAL SERVICES, 870 Winter Street, Waltham, Massachusetts Zip 02451–1449; tel. 781/522–3000; Dave Letts, Vice President and General Manager; www.raytheon.com

Information Systems:

ALLSCRIPTS HEALTHCARE SOLUTIONS, 222 Merchandise Mart Plaza, Suite 2024, Chicago, Illinois Zip 60654–1010; tel. 312/447–2412; Stephanie Kowalski, Vice President Central Marketing; www.allscripts.com

CERNER CORPORATION, 2800 Rockcreek Parkway, Kansas City, Missouri Zip 64117; tel. 816/221–1024; Laurel Vine, Program Manager, Industry Events; www.cerner.com

DESIGN CLINICALS, 5200 Southcenter Boulevard, Suite 250, Seattle, Washington Zip 98188–7911; tel. 888/633–7320; Dewey Howell, Chief Executive Officer; www.designclinicals.com

FLEMING AOD, INC., 816 Thayer Avenue, Floor 3rd, Silver Spring, Maryland Zip 20910–4508; tel. 202/872–1033; Mary Dalrymple, Managing Director; www.aod.cx

HEALTHLAND, 1600 Utica Avenue South, Suite 300, Minneapolis, Minnesota Zip 55416–1468; tel. 612/787–3120; Tracey Schroeder, Vice President Marketing

IMPRIVATA, INC., 10 Maguire Road Building 4, Lexington, Massachusetts Zip 02421–3110; tel. 781/674–2700; Ed Gaudel, Chief Marketing Officer; www.imprivata.com

KPMG LLP, 200 East Randolph Street, Suite 5500, Chicago, Illinois Zip 60601–6607; tel. 312/665–2073; Edward J. Giniat, National Line of Business Leader, Healthcare and Pharmaceuticals Practice

MEDHOST, 6100 West Plano Parkway, Suite 3100, Plano, Texas Zip 75093–8342; tel. 888/218–4678; Leslie LaFon, Departmental Segment Manager; www.medhost.com

MPOWR, A SUPPLYCORE SOLUTION, 303 North Main Street, Suite 800, Rockford, Illinois Zip 61101–1018; tel. 815/964–7940; Bryan Davis, Director; www.mpowr.com

QGENDA, INC., 3340 Peachtree Road N.E., Suite 1100, Atlanta, Georgia Zip 30326–1043; tel. 855/399–9945; Allison Aronson, Marketing Operations Associate; www.qgenda.com

SCC SOFT COMPUTER, 5400 Tech Data Drive, Clearwater, Florida Zip 33760–3116; tel. 727/789–0100; Gilbert Hakim, Chief Executive Officer; www.softcomputer.com

SHIFTWISE, 1800 S.W. 1st Avenue, Suite 510, Portland, Oregon Zip 97201–5322; tel. 503/548–2030; Nick Haselwander, Marketing Manager; www.shiftwise.com

VALENCE HEALTH, 600 West Jackson Boulevard, Chicago, Illinois Zip 60661–5636; tel. 312/273–6623; Kevin Weinstein, Chief Marketing Officer; www.valencehealth.com

Insurance Broker:

AMERICAN FIDELITY ASSURANCE COMPANY, 2000 North Classen Boulevard, Oklahoma City, Oklahoma Zip 73106; tel. 877/967–5748; Brian Mauck, National Sales Director; www.af–group.com

BOSTON MUTUAL LIFE INSURANCE COMPANY, 120 Royall Street, Canton, Massachusetts Zip 02021; tel. 781/828–7000; Peter Tillson, Vice President; www.bostonmutual.com

CHUBB INSURANCE, 82 Hopmeadow Street, Simsbury, Connecticut Zip 06070; tel. 860/408–2017; Kimberly Holmes, Assistant Vice President Healthcare; www.chubb.com

DYE & ESKIN, 1324 Vincent Place, Mc Lean, Virginia Zip 22101; tel. 703/556–0744; Rick Eskin, President

G. E. FINANCIAL, GE Appliance Park Building, Suite 100, Louisville, Kentucky Zip 40225; tel. 502/254–1756; Greg Miller, Director Business Development; www.ge.com

ING EMPLOYEE BENEFITS, 20 Washington Avenue South, Minneapolis, Minnesota Zip 55401; tel. 612/372–1122; Steve Pitzer, Vice President

IRONSHORE, 300 South Wacker Drive, Chicago, Illinois Zip 60606–6680; tel. 312/496–7535; Daniel R. Nash, Senior Vice President Field Operations and Business Development; www.ironshore.com

LOYAL INSURANCE, 423 Westport Road, Suite 201, Kansas City, Missouri Zip 64111; tel. 816/841–3597; Michael Reidy, Vice President

NEBCO, 1264 Knollwood Drive West, West Chester, Pennsylvania Zip 19380; tel. 877/739–3330; James M. Mattison, Vice President; www.nebenefit.com

THE ALLEN J. FLOOD COMPANIES, INC., 2 Madison Avenue, Larchmont, New York Zip 10538; tel. 914/834–9326; Allen J. Flood, President; www.ajfusa.com

UNITED CONCORDIA COMPANY, INC., 4401 Deer Path Road, Harrisburg, Pennsylvania Zip 17110; tel. 717/260–6800; Brett Altland, Product Development Analyst; www.ucci.com

Managed Care/Utilization:

CENTENE CORPORATION, 111 East Capitol Street, Suite 500, Jackson, Mississippi Zip 39201; tel. 601/863–0835; K. Michael Bailey, Vice President; www.centene.com

Manufacturer/Supplier:

3M, 3M Center, Building 275–4E–01, Saint Paul, Minnesota Zip 55144–1000; tel. 612/733–8183; Donald R. Brewer, Director Medical–Surgical Markets

© 2016 AHA Guide

AMERISOURCE BERGEN, 1300 Morris Drive, Chesterbrook, Pennsylvania Zip 19087–5559; tel. 610/727–2441; Elisa Moxley, Director, Health Systems Market Development; www.amerisourcebergen.com

BAXTER HEALTHCARE CORPORATION, Route 120 and Wilson Road, Round Lake, Illinois Zip 60073; tel. 224/948–2000; Tom Progar, Vice President Marketing Strategy and Operations; www.baxter.com

CAREFUSION CORPORATION, 3750 Torrey View Court, San Diego, California Zip 92130–2622; tel. 858/617–2000; Jocelyn Ochinang, Market Research Manager; www.carefusion.com

CORNING OPTICAL COMMUNICATIONS WIRELESS INC., 13221 Woodland Park Road, Suite 400, Herndon, Virginia Zip 20171–5505; tel. 202/230–3306; Grace Alcivar, Director Vertical Programs, Healthcare; www.corning.com

CUVERRO – OLIN BRASS, 4801 Olympia Park Plaza, Suite 3500, Louisville, Kentucky Zip 40241–2092; tel. 877/311–2883; Anthony Kulik, Director; www.cuverro.com

EXTENSION, INC, 6435 West Jefferson Boulevard, Suite 201, Fort Wayne, Indiana Zip 46804–6203; tel. 877/207–3753; Whitney St. Pierre, Director Marketing; www.opentheredbox.com

GE HEALTHCARE, 9900 West Innovation Drive, RP–2177, Wauwatosa, Wisconsin Zip 53226–4856; tel. 262/548–2088; Kimberly Rutherford, Business Partner and Director, Advertising & Promotion US–Canada Region

HD SUPPLY FACILITIES MAINTENANCE, tel. 858/831–2646; Jim Janclaes, Manager Healthcare National Account; www.HDsupplysolutions.com

HILL–ROM, 1069 State Route 46 East, Batesville, Indiana Zip 47006–9167; tel. 812/934–7958; Thomas J. Jeffers, Director Government Relations; www.hill–rom.com

JOHNSON & JOHNSON, 829 Williamsburg Boulevard, Downingtown, Pennsylvania Zip 19335–4124; tel. 610/518–7295; Larry Westfall, Director Healthcare Quality Alliances

Metro Hospital Assn:

HOSPITAL ASSOCIATION OF SOUTHERN CALIFORNIA, 515 South Figueroa Street, Suite 1300, Los Angeles, California Zip 90071–3300; tel. 213/538–0700; James D. Barber, President; www.hasc.org

National Health Care Prof Assn:

AMERICAN DENTAL ASSOCIATION, 211 East Chicago Avenue, Chicago, Illinois Zip 60611–2678; tel. 312/440–2500; Jane Grover, Director, Council on Access, Prevention and Interprofessional Relations; www.ada.org

Other:

AEROSCOUT, 1300 Island Drive, Suite 202, Redwood City, California Zip 94065; tel. 650/596–2994; Gabi Daniely, Vice President Marketing and Product Strategy; www.aeroscout.com

AGILITY RECOVERY SOLUTIONS, 11030 Circle Point Road, Suite 450, Westminster, Colorado Zip 80020–2791; tel. 877/495–9615; Jenny Boyd, Director Marketing Account; www.agilityrecovery.com

AIR METHODS CORPORATION, 7211 South Peoria Street, Englewood, Colorado Zip 80112–4133; tel. 303/792–7565; Ruthie Hubka, Government Relations Specialist; www.airmethods.com

AIRBOSS ENGINEERING PRODUCTS, 3341 75th Avenue, Suite GG, Landover, Maryland Zip 20785; tel. 240/334–6666; Adam H. Borcz, Associate; www.airbossofamerica.com

AMBIUS, 1125 Berkshire Boulevard, Suite 150, Reading, Pennsylvania Zip 19610–1211; tel. 610/372–9700; Cathy Hoffman, Marketing Assistant; www.ambius.com

AMC HEALTH, INC., 39 Broadway, Suite 540, New York, New York Zip 10006; tel. 877/776–1746; Joanna Haskin, Vice President Partner Development; www.amchealth.com

AMERICAN ASSOCIATION FOR WOUND CARE MANAGEMENT, 4109 Glenrose Street, Kensington, Maryland Zip 20895–3718; tel. 301/933–2200; Jule Crider, Executive Director; www.aawcm.org

AMERICAN ASSOCIATION OF NURSE ANESTHETISTS, 222 South Prospect Avenue, Park Ridge, Illinois Zip 60068–4001; tel. 847/655–1100; Wanda O. Wilson, Executive Director and Chief Executive Officer; www.aana.com

AMERICAN BOARD OF MEDICAL SPECIALTIES, 353 North Clark Street, Suite 1400, Chicago, Illinois Zip 60654–3454; tel. 312/436–2626; Lois Margaret Nora, President and Chief Executive Officer; www.abms.org

AMERICAN COLLEGE OF HEALTHCARE EXECUTIVES, One North Franklin, Suite 1700, Chicago, Illinois Zip 60606–4425; tel. 312/424–2800; Deborah Bowen, President and Chief Executive Officer; www.ache.org

AMERICAN DENTAL EDUCATION ASSOCIATION, 1400 K Street N.W., Suite 1100, Washington, District of Columbia Zip 20005; tel. 202/289–7201; Richard Valachovic, Executive Director; www.adea.org

AMERICAN HEALTH INFORMATION MANAGEMENT ASSOCIATION, 233 North Michigan Avenue, Suite 2150, Chicago, Illinois Zip 60601–5806; tel. 312/233–1100; David A. Sweet, Director Library Services

AMERICAN SOCIETY OF ANESTHESIOLOGISTS, 1061 American Lane, Schaumburg, Illinois Zip 60173; tel. 847/268–9160; Paul Pomerantz, Chief Executive Officer; www.asahq.org

AMN HEALTHCARE, INC., 12400 High Bluff Drive, Suite 100, San Diego, California Zip 92130–3581; tel. 866/871–8519; Steve Wehn, Senior Vice President of Corporate Development

APOGEE PHYSICIANS, 15059 North Scottsdale Road, Suite 600, Scottsdale, Arizona Zip 85254–2685; tel. 602/778–3600; Michael Gregory, Chairman; www.apogeephysicians.com

ARC GROUP ASSOCIATES, 330 South Warminster Road, Suite 345, Hatboro, Pennsylvania Zip 19040; tel. 215/881–9500; Eric Malakoff, Vice President Sales and Marketing; www.arcgroup.net

ARIS RADIOLOGY, 5655 Hudson Drive, Suite 210, Hudson, Ohio Zip 44236; tel. 330/655–3800; Stacey Christofferson, Chief Development Officer; www.arisradiology.com

ARJOHUNTLEIGH, 2349 West Lake Street, Suite 250, Addison, Illinois Zip 60101–6183; tel. 800/323–1245; Andrew Hepburn, Vice President; www.arjohuntleigh.com

ASSOCIATION OF PERIOPERATIVE REGISTERED NURSES, 2170 South Parker Road, Suite 400, Denver, Colorado Zip 80231; tel. 303/755–6304; Linda Kay Groah, Executive Director and Chief Executive Officer; www.aorn.org

AVATAR SOLUTIONS, 25 East Washington Street, Suite 600, Chicago, Illinois Zip 60602; tel. 312/236–7170; Jeffrey Brady, Chief Executive Officer; www.hrsolutionsinc.com

BACTES, 8344 Clairemont Mesa Boulevard, Suite 201, San Diego, California Zip 92111–1327; tel. 858/244–1811; Jeanie Pipitone, Senior Marketing Manager; www.bactes.com

BATTELLE MEMORIAL INSTITUTE, 505 King Avenue, Columbus, Ohio Zip 43201–2946; tel. 614/424–6424; Sean Deegan, Director; www.battelle.org

BERNARD HODES GROUP, 220 East 42nd Street, 14th Floor, New York, New York Zip 10017; tel. 888/438–9911; Karen Hart, Senior Vice President Healthcare Division; www.hodes.com

BEST UPON REQUEST, 8170 Corporate Park Drive, Suite 300, Cincinnati, Ohio Zip 45242; tel. 513/605–7800; Kirsten Lecky, Vice President Business Development; www.bestuponrequest.com

BLUE CROSS AND BLUE SHIELD ASSOCIATION, 225 North Michigan Avenue, Chicago, Illinois Zip 60601–7680; tel. 312/297–6000; Scott P. Serota, President and Chief Executive Officer; www.bcbs.com

BOARDVANTAGE, 4300 Bohannon Drive, Suite 110, Menlo Park, California Zip 94025; tel. 650/330–2444; Virginia Portillo, Conference and Events Coordinator; www.boardvantage.com

BUREAU OF MEDICINE AND SURGERY, DEPARTMENT OF THE NAVY, 7700 Arlington Boulevard, Suite 5126, Falls Church, Virginia Zip 22042; tel. 703/681–8489; Bryce H.P. Mendez, Healthcare Policy Analyst

CANON SOLUTIONS AMERICA, INC., 300 Commerce Square Boulevard, Burlington, New Jersey Zip 08016–1270; tel. 847/706–3411; Paul T. Murphy, Director Strategic Contract Support; www.solutions.canon.com

CAP SITE INC., 85 South Prospect Street, Burlington, Vermont Zip 05401–3444; tel. 802/383–0675; Gino Johnson, Senior Vice President; www.capsite.com

CARETECH SOLUTIONS, INC., tel. 248/823–0800; Paula Gwyn, Senior Manager Business Development; www.caretechsolutions.com

CCM ADVISORS, LLC, 190 South La Salle Street, Suite 2800, Chicago, Illinois Zip 60603; tel. 312/444–6200; Michael Randall, Director Sales and Marketing; www.ahafunds.org

CERTIPHI SCREENING, INC., 1105 Industrial Highway, Southampton, Pennsylvania Zip 18966; tel. 888/260–1370; Tony D'Orazio, President; www.certiphi.com

CHAMBERLIN EDMONDS, 14 Piedmont Center N.E., Atlanta, Georgia Zip 30305–1543; tel. 404/279–5000; Kim Williams, Chief Financial Officer; www.chamberlinedmonds.com

CISCO SYSTEMS, 165 Needletree Lane, Glastonbury, Connecticut Zip 06033; tel. 860/657–8127; Michael Haymaker, Director Healthcare Industry Marketing; www.cisco.com

CLAREDI CORPORATION, 2525 Lake Park Boulevard, Salt Lake City, Utah Zip 84120; tel. 801/982–3001; Kepa Zubeldia, Senior Vice President; www.claredi.com

COMPREHENSIVE PHARMACY SERVICES, 6409 North Quail Hollow Road, Memphis, Tennessee Zip 38120–1414; tel. 901/748–0470; Walker Upshaw, Chief Development Officer; www.cpspharm.com

COMPUTER ASSOCIATES, One Computer Associates Plaza, Islandia, New York Zip 11749; tel. 800/225–5224; Michael McDermand, Vice President Healthcare; www.ca.com

CONCUITY, INCORPORATED, 200 North Fairway Drive Suite 182, Vernon Hills, Illinois Zip 60061–1861; tel. 847/465–6003; James Farrar, Vice President Sales; www.concuity.com

CORNERSTONE ON DEMAND, 1601 Cloverfield Avenue, 6th Floor, Santa Monica, California Zip 90404; tel. 310/752–0200; Johnna Ehmke, Senior Marketing Manager; www.cornerstoneondemand.com

COVENANT HOSPICE, 5041 North 12th Avenue, Pensacola, Florida Zip 32504; tel. 850/433–2155; Dale O. Knee, President and Chief Executive Officer; www.covenanthospice.org

CYRACOM, 5780 North Swan Road, Tucson, Arizona Zip 85718–4527; tel. 800/713–4950; Jeremy Woan, President and Chief Executive Officer; www.cyracom.com

DEPARTMENT OF AIR FORCE MEDICAL SERVICE, HQ USAF/SG, Bolling AFB, District of Columbia Zip 20332–6188; tel. 202/545–6700

DEPARTMENT OF THE ARMY, OFFICE OF THE SURGEON GENERAL, 5109 Leesburg Pike, Falls Church, Virginia Zip 22041–3258; tel. 202/690–6467

DISH, PO Box 5096524, Englewood, Colorado Zip 80112–5905; tel. 720/514–6019; Steven Wilson, Manager; www.dish.com

DNV HEALTHCARE, INC., 400 Techne Center Drive, Suite 100, Milford, Ohio Zip 45150–2792; tel. 513/388–4863; Shannon Walker, Team Operator and Planner; www.dnvhealthcareinc.com

DONOR NETWORK WEST, 12667 Alcosta Boulevard, Suite 500, San Ramon, California Zip 94583–4427; tel. 925/480–3100; Laurie Boyer, External Affairs Officer; www.donornetworkwest.org

DRINKER BIDDLE & REATH LLP, 191 North Wacker Drive Suite 3700, Chicago, Illinois Zip 60606–1615; tel. 312/569–1000; Elisse Lassiter, Business Development Manager; www.drinkerbiddle.com

ECRI INSTITUTE, 5200 Butler Pike, Plymouth Meeting, Pennsylvania Zip 19462–1298; tel. 610/825–6000; Amy Schwartz, Founder; www.ecri.org

EKTRON, 542 Amherst Street, Nashua, New Hampshire Zip 03063–1016; tel. 603/594–0249; Deb Symons, Director, Field Marketing and Programs; www.ektron.com

EVICORE, 730 Cool Springs Boulevard, Suite 800, Franklin, Tennessee Zip 37067–7289; tel. 615/468–4116; Laura Lee, Marketing Project Manager, Providers; www.medsolutions.com

FIRST AMERICAN EQUIPMENT FINANCE, 255 Woodcliff Drive, Fairport, New York Zip 14450–4219; tel. 585/643–3266; Mike Wiedemer, Senior Vice President, Sales; www.faef.com

FIRST DATA USA, 5565 Glenridge Connector N.E., Atlanta, Georgia Zip 30342; tel. 914/450–4545; Andrew Finck, Vice President Healthcare Segment; www.firstdata.com

GENERAL DYNAMICS HEALTH SOLUTIONS, 3060 Williams Drive, Suite 100, Fairfax, Virginia Zip 22031–4655; tel. 888/545–8477; Anne Hughes, Director, Business Development; www.gdit.com/health

HEALTHCARE BUSINESS ASSOCIATES, P.O. Box 1188, Rancho Mirage, California Zip 92270–1188; tel. 888/292–6929; Jack C. Nixon, President

HEALTHGRID, 4203 Vineland Road, Suite K6, Orlando, Florida Zip 32811; tel. 855/624–2844; Raj Toleti, Founder and Chief Executive Officer; www.healthgrid.com

HEALTHTRUST PURCHASING GROUP INC, 155 Franklin Road, Suite 400, Brentwood, Tennessee Zip 37027–4693; tel. 615/344–3030; Beverly Wallace, President; www.healthtrustpg.com

HEALTHWAYS, INC, 701 Cool Springs Boulevard, Franklin, Tennessee Zip 37067–2697; tel. 800/327–3822; Karen Meyer, Principal; www.healthways.com

HENRY J. KAISER FAMILY FOUNDATION, 1330 G. Street N.W., Washington, District of Columbia Zip 20005–3004; tel. 202/347–5270; Drew Altman, President and Chief Executive Officer; www.kff.org

HMS, 355 Quartermaster Court, Jeffersonville, Indiana Zip 47130–3670; tel. 812/704–5747; Rich Flaherty, Vice President Sales and Marketing; www.hms.com

HOOPER, LUNDY & BOOKMAN, INC., 1875 Century Park East, Suite 1600, Los Angeles, California Zip 90067; tel. 310/551–8111; Lloyd Bookman, Partner; www.health-law.com

HOSPITAL RECRUITING.COM, 899 South College Mall Road, Suite 395, Bloomington, Indiana Zip 47401–6301; tel. 800/244–7236; Michael Jones, Managing Partner; www.hospitalrecruiting.com

HQ ACC/SGMS, 162 Dodd, Suite 100, Langley AFB, Virginia Zip 23665–1995

HQ AETC/SGAL, 63 Main Circle, Suite 3, Randolph AFB, Texas Zip 78150–4549

HQ AFMC/SGAR, 4225 Logistics Avenue, N–209, Dayton, Ohio Zip 45433–5761; tel. 937/656–3655; Alice Rohrbach

HQ AFSPC/SGAL, 150 Vandenberg Street, Suite 1105, Petterson AFB, Colorado Zip 80914–4550

HQ AMC/SGSL, 203 West Losey Street, Room 1180, Scott AFB, Illinois Zip 62225–5219

HQ PACAF/SGAL, 25 East Street, Suite D1, Hickam AFB, Hawaii Zip 96853–5418

HQ USAFA/SGAL, Pinion Drive, Building 4102, Suite 3, USAF Academy, Colorado Zip 80840

HURON CONSULTING GROUP, 550 West Van Buren, Chicago, Illinois Zip 60607; tel. 312/583–8700; Gordon Mountford, Executive Vice President; www.huronconsultinggroup.com

HYLAND SOFTWARE, INC., 28500 Clemens Road, Westlake, Ohio Zip 44145; tel. 440/788–5814; Michael Kortan, Director Health Care Solutions; www.onbase.com

ICRA SOLUTIONS LLC, 4034 Suwanee Trail Drive, Buford, Georgia Zip 30518–8771; tel. 678/412–5132; Amy Walker, Director; www.icrasolutions.com

ID EXPERTS, 10300 S.W. Greenburg Road, Suite 570, Portland, Oregon Zip 97223–5410; tel. 866/726–4271; Sally Gray, Manager Sales Support; www.idexpertscorp.com

IDENTITY FORCE, 1257 Worcester Road, Suite 308, Framingham, Massachusetts Zip 01701; tel. 508/788–6660; Mike Lawson, Vice President; www.identityforce.com

IHEALTHENGINES INC., tel. 650/248–9874; Harish P.K. Chidambaran, President and Chief Executive Officer; www.ihealthengines.com

INFORMATICS CORPORATION OF AMERICA, 1801 West End Avenue, Suite 1000, Nashville, Tennessee Zip 37203–2540; Rodney Hamilton, Chief Medical Information Officer

INNOVATIVE CAPITAL LLC, 1489 Baltimore Pike, Building 400, Springfield, Pennsylvania Zip 19064–3958; tel. 610/543–2490; Alan P. Richman, President and Chief Executive Officer; www.innovativecapital.com

INTALERE, 500 Commonwealth Drive, Warrendale, Pennsylvania Zip 15086–7516; tel. 877/711–5700; Laurie McGrath, Vice President Marketing; www.amerinet-gpo.com

INTERACTIVE HEALTH SOLUTIONS, 3800 North Wilke Road, Suite 155, Arlington Heights, Illinois Zip 60004–1278; tel. 847/754–2698; Joseph O'Brien, President; www.interactivesolutions.com

INTERNATIONAL ASSOCIATION FOR HEALTHCARE SECURITY AND SAFETY, P.O. Box 5038, Glendale Heights, Illinois Zip 60139; tel. 630/529–3913; Nancy Felesena, Executive Assistant; www.iahss.org

IP SERVICES, 2896 Crescent Avenue, Suite 201, Eugene, Oregon Zip 97408–7422; tel. 541/343–5974; Mark Allers, Vice President Business Development; www.ipservices.com

IRONPORT, 950 Elm Avenue, San Bruno, California Zip 94066; tel. 650/989–6500; Jeff Williams, Vice President Sales; www.ironport.com

JANI-KING, 16885 Dallas Parkway, Addison, Texas Zip 75001; tel. 972/991–0900; Bob Carabajal, Director Healthcare Services; www.janiking.com

JEWISH GUILD HEALTHCARE, 15 West 65th Street, New York, New York Zip 10023; tel. 212/769–6200; Alan R. Morse, President and Chief Executive Officer; www.jgb.org

LANCASTER POLLARD AND CO, 65 East State Street, Columbus, Ohio Zip 43215–4213; tel. 614/224–8800; Thomas Green, Chief Executive Officer; www.lancasterpollard.com

LITTLER MENDELSON, P.C., 1100 Superior Avenue, 20th Floor, Cleveland, Ohio Zip 44114–2530; tel. 216/623–6104; Angela Lupardus, Manager, Regional Business Development and Marketing; www.littler.com

MAGELLAN HEALTH SERVICES, 6950 Columbia Gateway Drive, Columbia, Maryland Zip 21046; tel. 314/387–4000; Rick Lee, President Employer Solutions; www.magellanhealth.com

MEDICAL INFORMATION TECHNOLOGY, INC., tel. 781/821–3000; Lynn Robblee, Supervisor of Event Coordination and Memberships; www.meditech.com

MEDISOLV, INC., 10440 Little Patuexent Parkway, Suite 1000, Columbia, Maryland Zip 21044–3630; tel. 443/539–0505; Erin Heilman, Marketing Specialist; www.medisolv.com

MEDNAX SERVICES INC., 1301 Concord Terrace, Sunrise, Florida Zip 33323–2843; tel. 954/384–0175; Roger J. Medel, President; www.mednax.com

MODERN HEALTHCARE, 150 North Michigan Avenue, 17th Floor, Chicago, Illinois Zip 60601–3806; tel. 312/649–5491; Fawn Lopez, Publisher; www.modernhealthcare.com

MUCH SHELIST, 191 North Wacker Drive, Chicago, Illinois Zip 60606–1615; tel. 312/521–2000; Christian Auty, Principal; www.muchshelist.com

NATIONAL COUNCIL OF STATE BOARDS OF NURSING, 111 East Wacker Drive, 29th Floor, Chicago, Illinois Zip 60601–4277; tel. 312/525–3600; David Charles Benton, Chief Executive Officer; www.ncsbn.org

NAVAL REGIONAL MEDICAL CENTER, PSC 1005, Box 36, FPO, Armed Forces Africa, Canada, E Zip 09593–0136

NEXTGEN HEALTHCARE, 3001 Farmington Drive Southeast, Atlanta, Georgia Zip 30339–4704; tel. 253/385–7630; Mike Swim, Vice President of Business Development; www.nextgen.com

NOBLIS, 3150 Fairview Park South, Falls Church, Virginia Zip 22042; tel. 703/610–2255; Alan Dowling, Executive Director; www.mitretek.org

NTRACTS, LLC., 101 West Ohio Street, Suite 400, Indianapolis, Indiana Zip 46204–1970; tel. 888/316–9805; Jeffrey W. Short, President and Chief Executive Officer; www.ntracts.com

OPTUM, 11000 Optum Circle, Eden Prairie, Minnesota Zip 55344–2503; tel. 888/445–8745; Kim Brooks, Marketing Director; www.optum.com

PACIFIC MEDICAL DATA SOLUTIONS INC, 4990 Wing Way, 2nd Floor, Paso Robles, California Zip 93446–8579; tel. 805/237–7387; Jessica Stewart, President and Chief Executive Officer; www.pacificmds.com

PASSAGEWAYS, LLC, 8 North 3rd Street, Lafayette, Indiana Zip 47901–1264; tel. 765/535–1880; Paroon Chadha, Chief Executive Officer; www.passageways.com

PATIENT POINT, 8230 Montgomery Road, Suite 300, Cincinnati, Ohio Zip 45236–2292; tel. 888/479–5600; Chris Martini, President Network Solutions; www.patientpoint.com

PILAT, 460 U.S. Highway 22 West Suite 408, Whitehouse Station, New Jersey Zip 08889–3447; tel. 908/823–9417; Travis Lupo, Director Business Development; www.pilat-nai.com

PINSTRIPE, 200 South Executive Drive, Suite 400, Brookfield, Wisconsin Zip 53005–4216; tel. 262/754–5061; Jill Schwieters, Executive Vice President; www.pinstripetalent.com

PROASSURANCE, 100 Brookwood Place, Birmingham, Alabama Zip 35209–6811; tel. 205/877–4400; W. Stancil Starnes, Chairman, Chief Executive Officer; www.proassurance.com

QUARLES AND BRADY LLP, 300 North LaSalle Street, Suite 4000, Chicago, Illinois Zip 60654–3422; tel. 312/715–2751; Susan Stewart, Director, Client Relations; www.quarles.com

REMEDY MEDICAL SERVICES, 1320 West Clairemont Avenue, Suite 118, Eau Claire, Wisconsin Zip 54701–6027; tel. 715/834–1555; Maria A. Fedele, Vice President Operations; www.remedymedicalservices.com

RENTOKIL STERITECH, 1125 Berkshire Boulevard, Suite 150, Reading, Pennsylvania Zip 19610–1211; tel. 610/372–9700; Erica Caceres, Manager; www.rentokil-steritech.com

RF TECHNOLOGIES, 3125 North 126th Street, Brookfield, Wisconsin Zip 53005; tel. 800/669–9946; Glenn Jonas, President and Chief Executive Officer; www.rft.com

RISESMART, INC., 2055 Gateway Place, Suite 150, San Jose, California Zip 95110–1015; tel. 877/384–0004; Komal Patel, Marketing Manager; www.risesmart.com

SENTRY DATA SYSTEMS, INC., 800 Fairway Drive, Suite 400, Deerfield Beach, Florida Zip 33441–1830; tel. 806/411–4566; Tim Lantz, Senior Vice President, Data Next; www.sentryds.com

SHAREDCLARITY, 4425 East Cotton Center Boulevard, Phoenix, Arizona Zip 85040–8854; tel. 916/781–0659; Mark West, President; www.sharedclarity.net

SIMPLEX GRINNELL, 50 Technology Drive, Westminster, Massachusetts Zip 01441; tel. 978/731–8486; Suzanne Rahall, Marketing Manager, Healthcare Communications; www.simplexgrinnell.com

SUBWAY, 325 Bic Drive, Milford, Connecticut Zip 06461; tel. 800/888–4848; Joanne Kilgore, Global Account Manager; www.subway.com

TANDBERG, 29 Norfolk Avenue, Peabody, Massachusetts Zip 01960; tel. 978/531–1516; Luke Leininger, Senior Product Manager, Healthcare TelePresence; www.tandberg.com

THE ADVISORY BOARD COMPANY, 2445 M Street N.W., Washington, District of Columbia Zip 20037–2403; tel. 202/266–5600; Kelsey Mahler, Associate Director, Information Resource Center; www.advisory.com

THE AMERICAN COLLEGE OF OBSTETRICIANS AND GYNECOLOGISTS, 409 12th Street, S.W., Washington, District of Columbia Zip 20024–2188; tel. 202/638–5577; Hal Lawrence, Executive Vice President; www.acog.org

THE CPI GROUP, 7400 East Orchard Road, Suite 270, Englewood, Colorado Zip 80111; tel. 303/504–9999; John Van Gulik, Business Development Manager; www.thecpigroup.net

THE WALKER COMPANY, 31090 S.W. Boones Bend Road, Wilsonville, Oregon Zip 97070–6412; tel. 503/694–8539; Larry W. Walker, Principal; www.walkercompany.com

THERMO USCS, 120 Bishop's Way, Brookfield, Wisconsin Zip 53008; tel. 262/784–5600; Christine Miller, Executive Vice President Healthcare Group; www.thermo.com

TRANSAMERICA RETIREMENT SOLUTIONS, 4 Manhattanville Road, Purchase, New York Zip 10577; tel. 914/697–8952; Peter Kunkel, President and Chief Executive Officer; www.https://www.trsretire.com

TRANSUNION, LLC, 445 Hutchinson Avenue, Suite 800, Columbus, Ohio Zip 43235; tel. 614/785–6411; Martin Callahan, Vice President Business Development; www.transunion.com

TRAVELERS INSURANCE COMPANY, One Tower Square, 6th Floor, Hartford, Connecticut Zip 06183–1134; tel. 860/277–9830; John Truhan, Operations Manager; www.travelers.com

U. S. ARMY MEDICAL COMMAND, 2050 Worth Road, Suite 10, San Antonio, Texas Zip 78234–6010; tel. 210/221–2212; Ann Russell Potter

UNIFORM DATA SYSTEM FOR MEDICAL REHABILITATION, 270 Northpointe Parkway, Suite 300, Amherst, New York Zip 14228; tel. 716/817–7800; Troy Hillman, Manager, Analytical Services Group; www.udsmr.org

VERGE SOLUTIONS, LLC, 710 Johnnie Dodds Boulevard, Suite 202, Mount Pleasant, South Carolina Zip 29464–3045; tel. 843/628–4166; Ashley Worrall, Director Field Marketing; www.verge-solutions.com

VERISYS CORPORATION, 1001 North Fairfax Avenue, Suite 640, Alexandria, Virginia Zip 22314–1798; tel. 703/535–1471; John Benson, Chief Operating Officer; www.verisys.com/

*The members listed in **bold** are Associate Advantage members.*   © 2016 AHA Guide

VERSUS TECHNOLOGY, INC., 2600 Miller Creek Road, Traverse City, Michigan Zip 49684; tel. 231/946–5868; Stephanie Bertschy, Director Marketing; www.versustech.com

VESTAGEN TECHNICAL TEXTILES, INC., tel. 407/781–2395; Brian Crawford, Chief Business Officer; www.vestagen.com

VIGILANZ CORPORATION, 5775 Wayzata Boulevard, Suite 970, Minneapolis, Minnesota Zip 55416–2669; tel. 855/525–9078; David Goldsteen, Chairman and Chief Executive Officer; www.vigilanzcorp.com

VIZIENT, 799 9th Street Northwest, Suite 210, Washington, District of Columbia Zip 20001–5325; tel. 202/354–2600; Shoshana Krilow, Vice President Public Policy and Government Relations

VMC, A CCMSI COMPANY, 12300 Perry Highway, Suite 300, Wexford, Pennsylvania Zip 15090–8380; tel. 800/501–6248; www.vcm–llc.com

VOCERA COMMUNICATIONS, 525 Race Street, Suite 150, San Jose, California Zip 95126–3495; tel. 408/882–5100; Diana Cropley, Marketing Program Specialist; www.vocera.com

WESTERN LITIGATION, INC, 9821 Katy Freeway, Suite 600, Houston, Texas Zip 77024–1206; tel. 800/588–0619; Robert B. Blasio, President and Chief Executive Officer; www.westernlitigation.com

WITT/KIEFFER, 2015 Spring Road, Suite 510, Oak Brook, Illinois Zip 60523; tel. 630/990–1370; James Gauss, Chairman of Board Services; www.wittkieffer.com/

XENEX DISINFECTION SERVICES, 121 Interpark Boulevard, Suite 104, San Antonio, Texas Zip 78216; tel. 800/553–0069; Morris Miller, Chief Executive Officer; www.xenex.com

YOURCARE UNIVERSE, INC, 6550 Carothers Parkway, Suite 100, Franklin, Tennessee Zip 37067; tel. 844/641–6800; Lauren Douglass, Brand Manager; www.yourcareuniverse.com

Other Health Related:

CENTER FOR MEDICAL INTEROPERABILITY, 618 Church Street Suite 220, Nashville, Tennessee Zip 37219–2453; tel. 202/617–6009; Kerry McDermott, Vice President for Public Policy and Communications; www.medicalinteroperability.org

Recruitment Services:

B. E. SMITH, 8801 Renner Avenue, Lenexa, Kansas Zip 66219–9746; tel. 855/296–6318; Allison Murphy, Marketing Manager; www.besmith.com

DOCCAFE.COM, tel. 715/302–8881; Laura Fitzsimmons, Managing Member; www.doccafe.com

FURST GROUP, 2902 McFarland Road, Rockford, Illinois Zip 61107–6801; tel. 800/642–9940; Patrick Kampert, Director of Communications; www.furstgroup.com

Regional Health Care Assn:

TEXAS ORGANIZATION OF RURAL & COMMUNITY HOSPITALS, P.O. Box 203878, Austin, Texas Zip 78720–3878; tel. 512/873–0045; David Pearson, President and Chief Executive Officer; www.torchnet.org

CANADA

Other:

HALOGEN SOFTWARE CORPORATION, 495 March Road, Suite 500, Ottawa, Ontario Zip K2K 3G1; tel. 613/270–1011; Lorna Daly, Channel Manager Healthcare; www.halogensoftware.com

PIVOTAL PAYMENTS, 1100 Rene Levesque West, Montreal, Zip H33–4N4; tel. 514/313–1190; Gigi Beyene, Vice President, Sales; www.pivotalpayments.com

Provincial Hospital Assn:

ONTARIO HOSPITAL ASSOCIATION, 200 Front Street West, Suite 2800, Toronto, Ontario Zip M5V 3L1; tel. 416/205–1300; Warren DiClemente, Chief Operating and Vice President Educational Services; www.oha.com

FOREIGN

BAHAMAS

Other:

PRINCESS MARGARET HOSPITAL, P.O. Box N–8200, Nassau, tel. 242/322–2861; Mary Elizabeth Lightbourne–Walker, Hospital Administrator; www.phabahamas.org

BAHRAIN

Other:

INTERNATIONAL HOSPITAL OF BAHRAIN, P.O. Box 1084, Manama, tel. 011/759–8222; F. S. Zeerah, President; www.ihb.net/

BRAZIL

Other:

HOSPITAL SAMARITANO, Rua Conselheiro Brotero, 1486, Sao Paulo, Zip 01232–010; tel. 551/821–5300; Luiz Alberto Oliveira De Luca, Corporate Superintendent; www.samaritano.com.br

COLOMBIA

Other:

ASOCIACION COLOMBIANA DE HOSPITALES Y CLINICAS, Carrera 4, No 73–15, Bogota, Juan Carlos Giraldo Valencia, Director General; www.achc.org.co

ECUADOR

Other:

JUNTA DE BENEFICENCIA DE GUAYAQUIL, P.O. Box 09–01–789, Guayaquil, tel. 011/432–0760; Lautaro Aspiazu Wright, Director; www.jbg.org.ec

GEORGIA

Other:

INNOVA MEDICAL CENTER, 7A Sandra Euli Street, Tbilisi, Zip 0105; Giorgi Kipiani, Director; www.innovamedical.ge

MARITIME HOSPITAL JSC, Melikishrin 102B, Batumi, Zip 60100; Tamari Kachlishvili, Medical Director; www.mh.com.ge

MEDI CLUB GEORGIA, 22A, Tashkenti Street, Tbilisi, Zip 0160; tel. 995/225–1991; Nugzar Abramishvili, General Director; www.mediclubgeorgia.ge

TBILISI CENTRAL HOSPITAL, Chachava Street 1, Tbilisi, Zip 0159; Ivane Martiashuili, Co–founder; www.tch.ge

GERMANY

Other:

HQ USAFE/SGPXL, Unit 3050, Box 130, Ramstein AB, Armed Forces Africa, Canada, E Zip 09094–5001

INDIA

Other:

SAMAST PATIDAR AAROGYA TRUST, Kirti Patel, Chief Executive Officer

ISRAEL

Other:

HADASSAH MEDICAL ORGANIZATION, P.O. Box 12000, Jerusalem, Zip 91120; tel. 972/677–7111; Tamar Peretz–Yablonski, Interim Director General; www.hadassah.org.il

JAPAN

Other:

KAMEDA MEDICAL CENTER AND CLINICS, 929 Higashi–Cho, Kamogawa City, Zip 296–8602; tel. 814/092–2211; John C. Wocher, Executive Vice President; www.kameda.com

U.S. NAVAL HOSPITAL OKINAWA, U.S. Naval Base, FPO, Zip 96362; tel. 011/743–7555; Commander Martin Kerr; www.med.navy.mil/sites/nhoki/Pages/default.aspx

JORDAN

Other:

SPECIALTY HOSPITAL, P.O. Box 930186, Amman, Zip 11193; Fawzi Al–Hammouri, General Manager; www.specialty–hospital.com

LEBANON

Other:

SAINT GEORGE HOSPITAL UNIVERSITY MEDICAL CENTER, P.O. Box 166378, Beirut, Zip 1100–2807; tel. 961/158–5700; Ziad Kamel, Administrative Director; www.stgeorgehospital.org

MEXICO

Other:

SHRINERS HOSPITAL FOR CHILDREN, Av Del Iman 257, Col Pedregal de Santa Ursula, Delegacion Coyoacan, Mexico City, Zip 04600; Araceli Nagore, Administrator

MYANMAR

Other:

ASIA ROYAL GENERAL HOSPITAL, 14 Baho Street, Sanchaung Township, Yangon, Zip 11162; tel. 951/153–8055; Myat Thu, Managing Director; www.asiaroyalmedical.com

NEPAL

Other:

SIDDHI VINAYAK HOSPITAL AND PRASUTI GRIHA PVT LTD, 44601 Indian SubContinent, Gongabu, Zip Kathmandu; Ram Prasad Aryal, Chairman

---

PANAMA

Other:

CLINICA HOSPITAL SAN FERNANDO, S. A., Dept PTY 1663, P.O. Box 25207, Miami, Florida Zip 33102–5207; tel. 507/305–6399; Edgardo Fernandez, Medical Director; www.hospitalsanfernando.com

PERU

Other:

BRITISH AMERICAN HOSPITAL, Avenue Alfredo Salazar 3 Era, Lima 27, tel. 511/712–3000; Gonzalo Garrido–Lecca, Director; www.angloamericana.com.pe

PHILIPPINES

Ambulatory Care Center:

DEPARTMENT OF VETERANS AFFAIRS, OUTPATIENT CLINIC, Pasay City, APO, Zip 96440; tel. 632/833–4566; Artemio Arugay, Commander; www.va.gov

Other:

ST. LUKE'S MEDICAL CENTER, 279 East Rodriguez Sr Boulevard, Quezon City, tel. 632/723–0101; Edgardo R. Cortez, President and Chief Executive Officer; www. stluke.com.ph/home

SAUDI ARABIA

Other:

ABDUL RAHMAN AL MISHARI GENERAL HOSPITAL, Olaya, P.O. Box 56929, Riyadh, Zip 11564; tel. 011/465–7700; Abdul Rahman Al Mishari, President; www.drabdulrahmanalmishari.com.sa/
MUHAMMAD SALEH BASHARAHIL HOSPITAL, P.O. Box 10505, Madinah Road, Omora Gadida, Makkah, tel. 009/520–4444; Turki M. Basharahil, General Manager; www.msbasharahil.com/
SANAD HOSPITAL, PO Box 91395, Riyadh, Khalid A. Al Ghamdi, General Manager; www.sanadhospital.com

SPAIN

Information Systems:

SIGESA, S.A., Calle Guatemala, 14, 4b, Madrid, Zip 28016; tel. 349/345–4018; Francisco Alvarez, Chief Financial Officer; www.sigesa.com

Other:

NEWIMAR S.A., Av De La Libertad, 24, Rota, Zip 11520; tel. 349/681–4003; Juan Miguel Margarito Monge, Project Manager, Hospital Services

UNITED ARAB EMIRATES

Other:

AMERICAN HOSPITAL–DUBAI, Oud Metha Road, P.O. Box 5566, Dubai, tel. 011/336–7777; Saeed M. Almulla, Chairman; www.ahdubai.com/main/index.aspx

UNITED KINGDOM

Consulting Firm:

I.G. ADVISORS, 201 Borough High Street, London, Zip SE11JA; tel. 440/234–0389; Carlos Miranda, Chief Executive Officer; www.impactandgrowth.com

Manufacturer/Supplier:

PRIMAL PICTURES LTD, Christchurch Court 10–15 Newgate Street, London, Zip ECIA7A2; tel. 442/017–5000; Peter Allan, Chief Executive Officer; www.primalpictures.com

Other:

FINANSCO HEALTHCARE, 11A Blacka Moor Road, Sheffield, Zip 00000; tel. 448/225–3844; Rukhsar Khan, Chief Executive Officer; www.finansco.com

*The members listed in **bold** are Associate Advantage members.* © 2016 AHA Guide

B

**Health Care Systems,
Networks
and Alliances**

Section B

Introduction

This section includes listings for networks, health care systems and alliances.

Health Care Systems

To reflect the diversity that exists among health care organizations, this publication uses the term health care system to identify both multihospital and diversified single hospital systems.

Multihospital Systems

A multihospital health care system is two or more hospitals owned, leased, sponsored, or contract managed by a central organization.

Single Hospital Systems

Single, freestanding member hospitals may be categorized as health care systems by bringing into membership three or more, and at least 25 percent, of their owned or leased non–hospital preacute and postacute health care organizations. (For purposes of definition, health care delivery is the availability of professional healthcare staff during all hours of the organization's operations). Organizations provide, or provide and finance, diagnostic, therapeutic, and/or consultative patient or client services that normally precede or follow acute, inpatient, hospitalization; or that serve to prevent or substitute for such hospitalization. These services are provided in either a freestanding facility not eligible for licensure as a hospital under state statue or through one that is a subsidiary of a hospital.

The first part of this section is an alphabetical list of health care systems which are listed under the system by state. Data for this section were compiled from the 2014 *Annual Survey* and the membership information base as published in section A of the *AHA Guide*.

One of the following codes appears after the name of each system listed to indicate the type of organizational control reported by that system:

CC	Catholic (Roman) church–related system, not–for–profit
CO	Other church–related system, not–for–profit
NP	Other not–for–profit system, including nonfederal, governmental systems
IO	Investor–owned, for profit system
FG	Federal Government

One of the following codes appears after the name of each hospital to indicate how that hospital is related to the system:

O	Owned
L	Leased
S	Sponsored
CM	Contract–managed

Health System Classification System

An identification system for Health Systems was developed jointly by the American Hospital Association's Health Research and Education Trust and Health Forum, and the University of California-Berkeley.[1] A health system is assigned to one of five categories based on how much they differentiate and centralized their hospital services, physician arrangements, and provider-based insurance products. Differentiation refers to the number of different products or services that the organization offers. Centralization refers to whether decision-making and service delivery emanate from the system level more so than individual hospitals.

Categories:

Centralized Health System: A delivery system in which the system centrally organizes individual hospital service delivery, physician arrangements, and insurance product development. The number of different products/services that are offered across the system is moderate.

Centralized Physician/Insurance Health System: A delivery system with highly centralized physician arrangements and insurance product development. Within this group, hospital services are relatively decentralized with individual hospitals having discretion over the array of services they offer. The number of different products/services that are offered across the system is moderate.

Moderately Centralized Health System: A delivery system that is distinguished by the presence of both centralized and decentralized activity for hospital services, physician arrangements, and insurance product development. For example, a system within this group may have centralized care of expensive, high technology services, such as open heart surgery, but allows individual hospitals to provide an array of other health services based on local needs. The number of different products/services that are offered across the system is moderate.

Decentralized Health System: A delivery system with a high degree of decentralized of hospital services, physician arrangements, and insurance product development. Within this group, systems may lack an overarching structure for coordination. Service and product differentiation is high, which may explain why centralization is hard to achieve. In this group, the system may simply service a role in sharing information and providing administrative support to highly developed local delivery systems centered around hospitals.

Independent Hospital System: A delivery system with limited differentiation in hospital services, physician arrangements, and insurance product development. These systems are largely horizontal affiliations of autonomous hospitals.

No Assignment: For some systems sufficient data from the Annual Survey were not available to determine a cluster assignment.

The second part of this section lists health care systems indexed geographically by state and city. Every effort has been made to be as inclusive and accurate as possible. However, as in all efforts of this type, there may be omissions. For further information, write to the Section for Health Care Systems, American Hospital Association, 155 N. Wacker Drive, Chicago, IL 60606.

Networks

The *AHA Guide* shows listings of networks. A network is defined as a group of hospitals, physicians, other providers, insurers and/or community agencies that work together to coordinate and deliver a broad spectrum of services to their community. Organizations listed represent the lead or hub of the network activity. Networks are listed by state, then alphabetically by name including participating partners.

The network identification process has purposely been designed to capture networks of varying organization type. Sources include but are not limited to the following: *AHA Annual Survey*, national, state and metropolitan associations, national news and periodical searches, and the networks and their health care providers themselves. Therefore, networks are included regardless of whether a hospital or healthcare system is the network lead. When an individual hospital does appear in the listing, it is indicative of the role the hospital plays as the network lead. In addition, the network listing is **not** mutually exclusive of the hospital, health care system or alliance listings within this publication.

Networks are very fluid in their composition as goals evolve and partners change. Therefore, some of the networks included in this listing may have dissolved, reformed, or simply been renamed as this section was being produced for publication.

The network identification process is an ongoing and responsive initiative. As more information is collected and validated, it will be made available in other venues, in addition to the *AHA Guide*. For more information concerning the network identification process, please contact The American Hospital Association Resource Center at 312/422–2050.

Alliances

An alliance is a formal organization, usually owned by shareholders/members, that works on behalf of its individual members in the provision of services and products and in the promotion of activities and ventures. The organization functions under a set of bylaws or other written rules to which each member agrees to abide.

Alliances are listed alphabetically by name. Its members are listed alphabetically by state, city, and then by member name.

[1] Bazzoli, CJ; Shortell, SM; Dubbs, N; Chan, C; and Kralovec, P; ''A Taxonomy of Health networks and Systems: Bringing Order Out of Chaos'' *Health Services Research*, February; 1999

Section B

Statistics for Health Care Systems and their Hospitals

The following tables describing health care systems refers to information in section B of the 2017 *AHA Guide.*

Table 1 shows the number of health care systems by type of control. Table 2 provides a breakdown of the number of systems that own, lease, sponsor or contract manage hospitals within each control category. Table 3 gives the number of hospitals and beds in each control category as well as total hospitals and beds. Finally, shows the percentage of hospitals and beds in each control category.

For more information on health care systems, please write to the Section for Health Care Systems, 155 N. Wacker Drive, Chicago, Illinois 60606 or call 312/422–3000.

Table 1. Multihospital Health Care Systems, by Type of Organizaton Control

Type of Control	Code	Number of Systems
Catholic (Roman) church–related	CC	30
Other church–related	CO	6
Subtotal, church–related		36
Other not–for–profit	NP	313
Subtotal, not–for–profit		349
Investor Owned	IO	75
Federal Government	FG	5
Total		429

Table 2. Multihospital Health Care Systems, by Type of Ownership and Control

Type of Ownership	Catholic Church–Related (CC)	Other Church–Related (CO)	Total Church–Related (CC + CO)	Other Not–for–Profit (NP)	Total Not–for–Profit (CC, CO, + NP)	Investor–Owned (IO)	Federal Government (FG)	All Systems
Systems that only own, lease or sponsor	22	4	26	270	296	66	5	367
Systems that only contract–manage	0	0	0	3	3	2	0	5
Systems that manage, own, lease, or sponsor	8	2	10	40	50	7	0	57
Total	30	6	36	313	349	75	5	429

Table 3. Hospitals and Beds in Multihospital Health Care Systems, by Type of Ownership and Control

Type of Ownership	Catholic Church–Related (CC) H	B	Other Church–Related (CO) H	B	Total Church–Related (CC + CO) H	B	Other Not–for–Profit (NP) H	B	Total Not–for–Profit (CC, CO, + NP) H	B	Investor–Owned (IO) H	B	Federal Government (FG) H	B	All Systems H	B
Owned, leased or sponsored	582	105,421	70	15,867	652	121,288	1,563	334,789	2,215	456,077	1,378	163,820	209	41,071	3,802	660,968
Contract–managed	44	2,317	2	465	46	2,782	113	10,179	159	12,961	97	5,152	0	0	256	18,113
Total	626	107,738	72	16,332	698	124,070	1,676	344,968	2,374	469,038	1,475	168,972	209	41,071	4,058	679,081

H = *hospitals;* **B** = *beds.*

Table 4. Hospitals and Beds in Multihospital Health Care Systems, by Type of Ownership and Control as a Percentage of All Systems

Type of Ownership	Catholic Church–Related (CC) H	B	Other Church–Related (CO) H	B	Total Church–Related (CC + CO) H	B	Other Not–for–Profit (NP) H	B	Total Not–for–Profit (CC, CO, + NP) H	B	Investor–Owned (IO) H	B	Federal Government (FG) H	B	All Systems H	B
Owned, leased or sponsored	15.3	15.9	1.8	2.4	17.1	18.4	41.1	50.7	58.3	69.0	36.2	24.8	5.5	6.2	100.0	100.0
Contract–managed	17.2	12.8	0.8	2.6	18.0	15.4	44.1	56.2	62.1	71.6	37.9	28.4	0.0	0.0	100.0	100.0
Total	15.4	15.9	1.8	2.4	17.2	18.3	41.3	50.8	58.5	69.1	36.3	24.9	5.2	6.0	100.0	100.0

H = *hospitals;* **B** = *beds.*
*Please note that figures may not always equal the provided subtotal or total percentages due to rounding.

Health Care Systems and Their Hospitals

0091: ACADIA HEALTHCARE COMPANY, INC. (IO)
830 Crescent Centre Drive, Suite 610, Franklin, TN
Zip 37067–7323; tel. 615/861–6000; Joey Jacobs, Chairman and
Chief Executive Officer
(Independent Hospital System)

ARIZONA: OASIS BEHAVIORAL HEALTH – CHANDLER (O, 47 beds) 2190
North Grace Boulevard, Chandler, AZ Zip 85225–3416;
tel. 480/917–9301; James Gallagher, Chief Executive Officer
Web address: www.obhhospital.com/about/location

SONORA BEHAVIORAL HEALTH HOSPITAL (O, 72 beds) 6050 North Corona
Road, #3, Tucson, AZ Zip 85704–1096; tel. 520/469–8700; Edeli Kinsala,
Chief Executive Officer

ARKANSAS: RIVERVIEW BEHAVIORAL HEALTH (O, 62 beds) 701 Arkansas
Boulevard, Texarkana, AR Zip 71854–2105; tel. 870/772–5028; Michael
A. Truman, Chief Executive Officer
Web address: www.riverviewbehavioralhealth.com

VALLEY BEHAVIORAL HEALTH SYSTEM (O, 75 beds) 10301 Mayo Drive,
Barling, AR Zip 72923–1660; tel. 479/494–5700; Anthony Walters, Chief
Executive Officer
Web address: www.valleybehavioral.com

VANTAGE POINT OF NORTHWEST ARKANSAS (O, 114 beds) 4253 North
Crossover Road, Fayetteville, AR Zip 72703–4596; tel. 479/521–5731;
Connie Borengasser, Chief Executive Officer
Web address: www.vantagepointnwa.com

CALIFORNIA: PACIFIC GROVE HOSPITAL (O, 68 beds) 5900 Brockton
Avenue, Riverside, CA Zip 92506–1862; tel. 951/275–8400; Nichol
Sheffield, Chief Executive Officer
Web address: www.pacificgrovehospital.com

SAN JOSE BEHAVORIAL HEALTH (O, 80 beds) 455 Silicon Valley Boulevard,
San Jose, CA Zip 95138–1858; tel. 888/210–2484; ,
Web address: www.sanjosebh.com

DELAWARE: MEADOW WOOD BEHAVIORAL HEALTH SYSTEM (O, 53 beds)
575 South Dupont Highway, New Castle, DE Zip 19720–4606;
tel. 302/328–3330; Bill A. Mason, Chief Executive Officer
Web address: www.meadowwoodhospital.com

FLORIDA: NORTH TAMPA BEHAVIORAL HEALTH (O, 75 beds) 29910 State
Road 56, Wesley Chapel, FL Zip 33543–8800; tel. 813/922–3300;
Jameson Norton, Chief Executive Officer
Web address: www.northtampabehavioralhealth.com

PARK ROYAL HOSPITAL (O, 103 beds) 9241 Park Royal Drive, Fort Myers, FL
Zip 33908–9204; tel. 239/985–2700; Michael K. Evans, Chief Executive
Officer
Web address: www.ParkRoyalHospital.com

GEORGIA: GREENLEAF CENTER (O, 73 beds) 2209 Pineview Drive, Valdosta,
GA Zip 31602–7316; tel. 229/247–4357; Stephen Register, Chief
Executive Officer
Web address: www.greenleafcounseling.net

LAKEVIEW BEHAVIORAL HEALTH (O, 70 beds) 1 Technology Parkway South,
Norcross, GA Zip 30092–2928; tel. 888/834–4195; ,
Web address: www.lakeviewbehavioralhealth.com

RIVERWOODS BEHAVIORAL HEALTH SYSTEM (O, 75 beds) 233 Medical
Center Drive, Riverdale, GA Zip 30274–2640; tel. 770/991–8500; Kirk
Kureska, Chief Executive Officer
Web address: www.riverwoodsbehavioral.com

INDIANA: OPTIONS BEHAVIORAL HEALTH SYSTEM (O, 42 beds) 5602 Caito
Drive, Indianapolis, IN Zip 46226–1346; tel. 317/544–4340; Matthew
Love, Chief Executive Officer
Web address: www.optionsbehavioralhealthsystem.com/

LOUISIANA: ACADIA OPTIMA HOSPITAL (O, 24 beds) 1131 Rue De Belier,
Lafayette, LA Zip 70506–6532; tel. 337/991–0571; Glynis R. DeRoche,
Administrator
Web address: www.optimaspecialtyhospital.com/

ACADIA VERMILION HOSPITAL (O, 54 beds) 2520 North University Avenue,
Lafayette, LA Zip 70507–5306; tel. 337/234–5614; Stephanie Bonin, Chief
Executive Officer
Web address: www.acadiavermilion.com

GREENBRIER BEHAVIOR HEALTH HOSPITAL (O, 60 beds) 201 Greenbrier
Boulevard, Covington, LA Zip 70433–7236; tel. 985/893–2970; Wes
Crawford, Chief Executive Officer
Web address: www.greenbrierhospital.com/

LONGLEAF HOSPITAL (O, 70 beds) 110 John Eskew Drive, Alexandria, LA
Zip 71303; tel. 318/445–5111; Monica Tatum, Chief Executive Officer and
Administrator
Web address: www.longleafhospital.com/

WESTEND HOSPITAL (O, 20 beds) 1530 Highway 90 West, Jennings, LA
Zip 70546–4022; tel. 337/616–8122; Luis Betances, Administrator
Web address: www.westendbh.com

MASSACHUSETTS: SOUTHCOAST BEHAVIORAL HEALTH (O, 120 beds) 581
Faunce Corner Road, Dartmouth, MA Zip 02747–1242;
tel. 888/210–2475; Kevin R. Burchill, Chief Executive Officer
Web address: www.southcoastbehavioral.com

MICHIGAN: HARBOR OAKS HOSPITAL (O, 45 beds) 35031 23 Mile Road,
New Baltimore, MI Zip 48047–3649; tel. 586/725–5777; Sari
Abromovich, Chief Executive Officer
Web address: www.harboroaks.com

STONECREST CENTER (O, 104 beds) 15000 Gratiot Avenue, Detroit, MI
Zip 48205–1973; tel. 313/245–0600; Steve Savage, Chief Executive Officer
Web address: www.stonecrestcenter.com

MISSOURI: LAKELAND BEHAVIORAL HEALTH SYSTEM (O, 132 beds) 440
South Market Street, Springfield, MO Zip 65806–2026;
tel. 417/865–5581; Nathan Duncan, Chief Executive Officer
Web address: www.lakeland–hospital.com

NEVADA: SEVEN HILLS HOSPITAL (O, 94 beds) 3021 West Horizon Ridge
Parkway, Henderson, NV Zip 89052–3990; tel. 702/646–5000; Robert L.
Turner, Ph.D., Chief Executive Officer
Web address: www.sevenhillsbi.com

OHIO: OHIO HOSPITAL FOR PSYCHIATRY (O, 90 beds) 880 Greenlawn Avenue,
Columbus, OH Zip 43223–2616; tel. 614/449–9664; Stanley Frank, Chief
Executive Officer
Web address: www.ohiohospitalforpsychiatry.com/

TEN LAKES CENTER (O, 16 beds) 819 North First Street, 3rd Floor,
Dennison, OH Zip 44621–1003; tel. 740/922–7499; Debra C. Gardner, R.N.,
MSN, Administrator
Web address: www.tenlakescenter.com/

OKLAHOMA: ROLLING HILLS HOSPITAL (O, 60 beds) 1000 Rolling Hills Lane,
Ada, OK Zip 74820–9415; tel. 580/436–3600; Anthony Guild, Chief
Executive Officer
Web address: www.rollinghillshospital.com

PENNSYLVANIA: BELMONT BEHAVIORAL HOSPITAL (O, 147 beds) 4200
Monument Road, Philadelphia, PA Zip 19131–1625; tel. 215/877–2000;
Mark Schor, Chief Executive Officer
Web address: www.einstein.edu/locations/belmont–behavioral–health/

SOUTHWOOD PSYCHIATRIC HOSPITAL (O, 112 beds) 2575 Boyce Plaza
Road, Pittsburgh, PA Zip 15241–3925; tel. 412/257–2290; Stephen J.
Quigley, Chief Executive Officer
Web address: www.southwoodhospital.com

PUERTO RICO: SAN JUAN CAPESTRANO HOSPITAL (O, 108 beds) Rural
Route 2, Box 11, San Juan, PR Zip 00926; tel. 787/625–2900; Marta
Rivera Plaza, Chief Executive Officer and Managing Director
Web address: www.sjcapestrano.com

SOUTH CAROLINA: REBOUND BEHAVIORAL HEALTH (O, 42 beds) 134 East
Rebound Road, Lancaster, SC Zip 29720–7712; tel. 877/914–1876;
George G. Boykin, Chief Executive Officer
Web address: www.reboundbehavioralhealth.com

For explanation of codes following names, see page B2.
★ Indicates Type III membership in the American Hospital Association.

TENNESSEE: CRESTWYN BEHAVIORAL HEALTH (O, 60 beds) 9485 Crestwyn Hills Cove, Memphis, TN Zip 38125–8515; tel. 877/241–1359; ,
Web address: www.crestwynbh.com

DELTA MEDICAL CENTER (O, 179 beds) 3000 Getwell Road, Memphis, TN Zip 38118–2299; tel. 901/369–8100; Phil Willcoxon, Chief Executive Officer
Web address: www.deltamedcenter.com

TRUSTPOINT HOSPITAL (O, 101 beds) 1009 North Thompson Lane, Murfreesboro, TN Zip 37129–4351; tel. 615/867–1111; Jeffrey Woods, Chief Executive Officer
Web address: www.trustpointhospital.com

TEXAS: ABILENE BEHAVIORAL HEALTH (O, 92 beds) 4225 Woods Place, Abilene, TX Zip 79602–7991, Mailing Address: P.O. Box 5559, Zip 79608–5559; tel. 325/698–6600; Anthony Guild, Chief Executive Officer
Web address: www.abilenebehavioralhealth.com/

CROSS CREEK HOSPITAL (O, 90 beds) 8402 Cross Park Drive, Austin, TX Zip 78754; tel. 512/215–3900; Jennifer Miller, Chief Executive Officer
Web address: www.cornerstonehealthcaregroup.com

RED RIVER HOSPITAL, LLC (O, 74 beds) 1505 Eighth Street, Wichita Falls, TX Zip 76301–3106; tel. 940/322–3171; John B. Warburton, Chief Executive Officer
Web address: www.redriverhospital.com

UTAH: HIGHLAND RIDGE HOSPITAL (O, 83 beds) 7309 South 180 West, Midvale, UT Zip 84047–3769; tel. 801/569–2153; Robert Beatty, Chief Operating Officer
Web address: www.highlandridgehospital.com

WASHINGTON: CASCADE BEHAVIORAL HOSPITAL (O, 63 beds) 12844 Military Road South, Tukwila, WA Zip 98168–3045; tel. 206/244–0180; Michael Uradnik, Chief Executive Officer
Web address: www.cascadebh.com

Owned, leased, sponsored:	39 hospitals	3049 beds
Contract–managed:	0 hospitals	0 beds
Totals:	39 hospitals	3049 beds

★0640: ACUITYHEALTHCARE, LP (IO)
10200 Mallard Creek Road, Suite 300, Charlotte, NC Zip 28262–9705; tel. 704/887–7280; Edwin H. Cooper, Jr., MS, President and Chief Executive Officer
(Independent Hospital System)

NEW JERSEY: ACUITY SPECIALTY HOSPITAL OF NEW JERSEY (O, 30 beds) 1925 Pacific Avenue, 7th Floor, Atlantic City, NJ Zip 08401–6713; tel. 609/441–2122; Monica Titus, President and Chief Executive Officer
Web address: www.acuityhealthcare.net

LOURDES SPECIALTY HOSPITAL OF SOUTHERN NEW JERSEY (O, 53 beds) 220 Sunset Road, Willingboro, NJ Zip 08046–1110; tel. 609/835–3650; Cheri Cowperthwait, R.N., Chief Executive Officer
Web address: www.lshnj.com

OHIO: ACUITY SPECIALTY HOSPITALS OHIO VALLEY (O, 65 beds) 380 Summit Avenue, 3rd Floor, Steubenville, OH Zip 43952–2667; tel. 740/283–7600; Judy K. Weaver, MS, Chief Executive Officer
Web address: www.acuityhealthcare.net

TEXAS: ACUITY HOSPITAL OF SOUTH TEXAS (O, 30 beds) 718 Lexington Avenue, San Antonio, TX Zip 78212–4768; tel. 210/572–4600; Kris Karns, Ph.D., FACHE, Chief Executive Officer
Web address: www.acuitysouthtexas.com

Owned, leased, sponsored:	4 hospitals	178 beds
Contract–managed:	0 hospitals	0 beds
Totals:	4 hospitals	178 beds

0895: ADENA HEALTH SYSTEM (NP)
272 Hospital Road, Chillicothe, OH Zip 45601–9031; tel. 740/779–7500; Mark H. Shuter, President and Chief Executive Officer
(Independent Hospital System)

OHIO: ADENA GREENFIELD MEDICAL CENTER (O, 25 beds) 550 Mirabeau Street, Greenfield, OH Zip 45123–1617; tel. 937/981–9400; Kathy Dye, Interim Administrator
Web address: www.adena.org

ADENA MEDICAL CENTER (O, 214 beds) 272 Hospital Road, Chillicothe, OH Zip 45601–9031; tel. 740/779–7500; Mark H. Shuter, President and Chief Executive Officer
Web address: www.adena.org

ADENA PIKE MEDICAL CENTER (O, 24 beds) 100 Dawn Lane, Waverly, OH Zip 45690–9138; tel. 740/947–2186; David M. Zanni, Associate Administrator
Web address: www.pikecommunityhospital.org

Owned, leased, sponsored:	3 hospitals	263 beds
Contract–managed:	0 hospitals	0 beds
Totals:	3 hospitals	263 beds

★0235: ADVENTIST HEALTH (CO)
2100 Douglas Boulevard, Roseville, CA Zip 95661–3898, Mailing Address: P.O. Box 619002, Zip 95661–9002; tel. 916/781–2000; Scott Reiner, President and Chief Executive Officer
(Decentralized Health System)

CALIFORNIA: ADVENTIST MEDICAL CENTER – HANFORD (O, 199 beds) 115 Mall Drive, Hanford, CA Zip 93230–3513; tel. 559/582–9000; Wayne Ferch, President and Chief Executive Officer
Web address: www.adventisthealthcv.com/hospital_newhanfordhospital.aspx

ADVENTIST MEDICAL CENTER–REEDLEY (L, 49 beds) 372 West Cypress Avenue, Reedley, CA Zip 93654–2199; tel. 559/638–8155; Wayne Ferch, President and Chief Executive Officer
Web address: www.skdh.org

CENTRAL VALLEY GENERAL HOSPITAL (O, 49 beds) 1025 North Douty Street, Hanford, CA Zip 93230–3722, Mailing Address: P.O. Box 480, Zip 93232–2113; tel. 559/583–2100; Wayne Ferch, President and Chief Executive Officer
Web address: www.hanfordhealth.com

FEATHER RIVER HOSPITAL (O, 86 beds) 5974 Pentz Road, Paradise, CA Zip 95969–5593; tel. 530/877–9361; Monty E. Knittel, Chief Executive Officer
Web address: www.frhosp.org

FRANK R. HOWARD MEMORIAL HOSPITAL (L, 25 beds) One Marcela Drive, Willits, CA Zip 95490–4298; tel. 707/459–6801; Rick Bockmann, Chief Executive Officer
Web address: www.howardhospital.com

GLENDALE ADVENTIST MEDICAL CENTER (O, 462 beds) 8700 Beverly Boulevard, NT–3138, Los Angeles, CA Zip 90048, Mailing Address: 1509 Wilson Terrace, Glendale, Zip 91206–4098; tel. 818/409–8000; Kevin A. Roberts, FACHE, President and Chief Executive Officer
Web address: www.glendaleadventist.com

LODI MEMORIAL HOSPITAL (O, 214 beds) 975 South Fairmont Avenue, Lodi, CA Zip 95240–5118, Mailing Address: P.O. Box 3004, Zip 95241–1908; tel. 209/334–3411; Daniel Wolcott, President and Chief Executive Officer
Web address: www.lodihealth.org

SAN JOAQUIN COMMUNITY HOSPITAL (O, 254 beds) 2615 Chester Avenue, Bakersfield, CA Zip 93301–2014, Mailing Address: P.O. Box 2615, Zip 93303–2615; tel. 661/395–3000; Douglas Duffield, President and Chief Executive Officer
Web address: www.sanjoaquinhospital.org

SIMI VALLEY HOSPITAL (O, 82 beds) 2975 North Sycamore Drive, Simi Valley, CA Zip 93065–1277; tel. 805/955–6000; Jennifer Swenson, President and Chief Executive Officer
Web address: www.simivalleyhospital.com

SONORA REGIONAL MEDICAL CENTER (O, 152 beds) 1000 Greenley Road, Sonora, CA Zip 95370–4819; tel. 209/536–5000; Andrew Jahn, President and Chief Executive Officer
Web address: www.sonoramedicalcenter.org/

ST. HELENA HOSPITAL CENTER FOR BEHAVIORAL HEALTH (O, 61 beds) 525 Oregon Street, Vallejo, CA Zip 94590–3201; tel. 707/648–2200; Steven Herber, M.D., President and Chief Executive Officer
Web address: www.sthelenahospitals.org/location/center–for–behavioral–health

For explanation of codes following names, see page B2.
★ Indicates Type III membership in the American Hospital Association.

ST. HELENA HOSPITAL CLEAR LAKE (O, 25 beds) 15630 18th Avenue, Clearlake, CA Zip 95422–9336, Mailing Address: P.O. Box 6710, Zip 95422; tel. 707/994–6486; David Santos, President and Chief Executive Officer
Web address: www.adventisthealth.org

ST. HELENA HOSPITAL NAPA VALLEY (O, 116 beds) 10 Woodland Road, Saint Helena, CA Zip 94574–9554; tel. 707/963–3611; Steven Herber, M.D., President and Chief Executive Officer
Web address: www.sthelenahospital.org

UKIAH VALLEY MEDICAL CENTER (O, 50 beds) 275 Hospital Drive, Ukiah, CA Zip 95482–4531; tel. 707/462–3111; Gwen Matthews, R.N., MSN, Chief Executive Officer
Web address: www.adventisthealth.org

WHITE MEMORIAL MEDICAL CENTER (O, 353 beds) 1720 Cesar Chavez Avenue, Los Angeles, CA Zip 90033–2414; tel. 323/268–5000; John Raffoul, Chief Executive Officer
Web address: www.whitememorial.com

HAWAII: CASTLE MEDICAL CENTER (O, 160 beds) 640 Ulukahiki Street, Kailua, HI Zip 96734–4454; tel. 808/263–5500; Kathryn A. Raethel, R.N., M.P.H., President and Chief Executive Officer
Web address: www.castlemed.org

OREGON: ADVENTIST MEDICAL CENTER–PORTLAND (O, 242 beds) 10123 S.E. Market Street, Portland, OR Zip 97216–2599; tel. 503/257–2500; David Russell, President and Chief Executive Officer
Web address: www.adventisthealthnw.com

TILLAMOOK REGIONAL MEDICAL CENTER (L, 25 beds) 1000 Third Street, Tillamook, OR Zip 97141–3430; tel. 503/842–4444; David Butler, President and Chief Executive Officer
Web address: www.tillamookregionalmc.com

WASHINGTON: WALLA WALLA GENERAL HOSPITAL (O, 38 beds) 1025 South Second Avenue, Walla Walla, WA Zip 99362–4116, Mailing Address: P.O. Box 1398, Zip 99362–0309; tel. 509/525–0480; Robert J. Beehler, Interim President and Chief Executive Officer
Web address: www.wwgh.com

Owned, leased, sponsored:	19 hospitals	2642 beds
Contract–managed:	0 hospitals	0 beds
Totals:	19 hospitals	2642 beds

★4165: ADVENTIST HEALTH SYSTEM SUNBELT HEALTH CARE CORPORATION (CO)
900 Hope Way, Altamonte Springs, FL Zip 32714–1502; tel. 407/357–1000; Donald L. Jernigan, Ph.D., President and Chief Executive Officer
(Decentralized Health System)

COLORADO: AVISTA ADVENTIST HOSPITAL (O, 114 beds) 100 Health Park Drive, Louisville, CO Zip 80027–9583; tel. 303/673–1000; Dennis Barts, Chief Executive Officer
Web address: www.avistahospital.org

CASTLE ROCK ADVENTIST HOSPITAL (O, 50 beds) 2350 Meadows Boulevard, Castle Rock, CO Zip 80109–8405; tel. 720/455–5000; Todd Folkenberg, Chief Executive Officer
Web address: www.castlerockhospital.org

LITTLETON ADVENTIST HOSPITAL (O, 201 beds) 7700 South Broadway Street, Littleton, CO Zip 80122–2628; tel. 303/730–8900; Brett Spenst, Chief Executive Officer
Web address: www.centura.org

PARKER ADVENTIST HOSPITAL (O, 145 beds) 9395 Crown Crest Boulevard, Parker, CO Zip 80138–8573; tel. 303/269–4000; Sam D. Huenergardt, Chief Executive Officer
Web address: www.parkerhospital.org

PORTER ADVENTIST HOSPITAL (O, 250 beds) 2525 South Downing Street, Denver, CO Zip 80210–5876; tel. 303/778–1955; Morre Dean, Chief Executive Officer
Web address: www.porterhospital.org/poh/home/

FLORIDA: FLORIDA HOSPITAL (O, 2654 beds) 601 East Rollins Street, Orlando, FL Zip 32803–1248; tel. 407/303–6611; Lars D. Houmann, President
Web address: www.flhosp.org

FLORIDA HOSPITAL AT CONNERTON LONG TERM ACUTE CARE (O, 50 beds) 9441 Health Center Drive, Land O'Lakes, FL Zip 34637–5837; tel. 813/903–3701; Brian Adams, President and Chief Executive Officer
Web address: www.elevatinghealthcare.org

FLORIDA HOSPITAL CARROLLWOOD (O, 96 beds) 7171 North Dale Mabry Highway, Tampa, FL Zip 33614–2665; tel. 813/932–2222; Joe Johnson, FACHE, Chief Executive Officer
Web address: www.elevatinghealthcare.org/locations/carrollwood

FLORIDA HOSPITAL DELAND (O, 156 beds) 701 West Plymouth Avenue, DeLand, FL Zip 32720–3236; tel. 386/943–4522; Lorenzo Brown, Chief Executive Officer
Web address: www.fhdeland.org

FLORIDA HOSPITAL FISH MEMORIAL (O, 175 beds) 1055 Saxon Boulevard, Orange City, FL Zip 32763–8468; tel. 386/917–5000; Robert Deininger, Chief Executive Officer
Web address: www.fhfishmemorial.org

FLORIDA HOSPITAL HEARTLAND MEDICAL CENTER (O, 189 beds) 4200 Sun'n Lake Boulevard, Sebring, FL Zip 33872–1986, Mailing Address: P.O. Box 9400, Zip 33871–9400; tel. 863/314–4466; Bruce Bergherm, Chief Executive Officer
Web address: www.fhheartland.org/

FLORIDA HOSPITAL MEMORIAL MEDICAL CENTER (O, 250 beds) 301 Memorial Medical Parkway, Daytona Beach, FL Zip 32117–5167; tel. 386/676–6000; Ed Noseworthy, Chief Executive Officer
Web address: www.floridahospitalmemorial.org

FLORIDA HOSPITAL NEW SMYRNA (O, 112 beds) 401 Palmetto Street, New Smyrna Beach, FL Zip 32168–7399; tel. 386/424–5000; Kenneth R. Mattison, Chief Executive Officer
Web address: www.https://www.floridahospital.com/new–smyrna

FLORIDA HOSPITAL NORTH PINELLAS (O, 168 beds) 1395 South Pinellas Avenue, Tarpon Springs, FL Zip 34689–3790; tel. 727/942–5000; Tricia Williams, President and Chief Executive Officer
Web address: www.fhnorthpinellas.com/

FLORIDA HOSPITAL TAMPA (O, 482 beds) 3100 East Fletcher Avenue, Tampa, FL Zip 33613–4688; tel. 813/971–6000; Brian Adams, President and CEO
Web address: www.floridahospital.com/tampa

FLORIDA HOSPITAL WATERMAN (O, 269 beds) 1000 Waterman Way, Tavares, FL Zip 32778–5266; tel. 352/253–3333; David Ottati, Chief Executive Officer
Web address: www.fhwat.org

FLORIDA HOSPITAL WAUCHULA (O, 25 beds) 533 West Carlton Street, Wauchula, FL Zip 33873–3407; tel. 863/773–3101; Denise Grimsley, R.N., Vice President and Administrator
Web address: www.fh.floridahospital.com/heartland/home.aspx

FLORIDA HOSPITAL WESLEY CHAPEL (O, 83 beds) 2600 Bruce B. Downs Bouelvard, Wesley Chapel, FL Zip 33544–9207; tel. 813/929–5000; Denyse Bales–Chubb, President and Chief Executive Officer
Web address: www.https://www.floridahospital.com/wesley–chapel

FLORIDA HOSPITAL ZEPHYRHILLS (O, 139 beds) 7050 Gall Boulevard, Zephyrhills, FL Zip 33541–1399; tel. 813/788–0411; Randy Surber, Chief Executive Officer
Web address: www.fhzeph.org

FLORIDA HOSPITAL–FLAGLER (O, 99 beds) 60 Memorial Medical Parkway, Palm Coast, FL Zip 32164–5980; tel. 386/586–2000; Ronald Jimenez, M.D., Chief Executive Officer
Web address: www.floridahospitalflagler.com/

GEORGIA: GORDON HOSPITAL (O, 82 beds) 1035 Red Bud Road, Calhoun, GA Zip 30701–2082, Mailing Address: P.O. Box 12938, Zip 30703–7013; tel. 706/629–2895; Pete M. Weber, President and Chief Executive Officer
Web address: www.gordonhospital.com

MURRAY MEDICAL CENTER (O, 33 beds) 707 Old Dalton Ellijay Road, Chatsworth, GA Zip 30705–2060, Mailing Address: P.O. Box 1406, Zip 30705–1406; tel. 706/695–4564; Karen Steely, Administrator
Web address: www.murraymedical.org/

ILLINOIS: ADVENTIST LA GRANGE MEMORIAL HOSPITAL (O, 200 beds) 5101 South Willow Spring Road, La Grange, IL Zip 60525–2600; tel. 708/245–9000; Michael Goebel, FACHE, Vice President and Chief Executive Officer
Web address: www.keepingyouwell.com

For explanation of codes following names, see page B2.
★ Indicates Type III membership in the American Hospital Association.

AMITA HEALTH ADVENTIST MEDICAL CENTER – HINSDALE (O, 275 beds) 120 North Oak Street, Hinsdale, IL Zip 60521–3890; tel. 630/856–6001; Michael Goebel, FACHE, Vice President and Chief Executive Officer
Web address: www.AMITAhealth.org

AMITA HEALTH ADVENTIST MEDICAL CENTER BOLINGBROOK (O, 144 beds) 500 Remington Boulevard, Bolingbrook, IL Zip 60440–4906; tel. 630/312–5000; Rick Mace, Chief Executive Officer
Web address: www.keepingyouwell.com/abh/

AMITA HEALTH GLENOAKS (O, 140 beds) 701 Winthrop Avenue, Glendale Heights, IL Zip 60139–1403; tel. 630/545–8000; Bruce Christian, President and Chief Executive Officer
Web address: www.AMITAHealth.org

KANSAS: SHAWNEE MISSION MEDICAL CENTER (O, 391 beds) 9100 West 74th Street, Shawnee Mission, KS Zip 66204–4004, Mailing Address: Box 2923, Zip 66201–1323; tel. 913/676–2000; Ken J. Bacon, President and Chief Executive Officer
Web address: www.shawneemission.org

KENTUCKY: MANCHESTER MEMORIAL HOSPITAL (O, 63 beds) 210 Marie Langdon Drive, Manchester, KY Zip 40962–6388; tel. 606/598–5104; Erika Skula, President and Chief Executive Officer
Web address: www.manchestermemorial.org

NORTH CAROLINA: PARK RIDGE HEALTH (O, 95 beds) 100 Hospital Drive, Hendersonville, NC Zip 28792–5272; tel. 828/684–8501; Jimm Bunch, President and Chief Executive Officer
Web address: www.parkridgehealth.org

TEXAS: CENTRAL TEXAS MEDICAL CENTER (O, 111 beds) 1301 Wonder World Drive, San Marcos, TX Zip 78666–7544; tel. 512/353–8979; Anthony Stahl, Chief Executive Officer
Web address: www.ctmc.org

METROPLEX ADVENTIST HOSPITAL (O, 177 beds) 2201 South Clear Creek Road, Killeen, TX Zip 76549–4110; tel. 254/526–7523; Carlyle L. E. Walton, FACHE, Chief Executive Officer
Web address: www.mplex.org

ROLLINS–BROOK COMMUNITY HOSPITAL (O, 35 beds) 608 North Key Avenue, Lampasas, TX Zip 76550–1106, Mailing Address: P.O. Box 589, Zip 76550–0032; tel. 512/556–3682; Carlyle L. E. Walton, FACHE, Chief Executive Officer
Web address: www.mplex.org

TEXAS HEALTH HUGULEY HOSPITAL FORT WORTH SOUTH (C, 197 beds) 11801 South Freeway, Burleson, TX Zip 76028–7021, Mailing Address: P.O. Box 6337, Fort Worth, Zip 76115–0337; tel. 817/293–9110; Kenneth A. Finch, President and Chief Executive Officer
Web address: www.TexasHealthHuguley.org

WISCONSIN: CHIPPEWA VALLEY HOSPITAL AND OAKVIEW CARE CENTER (O, 25 beds) 1220 Third Avenue West, Durand, WI Zip 54736–1600, Mailing Address: P.O. Box 224, Zip 54736–0224; tel. 715/672–4211; Douglas R. Peterson, President and Chief Executive Officer
Web address: www.chippewavalleyhospital.com/

Owned, leased, sponsored:	33 hospitals	7478 beds
Contract–managed:	1 hospital	197 beds
Totals:	34 hospitals	7675 beds

0214: ADVENTIST HEALTHCARE (NP)
820 West Diamond Avenue, Suite 600, Gaithersburg, MD Zip 20878–1419; tel. 301/315–3185; Terry Forde, President and Chief Executive Officer
(Independent Hospital System)

MARYLAND: ADVENTIST BEHAVIORAL HEALTH ROCKVILLE (O, 283 beds) 14901 Broschart Road, Rockville, MD Zip 20850–3318; tel. 301/251–4500; Kevin Young, FACHE, President
Web address: www.adventistbehavioralhealth.com

ADVENTIST HEALTHCARE SHADY GROVE MEDICAL CENTER (O, 321 beds) 9901 Medical Center Drive, Rockville, MD Zip 20850–3395; tel. 240/826–6000; John Sackett, President SGMC and Executive Vice President and Chief Operating Officer
Web address: www.adventisthealthcare.com

ADVENTIST REHABILITATION HOSPITAL OF MARYLAND (O, 77 beds) 9909 Medical Center Drive, Rockville, MD Zip 20850–6361; tel. 240/864–6000; Brent Reitz, President
Web address: www.adventistrehab.com

WASHINGTON ADVENTIST HOSPITAL (O, 230 beds) 7600 Carroll Avenue, Takoma Park, MD Zip 20912–6392; tel. 301/891–7600; Erik Wangsness, President
Web address: www.adventisthealthcare.com

Owned, leased, sponsored:	4 hospitals	911 beds
Contract–managed:	0 hospitals	0 beds
Totals:	4 hospitals	911 beds

★0064: ADVOCATE HEALTH CARE (NP)
3075 Highland Parkway, Suite 600, Downers Grove, IL Zip 60515–1206; tel. 630/929–8700; Jim H. Skogsbergh, President and Chief Executive Officer
(Moderately Centralized Health System)

ILLINOIS: ADVOCATE BROMENN MEDICAL CENTER (O, 198 beds) 1304 Franklin Avenue, Normal, IL Zip 61761–3558, Mailing Address: P.O. Box 2850, Bloomington, Zip 61702–2850; tel. 309/454–1400; Colleen Kannaday, FACHE, President
Web address: www.advocatehealth.com

ADVOCATE CHRIST MEDICAL CENTER (O, 659 beds) 4440 West 95th Street, Oak Lawn, IL Zip 60453–2699; tel. 708/684–8000; Kenneth W. Lukhard, President
Web address: www.advocatehealth.com/christ

ADVOCATE CONDELL MEDICAL CENTER (O, 277 beds) 801 South Milwaukee Avenue, Libertyville, IL Zip 60048–3199; tel. 847/362–2900; Dominica Tallarico, President
Web address: www.advocatehealth.com/condell/

ADVOCATE EUREKA HOSPITAL (O, 18 beds) 101 South Major Street, Eureka, IL Zip 61530–1246; tel. 309/467–2371; Colleen Kannaday, FACHE, President
Web address: www.advocatehealth.com/eureka/

ADVOCATE GOOD SAMARITAN HOSPITAL (O, 326 beds) 3815 Highland Avenue, Downers Grove, IL Zip 60515–1590; tel. 630/275–5900; David Fox, President
Web address: www.advocatehealth.com/gsam

ADVOCATE GOOD SHEPHERD HOSPITAL (O, 176 beds) 450 West Highway 22, Barrington, IL Zip 60010–1919; tel. 847/381–0123; Karen A. Lambert, President
Web address: www.advocatehealth.com/gshp/

ADVOCATE ILLINOIS MASONIC MEDICAL CENTER (O, 333 beds) 836 West Wellington Avenue, Chicago, IL Zip 60657–5147; tel. 773/975–1600; Susan Nordstrom Lopez, President
Web address: www.advocatehealth.com/masonic

ADVOCATE LUTHERAN GENERAL HOSPITAL (O, 625 beds) 1775 Dempster Street, Park Ridge, IL Zip 60068–1174; tel. 847/723–2210; Richard B. Floyd, President
Web address: www.advocatehealth.com/luth/

ADVOCATE SHERMAN HOSPITAL (O, 255 beds) 1425 North Randall Road, Elgin, IL Zip 60123–2300; tel. 847/742–9800; Linda Deering, MSN, R.N., President
Web address: www.advocatehealth.com/sherman

ADVOCATE SOUTH SUBURBAN HOSPITAL (O, 248 beds) 17800 South Kedzie Avenue, Hazel Crest, IL Zip 60429–0989; tel. 708/799–8000; Richard Heim, President
Web address: www.advocatehealth.com/ssub/

ADVOCATE TRINITY HOSPITAL (O, 186 beds) 2350 East 93rd Street, Chicago, IL Zip 60617; tel. 773/967–2000; Terika Richardson, M.P.H., President
Web address: www.advocatehealth.com/trinity

Owned, leased, sponsored:	11 hospitals	3301 beds
Contract–managed:	0 hospitals	0 beds
Totals:	11 hospitals	3301 beds

For explanation of codes following names, see page B2.
★ Indicates Type III membership in the American Hospital Association.

0312: AHMC & HEALTHCARE, INC. (IO)
55 South Raymond Avenue, Suite 105, Alhambra, CA
Zip 91801–7101; tel. 626/457–9600; Jonathan Wu, M.D., President
and Chairman
(Independent Hospital System)

CALIFORNIA: AHMC ANAHEIM REGIONAL MEDICAL CENTER (O, 223 beds)
1111 West La Palma Avenue, Anaheim, CA Zip 92801–2881;
tel. 714/774–1450; Patrick A. Petre, Chief Executive Officer
Web address: www.anaheimregionalmc.com

ALHAMBRA HOSPITAL MEDICAL CENTER (O, 144 beds) 100 South Raymond
Avenue, Alhambra, CA Zip 91801–3199, Mailing Address: P.O. Box 510,
Zip 91802–2510; tel. 626/570–1606; Iris Lai, Chief Executive Officer
Web address: www.alhambrahospital.com

GARFIELD MEDICAL CENTER (O, 195 beds) 525 North Garfield Avenue,
Monterey Park, CA Zip 91754–1205; tel. 626/573–2222; Paul J. Hensler,
Chief Executive Officer
Web address: www.garfieldmedicalcenter.com

GREATER EL MONTE COMMUNITY HOSPITAL (O, 46 beds) 1701 Santa Anita
Avenue, South El Monte, CA Zip 91733–3411; tel. 626/579–7777; Stanley
Toy, Jr., M.D., Chief Executive Officer
Web address: www.greaterelmonte.com

MONTEREY PARK HOSPITAL (O, 101 beds) 900 South Atlantic Boulevard,
Monterey Park, CA Zip 91754–4780; tel. 626/570–9000; Philip A. Cohen,
Chief Executive Officer
Web address: www.montereyparkhosp.com

WHITTIER HOSPITAL MEDICAL CENTER (O, 100 beds) 9080 Colima Road,
Whittier, CA Zip 90605–1600; tel. 562/945–3561; Richard Castro, Chief
Executive Officer
Web address: www.whittierhospital.com

Owned, leased, sponsored:	6 hospitals	809 beds
Contract–managed:	0 hospitals	0 beds
Totals:	6 hospitals	809 beds

0225: ALAMEDA HEALTH SYSTEM (NP)
15400 Foothill Boulevard, San Leandro, CA Zip 94578–1009;
tel. 510/677–7920; Daniel Boggan, Jr., Interim Chief Executive
Officer
(Moderately Centralized Health System)

ALAMEDA HOSPITAL (O, 126 beds) 2070 Clinton Avenue, Alameda, CA
Zip 94501–4397; tel. 510/522–3700; Bonnie Panlasigui, Chief Administrative
Officer
Web address: www.alamedahospital.org

HIGHLAND HOSPITAL (O, 387 beds) 1411 East 31st Street, Oakland, CA
Zip 94602–1018; tel. 510/437–4800; Delvecchio Finley, Chief Executive
Officer
Web address: www.alamedahealthsystem.org

SAN LEANDRO HOSPITAL (O, 45 beds) 13855 East 14th Street, San
Leandro, CA Zip 94578–2600; tel. 510/357–6500; James E. T. Jackson,
M.P.H., Chief Administrative Officer
Web address: www.sanleandrohospital.org

Owned, leased, sponsored:	3 hospitals	558 beds
Contract–managed:	0 hospitals	0 beds
Totals:	3 hospitals	558 beds

★0199: ALLEGHENY HEALTH NETWORK (NP)
30 Isabella Street, Suite 300, Pittsburgh, PA Zip 15212–5862;
tel. 412/359–3131; Cynthia Hundorfean, President and Chief
Executive Officer
(Moderately Centralized Health System)

NEW YORK: WESTFIELD MEMORIAL HOSPITAL (O, 4 beds) 189 East Main
Street, Westfield, NY Zip 14787–1195; tel. 716/326–4921; Scott
Whalen, Ph.D., FACHE, President and Chief Executive Officer
Web address: www.wmhinc.org

PENNSYLVANIA: ALLEGHENY GENERAL HOSPITAL (O, 381 beds) 320 East
North Avenue, Pittsburgh, PA Zip 15212–4756; tel. 412/359–3131;
Jeffrey Cohen, M.D., President
Web address: www.wpahs.org/locations/allegheny–general–hospital

ALLEGHENY VALLEY HOSPITAL (O, 228 beds) 1301 Carlisle Street, Natrona
Heights, PA Zip 15065–1152; tel. 724/224–5100; William Englert, Chief
Executive Officer
Web address: www.wpahs.org

CANONSBURG HOSPITAL (O, 104 beds) 100 Medical Boulevard, Canonsburg,
PA Zip 15317–9762; tel. 724/745–6100; David Goldberg, Interim President
and Chief Executive Officer
Web address: www.wpahs.org

FORBES HOSPITAL (O, 329 beds) 2570 Haymaker Road, Monroeville, PA
Zip 15146–3513; tel. 412/858–2000; Mark Rubino, M.D., President
Web address: www.ahn.org

JEFFERSON HOSPITAL (O, 341 beds) 565 Coal Valley Road, Jefferson Hills,
PA Zip 15025–3703, Mailing Address: Box 18119, Pittsburgh,
Zip 15236–0119; tel. 412/469–5000; Louise Urban, R.N., President and
Chief Executive Officer
Web address: www.jeffersonregional.com

SAINT VINCENT HOSPITAL (O, 400 beds) 232 West 25th Street, Erie, PA
Zip 16544–0002; tel. 814/452–5000; Scott Whalen, Ph.D., FACHE,
President and Chief Executive Officer
Web address: www.svhs.org

WEST PENN HOSPITAL (O, 317 beds) 4800 Friendship Avenue, Pittsburgh,
PA Zip 15224–1722; tel. 412/578–5000; Ronald J. Andro, President and
Chief Executive Officer
Web address: www.wpahs.org

Owned, leased, sponsored:	8 hospitals	2104 beds
Contract–managed:	0 hospitals	0 beds
Totals:	8 hospitals	2104 beds

0413: ALLEGIANCE HEALTH MANAGEMENT (IO)
504 Texas Street, Suite 200, Shreveport, LA Zip 71101–3526;
tel. 318/226–8202; Rock Bordelon, President and Chief Executive
Officer
(Independent Hospital System)

ARKANSAS: EUREKA SPRINGS HOSPITAL (O, 15 beds) 24 Norris Street,
Eureka Springs, AR Zip 72632–3541; tel. 479/253–7400; Peter Savoy,
III, Chief Executive Officer
Web address: www.eurekaspringshospital.com

NORTH METRO MEDICAL CENTER (O, 76 beds) 1400 West Braden Street,
Jacksonville, AR Zip 72076–3788; tel. 501/985–7000; Joe Farrer, Interim
Administrator
Web address: www.northmetromed.com

RIVER VALLEY MEDICAL CENTER (O, 35 beds) 200 North Third Street,
Dardanelle, AR Zip 72834–3802, Mailing Address: P.O. Box 578,
Zip 72834–0578; tel. 479/229–4677; Peter Savoy, III, Administrator

LOUISIANA: ALLEGIANCE HEALTH CENTER OF RUSTON (O, 14 beds) 1401
Ezell Street, Ruston, LA Zip 71270–7218; tel. 318/255–8085; Donna K.
Thompson, Chief Executive Officer
Web address: www.ahmgt.com

BIENVILLE MEDICAL CENTER (O, 21 beds) 1175 Pine Street, Suite 200,
Arcadia, LA Zip 71001–3122; tel. 318/263–4700; Kirk Lemoine, Chief
Executive Officer
Web address: www.bienvillemedicalcenter.net/

SABINE MEDICAL CENTER (O, 24 beds) 240 Highland Drive, Many, LA
Zip 71449–3718; tel. 318/256–5691; Chris Beddoe, Chief Executive Officer
Web address: www.sabinemedicalcenter.net

MISSISSIPPI: ALLEGIANCE SPECIALTY HOSPITAL OF GREENVILLE (O, 39
beds) 300 South Washington Avenue, 3rd Floor, Greenville, MS
Zip 38701–4719; tel. 662/332–7344; Vernail Herzog, Chief Executive
Officer
Web address: www.ahmgt.com

TEXAS: ALLEGIANCE BEHAVIORAL HEALTH CENTER OF PLAINVIEW (O, 20
beds) 2601 Dimmit Road, Suite 400, Plainview, TX Zip 79072–1833;
tel. 806/296–9191; Angie Alexander, Chief Executive Officer
Web address: www.ahmgt.com

ALLEGIANCE SPECIALTY HOSPITAL OF KILGORE (O, 60 beds) 1612 South
Henderson Boulevard, Kilgore, TX Zip 75662–3594; tel. 903/984–3505;
Karen Ross, Chief Executive Officer
Web address: www.ahmgt.com

For explanation of codes following names, see page B2.
★ Indicates Type III membership in the American Hospital Association.

Owned, leased, sponsored:	9 hospitals	304 beds
Contract–managed:	0 hospitals	0 beds
Totals:	9 hospitals	304 beds

0317: ALLIANT MANAGEMENT SERVICES (IO)

2650 Eastpoint Parkway, Suite 300, Louisville, KY Zip 40223–5164; tel. 502/992–3525; Timothy L. Jarm, President and Chief Executive Officer
(Moderately Centralized Health System)

FLORIDA: NORTHWEST FLORIDA COMMUNITY HOSPITAL (C, 59 beds) 1360 Brickyard Road, Chipley, FL Zip 32428–6303, Mailing Address: P.O. Box 889, Zip 32428–0889; tel. 850/638–1610; Mark E. Bush, Chief Executive Officer
Web address: www.nfch.org

ILLINOIS: FAIRFIELD MEMORIAL HOSPITAL (C, 55 beds) 303 N.W. 11th Street, Fairfield, IL Zip 62837–1203; tel. 618/842–2611; Katherine Bunting, Chief Executive Officer
Web address: www.fairfieldmemorial.org

FAYETTE COUNTY HOSPITAL (O, 110 beds) 650 West Taylor Street, Vandalia, IL Zip 62471–1296; tel. 618/283–1231; Gregory D. Starnes, Chief Executive Officer
Web address: www.fayettecountyhospital.org

GIBSON AREA HOSPITAL AND HEALTH SERVICES (C, 67 beds) 1120 North Melvin Street, Gibson City, IL Zip 60936–1477, Mailing Address: P.O. Box 429, Zip 60936–0429; tel. 217/784–4251; Robert C. Schmitt, II, Chief Executive Officer
Web address: www.gibsonhospital.org

PARIS COMMUNITY HOSPITAL (C, 25 beds) 721 East Court Street, Paris, IL Zip 61944–2460; tel. 217/465–4141; Oliver Smith, President and Chief Executive Officer
Web address: www.pariscommunityhospital.com

WABASH GENERAL HOSPITAL (C, 25 beds) 1418 College Drive, Mount Carmel, IL Zip 62863–2638; tel. 618/262–8621; Jay Purvis, President and Chief Executive Officer
Web address: www.wabashgeneral.com

INDIANA: GIBSON GENERAL HOSPITAL (C, 70 beds) 1808 Sherman Drive, Princeton, IN Zip 47670–1043; tel. 812/385–3401; Emmett C. Schuster, President and Chief Executive Officer
Web address: www.gibsongeneral.com

PERRY COUNTY MEMORIAL HOSPITAL (C, 25 beds) 8885 State Road 237, Tell City, IN Zip 47586–2750; tel. 812/547–7011; Brian J. Herwig, Chief Executive Officer
Web address: www.pchospital.org

KENTUCKY: BRECKINRIDGE MEMORIAL HOSPITAL (C, 43 beds) 1011 Old Highway 60, Hardinsburg, KY Zip 40143–2597; tel. 270/756–7000; Kent Giles, Interim Chief Executive Officer
Web address: www.breckinridgehealth.org/

CARROLL COUNTY MEMORIAL HOSPITAL (C, 25 beds) 309 11th Street, Carrollton, KY Zip 41008–1400; tel. 502/732–4321; Harry Hays, Chief Executive Officer
Web address: www.ccmhosp.com

JAMES B. HAGGIN MEMORIAL HOSPITAL (C, 25 beds) 464 Linden Avenue, Harrodsburg, KY Zip 40330–1862; tel. 859/734–5441; Victoria L. Reed, R.N., FACHE, Chief Executive Officer
Web address: www.hagginhosp.org

LIVINGSTON HOSPITAL AND HEALTHCARE SERVICES (C, 25 beds) 131 Hospital Drive, Salem, KY Zip 42078–8043; tel. 270/988–2299; Mark A. Edwards, Chief Executive Officer
Web address: www.lhhs.org

TWIN LAKES REGIONAL MEDICAL CENTER (C, 75 beds) 910 Wallace Avenue, Leitchfield, KY Zip 42754–2414; tel. 270/259–9400; Wayne Meriwether, Chief Executive Officer
Web address: www.tlrmc.com

NORTH CAROLINA: ALLEGHANY MEMORIAL HOSPITAL (C, 25 beds) 233 Doctors Street, Sparta, NC Zip 28675–9247; tel. 336/372–5511; Craig James, President
Web address: www.amhsparta.org

HUGH CHATHAM MEMORIAL HOSPITAL (C, 81 beds) 180 Parkwood Drive, Elkin, NC Zip 28621–2430, Mailing Address: P.O. Box 560, Zip 28621–0560; tel. 336/527–7000; Paul Hammes, Chief Executive Officer
Web address: www.hughchatham.org

Owned, leased, sponsored:	1 hospital	110 beds
Contract–managed:	14 hospitals	625 beds
Totals:	15 hospitals	735 beds

★0041: ALLINA HEALTH (NP)

2925 Chicago Avenue, Minneapolis, MN Zip 55407–1321, Mailing Address: P.O. Box 43, Zip 55440–0043; tel. 612/262–5000; Penny Ann Wheeler, M.D., Chief Executive Officer
(Moderately Centralized Health System)

MINNESOTA: ABBOTT NORTHWESTERN HOSPITAL (O, 675 beds) 800 East 28th Street, Minneapolis, MN Zip 55407–3799; tel. 612/863–4000; Ben Bache–Wiig, M.D., President
Web address: www.abbottnorthwestern.com

BUFFALO HOSPITAL (O, 44 beds) 303 Catlin Street, Buffalo, MN Zip 55313–1947; tel. 763/682–1212; Jennifer Myster, President
Web address: www.buffalohospital.org

CAMBRIDGE MEDICAL CENTER (O, 75 beds) 701 South Dellwood Street, Cambridge, MN Zip 55008–1920; tel. 763/689–7700; Gary Shaw, President
Web address: www.allina.com/ahs/cambridge.nsf

DISTRICT ONE HOSPITAL (O, 42 beds) 200 State Avenue, Faribault, MN Zip 55021–6345; tel. 507/334–6451; Stephen J. Pribyl, FACHE, President
Web address: www.allinahealth.org/District–One–Hospital/

HUTCHINSON HEALTH (C, 57 beds) 1095 Highway 15 South, Hutchinson, MN Zip 55350–3182; tel. 320/234–5000; Steven Mulder, M.D., President and Chief Executive Officer
Web address: www.hutchhealth.com

MERCY HOSPITAL (O, 258 beds) 4050 Coon Rapids Boulevard, Coon Rapids, MN Zip 55433–2586; tel. 763/236–6000; Sara J. Criger, President
Web address: www.allinamercy.org

NEW ULM MEDICAL CENTER (O, 45 beds) 1324 Fifth Street North, New Ulm, MN Zip 56073–1553; tel. 507/217–5000; Toby Freier, President
Web address: www.newulmmedicalcenter.com

OWATONNA HOSPITAL (O, 43 beds) 2250 N.W. 26th Street, Owatonna, MN Zip 55060–5503; tel. 507/451–3850; David L. Albrecht, President
Web address: www.owatonnahospital.com

PHILLIPS EYE INSTITUTE (O, 8 beds) 2215 Park Avenue, Minneapolis, MN Zip 55404–3756; tel. 612/775–8800; Daniel S. Conrad, M.D., President
Web address: www.allinahealth.org/ahs/pei.nsf/

REGINA HOSPITAL (O, 115 beds) 1175 Nininger Road, Hastings, MN Zip 55033–1098; tel. 651/480–4100; Thomas R. Thompson, Chief Executive Officer
Web address: www.reginamedical.org

ST. FRANCIS REGIONAL MEDICAL CENTER (O, 86 beds) 1455 St. Francis Avenue, Shakopee, MN Zip 55379–3380; tel. 952/428–3000; Mike McMahan, President
Web address: www.stfrancis–shakopee.com

UNITED HOSPITAL (O, 370 beds) 333 North Smith Avenue, Saint Paul, MN Zip 55102–2389; tel. 651/241–8000; Thomas O'Connor, President
Web address: www.allina.com

UNITY HOSPITAL (O, 167 beds) 550 Osborne Road N.E., Fridley, MN Zip 55432–2799; tel. 763/236–5000; Helen J. Strike, R.N., President
Web address: www.allina.com

WISCONSIN: RIVER FALLS AREA HOSPITAL (O, 10 beds) 1629 East Division Street, River Falls, WI Zip 54022–1571; tel. 715/425–6155; David R. Miller, President
Web address: www.allina.com

Owned, leased, sponsored:	13 hospitals	1938 beds
Contract–managed:	1 hospital	57 beds
Totals:	14 hospitals	1995 beds

For explanation of codes following names, see page B2.
★ Indicates Type III membership in the American Hospital Association.

0187: ALTA HEALTHCARE SYSTEM (IO)
10780 Santa Monica Boulevard, Suite 400, Los Angeles, CA
Zip 90025–7616; tel. 310/943–4500; David Topper, Chief Executive
Officer

CALIFORNIA: LOS ANGELES COMMUNITY HOSPITAL AT LOS ANGELES (O,
180 beds) 4081 East Olympic Boulevard, Los Angeles, CA
Zip 90023–3330; tel. 323/267–0477; Omar Ramirez, Chief Executive
Officer

SOUTHERN CALIFORNIA HOSPITAL AT CULVER CITY (O, 232 beds) 3828
Delmas Terrace, Culver City, CA Zip 90232–6806; tel. 310/836–7000;
Gerald B. Clute, Chief Executive Officer
Web address: www.sch–culvercity.com

SOUTHERN CALIFORNIA HOSPITAL AT HOLLYWOOD (O, 45 beds) 6245 De
Longpre Avenue, Los Angeles, CA Zip 90028–9001; tel. 323/462–2271;
Bruce P. Grimshaw, FACHE, Chief Executive Officer
Web address: www.hollywoodcommunityhospital.org/

Owned, leased, sponsored:	3 hospitals	457 beds
Contract–managed:	0 hospitals	0 beds
Totals:	3 hospitals	457 beds

0877: ALTAPOINTE HEALTH SYSTEMS (IO)
5750–A Southland Drive, Mobile, AL Zip 36693–3316;
tel. 251/473–4423; J. Tuerk Schlesinger, Chief Executive Officer

ALABAMA: BAYPOINTE BEHAVIORAL HEALTH (O, 60 beds) 5800 Southland
Drive, Mobile, AL Zip 36693–3313; tel. 251/661–0153; Phil Cusa,
Administrator
Web address: www.altapointe.org

EASTPOINTE HOSPITAL (O, 66 beds) 7400 Roper Lane, Daphne, AL
Zip 36526–5274; tel. 251/378–6500; Philip L. Cusa, Administrator
Web address: www.altapointe.org/eastpointe.php

Owned, leased, sponsored:	2 hospitals	126 beds
Contract–managed:	0 hospitals	0 beds
Totals:	2 hospitals	126 beds

**2295: AMERICAN PROVINCE OF LITTLE COMPANY OF MARY
SISTERS** (CC)
9350 South California Avenue, Evergreen Park, IL Zip 60805–2595;
tel. 708/229–5491; Sister Kathleen McIntyre, Province Leader
(Moderately Centralized Health System)

ILLINOIS: LITTLE COMPANY OF MARY HOSPITAL AND HEALTH CARE
CENTERS (O, 252 beds) 2800 West 95th Street, Evergreen Park, IL
Zip 60805–2795; tel. 708/422–6200; Dennis A. Reilly, President and
Chief Executive Officer
Web address: www.lcmh.org

INDIANA: MEMORIAL HOSPITAL AND HEALTH CARE CENTER (O, 143 beds)
800 West Ninth Street, Jasper, IN Zip 47546–2516; tel. 812/996–2345;
E. Kyle Bennett, President and Chief Executive Officer
Web address: www.mhhcc.org

Owned, leased, sponsored:	2 hospitals	395 beds
Contract–managed:	0 hospitals	0 beds
Totals:	2 hospitals	395 beds

0644: AMG INTEGRATED HEALTHCARE MANAGEMENT (IO)
101 La Rue France, Suite 500, Lafayette, LA Zip 70508–3144;
tel. 337/269–9828; August J. Rantz, III, Founder and Chief Executive
Officer
(Independent Hospital System)

KANSAS: AMG SPECIALTY HOSPITAL–WICHITA (O, 26 beds) 8080 East
Pawnee Street, Wichita, KS Zip 67207–5475; tel. 316/682–0004; Robert
A. Loepp, Jr., FACHE, Chief Executive Officer
Web address: www.amgwichita.com/

LOUISIANA: AMG SPECIALTY HOSPITAL – COVINGTON (O, 38 beds) 195
Highland Park Entrance, Covington, LA Zip 70433–7164;
tel. 985/867–3977; Tim Deaton, Chief Executive Officer
Web address: www.amgcovington.com/

AMG SPECIALTY HOSPITAL–DENHAM SPRINGS (O, 117 beds) 8375 Florida
Boulevard, Denham Springs, LA Zip 70726–7806; tel. 225/665–2664; Karen
Crayton, Administrator
Web address: www.amgdenham.com/

AMG SPECIALTY HOSPITAL–FELICIANA (O, 16 beds) 9725 Grace Lane,
Clinton, LA Zip 70722–4925; tel. 225/683–1600; Michael Sanders, Chief
Executive Officer
Web address: www.amgfeliciana.com/

AMG SPECIALTY HOSPITAL–HOUMA (O, 40 beds) 629 Dunn Street, Houma,
LA Zip 70360–4707; tel. 985/274–0001; Keith Carruth, Chief Executive
Officer
Web address: www.amghouma.com/

AMG SPECIALTY HOSPITAL–LAFAYETTE (O, 58 beds) 310 Youngsville
Highway, Lafayette, LA Zip 70508–4524; tel. 337/839–9880; Ben Miller,
Chief Executive Officer
Web address: www.amglafayette.com

LAFAYETTE PHYSICAL REHABILITATION HOSPITAL (O, 32 beds) 307 Polly
Lane, Lafayette, LA Zip 70508–4960; tel. 337/314–1111; Carol Washington,
R.N., MSN, Chief Executive Officer
Web address: www.lafayettephysicalrehab.com/

THE NEUROMEDICAL CENTER REHABILITATION HOSPITAL (O, 23 beds)
10101 Park Rowe Avenue, Suite 500, Baton Rouge, LA Zip 70810–1685;
tel. 225/906–2999; Elizabeth Wilson, Administrator
Web address: www.theneuromedicalcenter.com

MISSISSIPPI: AMG SPECIALTY HOSPITAL–GREENWOOD (O, 40 beds) 1401
River Road Floor 2, Greenwood, MS Zip 38930–4030;
tel. 662/459–2681; Jennifer Wallace, Chief Executive Officer
Web address: www.amggreenwood.com/

NEVADA: AMG SPECIALTY HOSPITAL – LAS VEGAS (O, 24 beds) 4015
Mcleod Drive, Las Vegas, NV Zip 89121–4305; tel. 702/433–2200;
William Fox, Chief Executive Officer
Web address: www.amgihm.com/locations/#map_top

NEW MEXICO: AMG SPECIALTY HOSPITAL–ALBUQUERQUE (O, 24 beds) 235
Elm Street N.E., Albuquerque, NM Zip 87102–3672; tel. 505/842–5550;
Susan Morgan, Chief Clinical Officer
Web address: www.amgalbuquerque.com/

OKLAHOMA: AMG SPECIALTY HOSPITAL–EDMOND (O, 37 beds) 1100 East
Ninth Street, Edmond, OK Zip 73034–5755; tel. 405/341–8150; Ricky
Higdon, Chief Executive Officer
Web address: www.amgedmond.com/

AMG SPECIALTY HOSPITAL–TULSA (O, 40 beds) 2408 East 81st Street, Suite
2800, Tulsa, OK Zip 74104–6510; tel. 918/710–3620; Elizabeth Rees, Chief
Executive Officer
Web address: www.amgoftulsa.com/

Owned, leased, sponsored:	13 hospitals	515 beds
Contract–managed:	0 hospitals	0 beds
Totals:	13 hospitals	515 beds

●0389: ANMED HEALTH (NP)
800 North Fant Street, Anderson, SC Zip 29621–5793;
tel. 864/512–1000; William T. Manson, III, Chief Executive Officer
(Moderately Centralized Health System)

SOUTH CAROLINA: ANMED HEALTH MEDICAL CENTER (O, 400 beds) 800
North Fant Street, Anderson, SC Zip 29621–5793; tel. 864/512–1000;
William T. Manson, III, Chief Executive Officer
Web address: www.anmedhealth.org

Owned, leased, sponsored:	1 hospital	400 beds
Contract–managed:	0 hospitals	0 beds
Totals:	1 hospital	400 beds

★0866: APPALACHIAN REGIONAL HEALTHCARE SYSTEM
(NP)
336 Deerfield Road, Boone, NC Zip 28607–5008, Mailing Address:
P.O. Box 2600, Zip 28607–2600; tel. 828/262–4100; Richard G.
Sparks, President and Chief Executive Officer
(Independent Hospital System)

For explanation of codes following names, see page B2.
★ Indicates Type III membership in the American Hospital Association.
● Single hospital health care system

Section B

NORTH CAROLINA: BLOWING ROCK REHABILITATION & DAVANT EXTENDED CARE CENTER (C, 72 beds) 418 Chestnut Street, Blowing Rock, NC Zip 28605–0148, Mailing Address: P.O. Box 148, Zip 28605–0148; tel. 828/295–3136; Elizabeth Hayes, R.N., Interim Administrator

CHARLES A. CANNON MEMORIAL HOSPITAL (C, 35 beds) 434 Hospital Drive, Newland, NC Zip 28646, Mailing Address: P.O. Box 767, Linville, Zip 28646–0767; tel. 828/737–7000; Carmen Lacey, MSN, R.N., President
Web address: www.https://apprhs.org/locations/cannon–memorial–hospital

WATAUGA MEDICAL CENTER (C, 99 beds) 336 Deerfield Road, Boone, NC Zip 28607–5008, Mailing Address: P.O. Box 2600, Zip 28607–2600; tel. 828/262–4100; Richard G. Sparks, Chief Executive Officer
Web address: www.https://apprhs.org/contact-us

Owned, leased, sponsored:	0 hospitals	0 beds
Contract–managed:	3 hospitals	206 beds
Totals:	3 hospitals	206 beds

0145: APPALACHIAN REGIONAL HEALTHCARE, INC. (NP)
2260 Executive Drive, Lexington, KY Zip 40505–4810, Mailing Address: P.O. Box 8086, Zip 40533–8086; tel. 859/226–2440; Jerry Haynes, President and Chief Executive Officer
(Decentralized Health System)

KENTUCKY: HARLAN ARH HOSPITAL (O, 145 beds) 81 Ball Park Road, Harlan, KY Zip 40831–1792; tel. 606/573–8100; Donald R. Fields, Community Chief Executive Officer
Web address: www.arh.org

HAZARD ARH REGIONAL MEDICAL CENTER (O, 358 beds) 100 Medical Center Drive, Hazard, KY Zip 41701–9421; tel. 606/439–6600; Dan Stone, Senior Community Chief Executive Officer
Web address: www.arh.org

MARY BRECKINRIDGE ARH HOSPITAL (O, 25 beds) 130 Kate Ireland Drive, Hyden, KY Zip 41749–9071, Mailing Address: P.O. Box 447–A, Zip 41749–0717; tel. 606/672–2901; Mallie S. Noble, Administrator
Web address: www.frontiernursing.org

MCDOWELL ARH HOSPITAL (O, 25 beds) Route 122, McDowell, KY Zip 41647, Mailing Address: P.O. Box 247, Zip 41647–0247; tel. 606/377–3400; Russell Barker, Community Chief Executive Officer
Web address: www.arh.org

MIDDLESBORO ARH HOSPITAL (O, 96 beds) 3600 West Cumberland Avenue, Middlesboro, KY Zip 40965–2614, Mailing Address: P.O. Box 340, Zip 40965–0340; tel. 606/242–1100; Michael Slusher, Community Chief Executive Officer
Web address: www.arh.org/middlesboro

MORGAN COUNTY ARH HOSPITAL (L, 25 beds) 476 Liberty Road, West Liberty, KY Zip 41472–2049, Mailing Address: P.O. Box 579, Zip 41472–0579; tel. 606/743–3186; Stephen M. Gavalchik, FACHE, Community Chief Executive Officer
Web address: www.arh.org

TUG VALLEY ARH REGIONAL MEDICAL CENTER (O, 141 beds) 260 Hospital Drive, South Williamson, KY Zip 41503–4072; tel. 606/237–1710; Timothy A. Hatfield, Community Chief Executive Officer
Web address: www.arh.org/locations/tug_valley/about_us.aspx

WHITESBURG ARH HOSPITAL (O, 87 beds) 240 Hospital Road, Whitesburg, KY Zip 41858–7627; tel. 606/633–3500; Dena C. Sparkman, FACHE, Community Chief Executive Officer
Web address: www.arh.org/whitesburg

WEST VIRGINIA: BECKLEY ARH HOSPITAL (O, 170 beds) 306 Stanaford Road, Beckley, WV Zip 25801–3142; tel. 304/255–3000; Rocco K. Massey, Community Chief Executive Officer
Web address: www.arh.org

SUMMERS COUNTY ARH HOSPITAL (L, 25 beds) Terrace Street, Hinton, WV Zip 25951–2407, Mailing Address: Drawer 940, Zip 25951–0940; tel. 304/466–1000; Wesley Dangerfield, Community Chief Executive Officer
Web address: www.arh.org

Owned, leased, sponsored:	10 hospitals	1097 beds
Contract–managed:	0 hospitals	0 beds
Totals:	10 hospitals	1097 beds

★**0104: ARCHBOLD MEDICAL CENTER** (NP)
910 South Broad Street, Thomasville, GA Zip 31792–6113; tel. 229/228–2739; J. Perry Mustian, President
(Moderately Centralized Health System)

GEORGIA: BROOKS COUNTY HOSPITAL (L, 25 beds) 903 North Court Street, Quitman, GA Zip 31643–1315, Mailing Address: P.O. Box 5000, Zip 31643–5000; tel. 229/263–4171; Nancy Fincher Williams, Administrator
Web address: www.archbold.org

GRADY GENERAL HOSPITAL (L, 48 beds) 1155 Fifth Street S.E., Cairo, GA Zip 39828–3142, Mailing Address: P.O. Box 360, Zip 39828–0360; tel. 229/377–1150; Crystal Ramm, Administrator
Web address: www.archbold.org

JOHN D. ARCHBOLD MEMORIAL HOSPITAL (O, 302 beds) 915 Gordon Avenue, Thomasville, GA Zip 31792–6614, Mailing Address: P.O. Box 1018, Zip 31799–1018; tel. 229/228–2000; J. Perry Mustian, President and Chief Executive Officer
Web address: www.archbold.org

MITCHELL COUNTY HOSPITAL (L, 181 beds) 90 East Stephens Street, Camilla, GA Zip 31730–1836, Mailing Address: P.O. Box 639, Zip 31730–0639; tel. 229/336–5284; James Womack, Administrator
Web address: www.archbold.org

Owned, leased, sponsored:	4 hospitals	556 beds
Contract–managed:	0 hospitals	0 beds
Totals:	4 hospitals	556 beds

★**0069: ARDENT HEALTH SERVICES** (IO)
1 Burton Hills Boulevard, Suite 250, Nashville, TN Zip 37215–6195; tel. 615/296–3000; David T. Vandewater, President and Chief Executive Officer
(Moderately Centralized Health System)

NEW MEXICO: LOVELACE MEDICAL CENTER (O, 263 beds) 601 Martin Luther King Avenue N.E., Albuquerque, NM Zip 87102–3619; tel. 505/727–8000; Troy Greer, Chief Executive Officer
Web address: www.lovelace.com/albuquerque–hospital/lovelace–medical–center#.UDZ1laDhf48

LOVELACE REGIONAL HOSPITAL – ROSWELL (O, 26 beds) 117 East 19th Street, Roswell, NM Zip 88201–5151; tel. 575/627–7000; Dawn M. Tschabrun, R.N., Chief Executive Officer
Web address: www.lovelace.com

LOVELACE REHABILITATION HOSPITAL (O, 62 beds) 505 Elm Street N.E., Albuquerque, NM Zip 87102–2500; tel. 505/727–4700; Derrick Jones, Chief Executive Officer
Web address: www.lovelace.com

LOVELACE WESTSIDE HOSPITAL (O, 80 beds) 10501 Golf Course Road N.W., Albuquerque, NM Zip 87114–5000, Mailing Address: P.O. Box 25555, Zip 87125–0555; tel. 505/727–8000; Farron Sneed, FACHE, Chief Executive Officer
Web address: www.lovelace.com/albuquerque–hospital/lovelace–westside–hospital#.UDZ1t6Dhf48

LOVELACE WOMEN'S HOSPITAL (O, 78 beds) 4701 Montgomery Boulevard N.E., Albuquerque, NM Zip 87109–1251, Mailing Address: P.O. Box 25555, Zip 87125–0555; tel. 505/727–7800; Sheri Milone, Chief Executive Officer and Administrator
Web address: www.lovelace.com/albuquerque–hospital/lovelace–womens–hospital#.UDZ17KDhf48

OKLAHOMA: BAILEY MEDICAL CENTER (O, 37 beds) 10502 North 110th East Avenue, Owasso, OK Zip 74055–6655; tel. 918/376–8000; Keith Mason, Chief Executive Officer
Web address: www.baileymedicalcenter.com

HILLCREST HOSPITAL – SOUTH (O, 160 beds) 8801 South 101st East Avenue, Tulsa, OK Zip 74133–5716; tel. 918/294–4000; Lynn M. Mergen, Chief Executive Officer
Web address: www.southcresthospital.com

HILLCREST HOSPITAL CLAREMORE (O, 67 beds) 1202 North Muskogee Place, Claremore, OK Zip 74017–3036; tel. 918/341–2556; David Chaussard, Chief Executive Officer
Web address: www.hillcrestclaremore.com

For explanation of codes following names, see page B2.
★ Indicates Type III membership in the American Hospital Association.

HILLCREST HOSPITAL CUSHING (O, 99 beds) 1027 East Cherry Street, Cushing, OK Zip 74023–4101, Mailing Address: P.O. Box 1409, Zip 74023–1409; tel. 918/225–2915; Kevin Hawk, Chief Executive Officer
Web address: www.hillcrestcushing.com/

HILLCREST HOSPITAL HENRYETTA (O, 41 beds) 2401 West Main Street, Henryetta, OK Zip 74437–3893, Mailing Address: P.O. Box 1269, Zip 74437–1269; tel. 918/650–1100; Dee Renshaw, Chief Executive Officer
Web address: www.hillcresthenryetta.com/

HILLCREST MEDICAL CENTER (O, 508 beds) 1120 South Utica Avenue, Tulsa, OK Zip 74104–4090; tel. 918/579–1000; Kevin J. Gross, FACHE, President and Chief Executive Officer
Web address: www.hillcrestmedicalcenter.com

TEXAS: BSA HOSPITAL, LLC (O, 318 beds) 1600 Wallace Boulevard, Amarillo, TX Zip 79106–1799; tel. 806/212–2000; Bob Williams, President and Chief Executive Officer
Web address: www.bsahs.org

PHYSICIANS SURGICAL HOSPITAL – PANHANDLE CAMPUS (O, 11 beds) 7100 West 9th Avenue, Amarillo, TX Zip 79106–1704; tel. 806/212–0247; Brad McCall, JD, Chief Executive Officer
Web address: www.physurg.com/

PHYSICIANS SURGICAL HOSPITAL – QUAIL CREEK (O, 41 beds) 6819 Plum Creek, Amarillo, TX Zip 79124–1602; tel. 806/354–6100; Brad McCall, JD, Chief Executive Officer
Web address: www.physurg.com

Owned, leased, sponsored:	14 hospitals	1791 beds
Contract–managed:	0 hospitals	0 beds
Totals:	14 hospitals	1791 beds

0809: ARNOT HEALTH (NP)
600 Roe Avenue, Elmira, NY Zip 14905–1629; tel. 607/737–4100; Robert K. Lambert, M.D., FACHE, President and Chief Executive Officer
(Independent Hospital System)

NEW YORK: ARNOT OGDEN MEDICAL CENTER (O, 244 beds) 600 Roe Avenue, Elmira, NY Zip 14905–1629; tel. 607/737–4100; Kerry Watson, Interim President and Chief Operating Officer
Web address: www.aomc.org

IRA DAVENPORT MEMORIAL HOSPITAL (O, 132 beds) 7571 State Route 54, Bath, NY Zip 14810–9590; tel. 607/776–8500; Richard Cleland, FACHE, Site Administrator
Web address: www.arnothealth.org

ST. JOSEPH'S HOSPITAL (O, 250 beds) 555 St. Joseph's Boulevard, Elmira, NY Zip 14901–3223; tel. 607/733–6541; Kerry Watson, Interim President and Chief Operating Officer
Web address: www.stjosephs.org

Owned, leased, sponsored:	3 hospitals	626 beds
Contract–managed:	0 hospitals	0 beds
Totals:	3 hospitals	626 beds

★0094: ASANTE HEALTH SYSTEM (NP)
2650 Siskiyou Boulevard, Suite 200, Medford, OR Zip 97504–8170; tel. 541/789–4100; Roy G. Vinyard, FACHE, President and Chief Executive Officer
(Moderately Centralized Health System)

OREGON: ASANTE ASHLAND COMMUNITY HOSPITAL (O, 36 beds) 280 Maple Street, Ashland, OR Zip 97520–1593; tel. 541/201–4000; Sheila Clough, Chief Executive Officer
Web address: www.ashlandhospital.org

ASANTE ROGUE REGIONAL MEDICAL CENTER (O, 320 beds) 2825 East Barnett Road, Medford, OR Zip 97504–8332; tel. 541/789–7000; Scott A. Kelly, Chief Executive Officer
Web address: www.asante.org

ASANTE THREE RIVERS MEDICAL CENTER (O, 111 beds) 500 S.W. Ramsey Avenue, Grants Pass, OR Zip 97527–5554; tel. 541/472–7000; Win Howard, Chief Executive Officer
Web address: www.asante.org/trmc/

Owned, leased, sponsored:	3 hospitals	467 beds
Contract–managed:	0 hospitals	0 beds
Totals:	3 hospitals	467 beds

★0198: ASCENSION HEALTH (CC)
101 South Hanley Road, Suite 450, Saint Louis, MO Zip 63105–3406; tel. 314/733–8000; Robert J. Henkel, FACHE, President and Chief Executive Officer
(Decentralized Health System)

ALABAMA: PROVIDENCE HOSPITAL (S, 302 beds) 6801 Airport Boulevard, Mobile, AL Zip 36608–3785, Mailing Address: P.O. Box 850429, Zip 36685–0429; tel. 251/633–1000; Todd S. Kennedy, President and Chief Executive Officer
Web address: www.providencehospital.org

ST. VINCENT'S BIRMINGHAM (S, 409 beds) 810 St. Vincent's Drive, Birmingham, AL Zip 35205–1695, Mailing Address: P.O. Box 12407, Zip 35202–2407; tel. 205/939–7000; Evan Ray, FACHE, President
Web address: www.stvhs.com

ST. VINCENT'S BLOUNT (S, 25 beds) 150 Gilbreath, Oneonta, AL Zip 35121–2827, Mailing Address: P.O. Box 1000, Zip 35121–0013; tel. 205/274–3000; Lisa Nichols, R.N., Interim Administrator
Web address: www.stvhs.com

ST. VINCENT'S EAST (S, 362 beds) 50 Medical Park East Drive, Birmingham, AL Zip 35235–9987; tel. 205/838–3000; Andrew Gnann, Vice President Operations
Web address: www.stvhs.com

ST. VINCENT'S ST. CLAIR (S, 40 beds) 7063 Veterans Parkway, Pell City, AL Zip 35125–1499; tel. 205/814–2105; Lisa Nichols, R.N., Administrator
Web address: www.stvhs.com

CONNECTICUT: ST. VINCENT'S MEDICAL CENTER (S, 403 beds) 2800 Main Street, Bridgeport, CT Zip 06606–4292; tel. 203/576–6000; Vincent C. Caponi, President and Chief Executive Officer
Web address: www.stvincents.org

DISTRICT OF COLUMBIA: PROVIDENCE HOSPITAL (S, 448 beds) 1150 Varnum Street N.E., Washington, DC Zip 20017–2104; tel. 202/269–7000; Darcy Burthay, MSN, R.N., President and Chief Executive Officer
Web address: www.provhosp.org

FLORIDA: SACRED HEART HOSPITAL ON THE EMERALD COAST (S, 58 beds) 7800 Highway 98 West, Miramar Beach, FL Zip 32550; tel. 850/278–3000; Roger L. Hall, President
Web address: www.sacredheartemerald.org

SACRED HEART HOSPITAL ON THE GULF (S, 19 beds) 3801 East Highway 98, Port St. Joe, FL Zip 32456–5318; tel. 850/229–5600; Roger L. Hall, President
Web address: www.sacred–heart.org/gulf/

SACRED HEART HOSPITAL PENSACOLA (S, 440 beds) 5151 North Ninth Avenue, Pensacola, FL Zip 32504–8795, Mailing Address: P.O. Box 2700, Zip 32513–2700; tel. 850/416–7000; Henry Stovall, President
Web address: www.sacred–heart.org

ST. VINCENT'S MEDICAL CENTER CLAY COUNTY (O, 64 beds) 1670 St. Vincent's Way, Middleburg, FL Zip 32068–8427, Mailing Address: 1670 St. Vincents Way, Zip 32068–8447; tel. 904/602–1000; James Machado, President
Web address: www.jaxhealth.com/

ST. VINCENT'S MEDICAL CENTER RIVERSIDE (S, 482 beds) 1 Shircliff Way, Jacksonville, FL Zip 32204–4748, Mailing Address: P.O. Box 2982, Zip 32203–2982; tel. 904/308–7300; Michael Schatzlein, M.D., President and Chief Executive Officer
Web address: www.jaxhealth.com

ST. VINCENT'S MEDICAL CENTER SOUTHSIDE (S, 288 beds) 4201 Belfort Road, Jacksonville, FL Zip 32216–1431; tel. 904/296–3700; Michael Schatzlein, M.D., President and Chief Executive Officer
Web address: www.jaxhealth.com

IDAHO: ST. JOSEPH REGIONAL MEDICAL CENTER (S, 123 beds) 415 Sixth Street, Lewiston, ID Zip 83501–2431; tel. 208/743–2511; Thomas E. Fitz, Jr., Interim President and Chief Executive Officer
Web address: www.sjrmc.org

For explanation of codes following names, see page B2.
★ Indicates Type III membership in the American Hospital Association.

Section B

ILLINOIS: ALEXIAN BROTHERS BEHAVIORAL HEALTH HOSPITAL (O, 141 beds) 1650 Moon Lake Boulevard, Hoffman Estates, IL Zip 60169–1010; tel. 847/882–1600; Clayton Ciha, President and Chief Executive Officer
Web address: www.abbhh.org

AMITA HEALTH ELK GROVE VILLAGE (O, 375 beds) 800 Biesterfield Road, Elk Grove Village, IL Zip 60007–3397; tel. 847/437–5500; John P. Werrbach, President and Chief Executive Officer
Web address: www.AMITAHealth.org

AMITA HEALTH HOFFMAN ESTATES (O, 286 beds) 1555 Barrington Road, Hoffman Estates, IL Zip 60169–1019; tel. 847/843–2000; Leonard Wilk, President and Chief Executive Officer
Web address: www.AMITAHealth.org

INDIANA: ST. MARY'S WARRICK HOSPITAL (S, 35 beds) 1116 Millis Avenue, Boonville, IN Zip 47601–2204; tel. 812/897–4800; Kathy J. Hall, Administrator
Web address: www.stmarys.org/warrick

ST. MARY'S MEDICAL CENTER OF EVANSVILLE (S, 436 beds) 3700 Washington Avenue, Evansville, IN Zip 47714–0541; tel. 812/485–4000; Keith Jewell, President
Web address: www.stmarys.org

ST. VINCENT ANDERSON REGIONAL HOSPITAL (S, 141 beds) 2015 Jackson Street, Anderson, IN Zip 46016–4339; tel. 765/649–2511; Mike Schroyer, FACHE, MSN, R.N., President
Web address: www.stvincent.org/andersonregional

ST. VINCENT CARMEL HOSPITAL (S, 107 beds) 13500 North Meridian Street, Carmel, IN Zip 46032–1456; tel. 317/582–7000; Michael D. Chittenden, President
Web address: www.stvincent.org

ST. VINCENT CLAY HOSPITAL (S, 25 beds) 1206 East National Avenue, Brazil, IN Zip 47834–2797, Mailing Address: P.O. Box 489, Zip 47834–0489; tel. 812/442–2500; Jerry Laue, Administrator
Web address: www.stvincent.org

ST. VINCENT DUNN HOSPITAL (S, 25 beds) 1600 23rd Street, Bedford, IN Zip 47421–4704; tel. 812/275–3331; Matt Balla, Chief Executive Officer
Web address: www.stvincent.org/St–Vincent–Dunn/Default.aspx

ST. VINCENT FISHERS HOSPITAL (S, 46 beds) 13861 Olio Road, Fishers, IN Zip 46037–3487; tel. 317/415–9000; Gary Fammartino, Administrator
Web address: www.stvincent.org

ST. VINCENT FRANKFORT HOSPITAL (S, 25 beds) 1300 South Jackson Street, Frankfort, IN Zip 46041–3313; tel. 765/656–3000; Kristi Bledsoe, R.N., Administrator
Web address: www.stvincent.org

ST. VINCENT HEART CENTER (S, 80 beds) 10580 North Meridian Street, Indianapolis, IN Zip 46290–1028; tel. 317/583–5000; Blake A. Dye, President
Web address: www.bestheartcare.com/

ST. VINCENT INDIANAPOLIS HOSPITAL (S, 909 beds) 2001 West 86th Street, Indianapolis, IN Zip 46260–1991, Mailing Address: P.O. Box 40970, Zip 46240–0970; tel. 317/338–2345; Joel Feldman, President
Web address: www.stvincent.org

ST. VINCENT JENNINGS HOSPITAL (S, 25 beds) 301 Henry Street, North Vernon, IN Zip 47265–1097; tel. 812/352–4200; ,
Web address: www.stvincent.org

ST. VINCENT KOKOMO (S, 138 beds) 1907 West Sycamore Street, Kokomo, IN Zip 46901–4197; tel. 765/452–5611; Margaret M. Johnson, President, St. Vincent Northwest Region
Web address: www.stvincent.org/stjoseph

ST. VINCENT MERCY HOSPITAL (S, 15 beds) 1331 South A Street, Elwood, IN Zip 46036–1942; tel. 765/552–4600; Francis G. Albarano, Administrator
Web address: www.stvincent.org

ST. VINCENT RANDOLPH HOSPITAL (S, 16 beds) 473 Greenville Avenue, Winchester, IN Zip 47394–9436; tel. 765/584–0004; Francis G. Albarano, Administrator
Web address: www.stvincent.org

ST. VINCENT SALEM HOSPITAL (S, 25 beds) 911 North Shelby Street, Salem, IN Zip 47167–1694; tel. 812/883–5881; Dana M. Muntz, Chief Executive Officer
Web address: www.stvincent.org/St–Vincent–Salem/Default.aspx

ST. VINCENT SETON SPECIALTY HOSPITAL (S, 74 beds) 8050 Township Line Road, Indianapolis, IN Zip 46260–2478; tel. 317/415–8500; Joel Feldman, President and Chief Executive Officer
Web address: www.stvincent.org/

ST. VINCENT WILLIAMSPORT HOSPITAL (S, 16 beds) 412 North Monroe Street, Williamsport, IN Zip 47993–1049; tel. 765/762–4000; Jane Craigin, Chief Executive Officer
Web address: www.stvincent.org

KANSAS: VIA CHRISTI HOSPITAL MANHATTAN, INC. (O, 96 beds) 1823 College Avenue, Manhattan, KS Zip 66502–3346; tel. 785/776–3322; Robert C. Copple, FACHE, Senior Administrator
Web address: www.https://www.viachristi.org/manhattan

VIA CHRISTI HOSPITAL ON ST. FRANCIS (O, 717 beds) 929 North St. Francis Street, Wichita, KS Zip 67214–3882; tel. 316/268–5000; Sherry Hausmann, Senior Administrator
Web address: www.via–christi.org

VIA CHRISTI HOSPITAL ON ST. TERESA (O, 40 beds) 14800 West St. Teresa, Wichita, KS Zip 67235–9602; tel. 316/796–7000; Claudio J. Ferraro, Senior Administrator
Web address: www.via–christi.org/st–teresa

VIA CHRISTI HOSPITAL PITTSBURG (O, 110 beds) 1 Mt. Carmel Way, Pittsburg, KS Zip 66762–7587; tel. 620/231–6100; Randall R. Cason, FACHE, Senior Administrator
Web address: www.viachristi.org/pittsburg

VIA CHRISTI REHABILITATION HOSPITAL (O, 58 beds) 1151 North Rock Road, Wichita, KS Zip 67206–1262; tel. 316/634–3400; Cindy LaFleur, Senior Administrator
Web address: www.via–christi.org

MARYLAND: SAINT AGNES HOSPITAL (S, 363 beds) 900 Caton Avenue, Baltimore, MD Zip 21229–5201; tel. 410/368–6000; Keith Vander Kolk, President and Chief Executive Officer
Web address: www.stagnes.org

MICHIGAN: BORGESS MEDICAL CENTER (S, 347 beds) 1521 Gull Road, Kalamazoo, MI Zip 49048–1640; tel. 269/226–7000; Kathlene A. Young, MS, FACHE, Chief Executive Officer
Web address: www.borgess.com

BORGESS–LEE MEMORIAL HOSPITAL (S, 25 beds) 420 West High Street, Dowagiac, MI Zip 49047–1943; tel. 269/782–8681; John E. Ryder, Chief Operating Officer
Web address: www.borgess.com

BORGESS–PIPP HOSPITAL (S, 43 beds) 411 Naomi Street, Plainwell, MI Zip 49080–1222; tel. 269/685–6811; John E. Ryder, Administrator and Chief Operating Officer
Web address: www.borgess.com

BRIGHTON CENTER FOR RECOVERY (S, 99 beds) 12851 Grand River Road, Brighton, MI Zip 48116–8506; tel. 810/227–1211; Raymond A. Waller, Director
Web address: www.brightonrecovery.org

CRITTENTON HOSPITAL MEDICAL CENTER (O, 254 beds) 1101 West University Drive, Rochester, MI Zip 48307–1831; tel. 248/652–5000; Margaret Dimond, Ph.D., President and Chief Executive Officer
Web address: www.crittenton.com

GENESYS REGIONAL MEDICAL CENTER (S, 415 beds) One Genesys Parkway, Grand Blanc, MI Zip 48439–8066; tel. 810/606–5000; Chris Palazzolo, President and Chief Executive Officer
Web address: www.genesys.org

PROVIDENCE – PROVIDENCE PARK HOSPITAL, SOUTHFIELD CAMPUS (S, 635 beds) 16001 West Nine Mile Road, Southfield, MI Zip 48075–4818, Mailing Address: P.O. Box 2043, Zip 48037–2043; tel. 248/424–3000; Michael Wiemann, M.D., President
Web address: www.providence-stjohnhealth.org

ST. JOHN HOSPITAL AND MEDICAL CENTER (S, 635 beds) 22101 Moross Road, Detroit, MI Zip 48236–2148; tel. 313/343–4000; Robert E. Hoban, Chief Executive Officer
Web address: www.stjohn.org

ST. JOHN MACOMB–OAKLAND HOSPITAL (S, 535 beds) 11800 East 12 Mile Road, Warren, MI Zip 48093–3472; tel. 586/573–5000; Terry Hamilton, President
Web address: www.stjohnprovidence.org/macomb–oakland/

ST. JOHN RIVER DISTRICT HOSPITAL (S, 68 beds) 4100 River Road, East China, MI Zip 48054–2909; tel. 810/329–7111; Frank W. Poma, President
Web address: www.stjohn.org

ST. JOSEPH HEALTH SYSTEM (S, 20 beds) 200 Hemlock Street, Tawas City, MI Zip 48763–9237, Mailing Address: P.O. Box 659, Zip 48764–0659; tel. 989/362–3411; Ann M. Balfour, R.N., President
Web address: www.sjhsys.org

For explanation of codes following names, see page B2.
★ Indicates Type III membership in the American Hospital Association.

Section B

ST. MARY'S OF MICHIGAN (S, 236 beds) 800 South Washington Avenue, Saginaw, MI Zip 48601–2594; tel. 989/907–8000; Chris Palazzolo, Health System President and Chief Executive Officer Mid–Michigan
Web address: www.stmarysofmichigan.org

ST. MARY'S OF MICHIGAN STANDISH HOSPITAL (S, 64 beds) 805 West Cedar Street, Standish, MI Zip 48658–9526; tel. 989/846–4521; Chris Palazzolo, President and Chief Executive Officer
Web address: www.stmarysofmichigan.org/standish

MINNESOTA: SAINT ELIZABETH'S MEDICAL CENTER (O, 164 beds) 1200 Grant Boulevard West, Wabasha, MN Zip 55981–1042; tel. 651/565–4531; Thomas Crowley, President and Chief Executive Officer
Web address: www.stelizabethswabasha.org

NEW YORK: OUR LADY OF LOURDES MEMORIAL HOSPITAL, INC. (S, 154 beds) 169 Riverside Drive, Binghamton, NY Zip 13905–4246; tel. 607/798–5111; Kathryn Connerton, President and Chief Executive Officer
Web address: www.lourdes.com

ST. MARY'S HEALTHCARE (S, 290 beds) 427 Guy Park Avenue, Amsterdam, NY Zip 12010–1054; tel. 518/842–1900; Victor Giulianelli, FACHE, President and Chief Executive Officer
Web address: www.smha.org

OKLAHOMA: JANE PHILLIPS MEMORIAL MEDICAL CENTER (O, 119 beds) 3500 East Frank Phillips Boulevard, Bartlesville, OK Zip 74006–2411; tel. 918/333–7200; Mike Moore, President and Chief Operating Officer
Web address: www.jpmc.org

JANE PHILLIPS NOWATA HEALTH CENTER (O, 15 beds) 237 South Locust Street, Nowata, OK Zip 74048–3660; tel. 918/273–3102; Jason McCauley, Administrator
Web address: www.jpmc.org

ST. JOHN BROKEN ARROW (O, 44 beds) 1000 West Boise Circle, Broken Arrow, OK Zip 74012–4900; tel. 918/994–8100; David L. Phillips, Chief Executive Officer
Web address: www.stjohnbrokenarrow.com

ST. JOHN MEDICAL CENTER (O, 546 beds) 1923 South Utica Avenue, Tulsa, OK Zip 74104–6502; tel. 918/744–2345; Jeffrey D. Nowlin, President and Chief Operating Officer
Web address: www.sjmc.org

ST. JOHN OWASSO (O, 45 beds) 12451 East 100th Street North, Owasso, OK Zip 74055–4600; tel. 918/274–5000; David L. Phillips, President and Chief Executive Officer
Web address: www.stjohnowasso.com

ST. JOHN SAPULPA (O, 25 beds) 519 South Division Street, Sapulpa, OK Zip 74066–4501, Mailing Address: P.O. Box 1368, Zip 74067–1368; tel. 918/224–4280; David L. Phillips, Chief Executive Officer
Web address: www.sjmc.org

TENNESSEE: SAINT THOMAS DEKALB HOSPITAL (O, 71 beds) 520 West Main Street, Smithville, TN Zip 37166–1138, Mailing Address: P.O. Box 640, Zip 37166–0640; tel. 615/215–5000; Craig Norris, Interim Chief Executive Officer
Web address: www.dekalbcommunityhospital.com

SAINT THOMAS HICKMAN HOSPITAL (S, 65 beds) 135 East Swan Street, Centerville, TN Zip 37033–1417; tel. 931/729–4271; Jack M. Keller, Chief Executive Officer
Web address: www.sths.com/hickman

SAINT THOMAS HIGHLANDS HOSPITAL (O, 60 beds) 401 Sewell Road, Sparta, TN Zip 38583–1299; tel. 931/738–9211; Craig Norris, Interim Chief Executive Officer
Web address: www.whitecountyhospital.com

SAINT THOMAS HOSPITAL FOR SPINAL SURGERY (S, 23 beds) 2011 Murphy Avenue, Suite 400, Nashville, TN Zip 37203–2065; tel. 615/341–7500; Kathy Watson, R.N., Administrator and Chief Nursing Officer
Web address: www.hospitalforspinalsurgery.com

SAINT THOMAS MIDTOWN HOSPITAL (S, 425 beds) 2000 Church Street, Nashville, TN Zip 37236–0002; tel. 615/284–5555; Don King, Chief Executive Officer
Web address: www.sths.com

SAINT THOMAS RIVER PARK HOSPITAL (O, 85 beds) 1559 Sparta Street, Mc Minnville, TN Zip 37110–1316; tel. 931/815–4000; Dale Humphrey, Chief Executive Officer
Web address: www.riverparkhospital.com

SAINT THOMAS RUTHERFORD HOSPITAL (S, 286 beds) 1700 Medical Center Parkway, Murfreesboro, TN Zip 37129–2245; tel. 615/396–4100; Gordon B. Ferguson, President and Chief Executive Officer
Web address: www.mtmc.org

SAINT THOMAS STONES RIVER HOSPITAL (O, 60 beds) 324 Doolittle Road, Woodbury, TN Zip 37190–1139; tel. 615/563–4001; Craig Norris, Interim Chief Executive Officer
Web address: www.stonesriverhospital.com

SAINT THOMAS WEST HOSPITAL (S, 395 beds) 4220 Harding Road, Nashville, TN Zip 37205–2095, Mailing Address: P.O. Box 380, Zip 37202–0380; tel. 615/222–2111; Don King, Chief Executive Officer
Web address: www.stthomas.org

TEXAS: DELL CHILDREN'S MEDICAL CENTER OF CENTRAL TEXAS (S, 248 beds) 4900 Mueller Boulevard, Austin, TX Zip 78723–3079; tel. 512/324–0000; Mark W. Shen, M.D., President and Chief Executive Officer
Web address: www.dellchildrens.net

PROVIDENCE HEALTHCARE NETWORK (S, 620 beds) 6901 Medical Parkway, Waco, TX Zip 76712–7998, Mailing Address: P.O. Box 2589, Zip 76702–2589; tel. 254/751–4000; Brett A. Esrock, President and Chief Executive Officer
Web address: www.providence.net

SETON EDGAR B. DAVIS HOSPITAL (S, 25 beds) 130 Hays Street, Luling, TX Zip 78648–3207; tel. 830/875–7000; Apryl Haynes, R.N., Vice President, Chief Operating Officer, Administrator
Web address: www.seton.net/locations/edgar_davis/

SETON HIGHLAND LAKES (S, 19 beds) 3201 South Water Street, Burnet, TX Zip 78611–4510, Mailing Address: P.O. Box 1219, Zip 78611–7219; tel. 512/715–3000; Karen Litterer, R.N., MSN, Administrator and Chief Operating Officer
Web address: www.seton.net

SETON MEDICAL CENTER AUSTIN (S, 422 beds) 1201 West 38th Street, Austin, TX Zip 78705–1006; tel. 512/324–1000; Katherine Henderson, President
Web address: www.seton.net/locations/smc/

SETON MEDICAL CENTER HAYS (O, 112 beds) 6001 Kyle Parkway, Kyle, TX Zip 78640–6112, Mailing Address: 6001 Kyle Prkway, Zip 78640–6112; tel. 512/504–5000; Christopher L. Hartle, President
Web address: www.seton.net/locations/seton_medical_center_hays/

SETON MEDICAL CENTER WILLIAMSON (S, 143 beds) 201 Seton Parkway, Round Rock, TX Zip 78665–8000; tel. 512/324–4000; Christopher L. Hartle, President
Web address: www.seton.net/williamson

SETON NORTHWEST HOSPITAL (S, 74 beds) 11113 Research Boulevard, Austin, TX Zip 78759–5236; tel. 512/324–6000; Margaret Butler, R.N., MSN, Administrator and Chief Operating Officer
Web address: www.seton.net

SETON SHOAL CREEK HOSPITAL (S, 94 beds) 3501 Mills Avenue, Austin, TX Zip 78731–6391; tel. 512/324–2000; William Henricks, Ph.D., Vice President and Chief Operating Officer
Web address: www.seton.net

SETON SMITHVILLE REGIONAL HOSPITAL (O, 10 beds) 800 East Highway 71, Smithville, TX Zip 78957–1730; tel. 512/237–3214; Robbie G. Rabe, Interim Vice President and Senior Director of Nursing
Web address: www.seton.org

SETON SOUTHWEST HOSPITAL (S, 33 beds) 7900 F. M. 1826, Austin, TX Zip 78737–1407; tel. 512/324–9000; Mary Faria, FACHE, Ph.D., Vice President and Chief Operating Officer
Web address: www.seton.net

UNIVERSITY MEDICAL CENTER AT BRACKENRIDGE (S, 208 beds) 601 East 15th Street, Austin, TX Zip 78701–1996; tel. 512/324–7000; Christann Vasquez, President
Web address: www.seton.net

WASHINGTON: LOURDES COUNSELING CENTER (S, 20 beds) 1175 Carondelet Drive, Richland, WA Zip 99354–3300; tel. 509/943–9104; Denise Clapp, Interim Executive Director
Web address: www.lourdeshealth.net

LOURDES MEDICAL CENTER (S, 53 beds) 520 North Fourth Avenue, Pasco, WA Zip 99301–5257; tel. 509/547–7704; John Serle, FACHE, President and Chief Executive Officer
Web address: www.lourdeshealth.net

For explanation of codes following names, see page B2.
★ Indicates Type III membership in the American Hospital Association.

WISCONSIN: CALUMET MEDICAL CENTER (O, 15 beds) 614 Memorial Drive, Chilton, WI Zip 53014–1597; tel. 920/849–2386; Timothy Richman, President
Web address: www.affinityhealth.org

COLUMBIA ST. MARY'S HOSPITAL MILWAUKEE (S, 266 beds) 2301 North Lake Drive, Milwaukee, WI Zip 53211–4508; tel. 414/291–1000; Travis Andersen, President and Chief Executive Officer
Web address: www.columbia–stmarys.org

COLUMBIA ST. MARY'S OZAUKEE HOSPITAL (S, 112 beds) 13111 North Port Washington Road, Mequon, WI Zip 53097–2416; tel. 262/243–7300; Travis Andersen, President and Chief Executive Officer
Web address: www.columbia–stmarys.org

HOWARD YOUNG MEDICAL CENTER (O, 38 beds) 240 Maple Street, Woodruff, WI Zip 54568–9190, Mailing Address: P.O. Box 470, Zip 54568–0470; tel. 715/356–8000; Sandra L. Anderson, President and Chief Executive Officer
Web address: www.ministryhealth.org

MERCY MEDICAL CENTER (O, 120 beds) 500 South Oakwood Road, Oshkosh, WI Zip 54904–7944; tel. 920/223–2000; Jeremy Normington–Slay, FACHE, Chief Executive Officer
Web address: www.affinityhealth.org

MIDWEST ORTHOPEDIC SPECIALTY HOSPITAL (O, 16 beds) 10101 South 27th Street, 2nd Floor, Franklin, WI Zip 53132–7209; tel. 414/817–5800; Coreen Dicus–Johnson, President
Web address: www.mymosh.com/

MINISTRY DOOR COUNTY MEDICAL CENTER (O, 55 beds) 323 South 18th Avenue, Sturgeon Bay, WI Zip 54235–1495; tel. 920/743–5566; Gerald M. Worrick, President and Chief Executive Officer
Web address: www.ministryhealth.org

MINISTRY EAGLE RIVER MEMORIAL HOSPITAL (O, 13 beds) 201 Hospital Road, Eagle River, WI Zip 54521–8835; tel. 715/479–7411; Sandra L. Anderson, President and Chief Executive Officer
Web address: www.ministryhealth.org

MINISTRY GOOD SAMARITAN HEALTH CENTER (O, 10 beds) 601 South Center Avenue, Merrill, WI Zip 54452–3404; tel. 715/536–5511; Mary T. Krueger, President
Web address: www.ministryhealth.org

MINISTRY OUR LADY OF VICTORY HOSPITAL (O, 5 beds) 1120 Pine Street, Stanley, WI Zip 54768–1297; tel. 715/644–5571; Vanessa Freitag, President
Web address: www.ministryhealth.org

MINISTRY SACRED HEART HOSPITAL (O, 11 beds) 401 West Mohawk Drive, Tomahawk, WI Zip 54487–2274; tel. 715/453–7700; Sandra L. Anderson, President and Chief Executive Officer
Web address: www.ministryhealth.org

MINISTRY SAINT CLARE'S HOSPITAL (O, 83 beds) 3400 Ministry Parkway, Weston, WI Zip 54476–5220; tel. 715/393–3000; Brian Kief, Interim President
Web address: www.ministryhealth.org

MINISTRY SAINT JOSEPH'S HOSPITAL (O, 275 beds) 611 St. Joseph Avenue, Marshfield, WI Zip 54449–1898; tel. 715/387–1713; Brian Kief, Regional Vice President Ministry Health Care and President Ministry Saint Joseph's Hospital
Web address: www.stjosephs–marshfield.org

MINISTRY SAINT MARY'S HOSPITALS (O, 60 beds) 2251 North Shore Drive, Rhinelander, WI Zip 54501–6710; tel. 715/361–2000; Sandra L. Anderson, President and Chief Executive Officer
Web address: www.ministryhealth.org

MINISTRY SAINT MICHAEL'S HOSPITAL (O, 50 beds) 900 Illinois Avenue, Stevens Point, WI Zip 54481–3196; tel. 715/346–5000; Jeffrey L. Martin, President
Web address: www.ministryhealth.org/SMH/home.nws

SACRED HEART REHABILITATION INSTITUTE (S, 31 beds) 2323 North Lake Drive, Milwaukee, WI Zip 53211–4508; tel. 414/298–6750; Bill Heart, Chief Operating Officer
Web address: www.columbia–stmarys.org/SHRI

ST. ELIZABETH HOSPITAL (O, 190 beds) 1506 South Oneida Street, Appleton, WI Zip 54915–1305; tel. 920/738–2000; Monica Hilt, President and Chief Executive Officer
Web address: www.affinityhealth.org

UNITED HOSPITAL SYSTEM, ST. CATHERINE'S MEDICAL CENTER CAMPUS (O, 202 beds) 9555 76th Street, Pleasant Prairie, WI Zip 53158–1984; tel. 262/656–2011; Richard O. Schmidt, Jr., President and Chief Executive Officer
Web address: www.uhsi.org

WHEATON FRANCISCAN HEALTHCARE – ALL SAINTS (O, 365 beds) 3801 Spring Street, Racine, WI Zip 53405–1690; tel. 262/687–4011; Susan Boland, R.N., MSN, President and Chief Executive Officer
Web address: www.allsaintshealth.com

WHEATON FRANCISCAN HEALTHCARE – ELMBROOK MEMORIAL (O, 120 beds) 19333 West North Avenue, Brookfield, WI Zip 53045–4198; tel. 262/785–2000; Debra K. Standridge, President
Web address: www.wfhealthcare.org

WHEATON FRANCISCAN HEALTHCARE – FRANKLIN (O, 37 beds) 10101 South 27th Street, Franklin, WI Zip 53132–7209; tel. 414/325–4700; Coreen Dicus–Johnson, President
Web address: www.mywheaton.org/

WHEATON FRANCISCAN HEALTHCARE – ST. FRANCIS (O, 177 beds) 3237 South 16th Street, Milwaukee, WI Zip 53215–4592; tel. 414/647–5000; Coreen Dicus–Johnson, President
Web address: www.mywheaton.org/stfrancis

WHEATON FRANCISCAN HEALTHCARE – ST. JOSEPH'S (O, 205 beds) 5000 West Chambers Street, Milwaukee, WI Zip 53210–1650; tel. 414/447–2000; Debra K. Standridge, President
Web address: www.mywheaton.org/stjoseph

Owned, leased, sponsored:	108 hospitals	18572 beds
Contract–managed:	0 hospitals	0 beds
Totals:	108 hospitals	18572 beds

★0519: ASPIRUS, INC. (NP)
425 Pine Ridge Boulevard, Wausau, WI Zip 54401–4123; tel. 715/847–2118; Matthew Heywood, Chief Executive Officer
(Moderately Centralized Health System)

MICHIGAN: ASPIRUS GRAND VIEW (O, 25 beds) N10561 Grand View Lane, Ironwood, MI Zip 49938–9622; tel. 906/932–2525; Paula L. Chermside, Chief Executive Officer
Web address: www.aspirus.org

ASPIRUS IRON RIVER HOSPITALS & CLINICS (O, 12 beds) 1400 West Ice Lake Road, Iron River, MI Zip 49935–9526; tel. 906/265–6121; Connie L. Koutouzos, R.N., MSN, Chief Executive Officer
Web address: www.aspirus.org

ASPIRUS KEWEENAW HOSPITAL (O, 25 beds) 205 Osceola Street, Laurium, MI Zip 49913–2134; tel. 906/337–6500; Michael Hauswirth, Chief Operating Officer
Web address: www.aspirus.org

ASPIRUS ONTONAGON HOSPITAL (O, 64 beds) 601 South Seventh Street, Ontonagon, MI Zip 49953–1459; tel. 906/884–8000; Michael Hauswirth, Chief Operating Officer
Web address: www.aspirus.org

WISCONSIN: ASPIRUS LANGLADE HOSPITAL (O, 17 beds) 112 East Fifth Avenue, Antigo, WI Zip 54409–2796; tel. 715/623–2331; David R. Schneider, Executive Director
Web address: www.aspirus.org

ASPIRUS MEDFORD HOSPITAL (O, 124 beds) 135 South Gibson Street, Medford, WI Zip 54451–1696; tel. 715/748–8100; Gregory A. Olson, President and Chief Executive Officer
Web address: www.aspirus.org

ASPIRUS RIVERVIEW HOSPITAL AND CLINICS, INC. (O, 69 beds) 410 Dewey Street, Wisconsin Rapids, WI Zip 54494–4715, Mailing Address: P.O. Box 8080, Zip 54495–8080; tel. 715/423–6060; Todd Burch, Chief Executive Officer
Web address: www.aspirus.org

ASPIRUS WAUSAU HOSPITAL (O, 229 beds) 333 Pine Ridge Boulevard, Wausau, WI Zip 54401–4187; tel. 715/847–2121; Darrell Lentz, President
Web address: www.aspirus.org

Owned, leased, sponsored:	8 hospitals	565 beds
Contract–managed:	0 hospitals	0 beds
Totals:	8 hospitals	565 beds

For explanation of codes following names, see page B2.
★ Indicates Type III membership in the American Hospital Association.

★**0865: ATLANTIC HEALTH SYSTEM** (NP)
475 South Street, Morristown, NJ Zip 07962, Mailing Address: P.O. Box 1905, Zip 07962–1905; tel. 973/660–3270; Brian A. Gragnolati, FACHE, President and Chief Executive Officer
(Decentralized Health System)

NEW JERSEY: CHILTON MEDICAL CENTER (O, 199 beds) 97 West Parkway, Pompton Plains, NJ Zip 07444–1696; tel. 973/831–5000; Stephanie L. Bloom, FACHE, President
Web address: www.chiltonmemorial.org

HACKETTSTOWN MEDICAL CENTER (O, 103 beds) 651 Willow Grove Street, Hackettstown, NJ Zip 07840–1799; tel. 908/852–5100; Jason C. Coe, President
Web address: www.hrmcnj.org

MORRISTOWN MEDICAL CENTER (O, 702 beds) 100 Madison Avenue, Morristown, NJ Zip 07960–6136; tel. 973/971–5000; Trish O'Keefe, Ph.D., R.N., President
Web address: www.atlantichealth.org/Morristown/

NEWTON MEDICAL CENTER (O, 148 beds) 175 High Street, Newton, NJ Zip 07860–1004; tel. 973/383–2121; Joseph DiPaolo, FACHE, President
Web address: www.atlantichealth.org/newton/

OVERLOOK MEDICAL CENTER (O, 320 beds) 99 Beauvoir Avenue, Summit, NJ Zip 07901–3533; tel. 908/522–2000; Alan R. Lieber, President
Web address: www.atlantichealth.org/Overlook

Owned, leased, sponsored:	5 hospitals	1472 beds
Contract–managed:	0 hospitals	0 beds
Totals:	5 hospitals	1472 beds

0894: AUDUBON BEHAVIORAL HEALTHCARE (IO)
100 West Hawkins, Suite D., Longview, TX Zip 75605; tel. 903/212–2930; William V. Brown, Chief Executive Officer

Owned, leased, sponsored:	0 hospitals	0 beds
Contract–managed:	0 hospitals	0 beds
Totals:	0 hospitals	0 beds

0859: AULTMAN HEALTH FOUNDATION (NP)
2600 Sixth Street S.W., Canton, OH Zip 44710–1702; tel. 330/363–6192; Edward J. Roth, III, President and Chief Executive Officer
(Moderately Centralized Health System)

OHIO: AULTMAN HOSPITAL (O, 532 beds) 2600 Sixth Street S.W., Canton, OH Zip 44710–1702; tel. 330/452–9911; Edward J. Roth, III, President and Chief Executive Officer
Web address: www.aultman.com

AULTMAN ORRVILLE HOSPITAL (O, 25 beds) 832 South Main Street, Orrville, OH Zip 44667–2208; tel. 330/682–3010; Marchelle Suppan, DPM, President and Chief Executive Officer
Web address: www.aultmanorrville.org

AULTMAN SPECIALTY HOSPITAL (O, 30 beds) 2600 Sixth Street, S.W., Canton, OH Zip 44710–1702; tel. 330/363–4000; Terry Regula, Chief Executive Officer
Web address: www.aultman.org

Owned, leased, sponsored:	3 hospitals	587 beds
Contract–managed:	0 hospitals	0 beds
Totals:	3 hospitals	587 beds

★**2215: AURORA HEALTH CARE** (NP)
750 Virginia Street, Milwaukee, WI Zip 53204, Mailing Address: P.O. Box 341880, Zip 53234–1880; tel. 414/299–1600; Nick Turkal, M.D., President and Chief Executive Officer
(Decentralized Health System)

WISCONSIN: AURORA BAYCARE MEDICAL CENTER (O, 167 beds) 2845 Greenbrier Road, Green Bay, WI Zip 54311–6519, Mailing Address: P.O. Box 8900, Zip 54308–8900; tel. 920/288–8000; Daniel T. Meyer, President
Web address: www.aurorabaycare.com

AURORA LAKELAND MEDICAL CENTER (O, 67 beds) W3985 County Road NN, Elkhorn, WI Zip 53121–4389; tel. 262/741–2000; Lisa Just, President

AURORA MEDICAL CENTER (O, 74 beds) 10400 75th Street, Kenosha, WI Zip 53142–7884; tel. 262/948–5600; Douglas E. Koch, Market President
Web address: www.aurorahealthcare.org

AURORA MEDICAL CENTER – MANITOWOC COUNTY (O, 62 beds) 5000 Memorial Drive, Two Rivers, WI Zip 54241–3900; tel. 920/794–5000; Cathie A. Kocourek, President
Web address: www.aurorahealthcare.org

AURORA MEDICAL CENTER GRAFTON (O, 127 beds) 975 Port Washington Road, Grafton, WI Zip 53024–9201; tel. 262/329–1000; Carrie Killoran, Interim President
Web address: www.aurorahealthcare.org

AURORA MEDICAL CENTER IN WASHINGTON COUNTY (O, 35 beds) 1032 East Sumner Street, Hartford, WI Zip 53027–1698; tel. 262/673–2300; Carrie Killoran, Interim President
Web address: www.aurorahealthcare.org

AURORA MEDICAL CENTER OF OSHKOSH (O, 61 beds) 855 North Westhaven Drive, Oshkosh, WI Zip 54904–7668; tel. 920/456–6000; Jeffrey Bard, President
Web address: www.aurorahealthcare.com

AURORA MEDICAL CENTER SUMMIT (O, 99 beds) 36500 Aurora Drive, Summit, WI Zip 53066–4899; tel. 262/434–1000; Michael Bergmann, President
Web address: www.aurorahealthcare.org

AURORA MEMORIAL HOSPITAL OF BURLINGTON (O, 55 beds) 252 McHenry Street, Burlington, WI Zip 53105–1828; tel. 262/767–6000; Lisa Just, President
Web address: www.aurorahealthcare.org

AURORA PSYCHIATRIC HOSPITAL (O, 81 beds) 1220 Dewey Avenue, Wauwatosa, WI Zip 53213–2598; tel. 414/454–6600; Peter Carlson, Administrator
Web address: www.aurorahealthcare.org

AURORA SHEBOYGAN MEMORIAL MEDICAL CENTER (O, 136 beds) 2629 North Seventh Street, Sheboygan, WI Zip 53083–4998; tel. 920/451–5000; David Graebner, President
Web address: www.aurorahealthcare.org

AURORA SINAI MEDICAL CENTER (O, 197 beds) 945 North 12th Street, Milwaukee, WI Zip 53233–1337, Mailing Address: P.O. Box 342, Zip 53201–0342; tel. 414/219–2000; Carolynn Glocka, R.N., President

AURORA ST. LUKE'S MEDICAL CENTER (O, 732 beds) 2900 West Oklahoma Avenue, Milwaukee, WI Zip 53215–4330, Mailing Address: P.O. Box 2901, Zip 53201–2901; tel. 414/649–6000; Marie Golanowski, R.N., MS, President
Web address: www.aurorahealthcare.org

AURORA WEST ALLIS MEDICAL CENTER (O, 218 beds) 8901 West Lincoln Avenue, West Allis, WI Zip 53227–2409, Mailing Address: P.O. Box 27901, Zip 53227–0901; tel. 414/328–6000; Richard A. Kellar, President
Web address: www.aurorahealthcare.org

Owned, leased, sponsored:	14 hospitals	2111 beds
Contract–managed:	0 hospitals	0 beds
Totals:	14 hospitals	2111 beds

0869: AVANTI HOSPITALS (IO)
222 North Sepulveda Boulevard, Suite 950, El Segundo, CA Zip 90245–5614; tel. 310/356–0550; Arnold R. Schaffer, Corporate Chief Executive Officer
(Independent Hospital System)

CALIFORNIA: COAST PLAZA HOSPITAL (O, 123 beds) 13100 Studebaker Road, Norwalk, CA Zip 90650–2500; tel. 562/868–3751; Richard Rowe, PharmD, Chief Executive Officer
Web address: www.coastplaza.com

COMMUNITY HOSPITAL OF HUNTINGTON PARK (O, 81 beds) 2623 East Slauson Avenue, Huntington Park, CA Zip 90255–2926; tel. 323/583–1931; Araceli Lonergan, Chief Executive Officer
Web address: www.chhplax.com

For explanation of codes following names, see page B2.
★ Indicates Type III membership in the American Hospital Association.

EAST LOS ANGELES DOCTORS HOSPITAL (O, 127 beds) 4060 Whittier Boulevard, Los Angeles, CA Zip 90023–2526; tel. 323/268–5514; Araceli Lonergan, Chief Executive Officer
Web address: www.avantihospitals.com

MEMORIAL HOSPITAL OF GARDENA (O, 172 beds) 1145 West Redondo Beach Boulevard, Gardena, CA Zip 90247–3528; tel. 310/532–4200; Kathy Wojno, R.N., MSN, Interim Administrator
Web address: www.mhglax.com/

Owned, leased, sponsored:	4 hospitals	503 beds
Contract–managed:	0 hospitals	0 beds
Totals:	4 hospitals	503 beds

★5255: **AVERA HEALTH** (CC)
3900 West Avera Drive, Suite 300, Sioux Falls, SD Zip 57108–5721; tel. 605/322–4700; John T. Porter, President and Chief Executive Officer
(Decentralized Health System)

IOWA: AVERA HOLY FAMILY HOSPITAL (O, 25 beds) 826 North Eighth Street, Estherville, IA Zip 51334–1598; tel. 712/362–2631; Dale Hustedt, Administrator
Web address: www.avera–holyfamily.org

FLOYD VALLEY HEALTHCARE (C, 25 beds) 714 Lincoln Street N.E., Le Mars, IA Zip 51031–3314; tel. 712/546–7871; Michael T. Donlin, FACHE, Administrator
Web address: www.floydvalley.org

HEGG MEMORIAL HEALTH CENTER AVERA (C, 85 beds) 1202 21st Avenue, Rock Valley, IA Zip 51247–1497; tel. 712/476–8000; Glenn Zevenbergen, Chief Executive Officer
Web address: www.hegghc.org

LAKES REGIONAL HEALTHCARE (C, 30 beds) 2301 Highway 71 South, Spirit Lake, IA Zip 51360–0159, Mailing Address: P.O. Box AB, Zip 51360–0159; tel. 712/336–1230; Jason Harrington, FACHE, President and Chief Executive Officer
Web address: www.lakeshealth.org

OSCEOLA COMMUNITY HOSPITAL (C, 25 beds) 600 Ninth Avenue North, Sibley, IA Zip 51249–1012, Mailing Address: P.O. Box 258, Zip 51249–0258; tel. 712/754–2574; Janet H. Dykstra, Chief Executive Officer
Web address: www.osceolacommunityhospital.org

SIOUX CENTER HEALTH (C, 88 beds) 1101 9th Street S.E., Sioux Center, IA Zip 51250; tel. 712/722–8107; Kayleen R. Lee, Chief Executive Officer
Web address: www.siouxcenterhealth.org

MINNESOTA: AVERA MARSHALL REGIONAL MEDICAL CENTER (O, 111 beds) 300 South Bruce Street, Marshall, MN Zip 56258–3900; tel. 507/532–9661; Mary B. Maertens, FACHE, President and Chief Executive Officer
Web address: www.avera.org

PIPESTONE COUNTY MEDICAL CENTER AVERA (C, 25 beds) 916 4th Avenue S.W., Pipestone, MN Zip 56164–1890; tel. 507/825–5811; Bradley D. Burris, Chief Executive Officer
Web address: www.pcmchealth.org

TYLER HEALTHCARE CENTER AVERA (C, 56 beds) 240 Willow Street, Tyler, MN Zip 56178–1166; tel. 507/247–5521; Jonathan Moe, Chief Executive Officer
Web address: www.www1.avera.org/amck/regionalfacilities/tyler/index.aspx

NEBRASKA: AVERA CREIGHTON HOSPITAL (O, 54 beds) 1503 Main Street, Creighton, NE Zip 68729–3007, Mailing Address: P.O. Box 186, Zip 68729–0186; tel. 402/358–5700; Jennifer Neukirch, Chief Executive Officer
Web address: www.avera.org/creighton/

AVERA ST. ANTHONY'S HOSPITAL (O, 25 beds) 300 North Second Street, O'Neill, NE Zip 68763–1514, Mailing Address: P.O. Box 270, Oneill, Zip 68763–0270; tel. 402/336–2611; Todd Consbruck, President and Chief Executive Officer
Web address: www.avera.org/st-anthonys

SOUTH DAKOTA: AVERA DE SMET MEMORIAL HOSPITAL (L, 6 beds) 306 Prairie Avenue S.W., De Smet, SD Zip 57231–2285, Mailing Address: P.O. Box 160, Zip 57231–0160; tel. 605/854–3329; Janice Schardin, R.N., MS, Administrator and Chief Executive Officer
Web address: www.desmetmemorial.org

AVERA DELLS AREA HOSPITAL (L, 23 beds) 909 North Iowa Avenue, Dell Rapids, SD Zip 57022–1231; tel. 605/428–5431; Scott James Hargens, Interim Administrator & Chief Executive Officer
Web address: www.avera.org/dell-rapids/

AVERA FLANDREAU HOSPITAL (L, 18 beds) 214 North Prairie Street, Flandreau, SD Zip 57028–1243; tel. 605/997–2433; Scott Hargens, Interim Administrator and Chief Executive Officer
Web address: www.avera.org/flandreau–medical/

AVERA GETTYSBURG HOSPITAL (O, 60 beds) 606 East Garfield Avenue, Gettysburg, SD Zip 57442–1398; tel. 605/765–2480; Robert L. Sheckler, Administrator
Web address: www.avera.org/st-marys–pierre/gettysburg–hospital/

AVERA GREGORY HOSPITAL (O, 67 beds) 400 Park Avenue, Gregory, SD Zip 57533–1302, Mailing Address: P.O. Box 408, Zip 57533–0408; tel. 605/835–8394; Anthony Timanus, Chief Executive Officer
Web address: www.gregoryhealthcare.org

AVERA HAND COUNTY MEMORIAL HOSPITAL (L, 9 beds) 300 West Fifth Street, Miller, SD Zip 57362–1238; tel. 605/853–2421; Bryan Breitling, Administrator
Web address: www.avera.org

AVERA HEART HOSPITAL OF SOUTH DAKOTA (O, 53 beds) 4500 West 69th Street, Sioux Falls, SD Zip 57108–8148; tel. 605/977–7000; Jon Soderholm, President
Web address: www.avera.org/heart–hospital

AVERA MCKENNAN HOSPITAL AND UNIVERSITY HEALTH CENTER (O, 415 beds) 1325 South Cliff Avenue, Sioux Falls, SD Zip 57105–1007, Mailing Address: P.O. Box 5045, Zip 57117–5045; tel. 605/322–8000; David Kapaska, D.O., Regional President and Chief Executive Officer
Web address: www.averamckennan.org

AVERA QUEEN OF PEACE HOSPITAL (O, 176 beds) 525 North Foster, Mitchell, SD Zip 57301–2999; tel. 605/995–2000; Thomas A. Clark, Regional President and Chief Executive Officer
Web address: www.averaqueenofpeace.org

AVERA SACRED HEART HOSPITAL (O, 293 beds) 501 Summit Avenue, Yankton, SD Zip 57078–3855; tel. 605/668–8000; Douglas R. Ekeren, Regional President and Chief Executive Officer
Web address: www.averasacredheart.com

AVERA ST. BENEDICT HEALTH CENTER (O, 99 beds) 401 West Glynn Drive, Parkston, SD Zip 57366–9605; tel. 605/928–3311; Gale N. Walker, President and Chief Executive Officer
Web address: www.averastbenedict.org

AVERA ST. LUKE'S HOSPITAL (O, 222 beds) 305 South State Street, Aberdeen, SD Zip 57401–4527; tel. 605/622–5000; Todd Forkel, President and Chief Executive Officer
Web address: www.avera.org/st-lukes–hospital/

AVERA ST. MARY'S HOSPITAL (O, 110 beds) 801 East Sioux Avenue, Pierre, SD Zip 57501–3323; tel. 605/224–3100; Todd Forkel, Interim Chief Executive Officer
Web address: www.avera.org/st-marys–pierre/

AVERA WESKOTA MEMORIAL HOSPITAL (L, 23 beds) 604 First Street N.E., Wessington Springs, SD Zip 57382–2166; tel. 605/539–1201; Gaea Blue, R.N., Administrator and Chief Executive Officer
Web address: www.averaweskota.org

EUREKA COMMUNITY HEALTH SERVICES AVERA (C, 6 beds) 410 Ninth Street, Eureka, SD Zip 57437–2182, Mailing Address: P.O. Box 517, Zip 57437–0517; tel. 605/284–2661; Carmen Weber, Administrator
Web address: www.avera.org

LANDMANN–JUNGMAN MEMORIAL HOSPITAL AVERA (C, 17 beds) 600 Billars Street, Scotland, SD Zip 57059–2026; tel. 605/583–2226; Darcy Permann, Interim Chief Executive Officer
Web address: www.ljmh.org

MARSHALL COUNTY HEALTHCARE CENTER AVERA (C, 18 beds) 413 Ninth Street, Britton, SD Zip 57430–2274; tel. 605/448–2253; Nick Fosness, Chief Executive Officer
Web address: www.avera.org

MILBANK AREA HOSPITAL AVERA (L, 25 beds) 901 East Virgil Avenue, Milbank, SD Zip 57252–2124; tel. 605/432–4538; Natalie Gauer, Administrator
Web address: www.averamilbank.org

For explanation of codes following names, see page B2.
★ Indicates Type III membership in the American Hospital Association.

PLATTE HEALTH CENTER AVERA (C, 65 beds) 601 East Seventh, Platte, SD Zip 57369–2123, Mailing Address: P.O. Box 200, Zip 57369–0200; tel. 605/337–3364; Mark Burket, Chief Executive Officer
Web address: www.phcavera.org

ST. MICHAEL'S HOSPITAL AVERA (C, 25 beds) 410 West 16th Avenue, Tyndall, SD Zip 57066–2318; tel. 605/589–2152; Carol Deurmier, Chief Executive Officer
Web address: www.stmichaels–bhfp.org

WAGNER COMMUNITY MEMORIAL HOSPITAL AVERA (C, 20 beds) 513 Third Street S.W., Wagner, SD Zip 57380–9675, Mailing Address: P.O. Box 280, Zip 57380–0280; tel. 605/384–3611; Bryan Slaba, Chief Executive Officer
Web address: www.avera.org/wagnerhospital

Owned, leased, sponsored:	19 hospitals	1814 beds
Contract–managed:	13 hospitals	485 beds
Totals:	32 hospitals	2299 beds

★**0633: AVITA HEALTH SYSTEM** (NP)
269 Portland Way South, Galion, OH Zip 44833–2399; tel. 419/468–4841; Jerome Morasko, President and Chief Executive Officer
(Independent Hospital System)

OHIO: BUCYRUS COMMUNITY HOSPITAL (O, 25 beds) 629 North Sandusky Avenue, Bucyrus, OH Zip 44820–1821; tel. 419/562–4677; Jerome Morasko, Chief Executive Officer
Web address: www.bchonline.org

GALION COMMUNITY HOSPITAL (O, 35 beds) 269 Portland Way South, Galion, OH Zip 44833–2399; tel. 419/468–4841; Jerome Morasko, President and Chief Executive Officer
Web address: www.avitahs.org

Owned, leased, sponsored:	2 hospitals	60 beds
Contract–managed:	0 hospitals	0 beds
Totals:	2 hospitals	60 beds

★**0194: BANNER HEALTH** (NP)
1441 North 12th Street, Phoenix, AZ Zip 85006–2837, Mailing Address: P.O. Box 25489, Zip 85002–5489; tel. 602/747–4000; Peter S. Fine, FACHE, President and Chief Executive Officer
(Decentralized Health System)

ALASKA: FAIRBANKS MEMORIAL HOSPITAL (L, 217 beds) 1650 Cowles Street, Fairbanks, AK Zip 99701–5998; tel. 907/452–8181; Gregory Johnson, D.D.S., Chief Executive Officer
Web address: www.bannerhealth.com/locations/alaska/fairbanks+memorial+Hospital

ARIZONA: BANNER – UNIVERSITY MEDICAL CENTER PHOENIX (O, 685 beds) 1111 East McDowell Road, Phoenix, AZ Zip 85006–2666, Mailing Address: P.O. Box 2989, Zip 85062–2989; tel. 602/239–2000; Steve Narang, M.D., Chief Executive Officer
Web address: www.bannerhealth.com/Locations/Arizona/Banner+Good+Samaritan+Medical+Center

BANNER – UNIVERSITY MEDICAL CENTER SOUTH (O, 167 beds) 2800 East Ajo Way, Tucson, AZ Zip 85713–6289; tel. 520/874–2000; Thomas C. Dickson, Chief Executive Officer
Web address: www.uahealth.com

BANNER – UNIVERSITY MEDICAL CENTER TUCSON (O, 451 beds) 1501 North Campbell Avenue, Tucson, AZ Zip 85724–5128; tel. 520/694–0111; Thomas C. Dickson, Chief Executive Officer
Web address: www.uahealth.com

BANNER BAYWOOD MEDICAL CENTER (O, 388 beds) 6644 East Baywood Avenue, Mesa, AZ Zip 85206–1797; tel. 480/321–2000; Julie Nunley, R.N., Chief Executive Officer
Web address: www.bannerhealth.com/locations/Arizona/banner+baywood+medical+center

BANNER BEHAVIORAL HEALTH HOSPITAL – SCOTTSDALE (O, 78 beds) 7575 East Earll Drive, Scottsdale, AZ Zip 85251–6915; tel. 480/941–7500; Brian Beutin, MS, Chief Executive Officer
Web address: www.bannerhealth.com/Locations/Arizona/Banner+Behavioral+Health

BANNER BOSWELL MEDICAL CENTER (O, 425 beds) 10401 West Thunderbird Boulevard, Sun City, AZ Zip 85351–3004, Mailing Address: P.O. Box 1690, Zip 85372–1690; tel. 623/832–4000; David Cheney, Chief Executive Officer
Web address: www.bannerhealth.com/Locations/Arizona/Banner+Boswell+Medical+Center

BANNER CASA GRANDE MEDICAL CENTER (O, 135 beds) 1800 East Florence Boulevard, Casa Grande, AZ Zip 85122–5399; tel. 520/381–6300; Rona Curphy, President and Chief Executive Officer
Web address: www.https://www.bannerhealth.com/Locations/Arizona/Banner+Casa+Grande+Medical+Center/_Banner+Casa+Grande+Medical+Center.htm

BANNER DEL E. WEBB MEDICAL CENTER (O, 365 beds) 14502 West Meeker Boulevard, Sun City West, AZ Zip 85375–5299; tel. 623/524–4000; Debbie Flores, Chief Executive Officer
Web address: www.bannerhealth.com/Locations/Arizona/Banner+Del+Webb+Medical+Center/

BANNER DESERT MEDICAL CENTER (O, 595 beds) 1400 South Dobson Road, Mesa, AZ Zip 85202–4707; tel. 480/412–3000; Laura Robertson, R.N., Chief Executive Officer
Web address: www.bannerhealth.com/Locations/Arizona/Banner+Desert+Medical+Center

BANNER ESTRELLA MEDICAL CENTER (O, 259 beds) 9201 West Thomas Road, Phoenix, AZ Zip 85037–3332; tel. 623/327–4000; Courtney Ophaug, FACHE, Chief Executive Officer
Web address: www.bannerhealth.com/Locations/Arizona/Banner+Estrella+Medical+Center/

BANNER GATEWAY MEDICAL CENTER (O, 177 beds) 1900 North Higley Road, Gilbert, AZ Zip 85234–1604; tel. 480/543–2000; Lamont M. Yoder, R.N., MSN, FACHE, Chief Executive Officer
Web address: www.bannerhealth.com/Locations/Arizona/Banner+Gateway+Medical+Center/

BANNER GOLDFIELD MEDICAL CENTER (O, 30 beds) 2050 West Southern Avenue, Apache Junction, AZ Zip 85120–7305; tel. 480/733–3300; Sharon Lind, MSN, FACHE, Chief Executive Officer
Web address: www.bannerhealth.com/Locations/Arizona/Banner+Goldfield+Medical+Center/_Welcome+to+Banner+Goldfield.htm

BANNER HEART HOSPITAL (O, 111 beds) 6750 East Baywood Avenue, Mesa, AZ Zip 85206–1749; tel. 480/854–5000; Julie Nunley, R.N., Chief Executive Officer
Web address: www.bannerhealth.com/Locations/Arizona/Banner+Heart+Hospital/

BANNER IRONWOOD MEDICAL CENTER (O, 53 beds) 37000 North Gantzel Road, San Tan Valley, AZ Zip 85140–7303; tel. 480/394–4000; Sharon Lind, MSN, FACHE, Chief Executive Officer
Web address: www.bannerhealth.com/Locations/Arizona/Banner+Ironwood/

BANNER PAYSON MEDICAL CENTER (O, 44 beds) 807 South Ponderosa Street, Payson, AZ Zip 85541–5599; tel. 928/474–3222; Lance Porter, Chief Executive Officer
Web address: www.paysonhospital.com

BANNER THUNDERBIRD MEDICAL CENTER (O, 476 beds) 5555 West Thunderbird Road, Glendale, AZ Zip 85306–4696; tel. 602/865–5555; Debra J. Krmpotic, R.N., Chief Executive Officer
Web address: www.bannerhealth.com/Locations/Arizona/Banner+Thunderbird+Medical+Center/

PAGE HOSPITAL (C, 25 beds) 501 North Navajo Drive, Page, AZ Zip 86040, Mailing Address: P.O. Box 1447, Zip 86040–1447; tel. 928/645–2424; Brian Kellar, Chief Executive Officer
Web address: www.bannerhealth.com/Locations/Arizona/Page+Hospital

CALIFORNIA: BANNER LASSEN MEDICAL CENTER (O, 25 beds) 1800 Spring Ridge Drive, Susanville, CA Zip 96130–6100; tel. 530/252–2000; Catherine S. Harshbarger, R.N., Chief Executive Officer
Web address: www.bannerhealth.com/California/Banner+Lassen+Medical+Center

COLORADO: BANNER FORT COLLINS MEDICAL CENTER (O, 22 beds) 4700 Lady Moon Drive, Fort Collins, CO Zip 80528–4426; tel. 970/229–4000; Margo Karsten, PhD, MSN, Chief Executive Officer
Web address: www.bannerhealth.com/Locations/Colorado/Banner+Fort+Collins+Medical+Center

EAST MORGAN COUNTY HOSPITAL (L, 19 beds) 2400 West Edison Street, Brush, CO Zip 80723–1640; tel. 970/842–6200; Linda Thorpe, Chief Executive Officer
Web address: www.emchbrush.com

For explanation of codes following names, see page B2.
★ Indicates Type III membership in the American Hospital Association.

B18 Health Care Systems, Networks and Alliances

© 2016 AHA Guide

MCKEE MEDICAL CENTER (O, 96 beds) 2000 Boise Avenue, Loveland, CO Zip 80538–4281; tel. 970/669–4640; Margo Karsten, PhD, MSN, Chief Executive Officer
Web address: www.mckeeloveland.com

NORTH COLORADO MEDICAL CENTER (L, 223 beds) 1801 16th Street, Greeley, CO Zip 80631–5154; tel. 970/352–4121; Margo Karsten, PhD, MSN, Chief Executive Officer
Web address: www.ncmcgreeley.com

STERLING REGIONAL MEDCENTER (O, 25 beds) 615 Fairhurst Street, Sterling, CO Zip 80751–4523; tel. 970/522–0122; Jeffrey Shelton, Chief Executive Officer
Web address: www.bannerhealth.com/Locations/Colorado/Sterling+Regional+MedCenter

NEBRASKA: OGALLALA COMMUNITY HOSPITAL (L, 18 beds) 2601 North Spruce Street, Ogallala, NE Zip 69153–2465; tel. 308/284–4011; Drew H. Dostal, R.N., FACHE, Chief Executive Officer
Web address: www.bannerhealth.com/Locations/Nebraska/Ogallala+Community+Hospital

NEVADA: BANNER CHURCHILL COMMUNITY HOSPITAL (O, 25 beds) 801 East Williams Avenue, Fallon, NV Zip 89406–3052; tel. 775/423–3151; Hoyt Skabelund, Chief Executive Officer
Web address: www.bannerhealth.com/churchill

WYOMING: COMMUNITY HOSPITAL (O, 20 beds) 2000 Campbell Drive, Torrington, WY Zip 82240–1597; tel. 307/532–4181; Shelby Nelson, Interim Chief Executive Officer
Web address: www.bannerhealth.com/Locations/Wyoming/Community+Hospital/

PLATTE COUNTY MEMORIAL HOSPITAL (L, 25 beds) 201 14th Street, Wheatland, WY Zip 82201–3201, Mailing Address: P.O. Box 848, Zip 82201–0848; tel. 307/322–3636; Shelby Nelson, Chief Executive Officer
Web address: www.bannerhealth.com/Locations/Wyoming/Platte+County+Memorial+Hospital

WASHAKIE MEDICAL CENTER (L, 22 beds) 400 South 15th Street, Worland, WY Zip 82401–3531, Mailing Address: P.O. Box 700, Zip 82401–0700; tel. 307/347–3221; Jay Stallings, Chief Executive Officer
Web address: www.washakiemedicalcenter.com

Owned, leased, sponsored:	28 hospitals	5176 beds
Contract–managed:	1 hospital	25 beds
Totals:	29 hospitals	5201 beds

★0005: BAPTIST HEALTH (NP)
841 Prudential Drive, Suite 1601, Jacksonville, FL Zip 32207–8202; tel. 904/202–2000; Hugh Greene, President and Chief Executive Officer
(Moderately Centralized Health System)

FLORIDA: BAPTIST MEDICAL CENTER BEACHES (O, 136 beds) 1350 13th Avenue South, Jacksonville Beach, FL Zip 32250–3205; tel. 904/627–2900; Joseph M. Mitrick, FACHE, President
Web address: www.community.e-baptisthealth.com/bmc/beaches/index.html

BAPTIST MEDICAL CENTER JACKSONVILLE (O, 903 beds) 800 Prudential Drive, Jacksonville, FL Zip 32207–8202; tel. 904/202–2000; Michael A. Mayo, FACHE, President
Web address: www.e-baptisthealth.com

Owned, leased, sponsored:	2 hospitals	1039 beds
Contract–managed:	0 hospitals	0 beds
Totals:	2 hospitals	1039 beds

0150: BAPTIST HEALTH (NP)
301 Brown Springs Road, Montgomery, AL Zip 36117–7005; tel. 334/273–4400; W. Russell Tyner, President and Chief Executive Officer
(Independent Hospital System)

ALABAMA: BAPTIST MEDICAL CENTER EAST (O, 164 beds) 400 Taylor Road, Montgomery, AL Zip 36117–3512, Mailing Address: P.O. Box 241267, Zip 36124–1267; tel. 334/277–8330; Jeff G. Rains, Chief Executive Officer
Web address: www.baptistfirst.org

BAPTIST MEDICAL CENTER SOUTH (O, 387 beds) 2105 East South Boulevard, Montgomery, AL Zip 36116–2409, Mailing Address: Box 11010, Zip 36111–0010; tel. 334/288–2100; J. Peter Selman, FACHE, Chief Executive Officer
Web address: www.baptistfirst.org

PRATTVILLE BAPTIST HOSPITAL (O, 50 beds) 124 South Memorial Drive, Prattville, AL Zip 36067–3619, Mailing Address: P.O. Box 681630, Zip 36068–1638; tel. 334/365–0651; Eric Morgan, Interim Chief Executive Officer
Web address: www.baptistfirst.org/facilities/prattville–baptist–hospital/default.aspx

Owned, leased, sponsored:	3 hospitals	601 beds
Contract–managed:	0 hospitals	0 beds
Totals:	3 hospitals	601 beds

★0315: BAPTIST HEALTH (CO)
2701 Eastpoint Parkway, Louisville, KY Zip 40223; tel. 502/896–5000; Stephen C. Hanson, Chief Executive Officer
(Centralized Physician/Insurance Health System)

KENTUCKY: BAPTIST HEALTH CORBIN (O, 273 beds) 1 Trillium Way, Corbin, KY Zip 40701–8420; tel. 606/528–1212; Larry Gray, President
Web address: www.baptisthealth.com/corbin

BAPTIST HEALTH FLOYD (O, 535 beds) 1850 State Street, New Albany, KY Zip 47150–4997; tel. 812/949–5500; Daniel J. Eichenberger, M.D., President and Chief Executive Officer
Web address: floydmemorial.com

BAPTIST HEALTH LA GRANGE (O, 65 beds) 1025 New Moody Lane, La Grange, KY Zip 40031–9154; tel. 502/222–5388; Christopher Roty, President
Web address: www.baptisthealthlagrange.com

BAPTIST HEALTH LEXINGTON (O, 344 beds) 1740 Nicholasville Road, Lexington, KY Zip 40503–1499; tel. 859/260–6100; William G. Sisson, President
Web address: www.baptisthealthlexington.com

BAPTIST HEALTH LOUISVILLE (O, 500 beds) 4000 Kresge Way, Louisville, KY Zip 40207–4676; tel. 502/897–8100; David L. Gray, FACHE, President
Web address: www.baptisthealthlouisville.com

BAPTIST HEALTH MADISONVILLE (O, 192 beds) 900 Hospital Drive, Madisonville, KY Zip 42431–1694; tel. 270/825–5100; Robert L. Ramey, President
Web address: www.baptisthealthmadisonville.com

BAPTIST HEALTH PADUCAH (O, 320 beds) 2501 Kentucky Avenue, Paducah, KY Zip 42003–3200; tel. 270/575–2100; William A. Brown, FACHE, President and CEO
Web address: www.baptisthealthpaducah.com

BAPTIST HEALTH RICHMOND (O, 69 beds) 801 Eastern Bypass, Richmond, KY Zip 40475–2405, Mailing Address: P.O. Box 1600, Zip 40476–2603; tel. 859/623–3131; Todd Jones, President
Web address: www.baptisthealthrichmond.com

HARDIN MEMORIAL HOSPITAL (C, 268 beds) 913 North Dixie Avenue, Elizabethtown, KY Zip 42701–2503; tel. 270/737–1212; Dennis B. Johnson, President and Chief Executive Officer
Web address: www.hmh.net

Owned, leased, sponsored:	8 hospitals	2298 beds
Contract–managed:	1 hospital	268 beds
Totals:	9 hospitals	2566 beds

★0355: BAPTIST HEALTH (NP)
9601 Interstate 630, Exit 7, Little Rock, AR Zip 72205–7299; tel. 501/202–2000; Troy R. Wells, Chief Executive Officer
(Centralized Physician/Insurance Health System)

ARKANSAS: BAPTIST HEALTH EXTENDED CARE HOSPITAL (O, 55 beds) 9601 Baptist Health Drive, Little Rock, AR Zip 72205–7202; tel. 501/202–1070; Mike Perkins, Vice President and Administrator
Web address: www.baptist–health.com/maps–directions/bh_extended_care/default.aspx

For explanation of codes following names, see page B2.
★ Indicates Type III membership in the American Hospital Association.

BAPTIST HEALTH MEDICAL CENTER – NORTH LITTLE ROCK (O, 225 beds) 3333 Springhill Drive, North Little Rock, AR Zip 72117–2922; tel. 501/202–3000; Steven B. Webb, FACHE, Vice President and Administrator
Web address: www.baptist–health.com/locations/accesspoint.aspx?accessPointID=190

BAPTIST HEALTH MEDICAL CENTER–ARKADELPHIA (L, 25 beds) 3050 Twin Rivers Drive, Arkadelphia, AR Zip 71923–4299; tel. 870/245–2622; John Bowen, Assistant Vice President and Administrator
Web address: www.baptist–health.com/locations/accesspoint.aspx?accessPointID=187

BAPTIST HEALTH MEDICAL CENTER–HEBER SPRINGS (O, 25 beds) 1800 Bypass Road, Heber Springs, AR Zip 72543–9135; tel. 501/887–3000; Edward L. Lacy, FACHE, Vice President and Administrator
Web address: www.baptist–health.com/maps–directions/bhmc–heber–springs

BAPTIST HEALTH MEDICAL CENTER–HOT SPRING COUNTY (L, 72 beds) 1001 Schneider Drive, Malvern, AR Zip 72104–4811; tel. 501/332–1000; Sheila Williams, Vice President and Administrator
Web address: www.https://www.baptist–health.org

BAPTIST HEALTH MEDICAL CENTER–LITTLE ROCK (O, 694 beds) 9601 Baptist Health Drive, Little Rock, AR Zip 72205–7299; tel. 501/202–2000; Greg Crain, FACHE, Vice President and Administrator
Web address: www.baptist–health.org/maps–directions/bhmc–lr

BAPTIST HEALTH MEDICAL CENTER–STUTTGART (L, 49 beds) 1703 North Buerkle Road, Stuttgart, AR Zip 72160–1905, Mailing Address: P.O. Box 1905, Zip 72160–1905; tel. 870/673–3511; Kevin L. Storey, Vice President and Administrator
Web address: www.https://www.baptist–health.com/location/baptist–health–medical–center–stuttgart–stuttgart

BAPTIST HEALTH REHABILITATION INSTITUTE (O, 120 beds) 9601 Interstate 630, Exit 7, Little Rock, AR Zip 72205–7202; tel. 501/202–7000; Lee Gentry, FACHE, Vice President and Administrator
Web address: www.baptist–health.com/locations/accesspoint.aspx?accessPointID=202

Owned, leased, sponsored:	8 hospitals	1265 beds
Contract–managed:	0 hospitals	0 beds
Totals:	8 hospitals	1265 beds

★0185: BAPTIST HEALTH CARE CORPORATION (NP) 1717 North E Street, Suite 402, Pensacola, FL Zip 32501–6377, Mailing Address: P.O. Box 17500, Zip 32522–7500; tel. 850/434–4011; Mark T. Faulkner, President
(Moderately Centralized Health System)

FLORIDA: BAPTIST HOSPITAL (O, 337 beds) 1000 West Moreno, Pensacola, FL Zip 32501–2316, Mailing Address: P.O. Box 17500, Zip 32522–7500; tel. 850/434–4011; Scott Raynes, President
Web address: www.ebaptisthealthcare.org

GULF BREEZE HOSPITAL (O, 65 beds) 1110 Gulf Breeze Parkway, Gulf Breeze, FL Zip 32561–4884; tel. 850/934–2000; Scott Raynes, President
Web address: www.ebaptisthealthcare.org/GulfBreezeHospital/

JAY HOSPITAL (L, 49 beds) 14114 South Alabama Street, Jay, FL Zip 32565–1219; tel. 850/675–8000; Michael T. Hutchins, Administrator
Web address: www.bhcpns.org/jayhospital/

Owned, leased, sponsored:	3 hospitals	451 beds
Contract–managed:	0 hospitals	0 beds
Totals:	3 hospitals	451 beds

★0122: BAPTIST HEALTH SOUTH FLORIDA (NP) 6855 Red Road, Suite 600, Coral Gables, FL Zip 33143–3632; tel. 786/662–7111; Brian E. Keeley, President and Chief Executive Officer
(Centralized Health System)

BAPTIST HEALTH SOUTH FLORIDA, BAPTIST HOSPITAL OF MIAMI (O, 720 beds) 8900 North Kendall Drive, Miami, FL Zip 33176–2197; tel. 786/596–1960; Albert Boulenger, Chief Executive Officer
Web address: www.baptisthealth.net

BAPTIST HEALTH SOUTH FLORIDA, DOCTORS HOSPITAL (O, 146 beds) 5000 University Drive, Coral Gables, FL Zip 33146–2094; tel. 786/308–3000; Nelson Lazo, Chief Executive Officer
Web address: www.baptisthealth.net

BAPTIST HEALTH SOUTH FLORIDA, HOMESTEAD HOSPITAL (O, 142 beds) 975 Baptist Way, Homestead, FL Zip 33033–7600; tel. 786/243–8000; William M. Duquette, Chief Executive Officer
Web address: www.baptisthealth.net

BAPTIST HEALTH SOUTH FLORIDA, MARINERS HOSPITAL (O, 25 beds) 91500 Overseas Highway, Tavernier, FL Zip 33070–2547; tel. 305/434–3000; Rick Freeburg, Chief Executive Officer
Web address: www.baptisthealth.net/en/facilities/mariners–hospital/Pages/default.aspx

BAPTIST HEALTH SOUTH FLORIDA, SOUTH MIAMI HOSPITAL (O, 335 beds) 6200 S.W. 73rd Street, Miami, FL Zip 33143–4679; tel. 786/662–4000; Lincoln S. Mendez, Chief Executive Officer
Web address: www.baptisthealth.net

BAPTIST HEALTH SOUTH FLORIDA, WEST KENDALL BAPTIST HOSPITAL (O, 133 beds) 9555 S.W. 162nd Avenue, Miami, FL Zip 33196–6408; tel. 786/467–2000; Javier Hernandez–Lichtl, Chief Executive Officer
Web address: www.baptisthealth.net/en/facilities/West–Kendall–Baptist–Hospital/Pages/default.aspx

Owned, leased, sponsored:	6 hospitals	1501 beds
Contract–managed:	0 hospitals	0 beds
Totals:	6 hospitals	1501 beds

★0336: BAPTIST HEALTH SYSTEMS (NP) 1225 North State Street, Jackson, MS Zip 39202–2064; tel. 601/968–1000; Chris Anderson, Chief Executive Officer
(Moderately Centralized Health System)

MISSISSIPPI: BAPTIST MEDICAL CENTER ATTALA (L, 25 beds) 220 Highway 12 West, Kosciusko, MS Zip 39090–3208, Mailing Address: P.O. Box 887, Zip 39090–0887; tel. 662/289–4311; John Dawson, Chief Executive Officer
Web address: www.mbhs.org/locations/baptist–medical–center–attala/

BAPTIST MEDICAL CENTER LEAKE (O, 69 beds) 1100 Highway 16 E., Carthage, MS Zip 39051–3809, Mailing Address: P.O. Box 909, Zip 39051–0909; tel. 601/267–1100; Daryl W. Weaver, Interim Chief Executive Officer
Web address: www.mbhs.com/locations/baptist–medical–center–leake/

BAPTIST MEDICAL CENTER YAZOO (O, 25 beds) 823 Grand Avenue, Yazoo City, MS Zip 39194–3233; tel. 662/746–2261; Sean Johnson, Chief Executive Officer
Web address: www.kdhyazoo.com

MISSISSIPPI BAPTIST MEDICAL CENTER (O, 483 beds) 1225 North State Street, Jackson, MS Zip 39202–2064; tel. 601/968–1000; Chris Anderson, President & Chief Executive Officer
Web address: www.mbhs.org

Owned, leased, sponsored:	4 hospitals	602 beds
Contract–managed:	0 hospitals	0 beds
Totals:	4 hospitals	602 beds

★1625: BAPTIST MEMORIAL HEALTH CARE CORPORATION (NP) 350 North Humphreys Boulevard, Memphis, TN Zip 38120–2177; tel. 901/227–5117; Jason Little, President and Chief Executive Officer
(Decentralized Health System)

ARKANSAS: NEA BAPTIST MEMORIAL HOSPITAL (O, 216 beds) 4800 East Johnson Avenue, Jonesboro, AR Zip 72401–8413; tel. 870/936–1000; Brad Parsons, FACHE, Administrator and Chief Executive Officer
Web address: www.neabaptist.com

MISSISSIPPI: BAPTIST MEMORIAL HOSPITAL–BOONEVILLE (L, 66 beds) 100 Hospital Street, Booneville, MS Zip 38829–3359; tel. 662/720–5000; James Grantham, Administrator and Chief Executive Officer
Web address: www.bmhcc.org/booneville

For explanation of codes following names, see page B2.
★ Indicates Type III membership in the American Hospital Association.

BAPTIST MEMORIAL HOSPITAL–DESOTO (O, 233 beds) 7601 Southcrest Parkway, Southaven, MS Zip 38671–4742; tel. 662/772–4000; James Huffman, Chief Executive Officer and Administrator
Web address: www.baptistonline.org/desoto/

BAPTIST MEMORIAL HOSPITAL–GOLDEN TRIANGLE (O, 236 beds) 2520 Fifth Street North, Columbus, MS Zip 39705–2095, Mailing Address: P.O. Box 1307, Zip 39703–1307; tel. 662/244–1000; Paul Cade, Administrator and Chief Executive Officer
Web address: www.baptistonline.org/golden–triangle/

BAPTIST MEMORIAL HOSPITAL–NORTH MISSISSIPPI (O, 217 beds) 2301 South Lamar Boulevard, Oxford, MS Zip 38655–5373, Mailing Address: P.O. Box 946, Zip 38655–6002; tel. 662/232–8100; William C. Henning, Administrator and Chief Executive Officer
Web address: www.baptistonline.org/north–mississippi/

BAPTIST MEMORIAL HOSPITAL–UNION COUNTY (L, 153 beds) 200 Highway 30 West, New Albany, MS Zip 38652–3112; tel. 662/538–7631; Walter Grace, Chief Executive Officer and Administrator
Web address: www.baptistonline.org/union–county/

TENNESSEE: BAPTIST MEMORIAL HOSPITAL – MEMPHIS (O, 555 beds) 6019 Walnut Grove Road, Memphis, TN Zip 38120–2173; tel. 901/226–5000; Dana Dye, R.N., Vice President, Administrator and Chief Executive Officer
Web address: www.baptistonline.org/memphis/

BAPTIST MEMORIAL HOSPITAL FOR WOMEN (O, 140 beds) 6225 Humphreys Boulevard, Memphis, TN Zip 38120–2373; tel. 901/227–9000; Kevin R. Hammeran, Chief Executive Officer and Administrator
Web address: www.baptistonline.org/womens/

BAPTIST MEMORIAL HOSPITAL–COLLIERVILLE (O, 61 beds) 1500 West Poplar Avenue, Collierville, TN Zip 38017–0601; tel. 901/861–9400; Lindsay Stencel, Chief Administrative Officer
Web address: www.baptistonline.org/collierville/

BAPTIST MEMORIAL HOSPITAL–HUNTINGDON (O, 35 beds) 631 R.B. Wilson Drive, Huntingdon, TN Zip 38344–1727; tel. 731/986–4461; Susan M. Breeden, Administrator and Chief Executive Officer
Web address: www.baptistonline.org/huntingdon/

BAPTIST MEMORIAL HOSPITAL–TIPTON (O, 44 beds) 1995 Highway 51 South, Covington, TN Zip 38019–3635; tel. 901/476–2621; Samuel Lynd, Administrator and Chief Executive Officer
Web address: www.baptistonline.org/tipton/

BAPTIST MEMORIAL HOSPITAL–UNION CITY (O, 65 beds) 1201 Bishop Street, Union City, TN Zip 38261–5403, Mailing Address: P.O. Box 310, Zip 38281–0310; tel. 731/885–2410; Barry Bondurant, Administrator and Chief Executive Officer
Web address: www.baptistonline.org/union–city/

BAPTIST MEMORIAL REHABILITATION HOSPITAL (O, 49 beds) 1240 South Germantown Road, Germantown, TN Zip 38138–2226; tel. 901/275–3300; Christopher L. Bariola, Chief Executive Officer
Web address: www.baptistrehab.com

BAPTIST MEMORIAL RESTORATIVE CARE HOSPITAL (O, 30 beds) 6019 Walnut Grove Road, Memphis, TN Zip 38120–2113; tel. 901/226–4200; Janice Hill, R.N., Administrator
Web address: www.baptistonline.org/restorative–care/

Owned, leased, sponsored:	14 hospitals	2100 beds
Contract–managed:	0 hospitals	0 beds
Totals:	14 hospitals	2100 beds

★**0528:** **BASSETT HEALTHCARE NETWORK** (NP)
1 Atwell Road, Cooperstown, NY Zip 13326–1301; tel. 607/547–3456; Vance Brown, M.D., President and Chief Executive Officer
(Independent Hospital System)

NEW YORK: AURELIA OSBORN FOX MEMORIAL HOSPITAL (O, 191 beds) 1 Norton Avenue, Oneonta, NY Zip 13820–2629; tel. 607/432–2000; Jeff Joyner, President
Web address: www.bassett.org/ao–fox–hospital/

BASSETT MEDICAL CENTER (O, 164 beds) One Atwell Road, Cooperstown, NY Zip 13326–1394; tel. 607/547–3100; Vance Brown, M.D., President and Chief Executive Officer
Web address: www.bassett.org

COBLESKILL REGIONAL HOSPITAL (O, 40 beds) 178 Grandview Drive, Cobleskill, NY Zip 12043–5144; tel. 518/254–3456; Eric H. Stein, FACHE, President and Chief Executive Officer
Web address: www.cobleskillhospital.org

LITTLE FALLS HOSPITAL (O, 25 beds) 140 Burwell Street, Little Falls, NY Zip 13365–1725; tel. 315/823–1000; Michael L. Ogden, President and Chief Executive Officer
Web address: www.bassett.org

O'CONNOR HOSPITAL (O, 16 beds) 460 Andes Road, State Route 28, Delhi, NY Zip 13753–7407; tel. 607/746–0300; Carlton Rule, M.D., Chief Executive Officer
Web address: www.bassett.org

Owned, leased, sponsored:	5 hospitals	436 beds
Contract–managed:	0 hospitals	0 beds
Totals:	5 hospitals	436 beds

★**0918:** **BAYLOR SCOTT & WHITE HEALTH** (NP)
4005 Crutcher Street, Suite 310, Dallas, TX Zip 75246–1779; tel. 214/820–0111; Joel T. Allison, Chief Executive Officer
(Centralized Physician/Insurance Health System)

TEXAS: BAYLOR ALL SAINTS MEDICAL CENTER AT FORT WORTH (O, 373 beds) 1400 Eighth Avenue, Fort Worth, TX Zip 76104–4192; tel. 817/926–2544; Janice Whitmire, Interim President
Web address: www.baylorhealth.com/PhysiciansLocations/AllSaints/Pages/Default.aspx

BAYLOR INSTITUTE FOR REHABILITATION (O, 89 beds) 909 North Washington Avenue, Dallas, TX Zip 75246–1520; tel. 214/820–9300; Fabian Polo, Chief Executive Officer
Web address: www.baylorhealth.com/PhysiciansLocations/BIR/Pages/Default.aspx

BAYLOR MEDICAL CENTER AT GARLAND (O, 112 beds) 2300 Marie Curie Drive, Garland, TX Zip 75042–5706; tel. 972/487–5000; Thomas J. Trenary, President
Web address: www.baylorhealth.com/PhysiciansLocations/Garland/Pages/Default.aspx

BAYLOR MEDICAL CENTER AT IRVING (L, 220 beds) 1901 North MacArthur Boulevard, Irving, TX Zip 75061–2220; tel. 972/579–8100; Cindy K. Schamp, President
Web address: www.baylorhealth.com/PhysiciansLocations/Irving/Pages/Default.aspx

BAYLOR MEDICAL CENTER AT MCKINNEY (O, 102 beds) 5252 West University Drive, McKinney, TX Zip 75071–7822; tel. 469/764–1000; Scott Peek, FACHE, President
Web address: www.baylorhealth.com/PhysiciansLocations/McKinney/Pages/Default.aspx

BAYLOR REGIONAL MEDICAL CENTER AT GRAPEVINE (O, 244 beds) 1650 West College Street, Grapevine, TX Zip 76051–3565; tel. 817/481–1588; Steven R. Newton, President
Web address: www.https://www.baylorhealth.com/PhysiciansLocations/Grapevine/Pages/Default.aspx

BAYLOR REGIONAL MEDICAL CENTER AT PLANO (O, 112 beds) 4700 Alliance Boulevard, Plano, TX Zip 75093–5323; tel. 469/814–2000; Jerri Garison, R.N., President
Web address: www.baylorhealth.com/PhysiciansLocations/Plano/Pages/Default.aspx

BAYLOR SCOTT & WHITE MEDICAL CENTER – CARROLLTON (O, 124 beds) 4343 North Josey Lane, Carrollton, TX Zip 75010–4691; tel. 972/394–1010; Michael Sanborn, FACHE, MS, President
Web address: www.baylorhealth.com

BAYLOR SCOTT & WHITE MEDICAL CENTER – HILLCREST (C, 275 beds) 100 Hillcrest Medical Boulevard, Waco, TX Zip 76712–8897; tel. 254/202–2000; Glenn A. Robinson, President
Web address: www.sw.org/hillcrest–medical–center

BAYLOR SCOTT & WHITE MEDICAL CENTER AT WAXAHACHIE (O, 86 beds) 2400 North I–35E, Waxahachie, TX Zip 75165; tel. 469/843–4000; Christopher York, FACHE, President
Web address: www.baylorhealth.com/PhysiciansLocations/Waxahachie/Pages/Default.aspx

For explanation of codes following names, see page B2.
★ Indicates Type III membership in the American Hospital Association.

Section B

BAYLOR UNIVERSITY MEDICAL CENTER (O, 893 beds) 3500 Gaston Avenue, Dallas, TX Zip 75246–2088; tel. 214/820–0111; John B. McWhorter, III, President
Web address: www.baylorhealth.
com/PhysiciansLocations/Dallas/Pages/Default.aspx

SCOTT & WHITE HOSPITAL – BRENHAM (O, 53 beds) 700 Medical Parkway, Brenham, TX Zip 77833–5498; tel. 979/337–5000; John R. Hughson, Vice President Operations
Web address: www.swbrenham.org

SCOTT & WHITE HOSPITAL – COLLEGE STATION (O, 119 beds) 700 Scott & White Drive, College Station, TX Zip 77845; tel. 979/207–0100; Jason Jennings, Chief Executive Officer
Web address: www.sw.org/location/college–station–hospital

SCOTT & WHITE HOSPITAL – LLANO (O, 13 beds) 200 West Ollie Street, Llano, TX Zip 78643–2628; tel. 325/247–5040; Eric N. Looper, Chief Executive Officer, Hill County Region
Web address: www.sw.org/location/llano–hospital

SCOTT & WHITE HOSPITAL – MARBLE FALLS (O, 84 beds) 800 West Highway 71, Marble Falls, TX Zip 78654; tel. 830/598–1204; Eric N. Looper, Chief Executive Officer
Web address: www.sw.org/location/marble–falls–hospital

SCOTT & WHITE HOSPITAL – TAYLOR (O, 25 beds) 305 Mallard Lane, Taylor, TX Zip 76574–1208; tel. 512/352–7611; Tim Tarbell, Director Operations
Web address: www.swtaylor.org

SCOTT & WHITE HOSPITAL AT ROUND ROCK (O, 101 beds) 300 University Boulevard, Round Rock, TX Zip 78665–1032; tel. 512/509–0100; Jay Fox, Chief Executive Officer
Web address: www.sw.org

SCOTT & WHITE MEMORIAL HOSPITAL (O, 648 beds) 2401 South 31st Street, Temple, TX Zip 76508–0002; tel. 254/724–2111; Shahin Motakef, FACHE, Chief Executive Officer
Web address: www.sw.org/location/temple–hospital

SCOTT AND WHITE CONTINUING CARE HOSPITAL (O, 50 beds) 546 North Kegley Road, Temple, TX Zip 76502–4069; tel. 254/215–0900; Kimberly K. Langston, R.N., Chief Executive Officer
Web address: www.sw.org/location/temple–cch

Owned, leased, sponsored:	18 hospitals	3448 beds
Contract–managed:	1 hospital	275 beds
Totals:	19 hospitals	3723 beds

★1095: BAYSTATE HEALTH, INC. (NP)
759 Chestnut Street, Springfield, MA Zip 01199–0001; tel. 413/794–0000; Mark A. Keroack, M.D., M.P.H., President and Chief Executive Officer
(Centralized Physician/Insurance Health System)

MASSACHUSETTS: BAYSTATE FRANKLIN MEDICAL CENTER (O, 89 beds) 164 High Street, Greenfield, MA Zip 01301–2613; tel. 413/773–0211; Cindy Russo, MS, President and Chief Administrative Officer
Web address: www.baystatehealth.org

BAYSTATE MEDICAL CENTER (O, 710 beds) 759 Chestnut Street, Springfield, MA Zip 01199–0001; tel. 413/794–0000; Mark A. Keroack, M.D., M.P.H., President and Chief Executive Officer
Web address: www.baystatehealth.org/bmc

BAYSTATE NOBLE HOSPITAL (O, 97 beds) 115 West Silver Street, Westfield, MA Zip 01085–3628; tel. 413/568–2811; Ronald Bryant, President
Web address: www.baystatehealth.org/locations/noble–hospital

BAYSTATE WING HOSPITAL (O, 74 beds) 40 Wright Street, Palmer, MA Zip 01069–1138; tel. 413/283–7651; Michael Francis Moran, Interim President and Chief Administrative Officer
Web address: www.baystatewinghospital.org/

Owned, leased, sponsored:	4 hospitals	970 beds
Contract–managed:	0 hospitals	0 beds
Totals:	4 hospitals	970 beds

★0940: BEACON HEALTH SYSTEM (NP)
615 North Michigan Street, South Bend, IN Zip 46601–1033; tel. 574/647–1000; Philip A. Newbold, Chief Executive Officer
(Centralized Physician/Insurance Health System)

INDIANA: ELKHART GENERAL HOSPITAL (O, 265 beds) 600 East Boulevard, Elkhart, IN Zip 46514–2499, Mailing Address: P.O. Box 1329, Zip 46515–1329; tel. 574/294–2621; Carl W. Risk, II, President
Web address: www.egh.org

MEMORIAL HOSPITAL OF SOUTH BEND (O, 445 beds) 615 North Michigan Street, South Bend, IN Zip 46601–1033; tel. 574/647–1000; Philip A. Newbold, Chief Executive Officer, Beacon Health System
Web address: www.qualityoflife.org

LOUISIANA: BEACON BEHAVIORAL HOSPITAL (O, 17 beds) 323 Evergreen Street, Bunkie, LA Zip 71322–1307; tel. 318/346–3143; Gene Amons, R.N., Adminstrator
Web address: www.beaconbh.com

Owned, leased, sponsored:	3 hospitals	727 beds
Contract–managed:	0 hospitals	0 beds
Totals:	3 hospitals	727 beds

★0953: BEAUMONT HEALTH (NP)
2000 Town Center, Suite 1200, Southfield, MI Zip 48075–1145, Mailing Address: 44201 Dequindre Road, Troy, Zip 48085–1117; tel. 248/898–5000; John T. Fox, President and Chief Executive Officer
(Moderately Centralized Health System)

MICHIGAN: BEAUMONT HOSPITAL – FARMINGTON HILLS (O, 330 beds) 28050 Grand River Avenue, Farmington Hills, MI Zip 48336–5933; tel. 248/471–8000; Constance O'Malley, President
Web address: www.beaumont.org

BEAUMONT HOSPITAL – GROSSE POINTE (O, 250 beds) 468 Cadieux Road, Grosse Pointe, MI Zip 48230–1507; tel. 313/473–1000; Richard P. Swaine, President
Web address: www.beaumont.org

BEAUMONT HOSPITAL – ROYAL OAK (O, 1070 beds) 3601 West Thirteen Mile Road, Royal Oak, MI Zip 48073–6712; tel. 248/898–5000; Rosanna Morris, Hospital President
Web address: www.beaumont.org

BEAUMONT HOSPITAL – TAYLOR (O, 189 beds) 10000 Telegraph Road, Taylor, MI Zip 48180–3330; tel. 313/295–5000; Lee Ann Odom, Division President
Web address: www.beaumont.org

BEAUMONT HOSPITAL – TRENTON (O, 193 beds) 5450 Fort Street, Trenton, MI Zip 48183–4625; tel. 734/671–3800; Chris Stesney–Ridenour, President
Web address: www.beaumont.org

BEAUMONT HOSPITAL – TROY (O, 458 beds) 44201 Dequindre Road, Troy, MI Zip 48085–1117; tel. 248/964–5000; Nancy Susick, MSN, President
Web address: www.beaumont.org

BEAUMONT HOSPITAL – WAYNE (O, 215 beds) 33155 Annapolis Street, Wayne, MI Zip 48184–2405; tel. 734/467–4000; Eric W. Widner, Division President
Web address: www.beaumont.org

BEAUMONT HOSPITAL–DEARBORN (O, 632 beds) 18101 Oakwood Boulevard, Dearborn, MI Zip 48124–4089, Mailing Address: P.O. Box 2500, Zip 48123–2500; tel. 313/593–7000; Kelly C. Smith, Senior Vice President and Division President
Web address: www.beaumont.org

Owned, leased, sponsored:	8 hospitals	3337 beds
Contract–managed:	0 hospitals	0 beds
Totals:	8 hospitals	3337 beds

0538: BENEFIS HEALTH SYSTEM (NP)
1101 26th Street South, Great Falls, MT Zip 59405–5161; tel. 406/455–5000; John H. Goodnow, Chief Executive Officer
(Moderately Centralized Health System)

MONTANA: BENEFIS HEALTH SYSTEM (O, 507 beds) 1101 26th Street South, Great Falls, MT Zip 59405–5104; tel. 406/455–5000; John H. Goodnow, Chief Executive Officer
Web address: www.benefis.org

For explanation of codes following names, see page B2.
★ Indicates Type III membership in the American Hospital Association.

BENEFIS TETON MEDICAL CENTER (O, 46 beds) 915 4th Street North West, Choteau, MT Zip 59422–9123; tel. 406/466–5763; Louie King, Chief Executive Officer
Web address: www.tetonmedicalcenter.net

MISSOURI RIVER MEDICAL CENTER (C, 52 beds) 1501 St. Charles Street, Fort Benton, MT Zip 59442–0249, Mailing Address: P.O. Box 249, Zip 59442–0249; tel. 406/622–3331; Louie King, President, Harry Bold Nursing Home Administrator
Web address: www.mrmcfb.org

Owned, leased, sponsored:	2 hospitals	553 beds
Contract–managed:	1 hospital	52 beds
Totals:	3 hospitals	605 beds

★2435: BERKSHIRE HEALTH SYSTEMS, INC. (NP)
725 North Street, Pittsfield, MA Zip 01201–4124; tel. 413/447–2750; David E. Phelps, President and Chief Executive Officer
(Moderately Centralized Health System)

MASSACHUSETTS: BERKSHIRE MEDICAL CENTER (O, 274 beds) 725 North ST, Pittsfield, MA Zip 01201–4124, Mailing Address: 725 North Street, Zip 01201–4124; tel. 413/447–2000; David E. Phelps, President and Chief Executive Officer
Web address: www.berkshirehealthsystems.org

FAIRVIEW HOSPITAL (O, 24 beds) 29 Lewis Avenue, Great Barrington, MA Zip 01230–1713; tel. 413/528–0790; Eugene A. Dellea, President
Web address: www.bhs1.org/body_fh.cfm?id=39

Owned, leased, sponsored:	2 hospitals	298 beds
Contract–managed:	0 hospitals	0 beds
Totals:	2 hospitals	298 beds

★0051: BJC HEALTHCARE (NP)
4901 Forest Park Avenue, Suite 1200, Saint Louis, MO Zip 63108–1402; tel. 314/747–9322; Steven H. Lipstein, President and Chief Executive Officer
(Centralized Health System)

ILLINOIS: ALTON MEMORIAL HOSPITAL (O, 230 beds) One Memorial Drive, Alton, IL Zip 62002–6722; tel. 618/463–7311; David A. Braasch, President
Web address: www.altonmemorialhospital.org

MEMORIAL HOSPITAL (O, 398 beds) 4500 Memorial Drive, Belleville, IL Zip 62226–5399; tel. 618/233–7750; Mark J. Turner, President and Chief Executive Officer
Web address: www.memhosp.com

MISSOURI: BARNES–JEWISH HOSPITAL (O, 1390 beds) 1 Barnes–Jewish Hospital Plaza, Saint Louis, MO Zip 63110–1003; tel. 314/747–3000; Robert W. Cannon, President
Web address: www.barnesjewish.org

BARNES–JEWISH ST. PETERS HOSPITAL (O, 101 beds) 10 Hospital Drive, Saint Peters, MO Zip 63376–1659; tel. 636/916–9000; Lee F. Fetter, Interim President
Web address: www.bjsph.org/

BARNES–JEWISH WEST COUNTY HOSPITAL (O, 77 beds) 12634 Olive Boulevard, Saint Louis, MO Zip 63141–6337; tel. 314/996–8000; Trisha Lollo, President
Web address: www.barnesjewishwestcounty.org

BOONE HOSPITAL CENTER (L, 311 beds) 1600 East Broadway, Columbia, MO Zip 65201–5844; tel. 573/815–8000; James J. Sinek, FACHE, President
Web address: www.boone.org

CHRISTIAN HOSPITAL (O, 220 beds) 11133 Dunn Road, Saint Louis, MO Zip 63136–6119; tel. 314/653–5000; Rick Stevens, President
Web address: www.christianhospital.org

MISSOURI BAPTIST MEDICAL CENTER (O, 448 beds) 3015 North Ballas Road, Saint Louis, MO Zip 63131–2329; tel. 314/996–5000; John Antes, President
Web address: www.missouribaptist.org

MISSOURI BAPTIST SULLIVAN HOSPITAL (O, 35 beds) 751 Sappington Bridge Road, Sullivan, MO Zip 63080–2354; tel. 573/468–4186; Tony Schwarm, President
Web address: www.missouribaptistsullivan.org

PARKLAND HEALTH CENTER – LIBERTY STREET (O, 103 beds) 1101 West Liberty Street, Farmington, MO Zip 63640–1921; tel. 573/756–6451; Thomas P. Karl, President
Web address: www.parklandhealthcenter.org

PARKLAND HEALTH CENTER–BONNE TERRE (O, 3 beds) 7245 Raider Road, Bonne Terre, MO Zip 63628–3767; tel. 573/358–1400; Christinia Jepsen, R.N., Administrator
Web address: www.parklandhealthcenter.org

PROGRESS WEST HOSPITAL (O, 44 beds) Two Progress Point Parkway, O'Fallon, MO Zip 63368–2208; tel. 636/344–1000; Lee F. Fetter, Interim President
Web address: www.progresswest.org

ST. LOUIS CHILDREN'S HOSPITAL (O, 280 beds) One Children's Place, Saint Louis, MO Zip 63110–1002; tel. 314/454–6000; Joan Magruder, President
Web address: www.stlouischildrens.org

Owned, leased, sponsored:	13 hospitals	3640 beds
Contract–managed:	0 hospitals	0 beds
Totals:	13 hospitals	3640 beds

★0852: BLANCHARD VALLEY HEALTH SYSTEM (NP)
1900 South Main Street, Findlay, OH Zip 45840–1214; tel. 419/423–4500; Scott C. Malaney, President and Chief Executive Officer
(Centralized Physician/Insurance Health System)

OHIO: BLANCHARD VALLEY HOSPITAL (O, 159 beds) 1900 South Main Street, Findlay, OH Zip 45840–1214; tel. 419/423–4500; Scott C. Malaney, President and Chief Executive Officer
Web address: www.bvhealthsystem.org

BLUFFTON HOSPITAL (O, 25 beds) 139 Garau Street, Bluffton, OH Zip 45817–1027; tel. 419/358–9010; Christine Keller, Chief Administrative Officer
Web address: www.bvhealthsystem.org/

Owned, leased, sponsored:	2 hospitals	184 beds
Contract–managed:	0 hospitals	0 beds
Totals:	2 hospitals	184 beds

★0300: BLUE MOUNTAIN HEALTH SYSTEM (NP)
211 North 12th Street, Lehighton, PA Zip 18235–1138; tel. 610/377–1300; Andrew E. Harris, President and Chief Executive Officer
(Independent Hospital System)

PENNSYLVANIA: BLUE MOUNTAIN HOSPITAL (O, 183 beds) 211 North 12th Street, Lehighton, PA Zip 18235–1138; tel. 610/377–1300; Andrew E. Harris, Chief Executive Officer
Web address: www.blmtn.org

PALMERTON HOSPITAL (O, 67 beds) 135 Lafayette Avenue, Palmerton, PA Zip 18071–1596; tel. 610/826–3141; Andrew E. Harris, Chief Executive Officer
Web address: www.ghmh.org/content/palmertoncampus.htm

Owned, leased, sponsored:	2 hospitals	250 beds
Contract–managed:	0 hospitals	0 beds
Totals:	2 hospitals	250 beds

★5085: BON SECOURS HEALTH SYSTEM, INC. (CC)
1505 Marriottsville Road, Marriottsville, MD Zip 21104–1399; tel. 410/442–5511; Richard Statuto, President and Chief Executive Officer
(Moderately Centralized Health System)

KENTUCKY: OUR LADY OF BELLEFONTE HOSPITAL (O, 147 beds) St. Christopher Drive, Ashland, KY Zip 41101, Mailing Address: P.O. Box 789, Zip 41105–0789; tel. 606/833–3333; Kevin Halter, Chief Executive Officer
Web address: www.olbh.com

Section B

For explanation of codes following names, see page B2.
★ Indicates Type III membership in the American Hospital Association.

MARYLAND: BON SECOURS BALTIMORE HEALTH SYSTEM (O, 93 beds) 2000 West Baltimore Street, Baltimore, MD Zip 21223–1558; tel. 410/362–3000; Samuel Lee Ross, M.D., MS, Chief Executive Officer
Web address: www.bonsecoursbaltimore.com

SOUTH CAROLINA: BON SECOURS ST. FRANCIS HEALTH SYSTEM (O, 394 beds) One St. Francis Drive, Greenville, SC Zip 29601–3207; tel. 864/255–1000; Craig McCoy, Chief Executive Officer
Web address: www.stfrancishealth.org

VIRGINIA: BON SECOURS MARYVIEW MEDICAL CENTER (O, 466 beds) 3636 High Street, Portsmouth, VA Zip 23707–3270; tel. 757/398–2200; Joseph M. Oddis, Chief Executive Officer
Web address: www.bonsecourshamptonroads.com

BON SECOURS MEMORIAL REGIONAL MEDICAL CENTER (O, 225 beds) 8260 Atlee Road, Mechanicsville, VA Zip 23116–1844; tel. 804/764–6000; Mark M. Gordon, Chief Executive Officer
Web address: www.bonsecours.com

BON SECOURS ST. FRANCIS MEDICAL CENTER (O, 124 beds) 13710 St. Francis Boulevard, Midlothian, VA Zip 23114–3267; tel. 804/594–7300; Chris Accashian, Chief Executive Officer
Web address: www.bonsecours.com/sfmc/default.asp

BON SECOURS ST. MARY'S HOSPITAL (O, 391 beds) 5801 Bremo Road, Richmond, VA Zip 23226–1907; tel. 804/285–2011; Francine Barr, R.N., MS, Chief Executive Officer
Web address: www.bonsecours.com

BON SECOURS–DEPAUL MEDICAL CENTER (O, 204 beds) 150 Kingsley Lane, Norfolk, VA Zip 23505–4650; tel. 757/889–5000; John E. Barrett, III, Chief Executive Officer
Web address: www.bonsecourshamptonroads.com

BON SECOURS–RICHMOND COMMUNITY HOSPITAL (O, 85 beds) 1500 North 28th Street, Richmond, VA Zip 23223–5396, Mailing Address: P.O. Box 27184, Zip 23261–7184; tel. 804/225–1700; Mark M. Gordon, Chief Executive Officer
Web address: www.bonsecours.com

MARY IMMACULATE HOSPITAL (O, 238 beds) 2 Bernardine Drive, Newport News, VA Zip 23602–4499; tel. 757/886–6000; Darlene Stephenson, Chief Executive Officer
Web address: www.bonsecourshamptonroads.com

RAPPAHANNOCK GENERAL HOSPITAL (O, 76 beds) 101 Harris Drive, Kilmarnock, VA Zip 22482–3880, Mailing Address: P.O. Box 1449, Zip 22482–1449; tel. 804/435–8000; Mark M. Gordon, Chief Executive Officer
Web address: www.rgh–hospital.com

Owned, leased, sponsored:	11 hospitals	2443 beds
Contract–managed:	0 hospitals	0 beds
Totals:	11 hospitals	2443 beds

● 1000: BOZEMAN HEALTH (IO)
915 Highland Boulevard, Bozeman, MT Zip 59715–6902; tel. 406/585–5000; John Hill, President and Chief Executive Officer

MONTANA: BOZEMAN HEALTH DEACONESS HOSPITAL (O, 86 beds) 915 Highland Boulevard, Bozeman, MT Zip 59715–6902; tel. 406/585–5000; John Hill, President and Chief Executive Officer
Web address: www.bozemandeaconess.org

Owned, leased, sponsored:	1 hospital	86 beds
Contract–managed:	0 hospitals	0 beds
Totals:	1 hospital	86 beds

2455: BRADFORD HEALTH SERVICES (IO)
2101 Magnolia Avenue South, Suite 518, Birmingham, AL Zip 35205–2853; tel. 205/251–7753; Jerry W. Crowder, President and Chief Executive Officer

ALABAMA: BRADFORD HEALTH SERVICES AT HUNTSVILLE (O, 84 beds) 1600 Browns Ferry Road, Madison, AL Zip 35758–9601, Mailing Address: P.O. Box 1488, Zip 35758–0176; tel. 256/461–7272; Bob Hinds, Executive Director
Web address: www.bradfordhealth.com

BRADFORD HEALTH SERVICES AT WARRIOR LODGE (O, 100 beds) 1189 Allbritt Road, Warrior, AL Zip 35180, Mailing Address: P.O. Box 129, Zip 35180–0129; tel. 205/647–1945; Roy M. Ramsey, Executive Director
Web address: www.bradfordhealth.com

Owned, leased, sponsored:	2 hospitals	184 beds
Contract–managed:	0 hospitals	0 beds
Totals:	2 hospitals	184 beds

0352: BRIDGEPOINT HEALTHCARE (IO)
155 Fleet Street, Portsmouth, NH Zip 03801–4050; tel. 603/570–4888; Marc C. Ferrell, President and Chief Executive Officer
(Independent Hospital System)

DISTRICT OF COLUMBIA: BRIDGEPOINT HOSPITAL CAPITOL HILL (O, 177 beds) 700 Constitution Avenue N.E., Washington, DC Zip 20002–6058; tel. 202/546–5700; James Linhares, Chief Executive Officer
Web address: www.bridgepointhealthcare.com/

BRIDGEPOINT HOSPITAL NATIONAL HARBOR (O, 82 beds) 4601 Martin Luther King Jr. Avenue, S.W., Washington, DC Zip 20032–1131; tel. 202/574–5700; Kevin Chavez, Chief Executive Officer
Web address: www.bridgepointhealthcare.com/

Owned, leased, sponsored:	2 hospitals	259 beds
Contract–managed:	0 hospitals	0 beds
Totals:	2 hospitals	259 beds

★0595: BRONSON HEALTHCARE GROUP (NP)
301 John Street, Kalamazoo, MI Zip 49007–5295; tel. 269/341–6000; Frank J. Sardone, President and Chief Executive Officer
(Centralized Health System)

MICHIGAN: BRONSON BATTLE CREEK (O, 198 beds) 300 North Avenue, Battle Creek, MI Zip 49017–3307; tel. 269/245–8000; Frank J. Sardone, President and Chief Executive Officer
Web address: www.bronsonhealth.com

BRONSON LAKEVIEW HOSPITAL (O, 35 beds) 408 Hazen Street, Paw Paw, MI Zip 49079–1019, Mailing Address: P.O. Box 209, Zip 49079–0209; tel. 269/657–3141; Kirk Richardson, R.N., Vice President, Chief Operating Officer, and Chief Nursing Officer
Web address: www.bronsonhealth.com/lakeview

BRONSON METHODIST HOSPITAL (O, 410 beds) 601 John Street, Kalamazoo, MI Zip 49007–5346; tel. 269/341–6000; Frank J. Sardone, President and Chief Executive Officer
Web address: www.bronsonhealth.com

Owned, leased, sponsored:	3 hospitals	643 beds
Contract–managed:	0 hospitals	0 beds
Totals:	3 hospitals	643 beds

★3115: BROWARD HEALTH (NP)
303 S.E. 17th Street, Fort Lauderdale, FL Zip 33316–2523; tel. 954/355–4400; Pauline Grant, FACHE, Interim President and Chief Executive Officer

FLORIDA: BROWARD HEALTH CORAL SPRINGS (O, 182 beds) 3000 Coral Hills Drive, Coral Springs, FL Zip 33065–4108; tel. 954/344–3000; Drew Grossman, Chief Executive Officer
Web address: www.browardhealth.org

BROWARD HEALTH IMPERIAL POINT (O, 180 beds) 6401 North Federal Highway, Fort Lauderdale, FL Zip 33308–1495; tel. 954/776–8500; Alice Taylor, R.N., MSN, Chief Executive Officer
Web address: www.browardhealth.org

BROWARD HEALTH MEDICAL CENTER (O, 648 beds) 1600 South Andrews Avenue, Fort Lauderdale, FL Zip 33316–2510; tel. 954/355–4400; Mark Sprada, R.N., Interim Chief Executive Officer
Web address: www.browardhealth.org

For explanation of codes following names, see page B2.
★ Indicates Type III membership in the American Hospital Association.
● Single hospital health care system

BROWARD HEALTH NORTH (O, 334 beds) 201 East Sample Road, Deerfield Beach, FL Zip 33064–3502; tel. 954/941–8300; Robert Bugg, Acting Chief Executive Officer
Web address: www.browardhealth.org

Owned, leased, sponsored:	4 hospitals	1344 beds
Contract–managed:	0 hospitals	0 beds
Totals:	4 hospitals	1344 beds

★0400: BRYAN HEALTH (NP)
1600 South 48th Street, Lincoln, NE Zip 68506–1283; tel. 402/481–1111; Kimberly A. Russel, FACHE, President and Chief Executive Officer
(Moderately Centralized Health System)

NEBRASKA: BRYAN MEDICAL CENTER (O, 540 beds) 1600 South 48th Street, Lincoln, NE Zip 68506–1299; tel. 402/489–0200; John T. Woodrich, President and Chief Operating Officer
Web address: www.bryanhealth.com

CRETE AREA MEDICAL CENTER (O, 24 beds) 2910 Betten Drive, Crete, NE Zip 68333–3084, Mailing Address: P.O. Box 220, Zip 68333–0220; tel. 402/826–2102; Rebekah Mussman, Chief Executive Officer
Web address: www.creteareamedicalcenter.com

SAUNDERS MEDICAL CENTER (C, 87 beds) 1760 County Road J., Wahoo, NE Zip 68066–4152; tel. 402/443–4191; Tyler Toline, FACHE, Chief Executive Officer
Web address: www.saundersmedicalcenter.com

Owned, leased, sponsored:	2 hospitals	564 beds
Contract–managed:	1 hospital	87 beds
Totals:	3 hospitals	651 beds

9655: BUREAU OF MEDICINE AND SURGERY, DEPARTMENT OF THE NAVY (FG)
7700 Arlington Boulevard, Suite 5126, Falls Church, VA Zip 22042; tel. 202/762–3701; Bryce H.P. Mendez, Healthcare Policy Analyst
(Moderately Centralized Health System)

CALIFORNIA: NAVAL HOSPITAL CAMP PENDLETON (O, 72 beds) Santa Margarita Road, Building H100, Camp Pendleton, CA Zip 92055–5191, Mailing Address: P.O. Box 555191, Zip 92055–5191; tel. 760/725–1304; Captain Lisa Mulligan, Commanding Officer
Web address: www.cpen.med.navy.mil/

NAVAL HOSPITAL LEMOORE (O, 16 beds) 937 Franklin Avenue, Lemoore, CA Zip 93246–0001; tel. 559/998–4481; Captain Mary A. Mahony, Commanding Officer
Web address: www.med.navy.mil/sites/nhlem/Pages/index.aspx

NAVAL MEDICAL CENTER SAN DIEGO (O, 285 beds) 34800 Bob Wilson Drive, San Diego, CA Zip 92134–5000; tel. 619/532–6400; Captain Joel A. Roos, Commanding Officer
Web address: www.med.navy.mil/sites/nmcsd/Pages/default.aspx

ROBERT E. BUSH NAVAL HOSPITAL (O, 39 beds) 1145 Sturgis Road, Twentynine Palms, CA Zip 92278, Mailing Address: Box 788250, MCAGCC, Zip 92278–8250; tel. 760/830–2190; Captain Jay C. Sourbeer, Commanding Officer
Web address: www.med.navy.mil/sites/nhtp/Pages/default.aspx

FLORIDA: NAVAL HOSPITAL JACKSONVILLE (O, 64 beds) 2080 Child Street, Jacksonville, FL Zip 32214–5000; tel. 904/542–7300; Commander Darryl Green, Director Administration
Web address: www.med.navy. mil/SITES/NAVALHOSPITALJAX/Pages/default.aspx

NAVAL HOSPITAL PENSACOLA (O, 28 beds) 6000 West Highway 98, Pensacola, FL Zip 32512–0003; tel. 850/505–6601; Commander Devin Morrison, Director Administration
Web address: www.med.navy.mil/sites/pcola/Pages/default.aspx

GUAM: U. S. NAVAL HOSPITAL GUAM (O, 55 beds) Agana, GU Zip 96910; FPO, tel. 671/344–9340; Captain Jeannie Comlish, Command Officer
Web address: www.med.navy.mil/sites/usnhguam/Pages/default.aspx

MARYLAND: WALTER REED NATIONAL MILITARY MEDICAL CENTER (O, 240 beds) 8901 Wisconsin Avenue, Bethesda, MD Zip 20889–5600; tel. 301/295–4611; Brigadier General Jeffrey B. Clark, Director
Web address: www.wrnmmc.capmed.mil/SitePages/home.aspx

NORTH CAROLINA: NAVAL HOSPITAL CAMP LEJEUNE (O, 117 beds) 100 Brewster Boulevard, Camp Lejeune, NC Zip 28547–2538, Mailing Address: P.O. Box 10100, Zip 28547–0100; tel. 910/450–4300; Captain Rick Freedman, Commanding Officer
Web address: www.med.navy.mil/sites/nhcl/Pages/default.aspx

SOUTH CAROLINA: NAVAL HOSPITAL BEAUFORT (O, 20 beds) 1 Pinckney Boulevard, Beaufort, SC Zip 29902–6122; tel. 843/228–5301; Lieutenant Commander Willie Brown, Director Administration
Web address: www.med.navy.mil/sites/nhbeaufort/Pages/Welcome_Page.aspx

VIRGINIA: NAVAL MEDICAL CENTER (O, 274 beds) 620 John Paul Jones Circle, Portsmouth, VA Zip 23708–2197; tel. 757/953–1980; Commander Matthew Case, MSC, USN, Director For Administration
Web address: www.nmcphc.med.navy.mil/

WASHINGTON: NAVAL HOSPITAL BREMERTON (O, 23 beds) One Boone Road, Bremerton, WA Zip 98312–1898; tel. 360/475–4000; Commander David Weiss, Commanding Officer
Web address: www.med.navy.mil/sites/nhbrem/Pages/default.aspx

NAVAL HOSPITAL OAK HARBOR (O, 29 beds) 3475 North Saratoga Street, Oak Harbor, WA Zip 98278–8800; tel. 360/257–9500; Commander Frederick Joseph McDonald, Commanding Officer
Web address: www.med.navy.mil/sites/nhoh/Pages/default.aspx

Owned, leased, sponsored:	13 hospitals	1262 beds
Contract–managed:	0 hospitals	0 beds
Totals:	13 hospitals	1262 beds

0113: CANCER TREATMENT CENTERS OF AMERICA (IO)
1336 Basswood Road, Schaumburg, IL Zip 60173–4544; tel. 847/342–7400; Rajesh K. Garg, M.D., JD, President and Chief Executive Officer

ARIZONA: WESTERN REGIONAL MEDICAL CENTER (O, 24 beds) 14200 West Celebrate Life way, Goodyear, AZ Zip 85338–3005; tel. 623/207–3000; Matthew McGuire, President and Chief Executive Officer
Web address: www.cancercenter.com/western–hospital.cfm

GEORGIA: SOUTHEASTERN REGIONAL MEDICAL CENTER (O, 50 beds) 600 Celebrate Life Parkway, Newnan, GA Zip 30265–8000; tel. 770/400–6000; Anne Meisner, MSN, President and Chief Executive Officer
Web address: www.cancercenter.com/southeastern–hospital.cfm

ILLINOIS: MIDWESTERN REGIONAL MEDICAL CENTER (O, 72 beds) 2520 Elisha Avenue, Zion, IL Zip 60099–2587; tel. 847/872–4561; Scott Jones, President and Chief Executive Officer
Web address: www.cancercenter.com

OKLAHOMA: SOUTHWESTERN REGIONAL MEDICAL CENTER (O, 40 beds) 10109 East 79th Street, Tulsa, OK Zip 74133–4564; tel. 918/286–5000; Richard Haldeman, President and Chief Executive Officer
Web address: www.cancercenter.com

PENNSYLVANIA: EASTERN REGIONAL MEDICAL CENTER (O, 74 beds) 1331 East Wyoming Avenue, Philadelphia, PA Zip 19124–3808; tel. 800/615–3055; John McNeil, President and Chief Executive Officer
Web address: www.cancercenter.com

Owned, leased, sponsored:	5 hospitals	260 beds
Contract–managed:	0 hospitals	0 beds
Totals:	5 hospitals	260 beds

★0124: CAPE COD HEALTHCARE, INC. (NP)
27 Park Street, Hyannis, MA Zip 02601–5230; tel. 508/862–5121; Michael K. Lauf, President and Chief Executive Officer
(Centralized Health System)

MASSACHUSETTS: CAPE COD HOSPITAL (O, 259 beds) 27 Park Street, Hyannis, MA Zip 02601–5230; tel. 508/771–1800; Michael K. Lauf, President and Chief Executive Officer
Web address: www.capecodhealth.org

For explanation of codes following names, see page B2.
★ Indicates Type III membership in the American Hospital Association.

Section B

FALMOUTH HOSPITAL (O, 95 beds) 100 Ter Heun Drive, Falmouth, MA Zip 02540–2599; tel. 508/548–5300; Michael K. Lauf, President and Chief Executive Officer
Web address: www.capecodhealth.org

Owned, leased, sponsored:	2 hospitals	354 beds
Contract–managed:	0 hospitals	0 beds
Totals:	2 hospitals	354 beds

0835: CAPE FEAR VALLEY HEALTH SYSTEM (NP)
1638 Owen Drive, Fayetteville, NC Zip 28304–3424, Mailing Address: P.O. Box 2000, Zip 28302–2000; tel. 910/615–4000; Michael Nagowski, President and Chief Executive Officer
(Moderately Centralized Health System)

NORTH CAROLINA: CAPE FEAR VALLEY – BLADEN COUNTY HOSPITAL (O, 25 beds) 501 South Poplar Street, Elizabethtown, NC Zip 28337–9375, Mailing Address: P.O. Box 398, Zip 28337–0398; tel. 910/862–5100; Daniel R. Weatherly, Interim Chief Executive Officer
Web address: www.bchn.org

CAPE FEAR VALLEY MEDICAL CENTER (O, 592 beds) 1638 Owen Drive, Fayetteville, NC Zip 28304–3431, Mailing Address: P.O. Box 2000, Zip 28302–2000; tel. 910/615–4000; Michael Nagowski, Chief Executive Officer
Web address: www.capefearvalley.com

HARNETT HEALTH SYSTEM (C, 96 beds) 800 Tilghman Drive, Dunn, NC Zip 28334–5599, Mailing Address: P.O. Box 1706, Zip 28335–1706; tel. 910/892–1000; Kevin Jackson, Interim Chief Executive Officer
Web address: www.myharnetthealth.org/

HIGHSMITH–RAINEY SPECIALTY HOSPITAL (O, 60 beds) 150 Robeson Street, Fayetteville, NC Zip 28301–5570; tel. 910/615–1000; Kevin Jackson, On Site Administrator
Web address: www.capefearvalley.com

HOKE HOSPITAL (O, 41 beds) 210 Medical Pavilion Drive, Raeford, NC Zip 28376–9111; tel. 910/904–8000; Roxie Wells, President
Web address: www.capefearvalley.com

Owned, leased, sponsored:	4 hospitals	718 beds
Contract–managed:	1 hospital	96 beds
Totals:	5 hospitals	814 beds

★0297: CAPITAL HEALTH (NP)
750 Brunswick Avenue, Trenton, NJ Zip 08638–4143; tel. 609/394–6000; Al Maghazehe, Ph.D., FACHE, President and Chief Executive Officer
(Independent Hospital System)

NEW JERSEY: CAPITAL HEALTH MEDICAL CENTER–HOPEWELL (O, 215 beds) 1 Capital Way, Pennington, NJ Zip 08534–2520; tel. 609/303–4000; Al Maghazehe, Ph.D., FACHE, President and Chief Executive Officer
Web address: www.capitalhealth.org

CAPITAL HEALTH REGIONAL MEDICAL CENTER (O, 204 beds) 750 Brunswick Avenue, Trenton, NJ Zip 08638–4143; tel. 609/394–6000; Al Maghazehe, Ph.D., FACHE, President and Chief Executive Officer
Web address: www.capitalhealth.org

Owned, leased, sponsored:	2 hospitals	419 beds
Contract–managed:	0 hospitals	0 beds
Totals:	2 hospitals	419 beds

★0099: CARE NEW ENGLAND HEALTH SYSTEM (NP)
45 Willard Avenue, Providence, RI Zip 02905–3218; tel. 401/453–7900; Dennis D. Keefe, President and Chief Executive Officer
(Centralized Health System)

RHODE ISLAND: BUTLER HOSPITAL (O, 143 beds) 345 Blackstone Boulevard, Providence, RI Zip 02906–4829; tel. 401/455–6200; Lawrence Price, M.D., President and Chief Operating Officer
Web address: www.butler.org

KENT COUNTY MEMORIAL HOSPITAL (O, 318 beds) 455 Tollgate Road, Warwick, RI Zip 02886–2770; tel. 401/737–7000; Michael J. Dacey, M.D., President and Chief Operating Officer
Web address: www.kentri.org

MEMORIAL HOSPITAL OF RHODE ISLAND (O, 150 beds) 111 Brewster Street, Pawtucket, RI Zip 02860–4499; tel. 401/729–2000; James E. Fanale, M.D., Interim Chief Operating Officer and Chief Medical Officer
Web address: www.mhri.org

WOMEN & INFANTS HOSPITAL OF RHODE ISLAND (O, 247 beds) 101 Dudley Street, Providence, RI Zip 02905–2499; tel. 401/274–1100; Mark R. Marcantano, President and Chief Operating Officer
Web address: www.womenandinfants.org

Owned, leased, sponsored:	4 hospitals	858 beds
Contract–managed:	0 hospitals	0 beds
Totals:	4 hospitals	858 beds

★0931: CAREPOINT HEALTH (IO)
10 Exchange Place, 15th Floor, Jersey City, NJ Zip 07302–3918; tel. 877/791–7000; Jeffrey M. Mandler, Chief Executive Officer

NEW JERSEY: BAYONNE MEDICAL CENTER (O, 205 beds) 29th Street & Avenue E., Bayonne, NJ Zip 07002–4699; tel. 201/858–5000; Jeffrey M. Mandler, Chief Executive Officer
Web address: www.carepointhealth.org

CAREPOINT HEALTH –CHRIST HOSPITAL (O, 376 beds) 176 Palisade Avenue, Jersey City, NJ Zip 07306–1196, Mailing Address: 176 Palisades Avenue, Zip 07306–1196; tel. 201/795–8200; Marie Theresa Duffy, Chief Operating Officer
Web address: www.carepointhealth.org

HOBOKEN UNIVERSITY MEDICAL CENTER (O, 204 beds) 308 Willow Avenue, Hoboken, NJ Zip 07030–3889; tel. 201/418–1000; Ann P. Logan, R.N., Ph.D., Chief Operating Officer
Web address: www.hobokenumc.com

Owned, leased, sponsored:	3 hospitals	785 beds
Contract–managed:	0 hospitals	0 beds
Totals:	3 hospitals	785 beds

★0070: CARILION CLINIC (NP)
1906 Belleview Avenue S.E., Roanoke, VA Zip 24014–1838, Mailing Address: P.O. Box 13727, Zip 24036–3727; tel. 540/981–7000; Nancy Howell Agee, President and Chief Executive Officer
(Moderately Centralized Health System)

VIRGINIA: CARILION FRANKLIN MEMORIAL HOSPITAL (O, 15 beds) 180 Floyd Avenue, Rocky Mount, VA Zip 24151–1389; tel. 540/483–5277; William D. Jacobsen, Vice President and Administrator
Web address: www.carilionclinic.org/Carilion/Franklin+Memorial+Hospital

CARILION GILES COMMUNITY HOSPITAL (O, 17 beds) 159 Hartley Way, Pearisburg, VA Zip 24134–2471; tel. 540/921–6000; William Flattery, Vice President and Administrator Western Division
Web address: www.carilionclinic.org/Carilion/cgch

CARILION NEW RIVER VALLEY MEDICAL CENTER (O, 82 beds) 2900 Lamb Circle, Christiansburg, VA Zip 24073–6344, Mailing Address: P.O. Box 5, Radford, Zip 24143–0005; tel. 540/731–2000; William Flattery, Vice President and Administrator Western Division
Web address: www.carilionclinic.org/Carilion/cnrv

CARILION ROANOKE MEMORIAL HOSPITAL (O, 655 beds) Belleview at Jefferson Street, Roanoke, VA Zip 24014, Mailing Address: P.O. Box 13367, Zip 24033–3367; tel. 540/981–7000; Steven C. Arner, President
Web address: www.carilionclinic.org

CARILION STONEWALL JACKSON HOSPITAL (O, 15 beds) 1 Health Circle, Lexington, VA Zip 24450–2492; tel. 540/458–3300; Charles E. Carr, Vice President and Administrator
Web address: www.carilionclinic.org/Carilion/csjh

CARILION TAZEWELL COMMUNITY HOSPITAL (O, 8 beds) 141 Ben Bolt Avenue, Tazewell, VA Zip 24651–9700; tel. 276/988–8700; Kathren Dowdy, MSN, Regional Hospital Senior Director
Web address: www.carilionclinic.org/Carilion/Carilion+Tazewell+Community+Hospital

---

For explanation of codes following names, see page B2.
★ Indicates Type III membership in the American Hospital Association.

Owned, leased, sponsored:	6 hospitals	792 beds
Contract–managed:	0 hospitals	0 beds
Totals:	6 hospitals	792 beds

★2575: **CARLE FOUNDATION** (NP)
611 West Park Street, Urbana, IL Zip 61801–2595;
tel. 217/383–3311; James C. Leonard, M.D., President and Chief
Executive Officer
(Moderately Centralized Health System)

ILLINOIS: CARLE FOUNDATION HOSPITAL (O, 376 beds) 611 West Park
Street, Urbana, IL Zip 61801–2595; tel. 217/383–3311; James C.
Leonard, M.D., President and Chief Executive Officer
Web address: www.carle.org

CARLE HOOPESTON REGIONAL HEALTH CENTER (O, 99 beds) 701 East
Orange Street, Hoopeston, IL Zip 60942–1801; tel. 217/283–5531; Harry
Brockus, Chief Executive Officer
Web address: www.carle.org

Owned, leased, sponsored:	2 hospitals	475 beds
Contract–managed:	0 hospitals	0 beds
Totals:	2 hospitals	475 beds

★0705: **CAROLINAS HEALTHCARE SYSTEM** (NP)
1000 Blythe Boulevard, Charlotte, NC Zip 28203–5871, Mailing
Address: P.O. Box 32861, Zip 28232–2861; tel. 704/355–2000;
Eugene A. Woods, FACHE, President and Chief Executive Officer
(Moderately Centralized Health System)

NORTH CAROLINA: CAROLINAS HEALTHCARE SYSTEM ANSON (O, 15 beds)
2301 U.S Highway 74 West, Wadesboro, NC Zip 28170;
tel. 704/994–4500; Michael Lutes, President
Web address: www.carolinashealthcare.org/anson

CAROLINAS HEALTHCARE SYSTEM BLUE RIDGE (C, 154 beds) 2201 South
Sterling Street, Morganton, NC Zip 28655–4058; tel. 828/580–5000; Kathy
C. Bailey, Ph.D., FACHE, President and Chief Executive Officer
Web address: www.blueridgehealth.org

CAROLINAS HEALTHCARE SYSTEM LINCOLN (O, 101 beds) 433 McAlister
Road, Lincolnton, NC Zip 28092–4147, Mailing Address: PO Box 677,
Zip 28093–0677; tel. 980/212–2000; Peter W. Acker, President and Chief
Executive Officer
Web address: www.carolinashealthcare.org/lincoln

CAROLINAS HEALTHCARE SYSTEM NORTHEAST (O, 455 beds) 920 Church
Street North, Concord, NC Zip 28025–2983; tel. 704/403–3000; Phyllis A.
Wingate, FACHE, President
Web address: www.carolinashealthcare.org/northeast

CAROLINAS HEALTHCARE SYSTEM PINEVILLE (O, 229 beds) 10628 Park
Road, Charlotte, NC Zip 28210–8407; tel. 704/543–2000; Christopher R.
Hummer, President
Web address: www.carolinashealthcare.org/pineville

CAROLINAS HEALTHCARE SYSTEM UNION (L, 224 beds) 600 Hospital Drive,
Monroe, NC Zip 28112–6000, Mailing Address: P.O. Box 5003,
Zip 28111–5003; tel. 980/993–3100; Michael Lutes, President
Web address: www.carolinashealthcare.org/union

CAROLINAS MEDICAL CENTER (O, 1132 beds) 1000 Blythe Boulevard,
Charlotte, NC Zip 28203–5871, Mailing Address: P.O. Box 32861,
Zip 28232–2861; tel. 704/355–2000; Spencer Lilly, President
Web address: www.carolinashealthcare.org/cmc

CAROLINAS MEDICAL CENTER–UNIVERSITY (O, 100 beds) 8800 North Tryon
Street, Charlotte, NC Zip 28262–3300, Mailing Address: P.O. Box 560727,
Zip 28256–0727; tel. 704/863–6000; William H. Leonard, President
Web address: www.carolinashealthcare.org/university

CAROLINAS REHABILITATION (O, 157 beds) 1100 Blythe Boulevard, Charlotte,
NC Zip 28203–5864; tel. 704/355–4300; Robert G. Larrison, Jr., President
Web address: www.carolinashealthcare.org/rehabilitation

CLEVELAND REGIONAL MEDICAL CENTER (L, 173 beds) 201 East Grover
Street, Shelby, NC Zip 28150–3917; tel. 980/487–3000; Brian Gwyn,
President and Chief Executive Officer
Web address: www.clevelandregional.org

COLUMBUS REGIONAL HEALTHCARE SYSTEM (C, 85 beds) 500 Jefferson
Street, Whiteville, NC Zip 28472–3634; tel. 910/642–8011; Carla Hollis,
President and Chief Executive Officer
Web address: www.crhealthcare.org/

KINGS MOUNTAIN HOSPITAL (O, 59 beds) 706 West King Street, Kings
Mountain, NC Zip 28086–2708; tel. 980/487–5000; Brian Gwyn, President
and Chief Executive Officer
Web address: www.clevelandregional.org/kings–mountain–hospital.html

MOSES H. CONE MEMORIAL HOSPITAL (C, 954 beds) 1200 North Elm
Street, Greensboro, NC Zip 27401–1020; tel. 336/832–7000; Mickey
Foster, President
Web address: www.conehealth.com/locations/moses–cone–hospital/

MURPHY MEDICAL CENTER (C, 191 beds) 3990 U.S. Highway 64 East Alt,
Murphy, NC Zip 28906–7917; tel. 828/837–8161; Michael Stevenson, Chief
Executive Officer
Web address: www.murphymedical.org

SCOTLAND HEALTH CARE SYSTEM (C, 104 beds) 500 Lauchwood Drive,
Laurinburg, NC Zip 28352–5599; tel. 910/291–7000; Gregory C. Wood,
President and Chief Executive Officer
Web address: www.scotlandhealth.org

ST. LUKE'S HOSPITAL (C, 35 beds) 101 Hospital Drive, Columbus, NC
Zip 28722–6418; tel. 828/894–3311; James B. Bross, President
Web address: www.saintlukeshospital.com

STANLY REGIONAL MEDICAL CENTER (C, 94 beds) 301 Yadkin Street,
Albemarle, NC Zip 28001–3441, Mailing Address: P.O. Box 1489,
Zip 28002–1489; tel. 704/984–4000; Alfred P. Taylor, President and Chief
Executive Officer
Web address: www.stanly.org

WILKES REGIONAL MEDICAL CENTER (C, 91 beds) 1370 West D Street,
North Wilkesboro, NC Zip 28659–3506, Mailing Address: P.O. Box 609,
Zip 28659–0609; tel. 336/651–8100; J. Gene Faile, Chief Executive Officer
and President
Web address: www.wilkesregional.com/

SOUTH CAROLINA: BON SECOURS ST. FRANCIS HOSPITAL (C, 172 beds)
2095 Henry Tecklenburg Drive, Charleston, SC Zip 29414–5733;
tel. 843/402–1000; Allen P. Carroll, Senior Vice President and Chief
Executive Officer
Web address: www.rsfh.com/

CANNON MEMORIAL HOSPITAL (C, 35 beds) 123 West G. Acker Drive,
Pickens, SC Zip 29671–2739, Mailing Address: P.O. Box 188,
Zip 29671–0188; tel. 864/878–4791; Norman G. Rentz, President and Chief
Executive Officer
Web address: www.cannonhospital.org

ROPER ST. FRANCIS (C, 298 beds) 316 Calhoun Street, Charleston, SC
Zip 29401–1125; tel. 843/724–2000; Matthew J. Severance, FACHE, Chief
Executive Officer
Web address: www.rsfh.com/

ROPER ST. FRANCIS MOUNT PLEASANT HOSPITAL (C, 50 beds) 3500
Highway 17 North, Mount Pleasant, SC Zip 29466–9123, Mailing Address:
3500 North Highway 17, Zip 29466–9123; tel. 843/606–7000; Anthony
Jackson, Chief Executive Officer
Web address: www.rsfh.com/mount–pleasant–hospital

Owned, leased, sponsored:	10 hospitals	2645 beds
Contract–managed:	12 hospitals	2263 beds
Totals:	22 hospitals	4908 beds

0656: **CARRUS HOSPITALS** (IO)
1810 West U.S. Highway 82, Sherman, TX Zip 75092–7069;
tel. 903/870–2600; Ronald E. Dorris, Chief Executive Officer
(Independent Hospital System)

TEXAS: CARRUS REHABILITATION HOSPITAL (O, 24 beds) 1810 West U.S.
Highway 82, Suite 100, Sherman, TX Zip 75092–7069;
tel. 903/870–2600; Jon–Michael Rains, Chief Executive Officer
Web address: www.carrushospital.com

For explanation of codes following names, see page B2.
★ Indicates Type III membership in the American Hospital Association.

Section B

CARRUS SPECIALTY HOSPITAL (O, 16 beds) 1810 West U.S. Highway 82, Sherman, TX Zip 75092-7069; tel. 903/870-2600; Jon-Michael Rains, Chief Executive Officer
Web address: www.carrushospital.com

Owned, leased, sponsored:	2 hospitals	40 beds
Contract-managed:	0 hospitals	0 beds
Totals:	2 hospitals	40 beds

★**0092: CATHOLIC HEALTH INITIATIVES** (CC)
198 Inverness Drive West, Suite 800, Englewood, CO Zip 80112-5202; tel. 303/298-9100; Kevin E. Lofton, FACHE, Chief Executive Officer
(Decentralized Health System)

ARKANSAS: CHI ST. VINCENT HOT SPRINGS (O, 262 beds) 300 Werner Street, Hot Springs, AR Zip 71913-6406; tel. 501/622-1000; Anthony Houston, FACHE, President
Web address: www.chistvincent.com/Hospitals/st-vincent-hot-springs

CHI ST. VINCENT INFIRMARY MEDICAL CENTER (S, 447 beds) Two St. Vincent Circle, Little Rock, AR Zip 72205-5499; tel. 501/552-3000; Polly J. Davenport, FACHE, R.N., President
Web address: www.chistvincent.com/

CHI ST. VINCENT MEDICAL CENTER-NORTH (S, 69 beds) 2215 Wildwood Avenue, Sherwood, AR Zip 72120-5089; tel. 501/552-7100; Polly J. Davenport, FACHE, R.N., Senior Vice President, Chief Operating Officer, President CHI St. Vincent Infirmary Medical Center and CHI St. Vincent M
Web address: www.stvincenthealth.com

CHI ST. VINCENT MORRILTON (S, 25 beds) 4 Hospital Drive, Morrilton, AR Zip 72110-4510; tel. 501/977-2300; Leslie Arnold, Chief Executive Officer and Administrator
Web address: www.chistvincent.com/Hospitals/st-vincent-morrilton

COLORADO: LONGMONT UNITED HOSPITAL (S, 146 beds) 1950 West Mountain View Avenue, Longmont, CO Zip 80501-3162, Mailing Address: P.O. Box 1659, Zip 80502-1659; tel. 303/651-5111; Mitchell C. Carson, President and Chief Executive Officer
Web address: www.luhcares.org

MERCY REGIONAL MEDICAL CENTER (S, 82 beds) 1010 Three Springs Boulevard, Durango, CO Zip 81301-8296; tel. 970/247-4311; Thomas Gessel, FACHE, President and Chief Executive Officer
Web address: www.mercydurango.org

ORTHOCOLORADO HOSPITAL (O, 48 beds) 11650 West 2nd Place, Lakewood, CO Zip 80228-1527; tel. 720/321-5000; Jude Torchia, Chief Executive Officer
Web address: www.orthocolorado.org

PENROSE-ST. FRANCIS HEALTH SERVICES (S, 405 beds) 2222 North Nevada Avenue, Colorado Springs, CO Zip 80907-6799; tel. 719/776-5000; Margaret D. Sabin, President and Chief Executive Officer
Web address: www.penrosestfrancis.org

ST. ANTHONY HOSPITAL (S, 224 beds) 11600 West Second Place, Lakewood, CO Zip 80228-1527; tel. 720/321-0000; Patrick Green, Interim Chief Executive Officer
Web address: www.stanthonyhosp.org

ST. ANTHONY NORTH HEALTH CAMPUS (S, 100 beds) 14300 Orchard Parkway, Westminster, CO Zip 80023-9206; tel. 720/627-0000; Carole Peet, R.N., MSN, President and Chief Executive Officer
Web address: www.stanthonynorth.org

ST. ANTHONY SUMMIT MEDICAL CENTER (S, 34 beds) 340 Peak One Drive, Frisco, CO Zip 80443, Mailing Address: P.O. Box 738, Zip 80443-0738; tel. 970/668-3300; Paul J. Chodkowski, Chief Executive Officer
Web address: www.summitmedicalcenter.org

ST. MARY-CORWIN MEDICAL CENTER (S, 125 beds) 1008 Minnequa Avenue, Pueblo, CO Zip 81004-3798; tel. 719/557-4000; Brian Moore, President and Chief Executive Officer
Web address: www.stmarycorwin.org

ST. THOMAS MORE HOSPITAL (S, 25 beds) 1338 Phay Avenue, Canon City, CO Zip 81212-2302; tel. 719/285-2000; Sheri Trahern, CPA, FACHE, Chief Executive Officer
Web address: www.stmhospital.org

INDIANA: SOUTHERN INDIANA REHABILITATION HOSPITAL (O, 60 beds) 3104 Blackiston Boulevard, New Albany, IN Zip 47150-9579; tel. 812/941-8300; Randy L. Napier, President
Web address: www.sirh.org

IOWA: CHI HEALTH MERCY CORNING (S, 22 beds) 603 Rosary Drive, Corning, IA Zip 50841-1683; tel. 641/322-3121; Debra Goldsmith, Chief Executive Officer
Web address: www.alegent.com

CHI HEALTH MERCY COUNCIL BLUFFS (S, 166 beds) 800 Mercy Drive, Council Bluffs, IA Zip 51503-3128, Mailing Address: P.O. Box 1C, Zip 51502-3001; tel. 712/328-5000; Marie E. Knedler, R.N., FACHE, President
Web address: www.chihealth.com/chi-health-mercy-council-bluffs

CHI HEALTH MISSOURI VALLEY (S, 16 beds) 631 North Eighth Street, Missouri Valley, IA Zip 51555-1102; tel. 712/642-2784; Robert A. Valentine, President
Web address: www.chihealth.com/chi-health-missouri-valley

KNOXVILLE HOSPITAL & CLINICS (C, 25 beds) 1002 South Lincoln Street, Knoxville, IA Zip 50138-3155; tel. 641/842-2151; Kevin Kincaid, Chief Executive Officer
Web address: www.knoxvillehospital.org

MADISON COUNTY HEALTH CARE SYSTEM (C, 25 beds) 300 West Hutchings Street, Winterset, IA Zip 50273-2109; tel. 515/462-2373; Marcia Hendricks, R.N., FACHE, Chief Executive Officer
Web address: www.madisonhealth.com

MERCY MEDICAL CENTER - WEST LAKES (O, 74 beds) 1755 59th Place, West Des Moines, IA Zip 50266-7737; tel. 515/358-8000; Robert P. Ritz, President
Web address: www.mercywestlakes.org/

MERCY MEDICAL CENTER-CENTERVILLE (S, 45 beds) 1 St. Joseph's Drive, Centerville, IA Zip 52544-8055; tel. 641/437-4111; Clinton J. Christianson, FACHE, President
Web address: www.mercycenterville.org

MERCY MEDICAL CENTER-DES MOINES (S, 539 beds) 1111 6th Avenue, Des Moines, IA Zip 50314-2611; tel. 515/247-3121; Robert P. Ritz, President
Web address: www.mercydesmoines.org

SKIFF MEDICAL CENTER (O, 48 beds) 204 North Fourth Avenue East, Newton, IA Zip 50208-3100, Mailing Address: P.O. Box 1006, Zip 50208-1006; tel. 641/792-1273; Brett Allen Altman, FACHE, President and Chief Executive Officer
Web address: www.skiffmed.com

KANSAS: BOB WILSON MEMORIAL GRANT COUNTY HOSPITAL (O, 26 beds) 415 North Main Street, Ulysses, KS Zip 67880-2133; tel. 620/356-1266; Deanna Mustin, R.N., Administrator
Web address: www.bwmgch.com

ST. CATHERINE HOSPITAL (S, 110 beds) 401 East Spruce Street, Garden City, KS Zip 67846-5679; tel. 620/272-2561; Scott J. Taylor, President and Chief Executive Officer
Web address: www.StCatherineHosp.org

KENTUCKY: CONTINUING CARE HOSPITAL (S, 43 beds) 150 North Eagle Creek Drive, 5th Floor, Lexington, KY Zip 40509-1805; tel. 859/967-5744; Tonja Williams, R.N., President

FLAGET MEMORIAL HOSPITAL (S, 42 beds) 4305 New Shepherdsville Road, Bardstown, KY Zip 40004-9019; tel. 502/350-5000; Beverly Sue Downs, R.N., MSN, FACHE, President
Web address: www.flaget.com

FRAZIER REHAB INSTITUTE (O, 87 beds) 220 Abraham Flexner Way, Louisville, KY Zip 40202-1887; tel. 502/582-7400; Randy L. Napier, President
Web address: www.frazierrehab.org

JEWISH HOSPITAL (O, 342 beds) 200 Abraham Flexner Way, Louisville, KY Zip 40202-1886; tel. 502/587-4011; Joseph Gilene, President
Web address: www.jewishhospital.org

JEWISH HOSPITAL-SHELBYVILLE (O, 30 beds) 727 Hospital Drive, Shelbyville, KY Zip 40065-1699; tel. 502/647-4000; Tonya Brady, Director of Operations
Web address: www.jhsmh.org

OUR LADY OF PEACE (O, 211 beds) 2020 Newburg Road, Louisville, KY Zip 40205-1879; tel. 502/479-4500; Jennifer Nolan, President
Web address: www.hopehasaplace.org

For explanation of codes following names, see page B2.
★ Indicates Type III membership in the American Hospital Association.

SAINT JOSEPH LONDON (S, 116 beds) 1001 Saint Joseph Lane, London, KY Zip 40741–8345; tel. 606/330–6000; Terrence G. Deis, CPA, FACHE, President
Web address: www.saintjosephhealthsystem.org

SAINT JOSEPH – MARTIN (S, 25 beds) 11203 Main Street, Martin, KY Zip 41649; tel. 606/285–6400; Kathy Stumbo, President
Web address: www.saintjosephmartin.org

SAINT JOSEPH BEREA (S, 25 beds) 305 Estill Street, Berea, KY Zip 40403–1909; tel. 859/986–3151; Eric Gilliam, Chief Executive Officer
Web address: www.kentuckyonehealth.org/berea

SAINT JOSEPH EAST (S, 150 beds) 150 North Eagle Creek Drive, Lexington, KY Zip 40509–1805; tel. 859/967–5000; Eric Gilliam, President
Web address: www.sjhlex.org

SAINT JOSEPH HOSPITAL (S, 307 beds) One St. Joseph Drive, Lexington, KY Zip 40504–3754; tel. 859/278–3436; Bruce J. Tassin, President
Web address: www.sjhlex.org

SAINT JOSEPH MOUNT STERLING (S, 42 beds) 225 Falcon Drive, Mount Sterling, KY Zip 40353–1158, Mailing Address: P.O. Box 7, Zip 40353–0007; tel. 859/497–5000; Benny Nolen, President
Web address: www.sjhlex.org

STS. MARY & ELIZABETH HOSPITAL (O, 174 beds) 1850 Bluegrass Avenue, Louisville, KY Zip 40215–1199; tel. 502/361–6000; Jennifer Nolan, President
Web address: www.jhsmh.org

TAYLOR REGIONAL HOSPITAL (C, 90 beds) 1700 Old Lebanon Road, Campbellsville, KY Zip 42718–9600; tel. 270/465–3561; Jane Wheatley, Chief Executive Officer
Web address: www.trhosp.org

UNIVERSITY OF LOUISVILLE HOSPITAL (C, 301 beds) 530 South Jackson Street, Louisville, KY Zip 40202–3611; tel. 502/562–3000; Charles W. Neumann, President
Web address: www.ulh.org

MINNESOTA: CHI LAKEWOOD HEALTH (S, 55 beds) 600 Main Avenue South, Baudette, MN Zip 56623–2855; tel. 218/634–2120; Benjamin Koppelman, Interim President
Web address: www.lakewoodhealthcenter.org

CHI ST. FRANCIS HEALTH (S, 105 beds) 2400 St. Francis Drive, Breckenridge, MN Zip 56520–1025; tel. 218/643–3000; David A. Nelson, President
Web address: www.sfcare.org

CHI ST. GABRIEL'S HEALTH (S, 25 beds) 815 Second Street S.E., Little Falls, MN Zip 56345–3596; tel. 320/632–5441; Lee Boyles, President
Web address: www.stgabriels.com

CHI ST. JOSEPH'S HEALTH (S, 25 beds) 600 Pleasant Avenue, Park Rapids, MN Zip 56470–1431; tel. 218/732–3311; Benjamin Koppelman, President
Web address: www.sjahs.org

NEBRASKA: CHI HEALTH BERGAN MERCY (S, 336 beds) 7500 Mercy Road, Omaha, NE Zip 68124–2319; tel. 402/398–6060; Marie E. Knedler, R.N., FACHE, President
Web address: www.alegent.com/bergan

CHI HEALTH GOOD SAMARITAN (S, 233 beds) 10 East 31st Street, Kearney, NE Zip 68847–2926, Mailing Address: P.O. Box 1990, Zip 68848–1990; tel. 308/865–7100; Michael H. Schnieders, FACHE, President
Web address: www.gshs.org

CHI HEALTH IMMANUEL (S, 289 beds) 6901 North 72nd Street, Omaha, NE Zip 68122–1799; tel. 402/572–2121; Ann Schumacher, R.N., MSN, FACHE, President
Web address: www.alegent.com/immanuel

CHI HEALTH LAKESIDE (S, 135 beds) 16901 Lakeside Hills Court, Omaha, NE Zip 68130–2318; tel. 402/717–8000; Cindy Alloway, President
Web address: www.CHIhealth.com

CHI HEALTH MIDLANDS (S, 54 beds) 11111 South 84th Street, Papillion, NE Zip 68046–4122; tel. 402/593–3000; Cindy Alloway, President
Web address: www.CHIhealth.com

CHI HEALTH NEBRASKA HEART (S, 52 beds) 7500 South 91st Street, Lincoln, NE Zip 68526–9437; tel. 402/327–2700; Dan Schonlau, Interim President
Web address: www.CHIhealthNebraskaHeart.com

CHI HEALTH PLAINVIEW (S, 15 beds) 704 North Third Street, Plainview, NE Zip 68769–2047, Mailing Address: P.O. Box 489, Zip 68769–0489; tel. 402/582–4245; Gregory Beckmann, Chief Executive Officer
Web address: www.alegentcreighton.com/plainview–hospital

CHI HEALTH SAINT FRANCIS (S, 159 beds) 2620 West Faidley Avenue, Grand Island, NE Zip 68803–4297, Mailing Address: P.O. Box 9804, Zip 68802–9804; tel. 308/384–4600; Daniel P. McElligott, FACHE, President
Web address: www.saintfrancisgi.org

CHI HEALTH SCHUYLER (S, 25 beds) 104 West 17th Street, Schuyler, NE Zip 68661–1304; tel. 402/352–2441; Connie Peters, R.N., President
Web address: www.alegent.org

CHI HEALTH ST ELIZABETH (S, 260 beds) 555 South 70th Street, Lincoln, NE Zip 68510–2494; tel. 402/219–8000; Kim S. Moore, FACHE, President
Web address: www.saintelizabethonline.com

CHI HEALTH ST. MARY'S (S, 18 beds) 1301 Grundman Boulevard, Nebraska City, NE Zip 68410; tel. 402/873–3321; Daniel J. Kelly, President
Web address: www.chihealthstmarys.com

NORTH DAKOTA: CHI LISBON HEALTH (S, 25 beds) 905 Main Street, Lisbon, ND Zip 58054–4334, Mailing Address: P.O. Box 353, Zip 58054–0353; tel. 701/683–6400; Peggy Reinke, R.N., Administrator
Web address: www.lisbonhospital.com

CHI MERCY HEALTH (S, 19 beds) 570 Chautauqua Boulevard, Valley City, ND Zip 58072–3199; tel. 701/845–6400; Keith E. Heuser, President
Web address: www.mercyhospitalvalleycity.org

CHI OAKES HOSPITAL (S, 20 beds) 1200 North Seventh Street, Oakes, ND Zip 58474–2502; tel. 701/742–3291; Becki Thompson, President
Web address: www.oakeshospital.com

CHI ST ALEXIUS HEALTH CARRINGTON MEDICAL CENTER (S, 25 beds) 800 North Fourth Street, Carrington, ND Zip 58421–1217, Mailing Address: P.O. Box 461, Zip 58421–0461; tel. 701/652–3141; Mariann Doeling, R.N., President
Web address: www.carringtonhealthcenter.org

CHI ST. ALEXIUS HEALTH (O, 271 beds) 900 East Broadway, Bismarck, ND Zip 58501–4586, Mailing Address: P.O. Box 5510, Zip 58506–5510; tel. 701/530–7000; Kurt Schley, Market Chief Executive Officer
Web address: www.st.alexius.org

CHI ST. ALEXIUS HEALTH DEVILS LAKE HOSPITAL (S, 25 beds) 1031 Seventh Street N.E., Devils Lake, ND Zip 58301–2798; tel. 701/662–2131; Andrew Lankowicz, FACHE, President
Web address: www.mercyhospitaldl.com

COMMUNITY MEMORIAL HOSPITAL (O, 25 beds) 220 Fifth Avenue, Turtle Lake, ND Zip 58575–4005, Mailing Address: P.O. Box 280, Zip 58575–0280; tel. 701/448–2331; Tod Graeber, Administrator
Web address: www.wrtc.com/cullum/hospital

GARRISON MEMORIAL HOSPITAL (O, 50 beds) 407 Third Avenue S.E., Garrison, ND Zip 58540–7235; tel. 701/463–2275; Tod Graeber, Administrator
Web address: www.garrisonmh.com

MERCY MEDICAL CENTER (S, 25 beds) 1301 15th Avenue West, Williston, ND Zip 58801–3896; tel. 701/774–7400; Matthew Grimshaw, President
Web address: www.mercy–williston.org

ST. JOSEPH'S HOSPITAL AND HEALTH CENTER (S, 25 beds) 2500 Fairway Street, Dickinson, ND Zip 58601–4399; tel. 701/456–4000; Reed Reyman, President
Web address: www.stjoeshospital.org

OHIO: GOOD SAMARITAN HOSPITAL (S, 504 beds) 375 Dixmyth Avenue, Cincinnati, OH Zip 45220–2489; tel. 513/862–1400; Jamie Easterling, Executive Director, Operations
Web address: www.trihealth.com

GOOD SAMARITAN HOSPITAL (S, 346 beds) 2222 Philadelphia Drive, Dayton, OH Zip 45406–1813; tel. 937/734–2612; Eloise Broner, President and Chief Executive Officer
Web address: www.goodsamdayton.org

PROVIDENCE CARE CENTER (O, 138 beds) 2025 Hayes Avenue, Sandusky, OH Zip 44870; Rick G. Ryan, Administrator and Chief Executive Officer

TRINITY HEALTH SYSTEM (O, 312 beds) 380 Summit Avenue, Steubenville, OH Zip 43952–2699; tel. 740/283–7000; Joseph M. Tasse, FACHE, Interim Chief Executive Officer
Web address: www.trinityhealth.com

For explanation of codes following names, see page B2.
★ Indicates Type III membership in the American Hospital Association.

TRINITY HOSPITAL TWIN CITY (O, 12 beds) 819 North First Street, Dennison, OH Zip 44621–1098; tel. 740/922–2800; Joseph J. Mitchell, President
Web address: www.trinitytwincity.org

OREGON: CHI ST. ANTHONY HOSPITAL (S, 25 beds) 2801 St. Anthony Way, Pendleton, OR Zip 97801–3800; tel. 541/276–5121; Harold S. Geller, Chief Executive Officer
Web address: www.sahpendleton.org

MERCY MEDICAL CENTER (S, 141 beds) 2700 Stewart Parkway, Roseburg, OR Zip 97471–1281; tel. 541/673–0611; Kelly C. Morgan, President and Chief Executive Officer
Web address: www.mercyrose.org

TENNESSEE: CHI MEMORIAL (S, 405 beds) 2525 De Sales Avenue, Chattanooga, TN Zip 37404–1161; tel. 423/495–2525; Larry P. Schumacher, R.N., MSN, Chief Executive Officer
Web address: www.memorial.org

TEXAS: BAYLOR ST. LUKE'S MEDICAL CENTER (O, 640 beds) 6720 Bertner Avenue, Houston, TX Zip 77030–2697, Mailing Address: P.O. Box 20269, Zip 77225–0269; tel. 832/355–1000; Michael H. Covert, FACHE, Chief Executive Officer
Web address: www.stlukestexas.com

BAYLOR ST. LUKE'S MEDICAL CENTER MCNAIR CAMPUS (O, 256 beds) One Baylor Plaza, BCM 100, Houston, TX Zip 77030–3411; tel. 713/798–4951; Michael H. Covert, FACHE, Chief Executive Officer
Web address: www.bcm.edu

BELLVILLE ST. JOSEPH HEALTH CENTER (O, 23 beds) 44 North Cummings Street, Bellville, TX Zip 77418–1347, Mailing Address: P.O. Box 977, Zip 77418–0977; tel. 979/413–7400; Reed Edmundson, Chief Executive Officer
Web address: www.st–joseph.org/body.cfm?id=773

BURLESON ST. JOSEPH HEALTH CENTER (O, 19 beds) 1101 Woodson Drive, Caldwell, TX Zip 77836–1052, Mailing Address: P.O. Box 360, Zip 77836–0360; tel. 979/567–3245; Brian Stanford, Administrator
Web address: www.st–joseph.org/

CHI ST. LUKE'S HEALTH – PATIENTS MEDICAL CENTER (O, 61 beds) 4600 East Sam Houston Parkway South, Pasadena, TX Zip 77505–3948; tel. 713/948–7000; Steven Foster, Chief Executive Officer
Web address: www.stlukestexas.com

CHI ST. LUKE'S HEALTH BRAZOSPORT (O, 103 beds) 100 Medical Drive, Lake Jackson, TX Zip 77566–5674; tel. 979/297–4411; Al Guevara, Jr., FACHE, President
Web address: www.chistlukesbrazosport.org

CHI ST. LUKE'S HEALTH MEMORIAL LIVINGSTON (O, 66 beds) 1717 Highway 59 Bypass, Livingston, TX Zip 77351–1257, Mailing Address: P.O. Box 1257, Zip 77351–0022; tel. 936/329–8700; Randy Slack, Chief Executive Officer
Web address: www.memorialhealth.org

CHI ST. LUKE'S HEALTH MEMORIAL LUFKIN (O, 217 beds) 1201 West Frank Avenue, Lufkin, TX Zip 75904–3357, Mailing Address: P.O. Box 1447, Zip 75902–1447; tel. 936/634–8111; Monte J. Bostwick, Market Chief Executive Officer
Web address: www.memorialhealth.us/centers/lufkin

CHI ST. LUKE'S HEALTH MEMORIAL SAN AUGUSTINE (O, 9 beds) 511 East Hospital Street, San Augustine, TX Zip 75972–2121, Mailing Address: P.O. Box 658, Zip 75972–0658; tel. 936/275–3446; Darlene Williams, R.N., Administrator
Web address: www.memorialhealth.org

CHI ST. LUKE'S HEALTH MEMORIAL SPECIALTY HOSPITAL (O, 20 beds) 1201 West Frank Avenue, Lufkin, TX Zip 75904–3357, Mailing Address: P.O. Box 1447, Zip 75902–1447; tel. 936/639–7530; Leslie Leach, Administrator
Web address: www.memorialhealth.org

GRIMES ST. JOSEPH HEALTH CENTER (O, 18 beds) 210 South Judson Street, Navasota, TX Zip 77868–3704; tel. 936/825–6585; Reed Edmundson, Administrator
Web address: www.st–joseph.org

MADISON ST. JOSEPH HEALTH CENTER (O, 25 beds) 100 West Cross Street, Madisonville, TX Zip 77864–2432, Mailing Address: Box 698, Zip 77864–0698; tel. 936/348–2631; Reed Edmundson, Administrator
Web address: www.st–joseph.org

ST. JOSEPH REGIONAL HEALTH CENTER (O, 228 beds) 2801 Franciscan Drive, Bryan, TX Zip 77802–2599; tel. 979/776–3777; Rick D. Napper, Market President
Web address: www.st–joseph.org

ST. LUKE'S HOSPITAL – THE VINTAGE HOSPITAL (O, 78 beds) 20171 Chasewood Park Drive, Houston, TX Zip 77070–1437; tel. 832/534–5000; Roland Cruickshank, President
Web address: www.stlukesvintage.com/

ST. LUKE'S LAKESIDE HOSPITAL (O, 30 beds) 17400 St. Luke's Way, The Woodlands, TX Zip 77384–8036; tel. 936/266–9000; David Argueta, Chief Executive Officer
Web address: www.stlukeslakeside.com/

ST. LUKE'S SUGAR LAND HOSPITAL (O, 58 beds) 1317 Lake Pointe Parkway, Sugar Land, TX Zip 77478–3997; tel. 281/637–7000; Robert A. Heifner, Chief Executive Officer
Web address: www.stlukessugarland.com

ST. LUKE'S THE WOODLANDS HOSPITAL (O, 192 beds) 17200 St. Luke's Way, The Woodlands, TX Zip 77384–8007; tel. 936/266–2000; David Argueta, Chief Executive Officer
Web address: www.stlukeswoodlands.com

WASHINGTON: HARRISON MEDICAL CENTER (O, 262 beds) 2520 Cherry Avenue, Bremerton, WA Zip 98310–4229; tel. 360/744–3911; David W. Schultz, FACHE, President
Web address: www.harrisonmedical.org

HIGHLINE MEDICAL CENTER (O, 128 beds) 16251 Sylvester Road S.W., Burien, WA Zip 98166–3052; tel. 206/244–9970; Anthony McLean, President
Web address: www.hchnet.org

ST. ANTHONY HOSPITAL (O, 80 beds) 11567 Canterwood Boulevard N.W., Gig Harbor, WA Zip 98332–5812; tel. 253/530–2000; David W. Schultz, FACHE, President
Web address: www.fhshealth.org/

ST. CLARE HOSPITAL (S, 104 beds) 11315 Bridgeport Way S.W., Lakewood, WA Zip 98499–3004; tel. 253/985–1711; Syd Bersante, R.N., President
Web address: www.fhshealth.org

ST. ELIZABETH HOSPITAL (S, 25 beds) 1455 Battersby Avenue, Enumclaw, WA Zip 98022–3634, Mailing Address: P.O. Box 218, Zip 98022–0218; tel. 360/802–8800; Syd Bersante, R.N., President
Web address: www.fhshealth.org

ST. FRANCIS HOSPITAL (S, 120 beds) 34515 Ninth Avenue South, Federal Way, WA Zip 98003–6799; tel. 253/944–8100; Anthony McLean, President
Web address: www.fhshealth.org

ST. JOSEPH MEDICAL CENTER (S, 363 beds) 1717 South J Street, Tacoma, WA Zip 98405–3004, Mailing Address: P.O. Box 2197, Zip 98401–2197; tel. 253/426–4101; Tim O'Haver, Chief Operating Officer
Web address: www.chifranciscan.org

Owned, leased, sponsored:	93 hospitals	11996 beds
Contract–managed:	4 hospitals	441 beds
Totals:	97 hospitals	12437 beds

0903: CATHOLIC HEALTH SERVICES (CC)
4790 North State Road 7, Lauderdale Lakes, FL Zip 33319–5860; tel. 954/484–1515; Joseph M. Catania, President and Chief Executive Officer

FLORIDA: ST. ANTHONY'S REHABILITATION HOSPITAL (S, 26 beds) 3485 N.W. 30th Street, Lauderdale Lakes, FL Zip 33311–1890; tel. 954/739–6233; Joseph M. Catania, Chief Executive Officer
Web address: www.catholichealthservices.org

ST. CATHERINE'S REHABILITATION HOSPITAL (S, 60 beds) 1050 N.E. 125th Street, North Miami, FL Zip 33161–5881; tel. 305/357–1735; Jaime Gonzalez, Administrator
Web address: www.catholichealthservices.org

Owned, leased, sponsored:	2 hospitals	86 beds
Contract–managed:	0 hospitals	0 beds
Totals:	2 hospitals	86 beds

0233: CATHOLIC HEALTH SERVICES OF LONG ISLAND (CC)
992 North Village Avenue, 1st Floor, Rockville Centre, NY Zip 11570–1002; tel. 516/705–3700; Alan D. Guerci, M.D., President and Chief Executive Officer
(Moderately Centralized Health System)

For explanation of codes following names, see page B2.
★ Indicates Type III membership in the American Hospital Association.

NEW YORK: GOOD SAMARITAN HOSPITAL MEDICAL CENTER (O, 537 beds) 1000 Montauk Highway, West Islip, NY Zip 11795–4927; tel. 631/376–3000; Nancy B. Simmons, Executive Vice President and Chief Administrative Officer
Web address: www.good–samaritan–hospital.org

MERCY MEDICAL CENTER (O, 191 beds) 1000 North Village Avenue, Rockville Centre, NY Zip 11570–1000; tel. 516/705–2525; Ronald Steimel, Executive Vice President and Chief Administrative Officer
Web address: www.mercymedicalcenter.chsli.org

ST. CATHERINE OF SIENA MEDICAL CENTER (O, 535 beds) 50 Route 25–A, Smithtown, NY Zip 11787–1348; tel. 631/862–3000; Paul J. Rowland, Executive Vice President and Chief Administrative Officer
Web address: www.stcatherines.chsli.org/

ST. CHARLES HOSPITAL (O, 243 beds) 200 Belle Terre Road, Port Jefferson, NY Zip 11777–1928; tel. 631/474–6000; James O'Connor, Executive Vice President and Chief Administrative Officer
Web address: www.stcharleshospital.chsli.org

ST. FRANCIS HOSPITAL, THE HEART CENTER (O, 306 beds) 100 Port Washington Boulevard, Roslyn, NY Zip 11576–1353; tel. 516/562–6000; Ruth Hennessey, Executive Vice President and Chief Administrative Officer
Web address: www.stfrancisheartcenter.com/index.html

ST. JOSEPH HOSPITAL (S, 128 beds) 4295 Hempstead Turnpike, Bethpage, NY Zip 11714–5769; tel. 516/579–6000; Ronald Steimel, Executive Vice President and Chief Administrative Officer
Web address: www.stjosephhospital.chsli.org

Owned, leased, sponsored:	6 hospitals	1940 beds
Contract–managed:	0 hospitals	0 beds
Totals:	6 hospitals	1940 beds

★0234: CATHOLIC HEALTH SYSTEM (CC)
144 Genesee Street, Buffalo, NY Zip 14203–1560; tel. 716/862–2410; Joseph D. McDonald, FACHE, President and Chief Executive Officer
(Centralized Physician/Insurance Health System)

FATHER BAKER MANOR (O, 160 beds) 6400 Powers Road, Orchard Park, NY Zip 14127; tel. 716/667–0001; Christine Kluckhohn, President, Continuing Care

KENMORE MERCY HOSPITAL (O, 288 beds) 2950 Elmwood Avenue, Kenmore, NY Zip 14217–1390, Mailing Address: 2950 Elmwood Avenue, Room 4024, Zip 14217–1390; tel. 716/447–6100; James M. Millard, President and Chief Executive Officer
Web address: www.chsbuffalo.org

MCAULEY RESIDENCE (O, 160 beds) 1503 Military Road, Kenmore, NY Zip 14217; tel. 716/447–6600; Christine Kluckhohn, President, Continuing Care

MERCY HOSPITAL (O, 438 beds) 565 Abbott Road, Buffalo, NY Zip 14220–2095; tel. 716/826–7000; Charles J. Urlaub, President and Chief Executive Officer
Web address: www.chsbuffalo.org

MERCY NURSING FACILITY (O, 74 beds) 565 Abbott Road, Buffalo, NY Zip 14220; tel. 716/828–2301; Christine Kluckhohn, President, Continuing Care

MOUNT ST. MARY'S HOSPITAL AND HEALTH CENTER (O, 127 beds) 5300 Military Road, Lewiston, NY Zip 14092–1903; tel. 716/297–4800; Gary C. Tucker, President and Chief Executive Officer
Web address: www.msmh.org

NAZARETH HOME (O, 125 beds) 291 West North Street, Buffalo, NY Zip 14201; tel. 716/881–2323; Christine Kluckhohn, President, Continuing Care

SISTERS OF CHARITY HOSPITAL OF BUFFALO (O, 467 beds) 2157 Main Street, Buffalo, NY Zip 14214–2692; tel. 716/862–1000; Peter U. Bergmann, President and Chief Executive Officer
Web address: www.chsbuffalo.org

ST. CATHERINE LABOURE (O, 80 beds) 2157 Main Street, Buffalo, NY Zip 14214; tel. 716/862–1451; Christine Kluckhohn, President, Continuing Care

ST. ELIZABETH'S HOME (O, 117 beds) 5539 Broadway, Lancaster, NY Zip 14086; tel. 716/683–5150; Christine Kluckhohn, President, Continuing Care

ST. FRANCIS OF BUFFALO (O, 120 beds) 34 Benwood Avenue, Buffalo, NY Zip 14214; tel. 716/862–2500; Christine Kluckhohn, President, Continuing Care

ST. FRANCIS OF WILLIAMSVILLE (O, 142 beds) 147 Reist Street, Williamsville, NY Zip 14221; tel. 716/633–5400; Christine Kluckhohn, President, Continuing Care

ST. JOSEPH MANOR (O, 22 beds) 2211 West State Street, Olean, NY Zip 14760; tel. 716/372–7810; Christine Kluckhohn, President, Continuing Care

Owned, leased, sponsored:	13 hospitals	2320 beds
Contract–managed:	0 hospitals	0 beds
Totals:	13 hospitals	2320 beds

★0991: CAYUGA HEALTH SYSTEM (NP)
101 Dates Drive, Ithaca, NY Zip 14850–1342; tel. 607/274–4011; John Rudd, President and Chief Executive Officer

CAYUGA MEDICAL CENTER AT ITHACA (O, 193 beds) 101 Dates Drive, Ithaca, NY Zip 14850–1342; tel. 607/274–4011
Web address: www.cayugamed.org

SCHUYLER HOSPITAL (O, 19) 220 Steuben Street, Montour Falls, NY Zip 14865–9709; tel. 607/535–7121
Web address: www.schuylerhospital.org

Owned, leased, sponsored:	2 hospitals	212 beds
Contract–managed:	0 hospitals	0 beds
Totals:	2 hospitals	212 beds

★0984: CEDARS–SINAI (NP)
8700 Beverly Boulevard, West Hollywood, CA Zip 90048–1865, Mailing Address: Box 48750, Los Angeles, Zip 90048–0750; tel. 310/423–5000; Thomas M. Priselac, President and Chief Executive Officer

CALIFORNIA: CEDARS–SINAI MEDICAL CENTER (O, 885 beds) 8700 Beverly Boulevard, Los Angeles, CA Zip 90048–1865, Mailing Address: Box 48750, Zip 90048–0750; tel. 310/423–5000; Thomas M. Priselac, President and Chief Executive Officer
Web address: www.cedars–sinai.edu

MARINA DEL REY HOSPITAL (O, 90 beds) 4650 Lincoln Boulevard, Marina Del Rey, CA Zip 90292–6306; tel. 310/823–8911; Paulette Heitmeyer, Administrator and Chief Operating Officer
Web address: www.marinahospital.com

Owned, leased, sponsored:	2 hospitals	975 beds
Contract–managed:	0 hospitals	0 beds
Totals:	2 hospitals	975 beds

★0298: CENTEGRA HEALTH SYSTEM (NP)
385 Millennium Drive, Crystal Lake, IL Zip 60012–3761; tel. 815/788–5800; Michael S. Eesley, Chief Executive Officer
(Centralized Health System)

ILLINOIS: CENTEGRA HOSPITAL – MCHENRY (O, 179 beds) 4201 Medical Center Drive, McHenry, IL Zip 60050–8409; tel. 815/344–5000; Michael S. Eesley, Chief Executive Officer
Web address: www.centegra.org

CENTEGRA HOSPITAL – WOODSTOCK (O, 96 beds) 3701 Doty Road, Woodstock, IL Zip 60098–7509, Mailing Address: P.O. Box 1990, Zip 60098–1990; tel. 815/338–2500; Michael S. Eesley, Chief Executive Officer
Web address: www.centegra.org

Owned, leased, sponsored:	2 hospitals	275 beds
Contract–managed:	0 hospitals	0 beds
Totals:	2 hospitals	275 beds

Section B

For explanation of codes following names, see page B2.
★ Indicates Type III membership in the American Hospital Association.

2265: CENTRA HEALTH, INC. (NP)
1920 Atherholt Road, Lynchburg, VA Zip 24501–1104;
tel. 434/200–3000; E. W. Tibbs, President and Chief Executive
Officer
(Moderately Centralized Health System)

VIRGINIA: CENTRA LYNCHBURG GENERAL HOSPITAL (O, 1045 beds) 1920
Atherholt Road, Lynchburg, VA Zip 24501–1104; tel. 434/200–4700; E.
W. Tibbs, President and Chief Executive Officer
Web address: www.centrahealth.com

CENTRA SOUTHSIDE COMMUNITY HOSPITAL (O, 86 beds) 800 Oak Street,
Farmville, VA Zip 23901–1199; tel. 434/392–8811; Thomas Angelo, Chief
Executive Officer
Web address: www.sch.centrahealth.com/

Owned, leased, sponsored:	2 hospitals	1131 beds
Contract–managed:	0 hospitals	0 beds
Totals:	2 hospitals	1131 beds

★0184: CENTRACARE HEALTH (NP)
1406 Sixth Avenue North, Saint Cloud, MN Zip 56303–1900;
tel. 320/251–2700; Kenneth D. Holmen, M.D., President and Chief
Executive Officer
(Moderately Centralized Health System)

MINNESOTA: CENTRACARE HEALTH–LONG PRAIRIE (O, 20 beds) 20 Ninth
Street S.E., Long Prairie, MN Zip 56347–1404; tel. 320/732–2141;
Daniel J. Swenson, FACHE, Administrator and Chief Executive Officer
Web address: www.centracare.com

CENTRACARE HEALTH–MELROSE (O, 93 beds) 525 Main Street West,
Melrose, MN Zip 56352–1043; tel. 320/256–4231; Gerry Gilbertson, FACHE,
Administrator
Web address: www.centracare.com

CENTRACARE HEALTH–MONTICELLO (O, 126 beds) 1013 Hart Boulevard,
Monticello, MN Zip 55362–8230; tel. 763/295–2945; Mary Ellen Wells,
FACHE, Administrator
Web address: www.newrivermedical.com

CENTRACARE HEALTH–PAYNESVILLE (O, 82 beds) 200 West 1st Street,
Paynesville, MN Zip 56362–1496; tel. 320/243–3767; Dennis C. Miley,
Administrator
Web address: www.centracare.com

CENTRACARE HEALTH–SAUK CENTRE (O, 85 beds) 425 North Elm Street,
Sauk Centre, MN Zip 56378–1010; tel. 320/352–2221; Delano Christianson,
Administrator
Web address: www.centracare.com/hospitals/sauk_centre/index.html

ST. CLOUD HOSPITAL (O, 487 beds) 1406 Sixth Avenue North, Saint Cloud,
MN Zip 56303–1901; tel. 320/251–2700; Craig J. Broman, FACHE,
President
Web address: www.centracare.com

Owned, leased, sponsored:	6 hospitals	893 beds
Contract–managed:	0 hospitals	0 beds
Totals:	6 hospitals	893 beds

0856: CENTRAL FLORIDA HEALTH (NP)
600 East Dixie Avenue, Leesburg, FL Zip 34748–5925;
tel. 352/323–5762; Donald G. Henderson, FACHE, Chief Executive
Officer

FLORIDA: LEESBURG REGIONAL MEDICAL CENTER (O, 330 beds) 600 East
Dixie Avenue, Leesburg, FL Zip 34748–5999; tel. 352/323–5762; Donald
G. Henderson, FACHE, President and Chief Executive Officer
Web address: www.cfhalliance.org

THE VILLAGES REGIONAL HOSPITAL (O, 277 beds) 1451 El Camino Real, The
Villages, FL Zip 32159–0041; tel. 352/751–8000; Donald G. Henderson,
FACHE, President and Chief Executive Officer
Web address: www.cfhalliance.org

Owned, leased, sponsored:	2 hospitals	607 beds
Contract–managed:	0 hospitals	0 beds
Totals:	2 hospitals	607 beds

1007: CENTRAL MAINE HEALTHCARE (NP)
300 Main Street, Lewiston, ME Zip 04240–7027;
tel. 207/795–0111; Jeff Brickman, President and Chief Executive
Officer

MAINE: BRIDGTON HOSPITAL (O, 25 beds) 10 Hospital Drive, Bridgton, ME
Zip 04009–1148; tel. 207/647–6000; R. David Frum, President
Web address: www.bridgtonhospital.org

CENTRAL MAINE MEDICAL CENTER (O, 190 beds) 300 Main Street, Lewiston,
ME Zip 04240–7027; tel. 207/795–0111; Tina Legere, President
Web address: www.cmmc.org

RUMFORD HOSPITAL (O, 21 beds) 420 Franklin Street, Rumford, ME
Zip 04276–2145; tel. 207/369–1000; R. David Frum, President
Web address: www.rumfordhospital.org

Owned, leased, sponsored:	3 hospitals	236 beds
Contract–managed:	0 hospitals	0 beds
Totals:	3 hospitals	236 beds

0934: CHARTERCARE HEALTH PARTNERS (NP)
825 Chalkstone Avenue, Providence, RI Zip 02908–4728;
tel. 410/456–2001; Lester P. Schindel, Chief Executive Officer
(Independent Hospital System)

RHODE ISLAND: ROGER WILLIAMS MEDICAL CENTER (O, 86 beds) 825
Chalkstone Avenue, Providence, RI Zip 02908–4735; tel. 401/456–2000;
Kimberly O'Connell, President
Web address: www.rwmc.com

ST. JOSEPH HEALTH SERVICES OF RHODE ISLAND (O, 125 beds) 200 High
Service Avenue, North Providence, RI Zip 02904–5199; tel. 401/456–3000;
Thomas Hughes, President
Web address: www.saintjosephri.com

Owned, leased, sponsored:	2 hospitals	211 beds
Contract–managed:	0 hospitals	0 beds
Totals:	2 hospitals	211 beds

0407: CHILDREN'S HOSPITAL AND HEALTH SYSTEM (NP)
9000 West Wisconsin Avenue, Milwaukee, WI Zip 53226–4810,
Mailing Address: P.O. Box 1997, Zip 53201–1997;
tel. 414/226–2000; Peggy N. Troy, President and Chief Executive
Officer
(Independent Hospital System)

WISCONSIN: CHILDREN'S HOSPITAL OF WISCONSIN (O, 297 beds) 9000
West Wisconsin Avenue, Milwaukee, WI Zip 53226–4810, Mailing Address:
P.O. Box 1997, Zip 53201–1997; tel. 414/266–2000; Peggy N. Troy,
President and Chief Executive Officer
Web address: www.chw.org

CHILDREN'S HOSPITAL OF WISCONSIN–FOX VALLEY (O, 42 beds) 130
Second Street, Neenah, WI Zip 54956–2883; tel. 920/969–7900; Peggy N.
Troy, President and Chief Executive Officer
Web address: www.chw.org

Owned, leased, sponsored:	2 hospitals	339 beds
Contract–managed:	0 hospitals	0 beds
Totals:	2 hospitals	339 beds

●★0131: CHRISTIANA CARE HEALTH SYSTEM (NP)
501 West 14th Street, Wilmington, DE Zip 19801–1013, Mailing
Address: P.O. Box 1668, Zip 19899–1668; tel. 302/733–1000;
Janice E. Nevin, M.D., M.P.H., Chief Executive Officer
(Moderately Centralized Health System)

DELAWARE: CHRISTIANA CARE HEALTH SYSTEM (O, 1049 beds) 4755
Ogletown–Stanton Road, Newark, DE Zip 19718–0002, Mailing Address:
P.O. Box 6001, Zip 19718; tel. 302/733–1000; Janice E. Nevin, M.D.,
M.P.H., Chief Executive Officer
Web address: www.christianacare.org

For explanation of codes following names, see page B2.
★ Indicates Type III membership in the American Hospital Association.
● Single hospital health care system

Owned, leased, sponsored:	1 hospital	1049 beds
Contract–managed:	0 hospitals	0 beds
Totals:	1 hospital	1049 beds

★**0192: CHRISTUS HEALTH** (CC)
919 Hidden Ridge Drive, Irving, TX Zip 75038; tel. 469/282–2000;
Ernie W. Sadau, Chief Executive Officer
(Moderately Centralized Health System)

ARKANSAS: CHRISTUS DUBUIS HOSPITAL OF FORT SMITH (C, 25 beds)
7301 Rogers Avenue, 4th Floor, Fort Smith, AR Zip 72903–4100;
tel. 479/314–4900; Keith Rogers, Administrator
Web address: www.christusdubuis.org/fortsmith

CHRISTUS DUBUIS HOSPITAL OF HOT SPRINGS (O, 26 beds) 300 Werner
Street, 3rd Floor East, Hot Springs National Park, AR Zip 71913–6406;
tel. 501/609–4300; Keith Rogers, Administrator
Web address: www.christusdubuis.org/hotsprings

GEORGIA: SOUTHERN CRESCENT HOSPITAL FOR SPECIALTY CARE (C, 30
beds) 11 Upper Riverdale Road S.W., 6th Floor, Riverdale, GA
Zip 30274–2615; tel. 770/897–7600; Fiona Adams, Interim Director
Web address: www.christusdubuis.
org/SouthernCrescentHospitalforSpecialtyCare

IOWA: CONTINUING CARE HOSPITAL AT ST. LUKE'S (C, 16 beds) 1026 A
Avenue N.E., 6th Floor, Cedar Rapids, IA Zip 52402–5036;
tel. 319/369–8142; Elly Steffen, Administrator
Web address: www.unitypoint.
org/cedarrapids/services–continuing–care–hospital.aspx

LOUISIANA: CHRISTUS COUSHATTA HEALTH CARE CENTER (O, 25 beds)
1635 Marvel Street, Coushatta, LA Zip 71019–9022, Mailing Address:
P.O. Box 589, Zip 71019–0589; tel. 318/932–2000; Brandon Hillman,
Interim Administrator, Director of Hospital Services
Web address: www.christuscoushatta.org

CHRISTUS DUBUIS HOSPITAL OF ALEXANDRIA (O, 25 beds) 3330 Masonic
Drive, 4th Floor, Alexandria, LA Zip 71301–3841; tel. 318/448–4938;
Kimberly Bennett, R.N., Interim Chief Executive Officer and Director of
Nursing
Web address: www.christusdubuis.
org/CHRISTUSDubuisHospitalofAlexandriaLA

CHRISTUS HEALTH SHREVEPORT–BOSSIER (O, 154 beds) 1453 East Bert
Koun Industrial Loop, Shreveport, LA Zip 71105–6800; tel. 318/681–5000;
Isaac Palmer, Chief Executive Officer
Web address: www.christushealthsb.org

CHRISTUS ST. FRANCES CABRINI HOSPITAL (O, 281 beds) 3330 Masonic
Drive, Alexandria, LA Zip 71301–3899; tel. 318/487–1122; Nancy R.
Hellyer, R.N., FACHE, Chief Executive Officer
Web address: www.cabrini.org/

CHRISTUS ST. PATRICK HOSPITAL OF LAKE CHARLES (O, 160 beds) 524 Dr.
Michael Debakey Drive, Lake Charles, LA Zip 70601–5799, Mailing Address:
P.O. Box 3401, Zip 70601; tel. 337/436–2511; Donald H. Lloyd, II, Chief
Executive Officer
Web address: www.stpatrickhospital.org

NATCHITOCHES REGIONAL MEDICAL CENTER (C, 91 beds) 501 Keyser
Avenue, Natchitoches, LA Zip 71457–6036, Mailing Address: P.O. Box 2009,
Zip 71457–2009; tel. 318/214–4200; D. Kirk Soileau, FACHE, Chief
Executive Officer
Web address: www.nrmchospital.org

SAVOY MEDICAL CENTER (C, 180 beds) 801 Poinciana Avenue, Mamou, LA
Zip 70554–2298; tel. 337/468–5261; Sherman Fookes, Chief Executive
Officer
Web address: www.savoymedical.com/

NEW MEXICO: CHRISTUS ST. VINCENT REGIONAL MEDICAL CENTER (O, 268
beds) 455 St. Michael's Drive, Santa Fe, NM Zip 87505–7663, Mailing
Address: P.O. Box 2107, Zip 87505; tel. 505/983–3361; Patrick Brian
Carrier, President and Chief Executive Officer
Web address: www.stvin.org

TEXAS: CHRISTUS CONTINUING CARE DBA DUBUIS HOSPITAL OF PARIS (C,
25 beds) 820 Clarksville Street, 6th Floor, Paris, TX Zip 75460–6027;
tel. 903/737–3600; Kathie Reese, R.N., Regional Administrator and Chief
Executive Officer
Web address: www.christusdubuis.org

CHRISTUS DUBUIS HOSPITAL OF BEAUMONT (O, 51 beds) 2830 Calder
Avenue, 4th Floor, Beaumont, TX Zip 77702–1809; tel. 409/899–8154;
Terry W. Kepler, Administrator
Web address: www.christusdubuis.
org/BeaumontandPortArthurSystem–CHRISTUSDubuisHospitalofBeaumont

CHRISTUS DUBUIS HOSPITAL OF PORT ARTHUR (C, 15 beds) 3600 Gates
Boulevard, 3rd Floor West, Port Arthur, TX Zip 77642–3858;
tel. 409/989–5300; Terry W. Kepler, Administrator
Web address: www.christusdubuis.org/CHRISTUSDubuisHospitalofPortArthur

CHRISTUS MOTHER FRANCES HOSPITAL – JACKSONVILLE (O, 21 beds) 2026
South Jackson, Jacksonville, TX Zip 75766–5822; tel. 903/541–4500; Anne
Pileggi, Administrator and Associate Vice President
Web address: www.tmfhs.org/jacksonville

CHRISTUS MOTHER FRANCES HOSPITAL – SULPHUR SPRINGS (O, 50 beds)
115 Airport Road, Sulphur Springs, TX Zip 75482–2105;
tel. 903/885–7671; Paul Harvery, President and Chief Executive Officer
Web address: www.tmfhc.org/maps–and–locations/locations–profile/?id=
72&searchId=8bcb329f–a152–e611–b37f–2c768a4e1b84&sort=11&page=
1&pageSize=10

CHRISTUS MOTHER FRANCES HOSPITAL – TYLER (O, 458 beds) 800 East
Dawson Street, Tyler, TX Zip 75701–2036; tel. 903/593–8441; John
McGreevy, Chief Executive Officer
Web address: www.tmfhc.org

CHRISTUS MOTHER FRANCES HOSPITAL – WINNSBORO (O, 25 beds) 719
West Coke Road, Winnsboro, TX Zip 75494–3011; tel. 903/342–5227; Janet
E. Coates, R.N., President and Chief Executive Officer
Web address: www.tmfhs.org

CHRISTUS SANTA ROSA HEALTH SYSTEM (O, 766 beds) 333 North Santa
Rosa Street, San Antonio, TX Zip 78207–3108; tel. 210/704–4184; Ken
Haynes, President and Chief Executive Officer
Web address: www.christussantarosa.org

CHRISTUS SOUTHEAST TEXAS HOSPITAL (O, 425 beds) 2830 Calder Avenue,
Beaumont, TX Zip 77702–1809, Mailing Address: P.O. Box 5405,
Zip 77726–5405; tel. 409/892–7171; Paul Trevino, Chief Executive Officer
Web address: www.christushospital.org

CHRISTUS SOUTHEAST TEXAS JASPER MEMORIAL (O, 40 beds) 1275 Marvin
Hancock Drive, Jasper, TX Zip 75951–4995; tel. 409/384–5461; Lance
Beus, Administrator
Web address: www.christusjasper.org

CHRISTUS SPOHN HOSPITAL ALICE (O, 73 beds) 2500 East Main Street,
Alice, TX Zip 78332–4169; tel. 361/661–8000; David LaMonte, Interim
President
Web address: www.christusspohn.org/locations_alice.htm

CHRISTUS SPOHN HOSPITAL BEEVILLE (O, 49 beds) 1500 East Houston
Street, Beeville, TX Zip 78102–5312; tel. 361/354–2000; Nathan Tudor,
Vice President and Chief Executive Officer
Web address: www.christusspohn.org

CHRISTUS SPOHN HOSPITAL CORPUS CHRISTI MEMORIAL (O, 576 beds)
2606 Hospital Boulevard, Corpus Christi, TX Zip 78405–1804, Mailing
Address: P.O. Box 5280, Zip 78405; tel. 361/902–4000; Pamela Robertson,
President and Chief Executive Officer
Web address: www.christusspohn.org

CHRISTUS SPOHN HOSPITAL KLEBERG (O, 50 beds) 1311 General Cavazos
Boulevard, Kingsville, TX Zip 78363–7130; tel. 361/595–1661; David
LeMonte, Vice President and Chief Operating Officer
Web address: www.christusspohn.org

CHRISTUS ST. MICHAEL HEALTH SYSTEM (O, 355 beds) 2600 St. Michael
Drive, Texarkana, TX Zip 75503–5220; tel. 903/614–1000; Chris Karam,
President and Chief Executive Officer
Web address: www.christusstmichael.org

CHRISTUS ST. MICHAEL REHABILITATION HOSPITAL (O, 50 beds) 2400 St.
Michael Drive, Texarkana, TX Zip 75503–2374; tel. 903/614–4000; Aloma
Gender, R.N., MSN, Administrator and Chief Nursing Officer
Web address: www.christusstmichael.org/rehab

Owned, leased, sponsored:	21 hospitals	3928 beds
Contract–managed:	7 hospitals	382 beds
Totals:	28 hospitals	4310 beds

For explanation of codes following names, see page B2.
★ Indicates Type III membership in the American Hospital Association.

Section B

★**0101: CITRUS VALLEY HEALTH PARTNERS** (NP)
210 West San Bernardino Road, Covina, CA Zip 91723–1515;
tel. 626/331–7331; Robert H. Curry, President and Chief Executive
Officer

CALIFORNIA: CITRUS VALLEY MEDICAL CENTER–INTER COMMUNITY
CAMPUS (O, 323 beds) 210 West San Bernadino Road, Covina, CA
Zip 91723–1515, Mailing Address: P.O. Box 6108, Zip 91722–5108;
tel. 626/331–7331; Robert H. Curry, President and Chief Executive
Officer
Web address: www.cvhp.org

FOOTHILL PRESBYTERIAN HOSPITAL (O, 75 beds) 250 South Grand Avenue,
Glendora, CA Zip 91741–4218; tel. 626/963–8411; Robert H. Curry,
President and Chief Executive Officer
Web address: www.cvhp.org/Our_Facilities/Foothill_Presbyterian.aspx

Owned, leased, sponsored:	2 hospitals	398 beds
Contract–managed:	0 hospitals	0 beds
Totals:	2 hospitals	398 beds

★**0212: CLEVELAND CLINIC HEALTH SYSTEM** (NP)
9500 Euclid, Cleveland, OH Zip 44195–5108; tel. 216/444–2200;
Delos Cosgrove, M.D., President and Chief Executive Officer
(Centralized Health System)

FLORIDA: CLEVELAND CLINIC FLORIDA (O, 155 beds) 2950 Cleveland Clinic
Boulevard, Weston, FL Zip 33331–3602; tel. 954/659–5000; Wael
Barsoum, President
Web address: www.clevelandclinic.org/florida

OHIO: AKRON GENERAL MEDICAL CENTER (O, 417 beds) 1 Akron General
Avenue, Akron, OH Zip 44307–2433; tel. 330/344–6000; Alan Papa,
President
Web address: www.akrongeneral.org

CLEVELAND CLINIC (O, 1280 beds) 9500 Euclid Avenue, Cleveland, OH
Zip 44195–5108; tel. 216/444–2200; Delos Cosgrove, M.D., President and
Chief Executive Officer
Web address: www.clevelandclinic.org

CLEVELAND CLINIC CHILDREN'S HOSPITAL FOR REHABILITATION (O, 25
beds) 2801 Martin Luther King Jr. Drive, Cleveland, OH Zip 44104–3865;
tel. 216/448–6400; Michael J. McHugh, M.D., Medical Director
Web address: www.my.clevelandclinic.org/childrens–hospital/default.aspx

CLEVELAND CLINIC FAIRVIEW HOSPITAL (O, 454 beds) 18101 Lorain Avenue,
Cleveland, OH Zip 44111–5656; tel. 216/476–7000; Neil Smith, D.O.,
President
Web address: www.fairviewhospital.org

CLEVELAND CLINIC, MEDINA HOSPITAL (O, 136 beds) 1000 East Washington
Street, Medina, OH Zip 44256–2170; tel. 330/725–1000; Thomas Tulisiak,
M.D., President
Web address: www.medinahospital.org

EDWIN SHAW REHAB (O, 35 beds) 330 Broadway Street East, Cuyahoga
Falls, OH Zip 44221–3312; tel. 330/436–0910; Alan Papa, President and
Chief Operating Officer
Web address: www.edwinshaw.com

EUCLID HOSPITAL (O, 221 beds) 18901 Lake Shore Boulevard, Euclid, OH
Zip 44119–1090; tel. 216/531–9000; Daniel Napierkowski, M.D., President
Web address: www.euclidhospital.org

HILLCREST HOSPITAL (O, 453 beds) 6780 Mayfield Road, Cleveland, OH
Zip 44124–2203; tel. 440/312–4500; Brian J. Harte, M.D., President
Web address: www.hillcresthospital.org

LODI COMMUNITY HOSPITAL (O, 20 beds) 225 Elyria Street, Lodi, OH
Zip 44254–1096; tel. 330/948–1222; Alan Papa, President and Chief
Operating Officer
Web address: www.lodihospital.org

LUTHERAN HOSPITAL (O, 198 beds) 1730 West 25th Street, Cleveland, OH
Zip 44113–3170; tel. 216/696–4300; Donald Malone, M.D., President
Web address: www.lutheranhospital.org

MARYMOUNT HOSPITAL (O, 286 beds) 12300 McCracken Road, Garfield
Heights, OH Zip 44125–2975; tel. 216/581–0500; Richard Parker, M.D.,
President
Web address: www.marymount.org

SOUTH POINTE HOSPITAL (O, 175 beds) 20000 Harvard Road, Warrensville
Heights, OH Zip 44122–6805; tel. 216/491–6000; Robert S. Juhasz, D.O.,
President
Web address: www.southpointehospital.org

Owned, leased, sponsored:	13 hospitals	3855 beds
Contract–managed:	0 hospitals	0 beds
Totals:	13 hospitals	3855 beds

0076: COLLEGE HEALTH ENTERPRISES (IO)
11627 Telegraph Road, Suite 200, Santa Fe Springs, CA
Zip 90670–6814; tel. 562/923–9449; Barry J. Weiss, Chairman of
the Board

CALIFORNIA: COLLEGE HOSPITAL CERRITOS (O, 157 beds) 10802 College
Place, Cerritos, CA Zip 90703–1579; tel. 562/924–9581; Stephen Witt,
President and Chief Executive Officer
Web address: www.collegehospitals.com

COLLEGE HOSPITAL COSTA MESA (O, 122 beds) 301 Victoria Street, Costa
Mesa, CA Zip 92627–7131; tel. 949/642–2734; Susan L. Taylor, JD, Chief
Executive Officer
Web address: www.collegehospitals.com/cosHome

Owned, leased, sponsored:	2 hospitals	279 beds
Contract–managed:	0 hospitals	0 beds
Totals:	2 hospitals	279 beds

0161: COLUMBUS REGIONAL HEALTHCARE SYSTEM (NP)
707 Center Street, Suite 400, Columbus, GA Zip 31901–1575;
tel. 706/660–6100; Scott Hill, Chief Executive Officer
(Independent Hospital System)

GEORGIA: AZALEA TRACE (O, 110 beds) 910 Talbotton Road, Columbus, GA
Zip 31901; tel. 706/323–9513; Todd West, Administrator

HAMILTON HOUSE NURSING CENTER/ADULT LIVING CENTER (O, 128 beds)
1911 Hamilton Road, Columbus, GA Zip 31901; tel. 706/571–1850; John
Sims, Administrator

MARION MEMORIAL NURSING HOME (O, 70 beds) Highway 41, Buena Vista,
GA Zip 31803, Mailing Address: P.O. Box 197, Zip 31803;
tel. 229/649–7100; Barbara Mitchell, Administrator

MIDTOWN MEDICAL CENTER (O, 497 beds) 710 Center Street, Columbus, GA
Zip 31901–1527, Mailing Address: P.O. Box 951, Zip 31902–0951;
tel. 706/571–1000; Ryan Chandler, President and Chief Executive Officer
Web address: www.columbusregional.com

MIDTOWN MEDICAL CENTER WEST (O, 171 beds) 616 19th Street,
Columbus, GA Zip 31901–1528, Mailing Address: P.O. Box 2188,
Zip 31902–2188; tel. 706/494–4262; Ryan Chandler, Chief Executive Officer
Web address: www.columbusregional.com

NORTHSIDE MEDICAL CENTER (O, 100 beds) 100 Frist Court, Columbus, GA
Zip 31909–3578, Mailing Address: P.O. Box 7188, Zip 31908–7188;
tel. 706/494–2100; Ryan Chandler, Interim Chief Executive Officer
Web address: www.columbusregional.com

Owned, leased, sponsored:	6 hospitals	1076 beds
Contract–managed:	0 hospitals	0 beds
Totals:	6 hospitals	1076 beds

0520: COMMONWEALTH HEALTH CORPORATION (NP)
800 Park Street, Bowling Green, KY Zip 42101–2356;
tel. 270/745–1500; Connie Smith, President and Chief Executive
Officer
(Centralized Physician/Insurance Health System)

KENTUCKY: COMMONWEALTH REGIONAL SPECIALTY HOSPITAL (O, 28 beds)
250 Park Drive, 6th Floor, Bowling Green, KY Zip 42101–1760, Mailing
Address: P.O. Box 90010, Zip 42102–9010; tel. 270/796–6200; Christa
Atkins, Administrator
Web address: www.commonwealthregionalspecialtyhospital.org

MEDICAL CENTER AT BOWLING GREEN (O, 337 beds) 250 Park Street,
Bowling Green, KY Zip 42101–1795, Mailing Address: P.O. Box 90010,
Zip 42102–9010; tel. 270/745–1000; Connie Smith, Chief Executive Officer
Web address: www.themedicalcenter.org

Section B

MEDICAL CENTER AT FRANKLIN (O, 25 beds) 1100 Brookhaven Road, Franklin, KY Zip 42134–2746; tel. 270/598–4800; Annette Runyon, Vice President and Administrator
Web address: www.themedicalcenterfranklin.org

MEDICAL CENTER AT SCOTTSVILLE (O, 135 beds) 456 Burnley Road, Scottsville, KY Zip 42164–6355; tel. 270/622–2800; Eric Hagan, R.N., Executive Vice President and Administrator
Web address: www.themedicalcenterscottsville.org/

THE MEDICAL CENTER ALBANY (C, 42 beds) 723 Burkesville Road, Albany, KY Zip 42602–1654; tel. 606/387–8000; Laura Belcher, Administrator
Web address: www.chc.net/services/hospitals/the_medical_center_at_albany.aspx

THE MEDICAL CENTER AT CAVERNA (O, 25 beds) 1501 South Dixie Street, Horse Cave, KY Zip 42749–1477; tel. 270/786–2191; Alan B. Alexander, FACHE, Vice President and Administrator
Web address: www.TheMedicalCenterCaverna.org

Owned, leased, sponsored:	5 hospitals	550 beds
Contract–managed:	1 hospital	42 beds
Totals:	6 hospitals	592 beds

★**0401: COMMUNITY HEALTH NETWORK** (NP)
7330 Shadeland Station, Indianapolis, IN Zip 46256–3957; tel. 317/355–1411; Bryan A. Mills, President and Chief Executive Officer
(Moderately Centralized Health System)

INDIANA: COMMUNITY HOSPITAL EAST (O, 335 beds) 1500 North Ritter Avenue, Indianapolis, IN Zip 46219–3095; tel. 317/355–1411; Scott L. Teffeteller, President
Web address: www.ecommunity.com/east/

COMMUNITY HOSPITAL NORTH (O, 308 beds) 7150 Clearvista Drive, Indianapolis, IN Zip 46256–1695, Mailing Address: 7250 Clearvista Drive, Suite 200, Zip 46256–1695; tel. 317/355–2469; Kathleen R. Krusie, FACHE, President
Web address: www.ecommunity.com/north

COMMUNITY HOSPITAL OF ANDERSON & MADISON COUNTY (O, 140 beds) 1515 North Madison Avenue, Anderson, IN Zip 46011–3453; tel. 765/298–4242; Beth S. Tharp, R.N., President and Chief Executive Officer
Web address: www.communityanderson.com

COMMUNITY HOSPITAL SOUTH (O, 158 beds) 1402 East County Line Road South, Indianapolis, IN Zip 46227–0963; tel. 317/887–7000; Anthony B. Lennen, President
Web address: www.ecommunity.com

COMMUNITY HOWARD REGIONAL HEALTH (O, 137 beds) 3500 South Lafountain Street, Kokomo, IN Zip 46902–3803, Mailing Address: P.O. Box 9011, Zip 46904–9011; tel. 765/453–0702; Joseph Hooper, President and Chief Executive Officer
Web address: www.howardregional.org

COMMUNITY HOWARD SPECIALTY HOSPITAL (O, 30 beds) 829 North Dixon Road, Kokomo, IN Zip 46901–7709; tel. 765/452–6700; Clayton L. Clement, Interim Administrator
Web address: www.communityhoward.org

Owned, leased, sponsored:	6 hospitals	1108 beds
Contract–managed:	0 hospitals	0 beds
Totals:	6 hospitals	1108 beds

★**0080: COMMUNITY HEALTH SYSTEMS, INC.** (IO)
4000 Meridian Boulevard, Franklin, TN Zip 37067–6325, Mailing Address: P.O. Box 689020, Zip 37068–9020; tel. 615/465–7000; Wayne T. Smith, Chairman, President and Chief Executive Officer
(Decentralized Health System)

ALABAMA: CRESTWOOD MEDICAL CENTER (O, 147 beds) One Hospital Drive, Huntsville, AL Zip 35801–3403; tel. 256/429–4000; Pamela Hudson, M.D., Chief Executive Officer
Web address: www.crestwoodmedcenter.com

FLOWERS HOSPITAL (O, 141 beds) 4370 West Main Street, Dothan, AL Zip 36305–4000, Mailing Address: P.O. Box 6907, Zip 36302–6907; tel. 334/793–5000; Suzanne Woods, President and Chief Executive Officer
Web address: www.flowershospital.com

GADSDEN REGIONAL MEDICAL CENTER (O, 274 beds) 1007 Goodyear Avenue, Gadsden, AL Zip 35903–1195; tel. 256/494–4000; Corey Ewing, FACHE, Chief Executive Officer
Web address: www.gadsdenregional.com

GRANDVIEW MEDICAL CENTER (O, 379 beds) 3690 Grandview Parkway, Birmingham, AL Zip 35243–3326; tel. 205/971–1000; Keith Granger, President and Chief Executive Officer
Web address: www.grandviewhealth.com

MEDICAL CENTER ENTERPRISE (O, 117 beds) 400 North Edwards Street, Enterprise, AL Zip 36330–2510; tel. 334/347–0584; Heath Phillips, Chief Executive Officer
Web address: www.mcehospital.com

SOUTH BALDWIN REGIONAL MEDICAL CENTER (L, 112 beds) 1613 North McKenzie Street, Foley, AL Zip 36535–2299; tel. 251/949–3400; Keith Newton, Chief Executive Officer
Web address: www.southbaldwinrmc.com

STRINGFELLOW MEMORIAL HOSPITAL (O, 75 beds) 301 East 18th Street, Anniston, AL Zip 36207–3952; tel. 256/235–8900; Jay Hinesley, FACHE, Chief Executive Officer
Web address: www.stringfellowhealth.com

ALASKA: MAT–SU REGIONAL MEDICAL CENTER (O, 74 beds) 2500 South Woodworth Loop, Palmer, AK Zip 99645–8984, Mailing Address: P.O. Box 1687, Zip 99645–1687; tel. 907/861–6000; John R. Lee, Chief Executive Officer
Web address: www.matsuregional.com

ARIZONA: NORTHWEST MEDICAL CENTER (O, 270 beds) 6200 North La Cholla Boulevard, Tucson, AZ Zip 85741–3599; tel. 520/742–9000; Kevin Stockton, Chief Executive Officer
Web address: www.northwestmedicalcenter.com

ORO VALLEY HOSPITAL (O, 144 beds) 1551 East Tangerine Road, Oro Valley, AZ Zip 85755–6213; tel. 520/901–3500; Jae Dale, Chief Executive Officer
Web address: www.orovalleyhospital.com

WESTERN ARIZONA REGIONAL MEDICAL CENTER (O, 139 beds) 2735 Silver Creek Road, Bullhead City, AZ Zip 86442–8303; tel. 928/763–2273; Aaron Hazzard, Interim Chief Executive Officer
Web address: www.warmc.com

ARKANSAS: MEDICAL CENTER OF SOUTH ARKANSAS (L, 120 beds) 700 West Grove Street, El Dorado, AR Zip 71730–4416; tel. 870/863–2000; Robert Rupp, Chief Executive Officer
Web address: www.themedcenter.net

NORTHWEST MEDICAL CENTER – SPRINGDALE (O, 358 beds) 609 West Maple Avenue, Springdale, AR Zip 72764–5394, Mailing Address: P.O. Box 47, Zip 72765–0047; tel. 479/751–5711; Sharif Omar, Chief Executive Officer
Web address: www.northwesthealth.com

PHYSICIANS' SPECIALTY HOSPITAL (O, 21 beds) 3873 North Parkview Drive, Fayetteville, AR Zip 72703, Mailing Address: 3875 North Parkview Drive, Zip 72703; tel. 479/571–7070; Rhonda McCabe, Chief Executive Officer
Web address: www.pshfay.com

SILOAM SPRINGS REGIONAL HOSPITAL (O, 44 beds) 603 North Progress Avenue, Siloam Springs, AR Zip 72761–4352; tel. 479/215–3000; Patrick Kerrwood, Chief Executive Officer
Web address: www.ssrh.net

SPARKS MEDICAL CENTER – VAN BUREN (L, 103 beds) East Main and South 20th Streets, Van Buren, AR Zip 72956–5715, Mailing Address: P.O. Box 409, Zip 72957–0409; tel. 479/474–3401; Daniel E. McKay, Chief Executive Officer
Web address: www.sparkshealth.com/locations/sparks–medical–center–van–buren

SPARKS REGIONAL MEDICAL CENTER (O, 303 beds) 100 Towson Avenue, Fort Smith, AR Zip 72901–2632, Mailing Address: P.O. Box 2406, Zip 72917–7006; tel. 479/441–4000; Daniel E. McKay, Chief Executive Officer
Web address: www.sparks.org

For explanation of codes following names, see page B2.
★ Indicates Type III membership in the American Hospital Association.

Section B

FLORIDA: BARTOW REGIONAL MEDICAL CENTER (O, 72 beds) 2200 Osprey Boulevard, Bartow, FL Zip 33830–3308, Mailing Address: P.O. Box 1050, Zip 33831–1050; tel. 863/533–8111; Philip Minden, Chief Executive Officer
Web address: www.bartowregional.com

BAYFRONT HEALTH BROOKSVILLE (L, 120 beds) 17240 Cortez Boulevard, Brooksville, FL Zip 34601–8921, Mailing Address: P.O. Box 37, Zip 34605–0037; tel. 352/796–5111; Kenneth R. Wicker, Chief Executive Officer
Web address: www.brooksvilleregionalhospital.org

BAYFRONT HEALTH DADE CITY (O, 120 beds) 13100 Fort King Road, Dade City, FL Zip 33525–5294; tel. 352/521–1100; Shauna McKinnon, Chief Executive Officer
Web address: www.pascoregionalmc.com

BAYFRONT HEALTH PORT CHARLOTTE (O, 190 beds) 2500 Harbor Boulevard, Port Charlotte, FL Zip 33952–5000; tel. 941/766–4122; Richard H. Satcher, Chief Executive Officer
Web address: www.bayfrontcharlotte.com

BAYFRONT HEALTH PUNTA GORDA (O, 190 beds) 809 East Marion Avenue, Punta Gorda, FL Zip 33950–3819, Mailing Address: P.O. Box 51–1328, Zip 33951–1328; tel. 941/639–3131; Andrew Emery, Chief Executive Officer
Web address: www.bayfrontcharlotte.com

BAYFRONT HEALTH ST. PETERSBURG (O, 395 beds) 701 Sixth Street South, Saint Petersburg, FL Zip 33701–4891; tel. 727/823–1234; Kathryn Gillette, President and Chief Executive Officer
Web address: www.bayfrontstpete.com

HEART OF FLORIDA REGIONAL MEDICAL CENTER (O, 193 beds) 40100 Highway 27, Davenport, FL Zip 33837–5906; tel. 863/422–4971; Ann Barnhart, Chief Executive Officer
Web address: www.heartofflorida.com

HIGHLANDS REGIONAL MEDICAL CENTER (L, 80 beds) 3600 South Highlands Avenue, Sebring, FL Zip 33870–5495, Mailing Address: Drawer 2066, Zip 33871–2066; tel. 863/385–6101; John D. Montois, Interim Chief Executive Officer
Web address: www.highlandsregional.com

LAKE WALES MEDICAL CENTER (O, 131 beds) 410 South 11th Street, Lake Wales, FL Zip 33853–4256; tel. 863/676–1433; Rebecca Brewer, FACHE, Chief Executive Officer
Web address: www.lakewalesmedicalcenter.com

LOWER KEYS MEDICAL CENTER (L, 90 beds) 5900 College Road, Key West, FL Zip 33040–4396, Mailing Address: P.O. Box 9107, Zip 33041–9107; tel. 305/294–5531; Stephen G. Pennington, Interim Chief Executive Officer
Web address: www.lkmc.com

MUNROE REGIONAL MEDICAL CENTER (O, 420 beds) 1500 S.W. 1st Avenue, Ocala, FL Zip 34471–6504, Mailing Address: P.O. Box 6000, Zip 34478–6000; tel. 352/351–7200; Bob Moore, FACHE, Chief Executive Officer
Web address: www.munroeregional.com

NORTH OKALOOSA MEDICAL CENTER (O, 110 beds) 151 Redstone Avenue S.E., Crestview, FL Zip 32539–6026; tel. 850/689–8100; Ronnie Daves, Chief Executive Officer
Web address: www.northokaloosa.com

PHYSICIANS REGIONAL – PINE RIDGE (O, 201 beds) 6101 Pine Ridge Road, Naples, FL Zip 34119–3900; tel. 239/348–4000; Scott Lowe, Interim Market Chief Executive Officer
Web address: www.physiciansregional.com

SANTA ROSA MEDICAL CENTER (L, 68 beds) 6002 Berryhill Road, Milton, FL Zip 32570–5062; tel. 850/626–7762; Doug Sills, Chief Executive Officer
Web address: www.santarosamedicalcenter.org

SEBASTIAN RIVER MEDICAL CENTER (O, 154 beds) 13695 North U.S. Highway 1, Sebastian, FL Zip 32958–3230, Mailing Address: Box 780838, Zip 32978–0838; tel. 772/589–3186; Kelly Enriquez, Chief Executive Officer
Web address: www.sebastianrivermedical.com

SEVEN RIVERS REGIONAL MEDICAL CENTER (O, 128 beds) 6201 North Suncoast Boulevard, Crystal River, FL Zip 34428–6712; tel. 352/795–6560; Austin Brown, Interim Chief Executive Officer
Web address: www.srrmc.com

SHANDS LAKE SHORE REGIONAL MEDICAL CENTER (O, 90 beds) 368 N.E. Franklin Street, Lake City, FL Zip 32055–3047; tel. 386/292–8000; Rhonda Kay Sherrod, R.N., MSN, Administrator
Web address: www.shandslakeshore.com

SHANDS LIVE OAK REGIONAL MEDICAL CENTER (O, 25 beds) 1100 S.W. 11th Street, Live Oak, FL Zip 32064–3608; tel. 386/362–0800; Bayode Omosaiye, FACHE, Chief Executive Officer
Web address: www.shandsliveoak.com/

SHANDS STARKE REGIONAL MEDICAL CENTER (O, 49 beds) 922 East Call Street, Starke, FL Zip 32091–3699; tel. 904/368–2300; ,
Web address: www.shandsstarke.com

ST. CLOUD REGIONAL MEDICAL CENTER (O, 84 beds) 2906 17th Street, Saint Cloud, FL Zip 34769–6099; tel. 407/892–2135; Brent Burish, Chief Executive Officer
Web address: www.stcloudregional.com

VENICE REGIONAL BAYFRONT HEALTH (O, 221 beds) 540 The Rialto, Venice, FL Zip 34285–2900; tel. 941/485–7711; John R. McLain, Chief Executive Officer
Web address: www.veniceregional.com

WUESTHOFF MEDICAL CENTER – MELBOURNE (O, 119 beds) 250 North Wickham Road, Melbourne, FL Zip 32935–8625; tel. 321/752–1200; Ron Gicca, Chief Executive Officer
Web address: www.wuesthoff.com/locations/wuesthoff–medical–center–melbourne

WUESTHOFF MEDICAL CENTER – ROCKLEDGE (O, 298 beds) 110 Longwood Avenue, Rockledge, FL Zip 32955–2887, Mailing Address: P.O. Box 565002, Mail Stop 1, Zip 32956–5002; tel. 321/636–2211; Gary Malaer, Chief Executive Officer
Web address: www.wuesthoff.org

GEORGIA: EAST GEORGIA REGIONAL MEDICAL CENTER (O, 149 beds) 1499 Fair Road, Statesboro, GA Zip 30458–1683, Mailing Address: P.O. Box 1048, Zip 30459–1048; tel. 912/486–1000; Paul Theriot, Chief Executive Officer
Web address: www.eastgeorgiaregional.com

INDIANA: BLUFFTON REGIONAL MEDICAL CENTER (O, 79 beds) 303 South Main Street, Bluffton, IN Zip 46714–2503; tel. 260/824–3210; Aaron Garofola, Chief Executive Officer
Web address: www.blufftonregional.com

DUKES MEMORIAL HOSPITAL (O, 25 beds) 275 West 12th Street, Peru, IN Zip 46970–1638; tel. 765/472–8000; Debra Close, Chief Executive Officer
Web address: www.dukesmemorialhosp.com

DUPONT HOSPITAL (O, 131 beds) 2520 East Dupont Road, Fort Wayne, IN Zip 46825–1675; tel. 260/416–3000; Chad Towner, Chief Executive Officer
Web address: www.thedupontdifference.com

KOSCIUSKO COMMUNITY HOSPITAL (O, 72 beds) 2101 East Dubois Drive, Warsaw, IN Zip 46580–3288; tel. 574/267–3200; Kirk M. Ray, Chief Executive Officer
Web address: www.kch.com

LA PORTE HOSPITAL (O, 110 beds) 1007 Lincolnway, La Porte, IN Zip 46350–3201, Mailing Address: P.O. Box 250, Zip 46352–0250; tel. 219/326–1234; G. Thor Thordarson, President and Chief Executive Officer
Web address: www.iuhealth.org

LUTHERAN HOSPITAL OF INDIANA (O, 379 beds) 7950 West Jefferson Boulevard, Fort Wayne, IN Zip 46804–4140; tel. 260/435–7001; Brian Bauer, Chief Executive Officer
Web address: www.lutheranhospital.com

ORTHOPAEDIC HOSPITAL OF LUTHERAN HEALTH NETWORK (O, 44 beds) 7952 West Jefferson Boulevard, Fort Wayne, IN Zip 46804–4140; tel. 260/435–2999; Lorie Ailor, Chief Executive Officer
Web address: www.theorthohospital.com

PORTER REGIONAL HOSPITAL (O, 276 beds) 85 East U.S. Highway 6, Valparaiso, IN Zip 46383–8947; tel. 219/983–8300; Stephen Lunn, Chief Executive Officer
Web address: www.porterhealth.com

REHABILITATION HOSPITAL OF FORT WAYNE (O, 36 beds) 7970 West Jefferson Boulevard, Fort Wayne, IN Zip 46804–4140; tel. 260/435–6100; Shelley Boxell, R.N., Chief Nursing Officer and Interim Chief Operating Officer
Web address: www.rehabhospital.com

ST. JOSEPH HOSPITAL (O, 182 beds) 700 Broadway, Fort Wayne, IN Zip 46802–1493; tel. 260/425–3000; Kenneth Jones, Chief Executive Officer
Web address: www.stjoehospital.com

For explanation of codes following names, see page B2.
★ Indicates Type III membership in the American Hospital Association.

STARKE HOSPITAL (O, 15 beds) 102 East Culver Road, Knox, IN
Zip 46534–2216, Mailing Address: P.O. Box 339, Zip 46534–0339;
tel. 574/772–6231; Craig Felty, Chief Executive Officer
Web address: www.iuhealth.org/starke/

LOUISIANA: BYRD REGIONAL HOSPITAL (O, 60 beds) 1020 West Fertitta
Boulevard, Leesville, LA Zip 71446–4645; tel. 337/239–9041; Roger C.
LeDoux, Chief Executive Officer
Web address: www.byrdregional.com

LAKE AREA MEDICAL CENTER (O, 88 beds) 4200 Nelson Road, Lake Charles,
LA Zip 70605–4118; tel. 337/474–6370; Bryan S. Bateman, Chief Executive
Officer
Web address: www.Lakeareamc.com

NORTHERN LOUISIANA MEDICAL CENTER (O, 104 beds) 401 East Vaughn
Avenue, Ruston, LA Zip 71270–5950; tel. 318/254–2100; Roy Finch, Chief
Executive Officer
Web address: www.northernlouisianamedicalcenter.com

MISSISSIPPI: MERIT HEALTH BATESVILLE (O, 112 beds) 303 Medical Center
Drive, Batesville, MS Zip 38606–8608; tel. 662/563–5611; Travis Sisson,
Chief Executive Officer
Web address: www.trilakesmc.com

MERIT HEALTH BILOXI (L, 198 beds) 150 Reynoir Street, Biloxi, MS
Zip 39530–4199, Mailing Address: P.O. Box 128, Zip 39533–0128;
tel. 228/432–1571; ,
Web address: www.merithealthbiloxi.com

MERIT HEALTH CENTRAL (L, 319 beds) 1850 Chadwick Drive, Jackson, MS
Zip 39204–3479, Mailing Address: P.O. Box 59001, Zip 39284–9001;
tel. 601/376–1000; Jon–Paul Croom, President and Chief Executive Officer
Web address: www.merithealthcentral.com/

MERIT HEALTH GILMORE MEMORIAL (O, 95 beds) 1105 Earl Frye Boulevard,
Amory, MS Zip 38821–5500, Mailing Address: P.O. Box 459,
Zip 38821–0459; tel. 662/256–7111; J. Allen Tyra, Chief Executive
Web address: www.gilmorehealth.com

MERIT HEALTH MADISON (L, 44 beds) 161 River Oaks Drive, Canton, MS
Zip 39046–5375, Mailing Address: PO Box 1607, Zip 39046–5375;
tel. 601/855–4000; Britton Phelps, Chief Executive Officer
Web address: www.merithealthmadison.com

MERIT HEALTH NATCHEZ (O, 104 beds) 54 Seargent S Prentiss Drive,
Natchez, MS Zip 39120–4726; tel. 601/443–2100; Eric Robinson, Chief
Executive Officer
Web address: www.natchezregional.com

MERIT HEALTH NORTHWEST MISSISSIPPI (L, 181 beds) 1970 Hospital Drive,
Clarksdale, MS Zip 38614–7202, Mailing Address: P.O. Box 1218,
Zip 38614–1218; tel. 662/627–3211; Joel Southern, R.N., MSN, Chief
Executive Officer
Web address: www.merithealthnorthwestms.com

MERIT HEALTH RANKIN (L, 134 beds) 350 Crossgates Boulevard, Brandon,
MS Zip 39042–2698; tel. 601/825–2811; Barry Moss, Chief Executive
Officer
Web address: www.crossgatesriveroaks.com

MERIT HEALTH RIVER OAKS (O, 158 beds) 1030 River Oaks Drive, Flowood,
MS Zip 39232–9553, Mailing Address: P.O. Box 5100, Jackson,
Zip 39296–5100; tel. 601/932–1030; L. Dwayne Blaylock, Chief Executive
Officer
Web address: www.riveroakshosp.com

MERIT HEALTH RIVER REGION (O, 361 beds) 2100 Highway 61 North,
Vicksburg, MS Zip 39183–8211, Mailing Address: P.O. Box 590,
Zip 39181–0590; tel. 601/883–5000; Gregory Pearson, Chief Executive
Officer
Web address: www.riverregion.com

MERIT HEALTH WESLEY (O, 211 beds) 5001 Hardy Street, Hattiesburg, MS
Zip 39402–1308, Mailing Address: P.O. Box 16509, Zip 39404–6509;
tel. 601/268–8000; Michael Neuendorf, Chief Executive Officer
Web address: www.wesley.com

MERIT HEALTH WOMAN'S HOSPITAL (O, 60 beds) 1026 North Flowood Drive,
Flowood, MS Zip 39232–9532, Mailing Address: 1026 North Flowood Drive,
Zip 39232; tel. 601/932–1000; Sherry J. Pitts, Chief Executive Officer
Web address: www.merithealthwomanshospital.com

NATCHEZ COMMUNITY HOSPITAL (O, 101 beds) 129 Jefferson Davis
Boulevard, Natchez, MS Zip 39120–5100, Mailing Address: P.O. Box 1203,
Zip 39121–1203; tel. 601/445–6200; Eric Robinson, Chief Executive Officer
Web address: www.natchezcommunityhospital.com/default.aspx

MISSOURI: MOBERLY REGIONAL MEDICAL CENTER (O, 94 beds) 1515 Union
Avenue, Moberly, MO Zip 65270–9449; tel. 660/263–8400; John M.
Dawes, FACHE, Chief Executive Officer
Web address: www.moberlyhospital.com

NORTHEAST REGIONAL MEDICAL CENTER (L, 93 beds) 315 South
Osteopathy, Kirksville, MO Zip 63501–6401, Mailing Address: P.O. Box
C8502, Zip 63501–8599; tel. 660/785–1000; Ranee C. Brayton, R.N., MSN,
Chief Executive Officer
Web address: www.nermc.com

POPLAR BLUFF REGIONAL MEDICAL CENTER (O, 252 beds) 3100 Oak Grove
Road, Poplar Bluff, MO Zip 63901, Mailing Address: P.O. Box 88,
Zip 63902–0088; tel. 573/776–2000; Larry Rodgers, Chief Executive Officer
Web address: www.poplarbluffregional.com

TWIN RIVERS REGIONAL MEDICAL CENTER (O, 100 beds) 1301 First Street,
Kennett, MO Zip 63857–2508, Mailing Address: P.O. Box 728,
Zip 63857–0728; tel. 573/888–4522; Gerald Faircloth, FACHE, Chief
Executive Officer
Web address: www.twinriversregional.com

NEW JERSEY: MEMORIAL HOSPITAL OF SALEM COUNTY (O, 110 beds) 310
Woodstown Road, Salem, NJ Zip 08079–2080; tel. 856/935–1000; Ryan
Jensen, Chief Executive Officer
Web address: www.salemhospitalnj.org

NEW MEXICO: CARLSBAD MEDICAL CENTER (O, 130 beds) 2430 West
Pierce Street, Carlsbad, NM Zip 88220–3597; tel. 575/887–4100; Cathy
Hibbs, Chief Executive Officer
Web address: www.carlsbadmedicalcenter.com

EASTERN NEW MEXICO MEDICAL CENTER (O, 149 beds) 405 West Country
Club Road, Roswell, NM Zip 88201–5209; tel. 575/622–8170; Rodney
Schumacher, Interim Chief Executive Officer
Web address: www.enmmc.com

LEA REGIONAL MEDICAL CENTER (O, 195 beds) 5419 North Lovington
Highway, Hobbs, NM Zip 88240–9125, Mailing Address: P.O. Box 3000,
Zip 88241–9501; tel. 575/492–5000; Timothy Thornell, FACHE, Chief
Executive Officer
Web address: www.learegionalmedical.com

MOUNTAINVIEW REGIONAL MEDICAL CENTER (O, 142 beds) 4311 East
Lohman Avenue, Las Cruces, NM Zip 88011–8255; tel. 575/556–7600;
Denten Park, Chief Executive Officer
Web address: www.mountainviewregional.com

NORTH CAROLINA: DAVIS REGIONAL MEDICAL CENTER (O, 130 beds) 218
Old Mocksville Road, Statesville, NC Zip 28625–1930, Mailing Address:
P.O. Box 1823, Zip 28687–1823; tel. 704/873–0281; William Chad
French, Chief Executive Officer
Web address: www.davisregional.com

LAKE NORMAN REGIONAL MEDICAL CENTER (O, 123 beds) 171 Fairview
Road, Mooresville, NC Zip 28117–9500, Mailing Address: P.O. Box 3250,
Zip 28117–3250; tel. 704/660–4000; Stephen L. Midkiff, Chief Executive
Officer
Web address: www.lnrmc.com

OHIO: HILLSIDE REHABILITATION HOSPITAL (O, 65 beds) 8747 Squires Lane
N.E., Warren, OH Zip 44484–1649; tel. 330/841–3700; Linda Case,
Administrator
Web address: www.valleycareofohio.net

NORTHSIDE MEDICAL CENTER (O, 373 beds) 500 Gypsy Lane, Youngstown,
OH Zip 44504–1315; tel. 330/884–1000; K. Robert Bauer, Jr., Interim Chief
Executive Officer
Web address: www.northsidemedicalcenter.net

TRUMBULL MEMORIAL HOSPITAL (O, 292 beds) 1350 East Market Street,
Warren, OH Zip 44483–6628; tel. 330/841–9011; John Walsh, Chief
Executive Officer
Web address: www.vchs.net

OKLAHOMA: ALLIANCEHEALTH BLACKWELL (O, 49 beds) 710 South 13th
Street, Blackwell, OK Zip 74631–3700; tel. 580/363–2311; Andrew
Wachtel, Chief Executive Officer
Web address: www.integris–health.com

ALLIANCEHEALTH CLINTON (O, 49 beds) 100 North 30th Street, Clinton, OK
Zip 73601–3117, Mailing Address: P.O. Box 1569, Zip 73601–1569;
tel. 580/323–2363; Cameron Lewis, Chief Executive Officer
Web address: www.alliancehealthclinton.com

For explanation of codes following names, see page B2.
★ Indicates Type III membership in the American Hospital Association.

ALLIANCEHEALTH DEACONESS (O, 238 beds) 5501 North Portland Avenue, Oklahoma City, OK Zip 73112–2099; tel. 405/604–6000; Devon Hyde, Chief Executive Officer
Web address: www.deaconessokc.com

ALLIANCEHEALTH DURANT (O, 148 beds) 1800 University Boulevard, Durant, OK Zip 74701–3006, Mailing Address: P.O. Box 1207, Zip 74702–1207; tel. 580/924–3080; Jeffrey S. Tarrant, FACHE, Chief Executive Officer
Web address: www.alliancehealthdurant.com/

ALLIANCEHEALTH MADILL (O, 21 beds) 901 South Fifth Avenue, Madill, OK Zip 73446–3640, Mailing Address: P.O. Box 827, Zip 73446–0827; tel. 580/795–3384; Minnie Burkhardt, Chief Executive Officer
Web address: www.myalliancehealth.com

ALLIANCEHEALTH MIDWEST (L, 255 beds) 2825 Parklawn Drive, Midwest City, OK Zip 73110–4258; tel. 405/610–4411; Damon Brown, Chief Executive Officer
Web address: www.alliancehealthmidwest.com

ALLIANCEHEALTH PONCA CITY (O, 74 beds) 1900 North 14th Street, Ponca City, OK Zip 74601–2099; tel. 580/765–3321; Christopher Mendoza, Chief Executive Officer
Web address: www.AllianceHealthPoncaCity.com

ALLIANCEHEALTH PRYOR (O, 24 beds) 111 North Bailey Street, Pryor, OK Zip 74361–4201, Mailing Address: P.O. Box 278, Zip 74362–0278; tel. 918/825–1600; Douglas K. Weaver, FACHE, President
Web address: www.integrismayescounty.com

ALLIANCEHEALTH SEMINOLE (O, 32 beds) 2401 Wrangler Boulevard, Seminole, OK Zip 74868–1917; tel. 405/303–4000; Adam Bracks, Chief Executive Officer
Web address: www.hma.com

ALLIANCEHEALTH WOODWARD (L, 40 beds) 900 17th Street, Woodward, OK Zip 73801–2448; tel. 580/256–5511; David Wallace, Chief Executive Officer
Web address: www.woodwardhospital.com

PENNSYLVANIA: BERWICK HOSPITAL CENTER (O, 341 beds) 701 East 16th Street, Berwick, PA Zip 18603–2397; tel. 570/759–5000; Diane Ljungquist, R.N., MS, Chief Executive Officer
Web address: www.berwick–hospital.com

BRANDYWINE HOSPITAL (O, 169 beds) 201 Reeceville Road, Coatesville, PA Zip 19320–1536; tel. 610/383–8000; W. Jeffrey Hunt, Chief Executive Officer
Web address: www.brandywinehospital.com

CARLISLE REGIONAL MEDICAL CENTER (O, 65 beds) 361 Alexander Spring Road, Carlisle, PA Zip 17015–6940; tel. 717/249–1212; David P. Steitz, Chief Executive Officer
Web address: www.carlislermc.com/default.aspx

CHESTNUT HILL HOSPITAL (O, 135 beds) 8835 Germantown Avenue, Philadelphia, PA Zip 19118–2718; tel. 215/248–8200; John D. Cacciamani, M.D., Chief Executive Officer
Web address: www.chhealthsystem.com

EASTON HOSPITAL (O, 196 beds) 250 South 21st Street, Easton, PA Zip 18042–3892; tel. 610/250–4000; John A. Zidansek, Chief Executive Officer
Web address: www.easton–hospital.com

FIRST HOSPITAL WYOMING VALLEY (O, 127 beds) 562 Wyoming Avenue, Kingston, PA Zip 18704–3721; tel. 570/552–3900; Ron Ziobro, Interim Chief Executive Officer
Web address: www.commonwealthhealth.net/locations/first–hospital

HEART OF LANCASTER REGIONAL MEDICAL CENTER (O, 148 beds) 1500 Highlands Drive, Lititz, PA Zip 17543–7694; tel. 717/625–5000; Deborah J. Willwerth, R.N., MSN, Chief Executive Officer
Web address: www.heartoflancaster.com

JENNERSVILLE REGIONAL HOSPITAL (O, 63 beds) 1015 West Baltimore Pike, West Grove, PA Zip 19390–9459; tel. 610/869–1000; Andrew Guz, Chief Executive Officer
Web address: www.jennersville.com

LANCASTER REGIONAL MEDICAL CENTER (O, 150 beds) 250 College Avenue, Lancaster, PA Zip 17603–3363, Mailing Address: P.O. Box 3434, Zip 17604–3434; tel. 717/291–8211; Brooks Turkel, Chief Executive Officer
Web address: www.lancasterregional.com

MEMORIAL HOSPITAL (O, 100 beds) 325 South Belmont Street, York, PA Zip 17403–2609, Mailing Address: P.O. Box 15118, Zip 17405–7118; tel. 717/843–8623; Sally J. Dixon, Chief Executive Officer
Web address: www.mhyork.org

MOSES TAYLOR HOSPITAL (O, 214 beds) 700 Quincy Avenue, Scranton, PA Zip 18510–1724; tel. 570/770–5000; Justin Davis, Chief Executive Officer
Web address: www.mth.org

PHOENIXVILLE HOSPITAL (O, 127 beds) 140 Nutt Road, Phoenixville, PA Zip 19460–3900, Mailing Address: P.O. Box 3001, Zip 19460–0916; tel. 610/983–1000; Stephen M. Tullman, Chief Executive Officer
Web address: www.phoenixvillehospital.com

POTTSTOWN MEMORIAL MEDICAL CENTER (O, 232 beds) 1600 East High Street, Pottstown, PA Zip 19464–5093; tel. 610/327–7000; Rich Newell, Chief Executive Officer
Web address: www.pottstownmemorial.com

REGIONAL HOSPITAL OF SCRANTON (O, 186 beds) 746 Jefferson Avenue, Scranton, PA Zip 18510–1624; tel. 570/348–7100; Justin Davis, Chief Executive Officer
Web address: www.regionalhospitalofscranton.net

SHARON REGIONAL HEALTH SYSTEM (O, 256 beds) 740 East State Street, Sharon, PA Zip 16146–3395; tel. 724/983–3911; Jason Roeback, Chief Executive Officer
Web address: www.sharonregional.com

TYLER MEMORIAL HOSPITAL (O, 44 beds) 5950 State Route 6, Tunkhannock, PA Zip 18657–7905; tel. 570/836–2161; Ann Marie Stevens, R.N., Chief Executive Officer
Web address: www.tylermemorialhospital.net

WILKES–BARRE GENERAL HOSPITAL (O, 374 beds) 575 North River Street, Wilkes–Barre, PA Zip 18764–0001; tel. 570/829–8111; Cornelio R. Catena, President and Chief Executive Officer
Web address: www.wvhc.org

SOUTH CAROLINA: CAROLINAS HOSPITAL SYSTEM (O, 416 beds) 805 Pamplico Highway, Florence, SC Zip 29505–6050, Mailing Address: P.O. Box 100550, Zip 29502–0550; tel. 843/674–5000; Darcy Craven, Chief Executive Officer
Web address: www.carolinashospital.com

CAROLINAS HOSPITAL SYSTEM MARION (O, 216 beds) 2829 East Highway 76, Mullins, SC Zip 29574–6035, Mailing Address: P.O. Drawer 1150, Marion, Zip 29571–1150; tel. 843/431–2000; Parkes Coggins, Chief Executive Officer
Web address: www.carolinashospitalmarion.com

CHESTER REGIONAL MEDICAL CENTER (L, 36 beds) 1 Medical Park Drive, Chester, SC Zip 29706–9769; tel. 803/581–3151; Page H. Vaughan, Chief Executive Officer
Web address: www.chesterregional.com

MARY BLACK HEALTH SYSTEM – GAFFNEY (O, 125 beds) 1530 North Limestone Street, Gaffney, SC Zip 29340–4738; tel. 864/487–4271; Joshua Self, Chief Executive Officer
Web address: www.upstatecarolina.org

MARY BLACK HEALTH SYSTEM–SPARTANBURG (O, 181 beds) 1700 Skylyn Drive, Spartanburg, SC Zip 29307–1061, Mailing Address: P.O. Box 3217, Zip 29304–3217; tel. 864/573–3000; Sean T. Dardeau, FACHE, Chief Executive Officer
Web address: www.maryblackhealthsystem.com

SPRINGS MEMORIAL HOSPITAL (O, 162 beds) 800 West Meeting Street, Lancaster, SC Zip 29720–2298; tel. 803/286–1214; Janice Dabney, Chief Executive Officer
Web address: www.springsmemorial.com

TENNESSEE: LAKEWAY REGIONAL HOSPITAL (O, 135 beds) 726 McFarland Street, Morristown, TN Zip 37814–3990; tel. 423/586–2302; Steve Simpson, Chief Executive Officer
Web address: www.tennova.com

TENNOVA HEALTHCARE – CLEVELAND (O, 208 beds) 2305 Chambliss Avenue N.W., Cleveland, TN Zip 37311–3847, Mailing Address: P.O. Box 3060, Zip 37320–3060; tel. 423/559–6000; R. Coleman Foss, Chief Executive Officer
Web address: www.skyridgemedicalcenter.net

TENNOVA HEALTHCARE DYERSBURG REGIONAL MEDICAL CENTER (O, 120 beds) 400 East Tickle Street, Dyersburg, TN Zip 38024–3120; tel. 731/285–2410; Reba Celsor, Chief Executive Officer
Web address: www.dyersburgregionalmc.com

TENNOVA HEALTHCARE REGIONAL HOSPITAL OF JACKSON (O, 134 beds) 367 Hospital Boulevard, Jackson, TN Zip 38305–2080; tel. 731/661–2000; Charles F. Miller, Chief Executive Officer
Web address: www.regionalhospitaljackson.com/Pages/Home.aspx

For explanation of codes following names, see page B2.
★ Indicates Type III membership in the American Hospital Association.

TENNOVA HEALTHCARE VOLUNTEER COMMUNITY HOSPITAL (O, 65 beds) 161 Mount Pelia Road, Martin, TN Zip 38237–3811; tel. 731/587–4261; Darrell Blaylock, Chief Executive Officer
Web address: www.volunteercommunityhospital.com

TENNOVA HEALTHCARE–CLARKSVILLE (O, 247 beds) 651 Dunlop Lane, Clarksville, TN Zip 37040–5015, Mailing Address: P.O. Box 31629, Zip 37040–0028; tel. 931/502–1000; Alex Villa, Chief Executive Officer
Web address: www.tennova.com/

TENNOVA HEALTHCARE–HARTON (O, 135 beds) 1801 North Jackson Street, Tullahoma, TN Zip 37388–8259; tel. 931/393–3000; Kenneth James, Chief Executive Officer
Web address: www.hartonmedicalcenter.com

TENNOVA HEALTHCARE–JAMESTOWN (O, 85 beds) 436 Central Avenue W., Jamestown, TN Zip 38556–3031, Mailing Address: P.O. Box 1500, Zip 38556–1500; tel. 931/879–8171; Lynette Pritchett, Chief Executive Officer
Web address: www.jamestownregional.org

TENNOVA HEALTHCARE–JEFFERSON MEMORIAL HOSPITAL (L, 54 beds) 110 Hospital Drive, Jefferson City, TN Zip 37760–5281; tel. 865/471–2500; Colin McRae, Chief Executive Officer
Web address: www.tennova.com/

TENNOVA HEALTHCARE–LAFOLLETTE MEDICAL CENTER (O, 164 beds) 923 East Central Avenue, La Follette, TN Zip 37766–2768, Mailing Address: P.O. Box 1301, Zip 37766–1301; tel. 423/907–1200; Mark Cain, Chief Executive Officer
Web address: www.tennova.com

TENNOVA HEALTHCARE–LEBANON (O, 245 beds) 1411 Baddour Parkway, Lebanon, TN Zip 37087–2513; tel. 615/444–8262; Matthew T. Caldwell, Chief Executive Officer
Web address: www.universitymedicalcenter.com

TENNOVA HEALTHCARE–SHELBYVILLE (O, 52 beds) 2835 Highway 231 North, Shelbyville, TN Zip 37160–7327; tel. 931/685–5433; Bill Rich, Chief Executive Officer
Web address: www.heritagemedicalcenter.com

TENNOVA NEWPORT MEDICAL CENTER (O, 47 beds) 435 Second Street, Newport, TN Zip 37821–3799; tel. 423/625–2200; Trevor Castaneda, Chief Executive Officer
Web address: www.tennova.com

TENNOVA PHYSICIANS REGIONAL MEDICAL CENTER (O, 220 beds) 900 East Oak Hill Avenue, Knoxville, TN Zip 37917–4556; tel. 865/545–8000; Neil Heatherly, Interim Chief Executive Officer
Web address: www.hma.com/content/physicians–regional–medical–center

TEXAS: ABILENE REGIONAL MEDICAL CENTER (O, 205 beds) 6250 U.S. Highway 83, Abilene, TX Zip 79606–5299; tel. 325/428–1000; Michael D. Murphy, Chief Executive Officer
Web address: www.abileneregional.com

BROWNWOOD REGIONAL MEDICAL CENTER (O, 188 beds) 1501 Burnet Road, Brownwood, TX Zip 76801–8520, Mailing Address: P.O. Box 760, Zip 76804–0760; tel. 325/646–8541; Claude E. Chip Camp, III, FACHE, Chief Executive Officer
Web address: www.brmc–cares.com

CEDAR PARK REGIONAL MEDICAL CENTER (O, 93 beds) 1401 Medical Parkway, Cedar Park, TX Zip 78613–7763; tel. 512/528–7000; Brad D. Holland, Chief Executive Officer
Web address: www.cedarparkregional.com

COLLEGE STATION MEDICAL CENTER (O, 148 beds) 1604 Rock Prairie Road, College Station, TX Zip 77845–8345; tel. 979/764–5100; Leslie Paul Luke, Interim Chief Executive Officer
Web address: www.csmedcenter.com

DETAR HEALTHCARE SYSTEM (O, 245 beds) 506 East San Antonio Street, Victoria, TX Zip 77901–6060, Mailing Address: P.O. Box 2089, Zip 77902–2089; tel. 361/575–7441; William R. Blanchard, Chief Executive Officer
Web address: www.detar.com

HILL REGIONAL HOSPITAL (O, 66 beds) 101 Circle Drive, Hillsboro, TX Zip 76645–2670; tel. 254/580–8500; Michael J. Ellis, FACHE, Chief Executive Officer
Web address: www.chs.net

LAKE GRANBURY MEDICAL CENTER (L, 73 beds) 1310 Paluxy Road, Granbury, TX Zip 76048–5655; tel. 817/573–2273; Derrick Cuenca, Chief Executive Officer
Web address: www.lakegranburymedicalcenter.com

LAREDO MEDICAL CENTER (O, 326 beds) 1700 East Saunders Avenue, Laredo, TX Zip 78041–5474, Mailing Address: P.O. Box 2068, Zip 78044–2068; tel. 956/796–5000; Enrique Gallegos, Chief Executive Officer
Web address: www.laredomedical.com

LONGVIEW REGIONAL MEDICAL CENTER (O, 230 beds) 2901 North Fourth Street, Longview, TX Zip 75605–5191, Mailing Address: P.O. Box 14000, Zip 75607–4000; tel. 903/758–1818; Casey Robertson, Chief Executive Officer
Web address: www.longviewregional.com

NAVARRO REGIONAL HOSPITAL (O, 148 beds) 3201 West State Highway 22, Corsicana, TX Zip 75110–2469; tel. 903/654–6800; Michael K. Stewart, Chief Executive Officer
Web address: www.navarrohospital.com

SAN ANGELO COMMUNITY MEDICAL CENTER (O, 131 beds) 3501 Knickerbocker Road, San Angelo, TX Zip 76904–7698; tel. 325/949–9511; Jeremy Riney, Chief Executive Officer
Web address: www.sacmc.com

SOUTH TEXAS REGIONAL MEDICAL CENTER (O, 67 beds) 1905 Highway 97 East, Jourdanton, TX Zip 78026–1504; tel. 830/769–3515; John E. Ulbricht, Chief Executive Officer
Web address: www.strmc.com

TOMBALL REGIONAL MEDICAL CENTER (O, 191 beds) 605 Holderrieth Street, Tomball, TX Zip 77375–6445; tel. 281/401–7500; Thomas W. Jackson, Chief Executive Officer
Web address: www.tomballregionalmedicalcenter.com

WEATHERFORD REGIONAL MEDICAL CENTER (O, 98 beds) 713 East Anderson Street, Weatherford, TX Zip 76086–5705; tel. 682/582–1000; David Orcutt, Chief Executive Officer
Web address: www.weatherfordregional.com

WOODLAND HEIGHTS MEDICAL CENTER (O, 115 beds) 505 South John Redditt Drive, Lufkin, TX Zip 75904–3157, Mailing Address: P.O. Box 150610, Zip 75904; tel. 936/634–8311; Kyle Swift, Chief Executive Officer
Web address: www.woodlandheights.net

VIRGINIA: SOUTHAMPTON MEMORIAL HOSPITAL (O, 72 beds) 100 Fairview Drive, Franklin, VA Zip 23851–1238, Mailing Address: P.O. Box 817, Zip 23851–0817; tel. 757/569–6100; Kimberly W. Marks, Chief Executive Officer
Web address: www.smhfranklin.com

SOUTHERN VIRGINIA REGIONAL MEDICAL CENTER (O, 80 beds) 727 North Main Street, Emporia, VA Zip 23847–1274; tel. 434/348–4400; Matt Tavenner, Chief Executive Officer
Web address: www.svrmc.com

SOUTHSIDE REGIONAL MEDICAL CENTER (O, 300 beds) 200 Medical Park Boulevard, Petersburg, VA Zip 23805–9274; tel. 804/765–5000; Douglas J. Moyer, Chief Executive Officer
Web address: www.srmconline.com

WASHINGTON: DEACONESS HOSPITAL (O, 352 beds) 800 West Fifth Avenue, Spokane, WA Zip 99204–2803, Mailing Address: P.O. Box 248, Zip 99210–0248; tel. 509/458–5800; Maurine Cate, Chief Executive Officer
Web address: www.deaconessspokane.com/Deaconess–Hospital/home.aspx

TOPPENISH COMMUNITY HOSPITAL (O, 48 beds) 502 West Fourth Avenue, Toppenish, WA Zip 98948–1616, Mailing Address: P.O. Box 672, Zip 98948–0672; tel. 509/865–3105; Chris Mendoza, Interim Chief Executive Officer
Web address: www.toppenishhospital.com

VALLEY HOSPITAL (O, 92 beds) 12606 East Mission Avenue, Spokane Valley, WA Zip 99216–1090; tel. 509/924–6650; Gregory George Repetti, III, FACHE, Chief Executive Officer
Web address: www.valleyhospital.org

YAKIMA REGIONAL MEDICAL AND CARDIAC CENTER (O, 167 beds) 110 South Ninth Avenue, Yakima, WA Zip 98902–3315; tel. 509/575–5000; Bryan Braegger, Interim Chief Executive Officer
Web address: www.yakimaregional.net

WEST VIRGINIA: BLUEFIELD REGIONAL MEDICAL CENTER (O, 92 beds) 500 Cherry Street, Bluefield, WV Zip 24701–3390; tel. 304/327–1100; Derek W. Cimala, Interim Chief Executive Officer
Web address: www.bluefield.org

For explanation of codes following names, see page B2.
★ Indicates Type III membership in the American Hospital Association.

GREENBRIER VALLEY MEDICAL CENTER (O, 113 beds) 202 Maplewood Avenue, Ronceverte, WV Zip 24970–1334, Mailing Address: P.O. Box 497, Zip 24970–0497; tel. 304/647–4411; Robert Calhoun, Chief Executive Officer
Web address: www.gvmc.com

PLATEAU MEDICAL CENTER (O, 25 beds) 430 Main Street, Oak Hill, WV Zip 25901–3455; tel. 304/469–8600; Derek W. Cimala, Interim Chief Executive Officer
Web address: www.plateaumedicalcenter.com

WILLIAMSON MEMORIAL HOSPITAL (O, 76 beds) 859 Alderson Street, Williamson, WV Zip 25661–3215, Mailing Address: P.O. Box 1980, Zip 25661–1980; tel. 304/235–2500; Cindy Segar–Miller, R.N., Chief Executive Officer
Web address: www.williamsonmemorial.net

Owned, leased, sponsored:	155 hospitals	23090 beds
Contract–managed:	0 hospitals	0 beds
Totals:	155 hospitals	23090 beds

0249: COMMUNITY HEALTHCARE SYSTEM (NP)
901 MacArthur Boulevard, Hammond, IN Zip 46321–2959; tel. 219/836–1600; Donald Powers, Chairman, President and Chief Executive Officer
(Independent Hospital System)

INDIANA: COMMUNITY HOSPITAL (O, 493 beds) 901 Macarthur Boulevard, Munster, IN Zip 46321–2959; tel. 219/836–1600; Luis F. Molina, Chief Executive Officer and Administrator
Web address: www.comhs.org

ST. CATHERINE HOSPITAL (O, 205 beds) 4321 Fir Street, East Chicago, IN Zip 46312–3097; tel. 219/392–1700; JoAnn Birdzell, Chief Executive Officer and Administrator
Web address: www.stcatherinehospital.org

ST. MARY MEDICAL CENTER (O, 200 beds) 1500 South Lake Park Avenue, Hobart, IN Zip 46342–6699; tel. 219/942–0551; Janice L. Ryba, JD, Chief Executive Officer
Web address: www.comhs.org

Owned, leased, sponsored:	3 hospitals	898 beds
Contract–managed:	0 hospitals	0 beds
Totals:	3 hospitals	898 beds

★0384: COMMUNITY HOSPITAL CORPORATION (NP)
7800 North Dallas Parkway, Suite 200, Plano, TX Zip 75024–6116; tel. 972/943–6400; Michael D. Williams, President and Chief Executive Officer
(Moderately Centralized Health System)

KENTUCKY: CONTINUECARE HOSPITAL AT BAPTIST HEALTH CORBIN (O, 32 beds) 1 Trillium Way, Lower Level, Corbin, KY Zip 40701–8727; tel. 606/523–5150; R. Alan Coppock, FACHE, President and CEO
Web address: www.continuecare.org

CONTINUECARE HOSPITAL AT BAPTIST HEALTH PADUCAH (O, 37 beds) 2501 Kentucky Avenue, 5th Floor, Paducah, KY Zip 42003–3813; tel. 270/575–2598; Arthur Rivas, Interim Chief Executive Officer
Web address: www.continuecare.org/paducah//

CONTINUECARE HOSPITAL AT MADISONVILLE (O, 36 beds) 900 Hospital Drive, 4th Floor, Madisonville, KY Zip 42431–1644; tel. 270/825–5450; Kathy DeVore, Administrator
Web address: www.continuecare.org/madisonville//

LOUISIANA: MOREHOUSE GENERAL HOSPITAL (C, 49 beds) 323 West Walnut Avenue, Bastrop, LA Zip 71220–4521, Mailing Address: P.O. Box 1060, Zip 71221–1060; tel. 318/283–3600; Gary G. Kendrick, Interim Chief Executive Officer
Web address: www.mghospital.com

NEW MEXICO: UNION COUNTY GENERAL HOSPITAL (C, 21 beds) 300 Wilson Street, Clayton, NM Zip 88415–3304, Mailing Address: P.O. Box 489, Zip 88415–0489; tel. 575/374–2585; Jerry Wiesner, Chief Executive Officer
Web address: www.ucgh.net/

NORTH CAROLINA: CAROLINAS CONTINUECARE HOSPITAL AT KINGS MOUNTAIN (O, 28 beds) 706 West King Street, 2nd Floor, Kings Mountain, NC Zip 28086–2708, Mailing Address: P.O. Box 159, Zip 28086–0159; tel. 980/487–5520; Denise R. Murray, Chief Executive Officer
Web address: www.continuecare.org/kings–mountain/

CAROLINAS CONTINUECARE HOSPITAL AT PINEVILLE (O, 40 beds) 10648 Park Road, Charlotte, NC Zip 28210; tel. 704/667–8050; Daniel C. Dunmyer, Chief Executive Officer
Web address: www.cshnc.com

CAROLINAS CONTINUECARE HOSPITAL AT UNIVERSITY (O, 35 beds) 8800 North Tryon Street, Charlotte, NC Zip 28262–3300; tel. 704/863–8300; Derek Murzyn, Chief Executive Officer
Web address: www.continuecare.org/charlotte//

SOUTH CAROLINA: CONTINUECARE HOSPITAL AT PALMETTO HEALTH BAPTIST (O, 35 beds) Taylor at Marion Street, Columbia, SC Zip 29220, Mailing Address: PO BOX 11069, Zip 29211–1069; tel. 803/296–3757; Larkin Virden, Interim Chief Executive Officer
Web address: www.continuecare.org/palmetto//

TENNESSEE: JELLICO COMMUNITY HOSPITAL (O, 31 beds) 188 Hospital Lane, Jellico, TN Zip 37762–4400; tel. 423/784–7252; Kim Dowell, R.N., Chief Executive Officer
Web address: www.jellicohospital.com

TEXAS: BAPTIST HOSPITALS OF SOUTHEAST TEXAS (O, 355 beds) 3080 College Street, Beaumont, TX Zip 77701–4689, Mailing Address: P.O. Box 1591, Zip 77704–1591; tel. 409/212–5000; David N. Parmer, Chief Executive Officer
Web address: www.bhset.net

CONTINUECARE HOSPITAL AT HENDRICK MEDICAL CENTER (O, 19 beds) 1900 Pine Street, Abilene, TX Zip 79601–2432; tel. 325/670–6251; Thomas P. Harlan, Chief Executive Officer
Web address: www.continuecare.org/hendrick/

CONTINUECARE HOSPITAL AT MEDICAL CENTER (ODESSA) (O, 25 beds) 500 West Fourth Street, 4th Floor, Odessa, TX Zip 79761–5001; tel. 432/640–4380; Judith Schiros, Chief Executive Officer
Web address: www.continuecare.org/odessa//

CONTINUECARE HOSPITAL AT MIDLAND MEMORIAL (O, 29 beds) 4214 Andrews Highway, 3rd Floor, Midland, TX Zip 79703–4822; tel. 432/221–3044; Judith Schiros, Chief Executive Officer
Web address: www.continuecare.org/midland/

ST. MARK'S MEDICAL CENTER (O, 65 beds) One St. Mark's Place, La Grange, TX Zip 78945; tel. 979/242–2200; Rick J. Montelongo, Chief Executive Officer
Web address: www.smmctx.org

TYLER CONTINUECARE HOSPITAL (O, 51 beds) 800 East Dawson, 4th Floor, Tyler, TX Zip 75701–2036; tel. 903/531–4080; Stephanie Hyde, R.N., MSN, Chief Executive Officer
Web address: www.continuecare.org

YOAKUM COMMUNITY HOSPITAL (O, 25 beds) 1200 Carl Ramert Drive, Yoakum, TX Zip 77995–4868; tel. 361/293–2321; Karen Barber, R.N., Chief Executive Officer
Web address: www.yoakumhospital.org

Owned, leased, sponsored:	15 hospitals	843 beds
Contract–managed:	2 hospitals	70 beds
Totals:	17 hospitals	913 beds

1085: COMMUNITY MEDICAL CENTERS (NP)
Fresno and Maddy Drive, Fresno, CA Zip 93721, Mailing Address: P.O. Box 1232, Zip 93715–1232; tel. 559/459–6000; Tim A. Joslin, President and Chief Executive Officer
(Independent Hospital System)

CALIFORNIA: CLOVIS COMMUNITY MEDICAL CENTER (O, 109 beds) 2755 Herndon Avenue, Clovis, CA Zip 93611–6801; tel. 559/324–4000; Craig Castro, Chief Executive Officer
Web address: www.communitymedical.org

COMMUNITY BEHAVIORAL HEALTH CENTER (O, 61 beds) 7171 North Cedar Avenue, Fresno, CA Zip 93720–3311; tel. 559/449–8000; Craig Wagoner, Chief Executive Officer
Web address: www.communitymedical.org

For explanation of codes following names, see page B2.
★ Indicates Type III membership in the American Hospital Association.

COMMUNITY REGIONAL MEDICAL CENTER (O, 808 beds) 2823 Fresno Street, Fresno, CA Zip 93721–1324, Mailing Address: P.O. Box 1232, Zip 93715–1232; tel. 559/459–6000; Craig Wagoner, Chief Executive Officer
Web address: www.communitymedical.org

FRESNO HEART AND SURGICAL HOSPITAL (O, 60 beds) 15 East Audubon Drive, Fresno, CA Zip 93720–1542; tel. 559/433–8000; Wanda Holderman, R.N., Chief Executive Officer
Web address: www.fresnoheartandsurgical.org

Owned, leased, sponsored:	4 hospitals	1038 beds
Contract–managed:	0 hospitals	0 beds
Totals:	4 hospitals	1038 beds

0990: COMMUNITY MEMORIAL HEALTH SYSTEM (NP)
147 North Brent Street, Ventura, CA Zip 93003–2809; tel. 805/652–5011; Gary Wilde, President and Chief Executive Officer

COMMUNITY MEMORIAL HOSPITAL (O, 345 beds) 147 North Brent Street, Ventura, CA Zip 93003–2809; tel. 805/652–5011; Gary Wilde, President and Chief Executive Officer
Web address: www.cmhshealth.org

OJAI VALLEY COMMUNITY HOSPITAL (O, 96 beds) 1306 Maricopa Highway, Ojai, CA Zip 93023–3163; tel. 805/646–1401; Haady Lashkari, Chief Administrative Officer
Web address: www.ojaihospital.org

Owned, leased, sponsored:	2 hospitals	441 beds
Contract–managed:	0 hospitals	0 beds
Totals:	2 hospitals	441 beds

0909: COMPASS HEALTH (NP)
713 North Avenue L., Crowley, LA Zip 70526–3832; tel. 337/788–3330; Mark J. Cullen, Chief Executive Officer
(Independent Hospital System)

LOUISIANA: COMPASS BEHAVIORAL CENTER OF ALEXANDRIA (O, 16 beds) 6410 Masonic Drve, Alexandria, LA Zip 71301–2319; tel. 318/442–3163; Phillip Maxwell, Administrator
Web address: www.compasshealthcare.com/site191.php

COMPASS BEHAVIORAL CENTER OF CROWLEY (O, 34 beds) 1526 North Avenue I., Crowley, LA Zip 70526–2434; tel. 337/788–3380; Allison Kidder–Tuck, Administrator
Web address: www.compasshealthcare.com

COMPASS BEHAVIORAL CENTER OF HOUMA (O, 20 beds) 4701 West Park Avenue, Houma, LA Zip 70364–4426; tel. 985/876–1715; Cheryl Turner, Administrator
Web address: www.compasshealthcare.com/site83.php

Owned, leased, sponsored:	3 hospitals	70 beds
Contract–managed:	0 hospitals	0 beds
Totals:	3 hospitals	70 beds

0999: CONCORD HEALTHCARE GROUP (IO)
111 Clifton AVenue, Lakewood, NJ Zip 08701; tel. 214/396–3462; Joe Neuman, Chief Executive Officer

OKLAHOMA: MIDWEST CITY SPECIALTY HOSPITAL (O, 31 beds) 8210 National Avenue, Midwest City, OK Zip 73110–8518; tel. 405/739–0800; Bobby Snyder, Chief Executive Officer
Web address: www.midwestcityspecialtyhospital.com/

TEXAS: MESA HILLS SPECIALTY HOSPITAL (O, 32 beds) 2311 North Oregon Street, 5th Floor, El Paso, TX Zip 79902–3216; tel. 915/545–1823; Jose Huerta, Chief Executive Officer
Web address: www.mesahillsspecialtyhospital.com/mesa_hills/index.aspx

PINE VALLEY SPECIALTY HOSPITAL (O, 35 beds) 6160 South Loop East, Houston, TX Zip 77087–1010; tel. 713/640–2400; Brent Hanson, Chief Executive Officer
Web address: www.promise–houston.com

PLANO SPECIALTY HOSPITAL (O, 43 beds) 1621 Coit Road, Plano, TX Zip 75075–6141; tel. 972/758–5200; Wayne Cook, Chief Executive Officer
Web address: www.specialtyhospital–plano.com

PLUM CREEK SPECIALTY HOSPITAL (O, 47 beds) 5601 Plum Creek Drive, Amarillo, TX Zip 79124–1801; tel. 806/351–1000; Bobby Snyder, Interim Chief Executive Officer
Web address: www.plumcreekspecialtyhosp.com/

Owned, leased, sponsored:	5 hospitals	188 beds
Contract–managed:	0 hospitals	0 beds
Totals:	5 hospitals	188 beds

0950: CONE HEALTH (NP)
1200 North Elm Street, Greensboro, NC Zip 27401–1004; tel. 336/832–7000; Terry Akin, President and Chief Executive Officer

MOSES H. CONE MEMORIAL HOSPITAL (C, 912 beds) 1200 North Elm Street, Greensboro, NC Zip 27401–1020; tel. 336/832–7000
Web address: http://www.conehealth.com/locations/moses-cone-hospital/

ALAMANCE REGIONAL MEDICAL CENTER (O, 218 beds) P.O. Box 202, Burlington, NC Zip 27216–0202; tel. 336/538–7000
Web address: http://www.armc.com

RANDOLPH HOSPITAL (C, 101 beds) P.O. Box 1048, Asheboro, NC Zip 27204–1048; tel. 336/625–5151
Web address: http://www.randolphhospital.org

Owned, leased, sponsored:	1 hospitals	218 beds
Contract–managed:	2 hospitals	1013 beds
Totals:	3 hospitals	1231 beds

0014: CONNECTICUT DEPARTMENT OF MENTAL HEALTH AND ADDICTION SERVICES (NP)
410 Capitol Avenue, Hartford, CT Zip 06106–1367, Mailing Address: P.O. Box 341431, Zip 06134–1431; tel. 860/418–7000; Miriam Delphin–Rittmon, Ph.D., Commissioner
(Independent Hospital System)

CONNECTICUT: CONNECTICUT MENTAL HEALTH CENTER (O, 32 beds) 34 Park Street, New Haven, CT Zip 06519–1109, Mailing Address: P.O. Box 1842, Zip 06508–1842; tel. 203/974–7144; Michael Sernyak, M.D., Director
Web address: www.ct.gov/dmhas/cwp/view.asp?a=2906&q=334596

CONNECTICUT VALLEY HOSPITAL (O, 596 beds) Eastern Drive, Middletown, CT Zip 06457–3947; tel. 860/262–5000; Helene M. Vartelas, MSN, Chief Executive Officer
Web address: www.ct.gov/dmhas/cwp/view.asp?a=3519&q=416778

SOUTHWEST CONNECTICUT MENTAL HEALTH SYSTEM (O, 62 beds) 1635 Central Avenue, Bridgeport, CT Zip 06610–2717; tel. 203/551–7400; Daniel Wartenberg, PsyD, M.P.H., Chief Executive Officer
Web address: www.ct.gov/dmhas/cwp/view.asp?a=2946&q=378936

Owned, leased, sponsored:	3 hospitals	690 beds
Contract–managed:	0 hospitals	0 beds
Totals:	3 hospitals	690 beds

0016: COOK COUNTY HEALTH AND HOSPITALS SYSTEM (NP)
1900 West Polk Street, Suite 220, Chicago, IL Zip 60612–3723; tel. 312/864–6820; John Jay Shannon, M.D., Chief Executive Officer
(Independent Hospital System)

ILLINOIS: JOHN H. STROGER JR. HOSPITAL OF COOK COUNTY (O, 464 beds) 1969 West Ogden Avenue, Chicago, IL Zip 60612–3714; tel. 312/864–6000; John Jay Shannon, M.D., Chief Executive Officer
Web address: www.cookcountyhealth.net

For explanation of codes following names, see page B2.
★ Indicates Type III membership in the American Hospital Association.

Section B

PROVIDENT HOSPITAL OF COOK COUNTY (O, 25 beds) 500 East 51st Street, Chicago, IL Zip 60615–2494; tel. 312/572–2000; John Jay Shannon, M.D., Chief Executive Officer
Web address: www.ccbhs.org/pages/ProvidentHospitalofCookCounty.htm

Owned, leased, sponsored:	2 hospitals	489 beds
Contract–managed:	0 hospitals	0 beds
Totals:	2 hospitals	489 beds

0905:   CORNERSTONE HEALTHCARE GROUP (IO)
2200 Ross Avenue, Suite 5400, Dallas, TX Zip 75201–7984; tel. 469/621–6700; David Smith, President and Chief Executive Officer
(Independent Hospital System)

ARIZONA: CHG HOSPITAL TUCSON, LLC (O, 34 beds) 7220 East Rosewood Drive, Tucson, AZ Zip 85710–1350; tel. 520/546–4595; Paul E. Qualls, Chief Executive Officer
Web address: www.chghospitals.com

ARKANSAS: CORNERSTONE HOSPITAL OF LITTLE ROCK (O, 40 beds) 2 St. Vincent Circle, 6th Floor, Little Rock, AR Zip 72205; tel. 501/265–0600; James H. Rogers, FACHE, Chief Executive Officer
Web address: www.chghospitals.com/littlerock/

LOUISIANA: CORNERSTONE HOSPITAL OF BOSSIER CITY (O, 54 beds) 4900 Medical Drive, Bossier City, LA Zip 71112–4521; tel. 318/747–9500; Sheri Burnette, R.N., Chief Executive Officer and Administrator
Web address: www.chghospitals.com/

CORNERSTONE HOSPITAL OF SOUTHWEST LOUISIANA (O, 30 beds) 703 Cypress Street, Sulphur, LA Zip 70663–5053; tel. 337/310–6000; David Smith, President
Web address: www.chghospitals.com/sulphur/

CORNERSTONE HOSPITAL–WEST MONROE (O, 40 beds) 6198 Cypress Street, West Monroe, LA Zip 71291–9010; tel. 318/396–5600; Chris Simpson, Chief Executive Officer
Web address: www.chghospitals.com/chwm.html

OKLAHOMA: CORNERSTONE HOSPITAL OF OKLAHOMA–MUSKOGEE (O, 41 beds) 351 South 40th Street, Muskogee, OK Zip 74401–4916; tel. 918/682–6161; Craig Koele, Chief Executive Officer
Web address: www.chghospitals.com/muskogee/

CORNERSTONE HOSPITAL OF OKLAHOMA–SHAWNEE (O, 34 beds) 1900 Gordon Cooper Drive, 2nd Floor, Shawnee, OK Zip 74801–8603, Mailing Address: P.O. Box 1245, Zip 74802–1245; tel. 405/395–5800; Elizabeth Waytula, Chief Executive Officer
Web address: www.chghospitals.com/shawnee/

TEXAS: CHG CORNERSTONE HOSPITAL CONROE (O, 41 beds) 1500 Grand Lake Drive, Conroe, TX Zip 77304–2891; tel. 936/523–1800; Suzanne Kretschmer, Chief Executive Officer
Web address: www.chghospitals.com/conroe/

CORNERSTONE HOSPITAL OF AUSTIN (O, 118 beds) 4207 Burnet Road, Austin, TX Zip 78756–3396; tel. 512/706–1900; Scott Galliardt, MSN, R.N., Chief Executive Officer
Web address: www.chghospitals.com/austin/

CORNERSTONE HOSPITAL OF HOUSTON AT CLEARLAKE (O, 148 beds) 709 Medical Center Boulevard, Webster, TX Zip 77598; tel. 281/332–3322; Amy Stasney, Chief Executive Officer
Web address: www.cornerstonehealthcaregroup.com

CORNERSTONE HOSPITAL–MEDICAL CENTER OF HOUSTON (O, 35 beds) 2001 Hermann Drive, Houston, TX Zip 77004; tel. 832/649–6200; Michael Higginbotham, Chief Executive Officer
Web address: www.chghospitals.com

SOLARA HOSPITAL HARLINGEN (O, 82 beds) 508 Victoria Lane, Harlingen, TX Zip 78550–3225; tel. 956/425–9600; Cary L. Montalvo, Chief Executive Officer
Web address: www.chghospitals.com/harlingen/

SOLARA HOSPITAL MCALLEN (O, 78 beds) 301 West Expressway 83, 8th Floor, McAllen, TX Zip 78503–3045; tel. 956/632–4880; Hari Namboodiri, Chief Executive Officer
Web address: www.chghospitals.com/mcallen/

WEST VIRGINIA: CORNERSTONE HOSPITAL OF HUNTINGTON (O, 25 beds) 2900 First Avenue, Two East, Huntington, WV Zip 25702–1241; tel. 304/399–2600; Cynthia Isaacs, Chief Executive Officer
Web address: www.chghospitals.com

Owned, leased, sponsored:	14 hospitals	800 beds
Contract–managed:	0 hospitals	0 beds
Totals:	14 hospitals	800 beds

★0103:   COTTAGE HEALTH (NP)
400 West Pueblo Street, Santa Barbara, CA Zip 93105–4353, Mailing Address: P.O. Box 689, Zip 93102–0689; tel. 805/569–7290; Ronald C. Werft, President and Chief Executive Officer
(Independent Hospital System)

CALIFORNIA: GOLETA VALLEY COTTAGE HOSPITAL (O, 28 beds) 351 South Patterson Avenue, Santa Barbara, CA Zip 93111–2496, Mailing Address: Box 6306, Zip 93160–6306; tel. 805/967–3411; Ronald C. Werft, President and Chief Executive Officer
Web address: www.sbch.org

SANTA BARBARA COTTAGE HOSPITAL (O, 351 beds) 400 West Pueblo Street, Santa Barbara, CA Zip 93105–4390, Mailing Address: P.O. Box 689, Zip 93102–0689; tel. 805/682–7111; Ronald C. Werft, President and Chief Executive Officer
Web address: www.cottagehealthsystem.org

SANTA YNEZ VALLEY COTTAGE HOSPITAL (O, 11 beds) 2050 Viborg Road, Solvang, CA Zip 93463–2295; tel. 805/688–6431; Ronald C. Werft, President and Chief Executive Officer
Web address: www.cottagehealthsystem.org

Owned, leased, sponsored:	3 hospitals	390 beds
Contract–managed:	0 hospitals	0 beds
Totals:	3 hospitals	390 beds

★0123:   COVENANT HEALTH (NP)
100 Fort Sanders West Boulevard, Knoxville, TN Zip 37922–3353; tel. 865/531–5555; James VanderSteeg, President and Chief Executive Officer
(Centralized Health System)

TENNESSEE: CLAIBORNE MEDICAL CENTER (L, 132 beds) 1850 Old Knoxville Road, Tazewell, TN Zip 37879–3625; tel. 423/626–4211; Patricia P. Ketterman, R.N., President and Chief Administrative Officer
Web address: www.claibornehospital.org

CUMBERLAND MEDICAL CENTER (O, 97 beds) 421 South Main Street, Crossville, TN Zip 38555–5031; tel. 931/484–9511; David V. Bunch, President and Chief Administrative Officer
Web address: www.cmchealthcare.org

FORT LOUDOUN MEDICAL CENTER (L, 30 beds) 550 Fort Loudoun Medical Center Drive, Lenoir City, TN Zip 37772–5673; tel. 865/271–6000; Jeffrey Feike, President and Chief Administrative Officer
Web address: www.covenanthealth.com

FORT SANDERS REGIONAL MEDICAL CENTER (O, 402 beds) 1901 West Clinch Avenue, Knoxville, TN Zip 37916–2307; tel. 865/541–1111; Keith Altshuler, President and Chief Administrative Officer
Web address: www.covenanthealth.com

LECONTE MEDICAL CENTER (O, 129 beds) 742 Middle Creek Road, Sevierville, TN Zip 37862–5019, Mailing Address: P.O. Box 8005, Zip 37864–8005; tel. 865/446–7000; Jennifer Hanson, MS, R.N., President and Chief Administrative Officer
Web address: www.lecontemedicalcenter.com

METHODIST MEDICAL CENTER OF OAK RIDGE (O, 210 beds) 990 Oak Ridge Turnpike, Oak Ridge, TN Zip 37830–6976, Mailing Address: P.O. Box 2529, Zip 37831–2529; tel. 865/835–1000; Jeremy Biggs, Chief Executive Officer
Web address: www.mmcoakridge.com

MORRISTOWN–HAMBLEN HEALTHCARE SYSTEM (O, 131 beds) 908 West Fourth North Street, Morristown, TN Zip 37814–3894, Mailing Address: P.O. Box 1178, Zip 37816–1178; tel. 423/492–9000; Gordon Lintz, Chief Administrative Officer
Web address: www.morristownhamblen.com

For explanation of codes following names, see page B2.
★ Indicates Type III membership in the American Hospital Association.

Section B

PARKWEST MEDICAL CENTER (O, 297 beds) 9352 Park West Boulevard, Knoxville, TN Zip 37923–4325, Mailing Address: P.O. Box 22993, Zip 37933–0993; tel. 865/373–1000; Rick Lassiter, President and Chief Administrative Officer
Web address: www.yesparkwest.com

ROANE MEDICAL CENTER (O, 36 beds) 8045 Roane Medical Center Drive, Harriman, TN Zip 37748–8333; tel. 865/316–1000; Gaye Jolly, FACHE, President/Chief Administrative Officer
Web address: www.roanemedical.com

Owned, leased, sponsored:	9 hospitals	1464 beds
Contract–managed:	0 hospitals	0 beds
Totals:	9 hospitals	1464 beds

★5885: COVENANT HEALTH (CC)
100 Ames Pond Drive, Suite 102, Tewksbury, MA Zip 01876–1240; tel. 978/654–6363; David R. Lincoln, FACHE, President and Chief Executive Officer
(Moderately Centralized Health System)

MAINE: ST. JOSEPH HOSPITAL (O, 84 beds) 360 Broadway, Bangor, ME Zip 04401–3979, Mailing Address: P.O. Box 403, Zip 04402–0403; tel. 207/262–1000; Mary Prybylo, President and Chief Executive Officer
Web address: www.sjhhealth.com

ST. MARY'S REGIONAL MEDICAL CENTER (O, 380 beds) 318 Sabattus Street, Lewiston, ME Zip 04240–5553, Mailing Address: P.O. Box 291, Zip 04243–0291; tel. 207/777–8100; Christopher A. Chekouras, President and Chief Executive Officer
Web address: www.stmarysmaine.com

NEW HAMPSHIRE: ST. JOSEPH HOSPITAL (O, 126 beds) 172 Kinsley Street, Nashua, NH Zip 03060–3648; tel. 603/882–3000; Richard Boehler, M.D., President and Chief Executive Officer
Web address: www.stjosephhospital.com

Owned, leased, sponsored:	3 hospitals	590 beds
Contract–managed:	0 hospitals	0 beds
Totals:	3 hospitals	590 beds

●★0036: COVENANT HEALTH SYSTEM (NP)
3615 19th Street, Lubbock, TX Zip 79410–1203; tel. 806/725–0447; Richard H. Parks, FACHE, President and Chief Executive Officer
(Centralized Health System)

TEXAS: COVENANT SPECIALTY HOSPITAL (O, 56 beds) 3815 20th Street, Lubbock, TX Zip 79410–1235; tel. 806/725–9200; Julie Bell, Interim Chief Executive Officer and Chief Nursing Officer
Web address: www.covenanthealth.org/view/Facilities/Specialty_Hospital

Owned, leased, sponsored:	1 hospital	56 beds
Contract–managed:	0 hospitals	0 beds
Totals:	1 hospital	56 beds

0179: COXHEALTH (NP)
1423 North Jefferson Avenue, Springfield, MO Zip 65802–1988; tel. 417/269–3108; Steven D. Edwards, President and Chief Executive Officer
(Centralized Physician/Insurance Health System)

MISSOURI: COX MEDICAL CENTER BRANSON (O, 113 beds) 251 Skaggs Road, Branson, MO Zip 65616–2031, Mailing Address: P.O. Box 650, Zip 65615–0650; tel. 417/335–7000; William K. Mahoney, President and Chief Executive Officer
Web address: www.coxhealth.com

COX MEDICAL CENTERS (O, 621 beds) 1423 North Jefferson Street, Springfield, MO Zip 65802–1988; tel. 417/269–3000; Steven D. Edwards, President and Chief Executive Officer
Web address: www.coxhealth.com

COX MONETT (O, 25 beds) 801 North Lincoln Avenue, Monett, MO Zip 65708–1641; tel. 417/235–3144; Darren Bass, President
Web address: www.coxhealth.com

	3 hospitals	759 beds
Contract–managed:	0 hospitals	0 beds
Totals:	3 hospitals	759 beds

0930: CRC HEALTH GROUP, INC. (IO)
20400 Stevens Creek Boulevard, Suite 600, Cupertino, CA Zip 95014–2217; tel. 866/540–5240; Jerome E. Rhodes, Chief Executive Officer
(Independent Hospital System)

ARIZONA: SIERRA TUCSON (O, 139 beds) 39580 South Lago Del Oro Parkway, Tucson, AZ Zip 85739–1091; tel. 520/624–4000; Stephen P. Fahey, Executive Director
Web address: www.sierratucson.com

NORTH CAROLINA: WILMINGTON TREATMENT CENTER (O, 44 beds) 2520 Troy Drive, Wilmington, NC Zip 28401–7643; tel. 910/762–2727; Robert Pitts, Executive Director
Web address: www.wilmtreatment.com

Owned, leased, sponsored:	2 hospitals	183 beds
Contract–managed:	0 hospitals	0 beds
Totals:	2 hospitals	183 beds

★0008: CROZER–KEYSTONE HEALTH SYSTEM (NP)
100 West Sproul Road, Springfield, PA Zip 19064–2033; tel. 610/338–8205; Patrick J. Gavin, President and Chief Executive Officer
(Moderately Centralized Health System)

PENNSYLVANIA: CROZER–CHESTER MEDICAL CENTER (O, 384 beds) One Medical Center Boulevard, Upland, PA Zip 19013–3995; tel. 610/447–2000; Patrick J. Gavin, President
Web address: www.crozer.org

DELAWARE COUNTY MEMORIAL HOSPITAL (O, 168 beds) 501 North Lansdowne Avenue, Drexel Hill, PA Zip 19026–1114; tel. 610/284–8100; Robert Haffey, R.N., President
Web address: www.crozer.org

Owned, leased, sponsored:	2 hospitals	552 beds
Contract–managed:	0 hospitals	0 beds
Totals:	2 hospitals	552 beds

0960: CURAE HEALTH (NP)
121 Leinart Street, Clinton, TN Zip 37716–3632, Mailing Address: P.O. Box 358, Zip 37717–0358; tel. 865/269–4074; Steve Clapp, President and Chief Executive Officer
(Independent Hospital System)

ALABAMA: LAKELAND COMMUNITY HOSPITAL (O, 56 beds) Highway 195 East, Haleyville, AL 35565–9536, Mailing Address: P.O. Box 780, Zip 35565–0780; tel. 205/486–5213; Cynthia Nichols, R.N., MSN, Chief Executive Officer
Web address: www.lakelandcommunityhospital.com/

NORTHWEST MEDICAL CENTER (O, 76 beds) 1530 U.S. Highway 43, Winfield, AL Zip 35594–5056; tel. 205/487–7000; Michael D. Windham, Chief Executive Officer
Web address: www.northwestmedcenter.com

RUSSELLVILLE HOSPITAL (O, 92 beds) 15155 Highway 43, Russellville, AL Zip 35653–1975, Mailing Address: P.O. Box 1089, Zip 35653–1089; tel. 256/332–1611; Christine R. Stewart, FACHE, Chief Executive Officer
Web address: www.russellvillehospital.com

Owned, leased, sponsored:	3 hospitals	224 beds
Contract–managed:	0 hospitals	0 beds
Totals:	3 hospitals	224 beds

★0864: DAVIS HEALTH SYSTEM (NP)
Reed Street and Gorman Avenue, Elkins, WV Zip 26241, Mailing Address: P.O. Box 1697, Zip 26241–1697; tel. 304/636–3300; Vance Jackson, FACHE, President and Chief Executive Officer
(Independent Hospital System)

For explanation of codes following names, see page B2.
★ Indicates Type III membership in the American Hospital Association.
● Single hospital health care system

WEST VIRGINIA: BROADDUS HOSPITAL (O, 72 beds) 1 Healthcare Drive, Philippi, WV Zip 26416–9405, Mailing Address: P.O. Box 930, Zip 26416–0930; tel. 304/457–1760; Jeffrey A. Powelson, Chief Executive Officer
Web address: www.davishealthsystem.org/

DAVIS MEDICAL CENTER (O, 80 beds) Gorman Avenue and Reed Street, Elkins, WV Zip 26241, Mailing Address: P.O. Box 1484, Zip 26241–1484; tel. 304/636–3300; Vance Jackson, FACHE, Chief Executive Officer
Web address: www.davishealthsystem.com

Owned, leased, sponsored:	2 hospitals	152 beds
Contract–managed:	0 hospitals	0 beds
Totals:	2 hospitals	152 beds

1825: DCH HEALTH SYSTEM (NP)
809 University Boulevard East, Tuscaloosa, AL Zip 35401–2029; tel. 205/759–7111; Bryan N. Kindred, FACHE, President and Chief Executive Officer
(Moderately Centralized Health System)

ALABAMA: DCH REGIONAL MEDICAL CENTER (O, 684 beds) 809 University Boulevard East, Tuscaloosa, AL Zip 35401–2029; tel. 205/759–7111; William H. Cassels, Administrator
Web address: www.dchsystem.com

FAYETTE MEDICAL CENTER (L, 167 beds) 1653 Temple Avenue North, Fayette, AL Zip 35555–1314, Mailing Address: P.O. Drawer 710, Zip 35555–0710; tel. 205/932–5966; Donald J. Jones, FACHE, Administrator
Web address: www.dchsystem.com

Owned, leased, sponsored:	2 hospitals	851 beds
Contract–managed:	0 hospitals	0 beds
Totals:	2 hospitals	851 beds

★0313: DEACONESS HEALTH SYSTEM (NP)
600 Mary Street, Evansville, IN Zip 47710–1658; tel. 812/450–5000; Linda E. White, President and Chief Executive Officer
(Moderately Centralized Health System)

INDIANA: DEACONESS HOSPITAL (O, 506 beds) 600 Mary Street, Evansville, IN Zip 47710–1658; tel. 812/450–5000; Shawn W. McCoy, Chief Administrative Officer
Web address: www.deaconess.com

THE HEART HOSPITAL AT DEACONESS GATEWAY (O, 24 beds) 4007 Gateway Boulevard, Newburgh, IN Zip 47630–8947; tel. 812/842–4784; Rebecca Malotte, Executive Director and Chief Nursing Officer
Web address: www.deaconess.com/

THE WOMEN'S HOSPITAL (O, 74 beds) 4199 Gateway Boulevard, Newburgh, IN Zip 47630–8940; tel. 812/842–4200; Christina M. Ryan, R.N., Chief Executive Officer
Web address: www.deaconess.com

Owned, leased, sponsored:	3 hospitals	604 beds
Contract–managed:	0 hospitals	0 beds
Totals:	3 hospitals	604 beds

0330: DEKALB REGIONAL HEALTH SYSTEM (NP)
2701 North Decatur Road, Decatur, GA Zip 30033–5918; tel. 404/501–1000; John Shelton, President and Chief Executive Officer
(Centralized Health System)

GEORGIA: DEKALB MEDICAL AT DOWNTOWN DECATUR (O, 44 beds) 450 North Candler Street, Decatur, GA Zip 30030–2671; tel. 404/501–6700; John Shelton, President and Chief Executive Officer
Web address: www.dekalbmedicalcenter.org

DEKALB MEDICAL AT HILLANDALE (O, 80 beds) 2801 DeKalb Medical Parkway, Lithonia, GA Zip 30058–4996; tel. 404/501–8700; John Shelton, President and Chief Executive Officer
Web address: www.dekalbmedical.org

DEKALB MEDICAL AT NORTH DECATUR (O, 417 beds) 2701 North Decatur Road, Decatur, GA Zip 30033–5995; tel. 404/501–1000; John Shelton, President and Chief Executive Officer
Web address: www.dekalbmedical.org

Owned, leased, sponsored:	3 hospitals	541 beds
Contract–managed:	0 hospitals	0 beds
Totals:	3 hospitals	541 beds

9495: DEPARTMENT OF THE AIR FORCE (FG)
1420 Pentagon, Room 4E1084, Washington, DC Zip 20330–1420; tel. 202/767–4765; Lieutenant General Thomas Travis, Surgeon General
(Independent Hospital System)

ALASKA: U. S. AIR FORCE REGIONAL HOSPITAL (O, 64 beds) 5955 Zeamer Avenue, Elmendorf AFB, AK Zip 99506–3702; tel. 907/580–3006; Major Mark Lamey, Commander
Web address: www.elmendorf.af.mil/

CALIFORNIA: DAVID GRANT USAF MEDICAL CENTER (O, 116 beds) 101 Bodin Circle, Travis AFB, CA Zip 94535–1809; tel. 707/423–7300; Colonel Brian T. Hayes, Commander
Web address: www.travis.af.mil/units/dgmc/index.asp

FLORIDA: U. S. AIR FORCE REGIONAL HOSPITAL (O, 57 beds) 307 Boatner Road, Suite 114, Eglin AFB, FL Zip 32542–1282; tel. 850/883–8221; Colonel Eveline F. Yao, Commander
Web address: www.eglin.af.mil

MISSISSIPPI: U. S. AIR FORCE MEDICAL CENTER KEESLER (O, 56 beds) 301 Fisher Street, Room 1A132, Keesler AFB, MS Zip 39534–2519; tel. 228/376–2550; Colonel Thomas Harrell, M.D., Commander
Web address: www.keesler.af.mil

NEVADA: MIKE O'CALLAGHAN FEDERAL HOSPITAL (O, 46 beds) 4700 Las Vegas Boulevard North, Suite 2419, Nellis AFB, NV Zip 89191–6600; tel. 702/653–2000; Colonel Christian Benjamin, USAF, MC, Commander
Web address: www.lasvegas.va.gov/

OHIO: WRIGHT PATTERSON MEDICAL CENTER (O, 52 beds) 4881 Sugar Maple Drive, Wright–Patterson AFB, OH Zip 45433–5529; tel. 937/257–9144; Colonel Brent J. Erickson, Administrator
Web address: www.wpafb.af.mil/units/wpmc/

VIRGINIA: U. S. AIR FORCE HOSPITAL (O, 65 beds) 77 Nealy Avenue, Hampton, VA Zip 23665–2040; tel. 757/764–6969; Colonel Wayne M. Pritt, Commander
Web address: www.jble.af.mil

Owned, leased, sponsored:	7 hospitals	456 beds
Contract–managed:	0 hospitals	0 beds
Totals:	7 hospitals	456 beds

9395: DEPARTMENT OF THE ARMY, OFFICE OF THE SURGEON GENERAL (FG)
5109 Leesburg Pike, Falls Church, VA Zip 22041–3215; tel. 703/681–3000; Lieutenant General Eric B. Schoomaker, Surgeon General
(Moderately Centralized Health System)

ALASKA: BASSETT ARMY COMMUNITY HOSPITAL (O, 24 beds) 1060 Gaffney Road, Box 7400, Fort Wainwright, AK Zip 99703–5001, Mailing Address: 1060 Gaffney Road, Box 7440, Zip 99703–5001; tel. 907/361–4000; Timothy Bergeron, Deputy Commander, Administration
Web address: www.alaska.amedd.army.mil

CALIFORNIA: WEED ARMY COMMUNITY HOSPITAL (O, 27 beds) Inner Loop Road and 4th Street, Building 166, Fort Irwin, CA Zip 92310–5065, Mailing Address: P.O. Box 105109, Zip 92310–5109; tel. 760/380–3108; Colonel Jason S. Wieman, Commander
Web address: www.irwin.amedd.army.mil

COLORADO: EVANS U. S. ARMY COMMUNITY HOSPITAL (O, 57 beds) 1650 Cochrane Circle, Building 7500, Fort Carson, CO Zip 80913–4613; tel. 719/526–7200; Patrick H. Garman, Commander
Web address: www.evans.amedd.army.mil

For explanation of codes following names, see page B2.
★ Indicates Type III membership in the American Hospital Association.

Section B

GEORGIA: DWIGHT DAVID EISENHOWER ARMY MEDICAL CENTER (O, 107 beds) 300 West Hospital Road, Fort Gordon, GA Zip 30905–5741; tel. 706/787–5811; Colonel John P. Lamoureux, Commander
Web address: www.ddeamc.amedd.army.mil

MARTIN ARMY COMMUNITY HOSPITAL (O, 57 beds) 7950 Martin Loop, Fort Benning, GA Zip 31905–5648, Mailing Address: 7950 Martin Loop, B9200, Room 010, Zip 31905–5648; tel. 706/544–2516; Colonel Marie Dominguez, Commander
Web address: www.martin.amedd.army.mil

WINN ARMY COMMUNITY HOSPITAL (O, 37 beds) 1061 Harmon Avenue, Hinesville, GA Zip 31314–5641, Mailing Address: 1061 Harmon Avenue, Suite 2311B, Zip 31314–5641; tel. 912/435–6965; Colonel Kirk W. Eggleston, Commanding Officer
Web address: www.winn.amedd.army.mil/

HAWAII: TRIPLER ARMY MEDICAL CENTER (O, 194 beds) 1 Jarret White Road, Honolulu, HI Zip 96859–5001; tel. 808/433–6661; Colonel David K. Dunning, Commanding Officer
Web address: www.tamc.amedd.army.mil

KANSAS: IRWIN ARMY COMMUNITY HOSPITAL (O, 44 beds) 600 Caisson Hill Road, Junction City, KS Zip 66442–7037; tel. 785/239–7000; Colonel Risa Ware, Commander
Web address: www.iach.amedd.army.mil

KENTUCKY: COLONEL FLORENCE A. BLANCHFIELD ARMY COMMUNITY HOSPITAL (O, 66 beds) 650 Joel Drive, Fort Campbell, KY Zip 42223–5318; tel. 270/798–8040; Colonel Telita Crosland, Commander
Web address: www.campbell.amedd.army.mil/

IRELAND ARMY COMMUNITY HOSPITAL (O, 17 beds) 289 Ireland Avenue, Fort Knox, KY Zip 40121–5111; tel. 502/624–9333; Colonel Robert S. Cornes, Commander
Web address: www.iach.knox.amedd.army.mil/

LOUISIANA: BAYNE–JONES ARMY COMMUNITY HOSPITAL (O, 22 beds) 1585 3rd Street, Fort Polk, LA Zip 71459–5102; tel. 337/531–3928; Colonel Carlene Blanding, Commander
Web address: www.polk.amedd.army.mil

MARSHALL ISLANDS: KWAJALEIN HOSPITAL (O, 14 beds) U.S. Army Kwajalein Atoll, Kwajalein Island, MH Zip 96960, Mailing Address: Box 1702, APO, UNITZip 96555–5000; tel. 805/355–2225; Elaine McMahon, Administrator

MISSOURI: GENERAL LEONARD WOOD ARMY COMMUNITY HOSPITAL (O, 54 beds) 126 Missouri Avenue, Fort Leonard Wood, MO Zip 65473–8952; tel. 573/596–0414; Colonel Christian Meko, Hospital Commander
Web address: www.glwach.amedd.army.mil/

NEW YORK: KELLER ARMY COMMUNITY HOSPITAL (O, 20 beds) 900 Washington Road, West Point, NY Zip 10996–1197, Mailing Address: U.S. Military Academy, Building 900, Zip 10996–1197; tel. 845/938–5169; Colonel Brian S. Burlingame, Commanding Officer
Web address: www.kach.amedd.army.mil/SitePages/Home.aspx

NORTH CAROLINA: WOMACK ARMY MEDICAL CENTER (O, 156 beds) Normandy Drive, Fort Bragg, NC Zip 28307–5000; tel. 910/907–6000; Colonel Ronald Stephens, Commander
Web address: www.wamc.amedd.army.mil/

OKLAHOMA: REYNOLDS ARMY COMMUNITY HOSPITAL (O, 24 beds) 4301 Wilson Street, Fort Sill, OK Zip 73503–4472; tel. 580/558–3000; Colonel Kenneth Lemons, Commander
Web address: www.rach.sill.amedd.army.mil

SOUTH CAROLINA: MONCRIEF ARMY COMMUNITY HOSPITAL (O, 60 beds) 4500 Stuart Street, Fort Jackson, SC Zip 29207–5700; tel. 803/751–2160; Colonel Traci Crawford, R.N., Commander
Web address: www.moncrief.amedd.army.mil

TEXAS: BROOKE ARMY MEDICAL CENTER (O, 226 beds) 3851 Roger Brookes Drive, Fort Sam Houston, TX Zip 78234–4501; tel. 210/916–4141; Colonel Evan Renz, Chief Executive Officer
Web address: www.bamc.amedd.army.mil

CARL R. DARNALL ARMY MEDICAL CENTER (O, 109 beds) 36000 Darnall Loop, Fort Hood, TX Zip 76544–5095; tel. 254/288–8000; Colonel Mark W. Thompson, M.D., Commanding Officer
Web address: www.crdamc.amedd.army.mil

WILLIAM BEAUMONT ARMY MEDICAL CENTER (O, 209 beds) 5005 North Piedras Street, El Paso, TX Zip 79920–5001; tel. 915/742–2121; Colonel Michael S. Heimall, Commander
Web address: www.wbamc.amedd.army.mil

VIRGINIA: FORT BELVOIR COMMUNITY HOSPITAL (O, 46 beds) 9300 Dewitt Loop, Fort Belvoir, VA Zip 22060–5285; tel. 571/231–3224; Captain Jennifer Vedral–Baron, Commander
Web address: www.fbch.capmed.mil/SitePages/Home.aspx

WASHINGTON: MADIGAN ARMY MEDICAL CENTER (O, 227 beds) Fitzsimmons Drive, Building 9040, Tacoma, WA Zip 98431–1100; tel. 253/968–1110; ,
Web address: www.mamc.amedd.army.mil

Owned, leased, sponsored:	22 hospitals	1797 beds
Contract–managed:	0 hospitals	0 beds
Totals:	22 hospitals	1797 beds

9295: DEPARTMENT OF VETERANS AFFAIRS (FG) 810 Vermont Avenue N.W., Washington, DC Zip 20420–0001; tel. 202/273–5781; Robert A. McDonald, Secretary, Veterans Affairs **(Decentralized Health System)**

ALABAMA: BIRMINGHAM VETERANS AFFAIRS MEDICAL CENTER (O, 151 beds) 700 South 19th Street, Birmingham, AL Zip 35233–1927; tel. 205/933–8101; Thomas C. Smith, III, FACHE, Director
Web address: www.birmingham.va.gov/

CENTRAL ALABAMA VETERANS HEALTH CARE SYSTEM (O, 245 beds) 215 Perry Hill Road, Montgomery, AL Zip 36109–3798; tel. 334/272–4670; Paul Bockelman, Director
Web address: www.centralalabama.va.gov/

TUSCALOOSA VETERANS AFFAIRS MEDICAL CENTER (O, 366 beds) 3701 Loop Road East, Tuscaloosa, AL Zip 35404–5015; tel. 205/554–2000; John F. Merkle, Medical Center Director
Web address: www.tuscaloosa.va.gov

ARIZONA: NORTHERN ARIZONA VETERANS AFFAIRS HEALTH CARE SYSTEM (O, 137 beds) 500 Highway 89 North, Prescott, AZ Zip 86313–5000; tel. 928/445–4860; Malcolm Keith Piatt, M.D., Interim Director
Web address: www.prescott.va.gov/

PHOENIX VETERANS AFFAIRS HEALTH CARE SYSTEM (O, 197 beds) 650 East Indian School Road, Phoenix, AZ Zip 85012–1892; tel. 602/277–5551; Deborah Amdur, Director
Web address: www.phoenix.va.gov/

SOUTHERN ARIZONA VETERANS AFFAIRS HEALTH CARE SYSTEM (O, 285 beds) 3601 South 6th Avenue, Tucson, AZ Zip 85723–0002; tel. 520/792–1450; Jennifer S. Gutowski, FACHE, Acting Director
Web address: www.tucson.va.gov

ARKANSAS: CENTRAL ARKANSAS VETERANS HEALTHCARE SYSTEM (O, 637 beds) 4300 West Seventh Street, Little Rock, AR Zip 72205–5446; tel. 501/257–1000; Cyril Ekeh, Interim Medical Center Director
Web address: www.littlerock.va.gov/

VETERANS HEALTH CARE SYSTEM OF THE OZARKS (O, 72 beds) 1100 North College Avenue, Fayetteville, AR Zip 72703–1944; tel. 479/443–4301; Bryan C. Matthews, Director
Web address: www.fayettevillear.va.gov

CALIFORNIA: SAN FRANCISCO VA MEDICAL CENTER (O, 244 beds) 4150 Clement Street, San Francisco, CA Zip 94121–1545; tel. 415/221–4810; Bonnie S. Graham, Director
Web address: www.sanfrancisco.va.gov/

VA GREATER LOS ANGELES HEALTHCARE SYSTEM (O, 1087 beds) 11301 Wilshire Boulevard, Los Angeles, CA Zip 90073–1003; tel. 310/478–3711; Ann R. Brown, M.D., Director
Web address: www.losangeles.va.gov/

VA LONG BEACH HEALTHCARE SYSTEM (O, 356 beds) 5901 East 7th Street, Long Beach, CA Zip 90822–5201; tel. 562/826–8000; Tracye B. Davis, Acting Director
Web address: www.longbeach.va.gov/

VA PALO ALTO HEALTH CARE SYSTEM (O, 808 beds) 3801 Miranda Avenue, Palo Alto, CA Zip 94304–1207; tel. 650/493–5000; Elizabeth Joyce Freeman, FACHE, Director
Web address: www.paloalto.va.gov/

For explanation of codes following names, see page B2.
★ Indicates Type III membership in the American Hospital Association.

VA SAN DIEGO HEALTHCARE SYSTEM (O, 248 beds) 3350 LaJolla Village Drive, San Diego, CA Zip 92161–0002; tel. 858/552–8585; Robert M. Smith, M.D., Director
Web address: www.sandiego.va.gov

VETERANS AFFAIRS CENTRAL CALIFORNIA HEALTH CARE SYSTEM (O, 117 beds) 2615 East Clinton Avenue, Fresno, CA Zip 93703–2223; tel. 559/225–6100; Wessel H. Meyer, M.D., Acting Director
Web address: www.fresno.va.gov/

VETERANS AFFAIRS LOMA LINDA HEALTHCARE SYSTEM (O, 268 beds) 11201 Benton Street, Loma Linda, CA Zip 92357–1000; tel. 909/825–7084; Barbara Fallen, FACHE, Director
Web address: www.lomalinda.va.gov

COLORADO: GRAND JUNCTION VETERANS HEALTH CARE SYSTEM (O, 23 beds) 2121 North Avenue, Grand Junction, CO Zip 81501–6428; tel. 970/242–0731; Marc Magill, Medical Center Director
Web address: www.grandjunction.va.gov/

SOUTHERN COLORADO HEALTHCARE SYSTEM (O, 299 beds) Las Animas, CO Zip 81054–0390; tel. 719/456–1260; Stuart C. Collyer, Director

VETERANS AFFAIRS EASTERN COLORADO HEALTH CARE SYSTEM (O, 271 beds) 1055 Clermont Street, Denver, CO Zip 80220–3877; tel. 303/399–8020; Sallie Houser–Hanfelder, FACHE, Director
Web address: www.denver.va.gov/

CONNECTICUT: VETERANS AFFAIRS CONNECTICUT HEALTHCARE SYSTEM (O, 197 beds) 950 Campbell Avenue, West Haven, CT Zip 06516–2770; tel. 203/932–5711; Gerald F. Culliton, Medical Center Director
Web address: www.connecticut.va.gov

DELAWARE: WILMINGTON VETERANS AFFAIRS MEDICAL CENTER (O, 120 beds) 1601 Kirkwood Highway, Wilmington, DE Zip 19805–4989; tel. 302/994–2511; Robin C. Aube–Warren, Director
Web address: www.va.gov/wilmington

DISTRICT OF COLUMBIA: WASHINGTON DC VETERANS AFFAIRS MEDICAL CENTER (O, 291 beds) 50 Irving Street N.W., Washington, DC Zip 20422–0002; tel. 202/745–8000; Brian A. Hawkins, Director
Web address: www.washingtondc.va.gov/

FLORIDA: BAY PINES VETERANS AFFAIRS HEALTHCARE SYSTEM (O, 396 beds) 10000 Bay Pines Boulevard, Bay Pines, FL Zip 33744–8200, Mailing Address: P.O. Box 5005, Zip 33744–5005; tel. 727/398–6661; Suzanne M. Klinker, Director
Web address: www.baypines.va.gov/

JAMES A. HALEY VETERANS' HOSPITAL–TAMPA (O, 499 beds) 13000 Bruce B. Downs Boulevard, Tampa, FL Zip 33612–4745; tel. 813/972–2000; Joe Battle, Director
Web address: www.tampa.va.gov/

MIAMI VETERANS AFFAIRS HEALTHCARE SYSTEM (O, 401 beds) 1201 N.W. 16th Street, Miami, FL Zip 33125–1624; tel. 305/575–7000; Paul M. Russo, FACHE, Director
Web address: www.miami.va.gov/

NORTH FLORIDA/SOUTH GEORGIA VETERAN'S HEALTH SYSTEM (O, 623 beds) 1601 S.W. Archer Road, Gainesville, FL Zip 32608–1135; tel. 352/376–1611; Thomas Wisnieski, FACHE, Director
Web address: www.northflorida.va.gov

WEST PALM BEACH VETERANS AFFAIRS MEDICAL CENTER (O, 297 beds) 7305 North Military Trail, West Palm Beach, FL Zip 33410–6400; tel. 561/422–8262; Charleen R. Szabo, FACHE, Director
Web address: www.westpalmbeach.va.gov/

GEORGIA: ATLANTA VETERANS AFFAIRS MEDICAL CENTER (O, 239 beds) 1670 Clairmont Road, Decatur, GA Zip 30033–4004; tel. 404/321–6111; Annette Walker, Director
Web address: www.atlanta.va.gov/

CARL VINSON VETERANS AFFAIRS MEDICAL CENTER (O, 178 beds) 1826 Veterans Boulevard, Dublin, GA Zip 31021–3620; tel. 478/272–1210; Maryalice Morro, MSN, R.N., Director
Web address: www.dublin.va.gov/

CHARLIE NORWOOD VETERANS AFFAIRS MEDICAL CENTER (O, 338 beds) 1 Freedom Way, Augusta, GA Zip 30904–6285; tel. 706/733–0188; Maria R. Andrews, MS, Director
Web address: www.augusta.va.gov/

HAWAII: VETERANS AFFAIRS PACIFIC ISLANDS HEALTH CARE SYSTEM (O, 0 beds) 459 Patterson Road, Honolulu, HI Zip 96819; tel. 808/433–0600; Wayne L. Pfeffer, FACHE, Director
Web address: www.hawaii.va.gov/

IDAHO: BOISE VETERANS AFFAIRS MEDICAL CENTER (O, 100 beds) 500 West Fort Street, Boise, ID Zip 83702–4598; tel. 208/422–1000; David P. Wood, FACHE, Director
Web address: www.boise.va.gov/

ILLINOIS: CAPTAIN JAMES A. LOVELL FEDERAL HEALTH CARE CENTER (O, 302 beds) 3001 Green Bay Road, North Chicago, IL Zip 60064–3049; tel. 847/688–1900; Stephen R. Holt, M.D., Director
Web address: www.lovell.fhcc.va.gov/

EDWARD HINES, JR. VETERANS AFFAIRS HOSPITAL (O, 485 beds) 5000 South Fifth Avenue, Hines, IL Zip 60141–3030, Mailing Address: P.O. Box 5000, Zip 60141–5000; tel. 708/202–8387; Drew Dewitt, FACHE, Acting Associate Director
Web address: www.hines.va.gov/

JESSE BROWN VETERANS AFFAIRS MEDICAL CENTER (O, 240 beds) 820 South Damen, Chicago, IL Zip 60612–3776; tel. 312/569–8387; Annette Walker, Acting Medical Center Director
Web address: www.chicago.va.gov/

MARION VETERANS AFFAIRS MEDICAL CENTER (O, 99 beds) 2401 West Main Street, Marion, IL Zip 62959–1188; tel. 618/997–5311; Frank Kehus, Interim Director
Web address: www.marion.va.gov

VETERANS AFFAIRS ILLIANA HEALTH CARE SYSTEM (O, 221 beds) 1900 East Main Street, Danville, IL Zip 61832–5198; tel. 217/554–3000; Diana Carranza, Interim Director
Web address: www.danville.va.gov/

INDIANA: RICHARD L. ROUDEBUSH VETERANS AFFAIRS MEDICAL CENTER (O, 209 beds) 1481 West Tenth Street, Indianapolis, IN Zip 46202–2884; tel. 317/554–0000; Brian Hancock, M.D., Director
Web address: www.indianapolis.va.gov

VETERANS AFFAIRS NORTHERN INDIANA HEALTH CARE SYSTEM (O, 217 beds) 2121 Lake Avenue, Fort Wayne, IN Zip 46805–5100; tel. 260/426–5431; Jay Miller, Acting Director
Web address: www.northernindiana.va.gov/

IOWA: IOWA CITY VETERANS AFFAIRS HEALTH CARE SYSTEM (O, 73 beds) 601 Highway 6 West, Iowa City, IA Zip 52246–2208; tel. 319/338–0581; Judith Johnson–Mekota, Director
Web address: www.iowacity.va.gov/

VETERANS AFFAIRS CENTRAL IOWA HEALTH CARE SYSTEM (O, 258 beds) 3600 30th Street, Des Moines, IA Zip 50310–5753; tel. 515/699–5999; Gail L. Graham, Director
Web address: www.centraliowa.va.gov/

KANSAS: ROBERT J. DOLE VETERANS AFFAIRS MEDICAL CENTER (O, 41 beds) 5500 East Kellogg, Wichita, KS Zip 67218–1607; tel. 316/685–2221; Francisco Vazquez, Director
Web address: www.wichita.va.gov

VETERANS AFFAIRS EASTERN KANSAS HEALTH CARE SYSTEM (O, 213 beds) 2200 South West Gage Boulevard, Topeka, KS Zip 66622–0002; tel. 785/350–3111; Anthony Rudy Klopfer, FACHE, Director
Web address: www.topeka.va.gov

KENTUCKY: LEXINGTON VETERANS AFFAIRS MEDICAL CENTER (O, 199 beds) 1101 Veterans Drive, Lexington, KY Zip 40502–2235; tel. 859/281–4901; Emma Metcalf, MSN, R.N., Director
Web address: www.lexington.va.gov/

ROBLEY REX VETERANS AFFAIRS MEDICAL CENTER (O, 116 beds) 800 Zorn Avenue, Louisville, KY Zip 40206–1499; tel. 502/287–4000; Martin J. Traxler, Chief Executive Officer
Web address: www.louisville.va.gov

LOUISIANA: ALEXANDRIA VETERANS AFFAIRS HEALTH CARE SYSTEM (O, 143 beds) 2495 Shreveport Highway, 71 N., Pineville, LA Zip 71360–4044, Mailing Address: P.O. Box 69004, Alexandria, Zip 71306–9004; tel. 318/473–0010; Peter Dancy, Director
Web address: www.alexandria.va.gov/

OVERTON BROOKS VETERANS AFFAIRS MEDICAL CENTER (O, 100 beds) 510 East Stoner Avenue, Shreveport, LA Zip 71101–4295; tel. 318/221–8411; Toby T. Mathew, Medical Center Director
Web address: www.shreveport.va.gov/

MAINE: MAINE VETERANS AFFAIRS MEDICAL CENTER (O, 167 beds) 1 VA Center, Augusta, ME Zip 04330–6719; tel. 207/623–8411; Ryan S. Lilly, Director
Web address: www.maine.va.gov/

For explanation of codes following names, see page B2.
★ Indicates Type III membership in the American Hospital Association.

B46 Health Care Systems, Networks and Alliances

© 2016 AHA Guide

Section B

MARYLAND: VETERANS AFFAIRS MARYLAND HEALTH CARE SYSTEM–BALTIMORE DIVISION (O, 727 beds) 10 North Greene Street, Baltimore, MD Zip 21201–1524; tel. 410/605–7001; Adam M. Robinson, Director
Web address: www.maryland.va.gov/

MASSACHUSETTS: BEDFORD VETERANS AFFAIRS MEDICAL CENTER, EDITH NOURSE ROGERS MEMORIAL VETERANS HOSPITAL (O, 461 beds) 200 Springs Road, Bedford, MA Zip 01730–1198; tel. 781/687–2000; Karen Acerra–Williams, Acting Director
Web address: www.bedford.va.gov

VETERANS AFFAIRS BOSTON HEALTHCARE SYSTEM (O, 361 beds) 1400 VFW Parkway, Boston, MA Zip 02132–4927; tel. 617/323–7700; Vincent Ng, Director
Web address: www.boston.va.gov/

VETERANS AFFAIRS BOSTON HEALTHCARE SYSTEM BROCKTON DIVISION (O, 375 beds) 940 Belmont Street, Brockton, MA Zip 02301–5596; tel. 508/583–4500; Vincent Ng, Interim Director
Web address: www.boston.va.gov/

VETERANS AFFAIRS CENTRAL WESTERN MASSACHUSETTS HEALTHCARE SYSTEM (O, 167 beds) 421 North Main Street, Leeds, MA Zip 01053–9764; tel. 413/582–3000; John P. Collins, Medical Center Director
Web address: www.centralwesternmass.va.gov/

MICHIGAN: ALEDA E. LUTZ VETERANS AFFAIRS MEDICAL CENTER (O, 89 beds) 1500 Weiss Street, Saginaw, MI Zip 48602–5298; tel. 989/497–2500; Ginny L. Creasman, Director
Web address: www.saginaw.va.gov/

BATTLE CREEK VETERANS AFFAIRS MEDICAL CENTER (O, 242 beds) 5500 Armstrong Road, Battle Creek, MI Zip 49037–7314; tel. 269/966–5600; Mary Beth Skupien, Director
Web address: www.battlecreek.va.gov/

JOHN D. DINGELL VETERANS AFFAIRS MEDICAL CENTER (O, 242 beds) 4646 John R Street, Detroit, MI Zip 48201–1932; tel. 313/576–1000; Pamela J. Reeves, M.D., Director
Web address: www.detroit.va.gov/

OSCAR G. JOHNSON VETERANS AFFAIRS MEDICAL CENTER (O, 17 beds) 325 East H Street, Iron Mountain, MI Zip 49801–4792; tel. 906/774–3300; James W. Rice, Director
Web address: www.ironmountain.va.gov/

VETERANS AFFAIRS ANN ARBOR HEALTHCARE SYSTEM (O, 109 beds) 2215 Fuller Road, Ann Arbor, MI Zip 48105–2399; tel. 734/769–7100; Robert P. McDivitt, FACHE, Director
Web address: www.annarbor.va.gov

MINNESOTA: MINNEAPOLIS VETERANS AFFAIRS HEALTH CARE SYSTEM (O, 305 beds) One Veterans Drive, Minneapolis, MN Zip 55417–2399; tel. 612/725–2000; Patrick J. Kelly, FACHE, Director
Web address: www.minneapolis.va.gov

ST. CLOUD VETERANS AFFAIRS HEALTH CARE SYSTEM (O, 388 beds) 4801 Veterans Drive, Saint Cloud, MN Zip 56303–2099; tel. 320/252–1670; Cheryl Thieschafer, Acting Director
Web address: www.stcloud.va.gov

MISSISSIPPI: G.V. (SONNY) MONTGOMERY VETERANS AFFAIRS MEDICAL CENTER (O, 323 beds) 1500 East Woodrow Wilson Drive, Jackson, MS Zip 39216–5199; tel. 601/362–4471; David M. Walker, M.D., Medical Center Director
Web address: www.jackson.va.gov/

VETERANS AFFAIRS GULF COAST VETERANS HEALTH CARE SYSTEM (O, 392 beds) 400 Veterans Avenue, Biloxi, MS Zip 39531–2410; tel. 228/523–5000; Anthony L. Dawson, FACHE, Director
Web address: www.biloxi.va.gov/

MISSOURI: HARRY S. TRUMAN MEMORIAL VETERANS HOSPITAL (O, 123 beds) 800 Hospital Drive, Columbia, MO Zip 65201–5275; tel. 573/814–6000; David Isaacks, Director
Web address: www.columbiamo.va.gov

JOHN J. PERSHING VETERANS AFFAIRS MEDICAL CENTER (O, 58 beds) 1500 North Westwood Boulevard, Poplar Bluff, MO Zip 63901–3318; tel. 573/686–4151; Patricia Ten Haaf, R.N., MSN, Ph.D., Director
Web address: www.poplarbluff.va.gov

KANSAS CITY VETERANS AFFAIRS MEDICAL CENTER (O, 157 beds) 4801 East Linwood Boulevard, Kansas City, MO Zip 64128–2226; tel. 816/861–4700; Kathleen R. Fogarty, MS, Director
Web address: www.kansascity.va.gov/

VETERANS AFFAIRS ST. LOUIS HEALTH CARE SYSTEM (O, 356 beds) 915 North Grand, Saint Louis, MO Zip 63106–1621; tel. 314/652–4100; Keith D. Repko, Director
Web address: www.stlouis.va.gov/

MONTANA: VETERANS AFFAIRS MONTANA HEALTH CARE SYSTEM (O, 65 beds) 3687 Veterans Drive, Fort Harrison, MT Zip 59636–9703, Mailing Address: P.O. Box 1500, Zip 59636–1500; tel. 406/442–6410; Dr. Kathy Berger, R.N., Interim Director
Web address: www.montana.va.gov/

NEBRASKA: VETERANS AFFAIRS NEBRASKA–WESTERN IOWA HEALTH CARE SYSTEM (O, 100 beds) 4101 Woolworth Avenue, Omaha, NE Zip 68105–1873; tel. 402/346–8800; Don Burman, Director
Web address: www.nebraska.va.gov/

VETERANS AFFAIRS NEBRASKA–WESTERN IOWA HEALTH CARE SYSTEM – LINCOLN (O, 132 beds) 600 South 70th Street, Lincoln, NE Zip 68510–2493; tel. 402/489–3802; Don Burman, Director
Web address: www.nebraska.va.gov/

NEVADA: VETERANS AFFAIRS SIERRA NEVADA HEALTH CARE SYSTEM (O, 124 beds) 975 Kirman Avenue, Reno, NV Zip 89502–0993; tel. 775/786–7200; Lisa M. Howard, Director
Web address: www.reno.va.gov/

VETERANS AFFAIRS SOUTHERN NEVADA HEALTHCARE SYSTEM (O, 90 beds) 6900 North Pecos Road, North Las Vegas, NV Zip 89086–4400; tel. 702/791–9000; Peggy W. Kearns, MS, FACHE, Executive Director
Web address: www.lasvegas.va.gov/

NEW HAMPSHIRE: MANCHESTER VETERANS AFFAIRS MEDICAL CENTER (O, 90 beds) 718 Smyth Road, Manchester, NH Zip 03104–4098; tel. 603/624–4366; Danielle Ocker, R.N., Director
Web address: www.manchester.va.gov/

NEW JERSEY: VETERANS AFFAIRS NEW JERSEY HEALTH CARE SYSTEM (O, 439 beds) 385 Tremont Avenue, East Orange, NJ Zip 07018–1095; tel. 973/676–1000; Mara Davis, Interim Director
Web address: www.newjersey.va.gov/

NEW MEXICO: NEW MEXICO VETERANS AFFAIRS HEALTH CARE SYSTEM – RAYMOND G. MURPHY MEDICAL CENTER (O, 203 beds) 1501 San Pedro S.E., Albuquerque, NM Zip 87108–5153; tel. 505/265–1711; Andrew Welch, Director
Web address: www.albuquerque.va.gov/

NEW YORK: ALBANY STRATTON VETERANS AFFAIRS MEDICAL CENTER (O, 155 beds) 113 Holland Avenue, Albany, NY Zip 12208–3473; tel. 518/626–5000; Deborah Spath, Interim Director
Web address: www.albany.va.gov/

BATH VETERANS AFFAIRS MEDICAL CENTER (O, 274 beds) 76 Veterans Avenue, Bath, NY Zip 14810–0842; tel. 607/664–4000; Michael J. Swartz, FACHE, Medical Center Director
Web address: www.bath.va.gov

CANANDAIGUA VETERANS AFFAIRS MEDICAL CENTER (O, 196 beds) 400 Fort Hill Avenue, Canandaigua, NY Zip 14424–1159; tel. 585/394–2000; Michael J. Swartz, FACHE, Medical Center Director
Web address: www.canandaigua.va.gov/

JAMES J. PETERS VETERANS AFFAIRS MEDICAL CENTER (O, 325 beds) 130 West Kingsbridge Road, Bronx, NY Zip 10468–3904; tel. 718/584–9000; Erik Langhoff, M.D., Ph.D., Director
Web address: www.bronx.va.gov/

NORTHPORT VETERANS AFFAIRS MEDICAL CENTER (O, 502 beds) 79 Middleville Road, Northport, NY Zip 11768–2200; tel. 631/261–4400; Philip C. Moschitta, Director
Web address: www.northport.va.gov/index.asp

SYRACUSE VETERANS AFFAIRS MEDICAL CENTER (O, 161 beds) 800 Irving Avenue, Syracuse, NY Zip 13210–2716; tel. 315/425–4400; James Cody, Director
Web address: www.syracuse.va.gov/

VETERANS AFFAIRS HUDSON VALLEY HEALTH CARE SYSTEM (O, 383 beds) 2094 Albany Post Road, Montrose, NY Zip 10548–1454, Mailing Address: P.O. Box 100, Zip 10548–0100; tel. 914/737–4400; Margaret B. Caplan, Director
Web address: www.hudsonvalley.va.gov/

VETERANS AFFAIRS NEW YORK HARBOR HEALTHCARE SYSTEM (O, 476 beds) 800 Poly Place, Brooklyn, NY Zip 11209–7104; tel. 718/630–3500; Martina A. Parauda, Director
Web address: www.nyharbor.va.gov

For explanation of codes following names, see page B2.
★ Indicates Type III membership in the American Hospital Association.

Section B

VETERANS AFFAIRS WESTERN NEW YORK HEALTHCARE SYSTEM–BATAVIA DIVISION (O, 128 beds) 222 Richmond Avenue, Batavia, NY 14020–1288; tel. 585/297–1000; Brian G. Stiller, Director Medical Center
Web address: www.buffalo.va.gov/batavia.asp

VETERANS AFFAIRS WESTERN NEW YORK HEALTHCARE SYSTEM–BUFFALO DIVISION (O, 113 beds) 3495 Bailey Avenue, Buffalo, NY Zip 14215–1129; tel. 716/834–9200; Brian G. Stiller, Director Medical Center
Web address: www.buffalo.va.gov/index.asp

NORTH CAROLINA: CHARLES GEORGE VETERANS AFFAIRS MEDICAL CENTER (O, 257 beds) 1100 Tunnel Road, Asheville, NC Zip 28805–2087; tel. 828/298–7911; Cynthia Breyfogle, FACHE, Director
Web address: www.asheville.va.gov/

DURHAM VETERANS AFFAIRS MEDICAL CENTER (O, 265 beds) 508 Fulton Street, Durham, NC Zip 27705–3897; tel. 919/286–0411; DeAnne Seekins, Director
Web address: www.durham.va.gov/

FAYETTEVILLE VETERANS AFFAIRS MEDICAL CENTER (O, 58 beds) 2300 Ramsey Street, Fayetteville, NC Zip 28301–3899; tel. 910/488–2120; Elizabeth Goolsby, Director
Web address: www.fayettevillenc.va.gov

W. G. (BILL) HEFFNER VETERANS AFFAIRS MEDICAL CENTER (O, 171 beds) 1601 Brenner Avenue, Salisbury, NC Zip 28144–2559; tel. 704/638–9000; Kaye Green, FACHE, Director
Web address: www.salisbury.va.gov

NORTH DAKOTA: FARGO VETERANS AFFAIRS HEALTH CARE SYSTEM (O, 77 beds) 2101 Elm Street North, Fargo, ND Zip 58102–2498; tel. 701/232–3241; Lavonne Liversage, Director
Web address: www.fargo.va.gov/

OHIO: CHILLICOTHE VETERANS AFFAIRS MEDICAL CENTER (O, 297 beds) 17273 State Route 104, Chillicothe, OH Zip 45601–9718; tel. 740/773–1141; Keith Sullivan, Director
Web address: www.chillicothe.va.gov/

CINCINNATI VETERANS AFFAIRS MEDICAL CENTER (O, 268 beds) 3200 Vine Street, Cincinnati, OH Zip 45220–2288; tel. 513/475–6300; Glenn A. Costie, FACHE, Interim Director
Web address: www.cincinnati.va.gov/

DAYTON VETERANS AFFAIRS MEDICAL CENTER (O, 471 beds) 4100 West Third Street, Dayton, OH Zip 45428–9000; tel. 937/268–6511; Glenn A. Costie, FACHE, Director
Web address: www.dayton.va.gov/

LOUIS STOKES CLEVELAND VETERANS AFFAIRS MEDICAL CENTER (O, 585 beds) 10701 East Boulevard, Cleveland, OH Zip 44106–1702; tel. 216/791–3800; Susan Fuehrer, Director
Web address: www.cleveland.va.gov/

OKLAHOMA: JACK C. MONTGOMERY VETERANS AFFAIRS MEDICAL CENTER (O, 99 beds) 1011 Honor Heights Drive, Muskogee, OK Zip 74401–1318; tel. 918/577–3000; Mark E. Carr, Medical Center Director
Web address: www.muskogee.va.gov

OKLAHOMA CITY VETERANS AFFAIRS MEDICAL CENTER (O, 192 beds) 921 N.E. 13th Street, Oklahoma City, OK Zip 73104–5028; tel. 405/456–1000; Wade Vlosich, Director
Web address: www.oklahoma.va.gov

OREGON: PORTLAND VETERANS AFFAIRS MEDICAL CENTER (O, 303 beds) 3710 S.W. U.S. Veterans Hospital Road, Portland, OR Zip 97239–2964, Mailing Address: P.O. Box 1034, Zip 97207–1034; tel. 503/220–8262; Michael W. Morgan, FACHE, Director
Web address: www.portland.va.gov/

SOUTHERN OREGON–WHITE CITY VETERANS AFFAIRS REHABILITATION CENTER AND CLINICS (O, 1075 beds) 8495 Crater Lake Highway, White City, OR Zip 97503; tel. 503/826–2111; Frank A. Drake, Director

VETERANS AFFAIRS ROSEBURG HEALTHCARE SYSTEM (O, 88 beds) 913 N.W. Garden Valley Boulevard, Roseburg, OR Zip 97471–6513; tel. 541/440–1000; Carol Bogedain, FACHE, Director
Web address: www.roseburg.va.gov/

PENNSYLVANIA: COATESVILLE VETERANS AFFAIRS MEDICAL CENTER (O, 118 beds) 1400 Black Horse Hill Road, Coatesville, PA Zip 19320–2040; tel. 610/384–7711; Gary W. Devansky, Director
Web address: www.coatesville.va.gov/

ERIE VETERANS AFFAIRS MEDICAL CENTER (O, 78 beds) 135 East 38th Street, Erie, PA Zip 16504–1559; tel. 814/860–2576; John Gennaro, FACHE, Director
Web address: www.erie.va.gov/

JAMES E. VAN ZANDT VETERANS AFFAIRS MEDICAL CENTER (O, 68 beds) 2907 Pleasant Valley Boulevard, Altoona, PA Zip 16602–4305; tel. 877/626–2500; Judy A. Hayman, Ph.D., Acting Director
Web address: www.altoona.va.gov/

LEBANON VETERANS AFFAIRS MEDICAL CENTER (O, 213 beds) 1700 South Lincoln Avenue, Lebanon, PA Zip 17042–7529; tel. 717/272–6621; Robert W. Callahan, Jr., Director
Web address: www.lebanon.va.gov

PHILADELPHIA VETERANS AFFAIRS MEDICAL CENTER (O, 280 beds) 3900 Woodland Avenue, Philadelphia, PA Zip 19104–4594; tel. 215/823–5800; Daniel Hendee, Director
Web address: www.philadelphia.va.gov/

VETERANS AFFAIRS PITTSBURGH HEALTHCARE SYSTEM (O, 549 beds) University Drive, Pittsburgh, PA Zip 15240–1001; tel. 866/482–7488; Karin L. McGraw, MSN, FACHE, Director
Web address: www.pittsburgh.va.gov/

WILKES–BARRE VETERANS AFFAIRS MEDICAL CENTER (O, 158 beds) 1111 East End Boulevard, Wilkes–Barre, PA Zip 18711–0030; tel. 570/824–3521; Michael Adelman, M.D., Medical Center Director
Web address: www.va.gov/vamcwb

PUERTO RICO: VETERANS AFFAIRS CARIBBEAN HEALTHCARE SYSTEM (O, 330 beds) 10 Casia Street, San Juan, PR Zip 00921–3201; tel. 787/641–7582; DeWayne Hamlin, Director
Web address: www.caribbean.va.gov/

RHODE ISLAND: PROVIDENCE VETERANS AFFAIRS MEDICAL CENTER (O, 73 beds) 830 Chalkstone Avenue, Providence, RI Zip 02908–4799; tel. 401/273–7100; Susan MacKenzie, Director
Web address: www.providence.va.gov/

SOUTH CAROLINA: RALPH H. JOHNSON VETERANS AFFAIRS MEDICAL CENTER (O, 98 beds) 109 Bee Street, Charleston, SC Zip 29401–5799; tel. 843/577–5011; Scott R. Isaacks, FACHE, Director and Chief Executive Officer
Web address: www.charleston.va.gov/

WM. JENNINGS BRYAN DORN VETERANS AFFAIRS MEDICAL CENTER (O, 216 beds) 6439 Garners Ferry Road, Columbia, SC Zip 29209–1639; tel. 803/776–4000; Timothy McMurry, Director
Web address: www.columbiasc.va.gov

SOUTH DAKOTA: SIOUX FALLS VETERANS AFFAIRS HEALTH CARE SYSTEM (O, 92 beds) 2501 West 22nd Street, Sioux Falls, SD Zip 57105–1305, Mailing Address: P.O. Box 5046, Zip 57117–5046; tel. 605/336–3230; Darwin Goodspeed, Director
Web address: www.siouxfalls.va.gov

VETERANS AFFAIRS BLACK HILLS HEALTH CARE SYSTEM (O, 308 beds) 113 Comanche Road, Fort Meade, SD Zip 57741–1099; tel. 605/347–2511; Sandra Horsman, Director
Web address: www.blackhills.va.gov/

TENNESSEE: JAMES H. QUILLEN VETERANS AFFAIRS MEDICAL CENTER (O, 98 beds) Corner of Lamont & Veterans Way, Mountain Home, TN Zip 37684, Mailing Address: P.O. Box 4000, Zip 37684–4000; tel. 423/926–1171; Daniel B. Snyder, FACHE, Acting Director
Web address: www.mountainhome.va.gov

MEMPHIS VETERANS AFFAIRS MEDICAL CENTER (O, 262 beds) 1030 Jefferson Avenue, Memphis, TN Zip 38104–2193; tel. 901/523–8990; C. Diane Knight, M.D., Director and Chief Executive Officer
Web address: www.memphis.va.gov/

TENNESSEE VALLEY HEALTHCARE SYSTEM (O, 546 beds) 1310 24th Avenue South, Nashville, TN Zip 37212–2637; tel. 615/327–4751; Suzanne L. Jene, Interim Executive Director
Web address: www.tennesseevalley.va.gov

TEXAS: AMARILLO VETERANS AFFAIRS HEALTH CARE SYSTEM (O, 55 beds) 6010 West Amarillo Boulevard, Amarillo, TX Zip 79106–1992; tel. 806/355–9703; Colonel Michael L. Kiefer, Director
Web address: www.amarillo.va.gov/

CENTRAL TEXAS VETERANS HEALTH CARE SYSTEM (O, 1532 beds) 1901 Veterans Memorial Drive, Temple, TX Zip 76504–7493; tel. 254/778–4811; Russell E. Lloyd, Acting Director
Web address: www.centraltexas.va.gov/

For explanation of codes following names, see page B2.
★ Indicates Type III membership in the American Hospital Association.

Section B

MICHAEL E. DEBAKEY VETERANS AFFAIRS MEDICAL CENTER (O, 479 beds) 2002 Holcombe Boulevard, Houston, TX Zip 77030–4298; tel. 713/791–1414; Adam C. Walmus, FACHE, Director
Web address: www.houston.va.gov

SOUTH TEXAS VETERANS HEALTH CARE SYSTEM (O, 838 beds) 7400 Merton Minter Boulevard, San Antonio, TX Zip 78229–4404; tel. 210/617–5300; Robert M. Walton, Healthcare System Director
Web address: www.southtexas.va.gov

VETERANS AFFAIRS NORTH TEXAS HEALTH CARE SYSTEM (O, 875 beds) 4500 South Lancaster Road, Dallas, TX Zip 75216–7167; tel. 214/742–8387; Jeffrey Milligan, Director
Web address: www.northtexas.va.gov/

WEST TEXAS VETERANS AFFAIRS HEALTH CARE SYSTEM (O, 149 beds) 300 Veterans Boulevard, Big Spring, TX Zip 79720–5500; Big Springs, tel. 432/263–7361; Colonel Michael L. Kiefer, Director
Web address: www.bigspring.va.gov/about/

UTAH: VETERANS AFFAIRS SALT LAKE CITY HEALTH CARE SYSTEM (O, 121 beds) 500 Foothill Drive, Salt Lake City, UT Zip 84148–0002; tel. 801/582–1565; Steven W. Young, Director
Web address: www.saltlakecity.va.gov/

VERMONT: WHITE RIVER JUNCTION VETERANS AFFAIRS MEDICAL CENTER (O, 60 beds) 215 North Main Street, White River Junction, VT Zip 05009–0001; tel. 802/295–9363; Al Montoya, Interim Medical Center Director
Web address: www.whiteriver.va.gov/

VIRGINIA: HAMPTON VETERANS AFFAIRS MEDICAL CENTER (O, 395 beds) 100 Emancipation Drive, Hampton, VA Zip 23667–0001; tel. 757/722–9961; Michael H. Dunfee, Director
Web address: www.hampton.va.gov/

HUNTER HOLMES MCGUIRE VETERANS AFFAIRS MEDICAL CENTER–RICHMOND (O, 381 beds) 1201 Broad Rock Boulevard, Richmond, VA Zip 23249–0002; tel. 804/675–5000; John A. Brandecker, M.P.H., Director
Web address: www.richmond.va.gov/

SALEM VETERANS AFFAIRS MEDICAL CENTER (O, 200 beds) 1970 Roanoke Boulevard, Salem, VA Zip 24153–6478; tel. 540/982–2463; Rebecca J. Stackhouse, Interim Director
Web address: www.salem.va.gov

WASHINGTON: JONATHAN M. WAINWRIGHT MEMORIAL VETERANS AFFAIRS MEDICAL CENTER (O, 14 beds) 77 Wainwright Drive, Walla Walla, WA Zip 99362–3994; tel. 509/525–5200; Brian W. Westfield, MSN, Director
Web address: www.wallawalla.va.gov/

MANN–GRANDSTAFF VETERANS AFFAIRS MEDICAL CENTER (O, 70 beds) 4815 North Assembly Street, Spokane, WA Zip 99205–6197; tel. 509/434–7000; Ronald J. Johnson, Director
Web address: www.spokane.va.gov/

VETERANS AFFAIRS PUGET SOUND HEALTH CARE SYSTEM (O, 358 beds) 1660 South Columbian Way, Seattle, WA Zip 98108–1597; tel. 206/762–1010; Michael J. Murphy, FACHE, Director
Web address: www.pugetsound.va.gov/

WEST VIRGINIA: BECKLEY VETERANS AFFAIRS MEDICAL CENTER (O, 173 beds) 200 Veterans Avenue, Beckley, WV Zip 25801–6499; tel. 304/255–2121; Daniel Bochicchio, M.D., Interim Director
Web address: www.beckley.va.gov/

HUNTINGTON VETERANS AFFAIRS MEDICAL CENTER (O, 80 beds) 1540 Spring Valley Drive, Huntington, WV Zip 25704–9300; tel. 304/429–6741; Brian Nimmo, Director
Web address: www.huntington.va.gov/

LOUIS A. JOHNSON VETERANS AFFAIRS MEDICAL CENTER (O, 71 beds) 1 Medical Center Drive, Clarksburg, WV Zip 26301–4199; tel. 304/623–3461; Glenn R. Snider, M.D., Interim Director
Web address: www.clarksburg.va.gov

MARTINSBURG VETERANS AFFAIRS MEDICAL CENTER (O, 495 beds) 510 Butler Avenue, Martinsburg, WV Zip 25405–9990; tel. 304/263–0811; Timothy J. Cooke, Medical Center Director and Chief Executive Officer
Web address: www.martinsburg.va.gov/

WISCONSIN: CLEMENT J. ZABLOCKI VETERANS AFFAIRS MEDICAL CENTER (O, 637 beds) 5000 West National Avenue, Milwaukee, WI Zip 53295–0001; tel. 414/384–2000; Daniel Zomchek, Ph.D., Executive Director
Web address: www.milwaukee.va.gov/

TOMAH VETERANS AFFAIRS MEDICAL CENTER (O, 71 beds) 500 East Veterans Street, Tomah, WI Zip 54660–3105; tel. 608/372–3971; Victoria Brahm, R.N., MSN, Acting Director
Web address: www.tomah.va.gov

WILLIAM S. MIDDLETON MEMORIAL VETERANS HOSPITAL (O, 87 beds) 2500 Overlook Terrace, Madison, WI Zip 53705–2286; tel. 608/256–1901; John J. Rohrer, Acting Director
Web address: www.madison.va.gov

WYOMING: CHEYENNE VETERANS AFFAIRS MEDICAL CENTER (O, 61 beds) 2360 East Pershing Boulevard, Cheyenne, WY Zip 82001–5392; tel. 307/778–7550; Paul L. Roberts, Director
Web address: www.cheyenne.va.gov/

SHERIDAN VETERANS AFFAIRS MEDICAL CENTER (O, 185 beds) 1898 Fort Road, Sheridan, WY Zip 82801–8320; tel. 307/672–3473; Gerald K. Darnell, PsyD, Interim Director
Web address: www.sheridan.va.gov/

Owned, leased, sponsored:	136 hospitals	36501 beds
Contract–managed:	0 hospitals	0 beds
Totals:	136 hospitals	36501 beds

0845: DEVEREUX (NP)
444 Devereux Drive, Villanova, PA Zip 19085–1932, Mailing Address: P.O. Box 638, Zip 19085–0638; tel. 610/520–3000; Robert Q. Kreider, President and Chief Executive Officer
(Independent Hospital System)

FLORIDA: DEVEREUX HOSPITAL AND CHILDREN'S CENTER OF FLORIDA (O, 100 beds) 8000 Devereux Drive, Melbourne, FL Zip 32940–7907; tel. 321/242–9100; Steven Murphy, Executive Director
Web address: www.devereux.org

GEORGIA: DEVEREUX GEORGIA TREATMENT NETWORK (O, 100 beds) 1291 Stanley Road N.W., Kennesaw, GA Zip 30152–4359; tel. 770/427–0147; Gwendolyn Skinner, Executive Director
Web address: www.devereuxga.org

PENNSYLVANIA: DEVEREUX CHILDREN'S BEHAVIORAL HEALTH CENTER (O, 49 beds) 655 Sugartown Road, Malvern, PA Zip 19355–3303, Mailing Address: 655 Sugartown Road, Zip 19355–3303; tel. 800/345–1292; David E. Woodward, Executive Director
Web address: www.devereux.org

TEXAS: DEVEREUX TEXAS TREATMENT NETWORK (O, 36 beds) 1150 Devereux Drive, League City, TX Zip 77573–2043; tel. 281/335–1000; Pamela E. Helm, Executive Director
Web address: www.devereux.org

Owned, leased, sponsored:	4 hospitals	285 beds
Contract–managed:	0 hospitals	0 beds
Totals:	4 hospitals	285 beds

★5205: DIGNITY HEALTH (CC)
185 Berry Street, Suite 300, San Francisco, CA Zip 94107–1773; tel. 415/438–5500; Lloyd H. Dean, President and Chief Executive Officer
(Decentralized Health System)

ARIZONA: CHANDLER REGIONAL MEDICAL CENTER (O, 338 beds) 1955 West Frye Road, Chandler, AZ Zip 85224–6282; tel. 480/728–3000; Tim Bricker, President and Chief Executive Officer
Web address: www.chandlerregional.com

MERCY GILBERT MEDICAL CENTER (S, 198 beds) 3555 South Val Vista Road, Gilbert, AZ Zip 85297–7323; tel. 480/728–8000; Tim Bricker, President and Chief Executive Officer
Web address: www.mercygilbert.org

ST. JOSEPH'S HOSPITAL AND MEDICAL CENTER (S, 595 beds) 350 West Thomas Road, Phoenix, AZ Zip 85013–4496, Mailing Address: P.O. Box 2071, Zip 85001–2071; tel. 602/406–3000; Patty White, R.N., MS, President
Web address: www.stjosephs–phx.org

CALIFORNIA: ARROYO GRANDE COMMUNITY HOSPITAL (O, 67 beds) 345 South Halcyon Road, Arroyo Grande, CA Zip 93420–3896; tel. 805/489–4261; Kenneth Dalebout, Site Administrator

For explanation of codes following names, see page B2.
★ Indicates Type III membership in the American Hospital Association.

Section B

BAKERSFIELD MEMORIAL HOSPITAL (O, 406 beds) 420 34th Street, Bakersfield, CA Zip 93301–2237; tel. 661/327–1792; Jon Van Boening, President and Chief Executive Officer
Web address: www.bakersfieldmemorial.org

CALIFORNIA HOSPITAL MEDICAL CENTER (O, 318 beds) 1401 South Grand Avenue, Los Angeles, CA Zip 90015–3010; tel. 213/748–2411; Margaret R. Peterson, Ph.D., R.N., President
Web address: www.chmcla.org

COMMUNITY HOSPITAL OF SAN BERNARDINO (O, 379 beds) 1805 Medical Center Drive, San Bernardino, CA Zip 92411–1214; tel. 909/887–6333; June Collison, President
Web address: www.dignityhealth.org/san–bernardino

DOMINICAN HOSPITAL (S, 275 beds) 1555 Soquel Drive, Santa Cruz, CA Zip 95065–1794; tel. 831/462–7700; Nanette Mickiewicz, M.D., President
Web address: www.dominicanhospital.org

FRENCH HOSPITAL MEDICAL CENTER (O, 72 beds) 1911 Johnson Avenue, San Luis Obispo, CA Zip 93401–4197; tel. 805/543–5353; Alan Iftiniuk, Chief Executive Officer
Web address: www.frenchmedicalcenter.org

GLENDALE MEMORIAL HOSPITAL AND HEALTH CENTER (O, 334 beds) 1420 South Central Avenue, Glendale, CA Zip 91204–2594; tel. 818/502–1900; Jack Ivie, President
Web address: www.glendalememorial.com

MARIAN REGIONAL MEDICAL CENTER (S, 286 beds) 1400 East Church Street, Santa Maria, CA Zip 93454–5906; tel. 805/739–3000; Charles J. Cova, Senior Vice President, Operations
Web address: www.marianmedicalcenter.org

MARK TWAIN MEDICAL CENTER (O, 25 beds) 768 Mountain Ranch Road, San Andreas, CA Zip 95249–9998; tel. 209/754–3521; Lawrence A. Philipp, Interim Chief Executive Officer
Web address: www.marktwainhospital.com

MERCY GENERAL HOSPITAL (S, 254 beds) 4001 J Street, Sacramento, CA Zip 95819–3600; tel. 916/453–4545; Edmundo Castaneda, President
Web address: www.mercygeneral.org

MERCY HOSPITAL OF FOLSOM (S, 106 beds) 1650 Creekside Drive, Folsom, CA Zip 95630–3400; tel. 916/983–7400; Edmundo Castaneda, President
Web address: www.mercyfolsom.org

MERCY HOSPITALS OF BAKERSFIELD (S, 187 beds) 2215 Truxtun Avenue, Bakersfield, CA Zip 93301–3698, Mailing Address: P.O. Box 119, Zip 93302–0119; tel. 661/632–5000; Bruce Peters, Chief Executive Officer
Web address: www.mercybakersfield.org

MERCY MEDICAL CENTER MERCED (S, 186 beds) 333 Mercy Avenue, Merced, CA Zip 95340–8319; tel. 209/564–5000; Charles Kassis, President
Web address: www.mercymercedcares.org

MERCY MEDICAL CENTER MOUNT SHASTA (S, 33 beds) 914 Pine Street, Mount Shasta, CA Zip 96067–2143; tel. 530/926–6111; Kenneth E. S. Platou, President
Web address: www.mercymtshasta.org

MERCY MEDICAL CENTER REDDING (S, 267 beds) 2175 Rosaline Avenue, Redding, CA Zip 96001–2549, Mailing Address: P.O. Box 496009, Zip 96049–6009; tel. 530/225–6000; Mark D. Korth, President
Web address: www.mercy.org

MERCY SAN JUAN MEDICAL CENTER (S, 359 beds) 6501 Coyle Avenue, Carmichael, CA Zip 95608–0306, Mailing Address: P.O. Box 479, Zip 95609–0479; tel. 916/537–5000; Brian K. Ivie, President
Web address: www.mercysanjuan.org

METHODIST HOSPITAL OF SACRAMENTO (O, 281 beds) 7500 Hospital Drive, Sacramento, CA Zip 95823–5477; tel. 916/423–3000; Brian K. Ivie, President and Chief Executive Officer
Web address: www.methodistsacramento.org

NORTHRIDGE HOSPITAL MEDICAL CENTER (O, 371 beds) 18300 Roscoe Boulevard, Northridge, CA Zip 91328–4167; tel. 818/885–8500; Saliba Salo, President
Web address: www.northridgehospital.org

SAINT FRANCIS MEMORIAL HOSPITAL (O, 239 beds) 900 Hyde Street, San Francisco, CA Zip 94109–4899, Mailing Address: P.O. Box 7726, Zip 94120–7726; tel. 415/353–6000; David G. Klein, M.D., President
Web address: www.saintfrancismemorial.org

SEQUOIA HOSPITAL (O, 131 beds) 170 Alameda De Las Pulgas, Redwood City, CA Zip 94062–2799; tel. 650/369–5811; Bill Graham, President
Web address: www.sequoiahospital.org

SIERRA NEVADA MEMORIAL HOSPITAL (O, 121 beds) 155 Glasson Way, Grass Valley, CA Zip 95945–5723, Mailing Address: P.O. Box 1029, Zip 95945–1029; tel. 530/274–6000; Katherine A. Medeiros, President and Chief Executive Officer
Web address: www.snmh.org

ST. BERNARDINE MEDICAL CENTER (S, 342 beds) 2101 North Waterman Avenue, San Bernardino, CA Zip 92404–4855; tel. 909/883–8711; Darryl VandenBosch, President
Web address: www.stbernardinemedicalcenter.com

ST. ELIZABETH COMMUNITY HOSPITAL (S, 65 beds) 2550 Sister Mary Columba Drive, Red Bluff, CA Zip 96080–4397; tel. 530/529–8000; G. Todd Smith, President
Web address: www.mercy.org

ST. JOHN'S PLEASANT VALLEY HOSPITAL (S, 127 beds) 2309 Antonio Avenue, Camarillo, CA Zip 93010–1414; tel. 805/389–5800; Darren W. Lee, President and Chief Executive Officer
Web address: www.dignityhealth.org/pleasantvalley

ST. JOHN'S REGIONAL MEDICAL CENTER (S, 161 beds) 1600 North Rose Avenue, Oxnard, CA Zip 93030–3723; tel. 805/988–2500; Darren W. Lee, President and Chief Executive Officer
Web address: www.stjohnshealth.org

ST. JOSEPH'S BEHAVIORAL HEALTH CENTER (S, 35 beds) 2510 North California Street, Stockton, CA Zip 95204–5568; tel. 209/461–2000; Paul Rains, R.N., MSN, President
Web address: www.stjosephscanhelp.org

ST. JOSEPH'S MEDICAL CENTER (S, 273 beds) 1800 North California Street, Stockton, CA Zip 95204–6019, Mailing Address: P.O. Box 213008, Zip 95213–9008; tel. 209/943–2000; Donald J. Wiley, President and Chief Executive Officer
Web address: www.stjosephsCARES.org

ST. MARY MEDICAL CENTER (S, 302 beds) 1050 Linden Avenue, Long Beach, CA Zip 90813–3321, Mailing Address: P.O. Box 887, Zip 90801–0887; tel. 562/491–9000; Joel P. Yuhas, FACHE, President and Chief Executive Officer
Web address: www.stmarymedicalcenter.org

ST. MARY'S MEDICAL CENTER (S, 232 beds) 450 Stanyan Street, San Francisco, CA Zip 94117–1079; tel. 415/668–1000; Michael C. Carter, Interim Chief Executive Officer
Web address: www.stmarysmedicalcenter.com

WOODLAND HEALTHCARE (O, 108 beds) 1325 Cottonwood Street, Woodland, CA Zip 95695–5199; tel. 530/662–3961; H. Kevin Vaziri, President
Web address: www.woodlandhealthcare.org

NEVADA: ST. ROSE DOMINICAN HOSPITALS – ROSE DE LIMA CAMPUS (S, 110 beds) 102 East Lake Mead Parkway, Henderson, NV Zip 89015–5524; tel. 702/616–5000; Teressa Conley, President and Chief Executive Officer
Web address: www.strosehospitals.org

ST. ROSE DOMINICAN HOSPITALS – SAN MARTIN CAMPUS (O, 147 beds) 8280 West Warm Springs Road, Las Vegas, NV Zip 89113–3612; tel. 702/492–8000; Lawrence Barnard, President and Chief Executive Officer
Web address: www.strosehospitals.org

ST. ROSE DOMINICAN HOSPITALS – SIENA CAMPUS (S, 230 beds) 3001 St. Rose Parkway, Henderson, NV Zip 89052; tel. 702/616–5000; Brian G. Brannman, President and Chief Executive Officer
Web address: www.strosehospitals.com

Owned, leased, sponsored:	36 hospitals	7960 beds
Contract–managed:	0 hospitals	0 beds
Totals:	36 hospitals	7960 beds

0029: DIMENSIONS HEALTHCARE SYSTEM (NP)
3001 Hospital Drive, 3rd Floor, Cheverly, MD Zip 20785–1189; tel. 301/583–4000; Neil J. Moore, President and Chief Executive Officer
(Moderately Centralized Health System)

MARYLAND: LAUREL REGIONAL HOSPITAL (O, 136 beds) 7300 Van Dusen Road, Laurel, MD Zip 20707–9463; tel. 301/725–4300; John Spearman, President and Chief Operating Officer
Web address: www.laurelregionalhospital.org

For explanation of codes following names, see page B2.
★ Indicates Type III membership in the American Hospital Association.

PRINCE GEORGE'S HOSPITAL CENTER (O, 156 beds) 3001 Hospital Drive, Cheverly, MD Zip 20785–1189; tel. 301/618–2000; K. Singh Taneja, Chief Operating Officer
Web address: www.princegeorgeshospital.org

Owned, leased, sponsored:	2 hospitals	292 beds
Contract–managed:	0 hospitals	0 beds
Totals:	2 hospitals	292 beds

0010: DIVISION OF MENTAL HEALTH AND ADDICTION SERVICES, DEPARTMENT OF HUMAN SERVICES, STATE OF NEW JERSEY (NP)
222 South Warren Street, Trenton, NJ Zip 08608–2306, Mailing Address: P.O. Box 700, Zip 08625–0700; tel. 609/777–0702; Lynn Kovich, Assistant Commissioner
(Independent Hospital System)

NEW JERSEY: ANCORA PSYCHIATRIC HOSPITAL (O, 450 beds) 301 Spring Garden Road, Hammonton, NJ Zip 08037–9699; tel. 609/561–1700; John Lubitsky, Chief Executive Officer
Web address: www.state.nj.us/humanservices/dmhs/oshm/aph/

ARTHUR BRISBANE CHILDREN TREATMENT CENTER (O, 92 beds) County Road 524, Farmingdale, NJ Zip 07727, Mailing Address: P.O. Box 625, Zip 07727; Vincent Giampeitro, Chief Executive Officer

GREYSTONE PARK PSYCHIATRIC HOSPITAL (O, 542 beds) 59 Koch Avenue, Morris Plains, NJ Zip 07950–4400; tel. 973/538–1800; Janet J. Monroe, R.N., Chief Executive Officer
Web address: www.state.nj.us/humanservices/dmhs/oshm/gpph/

TRENTON PSYCHIATRIC HOSPITAL (O, 431 beds) Route 29 and Sullivan Way, Trenton, NJ Zip 08628–3425, Mailing Address: P.O. Box 7500, West Trenton, Zip 08628–0500; tel. 609/633–1500; Teresa A. McQuaide, Chief Executive Officer
Web address: www.state.nj.us/humanservices/dmhs/oshm/tph/

Owned, leased, sponsored:	4 hospitals	1515 beds
Contract–managed:	0 hospitals	0 beds
Totals:	4 hospitals	1515 beds

0536: DIVISION OF MENTAL HEALTH, DEPARTMENT OF HUMAN SERVICES (NP)
319 East Madison Street, S–3B, Springfield, IL Zip 62701–1035; tel. 217/785–6023; Lorrie Rickman Jones, Ph.D., Director
(Independent Hospital System)

ILLINOIS: ALTON MENTAL HEALTH CENTER (O, 165 beds) 4500 College Avenue, Alton, IL Zip 62002–5099; tel. 618/474–3800; Brian E. Thomas, Administrator

ANDREW MCFARLAND MENTAL HEALTH CENTER (O, 118 beds) 901 East Southwind Road, Springfield, IL Zip 62703–5125; tel. 217/786–6994; Karen Schweighart, R.N., MS, Administrator

CHESTER MENTAL HEALTH CENTER (O, 245 beds) Chester Road, Chester, IL Zip 62233–0031, Mailing Address: Box 31, Zip 62233–0031; tel. 618/826–4571; Leah Hammel, Acting Administrator

CHICAGO–READ MENTAL HEALTH CENTER (O, 200 beds) 4200 North Oak Park Avenue, Chicago, IL Zip 60634–1457; tel. 773/794–4000; Thomas Simpatico, M.D., Facility Director and Network System Manager

CHOATE MENTAL HEALTH CENTER (O, 79 beds) 1000 North Main Street, Anna, IL Zip 62906–1699; tel. 618/833–5161; Elaine Ray, Administrator

ELGIN MENTAL HEALTH CENTER (O, 500 beds) 750 South State Street, Elgin, IL Zip 60123–7692; tel. 847/742–1040; Meredith Kiss, Administrator
Web address: www.dhs.state.il.us

JOHN J. MADDEN MENTAL HEALTH CENTER (O, 150 beds) 1200 South First Avenue, Hines, IL Zip 60141–0800; tel. 708/338–7202; Edith Newman, Interim Administrator

Owned, leased, sponsored:	7 hospitals	1457 beds
Contract–managed:	0 hospitals	0 beds
Totals:	7 hospitals	1457 beds

★**0861: DUKE LIFEPOINT HEALTHCARE** (IO)
103 Powell Court, Brentwood, TN Zip 37027–5079; tel. 615/372–8540; Jeffrey G. Seraphine, FACHE, Division President
(Moderately Centralized Health System)

MICHIGAN: UP HEALTH SYSTEM–MARQUETTE (O, 268 beds) 580 West College Avenue, Marquette, MI Zip 49855–2736; tel. 906/228–9440; Brian Sinotte, Chief Executive Officer
Web address: www.mgh.org

NORTH CAROLINA: CENTRAL CAROLINA HOSPITAL (O, 137 beds) 1135 Carthage Street, Sanford, NC Zip 27330–4162; tel. 919/774–2100; John Maxwell, Chief Executive Officer
Web address: www.centralcarolinahosp.com

FRYE REGIONAL MEDICAL CENTER (O, 256 beds) 420 North Center Street, Hickory, NC Zip 28601–5049; tel. 828/322–6070; Garfield Atchison, Chief Executive Officer
Web address: www.fryemedctr.com

HARRIS REGIONAL HOSPITAL (O, 86 beds) 68 Hospital Road, Sylva, NC Zip 28779–2722; tel. 828/586–7000; Steve Heatherly, Chief Executive Officer
Web address: www.westcare.org

HAYWOOD REGIONAL MEDICAL CENTER (O, 146 beds) 262 Leroy George Drive, Clyde, NC Zip 28721–7430; tel. 828/456–7311; Rod Harkleroad, R.N., Chief Executive Officer
Web address: www.haymed.org

MARIA PARHAM MEDICAL CENTER (O, 102 beds) 566 Ruin Creek Road, Henderson, NC Zip 27536–2927; tel. 252/438–4143; Bert Beard, Chief Executive Officer
Web address: www.mariaparham.com

PERSON MEMORIAL HOSPITAL (O, 106 beds) 615 Ridge Road, Roxboro, NC Zip 27573–4629; tel. 336/599–2121; David Ziolkowski, Chief Executive Officer
Web address: www.personhospital.com

RUTHERFORD REGIONAL HEALTH SYSTEM (O, 112 beds) 288 South Ridgecrest Avenue, Rutherfordton, NC Zip 28139–2838; tel. 828/286–5000; James Atkins, PharmD, Chief Executive Officer
Web address: www.rutherfordhosp.org

SWAIN COMMUNITY HOSPITAL (O, 25 beds) 45 Plateau Street, Bryson City, NC Zip 28713–4200; tel. 828/488–2155; Steve Heatherly, Chief Executive Officer
Web address: www.westcare.org

WILSON MEDICAL CENTER (O, 206 beds) 1705 Tarboro Street, S.W., Wilson, NC Zip 27893–3428; tel. 252/399–8040; William E. Caldwell, Jr., Chief Executive Officer
Web address: www.wilmed.org

PENNSYLVANIA: CONEMAUGH MEMORIAL MEDICAL CENTER (O, 539 beds) 1086 Franklin Street, Johnstown, PA Zip 15905–4398; tel. 814/534–9000; Steven E. Tucker, President
Web address: www.conemaugh.org

CONEMAUGH MEYERSDALE MEDICAL CENTER (O, 20 beds) 200 Hospital Drive, Meyersdale, PA Zip 15552–1249; tel. 814/634–5911; Heather Smith, President
Web address: www.conemaugh.org

CONEMAUGH MINERS MEDICAL CENTER (O, 30 beds) 290 Haida Avenue, Hastings, PA Zip 16646–5610, Mailing Address: P.O. Box 689, Zip 16646–0689; tel. 814/247–3100; William R. Crowe, President
Web address: www.conemaugh.org

VIRGINIA: TWIN COUNTY REGIONAL HEALTHCARE (O, 141 beds) 200 Hospital Drive, Galax, VA Zip 24333–2227; tel. 276/236–8181; Jon D. Applebaum, Chief Executive Officer
Web address: www.tcrh.org

Owned, leased, sponsored:	14 hospitals	2174 beds
Contract–managed:	0 hospitals	0 beds
Totals:	14 hospitals	2174 beds

★**0190: DUKE UNIVERSITY HEALTH SYSTEM** (NP)
201 Trent Drive, Durham, NC Zip 27710–3037, Mailing Address: P.O. Box 3701, Zip 27710–3701; tel. 919/684–2255; A. Eugene Washington, M.D., President and Chief Executive Officer
(Centralized Health System)

For explanation of codes following names, see page B2.
★ Indicates Type III membership in the American Hospital Association.

NORTH CAROLINA: DUKE RALEIGH HOSPITAL (O, 148 beds) 3400 Wake Forest Road, Raleigh, NC Zip 27609–7373; tel. 919/954–3000; David Zaas, M.D., Chief Executive Officer
Web address: www.dukehealthraleigh.org

DUKE REGIONAL HOSPITAL (L, 208 beds) 3643 North Roxboro Street, Durham, NC Zip 27704–2763; tel. 919/470–4000; Kathleen B. Galbraith, FACHE, President
Web address: www.dukehealth.org

DUKE UNIVERSITY HOSPITAL (O, 905 beds) 2301 Erwin Road, Durham, NC Zip 27705–4699, Mailing Address: P.O. Box 3814, Zip 27710–3708; tel. 919/684–8111; Kevin W. Sowers, R.N., MSN, President
Web address: www.dukehealth.org

Owned, leased, sponsored:	3 hospitals	1261 beds
Contract–managed:	0 hospitals	0 beds
Totals:	3 hospitals	1261 beds

★1895:   EAST TEXAS MEDICAL CENTER REGIONAL HEALTHCARE SYSTEM (NP)
1000 South Beckham Street, Tyler, TX Zip 75701–1908, Mailing Address: P.O. Box 6400, Zip 75711–6400; tel. 903/535–6211; Elmer G. Ellis, FACHE, President and Chief Executive Officer
(Independent Hospital System)

TEXAS: EAST TEXAS MEDICAL CENTER ATHENS (L, 127 beds) 2000 South Palestine Street, Athens, TX Zip 75751–5610; tel. 903/676–1000; Patrick L. Wallace, Administrator
Web address: www.etmc.org

EAST TEXAS MEDICAL CENTER CARTHAGE (L, 25 beds) 409 Cottage Road, Carthage, TX Zip 75633–1466; tel. 903/693–3841; Gary Mikeal Hudson, Administrator
Web address: www.etmc.org

EAST TEXAS MEDICAL CENTER HENDERSON (O, 41 beds) 300 Wilson Street, Henderson, TX Zip 75652–5956; tel. 903/657–7541; Mark Leitner, Administrator
Web address: www.etmc.org/etmchenderson/

EAST TEXAS MEDICAL CENTER JACKSONVILLE (O, 38 beds) 501 South Ragsdale Street, Jacksonville, TX Zip 75766–2413; tel. 903/541–5000; Jack R. Endres, FACHE, JD, Administrator
Web address: www.etmc.org

EAST TEXAS MEDICAL CENTER PITTSBURG (L, 25 beds) 2701 Highway 271 North, Pittsburg, TX Zip 75686–1032; tel. 903/946–5000; James Warren Robicheaux, FACHE, Senior Administrator
Web address: www.etmc.org/newpittsburg.htm

EAST TEXAS MEDICAL CENTER REHABILITATION HOSPITAL (O, 49 beds) 701 Olympic Plaza Circle, Tyler, TX Zip 75701–1950, Mailing Address: P.O. Box 7530, Zip 75711–7530; tel. 903/596–3000; Eddie L. Howard, Vice President and Chief Operating Officer
Web address: www.etmc.org

EAST TEXAS MEDICAL CENTER SPECIALTY HOSPITAL (O, 36 beds) 1000 South Beckham, 5th Floor, Tyler, TX Zip 75701–1908, Mailing Address: P.O. Box 7018, Zip 75711–7018; tel. 903/596–3600; Eddie L. Howard, Vice President and Chief Operating Officer
Web address: www.etmc.org

EAST TEXAS MEDICAL CENTER TRINITY (L, 22 beds) 317 Prospect Drive, Trinity, TX Zip 75862–6202, Mailing Address: P.O. Box 3169, Zip 75862–3169; tel. 936/744–1100; Ruth Cook, Administrator
Web address: www.etmc.org

EAST TEXAS MEDICAL CENTER TYLER (O, 412 beds) 1000 South Beckham Street, Tyler, TX Zip 75701–1908, Mailing Address: Box 6400, Zip 75711–6400; tel. 903/597–0351; Robert B. Evans, Administrator and Chief Executive Officer
Web address: www.etmc.org

EAST TEXAS MEDICAL CENTER–QUITMAN (L, 25 beds) 117 Winnsboro Street, Quitman, TX Zip 75783–2144, Mailing Address: P.O. Box 1000, Zip 75783–1000; tel. 903/763–6300; Patrick Swindle, Administrator
Web address: www.etmc.org/etmcquitman/

Owned, leased, sponsored:	10 hospitals	800 beds
Contract–managed:	0 hospitals	0 beds
Totals:	10 hospitals	800 beds

★0270:   EASTERN CONNECTICUT HEALTH NETWORK (NP)
71 Haynes Street, Manchester, CT Zip 06040–4131; tel. 860/533–3400; Peter J. Karl, President and Chief Executive Officer
(Centralized Health System)

CONNECTICUT: MANCHESTER MEMORIAL HOSPITAL (O, 156 beds) 71 Haynes Street, Manchester, CT Zip 06040–4188; tel. 860/646–1222; Peter J. Karl, President and Chief Executive Officer
Web address: www.echn.org

ROCKVILLE GENERAL HOSPITAL (O, 47 beds) 31 Union Street, Vernon, CT Zip 06066–3160; tel. 860/872–0501; Peter J. Karl, President and Chief Executive Officer
Web address: www.echn.org

Owned, leased, sponsored:	2 hospitals	203 beds
Contract–managed:	0 hospitals	0 beds
Totals:	2 hospitals	203 beds

★0555:   EASTERN MAINE HEALTHCARE SYSTEMS (NP)
43 Whiting Hill Road, Brewer, ME Zip 04412–1005; tel. 207/973–7045; M. Michelle Hood, FACHE, President and Chief Executive Officer
(Moderately Centralized Health System)

MAINE: BLUE HILL MEMORIAL HOSPITAL (O, 23 beds) 57 Water Street, Blue Hill, ME Zip 04614–5231; tel. 207/374–3400; John Ronan, President and Chief Executive Officer
Web address: www.bhmh.org

CHARLES A. DEAN MEMORIAL HOSPITAL (O, 23 beds) 364 Pritham Avenue, Greenville, ME Zip 04441–1395, Mailing Address: P.O. Box 1129, Zip 04441–1129; tel. 207/695–5200; Geno Murray, President and Chief Executive Officer
Web address: www.cadean.org

EASTERN MAINE MEDICAL CENTER (O, 361 beds) 489 State Street, Bangor, ME Zip 04401–6674, Mailing Address: P.O. Box 404, Zip 04402–0404; tel. 207/973–7000; Deborah Carey Johnson, R.N., President and Chief Executive Officer
Web address: www.emh.org

INLAND HOSPITAL (O, 29 beds) 200 Kennedy Memorial Drive, Waterville, ME Zip 04901–4595; tel. 207/861–3000; John Dalton, President and Chief Executive Officer
Web address: www.inlandhospital.org

MAINE COAST MEMORIAL HOSPITAL (O, 48 beds) 50 Union Street, Ellsworth, ME Zip 04605–1599; tel. 207/664–5311; Charles D. Therrien, President and Chief Executive Officer
Web address: www.mainehospital.org

MERCY HOSPITAL OF PORTLAND (O, 121 beds) 144 State Street, Portland, ME Zip 04101–3795; tel. 207/879–3000; Jay Eckersley, Interim Chief Executive Officer
Web address: www.mercyhospital.org

SEBASTICOOK VALLEY HEALTH (O, 25 beds) 447 North Main Street, Pittsfield, ME Zip 04967–3707; tel. 207/487–4000; Terri Vieira, President and Chief Executive Officer
Web address: www.sebasticookvalleyhealth.org

THE ACADIA HOSPITAL (O, 68 beds) 268 Stillwater Avenue, Bangor, ME Zip 04401–3945, Mailing Address: P.O. Box 422, Zip 04402–0422; tel. 207/973–6100; Daniel B. Coffey, President and Chief Executive Officer
Web address: www.acadiahospital.org

THE AROOSTOOK MEDICAL CENTER (O, 114 beds) 140 Academy Street, Presque Isle, ME Zip 04769–3171, Mailing Address: P.O. Box 151, Zip 04769–0151; tel. 207/768–4000; Glenda E. Dwyer, Interim President
Web address: www.tamc.org

Owned, leased, sponsored:	9 hospitals	812 beds
Contract–managed:	0 hospitals	0 beds
Totals:	9 hospitals	812 beds

For explanation of codes following names, see page B2.
★ Indicates Type III membership in the American Hospital Association.

Section B

★0926: EDWARD–ELMHURST HEALTHCARE (NP)
801 South Washington Street, Naperville, IL Zip 60540–7430;
tel. 630/527–3000; Pamela M. Davis, System President and Chief
Executive Officer
(Independent Hospital System)

ILLINOIS: EDWARD HOSPITAL (O, 350 beds) 801 South Washington Street,
Naperville, IL Zip 60540–7499; tel. 630/527–3000; Bill Kottmann,
President and Chief Executive Officer
Web address: www.eehealth.org

ELMHURST MEMORIAL HOSPITAL (O, 259 beds) 155 East Brush Hill Road,
Elmhurst, IL Zip 60126–5658; tel. 331/221–1000; Mary Lou Mastro, FACHE,
MS, R.N., President and Chief Executive Officer
Web address: www.emhc.org

LINDEN OAKS HOSPITAL (O, 108 beds) 852 South West Street, Naperville, IL
Zip 60540–6400; tel. 630/305–5500; Gina Sharp, FACHE, President
Web address: www.https://www.eehealth.org/services/behavioral–health

Owned, leased, sponsored:	3 hospitals	717 beds
Contract–managed:	0 hospitals	0 beds
Totals:	3 hospitals	717 beds

1685: EINSTEIN HEALTHCARE NETWORK (NP)
5501 Old York Road, Philadelphia, PA Zip 19141–3098;
tel. 215/456–7890; Barry R. Freedman, President and Chief
Executive Officer

PENNSYLVANIA: EINSTEIN MEDICAL CENTER MONTGOMERY (O, 171 beds)
559 West Germantown Pike, East Norriton, PA Zip 19403–4250;
tel. 484/622–1000; Beth Duffy, Chief Operating Officer

EINSTEIN MEDICAL CENTER PHILADELPHIA (O, 488 beds) 5501 Old York
Road, Philadelphia, PA Zip 19141–3098; tel. 215/456–7890; Barry R.
Freedman, President and Chief Executive Officer
Web address: www.einstein.edu

Owned, leased, sponsored:	2 hospitals	659 beds
Contract–managed:	0 hospitals	0 beds
Totals:	2 hospitals	659 beds

0879: EMERUS (IO)
10077 Grogan's Mill, Suite 100, The Woodlands, TX
Zip 77380–1022; tel. 281/292–2450; Toby Hamilton, Chief
Executive Officer

TEXAS: BAYLOR EMERGENCY MEDICAL CENTER AT AUBREY (O, 32 beds)
26791 Highway 380, Aubrey, TX Zip 76227; tel. 972/347–2525; Kyle
Kirkpatrick, Chief Executive Officer
Web address: www.bemcataubrey.com

BAYLOR EMERGENCY MEDICAL CENTERS – BURLESON (O, 8 beds) 12500
South Freeway Suite 100, Burleson, TX Zip 76028–7128;
tel. 214/294–6250; Kyle Kirkpatrick, Chief Executive Officer
Web address: www.bayloremc.com/burleson

BAYLOR EMERGENCY MEDICAL CENTERS – ROCKWALL (O, 8 beds) 1975
Alpha Drive Suite 100, Rockwall, TX Zip 75087–4951; tel. 214/294–6200;
Kyle Kirkpatrick, Chief Executive Officer
Web address: www.bayloremc.com/rockwall

EMERUS COMMUNITY HOSPITAL (O, 8 beds) 24429 State Highway 249,
Tomball, TX Zip 77375–8214; tel. 281/516–0911; Paula Gonzales,
Administrator
Web address: www.emerus.com/tomball/

EMERUS HOSPITAL – SUGAR LAND (O, 7 beds) 16000 Southwest Freeway,
Suite 100, Sugar Land, TX Zip 77479–2674; tel. 281/277–0911; Mike
Kohler, Chief Executive Officer
Web address: www.emerus.com

Owned, leased, sponsored:	5 hospitals	63 beds
Contract–managed:	0 hospitals	0 beds
Totals:	5 hospitals	63 beds

★0256: EMORY HEALTHCARE (NP)
1440 Clifton Road N.E., Suite 309, Atlanta, GA Zip 30322–1102;
tel. 404/778–5000; Jonathan S. Lewin, M.D., President
(Centralized Health System)

GEORGIA: EMORY JOHNS CREEK HOSPITAL (O, 113 beds) 6325 Hospital
Parkway, Johns Creek, GA Zip 30097–5775; tel. 678/474–7000; Marilyn
Margolis, MSN, Chief Executive Officer
Web address: www.emoryjohnscreek.com

EMORY REHABILITATION HOSPITAL (O, 46 beds) 1441 Clifton Road N.E.,
Atlanta, GA Zip 30322–1004; tel. 404/712–5512; Michael Eric Garrard,
FACHE, Chief Executive Officer
Web address: www.emoryhealthcare.org/rehabilitation

EMORY SAINT JOSEPH'S HOSPITAL OF ATLANTA (O, 262 beds) 5665
Peachtree Dunwoody Road N.E., Atlanta, GA Zip 30342–1701;
tel. 678/843–7001; Heather Dexter, Chief Executive Officer
Web address: www.stjosephsatlanta.org

EMORY UNIVERSITY HOSPITAL (O, 548 beds) 1364 Clifton Road N.E., atlanta,
GA Zip 30322; tel. 404/712–2000; Bryce D. Gartland, M.D., Chief Executive
Officer
Web address: www.emoryhealthcare.org

EMORY UNIVERSITY HOSPITAL MIDTOWN (O, 468 beds) 550 Peachtree
Street N.E., Atlanta, GA Zip 30308–2247; tel. 404/686–4411; Daniel Owens,
Chief Executive Officer
Web address: www.emoryhealthcare.org

Owned, leased, sponsored:	5 hospitals	1437 beds
Contract–managed:	0 hospitals	0 beds
Totals:	5 hospitals	1437 beds

0959: EPHRAIM MCDOWELL HEALTH (NP)
217 South Third Street, Danville, KY Zip 40422–1823;
tel. 859/239–1000; Sally M. Davenport, R.N., MS, Chief Executive
Officer
(Independent Hospital System)

KENTUCKY: EPHRAIM MCDOWELL FORT LOGAN HOSPITAL (O, 25 beds) 110
Metker Trail, Stanford, KY Zip 40484–1020; tel. 606/365–4600; Sally M.
Davenport, R.N., MS, Interim Chief Executive Officer
Web address: www.fortloganhospital.org

EPHRAIM MCDOWELL REGIONAL MEDICAL CENTER (O, 159 beds) 217 South
Third Street, Danville, KY Zip 40422–1823; tel. 859/239–1000; Sally M.
Davenport, R.N., MS, Chief Executive Officer
Web address: www.emrmc.org

Owned, leased, sponsored:	2 hospitals	184 beds
Contract–managed:	0 hospitals	0 beds
Totals:	2 hospitals	184 beds

0525: ERLANGER HEALTH SYSTEM (NP)
975 East Third Street, Chattanooga, TN Zip 37403–2147;
tel. 423/778–7000; Kevin M. Spiegel, President and Chief Executive
Officer
(Moderately Centralized Health System)

TENNESSEE: ERLANGER BLEDSOE HOSPITAL (C, 25 beds) 71 Wheeler
Avenue, Pikeville, TN Zip 37367, Mailing Address: P.O. Box 699,
Zip 37367–0699; tel. 423/447–2112; Stephanie Boynton, Administrator
Web address: www.erlanger.org

ERLANGER MEDICAL CENTER (O, 585 beds) 975 East Third Street,
Chattanooga, TN Zip 37403–2147; tel. 423/778–7000; Kevin M. Spiegel,
Chief Executive Officer
Web address: www.erlanger.org

Owned, leased, sponsored:	1 hospital	585 beds
Contract–managed:	1 hospital	25 beds
Totals:	2 hospitals	610 beds

Section B

For explanation of codes following names, see page B2.
★ Indicates Type III membership in the American Hospital Association.

0382: ERNEST HEALTH, INC. (IO)
7770 Jefferson Street N.E., Suite 320, Albuquerque, NM
Zip 87109–4386; tel. 505/856–5300; Darby Brockette, Chief
Executive Officer
(Independent Hospital System)

ARIZONA: MOUNTAIN VALLEY REGIONAL REHABILITATION HOSPITAL (O, 16
beds) 3700 North Windsong Drive, Prescott Valley, AZ Zip 86314–1253;
tel. 928/759–8800; Judy Baum, Chief Executive Officer
Web address: www.mvrrh.ernesthealth.com

COLORADO: NORTHERN COLORADO LONG TERM ACUTE HOSPITAL (O, 20
beds) 4401 Union Street, Johnstown, CO Zip 80534; tel. 970/619–3663;
Lamar McBride, Chief Operating Officer
Web address: www.ncltah.ernesthealth.com/

NORTHERN COLORADO REHABILITATION HOSPITAL (O, 40 beds) 4401 Union
Street, Johnstown, CO Zip 80534–2800; tel. 970/619–3400; Elizabeth
Bullard, Chief Executive Officer
Web address: www.ncrh.ernesthealth.com

IDAHO: NORTHERN IDAHO ADVANCED CARE HOSPITAL (O, 40 beds) 600
North Cecil Road, Post Falls, ID Zip 83854–6200; tel. 208/262–2800;
Maria Godley, R.N., Chief Executive Officer
Web address: www.niach.ernesthealth.com

SOUTHWEST IDAHO ADVANCED CARE HOSPITAL (O, 22 beds) 6651 West
Franklin Road, Boise, ID Zip 83709–0914; tel. 208/685–2400; Maureen
Fakinos, Interim Chief Executive Officer
Web address: www.siach.ernesthealth.com/

INDIANA: LAFAYETTE REGIONAL REHABILITATION HOSPITAL (O, 40 beds)
950 Park East Boulevard, Lafayette, IN Zip 47905–0792;
tel. 765/447–4040; Michelle Russell, Chief Executive Officer
Web address: www.lrrh.ernesthealth.com

MONTANA: ADVANCED CARE HOSPITAL OF MONTANA (O, 40 beds) 3528
Gabel Road, Billings, MT Zip 59102–7307; tel. 406/373–8000; Judi
Powers, Chief Executive Officer
Web address: www.achm.ernesthealth.com

NEW MEXICO: ADVANCED CARE HOSPITAL OF SOUTHERN NEW MEXICO (O,
40 beds) 4451 East Lohman Avenue, Las Cruces, NM Zip 88011–8267;
tel. 575/521–6600; Claudia Saiz, Chief Operating Officer
Web address: www.achsnm.ernesthealth.com

REHABILITATION HOSPITAL OF SOUTHERN NEW MEXICO (O, 40 beds) 4441
East Lohman Avenue, Las Cruces, NM Zip 88011–8267; tel. 575/521–6400;
Sabrina Martin, Chief Executive Officer
Web address: www.rhsnm.ernesthealth.com

SOUTH CAROLINA: GREENWOOD REGIONAL REHABILITATION HOSPITAL (O,
49 beds) 1530 Parkway, Greenwood, SC Zip 29646–4027;
tel. 864/330–9070; Kristin Manske, Chief Executive Officer
Web address: www.grrh.ernesthealth.com

TEXAS: LAREDO REHABILITATION HOSPITAL (O, 20 beds) 2005a East
Bustamante Street, Laredo, TX Zip 78041; tel. 956/764–8555; Larisa
Higgins, Administrator and Chief Operating Officer
Web address: www.lrh.ernesthealth.com

LAREDO SPECIALTY HOSPITAL (O, 40 beds) 2005 Bustamente Street,
Laredo, TX Zip 78041–5470; tel. 956/753–5353; Mario Rodriguez, Chief
Executive Officer
Web address: www.lsh.ernesthealth.com

MESQUITE REHABILITATION INSTITUTE (O, 20 beds) 1023 North Belt Line
Road, Mesquite, TX Zip 75149–1788; tel. 972/216–2400; Brian Abraham,
Chief Executive Officer
Web address: www.mesquiterehab.ernesthealth.com/

MESQUITE SPECIALTY HOSPITAL (O, 40 beds) 1024 North Galloway Avenue,
Mesquite, TX Zip 75149–2434; tel. 972/216–2300; Louis Bradley, Chief
Executive Officer
Web address: www.msh.ernesthealth.com

NEW BRAUNFELS REGIONAL REHABILITATION HOSPITAL (O, 40 beds) 2041
Sundance Parkway, New Braunfels, TX Zip 78130–2779;
tel. 830/625–6700; Jennifer Malatek, Chief Executive Officer
Web address: www.nbrrh.ernesthealth.com

SOUTH TEXAS REHABILITATION HOSPITAL (O, 40 beds) 425 East Alton Gloor
Boulevard, Brownsville, TX Zip 78526–3361; tel. 956/554–6000; Leo Garza,
Chief Executive Officer
Web address: www.strh.ernesthealth.com

TRUSTPOINT REHABILITATION HOSPITAL OF LUBBOCK (O, 60 beds) 4302A
Princeton Street, Lubbock, TX Zip 79415–1304; tel. 806/749–2222; Craig
Bragg, Chief Executive Officer
Web address: www.trustpointhospital.com/

UTAH: UTAH VALLEY SPECIALTY HOSPITAL (O, 40 beds) 306 River Bend
Lane, Provo, UT Zip 84604–5625; tel. 801/226–8880; Ezra Segura,
Chief Executive Officer
Web address: www.uvsh.ernesthealth.com

WYOMING: ELKHORN VALLEY REHABILITATION HOSPITAL (O, 40 beds) 5715
East 2nd Street, Casper, WY Zip 82609–4322; tel. 307/265–0005;
Michael Phillips, Chief Executive Officer
Web address: www.evrh.ernesthealth.com/

Owned, leased, sponsored:	19 hospitals	687 beds
Contract–managed:	0 hospitals	0 beds
Totals:	**19 hospitals**	**687 beds**

★**0396: ESSENTIA HEALTH** (NP)
502 East Second Street, Duluth, MN Zip 55805–1913;
tel. 218/786–8376; David C. Herman, M.D., Chief Executive Officer
(Moderately Centralized Health System)

IDAHO: CLEARWATER VALLEY HOSPITAL AND CLINICS (O, 23 beds) 301
Cedar, Orofino, ID Zip 83544–9029; tel. 208/476–4555; Lenne Bonner,
President
Web address: www.smh–cvhc.org

ST. MARY'S HOSPITAL (O, 28 beds) Lewiston and North Streets, Cottonwood,
ID Zip 83522–9750, Mailing Address: P.O. Box 137, Zip 83522–0137;
tel. 208/962–3251; Lenne Bonner, President
Web address: www.smh–cvhc.org/getpage.php?name=index

MINNESOTA: ESSENTIA HEALTH ADA (O, 14 beds) 201 9th Street West,
Ada, MN Zip 56510–1279; tel. 218/784–5000; Erin Stoltman,
Administrator
Web address: www.essentiahealth.org

ESSENTIA HEALTH DULUTH (O, 154 beds) 502 East Second Street, Duluth,
MN Zip 55805–1982; tel. 218/727–8762; James Garvey, Administrator
Web address: www.smdcmedicalcenter.org

ESSENTIA HEALTH FOSSTON (O, 75 beds) 900 Hilligoss Boulevard S.E.,
Fosston, MN Zip 56542–1599; tel. 218/435–1133; Kevin Gish, Administrator
and Vice President
Web address: www.essentiahealth.org

ESSENTIA HEALTH NORTHERN PINES MEDICAL CENTER (O, 58 beds) 5211
Highway 110, Aurora, MN Zip 55705–1599; tel. 218/229–2211; Laura
Ackman, Chief Operating Officer and Administrator
Web address: www.essentiahealth.
org/NorthernPines/FindaClinic/Essentia–HealthNorthern–Pines–36.aspx

ESSENTIA HEALTH SANDSTONE (O, 85 beds) 109 Court Avenue South,
Sandstone, MN Zip 55072–5120; tel. 320/245–2212; Michael D. Hedrix,
Administrator and President
Web address: www.pinemedicalcenter.org

ESSENTIA HEALTH ST. JOSEPH'S MEDICAL CENTER (O, 136 beds) 523 North
Third Street, Brainerd, MN Zip 56401–3098; tel. 218/829–2861; Adam
Rees, President
Web address: www.essentiahealth.org

ESSENTIA HEALTH ST. MARY'S – DETROIT LAKES (O, 131 beds) 1027
Washington Avenue, Detroit Lakes, MN Zip 56501–3409;
tel. 218/847–5611; Peter Jacobson, President
Web address: www.essentiahealth.org

ESSENTIA HEALTH ST. MARY'S MEDICAL CENTER (O, 306 beds) 407 East
Third Street, Duluth, MN Zip 55805–1984; tel. 218/786–4000; James
Garvey, Executive Vice President, Operations and Administrator
Web address: www.essentiahealth.
org/StMarysMedicalCenter/FindaClinic/Essentia–HealthSt–Marys–Medical–
Center–46.aspx

ESSENTIA HEALTH–DEER RIVER (O, 52 beds) 115 10th Avenue N.E., Deer
River, MN Zip 56636–8795; tel. 218/246–2900; Marsha Green, Chief
Executive Officer
Web address: www.essentiahealth.org

For explanation of codes following names, see page B2.
★ Indicates Type III membership in the American Hospital Association.

Section B

ESSENTIA HEALTH–GRACEVILLE (O, 65 beds) 115 West Second Street, Graceville, MN Zip 56240–4845, Mailing Address: P.O. Box 157, Zip 56240–0157; tel. 320/748–7223; Julie Rosenberg, Administrator **Web address:** www.essentiahealth. org/HolyTrinityHospital/FindaClinic/Essentia–HealthHoly–Trinity–Hospital–96. aspx

ESSENTIA HEALTH–VIRGINIA (L, 173 beds) 901 Ninth Street North, Virginia, MN Zip 55792–2398; tel. 218/741–3340; Daniel Milbridge, Administrator and Chief Operating Officer **Web address:** www.essentiahealth.org

MINNESOTA VALLEY HEALTH CENTER (O, 64 beds) 621 South Fourth Street, Le Sueur, MN Zip 56058–2298; tel. 507/665–3375; Pam Williams, Chief Executive Officer **Web address:** www.mvhc.org

NORTH DAKOTA: ESSENTIA HEALTH FARGO (O, 117 beds) 3000 32nd Avenue South, Fargo, ND Zip 58103–6132; tel. 701/364–8000; Timothy Sayler, Chief Operating Officer **Web address:** www.essentiahealth.com

WISCONSIN: ESSENTIA HEALTH ST. MARY'S HOSPITAL OF SUPERIOR (O, 25 beds) 3500 Tower Avenue, Superior, WI Zip 54880–5395; tel. 715/817–7000; Terry Jacobson, Administrator and Chief Executive Officer **Web address:** www.essentiahealth. org/EssentiaHealthStMarysHospitalofSuperiorFoundation/overview.aspx

Owned, leased, sponsored:	16 hospitals	1506 beds
Contract–managed:	0 hospitals	0 beds
Totals:	16 hospitals	1506 beds

2395: EXCELA HEALTH (NP)
532 West Pittsburgh Street, Greensburg, PA Zip 15601, Mailing Address: 134 Industrial Park Road, Zip 15601–7328; tel. 724/832–5050; Robert Rogalski, Chief Executive Officer **(Centralized Health System)**

PENNSYLVANIA: EXCELA FRICK HOSPITAL (O, 33 beds) 508 South Church Street, Mount Pleasant, PA Zip 15666–1790; tel. 724/547–1500; Ronald H. Ott, President **Web address:** www.excelahealth. org/PatientsandVisitors/HospitalsFacilities/Hospitals/Frick.aspx

EXCELA HEALTH WESTMORELAND HOSPITAL (O, 270 beds) 532 West Pittsburgh Street, Greensburg, PA Zip 15601–2282; tel. 724/832–4000; Ronald H. Ott, President **Web address:** www.excelahealth.org

EXCELA LATROBE AREA HOSPITAL (O, 114 beds) One Mellon Way, Latrobe, PA Zip 15650–1096; tel. 724/537–1000; Michael D. Busch, Executive Vice President and Chief Operating Officer **Web address:** www.excelahealth.org

Owned, leased, sponsored:	3 hospitals	417 beds
Contract–managed:	0 hospitals	0 beds
Totals:	3 hospitals	417 beds

★1325: FAIRVIEW HEALTH SERVICES (NP)
2450 Riverside Avenue, Minneapolis, MN Zip 55454–1400; tel. 612/672–6141; David Murphy, Interim Chief Executive Officer **(Centralized Physician/Insurance Health System)**

MINNESOTA: FAIRVIEW LAKES HEALTH SERVICES (O, 49 beds) 5200 Fairview Boulevard, Wyoming, MN Zip 55092–8013; tel. 651/982–7000; John W. Herman, President **Web address:** www.fairview.org/

FAIRVIEW NORTHLAND MEDICAL CENTER (O, 37 beds) 911 Northland Drive, Princeton, MN Zip 55371–2173; tel. 763/389–1313; John W. Herman, President **Web address:** www.northland.fairview.org

FAIRVIEW RIDGES HOSPITAL (O, 162 beds) 201 East Nicollet Boulevard, Burnsville, MN Zip 55337–5799; tel. 952/892–2000; Patrick Belland, President **Web address:** www.fairview.org

FAIRVIEW SOUTHDALE HOSPITAL (O, 338 beds) 6401 France Avenue South, Edina, MN Zip 55435–2199; tel. 952/924–5000; Bradley Beard, Regional President **Web address:** www.fairview.org

RANGE REGIONAL HEALTH SERVICES (O, 57 beds) 750 East 34th Street, Hibbing, MN Zip 55746–4600; tel. 218/262–4881; Debra K. Boardman, FACHE, President and Chief Executive Officer **Web address:** www.range.fairview.org

UNIVERSITY OF MINNESOTA MEDICAL CENTER, FAIRVIEW (O, 863 beds) 2450 Riverside Avenue, Minneapolis, MN Zip 55454–1400; tel. 612/672–6000; David Murphy, Interim Chief Executive Officer **Web address:** www.fairview.org

Owned, leased, sponsored:	6 hospitals	1506 beds
Contract–managed:	0 hospitals	0 beds
Totals:	6 hospitals	1506 beds

0814: FAITH REGIONAL HEALTH SERVICES (NP)
2700 West Norfolk Avenue, Norfolk, NE Zip 68701–4438, Mailing Address: P.O. Box 869, Zip 68702–0869; tel. 402/644–7201; Mark D. Klosterman, FACHE, President and Chief Executive Officer **(Independent Hospital System)**

NEBRASKA: FAITH REGIONAL HEALTH SERVICES (O, 146 beds) 2700 West Norfolk Avenue, Norfolk, NE Zip 68701–4438, Mailing Address: P.O. Box 869, Zip 68702–0869; tel. 402/644–7201; Mark D. Klosterman, FACHE, President and Chief Executive Officer **Web address:** www.frhs.org

NIOBRARA VALLEY HOSPITAL (C, 20 beds) 401 South Fifth Street, Lynch, NE Zip 68746–0118, Mailing Address: P.O. Box 118, Zip 68746–0118; tel. 402/569–2451; Kelly Kalkowski, Chief Executive Officer **Web address:** www.nvhcares.org

WEST HOLT MEMORIAL HOSPITAL (C, 17 beds) 406 West Neely Street, Atkinson, NE Zip 68713–4801; tel. 402/925–2811; Bradley D. Pfeifer, Chief Executive Officer **Web address:** www.westholtmed.org

Owned, leased, sponsored:	1 hospital	146 beds
Contract–managed:	2 hospitals	37 beds
Totals:	3 hospitals	183 beds

0397: FINGER LAKES HEALTH (NP)
196 North Street, Geneva, NY Zip 14456–1651; tel. 315/787–4000; Jose Acevedo, M.D., President and Chief Executive Officer **(Independent Hospital System)**

NEW YORK: GENEVA GENERAL HOSPITAL (O, 132 beds) 196 North Street, Geneva, NY Zip 14456–1694; tel. 315/787–4000; Jose Acevedo, M.D., President and Chief Executive Officer **Web address:** www.flhealth.org

SOLDIERS AND SAILORS MEMORIAL HOSPITAL OF YATES COUNTY (O, 186 beds) 418 North Main Street, Penn Yan, NY Zip 14527–1085; tel. 315/531–2000; Jose Acevedo, M.D., President and Chief Executive Officer **Web address:** www.flhealth.org

Owned, leased, sponsored:	2 hospitals	318 beds
Contract–managed:	0 hospitals	0 beds
Totals:	2 hospitals	318 beds

★0243: FIRSTHEALTH OF THE CAROLINAS (NP)
155 Memorial Drive, Pinehurst, NC Zip 28374–8710, Mailing Address: P.O. Box 3000, Zip 28374–3000; tel. 910/715–1000; David J. Kilarski, FACHE, Chief Executive Officer **(Centralized Physician/Insurance Health System)**

NORTH CAROLINA: FIRSTHEALTH MONTGOMERY MEMORIAL HOSPITAL (O, 25 beds) 520 Allen Street, Troy, NC Zip 27371–2802; tel. 910/571–5000; Beth Walker, R.N., President **Web address:** www.firsthealth.org

For explanation of codes following names, see page B2.
★ Indicates Type III membership in the American Hospital Association.

FIRSTHEALTH MOORE REGIONAL HOSPITAL (O, 371 beds) 155 Memorial Drive, Pinehurst, NC Zip 28374–8710, Mailing Address: P.O. Box 3000, Zip 28374–3000; tel. 910/715–1000; David J. Kilarski, FACHE, Chief Executive Officer
Web address: www.firsthealth.org

FIRSTHEALTH RICHMOND MEMORIAL HOSPITAL (O, 91 beds) 925 Long Drive, Rockingham, NC Zip 28379–4835; tel. 910/417–3000; John J. Jackson, President
Web address: www.firsthealth.org

Owned, leased, sponsored:	3 hospitals	487 beds
Contract–managed:	0 hospitals	0 beds
Totals:	3 hospitals	487 beds

0900:   FOUNDATION SURGICAL HOSPITAL AFFILIATES (IO)
14000 North Portland Avenue, Suite 204, Oklahoma City, OK Zip 73134–4002; tel. 405/608–1700; Thomas A. Michaud, Chief Executive Officer
(Independent Hospital System)

TEXAS: FOUNDATION SURGICAL HOSPITAL OF EL PASO (O, 20 beds) 1416 George Dieter Drive, El Paso, TX Zip 79936–7601; tel. 915/598–4240; Don Burris, Chief Executive Officer
Web address: www.physiciansmedcenter.com

FOUNDATION SURGICAL HOSPITAL OF SAN ANTONIO (O, 20 beds) 9522 Huebner Road, San Antonio, TX Zip 78240–1548; tel. 210/478–5400; Blake W. Hubbard, FACHE, Chief Executive Officer
Web address: www.fshsanantonio.com/bariatric–foundation–surgical.html

HERITAGE PARK SURGICAL HOSPITAL (O, 12 beds) 3601 North Calais Street, Sherman, TX Zip 75090–1785; tel. 903/870–0999; Marc Devorsetz, Chief Executive Officer
Web address: www.heritageparksurgicalhospital.com

Owned, leased, sponsored:	3 hospitals	52 beds
Contract–managed:	0 hospitals	0 beds
Totals:	3 hospitals	52 beds

5345:   FRANCISCAN ALLIANCE (CC)
1515 Dragoon Trail, Mishawaka, IN Zip 46544–4710, Mailing Address: P.O. Box 1290, Zip 46546–1290; tel. 574/256–3935; Kevin D. Leahy, President and Chief Executive Officer
(Moderately Centralized Health System)

ILLINOIS: FRANCISCAN ST. JAMES HOSPITAL AND HEALTH CENTERS (O, 398 beds) 20201 South Crawford Avenue, Olympia Fields, IL Zip 60461–1010; tel. 708/747–4000; Arnold Kimmel, Chief Executive Officer
Web address: www.franciscanalliance.org/hospitals/olympiafields/pages/default.aspx

INDIANA: FRANCISCAN HEALTHCARE – MUNSTER (O, 32 beds) 701 Superior Avenue, Munster, IN Zip 46321–4037; tel. 219/924–1300; Matthew Teolis, Interim President and Chief Executive Officer, Vice President of Medical Affairs
Web address: www.franciscanphysicianshospital.org

FRANCISCAN ST. ANTHONY HEALTH – CROWN POINT (O, 254 beds) 1201 South Main Street, Crown Point, IN Zip 46307–8483; tel. 219/738–2100; Barbara M. Anderson, President and Chief Executive Officer
Web address: www.franciscanalliance.org

FRANCISCAN ST. ANTHONY HEALTH – MICHIGAN CITY (O, 171 beds) 301 West Homer Street, Michigan City, IN Zip 46360–4358; tel. 219/879–8511; Dean Mazzoni, President and Chief Executive Officer
Web address: www.franciscanalliance.org

FRANCISCAN ST. ELIZABETH HEALTH – CRAWFORDSVILLE (O, 42 beds) 1710 Lafayette Road, Crawfordsville, IN Zip 47933–1099; tel. 765/362–2800; Terrance E. Wilson, President and CEO
Web address: www.stclaremedical.org

FRANCISCAN ST. ELIZABETH HEALTH – LAFAYETTE EAST (O, 187 beds) 1701 South Creasy Lane, Lafayette, IN Zip 47905–4972; tel. 765/502–4000; Terrance E. Wilson, President and CEO
Web address: www.ste.org

FRANCISCAN ST. FRANCIS HEALTH – INDIANAPOLIS (O, 455 beds) 8111 South Emerson Avenue, Indianapolis, IN Zip 46237–8601; tel. 317/528–5000; James Callaghan, III, M.D., President and Chief Executive Officer
Web address: www.stfrancishospitals.org

FRANCISCAN ST. FRANCIS HEALTH – MOORESVILLE (O, 115 beds) 1201 Hadley Road, Mooresville, IN Zip 46158–1789; tel. 317/831–1160; Peter J. Murphy, Senior Vice President and Chief Operating Officer
Web address: www.franciscanalliance.org/hospitals/mooresville/Pages/default.aspx

FRANCISCAN ST. FRANCIS HEALTH–CARMEL (O, 6 beds) 12188B North Meridian Street, Carmel, IN Zip 46032–4840; tel. 317/705–4500; Stephen J. Wheatley, Director of Operations
Web address: www.franciscanalliance.org/hospitals/carmel/Pages/default.aspx

FRANCISCAN ST. MARGARET HEALTH – HAMMOND (O, 406 beds) 5454 Hohman Avenue, Hammond, IN Zip 46320–1999; tel. 219/932–2300; Matthew Teolis, Interim President and Chief Executive Officer, Vice President of Medical Affairs
Web address: www.smmhc.com

Owned, leased, sponsored:	10 hospitals	2066 beds
Contract–managed:	0 hospitals	0 beds
Totals:	10 hospitals	2066 beds

★1475:   FRANCISCAN MISSIONARIES OF OUR LADY HEALTH SYSTEM, INC. (CC)
4200 Essen Lane, Baton Rouge, LA Zip 70809–2158; tel. 225/923–2701; John J. Finan, Jr., FACHE, President and Chief Executive Officer
(Moderately Centralized Health System)

LOUISIANA: ASSUMPTION COMMUNITY HOSPITAL (O, 6 beds) 135 Highway 402, Napoleonville, LA Zip 70390–2217; tel. 985/369–3600; Wayne M. Arboneaux, Chief Executive Officer

OUR LADY OF LOURDES REGIONAL MEDICAL CENTER (O, 186 beds) 4801 Ambassador Caffery Parkway, Lafayette, LA Zip 70508–6917; tel. 337/470–2000; William F. Barrow, II, President and Chief Executive Officer
Web address: www.lourdesrmc.com

OUR LADY OF THE ANGELS HOSPITAL (O, 57 beds) 433 Plaza Street, Bogalusa, LA Zip 70427–3793; tel. 985/730–6700; Rene Ragas, Chief Operating Officer
Web address: www.oloah.org

OUR LADY OF THE LAKE REGIONAL MEDICAL CENTER (O, 1111 beds) 5000 Hennessy Boulevard, Baton Rouge, LA Zip 70808–4375; tel. 225/765–6565; K. Scott Wester, FACHE, President and Chief Executive Officer
Web address: www.ololrmc.com

ST. ELIZABETH HOSPITAL (O, 44 beds) 1125 West Highway 30, Gonzales, LA Zip 70737–5004; tel. 225/647–5000; Robert L. Burgess, President and Chief Executive Officer
Web address: www.steh.com

ST. FRANCIS MEDICAL CENTER (O, 331 beds) 309 Jackson Street, Monroe, LA Zip 71201–7407, Mailing Address: P.O. Box 1901, Zip 71210–1901; tel. 318/966–4000; Kristin Wolkart, R.N., President and Chief Executive Officer
Web address: www.stfran.com

Owned, leased, sponsored:	6 hospitals	1735 beds
Contract–managed:	0 hospitals	0 beds
Totals:	6 hospitals	1735 beds

★1455:   FRANCISCAN SISTERS OF CHRISTIAN CHARITY SPONSORED MINISTRIES, INC. (CC)
1415 South Rapids Road, Manitowoc, WI Zip 54220–9302; tel. 920/684–7071; Daniel B. McGinty, President and Chief Executive Officer
(Moderately Centralized Health System)

NEBRASKA: ST. FRANCIS MEMORIAL HOSPITAL (O, 88 beds) 430 North Monitor Street, West Point, NE Zip 68788–1555; tel. 402/372–2404; Jerry Wordekemper, President and Chief Executive Officer
Web address: www.fcswp.org

For explanation of codes following names, see page B2.
★ Indicates Type III membership in the American Hospital Association.

Section B

OHIO: GENESIS HEALTHCARE SYSTEM (O, 321 beds) 2951 Maple Avenue, Zanesville, OH Zip 43701–1406; tel. 740/454–5000; Matthew J. Perry, President and Chief Executive Officer
Web address: www.genesishcs.org

WISCONSIN: HOLY FAMILY MEMORIAL (O, 67 beds) 2300 Western Avenue, Manitowoc, WI Zip 54220–3712, Mailing Address: P.O. Box 1450, Zip 54221–1450; tel. 920/320–2011; Mark P. Herzog, President and Chief Executive Officer
Web address: www.hfmhealth.org

Owned, leased, sponsored:	3 hospitals	476 beds
Contract–managed:	0 hospitals	0 beds
Totals:	3 hospitals	476 beds

★**0271: FREEMAN HEALTH SYSTEM** (NP)
1102 West 32nd Street, Joplin, MO Zip 64804–3503; tel. 417/347–1111; Paula F. Baker, President and Chief Executive Officer
(Centralized Health System)

MISSOURI: FREEMAN HEALTH SYSTEM (O, 396 beds) 1102 West 32nd Street, Joplin, MO Zip 64804–3503; tel. 417/347–1111; Paula F. Baker, President and Chief Executive Officer
Web address: www.freemanhealth.com

FREEMAN NEOSHO HOSPITAL (O, 25 beds) 113 West Hickory Street, Neosho, MO Zip 64850–1705; tel. 417/455–4352; Paula F. Baker, President and Chief Executive Officer
Web address: www.freemanhealth.com

Owned, leased, sponsored:	2 hospitals	421 beds
Contract–managed:	0 hospitals	0 beds
Totals:	2 hospitals	421 beds

0182: FUNDAMENTAL LONG TERM CARE HOLDINGS, LLC (IO)
930 Ridgebrook Road, Sparks Glencoe, MD Zip 21152–9390; tel. 410/773–1000; W. Bradley Bennett, President and Chief Executive Officer
(Independent Hospital System)

NEVADA: HARMON MEDICAL AND REHABILITATION HOSPITAL (O, 118 beds) 2170 East Harmon Avenue, Las Vegas, NV Zip 89119–7840; tel. 702/794–0100; Bonnie Essex Hillegass, Chief Executive Officer
HORIZON SPECIALTY HOSPITAL (O, 49 beds) 640 Desert Lane, Las Vegas, NV Zip 89106–4207; tel. 702/382–3155; Darrin Cook, Chief Executive Officer and Administrator
Web address: www.horizonspecialtyhosp.com/
SOUTHERN NEVADA MEDICAL AND REHABILITATION CENTER (O, 100 beds) 2945 Casa Vegas, Las Vegas, NV Zip 89169–2248; tel. 702/735–7179; Maureen Davis, Administrator

TEXAS: TEXAS SPECIALTY HOSPITAL AT LUBBOCK (O, 26 beds) 4302B Princeton Street, Lubbock, TX Zip 79415–1304; tel. 806/723–8700; Deanna Graves, Chief Executive Officer
Web address: www.texasspecialtylubbock.com/services.html

Owned, leased, sponsored:	4 hospitals	293 beds
Contract–managed:	0 hospitals	0 beds
Totals:	4 hospitals	293 beds

★**5570: GEISINGER HEALTH SYSTEM** (NP)
100 North Academy Avenue, Danville, PA Zip 17822–9800; tel. 570/271–6211; David T. Feinberg, M.D., President and Chief Executive Officer
(Independent Hospital System)

NEW JERSEY: ATLANTICARE REGIONAL MEDICAL CENTER (O, 530 beds) 1925 Pacific Avenue, Atlantic City, NJ Zip 08401–6713; tel. 609/441–8994; Lori Herndon, R.N., President and Chief Executive Officer
Web address: www.atlanticare.org

PENNSYLVANIA: GEISINGER MEDICAL CENTER (O, 545 beds) 100 North Academy Avenue, Danville, PA Zip 17822–2201; tel. 570/271–6211; Thomas P. Sokola, Chief Administrative Officer
Web address: www.geisinger.org

GEISINGER WYOMING VALLEY MEDICAL CENTER (O, 238 beds) 1000 East Mountain Boulevard, Wilkes Barre, PA Zip 18711–0027; tel. 570/808–7300; Ronald R. Beer, FACHE, Vice President, Clinical Operations
Web address: www.geisinger.org

GEISINGER–BLOOMSBURG HOSPITAL (O, 72 beds) 549 Fair Street, Bloomsburg, PA Zip 17815–1419; tel. 570/387–2100; Lissa Bryan–Smith, Chief Administrative Officer
Web address: www.bloomhealth.net

GEISINGER–COMMUNITY MEDICAL CENTER (O, 270 beds) 1800 Mulberry Street, Scranton, PA Zip 18510–2369; tel. 570/703–8000; David T. Feinberg, M.D., Chief Executive Officer
Web address: www.geisinger.org/for-patients/locations–directions/gcmc/

GEISINGER–LEWISTOWN HOSPITAL (O, 123 beds) 400 Highland Avenue, Lewistown, PA Zip 17044–1198; tel. 717/248–5411; Kay A. Hamilton, R.N., MS, Chief Administrative Officer
Web address: www.geisinger.org

Owned, leased, sponsored:	6 hospitals	1778 beds
Contract–managed:	0 hospitals	0 beds
Totals:	6 hospitals	1778 beds

★**0311: GENESIS HEALTH SYSTEM** (NP)
1227 East Rusholme Street, Davenport, IA Zip 52803–2498; tel. 563/421–1000; Douglas P. Cropper, President and Chief Executive Officer
(Centralized Physician/Insurance Health System)

ILLINOIS: GENESIS MEDICAL CENTER, ILLINI CAMPUS (O, 135 beds) 801 Illini Drive, Silvis, IL Zip 61282–1893; tel. 309/281–4000; Theresa Summers–Main, R.N., Interim President
Web address: www.genesishealth.com

GENESIS MEDICAL CENTER–ALEDO (O, 22 beds) 409 N.W. Ninth Avenue, Aledo, IL Zip 61231–1296; tel. 309/582–9100; Ted Rogalski, Administrator
Web address: www.genesishealth.com

IOWA: GENESIS MEDICAL CENTER, DEWITT (O, 86 beds) 1118 11th Street, De Witt, IA Zip 52742–1296; tel. 563/659–4200; Curt Coleman, FACHE, Chief Executive Officer
Web address: www.genesishealth.com

GENESIS MEDICAL CENTER–DAVENPORT (O, 352 beds) 1227 East Rusholme Street, Davenport, IA Zip 52803–2498; tel. 563/421–1000; Jordan Voigt, Administrator
Web address: www.genesishealth.com

JACKSON COUNTY REGIONAL HEALTH CENTER (C, 25 beds) 700 West Grove Street, Maquoketa, IA Zip 52060–2163; tel. 563/652–2474; Curt Coleman, FACHE, Administrator
Web address: www.jcrhc.org

Owned, leased, sponsored:	4 hospitals	595 beds
Contract–managed:	1 hospital	25 beds
Totals:	5 hospitals	620 beds

0283: GILLIARD HEALTH SERVICES (IO)
3091 Carter Hill Road, Montgomery, AL Zip 36111–1801; tel. 334/265–5009; William G. McKenzie, President, Chief Executive Officer and Chairman

ALABAMA: EVERGREEN MEDICAL CENTER (O, 42 beds) 101 Crestview Avenue, Evergreen, AL Zip 36401–3333, Mailing Address: P.O. Box 706, Zip 36401–0706; tel. 251/578–2480; Tom McLendon, Administrator
Web address: www.evergreenmedical.org

For explanation of codes following names, see page B2.
★ Indicates Type III membership in the American Hospital Association.

Section B

JACKSON MEDICAL CENTER (O, 26 beds) 220 Hospital Drive, Jackson, AL Zip 36545–2459, Mailing Address: P.O. Box 428, Zip 36545–0428; tel. 251/246–9021; Amy Gibson, Chief Executive Officer
Web address: www.jacksonmedicalcenter.org

Owned, leased, sponsored:	2 hospitals	68 beds
Contract–managed:	0 hospitals	0 beds
Totals:	2 hospitals	68 beds

0522: GOOD SHEPHERD HEALTH SYSTEM (NP)
700 East Marshall Avenue, Longview, TX Zip 75601–5580; tel. 903/315–2000; Steve Altmiller, President and Chief Executive Officer
(Independent Hospital System)

TEXAS: GOOD SHEPHERD MEDICAL CENTER (O, 393 beds) 700 East Marshall Avenue, Longview, TX Zip 75601–5580; tel. 903/315–2000; Steve Altmiller, President and Chief Executive Officer
Web address: www.gsmc.org

GOOD SHEPHERD MEDICAL CENTER–MARSHALL (O, 140 beds) 811 South Washington Avenue, Marshall, TX Zip 75670–5336, Mailing Address: P.O. Box 1599, Zip 75671–1599; tel. 903/927–6000; Russell J. Collier, FACHE, President and Chief Executive Officer
Web address: www.gsmcmarshall.org

Owned, leased, sponsored:	2 hospitals	533 beds
Contract–managed:	0 hospitals	0 beds
Totals:	2 hospitals	533 beds

0648: GOOD SHEPHERD REHABILITATION NETWORK (IO)
850 South Fifth Street, Allentown, PA Zip 18103–3308; tel. 610/776–3100; John Kristel, President and Chief Executive Officer
(Independent Hospital System)

PENNSYLVANIA: GOOD SHEPHERD REHABILITATION HOSPITAL (O, 106 beds) 850 South 5th Street, Allentown, PA Zip 18103–3308; tel. 610/776–3299; John Kristel, President and Chief Executive Officer
Web address: www.goodshepherdrehab.org

GOOD SHEPHERD SPECIALTY HOSPITAL (O, 32 beds) 2545 Schoenersville Road, 3rd Floor, Bethlehem, PA Zip 18017–7300; tel. 484/884–5051; Greg Wuchter, R.N., MSN, Administrator
Web address: www.goodshepherdrehab.org

Owned, leased, sponsored:	2 hospitals	138 beds
Contract–managed:	0 hospitals	0 beds
Totals:	2 hospitals	138 beds

★1535: GREAT PLAINS HEALTH ALLIANCE, INC. (NP)
250 North Rock Road, Suite 160, Wichita, KS Zip 67206–2241; tel. 316/685–1523; Dave Dellasega, President and Chief Executive Officer
(Decentralized Health System)

KANSAS: ASHLAND HEALTH CENTER (C, 45 beds) 709 Oak Street, Ashland, KS Zip 67831–0188, Mailing Address: P.O. Box 188, Zip 67831–0188; tel. 620/635–2241; Michael Mages, Chief Executive Officer
Web address: www.ashlandhc.org

CHEYENNE COUNTY HOSPITAL (L, 16 beds) 210 West First Street, Saint Francis, KS Zip 67756–3540, Mailing Address: P.O. Box 547, Zip 67756–0547; tel. 785/332–2104; Scott Jenkins, Administrator
Web address: www.cheyennecountyhospital.com

COMANCHE COUNTY HOSPITAL (C, 12 beds) 202 South Frisco Street, Coldwater, KS Zip 67029–9101, Mailing Address: HC 65, Box 8A, Zip 67029–9500; tel. 620/582–2144; Nancy Zimmerman, R.N., Administrator
Web address: www.gpha.com

ELLINWOOD DISTRICT HOSPITAL (L, 25 beds) 605 North Main Street, Ellinwood, KS Zip 67526–1440; tel. 620/564–2548; Kile Magner, Administrator
Web address: www.ellinwooddistricthospital.org

FREDONIA REGIONAL HOSPITAL (C, 34 beds) 1527 Madison Street, Fredonia, KS Zip 66736–1751, Mailing Address: P.O. Box 579, Zip 66736–0579; tel. 620/378–2121; John Hart, Chief Executive Officer
Web address: www.fredoniaregionalhospital.org

GRISELL MEMORIAL HOSPITAL DISTRICT ONE (C, 46 beds) 210 South Vermont Avenue, Ransom, KS Zip 67572–9525; tel. 785/731–2231; David Caudill, Administrator
Web address: www.grisellmemorialhospital.org

KIOWA COUNTY MEMORIAL HOSPITAL (L, 15 beds) 721 West Kansas Avenue, Greensburg, KS Zip 67054–1633; tel. 620/723–3341; Mary Sweet, Administrator
Web address: www.kcmh.net

LANE COUNTY HOSPITAL (C, 31 beds) 235 West Vine, Dighton, KS Zip 67839–0969, Mailing Address: P.O. Box 969, Zip 67839–0969; tel. 620/397–5321; Donna McGowan, Administrator

MEDICINE LODGE MEMORIAL HOSPITAL (C, 25 beds) 710 North Walnut Street, Medicine Lodge, KS Zip 67104–1019; tel. 620/886–3771; Kevin A. White, Administrator
Web address: www.mlmh.net/

MINNEOLA DISTRICT HOSPITAL (C, 54 beds) 212 Main Street, Minneola, KS Zip 67865–8511, Mailing Address: P.O. Box 127, Zip 67865–0127; tel. 620/885–4264; Deborah Bruner, Chief Executive Officer and Administrator
Web address: www.minneolahealthcare.com

OSBORNE COUNTY MEMORIAL HOSPITAL (C, 25 beds) 424 West New Hampshire Street, Osborne, KS Zip 67473–2314, Mailing Address: P.O. Box 70, Zip 67473–0070; tel. 785/346–2121; Rex D. Walk, Interim Chief Executive Officer
Web address: www.ocmh.org

OTTAWA COUNTY HEALTH CENTER (L, 42 beds) 215 East Eighth, Minneapolis, KS Zip 67467–1902, Mailing Address: P.O. Box 290, Zip 67467–0290; tel. 785/392–2122; Jody Parks, Administrator
Web address: www.ottawacountyhealthcenter.com

PHILLIPS COUNTY HOSPITAL (L, 25 beds) 1150 State Street, Phillipsburg, KS Zip 67661–1743, Mailing Address: P.O. Box 607, Zip 67661–0607; tel. 785/543–5226; David Engel, Chief Executive Officer
Web address: www.phillipshospital.org

RAWLINS COUNTY HEALTH CENTER (C, 24 beds) 707 Grant Street, Atwood, KS Zip 67730–1526, Mailing Address: P.O. Box 47, Zip 67730–0047; tel. 785/626–3211; Sharon K. Cox, FACHE, Chief Executive Officer
Web address: www.rchc.us

REPUBLIC COUNTY HOSPITAL (L, 63 beds) 2420 G Street, Belleville, KS Zip 66935–2400; tel. 785/527–2254; Blaine K. Miller, Administrator
Web address: www.rphospital.org

SABETHA COMMUNITY HOSPITAL (L, 25 beds) 14th and Oregon Streets, Sabetha, KS Zip 66534–0229, Mailing Address: P.O. Box 229, Zip 66534–0229; tel. 785/284–2121; Lora Key, Chief Executive Officer
Web address: www.sabethahospital.com

SATANTA DISTRICT HOSPITAL AND LONG TERM CARE (C, 57 beds) 401 South Cheyenne Street, Satanta, KS Zip 67870–0159, Mailing Address: P.O. Box 159, Zip 67870–0159; tel. 620/649–2761; Jeremy Clingenpeel, Administrator
Web address: www.satantahospital.org

SMITH COUNTY MEMORIAL HOSPITAL (L, 53 beds) 614 South Main Street, Smith Center, KS Zip 66967–3001; tel. 785/282–6845; Allen Van Driel, FACHE, Administrator
Web address: www.gpha.com

TREGO COUNTY–LEMKE MEMORIAL HOSPITAL (C, 62 beds) 320 North 13th Street, Wakeeney, KS Zip 67672–2099; tel. 785/743–2182; David Augustine, Chief Executive Officer
Web address: www.tclmh.org

NEBRASKA: HARLAN COUNTY HEALTH SYSTEM (C, 19 beds) 717 North Brown Street, Alma, NE Zip 68920–2132, Mailing Address: P.O. Box 836, Zip 68920–0836; tel. 308/928–2151; Manuela Wolf, R.N., Chief Executive Officer
Web address: www.harlancountyhealth.com

Owned, leased, sponsored:	8 hospitals	264 beds
Contract–managed:	12 hospitals	434 beds
Totals:	20 hospitals	698 beds

For explanation of codes following names, see page B2.
★ Indicates Type III membership in the American Hospital Association.

Section B

0144: GREATER HUDSON VALLEY HEALTH SYSTEM (NP)
60 Prospect Avenue, Middletown, NY Zip 10940–4133;
tel. 845/568–6050; Scott Batulis, President and Chief Executive
Officer
(Moderately Centralized Health System)

NEW YORK: CATSKILL REGIONAL MEDICAL CENTER (O, 165 beds) 68 Harris
Bushville Road, Harris, NY Zip 12742–5030, Mailing Address: P.O. Box
800, Zip 12742–0800; tel. 845/794–3300; Gerard Galarneau, M.D.,
Chief Executive Officer and Chief Medical Officer
Web address: www.crmcny.org

GROVER M. HERMANN HOSPITAL (O, 25 beds) 8881 Route 97, Callicoon, NY
Zip 12723; tel. 845/887–5530; Rolland Bojo, R.N., Administrator
Web address: www.crmcny.org

ORANGE REGIONAL MEDICAL CENTER (O, 301 beds) 707 East Main Street,
Middletown, NY Zip 10940–2650; tel. 845/333–1000; Scott Batulis,
President and Chief Executive Officer
Web address: www.ormc.org

Owned, leased, sponsored:	3 hospitals	491 beds
Contract–managed:	0 hospitals	0 beds
Totals:	3 hospitals	491 beds

★**1555: GREENVILLE HEALTH SYSTEM** (NP)
701 Grove Road, Greenville, SC Zip 29605–5611;
tel. 864/455–7000; Michael C. Riordan, President and Chief
Executive Officer
(Centralized Health System)

SOUTH CAROLINA: GHS GREENVILLE MEMORIAL HOSPITAL (O, 742 beds)
701 Grove Road, Greenville, SC Zip 29605–4295; tel. 864/455–7000;
Paul F. Johnson, President
Web address: www.ghs.org

GHS GREER MEMORIAL HOSPITAL (O, 70 beds) 830 South Buncombe Road,
Greer, SC Zip 29650–2400; tel. 864/797–8000; John F. Mansure, FACHE,
President
Web address: www.ghs.org

GHS HILLCREST MEMORIAL HOSPITAL (O, 43 beds) 729 S.E. Main Street,
Simpsonville, SC Zip 29681–3280; tel. 864/454–6100; Eric Bour, M.D.,
FACS, President
Web address: www.ghs.org

GREENVILLE HEALTH SYSTEM – LAURENS COUNTY MEMORIAL HOSPITAL (L,
67 beds) 22725 Highway 76 East, Clinton, SC Zip 29325–7527, Mailing
Address: P.O. Drawer 976, Zip 29325–0976; tel. 864/833–9100; Richard E.
D'Alberto, FACHE, Campus President
Web address: www.ghs.org/laurens

OCONEE MEMORIAL HOSPITAL (L, 252 beds) 298 Memorial Drive, Seneca,
SC Zip 29672–9499; tel. 864/882–3351; Hunter Kome, Campus President
Web address: www.oconeemed.org

PATEWOOD MEMORIAL HOSPITAL (O, 72 beds) 175 Patewood Drive,
Greenville, SC Zip 29615–3570; tel. 864/797–1000; Beverly J. Haines, R.N.,
President
Web address: www.ghs.org/patewood

Owned, leased, sponsored:	6 hospitals	1246 beds
Contract–managed:	0 hospitals	0 beds
Totals:	6 hospitals	1246 beds

★**0675: GUTHRIE CLINIC** (NP)
Guthrie Square, Sayre, PA Zip 18840; tel. 570/887–4312; Joseph A.
Scopelliti, M.D., President and Chief Executive Officer
(Moderately Centralized Health System)

NEW YORK: GUTHRIE CORNING HOSPITAL (O, 82 beds) One Guthrie Drive,
Corning, NY Zip 14830–3696; tel. 607/937–7200; Garrett W. Hoover,
FACHE, President
Web address: www.corninghospital.com

PENNSYLVANIA: GUTHRIE TOWANDA MEMORIAL HOSPITAL (O, 203 beds)
91 Hospital Drive, Towanda, PA Zip 18848–9702; tel. 570/265–2191;
Staci Covey, R.N., MS, President
Web address: www.memorialhospital.org

ROBERT PACKER HOSPITAL (O, 254 beds) 1 Guthrie Square, Sayre, PA
Zip 18840–1698; tel. 570/888–6666; Marie T. Droege, President
Web address: www.https://www.guthrie.org/location/robert–packer–hospital

TROY COMMUNITY HOSPITAL (O, 25 beds) 275 Guthrie Drive, Troy, PA
Zip 16947; tel. 570/297–2121; Staci Covey, R.N., MS, President
Web address: www.guthrie.org

Owned, leased, sponsored:	4 hospitals	564 beds
Contract–managed:	0 hospitals	0 beds
Totals:	4 hospitals	564 beds

★**1003: HACKENSACK MERIDIAN HEALTH** (NP)
343 Thornall Street, Edison, NJ Zip 08837–2206;
tel. 844/464–9355; Robert C. Garrett, FACHE, Co–Chief Executive
Officer

NEW JERSEY: BAYSHORE COMMUNITY HOSPITAL (O, 142 beds) 727 North
Beers Street, Holmdel, NJ Zip 07733–1598; tel. 732/739–5900; Timothy
J. Hogan, FACHE, Regional President
Web address: www.bchs.com

HACKENSACK UNIVERSITY MEDICAL CENTER (O, 711 beds) 30 Prospect
Avenue, Hackensack, NJ Zip 07601–1914; tel. 201/996–2000; Ihor S.
Sawczuk, M.D., President
Web address: www.hackensackumc.org

HACKENSACKUMC PALISADES (O, 228 beds) 7600 River Road, North
Bergen, NJ Zip 07047–6217; tel. 201/854–5000; Bruce J. Markowitz,
President and Chief Executive Officer
Web address: www.palisadesmedical.org

JERSEY SHORE UNIVERSITY MEDICAL CENTER (O, 554 beds) 1945 Route
33, Neptune, NJ Zip 07754–0397; tel. 732/775–5500; Kenneth N. Sable,
M.D., President
Web address: www.meridianhealth.com

OCEAN MEDICAL CENTER (O, 271 beds) 425 Jack Martin Boulevard, Brick
Township, NJ Zip 08724–7732; tel. 732/840–2200; Dean Q. Lin, FACHE,
President
Web address: www.meridianhealth.com

RARITAN BAY MEDICAL CENTER (O, 276 beds) 530 New Brunswick Avenue,
Perth Amboy, NJ Zip 08861–3654; tel. 732/442–3700; Michael R. D'Agnes,
FACHE, President and Chief Executive Officer
Web address: www.rbmc.org

RIVERVIEW MEDICAL CENTER (O, 281 beds) 1 Riverview Plaza, Red Bank, NJ
Zip 07701–1864; tel. 732/741–2700; Timothy J. Hogan, FACHE, Regional
President
Web address: www.riverviewmedicalcenter.com

SHORE REHABILITATION INSTITUTE (O, 40 beds) 425 Jack Martin Boulevard,
Brick, NJ Zip 08724–7732; tel. 732/836–4500; Marci Gietter, Interim
Executive Director
Web address: www.shorerehabilitationinstitute.com

SOUTHERN OCEAN MEDICAL CENTER (O, 153 beds) 1140 Route 72 West,
Manahawkin, NJ Zip 08050–2499; tel. 609/597–6011; Joseph P. Coyle,
President and Chief Executive Officer
Web address: www.soch.com

Owned, leased, sponsored:	9 hospitals	2656 beds
Contract–managed:	0 hospitals	0 beds
Totals:	9 hospitals	2656 beds

★**0541: HARTFORD HEALTHCARE** (NP)
One State Street, 19th Floor, Hartford, CT Zip 06103;
tel. 860/263–4100; Elliot T. Joseph, President and Chief Executive
Officer
(Centralized Health System)

CONNECTICUT: HARTFORD HOSPITAL (O, 870 beds) 80 Seymour Street,
Hartford, CT Zip 06102–8000, Mailing Address: P.O. Box 5037,
Zip 06102–5037; tel. 860/545–5000; Stuart Markowitz, M.D., President
Web address: www.harthosp.org

MIDSTATE MEDICAL CENTER (O, 88 beds) 435 Lewis Avenue, Meriden, CT
Zip 06451–2101; tel. 203/694–8200; Lucille A. Janatka, President and Chief
Executive Officer
Web address: www.midstatemedical.org

For explanation of codes following names, see page B2.
★ Indicates Type III membership in the American Hospital Association.

Section B

NATCHAUG HOSPITAL (O, 57 beds) 189 Storrs Road, Mansfield Center, CT Zip 06250–1683; tel. 860/456–1311; Patricia Rehmer, President
Web address: www.natchaug.org

THE HOSPITAL OF CENTRAL CONNECTICUT (O, 179 beds) 100 Grand Street, New Britain, CT Zip 06052–2017, Mailing Address: P.O. Box 100, Zip 06052–2017; tel. 860/224–5011; Lucille A. Janatka, President and Chief Executive Officer, Hartford HealthCare Central Region
Web address: www.thocc.org

THE WILLIAM W. BACKUS HOSPITAL (O, 184 beds) 326 Washington Street, Norwich, CT Zip 06360–2740; tel. 860/889–8331; Bimal Patel, President, Hartford HealthCare East Region
Web address: www.backushospital.org

WINDHAM HOSPITAL (O, 56 beds) 112 Mansfield Avenue, Willimantic, CT Zip 06226–2040; tel. 860/456–9116; Bimal Patel, President, Hartford Healthcare East Region
Web address: www.windhamhospital.org

Owned, leased, sponsored:	6 hospitals	1434 beds
Contract–managed:	0 hospitals	0 beds
Totals:	6 hospitals	1434 beds

0637:   HAVEN BEHAVIORAL HEALTHCARE (IO)
652 West Iris Drive, Nashville, TN Zip 37204–3191; tel. 615/250–9500; Michael Lindley, Chief Executive Officer

ARIZONA: HAVEN SENIOR HORIZONS (O, 30 beds) 1201 South 7th Avenue, Suite 200, Phoenix, AZ Zip 85007–4076; tel. 623/236–2000; Kathy Shaw, Chief Executive Officer
Web address: www.havenbehavioral.com

OHIO: HAVEN BEHAVIORAL SENIOR CARE OF DAYTON (O, 32 beds) One Elizabeth Place, 4th Floor Southwest Tower, Dayton, OH Zip 45417–3445; tel. 937/234–0100; Keith Kuhn, Chief Executive Officer
Web address: www.havenbehavioraldayton.com/

PENNSYLVANIA: HAVEN BEHAVIORAL HOSPITAL OF EASTERN PENNSYLVANIA (O, 48 beds) 145 North 6th Street, 3rd Floor, Reading, PA Zip 19601–3096; tel. 610/406–4340; Bryan W. Lett, Chief Executive Officer
Web address: www.https://havenbehavioral.com/

Owned, leased, sponsored:	3 hospitals	110 beds
Contract–managed:	0 hospitals	0 beds
Totals:	3 hospitals	110 beds

★**3555:   HAWAII HEALTH SYSTEMS CORPORATION** (NP)
3675 Kilauea Avenue, Honolulu, HI Zip 96816–2333; tel. 808/733–4151; Linda Rosen, M.D., Chief Executive Officer
(Independent Hospital System)

HAWAII: HALE HO'OLA HAMAKUA (O, 77 beds) 45–547 Plumeria Street, Honokaa, HI Zip 96727–6902; tel. 808/932–4100; Kerry Pitcher, Administrator
Web address: www.halehoolahamakua.org

HILO MEDICAL CENTER (O, 199 beds) 1190 Waianuenue Avenue, Hilo, HI Zip 96720–2089; tel. 808/932–3000; Dan Brinkman, R.N., Chief Executive Officer
Web address: www.https://www.hilomedicalcenter.org/

KAU HOSPITAL (O, 21 beds) 1 Kamani Street, Pahala, HI Zip 96777, Mailing Address: P.O. Box 40, Zip 96777–0040; tel. 808/932–4200; Merilyn Harris, Administrator
Web address: www.hhsc.org

KAUAI VETERANS MEMORIAL HOSPITAL (O, 45 beds) 4643 Waimea Canyon Road, Waimea, HI Zip 96796, Mailing Address: P.O. Box 337, Zip 96796–0337; tel. 808/338–9431; Peter Klune, Chief Executive Officer
Web address: www.kvmh.hhsc.org

KOHALA HOSPITAL (O, 28 beds) 54–383 Hospital Road, Kohala, HI Zip 96755, Mailing Address: P.O. Box 10, Kapaau, Zip 96755–0010; tel. 808/889–6211; Eugene Amar, Jr., Administrator
Web address: www.koh.hhsc.org

KONA COMMUNITY HOSPITAL (O, 94 beds) 79–1019 Haukapila Street, Kealakekua, HI Zip 96750–7920; tel. 808/322–9311; Jay E. Kreuzer, FACHE, Chief Executive Officer
Web address: www.kch.hhsc.org

KULA HOSPITAL (O, 6 beds) 100 Keokea Place, Kula, HI Zip 96790–7450; tel. 808/878–1221; Paul Harper–O'Connor, Interim Regional Administrator
Web address: www.hhsc.org

LANAI COMMUNITY HOSPITAL (O, 24 beds) 628 Seventh Street, Lanai City, HI Zip 96763–0650, Mailing Address: P.O. Box 630650, Zip 96763–0650; tel. 808/565–8450; Paul Harper–O'Connor, Interim Administrator
Web address: www.lch.hhsc.org

LEAHI HOSPITAL (O, 164 beds) 3675 Kilauea Avenue, Honolulu, HI Zip 96816–2398; tel. 808/733–8000; Reid Kondo, Interim Administrator
Web address: www.hhsc.org

MALUHIA HOSPITAL (O, 146 beds) 1027 Hala Drive, Honolulu, HI Zip 96817; tel. 808/832–5874; Derek Akiyoshi, Chief Executive Officer

MAUI MEMORIAL MEDICAL CENTER (O, 213 beds) 221 Mahalani Street, Wailuku, HI Zip 96793–2581; tel. 808/244–9056; Wesley Lo, Regional Chief Executive Officer
Web address: www.mmmc.hhsc.org

SAMUEL MAHELONA MEMORIAL HOSPITAL (O, 80 beds) 4800 Kawaihau Road, Kapaa, HI Zip 96746–1971; tel. 808/822–4961; Peter Klune, Chief Executive Officer
Web address: www.smmh.hhsc.org

Owned, leased, sponsored:	12 hospitals	1097 beds
Contract–managed:	0 hospitals	0 beds
Totals:	12 hospitals	1097 beds

0266:   HAWAII PACIFIC HEALTH (NP)
55 Merchant Street, Honolulu, HI Zip 96813–4306; tel. 808/949–9355; Raymond P. Vara, Jr., President and Chief Executive Officer
(Independent Hospital System)

KAPIOLANI MEDICAL CENTER FOR WOMEN & CHILDREN (O, 175 beds) 1319 Punahou Street, Honolulu, HI Zip 96826–1001; tel. 808/983–6000; Martha Smith, Chief Executive Officer
Web address: www.kapiolani.org

PALI MOMI MEDICAL CENTER (O, 128 beds) 98–1079 Moanalua Road, Aiea, HI Zip 96701–4713; tel. 808/486–6000; Art Gladstone, R.N., President and Chief Executive Officer
Web address: www.palimomi.org

STRAUB CLINIC & HOSPITAL (O, 108 beds) 888 South King Street, Honolulu, HI Zip 96813–3097; tel. 808/522–4000; Art Gladstone, R.N., Chief Executive Officer
Web address: www.straubhealth.org

WILCOX MEMORIAL HOSPITAL (O, 65 beds) 3–3420 Kuhio Highway, Lihue, HI Zip 96766–1099; tel. 808/245–1100; Jen Chahanovich, President and Chief Executive Officer
Web address: www.wilcoxhealth.org

Owned, leased, sponsored:	4 hospitals	476 beds
Contract–managed:	0 hospitals	0 beds
Totals:	4 hospitals	476 beds

★**0048:   HCA** (IO)
One Park Plaza, Nashville, TN Zip 37203–1548; tel. 615/344–5248; R. Milton Johnson, President and Chief Executive Officer
(Decentralized Health System)

ALASKA: ALASKA REGIONAL HOSPITAL (O, 132 beds) 2801 Debarr Road, Anchorage, AK Zip 99508–2997, Mailing Address: P.O. Box 143889, Zip 99514–3889; tel. 907/264–1754; Julie Taylor, FACHE, Chief Executive Officer
Web address: www.alaskaregional.com

CALIFORNIA: GOOD SAMARITAN HOSPITAL (O, 349 beds) 2425 Samaritan Drive, San Jose, CA Zip 95124–3997, Mailing Address: P.O. Box 240002, Zip 95154–2402; tel. 408/559–2011; Paul Beaupre, M.D., Chief Executive Officer
Web address: www.goodsamsanjose.com

LOS ROBLES HOSPITAL AND MEDICAL CENTER (O, 334 beds) 215 West Janss Road, Thousand Oaks, CA Zip 91360–1899; tel. 805/497–2727; Natalie Mussi, President and Chief Executive Officer
Web address: www.losrobleshospital.com

For explanation of codes following names, see page B2.
★ Indicates Type III membership in the American Hospital Association.

REGIONAL MEDICAL CENTER OF SAN JOSE (O, 216 beds) 225 North Jackson Avenue, San Jose, CA Zip 95116–1603; tel. 408/259–5000; Michael T. Johnson, FACHE, President and Chief Executive Officer
Web address: www.regionalmedicalsanjose.com

RIVERSIDE COMMUNITY HOSPITAL (O, 373 beds) 4445 Magnolia Avenue, Riverside, CA Zip 92501–4199; tel. 951/788–3000; Patrick D. Brilliant, President and Chief Executive Officer
Web address: www.riversidecommunityhospital.com

WEST HILLS HOSPITAL AND MEDICAL CENTER (O, 293 beds) 7300 Medical Center Drive, West Hills, CA Zip 91307–1900; tel. 818/676–4000; Douglas Long, President and Chief Executive Officer
Web address: www.westhillshospital.com

COLORADO: MEDICAL CENTER OF AURORA (O, 303 beds) 1501 South Potomac Street, Aurora, CO Zip 80012–5411; tel. 303/695–2600; Daniel Miller, Chief Executive Officer
Web address: www.auroramed.com

NORTH SUBURBAN MEDICAL CENTER (O, 139 beds) 9191 Grant Street, Thornton, CO Zip 80229–4341; tel. 303/451–7800; Jennifer Alderfer, Chief Executive Officer
Web address: www.northsuburban.com

PRESBYTERIAN–ST. LUKE'S MEDICAL CENTER (O, 395 beds) 1719 East 19th Avenue, Denver, CO Zip 80218–1281; tel. 303/839–6000; Maureen Tarrant, Chief Executive Officer
Web address: www.pslmc.com

ROSE MEDICAL CENTER (O, 262 beds) 4567 East Ninth Avenue, Denver, CO Zip 80220–3941; tel. 303/320–2121; Kenneth H. Feiler, Chief Executive Officer
Web address: www.rosebabies.com

SKY RIDGE MEDICAL CENTER (O, 276 beds) 10101 Ridge Gate Parkway, Lone Tree, CO Zip 80124–5522; tel. 720/225–1000; Susan Hicks, Chief Executive Officer
Web address: www.skyridgemedcenter.com

SPALDING REHABILITATION HOSPITAL (O, 40 beds) 900 Potomac Steet, Aurora, CO Zip 80011–6716; tel. 303/367–1166; Mark S. Deno, Chief Executive Officer
Web address: www.spaldingrehab.com

SWEDISH MEDICAL CENTER (O, 361 beds) 501 East Hampden Avenue, Englewood, CO Zip 80113–2702; tel. 303/788–5000; Richard A. Hammett, Chief Executive Officer
Web address: www.swedishhospital.com

FLORIDA: AVENTURA HOSPITAL AND MEDICAL CENTER (O, 359 beds) 20900 Biscayne Boulevard, Aventura, FL Zip 33180–1407; tel. 305/682–7000; Dianne Goldenberg, Chief Executive Officer
Web address: www.aventurahospital.com

BLAKE MEDICAL CENTER (O, 372 beds) 2020 59th Street West, Bradenton, FL Zip 34209–4669; tel. 941/792–6611; Daniel J. Friedrich, III, Chief Executive Officer
Web address: www.blakemedicalcenter.com

BRANDON REGIONAL HOSPITAL (O, 359 beds) 119 Oakfield Drive, Brandon, FL Zip 33511–5779; tel. 813/681–5551; Bland Eng, Chief Executive Officer
Web address: www.brandonhospital.com

CAPITAL REGIONAL MEDICAL CENTER (O, 198 beds) 2626 Capital Medical Boulevard, Tallahassee, FL Zip 32308–4499; tel. 850/325–5000; Mark Robinson, FACHE, President and Chief Executive Officer
Web address: www.capitalregionalmedicalcenter.com

CENTRAL FLORIDA REGIONAL HOSPITAL (O, 226 beds) 1401 West Seminole Boulevard, Sanford, FL Zip 32771–6764; tel. 407/321–4500; Wendy H. Brandon, Chief Executive Officer
Web address: www.centralfloridaregional.com

CITRUS MEMORIAL HEALTH SYSTEM (O, 204 beds) 502 West Highland Boulevard, Inverness, FL Zip 34452–4754; tel. 352/726–1551; Ralph A. Aleman, President and Chief Executive Officer
Web address: www.citrusmh.com

DOCTORS HOSPITAL OF SARASOTA (O, 168 beds) 5731 Bee Ridge Road, Sarasota, FL Zip 34233–5056; tel. 941/342–1100; Robert C. Meade, Chief Executive Officer
Web address: www.doctorsofsarasota.com

ENGLEWOOD COMMUNITY HOSPITAL (O, 100 beds) 700 Medical Boulevard, Englewood, FL Zip 34223–3978; tel. 941/475–6571; Valerie L. Powell–Stafford, Chief Executive Officer
Web address: www.englewoodcommunityhospital.com

FAWCETT MEMORIAL HOSPITAL (O, 237 beds) 21298 Olean Boulevard, Port Charlotte, FL Zip 33952–6765; tel. 941/629–1181; William Hawley, President and Chief Executive Officer
Web address: www.fawcetthospital.com

FORT WALTON BEACH MEDICAL CENTER (O, 257 beds) 1000 Mar–Walt Drive, Fort Walton Beach, FL Zip 32547–6795; tel. 850/862–1111; Mitchell P. Mongell, FACHE, Chief Executive Officer
Web address: www.fwbmc.com

GULF COAST MEDICAL CENTER (O, 176 beds) 449 West 23rd Street, Panama City, FL Zip 32405–4593, Mailing Address: P.O. Box 15309, Zip 32406–5309; tel. 850/769–8341; Carlton Ulmer, Chief Executive Officer
Web address: www.egulfcoastmedical.com

JFK MEDICAL CENTER (O, 424 beds) 5301 South Congress Avenue, Atlantis, FL Zip 33462–1197; tel. 561/965–7300; Gina Melby, Chief Executive Officer
Web address: www.jfkmc.com

JFK MEDICAL CENTER NORTH CAMPUS (O, 245 beds) 2201 45th Street, West Palm Beach, FL Zip 33407–2047; tel. 561/842–6141; Dana C. Oaks, Chief Executive Officer
Web address: www.westpalmhospital.com

KENDALL REGIONAL MEDICAL CENTER (O, 300 beds) 11750 Bird Road, Miami, FL Zip 33175–3530; tel. 305/223–3000; Scott A. Cihak, Chief Executive Officer
Web address: www.kendallmed.com

LAKE CITY MEDICAL CENTER (O, 67 beds) 340 N.W. Commerce Drive, Lake City, FL Zip 32055–4709; tel. 386/719–9000; Mark Miller, FACHE, Chief Executive Officer
Web address: www.lakecitymedical.com

LARGO MEDICAL CENTER (O, 243 beds) 201 14th Street S.W., Largo, FL Zip 33770–3133; tel. 727/588–5200; Anthony M. Degina, President and Chief Executive Officer
Web address: www.largomedical.com

LAWNWOOD REGIONAL MEDICAL CENTER & HEART INSTITUTE (O, 331 beds) 1700 South 23rd Street, Fort Pierce, FL Zip 34950–4803; tel. 772/461–4000; Greg Lowe, Chief Executive Officer
Web address: www.lawnwoodmed.com

MEDICAL CENTER OF TRINITY (O, 276 beds) 9330 State Road 54, Trinity, FL Zip 34655–1808; tel. 727/834–4900; Leigh Massengill, Chief Executive Officer
Web address: www.medicalcentertrinity.com

MEMORIAL HOSPITAL JACKSONVILLE (O, 418 beds) 3625 University Boulevard South, Jacksonville, FL Zip 32216–4207, Mailing Address: P.O. Box 16325, Zip 32245–6325; tel. 904/702–6111; James F. O'Loughlin, President and Chief Executive Officer
Web address: www.memorialhospitaljax.com

MEMORIAL HOSPITAL OF TAMPA (O, 139 beds) 2901 Swann Avenue, Tampa, FL Zip 33609–4057; tel. 813/873–6400; Ward Boston, III, Chief Executive Officer
Web address: www.memorialhospitaltampa.com

NORTH FLORIDA REGIONAL MEDICAL CENTER (O, 349 beds) 6500 Newberry Road, Gainesville, FL Zip 32605–4392, Mailing Address: P.O. Box 147006, Zip 32614–7006; tel. 352/333–4000; Brian Cook, FACHE, President and Chief Executive Officer
Web address: www.nfrmc.com

NORTHSIDE HOSPITAL (O, 217 beds) 6000 49th Street North, Saint Petersburg, FL Zip 33709–2145; tel. 727/521–4411; Dia Nichols, Chief Executive Officer
Web address: www.northsidehospital.com

NORTHWEST MEDICAL CENTER (O, 228 beds) 2801 North State Road 7, Margate, FL Zip 33063–5727; tel. 954/974–0400; Erica Gulrich, Chief Executive Officer
Web address: www.northwestmed.com

OAK HILL HOSPITAL (O, 262 beds) 11375 Cortez Boulevard, Brooksville, FL Zip 34613–5409; tel. 352/596–6632; Mickey Smith, Chief Executive Officer
Web address: www.oakhillhospital.com

OCALA REGIONAL MEDICAL CENTER (O, 270 beds) 1431 S.W. First Avenue, Ocala, FL Zip 34471–6500, Mailing Address: P.O. Box 2200, Zip 34478–2200; tel. 352/401–1000; Randy McVay, Chief Executive Officer
Web address: www.ocalaregional.com

ORANGE PARK MEDICAL CENTER (O, 297 beds) 2001 Kingsley Avenue, Orange Park, FL Zip 32073–5156; tel. 904/639–8500; Chad Patrick, President and Chief Executive Officer
Web address: www.opmedical.com

For explanation of codes following names, see page B2.
★ Indicates Type III membership in the American Hospital Association.

OSCEOLA REGIONAL MEDICAL CENTER (O, 235 beds) 700 West Oak Street, Kissimmee, FL Zip 34741–4996; tel. 407/846–2266; Robert M. Krieger, Chief Executive Officer
Web address: www.osceolaregional.com

PALMS OF PASADENA HOSPITAL (O, 187 beds) 1501 Pasadena Avenue South, Saint Petersburg, FL Zip 33707–3798; tel. 727/381–1000; Sharon Hayes, Chief Executive Officer
Web address: www.palmspasadena.com

PALMS WEST HOSPITAL (O, 204 beds) 13001 Southern Boulevard, Loxahatchee, FL Zip 33470–9203; tel. 561/798–3300; Eric Goldman, Chief Executive Officer
Web address: www.palmswesthospital.com

PLANTATION GENERAL HOSPITAL (O, 264 beds) 401 N.W. 42nd Avenue, Plantation, FL Zip 33317–2882; tel. 954/587–5010; Randy Gross, Chief Executive Officer
Web address: www.plantationgeneral.com

POINCIANA MEDICAL CENTER (O, 24 beds) 325 Cypress Parkway, Kissimmee, FL Zip 34758; tel. 407/530–2000; Joanna J. Conley, FACHE, Chief Executive Officer
Web address: www.poincianamedicalcenter.com

PUTNAM COMMUNITY MEDICAL CENTER (O, 99 beds) 611 Zeagler Drive, Palatka, FL Zip 32177–3810, Mailing Address: P.O. Box 778, Zip 32178–0778; tel. 386/328–5711; J. Christopher Mosley, Chief Executive Officer
Web address: www.pcmcfl.com

RAULERSON HOSPITAL (O, 100 beds) 1796 Highway 441 North, Okeechobee, FL Zip 34972–1918, Mailing Address: P.O. Box 1307, Zip 34973–1307; tel. 863/763–2151; Brian Melear, R.N., Chief Executive Officer
Web address: www.raulersonhospital.com

REGIONAL MEDICAL CENTER BAYONET POINT (O, 290 beds) 14000 Fivay Road, Hudson, FL Zip 34667–7199; tel. 727/869–5400; Shayne George, Chief Executive Officer
Web address: www.rmchealth.com

SOUTH BAY HOSPITAL (O, 112 beds) 4016 Sun City Center Boulevard, Sun City Center, FL Zip 33573–5298; tel. 813/634–3301; Sharon L. Roush, Chief Executive Officer
Web address: www.southbayhospital.com/

SPECIALTY HOSPITAL JACKSONVILLE (O, 62 beds) 4901 Richard Street, Jacksonville, FL Zip 32207–7328; tel. 904/737–3120; Barbara McCarthy, Chief Executive Officer
Web address: www.specialtyhospitaljax.com

ST. LUCIE MEDICAL CENTER (O, 194 beds) 1800 S.E. Tiffany Avenue, Port St. Lucie, FL Zip 34952–7521; tel. 772/335–4000; Jay Finnegan, Chief Executive Officer
Web address: www.stluciemed.com

ST. PETERSBURG GENERAL HOSPITAL (O, 219 beds) 6500 38th Avenue North, Saint Petersburg, FL Zip 33710–1629; tel. 727/384–1414; Janice Balzano, President and Chief Executive Officer
Web address: www.stpetegeneral.com

TAMPA COMMUNITY HOSPITAL (O, 201 beds) 6001 Webb Road, Tampa, FL Zip 33615–3291; tel. 813/888–7060; Jacob Fisher, Chief Executive Officer
Web address: www.tampacommunityhospital.com/

TWIN CITIES HOSPITAL (O, 57 beds) 2190 Highway 85 North, Niceville, FL Zip 32578–1045; tel. 850/678–4131; David Whalen, Chief Executive Officer
Web address: www.tchealthcare.com

UNIVERSITY HOSPITAL AND MEDICAL CENTER (O, 317 beds) 7201 North University Drive, Tamarac, FL Zip 33321–2996; tel. 954/721–2200; Joseph D. Melchiode, Chief Executive Officer
Web address: www.uhmchealth.com

WEST FLORIDA HOSPITAL (O, 339 beds) 8383 North Davis Highway, Pensacola, FL Zip 32514–6088; tel. 850/494–4000; Brian Baumgardner, Chief Executive Officer
Web address: www.westfloridahospital.com

WESTSIDE REGIONAL MEDICAL CENTER (O, 215 beds) 8201 West Broward Boulevard, Plantation, FL Zip 33324–2701; tel. 954/473–6600; Barbara Simmons, R.N., Chief Executive Officer
Web address: www.westsideregional.com

GEORGIA: CARTERSVILLE MEDICAL CENTER (O, 80 beds) 960 Joe Frank Harris Parkway, Cartersville, GA Zip 30120–2129; tel. 770/382–1530; Keith Sandlin, Chief Executive Officer
Web address: www.cartersvillemedical.com

COLISEUM MEDICAL CENTERS (O, 227 beds) 350 Hospital Drive, Macon, GA Zip 31217–3871; tel. 478/765–7000; Lance Jones, Chief Executive Officer
Web address: www.coliseumhealthsystem.com

COLISEUM NORTHSIDE HOSPITAL (O, 103 beds) 400 Charter Boulevard, Macon, GA Zip 31210–4853, Mailing Address: P.O. Box 4627, Zip 31208–4627; tel. 478/757–8200; Stephen J. Daugherty, Chief Executive Officer
Web address: www.coliseumhealthsystem.com

DOCTORS HOSPITAL (O, 307 beds) 3651 Wheeler Road, Augusta, GA Zip 30909–6426; tel. 706/651–3232; Douglas Welch, Chief Executive Officer
Web address: www.doctors–hospital.net

EASTSIDE MEDICAL CENTER (O, 294 beds) 1700 Medical Way, Snellville, GA Zip 30078–2195; tel. 770/979–0200; Trent Lind, Chief Executive Officer
Web address: www.eastsidemedical.com

FAIRVIEW PARK HOSPITAL (O, 168 beds) 200 Industrial Boulevard, Dublin, GA Zip 31021–2997, Mailing Address: P.O. Box 1408, Zip 31040–1408; tel. 478/275–2000; Donald R. Avery, FACHE, President and Chief Executive Officer
Web address: www.fairviewparkhospital.com

REDMOND REGIONAL MEDICAL CENTER (O, 230 beds) 501 Redmond Road, Rome, GA Zip 30165–1415, Mailing Address: P.O. Box 107001, Zip 30164–7001; tel. 706/291–0291; John Quinlivan, Chief Executive Officer
Web address: www.redmondregional.com

IDAHO: EASTERN IDAHO REGIONAL MEDICAL CENTER (O, 309 beds) 3100 Channing Way, Idaho Falls, ID Zip 83404–7533, Mailing Address: P.O. Box 2077, Zip 83403–2077; tel. 208/529–6111; Douglas Crabtree, Chief Executive Officer
Web address: www.eirmc.com

WEST VALLEY MEDICAL CENTER (O, 118 beds) 1717 Arlington, Caldwell, ID Zip 83605–4802; tel. 208/459–4641; Elizabeth Hunsicker, Chief Executive Officer
Web address: www.westvalleymedctr.com

INDIANA: TERRE HAUTE REGIONAL HOSPITAL (O, 208 beds) 3901 South Seventh Street, Terre Haute, IN Zip 47802–5709; tel. 812/232–0021; Mary Ann Conroy, Chief Executive Officer
Web address: www.regionalhospital.com

KANSAS: MENORAH MEDICAL CENTER (O, 158 beds) 5721 West 119th Street, Overland Park, KS Zip 66209–3722; tel. 913/498–6000; Charles Laird, Chief Executive Officer
Web address: www.menorahmedicalcenter.com

OVERLAND PARK REGIONAL MEDICAL CENTER (O, 277 beds) 10500 Quivira Road, Overland Park, KS Zip 66215–2306, Mailing Address: P.O. Box 15959, Zip 66215–5959; tel. 913/541–5000; Kevin J. Hicks, President and CEO
Web address: www.oprmc.com

WESLEY MEDICAL CENTER (O, 562 beds) 550 North Hillside, Wichita, KS Zip 67214–4976; tel. 316/962–2000; Bill Voloch, President and Chief Executive Officer
Web address: www.wesleymc.com

KENTUCKY: FRANKFORT REGIONAL MEDICAL CENTER (O, 128 beds) 299 King's Daughters Drive, Frankfort, KY Zip 40601–4186; tel. 502/875–5240; Chip Peal, Chief Executive Officer
Web address: www.frankfortregional.com

TRISTAR GREENVIEW REGIONAL HOSPITAL (O, 167 beds) 1801 Ashley Circle, Bowling Green, KY Zip 42104–3362; tel. 270/793–1000; Michael Sherrod, Chief Executive Officer
Web address: www.greenviewhospital.com

LOUISIANA: LAKEVIEW REGIONAL MEDICAL CENTER (O, 172 beds) 95 Judge Tanner Boulevard, Covington, LA Zip 70433–7507; tel. 985/867–3800; Bret G. Kolman, CPA, FACHE, Chief Executive Officer
Web address: www.lakeviewregional.com

RAPIDES REGIONAL MEDICAL CENTER (O, 357 beds) 211 Fourth Street, Alexandria, LA Zip 71301–8421; tel. 318/769–3000; Jason E. Cobb, FACHE, Chief Executive Officer
Web address: www.rapidesregional.com

TULANE MEDICAL CENTER (O, 294 beds) 1415 Tulane Avenue, New Orleans, LA Zip 70112–2600; tel. 504/988–5263; William Lunn, M.D., Chief Executive Officer
Web address: www.tuhc.com

For explanation of codes following names, see page B2.
★ Indicates Type III membership in the American Hospital Association.

WOMEN'S AND CHILDREN'S HOSPITAL (O, 161 beds) 4600 Ambassador Caffery Parkway, Lafayette, LA Zip 70508–6923, Mailing Address: P.O. Box 88030, Zip 70598–8030; tel. 337/521–9100; Kathy Bobbs, FACHE, President and Chief Executive Officer
Web address: www.womens–childrens.com

MISSISSIPPI: GARDEN PARK MEDICAL CENTER (O, 130 beds) 15200 Community Road, Gulfport, MS Zip 39503–3085, Mailing Address: P.O. Box 1240, Zip 39502–1240; tel. 228/575–7000; Brenda M. Waltz, FACHE, Chief Executive Officer
Web address: www.gpmedical.com

MISSOURI: BELTON REGIONAL MEDICAL CENTER (O, 46 beds) 17065 South 71 Highway, Belton, MO Zip 64012–4631; tel. 816/348–1200; Todd Krass, Chief Executive Officer
Web address: www.beltonregionalmedicalcenter.com

CENTERPOINT MEDICAL CENTER (O, 221 beds) 19600 East 39th Street, Independence, MO Zip 64057–2301; tel. 816/698–7000; David R. Williams, Chief Executive Officer
Web address: www.centerpointmedical.com

LAFAYETTE REGIONAL HEALTH CENTER (O, 25 beds) 1500 State Street, Lexington, MO Zip 64067–1107; tel. 660/259–2203; Darrel Box, Chief Executive Officer
Web address: www.lafayetteregionalhealthcenter.com

LEE'S SUMMIT MEDICAL CENTER (O, 64 beds) 2100 S.E. Blue Parkway, Lee's Summit, MO Zip 64063–1007; tel. 816/282–5000; Matt Sogard, Chief Executive Officer
Web address: www.leessummitmedicalcenter.com

RESEARCH MEDICAL CENTER (O, 456 beds) 2316 East Meyer Boulevard, Kansas City, MO Zip 64132–1136; tel. 816/276–4000; Jacqueline DeSouza, Chief Executive Officer
Web address: www.researchmedicalcenter.com

NEVADA: MOUNTAINVIEW HOSPITAL (O, 340 beds) 3100 North Tenaya Way, Las Vegas, NV Zip 89128–0436; tel. 702/255–5000; Chris Mowan, Chief Executive Officer
Web address: www.mountainview–hospital.com

SOUTHERN HILLS HOSPITAL AND MEDICAL CENTER (O, 134 beds) 9300 West Sunset Road, Las Vegas, NV Zip 89148–4844; tel. 702/880–2100; Adam Rudd, Chief Executive Officer
Web address: www.southernhillshospital.com

SUNRISE HOSPITAL AND MEDICAL CENTER (O, 668 beds) 3186 Maryland Parkway, Las Vegas, NV Zip 89109–2306, Mailing Address: P.O. Box 98530, Zip 89193; tel. 702/731–8000; Todd Sklamberg, President
Web address: www.sunrisehospital.com

NEW HAMPSHIRE: PARKLAND MEDICAL CENTER (O, 82 beds) One Parkland Drive, Derry, NH Zip 03038–2750; tel. 603/432–1500; Jeff Scionti, Interim Chief Executive Officer
Web address: www.parklandmedicalcenter.com

PORTSMOUTH REGIONAL HOSPITAL (O, 165 beds) 333 Borthwick Avenue, Portsmouth, NH Zip 03801–7128; tel. 603/436–5110; Dean Carucci, Chief Executive Officer
Web address: www.portsmouthhospital.com

OKLAHOMA: OU MEDICAL CENTER (O, 724 beds) 1200 Everett Drive, Oklahoma City, OK Zip 73104–5047, Mailing Address: P.O. Box 26307, Zip 73126–0307; tel. 405/271–3636; Charles Spicer, President and Chief Executive Officer
Web address: www.oumedicine.com/oumedicalcenter

SOUTH CAROLINA: COLLETON MEDICAL CENTER (O, 131 beds) 501 Robertson Boulevard, Walterboro, SC Zip 29488–5714; tel. 843/782–2000; Brad Griffin, Chief Executive Officer
Web address: www.colletonmedical.com

GRAND STRAND REGIONAL MEDICAL CENTER (O, 303 beds) 809 82nd Parkway, Myrtle Beach, SC Zip 29572–4607; tel. 843/692–1000; Mark E. Sims, Chief Executive Officer
Web address: www.grandstrandmed.com

TRIDENT MEDICAL CENTER (O, 421 beds) 9330 Medical Plaza Drive, Charleston, SC Zip 29406–9195; tel. 843/797–7000; Todd Gallati, FACHE, President and Chief Executive Officer
Web address: www.tridenthealthsystem.com

TENNESSEE: PARKRIDGE MEDICAL CENTER (O, 472 beds) 2333 McCallie Avenue, Chattanooga, TN Zip 37404–3258; tel. 423/698–6061; Darrell W. Moore, Chief Executive Officer
Web address: www.parkridgemedicalcenter.com

TRISTAR ASHLAND CITY MEDICAL CENTER (O, 12 beds) 313 North Main Street, Ashland City, TN Zip 37015–1347; tel. 615/792–3030; Darrell White, R.N., Administrator and Chief Nursing Officer
Web address: www.tristarashlandcity.com/

TRISTAR CENTENNIAL MEDICAL CENTER (O, 650 beds) 2300 Patterson Street, Nashville, TN Zip 37203–1528; tel. 615/342–1000; Heather J. Rohan, Chief Executive Officer
Web address: www.tristarcentennial.com

TRISTAR HENDERSONVILLE MEDICAL CENTER (O, 81 beds) 355 New Shackle Island Road, Hendersonville, TN Zip 37075–2479; tel. 615/338–1000; Regina Bartlett, Chief Executive Officer
Web address: www.hendersonvillemedicalcenter.com

TRISTAR HORIZON MEDICAL CENTER (O, 130 beds) 111 Highway 70 East, Dickson, TN Zip 37055–2080; tel. 615/446–0446; Dustin Greene, Chief Executive Officer
Web address: www.horizonmedicalcenter.com

TRISTAR SKYLINE MADISON CAMPUS (O, 284 beds) 500 Hospital Drive, Madison, TN Zip 37115–5032; tel. 615/769–5000; Steve Otto, Chief Executive Officer
Web address: www.skylinemadison.com

TRISTAR SKYLINE MEDICAL CENTER (O, 295 beds) 3441 Dickerson Pike, Nashville, TN Zip 37207–2539; tel. 615/769–2000; Steve Otto, Chief Executive Officer
Web address: www.skylinemedicalcenter.com

TRISTAR SOUTHERN HILLS MEDICAL CENTER (O, 101 beds) 391 Wallace Road, Nashville, TN Zip 37211–4859; tel. 615/781–4000; Thomas H. Ozburn, Chief Executive Officer
Web address: www.tristarsouthernhills.com

TRISTAR STONECREST MEDICAL CENTER (O, 101 beds) 200 StoneCrest Boulevard, Smyrna, TN Zip 37167–6810; tel. 615/768–2000; Louis Caputo, Chief Executive Officer
Web address: www.stonecrestmedical.com

TRISTAR SUMMIT MEDICAL CENTER (O, 196 beds) 5655 Frist Boulevard, Hermitage, TN Zip 37076–2053; tel. 615/316–3000; Jeffrey T. Whitehorn, Chief Executive Officer
Web address: www.summitmedctr.com

TEXAS: BAYSHORE MEDICAL CENTER (O, 461 beds) 4000 Spencer Highway, Pasadena, TX Zip 77504–1202; tel. 713/359–2000; Jeanna Barnard, FACHE, Chief Executive Officer
Web address: www.bayshoremedical.com

CLEAR LAKE REGIONAL MEDICAL CENTER (O, 683 beds) 500 Medical Center Boulevard, Webster, TX Zip 77598–4220; tel. 281/332–2511; Stephen K. Jones, Jr., FACHE, Chief Executive Officer
Web address: www.clearlakermc.com

CONROE REGIONAL MEDICAL CENTER (O, 301 beds) 504 Medical Boulevard, Conroe, TX Zip 77304, Mailing Address: P.O. Box 1538, Zip 77305–1538; tel. 936/539–1111; Matt Davis, Chief Executive Officer
Web address: www.conroeregional.com/

CORPUS CHRISTI MEDICAL CENTER (O, 416 beds) 3315 South Alameda Street, Corpus Christi, TX Zip 78411–1883, Mailing Address: P.O. Box 8991, Zip 78468–8991; tel. 361/761–1400; Jay Woodall, Chief Executive Officer
Web address: www.ccmedicalcenter.com

DENTON REGIONAL MEDICAL CENTER (O, 185 beds) 3535 South 1–35 East, Denton, TX Zip 76210; tel. 940/384–3535; Steven Edgar, President and Chief Executive Officer
Web address: www.dentonregional.com

GREEN OAKS HOSPITAL (O, 124 beds) 7808 Clodus Fields Drive, Dallas, TX Zip 75251–2206; tel. 972/991–9504; Thomas M. Collins, President, Chairman and Chief Executive Officer
Web address: www.greenoakspsych.com

KINGWOOD MEDICAL CENTER (O, 357 beds) 22999 U.S. Highway 59 North, Kingwood, TX Zip 77339; tel. 281/348–8000; Melinda Stephenson, Chief Executive Officer
Web address: www.kingwoodmedical.com

LAS COLINAS MEDICAL CENTER (O, 90 beds) 6800 North MacArthur Boulevard, Irving, TX Zip 75039–2422; tel. 972/969–2000; Daniela Decell, Chief Executive Officer
Web address: www.lascolinasmedical.com

LAS PALMAS MEDICAL CENTER (O, 570 beds) 1801 North Oregon Street, El Paso, TX Zip 79902–3591; tel. 915/521–1200; Don Karl, Interim Chief Executive Officer
Web address: www.laspalmashealth.com

For explanation of codes following names, see page B2.
★ Indicates Type III membership in the American Hospital Association.

Section B

MEDICAL CENTER ALLIANCE (O, 55 beds) 3101 North Tarrant Parkway, Fort Worth, TX Zip 76177; tel. 817/639–1000; Glenn Wallace, Chief Executive Officer
Web address: www.baylorhealth.com/PhysiciansLocations/BIR/Pages/Default.aspx

MEDICAL CENTER ARLINGTON (O, 265 beds) 3301 Matlock Road, Arlington, TX Zip 76015–2908; tel. 817/465–3241; Winston Borland, FACHE, President and Chief Executive Officer
Web address: www.medicalcenterarlington.com

MEDICAL CENTER OF LEWISVILLE (O, 166 beds) 500 West Main, Lewisville, TX Zip 75057–3699; tel. 972/420–1000; LaSharndra Barbarin, Chief Executive Officer
Web address: www.lewisvillemedical.com

MEDICAL CENTER OF MCKINNEY (O, 222 beds) 4500 Medical Center Drive, McKinney, TX Zip 75069–1650; tel. 972/547–8000; Ernest C. Lynch, III, President and Chief Executive Officer
Web address: www.medicalcenterofmckinney.com

MEDICAL CENTER OF PLANO (O, 395 beds) 3901 West 15th Street, Plano, TX Zip 75075–7738; tel. 972/596–6800; Charles Gressle, Chief Executive Officer
Web address: www.medicalcenterplano.com

MEDICAL CITY DALLAS HOSPITAL (O, 561 beds) 7777 Forest Lane, Dallas, TX Zip 75230–2598; tel. 972/566–7000; Chris Mowan, Chief Executive Officer
Web address: www.medicalcityhospital.com

METHODIST AMBULATORY SURGERY HOSPITAL – NORTHWEST (O, 23 beds) 9150 Huebner Road, Suite 100, San Antonio, TX Zip 78240–1545; tel. 210/575–5000; Scott Davis, Chief Executive Officer
Web address: www.sahealth.com

METHODIST HOSPITAL (O, 1593 beds) 7700 Floyd Curl Drive, San Antonio, TX Zip 78229–3993; tel. 210/575–4000; Gay Nord, Chief Executive Officer
Web address: www.sahealth.com

METHODIST STONE OAK HOSPITAL (O, 140 beds) 1139 East Sonterra Boulevard, San Antonio, TX Zip 78258–4347; tel. 210/638–2100; Marc Strode, Chief Executive Officer
Web address: www.sahealth.com/locations/methodist–stone–oak–hospital/

NORTH HILLS HOSPITAL (O, 164 beds) 4401 Booth Calloway Road, North Richland Hills, TX Zip 76180–7399; tel. 817/255–1000; Xavier Villarreal, FACHE, Chief Executive Officer
Web address: www.northhillshospital.com

PEARLAND MEDICAL CENTER (O, 33 beds) 11100 Shadow Creek Parkway, Pearland, TX Zip 77584–7285; tel. 713/770–7000; David S. Wagner, Chief Executive Officer
Web address: www.pearlandmc.com

PLAZA MEDICAL CENTER OF FORT WORTH (O, 212 beds) 900 Eighth Avenue, Fort Worth, TX Zip 76104–3902; tel. 817/336–2100; Clay Franklin, Chief Executive Officer
Web address: www.plazamedicalcenter.com

RIO GRANDE REGIONAL HOSPITAL (O, 320 beds) 101 East Ridge Road, McAllen, TX Zip 78503–1299; tel. 956/632–6000; Cristina Rivera, Chief Executive Officer
Web address: www.riohealth.com

ST. DAVID'S MEDICAL CENTER (O, 555 beds) 919 East 32nd Street, Austin, TX Zip 78705–2709, Mailing Address: P.O. Box 4039, Zip 78765–4039; tel. 512/476–7111; Donald H. Wilkerson, Chief Executive Officer
Web address: www.stdavids.com

ST. DAVID'S NORTH AUSTIN MEDICAL CENTER (O, 378 beds) 12221 North MoPac Expressway, Austin, TX Zip 78758–2496; tel. 512/901–1000; Allen Harrison, Chief Executive Officer
Web address: www.northaustin.com

ST. DAVID'S ROUND ROCK MEDICAL CENTER (O, 155 beds) 2400 Round Rock Avenue, Round Rock, TX Zip 78681–4097; tel. 512/341–1000; Deborah L. Ryle, Administrator and Chief Executive Officer
Web address: www.stdavids.com

ST. DAVID'S SOUTH AUSTIN MEDICAL CENTER (O, 270 beds) 901 West Ben White Boulevard, Austin, TX Zip 78704–6903; tel. 512/447–2211; Todd E. Steward, FACHE, Chief Executive Officer
Web address: www.southaustinmc.com

TEXAS ORTHOPEDIC HOSPITAL (O, 49 beds) 7401 South Main Street, Houston, TX Zip 77030–4509; tel. 713/799–8600; Eric Becker, Chief Executive Officer
Web address: www.texasorthopedic.com

VALLEY REGIONAL MEDICAL CENTER (O, 214 beds) 100A Alton Gloor Boulevard, Brownsville, TX Zip 78526–3354, Mailing Address: P.O. Box 3710, Zip 78523–3710; tel. 956/350–7101; Art Garza, Chief Executive Officer
Web address: www.valleyregionalmedicalcenter.com

WEST HOUSTON MEDICAL CENTER (O, 264 beds) 12141 Richmond Avenue, Houston, TX Zip 77082–2499; tel. 281/558–3444; Todd Caliva, Chief Executive Officer
Web address: www.westhoustonmedical.com

WOMAN'S HOSPITAL OF TEXAS (O, 345 beds) 7600 Fannin Street, Houston, TX Zip 77054–1906; tel. 713/790–1234; Ashley McClellan, Chief Executive Officer
Web address: www.womanshospital.com

UTAH: BRIGHAM CITY COMMUNITY HOSPITAL (O, 39 beds) 950 South Medical Drive, Brigham City, UT Zip 84302–4724; tel. 435/734–9471; Richard Spuhler, Chief Executive Officer
Web address: www.brighamcityhospital.com

CACHE VALLEY HOSPITAL (O, 22 beds) 2380 North 400 East, North Logan, UT Zip 84341–6000; tel. 435/713–9700; John C. Worley, III, Chief Executive Officer
Web address: www.cachevalleyhospital.com/

LAKEVIEW HOSPITAL (O, 119 beds) 630 East Medical Drive, Bountiful, UT Zip 84010–4908; tel. 801/299–2200; Troy Wood, Chief Executive Officer
Web address: www.lakeviewhospital.com

LONE PEAK HOSPITAL (O, 32 beds) 1925 South State Street, Draper, UT Zip 84020; tel. 801/545–8000; Mark Meadows, Chief Executive Officer
Web address: www.lonepeakhospital.com

MOUNTAIN VIEW HOSPITAL (O, 114 beds) 1000 East 100 North, Payson, UT Zip 84651–1600; tel. 801/465–7000; Kevin Johnson, Chief Executive Officer
Web address: www.mvhpayson.com

OGDEN REGIONAL MEDICAL CENTER (O, 167 beds) 5475 South 500 East, Ogden, UT Zip 84405–6905; tel. 801/479–2111; Mark B. Adams, Chief Executive Officer
Web address: www.ogdenregional.com

ST. MARK'S HOSPITAL (O, 277 beds) 1200 East 3900 South, Salt Lake City, UT Zip 84124–1390; tel. 801/268–7111; Steven B. Bateman, Chief Executive Officer
Web address: www.stmarkshospital.com

TIMPANOGOS REGIONAL HOSPITAL (O, 117 beds) 750 West 800 North, Orem, UT Zip 84057–3660; tel. 801/714–6000; Kimball S. Anderson, FACHE, Chief Executive Officer
Web address: www.timpanogosregionalhospital.com

VIRGINIA: CHIPPENHAM HOSPITAL (O, 765 beds) 7101 Jahnke Road, Richmond, VA Zip 23225–4044; tel. 804/320–3911; Tim McManus, President and Chief Executive Officer
Web address: www.cjwmedical.com

DOMINION HOSPITAL (O, 100 beds) 2960 Sleepy Hollow Road, Falls Church, VA Zip 22044–2030; tel. 703/536–2000; Lee Higginbotham, Chief Executive Officer
Web address: www.dominionhospital.com

HENRICO DOCTORS' HOSPITAL (O, 488 beds) 1602 Skipwith Road, Richmond, VA Zip 23229–5205; tel. 804/289–4500; William Wagnon, Executive Officer
Web address: www.henricodoctorshospital.com

JOHN RANDOLPH MEDICAL CENTER (O, 118 beds) 411 West Randolph Road, Hopewell, VA Zip 23860–2938; tel. 804/541–1600; Suzanne B. Jackson, FACHE, Chief Executive Officer
Web address: www.johnrandolphmed.com

LEWIS–GALE MEDICAL CENTER (O, 521 beds) 1900 Electric Road, Salem, VA Zip 24153–7494; tel. 540/776–4000; Jonathan L. Bartlett, Chief Executive Officer
Web address: www.lewis–gale.com

LEWISGALE HOSPITAL ALLEGHANY (O, 146 beds) One ARH Lane, Low Moor, VA Zip 24457, Mailing Address: P.O. Box 7, Zip 24457–0007; tel. 540/862–6011; Charlotte C. Tyson, Chief Executive Officer
Web address: www.alleghanyregional.com

LEWISGALE HOSPITAL MONTGOMERY (O, 103 beds) 3700 South Main Street, Blacksburg, VA Zip 24060–7081, Mailing Address: P.O. Box 90004, Zip 24062–9004; tel. 540/951–1111; Alan J. Fabian, Chief Executive Officer
Web address: www.lewisgale.com

For explanation of codes following names, see page B2.
★ Indicates Type III membership in the American Hospital Association.

Section B

LEWISGALE HOSPITAL PULASKI (O, 54 beds) 2400 Lee Highway, Pulaski, VA Zip 24301–2326, Mailing Address: P.O. Box 759, Zip 24301–0759; tel. 540/994–8100; Derek Vance, Chief Executive Officer
Web address: www.lewisgale.com/

RESTON HOSPITAL CENTER (O, 187 beds) 1850 Town Center Parkway, Reston, VA Zip 20190–3219; tel. 703/689–9000; John A. Deardorff, Chief Executive Officer
Web address: www.restonhospital.com

SPOTSYLVANIA REGIONAL MEDICAL CENTER (O, 100 beds) 4600 Spotsylvania Parkway, Fredericksburg, VA Zip 22408–7762; tel. 540/498–4000; Michael Clark, Chief Executive Officer
Web address: www.spotsrmc.com

Owned, leased, sponsored:	148 hospitals	36901 beds
Contract–managed:	0 hospitals	0 beds
Totals:	148 hospitals	36901 beds

0328: HEALTH FIRST, INC. (NP)
6450 U.S. Highway 1, Rockledge, FL Zip 32955–5747; tel. 321/434–7000; Steven P. Johnson, Ph.D., President and Chief Executive Officer
(Centralized Physician/Insurance Health System)

FLORIDA: HEALTH FIRST CAPE CANAVERAL HOSPITAL (O, 145 beds) 701 West Cocoa Beach Causeway, Cocoa Beach, FL Zip 32931–5595, Mailing Address: P.O. Box 320069, Zip 32932–0069; tel. 321/799–7111; William Calhoun, President, Community Hospitals
Web address: www.health–first.org

HEALTH FIRST HOLMES REGIONAL MEDICAL CENTER (O, 514 beds) 1350 South Hickory Street, Melbourne, FL Zip 32901–3224; tel. 321/434–7000; Sean Gregory, Chief Executive Officer
Web address: www.health–first.org

HEALTH FIRST PALM BAY HOSPITAL (O, 119 beds) 1425 Malabar Road N.E., Palm Bay, FL Zip 32907–2506; tel. 321/434–8000; William Calhoun, President, Community Hospitals
Web address: www.health–first.org/hospitals_services/pbch/index.cfm

HEALTH FIRST VIERA HOSPITAL (O, 84 beds) 8745 North Wickham Road, Melbourne, FL Zip 32940–5997; tel. 321/434–9164; William Calhoun, President, Community Hospitals
Web address: www.vierahospital.org

Owned, leased, sponsored:	4 hospitals	862 beds
Contract–managed:	0 hospitals	0 beds
Totals:	4 hospitals	862 beds

0307: HEALTH QUEST SYSTEMS, INC. (NP)
1351 Route 55 Suite 200, LaGrangeville, NY Zip 12540–5108, Mailing Address: 1351 Route 55, Zip 12540–5108; tel. 845/475–9500; Luke McGuinness, President and CEO
(Centralized Health System)

NEW YORK: NORTHERN DUTCHESS HOSPITAL (O, 68 beds) 6511 Springbrook Avenue, Rhinebeck, NY Zip 12572–3709, Mailing Address: P.O. Box 5002, Zip 12572–5002; tel. 845/876–3001; Denise George, R.N., President
Web address: www.health–quest.org/home_nd.cfm?id=9

PUTNAM HOSPITAL CENTER (O, 164 beds) 670 Stoneleigh Avenue, Carmel, NY Zip 10512–3997; tel. 845/279–5711; Peter Kelly, President
Web address: www.healthquest.org/carmel/putnam–hospital–center.aspx

VASSAR BROTHERS MEDICAL CENTER (O, 365 beds) 45 Reade Place, Poughkeepsie, NY Zip 12601–3947; tel. 845/454–8500; Ann McMackin, President
Web address: www.health–quest.org

Owned, leased, sponsored:	3 hospitals	597 beds
Contract–managed:	0 hospitals	0 beds
Totals:	3 hospitals	597 beds

★2185: HEALTHEAST CARE SYSTEM (NP)
559 Capitol Boulevard, 6–South, Saint Paul, MN Zip 55103–0000; tel. 651/232–2300; Kathryn G. Correia, President and Chief Executive Officer
(Centralized Physician/Insurance Health System)

MINNESOTA: BETHESDA HOSPITAL (O, 126 beds) 559 Capitol Boulevard, Saint Paul, MN Zip 55103–2101; tel. 651/232–2000; Catherine Barr, Chief Operating Officer
Web address: www.healtheast.org

ST. JOHN'S HOSPITAL (O, 192 beds) 1575 Beam Avenue, Maplewood, MN Zip 55109–1126; tel. 651/232–7000; Catherine Barr, Chief Operating Officer
Web address: www.stjohnshospital–mn.org

ST. JOSEPH'S HOSPITAL (O, 234 beds) 45 West 10th Street, Saint Paul, MN Zip 55102–1053; tel. 651/232–3000; Catherine Barr, Chief Operating Officer
Web address: www.healtheast.org

WOODWINDS HEALTH CAMPUS (O, 86 beds) 1925 Woodwinds Drive, Woodbury, MN Zip 55125–4445; tel. 651/232–0228; Catherine Barr, Chief Operating Officer
Web address: www.woodwinds.org

Owned, leased, sponsored:	4 hospitals	638 beds
Contract–managed:	0 hospitals	0 beds
Totals:	4 hospitals	638 beds

0342: HEALTHPARTNERS (NP)
8170 33rd Avenue South, Bloomington, MN Zip 55425–4516; tel. 952/883–7600; Mary K. Brainerd, President and Chief Executive Officer
(Moderately Centralized Health System)

GLENCOE REGIONAL HEALTH SERVICES (C, 135 beds) 1805 Hennepin Avenue North, Glencoe, MN Zip 55336–1416; tel. 320/864–3121; Jon D. Braband, FACHE, President and Chief Executive Officer
Web address: www.grhsonline.org

LAKEVIEW HOSPITAL (O, 54 beds) 927 Churchill Street West, Stillwater, MN Zip 55082–6605; tel. 651/439–5330; Theodore Wegleitner, Chief Executive Officer
Web address: www.lakeview.org

PARK NICOLLET METHODIST HOSPITAL (O, 393 beds) 6500 Excelsior Boulevard, Saint Louis Park, MN Zip 55426–4702; Minneapolis, tel. 952/993–5000; Steven Connelly, M.D., President and Chief Medical Officer
Web address: www.parknicollet.com

REGIONS HOSPITAL (O, 463 beds) 640 Jackson Street, Saint Paul, MN Zip 55101–2595; tel. 651/254–3456; Megan Remark, Chief Executive Officer
Web address: www.regionshospital.com

WISCONSIN: AMERY HOSPITAL AND CLINIC (O, 11 beds) 265 Griffin Street East, Amery, WI Zip 54001–1439; tel. 715/268–8000; Debra Rudquist, FACHE, President and Chief Executive Officer
Web address: www.amerymedicalcenter.org

HUDSON HOSPITAL AND CLINIC (O, 24 beds) 405 Stageline Road, Hudson, WI Zip 54016–7848; tel. 715/531–6000; Marian M. Furlong, R.N., FACHE, Chief Executive Officer
Web address: www.hudsonhospital.org

WESTFIELDS HOSPITAL (O, 25 beds) 535 Hospital Road, New Richmond, WI Zip 54017–1449; tel. 715/243–2600; Steven Massey, President and Chief Executive Officer
Web address: www.westfieldshospital.com

Owned, leased, sponsored:	6 hospitals	970 beds
Contract–managed:	1 hospital	135 beds
Totals:	7 hospitals	1105 beds

★0023: HEALTHSOUTH CORPORATION (IO)
3660 Grandview Parkway, Suite 200, Birmingham, AL Zip 35243–3332; tel. 205/967–7116; Jay F. Grinney, President and Chief Executive Officer
(Independent Hospital System)

For explanation of codes following names, see page B2.
★ Indicates Type III membership in the American Hospital Association.

Section B

ALABAMA: HEALTHSOUTH LAKESHORE REHABILITATION HOSPITAL (O, 100 beds) 3800 Ridgeway Drive, Birmingham, AL Zip 35209–5599; tel. 205/868–2000; Vickie Demers, Chief Executive Officer
Web address: www.healthsouthlakeshorerehab.com

HEALTHSOUTH REHABILITATION HOSPITAL (O, 51 beds) 1736 East Main Street, Dothan, AL Zip 36301–3040, Mailing Address: P.O. Box 6708, Zip 36302–6708; tel. 334/712–6333; Margaret A. Futch, Chief Executive Officer
Web address: www.healthsouthdothan.com

HEALTHSOUTH REHABILITATION HOSPITAL OF MONTGOMERY (O, 70 beds) 4465 Narrow Lane Road, Montgomery, AL Zip 36116–2900; tel. 334/284–7700; Thomas Roddy, Chief Executive Officer
Web address: www.healthsouthmontgomery.com

HEALTHSOUTH REHABILITATION HOSPITAL OF NORTH ALABAMA (O, 70 beds) 107 Governors Drive S.W., Huntsville, AL Zip 35801–4326; tel. 256/535–2300; Douglas H. Beverly, Chief Executive Officer
Web address: www.healthsouthhuntsville.com

HEALTHSOUTH REHABILITATION OF GADSDEN (O, 44 beds) 801 Goodyear Avenue, Gadsden, AL Zip 35903–1133; tel. 256/439–5000; Kayla Feazell, Chief Executive Officer
Web address: www.healthsouthgadsden.com

REGIONAL REHABILITATION HOSPITAL (O, 48 beds) 3715 Highway 280/431 North, Phenix City, AL Zip 36867; tel. 334/732–2200; Michael Bartell, Chief Executive Officer
Web address: www.regionalrehabhospital.com

ARIZONA: HEALTHSOUTH EAST VALLEY REHABILITATION HOSPITAL (O, 60 beds) 5652 East Baseline Road, Mesa, AZ Zip 85206–4713; tel. 480/567–0350; Jerry Gray, Interim Chief Executive Officer
Web address: www.healthsoutheastvalley.com

HEALTHSOUTH REHABILITATION OF SOUTHERN ARIZONA (O, 60 beds) 1921 West Hospital Drive, Tucson, AZ Zip 85704–7806; tel. 520/742–2800; Donna Beifus, Chief Executive Officer
Web address: www.healthsouthsouthernarizona.com

HEALTHSOUTH REHABILITATION INSTITUTE OF TUCSON (O, 80 beds) 2650 North Wyatt Drive, Tucson, AZ Zip 85712–6108; tel. 520/325–1300; Jeffrey Christensen, Chief Executive Officer
Web address: www.rehabinstituteoftucson.com

HEALTHSOUTH SCOTTSDALE REHABILITATION HOSPITAL (O, 60 beds) 9630 East Shea Boulevard, Scottsdale, AZ Zip 85260–6267; tel. 480/551–5400; Timothy T. Poore, Chief Executive Officer
Web address: www.healthsouthscottsdale.com

HEALTHSOUTH VALLEY OF THE SUN REHABILITATION HOSPITAL (O, 75 beds) 13460 North 67th Avenue, Glendale, AZ Zip 85304–1042; tel. 623/878–8800; Beth Bacher, Chief Executive Officer
Web address: www.healthsouthvalleyofthesun.com

YUMA REHABILITATION HOSPITAL (O, 41 beds) 901 West 24th Street, Yuma, AZ Zip 85364–6384; tel. 928/726–5000; Ian Hodge, Chief Executive Officer
Web address: www.yumarehabhospital.com

ARKANSAS: HEALTHSOUTH REHABILITATION HOSPITAL (O, 66 beds) 153 East Monte Painter Drive, Fayetteville, AR Zip 72703–4002; tel. 479/444–2200; Jack C. Mitchell, FACHE, Chief Executive Officer
Web address: www.healthsouthfayetteville.com

HEALTHSOUTH REHABILITATION HOSPITAL OF FORT SMITH (O, 60 beds) 1401 South J Street, Fort Smith, AR Zip 72901–5155; tel. 479/785–3300; Dawn Watts, Chief Executive Officer
Web address: www.healthsouthfortsmith.com

HEALTHSOUTH REHABILITATION HOSPITAL OF JONESBORO (O, 67 beds) 1201 Fleming Avenue, Jonesboro, AR Zip 72401–4311, Mailing Address: P.O. Box 1680, Zip 72403–1680; tel. 870/932–0440; Donna Harris, Chief Executive Officer
Web address: www.healthsouthjonesboro.com

ST. VINCENT REHABILITATION HOSPITAL (O, 71 beds) 2201 Wildwood Avenue, Sherwood, AR Zip 72120–5074; tel. 501/834–1800; Lisa Watson, Chief Executive Officer
Web address: www.stvincenthealth.com/svrehabhospital/index.html

CALIFORNIA: HEALTHSOUTH BAKERSFIELD REHABILITATION HOSPITAL (O, 66 beds) 5001 Commerce Drive, Bakersfield, CA Zip 93309–0689; tel. 661/323–5500; Martha Samora, R.N., FACHE, Chief Executive Officer
Web address: www.healthsouthbakersfield.com

HEALTHSOUTH TUSTIN REHABILITATION HOSPITAL (O, 48 beds) 14851 Yorba Street, Tustin, CA Zip 92780–2925; tel. 714/832–9200; Diana C. Hanyak, Chief Executive Officer
Web address: www.tustinrehab.com

COLORADO: HEALTHSOUTH REHABILITATION HOSPITAL OF COLORADO SPRINGS (O, 60 beds) 325 Parkside Drive, Colorado Springs, CO Zip 80910–3134; tel. 719/630–8000; Stephen Schaefer, Chief Executive Officer
Web address: www.healthsouthcoloradosprings.com

HEALTHSOUTH REHABILITATION HOSPITAL OF LITTLETON (O, 28 beds) 1001 West Mineral Avenue, Littleton, CO Zip 80120–4507; tel. 303/334–1100; David H. Shefte, Chief Executive Officer
Web address: www.healthsouthdenver.com

FLORIDA: HEALTHSOUTH EMERALD COAST REHABILITATION HOSPITAL (O, 75 beds) 1847 Florida Avenue, Panama City, FL Zip 32405–4640; tel. 850/914–8600; Tony N. Bennett, Chief Executive Officer
Web address: www.healthsouthpanamacity.com

HEALTHSOUTH REHABILITATION HOSPITAL (O, 70 beds) 901 North Clearwater–Largo Road, Largo, FL Zip 33770–4126; tel. 727/586–2999; Tripp Smith, Chief Executive Officer
Web address: www.healthsouthlargo.com

HEALTHSOUTH REHABILITATION HOSPITAL AT MARTIN HEALTH (O, 34 beds) 5850 S.E. Community Drive, Stuart, FL Zip 34997–6420; tel. 772/324–3500; Ivette Miranda, Chief Executive Officer
Web address: www.healthsouthmartin.com

HEALTHSOUTH REHABILITATION HOSPITAL OF ALTAMONTE SPRINGS (O, 50 beds) 831 South State Road 434, Altamonte Springs, FL Zip 32714–3502; tel. 407/587–8600; Jill Jordan, Chief Executive Officer
Web address: www.healthsouthaltamontesprings.com

HEALTHSOUTH REHABILITATION HOSPITAL OF MIAMI (O, 60 beds) 20601 Old Cutler Road, Cutler Bay, FL Zip 33189–2400; tel. 305/251–3800; Enrique A. Vicens–Rivera, Jr., JD, Chief Executive Officer
Web address: www.healthsouthmiami.com

HEALTHSOUTH REHABILITATION HOSPITAL OF OCALA (O, 40 beds) 2275 S.W. 22nd Lane, Ocala, FL Zip 34471–7710; tel. 352/282–4000; Ellen Witterstaeter, FACHE, Chief Executive Officer
Web address: www.healthsouthocala.com

HEALTHSOUTH REHABILITATION HOSPITAL OF SARASOTA (O, 96 beds) 6400 Edgelake Drive, Sarasota, FL Zip 34240–8813; tel. 941/921–8600; Marcus Braz, Chief Executive Officer
Web address: www.healthsouthsarasota.com

HEALTHSOUTH REHABILITATION HOSPITAL OF SPRING HILL (O, 80 beds) 12440 Cortez Boulevard, Brooksville, FL Zip 34613–2628; tel. 352/592–4250; Lori Bedard, Chief Executive Officer
Web address: www.healthsouthspringhill.com

HEALTHSOUTH REHABILITATION HOSPITAL OF TALLAHASSEE (O, 76 beds) 1675 Riggins Road, Tallahassee, FL Zip 32308–5315; tel. 850/656–4800; K. Dale Neely, FACHE, Chief Executive Officer
Web address: www.healthsouthtallahassee.com

HEALTHSOUTH SEA PINES REHABILITATION HOSPITAL (O, 90 beds) 101 East Florida Avenue, Melbourne, FL Zip 32901–8301; tel. 321/984–4600; Denise B. McGrath, Chief Executive Officer
Web address: www.healthsouthseapines.com

HEALTHSOUTH SUNRISE REHABILITATION HOSPITAL (O, 126 beds) 4399 North Nob Hill Road, Sunrise, FL Zip 33351–5899; tel. 954/749–0300; Stacy Modlin, Chief Executive Officer
Web address: www.healthsouthsunrise.com

HEALTHSOUTH TREASURE COAST REHABILITATION HOSPITAL (O, 80 beds) 1600 37th Street, Vero Beach, FL Zip 32960–4863; tel. 772/778–2100; Michael Kissner, Chief Executive Officer
Web address: www.healthsouthtreasurecoast.com

GEORGIA: HEALTHSOUTH WALTON REHABILITATION HOSPITAL (O, 58 beds) 1355 Independence Drive, Augusta, GA Zip 30901–1037; tel. 706/724–7746; Eric Crossan, Chief Executive Officer
Web address: www.healthsouthwalton.com/

ILLINOIS: VAN MATRE HEALTHSOUTH REHABILITATION HOSPITAL (O, 61 beds) 950 South Mulford Road, Rockford, IL Zip 61108–4274; tel. 815/381–8500; Ken Bowman, Chief Executive Officer
Web address: www.healthsouth.com

For explanation of codes following names, see page B2.
★ Indicates Type III membership in the American Hospital Association.

INDIANA: HEALTHSOUTH DEACONESS REHABILITATION HOSPITAL (O, 103 beds) 4100 Covert Avenue, Evansville, IN Zip 47714–5567, Mailing Address: P.O. Box 5349, Zip 47716–5349; tel. 812/476–9983; Blake Bunner, Chief Executive Officer
Web address: www.healthsouthdeaconess.com

KANSAS: KANSAS REHABILITATION HOSPITAL (O, 57 beds) 1504 S.W. Eighth Avenue, Topeka, KS Zip 66606–1632; tel. 785/235–6600; William J. Overbey, Chief Executive Officer
Web address: www.kansasrehabhospital.com

MID–AMERICA REHABILITATION HOSPITAL (O, 98 beds) 5701 West 110th Street, Shawnee Mission, KS Zip 66211–2503; tel. 913/491–2400; Troy DeDecker, FACHE, Chief Executive Officer
Web address: www.midamericarehabhospital.com

WESLEY REHABILITATION HOSPITAL (O, 65 beds) 8338 West 13th Street North, Wichita, KS Zip 67212–2984; tel. 316/729–9999; James F. Grocholski, FACHE, Chief Executive Officer
Web address: www.wesleyrehabhospital.com

KENTUCKY: CARDINAL HILL REHABILITATION HOSPITAL (O, 232 beds) 2050 Versailles Road, Lexington, KY Zip 40504–1405; tel. 859/254–5701; Gary Payne, Chief Executive Officer
Web address: www.cardinalhillhealthsouth.com

HEALTHSOUTH LAKEVIEW REHABILITATION HOSPITAL (O, 40 beds) 134 Heartland Drive, Elizabethtown, KY Zip 42701–2778; tel. 270/769–3100; Lori Jarboe, Chief Executive Officer
Web address: www.healthsouthlakeview.com

HEALTHSOUTH NORTHERN KENTUCKY REHABILITATION HOSPITAL (O, 40 beds) 201 Medical Village Drive, Edgewood, KY Zip 41017–3407; tel. 859/341–2044; Richard R. Evens, Chief Executive Officer
Web address: www.healthsouthkentucky.com

LOUISIANA: HEALTHSOUTH REHABILITATION HOSPITAL OF ALEXANDRIA (O, 47 beds) 104 North Third Street, Alexandria, LA Zip 71301–8581; tel. 318/449–1370; James W. McClung, Chief Executive Officer
Web address: www.healthsouthalexandria.com

MAINE: NEW ENGLAND REHABILITATION HOSPITAL OF PORTLAND (O, 90 beds) 335 Brighton Avenue, Portland, ME Zip 04102–2363; tel. 207/775–4000; Jeanine Chesley, Chief Executive Officer
Web address: www.nerhp.org

MARYLAND: HEALTHSOUTH CHESAPEAKE REHABILITATION HOSPITAL (O, 54 beds) 220 Tilghman Road, Salisbury, MD Zip 21804–1921; tel. 410/546–4600; Steven Walas, Chief Executive Officer
Web address: www.healthsouthchesapeake.com

MASSACHUSETTS: FAIRLAWN REHABILITATION HOSPITAL (O, 110 beds) 189 May Street, Worcester, MA Zip 01602–4339; tel. 508/791–6351; R. David Richer, Chief Executive Officer
Web address: www.fairlawnrehab.org

HEALTHSOUTH BRAINTREE REHABILITATION HOSPITAL (O, 187 beds) 250 Pond Street, Braintree, MA Zip 02184–5351; tel. 781/348–2500; Randy Doherty, CPA, Chief Executive Officer
Web address: www.braintreerehabhospital.com

HEALTHSOUTH NEW ENGLAND REHABILITATION HOSPITAL (O, 210 beds) Two Rehabilitation Way, Woburn, MA Zip 01801–6098; tel. 781/935–5050; Abraham Sims, FACHE, Chief Executive Officer
Web address: www.newenglandrehab.com

HEALTHSOUTH REHABILITATION HOSPITAL OF WESTERN MASSACHUSETTS (O, 53 beds) 222 State Street, Ludlow, MA Zip 01056–3437; tel. 413/308–3300; John R. Hunt, Chief Executive Officer
Web address: www.healthsouthrehab.org

MISSOURI: HOWARD A. RUSK REHABILITATION CENTER (O, 60 beds) 315 Business Loop 70 West, Columbia, MO Zip 65203–3248; tel. 573/817–2703; Larry Meeker, Chief Executive Officer
Web address: www.ruskrehab.com

THE REHABILITATION INSTITUTE OF ST. LOUIS (O, 96 beds) 4455 Duncan Avenue, Saint Louis, MO Zip 63110–1111; tel. 314/658–3800; Tara Diebling, Chief Executive Officer
Web address: www.rehabinstitutestl.com

NEVADA: HEALTHSOUTH DESERT CANYON REHABILITATION HOSPITAL (O, 50 beds) 9175 West Oquendo Road, Las Vegas, NV Zip 89148–1234; tel. 702/252–7342; Andrea Davis, Chief Executive Officer
Web address: www.healthsouthdesertcanyon.com

HEALTHSOUTH REHABILITATION HOSPITAL – HENDERSON (O, 90 beds) 10301 Jeffreys Street, Henderson, NV Zip 89052–3922; tel. 702/939–9400; Samantha Billig, Chief Executive Officer
Web address: www.hendersonrehabhospital.com

HEALTHSOUTH REHABILITATION HOSPITAL–LAS VEGAS (O, 79 beds) 1250 South Valley View Boulevard, Las Vegas, NV Zip 89102–1861; tel. 702/877–8898; Michael Ward, Chief Executive Officer
Web address: www.healthsouthlasvegas.com

NEW HAMPSHIRE: HEALTHSOUTH REHABILITATION HOSPITAL (O, 50 beds) 254 Pleasant Street, Concord, NH Zip 03301–2508; tel. 603/226–9800; Catherine Devaney, Chief Executive Officer
Web address: www.healthsouthrehabconcordnh.com

NEW JERSEY: HEALTHSOUTH REHABILITATION HOSPITAL OF TINTON FALLS (O, 60 beds) 2 Centre Plaza, Tinton Falls, NJ Zip 07724–9744; tel. 732/460–5320; Linda A. Savino, MS, Chief Executive Officer
Web address: www.rehabnj.com

HEALTHSOUTH REHABILITATION HOSPITAL OF TOMS RIVER (O, 92 beds) 14 Hospital Drive, Toms River, NJ Zip 08755–6470; tel. 732/244–3100; Patricia Ostaszewski, MS, Chief Executive Officer
Web address: www.rehabnjtomsriver.com/

HEALTHSOUTH REHABILITATION HOSPITAL OF VINELAND (O, 41 beds) 1237 West Sherman Avenue, Vineland, NJ Zip 08360–6920; tel. 856/696–7100; Tammy Feuer, Chief Executive Officer
Web address: www.healthsouthvineland.com

NEW MEXICO: HEALTHSOUTH REHABILITATION HOSPITAL (O, 87 beds) 7000 Jefferson Street N.E., Albuquerque, NM Zip 87109–4313; tel. 505/344–9478; David S. Nevill, Chief Executive Officer
Web address: www.healthsouthnewmexico.com

OHIO: HEALTHSOUTH REHABILITATION HOSPITAL AT DRAKE (O, 60 beds) 151 West Galbraith Road, Cincinnati, OH Zip 45216–1015; tel. 513/418–5600; Brad Kennedy, Chief Executive Officer
Web address: www.healthsouthatdrake.com

HEALTHSOUTH REHABILITATION HOSPITAL OF DAYTON (O, 50 beds) One Elizabeth Place, Dayton, OH Zip 45417–3445; tel. 937/424–8200; Brad Kennedy, Chief Executive Officer
Web address: www.reliantdayton.com

PENNSYLVANIA: GEISINGER HEALTHSOUTH REHABILITATION HOSPITAL (O, 42 beds) 2 Rehab Lane, Danville, PA Zip 17821–8498; tel. 570/271–6733; Lorie Dillon, Chief Executive Officer
Web address: www.geisingerhealthsouth.com

HEALTHSOUTH HARMARVILLE REHABILITATION HOSPITAL (O, 162 beds) Guys Run Road, Pittsburgh, PA Zip 15238–0460, Mailing Address: P.O. Box 11460, Zip 15238–0460; tel. 412/828–1300; Mark Van Volkenburg, Chief Executive Officer
Web address: www.healthsouthharmarville.com

HEALTHSOUTH NITTANY VALLEY REHABILITATION HOSPITAL (O, 73 beds) 550 West College Avenue, Pleasant Gap, PA Zip 16823–7401; tel. 814/359–3421; Susan Hartman, Chief Executive Officer
Web address: www.nittanyvalleyrehab.com

HEALTHSOUTH READING REHABILITATION HOSPITAL (O, 60 beds) 1623 Morgantown Road, Reading, PA Zip 19607–9455; tel. 610/796–6000; Amy Teal, Chief Executive Officer
Web address: www.healthsouthreading.com

HEALTHSOUTH REHABILITATION HOSPITAL OF ALTOONA (O, 80 beds) 2005 Valley View Boulevard, Altoona, PA Zip 16602–4598; tel. 814/944–3535; Scott Filler, Chief Executive Officer
Web address: www.healthsouthaltoona.com

HEALTHSOUTH REHABILITATION HOSPITAL OF ERIE (O, 100 beds) 143 East Second Street, Erie, PA Zip 16507–1501; tel. 814/878–1200; John Papalia, Chief Executive Officer
Web address: www.healthsoutherie.com

HEALTHSOUTH REHABILITATION HOSPITAL OF MECHANICSBURG (O, 75 beds) 175 Lancaster Boulevard, Mechanicsburg, PA Zip 17055–3562; tel. 717/691–3700; Mark Freeburn, Chief Executive Officer
Web address: www.healthsouthpa.com

HEALTHSOUTH REHABILITATION HOSPITAL OF SEWICKLEY (O, 44 beds) 303 Camp Meeting Road, Sewickley, PA Zip 15143–8322; tel. 412/741–9500; Leah Laffey, R.N., Chief Executive Officer
Web address: www.healthsouthsewickley.com

Section B

For explanation of codes following names, see page B2.
★ Indicates Type III membership in the American Hospital Association.

HEALTHSOUTH REHABILITATION HOSPITAL OF YORK (O, 90 beds) 1850 Normandie Drive, York, PA Zip 17408–1534; tel. 717/767–6941; Steven Alwine, Chief Executive Officer
Web address: www.healthsouthyork.com

PUERTO RICO: HEALTHSOUTH HOSPITAL OF MANATI (O, 40 beds) Carretera 2, Kilometro 47 7, Manati, PR Zip 00674; tel. 787/621–3800; Waleska Crespo–Rivera, Chief Executive Officer
Web address: www.healthsouth.com

HEALTHSOUTH REHABILITATION HOSPITAL OF SAN JUAN (O, 32 beds) University Hospital, 3rd Floor, San Juan, PR Zip 00923, Mailing Address: P.O. Box 70344, Zip 00923; tel. 787/274–5100; Daniel Del Castillo, Chief Executive Officer
Web address: www.healthsouthsanjuan.com

SOUTH CAROLINA: ANMED HEALTH REHABILITATION HOSPITAL (O, 45 beds) 1 Spring Back Way, Anderson, SC Zip 29621–2676; tel. 864/716–2600; Michele M. Skripps, R.N., Chief Executive Officer
Web address: www.anmedrehab.com

HEALTHSOUTH REHABILITATION HOSPITAL OF CHARLESTON (O, 49 beds) 9181 Medcom Street, Charleston, SC Zip 29406–9168; tel. 843/820–7777; Troy Powell, Chief Executive Officer
Web address: www.healthsouthcharleston.com

HEALTHSOUTH REHABILITATION HOSPITAL OF COLUMBIA (O, 96 beds) 2935 Colonial Drive, Columbia, SC Zip 29203–6811; tel. 803/254–7777; Catherine Landis, R.N., Chief Executive Officer
Web address: www.healthsouthcolumbia.com

HEALTHSOUTH REHABILITATION HOSPITAL OF FLORENCE (O, 88 beds) 900 East Cheves Street, Florence, SC Zip 29506–2704; tel. 843/679–9000; Jill Strawn, Chief Executive Officer
Web address: www.healthsouthflorence.com

HEALTHSOUTH REHABILITATION HOSPITAL OF ROCK HILL (O, 50 beds) 1795 Dr. Frank Gaston Boulevard, Rock Hill, SC Zip 29732–1190; tel. 803/326–3500; Deanna Martin, Chief Executive Officer
Web address: www.healthsouthrockhill.com

TENNESSEE: HEALTHSOUTH CANE CREEK REHABILITATION HOSPITAL (O, 40 beds) 180 Mount Pelia Road, Martin, TN Zip 38237–3812; tel. 731/587–4231; Rick Johnson, Chief Executive Officer
Web address: www.healthsouthcanecreek.com

HEALTHSOUTH CHATTANOOGA REHABILITATION HOSPITAL (O, 69 beds) 2412 McCallie Avenue, Chattanooga, TN Zip 37404–3398; tel. 423/698–0221; Scott Rowe, Chief Executive Officer
Web address: www.healthsouthchattanooga.com

HEALTHSOUTH REHABILITATION HOSPITAL (O, 50 beds) 113 Cassel Drive, Kingsport, TN Zip 37660–3775; tel. 423/246–7240; Troy Clark, Chief Executive Officer
Web address: www.healthsouthkingsport.com

HEALTHSOUTH REHABILITATION HOSPITAL MEMPHIS–NORTH (O, 50 beds) 4100 Austin Peay Highway, Memphis, TN Zip 38128–2502; tel. 901/213–5400; Adam Yoe, Chief Executive Officer
Web address: www.healthsouthnorthmemphis.com

HEALTHSOUTH REHABILITATION HOSPITAL OF MEMPHIS (O, 72 beds) 1282 Union Avenue, Memphis, TN Zip 38104–3414; tel. 901/722–2000; Kevin Spears, Chief Executive Officer
Web address: www.healthsouthmemphis.com

QUILLEN REHABILITATION HOSPITAL (O, 26 beds) 2511 Wesley Street, Johnson City, TN Zip 37601–1723; tel. 423/952–1700; Brian Luff, Chief Executive Officer
Web address: www.quillenrehabilitationhospital.com/

VANDERBILT STALLWORTH REHABILITATION HOSPITAL (O, 80 beds) 2201 Childrens Way, Nashville, TN Zip 37212–3165; tel. 615/320–7600; Armando Colombo, Chief Executive Officer
Web address: www.vanderbiltstallworthrehab.com

TEXAS: CHRISTUS TRINITY MOTHER FRANCES REHABILITATION HOSPITAL (O, 74 beds) 3131 Troup Highway, Tyler, TX Zip 75701–8352; tel. 903/510–7000; Sharla Anderson, Chief Executive Officer
Web address: www.tmfrehabhospital.com

HEALTHSOUTH CITY VIEW REHABILITATION HOSPITAL (O, 62 beds) 6701 Oakmont Boulevard, Fort Worth, TX Zip 76132–2957; tel. 817/370–4700; Janell Briscoe, Chief Executive Officer
Web address: www.healthsouthcityview.com

HEALTHSOUTH PLANO REHABILITATION HOSPITAL (O, 83 beds) 2800 West 15th Street, Plano, TX Zip 75075–7526; tel. 972/612–9000; Jennifer Lynn Brewer, Chief Executive Officer
Web address: www.healthsouthplano.com

HEALTHSOUTH REHABILITATION HOSPITAL – ABILENE (O, 30 beds) 6401 Directors Parkway, Abilene, TX Zip 79606–5869; tel. 325/691–1600; Joe Roberson, Chief Executive Officer
Web address: www.reliantabilene.com

HEALTHSOUTH REHABILITATION HOSPITAL – AUSTIN (O, 60 beds) 330 West Ben White Boulevard, Austin, TX Zip 78704; tel. 512/730–4800; Jack Boggess, Chief Executive Officer
Web address: www.reliantaustin.com

HEALTHSOUTH REHABILITATION HOSPITAL – DALLAS (O, 60 beds) 7930 Northaven Road, Dallas, TX Zip 75230–3331; tel. 214/706–8200; Daniel MacNicol, Chief Executive Officer
Web address: www.healthsouthdallas.com

HEALTHSOUTH REHABILITATION HOSPITAL – MID–CITIES (O, 60 beds) 2304 State Highway 121, Bedford, TX Zip 76021–5985; tel. 817/684–2000; Robert M. Smart, Chief Executive Officer
Web address: www.relianthcp.com

HEALTHSOUTH REHABILITATION HOSPITAL MIDLAND–ODESSA (O, 60 beds) 1800 Heritage Boulevard, Midland, TX Zip 79707–9750; tel. 432/520–1600; Christopher Wortham, Chief Executive Officer
Web address: www.healthsouthmidland.com

HEALTHSOUTH REHABILITATION HOSPITAL NORTH TEXAS (O, 50 beds) 3351 Waterview Parkway, Richardson, TX Zip 75080–1449; tel. 972/398–5700; Jim Ransom, Chief Executive Officer
Web address: www.relianthcp.com

HEALTHSOUTH REHABILITATION HOSPITAL OF ARLINGTON (O, 85 beds) 3200 Matlock Road, Arlington, TX Zip 76015–2911; tel. 817/468–4000; Sheril Appel, Chief Executive Officer
Web address: www.healthsoutharlington.com

HEALTHSOUTH REHABILITATION HOSPITAL OF AUSTIN (O, 40 beds) 1215 Red River Street, Austin, TX Zip 78701–1921; tel. 512/474–5700; Brad Dinsmore, Interim Chief Executive Officer
Web address: www.healthsouthaustin.com

HEALTHSOUTH REHABILITATION HOSPITAL OF BEAUMONT (O, 61 beds) 3340 Plaza 10 Boulevard, Beaumont, TX Zip 77707–2551; tel. 409/835–0835; H. J. Gaspard, Chief Executive Officer
Web address: www.healthsouthbeaumont.com

HEALTHSOUTH REHABILITATION HOSPITAL OF CYPRESS (O, 60 beds) 13031 Wortham Center Drive, Houston, TX Zip 77065–5662; tel. 832/280–2500; Sheila A. Bollier, Chief Executive Officer
Web address: www.healthsouthcypress.com

HEALTHSOUTH REHABILITATION HOSPITAL OF FORT WORTH (O, 60 beds) 1212 West Lancaster Avenue, Fort Worth, TX Zip 76102–4510; tel. 817/870–2336; Janell Briscoe, Chief Executive Officer
Web address: www.healthsouthfortworth.com

HEALTHSOUTH REHABILITATION HOSPITAL OF HUMBLE, LLC (O, 60 beds) 19002 McKay Drive, Humble, TX Zip 77338–5701; tel. 281/446–6148; Angela L. Simmons, Chief Executive Officer
Web address: www.healthsouthhumble.com

HEALTHSOUTH REHABILITATION HOSPITAL OF TEXARKANA (O, 60 beds) 515 West 12th Street, Texarkana, TX Zip 75501–4416; tel. 903/735–5000; Harlo McCall, Chief Executive Officer
Web address: www.healthsouthtexarkana.com

HEALTHSOUTH REHABILITATION HOSPITAL ROUND ROCK (O, 75 beds) 1400 Hester's Crossing, Round Rock, TX Zip 78681–8025; tel. 512/244–4400; Jack Boggess, Chief Executive Officer
Web address: www.healthsouthroundrock.com/

HEALTHSOUTH REHABILITATION HOSPITAL THE VINTAGE (O, 60 beds) 20180 Chasewood Park Drive, Houston, TX Zip 77070–1436; tel. 281/205–5100; Jeff Crawford, Chief Executive Officer
Web address: www.reliantnwhouston.com

HEALTHSOUTH REHABILITATION HOSPITAL THE WOODLANDS (O, 84 beds) 18550 'IH' 45 South, Conroe, TX Zip 77384; tel. 281/364–2000; Jeff Crawford, Chief Executive Officer
Web address: www.healthssouththewoodlands.com

HEALTHSOUTH REHABILITATION HOSPITAL VISION PARK (O, 60 beds) 117 Vision Park Boulevard, Shenandoah, TX Zip 77384–3001; tel. 936/444–1700; Jeff Crawford, Chief Executive Officer
Web address: www.healthsouthvisionpark.com/

For explanation of codes following names, see page B2.
★ Indicates Type III membership in the American Hospital Association.

HEALTHSOUTH REHABILITATION HOSPITAL–WICHITA FALLS (O, 63 beds) 3901 Armory Road, Wichita Falls, TX Zip 76302–2204; tel. 940/720–5700; Robbi Hudson, Chief Executive Officer
Web address: www.healthsouthwichitafalls.com

HEALTHSOUTH REHABILITATION INSTITUTE OF SAN ANTONIO (O, 96 beds) 9119 Cinnamon Hill, San Antonio, TX Zip 78240–5401; tel. 210/691–0737; Scott Butcher, Chief Executive Officer
Web address: www.hsriosa.com

HEALTHSOUTH SUGAR LAND REHABILITATION HOSPITAL (O, 50 beds) 1325 Highway 6, Sugar Land, TX Zip 77478–4906; tel. 281/276–7574; Nicholas Hardin, FACHE, Chief Executive Officer
Web address: www.healthsouthsugarland.com

UTAH: HEALTHSOUTH REHABILITATION HOSPITAL OF UTAH (O, 105 beds) 8074 South 1300 East, Sandy, UT Zip 84094–0743; tel. 801/561–3400; Jeff Frandsen, Chief Executive Officer
Web address: www.healthsouthutah.com

VIRGINIA: HEALTHSOUTH REHABILITATION HOSPITAL OF FREDERICKSBURG (O, 40 beds) 300 Park Hill Drive, Fredericksburg, VA Zip 22401–3387; tel. 540/368–7300; Gary J. Herbek, Chief Executive Officer
Web address: www.fredericksburgrehabhospital.com

HEALTHSOUTH REHABILITATION HOSPITAL OF NORTHERN VIRGINIA (O, 40 beds) 24430 Millstream Drive, Aldie, VA Zip 20105–3098; tel. 703/957–2000; Jason Waibel, Interim Chief Executive Officer
Web address: www.healthsouthnorthernvirginia.com

HEALTHSOUTH REHABILITATION HOSPITAL OF PETERSBURG (O, 53 beds) 95 Medical Park Boulevard, Petersburg, VA Zip 23805–9233; tel. 804/504–8100; Tracy Penn Turman, Chief Executive Officer
Web address: www.healthsouthpetersburg.com

HEALTHSOUTH REHABILITATION HOSPITAL OF VIRGINIA (O, 40 beds) 5700 Fitzhugh Avenue, Richmond, VA Zip 23226–1800; tel. 804/288–5700; David Cashwell, Chief Executive Officer
Web address: www.healthsouthrichmond.com

REHABILITATION HOSPITAL OF SOUTHWEST VIRGINIA (O, 25 beds) 103 North Street, Bristol, VA Zip 24201–3201; tel. 276/642–7900; Georgeanne Cole, Chief Executive Officer
Web address: www.rehabilitationhospitalswvirginia.com

UVA–HEALTHSOUTH REHABILITATION HOSPITAL (O, 50 beds) 515 Ray C. Hunt Drive, Charlottesville, VA Zip 22903–2981; tel. 434/244–2000; Thomas J. Cook, Chief Executive Officer
Web address: www.uvahealthsouth.com

WEST VIRGINIA: HEALTHSOUTH HUNTINGTON REHABILITATION HOSPITAL (O, 62 beds) 6900 West Country Club Drive, Huntington, WV Zip 25705–2000; tel. 304/733–1060; Michael E. Zuliani, Chief Executive Officer
Web address: www.healthsouthhuntington.com

HEALTHSOUTH MOUNTAINVIEW REGIONAL REHABILITATION HOSPITAL (O, 96 beds) 1160 Van Voorhis Road, Morgantown, WV Zip 26505–3437; tel. 304/598–1100; Lou Little, Chief Executive Officer
Web address: www.healthsouthmountainview.com

HEALTHSOUTH SOUTHERN HILLS REHABILITATION HOSPITAL (O, 45 beds) 120 Twelfth Street, Princeton, WV Zip 24740–2352; tel. 304/487–8000; Robert Williams, R.N., Chief Executive Officer
Web address: www.healthsouthsouthernhills.com

HEALTHSOUTH WESTERN HILLS REGIONAL REHABILITATION HOSPITAL (O, 40 beds) 3 Western Hills Drive, Parkersburg, WV Zip 26105–8122; tel. 304/420–1300; Alvin R. Lawson, JD, FACHE, Chief Executive Officer
Web address: www.healthsouthwesternhills.com

Owned, leased, sponsored:	117 hospitals	7984 beds
Contract–managed:	0 hospitals	0 beds
Totals:	117 hospitals	7984 beds

★**0585: HEALTHTECH MANAGEMENT SERVICES** (IO) 5110 Maryland Way Suite 200, Brentwood, TN Zip 37027–2307; tel. 615/309–6053; Derek Morkel, Chief Executive Officer
(Decentralized Health System)

ARIZONA: COBRE VALLEY REGIONAL MEDICAL CENTER (C, 25 beds) 5880 South Hospital Drive, Globe, AZ Zip 85501–9454; tel. 928/425–3261; Neal Jensen, Chief Executive Officer
Web address: www.cvrmc.org

GEORGIA: UPSON REGIONAL MEDICAL CENTER (C, 77 beds) 801 West Gordon Street, Thomaston, GA Zip 30286–3426, Mailing Address: P.O. Box 1059, Zip 30286–0027; tel. 706/647–8111; Tripp Penn, Chief Executive Officer
Web address: www.urmc.org

ILLINOIS: CARLINVILLE AREA HOSPITAL (C, 25 beds) 20733 North Broad Street, Carlinville, IL Zip 62626–1499; tel. 217/854–3141; Kenneth G. Reid, President and Chief Executive Officer
Web address: www.cahcare.com

HAMMOND–HENRY HOSPITAL (C, 61 beds) 600 North College Avenue, Geneseo, IL Zip 61254–1099; tel. 309/944–4625; Jeff Lingerfelt, Chief Executive Officer
Web address: www.hammondhenry.com

HILLSBORO AREA HOSPITAL (C, 25 beds) 1200 East Tremont Street, Hillsboro, IL Zip 62049–1900; tel. 217/532–6111; Rex H. Brown, President and Chief Executive Officer
Web address: www.hillsborohealth.org

LOUISIANA: IBERIA MEDICAL CENTER (C, 84 beds) 2315 East Main Street, New Iberia, LA Zip 70560–4031, Mailing Address: P.O. Box 13338, Zip 70562–3338; tel. 337/364–0441; Parker A. Templeton, FACHE, Chief Executive Officer
Web address: www.iberiamedicalcenter.com

MONTANA: BARRETT HOSPITAL & HEALTHCARE (C, 18 beds) 600 State Highway 91 South, Dillon, MT Zip 59725–7379; tel. 406/683–3000; Ken Westman, Chief Executive Officer
Web address: www.barretthospital.org

NEBRASKA: TRI VALLEY HEALTH SYSTEM (C, 52 beds) 1305 West Highway 6 and 34, Cambridge, NE Zip 69022–0488, Mailing Address: P.O. Box 488, Zip 69022–0488; tel. 308/697–3329; Deborah L. Herzberg, R.N., MS, FACHE, Chief Executive Officer
Web address: www.trivalleyhealth.com

NEW YORK: ADIRONDACK MEDICAL CENTER (C, 200 beds) 2233 State Route 86, Saranac Lake, NY Zip 12983–5644, Mailing Address: P.O. Box 471, Zip 12983–0471; tel. 518/891–4141; Sylvia Getman, President and Chief Executive Officer
Web address: www.adirondackhealth.org

OREGON: BLUE MOUNTAIN HOSPITAL (C, 45 beds) 170 Ford Road, John Day, OR Zip 97845–2009; tel. 541/575–1311; Stephen M. Erixon, Interim Chief Executive Officer
Web address: www.bluemountainhospital.org

WASHINGTON: SUNNYSIDE COMMUNITY HOSPITAL AND CLINICS (C, 25 beds) 1016 Tacoma Avenue, Sunnyside, WA Zip 98944–2263, Mailing Address: P.O. Box 719, Zip 98944–0719; tel. 509/837–1500; John Gallagher, Chief Executive Officer
Web address: www.sunnysidehospital.com

WISCONSIN: GRANT REGIONAL HEALTH CENTER (C, 5 beds) 507 South Monroe Street, Lancaster, WI Zip 53813–2054; tel. 608/723–2143; Nicole Clapp, R.N., MSN, FACHE, President and Chief Executive Officer
Web address: www.grantregional.com

SPOONER HEALTH (C, 25 beds) 1280 Chandler Drive, Spooner, WI Zip 54801–1299; tel. 715/635–2111; Michael Schafer, Chief Executive Officer and Administrator
Web address: www.spoonerhealth.com

TOMAH MEMORIAL HOSPITAL (C, 25 beds) 321 Butts Avenue, Tomah, WI Zip 54660–1412; tel. 608/372–2181; Philip J. Stuart, Administrator and Chief Executive Officer
Web address: www.tomahhospital.org

WYOMING: HOT SPRINGS COUNTY MEMORIAL HOSPITAL (C, 25 beds) 150 East Arapahoe Street, Thermopolis, WY Zip 82443–2498; tel. 307/864–3121; Margie Molitor, FACHE, R.N., Chief Executive Officer
Web address: www.hscmh.org

POWELL VALLEY HEALTHCARE (C, 125 beds) 777 Avenue H, Powell, WY Zip 82435–2296; tel. 307/754–2267; Terry Odom, Chief Executive Officer
Web address: www.pvhc.org

Owned, leased, sponsored:	0 hospitals	0 beds
Contract–managed:	16 hospitals	842 beds
Totals:	16 hospitals	842 beds

For explanation of codes following names, see page B2.
★ Indicates Type III membership in the American Hospital Association.

Section B

★9505:   HENRY FORD HEALTH SYSTEM (NP)
One Ford Place, Detroit, MI Zip 48202–3450; tel. 313/876–8708;
Nancy M. Schlichting, Chief Executive Officer
(Centralized Physician/Insurance Health System)

MICHIGAN: HENRY FORD ALLEGIANCE HEALTH (O, 302 beds) 205 North
East Avenue, Jackson, MI Zip 49201–1753; tel. 517/788–4800; Georgia
R. Fojtasek, R.N., President and Chief Executive Officer
Web address: www.allegiancehealth.org
HENRY FORD HOSPITAL (O, 681 beds) 2799 West Grand Boulevard, Detroit,
MI Zip 48202–2608; tel. 313/916–2600; John Popovich, M.D., President and
Chief Executive Officer
Web address: www.henryfordhealth.org
HENRY FORD KINGSWOOD HOSPITAL (O, 136 beds) 10300 West Eight Mile
Road, Ferndale, MI Zip 48220–2100; tel. 248/398–3200; DoreeAnn V.
Espiritu, M.D., Interim Chair, Behavioral Health Services
Web address: www.henryford.com
HENRY FORD MACOMB HOSPITALS (O, 418 beds) 15855 19 Mile Road,
Clinton Township, MI Zip 48038–6324; tel. 586/263–2300; Barbara W.
Rossmann, R.N., President and Chief Executive Officer
Web address: www.henryfordmacomb.com
HENRY FORD WEST BLOOMFIELD HOSPITAL (O, 198 beds) 6777 West Maple
Road, West Bloomfield, MI Zip 48322–3013; tel. 248/661–4100; Lynn M.
Torossian, President and Chief Executive Officer
Web address: www.henryford.com
HENRY FORD WYANDOTTE HOSPITAL (O, 351 beds) 2333 Biddle Avenue,
Wyandotte, MI Zip 48192–4668; tel. 734/246–6000; Denise
Brooks–Williams, President and Chief Executive Officer
Web address: www.henryfordhealth.org

Owned, leased, sponsored:	6 hospitals	2086 beds
Contract–managed:	0 hospitals	0 beds
Totals:	6 hospitals	2086 beds

0309:   HERITAGE VALLEY HEALTH SYSTEM (NP)
1000 Dutch Ridge Road, Beaver, PA Zip 15009–9727;
tel. 724/773–2024; Norman F. Mitry, President and Chief Executive
Officer
(Independent Hospital System)

PENNSYLVANIA: HERITAGE VALLEY HEALTH SYSTEM (O, 271 beds) 1000
Dutch Ridge Road, Beaver, PA Zip 15009–9727; tel. 724/728–7000;
Norman F. Mitry, President and Chief Executive Officer
Web address: www.heritagevalley.org
SEWICKLEY VALLEY HOSPITAL, (A DIVISION OF VALLEY MEDICAL FACILITIES)
(O, 179 beds) 720 Blackburn Road, Sewickley, PA Zip 15143–1459;
tel. 412/741–6600; Norman F. Mitry, President and Chief Executive Officer
Web address: www.heritagevalley.org

Owned, leased, sponsored:	2 hospitals	450 beds
Contract–managed:	0 hospitals	0 beds
Totals:	2 hospitals	450 beds

★0963:   HONORHEALTH (NP)
8125 North Hayden Road, Scottsdale, AZ Zip 85258–2463;
tel. 623/580–5800; Thomas J. Sadvary, FACHE, Chief Executive
Officer
(Independent Hospital System)

ARIZONA: HONORHEALTH DEER VALLEY MEDICAL CENTER (O, 204 beds)
19829 North 27th Avenue, Phoenix, AZ Zip 85027–4002;
tel. 623/879–6100; John L. Harrington, Jr., FACHE, Chief Executive
Officer
Web address: www.jcl.com
HONORHEALTH JOHN C. LINCOLN MEDICAL CENTER (O, 262 beds) 250 East
Dunlap Avenue, Phoenix, AZ Zip 85020–2825; tel. 602/943–2381; Margaret
Elizabeth Griffin, Chief Executive Officer
Web address: www.jcl.com
HONORHEALTH SCOTTSDALE OSBORN MEDICAL CENTER (O, 347 beds)
7400 East Osborn Road, Scottsdale, AZ Zip 85251–6403;
tel. 480/882–4000; Kimberly Post, Senior Vice President and Chief Executive
Officer
Web address: www.shc.org

HONORHEALTH SCOTTSDALE SHEA MEDICAL CENTER (O, 409 beds) 9003
East Shea Boulevard, Scottsdale, AZ Zip 85260–6771; tel. 480/323–3000;
Gary E. Baker, Senior Vice President and Chief Executive Officer
Web address: www.shc.org
HONORHEALTH SCOTTSDALE THOMPSON PEAK MEDICAL CENTER (O, 64
beds) 7400 East Thompson Peak Parkway, Scottsdale, AZ Zip 85255–4109;
tel. 480/324–7000; David Price, Chief Executive Officer
Web address: www.shc.org

Owned, leased, sponsored:	5 hospitals	1286 beds
Contract–managed:	0 hospitals	0 beds
Totals:	5 hospitals	1286 beds

★5355:   HOSPITAL SISTERS HEALTH SYSTEM (CC)
4936 LaVerna Road, Springfield, IL Zip 62707–9797, Mailing
Address: P.O. Box 19456, Zip 62794–9456; tel. 217/523–4747;
Mary Starmann–Harrison, FACHE, R.N., President and Chief Executive
Officer
(Decentralized Health System)

ILLINOIS: HSHS HOLY FAMILY HOSPITAL IN GREENVILLE (O, 42 beds) 200
Healthcare Drive, Greenville, IL Zip 62246–1154; tel. 618/664–1230;
Brian Nall, President and Chief Executive Officer
Web address: www.greenvilleregionalhospital.com
HSHS ST. ANTHONY'S MEMORIAL HOSPITAL (O, 133 beds) 503 North Maple
Street, Effingham, IL Zip 62401–2099; tel. 217/342–2121; Theresa
Rutherford, R.N., MS, FACHE, President and Chief Executive Officer
Web address: www.stanthonyshospital.org
HSHS ST. ELIZABETH'S HOSPITAL (O, 260 beds) 211 South Third Street,
Belleville, IL Zip 62220–1998; tel. 618/234–2120; Peggy A. Sebastian,
MSN, R.N., President and Chief Executive Officer
Web address: www.steliz.org
HSHS ST. FRANCIS HOSPITAL (O, 25 beds) 1215 Franciscan Drive, Litchfield,
IL Zip 62056–1799, Mailing Address: P.O. Box 1215, Zip 62056–0999;
tel. 217/324–2191; Patricia Fischer, FACHE, R.N., President and Chief
Executive Officer
Web address: www.stfrancis–litchfield.org
HSHS ST. JOSEPH'S HOSPITAL (O, 65 beds) 9515 Holy Cross Lane, Breese,
IL Zip 62230–3618, Mailing Address: PO Box 99, Zip 62230–0099;
tel. 618/526–4511; Paulette Evans, R.N., MSN, President and Chief
Executive Officer
Web address: www.stjoebreese.com
HSHS ST. JOSEPH'S HOSPITAL (O, 25 beds) 12866 Troxler Avenue,
Highland, IL Zip 62249–1698; tel. 618/651–2600; Elizabeth Govero, MSN,
R.N., Interim President and Chief Executive Officer
Web address: www.stjosephshighland.com
HSHS ST. MARY'S HOSPITAL (O, 244 beds) 1800 East Lake Shore Drive,
Decatur, IL Zip 62521–3883; tel. 217/464–2966; Daniel L. Perryman,
President and Chief Executive Officer
Web address: www.stmarysdecatur.org
ST. JOHN'S HOSPITAL (O, 432 beds) 800 East Carpenter Street, Springfield,
IL Zip 62769–0002; tel. 217/544–6464; Charles Lucore, M.D., President
and Chief Executive Officer
Web address: www.st–johns.org

WISCONSIN: HSHS ST. CLARE MEMORIAL HOSPITAL (O, 9 beds) 855 South
Main Street, Oconto Falls, WI Zip 54154–1296; tel. 920/846–3444;
Therese Handl, Chief Executive Officer
Web address: www.cmhospital.org/index.html
HSHS ST. JOSEPH'S HOSPITAL (O, 102 beds) 2661 County Highway I.,
Chippewa Falls, WI Zip 54729–5407; tel. 715/723–1811; Joan M. Coffman,
FACHE, President and Chief Executive Officer
Web address: www.stjoeschipfalls.com
HSHS ST. VINCENT HOSPITAL (O, 255 beds) 835 South Van Buren Street,
Green Bay, WI Zip 54301–3526, Mailing Address: P.O. Box 13508,
Zip 54307–3508; tel. 920/433–0111; Therese B. Pandl, President and Chief
Executive Officer
Web address: www.stvincenthospital.org
SACRED HEART HOSPITAL (O, 202 beds) 900 West Clairemont Avenue, Eau
Claire, WI Zip 54701–6122; tel. 715/717–4121; Julie Manas, President and
Chief Executive Officer
Web address: www.sacredhearteauclaire.org

For explanation of codes following names, see page B2.
★ Indicates Type III membership in the American Hospital Association.

ST. MARY'S HOSPITAL MEDICAL CENTER (O, 83 beds) 1726 Shawano Avenue, Green Bay, WI Zip 54303–3282; tel. 920/498–4200; Therese B. Pandl, President and Chief Executive Officer
Web address: www.stmgb.org

ST. NICHOLAS HOSPITAL (O, 46 beds) 3100 Superior Avenue, Sheboygan, WI Zip 53081–1948; tel. 920/459–8300; Andrew Bagnall, President and Chief Executive Officer
Web address: www.stnicholashospital.org

Owned, leased, sponsored:	14 hospitals	1923 beds
Contract–managed:	0 hospitals	0 beds
Totals:	14 hospitals	1923 beds

★**0642: HOUSTON HEALTHCARE SYSTEM** (NP)
1601 Watson Boulevard, Warner Robins, GA Zip 31093–3431, Mailing Address: P.O. Box 2886, Zip 31099–2886; tel. 478/922–4281; Cary Martin, Chief Executive Officer
(Independent Hospital System)

GEORGIA: HOUSTON MEDICAL CENTER (O, 237 beds) 1601 Watson Boulevard, Warner Robins, GA Zip 31093–3431, Mailing Address: P.O. Box 2886, Zip 31099–2886; tel. 478/922–4281; Cary Martin, Chief Executive Officer
Web address: www.hhc.org

PERRY HOSPITAL (O, 39 beds) 1120 Morningside Drive, Perry, GA Zip 31069–2906; tel. 478/987–3600; David Campbell, Administrator
Web address: www.hhc.org

Owned, leased, sponsored:	2 hospitals	276 beds
Contract–managed:	0 hospitals	0 beds
Totals:	2 hospitals	276 beds

★**7235: HOUSTON METHODIST** (CO)
6565 Fannin Street, D–200, Houston, TX Zip 77030–2707; tel. 713/441–2221; Marc L. Boom, M.D., Chief Executive Officer
(Centralized Health System)

TEXAS: HOUSTON METHODIST HOSPITAL (O, 861 beds) 6565 Fannin Street, D200, Houston, TX Zip 77030–2707; tel. 713/790–3311; Roberta Schwartz, Ph.D., Executive Vice President
Web address: www.methodisthealth.com

HOUSTON METHODIST SAN JACINTO HOSPITAL (O, 275 beds) 4401 Garth Road, Baytown, TX Zip 77521–2122; tel. 281/420–8600; David P. Bernard, FACHE, Chief Executive Officer
Web address: www.houstonmethodist.org

HOUSTON METHODIST ST. CATHERINE HOSPITAL (O, 44 beds) 701 Fry Road, Katy, TX Zip 77450–2255; tel. 281/599–5700; Gary L. Kempf, R.N., Administrator
Web address: www.houstonmethodist.org/katy–st–catherine–hospital

HOUSTON METHODIST ST. JOHN HOSPITAL (O, 137 beds) 18300 St. John Drive, Nassau Bay, TX Zip 77058–6302; tel. 281/333–5503; Dan Newman, Chief Executive Officer
Web address: www.houstonmethodist.org/st–john–clear–lake

HOUSTON METHODIST SUGAR LAND HOSPITAL (O, 243 beds) 16655 S.W. Freeway, Sugar Land, TX Zip 77479–2329; tel. 281/274–7000; Christopher Siebenaler, Chief Executive Officer
Web address: www.methodisthealth.com

HOUSTON METHODIST WEST HOSPITAL (O, 193 beds) 18500 Katy Freeway, Houston, TX Zip 77094–1110; tel. 832/522–1000; Wayne M. Voss, Chief Executive Officer
Web address: www.methodisthealth.com

HOUSTON METHODIST WILLOWBROOK HOSPITAL (O, 276 beds) 18220 Tomball Parkway, Houston, TX Zip 77070–4347; tel. 281/477–1000; Keith Barber, CPA, Chief Executive Officer
Web address: www.houstonmethodist.org/locations/willowbrook/

Owned, leased, sponsored:	7 hospitals	2029 beds
Contract–managed:	0 hospitals	0 beds
Totals:	7 hospitals	2029 beds

●**0907: HUNT REGIONAL HEALTHCARE** (NP)
4215 Joe Ramsey Boulevard, Greenville, TX Zip 75401–7852, Mailing Address: P.O. Box 1059, Zip 75403–1059; tel. 903/408–5000; Richard Carter, Chief Executive Officer
(Independent Hospital System)

HUNT REGIONAL MEDICAL CENTER (O, 206 beds) 4215 Joe Ramsey Boulevard, Greenville, TX Zip 75401–7899, Mailing Address: P.O. Box 1059, Zip 75403–1059; tel. 903/408–5000; Richard Carter, District Chief Executive Officer
Web address: www.huntregional.org

Owned, leased, sponsored:	1 hospital	206 beds
Contract–managed:	0 hospitals	0 beds
Totals:	1 hospital	206 beds

0117: HUNTSVILLE HOSPITAL HEALTH SYSTEM (NP)
101 Sivley Road S.W., Huntsville, AL Zip 35801–4421; tel. 265/256–1000; David S. Spillers, Chief Executive Officer
(Moderately Centralized Health System)

ALABAMA: ATHENS–LIMESTONE HOSPITAL (C, 101 beds) 700 West Market Street, Athens, AL Zip 35611–2457, Mailing Address: P.O. Box 999, Zip 35612–0999; tel. 256/233–9292; David Pryor, President
Web address: www.athenslimestonehospital.com

DECATUR MORGAN HOSPITAL (O, 203 beds) 1201 Seventh Street S.E., Decatur, AL Zip 35601–3303, Mailing Address: P.O. Box 2239, Zip 35609–2239; tel. 256/341–2000; Nathaniel Richardson, Jr., President
Web address: www.decaturgeneral.org

HELEN KELLER HOSPITAL (C, 145 beds) 1300 South Montgomery Avenue, Sheffield, AL Zip 35660–6334, Mailing Address: P.O. Box 610, Zip 35660–0610; tel. 256/386–4196; Paul Storey, FACHE, President and Chief Executive Officer
Web address: www.helenkeller.com

HUNTSVILLE HOSPITAL (O, 902 beds) 101 Sivley Road S.W., Huntsville, AL Zip 35801–4470; tel. 256/265–1000; David S. Spillers, Chief Executive Officer
Web address: www.huntsvillehospital.org

LAWRENCE MEDICAL CENTER (C, 53 beds) 202 Hospital Street, Moulton, AL Zip 35650–1218, Mailing Address: P.O. Box 39, Zip 35650–0039; tel. 256/974–2200; Kyle Buchanan, Chief Executive Officer
Web address: www.lawrencemedicalcenter.com

RED BAY HOSPITAL (C, 22 beds) 211 Hospital Road, Red Bay, AL Zip 35582–3858, Mailing Address: P.O. Box 490, Zip 35582–0490; tel. 256/356–9532; Glen M. Jones, FACHE, Administrator
Web address: www.redbayhospital.com

Owned, leased, sponsored:	2 hospitals	1105 beds
Contract–managed:	4 hospitals	321 beds
Totals:	6 hospitals	1426 beds

0201: IASIS HEALTHCARE (IO)
117 Seaboard Lane, Building E., Franklin, TN Zip 37067–2855; tel. 615/844–2747; Carl Whitmer, President and Chief Executive Officer
(Moderately Centralized Health System)

ARIZONA: MOUNTAIN VISTA MEDICAL CENTER (O, 172 beds) 1301 South Crismon Road, Mesa, AZ Zip 85209–3767; tel. 480/358–6100; Eric Paul, Interim Chief Executive Officer
Web address: www.mvmedicalcenter.com

ST. LUKE'S BEHAVIORAL HEALTH CENTER (O, 85 beds) 1800 East Van Buren, Phoenix, AZ Zip 85006–3742; tel. 602/251–8546; Gregory L. Jahn, R.N., Chief Executive Officer
Web address: www.iasishealthcare.com

ST. LUKE'S MEDICAL CENTER (O, 284 beds) 1800 East Van Buren Street, Phoenix, AZ Zip 85006–3742; tel. 602/251–8100; James Flinn, JD, FACHE, Chief Executive Officer
Web address: www.stlukesmedcenter.com

ARKANSAS: WADLEY REGIONAL MEDICAL CENTER AT HOPE (O, 79 beds) 2001 South Main Street, Hope, AR Zip 71801–8194; tel. 870/722–3800; Thomas D. Gilbert, FACHE, Chief Executive Officer
Web address: www.wadleyhealthathope.com

Section B

COLORADO: PIKES PEAK REGIONAL HOSPITAL (O, 15 beds) 16420 West Highway 24, Woodland Park, CO Zip 80863; tel. 719/687–9999; Kimberly Monjesky, Chief Executive Officer
Web address: www.pprmc.org

LOUISIANA: GLENWOOD REGIONAL MEDICAL CENTER (O, 278 beds) 503 McMillan Road, West Monroe, LA Zip 71291–5327; tel. 318/329–4200; Matthew S. Roberts, Chief Executive Officer
Web address: www.grmc.com

TEXAS: MEDICAL CENTER OF SOUTHEAST TEXAS (O, 17 beds) 6025 Metropolitan Drive, Beaumont, TX Zip 77706–2407; tel. 409/617–7700; Becky Ames, Chief Executive Officer
Web address: www.medicalcentersetexas.com/

ODESSA REGIONAL MEDICAL CENTER (O, 213 beds) 520 East Sixth Street, Odessa, TX Zip 79761–4565, Mailing Address: P.O. Box 4859, Zip 79760–4859; tel. 432/582–8000; Stacey L. Gerig, Chief Executive Officer
Web address: www.odessaregionalmedicalcenter.com

SOUTHWEST GENERAL HOSPITAL (O, 253 beds) 7400 Barlite Boulevard, San Antonio, TX Zip 78224–1399; tel. 210/921–2000; P. Craig Desmond, Chief Executive Officer
Web address: www.swgeneralhospital.com

ST. JOSEPH MEDICAL CENTER (O, 374 beds) 1401 St. Joseph Parkway, Houston, TX Zip 77002–8301; tel. 713/757–1000; Bryanie W. Swilley, Jr., Interim Chief Executive Officer
Web address: www.sjmctx.com

THE MEDICAL CENTER OF SOUTHEAST TEXAS (O, 168 beds) 2555 Jimmy Johnson Boulevard, Port Arthur, TX Zip 77640–2007; tel. 409/724–7389; Richard Gonzalez, Chief Executive Officer
Web address: www.medicalcentersetexas.com

WADLEY REGIONAL MEDICAL CENTER (O, 179 beds) 1000 Pine Street, Texarkana, TX Zip 75501–5170; tel. 903/798–8000; Thomas D. Gilbert, FACHE, Chief Executive Officer
Web address: www.wadleyhealth.com

UTAH: DAVIS HOSPITAL AND MEDICAL CENTER (O, 200 beds) 1600 West Antelope Drive, Layton, UT Zip 84041–1142; tel. 801/807–1000; Michael E. Jensen, Chief Executive Officer
Web address: www.davishospital.com

JORDAN VALLEY MEDICAL CENTER (O, 183 beds) 3580 West 9000 South, West Jordan, UT Zip 84088–8812; tel. 801/561–8888; Steven Anderson, Chief Executive Officer
Web address: www.jordanvalleymc.com

JORDAN VALLEY MEDICAL CENTER WEST VALLEY CAMPUS (O, 101 beds) 3460 South Pioneer Parkway, West Valley City, UT Zip 84120–2049; tel. 801/561–8888; Steven Anderson, Chief Executive Officer
Web address: www.pioneervalleyhospital.com

SALT LAKE REGIONAL MEDICAL CENTER (O, 132 beds) 1050 East South Temple, Salt Lake City, UT Zip 84102–1507; tel. 801/350–4111; Dale Johns, FACHE, Chief Executive Officer
Web address: www.saltlakeregional.com

Owned, leased, sponsored:	16 hospitals	2733 beds
Contract–managed:	0 hospitals	0 beds
Totals:	16 hospitals	2733 beds

★0231: INDIANA UNIVERSITY HEALTH (NP)
340 West 10th Street, Suite 6100, Indianapolis, IN Zip 46202–3082, Mailing Address: P.O. Box 1367, Zip 46206–1367; tel. 317/962–5900; Dennis M. Murphy, President
(Moderately Centralized Health System)

INDIANA: INDIANA UNIVERSITY HEALTH ARNETT HOSPITAL (O, 191 beds) 5165 McCarty Lane, Lafayette, IN Zip 47905–8764, Mailing Address: P.O. Box 5545, Zip 47903–5545; tel. 765/448–8000; Donald Clayton, M.D., President
Web address: www.iuhealth.org

INDIANA UNIVERSITY HEALTH BALL MEMORIAL HOSPITAL (O, 339 beds) 2401 University Avenue, Muncie, IN Zip 47303–3499; tel. 765/747–3111; Michael E. Haley, President
Web address: www.iuhealth.org

INDIANA UNIVERSITY HEALTH BEDFORD HOSPITAL (O, 25 beds) 2900 West 16th Street, Bedford, IN Zip 47421–3583; tel. 812/275–1200; Bradford W. Dykes, President and Chief Executive Officer
Web address: www.iuhealth.org

INDIANA UNIVERSITY HEALTH BLACKFORD HOSPITAL (O, 15 beds) 410 Pilgrim Boulevard, Hartford City, IN Zip 47348–1897; tel. 765/348–0300; Steven J. West, Chief Executive Officer
Web address: www.iuhealth.org/blackford

INDIANA UNIVERSITY HEALTH BLOOMINGTON HOSPITAL (O, 273 beds) 601 West Second Street, Bloomington, IN Zip 47403–2317, Mailing Address: P.O. Box 1149, Zip 47402–1149; tel. 812/336–6821; Mark E. Moore, President and Chief Executive Officer
Web address: www.iuhealth.org

INDIANA UNIVERSITY HEALTH GOSHEN HOSPITAL (O, 122 beds) 200 High Park Avenue, Goshen, IN Zip 46526–4899, Mailing Address: P.O. Box 139, Zip 46527–0139; tel. 574/533–2141; Randal Christophel, President and Chief Executive Officer
Web address: www.iuhealth.org

INDIANA UNIVERSITY HEALTH NORTH HOSPITAL (O, 161 beds) 11700 North Meridian Avenue, Carmel, IN Zip 46032–4656; tel. 317/688–2000; Jonathan R. Goble, FACHE, President and Chief Executive Officer
Web address: www.iuhealth.org/north

INDIANA UNIVERSITY HEALTH PAOLI HOSPITAL (O, 25 beds) 642 West Hospital Road, Paoli, IN Zip 47454–9672, Mailing Address: P.O. Box 499, Zip 47454–0499; tel. 812/723–2811; Larry Bailey, Chief Executive Officer
Web address: www.iuhealth.org/paoli

INDIANA UNIVERSITY HEALTH TIPTON HOSPITAL (O, 25 beds) 1000 South Main Street, Tipton, IN Zip 46072–9799; tel. 765/675–8500; Michael Harlowe, President and Chief Executive Officer
Web address: www.iuhealth.org

INDIANA UNIVERSITY HEALTH UNIVERSITY HOSPITAL (O, 1253 beds) 550 University Boulevard, Indianapolis, IN Zip 46202–5149, Mailing Address: P.O. Box 1367, Zip 46206–1367; tel. 317/944–5000; Herbert Buchanan, President
Web address: www.iuhealth.org

INDIANA UNIVERSITY HEALTH WEST HOSPITAL (O, 127 beds) 1111 North Ronald Reagan Parkway, Avon, IN Zip 46123–7085; tel. 317/217–3000; Doug Puckett, President
Web address: www.iuhealth.org

INDIANA UNIVERSITY HEALTH WHITE MEMORIAL HOSPITAL (O, 25 beds) 720 South Sixth Street, Monticello, IN Zip 47960–8182; tel. 574/583–7111; Jeffrey C. Zeh, President
Web address: www.iuhealth.org/white–memorial

JAY COUNTY HOSPITAL (C, 35 beds) 500 West Votaw Street, Portland, IN Zip 47371–1322; tel. 260/726–7131; David W. Hyatt, Chief Executive Officer
Web address: www.jaycountyhospital.com

REHABILITATION HOSPITAL OF INDIANA (O, 83 beds) 4141 Shore Drive, Indianapolis, IN Zip 46254–2607; tel. 317/329–2000; Daniel B. Woloszyn, Chief Executive Officer
Web address: www.rhin.com

Owned, leased, sponsored:	13 hospitals	2664 beds
Contract–managed:	1 hospital	35 beds
Totals:	14 hospitals	2699 beds

2025: INFIRMARY HEALTH SYSTEM (NP)
5 Mobile Infirmary Circle, Mobile, AL Zip 36607–3513; tel. 251/435–5500; D. Mark Nix, President and Chief Executive Officer

ALABAMA: ATMORE COMMUNITY HOSPITAL (O, 33 beds) 401 Medical Park Drive, Atmore, AL Zip 36502–3091; tel. 251/368–2500; Doug Tanner, Administrator
Web address: www.ebaptisthealthcare.org/AtmoreCommunityHospital/

INFIRMARY LONG TERM ACUTE CARE HOSPITAL (L, 38 beds) 5 Mobile Infirmary Circle, Mobile, AL Zip 36607–3513, Mailing Address: P.O. Box 2226, Zip 36652–2226; tel. 251/660–5239; Susanne Marmande, Administrator
Web address: www.theinfirmary.com/

For explanation of codes following names, see page B2.
★ Indicates Type III membership in the American Hospital Association.

MOBILE INFIRMARY MEDICAL CENTER (O, 526 beds) 5 Mobile Infirmary Drive North, Mobile, AL Zip 36607–3513, Mailing Address: P.O. Box 2144, Zip 36652–2144; tel. 251/435–2400; Jennifer Eslinger, President
Web address: www.infirmaryhealth.org

NORTH BALDWIN INFIRMARY (L, 50 beds) 1815 Hand Avenue, Bay Minette, AL Zip 36507–4110, Mailing Address: P.O. Box 1409, Zip 36507–1409; tel. 251/937–5521; Benjamin K. Hansert, Administrator
Web address: www.mobileinfirmary.org

THOMAS HOSPITAL (L, 136 beds) 750 Morphy Avenue, Fairhope, AL Zip 36532–1812, Mailing Address: P.O. Box 929, Zip 36533–0929; tel. 251/928–2375; Ormand P. Thompson, President
Web address: www.thomashospital.com

Owned, leased, sponsored:	5 hospitals	783 beds
Contract–managed:	0 hospitals	0 beds
Totals:	5 hospitals	783 beds

★1305: INOVA HEALTH SYSTEM (NP)
8110 Gatehouse Road, Suite 200 East, Falls Church, VA Zip 22042–1252; tel. 703/289–2069; J. Knox Singleton, President and Chief Executive Officer
(Centralized Health System)

VIRGINIA: INOVA ALEXANDRIA HOSPITAL (O, 334 beds) 4320 Seminary Road, Alexandria, VA Zip 22304–1535; tel. 703/504–3167; Susan Carroll, Chief Executive Officer
Web address: www.inova.org

INOVA FAIR OAKS HOSPITAL (O, 196 beds) 3600 Joseph Siewick Drive, Fairfax, VA Zip 22033–1798; tel. 703/391–3600; John L. Fitzgerald, Chief Executive Officer
Web address: www.inova.org

INOVA FAIRFAX HOSPITAL (O, 935 beds) 3300 Gallows Road, Falls Church, VA Zip 22042–3300; tel. 703/776–4001; Patrick Christiansen, Ph.D., Chief Executive Officer
Web address: www.inova.org

INOVA LOUDOUN HOSPITAL (O, 286 beds) 44045 Riverside Parkway, Leesburg, VA Zip 20176–5101, Mailing Address: P.O. Box 6000, Zip 20177–0600; tel. 703/858–6000; Patrick Walters, Chief Executive Officer
Web address: www.inova.org

INOVA MOUNT VERNON HOSPITAL (O, 237 beds) 2501 Parker's Lane, Alexandria, VA Zip 22306–3209; tel. 703/664–7000; Deborah Addo–Samuels, Chief Executive Officer
Web address: www.inova.org

Owned, leased, sponsored:	5 hospitals	1988 beds
Contract–managed:	0 hospitals	0 beds
Totals:	5 hospitals	1988 beds

★0151: INSPIRA HEALTH NETWORK (NP)
165 Bridgeton Pike, Mullica Hill, NJ Zip 08062; tel. 856/641–8000; John A. DiAngelo, President and Chief Executive Officer
(Moderately Centralized Health System)

NEW JERSEY: INSPIRA MEDICAL CENTER–ELMER (O, 88 beds) 501 West Front Street, Elmer, NJ Zip 08318–2101; tel. 856/363–1000; John A. DiAngelo, President and Chief Executive Officer
Web address: www.inspirahealthnetwork.org/?id=5281&sid=1

INSPIRA MEDICAL CENTER–VINELAND (O, 335 beds) 1505 West Sherman Avenue, Vineland, NJ Zip 08360–6912; tel. 856/641–8000; John A. DiAngelo, President and Chief Executive Officer
Web address: www.inspirahealthnetwork.org/?id=5280&sid=1

INSPIRA MEDICAL CENTER–WOODBURY (O, 261 beds) 509 North Broad Street, Woodbury, NJ Zip 08096–1697; tel. 856/845–0100; John A. DiAngelo, President and Chief Executive Officer
Web address: www.inspirahealthnetwork.org/?id=5282&sid=1

Owned, leased, sponsored:	3 hospitals	684 beds
Contract–managed:	0 hospitals	0 beds
Totals:	3 hospitals	684 beds

★0305: INTEGRIS HEALTH (NP)
3366 N.W. Expressway, Suite 800, Oklahoma City, OK Zip 73112–9756; tel. 405/949–6066; Bruce Lawrence, President and Chief Executive Officer
(Centralized Physician/Insurance Health System)

OKLAHOMA: INTEGRIS BAPTIST MEDICAL CENTER (O, 587 beds) 3300 N.W. Expressway, Oklahoma City, OK Zip 73112–4418; tel. 405/949–3011; Timothy J. Johnsen, MS, President
Web address: www.integrisok.com

INTEGRIS BASS BAPTIST HEALTH CENTER (O, 167 beds) 600 South Monroe Street, Enid, OK Zip 73701–7211, Mailing Address: P.O. Box 3168, Zip 73702–3168; tel. 580/233–2300; Edward Herrman, R.N., FACHE, President
Web address: www.integris–health.com

INTEGRIS CANADIAN VALLEY HOSPITAL (O, 75 beds) 1201 Health Center Parkway, Yukon, OK Zip 73099–6381; tel. 405/717–6800; Rex Van Meter, President
Web address: www.integris–health.com

INTEGRIS GROVE HOSPITAL (O, 58 beds) 1001 East 18th Street, Grove, OK Zip 74344–2907; tel. 918/786–2243; Tim Bowen, President
Web address: www.integris–health.com

INTEGRIS HEALTH EDMOND (O, 40 beds) 4801 Integris Parkway, Edmond, OK Zip 73034–8864; tel. 405/657–3000; Avilla Williams, MS, President
Web address: www.integrisok.com/edmond

INTEGRIS MIAMI HOSPITAL (O, 84 beds) 200 Second Street S.W., Miami, OK Zip 74354–6830; tel. 918/542–6611; Jordan Cash, President
Web address: www.integris–health.com

INTEGRIS SOUTHWEST MEDICAL CENTER (O, 352 beds) 4401 South Western, Oklahoma City, OK Zip 73109–3413; tel. 405/636–7000; Chris Hammes, Interim President
Web address: www.integris–health.com

LAKESIDE WOMEN'S HOSPITAL (O, 23 beds) 11200 North Portland Avenue, Oklahoma City, OK Zip 73120–5045; tel. 405/936–1500; Kelley Brewer, R.N., MSN, President
Web address: www.lakeside–wh.net

Owned, leased, sponsored:	8 hospitals	1386 beds
Contract–managed:	0 hospitals	0 beds
Totals:	8 hospitals	1386 beds

★1815: INTERMOUNTAIN HEALTHCARE, INC. (NP)
36 South State Street, 22nd Floor, Salt Lake City, UT Zip 84111–1453; tel. 801/442–2000; Charles W. Sorenson, Jr., M.D., President and Chief Executive Officer
(Moderately Centralized Health System)

IDAHO: CASSIA REGIONAL MEDICAL CENTER (O, 25 beds) 1501 Hiland Avenue, Burley, ID Zip 83318–2688; tel. 208/678–4444; Rod Barton, Administrator
Web address: www.cassiaregional.org

UTAH: ALTA VIEW HOSPITAL (O, 69 beds) 9660 South 1300 East, Sandy, UT Zip 84094–3793; tel. 801/501–2600; Bryan L. Johnson, Administrator
Web address: www.intermountainhealthcare.org

AMERICAN FORK HOSPITAL (O, 90 beds) 170 North 1100 East, American Fork, UT Zip 84003–2096; tel. 801/855–3300; Jason Wilson, Administrator and Chief Executive Officer
Web address: www.intermountainhealthcare.org

BEAR RIVER VALLEY HOSPITAL (O, 14 beds) 905 North 1000 West, Tremonton, UT Zip 84337–2497; tel. 435/207–4500; Ben Smalley, Chief Executive Officer
Web address: www.https://intermountainhealthcare. org/locations/bear–river–valley–hospital/

CEDAR CITY HOSPITAL (O, 48 beds) 1303 North Main Street, Cedar City, UT Zip 84721–9746; tel. 435/868–5000; Eric Packer, Chief Executive Officer
Web address: www.https://intermountainhealthcare. org/locations/cedar–city–hospital/

DELTA COMMUNITY MEDICAL CENTER (O, 18 beds) 126 South White Sage Avenue, Delta, UT Zip 84624–8937; tel. 435/864–5591; Lenny Lyons, Administrator
Web address: www.ihc.com

For explanation of codes following names, see page B2.
★ Indicates Type III membership in the American Hospital Association.

DIXIE REGIONAL MEDICAL CENTER (O, 261 beds) 1380 East Medical Center Drive, Saint George, UT Zip 84790–2123; tel. 435/251–1000; Terri Kane, Chief Executive Officer
Web address: www.intermountainhealthcare.org

FILLMORE COMMUNITY MEDICAL CENTER (O, 19 beds) 674 South Highway 99, Fillmore, UT Zip 84631–5013; tel. 435/743–5591; Lenny Lyons, Administrator
Web address: www.ihc.com

GARFIELD MEMORIAL HOSPITAL AND CLINICS (C, 41 beds) 200 North 400 East, Panguitch, UT Zip 84759, Mailing Address: P.O. Box 389, Zip 84759–0389; tel. 435/676–8811; Alberto Vasquez, Administrator
Web address: www.ihc.com/hospitals/garfield

HEBER VALLEY MEDICAL CENTER (O, 19 beds) 1485 South Highway 40, Heber City, UT Zip 84032–3522; tel. 435/654–2500; Shawn Morrow, Administrator
Web address: www.intermountainhealthcare.org

INTERMOUNTAIN MEDICAL CENTER (O, 468 beds) 5121 South Cottonwood Street, Murray, UT Zip 84107–5701; tel. 801/507–7000; Moody Chisholm, Regional Vice President
Web address: www.intermountainhealthcare.org

LDS HOSPITAL (O, 262 beds) Eighth Avenue and C Street, Salt Lake City, UT Zip 84143–0001; tel. 801/408–1100; Jim Sheets, Chief Executive Officer and Administrator
Web address: www.intermountainhealthcare.org

LOGAN REGIONAL HOSPITAL (O, 139 beds) 1400 North 500 East, Logan, UT Zip 84341–2455; tel. 435/716–1000; Kyle A. Hansen, Chief Executive Officer
Web address: www.loganregionalhospital.org

MCKAY–DEE HOSPITAL CENTER (O, 312 beds) 4401 Harrison Boulevard, Ogden, UT Zip 84403–3195; tel. 801/387–2800; Michael A. Clark, Administrator
Web address: www.mckay–dee.org

OREM COMMUNITY HOSPITAL (O, 18 beds) 331 North 400 West, Orem, UT Zip 84057–1999; tel. 801/224–4080; J. Francis Gibson, Administrator and Chief Executive Officer
Web address: www.intermountainhealthcare.org

PARK CITY MEDICAL CENTER (O, 37 beds) 900 Round Valley Drive, Park City, UT Zip 84060–7552; tel. 435/658–7000; Si William Hutt, Administrator
Web address: www.intermountainhealthcare.org

PRIMARY CHILDREN'S HOSPITAL (O, 289 beds) 100 North Mario Capecchi Drive, Salt Lake City, UT Zip 84113–1100; tel. 801/662–1000; Katy Welkie, MBA, R.N., Chief Executive Officer
Web address: www.intermountainhealthcare.org

RIVERTON HOSPITAL (O, 92 beds) 3741 West 12600 South, Riverton, UT Zip 84065–7215; tel. 801/285–4000; Blair Kent, Administrator
Web address: www.intermountainhealthcare.org/

SANPETE VALLEY HOSPITAL (O, 19 beds) 1100 South Medical Drive, Mount Pleasant, UT Zip 84647–2222; tel. 435/462–2441; Aaron C. Wood, Chief Executive Officer and Administrator
Web address: www.intermountainhealthcare.com

SEVIER VALLEY MEDICAL CENTER (O, 29 beds) 1000 North Main Street, Richfield, UT Zip 84701–1857; tel. 435/893–4100; Gary E. Beck, Administrator
Web address: www.sevierhospital.org

THE ORTHOPEDIC SPECIALTY HOSPITAL (O, 40 beds) 5848 South 300 East, Murray, UT Zip 84107–6121; tel. 801/314–4100; Barbara Ohm, Administrator
Web address: www.intermountainhealthcare.org

UTAH VALLEY REGIONAL MEDICAL CENTER (O, 344 beds) 1034 North 500 West, Provo, UT Zip 84604–3337; tel. 801/357–7850; Steve Smoot, Administrator
Web address: www.utahvalleyregional.org

Owned, leased, sponsored:	21 hospitals	2612 beds
Contract–managed:	1 hospital	41 beds
Totals:	22 hospitals	2653 beds

★**0902: IOWA SPECIALTY HOSPITALS** (NP)
1316 South Main Street, Clarion, IA Zip 50525–2019; tel. 515/532–2811; Steven J. Simonin, Chief Executive Officer
(Independent Hospital System)

IOWA: IOWA SPECIALTY HOSPITAL–BELMOND (C, 22 beds) 403 1st Street S.E., Belmond, IA Zip 50421–1201; tel. 641/444–3223; Amy McDaniel, Administrator and Chief Executive Officer
Web address: www.iowaspecialtyhospital.com

IOWA SPECIALTY HOSPITAL–CLARION (C, 25 beds) 1316 South Main Street, Clarion, IA Zip 50525–2019; tel. 515/532–2811; Steven J. Simonin, Chief Executive Officer
Web address: www.iowaspecialtyhospital.com

Owned, leased, sponsored:	0 hospitals	0 beds
Contract–managed:	2 hospitals	47 beds
Totals:	2 hospitals	47 beds

★**7775: JEFFERSON HEALTH** (NP)
259 Radnor–Chester Road, Suite 290, Radnor, PA Zip 19087–5288, Mailing Address: 111 South 11th Street, Philadelphia, Zip 19107; tel. 610/225–6200; Stephen K. Klasko, M.D., Chief Executive Officer
(Centralized Health System)

PENNSYLVANIA: ABINGTON HOSPITAL (O, 618 beds) 1200 Old York Road, Abington, PA Zip 19001–3720; tel. 215/481–2000; Margaret M. McGoldrick, President
Web address: www.abingtonhealth.org

ABINGTON–LANSDALE HOSPITAL JEFFERSON HEALTH (O, 140 beds) 100 Medical Campus Drive, Lansdale, PA Zip 19446–1200; tel. 215/368–2100; Gary R. Candia, Ph.D., FACHE, Chief Administrative Officer
Web address: www.abingtonhealth. org/find–a–location/abington–lansdale–hospital/#.V5dyVVL9yk4

ARIA – JEFFERSON HEALTH (O, 480 beds) 10800 Knights Road, Philadelphia, PA Zip 19114–4200; tel. 215/612–4101; Kathleen Kinslow, Ed.D., Chief Executive Officer
Web address: www.ariahealth.org

THOMAS JEFFERSON UNIVERSITY HOSPITALS (O, 893 beds) 111 South 11th Street, Philadelphia, PA Zip 19107–5084; tel. 215/955–6000; Richard Webster, R.N., President
Web address: www.jefferson.edu

Owned, leased, sponsored:	4 hospitals	2131 beds
Contract–managed:	0 hospitals	0 beds
Totals:	4 hospitals	2131 beds

★**8855: JFK HEALTH** (NP)
80 James Street, 2nd Floor, Edison, NJ Zip 08820–3938; tel. 732/632–1503; Raymond F. Fredericks, President and Chief Executive Officer

NEW JERSEY: JFK JOHNSON REHABILITATION INSTITUTE (O, 94 beds) 65 James Street, Edison, NJ Zip 08818; tel. 732/321–7050; Anthony Cuzzola, Vice President Administrator
Web address: www.njrehab.org

JFK MEDICAL CENTER (O, 334 beds) 65 James Street, Edison, NJ Zip 08818; tel. 732/321–7000; Raymond F. Fredericks, President and CEO
Web address: www.jfkmc.org

Owned, leased, sponsored:	2 hospitals	428 beds
Contract–managed:	0 hospitals	0 beds
Totals:	2 hospitals	428 beds

★**0324: JOHN MUIR HEALTH** (NP)
1400 Treat Boulevard, Walnut Creek, CA Zip 94597–2142; tel. 925/941–2100; Calvin K. Knight, President and Chief Executive Officer
(Independent Hospital System)

CALIFORNIA: JOHN MUIR BEHAVIORAL HEALTH CENTER (O, 73 beds) 2740 Grant Street, Concord, CA Zip 94520–2265; tel. 925/674–4100; Cindy Bolter, Chief Nursing and Operations Officer
Web address: www.johnmuirhealth.com

JOHN MUIR MEDICAL CENTER, CONCORD (O, 195 beds) 2540 East Street, Concord, CA Zip 94520–1906; tel. 925/682–8200; Michael S. Thomas, President and Chief Administrative Officer
Web address: www.johnmuirhealth.com

For explanation of codes following names, see page B2.
★ Indicates Type III membership in the American Hospital Association.

JOHN MUIR MEDICAL CENTER, WALNUT CREEK (O, 405 beds) 1601 Ygnacio Valley Road, Walnut Creek, CA Zip 94598–3194; tel. 925/939–3000; Jane Willemsen, President and Chief Administrative Officer
Web address: www.https://www.johnmuirhealth.com/

Owned, leased, sponsored:	3 hospitals	673 beds
Contract–managed:	0 hospitals	0 beds
Totals:	3 hospitals	673 beds

★**1015: JOHNS HOPKINS HEALTH SYSTEM** (NP)
733 North Broadway, BRB 104, Baltimore, MD Zip 21205–1832; tel. 410/955–5000; Ronald R. Peterson, President
(Centralized Physician/Insurance Health System)

DISTRICT OF COLUMBIA: SIBLEY MEMORIAL HOSPITAL (O, 246 beds) 5255 Loughboro Road N.W., Washington, DC Zip 20016–2633; tel. 202/537–4000; Richard O. Davis, Ph.D., President
Web address: www.sibley.org

FLORIDA: JOHNS HOPKINS ALL CHILDREN'S HOSPITAL (O, 259 beds) 501 6th Avenue South, Saint Petersburg, FL Zip 33701–4634; tel. 727/898–7451; Jonathan M. Ellen, M.D., President
Web address: www.allkids.org

MARYLAND: HOWARD COUNTY GENERAL HOSPITAL (O, 256 beds) 5755 Cedar Lane, Columbia, MD Zip 21044–2999; tel. 410/740–7890; Steven C. Snelgrove, President
Web address: www.hcgh.org

JOHNS HOPKINS BAYVIEW MEDICAL CENTER (O, 421 beds) 4940 Eastern Avenue, Baltimore, MD Zip 21224–2780; tel. 410/550–0100; Richard G. Bennett, M.D., President
Web address: www.hopkinsbayview.org

JOHNS HOPKINS HOSPITAL (O, 977 beds) 733 North Broadway MRB 104, Baltimore, MD Zip 21205–1832; tel. 410/955–5000; Redonda G. Miller, M.D., President
Web address: www.hopkinsmedicine.org

SUBURBAN HOSPITAL (O, 236 beds) 8600 Old Georgetown Road, Bethesda, MD Zip 20814–1497; tel. 301/896–3100; Jacky Schultz, R.N., MSN, Interim President
Web address: www.suburbanhospital.org

Owned, leased, sponsored:	6 hospitals	2395 beds
Contract–managed:	0 hospitals	0 beds
Totals:	6 hospitals	2395 beds

★**2105: KAISER FOUNDATION HOSPITALS** (NP)
One Kaiser Plaza, Oakland, CA Zip 94612–3600; tel. 510/271–5910; Bernard J. Tyson, Chairman and Chief Executive Officer
(Decentralized Health System)

CALIFORNIA: FREMONT MEDICAL CENTER (O, 106 beds) 39400 Paseo Padre Parkway, Fremont, CA Zip 94538–2310; tel. 510/248–3000; Victoria O'Gorman, Administrator
Web address: www.kp.org

KAISER PERMANENTE ANTIOCH MEDICAL CENTER (O, 150 beds) 4501 Sand Creek Road, Antioch, CA Zip 94531–8687; tel. 925/813–6500; Colleen McKeown, Senior Vice President and Area Manager
Web address: www.https://health.kaiserpermanente.org/wps/portal/facility/100382

KAISER PERMANENTE BALDWIN PARK MEDICAL CENTER (O, 257 beds) 1011 Baldwin Park Boulevard, Baldwin Park, CA Zip 91706–5806; tel. 626/851–1011; Margaret H. Pierce, Executive Director
Web address: www.kp.org

KAISER PERMANENTE DOWNEY MEDICAL CENTER (O, 342 beds) 9333 Imperial Highway, Downey, CA Zip 90242–2812; tel. 562/657–9000; James Branchick, R.N., MS, Executive Director
Web address: www.kaiserpermanente.org

KAISER PERMANENTE FONTANA MEDICAL CENTER (O, 490 beds) 9961 Sierra Avenue, Fontana, CA Zip 92335–6794; tel. 909/427–5000; Greg Christian, Executive Director
Web address: www.kaiserpermanente.org

KAISER PERMANENTE FRESNO MEDICAL CENTER (O, 169 beds) 7300 North Fresno Street, Fresno, CA Zip 93720–2942; tel. 559/448–4500; Debbie Hemker, Senior Vice President and Area Manager
Web address: www.kaiserpermanente.org

KAISER PERMANENTE LOS ANGELES MEDICAL CENTER (O, 528 beds) 4867 Sunset Boulevard, Los Angeles, CA Zip 90027–5961; tel. 323/783–4011; William N. Grice, Executive Director
Web address: www.kaiserpermanente.org

KAISER PERMANENTE MANTECA MEDICAL CENTER (O, 239 beds) 1777 West Yosemite Avenue, Manteca, CA Zip 95337–5187; tel. 209/825–3700; Deborah G. Friberg, Senior Vice President and Area Manager
Web address: www.kaiserpermanente.org

KAISER PERMANENTE MORENO VALLEY MEDICAL CENTER (O, 71 beds) 27300 Iris Avenue, Moreno Valley, CA Zip 92555–4800; tel. 951/243–0811; Vita M. Willett, Senior Vice President

KAISER PERMANENTE OAKLAND MEDICAL CENTER (O, 267 beds) 3600 Broadway, Oakland, CA Zip 94611–5693; tel. 510/752–1000; Mark Fratzke, R.N., Senior Vice President and Area Manager
Web address: www.kaiserpermanente.org

KAISER PERMANENTE ORANGE COUNTY ANAHEIM MEDICAL CENTER (O, 436 beds) 3440 East La Palma Avenue, Anaheim, CA Zip 92806–2020; tel. 714/644–2000; Mark E. Costa, Executive Director
Web address: www.kp.org

KAISER PERMANENTE PANORAMA CITY MEDICAL CENTER (O, 194 beds) 13652 Cantara Street, Panorama City, CA Zip 91402–5497; tel. 818/375–2000; Payman Roshan, Senior Vice President and Area Manager
Web address: www.kaiserpermanente.org

KAISER PERMANENTE REDWOOD CITY MEDICAL CENTER (O, 213 beds) 1100 Veterans Boulevard, Redwood City, CA Zip 94063–2087; tel. 650/299–2000; Michelle Gaskill-Hames, R.N., Senior Vice President & Area Manager
Web address: www.kaiserpermanente.org

KAISER PERMANENTE RIVERSIDE MEDICAL CENTER (O, 226 beds) 10800 Magnolia Avenue, Riverside, CA Zip 92505–3000; tel. 951/353–2000; Vita M. Willett, Executive Director
Web address: www.kaiserpermanente.org

KAISER PERMANENTE ROSEVILLE MEDICAL CENTER (O, 340 beds) 1600 Eureka Road, Roseville, CA Zip 95661–3027; tel. 916/784–4000; Jeffrey A. Collins, M.D., Senior Vice President and Area Manager
Web address: www.kp.org

KAISER PERMANENTE SACRAMENTO MEDICAL CENTER (O, 287 beds) 2025 Morse Avenue, Sacramento, CA Zip 95825–2100; tel. 916/973–5000; Sandy Sharon, Senior Vice President and Area Manager
Web address: www.kp.org

KAISER PERMANENTE SAN DIEGO MEDICAL CENTER (O, 414 beds) 4647 Zion Avenue, San Diego, CA Zip 92120–2507; tel. 619/528–5000; Jane Finley, Senior Vice President & Area Manager
Web address: www.kaiserpermanente.org

KAISER PERMANENTE SAN FRANCISCO MEDICAL CENTER (O, 215 beds) 2425 Geary Boulevard, San Francisco, CA Zip 94115–3358; tel. 415/833–2000; Ronald Groepper, Senior Vice President and Area Manager
Web address: www.kaiserpermanente.org

KAISER PERMANENTE SAN JOSE MEDICAL CENTER (O, 222 beds) 250 Hospital Parkway, San Jose, CA Zip 95119–1199; tel. 408/972–7000; Irene Chavez, Senior Vice President and Area Manager
Web address: www.kaiserpermanente.org

KAISER PERMANENTE SAN LEANDRO MEDICAL CENTER (O, 264 beds) 2500 Merced Street, San Leandro, CA Zip 94577–4201; tel. 510/454–1000; Thomas S. Hanenburg, Senior Vice President and Area Manager
Web address: www.kaiserpermanente.org

KAISER PERMANENTE SAN RAFAEL MEDICAL CENTER (O, 116 beds) 99 Montecillo Road, San Rafael, CA Zip 94903–3397; tel. 415/444–2000; Judy Coffey, R.N., Senior Vice President and Area Manager
Web address: www.kaiserpermanente.org

KAISER PERMANENTE SANTA CLARA MEDICAL CENTER (O, 327 beds) 700 Lawrence Expressway, Santa Clara, CA Zip 95051–5173; tel. 408/851–1000; Christopher L. Boyd, Senior Vice President and Area Manager
Web address: www.kaiserpermanente.org

For explanation of codes following names, see page B2.
★ Indicates Type III membership in the American Hospital Association.

KAISER PERMANENTE SANTA ROSA MEDICAL CENTER (O, 117 beds) 401 Bicentennial Way, Santa Rosa, CA Zip 95403–2192; tel. 707/571–4000; Judy Coffey, R.N., Senior Vice President and Area Manager
Web address: www.kaiserpermanente.org

KAISER PERMANENTE SOUTH BAY MEDICAL CENTER (O, 225 beds) 25825 Vermont Avenue, Harbor City, CA Zip 90710–3599; tel. 310/325–5111; Lesley A. Wille, Executive Director
Web address: www.kaiserpermanente.org

KAISER PERMANENTE SOUTH SACRAMENTO MEDICAL CENTER (O, 181 beds) 6600 Bruceville Road, Sacramento, CA Zip 95823–4691; tel. 916/688–2430; Patricia M. Rodriguez, Senior Vice President and Area Manager
Web address: www.kp.org

KAISER PERMANENTE SOUTH SAN FRANCISCO (O, 120 beds) 1200 El Camino Real, South San Francisco, CA Zip 94080–3208; tel. 650/742–2000; Ronald Groepper, Senior Vice President and Area Manager
Web address: www.kaiserpermanente.org

KAISER PERMANENTE VACAVILLE MEDICAL CENTER (O, 140 beds) 1 Quality Drive, Vacaville, CA Zip 95688–9494; tel. 707/624–4000; Joseph M. Mark, Interim Chief Executive Officer
Web address: www.kp.org

KAISER PERMANENTE VALLEJO MEDICAL CENTER (O, 248 beds) 975 Sereno Drive, Vallejo, CA Zip 94589–2441; tel. 707/651–1000; Corwin N. Harper, Senior Vice President and Area Manager
Web address: www.kaiserpermanente.org

KAISER PERMANENTE WALNUT CREEK MEDICAL CENTER (O, 233 beds) 1425 South Main Street, Walnut Creek, CA Zip 94596–5300; tel. 925/295–4000; Colleen McKeown, Senior Vice President and Area Manager
Web address: www.kaiserpermanente.org

KAISER PERMANENTE WEST LOS ANGELES MEDICAL CENTER (O, 133 beds) 6041 Cadillac Avenue, Los Angeles, CA Zip 90034–1700; tel. 323/857–2201; Georgina R. Garcia, R.N., Executive Director
Web address: www.kaiserpermanente.org

KAISER PERMANENTE WOODLAND HILLS MEDICAL CENTER (O, 128 beds) 5601 DeSoto Avenue, Woodland Hills, CA Zip 91367–6798; tel. 818/719–2000; Dennis C. Benton, Senior Vice President and Area Manager
Web address: www.kaiserpermanente.org

HAWAII: KAISER PERMANENTE MEDICAL CENTER (O, 235 beds) 3288 Moanalua Road, Honolulu, HI Zip 96819–1469; tel. 808/432–0000; Linda Puu, Hospital Administrator
Web address: www.kaiserpermanente.org

OREGON: KAISER FOUNDATION HOSPITAL WESTSIDE MEDICAL CENTER (O, 122 beds) 2875 N.W. Stucki Avenue, Hillsboro, OR Zip 97124–5806; tel. 971/310–1000; Brantley Dettmer, Administrator and Chief Operating Officer
Web address: www.kp.org

KAISER PERMANENTE SUNNYSIDE MEDICAL CENTER (O, 302 beds) 10180 S.E. Sunnyside Road, Clackamas, OR Zip 97015–8970; tel. 503/652–2880; Justin N. Evander, Administrator and Chief Operating Officer
Web address: www.kaiserpermanente.org

Owned, leased, sponsored:	34 hospitals	8057 beds
Contract–managed:	0 hospitals	0 beds
Totals:	34 hospitals	8057 beds

0954: KECK MEDICINE OF USC (NP)
1500 San Pablo Street, Los Angeles, CA Zip 90033–5313; tel. 323/442–8500; Paul A. Craig, R.N., JD, Interim Chief Executive Officer
(Independent Hospital System)

CALIFORNIA: KECK HOSPITAL OF USC (O, 316 beds) 1500 San Pablo Street, Los Angeles, CA Zip 90033–5313; tel. 323/442–8500; Rodney B. Hanners, Chief Executive Officer
Web address: www.keckhospitalofusc.org

USC NORRIS COMPREHENSIVE CANCER CENTER (O, 60 beds) 1441 Eastlake Avenue, Los Angeles, CA Zip 90089–0112; tel. 323/865–3000; Rodney B. Hanners, Chief Executive Officer
Web address: www.uscnorriscancerhospital.org

USC VERDUGO HILLS HOSPITAL (O, 81 beds) 1812 Verdugo Boulevard, Glendale, CA Zip 91208–1409; tel. 818/790–7100; Keith Hobbs, Chief Executive Officer
Web address: www.uscvhh.org

Owned, leased, sponsored:	3 hospitals	457 beds
Contract–managed:	0 hospitals	0 beds
Totals:	3 hospitals	457 beds

★0258: KETTERING HEALTH NETWORK (NP)
3965 Southern Boulevard, Dayton, OH Zip 45429–1229; tel. 937/395–8150; Fred M. Manchur, Chief Executive Officer
(Independent Hospital System)

OHIO: FORT HAMILTON HOSPITAL (O, 166 beds) 630 Eaton Avenue, Hamilton, OH Zip 45013–2770; tel. 513/867–2000; Michael Mewhirter, President
Web address: www.khnetwork.org/forthamilton

GRANDVIEW MEDICAL CENTER (O, 277 beds) 405 West Grand Avenue, Dayton, OH Zip 45405–4796; tel. 937/723–3200; Russell J. Wetherell, President
Web address: www.ketteringhealth.org/grandview/

GREENE MEMORIAL HOSPITAL (O, 49 beds) 1141 North Monroe Drive, Xenia, OH Zip 45385–1600; tel. 937/352–2000; Rick A. Dodds, President
Web address: www.ketteringhealth.org/greene

KETTERING MEDICAL CENTER (O, 395 beds) 3535 Southern Boulevard, Kettering, OH Zip 45429–1221; tel. 937/298–4331; Roy G. Chew, Ph.D., President
Web address: www.ketteringhealth.org/kettering

SOIN MEDICAL CENTER (O, 101 beds) 3535 Pentagon Boulevard, Beavercreek, OH Zip 45431–1705; tel. 937/702–4000; Rick A. Dodds, President
Web address: www.khnetwork.org/soin

SYCAMORE MEDICAL CENTER (O, 168 beds) 4000 Miamisburg–Centerville Road, Miamisburg, OH Zip 45342–7615; tel. 937/866–0551; Walter Sackett, President
Web address: www.khnetwork.org/sycamore

Owned, leased, sponsored:	6 hospitals	1156 beds
Contract–managed:	0 hospitals	0 beds
Totals:	6 hospitals	1156 beds

★0026: KINDRED HEALTHCARE (IO)
680 South Fourth Street, Louisville, KY Zip 40202–2412; tel. 502/596–7300; Kent Wallace, Chief Operating Officer
(Independent Hospital System)

CALIFORNIA: KINDRED HOSPITAL RANCHO (O, 55 beds) 10841 White Oak Avenue, Rancho Cucamonga, CA Zip 91730–3811; tel. 909/581–6400; Victor Carrasco, Chief Executive Officer
Web address: www.khrancho.com

KINDRED HOSPITAL RIVERSIDE (O, 40 beds) 2224 Medical Center Drive, Perris, CA Zip 92571–2638; tel. 951/436–3535; Jonathan Jean–Marie, Administrator and Chief Executive Officer
Web address: www.khriverside.com

KINDRED HOSPITAL SOUTH BAY (O, 84 beds) 1246 West 155th Street, Gardena, CA Zip 90247–4062; tel. 310/323–5330; Isaac Lin, Chief Executive Officer
Web address: www.khsouthbay.com/

KINDRED HOSPITAL–BALDWIN PARK (C, 91 beds) 14148 Francisquito Avenue, Baldwin Park, CA Zip 91706–6120; tel. 626/388–2700; Fiona Basa–Reyes, Chief Executive Officer
Web address: www.khbaldwinpark.com

KINDRED HOSPITAL–BREA (O, 48 beds) 875 North Brea Boulevard, Brea, CA Zip 92821–2699; tel. 714/529–6842; Diane Zeoli, Chief Executive Officer
Web address: www.kindredhospitalbrea.com/

KINDRED HOSPITAL–LA MIRADA (O, 216 beds) 14900 East Imperial Highway, La Mirada, CA Zip 90638–2172; tel. 562/944–1900; David Kowalski, Chief Executive Officer
Web address: www.kindredlamirada.com/

For explanation of codes following names, see page B2.
★ Indicates Type III membership in the American Hospital Association.

KINDRED HOSPITAL–LOS ANGELES (O, 81 beds) 5525 West Slauson Avenue, Los Angeles, CA Zip 90056–1067; tel. 310/642–0325; Phillip R. Wolfe, Chief Executive Officer
Web address: www.kindredhospitalla.com/

KINDRED HOSPITAL–ONTARIO (O, 81 beds) 550 North Monterey Avenue, Ontario, CA Zip 91764–3399; tel. 909/391–0333; Vincent Trac, Chief Executive Officer
Web address: www.khontario.com/

KINDRED HOSPITAL–SAN DIEGO (O, 70 beds) 1940 El Cajon Boulevard, San Diego, CA Zip 92104–1096; tel. 619/543–4500; Natalie Germuska, R.N., MSN, Market Chief Executive Officer
Web address: www.kindredsandiego.com

KINDRED HOSPITAL–SAN FRANCISCO BAY AREA (O, 78 beds) 2800 Benedict Drive, San Leandro, CA Zip 94577–6840; tel. 510/357–8300; Jacob M. McCarty, Chief Executive Officer
Web address: www.kindredhospitalsfba.com

KINDRED HOSPITAL–WESTMINSTER (O, 99 beds) 200 Hospital Circle, Westminster, CA Zip 92683–3910; tel. 714/893–4541; Scott Rifkin, Chief Executive Officer
Web address: www.khwestminster.com/

COLORADO: KINDRED HOSPITAL COLORADO SPRINGS (O, 30 beds) 6001 East Woodmen Road, 6th Floor, Colorado Springs, CO Zip 80923–2601; tel. 719/571–6000; Dawn Johantges, Chief Executive Officer
Web address: www.kindredcoloradosprings.com/

KINDRED HOSPITAL–AURORA (O, 37 beds) 700 Potomac Street 2nd Floor, Aurora, CO Zip 80011–6844; tel. 720/857–8333; Marc Lemon, Marketing Chief Executive Officer
Web address: www.khaurora.com/

KINDRED HOSPITAL–DENVER (O, 68 beds) 1920 High Street, Denver, CO Zip 80218–1213; tel. 303/320–5871; ,
Web address: www.kh–denver.com

KINDRED HOSPITAL–DENVER (O, 68 beds) 1719 East 19th Avenue, 5B, Denver, CO Zip 80218–1235; tel. 303/320–5871; George Welton, Chief Executive Officer
Web Address: www.kh-denver.com

KINDRED HOSPITAL DENVER South (O, 28 beds) 2525 South Downing, Street, 3 South, Denver, CO Zip 80210–5817; tel. 303/715–7373; George Welton, Chief Executive Officer
Web Address: www.kindreddenversouth.com

FLORIDA: KINDRED HOSPITAL BAY AREA–TAMPA (O, 73 beds) 4555 South Manhattan Avenue, Tampa, FL Zip 33611–2397; tel. 813/839–6341; Suthanthira M. Ratnasamy, R.N., FACHE, Chief Executive Officer
Web address: www.khtampa.com/

KINDRED HOSPITAL CENTRAL TAMPA (O, 96 beds) 4801 North Howard Avenue, Tampa, FL Zip 33603–1411; tel. 813/874–7575; Ralph Selner, Chief Executive Officer
Web address: www.kindredcentraltampa.com/

KINDRED HOSPITAL MELBOURNE (O, 60 beds) 765 West Nasa Boulevard, Melbourne, FL Zip 32901–1815; tel. 321/733–5725; Pamela R. Reed, Chief Executive Officer
Web address: www.khmelbourne.com

KINDRED HOSPITAL NORTH FLORIDA (O, 80 beds) 801 Oak Street, Green Cove Springs, FL Zip 32043–4317; tel. 904/284–9230; Susan Drago, R.N., Chief Executive Officer
Web address: www.khnorthflorida.com

KINDRED HOSPITAL OCALA (O, 31 beds) 1500 S.W. 1st Avenue, Ocala, FL Zip 34471–6504; tel. 352/369–0513; Merlene Bhoorasingh, Administrator
Web address: www.kindredocala.com/

KINDRED HOSPITAL SOUTH FLORIDA–FORT LAUDERDALE (O, 123 beds) 1516 East Las Olas Boulevard, Fort Lauderdale, FL Zip 33301–2399; tel. 954/764–8900; Michael S. Roffelsen, Chief Executive Officer
Web address: www.khfortlauderdale.com

KINDRED HOSPITAL THE PALM BEACHES (O, 70 beds) 5555 West Blue Heron Boulevard, Riviera Beach, FL Zip 33418–7813; tel. 561/840–0754; Mark Twilla, Chief Executive Officer
Web address: www.khthepalmbeaches.com/

GEORGIA: KINDRED HOSPITAL ROME (O, 45 beds) 304 Turner McCall Boulevard, Rome, GA Zip 30165–5621; tel. 706/378–6800; Al Diaz, M.D., Chief Executive Officer
Web address: www.kindredrome.com

ILLINOIS: KINDRED CHICAGO–CENTRAL HOSPITAL (O, 54 beds) 4058 West Melrose Street, Chicago, IL Zip 60641–4797; tel. 773/736–7000; Jonathan Cohee, Chief Executive Officer
Web address: www.khchicagocentral.com

KINDRED HOSPITAL CHICAGO–NORTHLAKE (O, 94 beds) 365 East North Avenue, Northlake, IL Zip 60164–2628; tel. 708/345–8100; Beverly Foster, Chief Executive Officer
Web address: www.kindrednorthlake.com

KINDRED HOSPITAL PEORIA (O, 50 beds) 500 West Romeo B. Garrett Avenue, Peoria, IL Zip 61605–2301; tel. 309/680–1500; Ted Paarlberg, Chief Executive Officer
Web address: www.khpeoria.com/

KINDRED HOSPITAL–SYCAMORE (O, 69 beds) 225 Edward Street, Sycamore, IL Zip 60178–2137; tel. 815/895–2144; Jim Cohick, Chief Executive Officer
Web address: www.kindredhospitalsyc.com/

INDIANA: KINDRED HOSPITAL INDIANAPOLIS SOUTH (O, 60 beds) 607 Greenwood Springs Drive, Greenwood, IN Zip 46143–6377; tel. 317/888–8155; Matthew Keppler, Market Chief Executive Officer
Web address: www.khindysouth.com/

KINDRED HOSPITAL INDIANAPOLIS NORTH (O , 45 beds) 8060 Knue Road, Indianapolis, IN Zip 46250–1976; Rick Ament, Chief Executive Officer
Web Address: www.kindredindynorth.com

KINDRED HOSPITAL NORTHWEST INDIANA (O, 70 beds) 5454 Hohman Avenue, 5th Floor, Hammond, IN Zip 46320–1931; tel. 219/937–9900; Frank A. Solare, Chief Executive Officer
Web address: www.khnwindiana.com

KINDRED HOSPITAL OF NORTHERN INDIANA (O, 32 beds) 215 West Fourth Street, Suite 200, Mishawaka, IN Zip 46544–1917; tel. 574/252–2000; Lori Skora, Chief Executive Officer
Web address: www.khnorthernindiana.com/

KINDRED HOSPITAL–INDIANAPOLIS (O, 59 beds) 1700 West 10th Street, Indianapolis, IN Zip 46222–3802; tel. 317/636–4400; Bryan Chatterton, Chief Executive Officer
Web address: www.kindredhospitalindy.com/

KENTUCKY: KINDRED HOSPITAL–LOUISVILLE (O, 164 beds) 1313 Saint Anthony Place, Louisville, KY Zip 40204–1740; tel. 502/587–7001; Wayne D. Blanchard, Chief Executive Officer
Web address: www.kindredlouisville.com/

MICHIGAN: KINDRED HOSPITAL DETROIT (O, 77 beds) 4777 East Outer Drive, Detroit, MI Zip 48234–3241; tel. 313/369–5800; Mary Hoskins, Chief Executive Officer
Web address: www.kindreddetroit.com/

MISSOURI: KINDRED HOSPITAL KANSAS CITY (O, 130 beds) 8701 Troost Avenue, Kansas City, MO Zip 64131–2767; tel. 816/995–2000; Alexander Gill, Chief Executive Officer
Web address: www.kindredhospitalkc.com

KINDRED HOSPITAL NORTHLAND (O, 35 beds) 500 Northwest 68th Street, Kansas City, MO Zip 64118–2455; tel. 816/420–6300; Jason Grundstrom, Chief Executive Officer
Web address: www.khnorthland.com

KINDRED HOSPITAL–ST. LOUIS (O, 98 beds) 4930 Lindell Boulevard, Saint Louis, MO Zip 63108–1510; tel. 314/361–8700; Stephanie Bridges, Chief Executive Officer
Web address: www.kindredstlouis.com/

KINDRED HOSPITAL–ST. LOUIS AT MERCY (O, 53 beds) 615 South New Ballas Road, 7th Floor, Saint Louis, MO Zip 63141–8221; tel. 314/567–4326; Robert S. Adcock, Chief Executive Officer
Web address: www.kindredstlouismercy.com

MERCY REHABILITATION HOSPITAL (O, 90 beds) 14561 North Outer Forty Road, Chesterfield, MO Zip 63017; tel. 314/881–4000; Donna M. Flannery, Chief Executive Officer
Web address: www.stjohnsmercyrehab.com

NEVADA: KINDRED HOSPITAL LAS VEGAS–SAHARA (O, 238 beds) 5110 West Sahara Avenue, Las Vegas, NV Zip 89146–3406; tel. 702/871–1418; Doug McCoy, Chief Executive Officer
Web address: www.kindredhospitallvs.com/

NEW JERSEY: KINDRED HOSPITAL–NEW JERSEY MORRIS COUNTY (O, 117 beds) 400 West Blackwell Street, Dover, NJ Zip 07801–2525; tel. 973/537–3818; Michael Pizzano, Chief Executive Officer
Web address: www.khmorriscounty.com/

Section B

For explanation of codes following names, see page B2.
★ Indicates Type III membership in the American Hospital Association.

NEW MEXICO: KINDRED HOSPITAL–ALBUQUERQUE (O, 61 beds) 700 High Street N.E., Albuquerque, NM Zip 87102–2565; tel. 505/242–4444; Bud Schawl, Chief Executive Officer
Web address: www.kindredalbuquerque.com/

NORTH CAROLINA: KINDRED HOSPITAL–GREENSBORO (O, 124 beds) 2401 Southside Boulevard, Greensboro, NC Zip 27406–3311; tel. 336/271–2800; Christopher Haynes, Chief Executive Officer
Web address: www.khgreensboro.com

OHIO: KINDRED HOSPITAL LIMA (O, 26 beds) 730 West Market Street, 6th Floor, Lima, OH Zip 45801–4602; tel. 419/224–1888; Susan Krinke, Chief Executive Officer
Web address: www.khlima.com

KINDRED HOSPITAL OF CENTRAL OHIO (O, 33 beds) 335 Glessner Avenue, 5th Floor, Mansfield, OH Zip 44903–2269; tel. 419/526–0777; Jeffrey Paul Weier, Chief Executive Officer
Web address: www.khcentralohio.com/

KINDRED HOSPITAL–DAYTON (O, 67 beds) 707 South Edwin C. Moses Boulevard, Dayton, OH Zip 45417–3462; tel. 937/222–5963; Lynn Schoen, Chief Executive Officer
Web address: www.khdayton.com

UH AVON REHABILITATION HOSPITAL (O, 50 beds) 37900 Chester Road, Avon, OH Zip 44011–1044; tel. 440/695–7100; Andrew Goldfrach, Chief Executive Officer
Web address: www.uhhospitals.org/uh–avon–rehabilitation–hospital

UH REHABILITATION HOSPITAL (O, 50 beds) 23333 Harvard Road, Beachwood, OH Zip 44122–6232; tel. 216/593–2200; Mirza Baig, M.D., Medical Director
Web address: www.uhhospitals.org

PENNSYLVANIA: KINDRED HOSPITAL SOUTH PHILADELPHIA (O, 58 beds) 1930 South Broad Street, Philadelphia, PA Zip 19145–2328; tel. 267/570–5200; Deborah Karn, Chief Executive Officer
Web address: www.khsouthphilly.com

KINDRED HOSPITAL–PHILADELPHIA (O, 57 beds) 6129 Palmetto Street, Philadelphia, PA Zip 19111–5729; tel. 215/722–8555; Sandra Larson, R.N., MSN, Chief Executive Officer
Web address: www.kindredphila.com/

TENNESSEE: KINDRED HOSPITAL–CHATTANOOGA (O, 44 beds) 709 Walnut Street, Chattanooga, TN Zip 37402–1916; tel. 423/266–7721; Steve Patterson, Chief Executive Officer
Web address: www.kindredchattanooga.com/

TEXAS: KINDRED HOSPITAL CLEAR LAKE (O, 147 beds) 350 Blossom Street, Webster, TX Zip 77598; tel. 281/316–7800; Mary Harbeson, R.N., Chief Executive Officer
Web address: www.khclearlake.com

KINDRED HOSPITAL DALLAS CENTRAL (O, 60 beds) 8050 Meadows Road, Dallas, TX Zip 75231–3406; tel. 469/232–6500; Kyron Kooken, Administrator
Web address: www.khdallascentral.com/

KINDRED HOSPITAL EL PASO (O, 72 beds) 1740 Curie Drive, El Paso, TX Zip 79902–2901; tel. 915/351–9044; ,
Web address: www.khelpaso.com

KINDRED HOSPITAL SUGAR LAND (O, 171 beds) 1550 First Colony Boulevard, Sugar Land, TX Zip 77479–4000; tel. 281/275–6000; John D. Cross, Chief Executive Officer
Web address: www.khsugarland.com

KINDRED HOSPITAL TARRANT COUNTY–ARLINGTON (O, 68 beds) 1000 North Cooper Street, Arlington, TX Zip 76011–5540; tel. 817/548–3400; Christina Richard, Market Chief Executive Officer
Web address: www.kindredhospitalarl.com/

KINDRED HOSPITAL TOMBALL (O, 75 beds) 505 Graham Drive, Tomball, TX Zip 77375–3368; tel. 281/255–5600; Tracy Kohler, Chief Executive Officer
Web address: www.khtomball.com/

KINDRED HOSPITAL–DALLAS (O, 50 beds) 9525 Greenville Avenue, Dallas, TX Zip 75243–4116; tel. 214/355–2600; James Mendez, Chief Executive Officer
Web address: www.khdallas.com

KINDRED HOSPITAL–FORT WORTH (O, 54 beds) 815 Eighth Avenue, Fort Worth, TX Zip 76104–2609; tel. 817/332–4812; Matthew Malinak, Chief Executive Officer
Web address: www.kindredfortworth.com/

KINDRED HOSPITAL–HOUSTON NORTHWEST (O, 84 beds) 11297 Fallbrook Drive, Houston, TX Zip 77065–4292; tel. 281/897–8114; Larkin Virden, Chief Executive Officer
Web address: www.khhoustonnw.com/

KINDRED HOSPITAL–MANSFIELD (O, 55 beds) 1802 Highway 157 North, Mansfield, TX Zip 76063–3923; tel. 817/473–6101; Jason Naranjo, Chief Executive Officer
Web address: www.kindredmansfield.com

KINDRED HOSPITAL–SAN ANTONIO (O, 59 beds) 3636 Medical Drive, San Antonio, TX Zip 78229–2183; tel. 210/616–0616; William Patton, Chief Executive Officer
Web address: www.khsanantonio.com/

KINDRED HOSPITAL SAN ANTONIO CENTRAL (O, 44 beds) 111 Dallas Street, 4th Floor, San Antonio, TX Zip 78205–1201; tel. 210/297–7185; Sean Stricker, Chief Executive Officer

KINDRED HOSPITAL TOWN AND COUNTRY (O, 65 beds) 1120 Business Center Drive, Houston, TX Zip 77043; tel. 713/932–2700; Randy Briones, Chief Executive Officer
Web Address: www.khtownandcountry.com

KINDRED HOSPITAL–WHITE ROCK (O, 25 beds) 9440 Poppy Drive, 5th Floor, Dallas, TX Zip 75218–3652; tel. 214/324–6562; Kelly Bailey, Chief Executive Officer and Administrator
Web address: www.khwhiterock.com

KINDRED HOSPITAL HOUSTON MEDICAL CENTER (O, 105 beds) 6441 Main Street, Houston, TX Zip 77030–1596; tel. 713/790–0500; Robert Stein, Chief Executive Officer
Web address: www.khhouston.com/

TEXAS REHABILITATION HOSPITAL OF FORT WORTH (O, 66 beds) 425 Alabama Avenue, Fort Worth, TX Zip 76104–1022; tel. 817/820–3400; Russell Bailey, Chief Executive Officer
Web address: www.texasrehabhospital.com/

WASHINGTON: KINDRED HOSPITAL SEATTLE–NORTHGATE (O, 80 beds) 10631 8th Avenue N.E., Seattle, WA Zip 98125–7213; tel. 206/364–2050; Jean Clark, Administrator
Web address: www.kindredhospitalseattle.com/

WISCONSIN: REHABILITATION HOSPITAL OF WISCONSIN (O, 40 beds) 1625 Coldwater Creek Drive, Waukesha, WI Zip 53188–8028; tel. 262/521–8800; Linda Newberry–Ferguson, Chief Executive Officer
Web address: www.rehabhospitalwi.com

Owned, leased, sponsored:	68 hospitals	4996 beds
Contract–managed:	1 hospital	91 beds
Totals:	69 hospitals	5087 beds

0333: KPC HEALTHCARE, INC. (IO)
1301 North Tustin Avenue, Santa Ana, CA Zip 92705–8619; tel. 714/953–3652; Suzanne Richards, R.N., M.P.H., FACHE, Chief Executive Officer
(Independent Hospital System)

CALIFORNIA: ANAHEIM GLOBAL MEDICAL CENTER (O, 181 beds) 1025 South Anaheim Boulevard, Anaheim, CA Zip 92805–5806; tel. 714/533–6220; Brian Cotter, Chief Executive Officer
Web address: www.westernmedanaheim.com

CHAPMAN GLOBAL MEDICAL CENTER (O, 100 beds) 2601 East Chapman Avenue, Orange, CA Zip 92869–3296; tel. 714/633–0011; Ronald J. Galonsky, Jr., Chief Executive Officer
Web address: www.Chapman–GMC.com

ORANGE COUNTY GLOBAL MEDICAL CENTER, INC. (O, 282 beds) 1001 North Tustin Avenue, Santa Ana, CA Zip 92705–3577; tel. 714/953–3500; Suzanne Richards, Chief Executive Officer
Web address: www.orangecounty–gmc.com

SOUTH COAST GLOBAL MEDICAL CENTER (O, 178 beds) 2701 South Bristol Street, Santa Ana, CA Zip 92704–6278; tel. 714/754–5454; Ronald J. Galonsky, Jr., Chief Executive Officer
Web address: www.SouthCoast–GMC.com

Owned, leased, sponsored:	4 hospitals	741 beds
Contract–managed:	0 hospitals	0 beds
Totals:	4 hospitals	741 beds

For explanation of codes following names, see page B2.
★ Indicates Type III membership in the American Hospital Association.

★**0904: L+M HEALTHCARE** (NP)
365 Montauk Avenue, New London, CT Zip 06320–4700;
tel. 860/442–0711; Bruce D. Cummings, President and Chief
Executive Officer
(Independent Hospital System)

CONNECTICUT: LAWRENCE + MEMORIAL HOSPITAL (O, 235 beds) 365
Montauk Avenue, New London, CT Zip 06320–4769; tel. 860/442–0711;
Bruce D. Cummings, President and Chief Executive Officer
Web address: www.lmhospital.org

RHODE ISLAND: WESTERLY HOSPITAL (O, 100 beds) 25 Wells Street,
Westerly, RI Zip 02891–2934; tel. 401/596–6000; Bruce D. Cummings,
President and Chief Executive Officer
Web address: www.westerlyhospital.org

Owned, leased, sponsored:	2 hospitals	335 beds
Contract–managed:	0 hospitals	0 beds
Totals:	2 hospitals	335 beds

0911: LAFAYETTE GENERAL HEALTH (NP)
1214 Coolidge Boulevard, Lafayette, LA Zip 70503–2621;
tel. 337/289–7991; David L. Callecod, President and Chief Executive
Officer
(Independent Hospital System)

LOUISIANA: ABROM KAPLAN MEMORIAL HOSPITAL (C, 35 beds) 1310 West
Seventh Street, Kaplan, LA Zip 70548–2910; tel. 337/643–8300; Bryce
Quebodeaux, Chief Executive Officer
Web address: www.lafayettegeneral.com

ACADIA GENERAL HOSPITAL (C, 178 beds) 1305 Crowley Rayne Highway,
Crowley, LA Zip 70526–8202; tel. 337/783–3222; Donald D. Trexler, Chief
Executive Officer
Web address: www.acadiageneral.com

LAFAYETTE GENERAL MEDICAL CENTER (O, 324 beds) 1214 Coolidge
Avenue, Lafayette, LA Zip 70503–2696, Mailing Address: P.O. Box 52009
OCS, Zip 70505–2009; tel. 337/289–7991; Patrick W. Gandy, CPA,
Executive Vice President and Chief Executive Officer
Web address: www.lafayettegeneral.com

LAFAYETTE GENERAL SURGICAL HOSPITAL (C, 10 beds) 1000 West Pinhook
Road, Lafayette, LA Zip 70503–2460; tel. 337/289–8088; Carrie E.
Templeton, FACHE, Chief Executive Officer
Web address: www.lgsh.us

ST. MARTIN HOSPITAL (C, 25 beds) 210 Champagne Boulevard, Breaux
Bridge, LA Zip 70517–3700, Mailing Address: P.O. Box 357,
Zip 70517–0357; tel. 337/332–2178; Karen Wyble, R.N., Chief Executive
Officer
Web address: www.stmartinhospital.org

UNIVERSITY HOSPITAL AND CLINICS (L, 100 beds) 2390 West Congress
Street, Lafayette, LA Zip 70506–4298; tel. 337/261–6000; Katherine D.
Hebert, Chief Executive Officer
Web address: www.lafayettegeneral.com

Owned, leased, sponsored:	2 hospitals	424 beds
Contract–managed:	4 hospitals	248 beds
Totals:	6 hospitals	672 beds

★**0891: LAHEY HEALTH** (NP)
41 Mall Road, Burlington, MA Zip 01805–0001; tel. 781/744–7100;
Howard R. Grant, JD, M.D., President and Chief Executive Officer
(Centralized Health System)

MASSACHUSETTS: BEVERLY HOSPITAL (O, 404 beds) 85 Herrick Street,
Beverly, MA Zip 01915–1777; tel. 978/922–3000; Philip M. Cormier,
Chief Executive Officer
Web address: www.beverlyhospital.org

LAHEY HOSPITAL & MEDICAL CENTER, BURLINGTON (O, 345 beds) 41 Mall
Road, Burlington, MA Zip 01805–0001; tel. 781/744–5100; Joanne Conroy,
M.D., Chief Executive Officer
Web address: www.lahey.org

WINCHESTER HOSPITAL (O, 197 beds) 41 Highland Avenue, Winchester, MA
Zip 01890–1496; tel. 781/729–9000; Dale M. Lodge, Chief Executive
Officer
Web address: www.winchesterhospital.org

Owned, leased, sponsored:	3 hospitals	946 beds
Contract–managed:	0 hospitals	0 beds
Totals:	3 hospitals	946 beds

0056: LAKELAND HEALTH (NP)
1234 Napier Avenue, Saint Joseph, MI Zip 49085–2158;
tel. 269/983–8300; Loren Hamel, M.D., President and Chief
Executive Officer
(Independent Hospital System)

MICHIGAN: LAKELAND HOSPITAL, WATERVLIET (O, 38 beds) 400 Medical
Park Drive, Watervliet, MI Zip 49098–9225; tel. 269/463–3111; Ray
Cruse, Chief Executive Officer

LAKELAND MEDICAL CENTER, ST. JOSEPH (O, 250 beds) 1234 Napier
Avenue, Saint Joseph, MI Zip 49085–2158; tel. 269/983–8300; Loren
Hamel, M.D., President and Chief Executive Officer
Web address: www.lakelandhealth.org

Owned, leased, sponsored:	2 hospitals	288 beds
Contract–managed:	0 hospitals	0 beds
Totals:	2 hospitals	288 beds

0393: LANDMARK HOSPITALS (IO)
3255 Independence Street, Cape Girardeau, MO Zip 63701–4914;
tel. 573/335–1091; William K. Kapp, III, M.D., President and Chief
Executive Officer
(Independent Hospital System)

FLORIDA: LANDMARK HOSPITAL OF SOUTHWEST FLORIDA (O, 50 beds)
1285 Creekside Boulevard East, Naples, FL Zip 34108;
tel. 239/529–1800; Jimmy Dascani, Chief Executive Officer
Web address: www.landmarkhospitals.com/naples.aspx

GEORGIA: LANDMARK HOSPITAL OF ATHENS (O, 42 beds) 775 Sunset Drive,
Athens, GA Zip 30606–2211; tel. 706/425–1500; Vivian Goff, R.N., Chief
Executive Officer
Web address: www.landmarkhospitals.com

LANDMARK HOSPITAL OF SAVANNAH (O, 50 beds) 800 East 68th Street,
Savannah, GA Zip 31405–4710; tel. 912/298–1000; John Salandi, Chief
Executive Officer
Web address: www.landmarkhospitals.com/savannah

MISSOURI: LANDMARK HOSPITAL OF CAPE GIRARDEAU (O, 30 beds) 3255
Independence Street, Cape Girardeau, MO Zip 63701–4914;
tel. 573/335–1091; Rodney Brown, Chief Executive Officer
Web address: www.landmarkhospitals.com

LANDMARK HOSPITAL OF COLUMBIA (O, 42 beds) 604 Old 63 North,
Columbia, MO Zip 65201–6308; tel. 573/499–6600; Deborah Sabella, R.N.,
Chief Executive Officer
Web address: www.landmarkhospitals.com

LANDMARK HOSPITAL OF JOPLIN (O, 30 beds) 2040 West 32nd Street,
Joplin, MO Zip 64804–3512; tel. 417/627–1300; Kevin J. Clement, Chief
Executive Officer
Web address: www.landmarkhospitals.com

UTAH: LANDMARK HOSPITAL OF SALT LAKE CITY (O, 38 beds) 4252 South
Birkhill Boulevard, Murray, UT Zip 84107–5715; tel. 801/268–5400; Ken
D'Amico, Chief Executive Officer
Web address: www.landmarkhospitals.com/utah.aspx

Owned, leased, sponsored:	7 hospitals	282 beds
Contract–managed:	0 hospitals	0 beds
Totals:	7 hospitals	282 beds

0932: LCMC HEALTH (NP)
200 Henry Clay Avenue, New Orleans, LA Zip 70118–5720;
tel. 504/899–9511; Greg Feirn, CPA, President and Chief Executive
Officer
(Moderately Centralized Health System)

LOUISIANA: CHILDREN'S HOSPITAL (O, 210 beds) 200 Henry Clay Avenue,
New Orleans, LA Zip 70118–5720; tel. 504/899–9511; Mary R. Perrin,
President and Chief Executive Officer
Web address: www.chnola.org

For explanation of codes following names, see page B2.
★ Indicates Type III membership in the American Hospital Association.

Section B

NEW ORLEANS EAST HOSPITAL (C, 34 beds) 5620 Read Boulevard, New Orleans, LA Zip 70127–3106, Mailing Address: 5620 Read Boulevard, Zip 70127–3106; tel. 504/592–6600; Takeisha C. Davis, M.D., M.P.H., President and Chief Executive Officer
Web address: www.noehospital.org

TOURO INFIRMARY (O, 280 beds) 1401 Foucher Street, New Orleans, LA Zip 70115–3593; tel. 504/897–7011; Susan E. Andrews, Chief Executive Officer
Web address: www.touro.com

UNIVERSITY MEDICAL CENTER (O, 255 beds) 2000 Canal Street, New Orleans, LA Zip 70112–3018; tel. 504/903–3000; William J. Masterson, President and Chief Executive Officer
Web address: www.umcno.org

Owned, leased, sponsored:	3 hospitals	745 beds
Contract–managed:	1 hospital	34 beds
Totals:	4 hospitals	779 beds

★**0369: LEE MEMORIAL HEALTH SYSTEM** (NP)
2776 Cleveland Avenue, Fort Myers, FL Zip 33901–5856, Mailing Address: P.O. Box 2218, Zip 33902–2218; tel. 239/343–2000; James R. Nathan, President and Chief Executive Officer
(Moderately Centralized Health System)

FLORIDA: CAPE CORAL HOSPITAL (O, 291 beds) 636 Del Prado Boulevard, Cape Coral, FL Zip 33990–2695; tel. 239/424–2000; James R. Nathan, President and Chief Executive Officer
Web address: www.leememorial.org

GULF COAST MEDICAL CENTER (O, 349 beds) 13681 Doctor's Way, Fort Myers, FL Zip 33912–4300; tel. 239/343–1000; James R. Nathan, President and Chief Executive Officer
Web address: www.leememorial.org

LEE MEMORIAL HOSPITAL (O, 857 beds) 2776 Cleveland Avenue, Fort Myers, FL Zip 33901–5855, Mailing Address: P.O. Box 2218, Zip 33902–2218; tel. 239/343–2000; James R. Nathan, President and Chief Executive Officer
Web address: www.leememorial.org

Owned, leased, sponsored:	3 hospitals	1497 beds
Contract–managed:	0 hospitals	0 beds
Totals:	3 hospitals	1497 beds

★**2755: LEGACY HEALTH** (NP)
1919 N.W. Lovejoy Street, Portland, OR Zip 97209–1503; tel. 503/415–5600; George J. Brown, M.D., President and Chief Executive Officer
(Centralized Health System)

OREGON: LEGACY EMANUEL HOSPITAL AND HEALTH CENTER (O, 427 beds) 2801 North Gantenbein Avenue, Portland, OR Zip 97227–1674; tel. 503/413–2200; Lori Morgan, M.D., Chief Administrative Officer
Web address: www.legacyhealth.org

LEGACY GOOD SAMARITAN HOSPITAL AND MEDICAL CENTER (O, 247 beds) 1015 N.W. 22nd Avenue, Portland, OR Zip 97210–3099; tel. 503/413–7711; Jonathan Avery, Chief Administrative Officer
Web address: www.legacyhealth.org

LEGACY MERIDIAN PARK MEDICAL CENTER (O, 130 beds) 19300 S.W. 65th Avenue, Tualatin, OR Zip 97062–9741; tel. 503/692–1212; Allyson Anderson, Chief Administrative Officer
Web address: www.legacyhealth.org

LEGACY MOUNT HOOD MEDICAL CENTER (O, 91 beds) 24800 S.E. Stark, Gresham, OR Zip 97030–3378; tel. 503/667–1122; Gretchen Nichols, R.N., Chief Administrative Officer
Web address: www.legacyhealth.org

WASHINGTON: LEGACY SALMON CREEK MEDICAL CENTER (O, 214 beds) 2211 N.E. 139th Street, Vancouver, WA Zip 98686–2742; tel. 360/487–1000; Bryce R. Helgerson, Chief Administrative Officer
Web address: www.legacyhealth.org

Owned, leased, sponsored:	5 hospitals	1109 beds
Contract–managed:	0 hospitals	0 beds
Totals:	5 hospitals	1109 beds

★**0370: LEHIGH VALLEY HEALTH NETWORK** (NP)
1200 South Cedar Crest Boulevard, Allentown, PA Zip 18103–6202, Mailing Address: P.O. Box 689, Zip 18105–1556; tel. 610/402–8000; Brian A. Nester, President and Chief Executive Officer
(Centralized Health System)

PENNSYLVANIA: LEHIGH VALLEY HOSPITAL (O, 833 beds) 1200 South Cedar Crest Boulevard, Allentown, PA Zip 18103–6248, Mailing Address: P.O. Box 689, Zip 18105–1556; tel. 610/402–8000; Brian A. Nester, President and Chief Executive Officer
Web address: www.lvhn.org

LEHIGH VALLEY HOSPITAL – HAZLETON (O, 120 beds) 700 East Broad Street, Hazleton, PA Zip 18201–6897; tel. 570/501–4000; John R. Fletcher, President
Web address: www.lvhn.org/hazleton/

LEHIGH VALLEY HOSPITAL–MUHLENBERG (O, 168 beds) 2545 Schoenersville Road, Bethlehem, PA Zip 18017–7300; tel. 484/884–2200; Brian A. Nester, President and Chief Executive Officer
Web address: www.lvhn.org

Owned, leased, sponsored:	3 hospitals	1121 beds
Contract–managed:	0 hospitals	0 beds
Totals:	3 hospitals	1121 beds

0412: LEHIGH VALLEY HOSPITAL - SCHUYLKILL (NP)
420 South Jackson Street, Pottsville, PA Zip 17901–3625; tel. 570/621–5000; Marc H. Lory, Interim President and Chief Executive Officer
(Independent Hospital System)

PENNSYLVANIA: LEHIGH VALLEY HOSPITAL – SCHUYLKILL EAST NORWEGIAN STREET (O, 109 beds) 700 East Norwegian Street, Pottsville, PA Zip 17901–2710; tel. 570/621–4000; Wiliam Reppy, Interim President and Chief Executive Officer
Web address: www.schuylkillhealth.com

LEHIGH VALLEY HOSPITAL – SCHUYLKILL SOUTH JACKSON STREET (O, 179 beds) 420 South Jackson Street, Pottsville, PA Zip 17901–3625; tel. 570/621–5000; Wiliam Reppy, Interim President and Chief Executive Officer
Web address: www.schuylkillhealth.com

Owned, leased, sponsored:	2 hospitals	288 beds
Contract–managed:	0 hospitals	0 beds
Totals:	2 hospitals	288 beds

0632: LHC GROUP (IO)
420 West Pinhook Road, Lafayette, LA Zip 70503–2131; tel. 337/233–1307; Keith G. Myers, Chairman and Chief Executive Officer

LOUISIANA: LOUISIANA EXTENDED CARE HOSPITAL OF LAFAYETTE (O, 42 beds) 1214 Coolidge Boulevard, Floors 9 & 10, Lafayette, LA Zip 70503–2621; tel. 337/289–8180; Kevin Frank, Administrator
Web address: www.lhcgroup.com

LOUISIANA EXTENDED CARE HOSPITAL OF NATCHITOCHES (O, 21 beds) 501 Keyser Avenue, Natchitoches, LA Zip 71457–6018; tel. 318/354–2044; John Rivoire, R.N., MSN, Administrator
Web address: www.lhcgroup.com

LOUISIANA EXTENDED CARE HOSPITAL WEST MONROE (O, 18 beds) 503 McMillan Road, 3rd Floor, West Monroe, LA Zip 71291–5327; tel. 318/329–4378; Cleta Munholland, Administrator

OCHSNER EXTENDED CARE HOSPITAL OF KENNER (O, 32 beds) 180 West Esplanade Avenue, 5th Floor, Kenner, LA Zip 70065–2467; tel. 504/464–8658; Frederick Nelson, Administrator
Web address: www.lhcgroup.com/

SPECIALTY HOSPITAL (O, 32 beds) 309 Jackson Street, 7th Floor, Monroe, LA Zip 71201–7407, Mailing Address: P.O. Box 1532, Zip 71210–1532; tel. 318/966–7045; Cleta Munholland, Administrator
Web address: www.lhcgroup.com

For explanation of codes following names, see page B2.
★ Indicates Type III membership in the American Hospital Association.

Section B

ST. LANDRY EXTENDED CARE HOSPITAL (O, 41 beds) 3983 1–49 South Service Road, 2nd Floor, Opelousas, LA Zip 70570; tel. 337/948–2251; Biff David, R.N., Administrator
Web address: www.lhcgroup.com

Owned, leased, sponsored:	6 hospitals	186 beds
Contract–managed:	0 hospitals	0 beds
Totals:	6 hospitals	186 beds

★**0394: LHP HOSPITAL GROUP** (IO)
2400 North Dallas Parkway, Suite 450, Plano, TX Zip 75093–5994; tel. 866/465–9222; John F. Holland, Chief Executive Officer
(Centralized Physician/Insurance Health System)

FLORIDA: BAY MEDICAL CENTER SACRED HEART HEALTH SYSTEM (O, 273 beds) 615 North Bonita Avenue, Panama City, FL Zip 32401–3600, Mailing Address: P.O. Box 59515, Zip 32412–0515; tel. 850/769–1511; Stephen Grubbs, Chief Executive Officer
Web address: www.baymedical.org

IDAHO: PORTNEUF MEDICAL CENTER (O, 175 beds) 777 Hospital Way, Pocatello, ID Zip 83201–5175; tel. 208/239–1000; Daniel Ordyna, Chief Executive Officer
Web address: www.portmed.org

NEW JERSEY: HACKENSACK UNIVERSITY MEDICAL CENTER AT PASCACK VALLEY (O, 128 beds) 250 Old Hook Road, Westwood, NJ Zip 07675–3123; tel. 201/383–1035; Emily L. Holliman, Chief Executive Officer
Web address: www.hackensackumcpv.com/

HACKENSACK UNIVERSITY MEDICAL CENTER MOUNTAINSIDE (O, 218 beds) 1 Bay Avenue, Montclair, NJ Zip 07042–4898; tel. 973/429–6000; John A. Fromhold, FACHE, Chief Executive Officer
Web address: www.mountainsidenow.com

TEXAS: SETON MEDICAL CENTER HARKER HEIGHTS (O, 83 beds) 850 West Central Texas Expressway, Harker Heights, TX Zip 76548–1890; tel. 254/690–0900; Matt T. Maxfield, FACHE, Chief Executive Officer
Web address: www.setonharkerheights.net

Owned, leased, sponsored:	5 hospitals	877 beds
Contract–managed:	0 hospitals	0 beds
Totals:	5 hospitals	877 beds

0158: LIFEBRIDGE HEALTH (NP)
2401 West Belvedere Avenue, Baltimore, MD Zip 21215–5216; tel. 410/601–5134; Neil M. Meltzer, President and Chief Executive Officer
(Independent Hospital System)

MARYLAND: CARROLL HOSPITAL (O, 147 beds) 200 Memorial Avenue, Westminster, MD Zip 21157–5799; tel. 410/848–3000; Leslie Simmons, R.N., FACHE, R.N., President and Chief Executive Officer
Web address: www.carrollhospitalcenter.org

LEVINDALE HEBREW GERIATRIC CENTER AND HOSPITAL (O, 490 beds) 2434 West Belvedere Avenue, Baltimore, MD Zip 21215–5267; tel. 410/601–2400; Idriz Limaj, Chief Operating Officer and Executive Director
Web address: www.sinai–balt.com

NORTHWEST HOSPITAL (O, 253 beds) 5401 Old Court Road, Randallstown, MD Zip 21133–5185; tel. 410/521–2200; Brian M. White, President
Web address: www.lifebridgehealth.org

Owned, leased, sponsored:	3 hospitals	890 beds
Contract–managed:	0 hospitals	0 beds
Totals:	3 hospitals	890 beds

★**0191: LIFECARE MANAGEMENT SERVICES** (IO)
5340 Legacy Drive, Suite 150, Plano, TX Zip 75024–3131; tel. 469/241–2100; Lew Little, Interim Chief Executive Officer
(Independent Hospital System)

COLORADO: COLORADO ACUTE LONG TERM HOSPITAL (O, 63 beds) 1690 North Meade Street, Denver, CO Zip 80204–1552; tel. 303/264–6900; Craig Bailey, MS, Administrator
Web address: www.lifecare–hospitals.com/hospital/colorado

FLORIDA: COMPLEX CARE HOSPITAL AT RIDGELAKE (O, 40 beds) 6150 Edgelake Drive, Sarasota, FL Zip 34240–8803; tel. 941/342–3000; Danny Mallicoat, Chief Executive Officer
Web address: www.lifecare–hospitals.com/hospital.php?id=23

LOUISIANA: LIFECARE HOSPITALS OF SHREVEPORT (O, 119 beds) 9320 Linwood Avenue, Shreveport, LA Zip 71106–7003; tel. 318/688–8504; Brent Martin, Administrator
Web address: www.lifecare–hospitals.com

LIFECARE SPECIALTY HOSPITAL OF NORTH LOUISIANA (O, 55 beds) 1401 Ezell Street, Ruston, LA Zip 71270–7218; tel. 318/251–3126; Brent Martin, Administrator
Web address: www.lifecare–hospitals.com/hospital.php?id=19

NEVADA: COMPLEX CARE HOSPITAL AT TENAYA (O, 70 beds) 2500 North Tenaya, Las Vegas, NV Zip 89128–0482; tel. 702/562–2021; Michael R. Shaw, Chief Executive Officer
Web address: www.lifecare–hospitals.com

TAHOE PACIFIC HOSPITALS (O, 60 beds) 2375 East Prater Way, Sparks, NV Zip 89434; tel. 775/355–5600; Matt Archer, Chief Executive Officer
Web address: www.lifecare–hospitals.com

NORTH CAROLINA: LIFECARE HOSPITALS OF NORTH CAROLINA (O, 41 beds) 1051 Noell Lane, Rocky Mount, NC Zip 27804–1761; tel. 252/451–2300; Robyn Perkerson, R.N., Administrator
Web address: www.lifecare–hospitals.com

OHIO: LIFECARE HOSPITAL OF DAYTON (O, 44 beds) 4000 Miamisburg–Centerville Road, Miamisburg, OH Zip 45342–7615; tel. 937/384–8300; William Bryant, Chief Executive Officer
Web address: www.lifecare–hospitals.com

PENNSYLVANIA: LIFECARE HOSPITALS OF CHESTER COUNTY (O, 39 beds) 400 East Marshall Street, West Chester, PA Zip 19380–5412; tel. 484/826–0400; Garrett Arneson, Chief Executive Officer
Web address: www.lifecare–hospitals.com

LIFECARE HOSPITALS OF MECHANICSBURG (O, 68 beds) 4950 Wilson Lane, Mechanicsburg, PA Zip 17055–4442; tel. 717/697–7706; Mary Ellen Kable, Chief Executive Officer
Web address: www.lifecare–hospitals.com/hospital.php?id=20

LIFECARE HOSPITALS OF PITTSBURGH (O, 236 beds) 225 Penn Avenue, Pittsburgh, PA Zip 15221–2148; tel. 412/247–2424; James Novak, Interim Chief Executive Officer
Web address: www.lifecare–hospitals.com

LIFECARE HOSPITALS OF PITTSBURGH – MONROEVILLE (O, 87 beds) 2380 McGinley Road, Monroeville, PA Zip 15146–4400; tel. 412/856–2400; James Novak, Interim Chief Executive Officer
Web address: www.lifecare–hospitals.com/hospital.php?id=8

TEXAS: LIFECARE HOSPITALS OF DALLAS (O, 60 beds) 1950 Record Crossing Road, Dallas, TX Zip 75235–6223; tel. 214/640–9600; Christy Carver, R.N., Chief Executive Officer
Web address: www.lifecare–hospitals.com/hospital/dallas

LIFECARE HOSPITALS OF SAN ANTONIO (O, 62 beds) 8902 Floyd Curl Drive, San Antonio, TX Zip 78240–1681; tel. 210/690–7000; Randell G. Stokes, Chief Executive Officer
Web address: www.lifecare–hospitals.com

LIFECARE HOSPITALS OF SOUTH TEXAS–NORTH MCALLEN (O, 84 beds) 5101 North Jackson, McAllen, TX Zip 78504–6343; tel. 956/926–7000; Angel Lozano, Chief Executive Officer
Web address: www.lifecare–hospitals.com/hospital/southtexas

WISCONSIN: LIFECARE HOSPITALS OF WISCONSIN (O, 27 beds) 2400 Golf Road, Pewaukee, WI Zip 53072–5590; tel. 262/524–2600; Gayla Campbell, Interim Chief Executive Officer
Web address: www.lifecare–hospitals.com

Owned, leased, sponsored:	16 hospitals	1155 beds
Contract–managed:	0 hospitals	0 beds
Totals:	16 hospitals	1155 beds

Section B

For explanation of codes following names, see page B2.
★ Indicates Type III membership in the American Hospital Association.

Section B

★0180:   **LIFEPOINT HEALTH** (IO)
330 Seven Springs Way, Brentwood, TN Zip 37027–4536;
tel. 615/920–7000; William F. Carpenter, III, Chairman and Chief
Executive Officer
(Decentralized Health System)

ALABAMA: ANDALUSIA HEALTH (O, 88 beds) 849 South Three Notch Street,
Andalusia, AL Zip 36420–5325, Mailing Address: P.O. Box 760,
Zip 36420–1214; tel. 334/222–8466; John C. Yanes, Chief Executive
Officer
Web address: www.andalusiahealth.com

VAUGHAN REGIONAL MEDICAL CENTER (O, 149 beds) 1015 Medical Center
Parkway, Selma, AL Zip 36701–6352; tel. 334/418–4100; J. David
McCormack, Chief Executive Officer
Web address: www.vaughanregional.com

ARIZONA: HAVASU REGIONAL MEDICAL CENTER (O, 162 beds) 101 Civic
Center Lane, Lake Havasu City, AZ Zip 86403–5683; tel. 928/855–8185;
Michael N. Patterson, Chief Executive Officer
Web address: www.havasuregional.com

VALLEY VIEW MEDICAL CENTER (O, 90 beds) 5330 South Highway 95, Fort
Mohave, AZ Zip 86426–9225; tel. 928/788–2273; Feliciano Jiron, Chief
Executive Officer
Web address: www.valleyviewmedicalcenter.net

COLORADO: COLORADO PLAINS MEDICAL CENTER (L, 50 beds) 1000
Lincoln Street, Fort Morgan, CO Zip 80701–3298; tel. 970/867–3391;
Gene L. O'Hara, Interim Chief Executive Officer
Web address: www.coloradoplainsmedicalcenter.com

GEORGIA: ROCKDALE MEDICAL CENTER (O, 138 beds) 1412 Milstead
Avenue N.E., Conyers, GA Zip 30012–3877; tel. 770/918–3000; Alan E.
George, Chief Executive Officer
Web address: www.rockdalemedicalcenter.org

ST. FRANCIS HOSPITAL (O, 304 beds) 2122 Manchester Expressway,
Columbus, GA Zip 31904–6878, Mailing Address: P.O. Box 7000,
Zip 31908–7000; tel. 706/596–4000; David Koontz, Chief Executive Officer
Web address: www.mystfrancis.com

INDIANA: CLARK MEMORIAL HOSPITAL (O, 185 beds) 1220 Missouri Avenue,
Jeffersonville, IN Zip 47130–3743, Mailing Address: P.O. Box 69,
Zip 47131–0600; tel. 812/282–6631; Martin Padgett, President and
Chief Executive Officer
Web address: www.clarkmemorial.org

SCOTT MEMORIAL HOSPITAL (O, 25 beds) 1415 North Gardner Street,
Scottsburg, IN Zip 47170, Mailing Address: Box 430, Zip 47170–0430;
tel. 812/752–3456; Michael Everett, Chief Executive Officer
Web address: www.scottmemorial.com

KANSAS: WESTERN PLAINS MEDICAL COMPLEX (O, 71 beds) 3001 Avenue
A, Dodge City, KS Zip 67801–6508, Mailing Address: P.O. Box 1478,
Zip 67801–1478; tel. 620/225–8400; Michael R. Burroughs, FACHE,
Chief Executive Officer
Web address: www.westernplainsmc.com

KENTUCKY: BLUEGRASS COMMUNITY HOSPITAL (O, 16 beds) 360 Amsden
Avenue, Versailles, KY Zip 40383–1286; tel. 859/873–3111; Tommy
Haggard, Chief Executive Officer
Web address: www.bluegrasscommunityhospital.com

BOURBON COMMUNITY HOSPITAL (O, 58 beds) 9 Linville Drive, Paris, KY
Zip 40361–2196; tel. 859/987–3600; Joseph G. Koch, Chief Executive
Officer
Web address: www.bourbonhospital.com

CLARK REGIONAL MEDICAL CENTER (O, 79 beds) 175 Hospital Drive,
Winchester, KY Zip 40391–9591; tel. 859/745–3500; Cherie Sibley, R.N.,
Chief Executive Officer
Web address: www.clarkregional.org

FLEMING COUNTY HOSPITAL (O, 52 beds) 55 Foundation Drive,
Flemingsburg, KY Zip 41041–9815, Mailing Address: P.O. Box 388,
Zip 41041–0388; tel. 606/849–5000; Brian Springate, Chief Executive
Officer
Web address: www.flemingcountyhospital.org

GEORGETOWN COMMUNITY HOSPITAL (O, 58 beds) 1140 Lexington Road,
Georgetown, KY Zip 40324–9362; tel. 502/868–1100; William Haugh,
Administrator
Web address: www.georgetowncommunityhospital.com

JACKSON PURCHASE MEDICAL CENTER (O, 227 beds) 1099 Medical Center
Circle, Mayfield, KY Zip 42066–1159; tel. 270/251–4100; David Anderson,
Chief Executive Officer
Web address: www.jacksonpurchase.com

LAKE CUMBERLAND REGIONAL HOSPITAL (O, 295 beds) 305 Langdon
Street, Somerset, KY Zip 42503–2750, Mailing Address: P.O. Box 620,
Zip 42502–0620; tel. 606/679–7441; Timothy A. Bess, Chief Executive
Officer
Web address: www.lakecumberlandhospital.com

LOGAN MEMORIAL HOSPITAL (O, 53 beds) 1625 South Nashville Road,
Russellville, KY Zip 42276–8834, Mailing Address: P.O. Box 10,
Zip 42276–0010; tel. 270/726–4011; James Bills, Chief Executive Officer
Web address: www.loganmemorial.com

MEADOWVIEW REGIONAL MEDICAL CENTER (O, 101 beds) 989 Medical Park
Drive, Maysville, KY Zip 41056–8750; tel. 606/759–5311; Robert Parker,
Chief Executive Officer
Web address: www.meadowviewregional.com

SPRING VIEW HOSPITAL (O, 60 beds) 320 Loretto Road, Lebanon, KY
Zip 40033–1300; tel. 270/692–3161; Timothy R. Trottier, Chief Executive
Officer
Web address: www.springviewhospital.com

LOUISIANA: MERCY REGIONAL MEDICAL CENTER (O, 109 beds) 800 East
Main Street, Ville Platte, LA Zip 70586–4618; tel. 337/363–5684; Scott
M. Smith, Chief Executive Officer
Web address: www.mercyregionalmedicalcenter.com

MINDEN MEDICAL CENTER (O, 161 beds) 1 Medical Plaza, Minden, LA
Zip 71055–3330, Mailing Address: P.O. Box 5003, Zip 71058–5003;
tel. 318/377–2321; Stephen R. Selzer, Interim Chief Executive Officer
Web address: www.mindenmedicalcenter.com

TECHE REGIONAL MEDICAL CENTER (L, 165 beds) 1125 Marguerite Street,
Morgan City, LA Zip 70380–1855, Mailing Address: P.O. Box 2308,
Zip 70381–2308; tel. 985/384–2200; James P. Frazier, III, Chief Executive
Officer
Web address: www.techeregional.com

MICHIGAN: UP HEALTH SYSTEM–BELL (O, 25 beds) 901 Lakeshore Drive,
Ishpeming, MI Zip 49849–1367; tel. 906/486–4431; Mitchell D. Leckelt,
Chief Executive Officer
Web address: www.bellhospital.org

MICHIGAN: UP HEALTH SYSTEM–MARQUETTE (O, 268 beds) 580 West
College Avenue, Marquette, MI Zip 49855–2736; tel. 906/228–9440; Brian
Sinotte, Chief Executive Officer
Web address: www.mgh.org

UP HEALTH SYSTEM–PORTAGE (O, 96 beds) 500 Campus Drive, Hancock, MI
Zip 49930–1569; tel. 906/483–1000; Jeff Lang, President
Web address: www.portagehealth.org

MISSISSIPPI: BOLIVAR MEDICAL CENTER (L, 127 beds) 901 East Sunflower
Road, Cleveland, MS Zip 38732–2833, Mailing Address: P.O. Box 1380,
Zip 38732–1380; tel. 662/846–0061; Robert L. Marshall, Jr., FACHE,
Chief Executive Officer
Web address: www.bolivarmedical.com

NEVADA: NORTHEASTERN NEVADA REGIONAL HOSPITAL (O, 50 beds) 2001
Errecart Boulevard, Elko, NV Zip 89801–8333; tel. 775/738–5151;
Richard L. Palagi, Chief Executive Officer
Web address: www.nnrhospital.com

NEW MEXICO: LOS ALAMOS MEDICAL CENTER (O, 38 beds) 3917 West
Road, Los Alamos, NM Zip 87544–2293; tel. 505/661–9500; John
Whiteside, Interim Chief Executive Officer,
Web address: www.losalamosmedicalcenter.com

MEMORIAL MEDICAL CENTER (L, 224 beds) 2450 South Telshor Boulevard,
Las Cruces, NM Zip 88011–5076; tel. 575/522–8641; John Harris, Chief
Executive Officer
Web address: www.mmclc.org

NORTH CAROLINA: CENTRAL CAROLINA HOSPITAL (O, 137 beds) 1135
Carthage Street, Sanford, NC Zip 27330–4162; tel. 919/774–2100; John
Maxwell, Chief Executive Officer
Web address: www.centralcarolinahosp.com

FRYE REGIONAL MEDICAL CENTER (O, 256 beds) 420 North Center Street,
Hickory, NC Zip 28601–5049; tel. 828/322–6070; Garfield Atchison, Chief
Executive Officer
Web address: www.fryemedctr.com

For explanation of codes following names, see page B2.
★ Indicates Type III membership in the American Hospital Association.

HARRIS REGIONAL HOSPITAL (O, 86 beds) 68 Hospital Road, Sylva, NC Zip 28779–2722; tel. 828/586–7000; Steve Heatherly, Chief Executive Officer
Web address: www.westcare.org

HAYWOOD REGIONAL MEDICAL CENTER (O, 146 beds) 262 Leroy George Drive, Clyde, NC Zip 28721–7430; tel. 828/456–7311; Rod Harkleroad, R.N., Chief Executive Officer
Web address: www.haymed.org

MARIA PARHAM MEDICAL CENTER (O, 102 beds) 566 Ruin Creek Road, Henderson, NC Zip 27536–2927; tel. 252/438–4143; Bert Beard, Chief Executive Officer
Web address: www.mariaparham.com

PERSON MEMORIAL HOSPITAL (O, 106 beds) 615 Ridge Road, Roxboro, NC Zip 27573–4629; tel. 336/599–2121; David Ziolkowski, Chief Executive Officer
Web address: www.personhospital.com

RUTHERFORD REGIONAL HEALTH SYSTEM (O, 112 beds) 288 South Ridgecrest Avenue, Rutherfordton, NC Zip 28139–2838; tel. 828/286–5000; James Atkins, PharmD, Chief Executive Officer
Web address: www.rutherfordhosp.org

SWAIN COMMUNITY HOSPITAL (O, 25 beds) 45 Plateau Street, Bryson City, NC Zip 28713–4200; tel. 828/488–2155; Steve Heatherly, Chief Executive Officer
Web address: www.westcare.org

WILSON MEDICAL CENTER (O, 206 beds) 1705 Tarboro Street, S.W., Wilson, NC Zip 27893–3428; tel. 252/399–8040; William E. Caldwell, Jr., Chief Executive Officer
Web address: www.wilmed.org

PENNSYLVANIA: CONEMAUGH MEMORIAL MEDICAL CENTER (O, 539 beds) 1086 Franklin Street, Johnstown, PA Zip 15905–4398; tel. 814/534–9000; Steven E. Tucker, President
Web address: www.conemaugh.org

CONEMAUGH MEYERSDALE MEDICAL CENTER (O, 20 beds) 200 Hospital Drive, Meyersdale, PA Zip 15552–1249; tel. 814/634–5911; Heather Smith, President
Web address: www.conemaugh.org

CONEMAUGH MINERS MEDICAL CENTER (O, 30 beds) 290 Haida Avenue, Hastings, PA Zip 16646–5610, Mailing Address: P.O. Box 689, Zip 16646–0689; tel. 814/247–3100; William R. Crowe, President
Web address: www.conemaugh.org

NASON HOSPITAL (O, 45 beds) 105 Nason Drive, Roaring Spring, PA Zip 16673–1202; tel. 814/224–2141; Timothy Harclerode, Chief Executive Officer
Web address: www.nasonhospital.com

SOUTH CAROLINA: PROVIDENCE HOSPITAL (O, 247 beds) 2435 Forest Drive, Columbia, SC Zip 29204–2098; tel. 803/865–4500; Terrence Kessler, Interim President and Chief Executive Officer
Web address: www.sistersofcharityhealth. org/health–care/providence–hospitals/

TENNESSEE: LIVINGSTON REGIONAL HOSPITAL (O, 114 beds) 315 Oak Street, Livingston, TN Zip 38570–1728, Mailing Address: P.O. Box 550, Zip 38570–0550; tel. 931/823–5611; Timothy W. McGill, Chief Executive Officer
Web address: www.MyLivingstonHospital.com

RIVERVIEW REGIONAL MEDICAL CENTER (O, 35 beds) 158 Hospital Drive, Carthage, TN Zip 37030–1096; tel. 615/735–1560; Michael Herman, Chief Executive Officer
Web address: www.myriverviewmedical.com/

SOUTHERN TENNESSEE REGIONAL HEALTH SYSTEM–LAWRENCEBURG (O, 99 beds) 1607 South Locust Avenue, Lawrenceburg, TN Zip 38464–4011, Mailing Address: P.O. Box 847, Zip 38464–0847; tel. 931/762–6571; Jeff Noblin, FACHE, Chief Executive Officer
Web address: www.crocketthospital.com

SOUTHERN TENNESSEE REGIONAL HEALTH SYSTEM–PULASKI (O, 42 beds) 1265 East College Street, Pulaski, TN Zip 38478–4541; tel. 931/363–7531; James H. Edmondson, Chief Executive Officer
Web address: www.hillsidehospital.com

SOUTHERN TENNESSEE REGIONAL HEALTH SYSTEM–WINCHESTER (O, 188 beds) 185 Hospital Road, Winchester, TN Zip 37398–2404; tel. 931/967–8200; Rob Followell, Chief Executive Officer
Web address: www.southerntennessee.com

STARR REGIONAL MEDICAL CENTER (O, 63 beds) 1114 West Madison Avenue, Athens, TN Zip 37303–4150, Mailing Address: P.O. Box 250, Zip 37371–0250; tel. 423/745–1411; Mark Nichols, FACHE, Chief Executive Officer
Web address: www.starrregional.com

SUMNER REGIONAL MEDICAL CENTER (O, 155 beds) 555 Hartsville Pike, Gallatin, TN Zip 37066–2400, Mailing Address: P.O. Box 1558, Zip 37066–1558; tel. 615/452–4210; Susan M. Peach, R.N., Chief Executive Officer
Web address: www.mysumnermedical.com

TROUSDALE MEDICAL CENTER (O, 25 beds) 500 Church Street, Hartsville, TN Zip 37074–1744; tel. 615/374–2221; Michael Herman, Chief Executive Officer
Web address: www.mytrousdalemedical.com

TEXAS: ENNIS REGIONAL MEDICAL CENTER (L, 58 beds) 2201 West Lampasas Street, Ennis, TX Zip 75119–5644; tel. 972/875–0900; Alan Daugherty, Chief Executive Officer
Web address: www.ennisregional.com

PALESTINE REGIONAL MEDICAL CENTER (O, 12 beds) 2900 South Loop 256, Palestine, TX Zip 75801–6958; tel. 903/731–1000; Richard Grogan, Interim Chief Executive Officer
Web address: www.palestineregional.com

PALESTINE REGIONAL MEDICAL CENTER–EAST (O, 139 beds) 2900 South Loop 256, Palestine, TX Zip 75801–6958; tel. 903/731–1000; Richard Grogan, Interim Chief Executive Officer
Web address: www.palestineregional.com

PARKVIEW REGIONAL HOSPITAL (L, 58 beds) 600 South Bonham, Mexia, TX Zip 76667–3603; tel. 254/562–5332; Alan Daugherty, Chief Executive Officer
Web address: www.parkviewregional.com

UTAH: ASHLEY REGIONAL MEDICAL CENTER (O, 39 beds) 150 West 100 North, Vernal, UT Zip 84078–2036; tel. 435/789–3342; Ben Cluff, Chief Executive Officer
Web address: www.ashleyregional.com

CASTLEVIEW HOSPITAL (O, 49 beds) 300 North Hospital Drive, Price, UT Zip 84501–4200; tel. 435/637–4800; Mark Holyoak, Chief Executive Officer
Web address: www.castleviewhospital.net

VIRGINIA: CLINCH VALLEY MEDICAL CENTER (O, 111 beds) 6801 Governor G. C. Peery Highway, Richlands, VA Zip 24641–2194; tel. 276/596–6000; Peter Mulkey, Chief Executive Officer
Web address: www.clinchvalleymedicalcenter.com

DANVILLE REGIONAL MEDICAL CENTER (O, 250 beds) 142 South Main Street, Danville, VA Zip 24541–2922; tel. 434/799–2100; Alan Larson, Chief Executive Officer
Web address: www.danvilleregional.org

FAUQUIER HOSPITAL (O, 86 beds) 500 Hospital Drive, Warrenton, VA Zip 20186–3099; tel. 540/316–5000; Rodger H. Baker, President and Chief Executive Officer
Web address: www.fauquierhospital.org

MEMORIAL HOSPITAL (O, 150 beds) 320 Hospital Drive, Martinsville, VA Zip 24112–1981, Mailing Address: P.O. Box 4788, Zip 24115–4788; tel. 276/666–7200; Michael Ehrat, Chief Executive Officer
Web address: www.martinsvillehospital.com

TWIN COUNTY REGIONAL HEALTHCARE (O, 141 beds) 200 Hospital Drive, Galax, VA Zip 24333–2227; tel. 276/236–8181; Jon D. Applebaum, Chief Executive Officer
Web address: www.tcrh.org

WYTHE COUNTY COMMUNITY HOSPITAL (L, 70 beds) 600 West Ridge Road, Wytheville, VA Zip 24382–1099; tel. 276/228–0200; Chad Melton, Chief Executive Officer
Web address: www.wcchcares.com

WEST VIRGINIA: LOGAN REGIONAL MEDICAL CENTER (O, 129 beds) 20 Hospital Drive, Logan, WV Zip 25601–3452; tel. 304/831–1101; Kevin Zachary, Chief Executive Officer
Web address: www.loganregionalmedicalcenter.com

RALEIGH GENERAL HOSPITAL (O, 229 beds) 1710 Harper Road, Beckley, WV Zip 25801–3397; tel. 304/256–4100; Harold L. Siglar, Interim Chief Executive Officer
Web address: www.raleighgeneral.com

For explanation of codes following names, see page B2.
★ Indicates Type III membership in the American Hospital Association.

Section B

WYOMING: SAGEWEST HEALTH CARE AT RIVERTON (O, 71 beds) 2100 West Sunset Drive, Riverton, WY Zip 82501–2274; tel. 307/856–4161; Stephen M. Erixon, Chief Executive Officer
Web address: www.sagewesthealthcare.com

Owned, leased, sponsored:	67 hospitals	7894 beds
Contract–managed:	0 hospitals	0 beds
Totals:	67 hospitals	7894 beds

0060: LIFESPAN CORPORATION (NP)
167 Point Street, Providence, RI Zip 02903–4771; tel. 401/444–3500; Timothy J. Babineau, M.D., President and Chief Executive Officer
(Centralized Health System)

RHODE ISLAND: EMMA PENDLETON BRADLEY HOSPITAL (O, 60 beds) 1011 Veterans Memorial Parkway, East Providence, RI Zip 02915–5099; tel. 401/432–1000; Daniel J. Wall, President and Chief Executive Officer
Web address: www.lifespan.org

MIRIAM HOSPITAL (O, 247 beds) 164 Summit Avenue, Providence, RI Zip 02906–2853; tel. 401/793–2500; Arthur J. Sampson, FACHE, President
Web address: www.lifespan.org

NEWPORT HOSPITAL (O, 119 beds) 11 Friendship Street, Newport, RI Zip 02840–2299; tel. 401/846–6400; Crista F. Durand, President
Web address: www.newporthospital.org

RHODE ISLAND HOSPITAL (O, 650 beds) 593 Eddy Street, Providence, RI Zip 02903–4900; tel. 401/444–4000; Timothy J. Babineau, M.D., President and Chief Executive Officer
Web address: www.rhodeislandhospital.org/

Owned, leased, sponsored:	4 hospitals	1076 beds
Contract–managed:	0 hospitals	0 beds
Totals:	4 hospitals	1076 beds

2175: LOMA LINDA UNIVERSITY ADVENTIST HEALTH SCIENCES CENTER (NP)
11175 Campus Street, Loma Linda, CA Zip 92350–1700; tel. 909/558–7572; Richard H. Hart, M.D., President and Chief Executive Officer
(Moderately Centralized Health System)

CALIFORNIA: LOMA LINDA UNIVERSITY BEHAVIORAL MEDICINE CENTER (O, 89 beds) 1710 Barton Road, Redlands, CA Zip 92373–5304; tel. 909/558–9200; Edward Field, Administrator
Web address: www.llu.edu

LOMA LINDA UNIVERSITY CHILDREN'S HOSPITAL (O, 337 beds) 11234 Anderson Street, Loma Linda, CA Zip 92354–2804; tel. 909/558–8000; Kerry Heinrich, JD, Chief Executive Officer
Web address: www.llu.edu/lluch

LOMA LINDA UNIVERSITY MEDICAL CENTER (O, 507 beds) 11234 Anderson Street, Loma Linda, CA Zip 92354–2804, Mailing Address: P.O. Box 2000, Zip 92354–0200; tel. 909/558–4000; Kerry Heinrich, JD, Chief Executive Officer
Web address: www.llumc.edu

LOMA LINDA UNIVERSITY MEDICAL CENTER–MURRIETA (O, 106 beds) 28062 Baxter Road, Murrieta, CA Zip 92563–1401; tel. 951/290–4000; Greg Henderson, Interim Administrator
Web address: www.llumcmurrieta.org

Owned, leased, sponsored:	4 hospitals	1039 beds
Contract–managed:	0 hospitals	0 beds
Totals:	4 hospitals	1039 beds

5755: LOS ANGELES COUNTY–DEPARTMENT OF HEALTH SERVICES (NP)
313 North Figueroa Street, Room 912, Los Angeles, CA Zip 90012–2691; tel. 213/240–8101; Mitchell H. Katz, M.D., Director
(Moderately Centralized Health System)

HARBOR–UCLA MEDICAL CENTER (O, 350 beds) 1000 West Carson Street, Torrance, CA Zip 90502–2059; tel. 310/222–2345; Kimberly McKenzie, R.N., MSN, Interim Chief Executive Officer
Web address: www.harbor–ucla.org

LAC+USC MEDICAL CENTER (O, 664 beds) 2051 Marengo Street, Los Angeles, CA Zip 90033–1352; tel. 323/409–1000; Dan A. Castillo, FACHE, Chief Executive Officer
Web address: www.lacusc.org

LAC–OLIVE VIEW–UCLA MEDICAL CENTER (O, 275 beds) 14445 Olive View Drive, Sylmar, CA Zip 91342–1438; tel. 818/364–1555; Carolyn F. Rhee, Chief Executive Officer
Web address: www.ladhs.org

RANCHO LOS AMIGOS NATIONAL REHABILITATION CENTER (O, 207 beds) 7601 East Imperial Highway, Downey, CA Zip 90242–3496; tel. 562/401–7111; Jorge Orozco, Chief Executive Officer
Web address: www.rancho.org

Owned, leased, sponsored:	4 hospitals	1496 beds
Contract–managed:	0 hospitals	0 beds
Totals:	4 hospitals	1496 beds

0047: LOUISIANA STATE HOSPITALS (NP)
628 North 4th Street, Baton Rouge, LA Zip 70802–5342, Mailing Address: P.O. Box 629, Zip 70821–0628; tel. 225/342–9500; Shelby Price, Chief Executive Officer
(Independent Hospital System)

LOUISIANA: CENTRAL LOUISIANA STATE HOSPITAL (O, 120 beds) 242 West Shamrock Avenue, Pineville, LA Zip 71360–6439, Mailing Address: P.O. Box 5031, Zip 71361–5031; tel. 318/484–6200; Ronald G. Williams, Administrator
Web address: www.dhh.louisiana.gov/index.cfm/directory/detail/217

EASTERN LOUISIANA MENTAL HEALTH SYSTEM (O, 473 beds) 4502 Highway 951, Jackson, LA Zip 70748–5842, Mailing Address: P.O. Box 498, Zip 70748–0498; tel. 225/634–0100; Hampton P. S. Lea, Acting Chief Executive Officer
Web address: www.wwprd.doa.louisiana.gov/laservices/publicpages/ServiceDetail.cfm?service_id=2445

Owned, leased, sponsored:	2 hospitals	593 beds
Contract–managed:	0 hospitals	0 beds
Totals:	2 hospitals	593 beds

★0320: LRGHEALTHCARE (NP)
80 Highland Street, Laconia, NH Zip 03246–3298; tel. 603/524–3211; Kevin Donovan, President and Chief Executive Officer
(Independent Hospital System)

NEW HAMPSHIRE: FRANKLIN REGIONAL HOSPITAL (O, 35 beds) 15 Aiken Avenue, Franklin, NH Zip 03235–1299; tel. 603/934–2060; Kevin Donovan, Chief Executive Officer
Web address: www.lrgh.org

LAKES REGION GENERAL HOSPITAL (O, 88 beds) 80 Highland Street, Laconia, NH Zip 03246–3298; tel. 603/524–3211; Kevin Donovan, Chief Executive Officer
Web address: www.lrgh.org

Owned, leased, sponsored:	2 hospitals	123 beds
Contract–managed:	0 hospitals	0 beds
Totals:	2 hospitals	123 beds

0614: MAINEHEALTH (NP)
110 Free Street, Portland, ME Zip 04101–3537; William L. Caron, Jr., President
(Moderately Centralized Health System)

MAINE: LINCOLNHEALTH (O, 79 beds) 35 Miles Street, Damariscotta, ME Zip 04543–4047; tel. 207/563–1234; James W. Donovan, President and Chief Executive Officer
Web address: www.lchcare.org

For explanation of codes following names, see page B2.
★ Indicates Type III membership in the American Hospital Association.

MAINE MEDICAL CENTER (O, 637 beds) 22 Bramhall Street, Portland, ME Zip 04102–3175; tel. 207/662–0111; Richard W. Petersen, President and Chief Executive Officer
Web address: www.mmc.org

PEN BAY MEDICAL CENTER (O, 165 beds) 6 Glen Cove Drive, Rockport, ME Zip 04856–4240; tel. 207/921–8000; Mark A. Biscone, Chief Executive Officer
Web address: www.penbayhealthcare.org

SPRING HARBOR HOSPITAL (O, 88 beds) 123 Andover Road, Westbrook, ME Zip 04092–3850; tel. 207/761–2200; Mary Jane Krebs, FACHE, President
Web address: www.springharbor.org

STEPHENS MEMORIAL HOSPITAL (O, 25 beds) 181 Main Street, Norway, ME Zip 04268–5664; tel. 207/743–5933; Timothy A. Churchill, President
Web address: www.wmhcc.com

WALDO COUNTY GENERAL HOSPITAL (O, 25 beds) 118 Northport Avenue, Belfast, ME Zip 04915–6072, Mailing Address: P.O. Box 287, Zip 04915–0287; tel. 207/338–2500; Mark A. Biscone, Chief Executive Officer
Web address: www.wcgh.org

NEW HAMPSHIRE: MEMORIAL HOSPITAL (O, 70 beds) 3073 White Mountain Highway, North Conway, NH 03860–7101; tel. 603/356–5461; Scott McKinnon, President and Chief Executive Officer
Web address: www.memorialhospitalnh.org

Owned, leased, sponsored:	7 hospitals	1089 beds
Contract–managed:	0 hospitals	0 beds
Totals:	7 hospitals	1089 beds

1975: MARSHALL HEALTH SYSTEM (NP)
227 Britany Road, Guntersville, AL Zip 35976–5766; tel. 256/894–6615; Gary R. Gore, Chief Executive Officer
(Independent Hospital System)

ALABAMA: MARSHALL MEDICAL CENTER NORTH (O, 90 beds) 8000 Alabama Highway 69, Guntersville, AL Zip 35976; tel. 256/753–8000; Cheryl M. Hays, FACHE, Administrator
Web address: www.mmcenters.com

MARSHALL MEDICAL CENTER SOUTH (O, 114 beds) U.S. Highway 431 North, Boaz, AL Zip 35957–0999, Mailing Address: P.O. Box 758, Zip 35957–0758; tel. 256/593–8310; John D. Anderson, FACHE, Administrator
Web address: www.mmcenters.com//index.php/facilities/marshall_south

Owned, leased, sponsored:	2 hospitals	204 beds
Contract–managed:	0 hospitals	0 beds
Totals:	2 hospitals	204 beds

★0523: MARY WASHINGTON HEALTHCARE (NP)
2300 Fall Hill Avenue, Suite 308, Fredericksburg, VA Zip 22401–3343; tel. 540/741–3100; Michael P. McDermott, M.D., President and Chief Executive Officer
(Centralized Physician/Insurance Health System)

VIRGINIA: MARY WASHINGTON HOSPITAL (O, 437 beds) 1001 Sam Perry Boulevard, Fredericksburg, VA Zip 22401–3354; tel. 540/741–1100; Michael P. McDermott, M.D., President and Chief Executive Officer
Web address: www.marywashingtonhealthcare.com

STAFFORD HOSPITAL (O, 100 beds) 101 Hospital Center Boulevard, Stafford, VA Zip 22554–6200; tel. 540/741–9000; Michael P. McDermott, M.D., President and Chief Executive Officer
Web address: www.mwhc.com

Owned, leased, sponsored:	2 hospitals	537 beds
Contract–managed:	0 hospitals	0 beds
Totals:	2 hospitals	537 beds

0013: MASSACHUSETTS DEPARTMENT OF MENTAL HEALTH (NP)
25 Staniford Street, Boston, MA Zip 02114–2575; tel. 617/626–8123; Joan Mikula, Interim Commissioner

MASSACHUSETTS: DR. J. CORRIGAN MENTAL HEALTH CENTER (O, 16 beds) 49 Hillside Street, Fall River, MA Zip 02720–5266; tel. 508/235–7200; Frank O'Reilly, Director

TAUNTON STATE HOSPITAL (O, 45 beds) 60 Hodges Avenue Extension, Taunton, MA Zip 02780–3034, Mailing Address: PO Box 4007, Zip 02780–0997; tel. 508/977–3000; Joyce O. Connor, Chief Operating Officer

WORCESTER RECOVERY CENTER AND HOSPITAL (O, 126 beds) 305 Belmont Street, Worcester, MA Zip 01604–1695; tel. 508/368–3300; Anthony Riccitelli, Chief Operating Officer

Owned, leased, sponsored:	3 hospitals	187 beds
Contract–managed:	0 hospitals	0 beds
Totals:	3 hospitals	187 beds

0280: MASSACHUSETTS DEPARTMENT OF PUBLIC HEALTH (NP)
250 Washington Street, Boston, MA Zip 02108–4619; tel. 617/624–6000; Sandra Akers, Bureau Director, Public Health Hospitals
(Independent Hospital System)

LEMUEL SHATTUCK HOSPITAL (O, 260 beds) 170 Morton Street, Jamaica Plain, MA Zip 02130–3735; tel. 617/522–8110; Rosette Martinez, Acting Chief Executive Officer
Web address: www.mass.gov/shattuckhospital

MASSACHUSETTS HOSPITAL SCHOOL (O, 93 beds) 3 Randolph Street, Canton, MA Zip 02021–2351; tel. 781/828–2440; Brian V. Devin, Chief Executive Officer
Web address: www.mhsf.us/

TEWKSBURY HOSPITAL (O, 381 beds) 365 East Street, Tewksbury, MA Zip 01876–1998; tel. 978/851–7321; Debra Tosti, Chief Executive Officer
Web address: www.mass.gov

WESTERN MASSACHUSETTS HOSPITAL (O, 80 beds) 91 East Mountain Road, Westfield, MA Zip 01085–1801; tel. 413/562–4131; Valenda M. Liptak, Chief Executive Officer
Web address: www.mass.gov/eohhs/gov/departments/dph/programs/western–massachusetts–hospital.html

Owned, leased, sponsored:	4 hospitals	814 beds
Contract–managed:	0 hospitals	0 beds
Totals:	4 hospitals	814 beds

★0882: MAURY REGIONAL HEALTH SYSTEM (NP)
1224 Trotwood Avenue, Columbia, TN Zip 38401–4802; tel. 931/381–1111; H. Alan Watson, FACHE, Chief Executive Officer
(Independent Hospital System)

TENNESSEE: MARSHALL MEDICAL CENTER (O, 12 beds) 1080 North Ellington Parkway, Lewisburg, TN Zip 37091–2227, Mailing Address: P.O. Box 1609, Zip 37091–1609; tel. 931/359–6241; Phyllis Brown, Chief Executive Officer
Web address: www.mauryregional.com

MAURY REGIONAL HOSPITAL (O, 211 beds) 1224 Trotwood Avenue, Columbia, TN Zip 38401–4802; tel. 931/381–1111; H. Alan Watson, FACHE, Chief Executive Officer
Web address: www.mauryregional.com

WAYNE MEDICAL CENTER (L, 78 beds) 103 J. V. Mangubat Drive, Waynesboro, TN Zip 38485–2440, Mailing Address: P.O. Box 580, Zip 38485–0580; tel. 931/722–5411; Teresa Grimmett, Chief Executive Officer
Web address: www.mauryregional.com

Owned, leased, sponsored:	3 hospitals	301 beds
Contract–managed:	0 hospitals	0 beds
Totals:	3 hospitals	301 beds

★1875: MAYO CLINIC (NP)
200 First Street S.W., Rochester, MN Zip 55905–0002; tel. 507/284–0288; John H. Noseworthy, MD, M.D., President and Chief Executive Officer
(Decentralized Health System)

For explanation of codes following names, see page B2.
★ Indicates Type III membership in the American Hospital Association.

ARIZONA: MAYO CLINIC HOSPITAL (O, 268 beds) 5777 East Mayo Boulevard, Phoenix, AZ Zip 85054–4502; tel. 480/342–0960; Wyatt Decker, Chief Executive Officer
Web address: www.mayoclinic.org/arizona/

FLORIDA: MAYO CLINIC JACKSONVILLE (O, 249 beds) 4500 San Pablo Road South, Jacksonville, FL Zip 32224–1865; tel. 904/953–2000; Gianrico Farrugia, M.D., Vice President and Chief Executive Officer
Web address: www.mayoclinic.org/jacksonville/

GEORGIA: MAYO CLINIC HEALTH SYSTEM IN WAYCROSS (O, 199 beds) 410 Darling Avenue, Waycross, GA Zip 31501–6357, Mailing Address: P.O. Box 139, Zip 31502–0139; tel. 912/283–3030; Roger Forgey, Interim Chief Executive Officer
Web address: www.mayoclinichealthsystem.org

IOWA: FLOYD COUNTY MEDICAL CENTER (C, 25 beds) 800 Eleventh Street, Charles City, IA Zip 50616–3499; tel. 641/228–6830; Bill D. Faust, Administrator
Web address: www.fcmc.us.com/

WINNESHIEK MEDICAL CENTER (C, 25 beds) 901 Montgomery Street, Decorah, IA Zip 52101–2325; tel. 563/382–2911; Lisa Radtke, Chief Administrative Officer
Web address: www.winmedical.org

MINNESOTA: MAYO CLINIC HEALTH SYSTEM IN ALBERT LEA (O, 129 beds) 404 West Fountain Street, Albert Lea, MN Zip 56007–2473; tel. 507/373–2384; Mark Ciota, M.D., Chief Executive Officer
Web address: www.almedcenter.org

MAYO CLINIC HEALTH SYSTEM IN CANNON FALLS (O, 15 beds) 32021 County Road 24 Boulevard, Cannon Falls, MN Zip 55009–1898; tel. 507/263–4221; Thomas J. Witt, M.D., President and Chief Executive Officer
Web address: www.mayoclinichealthsystem.org/locations/cannon–falls

MAYO CLINIC HEALTH SYSTEM IN FAIRMONT (O, 63 beds) 800 Medical Center Drive, Fairmont, MN Zip 56031–4575; tel. 507/238–8100; Robert Bartingale, Administrator
Web address: www.fairmontmedicalcenter.org

MAYO CLINIC HEALTH SYSTEM IN LAKE CITY (O, 101 beds) 500 West Grant Street, Lake City, MN Zip 55041–1143; tel. 651/345–3321; Thomas J. Witt, M.D., President and Chief Executive Officer
Web address: www.lakecitymedicalcenter.org

MAYO CLINIC HEALTH SYSTEM IN MANKATO (O, 166 beds) 1025 Marsh Street, Mankato, MN Zip 56001–4752; tel. 507/625–4031; Gregory Kutcher, M.D., President and Chief Executive Officer
Web address: www.isj–mhs.org

MAYO CLINIC HEALTH SYSTEM IN NEW PRAGUE (O, 25 beds) 301 Second Street N.E., New Prague, MN Zip 56071–1799; tel. 952/758–4431; Mary J. Klimp, FACHE, Administrator
Web address: www.mayoclinichealthsystem.org/locations/new–prague

MAYO CLINIC HEALTH SYSTEM IN RED WING (O, 22 beds) 701 Hewitt Boulevard, Red Wing, MN Zip 55066–2848, Mailing Address: P.O. Box 95, Zip 55066–0095; tel. 651/267–5000; Thomas J. Witt, M.D., President and Chief Executive Officer
Web address: www.mayoclinichealthsystem.org/locations/red–wing

MAYO CLINIC HEALTH SYSTEM IN SAINT JAMES (O, 13 beds) 1101 Moulton and Parsons Drive, Saint James, MN Zip 56081–5550; tel. 507/375–3261; Ryan J. Smith, Administrator
Web address: www.mayoclinichealthsystem.org/locations/st–james

MAYO CLINIC HEALTH SYSTEM IN SPRINGFIELD (O, 23 beds) 625 North Jackson Avenue, Springfield, MN Zip 56087–1714, Mailing Address: P.O. Box 146, Zip 56087–0146; tel. 507/723–6201; Scott D. Thoreson, FACHE, Administrator
Web address: www.mayoclinichealthsystem.org

MAYO CLINIC HEALTH SYSTEM IN WASECA (O, 25 beds) 501 North State Street, Waseca, MN Zip 56093–2811; tel. 507/835–1210; Thomas Borowski, Administrator
Web address: www.mayoclinichealthsystem.org

MAYO CLINIC HEALTH SYSTEM–ALBERT LEA AND AUSTIN (O, 69 beds) 1000 First Drive N.W., Austin, MN Zip 55912–2904; tel. 507/433–7351; Mark Ciota, M.D., Chief Executive Officer
Web address: www.austinmedicalcenter.org

MAYO CLINIC HOSPITAL – ROCHESTER (O, 1263 beds) 1216 Second Street S.W., Rochester, MN Zip 55902–1906; tel. 507/255–5123; F. Kenneth Ackerman, Chair, Hospital Operations
Web address: www.mayoclinic.org

WISCONSIN: MAYO CLINIC HEALTH SYSTEM – CHIPPEWA VALLEY IN BLOOMER (O, 19 beds) 1501 Thompson Street, Bloomer, WI Zip 54724–1299; tel. 715/568–2000; Edward A. Wittrock, Vice President Regional System
Web address: www.bloomermedicalcenter.org

MAYO CLINIC HEALTH SYSTEM – FRANCISCAN HEALTHCARE IN LA CROSSE (O, 81 beds) 700 West Avenue South, La Crosse, WI Zip 54601–4783; tel. 608/785–0940; Timothy J. Johnson, President and Chief Executive Officer
Web address: www.franciscanskemp.org

MAYO CLINIC HEALTH SYSTEM – FRANCISCAN HEALTHCARE IN SPARTA (O, 11 beds) 310 West Main Street, Sparta, WI Zip 54656–2171; tel. 608/269–2132; Kimberly Hawthorne, Administrator
Web address: www.mayoclinichealthsystem.org

MAYO CLINIC HEALTH SYSTEM – NORTHLAND IN BARRON (O, 15 beds) 1222 Woodland Avenue, Barron, WI Zip 54812–1798; tel. 715/537–3186; Maurita Sullivan, Vice President
Web address: www.luthermidelfortnorthland.org

MAYO CLINIC HEALTH SYSTEM – OAKRIDGE IN OSSEO (O, 39 beds) 13025 Eighth Street, Osseo, WI Zip 54758–7634, Mailing Address: P.O. Box 70, Zip 54758–0070; tel. 715/597–3121; Dean Eide, Vice President
Web address: www.mayoclinichealthsystem.org/locations/osseo

MAYO CLINIC HEALTH SYSTEM – RED CEDAR IN MENOMONIE (O, 23 beds) 2321 Stout Road, Menomonie, WI Zip 54751–2397; tel. 715/235–5531; Steven Lindberg, Chief Administrative Officer
Web address: www.rcmc–mhs.org

MAYO CLINIC HEALTH SYSTEM IN EAU CLAIRE (O, 185 beds) 1221 Whipple Street, Eau Claire, WI Zip 54703–5270, Mailing Address: P.O. Box 4105, Zip 54702–4105; tel. 715/838–3311; Randall L. Linton, M.D., President and Chief Executive Officer
Web address: www.mhs.mayo.edu

Owned, leased, sponsored:	22 hospitals	3003 beds
Contract–managed:	2 hospitals	50 beds
Totals:	24 hospitals	3053 beds

0252: MCLAREN HEALTH CARE CORPORATION (NP)
G3235 Beecher Road, Suite B., Flint, MI Zip 48532–3650; tel. 810/342–1100; Philip A. Incarnati, President and Chief Executive Officer
(Centralized Physician/Insurance Health System)

MICHIGAN: MARWOOD MANOR NURSING HOME (O, 106 beds) 1300 Beard Street, Port Huron, MI Zip 48060; tel. 818/982–2594; Brian Oberly, Administrator

MCLAREN BAY REGION (O, 338 beds) 1900 Columbus Avenue, Bay City, MI Zip 48708–6831; tel. 989/894–3000; Clarence Sevillian, President and Chief Executive Officer
Web address: www.bayregional.org

MCLAREN BAY SPECIAL CARE (O, 26 beds) 3250 East Midland Road, Suite 1, Bay City, MI Zip 48706–2835; tel. 989/667–6802; Cheryl A. Burzynski, MSN, President
Web address: www.bayspecialcare.org

MCLAREN CENTRAL MICHIGAN (O, 78 beds) 1221 South Drive, Mount Pleasant, MI Zip 48858–3257; tel. 989/772–6700; William P. Lawrence, President and Chief Executive Officer
Web address: www.cmch.org

MCLAREN FLINT (O, 348 beds) 401 South Ballenger Highway, Flint, MI Zip 48532–3685; tel. 810/342–2000; Donald C. Kooy, President and Chief Executive Officer
Web address: www.mclarenregional.org

MCLAREN GREATER LANSING (O, 321 beds) 401 West Greenlawn Avenue, Lansing, MI Zip 48910–2819; tel. 517/975–6000; Thomas Mee, R.N., President and Chief Executive Officer
Web address: www.mclaren.org

For explanation of codes following names, see page B2.
★ Indicates Type III membership in the American Hospital Association.

MCLAREN LAPEER REGION (O, 159 beds) 1375 North Main Street, Lapeer, MI Zip 48446–1350; tel. 810/667–5500; Barton Buxton, Ed.D., President and Chief Executive Officer
Web address: www.lapeerregional.org

MCLAREN MACOMB (O, 288 beds) 1000 Harrington Boulevard, Mount Clemens, MI Zip 48043–2992; tel. 586/493–8000; Thomas M. Brisse, President and Chief Executive Officer
Web address: www.mclaren.org/macomb/macomb.aspx

MCLAREN NORTHERN MICHIGAN (O, 188 beds) 416 Connable Avenue, Petoskey, MI Zip 49770–2297; tel. 231/487–4000; David M. Zechman, FACHE, President and Chief Executive Officer
Web address: www.northernhealth.org

MCLAREN OAKLAND (O, 263 beds) 50 North Perry Street, Pontiac, MI Zip 48342–2253; tel. 248/338–5000; Chad M. Grant, President and Chief Executive Officer
Web address: www.mclaren.org/oakland

MCLAREN PORT HURON (O, 186 beds) 1221 Pine Grove Avenue, Port Huron, MI Zip 48060–3511; tel. 810/987–5000; Jennifer Montgomery, R.N., FACHE, President and Chief Executive Officer
Web address: www.porthuronhospital.org

Owned, leased, sponsored:	11 hospitals	2301 beds
Contract–managed:	0 hospitals	0 beds
Totals:	11 hospitals	2301 beds

0874: MCLEOD HEALTH (NP)
555 East Cheves Street, Florence, SC Zip 29506–2617, Mailing Address: P.O. Box 100551, Zip 29502–0551; tel. 843/777–2000; Robert L. Colones, President and Chief Executive Officer
(Centralized Health System)

SOUTH CAROLINA: MCLEOD HEALTH CHERAW (O, 55 beds) 711 Chesterfield Highway, Cheraw, SC Zip 29520–7002; tel. 843/537–7881; Mib Scoggins, Chief Executive Officer
Web address: www.chesterfieldgeneral.com

MCLEOD HEALTH CLARENDON (C, 48 beds) 10 Hospital Street, Manning, SC Zip 29102–3153, Mailing Address: P.O. Box 550, Zip 29102–0550; tel. 803/433–3000; Deborah Locklair, FACHE, Administrator
Web address: www.clarendonhealth.com

MCLEOD LORIS SEACOAST HOSPITAL (O, 155 beds) 3655 Mitchell Street, Loris, SC Zip 29569–2827; tel. 843/716–7000; Edward D. Tinsley, III, Chief Executive Officer
Web address: www.mcleodhealth.org

MCLEOD MEDICAL CENTER DILLON (O, 58 beds) 301 East Jackson Street, Dillon, SC Zip 29536–2509, Mailing Address: P.O. Box 1327, Zip 29536–1327; tel. 843/774–4111; Deborah Locklair, FACHE, Administrator
Web address: www.mcleodhealth.org

MCLEOD MEDICAL CENTER–DARLINGTON (O, 72 beds) 701 Cashua Ferry Road, Darlington, SC Zip 29532–8488, Mailing Address: P.O. Box 1859, Zip 29540; tel. 843/395–1100; Tim Smoak, Administrator
Web address: www.mcleodhealth.org

MCLEOD REGIONAL MEDICAL CENTER (O, 493 beds) 555 East Cheves Street, Florence, SC Zip 29506–2617, Mailing Address: P.O. Box 100551, Zip 29502–0551; tel. 843/777–2000; Robert L. Colones, President and Chief Executive Officer
Web address: www.mcleodhealth.org

Owned, leased, sponsored:	5 hospitals	833 beds
Contract–managed:	1 hospital	48 beds
Totals:	6 hospitals	881 beds

1001: MEADVILLE MEDICAL CENTER (NP)
751 Liberty Street, Meadville, PA Zip 16335–2559; tel. 814/333–5000; Philip E. Pandolph, FACHE, Chief Executive Officer

PENNSYLVANIA: MEADVILLE MEDICAL CENTER (O, 210 beds) 751 Liberty Street, Meadville, PA Zip 16335–2559; tel. 814/333–5000; Philip E. Pandolph, FACHE, Chief Executive Officer
Web address: www.mmchs.org

TITUSVILLE AREA HOSPITAL (O, 50 beds) 406 West Oak Street, Titusville, PA Zip 16354–1404; tel. 814/827–1851; Lee Clinton, FACHE, Chief Executive Officer
Web address: www.titusvillehospital.org

Owned, leased, sponsored:	2 hospitals	260 beds
Contract–managed:	0 hospitals	0 beds
Totals:	2 hospitals	260 beds

★0971: MEDISYS HEALTH NETWORK (NP)
8900 Van Wyck Expressway, Jamaica, NY Zip 11418–2832; tel. 718/206–6000; Bruce J. Flanz, President and Chief Executive Officer
(Moderately Centralized Health System)

NEW YORK: FLUSHING HOSPITAL MEDICAL CENTER (C, 299 beds) 4500 Parsons Boulevard, Flushing, NY Zip 11355–2205; tel. 718/670–5000; Bruce J. Flanz, President and Chief Executive Officer
Web address: www.flushinghospital.org

JAMAICA HOSPITAL MEDICAL CENTER (C, 668 beds) 8900 Van Wyck Expressway, Jamaica, NY Zip 11418–2832; tel. 718/206–6000; Bruce J. Flanz, President and Chief Executive Officer
Web address: www.Jamaicahospital.org

Owned, leased, sponsored:	0 hospitals	0 beds
Contract–managed:	2 hospitals	967 beds
Totals:	2 hospitals	967 beds

★0154: MEDSTAR HEALTH (NP)
5565 Sterrett Place, 5th Floor, Columbia, MD Zip 21044–2665; tel. 410/772–6500; Kenneth A. Samet, President and Chief Executive Officer
(Centralized Health System)

DISTRICT OF COLUMBIA: MEDSTAR GEORGETOWN UNIVERSITY HOSPITAL (O, 415 beds) 3800 Reservoir Road N.W., Washington, DC Zip 20007–2197; tel. 202/444–2000; Michael Sachtleben, President
Web address: www.georgetownuniversityhospital.org

MEDSTAR NATIONAL REHABILITATION HOSPITAL (O, 137 beds) 102 Irving Street N.W., Washington, DC Zip 20010–2949; tel. 202/877–1000; John D. Rockwood, President
Web address: www.medstarnrh.org

MEDSTAR WASHINGTON HOSPITAL CENTER (O, 765 beds) 110 Irving Street N.W., Washington, DC Zip 20010–3017; tel. 202/877–7000; John Sullivan, President
Web address: www.whcenter.org

MARYLAND: MEDSTAR FRANKLIN SQUARE MEDICAL CENTER (O, 404 beds) 9000 Franklin Square Drive, Baltimore, MD Zip 21237–3901; tel. 443/777–7000; Samuel E. Moskowitz, President
Web address: www.medstarfranklin.org

MEDSTAR GOOD SAMARITAN HOSPITAL (O, 305 beds) 5601 Loch Raven Boulevard, Baltimore, MD Zip 21239–2995; tel. 443/444–8000; Bradley Chambers, President and Chief Executive Officer
Web address: www.goodsam–md.org

MEDSTAR HARBOR HOSPITAL (O, 150 beds) 3001 South Hanover Street, Baltimore, MD Zip 21225–1290; tel. 410/350–3200; Dennis W. Pullin, FACHE, President
Web address: www.harborhospital.org

MEDSTAR MONTGOMERY MEDICAL CENTER (O, 151 beds) 18101 Prince Philip Drive, Olney, MD Zip 20832–1512; tel. 301/774–8882; Thomas J. Senker, FACHE, Chief Executive Officer
Web address: www.medstarmontgomery.org

MEDSTAR SOUTHERN MARYLAND HOSPITAL CENTER (O, 255 beds) 7503 Surratts Road, Clinton, MD Zip 20735–3358; tel. 301/868–8000; Christine R. Wray, President
Web address: www.medstarsouthernmaryland.org

MEDSTAR ST. MARY'S HOSPITAL (O, 82 beds) 25500 Point Lookout Road, Leonardtown, MD Zip 20650–2015, Mailing Address: PO Box 527, Zip 20650–0527; tel. 301/475–6001; Christine R. Wray, President
Web address: www.medstarstmarys.org

For explanation of codes following names, see page B2.
★ Indicates Type III membership in the American Hospital Association.

MEDSTAR UNION MEMORIAL HOSPITAL (O, 218 beds) 201 East University Parkway, Baltimore, MD Zip 21218–2895; tel. 410/554–2000; Bradley Chambers, President
Web address: www.medstarunionmemorial.org

Owned, leased, sponsored:	10 hospitals	2882 beds
Contract–managed:	0 hospitals	0 beds
Totals:	10 hospitals	2882 beds

★0086: MEMORIAL HEALTH SYSTEM (NP)
701 North First Street, Springfield, IL Zip 62781–0001; tel. 217/788–3000; Edgar J. Curtis, FACHE, President and Chief Executive Officer
(Moderately Centralized Health System)

ILLINOIS: ABRAHAM LINCOLN MEMORIAL HOSPITAL (O, 25 beds) 200 Stahlhut Drive, Lincoln, IL Zip 62656–5066; tel. 217/732–2161; Dolan Dalpoas, President and Chief Executive Officer
Web address: www.almh.org

MEMORIAL MEDICAL CENTER (O, 470 beds) 701 North First Street, Springfield, IL Zip 62781–0001; tel. 217/788–3000; Edgar J. Curtis, FACHE, President and Chief Executive Officer
Web address: www.memorialmedical.com

PASSAVANT AREA HOSPITAL (O, 108 beds) 1600 West Walnut Street, Jacksonville, IL Zip 62650–1136; tel. 217/245–9541; Douglas L. Rahn, President and Chief Executive Officer
Web address: www.passavanthospital.com

TAYLORVILLE MEMORIAL HOSPITAL (O, 25 beds) 201 East Pleasant Street, Taylorville, IL Zip 62568–1597; tel. 217/824–3331; Kimberly L. Bourne, Chief Executive Officer
Web address: www.taylorvillememorial.org

Owned, leased, sponsored:	4 hospitals	628 beds
Contract–managed:	0 hospitals	0 beds
Totals:	4 hospitals	628 beds

0998: MEMORIAL HEALTH SYSTEM (NP)
401 Matthew Street, Marietta, OH Zip 45750–1635; tel. 740/374–1400; J. Scott Cantley, President and Chief Executive Officer

OHIO: MARIETTA MEMORIAL HOSPITAL (O, 152 beds) 401 Matthew Street, Marietta, OH Zip 45750–1699; tel. 740/374–1400; J. Scott Cantley, President and Chief Executive Officer
Web address: www.mhsystem.org

SELBY GENERAL HOSPITAL (O, 35 beds) 1106 Colegate Drive, Marietta, OH Zip 45750–1323; tel. 740/568–2000; Stephen Smith, President
Web address: www.selbygeneral.org

Owned, leased, sponsored:	2 hospitals	187 beds
Contract–managed:	0 hospitals	0 beds
Totals:	2 hospitals	187 beds

★0083: MEMORIAL HEALTHCARE SYSTEM (NP)
3501 Johnson Street, Hollywood, FL Zip 33021–5421; tel. 954/987–2000; Aurelio Fernandez, Chief Executive Officer
(Centralized Health System)

FLORIDA: MEMORIAL HOSPITAL MIRAMAR (O, 178 beds) 1901 S.W. 172nd Avenue, Miramar, FL Zip 33029–5592; tel. 954/538–5000; Leah A. Carpenter, Administrator and Chief Executive Officer
Web address: www.mhs.net

MEMORIAL HOSPITAL PEMBROKE (L, 157 beds) 7800 Sheridan Street, Pembroke Pines, FL Zip 33024–2536; tel. 954/883–8482; Mark Doyle, Administrator and Chief Executive Officer
Web address: www.memorialpembroke.com/

MEMORIAL HOSPITAL WEST (O, 384 beds) 703 North Flamingo Road, Pembroke Pines, FL Zip 33028–1014; tel. 954/436–5000; C. Kennon Hetlage, FACHE, Administrator and Chief Executive Officer
Web address: www.mhs.net

MEMORIAL REGIONAL HOSPITAL (O, 1037 beds) 3501 Johnson Street, Hollywood, FL Zip 33021–5421; tel. 954/987–2000; Zeff Ross, FACHE, Executive Vice President and Chief Executive Officer
Web address: www.mhs.net

Owned, leased, sponsored:	4 hospitals	1756 beds
Contract–managed:	0 hospitals	0 beds
Totals:	4 hospitals	1756 beds

★2645: MEMORIAL HERMANN HEALTH SYSTEM (NP)
929 Gessner, Suite 2700, Houston, TX Zip 77024–2593; tel. 713/242–2700; Benjamin K. Chu, M.D., President and Chief Executive Officer
(Centralized Health System)

TEXAS: MEMORIAL HERMANN – TEXAS MEDICAL CENTER (O, 973 beds) 6411 Fannin Street, Houston, TX Zip 77030–1501; tel. 713/704–4000; Brian Dean, FACHE, Chief Executive Officer
Web address: www.mhhs.org

MEMORIAL HERMANN GREATER HEIGHTS HOSPITAL (O, 1275 beds) 1635 North Loop West, Houston, TX Zip 77008–1532; tel. 713/867–3380; Susan Jadlowski, MSN, R.N., Chief Executive Officer
Web address: www.mhbh.org

MEMORIAL HERMANN KATY HOSPITAL (O, 142 beds) 23900 Katy Freeway, Katy, TX Zip 77494–1323; tel. 281/644–7000; James Parisi, Chief Executive Officer
Web address: www.memorialhermann.org/locations/katy/

MEMORIAL HERMANN MEMORIAL CITY MEDICAL CENTER (L, 382 beds) 921 Gessner Road, Houston, TX Zip 77024–2501; tel. 713/242–3000; Paul O'Sullivan, FACHE, Chief Executive Officer
Web address: www.memorialhermann.org

MEMORIAL HERMANN NORTHEAST (O, 218 beds) 18951 North Memorial Drive, Humble, TX Zip 77338–4297; tel. 281/540–7700; Heath Rushing, Chief Executive Officer
Web address: www.memorialhermann.org/locations/northeast/

MEMORIAL HERMANN ORTHOPEDIC AND SPINE HOSPITAL (O, 64 beds) 5410 West Loop South, Bellaire, TX Zip 77401–2103; tel. 713/314–4500; Andrew Knizley, Chief Executive Officer
Web address: www.memorialhermann.org/

MEMORIAL HERMANN REHABILITATION HOSPITAL – KATY (O, 35 beds) 21720 Kingsland Boulevard #102, Katy, TX Zip 77450–2550; Carl E. Josehart, Chief Executive Officer
Web address: www.oceanskaty.com/

MEMORIAL HERMANN SUGAR LAND HOSPITAL (O, 81 beds) 17500 West Grand Parkway South, Sugar Land, TX Zip 77479–2562; tel. 281/725–5000; Gregory Haralson, Chief Executive Officer
Web address: www.memorialhermann.org

MEMORIAL HERMANN SURGICAL HOSPITALG – FIRST COLONY (O, 6 beds) 16906 Southwest Freeway, Sugar Land, TX Zip 77479–2350; tel. 281/243–1000; Daniel Smith, Chief Executive Officer
Web address: www.memorialhermannfirstcolony.com

TIRR MEMORIAL HERMANN (O, 134 beds) 1333 Moursund Street, Houston, TX Zip 77030–3405; tel. 713/799–5000; Carl E. Josehart, Chief Executive Officer
Web address: www.memorialhermann.org/locations/tirr.html

Owned, leased, sponsored:	10 hospitals	3310 beds
Contract–managed:	0 hospitals	0 beds
Totals:	10 hospitals	3310 beds

0084: MEMORIALCARE (NP)
17360 Brookhurst Street, Fountain Valley, CA Zip 92708–3720, Mailing Address: P.O. Box 1428, Long Beach, Zip 90801–1428; tel. 714/377–2900; Barry S. Arbuckle, Ph.D., President and Chief Executive Officer
(Centralized Health System)

CALIFORNIA: COMMUNITY HOSPITAL LONG BEACH (O, 158 beds) 1720 Termino Avenue, Long Beach, CA Zip 90804–2104; tel. 562/498–1000; John Bishop, Chief Executive Officer
Web address: www.memorialcare.org

For explanation of codes following names, see page B2.
★ Indicates Type III membership in the American Hospital Association.

LONG BEACH MEMORIAL MEDICAL CENTER (O, 458 beds) 2801 Atlantic Avenue, Long Beach, CA Zip 90806–1701, Mailing Address: P.O. Box 1428, Zip 90801–1428; tel. 562/933–2000; John Bishop, Chief Executive Officer
Web address: www.memorialcare.org/LongBeach

MILLER CHILDREN'S & WOMEN'S HOSPITAL LONG BEACH (O, 371 beds) 2801 Atlantic Avenue, Long Beach, CA Zip 90806–1701; tel. 562/933–5437; John Bishop, Chief Executive Officer
Web address: www.memorialcare.org

ORANGE COAST MEMORIAL MEDICAL CENTER (O, 218 beds) 9920 Talbert Avenue, Fountain Valley, CA Zip 92708–5115; tel. 714/378–7000; Marcia Manker, Chief Executive Officer
Web address: www.memorialcare.org

SADDLEBACK MEMORIAL MEDICAL CENTER (O, 313 beds) 24451 Health Center Drive, Laguna Hills, CA Zip 92653–3689; tel. 949/837–4500; Marcia Manker, Chief Executive Officer
Web address: www.memorialcare.org

Owned, leased, sponsored:	5 hospitals	1518 beds
Contract–managed:	0 hospitals	0 beds
Totals:	5 hospitals	1518 beds

★**5155: MERCY HEALTH** (CC)
615 Elsinore Place, Cincinnati, OH Zip 45202–1459, Mailing Address: 1701 Mercy Health Place, Zip 45237; tel. 513/639–2800; John M. Starcher, President and Chief Executive Officer
(Moderately Centralized Health System)

KENTUCKY: LOURDES HOSPITAL (O, 280 beds) 1530 Lone Oak Road, Paducah, KY Zip 42003–7900, Mailing Address: P.O. Box 7100, Zip 42002–7100; tel. 270/444–2444; Steven Grinnell, Chief Executive Officer
Web address: www.lourdes–pad.org

MARCUM AND WALLACE MEMORIAL HOSPITAL (O, 25 beds) 60 Mercy Court, Irvine, KY Zip 40336–1331; tel. 606/723–2115; Susan Starling, President and Chief Executive Officer
Web address: www.marcumandwallace.org

OHIO: INSTITUTE FOR ORTHOPAEDIC SURGERY (O, 3 beds) 801 Medical Drive, Suite B., Lima, OH Zip 45804–4030; tel. 419/224–7586; Mark McDonald, M.D., President and Chief Executive Officer
Web address: www.ioshospital.com

MERCY ALLEN HOSPITAL (O, 25 beds) 200 West Lorain Street, Oberlin, OH Zip 44074–1077; tel. 440/775–1211; Joseph Sober, President
Web address: www.mercyonline.org/mercy_allen_hospital.aspx

MERCY HEALTH – ST. CHARLES HOSPITAL (O, 257 beds) 2600 Navarre Avenue, Oregon, OH Zip 43616–3297; tel. 419/696–7200; Jeffrey Dempsey, President and Chief Operating Officer
Web address: www.mercyweb.org

MERCY HEALTH – ANDERSON HOSPITAL (O, 188 beds) 7500 State Road, Cincinnati, OH Zip 45255–2492; tel. 513/624–4500; Jeff Graham, Market Leader and President
Web address: www.e–mercy.com

MERCY HEALTH – CLERMONT HOSPITAL (O, 119 beds) 3000 Hospital Drive, Batavia, OH Zip 45103–1921; tel. 513/732–8200; Jeff Graham, Market Leader and President
Web address: www.e–mercy.com

MERCY HEALTH – FAIRFIELD HOSPITAL (O, 236 beds) 3000 Mack Road, Fairfield, OH Zip 45014–5335; tel. 513/870–7000; Thomas S. Urban, Market Leader and President
Web address: www.e–mercy.com

MERCY HEALTH – ST. ELIZABETH BOARDMAN HOSPITAL (O, 193 beds) 8401 Market Street, Boardman, OH Zip 44512–6777; tel. 330/729–2929; Eugenia Aubel, President
Web address: www.ehealthconnection. com/regions/youngstown/content/show_facility.asp?facility_id=190

MERCY HEALTH – ST. ELIZABETH YOUNGSTOWN HOSPITAL (O, 379 beds) 1044 Belmont Avenue, Youngstown, OH Zip 44504–1096, Mailing Address: P.O. Box 1790, Zip 44501–1790; tel. 330/746–7211; Donald E. Kline, President and Chief Executive Officer
Web address: www.mercy.com

MERCY HEALTH – ST. JOSEPH WARREN HOSPITAL (O, 141 beds) 667 Eastland Avenue S.E., Warren, OH Zip 44484–4531; tel. 330/841–4000; Kathy Cook, FACHE, MSN, President
Web address: www.hmpartners.org

MERCY HEALTH – WEST HOSPITAL (O, 250 beds) 3300 Mercy Health Boulevard, Cincinnati, OH Zip 45211; tel. 513/215–5000; Michael Kramer, Chief Executive Officer
Web address: www.e–mercy.com/west–hospital

MERCY HEALTH – WILLARD HOSPITAL (O, 20 beds) 1100 Neal Zick Road, Willard, OH Zip 44890–9287; tel. 419/964–5000; B. Lynn Detterman, President and Chief Executive Officer
Web address: www.mercyweb.org

MERCY HOSPITAL OF DEFIANCE (O, 23 beds) 1404 East Second Street, Defiance, OH Zip 43512–2440; tel. 419/782–8444; B. Lynn Detterman, President and Chief Executive Officer
Web address: www.ehealthconnection.com/regions/toledo/

MERCY MEMORIAL HOSPITAL (O, 25 beds) 904 Scioto Street, Urbana, OH Zip 43078–2200; tel. 937/653–5231; Paul C. Hiltz, FACHE, President and Market Leader
Web address: www.health–partners.org

MERCY REGIONAL MEDICAL CENTER (O, 259 beds) 3700 Kolbe Road, Lorain, OH Zip 44053–1697; tel. 440/960–4000; Edwin M. Oley, President and Chief Executive Officer
Web address: www.community–health–partners.com

MERCY ST. ANNE HOSPITAL (O, 96 beds) 3404 West Sylvania Avenue, Toledo, OH Zip 43623–4467; tel. 419/407–2663; Bradley J. Bertke, President and Chief Ooperating Officer
Web address: www.mercyweb.org

MERCY ST. VINCENT MEDICAL CENTER (O, 381 beds) 2213 Cherry Street, Toledo, OH Zip 43608–2691; tel. 419/251–3232; Kerry Tirman, Chief Executive Officer
Web address: www.mercyweb.org

MERCY TIFFIN HOSPITAL (O, 51 beds) 45 St. Lawrence Drive, Tiffin, OH Zip 44883–8310; tel. 419/455–7000; B. Lynn Detterman, President and Chief Executive Officer
Web address: www.mercyweb.org

SPRINGFIELD REGIONAL MEDICAL CENTER (O, 259 beds) 100 Medical Center Drive, Springfield, OH Zip 45504–2687; tel. 937/523–1000; Paul C. Hiltz, FACHE, Market President and Chief Executive Officer
Web address: www.community–mercy.org

ST. RITA'S MEDICAL CENTER (O, 415 beds) 730 West Market Street, Lima, OH Zip 45801–4602; tel. 419/227–3361; Robert O. Baxter, Regional CEO, Lima
Web address: www.stritas.org

THE JEWISH HOSPITAL – MERCY HEALTH (O, 209 beds) 4777 East Galbraith Road, Cincinnati, OH Zip 45236–2725; tel. 513/686–3000; Patricia Davis–Hagens, R.N., Central Market Leader and President
Web address: www.jewishhospitalcincinnati.com/

Owned, leased, sponsored:	22 hospitals	3834 beds
Contract–managed:	0 hospitals	0 beds
Totals:	22 hospitals	3834 beds

★**5185: MERCY HEALTH** (CC)
14528 South Outer 40, Suite 100, Chesterfield, MO Zip 63017–5743; tel. 314/579–6100; Lynn Britton, President and Chief Executive Officer
(Decentralized Health System)

ARKANSAS: MERCY HOSPITAL BERRYVILLE (O, 25 beds) 214 Carter Street, Berryville, AR Zip 72616–4303; tel. 870/423–3355; Douglas M. Stroemel, Administrator
Web address: www.mercy.net/berryvillear

MERCY HOSPITAL BOONEVILLE (O, 25 beds) 880 West Main Street, Booneville, AR Zip 72927–3443, Mailing Address: P.O. Box 290, Zip 72927–0290; tel. 479/675–2800; Teresa Williams, R.N., Regional Administrator
Web address: www.mercy.net

MERCY HOSPITAL FORT SMITH (O, 370 beds) 7301 Rogers Avenue, Fort Smith, AR Zip 72903–4189, Mailing Address: P.O. Box 17000, Zip 72917–7000; tel. 479/314–6000; Ryan Gehrig, President
Web address: www.mercy.net/fortsmithar

For explanation of codes following names, see page B2.
★ Indicates Type III membership in the American Hospital Association.

Section B

MERCY HOSPITAL OZARK (O, 25 beds) 801 West River Street, Ozark, AR Zip 72949–3023; tel. 479/667–4138; Teresa Williams, R.N., Administrator and Director of Nursing
Web address: www.mercy.net/northwestarar/practice/mercy–hospital–ozark

MERCY HOSPITAL PARIS (O, 16 beds) 500 East Academy, Paris, AR Zip 72855–4040; tel. 479/963–6101; Sharon D. Sorey, R.N., Administrator
Web address: www.mercy.net/fortsmithar

MERCY HOSPITAL ROGERS (O, 189 beds) 2710 Rife Medical Lane, Rogers, AR Zip 72758–1452; tel. 479/338–8000; Eric Pianalto, President
Web address: www.mercyhealthnwa.smhs.com

MERCY HOSPITAL WALDRON (O, 24 beds) 1341 West 6th Street, Waldron, AR Zip 72958–7642; tel. 479/637–4135; Nick Hunt, Interim Director of Nursing
Web address: www.stedwardmercy.com

KANSAS: MERCY HOSPITAL COLUMBUS (O, 18 beds) 220 North Pennsylvania Avenue, Columbus, KS Zip 66725–1110; tel. 620/429–2545; Angie Saporito, Administrator
Web address: www.mercy.net/newsroom–mercy–maude–norton–hospital–quick–facts

MERCY HOSPITAL FORT SCOTT (O, 49 beds) 401 Woodland Hills Boulevard, Fort Scott, KS Zip 66701–8797; tel. 620/223–2200; Reta K. Baker, President
Web address: www.mercykansas.com

MISSOURI: MERCY HOSPITAL AURORA (L, 25 beds) 500 Porter Street, Aurora, MO Zip 65605–2365; tel. 417/678–2122; Douglas M. Stroemel, President
Web address: www.stjohns.com/aboutus/aurora.aspx

MERCY HOSPITAL CARTHAGE (L, 13 beds) 3125 Drive Russell Smith Way, Carthage, MO Zip 64836–7402; tel. 417/358–8121; Robert Watson, JD, Administrator
Web address: www.mercy.net

MERCY HOSPITAL CASSVILLE (L, 18 beds) 94 Main Street, Cassville, MO Zip 65625–1610; tel. 417/847–6000; Douglas M. Stroemel, President
Web address: www.mercy.net/northwestarar/practice/mercy–hospital–cassville

MERCY HOSPITAL JEFFERSON (O, 209 beds) Highway 61 South, Crystal City, MO Zip 63019, Mailing Address: P.O. Box 350, Zip 63019–0350; tel. 636/933–1000; Eric Ammons, President
Web address: www.mercy.net/crystalcitymo

MERCY HOSPITAL JOPLIN (O, 240 beds) 100 Mercy Way, Joplin, MO Zip 64804–1626; tel. 417/781–2727; Gary W. Pulsipher, President and Chief Executive Officer
Web address: www.mercy.net/joplinmo

MERCY HOSPITAL LEBANON (O, 58 beds) 100 Hospital Drive, Lebanon, MO Zip 65536–9210; tel. 417/533–6100; David R. Steinmann, Administrator
Web address: www.mercy.net/practice/mercy–hospital–lebanon

MERCY HOSPITAL LINCOLN (L, 25 beds) 1000 East Cherry Street, Troy, MO Zip 63379–1513; tel. 636/528–8551; Anthony Rothermich, Administrator
Web address: www.mercy.net

MERCY HOSPITAL SPRINGFIELD (O, 703 beds) 1235 East Cherokee Street, Springfield, MO Zip 65804–2263; tel. 417/820–2000; Alan Scarrow, M.D., President
Web address: www.mercy.net/springfieldmo

MERCY HOSPITAL ST. LOUIS (O, 962 beds) 615 South New Ballas Road, Saint Louis, MO Zip 63141–8277; tel. 314/569–6000; Jeffrey A. Johnston, President
Web address: www.mercy.net/stlouismo

MERCY HOSPITAL WASHINGTON (O, 166 beds) 901 East Fifth Street, Washington, MO Zip 63090–3127; tel. 636/239–8000; Eric J. Eoloff, President
Web address: www.mercy.net

MERCY ST. FRANCIS HOSPITAL (O, 20 beds) 100 West Highway 60, Mountain View, MO Zip 65548–7125; tel. 417/934–7000; David R. Steinmann, Administrator
Web address: www.stjohns.com/aboutus/stfrancis.aspx

OKLAHOMA: ARBUCKLE MEMORIAL HOSPITAL (C, 13 beds) 2011 West Broadway Street, Sulphur, OK Zip 73086–4221; tel. 580/622–2161; Darin Farrell, Chief Executive Officer
Web address: www.arbucklehospital.com/

MERCY HEALTH LOVE COUNTY (C, 25 beds) 300 Wanda Street, Marietta, OK Zip 73448–1200; tel. 580/276–3347; Richard Barker, Administrator
Web address: www.mercyhealthlovecounty.com

MERCY HOSPITAL ADA (L, 156 beds) 430 North Monte Vista, Ada, OK Zip 74820–4610; tel. 580/332–2323; Lori Wightman, R.N., MSN, FACHE, Chief Executive Officer
Web address: www.mercy.net/ada

MERCY HOSPITAL ARDMORE (O, 187 beds) 1011 14th Avenue N.W., Ardmore, OK Zip 73401–1828; tel. 580/223–5400; Daryle Voss, FACHE, President
Web address: www.mercyok.net

MERCY HOSPITAL EL RENO (L, 48 beds) 2115 Parkview Drive, El Reno, OK Zip 73036–2199, Mailing Address: P.O. Box 129, Zip 73036–0129; tel. 405/262–2640; Doug Danker, Administrator
Web address: www.mercyok.net

MERCY HOSPITAL HEALDTON (L, 22 beds) 918 South 8th Street, Healdton, OK Zip 73438–0928, Mailing Address: P.O. Box 928, Zip 73438–0928; tel. 580/229–0701; Jeremy A. Jones, Administrator
Web address: www.mercyok.com

MERCY HOSPITAL KINGFISHER (L, 25 beds) 1000 Kingfisher Regional Hospital Drive, Kingfisher, OK Zip 73750–3528, Mailing Address: P.O. Box 59, Zip 73750–0059; tel. 405/375–3141; Brian Denton, Administrator
Web address: www.kingfisherhospital.com

MERCY HOSPITAL LOGAN COUNTY (O, 25 beds) 200 South Academy Road, Guthrie, OK Zip 73044–8727, Mailing Address: P.O. Box 1017, Zip 73044–1017; tel. 405/282–6700; Joshua Tucker, Administrator
Web address: www.mercy.net

MERCY HOSPITAL OKLAHOMA CITY (O, 369 beds) 4300 West Memorial Road, Oklahoma City, OK Zip 73120–8362; tel. 405/755–1515; Jim Gebhart, Jr., FACHE, President
Web address: www.mercyok.net

MERCY HOSPITAL TISHOMINGO (L, 25 beds) 1000 South Byrd Street, Tishomingo, OK Zip 73460–3299; tel. 580/371–2327; Gary Sharum, Administrator
Web address: www.mercy.net/

MERCY HOSPITAL WATONGA (L, 17 beds) 500 North Clarence Nash Boulevard, Watonga, OK Zip 73772–2845, Mailing Address: P.O. Box 370, Zip 73772–0370; tel. 580/623–7211; Bobby Stitt, R.N., Administrator
Web address: www.mercy.net/watongaok/practice/mercy–hospital–watonga

SEILING MUNICIPAL HOSPITAL (C, 18 beds) Highway 60 N.E., Seiling, OK Zip 73663, Mailing Address: P.O. Box 720, Zip 73663–0720; tel. 580/922–7361; Jennifer Coons, Acting Chief Executive Officer
Web address: www.seilinghospital.com

Owned, leased, sponsored:	29 hospitals	4054 beds
Contract–managed:	3 hospitals	56 beds
Totals:	32 hospitals	4110 beds

0649: MERCY HEALTH SYSTEM (NP)
1000 Mineral Point Avenue, Janesville, WI Zip 53548–2940, Mailing Address: P.O. Box 5003, Zip 53547–5003; tel. 608/756–6000; Javon R. Bea, President and Chief Executive Officer
(Centralized Physician/Insurance Health System)

ILLINOIS: MERCY HARVARD HOSPITAL (O, 45 beds) 901 Grant Street, Harvard, IL Zip 60033–1898, Mailing Address: P.O. Box 850, Zip 60033–0850; tel. 815/943–5431; Javon R. Bea, Chief Executive Officer
Web address: www.mercyhealthsystem.org

MERCYHEALTH ROCKTON AVENUE HOSPITAL (O, 282 beds) 2400 North Rockton Avenue, Rockford, IL Zip 61103–3655; tel. 815/971–5000; Javon Bea, President and Chief Executive Officer
Web address: www.rhsnet.org

WISCONSIN: MERCY HOSPITAL AND TRAUMA CENTER (O, 148 beds) 1000 Mineral Point Avenue, Janesville, WI Zip 53548–2982, Mailing Address: P.O. Box 5003, Zip 53547–5003; tel. 608/756–6000; Javon R. Bea, President and Chief Executive Officer
Web address: www.mercyhealthsystem.org

MERCY WALWORTH HOSPITAL AND MEDICAL CENTER (O, 15 beds) N2950 State Road 67, Lake Geneva, WI Zip 53147–2655; tel. 262/245–0535; Jennifer Hallatt, Chief Operating Officer
Web address: www.mercyhealthsystem.org

For explanation of codes following names, see page B2.
★ Indicates Type III membership in the American Hospital Association.

Owned, leased, sponsored:	4 hospitals	490 beds
Contract–managed:	0 hospitals	0 beds
Totals:	4 hospitals	490 beds

★2735: **METHODIST HEALTH SYSTEM** (NP)
1441 North Beckley Avenue, Dallas, TX Zip 75203–1201, Mailing Address: P.O. Box 655999, Zip 75265–5999; tel. 214/947–8181; Stephen L. Mansfield, Ph.D., FACHE, President and Chief Executive Officer
(Centralized Physician/Insurance Health System)

TEXAS: METHODIST CHARLTON MEDICAL CENTER (O, 290 beds) 3500 West Wheatland Road, Dallas, TX Zip 75237–3460, Mailing Address: P.O. Box 225357, Zip 75222–5357; tel. 214/947–7777; Fran Laukaitis, R.N., President
Web address: www.methodisthealthsystem.org/charlton

METHODIST DALLAS MEDICAL CENTER (O, 432 beds) 1441 North Beckley Avenue, Dallas, TX Zip 75203–1201, Mailing Address: P.O. Box 655999, Zip 75265–5999; tel. 214/947–8181; David D. Clark, FACHE, President
Web address: www.methodisthealthsystem.org/Dallas

METHODIST MANSFIELD MEDICAL CENTER (O, 167 beds) 2700 East Broad Street, Mansfield, TX Zip 76063–5899; tel. 682/622–2000; John E. Phillips, FACHE, President
Web address: www.methodisthealthsystem.org/mansfield

METHODIST RICHARDSON MEDICAL CENTER (O, 249 beds) 2831 East President George Bush Highway, Richardson, TX Zip 75082–3561; tel. 469/204–1000; E. Kenneth Hutchenrider, Jr., FACHE, President
Web address: www.methodisthealthsystem.org/richardson

Owned, leased, sponsored:	4 hospitals	1138 beds
Contract–managed:	0 hospitals	0 beds
Totals:	4 hospitals	1138 beds

9345: **METHODIST LE BONHEUR HEALTHCARE** (CO)
1211 Union Avenue, Suite 700, Memphis, TN Zip 38104–6600; tel. 901/516–0791; Gary S. Shorb, President and Chief Executive Officer
(Centralized Health System)

MISSISSIPPI: METHODIST OLIVE BRANCH HOSPITAL (O, 67 beds) 4250 Bethel Road, Olive Branch, MS Zip 38654–8737; tel. 662/932–9000; David G. Baytos, Chief Executive Officer
Web address: www.methodisthealth.org/olivebranch

TENNESSEE: METHODIST HEALTHCARE MEMPHIS HOSPITALS (O, 1397 beds) 1265 Union Avenue, Memphis, TN Zip 38104–3415; tel. 901/516–7000; Michael O. Ugwueke, President and Chief Executive Officer
Web address: www.methodisthealth.org

Owned, leased, sponsored:	2 hospitals	1464 beds
Contract–managed:	0 hospitals	0 beds
Totals:	2 hospitals	1464 beds

★0001: **MIDMICHIGAN HEALTH** (NP)
4000 Wellness Drive, Midland, MI Zip 48670–0001; tel. 989/839–3000; Diane Postler–Slattery, Ph.D., President and Chief Executive Officer
(Centralized Health System)

MICHIGAN: MIDMICHIGAN MEDICAL CENTER – ALPENA (O, 125 beds) 1501 West Chisholm Street, Alpena, MI Zip 49707–1401; tel. 989/356–7390; Karmon T. Bjella, Chief Executive Officer
Web address: www.alpenaregionalmedicalcenter.org

MIDMICHIGAN MEDICAL CENTER–CLARE (O, 49 beds) 703 North McEwan Street, Clare, MI Zip 48617–1440; tel. 989/802–5000; Raymond Stover, President and Chief Executive Officer
Web address: www.midmichigan.org

MIDMICHIGAN MEDICAL CENTER–GLADWIN (O, 25 beds) 515 Quarter Street, Gladwin, MI Zip 48624–1959; tel. 989/426–9286; Raymond Stover, President and Chief Executive Officer
Web address: www.midmichigan.org

MIDMICHIGAN MEDICAL CENTER–GRATIOT (O, 79 beds) 300 East Warwick Drive, Alma, MI Zip 48801–1014; tel. 989/463–1101; Mark A. Santamaria, President
Web address: www.midmichigan.org/gratiot

MIDMICHIGAN MEDICAL CENTER–MIDLAND (O, 308 beds) 4000 Wellness Drive, Midland, MI Zip 48670–2000; tel. 989/839–3000; Gregory H. Rogers, President
Web address: www.midmichigan.org

Owned, leased, sponsored:	5 hospitals	586 beds
Contract–managed:	0 hospitals	0 beds
Totals:	5 hospitals	586 beds

0368: **MINNESOTA DEPARTMENT OF HUMAN SERVICES** (NP)
540 Cedar Street, Saint Paul, MN Zip 55101–2208, Mailing Address: P.O. Box 64998, Zip 55164–0998; tel. 651/431–3212; Anne Barry, Deputy Commissioner
(Independent Hospital System)

MINNESOTA: ANOKA–METROPOLITAN REGIONAL TREATMENT CENTER (O, 112 beds) 3301 Seventh Avenue, Anoka, MN Zip 55303–4516; tel. 651/431–5000; Wade Brost, Interim Executive Director
Web address: www.health.state.mn.us

COMMUNITY BEHAVIORAL HEALTH HOSPITAL – ALEXANDRIA (O, 16 beds) 1610 8th Avenue East, Alexandria, MN Zip 56308–2472; tel. 320/335–6201; Jennifer Westrum, Administrator
Web address: www.health.state.mn.us

COMMUNITY BEHAVIORAL HEALTH HOSPITAL – ANNANDALE (O, 16 beds) 400 Annandale Boulevard, Annandale, MN Zip 55302–3141; tel. 651/259–3850; Pamela R. Bajari, R.N., Interim Administrator
Web address: www.health.state.mn.us

COMMUNITY BEHAVIORAL HEALTH HOSPITAL – BAXTER (O, 16 beds) 14241 Grand Oaks Drive, Baxter, MN Zip 56425–8749; tel. 218/316–3101; Richard G. Slieter, Jr., Administrator

COMMUNITY BEHAVIORAL HEALTH HOSPITAL – BEMIDJI (O, 16 beds) 800 Bemidji Avenue North, Bemidji, MN Zip 56601–3054; tel. 218/308–2400; Larry A. Laudon, Administrator

COMMUNITY BEHAVIORAL HEALTH HOSPITAL – FERGUS FALLS (O, 16 beds) 1801 West Alcott Avenue, Fergus Falls, MN Zip 56537–2661, Mailing Address: P.O. Box 478, Zip 56538–0478; tel. 218/332–5001; Brenda Schleske, Administrator

COMMUNITY BEHAVIORAL HEALTH HOSPITAL – ROCHESTER (O, 8 beds) 251 Wood Lake Drive S.E., Rochester, MN Zip 55904–5530; tel. 507/206–2561; Stephanie Juhl, Administrator
Web address: www.health.state.mn.us

COMMUNITY BEHAVIORAL HEALTH HOSPITAL – ST. PETER (O, 10 beds) 2000 Klein Street, Saint Peter, MN Zip 56082–5800; tel. 507/933–5001; Christopher Schiffer, Administrator
Web address: www.health.state.mn.us

Owned, leased, sponsored:	8 hospitals	210 beds
Contract–managed:	0 hospitals	0 beds
Totals:	8 hospitals	210 beds

★0143: **MISSION HEALTH SYSTEM** (NP)
509 Biltmore Avenue, Asheville, NC Zip 28801–4601; tel. 828/213–1111; Ronald A. Paulus, M.D., President and Chief Executive Officer
(Moderately Centralized Health System)

NORTH CAROLINA: ANGEL MEDICAL CENTER (O, 43 beds) 120 Riverview Street, Franklin, NC Zip 28734–2612, Mailing Address: P.O. Box 1209, Zip 28744–0569; tel. 828/524–8411; Karen S. Gorby, R.N., MSN, FACHE, President and Chief Nursing Officer
Web address: www.angelmed.org

ASHEVILLE SPECIALTY HOSPITAL (O, 34 beds) 428 Biltmore Avenue, 4th Floor, Asheville, NC Zip 28801–4502; tel. 828/213–5400; Robert C. Desotelle, President and Chief Executive Officer
Web address: www.missionhospitals.org/acute–care

For explanation of codes following names, see page B2.
★ Indicates Type III membership in the American Hospital Association.

Section B

BLUE RIDGE REGIONAL HOSPITAL (O, 42 beds) 125 Hospital Drive, Spruce Pine, NC Zip 28777–3035; tel. 828/765–4201; Rebecca W. Carter, MSN, R.N., FACHE, Chief Executive Officer and Chief Nursing Officer
Web address: www.spchospital.org

CAREPARTNERS HEALTH SERVICES (O, 80 beds) 68 Sweeten Creek Road, Asheville, NC Zip 28803–2318, Mailing Address: P.O. Box 15025, Zip 28813–0025; tel. 828/277–4800; Tracy Buchanan, Chief Executive Officer and President
Web address: www.carepartners.org

HIGHLANDS–CASHIERS HOSPITAL (O, 104 beds) 190 Hospital Drive, Highlands, NC Zip 28741–7600, Mailing Address: P.O. Drawer 190, Zip 28741–0190; tel. 828/526–1200; Christina Derosa, Ph.D., Interim Chief Executive Officer and Chief Nursing Officer
Web address: www.hchospital.org

MCDOWELL HOSPITAL (O, 49 beds) 430 Rankin Drive, Marion, NC Zip 28752–6568, Mailing Address: P.O. Box 730, Zip 28752–0730; tel. 828/659–5000; Carol C. Wolfenbarger, FACHE, MSN, President and Chief Executive Officer
Web address: www.mission–health.org

MISSION HOSPITAL (O, 763 beds) 509 Biltmore Avenue, Asheville, NC Zip 28801–4690; tel. 828/213–1111; Jill Hoggard Green, Ph.D., R.N., President
Web address: www.mission–health.org

TRANSYLVANIA REGIONAL HOSPITAL (O, 30 beds) 260 Hospital Drive, Brevard, NC Zip 28712–3378; tel. 828/884–9111; Melina Arrowood, Interim President and Chief Nursing Officer
Web address: www.trhospital.org

Owned, leased, sponsored:	8 hospitals	1145 beds
Contract–managed:	0 hospitals	0 beds
Totals:	8 hospitals	1145 beds

★2475: MISSISSIPPI COUNTY HOSPITAL SYSTEM (NP)
1520 North Division Street, Blytheville, AR Zip 72315–1448, Mailing Address: P.O. Box 108, Zip 72316–0108; tel. 870/838–7300; Chris Raymer, R.N., Chief Executive Officer

GREAT RIVER MEDICAL CENTER (O, 73 beds) P.O. Box 108, Blytheville, AR Zip 72316–0108; tel. 870/838–7300; Chris Raymer, Chief Executive Officer
Web address: http://www.mchsys.org

SOUTH MISSISSIPPI COUNTY REGIONAL MEDICAL CENTER (O, 25 beds) P.O. Box 108, Blytheville, AR Zip 72316–0108; tel. 870/563–7000; Chris Raymer, Chief Executive Officer
Web address: http://www.mchsys.org

Owned, leased, sponsored:	2 hospitals	98 beds
Contract–managed:	0 hospitals	0 beds
Totals:	2 hospitals	98 beds

0017: MISSISSIPPI STATE DEPARTMENT OF MENTAL HEALTH (NP)
1101 Robert East Lee Building, 239 North Lamar Street, Jackson, MS Zip 39201–1101; tel. 601/359–1288; Edwin C. LeGrand, III, Executive Director
(Independent Hospital System)

MISSISSIPPI: EAST MISSISSIPPI STATE HOSPITAL (O, 411 beds) 1818 College Drive, Meridian, MS Zip 39307, Mailing Address: Box 4128, West Station, Zip 39304–4128; tel. 601/482–6186; Charles Carlisle, Director
Web address: www.emsh.state.ms.us

MISSISSIPPI STATE HOSPITAL (O, 395 beds) 3550 Highway 468 West, Whitfield, MS Zip 39193–5529, Mailing Address: P.O. Box 157–A, Zip 39193–0157; tel. 601/351–8000; James G. Chastain, FACHE, Director
Web address: www.msh.state.ms.us

NORTH MISSISSIPPI STATE HOSPITAL (O, 50 beds) 1937 Briar Ridge Road, Tupelo, MS Zip 38804–5963; tel. 662/690–4200; Paul A. Callens, Ph.D., Director
Web address: www.nmsh.state.ms.us

SOUTH MISSISSIPPI STATE HOSPITAL (O, 50 beds) 823 Highway 589, Purvis, MS Zip 39475–4194; tel. 601/794–0100; Clint Ashley, Director
Web address: www.smsh.state.ms.us

Owned, leased, sponsored:	4 hospitals	906 beds
Contract–managed:	0 hospitals	0 beds
Totals:	4 hospitals	906 beds

★0970: MONONGALIA HEALTH SYSTEM (NP)
1200 J. D. Anderson Drive, Morgantown, WV Zip 26505–3494; tel. 304/598–1200; Darryl L. Duncan, President and Chief Executive Officer
(Independent Hospital System)

WEST VIRGINIA: MONONGALIA GENERAL HOSPITAL (O, 185 beds) 1200 J. D. Anderson Drive, Morgantown, WV Zip 26505–3486; tel. 304/598–1200; Darryl L. Duncan, President and Chief Executive Officer
Web address: www.mongeneral.com

PRESTON MEMORIAL HOSPITAL (O, 25 beds) 150 Memorial Drive, Kingwood, WV Zip 26537–1495; tel. 304/329–1400; Melissa Lockwood, Chief Executive Officer
Web address: www.prestonmemorial.org

Owned, leased, sponsored:	2 hospitals	210 beds
Contract–managed:	0 hospitals	0 beds
Totals:	2 hospitals	210 beds

0343: MONTEFIORE HEALTH SYSTEM (NP)
111 East 210th Street, Bronx, NY Zip 10467–2490; tel. 718/920–4321; Steven M. Safyer, M.D., President and CEO
(Centralized Health System)

NEW YORK: MONTEFIORE MEDICAL CENTER (O, 1498 beds) 111 East 210th Street, Bronx, NY Zip 10467–2401; tel. 718/920–4321; Steven M. Safyer, M.D., President and Chief Executive Officer
Web address: www.montefiore.org

MONTEFIORE MOUNT VERNON (O, 65 beds) 12 North Seventh Avenue, Mount Vernon, NY Zip 10550–2098; tel. 914/664–8000; Jaccel Kouns, R.N., MS, Vice President and Executive Director
Web address: www.montefiorehealthsystem.org/landing.cfm?id=17

MONTEFIORE NEW ROCHELLE (O, 255 beds) 16 Guion Place, New Rochelle, NY Zip 10801–5502; tel. 914/632–5000; Anthony Alfano, Vice President Executive Director
Web address: www.montefiorehealthsystem.org

Owned, leased, sponsored:	3 hospitals	1818 beds
Contract–managed:	0 hospitals	0 beds
Totals:	3 hospitals	1818 beds

1335: MORTON PLANT MEASE HEALTH CARE (NP)
300 Pinellas Street, Clearwater, FL Zip 33756–3804, Mailing Address: P.O. Box 210, Zip 33757–0210; tel. 727/462–7000; Glenn D. Waters, FACHE, President

FLORIDA: MORTON PLANT HOSPITAL (O, 620 beds) 300 Pinellas Street, Clearwater, FL Zip 33756–3804, Mailing Address: P.O. Box 210, Zip 33757–0210; tel. 727/462–7000; N. Kristopher Hoce, President
Web address: www.mortonplant.com

MORTON PLANT NORTH BAY HOSPITAL (O, 226 beds) 6600 Madison Street, New Port Richey, FL Zip 34652–1900; tel. 727/842–8468; Michael Yungmann, President
Web address: www.mpmhealth.com

MORTON PLANT REHABILITATION CENTER (O, 126 beds) 400 Corbett Street, Belleair, FL Zip 34640; tel. 813/462–7600; Linda A. Kirk, Administrator

Owned, leased, sponsored:	3 hospitals	972 beds
Contract–managed:	0 hospitals	0 beds
Totals:	3 hospitals	972 beds

★0917: MOUNT SINAI HEALTH SYSTEM (NP)
One Gustave L. Levy Place, New York, NY Zip 10029; tel. 212/659–8888; Kenneth L. Davis, M.D., President and Chief Executive
(Centralized Health System)

For explanation of codes following names, see page B2.
★ Indicates Type III membership in the American Hospital Association.

NEW YORK: MOUNT SINAI BETH ISRAEL (O, 1028 beds) First Avenue and 16th Street, New York, NY Zip 10003–3803; tel. 212/420–2000; Susan Somerville, R.N., President
Web address: www.bethisraelny.org

MOUNT SINAI HOSPITAL (O, 1175 beds) One Gustave L. Levy Place, New York, NY Zip 10029–0310; tel. 212/241–6500; David L. Reich, M.D., President and Chief Operating Officer
Web address: www.mountsinai.org

MOUNT SINAI ST. LUKE'S – ROOSEVELT (O, 671 beds) 1111 Amsterdam Avenue, New York, NY Zip 10025–1716; tel. 212/523–4000; Arthur A. Gianelli, M.P.H., President
Web address: www.stlukeshospitalnyc.org

NEW YORK EYE AND EAR INFIRMARY OF MOUNT SINAI (O, 32 beds) 310 East 14th Street, New York, NY Zip 10003–4201; tel. 212/979–4000; James Tsai, M.D., President
Web address: www.nyee.edu

Owned, leased, sponsored:	4 hospitals	2906 beds
Contract–managed:	0 hospitals	0 beds
Totals:	4 hospitals	2906 beds

0167: MOUNTAIN STATES HEALTH ALLIANCE (NP)
400 North State of Franklin Road, Johnson City, TN Zip 37604–6035; tel. 423/302–3423; Alan M. Levine, President and Chief Executive Officer
(Centralized Health System)

TENNESSEE: FRANKLIN WOODS COMMUNITY HOSPITAL (O, 80 beds) 300 MedTech Parkway, Johnson City, TN Zip 37604–2277; tel. 423/302–1000; Lindy P. White, Chief Executive Officer
Web address: www.msha.com

INDIAN PATH MEDICAL CENTER (O, 239 beds) 2000 Brookside Drive, Kingsport, TN Zip 37660–4627; tel. 423/857–7000; Monty E. McLaurin, President and Chief Executive Officer
Web address: www.msha.com

JOHNSON CITY MEDICAL CENTER (O, 585 beds) 400 North State of Franklin Road, Johnson City, TN Zip 37604–6094; tel. 423/431–6111; Melody Trimble, Chief Executive Officer
Web address: www.msha.com

JOHNSON COUNTY COMMUNITY HOSPITAL (O, 2 beds) 1901 South Shady Street, Mountain City, TN Zip 37683–2271; tel. 423/727–1100; Chastity Trivette, Chief Executive Officer
Web address: www.msha.com

SYCAMORE SHOALS HOSPITAL (O, 121 beds) 1501 West Elk Avenue, Elizabethton, TN Zip 37643–2874; tel. 423/542–1300; Dwayne Taylor, Chief Executive Officer
Web address: www.msha.com

VIRGINIA: DICKENSON COMMUNITY HOSPITAL (O, 1 beds) 312 Hospital Drive, Clintwood, VA Zip 24228, Mailing Address: P.O. Box 1440, Zip 24228–1440; tel. 276/926–0300; Mark T. Leonard, Chief Executive Officer
Web address: www.msha.com/dch

JOHNSTON MEMORIAL HOSPITAL (O, 116 beds) 16000 Johnston Memorial Drive, Abingdon, VA Zip 24211–7659; tel. 276/258–1000; Stan Hickson, FACHE, President and Chief Executive Officer
Web address: www.jmh.org

NORTON COMMUNITY HOSPITAL (O, 129 beds) 100 15th Street N.W., Norton, VA Zip 24273–1616; tel. 276/679–9600; Mark T. Leonard, Chief Executive Officer
Web address: www.msha.com/nch

RUSSELL COUNTY MEDICAL CENTER (O, 78 beds) 58 Carroll Street, Lebanon, VA Zip 24266, Mailing Address: P.O. Box 3600, Zip 24266–0200; tel. 276/883–8000; Stephen K. Givens, Assistant Vice President and Administrator
Web address: www.mountainstateshealth.com/rcmc

SMYTH COUNTY COMMUNITY HOSPITAL (O, 153 beds) 245 Medical Park Drive, Marion, VA Zip 24354, Mailing Address: P.O. Box 880, Zip 24354–0880; tel. 276/378–1000; Stan Hickson, FACHE, President and Chief Executive Officer
Web address: www.msha.com/scch

Owned, leased, sponsored:	10 hospitals	1504 beds
Contract–managed:	0 hospitals	0 beds
Totals:	10 hospitals	1504 beds

6555: MULTICARE HEALTH SYSTEM (NP)
315 Martin Luther King Jr. Way, Tacoma, WA Zip 98405–4234, Mailing Address: P.O. Box 5299, Zip 98415–0299; tel. 253/403–1000; William G. Robertson, President and Chief Executive Officer
(Centralized Physician/Insurance Health System)

WASHINGTON: MULTICARE AUBURN MEDICAL CENTER (O, 133 beds) 202 North Division, Plaza One, Auburn, WA Zip 98001–4908; tel. 253/833–7711; Glenn Kasman, President and Market Leader
Web address: www.https://www.multicare.org/auburn-medical-center/

MULTICARE GOOD SAMARITAN HOSPITAL (O, 286 beds) 401 15th Avenue S.E., Puyallup, WA Zip 98372–3770, Mailing Address: P.O. Box 1247, Zip 98371–0192; tel. 253/697–4000; Glenn Kasman, President and Market Leader
Web address: www.multicare.org/good-samaritan-hospital/

MULTICARE MARY BRIDGE CHILDREN'S HOSPITAL AND HEALTH CENTER (O, 75 beds) 317 Martin Luther King Jr. Way, Tacoma, WA Zip 98405–4234, Mailing Address: P.O. Box 5299, Zip 98415–0299; tel. 253/403–1400; Linda Chen, President and Market Leader
Web address: www.multicare.org/marybridge

MULTICARE TACOMA GENERAL HOSPITAL (O, 366 beds) 315 Martin Luther King Jr. Way, Tacoma, WA Zip 98405–4234, Mailing Address: P.O. Box 5299, Zip 98415–0299; tel. 253/403–1000; Shelly Mullin, R.N., President and Market Leader
Web address: www.multicare.org

Owned, leased, sponsored:	4 hospitals	860 beds
Contract–managed:	0 hospitals	0 beds
Totals:	4 hospitals	860 beds

★1465: MUNSON HEALTHCARE (NP)
1105 Sixth Street, Traverse City, MI Zip 49684–2386; tel. 231/935–6703; Edwin Ness, President and Chief Executive Officer
(Centralized Health System)

MICHIGAN: KALKASKA MEMORIAL HEALTH CENTER (C, 96 beds) 419 South Coral Street, Kalkaska, MI Zip 49646–2503; tel. 231/258–7500; Kevin L. Rogols, FACHE, Administrator
Web address: www.munsonhealthcare.org

MUNSON HEALTHCARE CADILLAC HOSPITAL (O, 65 beds) 400 Hobart Street, Cadillac, MI Zip 49601–2389; tel. 231/876–7200; Tonya Smith, President
Web address: www.mercyhealthcadillac.com/welcome-cadillac

MUNSON HEALTHCARE CHARLEVOIX HOSPITAL (O, 25 beds) 14700 Lake Shore Drive, Charlevoix, MI Zip 49720–1999; tel. 231/547–4024; Lyn Jenks, Chief Executive Officer
Web address: www.cah.org

MUNSON HEALTHCARE GRAYLING HOSPITAL (O, 110 beds) 1100 East Michigan Avenue, Grayling, MI Zip 49738–1312; tel. 989/348–5461; Stephanie J. Riemer, President
Web address: www.mercygrayling.munsonhealthcare.org/

MUNSON MEDICAL CENTER (O, 391 beds) 1105 Sixth Street, Traverse City, MI Zip 49684–2386; tel. 231/935–5000; Alfred E. Pilong, Jr., FACHE, President, Munson Medical Center and Chief Operating Officer, Munson HEalthcare
Web address: www.munsonhealthcare.org

PAUL OLIVER MEMORIAL HOSPITAL (O, 47 beds) 224 Park Avenue, Frankfort, MI Zip 49635–9658; tel. 231/352–2200; Peter Marinoff, President
Web address: www.munsonhealthcare.org

Owned, leased, sponsored:	5 hospitals	638 beds
Contract–managed:	1 hospital	96 beds
Totals:	6 hospitals	734 beds

For explanation of codes following names, see page B2.
★ Indicates Type III membership in the American Hospital Association.

Section B

0261: NATIONAL SURGICAL HEALTHCARE (IO)
250 South Wacker Drive, Suite 500, Chicago, IL Zip 60606–5897; tel. 312/627–8400; David Crane, Chief Executive Officer
(Independent Hospital System)

ARIZONA: ARIZONA SPINE AND JOINT HOSPITAL (O, 23 beds) 4620 East Baseline Road, Mesa, AZ Zip 85206–4624; tel. 480/832–4770; Todd Greene, Chief Executive Officer
Web address: www.azspineandjoint.com

GEORGIA: OPTIM MEDICAL CENTER – SCREVEN (O, 25 beds) 215 Mims Road, Sylvania, GA Zip 30467–2097; tel. 912/564–7426; Robert R. Sellers, Chief Executive Officer
Web address: www.optimhealth.com

OPTIM MEDICAL CENTER – TATTNALL (O, 25 beds) 247 South Main Street, Reidsville, GA Zip 30453–4605; tel. 912/557–1000; Rob Snipes, Administrator
Web address: www.tattnallhospital.com

IDAHO: NORTHWEST SPECIALTY HOSPITAL (O, 34 beds) 1593 East Polston Avenue, Post Falls, ID Zip 83854–5326; tel. 208/262–2300; Rick Rasmussen, Chief Executive Officer
Web address: www.northwestspecialtyhospital.com

LOUISIANA: LAFAYETTE SURGICAL SPECIALTY HOSPITAL (O, 20 beds) 1101 Kaliste Saloom Road, Lafayette, LA Zip 70508–5705; tel. 337/769–4100; Buffy Domingue, Chief Executive Officer
Web address: www.lafayettesurgical.com

MICHIGAN: SOUTHEAST MICHIGAN SURGICAL HOSPITAL (O, 13 beds) 21230 Dequindre, Warren, MI Zip 48091–2287; tel. 586/427–1000; Yvonne Kughn, Chief Executive Officer
Web address: www.nshinc.com

NORTH CAROLINA: NORTH CAROLINA SPECIALTY HOSPITAL (O, 18 beds) 3916 Ben Franklin Boulevard, Durham, NC Zip 27704–2383, Mailing Address: PO Box 15819, Zip 27704–2383; tel. 919/956–9300; Randi L. Shults, Chief Executive Officer
Web address: www.ncspecialty.com

TEXAS: EL PASO SPECIALTY HOSPITAL (O, 27 beds) 1755 Curie Drive, El Paso, TX Zip 79902–2919; tel. 915/544–3636; James Wilcox, Chief Executive Officer
Web address: www.elpasospecialtyhospital.com

SOUTH TEXAS SPINE AND SURGICAL HOSPITAL (O, 30 beds) 18600 Hardy Oak Boulevard, San Antonio, TX Zip 78258–4206; tel. 210/507–4090; Thomas Klawiter, Chief Executive Officer
Web address: www.southtexassurgical.com

SOUTH TEXAS SURGICAL HOSPITAL (O, 20 beds) 6130 Parkway Drive, Corpus Christi, TX Zip 78414–2455; tel. 361/993–2000; James Murphy, Chief Executive Officer
Web address: www.southtexassurgicalhospital.com

WISCONSIN: OAKLEAF SURGICAL HOSPITAL (O, 13 beds) 3802 West Oakwood Mall Drive, Eau Claire, WI Zip 54701–3016; tel. 715/831–8130; Anne Hargrave–Thomas, Chief Executive Officer
Web address: www.oakleafmedical.com

WYOMING: MOUNTAIN VIEW REGIONAL HOSPITAL (O, 23 beds) 6550 East Second Street, Casper, WY Zip 82609–4321, Mailing Address: P.O. Box 51888, Zip 82605–1888; tel. 307/995–8100; Thomas Kopitnik, Acting Chief Executive Officer
Web address: www.mountainviewregionalhospital.com

Owned, leased, sponsored:	12 hospitals	271 beds
Contract–managed:	0 hospitals	0 beds
Totals:	12 hospitals	271 beds

0923: NAVICENT HEALTH (NP)
777 Hemlock Street, MSC 105, Macon, GA Zip 31201–2155, Mailing Address: 777 Hemlock Street, Zip 31201–2155; tel. 478/633–1000; Ninfa M. Saunders, Chief Executive Officer
(Centralized Health System)

GEORGIA: MEDICAL CENTER OF PEACH COUNTY, NAVICENT HEALTH (O, 25 beds) 1960 Highway 247 Connector, Bryon, GA Zip 31008; tel. 478/654–2000; Darren Pearce, Administrator and Chief Executive Officer
Web address: www.navicenthealth.org

MEDICAL CENTER, NAVICENT HEALTH (O, 659 beds) 777 Hemlock Street, Macon, GA Zip 31201–2155; tel. 478/633–1000; Ninfa M. Saunders, Chief Executive Officer
Web address: www.https://www.navicenthealth.org/

REHABILITATION HOSPITAL, NAVICENT HEALTH (O, 58 beds) 3351 Northside Drive, Macon, GA Zip 31210–2587; tel. 478/201–6500; Gina Tipton, Director of Operations
Web address: www.centralgarehab.com

Owned, leased, sponsored:	3 hospitals	742 beds
Contract–managed:	0 hospitals	0 beds
Totals:	3 hospitals	742 beds

★9265: NEBRASKA METHODIST HEALTH SYSTEM, INC. (CO)
8511 West Dodge Road, Omaha, NE Zip 68114–3403; tel. 402/354–5411; John M. Fraser, FACHE, President and Chief Executive Officer
(Centralized Physician/Insurance Health System)

IOWA: METHODIST JENNIE EDMUNDSON HOSPITAL (O, 114 beds) 933 East Pierce Street, Council Bluffs, IA Zip 51503–4652, Mailing Address: P.O. Box 2C, Zip 51502–3002; tel. 712/396–6000; Steven P. Baumert, President and Chief Executive Officer
Web address: www.bestcare.org

NEBRASKA: NEBRASKA METHODIST HOSPITAL (O, 377 beds) 8303 Dodge Street, Omaha, NE Zip 68114–4199; tel. 402/354–4000; Stephen L. Goeser, FACHE, President and Chief Executive Officer
Web address: www.bestcare.org

Owned, leased, sponsored:	2 hospitals	491 beds
Contract–managed:	0 hospitals	0 beds
Totals:	2 hospitals	491 beds

0892: NEMOURS (NP)
10140 Centurion Parkway North, Jacksonville, FL Zip 32256–0532; tel. 904/697–4100; David J. Bailey, M.D., President and Chief Executive Officer
(Independent Hospital System)

DELAWARE: ALFRED I. DUPONT HOSPITAL FOR CHILDREN (O, 194 beds) 1600 Rockland Road, Wilmington, DE Zip 19803–3616, Mailing Address: Box 269, Zip 19899–0269; tel. 302/651–4000; Roy Proujansky, M.D., Chief Executive Officer
Web address: www.nemours.org

FLORIDA: NEMOURS CHILDREN'S HOSPITAL (O, 64 beds) 13535 Nemours Parkway, Orlando, FL Zip 32827–7402; tel. 407/567–4000; Dana Bledsoe, MS, R.N., Chief Executive Officer
Web address: www.nemours.org

Owned, leased, sponsored:	2 hospitals	258 beds
Contract–managed:	0 hospitals	0 beds
Totals:	2 hospitals	258 beds

0620: NEUROPSYCHIATRIC HOSPITALS (IO)
1625 East Jefferson Boulevard, Mishawaka, IN Zip 46545–7103; tel. 574/255–1400; Cameron R. Gilbert, Ph.D., President and Chief Executive Officer

INDIANA: DOCTORS NEUROMEDICAL HOSPITAL (O, 20 beds) 411 South Whitlock Street, Bremen, IN Zip 46506–1626, Mailing Address: P.O. Box 36, Zip 46506–0036; tel. 574/546–3830; Alan Fisher, Chief Executive Officer
Web address: www.physicianshospitalsystem.net

DOCTORS NEUROPSYCHIATRIC HOSPITAL AND RESEARCH INSTITUTE (O, 20 beds) 417 South Whitlock Street, Bremen, IN Zip 46506–1626; tel. 574/546–0330; Christy Gilbert, Interim Chief Executive Officer

For explanation of codes following names, see page B2.
★ Indicates Type III membership in the American Hospital Association.

RIVERCREST SPECIALTY HOSPITAL (O, 30 beds) 1625 East Jefferson Boulevard, Mishawaka, IN Zip 46545–7103; tel. 574/255–1400; Christy Gilbert, Chief Executive Officer
Web address: www.physicianshospitalsystem.net/

Owned, leased, sponsored:	3 hospitals	70 beds
Contract–managed:	0 hospitals	0 beds
Totals:	3 hospitals	70 beds

★**0213: NEW HANOVER REGIONAL MEDICAL CENTER** (NP)
2131 South 17th Street, Wilmington, NC Zip 28401–7407; tel. 910/343–7040; John K. Barto, Jr., President and Chief Executive Officer
(Moderately Centralized Health System)

NORTH CAROLINA: NEW HANOVER REGIONAL MEDICAL CENTER (O, 692 beds) 2131 South 17th Street, Wilmington, NC Zip 28401–7483, Mailing Address: P.O. Box 9000, Zip 28402–9000; tel. 910/343–7000; John H. Gizdic, President and Chief Operating Officer
Web address: www.nhrmc.org

PENDER MEMORIAL HOSPITAL (C, 68 beds) 507 East Freemont Street, Burgaw, NC Zip 28425–5131; tel. 910/259–5451; Ruth Glaser, President
Web address: www.pendermemorial.org

Owned, leased, sponsored:	1 hospital	692 beds
Contract–managed:	1 hospital	68 beds
Totals:	2 hospitals	760 beds

0142: NEW YORK PRESBYTERIAN REGIONAL HOSPITAL NETWORK (NP)
525 East 68th Street, Box 182, New York, NY Zip 10065; tel. 212/746–3745; Steven J. Corwin, M.D., President and Chief Executive Officer
(Moderately Centralized Health System)

NEW YORK: NEW YORK–PRESBYTERIAN HOSPITAL (O, 2381 beds) 525 East 68th Street, New York, NY Zip 10065–4870; tel. 212/746–5454; Steven J. Corwin, M.D., President and Chief Executive Officer
Web address: www.nyp.org

NEW YORK–PRESBYTERIAN/HUDSON VALLEY HOSPITAL (O, 128 beds) 1980 Crompond Road, Cortlandt Manor, NY Zip 10567–4182; tel. 914/737–9000; Stacey Petrower, President
Web address: www.hvhc.org

NEW YORK–PRESBYTERIAN/LAWRENCE HOSPITAL (O, 205 beds) 55 Palmer Avenue, Bronxville, NY Zip 10708–3403; tel. 914/787–1000; Michael Fosina, M.P.H., FACHE, President
Web address: www.lawrencehealth.org

NEW YORK–PRESBYTERIAN/QUEENS (O, 519 beds) 56–45 Main Street, Flushing, NY Zip 11355–5045; tel. 718/670–1231; Jaclyn Mucaria, President and Chief Executive Officer
Web address: www.nyhq.org

Owned, leased, sponsored:	4 hospitals	3233 beds
Contract–managed:	0 hospitals	0 beds
Totals:	4 hospitals	3233 beds

0009: NEW YORK STATE OFFICE OF MENTAL HEALTH (NP)
44 Holland Avenue, Albany, NY Zip 12208–3411; tel. 518/474–7056; Kristin M. Woodlock, R.N., Acting Commissioner
(Independent Hospital System)

BRONX PSYCHIATRIC CENTER (O, 450 beds) 1500 Waters Place, Bronx, NY Zip 10461–2796; tel. 718/931–0600; Anita Daniels, Director
Web address: www.omh.ny.gov

BUFFALO PSYCHIATRIC CENTER (O, 240 beds) 400 Forest Avenue, Buffalo, NY Zip 14213–1298; tel. 716/885–2261; Thomas Dodson, Executive Director
Web address: www.omh.ny.gov

CAPITAL DISTRICT PSYCHIATRIC CENTER (O, 200 beds) 75 New Scotland Avenue, Albany, NY Zip 12208–3474; tel. 518/549–6000; William Dickson, Executive Director
Web address: www.omh.ny.gov/omhweb/facilities/cdpc/facility.htm

CENTRAL NEW YORK PSYCHIATRIC CENTER (O, 226 beds) 9005 Old River Road, Marcy, NY Zip 13403–3000, Mailing Address: P.O. Box 300, Zip 13403–0300; tel. 315/765–3600; Maureen Bosco, Executive Director
Web address: www.omh.ny.gov

CREEDMOOR PSYCHIATRIC CENTER (O, 380 beds) 79–25 Winchester Boulevard, Jamaica, NY Zip 11427–2128; tel. 718/264–3600; Ann Marie Barbarotta, Executive Director
Web address: www.omh.ny.gov

ELMIRA PSYCHIATRIC CENTER (O, 100 beds) 100 Washington Street, Elmira, NY Zip 14901–2898; tel. 607/737–4739; Mark Stephany, Executive Director
Web address: www.omh.ny.gov/omhweb/facilities/elpc/facility.htm

GREATER BINGHAMTON HEALTH CENTER (O, 115 beds) 425 Robinson Street, Binghamton, NY Zip 13904–1735; tel. 607/724–1391; Mark Stephany, Executive Director
Web address: www.omh.ny.gov/omhweb/facilities/bipc/facility.htm

KINGSBORO PSYCHIATRIC CENTER (O, 290 beds) 681 Clarkson Avenue, Brooklyn, NY Zip 11203–2125; tel. 718/221–7395; Deborah Parchment, Executive Director
Web address: www.omh.ny.gov/omhweb/facilities/kbpc/facility.htm

MANHATTAN PSYCHIATRIC CENTER–WARD'S ISLAND (O, 745 beds) 600 East 125th Street, New York, NY Zip 10035–6000; tel. 646/672–6767; Vincent Miccoli, Executive Director
Web address: www.omh.ny.gov

MID–HUDSON FORENSIC PSYCHIATRIC CENTER (O, 169 beds) Route 17M, New Hampton, NY Zip 10958, Mailing Address: P.O. Box 158, Zip 10958–0158; tel. 845/374–8700; Joseph Freebern, Executive Director
Web address: www.omh.ny.gov

MOHAWK VALLEY PSYCHIATRIC CENTER (O, 614 beds) 1400 Noyes Street, Utica, NY Zip 13502–3854; tel. 315/738–3800; Colleen A. Sawyer, R.N., MSN, Executive Director
Web address: www.omh.ny.gov/omhweb/facilities/mvpc/facility.htm

NEW YORK CITY CHILDREN'S CENTER (O, 84 beds) 74–03 Commonwealth Boulevard, Jamaica, NY Zip 11426–1890; tel. 718/264–4506; Anita Daniels, Executive Director
Web address: www.omh.ny.gov/omhweb/facilities/nyccc/

NEW YORK STATE PSYCHIATRIC INSTITUTE (O, 58 beds) 1051 Riverside Drive, New York, NY Zip 10032–1007; tel. 212/543–5000; Jeffrey A. Lieberman, M.D., Executive Director
Web address: www.nyspi.org

PILGRIM PSYCHIATRIC CENTER (O, 569 beds) 998 Crooked Hill Road, Brentwood, NY Zip 11717–1019; tel. 631/761–3500; Kathy O'Keefe, Executive Director
Web address: www.omh.ny.gov/omhweb/facilities/pgpc/facility.htm

RICHARD H. HUTCHINGS PSYCHIATRIC CENTER (O, 131 beds) 620 Madison Street, Syracuse, NY Zip 13210–2319; tel. 315/426–3632; Colleen A. Sawyer, R.N., MSN, Executive Director
Web address: www.omh.ny.gov

ROCHESTER PSYCHIATRIC CENTER (O, 180 beds) 1111 Elmwood Avenue, Rochester, NY Zip 14620–3005; tel. 585/241–1200; Philip Griffin, Director of Operations
Web address: www.omh.ny.gov/omhweb/facilities/ropc/facility.htm

ROCKLAND CHILDREN'S PSYCHIATRIC CENTER (O, 54 beds) 599 Convent Road, Orangeburg, NY Zip 10962–1162; tel. 845/359–7400; Christopher Tavella, Acting Executive Director
Web address: www.omh.ny.gov/

ROCKLAND PSYCHIATRIC CENTER (O, 525 beds) 140 Old Orangeburg Road, Orangeburg, NY Zip 10962–1157; tel. 845/359–1000; Christopher Tavella, Executive Director
Web address: www.omh.ny.gov/

SAGAMORE CHILDREN'S PSYCHIATRIC CENTER (O, 69 beds) 197 Half Hollow Road, Dix Hills, NY Zip 11746–5861; tel. 631/370–1700; Kathy O'Keefe, Interim Executive Director
Web address: www.omh.ny.gov

SOUTH BEACH PSYCHIATRIC CENTER (O, 340 beds) 777 Seaview Avenue, Staten Island, NY Zip 10305–3409; tel. 718/667–2300; Rosanne Gaylor, M.D., Acting Executive Director
Web address: www.omh.ny.gov/omhweb/facilities/sbpc/facility.htm

ST. LAWRENCE PSYCHIATRIC CENTER (O, 146 beds) 1 Chimney Point Drive, Ogdensburg, NY Zip 13669–2291; tel. 315/541–2001; Timothy Farrell, Executive Director
Web address: www.omh.ny.gov/omhweb/facilities/slpc/facility.htm

Section B

For explanation of codes following names, see page B2.
★ Indicates Type III membership in the American Hospital Association.

WESTERN NEW YORK CHILDREN'S PSYCHIATRIC CENTER (O, 46 beds) 1010 East and West Road, West Seneca, NY Zip 14224–3602; tel. 716/677–7000; Kathe Hayes, Executive Director
Web address: www.omh.ny.gov

Owned, leased, sponsored:	22 hospitals	5731 beds
Contract–managed:	0 hospitals	0 beds
Totals:	22 hospitals	5731 beds

0353: NEXUS HEALTH SYSTEMS (IO)
One Riverway, Suite 600, Houston, TX Zip 77056–1993; tel. 713/355–6111; John W. Cassidy, M.D., President, Chief Executive Officer and Chief Medical Officer
(Independent Hospital System)

CALIFORNIA: HEALTHBRIDGE CHILDREN'S HOSPITAL (O, 27 beds) 393 South Tustin Street, Orange, CA Zip 92866–2501; tel. 714/289–2400; Alex Villarruz, Chief Executive Officer
Web address: www.HealthBridgeOrange.com

TEXAS: HEALTHBRIDGE CHILDREN'S HOSPITAL OF HOUSTON (O, 37 beds) 2929 Woodland Park Drive, Houston, TX Zip 77082–2687; tel. 281/293–7774; Tony Bonilla, Chief Executive Officer
Web address: www.healthbridgehouston.com/

NEXUS SPECIALTY HOSPITAL (O, 75 beds) 123 Vision Park Boulevard, Shenandoah, TX Zip 77384–3001; tel. 281/364–0317; Mikael Simpson, Chief Executive Officer
Web address: www.nexusspecialty.com

Owned, leased, sponsored:	3 hospitals	139 beds
Contract–managed:	0 hospitals	0 beds
Totals:	3 hospitals	139 beds

0349: NOLAND HEALTH SERVICES, INC. (NP)
600 Corporate Parkway, Suite 100, Birmingham, AL Zip 35242–5451; tel. 205/783–8484; Gary M. Glasscock, President and Chief Executive Officer

ALABAMA: NOLAND HOSPITAL ANNISTON (O, 38 beds) 400 East 10th Street, 4th Floor, Anniston, AL Zip 36207–4716; tel. 256/741–6141; Trina Woods, Administrator
Web address: www.nolandhealth.com

NOLAND HOSPITAL BIRMINGHAM (O, 45 beds) 50 Medical Park East Drive, 8th Floor, Birmingham, AL Zip 35235; tel. 205/808–5100; Laura S. Wills, Administrator
Web address: www.nolandhealth.com

NOLAND HOSPITAL DOTHAN (O, 38 beds) 1108 Ross Clark Circle, 4th Floor, Dothan, AL Zip 36301–3022; tel. 334/699–4300; Kaye Burk, Administrator
Web address: www.nolandhealth.com

NOLAND HOSPITAL MONTGOMERY (O, 65 beds) 1725 Pine Street, 5 North, Montgomery, AL Zip 36106–1109; tel. 334/240–0532; Dale Jones, Administrator
Web address: www.nolandhealth.com

NOLAND HOSPITAL SHELBY (O, 15 beds) 1000 First Street North, 3rd Floor, Alabaster, AL Zip 35007–8703; tel. 205/620–8641; Laura S. Wills, Administrator
Web address: www.nolandhospitals.com

NOLAND HOSPITAL TUSCALOOSA (O, 32 beds) 809 University Boulevard E, 4th Floor, Tuscaloosa, AL Zip 35401–2029; tel. 205/759–7241; Jack Gibson, Administrator
Web address: www.nolandhealth.com

Owned, leased, sponsored:	6 hospitals	233 beds
Contract–managed:	0 hospitals	0 beds
Totals:	6 hospitals	233 beds

★0887: NORTH MEMORIAL HEALTH CARE (NP)
3300 Oakdale Avenue North, Robbinsdale, MN Zip 55422–2926; tel. 763/520–5200; J. Kevin Croston, M.D., Chief Executive Officer
(Centralized Physician/Insurance Health System)

MINNESOTA: MAPLE GROVE HOSPITAL (C, 108 beds) 9875 Hospital Drive, Maple Grove, MN Zip 55369–4648; tel. 763/581–1000; Andrew S. Cochrane, Chief Executive Officer
Web address: www.maplegrovehospital.org

NORTH MEMORIAL MEDICAL CENTER (O, 355 beds) 3300 Oakdale Avenue North, Robbinsdale, MN Zip 55422–2926; tel. 763/520–5200; Jeff Wicklander, President
Web address: www.northmemorial.com

Owned, leased, sponsored:	1 hospital	355 beds
Contract–managed:	1 hospital	108 beds
Totals:	2 hospitals	463 beds

★0032: NORTH MISSISSIPPI HEALTH SERVICES, INC. (NP)
830 South Gloster Street, Tupelo, MS Zip 38801–4996; tel. 662/377–3136; M. Shane Spees, President and Chief Executive Officer
(Centralized Physician/Insurance Health System)

ALABAMA: NORTH MISSISSIPPI MEDICAL CENTER–HAMILTON (O, 15 beds) 1256 Military Street South, Hamilton, AL Zip 35570–5003; tel. 205/921–6200; William Buck, Interim Chief Executive Officer
Web address: www.nmhs.net

MISSISSIPPI: CALHOUN HEALTH SERVICES (C, 145 beds) 140 Burke–Calhoun City Road, Calhoun City, MS Zip 38916–9690; tel. 662/628–6611; James P. Franklin, Administrator
Web address: www.nmhs.net/calhoun_city

NORTH MISSISSIPPI MEDICAL CENTER – TUPELO (O, 757 beds) 830 South Gloster Street, Tupelo, MS Zip 38801–4934; tel. 662/377–3000; David C. Wilson, Chief Executive Officer
Web address: www.nmhs.net

NORTH MISSISSIPPI MEDICAL CENTER–EUPORA (O, 73 beds) 70 Medical Plaza, Eupora, MS Zip 39744–4018; tel. 662/258–6221; Wes Sigler, Administrator
Web address: www.nmhs.net/eupora

NORTH MISSISSIPPI MEDICAL CENTER–IUKA (O, 48 beds) 1777 Curtis Drive, Iuka, MS Zip 38852–1001, Mailing Address: P.O. Box 860, Zip 38852–0860; tel. 662/423–6051; Fred A. Truesdale, Jr., Administrator
Web address: www.nmhs.net

NORTH MISSISSIPPI MEDICAL CENTER–PONTOTOC (L, 69 beds) 176 South Main Street, Pontotoc, MS Zip 38863–3311, Mailing Address: P.O. Box 790, Zip 38863–0790; tel. 662/488–7640; Leslia Carter, Administrator
Web address: www.nmhs.net

NORTH MISSISSIPPI MEDICAL CENTER–WEST POINT (O, 60 beds) 835 Medical Center Drive, West Point, MS Zip 39773–9320; tel. 662/495–2300; Barry L. Keel, Administration
Web address: www.nmhs.net/westpoint

Owned, leased, sponsored:	6 hospitals	1022 beds
Contract–managed:	1 hospital	145 beds
Totals:	7 hospitals	1167 beds

0867: NORTH OAKS HEALTH SYSTEM (NP)
15790 Paul Vega MD Drive, Hammond, LA Zip 70403–1436, Mailing Address: P.O. Box 2668, Zip 70404–2668; tel. 985/345–2700; Julie Bruhn, Administrative Operations Support Analyst
(Independent Hospital System)

LOUISIANA: NORTH OAKS MEDICAL CENTER (O, 248 beds) 15790 Paul Vega, MD, Drive, Hammond, LA Zip 70403–1436, Mailing Address: P.O. Box 2668, Zip 70404–2668; tel. 985/345–2700; Michele K. Sutton, FACHE, Administrator and Chief Executive Officer
Web address: www.northoaks.org

NORTH OAKS REHABILITATION HOSPITAL (O, 27 beds) 1900 South Morrison Boulevard, Hammond, LA Zip 70403–5742; tel. 985/542–7777; Sybil K. Paulson, Administrator
Web address: www.northoaks.org

Owned, leased, sponsored:	2 hospitals	275 beds
Contract–managed:	0 hospitals	0 beds
Totals:	2 hospitals	275 beds

For explanation of codes following names, see page B2.
★ Indicates Type III membership in the American Hospital Association.

★0281:   **NORTHERN ARIZONA HEALTHCARE** (NP)
1200 North Beaver Street, Flagstaff, AZ Zip 86001–3118;
tel. 928/779–3366; Robert P. Thames, President and Chief
Executive Officer
(Moderately Centralized Health System)

ARIZONA: FLAGSTAFF MEDICAL CENTER (O, 267 beds) 1200 North Beaver
Street, Flagstaff, AZ Zip 86001–3118; tel. 928/779–3366; Florence (Flo)
Spyrow, Chief Administrative Officer
Web address: www.nahealth.com
VERDE VALLEY MEDICAL CENTER (O, 110 beds) 269 South Candy Lane,
Cottonwood, AZ Zip 86326–4170; tel. 928/639–6000; Barbara Firminger,
Chief Administrative Officer
Web address: www.nahealth.com

Owned, leased, sponsored:	2 hospitals	377 beds
Contract–managed:	0 hospitals	0 beds
Totals:	2 hospitals	377 beds

★0410:   **NORTHSIDE HEALTHCARE SYSTEM** (NP)
1000 Johnson Ferry Road N.E., Atlanta, GA Zip 30342–1611;
tel. 404/851–8000; Robert Quattrocchi, President and Chief
Executive Officer

GEORGIA: NORTHSIDE HOSPITAL (O, 601 beds) 1000 Johnson Ferry Road
N.E., Atlanta, GA Zip 30342–1611; tel. 404/851–8000; Robert
Quattrocchi, President and Chief Executive Officer
Web address: www.northside.com
NORTHSIDE HOSPITAL–CHEROKEE (O, 88 beds) 201 Hospital Road, Canton,
GA Zip 30114–2408, Mailing Address: P.O. Box 906, Zip 30169–0906;
tel. 770/720–5100; William M. Hayes, Chief Executive Officer
Web address: www.northside.com
NORTHSIDE HOSPITAL–FORSYTH (O, 252 beds) 1200 Northside Forsyth
Drive, Cumming, GA Zip 30041–7659; tel. 770/844–3200; Lynn Jackson,
Administrator
Web address: www.northside.com

Owned, leased, sponsored:	3 hospitals	941 beds
Contract–managed:	0 hospitals	0 beds
Totals:	3 hospitals	941 beds

★0062:   **NORTHWELL HEALTH** (NP)
2000 Marcus Avenue, New Hyde Park, NY Zip 11042;
tel. 516/465–8100; Michael J. Dowling, President and Chief
Executive Officer
(Centralized Health System)

NEW YORK: GLEN COVE HOSPITAL (O, 140 beds) 101 St. Andrews Lane,
Glen Cove, NY Zip 11542–2254; tel. 516/674–7300; Susan Kwiatek,
R.N., Executive Director
Web address: www.northshorelij.com
HUNTINGTON HOSPITAL (O, 290 beds) 270 Park Avenue, Huntington, NY
Zip 11743–2799; tel. 631/351–2200; Gerard Brogan, Jr., M.D., Executive
Director
Web address: www.hunthosp.org
LENOX HILL HOSPITAL (O, 441 beds) 100 East 77th Street, New York, NY
Zip 10075–1850; tel. 212/434–2000; Dennis Connors, Executive Director
Web address: www.lenoxhillhospital.org
LONG ISLAND JEWISH MEDICAL CENTER (O, 900 beds) 270–05 76th
Avenue, New Hyde Park, NY Zip 11040–1496; tel. 718/470–7000; Michael
Goldberg, Executive Director
Web address: www.lij.edu
NORTH SHORE UNIVERSITY HOSPITAL (O, 764 beds) 300 Community Drive,
Manhasset, NY Zip 11030–3816; tel. 516/562–0100; Alessandro Bellucci,
M.D., Executive Director
Web address: www.northshorelij.com
NORTHERN WESTCHESTER HOSPITAL (O, 195 beds) 400 East Main Street,
Mount Kisco, NY Zip 10549–3477, Mailing Address: 400 East Main Street,
G–02, Zip 10549–3477; tel. 914/666–1200; Joel Seligman, President and
Chief Executive Officer
Web address: www.nwhc.net

PECONIC BAY MEDICAL CENTER (O, 176 beds) 1300 Roanoke Avenue,
Riverhead, NY Zip 11901–2031; tel. 631/548–6000; Andrew J. Mitchell,
President and Chief Executive Officer
Web address: www.pbmchealth.org
PHELPS MEMORIAL HOSPITAL CENTER (O, 158 beds) 701 North Broadway,
Sleepy Hollow, NY Zip 10591–1020; tel. 914/366–3000; Daniel Blum,
President
Web address: www.phelpshospital.org
PLAINVIEW HOSPITAL (O, 189 beds) 888 Old Country Road, Plainview, NY
Zip 11803–4978; tel. 516/719–3000; Michael Fener, Executive Director
Web address: www.northshorelij.com
SOUTH OAKS HOSPITAL (O, 258 beds) 400 Sunrise Highway, Amityville, NY
Zip 11701–2508; tel. 631/264–4000; Patricia Porter, Executive Director
Web address: www.longislandhome.org
SOUTHSIDE HOSPITAL (O, 287 beds) 301 East Main Street, Bay Shore, NY
Zip 11706–8458; tel. 631/968–3000; Donna Moravick, R.N., MSN,
Executive Director
Web address: www.southsidehospital.org
STATEN ISLAND UNIVERSITY HOSPITAL (O, 663 beds) 475 Seaview Avenue,
Staten Island, NY Zip 10305–3436; tel. 718/226–9000; Donna Proske, MS,
R.N., Executive Director
Web address: www.siuh.edu
SYOSSET HOSPITAL (O, 75 beds) 221 Jericho Turnpike, Syosset, NY
Zip 11791–4515; tel. 516/496–6500; Michael Fener, Executive Director
Web address: www.northshorelij.com

Owned, leased, sponsored:	13 hospitals	4536 beds
Contract–managed:	0 hospitals	0 beds
Totals:	13 hospitals	4536 beds

★0024:   **NORTHWESTERN MEMORIAL HEALTHCARE** (NP)
251 East Huron Street, Chicago, IL Zip 60611–2908;
tel. 312/926–2000; Dean M. Harrison, President and Chief Executive
Officer
(Centralized Health System)

ILLINOIS: NORTHWESTERN LAKE FOREST HOSPITAL (O, 183 beds) 660
North Westmoreland Road, Lake Forest, IL Zip 60045–1696;
tel. 847/234–5600; Thomas J. McAfee, President, North Market
Web address: www.lfh.org
NORTHWESTERN MEDICINE CENTRAL DUPAGE HOSPITAL (O, 379 beds) 25
North Winfield Road, Winfield, IL Zip 60190; tel. 630/933–1600; Brian J.
Lemon, President
Web address: www.cdh.org
NORTHWESTERN MEDICINE DELNOR HOSPITAL (O, 159 beds) 300 Randall
Road, Geneva, IL Zip 60134–4200; tel. 630/208–3000; Maureen A. Bryant,
FACHE, President
Web address: www.cadencehealth.org
NORTHWESTERN MEDICINE KISHWAUKEE HOSPITAL (O, 98 beds) 1 Kish
Hospital Drive, DeKalb, IL Zip 60115–9602, Mailing Address: P.O. Box 707,
Zip 60115–0707; tel. 815/756–1521; Kevin Poorten, President
Web address: www.kishhospital.org
NORTHWESTERN MEDICINE VALLEY WEST HOSPITAL (O, 25 beds) 1302
North Main Street, Sandwich, IL Zip 60548–2587; tel. 815/786–8484; Kevin
Poorten, President
Web address: www.kishhealth.org
NORTHWESTERN MEMORIAL HOSPITAL (O, 871 beds) 251 East Huron Street,
Chicago, IL Zip 60611–2908; tel. 312/926–2000; Dean M. Harrison, Chief
Executive Officer
Web address: www.nm.org

Owned, leased, sponsored:	6 hospitals	1715 beds
Contract–managed:	0 hospitals	0 beds
Totals:	6 hospitals	1715 beds

★2285:   **NORTON HEALTHCARE** (NP)
4967 U.S. Highway 42, Suite 100, Louisville, KY Zip 40222–6363,
Mailing Address: P.O. Box 35070, Zip 40232–5070;
tel. 502/629–8000; Stephen Williams, Chief Executive Officer
(Centralized Health System)

For explanation of codes following names, see page B2.
★ Indicates Type III membership in the American Hospital Association.

KENTUCKY: KOSAIR CHILDREN'S HOSPITAL (O, 267 beds) 231 East Chestnut Street, Louisville, KY Zip 40202–1821; tel. 502/629–6000; Thomas D. Kmetz, Division President
Web address: www.kosairchildrens.com/

NORTON AUDUBON HOSPITAL (O, 302 beds) One Audubon Plaza Drive, Louisville, KY Zip 40217–1300, Mailing Address: P.O. Box 17550, Zip 40217–0550; tel. 502/636–7111; Jon Cooper, Chief Administrative Officer
Web address: www.nortonhealthcare.com/NortonAudubonHospital

NORTON BROWNSBORO HOSPITAL (O, 124 beds) 4960 Norton Healthcare Boulevard, Louisville, KY Zip 40241–2831; tel. 502/446–8000; Andrew Strausbaugh, Chief Administrative Officer
Web address: www.nortonhealthcare.com/nortonbrownsborohospital

NORTON HOSPITAL (O, 382 beds) 200 East Chestnut Street, Louisville, KY Zip 40202–1800, Mailing Address: P.O. Box 35070, Zip 40232–5070; tel. 502/629–8000; Matthew Ayers, Chief Administrative Officer
Web address: www.nortonhealthcare.com/nortonhospital

NORTON WOMEN'S AND KOSAIR CHILDREN'S HOSPITAL (O, 359 beds) 4001 Dutchmans Lane, Louisville, KY Zip 40207–4799; tel. 502/893–1000; Charlotte Ipsan, Chief Administrative Officer
Web address: www.nortonhealthcare.com/nortonsuburbanhospital

Owned, leased, sponsored:	5 hospitals	1434 beds
Contract–managed:	0 hospitals	0 beds
Totals:	5 hospitals	1434 beds

★**0139: NOVANT HEALTH** (NP)
2085 Frontis Plaza Boulevard, Winston Salem, NC Zip 27103–5614; tel. 336/718–5600; Carl S. Armato, President and Chief Executive Officer
(Moderately Centralized Health System)

NORTH CAROLINA: ASHE MEMORIAL HOSPITAL (C, 25 beds) 200 Hospital Avenue, Jefferson, NC Zip 28640–9244; tel. 336/846–7101; Laura Lambeth, Chief Executive Officer
Web address: www.ashememorial.org

HALIFAX REGIONAL MEDICAL CENTER (C, 142 beds) 250 Smith Church Road, Roanoke Rapids, NC Zip 27870–4914, Mailing Address: P.O. Box 1089, Zip 27870–1089; tel. 252/535–8011; William Mahone, President and Chief Executive Officer
Web address: www.halifaxmedicalcenter.org

MOREHEAD MEMORIAL HOSPITAL (C, 188 beds) 117 East King's Highway, Eden, NC Zip 27288–5201; tel. 336/623–9711; Dana Weston, Chief Executive Officer
Web address: www.morehead.org

NOVANT HEALTH BRUNSWICK MEDICAL CENTER (O, 53 beds) 240 Hospital Drive N.E., Bolivia, NC Zip 28422–8346; tel. 910/721–1000; Shelbourn Stevens, President
Web address: www.brunswicknovant.org

NOVANT HEALTH CHARLOTTE ORTHOPAEDIC HOSPITAL (O, 33 beds) 1901 Randolph Road, Charlotte, NC Zip 28207–1195; tel. 704/316–2000; Jason Bernd, Vice President
Web address: www.novanthealth.org

NOVANT HEALTH FORSYTH MEDICAL CENTER (O, 706 beds) 3333 Silas Creek Parkway, Winston–Salem, NC Zip 27103–3090; tel. 336/718–5000; Sean M. Sanz, Chief Executive Officer
Web address: www.forsythmedicalcenter.org

NOVANT HEALTH HUNTERSVILLE MEDICAL CENTER (O, 78 beds) 10030 Gilead Road, Huntersville, NC Zip 28078–7545, Mailing Address: P.O. Box 3508, Zip 28070–3508; tel. 704/316–4000; Mike Riley, President
Web address: www.novanthealth.org

NOVANT HEALTH MATTHEWS MEDICAL CENTER (O, 111 beds) 1500 Matthews Township Parkway, Matthews, NC Zip 28105–4656; tel. 704/384–6500; Roland R. Bibeau, FACHE, President
Web address: www.https://www.novanthealth.org

NOVANT HEALTH MEDICAL PARK HOSPITAL (O, 14 beds) 1950 South Hawthorne Road, Winston–Salem, NC Zip 27103–3993; tel. 336/718–0600; Kirsten Royster, Chief Executive Officer
Web address: www.novanthealth.org

NOVANT HEALTH PRESBYTERIAN MEDICAL CENTER (O, 419 beds) 200 Hawthorne Lane, Charlotte, NC Zip 28204–2528, Mailing Address: P.O. Box 33549, Zip 28233–3549; tel. 704/384–4000; Paula Vincent, MSN, President and Chief Operating Officer
Web address: www.novanthealth.org

NOVANT HEALTH ROWAN MEDICAL CENTER (O, 147 beds) 612 Mocksville Avenue, Salisbury, NC Zip 28144–2799; tel. 704/210–5000; Dari Caldwell, R.N., Ph.D., FACHE, President and Chief Operating Officer
Web address: www.https://www.novanthealth.org/rowan–medical–center.aspx

NOVANT HEALTH THOMASVILLE MEDICAL CENTER (O, 80 beds) 207 Old Lexington Road, Thomasville, NC Zip 27360–3428, Mailing Address: P.O. Box 789, Zip 27361–0789; tel. 336/472–2000; Kathie A. Johnson, R.N., MS, Ph.D., Chief Executive Officer
Web address: www.thomasvillemedicalcenter.org

VIRGINIA: NOVANT HEALTH UVA HEALTH SYSTEM HAYMARKET MEDICAL CENTER (O, 18 beds) 15225 Heathcote Boulevard, Haymarket, VA Zip 20155–4023, Mailing Address: 14535 John Marshall Highway, Gainesville, Zip 20155–4023; tel. 571/284–1000; Don Sedgley, President
Web address: www.novanthealth.org

NOVANT HEALTH UVA HEALTH SYSTEM PRINCE WILLIAM MEDICAL CENTER (O, 90 beds) 8700 Sudley Road, Manassas, VA Zip 20110–4418, Mailing Address: P.O. Box 2610, Zip 20108–0867; tel. 703/369–8000; Melissa Robson, President
Web address: www.pwhs.org

Owned, leased, sponsored:	11 hospitals	1749 beds
Contract–managed:	3 hospitals	355 beds
Totals:	14 hospitals	2104 beds

★**3075: NYC HEALTH + HOSPITALS** (NP)
125 Worth Street, Room 514, New York, NY Zip 10013–4006; tel. 212/788–3321; Ramanathan Raju, M.D., President
(Moderately Centralized Health System)

NEW YORK: NYC HEALTH + HOSPITALS / BELLEVUE (O, 827 beds) 462 First Avenue, New York, NY Zip 10016–9198; tel. 212/562–4141; William Hicks, Interim Executive Director
Web address: www.nyc.gov/bellevue

NYC HEALTH + HOSPITALS / CARTER (O, 365 beds) 1752 Park Avenue, New York, NY Zip 10035; tel. 646/686–0000; Floyd R. Long, Chief Executive Officer
Web address: www.coler–goldwater.org

NYC HEALTH + HOSPITALS / CONEY ISLAND (O, 371 beds) 2601 Ocean Parkway, Brooklyn, NY Zip 11235–7795; tel. 718/616–3000; Anthony Rajkumar, Chief Executive Officer
Web address: www.nyc.gov/html/hhc/html/facilities/coneyisland.shtml

NYC HEALTH + HOSPITALS / ELMHURST (O, 525 beds) 79–01 Broadway, Elmhurst, NY Zip 11373–1329; tel. 718/334–4000; Israel Rocha, Chief Executive Officer
Web address: www.nyc.gov/html/hhc/ehc/html/home/home.shtml

NYC HEALTH + HOSPITALS / GOUVERNEUR (O, 196 beds) 227 Madison Street, New York, NY Zip 10002; tel. 212/238–7000; Gregory M. Kaladjian, Executive Director

NYC HEALTH + HOSPITALS / HARLEM (O, 272 beds) 506 Lenox Avenue, New York, NY Zip 10037–1802; tel. 212/939–1000; Ebone' Carrington, Interim Executive Director
Web address: www.nyc.gov/html/hhc/harlem

NYC HEALTH + HOSPITALS / JACOBI (O, 457 beds) 1400 Pelham Parkway South, Bronx, NY Zip 10461–1197; tel. 718/918–5000; John Morley, M.D., Acting Executive Director
Web address: www.nyc.gov/html/hhc/jacobi/home.html

NYC HEALTH + HOSPITALS / KINGS COUNTY (O, 599 beds) 451 Clarkson Avenue, Brooklyn, NY Zip 11203–2097; tel. 718/245–3131; Ernest Baptiste, Executive Director
Web address: www.nyc.gov/html/hhc/kchc/html/home/home.shtml

For explanation of codes following names, see page B2.
★ Indicates Type III membership in the American Hospital Association.

NYC HEALTH + HOSPITALS / LINCOLN (O, 355 beds) 234 East 149th Street, Bronx, NY Zip 10451–5504, Mailing Address: 234 East 149th Street, Room 923, Zip 10451–5504; tel. 718/579–5700; Milton Nunez, Executive Director
Web address: www.nyc.gov/html/hhc/lincoln/

NYC HEALTH + HOSPITALS / METROPOLITAN (O, 317 beds) 1901 First Avenue, New York, NY Zip 10029–7404; tel. 212/423–6262; Alina Moran, Chief Executive Officer
Web address: www.nyc.gov/html/hhc/mhc/html/home.shtml

NYC HEALTH + HOSPITALS / NORTH CENTRAL BRONX (O, 207 beds) 3424 Kossuth Avenue, Bronx, NY Zip 10467–2489; tel. 718/519–3500; Maureen Pode, Co–Interim Executive Director
Web address: www.nyc.gov/html/hhc/ncbh/html/home/home.shtml

NYC HEALTH + HOSPITALS / QUEENS (O, 259 beds) 82–68 164th Street, Jamaica, NY Zip 11432–1104; tel. 718/883–3000; Dona Green, Chief Operating Officer
Web address: www.nyc.gov/html/hhc/qhc/html/home/home.shtml

NYC HEALTH + HOSPITALS / SEA VIEW (O, 304 beds) 460 Brielle Avenue, Staten Island, NY Zip 10314; tel. 212/390–8181; Jane M. Lyons, Executive Director

NYC HEALTH + HOSPITALS / WOODHULL (O, 323 beds) 760 Broadway, Brooklyn, NY Zip 11206–5383; tel. 718/963–8000; Gregory Calliste, Ph.D., FACHE, Chief Executive Officer
Web address: www.nyc.gov/html/hhc

Owned, leased, sponsored:	14 hospitals	5377 beds
Contract–managed:	0 hospitals	0 beds
Totals:	14 hospitals	5377 beds

0616: OCEANS HEALTHCARE (IO)
2720 Rue de Jardin, Suite 100, Lake Charles, LA Zip 70605–4050; tel. 337/721–1900; Jason Reed, President and Chief Executive Officer
(Independent Hospital System)

LOUISIANA: OCEANS BEHAVIORAL HOSPITAL OF ALEXANDRIA (O, 24 beds) 2621 North Bolton Avenue, Alexandria, LA Zip 71303–4506; tel. 318/448–8473; Nicholas D. Guillory, MSN, Interim Administrator
Web address: www.obha.info/

OCEANS BEHAVIORAL HOSPITAL OF BATON ROUGE (O, 20 beds) 11135 Florida Boulevard, Baton Rouge, LA Zip 70815–2013; tel. 225/356–7030; Valerie Dalton, R.N., Administrator
Web address: www.obhbr.info/

OCEANS BEHAVIORAL HOSPITAL OF BROUSSARD (O, 38 beds) 418 Albertson Parkway, Broussard, LA Zip 70518–4971; tel. 337/237–6444; Amy Dysart–Credeur, Administrator
Web address: www.obhb.info/

OCEANS BEHAVIORAL HOSPITAL OF DE RIDDER (O, 20 beds) 1420 Blankenship Drive, Deridder, LA Zip 70634–4604; tel. 337/460–9472; Lynette Dhillon, Administrator
Web address: www.obhd.info/

OCEANS BEHAVIORAL HOSPITAL OF GREATER NEW ORLEANS (O, 30 beds) 716 Village Road, Kenner, LA Zip 70065–2751; tel. 504/464–8895; Deborah Spier, Administrator
Web address: www.obhgno.info/

OCEANS BEHAVIORAL HOSPITAL OF KENTWOOD (O, 16 beds) 921 Avenue G., Kentwood, LA Zip 70444–2636; tel. 985/229–0717; Sarah Chisholm, Administrator
Web address: www.obhk.info/

OCEANS BEHAVIORAL HOSPITAL OF LAKE CHARLES (O, 40 beds) 302 West Mcneese Street, Lake Charles, LA Zip 70605–5604; tel. 337/474–7581; William L. Willis, Administrator
Web address: www.obhlc.info/

OCEANS BEHAVIORAL HOSPITAL OF OPELOUSAS (O, 20 beds) 1310 Heather Drive, Opelousas, LA Zip 70570–7714; tel. 337/948–8820; Theresa Fontenot, Executive Director
Web address: www.obho.info/

TEXAS: OCEANS BEHAVIORAL HEALTH CENTER PERMIAN BASIN (O, 58 beds) 3300 South FM 1788, Midland, TX Zip 79706–2601; tel. 432/561–5915; Kristin Harris, Interim Chief Executive Officer
Web address: www.oceanspermianbasin.com/

OCEANS BEHAVIORAL HOSPITAL ABILENE (O, 35 beds) 6401 Directors Parkway, Suite 200, Abilene, TX Zip 79606–5869; tel. 325/691–0030; Stacy Sanford, Chief Executive Officer
Web address: www.oceansabilene.com

OCEANS BEHAVIORAL HOSPITAL FORT WORTH (O, 48 beds) 6200 Overton Ridge Boulevard, Fort Worth, TX Zip 76132–3614; tel. 817/361–1991; Scott Blakeley, Acting Administrator
Web address: www.oceanshealthcare.com

OCEANS BEHAVIORAL HOSPITAL KATY (O, 48 beds) 455 Park Grove Lane, Katy, TX Zip 77450–1572; tel. 281/492–8888; Stuart Archer, Chief Executive Officer
Web address: www.oceanskaty.com/

OCEANS BEHAVIORAL HOSPITAL LONGVIEW (O, 24 beds) 615 Clinic Drive, Longview, TX Zip 75605–5172; tel. 903/212–3105; Lauren Weber, Administrator
Web address: www.oceanslongview.com/

OCEANS BEHAVIORAL HOSPITAL LUFKIN (O, 24 beds) 302 Gobblers Knob Road, Lufkin, TX Zip 75904–5419; tel. 936/632–2276; Frances Dick, Chief Executive Officer
Web address: www.oceanslufkin.com/

OCEANS BEHAVIORAL HOSPITAL PLANO (O, 25 beds) 4301 Mapleshade Lane, Plano, TX Zip 75093–0010; tel. 972/596–5445; Rick Harding, Administrator
Web address: www.oceansplano.com

OCEANS BEHAVIORAL HOSPITAL SAN MARCOS (O, 25 beds) 1106 North Interstate 35, San Marcos, TX Zip 78666–7030; tel. 512/353–0194; Clara Hollis, Administrator
Web address: www.oceanssanmarcos.com

Owned, leased, sponsored:	16 hospitals	495 beds
Contract–managed:	0 hospitals	0 beds
Totals:	16 hospitals	495 beds

★0359: OCHSNER HEALTH SYSTEM (NP)
1514 Jefferson Highway, New Orleans, LA Zip 70121–2429; tel. 800/874–8984; Warner L. Thomas, FACHE, President and Chief Executive Officer
(Centralized Health System)

LOUISIANA: LEONARD J. CHABERT MEDICAL CENTER (C, 72 beds) 1978 Industrial Boulevard, Houma, LA Zip 70363–7094; tel. 985/873–2200; Timothy J. Allen, FACHE, Chief Executive Officer
Web address: www.ochsner.org/locations/leonard_j_chabert_medical_center/

OCHSNER MEDICAL CENTER (O, 813 beds) 1514 Jefferson Highway, New Orleans, LA Zip 70121–2429; tel. 504/842–3000; Robert K. Wolterman, Chief Executive Officer
Web address: www.ochsner.org

OCHSNER MEDICAL CENTER – KENNER (O, 110 beds) 180 West Esplanade Avenue, Kenner, LA Zip 70065–6001; tel. 504/468–8600; Stephen Robinson, Chief Executive Officer
Web address: www.ochsner.org/locations/ochsner_health_center_kenner_w_esplanade_ave/

OCHSNER MEDICAL CENTER – NORTH SHORE (L, 110 beds) 100 Medical Center Drive, Slidell, LA Zip 70461–5520; tel. 985/649–7070; John William Davis, Chief Executive Officer
Web address: www.https://www.ochsner.org/locations/ochsner–medical–center–north–shore/

OCHSNER MEDICAL CENTER–BATON ROUGE (O, 152 beds) 17000 Medical Center Drive, Baton Rouge, LA Zip 70816–3224; tel. 225/752–2470; Eric McMillen, Chief Executive Officer
Web address: www.ochsner.org/page.cfm?id=103

OCHSNER ST. ANNE GENERAL HOSPITAL (O, 38 beds) 4608 Highway 1, Raceland, LA Zip 70394–2623; tel. 985/537–6841; Timothy J. Allen, FACHE, Chief Executive Officer
Web address: www.ochsner.org/locations/ochsner–st–anne

ST. CHARLES PARISH HOSPITAL (C, 56 beds) 1057 Paul Maillard Road, Luling, LA Zip 70070–4349, Mailing Address: P.O. Box 87, Zip 70070–0087; tel. 985/785–6242; Ritchie Dupre, Chief Executive Officer
Web address: www.ochsner.org/locations/st_charles_parish_hospital/

For explanation of codes following names, see page B2.
★ Indicates Type III membership in the American Hospital Association.

MISSISSIPPI: HANCOCK MEDICAL CENTER (C, 102 beds) 149 Drinkwater Boulevard, Bay Saint Louis, MS Zip 39520–1658, Mailing Address: 149 Drinkwater Road, Zip 39520–1658; tel. 228/467–8600; Alan Hodges, Chief Executive Officer
Web address: www.hmc.org

Owned, leased, sponsored:	5 hospitals	1223 beds
Contract–managed:	3 hospitals	230 beds
Totals:	8 hospitals	1453 beds

0388:   OCONEE REGIONAL HEALTH SYSTEMS (NP)
821 North Cobb Street, Milledgeville, GA Zip 31061–2343; tel. 478/454–3505; Jean Aycock, President and Chief Executive Officer
(Independent Hospital System)

GEORGIA: JASPER MEMORIAL HOSPITAL (O, 67 beds) 898 College Street, Monticello, GA Zip 31064–1258; tel. 706/468–6411; Jan Gaston, Administrator
Web address: www.jaspermemorialhospital.org

OCONEE REGIONAL MEDICAL CENTER (O, 90 beds) 821 North Cobb Street, Milledgeville, GA Zip 31061–2351, Mailing Address: P.O. Box 690, Zip 31059–0690; tel. 478/454–3505; Steven Johnson, Interim Chief Executive Officer
Web address: www.oconeeregional.com

Owned, leased, sponsored:	2 hospitals	157 beds
Contract–managed:	0 hospitals	0 beds
Totals:	2 hospitals	157 beds

0537:   OHIO DEPARTMENT OF MENTAL HEALTH (NP)
30 East Broad Street, 8th Floor, Columbus, OH Zip 43215–3430; tel. 614/466–2297; Tracy Plouck, Director
(Independent Hospital System)

OHIO: APPALACHIAN BEHAVIORAL HEALTHCARE (O, 224 beds) 100 Hospital Drive, Athens, OH Zip 45701–2301; tel. 740/594–5000; Jane E. Krason, R.N., Chief Executive Officer
Web address: www.mh.state.oh.us

HEARTLAND BEHAVIORAL HEALTHCARE (O, 152 beds) 3000 Erie Stree South, Massillon, OH Zip 44646–7993, Mailing Address: 3000 Erie Street South, Zip 44646–7976; tel. 330/833–3135; Jeffrey Sims, Chief Executive Officer
Web address: www.mh.state.oh.us/ibhs/bhos/hoh.html

NORTHCOAST BEHAVIORAL HEALTHCARE (O, 260 beds) 1756 Sagamore Road, Northfield, OH Zip 44067–1086; tel. 330/467–7131; Douglas W. Kern, Chief Executive Officer
Web address: www.mha.ohio.gov

NORTHWEST OHIO PSYCHIATRIC HOSPITAL (O, 114 beds) 930 Detroit Avenue, Toledo, OH Zip 43614–2701; tel. 419/381–1881; Tamara Junge, Chief Executive Officer
Web address: www.mh.state.oh.us/

SUMMIT BEHAVIORAL HEALTHCARE (O, 291 beds) 1101 Summit Road, Cincinnati, OH Zip 45237–2652; tel. 513/948–3600; Elizabeth Banks, Chief Executive Officer
Web address: www.mh.state.oh.us/

TWIN VALLEY BEHAVIORAL HEALTHCARE (O, 228 beds) 2200 West Broad Street, Columbus, OH Zip 43223–1297; tel. 614/752–0333; Veronica Lofton, Acting Chief Executive Officer
Web address: www.mh.state.oh.us/ibhs/bhos/tvbh.html

Owned, leased, sponsored:	6 hospitals	1269 beds
Contract–managed:	0 hospitals	0 beds
Totals:	6 hospitals	1269 beds

★0251:   OHIO STATE UNIVERSITY HEALTH SYSTEM (NP)
370 West Ninth Avenue, Columbus, OH Zip 43210–1238; tel. 614/685–9015; David P. McQuaid, FACHE, Chief Executive Officer
(Centralized Physician/Insurance Health System)

JAMES CANCER HOSPITAL AND SOLOVE RESEARCH INSTITUTE (O, 304 beds) 460 West Tenth Avenue, Columbus, OH Zip 43210–1240; tel. 614/293–3300; Michael Caligiuri, Chief Executive Officer
Web address: www.jamesline.com

OHIO STATE UNIVERSITY WEXNER MEDICAL CENTER (O, 963 beds) 370 West 9th Avenue, Columbus, OH Zip 43210–1238; tel. 614/293–8000; Sheldon Retchin, M.D., Chief Executive Officer
Web address: www.medicalcenter.osu.edu

Owned, leased, sponsored:	2 hospitals	1267 beds
Contract–managed:	0 hospitals	0 beds
Totals:	2 hospitals	1267 beds

3315:   OHIO VALLEY HEALTH SERVICES AND EDUCATION CORPORATION (NP)
2000 Eoff Street, Wheeling, WV Zip 26003–3823; tel. 304/234–8383; Michael J. Caruso, President and Chief Executive Officer
(Moderately Centralized Health System)

EAST OHIO REGIONAL HOSPITAL (O, 139 beds) 90 North Fourth Street, Martins Ferry, OH Zip 43935–1648; tel. 740/633–1100; Michael J. Caruso, President and Chief Executive Officer
Web address: www.ovmc-eorh.com

WEST VIRGINIA: OHIO VALLEY MEDICAL CENTER (O, 189 beds) 2000 Eoff Street, Wheeling, WV Zip 26003–3870; tel. 304/234–0123; Michael J. Caruso, President and Chief Executive Officer
Web address: www.ovmc-eorh.com

Owned, leased, sponsored:	2 hospitals	328 beds
Contract–managed:	0 hospitals	0 beds
Totals:	2 hospitals	328 beds

★0162:   OHIOHEALTH (NP)
180 East Broad Street, Columbus, OH Zip 43215–3707; tel. 614/544–4455; David P. Blom, President and Chief Executive Officer
(Centralized Physician/Insurance Health System)

OHIO: MORROW COUNTY HOSPITAL (C, 23 beds) 651 West Marion Road, Mount Gilead, OH Zip 43338–1027; tel. 419/946–5015; Chad J. Miller, President and Chief Executive Officer
Web address: www.morrowcountyhospital.com

O'BLENESS MEMORIAL HOSPITAL (O, 64 beds) 55 Hospital Drive, Athens, OH Zip 45701–2302; tel. 740/593–5551; Mark R. Seckinger, President
Web address: www.obleness.org

OHIOHEALTH DOCTORS HOSPITAL (O, 176 beds) 5100 West Broad Street, Columbus, OH Zip 43228–1607; tel. 614/544–1000; Michael L. Reichfield, President
Web address: www.ohiohealth.com

OHIOHEALTH DUBLIN METHODIST HOSPITAL (O, 107 beds) 7500 Hospital Drive, Dublin, OH Zip 43016–8518; tel. 614/544–8000; Steve Bunyard, President
Web address: www.ohiohealth.com

OHIOHEALTH GRADY MEMORIAL HOSPITAL (O, 59 beds) 561 West Central Avenue, Delaware, OH Zip 43015–1410; tel. 740/615–1000; Steve Bunyard, President
Web address: www.ohiohealth.com

OHIOHEALTH GRANT MEDICAL CENTER (O, 434 beds) 111 South Grant Avenue, Columbus, OH Zip 43215–1898; tel. 614/566–9000; Michael Lawson, President and Chief Operating Officer
Web address: www.ohiohealth.com

OHIOHEALTH HARDIN MEMORIAL HOSPITAL (O, 25 beds) 921 East Franklin Street, Kenton, OH Zip 43326–2099; tel. 419/673–0761; Ron Snyder, Chief Operating Officer
Web address: www.hardinmemorial.org

OHIOHEALTH MARION GENERAL HOSPITAL (O, 170 beds) 1000 McKinley Park Drive, Marion, OH Zip 43302–6397; tel. 740/383–8400; Bruce P. Hagen, President
Web address: www.ohiohealth.com/mariongeneral

For explanation of codes following names, see page B2.
★ Indicates Type III membership in the American Hospital Association.

OHIOHEALTH MEDCENTRAL MANSFIELD HOSPITAL (O, 235 beds) 335 Glessner Avenue, Mansfield, OH Zip 44903–2265; tel. 419/526–8000; Jean Halpin, President
Web address: www.medcentral.org

OHIOHEALTH MEDCENTRAL SHELBY HOSPITAL (O, 25 beds) 199 West Main Street, Shelby, OH Zip 44875–1490; tel. 419/342–5015; Jean Halpin, President
Web address: www.medcentral.org/body.cfm?id=153

OHIOHEALTH RIVERSIDE METHODIST HOSPITAL (O, 817 beds) 3535 Olentangy River Road, Columbus, OH Zip 43214–3998; tel. 614/566–5000; Brian Jepson, President
Web address: www.ohiohealth.com

Owned, leased, sponsored:	10 hospitals	2112 beds
Contract–managed:	1 hospital	23 beds
Totals:	11 hospitals	2135 beds

0018: OKLAHOMA DEPARTMENT OF MENTAL HEALTH AND SUBSTANCE ABUSE SERVICES (NP)
1200 N.E. 13th Street, Oklahoma City, OK Zip 73117–1022, Mailing Address: P.O. Box 53277, Zip 73152–3277; tel. 405/522–3908; Terri White, Commissioner
(Independent Hospital System)

OKLAHOMA: GRIFFIN MEMORIAL HOSPITAL (O, 120 beds) 900 East Main Street, Norman, OK Zip 73071–5305, Mailing Address: P.O. Box 151, Zip 73070–0151; tel. 405/573–6600; Lori Jordan, Executive Director
Web address: www.odmhsas.org

NORTHWEST CENTER FOR BEHAVIORAL HEALTH (O, 24 beds) 1 Mi East Highway 270, Fort Supply, OK Zip 73841; tel. 580/766–2311; Trudy Hoffman, Executive Director
Web address: www.ncbhok.org/

OKLAHOMA FORENSIC CENTER (O, 200 beds) 24800 South 4420 Road, Vinita, OK Zip 74301–5544, Mailing Address: P.O. Box 69, Zip 74301–0069; tel. 918/256–7841; Kevan Finley, Chief Executive Officer
Web address: www.odmhsas.org

Owned, leased, sponsored:	3 hospitals	344 beds
Contract–managed:	0 hospitals	0 beds
Totals:	3 hospitals	344 beds

3355: ORLANDO HEALTH (NP)
1414 Kuhl Avenue, Orlando, FL Zip 32806–2093; tel. 321/843–7000; David W. Strong, President and Chief Executive Officer
(Centralized Health System)

FLORIDA: HEALTH CENTRAL HOSPITAL (O, 400 beds) 10000 West Colonial Drive, Ocoee, FL Zip 34761–3499; tel. 407/296–1000; Mark A. Marsh, President
Web address: www.healthcentral.org

ORLANDO REGIONAL MEDICAL CENTER (O, 1307 beds) 1414 Kuhl Avenue, Orlando, FL Zip 32806–2093; tel. 407/841–5111; Mark A. Jones, President
Web address: www.orlandohealth.com/facilities/orlando–regional–medical–center

SOUTH LAKE HOSPITAL (O, 170 beds) 1900 Don Wickham Drive, Clermont, FL Zip 34711–1979; tel. 352/394–4071; John Moore, President
Web address: www.southlakehospital.com

Owned, leased, sponsored:	3 hospitals	1877 beds
Contract–managed:	0 hospitals	0 beds
Totals:	3 hospitals	1877 beds

★**5335: OSF HEALTHCARE SYSTEM** (CC)
800 N.E. Glen Oak Avenue, Peoria, IL Zip 61603–3200; tel. 309/655–2850; Kevin D. Schoeplein, Chief Executive Officer
(Moderately Centralized Health System)

ILLINOIS: OSF HOLY FAMILY MEDICAL CENTER (O, 23 beds) 1000 West Harlem Avenue, Monmouth, IL Zip 61462–1007; tel. 309/734–3141; Patricia A. Luker, President
Web address: www.osfholyfamily.org

OSF SAINT ANTHONY MEDICAL CENTER (O, 235 beds) 5666 East State Street, Rockford, IL Zip 61108–2425; tel. 815/226–2000; Paula A. Carynski, MS, R.N., President
Web address: www.osfhealth.com

OSF SAINT ANTHONY'S HEALTH CENTER (O, 203 beds) 1 Saint Anthony's Way, Alton, IL Zip 62002–4579, Mailing Address: PO Box 340, Zip 62002–0340; tel. 618/465–2571; Ajay Pathak, President
Web address: www.osfsaintanthonys.org

OSF SAINT ELIZABETH MEDICAL CENTER (O, 87 beds) 1100 East Norris Drive, Ottawa, IL Zip 61350–1687; tel. 815/433–3100; Kenneth Beutke, President
Web address: www.osfsaintelizabeth.org

OSF SAINT FRANCIS MEDICAL CENTER (O, 609 beds) 530 N.E. Glen Oak Avenue, Peoria, IL Zip 61637–0001; tel. 309/655–2000; Michael A. Cruz, M.D., President
Web address: www.osfsaintfrancis.org

OSF SAINT JAMES – JOHN W. ALBRECHT MEDICAL CENTER (O, 42 beds) 2500 West Reynolds, Pontiac, IL Zip 61764–9774; tel. 815/842–2828; Bradley V. Solberg, FACHE, President
Web address: www.osfsaintjames.org

OSF SAINT LUKE MEDICAL CENTER (O, 25 beds) 1051 West South Street, Kewanee, IL Zip 61443–8354, Mailing Address: P.O. Box 747, Zip 61443–0747; tel. 309/852–7500; Lynn Fulton, President
Web address: www.osfsaintluke.org

OSF SAINT PAUL MEDICAL CENTER (O, 25 beds) 1401 East 12th Street, Mendota, IL Zip 61342–9216; tel. 815/539–7461; Jennifer Junis, MSN, R.N., President
Web address: www.https://www.osfhealthcare.org/saint-paul

OSF ST. JOSEPH MEDICAL CENTER (O, 149 beds) 2200 East Washington Street, Bloomington, IL Zip 61701–4323; tel. 309/662–3311; Chad Boore, President
Web address: www.osfstjoseph.org

OSF ST. MARY MEDICAL CENTER (O, 81 beds) 3333 North Seminary Street, Galesburg, IL Zip 61401–1299; tel. 309/344–3161; Roxanna Crosser, President
Web address: www.osfstmary.org

SAINT CLARE HOME (O, 0 beds) 5533 North Galena Road, Peoria Heights, IL Zip 61614–4499; tel. 309/682–5428; Candy Conover, Administrator

ST. ANTHONY'S CONTINUING CARE CENTER (O, 179 beds) 767 30th Street, Rock Island, IL Zip 61201; Sister Mary Anthony Mazzaferri, Administrator

MICHIGAN: OSF ST. FRANCIS HOSPITAL AND MEDICAL GROUP (O, 25 beds) 3401 Ludington Street, Escanaba, MI Zip 49829–1377; tel. 906/786–3311; David Lord, President
Web address: www.osfstfrancis.org

Owned, leased, sponsored:	13 hospitals	1683 beds
Contract–managed:	0 hospitals	0 beds
Totals:	13 hospitals	1683 beds

0982: OWENSBORO HEALTH (NP)
1201 Pleasant Valley Road, Owensboro, KY Zip 42303–9811; tel. 270/417–2000; Greg Strahan, Interim Chief Executive Officer

KENTUCKY: OWENSBORO HEALTH MUHLENBERG COMMUNITY HOSPITAL (O, 105 beds) 440 Hopkinsville Street, Greenville, KY Zip 42345–1172, Mailing Address: P.O. Box 387, Zip 42345–0378; tel. 270/338–8000; Ed Heath, FACHE, Chief Executive Officer
Web address: www.mchky.org

OWENSBORO HEALTH REGIONAL HOSPITAL (O, 356 beds) 1201 Pleasant Valley Road, Owensboro, KY Zip 42303; tel. 270/417–2000; Greg Strahan, Interim Chief Executive Officer
Web address: www.owensborohealth.org

Owned, leased, sponsored:	2 hospitals	461 beds
Contract–managed:	0 hospitals	0 beds
Totals:	2 hospitals	461 beds

0367: PACER HEALTH CORPORATION (IO)
14100 Palmetto Frontage Road, Suite 110, Miami Lakes, FL Zip 33016; tel. 305/828–7660; Rainier Gonzalez, Chairman and Chief Executive Officer

For explanation of codes following names, see page B2.
★ Indicates Type III membership in the American Hospital Association.

Section B

KENTUCKY: BARBOURVILLE ARH HOSPITAL (O, 25 beds) 80 Hospital Drive, Barbourville, KY Zip 40906–7363, Mailing Address: P.O. Box 10, Zip 40906–0010; tel. 606/546–4175; Charles D. Lovell, Jr., FACHE, Chief Executive Officer
Web address: www.knoxcohospital.com

LOUISIANA: CALCASIEU OAKS GERIATRIC PSYCHIATRIC HOSPITAL (O, 24 beds) 2837 Ernest Street, Lake Charles, LA Zip 70601–8785; tel. 337/439–8111; Charles Getwood, Assistant Chief Executive Officer

Owned, leased, sponsored:	2 hospitals	49 beds
Contract–managed:	0 hospitals	0 beds
Totals:	2 hospitals	49 beds

● ★**5235:   PALLOTTINE HEALTH SERVICES** (CC)
2900 First Avenue, Huntington, WV Zip 25702–1241; tel. 304/526–1234; Michael G. Sellards, Chief Executive Officer
(Independent Hospital System)

WEST VIRGINIA: ST. MARY'S MEDICAL CENTER (O, 393 beds) 2900 First Avenue, Huntington, WV Zip 25702–1272; tel. 304/526–1234; Michael G. Sellards, President and Chief Executive Officer
Web address: www.st-marys.org

Owned, leased, sponsored:	1 hospital	393 beds
Contract–managed:	0 hospitals	0 beds
Totals:	1 hospital	393 beds

★**4155:   PALMETTO HEALTH** (NP)
1301 Taylor Street, Suite 9–A, Columbia, SC Zip 29201–2942, Mailing Address: P.O. Box 2266, Zip 29202–2266; tel. 803/296–2100; Charles D. Beaman, Jr., Chief Executive Officer
(Centralized Health System)

SOUTH CAROLINA: PALMETTO HEALTH BAPTIST (O, 429 beds) Taylor at Marion Street, Columbia, SC Zip 29220–0001; tel. 803/296–5010; Gregory B. Gattman, Acute Care Executive
Web address: www.palmettohealth.org

PALMETTO HEALTH BAPTIST PARKRIDGE (O, 68 beds) 400 Palmetto Health Parkway, Columbia, SC Zip 29212–1760, Mailing Address: P.O. BOX 2266, Zip 29202–2266; tel. 803/907–7000; Sarah Kirby, R.N., MSN, FACHE, Chief Executive Officer
Web address: www.palmettohealth.org

PALMETTO HEALTH RICHLAND (O, 708 beds) Five Richland Medical Park Drive, Columbia, SC Zip 29203–6897; tel. 803/434–7000; Jay Hamm, R.N., FACHE, Chief Acute Care Executive
Web address: www.palmettohealth.org

PALMETTO HEALTH TUOMEY (O, 238 beds) 129 North Washington Street, Sumter, SC Zip 29150–4983; tel. 803/774–9000; Michelle Logan–Owens, Acting Chief Executive Officer
Web address: www.tuomey.com

Owned, leased, sponsored:	4 hospitals	1443 beds
Contract–managed:	0 hospitals	0 beds
Totals:	4 hospitals	1443 beds

★**7555:   PALOMAR HEALTH** (NP)
456 East Grand Avenue, Escondido, CA Zip 92025–3319; tel. 760/740–6393; Robert Hemker, President and Chief Executive Officer
(Moderately Centralized Health System)

CALIFORNIA: PALOMAR MEDICAL CENTER (O, 322 beds) 2185 West Citracado Parkway, Escondido, CA Zip 92029–4159; tel. 760/739–3000; Mariellena Sudak, R.N., MSN, Interim Vice President and Chief Nursing Officer
Web address: www.palomarhealth.org

POMERADO HOSPITAL (O, 229 beds) 15615 Pomerado Road, Poway, CA Zip 92064–2460; tel. 858/613–4000; Cheryl Olson, Interim Vice President
Web address: www.pph.org

Owned, leased, sponsored:	2 hospitals	551 beds
Contract–managed:	0 hospitals	0 beds
Totals:	2 hospitals	551 beds

★**0159:   PARKVIEW HEALTH** (NP)
10501 Corporate Drive, Fort Wayne, IN Zip 46845–1700; tel. 260/373–7001; Michael J. Packnett, President and Chief Executive Officer
(Centralized Physician/Insurance Health System)

INDIANA: PARKVIEW ORTHO HOSPITAL (O, 37 beds) 11130 Parkview Circle Drive, Fort Wayne, IN Zip 46845–1735; tel. 260/672–5000; Julie Fleck, Chief Operating Officer
Web address: www.parkview.com

PARKVIEW HUNTINGTON HOSPITAL (O, 36 beds) 2001 Stults Road, Huntington, IN Zip 46750–1291; tel. 260/355–3000; Juli Johnson, MSN, R.N., President
Web address: www.parkview.com

PARKVIEW LAGRANGE HOSPITAL (O, 25 beds) 207 North Townline Road, LaGrange, IN Zip 46761–1325; tel. 260/463–9000; Jordi K. Disler, President
Web address: www.parkview.com

PARKVIEW NOBLE HOSPITAL (O, 31 beds) 401 Sawyer Road, Kendallville, IN Zip 46755–2568; tel. 260/347–8700; Gary W. Adkins, President
Web address: www.parkview.com

PARKVIEW REGIONAL MEDICAL CENTER (O, 686 beds) 11109 Parkview Plaza Drive, Fort Wayne, IN Zip 46845–1701; tel. 260/266–1000; Ben Miles, President
Web address: www.parkview.com

PARKVIEW WABASH COUNTY HOSPITAL (O, 25 beds) 710 North East Street, Wabash, IN Zip 46992–1924, Mailing Address: P.O. Box 548, Zip 46992–0548; tel. 260/563–3131; Marilyn J. Custer–Mitchell, President
Web address: www.wchospital.com

PARKVIEW WHITLEY HOSPITAL (O, 30 beds) 1260 East State Road 205, Columbia City, IN Zip 46725–9492; tel. 260/248–9000; Scott F. Gabriel, President
Web address: www.parkview.com

Owned, leased, sponsored:	7 hospitals	870 beds
Contract–managed:	0 hospitals	0 beds
Totals:	7 hospitals	870 beds

★**1785:   PARTNERS HEALTHCARE SYSTEM, INC.** (NP)
800 Boylston Street, Suite 1150, Boston, MA Zip 02199–8123; tel. 617/278–1004; David Torchiana, M.D., Chief Executive Officer
(Moderately Centralized Health System)

MASSACHUSETTS: BRIGHAM AND WOMEN'S FAULKNER HOSPITAL (O, 83 beds) 1153 Centre Street, Boston, MA Zip 02130–3446; tel. 617/983–7000; Michael Gustafson, M.D., President
Web address: www.brighamandwomensfaulkner.org/index.asp

BRIGHAM AND WOMEN'S HOSPITAL (O, 741 beds) 75 Francis Street, Boston, MA Zip 02115–6110; tel. 617/732–5500; Elizabeth Nabel, M.D., President
Web address: www.brighamandwomens.org

COOLEY DICKINSON HOSPITAL (O, 86 beds) 30 Locust Street, Northampton, MA Zip 01060–2093, Mailing Address: P.O. Box 5001, Zip 01061–5001; tel. 413/582–2000; Joanne Marqusee, President and Chief Executive Officer
Web address: www.cooley-dickinson.org

MARTHA'S VINEYARD HOSPITAL (O, 25 beds) One Hospital Road, Oak Bluffs, MA Zip 02557, Mailing Address: P.O. Box 1477, Zip 02557–1477; tel. 508/693–0410; Joseph L. Woodin, Chief Executive Officer
Web address: www.marthasvineyardhospital.org

MASSACHUSETTS GENERAL HOSPITAL (O, 1016 beds) 55 Fruit Street, Boston, MA Zip 02114–2696; tel. 617/726–2000; Peter L. Slavin, M.D., President
Web address: www.massgeneral.org

MCLEAN HOSPITAL (O, 182 beds) 115 Mill Street, Belmont, MA Zip 02478–1064; tel. 617/855–2000; Scott L. Rauch, M.D., President
Web address: www.mcleanhospital.org

For explanation of codes following names, see page B2.
★ Indicates Type III membership in the American Hospital Association.
● Single hospital health care system

NANTUCKET COTTAGE HOSPITAL (O, 19 beds) 57 Prospect Street, Nantucket, MA Zip 02554–2799; tel. 508/825–8100; Margot Hartmann, M.D., Ph.D., President and Chief Executive Officer
Web address: www.nantuckethospital.org

NEWTON–WELLESLEY HOSPITAL (O, 264 beds) 2014 Washington Street, Newton Lower Falls, MA Zip 02462–1699; tel. 617/243–6000; Ellen Moloney, Interim President
Web address: www.nwh.org

NORTH SHORE MEDICAL CENTER (O, 406 beds) 81 Highland Avenue, Salem, MA Zip 01970–2714; tel. 978/741–1200; Robert G. Norton, President
Web address: www.nsmc.partners.org

SPAULDING HOSPITAL FOR CONTINUING MEDICAL CARE CAMBRIDGE (O, 128 beds) 1575 Cambridge Street, Cambridge, MA Zip 02138–4308; tel. 617/876–4344; Maureen Banks, FACHE, MS, R.N., President
Web address: www.spauldingnetwork.org

SPAULDING REHABILITATION HOSPITAL (O, 132 beds) 300 First Avenue, Charlestown, MA Zip 02129–3109; tel. 617/952–5000; David E. Storto, President
Web address: www.spauldingrehab.org

SPAULDING REHABILITATION HOSPITAL CAPE COD (O, 60 beds) 311 Service Road, East Sandwich, MA Zip 02537–1370; tel. 508/833–4000; Maureen Banks, FACHE, MS, R.N., President
Web address: www.spauldingrehab.org

Owned, leased, sponsored:	12 hospitals	3142 beds
Contract–managed:	0 hospitals	0 beds
Totals:	12 hospitals	3142 beds

★5415: PEACEHEALTH (CC)
1115 S.E. 164th Avenue, Vancouver, WA Zip 98683; tel. 360/729–1000; Elizabeth Dunne, President and Chief Executive Officer
(Moderately Centralized Health System)

ALASKA: PEACEHEALTH KETCHIKAN MEDICAL CENTER (L, 50 beds) 3100 Tongass Avenue, Ketchikan, AK Zip 99901–5746; tel. 907/225–5171; Ken Tonjes, Interim Chief Administrative Officer
Web address: www.peacehealth.org

OREGON: PEACEHEALTH COTTAGE GROVE COMMUNITY MEDICAL CENTER (O, 14 beds) 1515 Village Drive, Cottage Grove, OR Zip 97424–9700; tel. 541/942–0511; Tim Herrmann, R.N., Administrator
Web address: www.peacehealth.org

PEACEHEALTH PEACE HARBOR MEDICAL CENTER (O, 21 beds) 400 Ninth Street, Florence, OR Zip 97439–7398; tel. 541/997–8412; Rick Yecny, Chief Executive Officer and Chief Mission Officer
Web address: www.peacehealth.org

PEACEHEALTH SACRED HEART MEDICAL CENTER AT RIVERBEND (O, 379 beds) 3333 Riverbend Drive, Springfield, OR Zip 97477–8800; tel. 541/222–7300; Mary Anne McMurren, Chief Adminstrative Officer
Web address: www.peacehealth.org

PEACEHEALTH SACRED HEART MEDICAL CENTER UNIVERSITY DISTRICT (O, 104 beds) 1255 Hilyard Street, Eugene, OR Zip 97401–3700, Mailing Address: P.O. Box 10905, Zip 97440–2905; tel. 541/686–7300; Rand O'Leary, FACHE, Chief Executive Officer
Web address: www.peacehealth.org

WASHINGTON: PEACEHEALTH PEACE ISLAND MEDICAL CENTER (O, 10 beds) 1117 Spring Street, Friday Harbor, WA Zip 98250–9782; tel. 360/378–2141; Merry Ann Keane, Chief Administrative Officer
Web address: www.peacehealth.org

PEACEHEALTH SOUTHWEST MEDICAL CENTER (O, 450 beds) 400 N.E. Mother Joseph Place, Vancouver, WA Zip 98664–3200, Mailing Address: P.O. Box 1600, Zip 98668–1600; tel. 360/256–2000; Nancy Steiger, FACHE, R.N., Chief Executive
Web address: www.peacehealth.org

PEACEHEALTH ST. JOHN MEDICAL CENTER (O, 180 beds) 1615 Delaware Street, Longview, WA Zip 98632–2367, Mailing Address: P.O. Box 3002, Zip 98632–0302; tel. 360/414–2000; Kirk Raboin, Chief Administrative Officer
Web address: www.peacehealth.org

PEACEHEALTH ST. JOSEPH MEDICAL CENTER (O, 253 beds) 2901 Squalicum Parkway, Bellingham, WA Zip 98225–1851; tel. 360/734–5400; Dale Zender, President Hospital Services NW
Web address: www.peacehealth.org

PEACEHEALTH UNITED GENERAL MEDICAL CENTER (C, 25 beds) 2000 Hospital Drive, Sedro–Woolley, WA Zip 98284–4327; tel. 360/856–6021; Christopher Johnston, Interim Chief Administrative Officer
Web address: www.peacehealth.org/united–general/Pages/default.aspx

Owned, leased, sponsored:	9 hospitals	1461 beds
Contract–managed:	1 hospital	25 beds
Totals:	10 hospitals	1486 beds

0989: PENN STATE HERSHEY HEALTH SYSTEM (NP)
500 University Drive, Hershey, PA Zip 17033–2360; tel. 717/531–8521; A. Craig Hillemeier, M.D., Chief Executive Officer

PENNSYLVANIA: PENN STATE HEALTH ST. JOSEPH (O, 180 beds) 2500 Bernville Road, Reading, PA Zip 19605–9453, Mailing Address: P.O. Box 316, Zip 19603–0316; tel. 610/378–2000; John R. Morahan, President and Chief Executive Officer
Web address: www.thefutureofhealthcare.org

PENN STATE MILTON S. HERSHEY MEDICAL CENTER (O, 539 beds) 500 University Drive, Hershey, PA Zip 17033–2360, Mailing Address: P.O. Box 850, Zip 17033–0850; tel. 717/531–8323; A. Craig Hillemeier, M.D., Chief Executive Officer
Web address: www.pennstatehershey.org/

Owned, leased, sponsored:	2 hospitals	719 beds
Contract–managed:	0 hospitals	0 beds
Totals:	2 hospitals	719 beds

★0314: PHOEBE PUTNEY HEALTH SYSTEM (NP)
417 Third Avenue, Albany, GA Zip 31701–1943; tel. 229/312–1000; Joel Wernick, President and Chief Executive Officer
(Independent Hospital System)

GEORGIA: PHOEBE SUMTER MEDICAL CENTER (O, 44 beds) 126 Highway 280 West, Americus, GA Zip 31719; tel. 229/924–6011; Brandi Lunneborg, Chief Executive Officer
Web address: www.phoebesumter.org

PHOEBE WORTH MEDICAL CENTER (O, 18 beds) 807 South Isabella Street, Sylvester, GA Zip 31791–7554, Mailing Address: P.O. Box 545, Zip 31791–0545; tel. 229/776–6961; Kim Gilman, Chief Executive Officer
Web address: www.phoebeputney.com

SOUTHWEST GEORGIA REGIONAL MEDICAL CENTER (O, 105 beds) 361 Randolph Street, Cuthbert, GA Zip 39840–6127; tel. 229/732–2181; Kim Gilman, Chief Executive Officer and Chief Nursing Officer
Web address: www.phoebeputney.com

Owned, leased, sponsored:	3 hospitals	167 beds
Contract–managed:	0 hospitals	0 beds
Totals:	3 hospitals	167 beds

0043: PHYSICIANS FOR HEALTHY HOSPITALS (IO)
1117 East Devonshire Avenue, Hemet, CA Zip 92543–3083; tel. 951/652–2811; Joel M. Bergenfeld, Chief Executive Officer

CALIFORNIA: HEMET VALLEY MEDICAL CENTER (O, 159 beds) 1117 East Devonshire Avenue, Hemet, CA Zip 92543–3083; tel. 951/652–2811; Joel M. Bergenfeld, Chief Hospital Executive Officer
Web address: www.physiciansforhealthyhospitals.com

MENIFEE VALLEY MEDICAL CENTER (O, 74 beds) 28400 McCall Boulevard, Sun City, CA Zip 92585–9537; tel. 951/679–8888; Dan C. McLaughlin, Chief Executive Officer
Web address: www.valleyhealthsystem.com

Owned, leased, sponsored:	2 hospitals	233 beds
Contract–managed:	0 hospitals	0 beds
Totals:	2 hospitals	233 beds

For explanation of codes following names, see page B2.
★ Indicates Type III membership in the American Hospital Association.

Section B

0310: PIEDMONT HEALTHCARE (NP)
1800 Howell Mill Road N.W., Suite 850, Atlanta, GA
Zip 30318–0923; tel. 404/425–1314; Kevin Brown, President and
Chief Executive Officer
(Independent Hospital System)

GEORGIA: PIEDMONT FAYETTE HOSPITAL (O, 172 beds) 1255 Highway 54
West, Fayetteville, GA Zip 30214–4526; tel. 770/719–7000; Michael
Burnett, Chief Executive Officer
Web address: www.piedmont.org

PIEDMONT HENRY HOSPITAL (L, 214 beds) 1133 Eagle's Landing Parkway,
Stockbridge, GA Zip 30281–5099; tel. 678/604–1000; Charles F. Scott,
Chief Executive Officer
Web address: www.piedmonthenry.org

PIEDMONT HOSPITAL (O, 510 beds) 1968 Peachtree Road N.W., Atlanta, GA
Zip 30309–1281; tel. 404/605–5000; Patrick M. Battey, M.D., Chief
Executive Officer
Web address: www.piedmonthospital.org

PIEDMONT MOUNTAINSIDE HOSPITAL (O, 52 beds) 1266 Highway 515
South, Jasper, GA Zip 30143–4872; tel. 706/692–2441; Denise Ray,
President and Chief Executive Officer
Web address: www.piedmontmountainsidehospital.org

PIEDMONT NEWNAN HOSPITAL (O, 136 beds) 745 Poplar Road, Newnan, GA
Zip 30265–1618; tel. 770/400–1000; Michael Robertson, Chief Executive
Officer
Web address: www.piedmont.org/locations/piedmont–newnan/pnh–home

PIEDMONT NEWTON HOSPITAL (O, 101 beds) 5126 Hospital Drive,
Covington, GA Zip 30014–2567; tel. 770/786–7053; James F. Weadick,
Administrator and Chief Executive Officer
Web address: www.newtonmedical.com

Owned, leased, sponsored:	6 hospitals	1185 beds
Contract–managed:	0 hospitals	0 beds
Totals:	6 hospitals	1185 beds

★0958: PIH HEALTH (NP)
12401 Washington Boulevard, Whittier, CA Zip 90602–1006;
tel. 562/698–0811; James R. West, President and Chief Executive
Officer
(Moderately Centralized Health System)

CALIFORNIA: PIH HEALTH HOSPITAL – DOWNEY (O, 192 beds) 11500
Brookshire Avenue, Downey, CA Zip 90241–4917; tel. 562/904–5000;
James R. West, President and Chief Executive Officer
Web address: www.PIHHealth.org

PIH HEALTH HOSPITAL–WHITTIER (O, 548 beds) 12401 Washington
Boulevard, Whittier, CA Zip 90602–1099; tel. 562/698–0811; James R.
West, President and Chief Executive Officer
Web address: www.PIHHealth.org

Owned, leased, sponsored:	2 hospitals	740 beds
Contract–managed:	0 hospitals	0 beds
Totals:	2 hospitals	740 beds

★0326: PIONEER HEALTH SERVICES (IO)
110 Pioneer Way, Magee, MS Zip 39111–5501, Mailing Address:
P.O. Box 1100, Zip 39111–1100; tel. 601/849–6440; Joseph S.
McNulty, III, President and Chief Executive Officer
(Independent Hospital System)

GEORGIA: PIONEER COMMUNITY HOSPITAL OF EARLY (L, 152 beds) 11740
Columbia Street, Blakely, GA Zip 39823–2574; tel. 229/723–4241;
Ginger Cushing, Chief Executive Officer
Web address: www.pchearly.com

MISSISSIPPI: LACKEY MEMORIAL HOSPITAL (C, 45 beds) 330 Broad Street,
Forest, MS Zip 39074–3508, Mailing Address: P.O. Box 428,
Zip 39074–0428; tel. 601/469–4151; Mark Norman, Chief Executive
Officer
Web address: www.lackeymemorialhospital.com

PIONEER COMMUNITY HOSPITAL OF ABERDEEN (L, 35 beds) 400 South
Chestnut Street, Aberdeen, MS Zip 39730–3335, Mailing Address: P.O. Box
548, Zip 39730–0548; tel. 662/369–2455; Christopher Chandler, Chief
Executive Officer
Web address: www.pchaberdeen.com

NORTH CAROLINA: PIONEER COMMUNITY HOSPITAL OF STOKES (L, 65
beds) 1570 Highway 8 and 89 North, Danbury, NC Zip 27016, Mailing
Address: P.O. Box 10, Zip 27016–0010; tel. 336/593–2831; Pamela P.
Tillman, R.N., Chief Executive Officer
Web address: www.pchstokes.com

VIRGINIA: PIONEER COMMUNITY HOSPITAL OF PATRICK (O, 25 beds) 18688
Jeb Stuart Highway, Stuart, VA Zip 24171–1559; tel. 276/694–3151;
Jeanette Filpi, Chief Executive Officer
Web address: www.pchpatrick.com

Owned, leased, sponsored:	4 hospitals	277 beds
Contract–managed:	1 hospital	45 beds
Totals:	5 hospitals	322 beds

★0617: POST ACUTE MEDICAL, LLC (IO)
1828 Good Hope Road, Suite 102, Enola, PA Zip 17025–1233;
tel. 717/731–9660; Anthony F. Misitano, President and Chief
Executive Officer
(Independent Hospital System)

LOUISIANA: PAM SPECIALTY HOSPITAL OF COVINGTON (O, 58 beds) 20050
Crestwood Boulevard, Covington, LA Zip 70433–5207;
tel. 985/875–7525; J. Cullen Meyers, Chief Executive Officer
Web address: www.postacutemedical.com

PAM SPECIALTY HOSPITAL OF HAMMOND (O, 40 beds) 42074 Veterans
Avenue, Hammond, LA Zip 70403–1408; tel. 985/902–8148; Nicholas Paul
Mendez, Chief Executive Officer
Web address: www.postacutemedical.com

PAM SPECIALTY HOSPITAL OF LAFAYETTE (O, 50 beds) 204 Energy Parkway,
Lafayette, LA Zip 70508–3816; tel. 337/232–1905; Jason Branson, Chief
Executive Officer
Web address: www.postacutemedical.com

OKLAHOMA: POST ACUTE MEDICAL SPECIALTY HOSPITAL OF TULSA (O, 60
beds) 3219 South 79th East Avenue, Tulsa, OK Zip 74145–1343;
tel. 918/663–8183; Lee A. Simpson, Jr., Chief Executive Officer
Web address: www.postacutetulsa.com

TEXAS: CUMBERLAND SURGICAL HOSPITAL (O, 9 beds) 5330 N. Loop 1604
W., San Antonio, TX Zip 78249; tel. 210/877–8000; Michelle Patino,
Chief Executive Officer

POST ACUTE MEDICAL SPECIALTY HOSPITAL OF CORPUS CHRISTI – NORTH
(O, 22 beds) 600 Elizabeth Street, 3rd Floor, Corpus Christi, TX
Zip 78404–2235; tel. 361/881–3223; Hector Bernal, Chief Executive Officer
Web address: www.postacutemedical.com/our–facilities/hospitals/post–
acute–medical–specialty–hospital–corpus–christi/

POST ACUTE MEDICAL SPECIALTY HOSPITAL OF CORPUS CHRISTI – SOUTH
(O, 74 beds) 6226 Saratoga Boulevard, Corpus Christi, TX Zip 78414–3421;
tel. 361/986–1600; Michael L. Pierce, Chief Executive Officer
Web address: www.postacutemedical.com

POST ACUTE MEDICAL SPECIALTY HOSPITAL OF TEXARKANA – NORTH (O,
49 beds) 2400 St. Michael Drive, 2nd Floor, Texarkana, TX Zip 75503–2372;
tel. 903/614–7600; Benny Costello, Administrator
Web address: www.postacutemedical.com

POST ACUTE MEDICAL SPECIALTY HOSPITAL OF VICTORIA (O, 23 beds) 506
East San Antonio Street, 3rd Floor, Victoria, TX Zip 77901–6060;
tel. 361/575–1445; Portlyn Brogger, Chief Executive Officer
Web address: www.khvictoria.com

POST ACUTE/WARM SPRINGS REHABILITATION HOSPITAL OF ALLEN (O, 39
beds) 1001 Raintree Circle, Allen, TX Zip 75013–4912; tel. 972/908–2015;
Bill Kaupas, Chief Executive Officer
Web address: www.warmsprings.org

POST ACUTE/WARM SPRINGS REHABILITATION HOSPITAL OF SAN ANTONIO
(O, 138 beds) 5101 Medical Drive, San Antonio, TX Zip 78229–4801;
tel. 210/616–0100; Debra Bormann, Chief Executive Officer
Web address: www.postacutemedical.com/our–facilities/hospitals/warm–
springs–rehabilitation–hospital–san–antonio/

For explanation of codes following names, see page B2.
★ Indicates Type III membership in the American Hospital Association.

Section B

POST ACUTE/WARM SPRINGS SPECIALTY HOSPITAL OF LULING (O, 34 beds) 200 Memorial Drive, Luling, TX Zip 78648–3213; tel. 830/875–8400; Jana Kuykendall, Chief Executive Officer
Web address: www.warmsprings.org

POST ACUTE/WARM SPRINGS SPECIALTY HOSPITAL OF NEW BRAUNFELS (O, 40 beds) 1445 Hanz Drive, New Braunfels, TX Zip 78130–2567; tel. 830/627–7600; Shayne Goode, Administrator
Web address: www.warmsprings.org/locations/hos/h1/

POST ACUTE/WARM SPRINGS SPECIALTY HOSPITAL OF SAN ANTONIO (O, 26 beds) 7400 Barlite Boulevard, 2nd Floor, San Antonio, TX Zip 78224–1308; tel. 210/921–3550; James Asberry, Chief Executive Officer
Web address: www.postacutemedical.com

POST ACUTE/WARM SPRINGS SPECIALTY HOSPITAL OF VICTORIA (O, 26 beds) 102 Medical Drive, Victoria, TX Zip 77904–3101; tel. 361/576–6200; Portlyn Brogger, Chief Executive Officer
Web address: www.warmsprings.org

WISCONSIN: POST ACUTE MEDICAL SPECIALTY HOSPITAL OF MILWAUKEE (O, 56 beds) 5017 South 110Th Street, Greenfield, WI Zip 53228–3131; tel. 414/427–8282; Christine Peterson, Chief Executive Officer
Web address: www.postacutemedical.com/

Owned, leased, sponsored:	16 hospitals	744 beds
Contract–managed:	0 hospitals	0 beds
Totals:	16 hospitals	744 beds

0240: PREFERRED MANAGEMENT CORPORATION (IO)
120 West MacArthur, Suite 121, Shawnee, OK Zip 74804–2005; tel. 405/878–0202; Donald Freeman, President and Chief Executive Officer
(Independent Hospital System)

TEXAS: COLEMAN COUNTY MEDICAL CENTER (L, 25 beds) 310 South Pecos Street, Coleman, TX Zip 76834–4159; tel. 325/625–2135; Michael W. Pruitt, Administrator and Chief Executive Officer
Web address: www.colemantexas.org/hospital.html

COLLINGSWORTH GENERAL HOSPITAL (L, 13 beds) 1013 15th Street, Wellington, TX Zip 79095–3703, Mailing Address: P.O. Box 1112, Zip 79095–1112; tel. 806/447–2521; Candy Powell, Administrator
Web address: www.collingsworthgeneral.net

CULBERSON HOSPITAL (L, 14 beds) Eisenhower–Farm Market Road 2185, Van Horn, TX Zip 79855, Mailing Address: P.O. Box 609, Zip 79855–0609; tel. 432/283–2760; Jonathon Voelkel, Administrator
Web address: www.culbersonhospital.org

KIMBLE HOSPITAL (O, 15 beds) 349 Reid Road, Junction, TX Zip 76849–3049; tel. 325/446–3321; Jimmy D. Stuart, Administrator
Web address: www.kimblehospital.org/

PARMER MEDICAL CENTER (C, 15 beds) 1307 Cleveland Street, Friona, TX Zip 79035–1121; tel. 806/250–2754; Gayla Quillin, Administrator
Web address: www.parmermedicalcenter.com

SABINE COUNTY HOSPITAL (L, 25 beds) 2301 Worth Street, Hemphill, TX Zip 75948–7216, Mailing Address: P.O. Box 750, Zip 75948–0750; tel. 409/787–3300; Jerry Howell, Administrator
Web address: www.sabinecountyhospital.com/

SCHLEICHER COUNTY MEDICAL CENTER (L, 14 beds) 102 North U.S. Highway 277, Eldorado, TX Zip 76936–4010; tel. 325/853–2507; Paul Burke, Administrator
Web address: www.scmc.us

Owned, leased, sponsored:	6 hospitals	106 beds
Contract–managed:	1 hospital	15 beds
Totals:	7 hospitals	121 beds

★0977: PREMIER HEALTH (NP)
110 North Main Street Suite 390, Dayton, OH Zip 45402–3720; tel. 937/499–9401; Mary H. Boosalis, President
(Centralized Physician/Insurance Health System)

OHIO: ATRIUM MEDICAL CENTER (O, 302 beds) One Medical Center Drive, Middletown, OH Zip 45005–1066; tel. 513/424–2111; Carol Turner, President and Chief Executive Officer
Web address: www.PremierHealth.com

GOOD SAMARITAN HOSPITAL (O, 346 beds) 2222 Philadelphia Drive, Dayton, OH Zip 45406–1813; tel. 937/734–2612; Eloise Broner, President and Chief Executive Officer
Web address: www.goodsamdayton.org

MIAMI VALLEY HOSPITAL (O, 845 beds) One Wyoming Street, Dayton, OH Zip 45409–2793; tel. 937/208–8000; Mark S. Shaker, President and Chief Executive Officer
Web address: www.miamivalleyhospital.org

UPPER VALLEY MEDICAL CENTER (O, 449 beds) 3130 North County Road 25A, Troy, OH Zip 45373–1309; tel. 937/440–4000; Rebecca Rice, FACHE, Chief Executive Officer
Web address: www.uvmc.com

Owned, leased, sponsored:	4 hospitals	1942 beds
Contract–managed:	0 hospitals	0 beds
Totals:	4 hospitals	1942 beds

★3505: PRESBYTERIAN HEALTHCARE SERVICES (NP)
2501 Buena Vista Drive, S.E., Albuquerque, NM Zip 87106–4260, Mailing Address: P.O. Box 26666, Zip 87125–6666; tel. 505/841–1234; James H. Hinton, President and Chief Executive Officer
(Centralized Physician/Insurance Health System)

NEW MEXICO: DR. DAN C. TRIGG MEMORIAL HOSPITAL (L, 10 beds) 301 East Miel De Luna Avenue, Tucumcari, NM Zip 88401–3810, Mailing Address: P.O. Box 608, Zip 88401–0608; tel. 575/461–7000; Donald Weidemann, Administrator
Web address: www.phs.org

LINCOLN COUNTY MEDICAL CENTER (L, 25 beds) 211 Sudderth Drive, Ruidoso, NM Zip 88345–6043, Mailing Address: P.O. Box 8000, Zip 88355–8000; tel. 575/257–8200; Todd Oberheu, Administrator
Web address: www.phs.org

PLAINS REGIONAL MEDICAL CENTER (O, 59 beds) 2100 Martin Luther King Boulevard, Clovis, NM Zip 88101–9412, Mailing Address: P.O. Box 1688, Zip 88102–1688; tel. 575/769–2141; Vincent B. DiFranco, Chief Executive Officer
Web address: www.phs.org

PRESBYTERIAN ESPANOLA HOSPITAL (O, 42 beds) 1010 Spruce Street, Espanola, NM Zip 87532–2746; tel. 505/753–7111; Brenda Romero, Administrator
Web address: www.phs.org

PRESBYTERIAN HOSPITAL (O, 638 beds) 1100 Central Avenue S.E., Albuquerque, NM Zip 87106–4934, Mailing Address: P.O. Box 26666, Zip 87125–6666; tel. 505/841–1234; Sandra C. Podley, Administrator
Web address: www.phs.org

SOCORRO GENERAL HOSPITAL (O, 18 beds) 1202 Highway 60 West, Socorro, NM Zip 87801–3914, Mailing Address: P.O. Box 1009, Zip 87801–1009; tel. 575/835–1140; Veronica Pound, R.N., Administrator
Web address: www.phs.org

Owned, leased, sponsored:	6 hospitals	792 beds
Contract–managed:	0 hospitals	0 beds
Totals:	6 hospitals	792 beds

★0851: PRESENCE HEALTH (CC)
200 South Wacker Drive, Suite 1100, Chicago, IL Zip 60606–5829; tel. 312/308–3200; Michael Englehart, President and Chief Executive Officer
(Moderately Centralized Health System)

ILLINOIS: OUR LADY OF THE RESURRECTION–LONG TERM CARE (O, 50 beds) 5645 West Addison Street, Chicago, IL Zip 60634;

PRESENCE COVENANT MEDICAL CENTER (O, 181 beds) 1400 West Park Street, Urbana, IL Zip 61801–2396; tel. 217/337–2000; Jared Rogers, M.D., President and Chief Executive Officer
Web address: www.presencehealth.org/covenant

PRESENCE HOLY FAMILY MEDICAL CENTER (O, 128 beds) 100 North River Road, Des Plaines, IL Zip 60016–1255; tel. 847/297–1800; Yolande Wilson–Stubbs, Regional Chief Operating Officer
Web address: www.presencehealth.org

For explanation of codes following names, see page B2.
★ Indicates Type III membership in the American Hospital Association.

PRESENCE MERCY MEDICAL CENTER (O, 242 beds) 1325 North Highland Avenue, Aurora, IL Zip 60506–1449; tel. 630/859–2222; Michael L. Brown, Regional President and Chief Executive Officer
Web address: www.presencehealth.org/mercy/

PRESENCE RESURRECTION MEDICAL CENTER (O, 325 beds) 7435 West Talcott Avenue, Chicago, IL Zip 60631–3746; tel. 773/774–8000; Robert Dahl, President and Chief Executive Officer
Web address: www.presencehealth.org

PRESENCE SAINT FRANCIS HOSPITAL (O, 199 beds) 355 Ridge Avenue, Evanston, IL Zip 60202–3399; tel. 847/316–4000; Roberta Luskin–Hawk, M.D., Chief Executive Officer
Web address: www.reshealth.org

PRESENCE SAINT JOSEPH HOSPITAL (O, 327 beds) 2900 North Lake Shore Drive, Chicago, IL Zip 60657–6274; tel. 773/665–3000; Roberta Luskin–Hawk, M.D., President and Chief Executive Officer
Web address: www.reshealth.org

PRESENCE SAINT JOSEPH HOSPITAL (O, 184 beds) 77 North Airlite Street, Elgin, IL Zip 60123–4912; tel. 847/695–3200; Michael L. Brown, Regional President and Chief Executive Officer
Web address: www.provena.org

PRESENCE SAINT JOSEPH MEDICAL CENTER (O, 443 beds) 333 North Madison Street, Joliet, IL Zip 60435–8200; tel. 815/725–7133; Lowell W. Johnson, LFACHE, Chief Executive Officer
Web address: www.presencehealth.org/stjoes

PRESENCE SAINTS MARY & ELIZABETH MEDICAL CENTER (O, 492 beds) 2233 West Division Street, Chicago, IL Zip 60622–3086; tel. 312/770–2000; Martin H. Judd, Regional President and Chief Executive Officer
Web address: www.presencehealth.org/presence–saints–mary–and–elizabeth–medical–center–chicago

PRESENCE ST. MARY'S HOSPITAL (O, 156 beds) 500 West Court Street, Kankakee, IL Zip 60901–3661; tel. 815/937–2400; Kathleen Rhine, President and Chief Executive Officer
Web address: www.presencehealth.org/presence–st–marys–hospital–kankakee

PRESENCE UNITED SAMARITANS MEDICAL CENTER (O, 117 beds) 812 North Logan, Danville, IL Zip 61832–3788; tel. 217/443–5000; Jared Rogers, M.D., President and Chief Executive Officer
Web address: www.presencehealth.org/usmc

RESURRECTION NURSING PAVILION (O, 295 beds) 1001 North Greenwood, Park Ridge, IL Zip 60068; Patricia Tiernan, Administrator

Owned, leased, sponsored:	13 hospitals	3139 beds
Contract–managed:	0 hospitals	0 beds
Totals:	13 hospitals	3139 beds

★0357: PRIME HEALTHCARE SERVICES (IO)
3300 East Guasti Road, Ontario, CA Zip 91761–8655; tel. 909/235–4400; Prem Reddy, M.D., President and Chief Executive Officer
(Moderately Centralized Health System)

ALABAMA: RIVERVIEW REGIONAL MEDICAL CENTER (O, 280 beds) 600 South Third Street, Gadsden, AL Zip 35901–5399; tel. 256/543–5200; David Fuller, FACHE, Interim Chief Executive Officer
Web address: www.riverviewregional.com

CALIFORNIA: ALVARADO HOSPITAL MEDICAL CENTER (O, 306 beds) 6655 Alvarado Road, San Diego, CA Zip 92120–5208; tel. 619/287–3270; Robin Gomez, R.N., MSN, Administrator
Web address: www.alvaradohospital.com

CENTINELA HOSPITAL MEDICAL CENTER (O, 369 beds) 555 East Hardy Street, Inglewood, CA Zip 90301–4011, Mailing Address: P.O. Box 720, Zip 90312–6720; tel. 310/673–4660; Linda Bradley, Chief Executive Officer
Web address: www.centinelamed.com

CHINO VALLEY MEDICAL CENTER (O, 126 beds) 5451 Walnut Avenue, Chino, CA Zip 91710–2672; tel. 909/464–8600; James M. Lally, D.O., President and Chief Medical Officer
Web address: www.cvmc.com

DESERT VALLEY HOSPITAL (O, 75 beds) 16850 Bear Valley Road, Victorville, CA Zip 92395–5795; tel. 760/241–8000; Fred Hunter, R.N., Chief Executive Officer
Web address: www.dvmc.com

ENCINO HOSPITAL MEDICAL CENTER (O, 80 beds) 16237 Ventura Boulevard, Encino, CA Zip 91436–2272; tel. 818/995–5000; Bockhi Park, Chief Executive Officer
Web address: www.encinomed.com

GARDEN GROVE HOSPITAL AND MEDICAL CENTER (O, 167 beds) 12601 Garden Grove Boulevard, Garden Grove, CA Zip 92843–1959; tel. 714/537–5160; Edward Mirzabegian, Chief Executive Officer
Web address: www.gardengrovehospital.com

GLENDORA COMMUNITY HOSPITAL (O, 128 beds) 150 West Route 66, Glendora, CA Zip 91740–6207; tel. 626/852–5000; Edward Mirzabegian, Chief Executive Officer
Web address: www.evhmc.com

HUNTINGTON BEACH HOSPITAL (O, 131 beds) 17772 Beach Boulevard, Huntington Beach, CA Zip 92647–6896; tel. 714/843–5000; Edward Mirzabegian, Chief Executive Officer
Web address: www.hbhospital.com

LA PALMA INTERCOMMUNITY HOSPITAL (O, 140 beds) 7901 Walker Street, La Palma, CA Zip 90623–1764; tel. 714/670–7400; Virgis Narbutas, Chief Executive Officer
Web address: www.lapalmaintercommunityhospital.com

MONTCLAIR HOSPITAL MEDICAL CENTER (O, 102 beds) 5000 San Bernardino Street, Montclair, CA Zip 91763–2326; tel. 909/625–5411; Edward Mirzabegian, Chief Executive Officer
Web address: www.montclair–hospital.com

PARADISE VALLEY HOSPITAL (O, 256 beds) 2400 East Fourth Street, National City, CA Zip 91950–2099; tel. 619/470–4321; Neerav Jadeja, Administrator
Web address: www.paradisevalleyhospital.org

SAN DIMAS COMMUNITY HOSPITAL (O, 101 beds) 1350 West Covina Boulevard, San Dimas, CA Zip 91773–3219; tel. 909/599–6811; Kurt Weinmeister, Chief Executive Officer
Web address: www.sandimashospital.com/

SHASTA REGIONAL MEDICAL CENTER (O, 113 beds) 1100 Butte Street, Redding, CA Zip 96001–0853, Mailing Address: P.O. Box 496072, Zip 96049–6072; tel. 530/244–5400; Cynthia Gordon, R.N., Chief Executive Officer
Web address: www.shastaregional.com

SHERMAN OAKS HOSPITAL (O, 90 beds) 4929 Van Nuys Boulevard, Sherman Oaks, CA Zip 91403–1777; tel. 818/981–7111; Bockhi Park, Chief Executive Officer
Web address: www.shermanoakshospital.com

WEST ANAHEIM MEDICAL CENTER (O, 219 beds) 3033 West Orange Avenue, Anaheim, CA Zip 92804–3183; tel. 714/827–3000; Virgis Narbutas, Chief Executive Officer
Web address: www.westanaheimmedctr.com

FLORIDA: LEHIGH REGIONAL MEDICAL CENTER (O, 88 beds) 1500 Lee Boulevard, Lehigh Acres, FL Zip 33936–4835; tel. 239/369–2101; Thomas Marshall, Interim Chief Executive Officer
Web address: www.lehighregional.com

GEORGIA: SOUTHERN REGIONAL MEDICAL CENTER (O, 331 beds) 11 Upper Riverdale Road S.W., Riverdale, GA Zip 30274–2615; tel. 770/991–8000; Charlotte W. Dupre, Interim Chief Executive Officer
Web address: www.southernregional.org

INDIANA: MONROE HOSPITAL (O, 32 beds) 5811 East Slick Rock lane, Bloomfield, IN Zip 47424, Mailing Address: 4011 South Monroe Medical Park Boulevard, Bloomington, Zip 47403–8000; tel. 812/825–1111; Phillip W. Lowe, Chief Executive Officer
Web address: www.monroehospital.com

KANSAS: PROVIDENCE MEDICAL CENTER (O, 170 beds) 8929 Parallel Parkway, Kansas City, KS Zip 66112–1689; tel. 913/596–4000; Randall G. Nyp, FACHE, Chief Executive Officer
Web address: www.providencekc.com

SAINT JOHN HOSPITAL (O, 40 beds) 3500 South Fourth Street, Leavenworth, KS Zip 66048–5043; tel. 913/680–6000; Randall G. Nyp, FACHE, President and Chief Executive Officer
Web address: www.providence–health.org/sjh

MICHIGAN: GARDEN CITY HOSPITAL (O, 176 beds) 6245 Inkster Road, Garden City, MI Zip 48135–4001; tel. 734/421–3300; Saju George, Chief Executive Officer
Web address: www.gch.org

For explanation of codes following names, see page B2.
★ Indicates Type III membership in the American Hospital Association.

LAKE HURON MEDICAL CENTER (O, 119 beds) 2601 Electric Avenue, Port Huron, MI Zip 48060–6518; tel. 810/985–1500; Rebekah Smith, R.N., President and Chief Executive Officer
Web address: www.mymercy.us

MISSOURI: ST. JOSEPH MEDICAL CENTER (O, 185 beds) 1000 Carondelet Drive, Kansas City, MO Zip 64114–4673; tel. 816/942–4400; Robert J. Erickson, Chief Executive Officer
Web address: www.stjosephkc.com/

ST. MARY'S MEDICAL CENTER (O, 88 beds) 201 Northwest R. D. Mize Road, Blue Springs, MO Zip 64014–2518; tel. 816/228–5900; Debra Ohnoutka, Chief Executive Officer
Web address: www.stmaryskc.com/

NEVADA: NORTH VISTA HOSPITAL (O, 177 beds) 1409 East Lake Mead Boulevard, North Las Vegas, NV Zip 89030–7197; tel. 702/649–7711; Vincenzo Variale, Chief Executive Officer
Web address: www.northvistahospital.com

SAINT MARY'S REGIONAL MEDICAL CENTER (O, 293 beds) 235 West Sixth Street, Reno, NV Zip 89503–4548; tel. 775/770–3000; Helen Lidholm, Chief Executive Officer
Web address: www.saintmarysreno.org

NEW JERSEY: SAINT CLARE'S HEALTH SYSTEM (O, 478 beds) 25 Pocono Road, Denville, NJ Zip 07834–2954; tel. 973/625–6000; Brian Finestein, Chief Executive Officer
Web address: www.saintclares.org

SAINT MICHAEL'S MEDICAL CENTER (O, 162 beds) 111 Central Avenue, Newark, NJ Zip 07102–1909; tel. 973/877–5350; Robert C. Iannaccone, Chief Executive Officer
Web address: www.smmcnj.org

ST. MARY'S GENERAL HOSPITAL (O, 269 beds) 350 Boulevard, Passaic, NJ Zip 07055–2840; tel. 973/365–4300; Edward Condit, President and Chief Executive Officer
Web address: www.smh–passaic.org

OHIO: EAST LIVERPOOL CITY HOSPITAL (O, 109 beds) 425 West Fifth Street, East Liverpool, OH Zip 43920–2498; tel. 330/385–7200; Keith Richardson, President and Chief Executive Officer
Web address: www.elch.org

PENNSYLVANIA: LOWER BUCKS HOSPITAL (O, 104 beds) 501 Bath Road, Bristol, PA Zip 19007–3190; tel. 215/785–9200; Linda J. Grass, Chief Executive Officer
Web address: www.lowerbuckshosp.com

ROXBOROUGH MEMORIAL HOSPITAL (O, 140 beds) 5800 Ridge Avenue, Philadelphia, PA Zip 19128–1737; tel. 215/483–9900; Peter J. Adamo, Chief Executive Officer
Web address: www.roxboroughmemorial.com

SUBURBAN COMMUNITY HOSPITAL (O, 126 beds) 2701 DeKalb Pike, Norristown, PA Zip 19401–1820; tel. 610/278–2000; Peter J. Adamo, Chief Executive Officer
Web address: www.suburbanhosp.org

RHODE ISLAND: LANDMARK MEDICAL CENTER (O, 140 beds) 115 Cass Avenue, Woonsocket, RI Zip 02895–4731; tel. 401/769–4100; Richard Charest, President & Chief Executive Officer
Web address: www.landmarkmedcenter.com

REHABILITATION HOSPITAL OF RHODE ISLAND (O, 70 beds) 116 Eddie Dowling Highway, North Smithfield, RI Zip 02896–7327; tel. 401/766–0800; Richard Charest, Chief Executive Officer
Web address: www.rhri.net

TEXAS: DALLAS MEDICAL CENTER (O, 83 beds) Seven Medical Parkway, Dallas, TX Zip 75234–7823, Mailing Address: P.O. Box 819094, Zip 75381–9094; tel. 972/247–1000; J. T. Barnhart, Chief Executive Officer
Web address: www.dallasmedcenter.com

DALLAS REGIONAL MEDICAL CENTER (O, 100 beds) 1011 North Galloway Avenue, Mesquite, TX Zip 75149–2433; tel. 214/320–7000; Glenda Newby, Chief Executive Officer
Web address: www.dallasregionalmedicalcenter.com

HARLINGEN MEDICAL CENTER (O, 88 beds) 5501 South Expressway 77, Harlingen, TX Zip 78550–3213; tel. 956/365–1000; Brenda Ivory, Chief Executive Officer
Web address: www.harlingenmedicalcenter.com

KNAPP MEDICAL CENTER (O, 192 beds) 1401 East Eighth Street, Weslaco, TX Zip 78596–6640, Mailing Address: P.O. Box 1110, Zip 78599–1110; tel. 956/968–8567; Rene Lopez, Chief Executive Officer
Web address: www.knappmed.org

PAMPA REGIONAL MEDICAL CENTER (O, 32 beds) One Medical Plaza, Pampa, TX Zip 79065; tel. 806/665–3721; Brad S. Morse, Chief Executive Officer
Web address: www.prmctx.com

Owned, leased, sponsored:	41 hospitals	6475 beds
Contract–managed:	0 hospitals	0 beds
Totals:	41 hospitals	6475 beds

★0153: PROHEALTH CARE, INC. (NP)
N17 W24100 Riverwood Drive, Suite 130, Waukesha, WI Zip 53188; tel. 262/928–2242; Susan A. Edwards, President and Chief Executive Officer
(Centralized Health System)

WISCONSIN: OCONOMOWOC MEMORIAL HOSPITAL (O, 58 beds) 791 Summit Avenue, Oconomowoc, WI Zip 53066–3896; tel. 262/569–9400; Susan A. Edwards, Chief Executive Officer
Web address: www.prohealthcare.org/locations/locations–v2–detail/?id=1123

WAUKESHA MEMORIAL HOSPITAL (O, 287 beds) 725 American Avenue, Waukesha, WI Zip 53188–5099; tel. 262/928–1000; Susan A. Edwards, Chief Executive Officer
Web address: www.prohealthcare.org/locations/locations–v2–detail/?id=1119

Owned, leased, sponsored:	2 hospitals	345 beds
Contract–managed:	0 hospitals	0 beds
Totals:	2 hospitals	345 beds

★0197: PROMEDICA HEALTH SYSTEM (NP)
1801 Richards Road, Toledo, OH Zip 43607–1037; tel. 419/469–3800; Randall D. Oostra, FACHE, President and Chief Executive Officer
(Centralized Health System)

MICHIGAN: PROMEDICA BIXBY HOSPITAL (O, 66 beds) 818 Riverside Avenue, Adrian, MI Zip 49221–1446; tel. 517/265–0900; Julie Yaroch, D.O., President
Web address: www.promedica.org

PROMEDICA HERRICK HOSPITAL (O, 60 beds) 500 East Pottawatamie Street, Tecumseh, MI Zip 49286–2018; tel. 517/424–3000; Julie Yaroch, D.O., President
Web address: www.promedica.org

PROMEDICA MONROE REGIONAL HOSPITAL (O, 173 beds) 718 North Macomb Street, Monroe, MI Zip 48162–7815; tel. 734/240–8400; Daniel Schwanke, Interim President
Web address: www.promedica.org

OHIO: PROMEDICA BAY PARK HOSPITAL (O, 77 beds) 2801 Bay Park Drive, Oregon, OH Zip 43616–4920; tel. 419/690–7900; Holly L. Bristoll, President
Web address: www.promedica.org

PROMEDICA DEFIANCE REGIONAL HOSPITAL (O, 35 beds) 1200 Ralston Avenue, Defiance, OH Zip 43512–1396; tel. 419/783–6955; Darrin Arquette, President
Web address: www.promedica.org

PROMEDICA FLOWER HOSPITAL (O, 273 beds) 5200 Harroun Road, Sylvania, OH Zip 43560–2196; tel. 419/824–1444; Neeraj Kanwal, M.D., President
Web address: www.promedica.org

PROMEDICA FOSTORIA COMMUNITY HOSPITAL (O, 25 beds) 501 Van Buren Street, Fostoria, OH Zip 44830–1534, Mailing Address: P.O. Box 907, Zip 44830–0907; tel. 419/435–7734; Holly L. Bristoll, President
Web address: www.promedica.org

PROMEDICA MEMORIAL HOSPITAL (O, 49 beds) 715 South Taft Avenue, Fremont, OH Zip 43420–3237; tel. 419/332–7321; Pamela Jensen, FACHE, President
Web address: www.promedica.org

Section B

For explanation of codes following names, see page B2.
★ Indicates Type III membership in the American Hospital Association.

PROMEDICA ST. LUKE'S HOSPITAL (O, 172 beds) 5901 Monclova Road, Maumee, OH Zip 43537–1899; tel. 419/893–5911; Daniel L. Wakeman, President
Web address: www.stlukeshospital.com

PROMEDICA TOLEDO HOSPITAL (O, 609 beds) 2142 North Cove Boulevard, Toledo, OH Zip 43606–3896; tel. 419/291–4000; Arturo Polizzi, President
Web address: www.promedica.org

Owned, leased, sponsored:	10 hospitals	1539 beds
Contract–managed:	0 hospitals	0 beds
Totals:	10 hospitals	1539 beds

0230:   PROMISE HEALTHCARE (IO)
999 Yamato Road, 3rd Floor, Boca Raton, FL Zip 33431–4477; tel. 561/869–3100; Peter R. Baronoff, Chief Executive Officer
(Independent Hospital System)

ARIZONA: PROMISE HOSPITAL OF PHOENIX (L, 40 beds) 433 East 6th Street, Mesa, AZ Zip 85203–7104; tel. 480/427–3000; Scott Floden, Chief Executive Officer
Web address: www.promise–phoenix.com

CALIFORNIA: PROMISE HOSPITAL OF EAST LOS ANGELES (L, 36 beds) 443 South Soto Street, Los Angeles, CA Zip 90033–4398; tel. 323/261–1181; Michael D. Kerr, Chief Executive Officer
Web address: www.promiseeastla.com

PROMISE HOSPITAL OF SAN DIEGO (O, 100 beds) 5550 University Avenue, San Diego, CA Zip 92105–2307; tel. 619/582–3800; William Mitchell, Chief Executive Officer
Web address: www.promisesandiego.com

FLORIDA: PROMISE HOSPITAL OF FLORIDA AT THE VILLAGES (O, 40 beds) 5050 County Road, Oxford, FL Zip 34484; tel. 352/689–6400; Hoyt Ross, Chief Executive Officer
Web address: www.promise–villages.com

PROMISE HOSPITAL OF FORT MYERS (O, 60 beds) 3050 Champion Ring Road, Fort Myers, FL Zip 33905–5599; tel. 239/313–2900; Patrick G. Ryan, Chief Executive Officer
Web address: www.promisefortmyers.om

PROMISE HOSPITAL OF MIAMI (O, 60 beds) 14001 N.W. 82nd Avenue, Miami, FL Zip 33158; tel. 786/609–9200; Theodore L. Welding, Chief Executive Officer
Web address: www.promise–miami.com

KANSAS: PROMISE HOSPITAL OF OVERLAND PARK (O, 104 beds) 6509 West 103rd Street, Overland Park, KS Zip 66212–1728; tel. 913/649–3701; Karen Leverich, Chief Executive Officer
Web address: www.promise–overlandpark.com

LOUISIANA: PROMISE HOSPITAL BATON ROUGE – MAIN CAMPUS (L, 50 beds) 5130 Mancuso Lane, Baton Rouge, LA Zip 70809–3583; tel. 225/490–9600; Kiley P. Cedotal, FACHE, Chief Executive Officer
Web address: www.promise–batonrouge.com

PROMISE HOSPITAL OF BATON ROUGE – MID–CITY CAMPUS (O, 57 beds) 3600 Florida Boulevard, 4th Floor, Baton Rouge, LA Zip 70806–3842; tel. 225/387–7770; Kiley P. Cedotal, FACHE, Chief Executive Officer
Web address: www.promise–batonrougemidcity.com

PROMISE HOSPITAL OF BATON ROUGE – OCHSNER CAMPUS (O, 22 beds) 17000 Medical Center Drive, 3rd Floor, Baton Rouge, LA Zip 70816–3246; tel. 225/236–5440; Kiley P. Cedotal, FACHE, Chief Executive Officer
Web address: www.promise–batonrougeochsner.com

PROMISE HOSPITAL OF LOUISIANA – SHREVEPORT CAMPUS (O, 146 beds) 1800 Irving Place, Shreveport, LA Zip 71101–4608; tel. 318/425–4096; Rick Stockton, Chief Executive Officer
Web address: www.promise–shreveport.com

PROMISE HOSPITAL OF MISS LOU (O, 40 beds) 209 Front Street, Vidalia, LA Zip 71373–2837; tel. 318/336–6500; Michael Harrell, R.N., Chief Executive Officer
Web address: www.promise–misslou.com

MISSISSIPPI: PROMISE HOSPITAL OF VICKSBURG (L, 33 beds) 1111 North Frontage Road, 2nd Floor, Vicksburg, MS Zip 39180–5102; tel. 601/619–3526; Michael Harrell, R.N., Chief Executive Officer
Web address: www.promise–vicksburg.com

TEXAS: PROMISE HOSPITAL OF DALLAS (O, 62 beds) 7955 Harry Hines Boulevard, Dallas, TX Zip 75235–3305; tel. 214/637–0000; Louis P. Bradley, Jr., Chief Executive Officer
Web address: www.promise–dallas.com/

PROMISE HOSPITAL OF WICHITA FALLS (O, 31 beds) 1103 Grace Street, Wichita Falls, TX Zip 76301–4414; tel. 940/720–6633; Michael L. McEachern, Chief Executive Officer
Web address: www.promise–wichitafalls.com

UTAH: PROMISE HOSPITAL OF SALT LAKE (O, 41 beds) 8 Avenue, C. Street, Salt Lake City, UT Zip 84143; tel. 801/408–7110; Wayne Kinsey, Chief Executive Officer
Web address: www.promise–saltlake.com

Owned, leased, sponsored:	16 hospitals	922 beds
Contract–managed:	0 hospitals	0 beds
Totals:	16 hospitals	922 beds

★1006:   PROVIDENCE ST. JOSEPH HEALTH (CC)
181 Lind Avenue Southwest, 9016, Renton, WA Zip 98057–9016; tel. 425/525–3698; Rodney F. Hochman, M.D., President and Chief Executive Officer; 3345 Michelson Drive, Suite 100   Irvine, CA 92612

ALASKA: PROVIDENCE ALASKA MEDICAL CENTER (O, 401 beds) 3200 Providence Drive, Anchorage, AK Zip 99508–4615, Mailing Address: P.O. Box 196604, Zip 99519–6604; tel. 907/562–2211; Richard Mandsager, M.D., Executive Officer
Web address: www.providence.org/alaska/pamc/default.htm

PROVIDENCE KODIAK ISLAND MEDICAL CENTER (L, 25 beds) 1915 East Rezanof Drive, Kodiak, AK Zip 99615–6602; tel. 907/486–3281; Barbara Bigelow, Administrator
Web address: www.providence.org

PROVIDENCE SEWARD MEDICAL CENTER (L, 46 beds) 417 First Avenue, Seward, AK Zip 99664, Mailing Address: P.O. Box 365, Zip 99664–0365; tel. 907/224–5205; Joseph Fong, Administrator
Web address: www.providence.org

PROVIDENCE VALDEZ MEDICAL CENTER (C, 21 beds) 911 Meals Avenue, Valdez, AK Zip 99686–0550, Mailing Address: P.O. Box 550, Zip 99686–0550; tel. 907/835–2249; Jeremy O'Neil, Administrator
Web address: www.providence.org/alaska

CALIFORNIA: MISSION HOSPITAL (O, 235 beds) 27700 Medical Center Road, Mission Viejo, CA Zip 92691–6474; tel. 949/364–1400; Richard Afable, M.D., M.P.H., Interim President & Chief Executive Officer
Web address: www.mission4health.com

PETALUMA VALLEY HOSPITAL (L, 49 beds) 400 North McDowell Boulevard, Petaluma, CA Zip 94954–2366; tel. 707/778–1111; Todd Salnas, President
Web address: www.stjosephhealth.org/About–Us/Facilities/Petaluma–Valley–Hospital.aspx

PROVIDENCE HOLY CROSS MEDICAL CENTER (O, 377 beds) 15031 Rinaldi Street, Mission Hills, CA Zip 91345–1207; tel. 818/365–8051; Bernard Klein, M.D., Chief Executive
Web address: www.https://california.providence.org/holy–cross/Pages/default.aspx

PROVIDENCE LITTLE COMPANY OF MARY MEDICAL CENTER – TORRANCE (O, 376 beds) 4101 Torrance Boulevard, Torrance, CA Zip 90503–4664; tel. 310/540–7676; Mary E. Kingston, FACHE, R.N., Chief Executive Officer, South Bay Community
Web address: www.providence.org

PROVIDENCE LITTLE COMPANY OF MARY MEDICAL CENTER SAN PEDRO (O, 317 beds) 1300 West Seventh Street, San Pedro, CA Zip 90732–3505; tel. 310/832–3311; Mary E. Kingston, FACHE, R.N., Chief Executive Officer
Web address: www.https://california.providence.org/san–pedro

PROVIDENCE SAINT JOHN'S HEALTH CENTER (O, 234 beds) 2121 Santa Monica Boulevard, Santa Monica, CA Zip 90404–2091; tel. 310/829–5511; Marcel C. Loh, FACHE, Chief Executive Officer
Web address: www.providence.org/saintjohns

PROVIDENCE SAINT JOSEPH MEDICAL CENTER (O, 383 beds) 501 South Buena Vista Street, Burbank, CA Zip 91505–4866; tel. 818/843–5111; Julie Sprengel, Chief Executive Officer
Web address: www.providence.org

For explanation of codes following names, see page B2.
★ Indicates Type III membership in the American Hospital Association.

B108   Health Care Systems, Networks and Alliances

© 2016 AHA Guide

PROVIDENCE TARZANA MEDICAL CENTER (O, 249 beds) 18321 Clark Street, Tarzana, CA Zip 91356–3521; tel. 818/881–0800; Dale Surowitz, Chief Executive
Web address: www.providence.org/tarzana.com

QUEEN OF THE VALLEY MEDICAL CENTER (O, 120 beds) 1000 Trancas Street, Napa, CA Zip 94558–2906, Mailing Address: P.O. Box 2340, Zip 94558–0688; tel. 707/252–4411; Walt Mickens, FACHE, President and Chief Executive Officer
Web address: www.thequeen.org

REDWOOD MEMORIAL HOSPITAL (O, 25 beds) 3300 Renner Drive, Fortuna, CA Zip 95540–3198; tel. 707/725–3361; David O'Brien, M.D., President
Web address: www.redwoodmemorial.org/

SANTA ROSA MEMORIAL HOSPITAL (O, 278 beds) 1165 Montgomery Drive, Santa Rosa, CA Zip 95405–4897, Mailing Address: P.O. Box 522, Zip 95402–0522; tel. 707/546–3210; Todd Salnas, President
Web address: www.stjosephhealth.org

ST. JOSEPH HOSPITAL (O, 153 beds) 2700 Dolbeer Street, Eureka, CA Zip 95501–4799; tel. 707/445–8121; David O'Brien, M.D., President
Web address: www.stjosepheureka.org

ST. JOSEPH HOSPITAL (O, 379 beds) 1100 West Stewart Drive, Orange, CA Zip 92868–3849, Mailing Address: P.O. Box 5600, Zip 92863–5600; tel. 714/633–9111; Steven C. Moreau, President and Chief Executive Officer
Web address: www.sjo.org

ST. JUDE MEDICAL CENTER (O, 351 beds) 101 East Valencia Mesa Drive, Fullerton, CA Zip 92835–3875; tel. 714/992–3000; Lee Penrose, President and Chief Executive Officer
Web address: www.stjudemedicalcenter.org

ST. MARY MEDICAL CENTER (O, 210 beds) 18300 Highway 18, Apple Valley, CA Zip 92307–2206, Mailing Address: P.O. Box 7025, Zip 92307–0725; tel. 760/242–2311; Alan H. Garrett, President and Chief Executive Officer
Web address: www.stmaryapplevalley.com/

MONTANA: COMMUNITY HOSPITAL OF ANACONDA (C, 87 beds) 401 West Pennsylvania Street, Anaconda, MT Zip 59711; tel. 406/563–8500; Steve McNeece, Chief Executive Officer
Web address: www.communityhospitalofanaconda.org

PROVIDENCE ST. JOSEPH MEDICAL CENTER (S, 22 beds) 6 Thirteenth Avenue East, Polson, MT Zip 59860–5315, Mailing Address: P.O. Box 1010, Zip 59860–1010; tel. 406/883–5377; James R. Kiser, II, Chief Executive Officer
Web address: www.saintjoes.org

ST. PATRICK HOSPITAL (S, 200 beds) 500 West Broadway, Missoula, MT Zip 59802–4096, Mailing Address: P.O. Box 4587, Zip 59806–4587; tel. 406/543–7271; Jeff Fee, Chief Executive Officer
Web address: www.saintpatrick.org

OREGON: PROVIDENCE HOOD RIVER MEMORIAL HOSPITAL (O, 25 beds) 810 12th Street, Hood River, OR Zip 97031–1587, Mailing Address: P.O. Box 149, Zip 97031–0055; tel. 541/386–3911; Jeanie Vieira, Chief Executive Officer
Web address: www.providence.org/hoodriver

PROVIDENCE MEDFORD MEDICAL CENTER (O, 142 beds) 1111 Crater Lake Avenue, Medford, OR Zip 97504–6241; tel. 541/732–5000; Cindy Mayo, R.N., FACHE, Chief Executive Officer
Web address: www.providence.org

PROVIDENCE MILWAUKIE HOSPITAL (O, 51 beds) 10150 S.E. 32nd Avenue, Milwaukie, OR Zip 97222–6516; tel. 503/513–8300; Keith Hyde, Chief Executive
Web address: www.providence.org

PROVIDENCE NEWBERG MEDICAL CENTER (O, 40 beds) 1001 Providence Drive, Newberg, OR Zip 97132–7485; tel. 503/537–1555; Lorinda Van Zanten, MSN, Chief Executive Officer
Web address: www.phsor.org

PROVIDENCE PORTLAND MEDICAL CENTER (O, 417 beds) 4805 N.E. Glisan Street, Portland, OR Zip 97213–2933; tel. 503/215–5526; Paul Gaden, Chief Executive Officer
Web address: www.providence.org

PROVIDENCE SEASIDE HOSPITAL (L, 25 beds) 725 South Wahanna Road, Seaside, OR Zip 97138–7735; tel. 503/717–7000; Kendall Sawa, R.N., Chief Executive Officer
Web address: www.providence.org

PROVIDENCE ST. VINCENT MEDICAL CENTER (O, 552 beds) 9205 S.W. Barnes Road, Portland, OR Zip 97225–6661; tel. 503/216–1234; Janice Burger, Chief Executive
Web address: www.providence.org/portland/hospitals

PROVIDENCE WILLAMETTE FALLS MEDICAL CENTER (O, 111 beds) 1500 Division Street, Oregon City, OR Zip 97045–1597; tel. 503/656–1631; Russ Reinhard, Chief Executive
Web address: www.providence.org/pwfmc

TEXAS: COVENANT CHILDREN'S HOSPITAL (O, 73 beds) 4015 22nd Place, Lubbock, TX Zip 79410; tel. 806/725–1011; Amy Thompson, M.D., Chief Executive Officer
Web address: www.covenanthealth.
org/About–Us/Facilities/Childrens–Hospital.aspx

COVENANT HOSPITAL PLAINVIEW (L, 68 beds) 2601 Dimmitt Road, Plainview, TX Zip 79072–1833; tel. 806/296–5531; Robert Copeland, Interim Chief Executive Officer
Web address: www.covenantplainview.org

COVENANT HOSPITAL–LEVELLAND (L, 26 beds) 1900 South College Avenue, Levelland, TX Zip 79336–6508; tel. 806/894–4963; Bruce White, Administrator
Web address: www.covenanthospitallevelland.com/

COVENANT MEDICAL CENTER (O, 566 beds) 3615 19th Street, Lubbock, TX Zip 79410–4402, Mailing Address: P.O. Box 1201, Zip 79408–1201; tel. 806/725–0000; Walt Cathey, Chief Executive Officer
Web address: www.covenanthealth.org

WASHINGTON: KADLEC REGIONAL MEDICAL CENTER (O, 254 beds) 888 Swift Boulevard, Richland, WA Zip 99352–3514; tel. 509/946–4611; Rand J. Wortman, President and Chief Executive Officer
Web address: www.kadlecmed.org

PROVIDENCE CENTRALIA HOSPITAL (O, 91 beds) 914 South Scheuber Road, Centralia, WA Zip 98531–9027; tel. 360/736–2803; Medrice Coluccio, R.N., Southwest Region Chief Executive
Web address: www.providence.org

PROVIDENCE HOLY FAMILY HOSPITAL (S, 191 beds) 5633 North Lidgerwood Street, Spokane, WA Zip 99208–1224; tel. 509/482–0111; Alex Jackson, Chief Executive
Web address: www.providence.org

PROVIDENCE MOUNT CARMEL HOSPITAL (S, 25 beds) 982 East Columbia Avenue, Colville, WA Zip 99114–3352; tel. 509/685–5100; Ronald G. Rehn, Chief Executive Officer
Web address: www.mtcarmelhospital.org

PROVIDENCE REGIONAL MEDICAL CENTER EVERETT (O, 501 beds) 1321 Colby Avenue, Everett, WA Zip 98201–1665, Mailing Address: P.O. Box 1147, Zip 98206–1147; tel. 425/261–2000; Preston M. Simmons, FACHE, Chief Executive Officer
Web address: www.providence.org

PROVIDENCE SACRED HEART MEDICAL CENTER & CHILDREN'S HOSPITAL (S, 672 beds) 101 West Eighth Avenue, Spokane, WA Zip 99204–2364, Mailing Address: P.O. Box 2555, Zip 99220–2555; tel. 509/474–3131; Alex Jackson, Chief Executive
Web address: www.shmc.org

PROVIDENCE ST. JOSEPH'S HOSPITAL (S, 65 beds) 500 East Webster Street, Chewelah, WA Zip 99109–9523; tel. 509/935–8211; Ronald G. Rehn, Chief Executive Officer
Web address: www.washington.providence.
org/hospitals/st–josephs–hospital/

PROVIDENCE ST. MARY MEDICAL CENTER (S, 105 beds) 401 West Poplar Street, Walla Walla, WA Zip 99362–2846, Mailing Address: P.O. Box 1477, Zip 99362–0312; tel. 509/525–3320; Steven A. Burdick, Chief Executive Officer
Web address: www.washington.providence.org/hospitals/st–mary/

PROVIDENCE ST. PETER HOSPITAL (O, 347 beds) 413 Lilly Road N.E., Olympia, WA Zip 98506–5166; tel. 360/491–9480; Medrice Coluccio, R.N., Chief Executive Officer
Web address: www.providence.org/swsa/facilities/st_peter_hospital

ST. LUKE'S REHABILITATION INSTITUTE (O, 72 beds) 711 South Cowley Street, Spokane, WA Zip 99202–1388; tel. 509/473–6000; Nancy Webster, Chief Administrative Officer
Web address: www.st–lukes.org

For explanation of codes following names, see page B2.
★ Indicates Type III membership in the American Hospital Association.

SWEDISH MEDICAL CENTER–CHERRY HILL CAMPUS (O, 198 beds) 500 17th Avenue, Seattle, WA Zip 98122–5711; tel. 206/320–2000; June Altaras, R.N., Chief Executive Officer
Web address: www.swedish.org

SWEDISH MEDICAL CENTER–FIRST HILL (O, 620 beds) 747 Broadway, Seattle, WA Zip 98122–4307; tel. 206/386–6000; June Altaras, R.N., Chief Executive Officer
Web address: www.swedish.org

SWEDISH/EDMONDS (O, 161 beds) 21601 76th Avenue West, Edmonds, WA Zip 98026–7506; tel. 425/640–4000; Jennifer Graves, R.N., MS, Chief Executive
Web address: www.swedish.org

SWEDISH/ISSAQUAH (O, 49 beds) 751 N.E. Blakely Drive, Issaquah, WA Zip 98029–6201; tel. 425/313–4000; Rayburn Lewis, M.D., Chief Executive
Web address: www.swedish.org/issaquah

WHITMAN HOSPITAL AND MEDICAL CENTER (C, 25 beds) 1200 West Fairview Street, Colfax, WA Zip 99111–9579; tel. 509/397–3435; Hank Hanigan, MS, R.N., Chief Executive Officer
Web address: www.whitmanhospital.org

Owned, leased, sponsored:	46 hospitals	9877 beds
Contract–managed:	3 hospitals	133 beds
Totals:	49 hospitals	10010 beds

★**0011: PUERTO RICO DEPARTMENT OF HEALTH** (NP)
Building A – Medical Center, San Juan, PR Zip 00936, Mailing Address: Call Box 70184, Zip 00936; tel. 787/765–2929; Ana Rius, M.D., Secretary of Health
(Independent Hospital System)

PUERTO RICO: CARDIOVASCULAR CENTER OF PUERTO RICO AND THE CARIBBEAN (O, 154 beds) Americo Miranda Centro Medico, San Juan, PR Zip 00936, Mailing Address: P.O. Box 366528, Zip 00936–6528; tel. 787/754–8500; Carlos Cabrera, Executive Director
Web address: www.cardiovascular.gobierno.pr

HOSPITAL UNIVERSITARIO DR. RAMON RUIZ ARNAU (O, 102 beds) Avenue Laurel, Santa Juanita, Bayamon, PR Zip 00956; tel. 787/787–5151; Prudencio A. Laureano, Chief Executive Officer

UNIVERSITY HOSPITAL (O, 220 beds) Nineyas 869 Rio Piedras, San Juan, PR Zip 00922, Mailing Address: P.O. Box 2116, Zip 00922; tel. 787/754–0101; Jorge Matta Gonzalez, Executive Director

UNIVERSITY PEDIATRIC HOSPITAL (O, 145 beds) Barrio Monacenno, Carretera 22, Rio Piedras, PR Zip 00935, Mailing Address: P.O. Box 191079, San Juan, Zip 00910–1070; tel. 787/777–3535; Gloria Hernandez, Executive Director
Web address: www.md.rcm.upr.edu/pediatrics/university_pediatric_hospital.php

Owned, leased, sponsored:	4 hospitals	621 beds
Contract–managed:	0 hospitals	0 beds
Totals:	4 hospitals	621 beds

★**0002: QHR** (IO)
105 Continental Place, Brentwood, TN Zip 37027–1052; tel. 800/233–1470; Mickey Bilbrey, President and Chief Executive Officer
(Decentralized Health System)

ARKANSAS: GREAT RIVER MEDICAL CENTER (C, 73 beds) 1520 North Division Street, Blytheville, AR Zip 72315–1448, Mailing Address: P.O. Box 108, Zip 72316–0108; tel. 870/838–7300; Chris Raymer, R.N., Chief Executive Officer
Web address: www.mchsys.org

SOUTH MISSISSIPPI COUNTY REGIONAL MEDICAL CENTER (C, 25 beds) 611 West Lee Avenue, Osceola, AR Zip 72370–3001, Mailing Address: P.O. Box 108, Blytheville, Zip 72316–0108; tel. 870/563–7000; Chris Raymer, R.N., Chief Executive Officer
Web address: www.mchsys.org

CALIFORNIA: BEAR VALLEY COMMUNITY HOSPITAL (C, 30 beds) 41870 Garstin Drive, Big Bear Lake, CA Zip 92315, Mailing Address: P.O. Box 1649, Zip 92315–1649; tel. 909/866–6501; David M. Faulkner, Interim Chief Executive Officer
Web address: www.bvchd.com

COLORADO: ARKANSAS VALLEY REGIONAL MEDICAL CENTER (C, 145 beds) 1100 Carson Avenue, La Junta, CO Zip 81050–2799; tel. 719/383–6000; Lynn Crowell, Chief Executive Officer
Web address: www.avrmc.org

COMMUNITY HOSPITAL (C, 44 beds) 2351 G. Road, Grand Junction, CO Zip 81505; tel. 970/242–0920; Chris Thomas, FACHE, President and Chief Executive Officer
Web address: www.yourcommunityhospital.com

MONTROSE MEMORIAL HOSPITAL (C, 66 beds) 800 South Third Street, Montrose, CO Zip 81401–4212; tel. 970/249–2211; Steven Hannah, Chief Executive Officer
Web address: www.montrosehospital.com

PIONEERS MEDICAL CENTER (C, 40 beds) 100 Pioneers Medical Center Drive, Meeker, CO Zip 81641–3181; tel. 970/878–5047; Kenneth Harman, Chief Executive Officer
Web address: www.pioneershospital.org

PROWERS MEDICAL CENTER (C, 25 beds) 401 Kendall Drive, Lamar, CO Zip 81052–3993; tel. 719/336–4343; Craig Loveless, Chief Executive Officer
Web address: www.prowersmedical.com

THE MEMORIAL HOSPITAL AT CRAIG (C, 25 beds) 750 Hospital Loop, Craig, CO Zip 81625–8750; tel. 970/824–9411; Andrew Daniels, Chief Executive Officer
Web address: www.thememorialhospital.com

FLORIDA: FISHERMEN'S HOSPITAL (C, 25 beds) 3301 Overseas Highway, Marathon, FL Zip 33050–2329; tel. 305/743–5533; Hal W. Leftwich, FACHE, Chief Executive Officer
Web address: www.fishermenshospital.org

HENDRY REGIONAL MEDICAL CENTER (C, 25 beds) 524 West Sagamore Avenue, Clewiston, FL Zip 33440–3514; tel. 863/902–3000; R. D. Williams, Chief Executive Officer
Web address: www.hendryregional.org

JACKSON HOSPITAL (C, 68 beds) 4250 Hospital Drive, Marianna, FL Zip 32446–1917, Mailing Address: P.O. Box 1608, Zip 32447–5608; tel. 850/526–2200; Larry Meese, Chief Executive Officer
Web address: www.jacksonhosp.com

IDAHO: GRITMAN MEDICAL CENTER (C, 25 beds) 700 South Main Street, Moscow, ID Zip 83843–3056; tel. 208/882–4511; Kara Besst, President and Chief Executive Officer
Web address: www.gritman.org

STEELE MEMORIAL MEDICAL CENTER (C, 18 beds) 203 South Daisy Street, Salmon, ID Zip 83467–4709; tel. 208/756–5600; Jeanine Gentry, Chief Executive Officer
Web address: www.steelemh.org

ILLINOIS: CRAWFORD MEMORIAL HOSPITAL (C, 63 beds) 1000 North Allen Street, Robinson, IL Zip 62454–1167; tel. 618/544–3131; Donald E. Annis, Chief Executive Officer
Web address: www.crawfordmh.net

LAWRENCE COUNTY MEMORIAL HOSPITAL (C, 25 beds) 2200 West State Street, Lawrenceville, IL Zip 62439–1852; tel. 618/943–1000; Doug Florkowski, Chief Executive Officer
Web address: www.lcmhosp.org

PEKIN HOSPITAL (C, 107 beds) 600 South 13th Street, Pekin, IL Zip 61554–4936; tel. 309/347–1151; Bob J. Haley, Chief Executive Officer
Web address: www.pekinhospital.org

INDIANA: DAVIESS COMMUNITY HOSPITAL (C, 80 beds) 1314 East Walnut Street, Washington, IN Zip 47501–2860, Mailing Address: P.O. Box 760, Zip 47501–0760; tel. 812/254–2760; David Bixler, Chief Executive Officer
Web address: www.dchosp.org

SULLIVAN COUNTY COMMUNITY HOSPITAL (C, 25 beds) 2200 North Section Street, Sullivan, IN Zip 47882–7523, Mailing Address: P.O. Box 10, Zip 47882–0010; tel. 812/268–4311; Michelle Sly–Franklin, Chief Executive Officer
Web address: www.schosp.com

For explanation of codes following names, see page B2.
★ Indicates Type III membership in the American Hospital Association.

IOWA: BOONE COUNTY HOSPITAL (C, 32 beds) 1015 Union Street, Boone, IA Zip 50036–4821; tel. 515/432–3140; Joseph S. Smith, Chief Executive Officer
Web address: www.boonehospital.com

FORT MADISON COMMUNITY HOSPITAL (C, 50 beds) 5445 Avenue O, Fort Madison, IA Zip 52627–9611, Mailing Address: P.O. Box 174, Zip 52627–0174; tel. 319/372–6530; Lynn W. Beasley, FACHE, Interim Chief Executive Officer
Web address: www.fmchosp.com

KANSAS: GREELEY COUNTY HEALTH SERVICES (C, 50 beds) 506 Third Street, Tribune, KS Zip 67879–9684, Mailing Address: P.O. Box 338, Zip 67879–0338; tel. 620/376–4221; Lee Rhodes, Administrator and Chief Executive Officer
Web address: www.mygchs.com

NEOSHO MEMORIAL REGIONAL MEDICAL CENTER (C, 25 beds) 629 South Plummer, Chanute, KS Zip 66720–1928, Mailing Address: P.O. Box 426, Zip 66720–0426; tel. 620/431–4000; Dennis Franks, FACHE, Chief Executive Officer
Web address: www.nmrmc.com

WILSON MEDICAL CENTER (C, 15 beds) 2600 Ottawa Road, Neodesha, KS Zip 66757–1897, Mailing Address: P.O. Box 360, Zip 66757–0360; tel. 620/325–2611; Dennis R. Shelby, Chief Executive Officer
Web address: www.wilsonmedical.org

KENTUCKY: CALDWELL MEDICAL CENTER (C, 25 beds) 100 Medical Center Drive, Princeton, KY Zip 42445–2430, Mailing Address: P.O. Box 410, Zip 42445–0410; tel. 270/365–0300; Kelley J. Rushing, Chief Executive Officer
Web address: www.caldwellhosp.org

JENNIE STUART MEDICAL CENTER (C, 139 beds) 320 West 18th Street, Hopkinsville, KY Zip 42240–1965, Mailing Address: P.O. Box 2400, Zip 42241–2400; tel. 270/887–0100; Eric A. Lee, President and Chief Executive Officer
Web address: www.jsmc.org

MONROE COUNTY MEDICAL CENTER (C, 49 beds) 529 Capp Harlan Road, Tompkinsville, KY Zip 42167–1840; tel. 270/487–9231; Vicky McFall, Chief Executive Officer
Web address: www.mcmccares.com

OHIO COUNTY HOSPITAL (C, 25 beds) 1211 Main Street, Hartford, KY Zip 42347–1619; tel. 270/298–7411; Blaine Pieper, Chief Executive Officer
Web address: www.ohiocountyhospital.com

LOUISIANA: CLAIBORNE MEMORIAL MEDICAL CENTER (C, 57 beds) 620 East College Street, Homer, LA Zip 71040–3202; tel. 318/927–2024; Antonia M. Goodin, Interim Chief Executive Officer
Web address: www.claibornemedical.com/

FRANKLIN FOUNDATION HOSPITAL (C, 22 beds) 1097 Northwest Boulevard, Franklin, LA Zip 70538–3407, Mailing Address: P.O. Box 577, Zip 70538–0577; tel. 337/828–0760; Craig R. Cudworth, Chief Executive Officer
Web address: www.franklinfoundation.org

MAINE: CALAIS REGIONAL HOSPITAL (C, 25 beds) 24 Hospital Lane, Calais, ME Zip 04619–1398; tel. 207/454–7521; Rodney Boula, Chief Executive Officer
Web address: www.calaishospital.com

CARY MEDICAL CENTER (C, 49 beds) 163 Van Buren Road, Suite 1, Caribou, ME Zip 04736–3567; tel. 207/498–3111; Kris A. Doody, R.N., Chief Executive Officer
Web address: www.carymedicalcenter.org

PENOBSCOT VALLEY HOSPITAL (C, 25 beds) 7 Transalpine Road, Lincoln, ME Zip 04457–4222, Mailing Address: P.O. Box 368, Zip 04457–0368; tel. 207/794–3321; Gary R. Poquette, FACHE, Chief Executive Officer
Web address: www.pvhme.org

MICHIGAN: ALLEGAN GENERAL HOSPITAL (C, 25 beds) 555 Linn Street, Allegan, MI Zip 49010–1524; tel. 269/673–8424; Gerald J. Barbini, President and Chief Executive Officer
Web address: www.aghosp.org

HAYES GREEN BEACH MEMORIAL HOSPITAL (C, 25 beds) 321 East Harris Street, Charlotte, MI Zip 48813–1629; tel. 517/543–1050; Matthew Rush, FACHE, President and Chief Executive Officer
Web address: www.hgbhealth.com

STURGIS HOSPITAL (C, 49 beds) 916 Myrtle Street, Sturgis, MI Zip 49091–2326; tel. 269/651–7824; Robert J. LaBarge, President and Chief Executive Officer
Web address: www.sturgishospital.com

THREE RIVERS HEALTH (C, 35 beds) 701 South Health Parkway, Three Rivers, MI Zip 49093–8352; tel. 269/278–1145; William B. Russell, Chief Executive Officer
Web address: www.threerivershealth.org

MISSISSIPPI: KING'S DAUGHTERS MEDICAL CENTER (C, 122 beds) 427 Highway 51 North, Brookhaven, MS Zip 39601–2350, Mailing Address: P.O. Box 948, Zip 39602–0948; tel. 601/833–6011; Alvin Hoover, FACHE, Chief Executive Officer
Web address: www.kdmc.org

MISSOURI: NEVADA REGIONAL MEDICAL CENTER (C, 71 beds) 800 South Ash Street, Nevada, MO Zip 64772–3223; tel. 417/667–3355; Kevin Leeper, Chief Executive Officer
Web address: www.nrmchealth.com

MONTANA: NORTH VALLEY HOSPITAL (C, 25 beds) 1600 Hospital Way, Whitefish, MT Zip 59937–7849; tel. 406/863–3500; Tate J. Kreitinger, Interim Chief Executive Officer
Web address: www.nvhosp.org

NEBRASKA: PHELPS MEMORIAL HEALTH CENTER (C, 25 beds) 1215 Tibbals Street, Holdrege, NE Zip 68949–1255; tel. 308/995–2211; Mark Harrel, Chief Executive Officer
Web address: www.phelpsmemorial.com

NORTH CAROLINA: NORTHERN HOSPITAL OF SURRY COUNTY (C, 108 beds) 830 Rockford Street, Mount Airy, NC Zip 27030–5365, Mailing Address: P.O. Box 1101, Zip 27030–1101; tel. 336/719–7000; Ned Hill, President and Chief Executive Officer
Web address: www.northernhospital.com

OHIO: KNOX COMMUNITY HOSPITAL (C, 65 beds) 1330 Coshocton Road, Mount Vernon, OH Zip 43050–1495; tel. 740/393–9000; Bruce D. White, Chief Executive Officer
Web address: www.knoxcommhosp.org

WOOSTER COMMUNITY HOSPITAL (C, 150 beds) 1761 Beall Avenue, Wooster, OH Zip 44691–2342; tel. 330/263–8100; William E. Sheron, Chief Executive Officer
Web address: www.woosterhospital.org

OKLAHOMA: PERRY MEMORIAL HOSPITAL (C, 26 beds) 501 North 14th Street, Perry, OK Zip 73077–5099; tel. 580/336–3541; Daniel Odegaard, FACHE, Chief Executive Officer
Web address: www.pmh–ok.org

PENNSYLVANIA: CLARION HOSPITAL (C, 66 beds) One Hospital Drive, Clarion, PA Zip 16214–8501; tel. 814/226–9500; Byron Quinton, Chief Executive Officer
Web address: www.clarionhospital.org

JERSEY SHORE HOSPITAL (C, 25 beds) 1020 Thompson Street, Jersey Shore, PA Zip 17740–1794; tel. 570/398–0100; David A. Shannon, President and Chief Executive Officer
Web address: www.jsh.org

SOUTH CAROLINA: ABBEVILLE AREA MEDICAL CENTER (C, 25 beds) 420 Thomson Circle, Abbeville, SC Zip 29620–5656, Mailing Address: P.O. Box 887, Zip 29620–0887; tel. 864/366–5011; Howard D. Turner, Chief Executive Officer
Web address: www.abbevilleareamc.com

NEWBERRY COUNTY MEMORIAL HOSPITAL (C, 52 beds) 2669 Kinard Street, Newberry, SC Zip 29108–2911, Mailing Address: P.O. Box 497, Zip 29108–0497; tel. 803/276–7570; Bruce A. Baldwin, Chief Executive Officer
Web address: www.newberryhospital.org

REGIONAL MEDICAL CENTER (C, 286 beds) 3000 St. Matthews Road, Orangeburg, SC Zip 29118–1442; tel. 803/395–2200; Thomas C. Dandridge, President and Chief Executive Officer
Web address: www.trmchealth.org

TIDELANDS GEORGETOWN MEMORIAL HOSPITAL (C, 136 beds) 606 Black River Road, Georgetown, SC Zip 29440–3368, Mailing Address: Drawer 421718, Zip 29442–4203; tel. 843/527–7000; Gayle L. Resetar, Chief Operating Officer
Web address: www.georgetownhospitalsystem.org

For explanation of codes following names, see page B2.
★ Indicates Type III membership in the American Hospital Association.

TIDELANDS WACCAMAW COMMUNITY HOSPITAL (C, 169 beds) 4070 Highway 17 Bypass, Murrells Inlet, SC Zip 29576–5033, Mailing Address: P.O. Drawer 3350, Zip 29576–2673; tel. 843/652–1000; Gayle L. Resetar, Chief Operating Officer
Web address: www.tidelandshealth.org

SOUTH DAKOTA: HURON REGIONAL MEDICAL CENTER (C, 25 beds) 172 Fourth Street S.E., Huron, SD Zip 57350–2590; tel. 605/353–6200; David Dick, Chief Executive Officer
Web address: www.huronregional.org

TENNESSEE: MACON COUNTY GENERAL HOSPITAL (C, 25 beds) 204 Medical Drive, Lafayette, TN Zip 37083–1799, Mailing Address: P.O. Box 378, Zip 37083–0378; tel. 615/666–2147; Dennis A. Wolford, FACHE, Chief Executive Officer
Web address: www.mcgh.net

RHEA MEDICAL CENTER (C, 25 beds) 9400 Rhea County Highway, Dayton, TN Zip 37321–7922; tel. 423/775–1121; Kennedy L. Croom, Jr., Administrator and Chief Executive Officer
Web address: www.rheamedical.org

TEXAS: MATAGORDA REGIONAL MEDICAL CENTER (C, 58 beds) 104 7th Street, Bay City, TX Zip 77414–4853; tel. 979/245–6383; Steven L. Smith, Chief Executive Officer
Web address: www.matagordaregional.org

MEMORIAL HOSPITAL (C, 33 beds) 1110 Sarah Dewitt Drive, Gonzales, TX Zip 78629–3311, Mailing Address: P.O. Box 587, Zip 78629–0587; tel. 830/672–7581; Charles Norris, Chief Executive Officer
Web address: www.gonzaleshealthcare.com

VERMONT: NORTHWESTERN MEDICAL CENTER (C, 55 beds) 133 Fairfield Street, Saint Albans, VT Zip 05478–1726; tel. 802/524–5911; Jill Berry Bowen, President and Chief Executive Officer
Web address: www.northwesternmedicalcenter.org

WYOMING: MEMORIAL HOSPITAL OF CARBON COUNTY (C, 25 beds) 2221 West Elm Street, Rawlins, WY Zip 82301–5108, Mailing Address: P.O. Box 460, Zip 82301–0460; tel. 307/324–2221; Dana Barnett, Chief Executive Officer
Web address: www.imhcc.com

WEST PARK HOSPITAL (C, 112 beds) 707 Sheridan Avenue, Cody, WY Zip 82414–3409; tel. 307/527–7501; Douglas A. McMillan, Administrator and Chief Executive Officer
Web address: www.westparkhospital.org

Owned, leased, sponsored:	0 hospitals	0 beds
Contract–managed:	60 hospitals	3365 beds
Totals:	60 hospitals	3365 beds

★0040: QUEEN'S HEALTH SYSTEMS (NP)
1301 Punchbowl Street, Honolulu, HI Zip 96813–2402; tel. 808/535–5448; Arthur A. Ushijima, FACHE, President and Chief Executive Officer
(Moderately Centralized Health System)

HAWAII: MOLOKAI GENERAL HOSPITAL (O, 15 beds) 280 Home Olu Place, Kaunakakai, HI Zip 96748–0408, Mailing Address: P.O. Box 408, Zip 96748–0408; tel. 808/553–5331; Janice Kalanihuia, President
Web address: www.queens.org

NORTH HAWAII COMMUNITY HOSPITAL (O, 35 beds) 67–1125 Mamalahoa Highway, Kamuela, HI Zip 96743–8496; tel. 808/885–4444; Cynthia Kamikawa, R.N., MSN, President
Web address: www.nhch.com

QUEEN'S MEDICAL CENTER (O, 516 beds) 1301 Punchbowl Street, Honolulu, HI Zip 96813–2499; tel. 808/691–5100; Arthur A. Ushijima, FACHE, President
Web address: www.queensmedicalcenter.org

Owned, leased, sponsored:	3 hospitals	566 beds
Contract–managed:	0 hospitals	0 beds
Totals:	3 hospitals	566 beds

★0981: QUORUM HEALTH (IO)
1573 Mallory Lane, Suite 100, Brentwood, TN Zip 37027; tel. 615/221–1400; Thomas Miller, President and Chief Executive Officer

ALABAMA: CHEROKEE MEDICAL CENTER (O, 45 beds) 400 Northwood Drive, Centre, AL Zip 35960–1023; tel. 256/927–5531; Terry Long, Chief Executive Officer
Web address: www.cherokeemedicalcenter.com

DEKALB REGIONAL MEDICAL CENTER (O, 115 beds) 200 Medical Center Drive, Fort Payne, AL Zip 35968–3458, Mailing Address: P.O. Box 680778, Zip 35968–1608; tel. 256/845–3150; Patrick Trammell, Chief Executive Officer
Web address: www.dekalbregional.com

L. V. STABLER MEMORIAL HOSPITAL (O, 15 beds) 29 L. V. Stabler Drive, Greenville, AL Zip 36037–3800; tel. 334/382–2671; Donald R. Rentfro, Chief Executive Officer
Web address: www.lvstabler.com

ARKANSAS: FORREST CITY MEDICAL CENTER (L, 70 beds) 1601 Newcastle Road, Forrest City, AR Zip 72335–2218; tel. 870/261–0000; Kevin Decker, Chief Executive Officer
Web address: www.forrestcitymedicalcenter.com

HELENA REGIONAL MEDICAL CENTER (L, 105 beds) 1801 Martin Luther King Drive, Helena, AR Zip 72342, Mailing Address: P.O. Box 788, Zip 72342–0788; tel. 870/338–5800; Leah Osbahr, M.P.H., Chief Executive Officer
Web address: www.helenarmc.com

CALIFORNIA: BARSTOW COMMUNITY HOSPITAL (L, 30 beds) 820 East Mountain View Street, Barstow, CA Zip 92311–3004; tel. 760/256–1761; Steven Foster, Chief Executive Officer
Web address: www.barstowhospital.com

WATSONVILLE COMMUNITY HOSPITAL (O, 106 beds) 75 Nielson Street, Watsonville, CA Zip 95076–2468; tel. 831/724–4741; Audra Earle, FACHE, Chief Executive Officer
Web address: www.watsonvillehospital.com

GEORGIA: BARROW REGIONAL MEDICAL CENTER (O, 56 beds) 316 North Broad Street, Winder, GA Zip 30680–2150, Mailing Address: P.O. Box 688, Zip 30680–0688; tel. 770/867–3400; Chad Hatfield, Chief Executive Officer
Web address: www.barrowregional.com

CLEARVIEW REGIONAL MEDICAL CENTER (O, 77 beds) 2151 West Spring Street, Monroe, GA Zip 30655–3115, Mailing Address: PO BOX 1346, Zip 30655–1346; tel. 770/267–8461; Michael Johnson, Chief Executive Officer
Web address: www.clearviewregionalmedicalcenter.com/

FANNIN REGIONAL HOSPITAL (O, 50 beds) 2855 Old Highway 5, Blue Ridge, GA Zip 30513–6248; tel. 706/632–3711; David S. Sanders, Chief Executive Officer
Web address: www.fanninregionalhospital.com

TRINITY HOSPITAL OF AUGUSTA (O, 105 beds) 2260 Wrightsboro Road, Augusta, GA Zip 30904–4726; tel. 706/481–7000; Jason A. Studley, FACHE, President and Chief Executive Officer
Web address: www.trinityofaugusta.com

ILLINOIS: CROSSROADS COMMUNITY HOSPITAL (O, 47 beds) 8 Doctors Park Road, Mount Vernon, IL Zip 62864–6224; tel. 618/244–5500; Finny Mathew, Chief Executive Officer
Web address: www.crossroadshospital.com

GALESBURG COTTAGE HOSPITAL (O, 119 beds) 695 North Kellogg Street, Galesburg, IL Zip 61401–2885; tel. 309/343–8131; Barry S. Schneider, Chief Executive Officer
Web address: www.cottagehospital.com

GATEWAY REGIONAL MEDICAL CENTER (O, 268 beds) 2100 Madison Avenue, Granite City, IL Zip 62040–4799; tel. 618/798–3000; M. Edward Cunningham, Chief Executive Officer
Web address: www.gatewayregional.net

HEARTLAND REGIONAL MEDICAL CENTER (O, 92 beds) 3333 West DeYoung, Marion, IL Zip 62959–5884; tel. 618/998–7000; James Flynn, Chief Executive Officer
Web address: www.heartlandregional.com

For explanation of codes following names, see page B2.
★ Indicates Type III membership in the American Hospital Association.

B112 Health Care Systems, Networks and Alliances

© 2016 AHA Guide

METROSOUTH MEDICAL CENTER (O, 180 beds) 12935 South Gregory Street, Blue Island, IL Zip 60406–2470; tel. 708/597–2000; John D. Baird, Chief Executive Officer
Web address: www.metrosouthmedicalcenter.com

RED BUD REGIONAL HOSPITAL (O, 140 beds) 325 Spring Street, Red Bud, IL Zip 62278–1105; tel. 618/282–3831; Shane Watson, Chief Executive Officer
Web address: www.redbudregional.com

UNION COUNTY HOSPITAL (L, 47 beds) 517 North Main Street, Anna, IL Zip 62906–1696; tel. 618/833–4511; James R. Farris, FACHE, Chief Executive Officer
Web address: www.unioncountyhospital.com

VISTA MEDICAL CENTER EAST (O, 190 beds) 1324 North Sheridan Road, Waukegan, IL Zip 60085–2161; tel. 847/360–3000; Barbara J. Martin, R.N., President and Chief Executive Officer
Web address: www.vistahealth.com

VISTA MEDICAL CENTER WEST (O, 67 beds) 2615 Washington Street, Waukegan, IL Zip 60085–4988; tel. 847/249–3900; Barbara J. Martin, R.N., President and Chief Executive Officer
Web address: www.vistahealth.com

KENTUCKY: KENTUCKY RIVER MEDICAL CENTER (L, 54 beds) 540 Jett Drive, Jackson, KY Zip 41339–9622; tel. 606/666–6000; John Ballard, Ph.D., Chief Executive Officer
Web address: www.kentuckyrivermc.com

PAUL B. HALL REGIONAL MEDICAL CENTER (O, 72 beds) 625 James S. Trimble Boulevard, Paintsville, KY Zip 41240–0000; tel. 606/789–3511; Deborah Trimble, R.N., Chief Executive Officer
Web address: www.pbhrmc.com

THREE RIVERS MEDICAL CENTER (O, 90 beds) 2485 Highway 644, Louisa, KY Zip 41230–9242, Mailing Address: P.O. Box 769, Zip 41230–0769; tel. 606/638–9451; Greg Kiser, Chief Executive Officer
Web address: www.threeriversmedicalcenter.com

NEVADA: MESA VIEW REGIONAL HOSPITAL (O, 25 beds) 1299 Bertha Howe Avenue, Mesquite, NV Zip 89027–7500; tel. 702/346–8040; Patricia Holden, Chief Executive Officer
Web address: www.mesaviewhospital.com

NEW MEXICO: ALTA VISTA REGIONAL HOSPITAL (O, 54 beds) 104 Legion Drive, Las Vegas, NM Zip 87701–4804; tel. 505/426–3500; R. Chris Wolf, Chief Executive Officer
Web address: www.altavistaregionalhospital.com

MIMBRES MEMORIAL HOSPITAL (O, 75 beds) 900 West Ash Street, Deming, NM Zip 88030–4098, Mailing Address: P.O. Box 710, Zip 88031–0710; tel. 575/546–5800; Kelly Duke, Chief Executive Officer
Web address: www.mimbresmemorial.com

NORTH CAROLINA: MARTIN GENERAL HOSPITAL (L, 49 beds) 310 South McCaskey Road, Williamston, NC Zip 27892–2150, Mailing Address: P.O. Box 1128, Zip 27892–1128; tel. 252/809–6300; Taffy J. Arias, Chief Executive Officer
Web address: www.martingeneral.com

SANDHILLS REGIONAL MEDICAL CENTER (O, 64 beds) 1000 West Hamlet Avenue, Hamlet, NC Zip 28345–4522, Mailing Address: P.O. Box 1109, Zip 28345–1109; tel. 910/205–8000; David Clay, Chief Executive Officer
Web address: www.sandhillsregional.com

OHIO: AFFINITY MEDICAL CENTER (O, 112 beds) 875 Eighth Street N.E., Massillon, OH Zip 44646–8503, Mailing Address: P.O. Box 4805, Zip 44648–0805; tel. 330/832–8761; Ronald L. Bierman, Chief Executive Officer
Web address: www.affinitymedicalcenter.com

OREGON: MCKENZIE–WILLAMETTE MEDICAL CENTER (O, 113 beds) 1460 G Street, Springfield, OR Zip 97477–4197; tel. 541/726–4400; Chad Campbell, Chief Executive Officer
Web address: www.mckweb.com

PENNSYLVANIA: LOCK HAVEN HOSPITAL (O, 84 beds) 24 Cree Drive, Lock Haven, PA Zip 17745–2699; tel. 570/893–5000; Steven T. Davis, Chief Executive Officer
Web address: www.lockhavenhospital.com

SUNBURY COMMUNITY HOSPITAL AND OUTPATIENT CENTER (O, 76 beds) 350 North Eleventh Street, Sunbury, PA Zip 17801–1611; tel. 570/286–3333; Robert D. Williams, Chief Executive Officer
Web address: www.sunburyhospital.com

TENNESSEE: HENDERSON COUNTY COMMUNITY HOSPITAL (O, 36 beds) 200 West Church Street, Lexington, TN Zip 38351–2038; tel. 731/968–3646; Pamela W. Roberts, Chief Executive Officer
Web address: www.hendersoncchospital.com

MCKENZIE REGIONAL HOSPITAL (O, 35 beds) 161 Hospital Drive, McKenzie, TN Zip 38201–1636; tel. 731/352–5344; Michael Morrical, Chief Executive Officer
Web address: www.mckenzieregionalhospital.com

TEXAS: BIG BEND REGIONAL MEDICAL CENTER (O, 25 beds) 2600 Highway 118 North, Alpine, TX Zip 79830–2002; tel. 432/837–3447; Matthew van Leeuwe, Interim Chief Executive Officer
Web address: www.bigbendhealthcare.com

SCENIC MOUNTAIN MEDICAL CENTER (O, 75 beds) 1601 West 11th Place, Big Spring, TX Zip 79720–4198; tel. 432/263–1211; Emma Krabill, Chief Executive Officer
Web address: www.smmccares.com

UTAH: MOUNTAIN WEST MEDICAL CENTER (O, 44 beds) 2055 North Main Street, Tooele, UT Zip 84074–9819; tel. 435/843–3600; Philip Eaton, Interim Chief Executive Officer
Web address: www.mountainwestmc.com

WYOMING: EVANSTON REGIONAL HOSPITAL (O, 42 beds) 190 Arrowhead Drive, Evanston, WY Zip 82930–9266; tel. 307/789–3636; Jeremy Davis, Chief Executive Officer
Web address: www.evanstonregionalhospital.com

Owned, leased, sponsored:	38 hospitals	3049 beds
Contract–managed:	0 hospitals	0 beds
Totals:	38 hospitals	3049 beds

0996: RCCH HEALTHCARE PARTNERS (IO)
103 Continental Place Suite 200, Brentwood, TN Zip 37027–1042; tel. 615/844–9800; Michael Wiechart, President and Chief Executive Officer

ALABAMA: ELIZA COFFEE MEMORIAL HOSPITAL (O, 278 beds) 205 Marengo Street, Florence, AL Zip 35630–6033, Mailing Address: P.O. Box 818, Zip 35631–0818; tel. 256/768–9191; Russell Pigg, Chief Executive Officer
Web address: www.chgroup.org

SHOALS HOSPITAL (O, 137 beds) 201 Avalon Avenue, Muscle Shoals, AL Zip 35661–2805, Mailing Address: P.O. Box 3359, Zip 35662–3359; tel. 256/386–1600; Kidada Hawkins, Chief Executive Officer
Web address: www.shoalshospital.com

ARIZONA: CANYON VISTA MEDICAL CENTER (L, 100 beds) 5700 East Highway 90, Sierra Vista, AZ Zip 85635–9110; tel. 520/263–2000; Randy Anderson, Chief Executive Officer
Web address: www.canyonvistamedicalcenter.com/

ARKANSAS: NATIONAL PARK MEDICAL CENTER (O, 193 beds) 1910 Malvern Avenue, Hot Springs, AR Zip 71901–7799; tel. 501/321–1000; Jerry D. Mabry, FACHE, Chief Executive Officer
Web address: www.nationalparkmedical.com

SAINT MARY'S REGIONAL MEDICAL CENTER (O, 141 beds) 1808 West Main Street, Russellville, AR Zip 72801–2724; tel. 479/968–2841; James Davidson, Chief Executive Officer
Web address: www.saintmarysregional.com

CONNECTICUT: SHARON HOSPITAL (O, 78 beds) 50 Hospital Hill Road, Sharon, CT Zip 06069–2096, Mailing Address: P.O. Box 789, Zip 06069–0789; tel. 860/364–4000; Peter Cordeau, Chief Executive Officer
Web address: www.sharonhospital.com

IOWA: OTTUMWA REGIONAL HEALTH CENTER (O, 101 beds) 1001 Pennsylvania Avenue, Ottumwa, IA Zip 52501–2186; tel. 641/684–2300; Philip J. Noel, III, Chief Executive Officer
Web address: www.ottumwaregionalhealth.com

OHIO: CLINTON MEMORIAL HOSPITAL (O, 119 beds) 610 West Main Street, Wilmington, OH Zip 45177–2125; tel. 937/382–6611; Gregory A. Nielsen, FACHE, Chief Executive Officer
Web address: www.cmhregional.com

For explanation of codes following names, see page B2.
★ Indicates Type III membership in the American Hospital Association.

OKLAHOMA: EASTAR HEALTH SYSTEM (L, 222 beds) 300 Rockefeller Drive, Muskogee, OK Zip 74401–5081; tel. 918/682–5501; Anthony R. Young, Chief Executive Officer
Web address: www.eastarhealth.com

SOUTHWESTERN MEDICAL CENTER (O, 178 beds) 5602 S.W. Lee Boulevard, Lawton, OK Zip 73505–9635; tel. 580/531–4700; Stephen O. Hyde, FACHE, Chief Executive Officer
Web address: www.swmconline.com

OREGON: WILLAMETTE VALLEY MEDICAL CENTER (O, 88 beds) 2700 S.E. Stratus Avenue, McMinnville, OR Zip 97128–6255; tel. 503/472–6131; Peter A. Hofstetter, Chief Executive Officer
Web address: www.wvmcweb.com

SOUTH CAROLINA: CAROLINA PINES REGIONAL MEDICAL CENTER (O, 120 beds) 1304 West Bobo Newsom Highway, Hartsville, SC Zip 29550–4710; tel. 843/339–2100; J. Timothy Browne, FACHE, Chief Executive Officer
Web address: www.cprmc.com

KERSHAWHEALTH (O, 215 beds) 1315 Roberts Street, Camden, SC Zip 29020–3737, Mailing Address: P.O. Box 7003, Zip 29021–7003; tel. 803/432–4311; Terry Gunn, FACHE, Chief Executive Officer
Web address: www.kershawhealth.com

TEXAS: PARIS REGIONAL MEDICAL CENTER (O, 173 beds) 865 Deshong Drive, Paris, TX Zip 75460–9313, Mailing Address: P.O. Box 9070, Zip 75461–9070; tel. 903/785–4521; Patti Monczewski, Interim Chief Executive Officer
Web address: www.parisrmc.com

WASHINGTON: CAPITAL MEDICAL CENTER (O, 85 beds) 3900 Capital Mall Drive S.W., Olympia, WA Zip 98502–5026, Mailing Address: P.O. Box 19002, Zip 98507–0013; tel. 360/754–5858; Jim Geist, Chief Executive Officer
Web address: www.capitalmedical.com

Owned, leased, sponsored:	15 hospitals	2228 beds
Contract–managed:	0 hospitals	0 beds
Totals:	15 hospitals	2228 beds

★8495: REGIONAL HEALTH (NP)
353 Fairmont Boulevard, Rapid City, SD Zip 57701–7375, Mailing Address: P.O. Box 6000, Zip 57709–6000; tel. 605/719–1000; Brent R. Phillips, President and Chief Executive Officer
(Moderately Centralized Health System)

SOUTH DAKOTA: CUSTER REGIONAL HOSPITAL (L, 87 beds) 1039 Montgomery Street, Custer, SD Zip 57730–1397; tel. 605/673–2229; Veronica Schmidt, President
Web address: www.regionalhealth.com

LEAD–DEADWOOD REGIONAL HOSPITAL (O, 7 beds) 61 Charles Street, Deadwood, SD Zip 57732–1303; tel. 605/717–6000; Mark C. Schmidt, President
Web address: www.regionalhealth.com

PHILIP HEALTH SERVICES (C, 48 beds) 503 West Pine Street, Philip, SD Zip 57567–3300, Mailing Address: P.O. Box 790, Zip 57567–0790; tel. 605/859–2511; Kent Olson, Administrator and Chief Executive Officer

RAPID CITY REGIONAL HOSPITAL (O, 408 beds) 353 Fairmont Boulevard, Rapid City, SD Zip 57701–7393, Mailing Address: P.O. Box 6000, Zip 57709–6000; tel. 605/755–1000; Dennis C. Millirons, FACHE, Interim President
Web address: www.regionalhealth.com

SPEARFISH REGIONAL HOSPITAL (O, 35 beds) 1440 North Main Street, Spearfish, SD Zip 57783–1504; tel. 605/644–4000; Larry W. Veitz, President
Web address: www.regionalhealth. com/Our–Locations/Regional–Hospitals/Spearfish–Regional–Hospital.aspx

STURGIS REGIONAL HOSPITAL (O, 109 beds) 949 Harmon Street, Sturgis, SD Zip 57785–2452; tel. 605/720–2400; Mark Schulte, FACHE, President
Web address: www.regionalhealth. com/Our–Locations/Regional–Hospitals/Sturgis–Regional–Hospital.aspx

WYOMING: CROOK COUNTY MEDICAL SERVICES DISTRICT (C, 16 beds) 713 Oak Street, Sundance, WY Zip 82729, Mailing Address: P.O. Box 517, Zip 82729–0517; tel. 307/283–3501; Nathan Hough, Chief Executive Officer
Web address: www.ccmsd.org/

WESTON COUNTY HEALTH SERVICES (C, 75 beds) 1124 Washington Boulevard, Newcastle, WY Zip 82701–2972; tel. 307/746–4491; Maureen K. Cadwell, Chief Executive Officer
Web address: www.wchs–wy.org

Owned, leased, sponsored:	5 hospitals	646 beds
Contract–managed:	3 hospitals	139 beds
Totals:	8 hospitals	785 beds

★2625: RENOWN HEALTH (NP)
1155 Mill Street, Reno, NV Zip 89502–1576; tel. 775/982–5529; Anthony D. Slonim, M.D., Dr.PH, President and Chief Executive Officer
(Centralized Health System)

NEVADA: RENOWN REGIONAL MEDICAL CENTER (O, 643 beds) 1155 Mill Street, Reno, NV Zip 89502–1576; tel. 775/982–4100; Erik Olson, Chief Executive Officer
Web address: www.renown.org

RENOWN REHABILITATION HOSPITAL (O, 62 beds) 1495 Mill Street, Reno, NV Zip 89502–1479; tel. 775/982–3500; Chris Nicholas, Chief Executive Officer
Web address: www.renown.org

RENOWN SOUTH MEADOWS MEDICAL CENTER (O, 76 beds) 10101 Double R Boulevard, Reno, NV Zip 89521–5931; tel. 775/982–7000; Susan Davila, Chief Executive Officer
Web address: www.renown.org

Owned, leased, sponsored:	3 hospitals	781 beds
Contract–managed:	0 hospitals	0 beds
Totals:	3 hospitals	781 beds

★0964: RIDGEVIEW MEDICAL CENTER (IO)
500 South Maple Street, Waconia, MN Zip 55387–1752; tel. 952/442–2191; Robert Stevens, President and Chief Executive Officer
(Independent Hospital System)

MINNESOTA: RIDGEVIEW MEDICAL CENTER (O, 102 beds) 500 South Maple Street, Waconia, MN Zip 55387–1791; tel. 952/442–2191; Robert Stevens, President and Chief Executive Officer
Web address: www.ridgeviewmedical.org

RIDGEVIEW SIBLEY MEDICAL CENTER (L, 17 beds) 601 West Chandler Street, Arlington, MN Zip 55307–2127; tel. 507/964–2271; Todd Sandberg, Chief Executive Officer and Administrator
Web address: www.sibleymedical.org

Owned, leased, sponsored:	2 hospitals	119 beds
Contract–managed:	0 hospitals	0 beds
Totals:	2 hospitals	119 beds

4810: RIVERSIDE HEALTH SYSTEM (NP)
701 Town Center Drive, Suite 1000, Newport News, VA Zip 23606–4286; tel. 757/534–7000; William B. Downey, President and Chief Executive Officer
(Independent Hospital System)

VIRGINIA: HAMPTON ROADS SPECIALTY HOSPITAL (O, 25 beds) 245 Chesapeake Avenue, Newport News, VA Zip 23607–6038; tel. 757/534–5000; Courtney Detwiler, R.N., Administrator
Web address: www.hamptonroadsspecialtyhospital.com

RIVERSIDE DOCTORS' HOSPITAL (O, 13 beds) 1500 Commonwealth Avenue, Williamsburg, VA Zip 23185–5229; tel. 757/585–2200; Adria Vanhoosier, Administrator
Web address: www.riversideonline.com/rdhw

For explanation of codes following names, see page B2.
★ Indicates Type III membership in the American Hospital Association.

Section B

RIVERSIDE REGIONAL MEDICAL CENTER (O, 312 beds) 500 J. Clyde Morris Boulevard, Newport News, VA Zip 23601–1929; tel. 757/594–2000; Michael J. Doucette, Senior Vice President and Administrator
Web address: www.riverside–online.com

RIVERSIDE REHABILITATION INSTITUTE (O, 30 beds) 245 Chesapeake Avenue, Newport News, VA Zip 23607–6038; tel. 757/928–8000; Daniel Ballin, Administrator
Web address: www.riversideonline.com/rri/index.cfm

RIVERSIDE SHORE MEMORIAL HOSPITAL (O, 29 beds) 9507 Hospital Avenue, Nassawadox, VA Zip 23413–1821, Mailing Address: P.O. Box 17, Zip 23413–0017; tel. 757/414–8000; John Peterman, Vice President and Administrator
Web address: www.riversideonline.com

RIVERSIDE TAPPAHANNOCK HOSPITAL (O, 15 beds) 618 Hospital Road, Tappahannock, VA Zip 22560–5000; tel. 804/443–3311; Esther Desimini, Administrator
Web address: www.riverside–online.com

RIVERSIDE WALTER REED HOSPITAL (O, 28 beds) 7519 Hospital Drive, Gloucester, VA Zip 23061–4178, Mailing Address: P.O. Box 1130, Zip 23061–1130; tel. 804/693–8800; Megan Kleckner, Vice President and Administrator
Web address: www.riversideonline.com

Owned, leased, sponsored:	7 hospitals	452 beds
Contract–managed:	0 hospitals	0 beds
Totals:	7 hospitals	452 beds

★0046: ROCHESTER REGIONAL HEALTH (NP)
1425 Portland Avenue, 5th Floor, Rochester, NY Zip 14621–3001; tel. 585/922–4000; Eric Bieber, M.D., President and Chief Executive Officer
(Moderately Centralized Health System)

NEW YORK: CLIFTON SPRINGS HOSPITAL AND CLINIC (O, 214 beds) 2 Coulter Road, Clifton Springs, NY Zip 14432–1189; tel. 315/462–9561; Dustin Riccio, M.D., President
Web address: www.cliftonspringshospital.org

NEWARK–WAYNE COMMUNITY HOSPITAL (O, 280 beds) 1200 Driving Park Avenue, Newark, NY Zip 14513–1057, Mailing Address: P.O. Box 111, Zip 14513–0111; tel. 315/332–2022; Dustin Riccio, M.D., President Eastern Region
Web address: www.rochesterregional.org

ROCHESTER GENERAL HOSPITAL (O, 520 beds) 1425 Portland Avenue, Rochester, NY Zip 14621–3099; tel. 585/922–4000; Nancy Tinsley, President
Web address: www.rochestergeneral.org

UNITED MEMORIAL MEDICAL CENTER (O, 131 beds) 127 North Street, Batavia, NY Zip 14020–1631; tel. 585/343–6030; Daniel P. Ireland, FACHE, President
Web address: www.ummc.org

UNITY HOSPITAL (O, 487 beds) 1555 Long Pond Road, Rochester, NY Zip 14626–4182; tel. 585/723–7000; Douglas Stewart, PsyD, President
Web address: www.unityhealth.org

Owned, leased, sponsored:	5 hospitals	1632 beds
Contract–managed:	0 hospitals	0 beds
Totals:	5 hospitals	1632 beds

0348: RURAL COMMUNITY HOSPITALS OF AMERICA (IO)
1100 Main Street, Suite 2350, Kansas City, MO Zip 64105–5186; tel. 816/474–7800; Lawrence J. Arthur, President
(Independent Hospital System)

KANSAS: HILLSBORO COMMUNITY HOSPITAL (O, 10 beds) 701 South Main Street, Hillsboro, KS Zip 67063–1553; tel. 620/947–3114; Marion Regier, Chief Executive Officer
Web address: www.hchks.com

HORTON COMMUNITY HOSPITAL (O, 25 beds) 240 West 18th Street, Horton, KS Zip 66439–1245; tel. 785/486–2642; James D. Noble, Chief Executive Officer
Web address: www.horton–hospital.com

OSWEGO COMMUNITY HOSPITAL (O, 12 beds) 800 Barker Drive, Oswego, KS Zip 67356–9014; tel. 620/795–2921; Daniel Hiben, Chief Executive Officer
Web address: www.oswegocommunityhospital.com

MISSOURI: COOPER COUNTY MEMORIAL HOSPITAL (C, 32 beds) 17651 B Highway, Boonville, MO Zip 65233–2839, Mailing Address: P.O. Box 88, Zip 65233–0088; tel. 660/882–7461; Danielle Gearhart, Chief Executive Officer
Web address: www.coopercmh.com

I–70 COMMUNITY HOSPITAL (O, 15 beds) 105 Hospital Drive, Sweet Springs, MO Zip 65351–2229; tel. 660/335–4700; Jeff Bloemker, Chief Executive Officer
Web address: www.i70medcenter.com

NORTH CAROLINA: WASHINGTON COUNTY HOSPITAL (O, 25 beds) 958 U.S. Highway 64 East, Plymouth, NC Zip 27962–9591; tel. 252/793–4135; Cameron Highsmith, Chief Executive Officer

OKLAHOMA: DRUMRIGHT REGIONAL HOSPITAL (O, 15 beds) 610 West Bypass, Drumright, OK Zip 74030–5957; tel. 918/382–2300; William Holland, Chief Executive Officer
Web address: www.drumrighthospital.com/

FAIRFAX COMMUNITY HOSPITAL (O, 15 beds) 40 Hospital Road, Fairfax, OK Zip 74637–5084; tel. 918/642–3291; Tina Steele, Chief Executive Officer and Chief Financial Officer

HASKELL COUNTY COMMUNITY HOSPITAL (O, 32 beds) 401 Northwest H Street, Stigler, OK Zip 74462–1625; tel. 918/967–4682; Donald E. Buchanan, Interim Chief Executive Officer
Web address: www.haskellhospital.com

PRAGUE COMMUNITY HOSPITAL (O, 15 beds) 1322 Klabzuba Avenue, Prague, OK Zip 74864–9005, Mailing Address: P.O. Box S., Zip 74864–1090; tel. 405/567–4922; Randy Simmons, Chief Executive Officer
Web address: www.praguehospital.com

TENNESSEE: LAUDERDALE COMMUNITY HOSPITAL (O, 25 beds) 326 Asbury Avenue, Ripley, TN Zip 38063–5577; tel. 731/221–2200; Michael G. Layfield, Interim Chief Executive Officer
Web address: www.lauderdalehospital.com/

Owned, leased, sponsored:	10 hospitals	189 beds
Contract–managed:	1 hospital	32 beds
Totals:	11 hospitals	221 beds

★0109: RURAL HEALTH GROUP (IO)
48 West 1500 North, Nephi, UT Zip 84648–8900; tel. 435/623–4924; Mark R. Stoddard, President and Chairman
(Independent Hospital System)

NEVADA: DESERT VIEW HOSPITAL (O, 25 beds) 360 South Lola Lane, Pahrump, NV Zip 89048–0884; tel. 775/751–7500; Kelly H. Adams, Chief Executive Officer
Web address: www.desertviewhospital.com

UTAH: CENTRAL VALLEY MEDICAL CENTER (L, 27 beds) 48 West 1500 North, Nephi, UT Zip 84648–8900; tel. 435/623–3000; Mark R. Stoddard, President
Web address: www.cvmed.net

Owned, leased, sponsored:	2 hospitals	52 beds
Contract–managed:	0 hospitals	0 beds
Totals:	2 hospitals	52 beds

★0220: RUSH HEALTH SYSTEMS (NP)
1314 19th Avenue, Meridian, MS Zip 39301–4116; tel. 601/483–0011; Wallace Strickland, President and Chief Executive Officer
(Independent Hospital System)

ALABAMA: CHOCTAW GENERAL HOSPITAL (O, 25 beds) 401 Vanity Fair Avenue, Butler, AL Zip 36904–3032; tel. 205/459–9100; J. W. Cowan, Administrator
Web address: www.choctawgeneral.com/cgh/

For explanation of codes following names, see page B2.
★ Indicates Type III membership in the American Hospital Association.

Section B

MISSISSIPPI: H. C. WATKINS MEMORIAL HOSPITAL (O, 25 beds) 605 South Archusa Avenue, Quitman, MS Zip 39355–2331; tel. 601/776–6925; Michael Nester, Administrator
Web address: www.watkinsmemorialhospital.com/hcwmh/

JOHN C. STENNIS MEMORIAL HOSPITAL (O, 25 beds) 14365 Highway 16 West, De Kalb, MS Zip 39328–7974; tel. 769/486–1000; Justin Palmer, Administrator
Web address: www.johncstennismemorialhospital.com/jcsmh/

LAIRD HOSPITAL (O, 25 beds) 25117 Highway 15, Union, MS Zip 39365–9099; tel. 601/774–8214; Thomas G. Bartlett, III, Administrator
Web address: www.lairdhospital.com/lh/

RUSH FOUNDATION HOSPITAL (O, 182 beds) 1314 19th Avenue, Meridian, MS Zip 39301–4195; tel. 601/483–0011; Larkin Kennedy, Chief Executive Officer
Web address: www.rushhealthsystems.org/rfh/

SCOTT REGIONAL HOSPITAL (O, 25 beds) 317 Highway 13 South, Morton, MS Zip 39117–3353, Mailing Address: P.O. Box 259, Zip 39117–0259; tel. 601/732–6301; Michael R. Edwards, Administrator
Web address: www.scottregional.org/srh/

SPECIALTY HOSPITAL OF MERIDIAN (O, 49 beds) 1314 19th Avenue, Meridian, MS Zip 39301–4116; tel. 601/703–4211; Elizabeth C. Mitchell, Chief Executive Officer and Chief Operating Officer
Web address: www.specialtyhospitalofmeridian.com/shm/

Owned, leased, sponsored:	7 hospitals	356 beds
Contract–managed:	0 hospitals	0 beds
Totals:	7 hospitals	356 beds

★3855: RUSH UNIVERSITY MEDICAL CENTER (NP)
1653 West Congress Parkway, Chicago, IL Zip 60612–3864; tel. 312/942–5000; Larry J. Goodman, M.D., Chief Executive Officer
(Moderately Centralized Health System)

ILLINOIS: RUSH OAK PARK HOSPITAL (O, 95 beds) 520 South Maple Avenue, Oak Park, IL Zip 60304–1097; tel. 708/383–9300; Bruce M. Elegant, FACHE, President and Chief Executive Officer
Web address: www.roph.org

RUSH UNIVERSITY MEDICAL CENTER (O, 679 beds) 1653 West Congress Parkway, Chicago, IL Zip 60612–3833; tel. 312/942–5000; Larry J. Goodman, M.D., Chief Executive Officer
Web address: www.rush.edu

RUSH–COPLEY MEDICAL CENTER (O, 210 beds) 2000 Ogden Avenue, Aurora, IL Zip 60504–7222; tel. 630/978–6200; Barry C. Finn, President and Chief Executive Officer
Web address: www.rushcopley.com

Owned, leased, sponsored:	3 hospitals	984 beds
Contract–managed:	0 hospitals	0 beds
Totals:	3 hospitals	984 beds

★0994: RWJBARNABAS HEALTH (NP)
95 Old Short Hills Road, West Orange, NJ Zip 07052–1008; tel. 973/322–4000; Barry Ostrowsky, President and Chief Executive Officer

NEW JERSEY: BARNABAS HEALTH BEHAVIORAL HEALTH CENTER (O, 40 beds) 1691 Highway 9, Toms River, NJ Zip 08754; tel. 732/914–1688; Deanna Sperling, President and Chief Executive Officer
Web address: www.barnabashealth.org/hospitals/psychiatric/index.html

CHILDREN'S SPECIALIZED HOSPITAL–PSE&G (O, 140 beds) 200 Somerset Street, New Brunswick, NJ Zip 08901–1942; tel. 732/258–7000; Warren E. Moore, President and Chief Executive Officer
Web address: www.childrens–specialized.org

CLARA MAASS MEDICAL CENTER (O, 469 beds) One Clara Maass Drive, Belleville, NJ Zip 07109–3557; tel. 973/450–2000; Mary Ellen Clyne, MSN, Ph.D., R.N., President and Chief Executive Officer
Web address: www.barnabashealth.org/hospitals/clara_maass/index.html

COMMUNITY MEDICAL CENTER (O, 357 beds) 99 Route 37 West, Toms River, NJ Zip 08755–6423; tel. 732/557–8000; Michael Mimoso, FACHE, President and Chief Executive Officer
Web address: www.barnabashealth.org/hospitals/community_medical/index.html

JERSEY CITY MEDICAL CENTER (O, 316 beds) 355 Grand Street, Jersey City, NJ Zip 07302–4321; tel. 201/915–2000; Joseph F. Scott, FACHE, President and Chief Executive Officer
Web address: www.barnabashealth.org/Jersey–City–Medical–Center.aspx

MONMOUTH MEDICAL CENTER, LONG BRANCH CAMPUS (O, 305 beds) 300 Second Avenue, Long Branch, NJ Zip 07740–6303; tel. 732/222–5200; Bill Arnold, President and Chief Executive Officer
Web address: www.barnabashealth.org/hospitals/monmouth_medical/index.html

MONMOUTH MEDICAL CENTER, SOUTHERN CAMPUS (O, 124 beds) 600 River Avenue, Lakewood, NJ Zip 08701–5237; tel. 732/363–1900; Frank J. Vozos, M.D., FACS, President and Chief Executive Officer, Barnabas Health Behavioral Health Center
Web address: www.barnabashealth.org/monmouth–medical–center–southern–campus.aspx

NEWARK BETH ISRAEL MEDICAL CENTER (O, 338 beds) 201 Lyons Avenue, Newark, NJ Zip 07112–2027; tel. 973/926–7000; Darrell K. Terry, Sr., Interim President and Chief Executive Officer
Web address: www.barnabashealth.org/hospitals/newark_beth_israel/index.html

ROBERT WOOD JOHNSON UNIVERSITY HOSPITAL (O, 610 beds) 1 Robert Wood Johnson Place, New Brunswick, NJ Zip 08901–1928; tel. 732/828–3000; Michael A. Antoniades, President and Chief Executive Officer
Web address: www.rwjuh.edu

ROBERT WOOD JOHNSON UNIVERSITY HOSPITAL AT HAMILTON (O, 164 beds) One Hamilton Health Place, Hamilton, NJ Zip 08690–3599; tel. 609/586–7900; Richard Freeman, President and Chief Executive Officer
Web address: www.rwjhamilton.org

ROBERT WOOD JOHNSON UNIVERSITY HOSPITAL RAHWAY (O, 123 beds) 865 Stone Street, Rahway, NJ Zip 07065–2797; tel. 732/381–4200; Kirk C. Tice, President and Chief Executive Officer
Web address: www.rwjuhr.com

ROBERT WOOD JOHNSON UNIVERSITY HOSPITAL SOMERSET (O, 250 beds) 110 Rehill Avenue, Somerville, NJ Zip 08876–2598; tel. 908/685–2200; Michael A. Antoniades, President and Chief Executive Officer
Web address: www.rwjuh.edu

SAINT BARNABAS MEDICAL CENTER (O, 545 beds) 94 Old Short Hills Road, Livingston, NJ Zip 07039–5672; tel. 973/322–5000; Stephen P. Zieniewicz, FACHE, President and Chief Executive Officer
Web address: www.barnabashealth.org/hospitals/saint_barnabas/index.html

Owned, leased, sponsored:	13 hospitals	3781 beds
Contract–managed:	0 hospitals	0 beds
Totals:	13 hospitals	3781 beds

0912: SAFE HAVEN HEALTH CARE (IO)
2520 South 5th Avenue, Pocatello, ID Zip 83204–1923; tel. 800/261–2443; Scott Burpee, President

IDAHO: SAFE HAVEN HOSPITAL OF POCATELLO (O, 87 beds) 1200 Hospital Way, Pocatello, ID Zip 83201–2708; tel. 208/232–2570; Karen Neilson, Administrator
Web address: www.safehavenhealthcare.org/safehaven_hospital/index.html

SAFE HAVEN HOSPITAL OF TREASURE VALLEY (O, 22 beds) 8050 Northview Street, Boise, ID Zip 83704–7126; tel. 208/327–0504; Scott Proctor, Chief Executive Officer
Web address: www.boisepsychhospital.com

Owned, leased, sponsored:	2 hospitals	109 beds
Contract–managed:	0 hospitals	0 beds
Totals:	2 hospitals	109 beds

★0254: SAINT FRANCIS HEALTH SYSTEM (NP)
6161 South Yale Avenue, Tulsa, OK Zip 74136–1902; tel. 918/494–8454; Jake Henry Jr., President and Chief Executive Officer
(Centralized Health System)

For explanation of codes following names, see page B2.
★ Indicates Type III membership in the American Hospital Association.

Section B

OKLAHOMA: LAUREATE PSYCHIATRIC CLINIC AND HOSPITAL (O, 75 beds)
6655 South Yale Avenue, Tulsa, OK Zip 74136–3329;
tel. 918/481–4000; William Schloss, Senior Vice President, Administrator
Web address: www.laureate.com

SAINT FRANCIS HOSPITAL (O, 841 beds) 6161 South Yale Avenue, Tulsa, OK
Zip 74136–1902; tel. 918/494–2200; Lynn A. Sund, Senior Vice President,
Chief Nurse Executive, Saint Francis Health System and Administrator, Saint
Francis Hospital
Web address: www.saintfrancis.com

SAINT FRANCIS HOSPITAL SOUTH (O, 84 beds) 10501 East 91St. Streeet,
Tulsa, OK Zip 74133–5790; tel. 918/307–6010; David S. Weil, Senior Vice
President and Administrator
Web address: www.saintfrancis.com/south/

Owned, leased, sponsored:	3 hospitals	1000 beds
Contract–managed:	0 hospitals	0 beds
Totals:	3 hospitals	1000 beds

★0120: SAINT LUKE'S HEALTH SYSTEM (NP)
901 East 104th Street, Mailstop 900N, Kansas City, MO
Zip 64131–4517, Mailing Address: 901 East 104th Street,
Zip 64131–4517; tel. 816/932–2000; Melinda Estes, M.D.,
President and Chief Executive Officer
(Centralized Health System)

KANSAS: ANDERSON COUNTY HOSPITAL (L, 48 beds) 421 South Maple,
Garnett, KS Zip 66032–1334, Mailing Address: P.O. Box 309,
Zip 66032–0309; tel. 785/448–3131; Rick McKain, Chief Executive
Officer
Web address: www.saint–lukes.org

SAINT LUKE'S CUSHING HOSPITAL (O, 25 beds) 711 Marshall Street,
Leavenworth, KS Zip 66048–3235; tel. 913/684–1100; Adele Ducharme,
R.N., MSN, Chief Executive Officer
Web address: www.saintlukeshealthsystem.
org/locations/saint–lukes–cushing–hospital

SAINT LUKE'S SOUTH HOSPITAL (O, 110 beds) 12300 Metcalf Avenue,
Overland Park, KS Zip 66213–1324; tel. 913/317–7000; Bobby
Olm–Shipman, Chief Executive Officer
Web address: www.saintlukeshealthsystem.org/south

MISSOURI: CRITTENTON CHILDREN'S CENTER (O, 46 beds) 10918 Elm
Avenue, Kansas City, MO Zip 64134–4108; tel. 816/765–6600; Janine
Hron, Chief Executive Officer
Web address: www.crittentonkc.org

HEDRICK MEDICAL CENTER (L, 25 beds) 2799 North Washington Street,
Chillicothe, MO Zip 64601–2902; tel. 660/646–1480; Steven M. Schieber,
FACHE, Chief Executive Officer
Web address: www.saintlukeskc.org

SAINT LUKE'S EAST HOSPITAL (O, 161 beds) 100 N.E. Saint Luke's
Boulevard, Lee's Summit, MO Zip 64086–6000; tel. 816/347–5000; Ronald
L. Baker, Chief Executive Officer
Web address: www.saintlukeskc.org

SAINT LUKE'S HOSPITAL OF KANSAS CITY (O, 442 beds) 4401 Wornall Road,
Kansas City, MO Zip 64111–3220; tel. 816/932–3800; Jani L. Johnson,
R.N., MSN, Chief Executive Officer
Web address: www.saint–lukes.org

SAINT LUKE'S NORTH HOSPITAL – BARRY ROAD (O, 142 beds) 5830 N.W.
Barry Road, Kansas City, MO Zip 64154–2778; tel. 816/891–6000; Matthew
Wenzel, President and Chief Executive Officer
Web address: www.saint–lukes.org

WRIGHT MEMORIAL HOSPITAL (L, 25 beds) 191 Iowa Boulevard, Trenton, MO
Zip 64683–8343; tel. 660/358–5700; Gary W. Jordan, FACHE, Chief
Executive Officer
Web address: www.saintlukeshealthsystem.org

Owned, leased, sponsored:	9 hospitals	1024 beds
Contract–managed:	0 hospitals	0 beds
Totals:	9 hospitals	1024 beds

0403: SALEM HEALTH (NP)
890 Oak Street Building B. POB 14001, Salem, OR
Zip 97309–5014; tel. 503/561–5200; Norman F. Gruber, President
and Chief Executive Officer
(Independent Hospital System)

OREGON: SALEM HEALTH WEST VALLEY (O, 6 beds) 525 S.E. Washington
Street, Dallas, OR Zip 97338–2834, Mailing Address: P.O. Box 378,
Zip 97338–0378; tel. 503/623–8301; Bruce C. Rodgers, Chief
Administrative Officer
Web address: www.salemhealth.org/wvh/

SALEM HOSPITAL (O, 441 beds) 890 Oak Street S.E., Salem, OR
Zip 97301–3959, Mailing Address: P.O. Box 14001, Zip 97309–5014;
tel. 503/561–5200; Cheryl R. Nester Wolfe, President and Chief Executive
Officer
Web address: www.salemhealth.org

Owned, leased, sponsored:	2 hospitals	447 beds
Contract–managed:	0 hospitals	0 beds
Totals:	2 hospitals	447 beds

1002: SALINA REGIONAL HEALTH CENTER (NP)
400 South Santa Fe Avenue, Salina, KS Zip 67401–4198, Mailing
Address: PO Box 5080, Zip 67402–5080; tel. 785/452–7000;
Michael Terry, President and Chief Executive Officer

KANSAS: CLOUD COUNTY HEALTH CENTER (C, 25 beds) 1100 Highland
Drive, Concordia, KS Zip 66901–3923; tel. 785/243–1234; Cherri
Waites, Chief Executive Officer
Web address: www.cchc.com

LINDSBORG COMMUNITY HOSPITAL (C, 21 beds) 605 West Lincoln Street,
Lindsborg, KS Zip 67456–2328; tel. 785/227–3308; Larry VanDerWege,
Administrator
Web address: www.lindsborghospital.org

SALINA REGIONAL HEALTH CENTER (O, 205 beds) 400 South Santa Fe
Avenue, Salina, KS Zip 67401–4198, Mailing Address: P.O. Box 5080,
Zip 67402–5080; tel. 785/452–7000; Micheal Terry, President and Chief
Executive Officer
Web address: www.srhc.com

Owned, leased, sponsored:	1 hospital	205 beds
Contract–managed:	2 hospitals	46 beds
Totals:	3 hospitals	251 beds

★0186: SAMARITAN HEALTH SERVICES (NP)
3600 N.W. Samaritan Drive, Corvallis, OR Zip 97330–3737, Mailing
Address: P.O. Box 1068, Zip 97339–1068; tel. 541/768–5001;
Larry A. Mullins, FACHE, President and Chief Executive Officer
(Centralized Physician/Insurance Health System)

OREGON: GOOD SAMARITAN REGIONAL MEDICAL CENTER (O, 165 beds)
3600 N.W. Samaritan Drive, Corvallis, OR Zip 97330–3737, Mailing
Address: P.O. Box 1068, Zip 97339–1068; tel. 541/768–5111; Becky A.
Pape, R.N., Chief Executive Officer
Web address: www.samhealth.org

SAMARITAN ALBANY GENERAL HOSPITAL (O, 70 beds) 1046 Sixth Avenue,
S.W., Albany, OR Zip 97321–1999; tel. 541/812–4000; David G. Triebes,
Chief Executive Officer
Web address: www.samhealth.org

SAMARITAN LEBANON COMMUNITY HOSPITAL (O, 25 beds) 525 North
Santiam Highway, Lebanon, OR Zip 97355–4363, Mailing Address: P.O. Box
739, Zip 97355–0739; tel. 541/258–2101; Marty Cahill, Chief Executive
Officer
Web address: www.samhealth.org

SAMARITAN NORTH LINCOLN HOSPITAL (C, 25 beds) 3043 N.E. 28th Street,
Lincoln City, OR Zip 97367–4518, Mailing Address: P.O. Box 767,
Zip 97367–0767; tel. 541/994–3661; Lesley Ogden, M.D., Chief Executive
Officer
Web address: www.samhealth.org

For explanation of codes following names, see page B2.
★ Indicates Type III membership in the American Hospital Association.

Section B

SAMARITAN PACIFIC COMMUNITIES HOSPITAL (C, 25 beds) 930 S.W. Abbey Street, Newport, OR Zip 97365–4820, Mailing Address: P.O. Box 945, Zip 97365–0072; tel. 541/265–2244; David C. Bigelow, PharmD, Chief Executive Officer
Web address: www.samhealth.org

Owned, leased, sponsored:	3 hospitals	260 beds
Contract–managed:	2 hospitals	50 beds
Totals:	5 hospitals	310 beds

★**0914: SAN LUIS VALLEY HEALTH** (NP)
106 Blanca Avenue, Alamosa, CO Zip 81101–2340; tel. 719/589–2511; Konnie Martin, Chief Executive Officer
(Independent Hospital System)

COLORADO: SAN LUIS VALLEY HEALTH (O, 44 beds) 106 Blanca Avenue, Alamosa, CO Zip 81101–2393; tel. 719/589–2511; Konnie Martin, Chief Executive Officer
Web address: www.sanluisvalleyhealth.org

SAN LUIS VALLEY HEALTH CONEJOS COUNTY HOSPITAL (O, 17 beds) 19021 U.S. Highway 285, La Jara, CO Zip 81140–0639, Mailing Address: P.O. Box 639, Zip 81140–0639; tel. 719/274–5121; Konnie Martin, Chief Executive Officer
Web address: www.sanluisvalleyhealth.org/locations/conejos–county–hospital

Owned, leased, sponsored:	2 hospitals	61 beds
Contract–managed:	0 hospitals	0 beds
Totals:	2 hospitals	61 beds

★**0530: SANFORD HEALTH** (NP)
2301 East 60th Street North, Sioux Falls, SD Zip 57104–0569, Mailing Address: PO Box 5039, Zip 57117–5039; tel. 605/333–1000; Kelby K. Krabbenhoft, President and Chief Executive Officer
(Decentralized Health System)

IOWA: ORANGE CITY AREA HEALTH SYSTEM (C, 108 beds) 1000 Lincoln Circle S.E., Orange City, IA Zip 51041–1862; tel. 712/737–4984; Martin W. Guthmiller, Chief Executive Officer
Web address: www.ochealthsystem.org

SANFORD ROCK RAPIDS MEDICAL CENTER (L, 14 beds) 801 South Greene Street, Rock Rapids, IA Zip 51246–1998; tel. 712/472–2591; Tammy Loosbrock, Senior Director
Web address: www.sanfordrockrapids.org

SANFORD SHELDON MEDICAL CENTER (O, 95 beds) 118 North Seventh Avenue, Sheldon, IA Zip 51201–1235, Mailing Address: P.O. Box 250, Zip 51201–0250; tel. 712/324–5041; Richard E. Nordahl, Chief Executive Officer
Web address: www.sanfordsheldon.org

MINNESOTA: ARNOLD MEMORIAL HEALTH CARE CENTER (L, 50 beds) 601 Louisiana Avenue, Adrian, MN Zip 56110–0279, Mailing Address: P.O. Box 279, Zip 56110–0279; tel. 507/483–2668; Michele Roban, Administrator

MAHNOMEN HEALTH CENTER (C, 56 beds) 414 West Jefferson Avenue, Mahnomen, MN Zip 56557–4912, Mailing Address: P.O. Box 396, Zip 56557–0396; tel. 218/935–2511; Dale K. Kruger, Chief Executive Officer
Web address: www.mahnomenhealthcenter.com

MURRAY COUNTY MEDICAL CENTER (C, 18 beds) 2042 Juniper Avenue, Slayton, MN Zip 56172–1017; tel. 507/836–6111; Dennis Goebel, Chief Executive Officer
Web address: www.murraycountymed.org

ORTONVILLE AREA HEALTH SERVICES (C, 115 beds) 450 Eastvold Avenue, Ortonville, MN Zip 56278–1133; tel. 320/839–2502; David Rogers, Chief Executive Officer
Web address: www.oahs.us

PERHAM HEALTH (C, 121 beds) 1000 Coney Street West, Perham, MN Zip 56573–1108; tel. 218/347–4500; Chuck Hofius, Chief Executive Officer
Web address: www.perhamhealth.org

SANFORD BAGLEY MEDICAL CENTER (O, 25 beds) 203 Fourth Street N.W., Bagley, MN Zip 56621–8307; tel. 218/694–6501; Sammi Davidson, Administrative Director
Web address: www.sanfordhealth.org

SANFORD BEMIDJI MEDICAL CENTER (O, 196 beds) 1300 Anne Street N.W., Bemidji, MN Zip 56601–5103; tel. 218/751–5430; Bryan Nermoe, President
Web address: www.nchs.com

SANFORD CANBY MEDICAL CENTER (L, 93 beds) 112 St. Olaf Avenue South, Canby, MN Zip 56220–1433; tel. 507/223–7277; Lori Sisk, R.N., Chief Executive Officer
Web address: www.sanfordcanby.org

SANFORD JACKSON MEDICAL CENTER (O, 14 beds) 1430 North Highway, Jackson, MN Zip 56143–1093; tel. 507/847–2420; Mary J. Ruyter, Chief Executive Officer
Web address: www.sanfordjackson.org

SANFORD LUVERNE MEDICAL CENTER (O, 25 beds) 1600 North Kniss Avenue, Luverne, MN Zip 56156–1067; tel. 507/283–2321; Tammy Loosbrock, Senior Director
Web address: www.sanfordluverne.org

SANFORD MEDICAL CENTER THIEF RIVER FALLS (O, 35 beds) 3001 Sanford Parkway, Thief River Falls, MN Zip 56701–2700; tel. 218/681–4240; Brian J. Carlson, FACHE, Chief Executive Officer
Web address: www.sanfordhealth.org

SANFORD THIEF RIVER FALLS BEHAVIORAL HEALTH CENTER (O, 16 beds) 120 LaBree Avenue South, Thief River Falls, MN Zip 56701–2819, Mailing Address: 3001 Sanford Parkway, Zip 56701–2819; tel. 218/683–4349; Brian J. Carlson, FACHE, Chief Executive Officer
Web address: www.sanfordhealth.org/Locations/1766896362

SANFORD TRACY MEDICAL CENTER (O, 25 beds) 251 Fifth Street East, Tracy, MN Zip 56175–1536; tel. 507/629–3200; Stacy Barstad, Chief Executive Officer
Web address: www.sanfordtracy.org

SANFORD WESTBROOK MEDICAL CENTER (L, 6 beds) 920 Bell Avenue, Westbrook, MN Zip 56183–9669, Mailing Address: P.O. Box 188, Zip 56183–0188; tel. 507/274–6121; Stacy Barstad, Chief Executive Officer
Web address: www.sanfordwestbrook.org

SANFORD WHEATON MEDICAL CENTER (O, 15 beds) 401 12th Street North, Wheaton, MN Zip 56296–1099; tel. 320/563–8226; JoAnn M. Foltz, R.N., Chief Executive Officer
Web address: www.sanfordhealth.org

SANFORD WORTHINGTON MEDICAL CENTER (O, 48 beds) 1018 Sixth Avenue, Worthington, MN Zip 56187–2202, Mailing Address: P.O. Box 997, Zip 56187–0997; tel. 507/372–2941; Michael Hammer, Chief Executive Officer
Web address: www.sanfordhealth.org

WINDOM AREA HOSPITAL (C, 18 beds) 2150 Hospital Drive, Windom, MN Zip 56101–0339, Mailing Address: P.O. Box 339, Zip 56101–0339; tel. 507/831–2400; Shelby Medina, Chief Executive Officer
Web address: www.windomareahospital.com

NORTH DAKOTA: NORTHWOOD DEACONESS HEALTH CENTER (O, 73 beds) 4 North Park Street, Northwood, ND Zip 58267–4102, Mailing Address: P.O. Box 190, Zip 58267–0190; tel. 701/587–6060; Pete Antonson, Chief Executive Officer
Web address: www.ndhc.net

SANFORD BISMARCK (O, 208 beds) 300 North Seventh Street, Bismarck, ND Zip 58501–4439, Mailing Address: P.O. Box 5525, Zip 58506–5525; tel. 701/323–6000; Craig Lambrecht, M.D., President
Web address: www.bismarck.sanfordhealth.org/

SANFORD HILLSBORO MEDICAL CENTER (C, 52 beds) 12 Third Street S.E., Hillsboro, ND Zip 58045–4840, Mailing Address: P.O. Box 609, Zip 58045–0609; tel. 701/636–3200; Jac McTaggart, Chief Executive Officer
Web address: www.hillsboromedicalcenter.com

SANFORD MAYVILLE MEDICAL CENTER (O, 18 beds) 42 Sixth Avenue S.E., Mayville, ND Zip 58257–1598; tel. 701/786–3800; Roger Baier, Chief Executive Officer
Web address: www.unionhospital.com

SANFORD MEDICAL CENTER FARGO (O, 473 beds) 801 Broadway North, Fargo, ND Zip 58122–3641; tel. 701/234–2000; Paul F. Richard, Executive Vice President
Web address: www.sanfordhealth.org

For explanation of codes following names, see page B2.
★ Indicates Type III membership in the American Hospital Association.

SOUTH DAKOTA: COMMUNITY MEMORIAL HOSPITAL (C, 16 beds) 809 Jackson Street, Burke, SD Zip 57523–2065, Mailing Address: P.O. Box 319, Zip 57523–0319; tel. 605/775–2621; Mistie Sachtjen, Chief Executive Officer
Web address: www.sanfordhealth.org

PIONEER MEMORIAL HOSPITAL AND HEALTH SERVICES (C, 64 beds) 315 North Washington Street, Viborg, SD Zip 57070–2002, Mailing Address: P.O. Box 368, Zip 57070–0368; tel. 605/326–5161; Thomas V. Richter, Chief Executive Officer
Web address: www.pioneermemorial.org

SANFORD ABERDEEN MEDICAL CENTER (O, 16 beds) 2905 3rd Avenue S.E., Aberdeen, SD Zip 57401–5420; tel. 605/626–4200; Ashley M. Erickson, Chief Executive Officer
Web address: www.sanfordaberdeen.org/

SANFORD CANTON–INWOOD MEDICAL CENTER (O, 11 beds) 440 North Hiawatha Drive, Canton, SD Zip 57013–5800; tel. 605/764–1400; Scott C. Larson, Chief Executive Officer
Web address: www.sanfordcantoninwood.org

SANFORD CHAMBERLAIN MEDICAL CENTER (O, 69 beds) 300 South Byron Boulevard, Chamberlain, SD Zip 57325–9741; tel. 605/234–5511; Erica Peterson, Chief Executive Officer
Web address: www.sanfordchamberlain.org

SANFORD CLEAR LAKE MEDICAL CENTER (L, 10 beds) 701 Third Avenue South, Clear Lake, SD Zip 57226–2016; tel. 605/874–2141; Lori Sisk, R.N., Chief Executive Officer
Web address: www.sanforddeuelcounty.org

SANFORD USD MEDICAL CENTER (O, 483 beds) 1305 West 18th Street, Sioux Falls, SD Zip 57105–0496, Mailing Address: P.O. Box 5039, Zip 57117–5039; tel. 605/333–1000; Paul A. Hanson, FACHE, President
Web address: www.sanfordhealth.org

SANFORD VERMILLION MEDICAL CENTER (L, 114 beds) 20 South Plum Street, Vermillion, SD Zip 57069–3346; tel. 605/677–3500; Timothy J. Tracy, Chief Executive Officer
Web address: www.sanfordvermillion.org

SANFORD WEBSTER MEDICAL CENTER (L, 20 beds) 1401 West 1st Street, Webster, SD Zip 57274–1054, Mailing Address: P.O. Box 489, Zip 57274–0489; tel. 605/345–3336; Isaac Gerdes, Chief Executive Officer
Web address: www.sanfordhealth.org

WINNER REGIONAL HEALTHCARE CENTER (C, 104 beds) 745 East Eighth Street, Winner, SD Zip 57580–2631; tel. 605/842–7100; Kevin Coffey, Chief Executive Officer
Web address: www.winnerregional.org

Owned, leased, sponsored:	25 hospitals	2152 beds
Contract–managed:	10 hospitals	672 beds
Totals:	35 hospitals	2824 beds

★5095: SCL HEALTH (CC)
500 Eldorado Boulevard, Suite 100–D, Broomfield, CO Zip 80021; tel. 303/813–5180; Michael A. Slubowski, FACHE, Chief Executive Officer
(Moderately Centralized Health System)

COLORADO: GOOD SAMARITAN MEDICAL CENTER (S, 183 beds) 200 Exempla Circle, Lafayette, CO Zip 80026–3370; tel. 303/689–4000; David Hamm, President and Chief Executive Officer
Web address: www.goodsamaritancolorado.org/

LUTHERAN MEDICAL CENTER (S, 518 beds) 8300 West 38th Avenue, Wheat Ridge, CO Zip 80033–6005; tel. 303/425–4500; Grant Wicklund, President and Chief Executive Officer
Web address: www.exempla.org

PLATTE VALLEY MEDICAL CENTER (O, 70 beds) 1600 Prairie Center Parkway, Brighton, CO Zip 80601–4006; tel. 303/498–1600; John R. Hicks, President and Chief Executive Officer
Web address: www.pvmc.org

SAINT JOSEPH HOSPITAL (O, 400 beds) 1835 Franklin Street, Denver, CO Zip 80218–1126; tel. 303/837–7111; Jameson Smith, Chief Executive Officer
Web address: www.saintjosephdenver.org/

ST. MARY'S MEDICAL CENTER (O, 310 beds) 2635 North 7th Street, Grand Junction, CO Zip 81501–8209, Mailing Address: P.O. Box 1628, Zip 81502–1628; tel. 970/298–2273; Brian Davidson, M.D., Interim President
Web address: www.stmarygj.com

KANSAS: ST. FRANCIS HEALTH (O, 259 beds) 1700 S.W. 7th Street, Topeka, KS Zip 66606–1690; tel. 785/295–8000; David P. Setchel, President
Web address: www.stfrancistopeka.org

MONTANA: HOLY ROSARY HEALTHCARE (O, 90 beds) 2600 Wilson Street, Miles City, MT Zip 59301–5094; tel. 406/233–2600; Paul Lewis, Chief Executive Officer
Web address: www.holyrosaryhealthcare.org

ST. JAMES HEALTHCARE (O, 67 beds) 400 South Clark Street, Butte, MT Zip 59701–2328; tel. 406/723–2500; Charles T. Wright, President and Chief Executive Officer
Web address: www.stjameshealthcare.org

ST. VINCENT HEALTHCARE (O, 221 beds) 1233 North 30th Street, Billings, MT Zip 59101–0165, Mailing Address: P.O. Box 35200, Zip 59107–5200; tel. 406/237–7000; Steve Loveless, President and Chief Executive Officer
Web address: www.svh-mt.org

Owned, leased, sponsored:	9 hospitals	2118 beds
Contract–managed:	0 hospitals	0 beds
Totals:	9 hospitals	2118 beds

★1505: SCRIPPS HEALTH (NP)
4275 Campus Point Court CP112, San Diego, CA Zip 92121–1513, Mailing Address: 4275 Campus Point Court, Zip 92121–1513; tel. 858/678–7200; Chris D. Van Gorder, FACHE, President and Chief Executive Officer
(Centralized Health System)

CALIFORNIA: SCRIPPS GREEN HOSPITAL (O, 173 beds) 10666 North Torrey Pines Road, La Jolla, CA Zip 92037–1093; tel. 858/455–9100; Robin Brown, Chief Executive, Senior Vice President
Web address: www.scrippshealth.org

SCRIPPS MEMORIAL HOSPITAL–ENCINITAS (O, 194 beds) 354 Santa Fe Drive, Encinitas, CA Zip 92024–5182, Mailing Address: P.O. Box 230817, Zip 92023–0817; tel. 760/633–6501; Carl J. Etter, Chief Executive and Senior Vice President
Web address: www.scripps.org

SCRIPPS MEMORIAL HOSPITAL–LA JOLLA (O, 203 beds) 9888 Genesee Avenue, La Jolla, CA Zip 92037–1200, Mailing Address: P.O. Box 28, Zip 92038–0028; tel. 858/626–4123; Gary G. Fybel, FACHE, Chief Executive, Senior Vice President
Web address: www.scripps.org/locations/hospitals__ scripps–memorial–hospital–la–jolla

SCRIPPS MERCY HOSPITAL (O, 392 beds) 4077 Fifth Avenue, San Diego, CA Zip 92103–2105; tel. 619/294–8111; Thomas A. Gammiere, Chief Executive, Senior Vice President
Web address: www.scrippshealth.org

Owned, leased, sponsored:	4 hospitals	962 beds
Contract–managed:	0 hospitals	0 beds
Totals:	4 hospitals	962 beds

★0181: SELECT MEDICAL CORPORATION (IO)
4714 Gettysburg Road, Mechanicsburg, PA Zip 17055–4325; tel. 717/972–1100; David S. Chernow, President and Chief Executive Officer
(Independent Hospital System)

ALABAMA: SELECT SPECIALTY HOSPITAL–BIRMINGHAM (O, 38 beds) 2010 Brookwood Medical Center Drive, 3rd Floor, Birmingham, AL Zip 35209–6804; tel. 205/599–4600; Andrea White, Chief Executive Officer
Web address: www.selectspecialtyhospitals. com/company/locations/birmingham.aspx

ARIZONA: HONORHEALTH REHABILITATION HOSPITAL (O, 50 beds) 8850 East Pima Center Parkway, Scottsdale, AZ Zip 85258–4619; tel. 480/800–3900; Scott R. Keen, Chief Executive Officer
Web address: www.scottsdale–rehab.com/

For explanation of codes following names, see page B2.
★ Indicates Type III membership in the American Hospital Association.

SELECT SPECIALTY HOSPITAL–PHOENIX (O, 48 beds) 350 West Thomas Road, 3rd Floor Main, Phoenix, AZ Zip 85013–4409; tel. 602/406–6802; Sharon Anthony, Chief Executive Officer
Web address: www.phoenix.selectspecialtyhospitals.com/

ARKANSAS: REGENCY HOSPITAL OF NORTHWEST ARKANSAS – SPRINGDALE (O, 25 beds) 609 West Maple Avenue, 6th Floor, Springdale, AR Zip 72764; tel. 479/757–2600; Jerry Alexander, Chief Executive Officer
Web address: www.regencyhospital.com

SELECT SPECIALTY HOSPITAL–FORT SMITH (O, 34 beds) 1001 Towson Avenue, 6 Central, Fort Smith, AR Zip 72901–4921; tel. 479/441–3960; Cindy McLain, Chief Executive Officer
Web address: www.selectspecialtyhospitals. com/company/locations/fortsmith.aspx

DELAWARE: SELECT SPECIALTY HOSPITAL–WILMINGTON (O, 35 beds) 701 North Clayton Street, 5th Floor, Wilmington, DE Zip 19805–3948; tel. 302/421–4545; Donna Gares, R.N., FACHE, MSN, Chief Executive Officer
Web address: www.wilmington.selectspecialtyhospitals.com

FLORIDA: SELECT SPECIALTY HOSPITAL DAYTONA BEACH (O, 34 beds) 301 Memorial Medical Parkway, 11th Floor, Daytona Beach, FL Zip 32117–5167; tel. 386/231–3436; Adrianne Lutes, Chief Executive Officer
Web address: www.daytonabeach.selectspecialtyhospitals.com

SELECT SPECIALTY HOSPITAL–GAINESVILLE (O, 44 beds) 2708 S.W. Archer Road, Gainesville, FL Zip 32608–1316; tel. 352/337–3240; Kristopher Kitzke, Chief Executive Officer
Web address: www.selectspecialtyhospitals. com/company/locations/gainesville.aspx

SELECT SPECIALTY HOSPITAL–MIAMI (O, 47 beds) 955 N.W. 3rd Street, Miami, FL Zip 33128–1274; tel. 305/416–5700; Dionisio Bencomo, Chief Executive Officer
Web address: www.selectspecialtyhospitals.com/company/locations/miami. aspx

SELECT SPECIALTY HOSPITAL–ORLANDO (O, 75 beds) 2250 Bedford Road, Orlando, FL Zip 32803–1443; tel. 407/303–7869; Nellie Castroman, Chief Executive Officer
Web address: www.selectspecialtyhospitals. com/company/locations/orlando.aspx

SELECT SPECIALTY HOSPITAL–PALM BEACH (O, 60 beds) 3060 Melaleuca Lane, Lake Worth, FL Zip 33461–5174; tel. 561/357–7200; Larry Melby, Chief Executive Officer
Web address: www.selectspecialtyhospitals. com/company/locations/palmbeach.aspx

SELECT SPECIALTY HOSPITAL–PANAMA CITY (O, 30 beds) 615 North Bonita Avenue, 3rd Floor, Panama City, FL Zip 32401–3623; tel. 850/767–3180; Randal S. Hamilton, Chief Executive Officer
Web address: www.selectspecialtyhospitals. com/company/locations/panamacity.aspx

SELECT SPECIALTY HOSPITAL–PENSACOLA (O, 75 beds) 7000 Cobble Creek Drive, Pensacola, FL Zip 32504–8638; tel. 850/473–4800; David Goodson, Chief Executive Officer
Web address: www.selectspecialtyhospitals. com/company/locations/pensacola.aspx

SELECT SPECIALTY HOSPITAL–TALLAHASSEE (O, 29 beds) 1554 Surgeons Drive, Tallahassee, FL Zip 32308–4631; tel. 850/219–6950; Lora Davis, FACHE, Chief Executive Officer
Web address: www.tallahassee.selectspecialtyhospitals.com/

WEST GABLES REHABILITATION HOSPITAL (O, 60 beds) 2525 S.W. 75th Avenue, Miami, FL Zip 33155–2800; tel. 305/262–6800; Walter Concepcion, Chief Executive Officer
Web address: www.westgablesrehabhospital.com/

GEORGIA: REGENCY HOSPITAL OF CENTRAL GEORGIA (O, 60 beds) 535 Coliseum Drive, Macon, GA Zip 31217–0104; tel. 478/803–7300; Michael S. Boggs, Chief Executive Officer
Web address: www.regencyhospital.com

REGENCY HOSPITAL OF SOUTH ATLANTA (O, 40 beds) 1170 Cleveland Avenue, 4th Floor, East Point, GA Zip 30344–3615; tel. 404/466–6250; Kathy A. Felps, R.N., Chief Executive Officer
Web address: www.regencyhospital.com

SELECT SPECIALTY HOSPITAL – NORTHEAST ATLANTA (O, 18 beds) 1821 Clifton Road N.E., 2nd Floor, Atlanta, GA Zip 30329–4021; tel. 404/728–6200; Matthew Paul Pearson, Chief Executive Officer
Web address: www.selectspecialtyhospitals.com/

SELECT SPECIALTY HOSPITAL–ATLANTA (O, 30 beds) 550 Peachtree Street N.E., Atlanta, GA Zip 30308–2247; tel. 404/815–0348; Matthew Paul Pearson, Chief Executive Officer
Web address: www.selectspecialtyhospitals.com/company/locations/atlanta. aspx

SELECT SPECIALTY HOSPITAL–AUGUSTA (O, 80 beds) 1537 Walton Way, Augusta, GA Zip 30904–3764; tel. 706/731–1200; Curt L. Roberts, Chief Executive Officer
Web address: www.augusta.selectspecialtyhospitals.com

SELECT SPECIALTY HOSPITAL–SAVANNAH (O, 40 beds) 5353 Reynolds Street, 4 South, Savannah, GA Zip 31405–6015; tel. 912/819–7972; Patrick McVey, Chief Executive Officer
Web address: www.selectspecialtyhospitals. com/company/locations/savannah.aspx

SELECT SPECIALTY HOSPITAL MIDTOWN ATLANTA (O, 70 beds) 705 Juniper Street NE, Atlanta, GA Zip 30308–1307; tel. 404/873–2871; Jeffrey R. Fenn, MHA, Chief Executive Officer

INDIANA: REGENCY HOSPITAL OF NORTHWEST INDIANA (O, 61 beds) 4321 Fir Street, 4th Floor, East Chicago, IN Zip 46312–3049; tel. 219/392–7799; Cheryl G. Gentry, Chief Executive Officer
Web address: www.regencyhospital. com/company/locations/indiana–northwest–indiana.aspx

SELECT SPECIALTY HOSPITAL–EVANSVILLE (O, 60 beds) 400 S.E. 4th Street, Evansville, IN Zip 47713–1206; tel. 812/421–2500; Glen Winekauf, Chief Executive Officer
Web address: www.selectspecialtyhospitals. com/company/locations/evansville.aspx

SELECT SPECIALTY HOSPITAL–FORT WAYNE (O, 32 beds) 700 Broadway, 7th Floor, Fort Wayne, IN Zip 46802–1402; tel. 260/425–3810; Bill Underwood, Chief Executive Officer
Web address: www.fortwayne.selectspecialtyhospitals.com

IOWA: SELECT SPECIALTY HOSPITAL–DES MOINES (O, 30 beds) 1111 6th Avenue, 4th Floor Main, Des Moines, IA Zip 50314–2610; tel. 515/247–4400; Glen Griesheim, Chief Executive Officer
Web address: www.selectspecialtyhospitals.com

SELECT SPECIALTY HOSPITAL–QUAD CITIES (O, 50 beds) 1111 West Kimberly Road, Davenport, IA Zip 52806–5711; tel. 563/468–2000; Connie K. Siffring, Chief Executive Officer
Web address: www.selectmedicalcorp.com

KANSAS: SELECT SPECIALTY HOSPITAL–KANSAS CITY (O, 40 beds) 1731 North 90th Street, Kansas City, KS Zip 66112–1515; tel. 913/732–5900; Larry Niemann, Chief Executive Officer
Web address: www.selectspecialtyhospitals.com

SELECT SPECIALTY HOSPITAL–WICHITA (O, 48 beds) 929 North St. Francis Street, Wichita, KS Zip 67214–3821; tel. 316/261–8303; Peggy Cliffe, Chief Executive Officer
Web address: www.selectspecialtyhospitals.com/company/locations/wichita. aspx

KENTUCKY: SELECT SPECIALTY HOSPITAL–LEXINGTON (O, 41 beds) 310 South Limestone Street, 3rd Floor, Lexington, KY Zip 40508–3008; tel. 859/226–7096; Kim Pennington, Chief Executive Officer
Web address: www.lexington.selectspecialtyhospitals.com/

SELECT SPECIALTY HOSPITAL–NORTHERN KENTUCKY (O, 33 beds) 85 North Grand Avenue, Fort Thomas, KY Zip 41075–1793; tel. 859/572–3880; Teresa R. Detano, M.P.H., Chief Executive Officer
Web address: www.selectspecialtyhospitals.com

MICHIGAN: GREAT LAKES SPECIALTY HOSPITAL–GRAND RAPIDS (O, 20 beds) 200 S.E. Jefferson Avenue, 5th Floor, Grand Rapids, MI Zip 49503–4502; tel. 616/965–8650; Jevne Conover, Chief Executive Officer
Web address: www.selectmedicalcorp.com

SELECT SPECIALTY HOSPITAL–ANN ARBOR (O, 36 beds) 5301 East Huron River Drive, 5th Floor, Ypsilanti, MI Zip 48197–1051; tel. 734/712–6751; Bryan Cutliff, Chief Executive Officer
Web address: www.annarbor.selectspecialtyhospitals.com/

For explanation of codes following names, see page B2.
★ Indicates Type III membership in the American Hospital Association.

SELECT SPECIALTY HOSPITAL–BATTLE CREEK (O, 25 beds) 300 North Avenue, Battle Creek, MI Zip 49017–3307; tel. 269/245–4675; Salvatore Iweimrin, R.N., Chief Executive Officer
Web address: www.battlecreek.selectspecialtyhospitals.com/

SELECT SPECIALTY HOSPITAL–DOWNRIVER (O, 35 beds) 2333 Biddle Avenue, 8th Floor, Wyandotte, MI Zip 48192–4668; tel. 734/246–5500; Angela Kudla, MSN, R.N., Chief Nursing Officer
Web address: www.downriver.selectspecialtyhospitals.com/

SELECT SPECIALTY HOSPITAL–FLINT (O, 26 beds) 401 South Ballenger Highway, 5th Floor Central, Flint, MI Zip 48532–3638; tel. 810/342–4545; Christina DeBlouw, Chief Executive Officer
Web address: www.selectspecialtyhospitals.com/company/locations/flint.aspx

SELECT SPECIALTY HOSPITAL–GROSSE POINTE (O, 30 beds) 468 Cadieux Road, 3 North East, Grosse Pointe, MI Zip 48230–1507; tel. 313/473–6131; Zaahra Butt, Chief Executive Officer
Web address: www.grossepointe.selectspecialtyhospitals.com/

SELECT SPECIALTY HOSPITAL–MACOMB COUNTY (O, 30 beds) 215 North Avenue, Mount Clemens, MI Zip 48043–1700; tel. 586/307–9000; Jon P. O'Malley, Chief Executive Officer
Web address: www.macomb.selectspecialtyhospitals.com/

SELECT SPECIALTY HOSPITAL–MUSKEGON (O, 31 beds) 1700 Clinton Street, 3 South, Muskegon, MI Zip 49442–5502; tel. 231/728–5811; Sharon Purkis, Administrator
Web address: www.greatlakesspecialtyhospital.com

SELECT SPECIALTY HOSPITAL–NORTHWEST DETROIT (O, 36 beds) 6071 West Outer Drive, Detroit, MI Zip 48235–2624; tel. 313/966–4747; Marilouise Riska, Chief Executive Officer
Web address: www.selectspecialtyhospitals.com/company/locations/northwestdetroit.aspx

SELECT SPECIALTY HOSPITAL–PONTIAC (O, 30 beds) 44405 Woodward Avenue, 8th Floor, Pontiac, MI Zip 48341–5023; tel. 248/452–5252; Peggy Kingston, Chief Executive Officer
Web address: www.selectspecialtyhospitals.com/company/locations/pontiac.aspx

SELECT SPECIALTY HOSPITAL–SAGINAW (O, 32 beds) 1447 North Harrison Street, 8th Floor, Saginaw, MI Zip 48602–4785; tel. 989/583–4235; Matthew Cannon, Chief Executive Officer
Web address: www.selectspecialtyhospitals.com/company/locations/saginaw.aspx

MINNESOTA: REGENCY HOSPITAL OF MINNEAPOLIS (O, 64 beds) 1300 Hidden Lakes Parkway, Golden Valley, MN Zip 55422–4286; tel. 763/588–2750; Marshall E. Smith, Chief Executive Officer
Web address: www.regencyhospital.com

MISSISSIPPI: REGENCY HOSPITAL OF HATTIESBURG (O, 33 beds) 6051 U.S. Highway 49, 5th Floor, Hattiesburg, MS Zip 39401–6031; tel. 601/288–8510; William Heath, Chief Executive Officer
Web address: www.hattiesburg.regencyhospital.com/

REGENCY HOSPITAL OF MERIDIAN (O, 40 beds) 1102 Constitution Avenue, 2nd Floor, Meridian, MS Zip 39301–4001; tel. 601/484–7900; Clifton Quinn, Chief Executive Officer
Web address: www.regencyhospital.com

SELECT SPECIALTY HOSPITAL – BELHAVEN (O, 24 beds) 1225 North State Street, Jackson, MS Zip 39202–2097, Mailing Address: P.O. Box 23695, Zip 39225–3695; tel. 601/968–1000; Bobbie K. Ware, R.N., FACHE, Chief Executive Officer and Chief Nursing Officer
Web address: www.mbhs.org

SELECT SPECIALTY HOSPITAL–GULFPORT (O, 61 beds) 1520 Broad Avenue, Suite 300, Gulfport, MS Zip 39501–3601; tel. 228/575–7500; John O'Keefe, Chief Executive Officer
Web address: www.selectspecialtyhospitals.com/company/locations/gulfcoast.aspx

SELECT SPECIALTY HOSPITAL–JACKSON (O, 53 beds) 5903 Ridgewood Road, Suite 100, Jackson, MS Zip 39211–3700; tel. 601/899–3800; Chandler Ewing, Chief Executive Officer
Web address: www.selectspecialtyhospitals.com/company/locations/jackson.aspx

MISSOURI: SELECT SPECIALTY HOSPITAL–SPRINGFIELD (O, 44 beds) 1630 East Primrose Street, Springfield, MO Zip 65804–7929; tel. 417/885–4700; Mark S. Brodeur, FACHE, Chief Executive Officer
Web address: www.selectspecialtyhospitals.com/company/locations/springfield.aspx

SELECT SPECIALTY HOSPITAL–ST. LOUIS (O, 33 beds) 300 First Capitol Drive, Unit 1, Saint Charles, MO Zip 63301–2844; tel. 636/947–5010; Donna Mansard, Chief Executive Officer
Web address: www.selectspecialtyhospitals.com/company/locations/stlouis.aspx

SELECT SPECIALTY HOSPITAL–WESTERN MISSOURI (O, 34 beds) 2316 East Meyer Boulevard, 3 West, Kansas City, MO Zip 64132–1136; tel. 816/276–3300; Jeffrey Alexander, Chief Executive Officer
Web address: www.selectspecialtyhospitals.com/company/locations/westernmissouri.aspx

SSM SELECT REHABILITATION HOSPITAL (O, 95 beds) 1027 Bellevue Avenue, 3rd Floor, Richmond Heights, MO Zip 63117–1851, Mailing Address: 1027 Bellevue Avenue, Zip 63117–1851; tel. 314/768–5300; Timothy Wadman, Chief Executive Officer
Web address: www.ssm–select.com

NEBRASKA: SELECT SPECIALTY HOSPITAL – LINCOLN (O, 24 beds) 2300 South 16th Street, 7th Floor, Lincoln, NE Zip 68502–3704; tel. 402/483–8444; Scott Butterfield, Chief Executive Officer

SELECT SPECIALTY HOSPITAL–OMAHA (O, 52 beds) 1870 South 75th Street, Omaha, NE Zip 68124–1700; tel. 402/361–5700; Thomas N. Theroult, Chief Executive Officer
Web address: www.selectspecialtyhospitals.com/company/locations/omahacentral.aspx

NEW JERSEY: KESSLER INSTITUTE FOR REHABILITATION (O, 336 beds) 1199 Pleasant Valley Way, West Orange, NJ Zip 07052–1424; tel. 973/731–3600; Sue Kida, President
Web address: www.kessler–rehab.com

SELECT SPECIALTY HOSPITAL–NORTHEAST NEW JERSEY (O, 62 beds) 96 Parkway, Rochelle Park, NJ Zip 07662–4200; tel. 201/221–2358; Barbara E. Hannan, MS, R.N., Chief Executive Officer
Web address: www.selectspecialtyhospitals.com/company/locations/northeastnewjersey.aspx

NORTH CAROLINA: SELECT SPECIALTY HOSPITAL–DURHAM (O, 30 beds) 3643 North Roxboro Road, 6th Floor, Durham, NC Zip 27704–2702; tel. 919/470–9137; Theresa Hunkins, R.N., Chief Executive Officer
Web address: www.selectspecialtyhospitals.com/company/locations/durham.aspx

SELECT SPECIALTY HOSPITAL–GREENSBORO (O, 30 beds) 1200 North Elm Street, 5th Floor, Greensboro, NC Zip 27401–1004; tel. 336/832–8571; Deana Knight, Chief Executive Officer
Web address: www.selectspecialtyhospitals.com/company/locations/greensboro.aspx

SELECT SPECIALTY HOSPITAL–WINSTON–SALEM (O, 42 beds) 3333 Silas Creek Parkway, 6th Floor, Winston–Salem, NC Zip 27103–3013; tel. 336/718–6300; Leslie Deane, Chief Executive Officer
Web address: www.selectspecialtyhospitals.com/company/locations/winston–salem.aspx

OHIO: CLEVELAND CLINIC REHABILITATION HOSPITAL (O, 60 beds) 33355 Health Campus Boulevard, Avon, OH Zip 44011; tel. 440/937–9099; Sam Bayoumy, Chief Executive Officer
Web address: www.my.clevelandclinic.org

OHIOHEALTH REHABILITATION HOSPITAL (O, 44 beds) 1087 Dennison Avenue, 4th Floor, Columbus, OH Zip 43201–3201; tel. 614/484–9600; Eric Yap, Chief Executive Officer
Web address: www.ohiohealth–rehab.com

REGENCY HOSPITAL CLEVELAND EAST (O, 132 beds) 4200 Interchange Corporate Center Road, Warrensville Heights, OH Zip 44128–5631; tel. 216/910–3800; Thomas Knoske, Chief Executive Officer
Web address: www.regencyhospital.com/

REGENCY HOSPITAL OF COLUMBUS (O, 43 beds) 1430 South High Street, Columbus, OH Zip 43207–1045; tel. 614/456–0300; Lisa J. Pettrey, MSN, R.N., Chief Executive Officer
Web address: www.regencyhospital.com/

REGENCY HOSPITAL OF TOLEDO (O, 45 beds) 5220 Alexis Road, Sylvania, OH Zip 43560–2504; tel. 419/318–5700; Brett Johnson, Chief Executive Officer
Web address: www.regencyhospital.com

SELECT SPECIALTY HOSPITAL – BOARDMAN (O, 56 beds) 8401 Market Street, 7 South, Boardman, OH Zip 44512–6725; tel. 330/729–1750; Jodi Costello, Chief Executive Officer

For explanation of codes following names, see page B2.
★ Indicates Type III membership in the American Hospital Association.

Section B

SELECT SPECIALTY HOSPITAL – CINCINNATI NORTH (O, 25 beds) 10500 Montgomery Road, Cincinnati, OH Zip 45242–4402; tel. 513/865–5300; Susan Glen, Chief Executive Officer
Web address: www.cincinnatinorth.selectspecialtyhospitals.com/

SELECT SPECIALTY HOSPITAL OF SOUTHEAST OHIO (O, 35 beds) 2000 Tamarack Road, Newark, OH Zip 43055; tel. 740/588–7888; Linda Supplee, Chief Executive Officer
Web address: www.selectspecialtyhospitals.com/company/locations/zanesville.aspx

SELECT SPECIALTY HOSPITAL–AKRON (O, 60 beds) 200 East Market Street, Akron, OH Zip 44308–2015; tel. 330/761–7500; Sonda Burns, Chief Executive Officer
Web address: www.selectspecialtyhospitals.com/company/locations/akron.aspx

SELECT SPECIALTY HOSPITAL–CANTON (O, 30 beds) 1320 Mercy Drive N.W., 6th Floor, Canton, OH Zip 44708–2614; tel. 330/489–8189; Dawne Wheeler, Chief Executive Officer
Web address: www.selectspecialtyhospitals.com/company/locations/canton.aspx

SELECT SPECIALTY HOSPITAL–CINCINNATI (O, 36 beds) 375 Dixmyth Avenue, 15th Floor, Cincinnati, OH Zip 45220–2475; tel. 513/872–4444; Curtis Ohashi, Chief Executive Officer
Web address: www.selectspecialtyhospitals.com/company/locations/cincinnati.aspx

SELECT SPECIALTY HOSPITAL–COLUMBUS (O, 186 beds) 1087 Dennison Avenue, Columbus, OH Zip 43201–3201; tel. 614/458–9000; Patrick Tuer, Chief Executive Officer
Web address: www.selectspecialtyhospitals.com/company/locations/columbus.aspx

SELECT SPECIALTY HOSPITAL–YOUNGSTOWN (O, 51 beds) 1044 Belmont Avenue, Youngstown, OH Zip 44504–1006; tel. 330/480–2349; Jodi Costello, Chief Executive Officer
Web address: www.selectspecialtyhospitals.com/company/locations/youngstown.aspx

SELECT SPECIALTY HOSPITAL – CLEVELAND GATEWAY (O, 153 beds) 2351 East 22nd Street, 7th Floor, Cleveland, OH Zip 44115–3111; tel. 216/363–671; Cheryl G Gentry, Interim Chief Executive Officer

OKLAHOMA: SELECT SPECIALTY HOSPITAL–OKLAHOMA CITY (O, 72 beds) 3524 N.W. 56th Street, Oklahoma City, OK Zip 73112–4518; tel. 405/606–6700; Connie Strickland, Chief Executive Officer
Web address: www.selectspecialtyhospitals.com/company/locations/oklahomacity.aspx

SELECT SPECIALTY HOSPITAL–TULSA MIDTOWN (O, 56 beds) 1125 South Trenton Avenue, 3rd Floor, Tulsa, OK Zip 74120–5418; tel. 918/579–7300; Beth Culluh, Interim Chief Executive Officer
Web address: www.tulsa.selectspecialtyhospitals.com/

PENNSYLVANIA: HELEN M. SIMPSON REHABILITATION HOSPITAL (C, 55 beds) 4300 Londonderry Road, Harrisburg, PA Zip 17109–5317; tel. 717/920–4300; Melissa Gillis, Chief Executive Officer

PENN STATE HERSHEY REHABILITATION HOSPITAL (O, 32 beds) 1135 Old West Chocolate Avenue, Hummelstown, PA Zip 17036; tel. 717/832–2600; Scott Guevin, Chief Executive Officer
Web address: www.psh–rehab.com

SELECT SPECIALTY HOSPITAL–CENTRAL PENNSYLVANIA (O, 92 beds) 503 North 21st Street, 5th Floor, Camp Hill, PA Zip 17011–2204; tel. 717/972–4575; John E. Simodejka, Chief Executive Officer
Web address: www.camphill.selectspecialtyhospitals.com/

SELECT SPECIALTY HOSPITAL–DANVILLE (O, 30 beds) 100 North Academy Avenue, 3rd Floor, Danville, PA Zip 17822–3050; tel. 570/214–9653; Brian Mann, Chief Executive Officer
Web address: www.selectspecialtyhospitals.com/company/locations/danville.aspx

SELECT SPECIALTY HOSPITAL–ERIE (O, 50 beds) 252 West 11th Street, Erie, PA Zip 16501–1702; tel. 814/874–5300; Thomas Fucci, FACHE, Chief Executive Officer
Web address: www.erie.selectspecialtyhospitals.com/

SELECT SPECIALTY HOSPITAL–JOHNSTOWN (O, 39 beds) 320 Main Street, 3rd Floor, Johnstown, PA Zip 15901–1601; tel. 814/534–7300; Kelly Blake, Chief Executive Officer
Web address: www.selectspecialtyhospitals.com/company/locations/johnstown.aspx

SELECT SPECIALTY HOSPITAL–LAUREL HIGHLANDS (O, 40 beds) One Mellon Way, 3rd Floor, Latrobe, PA Zip 15650–1197; tel. 724/539–3230; Laurie Kozorosky, Chief Executive Officer
Web address: www.selectspecialtyhospitals.com/company/locations/laurelhighlands.aspx

SELECT SPECIALTY HOSPITAL–MCKEESPORT (O, 30 beds) 1500 Fifth Avenue, 6th Floor, McKeesport, PA Zip 15132–2422; tel. 412/664–2900; Angela Merryman, Chief Executive Officer
Web address: www.mckeesport.selectspecialtyhospitals.com/

SELECT SPECIALTY HOSPITAL–PITTSBURGH/UPMC (O, 32 beds) 200 Lothrop Street, E824, Pittsburgh, PA Zip 15213–2536; tel. 412/586–9800; John St. Leger, Chief Executive Officer
Web address: www.selectspecialtyhospitals.com/company/locations/pittsburghupmc.aspx

SOUTH CAROLINA: REGENCY HOSPITAL OF FLORENCE (O, 40 beds) 121 East Cedar Street, 4th Floor, Florence, SC Zip 29506–2576; tel. 843/661–3471; Amy Metz, Chief Executive Officer
Web address: www.regencyhospital.com

REGENCY HOSPITAL OF GREENVILLE (O, 32 beds) One St. Francis Drive, 4th Floor, Greenville, SC Zip 29601–3955; tel. 864/255–1438; Paige Beauregard, Chief Executive Officer
Web address: www.regencyhospital.com

SOUTH DAKOTA: SELECT SPECIALTY HOSPITAL–SIOUX FALLS (O, 24 beds) 1305 West 18th Street, Sioux Falls, SD Zip 57105–0401; tel. 605/312–9500; Carol Ulmer, Chief Executive Officer
Web address: www.selectspecialtyhospitals.com/company/locations/siouxfalls.aspx

TENNESSEE: SELECT SPECIALTY HOSPITAL–KNOXVILLE (O, 35 beds) 1901 Clinch Avenue, 4th Floor North, Knoxville, TN Zip 37916–2307; tel. 865/541–2615; Rita Wilder, Chief Executive Officer
Web address: www.knoxville.selectspecialtyhospitals.com/

SELECT SPECIALTY HOSPITAL–MEMPHIS (O, 39 beds) 5959 Park Avenue, 12th Floor, Memphis, TN Zip 38119–5200; tel. 901/765–1245; Marcia Taylor, Chief Executive Officer
Web address: www.selectspecialtyhospitals.com/company/locations/memphis.aspx

SELECT SPECIALTY HOSPITAL–NASHVILLE (O, 47 beds) 2000 Hayes Street, Nashville, TN Zip 37203–2318; tel. 615/284–4599; Jennifer Causey, Chief Executive Officer
Web address: www.selectspecialtyhospitals.com/company/locations/nashville.aspx

SELECT SPECIALTY HOSPITAL–NORTH KNOXVILLE (O, 33 beds) 7557B Dannaher Drive, Suite 145, Powell, TN Zip 37849–3568; tel. 865/512–2450; Steve Plumlee, Chief Executive Officer
Web address: www.northknoxville.selectspecialtyhospitals.com/

SELECT SPECIALTY HOSPITAL–TRI CITIES (O, 33 beds) One Medical Park Boulevard, 5th Floor, Bristol, TN Zip 37620–8964; tel. 423/844–5900; Jeffrey Radford, Chief Executive Officer
Web address: www.tricities.selectspecialtyhospitals.com/

TEXAS: BAYLOR INSTITUTE FOR REHABILITATION AT FORT WORTH (C, 42 beds) 6601 Harris Parkway, Fort Worth, TX Zip 76132–6108; Jeffrey D. Thompson, Chief Executive Officer
Web address: www.baylorhealth.com/PhysiciansLocations/BIR/Pages/Default.aspx

BAYLOR INSTITUTE FOR REHABILITATION AT FRISCO (O, 44 beds) 2990 Legacy Drive, Frisco, TX Zip 75034–6066; tel. 469/888–5100; Ryan Seymour, Chief Executive Officer
Web address: www.baylorhealth.com/bir

SELECT REHABILITATION HOSPITAL OF DENTON (O, 44 beds) 2620 Scripture Street, Denton, TX Zip 76201–4315; tel. 940/297–6500; Michelle Powell, Chief Executive Officer
Web address: www.selectrehab–denton.com/

SELECT SPECIALTY HOSPITAL – DALLAS DOWNTOWN (O, 46 beds) 3500 Gaston Avenue, Floors 3&4 Jonnson, Dallas, TX Zip 75246–2017; tel. 469/801–4500; Melody Nagel, Chief Executive Officer
Web address: www.dallasdowntown.selectspecialtyhospitals.com/

SELECT SPECIALTY HOSPITAL – DALLAS GARLAND (O, 40 beds) 2300 Marie Curie Drive, Floors 3E and 3W, Garland, TX Zip 75042–5706; tel. 469/440–5800; Ron Norris, Chief Executive Officer
Web address: www.dallasgarland.selectspecialtyhospitals.com/

For explanation of codes following names, see page B2.
★ Indicates Type III membership in the American Hospital Association.

Section B

SELECT SPECIALTY HOSPITAL–DALLAS (O, 60 beds) 2329 West Parker Road, Carrollton, TX Zip 75010–4713; Holly Powell, Chief Executive Officer
Web address: www.firsttexashospital.com/

SELECT SPECIALTY HOSPITAL–LONGVIEW (O, 32 beds) 700 East Marshall Avenue, 1st Floor, Longview, TX Zip 75601–5580; tel. 903/315–1100; Dennis Baker, Chief Executive Officer
Web address: www.selectspecialtyhospitals.com/company/locations/longview.aspx

SELECT SPECIALTY HOSPITAL–SOUTH DALLAS (O, 69 beds) 3500 West Wheatland Road, 4th Floor, Dallas, TX Zip 75237–3460; tel. 972/780–6500; Robert Dickens, Chief Executive Officer
Web address: www.selectspecialtyhospitals.com/company/locations/southdallas.aspx

WEST VIRGINIA: SELECT SPECIALTY HOSPITAL–CHARLESTON (O, 32 beds) 333 Laidley Street, 3rd Floor East, Charleston, WV Zip 25301–1614; tel. 304/720–7234; Frank Weber, Chief Executive Officer
Web address: www.selectspecialtyhospitals.com/company/locations/charleston.aspx

WISCONSIN: SELECT SPECIALTY HOSPITAL–MADISON (O, 58 beds) 801 Braxton Place, 2nd Floor, Madison, WI Zip 53715–1415; tel. 608/260–2700; Raymond F. Carnevale, Chief Executive Officer
Web address: www.madison.selectspecialtyhospitals.com

SELECT SPECIALTY HOSPITAL–MILWAUKEE (O, 34 beds) 8901 West Lincoln Avenue, 2nd Floor, Milwaukee, WI Zip 53227–2409; West Allis, tel. 414/328–7700; Mary Kay Diderrich, R.N., Chief Executive Officer
Web address: www.selectspecialtyhospitals.com/company/locations/milwaukee.aspx

Owned, leased, sponsored:	101 hospitals	4968 beds
Contract–managed:	2 hospitals	97 beds
Totals:	103 hospitals	5065 beds

★2565: SENTARA HEALTHCARE (NP)
6015 Poplar Hall Drive, Norfolk, VA Zip 23502–3819; tel. 757/455–7000; Howard P. Kern, Chief Executive Officer
(Centralized Health System)

NORTH CAROLINA: SENTARA ALBEMARLE MEDICAL CENTER (L, 83 beds) 1144 North Road Street, Elizabeth City, NC Zip 27909–3473, Mailing Address: P.O. Box 1587, Zip 27906–1587; tel. 252/335–0531; Coleen F. Santa Ana, President
Web address: www.albemarlehealth.org

VIRGINIA: MARTHA JEFFERSON HOSPITAL (O, 158 beds) 500 Martha Jefferson Drive, Charlottesville, VA Zip 22911–4668; tel. 434/654–7000; Jonathan S. Davis, FACHE, President
Web address: www.marthajefferson.org

SENTARA CAREPLEX HOSPITAL (O, 144 beds) 3000 Coliseum Drive, Hampton, VA Zip 23666–5963; tel. 757/736–1000; Debra A. Flores, R.N., MS, President and Administrator
Web address: www.sentara.com

SENTARA HALIFAX REGIONAL HOSPITAL (O, 413 beds) 2204 Wilborn Avenue, South Boston, VA Zip 24592–1638; tel. 434/517–3100; Chris A. Lumsden, Chief Executive Officer
Web address: www.hrhs.org

SENTARA LEIGH HOSPITAL (O, 250 beds) 830 Kempsville Road, Norfolk, VA Zip 23502–3920; tel. 757/261–6000; Teresa L. Edwards, President and Administrator
Web address: www.sentara.com

SENTARA NORFOLK GENERAL HOSPITAL (O, 495 beds) 600 Gresham Drive, Norfolk, VA Zip 23507–1904; tel. 757/388–3000; Kurt T. Hofelich, President
Web address: www.sentara.com

SENTARA NORTHERN VIRGINIA MEDICAL CENTER (O, 181 beds) 2300 Opitz Boulevard, Woodbridge, VA Zip 22191–3399; tel. 703/523–1000; Stephen D. Porter, President
Web address: www.sentara.com/northernvirginia

SENTARA OBICI HOSPITAL (O, 176 beds) 2800 Godwin Boulevard, Suffolk, VA Zip 23434–8038; tel. 757/934–4000; Steve Julian, M.D., President
Web address: www.sentara.com

SENTARA PRINCESS ANNE HOSPITAL (O, 160 beds) 2025 Glenn Mitchell Drive, Virginia Beach, VA Zip 23456–0178; tel. 757/507–1000; Thomas B. Thames, M.D., President
Web address: www.sentara.com

SENTARA RMH MEDICAL CENTER (O, 244 beds) 2010 Health Campus Drive, Harrisonburg, VA Zip 22801–3293; tel. 540/689–1000; James D. Krauss, President
Web address: www.rmhonline.com

SENTARA VIRGINIA BEACH GENERAL HOSPITAL (O, 259 beds) 1060 First Colonial Road, Virginia Beach, VA Zip 23454–3002; tel. 757/395–8000; Elwood Bernard Boone, III, FACHE, President
Web address: www.sentara.com

SENTARA WILLIAMSBURG REGIONAL MEDICAL CENTER (O, 145 beds) 100 Sentara Circle, Williamsburg, VA Zip 23188–5713; tel. 757/984–6000; David J. Masterson, President
Web address: www.sentara.com

Owned, leased, sponsored:	12 hospitals	2708 beds
Contract–managed:	0 hospitals	0 beds
Totals:	12 hospitals	2708 beds

★2065: SHARP HEALTHCARE (NP)
8695 Spectrum Center Boulevard, San Diego, CA Zip 92123–1489; tel. 858/499–4000; Michael Murphy, CPA, President & Chief Executive Officer
(Centralized Health System)

CALIFORNIA: SHARP CHULA VISTA MEDICAL CENTER (O, 343 beds) 751 Medical Center Court, Chula Vista, CA Zip 91911–6699, Mailing Address: P.O. Box 1297, Zip 91912–1297; tel. 619/502–5800; Pablo Velez, Chief Executive Officer
Web address: www.sharp.com

SHARP CORONADO HOSPITAL AND HEALTHCARE CENTER (L, 181 beds) 250 Prospect Place, Coronado, CA Zip 92118–1999; tel. 619/522–3600; Susan Stone, R.N., Ph.D., Senior Vice President and Chief Executive Officer
Web address: www.sharp.com

SHARP GROSSMONT HOSPITAL (L, 528 beds) 5555 Grossmont Center Drive, La Mesa, CA Zip 91942–3019, Mailing Address: P.O. Box 158, Zip 91944–0158; tel. 619/740–6000; Scott Evans, FACHE, PharmD, Senior Vice President and Chief Executive Officer
Web address: www.sharp.com

SHARP MEMORIAL HOSPITAL (O, 431 beds) 7901 Frost Street, San Diego, CA Zip 92123–2701; tel. 858/939–3400; Tim Smith, Senior Vice President and Chief Executive Officer
Web address: www.sharp.com

SHARP MESA VISTA HOSPITAL (O, 172 beds) 7850 Vista Hill Avenue, San Diego, CA Zip 92123–2717; tel. 858/278–4110; Trisha Khaleghi, Senior Vice President and Chief Executive Officer
Web address: www.sharp.com

Owned, leased, sponsored:	5 hospitals	1655 beds
Contract–managed:	0 hospitals	0 beds
Totals:	5 hospitals	1655 beds

4125: SHRINERS HOSPITALS FOR CHILDREN (NP)
2900 Rocky Point Drive, Tampa, FL Zip 33607–1435, Mailing Address: P.O. Box 31356, Zip 33631–3356; tel. 813/281–0300; John P. McCabe, Executive Vice President
(Independent Hospital System)

SHRINERS HOSPITALS FOR CHILDREN–LOS ANGELES (O, 30 beds) 3160 Geneva Street, Los Angeles, CA Zip 90020–1199; tel. 213/388–3151; Lou Lazatin, Administrator
Web address: www.shrinershospitalsforchildren.org/Hospitals/Locations/Losangeles.aspx

SHRINERS HOSPITALS FOR CHILDREN–NORTHERN CALIFORNIA (O, 70 beds) 2425 Stockton Boulevard, Sacramento, CA Zip 95817–2215; tel. 916/453–2000; Margaret Bryan, Administrator
Web address: www.shrinershospitalsforchildren.org/Hospitals/Locations/NorthernCalifornia.aspx

FLORIDA: SHRINERS HOSPITALS FOR CHILDREN–TAMPA (O, 60 beds) 12502 USF Pine Drive, Tampa, FL Zip 33612–9499; tel. 813/972–2250; ,
Web address: www.shrinershospitalsforchildren.org/Hospitals/Locations/Tampa.aspx

For explanation of codes following names, see page B2.
★ Indicates Type III membership in the American Hospital Association.

Section B

HAWAII: SHRINERS HOSPITALS FOR CHILDREN–HONOLULU (O, 16 beds) 1310 Punahou Street, Honolulu, HI Zip 96826–1099; tel. 808/941–4466; John R. White, Administrator
Web address: www.shrinershospitalsforchildren.org/Hospitals/Locations/Honolulu.aspx

ILLINOIS: SHRINERS HOSPITALS FOR CHILDREN–CHICAGO (O, 36 beds) 2211 North Oak Park Avenue, Chicago, IL Zip 60707–3392; tel. 773/622–5400; Mark L. Niederpruem, FACHE, Administrator
Web address: www.shrinershospitalsforchildren.org/Hospitals/Locations/Chicago.aspx

KENTUCKY: SHRINERS HOSPITALS FOR CHILDREN–LEXINGTON (O, 50 beds) 1900 Richmond Road, Lexington, KY Zip 40502–1298; tel. 859/266–2101; Tony Lewgood, Administrator
Web address: www.shrinershospitalsforchildren.org/Hospitals/Locations/Lexington.aspx

LOUISIANA: SHRINERS HOSPITALS FOR CHILDREN–SHREVEPORT (O, 45 beds) 3100 Samford Avenue, Shreveport, LA Zip 71103–4289; tel. 318/222–5704; Garry Kim Green, FACHE, Administrator
Web address: www.shrinershospitalsforchildren.org/Hospitals/Locations/Shreveport.aspx

MASSACHUSETTS: SHRINERS HOSPITALS FOR CHILDREN–BOSTON (O, 14 beds) 51 Blossom Street, Boston, MA Zip 02114–2601; tel. 617/722–3000; John Patrick ONeill, Administrator
Web address: www.shrinershospitalsforchildren.org/Hospitals/Locations/Boston

SHRINERS HOSPITALS FOR CHILDREN–SPRINGFIELD (O, 10 beds) 516 Carew Street, Springfield, MA Zip 01104–2396; tel. 413/787–2000; H. Lee Kirk, Jr., FACHE, Administrator
Web address: www.shrinershospitalsforchildren.org/Hospitals/Locations/Springfield.aspx

MINNESOTA: SHRINERS HOSPITALS FOR CHILDREN–TWIN CITIES (O, 40 beds) 2025 East River Parkway, Minneapolis, MN Zip 55414–3696; tel. 612/596–6100; Charles C. Lobeck, Administrator
Web address: www.shrinershospitalsforchildren.org/Hospitals/Locations/twincities.aspx

MISSOURI: SHRINERS HOSPITALS FOR CHILDREN–ST. LOUIS (O, 12 beds) 4400 Clayton Avenue, Saint Louis, MO Zip 63110–1624; tel. 314/432–3600; John Gloss, FACHE, Administrator
Web address: www.shrinershospitalsforchildren.org/Hospitals/Locations/Stlouis.aspx

OHIO: SHRINERS HOSPITALS FOR CHILDREN–CINCINNATI BURNS HOSPITAL (O, 30 beds) 3229 Burnet Avenue, Cincinnati, OH Zip 45229–3095; tel. 513/872–6000; Mark D. Shugarman, Administrator
Web address: www.shrinershospitalsforchildren.org/Hospitals/Locations/Cincinnati.aspx

OREGON: SHRINERS HOSPITALS FOR CHILDREN–PORTLAND (O, 12 beds) 3101 S.W. Sam Jackson Park Road, Portland, OR Zip 97239–3009; tel. 503/241–5090; J. Craig Patchin, Administrator
Web address: www.shrinershospitalsforchildren.org/Hospitals/Locations/Portland.aspx

PENNSYLVANIA: SHRINERS HOSPITALS FOR CHILDREN–PHILADELPHIA (O, 39 beds) 3551 North Broad Street, Philadelphia, PA Zip 19140–4160; tel. 215/430–4000; Ed Myers, Administrator
Web address: www.shrinershospitalsforchildren.org/Hospitals/Locations/Philadelphia.aspx

SOUTH CAROLINA: SHRINERS HOSPITALS FOR CHILDREN–GREENVILLE (O, 15 beds) 950 West Faris Road, Greenville, SC Zip 29605–4277; tel. 864/271–3444; Randall R. Romberger, Administrator
Web address: www.greenvilleshrinershospital.org

TEXAS: SHRINERS HOSPITALS FOR CHILDREN–GALVESTON (O, 15 beds) 815 Market Street, Galveston, TX Zip 77550–2725; tel. 409/770–6600; Mary Jaco, Administrator
Web address: www.shrinershospitalsforchildren.org/Hospitals/Locations/Galveston.aspx

SHRINERS HOSPITALS FOR CHILDREN–HOUSTON (O, 40 beds) 6977 Main Street, Houston, TX Zip 77030–3701; tel. 713/797–1616; Cathy Moniaci, MS, R.N., Administrator
Web address: www.shrinershospitalsforchildren.org/Locations/houston

UTAH: SHRINERS HOSPITALS FOR CHILDREN–SALT LAKE CITY (O, 45 beds) Fairfax Road & Virginia Street, Salt Lake City, UT Zip 84103–4399; tel. 801/536–3500; Kevin Martin, M.P.H., R.N., Administrator
Web address: www.shrinershospitalsforchildren.org/Hospitals/Locations/SaltLakeCity.aspx

WASHINGTON: SHRINERS HOSPITALS FOR CHILDREN–SPOKANE (O, 30 beds) 911 West Fifth Avenue, Spokane, WA Zip 99204–2901, Mailing Address: P.O. Box 2472, Zip 99210–2472; tel. 509/455–7844; Peter G. Brewer, Administrator
Web address: www.shrinershospitalsforchildren.org/Hospitals/Locations/Spokane.aspx

Owned, leased, sponsored:	19 hospitals	609 beds
Contract–managed:	0 hospitals	0 beds
Totals:	19 hospitals	609 beds

0360: SIGNATURE HEALTHCARE SERVICES (IO)
4238 Green River Road, Corona, CA Zip 92880–1669; tel. 951/549–8032; Soon K. Kim, M.D., President and Chief Executive Officer
(Independent Hospital System)

ARIZONA: AURORA BEHAVIORAL HEALTH SYSTEM EAST (O, 70 beds) 6350 South Maple Street, Tempe, AZ Zip 85283–2857; tel. 480/345–5400; Bruce Waldo, Chief Executive Officer
Web address: www.auroraarizona.com

AURORA BEHAVIORAL HEALTH SYSTEM WEST (O, 80 beds) 6015 West Peoria Avenue, Glendale, AZ Zip 85302–1213; tel. 623/344–4400; Bruce Waldo, Chief Executive Officer
Web address: www.aurorabehavioral.com

CALIFORNIA: AURORA BEHAVIORAL HEALTHCARE SAN DIEGO (O, 80 beds) 11878 Avenue of Industry, San Diego, CA Zip 92128–3490; tel. 858/487–3200; James S. Plummer, Chief Executive Officer
Web address: www.sandiego.aurorabehavioral.com/

AURORA CHARTER OAK HOSPITAL (O, 146 beds) 1161 East Covina Boulevard, Covina, CA Zip 91724–1599; tel. 626/966–1632; Todd A. Smith, Chief Executive Officer
Web address: www.charteroakhospital.com

LAS ENCINAS HOSPITAL (O, 138 beds) 2900 East Del Mar Boulevard, Pasadena, CA Zip 91107–4399; tel. 626/795–9901; Joseph Murphy, Chief Executive Officer
Web address: www.lasencinashospital.com

VISTA DEL MAR HOSPITAL (O, 87 beds) 801 Seneca Street, Ventura, CA Zip 93001–1411; tel. 805/653–6434; Mayla Krebsbach, Chief Executive Officer
Web address: www.vistadelmarhospital.com

ILLINOIS: CHICAGO LAKESHORE HOSPITAL (O, 115 beds) 4840 North Marine Drive, Chicago, IL Zip 60640–4296; tel. 773/878–9700; Patrick Moallemian, Chief Executive Officer
Web address: www.chicagolakeshorehospital.com

TEXAS: DALLAS BEHAVIORAL HEALTHCARE HOSPITAL (O, 116 beds) 800 Kirnwood Drive, Desoto, TX Zip 75115–2000; tel. 855/982–0897; Selene Q. Hammon, Chief Executive Officer
Web address: www.dallasbehavioral.com

GEORGETOWN BEHAVIORAL HEALTH INSTITUTE (O, 50 beds) 3101 South Austin Avenue, Georgetown, TX Zip 78626–7541; tel. 512/819–1100; Joseph R. Rodriguez, Chief Executive Officer
Web address: www.georgetownbehavioral.co

Owned, leased, sponsored:	9 hospitals	882 beds
Contract–managed:	0 hospitals	0 beds
Totals:	9 hospitals	882 beds

★0284: SINAI HEALTH SYSTEM (NP)
1500 South California Avenue, Chicago, IL Zip 60608–1729; tel. 773/542–2000; Karen Teitelbaum, President and Chief Executive Officer
(Independent Hospital System)

For explanation of codes following names, see page B2.
★ Indicates Type III membership in the American Hospital Association.

ILLINOIS: HOLY CROSS HOSPITAL (O, 213 beds) 2701 West 68th Street, Chicago, IL Zip 60629–1882; tel. 773/884–9000; Lori Pacura, MSN, R.N., President
Web address: www.holycrosshospital.org

MOUNT SINAI HOSPITAL (O, 290 beds) California Avenue at 15th Street, Chicago, IL Zip 60608–1729; tel. 773/542–2000; Loren Chandler, President
Web address: www.sinai.org

SCHWAB REHABILITATION HOSPITAL (O, 102 beds) 1401 South California Avenue, Chicago, IL Zip 60608–1858; tel. 773/522–2010; Karen Teitelbaum, Chief Executive Officer
Web address: www.schwabrehab.org

Owned, leased, sponsored:	3 hospitals	605 beds
Contract–managed:	0 hospitals	0 beds
Totals:	3 hospitals	605 beds

5125: SISTERS OF CHARITY HEALTH SYSTEM (CC)
2475 East 22nd Street, Cleveland, OH Zip 44115–3221; tel. 216/363–2797; Terrence Kessler, President and Chief Executive Officer
(Moderately Centralized Health System)

OHIO: MERCY MEDICAL CENTER (O, 329 beds) 1320 Mercy Drive N.W., Canton, OH Zip 44708–2641; tel. 330/489–1000; Thomas E. Cecconi, President and Chief Executive Officer
Web address: www.cantonmercy.org

ST. VINCENT CHARITY MEDICAL CENTER (O, 214 beds) 2351 East 22nd Street, Cleveland, OH Zip 44115–3111; tel. 216/861–6200; David F. Perse, M.D., President and Chief Executive Officer
Web address: www.stvincentcharity.com/

Owned, leased, sponsored:	2 hospitals	543 beds
Contract–managed:	0 hospitals	0 beds
Totals:	2 hospitals	543 beds

5805: SISTERS OF MARY OF THE PRESENTATION HEALTH SYSTEM (CC)
1202 Page Drive S.W., Fargo, ND Zip 58103–2340, Mailing Address: P.O. Box 10007, Zip 58106–0007; tel. 701/237–9290; Aaron K. Alton, President and Chief Executive Officer
(Moderately Centralized Health System)

ILLINOIS: ST. MARGARET'S HOSPITAL (O, 54 beds) 600 East First Street, Spring Valley, IL Zip 61362–1512; tel. 815/664–5311; Tim Muntz, President and Chief Executive Officer
Web address: www.aboutsmh.org

NORTH DAKOTA: PRESENTATION MEDICAL CENTER (O, 25 beds) 213 Second Avenue N.E., Rolla, ND Zip 58367–7153, Mailing Address: P.O. Box 759, Zip 58367–0759; tel. 701/477–3161; Mark Kerr, Chief Executive Officer
Web address: www.pmc-rolla.com

ST. ALOISIUS MEDICAL CENTER (O, 117 beds) 325 East Brewster Street, Harvey, ND Zip 58341–1653; tel. 701/324–4651; Gregory LaFrancois, President and Chief Executive Officer
Web address: www.staloisius.com

ST. ANDREW'S HEALTH CENTER (O, 25 beds) 316 Ohmer Street, Bottineau, ND Zip 58318–1045; tel. 701/228–9300; Jodi Atkinson, President and Chief Executive Officer
Web address: www.standrewshealth.com

Owned, leased, sponsored:	4 hospitals	221 beds
Contract–managed:	0 hospitals	0 beds
Totals:	4 hospitals	221 beds

● **5955: SISTERS OF SAINT FRANCIS** (CC)
2500 Grant Boulevard, Syracuse, NY Zip 13208–1782; tel. 315/634–7000; Sister Geraldine Ching, Assistant General Minister
(Independent Hospital System)

NEW YORK: ST. ELIZABETH MEDICAL CENTER (S, 181 beds) 2209 Genesee Street, Utica, NY Zip 13501–5999; tel. 315/798–8100; Scott H. Perra, FACHE, Chief Executive Officer
Web address: www.stemc.org

Owned, leased, sponsored:	1 hospital	181 beds
Contract–managed:	0 hospitals	0 beds
Totals:	1 hospital	181 beds

0997: SKAGIT REGIONAL HEALTH (NP)
1415 East Kincaid Street, Mount Vernon, WA Zip 98274–4126; tel. 360/424–4111; Gregg Agustin Davidson, FACHE, President and Chief Executive Officer

WASHINGTON: CASCADE VALLEY HOSPITAL AND CLINICS (L, 48 beds) 330 South Stillaguamish Avenue, Arlington, WA Zip 98223–1642; tel. 360/435–2133; Michael Liepman, Chief Executive Officer
Web address: www.cascadevalley.org

SKAGIT REGIONAL HEALTH (O, 137 beds) 1415 East Kincaid, Mount Vernon, WA Zip 98274–4126, Mailing Address: P.O. Box 1376, Zip 98273–1376; tel. 360/424–4111; Michael T. Liepman, Chief Executive Officer
Web address: www.skagitregionalhealth.org

Owned, leased, sponsored:	2 hospitals	185 beds
Contract–managed:	0 hospitals	0 beds
Totals:	2 hospitals	185 beds

★**0253: SOUTHEAST GEORGIA HEALTH SYSTEM** (NP)
2415 Parkwood Drive, Brunswick, GA Zip 31520–4722, Mailing Address: P.O. Box 1518, Zip 31521–1518; tel. 912/466–7000; Michael D. Scherneck, President and Chief Executive Officer

GEORGIA: SOUTHEAST GEORGIA HEALTH SYSTEM BRUNSWICK CAMPUS (O, 532 beds) 2415 Parkwood Drive, Brunswick, GA Zip 31520–4722, Mailing Address: P.O. Box 1518, Zip 31521–1518; tel. 912/466–7000; Michael D. Scherneck, President and Chief Executive Officer
Web address: www.sghs.org

SOUTHEAST GEORGIA HEALTH SYSTEM CAMDEN CAMPUS (O, 40 beds) 2000 Dan Proctor Drive, Saint Marys, GA Zip 31558–3810; tel. 912/576–6200; Howard W. Sepp, Jr., Vice President and Administrator
Web address: www.sghs.org

Owned, leased, sponsored:	2 hospitals	572 beds
Contract–managed:	0 hospitals	0 beds
Totals:	2 hospitals	572 beds

0628: SOUTHEASTHEALTH (NP)
1701 Lacey Street, Cape Girardeau, MO Zip 63701–5230; tel. 573/334–4822; Kenneth Bateman, CPA, Chief Executive Officer
(Independent Hospital System)

MISSOURI: SOUTHEAST HEALTH CENTER OF RIPLEY COUNTY (L, 10 beds) 109 Plum Street, Doniphan, MO Zip 63935–1299; tel. 573/996–2141; Cheryl Barton, R.N., Chief Executive Officer
Web address: www.sehealth.org/southeast–health–center–of–ripley–county/SoutheastHEALTH.aspx?nd=41

SOUTHEAST HEALTH CENTER OF STODDARD COUNTY (L, 16 beds) 1200 North One Mile Road, Dexter, MO Zip 63841–1000; tel. 573/624–5566; Sue Ann Williams, Chief Executive Officer
Web address: www.sehealth.org

SOUTHEAST HOSPITAL (O, 199 beds) 1701 Lacey Street, Cape Girardeau, MO Zip 63701–5230; tel. 573/334–4822; Kenneth Bateman, CPA, Chief Executive Officer
Web address: www.sehealth.org/

Owned, leased, sponsored:	3 hospitals	225 beds
Contract–managed:	0 hospitals	0 beds
Totals:	3 hospitals	225 beds

For explanation of codes following names, see page B2.
★ Indicates Type III membership in the American Hospital Association.
● Single hospital health care system

Section B

4175: SOUTHERN ILLINOIS HOSPITAL SERVICES (NP)
1239 East Main Street, Carbondale, IL Zip 62901–3114, Mailing Address: P.O. Box 3988, Zip 62902–3988; tel. 618/457–5200; Rex P. Budde, President and Chief Executive Officer
(Independent Hospital System)

ILLINOIS: HERRIN HOSPITAL (O, 114 beds) 201 South 14th Street, Herrin, IL Zip 62948–3631; tel. 618/942–2171; Terence Farrell, Vice President and Administrator
Web address: www.sih.net

MEMORIAL HOSPITAL OF CARBONDALE (O, 159 beds) 405 West Jackson Street, Carbondale, IL Zip 62901–1467, Mailing Address: P.O. Box 10000, Zip 62902–9000; tel. 618/549–0721; Bart Millstead, Administrator
Web address: www.sih.net

ST. JOSEPH MEMORIAL HOSPITAL (O, 25 beds) 2 South Hospital Drive, Murphysboro, IL Zip 62966–3333; tel. 618/684–3156; Susan Odle, Administrator
Web address: www.sih.net

Owned, leased, sponsored:	3 hospitals	298 beds
Contract–managed:	0 hospitals	0 beds
Totals:	3 hospitals	298 beds

0346: SOUTHERN PLAINS MEDICAL GROUP (IO)
4323 N.W. 63rd Street Suite 232, Oklahoma City, OK Zip 73116–1546; tel. 405/753–6770; Margie Homer, President

OKLAHOMA: PHYSICIANS' HOSPITAL IN ANADARKO (O, 25 beds) 1002 Central Boulevard East, Anadarko, OK Zip 73005–4496; tel. 405/247–2551; Travis A. Villani, FACHE, Chief Executive Officer and Administrator
Web address: www.anadarkohospital.com

STROUD REGIONAL MEDICAL CENTER (O, 25 beds) Highway 66 West, Stroud, OK Zip 74079, Mailing Address: P.O. Box 530, Zip 74079–0530; tel. 918/968–3571; Larry Troxell, Administrator
Web address: www.stroudhospital.com/

Owned, leased, sponsored:	2 hospitals	50 beds
Contract–managed:	0 hospitals	0 beds
Totals:	2 hospitals	50 beds

0652: SOUTHWEST HEALTH SYSTEMS (NP)
215 Marion Avenue, Mccomb, MS Zip 39648–2705, Mailing Address: P.O. Box 1307, Zip 39649–1307; tel. 601/249–5500; Norman M. Price, FACHE, Chief Executive Officer and Administrator
(Independent Hospital System)

MISSISSIPPI: LAWRENCE COUNTY HOSPITAL (O, 25 beds) Highway 84 East, Monticello, MS Zip 39654–0788, Mailing Address: P.O. Box 788, Zip 39654–0788; tel. 601/587–4051; Semmes Ross, Jr., Administrator
Web address: www.smrmc.com

SOUTHWEST MISSISSIPPI REGIONAL MEDICAL CENTER (O, 143 beds) 215 Marion Avenue, McComb, MS Zip 39648–2705, Mailing Address: P.O. Box 1307, Zip 39649–1307; tel. 601/249–5500; Norman M. Price, FACHE, Chief Executive Officer
Web address: www.smrmc.com

Owned, leased, sponsored:	2 hospitals	168 beds
Contract–managed:	0 hospitals	0 beds
Totals:	2 hospitals	168 beds

● 0164: SOUTHWEST HEALTHCARE SYSTEM (IO)
4400 North Scottsdale Road, Suite 9347, Scottsdale, AZ Zip 85251–3331; tel. 480/348–9800; Paul R. Tuft, President
(Independent Hospital System)

TEXAS: GULF COAST MEDICAL CENTER (O, 129 beds) 10141 Highway 59, Wharton, TX Zip 77488–3004; tel. 979/532–2500; Joy Janak, Interim Chief Executive Officer
Web address: www.gulfcoastmedical.com

Owned, leased, sponsored:	1 hospital	129 beds
Contract–managed:	0 hospitals	0 beds
Totals:	1 hospital	129 beds

★1245: SPARROW HEALTH SYSTEM (NP)
1215 East Michigan Avenue, Lansing, MI Zip 48912–1811; tel. 517/364–1000; Dennis A. Swan, JD, FACHE, President and Chief Executive Officer
(Centralized Physician/Insurance Health System)

MICHIGAN: SPARROW CARSON HOSPITAL (O, 62 beds) 406 East Elm Street, Carson City, MI Zip 48811–9693, Mailing Address: P.O. Box 879, Zip 48811–0879; tel. 989/584–3131; Matthew J. Thompson, Chief Executive Officer
Web address: www.carsoncityhospital.com

SPARROW CLINTON HOSPITAL (O, 25 beds) 805 South Oakland Street, Saint Johns, MI Zip 48879–2253; tel. 989/227–3400; Edward Bruun, President and Chief Executive Officer
Web address: www.sparrowclinton.org

SPARROW HOSPITAL (O, 666 beds) 1215 East Michigan Avenue, Lansing, MI Zip 48912–1811; tel. 517/364–1000; Dennis A. Swan, JD, FACHE, President and Chief Executive Officer
Web address: www.sparrow.org

SPARROW IONIA HOSPITAL (O, 22 beds) 3565 South State Road, Ionia, MI Zip 48846–1870, Mailing Address: Box 1001, Zip 48846–6001; tel. 616/523–1400; William Roeser, President and Chief Executive Officer
Web address: www.sparrow.org/sparrowionia

SPARROW SPECIALTY HOSPITAL (O, 30 beds) 8 West Sparrow Hospital Tower, Lansing, MI Zip 48912; tel. 517/364–4840; Lou Little, President and Chief Executive Officer
Web address: www.sparrowspecialty.org

Owned, leased, sponsored:	5 hospitals	805 beds
Contract–managed:	0 hospitals	0 beds
Totals:	5 hospitals	805 beds

★4195: SPARTANBURG REGIONAL HEALTHCARE SYSTEM (NP)
101 East Wood Street, Spartanburg, SC Zip 29303–3040; tel. 864/560–6000; Bruce Holstien, President and Chief Executive Officer
(Centralized Health System)

SOUTH CAROLINA: PELHAM MEDICAL CENTER (O, 46 beds) 250 Westmoreland Road, Greer, SC Zip 29651–9013; tel. 864/530–6000; Anthony Kouskolekas, FACHE, President
Web address: www.pelhammedicalcenter.com

SPARTANBURG HOSPITAL FOR RESTORATIVE CARE (O, 116 beds) 389 Serpentine Drive, Spartanburg, SC Zip 29303–3026; tel. 864/560–3280; Anita M. Butler, Chief Executive Officer
Web address: www.srhs.com

SPARTANBURG MEDICAL CENTER (O, 514 beds) 101 East Wood Street, Spartanburg, SC Zip 29303–3040; tel. 864/560–6000; J. Philip Feisal, President and Chief Executive Officer
Web address: www.spartanburgregional.com

UNION MEDICAL CENTER (O, 50 beds) 322 West South Street, Union, SC Zip 29379–2857, Mailing Address: P.O. Box 789, Zip 29379–0789; tel. 864/301–2000; Paul R. Newhouse, President
Web address: www.https://www.spartanburgregional. com/locations/union–medical–center/

Owned, leased, sponsored:	4 hospitals	726 beds
Contract–managed:	0 hospitals	0 beds
Totals:	4 hospitals	726 beds

★0177: SPECTRUM HEALTH (NP)
100 Michigan Street N.E., Grand Rapids, MI Zip 49503–2551; tel. 616/391–1774; Richard C. Breon, President and Chief Executive Officer
(Moderately Centralized Health System)

For explanation of codes following names, see page B2.
★ Indicates Type III membership in the American Hospital Association.
● Single hospital health care system

Section B

MICHIGAN: SPECTRUM HEALTH – BUTTERWORTH HOSPITAL (O, 1126 beds) 100 Michigan Street N.E., Grand Rapids, MI Zip 49503–2560; tel. 616/774–7444; Christina Freese–Decker, FACHE, President, Spectrum Health Hospital Group
Web address: www.spectrumhealth.org

SPECTRUM HEALTH BIG RAPIDS HOSPITAL (O, 61 beds) 605 Oak Street, Big Rapids, MI Zip 49307–2099; tel. 231/796–8691; Mary Kay VanDriel, President
Web address: www.mcmcbr.com

SPECTRUM HEALTH GERBER MEMORIAL (O, 25 beds) 212 South Sullivan Avenue, Fremont, MI Zip 49412–1548; tel. 231/924–3300; Randall Stasik, President
Web address: www.spectrumhealth.org

SPECTRUM HEALTH LUDINGTON HOSPITAL (O, 44 beds) One Atkinson Drive, Ludington, MI Zip 49431–1906; tel. 231/843–2591; Randall Stasik, Interim President
Web address: www.mmcwm.com

SPECTRUM HEALTH PENNOCK (O, 39 beds) 1009 West Green Street, Hastings, MI Zip 49058–1710; tel. 269/945–3451; Sheryl Lewis Blake, FACHE, President
Web address: www.spectrumhealth.org

SPECTRUM HEALTH REED CITY HOSPITAL (O, 75 beds) 300 North Patterson Road, Reed City, MI Zip 49677–8041, Mailing Address: P.O. Box 75, Zip 49677–0075; tel. 231/832–3271; Mary Kay VanDriel, President
Web address: www.spectrumhealth.org/reedcity

SPECTRUM HEALTH SPECIAL CARE HOSPITAL (O, 40 beds) 750 Fuller Avenue N.E., Grand Rapids, MI Zip 49503–1995; tel. 616/486–3000; Chad Tuttle, President
Web address: www.spectrum–health.org

SPECTRUM HEALTH UNITED HOSPITAL (O, 116 beds) 615 South Bower Street, Greenville, MI Zip 48838–2614; tel. 616/754–4691; Brian Brasser, President
Web address: www.spectrumhealth.org/

SPECTRUM HEALTH ZEELAND COMMUNITY HOSPITAL (O, 50 beds) 8333 Felch Street, Zeeland, MI Zip 49464–2608; tel. 616/772–4644; Ron Lewis, President
Web address: www.spectrumhealth.org/zeeland

Owned, leased, sponsored:	9 hospitals	1576 beds
Contract–managed:	0 hospitals	0 beds
Totals:	9 hospitals	1576 beds

★5455: SSM HEALTH (CC)
10101 Woodfield Lane, Saint Louis, MO Zip 63132–2937; tel. 314/994–7800; William P. Thompson, President and Chief Executive Officer
(Decentralized Health System)

ILLINOIS: CLAY COUNTY HOSPITAL (C, 18 beds) 911 Stacy Burk Drive, Flora, IL Zip 62839–3241, Mailing Address: P.O. Box 280, Zip 62839–0280; tel. 618/662–2131; Amanda J. Basso, President
Web address: www.claycountyhospital.org

GOOD SAMARITAN REGIONAL HEALTH CENTER (O, 134 beds) 1 Good Samaritan Way, Mount Vernon, IL Zip 62864–2402; tel. 618/242–4600; Michael D. Warren, President
Web address: www.smgsi.com

SSM HEALTH ST. MARY'S HOSPITAL CENTRALIA (O, 113 beds) 400 North Pleasant Avenue, Centralia, IL Zip 62801–3056; tel. 618/436–8000; John R. Sigsbury, President
Web address: www.ssmhealthillinois.com

MISSOURI: SSM CARDINAL GLENNON CHILDREN'S MEDICAL CENTER (O, 176 beds) 1465 South Grand Boulevard, Saint Louis, MO Zip 63104–1095; tel. 314/577–5600; Steven Burghart, President
Web address: www.cardinalglennon.com

SSM DEPAUL HEALTH CENTER (O, 477 beds) 12303 De Paul Drive, Bridgeton, MO Zip 63044–2512; tel. 314/344–6000; Sean Hogan, President
Web address: www.ssmdepaul.com

SSM HEALTH SAINT LOUIS UNIVERSITY HOSPITAL (O, 352 beds) 3635 Vista at Grand Boulevard, Saint Louis, MO Zip 63110–0250, Mailing Address: P.O. Box 15250, Zip 63110–0250; tel. 314/577–8000; Kathleen R. Becker, M.P.H., JD, President
Web address: www.sluhospital.com

SSM HEALTH ST. FRANCIS HOSPITAL – MARYVILLE (O, 56 beds) 2016 South Main Street, Maryville, MO Zip 64468–2655; tel. 660/562–2600; Michael A. Baumgartner, President
Web address: www.ssmhealthstfrancis.com

SSM HEALTH ST. JOSEPH HOSPITAL – LAKE SAINT LOUIS (O, 119 beds) 100 Medical Plaza, Lake Saint Louis, MO Zip 63367–1366; tel. 636/625–5200; Lisle Wescott, President
Web address: www.ssmstjoseph.com

SSM HEALTH ST. MARY'S HOSPITAL – AUDRAIN (O, 51 beds) 620 East Monroe Street, Mexico, MO Zip 65265–2919; tel. 573/582–5000; Donna K. Jacobs, FACHE, President
Web address: www.ssmhealthmidmo.com

SSM HEALTH ST. MARY'S HOSPITAL – JEFFERSON CITY (O, 154 beds) 2505 Mission Drive, Jefferson City, MO Zip 65109; tel. 573/681–3000; R. Brent VanConia, President
Web address: www.lethealingbegin.com

SSM ST. CLARE HOSPITAL (O, 184 beds) 1015 Bowles Avenue, Fenton, MO Zip 63026–2394; tel. 636/496–2000; Ellis Hawkins, President
Web address: www.ssmstclare.com

SSM ST. JOSEPH HEALTH CENTER (O, 331 beds) 300 First Capitol Drive, Saint Charles, MO Zip 63301–2844; tel. 636/947–5000; Michael E. Bowers, President
Web address: www.ssmstjoseph.com

SSM ST. MARY'S HEALTH CENTER (O, 381 beds) 6420 Clayton Road, Saint Louis, MO Zip 63117–1811; tel. 314/768–8000; Travis Capers, FACHE, President
Web address: www.stmarys–stlouis.com

OKLAHOMA: ST. ANTHONY HOSPITAL (O, 579 beds) 1000 North Lee Street, Oklahoma City, OK Zip 73102–1080, Mailing Address: P.O. Box 205, Zip 73101–0205; tel. 405/272–7000; Tammy Powell, FACHE, M.P.H., President
Web address: www.saintsok.com

ST. ANTHONY SHAWNEE HOSPITAL (O, 76 beds) 1102 West Macarthur ST, Shawnee, OK Zip 74804–1744, Mailing Address: 1102 West MacArthur Street, Zip 74804–1744; tel. 405/273–2270; Charles E. Skillings, President and Chief Executive Officer
Web address: www.stanthonyshawnee.com

WISCONSIN: ST. CLARE HOSPITAL (O, 60 beds) 707 14th Street, Baraboo, WI Zip 53913–1597; tel. 608/356–1400; Laura Jelle, President
Web address: www.stclare.com

ST. MARY'S HOSPITAL (O, 362 beds) 700 South Park Street, Madison, WI Zip 53715–1830; tel. 608/251–6100; Jon Rozenfeld, President
Web address: www.stmarysmadison.com

ST. MARY'S JANESVILLE HOSPITAL (O, 50 beds) 3400 East Racine Steeet, Janesville, WI Zip 53546–2344; tel. 608/373–8000; Kerry Swanson, President
Web address: www.stmarysjanesville.com

Owned, leased, sponsored:	17 hospitals	3655 beds
Contract–managed:	1 hospital	18 beds
Totals:	18 hospitals	3673 beds

★0250: ST. CHARLES HEALTH SYSTEM, INC. (NP)
2500 N.E. Neff Road, Bend, OR Zip 97701–6015; tel. 541/382–4321; Joseph Sluka, President and Chief Executive Officer
(Centralized Physician/Insurance Health System)

OREGON: ST. CHARLES BEND (O, 261 beds) 2500 N.E. Neff Road, Bend, OR Zip 97701–6015; tel. 541/382–4321; Joseph Sluka, Chief Executive Officer
Web address: www.stcharleshealthcare.org

ST. CHARLES MADRAS (O, 22 beds) 470 N.E. A Street, Madras, OR Zip 97741–1844; tel. 541/475–3882; John Bishop, President
Web address: www.mvhd.org

For explanation of codes following names, see page B2.
★ Indicates Type III membership in the American Hospital Association.

Section B

ST. CHARLES PRINEVILLE (O, 16 beds) 1201 N.E. Elm Street, Prineville, OR Zip 97754–1206; tel. 541/447–6254; John Bishop, President
Web address: www.stcharleshealthcare.org

ST. CHARLES REDMOND (O, 48 beds) 1253 N.W. Canal Boulevard, Redmond, OR Zip 97756–1395; tel. 541/548–8131; Joseph Sluka, Chief Executive Officer
Web address: www.stcharleshealthcare.org

Owned, leased, sponsored:	4 hospitals	347 beds
Contract–managed:	0 hospitals	0 beds
Totals:	4 hospitals	347 beds

0618: ST. ELIZABETH HEALTHCARE (NP)
1 Medical Village Drive, Edgewood, KY Zip 41017–3403; tel. 859/301–2000; Garren Colvin, Chief Executive Officer
(Independent Hospital System)

KENTUCKY: ST. ELIZABETH EDGEWOOD (O, 508 beds) 1 Medical Village Drive, Edgewood, KY Zip 41017–3403; tel. 859/301–2000; Garren Colvin, Chief Executive Officer
Web address: www.stelizabeth.com

ST. ELIZABETH FLORENCE (O, 169 beds) 4900 Houston Road, Florence, KY Zip 41042–4824; tel. 859/212–5200; Garren Colvin, Chief Executive Officer
Web address: www.stelizabeth.com

ST. ELIZABETH FORT THOMAS (O, 171 beds) 85 North Grand Avenue, Fort Thomas, KY Zip 41075–1796; tel. 859/572–3100; Garren Colvin, Chief Executive Officer
Web address: www.stelizabeth.com

ST. ELIZABETH GRANT (O, 16 beds) 238 Barnes Road, Williamstown, KY Zip 41097–9482; tel. 859/824–8240; Garren Colvin, Chief Executive Officer
Web address: www.stelizabeth.com

Owned, leased, sponsored:	4 hospitals	864 beds
Contract–managed:	0 hospitals	0 beds
Totals:	4 hospitals	864 beds

0928: ST. LAWRENCE HEALTH SYSTEM (NP)
50 Leroy Street, Potsdam, NY Zip 13676–1799; tel. 315/265–3300; David B. Acker, FACHE, President and CEO
(Independent Hospital System)

NEW YORK: CANTON–POTSDAM HOSPITAL (O, 87 beds) 50 Leroy Street, Potsdam, NY Zip 13676–1799; tel. 315/265–3300; David B. Acker, FACHE, President and CEO
Web address: www.cphospital.org

GOUVERNEUR HOSPITAL (O, 25 beds) 77 West Barney Street, Gouverneur, NY Zip 13642–1040; tel. 315/287–1000; Marlinda L. LaValley, Chief Executive Officer
Web address: www.gvnrhospital.org

Owned, leased, sponsored:	2 hospitals	112 beds
Contract–managed:	0 hospitals	0 beds
Totals:	2 hospitals	112 beds

★**0356: ST. LUKE'S HEALTH SYSTEM** (NP)
420 West Idaho Street, Boise, ID Zip 83702–6041; tel. 208/381–4200; David C. Pate, M.D., JD, President and Chief Executive Officer
(Moderately Centralized Health System)

IDAHO: NORTH CANYON MEDICAL CENTER (C, 18 beds) 267 North Canyon Drive, Gooding, ID Zip 83330–5500; tel. 208/934–4433; Tim Powers, Chief Executive Officer
Web address: www.ncm–c.org

ST. LUKE'S ELMORE (L, 63 beds) 895 North Sixth East Street, Mountain Home, ID Zip 83647–2207, Mailing Address: P.O. Box 1270, Zip 83647–1270; tel. 208/587–8401; Michael Blauer, Administrator
Web address: www.stlukesonline.org/elmore/

ST. LUKE'S JEROME (O, 25 beds) 709 North Lincoln Street, Jerome, ID Zip 83338–1851, Mailing Address: 709 North Lincoln Avenue, Zip 83338–1851; tel. 208/814–9500; Chris Roth, Chief Executive Officer East Region – Interim
Web address: www.stlukesonline.org/jerome/

ST. LUKE'S MAGIC VALLEY MEDICAL CENTER (O, 224 beds) 801 Pole Line Road West, Twin Falls, ID Zip 83301–5810, Mailing Address: P.O. Box 409, Zip 83303–0409; tel. 208/814–1000; Chris Roth, Chief Executive Officer East Region – Interim
Web address: www.stlukesonline.org

ST. LUKE'S MCCALL (L, 15 beds) 1000 State Street, McCall, ID Zip 83638–3704; tel. 208/634–2221; Sean McCallister, Administrator
Web address: www.https://www.stlukesonline.org/communities–and–locations/facilities/hospitals–and–medical–centers/st–lukes–mccall–medical–center

ST. LUKE'S REGIONAL MEDICAL CENTER (O, 604 beds) 190 East Bannock Street, Boise, ID Zip 83712–6241; tel. 208/381–2222; Kathy D. Moore, Chief Executive Officer
Web address: www.stlukesonline.org/boise

ST. LUKE'S REHABILITATION HOSPITAL (O, 31 beds) 600 North Robbins Road, Boise, ID Zip 83702–4565, Mailing Address: P.O. Box 1100, Zip 83701–1100; tel. 208/489–4444; Nolan Hoffer, Senior Director
Web address: www.idahoelksrehab.org

ST. LUKE'S WOOD RIVER MEDICAL CENTER (O, 25 beds) 100 Hospital Drive, Ketchum, ID Zip 83340, Mailing Address: P.O. Box 100, Zip 83340–0100; tel. 208/727–8800; Chris Roth, Chief Executive Officer East Region–Interim
Web address: www.slrmc.org

WEISER MEMORIAL HOSPITAL (C, 25 beds) 645 East Fifth Street, Weiser, ID Zip 83672–2202; tel. 208/549–0370; Steven D. Hale, Chief Executive Officer
Web address: www.weisermemorialhospital.org

Owned, leased, sponsored:	7 hospitals	987 beds
Contract–managed:	2 hospitals	43 beds
Totals:	9 hospitals	1030 beds

0862: ST. LUKE'S UNIVERSITY HEALTH NETWORK (NP)
801 Ostrum Street, Bethlehem, PA Zip 18015–1000; tel. 610/954–4000; Richard A. Anderson, President and Chief Executive Officer
(Moderately Centralized Health System)

NEW JERSEY: ST. LUKE'S HOSPITAL – WARREN CAMPUS (O, 94 beds) 185 Roseberry Street, Phillipsburg, NJ Zip 08865–1690; tel. 908/859–6700; Scott R. Wolfe, CPA, President
Web address: www.slhn.org

PENNSYLVANIA: ST. LUKE'S HOSPITAL – ANDERSON CAMPUS (O, 108 beds) 1872 Riverside Circle, Easton, PA Zip 18045–5669; tel. 484/503–3000; Edward Nawrocki, President
Web address: www.mystlukesonline.org

ST. LUKE'S HOSPITAL – MINERS CAMPUS (O, 92 beds) 360 West Ruddle Street, Coaldale, PA Zip 18218–1027; tel. 570/645–2131; William E. Moyer, President
Web address: www.slhn.org

ST. LUKE'S HOSPITAL – QUAKERTOWN CAMPUS (O, 57 beds) 1021 Park Avenue, Quakertown, PA Zip 18951–1573; tel. 215/538–4500; Edward Nawrocki, President
Web address: www.slhn.org

ST. LUKE'S UNIVERSITY HOSPITAL – BETHLEHEM CAMPUS (O, 540 beds) 801 Ostrum Street, Bethlehem, PA Zip 18015–1065; tel. 484/526–4000; Carol Kuplen, R.N., MSN, President and Chief Executive Officer
Web address: www.slhn–lehighvalley.org

Owned, leased, sponsored:	5 hospitals	891 beds
Contract–managed:	0 hospitals	0 beds
Totals:	5 hospitals	891 beds

For explanation of codes following names, see page B2.
★ Indicates Type III membership in the American Hospital Association.

★0156: **STANFORD HEALTH CARE** (NP)
300 Pasteur Drive, Palo Alto, CA Zip 94304–2299;
tel. 650/723–4000; David Entwistle, President and Chief Executive
Officer
(Moderately Centralized Health System)

CALIFORNIA: STANFORD HEALTH CARE (O, 491 beds) 300 Pasteur Drive,
Suite H3200, Palo Alto, CA Zip 94304–2203; tel. 650/723–4000;
Mariann Byerwalter, Interim President and Chief Executive Officer
Web address: www.stanfordhealthcare.org

STANFORD HEALTH CARE – VALLEYCARE (O, 207 beds) 5555 West Las
Positas Boulevard, Pleasanton, CA Zip 94588–4000; tel. 925/847–3000;
Scott Gregerson, President and Chief Executive Officer
Web address: www.valleycare.com

Owned, leased, sponsored:	2 hospitals	698 beds
Contract–managed:	0 hospitals	0 beds
Totals:	2 hospitals	698 beds

0141: **STEWARD HEALTH CARE SYSTEM, LLC** (IO)
500 Boylston Street, 5th Floor, Boston, MA Zip 02116–3740;
tel. 617/419–4700; Ralph de la Torre, M.D., Chairman and Chief
Executive Officer
(Independent Hospital System)

MASSACHUSETTS: CARNEY HOSPITAL (O, 120 beds) 2100 Dorchester
Avenue, Boston, MA Zip 02124–5615; tel. 617/296–4000; Walter J.
Ramos, President and Chief Executive Officer
Web address: www.carneyhospital.org

GOOD SAMARITAN MEDICAL CENTER (O, 189 beds) 235 North Pearl Street,
Brockton, MA Zip 02301–1794; tel. 508/427–3000; John A. Jurczyk,
FACHE, Interim President
Web address: www.stewardhealth.org/Good–Samaritan

HOLY FAMILY HOSPITAL (O, 329 beds) 70 East Street, Methuen, MA
Zip 01844–4597; tel. 978/687–0151; Joseph Roach, Chief Executive Officer
Web address: www.stewardhealth.org/Holy–Family–Hospital

MORTON HOSPITAL AND MEDICAL CENTER (O, 154 beds) 88 Washington
Street, Taunton, MA Zip 02780–2465; tel. 508/828–7000; Deborah Bitsoli,
CPA, President
Web address: www.mortonhospital.org

NASHOBA VALLEY MEDICAL CENTER (O, 48 beds) 200 Groton Road, Ayer,
MA Zip 01432–3300; tel. 978/784–9000; Salvatore Perla, President
Web address: www.nashobamed.com

NEW ENGLAND SINAI HOSPITAL AND REHABILITATION CENTER (O, 212 beds)
150 York Street, Stoughton, MA Zip 02072–1881; tel. 781/344–0600;
Judith C. Waterston, R.N., MS, President and Chief Executive Officer
Web address: www.newenglandsinai.org

NORWOOD HOSPITAL (O, 188 beds) 800 Washington Street, Norwood, MA
Zip 02062–3487; tel. 781/769–4000; Kimberly S. Bassett, R.N., Interim
President
Web address: www.stewardhealth.org/Norwood–Hospital

SAINT ANNE'S HOSPITAL (O, 160 beds) 795 Middle Street, Fall River, MA
Zip 02721–1798; tel. 508/674–5741; Craig A. Jesiolowski, FACHE,
President
Web address: www.saintanneshospital.org

ST. ELIZABETH'S MEDICAL CENTER (O, 338 beds) 736 Cambridge Street,
Brighton, MA Zip 02135–2997; tel. 617/789–3000; Beth Hughes, Chief
Executive Officer
Web address: www.stewardhealth.org/St_Elizabeths

Owned, leased, sponsored:	9 hospitals	1738 beds
Contract–managed:	0 hospitals	0 beds
Totals:	9 hospitals	1738 beds

0858: **STRATEGIC BEHAVIORAL HEALTH, LLC** (IO)
8295 Tournament Drive, Suite 201, Memphis, TN Zip 38125–8913;
tel. 901/969–3100; Jim Shaheen, President

COLORADO: PEAK VIEW BEHAVIORAL HEALTH (O, 92 beds) 7353 Sisters
Grove, Colorado Springs, CO Zip 80923–2615; tel. 719/444–8484; Lana
Currance, R.N., MSN, Chief Executive Officer
Web address: www.strategicbh.com/peakview.html

NEVADA: MONTEVISTA HOSPITAL (O, 162 beds) 5900 West Rochelle Avenue,
Las Vegas, NV Zip 89103–3327; tel. 702/364–1111; Richard Failla, Chief
Executive Officer
Web address: www.montevistahospital.com

RED ROCK BEHAVIORAL HOSPITAL (O, 21 beds) 5975 West Twain Avenue,
Las Vegas, NV Zip 89103–1237; tel. 702/214–8099; Richard Failla, Chief
Executive Officer
Web address: www.redrockhospital.com

NEW MEXICO: PEAK BEHAVIORAL HEALTH SERVICES (O, 120 beds) 5065
McNutt Road, Santa Teresa, NM Zip 88008–9442; tel. 575/589–3000;
Jose Santos–Roheu, Interim Chief Executive Officer
Web address: www.peakbehavioral.com/

NORTH CAROLINA: STRATEGIC BEHAVIORAL HEALTH – CHARLOTTE (O, 60
beds) 1715 Sharon Road West, Charlotte, NC Zip 28210–5663;
tel. 704/944–0650; Mercy Estevez, Chief Executive Officer
Web address: www.sbccharlotte.com/

STRATEGIC BEHAVIORAL HEALTH – RALEIGH (O, 50 beds) 3200 Waterfield
Drive, Garner, NC Zip 27529–7727; tel. 919/800–4400; Matt Doyle, Chief
Executive Officer
Web address: www.sbcraleigh.com/

STRATEGIC BEHAVIORAL HEALTH – WILMINGTON (O, 92 beds) 2050
Mercantile Drive, Leland, NC Zip 28451–4053; tel. 910/371–2500; Daniel
Kern, Chief Executive Officer
Web address: www.sbcwilmington.com/

TEXAS: ROCK PRAIRIE BEHAVIORAL HEALTH (O, 72 beds) 3550 Normand
Drive, College Station, TX Zip 77845–6399; tel. 979/703–8848; Jackie
St. Germain, Chief Executive Officer

Owned, leased, sponsored:	8 hospitals	669 beds
Contract–managed:	0 hospitals	0 beds
Totals:	8 hospitals	669 beds

0517: **SUCCESS HEALTHCARE** (IO)
999 Yamato Road, 3rd Floor, Boca Raton, FL Zip 33431–4477;
tel. 561/869–6300; Peter R. Baronoff, President and Chief Executive
Officer
(Independent Hospital System)

CALIFORNIA: SILVER LAKE MEDICAL CENTER (O, 150 beds) 1711 West
Temple Street, Los Angeles, CA Zip 90026–5421; tel. 213/989–6100;
Brent A. Cope, Chief Executive Officer
Web address: www.silverlakemc.com

MISSOURI: ST. ALEXIUS HOSPITAL – BROADWAY CAMPUS (O, 189 beds)
3933 South Broadway, Saint Louis, MO Zip 63118–4601;
tel. 314/865–7000; Michael J. Motte, Chief Executive Officer
Web address: www.stalexiushospital.com

Owned, leased, sponsored:	2 hospitals	339 beds
Contract–managed:	0 hospitals	0 beds
Totals:	2 hospitals	339 beds

0399: **SUMMA HEALTH** (NP)
1077 Gorge Boulevard, Akron, OH Zip 44310; tel. 330/375–3000;
Thomas Malone, M.D., President and Chief Executive Officer
(Centralized Physician/Insurance Health System)

OHIO: SUMMA HEALTH SYSTEM (O, 717 beds) 525 East Market Street,
Akron, OH Zip 44304–1619; tel. 330/375–3000; Thomas Malone, M.D.,
President and Chief Executive Officer
Web address: www.summahealth.org

SUMMA REHAB HOSPITAL (O, 60 beds) 29 North Adams Street, Akron, OH
Zip 44304–1641; tel. 330/572–7300; Cheryl Henthorn, Chief Executive
Officer
Web address: www.summarehabhospital.com/

For explanation of codes following names, see page B2.
★ Indicates Type III membership in the American Hospital Association.

SUMMA WESTERN RESERVE HOSPITAL (O, 72 beds) 1900 23rd Street, Cuyahoga Falls, OH Zip 44223–1499; tel. 330/971–7000; Robert Kent, D.O., President and Chief Executive Officer
Web address: www.westernreservehospital.org

Owned, leased, sponsored:	3 hospitals	849 beds
Contract–managed:	0 hospitals	0 beds
Totals:	3 hospitals	849 beds

★0189: SUMMIT HEALTH (NP)
112 North Seventh Street, Chambersburg, PA Zip 17201–1720; tel. 717/267–7138; Patrick W. O'Donnell, CPA, President and Chief Executive Officer
(Independent Hospital System)

PENNSYLVANIA: CHAMBERSBURG HOSPITAL (O, 248 beds) 112 North Seventh Street, Chambersburg, PA Zip 17201–1720; tel. 717/267–3000; Patrick W. O'Donnell, CPA, President and Chief Executive Officer
Web address: www.summithealth.org

WAYNESBORO HOSPITAL (O, 56 beds) 501 East Main Street, Waynesboro, PA Zip 17268–2394; tel. 717/765–4000; Melissa Dubrow, Chief Operating Officer
Web address: www.summithealth.org

Owned, leased, sponsored:	2 hospitals	304 beds
Contract–managed:	0 hospitals	0 beds
Totals:	2 hospitals	304 beds

0237: SUNLINK HEALTH SYSTEMS (IO)
900 Circle 75 Parkway, Suite 1120, Atlanta, GA Zip 30339–3005; tel. 770/933–7000; Robert M. Thornton, Jr., Chief Executive Officer
(Independent Hospital System)

GEORGIA: CHESTATEE REGIONAL HOSPITAL (O, 49 beds) 227 Mountain Drive, Dahlonega, GA Zip 30533–1606; tel. 706/864–6136; Jeanne Van Galder, Chief Executive Officer
Web address: www.chestateeregionalhospital.com

MISSISSIPPI: TRACE REGIONAL HOSPITAL (O, 84 beds) Highway 8 East, Houston, MS Zip 38851–9396, Mailing Address: P.O. Box 626, Zip 38851–0626; tel. 662/456–3700; Gary L. Staten, Chief Executive Officer
Web address: www.traceregional.com

Owned, leased, sponsored:	2 hospitals	133 beds
Contract–managed:	0 hospitals	0 beds
Totals:	2 hospitals	133 beds

★0066: SUSQUEHANNA HEALTH SYSTEM (NP)
700 High Street, Williamsport, PA Zip 17701–3100; tel. 570/321–1000; Steven P. Johnson, FACHE, President and Chief Executive Officer
(Centralized Health System)

PENNSYLVANIA: DIVINE PROVIDENCE HOSPITAL (O, 31 beds) 1100 Grampian Boulevard, Williamsport, PA Zip 17701–1995; tel. 570/326–8000; Robert E. Kane, President
Web address: www.susquehannahealth.org

MUNCY VALLEY HOSPITAL (O, 156 beds) 215 East Water Street, Muncy, PA Zip 17756–8700; tel. 570/546–8282; Ronald J. Reynolds, Vice President East Lycoming Operations and Chief Administrative Officer
Web address: www.susquehannahealth.org

SOLDIERS AND SAILORS MEMORIAL HOSPITAL (O, 67 beds) 32–36 Central Avenue, Wellsboro, PA Zip 16901–1899; tel. 570/724–1631; Janie Hilfiger, President
Web address: www.susquehannahealth.org

WILLIAMSPORT REGIONAL MEDICAL CENTER (O, 220 beds) 700 High Street, Williamsport, PA Zip 17701–3100; tel. 570/321–1000; Jan E. Fisher, Executive Vice President, Chief Operating Officer and Chief Administrative Officer
Web address: www.susquehannahealth.org

Owned, leased, sponsored:	4 hospitals	474 beds
Contract–managed:	0 hospitals	0 beds
Totals:	4 hospitals	474 beds

★8795: SUTTER HEALTH (NP)
2200 River Plaza Drive, Sacramento, CA Zip 95833–4134; tel. 916/733–8800; Sarah Krevans, President and Chief Executive Officer
(Centralized Health System)

CALIFORNIA: ALTA BATES SUMMIT MEDICAL CENTER (O, 441 beds) 2450 Ashby Avenue, Berkeley, CA Zip 94705–2067; tel. 510/204–4444; Charles Prosper, Chief Executive Officer
Web address: www.altabatessummit.org/

ALTA BATES SUMMIT MEDICAL CENTER – SUMMIT CAMPUS (O, 333 beds) 350 Hawthorne Avenue, Oakland, CA Zip 94609–3100; tel. 510/655–4000; Charles Prosper, Chief Executive Officer
Web address: www.altabatessummit.com

CALIFORNIA PACIFIC MEDICAL CENTER (O, 642 beds) 2333 Buchanan Street, San Francisco, CA Zip 94115–1925, Mailing Address: P.O. Box 7999, Zip 94120–7999; tel. 415/600–6000; Warren S. Browner, M.D., M.P.H., Chief Executive Officer
Web address: www.cpmc.org

CALIFORNIA PACIFIC MEDICAL CENTER–DAVIES CAMPUS (O, 205 beds) Castro and Duboce Streets, San Francisco, CA Zip 94114; tel. 415/600–6000; Mary Lanier, Vice President, Post Acute Services and Site Administrator
Web address: www.cpmc.org

EDEN MEDICAL CENTER (O, 130 beds) 20103 Lake Chabot Road, Castro Valley, CA Zip 94546–5305; tel. 510/537–1234; Theresa Glubka, R.N., Chief Executive Officer
Web address: www.edenmedcenter.org

MEMORIAL HOSPITAL LOS BANOS (O, 35 beds) 520 West I Street, Los Banos, CA Zip 93635–3498; tel. 209/826–0591; Doug Archer, Administrator
Web address: www.memoriallosbanos.org/

MEMORIAL MEDICAL CENTER (O, 196 beds) 1700 Coffee Road, Modesto, CA Zip 95355–2869, Mailing Address: P.O. Box 942, Zip 95353–0942; tel. 209/526–4500; Daryn J. Kumar, Chief Executive Officer
Web address: www.memorialmedicalcenter.org

MENLO PARK SURGICAL HOSPITAL (O, 12 beds) 570 Willow Road, Menlo Park, CA Zip 94025–2617; tel. 650/324–8500; Kathleen Palange, R.N., Chief Administrative Officer
Web address: www.pamf.org/mpsh

MILLS–PENINSULA HEALTH SERVICES (O, 258 beds) 1501 Trousdale Drive, Burlingame, CA Zip 94010–3282; tel. 650/696–5400; Janet Wagner, R.N., Chief Executive Officer
Web address: www.mills–peninsula.org

NOVATO COMMUNITY HOSPITAL (O, 40 beds) 180 Rowland Way, Novato, CA Zip 94945–5009, Mailing Address: P.O. Box 1108, Zip 94948–1108; tel. 415/209–1300; Brian Alexander, Chief Administrative Officer
Web address: www.novatocommunity.sutterhealth.org

ST. LUKE'S HOSPITAL (O, 175 beds) 3555 Cesar Chavez Street, San Francisco, CA Zip 94110–4403; tel. 415/600–6000; Warren S. Browner, M.D., M.P.H., Chief Executive Officer
Web address: www.stlukes–sf.org

STANISLAUS SURGICAL HOSPITAL (O, 23 beds) 1421 Oakdale Road, Modesto, CA Zip 95355–3356; tel. 209/572–2700; Douglas V. Johnson, Chief Executive Officer
Web address: www.stanislaussurgical.com

SUTTER AMADOR HOSPITAL (O, 52 beds) 200 Mission Boulevard, Jackson, CA Zip 95642–2564; tel. 209/223–7500; Anne Platt, Chief Executive Officer
Web address: www.sutteramador.org

SUTTER AUBURN FAITH HOSPITAL (O, 72 beds) 11815 Education Street, Auburn, CA Zip 95602–2410; tel. 530/888–4500; Mitchell J. Hanna, Chief Executive Officer
Web address: www.sutterhealth.org

For explanation of codes following names, see page B2.
★ Indicates Type III membership in the American Hospital Association.

© 2016 AHA Guide

SUTTER CENTER FOR PSYCHIATRY (O, 71 beds) 7700 Folsom Boulevard, Sacramento, CA Zip 95826–2608; tel. 916/386–3000; John W. Boyd, PsyD, Chief Executive Officer
Web address: www.sutterpsychiatry.org

SUTTER COAST HOSPITAL (O, 49 beds) 800 East Washington Boulevard, Crescent City, CA Zip 95531–8359; tel. 707/464–8511; Mitchell J. Hanna, Chief Executive Officer
Web address: www.sutterhealth.org

SUTTER DAVIS HOSPITAL (O, 48 beds) 2000 Sutter Place, Davis, CA Zip 95616–6201, Mailing Address: P.O. Box 1617, Zip 95617–1617; tel. 530/756–6440; Jennifer Maher, Chief Executive Officer
Web address: www.sutterhealth.org

SUTTER DELTA MEDICAL CENTER (O, 132 beds) 3901 Lone Tree Way, Antioch, CA Zip 94509–6253; tel. 925/779–7200; Dori Stevens, Chief Executive Officer
Web address: www.sutterdelta.org

SUTTER LAKESIDE HOSPITAL (O, 25 beds) 5176 Hill Road East, Lakeport, CA Zip 95453–6300; tel. 707/262–5000; Siri Nelson, Chief Administrative Officer
Web address: www.sutterlakeside.org

SUTTER MATERNITY AND SURGERY CENTER OF SANTA CRUZ (O, 30 beds) 2900 Chanticleer Avenue, Santa Cruz, CA Zip 95065–1816; tel. 831/477–2200; Stephen Gray, Chief Administrative Officer
Web address: www.suttersantacruz.org

SUTTER MEDICAL CENTER, SACRAMENTO (O, 523 beds) 2801 L Street, Sacramento, CA Zip 95816–5680; tel. 916/454–3333; Michael J. Cohill, Interim Chief Executive Officer
Web address: www.sutterhealth.org

SUTTER OAKS NURSING CENTER (O, 100 beds) 2600 L. Street, Sacramento, CA Zip 95816–5612; tel. 916/552–2200; John W. Boyd, PsyD, Chief Administrative Officer

SUTTER ROSEVILLE MEDICAL CENTER (O, 328 beds) One Medical Plaza Drive, Roseville, CA Zip 95661–3037; tel. 916/781–1000; Patrick R. Brady, Chief Executive Officer
Web address: www.sutterroseville.org

SUTTER SANTA ROSA REGIONAL HOSPITAL (O, 84 beds) 30 Mark West Springs Road, Santa Rosa, CA Zip 95403; tel. 707/576–4000; Mike Purvis, Chief Administrative Officer
Web address: www.sutterhealth.org

SUTTER SOLANO MEDICAL CENTER (O, 102 beds) 300 Hospital Drive, Vallejo, CA Zip 94589–2574, Mailing Address: P.O. Box 3189, Zip 94590–0669; tel. 707/554–4444; John W. Boyd, PsyD, Chief Executive Officer
Web address: www.suttersolano.org

SUTTER SURGICAL HOSPITAL – NORTH VALLEY (O, 14 beds) 455 Plumas Boulevard, Yuba City, CA Zip 95991–5074; tel. 530/749–5700; Shawndra Simpson, Interim Chief Executive Officer
Web address: www.sshnv.org

SUTTER TRACY COMMUNITY HOSPITAL (O, 81 beds) 1420 North Tracy Boulevard, Tracy, CA Zip 95376–3497; tel. 209/835–1500; David M. Thompson, Chief Executive Officer
Web address: www.suttertracy.org

HAWAII: KAHI MOHALA BEHAVIORAL HEALTH (O, 76 beds) 91–2301 Old Fort Weaver Road, Ewa Beach, HI Zip 96706–3602; tel. 808/671–8511; Leonard Licina, Chief Executive Officer
Web address: www.kahimohala.org

Owned, leased, sponsored:	28 hospitals	4277 beds
Contract–managed:	0 hospitals	0 beds
Totals:	28 hospitals	4277 beds

★**0871: SWEDISH HEALTH SERVICES** (NP)
747 Broadway, Seattle, WA Zip 98122–4379; tel. 206/386–6000; Anthony A. Armada, Senior Vice President, Chief Executive Officer of Swedish Health Services and Providence Health and Services

WASHINGTON: SWEDISH MEDICAL CENTER–CHERRY HILL CAMPUS (O, 198 beds) 500 17th Avenue, Seattle, WA Zip 98122–5711; tel. 206/320–2000; June Altaras, R.N., Chief Executive Officer
Web address: www.swedish.org

SWEDISH MEDICAL CENTER–FIRST HILL (O, 620 beds) 747 Broadway, Seattle, WA Zip 98122–4307; tel. 206/386–6000; June Altaras, R.N., Chief Executive Officer
Web address: www.swedish.org

SWEDISH/EDMONDS (O, 161 beds) 21601 76th Avenue West, Edmonds, WA Zip 98026–7506; tel. 425/640–4000; Jennifer Graves, R.N., MS, Chief Executive
Web address: www.swedish.org

SWEDISH/ISSAQUAH (O, 49 beds) 751 N.E. Blakely Drive, Issaquah, WA Zip 98029–6201; tel. 425/313–4000; Rayburn Lewis, M.D., Chief Executive
Web address: www.swedish.org/issaquah

Owned, leased, sponsored:	4 hospitals	1028 beds
Contract–managed:	0 hospitals	0 beds
Totals:	4 hospitals	1028 beds

★**0379: TAHOE FOREST HEALTH SYSTEM** (NP)
10121 Pine Avenue, Truckee, CA Zip 96161–4835; tel. 530/587–6011; Harry Weis, Chief Executive Officer

CALIFORNIA: TAHOE FOREST HOSPITAL DISTRICT (O, 62 beds) 10121 Pine Avenue, Truckee, CA Zip 96161–4856, Mailing Address: P.O. Box 759, Zip 96160–0759; tel. 530/587–6011; Harry Weis, Chief Executive Officer
Web address: www.tfhd.com

NEVADA: INCLINE VILLAGE COMMUNITY HOSPITAL (O, 6 beds) 880 Alder Avenue, Incline Village, NV Zip 89451–8335; tel. 775/833–4100; Judy Newland, R.N., Chief Nursing Officer
Web address: www.tfhd.com

Owned, leased, sponsored:	2 hospitals	68 beds
Contract–managed:	0 hospitals	0 beds
Totals:	2 hospitals	68 beds

★**0341: TANNER HEALTH SYSTEM** (NP)
705 Dixie Street, Carrollton, GA Zip 30117–3818; tel. 770/836–9580; Loy M. Howard, President and Chief Executive Officer

GEORGIA: TANNER HIGGINS GENERAL HOSPITAL (O, 23 beds) 200 Allen Memorial Drive, Bremen, GA Zip 30110–2012; tel. 770/824–2000; Bonnie Boles, M.D., Administrator
Web address: www.tanner.org/Main/HigginsGeneralHospitalBremen.aspx

TANNER MEDICAL CENTER–CARROLLTON (O, 162 beds) 705 Dixie Street, Carrollton, GA Zip 30117–3818; tel. 770/836–9666; James D. Griffith, Chief Operating Officer
Web address: www.tanner.org

TANNER MEDICAL CENTER–VILLA RICA (O, 109 beds) 601 Dallas Highway, Villa Rica, GA Zip 30180–1202; tel. 770/456–3000; Bonnie Boles, M.D., Administrator
Web address: www.tanner.org

Owned, leased, sponsored:	3 hospitals	294 beds
Contract–managed:	0 hospitals	0 beds
Totals:	3 hospitals	294 beds

★**0169: TEMPLE UNIVERSITY HEALTH SYSTEM** (NP)
3509 North Broad Street, 9th Floor, Philadelphia, PA Zip 19140–4105; tel. 215/707–0900; Larry Kaiser, M.D., President and Chief Executive Officer
(Centralized Health System)

PENNSYLVANIA: FOX CHASE CANCER CENTER–AMERICAN ONCOLOGIC HOSPITAL (O, 65 beds) 333 Cottman Avenue, Philadelphia, PA Zip 19111–2434; tel. 215/728–6900; Richard Fisher, President and Chief Executive Officer
Web address: www.fccc.org

JEANES HOSPITAL (O, 146 beds) 7600 Central Avenue, Philadelphia, PA Zip 19111–2499; tel. 215/728–2000; Marc P. Hurowitz, D.O., President and Chief Executive Officer
Web address: www.jeanes.com

For explanation of codes following names, see page B2.
★ Indicates Type III membership in the American Hospital Association.

TEMPLE UNIVERSITY HOSPITAL (O, 701 beds) 3401 North Broad Street, Philadelphia, PA Zip 19140–5103; tel. 215/707–2000; Verdi Disesa, M.D., President and Chief Executive Officer
Web address: www.tuh.templehealth.org/content/default.htm

Owned, leased, sponsored:	3 hospitals	912 beds
Contract–managed:	0 hospitals	0 beds
Totals:	3 hospitals	912 beds

★**0919:   TENET HEALTHCARE CORPORATION** (IO)
1445 Ross Avenue, Suite 1400, Dallas, TX Zip 75202–2703, Mailing Address: P.O. Box 1390369, Zip 75313–9036; tel. 469/893–2200; Trevor Fetter, President and Chief Executive Officer
(Decentralized Health System)

ALABAMA: BROOKWOOD BAPTIST MEDICAL CENTER (O, 607 beds) 2010 Brookwood Medical Center Drive, Birmingham, AL Zip 35209–6875; tel. 205/877–1000; Charles A. Stark, FACHE, President and Chief Executive Officer
Web address: www.https://www.brookwoodbaptisthealth.com/

CITIZENS BAPTIST MEDICAL CENTER (O, 72 beds) 604 Stone Avenue, Talladega, AL Zip 35160–2217, Mailing Address: P.O. Box 978, Zip 35161–0978; tel. 256/362–8111; Zach Abercombie, Interim Administrator
Web address: www.brookwoodbaptisthealth.org

PRINCETON BAPTIST MEDICAL CENTER (O, 309 beds) 701 Princeton Avenue S.W., Birmingham, AL Zip 35211–1303; tel. 205/783–3000; Betsy Postlethwait, President
Web address: www.bhsala.com

SHELBY BAPTIST MEDICAL CENTER (O, 231 beds) 1000 First Street North, Alabaster, AL Zip 35007–8703; tel. 205/620–8100; Robert A. Phillips, President
Web address: www.brookwoodbaptisthealth.com

WALKER BAPTIST MEDICAL CENTER (O, 158 beds) 3400 Highway 78 East, Jasper, AL Zip 35501–8907, Mailing Address: P.O. Box 3547, Zip 35502–3547; tel. 205/387–4000; John Langlois, Interim Administrator
Web address: www.bhsala.com

ARIZONA: ABRAZO ARROWHEAD CAMPUS (O, 234 beds) 18701 North 67th Avenue, Glendale, AZ Zip 85308–7100; tel. 623/561–1000; Frank L. Molinaro, Chief Executive Officer
Web address: www.arrowheadhospital.com

ABRAZO CENTRAL CAMPUS (O, 215 beds) 2000 West Bethany Home Road, Phoenix, AZ Zip 85015–2443; tel. 602/249–0212; Danny L. Jones, Jr., FACHE, Chief Executive Officer
Web address: www.abrazohealth.com

ABRAZO MARYVALE CAMPUS (O, 100 beds) 5102 West Campbell Avenue, Phoenix, AZ Zip 85031–1799; tel. 623/848–5000; Crystal Hamilton, R.N., Chief Executive Officer
Web address: www.maryvalehospital.com

ABRAZO SCOTTSDALE CAMPUS (O, 142 beds) 3929 East Bell Road, Phoenix, AZ Zip 85032–2196; tel. 602/923–5000; David Tupponce, M.D., Chief Executive Officer
Web address: www.abrazoscottsdale.com

ABRAZO WEST CAMPUS (O, 106 beds) 13677 West McDowell Road, Goodyear, AZ Zip 85395–2635; tel. 623/882–1500; Stan V. Holm, FACHE, Chief Executive Officer
Web address: www.wvhospital.com

CARONDELET HOLY CROSS HOSPITAL (O, 25 beds) 1171 West Target Range Road, Nogales, AZ Zip 85621–2415; tel. 520/285–3000; Debbie Knapheide, MSN, Site Administrator, Chief Nursing Officer and Chief Operating Officer
Web address: www.carondelet.org

CARONDELET ST. JOSEPH'S HOSPITAL (O, 486 beds) 350 North Wilmot Road, Tucson, AZ Zip 85711–2678; tel. 520/873–3000; Mark A. Benz, President and Chief Executive Officer
Web address: www.carondelet.org

CARONDELET ST. MARY'S HOSPITAL (O, 300 beds) 1601 West St. Mary's Road, Tucson, AZ Zip 85745–2682; tel. 520/872–3000; Amy Beiter, M.D., President and Chief Executive Officer
Web address: www.carondelet.org

CALIFORNIA: DESERT REGIONAL MEDICAL CENTER (L, 382 beds) 1150 North Indian Canyon Drive, Palm Springs, CA Zip 92262–4872; tel. 760/323–6511; Carolyn P. Caldwell, Chief Executive Officer
Web address: www.desertregional.com

DOCTORS HOSPITAL OF MANTECA (O, 56 beds) 1205 East North Street, Manteca, CA Zip 95336–4900; tel. 209/823–3111; Ikenna Mmeje, Chief Executive Officer
Web address: www.doctorsmanteca.com

DOCTORS MEDICAL CENTER OF MODESTO (O, 455 beds) 1441 Florida Avenue, Modesto, CA Zip 95350–4418, Mailing Address: P.O. Box 4138, Zip 95352–4138; tel. 209/578–1211; Warren J. Kirk, Chief Executive Officer
Web address: www.dmc–modesto.com

EMANUEL MEDICAL CENTER (O, 209 beds) 825 Delbon Avenue, Turlock, CA Zip 95382–2016, Mailing Address: P.O. Box 819005, Zip 95382; tel. 209/667–4200; Susan C. Micheletti, Chief Executive Officer
Web address: www.emanuelmed.org

FOUNTAIN VALLEY REGIONAL HOSPITAL AND MEDICAL CENTER (O, 400 beds) 17100 Euclid Street, Fountain Valley, CA Zip 92708–4043; tel. 714/966–7200; B. Joseph Badalian, Chief Executive Officer
Web address: www.fountainvalleyhospital.com

HI–DESERT MEDICAL CENTER (L, 179 beds) 6530 La Contenta, Suite 100, Yucca Valley, CA Zip 92284, Mailing Address: 6601 White Feather Road, Joshua Tree, Zip 92252–6607; tel. 760/366–3711; Karen Faulis, Chief Executive Officer
Web address: www.hdmc.org

JOHN F. KENNEDY MEMORIAL HOSPITAL (O, 145 beds) 47111 Monroe Street, Indio, CA Zip 92201–6799; tel. 760/347–6191; Gary Honts, Chief Executive Officer
Web address: www.jfkmemorialhosp.com

LAKEWOOD REGIONAL MEDICAL CENTER (O, 153 beds) 3700 East South Street, Lakewood, CA Zip 90712–1498, Mailing Address: P.O. Box 6070, Zip 90712; tel. 562/531–2550; John A. Grah, FACHE, Chief Executive Officer
Web address: www.lakewoodregional.com

LOS ALAMITOS MEDICAL CENTER (O, 167 beds) 3751 Katella Avenue, Los Alamitos, CA Zip 90720–3164; tel. 562/598–1311; Kent G. Clayton, Chief Executive Officer
Web address: www.losalamitosmedctr.com

PLACENTIA–LINDA HOSPITAL (O, 114 beds) 1301 North Rose Drive, Placentia, CA Zip 92870–3899; tel. 714/993–2000; Charles Orlando, Interim Chief Executive Officer
Web address: www.placentialinda.com

SAN RAMON REGIONAL MEDICAL CENTER (O, 123 beds) 6001 Norris Canyon Road, San Ramon, CA Zip 94583–5400; tel. 925/275–9200; Gary Sloan, Chief Executive Officer
Web address: www.sanramonmedctr.com

SIERRA VISTA REGIONAL MEDICAL CENTER (O, 164 beds) 1010 Murray Avenue, San Luis Obispo, CA Zip 93405–1806, Mailing Address: P.O. Box 1367, Zip 93405; tel. 805/546–7600; Joseph DeSchryver, Chief Executive Officer
Web address: www.sierravistaregional.com

TWIN CITIES COMMUNITY HOSPITAL (O, 89 beds) 1100 Las Tablas Road, Templeton, CA Zip 93465–9796; tel. 805/434–3500; Mark P. Lisa, FACHE, Chief Executive Officer
Web address: www.twincitieshospital.com

FLORIDA: CORAL GABLES HOSPITAL (O, 256 beds) 3100 Douglas Road, Coral Gables, FL Zip 33134–6914; tel. 305/445–8461; Patrick Downes, Chief Executive Officer
Web address: www.coralgableshospital.com

DELRAY MEDICAL CENTER (O, 439 beds) 5352 Linton Boulevard, Delray Beach, FL Zip 33484–6580; tel. 561/498–4440; Mark Bryan, Chief Executive Officer
Web address: www.delraymedicalctr.com

GOOD SAMARITAN MEDICAL CENTER (O, 174 beds) 1309 North Flagler Drive, West Palm Beach, FL Zip 33401–3499; tel. 561/655–5511; Mark Nosacka, Chief Executive Officer
Web address: www.goodsamaritanmc.com

HIALEAH HOSPITAL (O, 191 beds) 651 East 25th Street, Hialeah, FL Zip 33013–3878; tel. 305/693–6100; Ben A. Rodriguez, Chief Executive Officer
Web address: www.hialeahhosp.com

For explanation of codes following names, see page B2.
★ Indicates Type III membership in the American Hospital Association.

NORTH SHORE MEDICAL CENTER (O, 357 beds) 1100 N.W. 95th Street, Miami, FL Zip 33150–2098; tel. 305/835–6000; Manuel Linares, Chief Executive Officer
Web address: www.northshoremedical.com

PALM BEACH GARDENS MEDICAL CENTER (L, 199 beds) 3360 Burns Road, Palm Beach Gardens, FL Zip 33410–4323; tel. 561/622–1411; Jeffrey M. Welch, Chief Executive Officer
Web address: www.pbgmc.com

PALMETTO GENERAL HOSPITAL (O, 360 beds) 2001 West 68th Street, Hialeah, FL Zip 33016–1898; tel. 305/823–5000; Ana J. Mederos, Chief Executive Officer
Web address: www.palmettogeneral.com

ST. MARY'S MEDICAL CENTER (O, 464 beds) 901 45th Street, West Palm Beach, FL Zip 33407–2495; tel. 561/844–6300; Gabrielle Finley–Hazle, Chief Executive Officer
Web address: www.stmarysmc.com

WEST BOCA MEDICAL CENTER (O, 195 beds) 21644 State Road 7, Boca Raton, FL Zip 33428–1899; tel. 561/488–8000; Mitchell S. Feldman, Chief Executive Officer
Web address: www.westbocamedctr.com

ILLINOIS: LOUIS A. WEISS MEMORIAL HOSPITAL (O, 153 beds) 4646 North Marine Drive, Chicago, IL Zip 60640–5759; tel. 773/878–8700; Anthony Tedeschi, M.D., M.P.H., Chief Executive Officer and Chief Medical Officer
Web address: www.weisshospital.com

MACNEAL HOSPITAL (O, 357 beds) 3249 South Oak Park Avenue, Berwyn, IL Zip 60402–0715; tel. 708/783–9100; J. Scott Steiner, Chief Executive Officer
Web address: www.macneal.com

WEST SUBURBAN MEDICAL CENTER (O, 172 beds) 3 Erie Court, Oak Park, IL Zip 60302–2599; tel. 708/383–6200; Patrick J. Maloney, Chief Executive Officer
Web address: www.westsuburbanmc.com/Home.aspx

WESTLAKE HOSPITAL (O, 181 beds) 1225 Lake Street, Melrose Park, IL Zip 60160–4000; tel. 708/681–3000; Patrick J. Maloney, Chief Executive Officer
Web address: www.westlakehosp.com

MASSACHUSETTS: METROWEST MEDICAL CENTER (O, 155 beds) 115 Lincoln Street, Framingham, MA Zip 01702–6342; tel. 508/383–1000; Barbara J. Doyle, R.N., MS, Chief Executive Officer
Web address: www.mwmc.com

SAINT VINCENT HOSPITAL (O, 283 beds) 123 Summer Street, Worcester, MA Zip 01608–1216; tel. 508/363–5000; Steven MacLauchlan, Chief Executive Officer
Web address: www.stvincenthospital.com

MICHIGAN: DMC – CHILDREN'S HOSPITAL OF MICHIGAN (O, 225 beds) 3901 Beaubien Street, Detroit, MI Zip 48201–2119; tel. 313/745–5437; Luanne T. Ewald, Interim Chief Executive Officer
Web address: www.chmkids.org

DMC – DETROIT RECEIVING HOSPITAL (O, 191 beds) 4201 Saint Antoine Street, Detroit, MI Zip 48201–2153; tel. 313/745–3000; Reginald J. Eadie, M.D., Chief Executive Officer
Web address: www.dmc.org

DMC – REHABILITATION INSTITUTE OF MICHIGAN (O, 69 beds) 261 Mack Avenue, Detroit, MI Zip 48201–2495; tel. 313/745–1203; William H. Restum, Ph.D., Chief Executive Officer
Web address: www.rimrehab.org

DMC – SINAI–GRACE HOSPITAL (O, 295 beds) 6071 West Outer Drive, Detroit, MI Zip 48235–2679; tel. 313/966–3300; Paula R. Autry, FACHE, Chief Executive Officer
Web address: www.sinaigrace.org

DMC HARPER UNIVERSITY HOSPITAL (O, 397 beds) 3990 John R Street, Detroit, MI Zip 48201–2018; tel. 313/745–8040; Reginald J. Eadie, M.D., Chief Executive Officer
Web address: www.harperhospital.org

DMC HURON VALLEY–SINAI HOSPITAL (O, 148 beds) 1 William Carls Drive, Commerce Township, MI Zip 48382–2201; tel. 248/937–3300; Karen Fordham, President
Web address: www.hvsh.org

MISSOURI: DES PERES HOSPITAL (O, 143 beds) 2345 Dougherty Ferry Road, Saint Louis, MO Zip 63122–3313; tel. 314/966–9100; David E. Loving, Chief Executive Officer
Web address: www.despereshospital.com

PENNSYLVANIA: HAHNEMANN UNIVERSITY HOSPITAL (O, 496 beds) Broad and Vine Streets, Philadelphia, PA Zip 19102–1192; tel. 215/762–7000; Michael P. Halter, Chief Executive Officer
Web address: www.hahnemannhospital.com

ST. CHRISTOPHER'S HOSPITAL FOR CHILDREN (O, 181 beds) 3601 A. Street, Philadelphia, PA Zip 19134–1043; tel. 215/427–5000; J. Mark McLoone, FACHE, Chief Executive Officer
Web address: www.stchristophershospital.com

SOUTH CAROLINA: COASTAL CAROLINA HOSPITAL (O, 35 beds) 1000 Medical Center Drive, Hardeeville, SC Zip 29927–3446; tel. 843/784–8000; Jeremy L. Clark, Interim Chief Executive Officer
Web address: www.coastalhospital.com

EAST COOPER MEDICAL CENTER (O, 140 beds) 2000 Hospital Drive, Mount Pleasant, SC Zip 29464–3764; tel. 843/881–0100; Jason P. Alexander, FACHE, Chief Executive Officer
Web address: www.eastcoopermedctr.com

HILTON HEAD HOSPITAL (O, 93 beds) 25 Hospital Center Boulevard, Hilton Head Island, SC Zip 29926–2738; tel. 843/681–6122; Jeremy L. Clark, Market Chief Executive Officer
Web address: www.hiltonheadregional.com

PIEDMONT MEDICAL CENTER (O, 280 beds) 222 Herlong Avenue, Rock Hill, SC Zip 29732; tel. 803/329–1234; Bradley S. Talbert, FACHE, Chief Executive Officer
Web address: www.piedmontmedicalcenter.com

TENNESSEE: SAINT FRANCIS HOSPITAL (O, 511 beds) 5959 Park Avenue, Memphis, TN Zip 38119–5198, Mailing Address: P.O. Box 171808, Zip 38187–1808; tel. 901/765–1000; Audrey Gregory, R.N., MSN, Chief Executive Officer
Web address: www.saintfrancishosp.com

SAINT FRANCIS HOSPITAL–BARTLETT (O, 156 beds) 2986 Kate Bond Road, Bartlett, TN Zip 38133–4003; tel. 901/820–7000; Christopher Locke, Chief Executive Officer
Web address: www.saintfrancisbartlett.com

TEXAS: BAPTIST MEDICAL CENTER (O, 1619 beds) 111 Dallas Street, San Antonio, TX Zip 78205–1230; tel. 210/297–7000; Jonathan Turton, FACHE, President and Chief Executive Officer
Web address: www.baptisthealthsystem.com

BAYLOR SCOTT & WHITE MEDICAL CENTER – SUNNYVALE (O, 70 beds) 231 South Collins Road, Sunnyvale, TX Zip 75182–4624; tel. 972/892–3000; Collin LeMaistre, Chief Executive Officer
Web address: www.BaylorScottandWhite.com/Sunnyvale

BAYLOR SCOTT & WHITE MEDICAL CENTER – WHITE ROCK (O, 151 beds) 9440 Poppy Drive, Dallas, TX Zip 75218–3694; tel. 214/324–6100; Jaikumar Krishnaswamy, Chief Executive Officer
Web address: www.BaylorScottandWhite.com/WhiteRock

CENTENNIAL MEDICAL CENTER (O, 106 beds) 12505 Lebanon Road, Frisco, TX Zip 75035–8298; tel. 972/963–3333; Joe D. Thomason, Chief Executive Officer
Web address: www.centennialmedcenter.com

CYPRESS FAIRBANKS MEDICAL CENTER (O, 160 beds) 10655 Steepletop Drive, Houston, TX Zip 77065–4297; tel. 281/890–4285; Terry J. Wheeler, Chief Executive Officer
Web address: www.cyfairhospital.com

HOUSTON NORTHWEST MEDICAL CENTER (O, 339 beds) 710 FM 1960 Road West, Houston, TX Zip 77090–3402; tel. 281/440–1000; Timothy Puthoff, Chief Executive Officer
Web address: www.hnmc.com

LAKE POINTE MEDICAL CENTER (O, 112 beds) 6800 Scenic Drive, Rowlett, TX Zip 75088–4552, Mailing Address: P.O. Box 1550, Zip 75030–1550; tel. 972/412–2273; Brett D. Lee, Chief Executive Officer
Web address: www.lakepointemedical.com

NACOGDOCHES MEDICAL CENTER (O, 109 beds) 4920 N.E. Stallings Drive, Nacogdoches, TX Zip 75965–1200; tel. 936/569–9481; Jeff Patterson, Chief Executive Officer
Web address: www.nacmedicalcenter.com

For explanation of codes following names, see page B2.
★ Indicates Type III membership in the American Hospital Association.

PARK PLAZA HOSPITAL (O, 139 beds) 1313 Hermann Drive, Houston, TX Zip 77004–7092; tel. 713/527–5000; Steven D. Patonai, Interim Chief Executive Officer
Web address: www.parkplazahospital.com

PLAZA SPECIALTY HOSPITAL (O, 46 beds) 1300 Binz Street, Houston, TX Zip 77004–7016; tel. 713/285–1000; Richard Andrew Pletz, Chief Executive Officer
Web address: www.plazaspecialtyhospital.com

RESOLUTE HEALTH (O, 54 beds) 555 Creekside Crossing, New Braunfels, TX Zip 78130–2594; tel. 830/500–6000; Matt Stone, Chief Executive Officer
Web address: www.resolutehealth.com

THE HOSPITALS OF PROVIDENCE EAST CAMPUS (O, 182 beds) 3280 Joe Battle Boulevard, El Paso, TX Zip 79938–2622; tel. 915/832–2000; Nicholas R. Tejeda, FACHE, Chief Executive Officer
Web address: www.sphn.com

THE HOSPITALS OF PROVIDENCE MEMORIAL CAMPUS (O, 409 beds) 2001 North Oregon Street, El Paso, TX Zip 79902–3368; tel. 915/577–6625; Sally A. Hurt–Deitch, FACHE, R.N., Market Chief Executive Officer
Web address: www.thehospitalsofprovidence.com

THE HOSPITALS OF PROVIDENCE SIERRA CAMPUS (O, 225 beds) 1625 Medical Center Drive, El Paso, TX Zip 79902–5005; tel. 915/747–4000; Monica Vargas–Mahar, FACHE, Chief Executive Officer
Web address: www.thehospitalsofprovidence.com

VALLEY BAPTIST MEDICAL CENTER–BROWNSVILLE (O, 262 beds) 1040 West Jefferson Street, Brownsville, TX Zip 78520–6338, Mailing Address: P.O. Box 3590, Zip 78523–3590; tel. 956/698–5400; Leslie Bingham, Senior Vice President and Chief Executive Officer
Web address: www.valleybaptist.net/brownsville/index.htm

VALLEY BAPTIST MEDICAL CENTER–HARLINGEN (O, 416 beds) 2101 Pease Street, Harlingen, TX Zip 78550–8307, Mailing Address: P.O. Drawer 2588, Zip 78551–2588; tel. 956/389–1100; Manuel Vela, President and Chief Executive Officer
Web address: www.valleybaptist.net/harlingen/index.htm

Owned, leased, sponsored:	72 hospitals	17316 beds
Contract–managed:	0 hospitals	0 beds
Totals:	72 hospitals	17316 beds

0876: TENNESSEE HEALTH MANAGEMENT (IO)
52 West Eighth Street, Parsons, TN Zip 38363–4656, Mailing Address: PO Box 10, Zip 38363–0010; tel. 731/847–6343; Dennis Berry, Chief Executive Officer

ALABAMA: BEHAVIORAL HEALTHCARE CENTER AT HUNTSVILLE (O, 20 beds) 5315 Millennium Drive N.W., Huntsville, AL Zip 35806–2458; tel. 256/964–6700; Bradley Moss, Administrator
Web address: www.tnhealthmanagement.com/bhc/huntsville

TENNESSEE: BEHAVIORAL HEALTHCARE CENTER AT CLARKSVILLE (O, 26 beds) 930 Professional Park Drive, Clarksville, TN Zip 37040–5136; tel. 931/538–6420; Jennifer Robinson, Administrator
Web address: www.bhcclarksville.com

BEHAVIORAL HEALTHCARE CENTER AT COLUMBIA (O, 16 beds) 1400 Rosewood Drive, Columbia, TN Zip 38401–4878; tel. 931/388–6573; Paula Chennault, Administrator
Web address: www.thmgt.com/locations/behavioral–healthcare–center–at–columbia

BEHAVIORAL HEALTHCARE CENTER AT MARTIN (O, 16 beds) 458 Hannings Lane, Martin, TN Zip 38237–3308; tel. 731/588–2830; Carrie Brawley, Administrator
Web address: www.tnhealthmanagement.com/BHC/martin/

Owned, leased, sponsored:	4 hospitals	78 beds
Contract–managed:	0 hospitals	0 beds
Totals:	4 hospitals	78 beds

0020: TEXAS DEPARTMENT OF STATE HEALTH SERVICES (NP)
1100 West 49th Street, Austin, TX Zip 78756–3199; tel. 512/458–7111; Kirk Cole, Interim Commissioner
(Independent Hospital System)

TEXAS: AUSTIN STATE HOSPITAL (O, 299 beds) 4110 Guadalupe Street, Austin, TX Zip 78751–4296; tel. 512/452–0381; Cathy Nottebart, Interim Superintendent
Web address: www.dshs.state.tx.us/mhhospitals/austinsh/default.shtm

BIG SPRING STATE HOSPITAL (O, 200 beds) 1901 North Highway 87, Big Spring, TX Zip 79720–0283; tel. 432/267–8216; Lorie Dunnam, Superintendent
Web address: www.dshs.state.tx.us/mhhospitals/BigSpringSH/default.shtm

EL PASO PSYCHIATRIC CENTER (O, 74 beds) 4615 Alameda Avenue, El Paso, TX Zip 79905–2702; tel. 915/532–2202; Zulema Carrillo, Superintendent
Web address: www.dshs.state.tx.us/mhhospitals/ElPasoPC/default.shtm

KERRVILLE STATE HOSPITAL (O, 202 beds) 721 Thompson Drive, Kerrville, TX Zip 78028–5154; tel. 830/896–2211; Leigh Ann Fitzpatrick, Superintendent
Web address: www.dshs.state.tx.us/mhhospitals/KerrvilleSH/default.shtm

NORTH TEXAS STATE HOSPITAL (O, 640 beds) Highway 70 Northwest, Vernon, TX Zip 76384, Mailing Address: P.O. Box 2231, Zip 76385–2231; tel. 940/552–9901; James E. Smith, Superintendent
Web address: www.online.dshs.state.tx.us/northtexassh/default.htm

RIO GRANDE STATE CENTER/SOUTH TEXAS HEALTH CARE SYSTEM (O, 55 beds) 1401 South Rangerville Road, Harlingen, TX Zip 78552–7638; tel. 956/364–8000; Sonia Hernandez–Keeble, Superintendent
Web address: www.dshs.state.tx.us/mhhospitals/RioGrandeSC/default.shtm

RUSK STATE HOSPITAL (O, 325 beds) 805 North Dickinson, Rusk, TX Zip 75785–2333, Mailing Address: P.O. Box 318, Zip 75785–0318; tel. 903/683–3421; Brenda Slaton, Superintendent
Web address: www.dshs.state.tx.us/mhhospitals/RuskSH/default.shtm

SAN ANTONIO STATE HOSPITAL (O, 302 beds) 6711 South New Braunfels, Suite 100, San Antonio, TX Zip 78223–3006; tel. 210/531–7711; Robert C. Arizpe, Superintendent
Web address: www.dshs.state.tx.us/mhhospitals/SanAntonioSH/default.shtm

TERRELL STATE HOSPITAL (O, 288 beds) 1200 East Brin Street, Terrell, TX Zip 75160–2938, Mailing Address: P.O. Box 70, Zip 75160–9000; tel. 972/524–6452; Dorothy Floyd, Ph.D., Superintendent
Web address: www.dshs.state.tx.us/mhhospitals/terrellsh

TEXAS CENTER FOR INFECTIOUS DISEASE (O, 40 beds) 2303 S.E. Military Drive, San Antonio, TX Zip 78223–3597; tel. 210/534–8857; James N. Elkins, FACHE, Director
Web address: www.dshs.state.tx.us/tcid/default.shtm

Owned, leased, sponsored:	10 hospitals	2425 beds
Contract–managed:	0 hospitals	0 beds
Totals:	10 hospitals	2425 beds

★0129: TEXAS HEALTH RESOURCES (NP)
612 East Lamar Boulevard, Suite 900, Arlington, TX Zip 76011–4130; tel. 682/236–7900; Barclay E. Berdan, FACHE, Chief Executive Officer
(Moderately Centralized Health System)

TEXAS HEALTH ARLINGTON MEMORIAL HOSPITAL (O, 290 beds) 800 West Randol Mill Road, Arlington, TX Zip 76012–2503; tel. 817/548–6100; Blake Kretz, President
Web address: www.arlingtonmemorial.org

TEXAS HEALTH HARRIS METHODIST HOSPITAL ALLIANCE (O, 74 beds) 10864 Texas Health Trail, Fort Worth, TX Zip 76244–4897; tel. 682/212–2000; Clint Abernathy, President and Chief Operating Officer
Web address: www.https://www.texashealth.org/alliance/Pages/default.aspx

TEXAS HEALTH HARRIS METHODIST HOSPITAL AZLE (O, 31 beds) 108 Denver Trail, Azle, TX Zip 76020–3614; tel. 817/444–8600; Bob S. Ellzey, FACHE, President
Web address: www.texashealth.org/Azle

TEXAS HEALTH HARRIS METHODIST HOSPITAL CLEBURNE (O, 85 beds) 201 Walls Drive, Cleburne, TX Zip 76033–4007; tel. 817/641–2551; Lorrie Normand, R.N., Interim Chief Executive Officer and Chief Nursing Officer
Web address: www.texashealth.org

TEXAS HEALTH HARRIS METHODIST HOSPITAL FORT WORTH (O, 639 beds) 1301 Pennsylvania Avenue, Fort Worth, TX Zip 76104–2122; tel. 817/250–2000; Lillie Biggins, RN, R.N., President
Web address: www.texashealth.org

For explanation of codes following names, see page B2.
★ Indicates Type III membership in the American Hospital Association.

TEXAS HEALTH HARRIS METHODIST HOSPITAL HURST–EULESS–BEDFORD (O, 202 beds) 1600 Hospital Parkway, Bedford, TX Zip 76022–6913, Mailing Address: P.O. Box 669, Zip 76095–0669; tel. 817/685–4000; Deborah Paganelli, President
Web address: www.texashealth.org

TEXAS HEALTH HARRIS METHODIST HOSPITAL SOUTHWEST FORT WORTH (O, 199 beds) 6100 Harris Parkway, Fort Worth, TX Zip 76132–4199; tel. 817/433–5000; Joseph DeLeon, President
Web address: www.texashealth.org

TEXAS HEALTH HARRIS METHODIST HOSPITAL STEPHENVILLE (O, 54 beds) 411 North Belknap Street, Stephenville, TX Zip 76401–3415; tel. 254/965–1500; Christopher Leu, President
Web address: www.texashealth.org/landing.cfm?id=108

TEXAS HEALTH PRESBYTERIAN HOSPITAL ALLEN (O, 48 beds) 1105 Central Expressway North, Suite 140, Allen, TX Zip 75013–6103; tel. 972/747–1000; Jared Shelton, Chief Executive Officer
Web address: www.texashealth.org

TEXAS HEALTH PRESBYTERIAN HOSPITAL DALLAS (O, 611 beds) 8200 Walnut Hill Lane, Dallas, TX Zip 75231–4426; tel. 214/345–6789; James Berg, FACHE, President
Web address: www.texashealth.org

TEXAS HEALTH PRESBYTERIAN HOSPITAL DENTON (O, 208 beds) 3000 North I–35, Denton, TX Zip 76201–5119; tel. 940/898–7000; Jeff Reecer, FACHE, Chief Executive Officer
Web address: www.dentonhospital.com

TEXAS HEALTH PRESBYTERIAN HOSPITAL KAUFMAN (O, 68 beds) 850 Ed Hall Drive, Kaufman, TX Zip 75142–1861, Mailing Address: P.O. Box 1108, Zip 75142–5401; tel. 972/932–7200; Patsy Youngs, President
Web address: www.texashealth.org/Kaufman

TEXAS HEALTH PRESBYTERIAN HOSPITAL PLANO (O, 334 beds) 6200 West Parker Road, Plano, TX Zip 75093–8185; tel. 972/981–8000; Joshua Floren, President
Web address: www.texashealth.org

TEXAS HEALTH SPECIALTY HOSPITAL (O, 10 beds) 1301 Pennsylvania Avenue, 4th Floor, Fort Worth, TX Zip 76104–2190; tel. 817/250–5500; Cheryl Mobley, FACHE, President
Web address: www.texashealth.org

Owned, leased, sponsored:	14 hospitals	2853 beds
Contract–managed:	0 hospitals	0 beds
Totals:	14 hospitals	2853 beds

2445: THEDACARE, INC. (NP)
122 East College Avenue, Appleton, WI Zip 54911–5794, Mailing Address: P.O. Box 8025, Zip 54912–8025; tel. 920/830–5889; Dean Gruner, M.D., President and Chief Executive Officer
(Moderately Centralized Health System)

WISCONSIN: APPLETON MEDICAL CENTER (O, 147 beds) 1818 North Meade Street, Appleton, WI Zip 54911–3496; tel. 920/731–4101; Brian Burmeister, Senior Vice President
Web address: www.thedacare.org

BERLIN MEMORIAL HOSPITAL (O, 75 beds) 225 Memorial Drive, Berlin, WI Zip 54923–1295; tel. 920/361–1313; John Feeney, President and Chief Executive Officer
Web address: www.chnwi.org

THEDA CARE MEDICAL CENTER – WILD ROSE (O, 25 beds) 601 Grove Avenue, Wild Rose, WI Zip 54984–6903, Mailing Address: P.O. Box 243, Zip 54984–0243; tel. 920/622–3257; Craig A. Kantos, Chief Executive Officer
Web address: www.wildrosehospital.org

THEDA CLARK MEDICAL CENTER (O, 151 beds) 130 Second Street, Neenah, WI Zip 54956–2883, Mailing Address: P.O. Box 2021, Zip 54957–2021; tel. 920/729–3100; Brian Burmeister, Senior Vice President, ThedaCare Hospitals
Web address: www.thedacare.org

THEDACARE MEDICAL CENTER–NEW LONDON (O, 25 beds) 1405 Mill Street, New London, WI Zip 54961–0307, Mailing Address: P.O. Box 307, Zip 54961–0307; tel. 920/531–2000; William Schmidt, President and Chief Executive Officer
Web address: www.thedacare.org

THEDACARE MEDICAL CENTER–SHAWANO (O, 22 beds) 100 County Road B., Shawano, WI Zip 54166–2127; tel. 715/526–2111; Dorothy Erdmann, Chief Executive Officer
Web address: www.shawanomed.org

THEDACARE MEDICAL CENTER–WAUPACA (O, 25 beds) 800 Riverside Drive, Waupaca, WI Zip 54981–1999; tel. 715/258–1000; Craig A. Kantos, Chief Executive Officer
Web address: www.riversidemedical.org

Owned, leased, sponsored:	7 hospitals	470 beds
Contract–managed:	0 hospitals	0 beds
Totals:	7 hospitals	470 beds

★0643: THOMAS HEALTH SYSTEM, INC. (NP)
4605 MacCorkle Avenue S.W., South Charleston, WV Zip 25309–1311; tel. 304/766–3600; Daniel Lauffer, FACHE, President and Chief Executive Officer
(Centralized Health System)

WEST VIRGINIA: SAINT FRANCIS HOSPITAL (O, 118 beds) 333 Laidley Street, Charleston, WV Zip 25301–1628, Mailing Address: P.O. Box 471, Zip 25322–0471; tel. 304/347–6500; Daniel Lauffer, FACHE, President and Chief Executive Officer
Web address: www.stfrancishospital.com

THOMAS MEMORIAL HOSPITAL (O, 215 beds) 4605 MacCorkle Avenue S.W., South Charleston, WV Zip 25309–1398; tel. 304/766–3600; Daniel Lauffer, FACHE, President and Chief Executive Officer
Web address: www.thomaswv.org

Owned, leased, sponsored:	2 hospitals	333 beds
Contract–managed:	0 hospitals	0 beds
Totals:	2 hospitals	333 beds

★0812: TIDELANDS HEALTH (NP)
606 Black River Road, Georgetown, SC Zip 29440–3304, Mailing Address: P.O. Box 421718, Zip 29442–4203; tel. 843/527–7000; Bruce P. Bailey, President and Chief Executive Officer

TIDELANDS GEORGETOWN MEMORIAL HOSPITAL (O, 136 beds) Drawer 421718, Georgetown, SC Zip 29442–4203; tel. 843/527–7000
Web address: http://www.tidelandshealth.org/

TIDELANDS WACCAMAW COMMUNITY HOSPITAL (O, 169 beds) P.O. Drawer 3350, Murrells Inlet, SC Zip 29576–2673; tel. 843/652–1000
Web address: http://www.tidelandshealth.org/

Owned, leased, sponsored:	2 hospitals	305 beds
Contract–managed:	0 hospitals	0 beds
Totals:	2 hospitals	305 beds

★0910: TIFT REGIONAL HEALTH SYSTEM (NP)
901 East 18th Street, Tifton, GA Zip 31794–3648; tel. 229/353–6100; William T. Richardson, President and Chief Executive Officer
(Independent Hospital System)

GEORGIA: COOK MEDICAL CENTER–A CAMPUS OF TIFT REGIONAL MEDICAL CENTER (O, 155 beds) 706 North Parrish Avenue, Adel, GA Zip 31620–1511; tel. 229/896–8000; Michael L. Purvis, Chief Executive Officer
Web address: www.cookmedicalcenter.com

TIFT REGIONAL MEDICAL CENTER (O, 181 beds) 901 East 18th Street, Tifton, GA Zip 31794–3648, Mailing Address: Drawer 747, Zip 31793–0747; tel. 229/382–7120; William T. Richardson, President and Chief Executive Officer
Web address: www.tiftregional.com

Owned, leased, sponsored:	2 hospitals	336 beds
Contract–managed:	0 hospitals	0 beds
Totals:	2 hospitals	336 beds

For explanation of codes following names, see page B2.
★ Indicates Type III membership in the American Hospital Association.

Section B

★0906: TRINITY HEALTH (CC)
20555 Victor Parkway, Livonia, MI Zip 48152–7031;
tel. 734/343–1000; Richard J. Gilfillan, M.D., President and Chief
Executive Officer
(Decentralized Health System)

CALIFORNIA: SAINT AGNES MEDICAL CENTER (O, 436 beds) 1303 East
Herndon Avenue, Fresno, CA Zip 93720–3397; tel. 559/450–3000;
Nancy Hollingsworth, R.N., MSN, President and Chief Executive Officer
Web address: www.samc.org

CONNECTICUT: JOHNSON MEMORIAL MEDICAL CENTER (O, 72 beds) 201
Chestnut Hill Road, Stafford Springs, CT Zip 06076–4005;
tel. 860/684–4251; Stuart E. Rosenberg, President and Chief Executive
Officer
Web address: www.jmmc.com

MOUNT SINAI REHABILITATION HOSPITAL (O, 30 beds) 490 Blue Hills Avenue,
Hartford, CT Zip 06112–1513; tel. 860/714–3500; Robert J. Krug, M.D.,
Chief Executive Officer
Web address: www.stfranciscare.org

SAINT FRANCIS HOSPITAL AND MEDICAL CENTER (O, 581 beds) 114
Woodland Street, Hartford, CT Zip 06105–1208; tel. 860/714–4000; John F.
Rodis, M.D., President
Web address: www.saintfranciscare.com

SAINT MARY'S HOSPITAL (O, 156 beds) 56 Franklin Street, Waterbury, CT
Zip 06706–1281; tel. 203/709–6000; Chad W. Wable, President and Chief
Executive Officer
Web address: www.stmh.org

DELAWARE: ST. FRANCIS HOSPITAL (O, 214 beds) Seventh and Clayton
Streets, Wilmington, DE Zip 19805–0500, Mailing Address: P.O. Box
2500, Zip 19805–0500; tel. 302/421–4100; Brian E. Dietz, FACHE,
Interim President and Chief Executive officer
Web address: www.stfrancishealthcare.org

FLORIDA: HOLY CROSS HOSPITAL (O, 367 beds) 4725 North Federal
Highway, Fort Lauderdale, FL Zip 33308–4668, Mailing Address: P.O. Box
23460, Zip 33307–3460; tel. 954/771–8000; Patrick Taylor, M.D.,
President and Chief Executive Officer
Web address: www.holy–cross.com

MEASE COUNTRYSIDE HOSPITAL (C, 311 beds) 3231 McMullen–Booth Road,
Safety Harbor, FL Zip 34695–6607, Mailing Address: P.O. Box 1098,
Zip 34695–1098; tel. 727/725–6111; Lou Galdieri, R.N., President
Web address: www.mpmhealth.com

MEASE DUNEDIN HOSPITAL (C, 120 beds) 601 Main Street, Dunedin, FL
Zip 34698–5891, Mailing Address: P.O. Box 760, Zip 34697–0760;
tel. 727/733–1111; Lou Galdieri, R.N., President
Web address: www.mpmhealth.com

SOUTH FLORIDA BAPTIST HOSPITAL (S, 115 beds) 301 North Alexander
Street, Plant City, FL Zip 33563–4303; tel. 813/757–1200; Karen Kerr,
R.N., President
Web address: www.https://baycare.org/sfbh

ST. ANTHONY'S HOSPITAL (S, 393 beds) 1200 Seventh Avenue North, Saint
Petersburg, FL Zip 33705–1388, Mailing Address: P.O. Box 12588,
Zip 33733–2588; tel. 727/825–1100; M. Scott Smith, President
Web address: www.stanthonys.com/

ST. JOSEPH'S HOSPITAL (S, 1006 beds) 3001 West Martin Luther King Jr.
Boulevard, Tampa, FL Zip 33607–6387, Mailing Address: P.O. Box 4227,
Zip 33677–4227; tel. 813/870–4000; Lorraine Lutton, President
Web address: www.sjbhealth.org

WINTER HAVEN HOSPITAL (S, 350 beds) 200 Avenue F. N.E., Winter Haven,
FL Zip 33881–4193; tel. 863/293–1121; Stephen A. Nierman, President
Web address: www.winterhavenhospital.org

GEORGIA: ST. MARY'S GOOD SAMARITAN HOSPITAL (O, 25 beds) 5401 Lake
Oconee Parkway, Greensboro, GA Zip 30642–4232; tel. 706/453–7331;
D. Montez Carter, President
Web address: www.stmarysgoodsam.org

ST. MARY'S HEALTH CARE SYSTEM (O, 183 beds) 1230 Baxter Street,
Athens, GA Zip 30606–3791; tel. 706/389–3000; Donald McKenna,
President and Chief Executive Officer
Web address: www.stmarysathens.com

ST. MARY'S SACRED HEART HOSPITAL (O, 35 beds) 367 Clear Creek
Parkway, Lavonia, GA Zip 30553–4173; tel. 706/356–7800; Jeff English,
Interim Chief Executive Officer
Web address: www.stmaryssacredheart.org/

IDAHO: SAINT ALPHONSUS MEDICAL CENTER – NAMPA (O, 131 beds) 1512
12th Avenue Road, Nampa, ID Zip 83686–6008; tel. 208/463–5000; Karl
Keeler, Chief Executive Officer
Web address: www.mercynampa.org

SAINT ALPHONSUS REGIONAL MEDICAL CENTER (O, 399 beds) 1055 North
Curtis Road, Boise, ID Zip 83706–1309, Mailing Address: 1055 North Curtis
Road, Zip 83706–1309; tel. 208/367–2121; Rodney D. Reider, President
Web address: www.saintalphonsus.org

ILLINOIS: GOTTLIEB MEMORIAL HOSPITAL (O, 205 beds) 701 West North
Avenue, Melrose Park, IL Zip 60160–1612; tel. 708/681–3200; Lori
Price, President
Web address: www.gottliebhospital.org

LOYOLA UNIVERSITY MEDICAL CENTER (O, 519 beds) 2160 South First
Avenue, Maywood, IL Zip 60153–3328; tel. 708/216–9000; Larry M.
Goldberg, President and Chief Executive Officer
Web address: www.loyolamedicine.org/Medical_Services/index.cfm

MERCY HOSPITAL AND MEDICAL CENTER (O, 189 beds) 2525 South
Michigan Avenue, Chicago, IL Zip 60616–2333; tel. 312/567–2000; Carol L.
Schneider, President and Chief Executive Officer
Web address: www.mercy–chicago.org

INDIANA: SAINT JOSEPH REGIONAL MEDICAL CENTER (O, 294 beds) 5215
Holy Cross Parkway, Mishawaka, IN Zip 46545–1469;
tel. 574/335–5000; Albert Gutierrez, FACHE, President and Chief
Executive Officer
Web address: www.sjmed.com

SAINT JOSEPH REGIONAL MEDICAL CENTER–PLYMOUTH CAMPUS (O, 48
beds) 1915 Lake Avenue, Plymouth, IN Zip 46563–9366, Mailing Address:
P.O. Box 670, Zip 46563–0670; tel. 574/948–4000; Loretta Schmidt,
President
Web address: www.sjmed.com

IOWA: BAUM HARMON MERCY HOSPITAL (O, 11 beds) 255 North Welch
Avenue, Primghar, IA Zip 51245–7765, Mailing Address: P.O. Box 528,
Zip 51245–0528; tel. 712/957–2300; Angie Shilling, Chief Executive
Officer
Web address: www.baumharmon.org

CENTRAL COMMUNITY HOSPITAL (C, 25 beds) 901 Davidson Street N.W.,
Elkader, IA Zip 52043–9015; tel. 563/245–7000; Frances J. Zichal, Chief
Executive Officer
Web address: www.centralcommunityhospital.com

FRANKLIN GENERAL HOSPITAL (C, 77 beds) 1720 Central Avenue East, Suite
A., Hampton, IA Zip 50441–1867; tel. 641/456–5000; Kim Price, Chief
Executive Officer
Web address: www.franklingeneral.com

HANCOCK COUNTY HEALTH SYSTEM (C, 25 beds) 532 First Street N.W.,
Britt, IA Zip 50423–1227; tel. 641/843–5000; Jeffry Stampohar, Chief
Executive Officer
Web address: www.trustchs.com/hancock–county–health–system

HANSEN FAMILY HOSPITAL (C, 21 beds) 920 South Oak, Iowa Falls, IA
Zip 50126–9506; tel. 641/648–4631; Cherelle Montanye-Ireland, Chief
Executive Officer
Web address: www.hansenfamilyhospital.com

HAWARDEN REGIONAL HEALTHCARE (C, 18 beds) 1111 11th Street,
Hawarden, IA Zip 51023–1999; tel. 712/551–3100; Jayson Pullman, Chief
Executive Officer
Web address: www.hawardenregionalhealthcare.com/

KOSSUTH REGIONAL HEALTH CENTER (C, 23 beds) 1515 South Phillips
Street, Algona, IA Zip 50511–3649; tel. 515/295–2451; Scott A. Curtis,
Administrator and Chief Executive Officer
Web address: www.krhc.com

MERCY MEDICAL CENTER–CLINTON (O, 290 beds) 1410 North Fourth Street,
Clinton, IA Zip 52732–2940; tel. 563/244–5555; Sean J. Williams, President
and Chief Executive Officer
Web address: www.mercyclinton.com

MERCY MEDICAL CENTER–DUBUQUE (O, 235 beds) 250 Mercy Drive,
Dubuque, IA Zip 52001–7360; tel. 563/589–8000; Kay Takes, R.N.,
President
Web address: www.mercydubuque.com

MERCY MEDICAL CENTER–DYERSVILLE (O, 20 beds) 1111 Third Street S.W.,
Dyersville, IA Zip 52040–1725; tel. 563/875–7101; Kay Takes, R.N.,
President
Web address: www.mercydubuque.com/mercy–dyersville

For explanation of codes following names, see page B2.
★ Indicates Type III membership in the American Hospital Association.

MERCY MEDICAL CENTER–NEW HAMPTON (O, 18 beds) 308 North Maple Avenue, New Hampton, IA Zip 50659–1142; tel. 641/394–4121; Aaron Flugum, Chief Executive Officer
Web address: www.mercynewhampton.com

MERCY MEDICAL CENTER–NORTH IOWA (O, 205 beds) 1000 Fourth Street S.W., Mason City, IA Zip 50401–2800; tel. 641/428–7000; Daniel Varnum, President and Chief Executive Officer
Web address: www.mercynorthiowa.com

MERCY MEDICAL CENTER–SIOUX CITY (O, 192 beds) 801 Fifth Street, Sioux City, IA Zip 51101–1326, Mailing Address: P.O. Box 3168, Zip 51102–3168; tel. 712/279–2010; James G. Fitzpatrick, FACHE, Chief Executive Officer
Web address: www.mercysiouxcity.com

MITCHELL COUNTY REGIONAL HEALTH CENTER (C, 25 beds) 616 North Eighth Street, Osage, IA Zip 50461–1498; tel. 641/732–6000; Shelly Russell, Chief Executive Officer
Web address: www.mitchellcohospital–clinics.com

PALO ALTO COUNTY HEALTH SYSTEM (C, 47 beds) 3201 First Street, Emmetsburg, IA Zip 50536–2516; tel. 712/852–5500; Desiree Einsweiler, Chief Executive Officer
Web address: www.pachs.com

REGIONAL HEALTH SERVICES OF HOWARD COUNTY (C, 18 beds) 235 Eighth Avenue West, Cresco, IA Zip 52136–1098; tel. 563/547–2101; Robin M. Schluter, Chief Executive Officer
Web address: www.rhshc.com

MARYLAND: HOLY CROSS HOSPITAL (O, 425 beds) 1500 Forest Glen Road, Silver Spring, MD Zip 20910–1487; tel. 301/754–7000; Judith Rogers, R.N., Ph.D., President and Chief Executive Officer
Web address: www.holycrosshealth.org

MASSACHUSETTS: FARREN CARE CENTER (O, 72 beds) 340 Montague City Road, Turners Falls, MA Zip 01376–9983; tel. 413/774–3111; James Clifford, Administrator

MERCY MEDICAL CENTER (O, 336 beds) 271 Carew Street, Springfield, MA Zip 01104–2398, Mailing Address: P.O. Box 9012, Zip 01102–9012; tel. 413/748–9000; Scott A. Wolf, D.O., President and Chief Executive Officer
Web address: www.mercycares.com

MICHIGAN: MERCY HEALTH HACKLEY CAMPUS (O, 401 beds) 1700 Clinton Street, Muskegon, MI Zip 49442–5502, Mailing Address: P.O. Box 3302, Zip 49443–3302; tel. 231/726–3511; Greg Loomis, President
Web address: www.mercyhealthmuskegon.com

MERCY HEALTH SAINT MARY'S (O, 371 beds) 200 Jefferson Avenue S.E., Grand Rapids, MI Zip 49503–4598; tel. 616/685–5000; Bill Manns, President
Web address: www.mercyhealthsaintmarys.org

MERCY HEALTH, LAKESHORE CAMPUS (O, 24 beds) 72 South State Street, Shelby, MI Zip 49455–1299; tel. 231/861–2156; Jay Bryan, President and Chief Executive Officer
Web address: www.mercyhealthmuskegon.com

ST. JOSEPH MERCY ANN ARBOR (O, 481 beds) 5301 Mcauley Drive, Ypsilanti, MI Zip 48197–1051, Mailing Address: P.O. Box 995, Ann Arbor, Zip 48106–0995; tel. 734/712–3456; David Brooks, President
Web address: www.sjmercyhealth.org

ST. JOSEPH MERCY CHELSEA (O, 96 beds) 775 South Main Street, Chelsea, MI Zip 48118–1383; tel. 734/593–6000; Nancy Kay Graebner, President and Chief Executive Officer
Web address: www.cch.org

ST. JOSEPH MERCY LIVINGSTON HOSPITAL (O, 42 beds) 620 Byron Road, Howell, MI Zip 48843–1093; tel. 517/545–6000; David Brooks, President
Web address: www.stjoeslivingston.org/livingston

ST. JOSEPH MERCY OAKLAND (O, 413 beds) 44405 Woodward Avenue, Pontiac, MI Zip 48341–5023; tel. 248/858–3000; Shannon Striebich, Chief Executive Officer
Web address: www.stjoesoakland.com

ST. MARY MERCY HOSPITAL (O, 303 beds) 36475 Five Mile Road, Livonia, MI Zip 48154–1988; tel. 734/655–4800; David A. Spivey, President and Chief Executive Officer
Web address: www.stmarymercy.org

NEBRASKA: OAKLAND MERCY HOSPITAL (O, 18 beds) 601 East Second Street, Oakland, NE Zip 68045–1499; tel. 402/685–5601; John W. Werner, Chief Executive Officer
Web address: www.oaklandhospital.org

PENDER COMMUNITY HOSPITAL (C, 67 beds) 100 Hospital Drive, Pender, NE Zip 68047–0100, Mailing Address: P.O. Box 100, Zip 68047–0100; tel. 402/385–3083; Melissa Kelly, Administrator
Web address: www.pendercommunityhospital.com

NEW JERSEY: LOURDES MEDICAL CENTER OF BURLINGTON COUNTY (O, 169 beds) 218–A Sunset Road, Willingboro, NJ Zip 08046–1162; tel. 609/835–2900; Mark Nessel, Executive Vice President and Chief Operating Officer
Web address: www.lourdesnet.org

OUR LADY OF LOURDES MEDICAL CENTER (O, 350 beds) 1600 Haddon Avenue, Camden, NJ Zip 08103–3117; tel. 856/757–3500; Alexander J. Hatala, FACHE, President and Chief Executive Officer
Web address: www.lourdesnet.org

ST. FRANCIS MEDICAL CENTER (O, 142 beds) 601 Hamilton Avenue, Trenton, NJ Zip 08629–1986; tel. 609/599–5000; Vincent Costantino, Chief Administrative Officer
Web address: www.stfrancismedical.com

NEW YORK: ALBANY MEMORIAL HOSPITAL (O, 74 beds) 600 Northern Boulevard, Albany, NY Zip 12204–1083; tel. 518/471–3221; Virginia L. Golden, Chief Executive Officer
Web address: www.nehealth.com

SAMARITAN HOSPITAL (O, 134 beds) 2215 Burdett Avenue, Troy, NY Zip 12180–2475; tel. 518/271–3300; Norman E. Dascher, Jr., Chief Executive Officer
Web address: www.nehealth.com

ST. JAMES MERCY HOSPITAL (O, 222 beds) 411 Canisteo Street, Hornell, NY Zip 14843–2197; tel. 607/324–8000; Jennifer Sullivan, President and Chief Executive Officer
Web address: www.stjamesmercy.org

ST. JOSEPH'S HOSPITAL HEALTH CENTER (O, 431 beds) 301 Prospect Avenue, Syracuse, NY Zip 13203–1807; tel. 315/448–5111; Kathryn H. Ruscitto, President
Web address: www.sjhsyr.org

ST. MARY'S HOSPITAL (O, 173 beds) 1300 Massachusetts Avenue, Troy, NY Zip 12180–1695; tel. 518/268–5000; Norman E. Dascher, Jr., Chief Executive Officer
Web address: www.setonhealth.org

ST. PETER'S HOSPITAL (O, 442 beds) 315 South Manning Boulevard, Albany, NY Zip 12208–1789; tel. 518/525–1550; Virginia L. Golden, Chief Executive Officer
Web address: www.sphcs.org

SUNNYVIEW REHABILITATION HOSPITAL (O, 115 beds) 1270 Belmont Avenue, Schenectady, NY Zip 12308–2104; tel. 518/382–4500; Edward Eisenman, Chief Executive Officer
Web address: www.sunnyview.org

NORTH CAROLINA: ST. JOSEPH OF THE PINES HOSPITAL (O, 204 beds) 590 Central Drive, Southern Pines, NC Zip 28387; tel. 910/246–1000; Ken Cormier, President and Chief Executive Officer

OHIO: MOUNT CARMEL (O, 747 beds) 793 West State Street, Columbus, OH Zip 43222–1551; tel. 614/234–5000; Sean McKibben, President and Chief Operating Officer
Web address: www.mountcarmelhealth.com

MOUNT CARMEL NEW ALBANY SURGICAL HOSPITAL (O, 60 beds) 7333 Smith's Mill Road, New Albany, OH Zip 43054–9291; tel. 614/775–6600; Diane Doucette, R.N., President
Web address: www.mountcarmelhealth.com

MOUNT CARMEL ST. ANN'S (O, 281 beds) 500 South Cleveland Avenue, Westerville, OH Zip 43081–8998; tel. 614/898–4000; Roger Spoelman, Interim President and Chief Executive Officer
Web address: www.mountcarmelhealth.com

OREGON: SAINT ALPHONSUS MEDICAL CENTER – BAKER CITY (S, 25 beds) 3325 Pocahontas Road, Baker City, OR Zip 97814–1464; tel. 541/523–6461; H. Ray Gibbons, FACHE, Chief Executive Officer
Web address: www.saintalphonsus.org/bakercity

SAINT ALPHONSUS MEDICAL CENTER – ONTARIO (S, 49 beds) 351 S.W. Ninth Street, Ontario, OR Zip 97914–2693; tel. 541/881–7000; Karl Keeler, Chief Executive Officer
Web address: www.saintalphonsus.org/ontario

For explanation of codes following names, see page B2.
★ Indicates Type III membership in the American Hospital Association.

PENNSYLVANIA: MERCY FITZGERALD HOSPITAL (O, 366 beds) 1500 Lansdowne Avenue, Darby, PA Zip 19023–1200; tel. 610/237–4000; Susan Cusack, Executive Director
Web address: www.mercyhealth.org

NAZARETH HOSPITAL (O, 141 beds) 2601 Holme Avenue, Philadelphia, PA Zip 19152–2096; tel. 215/335–6000; Nancy Cherone, Executive Director and Administrator
Web address: www.nazarethhospital.org

ST. MARY MEDICAL CENTER (O, 307 beds) 1201 Langhorne–Newtown Road, Langhorne, PA Zip 19047–1201; tel. 215/710–2000; James L. Woodward, President and Chief Executive Officer
Web address: www.stmaryhealthcare.org

Owned, leased, sponsored:	59 hospitals	14133 beds
Contract–managed:	12 hospitals	777 beds
Totals:	71 hospitals	14910 beds

★**9255: TRUMAN MEDICAL CENTERS** (NP)
2301 Holmes Street, Kansas City, MO Zip 64108–2677; tel. 816/404–1000; Charlie Shields, President and Chief Executive Officer
(Independent Hospital System)

MISSOURI: TRUMAN MEDICAL CENTER–HOSPITAL HILL (O, 249 beds) 2301 Holmes Street, Kansas City, MO Zip 64108–2640; tel. 816/404–1000; Charlie Shields, President and Chief Executive Officer
Web address: www.trumed.org

TRUMAN MEDICAL CENTER–LAKEWOOD (O, 298 beds) 7900 Lee's Summit Road, Kansas City, MO Zip 64139–1236; tel. 816/404–7000; Charlie Shields, President and Chief Executive Officer
Web address: www.trumed.org

Owned, leased, sponsored:	2 hospitals	547 beds
Contract–managed:	0 hospitals	0 beds
Totals:	2 hospitals	547 beds

9195: U. S. INDIAN HEALTH SERVICE (FG)
801 Thompson Avenue, Rockville, MD Zip 20852–1627; tel. 301/443–1083; Yvette Roubideaux, M.D., M.P.H., Director
(Independent Hospital System)

ARIZONA: CHINLE COMPREHENSIVE HEALTH CARE FACILITY (O, 60 beds) Highway 191, Chinle, AZ Zip 86503, Mailing Address: P.O. Drawer PH, Zip 86503–8000; tel. 928/674–7001; Ron Tso, Chief Executive Officer
Web address: www.ihs.gov

HOPI HEALTH CARE CENTER (O, 6 beds) Highway 264 Mile Marker 388, Keams Canyon, AZ Zip 86042, Mailing Address: P.O. Box 4000, Polacca, Zip 86042–4000; tel. 928/737–6000; Daryl Melvin, Chief Executive Officer
Web address: www.ihs.gov/index.asp

SAN CARLOS APACHE HEALTHCARE CORPORATION (O, 8 beds) 103 Medicine Way Road, Peridot, AZ Zip 85542, Mailing Address: 10 Medicine Way Road, Zip 85542; tel. 928/475–2371; Deven Parlikar, President and Chief Executive Officer
Web address: www.ihs.gov

TSEHOOTSOOI MEDICAL CENTER (O, 52 beds) Highway 12 & Bonito Drive, Fort Defiance, AZ Zip 86504, Mailing Address: P.O. Box 649, Zip 86504–0649; tel. 928/729–8000; Sandi Aretino, Chief Executive Officer
Web address: www.fdihb.org

U. S. PUBLIC HEALTH SERVICE INDIAN HOSPITAL (O, 20 beds) 12033 Agency Road, Parker, AZ Zip 85344–7718; tel. 928/669–2137; Elizabeth Helsel, Chief Executive Officer
Web address: www.ihs.gov

U. S. PUBLIC HEALTH SERVICE INDIAN HOSPITAL–SELLS (O, 12 beds) Highway 86 & Topawa Road, Sells, AZ Zip 85634, Mailing Address: P.O. Box 548, Zip 85634–0548; tel. 520/383–7251; Angela Fallon, Acting Chief Executive Officer
Web address: www.ihs.gov

U. S. PUBLIC HEALTH SERVICE INDIAN HOSPITAL–WHITERIVER (O, 35 beds) 200 West Hospital Drive, Whiteriver, AZ Zip 85941–0860, Mailing Address: State Route 73, Box 860, Zip 85941–0860; tel. 928/338–4911; Michelle Martinez, Chief Executive Officer
Web address: www.ihs.gov

U. S. PUBLIC HEALTH SERVICE PHOENIX INDIAN MEDICAL CENTER (O, 127 beds) 4212 North 16th Street, Phoenix, AZ Zip 85016–5389; tel. 602/263–1200; Captain Michael Weakhee, Chief Executive Officer
Web address: www.ihs.gov

MARYLAND: NATIONAL INSTITUTES OF HEALTH CLINICAL CENTER (O, 146 beds) 9000 Rockville Pike, Building 10, Room 6–2551, Bethesda, MD Zip 20892–1504; tel. 301/496–4000; John I. Gallin, M.D., Director
Web address: www.clinicalcenter.nih.gov

MINNESOTA: RED LAKE INDIAN HEALTH SERVICE HOSPITAL (O, 19 beds) 24760 Hospital Drive, Red Lake, MN Zip 56671, Mailing Address: P.O. Box 497, Zip 56671–0497; tel. 218/679–3912; Norine Smith, Chief Executive Officer
Web address: www.rlnnredlakehospital.com/

U. S. PUBLIC HEALTH SERVICE INDIAN HOSPITAL (O, 9 beds) 425 7th Street North West, Cass Lake, MN Zip 56633; tel. 218/335–3200; Robert Malone, Chief Executive Officer
Web address: www.ihs.gov

MONTANA: CROW/NORTHERN CHEYENNE HOSPITAL (O, 24 beds) 10110 South 7650 East, Crow Agency, MT Zip 59022–0009, Mailing Address: P.O. Box 9, Zip 59022–0009; tel. 406/638–2626; Darren Crowe, Chief Executive Officer
Web address: www.ihs.gov/facilitiesservices/areaoffices/billings/crow/index.asp

FORT BELKNAP U. S. PUBLIC HEALTH SERVICE INDIAN HOSPITAL (O, 6 beds) 669 Agency Main Street, Harlem, MT Zip 59526–9455; tel. 406/353–3100; Alan Barlow, Chief Executive Officer
Web address: www.ihs.gov

U. S. PUBLIC HEALTH SERVICE BLACKFEET COMMUNITY HOSPITAL (O, 25 beds) 760 New Hospital Circle, Saint Mary, MT Zip 59417–0760, Mailing Address: P.O. Box 760, Browning, Zip 59417–0760; tel. 406/338–6100; Dee Hutchison, Chief Executive Officer
Web address: www.ihs.gov

NEBRASKA: U. S. PUBLIC HEALTH SERVICE INDIAN HOSPITAL (O, 30 beds) Highway 7577, Winnebago, NE Zip 68071; tel. 402/878–2231; Patricia Medina, Service Unit Director
Web address: www.ihs.gov

NEW MEXICO: ACOMA–CANONCITO–LAGUNA HOSPITAL (O, 25 beds) 80B Veterans Boulevard, Acoma, NM Zip 87034, Mailing Address: P.O. Box 130, San Fidel, Zip 87049–0130; tel. 505/552–5300; William Thorne, Jr., Chief Executive Officer
Web address: www.ihs.gov/albuquerque/index.cfm?module=dsp_abq_acoma_canoncito_laguna

GALLUP INDIAN MEDICAL CENTER (O, 58 beds) 516 East Nizhoni Boulevard, Gallup, NM Zip 87301–5748, Mailing Address: P.O. Box 1337, Zip 87305–1337; tel. 505/722–1000; Vida J. Khow, Chief Executive Officer
Web address: www.ihs.gov/navajo/index.cfm?module=nao_hcc_gallup

MESCALERO PUBLIC HEALTH SERVICE INDIAN HOSPITAL (O, 13 beds) 318 Abalone Loop, Mescalero, NM Zip 88340, Mailing Address: Box 210, Zip 88340–0210; tel. 505/464–3801; Dorlynn Simmons, Chief Executive Officer
Web address: www.ihs.gov

NORTHERN NAVAJO MEDICAL CENTER (O, 68 beds) Highway 491 North, Shiprock, NM Zip 87420–0160, Mailing Address: P.O. Box 160, Zip 87420–0160; tel. 505/368–6001; Fannessa Comer, Chief Executive Officer
Web address: www.ihs.gov/

PHS SANTA FE INDIAN HOSPITAL (O, 4 beds) 1700 Cerrillos Road, Santa Fe, NM Zip 87505–3554; tel. 505/988–9821; Leslie Dye, Chief Executive Officer

U. S. PUBLIC HEALTH SERVICE INDIAN HOSPITAL (O, 12 beds) Route 9 and State Road 371, Crownpoint, NM Zip 87313, Mailing Address: P.O. Box 358, Zip 87313–0358; tel. 505/786–5291; Anslem Roanhorse, Chief Executive Officer
Web address: www.ihs.gov

U. S. PUBLIC HEALTH SERVICE INDIAN HOSPITAL (O, 32 beds) Route 301 North B. Street, Zuni, NM Zip 87327, Mailing Address: P.O. Box 467, Zip 87327–0467; tel. 505/782–4431; Jean Othole, Chief Executive Officer
Web address: www.ihs.gov

For explanation of codes following names, see page B2.
★ Indicates Type III membership in the American Hospital Association.

NORTH DAKOTA: INDIAN HEALTH SERVICE – QUENTIN N. BURDICK MEMORIAL HEALTH CARE FACILITY (O, 27 beds) 1300 Hospital Loop, Belcourt, ND Zip 58316, Mailing Address: P.O. Box 160, Zip 58316–0160; tel. 701/477–6111; Shelly Harris, Chief Executive Officer
Web address: www.ihs.gov

STANDING ROCK SERVICE UNIT, FORT YATES HOSPITAL, INDIAN HEALTH SERVICE, DHHS (O, 12 beds) 10 North River Road, Fort Yates, ND Zip 58538, Mailing Address: P.O. Box J, Zip 58538; tel. 701/854–3831; Jana Gipp, Chief Executive Officer
Web address: www.ihs.gov

OKLAHOMA: CHEROKEE NATION W.W. HASTINGS INDIAN HOSPITAL (O, 58 beds) 100 South Bliss Avenue, Tahlequah, OK Zip 74464–2512; tel. 918/458–3100; Brian Hail, Chief Executive Officer
Web address: www.cherokee.org

CLAREMORE INDIAN HOSPITAL (O, 44 beds) 101 South Moore Avenue, Claremore, OK Zip 74017–5091; tel. 918/342–6200; George Valliere, Chief Executive Officer
Web address: www.ihs.gov

LAWTON INDIAN HOSPITAL (O, 26 beds) 1515 Lawrie Tatum Road, Lawton, OK Zip 73507–3099; tel. 580/353–0350; Greg Ketcher, Administrator
Web address: www.ihs.gov

SOUTH DAKOTA: INDIAN HEALTH SERVICE HOSPITAL (O, 9 beds) 3200 Canyon Lake Drive, Rapid City, SD Zip 57702–8197; tel. 605/355–2280; Kevin J. Stiffarm, Chief Executive Officer
Web address: www.ihs.gov

U. S. PUBLIC HEALTH SERVICE INDIAN HOSPITAL (O, 8 beds) 317 Main Street, Eagle Butte, SD Zip 57625–1012, Mailing Address: P.O. Box 1012, Zip 57625–1012; tel. 605/964–7724; Charles Fisher, Chief Executive Officer
Web address: www.ihs.gov

U. S. PUBLIC HEALTH SERVICE INDIAN HOSPITAL (O, 45 beds) East Highway 18, Pine Ridge, SD Zip 57770, Mailing Address: P.O. Box 1201, Zip 57770–1201; tel. 605/867–5131; Ellen Davis, Service Unit Director
Web address: www.ihs.gov

U. S. PUBLIC HEALTH SERVICE INDIAN HOSPITAL (O, 35 beds) Highway 18, Soldier Creek Road, Rosebud, SD Zip 57570; tel. 605/747–2231; Kathey Wilson, Acting Chief Executive Officer
Web address: www.ihs.gov

Owned, leased, sponsored:	31 hospitals	1055 beds
Contract–managed:	0 hospitals	0 beds
Totals:	31 hospitals	1055 beds

★9105: UAB HEALTH SYSTEM (NP)
500 22nd Street South, Suite 408, Birmingham, AL Zip 35233–3110; tel. 205/975–5362; William Ferniany, Ph.D., Chief Executive Officer
(Centralized Physician/Insurance Health System)

ALABAMA: MEDICAL WEST (O, 231 beds) 995 Ninth Avenue S.W., Bessemer, AL Zip 35022–4527; tel. 205/481–7000; Brian Keith Pennington, President and Chief Executive Officer
Web address: www.medicalwesthospital.org

UNIVERSITY OF ALABAMA HOSPITAL (O, 1062 beds) 619 19th Street South, Birmingham, AL Zip 35249–1900; tel. 205/934–4011; Anthony Patterson, FACHE, Senior Vice President Inpatient Services
Web address: www.uabmedicine.org

Owned, leased, sponsored:	2 hospitals	1293 beds
Contract–managed:	0 hospitals	0 beds
Totals:	2 hospitals	1293 beds

★0082: UC HEALTH (NP)
3200 Burnet Avenue, Cincinnati, OH Zip 45229–3019; tel. 513/585–6000; Richard P. Lofgren, M.D., M.P.H., President and CEO
(Moderately Centralized Health System)

OHIO: DANIEL DRAKE CENTER FOR POST ACUTE CARE (O, 202 beds) 151 West Galbraith Road, Cincinnati, OH Zip 45216–1015; tel. 513/418–2500; Amy Schroyer, Vice President Administration and Senior Site Executive
Web address: www.uchealth.com/danieldrakecenter/

UNIVERSITY OF CINCINNATI MEDICAL CENTER (O, 607 beds) 234 Goodman Street, Cincinnati, OH Zip 45219–2316; tel. 513/584–1000; Jennifer Jackson, R.N., MSN, Chief Administrative Officer, Chief Nursing Officer and Vice President
Web address: www.uchealth.com/university-of-cincinnati-medical-center/

WEST CHESTER HOSPITAL (O, 182 beds) 7700 University Drive, West Chester, OH Zip 45069–2505; tel. 513/298–3000; Tom G. Daskalakis, Chief Administrative Officer
Web address: www.uchealth.com/westchesterhospital

Owned, leased, sponsored:	3 hospitals	991 beds
Contract–managed:	0 hospitals	0 beds
Totals:	3 hospitals	991 beds

★0111: UF HEALTH SHANDS (NP)
1600 S.W. Archer Road, Gainesville, FL Zip 32610–0326; tel. 352/733–1500; Edward Jimenez, Chief Executive Officer
(Moderately Centralized Health System)

FLORIDA: UF HEALTH JACKSONVILLE (O, 620 beds) 655 West Eighth Street, Jacksonville, FL Zip 32209–6595; tel. 904/244–0411; Russell Armistead, Chief Executive Officer
Web address: www.ufhealthjax.org/

UF HEALTH SHANDS HOSPITAL (O, 972 beds) 1600 S.W. Archer Road, Gainesville, FL Zip 32610–3003, Mailing Address: PO Box 100326, Zip 32610–0326; tel. 352/265–0111; Edward Jimenez, Chief Executive Officer
Web address: www.https://ufhealth.org/

Owned, leased, sponsored:	2 hospitals	1592 beds
Contract–managed:	0 hospitals	0 beds
Totals:	2 hospitals	1592 beds

★0224: UMASS MEMORIAL HEALTH CARE, INC. (NP)
1 Biotech Park, Worcester, MA Zip 01605–2982; tel. 508/334–0100; Eric Dickson, M.D., President and Chief Executive Officer
(Moderately Centralized Health System)

MASSACHUSETTS: CLINTON HOSPITAL (O, 41 beds) 201 Highland Street, Clinton, MA Zip 01510–1096; tel. 978/368–3000; Lisa Colombo, R.N., Chief Executive Officer
Web address: www.clintonhospital.org

HEALTHALLIANCE HOSPITALS (O, 103 beds) 60 Hospital Road, Leominster, MA Zip 01453–2205; tel. 978/466–2000; Deborah K. Weymouth, FACHE, President and Chief Executive Officer
Web address: www.healthalliance.com

UMASS MEMORIAL MEDICAL CENTER (O, 654 beds) 119 Belmont Street, Worcester, MA Zip 01605–2982; tel. 508/334–1000; Patrick L. Muldoon, FACHE, President
Web address: www.umassmemorial.org

UMASS MEMORIAL–MARLBOROUGH HOSPITAL (O, 67 beds) 157 Union ST, Marlborough, MA Zip 01752–1297; tel. 508/481–5000; Steven P. Roach, FACHE, President and Chief Executive Officer
Web address: www.marlboroughhospital.org

Owned, leased, sponsored:	4 hospitals	865 beds
Contract–managed:	0 hospitals	0 beds
Totals:	4 hospitals	865 beds

★0901: UNC HEALTH CARE (NP)
101 Manning Drive, Chapel Hill, NC Zip 27514–4220; tel. 919/966–4131; William L. Roper, M.D., M.P.H., Chief Executive Officer
(Moderately Centralized Health System)

For explanation of codes following names, see page B2.
★ Indicates Type III membership in the American Hospital Association.

NORTH CAROLINA: CALDWELL MEMORIAL HOSPITAL (O, 82 beds) 321 Mulberry Street S.W., Lenoir, NC Zip 28645–5720, Mailing Address: P.O. Box 1890, Zip 28645–1890; tel. 828/757–5100; Laura J. Easton, R.N., President and Chief Executive Officer
Web address: www.caldwellmemorial.org

CHATHAM HOSPITAL (O, 25 beds) 475 Progress Boulevard, Siler City, NC Zip 27344–6787, Mailing Address: P.O. Box 649, Zip 27344–0649; tel. 919/799–4000; Robert A. Enders, Jr., President
Web address: www.chathamhospital.org

HIGH POINT REGIONAL HEALTH SYSTEM (O, 335 beds) 601 North Elm Street, High Point, NC Zip 27262–4398, Mailing Address: P.O. Box HP–5, Zip 27261–1899; tel. 336/878–6000; Ernest L. Bovio, Jr., Chief Executive Officer
Web address: www.highpointregional.com

JOHNSTON HEALTH (C, 145 beds) 509 North Bright Leaf Boulevard, Smithfield, NC Zip 27577–4407, Mailing Address: P.O. Box 1376, Zip 27577–1376; tel. 919/934–8171; Charles W. Elliott, Jr., Chief Executive Officer
Web address: www.johnstonhealth.org

MARGARET R. PARDEE MEMORIAL HOSPITAL (C, 138 beds) 800 North Justice Street, Hendersonville, NC Zip 28791–3410; tel. 828/696–1000; James M. Kirby, II, President and Chief Executive Officer
Web address: www.pardeehospital.org

NASH HEALTH CARE SYSTEMS (C, 303 beds) 2460 Curtis Ellis Drive, Rocky Mount, NC Zip 27804–2237; tel. 252/962–8000; Larry H. Chewning, III, President and Chief Executive Officer
Web address: www.nhcs.org

UNC LENOIR HEALTHCARE (C, 155 beds) 100 Airport Road, Kinston, NC Zip 28501–1634, Mailing Address: P.O. Box 1678, Zip 28503–1678; tel. 252/522–7000; Gary E. Black, President and Chief Executive Officer
Web address: www.lenoirmemorial.org

UNC REX HEALTHCARE (O, 660 beds) 4420 Lake Boone Trail, Raleigh, NC Zip 27607–6599; tel. 919/784–3100; Steve W. Burriss, Ph.D., President
Web address: www.rexhealth.com

UNIVERSITY OF NORTH CAROLINA HOSPITALS (O, 866 beds) 101 Manning Drive, Chapel Hill, NC Zip 27514–4220; tel. 984/974–1000; Gary L. Park, President
Web address: www.unchealthcare.org

WAYNE MEMORIAL HOSPITAL (C, 274 beds) 2700 Wayne Memorial Drive, Goldsboro, NC Zip 27534–9494, Mailing Address: P.O. Box 8001, Zip 27533–8001; tel. 919/736–1110; Robert A. Enders, Jr., Interim President and Chief Executive Officer
Web address: www.waynehealth.org

Owned, leased, sponsored:	5 hospitals	1968 beds
Contract–managed:	5 hospitals	1015 beds
Totals:	10 hospitals	2983 beds

0922: UNION GENERAL HOSPITAL, INC. (NP)
35 Hospital Road, Blairsville, GA Zip 30512–3139; tel. 706/745–2111; Mike Gowder, Chief Executive Officer

GEORGIA: CHATUGE REGIONAL HOSPITAL AND NURSING HOME (O, 137 beds) 110 Main Street, Hiawassee, GA Zip 30546–3408, Mailing Address: P.O. Box 509, Zip 30546–0509; tel. 706/896–2222; John Mark Gordon, Administrator
Web address: www.chatugeregionalhospital.org

UNION GENERAL HOSPITAL (O, 195 beds) 35 Hospital Road, Blairsville, GA Zip 30512–3139; tel. 706/745–2111; Lewis Kelley, Interim Chief Executive Officer
Web address: www.uniongeneralhospital.com

Owned, leased, sponsored:	2 hospitals	332 beds
Contract–managed:	0 hospitals	0 beds
Totals:	2 hospitals	332 beds

0288: UNITED HEALTH SERVICES (NP)
10–42 Mitchell Avenue, Binghamton, NY Zip 13903–1617; tel. 607/762–2200; Matthew J. Salanger, President and Chief Executive Officer
(Independent Hospital System)

NEW YORK: UHS CHENANGO MEMORIAL HOSPITAL (O, 138 beds) 179 North Broad Street, Norwich, NY Zip 13815–1097; tel. 607/337–4111; Drake M. Lamen, President, Chief Executive Officer and Chief Medical Officer
Web address: www.uhs.net/cmh

UHS DELAWARE VALLEY HOSPITAL (O, 25 beds) 1 Titus Place, Walton, NY Zip 13856–1498; tel. 607/865–2100; Paul Summers, President and Chief Executive Officer
Web address: www.uhs.net/locations/

UNITED HEALTH SERVICES HOSPITALS–BINGHAMTON (O, 466 beds) 10–42 Mitchell Avenue, Binghamton, NY Zip 13903–1678; tel. 607/763–6000; Matthew J. Salanger, President and Chief Executive Officer
Web address: www.uhs.net

Owned, leased, sponsored:	3 hospitals	629 beds
Contract–managed:	0 hospitals	0 beds
Totals:	3 hospitals	629 beds

9605: UNITED MEDICAL CORPORATION (IO)
603 Main Street, Windermere, FL Zip 34786–3548, Mailing Address: P.O. Box 1100, Zip 34786–1100; tel. 407/876–2200; Donald R. Dizney, Chairman and Chief Executive Officer

PUERTO RICO: HOSPITAL PAVIA–HATO REY (O, 180 beds) 435 Ponce De Leon Avenue, San Juan, PR Zip 00917–3428; tel. 787/641–2323; Guillermo Pastrana, Executive Director
Web address: www.paviahealth.com

HOSPITAL PAVIA–SANTURCE (O, 197 beds) 1462 Asia Street, San Juan, PR Zip 00909–2143, Mailing Address: Box 11137, Santurce Station, Zip 00910–1137; tel. 787/727–6060; Jose Luis Rodriguez, Chief Executive Officer
Web address: www.paviahealth.com

HOSPITAL PEREA (O, 103 beds) 15 Basora Street, Mayaguez, PR Zip 00681, Mailing Address: P.O. Box 170, Zip 00681; tel. 787/834–0101; Jorge I. Martinez, Executive Director
Web address: www.paviahealth.com/perea_hospital.htm

HOSPITAL SAN FRANCISCO (O, 150 beds) 371 Avenida De Diego, San Juan, PR Zip 00923–1711, Mailing Address: P.O. Box 29025, Zip 00929–0025; tel. 787/767–5100; Marcos Aguila, Chief Executive Officer
Web address: www.metropavia.com/SanFrancisco.cfm

SAN JORGE CHILDREN'S HOSPITAL (O, 125 beds) 252 San Jorge Street, Santurce, San Juan, PR Zip 00912–3310; tel. 787/727–1000; Domingo Cruz, Senior Vice President Operations
Web address: www.sanjorgechildrenshospital.com

TENNESSEE: TEN BROECK TENNESSEE TREATMENT FACILITY (O, 36 beds) 1 Medical Center Boulevard, 5 West, Cookeville, TN Zip 38501; tel. 931/783–2570; Kelly Tripp, Chief Executive Officer
Web address: www.tenbroeck.com

Owned, leased, sponsored:	6 hospitals	791 beds
Contract–managed:	0 hospitals	0 beds
Totals:	6 hospitals	791 beds

0937: UNITED MEDICAL REHABILITATION HOSPITALS (IO)
3201 Wall Boulevard, Suite B., Gretna, LA Zip 70056–7755; tel. 504/433–5551; John E.H. Mills, President & Chief Executive Officer

LOUISIANA: UNITED MEDICAL REHABILITATION HOSPITAL (O, 21 beds) 3201 Wall Boulevard, Suite B., Gretna, LA Zip 70056–7755; tel. 504/433–5551; John E.H. Mills, President and Chief Executive Officer
Web address: www.umrhospital.com/

UNITED MEDICAL REHABILITATION HOSPITAL (O, 20 beds) 15717 Belle Drive, Hammond, LA Zip 70403–1439; tel. 985/340–5998; Cyrilla Bonds, Administrator
Web address: www.umrhospital.com

Owned, leased, sponsored:	2 hospitals	41 beds
Contract–managed:	0 hospitals	0 beds
Totals:	2 hospitals	41 beds

For explanation of codes following names, see page B2.
★ Indicates Type III membership in the American Hospital Association.

0322: UNITED SURGICAL PARTNERS INTERNATIONAL (IO)
15305 Dallas Parkway, Suite 1600, Addison, TX Zip 75001–6491;
tel. 972/713–3500; William H. Wilcox, President and Chief Executive
Officer
(Independent Hospital System)

ARIZONA: ARIZONA ORTHOPEDIC SURGICAL HOSPITAL (O, 24 beds) 2905
West Warner Road, Chandler, AZ Zip 85224–1674; tel. 480/603–9000;
Patricia Alice, Chief Executive Officer
Web address: www.azosh.com

OKLAHOMA: OKLAHOMA CENTER FOR ORTHOPEDIC AND MULTI–SPECIALTY
SURGERY (O, 14 beds) 8100 South Walker, Suite C., Oklahoma City, OK
Zip 73139–9402, Mailing Address: P.O. Box 890609, Zip 73189–0609;
tel. 405/602–6500; Mike Kimzey, Chief Executive Officer and
Administrator
Web address: www.ocomhospital.com

TEXAS: BAYLOR MEDICAL CENTER AT FRISCO (O, 68 beds) 5601 Warren
Parkway, Frisco, TX Zip 75034–4069; tel. 214/407–5000; William A.
Keaton, Chief Executive Officer
Web address: www.bmcf.com

BAYLOR MEDICAL CENTER AT UPTOWN (O, 24 beds) 2727 East Lemmon
Avenue, Dallas, TX Zip 75204–2895; tel. 214/443–3000; Jon Duckert, Chief
Executive Officer
Web address: www.bmcuptown.com

BAYLOR SURGICAL HOSPITAL AT LAS COLINAS (O, 12 beds) 400 West
Interstate 635, Irving, TX Zip 75063; tel. 972/868–4000; Deonna Unell,
Chief Executive Officer
Web address: www.baylorhealth.
com/About/Community/Assessments/West/ICSH/Pages/Default.aspx

TOPS SURGICAL SPECIALTY HOSPITAL (O, 15 beds) 17080 Red Oak Drive,
Houston, TX Zip 77090–2602; tel. 281/539–2900; Samuel H. Rossmann,
Chief Executive Officer
Web address: www.tops–hospital.com

Owned, leased, sponsored:	6 hospitals	157 beds
Contract–managed:	0 hospitals	0 beds
Totals:	6 hospitals	157 beds

★0061: UNITYPOINT HEALTH (NP)
1776 Westlakes Parkway, Suite 400, West Des Moines, IA
Zip 50266–8239; tel. 515/241–6161; Kevin Vermeer, President and
Chief Executive Officer
(Decentralized Health System)

ILLINOIS: UNITYPOINT HEALTH – PEORIA (O, 277 beds) 221 N.E. Glen Oak
Avenue, Peoria, IL Zip 61636–4310; tel. 309/672–5522; Deborah R.
Simon, R.N., President and Chief Executive Officer
Web address: www.unitypoint.org/peoria

UNITYPOINT HEALTH – PROCTOR (O, 138 beds) 5409 North Knoxville
Avenue, Peoria, IL Zip 61614–5069; tel. 309/691–1000; Deborah R. Simon,
R.N., President and Chief Executive Officer
Web address: www.proctor.org

UNITYPOINT HEALTH – TRINITY ROCK ISLAND (O, 345 beds) 2701 17th
Street, Rock Island, IL Zip 61201–5393; tel. 309/779–5000; Richard A.
Seidler, FACHE, President and Chief Executive Officer
Web address: www.trinityqc.com

IOWA: BUENA VISTA REGIONAL MEDICAL CENTER (C, 35 beds) 1525 West
Fifth Street, Storm Lake, IA Zip 50588–3027, Mailing Address: P.O. Box
309, Zip 50588–0309; tel. 712/732–4030; Steven Colerick, Chief
Executive Officer
Web address: www.bvrmc.org

CLARKE COUNTY HOSPITAL (C, 25 beds) 800 South Fillmore Street, Osceola,
IA Zip 50213–1619; tel. 641/342–2184; Brian G. Evans, FACHE, Chief
Executive Officer
Web address: www.clarkehosp.org

COMMUNITY MEMORIAL HOSPITAL (C, 16 beds) 909 West First Street,
Sumner, IA Zip 50674–1203, Mailing Address: P.O. Box 148,
Zip 50674–0148; tel. 563/578–3275; Dustin Wright, Chief Executive Officer
Web address: www.cmhsumner.org

GREATER REGIONAL MEDICAL CENTER (C, 25 beds) 1700 West Townline
Street Suite 3, Creston, IA Zip 50801–1099; tel. 641/782–7091; Monte
Neitzel, Chief Executive Officer
Web address: www.greaterregional.org

GREENE COUNTY MEDICAL CENTER (C, 90 beds) 1000 West Lincolnway,
Jefferson, IA Zip 50129–1645; tel. 515/386–2114; Carl P. Behne,
Administrator and Chief Executive Officer
Web address: www.gcmchealth.com

GRUNDY COUNTY MEMORIAL HOSPITAL (C, 80 beds) 201 East J Avenue,
Grundy Center, IA Zip 50638–2096; tel. 319/824–5421; Jennifer Havens,
Chief Executive Officer and Director of Nursing Operations
Web address: www.grundycountyhospital.com

GUTHRIE COUNTY HOSPITAL (C, 17 beds) 710 North 12th Street, Guthrie
Center, IA Zip 50115–1544; tel. 641/332–2201; Patrick Peters, Chief
Executive Officer
Web address: www.guthriecountyhospital.org

GUTTENBERG MUNICIPAL HOSPITAL (C, 20 beds) 200 Main Street,
Guttenberg, IA Zip 52052–9108, Mailing Address: P.O. Box 550,
Zip 52052–0550; tel. 563/252–1121; Kimberley A. Gau, FACHE, Chief
Executive Officer
Web address: www.guttenberghospital.org

HUMBOLDT COUNTY MEMORIAL HOSPITAL (C, 49 beds) 1000 North 15th
Street, Humboldt, IA Zip 50548–1008; tel. 515/332–4200; Michelle Sleiter,
Chief Executive Officer
Web address: www.humboldthospital.org

LORING HOSPITAL (C, 25 beds) 211 Highland Avenue, Sac City, IA
Zip 50583–2424; tel. 712/662–7105; Brian Martin, Chief Executive Officer
Web address: www.loringhospital.org

MARENGO MEMORIAL HOSPITAL (O, 25 beds) 300 West May Street,
Marengo, IA Zip 52301–1261; tel. 319/642–5543; Barry Goettsch, FACHE,
Chief Executive Officer
Web address: www.marengohospital.org

POCAHONTAS COMMUNITY HOSPITAL (C, 20 beds) 606 N.W. Seventh Street,
Pocahontas, IA Zip 50574–1099; tel. 712/335–3501; James D. Roetman,
President and Chief Executive Officer
Web address: www.pocahontashospital.org

STEWART MEMORIAL COMMUNITY HOSPITAL (C, 25 beds) 1301 West Main,
Lake City, IA Zip 51449–1585; tel. 712/464–3171; Cynthia L. Carstens,
R.N., President and Chief Executive Officer
Web address: www.stewartmemorial.org

STORY COUNTY MEDICAL CENTER (C, 77 beds) 640 South 19th Street,
Nevada, IA Zip 50201–2902; tel. 515/382–2111; Nate Thompson, Chief
Executive Officer
Web address: www.storymedical.org

UNITYPOINT HEALTH – ALLEN HOSPITAL (O, 201 beds) 1825 Logan Avenue,
Waterloo, IA Zip 50703–1916; tel. 319/235–3941; Pamela K. Delagardelle,
President and Chief Executive Officer
Web address: www.allenhospital.org

UNITYPOINT HEALTH – FINLEY HOSPITAL (O, 109 beds) 350 North Grandview
Avenue, Dubuque, IA Zip 52001–6392; tel. 563/582–1881; David R.
Brandon, President and Chief Executive Officer
Web address: www.unitypoint.org

UNITYPOINT HEALTH – IOWA METHODIST MEDICAL CENTER (O, 432 beds)
1200 Pleasant Street, Des Moines, IA Zip 50309–1406; tel. 515/241–6212;
Eric T. Crowell, President and Chief Executive Officer
Web address: www.unitypoint.org

UNITYPOINT HEALTH – JONES REGIONAL MEDICAL CENTER (O, 22 beds)
1795 Highway 64 East, Anamosa, IA Zip 52205–2112; tel. 319/462–6131;
Eric Briesemeister, Chief Executive Officer
Web address: www.jonesregional.org

UNITYPOINT HEALTH – ST. LUKE'S (O, 155 beds) 2720 Stone Park
Boulevard, Sioux City, IA Zip 51104–3734; tel. 712/279–3500; Lynn Wold,
President and Chief Executive Officer
Web address: www.stlukes.org

UNITYPOINT HEALTH – ST. LUKE'S HOSPITAL (O, 347 beds) 1026 A Avenue
N.E., Cedar Rapids, IA Zip 52402–3026, Mailing Address: P.O. Box 3026,
Zip 52406–3026; tel. 319/369–7211; Theodore E. Townsend, FACHE,
President and Chief Executive Officer
Web address: www.unitypoint.org

For explanation of codes following names, see page B2.
★ Indicates Type III membership in the American Hospital Association.

UNITYPOINT HEALTH – TRINITY BETTENDORF (O, 76 beds) 4500 Utica Ridge Road, Bettendorf, IA Zip 52722–1626; tel. 563/742–5000; Richard A. Seidler, FACHE, President and Chief Executive Officer
Web address: www.trinityqc.com

UNITYPOINT HEALTH – TRINITY MUSCATINE (O, 45 beds) 1518 Mulberry Avenue, Muscatine, IA Zip 52761–3499; tel. 563/264–9100; James M. Hayes, Chief Executive Officer
Web address: www.unitypoint.org/quadcities/trinity–muscatine.aspx

UNITYPOINT HEALTH – TRINITY REGIONAL MEDICAL CENTER (O, 107 beds) 802 Kenyon Road, Fort Dodge, IA Zip 50501–5795; tel. 515/573–3101; Mike Dewerff, President and Chief Executive Officer
Web address: www.trmc.org

UNITYPOINT HEALTH–IOWA LUTHERAN HOSPITAL (O, 205 beds) 700 East University Avenue, Des Moines, IA Zip 50316–2392; tel. 515/263–5612; Eric T. Crowell, President and Chief Executive Officer
Web address: www.unitypoint.org

WISCONSIN: MERITER UNITYPOINT HEALTH (O, 304 beds) 202 South Park Street, Madison, WI Zip 53715–1507; tel. 608/417–6000; Arthur Nizza, Chief Executive Officer
Web address: www.meriter.com

Owned, leased, sponsored:	15 hospitals	2788 beds
Contract–managed:	13 hospitals	504 beds
Totals:	28 hospitals	3292 beds

9555: UNIVERSAL HEALTH SERVICES, INC. (IO)
367 South Gulph Road, King of Prussia, PA Zip 19406–3121, Mailing Address: P.O. Box 61558, Zip 19406–0958; tel. 610/768–3300; Alan B. Miller, Chairman and Chief Executive Officer
(Decentralized Health System)

ALABAMA: HILL CREST BEHAVIORAL HEALTH SERVICES (O, 94 beds) 6869 Fifth Avenue South, Birmingham, AL Zip 35212–1866; tel. 205/833–9000; Steve McCabe, Chief Executive Officer
Web address: www.hillcrestbhs.com

LAUREL OAKS BEHAVIORAL HEALTH CENTER (O, 38 beds) 700 East Cottonwood Road, Dothan, AL Zip 36301–3644; tel. 334/794–7373; Derek Johnson, Chief Executive Officer
Web address: www.laureloaksbhc.com

ALASKA: NORTH STAR BEHAVIORAL HEALTH SYSTEM (O, 200 beds) 2530 DeBarr Circle, Anchorage, AK Zip 99508–2948; tel. 907/258–7575; Andrew Mayo, Ph.D., Chief Executive Officer and Managing Director
Web address: www.northstarbehavioral.com

ARIZONA: PALO VERDE BEHAVIORAL HEALTH (O, 48 beds) 2695 North Craycroft Road, Tucson, AZ Zip 85712–2244; tel. 520/322–2888; P. P. Frayser, Chief Executive Officer
Web address: www.paloverdebh.com/

VALLEY HOSPITAL PHOENIX (O, 122 beds) 3550 East Pinchot Avenue, Phoenix, AZ Zip 85018–7434; tel. 602/957–4000; Michelle David, Chief Executive Officer
Web address: www.valleyhospital–phoenix.com

ARKANSAS: PINNACLE POINTE HOSPITAL (O, 124 beds) 11501 Financial Center Parkway, Little Rock, AR Zip 72211–3715; tel. 501/223–3322; Shane Frazier, Chief Executive Officer
Web address: www.pinnaclepointehospital.com

RIVENDELL BEHAVIORAL HEALTH SERVICES OF ARKANSAS (O, 77 beds) 100 Rivendell Drive, Benton, AR Zip 72019–9100; tel. 501/316–1255; Jay Shehi, Chief Executive Officer
Web address: www.rivendellofarkansas.com

THE BRIDGEWAY (L, 127 beds) 21 Bridgeway Road, North Little Rock, AR Zip 72113–9516; tel. 501/771–1500; Jason Miller, M.P.H., Chief Executive Officer
Web address: www.thebridgeway.com

CALIFORNIA: BHC ALHAMBRA HOSPITAL (O, 97 beds) 4619 North Rosemead Boulevard, Rosemead, CA Zip 91770–1478, Mailing Address: P.O. Box 369, Zip 91770–0369; tel. 626/286–1191; Peggy Minnick, R.N., Chief Executive Officer
Web address: www.bhcalhambra.com

CANYON RIDGE HOSPITAL (O, 106 beds) 5353 G Street, Chino, CA Zip 91710–5250; tel. 909/590–3700; Burt Harris, Acting Chief Executive Officer
Web address: www.canyonridgehospital.com

CORONA REGIONAL MEDICAL CENTER (O, 238 beds) 800 South Main Street, Corona, CA Zip 92882–3400; tel. 951/737–4343; Mark H. Uffer, Chief Executive Officer
Web address: www.coronaregional.com

DEL AMO HOSPITAL (O, 70 beds) 23700 Camino Del Sol, Torrance, CA Zip 90505–5000; tel. 310/530–1151; Steven Oppenheimer, Chief Executive Officer
Web address: www.delamohospital.com

FREMONT HOSPITAL (O, 148 beds) 39001 Sundale Drive, Fremont, CA Zip 94538–2005; tel. 510/796–1100; John C. Cooper, Chief Executive Officer
Web address: www.fremonthospital.com

HERITAGE OAKS HOSPITAL (O, 120 beds) 4250 Auburn Boulevard, Sacramento, CA Zip 95841–4164; tel. 916/489–3336; Shawn Silva, Chief Executive Officer
Web address: www.heritageoakshospital.com

PALMDALE REGIONAL MEDICAL CENTER (O, 157 beds) 38600 Medical Center Drive, Palmdale, CA Zip 93551–4483; tel. 661/382–5000; Richard Allen, Chief Executive Officer
Web address: www.palmdaleregional.com

SIERRA VISTA HOSPITAL (O, 120 beds) 8001 Bruceville Road, Sacramento, CA Zip 95823–2329; tel. 916/288–0300; Mike Zauner, Chief Executive Officer
Web address: www.sierravistahospital.com

SOUTHWEST HEALTHCARE SYSTEM (O, 242 beds) 25500 Medical Center Drive, Murrieta, CA Zip 92562–5965; tel. 951/696–6000; Bradley D. Neet, FACHE, Chief Executive Officer
Web address: www.swhealthcaresystem.com/

TEMECULA VALLEY HOSPITAL (O, 140 beds) 31700 Temecula Parkway, Temecula, CA Zip 92592–5896; tel. 951/331–2216; Darlene Wetton, R.N., Chief Executive Officer
Web address: www.temeculavalleyhospital.com

COLORADO: CEDAR SPRINGS HOSPITAL (O, 110 beds) 2135 Southgate Road, Colorado Springs, CO Zip 80906–2693; tel. 719/633–4114; A. Christopher Burke, Chief Executive Officer
Web address: www.cedarspringsbhs.com

CENTENNIAL PEAKS HOSPITAL (O, 72 beds) 2255 South 88th Street, Louisville, CO Zip 80027–9716; tel. 303/673–9990; Elicia Bunch, Chief Executive Officer
Web address: www.centennialpeaks.com

HIGHLANDS BEHAVIORAL HEALTH SYSTEM (O, 86 beds) 8565 South Poplar Way, Littleton, CO Zip 80130–3602; tel. 720/348–2800; Lisa Strub, Interim Chief Executive Officer
Web address: www.highlandsbhs.com

DELAWARE: DOVER BEHAVIORAL HEALTH SYSTEM (O, 72 beds) 725 Horsepond Road, Dover, DE Zip 19901–7232; tel. 302/741–0140; Jean–Charles Constant, Administrator
Web address: www.doverbehavioral.com

ROCKFORD CENTER (O, 128 beds) 100 Rockford Drive, Newark, DE Zip 19713–2121; tel. 302/996–5480; John F. McKenna, Chief Executive Officer and Managing Director
Web address: www.rockfordcenter.com

DISTRICT OF COLUMBIA: GEORGE WASHINGTON UNIVERSITY HOSPITAL (O, 385 beds) 900 23rd Street N.W., Washington, DC Zip 20037–2342; tel. 202/715–4000; Kimberly Russo, Chief Executive Officer
Web address: www.gwhospital.com

FLORIDA: ATLANTIC SHORES HOSPITAL (O, 72 beds) 4545 North Federal Highway, Fort Lauderdale, FL Zip 33308–5274; tel. 954/771–2711; Manuel R. Llano, Chief Executive Officer
Web address: www.atlanticshoreshospital.com

CENTRAL FLORIDA BEHAVIORAL HOSPITAL (O, 126 beds) 6601 Central Florida Parkway, Orlando, FL Zip 32821–8064; tel. 407/370–0111; Vickie Lewis, Chief Executive Officer
Web address: www.centralfloridabehavioral.com

For explanation of codes following names, see page B2.
★ Indicates Type III membership in the American Hospital Association.

B142 Health Care Systems, Networks and Alliances

© 2016 AHA Guide

EMERALD COAST BEHAVIORAL HOSPITAL (O, 80 beds) 1940 Harrison Avenue, Panama City, FL Zip 32405–4542; tel. 850/763–0017; Tim Bedford, Chief Executive Officer
Web address: www.emeraldcoastbehavioral.com

FORT LAUDERDALE HOSPITAL (L, 100 beds) 1601 East Las Olas Boulevard, Fort Lauderdale, FL Zip 33301–2393; tel. 954/463–4321; Manuel R. Llano, Chief Executive Officer
Web address: www.fortlauderdalehospital.org

LAKEWOOD RANCH MEDICAL CENTER (O, 120 beds) 8330 Lakewood Ranch Boulevard, Bradenton, FL Zip 34202–5174; tel. 941/782–2100; Linda S. Widra, FACHE, Ph.D., R.N., Interim Chief Executive Officer
Web address: www.lakewoodranchmedicalcenter.com

MANATEE MEMORIAL HOSPITAL (O, 319 beds) 206 Second Street East, Bradenton, FL Zip 34208–1000; tel. 941/746–5111; Kevin DiLallo, Chief Executive Officer
Web address: www.manateememorial.com

RIVER POINT BEHAVIORAL HEALTH (O, 92 beds) 6300 Beach Boulevard, Jacksonville, FL Zip 32216–2782; tel. 904/724–9202; Kevin McGee, Chief Executive Officer
Web address: www.riverpointbehavioral.com

SUNCOAST BEHAVIORAL HEALTH CENTER (O, 80 beds) 4480 51st Street West, Bradenton, FL Zip 34210–2855; tel. 941/251–5000; Brandy Hamilton, Chief Executive Officer
Web address: www.suncoastbhc.com

THE VINES (O, 64 beds) 3130 S.W. 27th Avenue, Ocala, FL Zip 34471–4306; tel. 352/671–3130; Stephen Quintyne, Chief Executive Officer
Web address: www.thevineshospital.com

WEKIVA SPRINGS (O, 60 beds) 3947 Salisbury Road, Jacksonville, FL Zip 32216–6115; tel. 904/296–3533; Sheila Carr, Chief Executive Officer
Web address: www.wekivacenter.com

WELLINGTON REGIONAL MEDICAL CENTER (L, 158 beds) 10101 Forest Hill Boulevard, West Palm Beach, FL Zip 33414–6199; tel. 561/798–8500; Robbin Lee, Chief Executive Officer
Web address: www.wellingtonregional.com

WINDMOOR HEALTHCARE OF CLEARWATER (O, 120 beds) 11300 U.S. 19 North, Clearwater, FL Zip 33764; tel. 727/541–2646; Wendy Merson, Chief Executive Officer
Web address: www.windmoor.com

GEORGIA: ANCHOR HOSPITAL (O, 122 beds) 5454 Yorktowne Drive, Atlanta, GA Zip 30349–5317; tel. 770/991–6044; Randall G. Hines, Ph.D., Chief Executive Officer
Web address: www.anchorhospital.com

COASTAL HARBOR TREATMENT CENTER (O, 191 beds) 1150 Cornell Avenue, Savannah, GA Zip 31406–2702; tel. 912/354–3911; Sally Perry, Chief Executive Officer
Web address: www.coastalharbor.com

PEACHFORD BEHAVIORAL HEALTH SYSTEM (O, 246 beds) 2151 Peachford Road, Atlanta, GA Zip 30338–6599; tel. 770/455–3200; Matthew Crouch, Chief Executive Officer and Managing Director
Web address: www.peachfordhospital.com

SAINT SIMONS BY–THE–SEA HOSPITAL (O, 101 beds) 2927 Demere Road, Saint Simons Island, GA Zip 31522–1620; tel. 912/638–1999; Maria Weese, Interim Chief Executive Officer
Web address: www.ssbythesea.com

TURNING POINT HOSPITAL (O, 59 beds) 3015 Veterans Parkway South, Moultrie, GA Zip 31788–6705, Mailing Address: P.O. Box 1177, Zip 31776–1177; tel. 229/985–4815; Judy H. Payne, Chief Executive Officer
Web address: www.turningpointcare.com

IDAHO: INTERMOUNTAIN HOSPITAL (O, 140 beds) 303 North Allumbaugh Street, Boise, ID Zip 83704–9208; tel. 208/377–8400; Jeffrey F. Morrell, Chief Executive Officer
Web address: www.intermountainhospital.com

ILLINOIS: GARFIELD PARK HOSPITAL (O, 43 beds) 520 North Ridgeway Avenue, Chicago, IL Zip 60624–1232; tel. 773/265–3700; Len Kirby, Chief Executive Officer
Web address: www.garfieldparkhospital.com

HARTGROVE HOSPITAL (O, 128 beds) 5730 West Roosevelt Road, Chicago, IL Zip 60644–1580; tel. 773/413–1700; Steven Airhart, Chief Executive Officer
Web address: www.hartgrovehospital.com

LINCOLN PRAIRIE BEHAVIORAL HEALTH CENTER (O, 97 beds) 5230 South Sixth Street, Springfield, IL Zip 62703–5128; tel. 217/585–1180; Mark Littrell, Chief Executive Officer
Web address: www.lincolnprairiebhc.com/

RIVEREDGE HOSPITAL (O, 224 beds) 8311 West Roosevelt Road, Forest Park, IL Zip 60130–2500; tel. 708/771–7000; Carey Carlock, Chief Executive Officer
Web address: www.riveredgehospital.com

STREAMWOOD BEHAVIORAL HEALTH CENTER (O, 177 beds) 1400 East Irving Park Road, Streamwood, IL Zip 60107–3203; tel. 630/837–9000; Ron Weglarz, Chief Executive Officer and Managing Director
Web address: www.streamwoodhospital.com

THE PAVILION (O, 46 beds) 809 West Church Street, Champaign, IL Zip 61820–3399; tel. 217/373–1700; Joseph Sheehy, Chief Executive Officer and Managing Director
Web address: www.pavilionhospital.com

INDIANA: BLOOMINGTON MEADOWS HOSPITAL (O, 67 beds) 3600 North Prow Road, Bloomington, IN Zip 47404–1616; tel. 812/331–8000; Jean Scallon, Chief Executive Officer
Web address: www.bloomingtonmeadows.com

MICHIANA BEHAVIORAL HEALTH CENTER (O, 75 beds) 1800 North Oak Drive, Plymouth, IN Zip 46563–3492; tel. 574/936–3784; Michael Perry, Chief Executive Officer
Web address: www.michianabhc.com

VALLE VISTA HOSPITAL (O, 102 beds) 898 East Main Street, Greenwood, IN Zip 46143–1400; tel. 317/887–1348; Sherri R. Jewett, Chief Executive Officer
Web address: www.vallevistahospital.com

WELLSTONE REGIONAL HOSPITAL (O, 100 beds) 2700 Vissing Park Road, Jeffersonville, IN Zip 47130–5989; tel. 812/284–8000; Greg Stewart, Chief Executive Officer
Web address: www.wellstonehospital.com

KENTUCKY: CUMBERLAND HALL HOSPITAL (O, 97 beds) 270 Walton Way, Hopkinsville, KY Zip 42240–6808; tel. 270/886–1919; Jason Staats, Chief Executive Officer
Web address: www.cumberlandhallhospital.com

LINCOLN TRAIL BEHAVIORAL HEALTH SYSTEM (O, 140 beds) 3909 South Wilson Road, Radcliff, KY Zip 40160–8944, Mailing Address: P.O. Box 369, Zip 40159–0369; tel. 270/351–9444; Charles L. Webb, Jr., Chief Executive Officer
Web address: www.lincolnbehavioral.com

RIDGE BEHAVIORAL HEALTH SYSTEM (O, 110 beds) 3050 Rio Dosa Drive, Lexington, KY Zip 40509–1540; tel. 859/269–2325; Nina W. Eisner, Chief Executive Officer and Managing Director
Web address: www.ridgebhs.com

RIVENDELL BEHAVIORAL HEALTH (O, 125 beds) 1035 Porter Pike, Bowling Green, KY Zip 42103–9581; tel. 270/843–1199; Matt Ours, Chief Executive Officer and Managing Director
Web address: www.rivendellbehavioral.com

THE BROOK AT DUPONT (O, 88 beds) 1405 Browns Lane, Louisville, KY Zip 40207–4608; tel. 502/896–0495; Paul Andrews, Chief Executive Officer
Web address: www.thebrookhospitals.com/

THE BROOK HOSPITAL – KMI (O, 110 beds) 8521 Old LaGrange Road, Louisville, KY Zip 40242–3800; tel. 502/426–6380; Paul Andrews, Chief Executive Officer
Web address: www.thebrookhospitals.com

LOUISIANA: BRENTWOOD HOSPITAL (O, 176 beds) 1006 Highland Avenue, Shreveport, LA Zip 71101–4103; tel. 318/678–7500; William Weaver, Chief Executive Officer
Web address: www.brentwoodbehavioral.com

RIVER OAKS HOSPITAL (O, 126 beds) 1525 River Oaks Road West, New Orleans, LA Zip 70123–2162; tel. 504/734–1740; Evelyn Nolting, Chief Executive Officer and Managing Director
Web address: www.riveroakshospital.com

MASSACHUSETTS: ARBOUR H. R. I. HOSPITAL (O, 68 beds) 227 Babcock Street, Brookline, MA Zip 02446–6799; tel. 617/731–3200; William Zella, Chief Executive Officer
Web address: www.arbourhealth.com

ARBOUR HOSPITAL (O, 118 beds) 49 Robinwood Avenue, Boston, MA Zip 02130–2156; tel. 617/522–4400; Laura Ames, Chief Executive Officer
Web address: www.arbourhealth.com

For explanation of codes following names, see page B2.
★ Indicates Type III membership in the American Hospital Association.

ARBOUR–FULLER HOSPITAL (O, 46 beds) 200 May Street, Attleboro, MA Zip 02703–5520; tel. 508/761–8500; James Rollins, Interim Chief Executive Officer
Web address: www.arbourhealth.com

PEMBROKE HOSPITAL (O, 115 beds) 199 Oak Street, Pembroke, MA Zip 02359–1953; tel. 781/829–7000; Thomas P. Hickey, Chief Executive Officer and Managing Director
Web address: www.arbourhealth.com/organizations/pembroke–hospital/

WESTWOOD LODGE HOSPITAL (O, 130 beds) 45 Clapboardtree Street, Westwood, MA Zip 02090–2903; tel. 781/762–7764; Gregory Brownstein, Chief Executive Officer
Web address: www.arbourhealth.com

MICHIGAN: FOREST VIEW PSYCHIATRIC HOSPITAL (O, 109 beds) 1055 Medical Park Drive S.E., Grand Rapids, MI Zip 49546–3607; tel. 616/942–9610; Andrew Hotaling, Chief Executive Officer
Web address: www.forestviewhospital.com

HAVENWYCK HOSPITAL (O, 235 beds) 1525 University Drive, Auburn Hills, MI Zip 48326–2673; tel. 248/373–9200; Diane Henneman, Chief Executive Officer
Web address: www.havenwyckhospital.com

MISSISSIPPI: ALLIANCE HEALTH CENTER (O, 154 beds) 5000 Highway 39 North, Meridian, MS Zip 39301–1021; tel. 601/483–6211; Brennan Francois, Chief Executive Officer
Web address: www.alliancehealthcenter.com

BRENTWOOD BEHAVIORAL HEALTHCARE OF MISSISSIPPI (O, 105 beds) 3531 East Lakeland Drive, Jackson, MS Zip 39232–8839; tel. 601/936–2024; Michael J. Carney, Chief Executive Officer
Web address: www.brentwoodjackson.com

PARKWOOD BEHAVIORAL HEALTH SYSTEM (O, 148 beds) 8135 Goodman Road, Olive Branch, MS Zip 38654–2103; tel. 662/895–4900; Ethan Permenter, Chief Executive Officer
Web address: www.parkwoodbhs.com

MISSOURI: HEARTLAND BEHAVIORAL HEALTH SERVICES (O, 69 beds) 1500 West Ashland Street, Nevada, MO Zip 64772–1710; tel. 417/667–2666; Alyson Wysong–Harder, Chief Executive Officer
Web address: www.heartlandbehavioral.com

TWO RIVERS BEHAVIORAL HEALTH SYSTEM (O, 105 beds) 5121 Raytown Road, Kansas City, MO Zip 64133–2141; tel. 816/382–6300; Terry Trafton, Chief Executive Officer
Web address: www.tworivershospital.com

NEVADA: CENTENNIAL HILLS HOSPITAL MEDICAL CENTER (O, 171 beds) 6900 North Durango Drive, Las Vegas, NV Zip 89149–4409; tel. 702/835–9700; Sajit Pullarkat, Chief Executive Officer and Managing Director
Web address: www.centennialhillshospital.com

DESERT SPRINGS HOSPITAL MEDICAL CENTER (O, 346 beds) 2075 East Flamingo Road, Las Vegas, NV Zip 89119–5121; tel. 702/733–8800; Jeremy Bradshaw, Chief Executive Officer
Web address: www.desertspringshospital.com

NORTHERN NEVADA MEDICAL CENTER (O, 108 beds) 2375 East Prater Way, Sparks, NV Zip 89434–9641; tel. 775/331–7000; Alan C. Olive, Chief Executive Officer
Web address: www.nnmc.com

SPRING MOUNTAIN SAHARA (O, 30 beds) 5460 West Sahara, Las Vegas, NV Zip 89146–3307; tel. 702/216–8900; Darryl S. Dubroca, Chief Executive Officer and Managing Director
Web address: www.springmountainsahara.com

SPRING MOUNTAIN TREATMENT CENTER (L, 110 beds) 7000 West Spring Mountain Road, Las Vegas, NV Zip 89117–3816; tel. 702/873–2400; C. Alan Eaks, Chief Executive Officer and Managing Director
Web address: www.springmountaintreatmentcenter.com/

SPRING VALLEY HOSPITAL MEDICAL CENTER (O, 169 beds) 5400 South Rainbow Boulevard, Las Vegas, NV Zip 89118–1859; tel. 702/853–3000; Leonard Freehof, Chief Executive Officer and Managing Director
Web address: www.springvalleyhospital.com

SUMMERLIN HOSPITAL MEDICAL CENTER (O, 148 beds) 657 Town Center Drive, Las Vegas, NV Zip 89144–6367; tel. 702/233–7000; Robert S. Freymuller, Chief Executive Officer
Web address: www.summerlinhospital.com

VALLEY HOSPITAL MEDICAL CENTER (O, 365 beds) 620 Shadow Lane, Las Vegas, NV Zip 89106–4119; tel. 702/388–4000; Elaine Glaser, Chief Executive Officer
Web address: www.valleyhospital.net

WEST HILLS HOSPITAL (O, 190 beds) 1240 East Ninth Street, Reno, NV Zip 89512–2964; tel. 775/323–0478; Allison Zednicek, Chief Executive Officer
Web address: www.westhillshospital.net

NEW JERSEY: HAMPTON BEHAVIORAL HEALTH CENTER (O, 110 beds) 650 Rancocas Road, Westampton, NJ Zip 08060–5613; tel. 609/267–7000; Craig Hilton, Chief Executive Officer
Web address: www.hamptonhospital.com

SUMMIT OAKS HOSPITAL (O, 90 beds) 19 Prospect Street, Summit, NJ Zip 07901–2530; tel. 908/522–7000; Oana Radu, Chief Executive Officer
Web address: www.summitoakshospital.com/

NEW MEXICO: MESILLA VALLEY HOSPITAL (O, 120 beds) 3751 Del Rey Boulevard, Las Cruces, NM Zip 88012–8526; tel. 575/382–3500; Diana Schultz, Chief Executive Officer
Web address: www.mesillavalleyhospital.com

NORTH CAROLINA: BRYNN MARR HOSPITAL (O, 99 beds) 192 Village Drive, Jacksonville, NC Zip 28546–7299; tel. 910/577–1400; Jay Kortemeyer, Chief Executive Officer
Web address: www.brynnmarr.org

HOLLY HILL HOSPITAL (O, 200 beds) 3019 Falstaff Road, Raleigh, NC Zip 27610–1812; tel. 919/250–7000; Michael S. McDonald, Jr., Chief Executive Officer
Web address: www.hollyhillhospital.com

OLD VINEYARD BEHAVIORAL HEALTH SERVICES (O, 104 beds) 3637 Old Vineyard Road, Winston–Salem, NC Zip 27104–4842; tel. 336/794–3550; Kevin Patton, Chief Executive Officer
Web address: www.oldvineyardbhs.com

NORTH DAKOTA: PRAIRIE ST. JOHN'S (O, 94 beds) 510 4th Street South, Fargo, ND Zip 58103–1914; tel. 701/476–7200; Jeff Herman, Chief Executive Officer
Web address: www.prairie–stjohns.com

OHIO: ARROWHEAD BEHAVIORAL HEALTH HOSPITAL (O, 48 beds) 1725 Timber Line Road, Maumee, OH Zip 43537–4015; tel. 419/891–9333; Joseph Denicola, Chief Executive Officer and Managing Director
Web address: www.arrowheadbehavioral.com

BELMONT PINES HOSPITAL (O, 46 beds) 615 Churchill–Hubbard Road, Youngstown, OH Zip 44505–1379; tel. 330/759–2700; Lisa Cocca, Chief Executive Officer
Web address: www.belmontpines.com

WINDSOR–LAURELWOOD CENTER FOR BEHAVIORAL MEDICINE (O, 159 beds) 35900 Euclid Avenue, Willoughby, OH Zip 44094–4648; tel. 440/953–3000; Ric McAllister, Chief Executive Officer
Web address: www.windsorlaurelwood.com

OKLAHOMA: CEDAR RIDGE HOSPITAL (O, 116 beds) 6501 N.E. 50th Street, Oklahoma City, OK Zip 73141–9118; tel. 405/605–6111; Rob Lake, Interim Chief Executive Officer
Web address: www.cedarridgebhs.com

SHADOW MOUNTAIN BEHAVIORAL HEALTH SYSTEM (O, 238 beds) 6262 South Sheridan Road, Tulsa, OK Zip 74133–4055; tel. 918/492–8200; Mike Kistler, Chief Executive Officer
Web address: www.shadowmountainbhs.com

ST. MARY'S REGIONAL MEDICAL CENTER (O, 164 beds) 305 South Fifth Street, Enid, OK Zip 73701–5899, Mailing Address: P.O. Box 232, Zip 73702–0232; tel. 580/233–6100; Stanley D. Tatum, FACHE, Chief Executive Officer
Web address: www.stmarysregional.com

OREGON: CEDAR HILLS HOSPITAL (O, 78 beds) 10300 S.W. Eastridge Street, Portland, OR Zip 97225–5004; tel. 503/944–5000; Elizabeth Hutter, Chief Executive Officer
Web address: www.cedarhillshospital.com

PENNSYLVANIA: BROOKE GLEN BEHAVIORAL HOSPITAL (O, 146 beds) 7170 Lafayette Avenue, Fort Washington, PA Zip 19034–2301; tel. 215/641–5300; Neil Callahan, Chief Executive Officer
Web address: www.brookeglenhospital.com

For explanation of codes following names, see page B2.
★ Indicates Type III membership in the American Hospital Association.

CLARION PSYCHIATRIC CENTER (O, 74 beds) 2 Hospital Drive, Clarion, PA Zip 16214–8502; tel. 814/226–9545; Michael Post, Chief Executive Officer
Web address: www.clarioncenter.com

FAIRMOUNT BEHAVIORAL HEALTH SYSTEM (O, 235 beds) 561 Fairthorne Avenue, Philadelphia, PA Zip 19128–2499; tel. 215/487–4000; Lisa M. McConlogue, MSN, Ph.D., Chief Executive Officer and Managing Director
Web address: www.fairmountbhs.com

FOUNDATIONS BEHAVIORAL HEALTH (O, 58 beds) 833 East Butler Avenue, Doylestown, PA Zip 18901–2280; tel. 215/345–0444; Robert Weinhold, Chief Executive Officer
Web address: www.fbh.com

FRIENDS HOSPITAL (O, 192 beds) 4641 Roosevelt Boulevard, Philadelphia, PA Zip 19124–2343; tel. 215/831–4600; R. John Repique, R.N., Chief Executive Officer
Web address: www.friendshospital.com

HORSHAM CLINIC (O, 138 beds) 722 East Butler Pike, Ambler, PA Zip 19002–2310; tel. 215/643–7800; Phyllis Weisfield, Chief Executive Officer and Managing Director
Web address: www.horshamclinic.com

MEADOWS PSYCHIATRIC CENTER (O, 107 beds) 132 The Meadows Drive, Centre Hall, PA Zip 16828–9231; tel. 814/364–2161; Ann Wayne, Interim Chief Executive Officer and Managing Director
Web address: www.themeadows.net

ROXBURY TREATMENT CENTER (O, 94 beds) 601 Roxbury Road, Shippensburg, PA Zip 17257–9302; tel. 800/648–4673; Shauna Mogerman, Chief Executive Officer
Web address: www.roxburyhospital.com

PUERTO RICO: FIRST HOSPITAL PANAMERICANO (O, 153 beds) State Road 787 KM 1 5, Cidra, PR Zip 00739, Mailing Address: P.O. Box 1400, Zip 00739; tel. 787/739–5555; Astro Munoz, Executive Director
Web address: www.hospitalpanamericano.com

SOUTH CAROLINA: AIKEN REGIONAL MEDICAL CENTERS (O, 271 beds) 302 University Parkway, Aiken, SC Zip 29801–6302; tel. 803/641–5000; Vance V. Reynolds, FACHE, CPA, Chief Executive Officer
Web address: www.aikenregional.com

CAROLINA CENTER FOR BEHAVIORAL HEALTH (O, 130 beds) 2700 East Phillips Road, Greer, SC Zip 29650–4816; tel. 864/235–2335; John Willingham, Chief Executive Officer and Managing Director
Web address: www.thecarolinacenter.com

LIGHTHOUSE CARE CENTER OF CONWAY (O, 78 beds) 152 Waccamaw Medical Park Drive, Conway, SC Zip 29526–8901; tel. 843/347–8871; Thomas L. Ryba, Chief Executive Officer
Web address: www.lighthousecarecenterofconway.com/

PALMETTO LOWCOUNTRY BEHAVIORAL HEALTH (O, 100 beds) 2777 Speissegger Drive, Charleston, SC Zip 29405–8229; tel. 843/747–5830; Shari Baker, Chief Executive Officer
Web address: www.palmettobehavioralhealth.com

THREE RIVERS BEHAVIORAL HEALTH (O, 118 beds) 2900 Sunset Boulevard, West Columbia, SC Zip 29169–3422; tel. 803/796–9911; Nannette M. Lewis, Chief Executive Officer
Web address: www.threeriversbehavioral.org

TENNESSEE: LAKESIDE BEHAVIORAL HEALTH SYSTEM (O, 319 beds) 2911 Brunswick Road, Memphis, TN Zip 38133–4199; tel. 901/377–4700; Joy Golden, Chief Executive Officer
Web address: www.lakesidebhs.com

ROLLING HILLS HOSPITAL (O, 80 beds) 2014 Quail Hollow Circle, Franklin, TN Zip 37067–5967; tel. 615/628–5700; Jim Spruyt, Chief Executive Officer
Web address: www.RollingHillsHospital.org/

TEXAS: AUSTIN LAKES HOSPITAL (O, 58 beds) 1025 East 32nd Street, Austin, TX Zip 78705–2714; tel. 512/544–5253; Rick Buckelew, Chief Executive Officer
Web address: www.austinlakeshospital.com

AUSTIN OAKS HOSPITAL (O, 80 beds) 1407 West Stassney Lane, Austin, TX Zip 78745–2947; tel. 512/440–4800; Steve Kelly, Interim Chief Executive Officer
Web address: www.austinoakshospital.com

BEHAVIORAL HOSPITAL OF BELLAIRE (O, 114 beds) 5314 Dashwood Drive, Houston, TX Zip 77081–4603; tel. 713/600–9500; Ethan Permenter, Chief Executive Officer
Web address: www.bhbhospital.com

CORNERSTONE REGIONAL HOSPITAL (L, 14 beds) 2302 Cornerstone Boulevard, Edinburg, TX Zip 78539–8471; tel. 956/618–4444; Roxanna M. Godinez, Chief Executive Officer
Web address: www.cornerstoneregional.com

CYPRESS CREEK HOSPITAL (O, 96 beds) 17750 Cali Drive, Houston, TX Zip 77090–2700; tel. 281/586–7600; Brian Brooker, Chief Executive Officer
Web address: www.cypresscreekhospital.com

DOCTORS HOSPITAL OF LAREDO (O, 183 beds) 10700 McPherson Road, Laredo, TX Zip 78045–6268; tel. 956/523–2000; James R. Resendez, Chief Executive Officer
Web address: www.doctorshosplaredo.com

EL PASO BEHAVIORAL HEALTH SYSTEM (O, 163 beds) 1900 Denver Avenue, El Paso, TX Zip 79902–3008; tel. 915/544–4000; David W. Morris, Chief Executive Officer
Web address: www.ubhelpaso.com/

FORT DUNCAN REGIONAL MEDICAL CENTER (O, 101 beds) 3333 North Foster Maldonado Boulevard, Eagle Pass, TX Zip 78852–5893; tel. 830/773–5321; Eladio Montalvo, Chief Executive Officer
Web address: www.fortduncanmedicalcenter.com

GLEN OAKS HOSPITAL (O, 54 beds) 301 Division Street, Greenville, TX Zip 75401–4101; tel. 903/454–6000; Jennifer Dedrick, Chief Executive Officer
Web address: www.glenoakshospital.com

HICKORY TRAIL HOSPITAL (O, 86 beds) 2000 Old Hickory Trail, Desoto, TX Zip 75115–2242; tel. 972/298–7323; Kay McKennery, Interim Chief Executive Officer
Web address: www.hickorytrail.com

KINGWOOD PINES HOSPITAL (O, 82 beds) 2001 Ladbrook Drive, Kingwood, TX Zip 77339–3004; tel. 281/404–1001; James Burroughs, Chief Executive Officer
Web address: www.kingwoodpines.com

LAUREL RIDGE TREATMENT CENTER (O, 208 beds) 17720 Corporate Woods Drive, San Antonio, TX Zip 78259–3500; tel. 210/491–9400; Jacob Cuellar, M.D., Chief Executive Officer
Web address: www.laurelridgetc.com

MAYHILL HOSPITAL (O, 59 beds) 2809 South Mayhill Road, Denton, TX Zip 76208–5910; tel. 940/239–3000; Adam Vincent, Chief Executive Officer
Web address: www.mayhillhospital.com

MILLWOOD HOSPITAL (O, 122 beds) 1011 North Cooper Street, Arlington, TX Zip 76011–5517; tel. 817/261–3121; Dwight A. Lacy, Chief Executive Officer
Web address: www.millwoodhospital.com

NORTHWEST TEXAS HEALTHCARE SYSTEM (O, 437 beds) 1501 South Coulter Avenue, Amarillo, TX Zip 79106–1770, Mailing Address: P.O. Box 1110, Zip 79105–1110; tel. 806/354–1000; Mark W. Crawford, Chief Executive Officer
Web address: www.nwtexashealthcare.com

RIVER CREST HOSPITAL (O, 80 beds) 1636 Hunters Glen Road, San Angelo, TX Zip 76901–5016; tel. 325/949–5722; Chris Rupert, Interim Chief Executive Officer
Web address: www.rivercresthospital.com

SOUTH TEXAS HEALTH SYSTEM (O, 788 beds) 1102 West Trenton Road, Edinburg, TX Zip 78539–9105; tel. 956/388–6000; Jennifer Garza, Chief Executive Officer
Web address: www.southtexashealthsystem.com

TEXAS NEUROREHAB CENTER (O, 47 beds) 1106 West Dittmar Road, Building 9, Austin, TX Zip 78745–6328, Mailing Address: P.O. Box 150459, Zip 78715–0459; tel. 512/444–4835; Edgar E. Prettyman, PsyD, Chief Executive Officer
Web address: www.texasneurorehab.com

TEXOMA MEDICAL CENTER (O, 326 beds) 5016 South U.S. Highway 75, Denison, TX Zip 75020–4584, Mailing Address: P.O. Box 890, Zip 75021–0890; tel. 903/416–4000; Ronald T. Seal, Chief Executive Officer
Web address: www.texomamedicalcenter.net

TIMBERLAWN MENTAL HEALTH SYSTEM (O, 19 beds) 4600 Samuell Boulevard, Dallas, TX Zip 75228–6800; tel. 214/381–7181; Shelah Adams, Chief Executive Officer
Web address: www.timberlawn.com

UNIVERSITY BEHAVIORAL HEALTH OF DENTON (O, 104 beds) 2026 West University Drive, Denton, TX Zip 76201–0644; tel. 940/320–8100; Samantha Castle, Chief Executive Officer
Web address: www.ubhdenton.com

For explanation of codes following names, see page B2.
★ Indicates Type III membership in the American Hospital Association.

WEST OAKS HOSPITAL (O, 144 beds) 6500 Hornwood Drive, Houston, TX Zip 77074–5095; tel. 713/995–0909; Mandy Westerman, Chief Executive Officer
Web address: www.westoakshospital.com

UTAH: PROVO CANYON BEHAVIORAL HOSPITAL (O, 80 beds) 1350 East 750 North, Orem, UT Zip 84097–4345; tel. 801/852–2273; Jeremy Cottle, Ph.D., Chief Executive Officer
Web address: www.pcbh.com

SALT LAKE BEHAVIORAL HEALTH (O, 118 beds) 3802 South 700 East, Salt Lake City, UT Zip 84106–1182; tel. 801/264–6000; Kreg Gillman, Chief Executive Officer
Web address: www.saltlakebehavioralhealth.com

VIRGINIA: CUMBERLAND HOSPITAL (O, 132 beds) 9407 Cumberland Road, New Kent, VA Zip 23124–2029; tel. 804/966–2242; Patrice Gay Brooks, Chief Executive Officer
Web address: www.cumberlandhospital.com

POPLAR SPRINGS HOSPITAL (O, 183 beds) 350 Poplar Drive, Petersburg, VA Zip 23805–9367; tel. 804/733–6874; Joseph Trapani, Chief Executive Officer
Web address: www.poplarsprings.com

VIRGINIA BEACH PSYCHIATRIC CENTER (O, 100 beds) 1100 First Colonial Road, Virginia Beach, VA Zip 23454–2403; tel. 757/496–6000; Dustin Davis, Chief Executive Officer
Web address: www.vbpcweb.com

WASHINGTON: FAIRFAX BEHAVIORAL HEALTH (O, 103 beds) 10200 N.E. 132nd Street, Kirkland, WA Zip 98034–2899; tel. 425/821–2000; Ron Escarda, Chief Executive Officer
Web address: www.fairfaxhospital.com

WEST VIRGINIA: RIVER PARK HOSPITAL (O, 175 beds) 1230 Sixth Avenue, Huntington, WV Zip 25701–2312, Mailing Address: P.O. Box 1875, Zip 25719–1875; tel. 304/526–9111; Terry A. Stephens, Chief Executive Officer
Web address: www.riverparkhospital.net

WYOMING: WYOMING BEHAVIORAL INSTITUTE (O, 129 beds) 2521 East 15th Street, Casper, WY Zip 82609–4126; tel. 307/237–7444; Joseph Gallagher, Chief Executive Officer
Web address: www.wbihelp.com

Owned, leased, sponsored:	141 hospitals	18785 beds
Contract–managed:	0 hospitals	0 beds
Totals:	141 hospitals	18785 beds

★**0896: UNIVERSITY HEALTH CARE SYSTEM** (NP)
1350 Walton Way, Augusta, GA Zip 30901–2629; tel. 706/722–9011; James R. Davis, President and Chief Executive Officer
(Independent Hospital System)

GEORGIA: UNIVERSITY HOSPITAL (O, 489 beds) 1350 Walton Way, Augusta, GA Zip 30901–2629; tel. 706/722–9011; James R. Davis, Chief Executive Officer
Web address: www.universityhealth.org

UNIVERSITY HOSPITAL MCDUFFIE (O, 12 beds) 2460 Washington Road, N.E., Thomson, GA Zip 30824; tel. 706/595–1411; Bob Kepshire, R.N., MS, Administrator and Chief Nursing Officer
Web address: www.universityhealth.org/mcduffie

Owned, leased, sponsored:	2 hospitals	501 beds
Contract–managed:	0 hospitals	0 beds
Totals:	2 hospitals	501 beds

0961: UNIVERSITY HEALTH SYSTEM (NP)
1501 Kings Highway, Shreveport, LA Zip 71103–4228; tel. 318/675–5000; Richard C. Cascio, Interim Chief Executive Officer
(Independent Hospital System)

LOUISIANA: UNIVERSITY HEALTH CONWAY (O, 108 beds) 4864 Jackson Street, Monroe, LA Zip 71202–6497, Mailing Address: P.O. Box 1881, Zip 71210–8005; tel. 318/330–7000; Larry Donner, Administrator
Web address: www.uhsystem.com

UNIVERSITY HEALTH SHREVEPORT (O, 459 beds) 1501 Kings Highway, Shreveport, LA Zip 71103–4228, Mailing Address: P.O. Box 33932, Zip 71130–3932; tel. 318/675–5000; Roderick L. Williams, M.P.H., President
Web address: www.lsuhscshreveport.edu

Owned, leased, sponsored:	2 hospitals	567 beds
Contract–managed:	0 hospitals	0 beds
Totals:	2 hospitals	567 beds

★**0112: UNIVERSITY HOSPITALS** (NP)
11100 Euclid Avenue, Cleveland, OH Zip 44106–5000; tel. 216/844–1000; Thomas F. Zenty, III, President and Chief Executive Officer
(Moderately Centralized Health System)

OHIO: ST. JOHN MEDICAL CENTER (O, 191 beds) 29000 Center Ridge Road, Westlake, OH Zip 44145–5293; tel. 440/835–8000; Robert G. David, President
Web address: www.sjws.net

UH PORTAGE MEDICAL CENTER (O, 117 beds) 6847 North Chestnut Street, Ravenna, OH Zip 44266–3929, Mailing Address: P.O. Box 1204, Zip 44266–1204; tel. 330/297–0811; M. Steven Jones, President
Web address: www.uhportage.org

UH REGIONAL HOSPITALS (O, 101 beds) 27100 Chardon Road, Cleveland, OH Zip 44143–1116; tel. 440/585–6500; Brian Monter, MSN, R.N., President
Web address: www.uhhospitals.org

UNIVERSITY HOSPITALS AHUJA MEDICAL CENTER (O, 138 beds) 3999 Richmond Road, Beachwood, OH Zip 44122–6046; tel. 216/593–5500; Susan V. Juris, President
Web address: www.uhhospitals.org/ahuja/tabid/7051/uhahujamedicalcenter.aspx

UNIVERSITY HOSPITALS CLEVELAND MEDICAL CENTER (O, 814 beds) 11100 Euclid Avenue, Cleveland, OH Zip 44106–1716; tel. 216/844–1000; Daniel I. Simon, M.D., President
Web address: www.UHhospitals.org

UNIVERSITY HOSPITALS CONNEAUT MEDICAL CENTER (O, 25 beds) 158 West Main Road, Conneaut, OH Zip 44030–2039; tel. 440/593–1131; M. Steven Jones, President
Web address: www.uhhospitals.org

UNIVERSITY HOSPITALS ELYRIA MEDICAL CENTER (O, 237 beds) 630 East River Street, Elyria, OH Zip 44035–5902; tel. 440/329–7500; Charlotte Wray, MSN, President
Web address: www.emh–healthcare.org

UNIVERSITY HOSPITALS GEAUGA MEDICAL CENTER (O, 142 beds) 13207 Ravenna Road, Chardon, OH Zip 44024–7032; tel. 440/269–6000; M. Steven Jones, President
Web address: www.uhhospitals.org/geauga/

UNIVERSITY HOSPITALS GENEVA MEDICAL CENTER (O, 25 beds) 870 West Main Street, Geneva, OH Zip 44041–1295; tel. 440/466–1141; M. Steven Jones, President
Web address: www.uhhs.com

UNIVERSITY HOSPITALS PARMA MEDICAL CENTER (O, 254 beds) 7007 Powers Boulevard, Parma, OH Zip 44129–5495; tel. 440/743–3000; Kristi M. Sink, Interim President
Web address: www.uhhospitals.org/parma

UNIVERSITY HOSPITALS SAMARITAN MEDICAL CENTER (O, 49 beds) 1025 Center Street, Ashland, OH Zip 44805–4011; tel. 419/289–0491; Danny L. Boggs, President and Chief Executive Officer
Web address: www.samaritanhospital.org

Owned, leased, sponsored:	11 hospitals	2093 beds
Contract–managed:	0 hospitals	0 beds
Totals:	11 hospitals	2093 beds

★**0915: UNIVERSITY HOSPITALS AND HEALTH SYSTEM** (NP)
2500 North State Street, Jackson, MS Zip 39216–4500; tel. 601/984–1000; Kevin S. Cook, Chief Executive Officer
(Decentralized Health System)

For explanation of codes following names, see page B2.
★ Indicates Type III membership in the American Hospital Association.

MISSISSIPPI: UNIVERSITY OF MISSISSIPPI MEDICAL CENTER (O, 680 beds) 2500 North State Street, Jackson, MS Zip 39216–4505; tel. 601/984–1000; Kevin S. Cook, Chief Executive Officer
Web address: www.umc.edu

UNIVERSITY OF MISSISSIPPI MEDICAL CENTER GRENADA (C, 93 beds) 960 Avent Drive, Grenada, MS Zip 38901–5230; tel. 662/227–7000; Donald Hutson, Chief Executive Officer
Web address: www.ummchealth.com/grenada

UNIVERSITY OF MISSISSIPPI MEDICAL CENTER HOLMES COUNTY (O, 25 beds) 239 Bowling Green Road, Lexington, MS Zip 39095–5167; tel. 601/496–5200; Donald Hutson, Chief Executive Officer
Web address: www.ummchealth.com/holmes/

Owned, leased, sponsored:	2 hospitals	705 beds
Contract–managed:	1 hospital	93 beds
Totals:	3 hospitals	798 beds

★6405:   UNIVERSITY OF CALIFORNIA SYSTEMWIDE ADMINISTRATION (NP)
1111 Franklin Street, 11th Floor, Oakland, CA Zip 94607–5200; tel. 510/987–9071; John D. Stobo, M.D., Executive Vice President and Chief Executive Officer
(Moderately Centralized Health System)

CALIFORNIA: RONALD REAGAN UCLA MEDICAL CENTER (O, 466 beds) 757 Westwood Plaza, Los Angeles, CA Zip 90095–8358; tel. 310/825–9111; Johnese Spisso, Chief Executive Officer
Web address: www.uclahealth.org

STEWART & LYNDA RESNICK NEUROPSYCHIATRIC HOSPITAL AT UCLA (O, 74 beds) 150 UCLA Medical Plaza, Los Angeles, CA Zip 90095–8353; tel. 310/825–9989; Peter Whybrow, M.D., Chief Executive Officer
Web address: www.semel.ucla.edu/resnick

UC IRVINE MEDICAL CENTER (O, 411 beds) 101 The City Drive South, Orange, CA Zip 92868–3298; tel. 714/456–6011; Howard Federoff, M.D., Vice Chancellor, Health Affairs & Chief Executive Officer, UC Irvine Health
Web address: www.ucirvinehealth.org

UC SAN DIEGO HEALTH (O, 542 beds) 200 West Arbor Drive, San Diego, CA Zip 92103–9000; tel. 619/543–6222; Patty Maysent, Interim Chief Executive Officer
Web address: www.health.ucsd.edu

UCLA MEDICAL CENTER–SANTA MONICA (O, 265 beds) 1250 16th Street, Santa Monica, CA Zip 90404–1249; tel. 310/319–4000; Paul Watkins, Chief Administrative Officer
Web address: www.healthcare.ucla.edu

UCSF MEDICAL CENTER (O, 745 beds) 500 Parnassus Avenue, San Francisco, CA Zip 94143–0296, Mailing Address: 500 Parnassus Avenue, Box 0296, Zip 94143–0296; tel. 415/476–1000; Mark R. Laret, Chief Executive Officer
Web address: www.ucsfhealth.org

UNIVERSITY OF CALIFORNIA, DAVIS MEDICAL CENTER (O, 583 beds) 2315 Stockton Boulevard, Sacramento, CA Zip 95817–2282; tel. 916/734–2011; Ann Madden Rice, Chief Executive Officer
Web address: www.ucdmc.ucdavis.edu

Owned, leased, sponsored:	7 hospitals	3086 beds
Contract–managed:	0 hospitals	0 beds
Totals:	7 hospitals	3086 beds

0058:   UNIVERSITY OF CHICAGO MEDICINE (NP)
5841 South Maryland Avenue, Chicago, IL Zip 60637–1447; tel. 773/702–6240; Sharon L. O'Keefe, President

ILLINOIS: INGALLS MEMORIAL HOSPITAL (O, 478 beds) One Ingalls Drive, Harvey, IL Zip 60426–3591; tel. 708/333–2300; Kurt E. Johnson, President and Chief Executive Officer
Web address: www.ingallshealthsystem.org

UNIVERSITY OF CHICAGO MEDICAL CENTER (O, 624 beds) 5841 South Maryland Avenue, Chicago, IL Zip 60637–1447; tel. 773/702–1000; Sharon L. O'Keefe, President
Web address: www.uchospitals.edu

Owned, leased, sponsored:	2 hospitals	1102 beds
Contract–managed:	0 hospitals	0 beds
Totals:	2 hospitals	1102 beds

★0381:   UNIVERSITY OF COLORADO HEALTH (NP)
2315 East Harmony Road, Suite 200, Fort Collins, CO Zip 80528–8620; tel. 970/848–0000; Elizabeth B. Concordia, President and Chief Executive Officer
(Moderately Centralized Health System)

COLORADO: MEDICAL CENTER OF THE ROCKIES (O, 174 beds) 2500 Rocky Mountain Avenue, Loveland, CO Zip 80538–9004; tel. 970/624–2500; Kevin L. Unger, FACHE, Ph.D., President and Chief Executive Officer
Web address: www.medctrrockies.org

MEMORIAL HOSPITAL (L, 548 beds) 1400 East Boulder Street, Colorado Springs, CO Zip 80909–5599; tel. 719/365–9888; George E. Hayes, FACHE, President and Chief Executive Officer
Web address: www.uchealth.org/southerncolorado

POUDRE VALLEY HOSPITAL (O, 253 beds) 1024 South Lemay Avenue, Fort Collins, CO Zip 80524–3998, Mailing Address: 2315 East Harmony Road, Zip 80528; tel. 970/495–7141; Kevin L. Unger, FACHE, Ph.D., President and Chief Executive Officer
Web address: www.uchealth.org

UNIVERSITY OF COLORADO HOSPITAL (O, 648 beds) 12401 East 17th Avenue, Aurora, CO Zip 80045–2545; tel. 720/848–0000; William Cook, President and Chief Executive Officer
Web address: www.uchealth.org

Owned, leased, sponsored:	4 hospitals	1623 beds
Contract–managed:	0 hospitals	0 beds
Totals:	4 hospitals	1623 beds

★0216:   UNIVERSITY OF MARYLAND MEDICAL SYSTEM (NP)
250 West Pratt Street, 24th Floor, Baltimore, MD Zip 21201–1595; tel. 410/328–8667; Robert A. Chrencik, President and Chief Executive Officer
(Moderately Centralized Health System)

MARYLAND: MT. WASHINGTON PEDIATRIC HOSPITAL (O, 61 beds) 1708 West Rogers Avenue, Baltimore, MD Zip 21209–4545; tel. 410/578–8600; Sheldon J. Stein, President and Chief Executive Officer
Web address: www.mwph.org

UNIVERSITY OF MARYLAND BALTIMORE WASHINGTON MEDICAL CENTER (O, 310 beds) 301 Hospital Drive, Glen Burnie, MD Zip 21061–5899; tel. 410/787–4000; Karen E. Olscamp, President and Chief Executive Officer
Web address: www.mybwmc.org

UNIVERSITY OF MARYLAND CHARLES REGIONAL MEDICAL CENTER (O, 115 beds) 5 Garrett Avenue, La Plata, MD Zip 20646–5960, Mailing Address: P.O. Box 1070, Zip 20646–1070; tel. 301/609–4000; Noel A. Cervino, President and Chief Executive Officer
Web address: www.charlesregional.org

UNIVERSITY OF MARYLAND HARFORD MEMORIAL HOSPITAL (O, 49 beds) 501 South Union Avenue, Havre De Grace, MD Zip 21078–3493; tel. 443/843–5000; Lyle Ernest Sheldon, FACHE, President and Chief Executive Officer
Web address: www.uchs.org

UNIVERSITY OF MARYLAND MEDICAL CENTER (O, 630 beds) 22 South Greene Street, Baltimore, MD Zip 21201–1595; tel. 410/328–8667; Mohan Suntha, M.D., President and Chief Executive Officer
Web address: www.umm.edu

UNIVERSITY OF MARYLAND MEDICAL CENTER MIDTOWN CAMPUS (O, 170 beds) 827 Linden Avenue, Baltimore, MD Zip 21201–4606; tel. 410/225–8000; John W. Ashworth, Interim President and Chief Executive Officer
Web address: www.ummidtown.org/

UNIVERSITY OF MARYLAND REHABILITATION & ORTHOPAEDIC INSTITUTE (O, 104 beds) 2200 Kernan Drive, Baltimore, MD Zip 21207–6697; tel. 410/448–2500; Cynthia Kelleher, M.P.H., President and Chief Executive Officer
Web address: www.umrehabortho.org

Section B

For explanation of codes following names, see page B2.
★ Indicates Type III membership in the American Hospital Association.

UNIVERSITY OF MARYLAND SHORE MEDICAL CENTER AT CHESTERTOWN (O, 124 beds) 100 Brown Street, Chestertown, MD Zip 21620–1499; tel. 410/778–3300; Kenneth D. Kozel, FACHE, President and Chief Executive Officer
Web address: www.umms.org/hospitals/shore–health–system.htm

UNIVERSITY OF MARYLAND SHORE MEDICAL CENTER AT DORCHESTER (O, 47 beds) 300 Byrn Street, Cambridge, MD Zip 21613–1908; tel. 410/228–5511; Kenneth D. Kozel, FACHE, President and Chief Executive Officer
Web address: www.shorehealth.org

UNIVERSITY OF MARYLAND SHORE MEDICAL CENTER AT EASTON (O, 132 beds) 219 South Washington Street, Easton, MD Zip 21601–2996; tel. 410/822–1000; Kenneth D. Kozel, FACHE, President and Chief Executive Officer
Web address: www.shorehealth.org

UNIVERSITY OF MARYLAND ST. JOSEPH MEDICAL CENTER (O, 314 beds) 7601 Osler Drive, Towson, MD Zip 21204–7582; tel. 410/337–1000; Thomas Smyth, President and Chief Executive Officer
Web address: www.stjosephtowson.com/home.aspx

UNIVERSITY OF MARYLAND UPPER CHESAPEAKE MEDICAL CENTER (O, 181 beds) 500 Upper Chesapeake Drive, Bel Air, MD Zip 21014–4324; tel. 443/643–1000; Lyle Ernest Sheldon, FACHE, President and Chief Executive Officer
Web address: www.uchs.org

Owned, leased, sponsored:	12 hospitals	2237 beds
Contract–managed:	0 hospitals	0 beds
Totals:	12 hospitals	2237 beds

0881:   UNIVERSITY OF MIAMI HEALTH SYSTEM (NP)
1400 N.W. 12th Avenue, Miami, FL Zip 33136–1003; tel. 305/243–4000; Pascal J. Goldschmidt, M.D., Chief Executive Officer
(Centralized Health System)

FLORIDA: BASCOM PALMER EYE INSTITUTE–ANNE BATES LEACH EYE HOSPITAL (O, 56 beds) 900 N.W. 17th Street, Miami, FL Zip 33136–1199, Mailing Address: Box 016880, Zip 33101–6880; tel. 305/326–6000; Michael B. Gittelman, Administrator
Web address: www.bascompalmer.org

UNIVERSITY OF MIAMI HOSPITAL (O, 464 beds) 1400 N.W. 12th Avenue, Miami, FL Zip 33136–1003; tel. 305/325–5511; Michael B. Gittelman, Interim Chief Executive Officer
Web address: www.umiamihospital.com

UNIVERSITY OF MIAMI HOSPITAL AND CLINICS (O, 40 beds) 1475 N.W. 12th Avenue, Miami, FL Zip 33136–1002; tel. 305/243–4000; Richard R. Ballard, Chief Executive Officer and Administrator
Web address: www.uhealthsystem.com

Owned, leased, sponsored:	3 hospitals	560 beds
Contract–managed:	0 hospitals	0 beds
Totals:	3 hospitals	560 beds

★0227:   UNIVERSITY OF MISSOURI HEALTH CARE (NP)
One Hospital Drive, DC 031, Columbia, MO Zip 65212–0001; tel. 573/884–8738; Mitchell L. Wasden, Ed.D., Chief Executive Officer and Chief Operating Officer
(Moderately Centralized Health System)

MISSOURI: CAPITAL REGION MEDICAL CENTER (O, 114 beds) 1125 Madison Street, Jefferson City, MO Zip 65101–5200, Mailing Address: P.O. Box 1128, Zip 65102–1128; tel. 573/632–5000; Gaspare Calvaruso, President
Web address: www.crmc.org

UNIVERSITY OF MISSOURI HOSPITALS AND CLINICS (O, 538 beds) One Hospital Drive, Columbia, MO Zip 65212–0001; tel. 573/882–4141; Mitchell L. Wasden, Ed.D., Chief Executive Officer and Chief Operating Officer
Web address: www.muhealth.org

Owned, leased, sponsored:	2 hospitals	652 beds
Contract–managed:	0 hospitals	0 beds
Totals:	2 hospitals	652 beds

0021:   UNIVERSITY OF NEW MEXICO HOSPITALS (NP)
915 Camino De Salud, Albuquerque, NM Zip 87131–0001; tel. 505/272–5849; Stephen W. McKernan, Chief Executive Officer
(Moderately Centralized Health System)

NEW MEXICO: UNIVERSITY OF NEW MEXICO HOSPITALS (O, 537 beds) 2211 Lomas Boulevard N.E., Albuquerque, NM Zip 87106–2745; tel. 505/272–2111; Stephen W. McKernan, Chief Executive Officer
Web address: www.unm.edu

UNM SANDOVAL REGIONAL MEDICAL CENTER (O, 72 beds) MSC09 5300 1 University of New Mexico, Albuquerque, NM Zip 87131, Mailing Address: 3001 Broadmoor Boulevard N.E., Rio Rancho, Zip 87144–2100; tel. 505/994–7000; Jamie A. Silva–Steele, R.N., President and Chief Executive Officer
Web address: www.hospitals.unm.edu/

Owned, leased, sponsored:	2 hospitals	609 beds
Contract–managed:	0 hospitals	0 beds
Totals:	2 hospitals	609 beds

★0168:   UNIVERSITY OF PENNSYLVANIA HEALTH SYSTEM (NP)
3400 Civic Center Bouelvard, Philadelphia, PA Zip 19104–5127; tel. 215/662–2203; Ralph W. Muller, President and Chief Executive Officer
(Moderately Centralized Health System)

PENNSYLVANIA: HOSPITAL OF THE UNIVERSITY OF PENNSYLVANIA (O, 789 beds) 3400 Spruce Street, Philadelphia, PA Zip 19104–4206; tel. 215/662–4000; Garry L. Scheib, Chief Executive Officer
Web address: www.pennmedicine.org

LANCASTER GENERAL HOSPITAL (O, 630 beds) 555 North Duke Street, Lancaster, PA Zip 17602–2250; tel. 717/544–5511; Jan L. Bergen, President and Chief Executive Officer
Web address: www.lancastergeneralhealth.org

PENN MEDICINE CHESTER COUNTY HOSPITAL (O, 211 beds) 701 East Marshall Street, West Chester, PA Zip 19380–4412; tel. 610/431–5000; Michael J. Duncan, President and Chief Executive Officer
Web address: www.chestercountyhospital.org

PENN PRESBYTERIAN MEDICAL CENTER (O, 354 beds) 51 North 39th Street, Philadelphia, PA Zip 19104–2699; tel. 215/662–8000; Michele M. Volpe, Chief Executive Officer
Web address: www.pennmedicine.org/pmc/

PENNSYLVANIA HOSPITAL (O, 397 beds) 800 Spruce Street, Philadelphia, PA Zip 19107–6192; tel. 215/829–3000; Theresa M. Larivee, Chief Executive Officer
Web address: www.pahosp.com

Owned, leased, sponsored:	5 hospitals	2381 beds
Contract–managed:	0 hospitals	0 beds
Totals:	5 hospitals	2381 beds

★0223:   UNIVERSITY OF ROCHESTER MEDICAL CENTER (NP)
601 Elmwood Avenue Box 623, Rochester, NY Zip 14642–0002, Mailing Address: 601 Elmwood Avenue, Zip 14642–0002; tel. 585/275–2100; Steven I. Goldstein, General Director and Chief Executive Officer
(Centralized Health System)

NEW YORK: F. F. THOMPSON HOSPITAL (O, 264 beds) 350 Parrish Street, Canandaigua, NY Zip 14424–1731; tel. 585/396–6000; Michael Stapleton, President and Chief Executive Officer
Web address: www.thompsonhealth.com

HIGHLAND HOSPITAL (O, 261 beds) 1000 South Avenue, Rochester, NY Zip 14620–2733; tel. 585/473–2200; Steven I. Goldstein, President and Chief Executive Officer
Web address: www.stronghealth.com

For explanation of codes following names, see page B2.
★ Indicates Type III membership in the American Hospital Association.

STRONG MEMORIAL HOSPITAL OF THE UNIVERSITY OF ROCHESTER (O, 818 beds) 601 Elmwood Avenue, Rochester, NY Zip 14642–0002, Mailing Address: 601 Elmwood Avenue, Box 612, Zip 14642–0002; tel. 585/275–2100; Steven I. Goldstein, President and Chief Executive Officer
Web address: www.urmc.rochester.edu

Owned, leased, sponsored:	3 hospitals	1343 beds
Contract–managed:	0 hospitals	0 beds
Totals:	3 hospitals	1343 beds

★0057: UNIVERSITY OF SOUTH ALABAMA HOSPITALS (NP)
2451 Fillingim Street, Mobile, AL Zip 36617–2238; tel. 251/471–7000; Owen Bailey, FACHE, Chief Operating Officer
(Independent Hospital System)

ALABAMA: UNIVERSITY OF SOUTH ALABAMA CHILDREN'S AND WOMEN'S HOSPITAL (O, 182 beds) 1700 Center Street, Mobile, AL Zip 36604–3301; tel. 251/415–1000; Chris Jett, Administrator
Web address: www.usahealthsystem.com/usacwh

UNIVERSITY OF SOUTH ALABAMA MEDICAL CENTER (O, 142 beds) 2451 Fillingim Street, Mobile, AL Zip 36617–2293; tel. 251/471–7000; A. Elizabeth Anderson, Administrator
Web address: www.usahealthsystem.com/usamc

Owned, leased, sponsored:	2 hospitals	324 beds
Contract–managed:	0 hospitals	0 beds
Totals:	2 hospitals	324 beds

★0033: UNIVERSITY OF TEXAS SYSTEM (NP)
601 Colorado Street, Suite 205, Austin, TX Zip 78701–2904; tel. 512/499–4224; Raymond Greenberg, M.D., Executive Vice Chancellor
(Moderately Centralized Health System)

TEXAS: UNIVERSITY OF TEXAS HARRIS COUNTY PSYCHIATRIC CENTER (C, 208 beds) 2800 South MacGregor Way, Houston, TX Zip 77021–1000, Mailing Address: P.O. Box 20249, Zip 77225–0249; tel. 713/741–7870; Jair C. Soares, M.D., Executive Director
Web address: www.hcpc.uth.tmc.edu

UNIVERSITY OF TEXAS HEALTH NORTHEAST (O, 130 beds) 11937 Highway 271, Tyler, TX Zip 75708–3154; tel. 903/877–7777; Kirk A. Calhoun, M.D., President
Web address: www.uthct.edu

UNIVERSITY OF TEXAS M.D. ANDERSON CANCER CENTER (O, 665 beds) 1515 Holcombe Boulevard, Unit 1491, Houston, TX Zip 77030–4000; tel. 713/792–2121; Ronald A. DePinho, M.D., President
Web address: www.mdanderson.org

UNIVERSITY OF TEXAS MEDICAL BRANCH (O, 562 beds) 301 University Boulevard, Galveston, TX Zip 77555–0128; tel. 409/772–1011; Donna K. Sollenberger, Executive Vice President and Chief Executive Officer
Web address: www.utmb.edu

Owned, leased, sponsored:	3 hospitals	1357 beds
Contract–managed:	1 hospital	208 beds
Totals:	4 hospitals	1565 beds

0137: UPMC (NP)
600 Grant Street, U.S. Steel Tower, Suite 6262, Pittsburgh, PA Zip 15219–2702; tel. 412/647–8762; Jeffrey A. Romoff, President and Chief Executive Officer
(Centralized Physician/Insurance Health System)

PENNSYLVANIA: CHILDREN'S HOSPITAL OF PITTSBURGH OF UPMC (O, 305 beds) One Children's Hospital Drive, Pittsburgh, PA Zip 15224–1334; tel. 412/692–5325; Christopher A. Gessner, President
Web address: www.chp.edu

JAMESON HOSPITAL (O, 238 beds) 1211 Wilmington Avenue, New Castle, PA Zip 16105–2516; tel. 724/658–9001; Douglas Danko, President and Chief Executive Officer
Web address: www.jamesonhealth.org

MAGEE–WOMENS HOSPITAL OF UPMC (O, 321 beds) 300 Halket Street, Pittsburgh, PA Zip 15213–3108; tel. 412/641–1000; Leslie C. Davis, President
Web address: www.magee.edu

UPMC ALTOONA (O, 380 beds) 620 Howard Avenue, Altoona, PA Zip 16601–4804; tel. 814/889–2011; Gerald Murray, President
Web address: www.altoonaregional.org

UPMC BEDFORD MEMORIAL (O, 27 beds) 10455 Lincoln Highway, Everett, PA Zip 15537–7046; tel. 814/623–6161; Gerald Murray, President
Web address: www.upmcbedfordmemorial.com

UPMC EAST (O, 155 beds) 2775 Mosside Boulevard, Monroeville, PA Zip 15146–2760; tel. 412/357–3000; Mark Sevco, President
Web address: www.upmc.com/locations/hospitals/east/Pages/default.aspx

UPMC HAMOT (O, 317 beds) 201 State Street, Erie, PA Zip 16550–0002; tel. 814/877–6000; V. James Fiorenzo, President
Web address: www.hamot.org

UPMC HORIZON (O, 121 beds) 110 North Main Street, Greenville, PA Zip 16125–1726, Mailing Address: 2200 Memorial Drive, Farrell, Zip 16121–1357; tel. 724/588–2100; Donald R. Owrey, President
Web address: www.upmc.com

UPMC MCKEESPORT (O, 184 beds) 1500 Fifth Avenue, McKeesport, PA Zip 15132–2422; tel. 412/664–2000; Mark Sevco, President
Web address: www.mckeesport.upmc.com

UPMC MERCY (O, 482 beds) 1400 Locust Street, Pittsburgh, PA Zip 15219–5166; tel. 412/232–8111; Michael A. Grace, President
Web address: www.upmc.com/HospitalsFacilities/HFHome/Hospitals/Mercy/

UPMC NORTHWEST (O, 128 beds) 100 Fairfield Drive, Seneca, PA Zip 16346–2130; tel. 814/676–7600; David Gibbons, President
Web address: www.upmc.com/locations/hospitals/northwest/Pages/default. aspx

UPMC PASSAVANT (O, 328 beds) 9100 Babcock Boulevard, Pittsburgh, PA Zip 15237–5815; tel. 412/748–6700; David T. Martin, President
Web address: www.upmc.edu/passavant

UPMC PRESBYTERIAN SHADYSIDE (O, 1482 beds) 200 Lothrop Street, Pittsburgh, PA Zip 15213–2536; tel. 412/647–2345; John Innocenti, Sr., President and Chief Executive Officer
Web address: www.upmc.edu

UPMC ST. MARGARET (O, 226 beds) 815 Freeport Road, Pittsburgh, PA Zip 15215–3301; tel. 412/784–4000; David J. Patton, President
Web address: www.upmc. com/locations/hospitals/st–margaret/Pages/default.aspx

Owned, leased, sponsored:	14 hospitals	4694 beds
Contract–managed:	0 hospitals	0 beds
Totals:	14 hospitals	4694 beds

0816: UPPER ALLEGHENY HEALTH SYSTEM (NP)
130 South Union Street, Suite 300, Olean, NY Zip 14760–3676; tel. 716/375–6190; Timothy J. Finan, FACHE, President and Chief Executive Officer
(Independent Hospital System)

NEW YORK: OLEAN GENERAL HOSPITAL (O, 186 beds) 515 Main Street, Olean, NY Zip 14760–1513; tel. 716/373–2600; Timothy J. Finan, FACHE, President and Chief Executive Officer
Web address: www.ogh.org

PENNSYLVANIA: BRADFORD REGIONAL MEDICAL CENTER (O, 182 beds) 116 Interstate Parkway, Bradford, PA Zip 16701–1036; tel. 814/368–4143; Timothy J. Finan, FACHE, President and Chief Executive Officer
Web address: www.brmc.com

Owned, leased, sponsored:	2 hospitals	368 beds
Contract–managed:	0 hospitals	0 beds
Totals:	2 hospitals	368 beds

For explanation of codes following names, see page B2.
★ Indicates Type III membership in the American Hospital Association.

0038: UPPER CHESAPEAKE HEALTH SYSTEM (NP)
520 Upper Chesapeake Drive, Suite 405, Bel Air, MD
Zip 21014–4381; tel. 443/643–3303; Lyle Ernest Sheldon, FACHE,
President and Chief Executive Officer

Owned, leased, sponsored:	0 hospitals	0 beds
Contract–managed:	0 hospitals	0 beds
Totals:	0 hospitals	0 beds

0868: USMD HEALTH SYSTEM (IO)
6333 North State Highway 161 Suite 200, Irving, TX
Zip 75038–2229; tel. 214/493–4000; Karen A. Fiducia, FACHE,
President, Hospital Division
(Independent Hospital System)

TEXAS: USMD HOSPITAL AT ARLINGTON (O, 34 beds) 801 West Interstate
20, Arlington, TX Zip 76017–5851; tel. 817/472–3400; Marcia Crim,
R.N., MSN, Chief Executive Officer
Web address: www.usmdarlington.com

USMD HOSPITAL AT FORT WORTH (O, 8 beds) 5900 Altamesa Boulevard,
Fort Worth, TX Zip 76132–5473; tel. 817/433–9100; Stephanie
Atkins–Guidry, Administrator and Chief Nursing Officer
Web address: www.usmdfortworth.com/

Owned, leased, sponsored:	2 hospitals	42 beds
Contract–managed:	0 hospitals	0 beds
Totals:	2 hospitals	42 beds

0860: UVA HEALTH SYSTEM (NP)
1215 Lee Street, Charlottesville, VA Zip 22908–0816;
tel. 434/924–0211; R. Edward Howell, Vice President and Chief
Executive Officer
(Centralized Health System)

VIRGINIA: NOVANT HEALTH UVA HEALTH SYSTEM CULPEPER MEDICAL
CENTER (O, 68 beds) 501 Sunset Lane, Culpeper, VA Zip 22701–3917,
Mailing Address: P.O. Box 592, Zip 22701–0500; tel. 540/829–4100;
Greg Napps, Chief Executive Officer
Web address: www.culpeperhealth.org

UNIVERSITY OF VIRGINIA MEDICAL CENTER (O, 585 beds) 1215 Lee Street,
Charlottesville, VA Zip 22908–0001, Mailing Address: P.O. Box 800809,
Zip 22908–0809; tel. 434/924–0211; Pamela Sutton–Wallace, Chief
Executive Officer
Web address: www.healthsystem.virginia.edu

UVA TRANSITIONAL CARE HOSPITAL (O, 40 beds) 2965 Ivy Road (250 West),
Charlottesville, VA Zip 22903–9330; tel. 434/924–7897; Michelle Hereford,
Chief
Web address: www.uvahealth.com/services/transitional–care–hospital

Owned, leased, sponsored:	3 hospitals	693 beds
Contract–managed:	0 hospitals	0 beds
Totals:	3 hospitals	693 beds

★6415: UW MEDICINE (NP)
1959 N.E. Pacific Street, Seattle, WA Zip 98195–0001, Mailing
Address: P.O. Box 356350, Zip 98195–6350; tel. 206/543–7718;
Paul G. Ramsey, M.D., Chief Executive Officer
(Independent Hospital System)

WASHINGTON: UNIVERSITY OF WASHINGTON MEDICAL CENTER (O, 438
beds) 1959 N.E. Pacific Street, Seattle, WA Zip 98195–6151;
tel. 206/598–3300; Geoff Austin, Interim Executive Director
Web address: www.uwmedicine.org/uw–medical–center

UW MEDICINE/HARBORVIEW MEDICAL CENTER (C, 413 beds) 325 Ninth
Avenue, Seattle, WA Zip 98104–2499, Mailing Address: P.O. Box 359717,
Zip 98195–9717; tel. 206/744–3000; Paul Hayes, R.N., Executive Director
Web address: www.uwmedicine.
org/Patient–Care/Locations/HMC/Pages/default.aspx

UW MEDICINE/NORTHWEST HOSPITAL & MEDICAL CENTER (O, 176 beds)
1550 North 115th Street, Seattle, WA Zip 98133–8401; tel. 206/364–0500;
Adam Parcher, Interim Executive Director
Web address: www.uwmedicine.
org/Patient–Care/Locations/nwh/Pages/default.aspx

UW MEDICINE/VALLEY MEDICAL CENTER (C, 283 beds) 400 South 43rd
Street, Renton, WA Zip 98055–5714, Mailing Address: P.O. Box 50010,
Zip 98058–5010; tel. 425/228–3450; Richard D. Roodman, Chief Executive
Officer
Web address: www.valleymed.org

Owned, leased, sponsored:	2 hospitals	614 beds
Contract–managed:	2 hospitals	696 beds
Totals:	4 hospitals	1310 beds

★0128: VALLEY HEALTH SYSTEM (NP)
220 Campus Boulevard, Suite 420, Winchester, VA Zip 22601–2889,
Mailing Address: P.O. Box 3340, Zip 22604–2540;
tel. 540/536–8024; Mark H. Merrill, President and Chief Executive
Officer
(Moderately Centralized Health System)

VIRGINIA: PAGE MEMORIAL HOSPITAL (O, 25 beds) 200 Memorial Drive,
Luray, VA Zip 22835–1005; tel. 540/743–4561; N. Travis Clark,
President
Web address: www.valleyhealthlink.com/page

SHENANDOAH MEMORIAL HOSPITAL (O, 25 beds) 759 South Main Street,
Woodstock, VA Zip 22664–1127; tel. 540/459–1100; N. Travis Clark,
President
Web address: www.valleyhealthlink.com/shenandoah

WARREN MEMORIAL HOSPITAL (O, 166 beds) 1000 North Shenandoah
Avenue, Front Royal, VA Zip 22630–3598; tel. 540/636–0300; Floyd Heater,
President and Chief Executive Officer
Web address: www.valleyhealthlink.com/WMH

WINCHESTER MEDICAL CENTER (O, 445 beds) 1840 Amherst Street,
Winchester, VA Zip 22601–2808, Mailing Address: P.O. Box 3340,
Zip 22604–2540; tel. 540/536–8000; Grady W. Philips, III, President
Web address: www.valleyhealthlink.com/WMC

WEST VIRGINIA: HAMPSHIRE MEMORIAL HOSPITAL (O, 44 beds) 363 Sunrise
Boulevard, Romney, WV Zip 26757–4607; tel. 304/822–4561; Thomas
S. Kluge, President
Web address: www.valleyhealthlink.com/hampshire

WAR MEMORIAL HOSPITAL (O, 41 beds) One Healthy Way, Berkeley Springs,
WV Zip 25411–7463; tel. 304/258–1234; Thomas S. Kluge, President
Web address: www.valleyhealthlink.com/war

Owned, leased, sponsored:	6 hospitals	746 beds
Contract–managed:	0 hospitals	0 beds
Totals:	6 hospitals	746 beds

● ★0387: VANDERBILT HEALTH (NP)
1211 22nd Avenue South, Nashville, TN Zip 37232;
tel. 615/322–5000; Charles Wright Pinson, M.D., Deputy Vice
Chancellor for Health Affairs and Chief Executive Officer of Vanderbilt
Health System
(Moderately Centralized Health System)

TENNESSEE: VANDERBILT UNIVERSITY MEDICAL CENTER (O, 1000 beds)
1211 22nd Avenue North, Nashville, TN Zip 37232–2102;
tel. 615/322–5000; Mitch Edgeworth, Chief Executive Officer
Web address: www.mc.vanderbilt.edu

Owned, leased, sponsored:	1 hospital	1000 beds
Contract–managed:	0 hospitals	0 beds
Totals:	1 hospital	1000 beds

0939: VCU HEALTH SYSTEM (NP)
1250 East Marshall Street, Richmond, VA Zip 23298–5051, Mailing
Address: P.O. Box 980510, Zip 23298–0510; tel. 804/828–9000;
Marsha Rappley, M.D., Chief Executive Officer and Vice President for
Health Sciences
(Moderately Centralized Health System)

For explanation of codes following names, see page B2.
★ Indicates Type III membership in the American Hospital Association.
● Single hospital health care system

© 2016 AHA Guide

Section B

VIRGINIA: CHILDREN'S HOSPITAL OF RICHMOND AT VCU–BROOK ROAD CAMPUS (O, 36 beds) 2924 Brook Road, Richmond, VA Zip 23220–1298; tel. 804/321–7474; Leslie G. Wyatt, Senior Vice President Children's Services and Executive Director
Web address: www.chrichmond.org

VCU COMMUNITY MEMORIAL HOSPITAL (O, 178 beds) 125 Buena Vista Circle, South Hill, VA Zip 23970–1431, Mailing Address: P.O. Box 90, Zip 23970–0090; tel. 434/447–3151; W. Scott Burnette, Chief Executive Officer
Web address: www.cmh–sh.org

VCU MEDICAL CENTER (O, 786 beds) 1250 East Marshall Street, Richmond, VA Zip 23298–5051, Mailing Address: P.O. Box 980510, Zip 23298–0510; tel. 804/828–9000; John Duval, Chief Executive Officer
Web address: www.vcuhealth.org

Owned, leased, sponsored:	3 hospitals	1000 beds
Contract–managed:	0 hospitals	0 beds
Totals:	3 hospitals	1000 beds

★**1075:   VERITY HEALTH SYSTEM** (CC)
2200 West Third Street, Suite 200, Los Angeles, CA Zip 90057–1935, Mailing Address: 203 Redwood Shores Parkway, Suite 800, Redwood City, Zip 94065; tel. 650/551–6650; Andrei Soran, MSN, Chief Executive Officer
(Independent Hospital System)

CALIFORNIA: O'CONNOR HOSPITAL (O, 202 beds) 2105 Forest Avenue, San Jose, CA Zip 95128–1471; tel. 408/947–2500; Robert Minkin, President and Chief Executive Officer
Web address: www.oconnorhospital.org

SAINT LOUISE REGIONAL HOSPITAL (O, 93 beds) 9400 No Name Uno, Gilroy, CA Zip 95020–3528; tel. 408/848–2000; Robert Minkin, Interim Chief Executive Officer
Web address: www.verity.org

SETON MEDICAL CENTER (O, 410 beds) 1900 Sullivan Avenue, Daly City, CA Zip 94015–2229; tel. 650/992–4000; John Ferrelli, Chief Executive Officer
Web address: www.setonmedicalcenter.org

SETON MEDICAL CENTER COASTSIDE (O, 116 beds) 600 Marine Boulevard, Moss Beach, CA Zip 94038–9641; tel. 650/563–7100; John Ferrelli, Chief Executive Officer

ST. FRANCIS MEDICAL CENTER (O, 323 beds) 3630 East Imperial Highway, Lynwood, CA Zip 90262–2636; tel. 310/900–8900; Gerald T. Kozai, PharmD, President and Chief Executive Officer
Web address: www.dochs.org

ST. VINCENT MEDICAL CENTER (O, 271 beds) 2131 West Third Street, Los Angeles, CA Zip 90057–1901, Mailing Address: P.O. Box 57992, Zip 90057–0992; tel. 213/484–7111; Frank J. Cracolici, President and Chief Executive Officer
Web address: www.stvincentmedicalcenter.com

Owned, leased, sponsored:	6 hospitals	1415 beds
Contract–managed:	0 hospitals	0 beds
Totals:	6 hospitals	1415 beds

★**0299:   VIBRA HEALTHCARE** (IO)
4550 Lena Drive, Suite 225, Mechanicsburg, PA Zip 17055–4920; tel. 717/591–5700; Brad Hollinger, Chairman and Chief Executive Officer
(Independent Hospital System)

BALLARD REHABILITATION HOSPITAL (O, 55 beds) 1760 West 16th Street, San Bernardino, CA Zip 92411–1160; tel. 909/473–1200; Mary Miles Hunt, Chief Executive Officer
Web address: www.ballardrehab.com

KENTFIELD REHABILITATION AND SPECIALTY HOSPITAL (O, 52 beds) 1125 Sir Francis Drake Boulevard, Kentfield, CA Zip 94904–1455; tel. 415/456–9680; Ann Gors, Chief Executive Officer
Web address: www.kentfieldrehab.com

SAN JOAQUIN VALLEY REHABILITATION HOSPITAL (O, 62 beds) 7173 North Sharon Avenue, Fresno, CA Zip 93720–3329; tel. 559/436–3600; Mary Jo Jacobson, Chief Executive Officer
Web address: www.sanjoaquinrehab.com

VIBRA HOSPITAL OF NORTHERN CALIFORNIA (O, 88 beds) 2801 Eureka Way, Redding, CA Zip 96001–0222; tel. 530/246–9000; Chris Jones, Chief Executive Officer
Web address: www.norcalrehab.com

VIBRA HOSPITAL OF SACRAMENTO (O, 34 beds) 330 Montrose Drive, Folsom, CA Zip 95630–2720; tel. 916/351–9151; Kimberly Horton, R.N., MSN, Chief Executive Officer
Web address: www.vhsacramento.com

VIBRA HOSPITAL OF SAN DIEGO (O, 110 beds) 555 Washington Street, San Diego, CA Zip 92103–2294; tel. 619/260–8300; Yameeka Jones, Chief Executive Officer
Web address: www.vhsandiego.com/

COLORADO: VIBRA HOSPITAL OF DENVER (O, 71 beds) 8451 Pearl Street, Thornton, CO Zip 80229–4804; tel. 303/288–3000; Linda Tautz, Interim Chief Executive Officer
Web address: www.vhdenver.com

IDAHO: VIBRA HOSPITAL OF BOISE (O, 35 beds) 2131 South Bonito Way, Meridian, ID Zip 83642–1659; tel. 877/801–2244; Cynthia Newsom, Chief Executive Officer
Web address: www.vhboise.com

ILLINOIS: VIBRA HOSPITAL OF SPRINGFIELD (O, 32 beds) 701 North Walnut Street, Springfield, IL Zip 62702–4931; tel. 217/528–1217; Larry Deal, R.N., Chief Executive Officer
Web address: www.vhspringfield.com

INDIANA: VIBRA HOSPITAL OF FORT WAYNE (O, 24 beds) 2200 Randallia Drive, Fort Wayne, IN Zip 46805–4638; tel. 260/399–2900; Ryan Cassedy, Chief Executive Officer
Web address: www.vhfortwayne.com

VIBRA HOSPITAL OF NORTHWESTERN INDIANA (O, 40 beds) 9509 Georgia Street, Crown Point, IN Zip 46307–6518; tel. 219/472–2200; Rodney Midkiff, Chief Executive Officer
Web address: www.vhnwindiana.com/

KENTUCKY: GATEWAY REHABILITATION HOSPITAL (C, 40 beds) 5940 Merchant Street, Florence, KY Zip 41042–1158; tel. 859/426–2400; Frank Schneider, FACHE, Chief Executive Officer
Web address: www.gatewayflorence.com/

SOUTHERN KENTUCKY REHABILITATION HOSPITAL (O, 60 beds) 1300 Campbell Lane, Bowling Green, KY Zip 42104–4162; tel. 270/782–6900; Stuart Locke, Chief Executive Officer
Web address: www.skyrehab.com

MASSACHUSETTS: VIBRA HOSPITAL OF SOUTHEASTERN MASSACHUSETTS (O, 90 beds) 4499 Acushnet Avenue, New Bedford, MA Zip 02745–4707; tel. 508/995–6900; Edward B. Leary, Chief Executive Officer
Web address: www.newbedfordrehab.com

VIBRA HOSPITAL OF WESTERN MASSACHUSETTS (O, 346 beds) 1400 State Street, Springfield, MA Zip 01109–2550; tel. 413/726–6700; Edward B. Leary, Interim Chief Executive Officer
Web address: www.vhwmass.com

MICHIGAN: VIBRA HOSPITAL OF SOUTHEASTERN MICHIGAN, LLC (O, 220 beds) 26400 West Outer Drive, Lincoln Park, MI Zip 48146–2088; tel. 313/386–2000; Denise Wayne, Chief Executive Officer
Web address: www.vhsemichigan.com/

NEW JERSEY: MARLTON REHABILITATION HOSPITAL (O, 61 beds) 92 Brick Road, Marlton, NJ Zip 08053–2177; tel. 856/988–8778; Phyllis J. Schlichtmann, Chief Executive Officer
Web address: www.marltonrehab.com

NORTH DAKOTA: VIBRA HOSPITAL OF CENTRAL DAKOTAS (O, 41 beds) 1000 18th Street N.W., Mandan, ND Zip 58554–1612; tel. 701/667–2000; Glynda Troyo–Sauviac, Chief Executive Officer
Web address: www.vhcentraldakotas.com

VIBRA HOSPITAL OF FARGO (O, 31 beds) 1720 University Drive South, Fargo, ND Zip 58103–4940; tel. 701/241–9099; Custer Huseby, Chief Executive Officer
Web address: www.vhfargo.com

OHIO: VIBRA HOSPITAL OF MAHONING VALLEY (O, 42 beds) 8049 South Avenue, Boardman, OH Zip 44512–6154; tel. 330/726–5000; Nathan Mast, Chief Executive Officer
Web address: www.vhmvalley.com

For explanation of codes following names, see page B2.
★ Indicates Type III membership in the American Hospital Association.

Section B

OREGON: VIBRA SPECIALTY HOSPITAL OF PORTLAND (O, 68 beds) 10300 N.E. Hancock Street, Portland, OR Zip 97220–3831; tel. 503/257–5500; David Tupper, Chief Executive Officer
Web address: www.vshportland.com

SOUTH CAROLINA: VIBRA HOSPITAL OF CHARLESTON (O, 94 beds) 1200 Hospital Drive, Mt. Pleasant, SC Zip 29464; tel. 843/375–4000; Pete R. Miller, Chief Executive Officer
Web address: www.vhcharleston.com

TEXAS: HIGHLANDS REHABILITATION HOSPITAL (O, 41 beds) 1395 George Dieter Drive, El Paso, TX Zip 79936–7410; tel. 915/298–7222; Mariaelena Carmona, Chief Executive Officer
Web address: www.vrhhighlands.com/

VIBRA HOSPITAL OF AMARILLO (O, 72 beds) 7501 Wallace Boulevard, Amarillo, TX Zip 79124–2150; tel. 806/467–7000; Jerry Jasper, Chief Executive Officer
Web address: www.vhamarillo.com

VIBRA REHABILITATION HOSPITAL LAKE TRAVIS (O, 36 beds) 2000 Medical Drive, Lakeway, TX Zip 78734–4200; tel. 512/263–4500; Deborah Hopps, Chief Executive Officer
Web address: www.vrhlaketravis.com

VIBRA REHABILITATION HOSPITAL OF AMARILLO (O, 44 beds) 7200 West 9th Avenue, Amarillo, TX Zip 79106–1703; tel. 806/468–2900; Jerry Jasper, Chief Executive Officer
Web address: www.vrhamarillo.com

VIBRA SPECIALTY HOSPITAL AT DESOTO (O, 40 beds) 2700 Walker Way, Desoto, TX Zip 75115–2088; tel. 972/298–1100; Thomas Alexander, Chief Executive Officer
Web address: www.vshdesoto.com

VIRGINIA: VIBRA HOSPITAL OF RICHMOND (O, 60 beds) 2220 Edward Holland Drive, Richmond, VA Zip 23230–2519; tel. 804/678–7000; Craig Johnson, Interim Chief Executive Officer
Web address: www.vhrichmond.com

Owned, leased, sponsored:	27 hospitals	1949 beds
Contract–managed:	1 hospital	40 beds
Totals:	28 hospitals	1989 beds

0920: VIBRANT HEALTHCARE (IO)
12222 North Central Expressway, Suite 440, Dallas, TX Zip 75243–3767; tel. 469/330–6745
(Independent Hospital System)

Owned, leased, sponsored:	0 hospitals	0 beds
Contract–managed:	0 hospitals	0 beds
Totals:	0 hospitals	0 beds

0897: VICTORY HEALTHCARE (IO)
2201 Timberloch Place, Suite 200, The Woodlands, TX Zip 77380; tel. 281/863–2100; Robert N. Helms, Jr., Board Chair, President and Chief Executive Officer
(Independent Hospital System)

Owned, leased, sponsored:	0 hospitals	0 beds
Contract–managed:	0 hospitals	0 beds
Totals:	0 hospitals	0 beds

★0217: VIDANT HEALTH (NP)
2100 Stantonsburg Road, Greenville, NC Zip 27834–2818, Mailing Address: P.O. Box 6028, Zip 27835–6028; tel. 252/847–4100; Michael Waldrum, M.D., Chief Executive Officer
(Moderately Centralized Health System)

NORTH CAROLINA: THE OUTER BANKS HOSPITAL (O, 21 beds) 4800 South Croatan Highway, Nags Head, NC Zip 27959–9704; tel. 252/449–4511; Ronald A. Sloan, FACHE, President
Web address: www.theouterbankshospital.com

VIDANT BEAUFORT HOSPITAL (L, 79 beds) 628 East 12th Street, Washington, NC Zip 27889–3409; tel. 252/975–4100; Harvey Case, President
Web address: www.vidanthealth.com

VIDANT BERTIE HOSPITAL (L, 6 beds) 1403 South King Street, Windsor, NC Zip 27983–9666, Mailing Address: P.O. Box 40, Zip 27983–0040; tel. 252/794–6600; Jeffrey Sackrison, President
Web address: www.vidanthealth.com

VIDANT CHOWAN HOSPITAL (L, 19 beds) 211 Virginia Road, Edenton, NC Zip 27932–9668, Mailing Address: P.O. Box 629, Zip 27932–0629; tel. 252/482–8451; Jeffrey Sackrison, President
Web address: www.vidanthealth.com

VIDANT DUPLIN HOSPITAL (L, 48 beds) 401 North Main Street, Kenansville, NC Zip 28349–8801, Mailing Address: P.O. Box 278, Zip 28349–0278; tel. 910/296–0941; Jay Briley, President
Web address: www.vidanthealth.com

VIDANT EDGECOMBE HOSPITAL (O, 94 beds) 111 Hospital Drive, Tarboro, NC Zip 27886–2011; tel. 252/641–7700; Wendell H. Baker, Jr., President
Web address: www.https://www.vidanthealth.com/edgecombe/default.aspx

VIDANT MEDICAL CENTER (O, 909 beds) 2100 Stantonsburg Road, Greenville, NC Zip 27834–2818, Mailing Address: P.O. Box 6028, Zip 27835–6028; tel. 252/847–4100; William Brian Floyd, President
Web address: www.https://www.vidanthealth.com/

VIDANT ROANOKE–CHOWAN HOSPITAL (L, 70 beds) 500 South Academy Street, Ahoskie, NC Zip 27910–3261, Mailing Address: P.O. Box 1385, Zip 27910–1385; tel. 252/209–3000; Susan S. Lassiter, FACHE, President and Chief Executive Officer
Web address: www.vidanthealth.com

Owned, leased, sponsored:	8 hospitals	1246 beds
Contract–managed:	0 hospitals	0 beds
Totals:	8 hospitals	1246 beds

0012: VIRGINIA DEPARTMENT OF MENTAL HEALTH (NP)
1220 Bank Street, Richmond, VA Zip 23219–3645, Mailing Address: P.O. Box 1797, Zip 23218–1797; tel. 804/786–3921; James S. Reinhard, M.D., Commissioner
(Independent Hospital System)

VIRGINIA: CATAWBA HOSPITAL (O, 110 beds) 5525 Catawba Hospital Drive, Catawba, VA Zip 24070–2115, Mailing Address: P.O. Box 200, Zip 24070–0200; tel. 540/375–4200; Walton F. Mitchell, III, Director
Web address: www.catawba.dbhds.virginia.gov

CENTRAL STATE HOSPITAL (O, 277 beds) 26317 West Washington Street, Petersburg, VA Zip 23803–2727, Mailing Address: P.O. Box 4030, Zip 23803–0030; tel. 804/524–7000; Vicki Montgomery, Director and Chief Executive Officer
Web address: www.csh.dbhds.virginia.gov

CENTRAL VIRGINIA TRAINING CENTER (O, 1112 beds) 210 East Colony Road, Madison Heights, VA Zip 24572–2005, Mailing Address: P.O. Box 1098, Lynchburg, Zip 24505–1098; tel. 434/947–6326; Denise D. Micheletti, R.N., Director
Web address: www.cvtc.dmhmrsas.virginia.gov/

COMMONWEALTH CENTER FOR CHILDREN AND ADOLESCENTS (O, 60 beds) 1355 Richmond Road, Staunton, VA Zip 24401–9146, Mailing Address: Box 4000, Zip 24402–4000; tel. 540/332–2100; William J. Tuell, MSN, Facility Director
Web address: www.ccca.dbhds.virginia.gov

EASTERN STATE HOSPITAL (O, 300 beds) 4601 Ironbound Road, Williamsburg, VA Zip 23188–2652; tel. 757/253–5161; John M. Favret, Director
Web address: www.esh.dmhmrsas.virginia.gov/

HIRAM W. DAVIS MEDICAL CENTER (O, 10 beds) 26317 West Washington Street, Petersburg, VA Zip 23803–2727, Mailing Address: P.O. Box 4030, Zip 23803–0030; tel. 804/524–7344; Brenda Buenvenida, Director

NORTHERN VIRGINIA MENTAL HEALTH INSTITUTE (O, 134 beds) 3302 Gallows Road, Falls Church, VA Zip 22042–3398; tel. 703/207–7110; James R. Newton, Facility Director
Web address: www.nvmhi.dmhmrsas.virginia.gov

PIEDMONT GERIATRIC HOSPITAL (O, 135 beds) 5001 East Patrick Henry Highway, Burkeville, VA Zip 23922–3460, Mailing Address: P.O. Box 427, Zip 23922–0427; tel. 434/767–4401; Stephen M. Herrick, Ph.D., Director
Web address: www.pgh.dmhmrsas.virginia.gov

For explanation of codes following names, see page B2.
★ Indicates Type III membership in the American Hospital Association.

SOUTHERN VIRGINIA MENTAL HEALTH INSTITUTE (O, 72 beds) 382 Taylor Drive, Danville, VA Zip 24541–4023; tel. 434/799–6220; William Cook, Director
Web address: www.svmhi.dbhds.virginia.gov

SOUTHWESTERN VIRGINIA MENTAL HEALTH INSTITUTE (O, 266 beds) 340 Bagley Circle, Marion, VA Zip 24354–3390; tel. 276/783–1200; Cynthia McClaskey, Ph.D., Director
Web address: www.swvmhi.dmhmrsas.virginia.gov/

WESTERN STATE HOSPITAL (O, 246 beds) 1301 Richmond Avenue, Staunton, VA Zip 24401–9146, Mailing Address: P.O. Box 2500, Zip 24402–2500; tel. 540/332–8000; Mary Clare Smith, M.D., Director
Web address: www.dbhds.virginia.gov

Owned, leased, sponsored:	11 hospitals	2722 beds
Contract–managed:	0 hospitals	0 beds
Totals:	11 hospitals	2722 beds

0986: VIRGINIA MASON HEALTH SYSTEM (NP)
1100 Ninth Avenue, Seattle, WA Zip 98101–2756, Mailing Address: P.O. Box 900, Zip 98111–0900; tel. 206/223–6600; Gary Kaplan, M.D., FACHE, Chief Executive Officer

WASHINGTON: VIRGINIA MASON MEDICAL CENTER (O, 280 beds) 1100 Ninth Avenue, Seattle, WA Zip 98101–2756, Mailing Address: P.O. Box 900, Zip 98111–0900; tel. 206/223–6600; Gary Kaplan, M.D., FACHE, Chairman and Chief Executive Officer
Web address: www.VirginiaMason.org

YAKIMA VALLEY MEMORIAL HOSPITAL (O, 226 beds) 2811 Tieton Drive, Yakima, WA Zip 98902–3761; tel. 509/575–8000; Russ Myers, Chief Executive Officer
Web address: www.yakimamemorial.org

Owned, leased, sponsored:	2 hospitals	506 beds
Contract–managed:	0 hospitals	0 beds
Totals:	2 hospitals	506 beds

★6725: VIRTUA HEALTH (NP)
50 Lake Center Executive Drive, Suite 401, Marlton, NJ Zip 08053; tel. 856/355–0010; Richard P. Miller, Chief Executive Officer
(Centralized Health System)

NEW JERSEY: VIRTUA MARLTON (O, 189 beds) 90 Brick Road, Marlton, NJ Zip 08053–2177; tel. 856/355–6000; Matthew Zuino, Senior Vice President Hospital Services
Web address: www.virtua.org

VIRTUA MEMORIAL (O, 334 beds) 175 Madison Avenue, Mount Holly, NJ Zip 08060–2099; tel. 609/267–0700; Matthew Zuino, Senior Vice President Hospital Services
Web address: www.virtua.org

VIRTUA VOORHEES (O, 398 beds) 100 Bowman Drive, Voorhees, NJ Zip 08043–9612; tel. 856/325–3000; Matthew Zuino, Senior Vice President Hospital Services
Web address: www.virtua.org

Owned, leased, sponsored:	3 hospitals	921 beds
Contract–managed:	0 hospitals	0 beds
Totals:	3 hospitals	921 beds

★0221: WAKE FOREST BAPTIST HEALTH (NP)
Medical Center Boulevard, Winston–Salem, NC Zip 27157; tel. 336/716–2011; John D. McConnell, M.D., Chief Executive Officer
(Moderately Centralized Health System)

NORTH CAROLINA: WAKE FOREST BAPTIST HEALTH–DAVIE MEDICAL CENTER (O, 25 beds) 223 Hospital Street, Mocksville, NC Zip 27028–2038, Mailing Address: 329 NC Highway 801 North, Bermuda Run, Zip 27006; tel. 336/998–1300; Chad J. Brown, M.P.H., President
Web address: www.wakehealth.edu/Davie–Medical–Center

WAKE FOREST BAPTIST HEALTH–LEXINGTON MEDICAL CENTER (O, 76 beds) 250 Hospital Drive, Lexington, NC Zip 27292–6728, Mailing Address: P.O. Box 1817, Zip 27293–1817; tel. 336/248–5161; William B. James, FACHE, President
Web address: www.lexington.wakehealth.edu

WAKE FOREST BAPTIST MEDICAL CENTER (O, 787 beds) Medical Center Boulevard, Winston–Salem, NC Zip 27157–0001; tel. 336/716–2011; John D. McConnell, M.D., Chief Executive Officer
Web address: www.wakehealth.edu

Owned, leased, sponsored:	3 hospitals	888 beds
Contract–managed:	0 hospitals	0 beds
Totals:	3 hospitals	888 beds

★6705: WAKEMED HEALTH & HOSPITALS (NP)
3000 New Bern Avenue, Raleigh, NC Zip 27610–1231; tel. 919/350–8000; Donald R. Gintzig, President and Chief Executive Officer
(Moderately Centralized Health System)

WAKEMED CARY HOSPITAL (O, 156 beds) 1900 Kildaire Farm Road, Cary, NC Zip 27518–6616; tel. 919/350–8000; Donald R. Gintzig, President and Chief Executive Officer
Web address: www.wakemed.org

WAKEMED RALEIGH CAMPUS (O, 681 beds) 3000 New Bern Avenue, Raleigh, NC Zip 27610–1295; tel. 919/350–8000; Donald R. Gintzig, President and Chief Executive Officer
Web address: www.wakemed.org

Owned, leased, sponsored:	2 hospitals	837 beds
Contract–managed:	0 hospitals	0 beds
Totals:	2 hospitals	837 beds

0979: WASHINGTON HEALTH SYSTEM (NP)
155 Wilson Avenue, Washington, PA Zip 15301–3336; tel. 724/225–7000; Gary B. Weinstein, Chief Executive Officer

PENNSYLVANIA: WASHINGTON HEALTH SYSTEM GREENE (O, 49 beds) 350 Bonar Avenue, Waynesburg, PA Zip 15370–1608; tel. 724/627–3101; Terry Wiltrout, President
Web address: www.southwestregionalmedical.com/

WASHINGTON HOSPITAL (O, 251 beds) 155 Wilson Avenue, Washington, PA Zip 15301–3398; tel. 724/225–7000; Gary B. Weinstein, President and Chief Executive Officer
Web address: www.washingtonhospital.org

Owned, leased, sponsored:	2 hospitals	300 beds
Contract–managed:	0 hospitals	0 beds
Totals:	2 hospitals	300 beds

★0188: WELLMONT HEALTH SYSTEM (NP)
1905 American Way, Kingsport, TN Zip 37660–5882; tel. 423/230–8200; Barton A. Hove, President and Chief Executive Officer
(Centralized Physician/Insurance Health System)

TENNESSEE: WELLMONT BRISTOL REGIONAL MEDICAL CENTER (O, 288 beds) 1 Medical Park Boulevard, Bristol, TN Zip 37620–7430; tel. 423/844–1121; Greg Neal, FACHE, President
Web address: www.wellmont.org

WELLMONT HANCOCK COUNTY HOSPITAL (O, 10 beds) 1519 Main Street, Sneedville, TN Zip 37869–3657; tel. 423/733–5000; Rebecca Beck, President
Web address: www.wellmont.org/Hospitals/Hancock–County–Hospital.aspx

WELLMONT HAWKINS COUNTY MEMORIAL HOSPITAL (L, 50 beds) 851 Locust Street, Rogersville, TN Zip 37857–2407, Mailing Address: P.O. Box 130, Zip 37857–0130; tel. 423/921–7000; Rebecca Beck, President
Web address: www.wellmont.org

WELLMONT HOLSTON VALLEY MEDICAL CENTER (O, 345 beds) 130 West Ravine Street, Kingsport, TN Zip 37660–3837, Mailing Address: P.O. Box 238, Zip 37662–0238; tel. 423/224–4000; Tim Attebery, Chief Executive Officer
Web address: www.wellmont.org

For explanation of codes following names, see page B2.
★ Indicates Type III membership in the American Hospital Association.

VIRGINIA: MOUNTAIN VIEW REGIONAL MEDICAL CENTER (O, 70 beds) 310 Third Street N.E., Norton, VA Zip 24273–1137; tel. 276/679–9100; Dale Clark, President
Web address: www.wellmont.org

WELLMONT LONESOME PINE HOSPITAL (O, 30 beds) 1990 Holton Avenue East, Big Stone Gap, VA Zip 24219–3350; tel. 276/523–3111; Dale Clark, President
Web address: www.wellmont.org

Owned, leased, sponsored:	6 hospitals	793 beds
Contract–managed:	0 hospitals	0 beds
Totals:	6 hospitals	793 beds

★0068: **WELLSPAN HEALTH** (NP)
45 Monument Road, Suite 200, York, PA Zip 17403–5071; tel. 717/851–2121; Kevin H. Mosser, M.D., President and Chief Executive Officer
(Centralized Physician/Insurance Health System)

PENNSYLVANIA: WELLSPAN EPHRATA COMMUNITY HOSPITAL (O, 130 beds) 169 Martin Avenue, Ephrata, PA Zip 17522–1724, Mailing Address: P.O. Box 1002, Zip 17522–1002; tel. 717/733–0311; ,
Web address: www.wellspan.org

WELLSPAN GETTYSBURG HOSPITAL (O, 76 beds) 147 Gettys Street, Gettysburg, PA Zip 17325–2534; tel. 717/334–2121; Jane E. Hyde, President
Web address: www.wellspan.org

WELLSPAN GOOD SAMARITAN HOSPITAL (O, 151 beds) Fourth and Walnut Streets, Lebanon, PA Zip 17042–1281, Mailing Address: P.O. Box 1281, Zip 17042–1281; tel. 717/270–7500; Thomas R. Harlow, FACHE, President
Web address: www.gshleb.org

WELLSPAN YORK HOSPITAL (O, 556 beds) 1001 South George Street, York, PA Zip 17403–3645; tel. 717/851–2345; Keith D. Noll, President
Web address: www.wellspan.org

Owned, leased, sponsored:	4 hospitals	913 beds
Contract–managed:	0 hospitals	0 beds
Totals:	4 hospitals	913 beds

★0995: **WELLSTAR HEALTH SYSTEM** (NP)
793 Sawyer Road, Marietta, GA Zip 30062; tel. 770/792–5012; Candice Saunders, President and Chief Executive Officer
(Centralized Health System)

GEORGIA: NORTH FULTON REGIONAL HOSPITAL (O, 196 beds) 3000 Hospital Boulevard, Roswell, GA Zip 30076–3899; tel. 770/751–2500; Deborah C. Keel, Chief Executive Officer
Web address: www.nfultonhospital.com

SPALDING REGIONAL HOSPITAL (O, 160 beds) 601 South Eighth Street, Griffin, GA Zip 30224–4294, Mailing Address: P.O. Drawer V, Zip 30224–1168; tel. 770/228–2721; Tamara Ison, Senior Vice President and President
Web address: www.spaldingregional.com

SYLVAN GROVE HOSPITAL (O, 24 beds) 1050 McDonough Road, Jackson, GA Zip 30233–1599; tel. 770/775–7861; Tamara Ison, Senior Vice President and President
Web address: www.sylvangrovehospital.com

WELLSTAR ATLANTA MEDICAL CENTER (O, 536 beds) 303 Parkway Drive N.E., Atlanta, GA Zip 30312–1212; tel. 404/265–4000; Kimberly Ryan, President
Web address: www.atlantamedcenter.com

WELLSTAR COBB HOSPITAL (O, 402 beds) 3950 Austell Road, Austell, GA Zip 30106–1121; tel. 770/732–4000; Amy Frey Carrier, President
Web address: www.wellstar.org

WELLSTAR DOUGLAS HOSPITAL (O, 108 beds) 8954 Hospital Drive, Douglasville, GA Zip 30134–2282; tel. 770/949–1500; Craig A. Owens, President
Web address: www.wellstar.org

WELLSTAR KENNESTONE HOSPITAL (O, 657 beds) 677 Church Street, Marietta, GA Zip 30060–1148; tel. 770/793–5000; Dan Woods, President
Web address: www.wellstar.org

WELLSTAR PAULDING HOSPITAL (O, 238 beds) 2518 Jimmy Lee Smith Parkway, Hiram, GA Zip 30141; tel. 470/644–7000; Mark Haney, President
Web address: www.wellstar.org

WELLSTAR WINDY HILL HOSPITAL (O, 55 beds) 2540 Windy Hill Road, Marietta, GA Zip 30067–8632; tel. 770/644–1000; Kem Mullins, FACHE, President
Web address: www.wellstar.org

WEST GEORGIA HEALTH (O, 390 beds) 1514 Vernon Road, Lagrange, GA Zip 30240–4131; tel. 706/882–1411; Gerald N. Fulks, President
Web address: www.wghealth.org/

Owned, leased, sponsored:	10 hospitals	2766 beds
Contract–managed:	0 hospitals	0 beds
Totals:	10 hospitals	2766 beds

★0004: **WEST TENNESSEE HEALTHCARE** (NP)
620 Skyline Drive, Jackson, TN Zip 38301–3923; tel. 731/541–5000; James E. Ross, Interim Chief Executive Officer
(Centralized Physician/Insurance Health System)

TENNESSEE: BOLIVAR GENERAL HOSPITAL (O, 21 beds) 650 Nuckolls Road, Bolivar, TN Zip 38008–1532, Mailing Address: PO Box 509, Zip 38008–0509; tel. 731/658–3100; Ruby Kirby, Administrator
Web address: www.wth.net

CAMDEN GENERAL HOSPITAL (O, 25 beds) 175 Hospital Drive, Camden, TN Zip 38320–1617; tel. 731/584–6135; Betty Haskins, Interim Administrator
Web address: www.wth.net

JACKSON–MADISON COUNTY GENERAL HOSPITAL (O, 635 beds) 620 Skyline Drive, Jackson, TN Zip 38301–3923; tel. 731/541–5000; James E. Ross, Interim Chief Executive Officer
Web address: www.wth.org

MILAN GENERAL HOSPITAL (O, 28 beds) 4039 Highland Street, Milan, TN Zip 38358–3483; tel. 731/686–1591; Sherry Scruggs, Administrator
Web address: www.wth.org

PATHWAYS OF TENNESSEE (O, 25 beds) 238 Summar Drive, Jackson, TN Zip 38301–3906; tel. 731/541–8200; Pam Henson, Executive Director
Web address: www.wth.net/pathways

Owned, leased, sponsored:	5 hospitals	734 beds
Contract–managed:	0 hospitals	0 beds
Totals:	5 hospitals	734 beds

★0119: **WEST VIRGINIA UNIVERSITY HEALTH SYSTEM** (NP)
3040 University Avenue, Suite 3400, Morgantown, WV Zip 26505; tel. 304/285–7150; Albert Wright, PharmD, President and Chief Executive Officer
(Moderately Centralized Health System)

WEST VIRGINIA: BERKELEY MEDICAL CENTER (O, 195 beds) 2500 Hospital Drive, Martinsburg, WV Zip 25401–3402; tel. 304/264–1000; Anthony Zelenka, President and Chief Operating Officer
Web address: www.cityhospital.org

CAMDEN CLARK MEDICAL CENTER (O, 254 beds) 800 Garfield Avenue, Parkersburg, WV Zip 26101–5378, Mailing Address: P.O. Box 718, Zip 26102–0718; tel. 304/424–2111; David K. McClure, President and Chief Executive Officer
Web address: www.camdenclark.org

JEFFERSON MEDICAL CENTER (O, 25 beds) 300 South Preston Street, Ranson, WV Zip 25438–1631; tel. 304/728–1600; Anthony Zelenka, Chief Executive Officer
Web address: www.wvuniversityhealthcare.com/locations/Jefferson–Medical–Center.aspx

POTOMAC VALLEY HOSPITAL (O, 25 beds) 100 Pin Oak Lane, Keyser, WV Zip 26726–5908; tel. 304/597–3500; Linda K. Shroyer, Administrator
Web address: www.potomacvalleyhospital.com

ST. JOSEPH'S HOSPITAL OF BUCKHANNON (O, 51 beds) 1 Amalia Drive, Buckhannon, WV Zip 26201–2276; tel. 304/473–2000; Skip Gjolberg, FACHE, Administrator
Web address: www.stj.net

For explanation of codes following names, see page B2.
★ Indicates Type III membership in the American Hospital Association.

UNITED HOSPITAL CENTER (O, 264 beds) 327 Medical Park Drive, Bridgeport, WV Zip 26330–9006; tel. 681/342–1000; Michael C. Tillman, President and Chief Executive Officer
Web address: www.thenewuhc.com

WEST VIRGINIA UNIVERSITY HOSPITALS (O, 524 beds) 1 Medical Center Drive, Morgantown, WV Zip 26506–4749; tel. 304/598–4000; Albert Wright, PharmD, President and Chief Executive Officer
Web address: www.health.wvu.edu

Owned, leased, sponsored:	7 hospitals	1338 beds
Contract–managed:	0 hospitals	0 beds
Totals:	7 hospitals	1338 beds

★**0811:   WESTERN CONNECTICUT HEALTH NETWORK** (NP)
24 Hospital Avenue, Danbury, CT Zip 06810–6099; tel. 203/739–7066; John M. Murphy, M.D., President and Chief Executive Officer
(Moderately Centralized Health System)

CONNECTICUT: DANBURY HOSPITAL (O, 417 beds) 24 Hospital Avenue, Danbury, CT Zip 06810–6099; tel. 203/739–7000; John M. Murphy, M.D., President and Chief Executive Officer, Western Connecticut Health Network
Web address: www.danburyhospital.org

NORWALK HOSPITAL (O, 311 beds) 34 Maple Street, Norwalk, CT Zip 06850–3894; tel. 203/852–2000; Michael Daglio, President
Web address: www.norwalkhospital.org

Owned, leased, sponsored:	2 hospitals	728 beds
Contract–managed:	0 hospitals	0 beds
Totals:	2 hospitals	728 beds

★**6745:   WHEATON FRANCISCAN HEALTHCARE** (CC)
26W171 Roosevelt Road, Wheaton, IL Zip 60187–6002, Mailing Address: P.O. Box 667, Zip 60187–0667; tel. 630/909–6900; John D. Oliverio, President and Chief Executive Officer
(Moderately Centralized Health System)

ILLINOIS: MARIANJOY REHABILITATION HOSPITAL (O, 127 beds) 26 West 171 Roosevelt Road, Wheaton, IL Zip 60187–0795, Mailing Address: P.O. Box 795, Zip 60187–0795; tel. 630/909–8000; Kathleen C. Yosko, President
Web address: www.marianjoy.org

IOWA: COVENANT MEDICAL CENTER (O, 229 beds) 3421 West Ninth Street, Waterloo, IA Zip 50702–5401; tel. 319/272–8000; Jack Dusenbery, President and Chief Executive Officer
Web address: www.wheatoniowa.org

MERCY HOSPITAL OF FRANCISCAN SISTERS (O, 64 beds) 201 Eighth Avenue S.E., Oelwein, IA Zip 50662–2447; tel. 319/283–6000; Terri Derflinger, Administrator
Web address: www.wheatoniowa.org

SARTORI MEMORIAL HOSPITAL (O, 50 beds) 515 College Street, Cedar Falls, IA Zip 50613–2500; tel. 319/268–3000; MaryJo Kavalier, Administrator
Web address: www.wheatoniowa.org

Owned, leased, sponsored:	4 hospitals	470 beds
Contract–managed:	0 hospitals	0 beds
Totals:	4 hospitals	470 beds

★**0468:   WHITE RIVER HEALTH SYSTEM** (NP)
1710 Harrison Street, Batesville, AR Zip 72501–7303; tel. 870/262–1200; Gary Bebow, FACHE, Administrator and Chief Executive Officer
(Independent Hospital System)

ARKANSAS: STONE COUNTY MEDICAL CENTER (O, 25 beds) 2106 East Main Street, Mountain View, AR Zip 72560–6439, Mailing Address: P.O. Box 510, Zip 72560–0510; tel. 870/269–4361; Stanley Townsend, Chief Executive Officer
Web address: www.whiteriverhealthsystem.com

WHITE RIVER MEDICAL CENTER (O, 210 beds) 1710 Harrison Street, Batesville, AR Zip 72501–7303, Mailing Address: P.O. Box 2197, Zip 72503–2197; tel. 870/262–1200; Gary Bebow, FACHE, Administrator and Chief Executive Officer
Web address: www.whiteriverhealthsystem.com

Owned, leased, sponsored:	2 hospitals	235 beds
Contract–managed:	0 hospitals	0 beds
Totals:	2 hospitals	235 beds

0646:   WHITTIER HEALTH NETWORK (IO)
25 Railroad Square, Haverhill, MA Zip 01832–5721; tel. 978/556–5858; Alfred L. Arcidi, M.D., President
(Independent Hospital System)

MASSACHUSETTS: WHITTIER PAVILION (O, 65 beds) 76 Summer Street, Haverhill, MA Zip 01830–5814; tel. 978/373–8222; Alfred L. Arcidi, M.D., Chief Executive Officer
Web address: www.whittierhealth.com

WHITTIER REHABILITATION HOSPITAL (O, 60 beds) 150 Flanders Road, Westborough, MA Zip 01581–1017; tel. 508/871–2000; Alfred J. Arcidi, M.D., Senior Vice President
Web address: www.whittierhealth.com

WHITTIER REHABILITATION HOSPITAL (O, 60 beds) 145 Ward Hill Avenue, Bradford, MA Zip 01835–6928; tel. 978/372–8000; Alfred J. Arcidi, M.D., Senior Vice President
Web address: www.whittierhealth.com

Owned, leased, sponsored:	3 hospitals	185 beds
Contract–managed:	0 hospitals	0 beds
Totals:	3 hospitals	185 beds

1945:   WILLIS–KNIGHTON HEALTH SYSTEM (NP)
2600 Greenwood Road, Shreveport, LA Zip 71103–3908; tel. 318/212–4000; James K. Elrod, FACHE, President and Chief Executive Officer
(Moderately Centralized Health System)

LOUISIANA: DE SOTO REGIONAL HEALTH SYSTEM (C, 10 beds) 207 Jefferson Street, Mansfield, LA Zip 71052–2603, Mailing Address: P.O. Box 1636, Zip 71052–1636; tel. 318/872–4610; Todd Eppler, FACHE, Chief Executive Officer
Web address: www.desotoregional.com

SPRINGHILL MEDICAL CENTER (C, 58 beds) 2001 Doctors Drive, Springhill, LA Zip 71075–4526, Mailing Address: P.O. Box 920, Zip 71075–0920; tel. 318/539–1000; Vince Sedminik, Chief Executive Officer
Web address: www.smccare.com

WILLIS–KNIGHTON MEDICAL CENTER (O, 720 beds) 2600 Greenwood Road, Shreveport, LA Zip 71103–3908, Mailing Address: P.O. Box 32600, Zip 71130–2600; tel. 318/212–4600; James K. Elrod, FACHE, Chief Executive Officer
Web address: www.wkhs.com

WK BOSSIER HEALTH CENTER (O, 166 beds) 2400 Hospital Drive, Bossier City, LA Zip 71111–2385; tel. 318/212–7000; Clifford M. Broussard, FACHE, Administrator
Web address: www.wkhs.com/wkb/

Owned, leased, sponsored:	2 hospitals	886 beds
Contract–managed:	2 hospitals	68 beds
Totals:	4 hospitals	954 beds

1004:   WMCHEALTH (NP)
100 Woods Road, Valhalla, NY Zip 10595–1530; tel. 914/493–7000; Michael D. Israel, President and Chief Executive Officer

NEW YORK: BON SECOURS COMMUNITY HOSPITAL (O, 143 beds) 160 East Main Street, Port Jervis, NY Zip 12771–2245, Mailing Address: P.O. Box 1014, Zip 12771–0268; tel. 845/858–7000; Jeff Reilly, Administrator
Web address: www.bonsecourscommunityhosp.org

For explanation of codes following names, see page B2.
★ Indicates Type III membership in the American Hospital Association.

Section B

GOOD SAMARITAN REGIONAL MEDICAL CENTER (O, 308 beds) 255 Lafayette Avenue, Suffern, NY Zip 10901–4869; tel. 845/368–5000; Mary Leahy, M.D., Chief Executive Officer
Web address: www.goodsamhosp.org

HEALTH ALLIANCE HOSPITAL – BROADWAY CAMPUS (O, 150 beds) 396 Broadway, Kingston, NY Zip 12401–4692; tel. 845/331–3131; David Scarpino, President and Chief Executive Officer
Web address: www.hahv.org

HEALTH ALLIANCE HOSPITAL – MARY'S AVENUE CAMPUS (O, 120 beds) 105 Marys Avenue, Kingston, NY Zip 12401–5894; tel. 845/338–2500; David Scarpino, President and Chief Executive Officer
Web address: www.hahv.org

MARGARETVILLE HOSPITAL (O, 15 beds) 42084 State Highway 28, Margaretville, NY Zip 12455–2820; tel. 845/586–2631; Sandra A. Horan, Executive Director
Web address: www.margaretvillehospital.org

ST. ANTHONY COMMUNITY HOSPITAL (O, 60 beds) 15 Maple Avenue, Warwick, NY Zip 10990–1028; tel. 845/986–2276; Jeff Reilly, Chief Operating Officer
Web address: www.stanthonycommunityhosp.org

WESTCHESTER MEDICAL CENTER (O, 895 beds) 100 Woods Road, Valhalla, NY Zip 10595–1530; tel. 914/493–7000; Michael D. Israel, President and Chief Executive Officer
Web address: www.wmchealth.org

Owned, leased, sponsored:	7 hospitals	1691 beds
Contract–managed:	0 hospitals	0 beds
Totals:	7 hospitals	1691 beds

★**0157:** **YALE NEW HAVEN HEALTH** (NP)
789 Howard Avenue, New Haven, CT Zip 06519–1304; tel. 203/688–4608; Marna P. Borgstrom, President and Chief Executive Officer
(Centralized Physician/Insurance Health System)
CONNECTICUT: BRIDGEPORT HOSPITAL (O, 357 beds) 267 Grant Street, Bridgeport, CT Zip 06610–2805, Mailing Address: P.O. Box 5000, Zip 06610–0120; tel. 203/384–3000; William M. Jennings, President and Chief Executive Officer
Web address: www.bridgeporthospital.org
GREENWICH HOSPITAL (O, 184 beds) 5 Perryridge Road, Greenwich, CT Zip 06830–4697; tel. 203/863–3000; Norman G. Roth, Chief Executive Officer
Web address: www.greenhosp.org
YALE–NEW HAVEN HOSPITAL (O, 1391 beds) 20 York Street, New Haven, CT Zip 06510–3202; tel. 203/688–4242; Marna P. Borgstrom, Chief Executive Officer
Web address: www.ynhh.org

Owned, leased, sponsored:	3 hospitals	1932 beds
Contract–managed:	0 hospitals	0 beds
Totals:	3 hospitals	1932 beds

For explanation of codes following names, see page B2.
★ Indicates Type III membership in the American Hospital Association.

B156 Health Care Systems, Networks and Alliances

© 2016 AHA Guide

Geographically

United States

ALABAMA

Birmingham: BRADFORD HEALTH SERVICES 2101 Magnolia Avenue South, Suite 518, Zip 35205–2853; tel. 205/251–7753; Jerry W. Crowder, President and Chief Executive Officer, p. B24

★ HEALTHSOUTH CORPORATION 3660 Grandview Parkway, Suite 200, Zip 35243–3332; tel. 205/967–7116; Jay F. Grinney, President and Chief Executive Officer, p. B65

NOLAND HEALTH SERVICES, INC. 600 Corporate Parkway, Suite 100, Zip 35242–5451; tel. 205/783–8484; Gary M. Glasscock, President and Chief Executive Officer, p. B96

★ UAB HEALTH SYSTEM 500 22nd Street South, Suite 408, Zip 35233–3110; tel. 205/975–5362; William Ferniany, Ph.D., Chief Executive Officer, p. B139

Guntersville: MARSHALL HEALTH SYSTEM 227 Britany Road, Zip 35976–5766; tel. 256/894–6615; Gary R. Gore, Chief Executive Officer, p. B85

Huntsville: HUNTSVILLE HOSPITAL HEALTH SYSTEM 101 Sivley Road S.W., Zip 35801–4421; tel. 265/256–1000; David S. Spillers, Chief Executive Officer, p. B71

Mobile: ALTAPOINTE HEALTH SYSTEMS 5750–A Southland Drive, Zip 36693–3316; tel. 251/473–4423; J. Tuerk Schlesinger, Chief Executive Officer, p. B10

INFIRMARY HEALTH SYSTEM 5 Mobile Infirmary Circle, Zip 36607–3513; tel. 251/435–5500; D. Mark Nix, President and Chief Executive Officer, p. B72

★ UNIVERSITY OF SOUTH ALABAMA HOSPITALS 2451 Fillingim Street, Zip 36617–2238; tel. 251/471–7000; Owen Bailey, FACHE, Chief Operating Officer, p. B149

Montgomery: BAPTIST HEALTH 301 Brown Springs Road, Zip 36117–7005; tel. 334/273–4400; W. Russell Tyner, President and Chief Executive Officer, p. B19

GILLIARD HEALTH SERVICES 3091 Carter Hill Road, Zip 36111–1801; tel. 334/265–5009; William G. McKenzie, President, Chief Executive Officer and Chairman, p. B57

Tuscaloosa: DCH HEALTH SYSTEM 809 University Boulevard East, Zip 35401–2029; tel. 205/759–7111; Bryan N. Kindred, FACHE, President and Chief Executive Officer, p. B44

ARIZONA

Flagstaff: ★ NORTHERN ARIZONA HEALTHCARE 1200 North Beaver Street, Zip 86001–3118; tel. 928/779–3366; Robert P. Thames, President and Chief Executive Officer, p. B97

Phoenix: ★ BANNER HEALTH 1441 North 12th Street, Zip 85006–2837, Mailing Address: P.O. Box 25489, Zip 85002–5489; tel. 602/747–4000; Peter S. Fine, FACHE, President and Chief Executive Officer, p. B18

Scottsdale: ★ HONORHEALTH 8125 North Hayden Road, Zip 85258–2463; tel. 623/580–5800; Thomas J. Sadvary, FACHE, Chief Executive Officer, p. B70

SOUTHWEST HEALTHCARE SYSTEM 4400 North Scottsdale Road, Suite 9347, Zip 85251–3331; tel. 480/348–9800; Paul R. Tuft, President, p. B126

ARKANSAS

Batesville: ★ WHITE RIVER HEALTH SYSTEM 1710 Harrison Street, Zip 72501–7303; tel. 870/262–1200; Gary Bebow, FACHE, Administrator and Chief Executive Officer, p. B155

Blytheville: ★ MISSISSIPPI COUNTY HOSPITAL SYSTEM 1520 North Division Street, Zip 72315–1448, Mailing Address: P.O. Box 108, Zip 72316–0108; tel. 870/838–7300; Chris Raymer, R.N., Chief Executive Officer, p. B92

Little Rock: ★ BAPTIST HEALTH 9601 Interstate 630, Exit 7, Zip 72205–7299; tel. 501/202–2000; Troy R. Wells, Chief Executive Officer, p. B19

CALIFORNIA

Alhambra: AHMC & HEALTHCARE, INC. 55 South Raymond Avenue, Suite 105, Zip 91801–7101; tel. 626/457–9600; Jonathan Wu, M.D., President and Chairman, p. B8

Corona: SIGNATURE HEALTHCARE SERVICES 4238 Green River Road, Zip 92880–1669; tel. 951/549–8032; Soon K. Kim, M.D., President and Chief Executive Officer, p. B124

Covina: ★ CITRUS VALLEY HEALTH PARTNERS 210 West San Bernardino Road, Zip 91723–1515; tel. 626/331–7331; Robert H. Curry, President and Chief Executive Officer, p. B34

Cupertino: CRC HEALTH GROUP, INC. 20400 Stevens Creek Boulevard, Suite 600, Zip 95014–2217; tel. 866/540–5240; Jerome E. Rhodes, Chief Executive Officer, p. B43

El Segundo: AVANTI HOSPITALS 222 North Sepulveda Boulevard, Suite 950, Zip 90245–5614; tel. 310/356–0550; Arnold R. Schaffer, Corporate Chief Executive Officer, p. B16

Escondido: ★ PALOMAR HEALTH 456 East Grand Avenue, Zip 92025–3319; tel. 760/740–6393; Robert Hemker, President and Chief Executive Officer, p. B102

Fountain Valley: MEMORIALCARE 17360 Brookhurst Street, Zip 92708–3720, Mailing Address: P.O. Box 1428, Long Beach, Zip 90801–1428; tel. 714/377–2900; Barry S. Arbuckle, Ph.D., President and Chief Executive Officer, p. B88

Fresno: COMMUNITY MEDICAL CENTERS Fresno and Maddy Drive, Zip 93721, Mailing Address: P.O. Box 1232, Zip 93715–1232; tel. 559/459–6000; Tim A. Joslin, President and Chief Executive Officer, p. B40

Hemet: PHYSICIANS FOR HEALTHY HOSPITALS 1117 East Devonshire Avenue, Zip 92543–3083; tel. 951/652–2811; Joel M. Bergenfeld, Chief Executive Officer, p. B103

Loma Linda: LOMA LINDA UNIVERSITY ADVENTIST HEALTH SCIENCES CENTER 11175 Campus Street, Zip 92350–1700; tel. 909/558–7572; Richard H. Hart, M.D., President and Chief Executive Officer, p. B84

Los Angeles: ALTA HEALTHCARE SYSTEM 10780 Santa Monica Boulevard, Suite 400, Zip 90025–7616; tel. 310/943–4500; David Topper, Chief Executive Officer, p. B10

KECK MEDICINE OF USC 1500 San Pablo Street, Zip 90033–5313; tel. 323/442–8500; Paul A. Craig, R.N., JD, Interim Chief Executive Officer, p. B76

LOS ANGELES COUNTY–DEPARTMENT OF HEALTH SERVICES 313 North Figueroa Street, Room 912, Zip 90012–2691; tel. 213/240–8101; Mitchell H. Katz, M.D., Director, p. B84

★ VERITY HEALTH SYSTEM 2200 West Third Street, Suite 200, Zip 90057–1935, Mailing Address: 203 Redwood Shores Parkway, Suite 800, Redwood City, Zip 94065; tel. 650/551–6650; Andrei Soran, MSN, Chief Executive Officer, p. B151

Oakland: ★ KAISER FOUNDATION HOSPITALS One Kaiser Plaza, Zip 94612–3600; tel. 510/271–5910; Bernard J. Tyson, Chairman and Chief Executive Officer, p. B75

★ UNIVERSITY OF CALIFORNIA SYSTEMWIDE ADMINISTRATION 1111 Franklin Street, 11th Floor, Zip 94607–5200; tel. 510/987–9071; John D. Stobo, M.D., Executive Vice President and Chief Executive Officer, p. B147

Ontario: ★ PRIME HEALTHCARE SERVICES 3300 East Guasti Road, Zip 91761–8655; tel. 909/235–4400; Prem Reddy, M.D., President and Chief Executive Officer, p. B106

Palo Alto: ★ STANFORD HEALTH CARE 300 Pasteur Drive, Zip 94304–2299; tel. 650/723–4000; David Entwistle, President and Chief Executive Officer, p. B129

Roseville: ★ ADVENTIST HEALTH 2100 Douglas Boulevard, Zip 95661–3898, Mailing Address: P.O. Box 619002, Zip 95661–9002; tel. 916/781–2000; Scott Reiner, President and Chief Executive Officer, p. B5

Sacramento: ★ SUTTER HEALTH 2200 River Plaza Drive, Zip 95833–4134; tel. 916/733–8800; Sarah Krevans, President and Chief Executive Officer, p. B130

San Diego: ★ SCRIPPS HEALTH 4275 Campus Point Court CP112, Zip 92121–1513, Mailing Address: 4275 Campus Point Court, Zip 92121–1513; tel. 858/678–7200; Chris D. Van Gorder, FACHE, President and Chief Executive Officer, p. B119

★ SHARP HEALTHCARE 8695 Spectrum Center Boulevard, Zip 92123–1489; tel. 858/499–4000; Michael Murphy, CPA, President & Chief Executive Officer, p. B123

San Francisco: ★ DIGNITY HEALTH 185 Berry Street, Suite 300, Zip 94107–1773; tel. 415/438–5500; Lloyd H. Dean, President and Chief Executive Officer, p. B49

San Leandro: ALAMEDA HEALTH SYSTEM 15400 Foothill Boulevard, Zip 94578–1009; tel. 510/677–7920; Daniel Boggan, Jr., Interim Chief Executive Officer, p. B8

Santa Ana: KPC HEALTHCARE, INC. 1301 North Tustin Avenue, Zip 92705–8619; tel. 714/953–3652; Suzanne Richards, R.N., M.P.H., FACHE, Chief Executive Officer, p. B78

Santa Barbara: ★ COTTAGE HEALTH 400 West Pueblo Street, Zip 93105–4353, Mailing Address: P.O. Box 689, Zip 93102–0689; tel. 805/569–7290; Ronald C. Werft, President and Chief Executive Officer, p. B42

Santa Fe Springs: COLLEGE HEALTH ENTERPRISES 11627 Telegraph Road, Suite 200, Zip 90670–6814; tel. 562/923–9449; Barry J. Weiss, Chairman of the Board, p. B34

Truckee: ★ TAHOE FOREST HEALTH SYSTEM 10121 Pine Avenue, Zip 96161–4835; tel. 530/587–6011; Harry Weis, Chief Executive Officer, p. B131

Ventura: COMMUNITY MEMORIAL HEALTH SYSTEM 147 North Brent Street, Zip 93003–2809; tel. 805/652–5011; Gary Wilde, President and Chief Executive Officer, p. B41

Walnut Creek: ★ JOHN MUIR HEALTH 1400 Treat Boulevard, Zip 94597–2142; tel. 925/941–2100; Calvin K. Knight, President and Chief Executive Officer, p. B74

West Hollywood: ★ CEDARS–SINAI 8700 Beverly Boulevard, Zip 90048–1865, Mailing Address: Box 48750, Los Angeles, Zip 90048–0750; tel. 310/423–5000; Thomas M. Priselac, President and Chief Executive Officer, p. B31

Whittier: ★ PIH HEALTH 12401 Washington Boulevard, Zip 90602–1006; tel. 562/698–0811; James R. West, President and Chief Executive Officer, p. B104

COLORADO

Alamosa: ★ SAN LUIS VALLEY HEALTH 106 Blanca Avenue, Zip 81101–2340; tel. 719/589–2511; Konnie Martin, Chief Executive Officer, p. B118

Broomfield: ★ SCL HEALTH 500 Eldorado Boulevard, Suite 100–D, Zip 80021; tel. 303/813–5180; Michael A. Slubowski, FACHE, Chief Executive Officer, p. B119

Englewood: ★ CATHOLIC HEALTH INITIATIVES 198 Inverness Drive West, Suite 800, Zip 80112–5202; tel. 303/298–9100; Kevin E. Lofton, FACHE, Chief Executive Officer, p. B28

Fort Collins: ★ UNIVERSITY OF COLORADO HEALTH 2315 East Harmony Road, Suite 200, Zip 80528–8620; tel. 970/848–0000; Elizabeth B. Concordia, President and Chief Executive Officer, p. B147

CONNECTICUT

Danbury: ★ WESTERN CONNECTICUT HEALTH NETWORK 24 Hospital Avenue, Zip 06810–6099; tel. 203/739–7066; John M. Murphy, M.D., President and Chief Executive Officer, p. B155

Hartford: CONNECTICUT DEPARTMENT OF MENTAL HEALTH AND ADDICTION SERVICES 410 Capitol Avenue, Zip 06106–1367, Mailing Address: P.O. Box 341431, Zip 06134–1431; tel. 860/418–7000; Miriam Delphin-Rittmon, Ph.D., Commissioner, p. B41

★ HARTFORD HEALTHCARE One State Street, 19th Floor, Zip 06103; tel. 860/263–4100; Elliot T. Joseph, President and Chief Executive Officer, p. B59

Manchester: ★ EASTERN CONNECTICUT HEALTH NETWORK 71 Haynes Street, Zip 06040–4131; tel. 860/533–3400; Peter J. Karl, President and Chief Executive Officer, p. B52

New Haven: ★ YALE NEW HAVEN HEALTH 789 Howard Avenue, Zip 06519–1304; tel. 203/688–4608; Marna P. Borgstrom, President and Chief Executive Officer, p. B156

New London: ★ L+M HEALTHCARE 365 Montauk Avenue, Zip 06320–4700; tel. 860/442–0711; Bruce D. Cummings, President and Chief Executive Officer, p. B79

DELAWARE

Wilmington: ★ CHRISTIANA CARE HEALTH SYSTEM 501 West 14th Street, Zip 19801–1013, Mailing Address: P.O. Box 1668, Zip 19899–1668; tel. 302/733–1000; Janice E. Nevin, M.D., M.P.H., Chief Executive Officer, p. B32

DISTRICT OF COLUMBIA

Washington: DEPARTMENT OF THE AIR FORCE 1420 Pentagon, Room 4E1084, Zip 20330–1420; tel. 202/767–4765; Lieutenant General Thomas Travis, Surgeon General, p. B44

DEPARTMENT OF VETERANS AFFAIRS 810 Vermont Avenue N.W., Zip 20420–0001; tel. 202/273–5781; Robert A. McDonald, Secretary, Veterans Affairs, p. B45

FLORIDA

Altamonte Springs: ★ ADVENTIST HEALTH SYSTEM SUNBELT HEALTH CARE CORPORATION 900 Hope Way, Zip 32714–1502; tel. 407/357–1000; Donald L. Jernigan, Ph.D., President and Chief Executive Officer, p. B6

Boca Raton: PROMISE HEALTHCARE 999 Yamato Road, 3rd Floor, Zip 33431–4477; tel. 561/869–3100; Peter R. Baronoff, Chief Executive Officer, p. B108

SUCCESS HEALTHCARE 999 Yamato Road, 3rd Floor, Zip 33431–4477; tel. 561/869–6300; Peter R. Baronoff, President and Chief Executive Officer, p. B129

Clearwater: MORTON PLANT MEASE HEALTH CARE 300 Pinellas Street, Zip 33756–3804, Mailing Address: P.O. Box 210, Zip 33757–0210; tel. 727/462–7000; Glenn D. Waters, FACHE, President, p. B92

Coral Gables: ★ BAPTIST HEALTH SOUTH FLORIDA 6855 Red Road, Suite 600, Zip 33143–3632; tel. 786/662–7111; Brian E. Keeley, President and Chief Executive Officer, p. B20

Fort Lauderdale: ★ BROWARD HEALTH 303 S.E. 17th Street, Zip 33316–2523; tel. 954/355–4400; Pauline Grant, FACHE, Interim President and Chief Executive Officer, p. B24

Fort Myers: ★ LEE MEMORIAL HEALTH SYSTEM 2776 Cleveland Avenue, Zip 33901–5856, Mailing Address: P.O. Box 2218, Zip 33902–2218; tel. 239/343–2000; James R. Nathan, President and Chief Executive Officer, p. B80

Gainesville: ★ UF HEALTH SHANDS 1600 S.W. Archer Road, Zip 32610–0326; tel. 352/733–1500; Edward Jimenez, Chief Executive Officer, p. B139

Hollywood: ★ MEMORIAL HEALTHCARE SYSTEM 3501 Johnson Street, Zip 33021–5421; tel. 954/987–2000; Aurelio Fernandez, Chief Executive Officer, p. B88

Jacksonville: ★ BAPTIST HEALTH 841 Prudential Drive, Suite 1601, Zip 32207–8202; tel. 904/202–2000; Hugh Greene, President and Chief Executive Officer, p. B19

NEMOURS 10140 Centurion Parkway North, Zip 32256–0532; tel. 904/697–4100; David J. Bailey, M.D., President and Chief Executive Officer, p. B94

Lauderdale Lakes: CATHOLIC HEALTH SERVICES 4790 North State Road 7, Zip 33319–5860; tel. 954/484–1515; Joseph M. Catania, President and Chief Executive Officer, p. B30

Leesburg: CENTRAL FLORIDA HEALTH 600 East Dixie Avenue, Zip 34748–5925; tel. 352/323–5762; Donald G. Henderson, FACHE, Chief Executive Officer, p. B32

Miami: UNIVERSITY OF MIAMI HEALTH SYSTEM 1400 N.W. 12th Avenue, Zip 33136–1003; tel. 305/243–4000; Pascal J. Goldschmidt, M.D., Chief Executive Officer, p. B148

Miami Lakes: PACER HEALTH CORPORATION 14100 Palmetto Frontage Road, Suite 110, Zip 33016; tel. 305/828–7660; Rainier Gonzalez, Chairman and Chief Executive Officer, p. B101

Orlando: ORLANDO HEALTH 1414 Kuhl Avenue, Zip 32806–2093; tel. 321/843–7000; David W. Strong, President and Chief Executive Officer, p. B101

Pensacola: ★ BAPTIST HEALTH CARE CORPORATION 1717 North E Street, Suite 402, Zip 32501–6377, Mailing Address: P.O. Box 17500, Zip 32522–7500; tel. 850/434–4011; Mark T. Faulkner, President, p. B20

Rockledge: HEALTH FIRST, INC. 6450 U.S. Highway 1, Zip 32955–5747; tel. 321/434–7000; Steven P. Johnson, Ph.D., President and Chief Executive Officer, p. B65

Tampa: SHRINERS HOSPITALS FOR CHILDREN 2900 Rocky Point Drive, Zip 33607–1435, Mailing Address: P.O. Box 31356, Zip 33631–3356; tel. 813/281–0300; John P. McCabe, Executive Vice President, p. B123

Windermere: UNITED MEDICAL CORPORATION 603 Main Street, Zip 34786–3548, Mailing Address: P.O. Box 1100, Zip 34786–1100; tel. 407/876–2200; Donald R. Dizney, Chairman and Chief Executive Officer, p. B140

GEORGIA

Albany: ★ PHOEBE PUTNEY HEALTH SYSTEM 417 Third Avenue, Zip 31701–1943; tel. 229/312–1000; Joel Wernick, President and Chief Executive Officer, p. B103

Atlanta: ★ EMORY HEALTHCARE 1440 Clifton Road N.E., Suite 309, Zip 30322–1102; tel. 404/778–5000; Jonathan S. Lewin, M.D., President, p. B53

★ NORTHSIDE HEALTHCARE SYSTEM 1000 Johnson Ferry Road N.E., Zip 30342–1611; tel. 404/851–8000; Robert Quattrocchi, President and Chief Executive Officer, p. B97

PIEDMONT HEALTHCARE 1800 Howell Mill Road N.W., Suite 850, Zip 30318–0923; tel. 404/425–1314; Kevin Brown, President and Chief Executive Officer, p. B104

SUNLINK HEALTH SYSTEMS 900 Circle 75 Parkway, Suite 1120, Zip 30339–3005; tel. 770/933–7000; Robert M. Thornton, Jr., Chief Executive Officer, p. B130

Augusta: ★ UNIVERSITY HEALTH CARE SYSTEM 1350 Walton Way, Zip 30901–2629; tel. 706/722–9011; James R. Davis, President and Chief Executive Officer, p. B146

Blairsville: UNION GENERAL HOSPITAL, INC. 35 Hospital Road, Zip 30512–3139; tel. 706/745–2111; Mike Gowder, Chief Executive Officer, p. B140

Brunswick: ★ SOUTHEAST GEORGIA HEALTH SYSTEM 2415 Parkwood Drive, Zip 31520–4722, Mailing Address: P.O. Box 1518, Zip 31521–1518; tel. 912/466–7000; Michael D. Scherneck, President and Chief Executive Officer, p. B125

Carrollton: ★ TANNER HEALTH SYSTEM 705 Dixie Street, Zip 30117–3818; tel. 770/836–9580; Loy M. Howard, President and Chief Executive Officer, p. B131

Columbus: COLUMBUS REGIONAL HEALTHCARE SYSTEM 707 Center Street, Suite 400, Zip 31901–1575; tel. 706/660–6100; Scott Hill, Chief Executive Officer, p. B34

Decatur: DEKALB REGIONAL HEALTH SYSTEM 2701 North Decatur Road, Zip 30033–5918; tel. 404/501–1000; John Shelton, President and Chief Executive Officer, p. B44

Macon: NAVICENT HEALTH 777 Hemlock Street, MSC 105, Zip 31201–2155, Mailing Address: 777 Hemlock Street, Zip 31201–2155; tel. 478/633–1000; Ninfa M. Saunders, Chief Executive Officer, p. B94

Marietta: ★ WELLSTAR HEALTH SYSTEM 793 Sawyer Road, Zip 30062; tel. 770/792–5012; Candice Saunders, President and Chief Executive Officer, p. B154

Milledgeville: OCONEE REGIONAL HEALTH SYSTEMS 821 North Cobb Street, Zip 31061–2343; tel. 478/454–3505; Jean Aycock, President and Chief Executive Officer, p. B100

Thomasville: ARCHBOLD MEDICAL CENTER 910 South Broad Street, Zip 31792–6113; tel. 229/228–2739; J. Perry Mustian, President, p. B11

Tifton: ★ TIFT REGIONAL HEALTH SYSTEM 901 East 18th Street, Zip 31794–3648; tel. 229/353–6100; William T. Richardson, President and Chief Executive Officer, p. B135

Warner Robins: ★ HOUSTON HEALTHCARE SYSTEM 1601 Watson Boulevard, Zip 31093–3431, Mailing Address: P.O. Box 2886, Zip 31099–2886; tel. 478/922–4281; Cary Martin, Chief Executive Officer, p. B71

HAWAII

Honolulu: ★ HAWAII HEALTH SYSTEMS CORPORATION 3675 Kilauea Avenue, Zip 96816–2333; tel. 808/733–4151; Linda Rosen, M.D., Chief Executive Officer, p. B60

HAWAII PACIFIC HEALTH 55 Merchant Street, Zip 96813–4306; tel. 808/949–9355; Raymond P. Vara, Jr., President and Chief Executive Officer, p. B60

★ QUEEN'S HEALTH SYSTEMS 1301 Punchbowl Street, Zip 96813–2402; tel. 808/535–5448; Arthur A. Ushijima, FACHE, President and Chief Executive Officer, p. B112

IDAHO

Boise: ★ ST. LUKE'S HEALTH SYSTEM 420 West Idaho Street, Zip 83702–6041; tel. 208/381–4200; David C. Pate, M.D., JD, President and Chief Executive Officer, p. B128

Pocatello: SAFE HAVEN HEALTH CARE 2520 South 5th Avenue, Zip 83204–1923; tel. 800/261–2443; Scott Burpee, President, p. B116

ILLINOIS

Carbondale: SOUTHERN ILLINOIS HOSPITAL SERVICES 1239 East Main Street, Zip 62901–3114, Mailing Address: P.O. Box 3988, Zip 62902–3988; tel. 618/457–5200; Rex P. Budde, President and Chief Executive Officer, p. B126

Chicago: COOK COUNTY HEALTH AND HOSPITALS SYSTEM 1900 West Polk Street, Suite 220, Zip 60612–3723; tel. 312/864–6820; John Jay Shannon, M.D., Chief Executive Officer, p. B41

NATIONAL SURGICAL HEALTHCARE 250 South Wacker Drive, Suite 500, Zip 60606–5897; tel. 312/627–8400; David Crane, Chief Executive Officer, p. B94

★ NORTHWESTERN MEMORIAL HEALTHCARE 251 East Huron Street, Zip 60611–2908; tel. 312/926–2000; Dean M. Harrison, President and Chief Executive Officer, p. B97

★ PRESENCE HEALTH 200 South Wacker Drive, Suite 1100, Zip 60606–5829; tel. 312/308–3200; Michael Englehart, President and Chief Executive Officer, p. B105

★ RUSH UNIVERSITY MEDICAL CENTER 1653 West Congress Parkway, Zip 60612–3864; tel. 312/942–5000; Larry J. Goodman, M.D., Chief Executive Officer, p. B116

★ SINAI HEALTH SYSTEM 1500 South California Avenue, Zip 60608–1729; tel. 773/542–2000; Karen Teitelbaum, President and Chief Executive Officer, p. B124

UNIVERSITY OF CHICAGO MEDICINE 5841 South Maryland Avenue, Zip 60637–1447; tel. 773/702–6240; Sharon L. O'Keefe, President, p. B147

Crystal Lake: ★ CENTEGRA HEALTH SYSTEM 385 Millennium Drive, Zip 60012–3761; tel. 815/788–5800; Michael S. Eesley, Chief Executive Officer, p. B31

Downers Grove: ★ ADVOCATE HEALTH CARE 3075 Highland Parkway, Suite 600, Zip 60515–1206; tel. 630/929–8700; Jim H. Skogsbergh, President and Chief Executive Officer, p. B7

Evergreen Park: AMERICAN PROVINCE OF LITTLE COMPANY OF MARY SISTERS 9350 South California Avenue, Zip 60805–2595; tel. 708/229–5491; Sister Kathleen McIntyre, Province Leader, p. B10

Naperville: ★ EDWARD–ELMHURST HEALTHCARE 801 South Washington Street, Zip 60540–7430; tel. 630/527–3000; Pamela M. Davis, System President and Chief Executive Officer, p. B53

Peoria: ★ OSF HEALTHCARE SYSTEM 800 N.E. Glen Oak Avenue, Zip 61603–3200; tel. 309/655–2850; Kevin D. Schoeplein, Chief Executive Officer, p. B101

Schaumburg: CANCER TREATMENT CENTERS OF AMERICA 1336 Basswood Road, Zip 60173–4544; tel. 847/342–7400; Rajesh K. Garg, M.D., JD, President and Chief Executive Officer, p. B25

Springfield: DIVISION OF MENTAL HEALTH, DEPARTMENT OF HUMAN SERVICES 319 East Madison Street, S–3B, Zip 62701–1035; tel. 217/785–6023; Lorrie Rickman Jones, Ph.D., Director, p. B51

★ HOSPITAL SISTERS HEALTH SYSTEM 4936 LaVerna Road, Zip 62707–9797, Mailing Address: P.O. Box 19456, Zip 62794–9456; tel. 217/523–4747; Mary Starmann–Harrison, FACHE, R.N., President and Chief Executive Officer, p. B70

★ MEMORIAL HEALTH SYSTEM 701 North First Street, Zip 62781–0001; tel. 217/788–3000; Edgar J. Curtis, FACHE, President and Chief Executive Officer, p. B88

Urbana: ★ CARLE FOUNDATION 611 West Park Street, Zip 61801–2595; tel. 217/383–3311; James C. Leonard, M.D., President and Chief Executive Officer, p. B27

Wheaton: ★ WHEATON FRANCISCAN HEALTHCARE 26W171 Roosevelt Road, Zip 60187–6002, Mailing Address: P.O. Box 667, Zip 60187–0667; tel. 630/909–6900; John D. Oliverio, President and Chief Executive Officer, p. B155

INDIANA

Evansville: ★ DEACONESS HEALTH SYSTEM 600 Mary Street, Zip 47710–1658; tel. 812/450–5000; Linda E. White, President and Chief Executive Officer, p. B44

Fort Wayne: ★ PARKVIEW HEALTH 10501 Corporate Drive, Zip 46845–1700; tel. 260/373–7001; Michael J. Packnett, President and Chief Executive Officer, p. B102

Hammond: COMMUNITY HEALTHCARE SYSTEM 901 MacArthur Boulevard, Zip 46321–2959; tel. 219/836–1600; Donald Powers, Chairman, President and Chief Executive Officer, p. B40

Indianapolis: ★ COMMUNITY HEALTH NETWORK 7330 Shadeland Station, Zip 46256–3957; tel. 317/355–1411; Bryan A. Mills, President and Chief Executive Officer, p. B35

★ INDIANA UNIVERSITY HEALTH 340 West 10th Street, Suite 6100, Zip 46202–3082, Mailing Address: P.O. Box 1367, Zip 46206–1367; tel. 317/962–5900; Dennis M. Murphy, President, p. B72

Mishawaka: FRANCISCAN ALLIANCE 1515 Dragoon Trail, Zip 46544–4710, Mailing Address: P.O. Box 1290, Zip 46546–1290; tel. 574/256–3935; Kevin D. Leahy, President and Chief Executive Officer, p. B56

NEUROPSYCHIATRIC HOSPITALS 1625 East Jefferson Boulevard, Zip 46545–7103; tel. 574/255–1400; Cameron R. Gilbert, Ph.D., President and Chief Executive Officer, p. B94

South Bend: ★ BEACON HEALTH SYSTEM 615 North Michigan Street, Zip 46601–1033; tel. 574/647–1000; Philip A. Newbold, Chief Executive Officer, p. B22

IOWA

Clarion: ★ IOWA SPECIALTY HOSPITALS 1316 South Main Street, Zip 50525–2019; tel. 515/532–2811; Steven J. Simonin, Chief Executive Officer, p. B74

Davenport: ★ GENESIS HEALTH SYSTEM 1227 East Rusholme Street, Zip 52803–2498; tel. 563/421–1000; Douglas P. Cropper, President and Chief Executive Officer, p. B57

West Des Moines: ★ UNITYPOINT HEALTH 1776 Westlakes Parkway, Suite 400, Zip 50266–8239; tel. 515/241–6161; Kevin Vermeer, President and Chief Executive Officer, p. B141

KANSAS

Salina: SALINA REGIONAL HEALTH CENTER 400 South Santa Fe Avenue, Zip 67401–4198, Mailing Address: PO Box 5080, Zip 67402–5080; tel. 785/452–7000; Michael Terry, President and Chief Executive Officer, p. B117

Wichita: ★ GREAT PLAINS HEALTH ALLIANCE, INC. 250 North Rock Road, Suite 160, Zip 67206–2241; tel. 316/685–1523; Dave Dellasega, President and Chief Executive Officer, p. B58

KENTUCKY

Bowling Green: COMMONWEALTH HEALTH CORPORATION 800 Park Street, Zip 42101–2356; tel. 270/745–1500; Connie Smith, President and Chief Executive Officer, p. B34

Danville: EPHRAIM MCDOWELL HEALTH 217 South Third Street, Zip 40422–1823; tel. 859/239–1000; Sally M. Davenport, R.N., MS, Chief Executive Officer, p. B53

Edgewood: ST. ELIZABETH HEALTHCARE 1 Medical Village Drive, Zip 41017–3403; tel. 859/301–2000; Garren Colvin, Chief Executive Officer, p. B128

Lexington: APPALACHIAN REGIONAL HEALTHCARE, INC. 2260 Executive Drive, Zip 40505–4810, Mailing Address: P.O. Box 8086, Zip 40533–8086; tel. 859/226–2440; Jerry Haynes, President and Chief Executive Officer, p. B11

Louisville: ALLIANT MANAGEMENT SERVICES 2650 Eastpoint Parkway, Suite 300, Zip 40223–5164; tel. 502/992–3525; Timothy L. Jarm, President and Chief Executive Officer, p. B9

★ BAPTIST HEALTH 2701 Eastpoint Parkway, Zip 40223; tel. 502/896–5000; Stephen C. Hanson, Chief Executive Officer, p. B19

★ KINDRED HEALTHCARE 680 South Fourth Street, Zip 40202–2412; tel. 502/596–7300; Kent Wallace, Chief Operating Officer, p. B76

★ NORTON HEALTHCARE 4967 U.S. Highway 42, Suite 100, Zip 40222–6363, Mailing Address: P.O. Box 35070, Zip 40232–5070; tel. 502/629–8000; Stephen Williams, Chief Executive Officer, p. B97

Owensboro: OWENSBORO HEALTH 1201 Pleasant Valley Road, Zip 42303–9811; tel. 270/417–2000; Greg Strahan, Interim Chief Executive Officer, p. B101

LOUISIANA

Baton Rouge: ★ FRANCISCAN MISSIONARIES OF OUR LADY HEALTH SYSTEM, INC. 4200 Essen Lane, Zip 70809–2158; tel. 225/923–2701; John J. Finan, Jr., FACHE, President and Chief Executive Officer, p. B56

LOUISIANA STATE HOSPITALS 628 North 4th Street, Zip 70802–5342, Mailing Address: P.O. Box 629, Zip 70821–0628; tel. 225/342–9500; Shelby Price, Chief Executive Officer, p. B84

Crowley: COMPASS HEALTH 713 North Avenue L., Zip 70526–3832; tel. 337/788–3330; Mark J. Cullen, Chief Executive Officer, p. B41

Gretna: UNITED MEDICAL REHABILITATION HOSPITALS 3201 Wall Boulevard, Suite B., Zip 70056–7755; tel. 504/433–5551; John E.H. Mills, President & Chief Executive Officer, p. B140

Hammond: NORTH OAKS HEALTH SYSTEM 15790 Paul Vega MD Drive, Zip 70403–1436, Mailing Address: P.O. Box 2668, Zip 70404–2668; tel. 985/345–2700; Julie Bruhn, Administrative Operations Support Analyst, p. B96

Lafayette: AMG INTEGRATED HEALTHCARE MANAGEMENT 101 La Rue France, Suite 500, Zip 70508–3144; tel. 337/269–9828; August J. Rantz, III, Founder and Chief Executive Officer, p. B10

LAFAYETTE GENERAL HEALTH 1214 Coolidge Boulevard, Zip 70503–2621; tel. 337/289–7991; David L. Callecod, President and Chief Executive Officer, p. B79

LHC GROUP 420 West Pinhook Road, Zip 70503–2131; tel. 337/233–1307; Keith G. Myers, Chairman and Chief Executive Officer, p. B80

Lake Charles: OCEANS HEALTHCARE 2720 Rue de Jardin, Suite 100, Zip 70605–4050; tel. 337/721–1900; Jason Reed, President and Chief Executive Officer, p. B99

New Orleans: LCMC HEALTH 200 Henry Clay Avenue, Zip 70118–5720; tel. 504/899–9511; Greg Feirn, CPA, President and Chief Executive Officer, p. B79

★ OCHSNER HEALTH SYSTEM 1514 Jefferson Highway, Zip 70121–2429; tel. 800/874–8984; Warner L. Thomas, FACHE, President and Chief Executive Officer, p. B99

Shreveport: ALLEGIANCE HEALTH MANAGEMENT 504 Texas Street, Suite 200, Zip 71101–3526; tel. 318/226–8202; Rock Bordelon, President and Chief Executive Officer, p. B8

UNIVERSITY HEALTH SYSTEM 1501 Kings Highway, Zip 71103–4228; tel. 318/675–5000; Richard C. Cascio, Interim Chief Executive Officer, p. B146

WILLIS–KNIGHTON HEALTH SYSTEM 2600 Greenwood Road, Zip 71103–3908; tel. 318/212–4000; James K. Elrod, FACHE, President and Chief Executive Officer, p. B155

MAINE

Brewer: ★ EASTERN MAINE HEALTHCARE SYSTEMS 43 Whiting Hill Road, Zip 04412–1005; tel. 207/973–7045; M. Michelle Hood, FACHE, President and Chief Executive Officer, p. B52

Lewiston: CENTRAL MAINE HEALTHCARE 300 Main Street, Zip 04240–7027; tel. 207/795–0111; , p. B32

Portland: MAINEHEALTH 110 Free Street, Zip 04101–3537; William L. Caron, Jr., President, p. B84

MARYLAND

Baltimore: ★ JOHNS HOPKINS HEALTH SYSTEM 733 North Broadway, BRB 104, Zip 21205–1832; tel. 410/955–5000; Ronald R. Peterson, President, p. B75

LIFEBRIDGE HEALTH 2401 West Belvedere Avenue, Zip 21215–5216; tel. 410/601–5134; Neil M. Meltzer, President and Chief Executive Officer, p. B81

★ UNIVERSITY OF MARYLAND MEDICAL SYSTEM 250 West Pratt Street, 24th Floor, Zip 21201–1595; tel. 410/328–8667; Robert A. Chrencik, President and Chief Executive Officer, p. B147

Bel Air: UPPER CHESAPEAKE HEALTH SYSTEM 520 Upper Chesapeake Drive, Suite 405, Zip 21014–4381; tel. 443/643–3303; Lyle Ernest Sheldon, FACHE, President and Chief Executive Officer, p. B150

Cheverly: DIMENSIONS HEALTHCARE SYSTEM 3001 Hospital Drive, 3rd Floor, Zip 20785–1189; tel. 301/583–4000; Neil J. Moore, President and Chief Executive Officer, p. B50

Columbia: ★ MEDSTAR HEALTH 5565 Sterrett Place, 5th Floor, Zip 21044–2665; tel. 410/772–6500; Kenneth A. Samet, President and Chief Executive Officer, p. B87

Gaithersburg: ADVENTIST HEALTHCARE 820 West Diamond Avenue, Suite 600, Zip 20878–1419; tel. 301/315–3185; Terry Forde, President and Chief Executive Officer, p. B7

Marriottsville: ★ BON SECOURS HEALTH SYSTEM, INC. 1505 Marriottsville Road, Zip 21104–1399; tel. 410/442–5511; Richard Statuto, President and Chief Executive Officer, p. B23

Rockville: U. S. INDIAN HEALTH SERVICE 801 Thompson Avenue, Zip 20852–1627; tel. 301/443–1083; Yvette Roubideaux, M.D., M.P.H., Director, p. B138

Sparks Glencoe: FUNDAMENTAL LONG TERM CARE HOLDINGS, LLC 930 Ridgebrook Road, Zip 21152–9390; tel. 410/773–1000; W. Bradley Bennett, President and Chief Executive Officer, p. B57

MASSACHUSETTS

Boston: MASSACHUSETTS DEPARTMENT OF MENTAL HEALTH 25 Staniford Street, Zip 02114–2575; tel. 617/626–8123; Joan Mikula, Interim Commissioner, p. B85

MASSACHUSETTS DEPARTMENT OF PUBLIC HEALTH 250 Washington Street, Zip 02108–4619; tel. 617/624–6000; Sandra Akers, Bureau Director, Public Health Hospitals, p. B85

★ PARTNERS HEALTHCARE SYSTEM, INC. 800 Boylston Street, Suite 1150, Zip 02199–8123; tel. 617/278–1004; David Torchiana, M.D., Chief Executive Officer, p. B102

STEWARD HEALTH CARE SYSTEM, LLC 500 Boylston Street, 5th Floor, Zip 02116–3740; tel. 617/419–4700; Ralph de la Torre, M.D., Chairman and Chief Executive Officer, p. B129

Burlington: ★ LAHEY HEALTH 41 Mall Road, Zip 01805–0001; tel. 781/744–7100; Howard R. Grant, JD, M.D., President and Chief Executive Officer, p. B79

Haverhill: WHITTIER HEALTH NETWORK 25 Railroad Square, Zip 01832–5721; tel. 978/556–5858; Alfred L. Arcidi, M.D., President, p. B155

Hyannis: ★ CAPE COD HEALTHCARE, INC. 27 Park Street, Zip 02601–5230; tel. 508/862–5121; Michael K. Lauf, President and Chief Executive Officer, p. B25

Pittsfield: ★ BERKSHIRE HEALTH SYSTEMS, INC. 725 North Street, Zip 01201–4124; tel. 413/447–2750; David E. Phelps, President and Chief Executive Officer, p. B23

Springfield: ★ BAYSTATE HEALTH, INC. 759 Chestnut Street, Zip 01199–0001; tel. 413/794–0000; Mark A. Keroack, M.D., M.P.H., President and Chief Executive Officer, p. B22

Tewksbury: ★ COVENANT HEALTH 100 Ames Pond Drive, Suite 102, Zip 01876–1240; tel. 978/654–6363; David R. Lincoln, FACHE, President and Chief Executive Officer, p. B43

Worcester: ★ UMASS MEMORIAL HEALTH CARE, INC. 1 Biotech Park, Zip 01605–2982; tel. 508/334–0100; Eric Dickson, M.D., President and Chief Executive Officer, p. B139

MICHIGAN

Detroit: ★ HENRY FORD HEALTH SYSTEM One Ford Place, Zip 48202–3450; tel. 313/876–8708; Nancy M. Schlichting, Chief Executive Officer, p. B70

Flint: MCLAREN HEALTH CARE CORPORATION G3235 Beecher Road, Suite B., Zip 48532–3650; tel. 810/342–1100; Philip A. Incarnati, President and Chief Executive Officer, p. B86

Grand Rapids: ★ SPECTRUM HEALTH 100 Michigan Street N.E., Zip 49503–2551; tel. 616/391–1774; Richard C. Breon, President and Chief Executive Officer, p. B126

Kalamazoo: ★ BRONSON HEALTHCARE GROUP 301 John Street, Zip 49007–5295; tel. 269/341–6000; Frank J. Sardone, President and Chief Executive Officer, p. B24

Lansing: ★ SPARROW HEALTH SYSTEM 1215 East Michigan Avenue, Zip 48912–1811; tel. 517/364–1000; Dennis A. Swan, JD, FACHE, President and Chief Executive Officer, p. B126

Livonia: ★ TRINITY HEALTH 20555 Victor Parkway, Zip 48152–7031; tel. 734/343–1000; Richard J. Gilfillan, M.D., President and Chief Executive Officer, p. B136

Midland: ★ MIDMICHIGAN HEALTH 4000 Wellness Drive, Zip 48670–0001; tel. 989/839–3000; Diane Postler-Slattery, Ph.D., President and Chief Executive Officer, p. B91

Saint Joseph: LAKELAND HEALTH 1234 Napier Avenue, Zip 49085–2158; tel. 269/983–8300; Loren Hamel, M.D., President and Chief Executive Officer, p. B79

Southfield: ★ BEAUMONT HEALTH 2000 Town Center, Suite 1200, Zip 48075–1145, Mailing Address: 44201 Dequindre Road, Troy, Zip 48085–1117; tel. 248/898–5000; John T. Fox, President and Chief Executive Officer, p. B22

Traverse City: ★ MUNSON HEALTHCARE 1105 Sixth Street, Zip 49684–2386; tel. 231/935–6703; Edwin Ness, President and Chief Executive Officer, p. B93

MINNESOTA

Bloomington: HEALTHPARTNERS 8170 33rd Avenue South, Zip 55425–4516; tel. 952/883–7600; Mary K. Brainerd, President and Chief Executive Officer, p. B65

Duluth: ★ ESSENTIA HEALTH 502 East Second Street, Zip 55805–1913; tel. 218/786–8376; David C. Herman, M.D., Chief Executive Officer, p. B54

Minneapolis: ★ ALLINA HEALTH 2925 Chicago Avenue, Zip 55407–1321, Mailing Address: P.O. Box 43, Zip 55440–0043; tel. 612/262–5000; Penny Ann Wheeler, M.D., Chief Executive Officer, p. B9

★ FAIRVIEW HEALTH SERVICES 2450 Riverside Avenue, Zip 55454–1400; tel. 612/672–6141; David Murphy, Interim Chief Executive Officer, p. B55

Robbinsdale: ★ NORTH MEMORIAL HEALTH CARE 3300 Oakdale Avenue North, Zip 55422–2926; tel. 763/520–5200; J. Kevin Croston, M.D., Chief Executive Officer, p. B96

Rochester: ★ MAYO CLINIC 200 First Street S.W., Zip 55905–0002; tel. 507/284–0288; John H. Noseworthy, MD, M.D., President and Chief Executive Officer, p. B85

Saint Cloud: ★ CENTRACARE HEALTH 1406 Sixth Avenue North, Zip 56303–1900; tel. 320/251–2700; Kenneth D. Holmen, M.D., President and Chief Executive Officer, p. B32

Saint Paul: ★ HEALTHEAST CARE SYSTEM 559 Capitol Boulevard, 6–South, Zip 55103–0000; tel. 651/232–2300; Kathryn G. Correia, President and Chief Executive Officer, p. B65

MINNESOTA DEPARTMENT OF HUMAN SERVICES 540 Cedar Street, Zip 55101–2208, Mailing Address: P.O. Box 64998, Zip 55164–0998; tel. 651/431–3212; Anne Barry, Deputy Commissioner, p. B91

Waconia: ★ RIDGEVIEW MEDICAL CENTER 500 South Maple Street, Zip 55387–1752; tel. 952/442–2191; Robert Stevens, President and Chief Executive Officer, p. B114

MISSISSIPPI

Jackson: ★ BAPTIST HEALTH SYSTEMS 1225 North State Street, Zip 39202–2064; tel. 601/968–1000; Chris Anderson, Chief Executive Officer, p. B20

MISSISSIPPI STATE DEPARTMENT OF MENTAL HEALTH 1101 Robert East Lee Building, 239 North Lamar Street, Zip 39201–1101; tel. 601/359–1288; Edwin C. LeGrand, III, Executive Director, p. B92

★ UNIVERSITY HOSPITALS AND HEALTH SYSTEM 2500 North State Street, Zip 39216–4500; tel. 601/984–1000; Kevin S. Cook, Chief Executive Officer, p. B146

Magee: ★ PIONEER HEALTH SERVICES 110 Pioneer Way, Zip 39111–5501, Mailing Address: P.O. Box 1100, Zip 39111–1100; tel. 601/849–6440; Joseph S. McNulty, III, President and Chief Executive Officer, p. B104

Mccomb: SOUTHWEST HEALTH SYSTEMS 215 Marion Avenue, Zip 39648–2705, Mailing Address: P.O. Box 1307, Zip 39649–1307; tel. 601/249–5500; Norman M. Price, FACHE, Chief Executive Officer and Administrator, p. B126

Meridian: ★ RUSH HEALTH SYSTEMS 1314 19th Avenue, Zip 39301–4116; tel. 601/483–0011; Wallace Strickland, President and Chief Executive Officer, p. B115

Tupelo: ★ NORTH MISSISSIPPI HEALTH SERVICES, INC. 830 South Gloster Street, Zip 38801–4996; tel. 662/377–3136; M. Shane Spees, President and Chief Executive Officer, p. B96

MISSOURI

Cape Girardeau: LANDMARK HOSPITALS 3255 Independence Street, Zip 63701–4914; tel. 573/335–1091; William K. Kapp, III, M.D., President and Chief Executive Officer, p. B79

SOUTHEASTHEALTH 1701 Lacey Street, Zip 63701–5230; tel. 573/334–4822; Kenneth Bateman, CPA, Chief Executive Officer, p. B125

Chesterfield: ★ MERCY HEALTH 14528 South Outer 40, Suite 100, Zip 63017–5743; tel. 314/579–6100; Lynn Britton, President and Chief Executive Officer, p. B89

Columbia: ★ UNIVERSITY OF MISSOURI HEALTH CARE One Hospital Drive, DC 031, Zip 65212–0001; tel. 573/884–8738; Mitchell L. Wasden, Ed.D., Chief Executive Officer and Chief Operating Officer, p. B148

Joplin: ★ FREEMAN HEALTH SYSTEM 1102 West 32nd Street, Zip 64804–3503; tel. 417/347–1111; Paula F. Baker, President and Chief Executive Officer, p. B57

Kansas City: RURAL COMMUNITY HOSPITALS OF AMERICA 1100 Main Street, Suite 2350, Zip 64105–5186; tel. 816/474–7800; Lawrence J. Arthur, President, p. B115

★ SAINT LUKE'S HEALTH SYSTEM 901 East 104th Street, Mailstop 900N, Zip 64131–4517, Mailing Address: 901 East 104th Street, Zip 64131–4517; tel. 816/932–2000; Melinda Estes, M.D., President and Chief Executive Officer, p. B117

★ TRUMAN MEDICAL CENTERS 2301 Holmes Street, Zip 64108–2677; tel. 816/404–1000; Charlie Shields, President and Chief Executive Officer, p. B138

Saint Louis: ★ ASCENSION HEALTH 101 South Hanley Road, Suite 450, Zip 63105–3406; tel. 314/733–8000; Robert J. Henkel, FACHE, President and Chief Executive Officer, p. B12

★ BJC HEALTHCARE 4901 Forest Park Avenue, Suite 1200, Zip 63108–1402; tel. 314/747–9322; Steven H. Lipstein, President and Chief Executive Officer, p. B23

★ SSM HEALTH 10101 Woodfield Lane, Zip 63132–2937; tel. 314/994–7800; William P. Thompson, President and Chief Executive Officer, p. B127

Springfield: COXHEALTH 1423 North Jefferson Avenue, Zip 65802–1988; tel. 417/269–3108; Steven D. Edwards, President and Chief Executive Officer, p. B43

MONTANA

Bozeman: BOZEMAN HEALTH 915 Highland Boulevard, Zip 59715–6902; tel. 406/585–5000; John Hill, President and Chief Executive Officer, p. B24

Great Falls: BENEFIS HEALTH SYSTEM 1101 26th Street South, Zip 59405–5161; tel. 406/455–5000; John H. Goodnow, Chief Executive Officer, p. B22

NEBRASKA

Lincoln: ★ BRYAN HEALTH 1600 South 48th Street, Zip 68506–1283; tel. 402/481–1111; Kimberly A. Russel, FACHE, President and Chief Executive Officer, p. B25

Norfolk: FAITH REGIONAL HEALTH SERVICES 2700 West Norfolk Avenue, Zip 68701–4438, Mailing Address: P.O. Box 869, Zip 68702–0869; tel. 402/644–7201; Mark D. Klosterman, FACHE, President and Chief Executive Officer, p. B55

Omaha: ★ NEBRASKA METHODIST HEALTH SYSTEM, INC. 8511 West Dodge Road, Zip 68114–3403; tel. 402/354–5411; John M. Fraser, FACHE, President and Chief Executive Officer, p. B94

NEVADA

Reno: ★ RENOWN HEALTH 1155 Mill Street, Zip 89502–1576; tel. 775/982–5529; Anthony D. Slonim, M.D., Dr.PH, President and Chief Executive Officer, p. B114

NEW HAMPSHIRE

Laconia: ★ LRGHEALTHCARE 80 Highland Street, Zip 03246–3298; tel. 603/524–3211; Kevin Donovan, President and Chief Executive Officer, p. B84

Portsmouth: BRIDGEPOINT HEALTHCARE 155 Fleet Street, Zip 03801–4050; tel. 603/570–4888; Marc C. Ferrell, President and Chief Executive Officer, p. B24

NEW JERSEY

Edison: ★ HACKENSACK MERIDIAN HEALTH 343 Thornall Street, Zip 08837–2206; tel. 844/464–9355; Robert C. Garrett, FACHE, Co–Chief Executive Officer, p. B59

★ JFK HEALTH 80 James Street, 2nd Floor, Zip 08820–3938; tel. 732/632–1503; Raymond F. Fredericks, President and Chief Executive Officer, p. B74

Jersey City: ★ CAREPOINT HEALTH 10 Exchange Place, 15th Floor, Zip 07302–3918; tel. 877/791–7000; Jeffrey M. Mandler, Chief Executive Officer, p. B26

Lakewood: CONCORD HEALTHCARE GROUP 111 Clifton AVenue, Zip 08701; tel. 214/396–3462; Joe Neuman, Chief Executive Officer, p. B41

Marlton: ★ VIRTUA HEALTH 50 Lake Center Executive Drive, Suite 401, Zip 08053; tel. 856/355–0010; Richard P. Miller, Chief Executive Officer, p. B153

Morristown: ★ ATLANTIC HEALTH SYSTEM 475 South Street, Zip 07962, Mailing Address: P.O. Box 1905, Zip 07962–1905; tel. 973/660–3270; Brian A. Gragnolati, FACHE, President and Chief Executive Officer, p. B16

Mullica Hill: ★ INSPIRA HEALTH NETWORK 165 Bridgeton Pike, Zip 08062; tel. 856/641–8000; John A. DiAngelo, President and Chief Executive Officer, p. B73

Trenton: ★ CAPITAL HEALTH 750 Brunswick Avenue, Zip 08638–4143; tel. 609/394–6000; Al Maghazehe, Ph.D., FACHE, President and Chief Executive Officer, p. B26

DIVISION OF MENTAL HEALTH AND ADDICTION SERVICES, DEPARTMENT OF HUMAN SERVICES, STATE OF NEW JERSEY 222 South Warren Street, Zip 08608–2306, Mailing Address: P.O. Box 700, Zip 08625–0700; tel. 609/777–0702; Lynn Kovich, Assistant Commissioner, p. B51

West Orange: ★ RWJBARNABAS HEALTH 95 Old Short Hills Road, Zip 07052–1008; tel. 973/322–4000; Barry Ostrowsky, President and Chief Executive Officer, p. B116

NEW MEXICO

Albuquerque: ERNEST HEALTH, INC. 7770 Jefferson Street N.E., Suite 320, Zip 87109–4386; tel. 505/856–5300; Darby Brockette, Chief Executive Officer, p. B54

★ PRESBYTERIAN HEALTHCARE SERVICES 2501 Buena Vista Drive, S.E., Zip 87106–4260, Mailing Address: P.O. Box 26666, Zip 87125–6666; tel. 505/841–1234; James H. Hinton, President and Chief Executive Officer, p. B105

UNIVERSITY OF NEW MEXICO HOSPITALS 915 Camino De Salud, Zip 87131–0001; tel. 505/272–5849; Stephen W. McKernan, Chief Executive Officer, p. B148

NEW YORK

Albany: NEW YORK STATE OFFICE OF MENTAL HEALTH 44 Holland Avenue, Zip 12208–3411; tel. 518/474–7056; Kristin M. Woodlock, R.N., Acting Commissioner, p. B95

Binghamton: UNITED HEALTH SERVICES 10–42 Mitchell Avenue, Zip 13903–1617; tel. 607/762–2200; Matthew J. Salanger, President and Chief Executive Officer, p. B140

Bronx: MONTEFIORE HEALTH SYSTEM 111 East 210th Street, Zip 10467–2490; tel. 718/920–4321; Steven M. Safyer, M.D., President and CEO, p. B92

Buffalo: ★ CATHOLIC HEALTH SYSTEM 144 Genesee Street, Zip 14203–1560; tel. 716/862–2410; Joseph D. McDonald, FACHE, President and Chief Executive Officer, p. B31

Cooperstown: ★ BASSETT HEALTHCARE NETWORK 1 Atwell Road, Zip 13326–1301; tel. 607/547–3456; Vance Brown, M.D., President and Chief Executive Officer, p. B21

Elmira: ARNOT HEALTH 600 Roe Avenue, Zip 14905–1629; tel. 607/737–4100; Robert K. Lambert, M.D., FACHE, President and Chief Executive Officer, p. B12

Geneva: FINGER LAKES HEALTH 196 North Street, Zip 14456–1651; tel. 315/787–4000; Jose Acevedo, M.D., President and Chief Executive Officer, p. B55

Ithaca: ★ CAYUGA HEALTH SYSTEM 101 Dates Drive, Zip 14850–1342; tel. 607/274–4011; John Rudd, President and Chief Executive Officer, p. B31

Jamaica: ★ MEDISYS HEALTH NETWORK 8900 Van Wyck Expressway, Zip 11418–2832; tel. 718/206–6000; Bruce J. Flanz, President and Chief Executive Officer, p. B87

LaGrangeville: HEALTH QUEST SYSTEMS, INC. 1351 Route 55 Suite 200, Zip 12540–5108, Mailing Address: 1351 Route 55, Zip 12540–5108; tel. 845/475–9500; Luke McGuinness, President and CEO, p. B65

Middletown: GREATER HUDSON VALLEY HEALTH SYSTEM 60 Prospect Avenue, Zip 10940–4133; tel. 845/568–6050; Scott Batulis, President and Chief Executive Officer, p. B59

New Hyde Park: ★ NORTHWELL HEALTH 2000 Marcus Avenue, Zip 11042; tel. 516/465–8100; Michael J. Dowling, President and Chief Executive Officer, p. B97

New York: ★ MOUNT SINAI HEALTH SYSTEM One Gustave L. Levy Place, Zip 10029; tel. 212/659–8888; Kenneth L. Davis, M.D., President and Chief Executive, p. B92

NEW YORK PRESBYTERIAN REGIONAL HOSPITAL NETWORK 525 East 68th Street, Box 182, Zip 10065; tel. 212/746–3745; Steven J. Corwin, M.D., President and Chief Executive Officer, p. B95

★ NYC HEALTH + HOSPITALS 125 Worth Street, Room 514, Zip 10013–4006; tel. 212/788–3321; Ramanathan Raju, M.D., President, p. B98

Olean: UPPER ALLEGHENY HEALTH SYSTEM 130 South Union Street, Suite 300, Zip 14760–3676; tel. 716/375–6190; Timothy J. Finan, FACHE, President and Chief Executive Officer, p. B149

Potsdam: ST. LAWRENCE HEALTH SYSTEM 50 Leroy Street, Zip 13676–1799; tel. 315/265–3300; David B. Acker, FACHE, President and CEO, p. B128

Rochester: ★ ROCHESTER REGIONAL HEALTH 1425 Portland Avenue, 5th Floor, Zip 14621–3001; tel. 585/922–4000; Eric Bieber, M.D., President and Chief Executive Officer, p. B115

★ UNIVERSITY OF ROCHESTER MEDICAL CENTER 601 Elmwood Avenue Box 623, Zip 14642–0002, Mailing Address: 601 Elmwood Avenue, Zip 14642–0002; tel. 585/275–2100; Steven I. Goldstein, General Director and Chief Executive Officer, p. B148

Rockville Centre: CATHOLIC HEALTH SERVICES OF LONG ISLAND 992 North Village Avenue, 1st Floor, Zip 11570–1002; tel. 516/705–3700; Alan D. Guerci, M.D., President and Chief Executive Officer, p. B30

Syracuse: SISTERS OF SAINT FRANCIS 2500 Grant Boulevard, Zip 13208–1782; tel. 315/634–7000; Sister Geraldine Ching, Assistant General Minister, p. B125

Valhalla: WMCHEALTH 100 Woods Road, Zip 10595–1530; tel. 914/493–7000; Michael D. Israel, President and Chief Executive Officer, p. B155

NORTH CAROLINA

Asheville: ★ MISSION HEALTH SYSTEM 509 Biltmore Avenue, Zip 28801–4601; tel. 828/213–1111; Ronald A. Paulus, M.D., President and Chief Executive Officer, p. B91

Boone: ★ APPALACHIAN REGIONAL HEALTHCARE SYSTEM 336 Deerfield Road, Zip 28607–5008, Mailing Address: P.O. Box 2600, Zip 28607–2600; tel. 828/262–4100; Richard G. Sparks, President and Chief Executive Officer, p. B10

Chapel Hill: ★ UNC HEALTH CARE 101 Manning Drive, Zip 27514–4220; tel. 919/966–4131; William L. Roper, M.D., M.P.H., Chief Executive Officer, p. B139

Charlotte: ★ ACUITYHEALTHCARE, LP 10200 Mallard Creek Road, Suite 300, Zip 28262–9705; tel. 704/887–7280; Edwin H. Cooper, Jr., MS, President and Chief Executive Officer, p. B5

★ CAROLINAS HEALTHCARE SYSTEM 1000 Blythe Boulevard, Zip 28203–5871, Mailing Address: P.O. Box 32861, Zip 28232–2861; tel. 704/355–2000; Eugene A. Woods, FACHE, President and Chief Executive Officer, p. B27

Durham: ★ DUKE UNIVERSITY HEALTH SYSTEM 201 Trent Drive, Zip 27710–3037, Mailing Address: P.O. Box 3701, Zip 27710–3701; tel. 919/684–2255; A. Eugene Washington, M.D., President and Chief Executive Officer, p. B51

Fayetteville: CAPE FEAR VALLEY HEALTH SYSTEM 1638 Owen Drive, Zip 28304–3424, Mailing Address: P.O. Box 2000, Zip 28302–2000; tel. 910/615–4000; Michael Nagowski, President and Chief Executive Officer, p. B26

Greensboro: CONE HEALTH 1200 North Elm Street, Zip 27401–1004; tel. 336/832–7000; Terry Akin, President and Chief Executive Officer, p. B41

Greenville: ★ VIDANT HEALTH 2100 Stantonsburg Road, Zip 27834–2818, Mailing Address: P.O. Box 6028, Zip 27835–6028; tel. 252/847–4100; Michael Waldrum, M.D., Chief Executive Officer, p. B152

Pinehurst: ★ FIRSTHEALTH OF THE CAROLINAS 155 Memorial Drive, Zip 28374–8710, Mailing Address: P.O. Box 3000, Zip 28374–3000; tel. 910/715–1000; David J. Kilarski, FACHE, Chief Executive Officer, p. B55

Raleigh: ★ WAKEMED HEALTH & HOSPITALS 3000 New Bern Avenue, Zip 27610–1231; tel. 919/350–8000; Donald R. Gintzig, President and Chief Executive Officer, p. B153

Wilmington: ★ NEW HANOVER REGIONAL MEDICAL CENTER 2131 South 17th Street, Zip 28401–7407; tel. 910/343–7040; John K. Barto, Jr., President and Chief Executive Officer, p. B95

Winston Salem: ★ NOVANT HEALTH 2085 Frontis Plaza Boulevard, Zip 27103–5614; tel. 336/718–5600; Carl S. Armato, President and Chief Executive Officer, p. B98

Winston–Salem: ★ WAKE FOREST BAPTIST HEALTH Medical Center Boulevard, Zip 27157; tel. 336/716–2011; John D. McConnell, M.D., Chief Executive Officer, p. B153

NORTH DAKOTA

Fargo: SISTERS OF MARY OF THE PRESENTATION HEALTH SYSTEM 1202 Page Drive S.W., Zip 58103–2340, Mailing Address: P.O. Box 10007, Zip 58106–0007; tel. 701/237–9290; Aaron K. Alton, President and Chief Executive Officer, p. B125

OHIO

Akron: SUMMA HEALTH 1077 Gorge Boulevard, Zip 44310; tel. 330/375–3000; Thomas Malone, M.D., President and Chief Executive Officer, p. B129

Canton: AULTMAN HEALTH FOUNDATION 2600 Sixth Street S.W., Zip 44710–1702; tel. 330/363–6192; Edward J. Roth, III, President and Chief Executive Officer, p. B16

Chillicothe: ADENA HEALTH SYSTEM 272 Hospital Road, Zip 45601–9031; tel. 740/779–7500; Mark H. Shuter, President and Chief Executive Officer, p. B5

Cincinnati: ★ MERCY HEALTH 615 Elsinore Place, Zip 45202–1459, Mailing Address: 1701 Mercy Health Place, Zip 45237; tel. 513/639–2800; John M. Starcher, President and Chief Executive Officer, p. B89

★ UC HEALTH 3200 Burnet Avenue, Zip 45229–3019; tel. 513/585–6000; Richard P. Lofgren, M.D., M.P.H., President and CEO, p. B139

Cleveland: ★ CLEVELAND CLINIC HEALTH SYSTEM 9500 Euclid, Zip 44195–5108; tel. 216/444–2200; Delos Cosgrove, M.D., President and Chief Executive Officer, p. B34

SISTERS OF CHARITY HEALTH SYSTEM 2475 East 22nd Street, Zip 44115–3221; tel. 216/363–2797; Terrence Kessler, President and Chief Executive Officer, p. B125

★ UNIVERSITY HOSPITALS 11100 Euclid Avenue, Zip 44106–5000; tel. 216/844–1000; Thomas F. Zenty, III, President and Chief Executive Officer, p. B146

Columbus: OHIO DEPARTMENT OF MENTAL HEALTH 30 East Broad Street, 8th Floor, Zip 43215–3430; tel. 614/466–2297; Tracy Plouck, Director, p. B100

★ OHIO STATE UNIVERSITY HEALTH SYSTEM 370 West Ninth Avenue, Zip 43210–1238; tel. 614/685–9015; David P. McQuaid, FACHE, Chief Executive Officer, p. B100

★ OHIOHEALTH 180 East Broad Street, Zip 43215–3707; tel. 614/544–4455; David P. Blom, President and Chief Executive Officer, p. B100

Dayton: ★ KETTERING HEALTH NETWORK 3965 Southern Boulevard, Zip 45429–1229; tel. 937/395–8150; Fred M. Manchur, Chief Executive Officer, p. B76

★ PREMIER HEALTH 110 North Main Street Suite 390, Zip 45402–3720; tel. 937/499–9401; Mary H. Boosalis, President, p. B105

Findlay: ★ BLANCHARD VALLEY HEALTH SYSTEM 1900 South Main Street, Zip 45840–1214; tel. 419/423–4500; Scott C. Malaney, President and Chief Executive Officer, p. B23

Galion: ★ AVITA HEALTH SYSTEM 269 Portland Way South, Zip 44833–2399; tel. 419/468–4841; Jerome Morasko, President and Chief Executive Officer, p. B18

Marietta: MEMORIAL HEALTH SYSTEM 401 Matthew Street, Zip 45750–1635; tel. 740/374–1400; J. Scott Cantley, President and Chief Executive Officer, p. B88

Toledo: ★ PROMEDICA HEALTH SYSTEM 1801 Richards Road, Zip 43607–1037; tel. 419/469–3800; Randall D. Oostra, FACHE, President and Chief Executive Officer, p. B107

OKLAHOMA

Oklahoma City: FOUNDATION SURGICAL HOSPITAL AFFILIATES 14000 North Portland Avenue, Suite 204, Zip 73134–4002; tel. 405/608–1700; Thomas A. Michaud, Chief Executive Officer, p. B56

★ INTEGRIS HEALTH 3366 N.W. Expressway, Suite 800, Zip 73112–9756; tel. 405/949–6066; Bruce Lawrence, President and Chief Executive Officer, p. B73

OKLAHOMA DEPARTMENT OF MENTAL HEALTH AND SUBSTANCE ABUSE SERVICES 1200 N.E. 13th Street, Zip 73117–1022, Mailing Address: P.O. Box 53277, Zip 73152–3277; tel. 405/522–3908; Terri White, Commissioner, p. B101

SOUTHERN PLAINS MEDICAL GROUP 4323 N.W. 63rd Street Suite 232, Zip 73116–1546; tel. 405/753–6770; Margie Homer, President, p. B126

Shawnee: PREFERRED MANAGEMENT CORPORATION 120 West MacArthur, Suite 121, Zip 74804–2005; tel. 405/878–0202; Donald Freeman, President and Chief Executive Officer, p. B105

Tulsa: ★ SAINT FRANCIS HEALTH SYSTEM 6161 South Yale Avenue, Zip 74136–1902; tel. 918/494–8454; Jake Henry Jr., President and Chief Executive Officer, p. B116

OREGON

Bend: ★ ST. CHARLES HEALTH SYSTEM, INC. 2500 N.E. Neff Road, Zip 97701–6015; tel. 541/382–4321; Joseph Sluka, President and Chief Executive Officer, p. B127

Corvallis: ★ SAMARITAN HEALTH SERVICES 3600 N.W. Samaritan Drive, Zip 97330–3737, Mailing Address: P.O. Box 1068, Zip 97339–1068; tel. 541/768–5001; Larry A. Mullins, FACHE, President and Chief Executive Officer, p. B117

Medford: ★ ASANTE HEALTH SYSTEM 2650 Siskiyou Boulevard, Suite 200, Zip 97504–8170; tel. 541/789–4100; Roy G. Vinyard, FACHE, President and Chief Executive Officer, p. B12

Portland: ★ LEGACY HEALTH 1919 N.W. Lovejoy Street, Zip 97209–1503; tel. 503/415–5600; George J. Brown, M.D., President and Chief Executive Officer, p. B80

Salem: SALEM HEALTH 890 Oak Street Building B. POB 14001, Zip 97309–5014; tel. 503/561–5200; Norman F. Gruber, President and Chief Executive Officer, p. B117

PENNSYLVANIA

Allentown: GOOD SHEPHERD REHABILITATION NETWORK 850 South Fifth Street, Zip 18103–3308; tel. 610/776–3100; John Kristel, President and Chief Executive Officer, p. B58

★ LEHIGH VALLEY HEALTH NETWORK 1200 South Cedar Crest Boulevard, Zip 18103–6202, Mailing Address: P.O. Box 689, Zip 18105–1556; tel. 610/402–8000; Brian A. Nester, President and Chief Executive Officer, p. B80

Beaver: HERITAGE VALLEY HEALTH SYSTEM 1000 Dutch Ridge Road, Zip 15009–9727; tel. 724/773–2024; Norman F. Mitry, President and Chief Executive Officer, p. B70

Bethlehem: ST. LUKE'S UNIVERSITY HEALTH NETWORK 801 Ostrum Street, Zip 18015–1000; tel. 610/954–4000; Richard A. Anderson, President and Chief Executive Officer, p. B128

Chambersburg: ★ SUMMIT HEALTH 112 North Seventh Street, Zip 17201–1720; tel. 717/267–7138; Patrick W. O'Donnell, CPA, President and Chief Executive Officer, p. B130

Danville: ★ GEISINGER HEALTH SYSTEM 100 North Academy Avenue, Zip 17822–9800; tel. 570/271–6211; David T. Feinberg, M.D., President and Chief Executive Officer, p. B57

Enola: ★ POST ACUTE MEDICAL, LLC 1828 Good Hope Road, Suite 102, Zip 17025–1233; tel. 717/731–9660; Anthony F. Misitano, President and Chief Executive Officer, p. B104

Greensburg: EXCELA HEALTH 532 West Pittsburgh Street, Zip 15601, Mailing Address: 134 Industrial Park Road, Zip 15601–7328; tel. 724/832–5050; Robert Rogalski, Chief Executive Officer, p. B55

Hershey: PENN STATE HERSHEY HEALTH SYSTEM 500 University Drive, Zip 17033–2360; tel. 717/531–8521; A. Craig Hillemeier, M.D., Chief Executive Officer, p. B103

Health Care Systems Index

King of Prussia: UNIVERSAL HEALTH SERVICES, INC. 367 South Gulph Road, Zip 19406–3121, Mailing Address: P.O. Box 61558, Zip 19406–0958; tel. 610/768–3300; Alan B. Miller, Chairman and Chief Executive Officer, p. B142

Lehighton: ★ BLUE MOUNTAIN HEALTH SYSTEM 211 North 12th Street, Zip 18235–1138; tel. 610/377–1300; Andrew E. Harris, President and Chief Executive Officer, p. B23

Meadville: MEADVILLE MEDICAL CENTER 751 Liberty Street, Zip 16335–2559; tel. 814/333–5000; Philip E. Pandolph, FACHE, Chief Executive Officer, p. B87

Mechanicsburg: ★ SELECT MEDICAL CORPORATION 4714 Gettysburg Road, Zip 17055–4325; tel. 717/972–1100; David S. Chernow, President and Chief Executive Officer, p. B119

★ VIBRA HEALTHCARE 4550 Lena Drive, Suite 225, Zip 17055–4920; tel. 717/591–5700; Brad Hollinger, Chairman and Chief Executive Officer, p. B151

Philadelphia: EINSTEIN HEALTHCARE NETWORK 5501 Old York Road, Zip 19141–3098; tel. 215/456–7890; Barry R. Freedman, President and Chief Executive Officer, p. B53

★ TEMPLE UNIVERSITY HEALTH SYSTEM 3509 North Broad Street, 9th Floor, Zip 19140–4105; tel. 215/707–0900; Larry Kaiser, M.D., President and Chief Executive Officer, p. B131

★ UNIVERSITY OF PENNSYLVANIA HEALTH SYSTEM 3400 Civic Center Bouelvard, Zip 19104–5127; tel. 215/662–2203; Ralph W. Muller, President and Chief Executive Officer, p. B148

Pittsburgh: ★ ALLEGHENY HEALTH NETWORK 30 Isabella Street, Suite 300, Zip 15212–5862; tel. 412/359–3131; Cynthia Hundorfean, President and Chief Executive Officer, p. B8

UPMC 600 Grant Street, U.S. Steel Tower, Suite 6262, Zip 15219–2702; tel. 412/647–8762; Jeffrey A. Romoff, President and Chief Executive Officer, p. B149

Pottsville: SCHUYLKILL HEALTH SYSTEM 420 South Jackson Street, Zip 17901–3625; tel. 570/621–5000; Marc H. Lory, Interim President and Chief Executive Officer, p. B80

Radnor: ★ JEFFERSON HEALTH 259 Radnor–Chester Road, Suite 290, Zip 19087–5288, Mailing Address: 111 South 11th Street, Philadelphia, Zip 19107; tel. 610/225–6200; Stephen K. Klasko, M.D., Chief Executive Officer, p. B74

Sayre: ★ GUTHRIE CLINIC Guthrie Square, Zip 18840; tel. 570/887–4312; Joseph A. Scopelliti, M.D., President and Chief Executive Officer, p. B59

Springfield: ★ CROZER–KEYSTONE HEALTH SYSTEM 100 West Sproul Road, Zip 19064–2033; tel. 610/338–8205; Patrick J. Gavin, President and Chief Executive Officer, p. B43

Villanova: DEVEREUX 444 Devereux Drive, Zip 19085–1932, Mailing Address: P.O. Box 638, Zip 19085–0638; tel. 610/520–3000; Robert Q. Kreider, President and Chief Executive Officer, p. B49

Washington: WASHINGTON HEALTH SYSTEM 155 Wilson Avenue, Zip 15301–3336; tel. 724/225–7000; Gary B. Weinstein, Chief Executive Officer, p. B153

Williamsport: ★ SUSQUEHANNA HEALTH SYSTEM 700 High Street, Zip 17701–3100; tel. 570/321–1000; Steven P. Johnson, FACHE, President and Chief Executive Officer, p. B130

York: ★ WELLSPAN HEALTH 45 Monument Road, Suite 200, Zip 17403–5071; tel. 717/851–2121; Kevin H. Mosser, M.D., President and Chief Executive Officer, p. B154

PUERTO RICO

San Juan: ★ PUERTO RICO DEPARTMENT OF HEALTH Building A – Medical Center, Zip 00936, Mailing Address: Call Box 70184, Zip 00936; tel. 787/765–2929; Ana Rius, M.D., Secretary of Health, p. B110

RHODE ISLAND

Providence: ★ CARE NEW ENGLAND HEALTH SYSTEM 45 Willard Avenue, Zip 02905–3218; tel. 401/453–7900; Dennis D. Keefe, President and Chief Executive Officer, p. B26

CHARTERCARE HEALTH PARTNERS 825 Chalkstone Avenue, Zip 02908–4728; tel. 410/456–2001; Lester P. Schindel, Chief Executive Officer, p. B32

LIFESPAN CORPORATION 167 Point Street, Zip 02903–4771; tel. 401/444–3500; Timothy J. Babineau, M.D., President and Chief Executive Officer, p. B84

SOUTH CAROLINA

Anderson: ANMED HEALTH 800 North Fant Street, Zip 29621–5793; tel. 864/512–1000; William T. Manson, III, Chief Executive Officer, p. B10

Columbia: ★ PALMETTO HEALTH 1301 Taylor Street, Suite 9–A, Zip 29201–2942, Mailing Address: P.O. Box 2266, Zip 29202–2266; tel. 803/296–2100; Charles D. Beaman, Jr., Chief Executive Officer, p. B102

Florence: MCLEOD HEALTH 555 East Cheves Street, Zip 29506–2617, Mailing Address: P.O. Box 100551, Zip 29502–0551; tel. 843/777–2000; Robert L. Colones, President and Chief Executive Officer, p. B87

Georgetown: ★ TIDELANDS HEALTH 606 Black River Road, Zip 29440–3304, Mailing Address: P.O. Box 421718, Zip 29442–4203; tel. 843/527–7000; Bruce P. Bailey, President and Chief Executive Officer, p. B135

Greenville: ★ GREENVILLE HEALTH SYSTEM 701 Grove Road, Zip 29605–5611; tel. 864/455–7000; Michael C. Riordan, President and Chief Executive Officer, p. B59

Spartanburg: ★ SPARTANBURG REGIONAL HEALTHCARE SYSTEM 101 East Wood Street, Zip 29303–3040; tel. 864/560–6000; Bruce Holstien, President and Chief Executive Officer, p. B126

SOUTH DAKOTA

Rapid City: ★ REGIONAL HEALTH 353 Fairmont Boulevard, Zip 57701–7375, Mailing Address: P.O. Box 6000, Zip 57709–6000; tel. 605/719–1000; Brent R. Phillips, President and Chief Executive Officer, p. B114

Sioux Falls: ★ AVERA HEALTH 3900 West Avera Drive, Suite 300, Zip 57108–5721; tel. 605/322–4700; John T. Porter, President and Chief Executive Officer, p. B17

★ SANFORD HEALTH 2301 East 60th Street North, Zip 57104–0569, Mailing Address: PO Box 5039, Zip 57117–5039; tel. 605/333–1000; Kelby K. Krabbenhoft, President and Chief Executive Officer, p. B118

TENNESSEE

Brentwood: ★ DUKE LIFEPOINT HEALTHCARE 103 Powell Court, Zip 37027–5079; tel. 615/372–8540; Jeffrey G. Seraphine, FACHE, Division President, p. B51

★ HEALTHTECH MANAGEMENT SERVICES 5110 Maryland Way Suite 200, Zip 37027–2307; tel. 615/309–6053; Derek Morkel, Chief Executive Officer, p. B69

★ LIFEPOINT HEALTH 330 Seven Springs Way, Zip 37027–4536; tel. 615/920–7000; William F. Carpenter, III, Chairman and Chief Executive Officer, p. B82

★ QHR 105 Continental Place, Zip 37027–1052; tel. 800/233–1470; Mickey Bilbrey, President and Chief Executive Officer, p. B110

★ QUORUM HEALTH 1573 Mallory Lane, Suite 100, Zip 37027; tel. 615/221–1400; Thomas Miller, President and Chief Executive Officer, p. B112

RCCH HEALTHCARE PARTNERS 103 Continental Place Suite 200, Zip 37027–1042; tel. 615/844–9800; Michael Wiechart, President and Chief Executive Officer, p. B113

Chattanooga: ERLANGER HEALTH SYSTEM 975 East Third Street, Zip 37403–2147; tel. 423/778–7000; Kevin M. Spiegel, President and Chief Executive Officer, p. B53

Clinton: CURAE HEALTH 121 Leinart Street, Zip 37716–3632, Mailing Address: P.O. Box 358, Zip 37717–0358; tel. 865/269–4074; Steve Clapp, President and Chief Executive Officer, p. B43

Columbia: ★ MAURY REGIONAL HEALTH SYSTEM 1224 Trotwood Avenue, Zip 38401–4802; tel. 931/381–1111; H. Alan Watson, FACHE, Chief Executive Officer, p. B85

Franklin: ACADIA HEALTHCARE COMPANY, INC. 830 Crescent Centre Drive, Suite 610, Zip 37067–7323; tel. 615/861–6000; Joey Jacobs, Chairman and Chief Executive Officer, p. B4

★ COMMUNITY HEALTH SYSTEMS, INC. 4000 Meridian Boulevard, Zip 37067–6325, Mailing Address: P.O. Box 689020, Zip 37068–9020; tel. 615/465–7000; Wayne T. Smith, Chairman, President and Chief Executive Officer, p. B35

IASIS HEALTHCARE 117 Seaboard Lane, Building E., Zip 37067–2855; tel. 615/844–2747; Carl Whitmer, President and Chief Executive Officer, p. B71

Jackson: ★ WEST TENNESSEE HEALTHCARE 620 Skyline Drive, Zip 38301–3923; tel. 731/541–5000; James E. Ross, Interim Chief Executive Officer, p. B154

Johnson City: MOUNTAIN STATES HEALTH ALLIANCE 400 North State of Franklin Road, Zip 37604–6035; tel. 423/302–3423; Alan M. Levine, President and Chief Executive Officer, p. B93

Kingsport: ★ WELLMONT HEALTH SYSTEM 1905 American Way, Zip 37660–5882; tel. 423/230–8200; Barton A. Hove, President and Chief Executive Officer, p. B153

Knoxville: ★ COVENANT HEALTH 100 Fort Sanders West Boulevard, Zip 37922–3353; tel. 865/531–5555; James VanderSteeg, President and Chief Executive Officer, p. B42

Memphis: ★ BAPTIST MEMORIAL HEALTH CARE CORPORATION 350 North Humphreys Boulevard, Zip 38120–2177; tel. 901/227–5117; Jason Little, President and Chief Executive Officer, p. B20

METHODIST LE BONHEUR HEALTHCARE 1211 Union Avenue, Suite 700, Zip 38104–6600; tel. 901/516–0791; Gary S. Shorb, President and Chief Executive Officer, p. B91

STRATEGIC BEHAVIORAL HEALTH, LLC 8295 Tournament Drive, Suite 201, Zip 38125–8913; tel. 901/969–3100; Jim Shaheen, President, p. B129

Nashville: ★ ARDENT HEALTH SERVICES 1 Burton Hills Boulevard, Suite 250, Zip 37215–6195; tel. 615/296–3000; David T. Vandewater, President and Chief Executive Officer, p. B11

HAVEN BEHAVIORAL HEALTHCARE 652 West Iris Drive, Zip 37204–3191; tel. 615/250–9500; Michael Lindley, Chief Executive Officer, p. B60

★ HCA One Park Plaza, Zip 37203–1548; tel. 615/344–5248; R. Milton Johnson, President and Chief Executive Officer, p. B60

★ VANDERBILT HEALTH 1211 22nd Avenue South, Zip 37232; tel. 615/322–5000; Charles Wright Pinson, M.D., Deputy Vice Chancellor for Health Affairs and Chief Executive Officer of Vanderbilt Health System, p. B150

Parsons: TENNESSEE HEALTH MANAGEMENT 52 West Eighth Street, Zip 38363–4656, Mailing Address: PO Box 10, Zip 38363–0010; tel. 731/847–6343; Dennis Berry, Chief Executive Officer, p. B134

TEXAS

Addison: UNITED SURGICAL PARTNERS INTERNATIONAL 15305 Dallas Parkway, Suite 1600, Zip 75001–6491; tel. 972/713–3500; William H. Wilcox, President and Chief Executive Officer, p. B141

Arlington: ★ TEXAS HEALTH RESOURCES 612 East Lamar Boulevard, Suite 900, Zip 76011–4130; tel. 682/236–7900; Barclay E. Berdan, FACHE, Chief Executive Officer, p. B134

Austin: TEXAS DEPARTMENT OF STATE HEALTH SERVICES 1100 West 49th Street, Zip 78756–3199; tel. 512/458–7111; Kirk Cole, Interim Commissioner, p. B134

★ UNIVERSITY OF TEXAS SYSTEM 601 Colorado Street, Suite 205, Zip 78701–2904; tel. 512/499–4224; Raymond Greenberg, M.D., Executive Vice Chancellor, p. B149

Dallas: ★ BAYLOR SCOTT & WHITE HEALTH 4005 Crutcher Street, Suite 310, Zip 75246–1779; tel. 214/820–0111; Joel T. Allison, Chief Executive Officer, p. B21

CORNERSTONE HEALTHCARE GROUP 2200 Ross Avenue, Suite 5400, Zip 75201–7984; tel. 469/621–6700; David Smith, President and Chief Executive Officer, p. B42

★ METHODIST HEALTH SYSTEM 1441 North Beckley Avenue, Zip 75203–1201, Mailing Address: P.O. Box 655999, Zip 75265–5999; tel. 214/947–8181; Stephen L. Mansfield, Ph.D., FACHE, President and Chief Executive Officer, p. B91

★ TENET HEALTHCARE CORPORATION 1445 Ross Avenue, Suite 1400, Zip 75202–2703, Mailing Address: P.O. Box 1390369, Zip 75313–9036; tel. 469/893–2200; Trevor Fetter, President and Chief Executive Officer, p. B132

VIBRANT HEALTHCARE 12222 North Central Expressway, Suite 440, Zip 75243–3767; tel. 469/330–6745; , p. B152

Greenville: HUNT REGIONAL HEALTHCARE 4215 Joe Ramsey Boulevard, Zip 75401–7852, Mailing Address: P.O. Box 1059, Zip 75403–1059; tel. 903/408–5000; Richard Carter, Chief Executive Officer, p. B71

Houston: ★ HOUSTON METHODIST 6565 Fannin Street, D–200, Zip 77030–2707; tel. 713/441–2221; Marc L. Boom, M.D., Chief Executive Officer, p. B71

★ MEMORIAL HERMANN HEALTH SYSTEM 929 Gessner, Suite 2700, Zip 77024–2593; tel. 713/242–2700; Benjamin K. Chu, M.D., President and Chief Executive Officer, p. B88

NEXUS HEALTH SYSTEMS One Riverway, Suite 600, Zip 77056–1993; tel. 713/355–6111; John W. Cassidy, M.D., President, Chief Executive Officer and Chief Medical Officer, p. B96

Irving: ★ CHRISTUS HEALTH 919 Hidden Ridge Drive, Zip 75038; tel. 469/282–2000; Ernie W. Sadau, Chief Executive Officer, p. B33

USMD HEALTH SYSTEM 6333 North State Highway 161 Suite 200, Zip 75038–2229; tel. 214/493–4000; Karen A. Fiducia, FACHE, President, Hospital Division, p. B150

Longview: AUDUBON BEHAVIORAL HEALTHCARE 100 West Hawkins, Suite D., Zip 75605; tel. 903/212–2930; William V. Brown, Chief Executive Officer, p. B16

GOOD SHEPHERD HEALTH SYSTEM 700 East Marshall Avenue, Zip 75601–5580; tel. 903/315–2000; Steve Altmiller, President and Chief Executive Officer, p. B58

Lubbock: ★ COVENANT HEALTH SYSTEM 3615 19th Street, Zip 79410–1203; tel. 806/725–0447; Richard H. Parks, FACHE, President and Chief Executive Officer, p. B43

Plano: ★ COMMUNITY HOSPITAL CORPORATION 7800 North Dallas Parkway, Suite 200, Zip 75024–6116; tel. 972/943–6400; Michael D. Williams, President and Chief Executive Officer, p. B40

★ LHP HOSPITAL GROUP 2400 North Dallas Parkway, Suite 450, Zip 75093–5994; tel. 866/465–9222; John F. Holland, Chief Executive Officer, p. B81

★ LIFECARE MANAGEMENT SERVICES 5340 Legacy Drive, Suite 150, Zip 75024–3131; tel. 469/241–2100; Lew Little, Interim Chief Executive Officer, p. B81

Sherman: CARRUS HOSPITALS 1810 West U.S. Highway 82, Zip 75092–7069; tel. 903/870–2600; Ronald E. Dorris, Chief Executive Officer, p. B27

The Woodlands: EMERUS 10077 Grogan's Mill, Suite 100, Zip 77380–1022; tel. 281/292–2450; Toby Hamilton, Chief Executive Officer, p. B53

VICTORY HEALTHCARE 2201 Timberloch Place, Suite 200, Zip 77380; tel. 281/863–2100; Robert N. Helms, Jr., Board Chair, President and Chief Executive Officer, p. B152

Tyler: ★ EAST TEXAS MEDICAL CENTER REGIONAL HEALTHCARE SYSTEM 1000 South Beckham Street, Zip 75701–1908, Mailing Address: P.O. Box 6400, Zip 75711–6400; tel. 903/535–6211; Elmer G. Ellis, FACHE, President and Chief Executive Officer, p. B52

UTAH

Nephi: ★ RURAL HEALTH GROUP 48 West 1500 North, Zip 84648–8900; tel. 435/623–4924; Mark R. Stoddard, President and Chairman, p. B115

Salt Lake City: ★ INTERMOUNTAIN HEALTHCARE, INC. 36 South State Street, 22nd Floor, Zip 84111–1453; tel. 801/442–2000; Charles W. Sorenson, Jr., M.D., President and Chief Executive Officer, p. B73

VIRGINIA

Charlottesville: UVA HEALTH SYSTEM 1215 Lee Street, Zip 22908–0816; tel. 434/924–0211; R. Edward Howell, Vice President and Chief Executive Officer, p. B150

Falls Church: BUREAU OF MEDICINE AND SURGERY, DEPARTMENT OF THE NAVY 7700 Arlington Boulevard, Suite 5126, Zip 22042; tel. 202/762–3701; Bryce H.P. Mendez, Healthcare Policy Analyst, p. B25

DEPARTMENT OF THE ARMY, OFFICE OF THE SURGEON GENERAL 5109 Leesburg Pike, Zip 22041–3215; tel. 703/681–3000; Lieutenant General Eric B. Schoomaker, Surgeon General, p. B44

★ INOVA HEALTH SYSTEM 8110 Gatehouse Road, Suite 200 East, Zip 22042–1252; tel. 703/289–2069; J. Knox Singleton, President and Chief Executive Officer, p. B73

Fredericksburg: ★ MARY WASHINGTON HEALTHCARE 2300 Fall Hill Avenue, Suite 308, Zip 22401–3343; tel. 540/741–3100; Michael P. McDermott, M.D., President and Chief Executive Officer, p. B85

Lynchburg: CENTRA HEALTH, INC. 1920 Atherholt Road, Zip 24501–1104; tel. 434/200–3000; E. W. Tibbs, President and Chief Executive Officer, p. B32

Newport News: RIVERSIDE HEALTH SYSTEM 701 Town Center Drive, Suite 1000, Zip 23606–4286; tel. 757/534–7000; William B. Downey, President and Chief Executive Officer, p. B114

Norfolk: ★ SENTARA HEALTHCARE 6015 Poplar Hall Drive, Zip 23502–3819; tel. 757/455–7000; Howard P. Kern, Chief Executive Officer, p. B123

Richmond: VCU HEALTH SYSTEM 1250 East Marshall Street, Zip 23298–5051, Mailing Address: P.O. Box 980510, Zip 23298–0510; tel. 804/828–9000; Marsha Rappley, M.D., Chief Executive Officer and Vice President for Health Sciences, p. B150

VIRGINIA DEPARTMENT OF MENTAL HEALTH 1220 Bank Street, Zip 23219–3645, Mailing Address: P.O. Box 1797, Zip 23218–1797; tel. 804/786–3921; James S. Reinhard, M.D., Commissioner, p. B152

Roanoke: ★ CARILION CLINIC 1906 Belleview Avenue S.E., Zip 24014–1838, Mailing Address: P.O. Box 13727, Zip 24036–3727; tel. 540/981–7000; Nancy Howell Agee, President and Chief Executive Officer, p. B26

Health Care Systems Index

Winchester: ★ VALLEY HEALTH SYSTEM 220 Campus Boulevard, Suite 420, Zip 22601–2889, Mailing Address: P.O. Box 3340, Zip 22604–2540; tel. 540/536–8024; Mark H. Merrill, President and Chief Executive Officer, p. B150

WASHINGTON

Mount Vernon: SKAGIT REGIONAL HEALTH 1415 East Kincaid Street, Zip 98274–4126; tel. 360/424–4111; Gregg Agustin Davidson, FACHE, President and Chief Executive Officer, p. B125

Renton: ★ PROVIDENCE ST. JOSEPH HEALTH 181 Lind Avenue Southwest, 9016, Zip 98057–9016; tel. 425/525–3698; Rodney F. Hochman, M.D., President and Chief Executive Officer, p. B108

Seattle: ★ SWEDISH HEALTH SERVICES 747 Broadway, Zip 98122–4379; tel. 206/386–6000; Anthony A. Armada, Senior Vice President, Chief Executive Officer of Swedish Health Services and Providence Health and Services, p. B131

★ UW MEDICINE 1959 N.E. Pacific Street, Zip 98195–0001, Mailing Address: P.O. Box 356350, Zip 98195–6350; tel. 206/543–7718; Paul G. Ramsey, M.D., Chief Executive Officer, p. B150

VIRGINIA MASON HEALTH SYSTEM 1100 Ninth Avenue, Zip 98101–2756, Mailing Address: P.O. Box 900, Zip 98111–0900; tel. 206/223–6600; Gary Kaplan, M.D., FACHE, Chief Executive Officer, p. B153

Tacoma: MULTICARE HEALTH SYSTEM 315 Martin Luther King Jr. Way, Zip 98405–4234, Mailing Address: P.O. Box 5299, Zip 98415–0299; tel. 253/403–1000; William G. Robertson, President and Chief Executive Officer, p. B93

Vancouver: ★ PEACEHEALTH 1115 S.E. 164th Avenue, Zip 98683; tel. 360/729–1000; Elizabeth Dunne, President and Chief Executive Officer, p. B103

WEST VIRGINIA

Elkins: ★ DAVIS HEALTH SYSTEM Reed Street and Gorman Avenue, Zip 26241, Mailing Address: P.O. Box 1697, Zip 26241–1697; tel. 304/636–3300; Vance Jackson, FACHE, President and Chief Executive Officer, p. B43

Huntington: ★ PALLOTTINE HEALTH SERVICES 2900 First Avenue, Zip 25702–1241; tel. 304/526–1234; Michael G. Sellards, Chief Executive Officer, p. B102

Morgantown: ★ MONONGALIA HEALTH SYSTEM 1200 J. D. Anderson Drive, Zip 26505–3494; tel. 304/598–1200; Darryl L. Duncan, President and Chief Executive Officer, p. B92

★ WEST VIRGINIA UNIVERSITY HEALTH SYSTEM 3040 University Avenue, Suite 3400, Zip 26505; tel. 304/285–7150; Albert Wright, PharmD, President and Chief Executive Officer, p. B154

South Charleston: ★ THOMAS HEALTH SYSTEM, INC. 4605 MacCorkle Avenue S.W., Zip 25309–1311; tel. 304/766–3600; Daniel Lauffer, FACHE, President and Chief Executive Officer, p. B135

Wheeling: OHIO VALLEY HEALTH SERVICES AND EDUCATION CORPORATION 2000 Eoff Street, Zip 26003–3823; tel. 304/234–8383; Michael J. Caruso, President and Chief Executive Officer, p. B100

WISCONSIN

Appleton: THEDACARE, INC. 122 East College Avenue, Zip 54911–5794, Mailing Address: P.O. Box 8025, Zip 54912–8025; tel. 920/830–5889; Dean Gruner, M.D., President and Chief Executive Officer, p. B135

Janesville: MERCY HEALTH SYSTEM 1000 Mineral Point Avenue, Zip 53548–2940, Mailing Address: P.O. Box 5003, Zip 53547–5003; tel. 608/756–6000; Javon R. Bea, President and Chief Executive Officer, p. B90

Manitowoc: ★ FRANCISCAN SISTERS OF CHRISTIAN CHARITY SPONSORED MINISTRIES, INC. 1415 South Rapids Road, Zip 54220–9302; tel. 920/684–7071; Daniel B. McGinty, President and Chief Executive Officer, p. B56

Milwaukee: ★ AURORA HEALTH CARE 750 Virginia Street, Zip 53204, Mailing Address: P.O. Box 341880, Zip 53234–1880; tel. 414/299–1600; Nick Turkal, M.D., President and Chief Executive Officer, p. B16

CHILDREN'S HOSPITAL AND HEALTH SYSTEM 9000 West Wisconsin Avenue, Zip 53226–4810, Mailing Address: P.O. Box 1997, Zip 53201–1997; tel. 414/226–2000; Peggy N. Troy, President and Chief Executive Officer, p. B32

Waukesha: ★ PROHEALTH CARE, INC. N17 W24100 Riverwood Drive, Suite 130, Zip 53188; tel. 262/928–2242; Susan A. Edwards, President and Chief Executive Officer, p. B107

Wausau: ★ ASPIRUS, INC. 425 Pine Ridge Boulevard, Zip 54401–4123; tel. 715/847–2118; Matthew Heywood, Chief Executive Officer, p. B15

ARIZONA

HONORHEALTH
8125 North Hayden Road, Scottsdale, AZ 85258–2463;
tel. 480/882–4000; Thomas J. Sadvary, FACHE, Chief Executive Officer

HONORHEALTH DEER VALLEY MEDICAL CENTER, 19829 North 27th Avenue, Phoenix, AZ, Zip 85027–4002; tel. 623/879–6100; John L. Harrington, Jr., FACHE, Chief Executive Officer

HONORHEALTH JOHN C. LINCOLN MEDICAL CENTER, 250 East Dunlap Avenue, Phoenix, AZ, Zip 85020–2825; tel. 602/943–2381; Margaret Elizabeth Griffin, Chief Executive Officer

HONORHEALTH REHABILITATION HOSPITAL, 8850 East Pima Center Parkway, Scottsdale, AZ, Zip 85258–4619; tel. 480/800–3900; Scott R. Keen, Chief Executive Officer

HONORHEALTH SCOTTSDALE OSBORN MEDICAL CENTER, 7400 East Osborn Road, Scottsdale, AZ, Zip 85251–6403; tel. 480/882–4000; Kimberly Post, Senior Vice President and Chief Executive Officer

HONORHEALTH SCOTTSDALE SHEA MEDICAL CENTER, 9003 East Shea Boulevard, Scottsdale, AZ, Zip 85260–6771; tel. 480/323–3000; Gary E. Baker, Senior Vice President and Chief Executive Officer

HONORHEALTH SCOTTSDALE THOMPSON PEAK MEDICAL CENTER, 7400 East Thompson Peak Parkway, Scottsdale, AZ, Zip 85255–4109; tel. 480/324–7000; David Price, Chief Executive Officer

NORTHERN ARIZONA HEALTHCARE
1200 North Beaver Street, Flagstaff, AZ 86001–3118;
tel. 928/779–3366; Robert P. Thames, President and Chief Executive Officer

FLAGSTAFF MEDICAL CENTER, 1200 North Beaver Street, Flagstaff, AZ, Zip 86001–3118; tel. 928/779–3366; Florence (Flo) Spyrow, Chief Administrative Officer

VERDE VALLEY MEDICAL CENTER, 269 South Candy Lane, Cottonwood, AZ, Zip 86326–4170; tel. 928/639–6000; Barbara Firminger, Chief Administrative Officer

CALIFORNIA

ADVENTIST HEALTH NORTHERN CALIFORNIA NETWORK
463 Aviation Boulevard, Santa Rosa, CA 95403–1079;
tel. 707/571–2893; Jeff Eller, President and Chief Executive Officer

FRANK R. HOWARD MEMORIAL HOSPITAL, One Marcela Drive, Willits, CA, Zip 95490–4298; tel. 707/459–6801; Rick Bockmann, Chief Executive Officer

ST. HELENA HOSPITAL CENTER FOR BEHAVIORAL HEALTH, 525 Oregon Street, Vallejo, CA, Zip 94590–3201; tel. 707/648–2200; Steven Herber, M.D., President and Chief Executive Officer

ST. HELENA HOSPITAL CLEAR LAKE, 15630 18th Avenue, Clearlake, CA, Zip 95422–9336, Mailing Address: P.O. Box 6710, Zip 95422; tel. 707/994–6486; David Santos, President and Chief Executive Officer

ST. HELENA HOSPITAL NAPA VALLEY, 10 Woodland Road, Saint Helena, CA, Zip 94574–9554; tel. 707/963–3611; Steven Herber, M.D., President and Chief Executive Officer

UKIAH VALLEY MEDICAL CENTER, 275 Hospital Drive, Ukiah, CA, Zip 95482–4531; tel. 707/462–3111; Gwen Matthews, R.N., MSN, Chief Executive Officer

PROVIDENCE HEALTH AND SERVICES – SOUTHERN CALIFORNIA
Regional Administration, 20555 Earl Street, Torrance, CA 90503–3006;
tel. 310/793–8087; Erik G. Wexler, Senior Vice President and Chief Executive

PROVIDENCE HOLY CROSS MEDICAL CENTER, 15031 Rinaldi Street, Mission Hills, CA, Zip 91345–1207; tel. 818/365–8051; Bernard Klein, M.D., Chief Executive

PROVIDENCE LITTLE COMPANY OF MARY MEDICAL CENTER – TORRANCE, 4101 Torrance Boulevard, Torrance, CA, Zip 90503–4664; tel. 310/540–7676; Mary E. Kingston, FACHE, R.N., Chief Executive Officer, South Bay Community

PROVIDENCE LITTLE COMPANY OF MARY MEDICAL CENTER SAN PEDRO, 1300 West Seventh Street, San Pedro, CA, Zip 90732–3505; tel. 310/832–3311; Mary E. Kingston, FACHE, R.N., Chief Executive Officer

PROVIDENCE SAINT JOHN'S HEALTH CENTER, 2121 Santa Monica Boulevard, Santa Monica, CA, Zip 90404–2091; tel. 310/829–5511; Marcel C. Loh, FACHE, Chief Executive Officer

PROVIDENCE SAINT JOSEPH MEDICAL CENTER, 501 South Buena Vista Street, Burbank, CA, Zip 91505–4866; tel. 818/843–5111; Julie Sprengel, Chief Executive Officer

PROVIDENCE TARZANA MEDICAL CENTER, 18321 Clark Street, Tarzana, CA, Zip 91356–3521; tel. 818/881–0800; Dale Surowitz, Chief Executive

ST. JOSEPH HOAG HEALTH
3345 Michelson Drive, Suite 100, Irvine, CA 92612–0693;
tel. 949/381–4019; Richard Afable, M.D., M.P.H., President and Chief Executive Officer

HOAG MEMORIAL HOSPITAL PRESBYTERIAN, One Hoag Drive, Newport Beach, CA, Zip 92663–4120, Mailing Address: P.O. Box 6100, Zip 92658–6100; tel. 949/764–4624; Robert Braithwaite, President and Chief Executive Officer

MISSION HOSPITAL, 27700 Medical Center Road, Mission Viejo, CA, Zip 92691–6474; tel. 949/364–1400; Richard Afable, M.D., M.P.H., Interim President & Chief Executive Officer

ST. JOSEPH HOSPITAL, 1100 West Stewart Drive, Orange, CA, Zip 92868–3849, Mailing Address: P.O. Box 5600, Zip 92863–5600; tel. 714/633–9111; Steven C. Moreau, President and Chief Executive Officer

ST. MARY MEDICAL CENTER, 18300 Highway 18, Apple Valley, CA, Zip 92307–2206, Mailing Address: P.O. Box 7025, Zip 92307–0725; tel. 760/242–2311; Alan H. Garrett, President and Chief Executive Officer

COLORADO

CENTURA HEALTH
188 Inverness Drive West, Suite 500, Englewood, CO 80112–5204;
tel. 303/290–6500; Jill Boyle, Interim Administrator and Director Clinical Operations

AVISTA ADVENTIST HOSPITAL, 100 Health Park Drive, Louisville, CO, Zip 80027–9583; tel. 303/673–1000; Dennis Barts, Chief Executive Officer

CASTLE ROCK ADVENTIST HOSPITAL, 2350 Meadows Boulevard, Castle Rock, CO, Zip 80109–8405; tel. 720/455–5000; Todd Folkenberg, Chief Executive Officer

LITTLETON ADVENTIST HOSPITAL, 7700 South Broadway Street, Littleton, CO, Zip 80122–2628; tel. 303/730–8900; Brett Spenst, Chief Executive Officer

PARKER ADVENTIST HOSPITAL, 9395 Crown Crest Boulevard, Parker, CO, Zip 80138–8573; tel. 303/269–4000; Sam D. Huenergardt, Chief Executive Officer

PENROSE–ST. FRANCIS HEALTH SERVICES, 2222 North Nevada Avenue, Colorado Springs, CO, Zip 80907–6799; tel. 719/776–5000; Margaret D. Sabin, President and Chief Executive Officer

PORTER ADVENTIST HOSPITAL, 2525 South Downing Street, Denver, CO, Zip 80210–5876; tel. 303/778–1955; Morre Dean, Chief Executive Officer

ST. ANTHONY HOSPITAL, 11600 West Second Place, Lakewood, CO, Zip 80228–1527; tel. 720/321–0000; Patrick Green, Interim Chief Executive Officer

ST. ANTHONY NORTH HEALTH CAMPUS, 14300 Orchard Parkway, Westminster, CO, Zip 80023–9206; tel. 720/627–0000; Carole Peet, R.N., MSN, President and Chief Executive Officer

ST. ANTHONY SUMMIT MEDICAL CENTER, 340 Peak One Drive, Frisco, CO, Zip 80443, Mailing Address: P.O. Box 738, Zip 80443–0738; tel. 970/668–3300; Paul J. Chodkowski, Chief Executive Officer

ST. MARY–CORWIN MEDICAL CENTER, 1008 Minnequa Avenue, Pueblo, CO, Zip 81004–3798; tel. 719/557–4000; Brian Moore, President and Chief Executive Officer

ST. THOMAS MORE HOSPITAL, 1338 Phay Avenue, Canon City, CO, Zip 81212–2302; tel. 719/285–2000; Sheri Trahern, CPA, FACHE, Chief Executive Officer

ST. VINCENT GENERAL HOSPITAL DISTRICT, 822 West 4th Street, Leadville, CO, Zip 80461–3897; tel. 719/486–0230; Sam Radke, Interim Chief Executive Officer and Interim Chief Financial Officer

COMMUNITY HEALTH PROVIDERS ORGANIZATION
2021 North 12th Street, Grand Junction, CO 81501–2980;
tel. 970/256–6200; Chris Thomas, FACHE, President and Chief Executive Officer

COMMUNITY HOSPITAL, 2351 G. Road, Grand Junction, CO, Zip 81505; tel. 970/242–0920; Chris Thomas, FACHE, President and Chief Executive Officer

HCA HEALTHONE, LLC
4900 South Monaco Street, Suite 380, Denver, CO 80237–3487;
tel. 303/788–2500; Sylvia Young, President

MEDICAL CENTER OF AURORA, 1501 South Potomac Street, Aurora, CO, Zip 80012–5411; tel. 303/695–2600; Daniel Miller, Chief Executive Officer

NORTH SUBURBAN MEDICAL CENTER, 9191 Grant Street, Thornton, CO, Zip 80229–4341; tel. 303/451–7800; Jennifer Alderfer, President and Chief Executive Officer

PRESBYTERIAN–ST. LUKE'S MEDICAL CENTER, 1719 East 19th Avenue, Denver, CO, Zip 80218–1281; tel. 303/839–6000; Maureen Tarrant, President and Chief Executive Officer

ROSE MEDICAL CENTER, 4567 East Ninth Avenue, Denver, CO, Zip 80220–3941; tel. 303/320–2121; Kenneth H. Feiler, President and Chief Executive Officer

SKY RIDGE MEDICAL CENTER, 10101 Ridge Gate Parkway, Lone Tree, CO, Zip 80124–5522; tel. 720/225–1000; Susan Hicks, Chief Executive Officer

SPALDING REHABILITATION HOSPITAL, 900 Potomac Steet, Aurora, CO, Zip 80011–6716; tel. 303/367–1166; Mark S. Deno, President and Chief Executive Officer

SWEDISH MEDICAL CENTER, 501 East Hampden Avenue, Englewood, CO, Zip 80113–2702; tel. 303/788–5000; Richard A. Hammett, Chief Executive Officer

CONNECTICUT

EASTERN CONNECTICUT HEALTH NETWORK
71 Haynes Street, Manchester, CT 06040–4131; tel. 860/533–3400; Peter J. Karl, President and Chief Executive Officer

MANCHESTER MEMORIAL HOSPITAL, 71 Haynes Street, Manchester, CT, Zip 06040–4188; tel. 860/646–1222; Peter J. Karl, President and Chief Executive Officer

ROCKVILLE GENERAL HOSPITAL, 31 Union Street, Vernon, CT, Zip 06066–3160; tel. 860/872–0501; Peter J. Karl, President and Chief Executive Officer

FLORIDA

BAYCARE HEALTH SYSTEM
2985 Drew Street, Clearwater, FL 33759–3012; tel. 877/692–2922; Tommy Inzina, President and Chief Executive Officer

BARTOW REGIONAL MEDICAL CENTER, 2200 Osprey Boulevard, Bartow, FL, Zip 33830–3308, Mailing Address: P.O. Box 1050, Zip 33831–1050; tel. 863/533–8111; Philip Minden, Chief Executive Officer

BAYCARE ALLIANT HOSPITAL, 601 Main Street, Dunedin, FL, Zip 34698–5848; tel. 727/736–9991; Jacqueline Arocho, Administrator

MEASE COUNTRYSIDE HOSPITAL, 3231 McMullen–Booth Road, Safety Harbor, FL, Zip 34695–6607, Mailing Address: P.O. Box 1098, Zip 34695–1098; tel. 727/725–6111; Lou Galdieri, R.N., President

MEASE DUNEDIN HOSPITAL, 601 Main Street, Dunedin, FL, Zip 34698–5891, Mailing Address: P.O. Box 760, Zip 34697–0760; tel. 727/733–1111; Lou Galdieri, R.N., President

MORTON PLANT HOSPITAL, 300 Pinellas Street, Clearwater, FL, Zip 33756–3804, Mailing Address: P.O. Box 210, Zip 33757–0210; tel. 727/462–7000; N. Kristopher Hoce, President

MORTON PLANT NORTH BAY HOSPITAL, 6600 Madison Street, New Port Richey, FL, Zip 34652–1900; tel. 727/842–8468; Michael Yungmann, President

SOUTH FLORIDA BAPTIST HOSPITAL, 301 North Alexander Street, Plant City, FL, Zip 33563–4303; tel. 813/757–1200; Karen Kerr, R.N., President

ST. ANTHONY'S HOSPITAL, 1200 Seventh Avenue North, Saint Petersburg, FL, Zip 33705–1388, Mailing Address: P.O. Box 12588, Zip 33733–2588; tel. 727/825–1100; M. Scott Smith, President

ST. JOSEPH'S HOSPITAL, 3001 West Martin Luther King Jr. Boulevard, Tampa, FL, Zip 33607–6387, Mailing Address: P.O. Box 4227, Zip 33677–4227; tel. 813/870–4000; Lorraine Lutton, President

WINTER HAVEN HOSPITAL, 200 Avenue F. N.E., Winter Haven, FL, Zip 33881–4193; tel. 863/293–1121; Stephen A. Nierman, President

GEORGIA

ST. JOSEPH'S/CANDLER HEALTH SYSTEM, INC.
5353 Reynolds Street, Savannah, GA 31405–6015; tel. 912/819–6000; Paul P. Hinchey, President and Chief Executive Officer

APPLING HEALTHCARE SYSTEM, 163 East Tollison Street, Baxley, GA, Zip 31513–0120; tel. 912/367–9841; Raymond J. Leadbetter, Jr., Interim Chief Executive Officer

CANDLER HOSPITAL, 5353 Reynolds Street, Savannah, GA, Zip 31405–6015; tel. 912/819–6000; Paul P. Hinchey, President and Chief Executive Officer

EFFINGHAM HOSPITAL, 459 Highway 119 South, Springfield, GA, Zip 31329–3021, Mailing Address: P.O. Box 386, Zip 31329–0386; tel. 912/754–6451; Francine Baker–Witt, R.N., Interim Chief Executive Officer

EMORY UNIVERSITY HOSPITAL, 1364 Clifton Road N.E., atlanta, GA, Zip 30322; tel. 404/712–2000; Bryce D. Gartland, M.D., Chief Executive Officer

LIBERTY REGIONAL MEDICAL CENTER, 462 Elma G. Miles Parkway, Hinesville, GA, Zip 31313–4000, Mailing Address: P.O. Box 919, Zip 31310–0919; tel. 912/369–9400; Michael Hester, Chief Executive Officer

MEADOWS REGIONAL MEDICAL CENTER, One Meadows Parkway, Vidalia, GA, Zip 30474–8759, Mailing Address: P.O. Box 1048, Zip 30475–1048; tel. 912/535–5555; Alan Kent, Chief Executive Officer

ST. JOSEPH'S HOSPITAL, 11705 Mercy Boulevard, Savannah, GA, Zip 31419–1791; tel. 912/819–4100; Paul P. Hinchey, President and Chief Executive Officer

WILLINGWAY HOSPITAL, 311 Jones Mill Road, Statesboro, GA, Zip 30458–4765; tel. 912/764–6236; Barbara S. Reid, Chief Executive Officer

IDAHO

THE HOSPITAL COOPERATIVE
500 South 11th Avenue Suite 503, Pocatello, ID 83201–4881; tel. 208/239–1951; Jon Smith, Executive Director

BEAR LAKE MEMORIAL HOSPITAL, 164 South Fifth Street, Montpelier, ID, Zip 83254–1597; tel. 208/847–1630; Rodney D. Jacobson, Administrator

BINGHAM MEMORIAL HOSPITAL, 98 Poplar Street, Blackfoot, ID, Zip 83221–1799; tel. 208/785–4100; D. Jeffery Daniels, Chief Executive Officer

CARIBOU MEMORIAL HOSPITAL AND LIVING CENTER, 300 South Third West, Soda Springs, ID, Zip 83276–1598; tel. 208/547–3341; Jon Smith, Chief Executive Officer

EASTERN IDAHO REGIONAL MEDICAL CENTER, 3100 Channing Way, Idaho Falls, ID, Zip 83404–7533, Mailing Address: P.O. Box 2077, Zip 83403–2077; tel. 208/529–6111; Douglas Crabtree, Chief Executive Officer

FRANKLIN COUNTY MEDICAL CENTER, 44 North First East Street, Preston, ID, Zip 83263–1399; tel. 208/852–0137; Alan Bird, Chief Executive Officer

LOST RIVERS MEDICAL CENTER, 551 Highland Drive, Arco, ID, Zip 83213–9771, Mailing Address: P.O. Box 145, Zip 83213–0145; tel. 208/527–8206; Brad Huerta, Chief Executive Officer and Administrator

MADISON MEMORIAL HOSPITAL, 450 East Main Street, Rexburg, ID, Zip 83440–2048, Mailing Address: P.O. Box 310, Zip 83440–0310; tel. 208/359–6900; Rachel Ann Gonzales, Chief Executive Officer

MINIDOKA MEMORIAL HOSPITAL, 1224 Eighth Street, Rupert, ID, Zip 83350–1599; tel. 208/436–0481; Tom Murphy, Chief Executive Officer

NELL J. REDFIELD MEMORIAL HOSPITAL, 150 North 200 West, Malad City, ID, Zip 83252–1239, Mailing Address: Box 126, Zip 83252–0126; tel. 208/766–2231; John Williams, Administrator and Chief Executive Officer

PORTNEUF MEDICAL CENTER, 777 Hospital Way, Pocatello, ID, Zip 83201–5175; tel. 208/239–1000; Daniel Ordyna, Chief Executive Officer

POWER COUNTY HOSPITAL DISTRICT, 510 Roosevelt Street, American Falls, ID, Zip 83211–1362, Mailing Address: P.O. Box 420, Zip 83211–0420; tel. 208/226–3200; Dallas Clinger, Administrator

STAR VALLEY MEDICAL CENTER, 901 Adams Street, Afton, WY, Zip 83110–9621, Mailing Address: P.O. Box 579, Zip 83110–0579; tel. 307/885–5800; Charlie A. Button, President and Chief Executive Officer

STEELE MEMORIAL MEDICAL CENTER, 203 South Daisy Street, Salmon, ID, Zip 83467–4709; tel. 208/756–5600; Jeanine Gentry, Chief Executive Officer

TETON VALLEY HEALTH CARE, 120 East Howard Street, Driggs, ID, Zip 83422–5112; tel. 208/354–2383; Keith Gnagey, Chief Executive Officer

ILLINOIS

AMITA HEALTH
120 North Oak Street, Hinsdale, IL 60521–3829; tel. 630/856–9000; Michael Goebel, FACHE, Vice President and Chief Executive Officer

ADVENTIST LA GRANGE MEMORIAL HOSPITAL, 5101 South Willow Spring Road, La Grange, IL, Zip 60525–2600; tel. 708/245–9000; Michael Goebel, FACHE, Vice President and Chief Executive Officer

ALEXIAN BROTHERS BEHAVIORAL HEALTH HOSPITAL, 1650 Moon Lake Boulevard, Hoffman Estates, IL, Zip 60169–1010; tel. 847/882–1600; Clayton Ciha, President and Chief Executive Officer

AMITA HEALTH ADVENTIST MEDICAL CENTER – HINSDALE, 120 North Oak Street, Hinsdale, IL, Zip 60521–3890; tel. 630/856–6001; Michael Goebel, FACHE, Vice President and Chief Executive Officer

AMITA HEALTH ADVENTIST MEDICAL CENTER BOLINGBROOK, 500 Remington Boulevard, Bolingbrook, IL, Zip 60440–4906; tel. 630/312–5000; Rick Mace, Chief Executive Officer

AMITA HEALTH GLENOAKS, 701 Winthrop Avenue, Glendale Heights, IL, Zip 60139–1403; tel. 630/545–8000; Bruce Christian, President and Chief Executive Officer

INDIANA

LUTHERAN HEALTH NETWORK
7950 West Jefferson Boulevard, Fort Wayne, IN 46804–4140; tel. 260/435–7001; Brian Bauer, Chief Executive Officer

BLUFFTON REGIONAL MEDICAL CENTER, 303 South Main Street, Bluffton, IN, Zip 46714–2503; tel. 260/824–3210; Aaron Garofola, Chief Executive Officer

DUKES MEMORIAL HOSPITAL, 275 West 12th Street, Peru, IN, Zip 46970–1638; tel. 765/472–8000; Debra Close, Chief Executive Officer

DUPONT HOSPITAL, 2520 East Dupont Road, Fort Wayne, IN, Zip 46825–1675; tel. 260/416–3000; Chad Towner, Chief Executive Officer

KOSCIUSKO COMMUNITY HOSPITAL, 2101 East Dubois Drive, Warsaw, IN, Zip 46580–3288; tel. 574/267–3200; Kirk M. Ray, Chief Executive Officer

LUTHERAN HOSPITAL OF INDIANA, 7950 West Jefferson Boulevard, Fort Wayne, IN, Zip 46804–4140; tel. 260/435–7001; Brian Bauer, Chief Executive Officer

ORTHOPAEDIC HOSPITAL OF LUTHERAN HEALTH NETWORK, 7952 West Jefferson Boulevard, Fort Wayne, IN, Zip 46804–4140; tel. 260/435–2999; Lorie Ailor, Chief Executive Officer

REHABILITATION HOSPITAL OF FORT WAYNE, 7970 West Jefferson Boulevard, Fort Wayne, IN, Zip 46804–4140; tel. 260/435–6100; Shelley Boxell, R.N., Chief Nursing Officer and Interim Chief Operating Officer

ST. JOSEPH HOSPITAL, 700 Broadway, Fort Wayne, IN, Zip 46802–1493; tel. 260/425–3000; Kenneth Jones, Chief Executive Officer

ST. VINCENT HEALTH
2001 North Meridian Street, Indianapolis, IN 46202;
tel. 317/338–2273; Jonathan Nalli, Chief Executive Officer

ST. MARY'S MEDICAL CENTER OF EVANSVILLE, 3700 Washington Avenue, Evansville, IN, Zip 47714–0541; tel. 812/485–4000; Keith Jewell, President

ST. MARY'S WARRICK HOSPITAL, 1116 Millis Avenue, Boonville, IN, Zip 47601–2204; tel. 812/897–4800; Kathy J. Hall, Administrator

ST. VINCENT ANDERSON REGIONAL HOSPITAL, 2015 Jackson Street, Anderson, IN, Zip 46016–4339; tel. 765/649–2511; Mike Schroyer, FACHE, MSN, R.N., President

ST. VINCENT CARMEL HOSPITAL, 13500 North Meridian Street, Carmel, IN, Zip 46032–1456; tel. 317/582–7000; Michael D. Chittenden, President

ST. VINCENT CLAY HOSPITAL, 1206 East National Avenue, Brazil, IN, Zip 47834–2797, Mailing Address: P.O. Box 489, Zip 47834–0489; tel. 812/442–2500; Jerry Laue, Administrator

ST. VINCENT DUNN HOSPITAL, 1600 23rd Street, Bedford, IN, Zip 47421–4704; tel. 812/275–3331; Matt Balla, Chief Executive Officer

ST. VINCENT FISHERS HOSPITAL, 13861 Olio Road, Fishers, IN, Zip 46037–3487; tel. 317/415–9000; Gary Fammartino, Administrator

ST. VINCENT FRANKFORT HOSPITAL, 1300 South Jackson Street, Frankfort, IN, Zip 46041–3313; tel. 765/656–3000; Kristi Bledsoe, R.N., Administrator

ST. VINCENT HEART CENTER, 10580 North Meridian Street, Indianapolis, IN, Zip 46290–1028; tel. 317/583–5000; Blake A. Dye, President

ST. VINCENT INDIANAPOLIS HOSPITAL, 2001 West 86th Street, Indianapolis, IN, Zip 46260–1991, Mailing Address: P.O. Box 40970, Zip 46240–0970; tel. 317/338–2345; Joel Feldman, President

ST. VINCENT JENNINGS HOSPITAL, 301 Henry Street, North Vernon, IN, Zip 47265–1097; tel. 812/352–4200

ST. VINCENT KOKOKO, 1907 West Sycamore Street, Kokono, IN, Zip 46901–4197; tel. 765/452–5611; Margaret M. Johnson, President, St. Vincent Northwest Region

ST. VINCENT MERCY HOSPITAL, 1331 South A Street, Elwood, IN, Zip 46036–1942; tel. 765/552–4600; Francis G. Albarano, Administrator

ST. VINCENT RANDOLPH HOSPITAL, 473 Greenville Avenue, Winchester, IN, Zip 47394–9436; tel. 765/584–0004; Francis G. Albarano, Administrator

ST. VINCENT SALEM HOSPITAL, 911 North Shelby Street, Salem, IN, Zip 47167–1694; tel. 812/883–5881; Dana M. Muntz, Chief Executive Officer

ST. VINCENT SETON SPECIALTY HOSPITAL, 8050 Township Line Road, Indianapolis, IN, Zip 46260–2478; tel. 317/415–8500; Joel Feldman, President and Chief Executive Officer

ST. VINCENT WILLIAMSPORT HOSPITAL, 412 North Monroe Street, Williamsport, IN, Zip 47993–1049; tel. 765/762–4000; Jane Craigin, Chief Executive Officer

SUBURBAN HEALTH ORGANIZATION
2780 Waterfront Parkway East Drive, Suite 300, Indianapolis, IN 46214;
tel. 317/692–5222; Dave Lippincott, President

HANCOCK REGIONAL HOSPITAL, 801 North State Street, Greenfield, IN, Zip 46140–1270, Mailing Address: P.O. Box 827, Zip 46140–0827; tel. 317/462–5544; Steven V. Long, FACHE, President and Chief Executive Officer

HENDRICKS REGIONAL HEALTH, 1000 East Main Street, Danville, IN, Zip 46122–1948, Mailing Address: P.O. Box 409, Zip 46122–0409; tel. 317/745–4451; Kevin Speer, Chief Executive Officer

HENRY COUNTY HOSPITAL, 1000 North 16th Street, New Castle, IN, Zip 47362–4319, Mailing Address: P.O. Box 490, Zip 47362–0490; tel. 765/521–0890; Paul Janssen, President and Chief Executive Officer

JOHNSON MEMORIAL HOSPITAL, 1125 West Jefferson Street, Franklin, IN, Zip 46131–2140, Mailing Address: P.O. Box 549, Zip 46131–0549; tel. 317/736–3300; Larry Heydon, President and Chief Executive Officer

MAJOR HOSPITAL, 150 West Washington Street, Shelbyville, IN, Zip 46176–1236; tel. 317/392–3211; John M. Horner, President and Chief Executive Officer

MARGARET MARY HEALTH, 321 Mitchell Avenue, Batesville, IN, Zip 47006–8909, Mailing Address: P.O. Box 226, Zip 47006–0226; tel. 812/934–6624; Timothy L. Putnam, FACHE, President and Chief Executive Officer

RIVERVIEW HEALTH, 395 Westfield Road, Noblesville, IN, Zip 46060–1425, Mailing Address: P.O. Box 220, Zip 46061–0220; tel. 317/773–0760; Seth Warren, President and Chief Executive Officer

RUSH MEMORIAL HOSPITAL, 1300 North Main Street, Rushville, IN, Zip 46173–1198, Mailing Address: P.O. Box 608, Zip 46173–0608; tel. 765/932–4111; Bradley Smith, President and Chief Executive Officer

WITHAM HEALTH SERVICES, 2605 North Lebanon Street, Lebanon, IN, Zip 46052–1476, Mailing Address: P.O. Box 1200, Zip 46052–3005; tel. 765/485–8000; Raymond V. Ingham, Ph.D., President and Chief Executive Officer

IOWA

GENESIS HEALTH SYSTEM
1227 East Rusholme Street, Davenport, IA 52803–2459;
tel. 563/421–1000; Douglas P. Cropper, President and Chief Executive Officer

GENESIS MEDICAL CENTER, DEWITT, 1118 11th Street, De Witt, IA, Zip 52742–1296; tel. 563/659–4200; Curt Coleman, FACHE, Chief Executive Officer

GENESIS MEDICAL CENTER, ILLINI CAMPUS, 801 Illini Drive, Silvis, IL, Zip 61282–1893; tel. 309/281–4000; Theresa Summers–Main, R.N., Interim President

GENESIS MEDICAL CENTER–ALEDO, 409 N.W. Ninth Avenue, Aledo, IL, Zip 61231–1296; tel. 309/582–9100; Ted Rogalski, Administrator

GENESIS MEDICAL CENTER–DAVENPORT, 1227 East Rusholme Street, Davenport, IA, Zip 52803–2498; tel. 563/421–1000; Jordan Voigt, Administrator

MERCY HEALTH NETWORK – CENTRAL IOWA
1755 59th Place, West Des Moines, IA 50266–7737;
tel. 515/358–8023; Michael Trachta, Vice President Network CAH Operations

ADAIR COUNTY MEMORIAL HOSPITAL, 609 S.E. Kent Street, Greenfield, IA, Zip 50849–9454; tel. 641/743–2123; Marcia Hendricks, R.N., FACHE, Chief Executive Officer

AUDUBON COUNTY MEMORIAL HOSPITAL, 515 Pacific Street, Audubon, IA, Zip 50025–1056; tel. 712/563–2611; Thomas G. Smith, Administrator and Chief Executive Officer

BOONE COUNTY HOSPITAL, 1015 Union Street, Boone, IA, Zip 50036–4821; tel. 515/432–3140; Joseph S. Smith, Chief Executive Officer

CENTRAL COMMUNITY HOSPITAL, 901 Davidson Street N.W., Elkader, IA, Zip 52043–9015; tel. 563/245–7000; Frances J. Zichal, Chief Executive Officer

DALLAS COUNTY HOSPITAL, 610 10th Street, Perry, IA, Zip 50220–2221; tel. 515/465–3547; Angela Mortoza, Chief Executive Officer

DAVIS COUNTY HOSPITAL, 509 North Madison Street, Bloomfield, IA, Zip 52537–1271; tel. 641/664–2145; Kirby Johnson, Chief Executive Officer

DECATUR COUNTY HOSPITAL, 1405 N.W. Church Street, Leon, IA, Zip 50144–1299; tel. 641/446–4871; Suzanne Cooner, R.N., MSN, Chief Executive Officer

GRINNELL REGIONAL MEDICAL CENTER, 210 Fourth Avenue, Grinnell, IA, Zip 50112–1898; tel. 641/236–7511; Todd C. Linden, President and Chief Executive Officer

KNOXVILLE HOSPITAL & CLINICS, 1002 South Lincoln Street, Knoxville, IA, Zip 50138–3155; tel. 641/842–2151; Kevin Kincaid, Chief Executive Officer

MADISON COUNTY HEALTH CARE SYSTEM, 300 West Hutchings Street, Winterset, IA, Zip 50273–2109; tel. 515/462–2373; Marcia Hendricks, R.N., FACHE, Chief Executive Officer

MANNING REGIONAL HEALTHCARE CENTER, 1550 6th Street, Manning, IA, Zip 51455–1093; tel. 712/655–2072; John O'Brien, Chief Executive Officer

MERCY MEDICAL CENTER–CENTERVILLE, 1 St. Joseph's Drive, Centerville, IA, Zip 52544–8055; tel. 641/437–4111; Clinton J. Christianson, FACHE, President

MERCY MEDICAL CENTER–DES MOINES, 1111 6th Avenue, Des Moines, IA, Zip 50314–2611; tel. 515/247–3121; Robert P. Ritz, President

MONROE COUNTY HOSPITAL AND CLINICS, 6580 165th Street, Albia, IA, Zip 52531–8793; tel. 641/932–2134; Veronica Fuhs, Chief Executive Officer

RINGGOLD COUNTY HOSPITAL, 504 North Cleveland Street, Mount Ayr, IA, Zip 50854–2201; tel. 641/464–3226; Gordon W. Winkler, Administrator and Chief Executive Officer

SKIFF MEDICAL CENTER, 204 North Fourth Avenue East, Newton, IA, Zip 50208–3100, Mailing Address: P.O. Box 1006, Zip 50208–1006; tel. 641/792–1273; Brett Allen Altman, FACHE, President and Chief Executive Officer

VAN DIEST MEDICAL CENTER, 2350 Hospital Drive, Webster City, IA, Zip 50595–6600, Mailing Address: P.O. Box 430, Zip 50595–0430; tel. 515/832–9400; Lori Rathbun, Chief Executive Officer

WAYNE COUNTY HOSPITAL, 417 South East Street, Corydon, IA, Zip 50060–1860, Mailing Address: P.O. Box 305, Zip 50060–0305; tel. 641/872–2260; Daren Relph, Chief Executive Officer

MERCY HEALTH NETWORK – NORTH IOWA
1000 4th Street S.W., Mason City, IA 50401–2800; tel. 641/428–7000; Daniel Varnum, Chief Executive Officer

FRANKLIN GENERAL HOSPITAL, 1720 Central Avenue East, Suite A., Hampton, IA, Zip 50441–1867; tel. 641/456–5000; Kim Price, Chief Executive Officer

HANCOCK COUNTY HEALTH SYSTEM, 532 First Street N.W., Britt, IA, Zip 50423–1227; tel. 641/843–5000; Jeffry Stampohar, Chief Executive Officer

HANSEN FAMILY HOSPITAL, 920 South Oak, Iowa Falls, IA, Zip 50126–9506; tel. 641/648–4631; Cherelle Montanye–Ireland, Chief Executive Officer

KOSSUTH REGIONAL HEALTH CENTER, 1515 South Phillips Street, Algona, IA, Zip 50511–3649; tel. 515/295–2451; Scott A. Curtis, Administrator and Chief Executive Officer

MERCY MEDICAL CENTER–NEW HAMPTON, 308 North Maple Avenue, New Hampton, IA, Zip 50659–1142; tel. 641/394–4121; Aaron Flugum, Chief Executive Officer

MERCY MEDICAL CENTER–NORTH IOWA, 1000 Fourth Street S.W., Mason City, IA, Zip 50401–2800; tel. 641/428–7000; Daniel Varnum, President and Chief Executive Officer

MITCHELL COUNTY REGIONAL HEALTH CENTER, 616 North Eighth Street, Osage, IA, Zip 50461–1498; tel. 641/732–6000; Shelly Russell, Chief Executive Officer

PALO ALTO COUNTY HEALTH SYSTEM, 3201 First Street, Emmetsburg, IA, Zip 50536–2516; tel. 712/852–5500; Desiree Einsweiler, Chief Executive Officer

REGIONAL HEALTH SERVICES OF HOWARD COUNTY, 235 Eighth Avenue West, Cresco, IA, Zip 52136–1098; tel. 563/547–2101; Robin M. Schluter, Chief Executive Officer

KANSAS

COTTONWOOD HEALTH ALLIANCE
1100 Columbine Drive, Holton, KS Zip 66436–8824;
Tel: 785/364–2115; Sara A. Larison, Director

F. W. HUSTON MEDICAL CENTER, 408 Delaware Street, Winchester, KS, Zip 66097–4003; tel. 913/774–2314; LaMont Cook, Administrator

HIAWATHA COMMUNITY HOSPITAL, 300 Utah Street, Hiawatha, KS, Zip 66434–2314; tel. 785/742–2131; Jenny Knudson, Controller

HOLTON COMMUNITY HOSPITAL, 1100 Columbine Drive, Holton KS, Zip 66436–8824; tel. 785/364–2116; Carrie L. Saia, Chief Executive Officer

NEMAHA VALLEY COMMUNITY HOSPITAL, 1600 Community Drive, Seneca, KS, Zip 66538–9739; Kiley Floyd, Chief Executive Officer

ST. FRANCIS HEALTH, 1700 SW 7th Street, Topeka, KS Zip 66606–1690; tel. 785/295–8000; David P. Setchel, President

HAYS MEDICAL CENTER
2220 Canterbury Drive, Hays, KS 67601–2370; tel. 785/623–2300;
John H. Jeter, M.D., President and Chief Executive Officer

PAWNEE VALLEY COMMUNITY HOSPITAL, 923 Carroll Avenue, Larned, KS, Zip 67550–2429; tel. 620/285–3161; Shae Veach, Vice President, Regional Operations

HEALTH INNOVATIONS NETWORK OF KANSAS
1500 S.W. 10th Avenue, Topeka, KS 66604–1301; tel. 785/354–6137;
Kristi Gosser, Network Operations Director

ATCHISON HOSPITAL, 800 Raven Hill Drive, Atchison, KS, Zip 66002–9204; tel. 913/367–2131; John L. Jacobson, Chief Executive Officer

CLAY COUNTY MEDICAL CENTER, 617 Liberty Street, Clay Center, KS, Zip 67432–1564, Mailing Address: P.O. Box 512, Zip 67432–0512; tel. 785/632–2144; Austin M. Gillard, Chief Executive Officer

COFFEY COUNTY HOSPITAL, 801 North 4th Street, Burlington, KS, Zip 66839–2602; tel. 620/364–2121; Leonard Hernandez, Chief Executive Officer

COMMUNITY HEALTHCARE SYSTEM, 120 West Eighth Street, Onaga, KS, Zip 66521–9574; tel. 785/889–4272; Todd Willert, Chief Executive Officer

F. W. HUSTON MEDICAL CENTER, 408 Delaware Street, Winchester, KS, Zip 66097–4003; tel. 913/774–4340; LaMont Cook, Administrator

GEARY COMMUNITY HOSPITAL, 1102 St. Mary's Road, Junction City, KS, Zip 66441–4196, Mailing Address: P.O. Box 490, Zip 66441–0490; tel. 785/238–4131; Joseph Stratton, FACHE, Chief Executive Officer

HERINGTON MUNICIPAL HOSPITAL, 100 East Helen Street, Herington, KS, Zip 67449–1606; tel. 785/258–2207; Alan Meisinger, Chief Financial Officer

HIAWATHA COMMUNITY HOSPITAL, 300 Utah Street, Hiawatha, KS, Zip 66434–2314; tel. 785/742–2131; Roger Barnhart, Chief Executive Officer

HORTON COMMUNITY HOSPITAL, 240 West 18th Street, Horton, KS, Zip 66439–1245; tel. 785/486–2642; James D. Noble, Chief Executive Officer

IRWIN ARMY COMMUNITY HOSPITAL, 600 Caisson Hill Road, Junction City, KS, Zip 66442–7037; tel. 785/239–7000; Colonel Risa Ware, Commander

KANSAS REHABILITATION HOSPITAL, 1504 S.W. Eighth Avenue, Topeka, KS, Zip 66606–1632; tel. 785/235–6600; William J. Overbey, Chief Executive Officer

MORRIS COUNTY HOSPITAL, 600 North Washington Street, Council Grove, KS, Zip 66846–1422; tel. 620/767–6811; James H. Reagan, Jr., Ph.D., Chief Executive Officer

NEMAHA VALLEY COMMUNITY HOSPITAL, 1600 Community Drive, Seneca, KS, Zip 66538–9739; tel. 785/336–6181; Kiley Floyd, Chief Executive Officer

NEWMAN REGIONAL HEALTH, 1201 West 12th Avenue, Emporia, KS, Zip 66801–2597; tel. 620/343–6800; Robert N. Wright, Chief Executive Officer

SABETHA COMMUNITY HOSPITAL, 14th and Oregon Streets, Sabetha, KS, Zip 66534–0229, Mailing Address: P.O. Box 229, Zip 66534–0229; tel. 785/284–2121; Lora Key, Chief Executive Officer

STORMONT VAIL HEALTH, 1500 S.W. Tenth Avenue, Topeka, KS, Zip 66604–1353; tel. 785/354–6000; Randall Peterson, President and Chief Executive Officer

VIA CHRISTI HOSPITAL MANHATTAN, INC., 1823 College Avenue, Manhattan, KS, Zip 66502–3346; tel. 785/776–3322; Robert C. Copple, FACHE, Senior Administrator

WAMEGO HEALTH CENTER, 711 Genn Drive, Wamego, KS, Zip 66547–1179; tel. 785/456–2295; Robert C. Copple, FACHE, Senior Administrator, Via Christi

WASHINGTON COUNTY HOSPITAL, 304 East Third Street, Washington, KS, Zip 66968–2033; tel. 785/325–2211; Roxanne Schottel, Chief Executive Officer

MED–OP, INC.
220 Canterbury Drive, Hays, KS 67601; tel. 785/623–2301; Shae Veach, Executive Director

CITIZENS MEDICAL CENTER, 100 East College Drive, Colby, KS, Zip 67701–3799; tel. 785/462–7511; Greg Unruh, Chief Executive Officer

CLARA BARTON HOSPITAL, 250 West Ninth Street, Hoisington, KS, Zip 67544–1706; tel. 620/653–2114; James Blackwell, President and Chief Executive Officer

GOODLAND REGIONAL MEDICAL CENTER, 220 West Second Street, Goodland, KS, Zip 67735–1602; tel. 785/890–3625; William Widener, Chief Executive Officer

GOVE COUNTY MEDICAL CENTER, 520 West Fifth Street, Quinter, KS, Zip 67752–0129, Mailing Address: P.O. Box 129, Zip 67752–0129; tel. 785/754–3341; Coleen Tummons, Chief Executive Officer

GRAHAM COUNTY HOSPITAL, 304 West Prout Street, Hill City, KS, Zip 67642–1435; tel. 785/421–2121; Melissa Atkins, CPA, Chief Executive Officer

HAYS MEDICAL CENTER, 2220 Canterbury Drive, Hays, KS, Zip 67601–2370, Mailing Address: P.O. Box 8100, Zip 67601–8100; tel. 785/623–5000; John H. Jeter, M.D., President and Chief Executive Officer

LOGAN COUNTY HOSPITAL, 211 Cherry Street, Oakley, KS, Zip 67748–1201; tel. 785/672–3211; Meldon L. Snow, Chief Executive Officer

NESS COUNTY HOSPITAL DISTRICT NO 2, 312 Custer Street, Ness City, KS, Zip 67560–1654; tel. 785/798–2291; Curt Thomas, Administrator

NORTON COUNTY HOSPITAL, 102 East Holme, Norton, KS, Zip 67654–1406, Mailing Address: P.O. Box 250, Zip 67654–0250; tel. 785/877–3351; Ryan Stover, Chief Executive Officer

PAWNEE VALLEY COMMUNITY HOSPITAL, 923 Carroll Avenue, Larned, KS, Zip 67550–2429; tel. 620/285–3161; Shae Veach, Vice President, Regional Operations

ROOKS COUNTY HEALTH CENTER, 1210 North Washington Street, Plainville, KS, Zip 67663–1632, Mailing Address: P.O. Box 389, Zip 67663–0389; tel. 785/434–4553; Michael Sinclair, Chief Executive Officer

RUSH COUNTY MEMORIAL HOSPITAL, 801 Locust Street, La Crosse, KS, Zip 67548–9673, Mailing Address: P.O. Box 520, Zip 67548–0520; tel. 785/222–2545; Brenda Legleiter, R.N., Chief Executive Officer

RUSSELL REGIONAL HOSPITAL, 200 South Main Street, Russell, KS, Zip 67665–2920; tel. 785/483–3131; Harold Courtois, Chief Executive Officer

SCOTT COUNTY HOSPITAL, 201 East Albert Avenue, Scott City, KS, Zip 67871–1203; tel. 620/872–5811; Mark Burnett, President and Chief Executive Officer

SHERIDAN COUNTY HEALTH COMPLEX, 826 18th Street, Hoxie, KS, Zip 67740–0167, Mailing Address: P.O. Box 167, Zip 67740–0167; tel. 785/675–3281; Niceta Farber, Chief Executive Officer

PIONEER HEALTH NETWORK, INC.
310 East Walnut Street, Suite 210, Garden City, KS 67846–5565; tel. 620/276–6100; Mary Adam, Executive Director

BOB WILSON MEMORIAL GRANT COUNTY HOSPITAL, 415 North Main Street, Ulysses, KS, Zip 67880–2133; tel. 620/356–1266; Deanna Mustin, R.N., Administrator

CITIZENS MEDICAL CENTER, 100 East College Drive, Colby, KS, Zip 67701–3799; tel. 785/462–7511; Greg Unruh, Chief Executive Officer

EDWARDS COUNTY HOSPITAL AND HEALTHCARE CENTER, 620 West Eighth Street, Kinsley, KS, Zip 67547–2329, Mailing Address: P.O. Box 99, Zip 67547–0099; tel. 620/659–3621; Jimmie W. Hansel, Ph.D., Chief Executive Officer

GREELEY COUNTY HEALTH SERVICES, 506 Third Street, Tribune, KS, Zip 67879–9684, Mailing Address: P.O. Box 338, Zip 67879–0338; tel. 620/376–4221; Lee Rhodes, Administrator and Chief Executive Officer

HAMILTON COUNTY HOSPITAL, 700 North Huser Street, Syracuse, KS, Zip 67878–0948, Mailing Address: P.O. Box 948, Zip 67878–0948; tel. 620/384–7461; Bart Daugherty, Chief Executive Officer

HODGEMAN COUNTY HEALTH CENTER, 809 Bramley Street, Jetmore, KS, Zip 67854–9320, Mailing Address: P.O. Box 310, Zip 67854–0310; tel. 620/357–8361; Teresa L. Deuel, Chief Executive Officer

KEARNY COUNTY HOSPITAL, 500 Thorpe Street, Lakin, KS, Zip 67860–9625; tel. 620/355–7111; Benjamin Anderson, Chief Executive Officer and Administrator

LANE COUNTY HOSPITAL, 235 West Vine, Dighton, KS, Zip 67839–0969, Mailing Address: P.O. Box 969, Zip 67839–0969; tel. 620/397–5321; Donna McGowan, Administrator

LOGAN COUNTY HOSPITAL, 211 Cherry Street, Oakley, KS, Zip 67748–1201; tel. 785/672–3211; Meldon L. Snow, Chief Executive Officer

MEADE DISTRICT HOSPITAL, 510 East Carthage Street, Meade, KS, Zip 67864–6401, Mailing Address: P.O. Box 820, Zip 67864–0820; tel. 620/873–2141; Steve Stewart, Administrator

MINNEOLA DISTRICT HOSPITAL, 212 Main Street, Minneola, KS, Zip 67865–8511, Mailing Address: P.O. Box 127, Zip 67865–0127; tel. 620/885–4264; Deborah Bruner, Chief Executive Officer and Administrator

MORTON COUNTY HEALTH SYSTEM, 445 Hilltop Street, Elkhart, KS, Zip 67950–0937, Mailing Address: P.O. Box 937, Zip 67950–0937; tel. 620/697–2141; Richard Q. Bergling, Chief Executive Officer

SATANTA DISTRICT HOSPITAL AND LONG TERM CARE, 401 South Cheyenne Street, Satanta, KS, Zip 67870–0159, Mailing Address: P.O. Box 159, Zip 67870–0159; tel. 620/649–2761; Jeremy Clingenpeel, Administrator

SCOTT COUNTY HOSPITAL, 201 East Albert Avenue, Scott City, KS, Zip 67871–1203; tel. 620/872–5811; Mark Burnett, President and Chief Executive Officer

SOUTHWEST MEDICAL CENTER, 315 West 15th Street, Liberal, KS, Zip 67901–2455, Mailing Address: Box 1340, Zip 67905–1340; tel. 620/624–1651; William Ermann, President and Chief Executive Officer

ST. CATHERINE HOSPITAL, 401 East Spruce Street, Garden City, KS, Zip 67846–5679; tel. 620/272–2561; Scott J. Taylor, President and Chief Executive Officer

STANTON COUNTY HOSPITAL, 404 North Chestnut Street, Johnson, KS, Zip 67855–5001, Mailing Address: P.O. Box 779, Zip 67855–0779; tel. 620/492–6250; Jay Tusten, Chief Executive Officer

STEVENS COUNTY HOSPITAL, 1006 South Jackson Street, Hugoton, KS, Zip 67951–2858, Mailing Address: P.O. Box 10, Zip 67951–0010; tel. 620/544–8511; Linda Stalcup, Chief Executive Officer

WICHITA COUNTY HEALTH CENTER, 211 East Earl Street, Leoti, KS, Zip 67861–9620; tel. 620/375–2233; Teresa Clark, Chief Executive Officer and Administrator

SOUTHERN PLAINS HEALTH NETWORK
203 South Main Street, Pratt, KS 67124–2714; tel. 620/672–7451; DeWayne Bryan, Executive Director

ASHLAND HEALTH CENTER, 709 Oak Street, Ashland, KS, Zip 67831–0188, Mailing Address: P.O. Box 188, Zip 67831–0188; tel. 620/635–2241; Michael Mages, Chief Executive Officer

COMANCHE COUNTY HOSPITAL, 202 South Frisco Street, Coldwater, KS, Zip 67029–9101, Mailing Address: HC 65, Box 8A, Zip 67029–9500; tel. 620/582–2144; Nancy Zimmerman, R.N., Administrator

MEDICINE LODGE MEMORIAL HOSPITAL, 710 North Walnut Street, Medicine Lodge, KS, Zip 67104–1019; tel. 620/886–3771; Kevin A. White, Administrator

PRATT REGIONAL MEDICAL CENTER, 200 Commodore Street, Pratt, KS, Zip 67124–2903; tel. 620/672–7451; Susan M. Page, President and Chief Executive Officer

STAFFORD COUNTY HOSPITAL, 502 South Buckeye Street, Stafford, KS, Zip 67578–2035, Mailing Address: P.O. Box 190, Zip 67578–0190; tel. 620/234–5221; Todd Taylor, Chief Executive Officer

SUNFLOWER HEALTH NETWORK
400 South Santa Fe Avenue, Salina, KS 67401–4144; tel. 785/452–6102; Heather Fuller, Executive Director

ANTHONY MEDICAL CENTER, 1101 East Spring Street, Anthony, KS, Zip 67003–2122; tel. 620/842–5111; Lori Allen, Chief Financial Officer and Interim Chief Executive Officer

CLAY COUNTY MEDICAL CENTER, 617 Liberty Street, Clay Center, KS, Zip 67432–1564, Mailing Address: P.O. Box 512, Zip 67432–0512; tel. 785/632–2144; Austin M. Gillard, Chief Executive Officer

CLOUD COUNTY HEALTH CENTER, 1100 Highland Drive, Concordia, KS, Zip 66901–3923; tel. 785/243–1234; Cherri Waites, Chief Executive Officer

ELLSWORTH COUNTY MEDICAL CENTER, 1604 Aylward Street, Ellsworth, KS, Zip 67439–0087, Mailing Address: P.O. Box 87, Zip 67439–0087; tel. 785/472–3111; Roger A. Masse, FACHE, Chief Executive Officer

HERINGTON MUNICIPAL HOSPITAL, 100 East Helen Street, Herington, KS, Zip 67449–1606; tel. 785/258–2207; Alan Meisinger, Chief Financial Officer

HILLSBORO COMMUNITY HOSPITAL, 701 South Main Street, Hillsboro, KS, Zip 67063–1553; tel. 620/947–3114; Marion Regier, Chief Executive Officer

HOSPITAL DISTRICT NO 1 OF RICE COUNTY, 619 South Clark Street, Lyons, KS, Zip 67554–3003, Mailing Address: P.O. Box 828, Zip 67554–0828; tel. 620/257–5173; George M. Stover, Chief Executive Officer

JEWELL COUNTY HOSPITAL, 100 Crestvue Avenue, Mankato, KS, Zip 66956–2407, Mailing Address: P.O. Box 327, Zip 66956–0327; tel. 785/378–3137; Doyle L. McKimmy, FACHE, Chief Executive Officer

LINCOLN COUNTY HOSPITAL, 624 North Second Street, Lincoln, KS, Zip 67455–1738, Mailing Address: P.O. Box 406, Zip 67455–0406; tel. 785/524–4403; Steven L. Granzow, Chief Executive Officer

LINDSBORG COMMUNITY HOSPITAL, 605 West Lincoln Street, Lindsborg, KS, Zip 67456–2328; tel. 785/227–3308; Larry VanDerWege, Administrator

MEMORIAL HEALTH SYSTEM, 511 N.E. Tenth Street, Abilene, KS, Zip 67410–2153; tel. 785/263–2100; Mark A. Miller, FACHE, Chief Executive Officer

MITCHELL COUNTY HOSPITAL HEALTH SYSTEMS, 400 West Eighth, Beloit, KS, Zip 67420–1605, Mailing Address: P.O. Box 399, Zip 67420–0399; tel. 785/738–2266; Jeremy Armstrong, FACHE, Chief Executive Officer

OSBORNE COUNTY MEMORIAL HOSPITAL, 424 West New Hampshire Street, Osborne, KS, Zip 67473–2314, Mailing Address: P.O. Box 70, Zip 67473–0070; tel. 785/346–2121; Rex D. Walk, Interim Chief Executive Officer

OTTAWA COUNTY HEALTH CENTER, 215 East Eighth, Minneapolis, KS, Zip 67467–1902, Mailing Address: P.O. Box 290, Zip 67467–0290; tel. 785/392–2122; Jody Parks, Administrator

REPUBLIC COUNTY HOSPITAL, 2420 G Street, Belleville, KS, Zip 66935–2400; tel. 785/527–2254; Blaine K. Miller, Administrator

SALINA REGIONAL HEALTH CENTER, 400 South Santa Fe Avenue, Salina, KS, Zip 67401–4198, Mailing Address: P.O. Box 5080, Zip 67402–5080; tel. 785/452–7000; Micheal Terry, President and Chief Executive Officer

SMITH COUNTY MEMORIAL HOSPITAL, 614 South Main Street, Smith Center, KS, Zip 66967–3001; tel. 785/282–6845; Allen Van Driel, FACHE, Administrator

KENTUCKY

COMMONWEALTH HEALTH CORPORATION
800 Park Street, Bowling Green, KY 42101–2356; tel. 270/745–1500; Connie Smith, Chief Executive Officer

COMMONWEALTH REGIONAL SPECIALTY HOSPITAL, 250 Park Drive, 6th Floor, Bowling Green, KY, Zip 42101–1760, Mailing Address: P.O. Box 90010, Zip 42102–9010; tel. 270/796–6200; Christa Atkins, Administrator

MEDICAL CENTER AT BOWLING GREEN, 250 Park Street, Bowling Green, KY, Zip 42101–1795, Mailing Address: P.O. Box 90010, Zip 42102–9010; tel. 270/745–1000; Connie Smith, Chief Executive Officer

MEDICAL CENTER AT FRANKLIN, 1100 Brookhaven Road, Franklin, KY, Zip 42134–2746; tel. 270/598–4800; Annette Runyon, Vice President and Administrator

MEDICAL CENTER AT SCOTTSVILLE, 456 Burnley Road, Scottsville, KY, Zip 42164–6355; tel. 270/622–2800; Eric Hagan, R.N., Executive Vice President and Administrator

COMMUNITY CARE NETWORK
110 A. Second Street, Henderson, KY 42420; tel. 619/278–2273; Roberta Alexander, Director

BAPTIST HEALTH MADISONVILLE, 900 Hospital Drive, Madisonville, KY, Zip 42431–1694; tel. 270/825–5100; Robert L. Ramey, President

BAPTIST HEALTH PADUCAH, 2501 Kentucky Avenue, Paducah, KY, Zip 42003–3200; tel. 270/575–2100; William A. Brown, FACHE, President and CEO

CALDWELL MEDICAL CENTER, 100 Medical Center Drive, Princeton, KY, Zip 42445–2430, Mailing Address: P.O. Box 410, Zip 42445–0410; tel. 270/365–0300; Kelley J. Rushing, Chief Executive Officer

CRITTENDEN COUNTY HOSPITAL, 520 West Gum Street, Marion, KY, Zip 42064–1516, Mailing Address: P.O. Box 386, Zip 42064–0386; tel. 270/965–5281; Greg R. McNeil, Chief Executive Officer

HEALTHSOUTH DEACONESS REHABILITATION HOSPITAL, 4100 Covert Avenue, Evansville, IN, Zip 47714–5567, Mailing Address: P.O. Box 5349, Zip 47716–5349; tel. 812/476–9983; Blake Bunner, Chief Executive Officer

JENNIE STUART MEDICAL CENTER, 320 West 18th Street, Hopkinsville, KY, Zip 42240–1965, Mailing Address: P.O. Box 2400, Zip 42241–2400; tel. 270/887–0100; Eric A. Lee, President and Chief Executive Officer

KOSAIR CHILDREN'S HOSPITAL, 231 East Chestnut Street, Louisville, KY, Zip 40202–1821; tel. 502/629–6000; Thomas D. Kmetz, Division President

LINCOLN TRAIL BEHAVIORAL HEALTH SYSTEM, 3909 South Wilson Road, Radcliff, KY, Zip 40160–8944, Mailing Address: P.O. Box 369, Zip 40159–0369; tel. 270/351–9444; Charles L. Webb, Jr., Chief Executive Officer

LIVINGSTON HOSPITAL AND HEALTHCARE SERVICES, 131 Hospital Drive, Salem, KY, Zip 42078–8043; tel. 270/988–2299; Mark A. Edwards, Chief Executive Officer

MEDICAL CENTER AT FRANKLIN, 1100 Brookhaven Road, Franklin, KY, Zip 42134–2746; tel. 270/598–4800; Annette Runyon, Vice President and Administrator

METHODIST HOSPITAL, 1305 North Elm Street, Henderson, KY, Zip 42420–2775, Mailing Address: P.O. Box 48, Zip 42419–0048; tel. 270/827–7700; Gary R. Colberg, FACHE, President and Chief Executive Officer

METHODIST HOSPITAL UNION COUNTY, 4604 Highway 60 West, Morganfield, KY, Zip 42437–9570; tel. 270/389–5000; Gary R. Colberg, FACHE, President and Chief Executive Officer

MURRAY–CALLOWAY COUNTY HOSPITAL, 803 Poplar Street, Murray, KY, Zip 42071–2432; tel. 270/762–1100; Colonel Jerome Penner, Chief Executive Officer

NORTON AUDUBON HOSPITAL, One Audubon Plaza Drive, Louisville, KY, Zip 40217–1300, Mailing Address: P.O. Box 17550, Zip 40217–0550; tel. 502/636–7111; Jon Cooper, Chief Administrative Officer

NORTON HOSPITAL, 200 East Chestnut Street, Louisville, KY, Zip 40202–1800, Mailing Address: P.O. Box 35070, Zip 40232–5070; tel. 502/629–8000; Matthew Ayers, Chief Administrative Officer

NORTON WOMEN'S AND KOSAIR CHILDREN'S HOSPITAL, 4001 Dutchmans Lane, Louisville, KY, Zip 40207–4799; tel. 502/893–1000; Charlotte Ipsan, Chief Administrative Officer

OHIO COUNTY HOSPITAL, 1211 Main Street, Hartford, KY, Zip 42347–1619; tel. 270/298–7411; Blaine Pieper, Chief Executive Officer

OWENSBORO HEALTH MUHLENBERG COMMUNITY HOSPITAL, 440 Hopkinsville Street, Greenville, KY, Zip 42345–1172, Mailing Address: P.O. Box 387, Zip 42345–0378; tel. 270/338–8000; Ed Heath, FACHE, Chief Executive Officer

RIVERVALLEY BEHAVIORAL HEALTH HOSPITAL, 1000 Industrial Drive, Owensboro, KY, Zip 42301–8715; tel. 270/689–6500; Gayle DiCesare, President and Chief Executive Officer

SAINT THOMAS WEST HOSPITAL, 4220 Harding Road, Nashville, TN, Zip 37205–2095, Mailing Address: P.O. Box 380, Zip 37202–0380; tel. 615/222–2111; Don King, Chief Executive Officer

ST. MARY'S MEDICAL CENTER OF EVANSVILLE, 3700 Washington Avenue, Evansville, IN, Zip 47714–0541; tel. 812/485–4000; Keith Jewell, President

STS. MARY & ELIZABETH HOSPITAL, 1850 Bluegrass Avenue, Louisville, KY, Zip 40215–1199; tel. 502/361–6000; Jennifer Nolan, President

TRIGG COUNTY HOSPITAL, 254 Main Street, Cadiz, KY, Zip 42211–9153, Mailing Address: P.O. Box 312, Zip 42211–0312; tel. 270/522–3215; John Sumner, Chief Executive Officer

KENTUCKYONE
200 Abraham Flexner Way, Louisville, KY 40202–2877; tel. 502/587–4011; Ruth W. Brinkley, RN, HSN, FACHE, President and Chief Executive Officer

CONTINUING CARE HOSPITAL, 150 North Eagle Creek Drive, 5th Floor, Lexington, KY, Zip 40509–1805; tel. 859/967–5744; Tonja Williams, R.N., President

FLAGET MEMORIAL HOSPITAL, 4305 New Shepherdsville Road, Bardstown, KY, Zip 40004–9019; tel. 502/350–5000; Beverly Sue Downs, R.N., MSN, FACHE, President

FRAZIER REHAB INSTITUTE, 220 Abraham Flexner Way, Louisville, KY, Zip 40202–1887; tel. 502/582–7400; Randy L. Napier, President

JEWISH HOSPITAL, 200 Abraham Flexner Way, Louisville, KY, Zip 40202–1886; tel. 502/587–4011; Joseph Gilene, President

JEWISH HOSPITAL–SHELBYVILLE, 727 Hospital Drive, Shelbyville, KY, Zip 40065–1699; tel. 502/647–4000; Tonya Brady, Director of Operations

OUR LADY OF PEACE, 2020 Newburg Road, Louisville, KY, Zip 40205–1879; tel. 502/479–4500; Jennifer Nolan, President

SAINT JOSEPH BEREA, 305 Estill Street, Berea, KY, Zip 40403–1909; tel. 859/986–3151; Eric Gilliam, Chief Executive Officer

SAINT JOSEPH EAST, 150 North Eagle Creek Drive, Lexington, KY, Zip 40509–1805; tel. 859/967–5000; Eric Gilliam, President

SAINT JOSEPH HOSPITAL, One St. Joseph Drive, Lexington, KY, Zip 40504–3754; tel. 859/278–3436; Bruce J. Tassin, President

SAINT JOSEPH LONDON, 1001 Saint Joseph Lane, London, KY, Zip 40741–8345; tel. 606/330–6000; Terrence G. Deis, CPA, FACHE, President

SAINT JOSEPH – MARTIN, 11203 Main Street, Martin, KY, Zip 41649; tel. 606/285–6400; Kathy Stumbo, President

SAINT JOSEPH MOUNT STERLING, 225 Falcon Drive, Mount Sterling, KY, Zip 40353–1158, Mailing Address: P.O. Box 7, Zip 40353–0007; tel. 859/497–5000; Benny Nolen, President

SOUTHERN INDIANA REHABILITATION HOSPITAL, 3104 Blackiston Boulevard, New Albany, IN, Zip 47150–9579; tel. 812/941–8300; Randy L. Napier, President

STS. MARY & ELIZABETH HOSPITAL, 1850 Bluegrass Avenue, Louisville, KY, Zip 40215–1199; tel. 502/361–6000; Jennifer Nolan, President

UNIVERSITY OF LOUISVILLE HOSPITAL, 530 South Jackson Street, Louisville, KY, Zip 40202–3611; tel. 502/562–3000; Charles W. Neumann, President

ST. ELIZABETH HEALTHCARE
1 Medical Village Drive, Edgewood, KY 41017–3403; tel. 859/301–2000; Garren Colvin, Chief Executive Officer

ST. ELIZABETH EDGEWOOD, 1 Medical Village Drive, Edgewood, KY, Zip 41017–3403; tel. 859/301–2000; Garren Colvin, Chief Executive Officer

ST. ELIZABETH FLORENCE, 4900 Houston Road, Florence, KY, Zip 41042–4824; tel. 859/212–5200; Garren Colvin, Chief Executive Officer

ST. ELIZABETH FORT THOMAS, 85 North Grand Avenue, Fort Thomas, KY, Zip 41075–1796; tel. 859/572–3100; Garren Colvin, Chief Executive Officer

ST. ELIZABETH GRANT, 238 Barnes Road, Williamstown, KY, Zip 41097–9482; tel. 859/824–8240; Garren Colvin, Chief Executive Officer

MAINE

MAINE NETWORK FOR HEALTH
Key Plaza, 23 Water Street, Bangor, ME 04401; tel. 207/942–2844; Stephen A. Ryan, President and Chief Executive Officer

BLUE HILL MEMORIAL HOSPITAL, 57 Water Street, Blue Hill, ME, Zip 04614–5231; tel. 207/374–3400; John Ronan, President and Chief Executive Officer

CHARLES A. DEAN MEMORIAL HOSPITAL, 364 Pritham Avenue, Greenville, ME, Zip 04441–1395, Mailing Address: P.O. Box 1129, Zip 04441–1129; tel. 207/695–5200; Geno Murray, President and Chief Executive Officer

EASTERN MAINE MEDICAL CENTER, 489 State Street, Bangor, ME, Zip 04401–6674, Mailing Address: P.O. Box 404, Zip 04402–0404; tel. 207/973–7000; Deborah Carey Johnson, R.N., President and Chief Executive Officer

HOULTON REGIONAL HOSPITAL, 20 Hartford Street, Houlton, ME, Zip 04730–1891; tel. 207/532–9471; Thomas J. Moakler, Chief Executive Officer

INLAND HOSPITAL, 200 Kennedy Memorial Drive, Waterville, ME, Zip 04901–4595; tel. 207/861–3000; John Dalton, President and Chief Executive Officer

MAYO REGIONAL HOSPITAL, 897 West Main Street, Dover–Foxcroft, ME, Zip 04426–1099; tel. 207/564–8401; Marie E. Vienneau, FACHE, President and Chief Executive Officer

MILLINOCKET REGIONAL HOSPITAL, 200 Somerset Street, Millinocket, ME, Zip 04462–1298; tel. 207/723–5161; Robert Peterson, Chief Executive Officer

MOUNT DESERT ISLAND HOSPITAL, 10 Wayman Lane, Bar Harbor, ME, Zip 04609–1625, Mailing Address: P.O. Box 8, Zip 04609–0008; tel. 207/288–5081; Arthur J. Blank, President and Chief Executive Officer

NORTHERN MAINE MEDICAL CENTER, 194 East Main Street, Fort Kent, ME, Zip 04743–1497; tel. 207/834–3155; Peter Sirois, Chief Executive Officer

SEBASTICOOK VALLEY HEALTH, 447 North Main Street, Pittsfield, ME, Zip 04967–3707; tel. 207/487–4000; Terri Vieira, President and Chief Executive Officer

THE ACADIA HOSPITAL, 268 Stillwater Avenue, Bangor, ME, Zip 04401–3945, Mailing Address: P.O. Box 422, Zip 04402–0422; tel. 207/973–6100; Daniel B. Coffey, President and Chief Executive Officer

THE AROOSTOOK MEDICAL CENTER, 140 Academy Street, Presque Isle, ME, Zip 04769–3171, Mailing Address: P.O. Box 151, Zip 04769–0151; tel. 207/768–4000; Glenda E. Dwyer, Interim President

MASSACHUSETTS

LAHEY HEALTH
41 Mall Road, Burlington, MA 01805–0001; tel. 781/744–7100; Howard R. Grant, JD, M.D., President and Chief Executive Officer

BEVERLY HOSPITAL, 85 Herrick Street, Beverly, MA, Zip 01915–1777; tel. 978/922–3000; Philip M. Cormier, Chief Executive Officer

LAHEY HOSPITAL & MEDICAL CENTER, BURLINGTON, 41 Mall Road, Burlington, MA, Zip 01805–0001; tel. 781/744–5100; Joanne Conroy, M.D., Chief Executive Officer

WINCHESTER HOSPITAL, 41 Highland Avenue, Winchester, MA, Zip 01890–1496; tel. 781/729–9000; Dale M. Lodge, Chief Executive Officer

WELLFORCE
1600 District Avenue, Suite 125, Burlington, MA 01803–5217; tel. 978/942–2220; Normand E. Deschene, FACHE, Chief Executive Officer

LOWELL GENERAL HOSPITAL, 295 Varnum Avenue, Lowell, MA, Zip 01854–2134; tel. 978/937–6000; Normand E. Deschene, FACHE, Chief Executive Officer

TUFTS MEDICAL CENTER, 800 Washington Street, Boston, MA, Zip 02111–1552; tel. 617/636–5000; Michael Wagner, M.D., President and Chief Executive Officer

MICHIGAN

GENESYS HEALTH SYSTEM
1 Genesys Parkway, Grand Blanc, MI 48439–8065; tel. 810/606–5000; Elizabeth Aderholdt, Chief Executive Officer

ST. JOHN MACOMB–OAKLAND HOSPITAL, 11800 East 12 Mile Road, Warren, MI, Zip 48093–3472; tel. 586/573–5000; Terry Hamilton, President

ST. JOSEPH HEALTH SYSTEM, 200 Hemlock Street, Tawas City, MI, Zip 48763–9237, Mailing Address: P.O. Box 659, Zip 48764–0659; tel. 989/362–3411; Ann M. Balfour, R.N., President

ST. MARY'S OF MICHIGAN, 800 South Washington Avenue, Saginaw, MI, Zip 48601–2594; tel. 989/907–8000; Chris Palazzolo, Health System President and Chief Executive Officer Mid–Michigan

LAKELAND REGIONAL HEALTH SYSTEM
1234 Napier Avenue, Saint Joseph, MI 49085–2112; tel. 269/983–8300; Loren Hamel, M.D., President and Chief Executive Officer

LAKELAND HOSPITAL, WATERVLIET, 400 Medical Park Drive, Watervliet, MI, Zip 49098–9225; tel. 269/463–3111; Ray Cruse, Chief Executive Officer

LAKELAND MEDICAL CENTER, ST. JOSEPH, 1234 Napier Avenue, Saint Joseph, MI, Zip 49085–2158; tel. 269/983–8300; Loren Hamel, M.D., Chief Executive Officer

ST. JOHN PROVIDENCE HEALTH SYSTEM
28000 Dequindre Drive, Warren, MI 48092; tel. 866/501–3627; Jean Meyer, President and Chief Executive Officer

BRIGHTON CENTER FOR RECOVERY, 12851 Grand River Road, Brighton, MI, Zip 48116–8506; tel. 810/227–1211; Raymond A. Waller, Director

PROVIDENCE – PROVIDENCE PARK HOSPITAL, SOUTHFIELD CAMPUS, 16001 West Nine Mile Road, Southfield, MI, Zip 48075–4818, Mailing Address: P.O. Box 2043, Zip 48037–2043; tel. 248/424–3000; Michael Wiemann, M.D., President

ST. JOHN HOSPITAL AND MEDICAL CENTER, 22101 Moross Road, Detroit, MI, Zip 48236–2148; tel. 313/343–4000; Robert E. Hoban, Chief Executive Officer

ST. JOHN MACOMB–OAKLAND HOSPITAL, 11800 East 12 Mile Road, Warren, MI, Zip 48093–3472; tel. 586/573–5000; Terry Hamilton, President

ST. JOHN RIVER DISTRICT HOSPITAL, 4100 River Road, East China, MI, Zip 48054–2909; tel. 810/329–7111; Frank W. Poma, President

UPPER PENINSULA HEALTH CARE NETWORK (UPHCN)
228 West Washington Street, Marquette, MI 49855–4330;
tel. 906/225–3146; Dennis Smith, Chief Executive Officer

ASPIRUS GRAND VIEW, N10561 Grand View Lane, Ironwood, MI, Zip 49938–9622; tel. 906/932–2525; Paula L. Chermside, Chief Executive Officer

ASPIRUS IRON RIVER HOSPITALS & CLINICS, 1400 West Ice Lake Road, Iron River, MI, Zip 49935–9526; tel. 906/265–6121; Connie L. Koutouzos, R.N., MSN, Chief Executive Officer

ASPIRUS KEWEENAW HOSPITAL, 205 Osceola Street, Laurium, MI, Zip 49913–2134; tel. 906/337–6500; Michael Hauswirth, Chief Operating Officer

ASPIRUS ONTONAGON HOSPITAL, 601 South Seventh Street, Ontonagon, MI, Zip 49953–1459; tel. 906/884–8000; Michael Hauswirth, Chief Operating Officer

BARAGA COUNTY MEMORIAL HOSPITAL, 18341 U.S. Highway 41, L'Anse, MI, Zip 49946–8024; tel. 906/524–3300; Margie Hale, R.N., MSN, Chief Executive Officer

DICKINSON COUNTY HEALTHCARE SYSTEM, 1721 South Stephenson Avenue, Iron Mountain, MI, Zip 49801–3637; tel. 906/774–1313; John Schon, Administrator and Chief Executive Officer

HELEN NEWBERRY JOY HOSPITAL, 502 West Harrie Street, Newberry, MI, Zip 49868–1209; tel. 906/293–9200; Scott Pillion, Chief Executive Officer

MACKINAC STRAITS HEALTH SYSTEM, INC., 1140 North State Street, Saint Ignace, MI, Zip 49781–1048; tel. 906/643–8585; Rodney M. Nelson, Chief Executive Officer

MUNISING MEMORIAL HOSPITAL, 1500 Sand Point Road, Munising, MI, Zip 49862–1406; tel. 906/387–4110; Kevin P. Calhoun, Chief Executive Officer

SCHOOLCRAFT MEMORIAL HOSPITAL, 7870W U.S. Highway 2, Manistique, MI, Zip 49854–8992; tel. 906/341–3200; Robert Crumb, Chief Executive Officer

UP HEALTH SYSTEM–BELL, 901 Lakeshore Drive, Ishpeming, MI, Zip 49849–1367; tel. 906/486–4431; Mitchell D. Leckelt, Chief Executive Officer

UP HEALTH SYSTEM–PORTAGE, 500 Campus Drive, Hancock, MI, Zip 49930–1569; tel. 906/483–1000; Jeff Lang, President

WAR MEMORIAL HOSPITAL, 500 Osborn Boulevard, Sault Sainte Marie, MI, Zip 49783–1884; tel. 906/635–4460; David B. Jahn, President and Chief Executive Officer

MINNESOTA

NORTHWEST METRO ALLIANCE
c/O Mercy Hospital, 4050 Coon Rapids Boulevard, Coon Rapids, MN
55433–2586; tel. 763/236–6000; Sara J. Criger, President

ABBOTT NORTHWESTERN HOSPITAL, 800 East 28th Street, Minneapolis, MN, Zip 55407–3799; tel. 612/863–4000; Ben Bache–Wiig, M.D., President

AMERY HOSPITAL AND CLINIC, 265 Griffin Street East, Amery, WI, Zip 54001–1439; tel. 715/268–8000; Debra Rudquist, FACHE, President and Chief Executive Officer

BUFFALO HOSPITAL, 303 Catlin Street, Buffalo, MN, Zip 55313–1947; tel. 763/682–1212; Jennifer Myster, President

CAMBRIDGE MEDICAL CENTER, 701 South Dellwood Street, Cambridge, MN, Zip 55008–1920; tel. 763/689–7700; Gary Shaw, President

DISTRICT ONE HOSPITAL, 200 State Avenue, Faribault, MN, Zip 55021–6345; tel. 507/334–6451; Stephen J. Pribyl, FACHE, President

GLENCOE REGIONAL HEALTH SERVICES, 1805 Hennepin Avenue North, Glencoe, MN, Zip 55336–1416; tel. 320/864–3121; Jon D. Braband, FACHE, President and Chief Executive Officer

HUDSON HOSPITAL AND CLINIC, 405 Stageline Road, Hudson, WI, Zip 54016–7848; tel. 715/531–6000; Marian M. Furlong, R.N., FACHE, Chief Executive Officer

HUTCHINSON HEALTH, 1095 Highway 15 South, Hutchinson, MN, Zip 55350–3182; tel. 320/234–5000; Steven Mulder, M.D., President and Chief Executive Officer

LAKEVIEW HOSPITAL, 927 Churchill Street West, Stillwater, MN, Zip 55082–6605; tel. 651/439–5330; Theodore Wegleitner, Chief Executive Officer

MERCY HOSPITAL, 4050 Coon Rapids Boulevard, Coon Rapids, MN, Zip 55433–2586; tel. 763/236–6000; Sara J. Criger, President

NEW ULM MEDICAL CENTER, 1324 Fifth Street North, New Ulm, MN, Zip 56073–1553; tel. 507/217–5000; Toby Freier, President

OWATONNA HOSPITAL, 2250 N.W. 26th Street, Owatonna, MN, Zip 55060–5503; tel. 507/451–3850; David L. Albrecht, President

PARK NICOLLET METHODIST HOSPITAL, 6500 Excelsior Boulevard, Saint Louis Park, MN, Zip 55426–4702; Mailing Address: Minneapolis, tel. 952/993–5000; Steven Connelly, M.D., President and Chief Medical Officer

PHILLIPS EYE INSTITUTE, 2215 Park Avenue, Minneapolis, MN, Zip 55404–3756; tel. 612/775–8800; Daniel S. Conrad, M.D., President

REGINA HOSPITAL, 1175 Nininger Road, Hastings, MN, Zip 55033–1098; tel. 651/480–4100; Thomas R. Thompson, Chief Executive Officer

REGIONS HOSPITAL, 640 Jackson Street, Saint Paul, MN, Zip 55101–2595; tel. 651/254–3456; Megan Remark, Chief Executive Officer

RIVER FALLS AREA HOSPITAL, 1629 East Division Street, River Falls, WI, Zip 54022–1571; tel. 715/425–6155; David R. Miller, President

ST. FRANCIS REGIONAL MEDICAL CENTER, 1455 St. Francis Avenue, Shakopee, MN, Zip 55379–3380; tel. 952/428–3000; Mike McMahan, President

UNITED HOSPITAL, 333 North Smith Avenue, Saint Paul, MN, Zip 55102–2389; tel. 651/241–8000; Thomas O'Connor, President

UNITY HOSPITAL, 550 Osborne Road N.E., Fridley, MN, Zip 55432–2799; tel. 763/236–5000; Helen J. Strike, R.N., President

WESTFIELDS HOSPITAL, 535 Hospital Road, New Richmond, WI, Zip 54017–1449; tel. 715/243–2600; Steven Massey, President and Chief Executive Officer

MISSOURI

HEALTH NETWORK OF MISSOURI
One Hospital Drive, Room C1213, DC 079.00, Columbia, MO 65212;
tel. 573/815–8000; Marty McCormick, Chief Executive Officer

BOTHWELL REGIONAL HEALTH CENTER, 601 East 14th Street, Sedalia, MO, Zip 65301–5972, Mailing Address: P.O. Box 1706, Zip 65302–1706; tel. 660/826–8833; James A. Robertson, Jr., Chief Executive Officer

CAPITAL REGION MEDICAL CENTER, 1125 Madison Street, Jefferson City, MO, Zip 65101–5200, Mailing Address: P.O. Box 1128, Zip 65102–1128; tel. 573/632–5000; Gaspare Calvaruso, President

HANNIBAL REGIONAL HOSPITAL, 6000 Hospital Drive, Hannibal, MO, Zip 63401–6887, Mailing Address: P.O. Box 551, Zip 63401–0551; tel. 573/248–1300; C. Todd Ahrens, President and Chief Executive Officer

LAKE REGIONAL HEALTH SYSTEM, 54 Hospital Drive, Osage Beach, MO, Zip 65065–3050; tel. 573/348–8000; Michael E. Henze, Chief Executive Officer

SAINT FRANCIS HEALTHCARE SYSTEM, 211 St. Francis Drive, Cape Girardeau, MO, Zip 63703–5049; tel. 573/331–3000; Steven C. Bjelich, President and Chief Executive Officer

UNIVERSITY OF MISSOURI HOSPITALS AND CLINICS, One Hospital Drive, Columbia, MO, Zip 65212–0001; tel. 573/882–4141; Mitchell L. Wasden, Ed.D., Chief Executive Officer and Chief Operating Officer

MERCY HEALTH EAST
615 South New Ballas Road, Saint Louis, MO 63141–8221;
tel. 314/364–3000; Donn Sorensen, President, East Region

MERCY HOSPITAL JEFFERSON, Highway 61 South, Crystal City, MO, Zip 63019, Mailing Address: P.O. Box 350, Zip 63019–0350; tel. 636/933–1000; Eric Ammons, President

MERCY HOSPITAL ST. LOUIS, 615 South New Ballas Road, Saint Louis, MO, Zip 63141–8277; tel. 314/569–6000; Jeffrey A. Johnston, President

MERCY HOSPITAL WASHINGTON, 901 East Fifth Street, Washington, MO, Zip 63090–3127; tel. 636/239–8000; Eric J. Eoloff, President

MOSAIC LIFE CARE
5325 Faraon Street, Saint Joseph, MO 64506–3488;
tel. 816/271–6000; Brady Dubois, President

LONG–TERM ACUTE CARE HOSPITAL, MOSAIC LIFE CARE AT ST. JOSEPH, 5325 Faraon Street, Saint Joseph, MO, Zip 64506–3488; tel. 816/271–6000; Dana Anderson, Administrator

MOSAIC LIFE CARE AT ST. JOSEPH, 5325 Faraon Street, Saint Joseph, MO, Zip 64506–3488; tel. 816/271–6000; Samuel Mark Laney, M.D., Chief Executive Officer

NORTHWEST MEDICAL CENTER, 705 North College Street, Albany, MO, Zip 64402–1433; tel. 660/726–3941; Jon D. Doolittle, President and Chief Executive Officer

MONTANA

MONTANA HEALTH NETWORK
11 South 7th Street, Suite 241, Miles City, MT 59301;
tel. 406/234–1420; Janet Bastian, Chief Executive Officer

BEARTOOTH BILLINGS CLINIC, 2525 North Broadway Avenue, Red Lodge, MT, Zip 59068–9222, Mailing Address: P.O. Box 590, Zip 59068–0590; tel. 406/446–2345; Kelley Evans, Chief Administrative Officer

BILLINGS CLINIC, 2800 10th Avenue North, Billings, MT, Zip 59101–0703, Mailing Address: P.O. Box 37000, Zip 59107–7000; tel. 406/657–4000; Nicholas Wolter, M.D., Chief Executive Officer

CENTRAL MONTANA MEDICAL CENTER, 408 Wendell Avenue, Lewistown, MT, Zip 59457–2261; tel. 406/535–7711; Michael Dowdy, Chief Executive Officer

DANIELS MEMORIAL HEALTHCARE CENTER, 105 Fifth Avenue East, Scobey, MT, Zip 59263, Mailing Address: P.O. Box 400, Zip 59263–0400; tel. 406/487–2296; David Hubbard, Chief Executive Officer

FALLON MEDICAL COMPLEX, 202 South 4th Street West, Baker, MT, Zip 59313–9156, Mailing Address: P.O. Box 820, Zip 59313–0820; tel. 406/778–3331; David Espeland, Chief Executive Officer

FRANCES MAHON DEACONESS HOSPITAL, 621 Third Street South, Glasgow, MT, Zip 59230–2699; tel. 406/228–3500; Randall G. Holom, Chief Executive Officer

GLENDIVE MEDICAL CENTER, 202 Prospect Drive, Glendive, MT, Zip 59330–1999; tel. 406/345–3306; Parker Powell, Chief Executive Officer

HOLY ROSARY HEALTHCARE, 2600 Wilson Street, Miles City, MT,. Zip 59301–5094; tel. 406/233–2600; Paul Lewis, Chief Executive Officer

MCCONE COUNTY HEALTH CENTER, 605 Sullivan Avenue, Circle, MT, Zip 59215, Mailing Address: P.O. Box 48, Zip 59215–0048; tel. 406/485–3381; Nancy Rosaaen, Chief Executive Officer

PHILLIPS COUNTY HOSPITAL, 311 South 8th Avenue East, Malta, MT, Zip 59538–0640, Mailing Address: P.O. Box 640, Zip 59538–0640; tel. 406/654–1100; Ward C. VanWichen, Chief Executive Officer

ROOSEVELT MEDICAL CENTER, 818 Second Avenue East, Culbertson, MT, Zip 59218, Mailing Address: P.O. Box 419, Zip 59218–0419; tel. 406/787–6401; Audrey Stromberg, Administrator

ROUNDUP MEMORIAL HEALTHCARE, 1202 Third Street West, Roundup, MT, Zip 59072–1816, Mailing Address: P.O. Box 40, Zip 59072–0040; tel. 406/323–2301; Bradley Howell, Chief Executive Officer

SHERIDAN MEMORIAL HOSPITAL, 440 West Laurel Avenue, Plentywood, MT, Zip 59254–1596; tel. 406/765–3700; Gregory L. Maurer, Chief Executive Officer

SIDNEY HEALTH CENTER, 216 14th Avenue S.W., Sidney, MT, Zip 59270–3586; tel. 406/488–2100; Richard Haraldson, Chief Executive Officer

STILLWATER COMMUNITY HOSPITAL, 44 West Fourth Avenue North, Columbus, MT, Zip 59019–0959, Mailing Address: P.O. Box 959, Zip 59019–0959; tel. 406/322–5316; Kelley Evans, Chief Administrative Officer

NEBRASKA

BLUE RIVER VALLEY HEALTH NETWORK
2222 North Lincoln Avenue, York, NE 68467–1030; tel. 402/362–0445; Charles K. Schulz, President

ANNIE JEFFREY MEMORIAL COUNTY HEALTH CENTER, 531 Beebe Street, Osceola, NE, Zip 68651–5537, Mailing Address: P.O. Box 428, Zip 68651–0428; tel. 402/747–2031; Joseph W. Lohrman, Chief Executive Officer

BOONE COUNTY HEALTH CENTER, 723 West Fairview Street, Albion, NE, Zip 68620–1725, Mailing Address: P.O. Box 151, Zip 68620–0151; tel. 402/395–2191; Victor N. Lee, FACHE, President and Chief Executive Officer

BRODSTONE MEMORIAL HOSPITAL, 520 East Tenth Street, Superior, NE, Zip 68978–1225, Mailing Address: P.O. Box 187, Zip 68978–0187; tel. 402/879–3281; John E. Keelan, Administrator and Chief Executive Officer

BUTLER COUNTY HEALTH CARE CENTER, 372 South Ninth Street, David City, NE, Zip 68632–2116; tel. 402/367–1200; Donald T. Naiberk, Administrator

COMMUNITY MEMORIAL HOSPITAL, 1579 Midland Street, Syracuse, NE, Zip 68446–9732, Mailing Address: P.O. Box N., Zip 68446–0518; tel. 402/269–2011; Michael Harvey, FACHE, President and Chief Executive Officer

CRETE AREA MEDICAL CENTER, 2910 Betten Drive, Crete, NE, Zip 68333–3084, Mailing Address: P.O. Box 220, Zip 68333–0220; tel. 402/826–2102; Rebekah Mussman, Chief Executive Officer

FILLMORE COUNTY HOSPITAL, 1900 F Street, Geneva, NE, Zip 68361–1325, Mailing Address: P.O. Box 193, Zip 68361–0193; tel. 402/759–3167; Paul Utemark, Chief Executive Officer

FRIEND COMMUNITY HEALTHCARE SYSTEM, 905 Second Street, Friend, NE, Zip 68359–1133; tel. 402/947–2541; Chad Thompson, Chief Executive Officer

HENDERSON HEALTH CARE SERVICES, 1621 Front Street, Henderson, NE, Zip 68371–8902; tel. 402/723–4512; Cheryl Brown, Administrator

HOWARD COUNTY MEDICAL CENTER, 1113 Sherman Street, Saint Paul, NE, Zip 68873–1546, Mailing Address: P.O. Box 406, Zip 68873–0406; tel. 308/754–4421; Arlan D. Johnson, Chief Executive Officer

JEFFERSON COMMUNITY HEALTH CENTER, 2200 H Street, Fairbury, NE, Zip 68352–1119, Mailing Address: P.O. Box 277, Zip 68352–0277; tel. 402/729–3351; Chad Jurgens, Chief Executive Officer

JOHNSON COUNTY HOSPITAL, 202 High Street, Tecumseh, NE, Zip 68450–2443, Mailing Address: P.O. Box 599, Zip 68450–0599; tel. 402/335–3361; Diane Newman, FACHE, Administrator

LITZENBERG MEMORIAL COUNTY HOSPITAL, 1715 26th Street, Central City, NE, Zip 68826–9620; tel. 308/946–3015; Julie Murray, Chief Executive Officer

MEMORIAL COMMUNITY HEALTH, 1423 Seventh Street, Aurora, NE, Zip 68818–1197; tel. 402/694–3171; Diane R. Keller, Chief Executive Officer

MEMORIAL HEALTH CARE SYSTEMS, 300 North Columbia Avenue, Seward, NE, Zip 68434–2228; tel. 402/643–2971; Roger J. Reamer, Chief Executive Officer

THAYER COUNTY HEALTH SERVICES, 120 Park Avenue, Hebron, NE, Zip 68370–2019, Mailing Address: P.O. Box 49, Zip 68370–0049; tel. 402/768–6041; Michael G. Burcham, Sr., FACHE, Chief Executive Officer

VALLEY COUNTY HEALTH SYSTEM, 2707 L. Street, Ord, NE, Zip 68862–1275; tel. 308/728–4200; Nancy Glaubke, Chief Executive Officer

YORK GENERAL HOSPITAL, 2222 North Lincoln Avenue, York, NE, Zip 68467–1095; tel. 402/362–6671; Charles K. Schulz, Chief Executive Officer

CHI HEALTH
12809 West Dodge Road, Omaha, NE 68154–2155; tel. 402/343–4300; Cliff Robertson, M.D., President and Chief Executive Officer

CHI HEALTH BERGAN MERCY, 7500 Mercy Road, Omaha, NE, Zip 68124–2319; tel. 402/398–6060; Marie E. Knedler, R.N., FACHE, President

CHI HEALTH GOOD SAMARITAN, 10 East 31st Street, Kearney, NE, Zip 68847–2926, Mailing Address: P.O. Box 1990, Zip 68848–1990; tel. 308/865–7100; Michael H. Schnieders, FACHE, President

CHI HEALTH IMMANUEL, 6901 North 72nd Street, Omaha, NE, Zip 68122–1799; tel. 402/572–2121; Ann Schumacher, R.N., MSN, FACHE, President

CHI HEALTH LAKESIDE, 16901 Lakeside Hills Court, Omaha, NE, Zip 68130–2318; tel. 402/717–8000; Cindy Alloway, President

CHI HEALTH MERCY CORNING, 603 Rosary Drive, Corning, IA, Zip 50841–1683; tel. 641/322–3121; Debra Goldsmith, Chief Executive Officer

CHI HEALTH MERCY COUNCIL BLUFFS, 800 Mercy Drive, Council Bluffs, IA, Zip 51503–3128, Mailing Address: P.O. Box 1C, Zip 51502–3001; tel. 712/328–5000; Marie E. Knedler, R.N., FACHE, President

CHI HEALTH MIDLANDS, 11111 South 84th Street, Papillion, NE, Zip 68046–4122; tel. 402/593–3000; Cindy Alloway, President

CHI HEALTH MISSOURI VALLEY, 631 North Eighth Street, Missouri Valley, IA, Zip 51555–1102; tel. 712/642–2784; Robert A. Valentine, President

CHI HEALTH NEBRASKA HEART, 7500 South 91st Street, Lincoln, NE, Zip 68526–9437; tel. 402/327–2700; Dan Schonlau, Interim President

CHI HEALTH PLAINVIEW, 704 North Third Street, Plainview, NE, Zip 68769–2047, Mailing Address: P.O. Box 489, Zip 68769–0489; tel. 402/582–4245; Gregory Beckmann, Chief Executive Officer

CHI HEALTH SAINT FRANCIS, 2620 West Faidley Avenue, Grand Island, NE, Zip 68803–4297, Mailing Address: P.O. Box 9804, Zip 68802–9804; tel. 308/384–4600; Daniel P. McElligott, FACHE, President

CHI HEALTH SCHUYLER, 104 West 17th Street, Schuyler, NE, Zip 68661–1304; tel. 402/352–2441; Connie Peters, R.N., President

CHI HEALTH ST ELIZABETH, 555 South 70th Street, Lincoln, NE, Zip 68510–2494; tel. 402/219–8000; Kim S. Moore, FACHE, President

CHI HEALTH ST. MARY'S, 1301 Grundman Boulevard, Nebraska City, NE, Zip 68410; tel. 402/873–3321; Daniel J. Kelly, President

NEBRASKA MEDICINE
987400 Nebraska Medical Center, Omaha, NE 68198–7400; tel. 877/763–0000; Daniel J. DeBehnke, M.D., Chief Executive Officer

NEBRASKA MEDICINE – BELLEVUE, 2500 Bellevue Medical Center Drive, Bellevue, NE, Zip 68123–1591; tel. 402/763–3000; Matt E. Pospisil, Vice President, Clinical Operations

NEBRASKA MEDICINE – NEBRASKA MEDICAL CENTER, 987400 Nebraska Medical Center, Omaha, NE, Zip 68198–7400; tel. 402/552–2000; Daniel J. DeBehnke, M.D., Chief Executive Officer

NORTHEAST HEALTH SERVICES
PO Box 186, Creighton, NE 68729–0186; tel. 402/358–5700; Jennifer Neukirch, Chief Executive Officer

AVERA CREIGHTON HOSPITAL, 1503 Main Street, Creighton, NE, Zip 68729–3007, Mailing Address: P.O. Box 186, Zip 68729–0186; tel. 402/358–5700; Jennifer Neukirch, Chief Executive Officer

CHI HEALTH PLAINVIEW, 704 North Third Street, Plainview, NE, Zip 68769–2047, Mailing Address: P.O. Box 489, Zip 68769–0489; tel. 402/582–4245; Gregory Beckmann, Chief Executive Officer

OSMOND GENERAL HOSPITAL, 402 North Maple Street, Osmond, NE, Zip 68765–5726, Mailing Address: P.O. Box 429, Zip 68765–0429; tel. 402/748–3393; Lon Knievel, Chief Executive Officer

NEW HAMPSHIRE

CARING COMMUNITY NETWORK OF THE TWIN RIVERS
c/o First Health, 841 Central Street, Franklin, NH 03235–2026; tel. 603/934–0177; Rick Silverberg, Managing Director

FRANKLIN REGIONAL HOSPITAL, 15 Aiken Avenue, Franklin, NH, Zip 03235–1299; tel. 603/934–2060; Kevin Donovan, Chief Executive Officer

NEW JERSEY

QUALCARE, INC.
242 Old New Brunswick Road, Piscataway, NJ 08854–3754; tel. 732/562–2800; Jerry Eisenberg, Network Contact

CAPITAL HEALTH MEDICAL CENTER–HOPEWELL, 1 Capital Way, Pennington, NJ, Zip 08534–2520; tel. 609/303–4000; Al Maghazehe, Ph.D., FACHE, President and Chief Executive Officer

CAREPOINT HEALTH –CHRIST HOSPITAL, 176 Palisade Avenue, Jersey City, NJ, Zip 07306–1196, Mailing Address: 176 Palisades Avenue, Zip 07306–1196; tel. 201/795–8200; Marie Theresa Duffy, Chief Operating Officer

CHILTON MEDICAL CENTER, 97 West Parkway, Pompton Plains, NJ, Zip 07444–1696; tel. 973/831–5000; Stephanie L. Bloom, FACHE, President

CLARA MAASS MEDICAL CENTER, One Clara Maass Drive, Belleville, NJ, Zip 07109–3557; tel. 973/450–2000; Mary Ellen Clyne, MSN, Ph.D., R.N., President and Chief Executive Officer

DEBORAH HEART AND LUNG CENTER, 200 Trenton Road, Browns Mills, NJ, Zip 08015–1705; tel. 609/893–6611; Joseph Chirichella, President and Chief Executive Officer

ENGLEWOOD HOSPITAL AND MEDICAL CENTER, 350 Engle Street, Englewood, NJ, Zip 07631–1898; tel. 201/894–3000; Warren Geller, President and Chief Executive Officer

HACKENSACK UNIVERSITY MEDICAL CENTER, 30 Prospect Avenue, Hackensack, NJ, Zip 07601–1914; tel. 201/996–2000; Ihor S. Sawczuk, M.D., President

HACKETTSTOWN MEDICAL CENTER, 651 Willow Grove Street, Hackettstown, NJ, Zip 07840–1799; tel. 908/852–5100; Jason C. Coe, President

INSPIRA MEDICAL CENTER–VINELAND, 1505 West Sherman Avenue, Vineland, NJ, Zip 08360–6912; tel. 856/641–8000; John A. DiAngelo, President and Chief Executive Officer

JFK MEDICAL CENTER, 65 James Street, Edison, NJ, Zip 08818; tel. 732/321–7000; Raymond F. Fredericks, President and CEO

MEMORIAL HOSPITAL OF SALEM COUNTY, 310 Woodstown Road, Salem, NJ, Zip 08079–2080; tel. 856/935–1000; Ryan Jensen, Chief Executive Officer

OCEAN MEDICAL CENTER, 425 Jack Martin Boulevard, Brick Township, NJ, Zip 08724–7732; tel. 732/840–2200; Dean Q. Lin, FACHE, President

PIEDMONT MOUNTAINSIDE HOSPITAL, 1266 Highway 515 South, Jasper, GA, Zip 30143–4872; tel. 706/692–2441; Denise Ray, President and Chief Executive Officer

RARITAN BAY MEDICAL CENTER, 530 New Brunswick Avenue, Perth Amboy, NJ, Zip 08861–3654; tel. 732/442–3700; Michael R. D'Agnes, FACHE, President and Chief Executive Officer

RIVERVIEW MEDICAL CENTER, 1 Riverview Plaza, Red Bank, NJ, Zip 07701–1864; tel. 732/741–2700; Timothy J. Hogan, FACHE, Regional President

ROBERT WOOD JOHNSON UNIVERSITY HOSPITAL, 1 Robert Wood Johnson Place, New Brunswick, NJ, Zip 08901–1928; tel. 732/828–3000; Michael A. Antoniades, President and Chief Executive Officer

SAINT MICHAEL'S MEDICAL CENTER, 111 Central Avenue, Newark, NJ, Zip 07102–1909; tel. 973/877–5350; Robert C. Iannaccone, Chief Executive Officer

ST. MARY'S GENERAL HOSPITAL, 350 Boulevard, Passaic, NJ, Zip 07055–2840; tel. 973/365–4300; Edward Condit, President and Chief Executive Officer

UNIVERSITY HOSPITAL, 150 Bergen Street, Newark, NJ, Zip 07103–2496; tel. 973/972–4300; John N. Kastanis, FACHE, President and Chief Executive Officer

UNIVERSITY MEDICAL CENTER OF PRINCETON AT PLAINSBORO, One Plainsboro Road, Plainsboro, NJ, Zip 08536–1913; tel. 609/853–7100; Barry S. Rabner, President and Chief Executive Officer, Princeton Healthcare System

VIRTUA MARLTON, 90 Brick Road, Marlton, NJ, Zip 08053–2177; tel. 856/355–6000; Matthew Zuino, Senior Vice President Hospital Services

NEW MEXICO

NEW MEXICO RURAL HOSPITAL NETWORK
7471 Pan American Freeway N.E., Albuquerque, NM 87109; tel. 505/346–0216; Stephen Stoddard, FACHE, Executive Director

ARTESIA GENERAL HOSPITAL, 702 North 13th Street, Artesia, NM, Zip 88210–1199; tel. 575/748–3333; Kenneth W. Randall, Chief Executive Officer

CIBOLA GENERAL HOSPITAL, 1016 East Roosevelt Avenue, Grants, NM, Zip 87020–2118; tel. 505/287–4446; Thomas Whelan, Chief Executive Officer

GUADALUPE COUNTY HOSPITAL, 117 Camino de Vida, Santa Rosa, NM, Zip 88435–2267; tel. 575/472–3417; Christina Campos, Administrator

HOLY CROSS HOSPITAL, 1397 Weimer Road, Taos, NM, Zip 87571–6253; tel. 575/758–8883; William D. Patten, Jr., Chief Executive Officer

MINERS' COLFAX MEDICAL CENTER, 200 Hospital Drive, Raton, NM, Zip 87740–2099; tel. 575/445–7700; Shawn Lerch, Chief Executive Officer

NOR–LEA GENERAL HOSPITAL, 1600 North Main Avenue, Lovington, NM, Zip 88260–2871; tel. 575/396–6611; David B. Shaw, Chief Executive Officer and Administrator

REHOBOTH MCKINLEY CHRISTIAN HEALTH CARE SERVICES, 1901 Red Rock Drive, Gallup, NM, Zip 87301–5683; tel. 505/863–7000; David Conejo, Chief Executive Officer

ROOSEVELT GENERAL HOSPITAL, 42121 U.S. Highway 70, Portales, NM, Zip 88130, Mailing Address: P.O. Box 868, Zip 88130–0868; tel. 575/359–1800; Larry E. Leaming, Ph.D., FACHE, Chief Executive Officer

SIERRA VISTA HOSPITAL, 800 East Ninth Avenue, Truth or Consequences, NM, Zip 87901–1961; tel. 575/894–2111; Michael P. Zimmerman, Chief Executive Officer

UNION COUNTY GENERAL HOSPITAL, 300 Wilson Street, Clayton, NM, Zip 88415–3304, Mailing Address: P.O. Box 489, Zip 88415–0489; tel. 575/374–2585; Jerry Wiesner, Chief Executive Officer

NEW YORK

ARDENT SOLUTIONS, INC.
85 North Main Street, Suite 4, Wellsville, NY 14895–1254; tel. 585/593–5223; Carrie Whitwood, Executive Director

JONES MEMORIAL HOSPITAL, 191 North Main Street, Wellsville, NY, Zip 14895–1150, Mailing Address: P.O. Box 72, Zip 14895–0072; tel. 585/593–1100; Eva Benedict, R.N., President and Chief Executive Officer

ST. JAMES MERCY HOSPITAL, 411 Canisteo Street, Hornell, NY, Zip 14843–2197; tel. 607/324–8000; Jennifer Sullivan, President and Chief Executive Officer

ARNOT HEALTH
600 Roe Avenue, Elmira, NY 14905–1629; tel. 607/737–4100; Richard Cleland, FACHE, Site Administrator

ARNOT OGDEN MEDICAL CENTER, 600 Roe Avenue, Elmira, NY, Zip 14905–1629; tel. 607/737–4100; Kerry Watson, Interim President and Chief Operating Officer

IRA DAVENPORT MEMORIAL HOSPITAL, 7571 State Route 54, Bath, NY, Zip 14810–9590; tel. 607/776–8500; Joseph Braunscheidel, Acting President

ST. JOSEPH'S HOSPITAL, 555 St. Joseph's Boulevard, Elmira, NY, Zip 14901–3223; tel. 607/733–6541; Kerry Watson, Interim President and Chief Operating Officer

BASSETT HEALTHCARE NETWORK
1 Atwell Road, Cooperstown, NY 13326–1301; tel. 607/547–3456; Vance Brown, M.D., President and Chief Executive Officer

AURELIA OSBORN FOX MEMORIAL HOSPITAL, 1 Norton Avenue, Oneonta, NY, Zip 13820–2629; tel. 607/432–2000; Jeff Joyner, President

BASSETT MEDICAL CENTER, One Atwell Road, Cooperstown, NY, Zip 13326–1394; tel. 607/547–3100; Vance Brown, M.D., President and Chief Executive Officer

COBLESKILL REGIONAL HOSPITAL, 178 Grandview Drive, Cobleskill, NY, Zip 12043–5144; tel. 518/254–3456; Eric H. Stein, FACHE, President and Chief Executive Officer

LITTLE FALLS HOSPITAL, 140 Burwell Street, Little Falls, NY, Zip 13365–1725; tel. 315/823–1000; Michael L. Ogden, President and Chief Executive Officer

O'CONNOR HOSPITAL, 460 Andes Road, State Route 28, Delhi, NY, Zip 13753–7407; tel. 607/746–0300; Carlton Rule, M.D., Chief Executive Officer

GREAT LAKES HEALTH SYSTEM OF WESTERN NEW YORK
726 Exchange Street, Suite 522, Buffalo, NY 14210–1485; tel. 716/859–8820; Jody Lomeo, Interim Chief Executive Officer

ERIE COUNTY MEDICAL CENTER, 462 Grider Street, Buffalo, NY, Zip 14215–3098; tel. 716/898–3000; Thomas J. Quatroche, Jr., Chief Executive Officer

KALEIDA HEALTH, 100 High Street, Buffalo, NY, Zip 14203–1154; tel. 716/859–5600; Jody Lomeo, Chief Executive Officer

LAKE ERIE REGIONAL HEALTH SYSTEM OF NEW YORK
529 Central Avenue, Dunkirk, NY 14048–2514; tel. 716/366–1111; J. Gary Rhodes, FACHE, Interim Chief Executive Officer

BROOKS MEMORIAL HOSPITAL, 529 Central Avenue, Dunkirk, NY, Zip 14048–2599; tel. 716/366–1111; Mary E. LaRowe, FACHE, President and Chief Executive Officer

TLC HEALTH NETWORK – LAKE SHORE HOSPITAL, 845 Route 5 and 20, Irving, NY, Zip 14081–9716; tel. 716/951–7000; John P. Galati, Chief Executive Officer

MOHAWK VALLEY NETWORK, INC.
1656 Champlin Avenue, Utica, NY 13502–4830; tel. 315/624–6002; Scott H. Perra, FACHE, President and Chief Executive Officer

FAXTON ST. LUKE'S HEALTHCARE, 1656 Champlin Avenue, Utica, NY, Zip 13502–4830, Mailing Address: P.O. Box 479, Zip 13503–0479; tel. 315/624–6000; Scott H. Perra, FACHE, President and Chief Executive Officer

ST. ELIZABETH MEDICAL CENTER, 2209 Genesee Street, Utica, NY, Zip 13501–5999; tel. 315/798–8100; Scott H. Perra, FACHE, Chief Executive Officer

MOUNT SINAI NYU HEALTH NETWORK
One Gustave L. Levy Place, New York, NY 10029; tel. 212/659–8888; Arthur A. Klein, M.D., President

ENGLEWOOD HOSPITAL AND MEDICAL CENTER, 350 Engle Street, Englewood, NJ, Zip 07631–1898; tel. 201/894–3000; Warren Geller, President and Chief Executive Officer

JAMES J. PETERS VETERANS AFFAIRS MEDICAL CENTER, 130 West Kingsbridge Road, Bronx, NY, Zip 10468–3904; tel. 718/584–9000; Erik Langhoff, M.D., Ph.D., Director

JERSEY CITY MEDICAL CENTER, 355 Grand Street, Jersey City, NJ, Zip 07302–4321; tel. 201/915–2000; Joseph F. Scott, FACHE, President and Chief Executive Officer

MEADOWLANDS HOSPITAL MEDICAL CENTER, 55 Meadowlands Parkway, Secaucus, NJ, Zip 07094–2977; tel. 201/392–3100; Felicia Karsos, R.N., President and Chief Executive Officer

MORRISTOWN MEDICAL CENTER, 100 Madison Avenue, Morristown, NJ, Zip 07960–6136; tel. 973/971–5000; Trish O'Keefe, Ph.D., R.N., President

MOUNT SINAI HOSPITAL, One Gustave L. Levy Place, New York, NY, Zip 10029–0310; tel. 212/241–6500; David L. Reich, M.D., President and Chief Operating Officer

NYC HEALTH + HOSPITALS / ELMHURST, 79–01 Broadway, Elmhurst, NY, Zip 11373–1329; tel. 718/334–4000; Israel Rocha, Chief Executive Officer

NYC HEALTH + HOSPITALS / QUEENS, 82–68 164th Street, Jamaica, NY, Zip 11432–1104; tel. 718/883–3000; Dona Green, Chief Operating Officer

OVERLOOK MEDICAL CENTER, 99 Beauvoir Avenue, Summit, NJ, Zip 07901–3533; tel. 908/522–2000; Alan R. Lieber, President

PHELPS MEMORIAL HOSPITAL CENTER, 701 North Broadway, Sleepy Hollow, NY, Zip 10591–1020; tel. 914/366–3000; Daniel Blum, President

ST. JOHN'S RIVERSIDE HOSPITAL, 967 North Broadway, Yonkers, NY, Zip 10701–1399; tel. 914/964–4444; Ronald J. Corti, President and Chief Executive Officer

ST. JOSEPH'S HEALTHCARE SYSTEM, 703 Main Street, Paterson, NJ, Zip 07503–2691; tel. 973/754–2000; Kevin J. Slavin, FACHE, President and Chief Executive Officer

ST. LUKE'S CORNWALL HOSPITAL, 70 Dubois Street, Newburgh, NY, Zip 12550–4851; tel. 845/561–4400; Joan Cusack–McGuirk, Interim President and Chief Executive Officer

VASSAR BROTHERS MEDICAL CENTER, 45 Reade Place, Poughkeepsie, NY, Zip 12601–3947; tel. 845/454–8500; Ann McMackin, President

NEW YORK PRESBYTERIAN REGIONAL HOSPITAL NETWORK
525 East 68th Street, Box 182, New York, NY 10065–4870; tel. 212/746–3745; Steven J. Corwin, M.D., President and Chief Executive Officer

GRACIE SQUARE HOSPITAL, 420 East 76th Street, New York, NY, Zip 10021–3396; tel. 212/988–4400; David Wyman, President and Chief Executive Officer

NEW YORK COMMUNITY HOSPITAL, 2525 Kings Highway, Brooklyn, NY, Zip 11229–1705; tel. 718/692–5300; Barry Stern, President and Chief Executive Officer

NEW YORK METHODIST HOSPITAL, 506 Sixth Street, Brooklyn, NY, Zip 11215–3609; tel. 718/780–3000; Mark J. Mundy, President and Chief Executive Officer

RURAL HEALTH NETWORK OF OSWEGO COUNTY
10 George Street, Oswego, NY 13126; tel. 315/592–0827; Brian Coleman, Coordinator

OSWEGO HOSPITAL, 110 West Sixth Street, Oswego, NY, Zip 13126–2507; tel. 315/349–5511; Charles Gijanto, President and Chief Executive Officer

STELLARIS HEALTH
135 Bedford Road, Armonk, NY 10504–1945; tel. 914/273–5454; Sharon A. Lucian, President and Chief Executive Officer

NEW YORK–PRESBYTERIAN/LAWRENCE HOSPITAL, 55 Palmer Avenue, Bronxville, NY, Zip 10708–3403; tel. 914/787–1000; Michael Fosina, M.P.H., FACHE, President

NORTHERN WESTCHESTER HOSPITAL, 400 East Main Street, Mount Kisco, NY, Zip 10549–3477, Mailing Address: 400 East Main Street, G–02, Zip 10549–3477; tel. 914/666–1200; Joel Seligman, President and Chief Executive Officer

PHELPS MEMORIAL HOSPITAL CENTER, 701 North Broadway, Sleepy Hollow, NY, Zip 10591–1020; tel. 914/366–3000; Daniel Blum, President

WHITE PLAINS HOSPITAL CENTER, 41 East Post Road, White Plains, NY, Zip 10601–4699; tel. 914/681–0600; Susan Fox, President and Chief Executive Officer

NORTH CAROLINA

COASTAL CAROLINAS HEALTH ALLIANCE
5305–M Wrightsville Avenue, Wilmington, NC 28403; tel. 910/332–8012; Yvonne Hughes, Chief Executive Officer

CAPE FEAR VALLEY – BLADEN COUNTY HOSPITAL, 501 South Poplar Street, Elizabethtown, NC, Zip 28337–9375, Mailing Address: P.O. Box 398, Zip 28337–0398; tel. 910/862–5100; Daniel R. Weatherly, Interim Chief Executive Officer

COLUMBUS REGIONAL HEALTHCARE SYSTEM, 500 Jefferson Street, Whiteville, NC, Zip 28472–3634; tel. 910/642–8011; Carla Hollis, President and Chief Executive Officer

J. ARTHUR DOSHER MEMORIAL HOSPITAL, 924 North Howe Street, Southport, NC, Zip 28461–3099; tel. 910/457–3800; Thomas R. Siemers, Chief Executive Officer

MCLEOD LORIS SEACOAST HOSPITAL, 3655 Mitchell Street, Loris, SC, Zip 29569–2827; tel. 843/716–7000; Edward D. Tinsley, III, Chief Executive Officer

MCLEOD REGIONAL MEDICAL CENTER, 555 East Cheves Street, Florence, SC, Zip 29506–2617, Mailing Address: P.O. Box 100551, Zip 29502–0551; tel. 843/777–2000; Robert L. Colones, President and Chief Executive Officer

NEW HANOVER REGIONAL MEDICAL CENTER, 2131 South 17th Street, Wilmington, NC, Zip 28401–7483, Mailing Address: P.O. Box 9000, Zip 28402–9000; tel. 910/343–7000; John H. Gizdic, President and Chief Operating Officer

PENDER MEMORIAL HOSPITAL, 507 East Freemont Street, Burgaw, NC, Zip 28425–5131; tel. 910/259–5451; Ruth Glaser, President

SAMPSON REGIONAL MEDICAL CENTER, 607 Beaman Street, Clinton, NC, Zip 28328–2697, Mailing Address: P.O. Box 260, Zip 28329–0260; tel. 910/592–8511; Shawn Howerton, M.D., Chief Executive Officer and President, Medical Staff

SCOTLAND HEALTH CARE SYSTEM, 500 Lauchwood Drive, Laurinburg, NC, Zip 28352–5599; tel. 910/291–7000; Gregory C. Wood, President and Chief Executive Officer

SOUTHEASTERN HEALTH, 300 West 27th Street, Lumberton, NC, Zip 28358–3075, Mailing Address: P.O. Box 1408, Zip 28359–1408; tel. 910/671–5000; Joann Anderson, President and Chief Executive Officer

VIDANT DUPLIN HOSPITAL, 401 North Main Street, Kenansville, NC, Zip 28349–8801, Mailing Address: P.O. Box 278, Zip 28349–0278; tel. 910/296–0941; Jay Briley, President

VIDANT MEDICAL CENTER, 2100 Stantonsburg Road, Greenville, NC, Zip 27834–2818, Mailing Address: P.O. Box 6028, Zip 27835–6028; tel. 252/847–4100; William Brian Floyd, President

MISSION HEALTH SYSTEM
509 Biltmore Avenue, Asheville, NC 28801–4601; tel. 828/213–1111; Ronald A. Paulus, M.D., President and Chief Executive Officer

ANGEL MEDICAL CENTER, 120 Riverview Street, Franklin, NC, Zip 28734–2612, Mailing Address: P.O. Box 1209, Zip 28744–0569; tel. 828/524–8411; Karen S. Gorby, R.N., MSN, FACHE, President and Chief Nursing Officer

ASHEVILLE SPECIALTY HOSPITAL, 428 Biltmore Avenue, 4th Floor, Asheville, NC, Zip 28801–4502; tel. 828/213–5400; Robert C. Desotelle, President and Chief Executive Officer

BLUE RIDGE REGIONAL HOSPITAL, 125 Hospital Drive, Spruce Pine, NC, Zip 28777–3035; tel. 828/765–4201; Rebecca W. Carter, MSN, R.N., FACHE, Chief Executive Officer and Chief Nursing Officer

CAREPARTNERS HEALTH SERVICES, 68 Sweeten Creek Road, Asheville, NC, Zip 28803–2318, Mailing Address: P.O. Box 15025, Zip 28813–0025; tel. 828/277–4800; Tracy Buchanan, Chief Executive Officer and President

HIGHLANDS–CASHIERS HOSPITAL, 190 Hospital Drive, Highlands, NC, Zip 28741–7600, Mailing Address: P.O. Drawer 190, Zip 28741–0190; tel. 828/526–1200; Christina Derosa, Ph.D., Interim Chief Executive Officer and Chief Nursing Officer

MCDOWELL HOSPITAL, 430 Rankin Drive, Marion, NC, Zip 28752–6568, Mailing Address: P.O. Box 730, Zip 28752–0730; tel. 828/659–5000; Carol C. Wolfenbarger, FACHE, MSN, President and Chief Executive Officer

MISSION HOSPITAL, 509 Biltmore Avenue, Asheville, NC, Zip 28801–4690; tel. 828/213–1111; Jill Hoggard Green, Ph.D., R.N., President

TRANSYLVANIA REGIONAL HOSPITAL, 260 Hospital Drive, Brevard, NC, Zip 28712–3378; tel. 828/884–9111; Melina Arrowood, Interim President and Chief Nursing Officer

WNC HEALTH NETWORK, INC.
1200 Ridgefield Boulevard Suite 200, Asheville, NC 28806–2280; tel. 828/667–8220; Heather Gates, Executive Director

ANGEL MEDICAL CENTER, 120 Riverview Street, Franklin, NC, Zip 28734–2612, Mailing Address: P.O. Box 1209, Zip 28744–0569; tel. 828/524–8411; Karen S. Gorby, R.N., MSN, FACHE, President and Chief Nursing Officer

BLUE RIDGE REGIONAL HOSPITAL, 125 Hospital Drive, Spruce Pine, NC, Zip 28777–3035; tel. 828/765–4201; Rebecca W. Carter, MSN, R.N., FACHE, Chief Executive Officer and Chief Nursing Officer

CAREPARTNERS HEALTH SERVICES, 68 Sweeten Creek Road, Asheville, NC, Zip 28803–2318, Mailing Address: P.O. Box 15025, Zip 28813–0025; tel. 828/277–4800; Tracy Buchanan, Chief Executive Officer and President

CHARLES GEORGE VETERANS AFFAIRS MEDICAL CENTER, 1100 Tunnel Road, Asheville, NC, Zip 28805–2087; tel. 828/298–7911; Cynthia Breyfogle, FACHE, Director

CHEROKEE INDIAN HOSPITAL, 1 Hospital Road, Cherokee, NC, Zip 28719; tel. 828/497–9163; Casey Cooper, Chief Executive Officer

HARRIS REGIONAL HOSPITAL, 68 Hospital Road, Sylva, NC, Zip 28779–2722; tel. 828/586–7000; Steve Heatherly, Chief Executive Officer

HAYWOOD REGIONAL MEDICAL CENTER, 262 Leroy George Drive, Clyde, NC, Zip 28721–7430; tel. 828/456–7311; Rod Harkleroad, R.N., Chief Executive Officer

HIGHLANDS–CASHIERS HOSPITAL, 190 Hospital Drive, Highlands, NC, Zip 28741–7600, Mailing Address: P.O. Drawer 190, Zip 28741–0190; tel. 828/526–1200; Christina Derosa, Ph.D., Interim Chief Executive Officer and Chief Nursing Officer

MARGARET R. PARDEE MEMORIAL HOSPITAL, 800 North Justice Street, Hendersonville, NC, Zip 28791–3410; tel. 828/696–1000; James M. Kirby, II, President and Chief Executive Officer

MCDOWELL HOSPITAL, 430 Rankin Drive, Marion, NC, Zip 28752–6568, Mailing Address: P.O. Box 730, Zip 28752–0730; tel. 828/659–5000; Carol C. Wolfenbarger, FACHE, MSN, President and Chief Executive Officer

MISSION HOSPITAL, 509 Biltmore Avenue, Asheville, NC, Zip 28801–4690; tel. 828/213–1111; Jill Hoggard Green, Ph.D., R.N., President

MURPHY MEDICAL CENTER, 3990 U.S. Highway 64 East Alt, Murphy, NC, Zip 28906–7917; tel. 828/837–8161; Michael Stevenson, Chief Executive Officer

PARK RIDGE HEALTH, 100 Hospital Drive, Hendersonville, NC, Zip 28792–5272; tel. 828/684–8501; Jimm Bunch, President and Chief Executive Officer

RUTHERFORD REGIONAL HEALTH SYSTEM, 288 South Ridgecrest Avenue, Rutherfordton, NC, Zip 28139–2838; tel. 828/286–5000; James Atkins, PharmD, Chief Executive Officer

ST. LUKE'S HOSPITAL, 101 Hospital Drive, Columbus, NC, Zip 28722–6418; tel. 828/894–3311; James B. Bross, President

SWAIN COMMUNITY HOSPITAL, 45 Plateau Street, Bryson City, NC, Zip 28713–4200; tel. 828/488–2155; Steve Heatherly, Chief Executive Officer

TRANSYLVANIA REGIONAL HOSPITAL, 260 Hospital Drive, Brevard, NC, Zip 28712–3378; tel. 828/884–9111; Melina Arrowood, Interim President and Chief Nursing Officer

NORTH DAKOTA

NORTHLAND HEALTHCARE ALLIANCE
3811 Lockport Street Suite 3, Bismarck, ND 58503–5554; tel. 701/250–0709; Timothy Cox, Director

ASHLEY MEDICAL CENTER, 612 North Center Avenue, Ashley, ND, Zip 58413–7013, Mailing Address: P.O. Box 450, Zip 58413–0450; tel. 701/288–3433; Jerry Lepp, Chief Executive Officer

CHI ST. ALEXIUS HEALTH, 900 East Broadway, Bismarck, ND, Zip 58501–4586, Mailing Address: P.O. Box 5510, Zip 58506–5510; tel. 701/530–7000; Kurt Schley, Market Chief Executive Officer

COMMUNITY MEMORIAL HOSPITAL, 220 Fifth Avenue, Turtle Lake, ND, Zip 58575–4005, Mailing Address: P.O. Box 280, Zip 58575–0280; tel. 701/448–2331; Tod Graeber, Administrator

GARRISON MEMORIAL HOSPITAL, 407 Third Avenue S.E., Garrison, ND, Zip 58540–7235; tel. 701/463–2275; Tod Graeber, Administrator

LINTON HOSPITAL, 518 North Broadway, Linton, ND, Zip 58552–7308, Mailing Address: P.O. Box 850, Zip 58552–0850; tel. 701/254–4511; Robert O. Black, Chief Executive Officer

MCKENZIE COUNTY HEALTHCARE SYSTEM, 516 North Main Street, Watford City, ND, Zip 58854–7310; tel. 701/842–3000; Daniel R. Kelly, Chief Executive Officer

MOBRIDGE REGIONAL HOSPITAL, 1401 Tenth Avenue West, Mobridge, SD, Zip 57601–1106, Mailing Address: P.O. Box 580, Zip 57601–0580; tel. 605/845–3692; Angelia K. Svihovec, Chief Executive Officer

PRESENTATION MEDICAL CENTER, 213 Second Avenue N.E., Rolla, ND, Zip 58367–7153, Mailing Address: P.O. Box 759, Zip 58367–0759; tel. 701/477–3161; Mark Kerr, Chief Executive Officer

SAKAKAWEA MEDICAL CENTER, 510 Eighth Avenue N.E., Hazen, ND, Zip 58545–4637; tel. 701/748–2225; Darrold Bertsch, Chief Executive Officer

SOUTHWEST HEALTHCARE SERVICES, 802 2nd Street Northwest, Bowman, ND, Zip 58623–4483, Mailing Address: P.O. Drawer C, Zip 58623; tel. 701/523–5265; Becky Hansen, Chief Executive Officer

ST. ALOISIUS MEDICAL CENTER, 325 East Brewster Street, Harvey, ND, Zip 58341–1653; tel. 701/324–4651; Gregory LaFrancois, President and Chief Executive Officer

ST. ANDREW'S HEALTH CENTER, 316 Ohmer Street, Bottineau, ND, Zip 58318–1045; tel. 701/228–9300; Jodi Atkinson, President and Chief Executive Officer

ST. JOSEPH'S HOSPITAL AND HEALTH CENTER, 2500 Fairway Street, Dickinson, ND, Zip 58601–4399; tel. 701/456–4000; Reed Reyman, President

WEST RIVER REGIONAL MEDICAL CENTER, 1000 Highway 12, Hettinger, ND, Zip 58639–7530; tel. 701/567–4561; Matthew Shahan, Chief Executive Officer

WISHEK COMMUNITY HOSPITAL AND CLINICS, 1007 Fourth Avenue South, Wishek, ND, Zip 58495–7527, Mailing Address: P.O. Box 647, Zip 58495–0647; tel. 701/452–2326; Beverly Vilhauer, Chief Executive Officer

OHIO

CLEVELAND HEALTH NETWORK
6000 West Creek Road, Suite 20, Independence, OH 44131–2139; tel. 216/986–1100; Fred M. DeGrandis, President

AKRON CHILDREN'S HOSPITAL, One Perkins Square, Akron, OH, Zip 44308–1063; tel. 330/543–1000; William H. Considine, President

ASHTABULA COUNTY MEDICAL CENTER, 2420 Lake Avenue, Ashtabula, OH, Zip 44004–4954; tel. 440/997–2262; Michael J. Habowski, President and Chief Executive Officer

CLEVELAND CLINIC, 9500 Euclid Avenue, Cleveland, OH, Zip 44195–5108; tel. 216/444–2200; Delos Cosgrove, M.D., President and Chief Executive Officer

CLEVELAND CLINIC CHILDREN'S HOSPITAL FOR REHABILITATION, 2801 Martin Luther King Jr. Drive, Cleveland, OH, Zip 44104–3865; tel. 216/448–6400; Michael J. McHugh, M.D., Medical Director

CLEVELAND CLINIC FAIRVIEW HOSPITAL, 18101 Lorain Avenue, Cleveland, OH, Zip 44111–5656; tel. 216/476–7000; Neil Smith, D.O., President

CLEVELAND CLINIC, MEDINA HOSPITAL, 1000 East Washington Street, Medina, OH, Zip 44256–2170; tel. 330/725–1000; Thomas Tulisiak, M.D., President

EUCLID HOSPITAL, 18901 Lake Shore Boulevard, Euclid, OH, Zip 44119–1090; tel. 216/531–9000; Daniel Napierkowski, M.D., President

FIRELANDS REGIONAL HEALTH SYSTEM, 1111 Hayes Avenue, Sandusky, OH, Zip 44870–3323; tel. 419/557–7400; Martin Tursky, President and Chief Executive Officer

FISHER–TITUS MEDICAL CENTER, 272 Benedict Avenue, Norwalk, OH, Zip 44857–2374; tel. 419/668–8101; Lorna Strayer, President and Chief Executive Officer

HILLCREST HOSPITAL, 6780 Mayfield Road, Cleveland, OH, Zip 44124–2203; tel. 440/312–4500; Brian J. Harte, M.D., President

LUTHERAN HOSPITAL, 1730 West 25th Street, Cleveland, OH, Zip 44113–3170; tel. 216/696–4300; Donald Malone, M.D., President

MARYMOUNT HOSPITAL, 12300 McCracken Road, Garfield Heights, OH, Zip 44125–2975; tel. 216/581–0500; Richard Parker, M.D., President

METROHEALTH MEDICAL CENTER, 2500 MetroHealth Drive, Cleveland, OH, Zip 44109–1998; tel. 216/778–7800; Akram Boutros, M.D., FACHE, President and Chief Executive Officer

SOUTH POINTE HOSPITAL, 20000 Harvard Road, Warrensville Heights, OH, Zip 44122–6805; tel. 216/491–6000; Robert S. Juhasz, D.O., President

SUMMA HEALTH SYSTEM, 525 East Market Street, Akron, OH, Zip 44304–1619; tel. 330/375–3000; Thomas Malone, M.D., President and Chief Executive Officer

SUMMA WESTERN RESERVE HOSPITAL, 1900 23rd Street, Cuyahoga Falls, OH, Zip 44223–1499; tel. 330/971–7000; Robert Kent, D.O., President and Chief Executive Officer

UNIVERSITY HOSPITALS ELYRIA MEDICAL CENTER, 630 East River Street, Elyria, OH, Zip 44035–5902; tel. 440/329–7500; Charlotte Wray, MSN, President

UNIVERSITY HOSPITALS PARMA MEDICAL CENTER, 7007 Powers Boulevard, Parma, OH, Zip 44129–5495; tel. 440/743–3000; Kristi M. Sink, Interim President

COMPREHENSIVE HEALTHCARE OF OHIO, INC.
630 East River Street, Elyria, OH 44035–5902; tel. 440/329–7700; Charlotte Wray, MSN, President

UNIVERSITY HOSPITALS ELYRIA MEDICAL CENTER, 630 East River Street, Elyria, OH, Zip 44035–5902; tel. 440/329–7500; Charlotte Wray, MSN, President

MERCY HEALTH – SOUTHWEST OHIO
4600 McAuley Place, Cincinnati, OH 45242; tel. 513/981–6000; John M. Starcher, President and Chief Executive Officer

MERCY HEALTH – ANDERSON HOSPITAL, 7500 State Road, Cincinnati, OH, Zip 45255–2492; tel. 513/624–4500; Jeff Graham, Market Leader and President

MERCY HEALTH – CLERMONT HOSPITAL, 3000 Hospital Drive, Batavia, OH, Zip 45103–1921; tel. 513/732–8200; Jeff Graham, Market Leader and President

MERCY HEALTH – FAIRFIELD HOSPITAL, 3000 Mack Road, Fairfield, OH, Zip 45014–5335; tel. 513/870–7000; Thomas S. Urban, Market Leader and President

MERCY HEALTH – WEST HOSPITAL, 3300 Mercy Health Boulevard, Cincinnati, OH, Zip 45211; tel. 513/215–5000; Michael Kramer, Chief Executive Officer

THE JEWISH HOSPITAL – MERCY HEALTH, 4777 East Galbraith Road, Cincinnati, OH, Zip 45236–2725; tel. 513/686–3000; Patricia Davis–Hagens, R.N., Central Market Leader and President

OHIO STATE HEALTH NETWORK
660 Ackerman Road, Suite 601F, Columbus, OH 43202–4500; tel. 614/293–3785; Joann Ort, Executive Director

BARNESVILLE HOSPITAL, 639 West Main Street, Barnesville, OH, Zip 43713–1039, Mailing Address: P.O. Box 309, Zip 43713–0309; tel. 740/425–3941; David D. Phillips, Chief Executive Officer and Administrator

MADISON HEALTH, 210 North Main Street, London, OH, Zip 43140–1115; tel. 740/845–7000; Dana E. Engle, Chief Executive Officer

MARY RUTAN HOSPITAL, 205 Palmer Avenue, Bellefontaine, OH, Zip 43311–2281; tel. 937/592–4015; Mandy C. Goble, President and Chief Executive Officer

MERCER HEALTH, 800 West Main Street, Coldwater, OH, Zip 45828–1698; tel. 419/678–2341; Lisa R. Klenke, R.N., Chief Executive Officer

OHIO STATE UNIVERSITY WEXNER MEDICAL CENTER, 370 West 9th Avenue, Columbus, OH, Zip 43210–1238; tel. 614/293–8000; Sheldon Retchin, M.D., Chief Executive Officer

Section B

OHIO VALLEY MEDICAL CENTER, 2000 Eoff Street, Wheeling, WV,
Zip 26003–3870; tel. 304/234–0123; Michael J. Caruso, President and
Chief Executive Officer

TRINITY HOSPITAL TWIN CITY, 819 North First Street, Dennison, OH,
Zip 44621–1098; tel. 740/922–2800; Joseph J. Mitchell, President

WILSON MEMORIAL HOSPITAL, 915 West Michigan Street, Sidney, OH,
Zip 45365–2491; tel. 937/498–2311; Mark J. Dooley, Chief Executive
Officer

WYANDOT MEMORIAL HOSPITAL, 885 North Sandusky Avenue, Upper Sandusky,
OH, Zip 43351–1098; tel. 419/294–4991; Joseph A. D'Ettorre, Chief
Executive Officer

PREMIER HEALTH
110 North Main Street, Suite 390, Dayton, OH 45402–3720;
tel. 937/499–9401; Mary H. Boosalis, President and Chief Executive
Officer

ATRIUM MEDICAL CENTER, One Medical Center Drive, Middletown, OH,
Zip 45005–1066; tel. 513/424–2111; Carol Turner, President and Chief
Executive Officer

GOOD SAMARITAN HOSPITAL, 2222 Philadelphia Drive, Dayton, OH,
Zip 45406–1813; tel. 937/734–2612; Eloise Broner, President and Chief
Executive Officer

MIAMI VALLEY HOSPITAL, One Wyoming Street, Dayton, OH, Zip 45409–2793;
tel. 937/208–8000; Mark S. Shaker, President and Chief Executive Officer

UPPER VALLEY MEDICAL CENTER, 3130 North County Road 25A, Troy, OH,
Zip 45373–1309; tel. 937/440–4000; Rebecca Rice, FACHE, Chief
Executive Officer

TRIHEALTH
619 Oak Street, Cincinnati, OH 45206; tel. 513/569–6507; Mark C.
Clement, President and Chief Executive Officer

BETHESDA NORTH HOSPITAL, 10500 Montgomery Road, Cincinnati, OH,
Zip 45242–4402; tel. 513/865–1111; Barbara Boyne, Executive Director,
Operations

GOOD SAMARITAN HOSPITAL, 375 Dixmyth Avenue, Cincinnati, OH,
Zip 45220–2489; tel. 513/862–1400; Jamie Easterling, Executive Director,
Operations

MCCULLOUGH–HYDE MEMORIAL HOSPITAL/TRIHEALTH, 110 North Poplar Street,
Oxford, OH, Zip 45056–1292; tel. 513/523–2111; Bryan D. Hehemann,
President and Chief Executive Officer

TRIHEALTH EVENDALE HOSPITAL, 3155 Glendale Milford Road, Cincinnati, OH,
Zip 45241–3134; tel. 513/454–2222; Kelvin Hanger, Chief Executive Officer

WEST CENTRAL OHIO, LLC
2615 Fort Amanda Road, Lima, OH Zip 45804–3704;
Tel: 419/226–9085; Ms. Robin Johnson, Executive Director

JOINT TOWNSHIP DISTRICT MEMORIAL HOSPITAL, 200 St. Clair Street, Saint
Marys, OH, Zip 45885–2400; tel. 419/394–3335; Kevin W. Harlan,
President

MARY RUTAN HOSPITAL, 205 Palmer Avenue, Bellefontaine, OH Zip 43311–2281;
tel. 937/592–4015; Mandy C. Goble, President and Chief Executive Officer

MERCER HEALTH, 800 West Main Street, Coldwater, OH Zip 45828–1698;
tel. 419/678–2341; Lisa R. Klenke, RN, Chief Executive Officer

ST. RITA'S MEDICAL CENTER, 730 West Market Street, Lima, OH
Zip 45801–4602; tel. 419/227–3361; Robert O. Baxter, Regional Chief
Executive Officer, Lima

VAN WERT COUNTY HOSPITAL, 1250 South Washington Street, Van Wert, OH
Zip 45891–2599; tel. 419/238–2390; James W. Pope, FACHE, President
and Chief Executive Officer

OKLAHOMA

MERCY HEALTH SYSTEM OF OKLAHOMA
4300 West Memorial Road, Oklahoma City, OK 73120–8304;
tel. 405/752–3756; Jennifer Coons, Acting Chief Executive Officer

ARBUCKLE MEMORIAL HOSPITAL, 2011 West Broadway Street, Sulphur, OK,
Zip 73086–4221; tel. 580/622–2161; Darin Farrell, Chief Executive Officer

MERCY HEALTH LOVE COUNTY, 300 Wanda Street, Marietta, OK,
Zip 73448–1200; tel. 580/276–3347; Richard Barker, Administrator

MERCY HOSPITAL ADA, 430 North Monte Vista, Ada, OK, Zip 74820–4610;
tel. 580/332–2323; Lori Wightman, R.N., MSN, FACHE, Chief Executive
Officer

MERCY HOSPITAL ARDMORE, 1011 14th Avenue N.W., Ardmore, OK,
Zip 73401–1828; tel. 580/223–5400; Daryle Voss, FACHE, President

MERCY HOSPITAL EL RENO, 2115 Parkview Drive, El Reno, OK,
Zip 73036–2199, Mailing Address: P.O. Box 129, Zip 73036–0129;
tel. 405/262–2640; Doug Danker, Administrator

MERCY HOSPITAL HEALDTON, 918 South 8th Street, Healdton, OK,
Zip 73438–0928, Mailing Address: P.O. Box 928, Zip 73438–0928;
tel. 580/229–0701; Jeremy A. Jones, Administrator

MERCY HOSPITAL KINGFISHER, 1000 Kingfisher Regional Hospital Drive,
Kingfisher, OK, Zip 73750–3528, Mailing Address: P.O. Box 59,
Zip 73750–0059; tel. 405/375–3141; Brian Denton, Administrator

MERCY HOSPITAL LOGAN COUNTY, 200 South Academy Road, Guthrie, OK,
Zip 73044–8727, Mailing Address: P.O. Box 1017, Zip 73044–1017;
tel. 405/282–6700; Joshua Tucker, Administrator

MERCY HOSPITAL OKLAHOMA CITY, 4300 West Memorial Road, Oklahoma City,
OK, Zip 73120–8362; tel. 405/755–1515; Jim Gebhart, Jr., FACHE,
President

MERCY HOSPITAL TISHOMINGO, 1000 South Byrd Street, Tishomingo, OK,
Zip 73460–3299; tel. 580/371–2327; Gary Sharum, Administrator

MERCY HOSPITAL WATONGA, 500 North Clarence Nash Boulevard, Watonga, OK,
Zip 73772–2845, Mailing Address: P.O. Box 370, Zip 73772–0370;
tel. 580/623–7211; Bobby Stitt, R.N., Administrator

MERCY REHABILITATION HOSPITAL OKLAHOMA CITY, 5401 West Memorial Road,
Oklahoma City, OK, Zip 73142–2026; tel. 405/752–3935; Sharon Smeltzer,
Chief Executive Officer

OKLAHOMA HEART HOSPITAL, 4050 West Memorial Road, Oklahoma City, OK,
Zip 73120–8382; tel. 405/608–3200; John Harvey, M.D., President and
Chief Executive Officer

OKLAHOMA HEART HOSPITAL SOUTH CAMPUS, 5200 East I–240 Service Road,
Oklahoma City, OK, Zip 73135; tel. 405/628–6000; John Harvey, M.D.,
President and Chief Executive Officer

OKLAHOMA STATE UNIVERSITY MEDICAL CENTER, 744 West Ninth Street, Tulsa,
OK, Zip 74127–9020; tel. 918/599–1000; Rhett Stover, Chief Executive
Officer

SEILING MUNICIPAL HOSPITAL, Highway 60 N.E., Seiling, OK, Zip 73663, Mailing
Address: P.O. Box 720, Zip 73663–0720; tel. 580/922–7361; Bobby Stitt,
R.N., Chief Executive Officer

PENNSYLVANIA

ALLEGHENY HEALTH NETWORK
30 Isabella Street, Suite 300, Pittsburgh, PA 15212–5862;
tel. 412/330–2400; Cynthia Hundorfean, President and Chief Executive
Officer

ALLEGHENY GENERAL HOSPITAL, 320 East North Avenue, Pittsburgh, PA,
Zip 15212–4756; tel. 412/359–3131; Jeffrey Cohen, M.D., President

ALLEGHENY VALLEY HOSPITAL, 1301 Carlisle Street, Natrona Heights, PA,
Zip 15065–1152; tel. 724/224–5100; William Englert, Chief Executive
Officer

CANONSBURG HOSPITAL, 100 Medical Boulevard, Canonsburg, PA,
Zip 15317–9762; tel. 724/745–6100; David Goldberg, Interim President
and Chief Executive Officer

FORBES HOSPITAL, 2570 Haymaker Road, Monroeville, PA, Zip 15146–3513;
tel. 412/858–2000; Mark Rubino, M.D., President

JEFFERSON HOSPITAL, 565 Coal Valley Road, Jefferson Hills, PA,
Zip 15025–3703, Mailing Address: Box 18119, Pittsburgh,
Zip 15236–0119; tel. 412/469–5000; Louise Urban, R.N., President and
Chief Executive Officer

SAINT VINCENT HOSPITAL, 232 West 25th Street, Erie, PA, Zip 16544–0002;
tel. 814/452–5000; Scott Whalen, Ph.D., FACHE, President and Chief
Executive Officer

WEST PENN HOSPITAL, 4800 Friendship Avenue, Pittsburgh, PA,
Zip 15224–1722; tel. 412/578–5000; Ronald J. Andro, President and Chief
Executive Officer

WESTFIELD MEMORIAL HOSPITAL, 189 East Main Street, Westfield, NY,
Zip 14787–1195; tel. 716/326–4921; Scott Whalen, Ph.D., FACHE,
President and Chief Executive Officer

COMMONWEALTH HEALTH
575 North River Street, Wilkes Barre, PA 18764–0999;
tel. 570/829–8111; Cornelio R. Catena, Chief Executive Officer

BERWICK HOSPITAL CENTER, 701 East 16th Street, Berwick, PA,
Zip 18603–2397; tel. 570/759–5000; Diane Ljungquist, R.N., MS, Chief
Executive Officer

FIRST HOSPITAL WYOMING VALLEY, 562 Wyoming Avenue, Kingston, PA,
Zip 18704–3721; tel. 570/552–3900; Ron Ziobro, Interim Chief Executive
Officer

MOSES TAYLOR HOSPITAL, 700 Quincy Avenue, Scranton, PA, Zip 18510–1724;
tel. 570/770–5000; Justin Davis, Chief Executive Officer

REGIONAL HOSPITAL OF SCRANTON, 746 Jefferson Avenue, Scranton, PA,
Zip 18510–1624; tel. 570/348–7100; Justin Davis, Chief Executive Officer

TYLER MEMORIAL HOSPITAL, 5950 State Route 6, Tunkhannock, PA,
Zip 18657–7905; tel. 570/836–2161; Ann Marie Stevens, R.N., Chief
Executive Officer

WILKES–BARRE GENERAL HOSPITAL, 575 North River Street, Wilkes–Barre, PA,
Zip 18764–0001; tel. 570/829–8111; Cornelio R. Catena, President and
Chief Executive Officer

PENN HIGHLANDS HEALTHCARE
204 Hospital Avenue, DuBois, PA 15801–1442; tel. 814/375–6431;
Raymond A. Graeca, Chief Executive Officer

PENN HIGHLANDS BROOKVILLE, 100 Hospital Road, Brookville, PA,
Zip 15825–1367; tel. 814/849–2312; Julie Peer, President

PENN HIGHLANDS CLEARFIELD, 809 Turnpike Avenue, Clearfield, PA,
Zip 16830–1232, Mailing Address: P.O. Box 992, Zip 16830–0992;
tel. 814/765–5341; Gary Macioce, President

PENN HIGHLANDS DUBOIS, 100 Hospital Avenue, DuBois, PA, Zip 15801–1440, Mailing Address: P.O. Box 447, Zip 15801–0447; tel. 814/371–2200; John Sutika, President

PENN HIGHLANDS ELK, 763 Johnsonburg Road, Saint Marys, PA, Zip 15857–3498; tel. 814/788–8000; Rose Campbell, R.N., President

VANTAGE HEALTHCARE NETWORK, INC.
18282 Technology Drive, Suite 202, Meadville, PA 16335–8378; tel. 814/337–0000; David Petrarca, Director Retail Operations

BRADFORD REGIONAL MEDICAL CENTER, 116 Interstate Parkway, Bradford, PA, Zip 16701–1036; tel. 814/368–4143; Timothy J. Finan, FACHE, President and Chief Executive Officer

CLARION HOSPITAL, One Hospital Drive, Clarion, PA, Zip 16214–8501; tel. 814/226–9500; Byron Quinton, Chief Executive Officer

JAMESON HOSPITAL, 1211 Wilmington Avenue, New Castle, PA, Zip 16105–2516; tel. 724/658–9001; Douglas Danko, President and Chief Executive Officer

KANE COMMUNITY HOSPITAL, 4372 Route 6, Kane, PA, Zip 16735–3060; tel. 814/837–8585; J. Gary Rhodes, FACHE, Chief Executive Officer

MEADVILLE MEDICAL CENTER, 751 Liberty Street, Meadville, PA, Zip 16335–2559; tel. 814/333–5000; Philip E. Pandolph, FACHE, Chief Executive Officer

PENN HIGHLANDS BROOKVILLE, 100 Hospital Road, Brookville, PA, Zip 15825–1367; tel. 814/849–2312; Julie Peer, President

PENN HIGHLANDS ELK, 763 Johnsonburg Road, Saint Marys, PA, Zip 15857–3498; tel. 814/788–8000; Rose Campbell, R.N., President

PUNXSUTAWNEY AREA HOSPITAL, 81 Hillcrest Drive, Punxsutawney, PA, Zip 15767–2616; tel. 814/938–1800; Daniel D. Blough, Jr., Chief Executive Officer

TITUSVILLE AREA HOSPITAL, 406 West Oak Street, Titusville, PA, Zip 16354–1404; tel. 814/827–1851; Lee Clinton, FACHE, Chief Executive Officer

UPMC BEDFORD MEMORIAL, 10455 Lincoln Highway, Everett, PA, Zip 15537–7046; tel. 814/623–6161; Gerald Murray, President

UPMC HAMOT, 201 State Street, Erie, PA, Zip 16550–0002; tel. 814/877–6000; V. James Fiorenzo, President

UPMC MCKEESPORT, 1500 Fifth Avenue, McKeesport, PA, Zip 15132–2422; tel. 412/664–2000; Mark Sevco, President

UPMC NORTHWEST, 100 Fairfield Drive, Seneca, PA, Zip 16346–2130; tel. 814/676–7600; David Gibbons, President

UPMC PASSAVANT, 9100 Babcock Boulevard, Pittsburgh, PA, Zip 15237–5815; tel. 412/748–6700; David T. Martin, President

UPMC ST. MARGARET, 815 Freeport Road, Pittsburgh, PA, Zip 15215–3301; tel. 412/784–4000; David J. Patton, President

WARREN GENERAL HOSPITAL, Two Crescent Park West, Warren, PA, Zip 16365–0068, Mailing Address: P.O. Box 68, Zip 16365–0068; tel. 814/723–4973; Richard Allen, Chief Executive Officer

SOUTH DAKOTA

REGIONAL HEALTH
353 Fairmont Boulevard, Rapid City, SD 57701–7375; tel. 605/719–1000; Brent R. Phillips, President and Chief Executive Officer

CUSTER REGIONAL HOSPITAL, 1039 Montgomery Street, Custer, SD, Zip 57730–1397; tel. 605/673–2229; Veronica Schmidt, President

LEAD–DEADWOOD REGIONAL HOSPITAL, 61 Charles Street, Deadwood, SD, Zip 57732–1303; tel. 605/717–6000; Mark C. Schmidt, President

PHILIP HEALTH SERVICES, 503 West Pine Street, Philip, SD, Zip 57567–3300, Mailing Address: P.O. Box 790, Zip 57567–0790; tel. 605/859–2511; Kent Olson, Administrator and Chief Executive Officer

RAPID CITY REGIONAL HOSPITAL, 353 Fairmont Boulevard, Rapid City, SD, Zip 57701–7393, Mailing Address: P.O. Box 6000, Zip 57709–6000; tel. 605/755–1000; Dennis C. Millirons, FACHE, Interim President

SPEARFISH REGIONAL HOSPITAL, 1440 North Main Street, Spearfish, SD, Zip 57783–1504; tel. 605/644–4000; Larry W. Veitz, President

STURGIS REGIONAL HOSPITAL, 949 Harmon Street, Sturgis, SD, Zip 57785–2452; tel. 605/720–2400; Mark Schulte, FACHE, President

WESTON COUNTY HEALTH SERVICES, 1124 Washington Boulevard, Newcastle, WY, Zip 82701–2972; tel. 307/746–4491; Maureen K. Cadwell, Chief Executive Officer

SANFORD HEALTH NETWORK
1305 West 18th Street, Sioux Falls, SD 57105–0401; tel. 605/328–5513; Jesse G. Tischer, President

BOZEMAN HEALTH DEACONESS HOSPITAL, 915 Highland Boulevard, Bozeman, MT, Zip 59715–6902; tel. 406/585–5000; John Hill, President and Chief Executive Officer

COMMUNITY MEMORIAL HOSPITAL, 809 Jackson Street, Burke, SD, Zip 57523–2065, Mailing Address: P.O. Box 319, Zip 57523–0319; tel. 605/775–2621; Mistie Sachtjen, Chief Executive Officer

DOUGLAS COUNTY MEMORIAL HOSPITAL, 708 Eighth Street, Armour, SD, Zip 57313–2102; tel. 605/724–2159; Heath Brouwer, Administrator

JAMESTOWN REGIONAL MEDICAL CENTER, 2422 20th Street S.W., Jamestown, ND, Zip 58401–6201; tel. 701/252–1050; K. C. DeBoer, President and Chief Executive Officer

KITTSON MEMORIAL HEALTHCARE CENTER, 1010 South Birch Street, Hallock, MN, Zip 56728–4215, Mailing Address: P.O. Box 700, Zip 56728–0700; tel. 218/843–3612; Cindy Urbaniak, Chief Executive Officer

LIBERTY MEDICAL CENTER, 315 West Madison Avenue, Chester, MT, Zip 59522, Mailing Address: P.O. Box 705, Zip 59522–0705; tel. 406/759–5181; Derek Daly, Chief Executive Officer

MAHNOMEN HEALTH CENTER, 414 West Jefferson Avenue, Mahnomen, MN, Zip 56557–4912, Mailing Address: P.O. Box 396, Zip 56557–0396; tel. 218/935–2511; Dale K. Kruger, Chief Executive Officer

MCKENZIE COUNTY HEALTHCARE SYSTEM, 516 North Main Street, Watford City, ND, Zip 58854–7310; tel. 701/842–3000; Daniel R. Kelly, Chief Executive Officer

MURRAY COUNTY MEDICAL CENTER, 2042 Juniper Avenue, Slayton, MN, Zip 56172–1017; tel. 507/836–6111; Dennis Goebel, Chief Executive Officer

NORTHWOOD DEACONESS HEALTH CENTER, 4 North Park Street, Northwood, ND, Zip 58267–4102, Mailing Address: P.O. Box 190, Zip 58267–0190; tel. 701/587–6060; Pete Antonson, Chief Executive Officer

ORANGE CITY AREA HEALTH SYSTEM, 1000 Lincoln Circle S.E., Orange City, IA, Zip 51041–1862; tel. 712/737–4984; Martin W. Guthmiller, Chief Executive Officer

ORTONVILLE AREA HEALTH SERVICES, 450 Eastvold Avenue, Ortonville, MN, Zip 56278–1133; tel. 320/839–2502; David Rogers, Chief Executive Officer

PERHAM HEALTH, 1000 Coney Street West, Perham, MN, Zip 56573–1108; tel. 218/347–4500; Chuck Hofius, Chief Executive Officer

PIONEER MEMORIAL HOSPITAL AND HEALTH SERVICES, 315 North Washington Street, Viborg, SD, Zip 57070–2002, Mailing Address: P.O. Box 368, Zip 57070–0368; tel. 605/326–5161; Thomas V. Richter, Chief Executive Officer

RIVERVIEW HEALTH, 323 South Minnesota Street, Crookston, MN, Zip 56716–1601; tel. 218/281–9200; Carrie Michalski, President and Chief Executive Officer

SANFORD ABERDEEN MEDICAL CENTER, 2905 3rd Avenue S.E., Aberdeen, SD, Zip 57401–5420; tel. 605/626–4200; Ashley M. Erickson, Chief Executive Officer

SANFORD BAGLEY MEDICAL CENTER, 203 Fourth Street N.W., Bagley, MN, Zip 56621–8307; tel. 218/694–6501; Sammi Davidson, Administrative Director

SANFORD BEMIDJI MEDICAL CENTER, 1300 Anne Street N.W., Bemidji, MN, Zip 56601–5103; tel. 218/751–5430; Bryan Nermoe, President

SANFORD BISMARCK, 300 North Seventh Street, Bismarck, ND, Zip 58501–4439, Mailing Address: P.O. Box 5525, Zip 58506–5525; tel. 701/323–6000; Craig Lambrecht, M.D., President

SANFORD CANBY MEDICAL CENTER, 112 St. Olaf Avenue South, Canby, MN, Zip 56220–1433; tel. 507/223–7277; Lori Sisk, R.N., Chief Executive Officer

SANFORD CANTON–INWOOD MEDICAL CENTER, 440 North Hiawatha Drive, Canton, SD, Zip 57013–5800; tel. 605/764–1400; Scott C. Larson, Chief Executive Officer

SANFORD CHAMBERLAIN MEDICAL CENTER, 300 South Byron Boulevard, Chamberlain, SD, Zip 57325–9741; tel. 605/234–5511; Erica Peterson, Chief Executive Officer

SANFORD CLEAR LAKE MEDICAL CENTER, 701 Third Avenue South, Clear Lake, SD, Zip 57226–2016; tel. 605/874–2141; Lori Sisk, R.N., Chief Executive Officer

SANFORD HILLSBORO MEDICAL CENTER, 12 Third Street S.E., Hillsboro, ND, Zip 58045–4840, Mailing Address: P.O. Box 609, Zip 58045–0609; tel. 701/636–3200; Jac McTaggart, Chief Executive Officer

SANFORD JACKSON MEDICAL CENTER, 1430 North Highway, Jackson, MN, Zip 56143–1093; tel. 507/847–2420; Mary J. Ruyter, Chief Executive Officer

SANFORD LUVERNE MEDICAL CENTER, 1600 North Kniss Avenue, Luverne, MN, Zip 56156–1067; tel. 507/283–2321; Tammy Loosbrock, Senior Director

SANFORD MAYVILLE MEDICAL CENTER, 42 Sixth Avenue S.E., Mayville, ND, Zip 58257–1598; tel. 701/786–3800; Roger Baier, Chief Executive Officer

SANFORD MEDICAL CENTER THIEF RIVER FALLS, 3001 Sanford Parkway, Thief River Falls, MN, Zip 56701–2700; tel. 218/681–4240; Brian J. Carlson, FACHE, Chief Executive Officer

SANFORD ROCK RAPIDS MEDICAL CENTER, 801 South Greene Street, Rock Rapids, IA, Zip 51246–1998; tel. 712/472–2591; Tammy Loosbrock, Senior Director

SANFORD SHELDON MEDICAL CENTER, 118 North Seventh Avenue, Sheldon, IA, Zip 51201–1235, Mailing Address: P.O. Box 250, Zip 51201–0250; tel. 712/324–5041; Richard E. Nordahl, Chief Executive Officer

SANFORD THIEF RIVER FALLS BEHAVIORAL HEALTH CENTER, 120 LaBree Avenue South, Thief River Falls, MN, Zip 56701–2819, Mailing Address: 3001 Sanford Parkway, Zip 56701–2819; tel. 218/683–4349; Brian J. Carlson, FACHE, Chief Executive Officer

SANFORD TRACY MEDICAL CENTER, 251 Fifth Street East, Tracy, MN, Zip 56175–1536; tel. 507/629–3200; Stacy Barstad, Chief Executive Officer

Section B

SANFORD USD MEDICAL CENTER, 1305 West 18th Street, Sioux Falls, SD, Zip 57105–0496, Mailing Address: P.O. Box 5039, Zip 57117–5039; tel. 605/333–1000; Paul A. Hanson, FACHE, President

SANFORD VERMILLION MEDICAL CENTER, 20 South Plum Street, Vermillion, SD, Zip 57069–3346; tel. 605/677–3500; Timothy J. Tracy, Chief Executive Officer

SANFORD WEBSTER MEDICAL CENTER, 1401 West 1st Street, Webster, SD, Zip 57274–1054, Mailing Address: P.O. Box 489, Zip 57274–0489; tel. 605/345–3336; Isaac Gerdes, Chief Executive Officer

SANFORD WESTBROOK MEDICAL CENTER, 920 Bell Avenue, Westbrook, MN, Zip 56183–9669, Mailing Address: P.O. Box 188, Zip 56183–0188; tel. 507/274–6121; Stacy Barstad, Chief Executive Officer

SANFORD WHEATON MEDICAL CENTER, 401 12th Street North, Wheaton, MN, Zip 56296–1099; tel. 320/563–8226; JoAnn M. Foltz, R.N., Chief Executive Officer

SANFORD WORTHINGTON MEDICAL CENTER, 1018 Sixth Avenue, Worthington, MN, Zip 56187–2202, Mailing Address: P.O. Box 997, Zip 56187–0997; tel. 507/372–2941; Michael Hammer, Chief Executive Officer

SIDNEY HEALTH CENTER, 216 14th Avenue S.W., Sidney, MT, Zip 59270–3586; tel. 406/488–2100; Richard Haraldson, Chief Executive Officer

WEST HOLT MEMORIAL HOSPITAL, 406 West Neely Street, Atkinson, NE, Zip 68713–4801; tel. 402/925–2811; Bradley D. Pfeifer, Chief Executive Officer

WINDOM AREA HOSPITAL, 2150 Hospital Drive, Windom, MN, Zip 56101–0339, Mailing Address: P.O. Box 339, Zip 56101–0339; tel. 507/831–2400; Shelby Medina, Chief Executive Officer

WINNER REGIONAL HEALTHCARE CENTER, 745 East Eighth Street, Winner, SD, Zip 57580–2631; tel. 605/842–7100; Kevin Coffey, Chief Executive Officer

TENNESSEE

TRISTAR HEALTH
110 Winners Circle, First Floor, Brentwood, TN 37027–5070; tel. 615/886–4900; Stephen Corbeil, President

CARTERSVILLE MEDICAL CENTER, 960 Joe Frank Harris Parkway, Cartersville, GA, Zip 30120–2129; tel. 770/382–1530; Keith Sandlin, Chief Executive Officer

EASTSIDE MEDICAL CENTER, 1700 Medical Way, Snellville, GA, Zip 30078–2195; tel. 770/979–0200; Scott Schmidly, Chief Executive Officer

PARKRIDGE MEDICAL CENTER, 2333 McCallie Avenue, Chattanooga, TN, Zip 37404–3258; tel. 423/698–6061; Darrell W. Moore, Chief Executive Officer

REDMOND REGIONAL MEDICAL CENTER, 501 Redmond Road, Rome, GA, Zip 30165–1415, Mailing Address: P.O. Box 107001, Zip 30164–7001; tel. 706/291–0291; John Quinlivan, Chief Executive Officer

TRISTAR ASHLAND CITY MEDICAL CENTER, 313 North Main Street, Ashland City, TN, Zip 37015–1347; tel. 615/792–3030; Darrell White, R.N., Administrator and Chief Nursing Officer

TRISTAR CENTENNIAL MEDICAL CENTER, 2300 Patterson Street, Nashville, TN, Zip 37203–1528; tel. 615/342–1000; Heather J. Rohan, Chief Executive Officer

TRISTAR GREENVIEW REGIONAL HOSPITAL, 1801 Ashley Circle, Bowling Green, KY, Zip 42104–3362; tel. 270/793–1000; Michael Sherrod, Chief Executive Officer

TRISTAR HENDERSONVILLE MEDICAL CENTER, 355 New Shackle Island Road, Hendersonville, TN, Zip 37075–2479; tel. 615/338–1000; Regina Bartlett, Chief Executive Officer

TRISTAR HORIZON MEDICAL CENTER, 111 Highway 70 East, Dickson, TN, Zip 37055–2080; tel. 615/446–0446; Dustin Greene, Chief Executive Officer

TRISTAR SKYLINE MADISON CAMPUS, 500 Hospital Drive, Madison, TN, Zip 37115–5032; tel. 615/769–5000; Steve Otto, Chief Executive Officer

TRISTAR SKYLINE MEDICAL CENTER, 3441 Dickerson Pike, Nashville, TN, Zip 37207–2539; tel. 615/769–2000; Steve Otto, Chief Executive Officer

TRISTAR SOUTHERN HILLS MEDICAL CENTER, 391 Wallace Road, Nashville, TN, Zip 37211–4859; tel. 615/781–4000; Thomas H. Ozburn, Chief Executive Officer

TRISTAR STONECREST MEDICAL CENTER, 200 StoneCrest Boulevard, Smyrna, TN, Zip 37167–6810; tel. 615/768–2000; Louis Caputo, Chief Executive Officer

TRISTAR SUMMIT MEDICAL CENTER, 5655 Frist Boulevard, Hermitage, TN, Zip 37076–2053; tel. 615/316–3000; Jeffrey T. Whitehorn, Chief Executive Officer

TEXAS

LITTLE RIVER HEALTHCARE
1700 Brazos Avenue, Rockdale, TX 76567–2517; tel. 512/446–4500; Jeffrey Madison, FACHE, Chief Executive Officer

LITTLE RIVER CAMERON HOSPITAL, 806 North Crockett Avenue, Cameron, TX, Zip 76520–2553; tel. 254/605–1300; Troy Zinn, Chief Executive Officer

ROCKDALE HOSPITAL, 1700 Brazos Street, Rockdale, TX, Zip 76567–2517, Mailing Address: Drawer 1010, Zip 76567–1010; tel. 512/446–4500; Jeffrey Madison, FACHE, Chief Executive Officer

METHODIST HEALTHCARE SYSTEM
8109 Fredericksburg Road, San Antonio, TX 78229–3311; tel. 210/575–0355; Jaime Wesolowski, President and Chief Executive Officer

METHODIST AMBULATORY SURGERY HOSPITAL – NORTHWEST, 9150 Huebner Road, Suite 100, San Antonio, TX, Zip 78240–1545; tel. 210/575–5000; Scott Davis, Chief Executive Officer

METHODIST HOSPITAL, 7700 Floyd Curl Drive, San Antonio, TX, Zip 78229–3993; tel. 210/575–4000; Gay Nord, Chief Executive Officer

METHODIST STONE OAK HOSPITAL, 1139 East Sonterra Boulevard, San Antonio, TX, Zip 78258–4347; tel. 210/638–2100; Marc Strode, Chief Executive Officer

REGIONAL HEALTHCARE ALLIANCE
530 South Beckham Avenue, Tyler, TX 75702–8310; tel. 903/531–4449; John Webb, President

ALLEGIANCE SPECIALTY HOSPITAL OF KILGORE, 1612 South Henderson Boulevard, Kilgore, TX, Zip 75662–3594; tel. 903/984–3505; Karen Ross, Chief Executive Officer

BAYLOR UNIVERSITY MEDICAL CENTER, 3500 Gaston Avenue, Dallas, TX, Zip 75246–2088; tel. 214/820–0111; John B. McWhorter, III, President

CHILDREN'S HEALTH SYSTEM OF TEXAS, 1935 Medical District Drive, Dallas, TX, Zip 75235; tel. 214/456–7000; Christopher J. Durovich, President and Chief Executive Officer

CHRISTUS MOTHER FRANCES HOSPITAL – JACKSONVILLE, 2026 South Jackson, Jacksonville, TX, Zip 75766–5822; tel. 903/541–4500; Anne Pileggi, Administrator and Associate Vice President

CHRISTUS MOTHER FRANCES HOSPITAL – SULPHUR SPRINGS, 115 Airport Road, Sulphur Springs, TX, Zip 75482–2105; tel. 903/885–7671; Paul Harvery, President and Chief Executive Officer

CHRISTUS MOTHER FRANCES HOSPITAL – TYLER, 800 East Dawson Street, Tyler, TX, Zip 75701–2036; tel. 903/593–8441; John McGreevy, Chief Executive Officer

CHRISTUS TRINITY MOTHER FRANCES REHABILITATION HOSPITAL, 3131 Troup Highway, Tyler, TX, Zip 75701–8352; tel. 903/510–7000; Sharla Anderson, Chief Executive Officer

EAST TEXAS MEDICAL CENTER HENDERSON, 300 Wilson Street, Henderson, TX, Zip 75652–5956; tel. 903/657–7541; Mark Leitner, Administrator

GOOD SHEPHERD MEDICAL CENTER, 700 East Marshall Avenue, Longview, TX, Zip 75601–5580; tel. 903/315–2000; Steve Altmiller, President and Chief Executive Officer

NACOGDOCHES MEDICAL CENTER, 4920 N.E. Stallings Drive, Nacogdoches, TX, Zip 75965–1200; tel. 936/569–9481; Jeff Patterson, Chief Executive Officer

PALESTINE REGIONAL MEDICAL CENTER–EAST, 2900 South Loop 256, Palestine, TX, Zip 75801–6958; tel. 903/731–1000; Richard Grogan, Interim Chief Executive Officer

PARIS REGIONAL MEDICAL CENTER, 865 Deshong Drive, Paris, TX, Zip 75460–9313, Mailing Address: P.O. Box 9070, Zip 75461–9070; tel. 903/785–4521; Patti Monczewski, Interim Chief Executive Officer

TITUS REGIONAL MEDICAL CENTER, 2001 North Jefferson Avenue, Mount Pleasant, TX, Zip 75455–2398; tel. 903/577–6000; John P. Allen, Chief Executive Officer

TYLER CONTINUECARE HOSPITAL, 800 East Dawson, 4th Floor, Tyler, TX, Zip 75701–2036; tel. 903/531–4080; Stephanie Hyde, R.N., MSN, Chief Executive Officer

UNIVERSITY OF TEXAS HEALTH NORTHEAST, 11937 Highway 271, Tyler, TX, Zip 75708–3154; tel. 903/877–7777; Kirk A. Calhoun, M.D., President

ST. DAVID'S HEALTH NETWORK
98 San Jacinto Boulevard, Austin, TX 78701–4082; tel. 512/708–9700; David Huffstutler, President and Chief Executive Officer

ST. DAVID'S MEDICAL CENTER, 919 East 32nd Street, Austin, TX, Zip 78705–2709, Mailing Address: P.O. Box 4039, Zip 78765–4039; tel. 512/476–7111; Donald H. Wilkerson, Chief Executive Officer

ST. DAVID'S NORTH AUSTIN MEDICAL CENTER, 12221 North MoPac Expressway, Austin, TX, Zip 78758–2496; tel. 512/901–1000; Allen Harrison, Chief Executive Officer

ST. DAVID'S ROUND ROCK MEDICAL CENTER, 2400 Round Rock Avenue, Round Rock, TX, Zip 78681–4097; tel. 512/341–1000; Deborah L. Ryle, Administrator and Chief Executive Officer

ST. DAVID'S SOUTH AUSTIN MEDICAL CENTER, 901 West Ben White Boulevard, Austin, TX, Zip 78704–6903; tel. 512/447–2211; Todd E. Steward, FACHE, Chief Executive Officer

THE HOSPITALS OF PROVIDENCE
2001 North Oregon, El Paso, TX 79902–5005; tel. 915/577–6625; Sally A. Hurt–Deitch, FACHE, R.N., Market Chief Executive Officer

THE HOSPITALS OF PROVIDENCE EAST CAMPUS, 3280 Joe Battle Boulevard, El Paso, TX, Zip 79938–2622; tel. 915/832–2000; Nicholas R. Tejeda, FACHE, Chief Executive Officer

THE HOSPITALS OF PROVIDENCE MEMORIAL CAMPUS, 2001 North Oregon Street, El Paso, TX, Zip 79902–3368; tel. 915/577–6625; Sally A. Hurt–Deitch, FACHE, R.N., Market Chief Executive Officer

THE HOSPITALS OF PROVIDENCE SIERRA CAMPUS, 1625 Medical Center Drive, El Paso, TX, Zip 79902–5005; tel. 915/747–4000; Monica Vargas–Mahar, FACHE, Chief Executive Officer

THE HOSPITALS OF PROVIDENCE TRANSMOUNTAIN CAMPUS, 2000 Transmountain Road, El Paso, TX Zip 79911; tel. 915/500–6560; Nicholas R. Tejada, FACHE, Chief Executive Officer

VERMONT

THE UNIVERSITY OF VERMONT HEALTH NETWORK
111 Colchester Avenue, Burlington, VT 05401–1473; tel. 802/847–3983; John R. Brumsted, M.D., President and Chief Executive Officer

THE UNIVERSITY OF VERMONT HEALTH NETWORK–CHAMPLAIN VALLEY PHYSICIANS HOSPITAL, 75 Beekman Street, Plattsburgh, NY, Zip 12901–1438; tel. 518/561–2000; Stephens M. Mundy, President and Chief Executive Officer

THE UNIVERSITY OF VERMONT HEALTH NETWORK CENTRAL VERMONT MEDICAL CENTER, 130 Fisher Road, Berlin, VT, Zip 05602–9516, Mailing Address: P.O. Box 547, Barre, Zip 05641–0547; tel. 802/371–4100; Judith C. Tartaglia, President and Chief Executive Officer

THE UNIVERSITY OF VERMONT HEALTH NETWORK ELIZABETHTOWN COMMUNITY HOSPITAL, 75 Park Street, Elizabethtown, NY, Zip 12932, Mailing Address: P.O. Box 277, Zip 12932–0277; tel. 518/873–6377; John R. Remillard, Interim Chief Executive Officer

THE UNIVERSITY OF VERMONT HEALTH NETWORK UNIVERSITY OF VERMONT MEDICAL CENTER, 111 Colchester Avenue, Burlington, VT, Zip 05401–1473; tel. 802/847–0000; Eileen Whalen, R.N., President and Chief Operating Officer

VIRGINIA

VIRGINIA HEALTH NETWORK
7400 Beaufont Springs Drive, Suite 505, Richmond, VA 23225–5521; tel. 804/320–3837; James Brittain, President

AUGUSTA HEALTH, 78 Medical Center Drive, Fishersville, VA, Zip 22939–2332, Mailing Address: P.O. Box 1000, Zip 22939–1000; tel. 540/932–4000; Mary N. Mannix, FACHE, President and Chief Executive Officer

BATH COMMUNITY HOSPITAL, 83 Park Drive, Hot Springs, VA, Zip 24445–2788, Mailing Address: P.O. Box Z., Zip 24445–0750; tel. 540/839–7000; Kathy Landreth, Interim Chief Executive Officer

BEDFORD MEMORIAL HOSPITAL, 1613 Oakwood Street, Bedford, VA, Zip 24523–1213, Mailing Address: P.O. Box 688, Zip 24523–0688; tel. 540/586–2441; Patti Jurkus, Chief Executive Officer

BON SECOURS–DEPAUL MEDICAL CENTER, 150 Kingsley Lane, Norfolk, VA, Zip 23505–4650; tel. 757/889–5000; John E. Barrett, III, Chief Executive Officer

BON SECOURS MARYVIEW MEDICAL CENTER, 3636 High Street, Portsmouth, VA, Zip 23707–3270; tel. 757/398–2200; Joseph M. Oddis, Chief Executive Officer

BON SECOURS MEMORIAL REGIONAL MEDICAL CENTER, 8260 Atlee Road, Mechanicsville, VA, Zip 23116–1844; tel. 804/764–6000; Mark M. Gordon, Chief Executive Officer

BON SECOURS–RICHMOND COMMUNITY HOSPITAL, 1500 North 28th Street, Richmond, VA, Zip 23223–5396, Mailing Address: P.O. Box 27184, Zip 23261–7184; tel. 804/225–1700; Mark M. Gordon, Chief Executive Officer

BON SECOURS ST. FRANCIS MEDICAL CENTER, 13710 St. Francis Boulevard, Midlothian, VA, Zip 23114–3267; tel. 804/594–7300; Chris Accashian, Chief Executive Officer

BON SECOURS ST. MARY'S HOSPITAL, 5801 Bremo Road, Richmond, VA, Zip 23226–1907; tel. 804/285–2011; Francine Barr, R.N., MS, Chief Executive Officer

BUCHANAN GENERAL HOSPITAL, 1535 Slate Creek Road, Grundy, VA, Zip 24614–6974; tel. 276/935–1000; Robert D. Ruchti, Chief Executive Officer

CARILION FRANKLIN MEMORIAL HOSPITAL, 180 Floyd Avenue, Rocky Mount, VA, Zip 24151–1389; tel. 540/483–5277; William D. Jacobsen, Vice President and Administrator

CARILION GILES COMMUNITY HOSPITAL, 159 Hartley Way, Pearisburg, VA, Zip 24134–2471; tel. 540/921–6000; William Flattery, Vice President and Administrator Western Division

CARILION NEW RIVER VALLEY MEDICAL CENTER, 2900 Lamb Circle, Christiansburg, VA, Zip 24073–6344, Mailing Address: P.O. Box 5, Radford, Zip 24143–0005; tel. 540/731–2000; William Flattery, Vice President and Administrator Western Division

CARILION ROANOKE MEMORIAL HOSPITAL, Belleview at Jefferson Street, Roanoke, VA, Zip 24014, Mailing Address: P.O. Box 13367, Zip 24033–3367; tel. 540/981–7000; Steven C. Arner, President

CARILION STONEWALL JACKSON HOSPITAL, 1 Health Circle, Lexington, VA, Zip 24450–2492; tel. 540/458–3300; Charles E. Carr, Vice President and Administrator

CARILION TAZEWELL COMMUNITY HOSPITAL, 141 Ben Bolt Avenue, Tazewell, VA, Zip 24651–9700; tel. 276/988–8700; Kathren Dowdy, MSN, Regional Hospital Senior Director

CENTRA SOUTHSIDE COMMUNITY HOSPITAL, 800 Oak Street, Farmville, VA, Zip 23901–1199; tel. 434/392–8811; Thomas Angelo, Chief Executive Officer

CHESAPEAKE REGIONAL HEALTHCARE, 736 Battlefield Boulevard North, Chesapeake, VA, Zip 23320–4941, Mailing Address: P.O. Box 2028, Zip 23327–2028; tel. 757/312–8121; Alton Stocks, M.D., Interim President and Chief Executive Officer

CHILDREN'S HOSPITAL OF RICHMOND AT VCU–BROOK ROAD CAMPUS, 2924 Brook Road, Richmond, VA, Zip 23220–1298; tel. 804/321–7474; Leslie G. Wyatt, Senior Vice President Children's Services and Executive Director

CHILDREN'S HOSPITAL OF THE KING'S DAUGHTERS, 601 Children's Lane, Norfolk, VA, Zip 23507–1910; tel. 757/668–7000; James D. Dahling, President and Chief Executive Officer

CHIPPENHAM HOSPITAL, 7101 Jahnke Road, Richmond, VA, Zip 23225–4044; tel. 804/320–3911; Tim McManus, President and Chief Executive Officer

CLINCH VALLEY MEDICAL CENTER, 6801 Governor G. C. Peery Highway, Richlands, VA, Zip 24641–2194; tel. 276/596–6000; Peter Mulkey, Chief Executive Officer

DOMINION HOSPITAL, 2960 Sleepy Hollow Road, Falls Church, VA, Zip 22044–2030; tel. 703/536–2000; Lee Higginbotham, Chief Executive Officer

FAUQUIER HOSPITAL, 500 Hospital Drive, Warrenton, VA, Zip 20186–3099; tel. 540/316–5000; Rodger H. Baker, President and Chief Executive Officer

HEALTHSOUTH REHABILITATION HOSPITAL OF VIRGINIA, 5700 Fitzhugh Avenue, Richmond, VA, Zip 23226–1800; tel. 804/288–5700; David Cashwell, Chief Executive Officer

HENRICO DOCTORS' HOSPITAL, 1602 Skipwith Road, Richmond, VA, Zip 23229–5205; tel. 804/289–4500; William Wagnon, Chief Executive Officer

INOVA ALEXANDRIA HOSPITAL, 4320 Seminary Road, Alexandria, VA, Zip 22304–1535; tel. 703/504–3167; Susan Carroll, Chief Executive Officer

INOVA FAIR OAKS HOSPITAL, 3600 Joseph Siewick Drive, Fairfax, VA, Zip 22033–1798; tel. 703/391–3600; John L. Fitzgerald, Chief Executive Officer

INOVA FAIRFAX HOSPITAL, 3300 Gallows Road, Falls Church, VA, Zip 22042–3300; tel. 703/776–4001; Patrick Christiansen, Ph.D., Chief Executive Officer

INOVA LOUDOUN HOSPITAL, 44045 Riverside Parkway, Leesburg, VA, Zip 20176–5101, Mailing Address: P.O. Box 6000, Zip 20177–0600; tel. 703/858–6000; Patrick Walters, Chief Executive Officer

INOVA MOUNT VERNON HOSPITAL, 2501 Parker's Lane, Alexandria, VA, Zip 22306–3209; tel. 703/664–7000; Deborah Addo–Samuels, Chief Executive Officer

JOHN RANDOLPH MEDICAL CENTER, 411 West Randolph Road, Hopewell, VA, Zip 23860–2938; tel. 804/541–1600; Suzanne B. Jackson, FACHE, Chief Executive Officer

JOHNSTON MEMORIAL HOSPITAL, 16000 Johnston Memorial Drive, Abingdon, VA, Zip 24211–7659; tel. 276/258–1000; Stan Hickson, FACHE, President and Chief Executive Officer

LEWISGALE HOSPITAL ALLEGHANY, One ARH Lane, Low Moor, VA, Zip 24457, Mailing Address: P.O. Box 7, Zip 24457–0007; tel. 540/862–6011; Charlotte C. Tyson, Chief Executive Officer

LEWISGALE HOSPITAL PULASKI, 2400 Lee Highway, Pulaski, VA, Zip 24301–2326, Mailing Address: P.O. Box 759, Zip 24301–0759; tel. 540/994–8100; Derek Vance, Chief Executive Officer

MARTHA JEFFERSON HOSPITAL, 500 Martha Jefferson Drive, Charlottesville, VA, Zip 22911–4668; tel. 434/654–7000; Jonathan S. Davis, FACHE, President

MARY IMMACULATE HOSPITAL, 2 Bernardine Drive, Newport News, VA, Zip 23602–4499; tel. 757/886–6000; Darlene Stephenson, Chief Executive Officer

MARY WASHINGTON HOSPITAL, 1001 Sam Perry Boulevard, Fredericksburg, VA, Zip 22401–3354; tel. 540/741–1100; Michael P. McDermott, M.D., President and Chief Executive Officer

MEMORIAL HOSPITAL, 320 Hospital Drive, Martinsville, VA, Zip 24112–1981, Mailing Address: P.O. Box 4788, Zip 24115–4788; tel. 276/666–7200; Michael Ehrat, Chief Executive Officer

MOUNTAIN VIEW REGIONAL MEDICAL CENTER, 310 Third Street N.E., Norton, VA, Zip 24273–1137; tel. 276/679–9100; Dale Clark, President

NORTHERN HOSPITAL OF SURRY COUNTY, 830 Rockford Street, Mount Airy, NC, Zip 27030–5365, Mailing Address: P.O. Box 1101, Zip 27030–1101; tel. 336/719–7000; Ned Hill, President and Chief Executive Officer

NOVANT HEALTH UVA HEALTH SYSTEM CULPEPER MEDICAL CENTER, 501 Sunset Lane, Culpeper, VA, Zip 22701–3917, Mailing Address: P.O. Box 592, Zip 22701–0500; tel. 540/829–4100; Greg Napps, Chief Executive Officer

NOVANT HEALTH UVA HEALTH SYSTEM PRINCE WILLIAM MEDICAL CENTER, 8700 Sudley Road, Manassas, VA, Zip 20110–4418, Mailing Address: P.O. Box 2610, Zip 20108–0867; tel. 703/369–8000; Melissa Robson, President

Section B

PIONEER COMMUNITY HOSPITAL OF PATRICK, 18688 Jeb Stuart Highway, Stuart, VA, Zip 24171–1559; tel. 276/694–3151; Jeanette Filpi, Chief Executive Officer

RAPPAHANNOCK GENERAL HOSPITAL, 101 Harris Drive, Kilmarnock, VA, Zip 22482–3880, Mailing Address: P.O. Box 1449, Zip 22482–1449; tel. 804/435–8000; Mark M. Gordon, Chief Executive Officer

RESTON HOSPITAL CENTER, 1850 Town Center Parkway, Reston, VA, Zip 20190–3219; tel. 703/689–9000; John A. Deardorff, Chief Executive Officer

RIVERSIDE REGIONAL MEDICAL CENTER, 500 J. Clyde Morris Boulevard, Newport News, VA, Zip 23601–1929; tel. 757/594–2000; Michael J. Doucette, Senior Vice President and Administrator

RIVERSIDE REHABILITATION INSTITUTE, 245 Chesapeake Avenue, Newport News, VA, Zip 23607–6038; tel. 757/928–8000; Daniel Ballin, Administrator

RIVERSIDE SHORE MEMORIAL HOSPITAL, 9507 Hospital Avenue, Nassawadox, VA, Zip 23413–1821, Mailing Address: P.O. Box 17, Zip 23413–0017; tel. 757/414–8000; John Peterman, Vice President and Administrator

RIVERSIDE TAPPAHANNOCK HOSPITAL, 618 Hospital Road, Tappahannock, VA, Zip 22560–5000; tel. 804/443–3311; Esther Desimini, Administrator

RIVERSIDE WALTER REED HOSPITAL, 7519 Hospital Drive, Gloucester, VA, Zip 23061–4178, Mailing Address: P.O. Box 1130, Zip 23061–1130; tel. 804/693–8800; Megan Kleckner, Vice President and Administrator

RUSSELL COUNTY MEDICAL CENTER, 58 Carroll Street, Lebanon, VA, Zip 24266, Mailing Address: P.O. Box 3600, Zip 24266–0200; tel. 276/883–8000; Stephen K. Givens, Assistant Vice President and Administrator

SENTARA CAREPLEX HOSPITAL, 3000 Coliseum Drive, Hampton, VA, Zip 23666–5963; tel. 757/736–1000; Debra A. Flores, R.N., MS, President and Administrator

SENTARA LEIGH HOSPITAL, 830 Kempsville Road, Norfolk, VA, Zip 23502–3920; tel. 757/261–6000; Teresa L. Edwards, President and Administrator

SENTARA NORFOLK GENERAL HOSPITAL, 600 Gresham Drive, Norfolk, VA, Zip 23507–1904; tel. 757/388–3000; Kurt T. Hofelich, President

SENTARA NORTHERN VIRGINIA MEDICAL CENTER, 2300 Opitz Boulevard, Woodbridge, VA, Zip 22191–3399; tel. 703/523–1000; Stephen D. Porter, President

SENTARA OBICI HOSPITAL, 2800 Godwin Boulevard, Suffolk, VA, Zip 23434–8038; tel. 757/934–4000; Steve Julian, M.D., President

SENTARA PRINCESS ANNE HOSPITAL, 2025 Glenn Mitchell Drive, Virginia Beach, VA, Zip 23456–0178; tel. 757/507–1000; Thomas B. Thames, M.D., President

SENTARA VIRGINIA BEACH GENERAL HOSPITAL, 1060 First Colonial Road, Virginia Beach, VA, Zip 23454–3002; tel. 757/395–8000; Elwood Bernard Boone, III, FACHE, President

SENTARA WILLIAMSBURG REGIONAL MEDICAL CENTER, 100 Sentara Circle, Williamsburg, VA, Zip 23188–5713; tel. 757/984–6000; David J. Masterson, President

SHELTERING ARMS REHABILITATION HOSPITAL, 8254 Atlee Road, Mechanicsville, VA, Zip 23116–1844; tel. 804/764–1000; Mary A. Zweifel, President and Chief Executive Officer

SMYTH COUNTY COMMUNITY HOSPITAL, 245 Medical Park Drive, Marion, VA, Zip 24354, Mailing Address: P.O. Box 880, Zip 24354–0880; tel. 276/378–1000; Stan Hickson, FACHE, President and Chief Executive Officer

SOUTHAMPTON MEMORIAL HOSPITAL, 100 Fairview Drive, Franklin, VA, Zip 23851–1238, Mailing Address: P.O. Box 817, Zip 23851–0817; tel. 757/569–6100; Kimberly W. Marks, Chief Executive Officer

SOUTHERN VIRGINIA REGIONAL MEDICAL CENTER, 727 North Main Street, Emporia, VA, Zip 23847–1274; tel. 434/348–4400; Matt Tavenner, Chief Executive Officer

SOUTHSIDE REGIONAL MEDICAL CENTER, 200 Medical Park Boulevard, Petersburg, VA, Zip 23805–9274; tel. 804/765–5000; Douglas J. Moyer, Chief Executive Officer

TWIN COUNTY REGIONAL HEALTHCARE, 200 Hospital Drive, Galax, VA, Zip 24333–2227; tel. 276/236–8181; Jon D. Applebaum, Chief Executive Officer

UNIVERSITY OF VIRGINIA MEDICAL CENTER, 1215 Lee Street, Charlottesville, VA, Zip 22908–0001, Mailing Address: P.O. Box 800809, Zip 22908–0809; tel. 434/924–0211; Pamela Sutton-Wallace, Chief Executive Officer

UVA–HEALTHSOUTH REHABILITATION HOSPITAL, 515 Ray C. Hunt Drive, Charlottesville, VA, Zip 22903–2981; tel. 434/244–2000; Thomas J. Cook, Chief Executive Officer

VCU COMMUNITY MEMORIAL HOSPITAL, 125 Buena Vista Circle, South Hill, VA, Zip 23970–1431, Mailing Address: P.O. Box 90, Zip 23970–0090; tel. 434/447–3151; W. Scott Burnette, Chief Executive Officer

VCU MEDICAL CENTER, 1250 East Marshall Street, Richmond, VA, Zip 23298–5051, Mailing Address: P.O. Box 980510, Zip 23298–0510; tel. 804/828–9000; John Duval, Chief Executive Officer

VIRGINIA HOSPITAL CENTER – ARLINGTON, 1701 North George Mason Drive, Arlington, VA, Zip 22205–3698; tel. 703/558–5000; James B. Cole, Chief Executive Officer

WYTHE COUNTY COMMUNITY HOSPITAL, 600 West Ridge Road, Wytheville, VA, Zip 24382–1099; tel. 276/228–0200; Chad Melton, Chief Executive Officer

WASHINGTON

GROUP HEALTH COOPERATIVE
320 Westlake Avenue North, Suite 100, Seattle, WA 98109–5233; tel. 206/448–5083; Scott Armstrong, Chief Executive Officer

CASCADE VALLEY HOSPITAL AND CLINICS, 330 South Stillaguamish Avenue, Arlington, WA, Zip 98223–1642; tel. 360/435–2133; Michael Liepman, Chief Executive Officer

COLUMBIA COUNTY HEALTH SYSTEM, 1012 South Third Street, Dayton, WA, Zip 99328–1696; tel. 509/382–2531; Shane McGuire, Chief Executive Officer

DEACONESS HOSPITAL, 800 West Fifth Avenue, Spokane, WA, Zip 99204–2803, Mailing Address: P.O. Box 248, Zip 99210–0248; tel. 509/458–5800; Maurine Cate, Chief Executive Officer

GROUP HEALTH COOPERATIVE CENTRAL HOSPITAL, 201 16th Avenue East, Seattle, WA, Zip 98112–5226; tel. 206/326–3000; Carol M. Taylor, R.N., Regional Director Clinical Operations

HARRISON MEDICAL CENTER, 2520 Cherry Avenue, Bremerton, WA, Zip 98310–4229; tel. 360/744–3911; David W. Schultz, FACHE, President

ISLAND HOSPITAL, 1211 24th Street, Anacortes, WA, Zip 98221–2562; tel. 360/299–1300; Vincent Oliver, FACHE, Administrator

KADLEC REGIONAL MEDICAL CENTER, 888 Swift Boulevard, Richland, WA, Zip 99352–3514; tel. 509/946–4611; Rand J. Wortman, President and Chief Executive Officer

KITTITAS VALLEY HEALTHCARE, 603 South Chestnut Street, Ellensburg, WA, Zip 98926–3875; tel. 509/962–7302; Julie Petersen, Interim Chief Executive Officer

KOOTENAI HEALTH, 2003 Kootenai Health Way, Coeur D'Alene, ID, Zip 83814–2677; tel. 208/625–4000; Jon Ness, Chief Executive Officer

LOURDES MEDICAL CENTER, 520 North Fourth Avenue, Pasco, WA, Zip 99301–5257; tel. 509/547–7704; John Serle, FACHE, President and Chief Executive Officer

MULTICARE MARY BRIDGE CHILDREN'S HOSPITAL AND HEALTH CENTER, 317 Martin Luther King Jr. Way, Tacoma, WA, Zip 98405–4234, Mailing Address: P.O. Box 5299, Zip 98415–0299; tel. 253/403–1400; Linda Chen, President and Market Leader

NORTHWEST SPECIALTY HOSPITAL, 1593 East Polston Avenue, Post Falls, ID, Zip 83854–5326; tel. 208/262–2300; Rick Rasmussen, Chief Executive Officer

OVERLAKE MEDICAL CENTER, 1035 116th Avenue N.E., Bellevue, WA, Zip 98004–4604; tel. 425/688–5000; J. Michael Marsh, President and Chief Executive Officer

PEACEHEALTH ST. JOSEPH MEDICAL CENTER, 2901 Squalicum Parkway, Bellingham, WA, Zip 98225–1851; tel. 360/734–5400; Dale Zender, President Hospital Services NW

PEACEHEALTH UNITED GENERAL MEDICAL CENTER, 2000 Hospital Drive, Sedro-Woolley, WA, Zip 98284–4327; tel. 360/856–6021; Christopher Johnston, Interim Chief Administrative Officer

PMH MEDICAL CENTER, 723 Memorial Street, Prosser, WA, Zip 99350–1524; tel. 509/786–2222; Craig J. Marks, FACHE, Chief Executive Officer

PROVIDENCE CENTRALIA HOSPITAL, 914 South Scheuber Road, Centralia, WA, Zip 98531–9027; tel. 360/736–2803; Medrice Coluccio, R.N., Southwest Region Chief Executive

PROVIDENCE HOLY FAMILY HOSPITAL, 5633 North Lidgerwood Street, Spokane, WA, Zip 99208–1224; tel. 509/482–0111; Alex Jackson, Chief Executive

PROVIDENCE REGIONAL MEDICAL CENTER EVERETT, 1321 Colby Avenue, Everett, WA, Zip 98201–1665, Mailing Address: P.O. Box 1147, Zip 98206–1147; tel. 425/261–2000; Preston M. Simmons, FACHE, Chief Executive Officer

PROVIDENCE SACRED HEART MEDICAL CENTER & CHILDREN'S HOSPITAL, 101 West Eighth Avenue, Spokane, WA, Zip 99204–2364, Mailing Address: P.O. Box 2555, Zip 99220–2555; tel. 509/474–3131; Alex Jackson, Chief Executive

PROVIDENCE ST. MARY MEDICAL CENTER, 401 West Poplar Street, Walla Walla, WA, Zip 99362–2846, Mailing Address: P.O. Box 1477, Zip 99362–0312; tel. 509/525–3320; Steven A. Burdick, Chief Executive Officer

PULLMAN REGIONAL HOSPITAL, 835 S.E. Bishop Boulevard, Pullman, WA, Zip 99163–5512; tel. 509/332–2541; Scott K. Adams, FACHE, Chief Executive Officer

SEATTLE CHILDREN'S HOSPITAL, 4800 Sand Point Way N.E., Seattle, WA, Zip 98105–3901, Mailing Address: P.O. Box 5371, Zip 98145–5005; tel. 206/987–2000; Jeff Sperring, M.D., Chief Executive Officer

SKAGIT REGIONAL HEALTH, 1415 East Kincaid, Mount Vernon, WA, Zip 98274–4126, Mailing Address: P.O. Box 1376, Zip 98273–1376; tel. 360/424–4111; Michael T. Liepman, Chief Executive Officer

ST. FRANCIS HOSPITAL, 34515 Ninth Avenue South, Federal Way, WA, Zip 98003–6799; tel. 253/944–8100; Anthony McLean, President

ST. JOSEPH MEDICAL CENTER, 1717 South J Street, Tacoma, WA, Zip 98405–3004, Mailing Address: P.O. Box 2197, Zip 98401–2197; tel. 253/426–4101; Tim O'Haver, Chief Operating Officer

SUNNYSIDE COMMUNITY HOSPITAL AND CLINICS, 1016 Tacoma Avenue, Sunnyside, WA, Zip 98944–2263, Mailing Address: P.O. Box 719, Zip 98944–0719; tel. 509/837–1500; John Gallagher, Chief Executive Officer

TOPPENISH COMMUNITY HOSPITAL, 502 West Fourth Avenue, Toppenish, WA, Zip 98948–1616, Mailing Address: P.O. Box 672, Zip 98948–0672; tel. 509/865–3105; Chris Mendoza, Interim Chief Executive Officer

TRIOS HEALTH, 900 South Auburn Street, Kennewick, WA, Zip 99336–5621, Mailing Address: P.O. Box 6128, Zip 99336–0128; tel. 509/586–6111; Glen Marshall, Chief Executive Officer

VALLEY HOSPITAL, 12606 East Mission Avenue, Spokane Valley, WA, Zip 99216–1090; tel. 509/924–6650; Gregory George Repetti, III, FACHE, Chief Executive Officer

VIRGINIA MASON MEDICAL CENTER, 1100 Ninth Avenue, Seattle, WA, Zip 98101–2756, Mailing Address: P.O. Box 900, Zip 98111–0900; tel. 206/223–6600; Gary Kaplan, M.D., FACHE, Chairman and Chief Executive Officer

WALLA WALLA GENERAL HOSPITAL, 1025 South Second Avenue, Walla Walla, WA, Zip 99362–4116, Mailing Address: P.O. Box 1398, Zip 99362–0309; tel. 509/525–0480; Robert J. Beehler, Interim President and Chief Executive Officer

WHIDBEYHEALTH, 101 North Main Street, Coupeville, WA, Zip 98239–3413; tel. 360/678–5151; Geri Forbes, Chief Executive Officer

WHITMAN HOSPITAL AND MEDICAL CENTER, 1200 West Fairview Street, Colfax, WA, Zip 99111–9579; tel. 509/397–3435; Hank Hanigan, MS, R.N., Chief Executive Officer

YAKIMA REGIONAL MEDICAL AND CARDIAC CENTER, 110 South Ninth Avenue, Yakima, WA, Zip 98902–3315; tel. 509/575–5000; Bryan Braegger, Interim Chief Executive Officer

YAKIMA VALLEY MEMORIAL HOSPITAL, 2811 Tieton Drive, Yakima, WA, Zip 98902–3761; tel. 509/575–8000; Russ Myers, Chief Executive Officer

LINCOLN COUNTY HEALTH DEPARTMENT
90 Nichols Street, Davenport, WA 99122–9729; tel. 509/725–1001; Ed Dzedzy, Public Health Administration

LINCOLN HOSPITAL, 10 Nicholls Street, Davenport, WA, Zip 99122–9729; tel. 509/725–7101; Tyson Lacy, Chief Executive Officer and Superintendent

ODESSA MEMORIAL HEALTHCARE CENTER, 502 East Amende Drive, Odessa, WA, Zip 99159–7003, Mailing Address: P.O. Box 368, Zip 99159–0368; tel. 509/982–2611; Mo P. Sheldon, FACHE, Chief Executive Officer and Administrator

WEST VIRGINIA

HEALTH PARTNERS NETWORK, INC.
1000 Technology Drive, Suite 2320, Fairmont, WV 26554–8834; tel. 304/368–2740; William G. MacLean, Executive Director

BROADDUS HOSPITAL, 1 Healthcare Drive, Philippi, WV, Zip 26416–9405, Mailing Address: P.O. Box 930, Zip 26416–0930; tel. 304/457–1760; Jeffrey A. Powelson, Chief Executive Officer

CAMDEN CLARK MEDICAL CENTER, 800 Garfield Avenue, Parkersburg, WV, Zip 26101–5378, Mailing Address: P.O. Box 718, Zip 26102–0718; tel. 304/424–2111; David K. McClure, President and Chief Executive Officer

DAVIS MEDICAL CENTER, Gorman Avenue and Reed Street, Elkins, WV, Zip 26241, Mailing Address: P.O. Box 1484, Zip 26241–1484; tel. 304/636–3300; Vance Jackson, FACHE, Chief Executive Officer

GRAFTON CITY HOSPITAL, 1 Hospital Plaza, Grafton, WV, Zip 26354–1283; tel. 304/265–0400; Patrick D. Shaw, Chief Executive Officer

HEALTHSOUTH MOUNTAINVIEW REGIONAL REHABILITATION HOSPITAL, 1160 Van Voorhis Road, Morgantown, WV, Zip 26505–3437; tel. 304/598–1100; Lou Little, Chief Executive Officer

MINNIE HAMILTON HEALTHCARE CENTER, 186 Hospital Drive, Grantsville, WV, Zip 26147–7100; tel. 304/354–9244; Steve Whited, Chief Executive Officer

ST. JOSEPH'S HOSPITAL OF BUCKHANNON, 1 Amalia Drive, Buckhannon, WV, Zip 26201–2276; tel. 304/473–2000; Skip Gjolberg, FACHE, Administrator

STONEWALL JACKSON MEMORIAL HOSPITAL, 230 Hospital Plaza, Weston, WV, Zip 26452–8558; tel. 304/269–8000; Avah Stalnaker, Chief Executive Officer

UNITED HOSPITAL CENTER, 327 Medical Park Drive, Bridgeport, WV, Zip 26330–9006; tel. 681/342–1000; Michael C. Tillman, President and Chief Executive Officer

WEBSTER COUNTY MEMORIAL HOSPITAL, 324 Miller Mountain Drive, Webster Springs, WV, Zip 26288–1087, Mailing Address: P.O. Box 312, Zip 26288–0312; tel. 304/847–5682; Robert M. Mace, M.D., Chief Executive Officer

WEST VIRGINIA UNIVERSITY HOSPITALS, 1 Medical Center Drive, Morgantown, WV, Zip 26506–4749; tel. 304/598–4000; Albert Wright, PharmD, President and Chief Executive Officer

PARTNERS IN HEALTH NETWORK, INC.
405 Capitol Street, Suite 505, Charleston, WV 25301–1783; tel. 304/388–7385; Robert D. Whitler, Executive Director

BOONE MEMORIAL HOSPITAL, 701 Madison Avenue, Madison, WV, Zip 25130–1699; tel. 304/369–1230; Virgil Underwood, Chief Executive Officer

BRAXTON COUNTY MEMORIAL HOSPITAL, 100 Hoylman DR, Gassaway, WV, Zip 26624–9318, Mailing Address: 100 Hoylman Drive, Zip 26624–9318; tel. 304/364–5156; Ben Vincent, FACHE, Chief Executive Officer

CHARLESTON AREA MEDICAL CENTER, 501 Morris Street, Charleston, WV, Zip 25301–1300, Mailing Address: P.O. Box 1547, Zip 25326–1547; tel. 304/388–5432; David L. Ramsey, President and Chief Executive Officer

EYE AND EAR CLINIC OF CHARLESTON, 1306 Kanawha Boulevard East, Charleston, WV, Zip 25301–3001, Mailing Address: P.O. Box 2271, Zip 25328–2271; tel. 304/343–4371; Christina Arvon, Administrator and Chief Executive Officer

HIGHLAND HOSPITAL, 300 56th Street S.E., Charleston, WV, Zip 25304–2361, Mailing Address: P.O. Box 4107, Zip 25364–4107; tel. 304/926–1600; Cynthia A. Persily, Ph.D., R.N., President and Chief Executive Officer

JACKSON GENERAL HOSPITAL, 122 Pinnell Street, Ripley, WV, Zip 25271–9101, Mailing Address: P.O. Box 720, Zip 25271–0720; tel. 304/372–2731; Stephanie McCoy, President and Chief Executive Officer

MINNIE HAMILTON HEALTHCARE CENTER, 186 Hospital Drive, Grantsville, WV, Zip 26147–7100; tel. 304/354–9244; Steve Whited, Chief Executive Officer

MONTGOMERY GENERAL HOSPITAL, 401 Sixth Avenue, Montgomery, WV, Zip 25136–2116, Mailing Address: P.O. Box 270, Zip 25136–0270; tel. 304/442–5151; Vickie Gay, Chief Executive Officer

POCAHONTAS MEMORIAL HOSPITAL, 150 Duncan Road, Buckeye, WV, Zip 24924, Mailing Address: Rural Route 2, Box 52 W, Zip 24924; tel. 304/799–7400; Barbara Lay, Chief Executive Officer

ROANE GENERAL HOSPITAL, 200 Hospital Drive, Spencer, WV, Zip 25276–1050; tel. 304/927–4444; Douglas E. Bentz, Chief Executive Officer

STONEWALL JACKSON MEMORIAL HOSPITAL, 230 Hospital Plaza, Weston, WV, Zip 26452–8558; tel. 304/269–8000; Avah Stalnaker, Chief Executive Officer

SUMMERSVILLE REGIONAL MEDICAL CENTER, 400 Fairview Heights Road, Summersville, WV, Zip 26651–9308; tel. 304/872–2891; Daniel M. Ayres, President and Chief Executive Officer

WEBSTER COUNTY MEMORIAL HOSPITAL, 324 Miller Mountain Drive, Webster Springs, WV, Zip 26288–1087, Mailing Address: P.O. Box 312, Zip 26288–0312; tel. 304/847–5682; Robert M. Mace, M.D., Chief Executive Officer

WISCONSIN

AFFINITY HEALTH SYSTEM
1506 South Oneida Street, Appleton, WI 54915–1305; tel. 920/831–8912; Monica Hilt, President and Chief Executive Officer

CALUMET MEDICAL CENTER, 614 Memorial Drive, Chilton, WI, Zip 53014–1597; tel. 920/849–2386; Timothy Richman, President

MERCY MEDICAL CENTER, 500 South Oakwood Road, Oshkosh, WI, Zip 54904–7944; tel. 920/223–2000; Jeremy Normington-Slay, FACHE, Chief Executive Officer

ST. ELIZABETH HOSPITAL, 1506 South Oneida Street, Appleton, WI, Zip 54915–1305; tel. 920/738–2000; Monica Hilt, President and Chief Executive Officer

ASPIRUS, INC.
425 Pine Ridge Boulevard, Wausau, WI 54401–4123; tel. 715/847–2118; Matthew Heywood, Chief Executive Officer

ASPIRUS GRAND VIEW, N10561 Grand View Lane, Ironwood, MI, Zip 49938–9622; tel. 906/932–2525; Paula L. Chermside, Chief Executive Officer

ASPIRUS IRON RIVER HOSPITALS & CLINICS, 1400 West Ice Lake Road, Iron River, MI, Zip 49935–9526; tel. 906/265–6121; Connie L. Koutouzos, R.N., MSN, Chief Executive Officer

ASPIRUS KEWEENAW HOSPITAL, 205 Osceola Street, Laurium, MI, Zip 49913–2134; tel. 906/337–6500; Michael Hauswirth, Chief Operating Officer

ASPIRUS LANGLADE HOSPITAL, 112 East Fifth Avenue, Antigo, WI, Zip 54409–2796; tel. 715/623–2331; David R. Schneider, Executive Director

ASPIRUS MEDFORD HOSPITAL, 135 South Gibson Street, Medford, WI, Zip 54451–1696; tel. 715/748–8100; Gregory A. Olson, President and Chief Executive Officer

ASPIRUS ONTONAGON HOSPITAL, 601 South Seventh Street, Ontonagon, MI, Zip 49953–1459; tel. 906/884–8000; Michael Hauswirth, Chief Operating Officer

ASPIRUS RIVERVIEW HOSPITAL AND CLINICS, INC., 410 Dewey Street, Wisconsin Rapids, WI, Zip 54494–4715, Mailing Address: P.O. Box 8080, Zip 54495–8080; tel. 715/423–6060; Todd Burch, Chief Executive Officer

ASPIRUS WAUSAU HOSPITAL, 333 Pine Ridge Boulevard, Wausau, WI, Zip 54401–4187; tel. 715/847–2121; Darrell Lentz, President

COLUMBIA ST. MARY'S
2025 East Newport Avenue, Milwaukee, WI 53211–2906; tel. 414/961–3300; Travis Andersen, President and Chief Executive Officer

COLUMBIA ST. MARY'S HOSPITAL MILWAUKEE, 2301 North Lake Drive, Milwaukee, WI, Zip 53211–4508; tel. 414/291–1000; Travis Andersen, President and Chief Executive Officer

COLUMBIA ST. MARY'S OZAUKEE HOSPITAL, 13111 North Port Washington Road, Mequon, WI, Zip 53097–2416; tel. 262/243–7300; Travis Andersen, President and Chief Executive Officer

SACRED HEART REHABILITATION INSTITUTE, 2323 North Lake Drive, Milwaukee, WI, Zip 53211–4508; tel. 414/298–6750; Bill Heart, Chief Operating Officer

COMMUNITY HEALTH NETWORK, INC.
225 Memorial Drive, Berlin, WI 54923–1243; tel. 920/361–5580; John Feeney, President and Chief Executive Officer

BERLIN MEMORIAL HOSPITAL, 225 Memorial Drive, Berlin, WI, Zip 54923–1295; tel. 920/361–1313; John Feeney, President and Chief Executive Officer

THEDA CARE MEDICAL CENTER – WILD ROSE, 601 Grove Avenue, Wild Rose, WI, Zip 54984–6903, Mailing Address: P.O. Box 243, Zip 54984–0243; tel. 920/622–3257; Craig A. Kantos, Chief Executive Officer

FROEDTERT HEALTH
9200 West Wisconsin Avenue, Milwaukee, WI 53226–3596; tel. 414/805–3000; Catherine A. Jacobson, President and Chief Executive Officer

COMMUNITY MEMORIAL HOSPITAL, W180 N8085 Town Hall Road, Menomonee Falls, WI, Zip 53051–3518, Mailing Address: P.O. Box 408, Zip 53052–0408; tel. 262/251–1000; Dennis Pollard, President of Community Memorial Hospital

FROEDTERT MEMORIAL LUTHERAN HOSPITAL, 9200 West Wisconsin Avenue, Milwaukee, WI, Zip 53226–3596, Mailing Address: P.O. Box 26099, Zip 53226–0099; tel. 414/805–3000; Catherine Buck, President

ST. JOSEPH'S HOSPITAL, 3200 Pleasant Valley Road, West Bend, WI, Zip 53095–9274; tel. 262/334–5533; Allen Ericson, Chief Operating Officer, Community Hospital Division and President, St. Joseph's Hospital

GUNDERSEN HEALTH SYSTEM
1900 South Avenue, La Crosse, WI 54601–5467; tel. 608/782–7300; Scott W. Rathgaber, M.D., Chief Executive Officer

GUNDERSEN BOSCOBEL AREA HOSPITAL AND CLINICS, 205 Parker Street, Boscobel, WI, Zip 53805–1698; tel. 608/375–4112; David Hartberg, Chief Executive Officer

GUNDERSEN HEALTH SYSTEM, 1900 South Avenue, La Crosse, WI, Zip 54601–5467; tel. 608/782–7300; Scott W. Rathgaber, M.D., Chief Executive Officer and Board Chair

GUNDERSEN ST. JOSEPH'S HOSPITAL AND CLINICS, 400 Water Avenue, Hillsboro, WI, Zip 54634–9054, Mailing Address: P.O. Box 527, Zip 54634–0527; tel. 608/489–8000; Debra Smith, Chief Executive Officer

GUNDERSEN TRI–COUNTY HOSPITAL AND CLINICS, 18601 Lincoln Street, Whitehall, WI, Zip 54773–8605; tel. 715/538–4361; Brian Theiler, President and Chief Executive Officer

PALMER LUTHERAN HEALTH CENTER, 112 Jefferson Street, West Union, IA, Zip 52175–1022; tel. 563/422–3811; Tanya Tysland, Chief Executive Officer

MERCY ALLIANCE, INC.
1000 Mineral Point Avenue, Janesville, WI 53548–2940; tel. 608/756–6000; Javon R. Bea, President and Chief Executive Officer

MERCY HARVARD HOSPITAL, 901 Grant Street, Harvard, IL, Zip 60033–1898, Mailing Address: P.O. Box 850, Zip 60033–0850; tel. 815/943–5431; Javon R. Bea, Chief Executive Officer

MERCY HOSPITAL AND TRAUMA CENTER, 1000 Mineral Point Avenue, Janesville, WI, Zip 53548–2982, Mailing Address: P.O. Box 5003, Zip 53547–5003; tel. 608/756–6000; Javon R. Bea, President and Chief Executive Officer

MERCY WALWORTH HOSPITAL AND MEDICAL CENTER, N2950 State Road 67, Lake Geneva, WI, Zip 53147–2655; tel. 262/245–0535; Jennifer Hallatt, Chief Operating Officer

MINISTRY HEALTH CARE
11925 West Lake Park Drive, Milwaukee, WI 53224–3002; tel. 414/359–1060; Daniel Neufelder, President

CALUMET MEDICAL CENTER, 614 Memorial Drive, Chilton, WI, Zip 53014–1597; tel. 920/849–2386; Timothy Richman, President

FLAMBEAU HOSPITAL, 98 Sherry Avenue, Park Falls, WI, Zip 54552–1467, Mailing Address: P.O. Box 310, Zip 54552–0310; tel. 715/762–2484; James R. Braun, Chief Administrative Officer and Chief Financial Officer

HOWARD YOUNG MEDICAL CENTER, 240 Maple Street, Woodruff, WI, Zip 54568–9190, Mailing Address: P.O. Box 470, Zip 54568–0470; tel. 715/356–8000; Sandra L. Anderson, President and Chief Executive Officer

MERCY MEDICAL CENTER, 500 South Oakwood Road, Oshkosh, WI Zip 54904–7944; tel. 920/223–3000; Jeremy Normington-Slay, FACHE, Chief Executive Officer

MINISTRY DOOR COUNTY MEDICAL CENTER, 323 South 18th Avenue, Sturgeon Bay, WI, Zip 54235–1495; tel. 920/743–5566; Gerald M. Worrick, President and Chief Executive Officer

MINISTRY EAGLE RIVER MEMORIAL HOSPITAL, 201 Hospital Road, Eagle River, WI, Zip 54521–8835; tel. 715/479–7411; Sandra L. Anderson, President and Chief Executive Officer

MINISTRY GOOD SAMARITAN HEALTH CENTER, 601 South Center Avenue, Merrill, WI, Zip 54452–3404; tel. 715/536–5511; Mary T. Krueger, President

MINISTRY OUR LADY OF VICTORY HOSPITAL, 1120 Pine Street, Stanley, WI, Zip 54768–1297; tel. 715/644–5571; Vanessa Freitag, President

MINISTRY SACRED HEART HOSPITAL, 401 West Mohawk Drive, Tomahawk, WI, Zip 54487–2274; tel. 715/453–7700; Sandra L. Anderson, President and Chief Executive Officer

MINISTRY SAINT CLARE'S HOSPITAL, 3400 Ministry Parkway, Weston, WI, Zip 54476–5220; tel. 715/393–3000; Brian Kief, Interim President

MINISTRY SAINT JOSEPH'S HOSPITAL, 611 St. Joseph Avenue, Marshfield, WI, Zip 54449–1898; tel. 715/387–1713; Brian Kief, Regional Vice President Ministry Health Care and President Ministry Saint Joseph's Hospital

MINISTRY SAINT MARY'S HOSPITALS, 2251 North Shore Drive, Rhinelander, WI, Zip 54501–6710; tel. 715/361–2000; Sandra L. Anderson, President and Chief Executive Officer

MINISTRY SAINT MICHAEL'S HOSPITAL, 900 Illinois Avenue, Stevens Point, WI, Zip 54481–3196; tel. 715/346–5000; Jeffrey L. Martin, President

SAINT ELIZABETH'S MEDICAL CENTER, 1200 Grant Boulevard West, Wabasha, MN, Zip 55981–1042; tel. 651/565–4531; Thomas Crowley, President and Chief Executive Officer

ST. ELIZABETH HOSPITAL, 1506 South Oneida Street, Appleton, WI, Zip 54915–1305; tel. 920/738–2000; Monica Hilt, President and Chief Executive Officer

WHEATON FRANCISCAN HEALTHCARE
400 West River Woods Parkway, Glendale, WI 53212–1060; tel. 414/465–3000; John D. Oliverio, President and Chief Executive Officer

MIDWEST ORTHOPEDIC SPECIALTY HOSPITAL, 10101 South 27th Street, 2nd Floor, Franklin, WI, Zip 53132–7209; tel. 414/817–5800; Coreen Dicus–Johnson, President

WHEATON FRANCISCAN HEALTHCARE – ALL SAINTS, 3801 Spring Street, Racine, WI, Zip 53405–1690; tel. 262/687–4011; Susan Boland, R.N., MSN, President and Chief Executive Officer

WHEATON FRANCISCAN HEALTHCARE – ELMBROOK MEMORIAL, 19333 West North Avenue, Brookfield, WI, Zip 53045–4198; tel. 262/785–2000; Debra K. Standridge, President

WHEATON FRANCISCAN HEALTHCARE – FRANKLIN, 10101 South 27th Street, Franklin, WI, Zip 53132–7209; tel. 414/325–4700; Coreen Dicus–Johnson, President

WHEATON FRANCISCAN HEALTHCARE – ST. FRANCIS, 3237 South 16th Street, Milwaukee, WI, Zip 53215–4592; tel. 414/647–5000; Coreen Dicus–Johnson, President

WHEATON FRANCISCAN HEALTHCARE – ST. JOSEPH'S, 5000 West Chambers Street, Milwaukee, WI, Zip 53210–1650; tel. 414/447–2000; Debra K. Standridge, President

Section B

Alliances

ALLIANCE OF INDEPENDENT ACADEMIC MEDICAL CENTERS

233 East Erie Street, Ste 306, Chicago, IL Zip 60611; tel. 312/836–3712; Kimberly Pierce–Boggs, Executive Director

ARIZONA
Phoenix
Member
  Maricopa Integrated Health System

Scottsdale
Member
  HonorHealth Scottsdale Osborn Medical Center

CALIFORNIA
Concord
Member
  John Muir Behavioral Health Center

Los Angeles
Member
  Cedars–Sinai Medical Center

Oakland
Member
  Kaiser Permanente Oakland Medical Center

Walnut Creek
Member
  John Muir Medical Center, Walnut Creek

COLORADO
Denver
Member
  Saint Joseph Hospital

CONNECTICUT
Danbury
Member
  Danbury Hospital

Hartford
Member
  Saint Francis Hospital and Medical Center

DELAWARE
Newark
Member
  Christiana Care Health System

FLORIDA
Orlando
Member
  Florida Hospital
  Orlando Health

ILLINOIS
Chicago
Member
  Advocate Illinois Masonic Medical Center

Oak Lawn
Member
  Advocate Christ Medical Center

Park Ridge
Member
  Advocate Lutheran General Hospital

Peoria
Member
  OSF Saint Francis Medical Center

IOWA
West Des Moines
Member
  UnityPoint Health

KENTUCKY
Louisville
Member
  Kosair Children's Hospital
  Norton Audubon Hospital
  Norton Brownsboro Hospital
  Norton Hospital
  Norton Women's and Kosair Children's Hospital

LOUISIANA
Baton Rouge
Member
  Baton Rouge General Medical Center
  Our Lady of the Lake Regional Medical Center

New Orleans
Member
  Ochsner Health System

MAINE
Portland
Member
  Maine Medical Center

MARYLAND
Annapolis
Member
  Anne Arundel Medical Center

Baltimore
Member
  Sinai Hospital of Baltimore

MASSACHUSETTS
Burlington
Member
  Lahey Hospital & Medical Center, Burlington

Springfield
Member
  Baystate Medical Center

MICHIGAN
Grand Rapids
Member
  Mercy Health Saint Mary's

Lansing
Member
  Sparrow Hospital

Rochester
Member
  Crittenton Hospital Medical Center

Royal Oak
Member
  Beaumont Hospital – Royal Oak

MONTANA
Billings
Member
  Billings Clinic

NEW JERSEY
Brick Township
Member
  Ocean Medical Center

Holmdel
Member
  Bayshore Community Hospital

Livingston
Member
  Saint Barnabas Medical Center

Long Branch
Member
  Monmouth Medical Center, Long Branch Campus

Manahawkin
Member
  Southern Ocean Medical Center

Neptune
Member
  Jersey Shore University Medical Center

Newark
Member
  Newark Beth Israel Medical Center

Phillipsburg
Member
  St. Luke's Hospital – Warren Campus

Red Bank
Member
  Riverview Medical Center

NEW YORK
Brooklyn
Member
  Maimonides Medical Center

Cooperstown
Member
  Bassett Medical Center

Mineola
Member
  Winthrop–University Hospital

NORTH CAROLINA
Charlotte
Member
  Carolinas Medical Center

Greensboro
Member
  Moses H. Cone Memorial Hospital

OHIO
Akron
Member
  Akron General Medical Center

Cincinnati
Member
  Christ Hospital
  TriHealth Evendale Hospital

Columbus
Member
  OhioHealth Grant Medical Center
  OhioHealth Riverside Methodist Hospital

OREGON
Hood River
Member
  Providence Hood River Memorial Hospital

Milwaukie
Member
  Providence Milwaukie Hospital

Portland
Member
  Providence Portland Medical Center
  Providence St. Vincent Medical Center

PENNSYLVANIA
Bethlehem
Member
  St. Luke's University Hospital – Bethlehem Campus

Bryn Mawr
Member
  Main Line Health

Johnstown
Member
  Conemaugh Memorial Medical Center

Philadelphia
Member
  Einstein Medical Center Philadelphia

Sayre
Member
  Robert Packer Hospital

West Reading
Member
  Reading Hospital

Wynnewood
Member
  Lankenau Medical Center

York
Member
  WellSpan York Hospital

TEXAS
Dallas
Member
  Parkland Health & Hospital System

Fort Worth
Member
  JPS Health Network

Garland
Member
Baylor Medical Center at Garland

WASHINGTON

Seattle
Member
Group Health Cooperative Central Hospital
Swedish Medical Center–Cherry Hill Campus
Swedish Medical Center–First Hill
Virginia Mason Medical Center

WEST VIRGINIA

Charleston
Member
Charleston Area Medical Center

WISCONSIN

Marshfield
Member
Ministry Saint Joseph's Hospital

Milwaukee
Member
Aurora Health Care

ALLIANCEHEALTH OKLAHOMA

5300 North Grand Boulevard, Oklahoma
City, OK Zip 73112–5647;
tel. 405/815–3900; Jim R. Kendrick,
Chief Executive Officer

OKLAHOMA

Blackwell
Member
AllianceHealth Blackwell

Clinton
Member
AllianceHealth Clinton

Durant
Member
AllianceHealth Durant

Madill
Member
AllianceHealth Madill

Midwest City
Member
AllianceHealth Midwest

Oklahoma City
Member
AllianceHealth Deaconess

Ponca City
Member
AllianceHealth Ponca City

Pryor
Member
AllianceHealth Pryor

Seminole
Member
AllianceHealth Seminole

Woodward
Member
AllianceHealth Woodward

CAPSTONE HEALTH ALLIANCE

1200 Ridgefield Boulevard, Suite 200,
Asheville, NC Zip 28806;
tel. 828/418–5050; Tim Bugg, President
and Chief Executive Officer

ALABAMA

Dothan
Member
Southeast Alabama Medical Center

Opelika
Member
East Alabama Medical Center

GEORGIA

Bremen
Member
Tanner Higgins General Hospital

Carrollton
Member
Tanner Medical Center–Carrollton

Lagrange
Member
West Georgia Health

Villa Rica
Member
Tanner Medical Center–Villa Rica

KENTUCKY

Bowling Green
Member
Commonwealth Regional Specialty Hospital
Medical Center at Bowling Green

Franklin
Member
Medical Center at Franklin

Scottsville
Member
Medical Center at Scottsville

NORTH CAROLINA

Asheboro
Member
Randolph Hospital

Asheville
Member
Asheville Specialty Hospital
CarePartners Health Services
Mission Hospital

Boone
Member
Watauga Medical Center

Brevard
Member
Transylvania Regional Hospital

Bryson City
Member
Swain Community Hospital

Cherokee
Member
Cherokee Indian Hospital

Clyde
Member
Haywood Regional Medical Center

Columbus
Member
St. Luke's Hospital

Elizabeth City
Member
Sentara Albemarle Medical Center

Elizabethtown
Member
Cape Fear Valley – Bladen County Hospital

Fayetteville
Member
Cape Fear Valley Medical Center
Highsmith–Rainey Specialty Hospital

Franklin
Member
Angel Medical Center

Gastonia
Member
CaroMont Regional Medical Center

Goldsboro
Member
Wayne Memorial Hospital

Hendersonville
Member
Margaret R. Pardee Memorial Hospital
Park Ridge Health

Hickory
Member
Catawba Valley Medical Center

Highlands
Member
Highlands–Cashiers Hospital

Kinston
Member
UNC Lenoir Healthcare

Lumberton
Member
Southeastern Health

Marion
Member
McDowell Hospital

Morehead City
Member
Carteret Health Care

Newland
Member
Charles A. Cannon Memorial Hospital

Oxford
Member
Granville Health System

Pinehurst
Member
FirstHealth Moore Regional Hospital

Roanoke Rapids
Member
Halifax Regional Medical Center

Rockingham
Member
FirstHealth Richmond Memorial Hospital

Rutherfordton
Member
Rutherford Regional Health System

Spruce Pine
Member
Blue Ridge Regional Hospital

Statesville
Member
Iredell Health System

Sylva
Member
Harris Regional Hospital

Troy
Member
FirstHealth Montgomery Memorial Hospital

PENNSYLVANIA

Erie
Member
Millcreek Community Hospital

Kittanning
Member
ACMH Hospital

Meadville
Member
Meadville Medical Center

SOUTH CAROLINA

Conway
Member
Conway Medical Center

Dillon
Member
McLeod Medical Center Dillon

Florence
Member
McLeod Regional Medical Center

Greenwood
Member
Self Regional Healthcare

Loris
Member
McLeod Loris Seacoast Hospital

Seneca
Member
Oconee Memorial Hospital

West Columbia
Member
Lexington Medical Center

Winnsboro
Member
Fairfield Memorial Hospital

TENNESSEE

Crossville
Member
Cumberland Medical Center

Elizabethton
Member
Sycamore Shoals Hospital

Erwin
Member
  Unicoi County Memorial Hospital

Greeneville
Member
  Laughlin Memorial Hospital

Johnson City
Member
  Franklin Woods Community Hospital
  Johnson City Medical Center

Kingsport
Member
  Indian Path Medical Center

Knoxville
Member
  University of Tennessee Medical Center

Maryville
Member
  Blount Memorial Hospital

Mountain City
Member
  Johnson County Community Hospital

VIRGINIA
Abingdon
Member
  Johnston Memorial Hospital

Bedford
Member
  Bedford Memorial Hospital

Chesapeake
Member
  Chesapeake Regional Healthcare

Christiansburg
Member
  Carilion New River Valley Medical Center

Clintwood
Member
  Dickenson Community Hospital

Gloucester
Member
  Riverside Walter Reed Hospital

Grundy
Member
  Buchanan General Hospital

Lebanon
Member
  Russell County Medical Center

Lexington
Member
  Carilion Stonewall Jackson Hospital

Marion
Member
  Smyth County Community Hospital

Nassawadox
Member
  Riverside Shore Memorial Hospital

Newport News
Member
  Riverside Regional Medical Center

Norton
Member
  Norton Community Hospital

Pearisburg
Member
  Carilion Giles Community Hospital

Radford
Member
  Carilion New River Valley Medical Center

Roanoke
Member
  Carilion Roanoke Memorial Hospital

Rocky Mount
Member
  Carilion Franklin Memorial Hospital

South Hill
Member
  VCU Community Memorial Hospital

Tappahannock
Member
  Riverside Tappahannock Hospital

Williamsburg
Member
  Riverside Doctors' Hospital

CATHOLIC CEO HEALTHCARE CONNECTION
  50 South Main Street, Suite 200,
  Naperville, IL Zip 60540–5484;
  tel. 630/352–2220; Roger N. Butler,
  Executive Director

CALIFORNIA
Orange
Member
  St. Joseph Hospital

San Francisco
Member
  Dignity Health

COLORADO
Broomfield
Member
  SCL Health

Englewood
Member
  Catholic Health Initiatives

ILLINOIS
Chicago
Member
  Presence Health

Peoria
Member
  OSF Healthcare System

Springfield
Member
  Hospital Sisters Health System

Wheaton
Member
  Wheaton Franciscan Healthcare

LOUISIANA
Baton Rouge
Member
  Franciscan Missionaries of Our Lady Health System, Inc.

MARYLAND
Marriottsville
Member
  Bon Secours Health System, Inc.

MASSACHUSETTS
Tewksbury
Member
  Covenant Health

MICHIGAN
Livonia
Member
  Trinity Healthy

MISSOURI
Chesterfield
Member
  Mercy Health

Saint Louis
Member
  Ascension Health
  SSM Health

OHIO
Cincinnati
Member
  Mercy Health

SOUTH DAKOTA
Sioux Falls
Member
  Avera Health

TEXAS
Irving
Member
  CHRISTUS Health

WASHINGTON
Vancouver
Member
  PeaceHealth

WISCONSIN
Manitowoc
Member
  Franciscan Sisters of Christian Charity Sponsored Ministries, Inc.

HEALTH ENTERPRISES COOPERATIVE
  5825 Dry Creek Lane NE, Cedar Rapids,
  IA Zip 52402–1225; tel. 319/368–3619;
  Judy L. Sadler, President and Chief
  Executive Officer

IOWA
Ames
Member
  Mary Greeley Medical Center

Chariton
Member
  Lucas County Health Center

Charles City
Member
  Floyd County Medical Center

Cherokee
Member
  Cherokee Regional Medical Center

Davenport
Member
  Genesis Health System

Denison
Member
  Crawford County Memorial Hospital

Des Moines
Member
  Broadlawns Medical Center

Fairfield
Member
  Jefferson County Health Center

Grinnell
Member
  Grinnell Regional Medical Center

Guthrie Center
Member
  Guthrie County Hospital

Humboldt
Member
  Humboldt County Memorial Hospital

Ida Grove
Member
  Horn Memorial Hospital

Independence
Member
  Buchanan County Health Center

Iowa City
Member
  Mercy Iowa City

Manchester
Member
  Regional Medical Center

Maquoketa
Member
  Jackson County Regional Health Center

Marshalltown
Member
  Central Iowa Healthcare

Mount Pleasant
Member
  Henry County Health Center

Newton
Member
  Skiff Medical Center

Oskaloosa
Member
  Mahaska Health Partnership

Section B

Pella
Member
   Pella Regional Health Center

Pocahontas
Member
   Pocahontas Community Hospital

Sac City
Member
   Loring Hospital

Waukon
Member
   Veterans Memorial Hospital

Waverly
Member
   Waverly Health Center

West Burlington
Member
   Great River Medical Center

MISSOURI

Bethany
Member
   Harrison County Community Hospital

Fairfax
Member
   Community Hospital - Fairfax

HOSPITAL NETWORK VENTURES, LLC
6212 American Avenue, Portage, MI
Zip 49002; tel. 269/329–3200; Gregory
L. Hedegore, President and Chief
Executive Officer

MICHIGAN

Allegan
Member
   Allegan General Hospital

Kalamazoo
Member
   Bronson Methodist Hospital

Marshall
Member
   Oaklawn Hospital

Sturgis
Member
   Sturgis Hospital

HOSPITAL SHARED SERVICES ASSOCIATION
P O Box 19741, Seattle, WA
Zip 98109–6741; tel. 206/399–0865;
Joe McNamee, Executive Director

OREGON

Salem
Member
   Oregon State Hospital

WASHINGTON

Bellevue
Member
   Overlake Medical Center

Chelan
Member
   Lake Chelan Community Hospital

Clarkston
Member
   Tri–State Memorial Hospital

Davenport
Member
   Lincoln Hospital

Edmonds
Member
   Swedish/Edmonds

Ephrata
Member
   Columbia Basin Hospital

Grand Coulee
Member
   Coulee Medical Center

Kirkland
Member
   EvergreenHealth

Medical Lake
Member
   Eastern State Hospital

Moses Lake
Member
   Samaritan Healthcare

Mount Vernon
Member
   Skagit Regional Health

Newport
Member
   Newport Hospital and Health Services

Odessa
Member
   Odessa Memorial Healthcare Center

Othello
Member
   Othello Community Hospital

Prosser
Member
   PMH Medical Center

Pullman
Member
   Pullman Regional Hospital

Quincy
Member
   Quincy Valley Medical Center

Republic
Member
   Ferry County Memorial Hospital

Ritzville
Member
   East Adams Rural Healthcare

Tacoma
Member
   Western State Hospital

Tonasket
Member
   North Valley Hospital

MEDI–SOTA, INC.
1280 Locust Street Suite 16, Dawson,
MN Zip 56232–2375;
tel. 320/769–2269; Deb Ranallo,
Executive Director

MINNESOTA

Appleton
Member
   Appleton Area Health Services

Arlington
Member
   Ridgeview Sibley Medical Center

Benson
Member
   Swift County–Benson Hospital

Blue Earth
Member
   United Hospital District

Canby
Member
   Sanford Canby Medical Center

Dawson
Member
   Johnson Memorial Health Services

Elbow Lake
Member
   Prairie Ridge Hospital and Health Services

Glencoe
Member
   Glencoe Regional Health Services

Glenwood
Member
   Glacial Ridge Health System

Graceville
Member
   Essentia Health–Graceville

Granite Falls
Member
   Granite Falls Municipal Hospital and Manor

Hendricks
Member
   Hendricks Community Hospital Association

Litchfield
Member
   Meeker Memorial Hospital

Long Prairie
Member
   CentraCare Health–Long Prairie

Madelia
Member
   Madelia Community Hospital

Madison
Member
   Madison Healthcare Services

Mahnomen
Member
   Mahnomen Health Center

Marshall
Member
   Avera Marshall Regional Medical Center

Montevideo
Member
   Chippewa County–Montevideo Hospital

Olivia
Member
   RC Hospital and Clinics

Ortonville
Member
   Ortonville Area Health Services

Paynesville
Member
   CentraCare Health–Paynesville

Perham
Member
   Perham Health

Pipestone
Member
   Pipestone County Medical Center Avera

Redwood Falls
Member
   Redwood Area Hospital

Saint Peter
Member
   River's Edge Hospital and Clinic

Slayton
Member
   Murray County Medical Center

Sleepy Eye
Member
   Sleepy Eye Medical Center

Staples
Member
   Lakewood Health System

Tracy
Member
   Sanford Tracy Medical Center

Tyler
Member
   Tyler Healthcare Center Avera

Wadena
Member
   Tri–County Hospital

Willmar
Member
   Rice Memorial Hospital

Windom
Member
   Windom Area Hospital

NORTHWEST KANSAS HEALTH ALLIANCE
2220 Canterbury Drive, Hays, KS
Zip 67601–2370; tel. 785/623–2300;
John H. Jeter M.D., President and Chief
Executive Officer

Section B

KANSAS

Ashland
Member
Ashland Health Center

Atwood
Member
Rawlins County Health Center

Beloit
Member
Mitchell County Hospital Health Systems

Colby
Member
Citizens Medical Center

Dighton
Member
Lane County Hospital

Dodge City
Member
Western Plains Medical Complex

Ellsworth
Member
Ellsworth County Medical Center

Garden City
Member
St. Catherine Hospital

Goodland
Member
Goodland Regional Medical Center

Great Bend
Member
Great Bend Regional Hospital

Greensburg
Member
Kiowa County Memorial Hospital

Hill City
Member
Graham County Hospital

Hoisington
Member
Clara Barton Hospital

Hoxie
Member
Sheridan County Health Complex

Hutchinson
Member
Hutchinson Regional Medical Center

Jetmore
Member
Hodgeman County Health Center

Kinsley
Member
Edwards County Hospital and Healthcare Center

La Crosse
Member
Rush County Memorial Hospital

Larned
Member
Pawnee Valley Community Hospital

Lawrence
Member
Lawrence Memorial Hospital

Leoti
Member
Wichita County Health Center

Lincoln
Member
Lincoln County Hospital

Lyons
Member
Hospital District No 1 of Rice County

Minneola
Member
Minneola District Hospital

Ness City
Member
Ness County Hospital District No 2

Norton
Member
Norton County Hospital

Oakley
Member
Logan County Hospital

Oberlin
Member
Decatur Health Systems

Osborne
Member
Osborne County Memorial Hospital

Ottawa
Member
Ransom Memorial Hospital

Phillipsburg
Member
Phillips County Hospital

Plainville
Member
Rooks County Health Center

Quinter
Member
Gove County Medical Center

Ransom
Member
Grisell Memorial Hospital District One

Russell
Member
Russell Regional Hospital

Saint Francis
Member
Cheyenne County Hospital

Salina
Member
Salina Regional Health Center

Satanta
Member
Satanta District Hospital and Long Term Care

Scott City
Member
Scott County Hospital

Smith Center
Member
Smith County Memorial Hospital

Stafford
Member
Stafford County Hospital

Tribune
Member
Greeley County Health Services

Wakeeney
Member
Trego County–Lemke Memorial Hospital

PENNANT HEALTH ALLIANCE

2122 Health Drive SW Suite 100,
Wyoming, MI Zip 49519–9698;
tel. 616/252–6800; Michael D. Faas,
Chief Executive Officer

MICHIGAN

Ann Arbor
Member
University of Michigan Hospitals and Health Centers

Cadillac
Member
Munson Healthcare Cadillac Hospital

Grand Rapids
Member
Mary Free Bed Rehabilitation Hospital
Mercy Health Saint Mary's

Grayling
Member
Munson Healthcare Grayling Hospital

Wyoming
Member
Metro Health Hospital

PREMIER, INC.

13034 Ballantyne Corporate Place,
Charlotte, NC Zip 28277–1498;
tel. 704/816–5353; Susan DeVore,
President and Chief Executive Officer

ALABAMA

Dothan
Member
Southeast Alabama Medical Center

Opelika
Member
East Alabama Medical Center

ARIZONA

Phoenix
Member
Banner Health

Scottsdale
Member
HonorHealth

ARKANSAS

Batesville
Member
White River Medical Center

Pine Bluff
Member
Jefferson Regional Medical Center

CALIFORNIA

Fresno
Member
Community Medical Centers

Loma Linda
Member
Loma Linda University Medical Center

Los Angeles
Member
Verity Health System

Mountain View
Member
El Camino Hospital

Rancho Mirage
Member
Eisenhower Medical Center

Roseville
Member
Adventist Health

San Francisco
Member
Dignity Health

CONNECTICUT

Hartford
Member
Saint Francis Hospital and Medical Center

Waterbury
Member
Saint Mary's Hospital

DELAWARE

Dover
Member
Bayhealth Medical Center

Lewes
Member
Beebe Healthcare

FLORIDA

Altamonte Springs
Member
Adventist Health System Sunbelt Health Care
Corporation

Clearwater
Member
BayCare Health System

Coral Gables
Member
Baptist Health South Florida

Dunedin
Member
BayCare Alliant Hospital

Gainesville
Member
AVMED-Sante Fe

Jacksonville
Member
Baptist Health
Nemours

Miami Beach
Member
   Mount Sinai Medical Center

Tampa
Member
   H. Lee Moffitt Cancer Center and Research Institute

Vero Beach
Member
   Indian River Medical Center

Winter Haven
Member
   Winter Haven Hospital

GEORGIA

Carrollton
Member
   Tanner Medical Center–Carrollton

Lagrange
Member
   West Georgia Health

Savannah
Member
   Memorial Health
   St. Joseph's Hospital

HAWAII

Honolulu
Member
   Kuakini Medical Center

ILLINOIS

Chicago
Member
   Mount Sinai Hospital
   Presence Health

Harvey
Member
   Ingalls Memorial Hospital

Naperville
Member
   Edward Hospital

Peoria
Member
   UnityPoint Health – Peoria

Urbana
Member
   Carle Foundation Hospital

Winfield
Member
   Cadence Health

INDIANA

Gary
Member
   Methodist Hospitals

KENTUCKY

Ashland
Member
   King's Daughters Medical Center

Bowling Green
Member
   Commonwealth Regional Specialty Hospital

Danville
Member
   Ephraim McDowell Regional Medical Center

Edgewood
Member
   St. Elizabeth Edgewood

Glasgow
Member
   T. J. Samson Community Hospital

Henderson
Member
   Methodist Hospital

Louisville
Member
   Alliant Management Services
   Baptist Health
   Norton Healthcare

Murray
Member
   Murray–Calloway County Hospital

LOUISIANA

Baton Rouge
Member
   Woman's Hospital

Hammond
Member
   North Oaks Health System

Houma
Member
   Terrebonne General Medical Center

Lafayette
Member
   Lafayette General Medical Center

Marrero
Member
   West Jefferson Medical Center

MAINE

Lewiston
Member
   Central Maine Medical Center

MARYLAND

Annapolis
Member
   Anne Arundel Medical Center

Baltimore
Member
   Greater Baltimore Medical Center
   Johns Hopkins Health System
   Mercy Medical Center
   Sinai Hospital of Baltimore

Cumberland
Member
   Western Maryland Regional Medical Center

Elkton
Member
   Union Hospital

Frederick
Member
   Frederick Memorial Hospital

Gaithersburg
Member
   Adventist HealthCare

Hagerstown
Member
   Meritus Medical Center

Lanham
Member
   Doctors Community Hospital

Marriottsville
Member
   Bon Secours Health System, Inc.

Randallstown
Member
   Northwest Hospital

Salisbury
Member
   Peninsula Regional Medical Center

Westminster
Member
   Carroll Hospital

MASSACHUSETTS

Boston
Member
   Tufts Medical Center

Fall River
Member
   Southcoast Hospitals Group

Springfield
Member
   Baystate Health, Inc.

MICHIGAN

Detroit
Member
   Henry Ford Health System

Flint
Member
   McLaren Health Care Corporation

Jackson
Member
   Henry Ford Allegiance Health

MINNESOTA

Minneapolis
Member
   Fairview Health Services

MISSISSIPPI

Jackson
Member
   Baptist Health Systems

Laurel
Member
   South Central Regional Medical Center

Meridian
Member
   Rush Health Systems

MISSOURI

Saint Joseph
Member
   Mosaic Life Care at St. Joseph

Saint Louis
Member
   SSM Health

MONTANA

Billings
Member
   Billings Clinic

NEW MEXICO

Albuquerque
Member
   Presbyterian Healthcare Services

NORTH CAROLINA

Asheboro
Member
   Randolph Hospital

Asheville
Member
   Mission Health System

Boone
Member
   Watauga Medical Center

Charlotte
Member
   Carolinas Healthcare System

Fayetteville
   Cape Fear Valley Health System

Gastonia
Member
   CaroMont Regional Medical Center

Goldsboro
Member
   Wayne Memorial Hospital

Greensboro
Member
   Moses H. Cone Memorial Hospital

Hendersonville
Member
   Margaret R. Pardee Memorial Hospital

Hickory
Member
   Catawba Valley Medical Center

Kinston
Member
   UNC Lenoir Healthcare

Lumberton
Member
   Southeastern Health

Morehead City
Member
   Carteret Health Care

Pinehurst
Member
   FirstHealth of the Carolinas

Roanoke Rapids
Member
   Halifax Regional Medical Center

Statesville
Member
  Iredell Health System

OHIO

Akron
Member
  Summa Health System

Cincinnati
Member
  Mercy Health

Cleveland
Member
  University Hospitals

Elyria
Member
  University Hospitals Elyria Medical Center

Kettering
Member
  Kettering Medical Center

Middleburg Heights
Member
  Southwest General Health Center

Parma
Member
  University Hospitals Parma Medical Center

Sandusky
Member
  Firelands Regional Health System

OKLAHOMA

Tulsa
Member
  Saint Francis Hospital

OREGON

Salem
Member
  Salem Hospital

PENNSYLVANIA

Beaver
Member
  Heritage Valley Health System

Bethlehem
Member
  St. Luke's University Health Network

Danville
Member
  Geisinger Health System

King of Prussia
Member
  Universal Health Services, Inc.

Philadelphia
Member
  Einstein Healthcare Network

Washington
Member
  Washington Hospital

SOUTH CAROLINA

Anderson
Member
  AnMed Health Medical Center

Conway
Member
  Conway Medical Center

West Columbia
Member
  Lexington Medical Center

SOUTH DAKOTA

Rapid City
Member
  Rapid City Regional Hospital

Sioux Falls
Member
  Avera Health

TENNESSEE

Crossville
Member
  Cumberland Medical Center

Greeneville
Member
  Laughlin Memorial Hospital

Johnson City
Member
  Mountain States Health Alliance

Knoxville
Member
  University of Tennessee Medical Center

Maryville
Member
  Blount Memorial Hospital

TEXAS

Arlington
Member
  Texas Health Resources

Dallas
Member
  Methodist Health System
  University of Texas Southwestern Medical Center

Galveston
Member
  University of Texas Medical Branch

Houston
Member
  Harris Health System
  University of Texas M.D. Anderson Cancer Center

Lubbock
Member
  University Medical Center

VIRGINIA

Abingdon
Member
  Johnston Memorial Hospital

Chesapeake
Member
  Chesapeake Regional Healthcare

Falls Church
Member
  Inova Health System

Marion
Member
  Smyth County Community Hospital

Newport News
Member
  Riverside Health System

Roanoke
Member
  Carilion Clinic

South Hill
Member
  VCU Community Memorial Hospital

Winchester
Member
  Valley Health System

WASHINGTON

Seattle
Member
  Group Health Cooperative Central Hospital

Vancouver
Member
  PeaceHealth

WEST VIRGINIA

Elkins
Member
  Davis Medical Center

Huntington
Member
  Cabell Huntington Hospital
  Pallottine Health Services

Morgantown
Member
  Monongalia General Hospital

Parkersburg
Member
  Camden Clark Medical Center

Point Pleasant
Member
  Pleasant Valley Hospital

South Charleston
Member
  Thomas Memorial Hospital

Weirton
Member
  Weirton Medical Center

WISCONSIN

Milwaukee
Member
  Aurora Health Care

SEAGATE ALLIANCE
3445 Winton Place, Sute 222, Rochester, NY Zip 14623–2950;
tel. 888/732–4284; Travis Heider, President and Chief Executive Officer

NEW JERSEY

Newark
Member
  Columbus Hospital LTACH

NEW YORK

Bath
Member
  Bath Veterans Affairs Medical Center
  Ira Davenport Memorial Hospital

Buffalo
Member
  BryLin Hospitals
  Catholic Health System
  Erie County Medical Center
  Roswell Park Cancer Institute

Canandaigua
Member
  F. F. Thompson Hospital

Carthage
Member
  Carthage Area Hospital

Clifton Springs
Member
  Clifton Springs Hospital and Clinic

Corning
Member
  Guthrie Corning Hospital

Cuba
Member
  Cuba Memorial Hospital

Dansville
Member
  Nicholas H. Noyes Memorial Hospital

Dunkirk
Member
  Brooks Memorial Hospital

Elmira
Member
  Arnot Ogden Medical Center
  Elmira Psychiatric Center
  St. Joseph's Hospital

Geneva
Member
  Geneva General Hospital

Hornell
Member
  St. James Mercy Hospital

Kenmore
Member
  Kenmore Mercy Hospital

Lockport
Member
  Eastern Niagara Hospital

Montour Falls
Member
  Schuyler Hospital

Newark
Member
  Newark–Wayne Community Hospital

Olean
Member
  Olean General Hospital

Penn Yan
Member
  Soldiers and Sailors Memorial Hospital of Yates
    County

Rochester
Member
  Highland Hospital
  Rochester General Hospital
  Rochester Psychiatric Center
  Strong Memorial Hospital of the University of
    Rochester
  Unity Hospital

Springville
Member
  Bertrand Chaffee Hospital

Syracuse
Member
  Upstate University Hospital

Wellsville
Member
  Jones Memorial Hospital

PENNSYLVANIA

Bradford
Member
  Bradford Regional Medical Center

Coudersport
Member
  Cole Memorial

SYNERNET, INC.
110 Free Street, Portland, ME
Zip 04101–3908; tel. 207/771–3456;
Gerry Vicenzi, President and Chief
Executive Officer

MAINE

Augusta
Member
  MaineGeneral Medical Center

Bangor
Member
  St. Joseph Hospital

Bar Harbor
Member
  Mount Desert Island Hospital

Brunswick
Member
  Mid Coast Hospital

Damariscotta
Member
  LincolnHealth

Farmington
Member
  Franklin Memorial Hospital

Fort Kent
Member
  Northern Maine Medical Center

Norway
Member
  Stephens Memorial Hospital

Portland
Member
  Maine Medical Center
  Mercy Hospital of Portland
  New England Rehabilitation Hospital of Portland

Rockport
Member
  Pen Bay Medical Center

Skowhegan
Member
  Redington–Fairview General Hospital

Westbrook
Member
  Spring Harbor Hospital

THE NEW JERSEY COUNCIL OF TEACHING HOSPITALS
154 West State Street, Trenton, NJ
Zip 08608; tel. 609/656–9600; Deborah
S. Briggs, President

NEW JERSEY

Camden
Member
  Cooper University Health Care

Hackensack
Member
  Hackensack University Medical Center

Marlton
Member
  Weisman Children's Rehabilitation Hospital

Montclair
Member
  Hackensack University Medical Center Mountainside

Morristown
Member
  Morristown Medical Center

New Brunswick
Member
  Children's Specialized Hospital–PSE&G

North Bergen
Member
  HackensackUMC Palisades

Paterson
Member
  St. Joseph's Healthcare System

Summit
Member
  Overlook Medical Center

UNITED IROQUOIS SHARED SERVICES, INC.
15 Executive Park Drive, Clifton Park, NY
Zip 12065–5631; tel. 518/383–5060;
Gary J. Fitzgerald, President

NEW YORK

Albany
Member
  Albany Memorial Hospital
  St. Peter's Hospital

Alexandria Bay
Member
  River Hospital

Amsterdam
Member
  St. Mary's Healthcare

Auburn
Member
  Auburn Community Hospital

Binghamton
Member
  Our Lady of Lourdes Memorial Hospital, Inc.
  United Health Services Hospitals–Binghamton

Buffalo
Member
  Roswell Park Cancer Institute

Carthage
Member
  Carthage Area Hospital

Cobleskill
Member
  Cobleskill Regional Hospital

Cooperstown
Member
  Bassett Medical Center

Cortland
Member
  Cortland Regional Medical Center

Cuba
Member
  Cuba Memorial Hospital

Delhi
Member
  O'Connor Hospital

Elizabethtown
Member
  The University of Vermont Health Network
  Elizabethtown Community Hospital

Glens Falls
Member
  Glens Falls Hospital

Glenville
Member
  Conifer Park

Gloversville
Member
  Nathan Littauer Hospital and Nursing Home

Hamilton
Member
  Community Memorial Hospital

Hudson
Member
  Columbia Memorial Hospital

Ithaca
Member
  Cayuga Medical Center at Ithaca

Little Falls
Member
  Little Falls Hospital

Lowville
Member
  Lewis County General Hospital

Malone
Member
  The University of Vermont Health Network – Alice
    Hyde Medical Center

Margaretville
Member
  Margaretville Hospital

Massena
Member
  Massena Memorial Hospital

Norwich
Member
  UHS Chenango Memorial Hospital

Ogdensburg
Member
  Claxton–Hepburn Medical Center

Olean
Member
  Olean General Hospital

Oneida
Member
  Oneida Healthcare

Oneonta
Member
  Aurelia Osborn Fox Memorial Hospital

Oswego
Member
  Oswego Hospital

Plattsburgh
Member
  The University of Vermont Health Network–Champlain
    Valley Physicians Hospital

Potsdam
Member
  Canton–Potsdam Hospital

Rome
Member
  Rome Memorial Hospital

Saranac Lake
Member
  Adirondack Medical Center

Saratoga Springs
Member
  Saratoga Hospital

Schenectady
Member
  Ellis Hospital
  Sunnyview Rehabilitation Hospital

Springville
Member
  Bertrand Chaffee Hospital

Star Lake
Member
  Clifton–Fine Hospital

Syracuse
Member
  Crouse Hospital
  Upstate University Hospital

Troy
Member
  Samaritan Hospital
  St. Mary's Hospital

Utica
Member
  Faxton St. Luke's Healthcare
  St. Elizabeth Medical Center

Walton
Member
  UHS Delaware Valley Hospital

Watertown
Member
  Samaritan Medical Center

UNIVERSITY OF IOWA HEALTH ALLIANCE
1755 59th Place, West Des Moines, IA
Zip 50266–7737; tel. 515/643–4000;
Jennifer Vermeer, President and Chief
Executive Officer

ILLINOIS
Aledo
Member
  Genesis Medical Center–Aledo

Silvis
Member
  Genesis Medical Center, Illini Campus

IOWA
Albia
Member
  Monroe County Hospital and Clinics

Algona
Member
  Kossuth Regional Health Center

Audubon
Member
  Audubon County Memorial Hospital

Belmond
Member
  Iowa Specialty Hospital–Belmond

Bloomfield
Member
  Davis County Hospital

Britt
Member
  Hancock County Health System

Cedar Falls
Member
  Sartori Memorial Hospital

Cedar Rapids
Member
  Mercy Medical Center–Cedar Rapids

Centerville
Member
  Mercy Medical Center–Centerville

Clarinda
Member
  Clarinda Regional Health Center

Clarion
Member
  Iowa Specialty Hospital–Clarion

Clinton
Member
  Mercy Medical Center–Clinton

Corydon
Member
  Wayne County Hospital

Cresco
Member
  Regional Health Services of Howard County

Davenport
Member
  Genesis Medical Center–Davenport

De Witt
Member
  Genesis Medical Center, DeWitt

Des Moines
Member
  Mercy Medical Center–Des Moines

Dubuque
Member
  Mercy Medical Center–Dubuque

Dyersville
Member
  Mercy Medical Center–Dyersville

Elkader
Member
  Central Community Hospital

Emmetsburg
Member
  Palo Alto County Health System

Fairfield
Member
  Jefferson County Health Center

Greenfield
Member
  Adair County Memorial Hospital

Grinnell
Member
  Grinnell Regional Medical Center

Hampton
Member
  Franklin General Hospital

Hawarden
Member
  Hawarden Regional Healthcare

Iowa City
Member
  University of Iowa Hospitals and Clinics

Iowa Falls
Member
  Hansen Family Hospital

Keosauqua
Member
  Van Buren County Hospital

Knoxville
Member
  Knoxville Hospital & Clinics

Leon
Member
  Decatur County Hospital

Manning
Member
  Manning Regional Healthcare Center

Maquoketa
Member
  Jackson County Regional Health Center

Mason City
Member
  Mercy Medical Center–North Iowa

Mount Ayr
Member
  Ringgold County Hospital

Mount Pleasant
Member
  Henry County Health Center

New Hampton
Member
  Mercy Medical Center–New Hampton

Oelwein
Member
  Mercy Hospital of Franciscan Sisters

Osage
Member
  Mitchell County Regional Health Center

Pella
Member
  Pella Regional Health Center

Perry
Member
  Dallas County Hospital

Primghar
Member
  Baum Harmon Mercy Hospital

Sigourney
Member
  Keokuk County Health Center

Sioux City
Member
  Mercy Medical Center–Sioux City

Vinton
Member
  Virginia Gay Hospital

Washington
Member
  Washington County Hospital and Clinics

Waterloo
Member
  Covenant Medical Center

Waverly
Member
  Waverly Health Center

Webster City
Member
  Van Diest Medical Center

West Des Moines
Member
  Mercy Medical Center – West Lakes

Winterset
Member
  Madison County Health Care System

NEBRASKA
Oakland
Member
  Oakland Mercy Hospital

Pender
Member
  Pender Community Hospital

VANTAGE HEALTHCARE NETWORK, INC.
18282 Technology Drive, Suite 202,
Meadville, PA Zip 16335;
tel. 814/337–0000; David Petrarca,
Director Retail Operations

PENNSYLVANIA
Corry
Member
  Corry Memorial Hospital

DuBois
Member
  Penn Highlands DuBois

Ellwood City
Member
  Ellwood City Hospital

Erie
Member
  Millcreek Community Hospital
  Saint Vincent Hospital

Farrell
Member
  UPMC Horizon

Kane
Member
  Kane Community Hospital

Kittanning
Member
  ACMH Hospital

Meadville
Member
  Meadville Medical Center

Saint Marys
Member
  Penn Highlands Elk

Seneca
Member
  UPMC Northwest

Titusville
Member
  Titusville Area Hospital

Warren
Member
  Warren General Hospital

VIZIENT, INC.
  290 East John Carpenter Freeway, Irving,
  TX Zip 75062–2730; tel. 972/830–0000;
  Curtis W. Nonomaque, President and
  Chief Executive Officer

ALABAMA
Alexander City
Member
  Russell Medical Center

Anniston
Member
  Northeast Alabama Regional Medical Center

Athens
Member
  Athens–Limestone Hospital

Atmore
Member
  Atmore Community Hospital

Bay Minette
Member
  North Baldwin Infirmary

Bessemer
Member
  Medical West

Birmingham
Member
  University of Alabama Hospital

Boaz
Member
  Marshall Medical Center South

Brewton
Member
  D. W. McMillan Memorial Hospital

Carrollton
Member
  Pickens County Medical Center

Decatur
Member
  Decatur Morgan Hospital

Fairhope
Member
  Thomas Hospital

Fayette
Member
  Fayette Medical Center

Guntersville
Member
  Marshall Health System
  Marshall Medical Center North

Huntsville
Member
  Huntsville Hospital

Mobile
Member
  Mobile Infirmary Medical Center
  University of South Alabama Children's and Women's
    Hospital
  University of South Alabama Medical Center

Montgomery
Member
  Baptist Medical Center East
  Baptist Medical Center South

Opp
Member
  Mizell Memorial Hospital

Ozark
Member
  Dale Medical Center

Prattville
Member
  Prattville Baptist Hospital

Red Bay
Member
  Red Bay Hospital

Scottsboro
Member
  Highlands Medical Center

Sheffield
Member
  Helen Keller Hospital

Tuscaloosa
Member
  DCH Health System
  DCH Regional Medical Center

Union Springs
Member
  Bullock County Hospital

ALASKA
Anchorage
Member
  Providence Alaska Medical Center
  St. Elias Specialty Hospital

Cordova
Member
  Cordova Community Medical Center

Kodiak
Member
  Providence Kodiak Island Medical Center

Seward
Member
  Providence Seward Medical Center

Valdez
Member
  Providence Valdez Medical Center

Wrangell
Member
  Wrangell Medical Center

AMERICAN SAMOA
Pago Pago
Member
  Lyndon B. Johnson Tropical Medical Center

ARIZONA
Benson
Member
  Benson Hospital

Bisbee
Member
  Copper Queen Community Hospital

Flagstaff
Member
  Flagstaff Medical Center

Green Valley
Member
  Green Valley Hospital

Kingman
Member
  Kingman Regional Medical Center

Phoenix
Member
  Maricopa Integrated Health System
  Mayo Clinic Hospital

Safford
Member
  Mt. Graham Regional Medical Center

Tucson
Member
  Banner – University Medical Center South
  Banner – University Medical Center Tucson
  TMC HealthCare

Willcox
Member
  Northern Cochise Community Hospital

ARKANSAS
Arkadelphia
Member
  Baptist Health Medical Center–Arkadelphia

Booneville
Member
  Mercy Hospital Booneville

Clinton
Member
  Ozark Health Medical Center

Conway
Member
  Conway Regional Medical Center

Fayetteville
Member
  Washington Regional Medical Center

Heber Springs
Member
  Baptist Health Medical Center–Heber Springs

Hot Springs
Member
  CHI St. Vincent Hot Springs

Jonesboro
Member
  NEA Baptist Memorial Hospital
  St. Bernards Medical Center

Little Rock
Member
  Baptist Health
  Baptist Health Extended Care Hospital
  Baptist Health Medical Center–Little Rock
  CHI St. Vincent Infirmary Medical Center

Malvern
Member
  Baptist Health Medical Center–Hot Spring County

Morrilton
Member
  CHI St. Vincent Morrilton

North Little Rock
Member
  Baptist Health Medical Center – North Little Rock

Paragould
Member
  Arkansas Methodist Medical Center

Piggott
Member
  Piggott Community Hospital

Stuttgart
Member
  Baptist Health Medical Center–Stuttgart

Walnut Ridge
Member
  Lawrence Memorial Hospital

Wynne
Member
  CrossRidge Community Hospital

CALIFORNIA
Alameda
Member
  Alameda Hospital

Antioch
Member
  Kaiser Permanente Antioch Medical Center

Arcadia
Member
  Methodist Hospital of Southern California

Auburn
Member
  Sutter Auburn Faith Hospital

Bakersfield
Member
  Kern Medical Center

Berkeley
Member
  Alta Bates Medical Center–Herrick Campus
  Alta Bates Summit Medical Center

Burbank
Member
  Providence Saint Joseph Medical Center

Burlingame
Member
  Mills–Peninsula Health Services

Castro Valley
Member
  Eden Medical Center

Colton
Member
  Arrowhead Regional Medical Center

Concord
Member
  John Muir Medical Center, Concord

Covina
Member
  Citrus Valley Health Partners
  Citrus Valley Medical Center–Inter Community Campus

Crescent City
Member
  Sutter Coast Hospital

Davis
Member
  Sutter Davis Hospital

Downey
Member
  PIH Health Hospital – Downey
  Rancho Los Amigos National Rehabilitation Center

El Centro
Member
  El Centro Regional Medical Center

Escondido
Member
  Palomar Health
  Palomar Medical Center

Fairfield
Member
  NorthBay Medical Center

Fremont
Member
  Fremont Medical Center
  Washington Hospital Healthcare System

French Camp
Member
  San Joaquin General Hospital

Fresno
Member
  Community Medical Centers
  Saint Agnes Medical Center

Glendora
Member
  Foothill Presbyterian Hospital

Jackson
Member
  Sutter Amador Hospital

King City
Member
  Mee Memorial Hospital

Lakeport
Member
  Sutter Lakeside Hospital

Lancaster
Member
  Antelope Valley Hospital

Los Angeles
Member
  Cedars–Sinai Medical Center
  LAC+USC Medical Center
  Martin Luther King, Jr. Community Hospital
  Ronald Reagan UCLA Medical Center
  Shriners Hospitals for Children–Los Angeles
  Stewart & Lynda Resnick Neuropsychiatric Hospital at
    UCLA
  USC Norris Comprehensive Cancer Center

Los Banos
Member
  Memorial Hospital Los Banos

Manteca
Member
  Kaiser Permanente Manteca Medical Center

Marina Del Rey
Member
  Marina Del Rey Hospital

Mariposa
Member
  John C. Fremont Healthcare District

Martinez
Member
  Contra Costa Regional Medical Center

Menlo Park
Member
  Menlo Park Surgical Hospital

Mission Hills
Member
  Providence Holy Cross Medical Center

Modesto
Member
  Memorial Medical Center

Monterey
Member
  Community Hospital of the Monterey Peninsula

Moreno Valley
Member
  Riverside University Health System–Medical Center

Mountain View
Member
  El Camino Hospital

Novato
Member
  Novato Community Hospital

Oakland
Member
  Alta Bates Summit Medical Center – Summit Campus
  Highland Hospital
  Kaiser Permanente Oakland Medical Center

Oceanside
Member
  Tri–City Medical Center

Ojai
Member
  Ojai Valley Community Hospital

Orange
Member
  UC Irvine Medical Center

Palo Alto
Member
  Lucile Salter Packard Children's Hospital Stanford
  Stanford Health Care

Pleasanton
Member
  Stanford Health Care – ValleyCare

Pomona
Member
  Pomona Valley Hospital Medical Center

Porterville
Member
  Sierra View Medical Center

Portola
Member
  Eastern Plumas Health Care

Poway
Member
  Pomerado Hospital

Redlands
Member
  Redlands Community Hospital

Redwood City
Member
  Kaiser Permanente Redwood City Medical Center

Roseville
Member
  Kaiser Permanente Roseville Medical Center
  Sutter Roseville Medical Center

Sacramento
Member
  Kaiser Permanente Sacramento Medical Center
  Kaiser Permanente South Sacramento Medical Center
  Shriners Hospitals for Children–Northern California
  Sutter Center for Psychiatry
  Sutter Health
  Sutter Medical Center, Sacramento
  University of California, Davis Medical Center

Salinas
Member
  Natividad Medical Center

San Diego
Member
  Scripps Health
  UC San Diego Health

San Francisco
Member
  California Pacific Medical Center
  California Pacific Medical Center–Davies Campus
  Chinese Hospital
  Kaiser Permanente San Francisco Medical Center
  St. Luke's Hospital
  UCSF Medical Center
  Zuckerberg San Francisco General Hospital and
    Trauma Center

San Jose
Member
  Kaiser Permanente San Jose Medical Center
  Santa Clara Valley Medical Center

San Leandro
Member
  San Leandro Hospital

San Mateo
Member
  San Mateo Medical Center

San Pedro
Member
  Providence Little Company of Mary Medical Center
    San Pedro

San Rafael
Member
  Kaiser Permanente San Rafael Medical Center

Santa Barbara
Member
  Cottage Health
  Goleta Valley Cottage Hospital
  Santa Barbara Cottage Hospital

Santa Clara
Member
  Kaiser Permanente Santa Clara Medical Center

Santa Cruz
Member
  Sutter Maternity and Surgery Center of Santa Cruz

Santa Monica
Member
  Providence Saint John's Health Center
  UCLA Medical Center–Santa Monica

Santa Rosa
Member
  Kaiser Permanente Santa Rosa Medical Center
  Sutter Santa Rosa Regional Hospital

Solvang
Member
  Santa Ynez Valley Cottage Hospital

South San Francisco
Member
  Kaiser Permanente South San Francisco

Stockton
Member
  Dameron Hospital

Sylmar
Member
  LAC–Olive View–UCLA Medical Center

Tarzana
Member
  Providence Tarzana Medical Center

Torrance
Member
  Harbor–UCLA Medical Center
  Providence Little Company of Mary Medical Center –
    Torrance
  Torrance Memorial Medical Center

Tracy
Member
  Sutter Tracy Community Hospital

Vacaville
Member
  Kaiser Permanente Vacaville Medical Center

Vallejo
Member
  Kaiser Permanente Vallejo Medical Center
  Sutter Solano Medical Center

Ventura
Member
  Community Memorial Hospital

Walnut Creek
Member
John Muir Health
John Muir Medical Center, Walnut Creek
Kaiser Permanente Walnut Creek Medical Center

Whittier
Member
PIH Health Hospital–Whittier

Yuba City
Member
Sutter Surgical Hospital – North Valley

COLORADO

Alamosa
Member
San Luis Valley Health

Aurora
Member
University of Colorado Hospital

Boulder
Member
Boulder Community Health

Canon City
Member
St. Thomas More Hospital

Colorado Springs
Member
Memorial Hospital
Penrose–St. Francis Health Services

Denver
Member
Denver Health
National Jewish Health

Durango
Member
Mercy Regional Medical Center

Englewood
Member
Craig Hospital

Estes Park
Member
Estes Park Medical Center

Fort Collins
Member
Poudre Valley Hospital

Grand Junction
Member
St. Mary's Medical Center

Gunnison
Member
Gunnison Valley Hospital

La Jara
Member
San Luis Valley Health Conejos County Hospital

Lakewood
Member
St. Anthony Hospital

Loveland
Member
Medical Center of the Rockies

Pueblo
Member
St. Mary–Corwin Medical Center

Steamboat Springs
Member
Yampa Valley Medical Center

Westminster
Member
St. Anthony North Health Campus

Yuma
Member
Yuma District Hospital

CONNECTICUT

Bridgeport
Member
Bridgeport Hospital

Bristol
Member
Bristol Hospital

Danbury
Member
Danbury Hospital

Farmington
Member
University of Connecticut Health Center, John Dempsey Hospital

Greenwich
Member
Greenwich Hospital

Hartford
Member
Hartford Hospital
Saint Francis Hospital and Medical Center

Manchester
Member
Eastern Connecticut Health Network
Manchester Memorial Hospital

Middletown
Member
Connecticut Valley Hospital
Middlesex Hospital

Milford
Member
Milford Hospital

New Haven
Member
Connecticut Mental Health Center
Yale New Haven Health
Yale–New Haven Hospital

New London
Member
Lawrence + Memorial Hospital

Norwalk
Member
Norwalk Hospital

Putnam
Member
Day Kimball Hospital

Stamford
Member
Stamford Hospital

Torrington
Member
The Charlotte Hungerford Hospital

Vernon
Member
Rockville General Hospital

DELAWARE

Wilmington
Member
St. Francis Hospital

DISTRICT OF COLUMBIA

Washington
Member
Howard University Hospital
MedStar Georgetown University Hospital
MedStar Washington Hospital Center
Sibley Memorial Hospital

FLORIDA

Apalachicola
Member
George E. Weems Memorial Hospital

Boca Raton
Member
Boca Raton Regional Hospital

Boynton Beach
Member
Bethesda Hospital East

Clermont
Member
South Lake Hospital

Cocoa Beach
Member
Health First Cape Canaveral Hospital

Coral Gables
Member
Baptist Health South Florida, Doctors Hospital

Daytona Beach
Member
Halifax Health Medical Center of Daytona Beach

Gainesville
Member
UF Health Shands Hospital

Gulf Breeze
Member
Gulf Breeze Hospital

Homestead
Member
Baptist Health South Florida, Homestead Hospital

Jacksonville
Member
Mayo Clinic Jacksonville

Jay
Member
Jay Hospital

Lakeland
Member
Lakeland Regional Health

Leesburg
Member
Leesburg Regional Medical Center

Melbourne
Member
Health First Holmes Regional Medical Center

Miami
Member
Baptist Health South Florida, Baptist Hospital of Miami
Baptist Health South Florida, West Kendall Baptist Hospital
Jackson Health System

Milton
Member
West Florida Community Care Center

Naples
Member
NCH Downtown Naples Hospital

Ocoee
Member
Health Central Hospital

Orlando
Member
Orlando Health
Orlando Regional Medical Center

Palm Bay
Member
Health First Palm Bay Hospital

Panama City
Member
Bay Medical Center Sacred Heart Health System

Pensacola
Member
Baptist Health Care Corporation
Baptist Hospital

Perry
Member
Doctor's Memorial Hospital

Rockledge
Member
Health First, Inc.

Starke
Member
Shands Starke Regional Medical Center

Stuart
Member
Martin Health System

Tallahassee
Member
Tallahassee Memorial HealthCare

Tampa
Member
H. Lee Moffitt Cancer Center and Research Institute
Shriners Hospitals for Children–Tampa
Tampa General Hospital

Tavernier
Member
Baptist Health South Florida, Mariners Hospital

The Villages
Member
   The Villages Regional Hospital

Titusville
Member
   Parrish Medical Center

Vero Beach
Member
   Indian River Medical Center

Weston
Member
   Cleveland Clinic Florida

GEORGIA

Adel
Member
   Cook Medical Center–A Campus of Tift Regional
      Medical Center

Albany
Member
   Phoebe Putney Health System
   Phoebe Putney Memorial Hospital

Americus
Member
   Phoebe Sumter Medical Center

Athens
Member
   Athens Regional Medical Center
   St. Mary's Health Care System

Atlanta
Member
   Emory Saint Joseph's Hospital of Atlanta
   Emory University Hospital
   Emory University Hospital Midtown
   Grady Memorial Hospital
   Northside Hospital
   Wellstar Atlanta Medical Center

Augusta
Member
   Augusta University Medical Center
   Charlie Norwood Veterans Affairs Medical Center
   University Hospital

Austell
Member
   WellStar Cobb Hospital

Braselton
Member
   Northeast Georgia Medical Center Braselton

Brunswick
Member
   Southeast Georgia Health System
   Southeast Georgia Health System Brunswick Campus

Bryon
Member
   Medical Center of Peach County, Navicent Health

Cairo
Member
   Grady General Hospital

Camilla
Member
   Mitchell County Hospital

Canton
Member
   Northside Hospital–Cherokee

Cedartown
Member
   Polk Medical Center

Claxton
Member
   Evans Memorial Hospital

Columbus
Member
   Columbus Regional Healthcare System
   Columbus Specialty Hospital
   Midtown Medical Center
   Northside Medical Center

Cordele
Member
   Crisp Regional Hospital

Cumming
Member
   Northside Hospital–Forsyth

Cuthbert
Member
   Southwest Georgia Regional Medical Center

Dalton
Member
   Hamilton Medical Center

Decatur
Member
   DeKalb Medical at Downtown Decatur

Douglas
Member
   Coffee Regional Medical Center

Douglasville
Member
   WellStar Douglas Hospital

Eatonton
Member
   Putnam General Hospital

Fitzgerald
Member
   Dorminy Medical Center

Gainesville
Member
   Northeast Georgia Medical Center

Hiram
Member
   WellStar Paulding Hospital

Homerville
Member
   Clinch Memorial Hospital

Jackson
Member
   Sylvan Grove Hospital

Johns Creek
Member
   Emory Johns Creek Hospital

Lakeland
Member
   South Georgia Medical Center Lanier Campus

Lawrenceville
Member
   Gwinnett Hospital System

Lithonia
Member
   DeKalb Medical at Hillandale

Macon
Member
   Medical Center, Navicent Health
   Rehabilitation Hospital, Navicent Health

Marietta
Member
   WellStar Health System
   WellStar Kennestone Hospital
   WellStar Windy Hill Hospital

Moultrie
Member
   Colquitt Regional Medical Center

Nashville
Member
   South Georgia Medical Center Berrien Campus

Newnan
Member
   Southeastern Regional Medical Center

Perry
Member
   Perry Hospital

Quitman
Member
   Brooks County Hospital

Riverdale
Member
   Southern Regional Medical Center

Rome
Member
   Floyd Medical Center

Roswell
Member
   North Fulton Regional Hospital

Saint Marys
Member
   Southeast Georgia Health System Camden Campus

Sandersville
Member
   Washington County Regional Medical Center

Savannah
Member
   Memorial Health

Swainsboro
Member
   Emanuel Medical Center

Sylvester
Member
   Phoebe Worth Medical Center

Thomasville
Member
   Archbold Medical Center
   John D. Archbold Memorial Hospital

Thomson
Member
   University Hospital McDuffie

Tifton
Member
   Tift Regional Medical Center

Valdosta
Member
   South Georgia Medical Center

Warm Springs
Member
   Roosevelt Warm Springs Rehabilitation and Specialty
      Hospitals – LTAC
   Roosevelt Warm Springs Rehabilitation and Specialty
      Hospitals – Rehab

Warner Robins
Member
   Houston Medical Center

Waycross
Member
   Mayo Clinic Health System in Waycross

GUAM

Dededo
Member
   Guam Regional Medical City

HAWAII

Aiea
Member
   Pali Momi Medical Center

Ewa Beach
Member
   Kahi Mohala Behavioral Health

Honolulu
Member
   Kaiser Permanente Medical Center
   Queen's Health Systems
   Queen's Medical Center
   Shriners Hospitals for Children–Honolulu
   Straub Clinic & Hospital

Kamuela
Member
   North Hawaii Community Hospital

Kaunakakai
Member
   Molokai General Hospital

Wahiawa
Member
   Wahiawa General Hospital

IDAHO

American Falls
Member
   Power County Hospital District

Blackfoot
Member
   Bingham Memorial Hospital

Boise
Member
   Saint Alphonsus Regional Medical Center
   St. Luke's Health System

Bonners Ferry
Member
Boundary Community Hospital

Cascade
Member
Cascade Medical Center

Coeur D'Alene
Member
Kootenai Health

Cottonwood
Member
St. Mary's Hospital

Emmett
Member
Valor Health

Orofino
Member
Clearwater Valley Hospital and Clinics

Preston
Member
Franklin County Medical Center

Rupert
Member
Minidoka Memorial Hospital

Sandpoint
Member
Bonner General Hospital

Weiser
Member
Weiser Memorial Hospital

ILLINOIS

Alton
Member
Alton Memorial Hospital

Arlington Heights
Member
Northwest Community Hospital

Aurora
Member
Rush–Copley Medical Center

Barrington
Member
Advocate Good Shepherd Hospital

Belleville
Member
Memorial Hospital

Bloomington
Member
OSF St. Joseph Medical Center

Canton
Member
Graham Hospital Association

Carbondale
Member
Memorial Hospital of Carbondale
Southern Illinois Hospital Services

Chester
Member
Memorial Hospital

Chicago
Member
Advocate Illinois Masonic Medical Center
Advocate Trinity Hospital
Ann & Robert H. Lurie Children's Hospital of Chicago
John H. Stroger Jr. Hospital of Cook County
La Rabida Children's Hospital
Louis A. Weiss Memorial Hospital
Mercy Hospital and Medical Center
Methodist Hospital of Chicago
Northwestern Memorial Hospital
Norwegian American Hospital
Presence Resurrection Medical Center
Provident Hospital of Cook County
Rush University Medical Center
Shriners Hospitals for Children–Chicago
Swedish Covenant Hospital
University of Chicago Medical Center
University of Illinois Hospital & Health Sciences
System

Decatur
Member
Decatur Memorial Hospital

Downers Grove
Member
Advocate Good Samaritan Hospital

Eldorado
Member
Ferrell Hospital

Elgin
Member
Advocate Sherman Hospital

Elmhurst
Member
Elmhurst Memorial Hospital

Evanston
Member
NorthShore University Health System

Evergreen Park
Member
Little Company of Mary Hospital and Health Care
Centers

Freeport
Member
FHN Memorial Hospital

Galesburg
Member
OSF St. Mary Medical Center

Geneva
Member
Northwestern Medicine Delnor Hospital

Greenville
Member
HSHS Holy Family Hospital in Greenville

Harvey
Member
Ingalls Memorial Hospital

Hazel Crest
Member
Advocate South Suburban Hospital

Herrin
Member
Herrin Hospital

Hinsdale
Member
AMITA Health Adventist Medical Center – Hinsdale
RML Specialty Hospital

Hoffman Estates
Member
Alexian Brothers Behavioral Health Hospital

Jacksonville
Member
Passavant Area Hospital

Jerseyville
Member
Jersey Community Hospital

Joliet
Member
Presence Saint Joseph Medical Center

Kewanee
Member
OSF Saint Luke Medical Center

Lake Forest
Member
Northwestern Lake Forest Hospital

Libertyville
Member
Advocate Condell Medical Center

Lincoln
Member
Abraham Lincoln Memorial Hospital

Macomb
Member
McDonough District Hospital

Maryville
Member
Anderson Hospital

Mattoon
Member
Sarah Bush Lincoln Health Center

Maywood
Member
Loyola University Medical Center

McHenry
Member
Centegra Hospital – McHenry

Monticello
Member
Kirby Medical Center

Murphysboro
Member
St. Joseph Memorial Hospital

New Lenox
Member
Silver Cross Hospital

Oak Lawn
Member
Advocate Christ Medical Center

Oak Park
Member
Rush Oak Park Hospital

Palos Heights
Member
Palos Community Hospital

Park Ridge
Member
Advocate Lutheran General Hospital

Peoria
Member
OSF Saint Francis Medical Center
UnityPoint Health – Peoria

Pittsfield
Member
Illini Community Hospital

Pontiac
Member
OSF Saint James – John W. Albrecht Medical Center

Quincy
Member
Blessing Hospital

Rock Island
Member
UnityPoint Health – Trinity Rock Island

Rockford
Member
OSF Saint Anthony Medical Center
SwedishAmerican – A Division of UW Health

Rushville
Member
Sarah D. Culbertson Memorial Hospital

Salem
Member
Salem Township Hospital

Shelbyville
Member
Shelby Memorial Hospital

Shiloh
Member
Memorial Hospital East

Springfield
Member
Memorial Health System
Memorial Medical Center

Taylorville
Member
Taylorville Memorial Hospital

Urbana
Member
Carle Foundation Hospital

Winfield
Member
Northwestern Medicine Central DuPage Hospital

INDIANA

Anderson
Member
Community Hospital of Anderson & Madison County

Angola
Member
Cameron Memorial Community Hospital

Auburn
Member
  DeKalb Health

Avon
Member
  Indiana University Health West Hospital

Batesville
Member
  Margaret Mary Health

Bedford
Member
  Indiana University Health Bedford Hospital

Bloomington
Member
  Indiana University Health Bloomington Hospital

Bremen
Member
  Doctors NeuroMedical Hospital

Carmel
Member
  Indiana University Health North Hospital

Clinton
Member
  Union Hospital Clinton

Columbia City
Member
  Parkview Whitley Hospital

Columbus
Member
  Columbus Regional Hospital

Danville
Member
  Hendricks Regional Health

Elkhart
Member
  Elkhart General Hospital

Evansville
Member
  Deaconess Health System
  Deaconess Hospital

Fort Wayne
Member
  Parkview Ortho Hospital
  Parkview Health
  Parkview Regional Medical Center

Franklin
Member
  Johnson Memorial Hospital

Goshen
Member
  Indiana University Health Goshen Hospital

Hartford City
Member
  Indiana University Health Blackford Hospital

Huntington
Member
  Parkview Huntington Hospital

Indianapolis
Member
  Community Health Network
  Community Hospital East
  Community Hospital North
  Community Hospital South
  Eskenazi Health
  Indiana University Health Methodist Hospital
  Indiana University Health University Hospital

Jasper
Member
  Memorial Hospital and Health Care Center

Kendallville
Member
  Parkview Noble Hospital

Knox
Member
  Starke Hospital

Kokomo
Member
  Community Howard Regional Health

La Porte
Member
  La Porte Hospital

Lafayette
Member
  Indiana University Health Arnett Hospital

LaGrange
Member
  Parkview LaGrange Hospital

Logansport
Member
  Logansport Memorial Hospital

Madison
Member
  King's Daughters' Health

Marion
Member
  Marion General Hospital

Monticello
Member
  Indiana University Health White Memorial Hospital

Muncie
Member
  Indiana University Health Ball Memorial Hospital

New Albany
Member
  Floyd Memorial Hospital and Health Services
  Southern Indiana Rehabilitation Hospital

New Castle
Member
  Henry County Hospital

Newburgh
Member
  The Heart Hospital at Deaconess Gateway
  The Women's Hospital

Noblesville
Member
  Riverview Health

Paoli
Member
  Indiana University Health Paoli Hospital

Portland
Member
  Jay County Hospital

Richmond
Member
  Reid Health

Rochester
Member
  Woodlawn Hospital

Seymour
Member
  Schneck Medical Center

Shelbyville
Member
  Major Hospital

South Bend
Member
  Healthwin Hospital
  Memorial Hospital of South Bend

Terre Haute
Member
  Union Hospital

Tipton
Member
  Indiana University Health Tipton Hospital

Vincennes
Member
  Good Samaritan Hospital

Wabash
Member
  Parkview Wabash County Hospital

IOWA

Anamosa
Member
  UnityPoint Health – Jones Regional Medical Center

Atlantic
Member
  Cass County Memorial Hospital

Bettendorf
Member
  UnityPoint Health – Trinity Bettendorf

Cedar Rapids
Member
  Continuing Care Hospital at St. Luke's
  UnityPoint Health – St. Luke's Hospital

Centerville
Member
  Mercy Medical Center–Centerville

Clarinda
Member
  Clarinda Regional Health Center

Clinton
Member
  Mercy Medical Center–Clinton

Corning
Member
  CHI Health Mercy Corning

Council Bluffs
Member
  Methodist Jennie Edmundson Hospital

Decorah
Member
  Winneshiek Medical Center

Des Moines
Member
  Mercy Medical Center–Des Moines
  UnityPoint Health–Iowa Lutheran Hospital

Dubuque
Member
  Mercy Medical Center–Dubuque
  UnityPoint Health – Finley Hospital

Fort Dodge
Member
  UnityPoint Health – Trinity Regional Medical Center

Grundy Center
Member
  Grundy County Memorial Hospital

Guttenberg
Member
  Guttenberg Municipal Hospital

Hamburg
Member
  George C Grape Community Hospital

Hampton
Member
  Franklin General Hospital

Harlan
Member
  Myrtue Medical Center

Iowa City
Member
  University of Iowa Hospitals and Clinics

Iowa Falls
Member
  Hansen Family Hospital

Jefferson
Member
  Greene County Medical Center

Keokuk
Member
  Keokuk Area Hospital

Keosauqua
Member
  Van Buren County Hospital

Lake City
Member
  Stewart Memorial Community Hospital

Le Mars
Member
  Floyd Valley Healthcare

Marengo
Member
  Marengo Memorial Hospital

Mason City
Member
  Mercy Medical Center–North Iowa

Missouri Valley
Member
  CHI Health Missouri Valley

Muscatine
Member
UnityPoint Health – Trinity Muscatine

Nevada
Member
Story County Medical Center

New Hampton
Member
Mercy Medical Center–New Hampton

Orange City
Member
Orange City Area Health System

Osceola
Member
Clarke County Hospital

Pella
Member
Pella Regional Health Center

Red Oak
Member
Montgomery County Memorial Hospital

Rock Rapids
Member
Sanford Rock Rapids Medical Center

Sheldon
Member
Sanford Sheldon Medical Center

Shenandoah
Member
Shenandoah Medical Center

Sigourney
Member
Keokuk County Health Center

Sioux City
Member
Mercy Medical Center–Sioux City
UnityPoint Health – St. Luke's

Sumner
Member
Community Memorial Hospital

Waverly
Member
Waverly Health Center

West Des Moines
Member
UnityPoint Health – Methodist West Hospital

West Union
Member
Palmer Lutheran Health Center

KANSAS

Abilene
Member
Memorial Health System

Anthony
Member
Anthony Medical Center

Ashland
Member
Ashland Health Center

Atchison
Member
Atchison Hospital

Atwood
Member
Rawlins County Health Center

Belleville
Member
Republic County Hospital

Beloit
Member
Mitchell County Hospital Health Systems

Clay Center
Member
Clay County Medical Center

Colby
Member
Citizens Medical Center

Coldwater
Member
Comanche County Hospital

Concordia
Member
Cloud County Health Center

Dighton
Member
Lane County Hospital

El Dorado
Member
Susan B. Allen Memorial Hospital

Ellinwood
Member
Ellinwood District Hospital

Ellsworth
Member
Ellsworth County Medical Center

Emporia
Member
Newman Regional Health

Fredonia
Member
Fredonia Regional Hospital

Garden City
Member
St. Catherine Hospital

Garnett
Member
Anderson County Hospital

Girard
Member
Girard Medical Center

Goodland
Member
Goodland Regional Medical Center

Great Bend
Member
Great Bend Regional Hospital

Greensburg
Member
Kiowa County Memorial Hospital

Hays
Member
Hays Medical Center

Herington
Member
Herington Municipal Hospital

Hiawatha
Member
Hiawatha Community Hospital

Hill City
Member
Graham County Hospital

Hoisington
Member
Clara Barton Hospital

Hoxie
Member
Sheridan County Health Complex

Junction City
Member
Geary Community Hospital

Kansas City
Member
The University of Kansas Hospital

La Crosse
Member
Rush County Memorial Hospital

Larned
Member
Pawnee Valley Community Hospital

Lawrence
Member
Lawrence Memorial Hospital

Leavenworth
Member
Saint Luke's Cushing Hospital

Lincoln
Member
Lincoln County Hospital

Lindsborg
Member
Lindsborg Community Hospital

Mankato
Member
Jewell County Hospital

Medicine Lodge
Member
Medicine Lodge Memorial Hospital

Minneapolis
Member
Ottawa County Health Center

Minneola
Member
Minneola District Hospital

Ness City
Member
Ness County Hospital District No 2

Norton
Member
Norton County Hospital

Oakley
Member
Logan County Hospital

Overland Park
Member
Menorah Medical Center
Overland Park Regional Medical Center
Saint Luke's South Hospital

Parsons
Member
Labette Health

Phillipsburg
Member
Phillips County Hospital

Plainville
Member
Rooks County Health Center

Pratt
Member
Pratt Regional Medical Center

Quinter
Member
Gove County Medical Center

Ransom
Member
Grisell Memorial Hospital District One

Russell
Member
Russell Regional Hospital

Sabetha
Member
Sabetha Community Hospital

Saint Francis
Member
Cheyenne County Hospital

Salina
Member
Salina Regional Health Center
Salina Surgical Hospital

Satanta
Member
Satanta District Hospital and Long Term Care

Scott City
Member
Scott County Hospital

Smith Center
Member
Smith County Memorial Hospital

Stafford
Member
Stafford County Hospital

Topeka
Member
Stormont Vail Health

Wakeeney
Member
Trego County–Lemke Memorial Hospital

Wichita
Member
Great Plains Health Alliance, Inc.
Kansas Spine and Specialty Hospital

KENTUCKY

Bardstown
Member
Flaget Memorial Hospital

Berea
Member
Saint Joseph Berea

Cynthiana
Member
Harrison Memorial Hospital

Florence
Member
St. Elizabeth Florence

Lexington
Member
Eastern State Hospital
Saint Joseph East
Saint Joseph Hospital
Shriners Hospitals for Children–Lexington
University of Kentucky Albert B. Chandler Hospital

London
Member
Saint Joseph London

Louisville
Member
Jewish Hospital
Our Lady of Peace
University of Louisville Hospital

Martin
Member
Saint Joseph – Martin

Morehead
Member
St. Claire Regional Medical Center

Mount Sterling
Member
Saint Joseph Mount Sterling

Mount Vernon
Member
Rockcastle Regional Hospital and Respiratory Care
Center

Owensboro
Member
Owensboro Health Regional Hospital

Pikeville
Member
Pikeville Medical Center

Shelbyville
Member
Jewish Hospital–Shelbyville

LOUISIANA

Baton Rouge
Member
Franciscan Missionaries of Our Lady Health System,
Inc.
Ochsner Medical Center–Baton Rouge
Our Lady of the Lake Regional Medical Center

Bogalusa
Member
Our Lady of the Angels Hospital

Bossier City
Member
WK Bossier Health Center

Church Point
Member
Acadia–St. Landry Hospital

Covington
Member
St. Tammany Parish Hospital

De Ridder
Member
Beauregard Memorial Hospital

Ferriday
Member
Riverland Medical Center

Gonzales
Member
St. Elizabeth Hospital

Jennings
Member
Jennings American Legion Hospital

Kenner
Member
Ochsner Medical Center – Kenner

Lafayette
Member
Lafayette General Medical Center
Our Lady of Lourdes Regional Medical Center

Lake Charles
Member
Lake Charles Memorial Hospital
Memorial Specialty Hospital

Mansfield
Member
De Soto Regional Health System

Monroe
Member
St. Francis Medical Center
University Health Conway

Napoleonville
Member
Assumption Community Hospital

Natchitoches
Member
Natchitoches Regional Medical Center

New Iberia
Member
Iberia Medical Center

New Orleans
Member
Touro Infirmary

Raceland
Member
Ochsner St. Anne General Hospital

Shreveport
Member
Shriners Hospitals for Children–Shreveport
University Health Shreveport
Willis–Knighton Health System
Willis–Knighton Medical Center

Slidell
Member
Ochsner Medical Center – North Shore

Springhill
Member
Springhill Medical Center

Sulphur
Member
West Calcasieu Cameron Hospital

Vivian
Member
North Caddo Medical Center

MAINE

Augusta
Member
MaineGeneral Medical Center
MaineGeneral Medical Center–Augusta Campus

Bangor
Member
Eastern Maine Medical Center
The Acadia Hospital

Bar Harbor
Member
Mount Desert Island Hospital

Belfast
Member
Waldo County General Hospital

Biddeford
Member
Southern Maine Health Care – Biddeford Medical
Center

Blue Hill
Member
Blue Hill Memorial Hospital

Brewer
Member
Eastern Maine Healthcare Systems

Brunswick
Member
Mid Coast Hospital

Damariscotta
Member
LincolnHealth

Dover–Foxcroft
Member
Mayo Regional Hospital

Ellsworth
Member
Maine Coast Memorial Hospital

Farmington
Member
Franklin Memorial Hospital

Fort Kent
Member
Northern Maine Medical Center

Greenville
Member
Charles A. Dean Memorial Hospital

Houlton
Member
Houlton Regional Hospital

Machias
Member
Down East Community Hospital

Millinocket
Member
Millinocket Regional Hospital

Norway
Member
Stephens Memorial Hospital

Pittsfield
Member
Sebasticook Valley Health

Portland
Member
Maine Medical Center
Mercy Hospital of Portland

Presque Isle
Member
The Aroostook Medical Center

Rockport
Member
Pen Bay Medical Center

Skowhegan
Member
Redington–Fairview General Hospital

Waterville
Member
Inland Hospital

Westbrook
Member
Spring Harbor Hospital

MARYLAND

Baltimore
Member
Greater Baltimore Medical Center
Johns Hopkins Bayview Medical Center
Johns Hopkins Hospital
MedStar Franklin Square Medical Center
MedStar Good Samaritan Hospital
MedStar Harbor Hospital
MedStar Union Memorial Hospital
Mercy Medical Center
Mt. Washington Pediatric Hospital
University of Maryland Medical Center
University of Maryland Medical Center Midtown
Campus
University of Maryland Rehabilitation & Orthopaedic
Institute

Alliances

Bel Air
Member
University of Maryland Upper Chesapeake Medical Center
Upper Chesapeake Health System

Bethesda
Member
Suburban Hospital

Cambridge
Member
University of Maryland Shore Medical Center at Dorchester

Chestertown
Member
University of Maryland Shore Medical Center at Chestertown

Cheverly
Member
Prince George's Hospital Center

Clinton
Member
MedStar Southern Maryland Hospital Center

Columbia
Member
Howard County General Hospital
MedStar Health

Easton
Member
University of Maryland Shore Medical Center at Easton

Elkton
Member
Union Hospital

Glen Burnie
Member
University of Maryland Baltimore Washington Medical Center

Hagerstown
Member
Meritus Medical Center

Havre De Grace
Member
University of Maryland Harford Memorial Hospital

La Plata
Member
University of Maryland Charles Regional Medical Center

Laurel
Member
Laurel Regional Hospital

Leonardtown
Member
MedStar St. Mary's Hospital

Olney
Member
MedStar Montgomery Medical Center

Prince Frederick
Member
Calvert Memorial Hospital

Randallstown
Member
Northwest Hospital

Rockville
Member
Adventist Behavioral Health Rockville
Adventist Healthcare Shady Grove Medical Center

Silver Spring
Member
Holy Cross Hospital

Takoma Park
Member
Washington Adventist Hospital

MASSACHUSETTS

Athol
Member
Athol Memorial Hospital

Ayer
Member
Nashoba Valley Medical Center

Belmont
Member
McLean Hospital

Beverly
Member
Beverly Hospital

Boston
Member
Beth Israel Deaconess Medical Center
Boston Medical Center
Brigham and Women's Faulkner Hospital
Brigham and Women's Hospital
Carney Hospital
Dana–Farber Cancer Institute
Massachusetts Eye and Ear Infirmary
Massachusetts General Hospital
Partners HealthCare System, Inc.
Shriners Hospitals for Children–Boston
Tufts Medical Center

Brighton
Member
St. Elizabeth's Medical Center

Brockton
Member
Good Samaritan Medical Center
Signature Healthcare Brockton Hospital

Burlington
Member
Lahey Hospital & Medical Center, Burlington

Cambridge
Member
Cambridge Health Alliance
Mount Auburn Hospital
Spaulding Hospital for Continuing Medical Care Cambridge

Charlestown
Member
Spaulding Rehabilitation Hospital

Clinton
Member
Clinton Hospital

Concord
Member
Emerson Hospital

East Sandwich
Member
Spaulding Rehabilitation Hospital Cape Cod

Fall River
Member
Saint Anne's Hospital

Gardner
Member
Heywood Hospital

Greenfield
Member
Baystate Franklin Medical Center

Holyoke
Member
Holyoke Medical Center

Hyannis
Member
Cape Cod Healthcare, Inc.

Leominster
Member
HealthAlliance Hospitals

Lowell
Member
Lowell General Hospital

Marlborough
Member
UMass Memorial–Marlborough Hospital

Melrose
Member
Melrose–Wakefield Hospital

Methuen
Member
Holy Family Hospital

Milton
Member
Beth Israel Deaconess Hospital–Milton

Nantucket
Member
Nantucket Cottage Hospital

Newton Lower Falls
Member
Newton–Wellesley Hospital

Northampton
Member
Cooley Dickinson Hospital

Norwood
Member
Norwood Hospital

Oak Bluffs
Member
Martha's Vineyard Hospital

Palmer
Member
Baystate Wing Hospital

Plymouth
Member
Beth Israel Deaconess Hospital Plymouth

Salem
Member
North Shore Medical Center

South Weymouth
Member
South Shore Hospital

Southbridge
Member
Harrington Memorial Hospital

Springfield
Member
Baystate Medical Center
Shriners Hospitals for Children–Springfield

Taunton
Member
Morton Hospital and Medical Center

Winchester
Member
Winchester Hospital

Worcester
Member
UMass Memorial Medical Center

MICHIGAN

Alma
Member
MidMichigan Medical Center–Gratiot

Alpena
Member
MidMichigan Medical Center – Alpena

Ann Arbor
Member
University of Michigan Hospitals and Health Centers

Battle Creek
Member
Bronson Battle Creek

Bay City
Member
McLaren Bay Region
McLaren Bay Special Care

Big Rapids
Member
Spectrum Health Big Rapids Hospital

Cadillac
Member
Munson Healthcare Cadillac Hospital

Carson City
Member
Sparrow Carson Hospital

Cass City
Member
Hills & Dales General Hospital

Chelsea
Member
St. Joseph Mercy Chelsea

Coldwater
Member
Community Health Center of Branch County

Dearborn
Member
  Beaumont Hospital–Dearborn

Detroit
Member
  Henry Ford Hospital

Farmington Hills
Member
  Beaumont Hospital – Farmington Hills

Flint
Member
  McLaren Flint

Fremont
Member
  Spectrum Health Gerber Memorial

Grand Haven
Member
  North Ottawa Community Hospital

Grand Rapids
Member
  Mary Free Bed Rehabilitation Hospital
  Pine Rest Christian Mental Health Services
  Spectrum Health
  Spectrum Health – Butterworth Hospital

Grayling
Member
  Munson Healthcare Grayling Hospital

Greenville
Member
  Spectrum Health United Hospital

Grosse Pointe
Member
  Beaumont Hospital – Grosse Pointe

Hastings
Member
  Spectrum Health Pennock

Holland
Member
  Holland Hospital

Ionia
Member
  Sparrow Ionia Hospital

Iron River
Member
  Aspirus Iron River Hospitals & Clinics

Ironwood
Member
  Aspirus Grand View

Kalamazoo
Member
  Bronson Healthcare Group
  Bronson Methodist Hospital

Lansing
Member
  Sparrow Hospital
  Sparrow Specialty Hospital

Laurium
Member
  Aspirus Keweenaw Hospital

Ludington
Member
  Spectrum Health Ludington Hospital

Marlette
Member
  Marlette Regional Hospital

Marshall
Member
  Oaklawn Hospital

Midland
Member
  MidMichigan Medical Center–Midland

Monroe
Member
  ProMedica Monroe Regional Hospital

Mount Clemens
Member
  McLaren Macomb

Mount Pleasant
Member
  McLaren Central Michigan

Muskegon
Member
  Mercy Health Hackley Campus

Ontonagon
Member
  Aspirus Ontonagon Hospital

Paw Paw
Member
  Bronson LakeView Hospital

Petoskey
Member
  McLaren Northern Michigan

Pontiac
Member
  McLaren Oakland
  St. Joseph Mercy Oakland

Port Huron
Member
  McLaren Port Huron

Reed City
Member
  Spectrum Health Reed City Hospital

Royal Oak
Member
  Beaumont Hospital – Royal Oak

Saginaw
Member
  Covenant Healthcare

Saint Johns
Member
  Sparrow Clinton Hospital

Saint Joseph
Member
  Lakeland Health
  Lakeland Medical Center, St. Joseph

Sheridan
Member
  Sheridan Community Hospital

South Haven
Member
  South Haven Health System

Taylor
Member
  Beaumont Hospital – Taylor

Tecumseh
Member
  ProMedica Herrick Hospital

Trenton
Member
  Beaumont Hospital – Trenton

Troy
Member
  Beaumont Hospital – Troy

Vicksburg
Member
  Bronson Vicksburg Hospital

Watervliet
Member
  Lakeland Hospital, Watervliet

Wayne
Member
  Beaumont Hospital – Wayne

West Branch
Member
  West Branch Regional Medical Center

Wyoming
Member
  Metro Health Hospital

Zeeland
Member
  Spectrum Health Zeeland Community Hospital

MINNESOTA

Ada
Member
  Essentia Health Ada

Albert Lea
Member
  Mayo Clinic Health System in Albert Lea

Arlington
Member
  Ridgeview Sibley Medical Center

Aurora
Member
  Essentia Health Northern Pines Medical Center

Austin
Member
  Mayo Clinic Health System–Albert Lea and Austin

Bagley
Member
  Sanford Bagley Medical Center

Baudette
Member
  CHI LakeWood Health

Bemidji
Member
  Sanford Bemidji Medical Center

Benson
Member
  Swift County–Benson Hospital

Blue Earth
Member
  United Hospital District

Brainerd
Member
  Essentia Health St. Joseph's Medical Center

Buffalo
Member
  Buffalo Hospital

Burnsville
Member
  Fairview Ridges Hospital

Cambridge
Member
  Cambridge Medical Center

Canby
Member
  Sanford Canby Medical Center

Cannon Falls
Member
  Mayo Clinic Health System in Cannon Falls

Coon Rapids
Member
  Mercy Hospital

Crookston
Member
  RiverView Health

Deer River
Member
  Essentia Health–Deer River

Detroit Lakes
Member
  Essentia Health St. Mary's – Detroit Lakes

Duluth
Member
  Essentia Health
  Essentia Health Duluth
  Essentia Health St. Mary's Medical Center
  St. Luke's Hospital

Fairmont
Member
  Mayo Clinic Health System in Fairmont

Faribault
Member
  District One Hospital

Fergus Falls
Member
  Lake Region Healthcare

Fosston
Member
  Essentia Health Fosston

Fridley
Member
  Unity Hospital

Glencoe
Member
  Glencoe Regional Health Services

Graceville
Member
Essentia Health–Graceville

Grand Rapids
Member
Grand Itasca Clinic and Hospital

Granite Falls
Member
Granite Falls Municipal Hospital and Manor

Hallock
Member
Kittson Memorial Healthcare Center

Hastings
Member
Regina Hospital

Hutchinson
Member
Hutchinson Health

Jackson
Member
Sanford Jackson Medical Center

Lake City
Member
Mayo Clinic Health System in Lake City

Little Falls
Member
CHI St. Gabriel's Health

Long Prairie
Member
CentraCare Health–Long Prairie

Luverne
Member
Sanford Luverne Medical Center

Madelia
Member
Madelia Community Hospital

Mahnomen
Member
Mahnomen Health Center

Mankato
Member
Mayo Clinic Health System in Mankato

Maple Grove
Member
Maple Grove Hospital

Melrose
Member
CentraCare Health–Melrose

Minneapolis
Member
Abbott Northwestern Hospital
Allina Health
Hennepin County Medical Center
Phillips Eye Institute
Shriners Hospitals for Children–Twin Cities

Monticello
Member
CentraCare Health–Monticello

New Prague
Member
Mayo Clinic Health System in New Prague

New Ulm
Member
New Ulm Medical Center

Ortonville
Member
Ortonville Area Health Services

Owatonna
Member
Owatonna Hospital

Park Rapids
Member
CHI St. Joseph's Health

Paynesville
Member
CentraCare Health–Paynesville

Perham
Member
Perham Health

Princeton
Member
Fairview Northland Medical Center

Red Wing
Member
Mayo Clinic Health System in Red Wing

Redwood Falls
Member
Redwood Area Hospital

Robbinsdale
Member
North Memorial Medical Center

Rochester
Member
Mayo Clinic
Mayo Clinic Hospital – Rochester

Roseau
Member
LifeCare Medical Center

Saint Cloud
Member
CentraCare Health
St. Cloud Hospital

Saint James
Member
Mayo Clinic Health System in Saint James

Saint Paul
Member
HealthEast Care System
Regions Hospital
United Hospital

Sandstone
Member
Essentia Health Sandstone

Sauk Centre
Member
CentraCare Health–Sauk Centre

Shakopee
Member
St. Francis Regional Medical Center

Slayton
Member
Murray County Medical Center

Springfield
Member
Mayo Clinic Health System in Springfield

Stillwater
Member
Lakeview Hospital

Thief River Falls
Member
Sanford Medical Center Thief River Falls
Sanford Thief River Falls Behavioral Health Center

Tracy
Member
Sanford Tracy Medical Center

Two Harbors
Member
Lake View Memorial Hospital

Virginia
Member
Essentia Health–Virginia

Waconia
Member
Ridgeview Medical Center

Warren
Member
North Valley Health Center

Waseca
Member
Mayo Clinic Health System in Waseca

Westbrook
Member
Sanford Westbrook Medical Center

Wheaton
Member
Sanford Wheaton Medical Center

Willmar
Member
Rice Memorial Hospital

Windom
Member
Windom Area Hospital

Worthington
Member
Sanford Worthington Medical Center

Wyoming
Member
Fairview Lakes Health Services

MISSISSIPPI

Booneville
Member
Baptist Memorial Hospital–Booneville

Columbia
Member
Marion General Hospital

Columbus
Member
Baptist Memorial Hospital–Golden Triangle

Corinth
Member
Magnolia Regional Health Center

Greenville
Member
Delta Regional Medical Center

Greenwood
Member
Greenwood Leflore Hospital

Grenada
Member
University of Mississippi Medical Center Grenada

Gulfport
Member
Memorial Hospital at Gulfport

Hattiesburg
Member
Forrest General Hospital

Indianola
Member
South Sunflower County Hospital

Jackson
Member
St. Dominic–Jackson Memorial Hospital
University of Mississippi Medical Center

Leakesville
Member
Greene County Hospital

Lexington
Member
University of Mississippi Medical Center Holmes
County

Lucedale
Member
George Regional Hospital

Magnolia
Member
Beacham Memorial Hospital

McComb
Member
Southwest Mississippi Regional Medical Center

Meridian
Member
Anderson Regional Health System
Anderson Regional Health System South

Monticello
Member
Lawrence County Hospital

New Albany
Member
Baptist Memorial Hospital–Union County

Olive Branch
Member
Methodist Olive Branch Hospital

Oxford
Member
Baptist Memorial Hospital–North Mississippi

Pascagoula
Member
Singing River Health System

Philadelphia
Member
  Neshoba County General Hospital

Picayune
Member
  Highland Community Hospital

Prentiss
Member
  Jefferson Davis Community Hospital

Southaven
Member
  Baptist Memorial Hospital–Desoto

Starkville
Member
  OCH Regional Medical Center

Tupelo
Member
  North Mississippi Health Services, Inc.

Tylertown
Member
  Walthall County General Hospital

MISSOURI

Appleton City
Member
  Ellett Memorial Hospital

Belton
Member
  Belton Regional Medical Center

Bolivar
Member
  Citizens Memorial Hospital

Bonne Terre
Member
  Parkland Health Center–Bonne Terre

Branson
Member
  Cox Medical Center Branson

Brookfield
Member
  General John J. Pershing Memorial Hospital

Cameron
Member
  Cameron Regional Medical Center

Cape Girardeau
Member
  Saint Francis Healthcare System

Chillicothe
Member
  Hedrick Medical Center

Clinton
Member
  Golden Valley Memorial Healthcare

Columbia
Member
  Boone Hospital Center
  University of Missouri Hospitals and Clinics

Farmington
Member
  Parkland Health Center – Liberty Street

Independence
Member
  Centerpoint Medical Center

Jefferson City
Member
  Capital Region Medical Center

Joplin
Member
  Freeman Health System
  Freeman Hospital East

Kansas City
Member
  Children's Mercy Hospitals and Clinics
  Crittenton Children's Center
  Research Medical Center
  Saint Luke's Health System
  Saint Luke's Hospital of Kansas City
  Saint Luke's North Hospital – Barry Road
  Truman Medical Center–Hospital Hill
  Truman Medical Center–Lakewood

Lamar
Member
  Barton County Memorial Hospital

Lee's Summit
Member
  Lee's Summit Medical Center
  Saint Luke's East Hospital

Lexington
Member
  Lafayette Regional Health Center

Liberty
Member
  Liberty Hospital

Macon
Member
  Samaritan Memorial Hospital

Marshall
Member
  Fitzgibbon Hospital

Milan
Member
  Sullivan County Memorial Hospital

Monett
Member
  Cox Monett

Neosho
Member
  Freeman Neosho Hospital

O'Fallon
Member
  Progress West Hospital

Osage Beach
Member
  Lake Regional Health System

Poplar Bluff
Member
  Black River Medical Center

Potosi
Member
  Washington County Memorial Hospital

Saint Louis
Member
  Barnes–Jewish Hospital
  Barnes–Jewish West County Hospital
  BJC HealthCare
  Christian Hospital
  Missouri Baptist Medical Center
  Shriners Hospitals for Children–St. Louis
  St. Louis Children's Hospital

Saint Peters
Member
  Barnes–Jewish St. Peters Hospital

Salem
Member
  Salem Memorial District Hospital

Sikeston
Member
  Missouri Delta Medical Center

Springfield
Member
  Cox Medical Center North
  Cox Medical Centers
  CoxHealth

Ste Genevieve
Member
  Ste. Genevieve County Memorial Hospital

Sullivan
Member
  Missouri Baptist Sullivan Hospital

Trenton
Member
  Wright Memorial Hospital

Warrensburg
Member
  Western Missouri Medical Center

MONTANA

Anaconda
Member
  Community Hospital of Anaconda

Bozeman
Member
  Bozeman Health Deaconess Hospital

Columbus
Member
  Stillwater Community Hospital

Conrad
Member
  Pondera Medical Center

Deer Lodge
Member
  Deer Lodge Medical Center

Ennis
Member
  Madison Valley Medical Center

Hamilton
Member
  Marcus Daly Memorial Hospital

Helena
Member
  St. Peter's Hospital

Kalispell
Member
  Kalispell Regional Healthcare
  The HealthCenter

Libby
Member
  Cabinet Peaks Medical Center

Missoula
Member
  St. Patrick Hospital

Philipsburg
Member
  Granite County Medical Center

Plains
Member
  Clark Fork Valley Hospital

Polson
Member
  Providence St. Joseph Medical Center

Ronan
Member
  St. Luke Community Healthcare

Sidney
Member
  Sidney Health Center

Townsend
Member
  Broadwater Health Center

White Sulphur Springs
Member
  Mountainview Medical Center

NEBRASKA

Alliance
Member
  Box Butte General Hospital

Alma
Member
  Harlan County Health System

Atkinson
Member
  West Holt Memorial Hospital

Beatrice
Member
  Beatrice Community Hospital and Health Center

Bellevue
Member
  Madonna Rehabilitation Specialty Hospital
  Nebraska Medicine – Bellevue

Blair
Member
  Memorial Community Hospital and Health System

Bridgeport
Member
  Morrill County Community Hospital

Broken Bow
Member
  Jennie M. Melham Memorial Medical Center

Section B

Columbus
Member
  Columbus Community Hospital

Crete
Member
  Crete Area Medical Center

Falls City
Member
  Community Medical Center, Inc.

Franklin
Member
  Franklin County Memorial Hospital

Gordon
Member
  Gordon Memorial Hospital

Grand Island
Member
  CHI Health Saint Francis

Hastings
Member
  Mary Lanning Healthcare

Kearney
Member
  CHI Health Good Samaritan

Lexington
Member
  Lexington Regional Health Center

Lincoln
Member
  Bryan Health
  Bryan Medical Center
  CHI Health Nebraska Heart
  CHI Health St Elizabeth
  Madonna Rehabilitation Hospital

Lynch
Member
  Niobrara Valley Hospital

Minden
Member
  Kearney County Health Services

Nebraska City
Member
  CHI Health St. Mary's

Neligh
Member
  Antelope Memorial Hospital

Norfolk
Member
  Faith Regional Health Services

O'Neill
Member
  Avera St. Anthony's Hospital

Omaha
Member
  CHI Health Bergan Mercy
  CHI Health Immanuel
  CHI Health Lakeside
  Nebraska Medicine – Nebraska Medical Center
  Nebraska Methodist Health System, Inc.
  Nebraska Methodist Hospital
  Nebraska Orthopaedic Hospital

Ord
Member
  Valley County Health System

Oshkosh
Member
  Regional West Garden County

Osmond
Member
  Osmond General Hospital

Papillion
Member
  CHI Health Midlands

Plainview
Member
  CHI Health Plainview

Schuyler
Member
  CHI Health Schuyler

Scottsbluff
Member
  Regional West Medical Center

York
Member
  York General Hospital

NEVADA
Las Vegas
Member
  Sunrise Hospital and Medical Center
  University Medical Center

NEW HAMPSHIRE
Claremont
Member
  Valley Regional Hospital

Colebrook
Member
  Upper Connecticut Valley Hospital

Dover
Member
  Wentworth–Douglass Hospital

Keene
Member
  Cheshire Medical Center

Lancaster
Member
  Weeks Medical Center

Lebanon
Member
  Alice Peck Day Memorial Hospital
  Dartmouth–Hitchcock Medical Center

Nashua
Member
  Southern New Hampshire Medical Center

New London
Member
  New London Hospital

North Conway
Member
  Memorial Hospital

Peterborough
Member
  Monadnock Community Hospital

Plymouth
Member
  Speare Memorial Hospital

Woodsville
Member
  Cottage Hospital

NEW JERSEY
Atlantic City
Member
  AtlantiCare Regional Medical Center

Camden
Member
  Cooper University Health Care

Cape May Court House
Member
  Cape Regional Medical Center

Denville
Member
  Saint Clare's Health System

Edison
Member
  JFK Health
  JFK Medical Center

Elmer
Member
  Inspira Medical Center–Elmer

Flemington
Member
  Hunterdon Medical Center

Hamilton
Member
  Robert Wood Johnson University Hospital at Hamilton

Marlton
Member
  Virtua Marlton

Morristown
Member
  Morristown Medical Center

Mount Holly
Member
  Virtua Memorial

Mullica Hill
Member
  Inspira Health Network

New Brunswick
Member
  Robert Wood Johnson University Hospital

Newark
Member
  University Hospital

Newton
Member
  Newton Medical Center

Pomona
Member
  Bacharach Institute for Rehabilitation

Pompton Plains
Member
  Chilton Medical Center

Rahway
Member
  Robert Wood Johnson University Hospital Rahway

Ridgewood
Member
  Valley Hospital

Somers Point
Member
  Shore Medical Center

Summit
Member
  Overlook Medical Center

Trenton
Member
  Capital Health

Vineland
Member
  Inspira Medical Center–Vineland

Voorhees
Member
  Virtua Voorhees

Woodbury
Member
  Inspira Medical Center–Woodbury

NEW MEXICO
Albuquerque
Member
  University of New Mexico Hospitals
  UNM Sandoval Regional Medical Center

Farmington
Member
  San Juan Regional Medical Center

Gallup
Member
  Rehoboth McKinley Christian Health Care Services

Santa Fe
Member
  CHRISTUS St. Vincent Regional Medical Center

NEW YORK
Albany
Member
  Albany Medical Center
  St. Peter's Hospital

Alexandria Bay
Member
  River Hospital

Binghamton
Member
  United Health Services Hospitals–Binghamton

Bronx
Member
  Montefiore Medical Center
  NYC Health + Hospitals / Jacobi
  NYC Health + Hospitals / North Central Bronx

Bronxville
Member
  New York–Presbyterian/Lawrence Hospital

Brooklyn
Member
  Brooklyn Hospital Center
  New York Community Hospital
  New York Methodist Hospital
  NYC Health + Hospitals / Coney Island
  NYC Health + Hospitals / Woodhull
  SUNY Downstate Medical Center University Hospital

Buffalo
Member
  Erie County Medical Center
  Roswell Park Cancer Institute

Canandaigua
Member
  F. F. Thompson Hospital

Cooperstown
Member
  Bassett Medical Center

Corning
Member
  Guthrie Corning Hospital

Cortlandt Manor
Member
  New York–Presbyterian/Hudson Valley Hospital

Elizabethtown
Member
  The University of Vermont Health Network
    Elizabethtown Community Hospital

Elmhurst
Member
  NYC Health + Hospitals / Elmhurst

Flushing
Member
  New York–Presbyterian/Queens

Geneva
Member
  Finger Lakes Health

Greenport
Member
  Eastern Long Island Hospital

Hamilton
Member
  Community Memorial Hospital

Ithaca
Member
  Cayuga Medical Center at Ithaca

Jamaica
Member
  NYC Health + Hospitals / Queens

Jamestown
Member
  Woman's Christian Association Hospital

Malone
Member
  The University of Vermont Health Network – Alice
    Hyde Medical Center

Mineola
Member
  Winthrop–University Hospital

Montour Falls
Member
  Schuyler Hospital

Mount Vernon
Member
  Montefiore Mount Vernon

New Rochelle
Member
  Montefiore New Rochelle

New York
Member
  Gracie Square Hospital
  Lenox Hill Hospital
  Mount Sinai Hospital
  New York–Presbyterian Hospital
  New York–Presbyterian/Columbia University Medical
    Center
  NYC Health + Hospitals / Bellevue
  NYC Health + Hospitals / Carter
  NYC Health + Hospitals / Harlem
  NYU Langone Medical Center
  Rockefeller University Hospital

Norwich
Member
  UHS Chenango Memorial Hospital

Nyack
Member
  Nyack Hospital

Ogdensburg
Member
  Claxton–Hepburn Medical Center

Plattsburgh
Member
  The University of Vermont Health Network–Champlain
    Valley Physicians Hospital

Riverhead
Member
  Peconic Bay Medical Center

Rochester
Member
  Highland Hospital
  Strong Memorial Hospital of the University of
    Rochester
  University of Rochester Medical Center

Sleepy Hollow
Member
  Phelps Memorial Hospital Center

Staten Island
Member
  Staten Island University Hospital

Stony Brook
Member
  Stony Brook University Hospital

Syracuse
Member
  Crouse Hospital
  Upstate University Hospital

Valhalla
Member
  Westchester Medical Center

Walton
Member
  UHS Delaware Valley Hospital

NORTH CAROLINA

Ahoskie
Member
  Vidant Roanoke–Chowan Hospital

Bolivia
Member
  Novant Health Brunswick Medical Center

Cary
Member
  WakeMed Cary Hospital

Chapel Hill
Member
  University of North Carolina Hospitals

Charlotte
Member
  Carolinas Healthcare System
  Novant Health Charlotte Orthopaedic Hospital
  Novant Health Presbyterian Medical Center

Clinton
Member
  Sampson Regional Medical Center

Dunn
Member
  Harnett Health System

Durham
Member
  Duke Regional Hospital
  Duke University Hospital

Eden
Member
  Morehead Memorial Hospital

Edenton
Member
  Vidant Chowan Hospital

Elizabeth City
Member
  Sentara Albemarle Medical Center

Elkin
Member
  Hugh Chatham Memorial Hospital

Greenville
Member
  Vidant Medical Center

Huntersville
Member
  Novant Health Huntersville Medical Center

Jefferson
Member
  Ashe Memorial Hospital

Kenansville
Member
  Vidant Duplin Hospital

Lexington
Member
  Wake Forest Baptist Health–Lexington Medical Center

Matthews
Member
  Novant Health Matthews Medical Center

Mocksville
Member
  Wake Forest Baptist Health–Davie Medical Center

Morehead City
Member
  Carteret Health Care

Nags Head
Member
  The Outer Banks Hospital

New Bern
Member
  CarolinaEast Health System

Raleigh
Member
  Duke Raleigh Hospital
  UNC REX Healthcare
  WakeMed Health & Hospitals
  WakeMed Raleigh Campus

Roanoke Rapids
Member
  Halifax Regional Medical Center

Rocky Mount
Member
  Nash Health Care Systems

Salisbury
Member
  Novant Health Rowan Medical Center

Siler City
Member
  Chatham Hospital

Sparta
Member
  Alleghany Memorial Hospital

Tarboro
Member
  Vidant Edgecombe Hospital

Thomasville
Member
  Novant Health Thomasville Medical Center

Washington
Member
  Vidant Beaufort Hospital

Wilson
Member
  Wilson Medical Center

Windsor
Member
  Vidant Bertie Hospital

Winston Salem
Member
  Novant Health

Winston–Salem
Member
  Novant Health Forsyth Medical Center
  Novant Health Medical Park Hospital
  Wake Forest Baptist Medical Center

Section B

NORTH DAKOTA

Bismarck
Member
Sanford Bismarck

Devils Lake
Member
CHI St. Alexius Health Devils Lake Hospital

Dickinson
Member
St. Joseph's Hospital and Health Center

Fargo
Member
Sanford Medical Center Fargo

Grand Forks
Member
Altru Health System

Hillsboro
Member
Sanford Hillsboro Medical Center

Jamestown
Member
Jamestown Regional Medical Center

Kenmare
Member
Kenmare Community Hospital

Lisbon
Member
CHI Lisbon Health

Mayville
Member
Sanford Mayville Medical Center

Mcville
Member
Nelson County Health System

Minot
Member
Trinity Health

Northwood
Member
Northwood Deaconess Health Center

Oakes
Member
CHI Oakes Hospital

Valley City
Member
CHI Mercy Health

OHIO

Akron
Member
Akron Children's Hospital
Akron General Medical Center

Alliance
Member
Alliance Community Hospital

Ashland
Member
University Hospitals Samaritan Medical Center

Ashtabula
Member
Ashtabula County Medical Center

Athens
Member
O'Bleness Memorial Hospital

Barnesville
Member
Barnesville Hospital

Bellaire
Member
Belmont Community Hospital

Bellefontaine
Member
Mary Rutan Hospital

Bluffton
Member
Bluffton Hospital

Bucyrus
Member
Bucyrus Community Hospital

Cadiz
Member
Harrison Community Hospital

Cambridge
Member
Southeastern Ohio Regional Medical Center

Canton
Member
Aultman Hospital

Chardon
Member
University Hospitals Geauga Medical Center

Cincinnati
Member
Christ Hospital
Cincinnati Children's Hospital Medical Center
Good Samaritan Hospital
Shriners Hospitals for Children–Cincinnati Burns Hospital
The Jewish Hospital – Mercy Health
UC Health
University of Cincinnati Medical Center

Circleville
Member
Berger Health System

Cleveland
Member
Cleveland Clinic
Cleveland Clinic Fairview Hospital
Lutheran Hospital
MetroHealth Medical Center
University Hospitals Cleveland Medical Center

Coldwater
Member
Mercer Health

Columbus
Member
Ohio State University Wexner Medical Center
OhioHealth
OhioHealth Doctors Hospital
OhioHealth Grant Medical Center
OhioHealth Riverside Methodist Hospital

Conneaut
Member
University Hospitals Conneaut Medical Center

Coshocton
Member
Coshocton County Memorial Hospital

Cuyahoga Falls
Member
Edwin Shaw Rehab

Dayton
Member
Good Samaritan Hospital
Miami Valley Hospital

Defiance
Member
ProMedica Defiance Regional Hospital

Delaware
Member
OhioHealth Grady Memorial Hospital

Dover
Member
Union Hospital

Dublin
Member
OhioHealth Dublin Methodist Hospital

Euclid
Member
Euclid Hospital

Findlay
Member
Blanchard Valley Hospital

Fostoria
Member
ProMedica Fostoria Community Hospital

Fremont
Member
ProMedica Memorial Hospital

Galion
Member
Galion Community Hospital

Garfield Heights
Member
Marymount Hospital

Geneva
Member
University Hospitals Geneva Medical Center

Greenville
Member
Wayne Hospital

Hamilton
Member
Fort Hamilton Hospital

Kenton
Member
OhioHealth Hardin Memorial Hospital

Lima
Member
Lima Memorial Health System

Lodi
Member
Lodi Community Hospital

Logan
Member
Hocking Valley Community Hospital

London
Member
Madison Health

Mansfield
Member
OhioHealth MedCentral Mansfield Hospital

Marion
Member
OhioHealth Marion General Hospital

Martins Ferry
Member
East Ohio Regional Hospital

Marysville
Member
Memorial Health

Mason
Member
Lindner Center of HOPE

Maumee
Member
ProMedica St. Luke's Hospital

Medina
Member
Cleveland Clinic, Medina Hospital

Middleburg Heights
Member
Southwest General Health Center

Millersburg
Member
Pomerene Hospital

Mount Gilead
Member
Morrow County Hospital

New Albany
Member
Mount Carmel New Albany Surgical Hospital

Newark
Member
Licking Memorial Hospital

Norwalk
Member
Fisher–Titus Medical Center

Orrville
Member
Aultman Orrville Hospital

Paulding
Member
Paulding County Hospital

Portsmouth
Member
Southern Ohio Medical Center

Rock Creek
Member
Glenbeigh Hospital and Outpatient Centers

Section B

Shelby
Member
OhioHealth MedCentral Shelby Hospital

Sidney
Member
Wilson Memorial Hospital

Sylvania
Member
ProMedica Flower Hospital

Toledo
Member
ProMedica Health System
ProMedica Toledo Hospital
The University of Toledo Medical Center

Troy
Member
Upper Valley Medical Center

Upper Sandusky
Member
Wyandot Memorial Hospital

Van Wert
Member
Van Wert County Hospital

Warrensville Heights
Member
South Pointe Hospital

Washington Court House
Member
Fayette County Memorial Hospital

Westerville
Member
Mount Carmel St. Ann's

Westlake
Member
St. John Medical Center

Zanesville
Member
Genesis HealthCare System

OKLAHOMA

Altus
Member
Jackson County Memorial Hospital

Antlers
Member
Pushmataha Hospital & Home Health

Atoka
Member
Atoka County Medical Center

Bethany
Member
The Children's Center Rehabilitation Hospital

Carnegie
Member
Carnegie Tri–County Municipal Hospital

Chickasha
Member
Grady Memorial Hospital

Duncan
Member
Duncan Regional Hospital

Edmond
Member
INTEGRIS Health Edmond

Elk City
Member
Great Plains Regional Medical Center

Enid
Member
Integris Bass Baptist Health Center
Integris Bass Pavilion

Grove
Member
Integris Grove Hospital

Hobart
Member
Elkview General Hospital

Hugo
Member
Choctaw Memorial Hospital

Lawton
Member
Comanche County Memorial Hospital

McAlester
Member
McAlester Regional Health Center

Miami
Member
INTEGRIS Miami Hospital

Norman
Member
Norman Regional Health System

Oklahoma City
Member
Integris Baptist Medical Center
INTEGRIS Health
Integris Southwest Medical Center
Lakeside Women's Hospital

Stillwater
Member
Stillwater Medical Center

Tahlequah
Member
Northeastern Health System

Waurika
Member
Jefferson County Hospital

Yukon
Member
INTEGRIS Canadian Valley Hospital

OREGON

Forest Grove
Member
Tuality Forest Grove Hospital

Grants Pass
Member
Asante Three Rivers Medical Center

Hillsboro
Member
Tuality Healthcare

Hood River
Member
Providence Hood River Memorial Hospital

Medford
Member
Asante Rogue Regional Medical Center
Providence Medford Medical Center

Milwaukie
Member
Providence Milwaukie Hospital

Newberg
Member
Providence Newberg Medical Center

Ontario
Member
Saint Alphonsus Medical Center – Ontario

Oregon City
Member
Providence Willamette Falls Medical Center

Pendleton
Member
CHI St. Anthony Hospital

Portland
Member
OHSU Hospital
Providence Portland Medical Center
Providence St. Vincent Medical Center
Shriners Hospitals for Children–Portland

Roseburg
Member
Mercy Medical Center

Salem
Member
Salem Hospital

Seaside
Member
Providence Seaside Hospital

Silverton
Member
Silverton Hospital

The Dalles
Member
Mid–Columbia Medical Center

PENNSYLVANIA

Abington
Member
Abington Hospital

Allentown
Member
Lehigh Valley Hospital

Bethlehem
Member
Lehigh Valley Hospital–Muhlenberg

Brookville
Member
Penn Highlands Brookville

Bryn Mawr
Member
Bryn Mawr Hospital

Butler
Member
Butler Health System

Chambersburg
Member
Chambersburg Hospital
Summit Health

Clearfield
Member
Penn Highlands Clearfield

Darby
Member
Mercy Fitzgerald Hospital

Drexel Hill
Member
Delaware County Memorial Hospital

DuBois
Member
Penn Highlands DuBois

East Norriton
Member
Einstein Medical Center Montgomery

East Stroudsburg
Member
Pocono Medical Center

Ephrata
Member
WellSpan Ephrata Community Hospital

Gettysburg
Member
WellSpan Gettysburg Hospital

Greensburg
Member
Excela Health Westmoreland Hospital

Hanover
Member
Hanover Hospital

Harrisburg
Member
Pinnacle Health System
PinnacleHealth at Community General Osteopathic
Hospital

Hazleton
Member
Lehigh Valley Hospital – Hazleton

Hershey
Member
Penn State Milton S. Hershey Medical Center

Huntingdon
Member
J. C. Blair Memorial Hospital

Indiana
Member
Indiana Regional Medical Center

Jefferson Hills
Member
Jefferson Hospital

Lancaster
Member
Lancaster General Hospital

Langhorne
Member
St. Mary Medical Center

Lansdale
Member
Abington–Lansdale Hospital Jefferson Health

Latrobe
Member
Excela Latrobe Area Hospital

Lebanon
Member
WellSpan Good Samaritan Hospital

Lehighton
Member
Blue Mountain Health System
Blue Mountain Hospital

Malvern
Member
Bryn Mawr Rehabilitation Hospital

Meadowbrook
Member
Holy Redeemer Hospital

Media
Member
Riddle Hospital

Monongahela
Member
Monongahela Valley Hospital

Mount Pleasant
Member
Excela Frick Hospital

Muncy
Member
Muncy Valley Hospital

New Castle
Member
Jameson Hospital

Palmerton
Member
Palmerton Hospital

Paoli
Member
Paoli Hospital

Philadelphia
Member
Aria – Jefferson Health
Children's Hospital of Philadelphia
Einstein Medical Center Philadelphia
Fox Chase Cancer Center–American Oncologic
Hospital
Hospital of the University of Pennsylvania
Jeanes Hospital
Magee Rehabilitation Hospital
Penn Presbyterian Medical Center
Pennsylvania Hospital
Temple University Hospital
University of Pennsylvania Health System

Pittsburgh
Member
St. Clair Hospital
UPMC Presbyterian Shadyside

Pottsville
Member
Schuylkill Medical Center – East Norwegian Street
Schuylkill Medical Center – South Jackson Street

Reading
Member
Penn State Health St. Joseph

Saint Marys
Member
Penn Highlands Elk

Sayre
Member
Guthrie Clinic
Robert Packer Hospital

Sellersville
Member
Grand View Health

Springfield
Member
Crozer–Keystone Health System

Towanda
Member
Guthrie Towanda Memorial Hospital

Troy
Member
Troy Community Hospital

Uniontown
Member
Uniontown Hospital

Upland
Member
Crozer–Chester Medical Center

Waynesboro
Member
Waynesboro Hospital

Wellsboro
Member
Soldiers and Sailors Memorial Hospital

West Chester
Member
Penn Medicine Chester County Hospital

West Reading
Member
Reading Hospital

Williamsport
Member
Divine Providence Hospital
Susquehanna Health System
Williamsport Regional Medical Center

Wynnewood
Member
Lankenau Medical Center

York
Member
WellSpan Health
WellSpan York Hospital

RHODE ISLAND

Newport
Member
Newport Hospital

Pawtucket
Member
Memorial Hospital of Rhode Island

Providence
Member
Butler Hospital
Care New England Health System
Lifespan Corporation
Miriam Hospital
Rhode Island Hospital
Women & Infants Hospital of Rhode Island

Warwick
Member
Kent County Memorial Hospital

Westerly
Member
Westerly Hospital

SOUTH CAROLINA

Charleston
Member
MUSC Medical Center of Medical University of South
Carolina

Cheraw
Member
McLeod Health Cheraw

Clinton
Member
Greenville Health System – Laurens County Memorial
Hospital

Columbia
Member
ContinueCARE Hospital at Palmetto Health Baptist
Palmetto Health Baptist
Palmetto Health Baptist Parkridge
Palmetto Health Richland
Providence Hospital

Darlington
Member
McLeod Medical Center–Darlington

Dillon
Member
McLeod Medical Center Dillon

Easley
Member
Baptist Easley Hospital

Florence
Member
McLeod Regional Medical Center

Georgetown
Member
Tidelands Georgetown Memorial Hospital

Greenville
Member
GHS Greenville Memorial Hospital
Patewood Memorial Hospital
Shriners Hospitals for Children–Greenville

Greenwood
Member
Self Regional Healthcare

Greer
Member
GHS Greer Memorial Hospital

Loris
Member
McLeod Loris Seacoast Hospital

Murrells Inlet
Member
Tidelands Waccamaw Community Hospital

Seneca
Member
Oconee Memorial Hospital

Simpsonville
Member
GHS Hillcrest Memorial Hospital

Sumter
Member
Palmetto Health Tuomey

Travelers Rest
Member
North Greenville Hospital

SOUTH DAKOTA

Aberdeen
Member
Sanford Aberdeen Medical Center

Armour
Member
Douglas County Memorial Hospital

Burke
Member
Community Memorial Hospital

Canton
Member
Sanford Canton–Inwood Medical Center

Chamberlain
Member
Sanford Chamberlain Medical Center

Clear Lake
Member
Sanford Clear Lake Medical Center

Sioux Falls
Member
Sanford Health
Sanford USD Medical Center

Vermillion
Member
Sanford Vermillion Medical Center

Viborg
Member
Pioneer Memorial Hospital and Health Services

Watertown
Member
Prairie Lakes Healthcare System

Webster
Member
Sanford Webster Medical Center

Winner
Member
Winner Regional Healthcare Center

TENNESSEE

Chattanooga
Member
Erlanger Health System
Erlanger North Hospital

Collierville
Member
Baptist Memorial Hospital–Collierville

Columbia
Member
Maury Regional Hospital

Covington
Member
Baptist Memorial Hospital–Tipton

Franklin
Member
Williamson Medical Center

Harriman
Member
Roane Medical Center

Huntingdon
Member
Baptist Memorial Hospital–Huntingdon

Knoxville
Member
Covenant Health
Fort Sanders Regional Medical Center
Parkwest Medical Center
University of Tennessee Medical Center

Lenoir City
Member
Fort Loudoun Medical Center

Lewisburg
Member
Marshall Medical Center

Louisville
Member
Peninsula Hospital

Memphis
Member
Baptist Memorial Health Care Corporation
Baptist Memorial Hospital – Memphis
Baptist Memorial Hospital for Women
Methodist Healthcare Memphis Hospitals
Regional One Health
St. Jude Children's Research Hospital

Morristown
Member
Morristown–Hamblen Healthcare System

Nashville
Member
Vanderbilt University Medical Center

Oak Ridge
Member
Methodist Medical Center of Oak Ridge

Sevierville
Member
LeConte Medical Center

Tazewell
Member
Claiborne Medical Center

Union City
Member
Baptist Memorial Hospital–Union City

Waynesboro
Member
Wayne Medical Center

TEXAS

Andrews
Member
Permian Regional Medical Center

Baytown
Member
Houston Methodist San Jacinto Hospital

Bellaire
Member
Memorial Hermann Orthopedic and Spine Hospital

Bellville
Member
Bellville St. Joseph Health Center

Dallas
Member
Baylor Scott & White Health
Children's Health System of Texas
Methodist Health System
Parkland Health & Hospital System
William P. Clements, Jr. University Hospital

El Paso
Member
University Medical Center of El Paso

Fort Worth
Member
JPS Health Network

Galveston
Member
Shriners Hospitals for Children–Galveston
University of Texas Medical Branch

Houston
Member
Baylor St. Luke's Medical Center
Harris Health System
Houston Methodist Hospital
Houston Methodist West Hospital
Houston Methodist Willowbrook Hospital
Memorial Hermann – Texas Medical Center
Memorial Hermann Greater Heights Hospital
Memorial Hermann Health System
Memorial Hermann Memorial City Medical Center
Shriners Hospitals for Children–Houston
St. Luke's Hospital – The Vintage Hospital
TIRR Memorial Hermann

Humble
Member
Memorial Hermann Northeast

Katy
Member
Houston Methodist St. Catherine Hospital
Memorial Hermann Katy Hospital

Livingston
Member
CHI St. Luke's Health Memorial Livingston

Lubbock
Member
Covenant Health System
Covenant Medical Center–Lakeside

Lufkin
Member
CHI St. Luke's Health Memorial Lufkin

Midland
Member
Midland Memorial Hospital

Pasadena
Member
CHI St. Luke's Health – Patients Medical Center

Pearsall
Member
Frio Regional Hospital

Plano
Member
Community Hospital Corporation

San Antonio
Member
University Health System

San Augustine
Member
CHI St. Luke's Health Memorial San Augustine

Sugar Land
Member
Houston Methodist Sugar Land Hospital
Memorial Hermann Sugar Land Hospital

Sweeny
Member
Sweeny Community Hospital

The Woodlands
Member
St. Luke's Lakeside Hospital
St. Luke's The Woodlands Hospital

Tyler
Member
CHRISTUS Mother Frances Hospital – Tyler
University of Texas Health Northeast

UTAH

Gunnison
Member
Gunnison Valley Hospital

Provo
Member
Utah State Hospital

Salt Lake City
Member
Shriners Hospitals for Children–Salt Lake City
University of Utah Health Care – Hospital and Clinics
University of Utah Neuropsychiatric Institute

VERMONT

Bennington
Member
Southwestern Vermont Medical Center

Berlin
Member
The University of Vermont Health Network Central
Vermont Medical Center

Brattleboro
Member
Brattleboro Memorial Hospital
Brattleboro Retreat

Burlington
Member
The University of Vermont Health Network University
of Vermont Medical Center

Morrisville
Member
Copley Hospital

Newport
Member
North Country Hospital and Health Center

Rutland
Member
Rutland Regional Medical Center

Saint Johnsbury
Member
Northeastern Vermont Regional Hospital

Springfield
Member
Springfield Hospital

Townshend
Member
Grace Cottage Hospital

Windsor
Member
Mt. Ascutney Hospital and Health Center

VIRGIN ISLANDS

Saint Thomas
Member
Schneider Regional Medical Center

VIRGINIA

Bedford
Member
Bedford Memorial Hospital

Charlottesville
Member
Martha Jefferson Hospital
University of Virginia Medical Center
UVA–HEALTHSOUTH Rehabilitation Hospital

Culpeper
Member
Novant Health UVA Health System Culpeper Medical
Center

Farmville
Member
Centra Southside Community Hospital

Fishersville
Member
Augusta Health

Fredericksburg
Member
Mary Washington Hospital
Snowden at Fredericksburg

Hampton
Member
Sentara CarePlex Hospital

Harrisonburg
Member
 Sentara RMH Medical Center

Lynchburg
Member
 Centra Lynchburg General Hospital

Manassas
Member
 Novant Health UVA Health System Prince William
  Medical Center

Norfolk
Member
 Hospital for Extended Recovery
 Sentara Healthcare
 Sentara Leigh Hospital
 Sentara Norfolk General Hospital

Richmond
Member
 Children's Hospital of Richmond at VCU–Brook Road
  Campus
 VCU Medical Center

South Boston
Member
 Sentara Halifax Regional Hospital

Stafford
Member
 Stafford Hospital

Suffolk
Member
 Sentara Obici Hospital

Virginia Beach
Member
 Sentara Princess Anne Hospital
 Sentara Virginia Beach General Hospital

Williamsburg
Member
 Sentara Williamsburg Regional Medical Center

Woodbridge
Member
 Sentara Northern Virginia Medical Center

WASHINGTON

Aberdeen
Member
 Grays Harbor Community Hospital

Auburn
Member
 MultiCare Auburn Medical Center

Bellingham
Member
 PeaceHealth St. Joseph Medical Center

Bremerton
Member
 Harrison Medical Center

Burien
Member
 Highline Medical Center

Centralia
Member
 Providence Centralia Hospital

Chewelah
Member
 Providence St. Joseph's Hospital

Colfax
Member
 Whitman Hospital and Medical Center

Colville
Member
 Providence Mount Carmel Hospital

Dayton
Member
 Columbia County Health System

Edmonds
Member
 Swedish/Edmonds

Enumclaw
Member
 St. Elizabeth Hospital

Everett
Member
 Providence Regional Medical Center Everett

Gig Harbor
Member
 St. Anthony Hospital

Ilwaco
Member
 Ocean Beach Hospital

Issaquah
Member
 Swedish/Issaquah

Lakewood
Member
 St. Clare Hospital

Morton
Member
 Morton General Hospital

Olympia
Member
 Providence St. Peter Hospital

Pomeroy
Member
 Garfield County Public Hospital District

Port Angeles
Member
 Olympic Medical Center

Prosser
Member
 PMH Medical Center

Puyallup
Member
 MultiCare Good Samaritan Hospital

Renton
Member
 UW Medicine/Valley Medical Center

Richland
Member
 Kadlec Regional Medical Center

Seattle
Member
 Swedish Medical Center–Cherry Hill Campus
 Swedish Medical Center–First Hill
 University of Washington Medical Center
 UW Medicine/Harborview Medical Center
 UW Medicine/Northwest Hospital & Medical Center

Spokane
Member
 Providence Holy Family Hospital
 Providence Sacred Heart Medical Center & Children's
  Hospital
 Shriners Hospitals for Children–Spokane
 St. Luke's Rehabilitation Institute

Tacoma
Member
 MultiCare Health System
 MultiCare Tacoma General Hospital
 St. Joseph Medical Center

Walla Walla
Member
 Providence St. Mary Medical Center

WEST VIRGINIA

Charleston
Member
 CAMC Women and Children's Hospital
 Charleston Area Medical Center

Gassaway
Member
 Braxton County Memorial Hospital

Madison
Member
 Boone Memorial Hospital

Martinsburg
Member
 Berkeley Medical Center

Montgomery
Member
 Montgomery General Hospital

Morgantown
Member
 West Virginia University Hospitals

Princeton
Member
 Princeton Community Hospital

Ranson
Member
 Jefferson Medical Center

Ripley
Member
 Jackson General Hospital

Spencer
Member
 Roane General Hospital

Wheeling
Member
 Ohio Valley Medical Center
 Wheeling Hospital

WISCONSIN

Antigo
Member
 Aspirus Langlade Hospital

Appleton
Member
 ThedaCare, Inc.

Barron
Member
 Mayo Clinic Health System – Northland in Barron

Beaver Dam
Member
 Beaver Dam Community Hospitals

Beloit
Member
 Beloit Health System

Bloomer
Member
 Mayo Clinic Health System – Chippewa Valley in
  Bloomer

Boscobel
Member
 Gundersen Boscobel Area Hospital and Clinics

Eau Claire
Member
 Mayo Clinic Health System in Eau Claire

Friendship
Member
 Moundview Memorial Hospital & Clinics

Green Bay
Member
 Bellin Memorial Hospital
 Bellin Psychiatric Center

Hillsboro
Member
 Gundersen St. Joseph's Hospital and Clinics

Hudson
Member
 Hudson Hospital and Clinic

La Crosse
Member
 Gundersen Health System
 Mayo Clinic Health System – Franciscan Healthcare in
  La Crosse

Madison
Member
 Meriter UnityPoint Health
 University of Wisconsin Hospitals and Clinics Authority

Marinette
Member
 Bay Area Medical Center

Medford
Member
 Aspirus Medford Hospital

Menomonee Falls
Member
 Community Memorial Hospital

Menomonie
Member
 Mayo Clinic Health System – Red Cedar in Menomonie

Milwaukee
Member
 Froedtert Memorial Lutheran Hospital

Neenah
Member
 Theda Clark Medical Center

Neillsville
Member
  Memorial Medical Center – Neillsville

New Richmond
Member
  Westfields Hospital

Oconomowoc
Member
  Oconomowoc Memorial Hospital

Oconto
Member
  Bellin Health Oconto Hospital

Osseo
Member
  Mayo Clinic Health System – Oakridge in Osseo

Portage
Member
  Divine Savior Healthcare

River Falls
Member
  River Falls Area Hospital

Sparta
Member
  Mayo Clinic Health System – Franciscan Healthcare in Sparta

Superior
Member
  Essentia Health St. Mary's Hospital of Superior

Waukesha
Member
  ProHealth Care, Inc.
  Waukesha Memorial Hospital

Waupaca
Member
  ThedaCare Medical Center–Waupaca

Wausau
Member
  Aspirus Wausau Hospital
  North Central Health Care

West Bend
Member
  St. Joseph's Hospital

Whitehall
Member
  Gundersen Tri–County Hospital and Clinics

Wild Rose
Member
  Theda Care Medical Center – Wild Rose

Wisconsin Rapids
Member
  Aspirus Riverview Hospital and Clinics, Inc.

WYOMING

Buffalo
Member
  Johnson County Healthcare Center

Casper
Member
  Wyoming Medical Center

Cheyenne
Member
  Cheyenne Regional Medical Center

Douglas
Member
  Memorial Hospital of Converse County

Laramie
Member
  Ivinson Memorial Hospital

Lusk
Member
  Niobrara Health and Life Center

Sheridan
Member
  Sheridan Memorial Hospital

YANKEE ALLIANCE
138 River Road, Andover, MA
Zip 01810–1083; tel. 978/470–2000;
James W. Oliver, President and Chief
Executive Officer

CALIFORNIA

Long Beach
Member
  College Medical Center

Oceanside
Member
  Tri–City Medical Center

CONNECTICUT

Derby
Member
  Griffin Hospital

Hartford
Member
  Saint Francis Hospital and Medical Center

New London
Member
  Lawrence + Memorial Hospital

Stafford Springs
Member
  Johnson Memorial Medical Center

FLORIDA

Boca Raton
Member
  Promise Healthcare

Coral Gables
Member
  Baptist Health South Florida, Doctors Hospital

Homestead
Member
  Baptist Health South Florida, Homestead Hospital

Miami
Member
  Baptist Health South Florida, Baptist Hospital of Miami
  Baptist Health South Florida, South Miami Hospital
  Baptist Health South Florida, West Kendall Baptist Hospital

Miami Beach
Member
  Mount Sinai Medical Center

Miramar
Member
  Memorial Hospital Miramar

Pembroke Pines
Member
  Memorial Hospital Pembroke
  Memorial Hospital West

South Miami
Member
  Larkin Community Hospital

Tavernier
Member
  Baptist Health South Florida, Mariners Hospital

ILLINOIS

Geneva
Member
  Northwestern Medicine Delnor Hospital

Winfield
Member
  Northwestern Medicine Central DuPage Hospital

INDIANA

Gary
Member
  Methodist Hospitals

Mishawaka
Member
  Unity Medical & Surgical Hospital

KENTUCKY

Ashland
Member
  King's Daughters Medical Center

Benton
Member
  Marshall County Hospital

Corbin
Member
  Baptist Health Corbin

Elizabethtown
Member
  Hardin Memorial Hospital

La Grange
Member
  Baptist Health La Grange

Lexington
Member
  Baptist Health Lexington

Louisville
Member
  Baptist Health Louisville

Madisonville
Member
  Baptist Health Madisonville

Paducah
Member
  Baptist Health Paducah

Prestonsburg
Member
  Highlands Regional Medical Center

Richmond
Member
  Baptist Health Richmond

MAINE

Bangor
Member
  St. Joseph Hospital

Lewiston
Member
  St. Mary's Regional Medical Center

MASSACHUSETTS

Attleboro
Member
  Sturdy Memorial Hospital

Boston
Member
  Boston Medical Center
  New England Baptist Hospital
  Tufts Medical Center

Brockton
Member
  Signature Healthcare Brockton Hospital

Burlington
Member
  Lahey Hospital & Medical Center, Burlington

Fall River
Member
  Southcoast Hospitals Group

Great Barrington
Member
  Fairview Hospital

Lowell
Member
  Lowell General Hospital

Milford
Member
  Milford Regional Medical Center

Newburyport
Member
  Anna Jaques Hospital

Oak Bluffs
Member
  Martha's Vineyard Hospital

Pittsfield
Member
  Berkshire Medical Center

Westfield
Member
  Baystate Noble Hospital

Winchester
Member
  Winchester Hospital

NEW HAMPSHIRE

Concord
Member
  Concord Hospital

Exeter
Member
  Exeter Hospital

Franklin
Member
  Franklin Regional Hospital

Laconia
Member
  Lakes Region General Hospital

Manchester
Member
  Catholic Medical Center
  Elliot Hospital

Nashua
Member
  St. Joseph Hospital

North Conway
Member
  Memorial Hospital

Rochester
Member
  Frisbie Memorial Hospital

Salem
Member
  Northeast Rehabilitation Hospital

NEW YORK

Batavia
Member
  United Memorial Medical Center

Bath
Member
  Ira Davenport Memorial Hospital

Elizabethtown
Member
  The University of Vermont Health Network
  Elizabethtown Community Hospital

Elmira
Member
  Arnot Ogden Medical Center
  St. Joseph's Hospital

Glens Falls
Member
  Glens Falls Hospital

Gloversville
Member
  Nathan Littauer Hospital and Nursing Home

Plattsburgh
Member
  The University of Vermont Health Network–Champlain
  Valley Physicians Hospital

Warsaw
Member
  Wyoming County Community Hospital

OHIO

Logan
Member
  Hocking Valley Community Hospital

Montpelier
Member
  Community Hospitals and Wellness
  Centers–Montpelier

Salem
Member
  Salem Regional Medical Center

Seaman
Member
  Adams County Regional Medical Center

Sidney
Member
  Wilson Memorial Hospital

Steubenville
Member
  Life Line Hospital

OKLAHOMA

Hugo
Member
  Lane Frost Health and Rehabilitation Center

PENNSYLVANIA

Honesdale
Member
  Wayne Memorial Hospital

Langhorne
Member
  Barix Clinics of Pennsylvania

Washington
Member
  Advanced Surgical Hospital

RHODE ISLAND

Pawtucket
Member
  Memorial Hospital of Rhode Island

Providence
Member
  Roger Williams Medical Center

Wakefield
Member
  South County Hospital

Westerly
Member
  Westerly Hospital

SOUTH CAROLINA

Columbia
Member
  Providence Hospital

Fairfax
Member
  Allendale County Hospital

TEXAS

Aransas Pass
Member
  Care Regional Medical Center

Austin
Member
  Arise Austin Medical Center

Houston
Member
  Healthbridge Children's Hospital of Houston

New Braunfels
Member
  Post Acute/Warm Springs Specialty Hospital of New
  Braunfels

Plainview
Member
  Covenant Hospital Plainview

WEST VIRGINIA

New Martinsville
Member
  Wetzel County Hospital

Abbreviations Used in the AHA Guide

AB, Army Base
ACSW, Academy of Certified Social Workers
AEC, Atomic Energy Commission
AFB, Air Force Base
AHA, American Hospital Association
AK, Alaska
AL, Alabama
AODA, Alcohol and Other Drug Abuse
APO, Army Post Office
AR, Arkansas
A.R.T., Accredited Record Technician
A.S.C., Ambulatory Surgical Center
A.T.C., Alcoholism Treatment Center
Ave., Avenue
AZ, Arizona

B.A., Bachelor of Arts
B.B.A., Bachelor of Business Administration
B.C., British Columbia
Blvd., Boulevard
B.S., Bachelor of Science
B.S.Ed., Bachelor of Science in Education
B.S.H.S., Bachelor of Science in Health Studies
B.S.N., Bachelor of Science in Nursing
B.S.W., Bachelor of Science and Social Worker
CA, California; Controller of Accounts

C.A.A.D.A.C., Certified Alcohol and Drug Abuse Counselor
CAC, Certified Alcoholism Counselor
CAE, Certified Association Executive
CAP, College of American Pathologists
CAPA, Certified Ambulatory Post Anesthesia
C.A.S., Certificate of Advanced Study
CCDC, Certified Chemical Dependency Counselor
C.D., Commander of the Order of Distinction
CDR, Commander
CDS, Chemical Dependency Specialist
CFACHE, Certified Fellow American College of Healthcare Executives
CFRE, Certified Fund Raising Executive
C.G., Certified Gastroenterology
CHC, Certified Health Consultant
CHE, Certified Healthcare Executive
C.L.D., Clinical Laboratory Director
CLU, Certified Life Underwriter, Chartered Life Underwriter
CMA, Certified Medical Assistant
C.M.H.A., Certified Mental Health Administrator
CNHA, Certified Nursing Home Administrator
CNM, Certified Nurse Midwife
CNOR, Certified Operating Room Nurse
C.N.S., Clinical Nurse Specialist
CO, Colorado; Commanding Officer
COA, Certified Ophthalmic Assistant
COMT, Commandant
C.O.M.T., Certified Ophthalmic Medical Technician
Conv., Conventions
Corp., Corporation; Corporate
C.O.T., Certified Ophthalmic Technician
CPA, Certified Public Accountant
C.P.H.Q., Certified Professional in Health Care Quality
CPM, Certified Public Manager
CRNA, Certified Registered Nurse Anesthetist
CRNH, Certified Registered Nurse Hospice
C.S.J.B, Catholic Saint John the Baptist
CSW, Certified Social Worker
CT, Connecticut
CWO, Chief Warrant Officer

D.B.A., Doctor of Business Administration
DC, District of Columbia
D.D., Doctor of Divinity
D.D.S., Doctor of Dental Surgery
DE, Delaware
Diet, Dietitian; Dietary; Dietetics
D.M.D., Doctor of Dental Medicine
D.MIN., Doctor of Ministry
D.O., Doctor of Osteopathic Medicine and Surgery, Doctor of Osteopathy
DPA, Doctorate Public Administration
D.P.M., Doctor of Podiatric Medicine
Dr., Drive
Dr.P.h., Doctor of Public Health
D.Sc., Doctor of Science
D.S.W., Doctor of Social Welfare
D.V.M., Doctor of Veterinary Medicine

E., East
Ed.D., Doctor of Education
Ed.S., Specialist in Education
ENS, Ensign
Esq., Esquire
Expwy., Expressway
ext., extension

FAAN, Fellow of the American Academy of Nursing
FACATA, Fellow of the American College of Addiction Treatment Administrators
FACHE, Fellow of the American College of Healthcare Executives
FACMGA, Fellow of the American College of Medical Group Administrators
FACP, Fellow of the American College of Physicians
FACS, Fellow of the American College of Surgeons
FAX, Facsimile
FL, Florida
FPO, Fleet Post Office
FRCPSC, Fellow of the Royal College of Physicians and Surgeons of Canada
FT, Full-time

GA, Georgia
Govt., Government; Governmental

HHS, Department of Health and Human Services
HI, Hawaii
HM, Helmsman
HMO, Health Maintenance Organization
Hon., Honorable; Honorary
H.S.A., Health System Administrator
Hts., Heights
Hwy., Highway

IA, Iowa
ID, Idaho
IL, Illinois
IN, Indiana
Inc., Incorporated

J.D., Doctor of Law
J.P., Justice of the Peace
Jr., Junior

KS, Kansas
KY, Kentucky

LA, Louisiana
LCDR, Lieutenant Commander
LCSW, Licensed Certified Social Worker
L.H.D., Doctor of Humanities

L.I.S.W., Licensed Independent Social Worker
LL.D., Doctor of Laws
L.L.P., Limited Licensed Practitioner
L.M.H.C., Licensed Master of Health Care
L.M.S.W., Licensed Master of Social Work
L.N.H.A., Licensed Nursing Home Administrator
L.P.C., Licensed Professional Counselor
LPN, Licensed Practical Nurse
L.P.N., Licensed Practical Nurse
L.S.W., Licensed Social Worker
Lt., Lieutenant
LTC, Lieutenant Colonel
Ltd., Limited
LT.GEN., Lieutenant General
LTJG, Lieutenant (junior grade)

MA, Massachusetts
M.A., Master of Arts
Maj., Major
M.B., Bachelor of Medicine
M.B.A., Masters of Business Administration
MC, Medical Corps; Marine Corps
M.C., Member of Congress
MD, Maryland
M.D., Doctor of Medicine
ME, Maine
M.Ed., Master of Education
MFCC, Marriage/Family/Child Counselor
MHA, Mental Health Association
M.H.S., Masters in Health Science; Masters in Human Service
MI, Michigan
MM, Masters of Management
MN, Minnesota
M.N., Master of Nursing
MO, Missouri
M.P.A., Master of Public Administration; Master Public Affairs
M.P.H., Master of Public Health
M.P.S., Master of Professional Studies; Master of Public Science
MS, Mississippi
M.S., Master of Science
MSC, Medical Service Corps
M.S.D., Doctor of Medical Science
MSHSA, Master of Science Health Service Administration
M.S.N., Master of Science in Nursing
M.S.P.H., Master of Science in Public Health
M.S.S.W., Master of Science in Social Work
M.S.W., Master of Social Work
MT, Montana
Mt., Mount

N., North
NC, North Carolina
N.C.A.D.C., National Certification of Alcohol and Drug Counselors
ND, North Dakota
NE, Nebraska
NH, New Hampshire
NHA, National Hearing Association; Nursing Home Administrator
NJ, New Jersey
NM, New Mexico
NPA, National Perinatal Association
NV, Nevada
NY, New York

OCN, Oncology Certified Nurse
O.D., Doctor of Optometry
O.F.M., Order Franciscan Monks, Order of Friars Minor
OH, Ohio
OK, Oklahoma
OR, Oregon
O.R., Operating Room

O.R.S., Operating Room Supervisor
OSF, Order of St. Francis

PA, Pennsylvania
P.A., Professional Association
P.C., Professional Corporation
Pharm.D., Doctor of Pharmacy
Ph.B., Bachelor of Philosophy
Ph.D., Doctor of Philosophy
PHS, Public Health Service
Pkwy., Parkway
Pl., Place
PR, Puerto Rico
PS, Professional Services
PSRO, Professional Standards Review Organization

RADM, Rear Admiral
RD, Rural Delivery
Rd., Road
R.F.D., Rural Free Delivery
RI, Rhode Island
R.M., Risk Manager
R.N., Registered Nurse
RNC, Republican National Committee; Registered Nurse or Board Certified
R.Ph., Registered Pharmacist
RRA, Registered Record Administrator
R.S.M., Religious Sisters of Mercy
Rte., Route

S., South
SC, South Carolina
S.C., Surgery Center
SCAC, Senior Certified Addiction Counselor
Sc.D., Doctor of Science
Sci., Science, Scientific
SD, South Dakota
SHCC, Statewide Health Coordinating Council
Sgt., Sergeant
SNA, Surgical Nursing Assistant
SNF, Skilled Nursing Facility
Sq., Square
Sr., Senior, Sister
St., Saint, Street
Sta., Station
Ste., Saint; Suite

Tel., Telephone
Terr., Terrace
TN, Tennessee
Tpke, Turnpike
Twp., Township
TX, Texas

USA, United States Army
USAF, United States Air Force
USMC, United States Marine Corps
USN, United States Navy
USPHS, United States Public Health Service
UT, Utah

VA, Virginia
VADM, Vice Admiral
VI, Virgin Islands
Vlg., Village
VT, Vermont

W., West
WA, Washington
WI, Wisconsin
WV, West Virginia
WY, Wyoming

Abbreviations

Index